Stanley Gibbons
STAMP CATALOGUE

PART 1

British Commonwealth 2000

Including post-independence issues of Ireland

102nd edition

VOLUME 1

Great Britain and Countries A to I

Stanley Gibbons Ltd
London and Ringwood

By Appointment to Her Majesty The Queen
Stanley Gibbons Ltd, London
Philatelists

Published by **Stanley Gibbons Ltd**
Editorial, Publications Sales Offices and Distribution Centre:
5 Parkside, Christchurch Road, Ringwood,
Hants BH24 3SH.

ISBN: 0-85259-473-9

Item No. 2811 (00)

Text assembled by Black Bear Press Limited, Cambridge

Made and Printed in Great Britain by William Clowes Limited, Beccles, Suffolk

Preface to the 2000 Edition

TO BOLDLY GO

ree months after this edition of the *Part 1 ritish Commonwealth) Catalogue* is published will be in the new Millennium.

This is clearly the time for predictions, but it quires a very efficient crystal ball to foresee the ture for both the postal service and philately. anges are afoot in the organisation of many stal authorities throughout the world, with an phasis on commercial operation and ternational competition. As vast sums of money e being poured into such projects it would seem at those involved do not subscribe to the theory at e-mail will replace the postal service within a cade or so. Although the use of postage stamps business in the developed economies is clining, the usefulness of Sir Rowland Hill's vention remains undiminished for personal ters and in developing countries where volumes mail are rapidly increasing.

The future of philately is a more complex bject. As a hobby with many diverse facets it ould continue to thrive, but in the opening years the new Millennium changes in emphasis are ely. The study of past issues, together with stal history, will certainly increase as more llectors are attracted to the serious side of the bby. Thematics will also remain popular, but e future for the collection of modern issues is uch more doubtful. The growing activity of post fice marketing departments threatens the tionale of the postage stamp with issues being oduced as "collectables" illustrating aspects of pular culture, rather than for postal purposes. the link with the postal service is lost, then such amps will become nothing more than stickers.

The criteria for listing stamps in the Stanley bbons catalogue are printed on pages x/xi of is edition. The point has already been reached here the Millennium series for one major postal ministration will not be included in the talogue as it does not fulfil these criteria.

Next May will see "The Stamp Show 2000" at arls Court. By tradition international stamp hibitions are only held in Great Britain once ery decade and so provide a fascinating insight to hobby trends. "Stamp Show 2000" will rtainly be worth watching!

PRICES

uring periods of low inflation it is unusual to find amp prices rising or falling across the board. In ch circumstances they will more accurately flect perceived changes in true scarcity, complicated by wider economic factors.

For this edition much work has been done on e prices for the **West Indies**, especially the larger ands, with increases extending either to 1935 or, in some cases, into the issues of King George VI.

Although further rises have taken place in recognised rare issues, such as those for **Batum**, there are interesting developments elsewhere, especially for the **Australian States**, in particular **Queensland**, **Victoria** and **Western Australia**, involving issues from 1870 onwards. Another area of activity covers issues for **Newfoundland** from 1880 onwards. Postal history interest is reflected in increased demand for many of the **Hong Kong** issues used in the Treaty Ports. **Indian States** remain popular, but show more emphasis on stamps from the King George VI period.

For the present reign it is clear that sufficient stocks are still in circulation for many issues up to the late 1980s. There are exceptions. **British Indian Ocean Territory** is up, and there is growing demand for values from the more complex definitive issues such as the **Fiji** 1979–94 set. Genuine scarcities do exist for some issues after 1988, but here demand is probably fuelled by thematic appeal. **Great Britain** sees the increases from the *GB Concise Catalogue* covering issues from the classic period up to 1937 repeated, but there are additional increases for King George VI issues and for the better Wilding definitives. It is reported that a number of commemorative and greetings stamp sets from the last ten years are difficult to find in quantity, and prices here may well have further to go.

REVISIONS IN THIS EDITION

The listing of pre-1953 watermark varieties, undertaken for the past two editions, has been completed with the inclusion of such items on issues from the 1860s to the end of the reign of Queen Victoria. No attempt has been made to provide such detail for those areas, such as the Australian States, where the position of the watermark is completely haphazard, but all of the De La Rue issues for this period, and a number of others, have been covered. In some instances the inclusion of these watermark varieties creates added interest to the listing and collectors will find the revisions for the Queen Victoria issues of **Antigua**, **Bahamas**, **Barbados**, **Bermuda**, **Egypt**, **Falkland Islands**, **Gambia** and **Hong Kong** well worth study.

Additional watermark varieties have also been included on post 1900 issues and we are particularly grateful to Charles Freeland and John Yorke for providing confirmed lists of such items.

The preparations for the new catalogue database have been responsible for the removal of many of the multiple price column listings from this edition. In some instances this has led to renumbering, but many of the revisions do provide a clearer impression of the issues than was previously possible.

In a number of instances the listings of new issues are not as up-to-date as they should be. Difficulties in obtaining stamps or information concerning them from the postal administrations or philatelic agents has led to such delays. This is, unfortunately, a growing trend, and in some instances it is proving almost impossible to confirm if stamps fulfil the criteria for catalogue listing.

There has been a most encouraging increase in the amount of philatelic literature published so that it has been possible to provide a separate bibliography for each volume.

Further study of the MCA watermark has identified a major variety in the form of a substitute Crown. This is illustrated in the introductory notes and listings for it can be found under **Bahamas**, **Barbados** and **Bermuda**. Others must exist.

Australia. Notes on the **New South Wales** letter sheets of 1838 have been included. Dates have been added to the listing of several states, particularly for the issues after 1880. The different perforations on the 1914 Commonwealth issue are now listed. The notes on Queen Elizabeth II papers have been improved and the 1972 white fluorescent paper printings given separate listing.

Botswana. The two types of 1989 Zebra postage dues printed in Zimbabwe are listed with illustrations based on information supplied by S. Jelgren.

Canada. Minor improvements have been made to the **Newfoundland** listing. The **Canada** 1868–90 Large Heads issue has been rewritten to provide a unified listing of both the Ottawa and Montreal printings.

Cyprus. More Key Type flaws have been added.

Falkland Islands. The comb and line perforations from the 1929–36 Whale and Penguins issue are now listed separately.

India. A new series of cover factors have been provided for **Soruth**.

Ireland. Further work has been done on the modern definitives with the help of Brian Warren. The current Birds series has required considerable revision to cover recent developments.

These are only the highlights for this volume. There are further corrections and additions throughout the listings and we are most grateful to those collectors, dealers and postal professionals who provide so much information for each new edition.

David J. Aggersberg

Stanley Gibbons Holdings Plc Addresses

STANLEY GIBBONS LIMITED, STANLEY GIBBONS AUCTIONS

399 Strand, London WC2R 0LX
Auction Room and Specialist Stamp Departments. Open Monday–Friday 9.30 a.m. to 5 p.m.
Shop. Open Monday–Friday 8.30 a.m. to 6 p.m. and Saturday 9.30 a.m. to 5.30 p.m.
Telephone 0171 (020 7 *from 22 April 2000*) **836 8444 and Fax 0171 (020 7) 836 7342 for all departments.**

STANLEY GIBBONS PUBLICATIONS

5 Parkside, Christchurch Road, Ringwood, Hants BH24 3SH.
Telephone 01425 472363 (24 hour answer phone service), Fax 01425 470247 and E-mail info@stangib.demon.co.uk
Publications Showroom (at above address). Open Monday–Friday 9 a.m. to 3 p.m.
Publications Mail Order. FREEPHONE 0800 611622. Monday–Friday 8.30 a.m. to 5 p.m.

FRASER'S

(a division of Stanley Gibbons Ltd)
399 Strand, London WC2R 0LX
Autographs, photographs, letters and documents.
Telephone 0171 (020 7 *from 22 April 2000*) **836 8444 and Fax 0171 (020 7) 836 7342**
Monday–Friday 9 a.m. to 5.30 p.m. and Saturday 10 a.m. to 4 p.m.

STANLEY GIBBONS PUBLICATIONS OVERSEAS REPRESENTATION

Stanley Gibbons Publications are represented overseas by the following sole distributors (*), distributors (**) or licensees (***).

Australia

Lighthouse Philatelic (Aust.) Pty Ltd*
PO Box 763
Strawberry Hills
New South Wales 2012
Australia

Stanley Gibbons (Australia) Pty Ltd***
Level 6, 36 Clarence Street
Sydney N.S.W. 2000
Australia

Belgium and Luxembourg**

Davo c/o Philac
Rue du Midi 48
Bruxelles 1000
Belgium

Canada*

Lighthouse Publications (Canada) Ltd
255 Duke Street
Montreal
Quebec
Canada H3C 2M2

Denmark**

Davo/Samlerforum
Ostergade 3
DK 7470 Karup
Denmark

Finland**

Davo
c/o Suomen Postimerkkeily
Ludvingkatu 5
SF-00130 Helsinki
Finland

France*

Davo France (Casteilla)
10 Rue Leon Foucault
78184 St Quentin Yvelines Cesex
France

Germany and Austria*

Leuchtturm Albenverlag Gmbh u. Co.
Am Spakenberg 45
Postfach 1340
D21495 Geesthacht
Germany

Hong Kong**

Po-on Stamp Service
GPO Box 2498
Hong Kong

Israel**

Capital Stamps
PO Box 3769
Jerusalem 91036
Israel

Italy*

Ernesto Marini SRL
Via Struppa 300
I-16165
Genova GE
Italy

Japan**

Japan Philatelic Co Ltd
PO Box 2
Suginami-Minami
Tokyo
Japan

Netherlands*

Davo Publications
PO Box 411
7400 AK Deventer
Netherlands

New Zealand***

Stanley Gibbons (New Zealand) Ltd
PO Box 80
Wellington
New Zealand

Norway**

Davo Norge A/S
PO Box 738 Sentrum
N-01 05 Oslo
Norway

Singapore***

Stanley Gibbons (Singapore) Pte Ltd
Raffles City
PO Box 1689
Singapore 9117

South Africa**

Republic Stamp and Coin Accessories cc
Republic House
54A, Silwood Road
Bramley 2090
Republic of South Africa

Sweden*

Chr Winther Sorensen AB
Box 43
S-310 Knaered
Sweden

Switzerland**

Phila Service
Burgstrasse 160
CH 4125 Riehen
Switzerland

West Indies/Caribbean**

Hugh Dunphy
PO Box 413
Kingston 10
Jamaica
West Indies

Stanley Gibbons Stamp Catalogue Complete List of Parts

1 British Commonwealth
(Annual in two volumes)

2 Austria & Hungary (5th edition, 1994)
Austria, Bosnia & Herzegovina, U.N. (Vienna), Hungary

3 Balkans (4th edition, 1998)
Albania, Bosnia & Herzegovina, Bulgaria, Croatia, Greece & Islands, Macedonia, Rumania, Slovenia, Yugoslavia

4 Benelux (4th edition, 1993)
Belgium & Colonies, Netherlands & Colonies, Luxembourg

5 Czechoslovakia & Poland (5th edition, 1994)
Czechoslovakia, Bohemia & Moravia, Slovakia, Poland

6 France (4th edition, 1993)
France, Colonies, Post Offices, Andorra, Monaco

7 Germany (5th edition, 1996)
Germany, States, Colonies, Post.Offices

8 Italy & Switzerland (5th edition, 1997)
Italy & Colonies, Fiume, San Marino, Vatican City, Trieste, Liechtenstein, Switzerland, U.N. (Geneva)

9 Portugal & Spain (4th edition, 1996)
Andorra, Portugal & Colonies, Spain & Colonies

10 Russia (5th edition, 1999)
Russia, Baltic States, Mongolia, Tuva

11 Scandinavia (4th edition, 1994)
Aland Island, Denmark, Faroe Islands, Finland, Greenland, Iceland, Norway, Sweden

12 Africa since Independence A-E (2nd edition, 1983)
Algeria, Angola, Benin, Bophuthatswana, Burundi, Cameroun, Cape Verde, Central African Republic, Chad, Comoro Islands, Congo, Djibouti, Equatorial Guinea, Ethiopia

13 Africa since Independence F-M (1st edition, 1981)
Gabon, Guinea, Guinea-Bissau, Ivory Coast, Liberia, Libya Malagasy Republic, Mali, Mauritania, Morocco, Mozambique

14 Africa since Independence N-Z (1st edition, 1981)
Niger Republic, Rwanda, St. Thomas & Prince, Senegal Somalia, Sudan, Togo, Transkei, Tunisia, Upper Volta, Venda Zaire

15 Central America (2nd edition, 1984)
Costa Rica, Cuba, Dominican Republic, El Salvador, Guatemala, Haiti, Honduras, Mexico, Nicaragua, Panama

16 Central Asia (3rd edition, 1992)
Afghanistan, Iran, Turkey

17 China (6th edition, 1998)
China, Taiwan, Tibet, Foreign P.O.'s, Hong Kong, Macao

18 Japan & Korea (4th edition, 1997)
Japan, Ryukyus, Korean Empire, South Korea, North Korea

19 Middle East (5th edition, 1996)
Bahrain, Egypt, Iraq, Israel, Jordan, Kuwait, Lebanon, Oman Qatar, Saudi Arabia, Syria, U.A.E., Yemen A.R., Yemen P.D.R.

20 South America (3rd edition, 1989)
Argentina, Bolivia, Brazil, Chile, Colombia, Ecuador, Paraguay, Peru, Surinam, Uruguay, Venezuela

21 South-East Asia (3rd edition, 1995)
Bhutan, Burma, Indonesia, Kampuchea, Laos, Nepal, Philippines, Thailand, Vietnam

22 United States (4th edition, 1994)
U.S. & Possessions, Canal Zone, Marshall Islands, Micronesia, Palau, U.N. (New York, Geneva, Vienna)

GREAT BRITAIN SPECIALISED CATALOGUES

Volume 1 Queen Victoria (11th edition, 1997)
Volume 2 King Edward VII to King George VI (11th edition, 1999)
Volume 3 Queen Elizabeth II Pre-decimal Issues (10th edition, 1998)
Volume 4 Queen Elizabeth II Decimal Definitive Issues (8th edition, 1996)
Volume 5 Queen Elizabeth II Decimal Special Issues (3rd edition, 1998)

THEMATIC CATALOGUES

Collect Aircraft on Stamps (1st edition, 1994)
Collect Birds on Stamps (4th edition, 1996)
Collect Chess on Stamps (2nd edition, 1999)
Collect Fish on Stamps (1st edition, 1999)
Collect Fungi on Stamps (2nd edition, 1997)
Collect Railways on Stamps (3rd edition, 1999)
Collect Shells on Stamps (1st edition, 1995)
Collect Ships on Stamps (new editon early 2000)

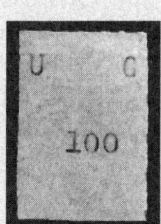

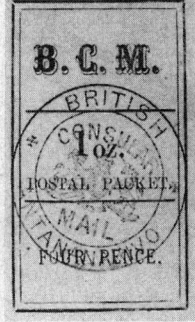

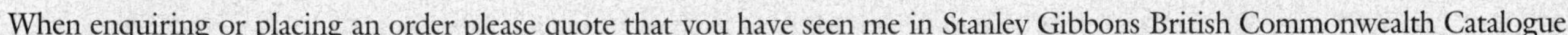

Catalogue Numbers Altered

The table below is a cross-reference of those catalogue numbers which have been altered in this edition.
For list of Numbers Added to this edition see page xxii.

Old	*New*
Great Britain	
623I/5I	623A/5A
623II/4II	623B/4B
624x	*Deleted*
814d	*Deleted*
Y1675*b*/bl	Y1675*c*/cl
NI79l	NI79al
Isle of Man	
111A/23A	111/23
111B/23B	111a/23a
773	775
774/5	778/9
776/7	781/2
Jersey	
204A/7A	204/7
204B/7B	204b/7b
776/80	777/81
782/3	783/4
784	786
785/6	790/1
787/90	794/8
801/57	807/63
Anguilla	
384B/8B	384a/8a
560B/3B	560a/3a
720B/4B	720a/4a
Antigua	
234/41	180a/95a
793B/810B	793a/810a
2394/575	2404/585
Barbuda	
677B/82B	677b/82b
Ascension	
SB3B/4B	SB3a/4a
Australia—New South Wales	
228ab/c	288b/d
O5c/e	O5ba/bc
South Australia	
195B/208B	195a/208a
Victoria	
135*a*/*g*	135*b*/*h*
Commonwealth of Australia	
20*a*/*c*	20*b*/d
21a/bw	21ca/dw
23*a*/w	23*ba*/bw
465ab	465b
468c	468bc
529a	529ab

Old	*New*
602B/7B	602a/7a
602c	602ab
1634c/7c	1634d/7d
O42w	O42aw
O42wa	O42b
O63w	*Deleted*
Cocos (Keeling) Islands	
235	236
236	235
Bahamas	
28*a*/31	29/30
39*a*	39*b*
Bangladesh	
368	369
369	376
376/81	370/5
O47	O50
O48	O51
O49	O47
Barbados	
184x	*Deleted*
187w/x	*Deleted*
188w/x	*Deleted*
189x	*Deleted*
190w	*Deleted*
221x	221y
351*a*	351*b*
399B/414B	399a/414a
Belize	
66B/9B	66c/9c
767B/78B	767a/78a
Bermuda	
27*a*	27*b*
29*a*	29*b*
34*a*	34*b*
Botswana	
713B/16B	713a/16a
Brunei	
26y	*Deleted*
Canada—Newfoundland	
63	63*a*
63*a*	63
91/3	80/2
164/77	*Rewritten*
225cw	225cbw
257/67	*Rewritten*
Dominion of Canada	
62/7*b*	72/89

Old	*New*
68	62
69/71*a*	90/6
72	63
73/4*a*	97/100
75/6*c*	64/70
77/82*b*	101/11
83	71
1756	1758
Cayman Islands	
69w	*Deleted*
75w	*Deleted*
Cook Islands	
1B/4B	1a/4a
194B/8B	194a/8a
327B	327a
335B/6B	335a/6a
1419/22	1424/7
Cyprus	
61*a*/b	61*b*/c
61w	61aw
68w	68aw
88w	*Deleted*
Turkish Cypriot Posts	
432/3	436/7
434/7	432/5
Dominica	
272B/86B	272a/86a
747B/9B	747a/9a
1241B/54B	1241a/54a
1241C/54C	1241b/54b
2318/405	2318/408
Egypt	
6e	6da
26/43	*Rewritten*
54c/ca	54d/da
55a/ab	55b/ba
56b	56c
58b/ba	58c/ca
59ab	59c
61ab	61c
63c	63d
64b	64c
93/5	95/7
96/7	93/4
O64a	O64c
Falkland Islands	
16*a*	16*b*
17*a*/*b*	17*b*/*c*
30*a*/*b*	30*b*/*c*
785/7	792/4
788/94	785/90
Falkland Is. Dependencies	
Z29*a*	Z29*b*

Old	*New*
Fiji	
138b/c	138c/d
580a/90a	580c/90c
Gambia	
17a	17c
18a	18c
Ghana	
27*a*	27*b*
54	54a
54a	54
79*b*/d	79*c*/*e*
120B/32B	120a/32a
2469/85	2497/513
2486/513	2469/96
SB1/5	SB2/6
Gibraltar	
110B/13B	110a/13a
Grenada	
47e	47f
128w	*Deleted*
650B/62B	650a/62a
1407B/25B	1407a/25a
1413*c*/21*c*	1425*c*/*g*
1420*c*	1420*b*
1425c/cd	1425b/ba
1994B/2007B	1994a/2007a
Grenadines of Grenada	
670B/88cB	670a/88ba
2293/497	2299/503
Guyana	
240a	240b
379/92	378/84
393A/407A	385/98
393B/407B	399/407*b*
769B	769c
770B	770d
770a	770da
781*a*	781*b*
808B	808a
808a	808ab
852	762a
869*a*	869*b*
874a	874b
875a	875c
1220B	1220a
1221*a*	1221*b*
1444a	1444c
2183/4c	*Rewritten*
Hong Kong	
156a/b	156b/c
553B/4B	554*a*/*b*
British Post Offices in China	
Z687	Z686

Old	*New*
India	
269*a*	269*b*
1575	1576
O216*a*	O216*b*
O261	O268
Convention States—Gw	
4/37	*Rewritten*
Feudatory States—Bho	
89B/98B	89a/98a
Charkhari	
31*c*/*d*	31*d*/*e*
Cochin	
4/5	8/9
6/9	4/7
28*a*	28*b*
67B/71B	67a/71a
74B	74a
79B	79a
81B	81a
85*a*/*c*	85*b*/*d*
O54B/6B	O54a/6a
O55a	O55ab
O56a	O56ab
Hyderabad	
24/36	*Rewritten*
O1/41	*Rewritten*
Jind	
J27*a*/34	J28/35
Kishangarh	
O25d/e	O25a/b
O25a/c	O25c/e
O29a	O29b
Nandgaon	
O2/5	O3/6
Nawanagar	
2a	2ab
2*b*/16	3/18
Travancore	
6*d*/*e*	6*e*/*f*
O96g	*Deleted*
Ireland	
8a/b	8b/c
1034/6	1035/7
1037	1053
1038	1056
1039/40	1059/60
1041	1062
1047	1080
1048/9	1084/5
1050/1	1088/9
1052/3	1092/3
1055/113	1100/58

Contents

General Philatelic Information

and Guidelines to the Scope of the Part 1 (British Commonwealth) Catalogue

The notes which follow seek to reflect current practice in compiling the Part 1 (British Commonwealth) Catalogue.

It scarcely needs emphasising that the *Stanley Gibbons Stamp Catalogue* has a very long history and that the vast quantity of information it contains has been carefully built up by successive generations through the work of countless individuals. Philately itself is never static and the Catalogue has evolved and developed during this long time-span. Thus, while these notes are important for today's criteria, they may be less precise the further back in the listings one travels. They are not intended to inaugurate some unwanted series of piecemeal alterations in a widely respected work, but it does seem to us useful that Catalogue users know as exactly as possible the policies currently in operation.

PRICES

The prices quoted in this Catalogue are the estimated selling prices of Stanley Gibbons Ltd at the time of publication. They are, *unless it is specifically stated otherwise*, for examples in fine condition for the issue concerned. Superb examples are worth more; those of a lower quality considerably less.

All prices are subject to change without prior notice and Stanley Gibbons Ltd may from time to time offer stamps below catalogue price. Individual low value stamps sold at 399, Strand are liable to an additional handling charge. Purchasers of new issues are asked to note that the prices charged for them contain an element for the service rendered and so may exceed the prices shown when the stamps are subsequently catalogued. Postage and handling charges are extra.

No guarantee is given to supply all stamps priced, since it is not possible to keep every catalogued item in stock. Commemorative issues may, at times, only be available in complete sets and not as individual values.

Quotation of prices. The prices in the left-hand column are for unused stamps and those in the right-hand column are for used.

A dagger (†) denotes that the item listed does not exist in that condition and a blank, or dash, that it exists, or may exist, but no market price is known.

Prices are expressed in pounds and pence sterling. One pound comprises 100 pence (£1 = 100p).

The method of notation is as follows: pence in numerals (e.g. 10 denotes ten pence); pound and pence, up to £100, in numerals (e.g. 4·25 denotes four pounds and twenty-five pence); prices above £100 expressed in whole pounds with the "£" sign shown.

Unused stamps. Great Britain and Commonwealth: the prices for unused stamps of Queen Victoria to King George V are for lightly hinged examples. Unused prices for King Edward VIII to Queen Elizabeth II issues are for unmounted mint.

Some stamps from the King George VI period are often difficult to find in unmounted mint condition. In such instances we would expect that collectors would need to pay a high proportion of the price quoted to obtain mounted mint examples. Generally speaking lightly mounted mint stamps from this reign, issued before 1945, are in considerable demand.

Mounted mint stamps from the reign of Queen Elizabeth II are frequently available at lower prices than those quoted for the stamps unmounted.

Used stamps. The used prices are normally for stamps postally used but may be for stamps cancelled-to-order where this practice exists.

A pen-cancellation on early issues can sometimes correctly denote postal use. Instances are individually noted in the Catalogue in explanation of the used price given.

Prices quoted for bisects on cover or on large piece are for those dated during the period officially authorised.

Stamps not sold unused to the public (e.g. some official stamps) are priced used only.

The use of "unified" designs, that is stamps inscribed for both postal and fiscal purposes, results in a number of stamps of very high face value. In some instances these may not have been primarily intended for postal purposes, but if they are so inscribed we include them. We only price such items used, however, where there is evidence of normal postal usage.

Cover prices. To assist collectors, cover prices are quoted for issues up to 1945 at the beginning of each country.

The system gives a general guide in the form of a factor by which the corresponding used price of the loose stamp should be multiplied when found in fine average condition on cover.

Care is needed in applying the factors and they relate to a cover which bears a single of the denomination listed; strips and blocks would need individual valuation outside the scope. If more than one denomination is present the most highly priced attracts the multiplier and the remainder are priced at the simple figure for used singles in arriving at a total.

The cover should be of non-philatelic origin, bearing the correct postal rate for the period and distance involved and cancelled with the markings normal to the offices concerned. Purely philatelic items have a cover value only slightly greater than the catalogue value for the corresponding used stamps. This applies generally to those high-value stamps used philatelically rather than in the normal course of commerce. Low-value stamps, e.g. ¼d. and ½d., are desirable when used as a single rate on cover and merit an increase in "multiplier" value.

First-day covers in the period up to 1945 are not within the scope of the system and the multiplier should not be used. As a special category of philatelic usage, with wide variations in valuation according to scarcity, they require separate treatment.

Oversized covers, difficult to accommodate on an album page, should be reckoned as worth little more than the corresponding value of the used stamps. The condition of a cover affects its value. Except for "wreck covers", serious damage or soiling reduce the value where the postal markings and stamps are ordinary ones. Conversely, visual appeal adds to the value and this can include freshness of appearance, important addresses, old-fashioned but legible hand-writing, historic town-names, etc.

The multipliers are a base on which further value would be added to take account of the cover's postal historical importance in demonstrating such things as unusual, scarce or emergency cancels, interesting routes, significant postal markings, combination usage, the development of postal rates, and so on.

For *Great Britain*, rather than multiplication factors, the cover price is shown as a third column, following the prices for unused and used stamps. It will be extended beyond King Edward VII in subsequent editions.

Minimum price. The minimum catalogue price quoted is 10p. For individual stamps prices between 10p. and 30p. are provided as a guide for catalogue users. The lowest price *charged* for individual stamps purchased from Stanley Gibbons Ltd is 30p.

Set prices. Set prices are generally for one of each value, excluding shades and varieties, but including major colour changes. Where there are alternative shades, etc., the cheapest is usually included. The number of stamps in the set is always stated for clarity. The mint prices for sets containing *se-tenant* pieces are based on the price quoted for such combinations, and not on those for the individual stamps.

Varieties. Where plate or cylinder varieties are priced in a used condition the price quoted is for a fine used example with the cancellation well clear of the listed flaw.

Specimen stamps. The pricing of these items is explained under that heading.

Stamp booklets. Prices are for complete assembled booklets in fine condition with those issued before 1945 showing normal wear and tear. Incomplete booklets and those which have been "exploded" will, in general, be worth less than the figure quoted.

Repricing. Collectors will be aware that the market factors of supply and demand directly influence the prices quoted in this Catalogue. Whatever the scarcity of a particular stamp, if there is no one in the market who wishes to buy it it cannot be expected to achieve a high price. Conversely, the same item actively sought by numerous potential buyers may cause the price to rise.

All the prices in this Catalogue are examined during the preparation of each new edition by expert staff of Stanley Gibbons and repriced as necessary. They take many factors into account, including supply and demand, and are in close touch with the international stamp market and the auction world.

Commonwealth cover prices and advice on postal history material originally provided by Edward B. Proud.

GUARANTEE

All stamps are guaranteed genuine originals in the following terms:

If not as described, and returned by the purchaser, we undertake to refund the price paid to us in the original transaction. If any stamp is certified as genuine by the Expert Committee of the Royal Philatelic Society, London, or by B.P.A. Expertising Ltd, the purchaser shall not be entitled to make any claim against us for any error, omission or mistake in such certificate.

Consumers' statutory rights are not affected by the above guarantee.

The recognised Expert Committees in this country are those of the Royal Philatelic Society, 41 Devonshire Place, London W1N 1PE, and B.P.A. Expertising Ltd, P.O. Box 137, Leatherhead, Surrey KT22 0RG. They do not undertake valuations under any circumstances and fees are payable for their services.

THE CATALOGUE IN GENERAL

Contents. The Catalogue is confined to adhesive postage stamps, including miniature sheets. For particular categories the rules are:

(*a*) Revenue (fiscal) stamps or telegraph stamps are listed only where they have been expressly authorised for postal duty.

(*b*) Stamps issued only precancelled are included, but normally issued stamps available additionally with precancel have no separate precancel listing unless the face value is changed.

(*c*) Stamps prepared for use but not issued, hitherto accorded full listing, are nowadays footnoted with a price (where possible).

(*d*) Bisects (trisects, etc.) are only listed where such usage was officially authorised.

(*e*) Stamps issued only on first day covers or in presentation packs and not available separately are not listed but may be priced in a footnote.

(*f*) New printings are only included in this Catalogue where they show a major philatelic variety, such as a change in shade, watermark or paper. Stamps which exist with or without imprint dates are listed separately; changes in imprint dates are mentioned in footnotes.

(*g*) Official and unofficial reprints are dealt with by footnote.

(*h*) Stamps from imperforate printings of modern issues which also occur perforated are covered by footnotes, but are listed where widely available for postal use.

Exclusions. The following are excluded: (*a*) non-postal revenue or fiscal stamps; (*b*) postage stamps used fiscally; (*c*) local carriage labels and private local issues; (*d*) telegraph stamps; (*e*) bogus or phantom stamps; (*f*) railway or airline letter fee stamps, bus or road transport company labels; (*g*) cut-outs; (*h*) all types of non-postal labels and souvenirs; (*i*) documentary labels for the postal service, e.g. registration, recorded delivery, air-mail etiquettes, etc.; (*j*) privately applied embellishments to official issues and privately commissioned items generally; (*k*) stamps for training postal officers.

Full listing. "Full listing" confers our recognition and implies allotting a catalogue number and (wherever possible) a price quotation.

In judging status for inclusion in the catalogue broad considerations are applied to stamps. They must be issued by a legitimate postal authority, recognised by the government concerned, and must be adhesives valid for proper postal use in the class of service for which they are inscribed. Stamps, with the exception of such categories as postage dues and officials, must be available to the general public, at face value, in reasonable quantities without any artificial restrictions being imposed on their distribution.

We record as abbreviated Appendix entries, without catalogue numbers or prices, stamps from countries which either persist in having far more issues than can be justified by postal need or have failed to maintain control over their distribution so that they have not been available to the public in reasonable quantities at face value. Miniature sheets and imperforate stamps are not mentioned in these entries.

The publishers of this catalogue have observed, with concern, the proliferation of "artificial" stamp-issuing territories. On several occasions this has resulted in separately inscribed issues for various component parts of otherwise united states or territories.

Stanley Gibbons Ltd have decided that where such circumstances occur, they will not, in the future, list these items in the SG catalogue without first satisfying themselves that the stamps represent a genuine political, historical or postal division within the country concerned. Any such issues which do not fulfil this stipulation will be recorded in the Catalogue Appendix only.

For errors and varieties the criterion is legitimate (albeit inadvertent) sale through a postal administration in the normal course of business. Details of provenance are always important; printers' waste and deliberately manufactured material are excluded.

Certificates. In assessing unlisted items due weight is given to Certificates from recognised Expert Committees and, where appropriate, we will usually ask to see them.

New issues. New issues are listed regularly in the Catalogue Supplement published in *Gibbons Stamp Monthly,* whence they are consolidated into the next available edition of the Catalogue.

Date of issue. Where local issue dates differ from dates of release by agencies, "date of issue" is the local date. Fortuitous stray usage before the officially intended date is disregarded in listing. For ease of reference, the Catalogue displays in the top corner the date of issue of the first set listed on each page.

Catalogue numbers. Stamps of each country are catalogued chronologically by date of issue. Subsidiary classes are placed at the end of the country, as separate lists, with a distinguishing letter prefix to the catalogue number, e.g. D for postage due, O for official and E for express delivery stamps.

The catalogue number appears in the extreme left column. The boldface Type numbers in the next column are merely cross-references to illustrations. Catalogue numbers in the *Gibbons Stamp Monthly* Supplement are provisional only and may need to be altered when the lists are consolidated. For the numbering of miniature sheets and sheetlets *see* section below.

Once published in the Catalogue, numbers are changed as little as possible; really serious renumbering is reserved for the occasions when a complete country or an entire issue is being rewritten. The edition first affected includes cross-reference tables of old and new numbers.

Our catalogue numbers are universally recognised in specifying stamps and as a hallmark of status.

Illustrations. Stamps are illustrated at three-quarters linear size. Stamps not illustrated are the same size and format as the value shown, unless otherwise indicated. Stamps issued only as miniature sheets have the stamp alone illustrated but sheet size is also quoted. Overprints, surcharges, watermarks and postmarks are normally actual size. Illustrations of varieties are often enlarged to show the detail. Stamp booklet covers are illustrated half-size, unless otherwise indicated.

Designers. Designers' names are quoted where known, though space precludes naming every individual concerned in the production of a set. In particular, photographers supplying material are usually named only where they also make an active contribution in the design stage; posed photographs of reigning monarchs are, however, an exception to this rule.

CONTACTING THE CATALOGUE EDITOR

The editor is always interested in hearing from people who have new information which will improve or correct the Catalogue. As a general rule he must see and examine the actual stamps before they can be considered for listing; photographs or photocopies are insufficient evidence.

Submissions should be made in writing to the Catalogue Editor, Stanley Gibbons Publications at the Ringwood office. The cost of return postage for items submitted is appreciated, and this should include the registration fee if required.

Where information is solicited purely for the benefit of the enquirer, the editor cannot undertake to reply if the answer is already contained in these published notes or if return postage is omitted. Written communications are greatly preferred to enquiries by telephone and the editor regrets that he or his staff cannot see personal callers without a prior appointment being made. Correspondence may be subject to delay during the production period of each new edition.

The editor welcomes close contact with study circles and is interested, too, in finding reliable local correspondents who will verify and supplement official information in countries where this is deficient.

We regret we do not give opinions as to the genuineness of stamps, nor do we identify stamps or number them by our Catalogue.

TECHNICAL MATTERS

The meanings of the technical terms used in the catalogue will be found in our *Philatelic Terms Illustrated* (*new edition in preparation*).

References below to "more specialised" listings are to be taken to indicate, as appropiate, the Stanley Gibbons *Great Britain Specialised Catalogue* in 5 volumes or the *Great Britain Concise Catalogue*.

1. Printing

Printing errors. Errors in printing are of major interest to the Catalogue. Authenticated items meriting consideration would include: background, centre or frame inverted or omitted; centre or subject transposed; error of colour; error or omission of value; double prints and impressions; printed both sides; and so on. Designs *tête-bêche,* whether intentionally or by accident, are listable. *Se-tenant* arrangements of stamps are recognised in the listings or footnotes. Gutter pairs (a pair of stamps separated by blank margin) are not included in this volume. Colours only partially omitted are not listed. Stamps with embossing omitted and (for Commonwealth countries) stamps printed on the gummed side are reserved for our more specialised listings.

Printing varieties. Listing is accorded to major changes in the printing base which lead to completely new types. In recess-printing this could be a design re-engraved; in photogravure or photolithography a screen altered in whole or in part. It can also encompass flat-bed and rotary printing if the results are readily distinguishable.

To be considered at all, varieties must be constant.

Early stamps, produced by primitive methods, were prone to numerous imperfections: the lists reflect this, recognising re-entries, retouches, broken frames, misshapen letters, and so on. Printing technology has, however, radically improved over the years, during which time photogravure and lithography have become predominant. Varieties nowadays are more in the nature of flaws and these, being too specialised for this general catalogue, are almost always outside the scope. The development of our range of specialised catalogues allows us now to list those items which have philatelic significance in their appropriate volume.

In no catalogue, however, do we list such items as: dry prints, kiss prints, doctor-blade flaws, colour shifts or registration flaws (unless they lead to the complete omission of a colour from an individual stamp), lithographic ring flaws, and so on. Neither do we recognise fortuitous happenings like paper creases or confetti flaws.

Overprints (and surcharges). Overprints of different types qualify for separate listing. These include overprints in different colours; overprints from different printing processes such as litho and typo; overprints in totally different typefaces, etc. Major errors in machine-printed overprints are important and listable. They include: overprint inverted or omitted; overprint double (treble, etc.); overprint diagonal; overprint double, one inverted; pairs with one overprint omitted, e.g. from a radical shift to an adjoining stamp; error of colour; error of type fount; letters inverted or omitted, etc. If the overprint is handstamped, few of these would qualify and a distinction is drawn. We continue, however, to list pairs of stamps where one has a handstamped overprint and the other has not.

Varieties occurring in overprints will often take the form of broken letters, slight differences in spacing, rising spaces, etc. Only the most important would be considered for footnote mention.

Sheet positions. If space permits we quote sheet positions of listed varieties and authenticated data is solicited for this purpose.

De La Rue plates. The Catalogue classifies the general plates used by De La Rue for printing British Colonial stamps as follows:

VICTORIAN KEY TYPE

Die I

1. The ball of decoration on the second point of the crown appears as a dark mass of lines.
2. Dark vertical shading separates the front hair from the bun.
3. The vertical line of colour outlining the front of the throat stops at the sixth line of shading on the neck.
4. The white space in the coil of the hair above the curl is roughly the shape of a pin's head.

Die II

1. There are very few lines of colour in the ball and it appears almost white.
2. A white vertical strand of hair appears in place of the dark shading.
3. The line stops at the eighth line of shading.
4. The white space is oblong, with a line of colour partially dividing it at the left end.

Plates numbered 1 and 2 are both Die I. Plates 3 and 4 are Die II.

GEORGIAN KEY TYPE

Die I

A. The second (thick) line below the name of the country is cut slanting, conforming roughly to the shape of the crown on each side.
B. The labels of solid colour bearing the words "POSTAGE" and "& REVENUE" are square at the inner top corners.
C. There is a projecting "bud" on the outer spiral of the ornament in each of the lower corners.

Die II

A. The second line is cut vertically on each side of the crown.
B. The labels curve inwards at the top.
C. There is no "bud" in this position.

Unless otherwise stated in the lists, all stamps with watermark Multiple Crown CA (w **8**) are Die I while those with watermark Multiple Crown Script CA (w **9**) are Die II. The Georgian Die II was introduced in April 1921 and was used for Plates 10 to 22 and 26 to 28. Plates 23 to 25 were made from Die I by mistake.

2. Paper

All stamps listed are deemed to be on "ordinary" paper of the wove type and white in colour; only departures from this are normally mentioned.

Types. Where classification so requires we distinguish such other types of paper as, for example, vertically and horizontally laid; wove and laid bâtonné; card(board); carton; cartridge; glazed; granite; native; pelure; porous; quadrillé; ribbed; rice; and silk thread.

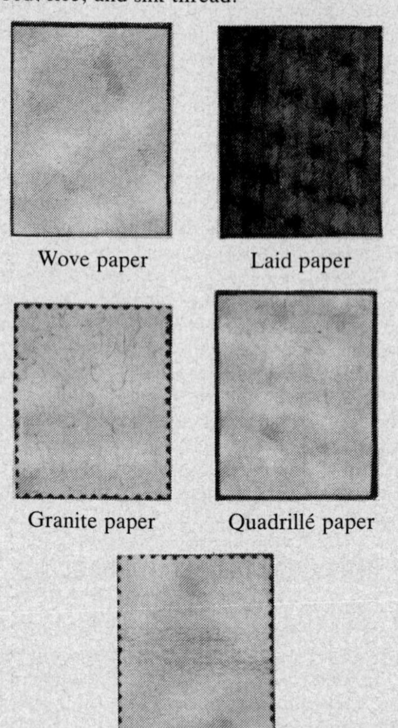

Wove paper — Laid paper — Granite paper — Quadrillé paper — Burelé band

The various makeshifts for normal paper are listed as appropriate. The varieties of double paper and joined paper are recognised. The security device of a printed burelé band on the back of a stamp, as in early Queensland, qualifies for listing.

Descriptive terms. The fact that a paper is handmade (and thus probably of uneven thickness) is mentioned where necessary. Such descriptive terms as "hard" and "soft"; "smooth" and 'rough"; "thick", "medium" and "thin" are applied where there is philatelic merit in classifying papers. We do not, for example, even in more specialised listings, classify paper thicknesses in the Wilding and Machin definitives of Great Britain. Weight standards for the paper apply to complete reels only, so that differences on individual stamps are acceptable to the printer provided the reel conforms overall.

Coloured, very white and toned papers. A coloured paper is one that is coloured right through (front and back of the stamp). In the Catalogue the colour of the paper is given in *italics,* thus:

black/*rose* = black design on rose paper.

Papers have been made specially white in recent years by, for example, a very heavy coating of chalk. We do not classify shades of whiteness of paper as distinct varieties. There does exist, however, a type of paper from early days called toned. This is off-white, often brownish or buffish, but it cannot be assigned any definite colour. A toning effect brought on by climate, incorrect storage or gum staining is disregarded here, as this was not the state of the paper when issued.

Modern developments. Two modern developments also affect the listings: printing on self-adhesive paper and the use of metallic foils. For self-adhesive stamps *see* under "Gum", below. Care should be taken not to damage the embossing on stamps impressed on metallic foils, such as Sierra Leone 1965–67, by subjecting the album pages to undue pressure. The possibility of faked "missing gold heads" is noted at the appropriat places in the listing of modern Great Britain.

"Ordinary" and "Chalk-surfaced" papers. Th availability of many postage stamps for revenu purposes made necessary some safeguard agains the illegitimate re-use of stamps with removabl cancellations. This was at first secured by usin fugitive inks and later by printing on chalk surfaced paper, both of which made it difficult t remove any form of obliteration without als damaging the stamp design.

This catalogue lists these chalk-surfaced pape varieties from their introduction in 1905. Wher no indication is given, the paper is "ordinary".

Our chalk-surfaced paper is specifically on which shows a black mark when touched with silver wire. The paper used during the Secon World War for high values, as in Bermuda, th Leeward Islands, etc., was thinly coated with som kind of surfacing which does not react to silver an is therefore regarded (and listed) as "ordinary" Stamps on chalk-surfaced paper can easily lose thi coating through immersion in water.

Another paper introduced during the War as substitute for chalk-surfaced is rather thick, ver white and glossy and shows little or no watermark nor does it show a black line when touched wit silver. In the Bahamas high values this paper migh be mistaken for the chalk-surfaced (which i thinner and poorer-looking) but for the silver test

Some modern coated papers show little or n reaction to the silver test and, therefore, canno be classed as chalk-surfaced.

Glazed paper. In 1969 the Crown Agent introduced a new general-purpose paper for use i conjunction with all current printing processes. I generally has a marked glossy surface but th degree varies according to the process used, bein more marked in recess-printing stamps. As it doe not respond to the silver test this presents a furthe test where previous printings were on chalk paper. A change of paper to the glazed variet merits separate listing.

Green and yellow papers. Issues of the Firs World War and immediate postwar period occu on green and yellow papers and these are give separate Catalogue listing. The original coloure papers (coloured throughout) gave way to surface coloured papers, the stamps having "white backs" other stamps show one colour on the front and different one at the back. Because of the numerou variations a grouping of colours is adopted a follows:

YELLOW PAPERS

(1) The original *yellow* paper (throughout) usually bright in colour. The gum is often sparse of harsh consistency and dull-looking. Use 1912–1920.

(2) The *white backs*. Used 1913–1914.

(3) A bright *lemon* paper. The colour must have a pronounced greenish tinge, different from th "yellow" in (1). As a rule, the gum on stamp using this lemon paper is plentiful, smooth an shiny, and the watermark shows distinctly. Care i needed with stamps printed in green on yellov paper (1) as it may appear that the paper is thi lemon. Used 1914–1916.

(4) An experimental *orange-buff* paper. Th colour must have a distinct brownish tinge. It i not to be confused with a muddy yellow (1) no the misleading appearance (on the surface) o stamps printed in red on yellow paper where ar engraved plate has been insufficiently wiped Used 1918–1921.

(5) An experimental *buff* paper. This lacks th brownish tinge of (4) and the brightness of th yellow shades. The gum is shiny when compare with the matt type used on (4). Used 1919–1920.

(6) A *pale yellow* paper that has a creamy ton to the yellow. Used from 1920 onwards.

GREEN PAPERS

(7) The original "green" paper, varying considerably through shades of *blue-green* and *yellow*

reen, the front and back sometimes differing. Jsed 1912–1916.

(8) The *white backs*. Used 1913–1914.

(9) A paper blue-green on the surface with *pale live* back. The back must be markedly paler than he front and this and the pronounced olive tinge the back distinguish it from (7). Used 916–1920.

(10) Paper with a vivid green surface, ommonly called *emerald-green*; it has the olive ack of (9). Used 1920.

(11) Paper with *emerald-green* both back and ont. Used from 1920 onwards.

3. Perforation and Rouletting

Perforation gauge. The gauge of a perforation is e number of holes in a length of 2 cm. For correct assification the size of the holes (large or small) ay need to be distinguished; in a few cases the ctual number of holes on each edge of the stamp eeds to be quoted.

Measurement. The Gibbons *Instanta* gauge is the andard for measuring perforations. The stamp is iewed against a dark background with the trans- arent gauge put on top of it. Though the gauge easures to decimal accuracy, perforations read om it are generally quoted in the Catalogue to the earest half. For example:

Just over perf $12\frac{3}{4}$ to just under $13\frac{1}{4}$ = perf 13
Perf $13\frac{1}{4}$ exactly, rounded up = perf $13\frac{1}{2}$
Just over perf $13\frac{1}{4}$ to just under $13\frac{3}{4}$ = perf $13\frac{1}{2}$
Perf $13\frac{3}{4}$ exactly, rounded up = perf 14

lowever, where classification depends on it, ctual quarter-perforations are quoted.

Notation. Where no perforation is quoted for an sue it is imperforate. Perforations are usually bbreviated (and spoken) as follows, though ometimes they may be spelled out for clarity. This otation for rectangular stamps (the majority) pplies to diamond shapes if "top" is read as the dge to the top right.

- 14: perforated alike on all sides (read: "perf 14").
- 14 × 15: the first figure refers to top and bottom, the second to left and right sides (read: "perf 14 by 15"). This is a compound perforation. For an upright triangular stamp the first figure refers to the two sloping sides and second to the base. In inverted triangulars the base is first and the second figure refers to the sloping sides.
- 14–15: perforation measuring anything between 14 and 15: the holes are irregularly spaced, thus the gauge may vary along a single line or even along a single edge of the stamp (read: "perf 14 to 15").
- 14 *irregular*: perforated 14 from a worn perfora- tor, giving badly aligned holes irregularly spaced (read: "irregular perf 14").
- *comp(ound)* 14 × 15: two gauges in use but not necessarily on opposite sides of the stamp. It could be one side in one gauge and three in the other; or two adjacent sides with the same gauge. (Read: "perf compound of 14 and 15".) For three gauges or more, abbreviated as "*P* 14, $14\frac{1}{2}$, 15 *or compound*" for example.
- 14, $14\frac{1}{2}$: perforated approximately $14\frac{1}{4}$ (read: "perf 14 or $14\frac{1}{2}$"). It does *not* mean two stamps, one perf 14 and the other perf $14\frac{1}{2}$. This obsolescent notation is gradually being replaced in the Catalogue.

mperf: imperforate (not perforated).

mperf × *P* 14: imperforate at top and bottom and perf 14 at sides.

Perf × imperf

P 14 × *imperf*: perf 14 at top and bottom and imperforate at sides.

Such headings as "*P* 13 × 14 (*vert*) and *P* 14 × 13 (*horiz*)" indicate which perforations apply to which stamp format—vertical or horizontal.

Some stamps are additionally perforated so that a label or tab is detachable; others have been perforated suitably for use as two halves. Listings are normally for whole stamps, unless stated otherwise.

Other terms. Perforation almost always gives circular holes; where other shapes have been used they are specified, e.g. square holes; lozenge perf. Interrupted perfs are brought about by the omission of pins at regular intervals. Perforations merely simulated by being printed as part of the design are of course ignored. With few exceptions, privately applied perforations are not listed.

In the nineteenth century perforations are often described as clean cut (clean, sharply incised holes), intermediate or rough (rough holes, imper- fectly cut, often the result of blunt pins).

Perforation errors and varieties. Authenticated errors, where a stamp normally perforated is accidentally issued imperforate, are listed provided no traces of perforation (blind holes or indentations) remain. They must be provided as pairs, both stamps wholly imperforate, and are only priced in that form.

In Great Britain, numerous of these part-perfo- rated stamps have arisen from the introduction of the Jumelle Press. This has a rotary perforator with rows of pins on one drum engaging with holes on another. Engagement is only gradual when the perforating unit is started up or stopped, giving rise to perforations "fading out", a variety mentioned above as not listed.

Stamps imperforate between stamp and sheet margin are not listed in this catalogue, but such errors on Great Britain stamps will be found in the *Great Britain Specialised Catalogue*.

Pairs described as "imperforate between" have the line of perforations between the two stamps omitted.

Imperf between (*horiz pair*): a horizontal pair of stamps with perfs all around the edges but none between the stamps.

Imperf between (*vert pair*): a vertical pair of stamps with perfs all around the edges but none between the stamps.

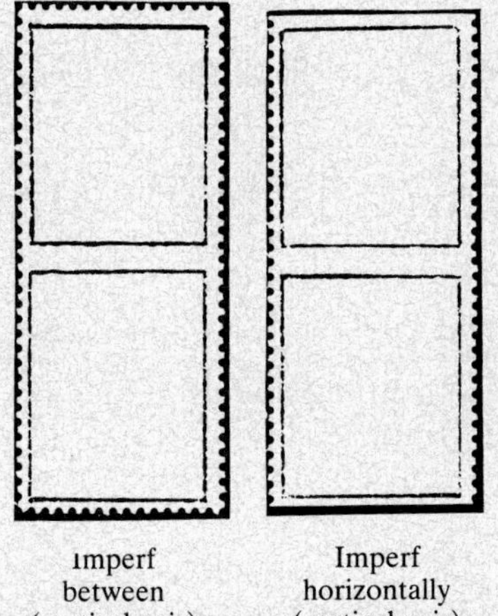

Imperf between (vertical pair) — Imperf horizontally (vertical pair)

Where several of the rows have escaped perfora- tion the resulting varieties are listable. Thus:

Imperf vert (*horiz pair*): a horizontal pair of stamps perforated top and bottom; all three vertical directions are imperf—the two outer edges and between the stamps.

Imperf horiz (*vert pair*): a vertical pair perforated at left and right edges; all three horizontal directions are imperf—the top, bottom and between the stamps.

Straight edges. Large sheets cut up before issue to post offices can cause stamps with straight edges, i.e. imperf on one side or on two sides at right angles. They are not usually listable in this condition and are worth less than corresponding stamps properly perforated all round. This does not, however, apply to certain stamps, mainly from coils and booklets, where straight edges on various sides are the manufacturing norm affecting every stamp. The listings and notes make clear which sides are correctly imperf.

Malfunction. Varieties of double, misplaced or partial perforation caused by error or machine malfunction are not listable, neither are freaks, such as perforations placed diagonally from paper folds, nor missing holes caused by broken pins.

Centering. Well-centred stamps have designs surrounded by equal opposite margins. Where this condition affects the price the fact is stated.

Types of perforating. Where necessary for classification, perforation types are distinguished. These include:

Line perforation from one line of pins punching single rows of holes at a time.

Comb perforation from pins disposed across the sheet in comb formation, punching out holes at three sides of the stamp a row at a time.

Harrow perforation applied to a whole pane or sheet at one stroke.

Rotary perforation from toothed wheels oper- ating across a sheet, then crosswise.

Sewing-machine perforation. The resultant condition, clean-cut or rough, is distinguished where required.

Pin-perforation is the commonly applied term for pin-roulette in which, instead of being punched out, round holes are pricked by sharp-pointed pins and no paper is removed.

Mixed perforation occurs when stamps with defective perforations are re-perforated in a dif- ferent gauge.

Punctured stamps. Perforation holes can be punched into the face of the stamp. Patterns of small holes, often in the shape of initial letters, are privately applied devices against pilferage. These "perfins" are outside the scope except for Australia, Canada, Cape of Good Hope, Papua and Sudan where they were used as official stamps by the national administration. Identification devices, when officially inspired, are listed or noted; they can be shapes, or letters or words formed from holes, sometimes converting one class of stamp into another.

Rouletting. In rouletting the paper is cut, for ease of separation, but none is removed. The gauge is measured, when needed, as for perforations. Tradi- tional French terms descriptive of the type of cut are often used and types include:

Arc roulette (*percé en arc*). Cuts are minute, spaced arcs, each roughly a semicircle.

Cross roulette (*percé en croix*). Cuts are tiny diagonal crosses.

Line roulette (*percé en ligne* or *en ligne droite*). Short straight cuts parallel to the frame of the stamp. The commonest basic roulette. Where not further described, "roulette" means this type.

Rouletted in colour or *coloured roulette* (*percé en lignes colorées* or *en lignes de couleur*). Cuts with coloured edges, arising from notched rule inked simultaneously with the printing plate.

Saw-tooth roulette (*percé en scie*). Cuts applied zigzag fashion to resemble the teeth of a saw.

Serpentine roulette (*percé en serpentin*). Cuts as sharply wavy lines.

Zigzag roulette (*percé en zigzags*). Short straight cuts at angles in alternate directions, producing sharp points on separation. U.S. usage favours "serrate(d) roulette" for this type.

Pin-roulette (originally *percé en points* and now *perforés trous d'epingle*) is commonly called pin- perforation in English.

4. Gum

All stamps listed are assumed to have gum of some kind; if they were issued without gum this is stated. Original gum (o.g.) means that which was present on the stamp as issued to the public. Deleterious climates and the presence of certain chemicals can cause gum to crack and, with early stamps, even make the paper deteriorate. Unscrupulous fakers are adept in removing it and regumming the stamp to meet the unreasoning demand often made for "full o.g." in cases where such a thing is virtually impossible.

The gum normally used on stamps has been gum arabic until the late 1960s when synthetic adhesives were introduced. Harrison and Sons Ltd for instance use *polyvinyl alcohol,* known to philatelists as PVA. This is almost invisible except for a slight yellowish tinge which was incorporated to make it possible to see that the stamps have been gummed. It has advantages in hot countries, as stamps do not curl and sheets are less likely to stick together. Gum arabic and PVA are not distinguished in the lists except that where a stamp exists with both forms this is indicated in footnotes. Our more specialised catalogues provide separate listing of gums for Great Britain.

Self-adhesive stamps are issued on backing paper, from which they are peeled before affixing to mail. Unused examples are priced as for backing paper intact, in which condition they are recommended to be kept. Used examples are best collected on cover or on piece.

5. Watermarks

Stamps are on unwatermarked paper except where the heading to the set says otherwise.

Detection. Watermarks are detected for Catalogue description by one of four methods: (1) holding stamps to the light; (2) laying stamps face down on a dark background; (3) adding a few drops of petroleum ether 40/60 to the stamp laid face down in a watermark tray; (4) by use of the Morley-Bright Detector, or other equipment, which work by revealing the thinning of the paper at the watermark (Note that petroleum ether is highly inflammable in use and can damage photogravure stamps.)

Listable types. Stamps occurring on both watermarked and unwatermarked papers are different types and both receive full listing.

Single watermarks (devices occurring once on every stamp) can be modified in size and shape as between different issues; the types are noted but not usually separately listed. Fortuitous absence of watermark from a single stamp or its gross displacement would not be listable.

To overcome registration difficulties the device may be repeated at close intervals (a *multiple watermark*), single stamps thus showing parts of several devices. Similarly, a large *sheet watermark* (or *all-over watermark*) covering numerous stamps can be used. We give informative notes and illustrations for them. The designs may be such that numbers of stamps in the sheet automatically lack watermark: this is not a listable variety. Multiple and all-over watermarks sometimes undergo modifications, but if the various types are difficult to distinguish from single stamps notes are given but not separate listings.

Papermakers' watermarks are noted where known but not listed separately, since most stamps in the sheet will lack them. Sheet watermarks which are nothing more than officially adopted papermakers' watermarks are, however, given normal listing.

Marginal watermarks, falling outside the pane of stamps, are ignored except where misplacement caused the adjoining row to be affected, in which case they are footnoted.

Watermark errors and varieties. Watermark errors are recognised as of major importance. They comprise stamps intended to be on unwatermarked paper but issued watermarked by mistake, or stamps printed on paper with the wrong watermark. Varieties showing letters omitted from the watermark are also included, but broken or deformed bits on the dandy roll are not listed unless they represent repairs.

Watermark positions. The diagram shows how watermark position is described in the Catalogue. Paper has a side intended for printing and watermarks are usually impressed so that they read normally when looked through from that printed side. However, since philatelists customarily detect watermarks by looking at the back of the stamp the watermark diagram also makes clear what is actually seen.

Illustrations in the Catalogue are of watermarks in normal positions (from the front of the stamps) and are actual size where possible.

Differences in watermark position are collectable as distinct varieties. This Catalogue now lists inverted, sideways inverted and reversed watermark varieties on Commonwealth stamps issued after 1900 *except* where the watermark position is completely haphazard. It is hoped to extend such listings to earlier issues in due course.

Great Britain inverted and sideways inverted watermarks can be found in the *Great Britain Specialised Catalogue* and the *Great Britain Concise Catalogue*.

Where a watermark comes indiscriminately in various positions our policy is to cover this by a general note: we do not give separate listings because the watermark position in these circumstances has no particular philatelic importance. There is a general note of this sort in modern Cyprus, for example. Issues printed since 1962 by Aspioti-Elka occur with the vertical stamps having the watermark normal or inverted, while horizontal stamps are likewise found with the watermark reading upwards or downwards.

AS DESCRIBED (Read through front of stamp)		AS SEEN DURING WATERMARK DETECTION (Stamp face down and back examined)
GvR	Normal	GvR (reversed)
GvR (inverted)	Inverted	GvR (reversed and inverted)
GvR (reversed)	Reversed	GvR
GvR (reversed and inverted)	Reversed and inverted	GvR (inverted)
GvR (sideways)	Sideways	GvR (sideways, reversed)
GvR (sideways inverted)	Sideways inverted	GvR (sideways inverted, reversed)

Standard types of watermark. Some watermarks have been used generally for various British possessions rather than exclusively for a single colony. To avoid repetition the Catalogue classifies 17 general types, as under, with references in the headings throughout the listings being given either in words or in the form "*W* w **14**" (meaning "watermark type w **14**"). In those cases where watermark illustrations appear in the listings themselves, the respective reference reads, for example, *W* **153**, thus indicating that tl watermark will be found in the normal sequence of illustrations as (type) **153**.

The general types are as follows, with a example of each quoted.

W	*Description*	*Example*
w **1**	Large Star	St. Helena No. 1
w **2**	Small Star	Turks Is. No. 4
w **3**	Broad (pointed) Star	Grenada No. 24
w **4**	Crown (over) CC, small stamp	Antigua No. 13
w **5**	Crown (over) CC, large stamp	Antigua No. 31
w **6**	Crown (over) CA, small stamp	Antigua No. 21
w **7**	Crown CA (CA over Crown), large stamp	Sierra Leone No. 54
w **8**	Multiple Crown CA	Antigua No. 41
w **9**	Multiple Crown Script CA	Seychelles No. 15
w **9***a*	do. Error	Seychelles No. 158a
w **9***b*	do. Error	Seychelles No. 158b
w **10**	V over Crown	N.S.W. No. 327
w **11**	Crown over A	N.S.W. No. 347
w **12**	Multiple St. Edward's Crown Block CA	Antigua No. 149
w **13**	Multiple PTM	Johore No. 166
w **14**	Multiple Crown CA Diagonal	Antigua No. 426
w **15**	Multiple POST OFFICE	Kiribati No. 141
w **16**	Multiple Crown Script CA Diagonal	Ascension No. 37
w **17**	Multiple CARTOR	Brunei No. 357

CC in these watermarks is an abbreviation f "Crown Colonies" and CA for "Crown Agents". Watermarks w **1**, w **2** and w **3** are on stamps printe by Perkins, Bacon; w **4** onwards on stamps fro De La Rue and other printers.

w **1**
Large Star

w **2**
Small Star

w **3**
Broad (pointed) Star

Watermark w **1**, *Large Star,* measures 15 t 16 mm across the star from point to point an about 27 mm from centre to centre verticall between stars in the sheet. It was made for lon stamps like Ceylon 1857 and St. Helena 1856.

Watermark w **2**, *Small Star,* is of similar desig but measures 12 to 13½ mm from point to point an 24 mm from centre to centre vertically. It was fo use with ordinary-size stamps such as Grenad 1863–71.

When the Large Star watermark was used wit the smaller stamps it only occasionally comes in th centre of the paper. It is frequently so misplaced a to show portions of two stars above and below an his eccentricity will very often help in determining he watermark.

Watermark w **3**, *Broad (pointed) Star*, esembles w **1** but the points are broader.

w **4**
Crown (over) CC

w **5**
Crown (over) CC

Two *Crown (over) CC* watermarks were used: v **4** was for stamps of ordinary size and w **5** for hose of larger size.

w **6**
Crown (over) CA

w **7**
CA over Crown

Two watermarks of *Crown CA* type were used, v **6** being for stamps of ordinary size. The other, v **7**, is properly described as *CA over Crown*. It was pecially made for paper on which it was intended o print long fiscal stamps: that some were used ostally accounts for the appearance of w **7** in the Catalogue. The watermark occupies twice the pace of the ordinary Crown CA watermark, w **6**. Stamps of normal size printed on paper with w **7** vatermark show it *sideways*; it takes a horizontal air of stamps to show the entire watermark.

w **8**
Multiple Crown CA

w **9**
Multiple Crown Script CA

Multiple watermarks began in 1904 with w **8**, *Multiple Crown CA*, changed from 1921 to w **9**, *Multiple Crown Script CA*. On stamps of ordinary ize portions of two or three watermarks appear nd on the large-sized stamps a greater number an be observed. The change to letters in script haracter with w **9** was accompanied by a Crown of listinctly different shape.

It seems likely that there were at least two landy rolls for each Crown Agents watermark in se at any one time with a reserve roll being mployed when the normal one was withdrawn or maintenance or repair.

Both the Mult Crown CA and the Mult Script CA types exist with one or other of the letters mitted from individual impressions. It is possible hat most of these occur from the reserve rolls as hey have only been found on certain issues. The MCA watermark experienced such problems during the early 1920s and the Script over a longer period from the early 1940s until 1951.

During the 1920s damage must also have occurred on one of the Crowns as a substituted Crown has been found on certain issues. This is smaller than the normal and consists of an oval base joined to two upright ovals with a circle positioned between their upper ends. The upper line of the Crown's base is omitted, as are the left and right-hand circles at the top and also the cross over the centre circle.

Substituted Crown

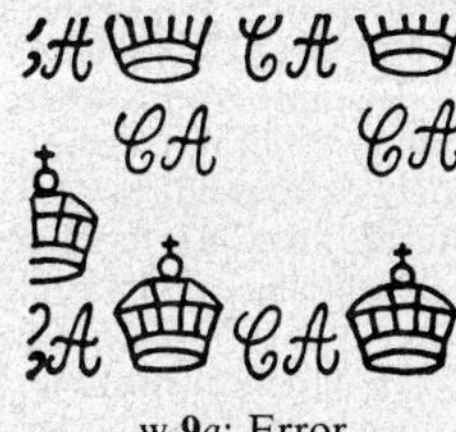

w **9a**: Error, Crown missing

w **9b**: Error, St. Edward's Crown

The *Multiple Crown Script CA* watermark, w **9**, is known with two errors recurring among the 1950–52 printings of several territories. In the first a crown has fallen away from the dandy-roll that impresses the watermark into the paper pulp. It gives w **9a**, *Crown missing*, but this omission has been found in both "Crown only" (*illustrated*) and "Crown CA" rows. The resulting faulty paper was used for Seychelles, Johore and the postage due stamps of nine colonies.

When the omission was noticed a second mishap occurred, which was to insert a wrong crown in the space, giving w **9b**, *St. Edward's Crown*. This produced varieties in Bahamas, St. Kitts-Nevis and Singapore and the incorrect crown likewise occurs in "Crown only" and "Crown CA" rows.

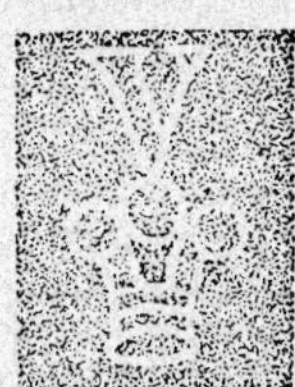

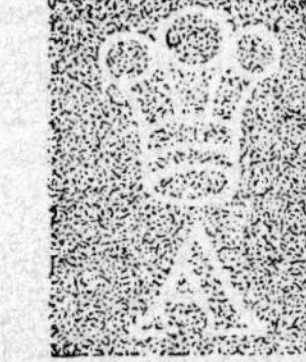

w **10**
V over Crown

w **11**
Crown over A

Resuming the general types, two watermarks found in issues of several Australian States are: w **10**, *V over Crown*, and w **11**, *Crown over A*.

w **12**
Multiple St. Edward's Crown Block CA

The *Multiple St. Edward's Crown Block CA* watermark, w **12**, was introduced in 1957 and besides the change in the Crown (from that used in *Multiple Crown Script CA*, w **9**) the letters reverted to block capitals. The new watermark began to appear sideways in 1966 and these stamps are generally listed as separate sets.

w **13**
Multiple PTM

The watermark w **13**, *Multiple PTM*, was introduced for new Malayan issues in November 1961.

w **14**
Multiple Crown CA Diagonal

By 1974 the two dandy-rolls (the "upright" and the "sideways") for w **12** were wearing out; the Crown Agents therefore discontinued using the sideways-watermark one and retained the other only as a stand-by. A new dandy-roll with the pattern of w **14**, *Multiple Crown CA Diagonal*, was introduced and first saw use with some Churchill Centenary issues.

The new watermark has the design arranged in gradually spiralling rows. It is improved in design to allow smooth passage over the paper (the gaps between letters and rows had caused jolts in previous dandy-rolls) and the sharp corners and angles, where fibres used to accumulate, have been eliminated by rounding.

This watermark has no "normal" sideways position amongst the different printers using it. To avoid confusion our more specialised listings do not rely on such terms as "sideways inverted" but describe the direction in which the watermark points.

w **15**
Multiple POST OFFICE

During 1981 w **15**, *Multiple POST OFFICE*, was introduced for certain issues prepared by Philatelists Ltd, acting for various countries in the Indian Ocean, Pacific and West Indies.

w **16**
Multiple Crown Script CA Diagonal

A new Crown Agents watermark was introduced during 1985, w **16**, *Multiple Crown Script CA Diagonal*. This was very similar to the previous w **14**, but showed "CA" in script rather than block letters. It was first used on the omnibus series of stamps commemorating the Life and Times of Queen Elizabeth the Queen Mother.

w **17**
Multiple CARTOR

Watermark w **17**, *Multiple CARTOR*, was used from 1985 for issues printed by this French firm for countries which did not normally use the Crown Agents watermark.

In recent years the use of watermarks has, to a small extent, been superseded by fluorescent security markings. These are often more visible from the reverse of the stamp (Cook Islands from 1970 onwards), but have occurred printed over the design (Hong Kong Nos. 415/30). In 1982 the Crown Agents introduced a new stock paper, without watermark, known as "C-Kurity" on which a fluorescent pattern of blue rosettes is visible on the reverse, beneath the gum. This paper was used for issues from Gambia and Norfolk Island.

6. Colours

Stamps in two or three colours have these named in order of appearance, from the centre moving outwards. Four colours or more are usually listed as multicoloured.

In compound colour names the second is the predominant one, thus:

orange-red = a red tending towards orange;

red-orange = an orange containing more red than usual.

Standard colours used. The 200 colours most used for stamp identification are given in the Stanley Gibbons Stamp Colour Key. The Catalogue has used the Stamp Colour Key as standard for describing new issues for some years. The names are also introduced as lists are rewritten, though exceptions are made for those early issues where traditional names have become universally established.

Determining colours. When comparing actual stamps with colour samples in the Stamp Colour Key, view in a good north daylight (or its best substitute: fluorescent "colour-matching" light). Sunshine is not recommended. Choose a solid portion of the stamp design; if available, marginal markings such as solid bars of colour or colour check dots are helpful. Shading lines in the design can be misleading as they appear lighter than solid colour. Postmarked portions of a stamp appear darker than normal. If more than one colour is present, mask off the extraneous ones as the eye tends to mix them.

Errors of colour. Major colour errors in stamps or overprints which qualify for listing are: wrong colours; one colour inverted in relation to the rest; albinos (colourless impressions), where these have Expert Committee certificates; colours completely omitted, but only on unused stamps (if found on used stamps the information is footnoted) and with good credentials, missing colours being frequently faked.

Colours only partially omitted are not recognised. Colour shifts, however spectacular, are not listed.

Shades. Shades in philately refer to variations in the intensity of a colour or the presence of differing amounts of other colours. They are particularly significant when they can be linked to specific printings. In general, shades need to be quite marked to fall within the scope of this Catalogue; it does not favour nowadays listing the often numerous shades of a stamp, but chooses a single applicable colour name which will indicate particular groups of outstanding shades. Furthermore, the listings refer to colours as issued: they may deteriorate into something different through the passage of time.

Modern colour printing by lithography is prone to marked differences of shade, even within a single run, and variations can occur within the same sheet. Such shades are not listed.

Aniline colours. An aniline colour meant originally one derived from coal-tar; it now refers more widely to colour of a particular brightness suffused on the surface of a stamp and showing through clearly on the back.

Colours of overprints and surcharges. All overprints and surcharges are in black unless stated otherwise in the heading or after the description of the stamp.

7. Specimen Stamps

Originally, stamps overprinted SPECIMEN were circulated to postmasters or kept in official records, but after the establishment of the Universal Postal Union supplies were sent to Berne for distribution to the postal administrations of member countries.

During the period 1884 to 1928 most of the stamps of British Crown Colonies required for this purpose were overprinted SPECIMEN in various shapes and sizes by their printers from typeset formes. Some locally produced provisionals were handstamped locally, as were sets prepared for presentation. From 1928 stamps were punched with holes forming the word SPECIMEN, each firm of printers using a different machine or machines. From 1948 the stamps supplied for U.P.U. distribution were no longer punctured.

Stamps of some other Commonwealth territorie were overprinted or handstamped locally, whil stamps of Great Britain and those overprinted fo use in overseas postal agencies (mostly of the highe denominations) bore SPECIMEN overprints an handstamps applied by the Inland Revenue or th Post Office.

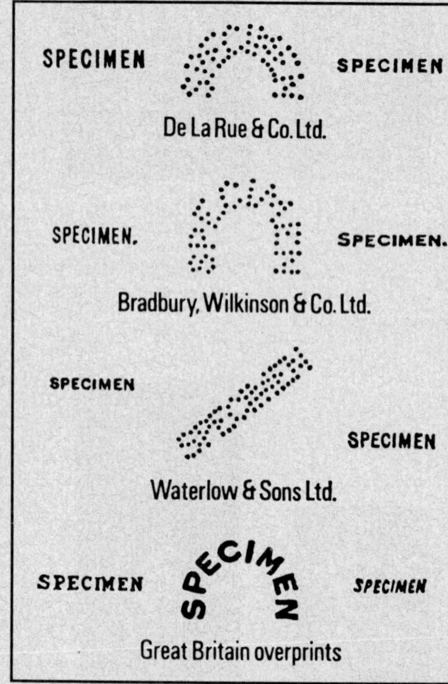

Some of the commoner types of overprints o punctures are illustrated here. Collectors are warned that dangerous forgeries of the puncture type exist.

The *Part* 1 (*British Commonwealth*) *Catalogu* records those Specimen overprints or perforation intended for distribution by the U.P.U. to membe countries. In addition the Specimen overprints o Australia and its dependent territories, whic were sold to collectors by the Post Office, are als included.

All other Specimens are outside the scope o this volume.

Specimens are not quoted in Great Britain a they are fully listed in the Stanley Gibbons *Grea Britain Specialised Catalogue.*

In specifying type of specimen for individua high-value stamps, "H/S" means handstamped "Optd" is overprinted and "Perf" is punctured Some sets occur mixed, e.g. "Optd/Perf". I unspecified, the type is apparent from the date or i is the same as for the lower values quoted as a set.

Prices. Prices for stamps up to £1 are quoted i sets; higher values are priced singly after th colours, thus "(S. £20)". Where specimens exist i more than one type the price quoted is for th cheapest. Specimen stamps have rarely survive even as pairs; these and strips of three, four or fiv are worth considerably more than singles.

8. Luminescence

Machines which sort mail electronically have bee introduced in recent years. In consequence som countries have issued stamps on fluorescent o phosphorescent papers, while others have marke their stamps with phosphor bands.

The various papers can only be distinguished b ultraviolet lamps emitting particular wavelengths They are separately listed only when the stamp have some other means of distinguishing them visible without the use of these lamps. Where this i not so, the papers are recorded in footnotes o headings.

For this Catalogue we do not consider i appropriate that collectors be compelled to hav ɜe of an ultraviolet lamp before being able to entify stamps by our listings. Some experience ill also be found necessary in interpreting the sults given by ultraviolet. Collectors using the mps, nevertheless, should exercise great care in eir use as exposure to their light is extremely ngerous to the eyes.

Phosphor bands are listable, since they are visible the naked eye (by holding stamps at an angle to e light and looking along them, the bands appear ırk). Stamps existing with and without phosphor ınds or with differing numbers of bands are given parate listings. Varieties such as double bands, ınds omitted, misplaced or printed on the back are ot listed.

Detailed descriptions appear at appropriate aces in the listings in explanation of luminescent apers; *see*, for example, Australia above No. 308, anada above Nos. 472 and 611, Cook Is. above o. 249, etc.

For Great Britain, where since 1959 phosphors ve played a prominent and intricate part in stamp sues, the main notes above Nos. 599, 723 and after e Decimal Machin issue (No. X841 onwards) ould be studied, as well as the footnotes to dividual listings where appropriate. In general e classification is as follows.

Stamps with *phosphor bands* are those where a parate cylinder applies the phosphor after the amps are printed. Issues with "all-over" phosphor ave the "band" covering the entire stamp. Parts of e stamp covered by phosphor bands, or the entire ırface for "all-over" phosphor versions, appear att. Stamps on *phosphorised paper* have the osphor added to the paper coating before the amps are printed. Issues on this paper have a mpletely shiny surface.

Further particularisation of phosphor—their ethods of printing and the colours they exhibit ıder ultraviolet—is outside the scope. The more ecialised listings should be consulted for this formation.

9. Coil Stamps

tamps issued only in coil form are given full listing. f stamps are issued in both sheets and coils the coil amps are listed separately only where there is ome feature (e.g. perforation or watermark ideways) by which singles can be distinguished. 'oil strips containing different stamps *se-tenant* are lso listed.

Coil join pairs are too random and too easily aked to permit of listing; similarly ignored are coil amps which have accidentally suffered an extra ow of perforations from the claw mechanism in a ıalfunctioning vending machine.

10. Stamp Booklets

tamp booklets (with the exception of those from reat Britain, the Channel Islands and the Isle of Ian, for which see the current editions of the *reat Britain Concise Catalogue* and *Collect 'hannel Islands and Isle of Man Stamps*) are now sted in this catalogue.

Single stamps from booklets are listed if they are istinguishable in some way (such as watermark or erforation) from similar sheet stamps.

Booklet panes are listed where they contain tamps of different denominations *se-tenant*, where tamp-size labels are included, or where such panes re otherwise identifiable. Booklet panes are laced in the listing under the lowest denomination resent.

Particular perforations (straight edges) are overed by appropriate notes.

11. Miniature Sheets and Sheetlets

Ve distinguish between "miniature sheets" and sheetlets" and this affects the catalogue numberıg. An item in sheet form that is postally valid, ontaining a single stamp, pair, block or set of tamps, with wide, inscribed and/or decorative margins, is a *miniature sheet* if it is sold at post offices as an indivisible entity. As such the Catalogue allots a single **MS** number and describes what stamps make it up. (*See* Great Britain 1978 Historic Buildings, No. **MS**1058, as an example.) The *sheetlet* or *small sheet* differs in that the individual stamps are intended to be purchased separately for postal purposes. For sheetlets, all the component postage stamps are numbered individually and the composition explained in a footnote. (The 1978 Christmas Island Christmas sheetlet, Nos. 99/107, is an example.) Note that the definitions refer to post office sale—not how items may be subsequently offered by stamp dealers.

Production as sheetlets is a modern marketing development chosen by postal administrations to interest collectors in purchasing the item complete; if he has done so he should, as with all *se-tenant* arrangements, keep the sheetlet intact in his collection.

The Catalogue will in future no longer give full listing to designs, originally issued in normal sheets, which subsequently appear in sheetlets showing changes of colour, perforation, printing process or face value. Such stamps will be covered by footnotes.

12. Forgeries and Fakes

Forgeries. Where space permits, notes are considered if they can give a concise description that will permit unequivocal detection of a forgery. Generalised warnings, lacking detail, are not nowadays inserted, since their value to the collector is problematic.

Fakes. Unwitting fakes are numerous, particularly "new shades" which are colour changelings brought about by exposure to sunlight, soaking in water contaminated with dyes from adherent paper, contact with oil and dirt from a pocketbook, and so on. Fraudulent operators, in addition, can offer to arrange: removal of hinge marks; repairs of thins on white or coloured papers; replacement of missing margins or perforations; reperforating in true or false gauges; removal of fiscal cancellations; rejoining of severed pairs, strips and blocks; and (a major hazard) regumming. Collectors can only be urged to purchase from reputable sources and to insist upon Expert Committee certification where there is any kind of doubt.

The Catalogue can consider footnotes about fakes where these are specific enough to assist in detection.

1935 SILVER JUBILEE CROWN COLONY ISSUE

The Crown Colony Windsor Castle design by Harold Fleury is, surely, one of the most impressive produced in the 20th-century and its reproduction in the recess process by three of the leading stamp-printing firms of the era has provided a subject for philatelic research which has yet to be exhausted.

Each of the three, Bradbury, Wilkinson & Co. and Waterlow and Sons, who both produced fifteen issues, together with De La Rue & Co. who printed fourteen, used a series of vignette (centre) plates coupled with individual frame plates for each value. All were taken from dies made by Waterlow. Several worthwhile varieties exist on the frame plates, but most interest has been concentrated on the centre plates, each of which was used to print a considerable number of different stamps.

Sheets printed by Bradbury, Wilkinson were without printed plate numbers, but research has now identified eleven centre plates which were probably used in permanent pairings. A twelfth plate awaits confirmation. Stamps from some of these centre plates have revealed a number of prominent plate flaws, the most famous of which, the extra flagstaff, has been eagerly sought by collectors for many years.

Extra flagstaff (Plate 1" R. 9/1)

Short extra flagstaff (Plate "2" R. 2/1)

Lightning conductor (Plate "3" R. 2/5)

Flagstaff on right-hand turret (Plate "5" R. 7/1)

Double flagstaff (Plate "6" R. 5/2)

De La Rue sheets were initially printed with plate numbers, but in many instances these were subsequently trimmed off. Surviving examples do, however, enable a positive identification of six centre plates, 2A, 2B, (2A), (2B), 4 and 4/ to be made. The evidence of sheet markings and plate flaws clearly demonstrates that there were two different pairs of plates numbered 2A 2B. The second pair is designated (2A) (2B) by specialist collectors to avoid further confusion. The number of major plate flaws is not so great as on the Bradbury, Wilkinson sheets, but four examples are included in the catalogue.

Diagonal line by turret (Plate 2A R. 10/1 and 10/2)

Dot to left of chapel (Plate 2B R. 8/3)

Dot by flagstaff (Plate 4 R. 8/4)

Dash by turret (Plate 4/ R. 3/6)

Much less is known concerning the Waterlow centre plate system as the sheets did not show plate numbers. Ten individual plates have, so far, been identified and it is believed that these were used in pairs. The two versions of the kite and log flaw from plate "2" show that this plate exists in two states.

Damaged turret (Plate "1" R. 5/6)

Kite and vertical log (Plate "2A" R. 10/6)

Kite and horizontal log (Plate "2B" R. 10/6)

Bird by turret (Plate "7" R. 1/5)

Abbreviations

Printers

A.B.N. Co	American Bank Note Co, New York.
A. & M.	Alden & Mowbray Ltd, Oxford.
Ashton-Potter	Ashton-Potter Ltd, Toronto.
Aspioti-Elka (Aspiotis)	Aspioti-Elka, Greece.
B.A.B.N.	British American Bank Note Co, Ottawa.
B.D.T.	B.D.T. International Security Printing Ltd, Dublin, Ireland.
B.W.	Bradbury Wilkinson & Co, Ltd.
Cartor	Cartor S.A., La Loupe, France.
C.B.N.	Canadian Bank Note Co, Ottawa.
Continental B.N. Co	Continental Bank Note Co.
Courvoisier	Imprimerie Courvoisier S.A., La-Chaux-de-Fonds, Switzerland.
D.L.R.	De La Rue & Co, Ltd, London, and (from 1961) Bogota, Colombia.
Edila	Editions de l'Aubetin, S.A.
Enschedé	Joh. Enschedé en Zonen, Haarlem, Netherlands.
Format	Format International Security Printers, Ltd, London.
Harrison	Harrison & Sons, Ltd, London
Heraclio Fournier	Heraclio Fournier S.A., Vitoria, Spain.
J.W.	John Waddington Security Print Ltd., Leeds
P.B.	Perkins Bacon Ltd, London.
Questa	Questa Colour Security Printers, Ltd., London
Ueberreuter	Ueberreuter (incorporating Bruder Rosenbaum), Korneuburg, Austria.
Walsall	Walsall Security Printers, Ltd.
Waterlow	Waterlow & Sons, Ltd, London.

General Abbreviations

Alph	Alphabet
Anniv	Anniversary
Comp	Compound (perforation)
Des	Designer; designed
Diag	Diagonal; diagonally
Eng	Engraver; engraved
F.C.	Fiscal Cancellation
H/S	Handstamped
Horiz	Horizontal; horizontally
Imp, Imperf	Imperforate
Inscr	Inscribed
L	Left
Litho	Lithographed
mm	Millimetres
MS	Miniature sheet
N.Y.	New York
Opt(d)	Overprint(ed)
P or P-c	Pen-cancelled
P, Pf or Perf	Perforated
Photo	Photogravure
Pl	Plate
Pr	Pair
Ptd	Printed
Ptg	Printing
R	Right
R.	Row
Recess	Recess-printed
Roto	Rotogravure
Roul	Rouletted
S	Specimen (overprint)
Surch	Surcharge(d)
T.C.	Telegraph Cancellation
T	Type
Typo	Typographed
Un	Unused
Us	Used
Vert	Vertical; vertically
W or wmk	Watermark
Wmk s	Watermark sideways

(†)=Does not exist.

(—) (or blank price column)=Exists, or may exis[t] but no market price is known.

/ between colours means "on" and the colo[ur] following is that of the paper on which the stamp [is] printed.

Colours of Stamps

Bl (blue); blk (black); brn (brown); car, car[mine] (carmine); choc (chocolate); clar (claret); eme[r] (emerald); grn (green); ind (indigo); ma[g] (magenta); mar (maroon); mult (multicoloured[)]; mve (mauve); ol (olive); orge (orange); pk (pink[)]; pur (purple); scar (scarlet); sep (sepia); tu[rq] (turquoise); ultram (ultramarine); verm (ve[r]milion); vio (violet); yell (yellow).

Colour of Overprints and Surcharges

(B.) = blue, (Blk.) = black, (Br.) = brown, (C.) = carmine, (G.) = green, (Mag.) = magenta, (Mve[.]) = mauve, (Ol.) = olive, (O.) = orange, (P.) = purple, (Pk.) = pink, (R.)=red, (Sil.) = silver, (V[.]) = violet, (Vm.) or (Verm.) = vermilion, (W.) = white, (Y.) = yellow.

Arabic Numerals

As in the case of European figures, the details of th[e] Arabic numerals vary in different stamp design[s] but they should be readily recognised with the aid o[f] this illustration.

٠	١	٢	٣	٤	٥	٦	٧	٨	٩
0	1	2	3	4	5	6	7	8	9

International Philatelic Glossary

English	*French*	*German*	*Spanish*	*Italian*
Agate	Agate	Achat	Agata	Agata
Air stamp	Timbre de la poste aérienne	Flugpostmarke	Sello de correo aéreo	Francobollo per posta aerea
Apple Green	Vert-pomme	Apfelgrün	Verde manzana	Verde mela
Barred	Annulé par barres	Balkenentwertung	Anulado con barras	Sbarrato
Bisected	Timbre coupé	Halbiert	Partido en dos	Frazionato
Bistre	Bistre	Bister	Bistre	Bistro
Bistre-brown	Brun-bistre	Bisterbraun	Castaño bistre	Bruno-bistro
Black	Noir	Schwarz	Negro	Nero
Blackish Brown	Brun-noir	Schwärzlichbraun	Castaño negruzco	Bruno nerastro
Blackish Green	Vert foncé	Schwärzlichgrün	Verde negruzco	Verde nerastro
Blackish Olive	Olive foncé	Schwärzlicholiv	Oliva negruzco	Oliva nerastro
Block of four	Bloc de quatre	Viererblock	Bloque de cuatro	Bloco di quattro
Blue	Bleu	Blau	Azul	Azzurro
Blue-green	Vert-bleu	Blaugrün	Verde azul	Verde azzurro
Bluish Violet	Violet bleuâtre	Bläulichviolett	Violeta azulado	Violetto azzurrastro
Booklet	Carnet	Heft	Cuadernillo	Libretto
Bright Blue	Bleu vif	Lebhaftblau	Azul vivo	Azzurro vivo
Bright Green	Vert vif	Lebhaftgrün	Verde vivo	Verde vivo
Bright Purple	Mauve vif	Lebhaftpurpur	Púrpura vivo	Porpora vivo
Bronze Green	Vert-bronze	Bronzegrün	Verde bronce	Verde bronzo
Brown	Brun	Braun	Castaño	Bruno
Brown-lake	Carmin-brun	Braunlack	Laca castaño	Lacca bruno
Brown-purple	Pourpre-brun	Braunpurpur	Púrpura castaño	Porpora bruno
Brown-red	Rouge-brun	Braunrot	Rojo castaño	Rosso bruno
Buff	Chamois	Sämisch	Anteado	Camoscio
Cancellation	Oblitération	Entwertung	Cancelación	Annullamento
Cancelled	Annulé	Gestempelt	Cancelado	Annullato
Carmine	Carmin	Karmin	Carmín	Carminio
Carmine-red	Rouge-carmin	Karminrot	Rojo carmín	Rosso carminio
Centred	Centré	Zentriert	Centrado	Centrato
Cerise	Rouge-cerise	Kirschrot	Color de ceresa	Color Ciliegia
Chalk-surfaced paper	Papier couché	Kreidepapier	Papel estucado	Carta gessata
Chalky Blue	Bleu terne	Kreideblau	Azul turbio	Azzurro smorto
Charity stamp	Timbre de bienfaisance	Wohltätigkeitsmarke	Sello de beneficenza	Francobollo di beneficenza
Chestnut	Marron	Kastanienbraun	Castaño rojo	Marrone
Chocolate	Chocolat	Schokolade	Chocolate	Cioccolato
Cinnamon	Cannelle	Zimtbraun	Canela	Cannella
Claret	Grenat	Weinrot	Rojo vinoso	Vinaccia
Cobalt	Cobalt	Kobalt	Cobalto	Cobalto
Colour	Couleur	Farbe	Color	Colore
Comb-perforation	Dentelure en peigne	Kammzähnung, Reihenzähnung	Dentado de peine	Dentellatura e pettine
Commemorative stamp	Timbre commémoratif	Gedenkmarke	Sello conmemorativo	Francobollo commemorativo
Crimson	Cramoisi	Karmesin	Carmesí	Cremisi
Deep Blue	Bleu foncé	Dunkelblau	Azul oscuro	Azzurro scuro
Deep Bluish Green	Vert-bleu foncé	Dunkelbläulichgrün	Verde azulado oscuro	Verde azzurro scuro
Design	Dessin	Markenbild	Diseño	Disegno
Die	Matrice	Urstempel, Type, Platte	Cuño	Conio, Matrice
Double	Double	Doppelt	Doble	Doppio
Drab	Olive terne	Trüboliv	Oliva turbio	Oliva smorto
Dull Green	Vert terne	Trübgrün	Verde turbio	Verde smorto
Dull Purple	Mauve terne	Trübpurpur	Púrpura turbio	Porpora smorto
Embossing	Impression en relief	Prägedruck	Impresión en relieve	Impressione a relievo
Emerald	Vert-eméraude	Smaragdgrün	Esmeralda	Smeraldo
Engraved	Gravé	Graviert	Grabado	Inciso
Error	Erreur	Fehler, Fehldruck	Error	Errore
Essay	Essai	Probedruck	Ensayo	Saggio
Express letter stamp	Timbre pour lettres par exprès	Eilmarke	Sello de urgencia	Francobollo per espresso
Fiscal stamp	Timbre fiscal	Stempelmarke	Sello fiscal	Francobollo fiscale
Flesh	Chair	Fleischfarben	Carne	Carnicino
Forgery	Faux, Falsification	Fälschung	Falsificación	Falso, Falsificazione
Frame	Cadre	Rahmen	Marco	Cornice
Granite paper	Papier avec fragments de fils de soie	Faserpapier	Papel con filamentos	Carto con fili di seta
Green	Vert	Grün	Verde	Verde
Greenish Blue	Bleu verdâtre	Grünlichblau	Azul verdoso	Azzurro verdastro

English	*French*	*German*	*Spanish*	*Italian*
Greenish Yellow	Jaune-vert	Grünlichgelb	Amarillo verdoso	Giallo verdastro
Grey	Gris	Grau	Gris	Grigio
Grey-blue	Bleu-gris	Graublau	Azul gris	Azzurro grigio
Grey-green	Vert gris	Graugrün	Verde gris	Verde grigio
Gum	Gomme	Gummi	Goma	Gomma
Gutter	Interpanneau	Zwischensteg	Espacio blanco entre dos grupos	Ponte
Imperforate	Non-dentelé	Geschnitten	Sin dentar	Non dentellato
Indigo	Indigo	Indigo	Azul indigo	Indaco
Inscription	Inscription	Inschrift	Inscripción	Dicitura
Inverted	Renversé	Kopfstehend	Invertido	Capovolto
Issue	Émission	Ausgabe	Emisión	Emissione
Laid	Vergé	Gestreift	Listado	Vergato
Lake	Lie de vin	Lackfarbe	Laca	Lacca
Lake-brown	Brun-carmin	Lackbraun	Castaño laca	Bruno lacca
Lavender	Bleu-lavande	Lavendel	Color de alhucema	Lavanda
Lemon	Jaune-citron	Zitrongelb	Limón	Limone
Light Blue	Bleu clair	Hellblau	Azul claro	Azzurro chiaro
Lilac	Lilas	Lila	Lila	Lilla
Line perforation	Dentelure en lignes	Linienzähnung	Dentado en linea	Dentellatura lineare
Lithography	Lithographie	Steindruck	Litografía	Litografia
Local	Timbre de poste locale	Lokalpostmarke	Emisión local	Emissione locale
Lozenge roulette	Percé en losanges	Rautenförmiger Durchstich	Picadura en rombos	Perforazione a losanghe
Magenta	Magenta	Magentarot	Magenta	Magenta
Margin	Marge	Rand	Borde	Margine
Maroon	Marron pourpré	Dunkelrotpurpur	Púrpura rojo oscuro	Marrone rossastro
Mauve	Mauve	Malvenfarbe	Malva	Malva
Multicoloured	Polychrome	Mehrfarbig	Multicolores	Policromo
Myrtle Green	Vert myrte	Myrtengrün	Verde mirto	Verde mirto
New Blue	Bleu ciel vif	Neublau	Azul nuevo	Azzurro nuovo
Newspaper stamp	Timbre pour journaux	Zeitungsmarke	Sello para periódicos	Francobollo per giornali
Obliteration	Oblitération	Abstempelung	Matasello	Annullamento
Obsolete	Hors (de) cours	Ausser Kurs	Fuera de curso	Fuori corso
Ochre	Ocre	Ocker	Ocre	Ocra
Official stamp	Timbre de service	Dienstmarke	Sello de servicio	Francobollo di servizio
Olive-brown	Brun-olive	Olivbraun	Castaño oliva	Bruno oliva
Olive-green	Vert-olive	Olivgrün	Verde oliva	Verde oliva
Olive-grey	Gris-olive	Olivgrau	Gris oliva	Grigio oliva
Olive-yellow	Jaune-olive	Olivgelb	Amarillo oliva	Giallo oliva
Orange	Orange	Orange	Naranja	Arancio
Orange-brown	Brun-orange	Orangebraun	Castaño naranja	Bruno arancio
Orange-red	Rouge-orange	Orangerot	Rojo naranja	Rosso arancio
Orange-yellow	Jaune-orange	Orangegelb	Amarillo naranja	Giallo arancio
Overprint	Surcharge	Aufdruck	Sobrecarga	Soprastampa
Pair	Paire	Paar	Pareja	Coppia
Pale	Pâle	Blass	Pálido	Pallido
Pane	Panneau	Gruppe	Grupo	Gruppo
Paper	Papier	Papier	Papel	Carta
Parcel post stamp	Timbre pour colis postaux	Paketmarke	Sello para paquete postal	Francobollo per pacchi postali
Pen-cancelled	Oblitéré à plume	Federzugentwertung	Cancelado a pluma	Annullato a penna
Percé en arc	Percé en arc	Bogenförmiger Durchstich	Picadura en forma de arco	Perforazione ad arco
Percé en scie	Percé en scie	Bogenförmiger Durchstich	Picado en sierra	Foratura a sega
Perforated	Dentelé	Gezähnt	Dentado	Dentellato
Perforation	Dentelure	Zähnung	Dentar	Dentellatura
Photogravure	Photogravure, Heliogravure	Rastertiefdruck	Fotograbado	Rotocalco
Pin perforation	Percé en points	In Punkten durchstochen	Horadado con alfileres	Perforato a punti
Plate	Planche	Platte	Plancha	Lastra, Tavola
Plum	Prune	Pflaumenfarbe	Color de ciruela	Prugna
Postage Due stamp	Timbre-taxe	Portomarke	Sello de tasa	Segnatasse
Postage stamp	Timbre-poste	Briefmarke, Freimarke, Postmarke	Sello de correos	Francobollo postale
Postal fiscal stamp	Timbre fiscal-postal	Stempelmarke als Postmarke verwendet	Sello fiscal-postal	Fiscale postale
Postmark	Oblitération postale	Poststempel	Matasello	Bollo
Printing	Impression, Tirage	Druck	Impresión	Stampa, Tiratura
Proof	Épreuve	Druckprobe	Prueba de impresión	Prova
Provisionals	Timbres provisoires	Provisorische Marken, Provisorien	Provisionales	Provvisori

nglish	*French*	*German*	*Spanish*	*Italian*
ussian Blue	Bleu de Prusse	Preussischblau	Azul de Prusia	Azzurro di Prussia
urple	Pourpre	Purpur	Púrpura	Porpora
urple-brown	Brun-pourpre	Purpurbraun	Castaño púrpura	Bruno porpora
ecess-printing	Impression en taille douce	Tiefdruck	Grabado	Incisione
ed	Rouge	Rot	Rojo	Rosso
ed-brown	Brun-rouge	Rotbraun	Castaño rojizo	Bruno rosso
eddish Lilac	Lilas rougeâtre	Rötlichlila	Lila rojizo	Lilla rossastro
eddish Purple	Pourpre-rouge	Rötlichpurpur	Púrpura rojizo	Porpora rossastro
eddish Violet	Violet rougeâtre	Rötlichviolett	Violeta rojizo	Violetto rossastro
ed-orange	Orange rougeâtre	Rotorange	Naranja rojizo	Arancio rosso
egistration stamp	Timbre pour lettre chargée (recommandée)	Einschreibemarke	Sello de certificado	Francobollo per lettere raccomandate
eprint	Réimpression	Neudruck	Reimpresión	Ristampa
eversed	Retourné	Umgekehrt	Invertido	Rovesciato
ose	Rose	Rosa	Rosa	Rosa
ose-red	Rouge rosé	Rosarot	Rojo rosado	Rosso rosa
osine	Rose vif	Lebhaftrosa	Rosa vivo	Rosa vivo
oulette	Percage	Durchstich	Picadura	Foratura
ouletted	Percé	Durchstochen	Picado	Forato
oyal Blue	Bleu-roi	Königblau	Azul real	Azzurro reale
age Green	Vert-sauge	Salbeigrün	Verde salvia	Verde salvia
almon	Saumon	Lachs	Salmón	Salmone
carlet	Écarlate	Scharlach	Escarlata	Scarlatto
epia	Sépia	Sepia	Sepia	Seppia
erpentine roulette	Percé en serpentin	Schlangenliniger Durchstich	Picado a serpentina	Perforazione a serpentina
hade	Nuance	Tönung	Tono	Gradazione de colore
heet	Feuille	Bogen	Hoja	Foglio
ate	Ardoise	Schiefer	Pizarra	Ardesia
ate-blue	Bleu-ardoise	Schieferblau	Azul pizarra	Azzurro ardesia
ate-green	Vert-ardoise	Schiefergrün	Verde pizarra	Verde ardesia
ate-lilac	Lilas-gris	Schieferlila	Lila pizarra	Lilla ardesia
ate-purple	Mauve-gris	Schieferpurpur	Púrpura pizarra	Porpora ardesia
ate-violet	Violet-gris	Schieferviolett	Violeta pizarra	Violetto ardesia
pecial delivery stamp	Timbre pour exprès	Eilmarke	Sello de urgencia	Francobollo per espressi
pecimen	Spécimen	Muster	Muestra	Saggio
teel Blue	Bleu acier	Stahlblau	Azul acero	Azzurro acciaio
trip	Bande	Streifen	Tira	Striscia
urcharge	Surcharge	Aufdruck	Sobrecarga	Soprastampa
ête-bêche	Tête-bêche	Kehrdruck	Tête-bêche	Tête-bêche
inted paper	Papier teinté	Getöntes Papier	Papel coloreado	Carta tinta
oo-late stamp	Timbre pour lettres en retard	Verspätungsmarke	Sello para cartas retardadas	Francobollo per le lettere in ritardo
urquoise-blue	Bleu-turquoise	Türkisblau	Azul turquesa	Azzurro turchese
urquoise-green	Vert-turquoise	Türkisgrün	Verde turquesa	Verde turchese
ypography	Typographie	Buchdruck	Tipografia	Tipografia
ltramarine	Outremer	Ultramarin	Ultramar	Oltremare
nused	Neuf	Ungebraucht	Nuevo	Nuovo
sed	Oblitéré, Usé	Gebraucht	Usado	Usato
enetian Red	Rouge-brun terne	Venezianischrot	Rojo veneciano	Rosso veneziano
ermilion	Vermillon	Zinnober	Cinabrio	Vermiglione
iolet	Violet	Violett	Violeta	Violetto
iolet-blue	Bleu-violet	Violettblau	Azul violeta	Azzurro violetto
Vatermark	Filigrane	Wasserzeichen	Filigrana	Filigrana
Vatermark sideways	Filigrane couché	Wasserzeichen liegend	Filigrana acostado	Filigrana coricata
Vove paper	Papier ordinaire, Papier uni	Einfaches Papier	Papel avitelado	Carta unita
ellow	Jaune	Gelb	Amarillo	Giallo
ellow-brown	Brun-jaune	Gelbbraun	Castaño amarillo	Bruno giallo
ellow-green	Vert-jaune	Gelbgrün	Verde amarillo	Verde giallo
ellow-olive	Olive jaunâtre	Gelboliv	Oliva amarillo	Oliva giallastro
ellow-orange	Orange jaunâtre	Gelborange	Naranja amarillo	Arancio giallastro
ig-zag roulette	Percé en zigzag	Sägezahnartiger Durchstich	Picado en zigzag	Perforazione a zigzag

Stamps Added

Excluding new issues which have appeared in *Gibbons Stamp Monthly* supplements, the following are the catalogue numbers of stamps listed in this edition for the first time. In addition watermark varieties have been added to Commonwealth countries from *circa* 1860 to 1900.

Great Britain. 713ab, 794g, 815c, 827d, 1994a, 2008a, 2021ab/ac, 2026ab, 2060a, 2064a, 2065a, 2067a

Australia—New South Wales. 228a, 241ba

Victoria. 135a, 334a, 384ba, 385ab, 409ba, 426ba

Commonwealth of Australia. 20a, 21a, 21bw, 21c, 23aw, 23b, 465ab, 467a, 468ba/bb, 468bd, 494a, 495b, 496a, 497a, 498b/504b, 514a, 516a, 523a, 524a, 525b, 526a, 527a, 528a, 529a, 643a, 647ab, 879ab, 1180b, O42c/cw, O67w

Bahamas. 106x, 107y, 108a, 109w, 110a, 110x, 162b

Bahrain. 2w, 11w, 16w

Bangladesh. **MS**352a, 368, O48/9, O52

Barbados. 191w/y, 201c, 202c, 205w, 205y, 208wa, 209y, 210x/y, 211x, 213x, 351aw

Belize. 121a

Bermuda. 53cx, 54w, 62w/x, 63a, 72b/c

Botswana. 58a, 76aw, 81a, 92w, 817a, D25ab/29ab

British Levant. Z176, 49a

British Virgin Islands. 80w

Brunei. 26w/x, 57x, 69x, 380a, 381a, 382a

Brunei (Japanese Occupation). J71a

Canada—Newfoundland. 199w, 200w, 209w, 210w, 211w, 212w, 226w, 227w, 228w, 246w, 247w

Dominion of Canada. 1162db, 1266b, 1267a

Cayman Islands. 56a, 59a, 69y, 87a, 123ab, 618w

Cyprus. 17a/b, 22a, 28c, 32a, 41a, 61bw, 63c, 69a, 75w, 81b, 82b, 103w

Dominica. 127b, 129c, 131c

Egypt. D71c, D72b, D73b, D74c, D76c, O64a

Falkland Islands. 74aw, 116a, 329w

Falkland Islands Dependencies. Z1, Z22a, Z22*d*, Z23a, Z23*d*, Z27*b*, Z29*a*, Z38*b*, Z86*b*, Z108

Fiji. 19f, 138*b*, 245h

Ghana. 40w, 62w, 77cw, 79bw, 79cw, 79ew, SB1, D8c, D10c, D13c, D15c, D18c, D20c, D23c, D24c

Grenada. 47e

Guyana. 16*a*, 240aw, 244aw, 273w, 781a, 812b, 814a, 815a, 820a, 821a, 823a, 827b, 844a/b, 845a, 859a, 860a, 869a, 872a, 874a, 874ba/bb, 875a/b, 880a/b, 894a, 933a, 937a, 992a, 1011a, 1221a, 1596a

Hong Kong. 156a, 156ba, 288a, 344a

British Post Offices in China. Z687

India. 210w, 233w, 234w, 236cw, 237w, 239w, 260w, 266w, 269aw, 271w, 929bb, 1525a, 1573a, O139w, O216a, O228a, O229a, O230a

China Expeditionary Force. C23a

Feudatory States—Bundi. 53b/ba, 58ab, O17ba, O31ba, O35*ba*
Charkhari. 28d, 31c
Cochin. 27w, 28aw, 28bw, 67aw, 68aw, 69aw, 70aw, 73aw, O3w, O11w, O69ba, O105a
Duttia. 38d, 39b, 40a/b
Jaipur. 23d
Jind. J15a
Kishangarh. 25b, 42b, O3ab, O6b, O19b, O25ca, O25da, O25ea, O29a, O29ba
Nandgaon. O2
Nawanagar. 2a
Orchha. 8bc
Poonch. 57a, 63a/b, O6a
Travancore. 6d
Travancore-Cochin. O5bb

Ireland. 8a, 295ada

Specialist Philatelic Societies

Requests for inclusion on this page should e sent to the Catalogue Editor.

ritish Decimal Stamps Study Circle
ecretary—Mr. S. van Kimmenade
2 Beaufort Heights, Beaufort Road,
t. George, Bristol BS5 8JX

reat Britain Philatelic Society
Membership Secretary—Mr. A. G. Lajer
he Old Post Office, Hurst,
erks RG10 0TR

reat Britain Decimal Stamp Book Study ircle
Membership Secretary—Mr. A. J. Wilkins
Buttermere Close, Brierley Hill, West
Midlands DY5 3SD

hannel Islands Specialists Society
Membership Secretary—Mr. T. Watkins
Iolmcroft, Lewes Road, Ringmer, Lewes,
ast Sussex, BN8 5ES

---

scension Study Circle
ecretary—Dr. R. C. F. Baker
reys, Tower Road, Whitstable, Kent
T5 2ER

ustralian States Study Circle
oyal Sydney Philatelic Club
Ionorary Secretary—Mr. B. Palmer
.P.O. Box 1751, Sydney, N.S.W. 1043,
ustralia

ritish Society of Australian Philately
ecretary—Mr. A. J. Griffiths
/o The British Philatelic Centre,
07 Charterhouse Street,
ondon EC1M 6PT

ociety of Australasian Specialists/Oceania
ecretary—Mr. S. Leven
.O. Box 24764, San Jose, CA 95154-4764,
J.S.A.

echuanalands and Botswana Society
Membership Secretary—Mr. J. Catterall
revessa, Upper Castle Road, St. Mawes,
ruro, Cornwall TR2 5BZ

ermuda Collectors Society
ecretary—Mr. T. J. McMahon
.O. Box 1949, Stuart, FL 34995, U.S.A.

ritish Caribbean Philatelic Study Group
Overseas Director—Mr. D. N. Druett
ennymead Auctions, 1 Brewerton Street,
naresborough, North Yorkshire HG5 8AZ

ritish West Indies Study Circle
Membership Secretary—Mr. S. A. Sharp
4 Lovelace Drive, Pyrford, Woking, Surrey
U22 8QY

urma Philatelic Study Circle
ecretary—Mr. A. Meech
208-91 Avenue, Edmonton, Alberta,
anada T6B 0R8

Ceylon Study Circle
Secretary—Mr. R.W.P. Frost
42 Lonsdale Road, Cannington, Bridgwater,
Somerset TA5 2JS

Cyprus Study Circle
Secretary—Mr. A. R. Everett
29 Diomed Drive, Great Barton,
Bury St. Edmunds, Suffolk IP31 2TN

Falklands Islands Study Group
Membership Secretary—Mr. D. W. A. Jeffery
38 Bradstock Road, Stoneleigh, Epsom,
Surrey KT17 2LH

Hong Kong Study Circle
Membership Secretary—Mr. P. V. Ball
37 Hart Court, Newcastle-under-Lyme,
Staffordshire ST5 2AL

Indian Ocean Study Circle
Secretary—Mr. K. B. Fitton
50 Firlands, Weybridge, Surrey KT13 0HR

India Study Circle
Secretary—Dr. W. Fincham
10 Vallis Way, London W13 0DD

Irish Philatelic Circle
General Secretary—Mr. P. J. Wood
21 Loftus Road, London W12 7EH

King George V Silver Jubilee Study Circle
Secretary—Mr. N. Levinge
80 Towcester Road, Northampton
NN4 8LQ

King George VI Collectors Society
Secretary—Mr. F. R. Lockyer, OBE
98 Albany, Manor Road, Bournemouth,
Dorset BH1 3EW

Kiribati and Tuvalu Philatelic Society
Honorary Secretary—Mr. M. J. Shaw
88 Stoneleigh Avenue, Worcester Park,
Surrey KT4 8XY

Malaya Study Group
Secretary—Mr. J. Robertson
12 Lisa Court, Downsland Road,
Basingstoke, Hampshire RG21 8TU

Malta Study Circle
Membership Secretary—Mr. A. Webster
50 Worcester Road
Sutton, Surrey SM2 6QB

New Zealand Society of Great Britain
General Secretary—Mr. K. C. Collins
13 Briton Crescent, Sanderstead,
Surrey CR2 0JN.

Orange Free State Study Circle
Secretary—Mr. J. R. Stroud
28 Oxford Street, Burnham-on-Sea,
Somerset TA8 1LQ

Pacific Islands Study Circle
Honorary Secretary—Mr. J. D. Ray
24 Woodvale Avenue, London SE25 4AE

Papuan Philatelic Society
Secretary—Mr. F. J. Prophet
5 Morcom Close, Menear Road, Boscoppa,
St. Austell, Cornwall PL25 3UF

Pitcairn Islands Study Group (U.K.)
Honorary Secretary—Mr. D. Sleep
6 Palace Gardens, 100 Court Road, Eltham,
London SE9 5NS

Rhodesian Study Circle
Secretary—Mr. R. G. Barnett
2 Cox Ley, Hatfield Heath,
Bishop's Stortford, Herts CM22 7ER

St. Helena, Ascension and Tristan da Cunha Philatelic Society
Secretary—Mr. J. Havill
205 N. Murray Blvd., #221, Colorado
Springs, CO 80916, U.S.A.

Sarawak Specialists Society (also Brunei, North Borneo and Labuan)
Secretary—Dr. J. Higgins
31 Grimston Road, South Wootton,
Kings Lynn, Norfolk PE30 3NR

South African Collectors' Society
General Secretary—Mr. R. Ross
28 Duddon Drive, Barrow-in-Furness,
Cumbria LA14 3TW

Philatelic Society of Sri Lanka
Secretary—Mr. H. Goonawardena
44A Hena Road, Mt. Lavinia 10370,
Sri Lanka.

Sudan Study Group
Secretary—Mr. N. D. Collier
34 Padleys Lane, Burton Joyce,
Nottingham NG14 5BZ

Tonga and Tin Can Mail Study Circle
Secretary/Treasurer—Mr. L. L. Benson
1832 Jean Avenue, Tallahassee
FL 32308-5227, U.S.A.

Transvaal Study Circle
Secretary—Mr. J. Woolgar
132 Dale Street, Chatham, Kent ME4 6QH

West Africa Study Circle
Secretary—Mr. J. Powell
23 Brook Street, Edlesborough, Dunstable,
Bedfordshire LU6 2JG

Select Bibliography

The literature on British Commonwealth tamps is vast, but works are often difficult to btain once they are out of print. The selection of ooks below has been made on the basis of uthority together with availability to the general eader, either as new or secondhand. Very pecialised studies, and those covering aspects of ostal history to which there are no references in he catalogue, have been excluded.

The following abbreviations are used to denote ublishers:
RL–Christie's Robson Lowe; HH–Harry Hayes; B–Proud Bailey Co. Ltd. and Postal History ublications Co.; PC–Philip Cockrill; RPSL–Royal Philatelic Society, London; G–Stanley Gibbons Ltd.

Where no publisher is quoted, the book is ublished by its author.

ENERAL. *Encyclopaedia of British Empire Postage Stamps.* Vols 1–6. Edited Robson Lowe. (CRL, 1951–1991)

pecimen Stamps of the Crown Colonies 1857–1948. Marcus Samuel. (RPSL, 1976 and 1984 Supplement)

ancelled by Perkins Bacon. P. Jaffé. (Spink & Son Ltd, 1998)

J.P.U. Specimen Stamps. J. Bendon. (1988)

King George V Key Plates of the Imperium Postage and Revenue Design. P. Fernbank. (West Africa Study Circle, 1997)

he Commemorative Stamps of the British Commonwealth. H.D.S. Haverbeck. (Faber, 1955)

ilver Jubilee of King George V Stamps Handbook. A.J. Ainscough. (Ainweel Developments, 1985)

he Printings of King George VI Colonial Stamps. W.J.W. Potter & Lt-Col R.C.M. Shelton. (1952 and later facsimile edition)

King George VI Large Key Type Stamps of Bermuda, Leeward Islands, Nyasaland. R.W. Dickgiesser and E.P. Yendall. (Triad Publications, 1985)

Madame Joseph Forged Postmarks. D. Worboys (RPSL, 1994)

G.B. Used Abroad: Cancellations and Postal Markings. J. Parmenter. (The Postal History Society, 1993)

GREAT BRITAIN. For extensive bibliographies see *G.B. Specialised Catalogues. Vols 1-5.*

tamps and Postal History of the Channel Islands. W. Newport. (Heineman, 1972)

ASCENSION. *Ascension. The Stamps and Postal History.* J.H. Attwood. (CRL, 1981)

AUSTRALIA. *The Postage History of New South Wales 1788–1901.* Edited J.S. White (Philatelic Assoc of New South Wales, 1988)

outh Australia. The Long Stamps 1902–12. J.R.W. Purves. (Royal Philatelic Society of Victoria, 1978)

he Departmental Stamps of South Australia. A.R. Butler. (RPSL, 1978)

tamps and Postal History of Tasmania. W.E. Tinsley. (RPSL, 1986)

The Pictorial Stamps of Tasmania 1899–1912. K.E. Lancaster. (Royal Philatelic Society of Victoria, 1986)

The Stamps of Victoria. G. Kellow. B. & K. Philatelic Publishing, 1990)

Western Australia. The Stamps and Postal History. Ed. M. Hamilton and B. Pope. (W. Australian Study Group, 1979)

Postage Stamps and Postal History of Western Australia. Vols 1–3. M. Juhl. (1981–83)

The Chapman Collection of Australian Commonwealth Stamps. R. Chapman. (Royal Philatelic Society of Victoria, 1999)

Cocos (Keeling) Islands. A Philatelic and Postal History to 1979. P. Collas & J. Hill. (B. & K. Philatelic Publishing, 1991)

Norfolk Island. A Postal and Philatelic History, 1788–1969. P. Collas & R. Breckon. (B.& K. Philatelic Publishing, 1997)

BAHAMAS. *The Postage Stamps and Postal History of the Bahamas.* H.G.D. Gisburn. (SG, 1950 and later facsimile edition)

BARBADOS. *The Stamps of Barbados.* E.A. Bayley. (1989)

Advanced Barbados Philately. H.F. Deakin. (B.W.I. Study Circle, 1997)

BATUM. *British Occupation of Batum.* P.T. Ashford. (1989)

BERMUDA. *The Postal History and Stamps of Bermuda.* M.H. Ludington (Quarterman Publications Inc., 1978)

The King George V High-value Stamps of Bermuda, 1917–1938. M. Glazer. (Calaby Publishers, 1994)

BOTSWANA. *The Postage Stamps, Postal Stationery and Postmarks of the Bechuanalands.* H.R. Holmes. (RPSL, 1971)

BRITISH OCCUPATION OF GERMAN COLONIES. *G.R.I.* R.M. Gibbs. (CRL, 1989)

BRITISH POSTAL AGENCIES IN EASTERN ARABIA. *The Postal Agencies in Eastern Arabia and the Gulf.* N. Donaldson (HH, 1975) and Supplement (Bridger & Kay Guernsey Ltd, 1994)

BRITISH WEST AFRICA. *The Postal History and Handstamps of British West Africa.* C. McCaig. (CRL, 1978)

BRUNEI. *Brunei. The Definitive Issues and Postal Cancellations to 1974.* E. Thorndike. (PC, 1983)

BURMA. *Burma Postal History.* G. Davis and D. Martin. (CRL, 1971 and 1987 Supplement).

CAMEROONS. *The Postal Arrangements of the Anglo-French Cameroons Expeditionary Force 1914–16.* R.J. Maddocks. (1996)

CANADA. *The Postage Stamps and Postal History of Newfoundland.* W.S. Boggs. (Quarterman Publications, 1975)

Stamps of British North America. F. Jarrett. (Quarterman Publications Inc, 1975)

The Postage Stamps and Postal History of Canada. W.S. Boggs. (Quarterman Publications Inc., 1974)

The First Decimal Issue of Canada 1859–68. G. Whitworth. (RPSL, 1966)

The Five Cents Beaver Stamp of Canada. G. Whitworth. (RPSL, 1985)

The Edward VII Issue of Canada. G.C. Marler. (National Postal Museum, Canada, 1975)

The Admiral Issue of Canada. G.C. Marler. (American Philatelic Society, 1982)

The Centennial Definitives of Canada. D. Gronbeck-Jones. (1972)

The Caricatures and Landscapes Definitives of Canada. D. Gronbeck-Jones (1979)

COOK ISLANDS. *The Early Cook Islands Post Office.* A.R. Burge. (Hawthorn Press, 1978)

CYPRUS. *Cyprus 1353–1986.* W. Castle. (CRL, 3rd edition, 1987)

DOMINICA. *Dominica Postal History, Stamps and Postal Stationery to 1935.* E.V. Toeg (B.W.I. Study Circle, 1994)

EGYPT. *Egypt Stamps & Postal History.* P.A.S. Smith. (James Bendon, 1999)

FALKLAND ISLANDS. *The Postage Stamps of the Falkland Islands and Dependencies.* B.S.H. Grant. (SG, 1952 and later facsimile edition)

The Falkland Islands Philatelic Digest. Nos. 1 & 2. M. Barton and R. Spafford. (HH, 1975 & 1979)

The De La Rue Definitives of the Falkland Islands 1901–29. J.P. Bunt. (1986 and 1996 Supplement)

The War Stamp Overprints of the Falkland Islands 1918–20. J.P. Bunt. (1981)

The Falkland Islands. Printings of the Pictorial Issue of 1938–49. C.E. Glass. (CRL, 1979)

The Falklands War. J.D. Davis. (1983)

FIJI. *Fiji Philatelics.* D.W.F. Alford. (Pacific Islands Study Circle, 1994)

The Postal History of Fiji 1911–1952. J.G. Rodger. (Pacific Islands Study Circle, 1991).

GAMBIA. *The Stamps and Postal History of the Gambia.* Edited J.O. Andrew. (CRL, 1985)

The Postal History of the Gambia. E.B. Proud (PB, 1994)

GHANA. *The Postal History of the Gold Coast.* E.B. Proud (PB, 1995)

The Postal Services of the Gold Coast, 1901–1957. Edited by M. Ensor. (West Africa Study Circle, 1998)

GIBRALTAR. *Posted in Gibraltar.* W. Hine-Haycock. (CRL, 1978)

Gibraltar. The Postal History and Postage Stamps. Vol 1 (to 1885). G. Osborn. (Gibraltar Study Circle, 1995)

GUYANA. *The Postage Stamps and Postal History of British Guiana.* W.A. Townsend and F.G. Howe. (RPSL, 1970)

HONG KONG. *The Philatelic History of Hong Kong. Vol 1.* (Hong Kong Study Circle, 1984)

Hong Kong Postage Stamps of the Queen Victoria Period. R.N. Gurevitch (1993)

Hong Kong. The 1898 10c. on 30c. Provisional Issue. A.M. Chu. (1998)

British Post Offices in the Far East. E.B. Proud. (PB, 1991)

Cancellations of the Treaty Ports of Hong Kong. H. Schoenfeld. (1988)

The Crown Colony of Wei Hai Wei. M. Goldsmith and C.W. Goodwyn. (RPSL, 1985)

INDIA. *C.E.F. The China Expeditionary Force 1900–1923.* D.S. Virk, J.C. Hume, D. Lang, G. Sattin. (Philatelic Congress of India, 1992)

India Used Abroad. V.S. Dastur. (Mysore Philatelics, 1982)

A Handbook on Gwalior Postal History and Stamps. V.K. Gupta. (1980)

The Stamps of Jammu & Kashmir. F. Staal. (The Collectors Club, 1983)

IRAQ. *The Postal History of Iraq.* P.C. Pearson and E.B. Proud. (PB, 1996)

IRELAND. *Irish Stamp Booklets 1931–1991.* C.I. Dulin (1998)

STANLEY GIBBONS STAMP CATALOGUE

Part 1: BRITISH COMMONWEALTH

VOLUME 1: GREAT BRITAIN AND COUNTRIES A TO I

102nd EDITION—2000

Great Britain

STAMPS ON COVER. Prices are quoted, as a third price column, for those Victorian and Edwardian issues usually found used on cover. In general these prices refer to the cheapest version of each basic stamp with other shades, plates or varieties, together with unusual frankings and postmarks, being worth more.

UNITED KINGDOM OF GREAT BRITAIN AND IRELAND

QUEEN VICTORIA
20 June 1837—22 January 1901

MULREADY ENVELOPES AND LETTER SHEETS, so called from the name of the designer, William Mulready, were issued concurrently with the first British adhesive stamps.

1d. black

Envelopes: £175 *unused*; £225 *used*.
Letter Sheets: £150 *unused*; £200 *used*.

2d. blue

Envelopes: £240 *unused*; £675 *used*.
Letter Sheets: £225 *unused*; £650 *used*.

LINE-ENGRAVED ISSUES

GENERAL NOTES

Brief notes on some aspects of the line-engraved stamps follow, but for further information and a full specialist treatment of these issues collectors are recommended to consult Volume 1 of the Stanley Gibbons *Great Britain Specialised Catalogue*.

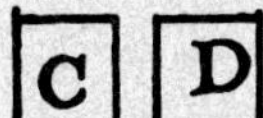
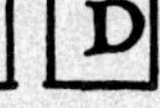

Alphabet I

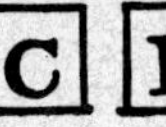

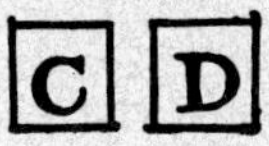

Alphabet II

Alphabet III

Alphabet IV

Typical Corner Letters of the four Alphabets

Alphabets. Four different styles were used for the corner letters on stamps prior to the issue with letters in all four corners, these being known to collectors as:

Alphabet I. Used for all plates made from 1840 to the end of 1851. Letters small.

Alphabet II. Plates from 1852 to mid-1855. Letters larger, heavier and broader.

Alphabet III. Plates from mid-1855 to end of period. Letters tall and more slender.

Alphabet IV. 1861. 1d. Die II, Plates 50 and 51 only. Letters were hand-engraved instead of being punched on the plate. They are therefore inconsistent in shape and size but generally larger and outstanding.

While the general descriptions and the illustrations of typical letters given above may be of some assistance, only long experience and published aids can enable every stamp to be allocated to its particular alphabet without hesitation, as certain letters in each are similar to those in one of the others.

Blue Paper. The blueing of the paper of the earlier issues is believed to be due to the presence of prussiate of potash in the printing ink, or in the paper, which, under certain conditions, tended to colour the paper when the sheets were damped for printing. An alternative term is bleuté paper.

Corner Letters. The corner letters on the early British stamps were intended as a safeguard against forgery, each stamp in the sheet having a different combination of letters. Taking the first 1d. stamp, printed in 20 horizontal rows of 12, as an example, the lettering is as follows:

Row 1. A A, A B, A C, etc. to A L.

Row 2. B A, B B, B C, etc. to B L.

and so on to

Row 20. T A, T B, T C, etc. to T L.

On the stamps with four corner letters, those in the upper corners are in the reverse positions to those in the lower corners. Thus in a sheet of 240 (12 × 20) the sequence is:

Row 1. AA/AA BA/AB CA/AC etc. to LA/AL

Row 2. AB/BA BB/BB CB/BC etc. to LB/BL

and so on to

Row 20. AT/TA BT/TB CT/TC etc. to LT/TL

Placing letters in all four corners was not only an added precaution against forgery but was meant to deter unmarked parts of used stamps being pieced together and passed off as an unused whole.

Dies. The first die of the 1d. was used for making the original die of the 2d., both the No Lines and White Lines issues. In 1855 the 1d. Die I was amended by retouching the head and deepening the lines on a transferred impression of the original. This later version, known to collectors as Die II, was used for making the dies for the 1d. and 2d. with letters in all four corners and also for the 1½d.

The two dies are illustrated above No. 17 in the catalogue.

Double letter

Guide line in corner

Guide line through value

Double Corner Letters. These are due to the workman placing his letter-punch in the wrong position at the first attempt, when lettering the plate, and then correcting the mistake; or to a slight shifting of the punch when struck. If a wrong letter was struck in the first instance, traces of a wrong letter may appear in a corner in addition to the correct one. A typical example is illustrated.

Guide Lines and Dots. When laying down the impressions of the design on the early plates, fine vertical and horizontal guide lines were marked on the plates to assist the operative. These were usually removed from the gutter margins, but could not be removed from the stamp impressions without damage to the plate, so that in such cases they appear on the printed stamps, sometimes in the corners, sometimes through "POSTAGE" or the value. Typical examples are illustrated.

Guide dots or cuts were similarly made to indicate the spacing of the guide lines. These too sometimes appear on the stamps.

Ivory Head

"Ivory Head." The so-called "ivory head" variety is one in which the Queen's Head shows white on the back of the stamp. It arises from the comparative absence of ink in the head portion of the design, with consequent absence of blueing. (*See* "Blued Paper" note above.)

Line-engraving. In this context "line-engraved" is synonymous with recess-printing, in which the engraver cuts recesses in a plate and printing (the coloured areas) is from these recesses. "Line-engraved" is the traditional philatelic description for these stamps; other equivalent terms found are "engraving in *taille-douce*" (French) or "in *intaglio*" (Italian).

Plates. Until the introduction of the stamps with letters in all four corners, the number of the plate was not indicated in the design of the stamp, but was printed on the sheet margin. By long study of identifiable blocks and the minor variations in the design, coupled with the position of the corner letters, philatelists are now able to allot many of these stamps to their respective plates. Specialist collectors often endeavour to obtain examples of a given stamp printed from its different plates and our catalogue accordingly reflects this depth of detail.

Maltese Cross — Type of Town postmark

Type of Penny Post cancellation

Example of 1844 type postmark

Postmarks. The so-called "Maltese Cross" design was the first employed for obliterating British postage stamps and was in use from 1840 to 1844. Being hand-cut, the obliterating stamps varied greatly in detail and some distinctive types can be allotted to particular towns or offices. Local types, such as those used at Manchester, Norwich, Leeds, etc., are keenly sought. A red ink was first employed, but was superseded by black, after some earlier experiments, in February 1841. Maltese Cross obliterations in other colours are rare.

Obliterations of this type, numbered 1 to 12 in the centre, were used at the London Chief Office in 1843 and 1844.

Some straight-line cancellations were in use in 1840 at the Penny Post receiving offices, normally applied on the envelope, the adhesives then being obliterated at the Head Office. They are nevertheless known, with or without Maltese Cross, on the early postage stamps.

In 1842 some offices in S.W. England used dated postmarks in place of the Maltese Cross, usually on the back of the letter since they were not originally intended as obliterators. These town postmarks have likewise been found on adhesives.

In 1844 the Maltese Cross design was superseded by numbered obliterators of varied type, one of which is illustrated. They are naturally comparatively scarce on the first 1d. and 2d. stamps. Like the Maltese Cross they are found in various colours, some of which are rare.

Re-entry

"Union Jack" re-entry

Re-entries. Re-entries on the plate show as a doubling of part of the design of the stamp generally at top or bottom. Many re-entries are very slight while others are most marked. A typical one is illustrated.

The "*Union Jack*" *re-entry*, so called owing to the effect of the re-entry on the appearance of the corner stars (*see illustration*) occurs on stamp L K of Plate 75 of the 1d. red, Die I.

T A (T L) M A (M L)
Varieties of Large Crown Watermark

I Two states of Large Crown Watermark II

Watermarks. Two watermark varieties, as illustrated, consisting of owns of entirely different shape, are found in sheets of the Large rown paper and fall on stamps lettered M A and T A (or M L and T L aen the paper is printed on the wrong side). Both varieties are found the 1d. rose-red of 1857, while the M A (M L) variety comes also on me plates of the 1d. of 1864 (Nos. 43, 44) up to about Plate 96. On e 2d. the T A (T L) variety is known on plates 8 and 9, and the M A 1 L) on later prints of plate 9. These varieties may exist inverted, or verted reversed on stamps lettered A A and A L and H A and H L, d some are known.

In 1861 a minor alteration was made in the Large Crown watermark the removal of the two vertical strokes, representing *fleurs-de-lis*, nich projected upwards from the uppermost of the three horizontal rves at the base of the Crown. Hence two states are distinguishable, illustrated.

ONDITION–IMPERFORATE LINE-ENGRAVED ISSUES

The prices quoted for the 1840 and 1841 imperforate Line-graved issues are for "fine" examples. As condition is most portant in assessing the value of a stamp, the following definitions ill assist collectors in the evaluation of individual examples.

Four main factors are relevant when considering quality.

(a) **Impression.** This should be clean and the surface free of any bbing or unnatural blurring which would detract from the opearance.

(b) **Margins.** This is perhaps the most difficult factor to evaluate. amps described as "fine", the standard adopted in this catalogue for ricing purposes, should have margins of the recognised width, efined as approximately one half of the distance between two djoining unsevered stamps. Stamps described as "very fine" or superb" should have margins which are proportionately larger than ose of a "fine" stamp. Examples with close margins should not, enerally, be classified as "fine".

(c) **Cancellation.** On a "fine" stamp this should be reasonably clear nd not noticeably smudged. A stamp described as "superb" should ave a neat cancellation, preferably centrally placed or to the right.

(d) **Appearance.** Stamps, at the prices quoted, should always be ithout any tears, creases, bends or thins and should not be toned on ther the front or back. Stamps with such defects are worth only a roportion of the catalogue price.

Good

Fine

Very Fine

Superb

The above actual size illustrations of 1840 1d. blacks show the arious grades of quality. When comparing these illustrations it hould be assumed that they are all from the same plate and that they re free of any hidden defects.

PRINTERS. Nos. 1/53*a* were recess-printed by Perkins, Bacon & Petch, known from 1852 as Perkins, Bacon & Co.

1

1*a*

2 Small Crown

(Eng Charles and Frederick Heath)

1840 (6 May). *Letters in lower corners. Wmk Small Crown. W* **2**. *Imperf.*

No.	Type		Un	Used	Used on cover
1	1	1d. intense black	£3750	£240	
2		1d. black	£3250	£175	£300
3		1d. grey-black (worn plate)	£3250	£240	
4	1*a*	2d. deep full blue	£7500	£425	
5		2d. blue	£6000	£350	£800
6		2d. pale blue	£7500	£400	

The 1d. stamp in black was printed from Plates 1 to 11. Plate 1 exists in two states (known to collectors as 1*a* and 1*b*), the latter being the result of extensive repairs.

Repairs were also made to Plates 2, 5, 6, 8, 9, 10 and 11, and certain impressions exist in two or more states.

The so-called "Royal reprint" of the 1d. black was made in 1864, from Plate 66, Die II, on paper with Large Crown watermark, inverted. A printing was also made in carmine, on paper with the same watermark, normal.

For 1d. black with "VR" in upper corners *see* No. V1 under Official Stamps.

The 2d. stamps were printed from Plates 1 and 2.

Plates of 1d. black

Plate	Un	Used
1*a*	£4750	£190
1*b*	£3250	£175
2	£3250	£175
3	£3750	£200
4	£3250	£190
5	£3250	£190
6	£3250	£190
7	£3500	£210
8	£3750	£240
9	£4250	£290
10	£4750	£375
11	£4750	£1700

Varieties of 1d. black

			Un	Used
a.	On *bleuté* paper (Plates 1 to 8)	*from*	—	£250
b.	Double letter in corner	*from*	£3500	£225
bb.	Re-entry		£3500	£240
bc.	"PB" re-entry (Plate 5, 3rd state)		—	£4000
cc.	Large letters in each corner (E J, I L, J C and P A) (Plate 1*b*)	*from*	£3500	£350
c.	Guide line in corner		£3500	£200
d.	,, ,, through value		£3500	£225
e.	Watermark inverted		£3750	£500
g.	Obliterated by Maltese Cross			
		In red	—	£190
		In black	—	£175
		In blue	—	£2250
		In magenta	—	£750
		In yellow	—	—
h.	Obliterated by Maltese Cross with number in centre	*from*		
		No. 1	—	£2750
		No. 2	—	£1750
		No. 3	—	£1750
		No. 4	—	£1750
		No. 5	—	£1750
		No. 6	—	£1750
		No. 7	—	£1750
		No. 8	—	£1750
		No. 9	—	£1750
		No. 10	—	£1750
		No. 11	—	—
		No. 12	—	£1750
i.	Obliterated "Penny Post" in black	*from*	—	£1300
j.	Obliterated by town postmark (without Maltese Cross)			
		In black *from*	—	£1300
		In yellow *from*	—	£7000
		In red *from*	—	£1500
k.	Obliterated by 1844 type postmark in black	*from*	—	£500

Plates of 2d. blue

Plate		Un	Used
1	*Shades from*	£6000	£350
2	*Shades from*	£7000	£400

Varieties of 2d. blue

			Un	Used
a.	Double letter in corner		—	£475
aa.	Re-entry		—	£525
b.	Guide line in corner		—	£425
c.	,, ,, through value		—	£425
d.	Watermark inverted		£7000	£675
e.	Obliterated by Maltese Cross			
		In red	—	£375
		In black	—	£350
		In blue	—	£3250
		In magenta	—	£2750
f.	Obliterated by Maltese Cross with number in centre	*from*		
		No. 1	—	£2750
		No. 2	—	£2750
		No. 3	—	£2750
		No. 4	—	£2750
		No. 5	—	£2750
		No. 6	—	£3000
		No. 7	—	£2750
		No. 8	—	£2750
		No. 9	—	£3250
		No. 10	—	£3000
		No. 11	—	£3000
		No. 12	—	£2750
g.	Obliterated "Penny Post" in black	*from*	—	£1800
h.	Obliterated by town postmark (without Maltese Cross) in black	*from*	—	£1500
i.	Obliterated by 1844 type postmark			
		In black *from*	—	£1000
		In blue *from*	—	£2500

1841 (10 Feb). *Printed from "black" plates. Wmk W* **2**. *Paper more or less blued. Imperf.*

No.	Type		Un	Used	Used on cover
7	1	1d. red-brown (*shades*)	£550	60·00	£100
		a. "PB" re-entry (Plate 5, 3rd state)	—	£1200	

The first printings of the 1d. in red-brown were made from Plates 1*b*, 2, 5 and 8 to 11 used for the 1d. black.

1d. red-brown from "black" plates

Plate	Un	Used
1*b*	£3250	£160
2	£1900	£110
5	£725	70·00
8	£575	60·00
9	£550	60·00
10	£575	60·00
11	£575	60·00

1841 (late Feb). *Plate* 12 *onwards. Wmk W* **2**. *Paper more or less blued. Imperf.*

No.	Type		Un	Used	Used on cover
8	1	1d. red-brown	£150	6·00	12·00
8*a*		1d. red-brown on very blue paper	£175	6·00	
9		1d. pale red-brown (worn plates)	£240	15·00	
10		1d. deep red-brown	£175	8·00	
11		1d. lake-red	£700	£250	
12		1d. orange-brown	£325	50·00	

Error. No letter "A" in right lower corner (*Stamp* B(A), *Plate* 77)

12*a*	1	1d. red-brown	—	£5250

The error "No letter A in right corner" was due to the omission to insert this letter on stamp B A of Plate 77. The error was discovered some months after the plate was registered and was then corrected.

There are innumerable variations in the colour and shade of the 1d. "red" and those given in the above list represent colour groups each covering a wide range.

Varieties of 1d. red-brown, etc.

			Un	Used
b.	Re-entry	*from*	—	27·00
c.	Double letter in corner	*from*	—	16·00
d.	Double Star (Plate 75) "Union Jack" re-entry		£7000	£650
e.	Guide line in corner		—	9·00
f.	,, ,, through value		—	16·00
g.	Thick outer frame to stamp		—	15·00
h.	Ivory head		£190	10·00
i.	Watermark inverted		£350	35·00
j.	Left corner letter "S" inverted (Plates 78, 105, 107)	*from*	—	60·00
k.	P converted to R (Plates 30, 33, 83, 86)	*from*	—	50·00
l.	Obliterated by Maltese Cross			
		In red	—	£1100
		In black	—	20·00
		In blue	—	£175
m.	Obliterated by Maltese Cross with number in centre			
		No. 1	—	40·00
		No. 2	—	40·00
		No. 3	—	60·00
		No. 4	—	£140
		No. 5	—	40·00
		No. 6	—	35·00
		No. 7	—	32·00
		No. 8	—	30·00
		No. 9	—	38·00
		No. 10	—	60·00
		No. 11	—	70·00
		No. 12	—	90·00
n.	Obliterated "Penny Post" in black		—	£225
o.	Obliterated by town postmark (without Maltese Cross)			
		In black *from*	—	£150
		In blue *from*	—	£300
		In green *from*	—	£450
		In yellow *from*	—	—
		In red *from*	—	£2000
p.	Obliterated by 1844 type postmark			
		In blue *from*	—	45·00
		In red *from*	—	£1000
		In green *from*	—	£250
		In violet *from*	—	£575
		In black *from*	—	6·00

Stamps with thick outer frame to the design are from plates on which the frame-lines have been strengthened or recut, particularly Plates 76 and 90.

For "Union Jack" re-entry *see* General Notes to Line-engraved Issues.

In "P converted to R" the corner letter "R" is formed from the "P", the distinctive long tail having been hand-cut.

KEY TO LINE-ENGRAVED ISSUES

s.	*Description*	*Date*	*Wmk*	*Perf*	*Die*	*Alphabet*
	THE IMPERFORATE ISSUES					
	1d. black	6.5.40	SC	Imp	I	I
	2d. no lines	8.5.40	SC	Imp	I	I
	PAPER MORE OR LESS BLUED					
	1d. red-brown	Feb 1841	SC	Imp	I	I
2	1d. red-brown	Feb 1841	SC	Imp	I	I
2	1d. red-brown	6.2.52	SC	Imp	I	II
15	2d. white lines	13.3.41	SC	Imp	I	I
	THE PERFORATED ISSUES					
	ONE PENNY VALUE					
a	1d. red-brown	1848	SC	Roul	I	I
b	1d. red-brown	1850	SC	16	I	I
c	1d. red-brown	1853	SC	16	I	II
d	1d. red-brown	1854	SC	14	I	I
'18	1d. red-brown	Feb 1854	SC	16	I	II
	1d. red-brown	Jan 1855	SC	14	I	II
'5	1d. red-brown	28.2.55	SC	14	II	II
	1d. red-brown	1.3.55	SC	16	II	II
	1d. red-brown	15.5.55	LC	16	II	II
'33	1d. red-brown	Aug 1855	LC	14	II	III
	NEW COLOURS ON WHITE PAPER					
41	1d. rose-red	Nov 1856	LC	14	II	III
	1d. rose-red	26.12.57	LC	16	II	III
	1d. rose-red	1861	LC	14	II	IV
	TWO PENCE VALUE					
20	2d. blue	1.3.54	SC	16	I	I
	2d. blue	22.2.55	SC	14	I	I
a	2d. blue	5.7.55	SC	14	I	II
a	2d. blue	18.8.55	SC	16	I	II
	2d. blue	20.7.55	LC	16	I	II
	2d. blue	20.7.55	LC	14	I	II
	2d. blue	2.7.57	LC	14	I	III
a	2d. blue	1.2.58	LC	16	I	III
	LETTERS IN ALL FOUR CORNERS					
'9	½d. rose-red	1.10.70	W **9**	14	—	
'4	1d. rose-red	1.4.64	LC	14	II	
a	1½d. rosy mauve	1860	LC	14	II	
'3	1½d. rose-red	1.10.70	LC	14	II	
	2d. blue	July 1858	LC	14	II	
'7	2d. thinner lines	7.7.69	LC	14	II	

Watermarks: SC = Small Crown, T **2**.
LC = Large Crown, T **4**.
Dies: *See* notes above No. 17 in the catalogue.
Alphabets: *See* General Notes to this section.

3 White lines added

41 (13 Mar)–**51**. *White lines added. Wmk W* **2**. *Paper more or less blued. Imperf.*

			Un	*Used*	*Used on cover*
	3	2d. pale blue	£1600	65·00	
		2d. blue	£1300	55·00	£200
		2d. deep full blue ..	£1600	65·00	
aa		2d. violet-blue (1851) ..	£7500	£600	

The 2d. stamp with white lines was printed from Plates 3 and 4.
No. 15*aa* came from Plate 4 and the price quoted is for examples on cker, lavender tinted paper.

Plates of 2d. blue

Plate		*Un*	*Used*
3	*Shades from*	£1300	60·00
4	*Shades from*	£1500	55·00

Varieties of 2d. blue

		Un	*Used*
Guide line in corner		—	60·00
,, ,, through value		£1700	60·00
Double letter in corner		—	60·00
Re-entry		£2000	75·00
Ivory head		£1800	55·00
Watermark inverted		£2250	£200
Obliterated by Maltese Cross			
	In red	—	£5500
	In black	—	80·00
	In blue	—	£1200
Obliterated by Maltese Cross with number in centre			
	No. 1	—	£210
	No. 2	—	£210
	No. 3	—	£210
	No. 4	—	£200
	No. 5	—	£290
	No. 6	—	£210
	No. 7	—	£400
	No. 8	—	£290
	No. 9	—	£400
	No. 10	—	£450
	No. 11	—	£290
	No. 12	—	£160
Obliterated by town postmark (without Maltese Cross)			
	In black *from*	—	£500
	In blue *from*	—	£850

h. Obliterated by 1844 type postmark

In black	*from*	—	55·00
In blue	*from*	—	£375
In red	*from*	—	£4500
In green	*from*	—	£700

1841 (April). *Trial printing* (*unissued*) *on Dickinson silk-thread paper. No wmk. Imperf.*

16 **1** 1d. red-brown (Plate 11) £2250

Eight sheets were printed on this paper, six being gummed, two ungummed, but we have only seen examples without gum.

1848. *Wmk Small Crown, W* **2**. *Rouletted approx* 11½ *by Henry Archer.*

16*a* **1** 1d. red-brown (Plates 70, 71) £4000

1850. *Wmk Small Crown, W* **2**. *P* 16 *by Henry Archer.*

16*b* **1** 1d. red-brown (Alph 1) (from Plates 90–101) .. .. .. *from* £650 £225

Stamp on cover, dated prior to February 1854 (*price* £375); dated during or after February 1854 (*price* £275).

1853. *Government Trial Perforations. Wmk Small Crown, W* **2**.

16*c*	**1**	1d. red-brown (*p* 16) (Alph II) (*on cover*)	†	£5250
16*d*		1d. red-brown (*p* 14) (Alph I)	£4250	

SEPARATION TRIALS. Although the various trials of machines for rouletting and perforating were unofficial, Archer had the consent of the authorities in making his experiments, and sheets so experimented upon were afterwards used by the Post Office.

As Archer ended his experiments in 1850 and plates with corner letters Alphabet II did not come into issue until 1852, perforated stamps with corner letters of Alphabet I may safely be assumed to be Archer productions, if genuine.

The Government trial perforations were done on Napier machines in 1853. As Alphabet II was by that time in use, the trials can only be distinguished from the perforated stamps listed below by being dated prior to 12 March 1854, the date when the perforated stamps were officially issued.

Die I

Die II

4 Large Crown

Die I: The features of the portrait are lightly shaded and consequently lack emphasis.

Die II (Die I retouched): The lines of the features have been deepened and appear stronger.

The eye is deeply shaded and made more lifelike. The nostril and lips are more clearly defined, the latter appearing much thicker. A strong downward stroke of colour marks the corner of the mouth. There is a deep indentation of colour between lower lip and chin. The band running from the back of the ear to the chignon has a bolder horizontal line below it than in Die I.

The original die (Die I) was used to provide roller dies for the laying down of all the line-engraved stamps from 1840 to 1855. In that year a new master die was laid down (by means of a Die I roller die) and the impression was retouched by hand engraving by William Humphrys. This retouched die, always known to philatelists as Die II, was from that time used for preparing all new roller dies.

One Penny. The numbering of the 1d. plates recommenced at 1 on the introduction of Die II. Plates 1 to 21 were Alphabet II from which a scarce plum shade exists. Corner letters of Alphabet III appear on Plate 22 and onwards.

As an experiment, the corner letters were engraved by hand on Plates 50 and 51 in 1856, instead of being punched (Alphabet IV), but punching was again resorted to from Plate 52 onwards. Plates 50 and 51 were not put into use until 1861.

Two Pence. Unlike the 1d. the old sequence of plate numbers continued. Plates 3 and 4 of the 2d. had corner letters of Alphabet I, Plate 5 Alphabet II and Plate 6 Alphabet III. In Plate 6 the white lines are thinner than before.

1854–57. *Paper more or less blued.* (*a*) *Wmk Small Crown, W* **2**. *P* 16.

			Un	★ *Used*	*Used on cover*
17	**1**	1d. red-brown (Die I) (12.3.54)	£160	10·00	20·00
		a. Imperf three sides (horiz pair)	†	—	
18		1d. yellow-brown (Die I) ..	£240	20·00	
19	**3**	2d. deep blue (Plate 4) (12.3.54)	£1600	60·00	80·00
		a. Imperf three sides (horiz pair)	†	—	
20		2d. pale blue (Plate 4)	£1700	75·00	
20*a*		2d. blue (Plate 5) (18.8.55) ..	£2100	£175	£300
21	**1**	1d. red-brown (Die II) (22.2.55)	£225	30·00	45·00
		a. Imperf			
		(*b*) *Wmk Small Crown, W* **2**. *P* 14			
22	**1**	1d. red-brown (Die I) (1.55) ..	£350	35·00	55·00
23	**3**	2d. blue (Plate 4) (22.2.55) ..	£2100	£150	£210
23*a*		2d. blue (Plate 5) (5.7.55) ..	£2100	£150	£210
		b. Imperf (Plate 5)			
24	**1**	1d. red-brown (Die II) (27.2.55)	£300	30·00	40·00
24*a*		1d. deep red-brown (very blue paper) (Die II)	£340	35·00	
25		1d. orange-brown (Die II) ..	£750	70·00	
		(*c*) *Wmk Large Crown, W* **4**. *P* 16			
26	**1**	1d. red-brown (Die II) (15.5.55)	£600	45·00	70·00
		a. Imperf (Plate 7)			
27	**3**	2d. blue (Plate 5) (20.7.55) ..	£2600	£175	£275
		a. Imperf	—	£2800	
		(*d*) *Wmk Large Crown, W* **4**. *P* 14			
29	**1**	1d. red-brown (Die II) (6.55) ..	£140	5·00	15·00
		a. Imperf (*shades*) (Plates 22, 24, 25, 32, 43)	£1200	£900	
30		1d. brick-red (Die II)	£225	25·00	
31	**1**	1d. plum (Die II) (2.56)	£1000	£325	
32		1d. brown-rose (Die II)	£225	25·00	
33		1d. orange-brown (Die II) (3.57)	£340	30·00	
34	**3**	2d. blue (Plate 5) (20.7.55) ..	£1300	40·00	£100
35		2d. blue (Plate 6) (2.7.57) ..	£1400	40·00	90·00
		a. Imperf	—	£3250	
		b. Imperf horiz (vert pair) ..	†	—	
★17/35a		**For well-centred, lightly used** ..		+125%	

1856–58. *Paper no longer blued.* (*a*) *Wmk Large Crown, W* **4**. *P* 16.

36	**1**	1d. rose-red (Die II) (26.12.57) ..	£750	40·00	70·00
36*a*	**3**	2d. blue (Plate 6) (1.2.58) ..	£3750	£175	£250
		(*b*) (Die II) *Wmk Large Crown, W* **4**. *P* 14			
37	**1**	1d. red-brown (11.56)	£325	80·00	
38		1d. pale red (9.4.57)	50·00	7·00	
		a. Imperf	£600	£500	
39		1d. pale rose (3.57)	50·00	15·00	
40		1d. rose-red (9.57)	35·00	7·00	12·00
		a. Imperf	£650	£500	
41		1d. deep-rose-red (7.57)	60·00	8·00	

1861. *Letters engraved on plate instead of punched* (*Alphabet IV*).

42	**1**	1d. rose-red (Die II) (Plates 50 and 51)	£160	20·00	40·00
		a. Imperf	—	£2000	
★36/42a		**For well-centred, lightly used** ..		+125%	

In both values, varieties may be found as described in the preceding issues—ivory heads, inverted watermarks, re-entries, and double letters in corners.

The change of perforation from 16 to 14 was decided upon late in 1854 since the closer holes of the former gauge tended to cause the sheets of stamps to break up when handled, but for a time both gauges were in concurrent use. Owing to faulty alignment of the impressions on the plates and to shrinkage of the paper when damped, badly perforated stamps are plentiful in the line-engraved issues.

5

6

Showing position of the plate number on the 1d. and 2d. values. (Plate 170 shown)

1858–79. *Letters in all four corners. Wmk Large Crown, W* **4**. *Die* II (1*d. and* 2*d.*). *P* 14.

			Un	★ *Used*	*Used on cover*
43	**5**	1d. rose-red (1.4.64)	5·00	1·50	4·00
44		1d. lake-red	5·00	1·50	
		a. Imperf .. .. *from*	£800	£625	
★43/4a		**For well-centred, lightly used** ..		+125%	

Plate	*Un*	*Used*	*Plate*	*Un*	*Used*
71	15·00	2·25	133	50·00	6·25
72	20·00	2·75	134	5·00	1·50
73	15·00	2·25	135	55·00	21·00
74	12·00	1·50	136	55·00	16·00
76	22·00	1·50	137	10·00	1·75
77	£100000	£80000	138	8·00	1·50
78	55·00	1·50	139	18·00	12·00
79	18·00	1·50	140	8·00	1·50
80	12·00	1·50	141	80·00	6·25
81	32·00	1·75	142	28·00	19·00
82	65·00	2·75	143	18·00	11·00
83	80·00	4·25	144	55·00	16·00
84	32·00	1·75	145	5·00	1·75
85	15·00	1·75	146	8·00	3·75
86	18·00	2·75	147	12·00	2·25
87	5·00	1·50	148	12·00	2·25
88	90·00	5·75	149	10·00	3·75
89	22·00	1·50	150	5·00	1·50
90	16·00	1·50	151	15·00	6·25
91	22·00	3·75	152	12·00	3·50
92	10·00	1·50	153	40·00	6·25
93	22·00	1·50	154	10·00	1·50
94	22·00	3·25	155	10·00	1·75
95	15·00	1·50	156	10·00	1·50
96	16·00	1·50	157	10·00	1·50
97	10·00	2·25	158	5·00	1·50
98	10·00	3·75	159	5·00	1·50
99	15·00	3·25	160	5·00	1·50
100	20·00	1·75	161	18·00	4·25
101	28·00	6·25	162	10·00	4·25
102	12·00	1·50	163	10·00	2·25
103	12·00	2·25	164	10·00	2·25
104	16·00	3·25	165	12·00	1·50
105	38·00	4·25	166	10·00	3·75
106	18·00	1·50	167	8·00	1·50
107	22·00	4·00	168	8·00	5·75
108	18·00	1·75	169	18·00	4·25
109	40·00	2·25	170	8·00	1·50
110	12·00	6·25	171	5·00	1·50
111	20·00	1·75	172	5·00	1·50
112	32·00	1·75	173	28·00	6·25
113	10·00	8·00	174	5·00	1·50
114	£190	8·50	175	20·00	2·25
115	55·00	1·75	176	15·00	1·75
116	40·00	6·25	177	8·00	1·50
117	10·00	1·50	178	10·00	2·25
118	15·00	1·50	179	10·00	1·75
119	8·00	1·50	180	10·00	3·25
120	5·00	1·50	181	10·00	1·50
121	22·00	6·25	182	55·00	3·25
122	5·00	1·50	183	15·00	2·25
123	8·00	1·50	184	5·00	1·75
124	8·00	1·50	185	10·00	2·25
125	8·00	1·75	186	18·00	1·75
127	20·00	1·75	187	8·00	1·50
129	8·00	5·25	188	12·00	7·50
130	12·00	1·75	189	20·00	4·25
131	40·00	12·00	190	10·00	3·75
132	55·00	17·00	191	5·00	4·25

Plate	Un	Used	Plate	Un	Used
192	15·00	1·50	209	10·00	6·25
193	5·00	1·50	210	12·00	8·50
194	10·00	5·25	211	25·00	16·00
195	10·00	5·25	212	10·00	8·00
196	8·00	3·25	213	10·00	8·00
197	10·00	6·25	214	15·00	14·00
198	6·00	3·75	215	15·00	14·00
199	12·00	3·75	216	15·00	14·00
200	12·00	1·50	217	12·00	4·25
201	5·00	3·25	218	8·00	5·25
202	10·00	5·25	219	32·00	55·00
203	5·00	11·00	220	5·00	4·25
204	8·00	1·75	221	18·00	11·00
205	8·00	2·25	222	28·00	27·00
206	8·00	6·25	223	32·00	45·00
207	8·00	6·25	224	38·00	38·00
208	8·00	11·00	225	£1100	£375

Error. Imperf. Issued at Cardiff (Plate 116)

		Un	Used
44*b* 5	1d. rose-red (18.1.70)	£2000	£1250

The following plate numbers are also known imperf and used (No. 44a); 72, 79, 80, 81, 82, 83, 86, 87, 88, 90, 91, 92, 93, 96, 97, 100, 102, 103, 104, 105, 107, 108, 109, 112, 114, 117, 120, 121, 122, 136, 137, 142, 146, 148, 158, 162, 164, 166, 171, 174, 191 and 202.

The numbering of this series of 1d. red plates follows after that of the previous 1d. stamp, last printed from Plate 68.

Plates 69, 70, 75, 126 and 128 were prepared for this issue but rejected owing to defects, and stamps from these plates do not exist, so that specimens which appear to be from these plates (like many of those which optimistic collectors believe to be from Plate 77) bear other plate numbers. Owing to faulty engraving or printing it is not always easy to identify the plate number. Plate 77 was also rejected but some stamps printed from it were used. One specimen is in the Tapling Collection and six or seven others are known. Plates 226 to 228 were made but not used.

Specimens from most of the plates are known with inverted watermark. The variety of watermark described in the General Notes to this section occurs on stamp M A (or M L) on plates up to about 96 (*Prices from £110 used*).

Re-entries in this issue are few, the best being on stamps M K and T K of Plate 71 and on S L and T L, Plate 83.

			Un	Used	★ Used on cover
45	6	2d. blue (thick lines) (7.58)	£190	7·00	20·00
		a. Imperf (Plate 9)	—	£3250	
		Plate			
		7	£475	30·00	
		8	£500	25·00	
		9	£190	7·00	
		12	£850	60·00	
46		2d. blue (thin lines) (1.7.69)	£190	12·00	22·00
47		2d. deep blue (thin lines)	£190	12·00	
		a. Imperf (Plate 13)	£2250		
		Plate			
		13	£200	12·00	
		14	£240	15·00	
		15	£190	15·00	
★45/7		**For well-centred, lightly used**		+125%	

Plates 10 and 11 of the 2d. were prepared but rejected. Plates 13 to 15 were laid down from a new roller impression on which the white lines were thinner.

There are some marked re-entries and repairs, particularly on Plates 7, 8, 9 and 12.

Stamps with inverted watermark may be found and also the T A (T L) and M A (M L) watermark varieties (*see* General Notes to this section).

Though the paper is normally white, some printings showed blueing and stamps showing the "ivory head" may therefore be found.

7

Showing the plate number (9)

9

1870 (1 Oct). *Wmk W* **9**, *extending over three stamps. P* 14.

			Un	Used	★ Used on cover
48	7	½d. rose-red	60·00	12·00	35·00
49		½d. rose	60·00	12·00	
		a. Imperf (Plates 1, 4, 5, 6, 8, 14) . . *from*	£1000	£675	
		Plate			
		1	£125	60·00	
		3	70·00	20·00	
		4	90·00	15·00	
		5	65·00	12·00	
		6	60·00	12·00	
		8	£110	60·00	
		9	£2400	£375	
		10	90·00	12·00	
		11	60·00	12·00	
		12	60·00	12·00	
		13	60·00	12·00	
		14	60·00	12·00	
		15	70·00	18·00	
		19	£110	32·00	
		20	£125	45·00	
★49/9a		**For well-centred, lightly used**		+200%	

The ½d. was printed in sheets of 480 (24 × 20) so that the check letters run from AA XT to AA TX.

Plates 2, 7, 16, 17 and 18 were not completed while Plates 21 and 22, though made, were not used.

Owing to the method of perforating, the outer side of stamps in either the A or X row (i e the left or right side of the sheet) is imperf.

Stamps may be found with watermark inverted or reversed, or without watermark, the latter due to misplacement of the paper when printing.

8

Position of plate Number

1870 (1 Oct). *Wmk W* **4**. *P* 14.

			Un	Used	★ Used on cover
51	8	1½d. rose-red	£200	30·00	£175
52		1½d. lake-red	£200	30·00	
		a. Imperf (Plates 1 and 3) *from*	£2000	†	
		Plate			
		(1)	£400	45·00	
		3	£200	30·00	
		Error of lettering. OP-PC for CP-PC (Plate 1)			
53	8	1½d. rose-red	£4500	£675	
★51/3		**For well-centred, lightly used**		+125%	

1860. *Prepared for use but not issued; blued paper. Wmk W* **4**. *P* 14.

			Un	Used
53*a*	8	1½d. rosy mauve (Plate 1)	£2250	
		b. Error of lettering, OP-PC for CP-PC		

Owing to a proposed change in the postal rates, 1½d. stamps were first printed in 1860, in rosy mauve, No. 53*a*, but the change was not approved and the greater part of the stock was destroyed.

In 1870 a 1½d. stamp was required and was issued in rose-red.

Plate 1 did not have the plate number in the design of the stamps, but on stamps from Plate 3 the number will be found in the frame as shown above.

Plate 2 was defective and was not used.

The error of lettering OP-PC on Plate 1 was apparently not noticed by the printers, and therefore not corrected.

EMBOSSED ISSUES

Volume 1 of the Stanley Gibbons *Great Britain Specialised Catalogue* gives further detailed information on the embossed issues.

PRICES. The prices quoted are for cut-square stamps with average to fine embossing. Stamps with exceptionally clear embossing are worth more.

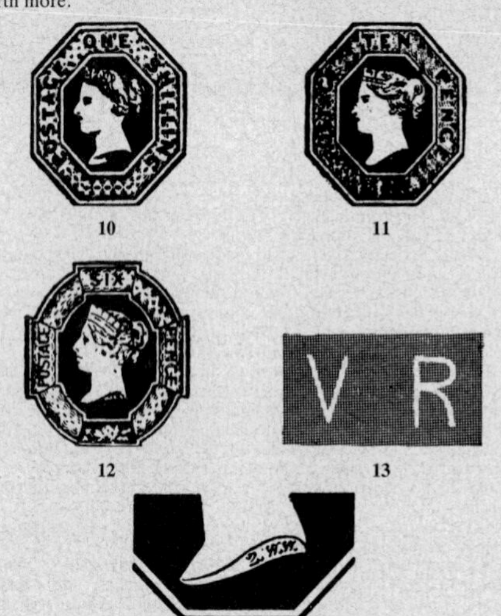

10 11 12 13

Position of die number

(Primary die engraved at the Royal Mint by William Wyon. Stamps printed at Somerset House)

1847–54. *Imperf.* (For paper and wmk see footnote.)

			Un	Used	Used on cover
54	10	1s. pale green (11.9.47)	£3250	£475	£575
55		1s. green	£3250	£525	
56		1s. deep green	£3750	£525	
		Die 1 (1847)	£3250	£475	
		Die 2 (1854)	£3750	£550	
57	11	10d. brown (6.11.48)	£2750	£700	£1200
		Die 1 (1848)	£3000	£750	
		Die 2 (1850)	£2750	£700	
		Die 3 (1853)	£2750	£700	
		Die 4 (1854)	£3000	£750	
		Die 5	£17000		
58	12	6d. mauve (1.3.54)	£3000	£550	
59		6d. dull lilac	£3000	£525	£650
60		6d. purple	£3000	£525	
61		6d. violet	£4250	£1000	

The 1s. and 10d. are on "Dickinson" paper with "silk" threads (actually a pale blue twisted cotton yarn). The 6d. is on paper watermarked V R in single-lined letters, W **13**, which may be found in four ways—upright, inverted, upright reversed, and inverted reversed, upright reversed being the most common.

The die numbers are indicated on the base of the bust. Only Die 1 (1 WW) of the 6d. was used for the adhesive stamps. The 10d. is from Die 1 (W.W.1 on stamps), and Dies 2 to 5 (2 W.W., 3 W.W., 4 W.W. and 5 W.W.) but the number and letters on stamps from Die 1 are seldom clear and many specimens are known without any trace of them. Because of this the stamp we previously listed as "No die number" has been deleted. That they are from Die 1 is proved by the existence of blocks showing stamps with and without the die number. The 1s. is from Dies 1 and 2 (W.W.1, W.W.2).

The normal arrangement of the "silk" threads in the paper was in pairs running down each vertical row of the sheet, the space betw the threads of each pair being approximately 5 mm and betw pairs of threads 20 mm. Varieties due to misplacement of the pa in printing show a single thread on the first stamp from the sh margin and two threads 20 mm apart on the other stamps of the r Faulty manufacture is the cause of stamps with a single thread in middle.

Through bad spacing of the impressions, which were handstru all values may be found with two impressions more or l overlapping. Owing to the small margin allowed for variation spacing, specimens with good margins on all sides are not comm

Double impressions are known of all values.

Later printings of the 6d. had the gum tinted green to enable printer to distinguish the gummed side of the paper.

SURFACE-PRINTED ISSUES

GENERAL NOTES

Volume 1 of the Stanley Gibbons *Great Britain Speciali Catalogue* gives further detailed information on the surface-prin issues.

"Abnormals". The majority of the great rarities in the surfa printed group of issues are the so-called "abnormals", wh existence is due to the practice of printing six sheets from every pl as soon as made, one of which was kept for record purposes Somerset House, while the others were perforated and usually issu If such plates were not used for general production or if, before t came into full use, a change of watermark or colour took place, six sheets originally printed would differ from the main issue in pla colour or watermark and, if issued, would be extremely rare.

The abnormal stamps of this class listed in this Catalogue distinguished, where not priced, by an asterisk (*), are:

No.	
78	3d. Plate 3 (with white dots)
152	4d. vermilion, Plate 16
153	4d. sage-green, Plate 17
109	6d. mauve, Plate 10
124/*a*	6d. chestnut and 6d. pale chestnut, Plate 12
145	6d. pale buff, Plate 13
88	9d. Plate 3 (hair lines)
98	9d. Plate 5 (*see* footnote to No. 98)
113	10d. Plate 2
91	1s. Plate 3 ("Plate 2")
148/50	1s. green, Plate 14
120	2s. blue, Plate 3

Those which may have been issued, but of which no specimens known, are 2½d. wmk Anchor, Plates 4 and 5; 3d. wmk Emble Plate 5; 3d. wmk Spray, Plate 21; 6d. grey, wmk Spray, Plate 18; orange, Plate 2; 1s. wmk Emblems, Plate 5. 5s. wmk Maltese Cro Plate 4.

The 10d. Plate 1, wmk Emblems (No. 99), is sometimes recko among the abnormals, but was an error, due to the use of the wr paper.

Corner Letters. With the exception of the 4d., 6d. and 1s. of 18 57, the ½d., 1½d., 2d. and 5d. of 1880, the 1d. lilac of 1881 and the (which had letters in lower corners only, and in the reverse orde the normal), all the surface-printed stamps issued prior to 1887 h letters in all four corners, as in the later line-engraved stamps. T arrangement is the same, the letters running in sequence right acr and down the sheets, whether these were divided into panes or r The corner letters existing naturally depend on the number of star in the sheet and their arrangement.

Imprimaturs and Imperforate Stamps. The Post Office retained their records (now in the National Postal Museum) one imperfor sheet from each plate, known as the Imprimatur (or offici approved) sheet. Some stamps were removed from time to time presentation purposes and have come on to the market, but th imperforates are not listed as they were not issued. Full details c be found in Volume I of the *Great Britain Specialised Catalogue.*

However, other imperforate stamps are known to have been issu and these are listed where it has been possible to prove that they not come from the Imprimatur sheets. It is therefore advisable purchase these only when acccompanied by an Expert Commit certificate of genuineness.

Plate Numbers. All stamps from No. 75 to No. 163 bear in th designs either the plate number or, in one or two earlier instanc some other indication by which one plate can be distinguished fr another. With the aid of these and of the corner letters it is t possible to "reconstruct" a sheet of stamps from any plate of a issue or denomination.

Surface-printing. In this context the traditional designat "surface-printing" is synonymous with typo(graphy)—a philate term—or letterpress—the printers' term—as meaning printing fr (the surface of) raised type. It is also called relief-printing, as image is in relief (in French, *en épargne*), unwanted parts of design having been cut away. Duplicate impressions can electrotyped or stereotyped from an original die, the resulting *clic* being locked together to form the printing plate.

Wing Margins. As the vertical gutters (spaces) between the pan into which sheets of stamps of most values were divided until introduction of the Imperial Crown watermark, were perfora through the centre with a single row of holes, instead of each verti row of stamps on the inner side of the panes having its own line perforation as is now usual, a proportion of the stamps in each sh have what is called a "wing margin" about 5 mm wide on one other side.

The stamps with "wing margins" are the watermark Emblems a Spray of Rose series (3d. 6d. 9d. 10d. 1s. and 2s.) with letters D, E or I in S.E. corner, and the watermark Garter series (4d. and 8 with letters F or G in S.E. corner. Knowledge of this lettering w enable collectors to guard against stamps with wing margin cut do and re-perforated, but note that wing margin stamps of Nos. 62 to are also to be found re-perforated.

PRINTERS. The issues of Queen Victoria, Nos. 62/214, were typo Thomas De La Rue & Co.

PERFORATIONS. All the surface-printed issues of Queen Victo are Perf 14, with the exception of Nos. 126/9.

ALTERED CATALOGUE NUMBERS

Any Catalogue numbers altered from the la edition are shown as a list in the introducto pages.

KEY TO SURFACE-PRINTED ISSUES 1855–83

.G. Nos.	Description	Watermark	Date of Issue
	NO CORNER LETTERS		
2	4d. carmine	Small Garter	31.7.55
3/5	4d. carmine	Medium Garter	25.2.56
6/*a*	4d. carmine	Large Garter	Jan 1857
9/70	6d. lilac	Emblems	21.10.56
1/3	1s. green	Emblems	1.11.56
	SMALL WHITE CORNER LETTERS		
5/7	3d. carmine	Emblems	1.5.62
8	3d. carmine (dots)	Emblems	Aug 1862
9/82	4d. red	Large Garter	15.1.62
3/5	6d. lilac	Emblems	1.12.62
6/8	9d. bistre	Emblems	15.1.62
9/91	1s. green	Emblems	1.12.62
	LARGE WHITE CORNER LETTERS		
2	3d. rose	Emblems	1.3.65
02/3	3d. rose	Spray	July 1867
3/5	4d. vermilion	Large Garter	4.7.65
6/7	6d. lilac	Emblems	7.3.65
04/7	6d. lilac	Spray	21.6.67
08/9	6d. lilac	Spray	8.3.69
22/4	6d. chestnut	Spray	12.4.72
25	6d. grey	Spray	24.4.73
8	9d. straw	Emblems	30.10.65
10/11	9d. straw	Spray	3.10.67
9	10d. brown	Emblems	11.11.67
12/14	10d. brown	Spray	1.7.67
01	1s. green	Emblems	19.1.65
15/17	1s. green	Spray	13.7.67
18/20*b*	2s. blue	Spray	1.7.67
21	2s. brown	Spray	27.2.80
26/7	5s. rose	Cross	1.7.67
28	10s. grey	Cross	26.9.78
29	£1 brown-lilac	Cross	26.9.78
30, 134	5s. rose	Anchor	25.11.82
31, 135	10s. grey-green	Anchor	Feb 1883
32, 136	£1 brown-lilac	Anchor	Dec 1882
33, 137	£5 orange	Anchor	21.3.82
	LARGE COLOURED CORNER LETTERS		
56	1d. Venetian red	Crown	1.1.80
38/9	2½d. rosy mauve	Anchor	1.7.75
41	2½d. rosy mauve	Orb	1.5.76
42	2½d. blue	Orb	5.2.80
57	2½d. blue	Crown	23.3.81
43/4	3d. rose	Spray	5.7.73
58	3d. rose	Crown	Jan 1881
59	3d. on 3d. lilac	Crown	1.1.83
52	4d. vermilion	Large Garter	1.3.76
53	4d. sage-green	Large Garter	12.3.77
54	4d. brown	Large Garter	15.8.80
60	4d. brown	Crown	9.12.80
45	6d. buff	Spray	15.3.73
46/7	6d. grey	Spray	20.3.74
61	6d. grey	Crown	1.1.81
62	6d. on 6d. lilac	Crown	1.1.83
56*a*	8d. purple-brown	Large Garter	July 1876
56	8d. orange	Large Garter	11.9.76
48/50	1s. green	Spray	1.9.73
51	1s. brown	Spray	14.10.80
63	1s. brown	Crown	24.5.81

Watermarks:		
	Anchor	W **40, 47**
	Cross	W **39**
	Crown	W **49**
	Emblems	W **20**
	Large Garter	W **17**
	Medium Garter	W **16**
	Orb	W **48**
	Small Garter	W **15**
	Spray	W **33**

14

15 Small Garter

16 Medium Garter

17 Large Garter

1855–57. *No corner letters.*

(a) *Wmk Small Garter, W* **15.** *Highly glazed, deeply blued paper* (31 July 1855)

			Un	★ Used	Used on cover
	14	4d. carmine (*shades*)	£2750	£250	£350
		a. Paper slightly blued ..	£3000	£250	
		b. White paper	£3500	£425	

(*b*) *Wmk Medium Garter, W* **16**

(i) *Thick, blued highly glazed paper* (25 February 1856)

			Un	Used	Used on cover
63	**14**	4d. carmine (*shades*)	£3250	£250	£350
		a. White paper	£3000		

(ii) *Ordinary thin white paper* (September 1856)

			Un	Used	Used on cover
64	**14**	4d. pale carmine	£2250	£225	£300
		a. Stamp printed double ..	†	—	

(iii) *Ordinary white paper, specially prepared ink* (1 November 1856)

			Un	Used	Used on cover
65	**14**	4d. rose *or* deep rose	£2250	£225	£325

(*c*) *Wmk Large Garter, W* **17.** *Ordinary white paper* (January 1857)

			Un	Used	Used on cover
66	**14**	4d. rose-carmine	£800	50·00	£110
		a. Rose	£700	50·00	
		b. Thick glazed paper	£1900	£150	
★62/6b		**For well-centred, lightly used** ..		+125%	

18

19

20 Emblems wmk (normal)

20*a* Wmk error, three roses and shamrock

20*b* Wmk error, three roses and thistle

(*d*) *Wmk Emblems, W* **20**

			Un	★ Used	Used on cover
69	**18**	6d. deep lilac (21.10.56) ..	£650	80·00	
70		6d. pale lilac	£575	60·00	£110
		a. Azure paper	£3000	£450	
		b. Thick paper	£850	£175	
		c. Error. Wmk W **20*a***			
71	**19**	1s. deep green (1.11.56) ..	£1500	£200	
72		1s. green	£725	£175	£200
73		1s. pale green	£725	£175	
		a. Azure paper	—	£625	
		b. Thick paper	—	£200	
		c. Imperf			
★69/73b		**For well-centred, lightly used** ..		+125%	

21

22

23

24

25 Plate 2

A. White dots added

B. Hair lines

1862–64. *A small uncoloured letter in each corner, the* 4*d. wmk Large Garter. W* **17**, *the others Emblems, W* **20**.

			Un	★ Used	Used on cover
75	**21**	3d. deep carmine-rose (Plate 2) (1.5.62)	£1600	£175	
76		3d. bright carmine-rose	£850	£150	£325
77		3d. pale carmine-rose	£850	£175	
		b. Thick paper	—	£225	
78		3d. rose (with white dots, Type A, Plate 3) (8.62)	£15000	£3000	
		a. Imperf (Plate 3)	£2500		
79	**22**	4d. bright red (Plate 3) (15.1.62)	£900	70·00	
80		4d. pale red	£600	50·00	£120
81		4d. bright red (Hair lines, Type B, Plate 4) (16.10.63)	£800	60·00	
82		4d. pale red (Hair lines, Type B, Plate 4)	£700	50·00	£140
		a. Imperf (Plate 4)	£2000		
83	**23**	6d. deep lilac (Plate 3) (1.12.62)	£950	80·00	
84	**23**	6d. lilac	£800	55·00	£125
		a. Azure paper	—	£375	
		b. Thick paper	—	90·00	
		c. Error. Wmk W **20*b*** (stamp TF)			
85		6d. lilac (Hair lines, Plate 4) (20.4.64)	£950	95·00	£200
		a. Imperf	£1400		
		c. Thick paper	£1400	£110	
		d. Error. Wmk W **20*b*** (stamp TF)			
86	**24**	9d. bistre (Plate 2) (15.1.62) ..	£1600	£190	£300
87		9d. straw	£1600	£175	
		a. On azure paper			
		b. Thick paper	£2000	£275	
		c. Error. Watermark W **20*b*** (stamp TF)	†	—	
88		9d. bistre (Hair lines, Plate 3) (5.62)	£6750	£2500	
89	**25**	1s. deep green (Plate No. 1 = Plate 2) (1.12.62)	£1100	£160	
90		1s. green (Plate No. 1 = Plate 2)	£900	£100	£200
		a. "K" in lower left corner in white circle (stamp KD) ..	£4500	£600	
		aa. "K" normal (stamp KD) ..	—	£850	
		b. On azure paper			
		c. Thick paper	—	£190	
		ca. Thick paper, "K" in circle as No. 90a	—	£1200	
91		1s. deep green (Plate No. 2 = Plate 3)	£12000		
		a. Imperf	£1800		
★75/91		**For well-centred, lightly used** ..		+125%	

The 3d. as Type **21**, but with network background in the spandrels which is found overprinted SPECIMEN, was never issued.

The plates of this issue may be distinguished as follows:

3d. Plate 2. No white dots.
 Plate 3. White dots as Illustration A.
4d. Plate 3. No hair lines. Roman I next to lower corner letters.
 Plate 4. Hair lines in corners. (Illustration B.). Roman II.
6d. Plate 3. No hair lines.
 Plate 4. Hair lines in corners.
9d. Plate 2. No hair lines.
 Plate 3. Hair lines in corners. Beware of faked lines.
1s. Plate 2. Numbered 1 on stamps.
 Plate 3. Numbered 2 on stamps and with hair lines.

The 9d. on azure paper (No. 87a) is very rare, only one confirmed example being known.

The variety "K" in circle, No. 90a, is believed to be due to a damaged letter having been cut out and replaced. It is probable that the punch was driven in too deeply, causing the flange to penetrate the surface, producing an indentation showing as an uncoloured circle.

The watermark variety "three roses and a shamrock" illustrated in W **20*a*** was evidently due to the substitution of an extra rose for the thistle in a faulty watermark bit. It is found on stamp TA of Plate 4 of the 3d., Plates 1 (No. 70c), 3, 5 and 6 of the 6d., Plate 4 of the 9d. and Plate 4 of the 1s.

A similar variety, W **20*b***, but showing three roses and a thistle is found on stamp TF of the 6d. (Nos. 84/5) and 9d. (Nos. 87, 97/8).

26

27

28 (with hyphen)

28*a* (without hyphen)

29

30

31

1865–67. *Large uncoloured corner letters. Wmk Large Garter* (4*d.*); *others Emblems.*

			Un	★ Used	Used on cover
92	**26**	3d. rose (Plate 4) (1.3.65) ..	£500	60·00	£125
		a. Error. Wmk W **20*a*** ..	£1200	£325	
		b. Thick paper	£625	70·00	
93	**27**	4d. dull vermilion (4.7.65) ..	£300	35·00	80·00
94		4d. vermilion	£275	35·00	
		a. Imperf (Plates 11, 12) ..	£600		
95		4d. deep vermilion	£300	32·00	
		Plate			
		7 (1865)	£375	38·00	
		8 (1866)	£325	38·00	
		9 (1867)	£325	35·00	
		10 (1868)	£375	50·00	
		11 (1869)	£375	30·00	
		12 (1870)	£275	35·00	
		13 (1872)	£325	35·00	
		14 (1873)	£375	60·00	
96	**28**	6d. deep lilac (with hyphen) (7.3.65)	£500	65·00	
97		6d. lilac (with hyphen) ..	£425	50·00	90·00
		a. Thick paper	£525	80·00	
		b. Stamp doubly printed (Pl 6)	—	£6000	
		c. Error. Wmk W **20*a*** (Pl 5, 6) .. .. .. *from*	—	£375	
		d. Error. Wmk W **20*b*** (Plate 5)			
		Plate			
		5 (1865)	£425	50·00	
		6 (1867)	£1300	90·00	

No.	Type	Description	Un	Used	Used on cover
8	**29**	9d. straw (Plate 4) (30.10.65) ..	£875	£300	£400
		a. Thick paper	£1300	£400	
		b. Error. Wmk W **20***a* ..	—	£450	
		c. Error. Wmk W **20***b* (stamp T F)			
9	**30**	10d. red-brown (Pl 1) (11.11.67)	†	£13000	
1	**31**	1s. green (Plate 4) (19.1.65) ..	£800	95·00	£150
		a. Error. Wmk W **20***a* ..	—	£425	
		b. Thick paper	£950	£190	
		c. Imperf between (vert pair)	—	£4500	
★92/101c		**For well-centred, lightly used** ..		+100%	

From mid-1866 to about the end of 1871 4d. stamps of this issue ppeared generally with watermark inverted.

Unused examples of No. 98 from Plate 5 exist, but this was never ut to press and all evidence points to such stamps originating from portion of the Imprimatur sheet which was perforated by De La ue in 1887 for insertion in albums to be presented to members of e Stamp Committee (*Price* £13000 *un*).

The 10d. stamps, No. 99, were printed in *error* on paper atermarked "Emblems" instead of on "Spray of Rose".

32

33 Spray of Rose

34

867–80. *Wmk Spray of Rose, W* **33**.

No.	Type	Description	Un	★ Used	Used on cover
02	**26**	3d. deep rose (12.7.67) ..	£275	35·00	
03		3d. rose	£275	25·00	50·00
		a. Imperf (Plates 5, 6, 8) *from*	£800		
		Plate			
		4 (1867)	£375	80·00	
		5 (1868)	£275	25·00	
		6 (1870)	£300	25·00	
		7 (1871)	£375	30·00	
		8 (1872)	£325	30·00	
		9 (1872)	£325	35·00	
		10 (1873)	£375	65·00	
04	**28**	6d. lilac (with hyphen) (Plate 6) (21.6.67)	£650	50·00	£125
		a. Imperf			
05		6d. deep lilac (with hyphen) (Plate 6)	£650	50·00	
06		6d. purple (with hyphen) (Pl 6)	£650	70·00	
07		6d. bright violet (with hyphen) (Plate 6) (22.7.68) ..	£650	55·00	
08	**28***a*	6d. dull violet (without hyphen) (Plate 8) (8.3.69) ..	£425	45·00	
09		6d. mauve (without hyphen)	£350	45·00	65·00
		a. Imperf (Plate Nos. 8 and 9)	£900	£800	
		Plate			
		8 (1869, mauve) ..	£350	45·00	
		9 (1870, mauve) ..	£350	45·00	
		10 (1869, mauve) ..	*	£13000	
10	**29**	9d. straw (Plate No. 4) (3.10.67)	£725	£150	£250
11		9d. pale straw (Plate No. 4) ..	£725	£160	
		a. Imperf (Plate 4)	£2250		
12	**30**	10d. red-brown (1.7.67) ..	£1200	£200	£400
13		10d. pale red-brown	£1200	£225	
14		10d. deep red-brown	£1400	£225	
		a. Imperf (Plate 1)	£2250		
		Plate			
		1 (1867)	£1200	£200	
		2 (1867)	£13000	£3000	
15	**31**	1s. deep green (13.7.67) ..	£500	22·00	
17		1s. green	£400	22·00	40·00
		a. Imperf between (horiz pair) (Plate 7)			
		b. Imperf (Plate 4) ..	£1300	£725	
		Plate			
		4 (1867)	£400	28·00	
		5 (1871)	£450	25·00	
		6 (1871)	£625	22·00	
		7 (1873)	£625	50·00	
18	**32**	2s. dull blue (1.7.67) ..	£1200	90·00	£400
19		2s. deep blue	£1200	90·00	
		a. Imperf (Plate 1)	£2500		
20		2s. pale blue	£1800	£150	
		aa. Imperf (Plate 1)	£2250		
20*a*		2s. cobalt	£5750	£1300	
20*b*		2s. milky blue	£3750	£550	
		Plate			
		1 (1867)	£1200	90·00	
		3 (1868)	*	£3500	
21		2s. brown (Plate No. 1) (27.2.80)	£7500	£1600	
		a. Imperf	£5500		
		b. No watermark	†	—	
★102/21		**For well-centred, lightly used** ..		+75%	

Examples of the 1s. from Plates 5 and 6 *without* watermark are ostal forgeries used at the Stock Exchange Post Office in the early 870's.

872–73. *Uncoloured letters in corners. Wmk Spray, W* **33**.

No.	Type	Description	Un	★ Used	Used on cover
22	**34**	6d. deep chestnut (Plate 11) (12.4.72)	£500	32·00	70·00
22*a*		6d. chestnut (Plate 11) (22.5.72)	£425	35·00	
22*b*		6d. pale chestnut (Plate 11) (1872)	£400	32·00	
23		6d. pale buff (19.10.72) ..	£425	60·00	£175
		Plate			
		11 (1872, pale buff) ..	£425	60·00	
		12 (1872, pale buff) ..	£900	95·00	
24		6d. chestnut (Plate 12) (1872) ..	*	£1500	
24*a*		6d. pale chestnut (Plate 12) (1872)	*	£1500	
25		6d. grey (Plate 12) (24.4.73) ..	£825	£150	£200
		a. Imperf	£1600		
122/5		**For well-centred, lightly used** ..		+50%	

35

36

37

38

39 Maltese Cross

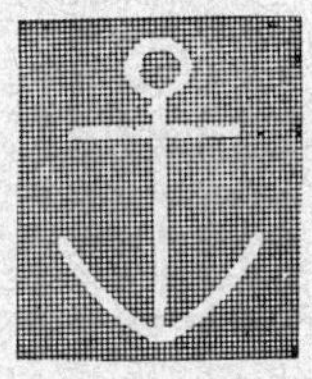

40 Large Anchor

1867–83. *Uncoloured letters in corners.*

(*a*) *Wmk Maltese Cross, W* **39**. *P* 15½ × 15

No.	Type	Description	Un	★ Used
126	**35**	5s. rose (1.7.67)	£3250	£375
127		5s. pale rose	£3500	£375
		a. Imperf (Plate 1)	£5000	
		Plate		
		1 (1867)	£3250	£375
		2 (1874)	£4250	£450
128	**36**	10s. greenish grey (Plate 1) (26.9.78) ..	£22000	£1200
129	**37**	£1 brown-lilac (Plate 1) (26.9.78) ..	£27000	£1700
		(*b*) *Wmk Anchor, W* **40**. *P* 14. (i) *Blued paper*		
130	**35**	5s. rose (Plate 4) (25.11.82)	£6500	£1300
131	**36**	10s. grey-green (Plate 1) (2.83)	£26000	£1900
132	**37**	£1 brown-lilac (Plate 1) (12.82) ..	£32000	£3250
133	**38**	£5 orange (Plate 1) (21.3.82)	£21000	£4750
		(ii) *White paper*		
134	**35**	5s. rose (Plate 4)	£6250	£1300
135	**36**	10s. greenish grey (Plate 1) .. .	£26000	£1900
136	**37**	£1 brown-lilac (Plate 1) .. .	£38000	£2750
137	**38**	£5 orange (Plate 1)	£5750	£1700
★126/37		**For well-centred, lightly used**		+75%

41

42

43

44 **45** **46**

47 Small Anchor

48 Orb

1873–80. *Large coloured letters in the corners.*

No.	Type	Description	Un	★ Used	Used on cover
		(*a*) *Wmk Anchor, W* **47**			
138	**41**	2½d. rosy mauve (*blued paper*) (1.7.75)	£475	65·00	
		a. Imperf			
139		2½d. rosy mauve (*white paper*) ..	£325	55·00	90·00
		Plate			
		1 (*blued paper*) (1875) ..	£475	65·00	
		1 (*white paper*) (1875) ..	£325	55·00	
		2 (*blued paper*) (1875) ..	£3500	£750	
		2 (*white paper*) (1875) ..	£325	55·00	
		3 (*white paper*) (1875) ..	£500	60·00	
		3 (*blued paper*) (1875) ..	—	£2750	
		Error of Lettering L H—F L for L H—H L (*Plate* 2)			
140	**41**	2½d. rosy mauve	£8500	£800	
		(*b*) *Wmk Orb, W* **48**			
141	**41**	2½d. rosy mauve (1.5.76) ..	£300	30·00	60·00
		Plate			
		3 (1876)	£650	60·00	
		4 (1876)	£300	30·00	
		5 (1876)	£300	35·00	
		6 (1876)	£300	30·00	
		7 (1877)	£300	30·00	
		8 (1877)	£300	35·00	
		9 (1877)	£300	30·00	
		10 (1878)	£350	45·00	
		11 (1878)	£300	30·00	
		12 (1878)	£300	35·00	
		13 (1878)	£300	35·00	
		14 (1879)	£300	30·00	
		15 (1879)	£300	30·00	
		16 (1879)	£300	30·00	
		17 (1880)	£725	£150	
142		2½d. blue (5.2.80)	£250	25·00	35·00
		Plate			
		17 (1880)	£250	35·00	
		18 (1880)	£300	28·00	
		19 (1880)	£250	25·00	
		20 (1880)	£250	25·00	
		(*c*) *Wmk Spray, W* **33**			
143	**42**	3d. rose (5.7.73)	£250	25·00	45·00
144		3d. pale rose	£250	25·00	
		Plate			
		11 (1873)	£250	25·00	
		12 (1873)	£300	25·00	
		14 (1874)	£325	28·00	
		15 (1874)	£250	25·00	
		16 (1875)	£250	25·00	
		17 (1875)	£300	25·00	
		18 (1875)	£300	25·00	
		19 (1876)	£250	25·00	
		20 (1879)	£250	45·00	
145	**43**	6d. pale buff (Plate 13) (15.3.73)	*	£5500	
146		6d. deep grey (20.3.74) ..	£325	40·00	70·00
147		6d. grey	£300	35·00	
		Plate			
		13 (1874)	£300	35·00	
		14 (1875)	£300	35·00	
		15 (1876)	£300	35·00	
		16 (1878)	£300	35·00	
		17 (1880)	£400	60·00	
148	**44**	1s. deep green (1.9.73) ..	£425	60·00	
150		1s. pale green	£350	45·00	75·00
		Plate			
		8 (1873)	£425	60·00	
		9 (1874)	£425	60·00	
		10 (1874)	£400	65·00	
		11 (1875)	£400	65·00	
		12 (1875)	£350	45·00	
		13 (1876)	£350	45·00	
		14 (—)	*	£13000	
151		1s. orange-brown (Plate 13) (14.10.80)	£15000	£300	£425
		(*d*) *Wmk Large Garter, W* **17**			
152	**45**	4d. vermilion (1.3.76)	£825	£225	£375
		Plate			
		15 (1876)	£825	£225	
		16 (1877)	*	£13000	
153		4d. sage-green (12.3.77) ..	£525	£150	£240
		Plate			
		15 (1877)	£600	£175	
		16 (1877)	£525	£150	
		17 (1877)	*	£7500	
154		4d. grey-brown (Plate 17) (15.8.80)	£775	£250	£350
		a. Imperf	£2750		
156	**46**	8d. orange (Plate 1) (11.9.76) ..	£675	£190	£250
★138/56		**For well-centred, lightly used** ..		+100%	

1876 (July). *Prepared for use but not issued.*

No.	Type	Description	Un
156*a*	**46**	8d. purple-brown (Plate 1) ..	£4000

49 Imperial Crown

3d

(**50**)

1880–83. *Wmk Imperial Crown, W* **49**.

No.	Type	Description	Un	★ Used	Used on cover
157	**41**	2½d. blue (23.3.81)	£250	15·00	30·00
		Plate			
		21 (1881)	£300	22·00	
		22 (1881)	£250	22·00	
		23 (1881)	£250	15·00	
158	**42**	3d. rose (3.81)	£300	50·00	70·00
		Plate			
		20 (1881)	£350	70·00	
		21 (1881)	£300	50·00	

			Un	Used	Used on cover
159	**42**	3d. on 3d. lilac (T **50**) (C.) (Plate 21) (1.1.83)	£300	95·00	£300
160	**45**	4d. grey-brown (8.12.80)	£250	40·00	95·00
		Plate			
		17 (1880)	£250	40·00	
		18 (1882)	£250	40·00	
161	**43**	6d. grey (1.1.81)	£225	45·00	70·00
		Plate			
		17 (1881)	£250	45·00	
		18 (1882)	£225	45·00	
162		6d. on 6d. lilac (as T **50**) (C.) (Plate 18) (1.1.83)	£250	95·00	£200
		a. Slanting dots (various) *from*	£300	£100	
		b. Opt double	—	£5250	
163	**44**	1s. orange-brown (24.5.81)	£325	90·00	£175
		Plate			
		13 (1881)	£375	90·00	
		14 (1881)	£325	90·00	
★157/63		**For well-centred, lightly used**		+75%	

The 1s. Plate 14 (line perf 14) exists in purple, but was not issued in this shade (*Price* £3000 *unused*). Examples were included in a few of the Souvenir Albums prepared for members of the "Stamp Committee of 1884".

52

53

54

55

56

1880–81. *Wmk Imperial Crown, W* **49**.

			Un	★ Used	Used on cover
164	**52**	½d. deep green (14.10.80)	30·00	8·00	15·00
		a. Imperf	£725		
		b. No watermark	£3250		
165		½d. pale green	30·00	12·00	
166	**53**	1d. Venetian red (1.1.80)	12·00	8·00	12·00
		a. Imperf	£725		
167	**54**	1½d. Venetian red (14.10.80)	£125	30·00	95·00
168	**55**	2d. pale rose (8.12.80)	£140	60·00	95·00
168*a*		2d. deep rose	£140	60·00	
169	**56**	5d. indigo (15.3.81)	£425	75·00	£160
		a. Imperf	£1500	£1100	
★164/9		**For well-centred, lightly used**		+75%	

Die I

57

Die II

1881. *Wmk Imperial Crown, W* **49**. (*a*) 14 *dots in each corner, Die* I (12 *July*).

			Un	★ Used	Used on cover
170	**57**	1d. lilac	95·00	22·00	30·00
171		1d. pale lilac	95·00	22·00	
		(*b*) 16 *dots in each corner, Die* II (13 *December*)			
172	**57**	1d. lilac	2·00	1·50	2·50
172*a*		1d. bluish lilac	£210	65·00	
173		1d. deep purple	2·00	1·00	
		a. Printed both sides	£425	†	
		b. Frame broken at bottom	£550	£250	
		c. Printed on gummed side	£450	†	
		d. Imperf three sides (pair)	£2750	†	
		e. Printed both sides but impression on back inverted	£475	†	
		f. No watermark	£800	†	
		g. Blued paper	£1900		
174		1d. mauve	2·00	1·00	
		a. Imperf (pair)	£1100		
★170/4		**For well-centred, lightly used**		+50%	

1d. stamps with the words "PEARS SOAP" printed on the back in *orange*, *blue* or *mauve* price *from* £400, *unused*.

The variety "frame broken at bottom" (No. 173b) shows a white space just inside the bottom frame-line from between the "N" and "E" of "ONE" to below the first "N" of "PENNY", breaking the pearls and cutting into the lower part of the oval below "PEN".

MINIMUM PRICE

The minimum price quote is 10p which represents a handling charge rather than a basis for valuing common stamps. For further notes about prices see introductory pages.

KEY TO SURFACE-PRINTED ISSUES 1880–1900

S.G. Nos.	Description	Date of Issue
164/5	½d. green	14.10.80
187	½d. slate-blue	1.4.84
197/*e*	½d. vermilion	1.1.87
213	½d. blue-green	17.4.1900
166	1d. Venetian red	1.1.80
170/1	1d. lilac, Die I	12.7.81
172/4	1d. lilac, Die II	12.12.81
167	1½d. Venetian red	14.10.80
188	1½d. lilac	1.4.84
198	1½d. purple and green	1.1.87
168/*a*	2d. rose	8.12.80
189	2d. lilac	1.4.84
199/200	2d. green and red	1.1.87
190	2½d. lilac	1.4.84
201	2½d. purple on blue paper	1.1.87
191	3d. lilac	1.4.84
202/4	3d. purple on yellow paper	1.1.87
192	4d. dull green	1.4.84
205/*a*	4d. green and brown	1.1.87
206	4½d. green and carmine	15.9.92
169	5d. indigo	15.3.81
193	5d. dull green	1.4.84
207	5d. purple and blue, Die I	1.1.87
207*a*	5d. purple and blue, Die II	1888
194	6d. dull green	1.4.84
208/*a*	6d. purple on rose-red paper	1.1.87
195	9d. dull green	1.8.83
209	9d. purple and blue	1.1.87
210/*b*	10d. purple and carmine	24.2.90
196	1s. dull green	1.4.84
211	1s. green	1.1.87
214	1s. green and carmine	11.7.1900
175	2s. 6d. lilac on blued paper	2.7.83
178/9	2s. 6d. lilac	1884
176	5s. rose on blued paper	1.4.84
180/1	5s. rose	1884
177/*a*	10s. ultramarine on blued paper	1.4.84
182/3*a*	10s. ultramarine	1884
185	£1 brown-lilac, wmk Crowns	1.4.84
186	£1 brown-lilac, wmk Orbs	2.88
212	£1 green	28.1.91

Note that the £5 value used with the above series is listed as Nos. 133 and 137.

58

59

60

1883–84. *Coloured letters in the corners. Wmk Anchor, W* **40**.

			Un	★ Used
		(*a*) *Blued paper*		
175	**58**	2s. 6d. lilac (2.7.83)	£2750	£700
176	**59**	5s. rose (1.4.84)	£4250	£1500
177	**60**	10s. ultramarine (1.4.84)	£14000	£3750
177*a*		10s. cobalt (5.84)	£16000	£5500
		(*b*) *White paper*		
178	**58**	2s. 6d. lilac	£300	90·00
179		2s. 6d. deep lilac	£300	90·00
		a. Error. On blued paper	£2000	£650
180	**59**	5s. rose	£500	£110
181		5s. crimson	£500	£110
182	**60**	10s. cobalt	£15000	£3750
183		10s. ultramarine	£1000	£325
183*a*		10s. pale ultramarine	£1000	£325
★175/83*a*		**For well-centred, lightly used**		+50%

For No. 180 perf 12 *see* second note below No. 196.

61

Broken frames, Plate 2

1884 (1 April). *Wmk Three Imperial Crowns, W* **49**.

			Un	★ Use
185	**61**	£1 brown-lilac	£13500	£13
		a. Frame broken	£20000	£20

1888 (Feb). *Wmk Three Orbs. W* **48**.

186	**61**	£1 brown-lilac	£24000	£20
		a. Frame broken	£30000	£35
★185/6a		**For well-centred, lightly used**		+50

The broken-frame varieties, Nos. 185a and 186a, are on Plate stamps JC and TA, as illustrated. *See also* No. 212a.

62

63

64

65

66

1883 (1 Aug) (9*d.*) *or* **1884** (1 April) (*others*). *Wmk Imperial Crow W* **49** (*sideways on horiz designs*).

			Un	★ Used	Used o cove
187	**52**	½d. slate-blue	16·00	6·00	11·
		a. Imperf	£700		
188	**62**	1½d. lilac	80·00	30·00	90·
		a. Imperf	£700		
189	**63**	2d. lilac	£125	60·00	£1
		a. Imperf	£800		
190	**64**	2½d. lilac	65·00	11·00	22·
		a. Imperf	£800		
191	**65**	3d. lilac	£150	80·00	£1
		a. Imperf	£800		
192	**66**	4d. dull green	£375	£160	£2
		a. Imperf	£850		
193	**62**	5d. dull green	£375	£160	£2
		a. Imperf	£850		
194	**63**	6d. dull green	£400	£175	£2
		a. Imperf	£850		
195	**64**	9d. dull green (1.8.83)	£725	£350	£8
196	**65**	1s. dull green	£525	£190	£3
		a. Imperf	£1750		
★187/96		**For well-centred, lightly used**		+100%	

The above prices are for stamps in the true dull green colou Stamps which have been soaked, causing the colour to run, a virtually worthless.

Stamps of the above set and No. 180 are also found perf 12; thes are official perforations, but were never issued. A second variety the 5d. is known with a line instead of a stop under the "d" in th value; this was never issued and is therefore only known *unuse* (*Price* £6000).

71

72

73

74

75

76

77

78

79

80

81

82

Die I

Die II

Die I: Square dots to right of "d".
Die II: Thin vertical lines to right of "d".

387 (1 Jan)–**1892.** *"Jubilee" issue. New types. The bicoloured stamps have the value tablets, or the frames including the value tablets, in the second colour. Wmk Imperial Crown, W* **49** (*Three Crowns on* £1).

			Un	★ *Used*	*Used on cover*
97	**71**	½d. vermilion	1·50	1·00	6·00
		a. Printed on gummed side ..	£1000	†	
		b. Printed both sides ..			
		c. Doubly printed	£5500		
		d. Imperf	£1250		
97e		½d. orange-vermilion	1·50	1·00	
98	**72**	1½d. dull purple and pale green	15·00	5·50	20·00
		a. Purple part of design double	—	£4000	
99	**73**	2d. green and scarlet ..	£325	£190	
00		2d. grey-green and carmine ..	22·00	10·00	22·00
01	**74**	2½d. purple/*blue*	15·00	2·50	6·00
		a. Printed on gummed side ..	£2500	†	
		b. Imperf three sides ..	£2250		
		c. Imperf	£2500		
02	**75**	3d. purple/*yellow*	20·00	3·00	22·00
		a. Imperf	£3500		
03		3d. deep purple/*yellow* ..	20·00	3·00	
04		3d. purple/*orange* (1890) ..	£400	£150	
05	**76**	4d. green and purple-brown ..	22·00	11·00	22·00
		aa. Imperf			
05a		4d. green and deep brown ..	22·00	11·00	
06	**77**	4½d. green and carmine (15.9.92)	8·00	30·00	65·00
06a		4½d. green & deep brt carmine	£475	£325	
07	**78**	5d. dull purple and blue (Die I)	£475	50·00	95·00
07a		5d. dull pur & bl (Die II) (1888)	25·00	10·00	28·00
08	**79**	6d. purple/*rose-red*	22·00	10·00	18·00
08a		6d. deep purple/*rose-red* ..	22·00	10·00	
09	**80**	9d. dull purple and blue ..	50·00	32·00	60·00
10	**81**	10d. dull purple and carmine (*shades*) (24.2.90) ..	40·00	32·00	65·00
		aa. Imperf	£4000		
10a		10d. dull purple & dp dull carm	£375	£175	
10b		10d. dull purple and scarlet ..	55·00	40·00	
11	**82**	1s. dull green	£190	55·00	85·00
12	**61**	£1 green (28.1.91)	£2250	£400	
		a. Frame broken	£5000	£1000	

197/212a **For well-centred, lightly used** .. +50%

The broken-frame varieties, No. 212a, are on Plate 2 stamps JC or A, as illustrated above No. 185.

½d. stamps with "PEARS SOAP" printed on the back in *orange,* 'ue or *mauve,* price *from* £400 each.

00. *Colours changed. Wmk Imperial Crown, W* **49**.

			Un	★ *Used*	*Used on cover*
13	**71**	½d. blue-green (17.4)	1·50	1·25	6·00
		a. Printed on gummed side	—	†	
		b. Imperf	£1750		
14	**82**	1s. green and carmine (11.7)	45·00	£110	£275
97/214		.. .. .. *Set of* 14	£425	£275	

213/14 **For well-centred, lightly used** .. +50%

The ½d., No. 213, in bright blue, is a colour changeling caused by constituent of the ink used for some months in 1900.

KING EDWARD VII
22 January 1901–6 May 1910

RINTINGS. Distinguishing De La Rue printings from the rovisional printings of the same values made by Harrison & Sons td. or at Somerset House may prove difficult in some cases. For very ıll guidance Volume 2 of the Stanley Gibbons *Great Britain pecialised Catalogue* should prove helpful.

Note that stamps perforated 15 × 14 must be Harrison; the 2½d., d. and 4d. in this perforation are useful reference material, their ıades and appearance in most cases matching the Harrison perf 14 rintings.

Except for the 6d. value, all stamps on chalk-surfaced paper were rinted by De La Rue.

Of the stamps on ordinary paper, the De La Rue impressions are sually clearer and of a higher finish than those of the other printers. he shades are markedly different except in some printings of the d., 6d. and 7d. and in the 5s., 10s. and £1.

Used stamps in good, clean, unrubbed condition and with dated ostmarks can form the basis of a useful reference collection, the ates often assisting in the assignment to the printers.

USED STAMPS. For well-centred, lightly used examples of King Edward VII stamps, add the following percentages to the used prices quoted below:

De La Rue printings (Nos. 215/66)—3d. values +35%, 4d. orange +100%, 6d. +75%, 7d. and 1s. +25%, all other values +50%.

Harrison printings (Nos. 267/86)—all values and perforations +75%

Somerset House printings (Nos. 287/320)—1s. values +25%, all other values +50%.

83

84

85

86

87

88

89

90

91

92

93

94

95

96

97

(Des E. Fuchs)

1902 (1 Jan)–**10**. *Printed by De La Rue & Co. Wmk Imperial Crown* (*½d. to* 1*s.*); *Anchor* (2*s.* 6*d. to* 10*s.*); *Three Crowns* (£1). *Ordinary paper. P* 14.

			Un	*Used*	*Used on cover*
215	**83**	½d. dull blue-green (1.1.02) ..	1·25	1·00	1·50
216		½d. blue-green	1·25	1·00	
217		½d. pale yellowish grn (26.11.04)	1·25	1·00	1·50
218		½d. yellowish green	1·25	1·00	
		a. Booklet pane. Five stamps plus St. Andrew's Cross label (6.06)	£175		
		b. Doubly printed (bottom row on one pane) (Control H9)	£15000		
219		1d. scarlet (1.1.02)	1·25	1·00	1·50
220		1d. bright scarlet	1·25	1·00	
		a. Imperf (pair)	£7000		
221	**84**	1½d. dull purple & grn (21.3.02)	20·00	12·00	
222		1½d. slate-purple and green ..	22·00	11·00	18·00
223		1½d. pale dull pur & grn (*chalk-surfaced paper*) (8.05) ..	30·00	12·00	
224		1½d. slate-purple & bluish green (*chalk-surfaced paper*) ..	30·00	9·00	
225	**85**	2d. yellowish green & carmine-red (25.3.02)	30·00	12·00	20·00
226		2d. grey-grn & carm-red (1904)	30·00	12·00	
227		2d. pale grey-green & carm-red (*chalk-surfaced paper*) (4.06)	30·00	15·00	
228		2d. pale grey-grn & scar (*chalk-surfaced paper*) (1909) ..	28·00	15·00	
229		2d. dull blue-grn & carm (*chalk-surfaced paper*) (1907) ..	55·00	35·00	
230	**86**	2½d. ultramarine (1.1.02) ..	11·00	6·00	15·00
231		2½d. pale ultramarine ..	11·00	6·00	
232	**87**	3d. dull pur/*orge-yell* (20.3.02)	28·00	6·00	25·00
		a. Chalk-surfaced paper (3.06)	£100	40·00	
232b		3d. deep purple/*orange-yellow*	28·00	7·00	
232c		3d. pale reddish pur/*orge-yell* (*chalk-surfaced paper*) (3.06)	95·00	30·00	
233		3d. dull reddish pur/*yell* (*lemon back*) (*chalk-surfaced paper*)	£100	45·00	
233b		3d. pale purple/*lemon* (*chalk-surfaced paper*)	25·00	11·00	
234		3d. pur/*lemon* (*chalk-surfaced paper*)	25·00	11·00	
235	**88**	4d. green & grey-brn (27.3.02)	35·00	22·00	
236		4d. green and chocolate-brown	35·00	22·00	
		a. Chalk-surfaced paper (1.06)	28·00	12·00	32·00
238		4d. dp green & choc-brn (*chalk-surfaced paper*) (1.06) ..	28·00	12·00	
239		4d. brown-orange (1.11.09) ..	£110	£100	
240		4d. pale orange (12.09) ..	15·00	12·00	30·00
241		4d. orange-red (12.09) ..	15·00	12·00	
242	**89**	5d. dull pur & ultram (14.5.02)	30·00	11·00	42·00
		a. Chalk-surfaced paper (5.06)	30·00	15·00	
244		5d. slate-pur & ultram (*chalk-surfaced paper*) (5.06) ..	30·00	15·00	
245	**83**	6d. pale dull purple (1.1.02) ..	25·00	11·00	35·00
		a. Chalk-surfaced paper (1.06)	25·00	11·00	
246		6d. slate-purple	25·00	11·00	
248		6d. dull purple (*chalk-surfaced paper*) (1.06)	25·00	11·00	
249	**90**	7d. grey-black (4.5.10) ..	9·00	11·00	£150
249a		7d. deep grey-black ..	80·00	80·00	
250	**91**	9d. dull pur & ultram (7.4.02)	55·00	40·00	£150
		a. Chalk-surfaced paper (6.05)	55·00	45·00	
251		9d. slate-purple & ultramarine	55·00	40·00	
		a. Chalk-surfaced paper (6.05)	55·00	45·00	
254	**92**	10d. dull purple & carm (3.7.02)	55·00	45·00	£150
		a. No cross on crown ..	£225	£140	
		b. Chalk-surfaced paper (9.06)	55·00	35·00	
255		10d. slate-purple & carm (*chalk-surfaced paper*) (9.06) ..	55·00	45·00	
		a. No cross on crown ..	£190	£140	
256		10d. dull purple & scarlet (*chalk-surfaced paper*) (9.10) ..	50·00	50·00	
		a. No cross on crown ..	£175	£120	
257	**93**	1s. dull green & carm (24.3.02)	48·00	20·00	£100
		a. Chalk-surfaced paper (9.05)	50·00	25·00	
259		1s. dull green & scarlet (*chalk-surfaced paper*) (9.10) ..	50·00	35·00	
260	**94**	2s. 6d. lilac (5.4.02) ..	£140	65·00	£575
261		2s. 6d. pale dull purple (*chalk-surfaced paper*) (7.10.05)	£140	£110	
262		2s. 6d. dull pur (*chalk-surfaced paper*)	£140	90·00	
263	**95**	5s. bright carmine (5.4.02)	£140	90·00	£625
264		5s. deep bright carmine ..	£160	90·00	
265	**96**	10s. ultramarine (5.4.02) ..	£400	£275	
266	**97**	£1 dull blue-green (16.6.02)	£1000	£400	

97a

1910 (May). *Prepared for use by De La Rue but not issued. Wmk Imperial Crown, W* **49**. *P* 14.

266a **97a** 2d. Tyrian plum £13000

One example of this stamp is known used, but it was never issued to the public.

1911. *Printed by Harrison & Sons. Ordinary paper. Wmk Imperial Crown.* (*a*) *P* 14.

			Un	*Used*	*Used on cover*
267	**83**	½d. dull yellow-green (3.5.11)	2·50	1·50	4·00
268		½d. dull green	2·75	1·50	
269		½d. deep dull green	9·00	3·50	
270		½d. pale bluish green ..	32·00	30·00	
		a. Booklet pane. Five stamps plus St. Andrew's Cross label	£240		
		b. Wmk sideways	—	£12000	
		c. Imperf (pair)	£12000		
271		½d. brt green (fine impression) (6.11)	£200	£125	
272		1d. rose-red (3.5.11)	5·00	9·00	10·00
		a. No wmk	40·00	40·00	
273		1d. deep rose-red	5·00	8·00	
274		1d. rose-carmine	45·00	22·00	
275		1d. aniline pink (5.11) ..	£325	£150	
275a		1d. aniline rose	£110	£100	
276	**86**	2½d. bright blue (10.7.11) ..	35·00	18·00	22·00
277	**87**	3d. purple/*lemon* (12.9.11) ..	50·00	£140	£425
277a		3d. grey/*lemon*	£2750		
278	**88**	4d. bright orange (12.7.11) ..	45·00	40·00	£125
		(*b*) *P* 15×14			
279	**83**	½d. dull green (30.10.11) ..	32·00	38·00	70·00
279a		½d. deep dull green	32·00	38·00	
280		1d. rose-red (4.10.11) ..	28·00	20·00	
281		1d. rose-carmine	11·00	10·00	20·00
282		1d. pale rose-carmine ..	16·00	9·00	
283	**86**	2½d. bright blue (14.10.11) ..	16·00	9·00	17·00
284		2½d. dull blue	16·00	9·00	
285	**87**	3d. purple/*lemon* (22.9.11) ..	28·00	9·00	20·00
285a		3d. grey/*lemon*	£2250		
286	**88**	4d. bright orange (11.11.11) ..	20·00	11·00	50·00
279/86		.. .. .. *Set of* 5	95·00	60·00	

1911–13. *Printed at Somerset House. Ordinary paper. Wmk as* 1902–10. *P* 14.

287	**84**	1½d. reddish purple and bright green (13.7.11) ..	32·00	25·00	
288		1½d. dull purple and green ..	18·00	18·00	35·00
289		1½d. slate-purple & grn (9.12)	20·00	18·00	
290	**85**	2d. dp dull grn & red (8.8.11)	18·00	10·00	35·00
291		2d. deep dull green & carmine	18·00	10·00	
292		2d. grey-green & bright carmine (carmine shows clearly on back) (11.3.12)	18·00	14·00	
293	**89**	5d. dull reddish purple and bright blue (7.8.11) ..	20·00	10·00	60·00
294		5d. deep dull reddish purple and bright blue	18·00	10·00	
295	**83**	6d. royal purple (31.10.11) ..	35·00	55·00	
296		6d. bright magenta (*chalk-surfaced paper*) (31.10.11)	£1900		
297		6d. dull purple	20·00	10·00	70·00
298		6d. reddish purple (11.11) ..	20·00	14·00	
		a. No cross on crown (*various shades*)	£240		
299		6d. very dp reddish pur (11.11)	32·00	28·00	
300		6d. dark purple (3.12) ..	22·00	22·00	
301		6d. dull purple ("Dickinson" coated paper*) (3.13) ..	£125	£100	
303		6d. deep plum (7.13) ..	18·00	55·00	
		a. No cross on crown ..	£275		
305	**90**	7d. slate-grey (1.8.12) ..	9·00	12·00	£100
306	**91**	9d. reddish purple and light blue (24.7.11)	60·00	45·00	

306*a*	**91**	9d. deep dull reddish purple & deep bright blue (9.11)	60·00	45·00	
307		9d. dull reddish purple & blue (10.11)	40·00	32·00	£120
307*a*		9d. deep plum and blue (7.13)	40·00	45·00	
308		9d. slate-pur & cobalt-bl (3.12)	75·00	55·00	
309	**92**	10d. dull purple & scar (9.10.11)	60·00	45·00	
310		10d. dull reddish pur & aniline pink	£210	£150	
311		10d. dull reddish purple & carm (5.12)	50·00	32·00	£140
		a. No cross on crown ..	£525		
312	**93**	1s. dark green & scar (13.7.11)	70·00	38·00	
313		1s. dp green & scar (9.10.11)	50·00	22·00	
314		1s. green & carmine (15.4.12)	38·00	22·00	£110
315	**94**	2s. 6d. dull greyish purple (15.9.11)	£350	£190	
316		2s. 6d. dull reddish purple ..	£140	85·00	
317		2s. 6d. dark purple	£140	85·00	
318	**95**	5s. carmine (29.2.12) ..	£190	85·00	
319	**96**	10s. blue (14.1.12)	£450	£325	
320	**97**	£1 deep green (3.9.11) ..	£1000	£450	

*No. 301 was on an experimental coated paper which does not respond to the silver test.

KING GEORGE V

6 May 1910–20 January 1936

Further detailed information on the issues of King George V will be found in Volume 2 of the Stanley Gibbons *Great Britain Specialised Catalogue*.

PRINTERS. Types **98** to **102** were typographed by Harrison & Sons Ltd, with the exception of certain preliminary printings made at Somerset House and distinguishable by the controls "A.11", B.11" or "B.12" (the Harrison printings do not have a full stop after the letter). The booklet stamps, Nos. 334/7, and 344/5 were printed by Harrisons only.

WATERMARK VARIETIES. Many British stamps to 1967 exist without watermark owing to misplacement of the paper, and with either inverted, reversed, or inverted and reversed watermarks. A proportion of the low-value stamps issued in booklets have the watermark inverted in the normal course of printing.

Low values with *watermark sideways* are normally from stamp rolls used in machines with sideways delivery or, from June 1940, certain booklets.

STAMPS WITHOUT WATERMARK. Stamps found without watermark, due to misplacement of the sheet in relation to the dandy roll, are not listed here, but will be found in the *Great Britain Specialised Catalogue*.

The 1½d. and 5d. 1912–22, and 2d. and 2½d., 1924–26, listed here, are from *whole* sheets completely without watermark.

98

99

For type differences with T **101/2** *see* notes below the latter.

Die A

Die B

Dies of Halfpenny

Die A. The three upper scales on the body of the right hand dolphin form a triangle; the centre jewel of the cross inside the crown is suggested by a comma.

Die B. The three upper scales are incomplete; the centre jewel is suggested by a crescent.

Die A

Die B

Dies of One Penny

Die A. The second line of shading on the ribbon to the right of the crown extends right across the wreath; the line nearest to the crown on the right hand ribbon shows as a short line at the bottom of the ribbon.

Die B. The second line of shading is broken in the middle; the first line is little more than a dot.

(Des Bertram Mackennal and G. W. Eve. Head from photograph by W. & D. Downey. Die eng J. A. C. Harrison)

1911–12. *Wmk Imperial Crown, W* **49**. *P* 15 × 14.

			Un	*Used*
321	**98**	½d. pale green (Die A) (22.6.11) ..	4·50	2·00
322		½d. green (Die A) (22.6.11)	4·50	2·00
		a. Error. Perf 14 (8.11)	—	£325
323		½d. bluish green (Die A)	£275	£160
324		½d. yellow-green (Die B)	8·00	1·50
325		½d. bright green (Die B)	4·50	1·50
		a. Wmk sideways	—	£2500
326		½d. bluish green (Die B)	£160	£100
327	**99**	1d. carmine-red (Die A) (22.6.11) ..	4·50	2·50
		c. Wmk sideways	†	—
328		1d. pale carmine (Die A) (22.6.11) ..	14·00	2·00
		a. No cross on crown	£325	£200
329		1d. carmine (Die B)	7·00	2·00
330		1d. pale carmine (Die B)	7·00	2·00
		a. No cross on crown	£425	£300
331		1d. rose-pink (Die B)	90·00	35·00
332		1d. scarlet (Die B) (6.12)	18·00	14·00
333		1d. aniline scarlet (Die B)	£125	80·00

For note on the aniline scarlet No. 333 see below No. 343.

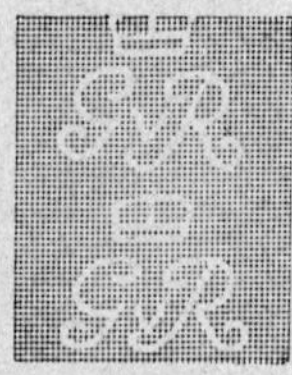

100 Simple Cypher

1912 (Aug). *Booklet stamps. Wmk Royal Cypher ("Simple"), W* **100**. *P* 15 × 14.

334	**98**	½d. pale green (Die B)	32·00	35·00
335		½d. green (Die B)	32·00	35·00
336	**99**	1d. scarlet (Die B)	25·00	25·00
337		1d. bright scarlet (Die B)	25·00	25·00

101

102

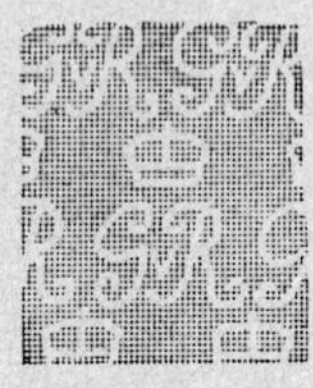

103 Multiple Cypher

Type differences

½d. In T **98** the ornament above "P" of "HALFPENNY" has two thin lines of colour and the beard is undefined. In T **101** the ornament has one thick line and the beard is well defined.

1d. In T **99** the body of the lion is unshaded and in T **102** it is shaded.

1912 (1 Jan). *Wmk Imperial Crown, W* **49**. *P* 15 × 14.

338	**101**	½d. deep green	12·00	6·00
339		½d. green	12·00	6·00
340		½d. yellow-green	12·00	6·00
		a. No cross on crown	65·00	25·00
341	**102**	1d. bright scarlet	4·00	2·00
		a. No cross on crown	55·00	25·00
		b. Printed double, one albino ..	£120	
342		1d. scarlet	4·00	2·00
343		1d. aniline scarlet*	£125	75·00
		a. No cross on crown	£750	

* Our prices for the aniline scarlet 1d. stamps, Nos. 333 and 343, are for specimens in which the colour is suffused on the surface of the stamp and shows through clearly on the back. Specimens without these characteristics but which show "aniline" reactions under the quartz lamp are relatively common.

1912 (Aug). *Wmk Royal Cypher ("Simple"), W* **100**. *P* 15 × 14.

344	**101**	½d. green	6·00	2·00
		a. No cross on crown	75·00	25·00
345	**102**	1d. scarlet	7·00	2·00
		a. No cross on crown	75·00	25·00

1912 (Sept–Oct). *Wmk Royal Cypher ("Multiple"), W* **103**. *P* 15 × 14.

346	**101**	½d. green (Oct)	10·00	7·00
		a. No cross on crown	75·00	45·00
		b. Imperf	£110	
		c. Wmk sideways	†	£1300
		d. Printed on gummed side ..	†	—
347		½d. yellow-green	9·00	7·00
348		½d. pale green	9·00	7·00
349	**102**	1d. bright scarlet	9·00	7·00
350		1d. scarlet	9·00	7·00
		a. No cross on crown	85·00	25·00
		b. Imperf	85·00	
		c. Wmk sideways	85·00	85·00
		d. Wmk sideways. No cross on crown	£600	

104

105

106

No. 357a

No. 357ab

No. 357ac

107

108

Die I

Die II

Dies of 2d.

Die I.— Inner frame-line at top and sides close to solid of backgroun… *Four* complete lines of shading between top of head and ov… frame-line. These four lines do *not* extend to the oval itse… White line round "TWOPENCE" thin.

Die II.— Inner frame-line farther from solid of background. Th… lines between top of head and extending to the oval. Wh… line round "TWOPENCE" thicker.

(Des Bertram Mackennal (heads) and G. W. Eve (frames). Coina… head (½, 1½, 2, 3 and 4d.); large medal head (1d., 2½d.); intermedia… medal head (5d. to 1s.); small medal head used for fiscal stamp… Dies eng J. A. C. Harrison)

(Typo by Harrison & Sons Ltd., except the 6d. printed by t… Stamping Department of the Board of Inland Revenue, Somers… House. The latter also made printings of the following which c… only be distinguished by the controls: ½d. B.13; 1½d. A.12; 2… C.13; 2½d. A.12; 3d. A.12, B.13, C.13; 4d. B.13; 5d. B.13; 7… C.13; 8d. C.13; 9d. agate B.13; 10d. C.13; 1s. C.13)

1912–24. *Wmk Royal Cypher, W* **100**. *Chalk-surfaced paper* (6d.… *P* 15×14.

351	**105**	½d. green (1.13)	1·00	
		a. Partial double print (half of bottom row from Control G15)	£15000	
		b. Gummed both sides		
352		½d. bright green	1·00	
353		½d. deep green	4·00	2·…
354		½d. yellow-green	5·00	3·…
355		½d. very yellow (Cyprus) green (1914)	£2000	
356		½d. blue-green	30·00	18·…
357	**104**	1d. bright scarlet (8.10.12)	1·00	
		a. "Q" for "O" (R.1/4) (Control E14)	£160	£1…
		ab. "Q" for "O" (R.4/11) (Control T22)	£325	£1…
		ac. Reversed "Q" for "O" (R.15/9) (Control T22)	£275	£1…
		ad. Inverted "Q" for "O" (R.20/3) ..	£350	£1…
		b. *Tête-bêche* (pair)	£50000	
358		1d. vermilion	3·00	2·…
359		1d. pale rose-red	10·00	2·…
360		1d. carmine-red	7·00	4·…
361		1d. scarlet-vermilion	90·00	30·…
		a. Printed on back†	£200	
362	**105**	1½d. red-brown (15.10.12)	2·00	1·…
		a. "PENCF" (R.15/12)	£180	£1…
		b. Booklet pane. Four stamps plus two printed labels (2.24)	£300	
363		1½d. chocolate-brown	3·25	1·…
		a. Without wmk	£150	£1…
364		1½d. chestnut	4·00	1·…
		a. "PENCF" (R.15/12)	£100	80·…
365		1½d. yellow-brown	14·00	14·…
366	**106**	2d. orange-yellow (Die I) (20.8.12) ..	6·00	3·…
367		2d. reddish orange (Die I) (11.13) ..	3·00	2·…
368		2d. orange (Die I)	3·00	2·…
369		2d. bright orange (Die I)	3·00	2·…
370		2d. orange (Die II) (9.21)	4·00	3·…
371	**104**	2½d. cobalt-blue (18.10.12)	7·00	3·…
371*a*		2½d. bright blue (1914)	7·00	3·…
372		2½d. blue	7·00	3·…
373		2½d. indigo-blue* (1920)	£900	£6…
373*a*		2½d. dull Prussian blue* (1921) ..	£500	£3…
374	**106**	3d. dull reddish violet (9.10.12) ..	8·00	2·…
375		3d. violet	4·00	3·…
376		3d. bluish violet (11.13)	5·00	2·…
377		3d. pale violet	6·00	2·…
378		4d. deep grey-green (15.1.13) ..	25·00	7·…
379		4d. grey-green	7·00	2·…
380		4d. pale grey-green	15·00	4·…
381	**107**	5d. brown (30.6.13)	6·00	5·…
382		5d. yellow-brown	7·00	5·…
		a. Without wmk	£500	
383		5d. bistre-brown	80·00	35·…
384		6d. dull purple (1.8.13)	18·00	7·…
385		6d. reddish purple	9·00	4·…
		a. Perf 14 (10.20)	75·00	£1…
386		6d. deep reddish purple	16·00	4·…
387		7d. olive (8.13)	11·00	6·…
388		7d. bronze-green (1915)	50·00	20·…
389		7d. sage-green (1917)	50·00	11·…
390		8d. black/*yellow* (1.8.13)	24·00	10·…
391		8d. black/*yellow-buff* (*granite*) (5.17)	28·00	13·…
392	**108**	9d. agate (30.6.13)	13·00	5·…
		a. Printed double, one albino ..		
393		9d. deep agate	15·00	5·…
393*a*		9d. olive-green (9.22)	85·00	30·…
393*b*		9d. pale olive-green	80·00	30·…
394		10d. turquoise-blue (1.8.13)	15·00	15·…
394*a*		10d. deep turquoise-blue	55·00	20·…

95	**108**	1s. bistre (1.8.13)	13·00	3·00
96		1s. bistre-brown	25·00	8·00
51/95		.. .. *Set of* 15	£175	80·00

Imperf stamps of this issue exist but may be war-time colour trials.

† The impression of No. 361a is set sideways and is very pale.

* No. 373 comes from Control O 20 and also exists on toned paper. o. 373*a* comes from Control R 21 and also exists on toned paper, ut both are unlike the rare Prussian blue shade of the 1935 2½d. ubilee issue.

See also Nos. 418/29.

For the 2d., T **106** bisected, see note under Guernsey, War ccupation Issues.

913 (Aug). *Wmk Royal Cypher* ("*Multiple*"). *W* **103**. *P* 15×14.

97	**105**	½d. bright green	£150	£180
		a. Wmk sideways	†	£18000
98	**104**	1d. dull scarlet	£225	£225

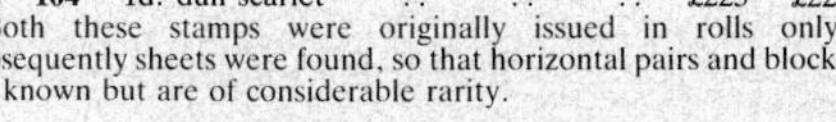

Both these stamps were originally issued in rolls only. ubsequently sheets were found, so that horizontal pairs and blocks e known but are of considerable rarity.

109

A

110 Single Cypher

Major Re-entries on 2s. 6d.

Nos. 400a and 408a

No. 415b

(Des Bertram Mackennal. Dies eng J. A. C. Harrison. Recess)

High values, so-called "Sea Horses" design: T **109**. *Background around portrait consists of horizontal lines, Type* A. *Wmk Single Cypher, W* **110.** *P* 11 × 12.

913 (30 June–Aug). *Printed by Waterlow Bros & Layton.*

99	2s. 6d. deep sepia-brown	£150	90·00
00	2s. 5d. sepia-brown	£140	80·00
	a. Re-entry (R. 2/1)	£750	£500
01	5s. rose-carmine	£250	£200
02	10s. indigo-blue (1 Aug)	£375	£300
03	£1 green (1 Aug)	£1250	£750
04	£1 dull blue-green (1 Aug)	£1250	£800
★399/404	**For well-centred, lightly used**		+35%

915 (Oct–Dec). *Printed by De La Rue & Co.*

05	2s. 6d. deep yellow-brown (Nov)	£160	85·00
06	2s. 6d. yellow-brown	£160	80·00
07	2s. 6d. pale brown (worn plate)	£150	80·00
08	2s. 6d. sepia (seal-brown)	£160	85·00
	a. Re-entry (R. 2/1)	£650	£425
09	5s. bright carmine	£240	£175
10	5s. pale carmine (worn plate)	£325	£200
11	10s. deep blue (Dec)	£1000	£500
12	10s. blue	£850	£450
13	10s. pale blue	£850	£450
★405/13	**For well-centred, lightly used**		+40%

918 (Dec)–**19.** *Printed by Bradbury, Wilkinson & Co, Ltd.*

13*a*	2s. 6d. olive-brown	70·00	40·00
14	2s. 6d. chocolate-brown	80·00	40·00
15	2s. 6d. reddish brown	90·00	40·00
15*a*	2s. 6d. pale brown	85·00	35·00
	b. Major re-entry (R.1/2)	£525	£300
16	5s. rose-red (1.19)	£190	60·00
17	10s. dull grey-blue (1.19)	£275	£100
99/417	.. .. *Set of* 4	£1600	£850
★413*a*/17	**For well-centred, lightly used**		+35%

DISTINGUISHING PRINTINGS. Note that the £1 value was only printed by Waterlow.

Waterlow and De La Rue stamps measure exactly 22 mm vertically. In the De La Rue printings the gum is usually patchy and yellowish, and the colour of the stamp, particularly in the 5s. tends to show through the back. The holes of the perforation are smaller than those of the other two printers, but there is a thick perforation tooth at the top of each vertical side.

In the Bradbury Wilkinson printings the height of the stamp is 22¾ or 23 mm. On most of the 22¾ mm high stamps a minute coloured guide dot appears in the margin just above the middle of the upper frame-line.

For (1934) re-engraved Waterlow printings *see* Nos. 450/2.

UNITED KINGDOM OF GREAT BRITAIN AND NORTHERN IRELAND

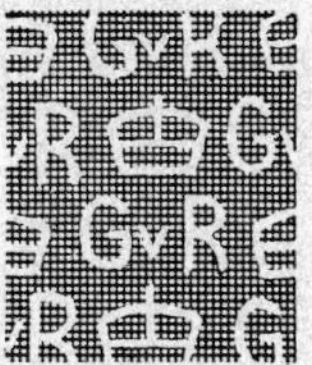

111 Block Cypher **111***a*

The watermark Type **111***a*, as compared with Type **111**, differs as follows: Closer spacing of horizontal rows (12½ mm instead of 14½ mm). Letters shorter and rounder. Watermark thicker.

(Typo by Waterlow & Sons, Ltd (all values except 6d.) and later, 1934–35, by Harrison & Sons, Ltd (all values). Until 1934 the 6d. was printed at Somerset House where a printing of the 1½d. was also made in 1926 (identifiable only by control E.26). Printings by Harrisons in 1934–35 can be identified, when in mint condition, by the fact that the gum shows a streaky appearance vertically, the Waterlow gum being uniformly applied, but Harrisons also used up the balance of the Waterlow "smooth gum" paper)

1924 (Feb)–**26**. *Wmk Block Cypher, W* **111**. *P* 15×14.

418	**105**	½d. green	50	50
		a. Wmk sideways (5.24)	5·00	2·75
		b. Doubly printed	£7500	
419	**104**	1d. scarlet	50	40
		a. Wmk sideways	14·00	14·00
		b. Experimental paper, W **111***a* (10.24)	22·00	
		c. Partial double print, one inverted		
		d. Inverted "Q" for "O" (R. 20/3)	£300	
420	**105**	1½d. red-brown	50	40
		a. *Tête-bêche* (pair)	£300	£525
		b. Wmk sideways (8.24)	6·00	3·00
		c. Printed on the gummed side ..	£325	†
		d. Booklet pane. Four stamps plus two printed labels (3.24) ..	90·00	
		e. Ditto. Wmk sideways	£3250	
		f. Experimental paper, W **111***a* (10.24)	40·00	70·00
		g. Double impression	£8500	
421	**106**	2d. orange (Die II) (7.24)	1·75	1·50
		a. No wmk	£500	
		b. Wmk sideways (7.26)	60·00	70·00
		c. Partial double print	£13000	
422	**104**	2½d. blue (10.24)	3·50	1·75
		a. No wmk	£650	
		b. Wmk sideways	†	£3750
423	**106**	3d. violet (10.24)	6·00	1·75
424		4d. grey-green (11.24)	7·50	1·50
		a. Printed on the gummed side ..	£1300	†
425	**107**	5d. brown (11.24)	12·00	2·25
426		6d. reddish purple (*chalk-surfaced paper*) (9.24)	7·00	1·75
426*a*		6d. purple (6.26)	2·25	1·00
427	**108**	9d. olive-green (12.24)	12·00	2·75
428		10d. turquoise-blue (11.24) ..	23·00	22·00
429		1s. bistre-brown (10.24)	14·00	2·00
418/29		.. .. *Set of* 12	75·00	32·00

There are numerous shades in this issue.

The 6d. on both chalk-surfaced and ordinary papers was printed by both Somerset House and Harrisons. The Harrisons printings have streaky gum, differ slightly in shade, and that on chalk-surfaced paper is printed in a highly fugitive ink. The prices quoted are for the commonest (Harrison) printing in each case.

112

(Des H. Nelson. Eng J. A. C. Harrison. Recess Waterlow)

1924–25. *British Empire Exhibition. W* **111**. *P* 14.

(*a*) *Dated* "1924" (23.4.24)

430	**112**	1d. scarlet	7·50	10·00
431		1½d. brown	11·00	14·00

(*b*) *Dated* "1925" (9.5.25)

432	**112**	1d. scarlet	12·00	22·00
433		1½d. brown	35·00	60·00

113

114

115

116 St. George and the Dragon

117

(Des J. Farleigh (T **113** and **115**), E. Linzell (T **114**) and H. Nelson (T **116**). Eng C. G. Lewis (T **113**), T. E. Storey (T **115**), both at the Royal Mint; J. A. C. Harrison, of Waterlow (T **114** and **116**). Typo by Waterlow from plates made at the Royal Mint, except T **116**, recess by Bradbury, Wilkinson from die and plate of their own manufacture)

1929 (10 May). *Ninth U.P.U. Congress, London.*

(*a*) *W* **111.** *P* 15 × 14

434	**113**	½d. green	2·25	2·25
		a. Wmk sideways	26·00	34·00
435	**114**	1d. scarlet	2·25	2·25
		a. Wmk sideways	45·00	48·00
436		1½d. purple-brown	2·25	1·75
		a. Wmk sideways	26·00	25·00
		b. Booklet pane. Four stamps plus two printed labels	£170	
437	**115**	2½d. blue	10·00	10·00

(*b*) *W* **117.** *P* 12

438	**116**	£1 black	£750	£550
434/7		.. .. *Set of* 4 (*to* 2½*d.*)	15·00	14·50

PRINTERS. All subsequent issues to 1997 were printed in photogravure by Harrison and Sons Ltd *except where otherwise stated.*

118

119

120

121

122

1934–36. *W* **111.** *P* 15 × 14.

439	**118**	½d. green (19.11.34)	30	40
		a. Wmk sideways	7·00	3·50
		b. Imperf three sides	£1250	
440	**119**	1d. scarlet (24.9.34)	30	40
		a. Imperf (pair)	£950	
		b. Printed on the gummed side ..	£400	†
		c. Wmk sideways	11·00	4·75
		d. Double impression	†	£12500
		e. Imperf between (pair)	£1750	
		f. Imperf three sides (pair)	£1250	
441	**118**	1½d. red-brown (20.8.34)	30	40
		a. Imperf (pair)	£275	
		b. Imperf three sides (lower stamp in vert pair)	£700	
		c. Imperf between (horiz pair) ..		
		d. Wmk sideways	6·00	4·00
		e. Booklet pane. Four stamps plus two printed labels (1.35)	60·00	
442	**120**	2d. orange (21.1.35)	50	75
		a. Imperf (pair)	£1500	
		b. Wmk sideways	65·00	55·00
443	**119**	2½d. ultramarine (18.3.35)	1·50	1·25
444	**120**	3d. violet (18.3.35)	1·50	1·25
445		4d. deep grey-green (2.12.35) ..	2·00	1·25
446	**121**	5d. yellow-brown (17.2.36)	6·00	2·75
447	**122**	9d. deep olive-green (2.12.35) ..	12·00	2·25
448		10d. turquoise-blue (24.2.36)	15·00	10·00
449		1s. bistre-brown (24.2.36)	15·00	1·25
		a. Double impression		
439/49		.. .. *Set of* 11	48·00	18·00

Owing to the need for wider space for the perforations the size of the designs of the ½d. and 2d. were once, and the 1d. and 1½d. twice reduced from that of the first printings.

There are also numerous minor variations, due to the photographic element in the process.

The ½d. imperf three sides, No. 439b, is known in a block of four, from a sheet, in which the bottom pair is imperf at top and sides.

For No. 442 bisected, see Guernsey, War Occupation Issues.

B

123

(Eng J. A. C. Harrison. Recess Waterlow)

1934 (16 Oct). *T* **109** (*re-engraved*). *Background around portrait consists of horizontal and diagonal lines. Type* B. *W* **110**. *P* 11×12.

450	**109**	2s. 6d. chocolate-brown	.. ..	60·00	30·00
451		5s. bright rose-red	.. ..	£125	75·00
452		10s. indigo	.. ..	£300	65·00
450/2		.. ..	*Set of* 3	£425	£150

There are numerous other minor differences in the design of this issue.

(Des B. Freedman)

1935 (7 May). *Silver Jubilee. W* **111**. *P* 15×14.

453	**123**	½d. green	.. ..	75	50
454		1d. scarlet	.. ..	1·25	1·50
455		1½d. red-brown	.. ..	75	50
456		2½d. blue	.. ..	4·50	5·50
456*a*		2½d. Prussian blue	.. ..	£3750	£3750
453/6		.. ..	*Set of* 4	6·00	7·00

The 1½d. and 2½d. values differ from T **123** in the emblem in the panel at right.

Four sheets of No. 456*a*, printed in the wrong shade, were issued in error by the Post Office Stores Department on 25 June 1935. It is known that three of the sheets were sold from the sub-office at 134 Fore Street, Upper Edmonton, London, between that date and 4 July.

KING EDWARD VIII
20 January–10 December 1936

Further detailed information on the stamps of King Edward VIII will be found in Volume 2 of the Stanley Gibbons *Great Britain Specialised Catalogue*.

124

125

(Des H. Brown, adapted Harrison using a photo by Hugh Cecil)

1936. *W* **125**. *P* 15×14.

457	**124**	½d. green (1.9.36)	.. .. ..	30	30
		a. Double impression	.. ..		
458		1d. scarlet (14.9.36)	.. .. ..	60	40
459		1½d. red-brown (1.9.36)	.. ..	30	30
		a. Booklet pane. Four stamps plus two printed labels (10.36)	.. ..	50·00	
460		2½d. bright blue (1.9.36)	.. ..	30	75
457/60		.. ..	*Set of* 4	1·25	1·60

KING GEORGE VI
11 December 1936–6 February 1952

Further detailed information on the stamps of King George VI will be found in Volume 2 of the Stanley Gibbons *Great Britain Specialised Catalogue*.

126 King George VI and Queen Elizabeth

(Des E. Dulac)

1937 (13 May). *Coronation. W* **127**. *P* 15×14.

461	**126**	1½d. maroon	.. ..	50	40

127

128

129

130

King George VI and National Emblems

(Des T **128/9**, E. Dulac (head) and E. Gill (frames). T **130**, E. Dulac (whole stamp))

1937–47. *W* **127**. *P* 15×14.

462	**128**	½d. green (10.5.37)	.. .. ..	10	25
		a. Wmk sideways (1.38)	.. ..	50	50
		ab. Booklet pane of 4 (6.40)	..	30·00	
463		1d. scarlet (10.5.37)	.. ..	10	25
		a. Wmk sideways (2.38)	.. ..	15·00	5·00
		ab. Booklet pane of 4 (6.40)	..	70·00	
464		1½d. red-brown (30.7.37)	.. ..	20	25
		a. Wmk sideways (2.38)	.. ..	1·00	1·25
		b. Booklet pane. Four stamps plus two printed labels (8.37)	..	48·00	
		c. Imperf three sides (pair)	..		
465		2d. orange (31.1.38)	.. ..	75	50
		a. Wmk sideways (2.38)	.. ..	70·00	30·00
		b. Bisected (on cover)	.. ..	†	22·00
466		2½d. ultramarine (10.5.37)	.. ..	25	15
		a. Wmk sideways (6.40)	.. ..	55·00	18·00
		b. *Tête-bêche* (horiz pair)	.. ..		
467		3d. violet (31.1.38)	.. .. ..	3·25	1·00
468	**129**	4d. grey-green (21.11.38)	.. ..	60	60
		a. Imperf (pair)	.. ..	£2000	
		b. Imperf three sides (horiz pair)	..	£2500	
469		5d. brown (21.11.38)	.. ..	2·50	75
		a. Imperf (pair)	.. ..	£2500	
		b. Imperf three sides (horiz pair)	..	£2000	
470		6d. purple (30.1.39)	.. ..	1·25	60
471	**130**	7d. emerald-green (27.2.39)	.. ..	3·25	60
		a. Imperf three sides (horiz pair)	..	£2000	
472		8d. bright carmine (27.2.39)	.. ..	3·50	70
473		9d. deep olive-green (1.5.39)	.. ..	5·50	80
474		10d. turquoise-blue (1.5.39)	.. ..	5·00	80
		aa. Imperf (pair)	.. ..	£3500	
474*a*		11d. plum (29.12.47)	.. ..	2·00	2·00
475		1s. bistre-brown (1.5.39)	.. ..	5·75	75
462/75		.. ..	*Set of* 15	30·00	8·75

For later printings of the lower values in apparently lighter shades and different colours, see Nos. 485/90 and 503/8.

No. 465b was authorised for use in Guernsey. See notes on War Occupation Issues.

Nos. 468b and 469b are perforated at foot only and each occurs in the same sheet as Nos. 468a and 469a.

No. 471a is also perforated at foot only, but occurs on the top row of a sheet.

131 King George VI

132 King George VI

133

(Des E. Dulac (T **131**) and Hon. G. R. Bellew (T **132**). Eng J. A. C. Harrison. Recess Waterlow)

1939–48. *W* **133**. *P* 14.

476	**131**	2s. 6d. brown (4.9.39)	.. ..	38·00	6·50
476*a*		2s. 6d. yellow-green (9.3.42)	.. ..	7·00	1·25
477		5s. red (21.8.39)	.. ..	14·00	1·75
478	**132**	10s. dark blue (30.10.39)	.. ..	£180	21·00
478*a*		10s. ultramarine (30.11.42)	.. ..	30·00	5·50
478*b*		£1 brown (1.10.48)	.. ..	10·00	23·00
476/8*b*		.. ..	*Set of* 6	£250	55·00

134 Queen Victoria and King George VI.

(Des H. L. Palmer)

1940 (6 May). *Centenary of First Adhesive Postage Stamps. W* **127**. *P* 14½×14.

479	**134**	½d. green	.. ..	30	30
480		1d. scarlet	.. ..	1·00	50
481		1½d. red-brown	.. ..	50	50
482		2d. orange	.. ..	50	50
		a. Bisected (on cover)	.. .. ..	†	16·00
483		2½d. ultramarine	.. ..	2·25	1·00
484		3d. violet	.. ..	3·00	3·25
479/84		.. ..	*Set of* 6	6·50	5·25

No. 482a was authorised for use in Guernsey. See notes on War Occupation Issues.

1941–42. *Head as Nos.* 462/7, *but lighter background. W* **127**. *P* 15×14.

485	**128**	½d. pale green (1.9.41)	.. ..	30	30
		a. *Tête-bêche* (horiz pair)	.. ..	£3000	
		b. Imperf (pair)	.. ..	£1750	
486		1d. pale scarlet (11.8.41)	.. ..	30	30
		a. Wmk sideways (10.42)	.. ..	4·00	6·00
		b. Imperf (pair)	.. ..	£2500	
		c. Imperf three sides (horiz pair)	..	£2500	
487	**128**	1½d. pale red-brown (28.9.42)	..	1·00	7
488		2d. pale orange (6.10.41)	.. ..	75	7
		a. Wmk sideways (6.42)	.. ..	25·00	16·(
		b. *Tête-bêche* (horiz pair)	.. ..	£2500	
		c. Imperf (pair)	.. ..	£2000	
		d. Imperf pane*	.. ..	£4500	
489		2½d. light ultramarine (21.7.41)	..	30	3
		a. Wmk sideways (8.42)	.. ..	13·00	11·(
		b. *Tête-bêche* (horiz pair)	.. ..	£2500	
		c. Imperf (pair)	.. ..	£2250	
		d. Imperf pane*	.. ..	£3500	
		e. Imperf three sides (horiz pair)	..	£3500	
490		3d. pale violet (3.11.41)	.. ..	2·00	9
485/90		.. ..	*Set of* 6	4·25	3·0

The *tête-bêche* varieties are from defectively made-up stam booklets.

Nos. 486c and 489e are perforated at foot only and occur in th same sheets as Nos. 486b and 489c.

*BOOKLET ERRORS. Those listed as "imperf panes" sho one row of perforations either at the top or at the bottom of th pane of 6.

WATERMARK VARIETIES. Please note that *inverted watermark* are outside the scope of this listing but are fully listed in the *Gre Britain Specialised* and *Great Britain Concise* Catalogues. See als the notes about watermarks at the beginning of the King George section.

135

136 Symbols of Peace and Reconstruction

(Des H. L. Palmer (T **135**) and R. Stone (T **136**))

1946 (11 June). *Victory. W* **127**. *P* 15×14.

491	**135**	2½d. ultramarine	.. ..	30	3
492	**136**	3d. violet	.. ..	30	3

137

138 King George VI and Queen Elizabeth

(Des G. Knipe and Joan Hassall from photographs by Doroth Wilding)

1948 (26 Apr). *Royal Silver Wedding. W* **127**. *P* 15×14 (2½*d.*) *c* 14×15 (£1).

493	**137**	2½d. ultramarine	.. .. ..	30	3
494	**138**	£1 blue	.. ..	38·00	35·

1948 (10 May). Stamps of 1d. and 2½d. showing seaweed-gatherin were on sale at eight Head Post Offices in Great Britain, but wer primarily for use in the Channel Islands and are listed there (se after Great Britain Postal Fiscals).

139 Globe and Laurel Wreath

140 "Speed"

141 Olympic Symbol

142 Winged Victory

)es P. Metcalfe (T **139**), A. Games (T **140**), S. D. Scott (T **141**) and E. Dulac (T **142**))

48 (29 July). *Olympic Games. W* **127.** *P* 15 × 14.

No.	Type	Description	Unused	Used
5	**139**	2½d. ultramarine	30	30
6	**140**	3d. violet	30	30
7	**141**	6d. bright purple	60	30
8	**142**	1s. brown	1·25	1·50
5/8		*Set of* 4	2·00	2·00

143 Two Hemispheres

144 U.P.U. Monument, Berne

145 Goddess Concordia, Globe and Points of Compass

146 Posthorn and Globe

)es Mary Adshead (T **143**), P. Metcalfe (T **144**), H. Fleury (T **145**) and Hon. G. R. Bellew (T **146**))

)49 (10 Oct). *75th Anniv of Universal Postal Union. W* **127.** *P* 15 × 14.

No.	Type	Description	Unused	Used
)9	**143**	2½d. ultramarine	30	30
)0	**144**	3d. violet	30	40
)1	**145**	6d. bright purple	60	75
)2	**146**	1s. brown	1·25	1·50
)9/502		*Set of* 4	2·00	2·75

)50–52. *4d. as Nos.* 468 *and others as Nos.* 485/9, *but colours changed. W* **127.** *P* 15×14.

No.	Type	Description	Unused	Used
)3	**128**	½d. pale orange (3.5.51)	30	30
		a. Imperf (pair)		
		b. *Tête-bêche* (horiz pair)	£3000	
		c. Imperf pane*	£4000	
)4		1d. light ultramarine (3.5.51)	30	30
		a. Wmk sideways (5.51)	1·00	1·25
		b. Imperf (pair)	£2000	
		c. Imperf three sides (horiz pair)	£1500	
		d. Booklet pane. Three stamps plus three printed labels (3.52)	18·00	
		e. Ditto. Partial *tête-bêche* pane	£2500	
)5		1½d. pale green (3.5.51)	50	60
		a. Wmk sideways (9.51)	2·50	4·00
)6		2d. pale red-brown (3.5.51)	50	40
		a. Wmk sideways (5.51)	1·50	1·75
		b. *Tête-bêche* (horiz pair)	£3000	
		c. Imperf three sides (horiz pair)	£1500	
)7		2½d. pale scarlet (3.5.51)	50	40
		a. Wmk sideways (5.51)	1·50	1·50
		b. *Tête-bêche* (horiz pair)		
)8	**129**	4d. light ultramarine (2.10.50)	2·50	1·75
		a. Double impression	†	£5000
)3/8		*Set of* 6	4·25	3·25

No. 504c is perforated at foot only and occurs in the same sheet s No. 504b.

No. 506c is also perforated at foot only.

*BOOKLET ERRORS. Those listed as "imperf panes" show one ɔw of perforations either at the top or at the bottom of the pane of

147 H.M.S. *Victory*

148 White Cliffs of Dover

149 St. George and the Dragon

150 Royal Coat of Arms

(Des Mary Adshead (T **147/8**), P. Metcalfe (T **149/50**). Recess Waterlow)

1951 (3 May). *W* **133.** *P* 11 × 12.

No.	Type	Description	Unused	Used
509	**147**	2s. 6d. yellow-green	6·00	1·00
510	**148**	5s. red	32·00	1·50
511	**149**	10s. ultramarine	21·00	8·50
512	**150**	£1 brown	32·00	20·00
509/12		*Set of* 4	80·00	25·00

151 "Commerce and Prosperity"

152 Festival Symbol

(Des E. Dulac (T **151**), A. Games (T **152**))

1951 (3 May). *Festival of Britain. W* **127.** *P* 15 × 14.

No.	Type	Description	Unused	Used
513	**151**	2½d. scarlet	30	30
514	**152**	4d. ultramarine	50	55

QUEEN ELIZABETH II
6 February 1952

Further detailed information on the stamps of Queen Elizabeth II will be found in volumes 3, 4 and 5 of the Stanley Gibbons *Great Britain Specialised Catalogue*.

USED PRICES. For Nos. 515 onwards the used prices quoted are for examples with circular dated postmarks.

153 Tudor Crown

154

155

156

157

158

159

160

Queen Elizabeth II and National Emblems

Types of 2½d. Type I:—In the frontal cross of the diadem, the top line is only half the width of the cross.

Type II:—The top line extends to the full width of the cross and there are signs of strengthening in other parts of the diadem.

(Des Enid Marx (T **154**), M. Farrar-Bell (T **155/6**), G. Knipe (T **157**), Mary Adshead (T **158**), E. Dulac (T **159/60**). Portrait by Dorothy Wilding)

1952–54. *W* **153.** *P* 15 × 14.

No.	Type	Description	Unused	Used
515	**154**	½d. orange-red (31.8.53)	10	15
516		1d. ultramarine (31.8.53)	20	20
		a. Booklet pane. Three stamps plus three printed labels	25·00	
517		1½d. green (5.12.52)	10	15
		a. Wmk sideways (15.10.54)	60	85
		b. Imperf pane*		
518		2d. red-brown (31.8.53)	20	15
		a. Wmk sideways (8.10.54)	1·25	2·00
519	**155**	2½d. carmine-red (Type I) (5.12.52)	10	15
		a. Wmk sideways (15.11.54)	10·00	10·00
		b. Type II (Booklets) (5.53)	1·50	1·25
520		3d. deep lilac (18.1.54)	1·00	75
521	**156**	4d. ultramarine (2.11.53)	3·00	1·25
522	**157**	5d. brown (6.7.53)	90	3·25
523		6d. reddish purple (18.1.54)	3·00	1·00
		a. Imperf three sides (pair)		
524		7d. bright green (18.1.54)	9·00	6·00
525	**158**	8d. magenta (6.7.53)	1·00	1·00
526		9d. bronze-green (8.2.54)	22·00	3·75
527		10d. Prussian blue (8.2.54)	18·00	3·75
528		11d. brown-purple (8.2.54)	30·00	20·00
529	**159**	1s. bistre-brown (6.7.53)	1·25	60
530	**160**	1s. 3d. green (2.11.53)	4·50	3·00
531	**159**	1s. 6d. grey-blue (2.11.53)	11·00	3·50
515/31		*Set of* 17	95·00	42·00

*BOOKLET ERRORS—This pane of 6 stamps is completely imperf (see No. 540*a*, etc.).

See also Nos. 540/56, 561/6, 570/94 and 599/618*a*.

For stamps as Type **157** with face values in decimal currency see Nos. 2031/3.

161

162

163

164

(Des E. Fuller (2½d.), M. Goaman (4d.), E. Dulac (1s. 3d.), M. Farrar-Bell (1s. 6d.), Portrait (except 1s. 3d.) by Dorothy Wilding)

1953 (3 June). *Coronation. W* **153.** *P* 15 × 14.

No.	Type	Description	Unused	Used
532	**161**	2½d. carmine-red	10	50
533	**162**	4d. ultramarine	40	1·75
534	**163**	1s. 3d. deep yellow-green	3·50	3·00
535	**164**	1s. 6d. deep grey-blue	7·00	3·75
532/5		*Set of* 4	10·00	8·00

165 St. Edward's Crown

166 Carrickfergus Castle

167 Caernarvon Castle

168 Edinburgh Castle

169 Windsor Castle

(Des L. Lamb. Portrait by Dorothy Wilding. Recess Waterlow (until 31.12.57) and De La Rue (subsequently))

1955–58. *W* **165.** *P* 11 × 12.

536 **166**	2s. 6d. black-brown (23.9.55) ..	10·00	2·00
	a. De La Rue printing (17.7.58) ..	30·00	3·00
537 **167**	5s. rose-carmine (23.9.55)	30·00	3·50
	a. De La Rue printing (30.4.58) ..	75·00	12·00
538 **168**	10s. ultramarine (1.9.55)	80·00	13·00
	a. De La Rue printing. *Dull ultramarine* (25.4.58)	£170	25·00
539 **169**	£1 black (1.9.55)	£130	42·00
	a. De La Rue printing (28.4.58) ..	£300	65·00
536/9	.. .. *Set of* 4	£225	55·00
536a/9a	.. .. *Set of* 4	£525	95·00

See also Nos. 595/8a and 759/62.

On 1 January 1958, the contract for printing the high values, T **166** to **169** was transferred to De La Rue & Co, Ltd.

The work of the two printers is very similar, but the following notes will be helpful to those attempting to identify Waterlow and De La Rue stamps of the W **165** issue.

The De La Rue sheets are printed in pairs and have a ⊣ or ⊢ shaped guide-mark at the centre of one side-margin, opposite the middle row of perforations, indicating left- and right-hand sheets respectively.

The Waterlow sheets have a small circle (sometimes crossed) instead of a "⊢" and this is present in both side-margins opposite the 6th row of stamps, though one is sometimes trimmed off. Short dashes are also present in the perforation gutter between the marginal stamps marking the middle of the four sides and a cross is at the centre of the sheet. The four corners of the sheet have two lines forming a right-angle as trimming marks, but some are usually trimmed off. All these gutter marks and sheet-trimming marks are absent in the De La Rue printings.

De La Rue used the Waterlow die and no alterations were made to it, so that no difference exists in the design or its size, but the making of new plates at first resulted in slight but measurable variations in the width of the gutters between stamps, particularly the horizontal, as follows:

	W.	D.L.R.
Horiz gutters, mm	3.8 to 4.0	3.4 to 3.8

Later D.L.R. plates were however less distinguishable in this respect.

For a short time in 1959 the D.L.R. 2s. 6d. appeared with one dot in the bottom margin below the first stamp.

It is possible to sort singles with reasonable certainty by general characteristics. The individual lines of the D.L.R. impression are cleaner and devoid of the whiskers of colour of Waterlow's, and the whole impression lighter and softer.

Owing to the closer setting of the horizontal rows the strokes of the perforating comb are closer; this results in the topmost tooth on each side of De La Rue stamps being narrower than the corresponding teeth in Waterlow's which were more than normally broad.

Shades also help. The 2s. 6d. D.L.R. is a warmer, more chocolate shade than the blackish brown of W.; the 5s. a lighter red with less carmine than W's; the 10s. more blue and less ultramarine; the £1 less intense black.

The paper of D.L.R. printings is uniformly white, identical with that of W. printings from February 1957 onwards, but earlier W. printings are on paper which is creamy by comparison.

In this and later issues of T **166/9** the dates of issue given for changes of watermark or paper are those on which supplies were first sent by the Supplies Department to Postmasters.

1955–58. *W* **165.** *P* 15 × 14.

540 **154**	½d. orange-red (booklets 8.55, sheets 12.12.55)	10	15
	a. Part perf pane*	£1200	
541	1d. ultramarine (19.9.55)	25	15
	a. Booklet pane. Three stamps plus three printed labels	15·00	
	b. *Tête-bêche* (horiz pair)		
542	1½d. green (booklets 8.55, sheets 11.10.55)	25	25
	a. Wmk sideways (7.3.56)	50	1·00
	b. *Tête-bêche* (horiz pair)	£900	
543	2d. red-brown (6.9.55)	20	25
	aa. Imperf between (vert pair) ..	£1500	
	a. Wmk sideways (31.7.56)	50	60
	ab. Imperf between (horiz pair) ..	£1500	
543*b*	2d. light red-brown (17.10.56) ..	20	25
	ba. *Tête-bêche* (horiz pair)	£600	
	bb. Imperf pane*		
	bc. Part perf pane*	£1200	
	d. Wmk sideways (5.3.57)	10·00	6·00
544 **155**	2½d. carmine-red (Type I) (28.9.55) ..	20	25
	a. Wmk sideways (Type I) (23.3.56)	1·50	1·50
	b. Type II (booklets 9.55, sheets 1957)	50	50
	ba. *Tête-bêche* (horiz pair)	£750	
	bb. Imperf pane*	£900	
	bc. Part perf pane*		
545	3d. deep lilac (17.7.56)	20	25
	aa. *Tête-bêche* (horiz pair)	£750	
	a. Imperf three sides (pair)	£500	
	b. Wmk sideways (22.11.57)	16·00	14·00
546 **156**	4d. ultramarine (14.11.55)	1·40	50
547 **157**	5d. brown (21.9.55)	5·50	5·50
548	6d. reddish purple (20.12.55)	4·00	1·00
	aa. Imperf three sides (pair)	£400	
	a. Deep claret (8.5.58)	4·00	1·25
	ab. Imperf three sides (pair)	£400	
549	7d. bright green (23.4.56)	50·00	10·00
550 **158**	8d. magenta (21.12.55)	6·00	1·00
551	9d. bronze-green (15.12.55)	23·00	3·00
552	10d. Prussian blue (22.9.55)	19·00	2·75
553	11d. brown-purple (28.10.55)	50	1·75
554 **159**	1s. bistre-brown (3.11.55)	19·00	75
555 **160**	1s. 3d. green (27.3.56)	27·00	1·75
556 **159**	1s. 6d. grey-blue (27.3.56)	19·00	1·50
540/56	.. .. *Set of* 18	£150	25·00

The dates given for Nos. 540/556 are those on which they were first issued by the Supplies Dept to postmasters.

In December 1956 a completely imperforate sheet of No. 543*b* was noticed by clerks in a Kent post office, one of whom purchased it against P.O. regulations. In view of this irregularity we do not consider it properly issued.

Types of 2½d. In this issue, in 1957, Type II formerly only found in stamps from booklets, began to replace Type I on sheet stamps.

*BOOKLET ERRORS. Those listed as "imperf panes" show one row of perforations either at top or bottom of the booklet pane; those as "part perf panes" have one row of 3 stamps imperf on three sides.

170 Scout Badge and "Rolling Hitch"

171 "Scouts coming to Britain"

172 Globe within a Compass

(Des Mary Adshead (2½d.), P. Keely (4d.), W. H. Brown (1s. 3d.))

1957 (1 Aug). *World Scout Jubilee Jamboree. W* **165.** *P* 15 × 14.

557 **170**	2½d. carmine-red	15	25
558 **171**	4d. ultramarine	50	1·25
559 **172**	1s. 3d. green	5·00	4·75
557/9	.. .. *Set of* 3	5·00	5·50

173

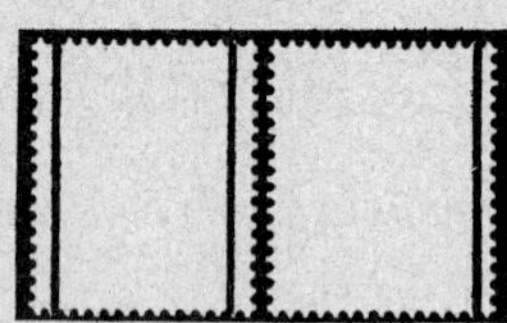

½d. to 1½d., 2½d., 3d. 2d.

Graphite-line arrangements (Stamps viewed from back)

(Adapted F. Langfield)

1957 (12 Sept). *46th Inter-Parliamentary Union Conference. W* **165.** *P* 15×14.

560 **173**	4d. ultramarine	1·00	1·25

GRAPHITE-LINED ISSUES. These were used in connection with automatic sorting machinery, first introduced experimentally at Southampton in December 1957.

The graphite lines were printed in black on the back, beneath the gum; two lines per stamp, except for the 2d.

In November 1959 phosphor bands were introduced (see notes after No. 598).

1957 (19 Nov). *Graphite-lined issue. Two graphite lines on the back, except 2d. value, which has one line. W* **165.** *P* 15 × 14.

561 **154**	½d. orange-red	30	30
562	1d. ultramarine	30	50
563	1½d. green	30	2·00
	a. Both lines at left	£800	£400
564	2d. light red-brown	2·50	2·75
	a. Line at left	£500	£175
565 **155**	2½d. carmine-red (Type II)	8·00	7·00
566	3d. deep lilac	30	70
561/6	.. .. *Set of* 6	10·50	11·50

No. 564a results from a misplacement of the line and horizontal pairs exist showing one stamp without line. No. 563a results from a similar misplacement.

See also Nos. 587/94.

176 Welsh Dragon

177 Flag and Games Emblem

178 Welsh Dragon

(Des R. Stone (3d.), W. H. Brown (6d.), P. Keely (1s. 3d.))

1958 (18 July). *Sixth British Empire and Commonwealth Games, Cardiff. W* **165.** *P* 15 × 14.

567 **176**	3d. deep lilac	15	1
568 **177**	6d. reddish purple	25	4
569 **178**	1s. 3d. green	3·00	3·0
567/9	.. .. *Set of* 3	3·00	3·0

179 Multiple Crowns

1958–65. *W* **179.** *P* 15×14.

570 **154**	½d. orange-red (25.11.58)	10	1
	a. Wmk sideways (26.5.61) ..	30	4
	c. Part perf pane*	£1000	
	k. Chalk-surfaced paper (15.7.63) ..	2·50	2·7
	l. Booklet pane. No. 570a×4 ..	3·50	
	m. Booklet pane. No. 570k×3 *se-tenant* with 574k	10·00	
	n. Booklet pane. No. 570a×2 *se-tenant* with 574l×2 (1.7.64)	2·50	
571	1d. ultramarine (booklets 11.58, sheets 24.3.59)	10	1
	aa. Imperf (vert pair from coil) ..		
	a. Wmk sideways (26.5.61) ..	1·25	1·0
	b. Part perf pane*	£1200	
	c. Imperf pane		
	l. Booklet pane. No. 571a×4 ..	4·50	
	m. Booklet pane. No. 571a×2 *se-tenant* with 575a×2 (1d. values at left) (16.8.65)	10·00	
	ma. Ditto. 1d. values at right ..	11·00	
572	1½d. grn (booklets 12.58, sheets 30.8.60)	10	1
	a. Imperf three sides (horiz strip of 3)		
	b. Wmk sideways (26.5.61) ..	9·00	4·5
	l. Booklet pane. No. 572b×4 ..	35·00	
573	2d. light red-brown (4.12.58) ..	10	1
	a. Wmk sideways (3.4.59)	60	1·2
574 **155**	2½d. carmine-red (Type II) (booklets 11.58, sheets 15.9.59)	10	1
	a. Imperf strip of 3		
	b. *Tête-bêche* (horiz pair)		
	c. Imperf pane	£1200	
	d. Wmk sideways (Type I) (10.11.60)	30	4
	da. Imperf strip of 6		
	e. Type I (wmk upright) (4.10.61) ..	30	6
	k. Chalk-surfaced paper (Type II) (15.7.63)	60	7
	l. Wmk sideways (Type II) Ord paper (1.7.64)	1·00	1·5
575	3d. deep lilac (booklets 11.58, sheets 8.12.58)	10	2
	a. Wmk sideways (24.10.58) ..	30	4
	b. Imperf pane*	£850	
	c. Part perf pane*		
	d. Phantom "R" (Cyl 41 no dot) ..	£275	
	e. Phantom "R" (Cyl 37 no dot) ..	30·00	
	l. Booklet pane. No. 575a×4 (26.5.61)	2·75	
576 **156**	4d. ultramarine (29.10.58)	50	2
	a. Deep ultramarine†† (28.4.65) ..	15	1
	ab. Wmk sideways (31.5.65) ..	60	5
	ac. Imperf pane*	£1200	
	ad. Part perf pane*	£800	
	al. Booklet pane. No. 576ab×4 (16.8.65)	2·75	
577	4½d. chestnut (9.2.59)	10	3
578 **157**	5d. brown (10.11.58)	25	4
579	6d. deep claret (23.12.58)	40	3
	a. Imperf three sides (pair) ..	£450	
	b. Imperf (pair)	£550	
580	7d. bright green (26.11.58)	50	7
581 **158**	8d. magenta (24.2.60)	50	4
582	9d. bronze-green (24.3.59)	50	6
583	10d. Prussian blue (18.11.58)	1·00	6
584 **159**	1s. bistre-brown (30.10.58)	50	4
585 **160**	1s. 3d. green (17.6.59)	40	4
586 **159**	1s. 6d. grey-blue (16.12.58)	4·00	5
570/86	.. .. *Set of* 17	8·00	4·2

*BOOKLET ERRORS. See note after No. 556.

††This "shade" was brought about by making more deeply etched cylinders, resulting in apparent depth of colour in parts of the design. There is no difference in the colour of the ink.

Sideways watermark. The 2d., 2½d., 3d. and 4d. come from coil and the ½d., 1d., 1½d., 2½d., 3d. and 4d. come from booklets. In *coi* stamps the sideways watermark shows the top of the watermark t the left *as seen from the front of the stamp*. In the *booklet* stamps i comes equally to the left or right.

Nos. 570k and 574k only come from 2s. "Holiday Resort" Experimental undated booklets issued in 1963, in which one page contained 1 × 2½d. *se-tenant* with 3 × ½d. (*See* No. 570l).

No. 574l comes from coils, and the "Holiday Resort" Experimental booklets dated "1964" comprising four panes each containing two of these 2½d. stamps *se-tenant* vertically with two ½d No. 570a (*See* No. 570m).

2½d. imperf No. 574a comes from a booklet with watermark upright. No. 574da is from a coil with sideways watermark.

No. 574e comes from *sheets* bearing cylinder number 42 and is also known on vertical delivery coils.

Nos. 575d and 615a occurred below the last stamp of the sheet from Cyl 41 (no dot), where an incomplete marginal rule revealed an "R". The cylinder was later twice retouched. The stamps listed show e original, unretouched "R". The rare variety, No. 575d, is best llected in a block of 4 or 6 with full margins in order to be sure that is not No. 615a with phosphor lines removed.

No. 575e is a similar variety but from Cyl. 37 (no dot). The arginal rule is much narrower and only a very small part of the "R" revealed. The cylinder was later retouched. The listed variety is for e original, unretouched state.

HITER PAPER. On 18 May 1962 the Post Office announced that whiter paper was being used for the current issue (including Nos. 5/8). This is beyond the scope of this catalogue, but the whiter apers are listed in Vol. 3 of the Stanley Gibbons *Great Britain ecialised Catalogue*.

58 (24 Nov)–**61.** *Graphite-lined issue. Two graphite lines on the back, except 2d. value, which has one line.* *W* **179.** *P* 15 × 14.

7	**154**	½d. orange-red (15.6.59)†	1·75	2·25
8		1d. ultramarine (18.12.58) .. .	1·00	1·50
		a. Misplaced graphite lines (7.61)*	1·00	1·25
9		1½d. green (4.8.59)†	40·00	40·00
0		2d. light red-brown (24.11.58) ..	6·00	3·25
1	**155**	2½d. carmine-red (Type II) (9.6.59) ..	8·00	10·00
2		3d. deep lilac (24.11.58)	75	50
		a. Misplaced graphite lines (5.61)*	£375	£350
3	**156**	4d. ultramarine (29.4.59)	3·50	4·50
		a. Misplaced graphite lines (1961)*	£1500	
4		4½d. chestnut (3.6.59)	5·00	4·00
7/94		.. .. *Set of* 8	60·00	60·00

Nos. 587/9 were only issued in booklets or coils (587/8).

*No. 588a (in coils), and Nos. 592a and 593a (both in sheets) result om the use of a residual stock of graphite-lined paper. As the use of aphite lines had ceased, the register of the lines in relation to the amps was of no importance and numerous misplacements ocrred—two lines close together, one line only, etc. No. 588a refers two lines at left or at right; No. 592a refers to stamps with two es only at left and both clear of the perforations and No. 593a to amps with two lines at left (with left line down perforations) and aces of a third line down the opposite perforations.

†The prices quoted are for stamps with the watermark inverted. *rices for upright watermark ½d.* £7.50 *un*, £7.50 *us*; 1½*d.* £95 *un*, 0 *us*.)

(Recess D.L.R. (until 31.12.62), then B.W.)

59–68. *W* **179.** *P* 11 × 12.

5	**166**	2s. 6d. black-brown (22.7.59) ..	10·00	75
		a. B.W. printing (1.7.63)	50	30
		k. Chalk-surfaced paper (30.5.68) ..	50	1·25
6	**167**	5s. scarlet-vermilion (15.6.59) ..	60·00	2·00
		a. B.W. ptg. *Red* (*shades*) (3.9.63) ..	1·00	60
		ab. Printed on the gummed side ..	£750	
7	**168**	10s. blue (21.7.59)	45·00	5·00
		a. B.W. ptg. *Bright ultram* (16.10.63)	3·00	3·50
8	**169**	£1 black (23.6.59)	95·00	12·00
		a. B.W. printing (14.11.63)	8·00	5·50
5/8		.. .. *Set of* 4	£180	17·00
5a/8a		.. .. *Set of* 4	11·00	9·00

The B.W. printings have a marginal Plate Number. They are enerally more deeply engraved than the D.L.R., showing more of e Diadem detail and heavier lines on Her Majesty's face. The rtical perf is 11.9 to 12 as against D.L.R. 11.8.

See also Nos. 759/62.

HOSPHOR BAND ISSUES. These are printed on the front and e wider than graphite lines. They are not easy to see but show as oad vertical bands at certain angles to the light.

Values representing the rate for printed papers (and when this was olished in 1968 for second class mail) have one band and others o, three or four bands as stated, according to the size and format.

In the small size stamps the bands are on each side with the single nd at left (*except where otherwise stated*). In the large-size mmemorative stamps the single band may be at left, centre or ght, varying in different designs. The bands are vertical on both rizontal and vertical designs *except where otherwise stated*.

The phosphor was originally applied typographically but later ually by photogravure and sometimes using flexography, a pographical process using rubber cylinders.

Three different types of phosphor have been used, distinguishable the colour emitted under an ultra-violet lamp, the first being een, then blue and now violet. Different sized bands are also own. All these are fully listed in Vol. 3 of the Stanley Gibbons *reat Britain Specialised Catalogue*.

Varieties. Misplaced and missing phosphor bands are known but ch varieties are beyond the scope of this Catalogue.

59 (18 Nov). *Phosphor-Graphite issue. Two phosphor bands on front and two graphite lines on back, except 2d. value, which has one band on front and one line on back.* *P* 15 × 14. (*a*) *W* **165.**

9	**154**	½d. orange-red	4·00	6·00
0		1d. ultramarine	9·00	7·00
1		1½d. green	2·00	6·00
		(*b*) W **179**		
5	**154**	2d. light red-brown (1 band)	4·50	4·00
		a. Error. W **165**	£180	£180
6	**155**	2½d. carmine-red (Type II)	20·00	13·00
7		3d. deep lilac	9·00	8·00
8	**156**	4d. ultramarine	12·00	25·00
9		4½d. chestnut	35·00	15·00
9/609		.. .. *Set of* 8	80·00	70·00

Examples of the 2½d., No. 606, exist showing watermark W **165** in ror. It is believed that phosphor-graphite stamps of this value ith this watermark were not used by the public for postal irposes.

960 (22 June)–**67.** *Phosphor issue. Two phosphor bands on front, except where otherwise stated.* *W* **179.** *P* 15 × 14.

10	**154**	½d. orange-red	10	15
		a. Wmk sideways (14.7.61) ..	10·00	10·00
		l. Booklet pane. No. 610a×4 ..	40·00	
11		1d. ultramarine	10	10
		a. Wmk sideways (14.7.61) ..	35	40
		l. Booklet pane. No. 611a×4 ..	9·00	
		m. Booklet pane. No. 611a×2 *se-tenant* with 615d×2† (16.8.65) ..	14·00	
		n. Booklet pane. No. 611a×2 *se-tenant* with 615b×2†† (11.67) ..	8·00	
12		1½d. green	10	20
		a. Wmk sideways (14.7.61) ..	10·00	10·00
		l. Booklet pane. No. 612a×4 ..	40·00	
13		2d. light red-brown (1 band) ..	22·00	19·00
13*a*		2d. lt red-brown (two bands) (4.10.61)	10	10
		aa. Imperf three sides***		
		ab. Wmk sideways (6.4.67) ..	25	75
614	**155**	2½d. carmine-red (Type II) (2 bands)*	10	50
614*a*		2½d. carmine-red (Type II) (1 band) (4.10.61)	50	1·00
614*b*		2½d. carmine-red (Type I) (1 band) (4.10.61)	38·00	32·00
615		3d. deep lilac (2 bands)	75	1·00
		a. Phantom "R" (Cyl 41 no dot)	30·00	
		b. Wmk sideways (14.7.61) ..	2·00	1·75
		l. Booklet pane. No. 615b×4 ..	7·00	
615*c*		3d. deep lilac (1 side band) (29.4.65)	60	1·00
		d. Wmk sideways (16.8.65) ..	6·00	5·00
		e. One centre band (8.12.66) ..	40	50
		ea. Wmk sideways (19.6.67) ..	50	1·00
616	**156**	4d. ultramarine	3·00	3·00
		a. Deep ultramarine (28.4.65) ..	30	30
		aa. Part perf pane		
		ab. Wmk sideways (16.8.65) ..	30	30
		al. Booklet pane. No. 616ab×4 ..	2·50	
616*b*		4½d. chestnut (13.9.61)	30	30
616*c*	**157**	5d. brown (9.6.67)	30	30
617		6d. deep claret (27.6.60)	50	30
617*a*		7d. bright green (15.2.67)	60	30
617*b*	**158**	8d. magenta (28.6.67)	30	30
617*c*		9d. bronze-green (29.12.66) ..	60	30
617*d*		10d. Prussian blue (30.12.66) ..	80	35
617*e*	**159**	1s. bistre-brown (28.6.67)	40	40
618	**160**	1s. 3d. green	2·00	2·75
618*a*	**159**	1s. 6d. grey-blue (12.12.66) ..	2·00	1·25
610/18*a*		.. .. *Set of* 17	8·00	7·50

The automatic facing equipment was brought into use on 6 July 1960 but the phosphor stamps may have been released a few days earlier.

The stamps with watermark sideways are from booklets except Nos. 613ab and 615ea which are from coils. No. 616ab comes from both booklets and coils.

No. 615a. See footnote after No. 586.

*No. 614 with two bands on the creamy paper was originally from cylinder 50 dot and no dot. When the change in postal rates took place in 1965 it was reissued from cylinder 57 dot and no dot on the whiter paper. Some of these latter were also released in error in districts of S.E. London in September 1964. The shade of the reissue is slightly more carmine.

***This comes from the bottom row of a sheet which is imperf at bottom and both sides.

†Booklet pane No. 611m comes in two forms, with the 1d. stamps on the left or on the right. This was printed in this manner to provide for 3d. stamps with only one band.

††Booklet pane No. 611n comes from 2s. booklets of January and March 1968. The two bands on the 3d. stamp were intentional because of the technical difficulties in producing one band and two band stamps *se-tenant*.

Unlike previous one-banded phosphor stamps, No. 615c has a broad band extending over two stamps so that alternate stamps have the band at left or right (same prices either way).

180 Postboy of 1660

181 Posthorn of 1660

(Des R. Stone (3d.), Faith Jaques (1s. 3d.))

1960 (7 July). *Tercentenary of Establishment of General Letter Office.* *W* **179** (*sideways on* 1*s.* 3*d.*). *P* 15 × 14 (3*d.*) *or* 14 × 15 (1*s.* 3*d.*).

619	**180**	3d. deep lilac	20	10
620	**181**	1s. 3d. green	4·00	4·00

182 Conference Emblem

(Des R. Stone (emblem, P. Rahikainen))

1960 (19 Sept). *First Anniv of European Postal and Telecommunications Conference. Chalk-surfaced paper.* *W* **179.** *P* 15 × 14.

621	**182**	6d. bronze-green and purple	50	60
622		1s. 6d. brown and blue	7·00	5·50

183 Thrift Plant

184 "Growth of Savings"

185 Thrift Plant

(Des P. Gauld (2½d.), M. Goaman (others))

1961 (28 Aug). *Centenary of Post Office Saving Bank. Chalk-surfaced paper.* *W* **179** (*sideways on* 2½*d.*). *P* 14×15 (2½*d.*) *or* 15×14 (*others*). A. "*Timson*" *Machine*

623A	**183**	2½d. black and red	20	20
		a. Black omitted	£6000	
624A	**184**	3d. orange-brown and violet ..	20	20
		a. Orange-brown omitted ..	£110	
625A	**185**	1s. 6d. red and blue	3·00	2·50
623A/5A		.. .. .. *Set of* 3	3·00	2·50
		B. "*Thrissell*" *Machine*		
623B	**183**	2½d. black and red	2·25	2·25
624B	**184**	3d. orange-brown and violet ..	25	25
		a. Orange-brown omitted ..	£250	

2½d. TIMSON. Cyls 1E–1F. Deeply shaded portrait (brownish black).

2½d. THRISSELL. Cyls 1D–1B or 1D (dot)–1B (dot). Lighter portrait (grey-black).

3d. TIMSON. Cyls 3D–3E. Clear, well-defined portrait with deep shadows and bright highlights.

3d. THRISSELL. Cyls 3C–3B or 3C (dot)–3B (dot). Dull portrait, lacking in contrast.

Sheet marginal examples *without* single extension perf hole on the short side of the stamp are always "Timson", as are those with large punch-hole *not* coincident with printed three-sided box guide mark.

The 3d. "Timson" perforated completely through the right-hand side margin comes from a relatively small part of the printing perforated on a sheet-fed machine.

Normally the "Timsons" were perforated in the reel, with three large punch-holes in both long margins and the perforations completely through both short margins. Only one punch-hole coincides with the guide-mark.

The "Thrissells" have one large punch-hole in one long margin, coinciding with guide-mark and one short margin imperf (except sometimes for encroachments).

186 C.E.P.T. Emblem

187 Doves and Emblem

188 Doves and Emblem

(Des M. Goaman (doves T. Kurpershoek))

1961 (18 Sept). *European Postal and Telecommunications* (*C.E.P.T.*) *Conference, Torquay. Chalk-surfaced paper.* *W* **179.** *P* 15 × 14.

626	**186**	2d. orange, pink and brown ..	25	20
		a. Orange omitted	£10000	
627	**187**	4d. buff, mauve and ultramarine	25	20
628	**188**	10d. turquoise, pale green & Prussian bl	60	75
		a. Pale green omitted	£3500	
		b. Turquoise omitted	£1800	
626/8		.. .. *Set of* 3	1·00	1·00

189 Hammer Beam Roof, Westminster Hall

190 Palace of Westminster

(Des Faith Jaques)

1961 (25 Sept). *Seventh Commonwealth Parliamentary Conference. Chalk-surfaced paper.* *W* **179** (*sideways on* 1*s.* 3*d.*). *P* 15 × 14 (6*d.*) *or* 14 × 15 (1*s.* 3*d.*).

629	**189**	6d. purple and gold	25	25
		a. Gold omitted	£475	
630	**190**	1s. 3d. green and blue	2·75	2·75
		a. Blue (Queen's head) omitted ..	£4500	

191 "Units of Productivity"

192 "National Productivity"

193 "Unified Productivity"

(Des D. Gentleman)

1962 (14 Nov). *National Productivity Year. Chalk-surfaced paper. W* **179** *(inverted on 2½d. and 3d.). P* 15 × 14.

631 **191** 2½d. myrtle-green & carm-red (*shades*) 20 10
p. One phosphor band .. .. 1·00 50
632 **192** 3d. light blue and violet (*shades*) .. 25 10
a. Light blue (Queen's head) omitted £725
p. Three phosphor bands .. .. 1·00 50
633 **193** 1s. 3d. carmine, light blue & dp green 1·75 2·00
a. Light blue (Queen's head) omitted £3750
p. Three phosphor bands .. .. 35·00 22·00
631/3 .. .. *Set of* 3 2·00 2·00
631p/3p .. .. *Set of* 3 35·00 22·00

194 Campaign Emblem and Family

195 Children of Three Races

(Des M. Goaman)

1963 (21 Mar). *Freedom from Hunger. Chalk-surfaced paper. W* **179** *(inverted). P* 15 × 14.

634 **194** 2½d. crimson and pink 10 10
p. One phosphor band .. .. 1·00 1·25
635 **195** 1s. 3d. bistre-brown and yellow .. 2·00 2·00
p. Three phosphor bands .. .. 35·00 22·00

196 "Paris Conference"

(Des R. Stone)

1963 (7 May). *Paris Postal Conference Centenary. Chalk-surfaced paper. W* **179** *(inverted). P* 15 × 14.

636 **196** 6d. green and mauve 50 50
a. Green omitted £1300
p. Three phosphor bands .. .. 6·50 6·50

197 Posy of Flowers

198 Woodland Life

(Des S. Scott (3d.), M. Goaman (4½d.))

1963 (16 May). *National Nature Week. Chalk-surfaced paper. W* **179**. *P* 15 × 14.

637 **197** 3d. yellow, green, brown and black .. 25 20
p. Three phosphor bands 50 60
638 **198** 4½d. black, blue, yellow, mag & brn-red 40 50
p. Three phosphor bands .. .. 2·50 2·50

199 Rescue at Sea

200 19th-century Lifeboat

201 Lifeboatmen

(Des D. Gentleman)

1963 (31 May). *Ninth International Lifeboat Conference, Edinburgh. Chalk-surfaced paper. W* **179**. *P* 15 × 14.

639 **199** 2½d. blue, black and red 10 10
p. One phosphor band 40 50
640 **200** 4d. red, yellow, brown, black and blue 40 30
p. Three phosphor bands 20 50
641 **201** 1s. 6d. sepia, yellow and grey-blue .. 2·75 3·00
p. Three phosphor bands .. .. 48·00 30·00
639/41 .. .. *Set of* 3 3·00 3·00
639p/41p .. .. *Set of* 3 48·00 30·00

202 Red Cross

203

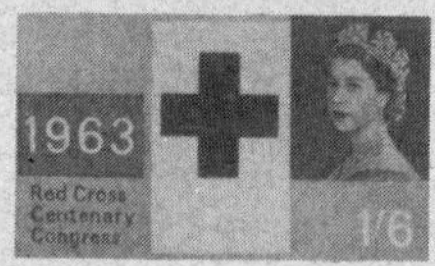

204

(Des H. Bartram)

1963 (15 Aug). *Red Cross Centenary Congress. Chalk-surfaced paper. W* **179**. *P* 15 × 14.

642 **202** 3d. red and deep lilac 10 10
a. Red omitted £2750
p. Three phosphor bands 60 60
pa. Red omitted £6000
643 **203** 1s. 3d. red, blue and grey .. .. 3·25 3·00
p. Three phosphor bands .. .. 40·00 38·00
644 **204** 1s. 6d. red, blue and bistre .. .. 3·00 3·00
p. Three phosphor bands .. .. 35·00 30·00
642/4 .. .. *Set of* 3 6·00 5·50
642p/4p .. .. *Set of* 3 70·00 60·00

205 Commonwealth Cable

(Des P. Gauld)

1963 (3 Dec). *Opening of COMPAC (Trans-Pacific Telephone Cable). Chalk-surfaced paper. W* **179**. *P* 15 × 14.

645 **205** 1s. 6d. blue and black .. .. .. 2·50 2·50
a. Black omitted £2500
p. Three phosphor bands .. .. 19·00 19·00

206 Puck and Bottom (*A Midsummer Night's Dream*)

207 Feste (*Twelfth Night*)

208 Balcony Scene (*Romeo and Juliet*)

209 "Eve of Agincourt" (*Henry V*)

210 Hamlet contemplating Yorick's Skull (*Hamlet*) and Queen Elizabeth II

(Des D. Gentleman. Photo Harrison & Sons (3d., 6d., 1s. 3d., 1s. 6d. Des C. and R. Ironside. Recess B.W. (2s. 6d.))

1964 (23 April). *Shakespeare Festival. Chalk-surfaced paper. W* **17**[9] *P* 11 × 12 *(2s. 6d.) or* 15 × 14 *(others).*

646 **206** 3d. yell-bistre, blk & dp vio-bl (*shades*) 10
p. Three phosphor bands 20
647 **207** 6d. yellow, orge, blk & yell-ol (*shades*) 20
p. Three phosphor bands 60
648 **208** 1s. 3d. cerise, bl-grn, blk & sep (*shades*) 90
p. Three phosphor bands .. .. 5·75
649 **209** 1s. 6d. violet, turq, blk & blue (*shades*) 1·25
p. Three phosphor bands .. .. 11·00
650 **210** 2s. 6d. deep slate-purple (*shades*) .. 2·00
646/50 .. .. *Set of* 5 4·00
646p/9p .. .. *Set of* 4 15·00

211 Flats near Richmond Park ("Urban Development")

212 Shipbuilding Yards, Belfast ("Industrial Activity")

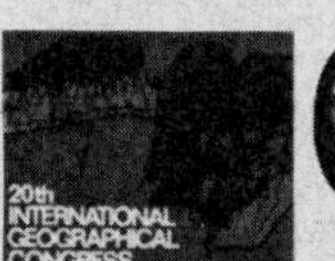

213 Beddgelert Forest Park, Snowdonia ("Forestry")

214 Nuclear Reactor, Dounreay ("Technological Development")

(Des D. Bailey)

1964 (1 July). *20th International Geographical Congress. Londo*[n]. *Chalk-surfaced paper. W* **179**. *P* 15×14.

651 **211** 2½d. black, olive-yell, ol-grey & turq-bl 10
p. One phosphor band 50
652 **212** 4d. orge-brn, red-brn, rose, blk & vio 25
a. Violet (face value) omitted .. £175
c. Violet and red-brown (dock walls) omitted £175
p. Three phosphor bands 75
653 **213** 8d. yellow-brown, emerald, grn & blk 60
a. Green (lawn) omitted £5500
p. Three phosphor bands .. .. 1·75
654 **214** 1s. 6d. yellow-brn, pale pk, blk & brn 3·25
p. Three phosphor bands .. .. 26·00
651/4 .. .. *Set of* 4 4·00
651p/4p .. .. *Set of* 4 26·00

A used example of the 4d. is known with the red-brown omitte[d]

215 Spring Gentian

216 Dog Rose

217 Honeysuckle

218 Fringed Water Lily

(Des M. and Sylvia Goaman)

964 (5 Aug). *Tenth International Botanical Congress, Edinburgh. Chalk-surfaced paper. W* **179.** *P* 15 × 14.

55	**215**	3d. violet, blue and sage-green	10	10
		a. Blue omitted	£4000	
		b. Sage-green omitted	£4000	
		p. Three phosphor bands	20	30
56	**216**	6d. apple-green, rose, scarlet and green	20	20
		p. Three phosphor bands	2·00	1·50
57	**217**	9d. lemon, green, lake and rose-red	1·60	2·50
		a. Green (leaves) omitted	£4000	
		p. Three phosphor bands	4·50	3·00
58	**218**	1s. 3d. yellow, emerald, reddish violet and grey-green	2·50	1·90
		a. Yellow (flowers) omitted	£8000	
		p. Three phosphor bands	24·00	20·00
55/8		.. .. *Set of* 4	4·00	4·00
55p/8p		.. .. *Set of* 4	28·00	22·00

219 Forth Road Bridge

220 Forth Road and Railway Bridges

(Des A. Restall)

964 (4 Sept). *Opening of Forth Road Bridge. Chalk-surfaced paper. W* **179.** *P* 15 × 14.

59	**219**	3d. black, blue and reddish violet	15	10
		p. Three phosphor bands	50	50
60	**220**	6d. blackish lilac, lt blue & carmine-red	45	40
		a. Light blue omitted	£1500	
		p. Three phosphor bands	4·75	4·75

221 Sir Winston Churchill

(Des D. Gentleman and Rosalind Dease, from photograph by Karsh)

965 (8 July). *Churchill Commemoration. Chalk-surfaced paper. W* **179.** *P* 15 × 14.

I. "REMBRANDT" Machine

61	**221**	4d. black and olive-brown	15	10
		p. Three phosphor bands	30	30

II. "TIMSON" Machine

61*a*	**221**	4d. black and olive-brown	50	50

III. "L. & M. 4" Machine

62	–	1s. 3d. black and grey	45	40
		p. Three phosphor bands	3·75	3·75

The 1s. 3d. shows a closer view of Churchill's head.

d. REMBRANDT. Cyls 1A–1B dot and no dot. Lack of shading detail on Churchill's portrait. Queen's portrait appears dull and coarse. This is a rotary machine which is sheet-fed.

4d. TIMSON. Cyls 5A–6B no dot. More detail on Churchill's portrait—furrow on forehead, his left eyebrow fully drawn and more shading on cheek. Queen's portrait lighter and sharper. This is a reel-fed, two-colour 12-in. wide rotary machine and the differences in impression are due to the greater pressure applied by this machine.

1s. 3d. Cyls 1A–1B no dot. The "Linotype and Machinery No. 4" machine is an ordinary sheet-fed rotary press machine. Besides being used for printing the 1s. 3d. stamps it was also employed for overprinting the phosphor bands on both values.

Two examples of the 4d. value exist with the Queen's head omitted, one due to something adhering to the cylinder and the other due to a paper fold. The stamp also exists with Churchill's head omitted, also due to a paper fold.

222 Simon de Montfort's Seal

223 Parliament Buildings (after engraving by Hollar, 1647)

(Des S. Black (6d.), R. Guyatt (2s. 6d.))

1965 (19 July). *700th Anniv of Simon de Montfort's Parliament. Chalk-surfaced paper. W* **179.** *P* 15 × 14.

663	**222**	6d. olive-green	10	10
		p. Three phosphor bands	1·00	1·00
664	**223**	2s. 6d. black, grey and pale drab ..	1·25	1·25

224 Bandsmen and Banner

225 Three Salvationists

(Des M. Farrar-Bell (3d.), G. Trenaman (1s. 6d.))

1965 (9 Aug). *Salvation Army Centenary. Chalk-surfaced paper. W* **179.** *P* 15 × 14.

665	**224**	3d. indigo, grey-blue, cerise, yell & brn	10	10
		p. One phosphor band	50	40
666	**225**	1s. 6d. red, blue, yellow and brown ..	1·00	1·00
		p. Three phosphor bands	3·00	3·25

226 Lister's Carbolic Spray

227 Lister and Chemical Symbols

(Des P. Gauld (4d.), F. Ariss (1s.))

1965 (1 Sept). *Centenary of Joseph Lister's Discovery of Antiseptic Surgery. Chalk-surfaced paper. W* **179.** *P* 15 × 14.

667	**226**	4d. indigo, brown-red and grey-black	10	10
		a. Brown-red (tube) omitted	£160	
		b. Indigo omitted	£1750	
		p. Three phosphor bands	15	20
		pa. Brown-red (tube) omitted	£1500	
668	**227**	1s. black, purple and new blue ..	1·00	1·50
		p. Three phosphor bands	2·75	2·75

228 Trinidad Carnival Dancers

229 Canadian Folk-dancers

(Des D. Gentleman and Rosalind Dease)

1965 (1 Sept). *Commonwealth Arts Festival. Chalk-surfaced paper. W* **179.** *P* 15 × 14.

669	**228**	6d. black and orange	10	10
		p. Three phosphor bands	30	30
670	**229**	1s. 6d. black and light reddish violet ..	1·25	1·50
		p. Three phosphor bands	2·50	2·50

230 Flight of Supermarine Spitfires

231 Pilot in Hawker Hurricane Mk I

232 Wing-tips of Supermarine Spitfire and Messerschmitt Bf 109

233 Supermarine Spitfires attacking Heinkel HE-111H Bomber

234 Supermarine Spitfire attacking Junkers Ju 87B "Stuka" Dive-bomber

235 Hawker Hurricanes Mk I over Wreck of Dornier Do-17Z Bomber

236 Anti-aircraft Artillery in Action

237 Air-battle over St. Paul's Cathedral

(Des D. Gentleman and Rosalind Dease (4d. × 6 and 1s. 3d.), A. Restall (9d.))

1965 (13 Sept). *25th Anniv of Battle of Britain. Chalk-surfaced paper. W* **179.** *P* 15 × 14.

671	**230**	4d. yellow-olive and black	30	35
		a. Block of 6. Nos. 671/6	8·00	10·00
		p. Three phosphor bands	40	50
		pa. Block of 6. Nos. 671p/6p	12·00	15·00
672	**231**	4d. yellow-olive, olive-grey and black	30	35
		p. Three phosphor bands	40	50
673	**232**	4d. red, new blue, yell-ol, ol-grey & blk	30	35
		p. Three phosphor bands	40	50
674	**233**	4d. olive-grey, yellow-olive and black	30	35
		p. Three phosphor bands	40	50
675	**234**	4d. olive-grey, yellow-olive and black	30	35
		p. Three phosphor bands	40	50
676	**235**	4d. olive-grey, yell-olive, new blue & blk	30	35
		a. New blue omitted	†	£3500
		p. Three phosphor bands	40	50

677 **236** 9d. bluish violet, orange and slate-purple .. 1·25 1·25
p. Three phosphor bands .. .. 1·25 80
678 **237** 1s. 3d. light grey, deep grey, black, light blue and bright blue .. .. 1·25 1·25
p. Three phosphor bands .. .. 1·25 80
671/8 .. .. *Set of* 8 9·50 4·25
671p/8p .. .. *Set of* 8 14·00 4·25

Nos. 671/6 were issued together *se-tenant* in blocks of 6 (3×2) within the sheet.

No. 676a is only known commercially used on cover from Truro.

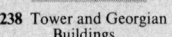

238 Tower and Georgian Buildings   **239** Tower and "Nash" Terrace, Regent's Park

(Des C. Abbott)

1965 (8 Oct). *Opening of Post Office Tower. Chalk-surfaced paper. W* **179** (*sideways on 3d.*). *P* 14 × 15 (*3d.*) *or* 15 × 14 (*1s. 3d.*).
679 **238** 3d. olive-yell, new blue & bronze-green 10 10
a. Olive-yellow (Tower) omitted .. £675
p. One phosphor band 10 10
680 **239** 1s. 3d. bronze-green, yellow-green & bl 65 85
p. Three phosphor bands 50 60

The one phosphor band on No. 679p was produced by printing broad phosphor bands across alternate vertical perforations. Individual stamps show the band at right or left (same prices either way).

240 U.N. Emblem

241 I.C.Y. Emblem

(Des J. Matthews)

1965 (25 Oct). *20th Anniv of U.N.O. and International Co-operation Year. Chalk-surfaced paper. W* **179**. *P* 15 × 14.
681 **240** 3d. black, yellow-orange and light blue 15 20
p. One phosphor band 25 50
682 **241** 1s. 6d. black, bright purple and lt blue 1·10 1·25
p. Three phosphor bands .. .. 3·50 3·75

242 Telecommunications Network

243 Radio Waves and Switchboard

(Des A. Restall)

1965 (15 Nov). *I.T.U. Centenary. Chalk-surfaced paper. W* **179**. *P* 15 × 14.
683 **242** 9d. red, ultram, dp slate, vio, blk & pk 20 25
p. Three phosphor bands 60 60
684 **243** 1s. 6d. red, greenish bl, ind, blk & lt pk 1·60 1·75
a. Light pink omitted £900
p. Three phosphor bands .. .. 5·25 5·50

Originally scheduled for issue on 17 May 1965, supplies from the Philatelic Bureau were sent in error to reach a dealer on that date and another dealer received his supply on 27 May.

244 Robert Burns (after Skirving chalk drawing)

245 Robert Burns (after Nasmyth portrait)

(Des G. Huntly)

1966 (25 Jan). *Burns Commemoration. Chalk-surfaced paper. W* **179**. *P* 15 × 14.
685 **244** 4d. black, deep violet-blue and new blue 15 15
p. Three phosphor bands 25 40
686 **245** 1s. 3d. black, slate-blue & yellow-orge 70 85
p. Three phosphor bands .. .. 2·25 2·50

246 Westminster Abbey

247 Fan Vaulting, Henry VII Chapel

(Des Sheila Robinson. Photo Harrison (3d.). Des and eng Bradbury, Wilkinson. Recess (2s. 6d.))

1966 (28 Feb). *900th Anniv of Westminster Abbey. Chalk-surfaced paper (3d.). W* **179**. *P* 15 × 14 (*3d.*) *or* 11 × 12 (*2s. 6d.*).
687 **246** 3d. black, red-brown and new blue .. 15 20
p. One phosphor band 30 40
688 **247** 2s. 6d. black .. .. 85 1·25

248 View near Hassocks, Sussex

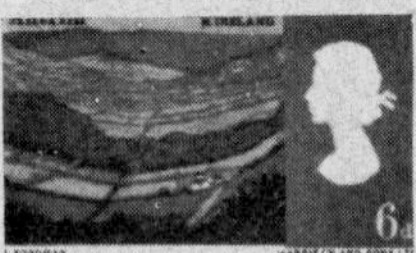

249 Antrim, Northern Ireland

250 Harlech Castle, Wales

251 Cairngorm Mountains, Scotland

(Des L. Rosoman. Queen's portrait, adapted by D. Gentleman from coinage)

1966 (2 May). *Landscapes. Chalk-surfaced paper. W* **179**. *P* 15 × 14.
689 **248** 4d. black, yellow-green and new blue 15 15
p. Three phosphor bands 15 15
690 **249** 6d. black, emerald and new blue 25 25
p. Three phosphor bands 25 25
691 **250** 1s. 3d. blk, greenish yell & greenish bl 40 45
p. Three phosphor bands 40 45
692 **251** 1s. 6d. black, orange and Prussian blue 60 60
p. Three phosphor bands 60 60
689/92 .. .. *Set of* 4 1·25 1·25
689p/92p .. .. *Set of* 4 1·25 1·25

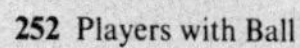

252 Players with Ball

253 Goalmouth Mêlée

254 Goalkeeper saving Goal

(Des D. Gentleman (4d.), W. Kempster (6d.), D. Caplan (1s. 3d.) Queen's portrait adapted by D. Gentleman from coinage)

1996 (1 June). *World Cup Football Championship. Chalk-surfaced paper. W* **179** (*sideways on 4d.*). *P* 14×15 (*4d.*) *or* 15×14 (*others*).
693 **252** 4d. red, reddish pur, brt bl, flesh & blk 15 1
p. Two phosphor bands 15 1
694 **253** 6d. black, sepia, red, apple-green & blue 20 3
a. Black omitted .. .. .. 85·00
b. Apple-green omitted £2000
c. Red omitted £2250
p. Three phosphor bands 20 3
pa. Black omitted £500
695 **254** 1s. 3d. black, blue, yell, red & lt yell-ol 75 9
a. Blue omitted £150
p. Three phosphor bands 75 9
693/5 .. .. *Set of* 3 1·00 1·2
693p/5p .. .. *Set of* 3 1·00 1·2

255 Black-headed Gull

256 Blue Tit

257 European Robin

258 Blackbird

(Des J. Norris Wood)

1966 (8 Aug). *British Birds. Chalk-surfaced paper. W* **179**. *P* 15 × 14.
696 **255** 4d. grey, black, red, emerald-green, brt blue, greenish yellow and bistre .. 10 1
a. Block of 4. Nos. 696/9 .. .. 1·00 1·5
ab. Black (value), etc. omitted* (*block of four*) £4000
ac. Black only omitted* £4000
p. Three phosphor bands 10 1
pa. Block of 4. Nos. 696p/9p .. .. 1·00 1·2
697 **256** 4d. black, greenish yellow, grey, emer-green, bright blue and bistre .. 10 1
p. Three phosphor bands 10 1
698 **257** 4d. red, greenish yellow, black, grey, bistre, reddish brown & emerald-grn 10 1
p. Three phosphor bands 10 1
699 **258** 4d. black, reddish brown, greenish yellow, grey and bistre** 10 1
p. Three phosphor bands 10 1
696/9 .. .. *Set of* 4 1·00 5
696p/9p .. .. *Set of* 4 1·00 5

Nos. 696/9 were issued together *se-tenant* in blocks of four within the sheet.

* In No. 696ab the blue, bistre and reddish brown are also omitted but in No. 696ac only the black is omitted.

** On No. 699 the black was printed over the bistre.

Other colours omitted, and the stamps affected:
d. Greenish yellow (Nos. 696/9) £400
pd. Greenish yellow (Nos. 696p/9) .. ..
e. Red (Nos. 696 and 698) £400
f. Emerald-green (Nos. 696/8) .. .. 75·00
pf. Emerald-green (Nos. 696p/8p) .. .. 75·00
g. Bright blue (Nos. 696/7) £300
pg. Bright blue (Nos. 696p/7p) £800
h. Bistre (Nos. 696/9) .. .. 90·00
ph. Bistre (Nos. 696p/9p) .. .. 90·00
j. Reddish brown (Nos. 698/9) .. .. 80·00
pj. Reddish brown (Nos. 698p/9p) .. .. 80·00
The prices quoted are for each stamp.

NEW INFORMATION

The editor is always interested to correspond with people who have new information that will improve or correct the Catalogue.

259 Cup Winners

966 (18 Aug). *England's World Cup Football Victory. Chalk-surfaced paper. W* **179** *(sideways). P* 14 × 15.

)0	**259**	4d. red, reddish pur, brt bl, flesh & blk	30	30

These stamps were only put on sale at post offices in England, the hannel Islands and the Isle of Man, and at the Philatelic Bureau in ondon and also, on 22 August, in Edinburgh on the occasion of the pening of the Edinburgh Festival as well as at Army post offices at ome and abroad.

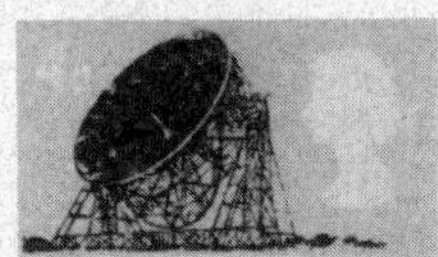

260 Jodrell Bank Radio Telescope

261 British Motor-cars

262 "SRN 6" Hovercraft

263 Windscale Reactor

(Des D. and A. Gillespie (4d., 6d.), A. Restall (others))

966 (19 Sept). *British Technology. Chalk-surfaced paper. W* **179.** *P* 15 × 14.

'01 **260**	4d.	black and lemon	15	15
	p.	Three phosphor bands	15	15
02 **261**	6d.	red, deep blue and orange	15	20
	a.	Red (Mini-cars) omitted	£4000	
	b.	Deep blue (Jaguar and inscr) omitted	£2500	
	p.	Three phosphor bands	15	20
03 **262**	1s.	3d. black, orange-red, slate and light greenish blue	30	50
	p.	Three phosphor bands	45	60
04 **263**	1s.	6d. black, yellow-green, bronze-green, lilac and deep blue	50	55
	p.	Three phosphor bands	65	70
01/4		*Set of* 4	1·00	1·25
01p/4p		*Set of* 4	1·25	1·50

264

265

266

267

268

269

All the above show battle scenes and they were issued together *se-tenant* in horizontal strips of six within the sheet.

270 Norman Ship

271 Norman Horsemen attacking Harold's Troops

(All the above are scenes from the Bayeux Tapestry)

(Des D. Gentleman. Photo, Queen's head die-stamped (6d., 1s. 3d.))

1966 (14 Oct). *900th Anniv of Battle of Hastings. Chalk-surfaced paper. W* **179** *(sideways on* 1s. 3d.*). P* 15 × 14.

705 **264**	4d.	black, olive-green, bistre, deep blue, orange, mag, grn, blue and grey	10	15
	a.	Strip of 6. Nos. 705/10	2·75	5·00
	p.	Three phosphor bands	10	25
	pa.	Strip of 6. Nos. 705p/10p	2·75	5·00
706 **265**	4d.	black, olive-green, bistre, deep blue, orange, mag, grn, blue and grey	10	15
	p.	Three phosphor bands	10	25
707 **266**	4d.	black, olive-green, bistre, deep blue, orange, mag, grn, blue and grey	10	15
	p.	Three phosphor bands	10	25
708 **267**	4d.	black, olive-green, bistre, deep blue, magenta, green, blue and grey	10	15
	p.	Three phosphor bands	10	25
709 **268**	4d.	black, olive-green, bistre, deep blue, orange, mag, grn, blue and grey	10	15
	p.	Three phosphor bands	10	25
710 **269**	4d.	black, olive-green, bistre, deep blue, orange, mag, grn, blue and grey	10	15
	p.	Three phosphor bands	10	25
711 **270**	6d.	black, olive-grn, vio, bl, grn & gold	10	10
	p.	Three phosphor bands	10	10
712 **271**	1s.	3d. black, lilac, bronze-green, rosine, bistre-brown and gold	20	20
	a.	Lilac omitted	£450	
	p.	Four phosphor bands	20	20
	pa.	Lilac omitted	£650	
705/12		*Set of* 8	3·00	1·50
705p/12p		*Set of* 8	3·00	1·90

Other colours omitted on the 4d. values and the stamps affected:

b.	Olive-green (Nos. 705/10)	40·00
pb.	Olive-green (Nos. 705p/10p)	40·00
c.	Bistre (Nos. 705/10)	40·00
pc.	Bistre (Nos. 705p/10p)	45·00
d.	Deep blue (Nos. 705/10)	50·00
pd.	Deep blue (Nos. 705p/10p)	50·00
e.	Orange (Nos. 705/7 and 709/10)	40·00
pe.	Orange (Nos. 705p/7p and 709p/10p)	35·00
f.	Magenta (Nos. 705/10)	45·00
pf.	Magenta (Nos. 705p/10p)	45·00
g.	Green (Nos. 705/10)	40·00
pg.	Green (Nos. 705p/10p)	40·00
h.	Blue (Nos. 705/10)	35·00
ph.	Blue (Nos. 705p/10p)	50·00
j.	Grey (Nos. 705/10)	35·00
pj.	Grey (Nos. 705p/10p)	35·00
pk.	Magenta and green (Nos. 705p/10p)	

The prices quoted are for each stamp.

Nos. 705 and 709, with grey and blue omitted, have been seen commercially used, posted from Middleton-in-Teesdale.

Three examples of No. 712 in a right-hand top corner block of 10 (2 × 5) are known with the Queen's head omitted as a result of a double paper fold prior to die-stamping. The perforation is normal. Of the other seven stamps, four have the Queen's head misplaced and three are normal.

MISSING GOLD HEADS. The 6d and 1s. 3d. were also issued with the die-stamped gold head omitted but as these can also be removed by chemical means we are not prepared to list them unless a way is found of distinguishing the genuine stamps from the fakes which will satisfy the Expert Committees.

The same remarks apply to Nos. 713/14.

272 King of the Orient **273** Snowman

(Des Tasveer Shemza (3d.), J. Berry (1s. 6d.) (winners of children's design competition). Photo, Queen's head die-stamped)

1966 (1 Dec). *Christmas. Chalk-surfaced paper. W* **179** *(sideways on* 3d.*). P* 14 × 15.

713 **272**	3d.	black, blue, green, yell, red & gold	10	10
	a.	Queen's head double	†	—
	ab.	Queen's head double, one albino		
	b.	Green omitted	—	£150
	p.	One phosphor band	10	10
714 **273**	1s.	6d. blue, red, pink, black and gold	40	40
	a.	Pink (hat) omitted	£750	
	p.	Two phosphor bands	40	40

See note below Nos. 679/80 which also applies to No. 713p.

274 Sea Freight

275 Air Freight

(Des C. Abbott)

1967 (20 Feb). *European Free Trade Association (E.F.T.A.). Chalk-surfaced paper. W* **179.** *P* 15 × 14.

715 **274**	9d.	deep blue, red, lilac, green, brown, new blue, yellow and black	20	20
	a.	Black (Queen's head, etc.), brown, new blue and yellow omitted	£650	
	b.	Lilac omitted	60·00	
	c.	Green omitted	60·00	
	d.	Brown (rail trucks) omitted	45·00	
	e.	New blue omitted	60·00	
	f.	Yellow omitted	60·00	
	p.	Three phosphor bands	20	20
	pb.	Lilac omitted	75·00	
	pc.	Green omitted	60·00	
	pd.	Brown omitted	45·00	
	pe.	New blue omitted	60·00	
	pf.	Yellow omitted	90·00	
716 **275**	1s.	6d. violet, red, deep blue, brown, green, blue-grey, new bl, yell & blk	30	30
	a.	Red omitted		
	b.	Deep blue omitted	£275	
	c.	Brown omitted	45·00	
	d.	Blue-grey omitted	60·00	
	e.	New blue omitted	60·00	
	f.	Yellow omitted	60·00	
	p.	Three phosphor bands	30	30
	pa.	Red omitted		
	pb.	Deep blue omitted	£275	
	pc.	Brown omitted	45·00	
	pd.	Blue-grey omitted	60·00	
	pf.	New blue omitted	60·00	

276 Hawthorn and Bramble

277 Larger Bindweed and Viper's Bugloss

278 Ox-eye Daisy, Coltsfoot and Buttercup

279 Bluebell, Red Campion and Wood Anemone

The above were issued together *se-tenant* in blocks of four within the sheet.

280 Dog Violet

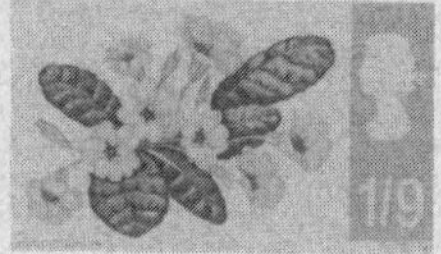

281 Primroses

(Des Rev. W. Keble Martin (T **276/9**), Mary Grierson (others))

1967 (24 Apr). *British Wild Flowers. Chalk-surfaced paper. W* **179**. *P* 15 × 14.

717 **276** 4d. grey, lemon, myrtle-green, red, agate and slate-purple 15 10
a. Block of 4. Nos. 717/20 .. .. 1·40 2·75
b. Grey double* .. .. ..
c. Red omitted £2000
f. Slate-purple omitted .. ..
p. Three phosphor bands 10 10
pa. Block of 4. Nos. 717p/20p .. 1·00 2·50
pd. Agate omitted £600
pf. Slate-purple omitted £150
718 **277** 4d. grey, lemon, myrtle-green, red, agate and violet 15 10
b. Grey double* .. .. ..
p. Three phosphor bands 10 10
pd. Agate omitted £600
pe. Violet omitted £2000
719 **278** 4d. grey, lemon, myrtle-green, red and agate 15 10
b. Grey double* .. .. ..
p. Three phosphor bands 10 10
pd. Agate omitted £600
720 **279** 4d. grey, lemon, myrtle-green, reddish purple, agate and violet 15 10
b. Grey double* .. .. ..
c. Reddish purple omitted £950
p. Three phosphor bands 10 10
pd. Agate omitted £650
pe. Violet omitted £2000
721 **280** 9d. lavender-grey, green, reddish violet and orange-yellow 15 10
p. Three phosphor bands 10 10
722 **281** 1s. 9d. lavender-grey, green, greenish yellow and orange 20 20
p. Three phosphor bands 30 20
717/22 .. .. *Set of* 6 1·50 65
717p/22p .. .. *Set of* 6 1·25 65

* The double impression of the grey printing affects the Queen's head, value and inscription.

PHOSPHOR BANDS. Issues from No. 723 are normally with phosphor bands only, except for the high values. However, most stamps have appeared with the phosphor bands omitted in error, but they are outside the scope of this catalogue. They are listed in Volumes 3, 4 and 5 of the Stanley Gibbons *Great Britain Specialised Catalogue* and in the *Great Britain Concise Catalogue*.
See also further notes after No. X1058.

PHOSPHORISED PAPER. Following the adoption of phosphor bands the Post Office started a series of experiments involving the addition of the phosphor to the paper coating before the stamps were printed. No. 743c was the first of these experiments to be issued for normal postal use. See also notes after No. X1058.

PVA GUM. Polyvinyl alcohol was introduced by Harrisons in place of gum Arabic in 1968. It is almost invisible except that a small amount of pale yellowish colouring matter was introduced to make it possible to see that the stamps had been gummed. Although this can be distinguished from gum arabic in unused stamps there is, of course, no means of detecting it in used examples. Such varieties are outside the scope of this catalogue, but they are listed in the *Great Britain Concise Catalogue*. See further notes *re* gum after Nos. 744 and 762.

282 **282a**

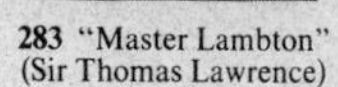

I II

Two types of the 2d.

I. Value spaced away from left side of stamp (cylinders 1 no dot and dot).
II. Value close to left side from new multipositive used for cylinders 5 no dot and dot onwards. The portrait appears in the centre, thus conforming to the other values.

(Des after plaster cast by Arnold Machin)

1967 (5 June)–**70.** *Chalk-surfaced paper. Two phosphor bands except where otherwise stated. No wmk. P* 15 × 14.

723 **282** ½d. orange-brown (5.2.68) 10 20
724 1d. lt olive (*shades*) (2 bands) (5.2.68) 10 10
a. Imperf (coil strip)† £1100
b. Part perf pane* .. .. ..
c. Imperf pane* £3750
d. Uncoated paper** .. .. 65·00
l. Booklet pane. No. 724×2 *se-tenant* with 730×2 (6.4.68) .. .. 3·00
m. Booklet pane. No. 724×4 *se-tenant* with 734×2 (6.1.69) .. .. 3·50
n. Booklet pane. No. 724×6, 734×6 and 735×3 *se-tenant* (1.12.69) .. 8·50
na. Uncoated paper** £900
725 1d. yellowish olive (1 centre band) (16.9.68) 25 30
l. Booklet pane. No. 725×4 *se-tenant* with 732×2 .. .. .. 4·00
m. Coil strip. No. 728×2 *se-tenant* with 729, 725 and 733 (27.8.69) .. 1·25
726 2d. lake-brown (Type I) (2 bands) (5.2.68) 10 15
727 2d. lake-brn (Type II) (2 bands) (1969) 15 15
728 2d. lake-brown (Type II) (1 centre band) (27.8.69) 50 75
729 3d. violet (*shades*) (1 centre band) (8.8.67) 10 10
a. Imperf (pair) £550
730 3d. violet (2 bands) (6.4.68) 30 30
a. Uncoated paper** £2000
731 4d. deep sepia (*shades*) (2 bands) .. 10 10
b. Part perf pane* £1000
732 4d. dp olive-brown (*shades*) (1 centre band) (16.9.68) 10 10
a. Part perf pane* £1000
l. Booklet pane. Two stamps plus two printed labels .. .. .. 1·00
733 4d. brt verm (1 centre band) (6.1.69) 10 10
a. *Tête-bêche* (horiz pair) £2500
b. Uncoated paper** .. .. 6·00
l. Booklet pane. Two stamps plus two printed labels (3.3.69) .. .. 1·00
734 4d. brt vermilion (1 side band) (6.1.69) 1·75 1·50
a. Uncoated paper** £175
735 5d. royal blue (*shades*) (1.7.68) .. 10 10
a. Imperf pane* £1200
b. Part perf pane* £800
c. Imperf (pair)†† £200
d. Uncoated paper** .. .. 15·00
736 6d. brt reddish pur (*shades*) (5.2.68) 20 20
737 **282a** 7d. bright emerald (1.7.68) 50 30
738 8d. bright vermilion (1.7.68) 20 30
739 8d. light turquoise-blue (6.1.69) .. 75 60
740 9d. myrtle-green (8.8.67) 60 30
741 **282** 10d. drab (1.7.68) 55 50
a. Uncoated paper** .. .. 23·00
742 1s. light bluish violet (*shades*) .. 50 30
743 1s. 6d. greenish blue and deep blue (*shades*) (8.8.67) 60 30
a. Greenish blue omitted .. .. 80·00
c. Phosphorised paper. *Prussian blue and indigo* (10.12.69) 85 90
ca. Prussian blue omitted £400
744 1s. 9d. dull orange and black (*shades*) 50 30
723/44 .. .. *Set of* 16 4·75 3·50

*BOOKLET ERRORS. See note after No. 556.

** Uncoated paper. This does not respond to the chalky test, and may be further distinguished from the normal chalk-surfaced paper by the fibres which clearly show on the surface, resulting in the printing impression being rougher, and by the screening dots which are not so evident. The 1d., 4d. and 5d. come from the £1 "Stamps for Cooks" Booklet (1970); and the 3d. and 10d. from sheets (1969). The 20p. and 50p. high values (Nos. 830/1) exist with similar errors.

† No. 724a occurs in a vertical strip of four, top stamp perforated on three sides, bottom stamp imperf three sides and the two middle stamps completely imperf.

†† No. 735c comes from the original state of cylinder 15 which is identifiable by the screening dots which extend through the gutters of the stamps and into the margins of the sheet. This must not be confused with imperforate stamps from cylinder 10, a large quantity of which was stolen from the printers early in 1970.

The 1d. with centre band (725) only came in the September 1968 booklets (PVA gum) and the coil strip (725m) (gum arabic); the 2d. with centre band (728) was only issued in the coil strip (725m); the 3d. (No. 730) appeared in booklets on 6.4.68, from coils during December 1968 and from sheets in January 1969; and the 4d. with one side band (734) only in 10s. (band at left) and £1 (band at left or right) booklets.

Gum. The 1d. (725), 3d. (729), 4d. (731 and 733), 9d., 1s., 1s. 6d. and 1s. 9d. exist with gum arabic as well as the PVA gum; the 2d. (728) and coil strip (725m) exist only with gum arabic; and the remainder exist with PVA gum only.

The 4d. (731) in shades of washed-out grey are colour changelings which we understand are caused by the concentrated solvents used in modern dry cleaning methods.

For decimal issue, see Nos. X841, etc.

283 "Master Lambton" (Sir Thomas Lawrence)

284 "Mares and Foals in a Landscape" (George Stubbs)

285 "Children Coming Out of School" (L. S. Lowry)

(Des S. Rose)

1967 (10 July). *British Paintings. Chalk-surfaced paper. Two phospho[r] bands. No wmk. P* 14 × 15 (4*d.*) *or* 15 × 14 (*others*).

748 **283** 4d. rose-red, lemon, brown, black, new blue and gold .. .. 10 1[0]
a. Gold (value and Queen's head) omitted £200
b. New blue omitted £2500
749 **284** 9d. Venetian red, ochre, grey-black, new blue, greenish yellow and black 20 2[0]
a. Black (Queen's head and value) omitted £400
b. Greenish yellow omitted £1300
750 **285** 1s. 6d. greenish yellow, grey, rose, new blue, grey-black and gold .. .. 60 6[0]
a. Gold (Queen's head) omitted .. £850
b. New blue omitted £160
c. Grey (clouds and shading) omitted 95·00
748/50 .. .. *Set of* 3 75 7[5]

286 *Gypsy Moth IV*

(Des M. and Sylvia Goaman)

1967 (24 July). *Sir Francis Chichester's World Voyage. Chalk-surfaced paper. Three phosphor bands. No wmk. P* 15 × 14.

751 **286** 1s. 9d. black, brown-red, lt emer & blue 25 2[0]

287 Radar Screen

288 *Penicillium notatum*

289 Vickers VC-10 Jet Engines

290 Television Equipmen[t]

(Des C. Abbott (4d., 1s.), Negus-Sharland team (others))

1967 (19 Sept). *British Discovery and Invention. Chalk-surface[d] paper. Three phosphor bands (4d.) or two phosphor bands (others) W* **179** (*sideways on* 1*s.* 9*d.*). *P* 14 × 15 (1*s.* 9*d.*) *or* 15 × 14 (*others*).

752 **287** 4d. greenish yellow, black and vermilion 10 1[0]
753 **288** 1s. blue-green, light greenish blue, slate-purple and bluish violet .. .. 15 1[0]
754 **289** 1s. 6d. black, grey, royal blue, ochre and turquoise-blue .. .. .. 35 3[5]
755 **290** 1s. 9d. black, grey-blue, pale olive-grey, violet and orange .. .. .. 50 5[0]
a. Grey-blue omitted .. ..
752/5 .. .. *Set of* 4 1·00 1·0[0]

WATERMARK. All issues from this date are on unwatermarke[d] paper.

291 "The Adoration of the Shepherds" (School of Seville)

292 "Madonna and Child" (Murillo)

293 "The Adoration of the Shepherds" (Louis le Nain)

(Des S. Rose)

67. *Christmas. Chalk-surfaced paper. One phosphor band (3d.) or two phosphor bands (others). P 15 × 14 (1s. 6d.) or 14 × 15 (others).*

5 **291** 3d. ol-yell, rose, bl, blk & gold (27.11) 10 20
a. Gold (value and Queen's head) omitted .. .. 75·00
b. Printed on the gummed side .. £300
c. Rose omitted .. .. ..
7 **292** 4d. bright purple, greenish yellow, new blue, grey-black and gold (18.10) 10 20
a. Gold (value and Queen's head) omitted .. .. 60·00
b. Gold ("4D" only) omitted .. £1000
c. Yellow (Child, robe and Madonna's face) omitted .. .. ..
8 **293** 1s. 6d. brt purple, bistre, lemon, black, orange-red, ultram & gold (27.11) 60 60
a. Gold (value and Queen's head) omitted £3500
b. Ultramarine omitted £350
c. Lemon omitted £10000
5/8 .. .. *Set of* 3 75 80

Distinct shades exist of the 3d. and 4d. values but are not listable there are intermediate shades. For the 4d. stamps from one achine show a darker background and give the appearance of the llow colour being omitted, but this is not so and these should not confused with the true missing yellow No. 757c.

No. 757b comes from stamps in the first vertical row of a sheet.

(Recess Bradbury, Wilkinson)

67–68. *No wmk. White paper. P 11 × 12.*

9 **166** 2s. 6d. black-brown (1.7.68) 40 50
0 **167** 5s. red (10.4.68) .. .. .. 1·00 1·00
1 **168** 10s. bright ultramarine (10.4.68) .. 5·50 7·00
2 **169** £1 black (4.12.67) .. .. .. 4·50 6·00
9/62 .. .. *Set of* 4 10·00 13·00

VA GUM. All the following issues from this date have PVA gum *cept where footnotes state otherwise.*

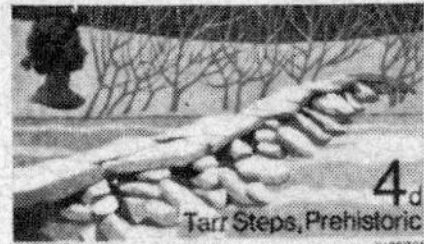

294 Tarr Steps, Exmoor

295 Aberfeldy Bridge

296 Menai Bridge

297 M4 Viaduct

(Des A. Restall (9d.), L. Rosoman (1s. 6d.), J. Matthews (others))

68 (29 Apr). *British Bridges. Chalk-surfaced paper. Two phosphor bands. P 15 × 14.*

53 **294** 4d. black, bluish violet, turq-blue & gold 10 10
a. Printed on gummed side .. .. 25·00
54 **295** 9d. red-brown, myrtle-green, ultramarine, olive-brown, black and gold .. 10 10
a. Gold (Queen's head) omitted .. £125
b. Ultramarine omitted .. .. † £3750
55 **296** 1s. 6d. olive-brown, red-orange, bright green, turquoise-green and gold .. 40 40
a. Gold (Queen's head) omitted .. £125
b. Red-orange (roof tops) omitted .. £150
56 **297** 1s. 9d. olive-brown, greenish yellow, dull green, deep ultramarine & gold 50 50
a. Gold (Queen's head) omitted .. £150
53/6 .. .. *Set of* 4 1·00 1·00

No. 764b is only known on first day covers posted from anterbury, Kent, or the Philatelic Bureau, Edinburgh.

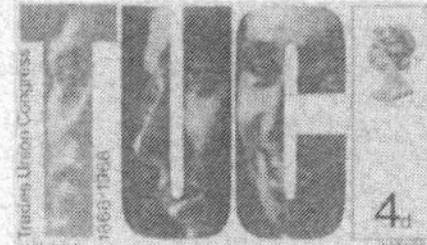

298 "T U C" and Trades Unionists

299 Mrs. Emmeline Pankhurst (statue)

300 Sopwith Camel and English Electric Lightning Fighters

301 Captain Cook's *Endeavour* and Signature

(Des D. Gentleman (4d.), C. Abbott (others))

1968 (29 May). *British Anniversaries. Events described on stamps. Chalk-surfaced paper. Two phosphor bands. P 15 × 14.*

767 **298** 4d. emerald, olive, blue and black .. 10 10
768 **299** 9d. reddish violet, bluish grey and black 10 15
769 **300** 1s. olive-brown, bl, red, slate-bl & blk 40 35
770 **301** 1s. 9d. yellow-ochre and blackish brown 50 50
767/70 .. .. *Set of* 4 1·00 1·00

302 "Queen Elizabeth I" (unknown artist)

303 "Pinkie" (Lawrence)

304 "Ruins of St. Mary Le Port" (Piper)

305 "The Hay Wain" (Constable)

(Des S. Rose)

1968 (12 Aug). *British Paintings. Queen's head embossed. Chalk-surfaced paper. Two phosphor bands. P 15 × 14 (1s. 9d.) or 14 × 15 (others).*

771 **302** 4d. blk, verm, greenish yell, grey & gold 10 10
a. Gold (value and Queen's head) omitted £125
b. Vermilion omitted* £225
772 **303** 1s. mauve, new blue, greenish yellow, black, magenta and gold 20 20
a. Gold (value and Queen's head) omitted £200
773 **304** 1s. 6d. slate, orange, black, mauve, greenish yellow, ultramarine & gold 30 30
a. Gold (value and Queen's head) omitted £100
774 **305** 1s. 9d. greenish yellow, black, new blue, red and gold 50 50
a. Gold (value and Queen's head) and embossing omitted £500
b. Red omitted £10000
771/4 .. .. *Set of* 4 1·00 1·00

*The effect of this is to leave the face and hands white and there is more yellow and olive in the costume.

The 4d., 1s. and 1s. 9d. are known with the embossing only omitted. No. 774a is only known with the phosphor also omitted. No. 772a exists both with or without embossing or phosphor bands.

306 Boy and Girl with Rocking Horse

307 Girl with Doll's House

308 Boy with Train Set

(Des Rosalind Dease. Head printed in gold and then embossed)

1968 (25 Nov). *Christmas. Chalk-surfaced paper. One centre phosphor band (4d.) or two phosphor bands (others). P 15 × 14 (4d.) or 14 × 15 (others).*

775 **306** 4d. black, orange, vermilion, ultramarine, bistre and gold 10 10
a. Gold omitted £2250
b. Vermilion omitted* £275
c. Ultramarine omitted £175
776 **307** 9d. yellow-olive, black, brown, yellow, magenta, orange, turq-green & gold 30 30
a. Yellow omitted .. .. .. 65·00
b. Turquoise-green (dress) omitted ..
777 **308** 1s. 6d. ultramarine, yellow-orange, brt purple, blue-green, black and gold 45 45
775/7 .. .. *Set of* 3 75 75

*The effect of the missing vermilion is shown on the rocking horse, saddle and faces which appear orange instead of red.

A single used example of the 4d. exists with the bistre omitted.

No. 775c is only known with the phosphor also omitted. All values exist with the embossing of Queen's head omitted.

309 *Queen Elizabeth 2*

310 Elizabethan Galleon

311 East Indiaman

312 *Cutty Sark*

313 *Great Britain*

314 *Mauretania I*

(Des D. Gentleman)

1969 (15 Jan). *British Ships. Chalk-surfaced paper. Two vertical phosphor bands at right (1s.), one horizontal phosphor band (5d.) or two phosphor bands (9d.). P 15×14.*

778 **309** 5d. black, grey, red and turquoise .. 10 10
a. Black (Queen's head, value, hull and inscr) omitted £700
b. Grey (decks, etc.) omitted .. 90·00
c. Red (inscription) omitted .. .. 50·00
779 **310** 9d. red, blue, ochre, brown, blk & grey 10 15
a. Strip of 3. Nos. 779/81 .. .. 1·75 3·00
ab. Red and blue omitted £1500
ac. Blue omitted £1500
780 **311** 9d. ochre, brown, black and grey .. 10 15
781 **312** 9d. ochre, brown, black and grey .. 10 15
782 **313** 1s. brown, blk, grey, grn & greenish yell 40 30
a. Pair. Nos. 782/3 .. .. .. 1·50 2·50
ab. Greenish yellow omitted .. ..
783 **314** 1s. red, black, brown, carmine and grey 40 30
a. Carmine (hull overlay) omitted .. £10000
b. Red (funnels) omitted £10000
c. Carmine and red omitted .. ..
778/83 .. .. *Set of* 6 2·50 1·00

The 9d. and 1s. values were arranged in horizontal strips of three and pairs respectively throughout the sheet.

No. 779ab is known only with the phosphor also omitted.

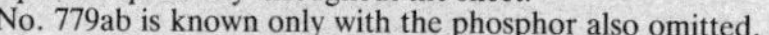

315 Concorde in Flight

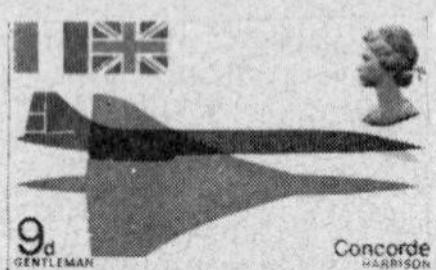

316 Plan and Elevation Views

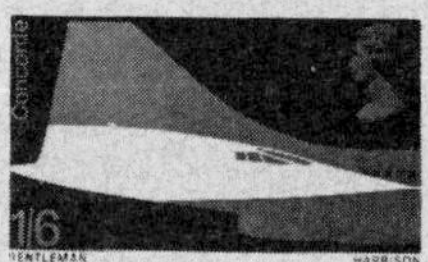

317 Concorde's Nose and Tail

(Des M. and Sylvia Goaman (4d.), D. Gentleman (9d., 1s. 6d.))

1969 (3 Mar). *First Flight of Concorde. Chalk-surfaced paper. Two phosphor bands. P 15×14.*

784 **315** 4d. yellow-orange, violet, greenish blue, blue-green and pale green 10 10
a. Violet (value, etc.) omitted .. £225
b. Yellow-orange omitted £110
785 **316** 9d. ultramarine, emerald, red & grey-bl 35 35
786 **317** 1s. 6d. deep blue, silver-grey & lt blue 50 50
a. Silver-grey omitted £275
784/6 .. .. *Set of* 3 85 85

No. 786a affects the Queen's head which appears in the light blue colour.

318 Queen Elizabeth II. (See also Type **357**)

(Des after plaster cast by Arnold Machin. Recess Bradbury, Wilkinson)

1969 (5 Mar). *P* 12.

787 **318** 2s. 6d. brown 50 30
788 5s. crimson-lake .. .. .. 2·25 60
789 10s. deep ultramarine .. .. .. 7·00 6·50
790 £1 bluish black .. .. .. 3·00 2·00
787/90 .. .. *Set of* 4 11·50 8·50

For decimal issue, see Nos. 829/31*b* and notes after No. 831*b*.

319 Page from *Daily Mail*, and Vickers FB-27 Vimy Aircraft

320 Europa and CEPT Emblems

321 ILO Emblem

322 Flags of NATO Countries

323 Vickers FB-27 Vimy Aircraft and Globe showing Flight

(Des P. Sharland (5d., 1s., 1s. 6d.), M. and Sylvia Goaman (9d., 1s. 9d.))

1969 (2 Apr). *Anniversaries. Events described on stamps. Chalk-surfaced paper. Two phosphor bands. P 15×14.*

791 **319** 5d. black, pale sage-green, chestnut and new blue 10 10
792 **320** 9d. pale turq, dp bl, lt emer-grn & blk 20 25
a. Uncoated paper* £1500
793 **321** 1s. bright purple, deep blue and lilac 25 25
794 **322** 1s. 6d. red, royal blue, yellow-green, black, lemon and new blue .. 25 30
e. Black omitted .. .. .. 60·00
f. Yellow-green (from flags) omitted 48·00
g. Lemon (from flags) omitted .. † —
795 **323** 1s. 9d. yellow-olive, greenish yellow and pale turquoise-green .. 30 35
a. Uncoated paper* £200
791/5 .. .. *Set of* 5 1·00 1·10

*Uncoated paper. The second note after No. 744 also applies here.

No. 794g is only known used on first day cover from Liverpool.

324 Durham Cathedral

325 York Minster

326 St. Giles' Cathedral, Edinburgh

327 Canterbury Cathedral

328 St. Paul's Cathedral

329 Liverpool Metropolitan Cathedral

(Des P. Gauld)

1969 (28 May). *British Architecture. Cathedrals. Chalk-surface paper. Two phosphor bands. P 15×14.*

796 **324** 5d. grey-blk, orge, pale bluish vio & blk 10
a. Block of 4. Nos. 796/9 .. .. 85 2·
ab. Block of 4. Uncoated paper** ..
b. Pale bluish violet omitted £2500
797 **325** 5d. grey-black, pale bluish violet, new blue and black 10
b. Pale bluish violet omitted £2500
798 **326** 5d. grey-black, purple, green and black 10
c. Green omitted* .. .. .. 40·00
799 **327** 5d. grey-black, green, new blue & black 10
800 **328** 9d. grey-blk, ochre, pale drab, vio & blk 15
a. Black (value) omitted £100
801 **329** 1s. 6d. grey-black, pale turquoise, pale reddish violet, pale yellow-ol & blk 15
a. Black (value) omitted £1600
b. Black (value) double .. ..
796/801 .. .. *Set of* 6 1·00

The 5d. values were issued together *se-tenant* in blocks of fo throughout the sheet.

*The missing green on the roof top is known on R. 2/5, R. 8/5 ar R. 10/5, but all from different sheets, and it only occurred in part the printing, being "probably caused by a batter on the impressic cylinder". Examples are also known with the green partly omitte

** Uncoated paper. The second note after No. 744 also appli here.

330 The King's Gate, Caernarvon Castle

331 The Eagle Tower, Caernarvon Castle

332 Queen Eleanor's Gate, Caernarvon Castle

333 Celtic Cross, Margam Abbey

334 H.R.H. The Prince of Wales (after photo by G. Argent)

(Des D. Gentleman)

1969 (1 July). *Investiture of H.R.H. The Prince of Wales. Chalk-surfaced paper. Two phosphor bands. P 14×15.*

802 **330** 5d. deep olive-grey, light olive-grey, deep grey, light grey, red, pale turquoise-green, black and silver .. 10
a. Strip of 3. Nos. 802/4 .. .. 70 1·
b. Black (value and inscr) omitted .. £150
c. Red omitted* £250
d. Deep grey omitted** .. .. 90·00
e. Pale turquoise-green omitted .. £325
803 **331** 5d. deep olive-grey, light olive-grey, deep grey, light grey, red, pale turquoise-green, black and silver .. 10
b. Black (value and inscr) omitted .. £150
c. Red omitted* £250
d. Deep grey omitted** .. .. 90·00
e. Pale turquoise-green omitted .. £325
f. Light grey (marks on walls, window frames, etc) omitted .. .. † £75
804 **332** 5d. deep olive-grey, light olive-grey, deep grey, light grey, red, pale turquoise-green, black and silver .. 10
b. Black (value and inscr) omitted .. £150
c. Red omitted* £250
d. Deep grey omitted** .. .. 90·00
e. Pale turquoise-green omitted .. £325
805 **333** 9d. deep grey, light grey, black and gold 20
806 **334** 1s. blackish yellow-olive and gold .. 20
802/6 .. .. *Set of* 5 1·00

The 5d. values were issued together, *se-tenant*, in strips of thre throughout the sheet.

*The 5d. value is also known with the red misplaced downwarc and where this occurs the red printing does not take very well on th silver background and in some cases is so faint that it could b mistaken for a missing red. However, the red can be seen under magnifying glass and caution should therefore be exercised whe purchasing copies of Nos. 802/4c.

**The deep grey affects the dark portions of the windows ar doors.

No. 803f is only known commercially used on cover.

335 Mahatma Gandhi

(Des B. Mullick)

69 (13 Aug). *Gandhi Centenary Year. Chalk-surfaced paper. Two phosphor bands. P* 15 × 14.
7 **335** 1s. 6d. black, green, red-orange & grey .. 30 30
a. Printed on the gummed side .. £325

336 National Giro "G" Symbol

337 Telecommunications—International Subscriber Dialling

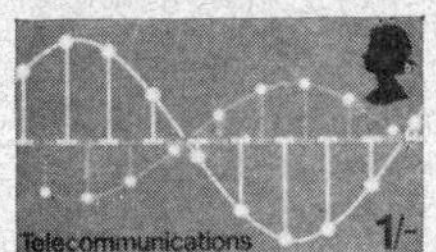

338 Telecommunications—Pulse Code Modulation

339 Postal Mechanisation—Automatic Sorting

(Des D. Gentleman. Litho De La Rue)

69 (1 Oct). *Post Office Technology Commemoration. Chalk-surfaced paper. Two phosphor bands. P* 13½ × 14.
8 **336** 5d. new bl, greenish bl, lavender & blk 10 10
9 **337** 9d. emerald, violet-blue and black .. 25 25
0 **338** 1s. emerald, lavender and black .. 25 25
1 **339** 1s. 6d. brt purple, lt blue, grey-bl & blk 50 50
8/11 .. .. *Set of* 4 1·00 1·00

340 Herald Angel

341 The Three Shepherds

342 The Three Kings

es F. Wegner. Queen's head (and stars 4d., 5d. and scroll-work 1s. 6d.) printed in gold and then embossed)

69 (26 Nov). *Christmas. Chalk-surfaced paper. Two phosphor bands* (*5d., 1s. 6d.*) *or one centre band* (*4d.*). *P* 15 × 14.
2 **340** 4d. vermilion, new blue, orange, bright purple, light green, bluish violet, blackish brown and gold 10 15
a. Gold (Queen's head etc.) omitted .. £2000
3 **341** 5d. magenta, light blue, royal blue, olive-brown, green, greenish yellow, red and gold 25 20
a. Light blue (sheep, etc) omitted .. 60·00
b. Red omitted* £550
c. Gold (Queen's head) omitted .. £450
d. Green omitted £200
e. Olive-brown, red and gold omitted £7000

814 **342** 1s. 6d. greenish yell, bright purple, bluish violet, deep slate, orange, green, new blue and gold .. 50 50
a. Gold (Queen's head etc.) omitted 90·00
b. Deep slate (value) omitted .. £250
c. Greenish yellow omitted .. £150
e. New blue omitted .. .. 60·00
812/14 .. .. *Set of* 3 75 75

*The effect of the missing red is shown on the hat, leggings and purse which appear as dull orange.

The 5d. and 1s. 6d. values are known with the embossing omitted.

No. 813e was caused by a paper fold and also shows the phosphor omitted.

Used copies of the 5d. have been seen with the olive-brown or greenish yellow (tunic at left) omitted.

343 Fife Harling

344 Cotswold Limestone

345 Welsh Stucco

346 Ulster Thatch

(Des D. Gentleman (5d., 9d.), Sheila Robinson (1s., 1s. 6d.))

1970 (11 Feb). *British Rural Architecture. Chalk-surfaced paper. Two phosphor bands. P* 15 × 14.
815 **343** 5d. grey, grey-blk, blk, lemon, greenish blue, orange-brown, ultram & grn 10 15
a. Lemon omitted .. .. .. 60·00
b. Grey (Queen's head and cottage shading) omitted £4000
c. Greenish blue (door) omitted .. † —
816 **344** 9d. orange-brown, olive-yellow, bright green, black, grey-black and grey 30 25
817 **345** 1s. dp bl, reddish lilac, drab & new bl 30 25
a. New blue omitted .. .. 55·00
818 **346** 1s. 6d. greenish yell, blk, turq-bl & lilac 40 45
a. Turquoise-blue omitted £4000
815/18 .. .. *Set of* 4 1·00 1·00

Used examples of the 5d. exist, one of which is on piece, with the greenish blue colour omitted.

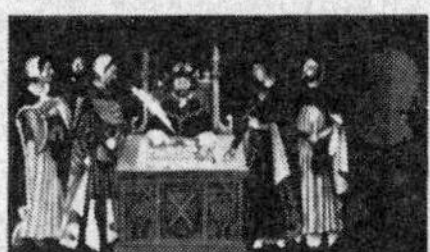

347 Signing the Declaration of Arbroath

348 Florence Nightingale attending Patients

349 Signing of International Co-operative Alliance

350 Pilgrims and *Mayflower*

351 Sir William Herschel, Francis Baily, Sir John Herschel and Telescope

(Des F. Wegner (5d., 9d., and 1s. 6d.), Marjorie Saynor (1s., 1s. 9d.). Queen's head printed in gold and then embossed)

1970 (1 Apr). *Anniversaries. Events described on stamps. Chalk-surfaced paper. Two phosphor bands. P* 15 × 14.
819 **347** 5d. blk, yell-olive, blue, emer, greenish yellow, rose-red, gold & orange-red 10 10
a. Gold (Queen's head) omitted .. £400
b. Emerald omitted £100
820 **348** 9d. ochre, deep blue, carmine, black, blue-green, yellow-olive, gold & bl 15 15
a. Ochre omitted £150
821 **349** 1s. green, greenish yellow, brown, black, cerise, gold and light blue .. 25 35
a. Gold (Queen's head) omitted .. 50·00
c. Green omitted .. .. .. 75·00
d. Brown omitted £100
822 **350** 1s. 6d. greenish yellow, carmine, deep yellow-olive, emerald, black, blue gold and sage-green 30 40
a. Gold (Queen's head) omitted .. 75·00
b. Emerald omitted .. .. .. 40·00
823 **351** 1s. 9d. blk, slate, lemon, gold & brt pur 30 40
a. Lemon (trousers and document) omitted £7500
819/23 .. .. *Set of* 5 1·00 1·25

The 9d., 1s. and 1s. 6d. are known with the embossing omitted.

No. 821c also exists with embossing omitted.

No. 823a is known mint, or used on first day cover postmarked London WC.

352 "Mr. Pickwick and Sam" (*Pickwick Papers*)

353 "Mr. and Mrs. Micawber" (*David Copperfield*)

354 "David Copperfield and Betsy Trotwood" (*David Copperfield*)

355 "Oliver asking for more" (*Oliver Twist*)

356 "Grasmere" (from engraving by J. Farrington, R.A.)

T **352/5** were issued together *se-tenant* in blocks of four throughout the sheet.

(Des Rosalind Dease. Queen's head printed in gold and then embossed)

1970 (3 June). *Literary Anniversaries. Death Centenary of Charles Dickens* (*novelist*) (*5d.* × *4*) *and Birth Bicentenary of William Wordsworth* (*poet*) (*1s. 6d.*). *Chalk-surfaced paper. Two phosphor bands. P* 14 × 15.
824 **352** 5d. black, orange, silver, gold and mag 10 10
a. Block of 4. Nos. 824/7 .. .. 1·00 2·00
ab. Imperf (block of four) £700
ac. Silver (inscr) omitted .. ..
825 **353** 5d. black, magenta, silver, gold & orge 10 10
826 **354** 5d. black, light greenish blue, silver, gold and yellow-bistre 10 10
b. Yellow-bistre (value) omitted .. £1200
827 **355** 5d. black, yellow-bistre, silver, gold and light greenish blue 10 10
b. Yell-bistre (background) omitted £3000
c. Lt greenish blue (value) omitted* £400
d. Light greenish blue and silver (inscr at foot) omitted .. .. ..
828 **356** 1s. 6d. light yellow-olive, black, silver, gold and bright blue 20 20
a. Gold (Queen's head) omitted .. £250
b. Silver ("Grasmere") omitted .. 70·00
c. Bright blue (face value) omitted ..
824/8 .. .. *Set of* 5 1·00 55

*No 827c (unlike No. 827b) comes from a sheet on which the colour was only partially omitted so that, although No. 827 was completely without the light greenish blue colour, it was still partially present on No. 826.

The 1s. 6d. is known with embossing omitted.

Essays exist of Nos. 824/7 showing the Queen's head in silver and with different inscriptions.

357 (Value redrawn)

(Des after plaster cast by Arnold Machin. Recess B.W.)

1970 (17 June)–**72.** *Decimal Currency. Chalk-surfaced paper or phosphorised paper* (10p.). *P* 12.

829 **357** 10p. cerise .. .. 1·00 85
830 20p. olive-green .. .. .. 1·00 30
831 50p. deep ultramarine .. .. .. 2·00 60
831*b* £1 bluish black (6.12.72) .. .. 4·00 1·00
829/31*b* .. .. *Set of* 4 7·00 2·50

The 20p. and 50p. exist on thinner, uncoated paper and are listed in the *Great Britain Concise Catalogue*.

A whiter paper was introduced in 1973. The £1 appeared on 27 Sept. 1973, the 20p. on 30 Nov. 1973 and the 50p. on 20 Feb. 1974.

The 50p. was issued on 1 Feb. 1973 on phosphorised paper. This cannot be distinguished from No. 831 with the naked eye.

The £1, T **318**, was also issued, on 17 June 1970, in sheets of 100 (10 × 10) instead of panes of 40 (8 × 5) but it is not easy to distinguish from No. 790 in singles. It can be readily differentiated when in large strips or marginal pieces showing sheet markings or plate numbers.

358 Runners

359 Swimmers

360 Cyclists

(Des A. Restall. Litho D.L.R.)

1970 (15 July). *Ninth British Commonwealth Games. Chalk-surfaced paper. Two phosphor bands. P* 13½ × 14.

832 **358** 5d. pk, emer, greenish yell & dp yell-grn 10 10
a. Greenish yellow omitted £4500
833 **359** 1s. 6d. light greenish blue, lilac, bistre-brown and Prussian blue .. 50 55
834 **360** 1s. 9d. yellow-orange, lilac, salmon and deep red-brown 50 55
832/4 .. .. *Set of* 3 1·00 1·10

361 1d. Black (1840)

362 1s. Green (1847)

363 4d. Carmine (1855)

(Des D. Gentleman)

1970 (18 Sept). *"Philympia 70" Stamp Exhibition. Chalk-surfaced paper. Two phosphor bands. P* 14 × 14½.

835 **361** 5d. grey-black, brownish bistre, black and dull purple 10 10
a. Grey-black (Queen's head) omitted £10000
836 **362** 9d. light drab, bluish green, stone, black and dull purple 50 50
837 **363** 1s. 6d. carmine, lt drab, blk & dull pur 50 60
835/7 .. .. *Set of* 3 1·00 1·10

364 Shepherds and Apparition of the Angel

365 Mary, Joseph, and Christ in the Manger

366 The Wise Men bearing gifts

(Des Sally Stiff after De Lisle Psalter. Queen's head printed in gold and then embossed)

1970 (25 Nov). *Christmas. Chalk-surfaced paper. One centre phosphor band* (4*d.*) *or two phosphor bands* (*others*). *P* 14 × 15.

838 **364** 4d. brown-red, turquoise-green, pale chestnut, brn, grey-blk, gold & verm 15 15
839 **365** 5d. emerald, gold, blue, brown-red, ochre, grey-black and violet .. 20 20
a. Gold (Queen's head) omitted .. † £2500
b. Emerald omitted .. .. .. 60·00
c. Imperf (pair) £250
840 **366** 1s. 6d. gold, grey-black, pale turq-grn, salmon, ultram, ochre & yellow-grn 50 50
a. Salmon omitted .. .. .. 80·00
b. Ochre omitted .. .. .. 50·00
838/40 .. .. *Set of* 3 75 75

The 4d. and 5d. are known with embossing omitted, and the 1s. 6d. is known with embossing and phosphor omitted.

(New Currency. 100 new pence = £1)

"X" NUMBERS. The following definitive series has been allocated "X" prefixes to the catalogue numbers to avoid re-numbering all subsequent issues.

367

367*a*

NO VALUE INDICATED. Stamps as Types **367**/*a* inscribed "2nd" or "1st" are listed as Nos. 1445/52, 1511/16, 1663*a*/6, 1979 and 2039/40.

ELLIPTICAL PERFORATIONS. These were introduced in 1993 and stamps showing them will be found listed as Nos. Y1667, etc.

PRINTING PROCESSES

Litho Photo

(*Illustrations enlarged* ×6)

Litho. Clear outlines to value and frame of stamp.

Photo. Uneven lines to value and frame formed by edges of screen.

Two types of the 3p., 10p. and 26p. (Nos. X930/c, X886/b and X971/b).

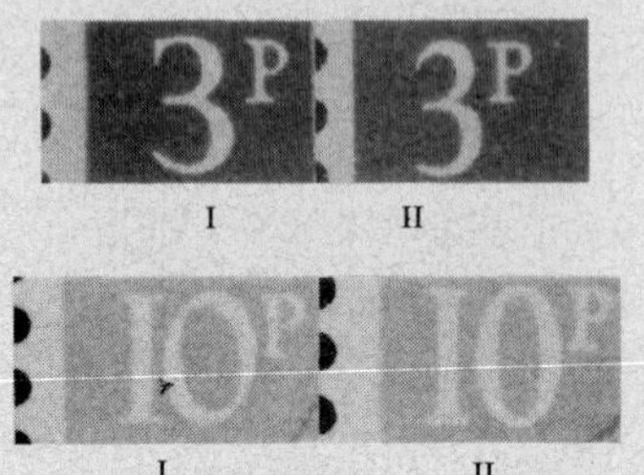

I II

I II

I II

Figures of face value as I (all ptgs of 3p. bright magenta exce multi-value coil No. 930cl and sheets from 21.1.92 onwards, 10 orange-brown except 1984 "Christian Heritage" £4 booklet a 26p. rosine except 1987 £1.04 "window" booklet).

Figures of face value narrower as in II (from coil No. X930cl ar in sheets from 21.1.92 (3p.), 1984 "Christian Heritage" £4 bookl (10p.) or 1987 £1.04 "window" booklet (26p.)).

This catalogue includes changes of figure styles on those stam where there is no other listable difference. Similar changes have al taken place on other values, but only in conjunction with list colour, paper or perforation differences.

(Des from plaster cast by Arnold Machin)

1971 (15 Feb)–**96.** *Decimal Currency. T* **367**. *Chalk-surfac paper.*

(*a*) *Photo Harrison* (*except for some printings of Nos.* X879 *a* X913 *in sheets produced by Enschedé and issued on* 12 Dec 19 (8*p.*) *and* 19 Nov 1991 (18*p.*)). *With phosphor bands. P* 15×14

X841 ½p. turquoise-blue (2 bands) 10
a. Imperf (pair)† £900
l. Booklet pane. No. X841 × 2 *se-tenant* vert with X849 × 2 .. .. .. 5·00
la. Ditto, *se-tenant* horiz (14.7.71) .. 80
m. Booklet pane. No. X841×5 plus label 3·50
n. Coil strip. No. X849, X841×2 and X844×2 35
o. Booklet pane. No. X841 × 3, X851 × 3 and X852 × 6 (24.5.72) .. .. 12·00
p. Booklet pane. No. X841 × 3, X842 and X852 × 2 (24.5.72) .. .. 75·00
q. Coil strip. No. X870, X849, X844 and X841 × 2 (3.12.75) 80
r. Booklet pane. No. X841 × 2, X844 × 3 and X870 (10.3.76) 70
s. Booklet pane. No. X841 × 2, X844 × 2, X873 × 2 and X881 × 4 (8½p. values at right) (26.1.77) .. .. 2·50
sa. Ditto. 8½p. values at left .. .. 2·50
t. Booklet pane. No. X841, X844, X894 × 3 and X902 (14p. value at right) (26.1.81) .. .. 2·00
ta. Ditto. 14p. value at left .. .. 2·00
u. Booklet pane. No. X841, X857 × 4 and X899 × 3 (12½p. values at left) (1.2.82) 2·50
ua. Ditto. 12½p. values at right .. .. 2·50
X842 ½p. turquoise-blue (1 side band) (24.5.72) 70·00 35·
X843 ½p. turquoise-bl (1 centre band) (14.12.77) 40
l. Coil strip. No. X843 × 2, X875 and X845 × 2 (14.12.77) 55
m. Booklet pane. No. X843 × 2, X845 × 2 and X875 plus label (8.2.78) .. 75
X844 1p. crimson (2 bands) 10
a. Imperf (vert coil) .. .. ..
b. Pair, one imperf 3 sides (vert coil) ..
c. Imperf (pair) .. .. ..
l. Booklet pane. No. X844 × 2 *se-tenant* vert with X848 × 2 .. .. .. 5·00
m. Ditto, *se-tenant* horiz (14.7.71) .. 80
n. Booklet pane. No. X844 × 2, X876 × 3 and X883 × 3 (9p. values at right) (13.6.77) .. .. 4·00
na. Ditto. 9p. values at left .. .. 2·50
X845 1p. crimson (1 centre band) (14.12.77) .. 20
l. Booklet pane. No. X879 and X845 × 2 plus label (17.10.79) 70
m. Coil strip. No. X879 and X845 × 2 plus 2 labels (16.1.80) 45
n. Booklet pane. No. X845 × 2, X860 and X898 each × 3 (5.4.83) .. .. 5·00
p. Booklet pane. No. X845× 3, X863 × 2 and X900 × 3 (3.9.84) .. .. 4·00
q. Booklet pane. No. X845 × 2 and X896 × 4 (29.7.86) .. .. .. 8·00
s. Booklet pane. No. X845, X867 × 2 and X900 × 3 (20.10.86) .. .. 3·00
sa. Ditto, but with vert edges of pane imperf (29.9.87) .. .. .. 3·00
X846 1p. crimson ("all-over") (10.10.79) .. 20
X847 1p. crimson (1 side band) (20.10.86) .. 1·10 1·
l. Booklet pane. X847, X901 and X912 ×2 .. .. 3·00
m. Booklet pane. No. X847, X901×2, X912×5 and X918 with margins all round (3.3.87) .. .. .. 13·00
X848 1½p. black (2 bands) 30
a. Uncoated paper (1971)* £110
b. Imperf (pair) .. .. ..
c. Imperf 3 sides (horiz pair) .. ..
X849 2p. myrtle-green (face value as T **367**) (2 bands) 20
a. Imperf (horiz pair) .. .. ..
l. Booklet pane. No. X849×2, X880×2 and X886×3 plus label (10p. values at right) (28.8.79) .. .. .. 2·50
la. Ditto. 10p. values at left .. .. 2·00
m. Booklet pane. No. X849×3, X889×2 and X895×2 plus label (12p. values at right) (4.2.80) .. .. .. 2·00
ma. Ditto. 12p. values at left .. .. 2·00
n. Booklet pane. No. X849, X888×3, X889 and X895×4 with margins all round (16.4.80) .. .. .. 3·75
o. Booklet pane. No. X849×6 with margins all round (16.4.80) .. 80
p. Booklet pane. No. X849, X857, X898 and X899×6 with margins all round (19.5.82) .. .. 4·50
X850 2p. myrtle-green (face value as T **367**) ("all-over") (10.10.79) 30

851 2½p. magenta (1 centre band) 25 10
a. Imperf (pair)† £250
l. Booklet pane. No. X851 × 5 plus label 2·75
m. Booklet pane. No. X851 × 4 plus two labels .. .. 4·00
n. Booklet pane. No. X851 × 3, X852 × 3 and X855 × 6 (24.5.72) .. .. 7·00
852 2½p. magenta (1 side band) .. .. 1·50 2·00
l. Booklet pane. No. X852 × 2 and X855 × 4 .. .. 5·00
853 2½p. magenta (2 bands) (21.5.75) .. 40 85
854 2½p. rose-red (2 bands) (26.8.81) .. 60 85
l. Booklet pane. No. X854 × 3, X862 × 2 and X894 × 3 (11½p. values at left) .. 5·00
la. Ditto. 11½p. values at right .. .. 6·50
855 3p. ultramarine (2 bands) 30 10
a. Imperf (coil strip of 5) £1000
b. Imperf (pair)† £250
c. Uncoated paper (1972)* .. .. 40·00
l. Booklet pane. No. X855 × 5 plus label 2·00
856 3p. ultramarine (1 centre band) (10.9.73) 30 25
a. Imperf (pair)† £250
b. Imperf between (vert pair)† .. £375
c. Imperf horiz (vert pair)† £200
857 3p. bright magenta (Type I) (2 bands) (1.2.82) 50 50
858 3½p. olive-grey (*shades*) (2 bands) .. 40 40
a. Imperf (pair) £350
859 3½p. olive-grey (1 centre band) (24.6.74) .. 40 15
860 3½p. purple-brown (1 centre band) (5.4.83) 1·50 1·75
861 4p. ochre-brown (2 bands) 30 30
a. Imperf (pair)† £950
862 4p. greenish blue (2 bands) (26.8.81) .. 1·75 1·75
863 4p. greenish blue (1 centre band) (3.9.84) 1·75 2·00
864 4p. greenish blue (1 side band) (8.1.85) 2·00 2·50
l. Booklet pane. No. X864×2, X901×4, X909×2 and X920 with margins all round .. .. 12·50
865 4½p. grey-blue (2 bands) (24.10.73) .. 30 25
a. Imperf (pair) £300
866 5p. pale violet (2 bands) 30 10
867 5p. claret (1 centre band) (20.10.86) .. 2·00 2·00
868 5½p. violet (2 bands) (24.10.73) 35 25
869 5½p. violet (1 centre band) (17.3.75) .. 30 20
a. Uncoated paper* £375
870 6p. light emerald (2 bands) 40 15
a. Uncoated paper* .. .. .. 17·00
871 6½p. greenish blue (2 bands) (4.9.74) .. 60 60
872 6½p. greenish blue (1 centre band) (24.9.75) 40 15
a. Imperf (vert pair) £300
b. Uncoated paper* £160
873 6½p. greenish blue (1 side band) (26.1.77) 80 85
874 7p. purple-brown (2 bands) (15.1.75) .. 70 85
a. Imperf (pair) £250
875 7p. purple-brown (1 centre band) (13.6.77) 40 30
a. Imperf (pair) £100
l. Booklet pane. No. X875 × 10 and X883 × 10 (15.11.78) .. .. 4·50
876 7p. purple-brown (1 side band) (13.6.77) 70 80
877 7½p. pale chestnut (2 bands) 40 30
878 8p. rosine (2 bands) (24.10.73) 30 30
a. Uncoated paper* .. .. .. 12·00
879 8p. rosine (1 centre band) (20.8.79) .. 30 30
a. Uncoated paper* £650
b. Imperf (pair) £600
l. Booklet pane. No. X879 and X886, each × 10 (14.11.79) .. .. 5·00
880 8p. rosine (1 side band) (28.8.79) .. 90 90
881 8½p. light yellowish green (*shades*) (2 bands) (24.9.75) 40 30
a. Imperf (pair) £750
882 9p. yellow-orange and black (2 bands) .. 70 40
883 9p. deep violet (2 bands) (25.2.76) .. 50 30
a. Imperf (pair) £200
884 9½p. purple (2 bands) (25.2.76) 50 40
885 10p. orge-brown & chest (2 bands) (11.8.71) 50 40
a. Orange-brown omitted £150
b. Imperf (horiz pair) £2000
886 10p. orange-brn (Type I) (2 bands) (25.2.76) 50 30
a. Imperf (pair) £250
b. Type II (4.9.84) .. .. .. 28·00 28·00
bl. Booklet pane. No. X886b, X901 and X909 × 7, with margins all round .. 29·00
887 10p. orange-brown (Type I) ("all-over") (3.10.79) 40 50
888 10p. orange-brown (Type I) (1 centre band) (4.2.80) 40 30
a. Imperf (pair) £275
l. Booklet pane. No. X888×9 with margins all round (16.4.80) .. .. 2·75
m. Booklet pane. No. X888 and X895, each × 10 (12.11.80) .. .. 6·00
889 10p. orange-brown (Type I) (1 side band) (4.2.80) .. .. 90 1·00
890 10½p. yellow (2 bands) (25.2.76) 60 40
891 10½p. deep dull blue (2 bands) (26.4.78) .. 80 50
892 11p. brown-red (2 bands) (25.2.76) .. 70 40
a. Imperf (pair) £1750
893 11½p. drab (1 centre band) (14.1.81) .. 60 40
a. Imperf (pair) £225
l. Booklet pane. No. X893 and X902, each × 10 (11.11.81) .. .. 7·00
894 11½p. drab (1 side band) (26.1.81) .. 70 90
l. Booklet pane. No. X894 × 4 and X902 × 6 (6.5.81) .. .. .. 4·00
895 12p. yellowish green (2 bands) (4.2.80) .. 70 50
l. Booklet pane. No. X895 × 9 with margins all round (16.4.80) .. .. 3·00
896 12p. bright emerald (1 centre band) (29.10.85) 70 50
a. Imperf (pair) .. .. ..
l. Booklet pane. No. X896 × 9 with margins all round (18.3.86) .. .. 3·00
897 12p. bright emerald (1 side band) (14.1.86) 1·00 1·00
l. Booklet pane. No. X897×4 and X909×6 (12p. values at left) .. 6·00
la. Ditto. 12p. values at right .. .. 6·00
m. Booklet pane. No. X897×6, X909×2 and X919 with margins all round (18.3.86) .. .. 14·00
898 12½p. light emerald (1 centre band) (27.1.82) 50 30
a. Imperf (pair) £100
l. Booklet pane. No. X898 and X907, each × 10 (10.11.82) .. .. 9·00

X899 12½p. light emerald (1 side band) (1.2.82) .. 70 70
l. Booklet pane. No. X899 × 4 and X907 × 6 (1.2.82) .. .. .. 5·00
m. Booklet pane. No. X899 × 6 with margins all round (19.5.82) .. .. 2·50
n. Booklet pane. No. X899 × 4 and X908 × 6 (12½p. values at left) (5.4.83) 8·00
na. Ditto. 12½p. values at right .. .. 8·00
X900 13p. pale chestnut (1 centre band) (28.8.84) 50 40
a. Imperf (pair) £500
l. Booklet pane. No. X900 × 9 with margins all round (8.1.85) .. .. 3·25
m. Booklet pane. No. X900 × 6 with margins all round (3.3.87) .. .. 2·50
n. Booklet pane. No. X900 × 4 with margins all round (4.8.87) .. .. 2·50
o. Booklet pane. No. X900 × 10 with margins all round (4.8.87) .. .. 5·00
X901 13p. pale chestnut (1 side band) (3.9.84) .. 70 70
l. Booklet pane. No. X901×4 and X909×6 (13p. values at left) .. 6·00
la. Ditto. 13p. values at right .. .. 6·00
m. Booklet pane. No. X901×6 with margins all round (4.9.84) .. .. 2·50
n. Booklet pane. No. X901 and X912×5 (20.10.86) .. .. 5·00
na. Ditto, but with vert edges of pane imperf (29.9.87) .. .. .. 5·00
X902 14p. grey-blue (2 bands) (26.1.81) .. 1·10 50
X903 14p. deep blue (1 centre band) (23.8.88) .. 70 50
a. Imperf (pair) £275
l. Booklet pane. No. X903 × 4 with margins all round .. .. .. 4·50
m. Booklet pane. No. X903 × 10 with margins all round .. .. .. 8·00
n. Booklet pane. No. X903 × 4 with horiz edges of pane imperf (11.10.88) .. 7·00
p. Booklet pane. No. X903 × 10 with horiz edges of pane imperf (11.10.88) 9·00
q. Booklet pane. No. X903×4 with three edges of pane imperf (24.1.89) .. 20·00
X904 14p. deep blue (1 side band) (5.9.88) .. 3·00 3·00
l. Booklet pane. No. X904 and X914×2 plus label .. .. 4·50
m. Booklet pane. No. X904×2 and X914×4 with vert edges of pane imperf 7·50
X905 15p. bright blue (1 centre band) (26.9.89) 75 50
a. Imperf (pair) £325
X906 15p. bright blue (1 side band) (2.10.89) .. 2·75 2·50
l. Booklet pane. No. X906×2 and X916 plus label .. .. 8·00
m. Booklet pane. No. X906, X916, X922, 1446, 1448, 1468, 1470 and 1472 plus label with margins all round (20.3.90) 18·00
X907 15½p. pale violet (2 bands) (1.2.82) .. 75 75
l. Booklet pane. No. X907×6 with margins all round (19.5.82) .. .. 3·00
m. Booklet pane. No. X907×9 with margins all round (19.5.82) .. .. 4·00
X908 16p. olive-drab (2 bands) (5.4.83) .. 1·50 1·50
X909 17p. grey-blue (2 bands) (3.9.84) .. 1·00 1·00
l. Booklet pane. No. X909×3 plus label (4.11.85) .. .. 3·00
X910 17p. deep blue (1 centre band) (4.9.90) .. 1·25 1·25
a. Imperf (pair) .. .. ..
X911 17p. deep blue (1 side band) (4.9.90) .. 1·50 1·50
l. Booklet pane. No. X911×3 plus label 3·00
m. Booklet pane. No. X911×2, X917×3 plus 3 labels with vert edges of pane imperf .. .. 4·00
X912 18p. deep olive-grey (2 bands) (20.10.86) 1·00 1·00
X913 18p. bright green (1 centre band) (10.9.91) 75 50
a. Imperf (pair) £375
X914 19p. bright orange-red (2 bands) (5.9.88) 1·50 1·50
X915 20p. dull purple (2 bands) (25.2.76) .. 1·25 75
X916 20p. brownish black (2 bands) (2.10.89) .. 1·75 2·00
X917 22p. bright orange-red (2 bands) (4.9.90) 1·50 1·50
X917*a* 25p. rose-red (2 bands) (6.2.96) .. .. 1·50 1·50
X918 26p. rosine (Type I) (2 bands) (3.3.87) .. 8·00 8·00
X919 31p. purple (2 bands) (18.3.86) .. .. 12·00 12·00
X920 34p. ochre-brown (2 bands) (8.1.85) .. 8·00 8·00
X921 50p. ochre-brown (2 bands) (2.2.77) .. 2·50 75
X922 50p. ochre (2 bands) (20.3.90) .. .. 5·50 5·50

(*b*) *Photo Harrison. On phosphorised paper. P* 15×14.

X924 ½p. turquoise-blue (10.12.80) 10 10
a. Imperf (pair) £130
l. Coil strip. No. X924 and X932×3 (30.12.81) .. .. 1·00
X925 1p. crimson (12.12.79) 20 20
a. Imperf (pair) £750
l. Coil strip. No. X925 and X932×3 (14.8.84) .. .. 1·00
m. Booklet pane. No. X925 and X969, each × 2 (10.9.91) .. .. .. 1·10
X926 2p. myrtle-green (face value as T **367**) (12.12.79) 20 20
a. Imperf (pair) £900
X927 2p. deep green (face value as T **367***a*) (26.7.88) 20 20
a. Imperf (pair) .. .. ..
l. Booklet pane. No. X927×2 and X969×4 plus 2 labels with vert edges of pane imperf (10.9.91) .. .. 1·50
X928 2p. myrtle-green (face value as T **367***a*) (5.9.88) .. .. 2·25 2·25
l. Coil strip. No. X928 and X932×3 .. 2·50
X929 2½p. rose-red (14.1.81) 30 30
l. Coil strip. No. X929 and X930×3 (6.81) .. .. 1·50
X930 3p. bright magenta (Type I) (22.10.80) .. 30 30
a. Imperf (horiz pair) £1000
b. Booklet pane. No. X930, X931×2 and X949×6 with margins all round (14.9.83) .. .. 4·50
c. Type II (10.10.89) .. .. .. 1·25 60
cl. Coil strip. No. X930c and X933×3 .. 2·75
X931 3½p. purple-brown (30.3.83) 60 60
X932 4p. greenish blue (30.12.81) 50 50

X933 4p. new blue (26.7.88) 30 30
a. Imperf (pair) £1500
l. Coil strip. No. X933×3 and X935 (27.11.90) .. .. 1·10
m. Coil strip. No. X933 and X935, each ×2 (1.10.91) 90
n. Coil strip. No. X933 and X935×3 (31.1.95) 40
X934 5p. pale violet (10.10.79) 40 30
X935 5p. dull red-brown (26.7.88) 30 30
a. Imperf (pair) £2000
X936 6p. yellow-olive (10.9.91) 30 30
X937 7p. brownish red (29.10.85) .. .. 2·00 2·00
X938 8½p. yellowish green (24.3.76) 50 60
X939 10p. orange-brown (Type I) (11.79) .. 50 30
X940 10p. dull orange (Type II) (4.9.90) .. 40 40
X941 11p. brown-red (27.8.80) .. .. 1·00 1·00
X942 11½p. ochre-brown (15.8.79) 60 50
X943 12p. yellowish green (30.1.80) 60 60
X944 13p. olive-grey (15.8.79) 70 50
X945 13½p. purple-brown (30.1.80) 70 70
X946 14p. grey-blue (14.1.81) 70 50
X947 15p. ultramarine (15.8.79) 70 50
X948 15½p. pale violet (14.1.81) 70 50
a. Imperf (pair) £200
X949 16p. olive-drab (30.3.83) 70 40
a. Imperf (pair) £130
l. Booklet pane. No. X949×9 with margins all round (14.9.83) .. .. 3·75
X950 16½p. pale chestnut (27.1.82) 90 80
X951 17p. light emerald (30.1.80) 80 50
X952 17p. grey-blue (30.3.83) 70 50
a. Imperf (pair) £275
l. Booklet pane. No. X952×6 with margins all round (4.9.84) .. .. 3·00
m. Booklet pane. No. X952×9 with margins all round (8.1.85) .. .. 4·50
X953 17½p. pale chestnut (30.1.80) 90 90
X954 18p. deep violet (14.1.81) 90 80
X955 18p. deep olive-grey (28.8.84) 90 70
a. Imperf (pair) £130
l. Booklet pane. No. X955×9 with margins all round (3.3.87) .. .. 4·50
m. Booklet pane. No. X955×4 with margins all round (4.8.87) .. .. 3·00
n. Booklet pane. No. X955×10 with margins all round (4.8.87) .. .. 6·50
X956 19p. bright orange-red (23.8.88) 90 75
a. Imperf (pair) £325
l. Booklet pane. No. X956×4 with margins all round .. .. .. 6·00
m. Booklet pane. No. X956×10 with margins all round .. .. .. 10·00
n. Booklet pane. No. X956×4 with horiz edges of pane imperf (11.10.88) .. 7·00
o. Booklet pane. No. X956×10 with horiz edges of pane imperf (11.10.88) 12·00
q. Booklet pane. No. X956×4 with three edges of pane imperf (24.1.89) .. 20·00
X957 19½p. olive-grey (27.1.82) .. .. .. 1·50 1·50
X958 20p. dull purple (10.10.79) .. .. 1·00 40
X959 20p. turquoise-green (23.8.88) .. .. 1·00 70
X960 20p. brownish black (26.9.89) .. .. 1·00 50
a. Imperf (pair) £650
l. Booklet pane. No. X960×5 plus label with vert edges of pane imperf (2.10.89) .. .. 7·00
X961 20½p. ultramarine (30.3.83) .. .. 1·40 1·25
a. Imperf (pair) £1100
X962 22p. blue (22.10.80) 90 50
a. Imperf (pair) £200
X963 22p. yellow-green (28.8.84) 90 65
a. Imperf (horiz pair) £900
X964 22p. bright orange-red (4.9.90) 90 60
a. Imperf (pair) .. .. ..
X965 23p. brown-red (30.3.83) .. .. 1·10 70
a. Imperf (horiz pair) £900
X966 23p. bright green (23.8.88) .. .. 1·25 70
X967 24p. violet (28.8.84) .. .. .. 1·40 1·10
X968 24p. Indian red (26.9.89) .. .. 1·75 1·10
a. Imperf (horiz pair) £2250
X969 24p. chestnut (10.9.91) .. .. .. 1·00 60
a. Imperf (pair) £200
X970 25p. purple (14.1.81) .. .. .. 1·10 1·10
X971 26p. rosine (Type I) (27.1.82) .. .. 1·00 40
a. Imperf (horiz pair) .. .. ..
b. Type II (4.8.87) .. .. .. 4·00 4·00
bl. Booklet pane. No. X971b×4 with margins all round .. .. .. 14·00
X972 26p. drab (4.9.90) .. .. .. 1·25 1·25
X973 27p. chestnut (23.8.88) .. .. .. 1·25 1·25
l. Booklet pane. No. X973×4 with margins all round .. .. .. 7·00
m. Booklet pane. No. X973×4 with horiz edges of pane imperf (11.10.88) .. 25·00
X974 27p. violet (4.9.90) .. .. .. 1·25 1·25
X975 28p. deep violet (30.3.83) .. .. 1·25 1·25
a. Imperf (pair) £1100
X976 28p. ochre (23.8.88) .. .. .. 1·25 1·25
X977 28p. deep bluish grey (10.9.91) .. .. 1·25 1·25
a. Imperf (pair) £1500
X978 29p. ochre-brown (27.1.82) .. .. 2·00 1·25
X979 29p. deep mauve (26.9.89) .. .. 2·00 1·25
X980 30p. deep olive-grey (26.9.89) .. .. 1·25 1·25
X981 31p. purple (30.3.83) .. .. .. 1·50 1·50
a. Imperf (pair) £1000
X982 31p. ultramarine (4.9.90) .. .. .. 1·50 1·50
X983 32p. greenish blue (23.8.88) .. .. 1·50 1·50
a. Imperf (pair) £1000
X984 33p. light emerald (4.9.90) .. .. 1·50 1·50
X985 34p. ochre-brown (28.8.84) .. .. 1·50 1·50
X986 34p. deep bluish grey (26.9.89) .. .. 1·75 1·50
X987 34p. deep mauve (10.9.91) .. .. 1·50 1·50
X988 35p. sepia (23.8.88) £1000
a. Imperf (pair) .. .. .. 1·75 1·50
X989 35p. yellow (10.9.91) .. .. .. 1·50 1·25
X990 37p. rosine (26.9.89) .. .. .. 1·75 1·75
X991 39p. bright mauve (10.9.91) .. .. 1·75 1·50

(*c*) *Photo Harrison. On ordinary paper. P* 15×14

X992 50p. ochre-brown (21.5.80) .. .. 2·00 1·00
a. Imperf (pair) £600
X993 75p. grey-black (face value as T **367***a*) (26.7.88) .. .. 2·50 2·50

(d) Photo Harrison. On ordinary or phosphorised paper. P 15×14

X994	50p. ochre (13.3.90)	1·75	80
	a. Imperf (pair)	£900	

(e) Litho J.W. P 14

X996	4p. greenish blue (2 phosphor bands) (30.1.80)	30	40
X997	4p. greenish blue (phosphorised paper) (11.81)	50	30
X998	20p. dull pur (2 phosphor bands) (21.5.80)	1·25	50
X999	20p. dull pur (phosphorised paper) (11.81)	1·75	50

(f) Litho Questa. P 14 *(No.* X1000, X1003/4 *and* X1023) *or* 15×14 *(others)*

X1000	2p. emerald-green (face value as T **367**) (phosphorised paper) (21.5.80)	30	30
	a. Perf 15×14 (10.7.84)	40	30
X1001	2p. bright green & dp green (face value as T **367***a*) (phosphorised paper) (23.2.88)	1·25	70
X1002	4p. greenish blue (phosphorised paper) (13.5.86)	70	70
X1003	5p. lt violet (phosphorised paper) (21.5.80)	50	30
X1004	5p. claret (phosphorised paper) (27.1.82)	60	30
	a. Perf 15×14 (21.2.84)	70	50
X1005	13p. pale chestnut (1 centre band) (9.2.88)	80	80
	l. Booklet pane. No. X1005×6 with margins all round	3·50	
X1006	13p. pale chestnut (1 side band) (9.2.88)	1·25	1·25
	l. Booklet pane. No. X1006×6, X1010, X1015 and X1021 with margins all round	22·00	
X1007	14p. deep blue (1 centre band) (11.10.88)	2·00	2·00
X1008	17p. deep blue (1 centre band) (19.3.91)	90	90
	l. Booklet pane. No. X1008×6 with margins all round	3·50	
X1009	18p. deep olive-grey (phosphorised paper) (9.2.88)	90	90
	l. Booklet pane. No. X1009×9 with margins all round	4·50	
	m. Booklet pane. No. X1009×6 with margins all round	3·00	
X1010	18p. dp ol-grey (2 phosphor bands) (9.2.88)	5·50	5·50
X1011	18p. bright green (1 centre band) (27.10.92)	1·50	1·50
	l. Booklet pane. No. X1011×6 with margins all round	7·50	
X1012	18p. bright green (1 side band) (27.10.92)	1·75	1·75
	l. Booklet pane X1012×2, X1018×2, X1022×2, 1451*a*, 1514*a* and central label with margins all round	10·00	
	m. Booklet pane. Nos. X1012, X1020, X1022 and 1451*a*, each × 2, and central label with margins all round (10.8.93)	11·00	
X1013	19p. brt orange-red (phosphorised paper) (11.10.88)	2·00	2·00
X1014	20p. dull pur (phosphorised paper) (13.5.86)	1·50	1·50
X1015	22p. yellow-grn (2 phosphor bands) (9.2.88)	8·50	8·50
X1016	22p. bright orange-red (phosphorised paper) (19.3.91)	1·25	1·25
	l. Booklet pane. No. X1016×9 with margins all round	5·50	
	m. Booklet pane. No. X1016×6, X1019×2 and central label with margins all round	8·00	
X1017	24p. chestnut (phosphorised paper) (27.10.92)	1·25	90
	l. Booklet pane. No. X1017×6 with margins all round	6·00	
X1018	24p. chestnut (2 bands) (27.10.92)	1·50	1·50
X1019	33p. lt emer (phosphorised paper) (19.3.91)	2·00	2·00
X1020	33p. lt emer (2 phosphor bands) (25.2.92)	1·50	1·50
X1021	34p. ochre-brn (2 phosphor bands) (9.2.88)	7·50	7·50
X1022	39p. bright mauve (2 bands) (27.10.92)	2·25	2·25
X1023	75p. black (face value as T **367**) (ordinary paper) (30.1.80)	3·50	2·00
	a. Perf 15×14 (21.2.84)	4·00	3·75
X1024	75p. brownish grey and black (face value as T **367***a*) (ordinary paper) (23.2.88)	10·00	9·00

(g) Litho Walsall. P 14

X1050	2p. dp green (phosphorised paper) (9.2.93)	1·25	1·25
	l. Booklet pane. No. X1050×2 and X1053×4 plus 2 labels with vert edges of the pane imperf	3·50	
X1051	14p. deep blue (1 side band) (25.4.89)	3·25	3·25
	l. Booklet pane. No. X1051×2 and X1052×4 with vert edges of pane imperf	10·00	
X1052	19p. bright orange-red (2 phosphor bands) (25.4.89)	1·75	2·00
X1053	24p. chestnut (phosphorised paper) (9.2.93)	1·50	1·50
X1054	29p. dp mauve (2 phosphor bands) (2.10.89)	5·50	5·50
	l. Booklet pane. No. X1054×4 with three edges of pane imperf	20·00	
X1055	29p. dp mve (phosphorised paper) (17.4.90)	6·50	6·50
	l. Booklet pane. No. X1055×4 with three edges of pane imperf	24·00	
X1056	31p. ultram (phosphorised paper) (17.9.90)	2·00	2·25
	l. Booklet pane. No. X1056×4 with horiz edges of pane imperf	7·00	
X1057	33p. lt emer (phosphorised paper) (16.9.91)	1·50	1·50
	l. Booklet pane. No. X1057×4 with horiz edges of pane imperf	5·00	
X1058	39p. brt mve (phosphorised paper) (16.9.91)	2·00	2·00
	l. Booklet pane. No. X1058×4 with horiz edges of pane imperf	7·00	

*See footnote after No. 744.

†These come from sheets with gum arabic.

Nos. X842, X847, X852, X854, X857, X860, X862/4, X867, X873, X876, X880, X886b, X889, X894/5, X897, X899, X901/2, X904, X906/9, X911/12, X914, X916/20, X922, X971b, X1005/13, X1015/22 and X1050/8 come from booklets; Nos. X843 and X845 come from booklets or coils, Nos. X917*a*, X928 and X932 come from coils: Nos. X852, X864, X873, X876, X880, X889, X894, X897, X899, X901, X911 and X1006 were each issued with the phosphor band at the right or left from the same stamp booklet, usually in equal quantities. Nos. X847, X906 and X1012 also exist with phosphor band at the left or right, but these come from different booklets.

In addition to booklet pane No. X1012m, No. X1020 also comes from the *se-tenant* pane in the Wales £6 booklet which is listed under No. W49a in the Wales Regional Section.

Nos. X844a/b come from a strip of eight of the vertical coil. It comprises two normals, one imperforate at sides and bottom, one completely imperforate, one imperforate at top, left and bottom and partly perforated at right due to the bottom stamps being perforated twice. No. X844b is also known from another strip having one stamp imperforate at sides and bottom.

Nos. X848b/c come from the same sheet, the latter having perforations at the foot of the stamps only.

Multi-value coil strips Nos. X924l, X925l, X928l, X929l, X930cl and X933l/n were produced by the Post Office for a large direct mail marketing firm. Use of the first coil strip, No. X929l, is known from June 1981. From 2 September 1981 No. X929l was available from the Philatelic Bureau, Edinburgh and, subsequently, from a number of other Post Office counters.

Later coil stamps were sold at the Philatelic Bureau and Post Office philatelic counters.

PANES OF SIX FROM STITCHED BOOKLETS. Nos. X841m, X851l/m and X855l include one or two printed labels showing commercial advertisements. These were originally perforated on all four sides, but from the August 1971 editions of the 25p. and 30p. booklets and December 1971 edition of the 50p. the line of perforations between the label and the binding margin was omitted. Similar panes, with the line of perforations omitted, exist for the 3p., 3½p. and 4½p. values (Nos. X856, X858 and X865), but these are outside the scope of this listing as the labels are blank.

PART-PERFORATED SHEETS. Since the introduction of the "Jumelle" press in 1972 a number of part-perforated sheets, both definitive and commemoratives, have been discovered. It is believed that these occur when the operation of the press is interrupted. Such sheets invariably show a number of "blind" perforations, where the pins have failed to cut the paper. Our listings of imperforate errors from these sheets are for pairs showing no trace whatsoever of the perforations. Examples showing "blind" perforations are outside the scope of this catalogue.

In cases where perforation varieties affect *se-tenant* stamps fuller descriptions will be found in Vol. 4 of the *G.B. Specialised Catalogue*.

WHITE PAPER. From 1972 printings appeared on fluorescent white paper giving a stronger chalk reaction than the original ordinary cream paper.

GUM ARABIC. The following exist with gum arabic as well as PVA gum (with or without added dextrin): Nos. X841, X841n, X851, X855, X856, X861 and X870. See notes after No. 722.

DEXTRIN GUM. From 1973 printings in photogravure appeared with PVA gum to which dextrin had been added. As the resulting gum was virtually colourless bluish green colouring matter was added to distinguish it from the previous PVA. Questa printings in lithography from 1988 onwards used PVA gum with dextrin, but did not show the colouring agent.

"ALL-OVER" PHOSPHOR. To improve mechanised handling most commemoratives from the 1972 Royal Silver Wedding 3p. value to the 1979 Rowland Hill Death Centenary set had the phosphor applied by printing cylinder across the entire surface of the stamp, giving a matt effect. Printing of the 1, 2 and 10p. definitives, released in October 1979, also had "all-over" phosphor, but these were purely a temporary expedient pending the adoption of phosphorised paper. Nos. X883, X890 and X921 have been discovered with "all over" phosphor in addition to the normal phosphor bands. These error are outside the scope of this catalogue.

PHOSPHORISED PAPER. Following the experiments on Nos. 743c and 829 a printing of the 4½p. definitive was issued on 13 November 1974, which had, in addition to the normal phosphor bands, phosphor included in the paper coating. Because of dfficulties in identifying the phosphorised paper with the naked eye this printing is not listed separately in this catalogue.

No. X938 was the first value printed on phosphorised paper without phosphor bands and was a further experiment issue to test the efficacy of this system. From 15 August 1979 phosphorised paper was accepted for use generally, the paper replacing phosphor bands on values other than those required in the second-class rate.

Stamps on phosphorised paper show a shiny surface instead of the matt areas of those printed with phosphor bands.

VARNISH COATING. Nos. X841 and X883 exist with and without a varnish coating. This cannot easily be detected without the use of an ultra-violet lamp as it merely reduces the fluorescent paper reaction.

POSTAL FORGERIES. In mid-1993 a number of postal forgeries of the 24p. chestnut were detected in the London area. These forgeries, produced by lithography, can be identified by the lack of phosphor in the paper, screening dots across the face value and by the perforations which were applied by a line machine gauging 11.

UNDERPRINTS. From 1982 various values appeared with underprints, printed on the reverse, in blue, over the gum. These were usually from special stamp booklets, sold at a discount by the Post Office, but in 1985 surplus stocks of such underprinted paper were used for other purposes.

The following Decimal Machin stamps exist with underprints:

- 12p. bright emerald (1 centre band)—double-lined star underprint from sheet printing (also exists without)
- 12½p. light emerald (1 centre band)—star with central dot underprint from booklet pane X898l
- 12½p. light emerald (1 centre band)—double-lined star underprint from booklet pane of 20
- 13p. pale chestnut (1 centre band)—double-lined star underprint from booklet pane of 10 (also exists without)
- 15½p. pale violet (2 bands)—star with central dot underprint from booklet pane X898l
- 16p. olive-drab (phosphorised paper)—double-lined D underprint from booklet pane of 10 (also exists without)
- 17p. grey-blue (2 bands)—double-lined star underprint from booklet pane X909l
- 17p. grey-blue (phosphorised paper)—double-lined D underprint from booklet pane of 10 (also exists without)

368 "A Mountain Road" (T. P. Flanagan)

369 "Deer's Meadow" (Tom Carr)

370 "Slieve na brock" (Colin Middleton)

(Layout des Stuart Rose)

71 (16 June). "*Ulster* 1971" *Paintings. Chalk-surfaced paper. Two phosphor bands. P* 15 × 14.
1 **368** 3p. yellow-buff, pale yellow, Venetian red, black, blue and drab .. 10 10
2 **369** 7½p. olive-brown, brownish grey, pale olive-grey, dp bl, cobalt & grey-bl 50 50
a. Pale olive-grey omitted* .. .. 60·00
3 **370** 9p. greenish yellow, orange, grey, lavender-grey, bistre, black, pale ochre-brown, and ochre-brown .. 50 50
a. Orange omitted £1500
1/3 .. .. *Set of* 3 1·00 1·00
A used example of the 3p. has been seen with the Venetian red itted.

371 John Keats (150th Death Anniv)

372 Thomas Gray (Death Bicentenary)

373 Sir Walter Scott (Birth Bicentenary)

es Rosalind Dease. Queen's head printed in gold and then embossed)

71 (28 July). *Literary Anniversaries. Chalk-surfaced paper. Two phosphor bands. P* 15 × 14.
4 **371** 3p. black, gold and greyish blue .. 10 10
a. Gold (Queen's head) omitted .. 90·00
5 **372** 5p. black, gold and yellow-olive .. 50 50
a. Gold (Queen's head) omitted .. £160
6 **373** 7½p. black, gold and yellow-brown .. 50 50
4/6 .. .. *Set of* 3 1·00 1·00
The 7½p. exists with embossing omitted.

374 Servicemen and Nurse of 1921

375 Roman Centurion

376 Rugby Football, 1871

(Des F. Wegner)

1971 (25 Aug). *British Anniversaries. Events described on stamps. Chalk-surfaced paper. Two phosphor bands. P* 15 × 14.
887 **374** 3p. red-orange, grey, deep blue, olive-grn, olive-brn, blk, rosine & vio-bl 10 10
a. Deep blue omitted* £600
b. Red-orange (nurse's cloak) omitted £275
c. Olive-brown (faces, etc.) omitted £160
d. Black omitted £10000
888 **375** 7½p. grey, yellow-brown, vermilion, mauve, grey-black, black, silver, gold and ochre 50 50
a. Grey omitted .. .. .. 75·00
889 **376** 9p. new blue, myrtle-green, grey-blk, lemon, olive-brn, mag & yell-ol 50 50
a. Olive-brown omitted £110
b. New blue omitted £2500
c. Myrtle-green omitted £2250
887/9 .. .. *Set of* 3 1·00 1·00
*The effect of the missing deep blue is shown on the sailor's uniform, which appears as grey.
Used examples have been seen of the 3p. with grey omitted and of the 9p. with the lemon (jerseys) omitted.

377 Physical Sciences Building, University College of Wales, Aberystwyth

378 Faraday Building, Southampton University

379 Engineering Department, Leicester University

380 Hexagon Restaurant, Essex University

(Des N. Jenkins)

1971 (22 Sept). *British Architecture. Modern University Buildings. Chalk-surfaced paper. Two phosphor bands. P* 15 × 14.
890 **377** 3p. olive-brn, ochre, lem, blk & yell-ol 10 10
a. Lemon omitted .. .. .. † £5000
b. Black (windows) omitted .. £10000
891 **378** 5p. rose, black, chestnut and lilac .. 20 20
892 **379** 7½p. ochre, black and purple-brown .. 50 50
893 **380** 9p. pale lilac, black, sepia-brn & dp bl 90 90
890/3 .. .. *Set of* 4 1·50 1·50
Mint examples of the 5p. exist with a larger "P" following the face value.
No. 890a is only known used on commercial cover from Wantage.

381 "Dream of the Wise Men"

382 "Adoration of the Magi"

383 "Ride of the Magi"

(Des Clarke-Clements-Hughes design team, from stained-glass windows, Canterbury Cathedral. Queen's head printed in gold and then embossed)

1971 (13 Oct). *Christmas. Ordinary paper. One centre phosphor band* (2½p.) *or two phosphor bands* (*others*). *P* 15×14.
894 **381** 2½p. new bl, blk, lemon, emer, reddish violet, carm-red, carm-rose & gold 10 10
a. Imperf (pair) £400
895 **382** 3p. black, reddish violet, lemon, new bl, carm-rose, emer, ultram & gold 10 10
a. Gold (Queen's head) omitted .. £500
b. Carmine-rose omitted £1750
c. Lemon (window panels) omitted 60·00
d. New blue omitted .. .. † £7000
e. Reddish violet (tunics etc) omitted
896 **383** 7½p. black, lilac, lemon, emerald, new blue, rose, green and gold .. 90 90
a. Gold (Queen's head) omitted .. 80·00
b. Lilac omitted £400
c. Emerald omitted £200
894/6 .. .. *Set of* 3 1·00 1·00
All three values are known with the embossing omitted and the 7½p. with embossing double. Used examples of the 3p. have been seen with reddish violet and embossing omitted or with lemon and carmine-rose omitted. A used example of the 7½p. exists with the lemon omitted.

WHITE CHALK-SURFACED PAPER. From No. 897 all issues, with the exception of Nos. 904/8, were printed on fluorescent white paper, giving a stronger chalk reaction than the original cream paper.

384 Sir James Clark Ross

385 Sir Martin Frobisher

386 Henry Hudson

387 Capt. Scott

(Des Marjorie Saynor. Queen's head printed in gold and then embossed)

1972 (16 Feb). *British Polar Explorers. Two phosphor bands. P* 14 × 15.
897 **384** 3p. yellow-brown, indigo, slate-black, flesh, lemon, rose, brt blue & gold 10 10
a. Gold (Queen's head) omitted .. 60·00
b. Slate-black (hair, etc.) omitted .. £2250
c. Lemon omitted £2000
898 **385** 5p. salmon, flesh, purple-brown, ochre, black and gold 20 20
a. Gold (Queen's head) omitted .. 90·00
899 **386** 7½p. reddish violet, blue, deep slate, yellow-brown, buff, black and gold 50 50
a. Gold (Queen's head) omitted .. £200

900 **387** 9p. dull blue, ultramarine, black, greenish yell, pale pink, rose-red & gold 90 90
897/900 .. .. *Set of* 4 1·50 1·50

The 3p. and 5p. are known with embossing omitted and the 3p. also exists with gold and embossing omitted. An example of the 3p. is known used on piece with the flesh colour omitted.

388 Statuette of Tutankhamun

389 19th-century Coastguard

390 Ralph Vaughan Williams and Score

(Des Rosalind Dease (3p.), F. Wegner (7½p.), C. Abbott (9p.). Queen's head printed in gold and then embossed (7½p., 9p.))

1972 (26 Apr). *General Anniversaries. Events described on stamps. Two phosphor bands. P* 15 × 14.

901 **388** 3p. black, grey, gold, dull bistre-brown, blackish brn, pale stone & lt brn 10 10
902 **389** 7½p. pale yellow, new blue, slate-blue, violet-blue, slate and gold .. 50 50
903 **390** 9p. bistre-brown, black, sage-green, dp slate, yellow-ochre, brown & gold 50 50
a. Gold (Queen's head) omitted .. £1250
b. Brown (facial features) omitted .. £750
c. Deep slate omitted .. ..
901/3 .. .. *Set of* 3 1·00 1·00

The 7½p. and 9p. exist with embossing omitted.

391 St. Andrew's, Greensted-juxta-Ongar, Essex

392 All Saints, Earls Barton, Northants

393 St. Andrew's, Letheringsett, Norfolk

394 St. Andrew's, Helpringham, Lincs

395 St. Mary the Virgin, Huish Episcopi, Somerset

(Des R. Maddox. Queen's head printed in gold and then embossed)

1972 (21 June). *British Architecture. Village Churches. Ordinary paper. Two phosphor bands. P* 14 × 15.

904 **391** 3p. violet-blue, black, lt yellow-olive, emerald-green, orange-verm & gold 10 10
a. Gold (Queen's head) omitted .. 75·00
905 **392** 4p. deep yellow-olive, black, emerald, violet-blue, orge-vermilion & gold 20 20
a. Gold (Queen's head) omitted .. £2500
b. Violet-blue omitted £110
906 **393** 5p. deep emerald, black, royal blue, lt yellow-olive, orange-verm & gold 30 25
a. Gold (Queen's head) omitted .. £150
907 **394** 7½p. orange-red, black, deep yellow-ol, royal blue, lt emerald & gold 75 80
908 **395** 9p. new blue, black, emerald-green, dp yellow-olive, orange-verm & gold 85 90
904/8 .. .. *Set of* 5 1·75 2·00

The 3p., 4p., 5p. and 9p. exist with embossing omitted.

An example of the 3p. is known used on piece with the orange-vermilion omitted.

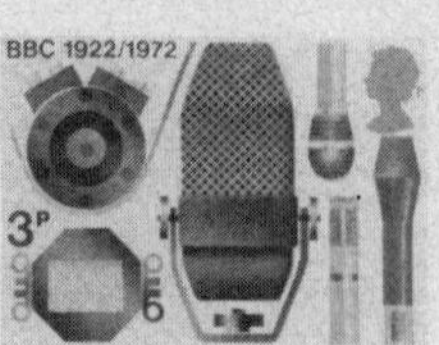

396 Microphones, 1924–69

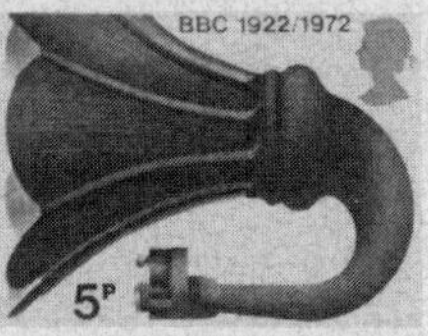

397 Horn Loudspeaker

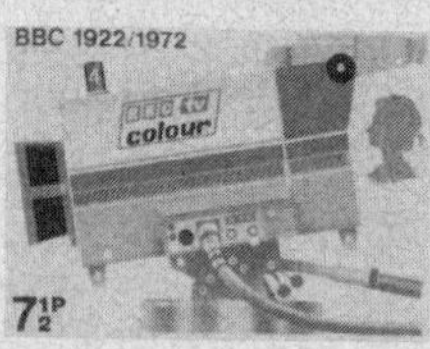

398 T.V. Camera, 1972

399 Oscillator and Spark Transmitter, 1897

(Des D. Gentleman)

1972 (13 Sept). *Broadcasting Anniversaries. 75th Anniv of Marconi and Kemp's Radio Experiments* (9*p.*), *and 50th Anniv of Daily Broadcasting by the B.B.C.* (*others*). *Two phosphor bands. P* 15 × 14.

909 **396** 3p. pale brown, black, grey, greenish yellow and brownish slate .. 10 10
a. Greenish yellow (terminals) omitted £2000
910 **397** 5p. brownish slate, lake-brown, salmon, lt brown, black & red-brn 15 20
911 **398** 7½p. light grey, slate, brownish slate, magenta and black 75 75
a. Brownish slate (Queen's head) omitted .. .. † £2000
912 **399** 9p. lemon, brown, brownish slate, deep brownish slate, bluish slate & blk 75 75
a. Brownish slate (Queen's head) omitted £1500
909/12 .. .. *Set of* 4 1·50 1·50

No. 911a is only known on first day covers posted from the Philatelic Bureau in Edinburgh.

400 Angel holding Trumpet

401 Angel playing Lute

402 Angel playing Harp

(Des Sally Stiff. Photo and embossed)

1972 (18 Oct). *Christmas. One centre phosphor band* (2½*p.*) *or tw phosphor bands* (*others*). *P* 14 × 15.

913 **400** 2½p. cerise, pale reddish brown, yellow-orange, orange-vermilion, lilac, gold, red-brown and deep grey .. 10
a. Gold omitted £250
c. Deep grey omitted .. ..
914 **401** 3p. ultram, lavender, lt turq-blue, brt green, gold, red-brown & bluish vio 10
a. Red-brown omitted £500
b. Bright green omitted .. .. 70·00
c. Bluish violet omitted .. .. 75·00
915 **402** 7½p. deep brown, pale lilac, lt cinnamon, ochre, gold, red-brn & blackish vio 90
a. Ochre omitted .. .. .. 55·00
b. Blackish violet (shadow) omitted
913/15 .. .. *Set of* 3 1·00 1·

All three values exist with embossing omitted.

403 Queen Elizabeth and Duke of Edinburgh

404 "Europe"

(Des J. Matthews from photo by N. Parkinson)

1972 (20 Nov). *Royal Silver Wedding. "All-over" phosphor* (3*p. or without phosphor* (20*p.*). *P* 14×15.

I. *"Rembrandt" Machine*

916 **403** 3p. brownish black, deep blue & silver 25 2
a. Silver omitted £300
917 20p. brownish blk, reddish pur & silver 1·00 1·(

II. *"Jumelle" Machine*

918 **403** 3p. brownish black, deep blue & silver 35 3

The 3p. "JUMELLE" has a lighter shade of the brownish blac than the 3p. "Rembrandt". It also has the brown cylinders less deep etched, which can be distinguished in the Duke's face which slightly lighter, and in the Queen's hair where the highlights a sharper.

3p. "REMBRANDT". Cyls. 3A-1B-11C no dot. Sheets of 100 (10 10).

3p. "JUMELLE". Cyls. 1A–1B–3C dot and no dot. Sheets of 1((two panes 5 × 10, separated by gutter margin).

(Des P. Murdoch)

1973 (3 Jan). *Britain's Entry into European Communities. Tw phosphor bands. P* 14 × 15.

919 **404** 3p. dull orange, bright rose-red, ultramarine, light lilac and black .. 10
920 5p. new blue, bright rose-red, ultramarine, cobalt-blue and black 25
a. Pair. Nos. 920/1 .. .. 1·25 1·
921 5p. light emerald-green, bright rose-red, ultramarine, cobalt-blue and black 25
919/21 .. .. *Set of* 3 1·25 1·

Nos. 920/1 were printed horizontally *se-tenant* throughout th sheet.

405 Oak Tree

(Des D. Gentleman)

1973 (28 Feb). *Tree Planting Year. British Trees* (1*st issue*). *Tw phosphor bands. P* 15 × 14.

922 **405** 9p. brownish black, apple-green, deep olive, sepia, blackish green and brownish grey 50 5
a. Brownish black (value and inscr) omitted £400
b. Brownish grey (Queen's head) omitted £250

See also No. 949.

[CH]ALK-SURFACED PAPER. The following issues are printed [on] chalk-surfaced paper but where "all-over" phosphor has been [ap]plied there is no chalk reaction except in the sheet margins outside [th]e phosphor area.

406 David Livingstone

407 H. M. Stanley

406/7 were printed together, horizontally *se-tenant* within the sheet)

408 Sir Francis Drake

409 Walter Raleigh

410 Charles Sturt

([D]es Marjorie Saynor. Queen's head printed in gold and then embossed)

[19]73 (18 Apr). *British Explorers. "All-over" phosphor. P* 14×15.

[92]3 **406** 3p. orange-yellow, lt orge-brown, grey-black, lt turq-blue, turq-blue & gold .. 25 20
 a. Pair. Nos. 923/4 .. .. .. 1·00 1·25
 b. Gold (Queen's head) omitted .. 40·00
 c. Turquoise-blue (background and inscr) omitted £350
 d. Light orange-brown omitted .. £300
[92]4 **407** 3p. orange-yellow, lt orge-brown, grey-black, lt turq-blue, turq-blue & gold 25 20
 b. Gold (Queen's head) omitted .. 40·00
 c. Turquoise-blue (background and inscr) omitted £350
 d. Light orange-brown omitted .. £300
[92]5 **408** 5p. light flesh, chrome-yellow, orange-yellow, sepia, brownish grey, grey-black, violet-blue and gold .. 20 30
 a. Gold (Queen's head) omitted .. 90·00
 b. Grey-black omitted £500
 c. Sepia omitted £450
[92]6 **409** 7½p. light flesh, reddish brown, sepia, ultram, grey-black, brt lilac & gold 20 30
 a. Gold (Queen's head) omitted .. £1750
 b. Ultramarine (eyes) omitted .. £2500
[92]7 **410** 9p. flesh, pale stone, grey-blue, grey-black, brown-grey, Venetian red, brown-red and gold 25 40
 a. Gold (Queen's head) omitted .. 90·00
 b. Brown-grey printing double .. *from* £800
 c. Grey-black omitted £1000
 d. Brown-red (rivers on map) omitted £500
[92]3/7 .. .. *Set of* 5 1·50 1·25

[C]aution is needed when buying missing gold heads in this issue as [the]y can be removed by using a hard eraser, etc., but this invariably [aff]ects the "all-over" phosphor. Genuine examples have the phosphor [int]act. Used examples off cover cannot be distinguished as much of [the] phosphor is lost in the course of floating.

[I]n the 5p. value the missing grey-black affects the doublet, which [ap]pears as brownish grey, and the lace ruff, which is entirely missing. [Th]e missing sepia affects only Drake's hair, which appears much [lig]hter.

[T]he double printing of the brown-grey (cylinder 1F) on the 9p. is [a m]ost unusual type of error to occur in a multicoloured photogravure [iss]ue. Two sheets are known and it is believed that they stuck to the [cyl]inder and went through a second time. This would result in the [foll]owing two sheets missing the colour but at the time of going to [pre]ss this error has not been reported. The second print is slightly [ask]ew and more prominent in the top half of the sheets. Examples [fro]m the upper part of the sheet showing a clear double impression [of t]he facial features are worth a substantial premium over the price [quo]ted.

[T]he 3p values, the 5p. and the 9p. exist with embossing omitted.

411

412

413

(T **411/13** show sketches of W. G. Grace by Harry Furniss)

(Des E. Ripley. Queen's head printed in gold and then embossed)

1973 (16 May). *County Cricket* 1873–1973. *"All-over" phosphor. P* 14 × 15.

928 **411** 3p. black, ochre and gold 10 10
 a. Gold (Queen's head) omitted .. £1800
929 **412** 7½p. black, light sage-green and gold .. 80 70
930 **413** 9p. black, cobalt and gold .. .. 1·00 90
928/30 .. .. *Set of* 3 1·75 1·50

All three values exist with embossing omitted.

414 "Self-portrait" (Reynolds)

415 "Self-portrait" (Raeburn)

416 "Nelly O'Brien" (Reynolds)

417 "Rev. R. Walker (The Skater)" (Raeburn)

(Des S. Rose. Queen's head printed in gold and then embossed)

1973 (4 July). *British Paintings.* 250*th Birth Anniv of Sir Joshua Reynolds and* 150*th Death Anniv of Sir Henry Raeburn. "All-over" phosphor. P* 14 × 15.

931 **414** 3p. rose, new blue, jet-black, magenta, greenish yellow, blk, ochre & gold 10 10
 a. Gold (Queen's head) omitted .. 60·00
932 **415** 5p. cinnamon, greenish yellow, new bl, lt magenta, blk, yellow-olive & gold 20 25
 a. Gold (Queen's head) omitted .. 75·00
 b. Greenish yellow omitted .. £350
933 **416** 7½p. greenish yellow, new blue, light magenta, black, cinnamon and gold 55 50
 a. Gold (Queen's head) omitted .. 75·00
 b. Cinnamon omitted £4000
934 **417** 9p brownish rose, black, dull rose, pale yell, brownish grey, pale bl & gold 60 60
 b. Brownish rose omitted .. .. 30·00
931/4 .. .. *Set of* 4 1·25 1·25

No. 931a is also known with the embossing also omitted or misplaced.

The 5p. and 7½p. are known with the embossing omitted.

The 9p. is known with the embossing and phosphor both omitted.

418 Court Masque Costumes

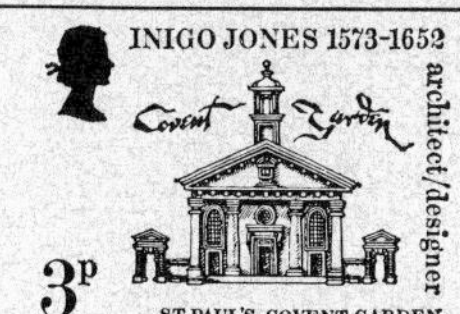

419 St. Paul's Church, Covent Garden

420 Prince's Lodging, Newmarket

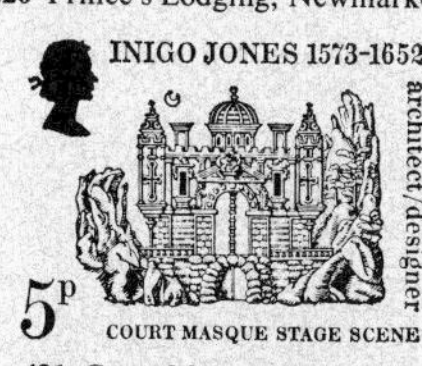

421 Court Masque Stage Scene

T **418/19** and T **420/1** were printed horizontally *se-tenant* within the sheet

(Des Rosalind Dease. Litho and typo B.W.)

1973 (15 Aug). 400*th Birth Anniv of Inigo Jones* (*architect and designer*). *"All-over" phosphor. P* 15 × 14.

935 **418** 3p. deep mauve, black and gold .. 10 15
 a. Pair. Nos. 935/6 .. .. .. 35 40
936 **419** 3p. deep brown, black and gold .. 10 15
937 **420** 5p. blue, black and gold 40 45
 a. Pair. Nos. 937/8 .. .. .. 1·50 1·50
938 **421** 5p. grey-olive, black and gold 40 45
935/8 .. .. *Set of* 4 1·60 1·10

422 Palace of Westminster seen from Whitehall

423 Palace of Westminster seen from Millbank

(Des R. Downer. Recess and typo B.W.)

1973 (12 Sept). 19*th Commonwealth Parliamentary Conference. "All-over" phosphor. P* 15 × 14.

939 **422** 8p. black, brownish grey and stone .. 50 60
940 **423** 10p. gold and black 50 40

424 Princess Anne and Capt. Mark Phillips.

(Des C. Clements and E. Hughes from photo by Lord Litchfield)

1973 (14 Nov). *Royal Wedding. "All-over" phosphor. P* 15 × 14.

941 **424** 3½p. dull violet and silver 10 10
 a. Imperf (horiz pair) £1000
942 20p. deep brown and silver 90 90
 a. Silver omitted £1200

425

426

427

428

429

T **425/9** depict the carol "Good King Wenceslas" and were printed horizontally *se-tenant* within the sheet.

430 "Good King Wenceslas, the Page and Peasant"

(Des D. Gentleman)

1973 (28 Nov). *Christmas. One centre phosphor band* (3p.) *or "all-over" phosphor* (3½p.). *P* 15 × 14.

943 **425** 3p. grey-black, blue, brownish grey, light brown, bright rose-red, turq-green, salmon-pink and gold 15 15
a. Strip of 5. Nos. 943/7 .. .. 2·75 4·00
b. Imperf (horiz strip of 5) £1250
944 **426** 3p. grey-black, violet-blue, slate, brown, rose-red, rosy mauve, turq-green, salmon-pink and gold 15 15
a. Rosy mauve omitted £625
945 **427** 3p. grey-black, violet-blue, slate, brown, rose-red, rosy mauve, turq-green, salmon-pink and gold 15 15
a. Rosy mauve omitted £625
946 **428** 3p. grey-black, violet-blue, slate, brown, rose-red, rosy mauve, turq-green, salmon-pink and gold 15 15
a. Rosy mauve omitted £625
947 **429** 3p. grey-black, violet-blue, slate, brown, rose-red, rosy mauve, turq-green, salmon-pink and gold 15 15
a. Rosy mauve omitted £625
948 **430** 3½p. salmon-pink, grey-black, red-brown, blue, turquoise-green, bright rose-red, rosy mauve, lavender-grey and gold 15 15
a. Imperf (pair) £400
b. Grey-black (value and inscr, etc) omitted .. .. 75·00
c. Salmon-pink omitted .. .. 70·00
d. Blue (leg, robes) omitted .. £130
e. Rosy mauve (robe at right) omitted .. .. 80·00
f. Blue and rosy mauve omitted .. £250
g. Bright rose-red (King's robe) omitted .. .. 75·00
h. Red-brown (logs, basket, etc) omitted .. ..
i. Turquoise-green (leg, robe, etc) omitted £2000
j. Gold (background) omitted .. † £750
943/8 .. .. *Set of* 6 2·75 80

Examples of No. 948j are only known used on cover from Gloucester. The 3½p. has also been seen with the lavender-grey omitted used on piece.

The 3p. and 3½p. are normally with PVA gum with added dextrin, but the 3½p. also exists with normal PVA gum and 3p. with gum arabic.

431 Horse Chestnut

(Des. D. Gentleman)

1974 (27 Feb). *British Trees* (*2nd issue*). *"All-over" phosphor. P* 15 × 14.

949 **431** 10p. light emerald, bright green, greenish yellow, brown-olive, black and brownish grey 50 50

432 First Motor Fire-engine, 1904

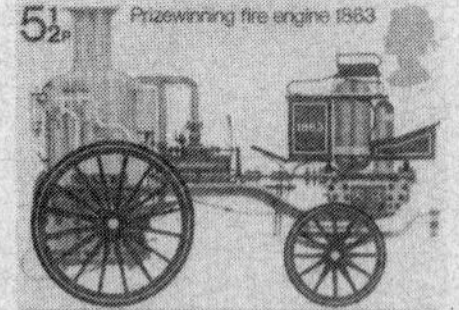

433 Prize-winning Fire-engine, 1863

434 First Steam Fire-engine, 1830

435 Fire-engine, 1766

(Des D. Gentleman)

1974 (24 Apr). *Bicentenary of the Fire Prevention* (*Metropolis*) *Act. "All-over" phosphor. P* 15 × 14.

950 **432** 3½p. grey-black, orange-yellow, greenish yellow, dull rose, ochre and grey 10 10
a. Imperf (pair) £800
951 **433** 5½p. greenish yellow, deep rosy magenta, orange-yellow, light emerald, grey-black and grey 35 35
952 **434** 8p. greenish yellow, light blue-green, light greenish blue, light chestnut, grey-black and grey 45 45
953 **435** 10p. grey-black, pale reddish brown, lt brown, orange-yellow and grey .. 50 50
950/3 .. .. *Set of* 4 1·25 1·25

The 3½p. exists with ordinary PVA gum.

436 P & O Packet, *Peninsular*, 1888

437 Farman H.F.III Biplane, 1911

438 Airmail-blue Van and Postbox, 1930

439 Imperial Airways Short S.21 Flying Boat *Maia*, 1937

(Des Rosalind Dease)

1974 (12 June). *Centenary of Universal Postal Union. "All-over" phosphor. P* 15 × 14.

954 **436** 3½p. deep brownish grey, bright mauve, grey-black and gold 10 10
955 **437** 5½p. pale orge, lt emer, grey-blk & gold 30 35
956 **438** 8p. cobalt, brown, grey-black and gold 40 45
957 **439** 10p. deep brownish grey, orange, grey-black and gold 60 50
954/7 .. .. *Set of* 4 1·25 1·25

440 Robert the Bruce

441 Owain Glyndŵr

442 Henry the Fifth

443 The Black Prince

(Des F. Wegner)

1974 (10 July). *Medieval Warriors. "All-over" phosphor. P* 15 × 1

958 **440** 4½p. greenish yellow, vermilion, slate-blue, red-brown, reddish brown, lilac-grey and gold 10
959 **441** 5½p. lemon, vermilion, slate-blue red-brn, reddish brn, ol-drab & gold 20
960 **442** 8p. deep grey, vermilion, greenish yellow, new blue, red-brown, deep cinnamon and gold 50
961 **443** 10p. vermilion, greenish yellow, new blue, red-brown, reddish brown, light blue and gold 55
958/61 .. .. *Set of* 4 1·25 1·

444 Churchill in Royal Yacht Squadron Uniform

445 Prime Minister, 1940

446 Secretary for War and Air, 1919

447 War Correspondent, South Africa, 1899

(Des C. Clements and E. Hughes)

1974 (9 Oct). *Birth Centenary of Sir Winston Churchill. "All-ove phosphor. P* 14 × 15.

962 **444** 4½p. Prussian blue, pale turquoise-green and silver 15
963 **445** 5½p. sepia, brownish grey and silver .. 30
964 **446** 8p. crimson, light claret and silver .. 60
965 **447** 10p. light brown, stone and silver .. 65
962/5 .. .. *Set of* 4 1·50 1·

448 "Adoration of the Magi" (York Minster, *circa* 1355)

449 "The Nativity" (St. Helen's Church, Norwich, *circa* 1480)

450 "Virgin and Child" (Ottery St. Mary Church, *circa* 1350)

451 "Virgin and Child" (Worcester Cathedral, *circa* 1224)

(Des Peter Hatch Partnership)

74 (27 Nov). *Christmas. Church Roof Bosses. One phosphor band* (3½*p.*) *or "all-over" phosphor* (*others*). *P* 15 × 14.
6 **448** 3½p. gold, light new blue, light brown, grey-black and light stone .. 10 10
a. Light stone (background shading) omitted £10000
7 **449** 4½p. gold, yellow-orange, rose-red, light brown, grey-black, & lt new blue 10 10
8 **450** 8p. blue, gold, light brown, rose-red, dull green and grey-black .. 45 45
9 **451** 10p. gold, dull rose, grey-black, light new blue, pale cinnamon and light brown 50 50
6/9 .. .. *Set of* 4 1·00 1·00

The phosphor band on the 3½p. was first applied down the centre the stamp but during the printing this was deliberately placed to e right between the roof boss and the value; however, intermediate ositions, due to shifts, are known.

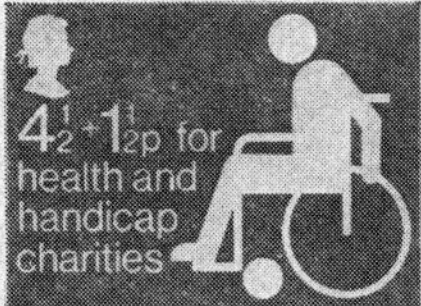

452 Invalid in Wheelchair

(Des P. Sharland)

75 (22 Jan). *Health and Handicap Funds. "All-over" phosphor. P* 15 × 14.
0 **452** 4½p. + 1½p. azure and grey-blue .. 25 25

453 "Peace—Burial at Sea"

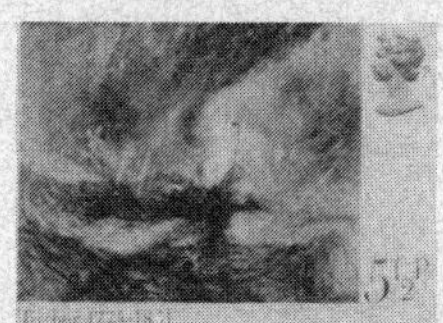

454 "Snowstorm—Steamer off a Harbour's Mouth"

455 "The Arsenal, Venice"

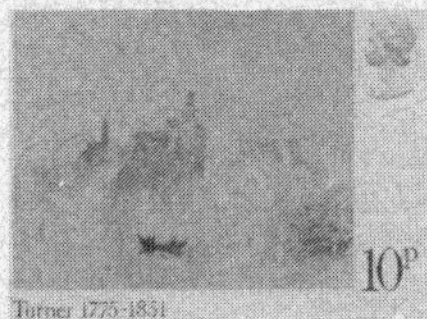

456 "St. Laurent"

(Des S. Rose)

75 (19 Feb). *Birth Bicentenary of J. M. W. Turner (painter). "All-over" phosphor. P* 15 × 14.
1 **453** 4½p. grey-blk, salmon, stone, bl & grey 10 10
2 **454** 5½p. cobalt, greenish yellow, light yellow-brown, grey-black and rose 15 15
3 **455** 8p. pale yellow-orange, greenish yellow, rose, cobalt and grey-black 40 40
4 **456** 10p. deep blue, light yellow-ochre, light brown, deep cobalt and grey-black 45 45
1/4 .. .. *Set of* 4 1·00 1·00

457 Charlotte Square, Edinburgh

458 The Rows, Chester

T **457/8** were printed horizontally *se-tenant* within the sheet.

459 Royal Observatory, Greenwich

460 St. George's Chapel, Windsor

461 National Theatre, London

(Des P. Gauld)

1975 (23 Apr). *European Architectural Heritage Year. "All-over" phosphor. P* 15 × 14.
975 **457** 7p. greenish yellow, bright orange, grey-black, red-brown, new blue, lavender and gold 50 55
a. Pair. Nos. 975/6 .. .. .. 1·00 1·10
976 **458** 7p. grey-black, greenish yellow, new blue, brt orange, red-brown & gold 50 55
977 **459** 8p. magenta, deep slate, pale magenta, lt yellow-olive, grey-black & gold 25 25
978 **460** 10p. bistre-brown, greenish yellow, deep slate, emer-green, grey-blk & gold 25 25
979 **461** 12p. grey-blk, new bl, pale mag & gold 25 35
975/9 .. .. *Set of* 5 1·50 1·50

462 Sailing Dinghies

463 Racing Keel Yachts

464 Cruising Yachts

465 Multihulls

(Des A. Restall. Recess and photo)

1975 (11 June). *Sailing. "All-over" phosphor. P* 15×14.
980 **462** 7p. black, bluish violet, scarlet, orange-vermilion, orange and gold .. 20 20
981 **463** 8p. black, orge-verm, orange, lavender, brt mauve, brt bl, dp ultram & gold 35 30
a. Black omitted .. .. .. 55·00
982 **464** 10p. black, orange, bluish emerald, light olive-drab, chocolate and gold .. 40 30
983 **465** 12p. black, ultramarine, turquoise-blue, rose, grey, steel-blue and gold .. 45 35
980/3 .. .. *Set of* 4 1·25 1·00

On No. 981a the recess-printed black colour is completely omitted.

466 Stephenson's *Locomotion*, 1825

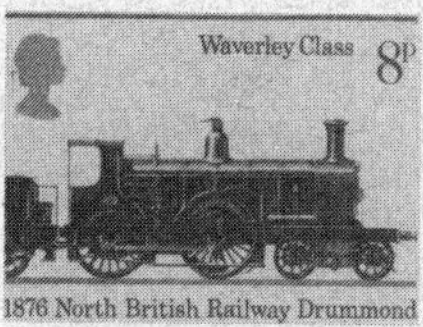

467 *Abbotsford*, 1876

468 *Caerphilly Castle*, 1923

469 High Speed Train, 1975

(Des B. Craker)

1975 (13 Aug). *150th Anniv of Public Railways. "All-over" phosphor. P* 15 × 14.
984 **466** 7p. red-brown, grey-black, greenish yellow, grey and silver 20 20
985 **467** 8p. brown, orange-yellow, vermilion, grey-black, grey and silver .. 45 35
986 **468** 10p. emerald-green, grey-black, yellow-orange, vermilion, grey and silver 50 40
987 **469** 12p. grey-black, pale lemon, vermilion, blue, grey and silver 55 45
984/7 .. .. *Set of* 4 1·50 1·25

470 Palace of Westminster

(Des R. Downer)

1975 (3 Sept). *62nd Inter-Parliamentary Union Conference. "All-over" phosphor. P* 15 × 14.
988 **470** 12p. light new blue, black, brownish grey and gold 50 50

471 Emma and Mr Woodhouse (*Emma*)

472 Catherine Morland (*Northanger Abbey*)

473 Mr. Darcy (*Pride and Prejudice*)

474 Mary and Henry Crawford (*Mansfield Park*)

(Des Barbara Brown)

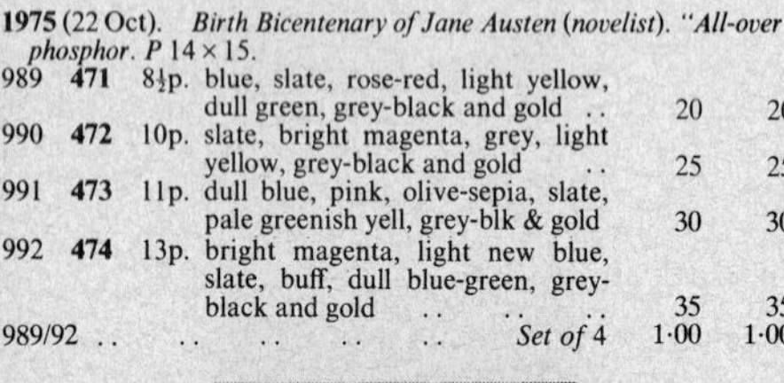

1975 (22 Oct). *Birth Bicentenary of Jane Austen (novelist). "All-over" phosphor. P* 14 × 15.

989 **471** 8½p. blue, slate, rose-red, light yellow, dull green, grey-black and gold .. 20 20
990 **472** 10p. slate, bright magenta, grey, light yellow, grey-black and gold .. 25 25
991 **473** 11p. dull blue, pink, olive-sepia, slate, pale greenish yell, grey-blk & gold 30 30
992 **474** 13p. bright magenta, light new blue, slate, buff, dull blue-green, grey-black and gold 35 35
989/92 .. .. *Set of* 4 1·00 1·00

475 Angels with Harp and Lute

476 Angel with Mandolin

477 Angel with Horn

478 Angel with Trumpet

(Des R. Downer)

1975 (26 Nov). *Christmas. One phosphor band (6½p.), phosphor-inked background (8½p.), "all-over" phosphor (others). P* 15 × 14.

993 **475** 6½p. bluish violet, bright reddish violet, light lavender and gold 20 15
994 **476** 8½p. turquoise-green, bright emerald-green, slate, lt turq-green & gold 20 20
995 **477** 11p. vermilion, cerise, pink and gold .. 30 35
996 **478** 13p. drab, brn, brt orge, buff & gold .. 40 40
993/6 .. .. *Set of* 4 1·00 1·00

479 Housewife

480 Policeman

481 District Nurse

482 Industrialist

(Des P. Sharland)

1976 (10 Mar). *Telephone Centenary. "All-over" phosphor. P* 15 × 14.

997 **479** 8½p. greenish blue, dp rose, black & bl 20 20
a. Deep rose (vase and picture frame) omitted £2000
998 **480** 10p. greenish blue, black & yellow-ol 25 25
999 **481** 11p. greenish bl, dp rose, blk & brt mve 30 30
1000 **482** 13p. olive-brn, dp rose, blk & orge-red 35 35
997/1000 .. .. *Set of* 4 1·00 1·00

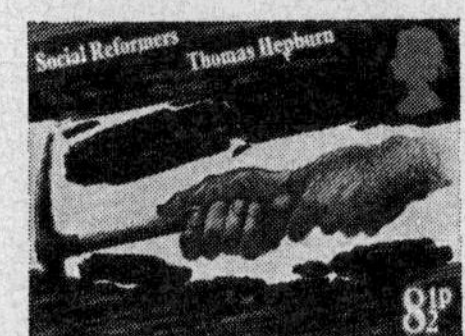

483 Hewing Coal (Thomas Hepburn)

484 Machinery (Robert Owen)

485 Chimney Cleaning (Lord Shaftesbury)

486 Hands clutching Prison Bars (Elizabeth Fry)

(Des D. Gentleman)

1976 (28 Apr). *Social Reformers. "All-over" phosphor. P* 15 × 14.

1001 **483** 8½p. lavender-grey, grey-black, black and slate-grey 20 20
1002 **484** 10p. lavender-grey, grey-black, grey and slate-violet 35 35
1003 **485** 11p. black, slate-grey and drab .. 40 40
1004 **486** 13p. slate-grey, black & deep dull grn 45 45
1001/4 .. .. *Set of* 4 1·25 1·25

487 Benjamin Franklin (bust by Jean-Jacques Caffieri)

(Des P. Sharland)

1976 (2 June). *Bicentenary of American Revolution. "All-ove phosphor. P* 14 × 15.

1005 **487** 11p pale bistre, slate-violet, pale blue-green, black and gold 50

488 "Elizabeth of Glamis"

489 "Grandpa Dickson"

490 "*Rosa Mundi*"

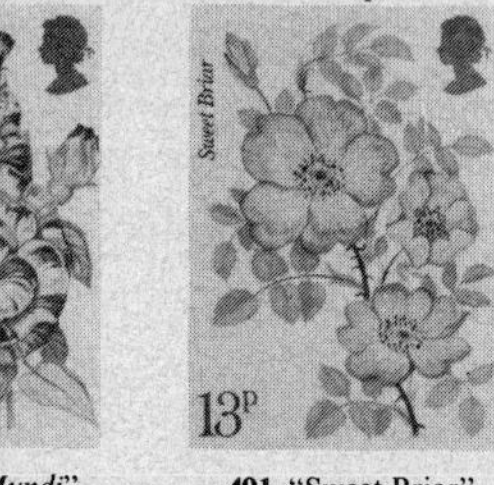

491 "Sweet Briar"

(Des Kristin Rosenberg)

1976 (30 June). *Centenary of Royal National Rose Society. "All-ove phosphor. P* 14 × 15.

1006 **488** 8½p. bright rose-red, greenish yellow, emerald, grey-black and gold .. 20
1007 **489** 10p. greenish yellow, bright green, reddish brown, grey-black and gold 30
1008 **490** 11p. bright magenta, greenish yellow, emerald, grey-blue, grey-black and gold 55
1009 **491** 13p. rose-pink, lake-brown, yellow-green, pale greenish yellow, grey-black and gold 60
a. Value omitted* £20000
1006/9 .. .. *Set of* 4 1·50 1·

*During repairs to the cylinder the face value on R. 1/9 w temporarily covered with copper. This covering was inadverten left in place during printing, but the error was discovered befo issue and most examples were removed from the sheets. Two m and one used examples have so far been reported, but only one the mint remains in private hands.

492 Archdruid

493 Morris Dancing

494 Scots Piper

495 Welsh Harpist

(Des Marjorie Saynor)

1976 (4 Aug). *British Cultural Traditions. "All-over" phosph P* 14 × 15.

1010 **492** 8½p. yellow, sepia, bright rose, dull ultramarine, black and gold .. 20
1011 **493** 10p. dull ultramarine, bright rose-red, sepia, greenish yellow, blk & gold 35
1012 **494** 11p. bluish green, yellow-brown, yell-orge, blk, brt rose-red & gold .. 40
1013 **495** 13p. dull violet-blue, yellow-orange, yell-brn, blk, bluish grn & gold 45
1010/13 .. .. *Set of* 4 1·25 1·

The 8½p. and 13p. commemorate the 800th Anniv of the Roy National Eisteddfod.

496 Woodcut from *The Canterbury Tales*

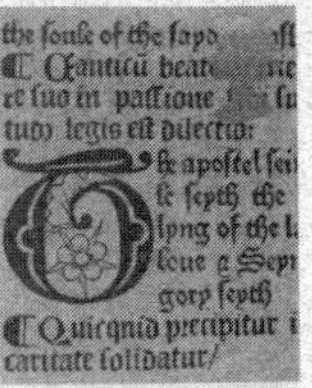

497 Extract from *The Tretyse of Love*

498 Woodcut from *The Game and Playe of Chesse*

499 Early Printing Press

(Des R. Gay. Queen's head printed in gold and then embossed)

76 (29 Sept). *500th Anniv of British Printing. "All-over" phosphor. P* 14 × 15.

14	**496**	8½p.	black, light new blue and gold ..	20	20
15	**497**	10p.	black, olive-green and gold ..	35	35
16	**498**	11p.	black, brownish grey and gold ..	40	40
17	**499**	13p.	chocolate, pale ochre and gold ..	45	45
14/17 ..			.. .. *Set of* 4	1·25	1·25

500 Virgin and Child

501 Angel with Crown

502 Angel appearing to Shepherds

503 The Three Kings

(Des Enid Marx)

76 (24 Nov). *Christmas. English Medieval Embroidery. One phosphor band* (6½*p.*), *"all-over" phosphor* (*others*). *P* 15 × 14.

18	**500**	6½p.	bl, bistre-yell, brn & brt orange	15	15
		a.	Imperf (pair)	£400	
19	**501**	8½p.	sage-green, yellow, brown-ochre, chestnut and olive-black ..	20	20
20	**502**	11p.	deep magenta, brown-orange, new blue, black and cinnamon ..	35	35
		a.	Uncoated paper*	60·00	30·00
21	**503**	13p.	bright purple, new blue, cinnamon, bronze-green and olive-grey	40	40
18/21 ..			.. .. *Set of* 4	1·00	1·00

* See footnote after No. 744.

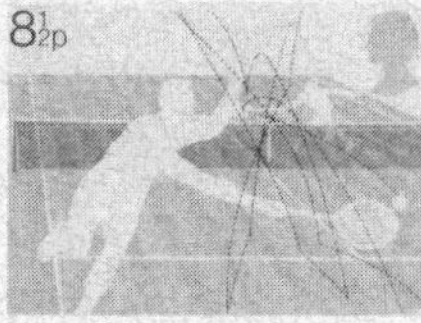

504 Lawn Tennis

505 Table Tennis

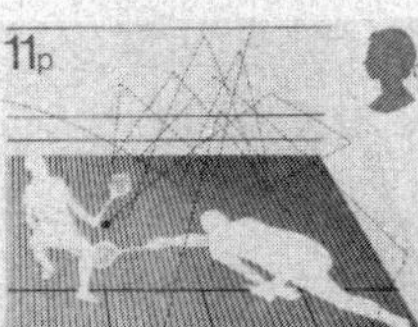

506 Squash

507 Badminton

(Des A. Restall)

1977 (12 Jan). *Racket Sports. Phosphorised paper. P* 15 × 14.

1022	**504**	8½p.	emer-grn, blk, grey & bluish grn	20	20
		a.	Imperf (horiz pair)	£850	
1023	**505**	10p.	myrtle-green, black, grey-black and deep blue-green	35	25
1024	**506**	11p.	orange, pale yellow, black, slate-black and grey	40	30
1025	**507**	13p.	brown, grey-black, grey and bright reddish violet	45	35
1022/5 ..			.. .. *Set of* 4	1·25	1·00

508

(Des after plaster cast by Arnold Machin)

1977 (2 Feb)–**87**. *P* 14 × 15.

1026	**508**	£1 brt yellow-green & blackish olive	3·25	30
		a. Imperf (pair)	£650	
1026*b*		£1.30, pale drab and deep greenish blue (3.8.83)	5·75	5·25
1026*c*		£1.33, pale mve & grey-blk (28.8.84)	6·00	6·00
1026*d*		£1.41, pale drab and deep greenish blue (17.9.85)	7·00	6·00
1026*e*		£1.50, pale mauve & grey-blk (2.9.86)	5·50	4·00
1026*f*		£1.60 pale drab and deep greenish blue (15.9.87)	5·75	6·00
1027		£2 light emerald and purple-brown ..	5·75	1·00
1028		£5 salmon and chalky blue	14·00	2·25
		a. Imperf (vert pair)	£2750	
1026/8 ..		.. .. *Set of* 8	48·00	28·00

509 Steroids—Conformational Analysis

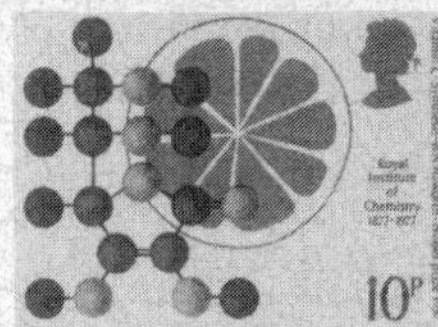

510 Vitamin C—Synthesis

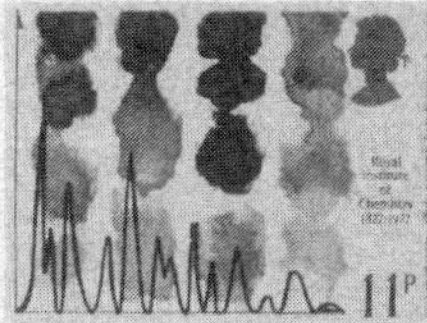

511 Starch—Chromatography

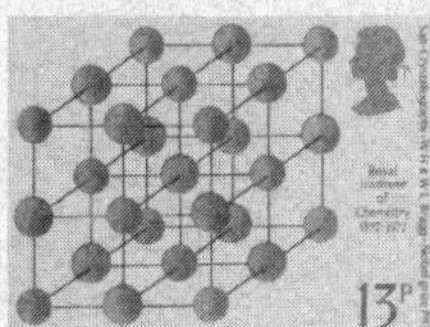

512 Salt—Crystallography

(Des J. Karo)

1977 (2 Mar). *Royal Institute of Chemistry Centenary. "All-over" phosphor. P* 15 × 14.

1029	**509**	8½p.	rosine, new blue, olive-yellow, brt mauve, yellow-brown, blk & gold	20	20
		a.	Imperf (horiz pair)	£850	
1030	**510**	10p.	bright orange, rosine, new blue, bright blue, black and gold ..	30	30
1031	**511**	11p.	rosine, greenish yellow, new blue, deep violet, black and gold ..	30	30
1032	**512**	13p.	new blue, brt green, black & gold	30	30
1029/32			.. .. *Set of* 4	1·00	1·00

513

514

515

516

T 513/16 differ in the decorations of "ER".

(Des R. Guyatt)

1977 (11 May–15 June). *Silver Jubilee. "All-over" phosphor. P* 15 × 14.

1033	**513**	8½p.	blackish green, black, silver, olive-grey and pale turquoise-green ..	20	20
		a.	Imperf (pair)	£700	
1034		9p.	maroon, black, silver, olive-grey and lavender (15 June)	25	25
1035	**514**	10p.	blackish blue, black, silver, olive-grey and ochre	25	25
		a.	Imperf (horiz pair)	£1300	
1036	**515**	11p.	brown-purple, black, silver, olive-grey and rose-pink	30	30
		a.	Imperf (horiz pair)	£1300	
1037	**516**	13p.	sepia, black, silver, olive-grey and bistre-yellow	40	40
		a.	Imperf (pair)	£1000	
1033/7 ..			.. .. *Set of* 5	1·25	1·25

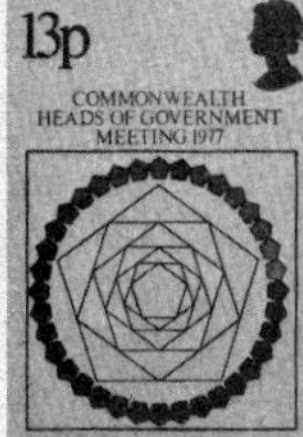

517 "Gathering of Nations"

(Des P. Murdoch. Recess and photo)

1977 (8 June). *Commonwealth Heads of Government Meeting, London. "All-over" phosphor. P* 14 × 15.

1038	**517**	13p.	black, blackish green, rose-carmine and silver	50	50

518 Hedgehog

519 Brown Hare

520 Red Squirrel

521 Otter

522 Badger

T **518/22** were printed horizontally *se-tenant* within the sheet.

(Des P. Oxenham)

1977 (5 Oct). *British Wildlife. "All-over" phosphor. P* 14 × 15.

1039 **518** 9p. reddish brown, grey-black, pale lemon, brt turq-bl, brt mag & gold .. 40 45
a. Horiz strip of 5. Nos. 1039/43 .. 1·75 2·00
b. Imperf (vert pair) £600
c. Imperf (horiz pair, Nos. 1039/40) .. £1000
1040 **519** 9p. reddish brown, grey-black, pale lemon, brt turq-bl, brt mag & gold 40 45
1041 **520** 9p. reddish brown, grey-black, pale lemon, brt turq-bl, brt mag & gold 40 45
1042 **521** 9p. reddish brown, grey-black, pale lemon, brt turq-bl, brt mag & gold 40 45
1043 **522** 9p. grey-black, reddish brown, pale lemon, brt turq-bl, brt mag & gold 40 45
1039/43 .. .. *Set of* 5 1·75 2·00

523 "Three French Hens, Two Turtle Doves and a Partridge in a Pear Tree"

524 "Six Geese a-laying, Five Gold Rings, Four Colly Birds"

525 "Eight Maids a-milking, Seven Swans a-swimming"

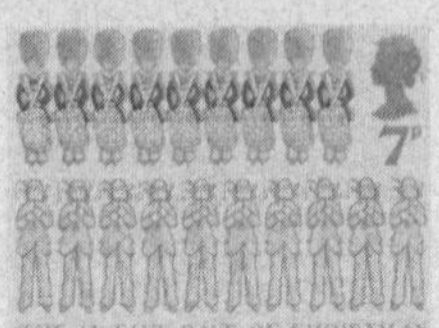

526 "Ten Pipers piping, Nine Drummers drumming"

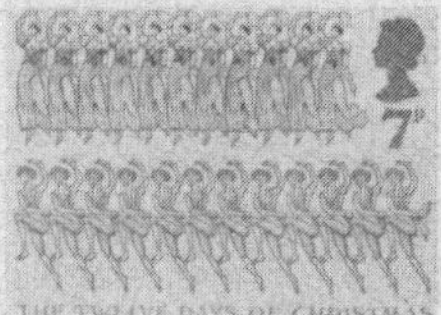

527 "Twelve Lords a-leaping, Eleven Ladies dancing"

T **523/7** depict the carol "The Twelve Days of Christmas" and were printed horizontally *se-tenant* within the sheet.

528 "A Partridge in a Pear Tree"

(Des D. Gentleman)

1977 (23 Nov). *Christmas. One centre phosphor band* (7*p.*) *or "all-over" phosphor* (9*p.*). *P* 15 × 14.

1044 **523** 7p. slate, grey, bright yellow-green, new blue, rose-red and gold 15 35
a. Horiz strip of 5. Nos. 1044/8 .. 1·25 1·50
ab. Imperf (strip of 5, Nos. 1044/8) .. £1100
1045 **524** 7p. slate, brt yellow-grn, new bl & gold 15 35
1046 **525** 7p. slate, grey, bright yellow-green, new blue, rose-red and gold 15 35
1047 **526** 7p. slate, grey, bright yellow-green, new blue, rose-red and gold 15 35
1048 **527** 7p. slate, grey, bright yellow-green, new blue, rose-red and gold 15 35
1049 **528** 9p. pale brown, pale orange, brt emer, pale greenish yell, slate-blk & gold 20 20
a. Imperf (pair) £800
1044/9 .. .. *Set of* 6 1·25 1·50

529 Oil—North Sea Production Platform

530 Coal—Modern Pithead

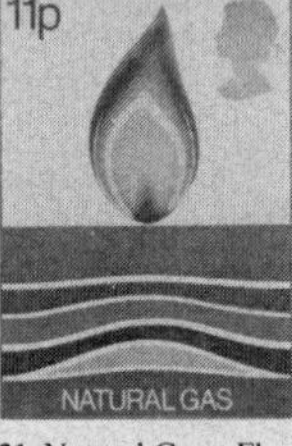

531 Natural Gas—Flame Rising from Sea

532 Electricity—Nuclear Power Station and Uranium Atom

(Des P. Murdoch)

1978 (25 Jan). *Energy Resources. "All-over" phosphor. P* 14 × 15.

1050 **529** 9p. deep brown, orange-vermilion, grey-black, greenish yellow, rose-pink, new blue and silver .. 25 20
1051 **530** 10½p. light emerald-green, grey-black, red-brown, slate-grey, pale apple-green and silver 25 30
1052 **531** 11p. greenish blue, bright violet, violet-blue, blackish brown, grey-black and silver 30 30
1053 **532** 13p. orange-vermilion, grey-black, deep brown, greenish yellow, light brown, light blue and silver .. 30 30
1050/3 .. .. *Set of* 4 1·00 1·00

533 The Tower of London

534 Holyroodhouse

535 Caernarvon Castle

536 Hampton Court Palace

(Des R. Maddox (stamps), J. Matthews (miniature sheet))

1978 (1 Mar). *British Architecture. Historic Buildings. "All-ov[er]" phosphor. P* 15 × 14.

1054 **533** 9p. black, olive-brown, new blue, brt green, lt yellow-olive & rose-red 25
1055 **534** 10½p. black, brown-olive, orange-yell, brt grn, lt yell-olive & vio-bl .. 25
1056 **535** 11p. black, brown-olive, violet-blue, brt green, lt yellow-olive & dull bl 30
1057 **536** 13p. black, orange-yellow, lake-brown, bright green and light yellow-olive 30
1054/7 .. .. *Set of* 4 1·00 1
MS1058 121×89 mm. Nos. 1054/7 (*sold at* 53½*p.*) 1·25 1
a. Imperforate £4250
b. Lt yellow-olive (Queen's head) omitted £3500
c. Rose-red (Union Jack on 9p.) omitted £2500
d. Orange-yellow omitted .. £2500
e. New blue (Union Jack on 9p.) omitted £10000

The premium on No. **MS**1058 was used to support the Lond[on] 1980 International Stamp Exhibition.

537 State Coach

538 St. Edward's Crown

539 The Sovereign's Orb

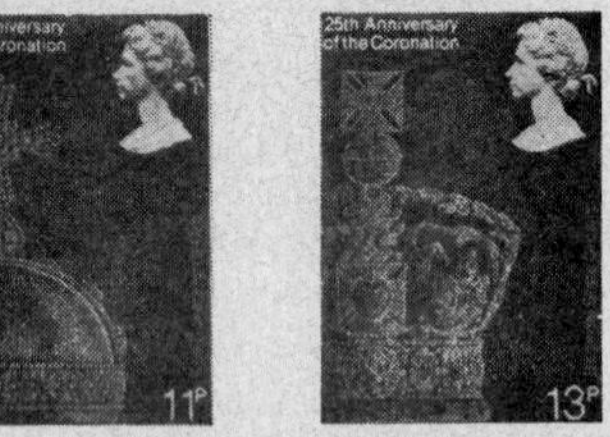

540 Imperial State Crown

(Des J. Matthews)

1978 (31 May). *25th Anniv of Coronation. "All-over" phosph[or]. P* 14 × 15.

1059 **537** 9p. gold and royal blue 20
1060 **538** 10½p. gold and brown-lake 25
1061 **539** 11p. gold and deep dull green .. 30
1062 **540** 13p. gold and reddish violet 35
1059/62 .. .. *Set of* 4 1·00 1·

541 Shire Horse

542 Shetland Pony

543 Welsh Pony

544 Thoroughbred

(Des P. Oxenham)

78 (5 July). *Horses. "All-over" phosphor. P* 15 × 14.

63	**541**	9p.	black, pale reddish brown, grey-black, greenish yellow, light blue, vermilion and gold	20	20
64	**542**	10½p.	pale chestnut, magenta, brownish grey, greenish yellow, greenish blue, grey-black and gold ..	35	25
65	**543**	11p.	reddish brown, black, light green, greenish yellow, bistre, grey-black and gold	40	30
66	**544**	13p.	reddish brown, pale reddish brown, emerald, greenish yellow, grey-black and gold	45	35
63/6 ..			.. .. *Set of* 4	1·25	1·00

545 "Penny-farthing" and 1884 Safety Bicycle

546 1920 Touring Bicycles

547 Modern Small-wheel Bicycles

548 1978 Road-racers

(Des F. Wegner)

78 (2 Aug). *Centenaries of Cyclists Touring Club and British Cycling Federation. "All-over" phosphor. P* 15 × 14.

67	**545**	9p.	brown, deep dull blue, rose-pink, pale olive, grey-black and gold ..	20	20
		a.	Imperf (pair)	£350	
68	**546**	10½p.	olive, pale yellow-orange, orange-vermilion, rose-red, light brown, grey-black and gold	25	25
69	**547**	11p.	orange-vermilion, greenish blue, light brown, pale greenish yellow, deep grey, grey-black and gold ..	30	30
70	**548**	13p.	new blue, orange-vermilion, light brn, olive-grey, grey-black & gold	35	35
		a.	Imperf (pair)	£750	
67/70 ..			.. .. *Set of* 4	1·00	1·00

549 Singing Carols round the Christmas Tree

550 The Waits

551 18th-century Carol Singers

552 "The Boar's Head Carol"

(Des Faith Jaques)

1978 (22 Nov). *Christmas. One centre phosphor band* (7p.) *or "all-over" phosphor* (*others*). *P* 15 × 14.

1071	**549**	7p.	bright green, greenish yellow, magenta, new blue, black and gold	20	20
		a.	Imperf (vert pair)	£350	
1072	**550**	9p.	magenta, greenish yellow, new blue, sage-green, black and gold	25	25
		a.	Imperf (pair)	£750	
1073	**551**	11p.	magenta, new blue, greenish yellow, yellow-brown, black & gold	30	30
		a.	Imperf (horiz pair)	£750	
1074	**552**	13p.	salmon-pink, new blue, greenish yellow, magenta, black and gold	35	35
1071/4 ..			.. .. *Set of* 4	1·00	1·00

553 Old English Sheepdog

554 Welsh Springer Spaniel

555 West Highland Terrier

556 Irish Setter

(Des P. Barrett)

1979 (7 Feb). *Dogs. "All-over" phosphor. P* 15 × 14.

1075	**553**	9p.	grey-black, sepia, turquoise-green, pale greenish yellow, pale greenish blue and grey	20	20
1076	**554**	10½p.	grey-black, lake-brown, apple-green, pale greenish yellow, pale greenish blue and grey	40	40
1077	**555**	11p.	grey-black, claret, yellowish grn, pale greenish yell, cobalt & grey	40	40
		a.	Imperf (horiz pair)	£900	
1078	**556**	13p.	grey-black, lake-brown, green, pale greenish yellow & dp turq-bl	40	40
1075/8 ..			.. .. *Set of* 4	1·25	1·25

557 Primrose

558 Daffodil

559 Bluebell

560 Snowdrop

(Des P. Newcombe)

1979 (21 Mar). *Spring Wild Flowers. "All-over" phosphor. P* 14 × 15.

1079	**557**	9p.	slate-black, deep brown, pale greenish yellow, deep olive, pale new blue and silver	20	20
		a.	Imperf (pair)	£400	
1080	**558**	10½p.	greenish yellow, grey-green, steel-blue, slate-blk, new blue & silver	40	40
		a.	Imperf (vert pair)	£1500	
1081	**559**	11p.	slate-black, deep brown, ultramarine, light greenish blue, pale greenish yellow and silver ..	40	30
		a.	Imperf (horiz pair)	£1200	
1082	**560**	13p.	slate-black, indigo, grey-green, sepia, ochre and silver	40	40
		a.	Imperf (horiz pair)	£750	
1079/82			.. .. *Set of* 4	1·25	1·25

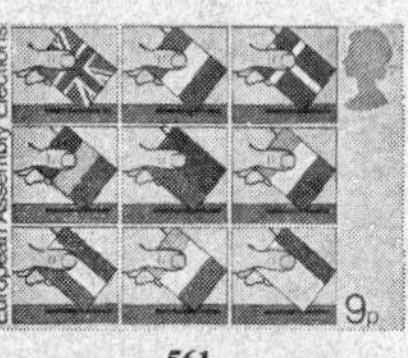

561

562

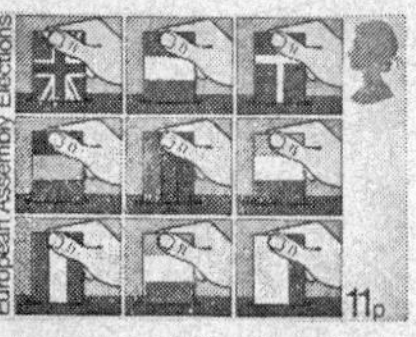

563

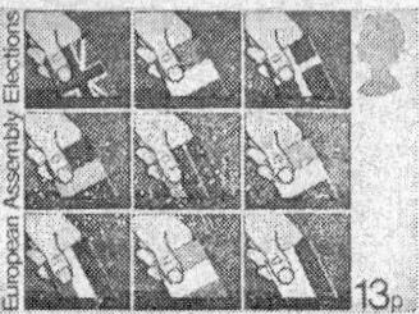

564

T **561/4** show Hands placing National Flags in Ballot Boxes.

(Des S. Cliff)

1979 (9 May). *First Direct Elections to European Assembly. Phosphorised paper. P* 15 × 14.

1083 **561** 9p. grey-black, vermilion, cinnamon, pale greenish yellow, pale turq-green and dull ultramarine .. 20 20
1084 **562** 10½p. grey-black, vermilion, cinnamon, pale greenish yellow, dull ultramarine, pale turq-grn & chestnut 30 30
1085 **563** 11p. grey-black, vermilion, cinnamon, pale greenish yellow, dull ultramarine, pale turq-grn & grey-grn 30 30
1086 **564** 13p. grey-black, vermilion, cinnamon, pale greenish yellow, dull ultramarine, pale turq-grn & brown 30 30
1083/6 .. .. *Set of* 4 1·00 1·00

565 "Saddling 'Mahmoud' for the Derby, 1936" (Sir Alfred Munnings)

566 "The Liverpool Great National Steeple Chase, 1839" (aquatint by F. C. Turner)

567 "The First Spring Meeting, Newmarket, 1793" (J. N. Sartorius)

568 "Racing at Dorsett Ferry, Windsor, 1684" (Francis Barlow)

(Des S. Rose)

1979 (6 June). *Horseracing Paintings. Bicentenary of the Derby* (9*p*.). *"All-over" phosphor. P* 15 × 14.

1087 **565** 9p. light blue, red-brown, rose-pink, pale greenish yellow, grey-black and gold 25 25
1088 **566** 10½p. bistre-yellow, slate-blue, salmon-pink, lt blue, grey-black and gold 30 30
1089 **567** 11p. rose, vermilion, pale greenish yellow, new blue, grey-black and gold 30 30
1090 **568** 13p. bistre-yellow, rose, turquoise, grey-black and gold 30 30
1087/90.. .. .. *Set of* 4 1·10 1·10

569 *The Tale of Peter Rabbit* (Beatrix Potter)

570 *The Wind in the Willows* (Kenneth Grahame)

571 *Winnie-the-Pooh* (A. A. Milne)

572 *Alice's Adventures in Wonderland* (Lewis Carroll)

(Des E. Hughes)

1979 (11 July). *International Year of the Child. Children's Book Illustrations. "All-over" phosphor. P* 14 × 15.

1091 **569** 9p. deep bluish green, grey-black, bistre-brown, bright rose, greenish yellow and silver 25 20
1092 **570** 10½p. dull ultramarine, grey-black, ol-brown, bright rose, yellow-orge, pale greenish yellow and silver .. 30 35
1093 **571** 11p. drab, grey-black, greenish yellow, new bl, yell-orge, agate & silver 35 40
1094 **572** 13p. pale greenish yellow, grey-black, bright rose, deep bluish green, olive-brown, new blue and silver 50 45
1091/4 .. .. *Set of* 4 1·25 1·25

573 Sir Rowland Hill

574 Postman, *circa* 1839

575 London Postman, *circa* 1839

576 Woman and Young Girl with Letters, 1840

(Des E. Stemp)

1979 (22 Aug–24 Oct). *Death Centenary of Sir Rowland Hill. "All-over" phosphor. P* 14 × 15.

1095 **573** 10p. grey-black, brown-ochre, myrtle-green, pale greenish yellow, rosine, bright blue and gold .. 25 25
a. Imperf (horiz pair) .. ..
1096 **574** 11½p. grey-black, brown-ochre, bright blue, rosine, bistre-brown, pale greenish yellow and gold .. 30 35
1097 **575** 13p. grey-black, brown-ochre, bright blue, rosine, bistre-brown, pale greenish yellow and gold .. 35 40
1098 **576** 15p. grey-black, brown-ochre, myrtle-green, bistre-brown, rosine, pale greenish yellow and gold .. 50 40
1095/8 .. .. *Set of* 4 1·25 1·25
MS1099 89×121 mm. Nos. 1095/8 (*sold at* 59½*p*.) (24 Oct) .. .. 1·25 1·25
a. Imperforate £1000
b. Brown-ochre (15p. background, etc) omitted £750
c. Gold (Queen's head) omitted .. £175
d. Brown-ochre, myrtle-green and gold omitted £3000
e. Bright blue (13p. background, etc) omitted £900
f. Myrtle-green (10p. (background), 15p.) omitted £1200
g. Pale greenish yellow omitted .. £140
h. Rosine omitted £500
i. Bistre-brown omitted £650
j. Grey-black and pale greenish yellow omitted £10000

The premium on No. **MS**1099 was used to support the London 1980 International Stamp Exhibition.

Examples of No. **MS**1099 showing face values on the stamps of 9p., 10½p., 11p. and 13p., with a sheet price of 53½p., were prepared, but not issued.

577 Policeman on the Beat

578 Policeman directing Traffic

579 Mounted Policewoman

580 River Patrol Boat

(Des B. Sanders)

1979 (26 Sept). 150*th Anniv of Metropolitan Police. Phosphoris paper. P* 15 × 14.

1100 **577** 10p. grey-black, red-brown, emerald, greenish yellow, brt blue & mag 25
1101 **578** 11½p. grey-black, bright orange, purple-brown, ultramarine, greenish yellow and deep bluish green .. 30
1102 **579** 13p. grey-black, red-brown, magenta, ol-grn, greenish yell & dp dull bl 35
1103 **580** 15p. grey-black, magenta, brown, slate-bl, dp brown & greenish blk 50
1100/3 .. .. *Set of* 4 1·25 1·

581 The Three Kings

582 Angel appearing to the Shepherds

583 The Nativity

584 Mary and Joseph travelling to Bethlehem

585 The Annunciation

(Des F. Wegner)

1979 (21 Nov). *Christmas. One centre phosphor band* (8*p*.) *phosphorised paper* (*others*). *P* 15 × 14.

1104 **581** 8p. blue, grey-black, ochre, slate-violet and gold 20
a. Imperf (pair) £500
1105 **582** 10p. bright rose-red, grey-black, chestnut, chrome-yell, dp vio & gold 25
a. Imperf between (vert pair) .. £450
b. Imperf (pair) £600
1106 **583** 11½p. orange-vermilion, steel-bl, drab, grey-black, deep blue-grn & gold 30
1107 **584** 13p. bright blue, orange-vermilion, bistre, grey-black and gold .. 40
1108 **585** 15p. orange-vermilion, blue, bistre, grey-black, green and gold .. 50
1104/8 .. .. *Set of* 5 1·50 1

586 Common Kingfisher

587 Dipper

588 Moorhen

589 Yellow Wagtails

(Des M. Warren)

80 (16 Jan). *Centenary of Wild Bird Protection Act. Phosphorised paper.* P 14 × 15.

09	**586**	10p.	bright blue, bright yellow-green, vermilion, pale greenish yellow, grey-black and gold	25	25
10	**587**	11½p.	sepia, grey-black, dull ultramarine, vermilion, grey-green, pale greenish yellow and gold ..	40	35
11	**588**	13p.	emerald-green, grey-black, bright bl, verm, pale greenish yell & gold	50	40
12	**589**	15p.	greenish yellow, brown, light green, slate-bl, grey-blk & gold	55	45
09/12			.. .. *Set of* 4	1·50	1·25

590 *Rocket* approaching Moorish Arch, Liverpool

591 First and Second Class Carriages passing through Olive Mount cutting

592 Third Class Carriage and Sheep Truck crossing Chat Moss

593 Horsebox and Carriage Truck near Bridgewater Canal

594 Goods Truck and Mail-Coach at Manchester

Г **590/4** were printed together, *se-tenant*, in horizontal strips of 5 oughout the sheet.

(Des D. Gentleman)

1980 (12 Mar). *150th Anniv of Liverpool and Manchester Railway. Phosphorised paper.* P 15 × 14.

1113	**590**	12p.	lemon, light brown, rose-red, pale blue and grey-black	25	40
		a.	Strip of 5. Nos. 1113/17	1·50	1·75
		ab.	Imperf (horiz strip of 5. Nos. 1113/17)	£1200	
		ac.	Lemon omitted (horiz strip of 5. Nos. 1113/17)	£7500	
1114	**591**	12p.	rose-red, light brown, lemon, pale blue and grey-black	25	40
1115	**592**	12p.	pale blue, rose-red, lemon, light brown and grey-black	25	40
1116	**593**	12p.	light brown, lemon, rose-red, pale blue and grey-black	25	40
1117	**594**	12p.	light brown, rose-red, pale blue, lemon and grey-black	25	40
1113/17			.. .. *Set of* 5	1·50	1·75

595 Montage of London Buildings

(Des J. Matthews. Recess)

1980 (9 Apr–7 May). *"London 1980" International Stamp Exhibition. Phosphorised paper.* P 14½ × 14.

1118	**595**	50p.	agate	1·50	1·50
MS1119			90 × 123 mm. No. 1118 (*sold at* 75*p.*) (7 May)	1·50	1·50
		a.	Error. Imperf	£700	

596 Buckingham Palace **597** The Albert Memorial

598 Royal Opera House **599** Hampton Court

600 Kensington Palace

(Des Sir Hugh Casson)

1980 (7 May). *London Landmarks. Phosphorised paper.* P 14 × 15.

1120	**596**	10½p.	grey, pale blue, rosine, pale greenish yell, yellowish green & silver	25	25
1121	**597**	12p.	grey-black, bistre, rosine, yellowish green, pale greenish yellow and silver	30	30
		a.	Imperf (vert pair)	£550	
1122	**598**	13½p.	grey-black, pale salmon, pale olgreen, slate-blue and silver ..	35	35
		a.	Imperf (pair)	£550	
1123	**599**	15p.	grey-black, pale salmon, slate-blue, dull yellowish green, olive-yellow and silver	40	40
1124	**600**	17½p.	grey, slate-blue, red-brown, sepia, yellowish green, pale greenish yellow and silver	40	40
		a.	Silver (Queen's head) omitted ..	£175	
1120/4			.. .. *Set of* 5	1·50	1·50

No. 1124a shows the Queen's head in pale greenish yellow, this colour being printed beneath the silver for technical reasons.

601 Charlotte Brontë (*Jane Eyre*)

602 George Eliot (*The Mill on the Floss*)

603 Emily Brontë (*Wuthering Heights*)

604 Mrs. Gaskell (*North and South*)

T **601/4** show authoresses and scenes from their novels. T **601/2** also include the "Europa" C.E.P.T. emblem.

(Des Barbara Brown)

1980 (9 July). *Famous Authoresses. Phosphorised paper.* P 15 × 14.

1125	**601**	12p.	red-brown, bright rose, bright bl, greenish yellow, grey and gold	30	30
1126	**602**	13½p.	red-brown, dull vermilion, pale bl, pale greenish yell, grey & gold	35	35
		a.	Pale blue omitted	£2500	
1127	**603**	15p.	red-brown, vermilion, blue, lemon, grey and gold	40	45
1128	**604**	17½p.	dull vermilion, slate-blue, ultram, pale greenish yell, grey and gold	60	60
		a.	Imperf and slate-blue omitted (pair)	£700	
1125/8			.. .. *Set of* 4	1·50	1·50

605 Queen Elizabeth the Queen Mother

(Des J. Matthews from photograph by N. Parkinson)

1980 (4 Aug). *80th Birthday of Queen Elizabeth the Queen Mother. Phosphorised paper.* P 14 × 15.

1129	**605**	12p.	bright rose, greenish yellow, new blue, grey and silver	75	75
		a.	Imperf (horiz pair)	£1200	

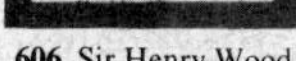

606 Sir Henry Wood **607** Sir Thomas Beecham

608 Sir Malcolm Sargent **609** Sir John Barbirolli

(Des P. Gauld)

1980 (10 Sept). *British Conductors. Phosphorised paper. P* 14 × 15.

No.	Type	Value	Description	Unused	Used
1130	**606**	12p.	slate, rose-red, greenish yellow, bistre and gold	30	30
1131	**607**	13½p.	grey-black, vermilion, greenish yellow, pale carmine-rose and gold	35	40
1132	**608**	15p.	grey-black, bright rose-red, greenish yellow, turquoise-grn & gold	45	45
1133	**609**	17½p.	black, bright rose-red, greenish yellow, dull violet-blue and gold	55	50
1130/3			.. .. *Set of* 4	1·50	1·50

610 Running

611 Rugby

612 Boxing

613 Cricket

(Des R. Goldsmith. Litho Questa)

1980 (10 Oct). *Sport Centenaries. Phosphorised paper. P* 14 × 14½.

No.	Type	Value	Description	Unused	Used
1134	**610**	12p.	pale new blue, greenish yellow, magenta, light brown, reddish purple and gold	30	30
			a. Gold (Queen's head) omitted ..	£10000	
1135	**611**	13½p.	pale new blue, olive-yellow, bright purple, orange-vermilion, blackish lilac and gold	35	40
1136	**612**	15p.	pale new blue, greenish yellow, bright purple, chalky blue & gold	40	40
			a. Gold (Queen's head) omitted ..	£10000	
1137	**613**	17½p.	pale new blue, greenish yellow, magenta, dp ol, grey-brn & gold	60	55
1134/7			.. .. *Set of* 4	1·50	1·50

Centenaries:—12p. Amateur Athletics Association; 13½p. Welsh Rugby Union; 15p. Amateur Boxing Association; 17½p. First England–Australia Test Match.

Nos. 1134a and 1136a were caused by paper folds.

614 Christmas Tree

615 Candles

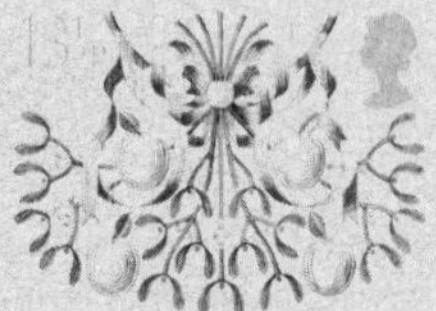

616 Apples and Mistletoe

617 Crown, Chains and Bell

618 Holly

(Des J. Matthews)

1980 (19 Nov). *Christmas. One centre phosphor band* (10*p.*) *or phosphorised paper* (*others*). *P* 15 × 14.

No.	Type	Value	Description	Unused	Used
1138	**614**	10p.	black, turquoise-green, greenish yellow, vermilion and blue ..	25	25
			a. Imperf (horiz pair)	£950	
1139	**615**	12p.	grey, magenta, rose-red, greenish grey and pale orange	30	35
1140	**616**	13½p.	grey-black, dull yellow-green, brown, greenish yellow and pale olive-bistre	35	40
1141	**617**	15p.	grey-black, bistre-yellow, bright orange, magenta and new blue ..	40	40
1142	**618**	17½p.	black, vermilion, dull yellowish green and greenish yellow ..	50	40
1138/42			.. .. *Set of* 5	1·60	1·60

619 St. Valentine's Day

620 Morris Dancers

621 Lammastide

622 Medieval Mummers

T **619/20** also include the "Europa" C.E.P.T. emblem.

(Des F. Wegner)

1981 (6 Feb). *Folklore. Phosphorised paper. P* 15 × 14.

No.	Type	Value	Description	Unused	Used
1143	**619**	14p.	cerise, green, yellow-orange, salmon-pink, black and gold ..	35	35
1144	**620**	18p.	dull ultramarine, lemon, lake-brown, brt green, black & gold	45	50
1145	**621**	22p.	chrome-yellow, rosine, brown, new blue, black and gold ..	60	60
1146	**622**	25p.	brt blue, red-brown, brt rose-red, greenish yellow, black and gold	75	70
1143/6			.. .. *Set of* 4	2·00	2·00

623 Blind Man with Guide Dog

624 Hands spelling "Deaf" in Sign Language

625 Disabled Man in Wheelchair

626 Disabled Artist painting with Foot

(Des J. Gibbs)

1981 (25 Mar). *International Year of the Disabled. Phosphorise- paper. P* 15 × 14.

No.	Type	Value	Description	Unused	Used
1147	**623**	14p.	drab, greenish yellow, bright rose-red, dull purple and silver ..	35	3
			a. Imperf (pair)	£600	
1148	**624**	18p.	deep blue-green, brt orange, dull vermilion, grey-black and silver	45	5
1149	**625**	22p.	brown-ochre, rosine, purple-brn, greenish blue, black and silver ..	60	6
1150	**626**	25p.	vermilion, lemon, pale salmon, olive-brn, new blue, blk & silver	75	7
1147/50			.. .. *Set of* 4	2·00	2·0

All known examples of No. 1147a are creased.

627 *Aglais urticae*

628 *Maculinea arion*

629 *Inachis io*

630 *Carterocephalus palaemon*

(Des G. Beningfield)

1981 (13 May). *Butterflies. Phosphorised paper. P* 14 × 15.

No.	Type	Value	Description	Unused	Used
1151	**627**	14p.	greenish yellow, yellow-green, brt rose, brt blue, emerald & gold ..	35	3
			a. Imperf (pair)	£950	
1152	**628**	18p.	black, greenish yellow, dull yellowish green, bright mauve, bright blue, bright green and gold ..	70	7
1153	**629**	22p.	black, greenish yell, bronze-grn, rosine, ultramarine, lt grn & gold	80	8
1154	**630**	25p.	black, greenish yellow, bronze-green, bright rose-red, ultramarine, bright emerald and gold ..	90	9
1151/4			.. .. *Set of* 4	2·50	2·5

631 Glenfinnan, Scotland

632 Derwentwater, England

633 Stackpole Head, Wales

634 Giant's Causeway, Northern Ireland

635 St. Kilda, Scotland

(Des M. Fairclough)

981 (24 June). *50th Anniv of National Trust for Scotland. British Landscapes. Phosphorised paper. P* 15 × 14.

155	**631**	14p.	lilac, dull blue, reddish brown, bistre-yellow, black and gold ..	30	30
156	**632**	18p.	bottle green, bright blue, brown, bistre-yellow, black and gold ..	40	40
157	**633**	20p.	deep turq-blue, dull blue, greenish yellow, reddish brn, black & gold	60	60
158	**634**	22p.	chrome-yellow, reddish brn, new blue, yellow-brown, black & gold	70	70
159	**635**	25p.	ultramarine, new blue, olive-green, olive-grey and gold ..	80	80
155/9 ..			.. .. *Set of* 5	2·50	2·50

636 Prince Charles and Lady Diana Spencer

(Des J. Matthews from photograph by Lord Snowdon)

981 (22 July). *Royal Wedding. Phosphorised paper. P* 14 × 15.

160	**636**	14p.	grey-blk, greenish yellow, brt rose-red, ultram, pale bl, blue & silver	2·00	1·75
161		25p.	drab, greenish yellow, bright rose-red, ultramarine, grey-brown, grey-black and silver	3·00	2·25

637 "Expeditions"

638 "Skills"

639 "Service"

640 "Recreation"

(Des P. Sharland. Litho J.W.)

1981 (12 Aug). *25th Anniv of Duke of Edinburgh Award Scheme. Phosphorised paper. P* 14.

1162	**637**	14p.	greenish yellow, magenta, pale new blue, black, emerald & silver	35	35
1163	**638**	18p.	greenish yellow, magenta, pale new blue, black, cobalt and gold	50	50
1164	**639**	22p.	greenish yellow, magenta, pale new blue, black, red-orge & gold	60	60
1165	**640**	25p.	bright orange, mauve, pale new blue, black, flesh and bronze ..	70	70
1162/5 ..			.. .. *Set of* 4	2·00	2·00

641 Cockle-dredging from *Linsey II*

642 Hauling in Trawl Net

643 Lobster Potting

644 Hoisting Seine Net

(Des B. Sanders)

1981 (23 Sept). *Fishing Industry. Phosphorised paper. P* 15 × 14.

1166	**641**	14p.	slate, greenish yellow, magenta, new blue, orange-brown, olive-grey and bronze-green	35	35
1167	**642**	18p.	slate, greenish yellow, brt crimson, ultramarine, blk & greenish slate	50	50
1168	**643**	22p.	grey, greenish yellow, bright rose, dull ultram, reddish lilac & black	60	60
1169	**644**	25p.	grey, greenish yellow, bright rose, cobalt and black	70	65
1166/9 ..			.. .. *Set of* 4	2·00	2·00

Nos. 1166/9 were issued on the occasion of the centenary of the Royal National Mission to Deep Sea Fishermen.

645 Father Christmas

646 Jesus Christ

647 Flying Angel

648 Joseph and Mary arriving at Bethlehem

649 Three Kings approaching Bethlehem

(Des Samantha Brown (11½p.), Tracy Jenkins (14p.), Lucinda Blackmore (18p.), Stephen Moore (22p.), Sophie Sharp (25p.))

1981 (18 Nov). *Christmas. Children's Pictures. One phosphor band (11½p.) or phosphorised paper (others). P* 15 × 14.

1170	**645**	11½p.	ultramarine, black, red, olive-bistre, bright green and gold ..	30	30
1171	**646**	14p.	bistre-yellow, brt magenta, blue, greenish blue, brt grn, blk & gold	40	40
1172	**647**	18p.	pale blue-green, bistre-yellow, brt magenta, ultramarine, blk & gold	50	50
1173	**648**	22p.	deep turquoise-blue, lemon, magenta, black and gold	60	60
1174	**649**	25p.	royal blue, lemon, bright magenta, black and gold	70	70
1170/4 ..			.. .. *Set of* 5	2·25	2·25

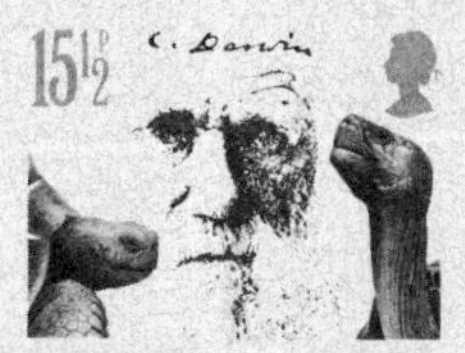

650 Charles Darwin and Giant Tortoises

651 Darwin and Marine Iguanas

652 Darwin, Cactus Ground Finch and Large Ground Finch

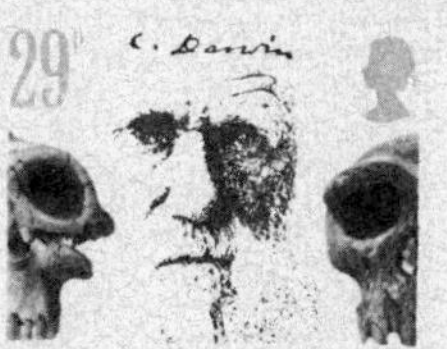

653 Darwin and Prehistoric Skulls

(Des D. Gentleman)

1982 (10 Feb). *Death Centenary of Charles Darwin. Phosphorised paper. P* 15 × 14.

1175	**650**	15½p.	dull purple, drab, bistre, black and grey-black	35	35
1176	**651**	19½p.	violet-grey, bistre-yellow, slate-black, red-brown, grey-blk & blk	60	60
1177	**652**	26p.	sage green, bistre-yellow, orange, chalky bl, grey-blk, red-brn & blk	70	70
1178	**653**	29p.	grey-brown, yellow-brn, brown-ochre, black and grey-black ..	75	75
1175/8 ..			.. .. *Set of* 4	2·25	2·25

654 Boys' Brigade **655** Girls' Brigade

656 Boy Scout Movement **657** Girl Guide Movement

(Des B. Sanders)

1982 (24 Mar). *Youth Organizations. Phosphorised paper. P* 15 × 14.
1179 **654** 15½p. gold, greenish yellow, pale orange, mauve, dull blue and grey-black 35 35
1180 **655** 19½p. gold, greenish yellow, pale orange, bright rose, deep ultramarine, olive-bistre and grey-black .. 60 50
1181 **656** 26p. gold, greenish yellow, olive-sepia, rosine, deep blue, deep dull green and grey-black 85 75
1182 **657** 29p. gold, yellow, dull orange, cerise, dull ultram, chestnut & grey-blk 1·00 90
1179/82 .. .. *Set of* 4 2·50 2·25

Nos. 1179/82 were issued on the occasion of the 75th anniversary of the Boy Scout Movement; the 125th birth anniversary of Lord Baden-Powell and the centenary of the Boys' Brigade (1983).

658 Ballerina **659** Harlequin

660 Hamlet **661** Opera Singer

(Des A. George)

1982 (28 Apr). *Europa. British Theatre. Phosphorised paper. P* 15 × 14.
1183 **658** 15½p. carm-lake, greenish bl, greenish yell, grey-blk, bottle grn & silver 35 35
1184 **659** 19½p. rosine, new blue, greenish yellow, black, ultramarine and silver .. 60 50
1185 **660** 26p. carmine-red, bright rose-red, greenish yellow, black, dull ultramarine, lake-brown and silver .. 90 75
1186 **661** 29p. rose-red, greenish yellow, bright blue, grey-black and silver .. 1·25 90
1183/6 .. .. *Set of* 4 2·75 2·25

662 Henry VIII and *Mary Rose*

663 Admiral Blake and *Triumph*

664 Lord Nelson and H.M.S. *Victory*

665 Lord Fisher and H.M.S. *Dreadnought*

666 Viscount Cunningham and H.M.S *Warspite*

(Des Marjorie Saynor. Eng C. Slania. Recess and photo)

1982 (16 June). *Maritime Heritage. Phosphorised paper. P* 15 × 14.
1187 **662** 15½p. black, lemon, bright rose, pale orange, ultramarine and grey .. 35 35
a. Imperf (pair) £750
1188 **663** 19½p. black, greenish yellow, bright rose-red, pale orange, ultram and grey 60 60
1189 **664** 24p. black, orange-yellow, bright rose-red, lake-brown, dp ultram & grey 70 70
1190 **665** 26p. black, orange-yellow, bright rose, lemon, ultramarine and grey .. 80 80
a. Imperf (pair) .. .. ..
1191 **666** 29p. black, olive-yellow, bright rose, orange-yellow, ultram & grey .. 90 90
1187/91 .. .. *Set of* 5 3·00 3·00

Nos. 1187/91 were issued on the occasion of Maritime England Year, the Bicentenary of the Livery Grant by City of London to Worshipful Company of Shipwrights and the raising of *Mary Rose* from Portsmouth Harbour.

Several used examples of the 15½p. have been seen with the black recess (ship and waves) omitted.

667 "Strawberry Thief" (William Morris)  **668** Untitled (Steiner and Co)

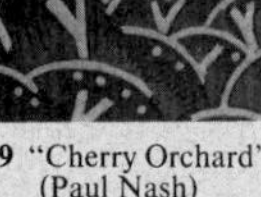

669 "Cherry Orchard" (Paul Nash) **670** "Chevron" (Andrew Foster)

(Des Peter Hatch Partnership)

1982 (23 July). *British Textiles. Phosphorised paper. P* 14 × 15.
1192 **667** 15½p. blue, olive-yellow, rosine, deep blue-green, bistre & Prussian blue 35 35
a. Imperf (horiz pair) £950
1193 **668** 19½p. olive-grey, greenish yellow, bright magenta, dull grn, yell-brn & blk 65 65
a. Imperf (vert pair) £1500
1194 **669** 26p. bright scarlet, dull mauve, dull ultramarine and bright carmine 80 80
1195 **670** 29p. bronze-green, orange-yellow, turq-green, stone, chestnut & sage-grn 1·00 1·00
1192/5 .. .. *Set of* 4 2·50 2·50

Nos. 1192/5 were issued on the occasion of the 250th birth anniversary of Sir Richard Arkwright (inventor of spinning machine).

671 Development of Communications

672 Modern Technological Aids

(Des Delaney and Ireland)

1982 (8 Sept). *Information Technology. Phosphorised paper. P* 14 × 15.
1196 **671** 15½p. black, greenish yellow, bright rose-red, bistre-brn, new bl & lt ochre 45 50
a. Imperf (pair) £200
1197 **672** 26p. black, greenish yellow, bright rose-red, ol-bistre, new bl & lt ol-grey 80 85
a. Imperf (pair) £1300

673 Austin "Seven" and "Metro"

674 Ford "Model T" and "Escort"

675 Jaguar "SS 1" and "XJ6"

676 Rolls-Royce "Silver Ghost" and "Silver Spirit"

(Des S. Paine. Litho Questa)

1982 (13 Oct). *British Motor Cars. Phosphorised paper. P* 14½ × 14.
1198 **673** 15½p. slate, orange-vermilion, bright orange, drab, yellow-green, olive-yellow, bluish grey and black .. 50 50
1199 **674** 19½p. slate, brt orange, olive-grey, rose-red, dull vermilion, grey & black 70 70
1200 **675** 26p. slate, red-brown, bright orange, turquoise-green, myrtle-green, dull blue-green, grey and olive .. 90 90
1201 **676** 29p. slate, bright orange, carmine-red, reddish purple, grey and black .. 1·25 1·25
1198/201 .. .. *Set of* 4 3·00 3·00

677 "While Shepherds Watched"

678 "The Holly and the Ivy"

679 "I Saw Three Ships"

680 "We Three Kings"

681 "Good King Wenceslas"

(Des Barbara Brown)

32 (17 Nov). *Christmas. Carols. One phosphor band* (12½*p.*) *or hosphorised paper* (*others*). *P* 15 × 14.

2 **677** 12½p. black, greenish yellow, brt scar, steel blue, red-brown & gold .. 30 30
3 **678** 15½p. black, bistre-yellow, brt rose-red, bright blue, bright green & gold 40 40
a. Imperf (pair) £950
4 **679** 19½p. black, bistre-yellow, brt rose-red, dull blue, deep brown & gold .. 70 70
a. Imperf (pair) £1300
5 **680** 26p. black, bistre-yellow, brt magenta, brt blue, choc, gold & orange-red 80 80
6 **681** 29p. black, bistre-yellow, magenta, brt blue, chestnut, gold and brt mag 90 90
2/6 .. .. *Set of* 5 2·75 2·75

682 Atlantic Salmon

683 Northern Pike

684 Brown Trout

685 Eurasian Perch

(Des A. Jardine)

3 (26 Jan). *British River Fishes. Phosphorised paper. P* 15 × 14.

7 **682** 15½p. grey-black, bistre-yellow, bright purple, new blue and silver .. 35 35
a. Imperf (pair) £1300
8 **683** 19½p. black, bistre-yellow, olive-bistre, dp claret, silver & dp bluish green 65 65
9 **684** 26p. grey-black, bistre-yell, chrome-yellow, magenta, silver & pale bl 80 80
a. Imperf (pair) £850
0 **685** 29p. black, greenish yellow, bright carmine, new blue and silver .. 1·00 1·00
7/10 .. .. *Set of* 4 2·50 2·50

ll known examples of No. 1209a are creased.

686 Tropical Island **687** Desert

688 Temperate Farmland **689** Mountain Range

(Des D. Fraser)

1983 (9 Mar). *Commonwealth Day. Geographical Regions. Phosphorised paper. P* 14 × 15.

1211 **686** 15½p. greenish blue, greenish yellow, bright rose, light brown, grey-black, deep claret and silver .. 35 35
1212 **687** 19½p. brt lilac, greenish yell, mag, dull blue, grey-blk, dp dull-bl & silver 65 65
1213 **688** 26p. lt blue, greenish yellow, brt mag, new blue, grey-blk, vio & silver 80 80
1214 **689** 29p. dull vio-bl, reddish vio, slate-lilac, new blue, myrtle-grn, blk & silver 1·00 1·00
1211/14 .. .. *Set of* 4 2·50 2·50

690 Humber Bridge

691 Thames Flood Barrier

692 *Iolair* (oilfield emergency support vessel)

(Des. M. Taylor)

1983 (25 May). *Europa. Engineering Achievements. Phosphorised paper. P* 15 × 14.

1215 **690** 16p. silver, orange-yellow, ultramarine, black and grey 45 45
1216 **691** 20½p. silver, greenish yellow, bright purple, blue, grey-black and grey .. 1·10 1·10
1217 **692** 28p. silver, lemon, brt rose-red, chestnut, dull ultramarine, blk & grey 1·25 1·25
1215/17 .. .. *Set of* 3 2·50 2·50

693 Musketeer and Pikeman, The Royal Scots (1633)

694 Fusilier and Ensign, The Royal Welch Fusiliers (mid-18th century)

695 Riflemen, 95th Rifles (The Royal Green Jackets) (1805)

696 Sergeant (khaki service uniform) and Guardsman (full dress), The Irish Guards (1900)

697 Paratroopers, The Parachute Regiment (1983)

(Des E. Stemp)

1983 (6 July). *British Army Uniforms. Phosphorised paper. P* 14 × 15.

1218 **693** 16p. black, buff, deep brown, slate-black, rose-red, gold & new blue 40 40
1219 **694** 20½p. black, buff, greenish yellow, slate-blk, brn-rose, gold & brt bl 70 70
1220 **695** 26p. black, buff, slate-purple, green, bistre and gold 85 85
a. Imperf (pair) £1300
1221 **696** 28p. black, buff, light brown, grey, dull rose, gold and new blue .. 85 85
1222 **697** 31p. black, buff, olive-yellow, grey, deep magenta, gold and new blue 1·10 1·10
1218/22 .. .. *Set of* 5 3·50 3·50

Nos. 1218/22 were issued on the occasion of the 350th anniversary of the Royal Scots, the senior line regiment of the British Army.

698 20th-century Garden, Sissinghurst

699 19th-century Garden, Biddulph Grange

700 18th-century Garden, Blenheim

701 17th-century Garden, Pitmedden

(Des Liz Butler, Litho J.W.)

1983 (24 Aug). *British Gardens. Phosphorised paper. P* 14.

1223 **698** 16p. greenish yellow, brt purple, new blue, black, bright green & silver 40 40
1224 **699** 20½p. greenish yellow, brt purple, new blue, black, bright green & silver 50 50
1225 **700** 28p. greenish yellow, brt purple, new blue, black, bright green & silver 90 90
1226 **701** 31p. greenish yellow, brt purple, new blue, black, bright green & silver 1·00 1·00
1223/6 .. .. *Set of* 4 2·50 2·50

Nos. 1223/6 were issued on the occasion of the death bicentenary of "Capability" Brown (landscape gardener)

702 Merry-go-round

703 Big Wheel, Helter-skelter and Performing Animals

704 Side Shows

705 Early Produce Fair

(Des A. Restall)

1983 (5 Oct). *British Fairs. Phosphorised paper. P* 15 × 14.

1227 **702** 16p. grey-black, greenish yellow, orange-red, ochre & turquoise-blue . . 40 40
1228 **703** 20½p. grey-black, yellow-ochre, yellow-orange, brt magenta, violet & blk 65 65
1229 **704** 28p. grey-black, bistre-yellow, orange-red, violet and yellow-brown . . 85 85
1230 **705** 31p. grey-black, greenish yellow, red, dp turq-green, slate-violet & brn 90 90
1227/30 . . . . *Set of* 4 2·50 2·50

706 "Christmas Post" (pillar-box)

707 "The Three Kings" (chimney-pots)

708 "World at Peace" (Dove and Blackbird)

709 "Light of Christmas" (street lamp)

710 "Christmas Dove" (hedge sculpture)

(Des T. Meeuwissen)

1983 (16 Nov). *Christmas. One phosphor band* (12½*p.*) *or phosphorised paper* (*others*). *P* 15 × 14.

1231 **706** 12½p. black, greenish yellow, bright rose-red, bright blue, gold and grey-black 30 30
a. Imperf (horiz pair) £750
1232 **707** 16p. black, greenish yellow, bright rose, pale new blue, gold & brown-pur 35 35
a. Imperf (pair) £850
1233 **708** 20½p. black, greenish yellow, bright rose, new blue, gold and blue 60 60
1234 **709** 28p. black, lemon, bright carmine, bluish violet, gold, deep turquoise-green and purple 70 80
1235 **710** 31p. black, greenish yellow, brt rose, new blue, gold, green & brn-olive 85 1·00
1231/5 . . . . *Set of* 5 2·50 2·75

711 Arms of the College of Arms

712 Arms of King Richard III (founder)

713 Arms of the Earl Marshal of England

714 Arms of the City of London

(Des J. Matthews)

1984 (17 Jan). *500th Anniv of College of Arms. Phosphorised paper. P* 14½.

1236 **711** 16p. black, chrome-yellow, reddish brn, scar-verm, brt bl & grey-blk 40 40
1237 **712** 20½p. black, chrome-yellow, rosine, bright blue and grey-black . . 60 60
1238 **713** 28p. black, chrome-yellow, rosine, brt blue, dull green and grey-black 85 85
1239 **714** 31p. black, chrome-yellow, rosine, brt blue and grey-black 95 95
a. Imperf (horiz pair) £1800
1236/9 . . . . *Set of* 4 2·50 2·50

715 Highland Cow

716 Chillingham Wild Bull

717 Hereford Bull

718 Welsh Black Bull

719 Irish Moiled Cow

(Des B. Driscoll)

1984 (6 Mar). *British Cattle. Phosphorised paper. P* 15 × 14.

1240 **715** 16p. grey-black, bistre-yellow, rosine, yellow-orge, new bl & pale drab 40
1241 **716** 20½p. grey-black, greenish yellow, magenta, bistre, dull blue-green, pale drab and light green 65
1242 **717** 26p. black, chrome-yellow, rosine, reddish brown, new blue & pale drab 70
1243 **718** 28p. black, greenish yellow, bright carmine, orange-brown, deep dull blue and pale drab 70
1244 **719** 31p. grey-black, bistre-yellow, rosine, red-brown, light blue & pale drab 90
1240/4 . . . . *Set of* 5 3·00 3·

Nos. 1240/4 were issued on the occasion of the centenary of th Highland Cattle Society and the bicentenary of the Royal Highlan and Agricultural Society of Scotland.

720 Liverpool Garden Festival Hall

721 Milburngate Centre, Durham

722 Bush House, Bristol

723 Commercial Street Development, Perth

(Des R. Maddox and Trickett and Webb Ltd)

1984 (10 Apr). *Urban Renewal. Phosphorised paper. P* 15 × 14.

1245 **720** 16p. bright emerald, greenish yellow, cerise, steel-bl, blk, silver & flesh 40
1246 **721** 20½p. bright orange, greenish yellow, deep dull blue, yellowish green, azure, black and silver . . 60
a. Imperf (horiz pair) £1000
1247 **722** 28p. rosine, greenish yellow, Prussian blue, pale blue-green, blk & silver 90
1248 **723** 31p. blue, greenish yell, cerise, grey-blue, bright green, black & silver 90
a. Imperf (pair) £1000
1245/8 . . . . *Set of* 4 2·50 2·

Nos. 1245/8 were issued on the occasion of 150th anniversaries of t Royal Institute of British Architects and the Chartered Institute Building, and to commemorate the first International Gardens Festiv Liverpool.

ROYAL MAIL POSTAGE LABELS

These imperforate labels, printed in red on phosphorised paper w grey-green background design, were issued on 1 May 1984 as an exp iment by the Post Office. Special microprocessor controlled machir were installed at post offices in Cambridge, London, Shirle (Southampton) and Windsor to provide an after-hours sales service the public. The machines printed and dispensed the labels according the coins inserted and the buttons operated by the customer. Valu were initially available in ½p steps to 16p and in addition, the labels we sold at philatelic counters in two packs containing either 3 values (12½, 16p) or 32 values (½p to 16p).

From 28 August 1984 the machines were adjusted to provide valu up to 17p. After 31 December 1984 labels including ½p values were wi drawn. The machines were withdrawn from service on 30 April 1985

24 C.E.P.T. 25th Aniversary Logo **725** Abduction of Europa

(Des J. Larrivière (T **724**), F. Wegner (T **725**)

84 (15 May). *25th Anniv of C.E.P.T. ("Europa") (T* **724***) and Second Elections to European Parliament (T* **725***). Phosphorised paper. P* 15 × 14.

49	**724**	16p. greenish slate, deep blue and gold	90	90
		a. Horiz pair. Nos. 1249/50	1·75	1·75
		ab. Imperf (horiz pair)	£1300	
50	**725**	16p. greenish slate, deep blue, black and gold	90	90
51	**724**	20½p. Venetian red, dp magenta & gold	1·60	1·60
		a. Horiz pair. Nos. 1251/2	3·25	3·25
		ab. Imperf (horiz pair)		
52	**725**	20½p. Venetian red, deep magenta, black and gold	1·60	1·60
49/52		*Set of* 4	4·50	4·50

Nos. 1249/50 and 1251/2 were each printed together, *se-tenant*, in orizontal pairs throughout the sheets.

726 Lancaster House

(Des P. Hogarth)

84 (5 June). *London Economic Summit Conference. Phosphorised paper. P* 14 × 15.

253	**726**	31p. silver, bistre-yellow, brown-ochre, black, rosine, bright blue and reddish lilac	1·00	1·00

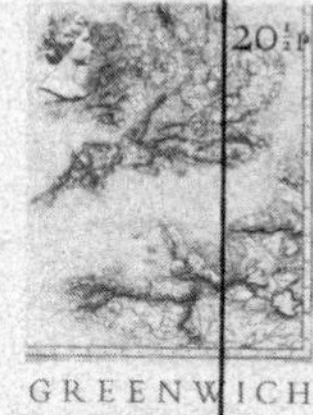

727 View of Earth from "Apollo 11" **728** Navigational Chart of English Channel

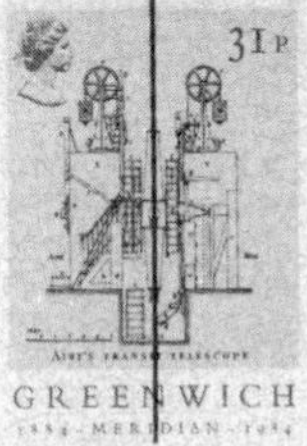

729 Greenwich Observatory **730** Sir George Airy's Transit Telescope

(Des. H. Waller. Litho Questa)

984 (26 June). *Centenary of the Greenwich Meridian. Phosphorised paper. P* 14 × 14½.

254	**727**	16p. new blue, greenish yellow, magenta, black, scar & blue-blk	40	40
255	**728**	20½p. olive-sepia, light brown, pale buff, black and scarlet	65	65
256	**729**	28p. new blue, greenish yellow, scarlet, black and bright purple	85	90
257	**730**	31p. deep blue, cobalt, scarlet & black	90	1·10
254/7		*Set of* 4	2·50	2·75

On Nos. 1254/7 the Meridian is represented by a scarlet line.

731 Bath Mail Coach, 1784

732 Attack on Exeter Mail, 1816

733 Norwich Mail in Thunderstorm, 1827

734 Holyhead and Liverpool Mails leaving London, 1828

735 Edinburgh Mail Snowbound, 1831

(Des K. Bassford and S. Paine. Eng C. Slania. Recess and photo)

1984 (31 July). *Bicentenary of First Mail Coach Run Bath and Bristol to London. Phosphorised paper. P* 15 × 14.

1258	**731**	16p. pale stone, black, grey-black and bright scarlet	65	65
		a. Horiz strip of 5 Nos. 1258/62	3·00	3·00
1259	**732**	16p. pale stone, black, grey-black and bright scarlet	65	65
1260	**733**	16p. pale stone, black, grey-black and bright scarlet	65	65
1261	**734**	16p. pale stone, black, grey-black and bright scarlet	65	65
1262	**735**	16p. pale stone, black, grey-black and bright scarlet	65	65
1258/62		*Set of* 5	3·00	3·00

Nos. 1258/62 were printed together, *se-tenant*, in horizontal strips of 5 throughout the sheet.

736 Nigerian Clinic

737 Violinist and Acropolis, Athens

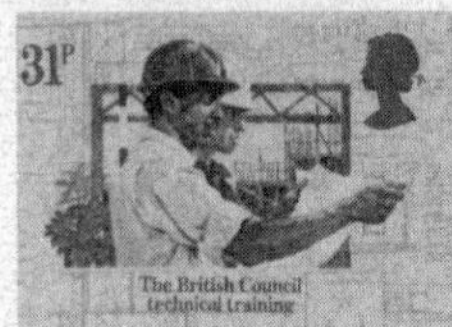

738 Building Project, Sri Lanka

739 British Council Library, Middle East

(Des F. Newell and J. Sorrell)

1984 (25 Sept). *50th Anniv of the British Council. Phosphorised paper. P* 15 × 14.

1263	**736**	17p. grey-green, greenish yellow, bright purple, dull blue, black, pale green and yellow-green	50	50
1264	**737**	22p. crimson, greenish yellow, bright rose-red, dull green, black, pale drab and slate-purple	65	65
1265	**738**	31p. sepia, olive-bistre, red, black, pale stone and olive-brown	90	90
1266	**739**	34p. steel blue, yellow, rose-red, new blue, black, azure and pale blue	1·00	1·00
1263/6		*Set of* 4	2·75	2·75

740 The Holy Family

741 Arrival in Bethlehem

742 Shepherd and Lamb

743 Virgin and Child

744 Offering of Frankincense

(Des Yvonne Gilbert)

1984 (20 Nov). *Christmas. One phosphor band* (13*p.*) *or phosphorised paper (others). P* 15 × 14.

1267	**740**	13p. pale cream, grey-black, bistre-yellow, mag, red-brn & lake-brn	30	30
1268	**741**	17p. pale cream, grey-black, yellow, magenta, dull blue & dp dull bl	50	50
		a. Imperf (pair)		
1269	**742**	22p. pale cream, grey-black, olive-yellow, bright magenta, bright blue and brownish grey	60	60
1270	**743**	31p. pale cream, grey-black, bistre-yellow, magenta, dull bl & lt brn	95	95
1271	**744**	34p. pale cream, olive-grey, bistre-yellow, magenta, turquoise-green and brown-olive	1·00	1·00
1267/71		*Set of* 5	3·00	3·00

Examples of No. 1267 from the Christmas £2.30 discount stamp booklet show a blue underprint of a double-lined star printed on the reverse over the gum.

745 "Flying Scotsman"

746 "Golden Arrow"

747 "Cheltenham Flyer"

748 "Royal Scot"

749 "Cornish Riviera"

(Des T. Cuneo)

1985 (22 Jan). *Famous Trains. Phosphorised paper. P* 15 × 14.

1272 **745** 17p. black, lemon, magenta, dull glue, grey-black and gold 50 50
a. Imperf (pair) £1800
1273 **746** 22p. black, greenish yellow, bright rose, dp dull blue, grey-blk & gold 85 70
1274 **747** 29p. black, greenish yellow, magneta, blue, grey-black and gold .. 1·00 90
1275 **748** 31p. black, bistre-yellow, bright magenta, new blue slate-black & gold 1·25 1·00
1276 **749** 34p. black, greenish yellow, bright rose, blue, slate-black and gold .. 1·40 1·10
1272/6 .. .. *Set of* 5 4·50 4·00

Nos. 1272/6 were issued on the occasion of the 150th anniversary of the Great Western Railway Company.

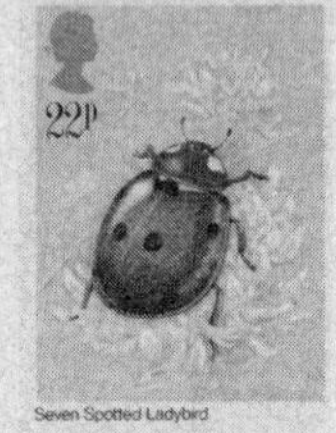

750 *Bombus terrestris* (bee)

751 *Coccinella septempunctata* (ladybird)

752 *Decticus verrucivorus* (bush-cricket)

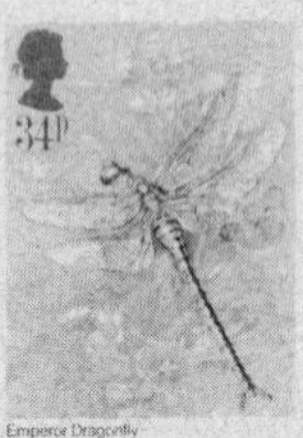

753 *Lucanus cervus* (stag beetle)

754 *Anax imperator* (dragonfly)

(Des G. Beningfield)

1985 (12 Mar). *Insects. Phosphorised paper. P* 14 × 15.

1277 **750** 17p. black, greenish yellow, magenta, blue, azure, gold and slate-black 40 40
1278 **751** 22p. black, greenish yellow, bright rose-red, dull blue-green, slate-black and gold 60 60
1279 **752** 29p. black, greenish yellow, bright rose, greenish blue, grey-black, gold and bistre-yellow.. .. .. 80 80
1280 **753** 31p. black, greenish yellow, rose, pale new blue and gold 90 90
1281 **754** 34p. black, greenish yellow, magenta, greenish blue, grey-black and gold .. 90 90
1277/81 .. .. *Set of* 5 3·25 3·25

Nos. 1277/81 were issued on the occasion of the centenaries of the Royal Entomological Society of London's Royal Charter, and of the Selborne Society.

755 "Water Music" (George Frideric Handel

756 "The Planets" Suite (Gustav Holst)

757 "The First Cuckoo" (Frederick Delius)

758 "Sea Pictures" (Edward Elgar)

(Des W. McLean)

1985 (14 May). *Europa. European Music Year. British Composers. Phosphorised paper. P* 14 × 14½.

1282 **755** 17p. black, brt yellow-grn, dp magenta, new blue, grey-black & gold .. 65 65
a. Imperf (vert pair) .. ..
1283 **756** 22p. black, greenish yellow, brt mag, new blue, grey-black and gold .. 90 90
a. Imperf (pair) £1300
1284 **757** 31p. black, greenish yellow, magenta, greenish blue, grey-black and gold 1·40 1·40
1285 **758** 34p. black, olive-yellow, bistre, turq-blue, slate and gold .. .. 1·50 1·50
1282/5 .. .. *Set of* 4 4·00 4·00

Nos. 1282/5 were issued on the occasion of the 300th birth anniversary of Handel.

759 R.N.L.I. Lifeboat and Signal Flags

760 Beachy Head Lighthouse and Chart

761 "Marecs A" Communications Satellite and Dish Aerials

762 Buoys

(Des F. Newell and J. Sorrel. Litho J.W.)

1985 (18 June). *Safety at Sea. Phosphorised paper. P* 14.

1286 **759** 17p. black, azure, emerald, ultramarine, orange-yellow, vermilion, bright blue, and chrome-yellow 50 50
1287 **760** 22p. black, azure, emerald, ultramarine, orange-yellow, vermilion, bright blue and chrome-yellow 65 65
1288 **761** 31p. black, azure, emerald, ultramarine, orange-yellow, vermilion, and bright blue .. .. 1·10 1·10
1289 **762** 34p. black, azure, emerald, ultramarine, orange-yellow, vermilion, bright blue and chrome-yellow .. .. .. 1·10 1·10
1286/9 .. .. *Set of* 4 3·00 3·00

Nos. 1286/9 were issued on the occasion of the Bicentenary of the unimmersible lifeboat and the 50th anniversary of radar.

763 Datapost Motorcyclist, City of London

764 Rural Postbus

765 Parcel Delivery in Winter

766 Town Letter Delivery

(Des P. Hogarth)

1985 (30 July). 350 *Years of Royal Mail Public Postal Service. Phosphorised paper. P* 14 × 15.

1290 **763** 17p. black, greenish yellow, bright carmine, greenish blue, yellow-brown, grey-black and silver .. 50 50
a. Imperf on 3 sides (vert pair) .. £1300
1291 **764** 22p. black, greenish yellow, cerise, steel bl, lt grn, grey-blk & silver 65 65
1292 **765** 31p. black, greenish yellow, brt carm, dull blue, drab, grey-blk & silver 1·10 1·10
a. Imperf (vert pair) £1300
1293 **766** 34p. black, greenish yellow, cerise, ultram, lt brn, grey-blk & silver 1·10 1·10
a. Imperf between (vert pair) ..
1290/3 .. .. *Set of* 4 3·00 3·00

Examples of No. 1290 from the commemorative £1.53 discount stamp booklet show a blue underprint of a double-lined D printed on the reverse over the gum.

No. 1290a shows perforation indentations at right, but is imperforate at top, bottom and on the left-hand side.

767 King Arthur and Merlin

768 Lady of the Lake

769 Queen Guinevere and Sir Lancelot

770 Sir Galahad

(Des Yvonne Gilbert)

985 (3 Sept). *Arthurian Legends. Phosphorised paper. P* 15 × 14.

294 **767** 17p. grey-black, lemon, brown-lilac, ultramarine, grey-black and silver 50 50
a. Imperf (pair) £1800

295 **768** 22p. black, lemon, brown-lilac, pale blue, grey-black, silver & grey-blk 75 75

296 **769** 31p. black, lemon, magenta, turquoise-blue, grey-black, silver & grey-blk 1·10 1·10

297 **770** 34p. grey, lemon, magenta, new blue, grey-black, silver and grey-black.. 1·25 1·25

294/7 .. .. *Set of* 4 3·25 3·25

Nos. 1294/7 were issued on the occasion of the 500th anniversary f the printing of Sir Thomas Malory's *Morte d'Arthur*.

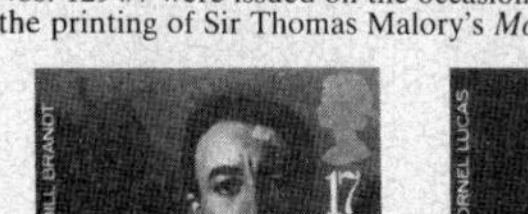

771 Peter Sellers (from photo by Bill Brandt)

772 David Niven (from photo by Cornell Lucas)

773 Charlie Chaplin (from photo by Lord Snowdon)

774 Vivien Leigh (from photo by Angus McBean)

775 Alfred Hitchcock (from photo by Howard Coster)

(Des K. Bassford)

985 (8 Oct). *British Film Year. Phosphorised paper. P* 14½.

298 **771** 17p. grey-black, ol-grey, gold & silver 50 50

299 **772** 22p. black, brown, gold and silver .. 75 75

300 **773** 29p. black, lavender, gold and silver .. 1·10 1·10

301 **774** 31p. black, pink, gold and silver .. 1·25 1·25

302 **775** 34p. black, greenish blue, gold & silver 1·40 1·40

298/302 .. .. *Set of* 5 4·50 4·50

776 Principal Boy

777 Genie

778 Dame

779 Good Fairy

780 Pantomime Cat

(Des A. George)

1985 (19 Nov). *Christmas. Pantomine Characters. One phosphor band* (12*p.*) *or phosphorised paper* (*others*). *P* 15 × 14.

1303 **776** 12p. new blue, greenish yellow, bright rose, gold, grey-black and silver 35 30
a. Imperf (pair) £1300

1304 **777** 17p. emerald, greenish yellow, bright rose, new blue, blk, gold & silver 45 40
a. Imperf (pair) £1800

1305 **778** 22p. bright carmine, greenish yellow, pale new blue, grey, gold & silver 70 80

1306 **779** 31p. bright orange, lemon, rose, slate-purple, silver and gold .. .. 95 1·00

1307 **780** 34p. brt reddish violet, brt blue, brt rose, blk, grey-brn, gold & silver 1·00 1·10

1303/7 .. .. *Set of* 5 3·00 3·25

Examples of No. 1303 from the Christmas £2.40 stamp booklet show a blue underprint of a double-lined star printed on the reverse over the gum.

781 Light Bulb and North Sea Oil Drilling Rig (Energy)

782 Thermometer and Pharmaceutical Laboratory (Health)

783 Garden Hoe and Steelworks (Steel)

784 Loaf of Bread and Cornfield (Agriculture)

(Des K. Bassford. Litho Questa)

1986 (14 Jan). *Industry Year. Phosphorised paper. P* 14½ × 14.

1308 **781** 17p. gold, black, magenta, greenish yellow and new blue 45 45

1309 **782** 22p. gold, pale turquoise-green, black, magenta, greenish yellow and blue 60 60

1310 **783** 31p. gold, black, magenta, greenish yellow and new blue .. .. 1·00 1·00

1311 **784** 34p. gold, black, magenta, greenish yellow and new blue .. .. 1·25 1·25

1308/11 .. .. *Set of* 4 3·00 3·00

785 Dr. Edmond Halley as Comet

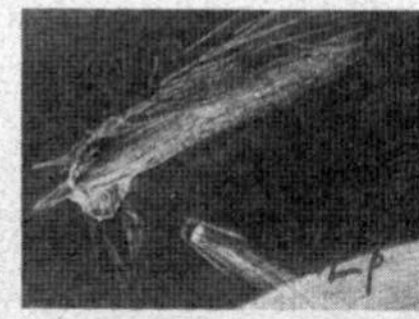

786 *Giotto* Spacecraft approaching Comet

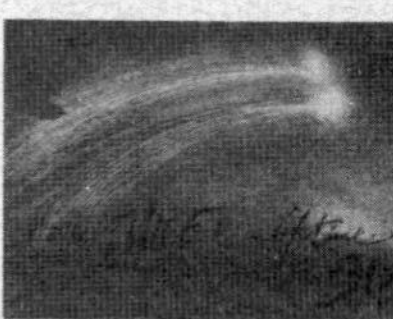

787 "Twice in a Lifetime"

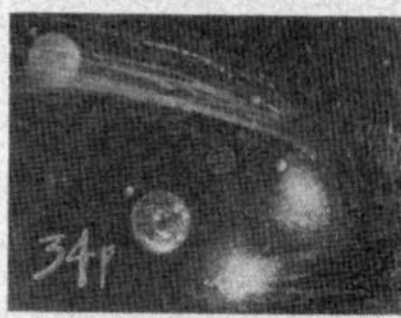

788 Comet orbiting Sun and Planets

(Des R. Steadman)

1986 (18 Feb). *Appearance of Halley's Comet. Phosphorised paper. P* 15 × 14.

1312 **785** 17p. black, bistre, rosine, blue, grey-black, gold and deep brown .. 45 45

1313 **786** 22p. orange-vermilion, greenish yellow, brt purple, new bl, blk & gold 70 70

1314 **787** 31p. black, greenish yellow, brt purple dp turquoise-blue, grey-blk & gold 1·10 1·10

1315 **788** 34p. blue, greenish yellow, magenta, deep turquoise-blue, black & gold 1·10 1·10

1312/15 .. .. *Set of* 4 3·00 3·00

789 Queen Elizabeth II in 1928, 1942 and 1952

790 Queen Elizabeth II in 1958, 1973 and 1982

(Des J. Matthews)

1986 (21 Apr). *60th Birthday of Queen Elizabeth II. Phosphorised paper. P* 15 × 14.

1316 **789** 17p. grey-black, turquoise-green, bright green, green and dull blue.. 70 40
a. Horiz pair. Nos. 1316/17.. .. 1·40 1·40

1317 **790** 17p. grey-black, dull blue, greenish blue and indigo 70 40

1318 **789** 34p. grey-black, deep dull purple, yellow-orange and red .. .. 1·50 1·50
a. Horiz pair. Nos. 1318/19.. .. 3·00 3·00

1319 **790** 34p. grey-black, olive-brown, yellow-brown, olive-grey and red .. 1·50 1·50

1316/19 .. .. *Set of* 4 4·00 4·00

Nos. 1316/17 and 1318/19 were printed together, *se-tenant*, in horizontal pairs throughout the sheets.

791 Barn Owl

792 Pine Marten

793 Wild Cat

794 Natterjack Toad

(Des K. Lilly)

1986 (20 May). *Europa. Nature Conservation. Endangered Species. Phosphorised paper. P* 14½×14.

1320	**791**	17p.	gold, greenish yellow, rose, yellow-brown, olive-grey, new blue & blk	50	50
1321	**792**	22p.	gold, greenish yellow, reddish brn, ol-yell, turq-bl, grey-blk & blk	90	75
1322	**793**	31p.	gold, brt yellow-green, magenta, lt brown, ultramarine, ol-brn & blk	1·40	1·25
1323	**794**	34p.	gold, greenish yellow, bright rose-red, brt green, grey-black & black	1·75	1·50
1320/3			.. .. *Set of* 4	4·00	3·50

795 Peasants working in Fields

796 Freemen working at Town Trades

797 Knight and Retainers

798 Lord at Banquet

(Des Tayburn Design Consultancy)

1986 (17 June). *900th Anniv of Domesday Book. Phosphorised paper. P* 15×14.

1324	**795**	17p.	yell-brn, verm, lemon, brt emer, orge-brn, grey & brownish grey	50	50
1325	**796**	22p.	yellow-ochre, red, greenish blue, chestnut, grey-blk & brownish grey	75	75
1326	**797**	31p.	yellow-brown, verm, grn, Indian red, grey-blk & brownish grey	1·10	1·10
1327	**798**	34p.	yellow-ochre, brt scar, grey-brn, new bl, lake-brn, grey-blk & grey	1·25	1·25
1324/7			.. .. *Set of* 4	3·25	3·25

MINIMUM PRICE

The minimum price quote is 10p which represents a handling charge rather than a basis for valuing common stamps. For further notes about prices see introductory pages.

799 Athletics

800 Rowing

801 Weightlifting

802 Rifle Shooting

803 Hockey

(Des N. Cudworth)

1986 (15 July). *Thirteenth Commonwealth Games, Edinburgh and World Hockey Cup for Men, London* (34*p*.). *Phosphorised paper. P* 15×14.

1328	**799**	17p.	black, greenish yellow, orange-vermilion, ultram, chestnut & emer	50	50
1329	**800**	22p.	black, lemon, scarlet, new blue, royal blue, chestnut & dp ultram	70	70
1330	**801**	29p.	grey-black, greenish yellow, scarlet, new blue, brown-ochre, brown-rose and pale chestnut ..	90	90
1331	**802**	31p.	black, greenish yellow, rose, blue, dull yell-grn, chestnut & yell-grn	1·10	1·10
1332	**803**	34p.	black, lemon, scarlet, brt blue, brt emerald, red-brown & vermilion	1·25	1·25
			a. Imperf (pair)	£1300	
1328/32			.. .. *Set of* 5	4·00	4·00

No. 1332 also commemorates the Centenary of the Hockey Association.

804 805
Prince Andrew and Miss Sarah Ferguson (from photo by Gene Nocon)

(Des J. Matthews)

1986 (22 July). *Royal Wedding. One phosphor band* (12*p*.) *or phosphorised paper* (17*p*.). *P* 14×15.

1333	**804**	12p.	lake, greenish yellow, cerise, ultramarine, black and silver	60	60
1334	**805**	17p.	steel blue, greenish yellow, cerise, ultramarine, black and gold ..	90	90
			a. Imperf (pair)	£850	

806 Stylised Cross on Ballot Paper

(Des J. Gibbs. Litho Questa)

1986 (19 Aug). *32nd Commonwealth Parliamentary Association Conference. Phosphorised paper. P* 14×14½.

1335	**806**	34p.	pale grey-lilac, black, vermilion, yellow and ultramarine	1·25	1·25

807 Lord Dowding and Hawker Hurricane Mk I

808 Lord Tedder and Hawker Typhoon 1B

809 Lord Trenchard and De Havilland D.H.9A

810 Sir Arthur Harris and Avro Type 683 Lancaster

811 Lord Portal and De Havilland D.H.98 Mosquito

(Des B. Sanders)

1986 (16 Sept). *History of the Royal Air Force. Phosphorised paper. P* 14½.

1336	**807**	17p.	pale blue, greenish yellow, bright rose, blue, black and grey-black	50	40
			a. Imperf (pair)	£950	
1337	**808**	22p.	pale turquoise-green, greenish yell, mag, new bl, blk & grey-blk	75	85
			a. Face value omitted*	£400	
			b. Queen's head omitted*	£400	
1338	**809**	29p.	pale drab, olive-yellow, magenta, blue, grey-black and black ..	1·00	1·00
1339	**810**	31p.	pale flesh, greenish yellow, magenta, ultram, blk & grey-blk	1·25	1·10
1340	**811**	34p.	buff, greenish yellow, magenta, blue, grey-black and black ..	1·50	1·25
1336/40			.. .. *Set of* 5	4·50	4·25

*Nos. 1337a/b come from three consecutive sheets on which the stamps in the first vertical row are without the face value and those in the second vertical row the Queen's head.

Nos. 1336/40 were issued to celebrate the 50th anniversary of the first R.A.F. Commands.

812 The Glastonbury Thorn

813 The Tanad Valley Plygain

814 The Hebrides Tribute

815 The Dewsbury Church Knell

816 The Hereford Boy Bishop

(Des Lynda Gray)

86 (18 Nov–2 Dec). *Christmas. Folk Customs. One phosphor band* (*12p., 13p.*) *or phosphorised paper* (*others*). *P* 15×14.

41 **812** 12p. gold, greenish yellow, vermilion, dp brown, emerald & dp bl (2.12) 50 50
a. Imperf (pair) £900
42 13p. deep blue, greenish yellow, verm, deep brown, emerald and gold .. 30 30
43 **813** 18p. myrtle-green, yellow, vermilion, dp blue, black, reddish brn & gold 45 45
44 **814** 22p. vermilion, olive-bistre, dull blue, deep brown, deep green and gold 65 65
45 **815** 31p. deep brown, yellow, vermilion, violet, dp dull green, black & gold 80 80
46 **816** 34p. violet, lemon, vermilion, deep dull blue, reddish brown and gold .. 90 90
41/6 .. .. *Set of* 6 3·25 3·25

No. 1341 represented a discount of 1p., available between 2 and 24 cember 1986, on the current second class postage rate.

Examples of the 13p. value from special folders, containing 36 mps and sold for £4.30, show a blue underprint of double-lined stars nted on the reverse over the gum.

817 North American Blanket Flower

818 Globe Thistle

819 *Echeveria*

820 Autumn Crocus

(Adapted J. Matthews)

87 (20 Jan). *Flower Photographs by Alfred Lammer. Phosphorised paper. P* 14½×14.

47 **817** 18p. silver, greenish yellow, rosine, deep green and black 50 50
48 **818** 22p. silver, greenish yellow, new blue, greenish blue and black 80 70
49 **819** 31p. silver, greenish yellow, scarlet, blue-green, deep green and black 1·25 1·10
a. Imperf (pair) £1600
50 **820** 34p. silver, greenish yellow, magenta, dull blue, deep green and black .. 1·40 1·25
47/50 .. .. *Set of* 4 3·50 3·25

OMNIBUS ISSUES

etails, together with prices for complete sets, f the various Omnibus issues from the 1935 ilver Jubilee series to date are included in a pecial section following Zimbabwe at the end of Volume 2.

821 *The Principia Mathematica*

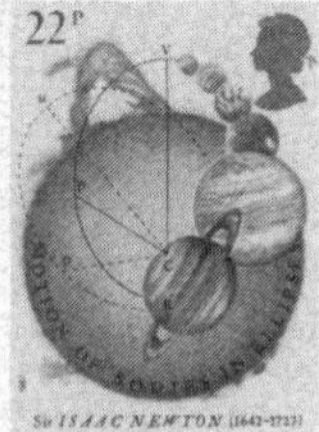

822 *Motion of Bodies in Ellipses*

823 *Optick Treatise*

824 *The System of the World*

(Des Sarah Godwin)

1987 (24 Mar). 300*th Anniv of* The Principia Mathematica *by Sir Isaac Newton. Phosphorised paper. P* 14×15.

1351 **821** 18p. black, greenish yellow, cerise, blue-green, grey-black and silver .. 50 50
1352 **822** 22p. black, greenish yellow, brt orange, blue, brt emer, silver & bluish vio 70 70
1353 **823** 31p. black, greenish yellow, scar, new bl, bronze-grn, silver & slate-grn 1·25 1·25
1354 **824** 34p. black, greenish yellow, red, bright blue, grey-black and silver .. 1·40 1·40
1351/4 .. .. *Set of* 4 3·50 3·50

825 Willis Faber & Dumas Building, Ipswich

826 Pompidou Centre, Paris

827 Staatsgalerie, Stuttgart

828 European Investment Bank, Luxembourg

(Des Brian Tattersfield)

1987 (12 May). *Europa. British Architects in Europe. Phosphorised paper. P* 15×14.

1355 **825** 18p. black, bistre-yellow, cerise, bright blue, deep grey and grey-black .. 50 50
1356 **826** 22p. black, greenish yellow, carmine, bright blue, dp grey & grey-black 70 70
1357 **827** 31p. grey-black, bistre-yellow, cerise, brt blue, brt green, black & dull vio 1·10 1·10
a. Imperf (horiz pair) £1000
1358 **828** 34p. black, greenish yellow, cerise, bright blue, grey-black & deep grey 1·25 1·25
1355/8 .. .. *Set of* 4 3·25 3·25

829 Brigade Members with Ashford Litter, 1887

830 Bandaging Blitz Victim, 1940

831 Volunteer with fainting Girl, 1965

832 Transport of Transplant Organ by Air Wing, 1987

(Des Debbie Cook. Litho Questa)

1987 (16 June). *Centenary of St. John Ambulance Brigade. Phosphorised paper. P* 14×14½.

1359 **829** 18p. new blue, greenish yellow, magenta, black, silver and pink .. 50 50
1360 **830** 22p. new blue, greenish yellow, magenta, black, silver and cobalt 65 65
1361 **831** 31p. new blue, greenish yellow, magenta, black, silver & bistre-brn 1·10 1·10
1362 **832** 34p. new blue, greenish yellow, mag, blk, silver & greenish grey 1·10 1·10
1359/62 .. .. *Set of* 4 3·00 3·00

833 Arms of the Lord Lyon King of Arms

834 Scottish Heraldic Banner of Prince Charles

835 Arms of Royal Scottish Academy of Painting, Sculpture and Architecture

836 Arms of Royal Society of Edinburgh

(Des J. Matthews)

1987 (21 July). 300*th Anniv of Revival of Order of the Thistle. Phosphorised paper. P* 14½.

1363 **833** 18p. black, lemon, scarlet, blue, deep green, slate and brown 50 50
1364 **834** 22p. black, greenish yellow, carmine, new blue, dp grn, grey & lake-brn 65 65
1365 **835** 31p. black, greenish yellow, scarlet, new blue, dull grn, grey & grey-blk 1·25 1·25
1366 **836** 34p. black, greenish yellow, scarlet, dp ultram, dull grn, grey & yell-brn 1·25 1·25
1363/6 .. .. *Set of* 4 3·25 3·25

837 Crystal Palace, "Monarch of the Glen" (Landseer) and Grace Darling

838 *Great Eastern, Beeton's Book of Household Management* and Prince Albert

839 Albert Memorial, Ballot Box and Disraeli

840 Diamond Jubilee Emblem, Newspaper Placard for Relief of Mafeking and Morse Key

(Des M. Dempsey. Eng C. Slania. Recess and photo)

1987 (8 Sept). *150th Anniv of Queen Victoria's Accession. Phosphorised paper. P* 15 × 14.

1367	**837**	18p.	pale stone, dp blue, lemon, rose, greenish bl, brn-ochre & grey-blk	50	50
1368	**838**	22p.	pale stone, deep brown, lemon, rose, grey-black and brown-ochre	75	75
1369	**839**	31p.	pale stone, dp lilac, lemon, cerise, brn-ochre, greenish bl & grey-blk	1·10	1·10
1370	**840**	34p.	pale stone, myrtle-green, yellow-ochre, reddish brown & brn-ochre	1·25	1·25
1367/70			.. .. *Set of* 4	3·25	3·25

841 Pot by Bernard Leach **842** Pot by Elizabeth Fritsch

843 Pot by Lucie Rie **844** Pot by Hans Coper

(Des T. Evans)

1987 (13 Oct). *Studio Pottery. Phosphorised paper. P* 14½ × 14.

1371	**841**	18p.	gold, lemon, light red-brown, chestnut, light grey and black ..	50	50
1372	**842**	26p.	blue over silver, yellow-orange, bright purple, lavender, bluish violet, grey-brown and black ..	70	70
1373	**843**	31p.	rose-lilac over silver, greenish yellow, cerise, new bl, grey-lilac & blk	1·10	1·10
1374	**844**	34p.	copper, yellow-brown, reddish brown, grey-lilac and black ..	1·25	1·25
1371/4			.. .. *Set of* 4	3·25	3·25

845 Decorating the Christmas Tree

846 Waiting for Father Christmas

847 Sleeping Child and Father Christmas in Sleigh

848 Child reading

849 Child playing Recorder and Snowman

(Des M. Foreman)

1987 (17 Nov). *Christmas. One phosphor band* (13*p.*) *or phosphorised paper* (*others*). *P* 15 × 14.

1375	**845**	13p.	gold, greenish yellow, rose, greenish blue and black	30	30
1376	**846**	18p.	gold, greenish yellow, bright purple, greenish blue, brt blue & blk	50	50
1377	**847**	26p.	gold, greenish yellow, bright purple, new blue, bright blue and black	75	75
1378	**848**	31p.	gold, greenish yellow, scarlet, brt mag, dull rose, greenish bl & blk	95	1·10
1379	**849**	34p.	gold, greenish yellow, dull rose, greenish blue, bright blue & black	1·10	1·25
1375/9			.. .. *Set of* 5	3·25	3·50

Examples of the 13p. value from special folders, containing 36 stamps and sold for £4.60, show a blue underprint of double-lined stars printed on the reverse over the gum.

850 Short-spined Seascorpion ("Bull-rout") (Jonathan Couch)

851 Yellow Waterlily (Major Joshua Swatkin)

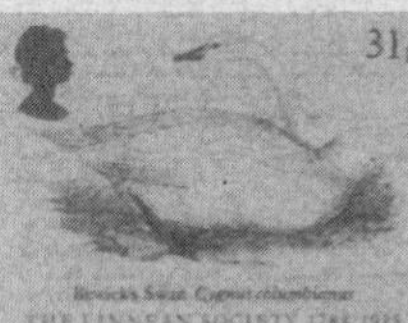

852 Whistling ("Bewick's") Swan (Edward Lear)

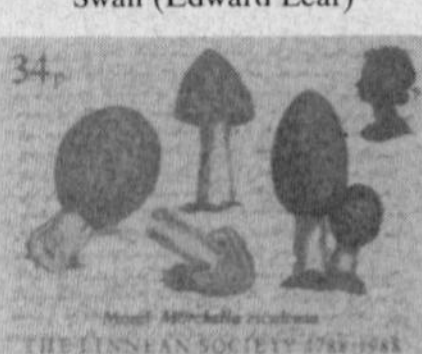

853 *Morchella esculenta* (James Sowerby)

(Des E. Hughes)

1988 (19 Jan). *Bicentenary of Linnean Society. Archive Illustrations. Phosphorised paper. P* 15 × 14.

1380	**850**	18p.	grey-black, stone, orange-yellow, bright purple, olive-bistre & gold	60	45
1381	**851**	26p.	black, stone, bistre-yellow, dull orange, greenish bl, gold & pale bis	80	70
1382	**852**	31p.	black, stone, greenish yellow, rose-red, dp blue, gold & olive-bis	1·25	1·10
		a.	Imperf (horiz pair)	£1300	
1383	**853**	34p.	black, stone, yellow, pale bistre, olive-grey, gold and olive-bistre. .	1·25	1·10
1380/3			.. .. *Set of* 4	3·50	3·00

854 Revd William Morgan (Bible translator, 1588) **855** William Salesbury (New Testament translator, 1567)

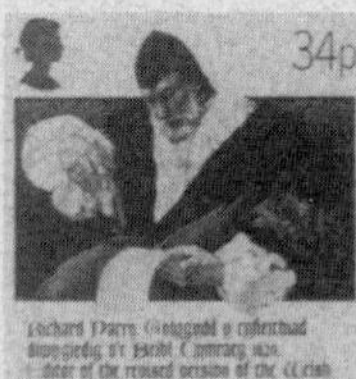

856 Bishop Richard Davies (New Testament translator, 1567) **857** Bishop Richard Parry (editor of Revised Welsh Bible, 1620)

(Des K. Bowen)

1988 (1 Mar). *400th Anniv of Welsh Bible. Phosphorised pape*
P 14½ × 14.

1384	**854**	18p.	grey-black, greenish yellow, cerise, blue, black and emerald ..	45	
		a.	Imperf (pair)	£1300	
1385	**855**	26p.	grey-black, yellow, bright rose-red, turquoise-blue, black & orge	70	
1386	**856**	31p.	black, chrome-yellow, carmine, new blue, grey-black and blue ..	1·10	1·
1387	**857**	34p.	grey-black, greenish yellow, cerise, turquoise-grn, blk & brt vio	1·10	1·
1384/7			.. .. *Set of* 4	3·00	3·

858 Gymnastics (Centenary of British Amateur Gymnastics Association) **859** Downhill Skiing (Ski Club of Great Britain)

860 Tennis (Centenary of Lawn Tennis Association) **861** Football (Centenary of Football League)

(Des J. Sutton)

1988 (22 Mar). *Sports Organizations. Phosphorised paper. P* 14

1388	**858**	18p.	violet-blue, greenish yellow, rosine, brt rose, new blue & silver	45	
1389	**859**	26p.	violet-blue, greenish yellow, vermilion, carmine, yell-orge & silver	70	
1390	**860**	31p.	violet-bl, greenish yell, rose, bl, pale greenish bl, silver & brt orge	1·10	1·
1391	**861**	34p.	violet-blue, greenish yellow, vermilion, bl, brt emer, silver & pink	1·10	1·
1388/91			.. .. *Set of* 4	3·00	3·0

862 *Mallard* and Mailbags on Pick-up Arms

863 Loading Transatlantic Mail on Liner *Queen Elizabeth*

864 Glasgow Tram No. 1173 and Pillar Box

865 Imperial Airways Handley Page H.P.45 *Horatius* and Airmail Van

(Des M. Dempsey)

988 (10 May). *Europa. Transport and Mail Services in* 1930s. *Phosphorised paper. P* 15×14.

392	**862**	18p. brown, yellow, rose-red, dull blue, dp brown, reddish vio & blk	50	50
393	**863**	26p. brown, yellow, orange-vermilion, dull blue, violet-bl, brt emer & blk	80	80
394	**864**	31p. brown, yellow-orange, carmine, dull purple, vio-bl, brt grn & blk	1·10	1·10
395	**865**	34p. brown, orange-yellow, carmine-rose, bluish vio, brt bl, sepia & blk	1·25	1·25
392/5		.. .. *Set of* 4	3·25	3·25

866 Early Settler and Sailing Clipper

867 Queen Elizabeth II with British and Australian Parliament Buildings

868 W. G. Grace (cricketer) and Tennis Racquet

869 Shakespeare, John Lennon (entertainer) and Sydney Landmarks

(Des G. Emery. Litho Questa)

988 (21 June). *Bicentenary of Australian Settlement. Phosphorised paper. P* 14½.

396	**866**	18p. deep ultramarine, orange-yellow, scarlet, black, bluish grey & emerald	60	60
		a. Horiz pair. Nos. 1396/7	1·25	1·25
397	**867**	18p. deep ultramarine, orange-yellow, black, bluish grey and emerald ..	60	60
398	**868**	34p. deep ultramarine, orange-yellow, scarlet, black, bluish grey & emerald	1·10	1·10
		a. Horiz pair. Nos. 1398/9	2·40	2·40
399	**869**	34p. deep ultramarine, orange-yellow, black, bluish grey and emerald ..	1·10	1·10
396/9		.. .. *Set of* 4	3·25	3·25

Nos. 1396/7 and 1398/9 were printed together, *se-tenant*, in orizontal pairs throughout the sheets, each pair showing a ackground design of the Australian flag.

Stamps in similar designs were also issued by Australia.

870 Spanish Galeasse off The Lizard

871 English Fleet leaving Plymouth

872 Engagement off Isle of Wight

873 Attack of English Fire-ships, Calais

874 Armada in Storm, North Sea

(Des G. Evernden)

1988 (19 July). *400th Anniv of Spanish Armada. Phosphorised paper. P* 15×14.

1400	**870**	18p. slate-black, yellow-orange, bright carm, brt bl, turq-bl, yell-grn & gold	65	65
		a. Horiz strip of 5. Nos. 1400/4 ..	3·00	3·00
1401	**871**	18p. slate-black, yellow-orange, bright carm, brt bl, turq-bl, yell-grn & gold	65	65
1402	**872**	18p. slate-black, yellow-orange, bright carm, brt bl, turq-bl, yell-grn & gold	65	65
1403	**873**	18p. slate-black, yellow-orange, bright carm, brt bl, turq-bl, yell-grn & gold	65	65
1404	**874**	18p. slate-black, yellow-orange, bright carm, brt bl, turq-bl, yell-grn & gold	65	65
1400/4		.. .. *Set of* 5	3·00	3·00

Nos. 1400/4 were printed together, *se-tenant*, in horizontal strips of 5 throughout the sheet, forming a composite design.

875 "The Owl and the Pussy-cat"

876 "Edward Lear as a Bird" (self-portrait)

877 "Cat" (from alphabet book)

878 "There was a Young Lady whose Bonnet .." (limerick)

(Des M. Swatridge and S. Dew)

1988 (6–27 Sept). *Death Centenary of Edward Lear (artist and author). Phosphorised paper. P* 15 × 14.

1405	**875**	19p black, pale cream and carmine ..	50	50
1406	**876**	27p black, pale cream and yellow ..	80	80
1407	**877**	32p black, pale cream and emerald ..	1·10	1·10
1408	**878**	35p black, pale cream and blue ..	1·25	1·25
1405/8		.. .. *Set of* 4	3·25	3·25
MS1409		122 × 90 mm. Nos. 1405/8 (*sold at* £1.35) (27 Sept)	8·00	7·00

The premium on No. **MS**1409 was used to support the "Stamp World London 90" International Stamp Exhibition.

879 Carrickfergus Castle

880 Caernarfon Castle

881 Edinburgh Castle

882 Windsor Castle

(Des from photos by Prince Andrew, Duke of York. Eng C. Matthews. Recess Harrison)

1988 (18 Oct). *Ordinary paper. P* 15 × 14.

1410	**879**	£1 deep green	3·00	50
1411	**880**	£1.50, maroon	4·50	1·25
1412	**881**	£2 indigo	6·50	1·75
1413	**882**	£5 deep brown	15·00	3·50
1410/13		.. .. *Set of* 4	26·00	6·25

For similar designs, but with silhouette Queen's head see Nos. 1611/14 and 1993/6.

883 Journey to Bethlehem

884 Shepherds and Star

885 Three Wise Men

886 Nativity

887 The Annunciation

(Des L. Trickett)

1988 (15 Nov). *Christmas. Christmas Cards. One phosphor band (14p.) or phosphorised paper (others). P* 15 × 14.
1414 **883** 14p. gold, orange-yellow, bright mauve, bluish violet, brt blue & grey-black 35 35
a. Error. "13p." instead of "14p." .. £5750
b. Imperf (pair) £750
1415 **884** 19p. gold, yell-orange, brt violet, ultram, rose-red, grey-black & bright blue .. 40 45
a. Imperf (pair) £600
1416 **885** 27p. gold, red, deep lavender, deep lilac, emerald, grey-black and bright blue 70 70
1417 **886** 32p. gold, orange-yellow, bright rose, dp mauve, violet, grey-black & brt blue 80 1·00
1418 **887** 35p. gold, green, reddish violet, bright blue, bright purple and grey-black .. 1·10 1·10
1414/18 .. .. *Set of* 5 3·25 3·25
Examples of No. 1414a were found in some 1988 Post Office Yearbooks.

888 Atlantic Puffin

889 Avocet

890 Oystercatcher

891 Northern Gannet

(Des D. Cordery)

1989 (17 Jan). *Centenary of Royal Society for the Protection of Birds. Phosphorised paper. P* 14 × 15.
1419 **888** 19p. grey, orange-yellow, orange-red, dull ultramarine, grey-black and silver .. 45 45
1420 **889** 27p. grey, bistre, rose, steel-blue, lavender, silver and grey-black .. 1·25 1·10
1421 **890** 32p. grey, bistre, scarlet, orange-red, lavender, silver and black .. 1·25 1·10
1422 **891** 35p. grey, lemon, rose-carmine, green, new blue, silver and black .. .. 1·50 1·25
1419/22 .. .. *Set of* 4 4·00 3·50

892 Rose

893 Cupid

894 Yachts

895 Fruit

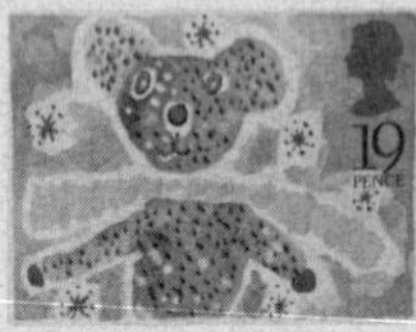

896 Teddy Bear

(Des P. Sutton)

1989 (31 Jan). *Greetings Stamps. Phosphorised paper. P* 15 × 14.
1423 **892** 19p. black, greenish yellow, bright rose, red, new blue, light green and gold .. 6·25 4·50
a. Booklet pane. Nos. 1423/7 × 2 plus 12 half stamp-size labels .. .. 55·00
1424 **893** 19p. black, greenish yellow, bright rose, red, new blue, light green and gold .. 6·25 4·50
1425 **894** 19p. black, greenish yellow, bright rose, red, new blue, light green and gold .. 6·25 4·50
1426 **895** 19p. black, greenish yellow, bright rose, red, new blue, light green and gold .. 6·25 4·50
1427 **896** 19p. black, greenish yellow, bright rose, red, new blue, light green and gold .. 6·25 4·50
1423/7 .. .. *Set of* 5 28·00 20·00
Nos. 1423/7 were only issued in £1.90 booklets.

897 Fruit and Vegetables

898 Meat Products

899 Dairy Produce

900 Cereal Products

(Des Sedley Place Ltd)

1989 (7 Mar). *Food and Farming Year. Phosphorised paper. P* 14 × 14½.
1428 **897** 19p. brownish grey, greenish yellow, rose, new blue, black, pale grey & emerald 50 50
1429 **898** 27p. brownish grey, greenish yellow, bright carmine, new blue, black, pale grey and bright orange 80 80
1430 **899** 32p. brownish grey, greenish yellow, rose-red, new blue, black, pale grey and bistre-yellow .. .. .. 1·10 1·10
1431 **900** 35p. brownish grey, greenish yellow, bright carmine, new blue, black, pale grey and brown-red .. .. 1·25 1·25
1428/31 .. .. *Set of* 4 3·25 3·25

901 Mortar Board (150th Anniv of Public Education in England)

902 Cross on Ballot Paper (3rd Direct Elections to European Parliament)

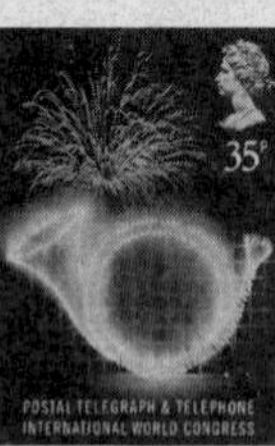

903 Posthorn (26th Postal, Telegraph and Telephone International Congress, Brighton)

904 Globe(Inter–Parliamentary Union Centenary Conference, London)

(Des Lewis Moberly from firework set-pieces. Litho Questa)

1989 (11 Apr). *Anniversaries. Phosphorised paper. P* 14 × 14½.
1432 **901** 19p. new blue, greenish yellow, mag & blk 1·25 1·25
a. Horiz pair. Nos. 1432/3 .. .. 2·50 2·50
1433 **902** 19p. new blue, greenish yellow, mag & blk 1·25 1·25
1434 **903** 35p. new blue, greenish yellow, mag & blk 1·75 1·75
a. Horiz pair. Nos. 1434/5 .. .. 3·50 3·50
1435 **904** 35p. new blue, greenish yellow, mag & blk 1·75 1·75
1432/5 .. .. *Set of* 4 5·50 5·50
Nos. 1432/3 and 1434/5 were each printed together, *se-tenant*, in horizontal pairs throughout the sheets.
Stamps as No. 1435, but inscribed "ONE HUNDREDTH CONFERENCE" were prepared, but not issued.

905 Toy Train and Airplane

906 Building Bricks

907 Dice and Board Games

908 Toy Robot, Boat and Doll's House

(Des D. Fern)

1989 (16 May). *Europa. Games and Toys. Phosphorised paper. P* 14 × 15.
1436 **905** 19p. black, greenish yellow, vermilion, blue-green, blue, gold and pale ochre 50 50
1437 **906** 27p. black, greenish yellow, reddish orange, blue-green, blue and gold .. 90 90
1438 **907** 32p. black, greenish yellow, orange-red, blue-green, blue, gold and pale ochre 1·25 1·25
1439 **908** 35p. black, greenish yellow, reddish orange, blue-green, bl, gold & stone 1·40 1·40
1436/9 .. .. *Set of* 4 3·50 3·50

909 Ironbridge, Shropshire

910 Tin Mine, St. Agnes Head, Cornwall

911 Cotton Mills, New Lanark, Strathclyde

912 Pontcysyllte Aqueduct, Clwyd

(Des R. Maddox)

1989 (4–25 July). *Industrial Archaeology. Phosphorised paper. P* 14×15.
1440 **909** 19p. black, bistre-yellow, rose-red, apple-green, lt blue, grey-black & emerald 50 50
1441 **910** 27p. black, bistre-yellow, rose-red, apple-green, lt blue, grey-black & dull blue 90 90
1442 **911** 32p. black, yellow-orange, apple-green, yellow, dull blue, grey-black and deep reddish violet .. .. 1·10 1·10
1443 **912** 35p. black, yellow, bright rose, apple-green, dull blue, grey-black & verm 1·10 1·10
1440/3 .. .. *Set of* 4 3·25 3·25
MS1444 122×90 mm. 19p., 27p., 32p., 35p. each black, olive-yellow, bright rose-red, dull blue, apple-green, grey-black and vermilion. P 15×14 (*sold at* £1.40) (25 July) .. .. .. 6·50 5·50
The stamps in No. **MS**1444 are horizontal versions of Nos. 1440/3 with each design continuing onto the sheet margins.
The premium on No. **MS**1444 was used to support "Stamp World London 90" International Stamp Exhibition.

913

914

›89 (22 Aug)–**93**. *Booklet Stamps.*

(*a*) *Photo Harrison. P* 15×14

45 **913** (2nd) bright blue (1 centre band) .. 1·50 50
a. Booklet pane. No. 1445×10 with horiz edges of pane imperf .. 8·00
b. Booklet pane. No. 1445×4 with three edges of pane imperf (28.11.89) .. .. 24·00
46 (2nd) bright blue (1 side band) (20.3.90) 2·50 2·50
47 **914** (1st) brownish black (phosphorised paper) .. .. 1·75 60
a. Booklet pane. No. 1447×10 with horiz edges of pane imperf .. 10·00
b. Booklet pane. No. 1447×4 with three edges of pane imperf (5.12.89) .. .. 24·00
48 (1st) brownish black (2 bands) (20.3.90) 2·50 2·50

(*b*) *Litho Walsall. P* 14

49 **913** (2nd) bright blue (1 centre band) .. 1·00 1·00
a. Imperf between (vert pair) ..
b. Booklet pane. No. 1449×4 with three edges of pane imperf .. 3·50
c. Booklet pane. No. 1449×4 with horiz edges of pane imperf (6.8.91) .. .. 3·00
d. Booklet pane. No. 1449×10 with horiz edges of pane imperf (6.8.91) .. .. 6·00
50 **914** (1st) blackish brown (2 bands) .. 2·50 2·00
a. Booklet pane. No. 1450×4 with three edges of pane imperf .. 9·00

(*c*) *Litho Questa. P* 15×14

51 **913** (2nd) brt blue (1 centre band) (19.9.89) 1·00 1·00
51*a* (2nd) brt blue (1 side band) (25.2.92) 2·50 2·50
al. Booklet pane. Nos. 1451*a* and 1514*a*, each × 3, with margins all round (10.8.93) .. .. 7·50
52 **914** (1st) brownish black (phosphorised paper) (19.9.89) .. .. 1·75 1·75

Nos. 1445, 1447, 1449/51 and 1452 were initially sold at 14p. ›nd) and 19p. (1st), but these prices were later increased to reflect ›w postage rates.

Nos. 1446 and 1448 come from the *se-tenant* pane in the 1990 ›ondon Life £5 booklet: This pane is listed as No. X906m.

No. 1449a occurred on a miscut example of pane No. 1449d ›hich showed an additional vertical pair beneath the last stamp in ›e bottom row.

No. 1451*a* with phosphor band at right comes from the *se-tenant* ›anes in the Wales and Tolkien £6 booklets. These panes are listed ›nder Nos. X1012l and W49a (Wales Regionals). The version with ›and at left which appears in No. 1451al comes from the £6 Beatrix ›otter booklet. No. 1446 only comes with band at right.

Nos. 1445, 1447 and 1449/50 do not exist perforated on all four ›des, but come with either one or two adjacent sides imperforate.

For illustrations showing the difference between photogravure ›nd lithography see beneath Type **367**.

For similar designs, but in changed colours, see Nos. 1511/16, for ›ose with elliptical perforations Nos. 1663*a*/6 and 1979 and for ›lf-adhesive versions Nos. 2039/40.

915 Snowflake (×10)

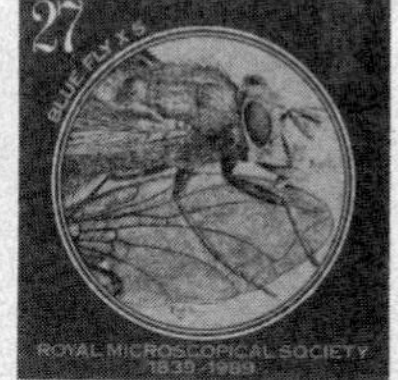

916 *Calliphora erythrocephala* (×5) (fly)

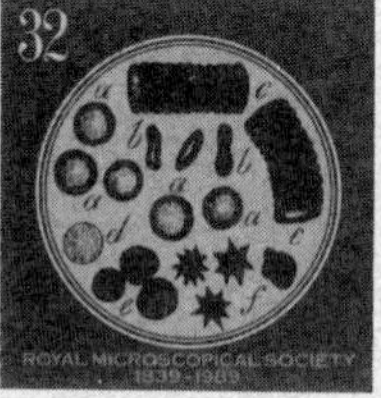

917 Blood Cells (×500)

918 Microchip (×600)

(Des K. Bassford. Litho Questa)

›**89** (5 Sept). *150th Anniv of Royal Microscopical Society. Phosphorised paper. P* 14½×14.

›53 **915** 19p. gold, lemon, pale blue, grey, black and grey-black 50 50
›54 **916** 27p. gold, lemon, drab, black & grey-blk 85 85
›55 **917** 32p. gold, lemon, orange-vermilion, flesh, black and grey-black .. .. .. 1·25 1·25
›56 **918** 35p. gold, lemon, blk, brt grn & grey-blk 1·40 1·40
›53/6 .. .. *Set of* 4 3·50 3·50

919 Royal Mail Coach

920 Escort of Blues and Royals

921 Lord Mayor's Coach

922 Coach Team passing St Paul's

923 Blues and Royals Drum Horse

(Des P. Cox)

1989 (17 Oct). *Lord Mayor's Show, London. Phosphorised paper. P* 14×15.

1457 **919** 20p. gold, lemon, rose, orge, pale bl & blk 80 80
a. Horiz strip of 5. Nos. 1457/61 .. 3·50 3·50
ab. Imperf (horiz strip of 5. Nos. 1457/61) £5000
ac. Imperf (horiz strip of 4. Nos. 1457/60) £2000
ad. Imperf (horiz strip of 3. Nos. 1457/9) £950
1458 **920** 20p. gold, lemon, rose, orge, pale bl & blk 80 80
1459 **921** 20p. gold, lemon, rose, orge, pale bl & blk 80 80
1460 **922** 20p. gold, lemon, rose, orge, pale bl & blk 80 80
1461 **923** 20p. gold, lemon, rose, orge, pale bl & blk 80 80
1457/61 .. .. *Set of* 5 3·50 3·50

This issue commemorates the 800th anniversary of the installation of the first Lord Mayor of London.

Nos. 1457/61 were printed together, *se-tenant*, in horizontal strips of 5 throughout the sheet.

Nos. 1457ab/ad come from a sheet partly imperforate at left.

924 14th-century Peasants from Stained-glass Window

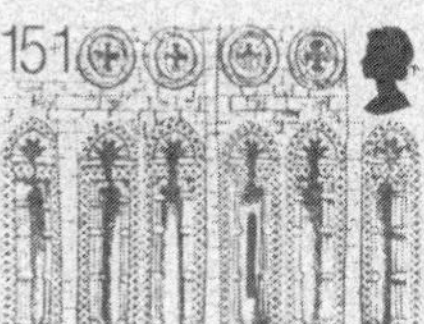

925 Arches and Roundels, West Front

926 Octagon Tower

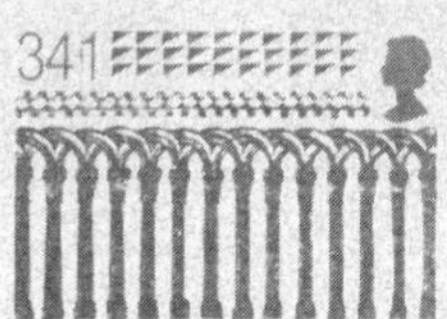

927 Arcade from West Transept

928 Triple Arch from West Front

(Des D. Gentleman)

1989 (14 Nov). *Christmas. 800th Anniversary of Ely Cathedral. One phosphor band (15p., 15p.+1p.) or phosphorised paper (others). P* 15×14.

1462 **924** 15p. gold, silver and blue 35 35
1463 **925** 15p. + 1p. gold, silver and blue .. 50 40
a. Imperf (pair) £1300
1464 **926** 20p. + 1p. gold, silver and rosine .. 60 50
a. Imperf (pair) £1300
1465 **927** 34p. + 1p. gold, silver and emerald .. 1·25 1·40
1466 **928** 37p. + 1p. gold, silver and yellow-olive 1·25 1·40
1462/6 .. .. *Set of* 5 3·50 3·50

929 Queen Victoria and Queen Elizabeth II

(Des J. Matthews (from plaster casts by Wyon and Machin))

1990 (10 Jan–12 June). *150th Anniv of the Penny Black.*

(*a*) *Photo Harrison. P* 15×14

1467 **929** 15p. bright blue (1 centre band) .. 50 50
a. Imperf (pair) £1250
l. Booklet pane. No. 1467×10 with horiz edges of pane imperf (30.1.90) 7·50
1468 15p. bright blue (1 side band) (30.1.90) 2·75 2·75
l. Booklet pane. No. 1468×2 and 1470 plus label .. .. .. 5·00
1469 20p. brownish black and cream (phosphorised paper) 75 75
a. Imperf (pair) £900
l. Booklet pane. No. 1469×5 plus label with vert sides of pane imperf (30.1.90) .. .. 7·00
m. Booklet pane. No. 1469×10 with horiz edges of pane imperf (30.1.90) 9·00
n. Booklet pane. No. 1469×6 with margins all round (20.3.90) .. 2·50
r. Booklet pane. No. 1469×4 with three edges of pane imperf (17.4.90) 6·00
1470 20p. brownish black and cream (2 bands) (30.1.90) .. .. 2·50 2·50
1471 29p. deep mauve (phosphorised paper) 1·25 1·25
1472 29p. deep mauve (2 bands) (20.3.90) .. 8·00 8·00
1473 34p. dp bluish grey (phosphorised paper) 1·50 1·25
1474 37p. rosine (phosphorised paper) .. 1·50 1·50

(*b*) *Litho Walsall. P* 14

1475 **929** 15p. bright blue (1 centre band) (30.1.90) 1·10 85
l. Booklet pane. No. 1475×4 with three edges of pane imperf .. 7·50
m. Booklet pane. No. 1475×10 with three edges of pane imperf (12.6.90) 8·00
1476 20p. brownish black and cream (phosphorised paper) (30.1.90) .. 1·25 90
l. Booklet pane. No. 1476×5 plus label with vertical edges of pane imperf .. .. 7·00
m. Booklet pane. No. 1476×4 with three edges of pane imperf .. 7·50
n. Booklet pane. No. 1476×10 with three edges of pane imperf (12.6.90) 10·00

(*c*) *Litho Questa. P* 15×14

1477 **929** 15p. bright blue (1 centre band) (17.4.90) 2·00 2·00
1478 20p. brownish black (phosphorised paper) (17.4.90) .. .. 2·00 2·00

Nos. 1475/6 do not exist perforated on all four sides, but come with either one or two adjacent sides imperforate.

Nos. 1468, 1470, 1472 and 1475/8 were only issued in stamp booklets. No. 1468 exists with the phosphor band at left or right. Nos. 1468 (band at right), 1470 and 1472 occur in the *se-tenant* pane from the 1990 London Life £5 booklet. This pane is listed as No. X906m.

For illustrations showing the difference between photogravure and lithography see beneath Type **367**.

For No. 1469 in miniature sheet see No. **MS**1501.

930 Kitten

931 Rabbit

932 Duckling

933 Puppy

(Des T. Evans. Litho Questa)

1990 (23 Jan). *150th Anniv of Royal Society for Prevention of Cruelty to Animals. Phosphorised paper. P* 14×14½.
1479 **930** 20p. new blue, greenish yellow, bright magenta, black and silver .. 65 70
a. Silver (Queen's head and face value) omitted £175
1480 **931** 29p. new blue, greenish yellow, bright magenta, black and silver .. 1·25 1·10
a. Imperf (horiz pair) £2500
1481 **932** 34p. new blue, greenish yellow, bright magenta, black and silver .. 1·50 1·25
a. Silver (Queen's head and face value) omitted £350
1482 **933** 37p. new blue, greenish yellow, bright magenta, black and silver .. 1·60 1·40
1479/82 .. .. *Set of* 4 4·50 4·00

934 Teddy Bear

935 Dennis the Menace

936 Punch

937 Cheshire Cat

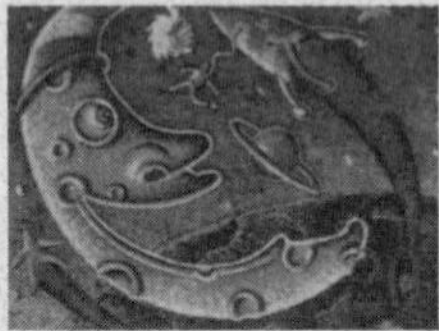

938 The Man in the Moon

939 The Laughing Policeman

940 Clown

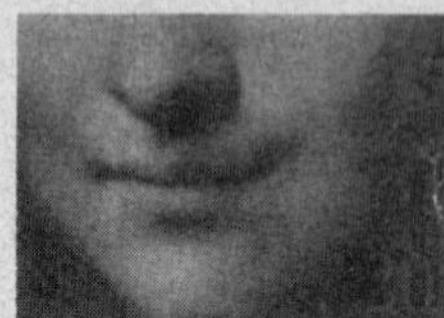

941 Mona Lisa

942 Queen of Hearts

943 Stan Laurel (comedian)

(Des Michael Peters and Partners Ltd)

1990 (6 Feb). *Greetings Stamps. "Smiles". Two phosphor bands. P* 15×14.
1483 **934** 20p. gold, greenish yellow, bright rose-red, new blue and grey-black .. 3·25 2·50
a. Booklet pane. Nos. 1483/92 with margins all round .. .. 28·00
1484 **935** 20p. gold, greenish yellow, brt rose-red, new blue, deep blue and grey-black 3·25 2·50
1485 **936** 20p. gold, greenish yellow, brt rose-red, new blue, deep blue and grey-black 3·25 2·50
1486 **937** 20p. gold, greenish yellow, brt rose-red, new blue and grey-black .. 3·25 2·50
1487 **938** 20p. gold, greenish yellow, brt rose-red, new blue and grey-black .. .. 3·25 2·50
1488 **939** 20p. gold, greenish yellow, brt rose-red, new blue and grey-black .. 3·25 2·50
1489 **940** 20p. gold, greenish yellow, brt rose-red, new blue and grey-black .. 3·25 2·50
1490 **941** 20p. gold, greenish yellow, bright rose-red, and grey-black .. .. 3·25 2·50
1491 **942** 20p. gold, greenish yellow, bright rose-red, new blue and grey-black .. 3·25 2·50
1492 **943** 20p. gold and grey-black .. .. 3·25 2·50
1483/92 .. .. *Set of* 10 28·00 22·00

Nos. 1483/92 were only issued in £2 booklets. The designs of Nos. 1483, 1485/7, 1489 and 1492 extend onto the pane margin.

For these designs with the face value expressed as "1st" see Nos. 1550/9.

944 Alexandra Palace ("Stamp World London 90" Exhibition)

945 Glasgow School of Art

946 British Philatelic Bureau, Edinburgh

947 Templeton Carpet Factory, Glasgow

(Des P. Hogarth)

1990 (6–20 Mar). *Europa (Nos.* 1493 *and* 1495) *and "Glasgow* 1990 *European City of Culture" (Nos.* 1494 *and* 1496). *Phosphorised paper. P* 14×15.
1493 **944** 20p. silver, lemon, flesh, grey-brown, blue, grey-black and black .. 50 50
a. Booklet pane. No. 1493×4 with margins all round (20 March) 2·00
1494 **945** 20p. silver, greenish yellow, dull orange, blue, grey-black and black .. 50 50
1495 **946** 29p. silver, stone, orange, olive-sepia, grey-blue, grey-black and black .. 1·10 1·10
1496 **947** 37p. silver, greenish yellow, brt emerald, salmon, olive-sepia, brt blue & black 1·25 1·25
1493/6 .. .. *Set of* 4 3·00 3·00

948 Export Achievement Award

949 Technological Achievement Award

(Des S. Broom. Litho Questa)

1990 (10 Apr). *25th Anniv of Queen's Awards for Export an Technology. Phosphorised paper. P* 14×14½.
1497 **948** 20p. new blue, greenish yellow, magenta, black and silver 75 7
a. Horiz pair. Nos. 1497/8 .. .. 1·50 1·5
1498 **949** 20p. new blue, greenish yellow, magenta, black and silver 75 7
1499 **948** 37p. new blue, greenish yellow, magenta, black and silver .. .. .. 1·40 1·4
a. Horiz pair. Nos. 1499/500 .. 2·75 2·7
1500 **949** 37p. new blue, greenish yellow, magenta, black and silver .. .. .. 1·40 1·4
1497/500 .. .. *Set of* 4 3·75 3·7

Nos. 1497/8 and 1499/500 were each printed together, *se-tenan* in horizontal pairs throughout the sheets.

(Des J. Matthews and Sedley Place Design Ltd. Eng C. Matthews Recess and photo)

1990 (3 May). *"Stamp World London* 90" *International Stam Exhibition, London. Sheet,* 122×90 *mm., containing No.* 146 *Phosphorised paper. P* 15×14.
MS1501 **929** 20p. brownish blk & cream (*sold at* £1) 4·25 4·2
a. Error. Imperf £6500
b. Black (recess printing) omitted £7500
c. Black (recess printing) inverted £7500

The premium on No. **MS**1501 was used to support the "Stam World London 90" International Stamp Exhibition.

On examples of No. **MS**1501b the 1d. black and seahors background are omitted due to a printer's sheet becoming attache to the underside before the recess part of the design was printed There is an albino impression visible on the reverse.

No. **MS**1501c shows the recess part of the design inverted i relation to the photogravure printing of Type **929**.

950 Cycad and Sir Joseph Banks Building

951 Stone Pine and Princess of Wales Conservatory

952 Willow Tree and Palm House

953 Cedar Tree and Pagoda

(Des P. Leith)

1990 (5 June). *150th Anniv of Kew Gardens. Phosphorised pape P* 14×15.
1502 **950** 20p. black, brt emerald, pale turquoise-green, light brown and lavender .. 50 5
1503 **951** 29p. black, brt emerald, turquoise-green, reddish orange and grey-black .. 80 8
1504 **952** 34p. Venetian red, brt green, cobalt, dull purple, turquoise-grn & yellow-green 1·25 1·2
1505 **953** 37p. pale violet-blue, bright emerald, red-brown, steel-blue and brown-rose .. 1·40 1·4
1502/5 .. .. *Set of* 4 3·50 3·5

954 Thomas Hardy and Clyffe Clump, Dorset

(Des J. Gibbs)

90 (10 July). *150th Birth Anniv of Thomas Hardy (author). Phosphorised paper. P* 14×15.
06 **954** 20p. vermilion, greenish yellow, pale lake-brown, deep brown, light red-brown and black 75 75
a. Imperf (pair) £950

955 Queen Elizabeth the Queen Mother

956 Queen Elizabeth

957 Elizabeth, Duchess of York

958 Lady Elizabeth Bowes-Lyon

)es J. Gorham from photographs by N. Parkinson (20p.), Dorothy Wilding (29p.), B. Park (34p.), Rita Martin (37p.))

90 (2 Aug). *90th Birthday of Queen Elizabeth the Queen Mother. Phosphorised paper. P* 14×15.

07	**955**	20p.	silver, greenish yellow, magenta, turquoise-blue and grey-black ..	70	70
08	**956**	29p.	silver, indigo and grey-blue ..	1·10	1·10
09	**957**	34p.	silver, lemon, red, new blue and grey-black	1·75	1·75
10	**958**	37p.	silver, sepia and stone	2·00	2·00
07/10			.. .. *Set of* 4	5·00	5·00

90 (7 Aug)–**92**. *Booklet Stamps. As T* **913/14**, *but colours changed.*

(*a*) *Photo Harrison. P* 15×14

11	**913**	(2nd)	deep blue (1 centre band) ..	1·00	1·00
			a. Booklet pane. No. 1511×10 with horiz edges of pane imperf ..	7·00	
12	**914**	(1st)	brt orge-red (phosphorised paper)	1·00	1·00
			a. Booklet pane. No. 1512×10 with horiz edges of pane imperf ..	5·25	

(*b*) *Litho Questa. P* 15×14

13	**913**	(2nd)	deep blue (1 centre band) ..	1·75	1·75
14	**914**	(1st)	brt orge-red (phosphorised paper)	1·00	1·00
14*a*		(1st)	brt orange-red (2 bands) (25.2.92)	2·00	2·00

(*c*) *Litho Walsall. P* 14

15	**913**	(2nd)	deep blue (1 centre band) ..	80	80
			a. Booklet pane. No. 1515×4 with horiz edges of pane imperf ..	3·00	
			b. Booklet pane. No. 1515×10 with horiz edges of pane imperf ..	6·00	
16	**914**	(1st)	brt orge-red (phosphorised paper)	1·00	1·00
			a. Booklet pane. No. 1516×4 with horiz edges of pane imperf ..	2·50	
			b. Booklet pane. No. 1516×10 with horiz edges of pane imperf ..	5·25	
			c. Perf 13	2·25	2·25
			ca. Booklet pane. No. 1516c×4 with horiz edges of pane imperf ..	10·00	

Nos. 1511/14 and 1515/16 were initially sold at 15p. (2nd) and 0p. (1st), but these prices were later increased to reflect new ostage rates.

Nos. 1511/12 and 1515/16 do not exist perforated on all four ides, but come with either the top or the bottom edge imperforate.

No. 1514*a* comes from the *se-tenant* panes in the £6 Wales, £6 olkien and £5.64 Beatrix Potter booklets. These panes are listed nder Nos. X1012l, 1451al and W49a (Wales Regionals).

No. 1516c was caused by the use of an incorrect perforation omb.

For similar stamps with elliptical perforations see Nos. 1663*a*/6.

For illustrations showing the difference between photogravure nd lithography see beneath Type **367**.

959 Victoria Cross

960 George Cross

961 Distinguished Service Cross and Distinguished Service Medal

962 Military Cross and Military Medal

963 Distinguished Flying Cross and Distinguished Flying Medal

(Des J. Gibbs and J. Harwood)

1990 (11 Sept). *Gallantry Awards. Phosphorised paper. P* 14×15 (*vert*) *or* 15×14 (*horiz*).

1517	**959**	20p.	grey-black, pale stone, stone, bistre-brown and bright carmine ..	80	80
1518	**960**	20p.	grey-black, pale stone, flesh, grey and ultramarine	80	80
1519	**961**	20p.	grey-black, pale stone, flesh, pale blue and ultramarine	80	80
			a. Imperf (pair)		
1520	**962**	20p.	grey-black, pale stone, ochre, pale blue, ultramarine, scarlet and violet	80	80
1521	**963**	20p.	grey-black, pale stone, yellow-brown, bluish grey and purple ..	80	80
1517/21			.. .. *Set of* 5	3·50	3·50

964 Armagh Observatory, Jodrell Bank Radio Telescope and La Palma Telescope

965 Newton's Moon and Tides Diagram with Early Telescopes

966 Greenwich Old Observatory and Early Astronomical Equipment

967 Stonehenge, Gyroscope and Navigating by Stars

(Des J. Fisher. Litho Questa)

1990 (16 Oct). *Astronomy. Phosphorised paper. P* 14×14½.

1522	**964**	22p.	cream, grey, dull blue-grn, slate-bl, blue-grn, orange-red, gold & black	50	40
			a. Gold (Queen's head) omitted ..	£350	
1523	**965**	26p.	black, yellow, dull purple, pale cream, brown-rose, new blue, greenish yellow, vermilion & gold	80	90
1524	**966**	31p.	black, cream, pale cream, yellow-orge, salmon, lemon, verm & gold	1·00	1·00
1525	**967**	37p.	black, pale buff, olive-bistre, pale cream, pale flesh, flesh, grey, rose-red and gold	1·10	1·10
1522/5			.. .. *Set of* 4	3·00	3·00

Nos. 1522/5 commemorate the Centenary of the British Astronomical Association and the Bicentenary of the Armagh Observatory.

968 Building a Snowman

969 Fetching the Christmas Tree

970 Carol Singing

971 Tobogganing

972 Ice-skating

(Des J. Gorham and A. Davidson)

1990 (13 Nov). *Christmas. One phosphor band* (17p) *or phosphorised paper* (*others*). *P* 15×14.

1526	**968**	17p.	gold, greenish yellow, rose, new blue and grey-black	45	35
			a. Booklet pane of 20 ..	9·00	
1527	**969**	22p.	gold, greenish yellow, magenta, new blue and black	55	65
			a. Imperf (horiz pair)	£450	
1528	**970**	26p.	gold, olive-yellow, pale magenta, agate, new blue, dull violet-bl & blk	80	80
1529	**971**	31p.	gold, greenish yellow, bright rose-red, dull mauve, new blue, turquoise-blue and grey-black ..	1·00	1·00
1530	**972**	37p.	gold, greenish yellow, rose, new blue and slate-green	1·10	1·10
1526/30			.. .. *Set of* 5	3·50	3·50

Booklet pane No. 1526a comes from a special £3.40 Christmas booklet and has the horizontal edges of the pane imperforate.

973 "King Charles Spaniel"

974 "A Pointer"

975 "Two Hounds in a Landscape"

976 "A Rough Dog"

977 "Fino and Tiny"

(Des Carroll, Dempsey & Thirkell Ltd)

1991 (8 Jan). *Dogs. Paintings by George Stubbs. Phosphorised paper. P* 14×14½.

1531 **973** 22p. gold, greenish yellow, magenta, new blue black and drab 75 75
a. Imperf (pair) £400
1532 **974** 26p. gold, greenish yellow, magenta, new blue, black and drab 90 90
1533 **975** 31p. gold, greenish yellow, magenta, new blue, black and drab . . . . 1·00 1·00
a. Imperf (pair) £950
1534 **976** 33p. gold, greenish yellow, magenta, new blue, black and drab . . . . 1·10 1·10
1535 **977** 37p. gold, greenish yellow, magenta, new blue, black and drab . . . . 1·25 1·25
1531/5 . . . . *Set of* 5 4·50 4·75

978 Thrush's Nest

979 Shooting Star and Rainbow

980 Magpies and Charm Bracelet

981 Black Cat

982 Common Kingfisher with Key

983 Mallard and Frog

984 Four-leaf Clover in Boot and Match Box

985 Pot of Gold at End of Rainbow

986 Heart-shaped Butterflies

987 Wishing Well and Sixpence

(Des T. Meeuwissen)

1991 (5 Feb). *Greetings Stamps. "Good Luck". Two phosphor bands. P* 15×14.

1536 **978** (1st) silver, greenish yellow, magenta new blue, olive-brown and black . . 1·60 1·60
a. Booklet pane. Nos. 1536/45 plus 12 half stamp-size labels with margins on 3 sides . . . . . . 14·00
1537 **979** (1st) silver, greenish yellow, magenta new blue, olive-brown and black . . 1·60 1·60
1538 **980** (1st) silver, greenish yellow, magenta new blue, olive-brown and black . . 1·60 1·60
1539 **981** (1st) silver, greenish yellow, magenta new blue, olive-brown and black . . 1·60 1·60
1540 **982** (1st) silver, greenish yellow, magenta new blue, olive-brown and black . . 1·60 1·60
1541 **983** (1st) silver, greenish yellow, magenta new blue, olive-brown and black . . 1·60 1·60
1542 **984** (1st) silver, greenish yellow, magenta new blue, olive-brown and black . . 1·60 1·60
1543 **985** (1st) silver, greenish yellow, magenta new blue, olive-brown and black . . 1·60 1·60
1544 **986** (1st) silver, greenish yellow, magenta new blue, olive-brown and black . . 1·60 1·60
1545 **987** (1st) silver, greenish yellow, magenta new blue, olive-brown and black . . 1·60 1·60
1536/45 . . . . *Set of* 10 14·00 14·00

Nos. 1536/45 were initially sold at 22p. each and were only issued in £2.20 booklets. It is intended that the price will be increased to reflect future alterations in postage rates. The backgrounds of the stamps form a composite design.

988 Michael Faraday (inventor of electric motor) (Birth Bicentenary)

989 Charles Babbage (computer science pioneer) (Birth Bicentenary)

990 Radar Sweep of East Anglia (50th anniv of operational radar network)

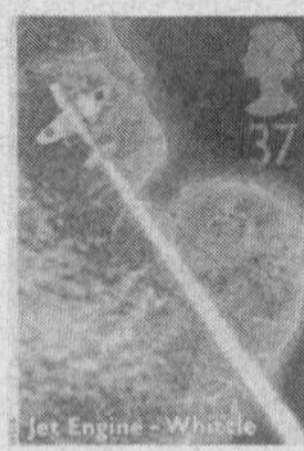

991 Gloster Whittle E28/39 Aircraft over East Anglia (50th anniv of first flight of Sir Frank Whittle's jet engine)

(Des P. Till (Nos. 1546/7), J. Harwood (Nos. 1548/9))

1991 (5 Mar). *Scientific Achievements. Phosphorised paper. P* 14×15.

1546 **988** 22p. silver, olive-brown greenish yellow, magenta, slate-blue, grey and black 65 65
a. Imperf (pair) £325
1547 **989** 22p. silver, chrome yellow, red, grey-black, brownish grey and sepia . . 65 6
1548 **990** 31p. silver, deep turquoise-green, violet-blue, steel blue and deep dull blue 95 9
1549 **991** 37p. silver, olive-bistre, rose-red, turq-blue, new blue and grey-black . . 1·10 1·1
1546/9 . . . . *Set of* 4 3·00 3·0

992 Teddy Bear

1991 (26 Mar). *Greetings Stamps. "Smiles". As Nos.* 1483/92, *b inscr* "1st" *as in T* **992**. *Two phosphor bands. P* 15×14.

1550 **992** (1st) gold, greenish yellow, bright rose-red, new blue and grey-black . . 1·00 1·0
a. Booklet pane. Nos. 1550/9 plus 12 half stamp-size labels with margins on 3 sides . . . . . . 9·00
1551 **935** (1st) gold, greenish yellow, brt rose-red, new blue, deep blue & grey-black 1·00 1·(
1552 **936** (1st) gold, greenish yellow, brt rose-red, new blue, deep blue & grey-black 1·00 1·(
1553 **937** (1st) gold, greenish yellow, bright rose-red, new blue and grey-black . . 1·00 1·(
1554 **938** (1st) gold, greenish yellow, bright rose-red, new blue and grey-black . . 1·00 1·(
1555 **939** (1st) gold, greenish yellow, bright rose-red, new blue and grey-black . . 1·00 1·(
1556 **940** (1st) gold, greenish yellow, bright rose-red, new blue and grey-black . . 1·00 1·0
1557 **941** (1st) gold, greenish yellow, bright rose-red and grey-black . . . . 1·00 1·(
1558 **942** (1st) gold, greenish yellow, bright rose-red, new blue and grey-black . . 1·00 1·(
1559 **943** (1st) gold and grey-black . . . . 1·00 1·(
1550/9 . . . . *Set of* 10 9·00 9·(

Nos. 1550/9 were only issued in £2.20 booklets (sold at £2.4 from 16 September 1991 and at £2.50 from 1 November 1993). Th designs of Nos. 1550, 1552/4, 1556 and 1559 extend onto the par margin.

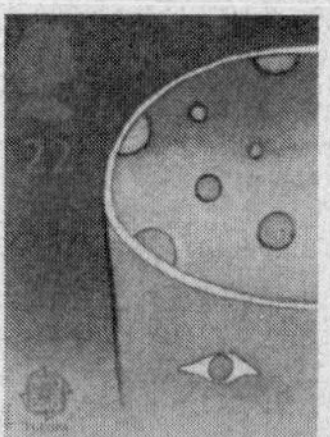

993 Man looking at Space **994**

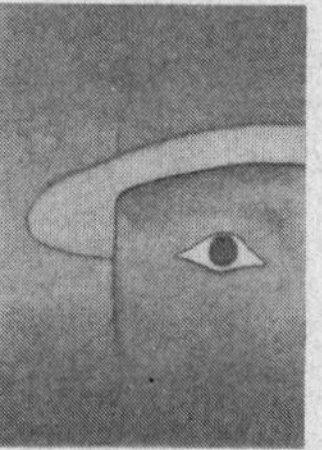

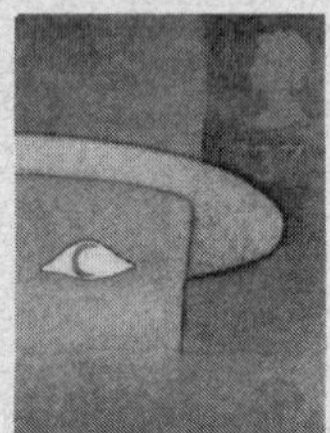

995 Space looking at Man **996**

(Des J.-M. Folon)

1991 (23 Apr). *Europa. Europe in Space. Phosphorised pape P* 14×15.

1560 **993** 22p. silver-mauve, greenish yellow, scar, violet-blue, brt blue, brt green & blk 55 5
a. Horiz pair. Nos. 1560/1 . . . . 1·10 1·1
1561 **994** 22p. silver-mauve, greenish yellow, scar, violet-blue, bright blue and black 55 5
1562 **995** 37p. silver-mauve, bistre-yellow, dull vermilion, blue and black . . 1·10 1·1
a. Horiz pair. Nos. 1562/3 . . . . 2·25 2·2
1563 **996** 37p. silver-mauve, bistre-yellow, dull vermilion, blue and black . . 1·10 1·1
1560/3 . . . . *Set of* 4 3·00 3·0

Nos. 1560/1 and 1562/3 were each printed together, *se-tenant*, i horizontal pairs throughout the sheets, each pair forming composite design.

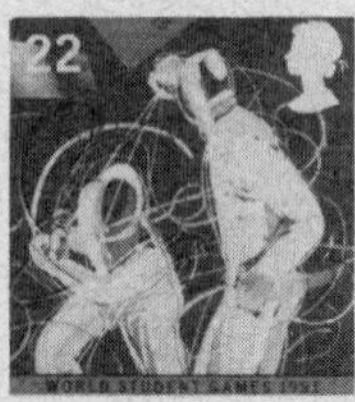

997 Fencing

998 Hurdling

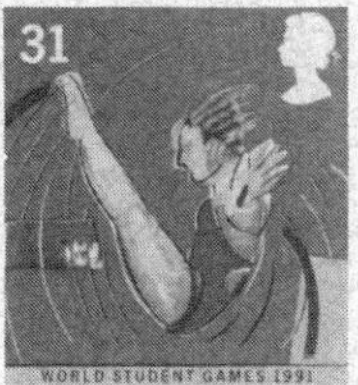

999 Diving

1000 Rugby

(Des Huntley Muir)

1 (11 June). *World Student Games, Sheffield* (*Nos.* 1564/6) *and Vorld Cup Rugby Championship* (*No.* 1567). *Phosphorised aper. P* 14½×14.

4 **997** 22p. black, greenish yellow, vermilion, bright orange, ultramarine and grey 50 50
5 **998** 26p. pale blue, greenish yellow, red, bright blue and black 80 80
6 **999** 31p. bright blue, bistre-yellow, rose, vermilion, new blue and black .. 95 95
7 **1000** 37p. yellow-orange, greenish yellow, rose, bright blue, emerald & black 1·10 1·10
4/7 .. .. *Set of* 4 3·00 3·00

1001 "Silver Jubilee"

1002 "Mme Alfred Carrière"

1003 *Rosa moyesii*

1004 "Harvest Fayre"

1005 "Mutabilis"

(Des Yvonne Skargon. Litho Questa)

91 (16 July). *9th World Congress of Roses, Belfast. Phosphorised paper. P* 14½×14.

58 **1001** 22p. new blue, greenish yellow, magenta, black and silver .. 80 80
a. Silver (Queen's head) omitted .. £750
69 **1002** 26p. new blue, greenish yellow, magenta, black and silver .. 1·00 1·00
70 **1003** 31p. new blue, greenish yellow, magenta, black and silver .. 1·10 1·10
71 **1004** 33p. new blue, greenish yellow, magenta, black and silver .. 1·25 1·25
72 **1005** 37p. new blue, greenish yellow, magenta, black and silver .. 1·40 1·40
58/72 .. .. *Set of* 5 5·00 5·00

1006 Iguanodon

1007 Stegosaurus

1008 Tyrannosaurus

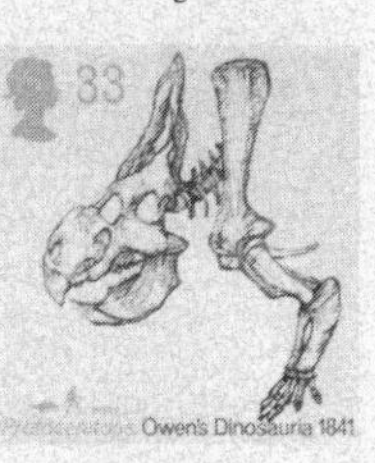

1009 Protoceratops

1010 Triceratops

(Des B. Kneale)

1991 (20 Aug). *150th Anniv of Dinosaurs' Identification by Owen. Phosphorised paper. P* 14½×14.

1573 **1006** 22p. grey, pale blue, magenta, bright blue, dull violet and grey-black .. 75 60
a. Imperf (pair) £1000
1574 **1007** 26p. grey, greenish yellow, pale emerald, bright blue-green, pale bright blue, grey-black and black 90 1·10
1575 **1008** 31p. grey, light blue, magenta, brt blue, pale blue, brown and grey-black .. 1·10 1·10
1576 **1009** 33p. grey, dull rose, pale brt bl, brt rose-red, yellow-orge, grey-blk & blk 1·40 1·25
1577 **1010** 37p. grey, greenish yellow, turquoise-blue, dull violet, yellow-brn & blk 1·50 1·50
1573/7 .. .. *Set of* 5 5·00 5·00

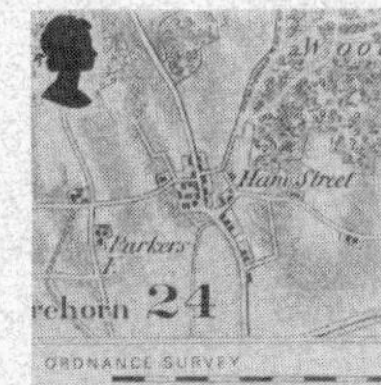

1011 Map of 1816

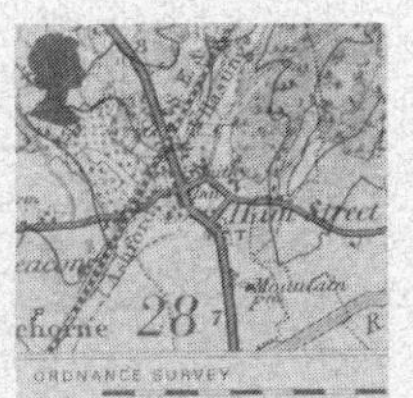

1012 Map of 1906

1013 Map of 1959

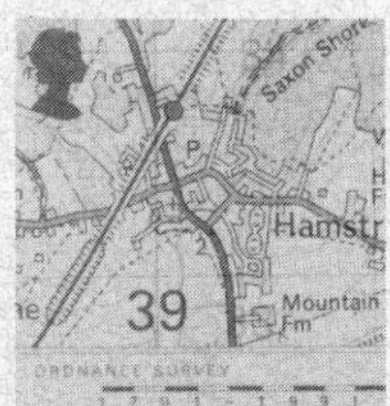

1014 Map of 1991

(Des H. Brown. Recess and litho Harrison (24p.), Litho Harrison (28p.), Questa (33p., 39p.))

1991 (17 Sept). *Bicentenary of Ordnance Survey. Maps of Hamstreet, Kent. Phosphorised paper. P* 14½×14.

1578 **1011** 24p. black, magenta, and cream .. 50 50
1579 **1012** 28p. blk, brt yellow-grn, new bl, reddish orge, magenta, olive-sepia & cream 85 85
1580 **1013** 33p. dull blue-green, orange-brown, magenta, olive-grey, greenish yellow, verm, greenish grey, pale bl, bl, dull orge, apple grn & blk 1·00 1·00
1581 **1014** 39p. black, mag, greenish yell & new bl 1·25 1·25
1578/81 .. .. *Set of* 4 3·25 3·25

Mint examples of Type **1012** exist with a face value of 26p.

1015 Adoration of the Magi

1016 Mary and Baby Jesus in the Stable

1017 The Holy Family and Angel

1018 The Annunciation

1019 The Flight into Egypt

(Des D. Driver)

1991 (12 Nov). *Christmas. Illuminated Letters from "Acts of Mary and Jesus" Manuscript in Bodleian Library. Oxford. One phosphor band* (18*p.*) *or phosphorised paper* (*others*). *P* 15×14.

1582 **1015** 18p. steel-blue, greenish yellow, rose-red, orange-red, black & gold .. 70 40
a. Imperf (pair) £1750
b. Booklet pane of 20 .. .. 8·25
1583 **1016** 24p. bright rose-red, greenish yellow, vermilion, slate-blue, yellow-green, grey-black and gold 80 50
1584 **1017** 28p. reddish brn, bistre-yellow, orange-vermilion, orange-red, deep dull blue, grey-black and gold .. 85 1·00
1585 **1018** 33p. green, greenish yell, red, orange-red, blue, grey and gold .. 95 1·10
1586 **1019** 39p. orange-red, greenish yell, orange-vermilion, deep dull blue, olive-sepia, black and gold .. 1·10 1·40
1582/6 .. .. *Set of* 5 4·00 4·00

Booklet pane No. 1582b comes from special £3.60 Christmas booklet and has margins at left, top and bottom.

1020 Fallow Deer in Scottish Forest

1021 Hare on North Yorkshire Moors

1022 Fox in the Fens

1023 Redwing and Home Counties Village

1024 Welsh Mountain Sheep in Snowdonia

(Des J. Gorham and K. Bowen)

1992 (14 Jan–25 Feb). *The Four Seasons. Wintertime. One phosphor band* (18*p.*) *or phosphorised paper* (*others*). *P* 15×14.

1587 **1020** 18p. silver, greenish yellow, grey, dull rose, new blue and black 50 50
1588 **1021** 24p. silver, lemon, rose, blue & grey-blk 70 70
a. Imperf (pair) £300
1589 **1022** 28p. silver, greenish yellow, bright rose, steel-blue and grey black 90 90
1590 **1023** 33p. silver, greenish yellow, brt orange, brt purple, greenish blue & grey 1·10 1·10
1591 **1024** 39p. silver, yellow, yellow-orange, grey, vermilion, new blue and black . . 1·25 1·25
a. Booklet pane. No. 1591×4 with margins all round (25 Feb) . . 3·25
1587/91 . . . . *Set of* 5 4·00 4·00

Booklet pane No. 1591a comes from the £6 "Cymru-Wales" booklet.

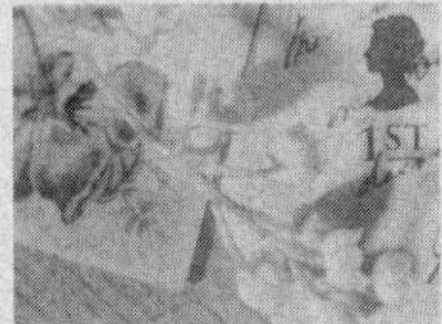

1025 Flower Spray

1026 Double Locket

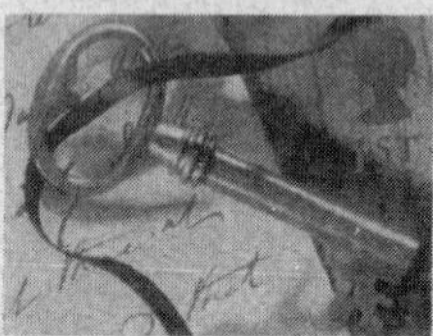

1027 Key

1028 Model Car and Cigarette Cards

1029 Compass and Map

1030 Pocket Watch

1031 1854 1d. Red Stamp and Pen

1032 Pearl Necklace

1033 Marbles

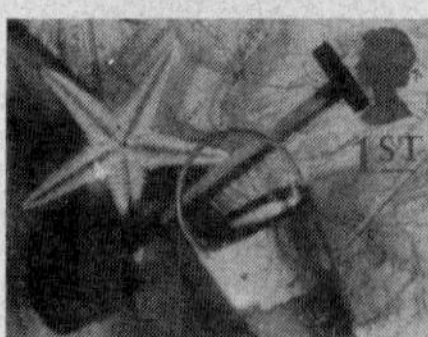

1034 Bucket, Spade and Starfish

(Des Trickett and Webb Ltd)

1992 (28 Jan). *Greetings Stamps. "Memories". Two phosphor bands. P* 15×14.

1592 **1025** (1st) gold, greenish yellow, magenta, ochre, light blue and grey-black . . 90 90
a. Booklet pane. Nos. 1592/1601 plus 12 half stamp-size labels with margins on 3 sides . . . . 8·00
1593 **1026** (1st) gold, greenish yellow, magenta, ochre, light blue and grey-black . . 90 90
1594 **1027** (1st) gold, greenish yellow, magenta, ochre, light blue and grey-black . . 90 90
1595 **1028** (1st) gold, greenish yellow, magenta, ochre, light blue and grey-black . . 90 90
1596 **1029** (1st) gold, greenish yellow, magenta, ochre, light blue and grey-black . . 90 90
1597 **1030** (1st) gold, greenish yellow, magenta, ochre, light blue and grey-black . . 90 90
1598 **1031** (1st) gold, greenish yellow, magenta, ochre, light blue and grey-black . . 90 90
1599 **1032** (1st) gold, greenish yellow, magenta, ochre, light blue and grey-black . . 90 90
1600 **1033** (1st) gold, greenish yellow, magenta, ochre, light blue and grey-black . . 90 90
1601 **1034** (1st) gold, greenish yellow, magenta, ochre, light blue and grey-black . . 90 90
1592/1601 . . . . *Set of* 10 8·00 8·00

Nos. 1592/1601 were only issued in £2.40 booklets (sold at £2.50 from 1 November 1993 and at £2.60 from 8 July 1996). The backgrounds of the stamps form a composite design.

1035 Queen Elizabeth in Coronation Robes and Parliamentary Emblem

1036 Queen Elizabeth in Garter Robes and Archiepiscopal Arms

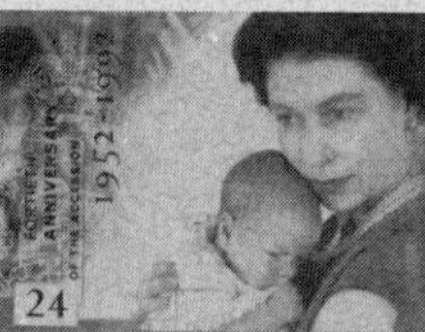

1037 Queen Elizabeth with Baby Prince Andrew and Royal Arms

1038 Queen Elizabeth at Trooping the Colour and Service Emblems

1039 Queen Elizabeth and Commonwealth Emblem

(Des Why Not Associates. Litho Questa)

1992 (6 Feb). 40*th Anniv of Accession. Two phosphor banc P* 14½×14.

1602 **1035** 24p. new blue, greenish yellow, magenta, black, silver and gold . . 1·40 1·
a. Horiz strip of 5. Nos. 1602/6 . . 6·00 6·
1603 **1036** 24p. new blue, greenish yellow, magenta, black, silver and gold . . 1·40 1·
1604 **1037** 24p. new blue, greenish yellow, magenta, black and silver . . 1·40 1·
1605 **1038** 24p. new blue, greenish yellow, magenta, black, silver and gold . . 1·40 1·
1606 **1039** 24p. new blue, greenish yellow, magenta, black, silver and gold . . 1·40 1·
1602/6 . . . . *Set of* 5 6·00 6·

Nos. 1602/6 were printed together, *se-tenant*, in horizontal stri of five throughout the sheet.

1040 Tennyson in 1888 and "The Beguiling of Merlin" (Sir Edward Burne-Jones)

1041 Tennyson in 1856 and "April Love" (Arthur Hughes)

1042 Tennyson in 1864 and "I am Sick of the Shadows" (John Waterhouse)

1043 Tennyson as a Young Man and "Mariana" (Dante Gabriel Rossetti)

(Des Irene von Treskow)

1992 (10 Mar). *Death Centenary of Alfred, Lord Tennyson (poe Phosphorised paper. P* 14½×14.

1607 **1040** 24p. gold, greenish yellow, magenta, new blue and black 50
1608 **1041** 28p. gold, greenish yellow, magenta, new blue and black 75
1609 **1042** 33p. gold, greenish yellow, magenta, new blue and black . . . . 1·25 1·
1610 **1043** 39p. gold, greenish yellow, magenta, new blue, bistre and black . . 1·40 1·
1607/10 . . . . *Set of* 4 3·50 3·

1044 Carrickfergus Castle

Elliptical hole in vertical perforations

GH CASTLE

Harrison Plates (Nos. 1611/14)

GH CASTLE

Enschedé Plates (Nos. 1993/6)

(Des from photos by Prince Andrew, Duke of York. Eng Matthews. Recess Harrison)

1992 (24 Mar)–**95.** *Designs as Nos.* 1410/13, *but showing Queen head in silhouette as T* **1044**. *P* 15×14 (*with one elliptical hole each vertical side*).

1611 **1044** £1 bottle green and gold† . . . . 5·00 1·
1612 **880** £1.50, maroon and gold† . . . . 3·75 2·
1613 **881** £2 indigo and gold† . . . . . . 5·00 2·

613*a* **1044** £3 reddish violet and gold† (22.8.95) 7·00 4·00
614 **882** £5 deep brown and gold† .. .. 12·00 6·00
a. Gold (Queen's head) omitted .. £275
611/14 .. .. *Set of* 5 30·00 14·00

† The Queen's head on these stamps is printed in optically variable ink which changes colour from gold to green when viewed from different angles.

The £1.50 (5 March 1996), £2 (2 May 1996) and £5 (17 September 1996) subsequently appeared on PVA (white gum) instead of the tinted PVAD previously used.

See also Nos. 1993/6.

1045 British Olympic Association Logo (Olympic Games, Barcelona)

1046 British Paralympic Association Symbol (Paralympics '92, Barcelona)

1047 *Santa Maria* (500th Anniv of Discovery of America by Columbus)

1048 *Kaisei* (Japanese cadet brigantine) (Grand Regatta Columbus, 1992)

1049 British Pavilion, "Expo '92", Seville

(Des K. Bassford (Nos. 1615/16, 1619), K. Bassford and S. Paine. Eng. C. Matthews (Nos. 1617/18). Litho Questa (Nos. 1615/16, 1619) or recess and litho Harrison (Nos. 1617/18))

1992 (7 Apr). *Europa. International Events. Phosphorised paper. P* 14×14½.

1615 **1045** 24p. new blue, lemon, magenta & black 75 75
a. Horiz pair. Nos. 1615/16 .. 1·50 1·50
1616 **1046** 24p. new blue, lemon, magenta & black 75 75
1617 **1047** 24p. black, grey, carmine, cream & gold 75 75
1618 **1048** 39p. black, grey, carmine, cream & gold 1·10 1·10
1619 **1049** 39p. new blue, lemon, magenta & black 1·10 1·10
1615/19 .. .. *Set of* 5 4·00 4·00

Nos. 1615/16 were printed together, *se-tenant*, throughout the sheet.

No. 1617 is known with the cream omitted used from Cornwall in September 1992.

1050 Pikeman

1051 Drummer

1052 Musketeer

1053 Standard Bearer

(Des J. Sancha)

1992 (16 June). *350th Anniv of the Civil War. Phosphorised paper. P* 14½×14.

1620 **1050** 24p. black, stone, bistre, scarlet, indigo, grey-green and yellow-ochre .. 55 55
a. Imperf (pair) £250
1621 **1051** 28p. black, yellow-ochre, ochre, rose-pink, bl, dull yell-grn & slate-lilac 70 70
1622 **1052** 33p. black, ochre, pale orange, lemon, reddish orange, new bl & olive-grn 1·25 1·25
1623 **1053** 39p. black, yellow-ochre, yell, greenish yellow, vermilion, ind & orge-brn 1·40 1·40
1620/3 .. .. *Set of* 4 3·50 3·50

1054 *The Yeomen of the Guard*

1055 *The Gondoliers*

1056 *The Mikado*

1057 *The Pirates of Penzance*

1058 *Iolanthe*

(Des Lynda Gray)

1992 (21 July). *150th Birth Anniv of Sir Arthur Sullivan (composer). Gilbert and Sullivan Operas. One phosphor band (18p.) or phosphorised paper (others). P* 14½×14.

1624 **1054** 18p. bluish violet, bistre-yellow, scarlet, stone, blue and grey-black .. 45 45
1625 **1055** 24p. purple-brown, lemon, scarlet, stone, blue, olive-bistre and black 60 60
a. Imperf (pair) £250
1626 **1056** 28p. rose-red, lemon, stone, new blue, bluish violet, brt emerald & black 75 75
1627 **1057** 33p. blue-green, orange-yellow, scarlet, olive-bistre, blue, brown-pur & blk 1·25 1·25
1628 **1058** 39p. deep blue, lemon, scarlet, stone, lavender, olive-bistre & lake-brown 1·40 1·40
1624/8 .. .. *Set of* 5 4·00 4·00

1059 "Acid Rain Kills"

1060 "Ozone Layer"

1061 "Greenhouse Effect"

1062 "Bird of Hope"

(Des Christopher Hall (24p.), Lewis Fowler (28p.), Sarah Warren (33p.), Alice Newton-Mold (39p.). Adapted Trickett and Webb Ltd)

1992 (15 Sept). *Protection of the Environment. Children's Paintings. Phosphorised paper. P* 14×14½.

1629 **1059** 24p. emerald, greenish yellow, pale olive-yellow, brt carmine & black 60 60
1630 **1060** 28p. vermilion, lemon, bright blue, new blue, brt green, ultramarine & blk 90 90
1631 **1061** 33p. greenish blue, greenish yellow, brt rose-red, brt green, emer, bl & blk 1·00 1·00
1632 **1062** 39p. emerald, greenish yellow, bright magenta, brt orange, brt blue & blk 1·10 1·10
1629/32 .. .. *Set of* 4 3·25 3·25

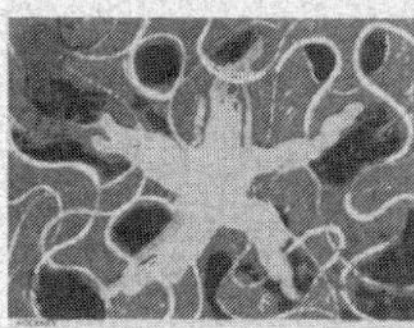

1063 European Star

(Des D. Hockney)

1992 (13 Oct). *Single European Market. Phosphorised paper. P* 15×14.

1633 **1063** 24p. gold, greenish yellow, bright magenta, dull ultramarine & black 75 75

1064 "Angel Gabriel", St. James's, Pangbourne

1065 "Madonna and Child", St. Mary's, Bibury

1066 "King with Gold", Our Lady and St. Peter, Leatherhead

1067 "Shepherds", All Saints, Porthcawl

1068 "Kings with Frankincense and Myrrh", Our Lady and St. Peter, Leatherhead

(Des Carroll, Dempsey and Thirkell Ltd from windows by Karl Parsons (18, 24, 33p.) and Paul Woodroffe (28, 39p.))

1992 (10 Nov). *Christmas. Stained Glass Windows. One centre band (18p.) or phosphorised paper (others). P* 15×14.

1634 **1064** 18p. black, greenish yellow, mauve, ultramarine, bright emerald & gold 40 40
a. Booklet pane of 20 .. .. 7·50
1635 **1065** 24p. blk, greenish yell, brt pur, ultram, new blue, brt greenish yell & gold 65 65
1636 **1066** 28p. black, lemon, rosine, ultramarine, reddish lilac, red-orange and gold 80 80
1637 **1067** 33p. bright ultramarine, greenish yell, rosine, brn, yellow-orge, blk & gold 95 95
1638 **1068** 39p. black, lemon, rosine, bright blue, deep violet, yellow-orange and gold 1·10 1·10
1634/8 .. .. *Set of* 5 3·50 3·50

Booklet pane No. 1634a comes from a special £3.60 Christmas booklet and has margins at left, top and bottom.

1069 Mute Swan Cob and St. Catherine's Chapel, Abbotsbury

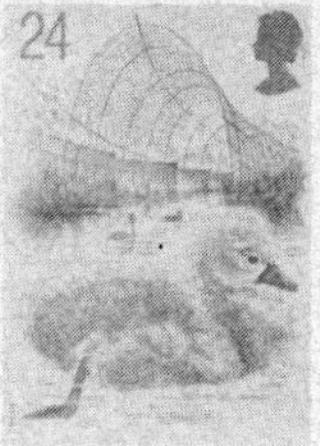

1070 Cygnet and Decoy

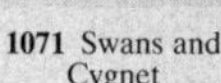

1071 Swans and Cygnet

1072 Eggs in Nest and Tithe Barn, Abbotsbury

1073 Young Swan and the Fleet

(Des D. Gentleman)

1993 (19 Jan). *600th Anniv of Abbotsbury Swannery. One phosphor band* (18*p*) *or phosphorised paper* (*others*). *P* 14×15.

1639	**1069**	18p.	gold, greenish yellow, bistre, green, vermilion and black	1·50	85
1640	**1070**	24p.	gold, cream, bright green, grey-brown, dull blue and grey-black . .	1·10	1·10
1641	**1071**	28p.	gold, greenish grey, yellow-brown, myrtle-green, brown, verm & blk	1·25	1·60
1642	**1072**	33p.	gold, ochre, apple-green, olive-brown, bright orange & grey-black	2·00	1·75
1643	**1073**	39p.	gold, cream, bright green, cobalt, light brown and black	2·25	2·25
1639/43			. . . . *Set of* 5	7·00	7·00

1074 Long John Silver and Parrot (*Treasure Island*)

1075 Tweedledum and Tweedledee (*Alice Through the Looking-Glass*)

1076 William (*William* books)

1077 Mole and Toad (*The Wind in the Willows*)

1078 Teacher and Wilfrid ("The Bash Street Kids")

1079 Peter Rabbit and Mrs. Rabbit (*The Tale of Peter Rabbit*)

1080 Snowman (*The Snowman*) and Father Christmas (*Father Christmas*)

1081 The Big Friendly Giant and Sophie (*The BFG*)

1082 Bill Badger and Rupert Bear

1083 Aladdin and the Genie

(Des Newell and Sorell)

1993 (2 Feb–10 Aug). *Greetings Stamps. "Gift Giving". Two phosphor bands. P* 15×14 (*with one elliptical hole on each vertical side*).

1644	**1074**	(1st)	gold, greenish yellow, magenta, pale brown, light blue and black	95	85
			a. Booklet pane. Nos. 1644/53 . .	8·50	
1645	**1075**	(1st)	gold, cream and black	95	85
1646	**1076**	(1st)	gold, greenish yellow, magenta, cream, new blue and black . .	95	85
1647	**1077**	(1st)	gold, greenish yellow, magenta, cream, new blue and black . .	95	85
1648	**1078**	(1st)	gold, greenish yellow, magenta, cream, new blue and black . .	95	85
1649	**1079**	(1st)	gold, greenish yellow, magenta, cream, new blue and black . .	95	85
			a. Booklet pane. No. 1649×4 with margins all round (10 Aug) . .	4·00	
1650	**1080**	(1st)	gold, greenish yellow, magenta, cream, new blue and black . .	95	85
1651	**1081**	(1st)	gold, greenish yellow, magenta, cream, new blue and black . .	95	85
1652	**1082**	(1st)	gold, greenish yellow, magenta, cream, new blue and black . .	95	85
1653	**1083**	(1st)	gold, greenish yellow, magenta, cream, new blue and black . .	95	85
1644/53			. . . . *Set of* 10	8·50	7·50

Nos. 1644/53 were only issued in £2.40 booklets (sold at £2.50 from 1 November 1993).

Booklet pane No. 1649a comes from the £6 (£5.64) Beatrix Potter booklet.

1084 Decorated Enamel Dial

1085 Escapement, Remontoire and Fusee

1086 Balance, Spring and Temperature Compensator

1087 Back of Movement

(Des H. Brown and D. Penny. Litho Questa)

1993 (16 Feb). *300th Birth Anniv of John Harrison (inventor of the marine chronometer). Details of "H4" Clock. Phosphorised paper. P* 14½×14.

1654	**1084**	24p.	new blue, greenish yellow, mag, black, grey-black and pale cream . .	50	50
1655	**1085**	28p.	new blue, greenish yellow, mag, black, grey-black and pale cream . .	85	85
1656	**1086**	33p.	new blue, greenish yellow, mag, black, grey-black and pale cream . .	1·10	1·10
1657	**1087**	39p.	new blue, greenish yellow, mag, black, grey-black and pale cream . .	1·25	1·25
1654/7			. . . . *Set of* 4	3·25	3·25

1088 Britannia

(Des B. Craddock, adapted Roundel Design Group. Litho (silver die-stamped, Braille symbol for "10" embossed) Questa)

1993 (2 Mar). *Granite paper. P* 14×14½ (*with two elliptical holes on each horizontal side*).

1658	**1088**	£10	greenish grey, rosine, yellow, new blue, reddish violet, vermilion, violet, bright green and silver . .	15·00	6·00
			a. Silver omitted	£950	

The paper used for No. 1658 contains fluorescent coloured fibres which, together with the ink on the shield, react under U.V. light.

1089 *Dendrobium hellwigianum*

1090 *Paphiopedilum* Maudiae "Magnificum"

1091 *Cymbidium lowianum*

1092 *Vanda* Rothschildiana

1093 *Dendrobium vexillarius* var *albiviride*

(Des Pandora Sellars)

)3 (16 Mar). *14th World Orchid Conference, Glasgow. One phosphor band* (18*p*.) *or phosphorised paper* (*others*). *P* 15×14.

59 **1089** 18p. green, greenish yellow, magenta, pale blue, apple-green and slate .. 40 40
a. Imperf (pair) £900
50 **1090** 24p. green, greenish yellow, bright green and grey-black 65 65
51 **1091** 28p. green, greenish yellow, red, bright turquoise-blue and drab 90 90
52 **1092** 33p. green, greenish yellow, pale mag, bright violet, bright green and grey 1·10 1·10
53 **1093** 39p. green, greenish yellow, red, pale olive-yell, brt grn, vio & grey-blk 1·40 1·40
59/63 .. .. *Set of* 5 4·00 4·00

.UORESCENT PHOSPHOR BANDS. Following the introduction new automatic sorting machinery in 1991 it was found necessary substantially increase the signal emitted by the phosphor bands. iis was achieved by adding a fluorescent element to the phosphor iich appears yellow under U.V. light. This combination was first ed on an experimental sheet printing of the 18p., No. X913, oduced by Enschedé in 1991. All values with phosphor bands om the elliptical perforations issue, including the No Value dicated design, originally showed this yellow fluor.

From mid-1995 printings of current sheet and booklet stamps gan to appear with the colour of the fluorescent element changed blue. As such differences in fluor colour can only be identified by e of a U.V. lamp they are outside the scope of this catalogue, but l details will be found in the *Great Britain Specialised Catalogue* *olume 4.*

The first commemorative/special stamp issue to show the change blue fluor was the Centenary of Rugby League set, Nos. 1891/5.

)MPUTER-ENGRAVED CYLINDERS. In 1991 Enschedé roduced a new method of preparing photogravure cylinders for reat Britain stamps. This new method utilised computer-graving instead of the traditional acid-etching and produced linders without the minor flaws which had long been a feature of e photogravure process. Such cylinders were first used on Great itain stamps for the printing of the 18p released on 19 November 91 (see No. X913).

Harrison and Sons continued to use the acid-etching method until d-1996 after which most Machin values, including N.V.I.'s, were oduced from computer-engraved cylinders using a very similar ocess to that of Enschedé. Some values exist in versions from th cylinder production methods and can often be identified by nor differences. Such stamps are, however, outside the scope of s listing, but full details can be found in the current edition of the *eat Britain Specialised Catalogue Volume 4.*

For commemorative stamps the first Harrison issue to use mputer-engraved cylinders was the Centenary of Cinema set os. 1920/4).

When Walsall introduced photogravure printing in 1997 their linders were produced using a similar computer-engraved ocess.

93 (6 Apr)–**99**. *Booklet stamps. As T* **913/14**, *but P* 14 (*No.* 1663*b*) *or* 15×14 (*others*) (*both with one elliptical hole on each vertical side*).

) *Photo Questa* (*Nos.* 1663ab, 1664ab), *Walsall* (*No.* 1663*b*, 1664*b*), *Harrison* (*No.* 1664), *De La Rue* (*No.* 1664al), *Harrison* (*later De La Rue*) *or Walsall* (*others*)

63*a* **913** (2nd) brt blue (1 centre band) (7.9.93) 30 35
ab. Perf 14 (1.12.98) 30 35
63*b* (2nd) brt blue (1 side band) (13.10.98) 50 50
bl. Booklet pane. Nos. 1663*b*×3 and NI79*a*, S91a and W80a with margins all round .. .. 3·75
64 **914** (1st) brt orge-red (phosphorised paper) 80 80
64*a* (1st) brt orange-red (2 phosphor bands) (4.4.95) 40 45
ab. Perf 14 (1.12.98) 40 45
al. Booklet pane. No. 1664*a*×8 with centre label and margins all round (16.2.99) .. .. .. 3·00
64*b* – (E) dp bl (2 phosphor bands) (19.1.99) 45 50

(*b*) *Litho Questa* (*Nos.* 1666l, 1666m, 1666n), *Walsall* (*No.* 1666la), *Enschedé* (*No.* 1666ma), *Questa or Walsall* (*others*)

65 **913** (2nd) bright blue (1 centre band) .. 60 60
66 **914** (1st) brt orange-red (2 phosphor bands) 40 45
l. Booklet pane. No. 1666×4 plus commemorative label at left (27.7.94) .. .. .. 6·00
la. Ditto, but with commemorative label at right (16.5.95) .. .. 1·50
m. Pane. No. 1666 with margins all round (roul 8 across top corners of pane) (17.8.94) 40
ma. Ditto, but roul 10 across top corners of pane (20.2.97) .. 40
n. Booklet pane. No. 1666×9 with margins all round (16.2.99) .. 3·50

Nos. 1663*a*/6, were issued in booklet panes showing perforations ı all four edges.

No. 1663*b* exists with the phosphor band at the left or right from parate panes (Nos. 1663bl and Y1672al) of the £6.16 Speed stamp ooklet.

No. 1664*b* was valid for the basic European airmail rate, initially p.

On 6 September 1993 Nos. 1665/6 printed in lithography by uesta were made available in sheets from post offices in rmingham, Coventry, Falkirk and Milton Keynes. These sheet amps became available nationally on 5 October 1993. On 29 April 97 No. 1663*a* printed in photogravure by Walsall became ailable in sheets. On the same date Nos. 1663*a* and 1664*a* were sued in coils printed by Harrison.

No. 1666l includes a commemorative label for the 300th nniversary of the Bank of England and No. 1666la exists with bels for the birth centenary of R. J. Mitchell, 70th birthday of ueen Elizabeth II, "Hong Kong '97" International Stamp xhibition, Commonwealth Heads of Government Meeting, dinburgh or 50th birthday of Prince of Wales.

No. 1666m, printed by Questa, was provided by the Royal Mail r inclusion in single pre-packed greetings cards. The pane shows rge margins at top and sides with lines of roulette gauging 8 retching from the bottom corners to the mid point of the top edge. xamples included with greetings cards show the top two corners of e pane folded over. The scheme was originally limited to Boots and their logo appeared on the pane margin. Other card retailers subsequently participated and later supplies omitted the logo. Unfolded examples were available from the British Philatelic Bureau and from other Post Office philatelic outlets. A further printing by Enschedé in 1997 showed the roulettes gauging 10 (No. 1666ma). Blank pieces of gummed paper have been found showing the perforation and rouletting of No. 1666ma, but no printing.

In mid-1994 a number of postal forgeries of the 2nd bright blue printed in lithography were detected, after having been rejected by the sorting equipment. These show the Queen's head in bright greenish blue, have a fluorescent, rather than a phosphor, band and show matt, colourless gum on the reverse. These forgeries come from booklets of ten which also have forged covers.

For 1st in gold see No. 1979 and for self-adhesive versions in these colours see Nos. 2039/40.

1993 (27 Apr)–**99**. *As No.* X841, *etc, but P* 15×14 (*with one elliptical hole on each vertical side*).

(*a*) *Photo*
Enschedé:—*20p.* (Y1674), *29p.*, *35p.* (Y1682), *36p.*, *38p.* (Y1686), *41p.* (Y1688), *43p.* (Y1690)
Harrison/De La Rue:—*7p.*, *20p.* (Y1675*c*/*d*), *25p.* (Y1676), 35p. (Y1683), *41p.* (Y1689), *43p.* (Y1691), *44p.*
Walsall:—10p. (Y1672a), 43p. (Y1691a)
Enschedé or Harrison/De La Rue:—*4p.*, *5p.*, *6p.*, *10p.* (Y1672), *25p.* (Y1677), *31p.*, *39p.*, *50p.*, *£1*
Enschedé, Harrison/De La Rue or Questa:—*1p.*, *2p.*
Enschedé, Harrison/De La Rue or Walsall:—*30p.*, *37p.*, *63p.*
Harrison/De La Rue or Questa:—*19p.*, *20p.* (Y1675), *26p.*
De La Rue or Walsall:—*38p.* (Y1686*b*), *64p.*

Y1667 **367** 1p. crimson (2 bands) (8.6.93) .. 10 10
l. Booklet pane. Nos. Y1667×2, Y1675 and Y1678×3 plus 2 labels (1.12.98) .. .. .. 1·50
m. Booklet pane. Nos. Y1667/8, Y1673, Y1678×3 plus 2 labels (24.4.99) .. .. .. 1·50
Y1668 2p. deep green (2 bands) (11.4.95) .. 10 10
Y1669 4p. new blue (2 bands) (14.12.93) .. 10 10
Y1670 5p. dull red-brown (2 bands) (8.6.93) 10 10
Y1671 6p. yellow-olive (2 bands) 10 15
Y1671*a* 7p. grey (2 bands) (20.4.99) 10 15
Y1672 10p. dull orange (2 bands) (8.6.93) .. 15 20
a. Perf 14 (13.10.98) 70 70
al. Booklet pane. Nos. Y1672a×2, 1663*b* and Y1691a, each × 3, with centre label and margins all round 5·00
Y1673 19p. bistre (1 centre band) (26.10.93) 30 35
a. Imperf (pair) £350
l. Booklet pane. Nos. Y1673 and Y1678×7 (24.4.99) .. .. 3·00
Y1674 20p. turquoise-grn (2 bands) (14.12.93) 60 60
Y1675 20p. brt green (1 centre band) (25.6.96) 30 35
a. Imperf (horiz pair) £350
bl. Booklet pane. Nos. Y1675 and Y1678×7 (1.12.98) .. .. 3·00
Y1675*c* 20p. bright green (1 side band) (23.9.97) 1·00 1·00
cl. Booklet pane. Nos. Y1675*c* and Y1678, each × 3, with margins all round .. .. 4·00
Y1675*d* 20p. bright green (2 bands) (20.4.99) .. 30 35
Y1676 25p. rose-red (phosphorised paper) (26.10.93) 80 80
a. Imperf (pair) £400
l. Booklet pane. No. Y1676×2 plus 2 labels (1.11.93) .. .. .. 1·25
Y1677 25p. rose-red (2 bands) (20.12.94) .. 80 80
l. Booklet pane. No. Y1677×2 plus 2 labels (6.6.95) .. .. .. 1·25
Y1678 26p. red-brown (2 bands) (25.6.96) .. 40 45
Y1679 29p. grey (2 bands) (26.10.93) .. 1·00 1·00
Y1680 30p. deep olive-grey (2 bands) (27.7.93) 45 50
Y1681 31p. deep mauve (2 bands) (25.6.96) .. 50 55
Y1682 35p. yellow (2 bands) (17.8.93) .. 1·00 1·00
Y1683 35p. yell (phosphorised paper) (1.11.93) 1·00 1·00
Y1684 36p. brt ultram (2 bands) (26.10.93) .. 1·00 1·00
Y1685 37p. bright mauve (2 bands) (25.6.96) 1·00 1·00
Y1686 38p. rosine (2 bands) (26.10.93) .. 1·00 1·00
a. Imperf (pair) £200
Y1686*b* 38p. ultramarine (2 bands) (20.4.99) .. 55 60
Y1687 39p. bright magenta (2 bands) (25.6.96) 60 65
Y1688 41p. grey-brown (2 bands) (26.10.93) 1·25 1·25
Y1689 41p. drab (phosphorised paper) (1.11.93) .. .. .. 1·25 1·25
Y1690 43p. dp olive-brown (2 bands) (25.6.96) 1·25 1·25
Y1691 43p. sepia (2 bands) (8.7.96) 65 70
a. Perf 14 (13.10.98) 70 70
Y1691*b* 44p. grey-brown (2 bands) (20.4.99) .. 65 70
Y1692 50p. ochre (2 bands) (14.12.93) .. 75 80
a. Imperf (pair) .. .. ..
Y1693 63p. light emerald (2 bands) (25.6.96) 95 1·00
Y1693*a* 64p. turquoise-green (2 bands) (20.4.99) 95 1·00
Y1694 £1 bluish violet (2 bands) (22.8.95) .. 1·50 1·60

(*b*) *Litho Walsall* (*37p.*, *60p.*, *63p.*), *Questa or Walsall* (*25p.*, *35p.*, *41p.*), *Questa* (*others*)

Y1743 **367** 1p. lake (2 bands) (8.7.96) 10 10
l. Booklet pane. Nos. Y1743×2, Y1751 and Y1753×3 plus 2 labels 1·50
Y1748 6p. yellow-olive (2 bands) (26.7.94) 7·50 7·50
l. Booklet pane. Nos. Y1748, Y1750 and Y1752×4 with margins all round .. .. 9·00
la. 6p. value misplaced .. ..
Y1749 10p. dull orange (2 bands) (25.4.95) 3·50 3·50
l. Booklet pane. Nos. Y1749, Y1750 ×2, Y1752×2, Y1754/5, Y1757 and centre label with margins all round 10·00
Y1750 19p. bistre (1 side band) (26.7.94) .. 1·00 1·00
l. Booklet pane. No. Y1750×6 with margins all round (25.4.95) .. 6·00
Y1751 20p. brt yell-grn (1 centre band) (8.7.96) 30 35
l. Booklet pane. Nos. Y1751 and Y1753×7 .. .. .. 3·00
Y1752 25p. red (2 bands) (1.11.93) 80 80
l. Booklet pane. Nos. Y1752, NI72, S84 and W73, each × 2 with centre label and margins all round (14.5.96) .. .. .. 3·00
Y1753 26p. chestnut (2 bands) (8.7.96) .. 40 45
Y1754 30p. olive-grey (2 bands) (25.4.95) .. 2·00 2·00
Y1755 35p. yellow (2 bands) (1.11.93) .. 1·25 1·25
Y1756 **367** 37p. bright mauve (2 bands) (8.7.96) 1·25 1·25
Y1757 41p. drab (*shades*) (2 bands) (1.11.93) 1·25 1·25
Y1758 60p. dull blue-grey (2 bands) (9.8.94) 2·00 2·00
Y1759 63p. light emerald (2 bands) (8.7.96) .. 2·00 2·00

(*c*) *Recess Enschedé*

Y1800 **367** £1.50, red (9.3.99) .. .. .. 2·25 2·40
Y1801 £2 dull blue (9.3.99) .. .. 3·00 3·25
Y1802 £3 dull violet (9.3.99) .. .. 4·50 4·75
Y1803 £5 brown (9.3.99) .. .. .. 7·50 7·75

No. Y1694 is printed in Iriodin ink which gives a shiny effect to the solid part of the background behind the Queen's head.

Nos. Y1683 and Y1689 were only issued in coils and Nos. Y1748/50, Y1752, Y1754/5 and Y1757/8 only in booklets.

No. Y1748la shows the 6p. value 22 mm to the left so that its position in the booklet pane is completely blank except for the phosphor bands. Other more minor misplacements exist.

No. Y1675*c* shows the phosphor band at right and No. Y1750 at left or right.

For 26p. in gold see No. 1978.

1094 "Family Group" (bronze sculpture) (Henry Moore)

1095 "Kew Gardens" (lithograph) (Edward Bawden)

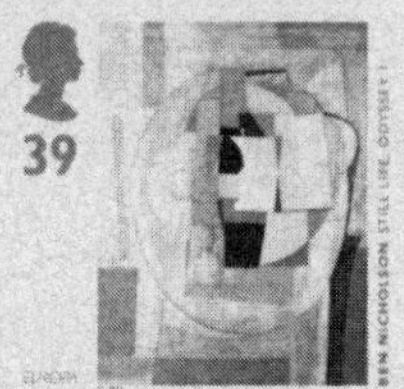

1096 "St. Francis and the Birds" (Stanley Spencer)

1097 "Still Life: Odyssey I" (Ben Nicholson)

(Des A. Dastor)

1993 (11 May). *Europa. Contemporary Art. Phosphorised paper. P* 14×14½.

1767 **1094** 24p. brownish grey, lemon, magenta, turquoise-blue, and grey-black .. 50 50
1768 **1095** 28p. brownish grey, buff, lt grn, yellow-brown, brt orge, new bl & grey-blk 80 80
1769 **1096** 33p. brownish grey, cream, greenish yellow, magenta, new bl & grey-blk 95 95
1770 **1097** 39p. brownish grey, cream, yell-ochre, rose-lilac, red, light blue & grey-blk 1·10 1·10
1767/70 .. .. *Set of* 4 3·00 3·00

1098 Emperor Claudius (from gold coin)

1099 Emperor Hadrian (bronze head)

1100 Goddess Roma (from gemstone)

1101 Christ (Hinton St. Mary mosaic)

(Des J. Gibbs)

1993 (15 June). *Roman Britain. Phosphorised paper with two phosphor bands. P* 14×14½.

1771 **1098** 24p. blk, pale orange, lt brown & silver 50 50
1772 **1099** 28p. black, greenish yellow, bright rose-red, silver, brt blue & grey-black 80 80
1773 **1100** 33p. black, greenish yellow, bright rose-red, silver and grey .. 95 95
1774 **1101** 39p. black, greenish yellow, rosine, silver, pale violet and grey .. 1·10 1·10
1771/4 .. .. *Set of* 4 3·00 3·00

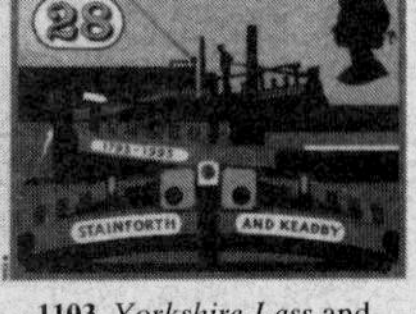

1102 *Midland Maid* and other Narrow Boats, Grand Junction Canal

1103 *Yorkshire Lass* and other Humber Keels, Stainforth and Keadby Canal

1104 *Valley Princess* and other Horse-drawn Barges, Brecknock and Abergavenny Canal

1105 Steam Barges, including *Pride of Scotland*, and Fishing Boats, Crinan Canal

(Des T. Lewery. Litho Questa)

1993 (20 July). *Inland Waterways. Two phosphor bands. P* 14½×14.

1775 **1102** 24p. new bl, greenish yell, brt mag, blk, bl, verm, brownish grey & sage-grn 50 50
1776 **1103** 28p. new bl, greenish yell, brt mag, blk, blue, bluish grey, verm & sage-grn 80 80
1777 **1104** 33p. new bl, greenish yell, brt mag, blk, bl, verm, greenish grey & sage-grn 95 95
1778 **1105** 39p. new blue, greenish yellow, brt mag, blk, bl, verm, sage-grn & dull mve 1·10 1·10
1775/8 .. .. *Set of* 4 3·00 3·00

Nos. 1775/8 commemorate the bicentenary of the Acts of Parliament authorising the canals depicted.

1106 Horse Chestnut

1107 Blackberry

1108 Hazel

1109 Rowan

1110 Pear

(Des Charlotte Knox)

1993 (14 Sept). *The Four Seasons. Autumn. Fruits and Leaves. One phosphor band* (18*p.*) *or phosphorised paper* (*others*). *P* 15×14.

1779 **1106** 18p. black, greenish yellow, cerise, bright green, gold and chestnut .. 40 40
1780 **1107** 24p. black, lemon, cerise, myrtle-green, gold, bright green and brown .. 65 65
1781 **1108** 28p. grey, lemon, emer, lake-brn & gold 90 90
1782 **1109** 33p. grey-black, greenish yellow, rosine, light green, gold and brown .. 1·10 1·10
1783 **1110** 39p. myrtle-green, greenish yellow, rosine, olive-sepia, gold, apple-green and deep myrtle-green .. 1·40 1·40
1779/83 .. .. *Set of* 5 4·00 4·00

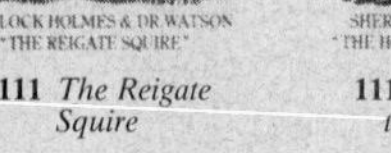

1111 *The Reigate Squire*

1112 *The Hound of the Baskervilles*

1113 *The Six Napoleons*

1114 *The Greek Interpreter*

1115 *The Final Problem*

(Des A. Davidson. Litho Questa)

1993 (12 Oct). *Sherlock Holmes. Centenary of the Publication* The Final Problem. *Phosphorised paper. P* 14×14½.

1784 **1111** 24p. new blue, greenish yellow, mag, black and gold .. .. .. 1·00 1
a. Horiz strip. Nos. 1784/8 .. 4·50 4
1785 **1112** 24p. new blue, greenish yellow, mag, black and gold .. .. .. 1·00 1
1786 **1113** 24p. new blue, greenish yellow, mag, black and gold .. .. .. 1·00 1·
1787 **1114** 24p. new blue, greenish yellow, mag, black and gold .. .. .. 1·00 1·
1788 **1115** 24p. new blue, greenish yellow, mag, black and gold .. .. .. 1·00 1·
1784/8 .. .. *Set of* 5 4·50 4·

Nos. 1785/8 were printed together, *se-tenant*, in horizontal stri of 5 throughout the sheet.

1116

(Des J. Matthews. Litho Walsall)

1993 (19 Oct). *Self-adhesive. Two phosphor bands. Die-c P* 14×15 (*with one elliptical hole on each vertical side*).

1789 **1116** (1st) orange-red .. .. .. 1·00 1·
a. Booklet pane. No. 1789×20 .. 15·00

No. 1789 was initially sold at 24p., which was increased to 25 from 1 November 1993. It was only issued in booklets containing stamps, each surrounded by die-cut perforations .

For similar 2nd and 1st designs printed in photogravure Enschedé see Nos. 1976/7.

1117 Bob Cratchit and Tiny Tim

1118 Mr. and Mrs. Fezziwig

1119 Scrooge

1120 The Prize Turkey

1121 Mr. Scrooge's Nephew

(Des Q. Blake)

3 (9 Nov). *Christmas. 150th Anniv of Publication of* A
:hristmas Carol *by Charles Dickens. One phosphor band (19p.)*
r phosphorised paper (others). P 15×14.
0 **1117** 19p. new blue, yellow, magenta, salmon, bright emerald & grey-blk 40 40
a. Imperf (pair) .. .. ..
1 **1118** 25p. yellow-orange, brn-lilac, steel-bl, lake-brown, lt grn, grey-blk & blk 70 70
2 **1119** 30p. cerise, bistre-yellow, dull blue, brn-rose, pale green, grey-black & blk 1·00 1·00
3 **1120** 35p. dp turquoise-green, lemon, verm, dull ultramarine, Indian red, bluish grey and black .. .. .. 1·10 1·10
4 **1121** 41p. reddish purple, lemon, purple, light blue, salmon, bright green & black 1·25 1·25
0/4 .. .. *Set of* 5 4·00 4·00

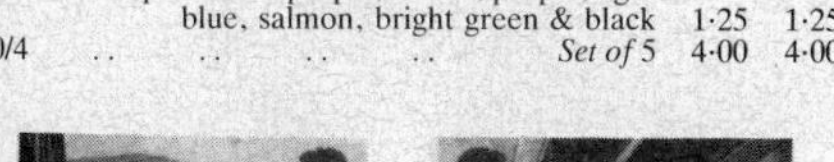

1122 Class 5 No. 44957 and Class B1 No. 61342 on West Highland Line

1123 Class A1 No. 60149 *Amadis* at Kings Cross

1124 Class 4 No. 43000 on Turntable at Blyth North

1125 Class 4 No. 42455 near Wigan Central

1126 Class "Castle" No. 7002 *Devizes Castle* on Bridge crossing Worcester and Birmingham Canal

(Des B. Delaney)

)4 (18 Jan). *The Age of Steam. Railway Photographs by Colin Gifford. One phosphor band (19p.) or phosphorised paper with* *wo bands (others). P* 14½.
)5 **1122** 19p. dp blue-green, grey-black & black 45 40
)6 **1123** 25p. slate-lilac, grey-black and black .. 75 65
)7 **1124** 30p. lake-brown, grey-black and black 1·00 90
)8 **1125** 35p. deep claret, grey-black and black 1·25 1·10
)9 **1126** 41p. indigo, grey-black and black .. 1·40 1·25
)5/9 .. .. *Set of* 5 4·50 4·00
Nos. 1796/9 are on phosphorised paper and also show two osphor bands.

MINIMUM PRICE

ıe minimum price quote is 10p which represents handling charge rather than a basis for valuing ımmon stamps. For further notes about prices see introductory pages.

1127 Dan Dare and the Mekon

1128 The Three Bears

1129 Rupert Bear

1130 Alice (*Alice in Wonderland*)

1131 Noggin and the Ice Dragon

1132 Peter Rabbit posting Letter

1133 Red Riding Hood and Wolf

1134 Orlando the Marmalade Cat

1135 Biggles

1136 Paddington Bear on Station

(Des Newell and Sorrell)

1994 (1 Feb). *Greetings Stamps. "Messages". Two phosphor bands. P* 15×14 *(with one elliptical hole on each vertical side).*
1800 **1127** (1st) gold, greenish yellow, brt purple, bistre-yellow, new blue and black 90 80
a. Booklet pane. Nos. 1800/9 .. 8·00
1801 **1128** (1st) gold, greenish yellow, brt purple, bistre-yellow, new blue and black 90 80
1802 **1129** (1st) gold, greenish yellow, brt purple, bistre-yellow, new blue and black 90 80
1803 **1130** (1st) gold, bistre-yellow and black .. 90 80
1804 **1131** (1st) gold, greenish yellow, brt purple, bistre-yellow, new blue and black 90 80
1805 **1132** (1st) gold, greenish yellow, brt purple, bistre-yellow, new blue and black 90 80
1806 **1133** (1st) gold, greenish yellow, brt purple, bistre-yellow, new blue and black 90 80
1807 **1134** (1st) gold, greenish yellow, brt purple, bistre-yellow, new blue and black 90 80
1808 **1135** (1st) gold, greenish yellow, brt purple, bistre-yellow, new blue and black 90 80
1809 **1136** (1st) gold, greenish yellow, brt purple, bistre-yellow, new blue and black 90 80
1800/9 .. .. *Set of* 10 8·00 7·00
Nos. 1800/9 were only issued in £2.50 stamp booklets (sold at £2.60 from 8 July 1996).

1137 Castell Y Waun (Chirk Castle), Clwyd, Wales

1138 Ben Arkle, Sutherland, Scotland

1139 Mourne Mountains, County Down, Northern Ireland

1140 Dersingham, Norfolk, England

1141 Dolwyddelan, Gwynedd, Wales

1994 (1 Mar–26 July). *25th Anniv of Investiture of the Prince of Wales. Paintings by Prince Charles. One phosphor band (19p.) or phosphorised paper (others). P* 15×14.
1810 **1137** 19p. grey-black, greenish yellow, magenta, new blue, black and silver 40 40
1811 **1138** 25p. grey-black, orange-yellow, bright magenta, new blue, silver and black 75 75

1812	**1139**	30p.	grey-black, greenish yellow, magenta, new blue, silver and black	1·00	1·00
		a.	Booklet pane. No. 1812×4 with margins all round (26 July) ..	3·50	
1813	**1140**	35p.	grey-black, greenish yellow, magenta, new blue, silver and black	1·10	1·10
1814	**1141**	41p.	grey-black, lemon, magenta, new blue, silver and black	1·25	1·25
1810/14			.. .. *Set of* 5	4·00	4·00

Booklet pane No. 1812a comes from the £6.04 "Northern Ireland" booklet.

1142 Bather at Blackpool

1143 "Where's my Little Lad?"

1144 "Wish You were Here!"

1145 Punch and Judy Show

1146 "The Tower Crane" Machine

(Des M. Dempsey and B. Dare. Litho Questa)

1994 (12 Apr). *Centenary of Picture Postcards. One side band* (19*p.*) *or two phosphor bands* (*others*). *P* 14×14½.

1815	**1142**	19p.	new blue, greenish yell, mag & blk	45	45
1816	**1143**	25p.	new blue, greenish yell, mag & blk	75	75
1817	**1144**	30p.	new blue, greenish yell, mag & blk	90	90
1818	**1145**	35p.	new blue, greenish yell, mag & blk	1·10	1·10
1819	**1146**	41p.	new blue, greenish yell, mag & blk	1·25	1·25
1815/19			.. .. *Set of* 5	4·00	4·00

1147 British Lion and French Cockerel over Tunnel

1148 Symbolic Hands over Train

(Des G. Hardie (T **1147**), J.-P. Cousin (T **1148**))

1994 (3 May). *Opening of Channel Tunnel. Phosphorised paper. P* 14×14½.

1820	**1147**	25p.	ultram, brt orange, scar, new blue, emerald, turquoise-blue & silver ..	75	75
		a.	Horiz pair. Nos. 1820/1	1·50	1·50
1821	**1148**	25p.	ultram, scar, new bl, emer & silver	75	75

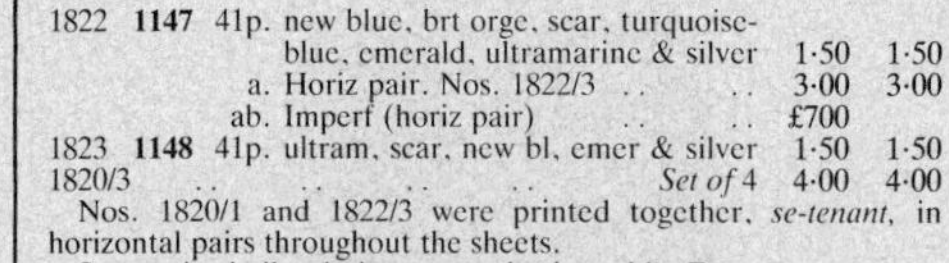

1822	**1147**	41p.	new blue, brt orge, scar, turquoise-blue, emerald, ultramarine & silver	1·50	1·50
		a.	Horiz pair. Nos. 1822/3	3·00	3·00
		ab.	Imperf (horiz pair)	£700	
1823	**1148**	41p.	ultram, scar, new bl, emer & silver	1·50	1·50
1820/3			.. .. *Set of* 4	4·00	4·00

Nos. 1820/1 and 1822/3 were printed together, *se-tenant*, in horizontal pairs throughout the sheets.

Stamps in similar designs were also issued by France.

1149 Groundcrew replacing Smoke Canisters on Douglas Boston of 88 Sqn

1150 H.M.S. *Warspite* (battleship) shelling Enemy Positions

1151 Commandos landing on Gold Beach

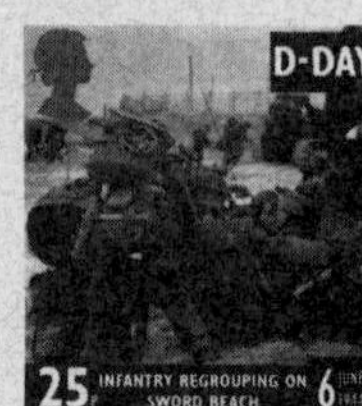

1152 Infantry regrouping on Sword Beach

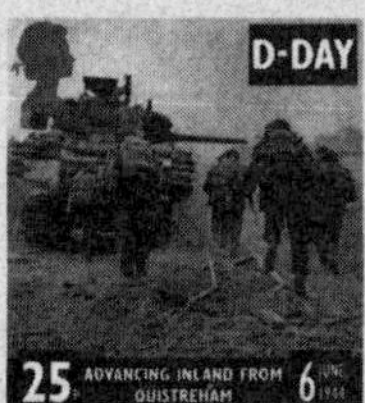

1153 Tank and Infantry advancing, Ouistreham

(Des K. Bassford from contemporary photographs. Litho Questa)

1994 (6 June). *50th Anniv of D-Day. Two phosphor bands. P* 14½×14.

1824	**1149**	25p.	pink, greenish yell, blackish lilac, slate-black, brt scarlet & silver-grey	1·00	1·00
		a.	Horiz strip of 5. Nos. 1824/8 ..	4·50	4·50
1825	**1150**	25p.	pink, greenish yell, blackish lilac, slate-black, brt scarlet & silver-grey	1·00	1·00
1826	**1151**	25p.	pink, greenish yell, blackish lilac, slate-black, brt scarlet & silver-grey	1·00	1·00
1827	**1152**	25p.	pink, greenish yell, blackish lilac, slate-black, brt scarlet & silver-grey	1·00	1·00
1828	**1153**	25p.	pink, greenish yell, blackish lilac, slate-black, brt scarlet & silver-grey	1·00	1·00
1824/8			.. .. *Set of* 5	4·50	4·50

Nos. 1824/8 were printed together, *se-tenant*, in horizontal strips of 5 throughout the sheet.

1154 The Old Course, St. Andrews

1155 The 18th Hole, Muirfield

1156 The 15th Hole ("Luckyslap"), Carnoustie

1157 The 8th Hole ("The Postage Stamp"), Royal Troon

1158 The 9th Hole, Turnberry

(Des P. Hogarth)

1994 (5 July). *Scottish Golf Courses. One phosphor band* (19*p.*) *phosphorised paper* (*others*). *P* 14½×14.

1829	**1154**	19p.	yellow-green, olive-grey, orange-verm, apple-green, blue & grey-blk	55	
1830	**1155**	25p.	yellow-green, lemon, brt orange, apple-green, blue, mag & grey-blk	80	
1831	**1156**	30p.	yellow-green, yellow, rosine, emer, blue-green, new blue & grey-black	1·00	1·
1832	**1157**	35p.	yellow-green, yellow, rosine, apple-green, new blue, dull bl & grey-blk	1·25	1·
1833	**1158**	41p.	yellow-grn, lemon, magenta, apple-green, dull blue, new bl & grey-blk	1·40	1·
1829/33			.. .. *Set of* 5	4·75	4·

Nos. 1829/33 commemorate the 250th anniversary of golf's fi set of rules produced by the Honourable Company of Edinbur Golfers.

1159 Royal Welsh Show, Llanelwedd

1160 All England Tennis Championships, Wimbledon

1161 Cowes Week

1162 Test Match, Lord's

1163 Braemar Gathering

(Des M. Cook)

1994 (2 Aug). *The Four Seasons. Summertime. One phosph band* (19*p.*) *or phosphorised paper* (*others*). *P* 15×14.

1834	**1159**	19p.	black, greenish yell, brt magenta, brown, yellow-brown & new blue	50	
1835	**1160**	25p.	black, greenish yellow, magenta, reddish violet, yellow-grn, myrtle-green and new blue	75	
1836	**1161**	30p.	black, greenish yellow, bright magenta, yellow-ochre, deep slate-blue, blue-green and blue ..	1·10	1·

837 **1162** 35p. black, greenish yellow, magenta, slate-lilac, yellow-green, deep bluish green and bright blue .. 1·25 1·25
838 **1163** 41p. black, greenish yellow, bright magenta, deep claret, light brown, myrtle-green and bright blue .. 1·40 1·40
834/8 .. .. *Set of* 5 4·50 4·50

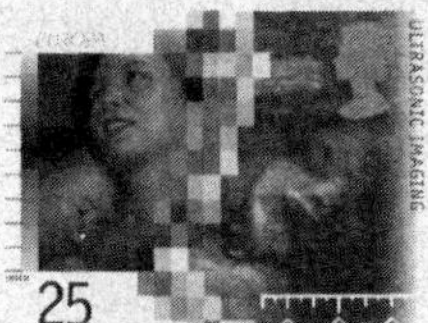

1164 Ultrasonic Imaging

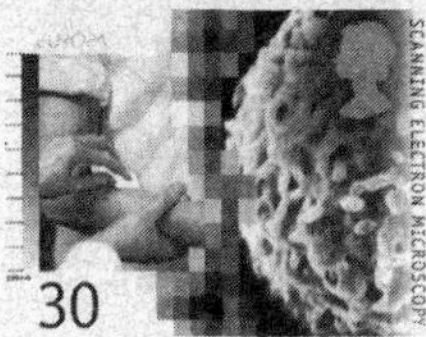

1165 Scanning Electron Microscopy

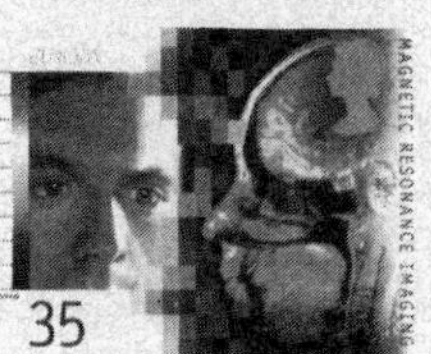

1166 Magnetic Resonance Imaging

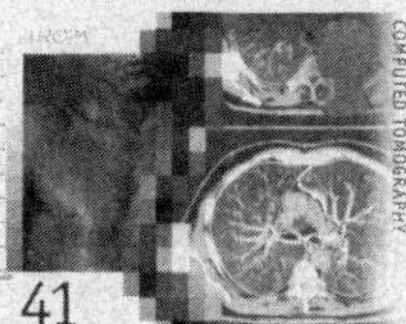

1167 Computed Tomography

(Des P. Vermier and J-P. Tibbles. Photo Enschedé)

994 (27 Sept). *Europa. Medical Discoveries. Phosphorised paper. P* 14×14½.
839 **1164** 25p. greenish yellow, bright magenta, new blue, black and silver .. 65 65
a. Imperf (vert pair) .. ..
840 **1165** 30p. greenish yellow, bright magenta, new blue, black and silver .. 85 85
841 **1166** 35p. greenish yellow, bright magenta, new blue, black and silver .. 90 90
842 **1167** 41p. greenish yellow, bright magenta, new blue, black and silver .. 1·00 1·00
839/42 .. .. *Set of* 4 3·00 3·00

1168 Mary and Joseph

1169 Three Wise Men

1170 Mary with Doll

1171 Shepherds

1172 Angels

(Des Yvonne Gilbert)

1994 (1 Nov). *Christmas. Children's Nativity Plays. One phosphor band* (19*p*) *or phosphorised paper* (*others*). *P* 15×14.
1843 **1168** 19p. turquoise-green, greenish yell, brt magenta, new bl, dull bl & grey-blk 60 60
a. Imperf (pair) £200
1844 **1169** 25p. orange-brown, greenish yellow, brt mag, new bl, lt bl, bistre & grey-blk 80 80
1845 **1170** 30p. lt brown, greenish yellow, brt mag, bl, turq-bl, new bl & brownish grey 90 90
1846 **1171** 35p. dp grey-brn, greenish yell, brt mag, turq-bl, dull violet-bl, ochre & brn 1·00 1·00
1847 **1172** 41p. blue, greenish yellow, brt magenta, turquoise-blue, light blue & dp grey 1·10 1·10
1843/7 .. .. *Set of* 5 4·00 4·00

1173 Sophie (black cat)

1174 Puskas (Siamese) and Tigger (tabby)

1175 Chloe (ginger cat)

1176 Kikko (tortoiseshell) and Rosie (Abyssinian)

1177 Fred (black and white cat)

(Des Elizabeth Blackadder. Litho Questa)

1995 (17 Jan). *Cats. One phosphor band* (19*p.*) *or two phosphor bands* (*others*). *P* 14½×14.
1848 **1173** 19p. new blue, greenish yellow, magenta, black and brown-red .. 60 60
1849 **1174** 25p. new blue, greenish yellow, mag, black and dull yellow-green .. 75 75
1850 **1175** 30p. new blue, greenish yellow, mag, black and yellow-brown .. .. 1·00 1·00
1851 **1176** 35p. new blue, greenish yellow, magenta, black and yellow .. 1·10 1·10
1852 **1177** 41p. new blue, greenish yellow, mag, black and reddish orange .. 1·25 1·25
1848/52 .. .. *Set of* 5 4·25 4·25

1178 Dandelions

1179 Sweet Chestnut Leaves

1180 Garlic Leaves

1181 Hazel Leaves

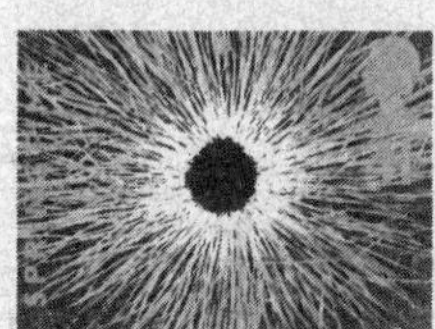

1182 Spring Grass

1995 (14 Mar). *The Four Seasons. Springtime. Plant Sculptures by Andy Goldsworthy. One phosphor band* (19*p.*) *or two phosphor bands* (*others*). *P* 15×14.
1853 **1178** 19p. silver, greenish yellow, magenta, green and grey-black 65 65
1854 **1179** 25p. silver, greenish yellow, magenta, new blue, and black 75 75
1855 **1180** 30p. silver, greenish yellow, magenta, new blue, and black .. .. 1·10 1·10
1856 **1181** 35p. silver, greenish yellow, magenta, new blue, and black .. .. 1·10 1·10
1857 **1182** 41p. silver, greenish yellow, magenta, new blue, blue-green and black .. 1·40 1·40
1853/7 .. .. *Set of* 5 4·50 4·50

1183 "La Danse a la Campagne" (Renoir)

1184 "Troilus and Criseyde" (Peter Brookes)

1185 "The Kiss" (Rodin)

1186 "Girls on the Town" (Beryl Cook)

1187 "Jazz" (Andrew Mockett)

1188 "Girls performing a Kathak Dance" (Aurangzeb period)

1189 "Alice Keppel with her Daughter" (Alice Hughes)

1190 "Children Playing" (L. S. Lowry)

1191 "Circus Clowns" (Emily Firmin and Justin Mitchell)

1192 Decoration from "All the Love Poems of Shakespeare" (Eric Gill)

(Des Newell and Sorrell. Litho Walsall)

1995 (21 Mar). *Greetings Stamps. "Greetings in Art". Two phosphor bands. P* 14½×14 (*with one elliptical hole on each vertical side*).

1858 **1183** (1st) greenish yellow, new blue, magenta, black and silver .. 40 45
a. Booklet pane. Nos. 1858/67 .. 4·00
ab. Silver (Queen's head and "1ST") omitted £5500
1859 **1184** (1st) greenish yellow, new blue, magenta, black and silver .. 40 45

1860 **1185** (1st) greenish yellow, new blue, magenta, black and silver .. 40 45
1861 **1186** (1st) greenish yellow, new blue, magenta, black and silver .. 40 45
1862 **1187** (1st) greenish yellow, new blue, magenta, black and silver .. 40 45
1863 **1188** (1st) greenish yellow, new blue, magenta, black and silver .. 40 45
1864 **1189** (1st) purple-brown and silver .. 40 45
1865 **1190** (1st) greenish yellow, new blue, magenta, black and silver .. 40 45
1866 **1191** (1st) greenish yellow, new blue, magenta, black and silver .. 40 45
1867 **1192** (1st) black, greenish yellow and silver 40 45
1858/67 .. .. *Set of* 10 4·00 4·25

Nos. 1858/67 were only available in £2.50 stamp booklets (sold at £2.60 from 8 July 1996).

No. 1858ab also shows the phosphor bands omitted.

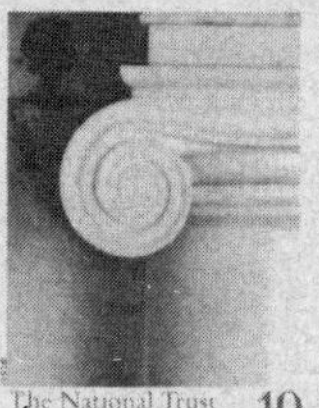

1193 Fireplace Decoration, Attingham Park, Shropshire

1194 Oak Seedling

1195 Carved Table Leg, Attingham Park

1196 St. David's Head, Dyfed, Wales

1197 Elizabethan Window, Little Moreton Hall, Cheshire

(Des T. Evans)

1995 (11–25 Apr). *Centenary of The National Trust. One phosphor band* (19*p.*), *two phosphor bands* (25*p.*, 35*p.*) *or phosphorised paper* (30*p.*, 41*p.*). *P* 14×15.

1868 **1193** 19p. grey-green, stone, grey-brown, grey-black and gold .. 55 55
1869 **1194** 25p. grey-green, greenish yellow, mag, new blue, gold and black .. 75 75
a. Booklet pane. No. 1869×6 with margins all round (25 April) .. 3·50
1870 **1195** 30p. grey-green, greenish yellow, mag, new blue, gold, black & slate-black 90 90
1871 **1196** 35p. grey-green, greenish yellow, magenta, blue, gold and black .. 1·00 1·00
1872 **1197** 41p. grey-green, greenish yell, brt green, slate-grn, gold, blackish brn & blk 1·25 1·25
1868/72 .. .. *Set of* 5 4·00 4·00

Booklet pane No. 1869a comes from the £6 "National Trust" booklet.

1198 British Troops and French Civilians celebrating

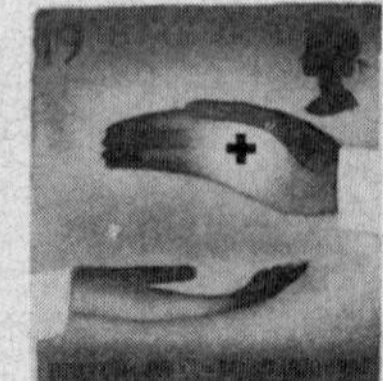

1199 Symbolic Hands and Red Cross

1200 St. Paul's Cathedral and Searchlights

1201 Symbolic Hand releasing Peace Dove

1202 Symbolic Hands

(Des J. Gorham (Nos. 1873, 1875), J-M. Folon (others))

1995 (2 May). *Europa. Peace and Freedom. One phosphor band* (*Nos.* 1873/4) *or two phosphor bands* (*others*). *P* 14½×14.

1873 **1198** 19p. silver, bistre-brown and grey-black 60 6
1874 **1199** 19p. silver, bistre-yellow, brt rose-red, vermilion, bright blue & slate-blue 60 6
1875 **1200** 25p. silver, blue and grey-black .. 85 8
1876 **1201** 25p. silver, verm, brt blue & grey-black 85 8
a. Imperf (vert pair) .. ..
1877 **1202** 30p. silver, bistre-yellow, brt magenta, pale greenish blue, grey-blk & flesh 1·00 1·0
1873/7 .. .. *Set of* 5 3·50 3·5

Nos. 1873 and 1875 commemorate the 50th anniversary of the end of the Second World War, No. 1874 the 125th anniversary of the British Red Cross Society and Nos. 1876/7 the 50th anniversary of the United Nations

Nos. 1876/7 include the "EUROPA" emblem.

1203 *The Time Machine*

1204 *The First Men in the Moon*

1205 *The War of the Worlds*

1206 *The Shape of Things to Come*

(Des Siobhan Keaney. Litho Questa)

1995 (6 June). *Science Fiction. Novels by H. G. Wells. Two phosphor bands. P* 14½×14.

1878 **1203** 25p. new blue, greenish yellow, magenta, black and rosine .. 65 65
1879 **1204** 30p. new blue, greenish yellow, black, rosine and violet 95 95
1880 **1205** 35p. rosine, greenish yellow, violet, black and bright blue-green .. 1·00 1·00
1881 **1206** 41p. new blue, greenish yellow, magenta, black and rosine .. 1·10 1·10
1878/81 .. .. *Set of* 4 3·25 3·25

Nos. 1878/81 commemorate the centenary of publication of Wells's *The Time Machine*.

1207 The Swan, 1595

1208 The Rose, 1592

1209 The Globe, 1599 **1210** The Hope, 1613

1211 The Globe, 1614

(Des C. Hodges. Litho Walsall)

5 (8 Aug). *Reconstruction of Shakespeare's Globe Theatre. wo phosphor bands. P* 14½.

2 **1207** 25p. brownish grey, black, magenta, new blue and greenish yellow .. 80 80
a. Horiz strip of 5. Nos. 1882/6 .. 3·50 3·50
3 **1208** 25p. brownish grey, black, magenta, new blue and greenish yellow .. 80 80
4 **1209** 25p. brownish grey, black, magenta, new blue and greenish yellow .. 80 80
5 **1210** 25p. brownish grey, black, magenta, new blue and greenish yellow .. 80 80
5 **1211** 25p. brownish grey, black, magenta, new blue and greenish yellow .. 80 80
2/6 .. .. *Set of* 5 3·50 3·50

os. 1882/6 were printed together, *se-tenant*, in horizontal strips 5 throughout the sheet with the backgrounds forming a posite design.

1212 Sir Rowland Hill and Uniform Penny Postage Petition **1213** Hill and Penny Black

1214 Guglielmo Marconi and Early Wireless **1215** Marconi and Sinking of *Titanic* (liner)

s The Four Hundred, Eng C. Slania. Recess and litho Harrison)

5 (5 Sept). *Pioneers of Communications. One phosphor band 9p.) or phosphorised paper (others). P* 14½×14.

7 **1212** 19p. silver, red and black 55 55
3 **1213** 25p. silver, brown and black 80 80
a. Silver (Queen's head and face value) omitted £200
9 **1214** 41p. silver, grey-green and black .. 1·10 1·10
) **1215** 60p. silver, deep ultramarine and black 1·50 1·50
7/90 .. .. *Set of* 4 3·50 3·50

os. 1887/8 mark the birth bicentenary of Sir Rowland Hill and . 1889/90 the centenary of the first radio transmissions.

1216 Harold Wagstaff **1217** Gus Risman

1218 Jim Sullivan **1219** Billy Batten

1220 Brian Bevan

(Des C. Birmingham)

1995 (3 Oct). *Centenary of Rugby League. One phosphor band (19p.) or two phosphor bands (others). P* 14×14½.

1891 **1216** 19p. blue, greenish yellow, magenta, new blue, grey-black and black .. 55 55
1892 **1217** 25p. slate-purple, greenish yellow, mag, new blue, grey-black & black .. 70 70
1893 **1218** 30p. slate-green, greenish yellow, bright purple, new blue, grey-black & blk 80 80
1894 **1219** 35p. slate-black, greenish yellow, mag, new blue and black .. .. 1·00 1·00
1895 **1220** 41p. bluish grey, orange-yellow, mag, new blue, grey-black and black .. 1·40 1·40
1891/5 .. .. *Set of* 5 4·00 4·00

1221 European Robin in Mouth of Pillar Box

1222 European Robin on Railings and Holly

1223 European Robin on Snow-covered Milk Bottles

1224 European Robin on Road Sign

1225 European Robin on Door Knob and Christmas Wreath

(Des K. Lilly)

1995 (30 Oct). *Christmas. Christmas Robins. One phosphor band (19p.) or two phosphor bands (others). P* 15×14.

1896 **1221** 19p. silver, greenish yellow, vermilion, orange-vermilion, bistre and black 45 45
1897 **1222** 25p. silver, greenish yellow, scarlet, pale blue, ochre and black 60 60
1898 **1223** 30p. silver, greenish yellow, rose-carmine, lt green, olive-brn & grey 80 80
1899 **1224** 41p. silver, greenish yellow, rose-red, dull blue, bistre and black .. 1·10 1·10
1900 **1225** 60p. silver, orange-yellow, red-orange, bistre and black .. .. .. 1·50 1·50
1896/1900 .. .. *Set of* 5 4·00 4·00

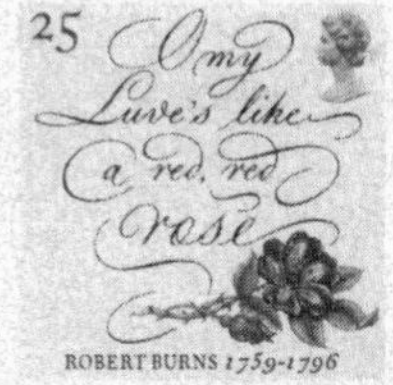

1226 Opening Lines of "To a Mouse" and Fieldmouse **1227** "O my Luve's like a red, red rose" and Wild Rose

1228 "Scots, wha hae wi Wallace bled" and Sir William Wallace **1229** "Auld Lang Syne" and Highland Dancers

(Des Tayburn Design Consultancy. Litho Questa)

1996 (25 Jan). *Death Bicentenary of Robert Burns (Scottish poet). One phosphor band (19p.) or 2 phosphor bands (others). P* 14½.

1901 **1226** 19p. cream, bistre-brown and black .. 55 55
1902 **1227** 25p. cream, bistre-brown, black, mag, bistre-yellow and new blue .. 80 80
1903 **1228** 41p. cream, bistre-brown, black, mag, bistre-yellow and new blue .. 1·10 1·10
1904 **1229** 60p. cream, bistre-brown, black, mag, bistre-yellow and new blue .. 1·50 1·50
1901/4 .. .. *Set of* 4 3·50 3·50

1230 "MORE! LOVE" (Mel Calman)

1231 "Sincerely" (Charles Barsotti)

1232 "Do you have something for the HUMAN CONDITION?" (Mel Calman)

1233 "MENTAL FLOSS" (Leo Cullum)

1234 "4.55 P.M." (Charles Barsotti)

1235 "Dear lottery prize winner" (Larry)

1236 "I'm writing to you because...." (Mel Calman)

1237 "FETCH THIS, FETCH THAT" (Charles Barsotti)

1238 "My day starts before I'm ready for it" (Mel Calman)

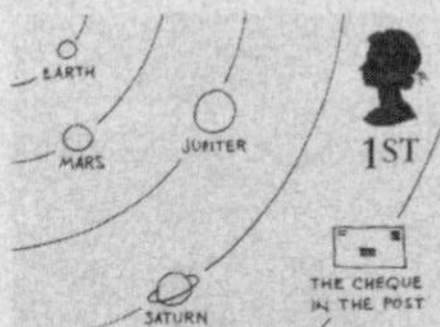

1239 "THE CHEQUE IN THE POST" (Jack Ziegler)

(Des M. Wolff. Litho Walsall)

1996 (26 Feb–11 Nov). *Greeting Stamps. Cartoons. "All-over" phosphor. P* 14½×14 (*with one elliptical hole on each vertical side*).

1905 **1230** (1st) black and bright mauve .. 40 45
a. Booklet pane. Nos. 1905/14 .. 4·00
p. Two phosphor bands (11 Nov) .. 40 45
pa. Booklet pane. Nos. 1905p/14p .. 4·00
1906 **1231** (1st) black and blue-green .. 40 45
p. Two phosphor bands (11 Nov) .. 40 45
1907 **1232** (1st) black and new blue .. 40 45
p. Two phosphor bands (11 Nov) .. 40 45
1908 **1233** (1st) black and bright violet .. 40 45
p. Two phosphor bands (11 Nov) .. 40 45
1909 **1234** (1st) black and vermilion .. 40 45
p. Two phosphor bands (11 Nov) .. 40 45
1910 **1235** (1st) black and new blue .. 40 45
p. Two phosphor bands (11 Nov) .. 40 45
1911 **1236** (1st) black and vermilion .. 40 45
p. Two phosphor bands (11 Nov) .. 40 45
1912 **1237** (1st) black and bright violet .. 40 45
p. Two phosphor bands (11 Nov) .. 40 45
1913 **1238** (1st) black and blue-green .. 40 45
p. Two phosphor bands (11 Nov) .. 40 45
1914 **1239** (1st) black and bright mauve .. 40 45
p. Two phosphor bands (11 Nov) .. 40 45
1905/14 .. .. *Set of* 10 4·00 4·50
1905p/14p .. .. *Set of* 10 4·00 4·50

Nos. 1905/14 were issued in £2.50 stamp booklets (sold at £2.60 from 8 July 1996), together with a pane of twenty half stamp-sized labels. The stamps and labels were attached to the booklet cover by a common gutter margin.

1240 "Muscovy Duck" **1241** "Lapwing"

1242 "White-fronted Goose" **1243** "Bittern"

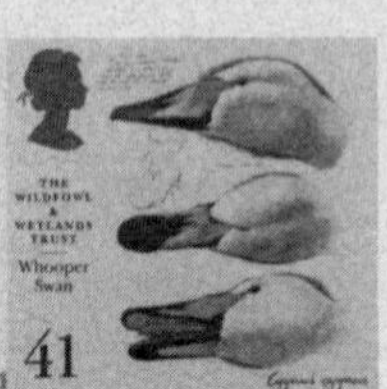

1244 "Whooper Swan"

(Des Moseley Webb)

1996 (12 Mar). 50*th Anniv of the Wildfowl and Wetlands Trust. Bird paintings by C. F. Tunnicliffe. One phosphor band* (19*p.*) *or phosphorised paper* (*others*). *P* 14×14½.

1915 **1240** 19p. sepia, orange-yellow, brown, pale buff, grey and gold 50 50
1916 **1241** 25p. bistre-brown, greenish yell, mag, new blue, pale buff, gold & black 70 70
1917 **1242** 30p. bistre-brown, greenish yell, mag, new bl, pale buff, gold & grey-blk 80 80
1918 **1243** 35p. sepia, pale orange, lake-brn, brn-olive, pale buff, gold & grey-black 1·10 1·10
1919 **1244** 41p. sepia, greenish yellow, magenta, new bl, pale buff, gold & grey-blk 1·40 1·40
1915/19 .. .. *Set of* 5 4·00 4·00

1245 The Odeon, Harrogate

1246 Laurence Olivier and Vivien Leigh in *Lady Hamilton* (film)

1247 Old Cinema Ticket

1248 Pathé News Still

1249 Cinema Sign, The Odeon, Manchester

(Des The Chase)

1996 (16 Apr). *Centenary of Cinema. One phosphor band* (19 *or two phosphor bands* (*others*). *P* 14×14½.

1920 **1245** 19p. black, greenish yellow, silver, bright magenta and new blue .. 50
1921 **1246** 25p. black, greenish yellow, silver, bright magenta and new blue .. 70
1922 **1247** 30p. black, greenish yellow, silver, bright magenta and new blue .. 80
1923 **1248** 35p. black, red and silver .. .. 1·10 1
1924 **1249** 41p. black, greenish yellow, silver, bright magenta and new blue .. 1·40 1
1920/4 .. .. *Set of* 5 4·00 4

1250 Dixie Dean

1251 Bobby Moore

1252 Duncan Edwards

1253 Billy Wright

1254 Danny Blanchflower

(Des H. Brown. Litho Questa)

1996 (14 May). *European Football Championship. One phosp band* (19*p.*) *or two phosphor bands* (*others*). *P* 14½×14.

1925 **1250** 19p. vermilion, black, pale grey and grey 40
a. Booklet pane. No. 1925×4 with margins all round .. .. 1·50
1926 **1251** 25p. brt emerald, blk, pale grey & grey 70
a. Booklet pane. No. 1926×4 with margins all round .. .. 2·25
1927 **1252** 35p. orge-yellow, blk, pale grey & grey 1·25
a. Booklet pane. No. 1927/9, each × 2, with margins all round .. 6·50
1928 **1253** 41p. new blue, black, pale grey and grey 1·25
1929 **1254** 60p. brt orange, black, pale grey & grey 1·60
1925/9 .. .. *Set of* 5 4·50

1255 Athlete on Starting Blocks

1256 Throwing the Javelin

1257 Basketball

1258 Swimming

1259 Athlete celebrating and Olympic Rings

(Des N. Knight. Litho Questa)

6 (9 July). *Olympic and Paralympic Games, Atlanta. Two hosphor bands. P* 14½×14.

0	**1255**	26p. greenish grey, silver, rosine, black, magenta, bistre-yellow & new blue	90	90
		a. Horiz strip of 5. Nos. 1930/4 ..	4·00	4·00
1	**1256**	26p. greenish grey, silver, rosine, black, magenta, bistre-yellow & new blue	90	90
2	**1257**	26p. greenish grey, silver, rosine, black, magenta, bistre-yellow & new blue	90	90
3	**1258**	26p. greenish grey, silver, rosine, black, magenta, bistre-yellow & new blue	90	90
4	**1259**	26p. greenish grey, silver, rosine, black, magenta, bistre-yellow & new blue	90	90
0/4		.. .. *Set of* 5	4·00	4·00

Nos. 1930/4 were printed together, *se-tenant*, in horizontal strips 5 throughout the sheet.

1260 Prof. Dorothy Hodgkin (scientist)

1261 Dame Margot Fonteyn (ballerina)

1262 Dame Elisabeth Frink (sculptress)

1263 Dame Daphne du Maurier (novelist)

1264 Dame Marea Hartman (sports administrator)

(Des Stephanie Nash)

1996 (6 Aug). *Europa. Famous Women. One phosphor band* (20*p*.) *or two phosphor bands* (*others*). *P* 14½.

1935	**1260**	20p. dull blue-grn, brownish grey & blk	50	50
1936	**1261**	26p. dull mauve, brownish grey & black	70	70
		a. Imperf (horiz pair)	£250	
1937	**1262**	31p. bronze, brownish grey and black	90	90
1938	**1263**	37p. silver, brownish grey and black ..	1·10	1·10
1939	**1264**	43p. gold, brownish grey and black ..	1·25	1·25
1935/9		.. .. *Set of* 5	4·00	4·00

Nos. 1936/7 include the "EUROPA" emblem.

1265 *Muffin the Mule*

1266 *Sooty*

1267 *Stingray*

1268 *The Clangers*

1269 *Dangermouse*

(Des Tutssells. Photo Enschedé)

1996 (3 Sept)–**97.** *50th Anniv of Children's Television. One phosphor band* (20*p*.) *or two phosphor bands* (*others*). *P* 14½×14.

1940	**1265**	20p. deep claret, black, magenta, rosine and greenish yellow	55	55
		a. Perf 15×14 (23.9.97)	1·00	1·00
		ab. Booklet pane. No. 1940a×4 with margins all round	4·00	
1941	**1266**	26p. bright blue, black, deep grey-blue, magenta and greenish yellow ..	80	80
1942	**1267**	31p. greenish blue, black, new blue, magenta and greenish yellow ..	1·00	1·00
1943	**1268**	37p. dull violet-blue, black, new blue, magenta and greenish yellow ..	1·25	1·25
1944	**1269**	43p. bright purple, black, new blue, magenta and greenish yellow ..	1·40	1·40
1940/4		.. .. *Set of* 5	4·50	4·50

No. 1940a comes from stamp booklets and was printed by Harrison & Sons Ltd.

1270 Triumph TR3

1271 MG TD

1272 Austin-Healey 100

1273 Jaguar XK120

1274 Morgan Plus 4

(Des S. Clay)

1996 (1 Oct). *Classic Sports Cars. One phosphor band* (20*p*.) *or two phosphor bands* (*others*). *P* 14½.

1945	**1270**	20p. silver, greenish yellow, bright scarlet, vermilion, new blue & blk	60	60
1946	**1271**	26p. silver, greenish yellow, magenta, greenish blue and black	70	70
		a. Imperf (pair)		
1947	**1272**	37p. silver, greenish yellow, brt mag, deep turq-blue, new blue & black	1·00	1·00
		a. Imperf (pair)		
1948	**1273**	43p. silver, greenish yellow, magenta, greenish blue and black	1·10	1·10
		a. Imperf (horiz pair)		
1949	**1274**	63p. silver, greenish yellow, magenta, greenish blue, stone and black ..	1·50	1·50
1945/9		.. .. *Set of* 5	4·50	4·50

On Nos. 1946/9 the left-hand phosphor band on each stamp is three times the width of that on the right.

1275 The Three Kings

1276 The Annunciation

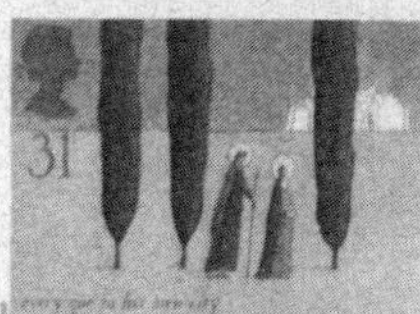

1277 The Journey to Bethlehem

1278 The Nativity

1279 The Shepherds

(Des Laura Stoddart)

1996 (28 Oct). *Christmas. One phosphor band (2nd class) or two phosphor bands (others). P* 15×14.

1950	**1275**	(2nd)	gold, greenish yellow, magenta, blue, black and light brown ..	60	60
1951	**1276**	(1st)	gold, yellow, cerise, new blue, black and light brown	75	75
1952	**1277**	31p.	gold, orange-yellow, cerise, blue, black and light brown	85	85
1953	**1278**	43p.	gold, greenish yellow, magenta, new blue, grey-black & lt brown	1·10	1·10
1954	**1279**	63p.	gold, greenish yellow, magenta, new blue, black and light brown	1·50	1·50
1950/4	..		.. .. .. *Set of* 5	4·50	4·50

1280 *Gentiana acaulis* (Georg Ehret)

1281 *Magnolia grandiflora* (Ehret)

1282 *Camellia japonica* (Alfred Chandler)

1283 *Tulipa* (Ehret)

1284 *Fuchsia* "Princess of Wales" (Augusta Withers)

1285 *Tulipa gesneriana* (Ehret)

1286 *Guzmania splendens* (Charlotte Sowerby)

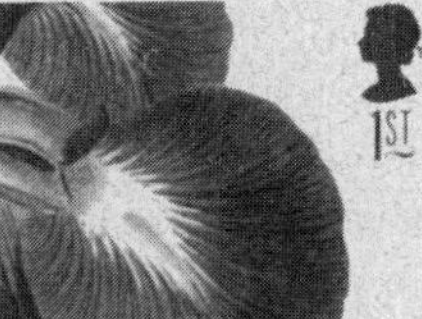

1287 *Iris latifolia* (Ehret)

1288 *Hippeastrum rutilum* (Pierre-Joseph Redoute)

1289 *Passiflora coerulea* (Ehret)

(Des Tutssels. Litho Walsall)

1997 (6 Jan). *Greeting Stamps. 19th-century Flower Paintings. Two phosphor bands. P* 14½×14 (*with one elliptical hole on each vertical side*).

1955	**1280**	(1st)	greenish yellow, new blue, magenta, black, blue-green & gold	40	45
		a.	Booklet pane. Nos. 1955/64 ..	4·00	
		ab.	Gold, blue-green and phosphor omitted		
1956	**1281**	(1st)	greenish yellow, new blue, magenta, black, blue-green & gold	40	45
1957	**1282**	(1st)	greenish yellow, new blue, magenta, black, blue-green & gold	40	45
1958	**1283**	(1st)	greenish yellow, new blue, magenta, black, blue-green & gold	40	45
1959	**1284**	(1st)	greenish yellow, new blue, magenta, black, blue-green & gold	40	45
1960	**1285**	(1st)	greenish yellow, new blue, magenta, black, blue-green & gold	40	45
1961	**1286**	(1st)	greenish yellow, new blue, magenta, black, blue-green & gold	40	45
1962	**1287**	(1st)	greenish yellow, new blue, magenta, black, blue-green & gold	40	45
1963	**1288**	(1st)	greenish yellow, new blue, magenta, black, blue-green & gold	40	45
1964	**1289**	(1st)	greenish yellow, new blue, magenta, black, blue-green & gold	40	45
1955/64	..		.. .. .. *Set of* 10	4·00	4·50

Nos. 1955/64 were issued in £2.60 stamp booklets together with a pane of twenty half-sized labels. The stamp and labels were attached to the booklet cover by a common gutter margin.

1290 "King Henry VIII"

1291 "Catherine of Aragon"

1292 "Anne Boleyn"

1293 "Jane Seymour"

1294 "Anne of Cleves"

1295 "Catherine Howard"

1296 "Catherine Parr"

(Des Kate Stephens from contemporary paintings. Photo Harrisor

1997 (21 Jan). *450th Death Anniv of King Henry VIII. Tw phosphor bands. P* 15 (*No.* 1965) *or* 14×15 (*others*).

1965	**1290**	26p.	gold, greenish yellow, bright purple, new blue and black ..	75	7
		a.	Imperf (pair)		
1966	**1291**	26p.	gold, greenish yellow, bright carmine, new blue and black ..	75	7
		a.	Horiz strip of 6. Nos. 1966/71 ..	4·25	4·2
1967	**1292**	26p.	gold, greenish yellow, bright carmine, new blue and black ..	75	7
1968	**1293**	26p.	gold, greenish yellow, bright carmine, new blue and black ..	75	7
1969	**1294**	26p.	gold, greenish yellow, bright carmine, new blue and black ..	75	7
1970	**1295**	26p.	gold, greenish yellow, bright carmine, new blue and black ..	75	7
1971	**1296**	26p.	gold, greenish yellow, bright carmine, new blue and black ..	75	7
1965/71	..		.. .. .. *Set of* 7	4·50	4·5

Nos. 1966/71 were printed together, *se-tenant*, in horizontal strip of six throughout the sheet.

1297 St. Columba in Boat

1298 St. Columba on Iona

1299 St. Augustine with King Ethelbert

1300 St. Augustine with Model of Cathedral

(Des Claire Melinsky. Photo Enschedé)

1997 (11 Mar). *Religious Anniversaries. Two phosphor band. P* 14½.

1972	**1297**	26p.	greenish yellow, magenta, new blue, grey-black and gold ..	70	7
		a.	Imperf (pair)		
1973	**1298**	37p.	greenish yellow, magenta, new blue, grey-black and gold ..	1·00	1·0
1974	**1299**	43p.	greenish yellow, magenta, new blue, grey-black and gold ..	1·25	1·2
1975	**1300**	63p.	greenish yellow, magenta, new blue, grey-black and gold ..	1·75	1·7
1972/5	..		.. .. .. *Set of* 4	4·25	4·2

Nos. 1972/3 commemorate the 1400th death anniversary of St Columba and Nos. 1974/5 the 1400th anniversary of the arrival c St. Augustine of Canterbury in Kent.

1301

1302

(Des J. Matthews. Photo Enschedé)

997 (18 Mar). *Self-adhesive. One centre phosphor band (2nd) or two phosphor bands (1st). P 14×15 die-cut (with one elliptical hole on each vertical side).*

976 **1301** (2nd) bright blue .. .. 1·00 1·00
977 **1302** (1st) bright orange-red .. .. .. 1·00 1·00

Nos. 1976/7, which were priced at 20p. and 26p. were each sold rolls of 100 with the stamps separate on the backing paper.

Photo Harrison (No. 1978), Harrison (booklets) or Walsall (sheets and booklets) (No. 1979))

997 (21 Apr–23 Sept). *Royal Golden Wedding (1st issue). Designs as T* **367** *and* **914** *but colours changed. Two phosphor bands. P 15×14 (with one elliptical hole on each vertical side).*

978 **367** 26p. gold 80 80
a. Imperf (horiz pair) £2000
l. Booklet pane Nos. 1978/9, each × 4, and centre label with margins all round (23 Sept) .. .. 3·50
979 **914** (1st) gold 80 80

See also Nos. 2011/14.

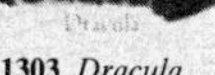

1303 *Dracula*

1304 *Frankenstein*

1305 *Dr. Jekyll and Mr. Hyde*

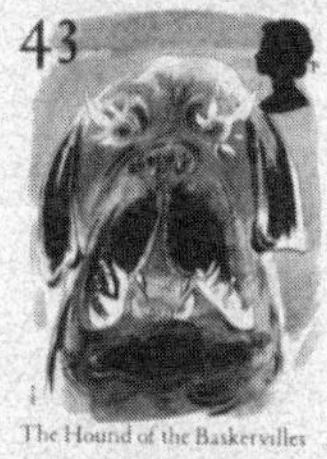

1306 *The Hound of the Baskervilles*

(Des I. Pollock. Photo Walsall)

997 (13 May). *Europa. Tales and Legends. Horror Stories. Two phosphor bands. P 14×15.*

980 **1303** 26p. grey-black, black, new blue, magenta and greenish yellow .. 1·00 1·00
981 **1304** 31p. grey-black, black, new blue, magenta and greenish yellow .. 1·10 1·10
982 **1305** 37p. grey-black, black, new blue, magenta and greenish yellow .. 1·25 1·25
983 **1306** 43p. grey-black, black, new blue, magenta and greenish yellow .. 1·25 1·25
980/3 .. .. *Set of* 4 4·25 4·25

Nos. 1980/3 commemorate the birth bicentenary of Mary Shelley reator of Frankenstein) with the 26p. and 31p. values corporating the "EUROPA" emblem.

Each value has features printed in fluorescent ink which are sible under ultra-violet light.

1307 Reginald Mitchell and Supermarine Spitfire MkIIA

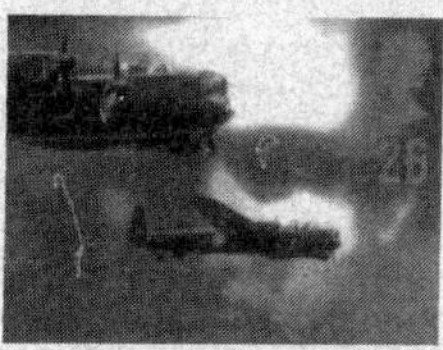

1308 Roy Chadwick and Avro Lancaster MkI

1309 Ronald Bishop and De Havilland Mosquito B MkXVI

1310 George Carter and Gloster Meteor T Mk 7

1311 Sir Sidney Camm and Hawker Hunter FGA Mk9

(Des Turner Duckworth. Photo Harrison)

1997 (10 June). *British Aircraft Designers. One phosphor band (20p.) or two phosphor bands (others). P 15×14.*

1984 **1307** 20p. silver, greenish yellow, magenta, new blue, black and grey .. 55 55
1985 **1308** 26p. silver, greenish yellow, magenta, new blue, black and grey .. 95 95
1986 **1309** 37p. silver, greenish yellow, magenta, new blue, black and grey .. 1·10 1·10
1987 **1310** 43p. silver, greenish yellow, magenta, new blue, black and grey .. 1·25 1·25
1988 **1311** 63p. silver, greenish yellow, magenta, new blue, black and grey .. 1·75 1·75
1984/8 .. .. *Set of* 5 5·00 5·00

1312 Carriage Horse and Coachman

1313 Lifeguards Horse and Trooper

1314 Blues and Royals Drum Horse and Drummer

1315 Duke of Edinburgh's Horse and Groom

(Des J.-L. Benard. Litho Walsall)

1997 (8 July). *"All the Queen's Horses". 50th Anniv of the British Horse Society. One phosphor band (20p.) or two phosphor bands (others). P 14½.*

1989 **1312** 20p. scarlet-vermilion, black, magenta, new blue and greenish yellow .. 70 70
1990 **1313** 26p. scarlet-vermilion, black, magenta, new blue and greenish yellow .. 1·00 1·00
1991 **1314** 43p. scarlet-vermilion, black, magenta, new blue and greenish yellow .. 1·25 1·25
1992 **1315** 63p. scarlet-vermilion, black, magenta, new blue and greenish yellow .. 1·75 1·75
1989/92 .. .. *Set of* 4 4·25 4·25

GH CASTLE

Harrison Nos. 1611/14

GH CASTLE

Enschedé Nos. 1993/6

Differences between Harrison and Enschedé:
Harrison – "C" has top serif and tail of letter points to right. "A" has flat top. "S" has top and bottom serifs.
Enschedé – "C" has no top serif and tail of letter points upwards. "A" has pointed top. "S" has no serifs.

(Des from photos by Prince Andrew, Duke of York. Eng Inge Madle. Recess (Queens head by silk screen process) Enschedé)

1997 (29 July). *Designs as Nos. 1612/14 with Queen's head in silhouette as T* **1044**, *but re-engraved with differences in inscription as shown above. P 15×14 (with one elliptical hole on each vertical side).*

1993 **880** £1.50, deep claret and gold† .. 2·25 2·40
1994 **881** £2 indigo and gold† .. .. .. 3·00 3·25
a. Gold (Queen's head) omitted .. £495
1995 **1044** £3 violet and gold† .. .. .. 4·50 4·75
a. Gold (Queen's head) omitted ..
1996 **882** £5 deep brown and gold† .. .. 7·50 7·75
a. Gold (Queen's head) omitted ..
1993/6 .. .. *Set of* 4 17·00 18·00

†The Queen's head on these stamps is printed in optically variable ink which changes colour from gold to green when viewed from different angles.

No. 1996a occurs on R. 5/8 and 6/8 from some sheets.

1316 Haroldswick, Shetland

1317 Painswick, Gloucestershire

1318 Beddgelert, Gwynedd

1319 Ballyroney, County Down

(Des T. Millington. Photo Enschedé)

1997 (12 Aug). *Sub-Post Offices. One phosphor band (20p.) or two phosphor bands (others). P 14½.*

1997 **1316** 20p. greenish yellow, brt magenta, new blue, grey-black, rosine & bl-grn 65 65
1998 **1317** 26p. greenish yellow, brt magenta, new blue, grey-black, rosine & bl-grn 80 80
1999 **1318** 43p. greenish yellow, brt magenta, new blue, grey-black, rosine & bl-grn 1·25 1·25
2000 **1319** 63p. greenish yellow, brt magenta, new blue, grey-black, rosine & bl-grn 1·75 1·75
1997/2000 .. .. *Set of* 4 4·00 4·00

Nos. 1997/2000 were issued on the occasion of the Centenary of the National Federation of Sub-Postmasters.

PRINTERS. Harrison and Sons Ltd became De La Rue Security Print on 8 September 1997. This was not reflected in the sheet imprints until mid-1998.

1320 *Noddy*

1321 *Famous Five*

1322 *Secret Seven*

1323 *Faraway Tree*

1324 *Malory Towers*

(Des C. Birmingham. Photo Enschedé)

1997 (9 Sept). *Birth Centenary of Enid Blyton (children's author). One phosphor band (20p) or two phosphor bands (others). P* 14×14½.

2001	**1320**	20p. greenish yellow, magenta, new blue, grey-black & deep grey-blue	55	55
2002	**1321**	26p. greenish yellow, magenta, new blue, grey-black & deep grey-blue	95	95
2003	**1322**	37p. greenish yellow, magenta, new blue, grey-black & deep grey-blue	1·10	1·10
2004	**1323**	43p. greenish yellow, magenta, new blue, grey-black & deep grey-blue	1·25	1·25
2005	**1324**	63p. greenish yellow, magenta, new blue, grey-black & deep grey-blue	1·75	1·75
2001/5		.. .. *Set of* 5	5·00	5·00

1325 Children and Father Christmas pulling Cracker

1326 Father Christmas with Traditional Cracker

1327 Father Christmas riding Cracker

1328 Father Christmas on Snowball

1329 Father Christmas and Chimney

(Des J. Gorham and M. Thomas (1st), J. Gorham (others). Photo Harrison)

1997 (27 Oct). *Christmas. 150th Anniv of the Christmas Cracker. One phosphor band (2nd) or two phosphor bands (others). P* 15×14.

2006	**1325**	(2nd) gold, greenish yellow, bright magenta, new blue & grey-black	70	70
		a. Imperf (pair)	£1100	
2007	**1326**	(1st) gold, greenish yellow, bright magenta, new blue & grey-black	80	80
2008	**1327**	31p. gold, greenish yellow, brt mag, new blue, brt blue & grey-black	90	90
		a. Imperf (pair)		
2009	**1328**	43p. gold, greenish yellow, brt mag, pale new blue & grey-black ..	1·10	1·10
2010	**1329**	63p. gold, greenish yellow, bright magenta, new blue & grey-black	1·50	1·50
2006/10		.. .. *Set of* 5	4·50	4·50

1330 Wedding Photograph, 1947

1331 Queen Elizabeth II and Prince Philip, 1997

(Des D. Driver (20p., 43p.), Lord Snowdon (26p., 63p.). Photo Harrison)

1997 (13 Nov). *Royal Golden Wedding (2nd issue). One phosphor band (20p.) or two phosphor bands (others). P* 15.

2011	**1330**	20p. gold, yellow-brown and grey-black	65	65
2012	**1331**	26p. gold, bistre-yellow, magenta, new blue, grey-black and greenish grey	80	80
2013	**1330**	43p. gold, bluish green and grey-black	1·25	1·25
2014	**1331**	63p. gold, bistre-yellow, magenta, new blue, grey-black & lavender-grey	1·75	1·75
2011/14		.. .. *Set of* 4	4·00	4·00

1332 Common Dormouse

1333 Lady's Slipper Orchid

1334 Song Thrush

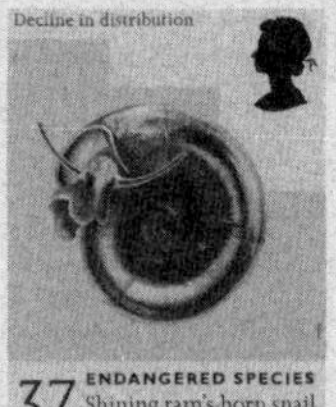

1335 Shining Ram's-horn Snail

1336 Mole Cricket

1337 Devil's Bolete

(Des R. Maude. Litho Questa)

1998 (20 Jan). *Endangered Species. One side phosphor band (20p.) or two phosphor bands (others). P* 14×14½.

2015	**1332**	20p. black, new blue, mag, greenish yellow, dp bl & pale lavender-grey	50	50
		a. Imperf (pair)		
2016	**1333**	26p. black, new blue, mag, greenish yellow, dp blue & pale yell-olive	60	60
2017	**1334**	31p. black, new blue, mag, greenish yellow, dp blue & pale bluish grey	80	80
2018	**1335**	37p. black, new blue, mag, greenish yellow, dp bl & pale greenish grey	90	90
2019	**1336**	43p. black, new blue, mag, greenish yellow, dp blue & pale dull mauve	1·00	1·00
2020	**1337**	63p. black, new blue, mag, greenish yellow, dp blue & pale grey-brown	1·50	1·50
2015/20		.. .. *Set of* 6	4·75	4·75

1338 Diana, Princess of Wales (photo by Lord Snowdon)

1339 At British Lung Foundation Function, April 1997 (photo by John Stillwell)

1340 Wearing Tiara, 1991 (photo by Lord Snowdon)

1341 On Visit to Birmingham, October 1995 (photo by Tim Graham)

1342 In Evening Dress, 1987 (photo by Terence Donovan)

(Des B. Robinson. Photo Harrison)

1998 (3 Feb). *Diana, Princess of Wales Commemoration. Two phosphor bands. P* 14×15.

2021	**1338**	26p. purple, greenish yellow, magenta, new blue and black	40	45
		a. Horiz strip of 5. Nos. 2021/5 ..	2·00	2·25
		ab. Imperf (horiz strip of 5. Nos. 2021/5)		
		ac. Imperf (horiz strip of 4. Nos. 2021/4)		
		ad. Imperf (horiz strip of 3. Nos. 2021/3)		
2022	**1339**	26p. purple, greenish yellow, magenta, new blue and black	40	45
2023	**1340**	26p. purple, greenish yellow, magenta, new blue and black	40	45
2024	**1341**	26p. purple, greenish yellow, magenta, new blue and black	40	45
2025	**1342**	26p. purple, greenish yellow, magenta, new blue and black	40	45
2021/5		.. .. *Set of* 5	2·00	2·25

Nos. 2021/5 were printed together, *se-tenant*, in horizontal strips of five throughout the sheet.

On No. 2021ac the right-hand stamp in the strip of 5 is perforated between the stamp and right margin only.

1343 Lion of England and Griffin of Edward III

1344 Falcon of Plantagenet and Bull of Clarence

1345 Lion of Mortimer and Yale of Beaufort

1346 Greyhound of Richmond and Dragon of Wales

1347 Unicorn of Scotland and Horse of Hanover

(Des J. Matthews. Recess and litho Harrison)

998 (24 Feb). 650*th Anniv of the Order of the Garter. The Queen's Beasts. Two phosphor bands. P* 15×14.

026	**1343**	26p. silver, green, brt blue, carmine-red, verm, lemon, grey-blk & blk	65	65
		a. Horiz strip of 5. Nos. 2026/30 ..	3·00	3·00
		ab. Missing green (on Nos. 2026, 2028/9) (horiz strip of 5) ..		
027	**1344**	26p. silver, green, brt blue, carm-red, verm, lemon, grey, grey-blk & blk	65	65
028	**1345**	26p. silver, green, brt blue, carm-red, verm, lemon, grey, grey-blk & blk	65	65
029	**1346**	26p. silver, green, brt blue, carm-red, verm, lemon, grey, grey-blk & blk	65	65
030	**1347**	26p. silver, green, brt blue, vermilion, lemon, grey, grey-black & black	65	65
026/30		.. .. *Set of* 5	3·00	3·00

Nos. 2026/30 were printed together, *se-tenant*, in horizontal strips f five throughout the sheet.

The phosphor bands on Nos. 2026/30 are only half the height of e stamps and do not cover the silver parts of the designs.

1348

Des G. Knipe, adapted Dew Gibbons Design Group. Photo Walsall)

998 (10 Mar). *As T* **157** (*Wilding definitive of* 1952–54) *but with face values in decimal currency as T* **1348**. *One side phosphor band* (20*p.*) *or two phosphor bands* (*others*). *P* 14 (*with one elliptical hole on each vertical side*).

031	**1348**	20p. light green	60	60
		b. Booklet pane. No. 2031×6 with margins all round	3·50	
		c. Booklet pane. Nos. 2031×4 and 2032/3, each × 2 and central label with margins all round	5·50	
032		26p. red-brown	60	60
		a. Booklet pane. No. 2032×9 ..	5·25	
		b. Booklet pane. Nos. 2032/3, each × 3	5·00	
033		37p. light purple	1·10	1·10
031/3		.. .. *Set of* 3	2·25	2·25

Nos. 2031/3 were only issued in £7.49 stamp booklets. No. 2031 xists with the phosphor band at left or right

1349 St. John's Point Lighthouse, County Down

1350 Smalls Lighthouse, Pembrokeshire

1351 Needles Rock Lighthouse, Isle of Wight, *c* 1900

1352 Bell Rock Lighthouse, Arbroath, mid-19th-century

1353 Eddystone Lighthouse, Plymouth, 1698

(Des D. Davis and J. Boon. Litho Questa)

1998 (24 Mar). *Lighthouses. One side phosphor band* (20*p.*) *or two phosphor bands* (*others*). *P* 14½×14.

2034	**1349**	20p. gold, greenish yellow, magenta, new blue and black	50	50
2035	**1350**	26p. gold, greenish yellow, magenta, new blue and black	70	70
2036	**1351**	37p. gold, greenish yellow, magenta, new blue and black	1·00	1·00
2037	**1352**	43p. gold, greenish yellow, magenta, new blue and black	1·10	1·10
2038	**1353**	63p. gold, greenish yellow, magenta, new blue and black	1·75	1·75
2034/8		.. .. *Set of* 5	4·50	4·50

Nos. 2034/8 commemorate the 300th anniversary of the first Eddystone Lighthouse and the final year of manned lighthouses.

(Photo Enschedé (coils) or Walsall) (sheets))

1998 (6 Apr). *Self-adhesive Coil Stamps. Designs as T* **913/14**. *One centre phosphor band* (2*nd*), *or two phosphor bands* (1*st*). *P* 15×14 *die-cut* (*with one elliptical hole on each vertical side*).

2039	(2nd) bright blue	30	35
2040	(1st) bright orange-red	40	45

Nos. 2039/40, initially sold for 20p. and 26p., were first issued in rolls of 200 with the surplus self-adhesive paper removed.

2nd and 1st self-adhesive stamps as Nos. 2039/40 were issued in sheets, printed in photogravure by Walsall Security Printers, on 15 June 1998. These are similar to the previous Enschedé coil printings, but the sheets retain the surplus self-adhesive paper around each stamp. Stamps from sheets have square perforation tips instead of the rounded versions to be found on the coils.

1354 Tommy Cooper

1355 Eric Morecambe

1356 Joyce Grenfell

1357 Les Dawson

1358 Peter Cook

(Des G. Scarfe. Litho Walsall)

1998 (23 Apr). *Comedians. One side phosphor band* (20*p.*) *or two phosphor bands* (*others*). *P* 14½×14.

2041	**1354**	20p. vermilion, black, rose-pink, new blue and greenish-yellow ..	50	50
2042	**1355**	26p. verm, black, rose-pink & new blue	70	70
2043	**1356**	37p. vermilion, black, rose-pink, new blue and greenish-yellow ..	1·00	1·00
2044	**1357**	43p. vermilion, black, rose-pink, new blue and pale orange	1·10	1·10
2045	**1358**	63p. vermilion, black, deep rose-pink, new blue and greenish-yellow ..	1·75	1·75
2041/5		.. .. *Set of* 5	4·50	4·50

Stamps as Type **1356** but with a face value of 30p., were prepared but not issued. Mint examples and a first day cover have been reported.

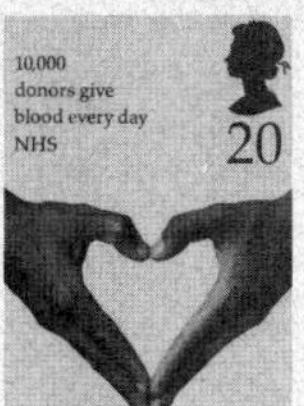

1359 Hands forming Heart

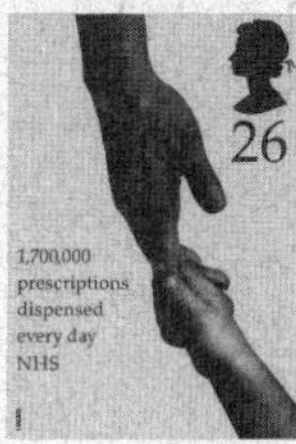

1360 Adult and Child holding Hands

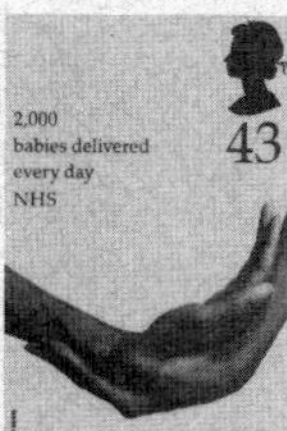

1361 Hands forming Cradle

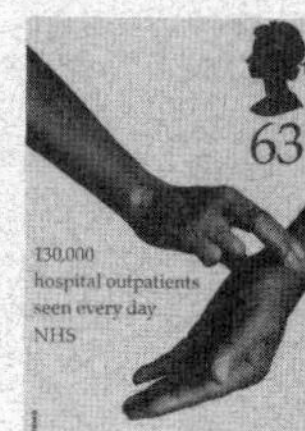

1362 Hand taking Pulse

(Des V. Frost from photos by A. Wilson. Litho Questa)

1998 (23 June). 50*th Anniv of the National Health Service. One side phosphor band* (20*p.*) *or two phosphor bands* (*others*). *P* 14×14½.

2046	**1359**	20p. deep claret, black, grey-brown, pale cream and cream	50	50
2047	**1360**	26p. deep grey-green, black, grey-brown, pale cream and cream ..	70	70
2048	**1361**	43p. deep lilac, black, grey-brown, pale cream and cream	1·10	1·10
2049	**1362**	63p. deep dull blue, black, grey-brown, pale cream and cream	1·75	1·75
2046/9		.. .. *Set of* 4	3·50	3·50

1363 *The Hobbit* (J. R. R. Tolkien)

1364 *The Lion, The Witch and the Wardrobe* (C. S. Lewis)

1365 *The Phoenix and the Carpet* (E. Nesbit)

1366 *The Borrowers* (Mary Norton)

1367 *Through the Looking Glass* (Lewis Carroll)

(Des P. Malone. Photo D.L.R.)

1998 (21 July). *Famous Children's Fantasy Novels. One centre phosphor band* (20*p.*) *or two phosphor bands* (*others*). *P* 15×14.

2050	**1363**	20p.	silver, greenish yellow, bright magenta, new blue, black and gold	50	50
2051	**1364**	26p.	silver, greenish yellow, bright magenta, new blue black and gold	70	70
2052	**1365**	37p.	silver, greenish yellow, bright magenta, new blue, black and gold	1·00	1·00
2053	**1366**	43p.	silver, greenish yellow, bright magenta, new blue, black and gold	1·10	1·10
2054	**1367**	63p.	silver, greenish yellow, bright magenta, new blue, black and gold	1·75	1·75
2050/4	..	..	.. .. .. *Set of* 5	4·50	4·50

Nos. 2050/4 commemorate the birth centenary of C. S. Lewis and the death centenary of Lewis Carroll.

1368 Woman in Yellow Feathered Costume

1369 Woman in Blue Costume and Headdress

1370 Group of Children in White and Gold Robes

1371 Child in "Tree" Costume

(Des T. Hazael. Photo Walsall)

1998 (25 Aug). *Europa. Festivals. Notting Hill Carnival. One centre phosphor band* (20*p.*) *or two phosphor bands* (*others*). *P* 14×14½.

2055	**1368**	20p.	gold, black, new blue, bright magenta and greenish yellow ..	30	35
2056	**1369**	26p.	gold, grey-black, new blue, bright magenta and greenish yellow ..	40	45
2057	**1370**	43p.	gold, grey-black, new blue, bright magenta and bistre-yellow ..	65	70
2058	**1371**	63p.	gold, grey-black, new blue, bright magenta and greenish yellow ..	95	1·00
2055/8	..	..	.. .. .. *Set of* 4	2·25	2·50

The 20p. and 26p. incorporate the "EUROPA" emblem.

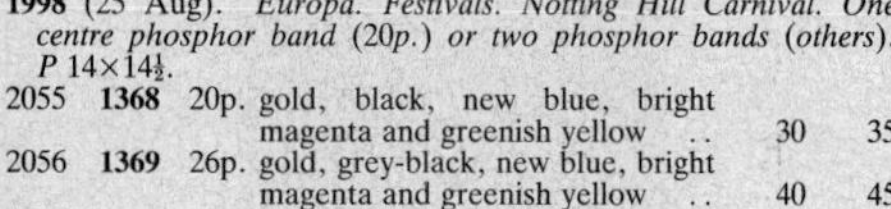

1372 Sir Malcolm Campbell's *Bluebird*, 1925

1373 Sir Henry Segrave's *Sunbeam*, 1926

1374 John G. Parry Thomas' *Babs*, 1926

1375 John R. Cobb's *Railton Mobil Special*, 1947

1376 Donald Campbell's *Bluebird CN7*, 1964

(Des Roundel Design Group. Photo De La Rue)

1998 (29 Sept–13 Oct). *British Land Speed Record Holders. One centre phosphor band* (20*p.*) *or two phosphor bands* (*others*). *P* 15×14.

2059	**1372**	20p.	rosine, greenish yellow, magenta, new blue, black and silver ..	30	35
		a.	Perf 14½×13½ (1 side phosphor band) (13 Oct)	50	50
		ac.	Booklet pane. No. 2059a×4 with margins all round	2·00	
2060	**1373**	26p.	rosine, greenish yellow, magenta, new blue, black and silver ..	40	45
		a.	Rosine (face value) omitted ..		
2061	**1374**	30p.	rosine, greenish yellow, magenta, new blue, black and silver ..	45	50
2062	**1375**	43p.	rosine, greenish yellow, magenta, new blue, black and silver ..	65	70
2063	**1376**	63p.	rosine, greenish yellow, magenta, new blue, black and silver ..	95	1·00
2059/63	..	..	.. .. .. *Set of* 5	2·75	3·00

Nos. 2059/63 commemorate the 50th death anniversary of Sir Malcolm Campbell.

No. 2059a, which occurs with the phosphor band at left or right, comes from stamp booklets and was printed by Walsall.

No. 2060a occurs on the fourth vertical row of several sheets. Other examples exist with either the "2" or the "6" omitted.

1377 Angel with Hands raised in Blessing

1378 Angel praying

1379 Angel playing Flute

1380 Angel playing Lute

1381 Angel praying

(Des Irene von Treskow. Photo De La Rue)

1998 (2 Nov). *Christmas. Angels. One centre phosphor band* (20*p.*) *or two phosphor bands* (*others*). *P* 15×14.

2064	**1377**	20p.	gold, greenish yellow, magenta, new blue and grey-black ..	30	35
		a.	Imperf (pair)		
2065	**1378**	26p.	gold, greenish yellow, magenta, new blue and grey-black ..	40	45
		a.	Imperf (pair)		
2066	**1379**	30p.	gold, greenish yellow, magenta, new blue and grey-black ..	45	50
2067	**1380**	43p.	gold, greenish yellow, magenta, new blue and grey-black ..	65	70
		a.	Imperf (pair)		
2068	**1381**	63p.	gold, greenish yellow, magenta, new blue and grey-black ..	95	1·00
2064/8	..	..	.. .. .. *Set of* 5	2·75	3·00

1382 Greenwich Meridian and Clock (John Harrison's chronometer)

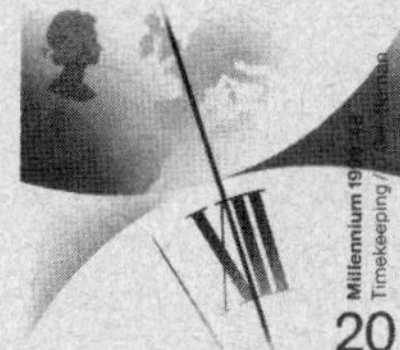

1383 Industrial Worker and Blast Furnace (James Watt's discovery of steam power)

1384 Early Photos of Leaves (Henry Fox-Talbot's photographic experiments)

1385 Computer inside Human Head (Alan Turing's work on computers)

(Des D. Gentleman (20p.), P. Howson (26p.), Z. and Barba Baran (43p.), E. Paolozzi (63p.). Photo Enschedé (26p.) or D La Rue (others))

1999 (12 Jan). *Millennium Series. The Inventors' Tale. One centr phosphor band* (20*p.*) *or two phosphor bands* (*others*). *P* 14×14

2069	**1382**	20p.	silver, deep grey, pale olive-grey, greenish grey, grey-black & bright rose-red	30	3
2070	**1383**	26p.	silver, black, new blue, bright magenta and greenish yellow ..	40	4
2071	**1384**	43p.	silver, greenish yellow, bright crimson, new blue, blk & brt mag	65	7
2072	**1385**	63p.	greenish blue, greenish yellow, cerise, new blue, blk & pale lemon	95	1·0
2069/72	..	..	.. .. .. *Set of* 4	2·25	2·5

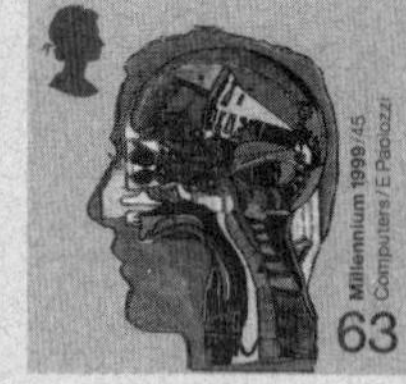

1386 Airliner hugging Globe (International air travel)

1387 Woman on Bicycle (Development of the bicycle)

1388 Victorian Railway Station (Growth of public transport)

1389 Captain Cook and Maori (Captain James Cook's voyages)

(Des G. Hardie (20p.), Sara Fanelli (26p.), J. Lawrence (43p. A. Klimowski (63p.). Photo Enschedé (20p., 63p.) or De La Ru (26p.). Litho Enschedé (43p.))

1999 (2 Feb). *Millennium Series. The Travellers' Tale. One centr phosphor band* (20*p.*) *or two phosphor bands* (*others*). *P* 14×14

2073	**1386**	20p.	silver, vermilion, grey-blk, bluish violet, greenish blue & pale grey	30	3
2074	**1387**	26p.	silver, greenish yellow, cerise, new blue, black and vermilion ..	40	4
2075	**1388**	43p.	grey-black, stone and bronze ..	65	7
2076	**1389**	63p.	silver, grey-black, new blue, brt magenta & greenish yellow ..	95	1·0
2073/6	..	..	.. .. .. *Set of* 4	2·25	2·5

1390

99 (16 Feb). (*a*) *Embossed and litho Walsall. Self-adhesive. Die-cut perf* 14×15.

77 **1390** (1st) grey (face value) (Queen's head in colourless relief) (phosphor background around head) 40 45
l. Booklet pane. No. 2077×4 with margins all round .. .. 1·60

(*b*) *Recess Enschedé. P* 14×14½.

78 **1390** (1st) grey-black (2 phosphor bands) 40 45
l. Booklet pane. No. 2078×4 with margins all round .. .. 1·60

(*c*) *Typo Harrison. P* 14×15

)79 **1390** (1st) black (2 phosphor bands) .. 40 45
l. Booklet pane. No. 2079×4 with margins all round .. .. 1·60

Nos. 2077/9 were only issued in £7.54 stamp booklets.

1391 Vaccinating Child (pattern in cow markings) (Jenner's development of smallpox vaccine)

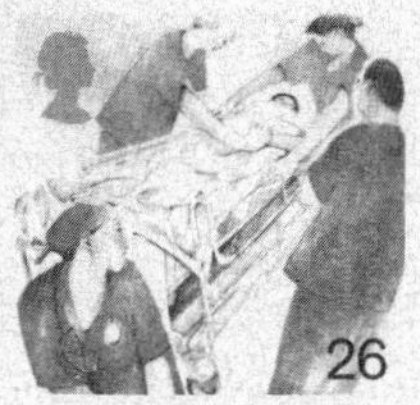

1392 Patient on Trolley (nursing care)

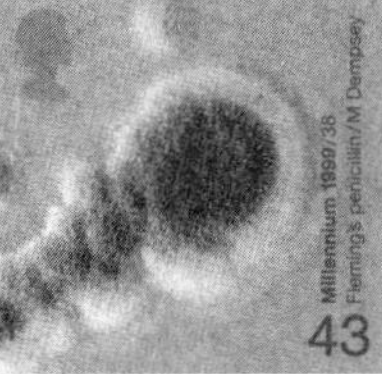

1393 Penicillin Mould (Fleming's discovery of penicillin)

1394 Sculpture of Test-tube Baby (development of in vitro fertilization)

)es P. Brookes (20p.), Susan Macfarlane (26p.), M. Dempsey (43p.), A. Gormley (63p.). Photo Questa)

99 (2 Mar). *Millennium Series. The Patients' Tale. One centre phosphor band* (20p.) *or two phosphor bands* (*others*). *P* 13½×14.

80 **1391** 20p. greenish yellow, bright magenta, new blue, black and silver .. 30 35
81 **1392** 26p. greenish yellow, bright magenta, new blue, blk, silver & dp turq-bl 40 45
82 **1393** 43p. greenish yell, brt mag, new blue, black, dp bluish green & silver 65 70
)83 **1394** 63p. greenish yellow, bright magenta, new blue, blk, silver & blue-blk 95 1·00
)80/3 .. .. *Set of* 4 2·25 2·50

1395 Dove and Norman Settler (medieval migration to Scotland)

1396 Pilgrim Fathers and Red Indian (17th-century migration to America)

1397 Sailing Ship and Aspects of Settlement (19th-century migration to Australia)

1398 Hummingbird and Superimposed Stylised Face (20th-century migration to Great Britain)

)es J. Byrne (20p.), W. McLean (26p.), J. Fisher (43p.), G. Powell (63p.). Litho (20p.) or photo (others) Walsall)

999 (6 Apr). *Millennium Series. The Settlers' Tale. One centre phosphor band* (20p.) *or two phosphor bands* (*others*). *P* 14×14½.

)84 **1395** 20p. gold, silver, black, magenta, blue and greenish yellow 30 35
)85 **1396** 26p. greenish yellow, magenta, new blue, grey-black and silver .. 40 45
)86 **1397** 43p. greenish yellow, magenta, new blue, grey-black, gold & chocolate 65 70
)87 **1398** 63p. greenish yellow, magenta, new bl, reddish vio, dp reddish vio & gold 95 1·00
)84/7 .. .. *Set of* 4 2·25 2·50

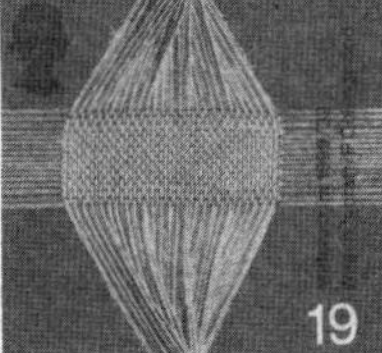

1399 Woven Threads (woollen industry)

1400 Northern Mill Town (cotton industry)

1401 Hull on Slipway (shipbuilding)

1402 Modern Office Block (City of London finance centre)

(Des P. Collingwood (19p.), D. Hockney (26p.), B. Sanderson (44p.), B. Neiland (64p.). Litho (19p.) or photo (others) De La Rue)

1999 (4 May). *Millennium Series. The Workers' Tale. One centre phosphor band* (19p.) *or two phosphor bands* (*others*). *P* 14×14½.

2088 **1399** 19p. drab, greenish yellow, cerise, new blue, grey-black and bronze .. 30 35
2089 **1400** 26p. silver, greenish yellow, rosine, new blue and grey-black .. 40 45
2090 **1401** 44p. silver, greenish yellow, orange-red, brt blue, yell-brn & grey-blk 70 75
2091 **1402** 64p. silver, greenish yellow, rosine, new blue and grey-black .. 1·00 1·10
2088/91 .. .. *Set of* 4 2·40 2·50

1403 Freddie Mercury (lead singer of Queen) ("Popular Music")

1404 Bobby Moore with World Cup, 1966 ("Sport")

1405 Dalek from *Dr. Who* (science-fiction series) ("Television")

1406 Charlie Chaplin (film star) ("Cinema")

(Des P. Blake (19p.), M. White (26p.), Lord Snowdon (44p.), R. Steadman (63p.). Photo Enschedé)

1999 (1 June). *Millennium Series. The Entertainers' Tale. One centre phosphor band* (19p.) *or two phosphor bands* (*others*). *P* 14×14½.

2092 **1403** 19p. greenish yellow, bright magenta, new blue, grey-black and gold .. 30 35
2093 **1404** 26p. greenish yellow, brt magenta, new blue, grey-black, gold & stone .. 40 45
2094 **1405** 44p. greenish yellow, bright magenta, new blue, grey-black and silver 70 75
2095 **1406** 64p. greenish yellow, bright magenta, new blue, grey-black and silver 1·00 1·10
2092/5 .. .. *Set of* 4 2·40 2·50

REGIONAL ISSUES

For Regional Issues of Guernsey, Jersey and the Isle of Man, *see* after Great Britain Postal Fiscals.

Printers (£ s. d. stamps of all regions):—Photo Harrison & Sons. Portrait by Dorothy Wilding Ltd.

DATES OF ISSUE. Conflicting dates of issue have been announced for some of the regional issues, partly explained by the stamps being released on different dates by the Philatelic Bureau in Edinburgh or the Philatelic Counter in London and in the regions. We have adopted the practice of giving the earliest known dates, since once released the stamps could have been used anywhere in the U.K.

I. NORTHERN IRELAND

N 1

N 2

N 3

(Des W. Hollywood (3d., 4d., 5d.), L. Pilton (6d., 9d.), T. Collins (1s. 3d., 1s. 6d.))

1958–67. *W* **179.** *P* 15 × 14.

NI1 **N 1** 3d. deep lilac (18.8.58) 20 10
p. One centre phosphor band (9.6.67) 20 15
NI2 4d. ultramarine (7.2.66) 20 15
p. Two phosphor bands (10.67) .. 20 15
NI3 **N 2** 6d. deep claret (29.9.58) 20 20
NI4 9d. bronze-green (2 phosphor bands) (1.3.67) 30 70
NI5 **N 3** 1s. 3d. green (29.9.58) 30 70
NI6 1s. 6d. grey-blue (2 phosphor bands) (1.3.67) 30 70

1968–69. *No wmk. Chalk-surfaced paper. One centre phosphor band (Nos.* NI8/9) *or two phosphor bands (others). P* 15 × 14.

NI 7 **N 1** 4d. deep bright blue (27.6.68) .. 20 15
NI 8 4d. olive-sepia (4.9.68) 20 15
NI 9 4d. bright vermilion (26.2.69) .. 20 20
NI10 5d. royal blue (4.9.68) 20 20
NI11 **N 3** 1s. 6d. grey-blue (20.5.69) .. 2·50 3·25

No. NI7 was only issued in Northern Ireland with gum arabic. After it had been withdrawn from Northern Ireland but whilst still on sale at the philatelic counters elsewhere, about fifty sheets with PVA gum were sold over the London Philatelic counter on 23 October 1968, and some were also on sale at the British Philatelic Exhibition Post Office in October, without any prior announcement. The other values exist with PVA gum only.

N 4

(Des J. Mathews after plaster cast by Arnold Machin)

1971 (7 July)–**93.** *Decimal Currency. Chalk-surfaced paper. Type* N **4.** *(a) Photo Harrison. With phosphor bands. P* 15×14.

NI12 2½p. bright magenta (1 centre band) .. 80 25
NI13 3p. ultramarine (2 bands) 40 15
NI14 3p. ultramarine (1 centre band) (23.1.74) 20 15
NI15 3½p. olive-grey (2 bands) (23.1.74) .. 20 20
NI16 3½p. olive-grey (1 centre band) (6.11.74) .. 20 25
NI17 4½p. grey-blue (2 bands) (6.11.74) .. 25 25
NI18 5p. reddish violet (2 bands) .. .. 1·50 1·50
NI19 5½p. violet (2 bands) (23.1.74) .. 20 20
NI20 5½p. violet (1 centre band) (21.5.75) .. 20 20
NI21 6½p. greenish blue (1 centre band) (14.1.76) 20 20
NI22 7p. purple-brown (1 centre band) (18.1.78) 35 25
NI23 7½p. chestnut (2 bands) .. .. .. 2·25 2·25
NI24 8p. rosine (2 bands) (23.1.74) .. 30 30
NI25 8½p. yellow-green (2 bands) (14.1.76) .. 30 30
NI26 9p. deep violet (2 bands) (18.1.78) .. 30 30
NI27 10p. orange-brown (2 bands) (20.10.76) .. 35 35
NI28 10p. orange-brown (1 centre band) (23.7.80) 35 35
NI29 10½p. steel-blue (2 bands) (18.1.78) .. 50 50
NI30 11p. scarlet (2 bands) (20.10.76) .. 50 50

(b) Photo Harrison. On phosphorised paper. P 15 × 14.

NI31 12p. yellowish green (23.7.80) 50 50
NI32 13½p. purple-brown (23.7.80) 70 80
NI33 15p. ultramarine (23.7.80) 70 70

(c) Litho Questa. P 14 *(11½p., 12½p., 14p. (No.* NI38), *15½p., 16p., 18p. (No.* NI45), *19½p., 20½p., 22p. (No.* NI53), *26p. (No.* NI60), *28p. (No.* NI62) *or* 15×14 *(others)*

NI34 11½p. drab (1 side band) (8.4.81) .. 70 70
NI35 12p. bright emerald (1 side band) (7.1.86) 70 70
NI36 12½p. light emerald (1 side band) (24.2.82) 60 60
a. Perf 15×14 (28.2.84) .. .. 4·25 4·25
NI37 13p. pale chestnut (1 side band) (23.10.84) 1·25 70
NI38 14p. grey-bl (phosphorised paper) (8.4.81) 70 60
NI39 14p. deep blue (1 centre band) (8.11.88) 70 60
NI40 15p. bright blue (1 centre band) (28.11.89) 70 60
NI41 15½p. pale violet (phosphorised paper) (24.2.82) 80 65
NI42 16p. drab (phosphorised paper) (27.4.83) 1·00 1·00
a. Perf 15×14 (28.2.84) .. .. 9·50 8·00
NI43 17p. grey-blue (phosphorised paper) (23.10.84) .. .. 1·00 80
NI44 17p. deep blue (1 centre band) (4.12.90) 70 80
NI45 18p. dp vio (phosphorised paper) (8.4.81) 90 90
NI46 18p. deep olive-grey (phosphorised paper) (6.1.87) 80 80
NI47 18p. bright green (1 centre band) (3.12.91) 70 70
a. Perf 14 (31.12.92*) .. .. 1·25 1·25
NI48 18p. bright green (1 side band) (10.8.93) 2·50 2·50
l. Booklet pane. Nos. NI48, NI59, S61, S71, W49 and W60 with margins all round .. .. 6·00
NI49 19p. bright orange-red (phosphorised paper) (8.11.88) 80 70
NI50 19½p. olive-grey (phosphorised paper) (24.2.82) .. .. 1·75 2·25
NI51 20p. brownish black (phosphorised paper) (28.11.89) 80 70
NI52 20½p. ultram (phosphorised paper) (27.4.83) 4·00 4·00
NI53 22p. blue (phosphorised paper) (8.4.81) 1·00 1·10
NI54 22p. yellow-green (phosphorised paper) (23.10.84) .. .. 1·00 1·10
NI55 22p. bright orange-red (phosphorised paper) (4.12.90) .. .. 1·00 85
NI56 23p. bright green (phosphorised paper) (8.11.88) .. .. 1·00 1·10
NI57 24p. Indian red (phosphorised paper) (28.11.89) .. .. 1·00 1·10
NI58 24p. chestnut (phosphorised paper) (3.12.91) 90 75
NI59 24p. chestnut (2 bands) (10.8.93) .. 2·00 2·00
NI60 26p. rosine (phosphorised paper) (24.2.82) 1·10 1·40
a. Perf 15×14 (27.1.87) .. .. 3·50 3·50
NI61 26p. drab (phosphorised paper) (4.12.90) 1·00 1·00
NI62 28p. deep violet-blue (phosphorised paper) (27.4.83) .. .. 1·10 1·10
a. Perf 15×14 (27.1.87) .. .. 1·10 1·10
NI63 28p. deep bluish grey (phosphorised paper) (3.12.91) .. .. 1·10 1·10
NI64 31p. bright purple (phosphorised paper) (23.10.84) .. .. 1·40 1·40
NI65 32p. greenish blue (phosphorised paper) (8.11.88) .. .. 1·25 1·25
NI66 34p. deep bluish grey (phosphorised paper) (28.11.89) .. .. 1·40 1·40
NI67 37p. rosine (phosphorised paper) (4.12.90) 1·40 1·40
NI68 39p. bright mauve (phosphorised paper) (3.12.91) .. .. 1·40 1·40

*Earliest known date of use.

No. NI47a was caused by the use of a reserve perforating machine for some printings in the second half of 1992.

Nos. NI48 and NI59 only come from booklets.

From 1972 printings were made on fluorescent white paper and from 1973 printings had dextrin added to the PVA gum (see notes after the 1971 Decimal Machin issue).

(Des J. Matthews after plaster cast by Arnold Machin)

1993 (7 Dec)–**98.** *Chalk-surfaced paper. (a) Litho Questa. One phosphor band (19p., 20p.) or two phosphor bands (others). P* 15×14 *(with one elliptical hole on each vertical side).*

NI69 **N 4** 19p. bistre (1 centre band) 50 50
NI70 19p. bistre (1 side band) (26.7.94) .. 2·50 2·50
a. Booklet pane. Nos. NI70×2, NI72×4, NI74, NI76 and centre label with margins all round .. 6·50
b. Booklet pane. Nos. NI70, NI72, NI74 and NI76 with margins all round .. .. 3·50
d. Booklet pane. Nos. NI70, NI72, S82, S84, W71 and W73 (25.4.95) 7·00
da. Part perf pane* .. .. ..
NI71 20p. brt green (1 centre band) (23.7.96) 70 70
NI72 25p. red 85 85
NI73 26p. red-brown (23.7.96) 90 90
NI74 30p. deep olive-grey .. .. .. 1·00 1·00
NI75 37p. bright mauve (23.7.96) .. .. 1·00 1·00
NI76 41p. grey-brown .. .. .. 1·25 1·25
NI77 63p. light emerald (23.7.96) .. .. 1·75 1·75

(b) Photo Walsall (20p., 26p. (No. NI79b), *63p.), Harrison or Walsall (26p. (No.* NI79), *37p.). P* 14 *(No.* NI78a) *or* 15×14 *(others) (both with one elliptical hole on each vertical side).*

NI78 **N 4** 20p. bright green (1 centre band) (1.7.97) 30 35
NI78*a* 20p. bright green (1 side band) (13.10.98) 80 80
al. Booklet pane. Nos. NI78*a*, S90*a* and W79*a*, and Y1691×3 with margins all round .. .. 4·50
NI79 26p. chestnut (2 bands) (1.7.97) .. 40 45
al. Booklet pane. Nos. NI79/80, S91/2 and W80/1 with margins all round (23.9.97) .. .. 2·75
b. Perf 14 (13.10.98) 80 80
NI80 37p. bright mauve (2 bands) (1.7.97) .. 60 65
NI81 63p. light emerald (2 bands) (1.7.97) .. 95 1·00

Nos. NI70, NI78*a* and NI79b only come from stamp booklets. No. NI70 exists with phosphor band at left or right.

*No, NI70da, which comes from the 1995 National Trust £6 booklet, shows the top two values in the pane of 6 (Nos. S82, S84) completely imperforate and the two Wales values below partly imperforate.

No. NI79al, which was printed by Harrison, comes from the 1997 B.B.C. £6.15 booklet.

II. SCOTLAND

S 1

S 2

S 3

(Des G. Huntly (3d., 4d., 5d), J. Fleming (6d., 9d.), A. Imrie (1s. 3d., 1s. 6d.))

1958–67. *W* **179.** *P* 15 × 14.

S1 **S 1** 3d. deep lilac (18.8.58) 20 15
p. Two phosphor bands (29.1.63) .. 13·00 1·25
pa. One side phosphor band (30.4.65) .. 20 25
pb. One centre phosphor band (9.11.67) 20 15
S2 4d. ultramarine (7.2.66) 20 10
p. Two phosphor bands 20 20
S3 **S 2** 6d. deep claret (29.9.58) 20 15
p. Two phosphor bands (29.1.63) .. 20 25
S4 9d. bronze-green (2 phosphor bands) (1.3.67) 30 30
S5 **S 3** 1s. 3d. green (29.9.58) 30 30
p. Two phosphor bands (29.1.63) .. 30 30
S6 1s. 6d. grey-blue (2 phosphor bands) (1.3.67) 35 30

The one phosphor band on No. S1pa was produced by printing broad phosphor bands across alternate vertical perforations. Individual stamps show the band at right or left (same prices either way).

1967–70. *No wmk. Chalk-surfaced paper. One centre phosphor ban*(S7, S9/10) *or two phosphor bands (others). P* 15 × 14.

S 7 **S 1** 3d. deep lilac (16.5.68) 10
S 8 4d. deep bright blue (28.11.67) .. 10
S 9 4d. olive-sepia (4.9.68) 10
S10 4d. bright vermilion (26.2.69) .. 10
S11 5d. royal blue (4.9.68) 20
S12 **S 2** 9d. bronze-green (28.9.70) .. .. 5·00 6·
S13 **S 3** 1s. 6d. grey-blue (12.12.68) .. .. 1·40 1·

Nos. S7/8 exist with both gum arabic and PVA gum; others wi PVA gum only.

S 4

(Des J. Matthews after plaster cast by Arnold Machin)

1971 (7 July)–**93.** *Decimal Currency. Chalk-surfaced paper. Typ* S **4.**

(a) Photo Harrison. With phosphor bands. P 15 × 14

S14 2½p. bright magenta (1 centre band) .. 25
S15 3p. ultramarine (2 bands) 30
a. Imperf (pair)† £400
S16 3p. ultramarine (1 centre band) (23.1.74) .. 15
S17 3½p. olive-grey (2 bands) (23.1.74) .. 20
S18 3½p. olive-grey (1 centre band) (6.11.74) .. 20
S19 4½p. grey-blue (2 bands) (6.11.74) .. 25
S20 5p. reddish violet (2 bands) .. .. 1·00 1·
S21 5½p. violet (2 bands) (23.1.74) .. 20
S22 5½p. violet (1 centre band) (21.5.75) .. 20
a. Imperf (pair) £350
S23 6½p. greenish blue (1 centre band) (14.1.76) 20
S24 7p. purple-brown (1 centre band) (18.1.78) 25
S25 7½p. chestnut (2 bands) .. .. 1·25 1·
S26 8p. rosine (2 bands) (23.1.74) .. 30
S27 8½p. yellow-green (2 bands) (14.1.76) .. 30
S28 9p. deep violet (2 bands) (18.1.78) .. 30
S29 10p. orange-brown (2 bands) (20.10.76) .. 35
S30 10p. orange-brown (1 centre band) (23.7.80) 35
S31 10½p. steel-blue (2 bands) (18.1.78) .. 50
S32 11p. scarlet (2 bands) (20.10.76) .. 50

(b) Photo Harrison. On phosphorised paper. P 15 × 14

S33 12p. yellowish green (23.7.80) 50
S34 13½p. purple-brown (23.7.80) 70
S35 15p. ultramarine (23.7.80) 60

(c) Litho J.W. One side phosphor band (11½p., 12p., 12½p., 13p.) phosphorised paper (others). P 14

S36 11½p. drab (8.4.81) 80
S37 12p. bright emerald (7.1.86) .. .. 1·75 1·
S38 12½p. light emerald (24.2.82) 60
S39 13p. pale chestnut (23.10.84) 70
S40 14p. grey-blue (8.4.81) 60
S41 15½p. pale violet (24.2.82) 70
S42 16p. drab (27.4.83) 70
S43 17p. grey-blue (23.10.84) .. .. 3·50 2·
S44 18p. deep violet (8.4.81) 80
S45 19½p. olive-grey (24.2.82) .. .. 1·75 1·
S46 20½p. ultramarine (27.4.83) .. .. 4·00 4·
S47 22p. blue (8.4.81) .. .. .. 90 1·
S48 22p. yellow-green (23.10.84) .. .. 2·25 2·
S49 26p. rosine (24.2.82) .. .. .. 1·10 1·
S50 28p. deep violet-blue (27.4.83) .. .. 1·10 1·
S51 31p. bright purple (23.10.84) .. .. 2·00 1·

(d) Litho Questa. P 15×14

S52 12p. bright emerald (1 side band) (29.4.86) 2·00 1·
S53 13p. pale chestnut (1 side band) (4.11.86) 70
S54 14p. deep blue (1 centre band) (8.11.88) .. 50
l. Booklet pane. No. S54×6 with margins all round (21.3.89) .. .. .. 2·75
S55 14p. deep blue (1 side band) (21.3.89) .. 80 1·
l. Booklet pane. No. S55×5, S63×2, S68 and centre label with margins all round 16·00
la. Error. Booklet pane imperf .. ..
S56 15p. bright blue (1 centre band) (28.11.89) 70
a. Imperf three sides (block of 4) .. £275
S57 17p. grey-bl (phosphorised paper) (29.4.86) 4·25 2·
S58 17p. deep blue (1 centre band) (4.12.90) .. 60
S59 18p. ol-grey (phosphorised paper) (6.1.87) 80
S60 18p. bright green (1 centre band) (3.12.91) 70
a. Perf 14 (26.9.92*) .. .. 1·00
S61 18p. brt green (1 side band) (10.8.93) .. 2·00 2·
S62 19p. bright orange-red (phosphorised paper) (8.11.88) 80
l. Booklet pane. No. S62×9 with margins all round (21.3.89) .. .. .. 5·50
m. Booklet pane. No S62×6 with margins all round (21.3.89) .. .. .. 3·50
S63 19p. bright orange-red (2 bands) (21.3.89) 1·50 1·
S64 20p. brownish black (phosphorised paper) (28.11.89) 80
S65 22p. yell-grn (phosphorised paper) (27.1.87) 90
S66 22p. bright orange-red (phosphorised paper) (4.12.90) .. .. 1·00
S67 23p. brt grn (phosphorised paper) (8.11.88) 1·00 1·
S68 23p. bright green (2 bands) (21.3.89) .. 12·00 11·
S69 24p. Indian red (phosphorised paper) (28.11.89) .. .. 1·00 1·
S70 24p. chestnut (phosphorised paper) (3.12.91) 75
a. Perf 14 (10.92*) .. .. .. 2·50 2·
S71 24p. chestnut (2 bands) (10.8.93) .. 2·00 2·
S72 26p. rosine (phosphorised paper) (27.1.87) 2·50 2·
S73 26p. drab (phosphorised paper) (4.12.90) 1·00 1·
S74 28p. deep violet-blue (phosphorised paper) (27.1.87) .. .. 1·10 1·
S75 28p. deep bluish grey (phosphorised paper) (3.12.91) .. .. 1·10 1·
a. Perf 14 (18.2.93*) .. .. .. 3·25 3·
S76 31p. brt pur (phosphorised paper) (29.4.86) 1·75 1·
S77 32p. greenish blue (phosphorised paper) (8.11.88) .. .. 1·25 1·
S78 34p. deep bluish grey (phosphorised paper) (28.11.89) .. .. 1·40 1·
S79 37p. rosine (phosphorised paper) (4.12.90) 1·40 1·

0 39p. brt mve (phosphorised paper) (3.12.91) 1·40 1·40
a. Perf 14 (11.92) 2·25 2·25

*Earliest known date of use.
†Exists only with gum arabic.
Nos. S55, S61, S63, S68 and S71 only come from booklets.
No. S56a occurred in the second vertical row on two sheets. The ror is best collected as a block of four to include the left-hand rtical pair imperforate on three sides.
Nos. S60a, S70a, S75a and S80a were caused by the use of a serve perforating machine for some printings in late 1992.
From 1972 printings were on fluorescent white paper. Nos. 4/15 exist with PVA and gum arabic and the remainder with PVA ıly. From 1973 printings had extra dextrin added (see notes after e 1971 Decimal Machin issue).

(Des J. Matthews after plaster cast by Arnold Machin)

93 (7 Dec)–98. *Chalk-surfaced paper. (a) Litho Questa. One phosphor band (19p., 20p.) or two phosphor bands (others). P 15×14 (with one elliptical hole on each vertical side).*

1 S 4 19p. bistre (1 centre band) 50 50
2 19p. bistre (1 side band) (25.4.95) 2·50 2·50
3 20p. bright green (1 centre band) (23.7.96) 70 70
4 4 25p. red 85 85
5 26p. red-brown (23.7.96) 90 90
6 30p. deep olive-grey 1·00 1·00
7 37p. bright mauve (23.7.96) 1·00 1·00
8 41p. grey-brown 1·25 1·25
9 63p. light emerald (23.7.96) 1·75 1·75

) *Photo Walsall (20p., 26p. (No. S91a), 63p.), Harrison or Walsall (26p. (No. S91), 37p.). P 14 (No. S90a) or 15×14 (others) (both with one elliptical hole on each vertical side).*

0 S 4 20p. bright green (1 centre band) (1.7.97) 30 35
0a 20p. bright green (1 side band) (13.10.98) 80 80
1 26p. chestnut (2 bands) (1.7.97) 40 45
a. Perf 14 (13.10.98) 80 80
2 37p. bright mauve (2 bands) (1.7.97) 60 65
3 63p. light emerald (2 bands) (1.7.97) 95 1·00

Nos. S82, S90*a* and S91a only come from booklets.
The Harrison printings of the Nos. S91/2 are from booklet pane). NI79al.

III. WALES

From the inception of the Regional stamps, the Welsh versions ere tendered to members of the public at all Post Offices within e former County of Monmouthshire but the national alternatives ere available on request. Offices with a Monmouthshire postal ldress but situated outside the County, namely Beachley, rockweir, Redbrook, Sedbury, Tutshill, Welsh Newton and 'oodcroft, were not supplied with the Welsh Regional stamps.
With the re-formation of Counties, Monmouthshire became ıown as Gwent and was also declared to be part of Wales. From July 1974, therefore, except for the offices mentioned above, only elsh Regional stamps were available at the offices under the risdiction of Newport, Gwent.

W 1 W 2 W 3

(Des R. Stone)

58–67. *W* **179.** *P* 15 × 14.

1 W 1 3d. deep lilac (18.8.58) 20 10
p. One centre phosphor band (16.5.67) 20 15
2 4d. ultramarine (7.2.66) 20 15
p. Two phosphor bands (10.67) 20 15
3 W 2 6d. deep claret (29.9.58) 40 20
4 9d. bronze-green (2 phosphor bands) (1.3.67) 40 40
5 W 3 1s. 3d. green (29.9.58) 30 30
6 1s. 6d. grey-blue (2 phosphor bands) (1.3.67) 35 40

67–69. *No wmk. Chalk-surfaced paper. One centre phosphor band (W7, W9/10) or two phosphor bands (others). P 15 × 14.*

7 W 1 3d. deep lilac (6.12.67) 20 10
8 4d. ultramarine (21.6.68) 20 10
9 4d. olive-sepia (4.9.68) 20 10
10 4d. bright vermilion (26.2.69) 20 20
11 5d. royal blue (4.9.68) 20 10
12 W 3 1s. 6d. grey-blue (1.8.69) 3·00 3·75

The 3d. exists with gum arabic only; the remainder with PVA m only.

W 4 With "p" W 5 Without "p"

(Des J. Matthews after plaster cast by Arnold Machin)

71 (7 July)–93. *Decimal Currency. Chalk-surfaced paper. Type* W 4. *(a) Photo Harrison. With phosphor bands. P* 15×14

13 2½p. bright magenta (1 centre band) 20 15
a. Imperf (pair)† £350
14 3p. ultramarine (2 bands) 25 15
15 3p. ultramarine (1 centre band) (23.1.74) 20 20
16 3½p. olive-grey (2 bands) (23.1.74) 20 25
17 3½p. olive-grey (1 centre band) (6.11.74) 20 25
18 4½p. grey-blue (2 bands) (6.11.74) 25 20
19 5p. reddish violet (2 bands) 1·00 1·00
20 5½p. violet (2 bands) (23.1.74) 20 25
21 5½p. violet (1 centre band) (21.5.75) 20 25
a. Imperf (pair) £400
22 6½p. greenish blue (1 centre band) (14.1.76) 20 20
23 7p. purple-brn (1 centre band) (18.1.78) 25 25
24 7½p. chestnut (2 bands) 1·25 1·50

W25 8p. rosine (2 bands) (23.1.74) 30 30
W26 8½p. yellow-green (2 bands) (14.1.76) 30 30
W27 9p. deep violet (2 bands) (18.1.78) 30 30
W28 10p. orange-brown (2 bands) (20.10.76) 35 30
W29 10p. orange-brn (1 centre band) (23.7.80) 35 30
W30 10½p. steel-blue (2 bands) (18.1.78) 50 50
W31 11p. scarlet (2 bands) (20.10.76) 50 50

(b) Photo Harrison. On phosphorised paper. P 15 × 14

W32 12p. yellow-green (23.7.80) 50 45
W33 13½p. purple-brown (23.7.80) 60 70
W34 15p. ultramarine (23.7.80) 60 50

(c) Litho Questa. P 14 (11½p., 12½p., 14p. (No. W39), 15½p., 16p., 18p. (No. W46), 19½p., 20½p., 22p. (No. W54), 26p. (No. W61), 28p. (No. W63)) or 15×14 (others).

W35 11½p. drab (1 side band) (8.4.81) 85 60
W36 12p. bright emerald (1 side band) (7.1.86) 1·25 1·10
W37 12½p. light emerald (1 side band) (24.2.82) 80 60
a. Perf 15×14 (10.1.84) 6·00 6·00
W38 13p. pale chestnut (1 side band) (23.10.84) 50 35
W39 14p. grey-bl (phosphorised paper) (8.4.81) 65 50
W40 14p. deep blue (1 centre band) (8.11.88) 55 50
W41 15p. bright blue (1 centre band) (28.11.89) 50 50
W42 15½p. pale violet (phosphorised paper) (24.2.82) 80 65
W43 16p. drab (phosphorised paper (27.4.83) 1·75 1·25
a. Perf 15×14 (10.1.84) 1·75 1·50
W44 17p. grey-blue (phosphorised paper) (23.10.84) 90 70
W45 17p. deep blue (1 centre band) (4.12.90) 70 55
W46 18p. deep violet (8.4.81) 80 75
W47 18p. deep olive-grey (phosphorised paper) (6.1.87) 80 70
W48 18p. bright green (1 centre band) (3.12.91) 55 55
a. Booklet pane. No. W48×6 with margins all round (25.2.92) 2·75
b. Perf 14 (12.1.93*) 2·25 2·25
W49 18p. bright green (1 side band) (25.2.92) 2·00 2·00
a. Booklet pane. No. X1020×2, 1451*a*, 1514*a*, W49×2, W60×2 and centre label with margins all round 10·00
W50 19p. bright orange-red (phosphorised paper) (8.11.88) 85 60
W51 19½p. olive-grey (phosphorised paper) (24.2.82) 2·00 2·00
W52 20p. brownish black (phosphorised paper) (28.11.89) 80 80
W53 20½p. ultram (phosphorised paper) (27.4.83) 4·00 4·00
W54 22p. blue (phosphorised paper) (8.4.81) 1·10 1·10
W55 22p. yellow-green (phosphorised paper) (23.10.84) 90 1·25
W56 22p. bright orange-red (phosphorised paper) (4.12.90) 80 70
W57 23p. brt grn (phosphorised paper) (8.11.88) 90 1·25
W58 24p. Indian red (phosphorised paper) (28.11.89) 1·00 1·25
W59 24p. chestnut (phosphorised paper) (3.12.91) 90 90
a. Booklet pane. No. W59×6 with margins all round (25.2.92) 4·75
b. Perf 14 (14.9.92*) 2·75 2·75
W60 24p. chestnut (2 bands) (25.2.92) 1·25 1·25
W61 26p. rosine (phosphorised paper) (24.2.82) 1·10 1·40
a. Perf 15×14 (27.1.87) 4·75 5·00
W62 26p. drab (phosphorised paper) (4.12.90) 1·00 1·00
W63 28p. deep violet-blue (phosphorised paper) (27.4.83) 1·10 1·25
a. Perf 15×14 (27.1.87) 1·10 1·10
W64 28p. deep bluish grey (phosphorised paper) (3.12.91) 1·10 1·10
W65 31p. bright purple (phosphorised paper) (23.10.84) 1·25 1·25
W66 32p. greenish blue (phosphorised paper) (8.11.88) 1·25 1·25
W67 34p. deep bluish grey (phosphorised paper) (28.11.89) 1·50 1·40
W68 37p. rosine (phosphorised paper) (4.12.90) 1·50 1·40
W69 39p. bright mauve (phosphorised paper) (3.12.91) 1·50 1·40

*Earliest known date of use.
†Exists with gum arabic.
Nos. W48b and W59b were caused by the use of a reserve perforating machine for some printings in late 1992.
Nos. W49 and W60 only come from booklets. No. W49 exists with phosphor band at left or right from different booklets.
From 1972 printings were on fluorescent white paper. Nos. W13/14 exist with PVA and gum arabic and the remainder with PVA only. From 1973 printings had extra dextrin added (see notes after the 1971 Decimal Machin issue).

(Des J. Matthews after plaster cast by Arnold Machin. Litho Questa)

1993 (7 Dec)–96. *Chalk-surfaced paper. One phosphor band (19p., 20p.) or two phosphor bands (others). P 15×14 (with one elliptical hole on each vertical side).*

W70 W 4 19p. bistre (1 centre band) 50 50
W71 19p. bistre (1 side band) (25.4.95) 2·50 2·50
W72 20p. brt green (1 centre band) (23.7.96) 70 70
W73 25p. red 85 85
W74 26p. red-brown (23.7.96) 90 90
W75 30p. deep olive-grey 1·00 1·00
W76 37p. bright mauve (23.7.96) 1·00 1·00
W77 41p. grey-brown 1·25 1·25
W78 63p. light emerald (23.7.96) 1·75 1·75

No. W71 only comes from booklets.

(Photo Walsall (20p., 26p. (No. W80a), 63p.), Harrison or Walsall (26p. (No. W80), 37p.))

1997 (1 July)–98. *Chalk-surfaced paper. One phosphor band (20p.) or two phosphor bands (others). P 14 (No. W79a) or 15×14 (others) (both with one elliptical hole on each vertical side).*

W79 W 5 20p. bright green (1 centre band) 30 35
W79*a* 20p. brt green (1 side band) (13.10.98) 80 80
W80 26p. chestnut 40 45
a. Perf 14 (13.10.98) 80 80
W81 37p. bright mauve 60 65
W82 63p. light emerald 95 1·00

Nos. W79a and W80a were only issued in booklets.
The Harrison printings of Nos. W80/1 come from booklet pane No. NI79al.

STAMP BOOKLETS

For a full listing of Great Britain stamp booklets see the *Great Britain Concise Catalogue* published each Spring.

POSTAGE DUE STAMPS

PERFORATIONS. All postage due stamps to No. D101 are perf 14×15.

D 1

D 2

(Des G. Eve. Typo Somerset House (early trial printings of ½d., 1d., 2d., and 5d.; all printings of 1s.) or Harrison (later printings of all values except 1s.)).

1914 (20 Apr)–22. *W* **100** *(Simple Cypher) sideways.*

D1 D 1 ½d. emerald 50 50
D2 1d. carmine 50 50
a. Pale carmine 75 75
D3 1½d. chestnut (1922) 40·00 12·00
D4 2d. agate 50 70
D5 3d. violet (1918) 2·50 1·00
a. Bluish violet 3·50 3·50
D6 4d. dull grey-green (12.20) 10·00 15·00
D7 5d. brownish cinnamon 5·00 3·25
D8 1s. bright blue (1915) 20·00 20·00
a. Deep bright blue 40·00 5·00
D1/8 *Set of* 8 90·00 28·00

The 1d. is known bisected and used to make up a 1½d. rate on understamped letters from Ceylon (1921) or Tasmania (1922, Palmers Green) and the 2d. bisected and used as 1d. at Christchurch, Malvern, Streatham and West Kensington in 1921.

1924. *As 1914–22, but on thick chalk-surfaced paper.*

D9 D 1 1d. carmine 2·25 3·50

(Typo Waterlow and (from 1934) Harrison)

1924–31. *W* **111** *(Block Cypher) sideways.*

D10 D 1 ½d. emerald (6.25) 90 75
D11 1d. carmine (4.25) 60 60
D12 1½d. chestnut (10.24) 40·00 18·00
D13 2d. agate (7.24) 1·00 40
D14 3d. dull violet (10.24) 1·50 40
a. Printed on gummed side 60·00 †
b. Experimental paper W **111*a*** 35·00 30·00
D15 4d. dull grey-green (10.24) 13·00 3·00
D16 5d. brownish cinnamon (1.31) 29·00 22·00
D17 1s. deep blue (9.24) 8·50 75
D18 D 2 2s. 6d. purple/*yellow* (5.24) 40·00 2·00
D10/18 *Set of* 9 £120 45·00

The 2d. is known bisected to make up the 2½d. rate at Perranwell Station, Cornwall, in 1932.

1936–37. *W* **125** *(E 8 R) sideways.*

D19 D 1 ½d. emerald (6.37) 7·50 7·00
D20 1d. carmine (5.37) 1·50 1·50
D21 2d. agate (5.37) 7·00 9·00
D22 3d. dull violet (3.37) 1·50 1·60
D23 4d. dull grey-green (12.36) 23·00 23·00
D24 5d. brownish cinnamon (11.36) 40·00 22·00
a. Yellow-brown (1937) 16·00 21·00
D25 1s. deep blue (12.36) 11·00 7·00
D26 D 2 2s. 6d. purple/*yellow* (5.37) £250 8·00
D19/26 *Set of* 8 *(cheapest)* £300 70·00

The 1d. is known bisected (Solihull, 3 July 1937).

1937–38. *W* **127** *(G VI R) sideways.*

D27 D 1 ½d. emerald (5.38) 8·00 4·50
D28 1d. carmine (5.38) 2·50 50
D29 2d. agate (5.38) 2·50 50
D30 3d. violet (12.37) 12·00 90
D31 4d. dull grey-green (9.37) 65·00 10·00
D32 5d. yellow-brown (11.38) 12·00 2·00
D33 1s. deep blue (10.37) 60·00 2·00
D34 D 2 2s. 6d. purple/*yellow* (9.38) 60·00 2·50
D27/34 *Set of* 8 £200 20·00

The 2d. is known bisected in June 1951 (Boreham Wood, Harpenden and St. Albans) and on 30 October 1954 (Harpenden).

DATES OF ISSUE. The dates for Nos. D35/68 are those on which stamps were first issued by the Supplies Department to postmasters.

1951–52. *Colours changed and new value (1½d.). W* **127** *(G VI R) sideways.*

D35 D 1 ½d. orange (18.9.51) 1·00 2·50
D36 1d. violet-blue (6.6.51) 1·50 1·25
D37 1½d. green (11.2.52) 1·75 2·50
D38 4d. blue (14.8.51) 30·00 11·00
D39 1s. ochre (6.12.51) 35·00 13·00
D35/9 *Set of* 5 60·00 22·00

The 1d. is known bisected (Dorking, 1952, and Camberley, 6 April 1954).

1954–55. *W* **153** *(Mult Tudor Crown and E 2 R) sideways.*

D40 D 1 ½d. orange (8.6.55) 6·00 4·50
D41 2d. agate (28.7.55) 4·00 4·00
D42 3d. violet (4.5.55) 50·00 32·00
D43 4d. blue (14.7.55) 18·00 19·00
a. Imperf (pair) £225
D44 5d. yellow-brown (19.5.55) 25·00 9·00
D45 D 2 2s. 6d. purple/*yellow* (11.54) £100 3·00
D40/5 *Set of* 6 £190 65·00

1955–57. *W* **165** *(Mult St. Edward's Crown and E 2 R) sideways.*

D46 D 1 ½d. orange (16.7.56) 1·25 2·25
D47 1d. violet-blue (7.6.56) 5·50 1·50
D48 1½d. green (13.2.56) 5·50 5·00
D49 2d. agate (22.5.56) 40·00 3·25
D50 3d. violet (5.3.56) 6·00 1·25
D51 4d. blue (24.4.56) 21·00 3·75
D52 5d. brown-ochre (23.3.56) 32·00 2·00
D53 1s. ochre (22.11.55) 70·00 2·00

D54 D 2 2s. 6d. purple/*yellow* (28.6.57) .. £140 8·00
D55 5s. scarlet/*yellow* (25.11.55) .. 80·00 25·00
D46/55 .. .. *Set of* 10 £350 48·00

The 1d. is known bisected in June 1957 (London S.E.D.O.), the 2d. in June 1956, the 3d. in April/May 1957 (London S.E.D.O.) and the 4d. in April 1957 (Poplar).

1959–63. *W* **179** *(Mult St Edward's Crown) sideways.*

D56 D 1 ½d. orange (18.10.61) .. .. .. 10 1·00
D57 1d. violet-blue (9.5.60) 10 50
D58 1½d. green (5.10.60) .. .. .. 90 2·75
D59 2d. agate (14.9.59) .. .. .. 1·25 50
D60 3d. violet (24.3.59) 40 30
D61 4d. blue (17.12.59) 40 30
D62 5d. yellow-brown (6.11.61) 45 75
D63 6d. purple (29.3.62) 60 30
D64 1s. ochre (11.4.60) .. .. .. 1·40 30
D65 D 2 2s. 6d. purple/*yellow* (11.5.61) .. 4·25 45
D66 5s. scarlet/*yellow* (8.5.61) .. .. 8·00 1·00
D67 10s. blue/*yellow* (2.9.63) .. .. 10·00 5·50
D68 £1 black/*yellow* (2.9.63) .. .. 45·00 8·50
D56/68 .. .. *Set of* 13 65·00 20·00

Whiter paper. The note after No. 586 also applies to Postage Due stamps.

The 1d. is known bisected (Newbury, December 1962 and March 1963).

1968–69. *Typo. No wmk. Chalk-surfaced paper.*

D69 D 1 2d. agate (11.4.68) 20 60
D70 3d. violet (9.9.68) 25 60
D71 4d. blue (6.5.68) 25 60
D72 5d. orange-brown (3.1.69) .. .. 5·00 7·00
D73 6d. purple (9.9.68) .. .. .. 60 1·00
D74 1s. ochre (19.11.68) .. .. .. 2·00 1·50
D69/74 .. .. *Set of* 6 7·50 10·00

The 2d. and 4d. exist with gum arabic and PVA gum; remainder with PVA gum only.

1968–69. *Photo. No wmk. Chalk-surfaced paper. PVA gum.*

D75 D 1 4d. blue (12.6.69) .. .. .. 5·00 5·50
D76 8d. red (3.10.68) .. .. .. 1·00 1·25

Nos. D75/6 are smaller, 21½×17½ mm.

D 3

D 4

(Des J. Matthews. Photo Harrison)

1970 (17 June)–**75.** *Decimal Currency. Chalk-surfaced paper.*

D77 D 3 ½p. turquoise-blue (15.2.71) 10 20
D78 1p. deep reddish purple (15.2.71) .. 10 15
D79 2p. myrtle-green (15.2.71) 10 15
D80 3p. ultramarine (15.2.71) 15 15
D81 4p. yellow-brown (15.2.71) 15 15
D82 5p. violet (15.2.71) 20 20
D83 7p. red-brown (21.8.74) 35 45
D84 D 4 10p. carmine 30 20
D85 11p. slate-green (18.6.75) 60 60
D86 20p. olive-brown 60 50
D87 50p. ultramarine .. .. 1·50 50
D88 £1 black .. .. 3·50 75
D89 £5 orange-yellow and black (2.4.73) 35·00 2·00
D77/89 .. .. *Set of* 13 38·00 5·00

Later printings were on fluorescent white paper, some with dextrin added to the PVA gum (see notes after X1058 of Great Britain).

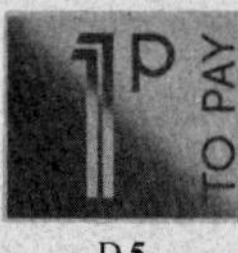

D 5

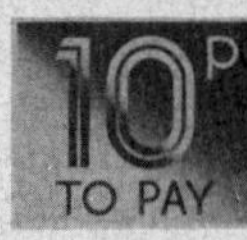

D 6

(Des Sedley Place Design Ltd. Photo Harrison)

1982 (9 June). *Chalk-surfaced paper.*

D 90 D 5 1p. lake 10 10
D 91 2p. bright blue 20 10
D 92 3p. deep mauve 10 15
D 93 4p. deep blue 10 20
D 94 5p. sepia 20 20
D 95 D 6 10p. light brown 20 25
D 96 20p. olive-green 40 30
D 97 25p. deep greenish blue 50 70
D 98 50p. grey-black .. .. 1·00 75
D 99 £1 red .. .. 2·00 50
D100 £2 turquoise-blue .. .. .. 4·50 50
D101 £5 dull orange .. .. 12·00 50
D90/101 .. .. *Set of* 12 19·00 3·75

D 7

(Des Sedley Place Design Ltd. Litho Questa)

1994 (15 Feb). *P* 15×14 *(with one elliptical hole on each vertical side).*

D102 D 7 1p. red, yellow and black 10 10
D103 2p. magenta, purple and black .. 10 10
D104 5p. yellow, red-brown and black .. 10 10
D105 10p. yellow, emerald and black .. 15 20
D106 20p. blue-green, violet and black .. 30 35
D107 25p. cerise, rosine and black 40 45
D108 £1 violet, magenta and black .. 1·50 1·60
D109 £1.20, greenish blue, blue-green & black 1·75 1·90
D110 £5 greenish black, blue-green and black 7·50 7·75
D102/10 .. .. *Set of* 9 11·50 12·50

Following changes in the method of collecting money due on unpaid or underpaid mail the use of postage due stamps was restricted from April 1995 to mail addressed to business customers and to Customs/V.A.T. charges levied by the Royal Mail on behalf of the Customs and Excise.

OFFICIAL STAMPS

In 1840 the 1d. black (Type **1**), with "V R" in the upper corners, was prepared for official use, but never issued for postal purposes. Obliterated specimens are those which were used for experimental trials of obliterating inks, or those that passed through the post by oversight.

V 1

1840. *Prepared for use but not issued; "V" "R" in upper corners. Imperf.*

				Un	Used	Used on cover
V1	V 1	1d. black		£6000	£6500	

The following Official stamps would be more correctly termed Departmental stamps as they were exclusively for the use of certain government departments. Until 1882 official mail used ordinary postage stamps purchased at post offices, the cash being refunded once a quarter. Later the government departments obtained Official stamps by requisition.

Official stamps were on sale to the public for a short time at Somerset House but they were not sold from post offices. The system of only supplying the Government departments was open to abuse so that all Official stamps were withdrawn on 13 May 1904.

OVERPRINTS, PERFORATIONS, WATERMARKS. All Official stamps were overprinted by Thomas De La Rue & Co. and are perf 14. They are on Crown watermarked paper unless otherwise stated.

INLAND REVENUE

These stamps were used by revenue officials in the provinces, mail to and from Head Office passing without a stamp. The London Office used these stamps only for foreign mail.

I.R.
OFFICIAL
(O 1)

I. R.
OFFICIAL
(O 2)

Optd with Types O **1** *(½d. to 1s.) or* O **2** *(others)*

1882–1901. *Stamps of Queen Victoria. (a) Issues of* 1880–81.

			Un	Used	★ Used on cover
O 1	½d. deep green (1.11.82)		15·00	5·00	50·00
O 2	½d. pale green		15·00	5·00	
O 3	1d. lilac (Die II) (1.10.82) ..		2·00	1·00	15·00
	a. Optd in blue-black		70·00	40·00	
	b. "OFFICIAL" omitted ..		—	£2500	
O 4	6d. grey (Plate 18) (3.11.82) ..		80·00	25·00	

No. O3 with the lines of the overprint transposed is an essay.

(b) Issues of 1884–88

		Un	Used	Used on cover
O 5	½d. slate-blue (8.5.85)	30·00	20·00	85·00
O 6	2½d. lilac (12.3.85)	£140	50·00	£650
O 7	1s. dull green (12.3.85)	£2600	£500	
O 8	5s. rose (*blued paper*) (wmk Anchor) (12.3.85)	£2900	£525	
O 9	5s. rose (wmk Anchor) (3.90) ..	£1500	£450	
	a. Raised stop after "R" ..	£1750	£450	
	b. Optd in blue-black	£2250	£500	
O 9*c*	10s. cobalt (*blued paper*) (wmk Anchor) (12.3.85)	£5500	£900	
O 9*d*	10s. ultramarine (*blued paper*) (wmk Anchor) (12.3.85)	£5500	£1750	
O10	10s. ultram (wmk Anchor) (3.90) ..	£2750	£600	
	a. Raised stop after "R" ..	£3500	£625	
	b. Optd in blue-black	£3750	£800	
O11	£1 brown-lilac (wmk Crowns) (12.3.85)	£20000		
	a. Frame broken	£25000		
O12	£1 brown-lilac (wmk Orbs) (3.90)	£27500		
	a. Frame broken	£30000		

(c) Issues of 1887–92

		Un	Used	Used on cover
O13	½d. vermilion (15.5.88)	2·00	1·00	25·00
	a. Without "I.R."	£2000		
	b. Imperf	£1250		
	c. Opt double (imperf)	£1500		
O14	2½d. purple/*blue* (2.92)	60·00	5·00	£200
O15	1s. dull green (9.89)	£225	25·00	£1200
O16	£1 green (6.92)	£3750	£500	
	a. No stop after "R"	—	£850	
	b. Frame broken	£6000	£1000	

Nos. O3, O13, O15 and O16 may be found with two varieties of overprint, namely, 1882 printings, *thin* letters, and 1894 printings, *thicker* letters.

(d) Issues of 1887 *and* 1900

		Un	Used	Used on cover
O17	½d. blue-green (4.01)	5·00	4·00	£100
O18	6d. purple/*rose-red* (1.7.01) ..	£125	25·00	
O19	1s. green and carmine (12.01) ..	£800	£175	
★O1/19	**For well-centred, lightly used** ..		+35%	

1902–04. *Stamps of King Edward VII. Ordinary paper.*

		Un	Used	Used on cover
O20	½d. blue-green (4.2.02)	20·00	2·00	£100
O21	1d. scarlet (4.2.02)	12·00	1·00	60·00
O22	2½d. ultramarine (19.2.02)	£450	90·00	
O23	6d. pale dull purple (14.3.04) ..	£85000	£65000	
O24	1s. dull green & carmine (29.4.02)	£550	95·00	
O25	5s. bright carmine (29.4.02) ..	£4500	£1500	
	a. Raised stop after "R" ..	£5000	£1600	
O26	10s. ultramarine (29.4.02)	£16000	£9500	
	a. Raised stop after "R" ..	£19000	£12000	
O27	£1 dull blue-green (29.4.02) ..	£13000	£7000	

OFFICE OF WORKS

These were issued to Head and Branch (local) offices in Londo and to Branch (local) offices at Birmingham, Bristol, Edinburg Glasgow, Leeds, Liverpool, Manchester and Southampton. Th overprints on stamps of value 2d. and upwards were created later i 1902, the 2d. for registration fees and the rest for overseas mail.

O.W.
OFFICIAL
(O 3)

Optd with Type O **3**

1896 (24 Mar)–**02.** *Stamps of Queen Victoria.*

		Un	Used	Used on cover
O31	½d. vermilion	£100	50·00	£25
O32	½d. blue-green (2.02)	£175	85·00	
O33	1d. lilac (Die II)	£175	50·00	£27
O34	5d. dull purple and blue (II) (29.4.02)	£850	£190	
O35	10d. dull purple and carmine (28.5.02)	£1400	£275	

1902 (11 Feb)–**03.** *Stamps of King Edward VII. Ordinary pape*

		Un	Used	Used on cover
O36	½d. blue-green (8.02)	£400	£100	£95
O37	1d. scarlet	£400	£100	£20
O38	2d. yellowish green and carmine-red (29.4.02)	£700	£100	£120
O39	2½d. ultramarine (29.4.02) ..	£800	£275	
O40	10d. dull purple & carmine (28.5.03)	£5250	£1750	
★O31/40	**For well-centred, lightly used** ..		+25%	

ARMY

Letters to and from the War Office in London passed witho postage. The overprinted stamps were distributed to District an Station Paymasters nationwide, including Cox and Co., the Arm Agents, who were paymasters to the Household Division.

ARMY
OFFICIAL
(O 4)

ARMY
OFFICIAL
(O 5)

ARMY
OFFICIAI
(O 6)

1896 (1 Sept)–**01.** *Stamps of Queen Victoria optd with Type* O **4** *(½d 1d.) or* O **5** *(2½d., 6d.).*

		Un	Used	Used on cover
O41	½d. vermilion	2·00	1·00	25·(
	a. "OFFICIAI" (R. 13/7) ..	40·00	20·00	
	b. Lines of opt transposed ..	£1100		
O42	½d. blue-green (6.00)	2·00	4·00	
O43	1d. lilac (Die II)	2·00	1·00	40·(
	a. "OFFICIAI" (R. 13/7) ..	40·00	20·00	
O44	2½d. purple/*blue*	5·00	3·00	£3(
O45	6d. purple/*rose-red* (20.9.01) ..	17·00	10·00	£5(

Nos. O41a and O43a occur on sheets overprinted by Forme 1.

1902–03. *Stamps of King Edward VII optd with Type* O **4** *(Nos O48/50) or Type* O **6** *(No. O52). Ordinary paper.*

		Un	Used	Used on cover
O48	½d. blue-green (11.2.02)	2·50	1·00	70·(
O49	1d. scarlet (11.2.02)	2·00	1·00	70·(
	a. "ARMY" omitted	†	—	
O50	6d. pale dull purple (23.8.02) ..	75·00	35·00	
O52	6d. pale dull purple (12.03) ..	£900	£325	

GOVERNMENT PARCELS

These stamps were issued to all departments, including the Hea Office, for use on parcels weighing over 3 lb. Below this weigh government parcels were sent by letter post to avoid the 55% of th postage paid from accruing to the railway companies, as laid dow by parcel-post regulations. Most government parcels stamps suffere heavy postmarks in use.

GOVT
PARCELS
(O 7)

Optd as Type O **7**

1883 (1 Aug)–**86.** *Stamps of Queen Victoria.*

		Un	★ Usec
O61	1½d. lilac (1.5.86)	£125	30·0(
	a. No dot under "T"	£150	32·0(
	b. Dot to left of "T"	£125	32·0(
O62	6d. dull green (1.5.86)	£825	£30(
O63	9d. dull green	£675	£19(
O64	1s. orange-brown (wmk Crown, Pl 13)	£450	80·0(
	a. No dot under "T"	£500	90·0(
	b. Dot to left of "T"	£500	90·0(
O64*c*	1s. orange-brown (Pl 14) ..	£775	£12
	ca. No dot under "T"	£850	£11(
	cb. Dot to left of "T"		

1887–90. *Stamps of Queen Victoria.*

		Un	Used
O65	1½d. dull purple and pale green (29.10.87)	15·00	3·(
	a. No dot under "T"	20·00	7·(
	b. Dot to right of "T"	18·00	6·(
	c. Dot to left of "T"	18·00	6·(
O66	6d. purple/*rose-red* (19.12.87) ..	30·00	12·(
	a. No dot under "T"	35·00	14·(
	b. Dot to right of "T"	35·00	14·(
	c. Dot to left of "T"	35·00	12·(
O67	9d. dull purple and blue (21.8.88)	60·00	16·(

68	1s. dull green (25.3.90)	£140	80·00
	a. No dot under "T"	£160	85·00
	b. Dot to right of "T"	£160	85·00
	c. Dot to left of "T"	£180	90·00
	d. Optd in blue-black		

91–1900. *Stamps of Queen Victoria.*

69	1d. lilac (Die II) (18.6.97)	30·00	9·00
	a. No dot under "T"	32·00	21·00
	b. Dot to left of "T"	32·00	21·00
	c. Opt inverted	£1000	£850
	d. Ditto. Dot to left of "T"	£1000	£550
70	2d. grey-green and carmine (24.10.91) ..	50·00	8·00
	a. No dot under "T"	60·00	10·00
	b. Dot to left of "T"	60·00	10·00
71	4½d. green and carmine (29.9.92) ..	£125	80·00
	b. Dot to right of "T"		
72	1s. green and carmine (11.00)	£175	55·00
	a. Opt inverted	†	£4000
★O61/72	**For well-centred lightly used**		**+100%**

The "no dot under T" variety occurred on R.12/3 and 20/2. The dot to left of T" comes four times in the sheet on R.2/7, 6/7, 7/9 nd 12/9. The best example of the "dot to right of T" is on R.20/1 . ll three varieties were corrected around 1897.

02. *Stamps of King Edward VII. Ordinary paper.*

74	1d. scarlet (30.10.02)	17·00	6·00
75	2d. yellowish green & carmine-red (29.4.02)	70·00	18·00
76	6d. pale dull purple (19.2.02)	£110	18·00
	a. Opt double, one albino	£4500	
77	9d. dull purple and ultramarine (28.8.02)	£240	60·00
78	1s. dull green and carmine (17.12.02) ..	£375	90·00

BOARD OF EDUCATION

BOARD

OF

EDUCATION

(O **8**)

Optd with Type O **8**

02 (19 Feb). *Stamps of Queen Victoria.*

		Un	*Used*	*Used on Cover*
81	5d. dull purple and blue (II) ..	£575	£120	
82	1s. green and carmine	£1000	£400	

02 (19 Feb)–**04.** *Stamps of King Edward VII. Ordinary paper.*

83	½d. blue-green	20·00	8·00	£275
84	1d. scarlet	20·00	7·00	£300
85	2½d. ultramarine	£550	60·00	
86	5d. dull purple & ultram (6.2.04)	£2250	£1000	
87	1s. dull green & carmine (23.12.02)	£40000	£30000	

ROYAL HOUSEHOLD

R.H.

OFFICIAL

(O **9**)

902. *Stamps of King Edward VII optd with Type* O **9**. *Ordinary paper.*

91	½d. blue-green (29.4.02)	£160	£100	£600
92	1d. scarlet (19.2.02)	£140	90·00	£400

ADMIRALTY

ADMIRALTY **ADMIRALTY**

OFFICIAL **OFFICIAL**

(O **10**) (O **11**) (with different "M")

903 (1 Apr). *Stamps of Edward VII optd with Type* O **10**. *Ordinary paper.*

101	½d. blue-green	11·00	5·00	
102	1d. scarlet	6·00	3·00	£200
103	1½d. dull purple and green ..	65·00	50·00	
104	2d. yellowish green & carmine-red	£125	60·00	
105	2½d. ultramarine	£140	50·00	
106	3d. purple/*yellow*	£125	50·00	

903–04. *Stamps of King Edward VII optd with Type* O **11**. *Ordinary paper.*

107	½d. blue-green (9.03)	10·00	6·00	£300
108	1d. scarlet (12.03)	9·00	5·00	60·00
109	1½d. dull purple and green (2.04)	£220	85·00	
110	2d. yellowish green and carmine-red (3.04)	£425	£110	
111	2½d. ultramarine (3.04)	£550	£300	
112	3d. dull purple/*orange-yell* (12.03)	£375	95·00	

Stamps of various issues perforated with a Crown and initials "H.M.O.W.", "O.W.", "B.T." or "S.O.") or with initials only "H.M.S.O." or "D.S.I.R.") have also been used for official purposes, ut these are outside the scope of the catalogue.

POSTAL FISCAL STAMPS

RICES. Prices in the used column are for stamps with genuine ostal cancellations dated from the time when they were authorised or use as postage stamps. Beware of stamps with fiscal cancellations emoved and fraudulent postmarks applied.

VALIDITY. The 1d. Surface-printed stamps were authorised for postal use from 1 June 1881 and at the same time the 1d. postage issue, No. 166, was declared valid for fiscal purposes. The 3d. and 6d. values, together with the Embossed issues were declared valid for postal purposes by another Act effective from 1 January 1883.

SURFACE-PRINTED ISSUES

(Typo Thomas De La Rue & Co)

F 1
Rectangular Buckle

F 2

F 3
Octagonal Buckle

F 4

F 5
Double-lined Anchor

F 6
Single-lined Anchor

1853–57. *P* 15½ × 15. (*a*) *Wmk* F **5** (*inverted*) (1853–55).

			Un	*Used*	*Used on cover*
F1	F **1**	1d. light blue (10.10.53) ..	15·00	18·00	80·00
F2	F **2**	1d. ochre (10.53)	60·00	40·00	£175
		a. *Tête-bêche* (in block of four)	£8000		
F3	F **3**	1d. pale turquoise-blue (12.53)	20·00	18·00	£140
F4		1d. light blue/*blue* (12.53) ..	40·00	25·00	£160
F5	F **4**	1d. reddish lilac/*blue glazed paper* (25.3.55)	60·00	14·00	£110

Only one example is known of No. F2a outside the National Postal Museum and the Royal Collection.

(*b*) *Wmk* F **6** (1856–57)

F6	F **4**	1d. reddish lilac (*shades*) ..	5·50	4·00	80·00
F7		1d. reddish lilac/*bluish* (*shades*) (1857)	5·50	4·00	80·00

INLAND **REVENUE**

(F 7)

1860 (3 Apr). *No.* F7 *optd with Type* F **7**, *in red.*

F8	F **4**	1d. dull reddish lilac/*blue* ..	£400	£325	£550

BLUE PAPER. In the following issues we no longer distinguish between bluish and white paper. There is a range of papers from white or greyish to bluish.

F 8

F 9

F 10

1860–67. *Bluish to white paper. P* 15½ × 15. (*a*) *Wmk* F **6** (1860).

F 9	F **8**	1d. reddish lilac (May) ..	6·00	6·00	80·00
F10	F **9**	3d. reddish lilac (June) ..	£250	90·00	£175
.F11	F **10**	6d. reddish lilac (Oct) ..	£100	75·00	£200

(*b*) *W* **40.** (*Anchor* 16 *mm high*) (1864)

F12	F **8**	1d. pale reddish lilac (Nov)	4·75	4·75	65·00
F13	F **9**	3d. pale reddish lilac ..	90·00	70·00	£160
F14	F **10**	6d. pale reddish lilac ..	90·00	70·00	£160

(*c*) *W* **40** (*Anchor* 18 *mm high*) (1867)

F15	F **8**	1d. reddish lilac	13·00	6·00	£130
F16	F **9**	3d. reddish lilac	70·00	65·00	£175
F17	F **10**	6d. reddish lilac	80·00	45·00	£170

For stamps perf 14, see Nos. F24/7.

F 11

F 12

Four Dies of Type F 12

Die 1. Corner ornaments small and either joined or broken; heavy shading under chin

Die 2. Ornaments small and always broken; clear line of shading under chin

Die 3. Ornaments larger and joined; line of shading under chin extended half way down neck

Die 4. Ornaments much larger; straight line of shading continued to bottom of neck

1867–81. *White to bluish paper. P* 14. (*a*) *W* **47** (*Small Anchor*).

F18	F **11**	1d. purple (1.9.67)	8·00	5·00	60·00
F19	F **12**	1d. purple (Die 1) (6.68) ..	1·75	1·50	40·00
F20		1d. purple (Die 2) (6.76) ..	10·00	10·00	£180
F21		1d. purple (Die 3) (3.77) ..	4·00	4·00	75·00
F22		1d. purple (Die 4) (7.78) ..	3·00	2·50	65·00

(*b*) *W* **48** (*Orb*)

F23	F **12**	1d. purple (Die 4) (1.81) ..	2·00	1·50	40·00

1881. *White to bluish paper. P* 14.

(*a*) *W* **40** (*Anchor* 18 *mm high*) (Jan)

F24	F **9**	3d. reddish lilac	£350	£225	£350
F25	F **10**	6d. reddish lilac	£190	75·00	£175

(*b*) *W* **40** (*Anchor* 20 *mm high*) (May)

F26	F **9**	3d. reddish lilac	£275	70·00	£175
F27	F **10**	6d. reddish lilac	£150	90·00	£275

ISSUES EMBOSSED IN COLOUR

(Made at Somerset House)

The embossed stamps were struck from dies not appropriated to any special purpose on paper which had the words "INLAND REVENUE" previously printed, and thus became available for payment of any duties for which no special stamps had been provided.

The die letters are included in the embossed designs and holes were drilled for the insertion of plugs showing figures indicating dates of striking.

F 13

F 14

INLAND REVENUE

(F 15)

INLAND REVENUE

(F 16)

1860 (3 Apr)–**71.** *Types* F **13/14** *and similar types embossed on bluish paper. Underprint Type* F **15.** *No wmk. Imperf.*

		Un	*Used*
F28	2d. pink (Die A) (1.1.71)	£140	£140
F29	3d. pink (Die C)	£100	95·00
	a. *Tête-bêche* (vert pair)	£1200	
F30	3d. pink (Die D)	£350	
F31	6d. pink (Die T)	£700	
F32	6d. pink (Die U)	£100	90·00
	a. *Tête-bêche* (vert pair)	£1400	
F33	9d. pink (Die C) (1.1.71)	£250	
F34	1s. pink (Die E) (28.6.61)	£350	£150
F35	1s. pink (Die F) (28.6.61)	£125	£100
	a. *Tête-bêche* (vert pair)	£600	
F36	2s. pink (Die K) (6.8.61)	£275	£175
F37	2s. 6d. pink (Die N) (28.6.61)	£850	
F38	2s. 6d. pink (Die O) (28.6.61)	85·00	85·00

1861–71. *As last but perf* 12½.

F39	2d. pink (Die A) (8.71)	£250	£130
F40	3d. pink (Die C)		
F41	3d. pink (Die D)		
F42	9d. pink (Die C) (8.71)	£275	£140
F43	1s. pink (Die E) (8.71)	£200	£130
F44	1s. pink (Die F) (8.71)	£180	£100
F45	2s. 6d. pink (Die O) (8.71)	£120	65·00

1874 (Nov). *Types as before embossed on white paper. Underprint Type* F **16,** *in green. W* **47** *(Small Anchor). P* 12½.

F46	2d. pink (Die A)	—	£175
F47	9d. pink (Die C)		
F48	1s. pink (Die F)	£190	£100
F49	2s. 6d. pink (Die O)	—	£150

1875 (Nov)–**80.** *As last but colour changed and on white or bluish paper.*

F50	2d. vermilion (Die A) (1880)	£275	£100
F51	9d. vermilion (Die C) (1876)	£275	£150
F52	1s. vermilion (Die E)	£175	75·00
F53	1s. vermilion (Die F)	£175	75·00
F54	2s. 6d. vermilion (Die O) (1878)	£225	£100

1882 (Oct). *As last but W* **48** *(Orbs).*

F55	2d. vermilion (Die A)		
F56	9d. vermilion (Die C)		
F57	1s. vermilion (Die E)		
F58	2s. 6d. vermilion (Die O)	£500	£250

The sale of Inland Revenue stamps up to the 2s. value ceased from 30 December 1882 and stocks were called in and destroyed. The 2s. 6d. value remained on sale until 2 July 1883 when it was replaced by the 2s. 6d. "Postage & Revenue" stamp. Inland Revenue stamps still in the hands of the public continued to be accepted for revenue and postal purposes.

CONTROLS. Since the 1967 edition of the Part 1 Catalogue the priced lists of stamps with control letters have been transferred to Volumes 1 and 2 of the Stanley Gibbons *Great Britain Specialised Catalogue.*

TELEGRAPH STAMPS. A priced listing of the Post Office telegraph stamps appears in Volume 1 of the Stanley Gibbons *Great Britain Specialised Catalogue.* The last listing for the private telegraph companies in the Part 1 Catalogue was in the 1940 edition and for military telegraphs the 1941 edition.

ISLAND ISSUES

Several islands off the coast of Great Britain have issued local stamps (usually termed British Private Local Issues or Local Carriage Labels) ostensibly to cover the cost of ferrying mail to the nearest mainland post office. No official post offices operate on most of these islands. As these stamps are not recognised as valid for national or international mail they are not listed here. The following islands are known to have issued stamps from the dates shown:
Bardsey, Gwynedd (from 1979); *Bernera*, Hebrides (from 1977); *Brecqhou*, Channel Is. (1969); *Caldey*, Dyfed (from 1973); *Calf of Man*, Isle of Man (1962–73); *Calve*, Hebrides (from 1984); *Canna*, Hebrides (from 1958); *Carn Iar*, Hebrides (1961–62); *Davaar*, Argyllshire (from 1964); *Drake's Island*, Devon (1973–82); *Easdale*, Argyllshire (from 1988); *Eynhallow*, Orkney (from 1973); *Gairsay*, Orkney (from 1980); *Grunay*, Shetland (from 1981); *Gugh*, Isles of Scilly (1972–80 and from 1995); *Herm*, Channel Is. (1949–69); *Heston*, Wigtownshire (1960s); *Hilbre*, Cheshire (1960s); *Hildasay*, Shetland (from 1997); *Jethou*, Channel Is. (1960–69); *Lihou*, Channel Is. (1966–69); *Lundy*, Devon (from 1929); *Pabay*, Skye (1962–70, 1972–81 and from 1982); *St. Kilda*, Hebrides (1968–71); *St. Martin's* and *St. Mary's*, Isles of Scilly (from 1995); *Sanda*, Argyllshire (from 1962); *Shuna*, Argyllshire (from 1949); *Soay*, Skye (1965–67); *Staffa*, Hebrides (from 1969); *Steep Holm*, Avon (1980–87); *Stroma*, Caithness (1962–70 and from 1988) and *Summer Isles*, Hebrides (1970–88 and from 1992). Those issued for Soay have been declared bogus by a committee of the Philatelic Traders Society.

Issues of the *Commodore Shipping Co* (1950–69), the *Alderney Shipping Co* (1969–75) and the *Isle of Sark Shipping Co* (from 1969) were/are for use on parcels carried by ship between Guernsey and Alderney and Sark. They are not valid for the carriage of letters and postcards.

Issues inscribed Alderney (1975–83 and from 1990) are issued in conjunction with an internal parcel delivery service. They are not valid for use on letters or postcards.

CHANNEL ISLANDS

GENERAL ISSUE

C 1 Gathering Vraic

C 2 Islanders gathering Vraic

(Des J. R. R. Stobie (1d.) or from drawing by E. Blampied (2½d.). Photo Harrison)

1948 (10 May). *Third Anniv of Liberation. W* **127** *of Great Britain. P* 15 × 14.

C1	C **1**	1d. scarlet	20	20
C2	C **2**	2½d. ultramarine	30	30

Supplies of these stamps were also available from eight head post offices on the mainland of Great Britain.

GUERNSEY

WAR OCCUPATION ISSUES

Stamps issued under British authority during the German Occupation

BISECTS. On 24 December 1940 authority was given, by Post Office notice, that prepayment of penny postage could be effected by using half a British 2d. stamp, diagonally bisected. Such stamps were first used on 27 December 1940.

The 2d. stamps generally available were those of the Postal Centenary issue, 1940 (S.G. 482) and the first colour of the King George VI issue (S.G. 465). These are listed under Nos. 482a and 465b. A number of the 2d. King George V, 1912–22, and of the King George V photogravure stamp (S.G. 442) which were in the hands of philatelists, were also bisected and used.

1

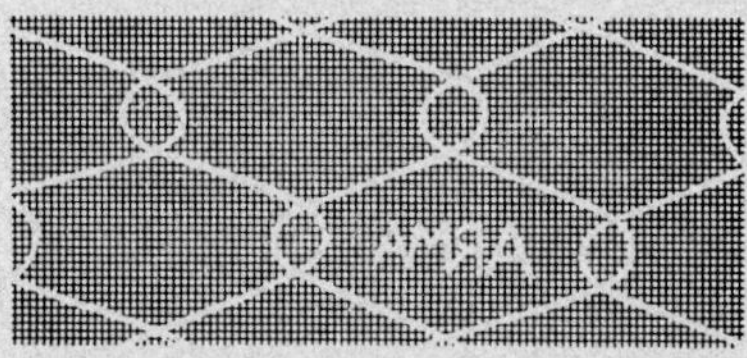

1*a* Loops (*half actual size*)

(Des E. W. Vaudin. Typo Guernsey Press Co Ltd)

1941–44. *Rouletted. (a) White paper. No wmk.*

1	**1**	½d. light green (7.4.41)	3·00	2·00
		a. *Emerald-green* (6.41)	4·00	2·25
		b. *Bluish green* (11.41)	42·00	16·00
		c. *Bright green* (2.42)	26·00	10·00
		d. *Dull green* (9.42)	4·00	2·75
		e. *Olive-green* (2.43)	30·00	18·00
		f. *Pale yellowish green* (7.43 and later) (*shades*)	3·00	2·50
		g. Imperf (pair)	£150	
		h. Imperf between (horiz pair)	£600	
		i. Imperf between (vert pair)	£700	
2		1d. scarlet (18.2.41)	2·50	1·25
		a. *Pale vermilion* (7.43) (etc.)	2·50	1·50
		b. *Carmine* (1943)	2·75	2·75
		c. Imperf (pair)	£150	75·00
		d. Imperf between (horiz pair)	£600	
		da. Imperf vert (centre stamp of horiz strip of 3)		
		e. Imperf between (vert pair)	£700	
		f. Printed double (scarlet shade)	75·00	
3		2½d. ultramarine (12.4.44)	4·25	4·50
		a. *Pale ultramarine* (7.44)	4·25	4·00
		b. Imperf (pair)	£350	
		c. Imperf between (horiz pair)	£800	

(*b*) *Bluish French bank-note paper. W* **1a** (*sideways*)

4	**1**	½d. bright green (11.3.42)	20·00	21·00
5		1d. scarlet (9.4.42)	10·00	23·00

The dates given for the shades of Nos. 1/3 are the months in which they were printed as indicated on the printer's imprints. Others are issue dates.

REGIONAL ISSUES

DATES OF ISSUE. Conflicting dates of issue have been announce for some of the regional issues, partly explained by the stamps bein released on different dates by the Philatelic Bureau in Edinburgh the Philatelic Counter in London and in the regions. We hav adopted the practice of giving the earliest known dates, since onc released the stamps could have been used anywhere in the U.K.

2

3

(Des E. A. Piprell. Portrait by Dorothy Wilding Ltd. Photo Harrisc & Sons)

1958 (18 Aug)–**67.** *W* **179** *of Great Britain. P* 15 × 14.

6	**2**	2½d. rose-red (8.6.64)	35	
7	**3**	3d. deep lilac	35	
		p. One centre phosphor band (24.5.67)	20	
8		4d. ultramarine (7.2.66)	25	
		p. Two phosphor bands (24.10.67)	20	
6/8p.		*Set of* 3	70	

1968–69. *No wmk. Chalk-surfaced paper. PVA gum*. One centr phosphor band (Nos. 10/11) or two phosphor bands (others P* 15 × 14.

9	**3**	4d. pale ultramarine (16.4.68)	10	
10		4d. olive-sepia (4.9.68)	15	
11		4d. bright vermilion (26.2.69)	15	
12		5d. royal blue (4.9.68)	15	
9/12		*Set of* 4	40	

No. 9 was not issued in Guernsey until 22 April.
* PVA Gum. See note after No. 722 of Great Britain.

INDEPENDENT POSTAL ADMINISTRATION

4 Castle Cornet and Edward the Confessor

5 View of Sark

Two Types of 1d. and 1s. 6d.:

I. Latitude inscr "40° 30′ N".
II. Corrected to "49° 30′ N".

(Des R. Granger Barrett. Photo Harrison (½d. to 2s. 6d.); Delrie (others))

1969 (1 Oct)–**70.** *Designs as T* **4/5.** *P* 14 (*½d. to 2s. 6d.*) *or* 12 (*others*).

13	½d. deep magenta and black	10	
14	1d. bright blue and black (I)	10	1
14*b*	1d. bright blue and black (II) (12.12.69)	30	3
	c. Booklet stamp with blank margins	40	4
15	1½d. yellow-brown and black	10	1
16	2d. gold, bright red, deep blue and black	10	1
17	3d. gold, pale greenish yellow, orge-red & blk	15	1
	a. Error. Wmk w **12**	£1200	
18	4d. multicoloured	25	2
	a. Booklet stamp with blank margins (12.12.69)	40	4
	ab. Yellow omitted	£250	
	ac. Emerald (stem) omitted	£110	
19	5d. gold, brt vermilion, bluish violet & black	25	1
	a. Booklet stamp with blank margins (12.12.69)	50	5
	b. Gold (inscr etc.) omitted (booklets)	£500	
20	6d. gold, pale greenish yellow, light bronze-green and black	30	3
21	9d. gold, bright red, crimson and black	40	3
22	1s. gold, bright vermilion, bistre and black	30	3
23	1s. 6d. turquoise-green and black (I)	30	3
23*b*	1s. 6d. turquoise-green and black (II) (4.2.70)	2·25	1·7
24	1s. 9d. multicoloured	1·25	1·5
	a. Emerald (stem) omitted	£325	
25	2s. 6d. bright reddish violet and black	5·00	4·2
26	5s. multicoloured	3·25	3·2
27	10s. multicoloured	26·00	22·0
	a. Perf 13½×13 (4.3.70)	48·00	40·0
28	£1 multicoloured	2·00	1·7
	a. Perf 13½×13 (4.3.70)	2·00	2·0
13/28	*Set of* 16	35·00	30·0

Designs: *Horiz as T* **4**—1d. (*both*), 1s. 6d. (*both*), Map and Williar I; 1½d. Martello Tower and Henry II; 2d. Arms of Sark and Kir John; 3d. Arms of Alderney and Edward III; 4d. Guernsey Lily an Henry V; 5d. Arms of Guernsey and Elizabeth I; 6d. Arms c Alderney and Charles II; 9d. Arms of Sark and George III; 1s. Arm of Guernsey and Queen Victoria; 1s. 9d. Guernsey Lily and Elizabe I; 2s. 6d. Martello Tower and King John. *Horiz as T* **5**—10s. View c Alderney; £1, View of Guernsey.

The booklet panes consist of single perforated stamps with wic margins all round intended to fit automatic machines designed fc the Great Britain 2s. booklets. They are therefore found with thre margins when detached from booklets or four margins whe complete.

There was no postal need for the ½d. and 1½d. values as the ½d. coin ad been withdrawn prior to their issue in anticipation of ecimalisation. These values were only on sale at the Philatelic ureau and the Crown Agents as well as in the U.S.A.

Nos. 14*b* and 23*b* are known only on thin paper and Nos. 13, 14, 5, 17, 20, 21, 22, 23, 24 and 25 also exist on thin paper.

19 Isaac Brock as Colonel

23 H.M.S. *L103* (landing craft) entering St. Peter's Harbour

(Litho Format)

969 (1 Dec). *Birth Bicentenary of Sir Isaac Brock. T* **19** *and similar multicoloured designs. P* 13½ × 14 (*2s. 6d.*) *or* 14 × 13½ (*others*).

) 4d. Type **19** 20 20
) 5d. Sir Isaac Brock as Major-General .. 20 20
1s. 9d. Isaac Brock as Ensign .. .. 1·40 1·25
2s. 6d. Arms and flags (*horiz*) .. .. 1·40 1·25
)/32 .. .. *Set of* 4 2·75 2·50

(Des and photo Courvoisier)

970 (9 May). *25th Anniv of Liberation. T* **23** *and similar designs. Granite paper. P* 11½.

3 4d. blue and pale blue 40 40
4 5d. brown-lake and pale grey 40 40
5 1s. 6d. bistre-brown and buff .. .. .. 3·25 2·50
3/5 .. .. *Set of* 3 3·50 3·00

Designs: *Horiz*—5d. British ships entering St. Peter's Port. *Vert*—s. 6d. Brigadier Snow reading Proclamation.

26 Guernsey "Toms"

32 St. Peter Church, Sark

(Des and photo Courvoisier)

970 (12 Aug). *Agriculture and Horticulture. T* **26** *and similar horiz designs. Multicoloured. Granite paper. P* 11½.

4d. Type **26** 80 20
5d. Guernsey Cow 90 20
9d. Guernsey Bull .. .. 5·00 2·75
1s. 6d. Freesias .. .. 6·00 3·00
/9 .. .. *Set of* 4 12·00 5·50

(Des and photo Courvoisier)

970 (11 Nov). *Christmas. Guernsey Churches* (*1st series*). *T* **32** *and similar multicoloured designs. Granite paper. P* 11½.

4d. St. Anne's Church, Alderney (*horiz*) .. 35 20
5d. St. Peter's Church (*horiz*) 45 25
9d. Type **32** .. .. 1·75 1·10
1s. 6d. St. Tugual Chapel, Herm .. .. 2·00 1·50
/3 .. .. *Set of* 4 4·00 2·75

See also Nos. 63/6.

INVALIDATION. The regional issues for Guernsey were invalidated r use in Guernsey and Jersey on 1 November 1969 but remained alid for use in the rest of the United Kingdom. Nos. 13/43 (except os. 28/a) and Nos. D1/7 were invalidated on 14 February 1972.

34 Martello Tower and King John

(Photo Harrison (½p. to 10p.), Delrieu (others))

971 (6 Jan)–**73**. *Decimal Currency. Designs as Nos. 13/27, but values inscr in decimal currency as in T* **34**. *Chalk-surfaced paper. P* 14 (*½ p. to 10p.*) *or* 13½×13 (*20p., 50p.*).

4 ½p. deep magenta and black (15.2.71) .. 10 15
a. Booklet stamp with margins (*glazed, ordinary paper*) 15 20
ab. Ditto. Chalk-surfaced paper (2.4.73) .. 15 20
5 1p. bright blue and black (II) (15.2.71) .. 10 10
6 1½p. yellow-brown and black (15.2.71) .. 15 15
7 2p. multicoloured (15.2.71) 15 15
a. Booklet stamp with margins (*glazed, ordinary paper*) 20 20
ab. Ditto. Chalk-surfaced paper (2.4.73) .. 20 20
ac. Emerald (stem) omitted £1200
b. Glazed, ordinary paper (15.2.71) .. 20 20
3 2½p. gold, brt verm, bluish vio & blk (15.2.71) 15 10
a. Bright vermilion omitted £500
b. Booklet stamp with margins (*glazed, ordinary paper*) 20 20
ba. Ditto. Chalk-surfaced paper (2.4.73) .. 20 20
) 3p. gold, pale greenish yellow, orange-red and black (15.2.71) 20 20
3½p. mult (*glazed, ordinary paper*) (15.2.71) .. 25 25
4p. multicoloured (15.2.71) 35 25

52 5p. turquoise-green and black (II) (15.2.71) 30 25
53 6p. gold, pale greenish yellow, light bronze-green and black (15.2.71) 30 35
54 7½p. gold, brt verm, bistre & black (15.2.71) 40 45
55 9p. gold, brt red, crimson & black (15.2.71) 50 75
56 10p. bright reddish violet and black .. .. 2·25 1·75
a. Ordinary paper. *Bright reddish violet and deep black* (1.9.72) .. .. 1·75 1·75
57 20p. multicoloured (*glazed, ordinary paper*) .. 1·00 1·00
*a. Shade** (25.1.73) .. .. 1·00 1·00
58 50p. multicoloured (*glazed, ordinary paper*) .. 2·00 2·00
44/58 .. .. *Set of* 15 7·00 7·00

*No. 57 has the sky in a pale turquoise-blue; on No. 57*a* it is pale turquoise-green.

35 Hong Kong 2 c. of 1862

(Des and recess D.L.R.)

1971 (2 June). *Thomas De La Rue Commemoration. T* **35** *and similar horiz designs. P* 14 × 13½.

59 2p. dull purple to brown-purple* 50 30
60 2½p. carmine-red 50 30
61 4p. deep bluish green .. .. 3·00 2·25
62 7½p. deep blue .. .. 3·25 2·25
59/62 .. .. *Set of* 4 6·50 4·50

Designs: (each incorporating portraits of Queen Elizabeth II and Thomas De La Rue as in T **35**)—2½p. Great Britain 4d. of 1855–7; 4p. Italy 5 c. of 1862; 7½p. Confederate States 5 c. of 1862.

* These colours represent the extreme range of shades of this value. The majority of the printing, however, is in an intermediate shade.

36 Ebenezer Church, St. Peter Port

(Des and photo Courvoisier)

1971 (27 Oct). *Christmas. Guernsey Churches* (*2nd series*). *T* **36** *and similar multicoloured designs. Granite paper. P* 11½.

63 2p. Type **36** 25 25
64 2½p. Church of St. Pierre du Bois 25 25
65 5p. St. Joseph's Church, St. Peter Port (*vert*) 2·50 2·00
66 7½d. Church of St. Philippe de Torteval (*vert*) 2·75 2·00
63/6 .. .. *Set of* 4 5·25 4·00

37 *Earl of Chesterfield* (1794)

(Des and photo Courvoisier)

1972 (10 Feb). *Mail Packet Boats* (*1st series*). *T* **37** *and similar horiz designs. Multicoloured. Granite paper. P* 11½.

67 2p. Type **37** 15 15
68 2½p. *Dasher* (1827) 20 20
69 7½p. *Ibex* (1891) .. .. 90 1·00
70 9p. *Alberta* (1900) .. .. 1·50 1·40
67/70 .. .. *Set of* 4 2·50 2·50

See also Nos. 80/3

38 Guernsey Bull

(Photo Courvoisier)

1972 (22 May). *World Conference of Guernsey Breeders, Guernsey. Granite paper. P* 11½.

71 **38** 5p. multicoloured 75 60

39 Bermuda Buttercup

40 Angels adoring Christ

(Des and photo Courvoisier)

1972 (24 May). *Wild Flowers. T* **39** *and similar multicoloured designs. Granite paper. P* 11½.

72 2p. Type **39** 15 20
73 2½p. Heath Spotted Orchid (*vert*) 15 20
74 7½p. Kaffir Fig .. .. 1·00 90
75 9p. Scarlet Pimpernel (*vert*) .. .. .. 1·40 1·25
72/5 .. .. *Set of* 4 2·50 2·25

(Des and photo Courvoisier)

1972 (20 Nov). *Royal Silver Wedding and Christmas. T* **40** *and similar vert designs showing stained-glass windows from Guernsey Churches. Multicoloured. Granite paper. P* 11½.

76 2p. Type **40** 10 10
77 2½p. The Epiphany 15 15
78 7½p. The Virgin Mary 60 55
79 9p. Christ 75 60
76/9 .. .. *Set of* 4 1·50 1·25

See also Nos. 89/92.

(Des and photo Courvoisier)

1973 (9 Mar). *Mail Packet Boats* (*2nd series*). *Multicoloured designs as T* **37**. *Granite paper. P* 11½.

80 2½p. *St. Julien* (1925) 20 10
81 3p. *Isle of Guernsey* (1930) 30 20
82 7½p. *St. Patrick* (1947) .. .. 1·10 60
83 9p. *Sarnia* (1961) .. .. 1·25 75
80/3 .. .. *Set of* 4 2·50 1·50

41 Supermarine Sea Eagle

42 "The Good Shepherd"

(Des and photo Courvoisier)

1973 (4 July). *50th Anniv of Air Service. T* **41** *and similar horiz designs. Multicoloured. Granite paper. P* 11½.

84 2½p. Type **41** 10 10
85 3p. Westland Wessex trimotor 15 15
86 5p. De Havilland D.H.89 Dragon Rapide .. 30 25
87 7½p. Douglas DC-3 .. .. 90 50
88 9p. Vickers Viscount 800 *Anne Marie* .. 1·00 55
84/8 .. .. *Set of* 5 2·25 1·40

(Des and photo Courvoisier)

1973 (24 Oct). *Christmas. T* **42** *and similar vert designs showing stained-glass windows from Guernsey Churches. Multicoloured. Granite paper. P* 11½.

89 2½p. Type **42** 10 10
90 3p. Christ at the well of Samaria 10 10
91 7½p. St. Dominic 30 30
92 20p. Mary and the Child Jesus 60 60
89/92 .. .. *Set of* 4 1·00 1·00

43 Princess Anne and Capt. Mark Phillips

(Des G. Anderson. Photo Courvoisier)

1973 (14 Nov). *Royal Wedding. Granite paper. P* 11½.

93 **43** 25p. multicoloured .. .. 1·00 75

44 *John Lockett*, 1875

(Des and photo Courvoisier)

1974 (15 Jan). *150th Anniv of Royal National Lifeboat Institution. T* **44** *and similar horiz designs. Multicoloured. Granite paper. P* 11½.

94 2½p. Type **44** 10 10
95 3p. *Arthur Lionel*, 1912 .. .. 10 10
96 8p. *Euphrosyne Kendal*, 1954 .. .. .. 45 45
97 10p. *Arun*, 1972 .. .. 45 45
94/7 .. .. *Set of* 4 1·00 1·00

MINIMUM PRICE

The minimum price quote is 10p which represents a handling charge rather than a basis for valuing common stamps. For further notes about prices see introductory pages.

45 Private, East Regt, 1815 **46** Driver, Field Battery, Royal Guernsey Artillery, 1848

(Photo Courvoisier (½ to 10p.) or Delrieu (others))

1974 (2 Apr)–**78.** *Designs as T* **45**/**6**. *Multicoloured.*

(*a*) *Vert designs as T* **45**. *Granite paper. P* 11½

98 ½p. Type **45** 10 10
a. Booklet strip of 8 (98 × 5 and 102 × 3)† 30
b. Booklet pane of 16 (98 × 4, 102 × 6 and 103 × 6)† 65
99 1p. Officer, 2nd North Regt, 1825 .. .. 10 10
a. Booklet strip of 8 (99 × 4, 103, 105 × 2 and 105*a*) (8.2.77)† 80
b. Booklet strip of 4 (99, 101 × 2 and 105*a*) (7.2.78)† 50
100 1½p. Gunner, Guernsey Artillery, 1787 .. 10 10
101 2p. Gunner, Guernsey Artillery, 1815 .. 10 10
102 2½p. Corporal, Royal Guernsey Artillery, 1868 .. .. 10 10
103 3p. Field Officer, Royal Guernsey Artillery, 1895 .. .. 10 10
104 3½p. Sergeant, 3rd Regt, 1867 .. .. 10 10
105 4p. Officer, East Regt, 1822 .. .. 15 15
105*a* 5p. Field Officer, Royal Guernsey Artillery, 1895 (29.5.76) 15 15
106 5½p. Colour-Sergeant of Grenadiers, East Regt, 1833 .. .. 20 25
107 6p. Officer, North Regt, 1832 .. .. 20 25
107*a* 7p. Officer, East Regt, 1822 (29.5.76) .. 25 25
108 8p. Field Officer, Rifle Company, 1868 .. 25 30
109 9p. Private, 4th West Regt, 1785 .. .. 30 30
110 10p. Field Officer, 4th West Regt, 1824 .. 30 30

(*b*) *Size as T* **46**. *P* 13 × 13½ (20, 50*p*.) *or* 13½ × 13 (£1)

111 20p. Type **46** (1.4.75) 55 40
112 50p. Officer, Field Battery, Royal Guernsey Artillery, 1868 (1.4.75) .. .. .. 1·50 1·25
113 £1 Cavalry Trooper, Light Dragoons, 1814 (*horiz*) (1.4.75) .. .. 3·25 2·50
98/113 .. .. *Set of* 18 7·00 6·00

The ½p. and 2½p. with the red colour omitted are chemically produced fakes.

† Nos. 98a/b come from special booklet sheets of 88 (8 × 11), and Nos. 99a/b from separate booklet sheets of 80 (2 panes 8 × 5). These sheets were put on sale in addition to the normal sheets. The strips and panes have the left-hand selvedge stuck into booklet covers, except for No. 99b which was loose, and then folded and supplied in plastic wallets.

47 Badge of Guernsey and U.P.U. Emblem

(Photo Courvoisier)

1974 (7 June). *U.P.U. Centenary. T* **47** *and similar horiz designs. Multicoloured. Granite paper. P* 11½.

114 2½p. Type **47** 10 10
115 3p. Map of Guernsey 10 10
116 8p. U.P.U. Building, Berne, and Guernsey flag 45 45
117 10p. "Salle des Etats" 45 45
114/17 .. .. *Set of* 4 1·00 1·00

48 "Cradle Rock" **49** Guernsey Spleenwort

(Des and photo Delrieu)

1974 (21 Sept). *Renoir Paintings. T* **48** *and similar multicoloured designs. P* 13.

118 3p. Type **48** 10 10
119 5½p. "Moulin Huet Bay" 15 15
120 8p. "Au Bord de la Mer" (*vert*) 40 40
121 10p. Self-portrait (*vert*) 45 45
118/21 .. .. *Set of* 4 1·00 1·00

(Des and photo Courvoisier)

1975 (7 Jan). *Guernsey Ferns. T* **49** *and similar vert designs. Multicoloured. Granite paper. P* 11½.

122 3½p. Type **49** 15 10
123 4p. Sand Quillwort 15 10
124 8p. Guernsey Quillwort 40 40
125 10p. Least Adder's Tongue 60 50
122/5 .. .. *Set of* 4 1·25 1·00

50 Victor Hugo House **51** Globe and Seal of Bailiwick

(Des and photo Courvoisier)

1975 (6 June). *Victor Hugo's Exile in Guernsey. T* **50** *and similar multicoloured designs. Granite paper. P* 11½.

126 3½p. Type **50** 10 10
127 4p. Candie Gardens (*vert*) 20 10
128 8p. United Europe Oak, Hauteville (*vert*) 40 40
129 10p. Tapestry Room, Hauteville 50 50
126/9 .. .. *Set of* 4 1·10 1·00
MS130 114 × 143 mm. Nos. 126/9 .. .. 1·10 1·00

(Des and photo Delrieu)

1975 (7 Oct). *Christmas. Multicoloured designs each showing Globe as T* **51**. *P* 13.

131 4p. Type **51** 10 10
132 6p. Guernsey flag 15 15
133 10p. Guernsey flag and Alderney shield (*horiz*) 45 35
134 12p. Guernsey flag and Sark shield (*horiz*) .. 50 50
131/4 .. .. *Set of* 4 1·10 1·00

52 Les Hanois

(Des and photo Courvoisier)

1976 (10 Feb). *Lighthouses. T* **52** *and similar horiz designs. Multicoloured. Granite paper. P* 11½.

135 4p. Type **52** 10 10
136 6p. Les Casquets 20 25
137 11p. Quesnard 50 45
138 13p. Point Robert 55 60
135/8 .. .. *Set of* 4 1·25 1·25

53 Milk Can

(Des and photo Courvoisier)

1976 (29 May). *Europa. T* **53** *and similar horiz design. Granite paper. P* 11½.

139 10p. chestnut and greenish black 40 40
140 25p. slate and deep dull blue 85 85

Design:—25p. Christening Cup.

54 Pine Forest, Guernsey

(Des and photo Courvoisier)

1976 (3 Aug). *Bailiwick Views. T* **54** *and similar multicoloured designs. Granite paper. P* 11½.

141 5p. Type **54** 15 10
142 7p. Herm and Jethou 15 20
143 11p. Grand Greve Bay, Sark (*vert*) .. 55 45
144 13p. Trois Vaux Bay, Alderney (*vert*) .. 55 65
141/4 .. .. *Set of* 4 1·25 1·25

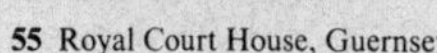

55 Royal Court House, Guernsey **56** Queen Elizabeth II

(Des and photo Courvoisier)

1976 (14 Oct). *Christmas. Buildings. T* **55** *and similar horiz designs. Multicoloured. Granite paper. P* 11½.

145 5p. Type **55** 15 1
146 7p. Elizabeth College, Guernsey 15 1
147 11p. La Seigneurie, Sark 55 5
148 13p. Island Hall, Alderney 55 6
145/8 .. .. *Set of* 4 1·25 1·2

(Des R. Granger Barrett. Photo Courvoisier)

1977 (8 Feb). *Silver Jubilee. T* **56** *and similar vert design. Multicoloured. Granite paper. P* 11½.

149 7p. Type **56** 25 2
150 35p. Queen Elizabeth (half-length portrait) 1·00 1·0

57 Woodland, Talbot's Valley **58** Statue-menhir, Caste

(Des and photo Courvoisier)

1977 (17 May). *Europa. T* **57** *and similar horiz design. Multicoloured. Granite paper. P* 11½.

151 7p. Type **57** 35 3
152 25p. Pastureland, Talbot's Valley 90 9

(Des and photo Courvoisier)

1977 (2 Aug). *Prehistoric Monuments. T* **58** *and similar multicoloured designs. Granite paper. P* 11½.

153 5p. Type **58** 10 1
154 7p. Megalithic tomb, St. Saviour (*horiz*) .. 15 1
155 11p. Cist, Tourgis (*horiz*) 55 5
156 13p. Statue-menhir, St. Martin 60 6
153/6 .. .. *Set of* 4 1·25 1·2

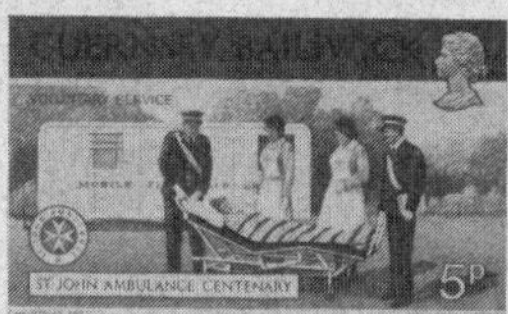

59 Mobile First Aid Unit

(Des P. Slade and M. Horder. Photo Courvoisier)

1977 (25 Oct). *Christmas and St. John Ambulance Centenary. T* **59** *and similar multicoloured designs. Granite paper. P* 11½.

157 5p. Type **59** 10 1
158 7p. Mobile radar unit 15 1
159 11p. Marine Ambulance *Flying Christine II* (*vert*) 55 5
160 13p. Cliff rescue (*vert*) 60 6
157/60 .. .. *Set of* 4 1·25 1·2

60 View from Clifton, *circa* 1830

(Des, recess and litho D.L.R.)

1978 (7 Feb). *Old Guernsey Prints* (1*st series*). *T* **60** *and similar horiz designs. P* 14 × 13½.

161 5p. black and pale apple-green 10 1
162 7p. black and stone 15 1
163 11p. black and light pink 55 5
164 13p. black and light azure 60 6
161/4 .. .. *Set of* 4 1·25 1·2

Designs:—7p. Market Square, St. Peter Port, *circa* 1838; 11p. Petit-Bo Bay, *circa* 1839; 13p. The Quay, St. Peter Port, *circa* 1830.

See also Nos. 249/52.

61 *Prosperity* Memorial **62** Queen Elizabeth II

(Des R. Granger Barrett. Litho Questa)

978 (2 May). *Europa. T* **61** *and similar vert design. Multicoloured. P* 14½.
65 5p. Type **61** 35 35
66 7p. Victoria Monument 40 40

)es R. Granger Barrett from bust by Arnold Machin. Photo Courvoisier)

978 (2 May). *25th Anniv of Coronation. Granite paper. P* 11½.
67 **62** 20p. black, grey and bright blue .. 75 75

978 (28 June). *Royal Visit. Design as No.* 167 *but inscr.* "VISIT OF H.M. THE QUEEN AND H.R.H. THE DUKE OF EDINBURGH JUNE 28–29, 1978 TO THE BAILIWICK OF GUERNSEY".
68 **62** 7p. black, grey and bright green .. 50 50

63 Northern Gannet

(Des J.W. Photo Courvoisier)

978 (29 Aug). *Birds. T* **63** *and similar horiz designs. Multicoloured. Granite paper. P* 11½.
69 5p. Type **63** 15 15
70 7p. Firecrest 25 25
71 11p. Dartford Warbler 60 45
72 13p. Spotted Redshank 70 55
69/72 .. .. *Set of* 4 1·50 1·25

64 Solanum

(Des and photo Courvoisier)

978 (31 Oct). *Christmas. T* **64** *and similar designs. Granite paper. P* 11½.
73 5p. multicoloured 10 10
74 7p. multicoloured 20 20
75 11p. multicoloured 40 40
76 13p. dp blue-green, grey & greenish yellow 50 50
73/6 .. .. *Set of* 4 1·10 1·10
Designs: *Horiz*—7p. Christmas Rose. *Vert*—11p. Holly; 13p. Mistletoe.

65 One Double Coin, 1830 **66** Ten Shillings William I Commemorative Coin, 1966

66a Seal of the Bailiwick

(Des R. Reed and Courvoisier (£5). Photo Courvoisier)

979 (13 Feb)–**83**. *Designs as T* **65/6a**. *Granite paper. P* 11½.
77 ½p. multicoloured 10 10
a. Booklet pane of 10. Nos. 177×2, 178×3, 179×2, 181, 183 and 187 (6.5.80) .. 1·00
b. Booklet pane of 10. Nos. 177×2, 178, 179×2, 183×2 and 187×3 (6.5.80) .. 1·25
78 1p. multicoloured 10 10
a. Booklet strip of 4. Nos. 178×2, 179 and 182 60
79 2p. multicoloured 10 10
a. Booklet strip of 5. Nos. 179, 182×2 and 184×2 .. .. 1·25

180 4p. multicoloured 10 10
a. Booklet pane of 10. Nos. 180 and 184, each × 5 (24.2.81) .. .. .. 1·75
b. Booklet pane of 15. Nos. 180, 184 and 190, each × 5 (24.2.81) .. .. 2·75
c. Booklet pane of 10. Nos. 180×2, 185×3 and 191×5 (14.3.83) .. .. 3·00
d. Booklet pane of 15. Nos. 180, 185 and 191, each × 5 (14.3.83) .. .. 3·75
181 5p. grey-black, silver and chestnut (*shades*) 15 10
b. Booklet pane. Nos. 181×5, 184×4 and 191 (2.2.82) .. .. 2·25
c. Booklet pane. Nos. 181, 184 and 191, each × 5 (2.2.82) .. .. .. 3·75
182 6p. grey-black, silver and brown-red .. 15 15
183 7p. grey-black, silver and green .. 15 20
184 8p. grey-black, silver and brown .. 20 20
185 9p. multicoloured 25 20
186 10p. multicoloured (green background) .. 50 50
187 10p. mult (orange background) (5.2.80) .. 35 30
188 11p. multicoloured 25 30
189 11½p. multicoloured (5.2.80) 25 30
190 12p. multicoloured 30 30
191 13p. multicoloured 30 30
192 14p. grey-black, silver and dull blue .. 30 30
193 15p. grey-black, silver and bistre 35 35
194 20p. grey-black, silver and dull brown .. 50 45
195 50p. grey-black, orange-red & silver (5.2.80) 1·00 75
196 £1 grey-blk, yellowish grn & silver (5.2.80) 2·00 1·50
197 £2 grey-black, new blue and silver (5.2.80) 4·00 2·50
198 £5 multicoloured (22.5.81) .. .. 10·00 7·50
177/98 .. .. *Set of* 22 19·00 14·50
Coins: *Vert as T* **65**—1p. Two doubles, 1899; 2p. Four doubles, 1902; 4p. Eight doubles 1959; 5p. Three pence, 1956; 6p. Five new pence, 1968; 7p. Fifty new pence, 1969; 8p. Ten new pence, 1970; 9p. Half new penny, 1971; 10p. (*both*), One new penny, 1971; 11p. Two new pence, 1971; 11½p. Half penny, 1979; 12p. One penny, 1977; 13p. Two pence, 1977; 14p. Five pence, 1977; 15p. Ten pence, 1977; 20p. Twenty-five pence, 1972. *Horiz as T* **66**—£1 Silver Jubilee commemorative crown, 1977; £2 Royal Silver Wedding crown, 1972.
Nos. 177a/b, 178a, 179a, 180a/d and 181b/c come from special booklet sheets of 40 (8 × 5) (Nos. 177a and 178a); 30 (6 × 5) (Nos. 177b, 180a/b, 180d and 181 b/c), 25 (5 × 5) (No. 179a) or 20 (4 × 5) No. 180c). These were put on sale in addition to the normal sheets, being first separated into strips, then folded and either affixed by the selvedge to booklet covers or supplied loose in plastic wallets.

67 Pillar-box and Postmark, 1853, Mail Van and Postmark, 1979 **68** Steam Tram, 1879

(Des R. Granger Barrett. Photo Courvoisier)

1979 (8 May). *Europa. Communications. T* **67** *and similar vert design. Multicoloured. Granite paper. P* 11½.
201 6p. Type **67** 30 30
202 8p. Telephone, 1897 and telex machine, 1979 30 30

(Photo Courvoisier)

1979 (7 Aug). *History of Public Transport. T* **68** *and similar horiz designs. Multicoloured. Granite paper. P* 11½.
203 6p. Type **68** 15 15
204 8p. Electric tram, 1896 .. .. .. 20 20
205 11p. Motor bus, 1911 .. .. .. 55 55
206 13p. Motor bus, 1979 .. .. .. 60 60
203/6 .. .. *Set of* 4 1·25 1·25

69 Bureau and Postal Headquarters **70** Major-General Le Marchant

(Des R. Granger Barrett. Photo Courvoisier)

1979 (1 Oct). *Christmas and 10th Anniv of Guernsey Postal Administration. T* **69** *and similar horiz designs. Multicoloured. Granite paper. P* 11½.
207 6p. Type **69** 15 15
208 8p. "Mails and telegrams" 25 15
209 13p. "Parcels" 50 55
210 15p. "Philately" 60 60
207/10 .. .. *Set of* 4 1·25 1·25
MS211 120 × 80 mm. Nos. 207/10 .. .. 1·00 70
One copy of a pre-release sample as No. 210, but with a face value of 11p., is known. Such stamps were not sold for postal purposes.

(Des and photo Courvoisier)

1980 (6 May). *Europa. Personalities. T* **70** *and similar vert design. Multicoloured. Granite paper. P* 11½.
212 10p. Type **70** 45 45
213 13½p. Admiral Lord De Saumarez 55 50

71 Policewoman with Lost Child

(Litho J.W.)

1980 (6 May). *60th Anniv of Guernsey Police Force. T* **71** *and similar horiz designs. Multicoloured. P* 13½ × 14.
214 7p. Type **71** 20 20
215 15p. Police motorcyclist escorting lorry .. 55 55
216 17½p. Police dog-handler 65 65
214/16 .. .. *Set of* 3 1·25 1·25

72 Golden Guernsey Goat

(Des P. Lambert. Photo Delrieu)

1980 (5 Aug). *Golden Guernsey Goats. T* **72** *and similar horiz designs showing goats. P* 13.
217 7p. multicoloured 20 20
218 10p. multicoloured 30 35
219 15p. multicoloured 55 45
220 17½p. multicoloured 65 60
217/20 .. .. *Set of* 4 1·50 1·40

73 "Sark Cottage"

(Photo Courvoisier)

1980 (15 Nov). *Christmas. Peter le Lievre Paintings. T* **73** *and similar multicoloured designs. Granite paper. P* 11½.
221 7p. Type **73** 25 20
222 10p. "Moulin Huet" 35 25
223 13½p. "Boats at Sea" 40 35
224 15p. "Cow Lane" (*vert*) 50 40
225 17½p. "Peter le Lievre" (*vert*) 65 50
221/5 .. .. *Set of* 5 2·00 1·50

74 *Polyommatus icarus* **75** Sailors paying respect to "Le Petit Bonhomme Andriou" (rock resembling head of a man)

(Photo Harrison)

1981 (24 Feb). *Butterflies. T* **74** *and similar horiz designs. Multicoloured. P* 14.
226 8p. Type **74** 25 25
227 12p. *Vanessa atalanta* 40 40
228 22p. *Aglais urticae* 90 70
229 25p. *Lasiommata megera* .. .. .. 1·00 90
226/9 .. .. *Set of* 4 2·25 2·00

(Des C. Abbott. Litho Questa)

1981 (22 May). *Europa. Folklore. T* **75** *and similar vert design. P* 14½.
230 12p. gold, red-brown and cinnamon .. 45 45
231 18p. gold, indigo and azure 55 55
Design:—18p. Fairies and Guernsey Lily.

76 Prince Charles **77** Sark Launch

(Des C. Abbott. Litho Questa)

1981 (29 July). *Royal Wedding. T* **76** *and similar multicoloured designs. P* 14½.
232 8p. Type **76** 50 50
a. Horiz strip of 3. Nos. 232/4 .. .. 1·50 1·50
233 8p. Prince Charles and Lady Diana Spencer 50 50
234 8p. Lady Diana 50 50

235	12p.	Type **76**	90	90
	a.	Horiz strip of 3. Nos. 235/7	2·75	2·75
236	12p.	As No. 233	90	90
237	12p.	As No. 234	90	90
238	25p.	Royal family (49 × 32 *mm*)	1·50	1·50
232/8		.. .. *Set of* 7	5·00	5·00
MS239		104 × 127 mm. Nos. 232/8. P 14	6·50	6·50

The 8 and 12p. values were each printed together, *se-tenant*, in horizontal strips of 3 throughout the sheets.

(Des and photo Courvoisier)

1981 (25 Aug). *Inter-island Transport. T* **77** *and similar horiz designs. Multicoloured. Granite paper. P* 11½.

240	8p.	Type **77**	20	20
241	12p.	Britten Norman "Short nose" Trislander airplane	40	40
242	18p.	Hydrofoil	60	50
243	22p.	Herm catamaran	75	65
244	25p.	*Sea Trent* (coaster)	90	75
240/4		.. .. *Set of* 5	2·50	2·25

78 Rifle Shooting

79 Sir Edgar MacCulloch (founder-president) and Guille-Allès Library, St. Peter Port

(Des P. le Vasseur. Litho Questa)

1981 (17 Nov). *International Year for Disabled Persons. T* **78** *and similar horiz designs. Multicoloured. P* 14½.

245	8p.	Type **78**	20	20
246	12p.	Riding	35	35
247	22p.	Swimming	65	55
248	25p.	"Work"	75	60
245/8		.. .. *Set of* 4	1·75	1·50

(Des, recess and litho D.L.R.)

1982 (2 Feb). *Old Guernsey Prints* (*2nd series*). *Prints from sketches by T. Compton. Horiz designs as T* **60**. *P* 14 × 13½.

249	8p.	black and pale blue	20	20
250	12p.	black and pale turquoise-green ..	35	35
251	22p.	black and pale yellow-brown	65	65
252	25p.	black and pale rose-lilac	75	75
249/52		.. .. *Set of* 4	1·75	1·75

Designs:—8p. Jethou; 12p. Fermain Bay; 22p. The Terres; 25p. St. Peter Port.

(Des G. Drummond. Photo Courvoisier)

1982 (28 Apr). *Centenary of La Société Guernesiaise. T* **79** *and similar horiz designs. Multicoloured. Granite paper. P* 11½.

253	8p.	Type **79**	20	20
254	13p.	French invasion fleet crossing English Channel, 1066 ("History")	35	35
255	20p.	H.M.S. *Crescent*, 1793 ("History") ..	45	45
256	24p.	Dragonfly ("Entomology")	70	70
257	26p.	Common Snipe caught for ringing ("Ornithology")	80	80
258	29p.	Samian Bowl, 160–200 A.D. ("Archaeology")	85	85
253/8		.. .. *Set of* 6	3·00	3·00

The 13 and 20p. values also include the Europa C.E.P.T. emblem in the designs.

80 "Sea Scouts"

81 Midnight Mass

(Des W.L.G. Creative Services Ltd. Litho Questa)

1982 (13 July). *75th Anniv of Boy Scout Movement. T* **80** *and similar vert designs. Multicoloured. P* 14½ × 14.

259	8p.	Type **80**	20	25
260	13p.	"Scouts"	50	50
261	26p.	"Cub Scouts"	70	70
262	29p.	"Air Scouts"	85	80
259/62		.. .. *Set of* 4	2·25	2·25

(Des Lynette Hemmant. Photo Harrison)

1982 (12 Oct). *Christmas. T* **81** *and similar horiz designs. Multicoloured. P* 14½.

263	8p.	Type **81**	20	20
	a.	Black (Queen's head, value and inscr) omitted		
264	13p.	Exchanging gifts	30	30
265	24p.	Christmas meal	75	75
266	26p.	Exchanging cards	75	75
267	29p.	Queen's Christmas message	80	80
263/7		.. .. *Set of* 5	2·50	2·50

NEW INFORMATION

The editor is always interested to correspond with people who have new information that will improve or correct the Catalogue.

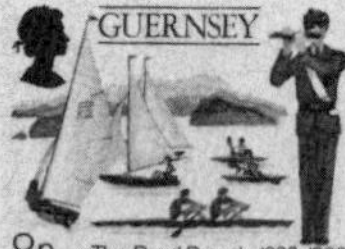

82 Flute Player and Boats

83 Building Albert Pier Extension, 1850s

(Des Sally Stiff. Photo Harrison)

1983 (18 Jan). *Centenary of Boys' Brigade. T* **82** *and similar horiz designs. Multicoloured. P* 14.

268	8p.	Type **82**	25	25
269	13p.	Cymbal player and tug 'o' war	40	40
270	24p.	Trumpet player and bible class ..	85	85
271	26p.	Drummer and cadets marching ..	90	90
272	29p.	Boys' Brigade band	95	95
268/72		.. .. *Set of* 5	3·00	3·00

(Des C. Abbott. Photo Courvoisier)

1983 (14 Mar). *Europa. Development of St. Peter Port Harbour. T* **83** *and similar horiz designs. Multicoloured. Granite paper. P* 11½.

273	13p.	Type **83**	35	35
	a.	Horiz pair. Nos. 273/4	70	70
274	13p.	St. Peter Port Harbour, 1983	35	35
275	20p.	St. Peter Port, 1680	75	75
	a.	Horiz pair. Nos. 275/6	1·50	1·50
276	20p.	Artist's impression of future development scheme	75	75
273/6		.. .. *Set of* 4	2·00	2·00

The two designs of each value were issued together, *se-tenant*, in horizontal pairs throughout the sheets.

84 "View at Guernsey" (Renoir)

(Des and photo Courvoisier)

1983 (6 Sept). *Centenary of Renoir's Visit to Guernsey. T* **84** *and similar multicoloured designs, showing paintings. Granite paper. P* 11 × 11½ (*13p.*) *or* 11½ (*others*).

277	9p.	Type **84**	25	25
278	13p.	"Children on the Seashore" (25 × 39 *mm*)	45	45
279	26p.	"Marine, Guernesey"	80	80
280	28p.	"La Baie du Moulin Huet à travers les Arbres"	1·10	1·10
281	31p.	"Brouillard à Guernesey"	1·25	1·25
277/81		.. .. *Set of* 5	3·50	3·50

85 Launching *Star of the West*, 1869, and Capt. J. Lenfestey

(Des R. Granger Barrett. Litho Questa)

1983 (15 Nov). *Guernsey Shipping* (*1st series*). *"Star of the West"* (*brigantine*). *T* **85** *and similar horiz designs. Multicoloured. P* 14.

282	9p.	Type **85**	25	25
283	13p.	Leaving St. Peter Port	40	40
284	26p.	Off Rio Grande Bar	80	80
285	28p.	Off St. Lucia	1·10	1·10
286	31p.	Map of 1879–80 voyage	1·25	1·25
282/6		.. .. *Set of* 5	3·50	3·50

See also Nos. 415/19.

86 Dame of Sark as Young Woman

(Des Jennifer Toombs. Litho Questa)

1984 (7 Feb). *Birth Centenary of Sibyl Hathaway, Dame of Sark. T* **86** *and similar horiz designs. Multicoloured. P* 14½.

287	9p.	Type **86**	25	25
288	13p.	German occupation, 1940–45	40	45
289	26p.	Royal Visit, 1957	90	90
290	28p.	Chief Pleas	95	95
291	31p.	The Dame of Sark rose	1·10	1·10
287/91		.. .. *Set of* 5	3·25	3·25

87 C.E.P.T. 25th Anniversary Logo

(Des J. Larrivière and C. Abbott. Litho Questa)

1984 (10 Apr). *Europa. P* 15 × 14½.

292	**87**	13p.	cobalt, dull ultramarine and black	65	65
293		20½p.	emerald, deep dull green and black	85	85

88 The Royal Court and St. George's Flag

89 St. Apolline Chape

(Des C. Abbott. Litho Questa)

1984 (10 Apr). *Links with the Commonwealth. T* **88** *and similar horiz design. Multicoloured. P* 14 × 14½.

294	9p.	Type **88**	40	40
295	31p.	Castle Cornet and Union flag	1·10	1·10

(Des C. Abbott. Litho Questa)

1984 (18 Sept)–**91**. *Views. T* **89** *and similar multicoloured designs. Chalk-surfaced paper. P* 14½.

296	1p.	Little Chapel (23.7.85)	20	10
297	2p.	Fort Grey (*horiz*) (23.7.85)	20	10
	a.	Booklet pane. Nos. 297×2, 299×4, 300×2 and 305×2 (2.12.85)	2·75	
298	3p.	Type **89**	20	10
	a.	Booklet pane. Nos. 298, 299×2, 306×4 and 309×3 (30.3.87)	4·25	
299	4p.	Petit Port (*horiz*)	20	10
	a.	Booklet pane. Nos. 299×2, 304×3 and 307×5	4·00	
	b.	Booklet pane. Nos. 299, 304 and 307, each × 5	4·75	
	c.	Booklet pane. Nos. 299×4, 306*b*×3 and 309*c*×3 (28.3.88)	4·00	
	d.	Booklet pane. Nos. 299, 301, 306*b*×3 and 309*d*×3 (28.2.89)	4·50	
300	5p.	Little Russel (*horiz*) (23.7.85) ..	20	10
	a.	Booklet pane. Nos. 300×2, 301×2, 309×3 and 310*b*×3 (2.4.91)	4·00	
301	6p.	The Harbour, Herm (*horiz*) (23.7.85)	20	15
	a.	Booklet pane. Nos. 301×4, 308×4 and 310×2 (27.12.89)	4·25	
	b.	Uncoated paper		
302	7p.	Saints (*horiz*) (23.7.85)	20	20
303	8p.	St. Saviour (23.7.85)	20	20
304	9p.	New jetty (inscr "Cambridge Berth") (*horiz*)	20	25
	a.	Booklet pane. Nos. 304×4 and 308×6 (19.3.85)	4·75	
	b.	Booklet pane. Nos. 304×2 and 308×8 (19.3.85)	4·50	
305	10p.	Belvoir, Herm (*horiz*)	25	25
	a.	Booklet pane. Nos. 305 and 308, each × 5 (1.4.86)	4·50	
306	11p.	La Seigneurie, Sark (*horiz*) (23.7.85)	25	25
	a.	Booklet pane. Nos. 306 and 309, each × 5 (30.3.87)	4·50	
306*b*	12p.	Petit Bot (28.3.88)	40	30
	ba.	Booklet pane. Nos. 306*b* and 309*c*, each × 5	4·25	
	bb.	Booklet pane. Nos. 306*b* and 309*d*, each × 4 (28.2.89)	4·75	
307	13p.	St. Saviours reservoir (*horiz*) ..	30	30
308	14p.	St. Peter Port	30	35
	a.	Booklet pane. Nos. 308 and 310, each × 5 (27.12.89)	4·75	
	b.	Uncoated paper		
309	15p.	Havelet (23.7.85)	30	35
	a.	Booklet pane. Nos. 309 and 310*b*, each × 5 (2.4.91)	5·25	
	b.	Imperf at sides and foot (horiz pair)		
309*c*	16p.	Hostel of St. John (*horiz*) (28.3.88)	30	35
309*d*	18p.	Le Variouf (28.2.89)	35	40
310	20p.	La Coupee, Sark (*horiz*)	50	45
	a.	Uncoated paper		
310*b*	21p.	King's Mills (*horiz*) (2.4.91)	50	45
310*c*	26p.	Town Church (2.4.91)	70	55
	ca.	Imperf at sides and foot (horiz pair)	£900	
311	30p.	Grandes Rocques (*horiz*) (23.7.85)	60	65
312	40p.	Torteval church	80	85
313	50p.	Bordeaux (*horiz*)	1·00	1·10
314	£1	Albecq (*horiz*)	2·00	2·10
315	£2	L'Ancresse (*horiz*) (23.7.85) ..	4·25	4·25
296/315		.. .. *Set of* 25	12·50	12·50

Booklet panes Nos. 297a, 298a, 299a/c, 304a/b, 305a, 306a and 306ba have margins all round and were issued, folded and loose, within the booklet covers.

Booklet panes Nos. 299d, 300a, 301a, 306bb, 308a and 309a have the outer edges imperforate on three sides and were also issued loose within the booklet covers.

The uncoated errors, Nos. 301b, 308b and 310a, come from examples of booklet panes Nos. 301a and 308a.

For 11p., 12p., 15p. and 16p. stamps in a smaller size see Nos. 398/9*a*.

90 "A Partridge in a Pear Tree' **91** Sir John Doyle and Coat of Arms

(Des R. Downer. Litho Questa)

1984 (20 Nov). *Christmas. "The Twelve Days of Christmas". T* **90** *and similar vert designs. Multicoloured. P* 14½.

No.	Description		Unused	Used
316	5p. Type **90**		20	20
	a. Sheetlet of 12. Nos. 316/27		2·50	
317	5p. "Two turtle doves"		20	20
318	5p. "Three French hens"		20	20
319	5p. "Four colly birds"		20	20
320	5p. "Five gold rings"		20	20
321	5p. "Six geese a-laying"		20	20
322	5p. "Seven swans a-swimming"		20	20
323	5p. "Eight maids a-milking"		20	20
324	5p. "Nine drummers drumming"		20	20
325	5p. "Ten pipers piping"		20	20
326	5p. "Eleven ladies dancing"		20	20
327	5p. "Twelve lords a-leaping"		20	20
316/27		*Set of* 12	2·50	2·50

Nos. 316/27 were printed, *se-tenant*, in sheetlets of 12.

(Des E. Stemp. Photo Courvoisier)

1984 (20 Nov). *150th Death Anniv of Lieut-General Sir John Doyle. T* **91** *and similar multicoloured designs. Granite paper. P* 11½.

No.	Description		Unused	Used
328	13p. Type **91**		40	40
329	29p. Battle of Germantown, 1777 (*horiz*)		1·00	1·00
330	31p. Reclamation of Braye du Valle, 1806 (*horiz*)		1·25	1·25
331	34p. Mail for Alderney, 1812 (*horiz*)		1·25	1·25
328/31		*Set of* 4	3·50	3·00

92 Cuckoo Wrasse **93** Dove

(Des P. Barrett. Photo Courvoisier)

1985 (22 Jan). *Fishes. T* **92** *and similar horiz designs. Multicoloured. Granite paper. P* 11½.

No.	Description		Unused	Used
332	9p. Type **92**		40	40
333	13p. Red Gurnard		60	60
334	29p. Red Mullet		1·50	1·10
335	31p. Mackerel		1·50	1·10
336	34p. Oceanic Sunfish		1·60	1·25
332/6		*Set of* 5	5·00	4·00

(Des C. Abbott. Litho Questa)

1985 (9 May). *40th Anniv of Peace in Europe. P* 14 × 14½.

No.	Type	Description	Unused	Used
337	**93**	22p. multicoloured	1·10	1·10

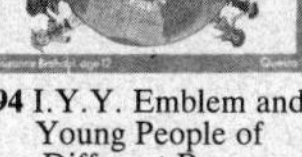

94 I.Y.Y. Emblem and Young People of Different Races **95** Stave of Music enclosing Flags

(Des Suzanne Brehaut (9p.), Mary Harrison (31p.). Litho Questa)

1985 (14 May). *International Youth Year. T* **94** *and similar square design. Multicoloured. P* 14.

No.	Description	Unused	Used
338	9p. Type **94**	40	40
339	31p. Girl Guides cooking over campfire	1·00	1·00

(Des Fiona Sloan (14p.), Katie Lillington (22p.). Litho Questa)

1985 (14 May). *Europa. European Music Year. T* **95** *and similar horiz design. Multicoloured. P* 14 × 14½.

No.	Description	Unused	Used
340	14p. Type **95**	45	40
341	22p. Stave of music and musical instruments	95	1·00

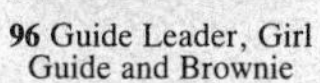

96 Guide Leader, Girl Guide and Brownie **97** Santa Claus

(Des Karon Mahy. Litho Questa)

1985 (14 May). *75th Anniv of Girl Guide Movement. P* 14.

No.	Type	Description	Unused	Used
342	**96**	34p. multicoloured	1·50	1·50

(Des C. Abbott. Photo Courvoisier)

1985 (19 Nov). *Christmas. Gift-bearers. T* **97** *and similar vert designs. Multicoloured. Granite paper. P* 12½.

No.	Description		Unused	Used
343	5p. Type **97**		25	25
	a. Sheetlet of 12. Nos. 343/54		4·25	
344	5p. Lussibruden (Sweden)		25	25
345	5p. King Balthazar		25	25
346	5p. Saint Nicholas (Netherlands)		25	25
347	5p. La Befana (Italy)		25	25
348	5p. Julenisse (Denmark)		25	25
349	5p. Christkind (Germany)		25	25
350	5p. King Wenceslas (Czechoslovakia)		25	25
351	5p. Shepherd of Les Baux (France)		25	25
352	5p. King Caspar		25	25
353	5p. Baboushka (Russia)		25	25
354	5p. King Melchior		25	25
343/54		*Set of* 12	4·25	4·00

Nos. 343/54 were printed, *se-tenant*, in sheetlets of 12.

98 "Vraicing"

(Des and photo Harrison)

1985 (19 Nov). *Paintings by Paul Jacob Naftel. T* **98** *and similar horiz designs. Multicoloured. P* 15 × 14.

No.	Description		Unused	Used
355	9p. Type **98**		30	30
356	14p. "Castle Cornet"		40	40
357	22p. "Rocquaine Bay"		90	90
358	31p. "Little Russel"		1·40	1·40
359	34p. "Seaweedgatherers"		1·50	1·50
355/9		*Set of* 5	4·00	4·00

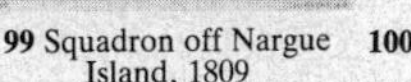

99 Squadron off Nargue Island, 1809 **100** Profile of Queen Elizabeth II (after R. Maklouf)

(Des T. Thompson. Photo Courvoisier)

1986 (4 Feb). *150th Death Anniv of Admiral Lord De Saumarez. T* **99** *and similar horiz designs. Multicoloured. Granite paper. P* 11½.

No.	Description		Unused	Used
360	9p. Type **99**		40	40
361	14p. Battle of the Nile, 1798		50	50
362	29p. Battle of St. Vincent, 1797		1·25	1·25
363	31p. H.M.S. *Crescent* off Cherbourg, 1793		1·40	1·40
364	34p. Battle of the Saints, 1782		1·40	1·40
360/4		*Set of* 5	4·50	4·00

(Des C. Abbott. Litho Questa)

1986 (21 Apr). *60th Birthday of Queen Elizabeth II. P* 14.

No.	Type	Description	Unused	Used
365	**100**	60p. multicoloured	2·50	2·50

101 Northern Gannet and Nylon Net ("Operation Gannet") **102** Prince Andrew and Miss Sarah Ferguson

(Des P. Newcombe. Photo Courvoisier)

1986 (22 May). *Europa. Nature and Environmental Protection. T* **101** *and similar vert designs. Multicoloured. Granite paper. P* 11½.

No.	Description		Unused	Used
366	10p. Type **101**		45	45
367	14p. Loose-flowered Orchid		75	75
368	22p. Guernsey Elm		1·00	1·00
366/8		*Set of* 3	2·00	2·00

(Des C. Abbott. Litho Questa)

1986 (23 July). *Royal Wedding. T* **102** *and similar multicoloured design. P* 14 (14*p.*) *or* 13½ × 14 (34*p.*).

No.	Description	Unused	Used
369	14p. Type **102**	75	75
370	34p. Prince Andrew and Miss Sarah Ferguson (*different*) (47 × 30 *mm*)	1·50	1·50

103 Bowls **104** Guernsey Museum and Art Gallery, Candie Gardens

(Des R. Goldsmith. Litho Questa)

1986 (24 July). *Sport in Guernsey. T* **103** *and similar multicoloured designs. P* 14½.

No.	Description		Unused	Used
371	10p. Type **103**		30	30
372	14p. Cricket		50	50
373	22p. Squash		75	75
374	29p. Hockey		1·25	1·25
375	31p. Swimming (*horiz*)		1·40	1·40
376	34p. Rifle-shooting (*horiz*)		1·50	1·50
371/6		*Set of* 6	5·00	5·00

(Des Sir Hugh Casson. Litho Questa)

1986 (18 Nov). *Centenary of Guernsey Museums. T* **104** *and similar horiz designs. Multicoloured. P* 14½.

No.	Description		Unused	Used
377	14p. Type **104**		60	60
378	29p. Fort Grey Maritime Museum		1·10	1·10
379	31p. Castle Cornet		1·10	1·10
380	34p. National Trust of Guernsey Folk Museum		1·40	1·40
377/80		*Set of* 4	3·75	3·75

105 "While Shepherds Watched their Flocks by Night"

(Des Wendy Bramall. Photo Courvoisier)

1986 (18 Nov). *Christmas. Carols. T* **105** *and similar vert designs. Multicoloured. Granite paper. P* 12½.

No.	Description		Unused	Used
381	6p. Type **105**		40	40
	a. Sheetlet of 12. Nos. 381/92		4·00	
382	6p. "In The Bleak Mid-Winter"		40	40
383	6p. "O Little Town of Bethlehem"		40	40
384	6p. "The Holly and the Ivy"		40	40
385	6p. "O Little Christmas Tree"		40	40
386	6p. "Away in a Manger"		40	40
387	6p. "Good King Wenceslas"		40	40
388	6p. "We Three Kings of Orient Are"		40	40
389	6p. "Hark the Herald Angels Sing"		40	40
390	6p. "I Saw Three Ships"		40	40
391	6p. "Little Donkey"		40	40
392	6p. "Jingle Bells"		40	40
381/92		*Set of* 12	4·00	4·00

Nos. 381/92 were printed, *se-tenant*, in sheetlets of 12.

106 Duke of Richmond and Portion of Map

(Des J. Cooter. Litho Questa)

1987 (10 Feb). *Bicentenary of Duke of Richmond's Survey of Guernsey. Sheet* 134 × 103 *mm containing T* **106** *and similar horiz designs showing sections of map. Multicoloured. P* 14½ × 14.

No.	Description	Unused	Used
MS393	14p. Type **106**; 29p. North-east; 31p. South-west; 34p. South-east	4·00	4·00

The stamps within No. **MS**393 show a composite design of the Duke of Richmond's map of Guernsey.

107 Post Office Headquarters **108** Sir Edmund Andros and La Plaiderie, Guernsey

(Des R. Reed. Litho Cartor)

1987 (5 May). *Europa. Modern Architecture. T* **107** *and similar vert designs. Multicoloured. P* 13×13½.

394 15p. Type **107** 55 55
 a. Horiz pair. Nos. 394/5 .. .. .. 1·10 1·10
395 15p. Architect's elevation of Post Office Headquarters 55 55
396 22p. Guernsey Grammar School 80 80
 a. Horiz pair. Nos. 396/7 .. .. .. 1·75 1·75
397 22p. Architect's elevation of Grammar School 80 80
394/7 .. .. *Set of* 4 2·50 2·50

Nos. 394/5 and 396/7 were each printed together, *se-tenant*, in horizontal pairs throughout the sheets.

(Photo Harrison)

1987 (15 May)–**88**. *Coil Stamps. Designs as Nos.* 306, 306*b*, 309 *and* 309*c*, *but smaller. P* 14×14½ (11*p*., 16*p*.) *or* 14½×14 (12*p*., 15*p*.).

398 11p. La Seigneurie, Sark (22×18 *mm*) .. 30 40
398*a* 12p. Petit Bot (18×22 *mm*) (28.3.88) .. 25 25
399 15p. Havelet (18×22 *mm*) 45 55
399*a* 16p. Hospital of St. John (22×18 *mm*) (28.3.88) 35 35
398/9*a* .. .. *Set of* 4 1·40 1·25

(Des B. Sanders. Photo Courvoisier)

1987 (7 July). *350th Birth Anniv of Sir Edmund Andros (colonial administrator). T* **108** *and similar horiz designs, each showing portrait. Multicoloured. Granite paper. P* 12.

400 15p. Type **108** 45 45
401 29p. Governor's Palace, Virginia .. .. 1·00 1·00
402 31p. Governor Andros in Boston .. .. 1·10 1·10
403 34p. Map of New Amsterdam (New York), 1661 .. .. 1·40 1·40
400/3 .. .. *Set of* 4 3·50 3·50

109 The Jester's Warning to Young William

110 John Wesley preaching on the Quay, Alderney

(Des P. le Vasseur. Litho Cartor)

1987 (9 Sept). *900th Death Anniv of William the Conqueror. T* **109** *and similar vert designs. Multicoloured. P* 13½×14.

404 11p. Type **109** 45 35
405 15p. Hastings battlefield 50 50
 a. Horiz pair. Nos. 405/6 .. .. .. 1·00 1·00
406 15p. Norman soldier with pennant 50 50
407 22p. William the Conqueror 80 75
 a. Horiz pair. Nos. 407/8 .. .. .. 1·60 1·50
408 22p. Queen Matilda and Abbaye aux Dames, Caen 80 80
409 34p. William's Coronation regalia and Halley's Comet .. .. 1·25 1·25
404/9 .. .. *Set of* 6 4·00 3·75

Nos. 405/6 and 407/8 were each printed together, *se-tenant*, in horizontal pairs throughout the sheets.

(Des R. Geary. Litho Questa)

1987 (17 Nov). *Bicentenary of John Wesley's Visit to Guernsey. T* **110** *and similar horiz designs. Multicoloured. P* 14½.

410 7p. Type **110** 30 30
411 15p. Wesley preaching at Mon Plaisir, St. Peter Port 45 45
412 29p. Preaching at Assembly Rooms .. .. 1·25 1·25
413 31p. Wesley and La Ville Baudu (early Methodist meeting place) .. .. 1·25 1·25
414 34p. Wesley and first Methodist Chapel, St. Peter Port .. .. 1·25 1·25
410/14 .. .. *Set of* 5 4·00 4·00

111 *Golden Spur* off St. Sampson Harbour

(Des R. Granger Barrett. Litho B.D.T.)

1988 (9 Feb). *Guernsey Shipping (2nd series). "Golden Spur" (full-rigged ship). T* **111** *and similar horiz designs. Multicoloured. P* 13½.

415 11p. Type **111** 35 35
416 15p. *Golden Spur* entering Hong Kong harbour 50 50
417 29p. Anchored off Macao .. .. .. 1·25 1·25
418 31p. In China Tea Race .. .. .. 1·25 1·25
419 34p. *Golden Spur* and map showing voyage of 1872–74 .. .. 1·25 1·25
415/19 .. .. *Set of* 5 4·00 4·00

112 Rowing Boat and Bedford "Rascal" Mail Van

113 Frederick Corbin Lukis and Lukis House, St. Peter Port

(Des C. Abbott. Litho Questa)

1988 (10 May). *Europa. Transport and Communications. T* **112** *and similar horiz designs. Multicoloured. P* 14½.

420 16p. Type **112** 60 60
 a. Horiz pair. Nos. 420/1 .. .. .. 1·25 1·25
421 16p. Rowing boat and Vickers Viscount 800 mail plane 60 60
422 22p. Postman on bicycle and horse-drawn carriages, Sark 95 95
 a. Horiz pair. Nos. 422/3 .. .. .. 1·90 1·90
423 22p. Postmen on bicycles and carriage .. 95 95
420/3 .. .. *Set of* 4 2·75 2·75

Nos. 420/1 and 422/3 were each printed together, *se-tenant*, in horizontal pairs throughout the sheets, the two stamps of each value forming a composite design.

(Des Wendy Bramall. Photo Courvoisier)

1988 (12 July). *Birth Bicentenary of Frederick Corbin Lukis (archaeologist). T* **113** *and similar horiz designs. Multicoloured. Granite paper. P* 12½.

424 12p. Type **113** 40 40
425 16p. Natural history books and reconstructed pot 50 50
426 29p. Lukis directing excavation of Le Creux ès Faies and prehistoric beaker .. .. 1·10 1·10
427 31p. Lukis House Observatory and garden .. 1·25 1·25
428 34p. Prehistoric artifacts .. .. .. 1·25 1·25
424/8 .. .. *Set of* 5 4·00 4·00

114 Powerboats and Westland Wessex Rescue Helicopter off Jethou

115 Joshua Gosselin and Herbarium

(Des and photo Courvoisier)

1988 (6 Sept). *World Offshore Powerboat Championships. T* **114** *and similar multicoloured designs. Granite paper. P* 12.

429 16p. Type **114** 60 60
430 30p. Powerboats in Gouliot Passage .. .. 1·10 1·10
431 32p. Start of race at St. Peter Port (*vert*) .. 1·25 1·25
432 35p. Admiralty chart showing course (*vert*) .. 1·50 1·50
429/32 .. .. *Set of* 4 4·00 4·00

(Des M. Oxenham. Litho Cartor)

1988 (15 Nov). *Bicentenary of Joshua Gosselin's* Flora Sarniensis. *T* **115** *and similar vert designs. Multicoloured. P* 13½×14.

433 12p. Type **115** 40 40
434 16p. Hares-tail Grass 55 55
 a. Horiz pair. Nos. 434/5 .. .. .. 1·10 1·10
435 16p. Dried Hares-tail Grass 55 55
436 23p. Variegated Catchfly 80 80
 a. Horiz pair. Nos. 436/7 .. .. .. 1·60 1·60
437 23p. Dried Variegated Catchfly 80 80
438 35p. Rock Sea Lavender .. .. .. 1·40 1·40
433/8 .. .. *Set of* 6 4·00 4·00

Nos. 434/5 and 436/7 were each printed together, *se-tenant*, in horizontal pairs throughout the sheets.

116 Coutances Cathedral, France

117 Lé Cat (Tip Cat)

(Des R. Downer. Litho Questa)

1988 (15 Nov). *Christmas. Ecclesiastical Links. T* **116** *and similar vert designs. Multicoloured. P* 14½.

439 8p. Type **116** 25 25
 a. Sheetlet of 12. Nos. 439/50 .. .. 3·50
440 8p. Interior of Notre Dame du Rosaire Church, Guernsey 25 25
441 8p. Stained glass, St. Sampson's Church, Guernsey 25 25
442 8p. Dol-de-Bretagne Cathedral, France .. 25 25
443 8p. Bishop's throne, Town Church, Guernsey 25 25
444 8p. Winchester Cathedral 25 25
445 8p. St. John's Cathedral, Portsmouth .. 25 25
446 8p. High altar, St. Joseph's Church, Guernsey 25 25
447 8p. Mont Saint-Michel, France 25 25
448 8p. Chancel, Vale Church, Guernsey .. 25 25
449 8p. Lychgate, Forest Church, Guernsey .. 25 25
450 8p. Marmoutier Abbey, France 25 25
439/50 .. .. *Set of* 12 3·50 3·50

Nos. 439/50 were printed, *se-tenant*, in sheetlets of 12.

(Des P. le Vasseur. Litho Cartor)

1989 (28 Feb). *Europa. Children's Toys and Games. T* **117** *and similar horiz designs. Multicoloured. P* 13½.

451 12p. Type **117** 40 40
452 16p. Girl with Cobo Alice doll 60 60
453 23p. Lé Colimachaön (hopscotch) .. .. 1·25 1·25
451/3 .. .. *Set of* 3 2·00 2·00

118 Outline Map of Guernsey

119 Guernsey Airways De Havilland D.H.86 Dragon Express and Mail Van

(Photo Harrison)

1989 (3 Apr–27 Dec). *Coil Stamps. No value expressed. P* 14½×14.

454 **118** (–) ultramarine (27.12.89) 40 40
455 (–) emerald 60 60

No. 454 is inscribed "MINIMUM BAILIWICK POSTAGE PAID" and No. 455 "MINIMUM FIRST CLASS POSTAGE TO UK PAID". They were initially sold at 14p. and 18p., but this was changed in line with postage rate rises.

In these coils every fifth stamp is numbered on the reverse.

(Des N. Foggo. Litho B.D.T.)

1989 (5 May). *50th Annivs of Guernsey Airport (Nos.* 456, 458, *and* 460*) and* 201 *Squadron's Affiliation with Guernsey (Nos.* 457, 459 *and* 461*). T* **119** *and similar horiz designs. Multicoloured. P* 13½.

456 12p. Type **119** 50 40
 a. Booklet pane. No. 456×6 .. .. 2·00
457 12p. Supermarine Southampton II flying boat at mooring 50 40
458 18p. B.E.A. De Havilland D.H.89 Dragon Rapide 75 75
 a. Booklet pane. No. 458×6 .. .. 3·00
459 18p. Short S.25 Sunderland Mk V flying boat taking off 75 75
460 35p. Air U.K. British Aerospace BAe 146 .. 1·25 1·25
 a. Booklet pane. No. 460×6 .. .. 6·00
461 35p. Avro Shackleton M.R.3 .. .. .. 1·25 1·25
456/61 .. .. *Set of* 6 4·50 4·50

Each booklet pane has margins all round with text printed at the foot.

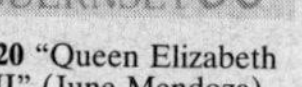

120 "Queen Elizabeth II" (June Mendoza)

121 *Ibex* at G.W.R. Terminal, St. Peter Port

(Des A. Theobald. Litho B.D.T.)

1989 (23 May). *Royal Visit. P* 15 × 14.

462 **120** 30p. multicoloured .. .. .. 1·25 1·25

(Des C. Jaques. Litho B.D.T.)

1989 (5 Sept). *Centenary of Great Western Railway Steamer Service to Channel Islands. T* **121** *and similar horiz designs. Multicoloured. P* 13½.

463 12p. Type **121** 30 30
464 18p. *Great Western* (paddle-steamer) in Little Russel 65 65
465 29p. *St. Julien* passing Casquets Light .. 90 90
466 34p. *Roebuck* off Portland .. .. .. 1·25 1·25
467 37p. *Antelope* and boat train on Weymouth Quay .. .. 1·40 1·40
463/7 .. .. *Set of* 5 4·00 4·00
MS468 115×117 mm. Nos. 463/7 .. .. 4·00 4·00

122 Two-toed Sloth

123 Star

(Des Anne Farncombe. Litho Cartor)

89 (17 Nov). *10th Anniv of Guernsey Zoological Trust. Animals of the Rainforest. T* **122** *and similar vert designs. Multicoloured. P* 13½×14.

9 18p. Type **122** .. .. 1·10 90
a. Horiz strip of 5. Nos. 469/73 .. 5·00
0 29p. Capuchin Monkey .. .. .. 1·10 90
1 32p. White-lipped Tamarin .. .. .. 1·10 90
2 34p. Common Squirrel-Monkey .. .. 1·10 90
3 37p. Common Gibbon .. .. .. 1·10 90
9/73 .. .. *Set of* 5 5·00 4·00

Nos. 469/73 were printed together, *se-tenant*, in horizontal strips five throughout the sheet.

(Des Wendy Bramall. Litho B.D.T.)

89 (17 Nov). *Christmas. Christmas Tree Decorations. T* **123** *and similar square designs. Multicoloured. P* 13.

4 10p. Type **123** 30 30
a. Sheetlet. Nos. 474/85 .. .. 4·00
5 10p. Fairy 30 30
6 10p. Candles 30 30
7 10p. Bird 30 30
8 10p. Present 30 30
9 10p. Carol-singer 30 30
0 10p. Christmas cracker 30 30
1 10p. Bauble 30 30
2 10p. Christmas stocking 30 30
3 10p. Bell 30 30
4 10p. Fawn 30 30
5 10p. Church 30 30
4/85 .. .. *Set of* 12 4·00 4·00

Nos. 474/85 were printed, *se-tenant*, in sheetlets of 12.

124 Sark Post Office, *c*. 1890

(Des C. Abbott. Litho Enschedé)

90 (27 Feb). *Europa. Post Office Buildings. T* **124** *and similar horiz designs. P* 13½×14.

6 20p. blackish brown, sepia and pale cinnamon 60 60
7 20p. multicoloured 60 60
8 24p. blackish brown, sepia and pale cinnamon 75 75
9 24p. multicoloured 75 75
6/9 .. .. *Set of* 4 2·50 2·50

Designs:—No. 487, Sark Post Office, 1990; 488, Arcade Post fice counter, St. Peter Port, *c*. 1840; 489, Arcade Post Office unter, St. Peter Port, 1990.

125 Penny Black and Mail Steamer off St. Peter Port, 1840

(Des Jennifer Toombs. Litho Questa)

90 (3 May). *150th Anniv of the Penny Black. T* **125** *and similar horiz designs. Multicoloured. P* 14.

0 14p. Type **125** 45 45
1 20p. Penny Red, 1841, and pillar box of 1853 60 60
2 32p. Bisected 2d., 1940, and German Army band .. .. 1·00 90
3 34p. Regional 3d., 1958, and Guernsey emblems .. .. 1·10 95
4 37p. Independent postal administration 1½d., 1969, and queue outside Main Post Office 1·10 1·00
0/4 .. .. *Set of* 5 3·75 3·50
S495 151×116 mm. Nos. 490/4 .. 4·00 3·75

No. **MS**495 also commemorates "Stamp World London 90" ternational Stamp Exhibition. It was reissued on 24 August 1990 verprinted for "NEW ZEALAND 1980" and sold at this ternational stamp exhibition in Auckland.

126 Lt. Philip Saumarez writing Log Book

(Des R. Granger Barrett. Litho Enschedé)

90 (26 July). *250th Anniv of Anson's Circumnavigation. T* **126** *and similar horiz designs. Multicoloured. P* 13½×14.

6 14p. Type **126** 45 45
7 20p. Anson's squadron leaving Portsmouth, 1740 .. .. 60 60
8 29p. Ships at St. Catherine's Island, Brazil .. 1·00 90
9 34p. H.M.S. *Tryal* (sloop) dismasted, Cape Horn, 1741 .. .. .. 1·10 95
0 37p. Crew of H.M.S. *Centurion* on Juan Fernandez .. .. 1·10 1·00
6/500 .. .. *Set of* 5 3·75 3·50

127 Grey Seal and Pup

128 Blue Tit and Great Tit

(Des Jennifer Toombs. Litho Questa)

1990 (16 Oct). *Marine Life. T* **127** *and similar horiz designs. Multicoloured. P* 14½.

501 20p Type **127** 60 60
502 26p Bottle-nosed Dolphin .. .. .. 1·10 1·10
503 31p Basking Shark .. .. 1·25 1·25
504 37p Common Porpoise .. .. .. 1·50 1·50
501/4 .. .. *Set of* 4 4·00 4·00

(Des Wendy Bramall. Litho B.D.T.)

1990 (16 Oct). *Christmas. Winter Birds. T* **128** *and similar square designs. Multicoloured. P* 13.

505 10p. Type **128** 40 40
a. Sheetlet of 12. Nos. 505/16 .. 4·50
506 10p. Snow Bunting 40 40
507 10p. Common Kestrel 40 40
508 10p. Common Starling 40 40
509 10p. Greenfinch 40 40
510 10p. European Robin 40 40
511 10p. Winter Wren 40 40
512 10p. Barn Owl 40 40
513 10p. Mistle Thrush 40 40
514 10p. Grey Heron 40 40
515 10p. Chaffinch 40 40
516 10p. Common Kingfisher 40 40
505/16 .. .. *Set of* 12 4·50 4·50

Nos. 505/16 were printed, *se-tenant*, in sheetlets of 12.

129 Air Raid and 1941 ½d. Stamp

(Des C. Abbott. Litho B.D.T.)

1991 (18 Feb). *50th Anniv of First Guernsey Stamps. T* **129** *and similar square designs. Multicoloured. P* 13½.

517 37p. Type **129** .. .. 1·25 1·25
a. Booklet pane. Nos. 517/19 .. 4·00
518 53p. 1941 1d. stamp .. .. .. 1·60 1·60
519 57p. 1944 2½d. stamp .. .. .. 1·60 1·60
517/19 .. .. *Set of* 3 4·00 4·00

Booklet pane No. 517a exists in three versions which differ in the order of the stamps from left to right and in the information printed on the pane margins.

130 Visit of Queen Victoria to Guernsey, and Discovery of Neptune, 1846

(Des Jennifer Toombs. Litho Enschedé)

1991 (30 Apr). *Europa. Europe in Space. T* **130** *and similar horiz designs. Multicoloured. P* 13½×14.

520 21p. Type **130** 65 65
521 21p. Visit of Queen Elizabeth II and Prince Philip to Sark, and "Sputnik" (first artificial satellite), 1957 .. .. 65 65
522 26p. Maiden voyage of *Sarnia* (ferry), and "Vostok 1" (first manned space flight), 1961 .. .. 90 75
523 26p. Cancelling Guernsey stamps, and first manned landing on Moon, 1969 .. 90 75
520/3 .. .. *Set of* 4 2·75 2·50

131 Children in Guernsey Sailing Trust "GP14" Dinghy

132 Pair of Oystercatchers

(Des C. Abbott. Litho B.D.T.)

1991 (2 July). *Centenary of Guernsey Yacht Club. T* **131** *and similar vert designs. Multicoloured. P* 14.

524 15p. Type **131** 50 50
525 21p. Guernsey Regatta 80 80
526 26p. Lombard Channel Islands Challenge race 90 90
527 31p. Rolex Swan Regatta .. .. .. 1·00 1·00
528 37p. Old Gaffers' Association gaff-rigged yacht 1·25 1·25
524/8 .. .. *Set of* 5 4·00 4·00
MS529 163×75 mm. As Nos. 524/8, but "GUERNSEY" and face values in yellow .. 4·00 4·00

(Des Wendy Bramall. Litho Questa)

1991 (15 Oct). *Nature Conservation. L'Eree Shingle Bank Reserve. T* **132** *and similar horiz designs. Multicoloured. P* 14½.

530 15p. Type **132** 40 40
a. Horiz strip of 5. Nos 530/4 .. 3·00
531 15p. Three Turnstones 40 40
532 15p. Dunlins and Turnstones 40 40
533 15p. Curlew and Turnstones 40 40
534 15p. Ringed Plover with chicks 40 40
535 21p. Gull, Sea Campion and Sea Radish .. 50 50
a. Horiz strip of 5. Nos. 535/9 .. 3·00
536 21p. Yellow Horned Poppy 50 50
537 21p. Pair of Stonechats, Hare's Foot Clover and Fennel 50 50
538 21p. Hare's Foot Clover, Fennel and Slender Oat 50 50
539 21p. Sea Kale on shore 50 50
530/9 .. .. *Set of* 10 5·50 4·00

Nos. 530/4 and 535/9 were each printed together, *se-tenant*, in horizontal strips of 5, throughout sheets of 20, with the backgrounds forming composite designs which continue onto the sheet margins.

133 "Rudolph the Red-nosed Reindeer" (Mclanie Sharpe)

134 Queen Elizabeth II in 1952

(Litho B.D.T.)

1991 (15 Oct). *Christmas. Children's Paintings. T* **133** *and similar square designs. Multicoloured. P* 13½×13.

540 12p. Type **133** 35 35
a. Sheetlet of 12. Nos. 540/51 .. 4·00
541 12p. "Christmas Pudding" (James Quinn) .. 35 35
542 12p. "Snowman" (Lisa Guille) 35 35
543 12p. "Snowman in Top Hat" (Jessica Ede-Golightly) 35 35
544 12p. "Robins and Christmas Tree" (Sharon Le Page) 35 35
545 12p. "Shepherds and Angels" (Anna Coquelin) 35 35
546 12p. "Nativity" (Claudine Lihou) 35 35
547 12p. "Three Wise Men" (Jonathan Le Noury) 35 35
548 12p. "Star of Bethlehem and Angels" (Marcia Mahy) 35 35
549 12p. "Christmas Tree" (Laurel Garfield) .. 35 35
550 12p. "Santa Claus" (Rebecca Driscoll) .. 35 35
551 12p. "Snowman and Star" (Ian Lowe) .. 35 35
540/51 .. .. *Set of* 12 4·00 4·00

Nos. 540/51 were printed, *se-tenant*, in sheetlets of 12.

(Des C. Abbott. Litho Questa)

1992 (6 Feb). *40th Anniv of Accession. T* **134** *and similar vert designs. Multicoloured. P* 14.

552 23p. Type **134** 70 70
553 28p. Queen Elizabeth in 1977 .. .. 75 75
554 33p. Queen Elizabeth in 1986 .. .. 85 85
555 39p. Queen Elizabeth in 1991 .. .. 1·10 1·10
552/5 .. .. *Set of* 4 3·00 3·00

135 Christopher Columbus

(Des R. Ollington. Litho Walsall)

1992 (6 Feb). *Europa. 500th Anniv of Discovery of America by Columbus. T* **135** *and similar horiz designs. Multicoloured. P* 13½×14.

556 23p. Type **135** 60 60
557 23p. Examples of Columbus's signature .. 60 60
558 28p. *Santa Maria* .. .. 1·10 1·10
559 28p. Map of first voyage .. .. .. 1·10 1·10
556/9 .. .. *Set of* 4 3·00 3·00
MS560 157×77 mm. Nos. 556/9 .. .. 3·00 3·00

No. **MS**560 was reissued on 22 May 1992 overprinted for "WORLD COLUMBIAN STAMP EXPO 92" and sold at this international stamp exhibition in Chicago.

136 Guernsey Calves

137 Stock

(Des R. Goldsmith. Litho Questa)

1992 (22 May). *150th Anniv of Royal Guernsey Agricultural and Horticultural Society. Sheet,* 93×71 *mm, containing T* **136.** *P* 14.
MS561 **136** 75p. multicoloured .. .. .. 2·00 2·00

(Des R. Gorringe, Litho Walsall (Nos. 572a, 572ba, 574a, 575a, 576ba, 577a), Questa (No. 576a), Cartor (No. 582*a*) or B.D.T. (others))

1992 (22 May)–**97.** *Horticultural Exports. T* **137** *and similar multicoloured designs. P* 14 (£1, £2) *or* 13 (*others*).
562 1p. *Stephanotis floribunda* (2.3.93) .. 10 10
563 2p. Potted Hydrangea (2.3.93) 10 10
564 3p. Type **137** 10 10
565 4p. Anemones 10 10
566 5p. Gladiolus 10 15
567 6p. *Asparagus plumosus* and *Gypsophila paniculata* (2.3.93) 10 15
568 7p. Guernsey Lily (2.3.93) 15 20
569 8p. Enchantment Lily (2.3.93) 15 20
570 9p. Clematis "Freckles" (2.3.93) 20 25
571 10p. Alstroemeria 20 25
572 16p. Standard Carnation (*horiz*) 30 35
a. Perf 14 .. .. 50 50
ac. Booklet pane. Nos. 572a×5 and 574a×3 4·00
ad. Booklet pane of 8 (2.3.93) .. .. 3·00
572*b* 18p. Standard Rose (2.1.97) 35 40
ba. Perf 14 .. .. 35 40
bb. Booklet pane of 8 .. .. .. 3·00
573 20p. Spray Rose 40 45
574 23p. Mixed Freesia (*horiz*) 45 50
a. Perf 14 .. .. 60 60
ac. Booklet pane of 8 .. .. .. 4·50
575 24p. Standard Rose (*horiz*) (2.3.93) .. 50 55
a. Perf 14 .. .. 50 55
ab. Booklet pane of 8 .. .. .. 4·00
576 25p. Iris "Ideal" (*horiz*) (18.2.94) .. 50 55
a. Perf 14½×15 .. .. .. 50 55
ab. Booklet pane of 4 .. .. .. 2·00
576*b* 26p. Freesia "Pink Glow" (*horiz*) (2.1.97) 55 60
ba. Perf 14 .. .. 55 60
bb. Booklet pane of 4 .. .. .. 2·10
577 28p. Lisianthus (*horiz*) (2.3.93) 55 60
a. Perf 14 .. .. 55 60
ab. Booklet pane of 4 .. .. .. 2·25
578 30p. Spray Chrysanthemum (*horiz*) (2.3.93) 60 65
579 40p. Spray Carnation 80 85
580 50p. Single Freesia (*horiz*) .. .. 1·00 1·10
581 £1 Floral arrangement (35×26½ *mm*) .. 2·00 2·10
582 £2 Chelsea Flower Show exhibit (35×26½ *mm*) (2.3.93) .. .. .. 4·00 4·25
582*a* £3 "Floral Fantasia" (exhibit) (35×28 *mm*) (24.1.96) .. .. 6·00 6·25
562/82*a* .. .. *Set of* 24 18·50 20·00

Imprint dates: "1992", Nos. 564/6, 571/2ac, 573/4ac, 579/81; "1993", Nos. 562/3, 567/70, 572ad, 575/ab, 577/ab, 578, 582; "1994", Nos. 576/ab; "1996", No. 582*a*; "1997", Nos. 572b/ba, 576b/ba.

Nos. 572a, 572ba, 574a, 575a, 576a, 576ba and 577a were only issued in booklets with the upper and lower edges of the panes imperforate.

For No. 581 in miniature sheets see Nos. **MS**644 and **MS**681.

138 Building the Ship

(Des Studio Legrain. Litho Cartor)

1992 (18 Sept). *"Operation Asterix" (excavation of Roman ship). T* **138** *and similar horiz designs showing Asterix cartoon characters. Multicoloured. P* 13.
583 16p. Type **138** 45 45
a. Booklet pane. Nos. 583/7 plus label with margins all round .. .. .. 3·50
584 23p. Loading the cargo 60 60
585 28p. Ship at sea 80 80
586 33p. Ship under attack 95 95
587 39p. Crew swimming ashore .. .. 1·10 1·10
583/7 .. .. *Set of* 5 3·50 3·50

Booklet pane No. 583a exists with marginal inscriptions in English, French, Italian or German.

139 Tram No. 10 decorated for Battle of Flowers

140 Man in Party Hat

(Des A. Peck. Litho Enschedé)

1992 (17 Nov). *Guernsey Trams. T* **139** *and similar horiz designs. Multicoloured. P* 13½.
588 16p. Type **139** 45 45
589 23p. Tram No.10 passing Hougue a la Perre 60 60
590 28p. Tram No. 1 at St. Sampsons 80 80
591 33p. First steam tram at St. Peter Port, 1879 95 95
592 39p. Last electric tram, 1934 .. .. 1·10 1·10
588/92 .. .. *Set of* 5 3·50 3·50

(Des Wendy Bramall. Litho B.D.T.)

1992 (17 Nov). *Christmas. Seasonal Fayre. T* **140** *and similar square designs. Multicoloured. P* 13.
593 13p. Type **140** 35 35
a. Sheetlet of 12. Nos. 593/604 .. .. 4·00
594 13p. Girl and Christmas tree 35 35
595 13p. Woman and balloons 35 35
596 13p. Mince pies and champagne 35 35
597 13p. Roast turkey 35 35
598 13p. Christmas pudding 35 35
599 13p. Christmas cake 35 35
600 13p. Fancy cakes 35 35
601 13p. Cheese 35 35
602 13p. Nuts 35 35
603 13p. Ham 35 35
604 13p. Chocolate log 35 35
593/604 .. .. *Set of* 12 4·00 4·00

Nos. 593/604 were printed together, *se-tenant*, in sheetlets of 12 forming a composite design.

141 Rupert Bear, Bingo and Dog

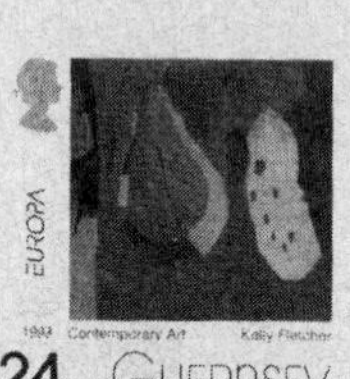

142 Tapestry by Kelly Fletcher

(Des J. Harrold. Litho Walsall)

1993 (2 Feb). *Rupert Bear and Friends (cartoon characters created by Mary and Herbert Tourtel). T* **141** *and similar vert designs. Multicoloured. P* 13½×13.
605 24p. Type **141** .. .. 1·00 1·00
MS606 116×97 mm. 16p. Airplane and castle; 16p. Professor's servant and Autumn Elf; 16p. Algy Pug; 16p. Baby Badger on sledge; 24p. Bill Badger, Willie Mouse, Reggie Rabbit and Podgy playing in snow; 24p. Type **141**; 24p. The Balloonist avoiding Gregory on toboggan; 24p. Tiger Lily and Edward Trunk .. .. 5·00 5·00

The 24p. values in No. **MS**606 are as Type **141**; the 16p. designs are smaller, each 25½×26 mm.

(Des B. Bell. Litho Enschedé)

1993 (7 May). *Europa. Contemporary Art. T* **142** *and similar multicoloured designs. P* 13½×14.
607 24p. Type **142** 80 80
608 24p. "Le Marchi a Paissaon" (etching and aquatint, Sally Reed) (48×33½ *mm*) .. 80 80
609 28p. "Red Abstract" (painting, Molly Harris) 90 90
610 28p. "Dress Shop, King's Road" (painting, Damon Bell) (48×33½ *mm*) 90 90
607/10 .. .. *Set of* 4 3·00 3·00

143 Arrest of Guernsey Parliamentarians, Fermain Bay

(Des C. Abbott. Litho Questa)

1993 (7 May). *350th Anniv of Siege of Castle Cornet. T* **143** *and similar horiz designs. Multicoloured. P* 14½×14.
611 16p. Type **143** 40 40
612 24p. Parliamentary ships attacking Castle Cornet 65 65
613 28p. Parliamentary captives escaping .. 85 85
614 33p. Castle cannon firing at St. Peter Port .. 95 95
615 39p. Surrender of Castle Cornet, 19 December 1651 .. .. 1·10 1·10
611/15 .. .. *Set of* 5 3·50 3·50
MS616 203×75 mm. Nos. 611/15 .. .. 3·50 3·50

OMNIBUS ISSUES

Details, together with prices for complete sets, of the various Omnibus issues from the 1935 Silver Jubilee series to date are included in a special section following Zimbabwe at the end of Volume 2.

144 Playing Cards

145 "The Twelve Pearls"

(Des J. Stephenson. Litho (16, 24, 28p.) or recess (33, 39p Enschedé)

1993 (27 July). *Birth Bicentenary of Thomas de la Rue (printe T* **144** *and similar vert designs. P* 13½.
617 16p. multicoloured 40
a. Booklet pane of 4 with margins all round 1·25
618 24p. multicoloured 65
a. Booklet pane of 4 with margins all round 1·90
619 28p. multicoloured 80
a. Booklet pane of 4 with margins all round 2·25
620 33p. carmine-lake 95
a. Booklet pane of 4 with margins all round 2·75
621 39p. blackish green .. .. 1·10 1·
a. Booklet pane of 4 with margins all round 3·00
617/21 .. .. *Set of* 5 3·50 3·

Designs:—24p. Fountain pens; 28p. Envelope-folding machin 33p. Great Britain 1855 4d. stamp; 39p. Thomas de la Rue a Mauritius £1 banknote.

(Des Jennifer Toombs. Litho B.D.T.)

1993 (2 Nov). *Christmas. Stained Glass Windows by Mary-Eily Putron from the Chapel of Christ the Healer. T* **145** *and simi square designs. Multicoloured. P* 13.
622 13p. Type **145** 45
a. Sheetlet. Nos. 622/33 .. .. .. 4·00
623 13p. "Healing rays" 45
624 13p. "Hand of God over the Holy City" .. 45
625 13p. "Wing and Seabirds" (facing left) .. 45
626 13p. "Christ the Healer" 45
627 13p. "Wing and Seabirds" (facing right) .. 45
628 13p. "The Young Jesus in the Temple" .. 45
629 13p. "The Raising of Jairus' Daughter" .. 45
630 13p. "Suffer little Children to come unto Me" 45
631 13p. "Pilgrim's Progress" 45
632 13p. "The Light of the World" 45
633 13p. "Raphael, the Archangel of Healing, with Tobias" 45
622/33 .. .. *Set of* 12 4·00 4·

Nos. 622/33 were printed together, *se-tenant*, in sheetlets of 12

146 Les Fouaillages (ancient burial ground)

(Des Miranda Schofield. Litho Cartor)

1994 (18 Feb). *Europa. Archaeological Discoveries. T* **146** *ar similar horiz designs. Multicoloured. P* 13½.
634 24p. Type **146** 60
635 24p. Mounted Celtic warrior 60
636 30p. Jars, arrow heads and stone axe from Les Fouaillages 80
637 30p. Sword, spear head and torque from King's Road burial 80
634/7 .. .. *Set of* 4 2·50 2·

Nos. 634/7 were each issued in small sheets of 10 (2×5) with large inscribed margin at left. Some sheets of No. 635 we overprinted with the "Hong Kong '94" emblem on the left marg for sale at this philatelic exhibition.

147 Canadian Supermarine Spitfires Mk V over Normandy Beaches

148 Peugeot "Type 3", 189

(Des N. Trudgian. Litho B.D.T.)

1994 (6 June). *50th Anniv of D-Day. Sheet* 93×71 *mm. P* 14.
MS638 **147** £2 multicoloured .. .. .. 5·00 5·

(Des R. Ollington. Litho B.D.T.)

1994 (19 July). *Centenary of First Car in Guernsey. T* **148** *ar similar horiz designs. Multicoloured. P* 14½×14.
639 16p. Type **148** 45 4
a. Booklet pane. No. 639×4 with margins all round .. .. 1·75

0 24p. Mercedes "Simplex", 1903 70 70
a. Booklet pane. No. 640×4 with margins all round 2·75
1 35p. Humber tourer, 1906 1·00 1·00
a. Booklet pane. No. 641×4 with margins all round 4·00
2 41p. Bentley sports tourer, 1936 1·10 1·10
a. Booklet pane. No. 642×4 with margins all round 4·25
3 60p. MG TC Midget, 1948 1·75 1·75
a. Booklet pane. No. 643×4 with margins all round 7·00
9/43 *Set of* 5 4·50 4·50

(Des R. Gorringe and M. Whyte. Litho Cartor)

94 (16 Aug). *"Philakorea '94" International Stamp Exhibition, Seoul. Sheet* 110×90 *mm containing stamp as No.* 581 *with changed imprint date. P* 13.
S644 £1 multicoloured 2·50 2·50

149 *Trident* (Herm ferry)

150 Dolls' House

(Des A. Copp. Litho Questa)

94 (1 Oct). *25th Anniv of Guernsey Postal Administration. T* **149** *and similar horiz designs. Multicoloured. P* 14.
5 16p. Type **149** 35 35
6 24p. Handley Page HPR-7 Super Dart Herald of Channel Express 55 55
7 35p. Britten Norman Trislander G-JOEY of Aurigny Air Services 75 75
8 41p. *Bon Marin de Serk* (Sark ferry) 85 85
) 60p. Map of Bailiwick 1·40 1·40
5/9 *Set of* 5 3·75 3·75
S650 150×100 mm. Nos. 645/9 3·75 3·75

(Des A. Peck. Litho B.D.T.)

94 (1 Oct). *Christmas. Bygone Toys. T* **150** *and similar square designs. Multicoloured. P* 13.
1 13p. Type **150** 40 40
a. Sheetlet. Nos. 651/6 2·00
2 13p. Doll 40 40
3 13p. Teddy in bassinette 40 40
4 13p. Sweets in pillar box and playing cards 40 40
5 13p. Spinning top 40 40
6 13p. Building blocks 40 40
7 24p. Rocking horse 75 75
a. Sheetlet. Nos. 657/62 3·50
8 24p. Teddy bear 75 75
9 24p. Tricycle 75 75
0 24p. Wooden duck 75 75
1 24p. Hornby toy locomotive 75 75
2 24p. Ludo game 75 75
1/62 *Set of* 12 5·00 5·00
Nos. 651/6 and 657/62 were each printed together, *se-tenant*, in eetlets of 6, each sheetlet forming a composite design.

151 Seafood "Face"

152 Winston Churchill and Wireless

(Des R. Ollington. Litho Questa)

95 (28 Feb). *Greetings Stamps. "The Welcoming Face of Guernsey". T* **151** *and similar vert designs. Multicoloured. P* 14.
3 24p. Type **151** 65 65
4 24p. Buckets and spade "face" 65 65
5 24p. Flowers "face" 65 65
6 24p. Fruit and vegetables "face" 65 65
7 24p. Sea shells and seaweed "face" 65 65
8 24p. Anchor and life belts "face" 65 65
9 24p. Glasses, cork and cutlery "face" 65 65
0 24p. Butterflies and caterpillars "face" 65 65
3/70 *Set of* 8 4·50 4·50
S671 137×109 mm. Nos. 663/70 4·50 4·50

(Des M. Whyte. Litho Enschedé)

95 (9 May). *50th Anniv of Liberation. T* **152** *and similar horiz designs. Multicoloured. P* 13½×14.
72 16p. Type **152** 50 50
73 24p. Union Jack and Royal Navy ships off St. Peter Port 75 75
74 35p. Royal Arms and military band 1·00 1·00
75 41p. *Vega* (Red Cross supply ship) 1·00 1·00
76 60p. Rejoicing crowd 1·75 1·75
72/6 *Set of* 5 4·50 4·50
S677 189×75 mm. Nos. 672/6 4·50 4·50

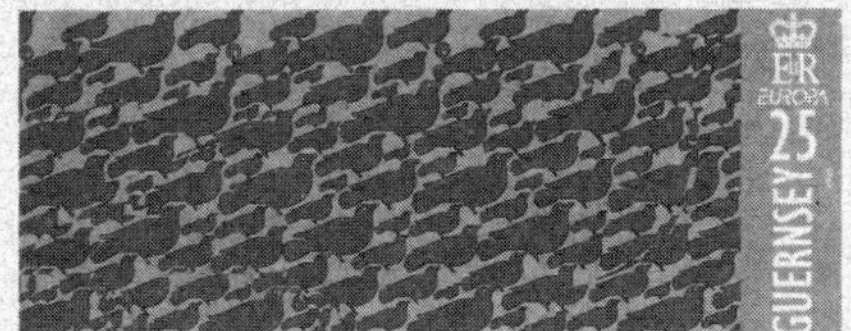

153 Silhouette of Doves on Ground

(Des K. Bassford. Litho Walsall)

1995 (9 May). *Europa. Peace and Freedom. T* **153** *and similar horiz design. Multicoloured. P* 14.
678 25p. Type **153** 65 65
679 30p. Silhouette of doves in flight 85 85
The designs of Nos. 678/9 each provide a stereogram or hidden three-dimensional image of a single dove designed by D. Burder.

154 Prince Charles, Castle Cornet and Bailiwick Arms

(Des C. Abbott. Litho Questa)

1995 (9 May). *Royal Visit. P* 14.
680 **154** £1.50, multicoloured 4·00 4·00

(Des R. Corringe and M. Whyte. Litho Cartor)

1995 (1 Sept). *"Singapore '95" International Stamp Exhibition. Sheet* 110×90 *mm containing stamp as No.* 581 *with changed imprint date. P* 13.
MS681 £1 multicoloured 2·50 2·50

155 Part of United Nations Emblem (face value at top left)

156 "Christmas Trees for Sale in Bern" (Cornelia Nussbrum-Weibel)

(Des K. Bassford. Litho and embossed Enschedé)

1995 (24 Oct). *50th Anniv of United Nations. T* **155** *and similar horiz designs showing different segments of the United Nations emblem. Each pale new blue and gold. P* 14×13½.
682 50p. Type **155** 1·25 1·25
a. Block of 4. Nos. 682/5 5·00
683 50p. Face value at top right 1·25 1·25
684 50p. Face value at bottom left 1·25 1·25
685 50p. Face value at bottom right 1·25 1·25
682/5 *Set of* 4 5·00 5·00
Nos. 682/5 were printed together, *se-tenant*, throughout the sheet with each block of 4 showing the complete emblem.

(Adapted M. Whyte from U.N.I.C.E.F. Christmas Cards. Litho B.D.T.)

1995 (16 Nov). *Christmas. 50th Anniv of U.N.I.C.E.F. T* **156** *and similar vert designs. Multicoloured. P* 13.
686 13p. Type **156** (face value at left) 40 40
a. Horiz pair. Nos. 686/7 80 80
687 13p. "Christmas Trees for Sale in Bern" (face value at right) 40 40
688 13p. + 1p. "Evening Snowfall" (Katerina Mertikas) (face value at left) 40 40
a. Horiz pair. Nos. 688/9 80 80
689 13p. + 1p. "Evening Snowfall) (face value at right) 40 40
690 24p. "It came upon a Midnight Clear" (Georgia Guback) (face value at left) 70 70
a. Horiz pair. Nos. 690/1 1·40 1·40
691 24p. "It came upon a Midnight Clear" (Georgia Guback) (face value at right) 70 70
692 24p. + 2p. "Children of the World" (face value at left) 70 70
a. Horiz pair. Nos. 692/3 1·40 1·40
693 24p. + 2p. "Children of the World" (face value at right) 70 70
686/93 *Set of* 8 4·00 4·00
Nos. 686/7, 688/9, 690/1 and 692/3 were printed together, *se-tenant*, as horizontal pairs in sheets of 12, each pair forming a composite design.

ALTERED CATALOGUE NUMBERS

Any Catalogue numbers altered from the last edition are shown as a list in the introductory pages.

157 Princess Anne (President, Save the Children Fund) and Children

(Des D. Miller. Litho B.D.T.)

1996 (21 Apr). *Europa. Famous Women. T* **157** *and similar horiz design. Multicoloured. P* 14.
694 25p. Type **157** 65 65
695 30p. Queen Elizabeth II and people of the Commonwealth 85 85
The background designs of Nos. 694/5 continue on to the vertical sheet margins.

158 England v. U.S.S.R., 1968 (value at right)

159 Maj-Gen. Brock meeting Tecumseh (Indian chief)

(Des M. Whyte. Litho Questa)

1996 (25 Apr). *European Football Championship. T* **158** *and similar horiz designs. Multicoloured. P* 14½×14.
696 16p. Type **158** 55 55
a. Horiz pair. Nos. 696/7 1·10 1·10
697 16p. England v. U.S.S.R., 1968 (value at left) 55 55
698 24p. Italy v. Belgium, 1972 (value at right) 75 75
a. Horiz pair. Nos. 698/9 1·50 1·50
699 24p. Italy v. Belgium, 1972 (value at left) 75 75
700 35p. Ireland v. Netherlands, 1988 (value at right) 80 80
a. Horiz pair. Nos. 700/1 1·60 1·60
701 35p. Ireland v. Netherlands, 1988 (value at left) 80 80
702 41p. Denmark v. Germany, 1992 final (value at right) 95 95
a. Horiz pair. Nos. 702/3 1·90 1·90
703 41p. Denmark v. Germany, 1992 final (value at left) 95 95
696/703 *Set of* 8 5·50 5·50
Nos. 696/7, 698/9, 700/1 and 702/3 were printed together, *se-tenant*, in horizontal pairs throughout the sheets of 8 which had illustrated margins.

(Des A. Peck. Litho Enschedé)

1996 (8 June). *"CAPEX '96" International Stamp Exhibition, Toronto. Sheet* 110×90 *mm containing T* **159** *and similar horiz design. P* 13½.
MS704 24p. Type **159**; £1 Major-General Sir Isaac Brock on horseback, 1812 2·50 2·75

160 Ancient Greek Runner

161 Humphrey Bogart as Philip Marlowe

(Des K. Bassford. Litho Questa)

1996 (19 July). *Centenary of Modern Olympic Games. T* **160** *and similar designs, each black, orange-yellow and orange, showing ancient Greek athletes. P* 14.
705 16p. Type **160** 50 50
706 24p. Throwing the javelin 95 95
707 41p. Throwing the discus 1·10 1·10
708 55p. Wrestling (52×31 *mm*) 1·40 1·40
709 60p. Jumping 1·60 1·60
705/9 *Set of* 5 5·00 5·00
MS710 192×75 mm. Nos. 705/9 5·00 5·00
No. 708 also includes the "OLYMPHILEX '96" International Stamp Exhibition, Atlanta, logo.

(Des R. Ollington. Litho Enschedé)

1996 (6 Nov). *Centenary of Cinema. Screen Detectives. T* **161** *and similar horiz designs. Multicoloured. P* 15×14.
711 16p. Type **161** 30 35
a. Booklet pane. No. 711×3 with margins all round 90
b. Booklet pane. Nos. 711/15 with margins all round 3·50
712 24p. Peter Sellers as Inspector Clouseau 50 55
a. Booklet pane. No. 712×3 with margins all round 1·50
713 35p. Basil Rathbone as Sherlock Holmes 70 75
a. Booklet pane. No. 713×3 with margins all round 2·10
714 41p. Margaret Rutherford as Miss Marple 80 85
a. Booklet pane. No. 714×3 with margins all round 2·40
715 60p. Warner Oland as Charlie Chan 1·25 1·40
a. Booklet pane. No. 715×3 with margins all round 3·75
711/15 *Set of* 5 3·50 4·00

162 The Annunciation

163 Holly Blue (*Celastrina argiolus*)

(Des P. le Vasseur. Litho B.D.T)

1996 (6 Nov). *Christmas. T* **162** *and similar multicoloured designs. P* 13.

716 13p. Type **162** 25 30
a. Sheetlet of 12. Nos. 716/29 .. .. 3·00
717 13p. Journey to Bethlehem 25 30
718 13p. Arrival at the inn 25 30
719 13p. Angel and shepherds 25 30
720 13p. Mary, Joseph and Jesus in stable .. 25 30
721 13p. Shepherds worshipping Jesus 25 30
722 13p. Three Kings following star 25 30
723 13p. Three Kings with gifts 25 30
724 13p. The Presentation in the Temple .. 25 30
725 13p. Mary and Jesus 25 30
726 13p. Joseph warned by angel 25 30
727 13p. The Flight into Egypt 25 30
728 24p. Mary cradling Jesus (*horiz*) 50 55
729 25p. The Nativity (*horiz*) 50 55
716/29 .. .. *Set of* 14 4·00 4·75

Nos. 716/27 were printed together, *se-tenant*, in sheetlets of 12.

(Des A. Peck. Litho B.D.T.)

1997 (12 Feb). *Endangered Species. Butterflies and Moths. T* **163** *and similar horiz designs. Multicoloured. P* 14.

730 18p. Type **163** 60 60
731 25p. Hummingbird Hawk-moth (*Macroglossum stellatarum*) 75 75
732 26p. Emperor Moth (*Saturnia pavonia*) .. 90 90
733 37p. Brimstone (*Gonepteryx rhamni*) .. 1·10 1·10
730/3 .. .. *Set of* 4 3·00 3·00
MS734 92×68 mm. £1 Painted Lady (*Cynthia cardui*). P 13½ .. .. 2·50 2·50

No. **MS**734 includes the "HONG KONG '97" International Stamp Exhibition logo on the sheet margin.

164 Gilliatt fighting Octopus

165 Shell Beach, Herm

(Des M. Wilkinson. Litho Cartor)

1997 (24 Apr). *Europa. Tales and Legends. Scenes from* Les Travailleurs de la Mer *by Victor Hugo. T* **164** *and similar horiz design. Multicoloured. P* 13½.

735 26p. Type **164** 65 65
736 31p. Gilliatt grieving on rock 75 75

Nos. 735/6 were each isued in small sheets of 10 (2×5) with an enlarged inscribed margin at left.

(Litho B.D.T.)

1997 (24 Apr). *Guernsey Scenes* (*1st series*). *T* **165** *and similar multicoloured designs. Self-adhesive. P* 9½ (*diecut*).

737 18p. Type **165** 40 45
a. Booklet pane of 8 .. .. .. 3·00
738 25p. La Seigneurie, Sark (*vert*) 60 60
a. Booklet pane of 8 .. .. .. 4·25
739 26p. Castle Cornet, Guernsey 60 60
a. Booklet pane of 4 .. .. .. 2·10
737/9 .. .. *Set of* 3 1·60 1·60

Nos. 737/9 were issued in stamp booklets or as rolls of 100 (18p. and 25p.).

See also Nos. 770/3.

166 19th-century Shipyard, St. Peter's Port

(Des C. Abbott. Litho Questa)

1997 (29 May). *"Pacific '97" World Philatelic Exhibition, San Francisco. Sheet* 110×90 *mm containing T* **166** *and similar horiz design. P* 14.

MS740 30p. brown-olive and gold; £1 multicoloured (*Costa Rica Packet* (coffee clipper)) .. .. 3·00 3·00

NEW INFORMATION

The editor is always interested to correspond with people who have new information that will improve or correct the Catalogue.

167 Transistor Radio, Microphone and Radio Logos

(Des Miranda Schofield. Litho Cartor)

1997 (21 Aug). *Methods of Communication. T* **167** *and similar horiz designs. Multicoloured. P* 13½×13.

741 18p. Type **167** 45 45
742 25p. Television, video camera and satellite dish 70 70
743 26p. Fax machine, telephones and mobile phone 70 70
744 37p. Printing press, newspaper and type .. 1·00 1·00
745 43p. Stamp, coding machine and postbox .. 1·10 1·10
746 63p. C.D., computer and disk .. .. 1·60 1·60
741/6 .. .. *Set of* 6 5·00 5·00

168 Teddy Bear making Cake

169 Visiting Guernsey, 1957

(Des Sally Diamond. Litho Walsall)

1997 (6 Nov). *Christmas. Teddy Bears. T* **168** *and similar vert designs. Multicoloured. P* 14½×14.

747 15p. Type **168** 45 45
748 25p. Teddy bears decorating Christmas tree .. 70 70
749 26p. Two teddy bears in armchair 70 70
750 37p. Teddy bear as Father Christmas .. 1·00 1·00
751 43p. Teddy bears unwrapping presents .. 1·10 1·10
752 63p. Teddy bears eating Christmas dinner .. 1·60 1·60
747/52 .. .. *Set of* 6 5·00 5·00
MS753 123×107 mm. Nos. 747/52 .. .. 5·00 5·00

(Des M. Whyte. Litho Questa)

1997 (20 Nov). *Golden Wedding of Queen Elizabeth and Prince Philip. T* **169** *and similar square designs. Multicoloured. P* 14½.

754 18p. Type **169** 45 45
a. Booklet pane. Nos. 754/5, each × 3 with margins all round .. .. .. 2·50
b. Booklet pane. Nos. 754/9 with margins all round .. .. 4·25
755 25p. Coronation Day, 1953 .. .. .. 70 70
756 26p. Royal family, 1957 .. .. .. 70 70
a. Booklet pane. Nos. 756/7, each × 3 with margins all round .. .. .. 3·75
757 37p. On royal yacht, 1972 .. .. .. 1·00 1·00
758 43p. Queen Elizabeth and Prince Philip at Trooping the Colour, 1987 .. .. 1·10 1·10
a. Booklet pane. Nos. 758/9, each × 3 with margins all round .. .. .. 6·25
759 63p. Queen Elizabeth and Prince Philip, 1997 1·60 1·60
754/9 .. .. *Set of* 6 5·00 5·00

No. 755 is inscribed "1947" in error.

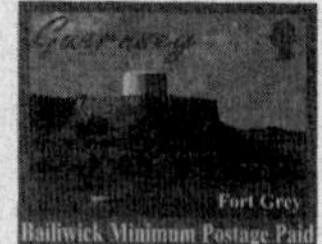

170 Tapestry of 11th-century Guernsey (St. Martin)

171 Fort Grey

(Des Sally Diamond. Litho Questa)

1998 (10 Feb). *The Millennium Tapestries Project. T* **170** *and similar vert designs each showing a different century contributed by individual parishes. Multicoloured. P* 15×14½.

760 25p. Type **170** 50 55
a. Horiz strip of 10 or two strips of 5. Nos. 760/9 .. .. 5·00
b. Booklet pane. Nos. 760/1, each × 2, and 762/3 with margins all round .. 3·00
c. Booklet pane. Nos. 760/1, and 768/9 each × 2 with margins all round .. .. 3·00
761 25p. 12th-century (St. Saviour) 50 55
762 25p. 13th-century (Vale) 50 55
a. Booklet pane. Nos. 762/3, each × 2, and 764/5 with margins all round .. .. 3·00
763 25p. 14th-century (St. Sampson) 50 55
764 25p. 15th-century (Torteval) 50 55
a. Booklet pane. Nos. 764/5, each × 2, and 766/7 with margins all round .. .. 3·00
765 25p. 16th-century (Castel) 50 55
766 25p. 17th-century (St. Andrew) 50 5
a. Booklet pane. Nos. 766/7, each × 2, and 768/9 with margins all round .. .. 3·00
767 25p. 18th-century (Forest) 50 5
768 25p. 19th-century (St. Pierre du Bois) .. 50 5
769 25p. 20th-century (St. Peter Port) 50 5
760/9 .. .. *Set of* 10 5·00 5·5

Nos. 760/9 were printed together, *se-tenant*, in horizontal strips o 10 throughout the sheet. These stamps were often supplied by th Guernsey Philatelic Bureau as two horizontal strips of 5.

(Des Joanna Brehaut. Litho B.D.T.)

1998 (25 Mar). *Guernsey Scenes* (*2nd series*). *T* **171** *and simil horiz designs. Multicoloured. Self-adhesive. P* 9½.

770 (20p.) Type **171** 40 4
a. Horiz pair. Nos. 770/1 80
b. Booklet pane. Nos. 770/1, each × 4 with margins all round .. .. .. 3·25
771 (20p.) Grand Havre 40 4
772 (25p.) Little Chapel 50 5
a. Horiz pair. Nos. 772/3 90
b. Booklet pane. Nos. 772/3, each × 4 with margins all round .. .. .. 4·00
773 (25p.) Guernsey Cow 50 5
770/3 .. .. *Set of* 4 1·75 2·(

Nos. 770/1 are inscribed "Bailiwick Minimum Postage Paid" an were initially sold at 20p. Nos. 772/3 are inscribed "UK Minimu Postage Paid" and were initially sold at 25p.

Nos. 770/3 were issued in stamp booklets or as rolls of 100, eac roll containing two designs.

172 Fairey IIIC, Balloon, Sopwith Camel and Avro 504

(Des C. Abbott. Litho Cartor)

1998 (7 May). *80th Anniv of the Royal Air Force. T* **172** *a similar horiz designs. Multicoloured. P* 13½×13.

774 20p. Type **172** 40 4
775 25p. Fairey Swordfish, Tiger Moth, Supermarine Walrus and Gloster Gladiator 50 5
776 30p. Hawker Hurricane, Supermarine Spitfire, Vickers Wellington, Short Sunderland (flying boat), Westland Lysander and Bristol Blenheim 60 6
777 37p. De Havilland Mosquito, Avro Lancaster, Auster III, Gloster Meteor and Horsa glider 75 8
778 43p. Canberra, Hawker Sea Fury, Bristol Sycamore, Hawker Hunter, Handley Page Victor and BAe Lightning 85 9
779 63p. Panavia Tornado GRI, BAe Hawk, BAe Sea Harrier, Westland Lynx (helicopter) and Hawker Siddeley Nimrod .. .. 1·25 1·4
774/9 .. .. *Set of* 6 4·25 4·7

173 Jules Rimet (first President of F.I.F.A.)

(Des A. Peck. Litho Enschedé)

1998 (7 May). *150th Anniv of the Cambridge Rules for Footbal Sheet* 110×90 *mm containing T* **173** *and similar horiz design P* 13½×14.

MS780 30p. Type **173**; £1.75, Bobby Moore and Queen Elizabeth II, 1966 .. .. .. 4·00 4·2

174 Girls in Traditional Costume watching Sheep Display, West Show

(Des Sally Diamond. Litho Enschedé)

1998 (11 Aug). *Europa. Festivals. T* **174** *and similar horiz design Multicoloured. P* 13½.

781 20p. Type **174** 40 4
782 25p. Marching band and "Battle of Flowers" exhibit, North Show 50 5
783 30p. Prince Charles, monument and tank, Liberation Day 60 6
784 37p. Goat, dahlias and show-jumping, South Show 75 8
781/4 .. .. *Set of* 4 2·25 2·5

The 25p. and 30p. incorporate the "EUROPA" emblem.

176 Royal Yacht *Britannia*

(Des M. Wilkinson. Litho and embossed Questa)

98 (11 Aug). *Maritime Heritage. P* 15×14½.
9 **176** £5 multicoloured .. .. .. 10·00 10·50
Numbers have been left for further values in this new definitive ries.

177 Modern Tree, Teletubby and Playstation

178 Elizabeth Bowes Lyon, 1907

(Des R. Ollington. Litho B.D.T)

98 (10 Nov). 150*th Anniv of the Introduction of the Christmas Tree. T* **177** *and similar horiz designs. Multicoloured. P* 13½.
0 17p. Type **177** 35 40
1 25p. 1960s tinsel tree, toy bus and doll .. 50 55
2 30p. 1930s gold foil tree, panda and toy tank 60 65
3 37p. 1920s tree, model of *Bluebird* and doll .. 75 80
4 43p. 1900 tree, teddy bear and toy train .. 85 90
5 63p. 1850's tree, wooden doll and spinning top 1·25 1·40
0/15 .. .. *Set of* 6 4·25 4·75
S816 160×94 mm. Nos. 810/15 .. .. 4·25 4·75

(Des R. Ollington. Litho Cartor)

99 (4 Feb). *Life and Times of Queen Elizabeth the Queen Mother. T* **178** *and similar vert designs. Multicoloured. P* 13.
17 25p. Type **178** 50 55
a. Horiz strip of 10 or two strips of 5. Nos. 817/26 .. .. 5·00
b. Booklet pane. Nos. 817/18, each × 2, and 819/20 with margins all round .. .. 3·00
c. Booklet pane. Nos. 817/18, and 825/6, each × 2, with margins all round .. 3·00
8 25p. On wedding day, 1923 .. .. .. 50 55
9 25p. Holding Princess Elizabeth, 1926 .. 50 55
b. Booklet pane. Nos. 819/20, each × 2, and 821/2 with margins all round .. .. 3·00
0 25p. At Coronation, 1937 .. .. .. 50 55
1 25p. Visiting bombed areas of London, 1940 (wearing green hat) 50 55
b. Booklet pane. Nos. 821/2, each × 2, and 823/4 with margins all round .. .. 3·00
2 25p. Fishing near Auckland, New Zealand, 1966 .. .. 50 55
3 25p. At Guernsey function, 1963 (wearing tiara) 50 55
b. Booklet pane. Nos. 823/4, each × 2, and 825/6 with margins all round .. .. 3·00
4 25p. Receiving flowers on her birthday, 1992 50 55
5 25p. Presenting trophy, Sandown Park races, 1989 .. .. 50 55
6 25p. Opening Royal Norfolk Regimental Museum, Norwich, 1990 (wearing blue hat) 50 55
17/26 .. .. *Set of* 10 5·00 5·25
Nos. 817/26 were printed together, *se-tenant*, in horizontal strips f 10 throughout the sheet.

179 *Spirit of Guernsey*, 1995

(Des K. Wisdom. Litho Cartor)

99 (27 Apr). 175*th Anniv of Royal National Lifeboat Institution. T* **179** *and similar horiz designs. Multicoloured. P* 13½×13.
27 20p. Type **179** 40 45
28 25p. *Sir William Arnold*, 1973 .. .. 50 55
29 30p. *Euphrosyne Kendal*, 1954 .. .. 60 65
30 38p. *Queen Victoria*, 1929 .. .. .. 75 80
31 44p. *Arthur Lionel*, 1912 .. .. .. 90 95
32 64p. *Vincent Kirk Ella*, 1888 .. .. 1·25 1·40
27/32 .. .. *Set of* 6 4·25 4·75

180 Burnet Rose and Local Carriage Label

(Des Colleen Corlett. Litho Walsall)

1999 (27 Apr). *Europa. Parks and Gardens. Herm Island. T* **180** *and similar square designs, each showing a different local carriage label. Multicoloured. P* 13½×13.
833 20p. Type **180** 40 45
834 25p. Puffin 50 55
835 30p. Small Heath Butterfly 60 65
836 38p. Shells on Shell Beach 75 80
833/6 .. .. *Set of* 4 2·25 2·40
Nos. 833/6 were each issued in small sheets of 10 (2×5) with an enlarged inscribed margin at left or right.

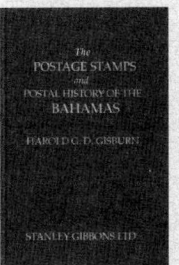

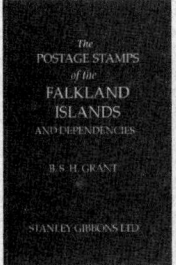

STAMP BOOKLETS

For a full listing of Guernsey stamp booklets see *Collect Channel Islands and Isle of Man Stamps* published each January.

POSTAGE DUE STAMPS

D 1 Castle Cornet

D 2 St. Peter Port

(Des R. Granger Barrett. Photo Delrieu)

1969 (1 Oct). *Value in black; background colour given. No wmk. P* 12½ × 12.

D1	**D 1**	1d. plum	2·25	1·25
D2		2d. bright green	2·25	1·25
D3		3d. vermilion	3·75	4·00
D4		4d. ultramarine	5·00	5·00
D5		5d. yellow-ochre	5·50	5·50
D6		6d. turquoise-blue	6·50	6·00
D7		1s. lake-brown	17·00	17·00
D1/7		*Set of* 7	35·00	35·00

1971 (15 Feb)–**76**. *As Type* **D 1** *but values in decimal currency.*

D 8	**D 1**	½p. plum	10	10
D 9		1p. bright green	10	10
D10		2p. vermilion	10	10
D11		3p. ultramarine	10	15
D12		4p. yellow-ochre	10	15
D13		5p. turquoise-blue	10	15
D14		6p. violet (10.2.76)	15	20
D15		8p. light yellow-orange (7.10.75)	25	20
D16		10p. lake-brown	30	30
D17		15p. grey (10.2.76)	40	40
D8/17		*Set of* 10	1·50	1·60

(Photo Delrieu)

1977 (2 Aug)–**80**. *Face value in black; background colour given. P* 13.

D18	**D 2**	½p. lake-brown	10	10
D19		1p. bright purple	10	10
D20		2p. bright orange	10	10
D21		3p. vermilion	10	10
D22		4p. turquoise-blue	15	15
D23		5p. yellow-green	15	15
D24		6p. turquoise-green	20	20
D25		8p. brown-ochre	25	25
D26		10p. ultramarine	40	40
D27		14p. green (5.2.80)	45	45
D28		15p. bright violet	45	45
D29		16p. rose-red (5.2.80)	55	55
D18/29		*Set of* 12	2·50	2·50

D 3 Milking Cow

(Litho Questa)

1982 (13 July). *Guernsey Scenes, circa* 1900. *Horiz designs as Type* **D 3**. *P* 14½.

D30	1p. indigo, blue-black and bright green	10	10
D31	2p. sepia, yellow-brown and azure	10	10
D32	3p. blackish green, black and lilac	10	10
D33	4p. bottle-green, black and dull orange	10	10
D34	5p. dp violet-blue, blue-black & turq-grn	10	10
D35	16p. deep grey-blue, deep blue and cobalt	30	35
D36	18p. steel-blue, indigo and apple-green	35	40
D37	20p. brown-olive, agate and pale blue	40	45
D38	25p. Prussian blue, blue-black and rose-pink	50	55
D39	30p. dp bluish grn, blackish ol & bistre-yell	60	65
D40	50p. olive-brown, sepia and dull violet-blue	1·00	1·10
D41	£1 light brown, brown and pale brown	2·00	2·10
D30/41	*Set of* 12	5·25	5·75

Designs:—2p. Vale Mill; 3p. Sark cottage; 4p. Quay-side, St. Peter Port; 5p. Well, Water Lane, Moulin Huet; 16p. Seaweed gathering; 18p. Upper Walk, White Rock; 20p. Cobo Bay; 25p. Saint's Bay; 30p. La Coupee, Sark; 50p. Old Harbour, St. Peter Port; £1 Greenhouses, Doyle Road, St. Peter Port.

ALDERNEY

The following issues are provided by the Guernsey Post Office for use on Alderney. They are also valid for postal purposes throughout the rest of the Bailiwick of Guernsey.

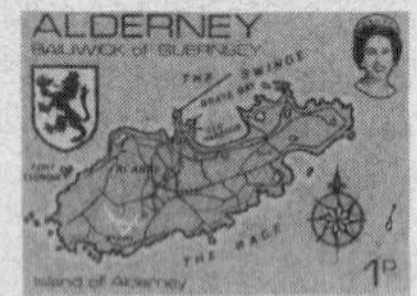

A 1 Island Map

(Des G. Drummond. Litho B.D.T. (20p. to 28p.). Photo Courvoisier (others))

1983 (14 June)–**93**. *Island Scenes. Type* A **1** *and similar horiz designs. Multicoloured. Granite paper (Nos.* A1/12). *P* 15×14 (*20p. to 28p.*) *or* 11½ (*others*).

A 1	1p. Type A **1**	10	10
A 2	4p. Hanging Rock	10	10
A 3	9p. States' Building, St. Anne	20	25
A 4	10p. St. Anne's Church	25	25
A 5	11p. Yachts in Braye Bay	25	25
A 6	12p. Victoria St., St. Anne	25	30
A 7	13p. Map of Channel	25	30
A 8	14p. Fort Clonque	30	35
A 9	15p. Corblets Bay and Fort	30	35
A10	16p. Old Tower, St. Anne	30	35
A11	17p. Golf course and Essex Castle	35	40
A12	18p. Old Harbour	35	40
A12*a*	20p. Quesnard Lighthouse (27.12.89)	80	80
A12*b*	21p. Braye Harbour (2.4.91)	80	80
A12*c*	23p. Island Hall (6.2.92)	70	70
A12*d*	24p. *J. T. Daly* (steam locomotive) (2.3.93)	1·75	1·75
A12*e*	28p. *Louis Marchesi of Round Table* (lifeboat) (2.3.93)	2·00	2·00
A1/12*e*	*Set of* 17	8·00	8·00

Nos. A12*a*/*e* are larger, 38×27 mm.

A2 Oystercatcher

(Des and photo Harrison)

1984 (12 June). *Birds. Type* **A2** *and similar horiz designs. Multicoloured. P* 14½.

A13	9p. Type **A2**	1·50	1·50
A14	13p. Turnstone	1·50	2·00
A15	26p. Ringed Plover	5·00	4·00
A16	28p. Dunlin	5·00	4·00
A17	31p. Curlew	5·00	4·00
A13/17	*Set of* 5	16·00	14·00

A 3 Westland Wessex HU Mk 5 Helicopter of the Queen's Flight

A 4 Royal Engineers, 1890

(Des A. Theobald. Photo Courvoisier)

1985 (19 Mar). *50th Anniv of Alderney Airport. Type* **A 3** *and similar horiz designs. Multicoloured. Granite paper. P* 11½.

A18	9p. Type A **3**	2·50	2·25
A19	13p. Britten Norman "long nose" Trislander	2·50	3·00
A20	29p. De Havilland D.H.114 Heron 1B	6·00	5·00
A21	31p. De Havilland D.H.89A Dragon Rapide *Sir Henry Lawrence*	6·50	5·50
A22	34p. Saro A.21 Windhover flying boat *City of Portsmouth*	7·00	5·50
A18/22	*Set of* 5	22·00	19·00

(Des E. Stemp. Litho Harrison)

1985 (24 Sept). *Regiments of the Alderney Garrison. Type* A **4** *and similar vert designs. Multicoloured. P* 14½.

A23	9p. Type A **4**	45	45
A24	14p. Duke of Albany's Own Highlanders (72nd Highland Regt), 1856	1·00	1·00
A25	29p. Royal Artillery, 1855	1·50	1·50
A26	31p. South Hampshire Regiment, 1810	1·75	1·75
A27	34p. Royal Irish Regiment, 1782	2·00	2·00
A23/7	*Set of* 5	6·00	6·00

No. A24 shows the tartan and insignia of the 78th Highland Regiment in error.

A 5 Fort Grosnez

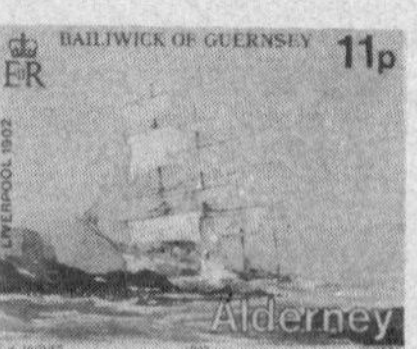

A 6 *Liverpool* (full-rigged ship) 1902

(Des R. Reed. Litho Cartor)

1986 (23 Sept). *Alderney Forts. Type* A **5** *and similar vert designs. Multicoloured. P* 13×13½.

A28	10p. Type A **5**	1·10	1·10
A29	14p. Fort Tourgis	1·75	1·75
A30	31p. Fort Clonque	4·00	4·00
A31	34p. Fort Albert	4·25	4·25
A28/31	*Set of* 4	10·00	10·00

(Des C. Jaques. Litho Questa)

1987 (5 May). *Alderney Shipwrecks. Type* A **6** *and similar horiz designs. Multicoloured. P* 14 × 14½.

A32	11p. Type A **6**	2·00	1·50
A33	15p. *Petit Raymond* (schooner), 1906	2·25	2·00
A34	29p. *Maina* (yacht), 1910	5·50	5·00
A35	31p. *Burton* (steamer), 1911	6·00	5·50
A36	34p. *Point Law* (oil tanker), 1975	6·50	6·00
A32/6	*Set of* 5	20·00	18·00

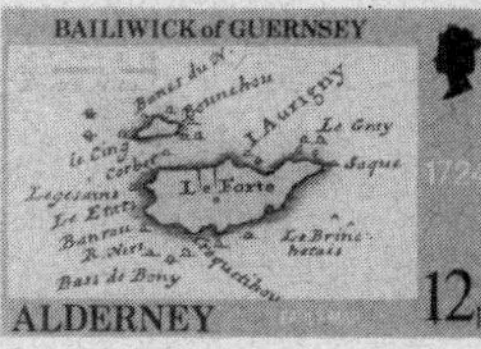

A 7 Moll's Map of 1724

(Des J. Cooter. Litho Enschedé)

1989 (7 July). *250th Anniv of Bastide's Survey of Alderney. Type* A **7** *and similar horiz designs. P* 13½×14.

A37	12p. multicoloured	40	4
A38	18p. black, greenish blue and orange-brown	60	6
A39	27p. black, greenish blue & dull yellow-green	1·10	1·1
A40	32p. black, greenish blue and bright rose-red	1·25	1·2
A41	35p. multicoloured	1·40	1·4
A37/41	*Set of* 5	4·25	4·2

Designs:—18p. Bastide's survey of 1739; 27p. Goodwin's map o 1831; 32p. General Staff map of 1943; 35p. Ordnance Survey map 1988.

A 8 H.M.S. *Alderney* (bomb ketch), 1738

(Des A. Theobald. Litho B.D.T.)

1990 (3 May). *Royal Navy Ships named after Alderney. Type* A *and similar horiz designs. P* 13½.

A42	14p. black and olive-bistre	45	4
A43	20p. black and orange-brown	60	6
A44	29p. black and cinnamon	1·10	1·1
A45	34p. black and pale turquoise-blue	1·10	1·1
A46	37p. black and cobalt	1·25	1·2
A42/6	*Set of* 5	4·00	4·0

Designs:—20p. H.M.S. *Alderney* (frigate), 1742; 29p. H.M.S *Alderney* (sloop), 1755; 34p H.M.S. *Alderney* (submarine), 194 37p. H.M.S. *Alderney* (patrol vessel), 1979.

A 9 Wreck of H.M.S. *Victory*, 1744

A 10 Two French Warships on Fire

(Des A. Theobald. Litho Cartor)

1991 (30 Apr). *Automation of The Casquets Lighthouse. Type* A *and similar horiz designs. Multicoloured. P* 14×13½.

A47	21p. Type A **9**	1·60	2·0
A48	26p. Lighthouse keeper's daughter rowing back to the Casquets	2·00	2·2
A49	31p. MBB-Bolkow Bo 105D helicopter leaving pad on St. Thomas Tower	2·50	2·7
A50	37p. Migrating birds over lighthouse	3·50	3·7
A51	50p. Trinity House vessel *Patricia* and arms	6·00	5·0
A47/51	*Set of* 5	14·00	14·0

(Des C. Abbott. Litho B.D.T.)

1992 (18 Sept). *300th Anniv of the Battle of La Hogue. Type* A 1 *and similar multicoloured designs. P* 14×15 (*50p.*) *or* 13½ (*others*)

A52	23p. Type A **10**	1·50	1·5
A53	28p. Crews leaving burning ships	2·25	2·2
A54	33p. French warship sinking	2·50	2·5
A55	50p. "The Battle of La Hogue" (47×32 *mm*)	3·75	3·7
A52/5	*Set of* 4	9·00	9·0

Nos. A52/4 show details of the painting on the 50p. value.

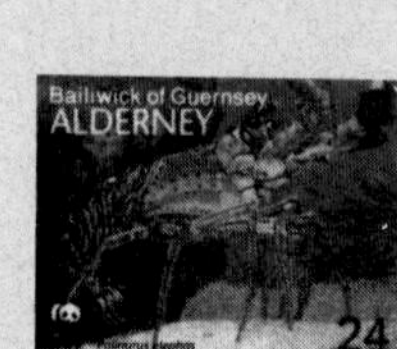

A 11 Spiny Lobster

A 12 Blue-tailed Damselfly, Dark Hair Water Crowfoot and Branched Bur-reed

(Des A. Peck. Litho Questa)

1993 (2 Nov). *Endangered Species. Marine Life. Type* A **11** *and similar horiz designs. Multicoloured. P* 14½.

A56 24p. Type A **11** 90 90
a. Horiz strip of 4. Nos. A56/9 .. .. 4·25
A57 28p. Plumose Anemone .. .. 1·00 1·00
A58 33p. Starfish .. .. 1·25 1·25
A59 39p. Sea Urchin .. .. 1·60 1·60
A56/9 .. .. *Set of* 4 4·25 4·25

Nos. A56/9 were printed together, *se-tenant*, in horizontal strips of 4, throughout the sheet, the backgrounds of each strip forming a composite design.

(Des Wendy Bramall. Litho B.D.T. (No. A71a) or Questa (others))

1994 (5 May)–**98**. *Flora and Fauna. Type* A **12** *and similar multicoloured designs. P* 14½.

A60 1p. Type A **12** 10 10
A61 2p. White-toothed Shrew and Flax-leaved St. John's Wort 10 10
A62 3p. Fulmar and Kaffir Fig 10 10
A63 4p. Clouded Yellow (butterfly) and Red Clover 10 10
A64 5p. Bumble Bee, Prostrate Broom and Giant Broomrape 10 10
A65 6p. Dartford Warbler and Lesser Dodder .. 15 20
A66 7p. Peacock (butterfly) and Stemless Thistle 15 20
A67 8p. Mole and Bluebell 15 20
A68 9p. Great Green Grasshopper and Common Gorse 20 25
A69 10p. Six-spot Burnet (moth) and Viper's Bugloss 20 25
A70 16p. Common Blue (butterfly) and Pyramidal Orchid 30 35
a. Perf 14×15 .. .. 30 35
ab. Booklet pane of 8 .. .. .. 2·50
A70*b* 18p. Small Tortoiseshell (butterfly) and Buddleia (2.1.97) 35 40
ba. Perf 14×15 .. .. 35 40
bb. Booklet pane of 8 .. .. .. 3·00
A71 20p. Common Rabbit and Creeping Buttercup 40 45
a. Perf 14×15 (25.3.98) 40 45
ab. Booklet pane of 8 .. .. .. 3·25
A72 24p. Great Black-backed Gull and Sand Crocus 50 55
a. Perf 14×15 .. .. 50 55
ab. Booklet pane of 8 .. .. .. 3·75
A72*b* 25p. Rock Pipit and Sea Stock (2.1.97) .. 50 55
ba. Perf 14×15 .. .. 50 55
bb. Booklet pane of 8 .. .. .. 4·00
A72*c* 26p. Sand Digger Wasp and Sea Bindweed (*horiz*) (2.1.97) 50 55
A73 30p. Atlantic Puffin and English Stonecrop 60 65
A74 40p. Emperor (moth) and Bramble .. 80 85
A75 50p. Pale-spined Hedgehog and Pink Oxalis 1·00 1·10
A76 £1 Common Tern and Bermuda Grass (*horiz*) .. .. 2·00 2·10
A77 £2 Northern Gannet and *Fucus vesiculosus* (seaweed) (*horiz*) (28.2.95) .. .. 4·00 4·25
A60/77 .. .. *Set of* 21 11·50 12·50

Nos. A70a, A70ba, A71a, A72a, and A72ba were only issued in booklets with the upper and lower edges imperforate.

A **13** Royal Aircraft Factory SE5A

(Des C. Abbott. Litho B.D.T.)

1995 (1 Sept). *Birth Centenary of Tommy Rose* (*aviator*). *Type* A **13** *and similar horiz designs. Multicoloured. P* 14×15.

A78 35p. Type A **13** 85 85
a. Horiz strip of 3. Nos. A78/80 .. .. 2·50
A79 35p. Miles Master II and other Miles aircraft 85 85
A80 35p. Miles Aerovan and Miles Monitor .. 85 85
A81 41p. Miles Falcon Six winning King's Cup air race, 1935 .. .. 1·00 1·00
a. Horiz strip of 3. Nos. A81/3 .. .. 3·00
A82 41p. Miles Hawk Speed Six winning Manx Air Derby, 1947 .. .. 1·00 1·00
A83 41p. Miles Falcon Six breaking U.K.–Cape record, 1936 .. .. 1·00 1·00
A78/83 .. .. *Set of* 6 5·50 5·50

Nos. A78/80 and A81/3 were printed together, *se-tenant*, as horizontal strips of 3 in sheets of 12 (2 panes 3×2).

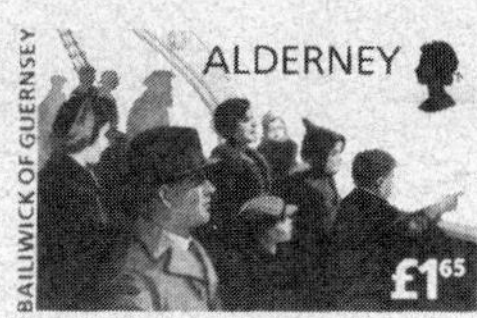

A **14** Returning Islanders

(Des C. Abbott. Litho B.D.T.)

1995 (16 Nov). *50th Anniv of Return of Islanders to Alderney. Sheet* 93×70 *mm. P* 13½.

MSA84 A **14** £1.65, multicoloured .. .. 4·00 4·00

A **15** Signallers training on Alderney

A **16** Cat with Butterfly

(Des A. Theobald. Litho Walsall)

1996 (24 Jan). *25th Anniv of Adoption of 30th Signal Regiment by Alderney. Type* A **15** *and similar horiz designs. Multicoloured. P* 14.

A85 24p. Type A **15** 65 65
a. Horiz strip of 4. Nos. A85/8 .. .. 5·00
A86 41p. Communications station, Falkland Islands .. .. 1·10 1·10
A87 60p. Dish aerial and Land Rover, Gulf War 1·50 1·50
A88 75p. Service with United Nations .. .. 1·75 1·75
A85/8 .. .. *Set of* 4 5·00 5·00

Nos. A85/8 were printed together, *se-tenant*, in horizontal strips of 4 throughout the sheet, each strip forming a composite design.

(Des P. le Vasseur. Litho B.D.T.)

1996 (19 July). *Cats. Type* A **16** *and similar square designs. Multicoloured. P* 13½.

A89 16p. Type A **16** 45 45
A90 24p. Blue and White on table 65 65
A91 25p. Tabby kitten grooming Blue and White Persian kitten 65 65
A92 35p. Red Persian under table 95 95
A93 41p. White cat with Tortoiseshell and White in toy cart .. .. 1·10 1·10
A94 60p. Siamese playing with wool .. .. 1·75 1·75
A89/94 .. .. *Set of* 6 5·00 5·00
MSA95 144×97 mm. Nos. A89/94 .. .. 5·00 5·00

A **17** Harold Larwood

A **18** Railway under Construction

(Des R. Ollington. Litho Walsall)

1997 (21 Aug). *150th Anniv of Cricket on Alderney. Type* A **17** *and similar vert designs. Multicoloured. P* 13½.

A 96 18p. Type A **17** 50 50
A 97 25p. John Arlott 65 65
A 98 37p. Pelham J. Warner .. .. .. 1·00 1·00
A 99 43p. W. G. Grace .. .. 1·25 1·25
A100 63p. John Wisden .. .. 1·60 1·60
A96/100 .. .. *Set of* 5 4·50 4·50
MSA101 190×75 mm. Nos. A96/100 and label .. 4·50 4·50

(Des R. Carter. Litho Questa)

1997 (20 Nov)–**98**. *Garrison Island* (*1st series*). *150th Anniv of Harbour. Type* A **18** *and similar horiz designs. Multicoloured. P* 14½×14.

A102 18p. Type A **18** 45 45
a. Horiz pair. Nos. A102/3 .. .. 90 90
b. Booklet pane. Nos. A102/5 with margins all round (10.11.98) .. .. 1·75
c. Booklet pane. Nos. A102/3 and A106/7 with margins all round .. .. 1·75
A103 18p. *Ariadne* (paddle steamer) at anchor .. 45 45
A104 25p. Quarrying stone 65 65
a. Horiz pair. Nos. A104/5 .. .. 1·25 1·25
b. Booklet pane. Nos. A104/5 and A108/9 with margins all round (10.11.98) .. 2·25
A105 25p. Quarry railway 65 65
A106 26p. Queen Victoria and Prince Albert on Alderney 70 70
a. Horiz pair. Nos. A106/7 .. .. 1·40 1·40
b. Booklet pane. Nos. A106/9 with margins all round (10.11.98) .. .. 2·25
A107 26p. Royal Yacht *Victoria and Albert* and guard of honour 70 70
A108 31p. Railway workers greet Queen Victoria 80 80
a. Horiz pair. Nos. A108/9 .. .. 1·60 1·60
A109 31p. Royal party in railway wagons .. 80 80
A102/9 .. .. *Set of* 8 4·75 4·75

Nos. A102/3, A104/5, A106/7 and A108/9 were each printed together, *se-tenant*, as horizontal pairs throughout sheets of 10.

See also Nos. A116/23.

MINIMUM PRICE

The minimum price quote is 10p which represents a handling charge rather than a basis for valuing common stamps. For further notes about prices see introductory pages.

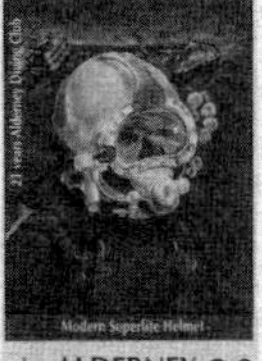

A **19** Modern Superlite Helmet and Wreck of *Point Law* (oil tanker)

A **20** Stained Glass Window commemorating Mary Rogers (Chief Stewardess)

(Des Victoria Kinnersly. Litho B.D.T.)

1998 (10 Feb). *21st Anniv of Alderney Diving Club. Type* A **19** *and similar vert designs. Multicoloured. P* 13.

A110 20p. Type A **19** 40 45
A111 30p. Cousteau-Gagnan Demand Valve and wreck of *Stella* (steamer) 60 65
A112 37p. Heinke Closed Helmet and *Liverpool* (full-rigged ship) 75 80
A113 43p. Siebe Closed Helmet 85 90
A114 63p. Deane Open Helmet .. .. 1·25 1·40
A110/14 .. .. *Set of* 5 3·75 4·25
MSA115 190×75 mm. Nos. A110/14 and label .. 3·75 4·25

(Des R. Carter. Litho Questa)

1998 (10 Nov). *Garrison Island* (*2nd series*). *Horiz designs as Type* A **18**. *Multicoloured. P* 14½×14.

A116 20p. Alderney Post Office 40 45
a. Horiz pair. Nos. A116/17 .. .. 80 90
b. Booklet pane. Nos. A116/19 with margins all round .. .. .. 1·75
c. Booklet pane. Nos. A116/17 and A120/1 with margins all round .. .. 2·00
A117 20p. Traders in Victoria Street 40 45
A118 25p. Court House 50 55
a. Horiz pair. Nos. A118/19 .. .. 1·00 1·10
b. Booklet pane. Nos. A118/19 and A122/3 with margins all round .. .. 2·50
A119 25p. Police Station and fire engine .. 50 55
A120 30p. St. Anne's Church 60 65
a. Horiz pair. Nos. A120/1 .. .. 1·25 1·40
b. Booklet pane. Nos. A120/3 with margins all round .. .. .. 2·75
A121 30p. Wedding party at Albert Gate .. 60 65
A122 37p. *Courier* (ferry) at Braye Bay .. 75 80
a. Horiz pair. Nos. A122/3 .. .. 1·50 1·60
A123 37p. Fishermen at quay 75 80
A116/23 .. .. *Set of* 8 4·50 5·00

Nos. A116/17, A118/19, A120/1 and A122/3 were each printed together, *se-tenant*, as horizontal pairs throughout sheets of 10.

(Des Joanna Brehaut. Litho B.D.T.)

1999 (4 Feb). *Centenary of the Wreck of* Stella (*mail steamer*). *Sheet* 110×90 *mm containing Type* A **20** *and similar horiz design. P* 14.

MSA124 25p. Type A **20**; £1.75, *Stella* leaving Southampton .. .. 2·00 2·25

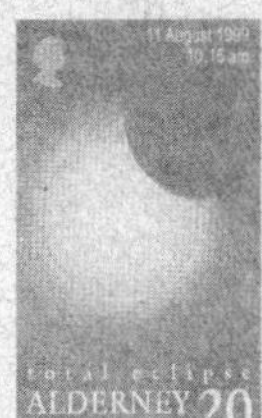

A **21** Solar Eclipse at 10.15 am

(Des Victoria Kinnersley. Litho Enschedé)

1999 (27 Apr). *Total Eclipse of the Sun* (11 *August*). *Type* A **21** *and similar vert designs, showing stages of the eclipse. Multicoloured. P* 13¼×13.

A125 20p. Type A **21** 40 45
A126 25p. At 10.51 am 50 55
A127 30p. At 11.14 am 60 65
A128 38p. At 11.16 am 75 80
A129 44p. At 11.17 am 90 95
A130 64p. At 11.36 am .. .. 1·25 1·40
A125/30 .. .. *Set of* 6 4·25 4·75
MSA131 191×80 mm. Nos. A125/30 and label .. 4·25 4·75

No. **MS**A131 also includes the "PHILEX FRANCE '99", Paris, and the "iBRA '99", Nuremberg, emblems on the sheet margin.

ISLE OF MAN

REGIONAL ISSUES

Although specifically issued for use in the Isle of Man, these issues were also valid for use throughout Great Britain.

DATES OF ISSUE: The note at the beginning of Guernsey also applies here.

Nos. 8/11 and current stamps of Great Britain were withdrawn from sale on the island from 5 July 1973 when the independent postal administration was established but remained valid for use there until 5 August 1973. They also remained on sale at the Philatelic Sales counters in the United Kingdom until 4 July 1974.

1

2

3

(Des J. Nicholson. Portrait by Dorothy Wilding Ltd. Photo Harrison)

1958 (18 Aug)–**68**. *W* **179**. *P* 15 × 14.

1	**1**	2½d.	carmine-red (8.6.64)	45	90
2	**2**	3d.	deep lilac	20	10
			a. Chalk-surfaced paper (17.5.63)	11·00	9·00
			p. One centre phosphor band (27.6.68)	20	40
3		4d.	ultramarine (7.2.66)	1·50	1·50
			p. Two phosphor bands (5.7.67)	20	25
1/3p			*Set of* 3	75	1·00

No. 2a was released in London sometime after 17 May 1963, this being the date of issue in Douglas.

1968–69. *No wmk. Chalk-surfaced paper. PVA gum. One centre phosphor band (Nos. 5/6) or two phosphor bands (others). P* 15 × 14.

4	**2**	4d.	blue (24.6.68)	20	25
5		4d.	olive-sepia (4.9.68)	20	30
6		4d.	bright vermilion (26.2.69)	45	75
7		5d.	royal blue (4.9.68)	45	75
4/7			*Set of* 4	1·00	1·75

(Des J. Matthews. Portrait after plaster cast by Arnold Machin. Photo Harrison)

1971 (7 July). *Decimal Currency. Chalk-surfaced paper. One centre phosphor band (2½p.) or two phosphor bands (others). P* 15 × 14.

8	**3**	2½p.	bright magenta	20	15
9		3p.	ultramarine	20	15
10		5p.	reddish violet	40	50
11		7½p.	chestnut	40	65
8/11			*Set of* 4	1·10	1·25

All values exist with PVA gum on ordinary cream paper and the 2½p. and 3p. also on fluorescent white paper.

INDEPENDENT POSTAL ADMINISTRATION

4 Castletown

5 Manx Cat

(Des J. Nicholson. Photo Courvoisier)

1973 (5 July)–**75**. *Horiz designs as T* **4** (*½p. to 9p., 11p. and 13p.*) *or vert designs as T* **5** (*others*). *Multicoloured. Granite paper. P* 11½.

12	½p.	Type **4**	10	10
13	1p.	Port Erin	10	10
14	1½p.	Snaefell	10	10
15	2p.	Laxey	10	10
16	2½p.	Tynwald Hill	10	10
17	3p.	Douglas Promenade (sage-green border)	10	10
		a. Error. Olive-bistre border†	£150	£100
18	3½p.	Port St. Mary (olive-brown border)	15	15
		a. Error. Grey-brown border†	£150	£100
19	4p.	Fairy Bridge	15	15
20	4½p.	As 2½p. (8.1.75)	20	20
21	5p.	Peel	20	20
22	5½p.	As 3p. (28.5.75)	25	25
23	6p.	Cregneish	25	25
24	7p.	As 2p. (28.5.75)	30	30
25	7½p.	Ramsey Bay	25	25
26	8p.	As 7½p. (8.1.75)	35	35
27	9p.	Douglas Bay	30	35
28	10p.	Type **5**	40	35
29	11p.	Monk's Bridge, Ballasalla (29.10.75)	30	30
30	13p.	Derbyhaven (29.10.75)	40	40
31	20p.	Manx Loaghtyn Ram	40	50
32	50p.	Manx Shearwater	1·50	1·25
33	£1	Viking longship	3·00	2·50
12/33		*Set of* 22	8·00	7·50

†These errors occur on printings in 1974. That on the 3p. resembles the border of the ½p. and that on the 3½p. the 2p.

Some printings from late 1973 have invisible gum.

Imprint dates: "1973", Nos. 12/19, 21, 23, 25, 27/8, 31/3; "1975", Nos. 20, 22, 24, 26, 29/30.

MINIMUM PRICE

The minimum price quote is 10p which represents a handling charge rather than a basis for valuing common stamps. For further notes about prices see introductory pages.

6 Viking landing on Man, A.D. 938

7 No. 1 *Sutherland*, 1873

(Des J. Nicholson. Photo Harrison)

1973 (5 July). *Inauguration of Postal Independence. P* 14.

34	**6**	15p.	multicoloured	60	60

(Des J. Nicholson. Photo Harrison)

1973 (4 Aug). *Steam Railway Centenary. T* **7** *and similar horiz designs showing steam locomotives. Multicoloured. P* 15 × 14.

35	2½p.	Type **7**	20	20
36	3p.	No. 4 *Caledonia*, 1885	20	20
37	7½p.	No. 13 *Kissack*, 1910	80	90
38	9p.	No. 3 *Pender*, 1873	1·00	90
35/8		*Set of* 4	2·00	2·00

8 Leonard Randles, First Winner, 1923

(Des J. Nicholson. Litho J.W.)

1973 (4 Sept). *Golden Jubilee of the Manx Grand Prix. T* **8** *and similar horiz design. Multicoloured. P* 14.

39	3p.	Type **8**	30	20
40	3½p.	Alan Holmes, Double Winner, 1957	30	20

9 Princess Anne and Capt. Mark Phillips

(Des A. Larkins. Recess and litho D.L.R.)

1973 (14 Nov). *Royal Wedding. P* 13½.

41	**9**	25p.	multicoloured	1·00	1·00

10 Badge, Citation and Sir William Hillary (Founder)

(Des J. Nicholson. Photo Courvoisier)

1974 (4 Mar). *150th Anniv of Royal National Lifeboat Institution. T* **10** *and similar horiz designs. Multicoloured. Granite paper. P* 11½.

42	3p.	Type **10**	10	10
43	3½p.	Wreck of *St. George*, 1830	15	15
44	8p.	R.N.L.B. *Manchester & Salford*, 1868–87	40	40
45	10p.	R.N.L.B. *Osman Gabriel*	45	45
42/5		*Set of* 4	1·00	1·00

11 Stanley Woods, 1935

(Des J. Nicholson. Litho D.L.R.)

1974 (29 May). *Tourist Trophy Motor-cycle Races* (1*st issue*). *T* **11** *and similar horiz designs. Multicoloured. P* 13 × 13½.

46	3p.	Type **11**	10	10
47	3½p.	Freddy Frith, 1937	10	10
48	8p.	Max Deubel and Emil Horner, 1961	45	45
49	10p.	Mike Hailwood, 1961	60	45
46/9		*Set of* 4	1·10	1·00

See also Nos. 63/6.

12 Rushen Abbey and Arms

(Des J. Nicholson from ideas by G. Kneale. Litho Questa (3½p., 10p or J.W. (others))

1974 (18 Sept). *Historical Anniversaries. T* **12** *and similar hor designs. Multicoloured. P* 14.

50	3½p.	Type **12**	10	
51	4½p.	Magnus Haraldson rows King Edgar on the Dee	10	
52	8p.	King Magnus and Norse fleet	40	
53	10p.	Bridge at Avignon and bishop's mitre	50	
50/3		*Set of* 4	1·00	

Nos. 50 and 53 mark the 600th Death Anniv of William Russe Bishop of Sodor and Man, and Nos. 51/2 the 1000th Anniv of th rule of King Magnus Haraldson.

13 Churchill and Bugler Dunne at Colenso, 1899

(Des G. Kneale. Photo Courvoisier)

1974 (22 Nov). *Birth Centenary of Sir Winston Churchill. T* **13** *ar similar horiz designs. Multicoloured. Granite paper. P* 11½.

54	3½p.	Type **13**	10	
55	4½p.	Churchill and Government Buildings, Douglas	10	
56	8p.	Churchill and Manx ack-ack crew	25	
57	20p.	Churchill as Freeman of Douglas	75	
54/7		*Set of* 4	1·10	
MS58		121 × 91 mm. Nos. 54/7	1·10	

No. **MS**58 is inscribed "30th Nov. 1974".

14 Cabin School and Names of Pioneers

(Des J. Nicholson. Photo Courvoisier)

1975 (14 Mar). *Manx Pioneers in Cleveland, Ohio. T* **14** *and simil horiz designs. Multicoloured. Granite paper. P* 11½.

59	4½p.	Type **14**	10	
60	5½p.	Terminal Tower Building, J. Gill and R. Carran	15	
61	8p.	Clague House Museum, and Robert and Margaret Clague	35	
62	10p.	S.S. *William T. Graves* and Thomas Quayle	50	
59/62		*Set of* 4	1·00	

15 Tom Sheard, 1923

(Des J. Nicholson. Litho J.W.)

1975 (28 May). *Tourist Trophy Motor-cycle Races* (2*nd issue*). *T* **1** *and similar horiz designs. Multicoloured. P* 13½.

63	5½p.	Type **15**	20	
64	7p.	Walter Handley, 1925	30	
65	10p.	Geoff Duke, 1955	50	
66	12p.	Peter Williams, 1973	50	
63/6		*Set of* 4	1·25	

16 Sir George Goldie and Birthplace

17 Title Page of Manx Bible

(Des G. Kneale. Photo Courvoisier)

1975 (9 Sept). *50th Death Anniv of Sir George Goldie. T* **16** *an similar multicoloured designs. Granite paper. P* 11½.

67	5½p.	Type **16**	10	1
68	7p.	Goldie and map of Africa (*vert*)	20	2
69	10p.	Goldie as President of Geographical Society (*vert*)	40	
70	12p.	River scene on the Niger	40	
67/70		*Set of* 4	1·00	

(Des J. Nicholson. Litho Questa)

75 (29 Oct). *Christmas and Bicentenary of Manx Bible. T* **17** *and similar horiz designs. Multicoloured. P* 14.

	5½p. Type **17**	15	15
	7p. Rev. Philip Moore and Ballaugh Old Church	20	20
	11p. Bishop Hildesley and Bishops Court ..	35	35
	13p. John Kelly saving Bible manuscript ..	40	40
/4	.. .. *Set of* 4	1·00	1·00

18 William Christian listening to Patrick Henry

19 First Horse Tram, 1876

(Des and litho J.W.)

76 (12 Mar). *Bicentenary of American Revolution. T* **18** *and similar vert designs. Multicoloured. P* 13½.

	5½p. Type **18**	15	15
	7p. Conveying the Fincastle Resolutions ..	20	20
	13p. Patrick Henry and William Christian ..	35	35
	20p. Christian as an Indian fighter	50	50
5/8	.. .. *Set of* 4	1·10	1·10
S79	153 × 89 mm. Nos. 75/8. P 14	1·50	1·60

(Des J. Nicholson. Photo Courvoisier)

76 (26 May). *Douglas Horse Trams Centenary. T* **19** *and similar horiz designs. Multicoloured. Granite paper. P* 11½.

	5½p. Type **19**	10	15
	7p. "Toast-rack" tram, 1890	15	15
	11p. Horse-bus, 1895	45	35
	13p. Royal tram, 1972	50	45
/3	.. .. *Set of* 4	1·10	1·00

20 Barroose Beaker

21 Diocesan Banner

(Des J. Nicholson. Photo Courvoisier)

976 (28 July). *Europa. Ceramic Art. T* **20** *and similar multicoloured designs. Granite paper. P* 11½.

4	5p. Type **20**	25	20
	a. Strip of 3. Nos. 84/6	70	60
5	5p. Souvenir teapot	25	20
6	5p. Laxey jug	25	20
7	10p. Cronk Aust food vessel (*horiz*)	40	35
	a. Strip of 3. Nos. 87/9	1·25	1·10
8	10p. Sansbury bowl (*horiz*)	40	35
9	10p. Knox urn (*horiz*)	40	35
4/9	.. .. *Set of* 6	1·75	1·50

Nos. 84/6 and 87/9 were each printed in sheets of 9 (3 × 3) the three signs being horizontally and vertically *se-tenant*.

(Des G. Kneale. Litho Questa)

976 (14 Oct). *Christmas and Centenary of Mothers' Union. T* **21** *and similar vert designs. Multicoloured. P* 14½.

0	6p. Type **21**	15	15
1	7p. Onchan banner	15	15
2	11p. Castletown banner	40	35
3	13p. Ramsey banner	40	45
/3	.. .. *Set of* 4	1·00	1·00

22 Queen Elizabeth II

(Des A. Larkins. Litho and recess D.L.R.)

977 (1 Mar). *Silver Jubilee. T* **22** *and similar multicoloured designs. P* 14 × 13 (*7p.*) *or* 13 × 14 (*others*).

4	6p. Type **22**	20	20
5	7p. Queen Elizabeth and Prince Philip (*vert*)	20	20
6	25p. Queen Elizabeth	80	70
4/6	.. .. *Set of* 3	1·10	1·00

The 25p. is similar to T **22** but has the portrait on the right.

23 Carrick Bay from "Tom-the-Dipper"

(Des J. Nicholson. Litho Questa)

1977 (26 May). *Europa. Landscapes. T* **23** *and similar horiz design. Multicoloured. P* 13½ × 14.

97	6p. Type **23**	20	20
98	10p. View from Ramsey	30	30

24 F. A. Applebee, 1912

(Des J. Nicholson. Litho J.W.)

1977 (26 May). *Linked Anniversaries. T* **24** *and similar horiz designs. Multicoloured. P* 13½.

99	6p. Type **24**	20	15
100	7p. St. John Ambulance Brigade at Governor's Bridge, *c.* 1938	20	20
101	11p. Scouts working scoreboard	50	40
102	13p. John Williams, 1976	50	40
99/102	.. .. *Set of* 4	1·25	1·00

The events commemorated are: 70th Anniv of Manx TT; 70th Anniv of Boy Scouts; Centenary of St John Ambulance Brigade.

25 Old Summer House, Mount Morrison, Peel

(Des and photo Courvoisier)

1977 (19 Oct). *Bicentenary of the First Visit of John Wesley. T* **25** *and similar horiz designs. Multicoloured. Granite paper. P* 11½.

103	6p. Type **25**	15	15
104	7p. Wesley preaching in Castletown Square	20	20
105	11p. Wesley preaching outside Braddan Church	35	35
106	13p. New Methodist Church, Douglas ..	40	40
103/6	.. .. *Set of* 4	1·00	1·00

Nos. 104/5 are larger, 38 × 26 mm.

26 H.M.S. *Ben-My-Chree* and Short Type 184 Seaplane, 1915

(Des A. Theobald. Litho J.W.)

1978 (28 Feb). *R.A.F. Diamond Jubilee. T* **26** *and similar horiz designs. Multicoloured. P* 13½ × 14.

107	6p. Type **26**	20	15
108	7p. H.M.S. *Vindex* and Bristol Scout C, 1915	30	20
109	11p. Boulton Paul Defiant over Douglas Bay, 1941	45	35
110	13p. Sepecat Jaguar over Ramsey, 1977 ..	50	40
107/10	.. .. *Set of* 4	1·25	1·00

27 Watch Tower, Langness

27a Queen Elizabeth II

(Des J. Nicholson (½p. to £1), G. Kneale (£2). Litho Questa (½p. to 16p.). Photo Courvoisier (20p. to £2))

1978 (28 Feb)–**81**. *Various multicoloured designs.* (*a*) *As T* **27**. *P* 14.

111	½p. Type **27**	10	10
	a. Perf 14½	20	10
112	1p. Jurby Church (*horiz*)	10	10
	a. Perf 14½	20	10
113	6p. Government Buildings	30	30
114	7p. Tynwald Hill (*horiz*)	35	35
	a. Perf 14½	8·00	6·50
115	8p. Milner's Tower	25	25
	a. Perf 14½	35	35
116	9p. Laxey Wheel	35	35
	a. Perf 14½	35	35
117	10p. Castle Rushen	40	40
	a. Perf 14½	35	35
118	11p. St. Ninian's Church	40	40
	a. Perf 14½	40	40
119	12p. Tower of Refuge (*horiz*)	50	50
	a. Perf 14½	50	40
120	13p. St. German's Cathedral (*horiz*) ..	60	60
	a. Perf 14½	40	40
121	14p. Point of Ayre Lighthouse (*horiz*) ..	60	60
	a. Perf 14½	50	50
122	15p. Corrin's Tower (*horiz*)	75	75
	a. Perf 14½	40	40
123	16p. Douglas Head Lighthouse (*horiz*) ..	90	90
	a. Perf 14½	25·00	21·00

(*b*) *As T* **27** *but size* 25×31 *mm. Granite paper. P* 11½ (18.10.78)

124	20p. Fuchsia	40	40
125	25p. Manx cat	50	50
126	50p. Chough	1·00	1·00
127	£1 Viking warrior	2·00	2·00

(*c*) *T* **27a**. *P* 11½ (29.9.81)

128	£2 multicoloured	4·25	4·25
111/28	.. .. *Set of* 18	11·50	11·50

Although both perforations of Nos. 111/23 were printed at the same time some did not appear in use until some time after 28 February 1978. Earliest dates for these are as follows: 1p. (112a) 8.79, 7p. (114a) 8.78, 8p. (115a) 6.80, 10p. (117a) 8.79, 12p. (119) 9.80.

28 Queen Elizabeth in Coronation Regalia

29 Wheel-headed Cross-slab

(Des G. Kneale. Litho Questa)

1978 (24 May). *25th Anniv of Coronation. P* 14½ × 14.

132	**28** 25p. multicoloured	75	75

(Des J. Nicholson. Photo Courvoisier)

1978 (24 May). *Europa. Sculpture. T* **29** *and similar vert designs showing Celtic and Norse Crosses. Multicoloured. Granite paper. P* 11½.

133	6p. Type **29**	20	15
	a. Strip of 3. Nos. 133/5	60	50
134	6p. Celtic wheel-cross	20	15
135	6p. Keeil Chiggyrt Stone	20	15
136	11p. Olaf Liotulfson Cross	35	30
	a. Strip of 3. Nos. 136/8	1·10	90
137	11p. Odd's and Thorleif's Crosses	35	30
138	11p. Thor Cross	35	30
133/8	.. .. *Set of* 6	1·50	1·25

Nos. 133/5 and 136/8 were each printed together, *se-tenant*, in horizontal and vertical strips of 3 throughout the sheet.

30 J. K. Ward and Ward Library, Peel

31 Hunt the Wren

(Des J.W. (7p.), G. Kneale (11p.), J. Nicholson (others). Litho J.W.)

1978 (10 June). *Anniversaries and Events. T* **30** *and similar horiz designs. Multicoloured. Invisible gum. P* 13½.

139	6p. Type **30**	15	15
140	7p. Swimmer, cyclist and walker (42 × 26 *mm*)	20	20
141	11p. American Bald Eagle, Manx arms and maple leaf (42 × 26 *mm*)	35	35
142	13p. Lumber camp at Three Rivers, Quebec	40	40
139/42	.. .. *Set of* 4	1·00	1·00

Commemorations:—6, 13p. James Kewley Ward (Manx pioneer in Canada); 7p. Commonwealth Games, Edmonton; 11p. 50th anniversary of North American Manx Association.

(Des J. Nicholson. Litho J.W.)

1978 (18 Oct). *Christmas. P* 13.

143	**31** 5p. multicoloured	50	50

32 P. M. C. Kermode (founder) and *Nassa kermodei*

33 Postman, 1859

(Des J. Nicholson. Litho Questa)

1979 (27 Feb). *Centenary of Natural History and Antiquarian Society. T* **32** *and similar horiz designs. Multicoloured. P* 14.

144	6p.	Type **32**	15	15
145	7p.	Peregrine Falcon	20	20
146	11p.	Fulmar	35	35
147	13p.	*Epitriptus cowini* (fly)	40	40
144/7		.. .. *Set of* 4	1·00	1·00

(Des A. Theobald. Litho Questa)

1979 (16 May). *Europa. Communications. T* **33** *and similar vert design. Multicoloured. P* 14½.

148	6p.	Type **33**	25	25
149	11p.	Postman, 1979	50	50

34 Viking Longship Emblem

35 Viking Raid at Garwick

Two types of No. 150:

Type I. Wrongly inscribed "INSULAREM". "1979" imprint date.

Type II. Inscription corrected to "INSULARUM". "1980" imprint date.

(Des J. Nicholson. Litho Harrison (3, 4p.), J.W. (others))

1979 (16 May)–**80**. *Millenium of Tynwald. Multicoloured.*

(*a*) *Vert designs as T* **34.** *P* 14½ × 14

150	3p.	Type **34** (Type I)	15	15
		a. Booklet pane. Nos. 150 × 4, 151 × 2 (4p. stamps at top)	80	
		ab. Ditto (4p. stamps in centre)	1·50	
		b. Type II (29.9.80)	10	10
		ba. Booklet pane. Nos. 150b × 4, 151 × 2 (4p. stamps at bottom)	75	
151	4p.	"Three Legs of Man" emblem	15	15
		(*b*) *Horiz designs as T* **35.** *P* 13		
152	6p.	Type **35**	15	15
153	7p.	10th-century meeting of Tynwald ..	20	20
154	11p.	Tynwald Hill and St. John's Church ..	30	30
155	13p.	Procession to Tynwald Hill	45	35
150/5		.. .. *Set of* 6	1·25	1·10

See also Nos. 188/9.

The 3 and 4p. values were printed in sheets containing ten blocks of 6 and five blocks of 4 separated by blank margins. The blocks of 6 contained four 3p. values and two 4p., *se-tenant*, with the 4p. in either the top or centre rows. The blocks of 4 contain the 4p. value only.

No. 151 exists with different dates below the design.

For details of No. 150ba see after No. 189.

36 Queen and Court on Tynwald Hill

(Des G. Kneale. Litho Questa)

1979 (5 July). *Royal Visit. T* **36** *and similar horiz design. Multicoloured. P* 14½.

156	7p.	Type **36**	35	35
157	13p.	Queen and procession from St. John's Church to Tynwald Hill	50	50

OMNIBUS ISSUES

Details, together with prices for complete sets, of the various Omnibus issues from the 1935 Silver Jubilee series to date are included in a special section following Zimbabwe at the end of Volume 2.

37 *Odin's Raven*

(Des J. Nicholson. Litho Questa)

1979 (19 Oct). *Voyage of "Odin's Raven". P* 14 × 14½.

158	**37**	15p.	multicoloured	70	70

38 John Quilliam seized by the Press Gang

39 Young Girl with Teddybear and Cat

(Des A. Theobald. Litho Questa)

1979 (19 Oct). *150th Death Anniv of Captain John Quilliam. T* **38** *and similar horiz designs. Multicoloured. P* 14.

159	6p.	Type **38**	15	15
160	8p.	Steering H.M.S. *Victory*, Battle of Trafalgar	20	20
161	13p.	Capt. John Quilliam and H.M.S. *Spencer*	35	35
162	15p.	Capt. John Quilliam (member of the House of Keys)	40	40
159/62		.. .. *Set of* 4	1·00	1·00

(Des Mrs E. Moore. Litho J.W.)

1979 (19 Oct). *Christmas. International Year of the Child. T* **39** *and similar vert design. Multicoloured. P* 13.

163	5p.	Type **39**	25	25
164	7p.	Father Christmas with young children	35	35

40 Conglomerate Arch, Langness

(Des J. Nicholson. Litho Questa)

1980 (5 Feb). *150th Anniv of Royal Geographical Society. T* **40** *and similar horiz designs. Multicoloured. P* 14½.

165	7p.	Type **40**	20	20
166	8p.	Braaid Circle	20	20
167	12p.	Cashtal-yn-Ard	25	25
168	13p.	Volcanic Rocks at Scarlett	35	35
169	15p.	Sugar-loaf Rock	40	40
165/9		.. .. *Set of* 5	1·25	1·25

41 *Mona's Isle I*

(Des J. Nicholson. Photo Courvoisier)

1980 (6 May). *150th Anniv of Isle of Man Steam Packet Company. T* **41** *and similar horiz designs. Multicoloured. Granite paper. P* 11½.

170	7p.	Type **41**	20	20
171	8p.	*Douglas I*	20	20
172	11½p.	H.M.S. *Mona's Queen II* sinking U-boat	30	30
173	12p.	H.M.S. *King Orry III* at surrender of German fleet	30	30
174	13p.	*Ben-My-Chree IV*	40	35
175	15p.	*Lady of Mann II*	50	40
170/5		.. .. *Set of* 6	1·75	1·60
MS176		180×125 mm. Nos. 170/5	1·75	1·75

No. **MS**176 was issued to commemorate the "London 1980" International Stamp Exhibition.

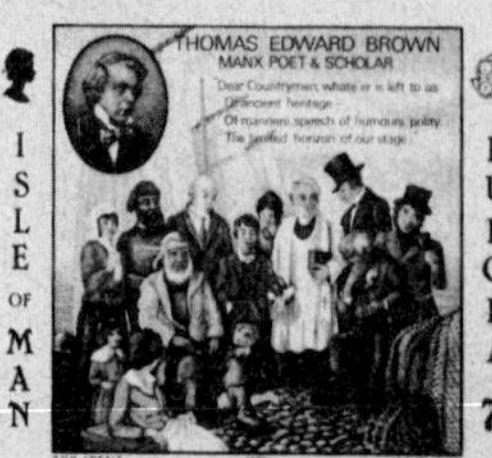

42 Stained Glass Window, T. E. Brown Room, Manx Museum

(Des G. Kneale. Photo Courvoisier)

1980 (6 May). *Europa. Personalities. Thomas Edward Brown (poe and scholar) Commemoration. T* **42** *and similar horiz design Multicoloured. Granite paper. P* 11½.

177	7p.	Type **42**	20	2
178	13½p.	Clifton College, Bristol	40	4

43 King Olav V and *Norge* (Norwegian royal yacht)

(Des J. Nicholson. Litho Questa)

1980 (13 June). *Visit of King Olav of Norway, August 1979. P* 14×14½.

179 **43**	12p.	multicoloured	50	5
MS180		125×157 mm. Nos. 158 and 179 ..	1·00	1·0

No. **MS**180 also commemorates the "NORWEX 80" Stam Exhibition, Oslo.

44 Winter Wren and View of Calf of Man

(Des J. Nicholson. Litho J.W.)

1980 (29 Sept). *Christmas and Wildlife Conservation Year. T* **44** *an similar horiz design. Multicoloured. P* 13½ × 14.

181	6p.	Type **44**	20	2
182	8p.	European Robin and view of Port Erin Marine Biological Station	30	3

45 William Kermode and Brig *Robert Quayle*, 1819

46 Peregrine Falcon

(Des A. Theobald. Litho Questa)

1980 (29 Sept). *Kermode Family in Tasmania Commemoration. T* **45** *and similar horiz designs. Multicoloured. P* 14½.

183	7p.	Type **45**	20	20
184	9p.	"Mona Vale", Van Diemen's Land, 1834	25	25
185	13½p.	Ross Bridge, Tasmania	40	35
186	15p.	"Mona Vale", Tasmania (completed 1868)	45	40
187	17½p.	Robert Q. Kermode and Parliament Buildings, Tasmania	50	45
183/7		.. .. *Set of* 5	1·60	1·50

(Des J. Nicholson. Litho Harrison)

1980 (29 Sept). *Booklet stamps. Vert designs as T* **46.** *Multicoloure P* 14½ × 14.

188	1p.	Type **46**	40	4
		a. Booklet pane. Nos. 151, 188 and 189 each × 2	75	
189	5p.	Loaghtyn Ram	40	4

In addition to 40p. and 80p. booklets Nos. 188/9 also come fron special booklet sheets of 60. These sheets contained No. 150ba an 188a, each × 5.

47 Luggers passing Red Pier, Douglas

(Des J. Nicholson. Litho Questa)

1981 (24 Feb). *Centenary of Royal National Mission to Deep Se Fishermen. T* **47** *and similar horiz designs. Multicoloured. P* 14.

190	8p.	Type **47**	25	25
191	9p.	Peel Lugger *Wanderer* rescuing survivors from the *Lusitania*	30	30
192	18p.	Nickeys leaving Port St. Mary Harbour	45	45
193	20p.	Nobby entering Ramsey Harbour ..	50	50
194	22p.	Nickeys *Sunbeam* and *Zebra* at Port Erin	50	50
190/4		.. .. *Set of* 5	1·75	1·75

48 "Crosh Cuirn" Superstition

(Des J. Nicholson. Litho Questa)

)81 (22 May). *Europa. Folklore. T* **48** *and similar horiz design. Multicoloured. P* 14½.

)5	8p. Type **48**	25	25
)6	18p. "Bollan Cross" superstition	75	75

49 Lt. Mark Wilks (Royal Manx Fencibles) and Peel Castle

(Des A. Theobald. Litho Questa)

)81 (22 May). *150th Death Anniv of Colonel Mark Wilks. T* **49** *and similar horiz designs. Multicoloured. P* 14.

)7	8p. Type **49**	25	25
)8	20p. Ensign Mark Wilks and Fort St. George, Madras	50	50
)9	22p. Governor Mark Wilks and Napoleon, St. Helena	70	55
)0	25p. Col. Mark Wilks (Speaker of the House of Keys) and estate, Kirby	80	80
)7/200 ..	.. .. *Set of* 4	2·00	1·90

50 Miss Emmeline Goulden (Mrs. Pankhurst) and Mrs. Sophia Jane Goulden

(Des A. Theobald. Litho Questa)

)81 (22 May). *Centenary of Manx Women's Suffrage. P* 14.

)1 **50**	9p. black, olive-grey and stone	50	50

51 Prince Charles and Lady Diana Spencer

(Des G. Kneale. Litho Harrison)

)81 (29 July). *Royal Wedding. P* 14.

)2 **51**	9p. black, bright blue and pale blue ..	50	50
)3	25p. black, bright blue and pink ..	1·50	1·50
IS204	130 × 183 mm. Nos. 202/3 × 2	4·50	4·50

52 Douglas War Memorial, Poppies and Commemorative Inscription

(Des A. Theobald. Photo Courvoisier)

)81 (29 Sept). *60th Anniv of The Royal British Legion. T* **52** *and similar horiz designs. Multicoloured. Granite paper. P* 11½.

)5	8p. Type **52**	25	25
)6	10p. Major Robert Cain (war hero)	30	35
)7	18p. Festival of Remembrance, Royal Albert Hall	65	65
)8	20p. T.S.S. *Tynwald* at Dunkirk, May 1940	75	75
)5/8 ..	.. .. *Set of* 4	1·75	1·75

ALTERED CATALOGUE NUMBERS

Any Catalogue numbers altered from the last edition are shown as a list in the introductory pages.

53 Nativity Scene (stained-glass window, St. George's Church)

(Des J.W. (7p.), G. Kneale (9p.). Litho J.W.)

1981 (29 Sept). *Christmas. T* **53** *and similar multicoloured design. P* 14.

209	7p. Type **53**	25	25
210	9p. Children from Special School performing nativity play (48 × 30 *mm*)	35	35

The 7p. value also commemorates the bicentenary of St. George's Church, Douglas and the 9p. the International Year for Disabled Persons.

54 Joseph and William Cunningham (founders of Isle of Man Boy Scout Movement) and Cunningham House Headquarters

(Des G. Kneale. Litho Questa)

1982 (23 Feb). *75th Anniv of Boy Scout Movement and 125th Birth Anniv of Lord Baden-Powell. T* **54** *and similar multicoloured designs. P* 14 × 14½ (19½*p.*) *or* 13½ × 14 (*others*).

211	9p. Type **54**	30	30
212	10p. Baden-Powell visiting Isle of Man, 1911	30	30
213	19½p. Baden-Powell and Scout emblem (40 × 31 *mm*)	60	60
214	24p. Scouts and Baden-Powell's last message	70	70
215	29p. Scout salute, handshake, emblem and globe	90	90
211/15 ..	.. .. *Set of* 5	2·50	2·50

55 *The Principals and Duties of Christianity* (Bishop T. Wilson) (first book printed in Manx, 1707)

(Des A. Theobald. Photo Courvoisier)

1982 (1 June). *Europa. Historic Events. T* **55** *and similar horiz design. Multicoloured. Granite paper. P* 12 × 12½.

216	9p. Type **55**	25	25
217	19½p. Landing at Derbyhaven (visit of Thomas, 2nd Earl of Derby, 1507) ..	50	50

56 Charlie Collier (first TT race (single cylinder) winner) and Tourist Trophy Race, 1907

(Des J. Nicholson. Litho Questa)

1982 (1 June). *75th Anniv of Tourist Trophy Motorcycle Racing. T* **56** *and similar horiz designs. Multicoloured. P* 14.

218	9p. Type **56**	20	20
219	10p. Freddie Dixon (Sidecar and Junior TT winner) and Junior TT race, 1927 ..	25	25
220	24p. Jimmie Simpson (TT winner and first to lap at 60, 70 and 80 mph) and Senior TT, 1932	80	70
221	26p. Mike Hailwood (winner of fourteen TT's) and Senior TT, 1961	85	75
222	29p. Jock Taylor (Sidecar TT winner, 1978, 1980 and 1981) and Sidecar TT (with Benga Johansson), 1980	1·00	90
218/22 ..	.. .. *Set of* 5	2·75	2·50

57 *Mona I*

(Des J. Nicholson. Litho Questa)

1982 (5 Oct). *150th Anniv of Isle of Man Steam Packet Company Mail Contract. T* **57** *and similar horiz design. Multicoloured. P* 13½ × 14.

223	12p. Type **57**	50	50
224	19½p. *Manx Maid II*	75	75

58 Three Wise Men bearing Gifts

59 Princess Diana with Prince William

(Des and litho J.W.)

1982 (5 Oct). *Christmas. T* **58** *and similar multicoloured design. P* 13 × 13½ (8*p.*) *or* 13½ × 13 (11*p.*).

225	8p. Type **58**	50	50
226	11p. Christmas snow scene (*vert*)	50	50

(Des G. Kneale. Litho Questa)

1982 (12 Oct). *21st Birthday of Princess of Wales and Birth of Prince William. Sheet* 100 × 83 *mm. P* 14½ × 14.

MS227 **59**	50p. multicoloured	3·50	3·50

60 Opening of Salvation Army Citadel, and T.H. Cannell, J.P.

(Des A. Theobald. Photo Courvoisier)

1983 (15 Feb). *Centenary of Salvation Army in Isle of Man. T* **60** *and similar horiz designs. Multicoloured. Granite paper. P* 11½.

228	10p. Type **60**	30	30
229	12p. Early meeting place and Gen. William Booth	40	40
230	19½p. Salvation Army band	60	60
231	26p. Treating lepers and Lt.-Col. Thomas Bridson	90	90
228/31 ..	.. .. *Set of* 4	2·00	2·00

61 Atlantic Puffins

61a "Queen Elizabeth II" (Ricardo Macarron)

(Des Colleen Corlett (£5), J. Nicholson (others). Litho Questa)

1983 (15 Feb)–**85**. *Horiz designs as T* **61**, *showing sea birds, and T* **61a**. *Multicoloured. P* 14 (20*p.* to £1), 14 × 13½ (£5) *or* 14½ (*others*).

232	1p. Type **61**	30	30
233	2p. Northern Gannets	30	30
234	5p. Lesser Black-backed Gulls	60	40
235	8p. Common Cormorants	60	40
236	10p. Kittiwakes	60	35
237	11p. Shags	60	35
238	12p. Grey Herons	70	40
239	13p. Herring Gulls	70	40
240	14p. Razorbills	70	40
241	15p. Great Black-backed Gulls	80	50
242	16p. Common Shelducks	80	50
243	18p. Oystercatchers	80	60
244	20p. Arctic Terns (14.9.83)	90	1·00
245	25p. Common Guillemots (14.9.83)	1·00	1·00
246	50p. Redshanks (14.9.83)	1·75	1·75
247	£1 Mute Swans (14.9.83)	3·25	3·00
248	£5 Type **61a** (31.1.85)	10·00	10·00
232/48 ..	.. .. *Set of* 17	21·00	19·00

Nos. 244/7 are larger, 39×26 mm.

62 Design Drawings by Robert Casement for the Great Laxey Wheel

(Des J. Nicholson. Litho Questa)

1983 (18 May). *Europa. The Great Laxey Wheel. T* **62** *and similar horiz design. P* 14.
249 10p. black, azure and buff 40 35
250 20½p. multicoloured 60 70
Design:—20½p. Robert Casement and the Great Laxey Wheel.

63 Nick Keig (international yachtsman) and Trimaran *Three Legs of Man III*

64 New Post Office Headquarters, Douglas

(Des J. Nicholson (10p., 31p.), Colleen Corlett (12p., 28p.). Photo Courvoisier)

1983 (18 May). *150th Anniv of King William's College. T* **63** *and similar horiz designs. Multicoloured. Granite paper. P* 11½.
251 10p. Type **63** 20 20
252 12p. King William's College, Castletown .. 30 30
253 28p. Sir William Bragg (winner of Nobel Prize for Physics) and spectrometer .. 80 80
254 31p. General Sir George White V.C. and action at Charasiah .. .. .. 1·00 1·00
251/4 .. .. *Set of* 4 2·00 2·00

(Des Colleen Corlett (10p.), J. Nicholson (15p.). Litho Questa)

1983 (5 July). *World Communications Year and 10th Anniv of Isle of Man Post Office Authority. T* **64** *and similar vert design. Multicoloured. P* 14½.
255 10p. Type **64** 40 40
256 15p. As Type **6**, but inscr "POST OFFICE DECENNIUM 1983" 60 60

65 Shepherds

(Des Colleen Corlett. Litho J.W.)

1983 (14 Sept). *Christmas. T* **65** *and similar horiz design. Multicoloured. P* 13.
257 9p. Type **65** 50 50
258 12p. Three Kings 50 50

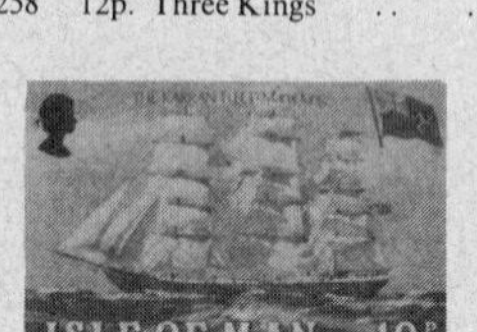

66 *Manx King* (full-rigged ship)

67 C.E.P.T. 25th Anniversary Logo

(Des J. Nicholson (10p. to 31p.); Colleen Corlett, J. Nicholson and J. Smith (miniature sheet). Litho Questa)

1984 (14 Feb). *The Karran Fleet. T* **66** *and similar horiz designs. Multicoloured. P* 14.
259 10p. Type **66** 40 40
260 13p. *Hope* (barque) 55 55
261 20½p. *Rio Grande* (brig) 85 85
262 28p. *Lady Elizabeth* (barque) .. .. .. 1·00 1·00
263 31p. *Sumatra* (barque) .. .. 1·10 1·10
259/63 .. .. *Set of* 5 3·50 3·50
MS264 103 × 94 mm. 28p. As No. 262, 31p. *Lady Elizabeth* (as shown on Falkland Islands No. 417) (*sold at* 60p.) .. .. 3·00 3·00
No. **MS**264 was issued to commemorate links between the Isle of Man and Falkland Islands.

(Des J. Larrivière, adapted Colleen Corlett. Photo Courvoisier)

1984 (27 Apr). *Europa. Granite paper. P* 12 × 11½.
265 **67** 10p. dull orange, deep reddish brown and pale orange 35 35
266 20½p. light blue, deep blue and pale blue 70 70

68 Railway Air Services De Havilland D.H.84 Dragon Mk 2

69 Window from Glencrutchery House, Douglas

(Des A. Theobald, Litho Questa)

1984 (27 Apr). *50th Anniv of First Official Airmail to the Isle of Man and 40th Anniv of International Civil Aviation Organization. T* **68** *and similar horiz designs. Multicoloured. P* 14.
267 11p. Type **68** 45 45
268 13p. West Coast Air Services De Havilland D.H.86A Dragon Express *Ronaldsway* 55 55
269 26p. B.E.A. Douglas DC-3 .. .. .. 95 95
270 28p. B.E.A. Vickers Viscount 800 .. .. 1·00 1·00
271 31p. Telair Britten Norman Islander .. 1·25 1·25
267/71 .. .. *Set of* 5 3·75 3·75

(Des D. Swinton. Litho J.W.)

1984 (21 Sept). *Christmas. Stained-glass Windows. T* **69** *and similar vert design. Multicoloured. P* 14.
272 10p. Type **69** 50 50
273 13p. Window from Lonan Old Church.. .. 50 50

70 William Cain's Birthplace, Ballasalla

(Des J. Nicholson. Litho Questa)

1984 (21 Sept). *William Cain (civic leader, Victoria) Commemoration. T* **70** *and similar horiz designs. Multicoloured. P* 14½ × 14.
274 11p. Type **70** 35 35
275 22p. The *Anna* leaving Liverpool, 1852 .. 75 75
276 28p. Early Australian railway .. .. .. 1·00 1·00
277 30p. William Cain as Mayor of Melbourne, and Town Hall .. .. 1·10 1·10
278 33p. Royal Exhibition Building, Melbourne .. 1·25 1·25
274/8 .. .. *Set of* 5 4·00 4·00

71 Queen Elizabeth II and Commonwealth Parliamentary Association Badge

(Des and litho J.W.)

1984 (21 Sept). *Links with the Commonwealth. 30th Commonwealth Parliamentary Association Conference. T* **71** *and similar horiz design. Multicoloured. P* 14.
279 14p. Type **71** 50 50
280 33p. Queen Elizabeth II and Manx emblem .. 1·10 1·10

72 Cunningham House Headquarters, and Mrs. Willie Cunningham and Mrs. Joseph Cunningham (former Commissioners)

(Des Colleen Corlett. Photo Courvoisier)

1985 (31 Jan). *75th Anniv of Girl Guide Movement. T* **72** *and similar horiz designs. Multicoloured. Granite paper. P* 11½.
281 11p. Type **72** 45 45
282 14p. Princess Margaret, Isle of Man standard and guides 75 75
283 29p. Lady Olave Baden-Powell opening Guide Headquarters, 1955 .. .. .. 1·10 1·10
284 31p. Guide uniforms from 1910 to 1985 .. 1·40 1·40
285 34p. Guide handclasp, salute and early badge .. 1·60 1·60
281/5 .. .. *Set of* 5 4·75 4·75

73 Score of Manx National Anthem

(Des D. Swinton. Photo Courvoisier)

1985 (24 Apr). *Europa. European Music Year. T* **73** *and similar horiz designs. Granite paper. P* 11½.
286 12p. black, orange-brown and chestnut .. 50 45
a. Horiz pair. Nos. 286/7 .. .. .. 1·00 90
287 12p. black, orange-brown and chestnut .. 50 45
288 22p. black, bright new blue and new blue .. 1·00 95
a. Horiz pair. Nos. 288/9 .. .. .. 2·10 1·90
289 22p. black, bright new blue and new blue .. 1·00 95
286/9 .. .. *Set of* 4 2·75 2·50
Designs:—No. 287, William H. Gill (lyricist); 288, Score of hymn "Crofton"; 289, Dr. John Clague (composer).
Nos. 286/7 and 288/9 were printed together, *se-tenant*, in horizontal pairs throughout the sheets.

74 Charles Rolls in 20 h.p. Rolls-Royce (1906 Tourist Trophy Race)

(Des A. Theobald. Litho Questa)

1985 (25 May). *Century of Motoring. T* **74** *and similar hor designs. Multicoloured. P* 14.
290 12p. Type **74** 40 4
a. Horiz pair. Nos. 290/1 .. .. .. 85 8
291 12p. W. Bentley in 3 litre Bentley (1922 Tourist Trophy Race) 40 4
292 14p. F. Gerrard in E.R.A. (1950 British Empire Trophy Race) 55 5
a. Horiz pair. Nos. 292/3 .. .. .. 1·10 1·
293 14p. Brian Lewis in Alfa Romeo (1934 Mannin Moar Race) 55 5
294 31p. Jaguar "XJ-SC" ("Roads Open" car, 1984 Motor Cycle T.T. Races) .. .. 1·40 1·
a. Horiz pair. Nos. 294/5 .. .. .. 2·75 2·
295 31p. Tony Pond and Mike Nicholson in Vauxhall "Chevette" (1981 Rothmans International Rally) .. .. 1·40 1·
290/5 .. .. *Set of* 6 4·25 4·
Nos. 290/1, 292/3 and 294/5 were printed together, *se-tenant*, horizontal pairs throughout the sheets.

75 Queen Alexandra and Victorian Sergeant with Wife

(Des Colleen Corlett. Litho Questa)

1985 (4 Sept). *Centenary of the Soldiers', Sailors' and Airmen Families Association. T* **75** *and similar horiz designs showir Association Presidents. Multicoloured. P* 14.
296 12p. Type **75** 40
297 15p. Queen Mary and Royal Air Force family 55
298 29p. Earl Mountbatten and Royal Navy family 1·10 1·
299 34p. Prince Michael of Kent and Royal Marine with parents, 1982 .. .. .. 1·25 1·
296/9 .. .. *Set of* 4 3·00 3·

76 Kirk Maughold (Birthplace)

(Des A. Theobald. Litho Questa)

1985 (2 Oct). *Birth Bicentenary of Lieutenant-General Sir Ma Cubbon (Indian administrator). T* **76** *and similar multicolour designs. P* 14.
300 12p. Type **76** 45
301 22p. Lieutenant-General Sir Mark Cubbon (*vert*) .. .. 1·10 1·
302 45p. Memorial Statue, Bangalore, India (*vert*) 1·90 1·
300/2 .. .. *Set of* 3 3·00 3·

77 St. Peter's Church, Onchan

(Des A. Theobald. Litho J.W.)

1985 (2 Oct). *Christmas. Manx Churches. T* **77** *and similar hor designs. Multicoloured. P* 13 × 13½.
303 11p. Type **77** 45
304 14p. Royal Chapel of St. John, Tynwald .. 55
305 31p. Bride Parish Church .. .. .. 1·25 1·
303/5 .. .. *Set of* 3 2·00 2·

78 Swimming

(Des C. Abbott. Litho Questa)

86 (5 Feb). *Commonwealth Games, Edinburgh. T* **78** *and similar horiz designs. Multicoloured. P* 14.

6 12p. Type **78** 40 40
7 15p. Race walking 50 50
8 31p. Rifle-shooting .. .. 1·50 1·50
9 34p. Cycling .. .. 1·50 1·50
6/9 .. .. *Set of* 4 3·50 3·50

No. 309 also commemorates the 50th anniversary of Manx ternational Cycling Week.

79 Viking Necklace and Peel Castle **80** Viking Longship

(Des J. Nicholson. Litho Questa)

86 (5 Feb). *Centenary of the Manx Museum. T* **79** *and similar multicoloured designs. P* 14.

0 12p. Type **79** 35 35
1 15p. Meayll Circle, Rushen 45 45
2 22p. Skeleton of Great Deer and Manx Museum (*vert*) 85 85
3 26p. Viking longship model (*vert*) .. .. 1·00 1·00
4 29p. Open Air Museum, Cregneash .. .. 1·25 1·25
0/14 .. .. *Set of* 5 3·50 3·50

(Des Colleen Corlett. Litho Harrison)

86 (10 Apr). *Manx Heritage Year. Booklet stamps. T* **80** *and similar vert design. P* 14½ × 14.

5 2p. multicoloured 20 20
a. Booklet pane. Nos. 315 × 2 and 316 × 4 .. 2·50
6 10p. black, apple green and brownish grey .. 55 55
a. Booklet pane. No. 316 × 3 and 3 stamp-size labels .. .. 2·50

Design:—10p. Celtic cross logo.

In addition to 50p. and £1.14 booklets Nos. 315/16 also come om special booklet sheets of 60 containing five each of Nos. 315a d 316a.

81 *Usnea articulata* (lichen) and *Neotinea intacta* (orchid), The Ayres **82** Ellanbane (home of Myles Standish)

(Des J. Nicholson and Nancy Corkish. Photo Courvoisier)

86 (10 Apr). *Europa. Protection of Nature and the Environment. T* **81** *and similar horiz designs. Multicoloured. Granite paper. P* 11½.

7 12p. Type **81** 60 60
a. Horiz pair. Nos. 317/18 .. .. .. 1·25 1·25
8 12p. Hen Harrier, Calf of Man 60 60
9 22p. Manx Stoat, Eary Cushlin 95 95
a. Horiz pair. Nos. 319/20 .. .. .. 1·90 1·90
0 22p. *Stenobothus stigmaticus* (grasshopper), St. Michael's Isle 95 95
7/20 .. .. *Set of* 4 2·75 2·75

The two designs of each value were printed together, *se-tenant*, in orizontal pairs throughout the sheets.

(Des C. Abbott. Litho Cartor)

86 (22 May). *"Ameripex '86" International Stamp Exhibition, Chicago. Captain Myles Standish of the* "Mayflower". *T* **82** *and similar vert designs. Multicoloured. P* 13½.

1 12p. Type **82** 35 35
2 15p. *Mayflower* crossing the Atlantic, 1620 .. 55 55
3 31p. Pilgrim Fathers landing at Plymouth, 1620 .. .. 1·40 1·40
4 34p. Captain Myles Standish .. .. .. 1·60 1·60
21/4 .. .. *Set of* 4 3·50 3·50
S325 100 × 75 mm. Nos. 323/4. P 12½ .. .. 2·75 2·75

No. **MS**325 also commemorates the 75th anniversary of the World anx Association.

83 Prince Andrew in Naval Uniform and Miss Sarah Ferguson **84** Prince Philip (from photo by Karsh)

(Des Colleen Corlett. Litho B.D.T.)

86 (23 July). *Royal Wedding. T* **83** *and similar horiz design. Multicoloured. P* 15 × 14.

6 15p. Type **83** 75 75
7 40p. Engagement photograph .. .. .. 1·75 1·50

(Des Colleen Corlett. Photo Courvoisier)

1986 (28 Aug). *Royal Birthdays. T* **84** *and similar multicoloured designs. Granite paper. P* 11½.

328 15p. Type **84** 80 80
a. Horiz pair. Nos. 328/9 .. .. .. 1·60 1·60
329 15p. Queen Elizabeth II (from photo by Karsh) 80 80
330 34p. Queen Elizabeth and Prince Philip (from photo by Karsh) (48 × 35 *mm*) .. .. 1·75 1·75
328/30 .. .. *Set of* 3 3·00 3·00

Nos. 328/9 were printed together, *se-tenant*, in horizontal pairs throughout the sheet.

Nos. 328/30 also commemorate "Stockholmia '86" International Stamp Exhibition, Sweden and the 350th anniversary of the Swedish Post Office and are so inscribed on the margins of the sheet of twelve (Nos. 328/9) and six (No. 330).

85 European Robins on Globe and "Peace and Goodwill" in Braille **86** North Quay

(Des Colleen Corlett. Litho Questa)

1986 (25 Sept). *Christmas. International Peace Year. T* **85** *and similar vert designs. Multicoloured. P* 14.

331 11p. Type **85** 50 50
332 14p. Hands releasing peace dove 55 55
333 31p. Clasped hands and "Peace" in sign language .. .. 1·25 1·25
331/3 .. .. *Set of* 3 2·00 2·00

(Des A. Theobald. Litho Questa)

1987 (21 Jan–26 Mar). *Victorian Douglas. T* **86** *and similar horiz designs. Multicoloured. P* 14 × 14½.

334 2p. Type **86** 10 10
a. Booklet pane. Nos. 334 × 2, 335 × 2 and 336 × 4 (2p. stamps at top) (26.3) .. 3·50
ab. Ditto, but 2p. stamps at bottom (26.3) .. 3·50
b. Booklet pane. Nos. 334/7, each × 2 (26.3) 3·50
335 3p. Old Fishmarket 10 10
336 10p. The Breakwater 35 35
337 15p. Jubilee Clock 50 50
338 31p. Loch Promenade .. .. 1·50 1·50
339 34p. Beach .. .. 1·75 1·75
334/9 .. .. *Set of* 6 3·75 3·75

87 "The Old Fishmarket and Harbour, Douglas"

(Des A. Theobald. Litho Cartor)

1987 (18 Feb). *Paintings by John Miller Nicholson. T* **87** *and similar horiz designs. Multicoloured. P* 13½.

340 12p. Type **87** 35 35
341 26p. "Red Sails at Douglas" 90 90
342 29p. "The Double Corner, Peel" .. .. 1·40 1·40
343 34p. "Peel Harbour" .. .. 1·60 1·60
340/3 .. .. *Set of* 4 3·75 3·75

88 Sea Terminal, Douglas

(Des R. Maddox. Litho B.D.T.)

1987 (29 Apr). *Europa. Architecture. T* **88** *and similar horiz designs. Multicoloured. P* 13½.

344 12p. Type **88** 60 60
a. Horiz pair. Nos. 344/5 .. .. .. 1·25 1·25
345 12p. Tower of Refuge, Douglas 60 60
346 22p. Gaiety Theatre, Douglas .. .. .. 1·10 1·10
a. Horiz pair. Nos. 346/7 .. .. .. 2·10 2·10
347 22p. Villa Marina, Douglas .. .. .. 1·10 1·10
344/7 .. .. *Set of* 4 3·00 3·00

Nos. 344/5 and 346/7 were each printed, *se-tenant*, in horizontal pairs throughout the sheets.

89 Supercharged BMW 500cc Motor Cycle, 1939

(Des B. Dix. Litho Cartor)

1987 (27 May). *80th Anniv of Tourist Trophy Motor Cycle Races. T* **89** *and similar horiz designs. Multicoloured. P* 13½ × 13.

348 12p. Type **89** 40 40
349 15p. Manx "Kneeler" Norton 350cc, 1953 .. 60 60
350 29p. MV Agusta 500cc 4, 1956 .. .. .. 1·00 1·00
351 31p. Guzzi 500cc V8, 1957 .. .. .. 1·10 1·10
352 34p. Honda 250cc 6, 1967 .. .. .. 1·40 1·40
348/52 .. .. *Set of* 5 4·00 4·00
MS353 150 × 140 mm. Nos. 348/52. P 14 × 13½ .. 4·75 4·75

Nos. 348/53 also commemorate the Centenary of the St. John Ambulance Brigade and the miniature sheet also carries the logo of "Capex '87" International Stamp Exhibition, Toronto, on its margin.

90 Fuchsia and Wild Roses **91** Stirring the Christmas Pudding

(Des Nancy Corkish. Litho Enschedé)

1987 (9 Sept). *Wild Flowers. T* **90** *and similar vert designs. Multicoloured. P* 14½ × 13.

354 16p. Type **90** 60 60
355 29p. Field Scabious and Ragwort .. .. 1·10 1·10
356 31p. Wood Anemone and Celandine .. .. 1·25 1·25
357 34p. Violets and Primroses .. .. .. 1·50 1·50
354/7 .. .. *Set of* 4 4·00 4·00

(Des Colleen Corlett. Litho Questa)

1987 (16 Oct). *Christmas. Victorian Scenes. T* **91** *and similar vert designs. Multicoloured. P* 14.

358 12p. Type **91** 50 50
359 15p. Bringing home the Christmas tree .. 75 75
360 31p. Decorating the Christmas tree .. .. 1·25 1·25
358/60 .. .. *Set of* 3 2·25 2·25

92 Russell Brookes in Vauxhall Opel (Manx Rally winner, 1985)

(Des C. Abbott. Litho Enschedé)

1988 (10 Feb). *Motor Sport. T* **92** *and similar horiz designs. Multicoloured. P* 13½ × 14½.

361 13p. Type **92** 75 70
362 26p. Ari Vatanen in Ford "Escort" (Manx Rally winner, 1976) .. .. 1·25 1·10
363 31p. Terry Smith in Repco "March 761" (Hill Climb winner, 1980) .. .. 1·40 1·25
364 34p. Nigel Mansell in Williams/Honda (British Grand Prix winner, 1986 and 1987) .. 1·60 1·40
361/4 .. .. *Set of* 4 4·50 4·00

93 Horse Tram Terminus, Douglas Bay Tramway **93a** Queen Elizabeth II taking Salute at Trooping the Colour

(Des Colleen Corlett (£2). A. Theobald (others). Litho B.D.T. (1p. to 19p., 21p., 23p.), Questa (20p. and 25p. to £2))

1988 (10 Feb)–**92**. *Manx Railways and Tramways. Horiz designs as T* **93**, *and T* **93a**. *Multicoloured. P* 13 (*1p. to 19p., 21p., 23p.*), 14½ × 15 (*20p., 25p. to £1*) *or* 14½ (*£2*).

365 1p. Type **93** 10 10
366 2p. Snaefell Mountain Railway 10 10
367 3p. Marine Drive Tramway 10 10
a. Booklet pane. Nos. 367×2, 370 and 373×2 (16.3.88) .. .. 3·00
b. Booklet pane. Nos. 367×2, 371×2 and 374 (16.10.89) .. .. 2·50
367*c* 4p. Douglas Cable Tramway (9.1.91) 10 10
ca. Booklet pane. Nos. 367*c*×3, 374 and 377*a* .. .. 2·75
cb. Booklet pane. Nos. 367*c*×3, 374×4 and 377*a* .. .. 4·25
368 5p. Douglas Head Incline Railway 20 20
369 10p. Douglas & Laxey Coast Electric Tramway car at Maughold Head 30 30

370 13p. As 4p. 50 50
 a. Booklet pane. Nos. 370×4 and 373×6 (16.3.88) .. .. 5·50
371 14p. Manx Northern Railway No. 4, *Caledonia*, at Gob-y-Deigan 50 50
 a. Booklet pane. Nos. 371×4 and 374×6 (16.10.89) .. .. 4·50
372 15p. Laxey Mine Railway Lewin locomotive *Ant* 50 50
 a. Booklet pane. Nos. 372 and 376×2 (14.2.90) .. .. 2·50
 b. Booklet pane. Nos. 372×4 and 376×6 (14.2.90) .. .. 6·00
373 16p. Port Erin Breakwater Tramway locomotive *Henry B. Loch* 50 50
374 17p. Ramsey Harbour Tramway 50 50
375 18p. Locomotive No. 7, *Tynwald*, on Foxdale line 55 55
375*a* 18p. T.P.O. Special leaving Douglas, 3 July 1991 (8.1.92) 55 55
 ab. Booklet pane. Nos. 375*a*×3 and 377*b*×2 .. .. 3·00
 ac. Booklet pane. Nos. 375*a*×6 and 377*b*×4 .. .. 5·50
376 19p. Baldwin Reservoir Tramway steam locomotive No. 1, *Injebreck* 60 60
377 20p. I.M.R. No. 13, *Kissack*, near St. Johns (21.9.88) 60 60
377*a* 21p. As 14p. (9.1.91) 60 60
377*b* 23p. Double-deck horse tram, Douglas (8.1.92) 60 60
378 25p. I.M.R. No. 12, *Hutchinson*, leaving Douglas (21.9.88) 70 70
379 50p. Groudle Glen Railway locomotive *Polar Bear* (21.9.88) .. .. .. 1·50 1·50
380 £1 I.M.R. No. 11, *Maitland*, pulling Royal Train, 1963 (21.9.88) .. .. 3·00 3·00
380*a* £2 Type **93*a*** (14.2.90) .. .. .. 6·00 6·00
365/80*a* .. .. *Set of* 21 16·00 16·00

In addition to stamp booklets Nos. 367a/b, 370a, 371a, 372a/b and 375ab/ac also come from special booklet sheets of 50 containing either ten examples of the strips of five or five examples of the strips of ten.

Nos. 367*c* and 377*a* show the Queen's head in white. The 4p. value was only issued in 50p. and £1 stamp booklets or in special booklet sheets of 50 containing five vertical strips of No. 367cb and five extra examples of both Nos. 367*c* and 377*a*.

Imprint dates: "1988", Nos. 365/7, 368/75, 376/7, 378/80; "1989", Nos. 367, 371, 374; "1990", Nos. 372, 376, 380*a*; "1991", Nos. 367*c*, 374, 377*a*; "1992", Nos. 375*a*, 377*b*, 379/80.

For miniature sheet containing Nos. 367c and 377*a* see No. **MS**484.

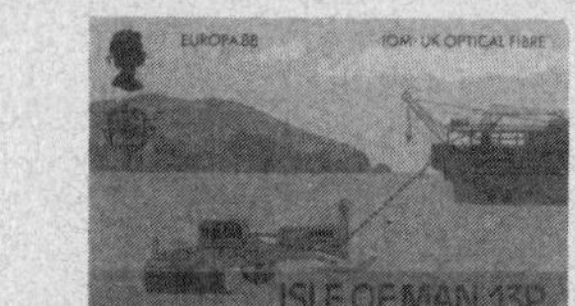

94 Laying Isle of Man—U.K. Submarine Cable

(Des C. Abbott. Litho Cartor)

1988 (14 Apr). *Europa. Transport and Communications. T* **94** *and similar horiz designs. Multicoloured. P* 14×13½.
381 13p. Type **94** 50 50
 a. Horiz pair. Nos. 381/2 .. .. .. 1·00 1·00
382 13p. *Flex Service 3* (cable ship) 50 50
383 22p. Earth station, Braddan 90 90
 a. Horiz pair. Nos. 383/4 .. .. .. 1·75 1·75
384 22p. "INTELSAT 5" satellite 90 90
381/4 .. .. *Set of* 4 2·50 2·50

Nos. 381/2 and 383/4 were each printed together, *se-tenant*, in horizontal pairs throughout the sheets. Nos. 381/2 form a composite design.

95 *Euterpe* (full-rigged ship) off Ramsey, 1863

96 "Magellanica"

(Des J. Nicholson. Litho Questa)

1988 (11 May). *Manx Sailing Ships. T* **95** *and similar horiz designs. Multicoloured. P* 14.
385 16p. Type **95** 50 50
386 29p. *Vixen* (topsail schooner) leaving Peel for Australia, 1853 .. .. .. 1·00 1·00
387 31p. *Ramsey* (full-rigged ship) off Brisbane, 1870 .. .. 1·25 1·25
388 34p. *Star of India* (formerly *Euterpe*) (barque) off San Diego, 1976 .. .. 1·40 1·40
385/8 .. .. *Set of* 4 3·75 3·75
MS389 110 × 85 mm. Nos. 385 and 388 .. .. 2·50 2·50

Nos. 386/7 also commemorate the Bicentenary of Australian Settlement.

(Des Colleen Corlett. Litho Enschedé)

1988 (21 Sept). *50th Anniv of British Fuchsia Society. T* **96** *and similar vert designs. Multicoloured. P* 13½ × 14.
390 13p. Type **96** 50 50
391 16p. "Pink Cloud" 60 60
392 22p. "Leonora" 80 70
393 29p. "Satellite" .. .. 1·00 1·00
394 31p. "Preston Guild" .. .. 1·25 1·25
395 34p. "Thalia" .. .. 1·40 1·40
390/5 .. .. *Set of* 6 5·00 5·00

97 Long-eared Owl

(Des Audrey North. Litho Questa)

1988 (12 Oct). *Christmas. Manx Birds. T* **97** *and similar horiz designs. Multicoloured. P* 14.
396 12p. Type **97** 55 55
397 15p. European Robin 85 85
398 31p. Grey Partridge .. .. 1·40 1·40
396/8 .. .. *Set of* 3 2·50 2·50

98 Ginger Cat

99 Tudric Pewter Clock, *c*. 1903

(Des P. Layton. Litho Questa)

1989 (8 Feb). *Manx Cats. T* **98** *and similar horiz designs. Multicoloured. P* 14.
399 16p. Type **98** 50 50
400 27p. Black and white cat .. .. .. 1·00 1·00
401 30p. Tortoiseshell and white cat .. .. 1·40 1·40
402 40p. Tortoiseshell cat .. .. .. 1·60 1·60
399/402 .. .. *Set of* 4 4·00 4·00

(Des Colleen Corlett. Litho Cartor)

1989 (8 Feb). *125th Birth Anniv of Archibald Knox (artist and designer). T* **99** *and similar multicoloured designs. P* 13.
403 13p. Type **99** 35 35
404 16p. "Celtic Cross" watercolour 45 45
405 23p. Silver cup and cover, 1902-03 .. .. 75 75
406 32p. Gold and silver brooches from Liberty's Cymric range (*horiz*) .. .. .. 1·40 1·40
407 35p. Silver jewel box, 1900 (*horiz*) .. .. 1·50 1·50
403/7 .. .. *Set of* 5 4·00 4·00

100 William Bligh and Old Church, Onchan

(Des C. Abbott. Litho B.D.T.)

1989 (28 Apr). *Bicentenary of the Mutiny on the Bounty. T* **100** *and similar horiz designs. Multicoloured. P* 14.
408 13p. Type **100** 25 30
 a. Booklet pane. Nos. 408/10 and 412/14 .. 3·00
 b. Booklet pane. Nos. 408/9 and 411/14 .. 3·00
409 16p. Bligh and loyal crew cast adrift 30 35
410 23p. Pitcairn Islands 1989 Settlement Bicentenary 90 c., No. 345 .. .. 1·10 1·10
 a. Booklet pane. Nos. 410/11, each × 3 .. 5·00
411 27p. Norfolk Island 1989 Bicentenary 39 c., No. 461 .. .. 1·10 1·10
412 30p. Midshipman Peter Heywood and Tahiti 70 70
413 32p. H.M.S. *Bounty* anchored off Pitcairn Island 75 75
414 35p. Fletcher Christian and Pitcairn Island .. 80 80
408/14 .. .. *Set of* 7 4·50 4·50
MS415 110×85 mm. Nos. 410/11 and 414 .. 5·00 4·75

Nos. 410/11 were only issued in £5.30 booklets and as part of No. **MS**415.

Booklet panes Nos. 408a/b and 410a each contain two vertical rows of three stamps, separated by a central gutter.

101 Skipping and Hopscotch

102 Atlantic Puffin

(Des Colleen Corlett. Litho Enschedé)

1989 (17 May). *Europa. Children's Games. T* **101** *and simil horiz designs. Multicoloured. P* 13½.
416 13p. Type **101** 60
 a. Horiz pair. Nos. 416/17 .. .. .. 1·25 1·
417 13p. Wheelbarrow, leapfrog and piggyback .. 60
418 23p. Completing model house and blowing bubbles 95
 a. Horiz pair. Nos. 418/19 .. .. .. 1·90 1·
419 23p. Girl with doll and doll's house 95
416/19 .. .. *Set of* 4 2·75 2·

Nos. 416/17 and 418/19 were printed together, *se-tenant* composite designs, in horizontal pairs throughout the sheets.

(Des W. Oliver. Litho Questa)

1989 (20 Sept). *Sea Birds. T* **102** *and similar vert design Multicoloured. P* 14.
420 13p. Type **102** 80
 a. Strip of 4. Nos. 420/3 .. .. .. 3·00
421 13p. Black Guillemot 80
422 13p. Common Cormorant 80
423 13p. Kittiwake 80
420/3 .. .. *Set of* 4 3·00 3·

Nos. 420/3 were printed together, *se-tenant*, in horizontal a vertical strips of 4 throughout the sheet. The sheet exists with without perforations across the side margins.

Examples of Nos. 420/3 sold at "World Stamp Expo '89", held Washington D.C. between 17 November and 8 December 198 carried a commemorative inscription on the bottom sheet margin

103 Red Cross Cadets learning Resuscitation

104 Mother with Baby, Jane Crookall Maternity Home

(Des A. Theobald. Litho Questa)

1989 (16 Oct). *125th Anniversary of International Red Cross a Centenary of Noble's Hospital, Isle of Man. T* **103** *and simil horiz designs. P* 14.
424 14p. multicoloured 40
425 17p. grey and orange-vermilion 65
426 23p. multicoloured 90
427 30p. multicoloured .. .. 1·25 1·
428 35p. multicoloured .. .. 1·50 1·
424/8 .. .. *Set of* 5 4·25 4·

Designs:—17p. Anniversary logo; 23p. Signing Gene Convention, 1864; 30p. Red Cross ambulance; 35p. Henri Duna (founder).

(Des Colleen Corlett. Litho Questa)

1989 (16 Oct). *Christmas. 50th Anniversary of Jane Crook Maternity Home and 75th Anniversary of St. Ninian's Churc Douglas. T* **104** *and similar vert designs. Multicoloured. P* 14½
429 13p. Type **104** 45
430 16p. Mother with child 55
431 34p. Madonna and Child .. .. .. 1·10 1·
432 37p. Baptism, St. Ninian's Church .. .. 1·25 1·
429/32 .. .. *Set of* 4 3·00 3·

105 "The Isle of Man Express going up a Gradient"

106 Modern Postman

(Des D. Swinton. Litho B.D.T.)

1990 (14 Feb). *Isle of Man Edwardian Postcards. T* **105** *a similar horiz designs. Multicoloured. P* 14.
433 15p. Type **105** 30
434 19p. "A way we have in the Isle of Man" .. 55
435 32p. "Douglas–waiting for the male boat" .. 1·00 1·
436 34p. "The last toast rack home, Douglas Parade" .. .. 1·40 1·
437 37p. "The last Isle of Man boat" .. .. 1·50 1·
433/7 .. .. *Set of* 5 4·25 4·

(Des A. Kellett. Litho Cartor)

1990 (18 Apr). *Europa. Post Office Buildings. T* **106** *and simil multicoloured designs. P* 13½.
438 15p. Type **106** 55
 a. Horiz pair. Nos. 438/9 .. .. .. 1·10 1·
439 15p. Ramsey Post Office, 1990 (40×26 *mm*) 55
440 24p. Postman, 1890 95
 a. Horiz pair. Nos. 440/1 .. .. .. 1·90 1·
441 24p. Douglas Post Office, 1890 (40×26 *mm*) .. 95
438/41 .. .. *Set of* 4 2·75 2·

Nos. 438/9 and 440/1 were each printed together, *se-tenant*, horizontal pairs throughout the sheets.

107 Penny Black

108 Queen Elizabeth the Queen Mother

s Colleen Corlett. Eng Inge Madle (No. **MS**447). Recess and litho (No. **MS**447) or litho (others) Enschedé)

0 (3 May). *150th Anniv of the Penny Black. T* **107** *and similar ert designs. P* 14×13½.

	1p. black, buff and gold	10	10
	a. Sheetlet. Horiz strip of 5. Nos. 442/6 ..	4·50	
	b. Sheetlet. No. 442×25	2·50	
	c. Booklet pane. No. 442×8 with margins all round	50	
	19p. gold, black and buff	65	65
	a. Booklet pane. Nos. 443/6×2 with margins all round	6·50	
	32p. multicoloured	1·25	1·25
	34p. multicoloured	1·25	1·25
	37p. multicoloured	1·40	1·40
/6	.. .. *Set of* 5	4·00	4·00
447	100×71 mm. £1 black, gold and buff (50×60 *m*)	3·75	3·75

)esigns:—19p. Wyon Medal, 1837; 32p. Wyon's stamp essay; . Perkins Bacon engine-turned essay, 1839; 37p. Twopence e, 1840; £1 Block of four Penny Black stamps lettered IM–JN. heetlet No. 442a was reissued on 24 August 1990 overprinted om STAMP WORLD LONDON '90 to NEW ZEALAND 0" for sale at the New Zealand exhibition.

'he Penny Black stamps shown on Nos. 442b/c each have erent corner letters at foot. The sheetlet of 25 was issued in junction with a special postal concession which allowed hand-ressed personal mail for the island to be posted for 1p. between am. and 12 noon on 6 May 1990.

lo. **MS**447 also commemorates "Stamp World London 90" ernational Stamp Exhibition, London.

(Des Colleen Corlett. Litho B.D.T.)

0 (4 Aug). *90th Birthday of Queen Elizabeth the Queen Aother. P* 13×13½.

108	90p. multicoloured	3·00	3·00

lo. 448 was printed in sheets of ten stamps and ten *se-tenant* ribed labels.

109 Hawker Hurricane Mk 1, Bristol Type 142 Blenheim Mk 1 and Home Defence

(Des A. Theobald. Litho Questa)

0 (5 Sept). *50th Anniv of Battle of Britain. T* **109** *and similar ioriz designs. Multicoloured. P* 14.

9	15p. Type **109**	40	40
	a. Horiz pair. Nos. 449/50	80	80
0	15p. Supermarine Spitfire with Westland Lysander Mk I rescue aircraft and launch	40	40
1	24p. Rearming Hawker Hurricane Mk I fighters	90	90
	a. Horiz pair. Nos. 451/2	1·75	1·75
2	24p. Ops room and scramble	90	90
3	29p. Civil Defence personnel	95	95
	a. Horiz pair. Nos. 453/4	1·90	1·90
4	29p. Anti-aircraft battery	95	95
)/54	.. .. *Set of* 6	4·00	4·00

The two designs of each value were printed together, *se-tenant*, in rizontal pairs throughout the sheets of 8.

110 Churchill with Freedom of Douglas Casket

111 Boy on Toboggan and Girl posting Letter

(Des C. Abbott. Litho Cartor)

0 (5 Sept). *25th Death Anniv of Sir Winston Churchill. T* **110** *and similar horiz designs. Multicoloured. P* 13½.

	19p. Type **110**	60	60
	32p. Churchill and London blitz	1·10	1·10
	34p. Churchill and searchlights over West-minster	1·40	1·40
	37p. Churchill with R.A.F. Hawker Hurricane Mk I fighters	1·40	1·40
5/8	.. .. *Set of* 4	4·25	4·25

(Des C. Abbott. Litho B.D.T)

1990 (10 Oct). *Christmas. T* **111** *and similar vert designs. Multicoloured. P* 13×13½.

459	14p. Type **111**	40	40
460	18p. Girl on toboggan and skaters	60	60
461	34p. Boy with snowman	1·25	1·25
462	37p. Children throwing snowballs	1·40	1·40
459/62	.. .. *Set of* 4	3·50	3·50
MS463	123×55 mm. As Nos. 459/62, but face values in black	3·50	3·50
	a. Blue (inscriptions) omitted	£600	

112 Henry Bloom Noble and Orphans (Marshall Wane)

113 Lifeboat *Sir William Hillary*, Douglas

(Des Colleen Corlett. Litho Walsall)

1991 (9 Jan). *Manx Photography. T* **112** *and similar horiz designs. P* 14.

464	17p. blackish brown, pale brownish grey & blk	45	45
465	21p. deep brown and ochre	60	60
466	26p. blackish brown, stone and brownish black	90	90
467	31p. agate, pale grey-brown and black ..	1·25	1·25
468	40p. multicoloured	1·50	1·50
464/8	.. .. *Set of* 5	4·25	4·25

Designs:—21p. Douglas (Frederick Frith); 26p. Studio portrait of three children (Hilda Newby); 31p. Cashtal yn Ard (Christopher Killip); 40p. Peel Castle (Colleen Corlett).

(Des A. Peck. Litho Questa)

1991 (13 Feb). *Manx Lifeboats. T* **113** *and similar horiz designs. Multicoloured. P* 14.

469	17p. Type **113**	45	45
470	21p. *Osman Gabriel*, Port Erin	60	60
471	26p. *Ann and James Ritchie*, Ramsey ..	90	90
472	31p. *The Gough Ritchie*, Port St. Mary ..	1·25	1·25
473	37p. *John Batstone*, Peel	1·50	1·50
469/73	.. .. *Set of* 5	4·25	4·25

No. 469 is inscribed "HILARY" and No. 471 "JAMES & ANN RITCHIE", both in error.

114 "Intelsat" Communications Satellite

115 Oliver Godfrey with Indian 500cc at Start, 1911

(Des D. Miller. Litho B.D.T.)

1991 (24 Apr). *Europa. Europe in Space. T* **114** *and similar vert designs. Multicoloured. P* 14.

474	17p. Type **114**	70	70
	a. Vert pair. Nos. 474/5	1·40	1·40
475	17p. "Ariane" rocket launch and fishing boats in Douglas harbour	70	70
476	26p. Weather satellite and space station ..	1·00	1·00
	a. Vert pair. Nos. 476/7	2·00	2·00
477	26p. Ronaldsway Airport, Manx Radio trans-mitter and Space shuttle launch ..	1·00	1·00
474/7	.. .. *Set of* 4	3·00	3·00

Nos. 474/5 and 476/7 were each printed together, *se-tenant*, in vertical pairs throughout the sheets, each pair forming a composite design.

(Des A. Theobald. Litho Enschedé)

1991 (30 May). *80th Anniv of Tourist Trophy Mountain Course. T* **115** *and similar horiz designs. Multicoloured. P* 14½×13.

478	17p. Type **115**	40	40
479	21p. Freddie Dixon on Douglas "banking" sidecar, 1923	60	60
480	26p. Bill Ivy on Yamaha 125cc, 1968 ..	85	85
481	31p. Giacomo Agostini on MV Agusta 500cc, 1972	1·25	1·25
482	37p. Joey Dunlop on RVF Honda 750cc, 1985	1·40	1·40
478/82	.. .. *Set of* 5	4·00	4·00
MS483	149×144 mm. Nos. 478/82	4·25	4·25

No. **MS**483 was reissued on 16 November 1991 overprinted for the Phila Nippon Exhibition, Japan.

(Des Colleen Corlett. Litho B.D.T.)

1991 (1 July). *9th Conference of Commonwealth Postal Administrations, Douglas. Sheet* 119×77 *mm containing Nos.* 367*c and* 377*a, each* × 2. *Multicoloured. P* 13.

MS484	Nos. 367*c* and 377*a*, each × 2	1·50	1·50

MINIMUM PRICE

The minimum price quote is 10p which represents a handling charge rather than a basis for valuing common stamps. For further notes about prices see introductory pages.

116 Laxey Hand-cart, 1920

117 Mute Swans, Douglas Harbour

(Des C. Abbott. Litho Questa)

1991 (18 Sept). *Fire Engines. T* **116** *and similar square designs. Multicoloured. P* 14½.

485	17p. Type **116**	40	40
486	21p. Horse-drawn steamer, Douglas, 1909 ..	60	60
487	30p. Merryweather "Hatfield" pump, 1936 ..	85	85
488	33p. Dennis "F8" pumping appliance, Peel, 1953	1·25	1·25
489	37p. Volvo turntable ladder, Douglas, 1989 ..	1·40	1·40
485/9	.. .. *Set of* 5	4·00	4·00

(Des Colleen Corlett. Litho Cartor)

1991 (18 Sept). *Swans. T* **117** *and similar horiz designs. Multicoloured. P* 13.

490	17p. Type **117**	55	55
	a. Horiz pair. Nos. 490/1	1·10	1·10
491	17p. Black Swans, Curraghs Wildlife Park ..	55	55
492	26p. Whooper Swans, Bishop's Dub, Ballaugh	1·10	1·10
	a. Horiz pair. Nos. 492/3	2·25	2·25
493	26p. Whistling ("Bewick's") Swans, Eairy Dam, Foxdale	1·10	1·10
494	37p. Coscoroba Swans, Curraghs Wildlife Park	1·40	1·40
	a. Horiz pair. Nos. 494/5	2·75	2·75
495	37p. Whooper ("Trumpeter") Swans, Curraghs Wildlife Park	1·40	1·40
490/5	.. .. *Set of* 6	5·50	5·50

The two designs of each value were printed together, *se-tenant*, in horizontal pairs throughout the sheets with the backgrounds forming composite designs.

118 The Three Kings

119 North African and Italian Campaigns, 1942–43

(Des D. Swinton. Litho Walsall)

1991 (14 Oct). *Christmas. Paper Sculptures. T* **118** *and similar square designs. Multicoloured.* (a) *Sheet stamps. P* 14×14½.

496	16p. Type **118**	50	40
497	20p. Mary with manger	65	70
498	26p. Shepherds with sheep	80	85
499	37p. Choir of angels	1·10	1·10
496/9	.. .. *Set of* 4	2·75	2·75
	(b) Booklet stamps. Self-adhesive. Stamps die-cut		
500	16p. Type **118**	75	75
	a. Booklet pane. Nos. 500×8 and 501×4 ..	10·00	
501	20p. As No. 497	1·00	1·00

(Des A. Theobald. Litho Questa)

1992 (6 Feb). *50th Anniv of Parachute Regiment. T* **119** *and similar horiz designs. Multicoloured. P* 14.

502	23p. Type **119**	75	75
	a. Horiz pair. Nos. 502/3	1·50	1·50
503	23p. D-Day, 1944	75	75
504	28p. Arnhem, 1944	80	80
	a. Horiz pair. Nos. 504/5	1·60	1·60
505	28p. Rhine crossing, 1945	80	80
506	39p. Operations in Near, Middle and Far East, 1945–68	1·25	1·25
	a. Horiz pair. Nos. 506/7	2·50	2·50
507	39p. Liberation of Falkland Islands, 1982 ..	1·25	1·25
502/7	.. .. *Set of* 6	5·00	5·00

The two designs of each value were printed together, *se-tenant*, in horizontal pairs throughout the sheets of 8.

120 Queen Elizabeth II at Coronation, 1953

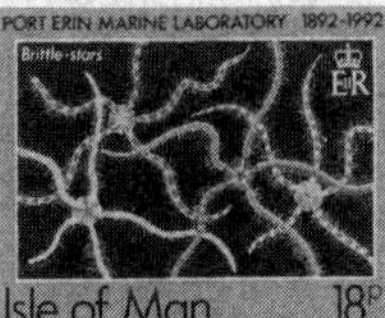

121 Brittle-stars

(Des D. Miller. Litho B.D.T.)

1992 (6 Feb). *40th Anniv of Accession. T* **120** *and similar vert designs. Multicoloured. P* 14.

508	18p. Type **120**	50	50
509	23p. Queen visiting Isle of Man, 1979 ..	60	60
510	28p. Queen in evening dress	70	70
511	33p. Queen visiting Isle of Man, 1989 ..	1·25	1·25
512	39p. Queen arriving for film premiere, 1990	1·40	1·40
508/12	.. .. *Set of* 5	4·00	4·00

(Des Jennifer Toombs. Litho Questa)

1992 (16 Apr). *Centenary of Port Erin Marine Laboratory. T* **121** *and similar horiz designs. Multicoloured. P* 14×14½.
513 18p. Type **121** 50 50
514 23p. Phytoplankton 60 60
515 28p. Atlantic Herring 70 70
516 33p. Great Scallop .. .. 1·25 1·25
517 39p. Dahlia Anemone and Delesseria .. 1·40 1·40
513/17 .. .. *Set of* 5 4·00 4·00

122 The Pilgrim Fathers embarking at Delfshaven

123 Central Pacific Locomotive *Jupiter*, 1869

(Des C. Abbott. Litho Enschedé)

1992 (16 Apr). *Europa. 500th Anniv of Discovery of America by Columbus. T* **122** *and similar square designs. Multicoloured. P* 14×13½.
518 18p. Type **122** 60 60
a. Horiz pair. Nos. 518/19 .. .. 1·25 1·25
519 18p. *Speedwell* leaving Delfshaven .. 60 60
520 28p. *Mayflower* setting sail for America .. 1·00 1·00
a. Horiz pair. Nos. 520/1 .. .. 2·00 2·00
521 28p. *Speedwell* anchored at Dartmouth .. 1·00 1·00
518/21 .. .. *Set of* 4 2·75 2·75
Nos. 518/19 and 520/1 were each printed together, *se-tenant*, in separate sheets, each horizontal pair forming a composite design.
The designs of Nos. 520/1 are after the painting by L. Wilcox.

(Des A. Peck. Litho Enschedé)

1992 (22 May). *Construction of the Union Pacific Railroad, 1866–69. T* **123** *and similar horiz designs. P* 13½×14.
522 33p. Type **123** 95 95
a. Horiz pair. Nos. 522/3 plus label .. 1·90 1·90
b. Booklet pane. Nos. 522/5×2 and **MS**526 10·00
523 33p. Union Pacific locomotive No. 119, 1869 95 95
524 39p. Union Pacific locomotive No. 844, 1992 1·25 1·25
a. Horiz pair. Nos. 524/5 plus label .. 2·50 2·50
525 39p. Union Pacific locomotive No. 3985, 1992 1·25 1·25
522/5 .. .. *Set of* 4 4·00 4·00
MS526 105×78 mm. £1.50, Golden Spike ceremony, 10 May 1869 (60×50 *mm*) .. .. 5·25 5·25
The two designs for each value were printed in small sheets of 10 (2×5) with each horizontal pair separated by a half stamp-size label showing Union Pacific emblem or portraits of Dan and Jack Casement (railroad contractors).
Booklet pane No. 522b contains two blocks of four of Nos. 522/5 with No. **MS**526 between them. Miniature sheets from the booklet show a white margin and line of roulettes at left and right. In the blocks of four each horizontal pair is separated by a half stamp-size label.

124 *King Orry V* in Douglas Harbour

(Des Colleen Corlett. Litho Walsall)

1992 (18 Sept). *Manx Harbours. T* **124** *and similar horiz designs. Multicoloured. P* 14½×14.
527 18p. Type **124** 50 50
528 23p. Castletown 60 60
529 37p. Port St. Mary .. .. 1·25 1·25
530 40p. Ramsey .. .. 1·25 1·25
527/30 .. .. *Set of* 4 3·25 3·25

125 *Saint Eloi* in 1972

126 Stained Glass Window, St. German's Cathedral, Peel

(Des Colleen Corlett. Litho Walsall)

1992 (18 Sept). *"Genova '92" International Thematic Stamp Exhibition. Sheet* 111×68 *mm containing T* **125** *and similar horiz design. Multicoloured. P* 14½×14.
MS531 18p. *King Orry V* in 1992 (as in Type **124**); £1 Type **125** .. .. 3·50 3·50

(Des Colleen Corlett. Litho Questa)

1992 (13 Oct). *Christmas. Manx Churches. T* **126** *and similar vert designs. Multicoloured. P* 14½.
532 17p. Type **126** 50 50
533 22p. Reredos, St. Matthew the Apostle Church, Douglas 70 70
534 28p. Stained glass window, St. George's Church, Douglas 85 85
535 37p. Reredos, St. Mary of the Isle Catholic Church, Douglas .. .. .. 1·00 1·00
536 40p. Stained glass window, Trinity Methodist Church, Douglas .. .. .. 1·10 1·10
532/6 .. .. *Set of* 5 3·75 3·75

127 Mansell on Lap of Honour, British Grand Prix, 1992

(Des A. Theobald. Litho Walsall)

1992 (8 Nov). *Nigel Mansell's Victory in Formula* 1 *World Motor Racing Championship. T* **127** *and similar horiz design. Multicoloured. P* 13½.
537 20p. Type **127** 70 70
538 24p. Mansell in French Grand Prix, 1992 .. 80 80

128 H.M.S. *Amazon* (frigate)

128*a* Manx Red Ensign

128*b* Queen Elizabeth II (hologram)

(Des A. Theobald (1p. to 27p.), J. Nicholson (30p. and 40p. to £1), Colleen Corlett (£2, £5). Litho Enschedé (1p. to £1), Questa (£2) or Walsall (£5) (hologram by Applied Holographics))

1993 (4 Jan)–**97**. *Ships. Horiz designs as T* **128** *and* **128*a/b***. *Multicoloured. P* 13½×13 (1p. *to* £1), 14½ (£2) *or* 14½×14 (£5).
539 1p. Type **128** 10 10
540 2p. *Fingal* (lighthouse tender) 10 10
541 4p. *Sir Winston Churchill* (cadet schooner) 10 10
a. Booklet pane. Nos. 541, 544 and 548, each × 2 (14.5.97) .. .. 2·50
542 5p. *Dar Mlodziezy* (full-rigged cadet ship) .. 10 10
543 20p. *Tynwald I* (paddle-steamer), 1846 .. 40 45
a. Booklet pane. Nos. 543×2 and 547×3 .. 3·00
b. Booklet pane. Nos. 543×4 and 547×6 .. 5·50
544 21p. *Ben Veg* (freighter) 40 45
545 22p. *Waverley* (paddle-steamer) 45 50
546 23p. Royal Yacht *Britannia* 45 50
547 24p. *Francis Drake* (ketch) 50 55
548 25p. *Royal Viking Sky* (liner) 50 55
549 26p. *Lord Nelson* (cadet barque) 55 60
550 27p. *Europa* (liner) 55 60
551 30p. *Snaefell V* (ferry) leaving Ardrossan (15.9.93) 60 65
552 35p. *Seacat* (catamaran ferry) (11.1.96) .. 70 75
553 40p. *Lady of Mann I* (ferry) off Ramsey (15.9.93) 80 85
554 50p. *Mona's Queen II* (paddle ferry) leaving Fleetwood (15.9.93) .. .. .. 1·00 1·10
555 £1 *Queen Elizabeth 2* (liner) and *Mona's Queen V* (ferry) off Liverpool (15.9.93) 2·00 2·10
556 £2 Type **128*a*** (12.1.94) .. .. .. 4·00 4·25
557 £5 Type **128*b*** (5.7.94) .. .. .. 10·00 10·50
539/57 .. .. *Set of* 19 23·00 24·00
In addition to stamp booklets Nos. 543a/b also come from a special booklet sheet of 50 (5×10) which provides either 5 examples of No. 543b or 10 of No. 543a. No. 541a comes from a special booklet sheet of 30 (5×6).
Imprint dates: "1993", Nos. 539/51, 553/5; "1994", Nos. 556/7; "1995", Nos. 543 and 547; "1996", No. 552; "1997", Nos. 541, 544, 548 and 555.
For 4p. 20p. and 24p. in similar designs, but smaller, see Nos. 687/93.
For miniature sheet containing the 23p. see No. **MS**760.

129 No. 1 Motor Car and No. 13 Trailer at Groudle Glen Hotel

(Des A. Theobald. Litho B.D.T.)

1993 (3 Feb). *Centenary of Manx Electric Railway. T* **129** *a[nd] similar horiz designs. Multicoloured. P* 14.
559 20p. Type **129** 50
a. Booklet pane. Nos. 559/62 .. .. 3·00
560 24p. No. 9 Tunnel Car and No. 19 Trailer at Douglas Bay Hotel 75
561 28p. No. 19 Motor Car and No. 59 Royal Trailer Special at Douglas Bay 85
562 39p. No. 33 Motor Car, No. 45 Trailer and No. 13 Van at Derby Castle .. .. 1·25 1
559/62 .. .. *Set of* 4 3·00 3
Booklet pane. No. 559a exists in four versions, which differ in [the] order of the stamps within the block of four and in the informati[on] printed on the pane margins.

130 "Sir Hall Caine" (statue) (Bryan Kneale)

(Des Colleen Corlett. Litho B.D.T.)

1993 (14 Apr). *Europa. Contemporary Art. Works by Bry[an] Kneale. T* **130** *and similar square designs. Multicoloured. P* 14
563 20p. Type **130** 55
a. Horiz pair. Nos. 563/4 .. .. .. 1·10 1
564 20p. "The Brass Bedstead" (painting) .. 55
565 28p. Abstract bronze sculpture 90
a. Horiz pair. Nos. 565/6 .. .. .. 1·75 1·
566 28p. "Polar Bear Skeleton" (drawing) .. 90
563/6 .. .. *Set of* 4 2·50 2·
Nos. 563/4 and 565/6 were each printed together, *se-tenant*, [in] horizontal pairs throughout the sheets.

131 Graham Oates and Bill Marshall (1933 International Six Day Trial) on Ariel Square Four

(Des C. Abbott. Litho Walsall)

1993 (3 June). *Manx Motor Cycling Events. T* **131** *and simi[lar] horiz designs. Multicoloured. P* 13½×14.
567 20p. Type **131** 50
568 24p. Sergeant Geoff Duke (1947 Royal Signals Display Team) on Triumph 3T Twin .. 70
569 28p. Denis Parkinson (1953 Senior Manx Grand Prix) on Manx Norton 90
570 33p. Richard Swallow (1991 Junior Classic MGP) on Aermacchi .. .. .. 1·25 1·
571 39p. Steve Colley (1992 Scottish Six Day Trial) on Beta Zero .. .. 1·40 1·
567/71 .. .. *Set of* 5 4·25 4·
MS572 165×120 mm. Nos. 567/71 .. .. 4·25 4·

132 *Inachis io* (Peacock)

133 Children decorating Christmas Tree

(Des Colleen Corlett. Litho Questa)

1993 (15 Sept). *Butterflies. T* **132** *and similar square design[s]. Multicoloured. P* 14½.
573 24p. Type **132** 80
a. Horiz strip of 5. Nos. 573/7 .. .. 3·50
574 24p. *Argynnis aglaja* (Dark Green Fritillary) 80
575 24p. *Cynthia cardui* (Painted Lady) 80
576 24p. *Celastrina argiolus* (Holly Blue) .. 80
577 24p. *Vanessa atalanta* (Red Admiral) .. 80
573/7 .. .. *Set of* 5 3·50 3·
Nos. 573/7 were printed together, *se-tenant*, both horizonta[lly] and vertically within the sheet of 20 (5×4).
Examples of Nos. 573/7 sold at "Philakorea '94" and "Singp[ex] '94" come with commemorative cachets on the bottom margin.

(Des Christine Haworth. Litho Questa)

1993 (12 Oct). *Christmas. T* **133** *and similar vert design[s]. Multicoloured. P* 14.
578 19p. Type **133** 55
579 23p. Girl with snowman 65
580 28p. Boy opening presents 80
581 39p. Girl with teddy bear .. .. .. 1·10 1·
582 40p. Children with toboggan .. .. 1·10 1·
578/82 .. .. *Set of* 5 3·75 3·

134 White-throated Robin

(Des Colleen Corlett. Litho B.D.T.)

94 (18 Feb). *Calf of Man Bird Observatory. T* **134** *and similar multicoloured designs. P* 14.

3 20p. Type **134** 60 60
a. Pair. Nos. 583/4 .. .. 1·25 1·25
4 20p. Black-eared Wheatear 60 60
5 24p. Goldcrest 90 90
a. Pair. Nos. 585/6 .. .. 1·75 1·75
6 24p. Northern Oriole 90 90
7 30p. Common Kingfisher .. .. 1·00 1·00
a. Pair. Nos. 587/8 .. .. 2·00 2·00
8 30p. Hoopoe .. .. 1·00 1·00
3/8 .. .. *Set of* 6 4·25 4·25
S589 100×71 mm. £1 Magpie (51½×61 *mm*). P 13½×13 .. .. 3·00 3·00

Nos. 583/4, 585/6 and 587/8 were printed together, *se-tenant*, in rizontal and vertical pairs throughout the sheets of 10.

No. **MS**589 also commemorates the "Hong Kong '94" philatelic hibition.

135 Gaiety Theatre, Douglas

(Des Colleen Corlett. Litho Cartor)

94 (18 Feb). *Booklet Stamps. Manx Tourism Centenary. T* **135** *and similar horiz designs. Multicoloured. P* 13½.

0 24p. Type **135** 60 60
a. Booklet pane. Nos. 590/9 with margins all round .. .. 5·50
1 24p. Sports 60 60
2 24p. Artist at work and yachts racing .. 60 60
3 24p. TT Races and British Aerospace Hawk T.1's of Red Arrows display team .. 60 60
4 24p. Musical instruments 60 60
5 24p. Laxey Wheel and Manx cat 60 60
6 24p. Tower of Refuge, Douglas, with bucket and spade 60 60
7 24p. Cyclist 60 60
8 24p. Tynwald Day and classic car 60 60
9 24p. Santa Mince Pie train, Groudle Glen .. 60 60
0/9 .. .. *Set of* 10 5·50 5·50

Nos. 590/9 were only issued in £2.40 stamp booklets.

136 *Eubranchus tricolor* (sea slug)

(Des Jennifer Toombs. Litho Enschedé)

94 (5 May). *Europa. Discoveries of Edward Forbes (marine biologist). T* **136** *and similar horiz designs. Multicoloured. P* 13×14½.

0 20p. Type **136** 50 50
a. Horiz strip of 3. Nos. 600/2 .. .. 1·50
1 20p. *Loligo forbesii* (Common Squid) .. 50 50
2 20p. Edward Forbes and signature 50 50
3 30p. *Solaster moretonis* (fossil starfish) .. 90 90
a. Horiz strip of 3. Nos. 603/5 .. .. 2·75
4 30p. *Adamsia carciniopados* (anemone) on Hermit Crab 90 90
5 30p. *Solaster endeca* (starfish) 90 90
0/5 .. .. *Set of* 6 3·75 3·75

Nos. 600/2 and 603/5 were printed together, *se-tenant*, in rizontal strips of 3 throughout the sheets of 15.

137 Maj-Gen. Bedell Smith and Naval Landing Force including *Ben-My-Chree IV* (ferry)

(Des A. Theobald. Litho Questa)

94 (6 June). *50th Anniv of D-Day. T* **137** *and similar horiz designs. Multicoloured. P* 14.

6 4p. Type **137** 15 15
a. Horiz pair. Nos. 606/7 .. .. .. 30 30
7 4p. Admiral Ramsay and naval ships including *Victoria* and *Lady of Mann* (ferries) .. 15 15
608 20p. Gen. Montgomery and British landings 70 70
a. Horiz pair. Nos. 608/9 .. .. 1·40 1·40
609 20p. Lt-Gen. Dempsey and 2nd Army landings 70 70
610 30p. Air Chief Marshal Leigh-Mallory and U.S. paratroops and aircraft .. .. .. 1·00 1·00
a. Horiz pair. Nos. 610/11 .. .. .. 2·00 2·00
611 30p. Air Chief Marshal Tedder and British paratroops and aircraft .. .. .. 1·00 1·00
612 41p. Lt-Gen. Bradley and U.S. 1st Army landings .. .. 1·25 1·25
a. Horiz pair. Nos. 612/13 .. .. .. 2·50 2·50
613 41p. Gen. Eisenhower and American landings 1·25 1·25
606/13 .. .. *Set of* 8 5·50 5·50

The two designs for each value were printed together, *se-tenant*, in horizontal pairs throughout sheets of 8.

138 Postman Pat, Jess and Ffinlo at Sea Terminal, Douglas

139 Cycling

(Des Colleen Corlett. Litho B.D.T.)

1994 (14 Sept). *Postman Pat visits the Isle of Man. T* **138** *and similar multicoloured designs. P* 15×14.

614 1p. Type **138** 10 10
a. Booklet pane. No. 614×2 with margins all round 20
615 20p. Laxey Wheel 60 60
a. Booklet pane. No. 615×2 with margins all round .. .. 1·25
616 24p. Cregneash 80 80
a. Booklet pane. No. 616×2 with margins all round .. .. 1·60
617 30p. Manx Electric Railway trains 90 90
a. Booklet pane. No. 617×2 with margins all round .. .. 1·75
618 36p. Peel Harbour .. .. 1·10 1·10
a. Booklet pane. No. 618×2 with margins all round .. .. 2·25
619 41p. Douglas Promenade .. .. 1·25 1·25
a. Booklet pane. No. 619×2 with margins all round .. .. 2·50
614/19 .. .. *Set of* 6 4·25 4·25
MS620 110×85 mm. £1 Postman Pat (25×39 *mm*). P 13 .. .. 3·00 3·00

Examples of No. **MS**620 from stamp booklets show a line of roulettes at left.

(Des D. Miller. Litho Walsall)

1994 (11 Oct). *Centenary of International Olympic Committee. T* **139** *and similar square designs. Multicoloured. P* 14×14½.

621 10p. Type **139** 30 30
622 20p. Downhill skiing 55 55
623 24p. Swimming 70 70
624 35p. Hurdling 95 95
625 48p. Centenary logo .. .. 1·40 1·40
621/5 .. .. *Set of* 5 3·50 3·50

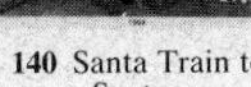

140 Santa Train to Santon

141 Foden Steam Wagon, Highway Board Depot, Douglas

(Des Colleen Corlett. Litho Cartor)

1994 (11 Oct). *Christmas. Father Christmas in the Isle of Man. T* **140** *and similar multicoloured designs. P* 13½×14 (23*p.*) *or* 14×13½ (*others*).

626 19p. Type **140** 50 50
627 23p. Father Christmas and Postman Pat on mini tractor, Douglas (*vert*) 70 70
628 60p. Father Christmas and majorettes in sleigh, Port St. Mary .. .. 1·60 1·60
626/8 .. .. *Set of* 3 2·50 2·50

(Des A. Peck. Litho Enschedé)

1995 (8 Feb). *Steam Traction Engines. T* **141** *and similar horiz designs. Multicoloured. P* 13½×13.

629 20p. Type **141** 60 60
630 24p. Clayton & Shuttleworth and Fowler engines pulling dead whale 70 70
631 30p. Wallis and Steevens engine at Ramsey Harbour 85 85
632 35p. Marshall engine with threshing machine, Ballarhenny .. .. 1·10 1·10
633 41p. Marshall convertible steam roller .. 1·25 1·25
629/33 .. .. *Set of* 5 4·00 4·00

COVER PRICES

Cover factors are quoted at the beginning of each country for most issues to 1945. An explanation of the system can be found on page x. The factors quoted do not, however, apply to philatelic covers.

142 Car No. 2 and First Train, 1895

(Des A. Theobald. Litho B.D.T.)

1995 (8 Feb). *Centenary of Snaefell Mountain Railway. T* **142** *and similar horiz designs. Multicoloured. P* 14.

634 20p. Type **142** 60 60
a. Booklet pane. Nos. 634/7 with margins all round .. .. 3·00
635 24p. Car No. 4 in green livery and Car No. 3 in Laxey Valley 70 70
636 35p. Car No. 6 and Car No. 5 in 1971 .. 95 95
637 42p. Goods Car No. 7 and *Caledonia* steam locomotive pulling construction train .. 1·10 1·10
634/7 .. .. *Set of* 4 3·00 3·00
MS638 110×87 mm. £1 Passenger car and Argus char-a-banc at Bungalow Hotel (60×37 *mm*) .. 3·00 3·00
a. Booklet pane. As No. **MS**638 with additional margins all round showing further inscriptions at right and left .. 3·00

Booklet pane No. 634a exists in three versions, which differ in the order of the stamps within the block of four.

No. **MS**638a from stamp booklets shows a white margin, description of the design and line of roulettes at left and an additional inscription, "1895. CENTENARY SNAEFELL MOUNTAIN RAILWAY. 1995", vertically in the margin at right.

143 Peace Doves forming Wave and Tower of Refuge, Douglas Bay

144 Spitfire, Tank and Medals

(Des Colleen Corlett and M. Magleby (20p.), Colleen Corlett (30p.). Litho Enschedé)

1995 (28 Apr). *Europa. Peace and Freedom. T* **143** *and similar vert design. Multicoloured. P* 14×13½.

639 20p. Type **143** 50 50
640 30p. Peace dove breaking barbed wire .. 75 75

(Des A. Theobald. Litho B.D.T.)

1995 (8 May). *50th Anniv of End of Second World War. T* **144** *and similar horiz designs. Multicoloured. P* 14.

641 10p. Type **144** 30 30
a. Horiz pair. Nos. 641/2 .. .. .. 60 60
642 10p. Typhoon, anti-aircraft gun and medals 30 30
643 20p. Lancaster, escort carrier and medals 55 55
a. Horiz pair. Nos. 643/4 .. .. .. 1·10 1·10
644 20p. U.S. Navy aircraft, jungle patrol and medals 55 55
645 24p. Celebrations in Parliament Square .. 70 70
a. Horiz pair. Nos. 645/6 .. .. .. 1·40 1·40
646 24p. V.E. Day bonfire 70 70
647 40p. Street party .. .. 1·10 1·10
a. Horiz pair. Nos. 647/8 .. .. .. 2·25 2·25
648 40p. King George VI and Queen Elizabeth on Isle of Man in July 1945 .. .. .. 1·10 1·10
641/8 .. .. *Set of* 8 4·75 4·75

The two designs for each value were printed together, *se-tenant*, in horizontal pairs throughout sheets of 8.

145 Reg Parnell in Maserati "4 CLT", 1951

(Des N. Sykes. Litho Questa)

1995 (8 May). *90th Anniv of Motor Racing on Isle of Man. T* **145** *and similar multicoloured designs. P* 14.

649 20p. Type **145** 60 60
650 24p. Stirling Moss in Frazer Nash, 1951 .. 75 75
651 30p. Richard Seaman in Delage, 1936 .. 85 85
652 36p. Prince Bira in ERA R2B "Romulus", 1937 .. .. 1·00 1·00
653 41p. Kenelm Guinness in Sunbeam 1, 1914 1·10 1·10
654 42p. Freddie Dixon in Riley, 1934 .. 1·10 1·10
649/54 .. .. *Set of* 6 4·75 4·75
MS655 103×73 mm. £1 John Napier in Arrol Johnston, 1905 (47×58 *mm*) .. .. .. 2·50 2·50

146 Thomas the Tank Engine and Bertie Bus being Unloaded

147 *Amanita muscaria*

(Des O. Bell. Litho B.D.T.)

1995 (15 Aug). *50th Anniv of Thomas the Tank Engine Stories by Revd. Awdry.* "Thomas the Tank Engine's Dream". *T* **146** *and similar horiz designs. Multicoloured. P* 14.
656 20p. Type **146** 60 60
a. Booklet pane. Nos. 656/7 with margins all round .. .. 1·25
b. Booklet pane. Nos. 656 and 661 with margins all round .. .. .. 1·75
657 24p. Mail train 75 75
a. Booklet pane. Nos. 657/8 with margins all round .. .. 1·50
658 30p. Bertie and engines at Ballasalla .. 85 85
a. Booklet pane. Nos. 658/9 with margins all round .. .. 1·75
659 36p. *Viking*, the diesel engine, Port Erin .. 1·00 1·00
a. Booklet pane. Nos. 659/60 with margins all round .. .. 2·00
660 41p. Thomas and railcar at Snaefell summit 1·10 1·10
a. Booklet pane. Nos. 660/1 with margins all round .. .. 2·25
661 45p. Engines racing past Laxey Wheel .. 1·25 1·25
656/61 .. .. *Set of* 6 5·00 5·00

(Des Colleen Corlett. Litho Enschedé)

1995 (1 Sept). *Fungi. T* **147** *and similar multicoloured designs. P* 13½.
662 20p. Type **147** 50 50
663 24p. *Boletus edulis* 65 65
664 30p. *Coprinus disseminatus* 85 85
665 35p. *Pleurotus ostreatus* 95 95
666 45p. *Geastrum triplex* .. .. 1·50 1·50
662/6 .. .. *Set of* 5 4·00 4·00
MS667 100×71 mm. £1 Shaggy Ink Cap and Bee Orchid (50×59 *mm*) .. .. 3·00 3·00
No. **MS**667 is inscribed "Singapore World Stamp Exhibition 1st–10th September 1995" on the sheet margin.

148 St. Catherine's Church, Port Erin

149 Langness Lighthouse

(Des Colleen Corlett. Litho B.D.T.)

1995 (10 Oct). *Christmas. T* **148** *and similar square designs. Multicoloured. P* 14.
668 19p. Type **148** 50 50
669 23p. European Robin on Holly branch .. 60 60
670 42p. St. Peter's Church and wild flowers .. 1·10 1·10
671 50p. Hedgehog hibernating under farm machinery .. .. 1·40 1·40
668/71 .. .. *Set of* 4 3·25 3·25

(Des D. Swinton. Litho Questa)

1996 (24 Jan). *Lighthouses. T* **149** *and similar multicoloured designs. P* 14.
672 20p. Type **149** 55 55
a. Booklet pane. No. 672×4 with margins all round .. .. 1·75
673 24p. Point of Ayre lighthouse (*horiz*) .. 65 65
a. Booklet pane. No. 673×4 with margins all round .. .. 2·25
674 30p. Chicken Rock lighthouse 85 85
a. Booklet pane. Nos. 674 and 676 each × 2 with margins all round .. .. 3·25
675 36p. Calf of Man lighthouse (*horiz*) .. .. 1·00 1·00
a. Booklet pane. Nos. 675 and 677 each × 2 with margins all round .. .. 3·50
676 41p. Douglas Head lighthouse .. .. 1·10 1·10
677 42p. Maughold Head lighthouse (*horiz*) .. 1·10 1·10
672/7 .. .. *Set of* 6 4·75 4·75

150 White Manx Cat and Celtic Interlaced Ribbons

151 Douglas Borough Arms

(Des Nancy Corkish. Litho B.D.T.)

1996 (14 Mar). *Manx Cats. T* **150** *and similar multicoloured designs. P* 14.
678 20p. Type **150** 60 60
679 24p. Cat and Union Jack ribbons 75 75
680 36p. Cat on rug in German colours, mouse and Brandenburg Gate .. .. 1·00 1·00
681 42p. Cat, U.S.A. flag and Statue of Liberty .. 1·10 1·10
682 48p. Cat, map of Australia and kangaroo .. 1·25 1·25
678/82 .. .. *Set of* 5 4·25 4·25
MS683 100×71 mm. £1.50, Cat with kittens (51×61 *mm*). P 13½×13 .. .. 4·00 4·00
For No. **MS**683 with "CAPEX '96" logo see No. **MS**712.

(Des Colleen Corlett. Litho B.D.T.)

1996 (14 Mar). *Centenary of Douglas Borough. Self-adhesive. Die-cut perf* 9×10.
684 **151** (20p.) multicoloured 50 50
No. 684 was printed in sheets of 40, each stamp surrounded by white backing paper divided by roulettes. The actual stamps are separated from the backing paper by die-cut perforations. It was initially sold for 20p. and was only valid for postage within the Isle of Man.

(Des A. Theobald. Litho Walsall)

1996 (21 Apr). *Ships. As Nos.* 541, 543 *and* 547, *but smaller,* 21×18 *mm. Multicoloured. P* 14.
687 4p. *Sir Winston Churchill* (cadet schooner) 10 10
a. Booklet pane. Nos. 687, 689 and 693, each × 2 .. .. 2·50
689 20p. *Tynwald I* (paddle-steamer), 1846 .. 60 60
693 24p. *Francis Drake* (ketch) 75 75
687/93 .. .. *Set of* 3 1·25 1·25
The 20p. and 24p. show the positions of the face value and Queen's head reversed.

152 Princess Anne (President, Save the Children Fund) and Children

(Des D. Miller. Litho B.D.T.)

1996 (21 Apr). *Europa. Famous Women. T* **152** *and similar horiz design. Multicoloured. P* 14.
701 24p. Type **152** 60 60
702 30p. Queen Elizabeth II and people of the Commonwealth 90 90
The background designs of Nos. 701/2 continue onto the vertical sheet margins.

153 Alec Bennett

154 National Poppy Appeal Trophy

(Des J. Dunne. Litho Questa)

1996 (30 May). *Tourist Trophy Motorcycle Races. Irish Winners. T* **153** *and similar multicoloured designs. P* 14.
703 20p. Type **153** 65 65
704 24p. Stanley Woods 70 70
705 45p. Artie Bell .. .. 1·25 1·25
706 60p. Joey and Robert Dunlop .. .. .. 1·50 1·50
703/6 .. .. *Set of* 4 3·75 3·75
MS707 100×70 mm. £1 R.A.F. Red Arrows display team (*vert*) .. .. 2·50 2·50

(Des C. Abbott. Litho B.D.T.)

1996 (8 June). *75th Anniv of Royal British Legion. T* **154** *and similar square designs. Multicoloured. P* 14.
708 20p. Type **154** 60 60
709 24p. Manx War Memorial, Braddan 65 65
710 42p. Poppy appeal collection box .. .. 1·10 1·10
711 75p. Royal British Legion badge .. .. 2·10 2·10
708/11 .. .. *Set of* 4 4·00 4·00

1996 (8 June). *"CAPEX '96" International Stamp Exhibition, Toronto. No.* **MS**683 *additionally inscribed with "CAPEX '96" exhibition logo on sheet margin.*
MS712 100×71 mm. £1.50 Cat with kittens (51×61 *mm*) .. .. 3·50 3·50

155 U.N.I.C.E.F. Projects in Mexico

156 Labrador

(Des C. Abbott. Litho Enschedé)

1996 (18 Sept). *50th Anniv of U.N.I.C.E.F. T* **155** *and simi horiz designs. Multicoloured. P* 13½×14.
713 24p. Type **155** 50
a. Horiz pair. Nos. 713/14 .. .. .. 1·00 1·
714 24p. Projects in Sri Lanka 50
715 30p. Projects in Colombia 60
a. Horiz pair. Nos. 715/16 .. .. .. 1·25 1
716 30p. Projects in Zambia 60
717 42p. Projects in Afghanistan 85
a. Horiz pair. Nos. 717/18 .. .. .. 1·75 1·
718 42p. Projects in Vietnam 85
713/18 .. .. *Set of* 6 3·75 3·
Nos. 713/14, 715/16 and 717/18 were each printed togeth *se-tenant*, in horizontal pairs throughout the sheets.

(Des Colleen Corlett. Litho Questa)

1996 (18 Sept). *Dogs. T* **156** *and similar multicoloured desig P* 14½.
719 20p. Type **156** 55
a. Booklet pane. No. 719×4 with margins all round .. .. 1·60
720 24p. Border Collie 65
a. Booklet pane. No. 720×4 with margins all round .. .. 2·00
721 31p. Dalmatian 75
a. Booklet pane. Nos. 721/4 with margins all round .. .. 3·50
722 38p. Mongrel 90
723 43p. English Setter .. .. 1·10 1·
724 63p. Alsatian .. .. 1·60 1
719/24 .. .. *Set of* 6 5·00 5
MS725 100×71 mm. £1.20, Labrador guide dog and working Border Collie (38×50 *mm*). P 13½×14 .. 3·00 3·
a. Booklet pane. As No. **MS**725, but with additional white margins all round separated by roulette .. .. 3·00

157 "Snowman and Pine Trees" (David Bennett)

158 Primroses and Cashtyl ny Ard

(Adapted Colleen Corlett. Litho Walsall)

1996 (2 Nov). *Christmas. Children's Paintings. T* **157** *and simi square designs. Multicoloured. P* 14×14½.
726 19p. Type **157** 50
727 23p. "Three-legged Father Christmas" (Louis White) 65
728 50p. "Family around Christmas Tree" (Robyn Whelan) .. .. 1·25 1·
729 75p. "Father Christmas in Sleigh" (Claire Bradley) .. .. 1·75 1·
726/9 .. .. *Set of* 4 3·75 3·

(Des Colleen Corlett. Litho B.D.T.)

1997 (12 Feb). *Spring in Man. T* **158** *and similar square desig Multicoloured. P* 14.
730 20p. Type **158** 40
731 24p. Lochtan sheep and lambs 50
732 43p. Daffodils, duck and ducklings 85
733 63p. Dabchick with young and frog on lily pad 1·25 1·
730/3 .. .. *Set of* 4 3·00 3·

159 Barn Owl

160 Moddey Dhoo, Peel Castle

(Des J. Paul. Litho B.D.T.)

1997 (12 Feb). *Owls. T* **159** *and similar vert desig Multicoloured. P* 14.
734 20p. Type **159** 60
a. Booklet pane. No. 734×4 with margins all round .. .. 1·60
735 24p. Short-eared Owl 75
a. Booklet pane. No. 735×4 with margins all round .. .. 2·00
736 31p. Long-eared Owl 90
a. Booklet pane. Nos. 736/9 with margins all round .. .. 3·50
737 36p. Little Owl .. .. 1·10 1
738 43p. Snowy Owl .. .. 1·25 1
739 56p. Tawny Owl .. .. 1·50 1
734/9 .. .. *Set of* 6 5·50 5
MS740 100×71 mm. £1.20, Long-eared Owl (*different*) (51×60 *mm*). P 13 .. .. .. 3·75 3
a. Booklet pane. As No. **MS**740 but with additional white margins all round and with line of roulettes at left .. .. 3·75
No. **MS**740 includes the "HONG KONG '97" Internatio Stamp Exhibition Logo on the sheet margin.

(Des Colleen Corlett. Litho Enschedé)

97 (24 Apr). *Europa. Tales and Legends. T* **160** *and similar horiz designs. Multicoloured. P* 13½×14.
1 21p. Type **160** 50 50
2 25p. Fairies in tree and cottage 60 60
3 31p. Fairies at Fairy bridge 70 70
4 36p. Giant Finn MacCooil and Calf of Man 80 80
5 37p. The Buggane of St. Trinian's 85 85
6 43p. Fynoderee and farm .. .. .. 1·00 1·00
1/6 .. .. *Set of* 6 4·00 4·00
Nos. 742/3 include the "EUROPA" emblem.

161 Sopwith Tabloid

(Des R. Carter. Litho Questa)

97 (24 Apr). *Manx Aircraft. T* **161** *and similar horiz designs. Multicoloured. P* 14.
7 21p. Type **161** 50 50
a. Horiz pair. Nos. 747/8 .. .. .. 1·00 1·00
8 21p. Grumman Tiger (winner of 1996 Schneider Trophy) 50 50
9 25p. BAe ATP (15th anniv of Manx Airlines) 60 60
a. Horiz pair. Nos. 749/50 .. .. 1·25 1·25
0 25p. BAe 146-200 (15th anniv of Manx Airlines) 60 60
1 31p. Boeing 757 200 (largest aircraft to land on Isle of Man) 75 75
a. Horiz pair. Nos. 751/2 .. .. .. 1·50 1·50
2 31p. Farman Biplane (1st Manx flight, 1911) 75 75
3 36p. Spitfire 90 90
a. Horiz pair. Nos. 753/4 .. .. .. 1·75 1·75
4 36p. Hawker Hurricane 90 90
7/54 .. .. *Set of* 8 5·00 5·00
Nos. 747/8, 749/50, 751/2 and 753/4 were each printed together, *-tenant*, in horizontal pairs, the backgrounds forming composite signs.
No. 752 is inscribed "EARMAN BIPLANE" in error.

162 14th Hole, Ramsey Golf Club

(Des D. Swinton. Litho Questa)

97 (29 May). *Golf. T* **162** *and similar multicoloured designs. P* 14.
5 21p. Type **162** 50 50
a. Booklet pane. No. 755×3 with margins all round .. .. 1·50
6 25p. 15th Hole, King Edward Bay Golf and Country Club 60 60
a. Booklet pane. No. 756×3 with margins all round .. .. 1·75
7 43p. 17th Hole, Rowany Golf Club .. .. 1·10 1·10
a. Booklet pane. Nos. 757/8 each × 2 with margins all round .. .. .. 4·00
8 50p. 8th Hole, Castletown Golf Links .. 1·50 1·50
5/8 .. .. *Set of* 4 3·25 3·25
S759 100×71 mm. £1.30, Golf ball (*circular, diameter 39 mm*) .. .. 3·00 3·00
a. Booklet pane. As No. **MS**759, but with additional white margins all round .. 3·00
No. **MS**759 includes the "Pacific 97" International Stamp hibition logo on the sheet margin.

(Litho Walsall)

97 (1 July). *Return of Hong Kong to China. Sheet* 130×90 *mm, containing design as No.* 546 *with changed imprint date. Multicoloured. W* w **14**. *P* 13×13½.
S760 23p. Royal Yacht *Britannia* .. .. 1·00 1·00

163 Steve Colley

164 Angel and Shepherd

(Des R. Organ. Litho Cartor)

97 (17 Sept). *F.I.M. "Trial des Nations" Motorcycle Team Trials. T* **163** *and similar multicoloured design. P* 13½.
1 21p. Type **163** 50 50
2 25p. Steve Saunders (*vert*) 60 60
3 37p. Sammy Miller (*vert*) .. .. .. 1·00 1·00
4 44p. Don Smith .. .. 1·25 1·25
1/4 .. .. *Set of* 4 3·00 3·00

(Des Jennifer Toombs. Litho B.D.T.)

1997 (3 Nov). *Christmas. T* **164** *and similar multicoloured designs. P* 14.
765 20p. Type **164** 55 55
766 24p. Angel and King 70 70
767 63p. The Nativity (54×39 *mm*) .. .. 1·50 1·50
765/7 .. .. *Set of* 3 2·50 2·50

165 Engagement of Princess Elizabeth and Lieut. Philip Mountbatten, 1947

(Des Colleen Corlett. Litho and die-stamped Questa)

1997 (3 Nov). *Golden Wedding of Queen Elizabeth and Prince Philip. T* **165** *and similar vert designs. Multicoloured (except No.* 768). *P* 14×14½.
768 50p. Type **165** (sepia and gold) .. .. 1·25 1·25
a. Strip of 4. Nos. 768/71 .. .. .. 4·50
769 50p. Wedding photograph, 1947 .. .. 1·25 1·25
770 50p. At Ascot, 1952 .. .. .. 1·25 1·25
771 50p. Golden Wedding photograph, 1997 .. 1·25 1·25
768/71 .. .. *Set of* 4 4·50 4·50
MS772 100×72 mm. £1 Queen Elizabeth and Prince Philip at Peel, 1989 (47×58 *mm*). P 14 .. .. 3·00 3·00
Nos. 768/71 were printed together, *se-tenant*, as horizontal or vertical strips of 4 throughout the sheet of 16.

166 Shamrock

167 Queen Elizabeth II and Queen Elizabeth the Queen Mother

(Des Colleen Corlett (1p. to £1). Litho Cartor (£2.50) or Walsall (others))

1998 (12 Feb–2 July). *Flowers. Vert designs as T* **166**, *and T* **167**. *Multicoloured. P* 13 (1, 2, 10, 20, 30*p.*) *or* 13×13½ (*others*).
773 1p. Bearded Iris (2 July) 10 10
774 2p. Daisy (2 July) 10 10
775 4p. Type **166** 10 10
a. Booklet pane. Nos. 775 and 778/9 each × 2 2·00
776 10p. Oriental Poppy (2 July) 20 25
777 20p. Heath Spotted Orchid (2 July) 40 45
778 21p. Cushag 40 45
779 25p. Princess of Wales Rose 50 55
780 30p. Fuchsia "Lady Thumb" (2 July) 60 65
781 50p. Daffodil .. .. 1·00 1·10
782 £1 Spear Thistle .. .. 2·00 2·10
790 £2.50, Type **167** (2 July) .. .. .. 5·00 5·25
773/90 .. .. *Set of* 11 10·00 11·00

168 Viking Figurehead

169 Bottle-nosed Dolphins

(Des A. Bell. Litho B.D.T.)

1998 (14 Feb). *Viking Longships. T* **168** *and similar vert designs. Multicoloured. P* 14.
793 21p. Type **168** 40 45
794 25p. Viking longship at sea 50 55
795 31p. Viking longship on beach 60 65
796 75p. Stern of ship .. .. 1·50 1·60
793/6 .. .. *Set of* 4 3·00 3·25
MS797 100×71 mm. £1 Viking ship at Peel Castle 2·00 2·10

(Des J. Paul. Litho Questa)

1998 (14 Mar). *U.N.E.S.C.O. International Year of the Ocean. T* **169** *and similar horiz designs. Multicoloured. P* 14.
798 10p. Type **169** 20 25
a. Booklet pane. Nos. 798/9, each × 3 and 3 labels with margins all round .. .. 1·75
b. Booklet pane. Nos. 798/9, 800/2 each × 2 and 1 central label with margins all round 3·50
799 21p. Basking Shark 40 45
800 25p. Front view of Basking Shark 50 55
801 31p. Minke Whale 60 65
802 63p. Killer Whale and calf .. .. .. 1·25 1·40
798/802 .. .. *Set of* 5 3·00 3·25

170 Locomotive No. 12 *Hutchinson*

(Des A. Peck. Litho Questa)

1998 (2 May). *125th Anniv of Isle of Man Steam Railway. T* **170** *and similar horiz designs. Multicoloured. P* 14½×14.
803 21p. Type **170** 40 45
a. Booklet pane. Nos. 803/6 with margins all round .. .. 2·75
804 25p. Locomotive No. 10 *G. H. Wood* 50 55
805 31p. Locomotive No. 11 *Maitland* 60 65
806 63p. Locomotive No. 4 *Loch* .. .. .. 1·25 1·40
803/6 .. .. *Set of* 4 2·75 3·00
MS807 119×54 mm. 25p. Pillar box and train at Douglas Station; £1 Locomotive No. 1 *Sutherland* 2·50 2·75
a. Booklet pane. As No. **MS**807 with additional margins showing diagram all round .. .. 2·50
Booklet pane No. 803a exists in two versions, which differ in the order of the stamps within the block of four.

171 Purple Helmets Display Team

172 Princess Diana wearing Protective Clothing, Angola

(Des The Agency. Litho B.D.T.)

1998 (1 June). *Isle of Man T.T. Races and 50th Anniv of Honda (manufacturer). T* **171** *and similar horiz designs. Multicoloured. P* 14.
808 21p. Type **171** 40 45
809 25p. Joey Dunlop 50 55
810 31p. Dave Molyneux 60 65
811 43p. Naomi Taniguchi 85 90
812 63p. Mike Hailwood .. .. 1·25 1·40
808/12 .. .. *Set of* 5 3·50 4·00

(Litho Cartor)

1998 (19 June). *Diana, Princess of Wales Commemoration. T* **172** *and similar vert designs. Multicoloured. P* 13½×13.
813 25p. Type **172** 50 55
a. Strip of 4. Nos. 813/16 .. .. .. 2·00
814 25p. Receiving award from United Cerebral Palsy Charity, New York, 1995 .. 50 55
815 25p. With children, South Korea, 1992 .. 50 55
816 25p. Wearing blue jacket, July 1993 .. 50 55
813/16 .. .. *Set of* 4 2·00 2·10
Nos. 813/16 were printed together, *se-tenant*, both horizontally and vertically, within the sheet of 16.

173 Tynwald Day Ceremony

(Des. M. Thompson. Litho Cartor)

1998 (2 July). *Europa. Festivals. T* **173** *and similar horiz design. Multicoloured. P* 13×13½.
817 25p. Type **173** 50 60
818 30p. Traditional dancers, Tynwald Fair .. 60 65

174 Father Christmas at North Pole

175 Large Oval Pillar Box, Kirk Onchan

(Des A. Bell. Litho Enschedé)

1998 (25 Sept). *Christmas. "A Very Special Delivery". T* **174** *and similar horiz designs. Multicoloured. P* 14½×14.
819 20p. Type **174** 40 45
820 24p. Father Christmas checking list 50 55
821 30p. Flying over Spring Valley Sorting Office 60 65
822 43p. Passing through Baldrine village .. 85 90
823 63p. Father Christmas delivering presents .. 1·25 1·40
819/23 .. .. *Set of* 5 3·50 4·00

(Des The Agency Ltd. Litho Walsall)

1999 (4 Mar). *Local Post Boxes. T* **175** *and similar vert designs. Multicoloured. P* 14.

824	10p. Type **175**	20	25
825	20p. Wall box, Ballaterson	40	45
826	21p. King Edward VII pillar box, Laxey Station	45	50
827	25p. Wall box, Spaldrick	50	55
828	44p. Small oval pillar box, Derby Road, Douglas	90	95
829	63p. Wall box, Baldrine Station	1·25	1·40
824/9	*Set of* 6	3·50	4·00

176 Cottage, Ballaglass Glen

177 *Ann and James Ritchie*, Ramsey

(Des Julia Ashby-Smyth. Litho B.D.T.)

1999 (4 Mar). *Europa. Parks and Gardens. T* **176** *and similar vert design. Multicoloured. P* 14.

830	25p. Type **176**	50	55
831	30p. Glen Maye Waterfall	60	65

(Des Mainstream Media (No. **MS**839), R. Tomlinson (others). Litho Questa)

1999 (4 Mar). *175th Anniv of Royal National Lifeboat Institution. T* **177** *and similar multicoloured designs. P* 14.

832	21p. Type **177**	45	50
	a. Booklet pane. Nos. 832/5 and 837, plus four printed labels, with margins all round	3·50	
	b. Booklet pane. Nos. 832/4, 836 and 838, plus four printed labels, with margins all round	3·50	
833	25p. *Sir William Hillary*, Douglas	50	55
834	37p. *Ruby Clery*, Peel	75	80
835	43p. Inshore lifeboat, Port Erin	85	90
836	43p. 1974 150th Anniv 8p. stamp	85	90
837	56p. *Gough Ritchie II*, Port St. Mary	1·10	1·25
838	56p. 1991 Manx Lifeboats 21p. stamp	1·10	1·25
832/8	*Set of* 7	5·50	5·75
MS839	100×70 mm. £1 Sir William Hillary (founder) (37×50 *mm*). P 13½×14	2·00	2·10
	a. Booklet pane. As No. **MS**839, but with additional margins showing lifeboats all round	2·00	

Nos. 836 and 838 were only available in £4.64 stamp booklets.

No. **MS**839 includes the "Australia '99" World Stamp Exhibition emblem on the sheet margin.

STAMP BOOKLETS

For a full listing of Isle of Man stamp booklets see *Collect Channel Islands and Isle of Man Stamps* published each January.

POSTAGE DUE STAMPS

D 1

D 2

D 3

(Litho Questa)

1973 (5 July). *P* 13½ × 14.

D1	**D 1**	½p. red, black and bistre-yellow	1·75	1·50
D2		1p. red, black and cinnamon	65	65
D3		2p. red, black and light apple-green	15	20
D4		3p. red, black and grey	25	25
D5		4p. red, black and carmine-rose	35	35
D6		5p. red, black and cobalt	40	40
D7		10p. red, black and light lavender	50	50
D8		20p. red, black and pale turquoise-green	90	90
D1/8		*Set of* 8	4·50	4·25

A second printing of all values was put on sale by the Philatelic Bureau from 1 September 1973, although examples are known used from mid-August onwards. These can be distinguished by the addition of a small "A" after the date "1973" in the bottom left margin of the stamps. Spurious examples of the second printing exist with the "A" removed.

Prices quoted above are for the second printing. *Prices for set of* 8 *original printing* £40 *mint*; £40 *used*.

(Des and litho Questa)

1975 (8 Jan). *Arms and inscriptions in black and red; background colour given. P* 14 × 13½.

D 9	**D 2**	½p. greenish yellow	10	10
D10		1p. flesh	10	10
D11		4p. rose-lilac	10	10
D12		7p. light greenish blue	20	20
D13		9p. brownish grey	25	25
D14		10p. bright mauve	30	30
D15		50p. orange-yellow	1·25	1·25
D16		£1 turquoise-green	2·50	2·50
D9/16		*Set of* 8	4·00	4·00

(Litho B.D.T.)

1982 (5 Oct). *P* 15 × 14.

D17	**D 3**	1p. multicoloured	10	10
D18		2p. multicoloured	10	10
D19		5p. multicoloured	10	10
D20		10p. multicoloured	20	25
D21		20p. multicoloured	40	45
D22		50p. multicoloured	1·00	1·10
D23		£1 multicoloured	2·00	2·10
D24		£2 multicoloured	4·00	4·25
D17/24		*Set of* 8	7·75	8·25

D 4

(Des Colleen Corlett. Litho B.D.T.)

1992 (18 Sept). *P* 13×13½.

D25	**D 4**	£5 multicoloured	10·00	10·50

JERSEY

WAR OCCUPATION ISSUES

amps issued under British authority during the German Occupation

1

)es Major N. V. L. Rybot. Typo *Jersey Evening Post*, St. Helier)

41–43. *White paper (thin to thick). No wmk. P* 11.
1 ½d. bright green (29.1.42) .. .. 4·00 3·25
 a. Imperf between (vert pair) £700
 b. Imperf between (horiz pair) £600
 c. Imperf (pair) £200
 d. On greyish paper (1.43) .. .. 5·00 5·75
 1d. scarlet (1.4.41) .. .. .. 4·25 3·25
 a. Imperf between (vert pair) £700
 b. Imperf between (horiz pair) £600
 c. Imperf (pair) £225
 d. On chalk-surfaced paper .. .. 40·00 38·00
 e. On greyish paper (1.43) .. .. 5·00 5·75

2 Old Jersey Farm — 3 Portelet Bay

4 Corbière Lighthouse — 5 Elizabeth Castle

6 Mont Orgueil Castle — 7 Gathering Vraic (seaweed)

)es E. Blampied. Eng H. Cortot. Typo French Govt Works, Paris)

43–44. *No wmk. P* 13½.
2 ½d. green (1 June) .. .. .. 7·00 5·50
 a. Rough, grey paper (6.10.43) .. 8·50 8·50
3 1d. scarlet (1 June) .. .. .. 1·50 75
 a. On newsprint (28.2.44) .. .. 2·50 2·00
4 1½d. brown (8 June) .. .. .. 3·00 3·00
5 2d. orange-yellow (8 June) .. .. 4·00 3·00
6 2½d. blue (29 June) .. .. .. 2·00 1·75
 a. On newsprint (25.2.44) .. .. 1·00 1·50
 ba. Thin paper* £200
7 3d. violet (29 June) .. .. .. 1·00 2·75
8 .. .. *Set of* 6 15·00 16·00

*On No. 7ba the design shows clearly through the back of the amp.

REGIONAL ISSUES

ATES OF ISSUE. The note at the beginning of the Guernsey egional Issues also applies here.

8 — 9

)es E. Blampied (T **8**), W. Gardner (T **9**). Portrait by Dorothy Wilding Ltd. Photo Harrison & Sons)

58 (18 Aug)–**67.** *W* **179** *of Great Britain. P* 15 × 14.
8 2½d. carmine-red (8.6.64) 35 75
 a. Imperf three sides (pair) £2000
9 3d. deep lilac 35 30
 p. One centre phosphor band (9.6.67) 20 20
 4d. ultramarine (7.2.66) 25 30
 p. Two phosphor bands (5.9.67) .. 20 25
11p .. .. *Set of* 3 60 1·00

68–69. *No wmk. Chalk-surfaced paper. PVA gum* One centre phosphor band (4d. values) or two phosphor bands (5d.). P* 15 × 14.
9 4d. olive-sepia (4.9.68) 20 25
 4d. bright vermilion (26.2.69) 20 35
 5d. royal blue (4.9.68) 20 50
/14 .. .. *Set of* 3 50 1·00

*PVA Gum. See note after No. 722 of Great Britain.

INDEPENDENT POSTAL ADMINISTRATION

10 Elizabeth Castle

11 Queen Elizabeth II (after Cecil Beaton)

13 Queen Elizabeth II (after Cecil Beaton)

12 Jersey Airport

(Des V. Whiteley. Photo Harrison (½d. to 1s. 9d.); Courvoisier (others))

1969 (1 Oct). *T* **10/13** *and similar horiz designs as T* **10** *(½d. to 1s. 6d.) or T* **12** *(5s., 10s., £1). Multicoloured. Granite paper (2s. 6d. to £1). P* 14 *(½d. to 1s. 9d.) or* 12 *(others).*
15 ½d. Type **10** 10 70
16 1d. La Hougue Bie (prehistoric tomb) (*shades*) 15 20
 a. Booklet stamp with blank margins .. 75
17 2d. Portelet Bay 10 15
18 3d. La Corbière Lighthouse 20 15
 b. Orange omitted £120
19 4d. Mont Orgueil Castle by night 15 10
 a. Booklet stamp with blank margins .. 40
20 5d. Arms and Royal Mace 15 10
21 6d. Jersey Cow 25 30
22 9d. Chart of English Channel 40 75
23 1s. Mont Orgueil Castle by day 75 75
24 1s. 6d. As 9d. .. .. 1·25 1·25
25 1s. 9d. Type **11** .. .. 1·25 1·25
26 2s. 6d. Type **12** .. .. 2·00 1·75
27 5s. Legislative Chamber .. .. .. 11·00 7·00
28 10s. The Royal Court .. .. .. 26·00 17·00
 a. Error. Green border* £4500
29 £1 Type **13** (*shades*) .. .. .. 2·00 1·50
15/29 .. .. *Set of* 15 40·00 27·00

*During the final printing of the 10s. a sheet was printed in the colours of the 50p., No. 56, i.e. green border instead of slate.

The 3d. is known with the orange omitted.

There was no postal need for the ½d. value as the ½d. coin had been withdrawn prior to its issue in anticipation of decimalisation.

Nos. 16a and 19a come from 2s. booklets for the automatic machines formerly used for the Great Britain 2s. booklets (see also note after Guernsey No. 28).

Various papers were used by Harrisons. The ½d. and 1d. exist on much thicker paper from 2s. booklets and the 2d. to 1s. 9d. exist on thinner paper having white instead of creamy gum.

24 First Day Cover — 25 Lord Coutanche, former Bailiff of Jersey

(Des R. Sellar. Photo Harrison)

1969 (1 Oct). *Inauguration of Post Office. P* 14.
30 **24** 4d. multicoloured 25 20
31 5d. multicoloured 30 30
32 1s. 6d. multicoloured .. .. .. 1·25 1·60
33 1s. 9d. multicoloured .. .. .. 1·25 1·60
30/3 .. .. *Set of* 4 2·75 3·25

(Des Rosalind Dease. Photo Courvoisier)

1970 (9 May). *25th Anniv of Liberation. T* **25** *and similar multicoloured designs. Granite paper P* 11½.
34 4d. Type **25** 25 25
35 5d. Sir Winston Churchill 25 25
36 1s. 6d. "Liberation" (Edmund Blampied) (*horiz*) .. .. 1·75 1·75
37 1s. 9d. S.S. *Vega* (*horiz*) .. .. 1·75 1·75
34/7 .. .. *Set of* 4 3·50 3·50

29 "A Tribute to Enid Blyton"

(Des Jennifer Toombs. Photo Courvoisier)

1970 (28 July). *"Battle of Flowers" Parade. T* **29** *and similar horiz designs. Multicoloured. Granite paper. P* 11½.
38 4d. Type **29** 25 25
39 5d. "Rags to Riches" (Cinderella and pumpkin) 40 40
40 1s. 6d. "Gourmet's Delight" (lobster and cornucopia) .. .. 7·00 2·50
41 1s. 9d. "We're the Greatest" (ostriches) .. 7·25 2·50
38/41 .. .. *Set of* 4 13·00 5·00

INVALIDATION. The regional issues for Jersey were invalidated for use in Jersey and Guernsey on 1 November 1969 but remained valid for use in the rest of the United Kingdom. Nos. 15/41 (except No. 29) and Nos. D1/6 were invalidated on 14 February 1972.

33 Jersey Airport

(Des V. Whiteley. Photo Harrison (½ to 9p.), Courvoisier (others))

1970 (1 Oct)–**74.** *Decimal Currency. Designs as Nos.* 15/28, *but with values inscr in decimal currency as in T* **33**, *and new horiz design as T* **10** *(6p.). Chalk-surfaced paper (4½, 5½, 8p.), granite paper (10, 20, 50p.).*
42 ½p. Type **10** (15.2.71) 10 10
 a. Booklet stamp with blank margins .. 40
43 1p. La Corbière Lighthouse (*shades*) (15.2.71) 10 10
 a. Orange omitted .. ..
44 1½p. Jersey Cow (15.2.71) 10 10
45 2p. Mont Orgueil Castle by night (15.2.71) 10 10
 a. Booklet stamp with blank margins .. 1·25
46 2½p. Arms and Royal Mace (15.2.71) .. 10 10
 a. Booklet stamp with blank margins .. 40
 ab. Gold (Mace) omitted £375
 ac. Gold (Mace) printed double £300
47 3p. La Hougue Bie (prehistoric tomb) (15.2.71) 10 10
 a. Booklet stamp with blank margins (1.12.72) 50
48 3½p. Portelet Bay (15.2.71) 15 15
 a. Booklet stamp with blank margins (1.7.74) 50
49 4p. Chart of English Channel (15.2.71) .. 15 15
49a 4½p. Arms and Royal Mace (1.11.74) .. 20 20
 ab. Uncoated paper £375
50 5p. Mont Orgueil Castle by day (15.2.71) .. 10 15
50a 5½p. Jersey Cow (1.11.74) 40 25
51 6p. Martello Tower, Archirondel (15.2.71) 25 30
52 7½p. Chart of English Channel (15.2.71) .. 30 40
52a 8p. Mont Orgueil Castle by night (1.11.74) 25 25
53 9p. Type **11** (15.2.71) 50 30
54 10p. Type **33** 50 55
55 20p. Legislative Chamber 75 75
56 50p. The Royal Court .. .. .. 1·75 1·75
42/56 .. .. *Set of* 18 5·00 5·00

Original printings of the ½p. to 4p., 5p. and 6p. to 9p. were with PVA gum; printings from 1974 (including original printings of the 4½p. and 5½p.) have dextrin added (see notes after 1971 Great Britain Decimal Machin issue). The 10p. to 50p. have gum arabic.

The border of No. 56 has been changed from turquoise-blue to dull green.

34 White Eared-Pheasant

(Des Jennifer Toombs. Photo Courvoisier)

1971 (12 Mar). *Wildlife Preservation Trust (1st series). T* **34** *and similar multicoloured designs. Granite paper. P* 11½.
57 2p. Type **34** 75 25
58 2½p. Thick-billed Parrot (*vert*) 75 25
59 7½p. Western Black and White Colobus Monkey (*vert*) .. .. .. 7·75 3·75
60 9p. Ring-tailed Lemur .. .. .. 8·00 3·75
57/60 .. .. *Set of* 4 15·50 7·25

See also Nos. 73/6, 217/21, 324/9, 447/51 and 818/23.

35 Poppy Emblem and Field — 36 "Tante Elizabeth" (E. Blampied)

(Des G. Drummond. Litho Questa)

1971 (15 June). *50th Anniv of Royal British Legion. T* **35** *and similar horiz designs. Multicoloured. P* 14.

61 2p. Royal British Legion Badge 50 50
62 2½p. Type **35** 50 50
63 7½p. Jack Counter, V.C., and Victoria Cross 2·40 2·40
64 9p. Crossed Tricolour and Union Jack .. 2·40 2·40
61/4 .. .. *Set of* 4 5·00 5·00

(Des and photo Courvoisier)

1971 (5 Oct). *Paintings. T* **36** *and similar multicoloured designs. Granite paper. P* 11½.

65 2p. Type **36** 15 15
66 2½p. "English Fleet in the Channel" (P. Monamy) (*horiz*) 25 20
67 7½p. "The Boyhood of Raleigh" (Millais) (*horiz*) .. .. 3·00 2·50
68 9p. "The Blind Beggar" (W. W. Ouless) .. 3·25 2·75
65/8 .. .. *Set of* 4 6·00 5·00

See also Nos. 115/18 and 213/16.

37 Jersey Fern **38** Artillery Shako

(Des G. Drummond. Photo Courvoisier)

1972 (18 Jan). *Wild Flowers of Jersey. T* **37** *and similar vert designs. Multicoloured. Granite paper. P* 11½.

69 3p. Type **37** 25 15
70 5p. Jersey Thrift 60 45
71 7½p. Jersey Orchid .. .. 2·25 2·25
72 9p. Jersey Viper's Bugloss .. .. .. 2·50 2·25
69/72 .. .. *Set of* 4 5·00 4·50

(Des Jennifer Toombs. Photo Courvoisier)

1972 (17 Mar). *Wildlife Preservation Trust (2nd series). Multicoloured designs similar to T* **34**. *Granite paper. P* 11½.

73 2½p. Cheetah 65 20
74 3p. Rothschild's Mynah (*vert*) 40 35
75 7½p. Spectacled Bear .. .. 1·40 1·50
76 9p. Tuatara .. .. 2·00 1·75
73/6 .. .. *Set of* 4 4·00 3·25

(Des and photo Courvoisier)

1972 (27 June). *Royal Jersey Militia. T* **38** *and similar vert designs. Multicoloured. Granite paper. P* 11½.

77 2½p. Type **38** 15 15
78 3p. Shako (2nd North Regt) 20 20
79 7½p. Shako (5th South-West Regt) 85 50
80 9p. Helmet (3rd Jersey Light Infantry) .. 1·00 60
77/80 .. .. *Set of* 4 2·00 1·25

39 Princess Anne **40** Armorican Bronze Coins

(Des G. Drummond from photographs by D. Groves. Photo Courvoisier)

1972 (1 Nov). *Royal Silver Wedding. T* **39** *and similar multicoloured designs. Granite paper. P* 11½.

81 2½p. Type **39** 10 10
82 3p. Queen Elizabeth and Prince Philip (*horiz*) 10 10
83 7½p. Prince Charles 40 40
84 20p. The Royal Family (*horiz*) 60 50
81/4 .. .. *Set of* 4 1·10 1·00

(Des G. Drummond. Photo Courvoisier)

1973 (23 Jan). *Centenary of La Société Jersiaise. T* **40** *and similar multicoloured designs. Granite paper. P* 11½.

85 2½p. Silver cups 10 10
86 3p. Gold torque (*vert*) 10 10
87 7½p. Royal Seal of Charles II (*vert*) 40 40
88 9p. Type **40** 50 50
85/8 .. .. *Set of* 4 1·00 1·00

41 Balloon *L'Armee de la Loire* and Letter, Paris, 1870 **42** *North Western*, 1870

(Des and photo Courvoisier)

1973 (16 May). *Jersey Aviation History. T* **41** *and similar horiz designs. Multicoloured. Granite paper. P* 11½.

89 3p. Type **41** 10 10
90 5p. Astra seaplane, 1912 .. .. .. 15 15
91 7½p. Supermarine Sea Eagle 60 40
92 9p. De Havilland D.H.86 Dragon Express *Giffard Bay* 80 50
89/92 .. .. *Set of* 4 1·50 1·00

(Des G. Drummond. Photo Courvoisier)

1973 (6 Aug). *Centenary of Jersey Eastern Railway. T* **42** *and similar designs showing early locomotives. Multicoloured. Granite paper. P* 11½.

93 2½p. Type **42** 10 10
94 3p. *Calvados*, 1873 .. .. 10 10
95 7½p. *Carteret* at Grouville Station, 1898 .. 60 40
96 9p. *Caesarea*, 1873, and route map .. 80 50
93/6 .. .. *Set of* 4 1·50 1·00

43 Princess Anne and Capt. Mark Phillips

(Des and photo Courvoisier)

1973 (14 Nov). *Royal Wedding. Granite paper. P* 11½.

97 **43** 3p. multicoloured 10 10
98 20p. multicoloured 90 90

44 Spider Crab **45** Freesias

(Des Jennifer Toombs. Photo Courvoisier)

1973 (15 Nov). *Marine Life. T* **44** *and similar horiz designs. Multicoloured. Granite paper. P* 11½.

99 2½p. Type **44** 10 10
100 3p. Conger Eel 10 10
101 7½p. Lobster 45 35
102 20p. Tuberculate Ormer 70 55
99/102 .. .. *Set of* 4 1·25 1·00

(Des G. Drummond. Photo Courvoisier)

1974 (13 Feb). *Spring Flowers. T* **45** *and similar vert designs. Multicoloured. Granite paper. P* 11½.

103 3p. Type **45** 10 10
104 5½p. Anemones 20 10
105 8p. Carnations and Gladioli 60 40
106 10p. Daffodils and Iris 80 50
103/6 .. .. *Set of* 4 1·50 1·00

46 First Letter-Box and Contemporary Cover **47** John Wesley

(Des G. Drummond. Photo Courvoisier)

1974 (7 June). *U.P.U. Centenary. T* **46** *and similar horiz designs. Multicoloured. Granite paper. P* 11½.

107 2½p. Type **46** 10 10
108 3p. Postmen, 1862 and 1969 .. .. .. 10 10
109 5½p. Letter-box and letter, 1974 .. .. 35 30
110 20p. R.M.S. *Aquila* (1874) and B.A.C. One Eleven 200 (1974) 85 60
107/10 .. .. *Set of* 4 1·25 1·00

(Des, recess and litho D.L.R.)

1974 (31 July). *Anniversaries. T* **47** *and similar vert designs. P* 13 × 14.

111 3p. agate and light cinnamon 10 10
112 3½p. blackish violet and light azure 10 10
113 8p. blue-black and pale rose-lilac 30 35
114 20p. black and pale buff 70 65
a. Pale buff (background) omitted .. ..
111/14 .. .. *Set of* 4 1·00 1·00

Portraits and events:—3p. Type **47** (Bicentenary of Methodism in Jersey); 3½p. Sir William Hillary, founder (150th Anniv of R.N.L.I.); 8p. Cannon Wace, poet and historian (800th Death Anniv); 20p. Sir Winston Churchill (Birth Centenary).

48 *Catherine* and *Mary* (Royal yachts) **49** Potato Digger

(Des and photo Courvoisier)

1974 (22 Nov). *Marine Paintings by Peter Monamy. T* **48** *and similar multicoloured designs. Granite paper. P* 11½.

115 3½p. Type **48** 10 1
116 5½p. French two-decker 20 1
117 8p. Dutch vessel (*horiz*) 30 3
118 25p. Battle of Cap La Hague, 1692 (55 × 27 mm) 80 6
115/18 .. .. *Set of* 4 1·25 1·0

(Des G. Drummond. Photo Courvoisier)

1975 (25 Feb). *19th-Century Farming. T* **49** *and similar horiz designs. Multicoloured. Granite paper. P* 11½.

119 3p. Type **49** 10 10
120 3½p. Cider crusher 10 15
121 8p. Six-horse plough 35 35
122 10p. Hay cart 55 50
119/22 .. .. *Set of* 4 1·00 1·00

50 H.M. Queen Elizabeth, the Queen Mother (photograph by Cecil Beaton) **51** Nautilus Shell

(Des and photo Courvoisier)

1975 (30 May). *Royal Visit. Granite paper. P* 11½.

123 **50** 20p. multicoloured .. .. .. 1·00 1·0

(Des A. Games. Photo Courvoisier)

1975 (6 June). *Jersey Tourism. T* **51** *and similar vert designs based o holiday posters. Multicoloured. Granite paper. P* 11½.

124 5p. Type **51** 10 1
125 8p. Parasol 15 1
126 10p. Deckchair 35 3
127 12p. Sandcastle with flags of Jersey and the U.K. 50 5
124/7 .. .. *Set of* 4 1·00 1·0
MS128 146 × 68 mm. Nos. 124/7 .. .. .. 1·00 1·1

52 Common Tern **53** Armstrong Whitworth Siskin IIIA

(Des Jennifer Toombs. Photo Courvoisier)

1975 (28 July). *Sea Birds. T* **52** *and similar vert designs. Multicoloured. Granite paper. P* 11½.

129 4p. Type **52** 15 15
130 5p. British Storm Petrel 15 15
131 8p. Brent Geese 50 35
132 25p. Shag 85 45
129/32 .. .. *Set of* 4 1·50 1·00

(Des A. Theobald. Photo Courvoisier)

1975 (30 Oct). *50th Anniv of Royal Air Forces Association, Jersey Branch. T* **53** *and similar horiz designs. Multicoloured. Granit paper. P* 11½.

133 4p. Type **53** 10 10
134 5p. Supermarine Southampton I flying boat 15 15
135 10p. Supermarine Spitfire Mk 1 .. .. 50 30
136 25p. Folland Fo.141 Gnat T.1 .. .. 95 60
133/6 .. .. *Set of* 4 1·50 1·00

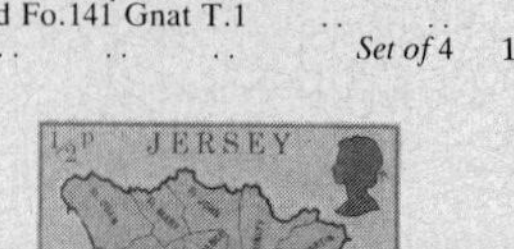

54 Map of Jersey Parishes

55 Parish Arms and Island Scene

(Des Courvoisier (£2). G. Drummond (others). Litho Questa (½ to 15p.). Photo Courvoisier (others))

1976–80. *Various multicoloured designs as T* **54/5**.

(*a*) *Parish Arms and Views as T* **54**. *P* 14½. (29 Jan)

137 ½p. Type **54** 10 10
138 1p. Zoological Park 10 10
a. Booklet pane of 2 plus 2 *se-tenant* labels (5.4.76) .. .. 1·00
b. Booklet pane of 4 (5.4.76) .. .. .. 1·00
139 5p. St. Mary's Church 15 15
a. Booklet pane of 4 (5.4.76) 50
140 6p. Seymour Tower 15 15
a. Booklet pane of 4 (28.2.78) 60
141 7p. La Corbière Lighthouse 20 20
a. Booklet pane of 4 (5.4.76) 60
142 8p. St. Saviour's Church 20 20
a. Booklet pane of 4 (28.2.78) 80
143 9p. Elizabeth Castle 25 25
a. Booklet pane of 4 (6.5.80) .. .. .. 1·00
144 10p. Gorey Harbour 25 25
145 11p. Jersey Airport 30 25
146 12p. Grosnez Castle 30 30
147 13p. Bonne Nuit Harbour 35 35
148 14p. Le Hocq Tower 35 40
149 15p. Morel Farm 40 45

(*b*) *Emblems as T* **55**. *Granite paper. P* 12 (20 Aug 1976–16 Nov 1977)

150 20p. Type **55** 50 50
151 30p. Flag and map 75 75
152 40p. Postal H.Q. and badge .. .. 1·00 1·00
153 50p. Parliament, Royal Court and arms .. 1·25 1·00
154 £1 Lieutenant-Governor's flag and Government House .. .. 2·50 2·25
155 £2 Queen Elizabeth II (photograph by Alex Wilson) (*vert*) (16.11.77) .. .. .. 4·50 4·25
137/55 .. .. *Set of* 19 12·00 11·50

Nos. 156/9 are vacant.

56 Sir Walter Ralegh and Map of Virginia

(Des M. Orbell. Photo Courvoisier)

1976 (29 May). *"Links with America". T* **56** *and similar horiz designs. Multicoloured. Granite paper. P* 11½.

160 5p. Type **56** 10 10
161 7p. Sir George Carteret and map of New Jersey 15 15
162 11p. Philippe Dauvergne and Long Island Landing 40 35
163 13p. John Copley and sketch 45 50
160/3 .. .. *Set of* 4 1·00 1·00

57 Dr. Grandin and Map of China

58 Coronation, 1953 (photographed by Cecil Beaton)

(Des Jennifer Toombs. Photo Courvoisier)

1976 (25 Nov). *Birth Centenary of Dr. Lilian Grandin (medical missionary). T* **57** *and similar horiz designs. Granite paper. P* 11½.

164 5p. multicoloured 10 10
165 7p. light yellow, yellow-brown and black .. 15 15
166 11p. multicoloured 50 35
167 13p. multicoloured 50 50
164/7 .. .. *Set of* 4 1·10 1·00

Designs:—7p. Sampan on the Yangtze; 11p. Overland trek; 13p. Dr. Grandin at work.

(Des G. Drummond. Photo Courvoisier)

1977 (7 Feb). *Silver Jubilee. T* **58** *and similar vert designs. Multicoloured. Granite paper. P* 11½.

168 5p. Type **58** 25 15
169 7p. Visit to Jersey, 1957 .. .. 30 20
170 25p. Queen Elizabeth II (photo by Peter Grugeon) 90 80
168/70 .. .. *Set of* 3 1·25 1·00

59 Coins of 1871 and 1877

(Des D. Henley. Litho Questa)

1977 (25 Mar). *Centenary of Currency Reform. T* **59** *and similar horiz designs. Multicoloured. P* 14.

171 5p. Type **59** 10 10
172 7p. One-twelfth shilling, 1949 .. .. .. 15 15
173 11p. Silver Crown, 1966 .. .. 40 35
174 13p. £2 piece, 1972 .. .. 45 50
171/4 .. .. *Set of* 4 1·00 1·00

60 Sir William Weston and *Santa Anna*, 1530

(Des A. Theobald. Litho Questa)

1977 (24 June). *St. John Ambulance Centenary. T* **60** *and similar horiz designs each showing a Grand Prior of the Order. Multicoloured. P* 14 × 13½.

175 5p. Type **60** 10 10
176 7p. Sir William Drogo and ambulance, 1877 15 15
177 11p. Duke of Connaught and ambulance, 1917 .. .. 40 35
178 13p. Duke of Gloucester and stretcher-team, 1977 .. .. 45 50
175/8 .. .. *Set of* 4 1·00 1·00

61 Arrival of Queen Victoria, 1846

(Des R. Granger Barrett. Litho Questa)

1977 (29 Sept). *125th Anniv of Victoria College. T* **61** *and similar multicoloured designs. P* 14½.

179 7p. Type **61** 20 20
180 10½p. Victoria College, 1852 .. .. 25 20
181 11p. Sir Galahad statue, 1924 (*vert*) 30 35
182 13p. College Hall (*vert*) 35 35
179/82 .. .. *Set of* 4 1·00 1·00

62 Harry Vardon Statuette and Map of Royal Jersey Course

(Des Jennifer Toombs. Litho Questa)

1978 (28 Feb). *Centenary of Royal Jersey Golf Club. T* **62** *and similar horiz designs. Multicoloured. P* 14.

183 6p. Type **62** 15 15
184 8p. Harry Vardon's grip and swing 20 20
185 11p. Harry Vardon's putt 65 35
186 13p. Golf trophies and book by Harry Vardon 65 40
183/6 .. .. *Set of* 4 1·50 1·00

63 Mont Orgueil Castle

64 "Gaspé Basin" (P. J. Ouless)

(Des from paintings by Thomas Phillips. Photo Courvoisier)

1978 (1 May). *Europa. Castles. T* **63** *and similar horiz designs. Multicoloured. Granite paper. P* 11½.

187 6p. Type **63** 20 20
188 8p. St. Aubin's Fort 40 40
189 10½p. Elizabeth Castle 50 50
187/9 .. .. *Set of* 3 1·00 1·00

(Des R. Granger Barrett. Litho Questa)

1978 (9 June). *Links with Canada. T* **64** *and similar horiz designs. Multicoloured. P* 14½.

190 6p. Type **64** 15 15
191 8p. Map of Gaspé Peninsula 20 20
192 10½p. *Century* (brigantine) 25 25
193 11p. Early map of Jersey 40 30
194 13p. St. Aubin's Bay, town and harbour .. 45 35
190/4 .. .. *Set of* 5 1·25 1·10

65 Queen Elizabeth and Prince Philip

66 Mail Cutter, 1778–1827

(Des and photo Courvoisier)

1978 (26 June). *25th Anniv of Coronation. T* **65** *and similar vert design. Granite paper. P* 11½.

195 8p. silver, black and cerise 30 30
196 25p. silver, black and new blue 70 70

Design:—25p. Hallmarks of 1953 and 1977.

(Des Jersey P.O. Litho Harrison)

1978 (18 Oct). *Bicentenary of England-Jersey Government Mail Packet Service. T* **66** *and similar horiz designs. P* 14½ × 14.

197 6p. black, yellow-brown and greenish yellow 15 15
198 8p. black, dull yellowish grn & pale yell-grn 20 20
199 10½p. black, ultramarine and cobalt 40 30
200 11p. black, purple and pale rose-lilac .. 45 35
201 13p. black, Venetian red and pink 50 45
197/201 .. .. *Set of* 5 1·50 1·25

Designs:—8p. *Flamer*, 1831–37; 10½p. *Diana*, 1877–90; 11p. *Ibex*, 1891–1925; 13p. *Caesarea*, 1960–75.

67 Jersey Calf

68 Jersey Pillar Box, *circa* 1860

(Des Jersey P.O. and Questa. Litho Questa)

1979 (1 Mar). *9th World Jersey Cattle Bureau Conference. T* **67** *and similar horiz design. Multicoloured. P* 13½.

202 6p. Type **67** 20 20
203 25p. "Ansom Designette" (cow presented to the Queen, 27 June 1978) (46 × 29 *mm*) 80 80

(Des Jennifer Toombs. Litho Questa)

1979 (1 Mar). *Europa. T* **68** *and similar vert designs. Multicoloured. P* 14.

204 8p. Type **68** 25 25
a. Horiz pair. Nos. 204/5 .. .. .. 50 50
b. Perf 14½ 25 25
ba. Horiz pair. Nos. 204b/5b 50 50
205 8p. Clearing a modern Jersey post box .. 25 25
b. Perf 14½ 25 25
206 10½p. Telephone switchboard, *circa* 1900 .. 30 30
a. Horiz pair. Nos. 206/7 .. .. .. 60 65
b. Perf 14½ 30 30
ba. Horiz pair. Nos. 206b/7b 60 60
207 10½p. Modern S.P.C. telephone system .. 30 30
b. Perf 14½ 30 30
204/7 .. .. *Set of* 4 1·00 1·00

Nos. 204/5 and 206/7 were each printed together, *se-tenant*, in horizontal pairs throughout the sheets.

Although both perforations were supplied to Jersey at the same time the 8p perforated 14½ is not known used before early April.

69 Percival Mew Gull *Golden City*

70 "My First Sermon"

(Des A. Theobald. Photo Courvoisier)

1979 (24 Apr). *25th Anniv of International Air Rally. T* **69** *and similar horiz designs. Multicoloured. Granite paper. P* 11½.

208 6p. Type **69** 15 15
209 8p. De Havilland D.H.C.1 Chipmunk .. 20 20
210 10½p. Druine D.31 Turbulent 40 20
211 11p. De Havilland D.H.82A Tiger Moth .. 45 25
212 13p. North American AT-6 Harvard 50 30
208/12 .. .. *Set of* 5 1·50 1·00

(Des Jersey P.O. and Courvoisier. Photo Courvoisier)

1979 (13 Aug). *International Year of the Child and 150th Birth Anniv of Millais. Paintings. T* **70** *and similar multicoloured designs. Granite paper. P* 12 × 12½ (25*p.*) *or* 12 × 11½ (*others*).

213 8p. Type **70** 25 15
214 10½p. "Orphans" 30 25
215 11p. "The Princes in the Tower" 30 25
216 25p. "Christ in the House of His Parents" (50 × 32 *mm*) 55 45
213/16 .. .. *Set of* 4 1·25 1·00

(Des Jennifer Toombs. Photo Courvoisier)

1979 (8 Nov). *Wildlife Preservation Trust (3rd series). Multicoloured designs as T* **34**. *Granite paper. P* 11½.

217	6p.	Pink Pigeon (*vert*)	15	15
218	8p.	Orang-Utan (*vert*)	20	20
219	11½p.	Waldrapp	50	25
220	13p.	Lowland Gorilla (*vert*)	65	25
221	15p.	Rodriguez Flying Fox (*vert*)	75	30
217/21		*Set of* 5	2·00	1·00

71 Plan of Mont Orgueil

(Litho Enschedé)

1980 (5 Feb). *Fortresses. T* **71** *and similar multicoloured designs showing drawings by Thomas Phillips. P* 13 × 13½ (25*p.*) *or* 13½ × 13 (*others*).

222	8p.	Type **71**	30	25
223	11½p.	Plan of La Tour de St. Aubin	35	30
224	13p.	Plan of Elizabeth Castle	55	45
225	25p.	Map of Jersey showing fortresses (38 × 27 *mm*)	80	70
222/5		*Set of* 4	1·75	1·50

72 Sir Walter Raleigh and Paul Ivy (engineer) discussing Elizabeth Castle

(Des Jersey Post Office and Questa. Litho Questa)

1980 (6 May). *Europa. Personalities. Links with Britain. T* **72** *and similar vert design. Multicoloured. P* 14.

226	9p.	Type **72**	20	20
227	9p.		20	20
	a.	Horiz pair. Nos. 226/7	50	50
228	13½p.	Sir George Carteret receiving rights to Smith's Island, Virginia from King	40	35
229	13½p.	Charles II	40	35
	a.	Horiz pair. Nos. 228/9	80	70
226/9		*Set of* 4	1·25	1·10

Nos. 226/7 and 228/9 were each printed together, *se-tenant*, in horizontal pair throughout the sheet, forming composite designs.

73 Planting

74 Three Lap Event

(Des R. Granger Barrett. Litho Questa)

1980 (6 May). *Centenary of Jersey Royal Potato. T* **73** *and similar vert designs. Multicoloured. P* 14.

230	7p.	Type **73**	15	15
231	15p.	Digging	35	35
232	17½p.	Weighbridge	60	60
230/2		*Set of* 3	1·00	1·00

(Des A. Theobald. Photo Courvoisier)

1980 (24 July). *60th Anniv of Jersey Motor-cycle and Light Car Club. T* **74** *and similar horiz designs. Multicoloured. Granite paper. P* 11½.

233	7p.	Type **74**	25	25
234	9p.	Jersey International Road Race	25	25
235	13½p.	Scrambling	45	45
236	15p.	Sand racing (saloon cars)	50	50
237	17½p.	National Hill Climb	55	55
233/7		*Set of* 5	1·75	1·75

75 *Eye of the Wind*

76 Detail of "The Death of Major Peirson"

(Des G. Drummond. Litho Questa)

1980 (1 Oct). *"Operation Drake" Round the World Expedition and 150th Anniv of Royal Geographical Society* (14*p.*). *P* 14.

238	7p.	Type **75**	20	20
239	9p.	Diving from inflatable dinghy	25	25
240	13½p.	Exploration of Papua New Guinea	35	35
241	14p.	Captain Scott's *Discovery*	45	35
242	15p.	Using aerial walkways, Conservation Project, Sulawesi	45	35
243	17½p.	*Eye of the Wind* and Goodyear Aerospace airship *Europa*	55	45
238/43		*Set of* 6	2·00	1·75

(Photo Courvoisier)

1981 (6 Jan). *Bicentenary of Battle of Jersey. Painting "The Death of Major Peirson" by J. S. Copley. T* **76** *and similar vert designs showing details of the work. Granite paper. P* 12½ × 12.

244	7p.	multicoloured	25	25
245	10p.	multicoloured	30	30
246	15p.	multicoloured	60	60
247	17½p.	multicoloured	80	80
244/7		*Set of* 4	1·75	1·75
MS248		144 × 97 mm. Nos. 244/7	2·00	2·00

Stamps from No. **MS**248 are without white margins.

77 De Bagot

78 Jersey Crest and Map of Channel

78a "Queen Elizabeth II" (Norman Hepple)

(Des and photo Courvoisier (£5). Des G. Drummond. Litho Questa (others))

1981 (24 Feb)–**88**. *Arms of Jersey Families. T* **77** *and similar designs in black, silver and turquoise-green* (½*p.*), *black, silver and mauve* (4*p.*), *black, silver and lemon* (20*p.*), *black and dull blue* (25*p.*), *black, silver and carmine* (26*p.*) *or multicoloured* (*others*) *with T* **78/a**. *Granite paper* (£5). *P* 12½×12 (£5), 15×14 (16*p.*, 17*p.*, 18*p.*, 19*p.*, 26*p.*, 75*p.*) *or* 14 (*others*).

249	½p.	Type **77**	20	20
250	1p.	De Carteret	10	10
	a.	Booklet pane of 6	20	
	b.	Perf 15 × 14 (12.1.88)	25	25
251	2p.	La Cloche	10	10
	a.	Booklet pane of 6 (1.12.81)	70	
	b.	Perf 15 × 14 (15.11.84)	20	20
	ba.	Booklet pane of 6 (1.4.86)	1·00	
252	3p.	Dumaresq	20	30
	a.	Booklet pane of 6	60	
	b.	Perf 15 × 14 (27.4.84)	10	10
	ba.	Booklet pane of 6	85	
253	4p.	Payn	25	15
	a.	Perf 15 × 14 (4.3.86)	20	25
	ab.	Booklet pane of 6 (6.4.87)	70	
254	5p.	Janvrin	15	15
	a.	Perf 15 × 14 (4.3.86)	35	35
255	6p.	Poingdestre	20	20
	a.	Perf 15 × 14 (4.3.86)	50	20
256	7p.	Pipon	20	20
	a.	Booklet pane of 6	90	
257	8p.	Marett	25	25
	a.	Booklet pane of 6 (19.4.83)	1·50	
258	9p.	Le Breton	30	30
	a.	Perf 15 × 14 (27.4.84)	35	35
	ab.	Booklet pane of 6	2·25	
259	10p.	Le Maistre	30	30
	a.	Booklet pane of 6	1·50	
	b.	Perf 15 × 14 (1.4.86)	35	35
	ba.	Booklet pane of 6	1·60	
260	11p.	Bisson (28.7.81)	35	35
	a.	Booklet pane of 6 (19.4.83)	1·75	
	b.	Perf 15 × 14 (6.4.87)	40	45
	ba.	Booklet pane of 6	1·75	
261	12p.	Robin (28.7.81)	50	40
	a.	Perf 15 × 14 (27.4.84)	40	25
	ab.	Booklet pane of 6	1·75	
262	13p.	Herault (28.7.81)	40	40
	a.	Perf 15 × 14 (15.11.84)	60	60
263	14p.	Messervy (28.7.81)	45	45
	a.	Perf 15 × 14 (15.11.84)	50	50
	ab.	Booklet pane of 6 (1.4.86)	2·25	
264	15p.	Fiott (28.7.81)	45	45
	a.	Perf 15 × 14 (6.4.87)	45	45
	ab.	Booklet pane of 6	2·25	
265	16p.	Malet (25.10.85)	45	45
	a.	Booklet pane of 6 (17.5.88)	2·25	
266	17p.	Mabon (25.10.85)	50	50
266*a*	18p.	De St. Martin (26.4.88)	75	75
266*b*	19p.	Hamptonne (26.4.88)	80	80
267	20p.	Badier (28.7.81)	60	60
	a.	Perf 15 × 14 (4.3.86)	90	90
268	25p.	L'Arbalestier (23.2.82)	60	60
268*a*	26p.	Type **77** (26.4.88)	60	60
269	30p.	Journeaux (23.2.82)	90	90
	a.	Perf 15×14 (4.3.86)	1·10	1·10
270	40p.	Lempriere (23.2.82)	1·25	1·25
	a.	Perf 15×14 (6.4.87)	1·25	1·25
271	50p.	Auvergne (23.2.82)	1·50	1·50
	a.	Perf 15×14 (6.4.87)	1·60	1·60
272	75p.	Remon (23.4.87)	2·25	1·75
273	£1	Type **78** (23.2.82)	3·25	3·00
274	£5	Type **78a** (17.11.83)	15·00	10·50
249/74		*Set of* 29	28·00	23·00

No. 258a only occurs in the £2.16 stamp booklet issued 27 April 1984, No. 259b from the £3.12 booklet of 1 April 1986, No. 260b from the £3.60 booklet of 6 April 1987 and No. 261a from the £2.16 booklet of 27 April 1984 and the £3.84 booklet of 17 May 1988.

79 Knight of Hambye slaying Dragon

(Des Jennifer Toombs. Litho Questa)

1981 (7 Apr). *Europa. Folklore. T* **79** *and similar horiz designs. Multicoloured. P* 14½.

275	10p.	Type **79**	25	25
	a.	Horiz pair. Nos. 275/6	55	55
276	10p.	Servant slaying Knight of Hambye, and awaiting execution	25	25
277	18p.	St. Brelade celebrating Easter on island	50	50
	a.	Horiz pair. Nos. 277/8	1·10	1·10
278	18p.	Island revealing itself as a huge fish	50	50
275/8		*Set of* 4	1·50	1·40

Legends:—10p. (*both*), Slaying of the Dragon of Lawrence by the Knight of Hambye; 18p. (*both*), Voyages of St. Brelade.

Nos. 275/6 and 277/8 were each printed together, *se-tenant*, in horizontal pairs throughout the sheet.

80 The Harbour by Gaslight

81 Prince Charles and Lady Diana Spencer

(Des R. Granger Barrett. Photo Courvoisier)

1981 (22 May). *150th Anniv of Gas Lighting in Jersey. T* **80** *and similar horiz designs showing Jersey by gaslight. Multicoloured. Granite paper. P* 11½.

279	7p.	Type **80**	25	25
280	10p.	The Quay	30	30
281	18p.	Royal Square	45	45
282	22p.	Halkett Place	55	55
283	25p.	Central Market	65	65
279/83		*Set of* 5	2·00	2·00

(Des Jersey P.O. and Courvoisier. Photo Courvoisier)

1981 (28 July). *Royal Wedding. Granite paper. P* 11½.

284	**81**	10p.	multicoloured	75	75
285		25p.	multicoloured	1·75	1·75

82 Christmas Tree in Royal Square

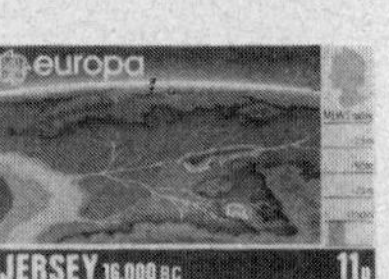

83 Jersey, 16,000 B.C.

(Des A. Copp. Litho Questa)

1981 (29 Sept). *Christmas. T* **82** *and similar vert designs. Multicoloured. P* 14½.

286	7p.	Type **82**	25	25
287	10p.	East window, Parish Church, St. Helier	40	40
288	18p.	Boxing Day meet of Jersey Drag Hunt	50	50
286/8		*Set of* 3	1·00	1·00

(Des A. Copp. Litho Questa)

1982 (20 Apr). *Europa. Historic Events. Formation of Jersey. T* **83** *and similar multicoloured designs. P* 14½.

289	11p.	Type **83**	30	30
290	11p.	Jersey, 10,000 B.C. (*vert*)	30	30
291	19½p.	7,000 B.C. (*vert*)	70	60
292	19½p.	4,000 B.C.	70	60
289/92		*Set of* 4	1·75	1·60

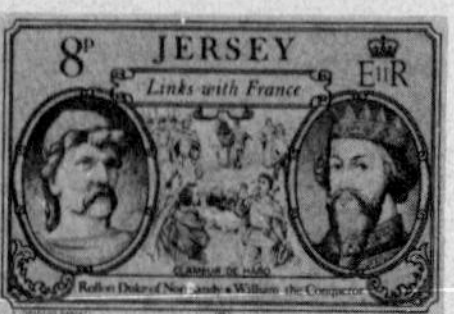

84 Duke Rollo of Normandy, William the Conqueror and "Clameur de Haro" (traditional procedure for obtaining justice)

(Des R. Granger Barrett. Litho Questa)

982 (11 June–7 Sept). *Links with France. T* **84** *and similar horiz designs. Multicoloured. P* 14.

93 8p. Type **84** .. 25 25
a. Horiz pair. Nos. 293/4 .. 50 50
b. Booklet pane. Nos. 293 and 294 each × 2 (7 Sept) .. 1·00
94 8p. John of England, Philippe Auguste of France and Siege of Rouen .. 25 25
95 11p. Jean Martell (brandy merchant), early still and view of Cognac .. 35 35
a. Horiz pair. Nos. 295/6 .. 70 70
b. Booklet pane. Nos. 295 and 296 each × 2 (7 Sept) .. 1·40
96 11p. Victor Hugo, "Le Rocher des Proscrits" (rock where he used to meditate) and Marine Terrace .. 35 35
97 19½p. Pierre Teilhard de Chardin (philosopher) and "Maison Saint Louis" (science institute) .. 60 60
a. Horiz pair. Nos. 297/8 .. 1·25 1·25
b. Booklet pane. Nos. 297 and 298 each × 2 (7 Sept) .. 2·50
98 19½p. Père Charles Rey (scientist), anemotachymeter and The Observatory, St. Louis .. 60 60
93/8 .. *Set of* 6 2·25 2·25

The two designs of each value were printed together, *se-tenant*, in orizontal pairs throughout the sheet.

Each booklet pane has margins all round and text, in English or rench, printed on the binding selvedge.

85 Sir William Smith, Founder of Boys' Brigade

86 H.M.S. *Tamar* with H.M.S. *Dolphin* at Port Egmont

(Des A. Theobald. Photo Courvoisier)

982 (18 Nov). *75th Anniv of Boy Scout Movement (Nos.* 301/3) *and Centenary of Boys' Brigade (Nos.* 299/301). *T* **85** *and similar multicoloured designs. Granite paper. P* 11½.

99 8p. Type **85** .. 25 25
00 11p. Boys' Brigade "Old Boys" band, Liberation Parade, 1945 (*vert*) .. 30 30
01 24p. William Smith and Lord Baden-Powell at Royal Albert Hall, 1903 .. 60 60
02 26p. Lord and Lady Baden-Powell in St. Helier, 1924 (*vert*) .. 75 75
03 29p. Scouts at "Westward Ho" campsite, St. Ouen's Bay .. 90 90
99/303 .. *Set of* 5 2·50 2·50

(Des R. Granger Barrett. Litho Questa)

983 (15 Feb). *Jersey Adventurers* (1*st series*). 250*th Birth Anniv of Philippe de Carteret. T* **86** *and similar horiz designs. Multicoloured. P* 14 × 14½.

04 8p. Type **86** .. 25 25
05 11p. H.M.S. *Dolphin* and H.M.S. *Swallow* off Magellan Strait .. 30 30
06 19½p. Discovering Pitcairn Island .. 50 50
07 24p. Carteret taking possession of English Cove, New Ireland .. 70 70
08 26p. H.M.S. *Swallow* sinking a pirate, Macassar Strait .. 85 75
09 29p. H.M.S. *Endymion* leading convoy from West Indies .. 1·00 85
04/9 .. *Set of* 6 3·25 3·00

See also Nos. 417/21 and 573/8.

87 1969 5s. Legislative Chamber Definitive

(Des G. Drummond. Litho Questa)

983 (19 Apr). *Europa. T* **87** *and similar multicoloured designs. P* 14½.

10 11p. Type **87** .. 50 50
a. Horiz pair. Nos. 310/11 .. 1·00 1·00
11 11p. Royal Mace (23 × 32 *mm*) .. 50 50
12 19½p. 1969 10s. Royal Court definitive showing green border error .. 75 75
a. Horiz pair. Nos. 312/13 .. 1·50 1·50
13 19½p. Bailiff's Seal (23 × 32 *mm*) .. 75 75
10/13 .. *Set of* 4 2·25 2·25

The two designs of each value were issued together, *se-tenant*, in orizontal pairs throughout the sheets.

88 Charles Le Geyt and Battle of Minden (1759)

(Des A. Copp. Litho Questa)

1983 (21 June). *World Communications Year and* 250*th Birth Anniv of Charles Le Geyt (first Jersey postmaster). T* **88** *and similar horiz designs. Multicoloured. P* 14.

314 8p. Type **88** .. 25 25
315 11p. London to Weymouth mail coach .. 35 35
316 24p. P.O. Mail Packet *Chesterfield* attacked by French privateer .. 75 75
317 26p. Mary Godfray and the Hue Street Post Office .. 90 90
318 29p. Mail steamer leaving St. Helier harbour 1·10 1·10
314/18 .. *Set of* 5 3·00 3·00

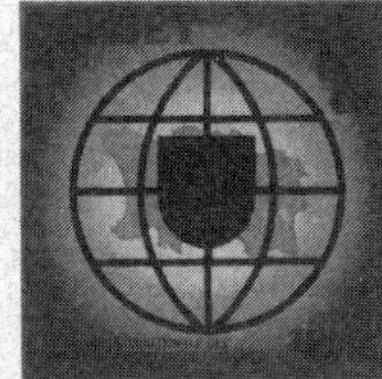

89 Assembly Emblem

90 "Cardinal Newman"

(Des A. Copp. Litho Questa)

1983 (21 June). 13*th General Assembly of the A.I.P.L.F. (Association Internationale des Parlementaires de Langue Francaise), Jersey. P* 14½.

319 **89** 19½p. multicoloured .. 75 75

(Des and photo Courvoisier)

1983 (20 Sept). 50*th Death Anniv of Walter Ouless (artist). T* **90** *and similar multicoloured designs, showing paintings. Granite paper. P* 11½.

320 8p. Type **90** .. 25 25
321 11p. "Incident in the French Revolution" .. 45 45
322 20½p. "Thomas Hardy" .. 85 85
323 31p. "David with the head of Goliath" (38 × 32 *mm*) .. 1·25 1·25
320/3 .. *Set of* 4 2·50 2·50

91 Golden Lion Tamarin

92 C.E.P.T. 25th Anniversary Logo

(Des W. Oliver. Litho Questa)

1984 (17 Jan). *Wildlife Preservation Trust* (4*th series*). *T* **91** *and similar vert designs. Multicoloured. P* 13½ × 14.

324 9p. Type **91** .. 30 30
325 12p. Snow Leopard .. 40 40
326 20½p. Jamaican Boa .. 60 60
327 26p. Round Island Gecko .. 95 75
328 28p. Coscoroba Swan .. 1·10 90
329 31p. St. Lucia Amazon .. 1·10 90
324/9 .. *Set of* 6 4·00 3·50

(Des J. Larrivière. Litho Questa)

1984 (12 Mar). *Europa. P* 14½ × 15.

330 **92** 9p. cobalt, dull ultramarine and black .. 30 30
331 12p. light green, green and black .. 40 40
332 20½p. rose-lilac, deep magenta and black .. 70 70
330/2 .. *Set of* 3 1·25 1·25

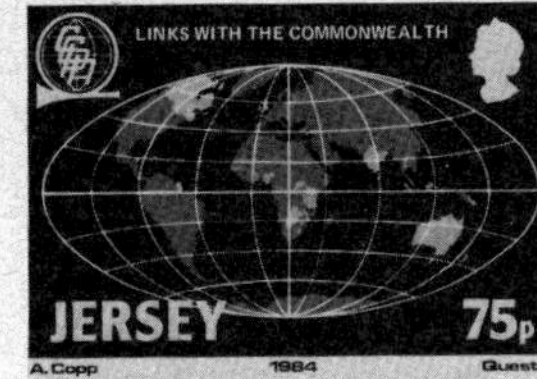

93 Map showing Commonwealth

(Des A. Copp. Litho Questa)

1984 (12 Mar). *Links with the Commonwealth. Sheet* 108 × 74 *mm. P* 15 × 14½.

MS333 **93** 75p. multicoloured .. 2·50 2·50

94 *Sarah Bloomshoft* at Demie de Pas Light, 1906

(Des G. Palmer. Litho Questa)

1984 (1 June). *Centenary of the Jersey R.N.L.I. Lifeboat Station T* **94** *and similar horiz designs showing famous rescues. Multicoloured. P* 14½.

334 9p. Type **94** .. 40 40
335 9p. *Hearts of Oak* and *Maurice Georges*, 1949 40 40
336 12p. *Elizabeth Rippon* and *Hanna*, 1949 .. 50 50
337 12p. *Elizabeth Rippon* and *Santa Maria*, 1951 50 50
338 20½p. *Elizabeth Rippon and Bacchus*, 1973 .. 90 75
339 20½p. *Thomas James King* and *Cythara*, 1983 .. 90 75
334/9 .. *Set of* 6 3·25 3·00

95 Bristol Type 170 Freighter Mk 32

(Des G. Drummond. Litho Questa)

1984 (24 July). 40*th Anniversary of International Civil Aviation Organization. T* **95** *and similar horiz designs. Multicoloured. P* 14.

340 9p. Type **95** .. 30 30
341 12p. Airspeed A.S.57 Ambassador 2 .. 40 40
342 26p. De Havilland D.H. 114 Heron 1B .. 1·10 90
343 31p. De Havilland D.H.89A Dragon Rapide 1·40 1·10
340/3 .. *Set of* 4 3·00 2·50

96 "Robinson Crusoe leaves the Wreck"

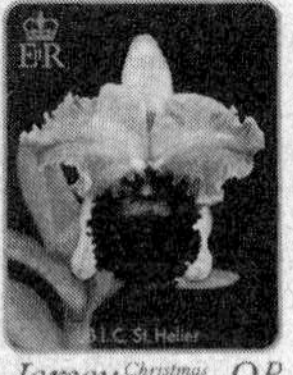

97 "B.L.C. St Helier" Orchid

(Des R. Granger Barrett. Photo Courvoisier)

1984 (21 Sept). *Links with Australia. Paintings by John Alexander Gilfillan. T* **96** *and similar horiz designs. Multicoloured. Granite paper. P* 11½ × 12.

344 9p. Type **96** .. 30 30
345 12p. "Edinburgh Castle" .. 40 40
346 20½p. "Maori Village" .. 75 75
347 26p. "Australian Landscape" .. 95 95
348 28p. "Waterhouse's Corner, Adelaide" .. 1·00 1·00
349 31p. "Captain Cook at Botany Bay" .. 1·10 1·10
344/9 .. *Set of* 6 4·00 4·00

(Photo Courvoisier)

1984 (15 Nov). *Christmas. Jersey Orchids* (1*st series*). *T* **97** *and similar vert design. Multicoloured. Granite paper. P* 12 × 11½.

350 9p. Type **97** .. 50 45
351 12p. "Oda Mt Bingham" .. 75 65

See also Nos. 433/7 and 613/17.

98 "*Hebe* off Corbiere, 1874"

(Photo Harrison)

1985 (26 Feb). *Death Centenary of Philip John Ouless (artist). T* **98** *and similar horiz designs. Multicoloured. P* 14 × 15.

352 9p. Type **98** .. 30 30
353 12p. "The *Gaspe* engaging the *Diomede*" .. 40 40
354 22p. "The Paddle-steamer *London* entering Naples, 1856" .. 80 80
355 31p. "The *Rambler* entering Cape Town, 1840" .. 1·40 1·10
356 34p. "St. Aubin's Bay from Mount Bingham, 1872" .. 1·50 1·25
352/6 .. *Set of* 5 4·00 3·50

99 John Ireland (composer) and Faldouet Dolmen

100 Girls' Brigade

(Des Jennifer Toombs. Litho Questa)

1985 (23 Apr). *Europa. European Music Year. T* **99** *and similar horiz designs. Multicoloured. P* 14.

357 10p. Type **99** .. 40 40
358 13p. Ivy St. Helier (actress) and His Majesty's Theatre, London .. 55 55
359 22p. Claude Debussy (composer) and Elizabeth Castle .. 1·00 90
357/9 .. *Set of* 3 1·75 1·60

(Des A. Theobald. Litho Questa)

1985 (30 May). *International Youth Year. T* **100** *and similar vert designs. Multicoloured. P* 14½×14.
360 10p. Type **100** 30 30
361 13p. Girl Guides (75th anniversary) 50 50
362 29p. Prince Charles and Jersey Youth Service Activities Base .. .. 1·00 1·00
363 31p. Sea Cadet Corps .. .. 1·10 1·00
364 34p. Air Training Corps .. .. 1·25 1·10
360/4 .. .. *Set of* 5 3·75 3·50

101 *Duke of Normandy* at Cheapside

(Des G. Palmer. Photo Courvoisier)

1985 (16 July). *The Jersey Western Railway. T* **101** *and similar horiz designs. Multicoloured. Granite paper. P* 11½.
365 10p. Type **101** 55 55
366 13p. Saddletank at First Tower 70 70
367 22p. *La Moye* at Millbrook .. .. 1·10 1·10
368 29p. *St. Heliers* at St. Aubin .. .. .. 1·25 1·25
369 34p. *St. Aubyns* at Corbière .. .. .. 1·40 1·40
365/9 .. .. *Set of* 5 4·50 4·50

102 Memorial Window to Revd. James Hemery (former Dean) and St. Helier Parish Church

(Des R. Granger Barrett. Litho Questa)

1985 (10 Sept). *300th Anniv of Huguenot Immigration. T* **102** *and similar horiz designs. Multicoloured. P* 14.
370 10p. Type **102** 30 30
a. Booklet pane of 4.. .. .. 1·25
371 10p. Judge Francis Jeune, Baron St. Helier, and Houses of Parliament 30 30
a. Booklet pane of 4.. .. .. 1·25
372 13p. Silverware by Pierre Amiraux 45 45
a. Booklet pane of 4.. .. .. 1·75
373 13p. Francis Voisin (merchant) and Russian port.. .. .. 45 45
a. Booklet pane of 4.. .. .. 1·75
374 22p. Robert Brohier, Schweppes carbonation plant and bottles 75 75
a. Booklet pane of 4.. .. .. 2·50
375 22p. George Ingouville, V.C., R.N., and attack on Viborg 75 75
a. Booklet pane of 4.. .. .. 2·50
370/5 .. .. *Set of* 6 2·75 2·75

Each booklet pane has margins all round and text printed on the binding selvedge.

103 Howard Davis Hall, Victoria College

(Des A. Copp. Litho Cartor)

1985 (25 Oct). *Thomas Benjamin Davis (philanthropist) Commemoration. T* **103** *and similar horiz designs. Multicoloured. P* 13½.
376 10p. Type **103** 40 40
377 13p. Racing schooner *Westward* 60 60
378 31p. Howard Davis Park, St. Helier .. .. 1·10 1·10
379 34p. Howard Davis Experimental Farm, Trinity .. .. 1·25 1·25
376/9 .. .. *Set of* 4 3·00 3·00

104 "*Amaryllis belladonna*" (Pandora Sellars)

105 King Harold, William of Normandy and Halley's Comet, 1066 (from Bayeux Tapestry)

(Des C. Abbott. Litho Questa)

1986 (28 Jan). *Jersey Lilies. T* **104** *and similar multicoloured design. P* 15×14½.
380 13p. Type **104** 75 75
381 34p. "A Jersey Lily" (Lily Langtry) (Sir John Millais) (30×48 *mm*) .. .. 1·75 1·75
MS382 140×96 mm. Nos. 380×4 and 381 .. 4·25 4·25

(Des Jennifer Toombs. Litho Cartor)

1986 (4 Mar). *Appearance of Halley's Comet. T* **105** *and similar horiz designs. Multicoloured. P* 13½×13.
383 10p. Type **105** 40 40
384 22p. Lady Carteret, Edmond Halley, map and Comet .. .. 1·00 1·00
385 31p. Aspects of communications in 1910 and 1986 on TV screen .. .. .. 1·40 1·40
383/5 .. .. *Set of* 3 2·50 2·50

106 Dwarf Pansy

107 Queen Elizabeth II (from photo by Karsh)

(Des Pandora Sellars. Litho Questa)

1986 (21 Apr). *Europa. Environmental Conservation. T* **106** *and similar vert designs. Multicoloured. P* 14½×14.
386 10p. Type **106** 40 40
387 14p. Sea Stock 75 75
388 22p. Sand Crocus .. .. 1·10 1·10
386/8 .. .. *Set of* 3 2·00 2·00

(Photo Courvoisier)

1986 (21 Apr). *60th Birthday of Queen Elizabeth II. Granite paper. P* 11½.
389 **107** £1 multicoloured .. .. 3·25 3·25

No. 389 was retained in use as part of the current definitive series until replaced by No. 500.

For a £2 value in this design see No. 491*b*.

108 Le Rât Cottage

109 Prince Andrew and Miss Sarah Ferguson

(Des A. Copp. Litho Cartor)

1986 (17 June). *50th Anniv of National Trust for Jersey. T* **108** *and similar horiz designs. Multicoloured. P* 13½×13.
390 10p. Type **108** 30 30
391 14p. The Elms (Trust headquarters) 45 45
392 22p. Morel Farm 80 80
393 29p. Quétivel Mill 90 90
394 31p. La Vallette 95 95
390/4 .. .. *Set of* 5 3·00 3·00

(Des A. Copp. Litho Cartor)

1986 (23 July). *Royal Wedding. P* 13½.
395 **109** 14p. multicoloured 50 50
396 40p. multicoloured .. .. 1·50 1·50

110 "Gathering Vraic"

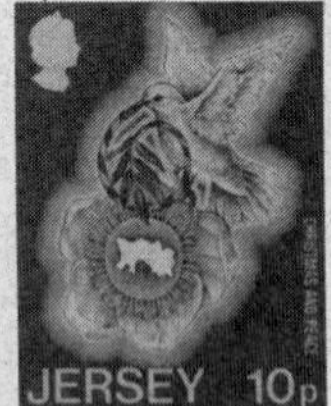

111 Island Map on Jersey Lily, and Dove holding Olive Branch

(Des A. Copp. Litho Questa)

1986 (28 Aug). *Birth Centenary of Edmund Blampied (artist). T* **110** *and similar vert designs. P* 14.
397 10p. multicoloured 40 40
398 14p. black, light blue and brownish grey .. 70 70
399 29p. multicoloured .. .. 1·00 1·00
400 31p. black, pale orange and brownish grey .. 1·25 1·25
401 34p. multicoloured .. .. 1·40 1·40
397/401 .. .. *Set of* 5 4·25 4·25

Designs:—14p. "Driving Home in the Rain"; 29p. "The Miller"; 31p. "The Joy Ride"; 34p. "Tante Elizabeth".

(Des G. Taylor. Litho Questa)

1986 (4 Nov). *Christmas. International Peace Year. T* **111** *and similar vert designs. Multicoloured. P* 14½.
402 10p. Type **111** 40 40
403 14p. Mistletoe wreath encircling European Robin and dove 60 60
404 34p. Christmas cracker releasing dove .. 1·25 1·25
402/4 .. .. *Set of* 3 2·00 2·00

112 *Westward* under Full Sail

(Des A. Copp. Litho Cartor)

1987 (15 Jan). *Racing Schooner "Westward". T* **112** *and similar horiz designs. Multicoloured. P* 13½.
405 10p. Type **112** 40 40
406 14p. T. B. Davis at the helm 60 60
407 31p. *Westward* overhauling *Britannia* .. 1·25 1·10
408 34p. *Westward* fitting-out at St. Helier .. 1·40 1·25
405/8 .. .. *Set of* 4 3·25 3·00

113 De Havilland D.H.86 Dragon Express *Belcroute Bay*

(Des G. Palmer. Litho Questa)

1987 (3 Mar). *50th Anniv of Jersey Airport. T* **113** *and similar horiz designs. Multicoloured. P* 14.
409 10p. Type **113** 30 30
410 14p. Boeing 757 and Douglas DC-9-15 .. 50 50
411 22p. Britten Norman "long nose" Trislander and Islander aircraft 70 70
412 29p. Short 330 and Vickers Viscount 800 .. 1·10 1·10
413 31p. B.A.C. One Eleven 500 and Handley Page H.P.R.7 Dart Herald .. .. 1·25 1·25
409/13 .. .. *Set of* 5 3·50 3·50

114 St. Mary and St. Peter's Roman Catholic Church

(Des A. Copp. Litho Questa)

1987 (23 Apr). *Europa. Modern Architecture. T* **114** *and similar horiz designs. Multicoloured. P* 15×14.
414 11p. Type **114** 45 45
415 15p. Villa Devereux, St. Brelade 65 65
416 22p. Fort Regent Leisure Centre, St. Helier (57×29 *mm*) 90 90
414/16 .. .. *Set of* 3 1·75 1·75

115 H.M.S. *Racehorse* and H.M.S. *Carcass* (bomb-ketches) trapped in Arctic

(Des R. Granger Barrett. Litho Questa)

1987 (9 July). *Jersey Adventurers (2nd series). Philippe D'Auvergne. T* **115** *and similar horiz designs. Multicoloured. P* 14.
417 11p. Type **115** 40 40
418 15p. H.M.S. *Alarm* on fire, Rhode Island .. 50 50
419 29p. H.M.S. *Arethusa* wrecked off Ushant .. 90 80
420 31p. H.M.S. *Rattlesnake* stranded on Isle de Trinidad .. .. 1·00 90
421 34p. Mont Orgueil Castle and fishing boats .. 1·10 1·00
417/21 .. .. *Set of* 5 3·50 3·25

See also Nos. 501/6 and 539/44.

116 Grant of Lands to Normandy, 911 and 933

(Des Jennifer Toombs. Litho Cartor)

1987 (9 Sept–16 Oct). *900th Death Anniv of William the Conqueror. T* **116** *and similar horiz designs. Multicoloured. P* 13½.
422 11p. Type **116** 40 40
a. Booklet pane of 4 (16 Oct) .. .. 2·00
423 15p. Edward the Confessor and Duke Robert I of Normandy landing on Jersey, 1030 .. 45 45
a. Booklet pane of 4 (16 Oct) .. .. 2·25

24 22p. King William's coronation, 1066, and fatal fall, 1087 .. .. 80 80
a. Booklet pane of 4 (16 Oct) .. .. 3·50
25 29p. Death of William Rufus, 1100, and Battle of Tinchebrai, 1106 .. .. 95 95
a. Booklet pane of 4 (16 Oct) .. .. 4·50
26 31p. Civil war between Matilda and Stephen, 1135–41 .. .. 1·10 1·10
a. Booklet pane of 4 (16 Oct) .. .. 5·00
27 34p. Henry inherits Normandy, 1151; John asserts ducal rights in Jersey, 1213 .. 1·25 1·25
a. Booklet pane of 4 (16 Oct) .. .. 5·50
22/7 .. .. *Set of* 6 4·50 4·50

Each booklet pane has margins all round and text printed on the inding selvedge.

117 "Grosnez Castle"

(Photo Courvoisier)

987 (3 Nov). *Christmas. Paintings by John Le Capelain. T* **117** *and similar horiz designs. Multicoloured. Granite paper. P* 11½.
28 11p. Type **117** 40 40
29 15p. "St. Aubin's Bay" 60 60
30 22p. "Mont Orgueil Castle" 80 80
31 31p. "Town Fort and Harbour, St. Helier" .. 1·10 1·10
32 34p. "The Hermitage" .. .. 1·25 1·25
28/32 .. .. *Set of* 5 3·75 3·75

118 *Cymbidium pontac*

(Litho Questa)

988 (12 Jan). *Jersey Orchids* (2*nd series*). *T* **118** *and similar multicoloured designs. P* 14.
33 11p. Type **118** 50 50
34 15p. *Odontioda Eric Young* (*vert*) 60 60
35 29p. *Lycaste auburn* "Seaford" and "Ditchling" .. .. 1·00 1·00
36 31p. *Odontoglossum St. Brelade* (*vert*) .. 1·10 1·10
37 34p. *Cymbidium mavourneen* "Jester" .. 1·25 1·25
33/7 .. .. *Set of* 5 4·00 4·00

119 Labrador Retriever

(Des P. Layton. Litho Questa)

988 (2 Mar). *Centenary of Jersey Dog Club. T* **119** *and similar horiz designs. Multicoloured. P* 14.
38 11p. Type **119** 50 50
39 15p. Wire-haired Dachshund 75 75
40 22p. Pekingese .. .. 1·10 1·10
41 31p. Cavalier King Charles Spaniel .. .. 1·10 1·10
42 34p. Dalmatian .. .. 1·25 1·25
38/42 .. .. *Set of* 5 4·25 4·25

120 De Havilland D.H.C.7 Dash Seven Aircraft, London Landmarks and Jersey Control Tower

121 Rodriguez Fody

(Des A. Copp. Litho Cartor)

988 (26 Apr). *Europa. Transport and Communications. T* **120** *and similar multicoloured designs. P* 14×13½ (*horiz*) *or* 13½×14 (*vert*).
43 16p. Type **120** 50 50
44 16p. Weather radar and Jersey airport landing system (*vert*) 50 50
45 22p. Hydrofoil, St. Malo and Elizabeth Castle, St. Helier 90 90
46 22p. Port control tower and Jersey Radio maritime communication centre, La Moye (*vert*) 90 90
43/6 .. .. *Set of* 4 2·50 2·50

(Des W. Oliver. Litho Cartor)

1988 (6 July). *Wildlife Preservation Trust* (5*th series*). *T* **121** *and similar multicoloured designs. P* 13½×14 (*vert*) *or* 14×13½ (*horiz*).
447 12p. Type **121** 55 55
448 16p. Volcano Rabbit (*horiz*) 70 70
449 29p. White-faced Marmoset .. .. .. 1·10 1·10
450 31p. Ploughshare Tortoise (*horiz*) .. .. 1·25 1·25
451 34p. Mauritius Kestrel .. .. .. 1·40 1·40
447/51 .. .. *Set of* 5 4·50 4·50

122 Rain Forest Leaf Frog, Costa Rica

123 St. Clement Parish Church

(Des V. Ambrus. Photo Courvoisier)

1988 (27 Sept). *Operation Raleigh. T* **122** *and similar horiz designs. Multicoloured. Granite paper. P* 12.
452 12p. Type **122** 45 45
453 16p. Archaelogical survey, Peru 55 55
454 22p. Climbing glacier, Chile 80 80
455 29p. Red Cross Centre, Solomon Islands .. 1·00 1·00
456 31p. Underwater exploration, Australia .. 1·10 1·10
457 34p. *Zebu* (brigantine) returning to St. Helier 1·25 1·25
452/7 .. .. *Set of* 6 4·50 4·50

(Des P. Layton. Litho B.D.T.)

1988 (15 Nov). *Christmas. Jersey Parish Churches* (1*st series*). *T* **123** *and similar horiz designs. Multicoloured. P* 13½.
458 12p. Type **123** 35 35
459 16p. St. Ouen 60 60
460 31p. St. Brelade 90 90
461 34p. St. Lawrence 95 95
458/61 .. .. *Set of* 4 2·50 2·50

See also Nos. 535/8 and 597/600.

124 Talbot "Type 4 CT Tourer", 1912

(Des A. Copp. Litho Questa)

1989 (31 Jan). *Vintage Cars* (1*st series*). *T* **124** *and similar horiz designs. Multicoloured. P* 14.
462 12p. Type **124** 40 40
463 16p. De Dion "Bouton Type 1-D", 1920 .. 60 60
464 23p. Austin 7 "Chummy", 1926 .. .. 75 75
465 30p. Ford "Model T", 1926 .. .. .. 90 90
466 32p. Bentley 8 litre, 1930 .. .. .. 1·10 1·10
467 35p. Cadillac "452A -V16 Fleetwood Sports Phaeton", 1931 .. .. 1·25 1·25
462/7 .. .. *Set of* 6 4·50 4·50

See also Nos. 591/6.

125 Belcroute Bay

125a Arms of King George VI

(Des G. Drummond (1p. to 75p.). Photo Courvoisier (£2), Litho Questa (£4), B.D.T. (others))

1989 (21 Mar)–**95**. *Jersey Scenes. T* **125** *and similar horiz designs, Queen's portrait as T* **107** *and T* **125a**. *Multicoloured. P* 11½×12 (£2), 15×14 (£4) *or* 13×13½ (*others*).
468 1p. Type **125** 10 10
469 2p. High Street, St. Aubin 10 10
470 4p. Royal Jersey Golf Course 10 10
a. Booklet pane of 6 with margins all round (3.5.90) 60
471 5p. Portelet Bay 10 10
a. Booklet pane of 6 with margins all round (12.2.91) 75
472 10p. Les Charrières D'Anneport 20 25
473 13p. St. Helier Marina 25 30
474 14p. Sand yacht racing, St. Ouen's Bay .. 30 35
a. Booklet pane of 6 with margins all round (3.5.90) .. .. 2·00
b. Booklet pane of 8 with margins all round (22.5.92) .. .. 2·75
475 15p. Rozel Harbour 30 35
a. Booklet pane of 6 with margins all round (12.2.91) .. .. 2·00
476 16p. St. Aubin's Harbour 30 35
a. Booklet pane of 8 with margins all round (22.5.92) .. .. 3·50
477 17p. Jersey Airport 35 40
478 18p. Corbière Lighthouse 35 40
a. Booklet pane of 6 with margins all round (3.5.90) .. .. 2·50
479 19p. Val de la Mare 40 45
480 20p. Elizabeth Castle 40 45
a. Booklet pane of 6 with margins all round (12.2.91) .. .. 3·00
481 21p. Greve de Lecq (16.1.90) 40 45
482 22p. Samarès Manor (16.1.90) 45 50
a. Booklet pane of 8 with margins all round (22.5.92) .. .. 4·25
483 23p. Bonne Nuit Harbour (16.1.90) 45 50
484 24p. Grosnez Castle (16.1.90) 50 55
485 25p. Augrès Manor (16.1.90) 50 55
486 26p. Central Market (16.1.90) 50 55
487 27p. St. Brelade's Bay (16.1.90) 55 60
488 30p. St. Ouen's Manor (13.3.90) 60 65
489 40p. La Hougue Bie (13.3.90) 80 85
490 50p. Mont Orgueil Castle (13.3.90) .. .. 1·00 1·10
491 75p. Royal Square, St Helier (13.3.90) .. 1·50 1·60
491*b* £2 Type **107** (19.3.91) .. .. .. 4·50 4·25
491*c* £4 Type **125a** (24.1.95) .. .. .. 8·00 8·25
468/91*c* .. .. *Set of* 26 22·00 23·00

126 Agile Frog

127 Toddlers' Toys

(Des W. Oliver. Litho Cartor)

1989 (25 Apr). *Endangered Jersey Fauna. T* **126** *and similar multicoloured designs. P* 13½×13 (*Nos.* 492 *and* 495), 13×13½ (*No.* 493) *or* 13½×14 (*No.* 494).
492 13p. Type **126** .. .. 1·00 1·00
493 13p. *Heteropterus morpheus* (butterfly) (*vert*) 1·00 1·00
494 17p. Barn Owl (*vert*) .. .. 1·10 1·10
495 17p. Green Lizard .. .. 1·10 1·10
492/5 .. .. *Set of* 4 3·75 3·75

(Des Clare Luke. Litho Questa)

1989 (25 Apr). *Europa. Children's Toys and Games. T* **127** *and similar square designs showing clay plaques. Multicoloured. P* 14.
496 17p. Type **127** 50 50
497 17p. Playground games 50 50
498 23p. Party games 90 90
499 23p. Teenage sports 90 90
496/9 .. .. *Set of* 4 2·50 2·50

128 Queen Elizabeth II and Royal Yacht *Britannia* in Elizabeth Harbour

(Des A. Copp. Litho Questa)

1989 (24 May). *Royal Visit. P* 14½.
500 **128** £1 multicoloured .. .. 3·00 3·00

No. 500 was retained in use as part of the current definitive series until replaced by No. 634.

129 Philippe D'Auvergne presented to Louis XVI, 1786

(Des V. Ambrus. Litho Cartor)

1989 (7 July). *Bicentenary of the French Revolution. Philippe D'Auvergne. T* **129** *and similar horiz designs. Multicoloured. P* 13½.
501 13p. Type **129** 45 45
a. Booklet pane of 4 .. .. .. 1·25
502 17p. Storming the Bastille, 1789 .. .. 60 60
a. Booklet pane of 4 .. .. .. 2·00
503 23p. Marie de Bouillon and revolutionaries, 1790 .. .. 80 80
a. Booklet pane of 4 .. .. .. 2·50
504 30p. Auvergne's headquarters at Mont Orgueil, 1795 .. .. 1·10 1·10
a. Booklet pane of 4 .. .. .. 4·25
505 32p. Landing arms for Chouan rebels, 1796 .. 1·25 1·25
a. Booklet pane of 4 .. .. .. 4·25
506 35p. The last Chouan revolt, 1799 .. .. 1·40 1·40
a. Booklet pane of 4 .. .. .. 4·75
501/6 .. .. *Set of* 6 5·00 5·00

Each booklet pane has margins all round and text printed on the binding selvedge.

See also Nos. 539/44.

130 *St. Helier* off Elizabeth Castle

(Des G. Palmer. Litho Questa)

1989 (5 Sept). *Centenary of Great Western Railway Steamer Service to Channel Islands. T* **130** *and similar horiz designs. Multicoloured. P* 13½×14.

507 13p. Type **130** 40 40
508 17p. *Caesarea II* off Corbière Lighthouse .. 50 50
509 27p. *Reindeer* in St. Helier harbour .. 1·00 1·00
510 32p. *Ibex* racing *Frederica* off Portelet .. 1·25 1·25
511 35p. *Lynx* off Noirmont .. .. .. 1·40 1·40
507/11 .. .. *Set of* 5 4·00 4·00

131 "Gorey Harbour"

132 Head Post Office, Broad Street, 1969

(Litho Enschedé)

1989 (24 Oct). *150th Birth Anniv of Sarah Louisa Kilpack (artist). T* **131** *and similar horiz designs. Multicoloured. P* 13×12½.

512 13p. Type **131** 40 40
513 17p. "La Corbière" 50 50
514 23p. "Grève de Lecq" .. .. 1·00 1·00
515 32p. "Bouley Bay" .. .. 1·25 1·25
516 35p. "Mont Orgueil" .. .. 1·40 1·40
512/16 .. .. *Set of* 5 4·00 4·00

(Des P. Layton. Litho Cartor, France)

1990 (13 Mar). *Europa. Post Office Buildings. T* **132** *and similar multicoloured designs. P* 13½×14 (*vert*) *or* 14×13½ (*horiz*).

517 18p. Type **132** 50 50
518 18p. Postal Headquarters, Mont Millais, 1990 50 50
519 24p. Hue Street Post Office, 1815 (*horiz*) .. 90 90
520 24p. Head Post Office, Halkett Place, 1890 (*horiz*) 90 90
517/20 .. .. *Set of* 4 2·50 2·50

133 "Battle of Flowers" Parade

134 Early Printing Press and Jersey Newspaper Mastheads

(Des A. Copp. Litho Enschedé)

1990 (3 May). *Festival of Tourism. T* **133** *and similar vert designs. Multicoloured. P* 14×13½.

521 18p. Type **133** 60 60
522 24p. Sports 75 75
523 29p. Mont Orgueil Castle and German Underground Hospital Museum 95 95
524 32p. Salon Culinaire .. .. 1·00 1·00
521/4 .. .. *Set of* 4 3·00 3·00
MS525 151×100 mm. Nos. 521/4 .. .. 3·00 3·00

(Des A. Copp. Litho Cartor)

1990 (26 June). *International Literacy Year. Jersey News Media. T* **134** *and similar horiz designs. Multicoloured. P* 13½.

526 14p. Type **134** 55 55
527 18p. Modern press, and offices of *Jersey Evening Post* in 1890 and 1990 .. .. 60 60
528 34p. Radio Jersey broadcaster .. .. 1·10 1·10
529 37p. Channel Television studio cameraman .. 1·10 1·10
526/9 .. .. *Set of* 4 3·00 3·00

PRICES OF SETS

Set prices are given for many issues, generally those containing three stamps or more. Definitive sets include one of each value or major colour change, but do not cover different perforations, die types or minor shades. Where a choice is possible the set prices are based on the cheapest versions of the stamps included in the listings.

135 British Aerospace Hawk T.1

136 "Landsat 5" and Thematic Mapper Image over Jersey

(Des G. Palmer. Litho Questa)

1990 (4 Sept). *50th Anniv of Battle of Britain. T* **135** *and similar horiz designs. Multicoloured. P* 14.

530 14p. Type **135** 45 45
531 18p. Supermarine Spitfire 60 60
532 24p. Hawker Hurricane Mk I 85 85
533 34p. Vickers-Armstrong Wellington .. .. 1·50 1·50
534 37p. Avro Type 683 Lancaster .. .. 1·60 1·60
530/4 .. .. *Set of* 5 4·50 4·50

(Des P. Layton. Litho B.D.T.)

1990 (13 Nov). *Christmas. Jersey Parish Churches* (2*nd series*). *Horiz designs as T* **123**. *Multicoloured. P* 13½.

535 14p. St. Helier 40 40
536 18p. Grouville 60 60
537 34p. St. Saviour .. .. 1·10 1·10
538 37p. St. John .. .. 1·25 1·25
535/8 .. .. *Set of* 4 3·00 3·00

(Des V. Ambrus. Litho Cartor)

1991 (22 Jan). *175th Death Anniv of Philippe d'Auvergne. Horiz designs as T* **129**. *Multicoloured. P* 13½.

539 15p. Prince's Tower, La Hougue Bie 50 50
540 20p. Auvergne's arrest in Paris 60 60
541 26p. Auvergne plotting against Napoleon .. 80 80
542 31p. Execution of George Cadoudal .. 1·00 1·00
543 37p. H.M.S. *Surly* (cutter) attacking French convoy .. .. 1·25 1·25
544 44p. Auvergne's last days in London .. 1·40 1·40
539/44 .. .. *Set of* 6 5·00 5·00

(Des A. Copp. Litho Enschedé)

1991 (19 Mar). *Europa. Europe in Space. T* **136** *and similar vert designs. Multicoloured. P* 14½×13.

545 20p. Type **136** 55 55
546 20p. "ERS-1" earth resources remote sensing satellite 55 55
547 26p. "Meteosat" weather satellite 85 85
548 26p. "Olympus" direct broadcasting satellite 85 85
545/8 .. .. *Set of* 4 2·50 2·50

137 1941 1d. Stamp (50th anniv of first Jersey postage stamp)

138 *Melitaea cinxia*

(Des A. Copp. Litho Cartor)

1991 (16 May). *Anniversaries. T* **137** *and similar vert designs. Multicoloured. P* 13½.

549 15p. Type **137** 40 40
550 20p. Steam train (centenary of Jersey Eastern Railway extension to Gorey Pier) .. 60 60
551 26p. Jersey cow and Herd Book (125th anniv of Jersey Herd Book) 80 80
552 31p. Stone-laying ceremony (from painting by P. J. Ouless) (150th anniv of Victoria Harbour) 90 90
553 53p. Marie Bartlett and hospital (250th anniv of Marie Bartlett's hospital bequest) .. 1·75 1·75
549/53 .. .. *Set of* 5 4·00 4·00

(Des W. Oliver. Litho Enschedé)

1991 (9 July). *Butterflies and Moths. T* **138** *and similar horiz designs. Multicoloured. P* 13×12½.

554 15p. Type **138** 40 40
555 20p. *Euplagia quadripunctaria* 50 50
556 37p. *Deilephilia porcellus* .. .. .. 1·60 1·60
557 57p. *Inachis io* .. .. 2·00 2·00
554/7 .. .. *Set of* 4 4·00 4·00

139 Drilling for Water, Ethiopia

140 "This is the Place for Me"

(Des A. Theobald. Litho B.D.T.)

1991 (3 Sept). *Overseas Aid. T* **139** *and similar horiz designs. Multicoloured. P* 13½×14.

558 15p. Type **139** 50 4
559 20p. Building construction, Rwanda 60 6
560 26p. Village polytechnic, Kenya 80 8
561 31p. Treating leprosy, Tanzania .. .. 1·00 1·0
562 37p. Ploughing, Zambia .. .. .. 1·25 1·2
563 44p. Immunisation clinic, Lesotho .. .. 1·40 1·4
558/63 .. .. *Set of* 6 5·00 5·0

(Litho Questa)

1991 (5 Nov). *Christmas. Illustrations by Edmund Blampied fo J.M. Barrie's* Peter Pan. *T* **140** *and similar vert designs Multicoloured. P* 14.

564 15p. Type **140** 40 4
565 20p. "The Island Come True" 65 6
566 37p. "The Never Bird" .. .. 1·25 1·2
567 53p. "The Great White Father" .. .. 1·60 1·6
564/7 .. .. *Set of* 4 3·50 3·5

141 Pied Wagtail

142 Shipping at Shanghai, 1860

(Des W. Oliver. Litho Cartor)

1992 (7 Jan). *Winter Birds. T* **141** *and similar vert designs Multicoloured. P* 13½×14.

568 16p. Type **141** 55 4
569 22p. Firecrest 80 6
570 28p. Common Snipe 90 7
571 39p. Lapwing .. .. 1·40 1·0
572 57p. Fieldfare .. .. 1·90 1·5
568/72 .. .. *Set of* 5 5·00 4·2

See also Nos. 635/9.

(Des V. Ambrus. Litho Cartor)

1992 (25 Feb). *Jersey Adventurers* (3*rd series*). *150th Birth Ann of William Mesny. T* **142** *and similar horiz design Multicoloured. P* 13½.

573 16p. Type **142** 50
b. Booklet pane of 4 .. .. 1·25
574 16p. Mesny's junk running Taiping blockade, 1862 .. .. 50 5
a. Booklet pane of 4 .. .. 1·25
575 22p. General Mesny outside river gate, 1874 75 7
a. Booklet pane of 4 .. .. 1·75
576 22p. Mesny in Burma, 1877 .. .. .. 75 7
a. Booklet pane of 4 .. .. 1·75
577 33p. Mesny and Governor Chang, 1882 .. 1·00 1·0
a. Booklet pane of 4 .. .. 2·50
578 33p. Mesny in mandarin's sedan chair, 1886 .. 1·00 1·0
a. Booklet pane of 4 .. .. 2·50
573/8 .. .. *Set of* 6 4·00 4·0

Each booklet pane has margins all round and text printed on th binding selvedge.

143 *Tickler* (brigantine)

(Des A. Copp. Litho Questa)

1992 (14 Apr). *Jersey Shipbuilding. T* **143** *and similar hor designs. Multicoloured. P* 14.

579 16p. Type **143** 50
580 22p. *Hebe* (brig) 80
581 50p. *Gemini* (barque) .. .. 1·60 1·
582 57p. *Percy Douglas* (full-rigged ship) .. 1·90 1·
579/82 .. .. *Set of* 4 4·25 4·
MS583 148×98 mm. Nos. 579/82 .. .. 4·25 4·

144 John Bertram (ship owner) and Columbus

145 "Snow Leopards" (Allison Griffiths)

(Des V. Ambrus. Litho Questa)

992 (14 Apr). *Europa. 500th Anniv of Discovery of America by Columbus. T* **144** *and similar horiz designs. P* 14×14½.

84 22p. Type **144** — 70 70
85 28p. Sir George Carteret (founder of New Jersey) — 85 85
86 39p. Sir Walter Ralegh (founder of Virginia) — 1·25 1·25
84/6 *Set of* 3 — 2·50 2·50

(Litho Questa)

992 (23 June). *Batik Designs. T* **145** *and similar vert designs. Multicoloured. P* 14½.

87 16p. Type **145** — 50 50
88 22p. "Three Elements" (Nataly Miorin) — 70 70
89 39p. "Three Men in a Tub" (Amanda Crocker) — 1·25 1·25
90 57p. "Cockatoos" (Michelle Millard) — 1·75 1·75
87/90 *Set of* 4 — 3·75 3·75

(Des A. Copp. Litho Enschedé)

1992 (8 Sept). *Vintage Cars* (*2nd series*). *Horiz designs as T* **124.** *Multicoloured. P* 13×12½.

591 16p. Morris Cowley "Bullnose", 1925 — 35 35
592 22p. Rolls Royce "20/25", 1932 — 50 50
593 28p. Chenard and Walcker "T5", 1924 — 80 80
594 33p. Packard 900 series "Light Eight", 1932 — 90 90
595 39p. Lanchester "21", 1927 — 1·10 1·10
596 50p. Buick "30 Roadster", 1913 — 1·50 1·50
591/6 *Set of* 6 — 4·50 4·50

(Des P. Layton. Litho B.D.T.)

1992 (3 Nov). *Christmas. Jersey Parish Churches* (3*rd series*). *Horiz designs as T* **123.** *Multicoloured. P* 13½.

597 16p. Trinity — 40 35
598 22p. St. Mary — 55 60
599 39p. St. Martin — 1·00 1·00
600 57p. St. Peter — 1·40 1·40
597/600 *Set of* 4 — 3·00 3·00

146 Farmhouse

147 *Phragmipedium* Eric Young "Jersey"

(Des A. Copp. Litho B.D.T.)

1993 (11 Jan). *Booklet Stamps. T* **146** *and similar horiz designs. Multicoloured. P* 13.

601 (–) Type **146** — 40 45
 a. Booklet pane. Nos. 601/4, each × 2, with margins all round — 3·25
602 (–) Trinity Church — 40 45
603 (–) Daffodils and cows — 40 45
604 (–) Jersey cows — 40 45
605 (–) Sunbathing — 50 55
 a. Booklet pane. Nos. 605/8, each × 2, with margins all round — 4·00
606 (–) Windsurfing — 50 55
607 (–) Crab (Queen's head at left) — 50 55
608 (–) Crab (Queen's head at right) — 50 55
609 (–) "Singin' in the Rain" float — 60 65
 a. Booklet pane. Nos. 609/12, each × 2, with margins all round — 5·00
610 (–) "Dragon Dance" float — 60 65
611 (–) "Bali, Morning of the World" float — 60 65
612 (–) "Zulu Fantasy" float — 60 65
601/12 *Set of* 12 — 5·75 6·25

The above do not show face values, but are inscribed "BAILIWICK POSTAGE PAID" (Nos. 601/4), "U.K. MINIMUM POSTAGE PAID" (Nos. 605/8) or "EUROPE POSTAGE PAID" (Nos. 609/12). They were initially sold at 17p., 23p, or 28p, but Nos. 601/4 and 609/12 were increased to 18p. and 30p. on 10 January 1994 and Nos. 601/4 to 19p. on 4 July 1995. On 10 March 1997 Nos. 601/4 were increased to 20p., Nos. 605/8 to 24p. and Nos. 609/12 to 31p.

(Litho Enschedé)

1993 (26 Jan). *Jersey Orchids* (3*rd series*). *T* **147** *and similar vert designs. Multicoloured. P* 14×13.

613 17p. Type **147** — 50 35
614 23p. *Odontoglossum* Augres "Trinity" — 75 45
615 28p. *Miltonia* St. Helier "Colomberie" — 90 65
616 39p. *Phragmipedium pearcei* — 1·25 1·25
617 57p. *Calanthe* Grouville "Grey" — 1·75 1·75
613/17 *Set of* 5 — 4·50 4·00

148 Douglas DC-3 Dakota

149 "Jersey's Opera House" (Ian Rolls)

(Des A. Theobald. Litho Questa)

1993 (1 Apr). *75th Anniv of Royal Air Force. T* **148** *and similar horiz designs. Multicoloured. P* 14.

618 17p. Type **148** — 50 50
619 23p. Wight seaplane — 70 70
620 28p. Avro Shackleton A.E.W.2 — 80 80
621 33p. Gloster Meteor Mk III and De Havilland D.H.100 Vampire FB.5 — 90 90
622 39p. Hawker Siddeley Harrier GR.1A — 1·10 1·10
623 57p. Panavia Tornado F Mk 3 — 1·60 1·60
618/23 *Set of* 6 — 5·00 5·00
MS624 147×98 mm. Nos. 619 and 623 — 3·50 3·50

Nos. 618/24 also commemorate the 50th anniversary of the Royal Air Force Association and the 40th anniversary of the first air display on Jersey.

(Litho Cartor)

1993 (1 Apr). *Europa. Contemporary Art. T* **149** *and similar vert designs. Multicoloured. P* 13½×14.

625 23p. Type **149** — 70 70
626 28p. "The Ham and Tomato Bap" (Jonathan Hubbard) — 85 85
627 39p. "Vase of Flowers" (Neil MacKenzie) — 1·25 1·25
625/7 *Set of* 3 — 2·50 2·50

150 1943 ½d. Occcupation Stamp

151 Queen Elizabeth II (from painting by Marca McGregor)

(Des G. Drummond. Litho Cartor)

1993 (2 June). *50th Anniv of Edmund Blampied's Occupation Stamps. T* **150** *and similar horiz designs showing stamps from the 1943 issue. P* 13½.

628 17p. myrtle-green, pale green and black — 40 45
629 23p. vermilion, salmon-pink and black — 55 55
630 28p. chocolate, cinnamon and black — 75 75
631 33p. reddish orange, salmon and black — 90 90
632 39p. royal blue, cobalt and black — 1·25 1·25
633 50p. bright magenta, pale mauve and black — 1·40 1·40
628/33 *Set of* 6 — 4·75 4·75

Designs:—23p. 1d. value; 28p. 1½d. value; 33p. 2d. value; 39p. 2½d. value; 50p. 3d. value.

(Litho Questa)

1993 (2 June). *40th Anniv of Coronation. P* 14½.

634 **151** £1 multicoloured — 2·50 2·50

No. 634 was retained in use as part of the current definitive series until replaced by No. 796.

152 Short-toed Treecreeper

153 Two Angels holding "Hark the Herald Angels Sing" Banner

(Des W. Oliver. Litho Cartor)

1993 (7 Sept). *Summer Birds. T* **152** *and similar vert designs. Multicoloured. P* 13½×14.

635 17p. Type **152** — 50 50
636 23p. Dartford Warbler — 75 75
637 28p. Common Wheatear — 85 85
638 39p. Cirl Bunting — 1·25 1·25
639 57p. Jay — 1·75 1·75
635/9 *Set of* 5 — 4·50 4·50

(Des N. MacKenzie. Litho Enschedé)

1993 (2 Nov). *Christmas. Stained Glass Windows by Henry Bosdet from St. Aubin on the Hill Church. T* **153** *and similar vert designs. Multicoloured. P* 14×13.

640 17p. Type **153** — 45 45
641 23p. Two angels playing harps — 65 65
642 39p. Two angels playing violins — 1·25 1·25
643 57p. Two angels holding "Once in Royal David's City" banner — 1·90 1·90
640/3 *Set of* 4 — 3·75 3·75

154 *Coprinus comatus*

(Des W. Oliver. Litho Questa)

1994 (11 Jan). *Fungi. T* **154** *and similar vert designs. Multicoloured. P* 14½.

644 18p. Type **154** — 45 45
645 23p. *Amanita muscaria* — 70 70
646 30p. *Cantharellus cibarius* — 90 90
647 41p. *Macrolepiota procera* — 1·25 1·25
648 60p. *Clathrus ruber* — 1·75 1·75
644/8 *Set of* 5 — 4·50 4·50

155 Pekingese

(Des P. Layton, adapted A. Copp. Litho Questa)

1994 (18 Feb). *"Hong Kong '94" International Stamp Exhibition. "Chinese Year of the Dog". Sheet* 110×75 *mm. P* 15×14½.

MS649 **155** £1 multicoloured — 3·00 3·00

156 Maine Coon

157 Mammoth Hunt, La Cotte de St. Brelade

(Des P. Layton. Litho B.D.T.)

1994 (5 Apr). *21st Anniv of Jersey Cat Club. T* **156** *and similar multicoloured designs. P* 14.

650 18p. Type **156** — 45 45
651 23p. British Shorthair (*horiz*) — 70 60
652 35p. Persian — 90 80
653 41p. Siamese (*horiz*) — 1·25 1·10
654 60p. Non-pedigree — 1·75 1·75
650/4 *Set of* 5 — 4·50 4·25

(Des A. Copp. Litho Enschedé)

1994 (5 Apr). *Europa. Archaeological Discoveries. T* **157** *and similar horiz designs. Multicoloured. P* 13½×14.

655 23p. Type **157** — 50 50
 a. Horiz pair. Nos. 655/6 — 1·00 1·00
656 23p. Stone Age hunters pulling mammoth into cave — 50 50
657 30p. Chambered passage, La Hougue Bie — 75 75
 a. Horiz pair. Nos. 657/8 — 1·50 1·50
658 30p. Transporting stones — 75 75
655/8 *Set of* 4 — 2·25 2·25

Nos. 655/6 and 657/8 were printed together, *se-tenant*, in horizontal pairs throughout the sheets.

158 Gliders and Towing Aircraft approaching France

(Des A. Theobald. Litho B.D.T.)

1994 (6 June). *50th Anniv of D-Day. T* **158** *and similar horiz designs. Multicoloured. P* 13½×14.

659	18p. Type **158**	60	50
	a. Booklet pane. Nos. 659/60, each × 3, with margins all round	2·75	
	b. Booklet pane. Nos. 659/64, with margins all round	6·00	
660	18p. Landing craft approaching beaches	60	50
661	23p. Disembarking from landing craft on Gold Beach	80	70
	a. Booklet pane. Nos. 661/2, each × 3, with margins all round	5·50	
662	23p. British troops on Sword Beach	80	70
663	30p. Spitfires over beaches	90	80
	a. Booklet pane. Nos. 663/4, each × 3, with margins all round	6·00	
664	30p. Invasion map	90	80
659/64	*Set of* 6	4·00	3·50

No. 659b was also available as a loose pane from the Philatelic Bureau.

159 Sailing

(Des A. Theobald. Litho Questa)

1994 (6 June). *Centenary of International Olympic Committee. T* **159** *and similar horiz designs. Multicoloured. P* 14.

665	18p. Type **159**	45	45
666	23p. Rifle shooting	60	60
667	30p. Hurdling	85	85
668	41p. Swimming	1·25	1·25
669	60p. Hockey	1·60	1·60
665/9	*Set of* 5	4·25	4·25

160 Strawberry Anemone

(Des W. Oliver. Litho Cartor)

1994 (2 Aug). *Marine Life. T* **160** *and similar horiz designs. Multicoloured. P* 13½.

670	18p. Type **160**	50	50
671	23p. Hermit Crab and parasitic anemone	75	75
672	41p. Velvet Swimming Crab	1·40	1·40
673	60p. Common Jellyfish	1·75	1·75
670/3	*Set of* 4	4·00	4·00

161 Condor 10 Wavepiercer Catamaran

(Des A. Copp. Litho Questa)

1994 (1 Oct). *25th Anniv of Jersey Postal Administration. T* **161** *and similar horiz designs. Multicoloured. P* 14.

674	18p. Type **161**	45	45
675	23p. Map of Jersey and pillar box	60	60
676	35p. Vickers Type 953 Vanguard of B.E.A.	85	75
677	41p. Shorts 360 of Aurigny Air Services	1·10	1·00
678	60p. *Caesarea* (Sealink ferry)	1·50	1·40
674/8	*Set of* 5	4·00	3·75
MS679	150×100 mm. Nos. 674/8	4·00	3·75

162 "Away in a Manger"

163 Dog and "GOOD LUCK"

(Des A. Copp. Litho Questa)

1994 (8 Nov). *Christmas. Carols. T* **162** *and similar horiz designs. Multicoloured. P* 14.

680	18p. Type **162**	45	45
681	23p. "Hark! the Herald Angels Sing"	60	60
682	41p. "While Shepherds watched"	1·25	1·25
683	60p. "We Three Kings of Orient Are"	1·60	1·60
680/3	*Set of* 4	3·50	3·50

(Des A. Copp. Litho B.D.T.)

1995 (24 Jan). *Greetings Stamps. T* **163** *and similar vert designs. Multicoloured. P* 13.

684	18p. Type **163**	45	45
	a. Horiz strip of 4. Nos. 684/7	1·75	
	b. Booklet pane of 9. Nos. 684/92	5·00	
685	18p. Rose and "WITH LOVE"	45	45
686	18p. Chick and "CONGRATULATIONS"	45	45
687	18p. Bouquet of flowers and "THANK YOU"	45	45
688	23p. Dove with letter and "WITH LOVE"	55	55
	a. Horiz strip of 4. Nos. 688/91	2·25	
689	23p. Cat and "GOOD LUCK"	55	55
690	23p. Carnations and "THANK YOU"	55	55
691	23p. Parrot and "CONGRATULATIONS"	55	55
692	60p. Pig and "HAPPY NEW YEAR" (25×63 *mm*)	1·40	1·40
684/92	*Set of* 9	5·00	5·00

Nos. 684/7 and 688/91 were printed together, *se-tenant*, in horizontal strips of 4 throughout sheets of 20 (4×5).

No. 692 commemorates the Chinese New Year of the Pig and was also printed in sheets of 10 (5×2).

164 Camellia "Captain Rawes"

165 "Liberation" (sculpture, Philip Jackson)

(Des and litho Questa)

1995 (21 Mar). *Camellias. T* **164** *and similar horiz designs. Multicoloured. P* 14½.

693	18p. Type **164**	60	60
694	23p. "Brigadoon"	80	80
695	30p. "Elsie Jury"	95	95
696	35p. "Augusto L'Gouveia Pinto"	1·00	1·00
697	41p. "Bella Romana"	1·10	1·10
693/7	*Set of* 5	4·00	4·00

(Des A. Theobald. Litho Cartor)

1995 (9 May). *Europa. Peace and Freedom. P* 13½.

698 **165**	23p. black and dull violet-blue	55	55
699	30p. black and rose-pink	70	75

166 Bailiff and Crown Officers in Launch

167 Bell Heather

(Des A. Theobald. Litho B.D.T.)

1995 (9 May). *50th Anniv of Liberation. T* **166** *and similar horiz designs. Multicoloured. P* 15×14.

700	18p. Type **166**	40	40
	a. Booklet pane. Nos. 700/1, each × 3, with margins all round	2·00	
701	18p. *Vega* (Red Cross supply ship)	40	40
702	23p. H.M.S. *Beagle* (destroyer)	60	60
	a. Booklet pane. Nos. 702/3, each × 3, with margins all round	2·75	
703	23p. British troops in Ordnance Yard, St. Helier	60	60
704	60p. King George VI and Queen Elizabeth in Jersey	1·50	1·50
	a. Booklet pane. Nos. 704/5, each × 3, with margins all round	7·50	
705	60p. Unloading supplies from landing craft, St. Aubin's	1·50	1·50
700/5	*Set of* 6	4·50	4·50
MS706	110×75 mm. £1 Royal Family with Winston Churchill on Buckingham Palace balcony, V.E. Day (80×39 *mm*)	2·50	2·50
	a. Booklet pane. As No. **MS**706 with additional margins all round showing arms, mace and inscriptions	2·50	

(Des N. Parlett. Litho B.D.T.)

1995 (4 July). *European Nature Conservation Year. Wild Flowers. T* **167** *and similar vert designs. Multicoloured. P* 13.

707	19p. Type **167**	45	45
	a. Horiz strip of 5. Nos. 707/11	2·25	
708	19p. Sea Campion	45	45
709	19p. Spotted Rock-rose	45	45
710	19p. Thrift	45	45
711	19p. Sheep's-bit Scabious	45	45
712	23p. Field Bind-weed	50	50
	a. Horiz strip of 5. Nos. 712/16	2·50	
713	23p. Common Bird's-foot-trefoil	50	50
714	23p. Sea-holly	50	50
715	23p. Common Centaury	50	50
716	23p. Dwarf Pansy	50	50
707/16	*Set of* 10	4·75	4·75

Nos. 707/11 and 712/16 were printed together, *se-tenant*, in horizontal strips of 5 throughout sheets of 20, the backgrounds forming composite designs.

168 *Precis almana*

(Des W. Oliver. Litho Questa)

1995 (1 Sept). *Butterflies. T* **168** *and similar horiz designs. Multicoloured. P* 14.

717	19p. Type **168**	55	5
718	23p. *Papilio palinurus*	70	7
719	30p. *Catopsilia scylla*	90	9
720	41p. *Papilio rumanzovia*	1·10	1·1
721	60p. *Troides helena*	1·75	1·7
717/21	*Set of* 5	4·50	4·5
MS722	150×100 mm. Nos. 720/1	3·00	3·0
	a. 41p. value imperforate		

No. **MS**722 includes the "Singapore '95" International Stam Exhibition logo on the sheet margin and shows the two stam designs without frames.

169 Peace Doves and United Nations Anniversary Emblem

(Des A. Copp. Litho Enschedé)

1995 (24 Oct). *50th Anniv of United Nations. T* **169** *and simila horiz design. P* 13×14½.

723 **169**	19p. cobalt and royal blue	45	4
724 –	23p. turquoise-green and deep blue-green	50	5
725 –	41p. deep blue-green and turquoise-green	85	8
726 **169**	60p. royal blue and cobalt	1·40	1·4
723/6	*Set of* 4	3·00	3·0

Design:—23p., 41p. Symbolic wheat and anniversary emblem.

170 "Puss in Boots"

(Des V. Ambrus. Litho Cartor)

1995 (24 Oct). *Christmas. Pantomimes. T* **170** *and similar hori designs. Multicoloured. P* 13½.

727	19p. Type **170**	45	4
728	23p. "Cinderella"	50	5
729	41p. "Sleeping Beauty"	85	8
730	60p. "Aladdin"	1·40	1·4
727/30	*Set of* 4	3·25	3·2

171 Rat with Top Hat

(Des V. Ambrus. Litho Questa)

1996 (19 Feb). *Chinese New Year* (*"Year of the Rat"*). *Shee 110×75 mm. P* 13½×14.

MS731 **171**	£1 multicoloured	3·00	3·0

172 African Child and Map

(Des A. Copp. Litho Questa)

1996 (19 Feb). *50th Anniv of U.N.I.C.E.F. T* **172** *and simila horiz designs. Multicoloured. P* 14½.

732	19p. Type **172**	50	5
733	23p. Children and Globe	60	6
734	30p. European child and map	80	8
735	35p. South American child and map	95	9
736	41p. Asian child and map	1·10	1·1
737	60p. South Pacific child and map	1·60	1·6
732/7	*Set of* 6	5·00	5·0

173 Queen Elizabeth II (from photo by T. O'Neill)

(Litho Questa)

996 (21 Apr). *70th Birthday of Queen Elizabeth II. P* 14×15.
38 **173** £5 multicoloured . . . . . . 10·00 10·50
No. 738 will be retained in use as part of the current definitive ries.

174 Elizabeth Garrett (first British woman doctor)

175 Player shooting at Goal

(Des Jennifer Toombs. Litho B.D.T.)

996 (25 Apr). *Europa. Famous Women. T* **174** *and similar horiz design. Multicoloured. P* 13½×14.
39 23p. Type **174** 60 60
40 30p. Emmeline Pankhurst (suffragette) . . 80 80

(Des A. Theobald. Litho B.D.T.)

996 (25 Apr). *European Football Championship, England. T* **175** *and similar horiz designs. Multicoloured. P* 13½×14.
41 19p. Type **175** 50 50
42 23p. Two players chasing ball 70 70
43 35p. Player avoiding tackle 95 95
44 41p. Two players competing for ball . . 1·10 1·10
45 60p. Players heading ball . . . . . . 1·75 1·75
41/5 . . . . *Set of* 5 4·50 4·50

176 Rowing

(Des A. Theobald. Litho Questa)

996 (8 June). *Sporting Anniversaries. T* **176** *and similar horiz designs. Multicoloured. P* 14.
46 19p. Type **176** 50 50
47 23p. Judo 70 70
48 35p. Fencing 95 95
49 41p. Boxing . . . . 1·10 1·10
50 60p. Basketball . . . . 1·75 1·75
46/50 . . . . *Set of* 5 4·50 4·50
1S751 150×100 mm. £1 Olympic torch (50×37 *mm*). P 13½ . . . . 2·50 2·50
Anniversaries:—Nos. 746/8, 750/1, Centenary of Modern)lympic Games; No. 749, 50th anniv of International Amateur oxing Association.
No. **MS**751 also includes the "CAPEX '96" International Stamp xhibition logo.

177 Bay on North Coast

(Des A. Copp. Litho B.D.T.)

996 (8 June). *Tourism. Beaches. T* **177** *and similar horiz designs. Multicoloured. P* 14.
52 19p. Type **177** 50 50
a. Booklet pane. Nos. 752/3, each × 3, with margins all round . . . . . . 2·50
b. Booklet pane. Nos. 752/7, with margins all round . . . . 4·25
53 23p. Portelet Bay 60 60
54 30p. Greve de Lecq Bay 80 80
a. Booklet pane. Nos. 754/5, each × 3, with margins all round . . . . . . 4·00
55 35p. Beauport Beach 95 95
56 41p. Plemont Bay . . . . 1·10 1·10
a. Booklet pane. Nos. 756/7, each × 3, with margins all round . . . . . . 6·00
57 60p. St. Brelade's Bay . . . . . . 1·60 1·60
52/7 . . . . *Set of* 6 5·00 5·00

178 Drag Hunt

179 The Journey to Bethlehem

(Des P. Layton. Litho Enschedé)

1996 (13 Sept). *Horses. T* **178** *and similar horiz designs. Multicoloured. P* 13½×14.
758 19p. Type **178** 50 50
759 23p. Pony and trap 60 60
760 30p. Training racehorses on beach 80 80
761 35p. Show jumping 95 95
762 41p. Pony Club event . . . . . . 1·10 1·10
763 60p. Shire mare and foal . . . . . . 1·60 1·60
758/63 . . . . *Set of* 6 5·00 5·00

(Des V. Ambrus. Litho Cartor)

1996 (12 Nov). *Christmas. T* **179** *and similar horiz designs. Multicoloured. P* 13×13½.
764 19p. Type **179** 40 45
765 23p. The Shepherds 45 50
766 30p. The Nativity 60 65
767 60p. The Three Kings . . . . . . 1·40 1·40
764/7 . . . . *Set of* 4 2·50 3·00

180 Jersey Cow wearing Scarf

(Des V. Ambrus. Litho Questa)

1997 (7 Feb). *Chinese New Year ("Year of the Ox"). Sheet* 110×74 *mm. P* 14×13½.
MS768 **180** £1 multicoloured . . . . . . 3·00 3·00

1997 (7 Feb). *"HONG KONG '97" International Stamp Exhibition. No.* **MS**768 *optd with exhibition emblem in black and* "JERSEY AT HONG KONG '97" *in red, both on sheet margin.*
MS769 **180** £1 multicoloured . . . . . . 3·00 3·00

181 Lillie the Cow on the Beach

182 Red-breasted Merganser

(Des A. Copp. Litho B.D.T.)

1997 (12 Feb). *Tourism. "Lillie the Cow". T* **181** *and similar horiz designs. Multicoloured. Self-adhesive. P* 9½.
770 (23p.) Type **181** 45 50
771 (23p.) Lillie taking photograph 45 50
772 (23p.) Carrying bucket and spade 45 50
773 (23p.) Eating meal at Mont Orgueil 45 50
770/3 . . . . *Set of* 4 1·75 2·00
Nos. 770/3, which are inscribed "UK MINIMUM POSTAGE PAID", come, *se-tenant*, in strips of 4 or rolls of 100 with the surplus self-adhesive paper around each stamp removed.

(Des N. Parlett. Litho Questa)

1997 (12 Feb)–**98**. *Seabirds and Waders. T* **182** *and similar horiz designs. Multicoloured. P* 14½.
774 1p. Type **182** 10 10
775 2p. Sanderling (28.1.98) 10 10
776 4p. Northern Gannet (11.8.98) 10 10
777 5p. Great Crested Grebe (28.1.98) 10 15
778 10p. Common Tern 20 25
779 15p. Black-headed Gull 30 35
780 20p. Dunlin 40 45
a. With copyright symbol after date (2.4.98) 40 45
781 21p. Sandwich Tern (28.1.98) 40 45
782 22p. Ringed Plover (11.8.98) 45 50
783 24p. Puffin 45 50
a. With copyright symbol after date (2.4.98) 45 50
784 25p. Brent Goose (28.1.98) 50 55
785 26p. Grey Plover (11.8.98) 50 55
786 30p. Fulmar (28.1.98) 60 65
787 31p. Golden Plover (11.8.98) 60 65
788 32p. Greenshank (11.8.98) 65 70
789 35p. Curlew (11.8.98) 70 75
790 37p. Oystercatcher 75 80
791 40p. Turnstone (28.1.98) 80 85
792 44p. Herring Gull (11.8.98) 90 95
793 50p. Great Black-backed Gull (11.8.98) . . 1·00 1·10
794 60p. Avocet (28.1.98) . . . . . . 1·25 1·40
795 75p. Redshank . . . . 1·50 1·60
796 £1 Razorbill (28.1.98) . . . . . . 2·00 2·10
797 £2 Shag . . . . 4·00 4·25
774/97 . . . . *Set of* 24 18·00 19·00
MS798 Three sheets, each 136×130 mm. (a) Nos. 774, 778/80, 783, 790, 795 and 797. (b) Nos. 775, 777, 781, 784, 786, 791, 794 and 796 (28.1.98). (c) Nos. 776, 782, 785, 787/9 and 792/3 (11.8.98)
Set of 3 *sheets* 18·00 19·00
Imprint dates: "1997" (without copyright symbol), Nos. 774, 778/80, 783, 790, 795, 797; "1998" (with copyright symbol), Nos. 775/7, 780a, 781/2, 783a, 784/9, 791/4, 796.

183 De Havilland D.H.95 Flamingo

(Des A. Theobald. Litho Enschedé)

1997 (10 Mar). *60th Anniv of Jersey Airport. T* **183** *and similar horiz designs. Multicoloured. P* 13½×14.
807 20p. Type **183** 55 55
808 24p. Handley Page H.P.R. Marathon . . 65 65
809 31p. De Havilland D.H.114 Heron 80 80
810 37p. Boeing 737-236 . . . . . . 1·00 1·00
811 43p. Britten Norman Trislander . . . . 1·10 1·10
812 63p. BAe 146-200 . . . . 1·75 1·75
807/12 . . . . *Set of* 6 5·25 5·25

184 The Bull of St. Clement

185 Cycling

(Des Jennifer Toombs. Litho B.D.T.)

1997 (15 Apr). *Europa. Tales and Legends. T* **184** *and similar horiz designs. Multicoloured. P* 15×14.
813 20p. Type **184** 50 50
814 24p. The Black Horse of St. Ouen 60 60
815 31p. The Black Dog of Bouley Bay 70 70
816 63p. Les Fontaines des Mittes . . . . 1·40 1·40
813/16 . . . . *Set of* 4 3·00 3·00
Nos. 814/15 include the "EUROPA" emblem.

1997 (29 May). *"Pacific 97" International Stamp Exhibition, San Francisco. No.* **MS**798a *optd with exhibition emblem on sheet margin.*
MS817 136×130 mm. Nos. 774, 778/80, 783, 790, 795 and 797 . . . . 7·50 8·00

(Des A. Theobald. Litho B.D.T.)

1997 (28 June). *7th Island Games, Jersey. T* **185** *and similar horiz designs. Multicoloured. P* 13½.
818 20p. Type **185** 55 55
a. Booklet pane. Nos. 818/19, each × 3, with margins all round . . . . . . 2·50
b. Booklet pane. Nos. 818/23, with margins all round . . . . 5·25
819 24p. Archery 65 65
820 31p. Windsurfing 80 80
a. Booklet pane. Nos. 820/1, each × 3, with margins all round . . . . . . 4·00
821 37p. Gymnastics . . . . 1·00 1·00
822 43p. Volleyball . . . . 1·10 1·10
a. Booklet pane. Nos. 822/3, each × 3, with margins all round . . . . . . 6·25
823 63p. Running . . . . 1·75 1·75
818/23 . . . . *Set of* 6 5·25 5·25

186 Mallorcan Midwife Toad

187 Ash

(Des W. Oliver. Litho Cartor)

1997 (2 Sept). *Wildlife Preservation Trust (6th series). T* **186** *and similar horiz designs. Multicoloured. P* 13.
824 20p. Type **186** 55 50
825 24p. Aye-Aye 65 65
826 31p. Echo Parakeet 80 80
827 37p. Pigmy Hog . . . . 1·00 1·00
828 43p. St. Lucia Whip-tail . . . . . . 1·10 1·10
829 63p. Madagascar Teal . . . . . . 1·75 1·75
824/9 . . . . *Set of* 6 5·25 5·25

(Des Norah Bryan. Litho Questa)

1997 (2 Sept). *Trees. T* **187** *and similar vert designs. Multicoloured. P* 14½.
830 20p. Type **187** 55 55
831 24p. Elder 65 65
832 31p. Beech 80 80
833 37p. Sweet Chestnut .. .. 1·00 1·00
834 43p. Hawthorn .. .. 1·10 1·10
835 63p. Common Oak .. .. 1·75 1·75
830/5 .. .. *Set of* 6 5·25 5·25

188 Father Christmas and Reindeer outside Jersey Airport

(Des Colleen Corlett. Litho B.D.T.)

1997 (11 Nov). *Christmas. T* **188** *and similar horiz designs. Multicoloured. P* 14.
836 20p. Type **188** 55 55
837 24p. Father Christmas with presents, St. Aubin's Harbour 65 65
838 31p. Father Christmas in sleigh, Mont Orgueil Castle 80 80
839 63p. Father Christmas with children, Royal Square, St. Helier .. .. .. 1·60 1·60
836/9 .. .. *Set of* 4 3·25 3·25

189 Wedding Photograph, 1947

(Des G. Drummond. Litho Questa)

1997 (20 Nov). *Golden Wedding of Queen Elizabeth and Prince Philip. T* **189** *and similar multicoloured designs. P* 14½.
840 50p. Type **189** .. .. 1·50 1·50
a. Horiz pair. Nos. 840/1 .. .. 3·00
841 50p. Queen Elizabeth and Prince Philip, 1997 1·50 1·50
MS842 150×100 mm. £1.50, Full-length Wedding photograph, 1947 (38×50 *mm*). P 13½ .. .. 4·50 4·50
Nos. 840/1 were printed together, *se-tenant*, in horizontal pairs throughout the sheet.

190 Tiger wearing Scarf

(Des V. Ambrus. Litho Questa)

1998 (28 Jan). *Chinese New Year ("Year of the Tiger"). Sheet 110×75 mm. P* 14×13½.
MS843 **190** £1 multicoloured .. .. .. 2·00 2·10

191 J.M.T. Bristol 4 Tonner, 1923

192 Creative Arts Festival

(Des A. Copp. Litho B.D.T.)

1998 (2 Apr). *75th Anniv of Jersey Motor Transport Company. Buses. T* **191** *and similar horiz designs. Multicoloured. P* 14.
844 20p. Type **191** 40 45
a. Booklet pane. Nos. 844/5, each × 3 with margins all round .. .. 2·75
b. Booklet pane. Nos. 844/9 with margins all round .. .. 4·25
845 24p. Safety Coach Service Regent double decker, 1934 .. .. 50 55
846 31p. Slade's Dennis Lancet, *c.* 1936 .. .. 60 65
a. Booklet pane. Nos. 846/7 each × 3 with margins all round .. .. 4·00
847 37p. Tantivy Leyland PLSC Lion, 1947 .. 75 80
848 43p. J.B.S. Morris, *c.* 1958 .. .. 85 90
a. Booklet pane. Nos. 848/9 each × 3 with margins all round .. .. 6·25
849 63p. J.M.T. Titan TD4 double decker, *c.* 1961 1·25 1·40
844/9 .. .. *Set of* 6 4·25 4·75

(Des A. Copp. Litho Enschedé)

1998 (2 Apr). *Europa. National Festivals. T* **192** *and similar vert designs. Multicoloured. P* 14×13½.
850 20p. Type **192** 40 45
851 24p. Jazz Festival 50 55
852 31p. Good Food Festival 60 65
853 63p. Floral Festival .. .. 1·25 1·40
850/3 .. .. *Set of* 4 2·75 3·00
Nos. 851/2 include the "EUROPA" emblem.

193 Hobie Cat and *Duke of Normandy* (launch)

194 Bass

(Des A. Theobald. Litho Cartor)

1998 (15 May). *Opening of Elizabeth Marina, St. Helier. T* **193** *and similar vert designs. Multicoloured. P* 13.
854 20p. Type **193** 40 45
a. Horiz strip of 5. Nos. 854/8 .. .. 2·00
855 20p. Hobie Cat with white, yellow, red and green sails 40 45
856 20p. Hobie Cats with pink, purple and orange sails 40 45
857 20p. Bow of Hobie Cat with yellow, blue and purple sail 40 45
858 20p. Hobie Cat heeling 40 45
859 24p. Yacht with red, white and blue spinnaker 40 45
a. Horiz strip of 5. Nos. 859/63 .. .. 2·00
860 24p. Yacht with pink spinnaker 40 45
861 24p. Yacht with two white sails 40 45
862 24p. Trimaran 40 45
863 24p. Yacht with blue, white and yellow spinnaker in foreground 40 45
854/63 .. .. *Set of* 10 4·00 4·50
Nos. 854/8 and 859/63 were each printed together, *se-tenant*, in horizontal strips of five throughout the sheets and form composite designs of yacht races.

(Des W. Oliver. Litho B.D.T.)

1998 (11 Aug). *International Year of the Ocean. Fishes. T* **194** *and horiz designs. Multicoloured. P* 15×14.
864 20p. Type **194** 40 45
865 24p. Red Gurnard 50 55
866 31p. Skate 60 65
867 37p. Mackerel 75 80
868 43p. Tope 85 90
869 63p. Cuckoo Wrasse .. .. 1·25 1·40
864/9 .. .. *Set of* 6 4·25 4·75

195 Cider-making

196 Irises

(Des A. Copp. Litho SNP Cambec, Melbourne)

1998 (11 Aug). *Days Gone By. T* **195** *and similar horiz designs. Multicoloured. Self-adhesive. P* 11 (*die-cut*).
870 (20p.) Type **195** 40 45
871 (20p.) Potato barrels on cart 40 45
872 (20p.) Collecting seaweed for fertiliser 40 45
873 (20p.) Milking Jersey cows 40 45
870/3 .. .. *Set of* 4 1·60 1·75
Nos. 870/3, which are inscribed "BAILIWICK MINIMUM POSTAGE PAID" and were initially sold at 20p. each, come *se-tenant* in strips of 4 or rolls of 100 with the surplus self-adhesive paper around each stamp removed.

(Des Wendy Tait. Litho Questa)

1998 (23 Oct). *Flowers. T* **196** *and similar multicoloured designs. P* 14½.
874 20p. Type **196** 40 45
875 24p. Carnations 50 55
876 31p. Chrysanthemums 60 65
877 37p. Pinks 75 80
878 43p. Roses 85 90
879 63p. Lilies .. .. 1·25 1·40
874/9 .. .. *Set of* 6 4·25 4·75
MS880 150×100 mm. £1.50, *Lilium* "Star Gazer" (50×37 *mm*). P 14×13½ .. .. .. 3·00 3·25
No. **MS**880 includes the "ITALIA '98" stamp exhibition emblem on the margin.

197 Central Market Crib

(Des Colleen Corlett. Litho Cartor)

1998 (10 Nov). *Christmas. Cribs. T* **197** *and similar horiz designs. Multicoloured. P* 13.
881 20p. Type **197** 40 45
882 24p. St. Thomas' Church crib 50 55
883 31p. Trinity Parish Church crib 60 65
884 63p. Royal Square crib .. .. 1·25 1·40
881/4 .. .. *Set of* 4 2·75 3·00

198 Rabbit

(Des V. Ambrus. Litho Questa)

1999 (16 Feb). *Chinese New Year ("Year of the Rabbit"). Sheet 110×75 mm. P* 14×13½.
MS885 **198** £1 multicoloured .. .. .. 2·00 2·10

199 Jersey Eastern Railway Mail Train

(Des A. Theobald. Litho B.D.T.)

1999 (16 Feb). *125th Anniv of U.P.U. T* **199** *and similar horiz designs. Multicoloured. P* 14.
886 20p. Type **199** 40 45
887 24p. *Brighton* (paddle-steamer) 50 55
888 43p. De Havilland D.H.86 Dragon Express at Jersey Airport 85 90
889 63p. Jersey Postal Service Morris Minor van 1·25 1·40
886/9 .. .. *Set of* 4 3·00 3·25

200 *Jessie Eliza*, St. Catherine

201 *Cymbidium* Maufant "Jersey"

(Litho Questa)

1999 (16 Feb). *175th Anniv of Royal National Lifeboat Institute. T* **200** *and similar horiz design. Multicoloured. P* 14½.
890 75p. Type **200** .. .. 1·50 1·60
a. Horiz pair. Nos. 890/1 .. .. 3·50
891 £1 *Alexander Coutanche*, St. Helier .. .. 2·00 2·10
Nos. 890/1 were printed together, *se-tenant*, in horizontal pairs throughout the sheet.

(Litho Enschedé)

1999 (19 Mar). *Jersey Orchids (4th series). T* **201** *and similar vert designs. Multicoloured. P* 14×13.
892 21p. Type **201** 45 50
893 25p. *Miltonia* Millbrook "Jersey" 50 55
894 31p. *Paphiopedilum* Transvaal 65 70
895 37p. *Paphiopedilum* Elizabeth Castle 75 80
896 43p. *Calanthe* Five Oaks 85 90
897 63p. *Cymbidium* Icho Tower "Trinity" .. .. 1·25 1·40
892/7 .. .. *Set of* 6 4·25 4·75
MS898 150×100 mm. £1.50, *Miltonia* Portelet. P 13½ .. .. 3·00 3·25
No. **MS**898 also includes the "Australia '99" World Stamp Exhibition, Melbourne, emblem on the margin at top left.

202 Howard Davis Park

(Des Ariel Luke. Litho Cartor)

999 (27 Apr). *Europa. Parks and Gardens. T* **202** *and similar horiz designs. Multicoloured. P* 13×13½.

)9	21p. Type **202**	45	50
)0	25p. Sir Winston Churchill Memorial Park . .	50	55
)1	31p. Coronation Park	65	70
)2	63p. La Collette Gardens	1·25	1·40
)9/902	. . . . *Set of* 4	2·75	3·00

Nos. 899/902 include the "EUROPA" logo at top left and all four alues show the "iBRA '99" International Stamp Exhibition, luremberg, emblem at top right.

STAMP BOOKLETS

For a full listing of Jersey stamp booklets see *Collect Channel Islands and Isle of Man Stamps* published each January.

POSTAGE DUE STAMPS

D **1**　　D **2** Map

(Des F. Guénier. Litho Bradbury, Wilkinson)

1969 (1 Oct). *P* 14 × 13½.

D1	D **1**	1d. bluish violet	1·50	1·50
D2		2d. sepia	2·25	2·00
D3		3d. magenta	3·00	2·75
D4	D **2**	1s. bright emerald	9·00	7·50
D5		2s. 6d. olive-grey	21·00	16·00
D6		5s. vermilion	30·00	27·00
D1/6		. . . . *Set of* 6	60·00	50·00

1971 (15 Feb)–**75.** *As Type* D **2** *but values in decimal currency.*

D 7	½p. black	10	10
D 8	1p. violet-blue	10	10
D 9	2p. olive-grey	10	10
D10	3p. reddish purple	10	10
D11	4p. pale red	10	10
D12	5p. bright emerald	15	15
D13	6p. yellow-orange (12.8.74)	20	15
D14	7p. bistre-yellow (12.8.74)	20	15
D15	8p. light greenish blue (1.5.75)	30	25
D16	10p. pale olive-grey	40	35
D17	11p. ochre (1.5.75)	40	40
D18	14p. violet	45	45
D19	25p. myrtle-green (12.8.74)	90	90
D20	50p. dull purple (1.5.75)	1·50	1·50
D7/20	. . . . *Set of* 14	4·50	4·25

D **3** Arms of St. Clement and Dovecote at Samares　　D **4** St. Brelade

(Des G. Drummond. Litho Questa)

1978 (17 Jan). *Type* D **3** *and similar horiz designs showing the Parish Arms given. P* 14.

D21	1p. blue-green and black	10	10
D22	2p. orange-yellow and black (St. Lawrence)	10	10
D23	3p. lake-brown and black (St. John) . .	10	10
D24	4p. orange-vermilion and black (St. Ouen)	10	10
D25	5p. ultramarine and black (St. Peter) . .	10	10
D26	10p. brown-olive and black (St. Martin) . .	30	20
D27	12p. greenish blue and black (St. Helier) . .	35	25
D28	14p. red-orange and black (St. Saviour) . .	35	30
D29	15p. bright magenta and black (St. Brelade)	35	30
D30	20p. yellow-green and black (Grouville) . .	50	40
D31	50p. deep brown and black (St. Mary) . .	1·10	1·10
D32	£1 chalky blue and black (Trinity) . .	2·25	2·25
D21/32	. . . . *Set of* 12	5·00	4·75

Parish Views shown:—2p. Handois Reservoir; 3p. Sorel Point; 4p. Pinnacle Rock; 5p. Quetivel Mill; 10p. St. Catherine's Breakwater; 12p. St. Helier Harbour; 14p. Highlands College; 15p. Beauport Bay; 20p. La Hougue Bie; 50p. Perry Farm; £1 Bouley Bay.

(Des G. Drummond. Litho Questa)

1982 (7 Sept). *Type* D **4** *and similar vert designs depicting Jersey Harbours. P* 14.

D33	1p. bright turquoise-green and black . .	10	10
D34	2p. chrome-yellow and black	10	10
D35	3p. lake-brown and black	10	10
D36	4p. red and black	10	10
D37	5p. bright blue and black	10	10
D38	6p. yellow-olive and black	10	15
D39	7p. bright reddish mauve and black	15	20
D40	8p. bright orange-red and black	15	20
D41	9p. bright green and black	20	25
D42	10p. turquoise-blue and black	20	25
D43	20p. apple-green and black	40	45
D44	30p. bright purple and black	60	65
D45	40p. dull orange and black	80	85
D46	£1 bright reddish violet and black	2·00	2·10
D33/46	. . . . *Set of* 14	4·50	5·00

Designs:—2p. St. Aubin; 3p. Rozel; 4p. Greve de Lecq; 5p. Bouley Bay; 6p. St. Catherine; 7p. Gorey; 8p. Bonne Nuit; 9p. La Roque; 10p. St. Helier; 20p. Ronez; 30p. La Collette; 40p. Elizabeth Castle; £1 Upper Harbour Marina.

British Post Offices Abroad

The origins of the network of Post Offices, Postal Agencies and Packet Agents can be recognised from the 18th century, but the system did not become established until the expansion of trade, following the end of the Napoleonic Wars in 1815.

Many offices were provided in newly acquired dependent territories, and were then, eventually, transferred from the control of the British Post Office to the evolving local administrations.

Those in foreign countries, nearly always based on existing British Consular appointments, were mostly connected to the network of British Packet lines which had been re-established in 1814. They tended to survive until the country in which they were situated established its own efficient postal service or joined the U.P.U. The term "Post Office Agent" was employed by the British G.P.O. and "Packet Agent" by the shipping lines to describe similar functions.

Listed in this section are the Crowned-circle handstamps and G.B. stamps used in the Post Offices and Agencies situated in foreign countries. Those for the territories within the scope of this catalogue will be found under the following headings:

Prices. Catalogue prices quoted in this section, and throughout the volume, covering Crowned-circle handstamps and stamps of Great Britain used abroad are for fine used examples with the cancellation or handstamp clearly legible. Poor impressions of the cancellations and handstamps are worth much less than the prices quoted.

CROWNED-CIRCLE HANDSTAMPS

Following the introduction, in 1840, of adhesive stamps in Great Britain there was considerable pressure from a number of the dependent territories for the British Post Office to provide something similar for their use.

Such suggestions were resisted, however, because of supposed operational problems, but the decision was taken, in connection with an expansion of the Packet Service, to issue a uniform series of handstamps and date stamps to the offices abroad, both in the dependent territories and in foreign countries.

Under the regulations circulated in December 1841, letters and packets forwarded through these offices to the United Kingdom or any of its territories were to be sent unpaid, the postage being collected on delivery. Where this was not possible, for example from a British colony to a foreign country or between two foreign ports, then a *crowned-circle handstamp* was to be applied with the postage, paid in advance, noted alongside in manuscript.

Examples of these handstamps were supplied over twenty years from 1842, but many continued to fulfil other functions long after the introduction of adhesive stamps in the colony concerned.

Our listings cover the use of these handstamps for their initial purpose and the prices quoted are for examples used on cover during the pre-adhesive period.

In most instances the dates quoted are those on which the handstamp appears in the G.P.O. Record Books, but it seems to have been normal for the handstamps to be sent to the office concerned immediately following this registration.

Many of the handstamps were individually cut by hand, so that each has its own characteristics, but for the purposes of the listing they have been grouped into nine Types as shown in the adjacent column. No attempt has been made to identify them by anything but the most major differences, so that minor differences in size and in the type of the crown have been ignored.

DOUBLE CIRCLE

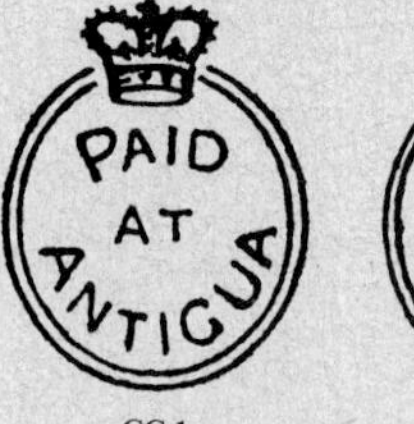

CC 1 CC 1a

Curved "PAID"

CC 1b CC 1c

Curved "PAID"

CC 2

Straight "PAID"

SINGLE CIRCLE

CC 3 CC 4

Straight "PAID"

CC 5

Curved "PAID"

CC 6 CC 7

Straight "PAID" Curved "PAID"

GREAT BRITAIN STAMPS USED ABROAD

Prices quoted are for single stamps not on cover unless otherwise stated. Stamps on cover are worth considerably more in most cases.

In many instances obliterators allocated to post offices abroad were, at a later date re-allocated to offices at home. Postmarks on issues later than those included in our lists can therefore safely be regarded as *not* having been "used abroad".

INDEX

ALTERED CATALOGUE NUMBERS

Any Catalogue numbers altered from the last edition are shown as a list in the introductory pages.

TYPES OF OBLITERATOR FOR GREAT BRITAIN STAMPS USED ABROAD

HORIZONTAL OVAL

(1)

(2)

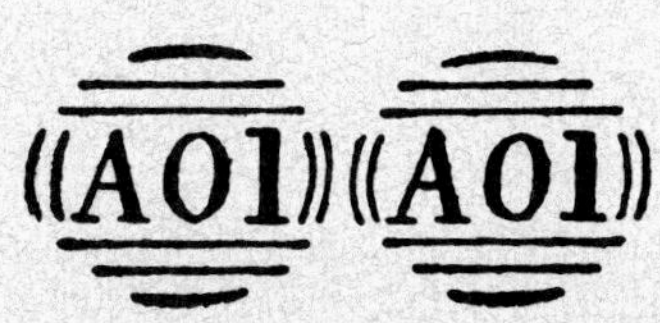

(3)

(4)

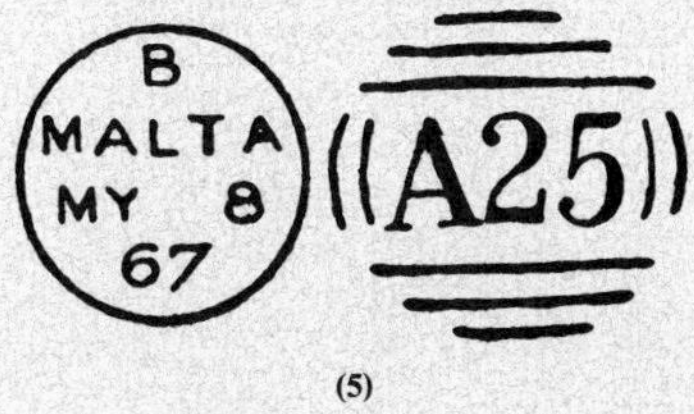

(5)

(6)

(7)

VERTICAL OVAL

(8)

(9)

(10)

(11)

(12)

(13)

(14)

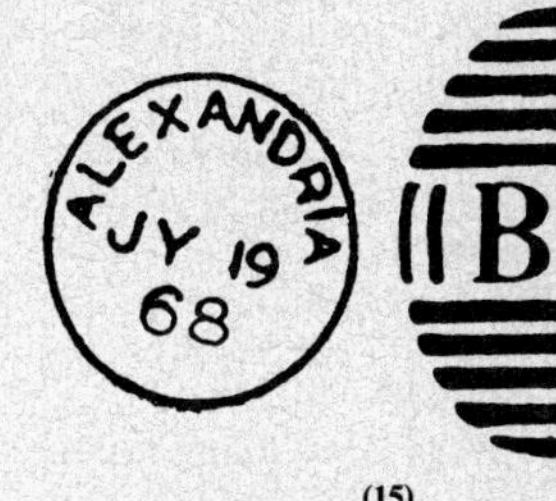

(15)

CIRCULAR DATE STAMPS

(16)

(17)

(18)

(19)

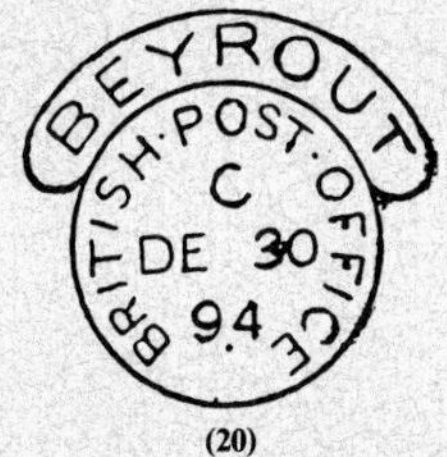

(20)

ARGENTINE REPUBLIC

BUENOS AYRES

The first regular monthly British mail packet service was introduced in 1824, replacing a private arrangement which had previously existed for some years.

Great Britain stamps were used from 1860 until the office closed at the end of June 1873. Until 1878 the British Consul continued to sell stamps which were used in combination with an Argentine value prepaying the internal rate. The British stamps on such covers were cancelled on arrival in England.

CROWNED-CIRCLE HANDSTAMPS

CC1 CC **7** BUENOS AYRES (Black or R.) (5.1.1851) *Price on cover* £700

Stamps of GREAT BRITAIN *cancelled* "B 32" *as in Types* **2, 12** *or* **13.**

1860 *to* **1873.**

Z 1 1d. rose-red (1857)
Z 2 1d. rose-red (1864) *From* 14·00
Plate Nos. 71, 72, 73, 74, 76, 78, 79, 80, 81, 82, 85, 87, 89, 90, 91, 92, 93, 94, 95, 96, 97, 99, 101, 103, 104, 107, 108, 110, 112, 113, 114, 117, 118, 119, 120, 121, 123, 125, 127, 129, 130, 131, 135, 136, 138, 139, 140, 142, 143, 145, 147, 149, 150, 151, 155, 159, 163, 164, 166, 169, 172.
Z 3 2d. blue (1858–69) *From* 22·00
Plate Nos. 8, 9, 12, 13, 14.
Z 4 3d. carmine-rose (1862) £160
Z 5 3d. rose (1865) (Plate No. 4) 70·00
Z 6 3d. rose (1867–73) *From* 32·00
Plate Nos. 4, 5, 6, 7, 8, 9, 10.
Z 7 4d. rose (1857) 55·00
Z 8 4d. red (1862) (Plate Nos. 3, 4) 60·00
Z 9 4d. vermilion (1865–73) *From* 32·00
Plate Nos. 7, 8, 9, 10, 11, 12, 13.
Z10 6d. lilac (1856) 65·00
Z11 6d. lilac (1862) (Plate Nos. 3, 4)
Z12 6d. lilac (1865–67) (Plate Nos. 5, 6) *From* 48·00
Z13 6d. lilac (1867) (Plate No. 6) 80·00
Z14 6d. violet (1867–70) (Plate Nos. 6, 8, 9) *From* 45·00
Z15 6d. buff (1872) (Plate No. 11) 75·00
Z16 6d. chestnut (1872) (Plate No. 11) 38·00
Z17 9d. bistre (1862) £275
Z18 9d. straw (1862) £225
Z19 9d. straw (1865) £400
Z20 9d. straw (1867) £250
Z21 10d. red-brown (1867) £275
Z22 1s. green (1856) £175
Z23 1s. green (1862) £140
Z24 1s. green (1865) (Plate No. 4) 95·00
Z25 1s. green (1867–73) (Plate Nos. 4, 5, 6, 7) *From* 22·00
Z26 1s. green (1873–77) (Plate No. 8)
Z27 2s. blue (1867) £120
Z28 5s. rose (1867) (Plate No. 1) £350

A "B 32" obliteration was later used by Mauritius on its own stamps.

AZORES

ST. MICHAELS (SAN MIGUEL)

A British Postal Agency existed at Ponta Delgada, the chief port of the island, to operate with the services of the Royal Mail Steam Packet Company.

CROWNED-CIRCLE HANDSTAMPS

CC1 CC **1b** ST. MICHAELS (27.5.1842)

BOLIVIA

COBIJA

It is believed that the British Postal Agency opened in 1862. The stamps of Great Britain were used between 1865 and 1878. They can be found used in combination with Bolivia adhesive stamps paying the local postage. The Agency closed in 1881, the town having been occupied by Chile in 1879.

CROWNED-CIRCLE HANDSTAMPS

CC1 CC **4** COBIJA (29.3.1862) *Price on cover* £4500

Stamps of GREAT BRITAIN *cancelled* "C 39" *as Types* **4, 8** *or* **12.**

1865 *to* **1878.**

Z 1 1d. rose-red (Plate Nos. 93, 95)
Z 2 2d. blue (1858–69) (Plate No. 14)
Z 3 3d. rose (1867–73) (Plate No. 6)
Z 4 3d. rose (1873–76) (Plate Nos. 16, 19)
Z 5 4d. sage-green (1877) (Plate No. 15)
Z 6 6d. violet (1867–70) (Plate No. 9) £350
Z 7 6d. buff (1872) (Plate No. 11)
Z 8 6d. grey (1874–76) (Plate Nos. 13, 14, 15, 16) £275
Z 9 1s. green (1867–73) (Plate Nos. 4, 5)
Z10 1s. green (1873–77) (Plate Nos. 10, 11, 12, 13) £275
Z11 2s. blue (1867) £450
Z12 5s. rose (1867–74) (Plate No. 2)

BRAZIL

The first packets ran to Brazil in 1808 when the Portuguese royal family went into exile at Rio de Janeiro. The Agencies at Bahia and Pernambuco did not open until 1851. All three agencies used the stamps of Great Britain from 1866 and these can be found used in combination with Brazil adhesive stamps paying the local postage. The agencies closed on 30 June 1874.

BAHIA

CROWNED-CIRCLE HANDSTAMPS

CC1 CC **7** BAHIA (Black, G. *or* R.) (6.1.1851) *Price on cover* £1700

Stamps of GREAT BRITAIN *cancelled* "C 81" *as Type* **12.**

1866 *to* **1874.**

Z 1 1d. rose-red (1864–79) *From* 30·00
Plate Nos. 90, 93, 96, 108, 113, 117, 135, 140, 147, 155.
Z 2 1½d. lake-red (1870–74) (Plate No. 3) 75·00
Z 3 2d. blue (1858–69) (Plate Nos. 9, 12, 13, 14) 55·00
Z 4 3d. rose (1865) (Plate No. 4)
Z 5 3d. rose (1867–73) (Plate Nos. 4, 6, 8, 9, 10) 50·00
Z 6 3d. rose (1873–79) (Plate No. 11)
Z 7 4d. vermilion (1865–73) *From* 32·00
Plate Nos. 8, 9, 10, 11, 12, 13.
Z 8 6d. lilac (1865–67) (Plate No. 5)
Z 9 6d. lilac (1867) (Plate No. 6) 75·00
Z10 6d. violet (1867–70) (Plate Nos. 6, 8, 9) *From* 50·00
Z11 6d. buff (1872–73) (Plate Nos. 11, 12) *From* 90·00
Z12 6d. chestnut (1872) (Plate No. 11)
Z13 6d. grey (1873) (Plate No. 12)
Z14 6d. grey (1874–76) (Plate No. 13)
Z15 9d. straw (1865) £350
Z16 9d. straw (1867) £200
Z17 1s. green (1865) (Plate No. 4) 90·00
Z18 1s. green (1867–73) (Plate Nos. 4, 5, 6, 7) *From* 35·00
Z19 1s. green (1873–77) (Plate Nos. 8, 9) *From* 60·00
Z20 2s. blue (1867) £200
Z21 5s. rose (1867) (Plate No. 1) £400

PERNAMBUCO

CROWNED-CIRCLE HANDSTAMPS

CC2 CC **7** PERNAMBUCO (Black *or* R.) (6.1.1851) *Price on cover* £1700

Stamps of GREAT BRITAIN *cancelled* "C 82" *as Type* **12.**

1866 *to* **1874.**

Z22 1d. rose-red (1864–79) *From* 30·00
Plate Nos. 85, 108, 111, 130, 131, 132, 149, 157, 159, 160, 187
Z23 2d. blue (1858–69) (Plate Nos. 9, 12, 13, 14) *From* 40·00
Z23*a* 3d. rose (1865) (Plate No. 4) 70·00
Z24 3d. rose (1867–73) (Plate Nos. 4, 5, 6, 7, 10) 40·00
Z25 3d. rose (1873–77) (Plate No. 11)
Z26 4d. vermilion (1865–73) *From* 30·00
Plate Nos. 9, 10, 11, 12, 13, 14.
Z27 6d. lilac (1865–67) (Plate Nos. 5, 6)
Z28 6d. lilac (1867) (Plate No. 6) 60·00
Z29 6d. violet (1867–70) (Plate Nos. 8, 9) *From* 35·00
Z30 6d. buff (1872–73) (Plate Nos. 11, 12) 50·00
Z31 6d. chestnut (1872) (Plate No. 11) 38·00
Z32 6d. grey (1873) (Plate No. 12)
Z33 9d. straw (1865) £350
Z34 9d. straw (1867) £140
Z35 10d. red-brown (1867) £200
Z36 1s. green (1865) (Plate No. 4) 80·00
Z37 1s. green (1867–73) (Plate Nos. 4, 5, 6, 7) 30·00
Z38 2s. blue (1867) £225
Z39 5s. rose (1867–74) (Plate Nos. 1, 2) £425

RIO DE JANEIRO

CROWNED-CIRCLE HANDSTAMPS

CC3 CC **7** RIO DE JANEIRO (Black, B., G. *or* R.) (6.1.1851) *Price on cover* £450

Stamps of GREAT BRITAIN *cancelled* "C 83" *as Type* **12.**

1866 *to* **1874.**

Z40 1d. rose-red (1857) 38·00
Z41 1d. rose-red (1864–79) *From* 20·00
Plate Nos. 71, 76, 80, 82, 86, 94, 103, 113, 117, 119, 123, 130, 132, 134, 135, 146, 148, 159, 161, 166, 185, 200, 204.
Z42 2d. blue (1858–69) (Plate Nos. 9, 12, 13, 14) *From* 22·00
Z43 3d. rose (1867–73) (Plate Nos. 4, 5, 6, 7, 8) *From* 30·00
Z44 3d. rose (1873–77) (Plate No. 11)
Z45 4d. vermilion (1865–73) *From* 30·00
Plate Nos. 8, 9, 10, 11, 12, 13, 14.
Z46 6d. lilac (1865–67) (Plate No. 5)
Z47 6d. lilac (1867) (Plate No. 6) 60·00
Z48 6d. violet (1867–70) (Plate Nos. 6, 8, 9) *From* 30·00
Z49 6d. buff (1872) (Plate No. 11) 65·00
Z50 6d. chestnut (1872) (Plate No. 11) 35·00
Z51 6d. grey (1873) (Plate No. 12)
Z52 9d. straw (1865) £250
Z53 9d. straw (1867) £120
Z54 10d. red-brown (1867) £150
Z55 1s. green (1865) (Plate No. 4) 80·00
Z56 1s. green (1867–73) (Plate Nos. 4, 5, 6, 7) *From* 18·00
Z57 1s. green (1873–77) (Plate Nos. 8, 9) 50·00
Z58 2s. blue (1867) 95·00
Z59 5s. rose (1867–74) (Plate Nos. 1, 2) *From* £300

CAPE VERDE ISLANDS

The British Packet Agency at St. Vincent opened in 1851 as part of the revised service to South America. The agency was closed by 1860.

CROWNED-CIRCLE HANDSTAMPS

CC1 CC **6** ST. VINCENT C.DE.V. (6.1.1851) *Price on cover* £4250

CHILE

The British Postal Agency at Valparaiso opened on 7 May 1846, to be followed by further offices at Caldera (1858) and Coquimbo (1863). The stamps of Great Britain were introduced in 1865 and can be found used in combination with Chile adhesives paying the local postage. All three offices closed on 31 March 1881 when Chile joined the U.P.U.

CALDERA

Stamps of GREAT BRITAIN *cancelled* "C 37" *as in Type* **4.**

1865 *to* **1881.**

Z 1 1d. rose-red (1864–79) *From* 25·00
Plate Nos. 71, 72, 88, 90, 95, 160, 195.
Z 2 1½d. lake-red (1870–74) (Plate No. 3)
Z 3 2d. blue (1858–69) (Plate No. 9) 35·00
Z 4 3d. rose (1865) (Plate No. 4) 80·00
Z 5 3d. rose (1867–73) (Plate Nos. 5, 7)
Z 6 3d. rose (1873–76) *From* 28·00
Plate Nos. 11, 12, 16, 17, 18, 19.
Z 7 4d. red (1862) (Plate No. 4)
Z 8 4d. vermilion (1865–73) *From* 42·00
Plate Nos. 8, 11, 12, 13, 14.
Z 9 4d. sage-green (1877) (Plate No. 16)
Z10 6d. lilac (1862) (Plate No. 4) 80·00
Z11 6d. lilac (1865–67) (Plate Nos. 5, 6)
Z12 6d. violet (1867–70) (Plate Nos. 6, 8, 9) *From* 40·00
Z13 6d. buff (1872) (Plate No. 11)
Z14 6d. chestnut (1872) (Plate No. 11)
Z15 6d. grey (1873) (Plate No. 12)
Z16 6d. grey (1874–80) *From* 30·
Plate Nos. 13, 14, 15, 16, 17.
Z17 8d. orange (1876) £2
Z18 9d. straw (1867) £1
Z19 10d. red-brown (1867) £2
Z20 1s. green (1865) (Plate No. 4)
Z21 1s. green (1867–73) (Plate Nos. 4, 5, 6) *From* 24·
Z22 1s. green (1873–77) *From* 45·
Plate Nos. 8, 10, 11, 12, 13.
Z23 2s. blue (1867) £2
Z23*a* 2s. cobalt (1867)
Z24 2s. brown (1880) £16
Z25 5s. rose (1867–74) (Plate No. 2) £4

COQUIMBO

Stamps of GREAT BRITAIN *cancelled* "C 40" *as in Type* **4.**

1865 *to* **1881.**

Z26 ½d. rose-red (1870–79) (Plate No. 14)
Z27 1d. rose-red (1857)
Z28 1d. rose-red (1864–79) (Plate Nos. 85, 204)
Z29 2d. blue (1858–69) (Plate Nos. 9, 14)
Z30 3d. rose (1865)
Z31 3d. rose (1872) (Plate No. 8)
Z32 3d. rose (1873–76) (Plate Nos. 18, 19) *From* 28·
Z33 4d. red (1863) (Plate No. 4) 50·
Z34 4d. vermilion (1865–73) (Plate Nos. 12, 14)
Z35 4d. sage-green (1877) (Plate Nos. 15, 16) £1
Z36 6d. lilac (1862) (Plate Nos. 3, 4) 65·
Z37 6d. lilac (1865–67) (Plate No. 5)
Z38 6d. lilac (1867) (Plate No. 6) 60·
Z39 6d. violet (1867–70) (Plate Nos. 6, 8, 9) *From* 35·
Z40 6d. buff (1872–73) (Plate Nos. 11, 12) *From* 60·
Z41 6d. chestnut (1872) (Plate No. 11)
Z42 6d. grey (1873) (Plate No. 12) £12
Z43 6d. grey (1874–76) (Plate Nos. 13, 14, 15, 16) *From* 25·
Z44 8d. orange (1876)
Z45 9d. straw (1862) £22
Z46 9d. straw (1867) £1
Z47 10d. red-brown (1867)
Z48 1s. green (1865) (Plate No. 4) 80·
Z49 1s. green (1867–73) (Plate Nos. 4, 5, 6) 25·
Z50 1s. green (1873–77) *From* 40·
Plate Nos. 8, 10, 11, 12, 13.
Z51 2s. blue (1867) £1
Z51*a* 2s. cobalt (1867)
Z52 2s. brown (1880) £170
Z53 5s. rose (1867–74) (Plate Nos. 1, 2) £37

VALPARAISO

CROWNED-CIRCLE HANDSTAMPS

CC1 CC **2** VALPARAISO (R.) (13.1.1846) *Price on cover* £3
CC2 CC **1** VALPARAISO. (R.) (16.7.1846) *Price on cover* £4

Stamps of GREAT BRITAIN *cancelled* "C 30", *as in Types* **12** *and* **1** *or circular date stamp as Type* **16.**

1865 *to* **1881.**

Z54 ½d. rose-red (1870–79) *From* 55·
Plate Nos. 6, 11, 12, 13, 14.
Z55 1d. rose-red (1864–79) *From* 16·0
Plate Nos. 80, 84, 85, 89, 91, 101, 106, 113, 116, 122, 123, 138, 140, 141, 146, 148, 149, 152, 157, 158, 162, 167, 175, 178, 181, 185, 186, 187, 189, 190, 195, 197, 198, 199, 200, 201, 207, 209, 210, 211, 212, 213, 214, 215, 217.
Z56 1½d. lake-red (1870–74) (Plate Nos. 1, 3) *From* 55·
Z57 2d. blue (1858–69) (Plate Nos. 9, 13, 14, 15) 35·
Z58 2½d. rosy mauve (1875), white paper (Plate No. 2) 65·
Z59 2½d. rosy mauve (1876) (Plate Nos. 4, 8) 50·
Z60 3d. carmine-rose (1862)
Z61 3d. rose (1865) (Plate No. 4)
Z62 3d. rose (1867–73) *From* 24·
Plate Nos. 5, 6, 7, 8, 9, 10.
Z63 3d. rose (1873–76) *From* 24·
Plate Nos. 11, 12, 14, 16, 17, 18, 19.
Z63*a* 4d. red (1862) (Plate No. 4)
Z63*b* 4d. red (1863) (Plate No. 4) (*Hair lines*)
Z64 4d. vermilion (1865–73) *From* 28·
Plate Nos. 9, 10, 11, 12, 13, 14.
Z65 4d. vermilion (1876) (Plate No. 15) £1
Z66 4d. sage-green (1877) (Plate Nos. 15, 16) £1
Z67 4d. grey-brown (1880) *wmk* Large Garter
Plate No. 17.
Z68 6d. lilac (1862) (Plate Nos. 3, 4) *From* 55·
Z69 6d. lilac (1865) (Plate Nos. 5, 6)
Z70 6d. lilac (1867) (Plate No. 6)
Z71 6d. violet (1867–70) (Plate Nos. 6, 8, 9) *From* 32·
Z72 6d. buff (1872–73) (Plate Nos. 11, 12) *From* 45·
Z73 6d. chestnut (1872) (Plate Nos. 11, 12) 28·
Z74 6d. grey (1873) (Plate No. 12) £1
Z75 6d. grey (1874–80) *From* 24·
Plate Nos. 13, 14, 15, 16, 17.
Z76 6d. grey (1881) (Plate No. 17)
Z77 8d. orange (1876) £1
Z78 9d. straw (1862)
Z79 9d. straw (1865)
Z80 9d. straw (1867) £1
Z81 10d. red-brown (1867) £1
Z82 1s. green (1865) (Plate No. 4)
Z83 1s. green (1867–73) (Plate Nos. 4, 5, 6, 7) *From* 20·
Z84 1s. green (1873–77) *From* 40·
Plate Nos. 8, 9, 10, 11, 12, 13.
Z85 1s. orange-brown (1880) (Plate No. 13) £2
Z86 2s. blue (1867) 80·
Z86*a* 2s. cobalt (1867) £10
Z87 2s. brown (1880) £14
Z88 5s. rose (1867–74) (Plate Nos. 1, 2) *From* £3
Z89 10s. grey-green (1878) (*wmk* Cross) £15
Z90 £1 brown-lilac (1878) (*wmk* Cross) £25

1880.

Z91 1d. Venetian red
Z92 1½d. Venetian red

COLOMBIA

The system of British Postal Agencies in the area was inaugurate by the opening of the Carthagena office in 1825. In 1842 agencies a Chagres, Panama and Santa Martha were added to the system. A further office opened at Colon in 1852, this port also being known a Aspinwall. During 1872 the system was further enlarged by an offic t Savanilla, although this agency was later, 1878, transferred to 3arranquilla.

Stamps of Great Britain were supplied to Carthagena, Panama and Santa Martha in 1865, Colon in 1870 and Savanilla in 1872. Combination covers with Colombia stamps paying the local postage re known from Santa Martha and Savanilla as are similar covers rom Panama showing Costa Rica and El Salvador stamps.

All offices, except Chagres which had ceased to operate in 1855, losed for public business on 30 June 1881. Colon and Panama ontinued to exist as transit offices to deal with the mail across the sthmus. Both finally closed on 31 March 1921.

CARTHAGENA

CROWNED-CIRCLE HANDSTAMPS

CC1 CC **1b** CARTHAGENA (R.) (15.1.1841) *Price on cover* £800
CC2 CC **1** CARTHAGENA (1.7.1846) *Price on cover* £700

Stamps of GREAT BRITAIN *cancelled* "C 56" *as in Type* **4**.

1865 *to* **1881.**
Z 1 ½d. rose-red (1870–79) (Plate No. 10)
Z 2 1d. rose-red (1864–79) *From* 34·00
Plate Nos. 78, 87, 100, 111, 113, 117, 119, 125, 172, 189, 217.
Z 3 2d. blue (1858–69) (Plate Nos. 9, 14) *From* 30·00
Z 4 3d. rose (1865) (Plate No. 4)
Z 5 3d. rose (1865–68) (Plate Nos. 4, 5)
Z 6 3d. rose (1873–79) (Plate Nos. 12, 17, 18) *From* 40·00
Z 7 4d. vermilion (1865–73) *From* 30·00
Plate Nos. 7, 8, 9, 10, 11, 12, 13, 14.
Z 8 4d. vermilion (1876) (Plate No. 15) £180
Z 9 4d. sage-green (1877) (Plate Nos. 15, 16) *From* £160
Z10 6d. lilac (1865–67) (Plate Nos. 5, 6)
Z11 6d. violet (1867–70) (Plate Nos. 6, 8) *From* 48·00
Z12 6d. grey (1873) (Plate No. 12) £130
Z13 6d. grey (1874–76) (Plate Nos. 13, 14, 15, 16) *From* 34·00
Z14 8d. orange (1876) £200
Z15 9d. straw (1865)
Z16 1s. green (1865)
Z17 1s. green (1867–73) (Plate Nos. 4, 5, 7) 36·00
Z18 1s. green (1873–77) (Plate Nos. 8, 9, 10, 11, 12, 13) 40·00
Z19 1s. orange-brown (1880)
Z20 2s. blue (1867) £200
Z21 5s. rose (1867) (Plate No. 1) £400

Cancelled "C 65" (*incorrect handstamp, supplied in error*) *as T* **12**.

1866 *to* **1881.**
Z22 ½d. rose-red (1870–79) (Plate No. 10)
Z23 1d. rose-red (1864–79) (Plate Nos. 100, 106, 111, 123) *From* 42·00
Z23*a* 1½d. lake-red (1870) (Plate No. 3)
Z24 2d. blue (1858–69) (Plate No. 9) 40·00
Z25 2d. rose (1880)
Z26 2½d. blue (1880) (Plate No. 19)
Z27 3d. rose (1867–73) (Plate No. 9)
Z28 3d. rose (1873–79) (Plate Nos. 14, 17, 19, 20)
Z29 4d. vermilion (1865–73) *From* 40·00
Plate Nos. 7, 8, 9, 11, 12, 13, 14.
Z30 4d. vermilion (1876) (Plate No. 15) £200
Z31 4d. sage-green (1877) (Plate Nos. 15, 16) *From* £175
Z32 6d. violet (1867–70) (Plate Nos. 6, 8) 80·00
Z33 6d. pale buff (1872) (Plate No. 11)
Z34 6d. grey (1873) (Plate No. 12) £120
Z35 6d. grey (1874–80) (Plate Nos. 13, 15, 16, 17) 40·00
Z36 8d. orange (1876) £275
Z37 9d. straw (1865) £275
Z38 1s. green (1865) (Plate No. 4) 85·00
Z39 1s. green (1867) (Plate Nos. 4, 5, 6, 7) 30·00
Z40 1s. green (1873–77) (Plate Nos. 8, 11, 12, 13) *From* 38·00
Z41 1s. orange-brown (1880)
Z42 2s. blue (1867) £350
Z43 2s. brown (1880) £2000
Z44 5s. rose (1867) (Plate Nos. 1, 2) £425

CHAGRES

CROWNED-CIRCLE HANDSTAMPS

CC3 CC **1** CHAGRES (16.9.1846)

COLON

CROWNED-CIRCLE HANDSTAMPS

CC4 CC **5** COLON (R.) (21.6.1854) *Price on cover* £3500

Stamps of GREAT BRITAIN *cancelled* "E 88" *as in Type* **12**.

1870 *to* **1881.**
Z45 1d. rose-red (1864–79) *From* 25·00
Plate Nos. 107, 121, 122, 123, 125, 127, 130, 131, 133, 136, 138, 142, 150, 151, 152, 153, 155, 156, 157, 158, 160, 169, 170, 171, 174, 176, 178, 179, 184, 187, 188, 194, 195, 201, 209, 213, 214, 217.
Z46 1d. Venetian red (1880)
Z47 1½d. lake-red (1870–74) (Plate No. 3) 90·00
Z48 2d. blue (1858–69) (Plate Nos. 14, 15) 28·00
Z49 2d. pale rose (1880)
Z50 3d. rose (1867–73) (Plate Nos. 6, 9)
Z51 3d. rose (1873–76) 35·00
Plate Nos. 11, 12, 16, 18, 19, 20.
Z52 4d. vermilion (1865–73) *From* 32·00
Plate Nos. 10, 11, 12, 13, 14.
Z53 4d. vermilion (1876) (Plate No. 15)
Z54 4d. sage-green (1877) (Plate Nos. 15, 16) £150
Z55 4d. grey-brown (1880) *wmk* Large Garter £200
Plate No. 17.
Z56 4d. grey-brown (1880) *wmk* Crown (Plate No. 17)
Z57 6d. violet (1867–70) (Plate Nos. 6, 8, 9)
Z58 6d. buff (1872) (Plate No. 11)
Z59 6d. chestnut (1872) (Plate No. 11) 50·00
Z60 6d. grey (1873) (Plate No. 12)
Z61 6d. grey (1874–80) *From* 28·00
Plate Nos. 13, 14, 15, 16, 17.
Z62 8d. orange (1876)
Z63 9d. straw (1867) £150
Z63*a* 10d. red-brown (1867)
Z64 1s. green (1867–73) (Plate Nos. 4, 5, 6, 7) 28·00
Z65 1s. green (1873–77) *From* 35·00
Plate Nos. 8, 9, 10, 11, 12, 13.
Z66 1s. orange-brown (1880) (Plate 13) £250
Z67 1s. orange-brown (1881) (Plate 13) 60·00
Z68 2s. blue (1867) £120
Z69 2s. brown (1880) £1700
Z70 5s. rose (1867) (Plate Nos. 1, 2) £400

PANAMA

CROWNED-CIRCLE HANDSTAMPS

CC5 CC **1** PANAMA (R.) (24.8.1846) *Price on cover* £1200

Stamps of GREAT BRITAIN *cancelled* "C 35" *as in Types* **4, 11** *or* **14**.

1865 *to* **1881.**
Z 71 ½d. rose-red (1870–79) *From* 27·00
Plate Nos. 10, 11, 12, 13, 14, 15, 19
Z 72 1d. rose-red (1864–79) *From* 18·00
Plate Nos. 71, 72, 76, 81, 85, 87, 88, 89, 93, 95, 96, 101, 104, 114, 122, 124, 130, 138, 139, 142, 159, 168, 171, 172, 174, 177, 179, 180, 184, 185, 187, 189, 191, 192, 193, 196, 197, 200, 203, 204, 205, 207, 208, 209, 210, 211, 213, 214, 215, 218, 224
Z 73 1½d. lake-red (1870–74) (Plate No. 3) 50·00
Z 74 2d. blue (1858–69) *From* 24·00
Plate Nos. 9, 12, 13, 14, 15.
Z 75 2½d. rosy mauve (1875) (Plate No. 1)
Z 76 2½d. rosy mauve (1876–80) (Plate Nos. 4, 12, 16)
Z 77 2½d. blue (1880) (Plate No. 19)
Z 78 2½d. blue (1881) (Plate Nos. 22, 23)
Z 79 3d. carmine-red (1862) £120
Z 80 3d. rose (1865) (Plate No. 4)
Z 81 3d. rose (1867–73) *From* 24·00
Plate Nos. 4, 5, 6, 7, 8, 9.
Z 82 3d. rose (1873–76) *From* 24·00
Plate Nos. 12, 14, 15, 16, 17, 18, 19, 20.
Z 83 3d. rose (1881) (Plate Nos. 20, 21)
Z 84 4d. red (1863) (Plate No. 4) 65·00
Z 85 4d. vermilion (1865–73) *From* 28·00
Plate Nos. 7, 8, 9, 10, 11, 12, 13, 14.
Z 86 4d. vermilion (1876) (Plate No. 15) £175
Z 87 4d. sage-green (1877) (Plate Nos. 15, 16) £130
Z 88 4d. grey-brown (1880) *wmk* Crown *From* 45·00
Plate Nos. 17, 18.
Z 89 6d. lilac (1862) (Plate Nos. 3, 4) *From* 55·00
Z 90 6d. lilac (1865–67) (Plate Nos. 5, 6) *From* 35·00
Z 91 6d. lilac (1867) (Plate No. 6)
Z 92 6d. violet (1867–70) (Plate Nos. 6, 8, 9) 28·00
Z 93 6d. buff (1872–73) (Plate Nos. 11, 12) *From* 45·00
Z 94 6d. chestnut (Plate No. 11) 28·00
Z 95 6d. grey (1873) (Plate No. 12) £120
Z 96 6d. grey (1874–80) *From* 28·00
Plate Nos. 13, 14, 15, 16, 17.
Z 97 6d. grey (1881) (Plate No. 17) 65·00
Z 98 8d. orange (1876) £175
Z 99 9d. straw (1862) £200
Z100 9d. straw (1867) £225
Z101 10d. red-brown (1867) £190
Z102 1s. green (1865) (Plate No. 4) 80·00
Z103 1s. green (1867–73) (Plate Nos. 4, 5, 6, 7) *From* 20·00
Z104 1s. green (1873–77) *From* 35·00
Plate Nos. 8, 9, 10, 11, 12, 13.
Z105 1s. orange-brown (1880) (Plate No. 13) £250
Z106 1s. orange-brown (1881) (Plate No. 13) 55·00
Z107 2s. blue (1867) 80·00
Z108 2s. brown (1880) £1500
Z109 5s. rose (1867–74) (Plate Nos. 1, 2) *From* £300

1880.
Z110 1d. Venetian red 16·00
Z111 2d. rose 45·00
Z112 5d. indigo 80·00

Later stamps cancelled "C 35" are believed to originate from sailors' letters or other forms of maritime mail.

SANTA MARTHA

CROWNED-CIRCLE HANDSTAMPS

CC6 CC **1b** SANTA MARTHA (R.) (15.12.1841) *Price on cover* £1200

Stamps of GREAT BRITAIN *cancelled* "C 62" *as in Type* **4**.

1865 *to* **1881.**
Z113 ½d. rose-red (1870–79) (Plate No. 6) 70·00
Z114 1d. rose-red (1864–79) (Plate No. 106) 50·00
Z115 2d. blue (1858–69) (Plate Nos. 9, 13) 70·00
Z116 4d. vermilion (1865–73) *From* 32·00
Plate Nos. 7, 8, 9, 11, 12, 13, 14.
Z117 4d. sage-green (1877) (Plate No. 15) £140
Z118 4d. grey-brown (1880) *wmk* Large Garter £200
Plate No. 17.
Z119 4d. grey-brown (1880) *wmk* Crown (Plate No. 17) 55·00
Z120 6d. lilac (1865–67) (Plate No. 5) 55·00
Z121 6d. grey (1873) (Plate No. 12)
Z122 6d. grey (1874–76) (Plate No. 14)
Z123 8d. orange (1876) £225
Z123*a* 9d. bistre (1862)
Z124 1s. green (1865) (Plate No. 4) 90·00
Z125 1s. green (1867–73) (Plate Nos. 5, 7) 50·00
Z126 1s. green (1873–77) (Plate No. 8)
Z127 2s. blue (1867) £275
Z128 5s. rose (1867) (Plate No. 2) £425

SAVANILLA (BARRANQUILLA)

Stamps of GREAT BRITAIN *cancelled* "F 69" *as in Type* **12**.

1872 *to* **1881.**
Z129 ½d. rose-red (1870–79) (Plate No. 6) 55·00
Z130 1d. rose-red (1864–79) (Plate Nos. 122, 171) 50·00
Z131 1½d. lake-red (1870–74) (Plate No. 3) 90·00
Z132 3d. rose (1867–73) (Plate No. 7)
Z133 3d. rose (1873–76) (Plate No. 20) 85·00
Z134 3d. rose (1881) (Plate No. 20) 85·00
Z135 4d. vermilion (1865–73) (Plate Nos. 12, 13, 14) 32·00
Z136 4d. vermilion (1876) (Plate No. 15) £175
Z137 4d. sage-green (1877) (Plate Nos. 15, 16) £140
Z138 4d. grey-brown (1880) *wmk* Large Garter £200
Plate No. 17.
Z139 4d. grey-brown (1880) *wmk* Crown (Plate No. 17) 50·00
Z140 6d. buff (1872) (Plate No. 11)
Z141 6d. grey (1878) (Plate Nos. 16, 17) *From* 60·00
Z142 8d. orange (1876) £225
Z143 1s. green (1867–73) (Plate Nos. 5, 7) 40·00
Z144 1s. green (1873–77) (Plate Nos. 8, 11, 12, 13) 50·00
Z145 1s. orange-brown (1880) £250
Z146 2s. blue (1867) £170
Z147 5s. rose (1867–74) (Plate No. 2) £425

CUBA

The British Postal Agency at Havana opened in 1762, the island then being part of the Spanish Empire. A further office, at St. Jago de Cuba, was added in 1841.

Great Britain stamps were supplied to Havana in 1865 and to St. Jago de Cuba in 1866. They continued in use until the offices closed on 30 May 1877.

HAVANA

CROWNED-CIRCLE HANDSTAMPS

CC1 CC **1b** HAVANA (13.11.1841) *Price on cover* £800
CC2 CC **1c** HAVANA (1848) *Price on cover* £800
CC3 CC **2** HAVANA (14.7.1848) *Price on cover* £675

Stamps of GREAT BRITAIN *cancelled* "C 58" *as in Types* **4, 12** *or* **14**.

1865 *to* **1877.**
Z 1 ½d. rose-red (1870) (Plate Nos. 6, 12) 50·00
Z 2 1d. rose-red (1864–79) 30·00
Plate Nos. 86, 90, 93, 115, 120, 123, 144, 146, 171, 174, 208.
Z 3 2d. blue (1858–69) (Plate Nos. 9, 14, 15) 35·00
Z 4 3d. rose (1867–73) (Plate No. 4) 80·00
Z 5 3d. rose (1873–76) (Plate Nos. 18, 19)
Z 6 4d. vermilion (1865–73) *From* 32·00
Plate Nos. 7, 8, 10, 11, 12, 13, 14.
Z 7 4d. vermilion (1876) (Plate No. 15)
Z 8 6d. lilac (1865) (with hyphen) (Plate No. 5)
Z 9 6d. grey (1874–76) (Plate No. 15)
Z10 8d. orange (1876)
Z11 9d. straw (1867) £200
Z12 10d. red-brown (1867) £250
Z13 1s. green (1865) (Plate No. 4) 85·00
Z14 1s. green (1867–73) (Plate Nos. 4, 5, 7) *From* 35·00
Z15 1s. green (1873–77) (Plate Nos. 10, 12, 13) *From* 50·00
Z16 2s. blue (1867) £160
Z17 5s. rose (1867–74) (Plate Nos. 1, 2) £425

ST. JAGO DE CUBA

CROWNED-CIRCLE HANDSTAMPS

CC4 CC **1b** ST. JAGO-DE-CUBA (R.) (15.12.1841) *Price on cover* £4750

Stamps of GREAT BRITAIN *cancelled* "C 88" *as Type* **12**.

1866 *to* **1877.**
Z18 ½d. rose-red (1870–79) (Plate Nos. 4, 6, 14)
Z19 1d. rose-red (1864–79) *From* 75·00
Plate Nos. 100, 105, 106, 109, 111, 120, 123, 138, 144, 146, 147, 148, 171, 208.
Z20 1½d. lake-red (1870–74) (Plate No. 3)
Z21 2d. blue (1858–69) (Plate Nos. 9, 12, 13, 14)
Z22 3d. rose (1867) (Plate No. 5)
Z23 4d. vermilion (1865–73) *From* 75·00
Plate Nos. 9, 10, 11, 12, 13, 14.
Z24 4d. vermilion (1876) (Plate No. 15) £225
Z25 6d. violet (1867–70) (Plate Nos. 6, 8, 9) *From* £225
Z26 6d. buff (Plate No. 11)
Z27 9d. straw (1865)
Z27*a* 9d. straw (1867)
Z28 10d. red-brown (1867) £350
Z29 1s. green (1867–73) (Plate Nos. 4, 5, 6) *From* £225
Z30 1s. green (1873–77) (Plate Nos. 9, 10, 12, 13)
Z31 2s. blue (1867)
Z32 5s. rose (1867) (Plate 1)

DANISH WEST INDIES

ST. THOMAS

The British Postal Agency at St. Thomas opened in January 1809 and by 1825 was the office around which many of the packet routes were organised.

Great Britain stamps were introduced on 3 July 1865 and can be found used in combination with Danish West Indies adhesives paying the local postage.

Following a hurricane in October 1867 the main British packet office was moved to Colon in Colombia.

The British Post Office at St. Thomas closed to the public on 1 September 1877, but continued to operate as a transit office for a further two years.

CROWNED-CIRCLE HANDSTAMPS

CC1 CC **1** ST. THOMAS (R.) (20.2.49) *Price on cover* £450
CC2 CC **6** ST. THOMAS (R.) (1.5.1855) *Price on cover* £900

Stamps of GREAT BRITAIN *cancelled* "C 51" *as in Types* **4, 12** *or* **14**.

1865 *to* **1879.**
Z 1 ½d. rose-red (1870–79) 32·00
Plate Nos. 5, 6, 8, 10, 11, 12.
Z 2 1d. rose-red (1857)
Z 3 1d. rose-red (1864–79) *From* 20·00
Plate Nos. 71, 72, 79, 81, 84, 85, 86, 87, 88, 89, 90, 93, 94, 95, 96, 97, 98, 99, 100, 101, 102, 105, 106, 107, 108, 109, 110, 111, 112, 113, 114, 116, 117, 118, 119, 120, 121, 122, 123, 124, 125, 127, 129, 130, 131, 133, 134, 136, 137, 138, 139, 140, 141, 142, 144, 145, 146, 147, 148, 149, 150, 151, 152, 154, 155, 156, 157, 158, 159, 160, 161, 162, 163, 164, 165, 166, 167, 169, 170, 171, 172, 173, 174, 175, 176, 177, 178, 179, 180, 181, 182, 184, 185, 186, 187, 189, 190, 197.
Z 4 1½d. lake-red (1870–74) (Plate Nos. 1, 3) 60·00
Z 5 2d. blue (1858–69) *From* 26·00
Plate Nos. 9, 12, 13, 14, 15.
Z 6 3d. rose (1865) (Plate No. 4) 65·00
Z 7 3d. rose (1867–73) *From* 28·00
Plate Nos. 4, 5, 6, 7, 8, 9, 10.
Z 8 3d. rose (1873–76) *From* 28·00
Plate Nos. 11, 12, 14, 15, 16, 17, 18, 19.
Z 9 4d. red (1862) (Plate Nos. 3, 4) 45·00
Z10 4d. vermilion (1865–73) *From* 30·00
Plate Nos. 7, 8, 9, 10, 11, 12, 13, 14.
Z11 4d. vermilion (1876) (Plate No. 15) £175
Z12 4d. sage-green (1877) (Plate Nos. 15, 16) *From* £140

Z14 6d. lilac (1864) (Plate No. 4) £100
Z15 6d. lilac (1865–67) (Plate Nos. 5, 6) .. *From* 40·00
Z16 6d. lilac (1867) (Plate No. 6) .. .. .. 60·00
Z17 6d. violet (1867–70) (Plate Nos. 6, 8, 9) .. *From* 30·00
Z18 6d. buff (1872–73) (Plate Nos. 11, 12) .. *From* 65·00
Z19 6d. chestnut (1872) (Plate No. 11) .. .. .. 28·00
Z20 6d. grey (1873) (Plate No. 12) £120
Z21 6d. grey (1874–76) (Plate Nos. 13, 14, 15, 16) .. 30·00
Z22 8d. orange (1876) £200
Z23 9d. straw (1862) £175
Z24 9d. bistre (1862) £175
Z25 9d. straw (1865) £250
Z26 9d. straw (1867) £150
Z27 10d. red-brown (1867) £200
Z28 1s. green (1865) (Plate No. 4) .. .. .. 90·00
Z29 1s. green (1867–73) (Plate Nos. 4, 5, 6, 7) .. *From* 22·00
Z30 1s. green (1873–77) .. .. *From* 55·00
Plate Nos, 8, 9, 10, 11, 12, 13.
Z31 2s. blue (1867) £120
Z32 5s. rose (1867–74) (Plate Nos. 1, 2) .. *From* £350

DOMINICAN REPUBLIC

British Postal Agencies may have existed in the area before 1867, but it is only from that year that details can be found concerning offices at Porto Plata and St. Domingo. Both were closed in 1871, but re-opened in 1876.

Although postmarks were supplied in 1866 it seems likely that Great Britain stamps were not sent until the offices re-opened in 1876.

Covers exist showing Great Britain stamps used in combination with those of Dominican Republic with the latter paying the local postage. Both agencies finally closed in 1881.

PORTO PLATA

Stamps of GREAT BRITAIN *cancelled* "C 86" *or circular date stamp as in Types* **8** *or* **17**.

1876 *to* **1881**
Z 1 ½d. rose-red (1870–79) (Plate Nos. 10, 12, 14) *From* 60·00
Z 2 1d. rose-red (1864–79) .. .. .. *From* 32·00
Plate Nos. 123, 130, 136, 146, 151, 178, 199, 200, 205, 217.
Z 3 1½d. lake-red (1870–74) (Plate No. 3) £100
Z 4 2d. blue (1858–69) (Plate Nos. 14, 15) .. .. 40·00
Z 5 2½d. rosy mauve (1876–79) (Plate Nos. 13, 14) *From* £140
Z 6 3d. rose (1873–76) (Plate No. 18) .. .. .. 80·00
Z 7 4d. vermilion (1873) (Plate No. 14) .. .. 80·00
Z 8 4d. vermilion (1876) (Plate No. 15) £200
Z 9 4d. sage-green (1877) (Plate No. 15) £160
Z10 6d. violet (1867–70) (Plate No. 8) .. .. ..
Z11 6d. grey (1874–76) (Plate No. 15) .. .. 60·00
Z12 8d. orange (1876) £275
Z13 1s. green (1867–73) (Plate Nos. 4, 7) .. *From* 40·00
Z14 1s. green (1873–77) (Plate Nos. 11, 12, 13) *From* 42·00
Z15 2s. blue (1867) £200
Z15*a* 5s. rose (1867–83) (Plate No. 2) .. .. ..

ST. DOMINGO

Stamps of GREAT BRITAIN *cancelled* "C 87" *or circular date stamp as in Types* **12** *or* **16**.

1876 *to* **1881**
Z16 ½d. rose-red (1870–79) .. .. .. *From* 60·00
Plate Nos. 5, 6, 8, 10, 11, 13.
Z17 1d. rose-red (1864–79) .. .. .. *From* 40·00
Plate Nos. 146, 154, 171, 173, 174, 176, 178, 186, 190, 197, 220.
Z18 1½d. lake-red (1870–74) (Plate No. 3) £100
Z19 2d. blue (1858–69) (Plate Nos. 13, 14) .. .. 70·00
Z20 3d. rose (1873–76) (Plate No. 18) .. .. ..
Z21 4d. vermilion (1865–73) .. .. .. *From* 48·00
Plate Nos. 11, 12, 14.
Z22 4d. vermilion (1876) (Plate No. 15) £225
Z23 4d. sage-green (1877) (Plate No. 15) £160
Z24 6d. grey (1874–76) (Plate No. 15) .. .. ..
Z25 9d. straw (1867) .. ..
Z26 1s. green (1867) (Plate No. 4) .. .. ..
Z27 1s. green (1873–77) .. .. .. *From* 70·00
Plate Nos. 10, 11, 12, 13.
Z28 2s. blue (1867) .. ..

ECUADOR

GUAYAQUIL

The first British Postal Agent in Guayaquil was appointed in 1848.

Great Britain stamps were supplied in 1865 and continued to be used until the agency closed on 30 June 1880. They can be found used in combination with stamps of Ecuador with the latter paying the local postage.

Stamps of GREAT BRITAIN *cancelled* "C 41" *as Type* **4**.

1865 *to* **1880**.
Z 1 ½d. rose-red (1870–79) (Plate Nos. 5, 6) .. .. 55·00
Z 2 1d. rose-red (1857) .. ..
Z 3 1d. rose-red (1864–79) .. .. .. *From* 27·00
Plate Nos. 74, 78, 85, 92, 94, 105, 110, 115, 133, 140, 145, 166, 174, 180, 216.
Z 4 1½d. lake-red (1870–74) (Plate No. 3) .. .. 75·00
Z 5 2d. blue (1858–69) (Plate Nos. 9, 13, 14) .. *From* 30·00
Z 6 3d. carmine-rose (1862) £175
Z 7 3d. rose (1865) (Plate No. 4) .. .. .. 60·00
Z 8 3d. rose (1867–73) (Plate Nos. 6, 7, 9, 10) .. *From* 28·00
Z 9 3d. rose (1873–76) .. .. *From* 28·00
Plate Nos. 11, 12, 15, 16, 17, 18, 19, 20.
Z10 4d. red (1862) (Plate Nos. 3, 4) .. .. .. 70·00
Z11 4d. vermilion (1865–73) .. .. .. *From* 28·00
Plate Nos. 7, 8, 9, 10, 11, 12, 13, 14.
Z12 4d. vermilion (1876) (Plate No. 15) £175
Z13 4d. sage-green (1877) (Plate Nos. 15, 16) £150
Z14 6d. lilac (1864) (Plate No. 4) .. .. .. 70·00
Z15 6d. lilac (1865–67) (Plate Nos. 5, 6) .. .. 40·00
Z16 6d. lilac (1867) (Plate No. 6) .. .. ..
Z17 6d. violet (1867–70) (Plate Nos. 6, 8, 9) .. *From* 32·00
Z18 6d. buff (1872–73) (Plate Nos. 11, 12) .. .. 75·00

Z19 6d. chestnut (1872) .. ..
Z20 6d. grey (1873) (Plate No. 12) .. .. ..
Z21 6d. grey (1874–76) (Plate Nos. 13, 14, 15, 16) *From* 30·00
Z22 8d. orange (1876) £200
Z23 9d. straw (1862) £200
Z24 9d. straw (1867) £150
Z25 10d. red-brown (1867) £160
Z26 1s. green (1865) (Plate No. 4) .. .. .. 90·00
Z27 1s. green (1867–73) (Plate Nos. 4, 5, 6, 7) .. *From* 25·00
Z28 1s. green (1873–77) .. .. *From* 48·00
Plate Nos. 8, 9, 10, 11, 12, 13.
Z29 2s. blue (1867) £125
Z30 2s. brown (1880) £2000
Z31 5s. rose (1867–74) (Plate Nos. 1, 2) .. *From* £400

FERNANDO PO

The British government leased naval facilities on this Spanish island from 1827 until 1834. A British Consul was appointed in 1849 and a postal agency was opened on 1 April 1858.

The use of Great Britain stamps was authorised in 1858, but a cancellation was not supplied until 1874. The office remained open until 1877.

CROWNED-CIRCLE HANDSTAMPS

CC1 CC **4** FERNANDO-PO (R.) (19.2.1859)
Price on cover £3750

Stamps of GREAT BRITAIN *cancelled* "247" *as Type* **9**.

1874 *to* **1877**.
Z1 4d. vermilion (1865–72) (Plate Nos. 13, 14) .. £750
Z2 4d. vermilion (1876) (Plate No. 15) .. .. ..
Z3 6d. grey (1874–76) (Plate Nos. 13, 14, 15, 16) .. £700

GUADELOUPE

A British Packet Agency was established on Guadeloupe on 1 October 1848 and continued to function until 1874.

No. CC1 is often found used in conjunction with French Colonies (General Issues) adhesive stamps.

A similar packet agency existed on Martinique from 1 October 1848 until 1879, but no crowned-circle handstamp was issued for it.

CROWNED-CIRCLE HANDSTAMPS

CC1 CC **1** GUADALOUPE (R., B. or Black) (9.3.1849)
Price on cover £1800

HAITI

The original British Postal Agencies in Haiti date from 1830 when it is known a Packet Agency was established at Jacmel. An office at Port-au-Prince followed in 1842, both these agencies remaining in operation until 30 June 1881.

During this period short-lived agencies also operated in the following Haitian towns: Aux Cayes (1848 to 1863), Cap Haitien (1842 to 1863), Gonaives (1849 to 1857) and St. Marc (1854 to 1861). A further agency may have operated at Le Mole around the year 1841.

Great Britain stamps were supplied to Jacmel in 1865 and to Port-au-Prince in 1869.

CAP HAITIEN

CROWNED-CIRCLE HANDSTAMPS

CC1 CC **1b** CAPE-HAITIEN (R.) (31.12.1841)
Price on cover £3000

JACMEL

CROWNED-CIRCLE HANDSTAMPS

CC2 CC **1b** JACMEL (R.) (29.6.1843) .. *Price on cover* £1000

Stamps of GREAT BRITAIN *cancelled* "C 59" *as Type* **4**.

1865 *to* **1881**.
Z 1 ½d. rose-red (1870–79) .. .. .. *From* 40·00
Plate Nos. 4, 5, 6, 10, 11, 12, 14, 15.
Z 2 1d. rose-red (1864–79) .. .. .. *From* 30·00
Plate Nos. 74, 81, 84, 87, 95, 106, 107, 109, 122, 136, 137, 139, 148, 150, 151, 152, 156, 157, 159, 160, 162, 164, 166, 167, 170, 171, 179, 181, 183, 184, 186, 187, 189, 192, 194, 198, 200, 204, 206, 215, 219.
Z 3 1½d. lake-red (1870–74) (Plate No. 3) .. .. 60·00
Z 4 2d. blue (1858–69) (Plate Nos. 9, 13, 14, 15) .. 40·00
Z 5 2½d. rosy mauve (1876) (Plate No. 4) .. ..
Z 6 3d. rose (1867–73) (Plate Nos. 5, 6, 7, 8, 9, 10) *From* 38·00
Z 7 3d. rose (1873–76) .. .. 38·00
Plate Nos. 11, 12, 14, 16, 17, 18, 19.
Z 8 4d. red (1863) (Plate No. 4) (*Hair lines*) .. .. 80·00
Z 9 4d. vermilion (1865–73) .. .. .. *From* 38·00
Plate Nos. 7, 8, 9, 10, 11, 12, 13, 14.
Z10 4d. vermilion (1876) (Plate No. 15) £200
Z11 4d. sage-green (1877) (Plate Nos. 15, 16) .. £150
Z12 4d. grey-brown (1880) *wmk* Large Garter .. £250
Plate No. 17.
Z13 4d. grey-brown (1880) *wmk* Crown (Plate No. 17) 35·00
Z14 6d. lilac (1867) (Plate Nos. 5, 6) .. .. 42·00
Z15 6d. violet (1867–70) (Plate Nos. 8, 9) .. .. 35·00
Z16 6d. buff (1872–73) (Plate Nos. 11, 12) .. *From* 60·00
Z17 6d. chestnut (1872) (Plate No. 11) .. ..
Z18 6d. grey (1873) (Plate No. 12) .. .. ..
Z19 6d. grey (1874–76) .. .. *From* 35·00
Plate Nos. 13, 14, 15, 16, 17.
Z20 8d. orange (1876) £250
Z21 9d. straw (1862) £200
Z22 9d. straw (1867) £175
Z23 10d. red-brown (1867) £160
Z24 1s. green (1865) (Plate No. 4) £100
Z25 1s. green (1867–73) (Plate Nos. 4, 5, 6, 7) .. *From* 30·00
Z26 1s. green (1873–77) .. .. *From* 48·00
Plate Nos. 8, 9, 10, 11, 12, 13.
Z27 1s. orange-brown (1880) (Plate No. 13) £300
Z28 2s. blue (1867) £100
Z29 2s. brown (1880) £2000
Z30 5s. rose (1867–74) (Plate Nos. 1, 2) .. *From* £300

1880.
Z31 ½d. green (1880) .. .. 28·0
Z32 1d. Venetian red .. .. 24·0
Z33 1½d. Venetian red .. .. 40·0
Z34 2d. rose .. .. 65·0

PORT-AU-PRINCE

CROWNED-CIRCLE HANDSTAMPS

CC3 CC **1b** PORT-AU-PRINCE (R.) (29.6.1843)
Price on cover £150

Stamps of GREAT BRITAIN *cancelled* "E 53" *as in Types* *or* **12**.

1869 *to* **1881.**
Z35 ½d. rose-red (1870-79) .. .. .. *From* 42·0
Plate Nos. 5, 6, 10, 11, 12, 13, 14.
Z36 1d. rose-red (1864–79) .. .. .. *From* 28·0
Plate Nos. 87, 134, 154, 159, 167, 171, 173, 174, 177, 183, 187, 189, 193, 199, 200, 201, 202, 206, 209, 210, 218, 219.
Z37 1½d. lake-red (1870–74) (Plate No. 3) .. .. 70·0
Z38 2d. blue (1858–69) (Plate Nos. 9, 14, 15) .. .. 38·0
Z40 2½d. rosy mauve (1876–79) (Plate Nos. 3, 9) .. 80·0
Z41 3d. rose (1867–73) (Plate Nos. 6, 7) .. ..
Z42 3d. rose (1873–79) (Plate Nos. 17, 18, 20) .. 30·0
Z43 4d. vermilion (1865–73) .. .. .. *From* 38·0
Plate Nos. 11, 12, 13, 14.
Z44 4d. vermilion (1876) (Plate No. 15) £20
Z45 4d. sage-green (1877) (Plate Nos. 15, 16) .. *From* £13
Z46 4d. grey-brown (1880) *wmk* Large Garter .. £25
Plate No. 17.
Z47 4d. grey-brown (1880) *wmk* Crown (Plate No. 17) 32·0
Z48 6d. grey (1874–76) (Plate Nos. 15, 16) .. ..
Z49 8d. orange (1876) £19
Z50 1s. green (1867–73) (Plate Nos. 4, 5, 6, 7) *From* 30·0
Z51 1s. green (1873–77) .. .. .. *From* 45·0
Plate Nos. 8, 9, 10, 11, 12, 13
Z52 1s. orange-brown (1880) (Plate No. 13) £30
Z53 1s. orange-brown (1881) (Plate No. 13) .. .. 70·0
Z54 2s. blue (1867) £10
Z55 2s. brown (1880) £200
Z56 5s. rose (1867–74) (Plate Nos. 1, 2) £37
Z57 10s. greenish grey (1878) £250

1880.
Z58 ½d. green .. .. 40·0
Z59 1d. Venetian red .. .. 30·0
Z60 1½d. Venetian red .. .. 40·0
Z61 2d. rose .. ..

MACAO

A British Consular Post Office opened in 1841. It had bee preceded by the Macao Boat Office, possibly a private ventur which operated in the 1830s. The office closed when the consula closed on 30 September 1845, but was back in operation by 1854.

The Agency continued to function, in conjunction with the Hor Kong Post Office, until 28 February 1884 when Portugal joined th U.P.U.

CROWNED-CIRCLE HANDSTAMPS

Z 2

CC1 – PAID AT MACAO (crowned-oval 20 mm wide) (R.) (1844) .. .. *Price on cover* £1400
CC2 Z **2** Crown and Macao (1881) .. .. ..

No. CC2 with the Crown removed was used by the Portugues post office in Macao as a cancellation until 1890.

A locally-cut mark, as Type CC **2**, inscribed "PAGO E MACAO" is known on covers between 1870 and 1877. It w probably used by the Portuguese postmaster to send letters via th British Post Office (*Price* £10000).

MADEIRA

The British Packet Agency on this Portuguese island was open in 1767 and was of increased importance from 1808 following th exile of the Portuguese royal family to Brazil. The South America packets ceased to call in 1858. It appears to have closed sometir around 1860.

CROWN-CIRCLE HANDSTAMPS

CC1 CC **1b** MADEIRA (R.) (28.2.1842) .. *Price on cover* £120

MEXICO

The British Postal Agency at Vera Cruz opened in 1825, followin the introduction of the Mexican Packet service. No handstamp were supplied, however, until 1842, when a similar agency Tampico was set up.

Great Britain stamps were used at Tampico from 1867, bu apparently, were never sent to the Vera Cruz office. Combinatio covers exist showing the local postage paid by Mexican adhesives The Agency at Vera Cruz closed in 1874 and that at Tampico i 1876.

TAMPICO

CROWNED-CIRCLE HANDSTAMPS

C1 CC **1b** TAMPICO (R.) (13.11.1841). . *Price on cover* £1600

No. CC1 may be found on cover, used in conjunction with Mexico hesive stamps.

amps of GREAT BRITAIN *cancelled* "C 63" *as Type* **4**.

67 *to* **1876**.
1 1d. rose-red (1864–79) . . . . . . *From* 80·00
Plate Nos. 81, 89, 103, 117, 139, 147.
2 2d. blue (1858–69) (Plate Nos. 9, 14) £100
3 4d. vermilion (1865–73) . . . . *From* 55·00
Plate Nos. 7, 8, 10, 11, 12, 13, 14.
4 1s. green (1867–73) (Plate Nos. 4, 5, 7, 8) . . . . 70·00
5 2s. blue (1867) £350

VERA CRUZ

CROWNED-CIRCLE HANDSTAMPS

2 CC **1b** VERA CRUZ (R.) (13.11.1841) *Price on cover* £1600
3 VERA CRUZ (Black) (*circa* 1845)
Price on cover £800

No. CC3 can also be found used in conjunction with Mexico hesive stamps.

NICARAGUA

GREYTOWN

British involvement on the Mosquito Coast of Nicaragua dates om 1655 when contacts were first made with the indigenous isquito Indians. A formal alliance was signed in 1740 and the area as considered as a British dependency until the Spanish authorities gotiated a withdrawal in 1786.

The Misquitos remained under British protection, however, and, lowing the revolutionary period in the Spanish dominions, this entually led to the appropriation, by the Misquitos with British cking, of the town of San Juan del Norte, later renamed Greytown. The port was included in the Royal West Indian Mail Steam cket Company's mail network from January 1842, forming part of e Jamaica District. This arrangement only lasted until September that year, however, although packets were once again calling at eytown by November 1844. Following the discovery of gold in alifornia the office increased in importance, owing to the overland ffic, although the first distinctive postmark is not recorded in use til February 1856.

A subsidiary agency, without its own postmark, operated at uefields from 1857 to 1863.

The British Protectorate over the Misquitos ended in 1860, but the itish Post Office at Greytown continued to operate, being supplied th Great Britain stamps in 1865. These are occasionally found ed in combination with Nicaraguan issues, which had only internal lidity.

The British Post Office at Greytown closed on 1 May 1882 when e Republic of Nicaragua joined the U.P.U.

CROWNED-CIRCLE HANDSTAMPS

Z 1

1 Z **1** GREYTOWN (R.) (14.4.1859) . . . .

Z 2 Z 4

Z 3

amps of GREAT BRITAIN *cancelled* "C 57" *as in Types* Z **2** (*issued* 1865), Z **3** (*issued* 1875), *or with circular postmark as Type* Z **4** (*issued* 1864).

65 *to* **1882**.
1 ½d. rose-red (1870–79) (Plate Nos. 5, 10, 11) . . 50·00
2 1d. rose-red (1864–79) (Plate Nos. 180, 197, 210) . . 30·00
3 1½d. lake-red (1870) (Plate No. 3) . . . . 60·00
4 2d. blue (1858–69) (Plate Nos. 9, 14, 15) . . . .
5 3d. rose (1873–76) (Plate Nos. 17, 18, 19, 20) . . 40·00
Z 6 3d. rose (1881) (Plate No. 20) . . . . . .
Z 7 4d. vermilion (1865–73) . . . . *From* 35·00
Plate Nos. 8, 10, 11, 12, 13, 14.
Z 8 4d. vermilion (1876) (Plate No. 15) £200
Z 9 4d. sage-green (1877) (Plate Nos. 15, 16) . . £140
Z10 4d. grey-brown (1880) *wmk* Large Garter £250
Plate No. 17.
Z11 4d. grey-brown (1880) *wmk* Crown (Plate No. 17) 85·00
Z12 6d. grey (1874–76) (Plate Nos. 14, 15, 16) . . . . 50·00
Z13 8d. orange (1876) . . . .
Z14 1s. green (1865) (Plate No. 4) . . . .
Z15 1s. green (1867–73) (Plate Nos. 6, 7) . . . .
Z16 1s. green (1873–77) (Plate Nos. 8, 10, 12, 13) . . 45·00
Z17 1s. orange-brown (1880) (Plate No. 13) . . £250
Z18 1s. orange-brown (1881) (Plate No. 13) . . 70·00
Z19 2s. blue (1867) £150
Z20 2s. brown (1880) £2000
Z21 5s. rose (1867–74) (Plate Nos. 1, 2) . . £300
Z22 5s. rose (1882) (Plate No. 4), blue *paper* . . £1100
Z23 10s. greenish grey (1878) £1800

1880.
Z24 1d. Venetian red . . . .
Z25 1½d. Venetian red . . . . 45·00

PERU

British Agencies in Peru date from 1846 when offices were established at Arica and Callao. The network was later expanded to include agencies at Paita (1848), Pisco (1868) and Iquique and Islay (both 1869). This last office was transferred to Mollendo in 1877.

It is believed that a further agency existed at Pisagua, but no details exist.

Great Britain stamps were supplied from 1865 and can be found used in combination with Peru adhesives paying the local postage. The Postal Agency at Pisco closed in 1870 and the remainder in 1879, the towns of Arica, Iquique and Pisagua passing to Chile by treaty in 1883.

ARICA

CROWNED-CIRCLE HANDSTAMPS

CC1 CC **1** ARICA (Black or R.) (5.11.1850)
Price on cover £2750

Stamps of GREAT BRITAIN *cancelled* "C 36" *as in Types* **4**, **12** *or* **14**.

1865 *to* **1879**.
Z 1 ½d. rose-red (1870–79) . . . . *From* 50·00
Plate Nos. 5, 6, 10, 11, 13.
Z 2 1d. rose-red (1864–79) . . . . *From* 40·00
Plate Nos. 102, 139, 140, 163, 167.
Z 3 1½d. lake-red (1870–74) (Plate No. 3) . . . .
Z 4 2d. blue (1858–69) (Plate No. 14) . . . . 70·00
Z 5 3d. rose (1867–73) (Plate Nos. 5, 9) . . . .
Z 6 3d. rose (1873–76) . . . . . . *From* 30·00
Plate Nos. 11, 12, 17, 18, 19.
Z 7 4d. vermilion (1865–73) . . . . *From* 32·00
Plate Nos. 10, 11, 12, 13, 14.
Z 8 4d. vermilion (1876) (Plate No. 15) . . . .
Z 9 4d. sage-green (1877) (Plate Nos. 15, 16) . . £140
Z10 6d. lilac (1862) (Plate Nos. 3, 4) . . . .
Z11 6d. lilac (1865–67) (Plate No. 5) . . . .
Z12 6d. violet (1867–70) (Plate Nos. 6, 8, 9) . . 35·00
Z13 6d. buff (1872) (Plate No. 11) . . . . 80·00
Z14 6d. chestnut (1872) (Plate No. 11) . . . .
Z15 6d. grey (1873) (Plate No. 12) £120
Z16 6d. grey (1874–76) (Plate Nos. 13, 14, 15, 16) *From* 28·00
Z17 8d. orange (1876) . . . .
Z18 9d. straw (1862) . . . .
Z19 9d. straw (1865) . . . .
Z20 9d. straw (1867) £150
Z21 10d. red-brown (1867) . . . . . .
Z22 1s. green (1862) . . . .
Z23 1s. green (1865) . . . .
Z24 1s. green (1867–73) (Plate Nos. 4, 5, 6, 7) . . *From* 26·00
Z25 1s. green (1873–77) . . . . . . *From* 50·00
Plate Nos. 8, 9, 10, 11, 12, 13.
Z26 2s. blue (1867) £150
Z27 5s. rose (1867–74) (Plate Nos. 1, 2) £350

CALLAO

CROWNED-CIRCLE HANDSTAMPS

CC2 CC **2** CALLAO (R.) (13.1.1846) . . *Price on cover* £1000
CC3 CC **1** CALLAO (R.) (16.7.1846) . . *Price on cover* £550

Nos. CC2/3 can be found used on covers from 1865 showing the local postage paid by a Peru adhesive.

Stamps of GREAT BRITAIN *cancelled* "C 38" *as in Types* **4**, **12** *or with circular date stamp as Type* **5**.

1865 *to* **1879**.
Z28 ½d. rose-red (1870–79) . . . . *From* 35·00
Plate Nos. 5, 6, 10, 11, 12, 13, 14.
Z29 1d. rose-red (1864–79) . . . . *From* 14·00
Plate Nos. 74, 88, 89, 93, 94, 97, 108, 123, 127, 128, 130, 134, 137, 139, 140, 141, 143, 144, 145, 146, 148, 149, 156, 157, 160, 163, 167, 171, 172, 173, 175, 176, 180, 181, 182, 183, 185, 187, 190, 193, 195, 198, 199, 200, 201, 204, 206, 209, 210, 212, 213, 215.
Z30 1½d. lake-red (1870–74) (Plate No. 3) . . . .
Z31 2d. blue (1858–69) . . . . . . *From* 18·00
Plate Nos. 9, 12, 13, 14, 15.
Z32 3d. carmine-rose (1862) . . . . . .
Z33 3d. rose (1865) (Plate No. 4) . . . . 55·00
Z34 3d. rose (1867–73) . . . . . . *From* 24·00
Plate Nos. 5, 6, 7, 8, 9, 10.
Z35 3d. rose (1873–76) . . . . . . *From* 30·00
Plate Nos. 11, 12, 14, 15, 16, 17, 18, 19.
Z36 4d. red (1862) (Plate Nos. 3, 4) . . . .
Z37 4d. vermilion (1865–73) . . . . *From* 28·00
Plate Nos. 8, 10, 11, 12, 13, 14.
Z38 4d. vermilion (1876) (Plate No. 15) £175
Z39 4d. sage-green (1877) (Plate Nos. 15, 16) . . £140
Z40 6d. lilac (1862) (Plate Nos. 3, 4) . . . .
Z40*a* 6d. lilac (1865) (Plate No. 5) . . . .
Z41 6d. lilac (1867) . . . .
Z42 6d. violet (1867–70) (Plate Nos. 6, 8, 9) . . *From* 38·00
Z43 6d. buff (1872–73) (Plate Nos. 11, 12) . . *From* 55·00
Z44 6d. chestnut (1872) (Plate No. 11) . . . . 30·00
Z45 6d. grey (1873) (Plate No. 12) £120
Z46 6d. grey (1874–80) (Plate Nos. 13, 14, 15, 16) *From* 28·00
Z47 8d. orange (1876) £175
Z48 9d. straw (1862) . . . .
Z49 9d. straw (1865) £275
Z50 9d. straw (1867) £160
Z51 10d. red-brown (1867) £200
Z52 1s. green (1865) . . . .
Z53 1s. green (1867–73) (Plate Nos. 4, 5, 6, 7) . . *From* 22·00
Z54 1s. green (1873–77) . . . . . . *From* 38·00
Plate Nos. 8, 9, 10, 11, 12, 13.
Z55 2s. blue (1867) £110
Z56 5s. rose (1867–74) (Plate Nos. 1, 2) . . *From* £300

IQUIQUE

Stamps of GREAT BRITAIN *cancelled* "D 87" *as Type* **12**.

1865 *to* **1879**.
Z57 ½d. rose-red (1870–79) (Plate Nos. 5, 6, 13, 14) . . 70·00
Z58 1d. rose-red (1864–79) (Plate Nos. 76, 179, 185, 205) 42·00
Z59 2d. blue (1858–69) (Plate Nos. 9, 12, 13, 14) . .
Z60 3d. rose (1867–73) (Plate Nos. 5, 6, 7, 8, 9) *From* 40·00
Z61 3d. rose (1873–76) (Plate Nos. 12, 18, 19) . . 60·00
Z62 4d. vermilion (1865–73) (Plate Nos. 12, 13, 14) . . 42·00
Z63 4d. vermilion (1876) (Plate No. 15) £200
Z64 4d. sage-green (1877) (Plate Nos. 15, 16) . . *From* £150
Z65 6d. mauve (1869) (Plate Nos. 8, 9) . . . .
Z66 6d. buff (1872–73) (Plate Nos. 11, 12) . . *From* 85·00
Z67 6d. chestnut (1872) (Plate No. 11) . . . .
Z68 6d. grey (1873) (Plate No. 12) £120
Z69 6d. grey (1874–76) (Plate Nos. 13, 14, 15, 16) . .
Z70 8d. orange (1876) £275
Z71 9d. straw (1867) £175
Z72 10d. red-brown (1867) . . . . . .
Z73 1s. green (1867–73) (Plate Nos. 4, 6, 7) . . *From* 38·00
Z74 1s. green (1873–77) . . . . . . *From* 48·00
Plate Nos. 8, 9, 10, 11, 12, 13.
Z75 2s. blue (1867) . . . .

ISLAY (*later* MOLLENDO)

CROWNED-CIRCLE HANDSTAMPS

CC4 CC **1** ISLAY (Black or R.) (23.10.1850) . . . .

Stamps of GREAT BRITAIN *cancelled* "C 42" *as Types* **4** *or* **12**.

1865 *to* **1879**.
Z76 1d. rose-red (1864–79) . . . . *From* 38·00
Plate Nos. 78, 84, 87, 88, 96, 103, 125, 134.
Z77 1½d. lake-red (1870–74) (Plate No. 3) . . . .
Z78 2d. blue (1858–69) (Plate Nos. 9, 13, 15) . . 30·00
Z79 3d. carmine-rose (1862) . . . . . .
Z80 3d. rose (1865) . . . . 75·00
Z81 3d. rose (1867–73) (Plate Nos. 4, 5, 6, 10) . . 40·00
Z82 4d. red (1862) (Plate Nos. 3, 4) . . . . 80·00
Z83 4d. vermilion (1867–73) . . . . *From* 40·00
Plate Nos. 9, 10, 11, 12, 13.
Z84 4d. vermilion (1876) (Plate No. 15) . . . .
Z85 4d. sage-green (1877) (Plate Nos. 15, 16) . . £150
Z86 6d. lilac (1862) (Plate Nos. 3, 4) . . . . 80·00
Z87 6d. lilac (1865) (Plate No. 5) . . . . 60·00
Z88 6d. violet (1867–70) (Plate Nos. 6, 8, 9) . . *From* 45·00
Z89 6d. buff (1873) (Plate No. 12) . . . .
Z90 6d. grey (1873) (Plate No. 12) . . . .
Z91 6d. grey (1874–76) (Plate Nos. 13, 14, 15, 16) *From* 38·00
Z92 9d. straw (1865) £275
Z93 9d. straw (1867) £160
Z94 10d. red-brown (1867) £180
Z95 1s. green (1865) (Plate No. 4) . . . .
Z96 1s. green (1867–73) (Plate Nos. 4, 5, 6, 7) . . *From* 32·00
Z97 1s. green (1873–77) (Plate Nos. 8, 10, 12, 13) *From* 44·00
Z98 2s. blue (1867) . . . .
Z99 5s. rose (1867) (Plate No. 1) . . . .

PAITA

CROWNED-CIRCLE HANDSTAMPS

CC5 CC **1** PAITA (Black *or* R.) (5.11.1850)
Price on cover £3750

Stamps of GREAT BRITAIN *cancelled* "C 43" *as Type* **4**.

1865 *to* **1879**.
Z100 1d. rose-red (1864–79) (Plate Nos. 127, 147) . .
Z101 2d. blue (1858–69) (Plate Nos. 9, 14) . . . .
Z102 3d. rose (1867–73) (Plate Nos. 5, 6) . . . . 40·00
Z103 3d. rose (1876) (Plate Nos. 17, 18, 19) . . . . 40·00
Z104 4d. vermilion (1865–73) . . . . *From* 40·00
Plate Nos. 10, 11, 12, 13, 14.
Z105 4d. sage-green (1877) (Plate No. 15) . . . .
Z106 6d. lilac (1862) (Plate No. 3) . . . . 85·00
Z107 6d. lilac (1865–67) (Plate Nos. 5, 6) . . . . 50·00
Z108 6d. violet (1867–70) (Plate Nos. 6, 8, 9) . . 42·00
Z109 6d. buff (1872–73) (Plate Nos. 11, 12) . . *From* 70·00
Z110 6d. chestnut (Plate No. 11) . . . . . . 42·00
Z111 6d. grey (1873) . . . .
Z112 6d. grey (1874–76) (Plate Nos. 13, 14, 15) . .
Z113 9d. straw (1862) . . . .
Z114 10d. red-brown (1867) £275
Z115 1s. green (1865) (Plate No. 4) . . . .
Z116 1s. green (1867–73) (Plate No. 4) . . . . 40·00
Z117 1s. green (1873–77) (Plate Nos. 8, 9, 10, 13) . . 42·00
Z118 2s. blue (1867) £175
Z119 5s. rose (1867) (Plate No. 1) £450

PISAGUA(?)

Stamp of GREAT BRITAIN *cancelled* "D 65" *as Type* **12**.

Z120 2s. blue (1867) . . . .

PISCO AND CHINCHA ISLANDS

Stamps of GREAT BRITAIN *cancelled* "D 74" *as Type* **12**.

1865 *to* **1870**.
Z121 2d. blue (1858–69) (Plate No. 9) . . . .
Z122 4d. vermilion (1865–73) (Plate Nos. 10, 12) . . £200
Z123 6d. violet (1868) (Plate No. 6) £800
Z124 1s. green (1867) (Plate No. 4) . . . .
Z125 2s. blue (1867) £700

PORTO RICO

A British Postal Agency operated at San Juan from 1844. On 24 October 1872 further offices were opened at Aguadilla, Arroyo, Mayaguez and Ponce, with Naguabo added three years later.

Great Britain stamps were used during 1865–66 and from 1873 to 1877. All the British Agencies closed on 1 May 1877.

AGUADILLA

Stamps of GREAT BRITAIN *cancelled* "F 84" *as Type* **8**.

1873 *to* **1877**.

No.	Description	Price
Z 1	½d. rose-red (1870) (Plate No. 6)	80·00
Z 2	1d. rose-red (1864–79) Plate Nos. 119, 122, 139, 149, 156, 160.	42·00
Z 3	2d. blue (1858–69) (Plate No. 14)	
Z 4	3d. rose (1867–73) (Plate Nos. 7, 8, 9)	
Z 5	3d. rose (1873–76) (Plate No. 12)	
Z 6	4d. vermilion (1865–73) (Plate Nos. 12, 13, 14)	50·00
Z 7	4d. vermilion (1876) (Plate No. 15)	£175
Z 7*a*	6d. pale buff (1872–73) (Plate No. 11)	
Z 8	6d. grey (1874–76) (Plate Nos. 13, 14)	
Z 9	9d. straw (1867)	£300
Z10	10d. red-brown (1867)	£200
Z11	1s. green (1867–73) (Plate Nos. 4, 5, 6, 7)	*From* 40·00
Z12	1s. green (1873–77) Plate Nos. 8, 9, 10, 11, 12.	*From* 55·00
Z13	2s. blue (1867)	£225

ARROYO

Stamps of GREAT BRITAIN *cancelled* "F 83" *as Type* **8**.

1873 *to* **1877**.

No.	Description	Price
Z14	½d. rose-red (1870) (Plate No. 5)	55·00
Z15	1d. rose-red (1864–79) Plate Nos. 149, 150, 151, 156, 164, 174, 175.	45·00
Z16	1½d. lake-red (1870) (Plate Nos. 1, 3)	
Z17	2d. blue (1858–69) (Plate No. 14)	
Z18	3d. rose (1867–73) (Plate Nos. 5, 7, 10)	40·00
Z19	3d. rose (1873–76) (Plate Nos. 11, 12, 14, 16, 18)	45·00
Z20	4d. vermilion (1865–73) (Plate Nos. 12, 13, 14)	40·00
Z21	4d. vermilion (1876) (Plate No. 15)	£175
Z22	6d. chestnut (1872) (Plate No. 11)	55·00
Z23	6d. pale-buff (1872) (Plate No. 11)	60·00
Z23*a*	6d. grey (1873) (Plate No. 12)	
Z24	6d. grey (1874–76) (Plate Nos. 13, 14, 15)	50·00
Z25	9d. straw (1867)	£225
Z26	10d. red-brown (1867)	£175
Z27	1s. green (1865) (Plate No. 4)	
Z28	1s. green (1867–73) (Plate Nos. 4, 5, 6, 7)	40·00
Z29	1s. green (1873–77) Plate Nos. 8, 9, 10, 11, 12, 13.	50·00
Z30	2s. blue (1867)	£180
Z31	5s. rose (1867–74) (Plate No. 2)	

MAYAGUEZ

Stamps of GREAT BRITAIN *cancelled* "F 85" *as Type* **8**.

1873 *to* **1877**.

No.	Description	Price
Z32	½d. rose-red (1870) Plate Nos. 4, 5, 6, 8, 10, 11.	*From* 45·00
Z33	1d. rose-red (1864–79) Plate Nos. 76, 120, 121, 122, 124, 134, 137, 140, 146, 149, 150, 151, 154, 155, 156, 157, 160, 167, 170, 171, 174, 175, 176, 178, 180, 182, 185, 186, 189.	*From* 24·00
Z34	1½d. lake-red (1870–74) (Plate Nos. 1, 3)	40·00
Z35	2d. blue (1858–69) (Plate Nos. 13, 14, 15)	38·00
Z36	3d. rose (1867–73) (Plate Nos. 7, 8, 9, 10)	30·00
Z37	3d. rose (1873–76) Plate Nos. 11, 12, 14, 15, 16, 17, 18, 19.	30·00
Z38	4d. vermilion (1865–73) (Plate Nos. 11, 12, 13, 14)	32·00
Z39	4d. vermilion (1876) (Plate No. 15)	£160
Z40	4d. sage-green (1877) (Plate No. 15)	
Z41	6d. mauve (1870) (Plate No. 9)	
Z42	6d. buff (1872) (Plate No. 11)	75·00
Z43	6d. chestnut (1872) (Plate No. 11)	65·00
Z44	6d. grey (1873) (Plate No. 12)	
Z45	6d. grey (1874–80) (Plate Nos. 13, 14, 15, 16)	38·00
Z46	8d. orange (1876)	£175
Z47	9d. straw (1867)	£140
Z48	10d. red-brown (1867)	£175
Z49	1s. green (1867–73) (Plate Nos. 4, 5, 6, 7)	25·00
Z50	1s. green (1873–77) Plate Nos. 8, 9, 10, 11, 12.	*From* 45·00
Z51	2s. blue (1867)	£160
Z52	5s. rose (1867–74) (Plate Nos. 1, 2)	

NAGUABO

Stamps of GREAT BRITAIN *cancelled* "582" *as Type* **9**.

1875 *to* **1877**.

No.	Description	Price
Z53	½d. rose-red (1870–79) (Plate Nos. 5, 12, 14)	
Z54	1d. rose-red (1864–79) (Plate Nos. 159, 165)	
Z55	3d. rose (1873–76) (Plate Nos. 17, 18)	£400
Z56	4d. vermilion (1872–73) (Plate Nos. 13,14)	*From* £375
Z57	4d. vermilion (1876) (Plate No. 15)	
Z58	6d. grey (1874–76) (Plate Nos. 14, 15)	
Z59	9d. straw (1867)	
Z60	10d. red-brown (1867)	£800
Z61	1s. green (1873–77) (Plate Nos. 11, 12)	
Z62	2s. dull blue (1867) (Plate No. 1)	£600

PONCE

Stamps of GREAT BRITAIN *cancelled* "F 88" *as Type* **8**.

1873 *to* **1877**.

No.	Description	Price
Z63	½d. rose-red (1870) (Plate Nos. 5, 10, 12)	50·00
Z64	1d. rose-red (1864–79) Plate Nos. 120, 121, 122, 123, 124, 146, 148, 154, 156, 157, 158, 160, 167, 171, 174, 175, 179, 186, 187.	*From* 30·00
Z65	1½d. lake-red (1870–74) (Plate No. 3)	£100
Z66	2d. blue (1858–69) (Plate Nos. 13, 14)	40·00
Z67	3d. rose (1867–73) (Plate Nos. 7, 8, 9)	
Z68	3d. rose (1873–76) (Plate Nos. 12, 16, 17, 18, 19)	35·00
Z69	4d. vermilion (1865–73) Plate Nos. 8, 9, 12, 13, 14.	*From* 35·00
Z70	4d. vermilion (1876) (Plate No. 15)	£175
Z71	4d. sage-green (1877) (Plate Nos. 15, 16)	£140
Z72	6d. buff (1872–73) (Plate Nos. 11, 12)	70·00
Z73	6d. chestnut (1872) (Plate No. 11)	50·00
Z74	6d. grey (1873) (Plate No. 12)	
Z75	6d. grey (1874–76) (Plate Nos. 13, 14, 15)	*From* 35·00
Z76	9d. straw (1867)	£200
Z77	10d. red-brown (1867)	£150
Z78	1s. green (1867–73) (Plate Nos. 4, 6, 7)	30·00
Z79	1s. green (1873–77) Plate Nos. 8, 9, 10, 11, 12, 13.	*From* 45·00
Z80	2s. blue (1867)	
Z81	5s. rose (1867–74) (Plate Nos. 1, 2)	*From* £350

SAN JUAN

CROWNED-CIRCLE HANDSTAMPS

CC1 CC **1** SAN JUAN PORTO RICO (R. *or* Black) (25.5.1844) .. .. .. *Price on cover* £800

No. CC1 may be found on cover, used in conjunction with Spanish colonial adhesive stamps paying the local postage.

Stamps of GREAT BRITAIN *cancelled* "C 61" *as in Types* **4**, **8** *or* **14**.

1865 *to* **1866** *and* **1873** *to* **1877**.

No.	Description	Price
Z 82	½d. rose-red (1870) (Plate Nos. 5, 10, 15)	*From* 30·00
Z 83	1d. rose-red (1857)	
Z 84	1d. rose-red (1864–79) Plate Nos. 73, 74, 81, 84, 90, 94, 100, 101, 102, 107, 117, 122, 124, 125, 127, 130, 137, 138, 139, 140, 145, 146, 149, 153, 156, 159, 160, 162, 163, 169, 171, 172, 173, 174, 175, 179, 180, 182, 186.	*From* 20·00
Z 85	1½d. lake-red (1870–74) (Plate Nos. 1, 3)	*From* 60·00
Z 86	2d. blue (1858–69) (Plate Nos. 9, 13, 14)	*From* 25·00
Z 87	3d. rose (1865) (Plate No. 4)	55·00
Z 88	3d. rose (1867–73) Plate Nos. 5, 6, 7, 8, 9, 10.	*From* 25·00
Z 89	3d. rose (1873–76) Plate Nos. 11, 12, 14, 15, 16, 17, 18.	*From* 25·00
Z 90	4d. vermilion (1865–73) Plate Nos. 7, 8, 9, 10, 11, 12, 13, 14.	*From* 30·00
Z 91	4d. vermilion (1876) (Plate No. 15)	£175
Z 92	6d. lilac (1865–67) (Plate Nos. 5, 6)	*From* 35·00
Z 93	6d. lilac (1867) (Plate No. 6)	40·00
Z 94	6d. violet (1867–70) (Plate Nos. 6, 8, 9)	*From* 30·00
Z 95	6d. buff (1872–73) (Plate Nos. 11, 12)	60·00
Z 96	6d. chestnut (1872) (Plate No. 11)	40·00
Z 97	6d. grey (1873) (Plate No. 12)	
Z 98	6d. grey (1874–76) (Plate Nos. 13, 14, 15)	*From* 24·00
Z 99	9d. straw (1862)	£175
Z100	9d. straw (1865)	£275
Z101	9d. straw (1867)	£150
Z102	10d. red-brown (1867)	£200
Z103	1s. green (1865) (Plate No. 4)	90·00
Z104	1s. green (1867–73) (Plate Nos. 4, 5, 6, 7)	*From* 24·00
Z105	1s. green (1873–77) Plate Nos. 8, 9, 10, 11, 12, 13.	*From* 40·00
Z106	2s. blue (1867)	£110
Z107	5s. rose (1867) (Plate Nos. 1, 2)	*From* £300

RUSSIA

ARMY FIELD OFFICES IN THE CRIMEA

1854 *to* **1857**.

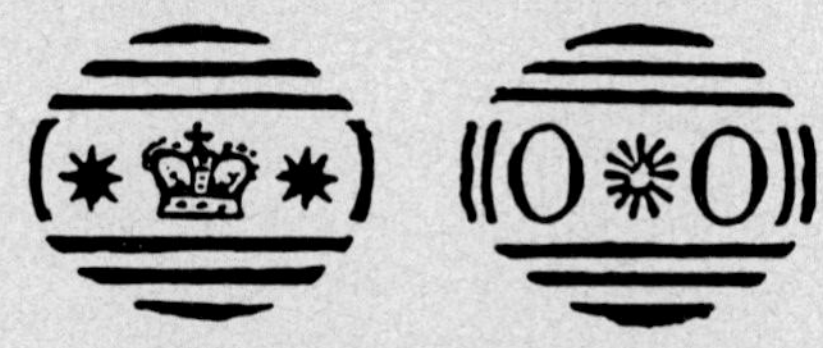

Crown between Stars

No.	Description	Price
Z 1	1d. red-brown (1841), *imperf*	£475
Z 2	1d. red-brown (1854), Die I, *wmk* Small Crown, *perf* 16	
Z 3	1d. red-brown (1855), Die II, *wmk* Small Crown, *perf* 16	£150
Z 4	1d. red-brown, Die I, *wmk* Small Crown, *perf* 14	
Z 5	1d. red-brown (1855), Die II, Small Crown, *perf* 14	
Z 6	2d. blue (1841) *imperf*	£900
Z 7	2d. blue, Small Crown (1854), *perf* 16 (Plate No. 4)	
Z 8	1s. green (1847), embossed	£1400

Star between Cyphers

No.	Description	Price
Z 9	1d. red-brown (1841), *imperf*	
Z10	1d. red-brown (1854), Die I, *wmk* Small Crown, *perf* 16	70·00
Z11	1d. red-brown (1855), Die II, *wmk* Small Crown, *perf* 16	70·00
Z12	1d. red-brown (1855), Die I, *wmk* Small Crown, *perf* 14	70·00
Z13	1d. red-brown (1855), Die II, *wmk* Small Crown, *perf* 14	70·00
Z14	1d. red-brown (1855), Die II, *wmk* Large Crown, *perf* 16	90·00
Z15	1d. red-brown (1855), Die II, *wmk* Large Crown, *perf* 14	42·00
Z16	2d. blue (1841), *imperf*	£1000
Z17	2d. blue (1854) *wmk* Small Crown, *perf* 16 Plate Nos. 4, 5.	*From* £130
Z18	2d. blue (1855) *wmk* Small Crown, *perf* 14 Plate No. 4.	£175
Z19	2d. blue (1855), *wmk* Large Crown, *perf* 16 Plate No. 5.	£200
Z20	2d. blue (1855), *wmk* Large Crown, *perf* 14 Plate No. 5.	£120
Z21	4d. rose (1857)	£800
Z22	6d. violet (1854), embossed	£1100
Z23	1s. green (1847), embossed	£1100

SPAIN

Little is known about the operation of British Packet Agencies Spain, other than the dates recorded for the various pos markings in the G.P.O. Proof Books. The Agency at Corunna said to date from the late 17th century when the Spanish packets South America were based there. No. CC1 was probably issued connection with the inauguration of the P & O service to Spain 1843. The Spanish port of call was changed to Vigo in 1846 and office at Corunna was then closed. Teneriffe became a port-of-c for the South American packets in 1817 and this arrangem continued until 1858.

CORUNNA

CROWNED-CIRCLE HANDSTAMPS

CC1 CC **1b** CORUNNA (28.2.1842) .. .. ..

Although recorded in the G.P.O. Proof Books no example of N CC1 on cover is known.

TENERIFFE (CANARY ISLANDS)

CROWNED-CIRCLE HANDSTAMPS

CC2 CC **7** TENERIFFE (6.1.1851) .. *Price on cover* £35

CC3 CC **4** TENERIFFE (23.10.1857) .. *Price on cover* £35

No. CC2/3 can be found used on covers from Spain to Sou America with the rate from Spain to Teneriffe paid in Spani adhesive stamps.

UNITED STATES OF AMERICA

The network of British Packet Agencies, to operate the tra Atlantic Packet system, was re-established in 1814 after the War 1812.

The New York Agency opened in that year to be followed further offices at Boston, Charleston (South Carolina), New Orlea Savannah (Georgia) (all in 1842), Mobile (Alabama) (1848) and S Francisco (1860). Of these agencies Charleston and Savann closed the same year (1842) as did New Orleans, although the lat was re-activated from 1848 to 1850. Mobile closed 1850, Boston 1865, New York in 1882 and San Francisco, for which no post markings have been recorded, in 1883.

Although recorded in the G.P.O. Proof Books no actual examp of the Crowned-circle handstamps for Charleston, Mobile, Ne Orleans and Savannah are known on cover.

The G.P.O. proof books record, in error, a Crowned-circ handstamp for St. Michaels, Maryland. This handstamp w intended for the agency on San Miguel in the Azores.

CHARLESTON

CROWNED-CIRCLE HANDSTAMPS

CC1 CC **1b** CHARLESTON (15.12.1841) .. ..

MOBILE

CROWNED-CIRCLE HANDSTAMPS

CC2 CC **1b** MOBILE (15.12.1841) .. .. ..

NEW ORLEANS

CROWNED-CIRCLE HANDSTAMPS

CC3 CC **1b** NEW ORLEANS (15.12.1841) .. ..

CC4 CC **1** NEW ORLEANS (27.4.1848) .. ..

NEW YORK

CROWNED-CIRCLE HANDSTAMPS

CC5 CC **1b** NEW YORK (R.) (15.12.1841) ..

SAVANNAH

CROWNED-CIRCLE HANDSTAMPS

CC6 CC **1b** SAVANNAH (15.12.1841) .. ..

URUGUAY

MONTEVIDEO

British packets commenced calling at Montevideo in 1824 passage to and from Buenos Aires.

Great Bitain stamps were in use from 1864. Combination cove exist with the local postage paid by Uruguay adhesive stamps. T agency was closed on 31 July 1873.

CROWNED-CIRCLE HANDSTAMPS

CC1 CC **5** MONTEVIDEO (Black *or* R.) (6.1.1851) *Price on cover* £7

Stamps of GREAT BRITAIN *cancelled* "C 28" *as in Types* **4** *or* **12**.

1864 *to* **1873**.

No.	Description	Price
Z 1	1d. rose-red (1864) Plate Nos. 73, 92, 93, 94, 119, 148, 154, 157, 171.	45·
Z 2	2d. blue (1858–69) (Plate Nos. 9, 13)	38·
Z 3	3d. rose (1865) (Plate No. 4)	
Z 4	3d. rose (1867–71) (Plate Nos. 4, 5, 7)	38·
Z 6	4d. rose (1857)	
Z 7	4d. red (1862) (Plate No. 4)	
Z 8	4d. vermilion (1865–70) Plate Nos. 7, 8, 9, 10, 11, 12.	*From* 35·
Z 9	6d. lilac (1856)	
Z10	6d. lilac (1862) (Plate No. 4)	
Z11	6d. lilac (1865–67) (Plate Nos. 5, 6)	48·
Z12	6d. lilac (1867) (Plate No. 6)	
Z13	6d. violet (1867–70) (Plate Nos. 8, 9)	*From* 38·
Z14	6d. buff (1872)	
Z15	6d. chestnut (1872)	
Z16	9d. straw (1862)	
Z17	9d. straw (1865)	
Z18	9d. straw (1867)	£1
Z19	10d. red-brown (1867)	£1
Z20	1s. green (1862)	£1
Z21	1s. green (1865) (Plate No. 4)	90·
Z22	1s. green (1867–73) (Plate Nos. 4, 5)	30·
Z23	2s. blue (1867)	95·
Z24	5s. rose (1867) (Plate No. 1)	£3

VENEZUELA

British Postal Agencies were initially opened at La Guayra and
rto Cabello on 1 January 1842. Further offices were added at
aracaibo in 1842 and Ciudad Bolivar during January 1868. Porto
abello closed in 1858 and Maracaibo was also short-lived. The
maining offices closed at the end of 1879 when Venezuela joined
e U.P.U.

Great Britain stamps were used at La Guayra from 1865 and at
udad Bolivar from its establishment in 1868. They can be found
ed in combination with Venezuela adhesives paying the local
stage.

CIUDAD BOLIVAR

amps of GREAT BRITAIN *cancelled* "D 22" *as Type* **12**, *or circular date stamp as Type* **17**.

58 *to* **1879**.

1 1d. rose-red (1864–79) (Plate No. 133) .. .. 75·00
2 2d. blue (1858–69) (Plate No. 13) .. ..
3 3d. rose (1867–73) (Plate No. 5) .. ..
4 3d. rose (1873–79) (Plate No. 11) £130
5 4d. vermilion (1865–73) (Plate Nos. 9, 11, 12, 14) 45·00
6 4d. sage-green (1877) (Plate Nos. 15, 16) *From* £140
7 4d. grey-brown (1880) *wmk* Crown (Plate No. 17)
8 9d. straw (1867) .. ..
9 10d. red-brown (1867) .. ..
10 1s. green (1867–73) (Plate Nos. 4, 5, 7) .. *From* 95·00
11 1s. green (1873–77) (Plate Nos. 10, 12, 13) .. 70·00
12 2s. blue (1867) £300
3 5s. rose (1867–74) (Plate Nos. 1, 2) £450

LA GUAYRA

CROWNED-CIRCLE HANDSTAMPS

1 CC **1b** LA GUAYRA (R.) (15.12.1841) *Price on cover* £850

amps of GREAT BRITAIN *cancelled* "C 60" *as Type* **4**, *circular date stamp as Type* **16** *or with No.* CC1.

65 *to* **1880**.

4 ½d. rose-red (1870) (Plate No. 6) .. .. ..
5 1d. rose-red (1864–79) .. .. .. *From* 40·00
Plate Nos. 81, 92, 96, 98, 111, 113, 115, 131, 138, 144, 145, 154, 177, 178, 180, 196.
6 1½d. lake-red (1870–74) (Plate No. 3) .. ..
17 2d. blue (1858–69) (Plate Nos. 13, 14) .. .. 42·00
8 3d. rose (1873–76) .. .. *From* 50·00
Plate Nos. 14, 15, 17, 18, 19.
9 4d. vermilion (1865–73) .. .. .. *From* 40·00
Plate Nos. 7, 9, 11, 12, 13, 14.
0 4d. vermilion (1876) (Plate No. 15) £175
1 4d. sage-green (1877) (Plate Nos. 15, 16) £140
2 6d. lilac (1865) (Plate No. 5) .. .. ..
3 6d. violet (1867–70) (Plate Nos. 6, 8) .. ..
24 6d. buff (1872–73) (Plate Nos. 11, 12) .. *From* 90·00
25 6d. grey (1873) (Plate No. 12) £120
26 6d. grey (1874–76) (Plate Nos. 13, 14, 15, 16) .. 42·00
27 8d. orange (1876) £250
28 9d. straw (1862) .. ..
29 9d. straw (1867) .. ..
30 10d. red-brown (1867) .. ..
31 1s. green (1865) (Plate No. 4) .. .. .. 90·00
32 1s. green (1867–73) (Plate Nos. 4, 7) .. ..
33 1s. green (1873–77) .. .. .. *From* 34·00
Plate Nos. 8, 9, 10, 11, 12, 13.
34 2s. blue (1867) £200
35 5s. rose (1867–74) (Plate No. 1, 2) .. .. *From* £400

MARACAIBO

CROWNED-CIRCLE HANDSTAMPS

C2 CC **1b** MARACAIBO (31.12.1841) .. ..
No examples of No. CC2 on cover have been recorded.

PORTO CABELLO

CROWNED-CIRCLE HANDSTAMPS

C3 CC **1b** PORTO-CABELLO (R.) (15.12.1841)
Price on cover £1500

MAIL BOAT OBLITERATIONS

The following cancellations were supplied to G.P.O. sorters
erating on ships holding mail contracts from the British Post
ffice. They were for use on mail posted on board, but most
amples occur on letters from soldiers and sailors serving overseas
hich were forwarded to the mailboats without postmarks.

P. & O. MEDITERRANEAN AND FAR EAST MAILBOATS

The first such cancellation, "A 17" as Type **2**, was issued to the
uthampton–Alexandria packet in April 1858, but no examples
ve been recorded.

The G.P.O. Proof Book also records "B 16", in Type **2**, as being
sued for marine sorting in November 1859, but this postmark was
bsequently used by the Plymouth and Bristol Sorting Carriage.

Sorting on board P. & O. packets ceased in June 1870 and many
the cancellation numbers were subsequently reallocated using
ypes **9**, **11** or **12**.

amps of GREAT BRITAIN *cancelled* "A 80" *as Type* **2**.

59 (Mar) *to* **1870**.

1d. rose-red (1857), Die II, *wmk* Large Crown, *perf* 14 .. ..
6d. lilac (1856) .. ..

amps of GREAT BRITAIN *cancelled* "A 81" *as Type* **2**.

59 (Mar) *to* **1870**.

3 1d. rose-red (1857), Die II, *wmk* Large Crown, *perf* 14 .. ..
4 1d. rose-red (1864–79) .. ..
Plate Nos. 84, 85, 86, 91, 97.
5 2d. blue (1858–69) (Plate No. 9) .. ..
6 4d. red (1862) (Plate No. 4) .. .. ..

Z 7 4d. vermilion (1865–73) (Plate No. 8) .. ..
Z 8 6d. lilac (1856) .. ..
Z 9 6d. lilac (1862) (Plate No. 3) .. .. ..
Z10 6d. lilac (1865–67) .. ..
Plate Nos. 5, 6.
Z11 6d. lilac (1867) (Plate No. 6) .. .. ..
Z12 6d. violet (1867–70) .. ..
Plate Nos. 6, 8.
Z13 10d. red-brown (1867) .. ..
Z14 1s. green (1856) .. ..

Stamps of GREAT BRITAIN *cancelled* "A 82" *as Type* **2**.

1859 (Mar) *to* **1870**.

Z15 1d. rose-red (1857), Die II, *wmk* Large Crown, *perf* 14 .. ..
Z16 2d. blue (1858) (Plate No. 7) .. ..
Z17 4d. rose (1856) .. ..
Z18 6d. lilac (1856) .. ..
Z19 6d. lilac (1865–67) .. ..
Plate Nos. 5, 6.
Z20 6d. lilac (1867) (Plate No. 6) .. .. ..

Stamps of GREAT BRITAIN *cancelled* "A 83" *as Type* **2**.

1859 (Apr) *to* **1870**.

Z21 1d. rose-red (1857), Die II, *wmk* Large Crown, *perf* 14 .. ..
Z22 1d. rose-red (1864–79) .. ..
Plate Nos. 73, 74, 84, 91, 109.
Z23 3d. carmine-rose (1862) .. ..
Z24 4d. rose (1857) .. ..
Z25 4d. red (1862) .. ..
Z26 4d. vermilion (1865–73) .. ..
Plate Nos. 9, 10.
Z27 6d. lilac (1856) .. ..
Z28 6d. lilac (1862) .. ..
Z29 6d. lilac (1865–67) .. ..
Plate Nos. 5, 6.
Z30 6d. violet (1867–70) .. ..
Plate Nos. 6, 8.
Z31 10d. red-brown (1867) .. ..
Z32 1s. green (1862) .. ..

Stamps of GREAT BRITAIN *cancelled* "A 84" *as Type* **2**.

1859 (Apr) *to* **1870**.

Z33 1d. rose-red (1857), Die II, *wmk* Large Crown, *perf* 14 .. ..

Stamps of GREAT BRITAIN *cancelled* "A 85" *as Type* **2**.

1859 (Apr) *to* **1870**.

Z34 1d. rose-red (1857), Die II, *wmk* Large Crown, *perf* 14 .. ..
Z35 1d. rose-red (1864–79) .. ..
Plate Nos. 79, 97, 103.
Z36 3d. carmine-rose (1862) .. ..
Z37 4d. red (1862) .. ..
Z38 6d. lilac (1856) .. ..
Z39 6d. lilac (1862) .. ..
Plate Nos. 3, 4.
Z40 6d. lilac (1865–67) (Plate No. 5) .. ..
Z41 6d. lilac (1867) (Plate No. 6) .. ..
Z42 1s. green (1862) .. ..

Stamps of GREAT BRITAIN *cancelled* "A 86" *as Type* **2**.

1859 (Apr) *to* **1870**.

Z43 1d. rose-red (1857), Die II, *wmk* Large Crown, *perf* 14 .. ..
Z44 1d. rose-red (1864–79) .. ..
Plate Nos. 73, 84, 94, 97, 114, 118.
Z45 3d. rose (1865) .. ..
Z46 3d. rose (1867–73) .. ..
Plate Nos. 4, 5.
Z47 4d. rose (1857) .. ..
Z48 4d. red (1862) (Plate No. 4) .. ..
Z49 4d. vermilion (1865–73) (Plate No. 10) .. ..
Z50 6d. lilac (1856) .. ..
Z51 6d. lilac (1862) .. ..
Plate Nos. 3, 4.
Z52 6d. lilac (1865–67) .. ..
Plate Nos. 5, 6.
Z53 6d. lilac (1867) .. ..
Plate Nos. 6, 8.
Z54 10d. red-brown (1867) .. ..
Z55 1s. green (1862) .. ..

Stamps of GREAT BRITAIN *cancelled* "A 87" *as Type* **2**.

1859 (Apr) *to* **1870**.

Z56 1d. rose-red (1857), Die II, *wmk* Large Crown, *perf* 14 .. ..
Z57 4d. rose (1856) .. ..
Z58 6d. lilac (1867) (Plate No. 6) .. ..

Stamps of GREAT BRITAIN *cancelled* "A 88" *as Type* **2**.

1859 (Apr) *to* **1870**.

Z59 1d. rose-red (1857), Die II, *wmk* Large Crown, *perf* 14 .. ..
Z60 1d. rose-red (1864–79) .. ..
Plate Nos. 74, 80, 85.
Z61 4d. rose (1857) .. ..
Z62 4d. red (1862) .. ..
Z63 4d. vermilion (1865–73) (Plate No. 8) .. ..
Z64 6d. lilac (1856) .. ..
Z65 6d. lilac (1862) (Plate No. 4) .. ..
Z66 6d. lilac (1865–67) (Plate No. 5) .. ..
Z67 6d. lilac (1867) (Plate No. 6) .. ..
Z68 6d. violet (1867–70) (Plate No. 8) .. ..
Z69 10d. red-brown (1867) .. ..
Z70 1s. green (1856) .. ..

Stamps of GREAT BRITAIN *cancelled* "A 89" *as Type* **2**.

1859 (Apr) *to* **1870**.

Z71 1d. rose-red (1857), Die II, *wmk* Large Crown, *perf* 14 .. ..
Z72 6d. lilac (1856) .. ..

Stamps of GREAT BRITAIN *cancelled* "A 90" *as Type* **2**.

1859 (June) *to* **1870**.

Z73 1d. rose-red (1857), Die II, *wmk* Large Crown, *perf* 14 .. ..
Z74 4d. rose (1856) .. ..
Z75 6d. lilac (1856) .. ..
Z76 6d. lilac (1865–67) .. ..
Plate Nos. 5, 6.
Z77 9d. straw (1867) .. ..

Stamps of GREAT BRITAIN *cancelled* "A 99" *as Type* **2**.

1859 (June) *to* **1870**.

Z78 1d. rose-red (1857), Die II, *wmk* Large Crown, *perf* 14 .. ..
Z79 1d. rose-red (1864–79) .. ..
Plate Nos. 93, 97, 99, 118.
Z80 4d. rose (1857) .. ..
Z81 4d. red (1862) .. ..
Z82 4d. vermilion (1865–73) (Plate No. 11) .. ..
Z83 6d. lilac (1856) .. ..
Z84 6d. lilac (1862) .. ..
Z85 6d. lilac (1865–67) .. ..
Plate Nos. 5, 6.
Z86 10d. red-brown (1867) .. ..

Stamps of GREAT BRITAIN *cancelled* "B 03" *as Type* **2**.

1859 (Aug) *to* **1870**.

Z87 1d. rose-red (1857), Die II, *wmk* Large Crown, *perf* 14 .. ..
Z88 1d. rose-red (1864–79) .. ..
Plate Nos. 109, 116.
Z89 3d. rose (1865) (Plate No. 4) .. ..
Z90 6d. lilac (1856) .. ..
Z91 6d. lilac (1867) (Plate No. 6) .. ..
Z92 6d. violet (1867–70) .. ..
Plate Nos. 6, 8.
Z93 10d. red-brown (1867) .. ..

Stamps of GREAT BRITAIN *cancelled* "B 12" *as Type* **2**.

1859 (Oct) *to* **1870**.

Z 94 1d. rose-red (1857), Die II, *wmk* Large Crown, *perf* 14 .. ..
Z 95 1d. rose-red (1864–79) (Plate No. 94) .. ..
Z 96 3d. rose (1865) (Plate No. 4) .. ..
Z 97 4d. red (1862) .. ..
Z 98 4d. vermilion (1865–73) (Plate No. 8) .. ..
Z 99 6d. lilac (1856) .. ..
Z100 6d. lilac (1862) .. ..
Z101 6d. lilac (1865–67) .. ..
Plate Nos. 5, 6.
Z102 6d. violet (1867–70) (Plate No. 8) .. ..

Stamps of GREAT BRITAIN *cancelled* "B 56" *as Type* **2**.

1861 (July) *to* **1870**.

Z103 1d. rose-red (1864–70) (Plate No. 84) .. ..
Z104 2d. blue (1858–69) (Plate No. 9) .. ..
Z105 4d. red (1862) (Plate No. 4) .. ..
Z106 4d. vermilion (1865–73) .. .. ..
Plate Nos. 7, 8.
Z107 6d. lilac (1862) .. ..
Plate Nos. 3, 4.
Z108 6d. lilac (1865–67) .. ..
Plate Nos. 5, 6.
Z109 6d. violet (1867–70) .. ..
Plate Nos. 6, 8.

Stamps of GREAT BRITAIN *cancelled* "B 57" *as Type* **2**.

1861 (July) *to* **1870**.

Z110 1d. rose-red (1857), Die II, *wmk* Large Crown, *perf* 14 .. ..
Z111 1d. rose-red (1864–79) (Plate No. 81) .. ..
Z112 2d. blue (1858–69) (Plate No. 9) .. ..
Z113 4d. red (1862) .. ..
Z114 4d. vermilion (1865–73) .. .. ..
Plate Nos. 7, 8.
Z115 6d. lilac (1865–67) .. ..
Plate Nos. 5, 6.

Stamps of GREAT BRITAIN *cancelled* "C 79" *as Type* **12**.

1866 (June) *to* **1870**.

Z116 6d. violet (1867–70) .. ..
Plate Nos. 6, 8.
Z117 10d. red-brown (1867) .. ..

CUNARD LINE ATLANTIC MAILBOATS

These were all issued in June 1859. No examples are known used after August 1868. "B 61" is recorded as being issued in March 1862, but no examples are known. Cancellation numbers were subsequently reallocated to offices in Great Britain or, in the case of "A 91", the British Virgin Islands.

Stamps of GREAT BRITAIN *cancelled* "A 91" *as Type* **2**.

1859 (June) *to* **1868**.

Z130 1d. rose-red (1857), Die II, *wmk* Large Crown, *perf* 14 .. ..
Z131 1d. rose-red (1864–79) (Plate No. 121) .. ..
Z132 2d. blue (1855), *wmk* Small Crown, *perf* 14 ..

Z133 2d. blue (1858–69) .. ..
Plate Nos. 8, 9.
Z134 4d. rose (1857) .. ..
Z135 4d. red (1862) .. ..
Z136 6d. lilac (1856) .. ..
Z137 6d. lilac (1862) .. ..
Z138 6d. lilac (1865–67) .. ..
Z139 9d. straw (1862) .. ..
Z140 1s. green (1856) .. ..

Stamps of GREAT BRITAIN *cancelled* "A 92" *as Type* **2**.

1859 (June) *to* **1868**.
Z141 1d. rose-red (1857), Die II, *wmk* Large Crown, *perf* 14 .. ..
Z142 1d. rose-red (1864–79) .. ..
Plate Nos. 93, 97.
Z143 6d. lilac (1856) .. ..
Z144 6d. lilac (1862) (Plate No. 3) .. .. ..
Z145 6d. lilac (1865–67) .. ..
Plate Nos. 5, 6.

Stamps of GREAT BRITAIN *cancelled* "A 93" *as Type* **2**.

1859 (June) *to* **1868**.
Z146 1d. rose-red (1857), Die II, *wmk* Large Crown, *perf* 14 .. ..
Z147 1d. rose-red (1864–79) (Plate No. 85) .. ..
Z148 6d. lilac (1856) .. ..
Z149 6d. lilac (1865–67) (Plate No. 6) .. ..
Z150 10d. red-brown (1867) .. ..

Stamps of GREAT BRITAIN *cancelled* "A 94" *as Type* **2**.

1859 (June) *to* **1868**.
Z151 1d. rose-red (1857), Die II, *wmk* Large Crown, *perf* 14 .. ..
Z152 1d. rose-red (1864–79) .. ..
Plate Nos. 74, 97.
Z153 4d. vermilion (1865–73) (Plate No. 7) .. ..
Z154 6d. lilac (1856) .. ..
Z155 6d. lilac (1862) .. ..
Z156 6d. lilac (1865–67) .. ..
Plate Nos. 5, 6.

Stamps of GREAT BRITAIN *cancelled* "A 95" *as Type* **2**.

1859 (June) *to* **1868**.
Z157 1d. rose-red (1857), Die II, *wmk* Large Crown, *perf* 14 .. ..
Z158 1d. rose-red (1864–79) .. ..
Plate Nos. 72, 89, 97.
Z159 3d. rose (1867–73) (Plate No. 5) .. ..
Z160 4d. red (1862) .. ..
Z161 4d. vermilion (1865–73) (Plate No. 8) .. ..
Z162 6d. lilac (1862) .. ..
Z163 6d. lilac (1865–67) (Plate No. 5) .. ..
Z164 6d. lilac (1867) (Plate No. 6) .. .. ..
Z165 1s. green (1856) .. ..

Stamps of GREAT BRITAIN *cancelled* "A 96" *as Type* **2**.

1859 (June) *to* **1868**.
Z166 1d. rose-red (1857), Die II, *wmk* Large Crown, *perf* 14 .. ..
Z167 4d. vermilion (1865–73) (Plate No. 7) .. ..
Z168 6d. lilac (1856) .. ..
Z169 1s. green (1856) .. ..

Stamps of GREAT BRITAIN *cancelled* "A 97" *as Type* **2**.

1859 (June) *to* **1868**.
Z170 1d. rose-red (1857), Die II, *wmk* Large Crown, *perf* 14 .. ..
Z171 1d. rose-red (1864–79) (Plate No. 71) .. ..
Z172 4d. red (1862) (Plate No. 3) .. .. ..

Stamps of GREAT BRITAIN *cancelled* "A 98" *as Type* **2**.

1859 (June) *to* **1868**.
Z173 1d. rose-red (1857), Die II, *wmk* Large Crown, *perf* 14 .. ..
Z174 4d. red (1862) .. ..
Z175 6d. lilac (1856) .. ..
Z176 6d. lilac (1862) (Plate No. 4) .. .. ..
Z177 6d. lilac (1865–67) .. ..
Plate Nos. 5, 6.

ALLAN LINE ATLANTIC MAILBOATS

British G.P.O. sorters worked on these Canadian ships betwe November 1859 and April 1860. Cancellations as Type **2** numbe "B 17", "B 18", "B 27", "B 28", "B 29" and "B 30" were issued them, but have not been reported used during this period. All w subsequently reallocated to British post offices.

SPANISH WEST INDIES MAILBOATS

"D 26" was supplied for use by British mail clerks employed ships of the Herrara Line operating between St. Thomas (Dani West Indies), Cuba, Dominican Republic and Porto Rico.

1868 *to* **1871**.
Z190 1d. rose-red (1864–79) .. ..
Plate Nos. 98, 125.
Z191 4d. vermilion (1865–73) £6
Plate Nos. 9, 10, 11.
Z192 6d. violet (1867–70) (Plate No. 8) .. ..
Z193 1s. green (1867) (Plate No. 4) .. .. ..

Abu Dhabi

Stamps of the BRITISH POSTAL AGENCIES IN EASTERN ARABIA were used from the oil installation on Das Island from December 1960 onwards, being postmarked at Bahrain. A British postal agency, using the same issues, postmarked "ABU DHABI" or "DAS ISLAND", operated in the shaikdom from 30 March 1963 until the introduction of Abu Dhabi issues in 1964.

An independent Arab Shaikhdom (one of the Trucial States), ith a British postal administration until 31 December 1966.

(Currency. 100 naye paise = 1 rupee)

1 Shaikh Shakhbut bin Sultan

3 Ruler's Palace

es M. Farrar Bell. Photo Harrison (5 n.p. to 75 n.p.). Des C. T. Kavanagh (1, 2 r.), Miss P. M. Goth (5, 10 r.). Recess B.W.)

64 (30 Mar). *T* **1**, **3** *and similar designs. P* 14½ (5 *to* 75 *n.p.*) *or* 13 × 13½ (*others*).

1	**1**	5 n.p. green	1·50	1·75
2		15 n.p. red-brown	2·00	1·25
3		20 n.p. ultramarine	2·00	85
		a. Perf 13×13½	£200	
4		30 n.p. red-orange	3·00	1·50
5	–	40 n.p. reddish violet	3·25	60
6	–	50 n.p. bistre	3·50	1·75
7	–	75 n.p. black	3·50	3·00
8	**3**	1 r. emerald	4·00	1·25
9		2 r. black	7·50	3·25
0	–	5 r. carmine-red	16·00	8·50
1	–	10 r. deep ultramarine	23·00	14·00
'11		.. .. *Set of* 11	60·00	35·00

Designs: *As Type* **1**—40, 50, 75 n.p. Mountain Gazelle. *As 'ype* **3**—5, 10 r. Oil rig and camels.

5

6

7

Saker Falcon

(Des V. Whiteley. Photo Harrison)

65 (30 Mar). *Falconry. P* 14½.

5		20 n.p. light brown and grey-blue ..	10·00	1·75
6		40 n.p. light brown and blue	13·00	2·75
7		2 r. sepia and turquoise-green ..	22·00	13·00
'14		.. .. *Set of* 3	40·00	16·00

(New Currency. 1,000 fils = 1 dinar)

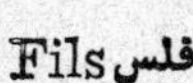

(8)

66 (1 Oct). *Nos.* 1/11 *such as T* 8 ("FILS" *only on* 40 *f. to* 70 *f.*) *with new value expressed on remainder), by Arabian Printing and Publishing House, Bahrain. P* 13 × 13½ (20 *f.*), *others as before.*

	1	5 f. on 5 n.p. green	8·00	5·50
		15 f. on 15 n.p. red-brown	8·00	4·50
		20 f. on 20 n.p. ultramarine	9·50	6·50
		b. Perf 14½	£100	
		ba. Surch inverted	£225	£375
		30 f. on 30 n.p. red-orange	9·00	13·00
		a. Arabic "2" for "3" in surch	£1700	
		b. Surch double, one albino	£160	
	–	40 f. on 40 n.p. reddish violet	13·00	85
	–	50 f. on 50 n.p. bistre	20·00	20·00
	–	75 f. on 75 n.p. black	20·00	17·00
		a. Surch double, one albino	£160	
	3	100 f. on 1 r. emerald	16·00	3·50
		200 f. on 2 r. black	18·00	12·00
	–	500 f. on 5 r. carmine-red	30·00	38·00
	–	1 d. on 10 r. deep ultramarine	40·00	65·00
		a. Short extra bar below portrait (R. 7/3)	£300	
/25		.. .. *Set of* 11	£170	£160

The Abu Dhabi Post Department took over the postal services 1 January 1967. Later stamp issues will be found in Part 19 'iddle East) of this Catalogue.

Aden
see South Arabian Federation

Anguilla

Following the grant of Associated Statehood to St. Christopher, Nevis and Anguilla on 27 February 1967 the population of Anguilla agitated for independence and the St. Kitts-Nevis authorities left the island on 30 May 1967. Nos. 1/16 were issued by the Island Council and were accepted for international mail. On 7 July 1969 the Anguilla post office was officially recognised by the Government of St. Christopher, Nevis and Anguilla and normal postal communications via St. Christopher were resumed. By the Anguilla Act of 27 July 1971, Anguilla was restored to direct British control.

A degree of internal self-government with an Executive Council was introduced on 10 February 1976 and the links with St. Kitts-Nevis were officially severed on 18 December 1980.

(Currency. 100 cents = 1 Eastern Caribbean dollar)

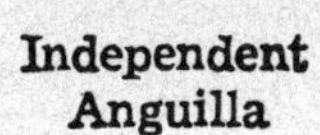

(1)

2 Mahogany Tree, The Quarter

1967 (4 Sept). *Nos.* 129/44 *of St. Kitts-Nevis optd as T* **1**, *by Island Press Inc, St. Thomas, U.S. Virgin Islands.*

1	½ c. New lighthouse, Sombrero	26·00	20·00
2	1 c. Loading sugar cane, St. Kitts	27·00	6·50
3	2 c. Pall Mall Square, Basseterre	28·00	1·25
4	3 c. Gateway, Brimstone Hill Fort, St. Kitts	28·00	4·50
	w. Wmk inverted	—	32·00
5	4 c. Nelson's Spring, Nevis	28·00	5·50
6	5 c. Grammar School, St. Kitts	£100	18·00
7	6 c. Crater, Mt Misery, St. Kitts	50·00	9·00
8	10 c. Hibiscus	28·00	6·50
9	15 c. Sea Island cotton, Nevis	60·00	11·00
10	20 c. Boat building, Anguilla	95·00	13·00
11	25 c. White-crowned Pigeon	85·00	22·00
	w. Wmk inverted	£110	38·00
12	50 c. St. George's Church Tower, Basseterre	£1800	£450
13	60 c. Alexander Hamilton	£2000	£850
14	$1 Map of St. Kitts–Nevis	£1600	£400
15	$2.50, Map of Anguilla	£1500	£300
16	$5 Arms of St. Christopher, Nevis and Anguilla	£1500	£300
1/16	.. .. *Set of* 16	£8000	£2250

Owing to the limited stocks available for overprinting, the sale of the above stamps was personally controlled by the Postmaster and no orders from the trade were accepted.

(Des John Lister Ltd. Litho A. & M.)

1967 (27 Nov)–**68**. *T* **2** *and similar horiz designs. P* 12½ × 13.

17	1 c. dull green, bistre-brown and pale orange	10	20
18	2 c. bluish green and black (21.3.68).. ..	10	20
19	3 c. black and light emerald (10.2.68) ..	10	10
20	4 c. cobalt-blue and black (10.2.68)	10	10
21	5 c. multicoloured	10	10
22	6 c. light vermilion and black (21.3.68) ..	10	10
23	10 c. multicoloured	15	10
24	15 c. multicoloured (10.2.68)	60	20
25	20 c. multicoloured	80	55
26	25 c. multicoloured	60	20
27	40 c. apple green, light greenish blue and black	80	25
28	60 c. multicoloured (10.2.68)	3·00	2·50
29	$1 multicoloured (10.2.68)	1·75	3·00
30	$2.50, multicoloured (21.3.68)	2·00	3·25
31	$5 multicoloured (10.2.68)	3·00	4·25
17/31	.. .. *Set of* 15	11·50	13·00

Designs:—2 c. Sombrero Lighthouse; 3 c. St. Mary's Church; 4 c. Valley Police Station; 5 c. Old Plantation House, Mt Fortune; 6 c. Valley Post Office; 10 c. Methodist Church, West End; 15 c. Wall-Blake Airport; 20 c. Beech A90 King Air aircraft over Sandy Ground; 25 c. Island Harbour; 40 c. Map of Anguilla; 60 c. Hermit Crab and Starfish; $1 Hibiscus; $2.50, Local scene; $5, Spiny Lobster.

The Interim Agreement, under which a British official "advised" the Island Council, expired on 9 January 1969 and, pending the subsequent permanent settlement, Nos. 17/31 were overprinted in black "INDEPENDENCE JANUARY 1969" in two lines. There is considerable doubt that these overprinted stamps were available for postal purposes on the island.

17 Yachts in Lagoon

18 Purple-throated Carib

(Des John Lister Ltd. Litho A. & M.)

1968 (11 May). *Anguillan Ships. T* **17** *and similar horiz designs. Multicoloured. P* 14.

32	10 c. Type **17**	30	10
33	15 c. Boat on beach	35	10
34	25 c. *Warspite* (schooner)	50	15
35	40 c. *Atlantic Star* (schooner)	60	20
32/5	.. .. *Set of* 4	1·60	40

(Des John Lister Ltd. Litho A. & M.)

1968 (8 July). *Anguillan Birds. T* **18** *and similar multicoloured designs. P* 14.

36	10 c. Type **18**	85	15
37	15 c. Bananaquit	1·10	20
38	25 c. Black-necked Stilt (*horiz*)	1·40	20
39	40 c. Royal Tern (*horiz*)	1·60	30
36/9	.. .. *Set of* 4	4·50	75

19 Guides' Badge and Anniversary Years

(Des John Lister Ltd. Litho A. & M.)

1968 (14 Oct). *35th Anniv of Anguillan Girl Guides. T* **19** *and similar multicoloured designs. P* 13 × 13½ (10, 25 *c.*) *or* 13½ × 13 (*others*).

40	10 c. Type **19**	10	10
41	15 c. Badge and silhouettes of Guides (*vert*) ..	15	10
42	25 c. Guides' badge and Headquarters ..	20	15
43	40 c. Association and Proficiency badges (*vert*)	25	15
40/3	.. .. *Set of* 4	65	35

20 The Three Kings

(Des John Lister Ltd. Litho A. & M.)

1968 (18 Nov). *Christmas. T* **20** *and similar designs. P* 13.

44	1 c. black and cerise	10	10
45	10 c. black and light greenish blue	10	10
46	15 c. black and chestnut	15	10
47	40 c. black and blue	15	10
48	50 c. black and dull green	20	15
44/8	.. .. *Set of* 5	55	30

Designs: *Vert*—10 c. The Wise Men; 15 c. Holy Family and manger. *Horiz*—40 c. The Shepherds; 50 c. Holy Family and donkey.

21 Bagging Salt

22 "The Crucifixion" (Studio of Massys)

(Des John Lister Ltd. Litho A. & M.)

1969 (4 Jan). *Anguillan Salt Industry. T* **21** *and similar horiz designs. Multicoloured. P* 13.

49	10 c. Type **21**	25	10
50	15 c. Packing salt	30	10
51	40 c. Salt pond	35	10
52	50 c. Loading salt	35	10
49/52	.. .. *Set of* 4	1·10	30

(Des John Lister Ltd. Litho Format)

1969 (31 Mar). *Easter Commemoration. T* **22** *and similar vert design. P.* 13½.

53	25 c. multicoloured	25	15
54	40 c. multicoloured	35	15

Design:—40 c. "The Last Supper" (ascribed to Roberti).

23 Amaryllis

(Des John Lister Ltd. Litho Format)

1969 (10 June). *Flowers of the Caribbean. T* **23** *and similar horiz designs. Multicoloured. P* 14.

55 10 c. Type **23** 20 20
56 15 c. Bougainvillea 25 20
57 40 c. Hibiscus 50 40
58 50 c. *Cattleya* orchid .. .. 1·50 1·00
55/8 .. .. *Set of* 4 2·25 1·75

24 Superb Gaza, Channelled Turban, Chestnut Turban and Carved Star Shell

(Des John Lister Ltd. Litho A. & M.)

1969 (22 Sept). *Sea Shells. T* **24** *and similar horiz designs. Multicoloured. P* 14.

59 10 c. Type **24** 20 15
60 15 c. American Thorny Oyster 20 15
61 40 c. Scotch, Royal and Smooth Scotch Bonnets 30 25
62 50 c. Atlantic Trumpet Triton 40 30
59/62 .. .. *Set of* 4 1·00 75

(25)

(26)

(27)

(28)

(29)

1969 (Oct). *Christmas. Nos.* 17, 25/8 *optd with T* **25/29**.

63 1 c. dull green, bistre-brown & light orange 10 10
64 20 c. multicoloured 20 10
65 25 c. multicoloured 20 10
66 40 c. apple-green, light greenish blue & black 25 15
67 60 c. multicoloured 40 20
63/7 .. .. *Set of* 5 1·00 45

30 Spotted Goatfish

31 "Morning Glory"

(Des John Lister Ltd. Litho A. & M.)

1969 (1 Dec). *Fishes. T* **30** *and similar horiz designs. Multicoloured. P* 14.

68 10 c. Type **30** 30 15
69 15 c. Blue-striped Grunt 45 15
70 40 c. Nassau Grouper 55 20
71 50 c. Banded Butterflyfish 65 20
68/71 .. .. *Set of* 4 1·75 65

(Des John Lister Ltd. Litho A. & M.)

1970 (23 Feb). *Flowers. T* **31** *and similar vert designs. Multicoloured, P* 14.

72 10 c. Type **31** 30 10
73 15 c. Blue Petrea 45 10
74 40 c. Hibiscus 70 20
75 50 c. "Flame Tree" 80 25
72/5 .. .. *Set of* 4 2·00 55

32 "The Crucifixion" (Masaccio)

33 Scout Badge and Map

(Des John Lister Ltd. Litho Format)

1970 (26 Mar). *Easter. T* **32** *and similar multicoloured designs. P* 13½.

76 10 c. "The Ascent to Calvary" (Tiepolo) (*horiz*) 15 10
77 20 c. Type **32** 20 10
78 40 c. "Deposition" (Rosso Fiorentino) .. 25 15
79 60 c. "The Ascent to Calvary" (Murillo) (*horiz*) 25 15
76/9 .. .. *Set of* 4 75 40

(Des John Lister Ltd. Litho A. & M.)

1970 (10 Aug). *40th Anniv of Scouting in Anguilla. T* **33** *and similar horiz designs. Multicoloured. P* 13.

80 10 c. Type **33** 15 15
81 15 c. Scout camp and cubs practising first-aid 20 15
82 40 c. Monkey Bridge 25 25
83 50 c. Scout H.Q. Building and Lord Baden-Powell 35 25
80/3 .. .. *Set of* 4 85 70

34 Boatbuilding

(Des John Lister Ltd. Litho Format)

1970 (23 Nov). *Various horiz designs as T* **34**. *Multicoloured. P* 14.

84 1 c. Type **34** 30 30
85 2 c. Road Construction 30 30
86 3 c. Quay, Blowing Point 30 20
87 4 c. Broadcaster, Radio Anguilla 30 40
88 5 c. Cottage Hospital Extension 40 40
89 6 c. Valley Secondary School 30 40
90 10 c. Hotel Extension 30 30
91 15 c. Sandy Ground 30 30
92 20 c. Supermarket and Cinema 55 30
93 25 c. Bananas and Mangoes 35 80
94 40 c. Wall Blake Airport .. .. .. 2·50 2·25
95 60 c. Sandy Ground Jetty .. .. .. 65 2·25
96 $1 Administration Buildings .. .. 1·25 1·40
97 $2.50, Livestock .. .. 1·50 3·75
98 $5 Sandy Hill Bay .. .. 2·75 3·75
84/98 .. .. *Set of* 15 11·00 15·00

35 "The Adoration of the Shepherds" (Reni)

36 "Ecce Homo" (detail, Correggio)

(Des John Lister Ltd. Litho Questa)

1970 (11 Dec). *Christmas. T* **35** *and similar vert designs. Multicoloured. P* 13½.

99 1 c. Type **35** 10 10
100 20 c. "The Virgin and Child" (Gozzoli) .. 30 20
101 25 c. "Mystic Nativity" (detail, Botticelli) .. 30 20
102 40 c. "The Santa Margherita Madonna" (detail, Mazzola) 40 25
103 50 c. "The Adoration of the Magi" (detail, Tiepolo) 40 25
99/103 .. .. *Set of* 5 1·25 85

(Des John Lister Ltd. Litho Format)

1971 (29 Mar). *Easter. T* **36** *and similar designs. P* 13½.

104 10 c. multicoloured 15 10
105 15 c. multicoloured 25 10
106 40 c. multicoloured 30 10
107 50 c. multicoloured 30 15
104/7 .. .. *Set of* 4 90 30

Designs: *Vert*—15 c. "Christ appearing to St. Peter" (detail, Carracci). *Horiz*—40 c. "Angels weeping over the Dead Christ" (detail, Guercino); 50 c. "The Supper at Emmaus" (detail, Caravaggio).

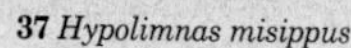

37 *Hypolimnas misippus*

38 *Magnanime and Aimable* in Battle

(Des John Lister Ltd. Litho Questa)

1971 (21 June). *Butterflies. T* **37** *and similar horiz designs. Multi-coloured. P* 14 × 14½.

108 10 c. Type **37** .. .. 1·25 7
109 15 c. *Junonia evarete* .. .. .. 1·40 8
110 40 c. *Agraulis vanillae* .. .. .. 2·00 1·2
111 50 c. *Danaus plexippus* .. .. .. 2·00 1·5
108/11 .. .. *Set of* 4 6·00 3·7

(Des John Lister Ltd. Litho Format)

1971 (30 Aug). *Sea-battles of the West Indies. T* **38** *and similar ve[rt] designs. Multicoloured. P* 14.

112 10 c. Type **38** 85 9
a. Horiz strip of 5. Nos. 112/16 .. .. 6·00
113 15 c. H.M.S. *Duke, Glorieux* and H.M.S. *Agamemnon* .. .. 1·00 1·1
114 25 c. H.M.S. *Formidable* and H.M.S. *Namur* against *Ville de Paris* .. .. .. 1·40 1·5
115 40 c. H.M.S. *Canada* .. .. 1·50 1·6
116 50 c. H.M.S. *St. Albans* and wreck of *Hector* 1·75 1·9
112/16 .. .. *Set of* 5 6·00 6·5

Nos. 112/16 were issued in horizontal *se-tenant* strips within th[e] sheet, to form a composite design in the order listed.

ADMINISTRATION BY BRITISH COMMISSION

39 "The Ansidei Madonna" (detail, Raphael)

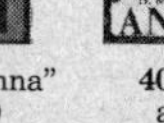

40 Map of Anguilla and St. Martins by Thomas Jefferys (1775)

(Des John Lister Ltd. Litho Questa)

1971 (29 Nov). *Christmas. T* **39** *and similar vert designs. P* 13½

117 20 c. multicoloured 20 2
118 25 c. multicoloured 20 2
119 40 c. multicoloured 30 3
120 50 c. multicoloured 35 4
117/20 .. .. *Set of* 4 95 1·1

Designs:—25 c. "Mystic Nativity" (detail, Botticelli); 40 c. "Ador-ation of the Shepherds" (detail; ascr to Murillo); 50 c. "Th[e] Madonna of the Iris" (detail; ascr to Dürer).

(Litho Format)

1972 (24 Jan). *Maps. T* **40** *and similar multicoloured design[s] showing maps by the cartographers given. P* 14.

121 10 c. Type **40** 25 1
122 15 c. Samuel Fahlberg (1814) 35 1
123 40 c. Thomas Jefferys (1775) (*horiz*) 50 2
124 50 c. Capt. E. Barnett (1847) (*horiz*) 60 2
121/4 .. .. *Set of* 4 1·50 6

41 "Jesus Buffeted"

42 Loblolly Tree

(Des John Lister Ltd. Litho Format)

1972 (14 Mar). *Easter. Stained Glass Windows from Church of St. Michael, Bray, Berkshire. T* **41** *and similar vert designs. Multicoloured. P* 14 × 13½.

125 10 c. Type **41** 25 2
a. Horiz strip of 5. Nos. 125/9 .. .. 1·40
126 15 c. "The Way of Sorrows" 30 3
127 25 c. "The Crucifixion" 30 3
128 40 c. "Descent from the Cross' 35 3
129 50 c. "The Burial" 40 4
125/9 .. .. *Set of* 5 1·40 1·4

Nos. 125/9 were printed horizontally *se-tenant* within the sheet

(Litho Questa ($10), Format (others))

1972 (30 Oct)–**75**. *T* **42** *and similar multicoloured designs (horiz except* 2, 4 *and* 6 *c.). P* 13½.

130 1 c. Spear fishing 10 4
131 2 c. Type **42** 10 4
132 3 c. Sandy Ground 10 4
133 4 c. Ferry at Blowing Point 75 2
134 5 c. Agriculture 15 5
135 6 c. St. Mary's Church 25 2
136 10 c. St. Gerard's Church 25 4
137 15 c. Cottage Hospital extension 25 3
138 20 c. Public library 30 3

25 c. Sunset at Blowing Point .. .. 40 1·25
40 c. Boat building .. .. 3·25 1·50
60 c. Hibiscus .. .. 4·00 3·50
$1 Magnificent Frigate Bird .. .. 8·50 7·00
$2.50, Frangipani .. .. 6·00 8·00
$5 Brown Pelican .. .. .. 15·00 14·00
a $10 Green-back turtle (20.5.75) .. .. 15·00 18·00
/44a .. .. *Set of* 16 48·00 50·00

43 *Malcolm Miller* (schooner) and Common Dolphin

(Des (from photograph by D. Groves) and photo Harrison)

'**2** (20 Nov). *Royal Silver Wedding. Multicoloured; background olour given. W* w **12.** *P* 14 × 14½.
43 25 c. yellow-olive (*shades*) 55 75
40 c. chocolate 55 75
w. Wmk inverted .. .. .. 1·75

44 Flight into Egypt **45** "The Betrayal of Christ"

(Des John Lister Ltd. Litho Questa)

'**2** (4 Dec). *Christmas. T* **44** *and similar vert designs. Multi-oloured. P* 13½.
1 c. Type **44** 10 10
20 c. Star of Bethlehem 20 20
a. Vert strip of 4. Nos. 148/51 75
25 c. Holy Family 20 20
40 c. Arrival of the Magi 20 25
50 c. Adoration of the Magi 25 25
'/51 .. .. *Set of* 5 75 85
Nos. 148/51 were printed vertically *se-tenant* within a sheet of 20 mps.

(Des John Lister Ltd. Litho Questa)

'**3** (26 Mar). *Easter. T* **45** *and similar vert designs. Multi-oloured; bottom panel in gold and black. P* 13½.
1 c. Type **45** 10 10
10 c. "The Man of Sorrows" 10 10
a. Vert strip of 5. Nos. 153/7 55
20 c. "Christ bearing the Cross" 10 15
25 c. "The Crucifixion" 15 15
40 c. "The Descent from the Cross" 15 15
50 c. "The Resurrection" 15 20
2/7 .. .. *Set of* 6 55 70
S158 140 × 141 mm. Nos. 152/7. Bottom panel in gold and mauve 70 80
Nos. 153/7 were printed within one sheet, vertically *se-tenant*.

46 *Santa Maria* **47** Princess Anne and Captain Mark Phillips

(Des John Lister Ltd. Litho Questa)

73 (10 Sept). *Columbus Discovers the West Indies. T* **46** *and similar horiz designs. Multicoloured. P* 13½.
9 1 c. Type **46** 10 10
0 20 c. Early map .. .. 1·25 1·25
a. Horiz strip of 4. Nos. 160/3 .. .. 6·00
1 40 c. Map of voyages .. .. 1·40 1·40
2 70 c. Sighting land .. .. 1·75 1·75
3 $1.20, Landing of Columbus .. .. .. 2·25 2·25
9/63 .. .. *Set of* 5 6·00 6·00
S164 193 × 93 mm. Nos. 159/63 .. .. .. 6·00 7·00
Nos. 160/3 were printed horizontally *se-tenant* within the sheet.

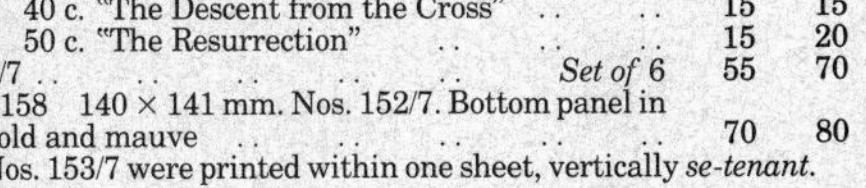

(Des PAD Studio. Litho Questa)

1973 (14 Nov). *Royal Wedding. Centre multicoloured. W* w **12** *(sideways). P* 13½.
165 **47** 60 c. turquoise-green 20 15
166 $1.20, deep mauve 30 15

48 "The Adoration of the Shepherds" (Reni) **49** "The Crucifixion" (Raphael)

(Des John Lister Ltd. Litho Questa)

1973 (2 Dec). *Christmas. T* **48** *and similar horiz designs. Multi-coloured. P* 13½.
167 1 c. Type **48** 10 10
168 10 c. "The Madonna and Child with Saints Jerome and Dominic" (Lippi) 10 10
a. Horiz strip of 5. Nos. 168/72 75
169 20 c. "The Nativity" (Master of Brunswick) .. 15 15
170 25 c. "Madonna of the Meadow" (Bellini) .. 15 15
171 40 c. "Virgin and Child" (Cima) 20 20
172 50 c. "Adoration of the Kings" (Geertgen) .. 20 20
167/72 .. .. *Set of* 6 75 75
MS173 148 × 149 mm. Nos. 167/72 .. .. 80 1·60
Nos. 168/72 were printed within the sheet, horizontally *se-tenant*.

(Des John Lister Ltd. Litho Questa)

1974 (30 Mar). *Easter. T* **49** *and similar vert designs showing various details of Raphael's "Crucifixion". P* 13½.
174 1 c. multicoloured 10 10
175 15 c. multicoloured 10 10
a. Vert strip of 5. Nos. 175/9 70
176 20 c. multicoloured 15 15
177 25 c. multicoloured 15 15
178 40 c. multicoloured 15 15
179 $1 multicoloured 20 25
174/9 .. .. *Set of* 6 70 70
MS180 123 × 141 mm. Nos. 174/9 .. .. 95 1·25
Nos. 175/9 were printed vertically *se-tenant* within one sheet.

50 Churchill making "Victory" Sign

(Des John Lister Ltd. Litho Questa)

1974 (24 June). *Birth Centenary of Sir Winston Churchill. T* **50** *and similar horiz designs. Multicoloured. P* 13½.
181 1 c. Type **50** 10 10
182 20 c. Churchill with Roosevelt 20 20
a. Horiz strip of 5. Nos. 182/6 .. .. 1·50
183 25 c. Wartime broadcast 20 20
184 40 c. Birthplace, Blenheim Palace 30 30
185 60 c. Churchill's statue 40 35
186 $1.20, Country residence, Chartwell .. 60 55
181/6 .. .. *Set of* 6 1·50 1·50
MS187 195 × 96 mm. Nos. 181/6 .. .. 1·75 2·25
Nos. 182/6 were printed horizontally *se-tenant* within the sheet.

51 U.P.U. Emblem

(Des John Lister Ltd. Litho Questa)

1974 (27 Aug). *Centenary of Universal Postal Union. P* 13½*.
188 **51** 1 c. black and bright blue 10 10
189 20 c. black and pale orange 15 15
a. Horiz strip of 5. Nos. 189/93 .. 1·10
190 25 c. black and light yellow 15 15
191 40 c. black and bright mauve 20 25
192 60 c. black and light emerald 30 40
193 $1.20, black and light blue 50 60
188/93 .. .. *Set of* 6 1·10 1·40
MS194 195 × 96 mm. Nos. 188/93 .. .. 1·25 2·00
Nos. 189/93 were printed horizontally *se-tenant* within the sheet.
*In No. **MS**194 the lower row of three stamps, 40 c., 60 c. and $1.20 values, are line-perforated 15 at foot, the remaining 3 stamps being comb-perforated 13½.

52 Anguillan pointing to Star **53** "Mary, John and Mary Magdalene" (Matthias Grünewald)

(Litho Questa)

1974 (16 Dec). *Christmas. T* **52** *and similar horiz designs. Multi-coloured. P* 14.
195 1 c. Type **52** 10 10
196 20 c. Child in Manger 10 15
a. Horiz strip of 5. Nos. 196/200 70
197 25 c. King's offering 10 15
198 40 c. Star over Map of Anguilla 15 15
199 60 c. Family looking at star 15 20
200 $1.20, Angels of Peace 20 30
195/200 .. .. *Set of* 6 70 95
MS201 177 × 85 mm. Nos. 195/200 .. .. 1·40 1·75
Nos. 196/200 were printed horizontally *se-tenant* within the sheet.

(Litho Questa)

1975 (25 Mar). *Easter. T* **53** *and similar multicoloured designs showing details of the Isenheim altarpiece. P* 14.
202 1 c. Type **53** 10 10
203 10 c. "The Crucifixion" 15 15
a. Horiz strip of 5. Nos. 203/7 .. .. 1·00
204 15 c. "St. John the Baptist" 15 15
205 20 c. "St. Sebastian and Angels" 20 20
206 $1 "The Entombment" 25 35
207 $1.50, "St. Anthony the Hermit" 35 45
202/7 .. .. *Set of* 6 1·00 1·25
MS208 134 × 127 mm. Nos. 202/7. Imperf. .. 1·00 1·75
Nos. 203/7 were printed horizontally *se-tenant* within the sheet.

54 Statue of Liberty **55** "Madonna, Child and the Infant John the Baptist" (Raphael)

(Des John Lister Ltd. Litho Questa)

1975 (10 Nov). *Bicentenary of American Revolution. T* **54** *and similar horiz designs. Multicoloured. P* 13½*.
209 1 c. Type **54** 10 10
210 10 c. The Capitol 20 10
a. Horiz strip of 5. Nos. 210/14 .. .. 1·60
211 15 c. "Congress voting for Independence" (Pine and Savage) 30 15
212 20 c. Washington and map 30 15
213 $1 Boston Tea Party 45 40
214 $1.50, Bicentenary logo 50 60
209/14 .. .. *Set of* 6 1·60 1·25
MS215 198 × 97 mm. Nos. 209/14 .. .. 1·60 2·50
Nos. 210/14 were printed horizontally *se-tenant* within the sheet.
*In No. **MS**215 the lower row of three stamps, 20 c., $1 and $1.50 values, are line-perforated 15 at foot, the remaining 3 stamps being comb-perforated 13½.

(Des John Lister Ltd. Litho Questa)

1975 (8 Dec). *Christmas. T* **55** *and similar vert designs showing the "Madonna and Child". Multicoloured. P* 13½.
216 1 c. Type **55** 10 10
217 10 c. Cima 15 10
a. Horiz strip of 5. Nos. 217/21 .. .. 1·25
218 15 c. Dolci 20 15
219 20 c. Dürer 20 15
220 $1 Bellini 35 25
221 $1.50, Botticelli 45 35
216/21 .. .. *Set of* 6 1·25 90
MS222 130 × 145 mm. Nos. 216/21 .. .. 2·00 2·25
Nos. 217/21 were printed horizontally *se-tenant* within the sheet.

PRICES OF SETS

Set prices are given for many issues, generally those containing three stamps or more. Definitive sets include one of each value or major colour change, but do not cover different perforations, die types or minor shades. Where a choice is possible the set prices are based on the cheapest versions of the stamps included in the listings.

EXECUTIVE COUNCIL

NEW CONSTITUTION 1976

(56)

57 Almond

TION

Italic second "O" in "CONSTITUTION". Occurs on Row 2/2 (Nos. 226, 228, 232, 235, 239), Row 3/2 (Nos. 230/1, 233/4, 236/8), Row 4/5 (Nos. 223/4, 240) or Row 5/2 (Nos. 225, 227, 229).

1976 (10 Feb–1 July). *New Constitution. Nos.* 130 *etc. optd with T* **56** *or surch also.*

No.	Description		Unused	Used
223	1 c.	Spear fishing	30	40
	a.	Italic "O"	3·00	
224	2 c.	on 1 c. Spear fishing	30	40
	a.	Italic "O"	3·00	
225	2 c.	Type **42** (1.7.76)	4·50	1·75
	a.	Italic "O"	16·00	
226	3 c.	on 40 c. Boat building	75	70
	a.	"3 c" omitted	£300	
	b.	Typo. "3 c"*	9·00	10·00
	c.	Italic "O"	5·50	
227	4 c.	Ferry at Blowing Point	1·00	1·00
	a.	Italic "O"	6·00	
228	5 c.	on 40 c. Boat building	30	50
	a.	Italic "O"	3·00	
229	6 c.	St. Mary's Church	30	50
	a.	Italic "O"	3·00	
230	10 c.	on 20 c. Public Library	30	50
	a.	Italic "O"	3·00	
231	10 c.	St. Gerard's Church (1.7.76)	4·50	3·50
	a.	Italic "O"	16·00	
232	15 c.	Cottage Hospital extension	30	90
	a.	Italic "O"	3·00	
233	20 c.	Public Library	30	50
	a.	Italic "O"	3·00	
234	25 c.	Sunset at Blowing Point	30	50
	a.	Italic "O"	3·00	
235	40 c.	Boat building	1·00	70
	a.	Italic "O"	6·00	
236	60 c.	Hibiscus	70	70
	a.	Italic "O"	4·50	
237	$1	Magnificent Frigate Bird	6·00	2·25
	a.	Italic "O"	20·00	
238	$2.50,	Frangipani	2·25	2·25
	a.	Italic "O"	8·00	
239	$5	Brown Pelican	7·50	6·50
	a.	Italic "O"	24·00	
240	$10	Green-back turtle	4·00	6·00
	a.	Italic "O"	17·00	
223/40		*Set of* 18	30·00	27·00

*No. 226a/b occur on R. 5/2, the "3 c" having been omitted during the normal litho surcharging.

(Des John Lister Ltd. Litho Questa)

1976 (16 Feb). *Flowering Trees. T* **57** *and similar horiz designs. Multicoloured. P* 13½.

No.	Description		Unused	Used
241	1 c.	Type **57**	10	10
242	10 c.	Autograph	20	20
	a.	Horiz strip of 5. Nos. 242/6	1·25	
243	15 c.	Calabash	20	20
244	20 c.	Cordia	20	20
245	$1	Papaya	30	45
246	$1.50,	Flamboyant	35	55
241/6		*Set of* 6	1·25	1·50
MS247		194 × 99 mm. Nos. 241/6	1·50	2·00

Nos. 242/6 were printed horizontally *se-tenant* within the sheet.

58 The Three Marys

59 French Ships approaching Anguilla

(Litho Questa)

1976 (5 Apr). *Easter. T* **58** *and similar multicoloured designs showing portions of the Altar Frontal Tapestry, Rheinau. P* 13½.

No.	Description		Unused	Used
248	1 c.	Type **58**	10	10
249	10 c.	The Crucifixion	10	10
	a.	Horiz strip of 5. Nos. 249/53	1·75	
250	15 c.	Two Soldiers	15	15
251	20 c.	The Annunciation	15	15
252	$1	The complete tapestry (*horiz*)	65	65
253	$1.50,	The Risen Christ	80	80
248/53		*Set of* 6	1·75	1·75
MS254		138 × 130 mm. Nos. 248/53. Imperf	1·75	2·10

Nos. 249/53 were printed horizontally *se-tenant* within the sheet.

(Des John Lister Ltd. Litho Questa)

1976 (8 Nov). *Battle for Anguilla,* 1796. *T* **59** *and similar horiz designs. Multicoloured. P* 13½.

No.	Description		Unused	Used
255	1 c.	Type **59**	10	10
256	3 c.	*Margaret* (sloop) leaving Anguilla	90	35
	a.	Horiz strip of 5. Nos. 256/60	7·00	
257	15 c.	Capture of *Le Desius*	1·25	55
258	25 c.	*La Vaillante* forced aground	1·50	80
259	$1	H.M.S. *Lapwing*	2·00	1·25
260	$1.50,	*Le Desius* burning	2·25	1·75
255/60		*Set of* 6	7·00	4·25
MS261		205×103 mm. Nos. 255/60	7·00	6·00

Nos. 256/60 were printed horizontally *se-tenant* within the sheet.

60 "Christmas Carnival" (A. Richardson)

(Litho Questa)

1976 (22 Nov). *Christmas. T* **60** *and similar horiz designs showing children's paintings. Multicoloured. P* 13½.

No.	Description		Unused	Used
262	1 c.	Type **60**	10	10
263	3 c.	"Dreams of Christmas Gifts" (J. Connor)	10	10
	a.	Horiz strip of 5, Nos. 263/7	1·00	
264	15 c.	"Carolling" (P. Richardson)	15	15
265	25 c.	"Candle-light Procession" (A. Mussington)	20	20
266	$1	"Going to Church" (B. Franklin)	30	30
267	$1.50,	"Coming Home for Christmas" (E. Gumbs)	40	40
262/7		*Set of* 6	1·00	1·10
MS268		232 × 147 mm. Nos. 262/7	1·50	1·75

Nos. 263/7 were printed horizontally *se-tenant* within the sheet.

61 Prince Charles and H.M.S. *Minerva* (frigate)

(Des John Lister Ltd. Litho Questa)

1977 (9 Feb). *Silver Jubilee. T* **61** *and similar horiz designs. Multicoloured. P* 13½.

No.	Description		Unused	Used
269	25 c.	Type **61**	15	10
270	40 c.	Prince Philip landing at Road Bay, 1964	15	10
271	$1.20,	Coronation scene	20	20
272	$2.50,	Coronation regalia and map of Anguilla	25	30
269/72		*Set of* 4	65	55
MS273		145 × 96 mm. Nos. 269/72	65	90

62 Yellow-crowned Night Heron

(Des John Lister Ltd. Litho Questa)

1977 (18 Apr)–78. *T* **62** *and similar horiz designs. Multicoloured. P* 13½.

No.	Description		Unused	Used
274	1 c.	Type **62**	30	70
275	2 c.	Great Barracuda	30	1·10
276	3 c.	Queen or Pink Conch	90	1·50
277	4 c.	Spanish Bayonet	40	30
278	5 c.	Honeycomb Trunkfish	1·50	30
279	6 c.	Cable and Wireless Building	30	30
280	10 c.	American Kestrel (20.2.78)	3·75	1·75
281	15 c.	Ground Orchid (20.2.78)	2·75	1·75
282	20 c.	Stop-light Parrotfish (20.2.78)	2·00	75
283	22 c.	Lobster fishing boat (20.2.78)	45	60
284	35 c.	Boat race (20.2.78)	1·40	70
285	50 c.	Sea Bean (20.2.78)	90	45
286	$1	Sandy Island (20.2.78)	60	45
287	$2.50	Manchineel (20.2.78)	1·00	1·00
288	$5	Ground Lizard (20.2.78)	2·00	1·75
289	$10	Red-billed Tropic Bird	9·00	4·25
274/89		*Set of* 16	25·00	16·00

63 "The Crucifixion" (Massys)

(Des John Lister Ltd. Litho Questa)

1977 (25 Apr). *Easter. T* **63** *and similar horiz designs showi[ng] paintings by Castagno* ($1.50) *or Ugolino* (*others*). *Multicolour[ed]. P* 13½.

No.	Description		Unused	Used
291	1 c.	Type **63**	10	
292	3 c.	"The Betrayal"	10	
	a.	Horiz strip of 5. Nos. 292/6	1·60	
293	22 c.	"The Way to Calvary"	20	2
294	30 c.	"The Deposition"	25	2
295	$1	"The Resurrection"	50	5
296	$1.50,	"The Crucifixion"	65	6
291/6		*Set of* 6	1·60	1·6
MS297		192 × 126 mm. Nos. 291/6	1·60	1·7

Nos. 292/6 were printed horizontally *se-tenant* within the shee[t].

ROYAL VISIT TO WEST INDIES

(64)

65 "Le Chapeau de Paille"

1977 (26 Oct). *Royal Visit. Nos.* 269/**MS**273 *optd with T* **64**.

No.	Description		Unused	Used
298	25 c.	Type **61**	10	
299	40 c.	Prince Philip landing at Road Bay, 1964	10	2
300	$1.20,	Coronation scene	20	3
301	$2.50,	Coronation regalia and map of Anguilla	25	5
298/301		*Set of* 4	60	1·0
MS302		145 × 96 mm. Nos. 298/301	80	9

(Des John Lister Ltd. Litho Questa)

1977 (1 Nov). *400th Birth Anniv of Rubens. T* **65** *and similar ve[rt] designs. Multicoloured. P* 13½.

No.	Description		Unused	Used
303	25 c.	Type **65**	15	
304	40 c.	"Helène Fourment and her Two Children"	20	
305	$1.20,	"Rubens and his Wife"	60	
306	$2.50,	"Marchesa Brigida Spinola-Doria"	75	
303/6		*Set of* 4	1·50	1·
MS307		93 × 145 mm. Nos. 303/6	1·75	2·

Each value was issued in sheets of 5 stamps and 1 label.

5c

(66)

EASTER 1978

(67)

1977 (14 Nov). *Christmas. Nos.* 262/8 *with old date blocked ou[t] and additionally inscr* "1977", *some surch also as T* **66**.

No.	Description		Unused	Used
308	1 c.	Type **60**	10	
309	5 c.	on 3 c. "Dreams of Christmas Gifts"	10	
	a.	Horiz strip of 5. Nos. 309/13	1·75	
310	12 c.	on 15 c. "Carolling"	15	
311	18 c.	on 25 c. "Candle-light Procession"	20	2
312	$1	"Going to Church"	45	4
313	$2.50	on $1.50, "Coming Home for Christmas'	90	
308/13		*Set of* 6	1·75	1·7
MS314		232 × 147 mm. Nos. 308/13	2·50	2·

1978 (6 Mar). *Easter. Nos.* 303/7 *optd with T* **67**, *in gold.*

No.	Description		Unused	Used
315	25 c.	Type **65**	15	2
316	40 c.	"Helène Fourment and her Two Children"	15	2
317	$1.20,	"Rubens and his Wife"	30	4
318	$2.50,	"Marchesa Brigida Spinola-Doria"	40	6
315/18		*Set of* 4	90	1·
MS319		93 × 145 mm. Nos. 315/18	1·25	1·

68 Coronation Coach at Admiralty Arch

VALLEY SECONDARY SCHOOL 1953-1978

(69)

ROAD METHODIST CHURCH 1878-1978

$1.20

(70)

(Des John Lister Ltd. Litho Questa)

978 (6 Apr). *25th Anniv of Coronation. T* **68** *and similar horiz designs. Multicoloured. P* 14.

20 22 c. Buckingham Palace 10 10
21 50 c. Type **68** 10 10
22 $1.50, Balcony scene 15 15
23 $2.50, Royal coat of arms 25 25
20/3 .. .. *Set of* 4 50 50
IS324 138 × 92 mm. Nos. 320/3 .. .. .. 60 60

978 (14 Aug). *Anniversaries. Nos.* 283/8 *optd as T* **69** *or surch as T* **70**.

25 22 c. Lobster fishing boat 20 15
a. Opt double £130
b. "C" omitted from "SECONDARY" .. 3·50
26 35 c. Boat race 30 20
a. "C" omitted from "SECONDARY" .. 3·75
27 50 c. Sea Bean 30 30
a. "I" omitted from "METHODIST" .. 3·75
28 $1 Sandy Island 40 40
a. "I" omitted from "METHODIST" .. 4·00
29 $1.20 on $5 Ground Lizard 45 45
a. "I" omitted from "METHODIST" .. 5·00
30 $1.50 on $2.50, Manchineel 60 55
a. "C" omitted from "SECONDARY" .. 6·00
25/30 .. .. *Set of* 6 2·00 1·75

The 22, 35 c. and $1.50 values commemorate the 25th anniversary of Valley Secondary School; the other values commemorate the Centenary of Road Methodist Church.

Nos. 325b, 326a and 330a occur on R. 4/1 and Nos. 327a, 328a and 329a on R. 2/4.

71 Mother and Child

(Des and litho Questa)

978 (11 Dec). *Christmas. Children's Paintings. T* **71** *and similar horiz designs. Multicoloured. P* 13½.

31 5 c. Type **71** 10 10
32 12 c. Christmas masquerade 15 10
33 18 c. Christmas dinner 15 10
34 22 c. Serenading 15 10
35 $1 Child in manger 45 20
36 $2.50, Family going to church 90 40
31/6 .. .. *Set of* 6 1·60 70
IS337 191 × 101 mm. Nos. 331/6 .. .. .. 1·60 1·75

979 (15 Jan). *International Year of the Child. As Nos.* 331/7 *but additionally inscr with emblem and* "1979 INTERNATIONAL YEAR OF THE CHILD". *Borders in different colours.*

38 5 c. Type **71** 10 10
39 12 c. Christmas masquerade 10 10
40 18 c. Christmas dinner 10 10
41 22 c. Serenading 10 10
42 $1 Child in manger 30 30
43 $2.50, Family going to church 50 50
38/43 .. .. *Set of* 6 90 90
IS344 205 × 112 mm. Nos. 338/43 .. .. .. 2·25 2·50

(**72**) **73** Valley Methodist Church

979 (12 Feb). *Nos.* 274/7 *and* 279/80 *surch as T* **72**.

45 12 c. on 2 c. Great Barracuda 50 50
46 14 c. on 4 c. Spanish Bayonet 40 50
a. Surch inverted .. .. 32·00
47 18 c. on 3 c. Queen or Pink Conch .. 80 55
48 25 c. on 6 c. Cable and Wireless Building .. 55 50
49 38 c. on 10 c. American Kestrel .. .. 2·00 70
50 40 c. on 1 c. Type **62** .. .. .. 2·00 70
45/50 .. .. *Set of* 6 5·50 3·00

(Des John Lister Ltd. Litho Questa)

979 (30 Mar). *Easter. Church Interiors. T* **73** *and similar horiz designs. Multicoloured. P* 14.

51 5 c. Type **73** 10 10
a. Horiz strip of 6. Nos. 351/6 .. .. 1·60
52 12 c. St. Mary's Anglican Church, The Valley 10 10
53 18 c. St. Gerard's Roman Catholic Church, The Valley 15 15
54 22 c. Road Methodist Church 15 15
55 $1.50, St. Augustine's Anglican Church, East End 60 60
56 $2.50, West End Methodist Church 75 75
51/6 .. .. *Set of* 6 1·60 1·60
IS357 190 × 105 mm. Nos. 351/6 .. .. .. 1·75 2·25

Nos. 351/6 were printed together horizontally *se-tenant*, within the sheet.

74 Cape of Good Hope 1d. "Woodblock" of 1881

(Des Stanley Gibbons Ltd. Litho Questa)

1979 (23 Apr). *Death Centenary of Sir Rowland Hill. T* **74** *and similar horiz designs showing stamps. Multicoloured. P* 14.

358 1 c. Type **74** 10 10
359 1 c. U.S.A. "inverted Jenny" of 1918 .. .. 10 10
360 22 c. Penny Black ("V.R. Official") 15 15
361 35 c. Germany 2 m. *Graf Zeppelin* of 1928 .. 20 20
362 $1.50, U.S.A. $5 Columbus of 1893 .. .. 45 60
363 $2.50, Great Britain £5 orange of 1882 .. 75 95
358/63 .. .. *Set of* 6 1·50 1·75
MS364 187 × 123 mm. Nos. 358/63 .. .. 1·50 2·10

75 Wright *Flyer I* (1st powered flight, 1903)

(Des John Lister Ltd. Litho Questa)

1979 (21 May). *History of Powered Flight. T* **75** *and similar horiz designs. Multicoloured. P* 14.

365 5 c. Type **75** 15 10
366 12 c. Louis Blériot at Dover after Channel crossing, 1909 .. .. 20 10
367 18 c. Vickers FB-27 Vimy (1st non-stop crossing of Atlantic, 1919) 25 15
368 22 c. Ryan NYP Special *Spirit of St. Louis* (1st solo Atlantic flight by Charles Lindbergh, 1927) 25 20
369 $1.50, Airship LZ-127 *Graf Zeppelin*, 1928 60 60
370 $2.50, Concorde, 1979 .. .. .. 2·00 90
365/70 .. .. *Set of* 6 3·00 1·75
MS371 200×113 mm. Nos. 365/70 .. .. 3·00 2·50

76 Sombrero Island

(Des John Lister Ltd. Litho Questa)

1979 (20 Aug). *Outer Islands. T* **76** *and similar horiz designs. Multicoloured. P* 14.

372 5 c. Type **76** 10 10
373 12 c. Anguillita Island 10 10
374 18 c. Sandy Island 15 15
375 25 c. Prickly Pear Cays 15 15
376 $1 Dog Island 30 40
377 $2.50, Scrub Island 50 70
372/7 .. .. *Set of* 6 1·10 1·40
MS378 180×91 mm. Nos. 372/7 .. .. 2·25 2·25

77 Red Poinsettia

(Des John Lister Ltd. Litho Format)

1979 (22 Oct). *Christmas. Flowers. T* **77** *and similar diamond-shaped designs. Multicoloured. P* 14½.

379 22 c. Type **77** 15 20
380 35 c. Kalanchoe 20 30
381 $1.50, Cream Poinsettia 40 50
382 $2.50, White Poinsettia 60 70
379/82 .. .. *Set of* 4 1·25 1·50
MS383 146 × 164 mm. Nos. 379/82 .. .. 1·75 2·25

78 Exhibition Scene

(Des R. Granger Barrett. Litho Format)

1979 (10 Dec). *"London 1980" International Stamp Exhibition (1st issue). T* **78** *and similar horiz designs. Multicoloured. P* 13.

384 35 c. Type **78** 15 20
a. Perf 14½ 15 20
385 50 c. Earls Court Exhibition Centre 15 25
a. Perf 14½ 20 25
386 $1.50, Penny Black and Two-penny Blue stamps 25 60
a. Perf 14½ 30 60
387 $2.50, Exhibition logo 45 95
a. Perf 14½ 50 95
384/7 .. .. *Set of* 4 90 1·75
MS388 150×94 mm. Nos. 384/7 .. .. 1·40 2·00
a. Perf 14½ .. .. 1·40 2·00

Nos. 384a/7a come from booklets and also exist from uncut booklet sheets of 10.

See also Nos. 407/10

79 Games Site

(Des John Lister Ltd. Litho Format)

1980 (14 Jan). *Winter Olympic Games, Lake Placid, U.S.A. T* **79** *and similar horiz designs. Multicoloured. P* 13.

389 5 c. Type **79** 10 10
390 18 c. Ice-hockey 10 10
391 35 c. Ice-skating 15 20
392 50 c. Bobsleighing 15 20
393 $1 Skiing 20 35
394 $2.50, Luge-tobogganing 40 80
389/94 .. .. *Set of* 6 80 1·50
MS395 136 × 128 mm. Nos. 389/94 .. .. 1·25 2·00

Nos. 389/94 also exist perforated 14½ (*Price for set of* 6 £1.60 *mint*, £1.90 *used*) from additional sheetlets of 10. Stamps perforated 13 are from normal sheets of 40.

50th Anniversary Scouting 1980 75th Anniversary Rotary 1980

80 Salt ready for Reaping (**81**) (**82**)

(Des John Lister Ltd. Litho Questa)

1980 (14 Apr). *Salt Industry. T* **80** *and similar horiz designs. Multicoloured. P* 14.

396 5 c. Type **80** 10 10
397 12 c. Tallying salt 10 10
398 18 c. Unloading salt flats 15 15
399 22 c. Salt storage heap 15 15
400 $1 Salt for bagging and grinding 30 40
401 $2.50, Loading salt for export 50 70
396/401 .. .. *Set of* 6 1·10 1·40
MS402 180 × 92 mm. Nos. 396/401 .. .. 1·10 1·75

Nos. 396/7, 398/9 and 400/1 were each printed in the same sheet, but with the values in separate panes.

1980 (16 Apr). *Anniversaries. Nos.* 280, 282 *and* 287/8 *optd with T* **81** (10 c., $2.50) *or* **82** (*others*).

403 10 c. American Kestrel .. .. .. 1·00 15
404 20 c. Stop-light Parrotfish 80 20
405 $2.50, Manchineel .. .. 1·75 1·25
406 $5 Ground Lizard .. .. 2·50 1·90
403/6 .. .. *Set of* 4 5·50 3·25

Commemorations:—10 c., $2.50, 50th anniversary of Anguilla Scout Movement; others, 75th anniversary of Rotary International.

83 Palace of Westminster and Great Britain 1970 9d. "Philympia" Commemorative **84** Queen Elizabeth the Queen Mother

(Des Stamp Magazine. Litho Rosenbaum Bros, Vienna)

1980 (6 May). *"London 1980" International Stamp Exhibition (2nd issue). T* **83** *and similar horiz designs showing famous landmarks and various international stamp exhibition commemorative stamps. Multicoloured. P* 13½.

407 50 c. Type **83** 55 65
408 $1.50, City Hall, Toronto and Canada 1978 $1.50, "CAPEX" .. .. 85 1·00
409 $2.50, Statue of Liberty and U.S.A. 1976 13 c. "Interphil" .. .. 1·10 1·40
407/9 .. .. *Set of* 3 2·25 2·75
MS410 157 × 130 mm. Nos. 407/9 .. .. 2·25 2·75

(Des R. Granger Barrett from photograph by N. Parkinson. Litho Rosenbaum Bros, Vienna)

1980 (4 Aug). *80th Birthday of Queen Elizabeth the Queen Mother. P* 13½.

411 **84** 35 c. multicoloured 30 30
412 50 c. multicoloured 45 40
413 $1.50, multicoloured .. .. .. 90 1·00
414 $3 multicoloured .. .. .. 2·25 2·00
411/14 .. .. *Set of* 4 3·50 3·25
MS415 160×110 mm. Nos. 411/14 .. .. 4·75 3·50

SEPARATION 1980

85 Brown Pelicans (**86**)

(Des John Lister Ltd. Litho Questa)

1980 (13 Nov). *Christmas. Birds. T* **85** *and similar vert designs. Multicoloured. P* 13½.
416 5 c. Type **85** .. 30 10
417 22 c. Great Blue Heron .. 75 20
418 $1.50, Barn Swallow .. 1·75 60
419 $3 Ruby-throated Hummingbird .. 2·25 1·40
416/19 *Set of* 4 4·50 2·10
MS420 126 × 160 mm. Nos. 416/19 .. 8·50 6·50

1980 (18 Dec). *Separation of Anguilla from St. Kitts-Nevis. Nos.* 274, 277, 279/89, 341 *and* 418/19 *optd as T* **86** *or surch also.*
421 1 c. Type **62** .. 10 40
422 2 c. on 4 c. Spanish Bayonet .. 10 40
423 5 c. on 15 c. Ground orchid .. 15 45
424 5 c. on $1.50, Barn Swallow .. 15 45
425 5 c. on $3 Ruby-throated Hummingbird .. 15 45
426 10 c. American Kestrel .. 20 60
427 12 c. on $1 Sandy Island .. 20 60
428 14 c. on $2.50, Manchineel .. 20 60
429 15 c. Ground orchid .. 25 60
430 18 c. on $5 Ground Lizard .. 25 60
431 20 c. Stop-light Parrotfish .. 25 60
432 22 c. Lobster fishing boat .. 25 60
433 25 c. on 15 c. Ground orchid .. 30 65
434 35 c. Boat race .. 30 65
435 38 c. on 22 c. Serenading .. 30 65
436 40 c. on 1 c. Type **62** .. 30 65
437 50 c. Sea Bean .. 35 75
438 $1 Sandy Island .. 50 1·00
439 $2.50, Manchineel .. 1·00 2·25
440 $5 Ground Lizard .. 2·25 3·75
441 $10 Red-billed Tropic Bird .. 5·00 6·00
442 $10 on 6 c. Cable and Wireless Building .. 5·00 6·00
421/42 *Set of* 22 16·00 26·00

87 First Petition for Separation, 1825

(Des John Lister Ltd. Litho Format)

1980 (18 Dec). *Separation of Anguilla from St. Kitts-Nevis. T* **87** *and similar horiz designs. Multicoloured. P* 14.
443 18 c. Type **87** .. 10 10
444 22 c. Referendum ballot paper, 1967 .. 15 10
445 35 c. Airport blockade, 1967 .. 15 15
446 50 c. Anguilla flag .. 20 20
447 $1 Separation celebrations, 1980 .. 30 35
443/7 *Set of* 5 80 85
MS448 178 × 92 mm. Nos. 443/7 .. 80 1·25

Nos. 443/4 and 445/6 were each printed in the same sheet with the two values in separate panes.

88 "Nelson's Dockyard" (R. Granger Barrett)

89 Minnie Mouse being chased by Bees

(Litho Rosenbaum Bros, Vienna)

1981 (2 Mar). *175th Death Anniv of Lord Nelson. Paintings. T* **88** *and similar horiz designs. Multicoloured. P* 14.
449 22 c. Type **88** .. 1·25 30
450 35 c. "Ships in which Nelson served" (Nicholas Pocock) .. 1·50 50
451 50 c. "H.M.S. *Victory*" (Monamy Swaine) .. 1·75 65
452 $3 "Battle of Trafalgar" (Clarkson Stanfield) 2·25 2·25
449/52 *Set of* 4 6·00 3·25
MS453 82 × 63 mm. $5 "Horatio Nelson" (L. F. Abbott) and coat of arms .. 3·00 3·25

(Litho Questa)

1981 (30 Mar). *Easter. Walt Disney Cartoon Characters. T* **89** *and similar vert designs. Multicoloured. P* 13½ × 14.
454 1 c. Type **89** .. 10 10
455 2 c. Pluto laughing at Mickey Mouse .. 10 10
456 3 c. Minnie Mouse tying ribbon round Pluto's neck .. 10 10
457 5 c. Minnie Mouse confronted by love-struck bird who fancies her bonnet .. 10 10
458 7 c. Dewey and Huey admiring themselves in mirror .. 10 10
459 9 c. Horace Horsecollar and Clarabelle Cow out for a stroll .. 10 10
460 10 c. Daisy Duck with hat full of Easter eggs 10 10
461 $2 Goofy unwrapping Easter hat .. 1·40 1·40
462 $3 Donald Duck in his Easter finery .. 1·60 1·60
454/62 *Set of* 9 2·75 3·00
MS463 134 × 108 mm. $5 Chip and Dale making off with hat .. 3·50 3·50

90 Prince Charles, Lady Diana Spencer and St. Paul's Cathedral

Extra flagstaff at right of Windsor Castle (R. 1/5 of each pane)

(Des R. Granger Barrett. Litho Rosenbaum Bros, Vienna)

1981 (15 June). *Royal Wedding. T* **90** *and similar horiz designs showing Prince Charles, Lady Diana Spencer and buildings. Multicoloured. P* 14. (a) *No wmk.*
464 50 c. Type **90** .. 15 20
465 $2.50, Althorp .. 30 50
466 $3 Windsor Castle .. 35 60
a. Extra flagstaff .. 8·50
464/6 *Set of* 3 70 1·25
MS467 90 x 72 mm. $5 Buckingham Palace .. 1·25 1·50

(b) *Booklet stamps. W w* **15** *(sideways*)*
468 50 c. Type **90** .. 25 45
a. Booklet pane of 4 .. 75
ab. Black printed twice .. 7·00
w. Wmk reading upwards .. 25
wa. Booklet pane of 4 .. 75
469 $3 As No. 466 .. 40 85
a. Booklet pane of 4 .. 1·40
ab. Black printed twice .. 7·00
w. Wmk reading upwards .. 40
wa. Booklet pane of 4 .. 1·40

*On Nos. 468/9 the normal sideways watermark reads downwards.

Nos. 464/6 also exist from additional sheetlets of two stamps and one label with changed background colours (*Price for set of* 3 80*p mint or used*).

Nos. 468/9 come from $14 stamp booklets.

Nos. 468ab and 469ab show the black features of the portraits strengthened by a further printing applied by typography. This is particularly visible on the Prince's suit and on the couple's hair.

91 Children playing in Tree

(Des Susan Csomer. Litho Rosenbaum Bros, Vienna)

1981 (31 July–30 Sept). *35th Anniv of U.N.I.C.E.F. T* **91** *and similar horiz designs. Multicoloured. P* 14.
470 5 c. Type **91** .. 20 30
471 10 c. Children playing by pool .. 20 30
472 15 c. Children playing musical instruments .. 20 30
473 $3 Children playing with pets (30 Sept) .. 2·50 3·00
470/3 *Set of* 4 2·75 3·50
MS474 78 × 106 mm. $4 Children playing football (*vert*) (30 Sept) .. 3·50 4·50

(Litho Questa)

1981 (2 Nov). *Christmas. Horiz designs as T* **89** *showing scenes from Walt Disney's cartoon film "The Night before Christmas". P* 13½.
475 1 c. multicoloured .. 10 10
476 2 c. multicoloured .. 10 10
477 3 c. multicoloured .. 10 10
478 5 c. multicoloured .. 10 10
479 7 c. multicoloured .. 10 10
480 10 c. multicoloured .. 10 10
481 12 c. multicoloured .. 10 10
482 $2 multicoloured .. 3·00 1·25
483 $3 multicoloured .. 3·00 1·60
475/83 *Set of* 9 5·50 2·75
MS484 130 × 105 mm. $5 multicoloured .. 5·50 3·50

92 Red Grouper (**93**)

(Des R. Granger Barrett. Litho Questa)

1982 (1 Jan). *Horiz designs as T* **92**. *Multicoloured. P* 13½×14
485 1 c. Type **92** .. 15 6
486 5 c. Ferry service, Blowing Point .. 30 6
487 10 c. Island dinghies .. 20 6
488 15 c. Majorettes .. 20 6
489 20 c. Launching boat, Sandy Hill .. 40 6
490 25 c. Corals .. 1·25 6
491 30 c. Little Bay cliffs .. 30 7
492 35 c. Fountain Cave interior .. 1·25 8
493 40 c. Sunset over Sandy Island .. 30 7
494 45 c. Landing at Sombrero .. 50 8
495 60 c. Seine fishing .. 3·00 2·2
496 75 c. Boat race at sunset, Sandy Ground .. 80 1·7
497 $1 Bagging lobster at Island Harbour .. 2·25 1·7
498 $5 Brown Pelicans .. 14·00 10·0
499 $7.50, Hibiscus .. 11·00 11·0
500 $10 Queen Triggerfish .. 14·00 12·0
485/500 *Set of* 16 45·00 40·0

1982 (22 Mar). *No.* 494 *surch with T* **93**.
501 50 c. on 45 c. Landing at Sombrero .. 50 3

94 Anthurium and *Heliconius charithonia*

95 Lady Diana Spencer in 1961

(Des R. Granger Barrett. Litho Questa)

1982 (5 Apr). *Easter. Flowers and Butterflies. T* **94** *and simil vert designs. Multicoloured. P* 14.
502 10 c. Type **94** .. 45
503 35 c. Bird of Paradise and *Junonia evarete* 1·10 4
504 75 c. Allamanda and *Danaus plexippus* .. 1·50 7
505 $3 Orchid Tree and *Biblis hyperia* .. 2·25 2·2
502/5 *Set of* 4 4·75 3·2
MS506 65×79 mm. $5 Amaryllis and *Dryas julia* 2·75 3·5

(Des R. Granger Barrett. Litho Ueberreuter)

1982 (17 May–30 Aug). *21st Birthday of Princess of Wale T* **95** *and similar vert designs. Multicoloured. P* 14.
507 10 c. Type **95** .. 30 2
a. Booklet pane of 4 (30 Aug) .. 1·00
508 30 c. Lady Diana Spencer in 1968 .. 50 2
509 40 c. Lady Diana in 1970 .. 50 3
a. Booklet pane of 4 (30 Aug) .. 1·75
510 60 c. Lady Diana in 1974 .. 55 3
a. Booklet pane of 4 (30 Aug) .. 2·00
511 $2 Lady Diana in 1981 .. 80 1·1
a. Booklet pane of 4 (30 Aug) .. 3·00
512 $3 Lady Diana in 1981 (*different*) .. 2·25 1·4
507/12 *Set of* 6 4·50 3·2
MS513 72×90 mm. $5 Princess of Wales .. 5·50 3·0
MS514 125×125 mm. As Nos. 507/12, but with buff borders .. 6·00 4·7

96 Pitching Tent

(Litho Ueberreuter)

1982 (5 July). *75th Anniv of Boy Scout Movement. T* **96** *an similar horiz designs. Multicoloured. P* 14.
515 10 c. Type **96** .. 45 2
516 35 c. Scout band .. 85 5
517 75 c. Yachting .. 1·25 9
518 $3 On parade .. 3·00 2·7
515/18 *Set of* 4 5·00 4·(
MS519 90 × 72 mm. $5 Cooking .. 4·50 4·

(Litho Format)

1982 (3 Aug). *World Cup Football Championship, Spain. Hor designs as T* **89** *showing scenes from Walt Disney's cartoon fil "Bedknobs and Broomsticks". P* 11.
520 1 c. multicoloured .. 10
521 3 c. multicoloured .. 10
522 4 c. multicoloured .. 10 1
523 5 c. multicoloured .. 10 1
524 7 c. multicoloured .. 10 1
525 9 c. multicoloured .. 10 1
526 10 c. multicoloured .. 10 1
527 $2.50 multicoloured .. 2·25 1·7
528 $3 multicoloured .. 2·25 2·(
520/8 *Set of* 9 4·50 3·7
MS529 126×101 mm. $5 mult. P 14×13½ .. 5·00 5·5

COMMONWEALTH GAMES 1982

(97)

82 (18 Oct). *Commonwealth Games, Brisbane. Nos.* 487, 495/6 *and* 498 *optd with T* **97**.

0 10 c. Island dinghies 15 25
a. "S" omitted from "GAMES" .. .. 1·75
1 60 c. Seine fishing 45 60
a. "S" omitted from "GAMES" .. .. 2·75
2 75 c. Boat race at sunset, Sandy Ground 60 80
a. "S" omitted from "GAMES" .. .. 3·25
3 $5 Brown Pelicans .. .. 3·25 3·75
a. "S" omitted from "GAMES" .. .. 9·00
30/3 .. .. *Set of* 4 4·00 4·75

The "S" omitted variety occurs on R.2/2 of the right-hand pane all values.

(Litho Questa)

82 (29 Nov). *Birth Centenary of A. A. Milne (author). Horiz designs as T* **89** *showing scenes from various "Winnie the Pooh" stories. P* 14 × 13½.

4 1 c. multicoloured 10 10
5 2 c. multicoloured 15 10
6 3 c. multicoloured 20 10
7 5 c. multicoloured 25 15
8 7 c. multicoloured 25 20
9 10 c. multicoloured 25 15
0 12 c. multicoloured 35 20
1 20 c. multicoloured 55 25
2 $5 multicoloured .. .. 5·50 6·50
4/42 .. .. *Set of* 9 6·75 7·00
IS543 120 × 93 mm. $5 multicoloured .. .. 6·50 7·00

98 Culture

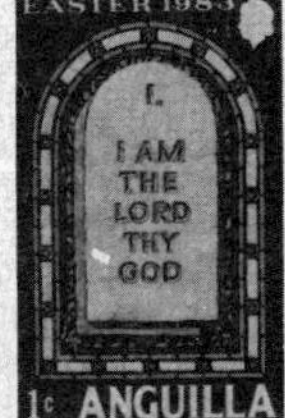

99 "I am the Lord Thy God"

(Des R. Granger Barrett. Litho Ueberreuter)

83 (28 Feb). *Commonwealth Day. T* **98** *and similar horiz designs. Multicoloured. P* 14.

4 10 c. Type **98** 10 15
5 35 c. Anguilla and British flags 30 30
6 75 c. Economic co-operation 60 80
7 $2.50, Salt industry (salt pond) .. .. 3·75 4·25
4/7 .. .. *Set of* 4 4·25 5·00
S548 76 × 61 mm. $5 World map showing position of Commonwealth countries .. .. .. 3·00 2·50

(Litho Questa)

83 (31 Mar). *Easter. The Ten Commandments. T* **99** *and similar vert designs. Multicoloured. P* 14.

9 1 c. Type **99** 10 10
0 2 c. "Thou shalt not make any graven image" 10 10
1 3 c. "Thou shalt not take My Name in vain" 10 10
2 10 c. "Remember the Sabbath Day" 20 10
3 35 c. "Honour thy father and mother" 45 20
4 60 c. "Thou shalt not kill" 80 40
5 75 c. "Thou shalt not commit adultery" .. 90 50
6 $2 "Thou shalt not steal" .. .. .. 2·25 1·50
7 $2.50, "Thou shalt not bear false witness" .. 2·50 1·50
8 $5 "Thou shalt not covet" .. .. .. 3·75 2·75
9/58 .. .. *Set of* 10 10·00 6·50
IS559 126×102 mm. $5 "Moses receiving the Tablets" (16th-century woodcut) .. .. 2·50 3·00

100 Leatherback Turtle

101 Montgolfier Hot Air Balloon, 1783

(Des R. Granger Barrett. Litho Questa)

983 (10 Aug). *Endangered Species. Turtles. T* **100** *and similar horiz designs. Multicoloured. P* 13½.

60 10 c. Type **100** .. .. 1·00 40
a. Perf 12 .. .. 2·00 70
61 35 c. Hawksbill Turtle .. .. 2·00 85
a. Perf 12 .. .. 3·50 2·00
62 75 c. Green Turtle .. .. 2·75 2·00
a. Perf 12 .. .. 4·50 3·75
63 $1 Loggerhead Turtle .. .. 3·25 3·50
a. Perf 12 .. .. 5·50 4·50
60/3 .. .. *Set of* 4 8·00 6·00
IS564 93×72 mm. $5 Leatherback Turtle (*different*) .. .. 5·50 3·00

(Des R. Granger Barrett. Litho Questa)

1983 (22 Aug). *Bicentenary of Manned Flight. T* **101** *and similar vert designs. Multicoloured. P* 13½.

565 10 c. Type **101** 30 20
566 60 c. Blanchard and Jeffries crossing English Channel by balloon, 1785 .. 85 55
567 $1 Henri Giffard's steam-powered dirigible airship, 1852 .. .. 1·25 75
568 $2.50, Otto Lilienthal and biplane glider, 1890–96 .. .. 2·00 1·50
565/8 .. .. *Set of* 4 4·00 2·75
MS569 72×90 mm. $5 Wilbur Wright flying round Statue of Liberty, 1909 .. .. .. 2·75 3·25

102 Boys' Brigade Band and Flag

(Des R. Granger Barrett. Litho Questa)

1983 (12 Sept). *Centenary of Boys' Brigade. T* **102** *and similar horiz design. Multicoloured. P* 13½.

570 10 c. Type **102** 25 15
571 $5 Brigade members marching .. .. 3·00 2·75
MS572 96 × 115 mm. Nos. 570/1 .. .. .. 3·25 3·75

150TH ANNIVERSARY ABOLITION OF SLAVERY ACT

(103)

1983 (24 Oct). *150th Anniv of the Abolition of Slavery* (*1st issue*). *Nos.* 487, 493 *and* 497/8 *optd with T* **103**.

573 10 c. Island dinghies 10 10
a. Opt inverted .. .. 35·00
574 40 c. Sunset over Sandy Island 25 25
575 $1 Bagging lobster at Island Harbour .. 60 50
576 $5 Brown Pelicans .. .. 4·75 2·75
573/6 .. .. *Set of* 4 5·00 3·25

See also Nos. 616/24.

104 Jiminy on Clock (*Cricket on the Hearth*)

(Litho Format)

1983 (14 Nov). *Christmas. Walt Disney Cartoon Characters. T* **104** *and similar vert designs depicting scenes from Dickens' Christmas stories. Multicoloured. P* 13½.

577 1 c. Type **104** 10 10
578 2 c. Jiminy with fiddle (*Cricket on the Hearth*) 10 10
579 3 c. Jiminy among toys (*Cricket on the Hearth*) 10 10
580 4 c. Mickey as Bob Cratchit (*A Christmas Carol*) 10 10
581 5 c. Donald Duck as Scrooge (*A Christmas Carol*) 10 10
582 6 c. Mini and Goofy in *The Chimes* 10 10
583 10 c. Goofy sees an imp appearing from bells (*The Chimes*) 10 10
584 $2 Donald Duck as Mr. Pickwick (*The Pickwick Papers*) .. .. 3·00 2·00
585 $3 Disney characters as Pickwickians (*The Pickwick Papers*) .. .. 3·25 2·25
577/85 .. .. *Set of* 9 6·25 4·25
MS586 130 × 104 mm. $5 Donald Duck as Mr. Pickwick with gifts (*The Pickwick Papers*) .. 6·00 8·00

105 100 Metres Race

(Litho Questa)

1984 (20 Feb–24 Apr). *Olympic Games, Los Angeles. T* **105** *and similar horiz designs showing Mickey Mouse in Decathlon events. Multicoloured. A. Inscr.* "1984 Los Angeles". *P* 14 × 13½.

587A 1 c. Type **105** 10 10
588A 2 c. Long jumping 10 10
589A 3 c. Shot-putting 10 10
590A 4 c. High jumping 10 10
591A 5 c. 400 metres race 10 10
592A 6 c. Hurdling 10 10
593A 10 c. Discus-throwing 10 10
594A $1 Pole-vaulting .. .. 3·00 1·25
595A $4 Javelin-throwing .. .. 5·50 3·50
587A/95A .. .. *Set of* 9 8·00 4·75
MS596A 117×93 mm. $5 1500 metres race .. 6·50 4·00

B. *Inscr* "1984 Olympics Los Angeles" *and Olympic emblem. P* 14×13½ (*No.* **MS**596B) *or* 12 (*others*) (24 Apr)

587B 1 c. Type **105** 10 10
588B 2 c. Long jumping 10 10
589B 3 c. Shot-putting 10 10
590B 4 c. High jumping 10 10
591B 5 c. 400 metres race 10 10
592B 6 c. Hurdling 10 10
593B 10 c. Discus-throwing 10 10
594B $1 Pole-vaulting .. .. 3·50 2·75
595B $4 Javelin-throwing .. .. 7·00 7·00
587B/95B .. .. *Set of* 9 10·00 9·00
MS596B 117×93 mm. $5 1500 metres race .. 6·50 4·00

Nos. 587B/95B were each printed in small sheets of 6 stamps including one *se-tenant* stamp-size label in position 2.

106 "Justice"

35c

(107)

(Des and litho Questa)

1984 (19 Apr). *Easter. T* **106** *and similar vert designs showing details from "La Stanza della Segnatura" by Raphael. Multicoloured. P* 13½ × 14.

597 10 c. Type **106** 15 10
598 25 c. "Poetry" 20 20
599 35 c. "Philosophy" 30 30
600 40 c. "Theology" 30 30
601 $1 "Abraham and Paul" 85 95
602 $2 "Moses and Matthew" .. .. .. 1·60 2·00
603 $3 "John and David" .. .. 2·25 2·75
604 $4 "Peter and Adam" .. .. 2·50 3·00
597/604 .. .. *Set of* 8 7·25 8·50
MS605 83 × 110 mm. $5 "Astronomy" .. .. 3·50 3·00

1984 (24 Apr–17 May). *Nos.* 485, 491 *and* 498/500 *surch as T* **107**.

606 25 c. on $7.50, Hibiscus (17 May) 45 35
607 35 c. on 30 c. Little Bay cliffs 50 40
608 60 c. on 1 c. Type **92** 55 45
609 $2.50 on $5 Brown Pelicans .. .. .. 2·25 1·50
a. Surch at left with decimal point* .. 18·00
610 $2.50 on $10 Queen Triggerfish .. .. 1·75 1·50
a. Surch at right without decimal point* .. 18·00
606/10 .. .. *Set of* 5 5·00 3·75

*The surcharge on No. 609 shows the figures at right of the design and without a decimal point. On No. 610 they are to the left and include a decimal point. No. 609a shows, in error, the surcharge for No. 610 and No. 610a that intended for No. 609.

108 Australia 1913 1d. Kangaroo Stamp

(Des K. Cato. Litho Leigh-Mardon Ltd, Melbourne)

1984 (16 July). *"Ausipex 84" International Stamp Exhibition, Melbourne. T* **108** *and similar horiz designs showing Australian stamps. Multicoloured. P* 13½ × 14.

611 10 c. Type **108** 40 20
612 75 c. 1914 6d. Laughing Kookaburra .. .. 1·25 85
613 $1 1932 2d. Sydney Harbour Bridge .. 1·75 1·25
614 $2.50, 1938 10s. King George VI .. .. 2·25 2·25
611/14 .. .. *Set of* 4 5·00 4·00
MS615 95 × 86 mm. $5 £1 Bass and £2 Admiral King .. .. 4·50 6·00

109 Thomas Fowell Buxton

(Des R. Granger Barrett. Litho Questa)

1984 (1 Aug). *150th Anniv of Abolition of Slavery* (*2nd issue*). *T* **109** *and similar horiz designs. Multicoloured. P* 14.

616 10 c. Type **109** 10 10
617 25 c. Abraham Lincoln 25 25
618 35 c. Henri Christophe 35 35
619 60 c. Thomas Clarkson 50 50
620 75 c. William Wilberforce 60 60
621 $1 Olaudah Equiano 70 70

622 $2.50, General Charles Gordon .. .. 1·60 1·60
623 $5 Granville Sharp .. .. 3·00 3·00
616/23 .. .. *Set of* 8 6·50 6·50
MS624 150 × 121 mm. Nos. 616/23. P 12 .. .. 6·50 8·00

U.P.U. CONGRESS
HAMBURG 1984

(**110**)

PRINCE HENRY
BIRTH 15.9.84

(**111**)

1984 (13 Aug). *Universal Postal Union Congress, Hamburg. Nos. 486/7 and 498 optd as T* **110** *or surch also (No. 626).*
625 5 c. Ferry services, Blowing Point 20 10
626 20 c. on 10 c. Island dinghies 30 15
627 $5 Brown Pelicans .. .. .. 4·50 3·50
625/7 .. .. *Set of* 3 4·50 3·50

1984 (31 Oct). *Birth of Prince Henry. Nos. 507/14 optd as T* **111**.
628 10 c. Type **95** 10 10
a. Booklet pane of 4 90
629 30 c. Lady Diana Spencer in 1968 .. .. 20 25
630 40 c. Lady Diana in 1970 .. .. .. 25 30
a. Booklet pane of 4 .. .. 1·25
631 60 c. Lady Diana in 1974 .. .. .. 40 45
a. Booklet pane of 4 .. .. 1·60
632 $2 Lady Diana in 1981 .. .. .. 1·00 1·25
a. Booklet pane of 4 .. .. 4·00
633 $3 Lady Diana in 1981 *(different)* .. 1·10 1·75
628/33 .. .. *Set of* 6 2·75 3·75
MS634 72 × 90 mm. $5 Princess of Wales .. 2·00 3·00
MS635 125 × 125 mm. As Nos. 628/33, but with buff borders .. .. 2·50 4·00
On No. **MS**634 the lines of overprint are larger, being placed vertically each side of the portrait.

112 Christmas in Sweden

(Litho Questa)

1984 (12 Nov). *Christmas. Walt Disney Cartoon Characters. T* **112** *and similar horiz designs showing national scenes. Multicoloured. P 12 ($2) or 14 × 13½ (others).*
636 1 c. Type **112** 10 10
637 2 c. Italy 10 10
638 3 c. Holland 10 10
639 4 c. Mexico 10 10
640 5 c. Spain 10 10
641 10 c. Disneyland, U.S.A. 10 10
642 $1 Japan .. .. 2·75 2·00
643 $2 Anguilla .. .. 3·50 4·00
644 $4 Germany .. .. 5·50 6·50
636/44 .. .. *Set of* 9 11·00 11·50
MS645 126 × 102 mm. $5 England .. .. 7·00 5·00
No. 643 was printed in sheetlets of 8 stamps.

113 Icarus in Flight

114 Barn Swallow

(Des H. Herni (60 c.), S. Diouf (75 c.), adapted R. Granger Barrett. Litho Ueberreuter)

1984 (3 Dec). *40th Anniv of International Civil Aviation Organization. T* **113** *and similar multicoloured designs. P 14.*
646 60 c. Type **113** 60 75
647 75 c. "Solar Princess" (abstract) 80 90
648 $2.50, I.C.A.O. emblem *(vert)* .. .. 2·25 3·00
646/8 .. .. *Set of* 3 3·25 4·25
MS649 65 × 49 mm. $5 Map of air routes serving Anguilla .. .. 3·00 4·25

(Litho Questa)

1985 (29 Apr). *Birth Bicentenary of John J. Audubon (ornithologist). T* **114** *and similar multicoloured designs. P 14.*
650 10 c. Type **114** 70 45
651 60 c. American Wood Stork .. .. .. 1·25 90
652 75 c. Roseate Tern .. .. 1·25 1·00
653 $5 Osprey .. .. 4·50 4·50
650/3 .. .. *Set of* 4 7·00 6·25
MS654 Two sheets, each 73 × 103 mm. (a) $4 Western Tanager *(horiz)*; (b) $4 Solitary Vireo *(horiz)* .. .. .. *Set of* 2 *sheets* 7·50 5·00
Nos. 650/3 were each issued in sheetlets of five stamps and one stamp-size label, which appears in the centre of the bottom row.

115 The Queen Mother visiting King's College Hospital, London

116 White-tailed Tropic Bird

(Des J.W. Litho Questa)

1985 (2 July). *Life and Times of Queen Elizabeth the Queen Mother. T* **115** *and similar vert designs. Multicoloured. P 14.*
655 10 c. Type **115** 10 10
656 $2 The Queen Mother inspecting Royal Marine Volunteer Cadets, Deal .. 80 1·25
657 $3 The Queen Mother outside Clarence House .. .. 1·10 1·50
655/7 .. .. *Set of* 3 1·75 2·50
MS658 56 × 85 mm. $5 At Ascot, 1979 .. .. 1·75 2·50
Nos. 655/7 also exist perforated 12 × 12½ from additional sheetlets of five stamps and one label *(Price for set of* 3 £1.75 *mint, £2.50 used).*

(Des R. Granger Barrett. Litho Questa)

1985 (22 July)–**86**. *Birds. T* **116** *and similar horiz designs. Multicoloured. P 13½ × 14.*
659 5 c. Brown Pelican (11.11.85) .. .. 1·25 1·25
660 10 c. Mourning Dove (11.11.85) .. .. 1·25 1·25
661 15 c. Magnificent Frigate Bird (inscr "Man-o-War") (11.11.85) .. .. .. 1·25 1·25
662 20 c. Antillean Crested Hummingbird (11.11.85) .. .. 1·25 1·25
663 25 c. Type **116** .. .. 1·25 1·25
664 30 c. Caribbean Elaenia (11.11.85) .. .. 1·25 1·25
665 35 c. Black-whiskered Vireo (11.11.85) .. 5·50 5·00
665*a* 35 c. Lesser Antillean Bullfinch (10.3.86) .. 1·25 1·25
666 40 c. Yellow-crowned Night Heron (11.11.85) 1·25 1·25
667 45 c. Pearly-eyed Thrasher (30.9.85) .. 1·25 1·25
668 50 c. Laughing Gull (30.9.85) .. .. 1·25 1·25
669 65 c. Brown Booby .. .. 1·25 1·25
670 80 c. Grey Kingbird (30.9.85) .. .. 2·00 2·75
671 $1 Audubon's Shearwater (30.9.85) .. 2·00 2·75
672 $1.35, Roseate Tern .. .. .. 1·50 2·75
673 $2.50, Bananaquit (11.11.85) .. .. 4·50 6·00
674 $5 Belted Kingfisher .. .. .. 3·75 7·00
675 $10 Green Heron (30.9.85) .. .. .. 6·50 9·00
659/75 .. .. *Set of* 18 35·00 45·00

GIRL GUIDES 75TH ANNIVERSARY
1910–1985

(**117**)

1985 (14 Oct). *75th Anniv of Girl Guide Movement. Nos. 486, 491, 496 and 498 optd with T* **117**.
676 5 c. Ferry service, Blowing Point 20 20
677 30 c. Little Bay cliffs 40 35
678 75 c. Boat race at sunset, Sandy Ground .. 60 85
679 $5 Brown Pelicans .. .. 6·00 5·25
a. Opt double .. .. 85·00
676/9 .. .. *Set of* 4 6·50 6·00

118 Goofy as Huckleberry Finn Fishing

(Des Walt Disney Productions. Litho Questa)

1985 (11 Nov). *150th Birth Anniv of Mark Twain (author). T* **118** *and similar horiz designs showing Walt Disney cartoon characters in scenes from "Huckleberry Finn". Multicoloured. P 12 ($1) or 14 × 13½ (others).*
680 10 c. Type **118** 25 15
681 60 c. Pete as Pap surprising Huck .. .. 1·00 85
682 $1 "Multiplication tables" .. .. .. 1·60 1·25
683 $3 The Duke reciting Shakespeare .. 3·00 3·50
680/3 .. .. *Set of* 4 5·25 5·25
MS684 127 × 102 mm. $5 "In school but out" 6·00 6·00
No. 682 was printed in sheetlets of 8 stamps.

119 Hansel and Gretel (Mickey and Minnie Mouse) awakening in Forest

(Des Walt Disney Productions. Litho Questa)

1985 (11 Nov). *Birth Bicentenaries of Grimm Brothers (fol- lorists). T* **119** *and similar horiz designs showing Walt Disne cartoon characters in scenes from "Hansel and Gretel". Mult coloured. P 12 (90 c.) or 14 × 13½ (others).*
685 5 c. Type **119** 10
686 50 c. Hansel and Gretel find the gingerbread house 55 4
687 90 c. Hansel and Gretel meeting the Witch .. 90 7
688 $4 Hansel and Gretel captured by the Witch .. .. 3·00 3·(
685/8 .. .. *Set of* 4 4·00 3·7
MS689 126 × 101 mm. $5 Hansel and Gretel riding on swan .. .. 6·00 6·5
No. 687 was printed in sheetlets of 8 stamps.

120 Statue of Liberty and *Danmark* (Denmark)

(Litho Format)

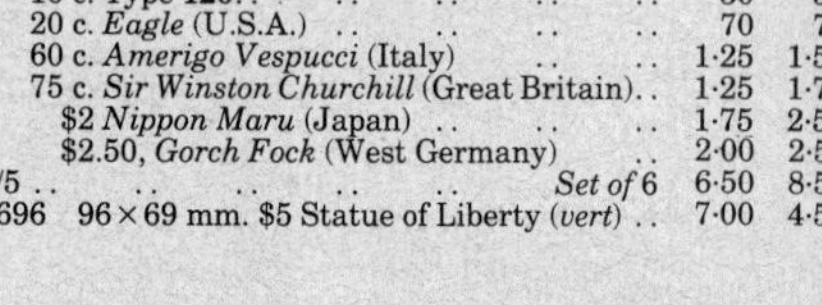

1985 (14 Nov). *Centenary of the Statue of Liberty (1986). T* **12** *and similar multicoloured designs showing the Statue c Liberty and cadet ships. P 15.*
690 10 c. Type **120** 50 5
691 20 c. *Eagle* (U.S.A.) 70 7
692 60 c. *Amerigo Vespucci* (Italy) .. .. 1·25 1·5
693 75 c. *Sir Winston Churchill* (Great Britain) .. 1·25 1·7
694 $2 *Nippon Maru* (Japan) .. .. .. 1·75 2·5
695 $2.50, *Gorch Fock* (West Germany) .. 2·00 2·5
690/5 .. .. *Set of* 6 6·50 8·5
MS696 96 × 69 mm. $5 Statue of Liberty *(vert)* .. 7·00 4·5

(**121**)

(**122**)

1985 (18 Nov). *80th Anniv of Rotary (10, 35 c.) and Inte national Youth Year (others). Nos. 487, 491 and 497 surch c optd as T* **121** *(10 c., 35 c.) or* **122** *(others).*
697 10 c. Island dinghies 10 1
698 35 c. on 30 c. Little Bay cliffs 25 2
699 $1 Bagging lobster at Island Harbour .. 70 7
700 $5 on 30 c. Little Bay cliffs .. .. 3·50 3·5
697/700 .. .. *Set of* 4 4·00 4·0

123 Johannes Hevelius (astronomer) and Mayan Temple Observatory

124 The Crucifixion

(Des W. Hanson. Litho Questa)

1986 (17 Mar). *Appearance of Halley's Comet. T* **123** *an similar horiz designs. Multicoloured. P 14.*
701 5 c. Type **123** 25 2
702 10 c. "Viking Lander" space vehicle on Mars, 1976 .. .. 25 2
703 60 c. Comet in 1664 (from *Theatri Cosmicum*, 1668) 85 8
704 $4 Comet over Mississippi riverboat, 1835 (150th birth anniv of Mark Twain) .. 3·50 3·
701/4 .. .. *Set of* 4 4·25 4·2
MS705 101 × 70 mm. $5 Halley's Comet over Anguilla .. .. 4·50 5·5

(Des R. Granger Barrett. Litho Questa)

1986 (27 Mar). *Easter. T* **124** *and similar designs showin stained glass windows from Chartres Cathedral. P 14 × 13½*
706 10 c. multicoloured 20 2
707 25 c. multicoloured 35 3
708 45 c. multicoloured 65 6
709 $4 multicoloured .. .. 3·25 3·7
706/9 .. .. *Set of* 4 4·00 4·5
MS710 93 × 75 mm. $5 multicoloured *(horiz)*. P 13½ × 14 .. .. 5·50 7·0

AMERIPEX 1986

125 Princess Elizabeth inspecting Guards, 1946

(126)

(Litho Questa)

986 (21 Apr). *60th Birthday of Queen Elizabeth II. T* **125** *and similar vert designs. P* 14.
11 20 c. black and yellow 15 15
12 $2 multicoloured .. .. 1·25 1·25
13 $3 multicoloured .. .. 1·75 1·75
11/13 .. .. *Set of* 3 2·75 2·75
MS714 120 × 85 mm. $5 black and grey-brown .. 2·75 3·50
Designs:—$2 Queen at Garter Ceremony; $3 At Trooping the Colour; $5 Duke and Duchess of York with baby Princess Elizabeth, 1926.

986 (22 May). *"Ameripex" International Stamp Exhibition, Chicago. Nos.* 659, 667, 671, 673 *and* 675 *optd with T* **126**.
15 5 c. Brown Pelican 40 40
16 45 c. Pearly-eyed Thrasher 70 45
17 $1 Audubon's Shearwater .. .. .. 1·25 85
18 $2.50, Bananaquit .. .. 2·25 2·50
19 $10 Green Heron .. .. 6·00 7·50
15/19 .. .. *Set of* 5 9·50 10·50

INTERNATIONAL YEAR OF PEACE

127 Prince Andrew and Miss Sarah Ferguson

(128)

(Des and litho Questa)

1986 (23 July). *Royal Wedding. T* **127** *and similar vert designs. Multicoloured. P* 14.
720 10 c. Type **127** 20 15
a. Perf 12 .. .. 15 15
721 35 c. Prince Andrew 45 35
a. Perf 12 .. .. 35 35
722 $2 Miss Sarah Ferguson .. .. .. 1·50 1·50
a. Perf 12 .. .. 1·60 1·60
723 $3 Prince Andrew and Miss Sarah Ferguson (*different*) .. .. .. 2·00 2·00
a. Perf 12 .. .. 2·25 2·25
720/3 .. .. *Set of* 4 3·75 3·50
MS724 119×90 mm. $6 Westminster Abbey .. 5·50 6·50
a. Perf 12 .. .. 5·50 6·50

986 (29 Sept). *International Peace Year. Nos.* 616/24 *optd with T* **128**.
25 10 c. Type **109** 25 25
26 25 c. Abraham Lincoln 45 45
27 35 c. Henri Christophe 55 55
28 60 c. Thomas Clarkson 80 80
29 75 c. William Wilberforce 90 90
30 $1 Olaudah Equiano .. .. 1·00 1·00
31 $2.50, General Gordon .. .. 2·00 2·00
32 $5 Granville Sharp .. .. 3·00 3·00
25/32 .. .. *Set of* 8 8·00 8·00
MS733 150 × 121 mnm. Nos. 725/32 .. .. 11·00 13·00

129 Trading Sloop

130 Christopher Columbus with Astrolabe

(Des R. Granger Barrett. Litho Questa)

1986 (25 Nov). *Christmas. Ships. T* **129** *and similar multicoloured designs. P* 14.
734 10 c. Type **129** 90 50
735 45 c. *Lady Rodney* (cargo liner) .. 1·75 1·10
736 80 c. *West Derby* (19th-century sailing ship) 2·50 2·50
737 $3 *Warspite* (local sloop) .. .. 4·75 5·50
734/7 .. .. *Set of* 4 9·00 8·50
MS738 130 × 100 mm. $6 Boat race day (*vert*) .. 12·00 14·00

(Des Mary Walters. Litho Questa)

1986 (22 Dec). *500th Anniv of Discovery of America* (1992) (*1st issue*). *T* **130** *and similar multicoloured designs. P* 14.
739 5 c. Type **130** 30 30
740 10 c. Columbus on board ship 50 35
741 35 c. *Santa Maria* .. .. 1·25 90
742 80 c. King Ferdinand and Queen Isabella of Spain (*horiz*) .. .. 1·50 1·60
743 $4 Caribbean Indians smoking tobacco (*horiz*) .. .. 3·25 4·25
739/43 .. .. *Set of* 5 6·00 6·50
MS744 Two sheets, each 96 × 66 mm. (a) $5 Caribbean Manatee (*horiz*). (b) $5 Dragon Tree .. .. .. *Set of* 2 *sheets* 12·00 14·00
See also Nos. 902/6.

131 *Danaus plexippus*

(Des R. Vigurs. Litho Questa)

1987 (14 Apr). *Easter. Butterflies. T* **131** *and similar horiz designs. Multicoloured. P* 14.
745 10 c. Type **131** 75 40
746 80 c. *Anartia jatrophae* .. .. .. 2·25 2·25
747 $1 *Heliconius charithonia* .. .. 2·50 2·50
748 $2 *Junonia evarete* .. .. .. 4·00 4·50
745/8 .. .. *Set of* 4 8·50 8·50
MS749 90×69 mm. $6 *Dryas julia* .. .. 10·00 12·00

CAPEX'87

132 Old Goose Iron and Modern Electric Iron

(133)

(Des R. Vigurs. Litho Questa)

1987 (25 May). *20th Anniv of Separation from St. Kitts–Nevis. T* **132** *and similar horiz designs. Multicoloured. P* 14.
750 10 c. Type **132** 15 20
751 35 c. Old East End School and Albena Lake-Hodge Comprehensive College .. 20 20
752 45 c. Past and present markets 25 25
753 80 c. Previous sailing ferry and new motor ferry, Blowing Point 45 55
754 $1 Original mobile office and new telephone exchange 55 75
755 $2 Open-air meeting, Burrowes Park, and House of Assembly in session .. 1·10 1·75
750/5 .. .. *Set of* 6 2·40 3·25
MS756 159 × 127 mm. Nos. 750/5 .. .. 5·50 7·00

1987 (13 June). *"Capex '87" International Stamp Exhibition, Toronto. Nos.* 665*a*, 667, 670 *and* 675 *optd with T* **133** *in red.*
757 35 c. Lesser Antillean Bullfinch 70 60
758 45 c. Pearly-eyed Thrasher 80 60
759 80 c. Grey Kingbird .. .. 1·25 1·25
760 $10 Green Heron .. .. 6·75 8·00
757/60 .. .. *Set of* 4 8·50 9·50

20 YEARS OF PROGRESS

1967 - 1987

(134)

1987 (4 Sept). *20th Anniv of Independence. Nos.* 659, 661/4 *and* 665*a*/75 *optd as T* **134** *in red or surch additionally in black* (*No.* 762).
761 5 c. Brown Pelican .. .. 1·00 1·00
762 10 c. on 15 c. Magnificent Frigate Bird .. 1·00 1·00
763 15 c. Magnificent Frigate Bird .. .. 1·25 1·25
764 20 c. Antillean Crested Hummingbird .. 1·25 1·25
765 25 c. Type **116** .. .. 1·25 1·25
766 30 c. Caribbean Elaenia .. .. .. 1·25 1·25
767 35 c. Lesser Antillean Bullfinch .. .. 1·25 1·25
768 40 c. Yellow-crowned Night Heron .. .. 1·25 1·25
769 45 c. Pearly-eyed Thrasher .. .. .. 1·25 1·25
a. Opt double, one albino .. .. 42·00
770 50 c. Laughing Gull .. .. 1·25 1·25
771 65 c. Brown Booby .. .. 1·50 1·75
772 80 c. Grey Kingbird .. .. 1·50 1·75
773 $1 Audubon's Shearwater .. .. .. 1·50 1·75
774 $1.35, Roseate Tern .. .. 2·00 2·25
775 $2.50, Bananaquit .. .. 2·25 3·50
776 $5 Belted Kingfisher .. .. 3·50 5·00
777 $10 Green Heron .. .. 6·00 8·50
761/77 .. .. *Set of* 17 27·00 32·00

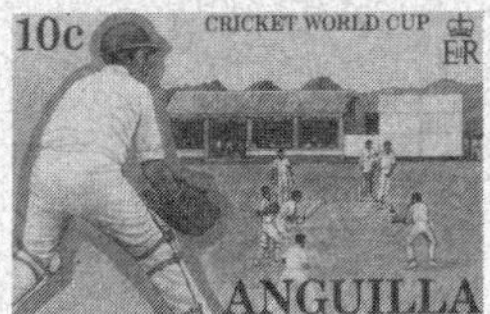

135 Wicket Keeper and Game in Progress

(Des R. Granger Barrett. Litho Questa)

1987 (5 Oct). *Cricket World Cup. T* **135** *and similar horiz designs. Multicoloured. P* 13½ × 14.
778 10 c. Type **135** 65 50
779 35 c. Batsman and local Anguilla team .. 1·10 60
780 45 c. Batsman and game in progress .. 1·25 70
781 $2.50, Bowler and game in progress .. 3·00 4·00
778/81 .. .. *Set of* 4 5·50 5·25
MS782 100 × 75 mm. $6 Batsman and game in progress (*different*) .. .. 9·50 11·00

136 West Indian Top Shell

(Des R. Granger Barrett. Litho Questa)

1987 (2 Nov). *Christmas. Sea Shells and Crabs. T* **136** *and similar horiz designs. Multicoloured. P* 13½ × 14.
783 10 c. Type **136** 65 40
784 35 c. Ghost Crab .. .. 1·00 60
785 50 c. Spiny Caribbean Vase .. .. .. 1·75 1·25
786 $2 Great Land Crab .. .. 3·00 4·25
783/6 .. .. *Set of* 4 5·75 6·00
MS787 101 × 75 mm. $6 Queen or Pink Conch 7·00 9·00

40TH WEDDING ANNIVERSARY

H.M. QUEEN ELIZABETH II

H.R.H. THE DUKE OF EDINBURGH

(137)

1987 (16 Dec). *Royal Ruby Wedding. Nos.* 665*a*, 671/2 *and* 675 *optd with T* **137** *in carmine.*
788 35 c. Lesser Antillean Bullfinch 40 30
789 $1 Audubon's Shearwater .. .. .. 1·00 80
790 $1.35, Roseate Tern .. .. 1·10 90
791 $10 Green Heron .. .. 5·25 6·00
788/91 .. .. *Set of* 4 7·00 7·25

138 *Crinum erubescens*

139 Relay Racing

(Des R. Vigurs. Litho Questa)

1988 (28 Mar). *Easter. Lilies. T* **138** *and similar vert designs. Multicoloured. P* 14×13½.
792 30 c. Type **138** 20 15
793 45 c. Spider Lily 30 25
794 $1 *Crinum macowanii* 75 60
795 $2.50, Day Lily .. .. 1·25 2·00
792/5 .. .. *Set of* 4 2·25 2·75
MS796 100×75 mm. $6 Easter Lily .. .. 2·75 3·75

(Des R. Vigurs. Litho Questa)

1988 (25 July). *Olympic Games, Seoul. T* **139** *and similar vert designs. Multicoloured. P* 14×13½.
797 35 c. Type **139** 40 30
798 45 c. Windsurfing 55 45
799 50 c. Tennis .. .. 1·25 1·00
800 80 c. Basketball .. .. 2·50 2·50
797/800 .. .. *Set of* 4 4·25 3·75
MS801 104×78 mm. $6 Athletics .. .. 3·00 4·00

140 Common Sea Fan

(Des R. Vigurs. Litho Questa)

1988 (28 Nov). *Christmas. Marine Life. T* **140** *and similar horiz designs. Multicoloured. P* 13½ × 14.

802	35 c. Type **140**	30	30
803	80 c. Coral Crab	70	70
804	$1 Grooved Brain Coral	85	85
805	$1.60, Queen Triggerfish	1·40	2·00
802/5	.. .. *Set of* 4	3·00	3·50
MS806	103 x 78 mm. $6 West Indies Spiny Lobster	3·00	4·00

H.R.H. PRINCESS
ALEXANDRA'S
VISIT NOVEMBER 1988

(**141**)

1988 (14 Dec). *Visit of Princess Alexandra. Nos.* 665*a*, 670/1 *and* 673 *optd with T* **141**.

807	35 c. Lesser Antillean Bullfinch	80	60
808	80 c. Grey Kingbird	1·40	1·40
809	$1 Audubon's Shearwater	1·60	1·60
810	$2.50, Bananaquit	2·75	3·75
807/10	.. .. *Set of* 4	6·00	6·50

142 Wood Slave

143 "Christ Crowned with Thorns" (detail) (Bosch)

(Des R. Vigurs. Litho Questa)

1989 (20 Feb). *Lizards. T* **142** *and similar horiz designs. Multicoloured. P* 13½ × 14.

811	45 c. Type **142**	45	35
812	80 c. Slippery Back	70	70
813	$2.50, *Iguana delicatissima*	2·00	2·75
811/13	.. .. *Set of* 3	2·75	3·50
MS814	101 × 75 mm. $6 Tree Lizard	2·75	3·50

(Des R. Vigurs. Litho Questa)

1989 (23 Mar). *Easter. Religious Paintings. T* **143** *and similar vert designs. Multicoloured. P* 14 × 13½.

815	35 c. Type **143**	20	20
816	80 c. "Christ bearing the Cross" (detail) (Gerard David)	45	55
817	$1 "The Deposition" (detail) (Gerard David)	50	60
818	$1.60, "Pietà" (detail) (Rogier van der Weyden)	85	1·40
815/18	.. .. *Set of* 4	1·75	2·50
MS819	103 × 77 mm. $6 "Crucified Christ with the Virgin Mary and Saints" (detail) (Raphael)	2·75	3·50

144 University Arms

20th
ANNIVERSARY
MOON
LANDING

(**145**)

(Des R. Vigurs. Litho Questa)

1989 (24 Apr). *40th Anniv of University of the West Indies. P* 14 × 13½.

820	**144** $5 multicoloured	2·40	3·00

1989 (31 July). *20th Anniv of First Manned Landing on Moon. Nos.* 670/2 *and* 674 *optd with T* **145**.

821	80 c. Grey Kingbird	80	80
822	$1 Audubon's Shearwater	90	90
823	$1.35, Roseate Tern	1·10	1·25
824	$5 Belted Kingfisher	3·75	4·25
821/4	.. .. *Set of* 4	6·00	6·50

146 Lone Star House, 1930

(Des J. Vigurs. Litho Questa)

1989 (11 Dec). *Christmas. Historic Houses. T* **146** *and similar horiz designs. Multicoloured. P* 13½×14.

825	5 c. Type **146**	15	15
826	35 c. Whitehouse, 1906	35	35
827	45 c. Hodges House	45	45
828	80 c. Warden's Place	80	1·25
825/8	.. .. *Set of* 4	1·60	2·00
MS829	102×77 mm. $6 Wallblake House, 1787	3·00	4·00

147 Bigeye ("Blear Eye")

148 The Last Supper

(Des J. Vigurs. Litho Questa)

1990 (2 Apr)–**92.** *Fishes. T* **147** *and similar horiz designs. Multicoloured. P* 13½×14. A. *Without imprint date at foot.*

830A	5 c. Type **147**	45	55
831A	10 c. Long-spined Squirrelfish ("Redman")	45	55
832A	15 c. Stop-light Parrotfish ("Speckletail")	30	40
833A	25 c. Blue-striped Grunt	40	50
834A	30 c. Yellow Jack	50	60
835A	35 c. Red Hind	60	70
836A	40 c. Spotted Goatfish	40	40
837A	45 c. Queen Triggerfish ("Old Wife") ..	40	40
838A	50 c. Coney ("Butter Fish")	40	40
839A	65 c. Smooth Trunkfish ("Shell Fish") ..	45	45
840A	80 c. Yellow-tailed Snapper	50	55
841A	$1 Banded Butterflyfish ("Katy") ..	55	60
842A	$1.35, Nassau Grouper	70	80
843A	$2.50 Blue Tang ("Doctor Fish") ..	1·10	1·40
844A	$5 Queen Angelfish	2·25	3·00
845A	$10 Great Barracuda	4·50	5·50
830A/45A	.. .. .. *Set of* 16	12·50	15·00

B. *With imprint date* (10.6.92)

830B	5 c. Type **147**	30	30
831B	10 c. Long-spined Squirrelfish ("Redman")	30	30
835B	35 c. Red Hind	40	40
830B/5B	.. .. *Set of* 3	90	90

(Des M. Pollard. Litho Questa)

1990 (2 Apr). *Easter. T* **148** *and similar vert designs. Multicoloured. P* 14×13½.

846	35 c. Type **148**	55	20
847	45 c. The Trial	55	25
848	$1.35, The Crucifixion	1·50	1·60
849	$2.50, The Empty Tomb	2·00	3·00
846/9	.. .. *Set of* 4	4·25	4·50
MS850	114×84 mm. $6 The Resurrection ..	5·50	6·50

149 G.B. 1840 Penny Black

WORLD CUP FOOTBALL
CHAMPIONSHIPS 1990

(**150**)

(Litho Questa)

1990 (30 Apr). *"Stamp World London 90" International Stamp Exhibition. T* **149** *and similar multicoloured designs showing stamps. P* 14.

851	25 c. Type **149**	40	25
852	50 c. G.B. 1840 Twopenny Blue	70	50
853	$1.50, Cape of Good Hope 1861 1d. "woodblock" (*horiz*)	1·50	1·75
854	$2.50, G.B. 1882 £5 (*horiz*)	2·00	2·50
851/4	.. .. *Set of* 4	4·25	4·50
MS855	86×71 mm. $6 Penny Black and Twopence Blue (*horiz*)	6·00	7·00

1990 (24 Sept). *Anniversaries and Events. Nos.* 841A/4A *optd as T* **150**.

856	$1 Banded Butterflyfish (optd "EXPO '90")	1·00	1·00
857	$1.35, Nassau Grouper (optd "1990 INTERNATIONAL LITERACY YEAR")	1·25	1·25
858	$2.50, Blue Tang (optd with T **150**) ..	2·50	3·00
859	$5 Queen Angelfish (optd "90TH BIRTHDAY H.M. THE QUEEN MOTHER")	4·00	4·50
856/9	.. .. *Set of* 4	8·00	8·75

151 Mermaid Flag

(Des R. Vigurs. Litho Questa)

1990 (5 Nov). *Island Flags. T* **151** *and similar horiz designs. Multicoloured. P* 13½×14.

860	50 c. Type **151**	70	40
861	80 c. New Anguilla official flag	1·00	90
862	$1 Three Dolphins flag	1·10	95
863	$5 Governor's official flag	3·75	5·00
860/3	.. .. *Set of* 4	6·00	6·50

152 Laughing Gulls

1991

(**153**)

(Des R. Vigurs. Litho Questa)

1990 (26 Nov). *Christmas. Sea Birds. T* **152** *and similar horiz designs. Multicoloured. P* 13½×14.

864	10 c. Type **152**	50	30
865	35 c. Brown Booby	85	50
866	$1.50, Bridled Tern	1·75	1·75
867	$3.50, Brown Pelican	3·00	3·50
864/7	.. .. *Set of* 4	5·50	5·50
MS868	101×76 mm. $6 Little Tern	6·50	8·50

1991 (30 Apr). *Easter. Nos.* 846/50 *optd with T* **153**.

869	35 c. Type **148**	45	35
870	45 c. The Trial	55	45
871	$1.35, The Crucifixion	1·25	1·50
872	$2.50, The Empty Tomb	2·00	3·00
869/72	.. .. *Set of* 4	3·75	4·75
MS873	114 × 84 mm. $6 The Resurrection ..	5·50	6·50

On No. **MS**873 the "1990" inscription on the sheet margin has also been obliterated.

154 Angel

155 Angels with Palm Branches outside St. Gerard's Church

(Des Michele Lavalette. Litho Questa)

1991 (16 Dec). *Christmas. T* **154** *and similar designs P* 14×13½ (5 *c.*, 35 *c.*) *or* 13½×14 (*others*).

874	5 c. dull violet, chestnut and black ..	20	20
875	35 c. multicoloured	65	45
876	80 c. multicoloured	1·40	1·40
877	$1 multicoloured	1·50	1·50
874/7	.. .. *Set of* 4	3·25	3·25
MS878	131×97 mm. $5 mult. P 13½×14 ..	4·25	5·00

Designs: *Vert*—35 c. Father Christmas. *Horiz*—80 c. Church and house; $1 Palm trees at night; $5 Anguilla village.

(Des Lucia Butler. Litho Questa)

1992 (21 Apr). *Easter. T* **155** *and similar multicoloured designs. P* 13½×14 (80 *c.*, $5) *or* 14×13½ (*others*).

879	35 c. Type **155**	35	2
880	45 c. Angels singing outside Methodist Church	45	3
881	80 c. Village (*horiz*)	90	9
882	$1 Congregation going to St. Mary's Church	1·00	1·0
883	$5 Dinghy regatta (*horiz*)	3·75	5·0
879/83	.. .. *Set of* 5	5·75	6·7

$1.60

(**156**)

157 Anguillan Flags

1992 (10 June). *As No.* 834, *but with imprint date, surch with T* **156**.

884	$1.60 on 30 c. Yellow Jack	1·10	1·1

(Litho Questa)

1992 (10 Aug). *25th Anniv of Separation from St. Kitts-Nevis. T* **157** *and similar square designs. Multicoloured. P* 14.

885	80 c. Type **157**	90	9
886	$1 Present official seal	1·10	1·1
887	$1.60, Anguillan flags at airport	2·00	2·0
888	$2 Royal Commissioner's official seal ..	2·00	2·0
885/8	.. .. *Set of* 4	5·50	5·5
MS889	116×117 mm. $10 "Independent Anguilla" overprinted stamps of 1967 (85×85 *mm*)	6·00	7·0

158 Dinghy Race

(Des Michele Lavalette. Litho Questa)

1992 (12 Oct). *Sailing Dinghy Racing. T* **158** *and similar designs. P* 13½×14 (*horiz*) *or* 14×13½ (*vert*).

890 20 c. multicoloured 60 45
891 35 c. multicoloured 80 50
892 45 c. multicoloured 85 50
893 80 c. multicoloured .. .. 1·50 2·00
a. Vert pair. Nos. 893/4 .. .. .. 3·00 4·00
894 80 c. black and pale azure .. .. .. 1·50 2·00
895 $1 multicoloured .. .. 1·50 1·75
890/5 .. .. *Set of* 6 6·00 6·50
MS896 129×30 mm. $6 multicoloured .. .. 3·75 4·50

Designs: *Vert*—35 c. Stylized poster; 80 c. (No. 893) *Blue Bird* in race; 80 c. (No. 894) Construction drawings of *Blue Bird* by Douglas Pyle; $1 Stylized poster (*different*). *Horiz* (*as T* **158**)—45 c. Dinghies on beach. (97×32 *mm*)–$6 Composite design as 20 and 45 c. values.

Nos. 893/4 were printed together, *se-tenant*, in vertical pairs throughout the sheet.

159 Mucka Jumbie on Stilts

(Litho Questa)

1992 (7 Dec). *Christmas. Local Traditions. T* **159** *and similar horiz dsigns. Multicoloured. P* 14.

897 20 c. Type **159** 15 15
898 70 c. Masqueraders 45 50
899 $1.05, Baking in old style oven 65 80
900 $2.40, Collecting presents from Christmas tree .. .. 1·25 1·90
897/900 .. .. *Set of* 4 2·25 3·00
MS901 128×101 $5 As No. 900 .. .. 3·50 4·50

No. **MS**901 also contains labels in designs as Nos. 897/9, but without face values.

160 Columbus landing in New World

161 "Kite Flying" (Kyle Brooks)

(Des Michele Lavalette. Litho Questa)

1992 (15 Dec). *500th Anniv of Discovery of America by Columbus* (*2nd issue*). *T* **160** *and similar designs. P* 14.

902 80 c. multicoloured .. .. 1·10 1·10
903 $1 brownish black and yellow-brown .. 1·10 1·10
904 $2 multicoloured .. .. 2·00 2·50
905 $3 multicoloured .. .. 2·50 3·00
902/5 .. .. *Set of* 4 6·00 7·00
MS906 78×54 mm. $6 multicoloured .. .. 6·50 7·00

Designs: *Vert*—$1 Christopher Columbus; $6 Columbus and map of West Indies. *Horiz*—$2 Fleet of Columbus; $3 *Pinta*.

(Litho Questa)

1993 (29 Mar). *Easter. Children's Paintings. T* **161** *and similar vert designs. Multicoloured. P* 14.

907 20 c. Type **161** 55 30
908 45 c. "Clifftop Village Service" (Kara Connor) 75 45
909 80 c. "Morning Devotion on Sombrero" (Junior Carty) .. .. .. 1·40 1·40
910 $1.50, "Hill Top Church Service" (Leana Harris) .. .. 2·00 2·75
907/10 .. .. *Set of* 4 4·25 4·50
MS911 90×110 mm. $5 "Good Friday Kites" (Marvin Hazel and Kyle Brooks) (39×53 *mm*) 4·50 5·50

162 Salt Picking

163 Lord Great Chamberlain presenting Spurs of Chivalry to Queen

(Des Penny Slinger. Litho Questa)

1993 (23 June). *Traditional Industries. T* **162** *and similar horiz designs. Multicoloured. P* 14.

912 20 c. Type **162** 75 40
913 80 c. Tobacco growing 90 90
914 $1 Cotton picking .. .. 1·00 1·00
915 $2 Harvesting sugar cane .. .. .. 1·75 2·50
912/15 .. .. *Set of* 4 4·00 4·25
MS916 111×85 mm. $6 Fishing .. .. 6·50 8·00

(Des John Lister Ltd. Litho Questa)

1993 (16 Aug). *40th Anniv of Coronation. T* **163** *and similar vert designs. Multicoloured. P* 14.

917 80 c. Type **163** 60 50
918 $1 The Benediction 75 70
919 $2 Queen Elizabeth II in Coronation robes 1·25 1·40
920 $3 St. Edward's Crown .. .. .. 1·75 2·00
917/20 .. .. *Set of* 4 4·00 4·25
MS921 114×95 mm. $6 The Queen and Prince Philip in Coronation coach .. .. .. 6·00 7·00

164 Carnival Pan Player

165 Mucka Jumbies Carnival Characters

(Des Penny Slinger. Litho Questa)

1993 (23 Aug). *Anguilla Carnival. T* **164** *and similar horiz designs. Multicoloured. P* 13½×14.

922 20 c. Type **164** 20 15
923 45 c. Revellers dressed as pirates 40 30
924 80 c. Revellers dressed as stars 65 65
925 $1 Mas dancing 75 75
926 $2 Masked couple .. .. 1·50 2·00
927 $3 Revellers dressed as commandos .. 2·00 2·50
922/7 .. .. *Set of* 6 5·00 5·75
MS928 123×94 mm. $5 Revellers in fantasy costumes .. .. 5·00 6·00

(Litho Questa)

1993 (7 Dec). *Christmas. T* **165** *and similar multicoloured designs. P* 14×13½.

929 20 c. Type **165** 15 20
930 35 c. Local carol singers 25 25
931 45 c. Christmas home baking 35 35
932 $3 Decorating Christmas tree .. .. 1·90 2·75
929/32 .. .. *Set of* 4 2·40 3·25
MS933 123×118 mm. $4 Mucka Jumbies and carol singers (58½×47 *mm*). P 14 .. .. 2·75 3·50

166 Travelling Branch Mail Van at Sandy Ground

167 Princess Alexandra, 1988

(Litho Questa)

1994 (11 Feb). *Delivering the Mail. T* **166** *and similar multicoloured designs. P* 14.

934 20 c. Type **166** 60 45
935 45 c. *Betsy R* (mail schooner) at The Forest (*vert*) 85 50
936 80 c. Mail van at old Post Office .. .. 1·25 1·25
937 $1 Jeep on beach, Island Harbour (*vert*) 1·25 1·25
938 $4 New Post Office .. .. .. 3·50 4·50
934/8 .. .. *Set of* 5 6·75 7·25

(Litho Questa)

1994 (18 Feb). *Royal Visitors. T* **167** *and similar vert designs. Multicoloured. P* 14.

939 45 c. Type **167** 45 35
940 50 c. Princess Alice, 1960 .. .. .. 50 45
941 80 c. Prince Philip, 1993 .. .. .. 75 75
942 $1 Prince Charles, 1973 .. .. .. 85 85
943 $2 Queen Elizabeth II, 1994 .. .. 1·50 2·00
939/43 .. .. *Set of* 5 3·50 4·00
MS944 162×90 mm. Nos. 939/43 .. .. 5·00 6·00

168 "The Crucifixion"

169 Cameroun Player and Pontiac Silverdome, Detroit

(Litho Questa)

1994 (6 Apr). *Easter. Stained-glass Windows. T* **168** *and similar vert designs. Multicoloured. P* 14×15.

945 20 c. Type **168** 30 30
946 45 c. "The Empty Tomb" 45 45
947 80 c. "The Resurrection" 80 90
948 $3 "Risen Christ with Disciples" .. 2·75 3·25
945/8 .. .. *Set of* 4 3·75 4·50

(Des R. Vigurs. Litho Questa)

1994 (3 Oct). *World Cup Football Championship, U.S.A. T* **169** *and similar horiz designs. Multicoloured. P* 14.

949 20 c. Type **169** 30 20
950 70 c. Argentine player and Foxboro Stadium, Boston 70 65
951 $1.80, Italian player and RFK Memorial Stadium, Washington .. .. 1·50 1·75
952 $2.40, German player and Soldier Field, Chicago .. .. 1·90 2·50
949/52 .. .. *Set of* 4 4·00 4·50
MS953 112×85 mm. $6 American and Colombian players .. .. .. 5·50 6·00

170 "The Nativity" (Gustave Doré)

171 Pair of Zenaida Doves

(Des R. Vigurs. Litho Questa)

1994 (22 Nov). *Christmas. Religious Paintings. T* **170** *and similar vert designs. Multicoloured. P* 14.

954 20 c. Type **170** 30 20
955 30 c. "The Wise Men guided by the Star" (Doré) 40 30
956 35 c. "The Annunciation" (Doré) 45 35
957 45 c. "Adoration of the Shepherds" (detail) (Poussin) 50 45
958 $2.40, "The Flight into Egypt" (Doré) .. 1·50 2·50
954/8 .. .. *Set of* 5 2·75 3·50

(Des R. Vigurs. Litho Questa)

1995 (10 Apr). *Easter. Zenaida Doves. T* **171** *and similar horiz designs. Multicoloured. P* 13½×14.

959 20 c. Type **171** 30 20
960 45 c. Dove on branch 50 40
961 50 c. Guarding nest 60 45
962 $5 With chicks .. .. 4·50 5·50
959/62 .. .. *Set of* 4 5·50 6·00

172 Trygve Lie (first Secretary-General) and General Assembly

(Des R. Vigurs. Litho Questa)

1995 (26 June). *50th Anniv of United Nations. T* **172** *and similar multicoloured designs. P* 14×13½ (*vert*) *or* 13½×14 (*others*).

963 20 c. Type **172** 20 20
964 80 c. Flag and building showing "50" .. 60 60
965 $1 Dag Hammarskjöld and U. Thant (former Secretary-Generals) and U.N. Charter 70 70
966 $5 U.N. Building (*vert*) .. .. .. 4·00 5·00
963/6 .. .. *Set of* 4 5·00 6·00

173 Anniversary Emblem and Map of Anguilla

(Des R. Vigurs. Litho Questa)

1995 (15 Aug). *25th Anniv of Caribbean Development Bank. T* **173** *and similar horiz design. Multicoloured. P* 13½×14.

967 45 c. Type **173** .. .. 1·50 1·75
a. Horiz pair. Nos. 967/8 .. .. .. 4·50 5·50
968 $5 Bank building and launches .. .. 3·00 3·75

Nos. 967/8 were printed together, *se-tenant*, in horizontal pairs throughout sheets of 10.

174 Blue Whale

(Litho Questa)

1995 (24 Nov). *Endangered Species. Whales. T* **174** *and similar multicoloured designs. P* 14×13½ (45 *c.*) *or* 13½×14 (*others*).

969 20 c. Type **174** 55 40
970 45 c. Right Whale (*vert*) 90 50
971 $1 Sperm Whale .. .. 1·50 1·50
972 $5 Humpback Whale .. .. 5·50 6·50
969/72 .. .. *Set of* 4 7·50 8·00

175 Palm Tree

176 Deep Water Gorgonia

(Litho Questa)

1995 (12 Dec). *Christmas. T* **175** *and similar square designs. Multicoloured. P* 14½.

973 10 c. Type **175** 25 20
974 25 c. Balloons and fishes 40 30
975 45 c. Shells 55 30
976 $5 Fishes in shape of Christmas Tree .. 5·50 6·50
973/6 .. .. *Set of* 4 6·00 6·50

(Des Michele Lavalette. Litho Cot Printery Ltd, Barbados)

1996 (21 June). *Corals. T* **176** *and similar horiz designs. Multicoloured. P* 14×14½.

977 20 c. Type **176** 50 30
978 80 c. Common Sea Fan .. .. 1·10 90
979 $5 Venus Sea Fern .. .. 4·50 5·50
977/9 .. .. *Set of* 3 5·50 6·00

177 Running

178 Siege of Sandy Hill Fort

(Des Iris Lewis. Litho Cot Printery Ltd, Barbados)

1996 (12 Dec). *Olympic Games, Atlanta. T* **177** *and similar vert designs. Multicoloured. P* 14.

980 20 c. Type **177** 30 20
981 80 c. Javelin throwing and wheelchair basketball 80 70
982 $1 High jumping and hurdles 85 85
983 $3.50, Olympic rings and torch with Greek and American flags .. .. .. 2·75 3·25
980/3 .. .. *Set of* 4 4·25 4·50

(Des Iris Lewis. Litho Cot Printery Ltd, Barbados)

1996 (12 Dec). *Bicentenary of the Battle for Anguilla. T* **178** *and similar multicoloured designs. P* 14.

984 60 c. Type **178** 60 60
985 75 c. French troops destroying church (*horiz*) 70 70
986 $1.50, Naval battle (*horiz*) .. .. .. 1·40 1·60
987 $4 French troops landing at Rendezvous Bay .. .. 2·75 3·50
984/7 .. .. *Set of* 4 5·00 5·75

179 Gooseberry

(Des Michele Lavalette. Litho Questa)

1997 (30 Apr). *Fruit. T* **179** *and similar horiz designs. Multicoloured. P* 14.

988 10 c. Type **179** 10 10
989 20 c. West Indian Cherry 10 10
990 40 c. Tamarind 15 20
991 50 c. Pomme-surette 20 25
992 60 c. Sea Almond 25 30
993 75 c. Sea Grape 35 40
994 80 c. Banana 35 40
995 $1 Genip 45 50
996 $1.10, Coco Plum 50 55
997 $1.25, Pope 55 60
998 $1.50, Pawpaw 65 70
999 $2 Sugar Apple 85 90
1000 $3 Soursop .. .. 1·25 1·40
1001 $4 Pomegranate .. .. 1·75 1·90
1002 $5 Cashew .. .. 2·10 2·25
1003 $10 Mango .. .. 4·25 4·50
998/1003 .. .. *Set of* 16 13·50 14·50

180 West Indian Iguanas hatching

1997 (13 Oct). *Endangered Species. West Indian Iguanas. T* **180** *and similar horiz designs. Multicoloured. Litho. P* 13½×14.

1004 20 c. Type **180** 35 40
a. Strip of 4. Nos. 1004/7 .. .. 2·75
1005 50 c. On rock 55 60
1006 75 c. On branch 60 70
1007 $3 Head of West Indian Iguana .. .. 1·50 1·75
1004/7 .. .. *Set of* 4 2·75 3·00

Nos. 1004/7 were printed together, *se-tenant*, in horizontal and vertical strips of 4 throughout the sheet.

181 "Juluca, Rainbow Deity"

182 Diana, Princess of Wales

(Des Clair Twaron and N. Graulke. Litho Cot Printery Ltd, Barbados)

1997 (17 Nov). *Ancient Stone Carvings from Fountain Cavern. T* **181** *and similar horiz designs. Multicoloured. P* 14×14½.

1008 30 c. Type **181** 30 35
1009 $1.25, "Lizard with front legs extended" 75 80
1010 $2.25, "Chief" .. .. 1·40 1·60
1011 $2.75, "Jocahu, the Creator" .. .. 1·75 2·00
1008/11 .. .. *Set of* 4 3·75 4·25

(Des R. Vigurs. Litho Questa)

1998 (14 Apr). *Diana, Princess of Wales Commemoration. T* **182** *and similar vert designs. Multicoloured. P* 14×13½.

1012 15 c. Type **182** 30 35
a. Strip of 4. Nos. 1012/15 .. .. 3·25
1013 $1 Wearing yellow blouse 80 85
1014 $1.90, Wearing tiara .. .. .. 1·25 1·40
1015 $2.25, Wearing blue short-sleeved Red Cross blouse .. .. 1·40 1·60
1012/15 .. .. *Set of* 4 3·25 3·75

Nos. 1012/15 were printed together, *se-tenant*, in horizontal and vertical strips of 4 throughout the sheet.

183 "Treasure Island" (Valarie Alix)

(Litho Cot Printery Ltd, Barbados)

1998 (24 Aug). *International Arts Festival. T* **183** *and similar multicoloured designs. P* 14.

1016 15 c. Type **183** 25 30
1017 30 c. "Posing in the Light" (Melsadis Fleming) (*vert*) 35 40
1018 $1 "Pescadores de Anguilla" (Juan Garcia) (*vert*) 70 80
1019 $1.50, "Fresh Catch" (Verna Hart) .. 1·00 1·25
1020 $1.90, "The Bell Tower of St. Mary's" (Ricky Racardo Edwards) (*vert*) .. 1·25 1·50
1016/20 .. .. *Set of* 5 3·25 3·75

STAMP BOOKLETS

1977 (9 Feb). *Silver Jubilee. Multicoloured cover showing Crown and map of Anguilla. Stapled.*

SB1 $8.70, booklet containing 25 c., 40 c., $1.20 and $2.50 (Nos. 269/72), each in pair .. .. 2·25
a. Stamps with margin at right .. .. 4·00

No. SB1 was produced from normal sheets and can be found stapled at the left or the right. A further printing was later produced from specially prepared sheets, so that stamps from Booket No. SB1a occur with small vertical margins at the right of each pair, in addition to the binding margin at left.

1978. *25th Anniv of Coronation. Multicoloured cover, 105×38 mm, showing Royal coat-of-arms and map of Anguilla. Stapled.*

SB2 $9.44, booklet containing 22 c., 50 c., $1.50 and $2.50 (Nos. 320/3), each in pair .. .. 1·75
a. Stamps with margin at right .. .. 2·00

No. SB2 exists with three different scenes on the back cover.

A second printing of No. SB2 exists with a sheet arrangement as described for No. SB1a.

1979. *Death Centenary of Sir Rowland Hill. Multicoloured cover, 104×39 mm, showing design from "Mulready" envelope on the front and coral beaches on the back. Stapled.*

SB3 $9.18, booklet containing 1 c. ×2, 22 c., 35 c., $1.50 and $2.50 (Nos. 358/63), each in pair .. 3·00

No. SB3 exists with three different scenes on the back cover.

1980. *"London 1980" International Stamp Exhibition. Three multicoloured covers, each 109×39 mm, showing designs from Anguilla stamps, either No. 384, 385 or 387, on front and different views of Anguilla on back. Stapled.*

SB4 $9.70, booklet (*any cover*) containing 35 c., 50 c., $1.50 and $2.50 (Nos. 384a/7a), each in pair 2·50
Set of 3 different cover designs .. .. 7·00

1981 (15 June). *Royal Wedding. Multicoloured covers, each 105×65 mm, showing Prince of Wales emblem on front and local scene on back. Stapled.*

SB5 $14 booklet containing two panes of 4 (either Nos. 468a, 469a or Nos. 468wa, 469wa) .. .. 2·00

No. SB5 exists with three different scenes on the back cover.

1982 (30 Aug). *21st Birthday of Princess of Wales. Multicoloured cover, 105×65 mm, showing Prince of Wales emblem on front and coral beach on back. Stapled.*

SB6 $12.40, booklet containing four panes of 4 (Nos. 507a, 509a, 510a, 511a) .. .. .. 7·00

1984 (31 Oct). *Birth of Prince Henry. Booklet No.* SB6 *optd* "PRINCE HENRY BIRTH 15.9.84" *on cover.*

SB7 $12.40, booklet containing four panes of 4 (Nos. 628a, 630a, 631a, 632a) .. .. .. 7·50

1996 (5 June). *Black on salmon cover, 105×71 mm, showing flag and map of Anguilla. Stamps attached by selvedge.*

SB8 $5 booklet containing Nos. 894 and 959, each ×5 2·10

It is understood that fourteen other combinations of contents with 20 c. and 80 c. face values exist.

1998 (13 Mar). *Cover as No.* SB8, *but surch* "EC $9.00".

SB9 $9 booklet containing Nos. 792 and 998, each ×5 4·00

It is understood that other combinations of contents with 30 c. and $1.50 face values exist.

1998 (12 Nov). *Multicoloured cover, 105×71 mm, showing outline map of Anguilla and flag emblem. Stamps attached by selvedge.*

SB10 $6.50, booklet containing Nos. 1017/18, each ×5, plus 5 printed labels .. .. .. 2·50

It is understood that other combinations of contents with 30 c. and $1 face values exist.

Antigua

The first mention of a local postmaster for Antigua is in 1760, ›ut the earliest straight-line mark, inscribed "ANTE/GOA", is ›nown on a letter of 1757. Mail services before 1850 were omewhat haphazard, until St. John's was made a branch office f the British G.P.O. in 1850. A second office, at English larbour, opened in 1857.

The stamps of Great Britain were used between May 1858 nd the end of April 1860, when the island postal service became he responsibility of the local colonial authorities. In the interim eriod, between the take-over and the appearance of Antiguan tamps, the crowned-circle handstamps were again utilised and Jo. CC1 can be found used as late as 1869.

For illustrations of the handstamp and postmark types see BRITISH POST OFFICES ABROAD notes, following GREAT BRITAIN.

ST. JOHN'S

CROWNED-CIRCLE HANDSTAMPS

CC1 CC 1 ANTIGUA (St. John's) (22.3.1850) (R.)
Price on cover £550

Stamps of GREAT BRITAIN *cancelled* "A 02" *as Type* **2**.

1858 *to* **1860**.
Z1 1d. rose-red (1857), *perf* 14 .. £475
Z2 2d. blue (1855), *perf* 14 (Plate No. 6) .. £900
Z3 2d. blue (1858) (Plate Nos. 7, 8, 9) .. £600
Z4 4d. rose (1857) .. £475
Z5 6d. lilac (1856) .. £160
Z6 1s. green (1856) .. £1500

ENGLISH HARBOUR

CROWNED-CIRCLE HANDSTAMPS

CC2 CC **3** ENGLISH HARBOUR (10.12.1857)
Price on cover £4250

Stamps of GREAT BRITAIN *cancelled* "A 18" *as Type* **2**.

1858 to **1860**.
Z7 2d. blue (1858) (Plate No. 7) .. £5000
Z8 4d. rose (1857) .. £5000
Z9 6d. lilac .. £2000
Z10 1s. green (1856) ..

PRICES FOR STAMPS ON COVER TO 1945

No. 1	*from* × 8
Nos. 2/4	†
Nos. 5/10	*from* × 15
Nos 13/14	*from* × 20
No. 15	*from* × 50
Nos. 16/18	*from* × 30
Nos. 19/23	*from* × 12
No. 24	*from* × 40
Nos. 25/30	*from* × 10
Nos. 31/51	*from* × 4
Nos. 52/4	*from* × 10
Nos. 55/61	*from* × 4
Nos. 62/80	*from* × 3
Nos. 81/90	*from* × 4
Nos. 91/4	*from* × 5
Nos. 95/7	*from* × 4
Nos. 98/109	*from* × 3

CROWN COLONY

1

3 (Die I)

(Eng C. Jeens after drawing by Edward Corbould. Recess P.B.)

1862 (Aug). *No wmk.* (*a*) *Rough perf* 14 *to* 16.
1 1 6d. blue-green .. £800 £500

(*b*) *P* 11 *to* 12½
2 1 6d. blue-green .. £4250

(*c*) *P* 14 *to* 16 × 11 *to* 12½
3 1 6d. blue-green .. £2750

(*d*) *P* 14 *to* 16 *compound with* 11 *to* 12½
4 1 6d. blue-green .. £3000

Nos. 2/4 may be trial perforations. They are not known used.

1863 (Jan)–**67**. *Wmk Small Star. W* w **2** (*sideways on* 6*d.*). *Rough perf* 14 *to* 16.
5 1 1d. rosy mauve .. £110 42·00
6 1d. dull rose (1864) .. 90·00 35·00
a. Imperf between (vert pair) .. £15000
7 1d. vermilion (1867) .. £140 22·00
a. Imperf between (horiz pair) .. £15000
b. Wmk sideways .. £180 38·00
8 6d. green (*shades*) .. £400 22·00
a. Wmk upright .. — 75·00
9 6d. dark green .. £425 22·00
10 6d. yellow-green .. £2750 75·00

Caution is needed in buying No. 10 as some of the shades of No. 8 verge on yellow-green.

The 1d. rosy mauve exists showing trial perforations of 11 to 12½ and 14 to 16.

(Recess D.L.R. from P.B. plates)

1872. *Wmk Crown CC. P* 12½.
13 1 1d. lake .. £100 15·00
w. Wmk inverted
x. Wmk reversed .. £100 15·00
y. Wmk inverted and reversed
14 1d. scarlet .. £140 17·00
w. Wmk inverted .. £200 75·00
x. Wmk reversed
15 6d. blue-green .. £500 7·50
w. Wmk inverted
x. Wmk reversed .. £500 7·50
y. Wmk inverted and reversed

1876. *Wmk Crown CC. P* 14.
16 1 1d. lake .. £100 9·00
a. Bisected (½d.) (1883) (on cover) .. † £2750
x. Wmk reversed
17 1d. lake-rose .. £100 9·00
w. Wmk inverted .. £150 60·00
x. Wmk reversed
y. Wmk inverted and reversed
18 6d. blue-green .. £300 13·00
x. Wmk reversed .. £300 13·00
y. Wmk inverted and reversed .. — 50·00

(Recess (T 1); typo (T 3) De La Rue & Co)

1879. *Wmk Crown CC. P* 14.
19 3 2½d. red-brown .. £600 £160
a. Large "2" in "2½" with slanting foot £7500 £2250
20 4d. blue .. £250 14·00

Top left triangle detached
(Pl 2 R. 3/3 of right pane)

1882. *Wmk Crown CA. P* 14.
21 3 ½d. dull green .. 2·25 10·00
a. Top left triangle detached .. £120
22 2½d. red-brown .. £130 55·00
a. Large "2" in "2½" with slanting foot £2500 £1100
23 4d. blue .. £275 15·00
a. Top left triangle detached .. — £375

1884. *Wmk Crown CA. P* 12.
24 1 1d. carmine-red .. 50·00 15·00
w. Wmk inverted
y. Wmk inverted and reversed

The 1d. scarlet is a colour changeling.

1884–86. *Wmk Crown CA. P* 14.
25 1 1d. carmine-red .. 1·40 2·50
x. Wmk reversed
y. Wmk inverted and reversed
26 1d. rose .. 55·00 12·00
27 3 2½d. ultramarine (1886) .. 6·00 11·00
a. Large "2" in "2½" with slanting foot £160 £250
b. Top left triangle detached .. £275
28 4d. chestnut (1886) .. 1·50 2·25
a. Top left triangle detached .. £110
29 1 6d. deep green .. 60·00 £120
30 3 1s. mauve (1886) .. £160 £120
a. Top left triangle detached .. £750
27/28, 30 Optd "Specimen" .. *Set of* 3 £150

Nos. 25 and 26 postmarked "A 12" in place of "A 02" were used in St. Christopher.

2½ 2½ 2½
A B C

The variety "Large '2' in '2½' with slanting foot" occurs on the first stamp of the seventh row in both left (A) and right (B) panes (in which positions the "NN" of "PENNY" have three vertical strokes shortened) and on the first stamp of the third row of the right-hand pane (C). The "2" varies slightly in each position.

From 31 October 1890 until July 1903 Leeward Islands general issues were used. Subsequently both general issues and the following separate issues were in concurrent use until July 1956, when the general Leewards Island stamps were withdrawn.

PRICES OF SETS

Set prices are given for many issues, generally those containing three stamps or more. Definitive sets include one of each value or major colour change, but do not cover different perforations, die types or minor shades. Where a choice is possible the set prices are based on the cheapest versions of the stamps included in the listings.

4

5

(Typo D.L.R.)

1903 (July)–**09**. *Wmk Crown CC. Ordinary paper. P* 14.
31 4 ½d. grey-black and grey-green .. 3·25 5·00
32 1d. grey-black and rose-red .. 5·00 80
a. Bluish paper (1909) .. 95·00 95·00
33 2d. dull purple and brown .. 6·00 24·00
34 2½d. grey-black and blue .. 8·00 14·00
a. Chalk-surfaced paper (1907) .. 16·00 38·00
35 3d. grey-green and orange-brown .. 9·50 20·00
36 6d. purple and black .. 28·00 48·00
w. Wmk inverted .. £100
37 1s. blue and dull purple .. 38·00 48·00
a. Chalk-surfaced paper (1907) .. 40·00 80·00
38 2s. grey-green and pale violet .. 65·00 85·00
39 2s. 6d. grey-black and purple .. 17·00 48·00
40 5 5s. grey-green and violet .. 70·00 90·00
a. Chalk-surfaced paper (1907) .. 75·00 95·00
31/40 .. *Set of* 10 £200 £350
31/40 Optd "Specimen" .. *Set of* 10 £150

1908–17. *Wmk Mult Crown CA. Chalk-surfaced paper* (2*d.*, 3*d. to* 2*s.*). *P* 14.
41 4 ½d. green .. 2·25 3·75
w. Wmk inverted
42 ½d. blue-green (1917) .. 3·00 5·00
43 1d. red (1909) .. 4·50 1·75
44 1d. scarlet (5.8.15) .. 4·75 2·75
45 2d. dull purple and brown (1912) .. 3·75 25·00
46 2½d. ultramarine .. 9·50 15·00
a. Blue .. 15·00 20·00
47 3d. grey-green and orange-brown (1912) 6·50 18·00
48 6d. purple and black (1911) .. 7·50 35·00
49 1s. blue and dull purple .. 15·00 65·00
50 2s. grey-green and violet (1912) .. 65·00 80·00
41/50 .. *Set of* 8 £100 £225
41, 43, 46 Optd "Specimen" .. *Set of* 3 65·00

1913. *As T* **5**, *but portrait of King George V. Wmk Mult Crown CA. Chalk-surfaced paper. P* 14.
51 5s. grey-green and violet (Optd S. £60) .. 70·00 £110

WAR STAMP
(7)

8

1916 (Sept)–**17**. *No.* 41 *optd in London with T* **7**.
52 4 ½d. green (Bk.) .. 65 1·50
53 ½d. green (R.) (1.10.17) .. 1·00 1·50

1918 (July). *Optd with T* **7**. *Wmk Mult Crown CA. P* 14.
54 4 1½d. orange .. 65 85
52/4 Optd "Specimen" .. *Set of* 3 70·00

(Typo D.L.R.)

1921–29. *P* 14. (*a*) *Wmk Mult Crown CA. Chalk-surfaced paper.*
55 8 3d. purple/*pale yellow* .. 3·75 11·00
56 4d. grey-black and red/*pale yellow* (1922) 1·50 5·00
57 1s. black/*emerald* .. 3·75 7·50
y. Wmk inverted and reversed
58 2s. purple and blue/*blue* .. 11·00 19·00
59 2s. 6d. black and red/*blue* .. 13·00 45·00
60 5s. green and red/*pale yellow* (1922) .. 8·00 42·00
61 £1 purple and black/*red* (1922) .. £170 £275
55/61 .. *Set of* 7 £190 £350
55/61 Optd "Specimen" .. *Set of* 7 £170

(*b*) *Wmk Mult Script CA. Chalk-surfaced paper* (3*d. to* 4*s.*).
62 8 ½d. dull green .. 1·25 20
63 1d. carmine-red .. 1·00 20
64 1d. bright violet (1923) .. 2·25 1·50
a. Mauve .. 8·50 6·50
65 1d. bright scarlet (1929) .. 12·00 2·75
67 1½d. dull orange (1922) .. 2·00 7·00
68 1½d. carmine-red (1926) .. 3·50 1·75
69 1½d. pale red-brown (1929) .. 2·00 60
70 2d. grey (1922) .. 1·50 75
a. Wmk sideways
71 2½d. bright blue (1922) .. 6·00 16·00
72 2½d. orange-yellow (1923) .. 1·50 17·00
73 2½d. ultramarine (1927) .. 3·25 5·50
74 3d. purple/*pale yellow* (1925) .. 4·00 8·50
75 6d. dull and bright purple (1922) .. 2·75 6·50
76 1s. black/*emerald* (1929) .. 6·00 8·00
77 2s. purple and blue/*blue* (1927) .. 10·00 50·00
78 2s. 6d. black and red/*blue* (1927) .. 18·00 24·00
79 3s. green and violet (1922) .. 24·00 75·00
80 4s. grey-black and red (1922) .. 48·00 60·00
62/80 .. *Set of* 16 £110 £225
62/80 Optd/Perf "Specimen" .. *Set of* 18 £325

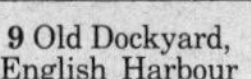

9 Old Dockyard, English Harbour

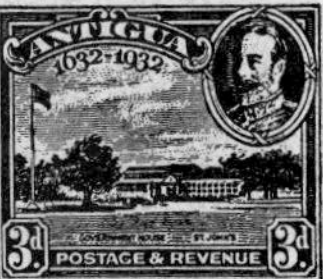

10 Government House, St. John's

(Des Mrs. J. Goodwin (5s.), Waterlow (others). Recess Waterlow)

1932 (27 Jan). *Tercentenary. T* **9/10** *and similar designs. Wmk Mult Script CA. P* 12½.

No.	Type	Description		
81	9	½d. green	1·75	5·50
82		1d. scarlet	2·50	4·25
83		1½d. brown	3·00	4·25
84	10	2d. grey	3·75	15·00
85		2½d. deep blue	3·75	8·50
86		3d. orange	3·75	12·00
87	–	6d. violet	13·00	12·00
88	–	1s. olive-green	18·00	25·00
89	–	2s. 6d. claret	38·00	48·00
90	–	5s. black and chocolate	75·00	£110
81/90		*Set of* 10	£140	£200
81/90 Perf "Specimen"		*Set of* 10	£200	

Designs: *Horiz*—6d., 1s., 2s. 6d. Nelson's *Victory*. *Vert*—5s. Sir Thomas Warner's *Concepcion*.

Examples of all values are known showing a forged St. Johns postmark dated "MY 18 1932".

13 Windsor Castle

(Des H. Fleury. Recess D.L.R.)

1935 (6 May). *Silver Jubilee. Wmk Mult Script CA. P* 13½ × 14.

No.	Type	Description		
91	13	1d. deep blue and carmine	2·00	2·25
		f. Diagonal line by turret	45·00	
92		1½d. ultramarine and grey	2·75	45
93		2½d. brown and deep blue	5·50	1·00
		g. Dot to left of chapel	£120	
94		1s. slate and purple	8·50	12·00
		h. Dot by flagstaff	£160	
91/4		*Set of* 4	17·00	14·00
91/4 Perf "Specimen"		*Set of* 4	70·00	

For illustrations of plate varieties see Catalogue Introduction.

14 King George VI and Queen Elizabeth

(Des D.L.R.. Recess B.W.)

1937 (12 May). *Coronation. Wmk Mult Script CA. P* 11×11½.

No.	Type	Description		
95	14	1d. carmine	50	80
96		1½d. yellow-brown	60	90
97		2½d. blue	1·25	1·60
95/7		*Set of* 3	2·10	3·00
95/7 Perf "Specimen"		*Set of* 3	50·00	

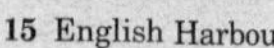

15 English Harbour

16 Nelson's Dockyard

(Recess Waterlow)

1938 (15 Nov)–**51**. *T* **15, 16** *and similar designs. Wmk Mult Script CA. P* 12½.

No.	Type	Description		
98	15	½d. green	30	90
99	16	1d. scarlet	2·75	1·75
		a. Red (8.42 and 11.47)	3·25	1·75
100		1½d. chocolate-brown	4·75	50
		a. Dull reddish brown (12.43)	2·25	1·25
		b. Lake-brown (7.49)	25·00	13·00
101	15	2d. grey	50	50
		a. Slate-grey (6.51)	6·00	4·50
102	16	2½d. deep ultramarine	70	80
103	–	3d. orange	60	80
104	–	6d. violet	1·40	80
105	–	1s. black and brown	3·00	95
		a. Black and red-brown (7.49)	30·00	9·50
		ab. Frame ptd double, once albino	£2500	
106	–	2s. 6d. brown-purple	42·00	8·00
		a. Maroon (8.42)	22·00	8·00
107	–	5s. olive-green	14·00	7·00
108	16	10s. magenta (1.4.48)	16·00	25·00
109	–	£1 slate-green (1.4.48)	25·00	35·00
98/109		*Set of* 12	75·00	70·00
98/109 Perf "Specimen"		*Set of* 12	£180	

Designs: *Horiz*—3d., 2s. 6d., £1 Fort James. *Vert*—6d., 1s., 5s. St. John's Harbour.

17 Houses of Parliament, London

(Des and recess D.L.R.)

1946 (1 Nov). *Victory. Wmk Mult Script CA. P* 13½×14.

No.	Type	Description		
110	17	1½d. brown	15	10
111		3d. red-orange	15	30
110/111 Perf "Specimen"		*Set of* 2	50·00	

18 19
King George VI and Queen Elizabeth

(Des and photo Waterlow (T **18**). Design recess; name typo B.W. (T **19**))

1949 (3 Jan). *Royal Silver Wedding. Wmk Mult Script CA.*

No.	Type	Description		
112	18	2½d. ultramarine (*p* 14×15)	40	1·00
113	19	5s. grey-olive (*p* 11½×11)	8·00	5·50

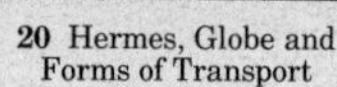

20 Hermes, Globe and Forms of Transport

21 Hemispheres, Jet-powered Vickers Viking Airliner and Steamer

22 Hermes and Globe

23 U.P.U. Monument

(Recess Waterlow (T **20, 23**). Designs recess, name typo B.W. (T **21/2**))

1949 (10 Oct). *75th Anniv of Universal Postal Union. Wmk Mult Script CA.*

No.	Type	Description		
114	20	2½d. ultramarine (*p* 13½–14)	40	50
115	21	3d. orange (*p* 11 × 11½)	1·50	1·75
116	22	6d. purple (*p* 11 × 11½)	45	1·25
117	23	1s. red-brown (*p* 13½–14)	45	75
114/17		*Set of* 4	2·50	3·75

(New Currency. 100 cents = 1 West Indian, later Eastern Caribbean, dollar)

24 Arms of University

25 Princess Alice

(Recess Waterlow)

1951 (16 Feb). *Inauguration of B.W.I. University College. Wmk Mult Script CA. P* 14×14½.

No.	Type	Description		
118	24	3 c. black and brown	45	50
119	25	12 c. black and violet	45	80

26 Queen Elizabeth II

27 Martello Tower

(Des and eng B.W. Recess D.L.R.)

1953 (2 June). *Coronation. Wmk Mult Script CA. P* 13½×13.

No.	Type	Description		
120	26	2 c. black and deep yellow-green	30	6

(Recess Waterlow until 1961, then D.L.R.)

1953 (2 Nov)–**62**. *Designs previously used for King George VI issue, but with portrait of Queen Elizabeth II as in T* **27**. *Wmk Mult Script CA. P* 13×13½ (*horiz*) *or* 13½×13 (*vert*).

No.	Type	Description		
120*a*	–	½ c. brown (3.7.56)	20	30
121	–	1 c. slate-grey	30	70
		a. Slate (7.11.61)	1·50	1·50
122	–	2 c. green	30	10
123	–	3 c. black and orange-yellow	40	20
		a. Black and yellow-orange (5.12.61)	1·75	2·00
124	–	4 c. scarlet	1·25	10
		a. Brown-red (11.12.62)	1·25	30
125	–	5 c. black and slate-lilac	2·50	40
126	–	6 c. yellow-ochre	2·00	10
		a. Dull yellow-ochre (5.12.61)	4·50	1·25
127	27	8 c. deep blue	2·25	10
128	–	12 c. violet	2·25	10
129	–	24 c. black and chocolate	2·50	15
130	27	48 c. purple and deep blue	7·00	2·50
131	–	60 c. maroon	7·50	80
132	–	$1.20, olive-green	2·25	70
		a. Yellowish olive (10.8.55)	2·25	70
133	–	$2.40, bright reddish purple	10·00	12·00
134	–	$4.80, slate-blue	15·00	23·00
120*a*/134		*Set of* 15	48·00	35·00

Designs: *Horiz*—½ c., 6 c., 60 c., $4.80, Fort James; 2 c., 3 c., 5 c. $2.40, Nelson's Dockyard. *Vert*—1 c., 4 c., English Harbour; 12 c. 24 c., $1.20, St. John's Harbour.

See also Nos. 149/58.

28 Federation Map

COMMEMORATION
ANTIGUA
CONSTITUTION
1960

(29)

(Recess B.W.)

1958 (22 Apr). *Inauguration of British Caribbean Federation W* w **12.** *P* 11½ × 11.

No.	Type	Description		
135	28	3 c. deep green	1·00	3
136		6 c. blue	1·40	2·2
137		12 c. scarlet	1·60	7
135/7		*Set of* 3	3·50	3·0

MINISTERIAL GOVERNMENT

1960 (1 Jan). *New Constitution. Nos.* 123 *and* 128 *optd with T* **29**.

138	3 c. black and orange-yellow (R.)	15	1
139	12 c. violet	15	1

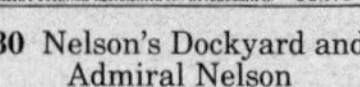

30 Nelson's Dockyard and Admiral Nelson

31 Stamp of 1862 and R.M.S.P. *Solent I* at English Harbour

(Recess B.W.)

1961 (14 Nov). *Restoration of Nelson's Dockyard. W* w **12** *P* 11½ × 11.

No.	Type	Description		
140	30	20 c. purple and brown	90	1·0
141		30 c. green and blue	1·10	1·2

(Des A. W. Morley. Recess B.W.)

1962 (1 Aug). *Stamp Centenary. W* w **12.** *P* 13½.

No.	Type	Description		
142	31	3 c. purple and deep green	60	1
143		10 c. blue and deep green	70	1
144		12 c. deep sepia and deep green	80	1
145		50 c. orange-brown and deep green	1·50	1·7
142/5		*Set of* 4	3·25	1·7

32 Protein Foods

33 Red Cross Emblem

(Des M. Goaman. Photo Harrison)

963 (4 June). *Freedom from Hunger. W* w **12**. *P* 14×14½.
46 **32** 12 c. bluish green 15 15

(Des V. Whiteley. Litho B.W.)

963 (2 Sept). *Red Cross Centenary. W* w **12.** *P* 13½.
47 **33** 3 c. red and black 40 50
48 12 c. red and blue . . . . . . 60 1·00

(Recess D.L.R.)

963 (16 Sept)–**65**. *As* 1953—61 *but wmk* w **12**.
49 – ½ c. brown (13.4.65) . . . . . . 1·50 75
50 – 1 c. slate (13.4.65) . . . . . . 1·00 1·00
51 – 2 c. green 60 20
52 – 3 c. black and yellow-orange 45 20
53 – 4 c. brown-red 30 30
54 – 5 c. black and slate-lilac 20 10
a. Black and reddish violet (15.1.65) 20 10
55 – 6 c. yellow-ochre 60 30
56 **27** 8 c. deep blue 30 20
57 – 12 c. violet 40 20
58 – 24 c. black and deep chocolate . . . . 4·00 70
a. Black and chocolate-brown (28.4.65) 4·75 2·50
49/158 . . . . *Set of* 10 8·50 3·50

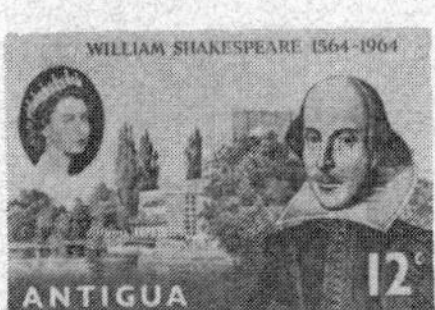

34 Shakespeare and Memorial Theatre, Stratford-upon-Avon

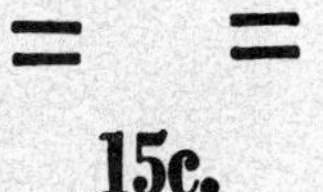

(35)

(Des R. Granger Barrett. Photo Harrison)

1964 (23 April). *400th Birth Anniv of William Shakespeare. W* w **12.** *P* 14 × 14½.
164 **34** 12 c. orange-brown 20 10
w. Wmk inverted . . . . . . 48·00

1965 (1 April). *No.* 157 *surch with T* **35**.
165 15 c. on 12 c. violet 10 10

36 I.T.U. Emblem

(Des M. Goaman. Litho Enschedé)

1965 (17 May). *I.T.U. Centenary. W* w **12.** *P* 11 × 11½.
166 **36** 2 c. light blue and light red 20 15
167 50 c. orange-yellow and ultramarine . . 90 80

37 I.C.Y. Emblem

(Des V. Whiteley. Litho Harrison)

1965 (25 Oct). *International Co-operation Year. W* w **12.** *P* 14½.
168 **37** 4 c. reddish purple and turquoise-green 15 10
169 15 c. deep bluish green and lavender . . 25 20

38 Sir Winston Churchill, and St. Paul's Cathedral in Wartime

(Des Jennifer Toombs. Photo Harrison)

1966 (24 Jan). *Churchill Commemoration. Printed in black, cerise and gold and with background in colours stated. W* w **12.** *P* 14.
170 **38** ½ c. new blue . . . . 10 1·50
a. Value omitted £300
171 4 c. deep green 30 10
172 25 c. brown 75 45
173 35 c. bluish violet 85 55
170/3 . . . . *Set of* 4 1·75 2·25
No. 170a was caused by misplacement of the gold and also shows "ANTIGUA" moved to the right.

39 Queen Elizabeth II and Duke of Edinburgh

(Des H. Baxter. Litho B.W.)

1966 (4 Feb). *Royal Visit. W* w **12.** *P* 11 × 12.
174 **39** 6 c. black and ultramarine . . . . 1·75 1·10
175 15 c. black and magenta . . . . . . 1·75 1·40

40 Footballer's Legs, Ball and Jules Rimet Cup

(Des V. Whiteley. Litho Harrison)

1966 (1 July). *World Football Cup Championships. W* w **12** (*sideways*). *P* 14.
176 **40** 6 c. violet, yellow-green, lake & yell-brn 20 25
177 35 c. chocolate, blue-grn, lake & yell-brn 60 25

41 W.H.O. Building

(Des M. Goaman. Litho Harrison)

1966 (20 Sept). *Inauguration of W.H.O. Headquarters, Geneva. W* w **12** (*sideways*). *P* 14.
178 **41** 2 c. black, yellow-green and light blue 15 15
179 15 c. black, light purple and yellow-brown 70 25

42 Nelson's Dockyard

(Des, eng and recess B.W.)

1966 (1 Nov)–**70**. *Horiz designs as T* **42**. *W* w **12**. *Ordinary paper. P* 11½×11.
180 ½ c. green and turquoise-blue 10 40
a. Perf 13½ (24.6.69) 10 95
181 1 c. purple and cerise 10 30
a. Perf 13½ (24.6.69) 10 80
ab. Glazed paper (30.9.69) 60 15
182 2 c. slate-blue and yellow-orange . . 10 20
a. Perf 13½ (24.6.69) 10 40
ab. Glazed paper (30.9.69) 70 10
183 3 c. rose-red and black 10 30
a. Perf 13½ (24.6.69) 15 15
184 4 c. slate-violet and brown 30 10
a. Perf 13½ (24.6.69) 15 15
ab. Glazed paper (6.4.70) . . . . 16·00 9·00
185 5 c. ultramarine and yellow-olive . . 10 10
a. Perf 13½ (24.6.69) 15 10
ab. Glazed paper (30.9.69) 40 10
186 6 c. salmon and purple 15 10
a. Perf 13½ (24.6.69) 15 70
187 10 c. emerald and rose-red 15 10
a. Perf 13½ (24.6.69) 15 15
ab. Glazed paper (30.9.69) . . . . 2·50 10
188 15 c. brown and new blue . . . . 1·25 10
a. Perf 13½ (*glazed paper*) (30.9.69) 55 10
189 25 c. slate-blue and sepia 35 20
a. Perf 13½ (*glazed paper*) (30.9.69) 45 10
190 35 c. cerise and blackish brown . . . . 1·50 55
a. Perf 13½ (*glazed paper*) (30.9.69) 60 1·00
191 50 c. dull green and black . . . . 1·50 2·50
a. Perf 13½ (*glazed paper*) (30.9.69) 70 2·25
192 75 c. greenish blue and ultramarine . . 1·50 2·50
193 $1 cerise and yellow-olive . . . . 4·75 2·50
a. Carmine and yellow-olive (14.5.68) . . 18·00 12·00
b. Perf 13½ (*glazed paper*) (30.9.69) 1·25 4·50
194 $2.50, black and cerise . . . . 3·50 5·50
a. Perf 13½ (*glazed paper*) (30.9.69) 1·50 8·00
195 $5 olive-green and slate-violet . . 5·50 6·50
a. Perf 13½ (*glazed paper*) (30.9.69) . . 12·00 24·00
180/195 . . . . . . *Set of* 16 18·00 19·00
Designs:—1 c. Old Post Office, St. John's; 2 c. Health Centre; 3 c. Teachers' Training College; 4 c. Martello Tower, Barbuda; 5 c. Ruins of Officers' Quarters, Shirley Heights; 6 c. Government House, Barbuda; 10 c. Princess Margaret School; 15 c. Air Terminal building; 25 c. General Post Office; 35 c. Clarence House; 50 c. Government House, St. John's; 75 c. Administration Building; $1, Courthouse, St. John's; $2.50, Magistrates' Court; $5, St. John's Cathedral.

NEW INFORMATION

The editor is always interested to correspond with people who have new information that will improve or correct the Catalogue.

54 "Education"

55 "Science"

56 "Culture"

(Des Jennifer Toombs. Litho Harrison)

1966 (1 Dec). *20th Anniv of U.N.E.S.C.O. W* w **12** (*sideways*). *P* 14.
196 **54** 4 c. slate-violet, red, yellow and orange 15 10
197 **55** 25 c. orange-yellow, violet and deep olive 35 10
198 **56** $1 black, bright purple and orange 1·10 2·25
196/8 . . . . *Set of* 3 1·40 2·25

ASSOCIATED STATEHOOD

57 State Flag and Maps

(Des W. D. Cribbs. Photo Harrison)

1967 (27 Feb). *Statehood. T* **57** *and similar horiz designs. Multicoloured. W* w **12** (*sideways**). *P* 14.
199 4 c. Type **57** 10 10
200 15 c. State Flag 10 20
w. Wmk Crown to right of CA . . . . 1·75
201 25 c. Premier's Office and State Flag . . 10 25
202 35 c. As 15 c. 15 25
199/202 . . . . . . *Set of* 4 30 65
*The normal sideways watermark shows Crown to left of CA, *as seen from the back of the stamp.*

60 Gilbert Memorial Church

(Des G. Drummond (from sketches by W. D. Cribbs). Photo Harrison)

1967 (18 May). *Attainment of Autonomy by the Methodist Church. T* **60** *and similar horiz designs. W* w **12.** *P* 14½ × 13½.
203 4 c. black and orange-red 10 10
204 25 c. black and bright green 15 15
205 35 c. black and bright blue 15 15
203/5 . . . . *Set of* 3 30 30
Designs:—25 c. Nathaniel Gilbert's House; 35 c. Caribbean and Central American map.

63 Coat of Arms

64 *Susan Constant* (settlers' ship)

(Des V. Whiteley (from sketches by W. D. Cribbs). Photo Harrison)

1967 (21 July). *300th Anniv of Treaty of Breda and Grant of New Arms. W* w **12** (*sideways**). *P* 14½×14.

206 **63** 15 c. multicoloured 15 10
w. Wmk Crown to right of CA .. 10·00 10·00
207 – 35 c. multicoloured 15 10

*The normal sideways watermark shows Crown to left of CA, *as seen from the back of the stamp.*

(Des and recess B.W.)

1967 (14 Dec). *300th Anniv of Barbuda Settlement. T* **64** *and similar horiz design. W* w **12.** *P* 11½ × 11.

208 **64** 4 c. deep ultramarine 30 10
209 – 6 c. purple 30 90
210 **64** 25 c. emerald 40 20
211 – 35 c. black 40 25
208/11 .. .. *Set of* 4 1·25 1·25

Design:—6, 35 c. Blaeu's map of 1665.

66 Tracking Station

70 Limbo-dancing

(Des G. Vasarhelyi. Photo Harrison)

1968 (29 Mar). *N.A.S.A. Apollo Project. Inauguration of Dow Hill Tracking Station. T* **66** *and similar vert designs in deep blue, orange-yellow and black. W* w **12** (*sideways*). *P* 14½ × 14.

212 4 c. Type **66** 10 10
213 15 c. Antenna and spacecraft taking off .. 20 10
214 25 c. Spacecraft approaching Moon 20 10
215 50 c. Re-entry of space capsule 30 30
212/15 .. .. *Set of* 4 70 40

(Des and photo Harrison)

1968 (1 July). *Tourism. T* **70** *and similar horiz designs. Multicoloured. W* w **12.** *P* 14½ × 14.

216 ½ c. Type **70** 10 10
217 15 c. Water-skiing and bathers 30 10
218 25 c. Yachts and beach 40 10
219 35 c. Underwater swimming 40 10
220 50 c. Type **70** 60 85
216/20 .. .. *Set of* 5 1·50 1·10

74 Old Harbour in 1768

(Des R. Granger Barrett. Recess B.W.)

1968 (31 Oct). *Opening of St. John's Deep Water Harbour. T* **74** *and similar horiz designs. W* w **12.** *P* 13.

221 2 c. light blue and carmine 10 30
222 15 c. light yellow-green and sepia 35 10
223 25 c. olive-yellow and blue 40 10
224 35 c. salmon and emerald 50 10
225 $1 black .. .. 90 1·75
221/5 .. .. *Set of* 5 2·00 2·00

Designs:—15 c. Old Harbour in 1829; 25 c. Freighter and chart of New Harbour; 35 c. New Harbour, 1968; $1, Type **74**.

78 Parliament Buildings

(Des R. Granger Barrett. Photo Harrison)

1969 (3 Feb). *Tercentenary of Parliament. T* **78** *and similar square designs. Multicoloured. W* w **12** (*sideways*). *P* 12½.

226 4 c. Type **78** 10 10
227 15 c. Antigua Mace and bearer 20 10
228 25 c. House of Representatives' Room .. 20 10
229 50 c. Coat of arms and Seal of Antigua .. 30 1·10
226/9 .. .. *Set of* 4 70 1·25

82 Freight Transport

(Des Jennifer Toombs. Litho D.L.R.)

1969 (14 Apr). *1st Anniv of CARIFTA (Caribbean Free Trade Area). T* **82** *and similar design. W* w **12** (*sideways on* 4 *c.,* 15 *c*). *P* 13.

230 4 c. black and reddish purple 10 10
231 15 c. black and turquoise-blue 20 30
232 25 c. chocolate, black and yellow-ochre .. 25 30
233 35 c. chocolate, black and yellow-brown .. 25 30
230/3 .. .. *Set of* 4 65 85

Designs: *Horiz*—4, 15 c. Type **82**. *Vert*—25, 35 c. Crate of cargo.

84 Island of Redonda (Chart)

(Des R. Granger Barrett. Photo Enschedé)

1969 (1 Aug). *Centenary of Redonda Phosphate Industry. T* **84** *and similar horiz design. W* w **12** (*sideways*). *P* 13 × 13½.

249 15 c. Type **84** 20 10
250 25 c. Redonda from the sea 20 10
251 50 c. Type **84** 45 75
249/51 .. .. *Set of* 3 75 80

86 "The Adoration of the Magi" (Marcillat)

20¢

(**88**)

(Des adapted by V. Whiteley. Litho Enschedé)

1969 (15 Oct). *Christmas. Stained-glass Windows. T* **86** *and similar vert design. Multicoloured. W* w **12** (*sideways**). *P* 13×14.

252 6 c. Type **86** 10 10
253 10 c. "The Nativity" (unknown German artist, 15th-century) 10 10
254 35 c. Type **86** 25 10
255 50 c. As 10 c. 50 40
w. Wmk Crown to right of CA .. .. 13·00
252/5 .. .. *Set of* 4 80 55

*The normal sideways watermark shows Crown to left of CA, *as seen from the back of the stamp.*

1970 (2 Jan). *No.* 189 *surch with T* **88**.

256 20 c. on 25 c. slate-blue and sepia 10 10

89 Coat of Arms

90 Sikorsky S-38 Flying Boat

(Des and photo Harrison)

1970 (30 Jan)–**73.** *Coil Stamps. W* w **12.** *P* 14½×14.

A. *Chalk-surfaced paper. Wmk upright* (30.1.70)

257A **89** 5 c. blue 10 10
258A 10 c. emerald 10 15
259A 25 c. crimson 20 25
257A/9A .. .. *Set of* 3 35 45

B. *Glazed paper. Wmk sideways* (8.3.73)

257B **89** 5 c. blue .. .. 1·00 1·50
258B 10 c. emerald .. .. 1·10 1·50
259B 75 c. crimson .. .. 1·75 2·00
257B/9B .. .. *Set of* 3 3·50 4·50

For these stamps with watermark W w **14**, see Nos. 541*a/c*.

(Des R. Granger Barrett. Litho J.W.)

1970 (16 Feb). *40th Anniv of Antiguan Air Services. T* **90** *and similar designs. Multicoloured. W* w **12** (*sideways*). *P* 14½.

260 5 c. Type **90** 50 10
261 20 c. Dornier Do-X flying boat .. .. 1·25 10
262 35 c. Hawker Siddeley H.S. 748 .. .. 1·50 10
263 50 c. Douglas C-124C Globemaster II .. 1·60 1·50
264 75 c. Vickers Super VC-10 .. .. 1·75 2·00
260/4 .. .. *Set of* 5 6·00 3·50

91 Dickens and Scene from *Nicholas Nickleby*

(Des Jennifer Toombs. Litho Walsall)

1970 (19 May). *Death Centenary of Charles Dickens. T* **91** *an similar horiz designs. W* w **12** (*sideways*). *P* 14.

265 5 c. bistre, sepia and black 10
266 20 c. light turquoise-blue, sepia and black .. 20
267 35 c. violet-blue, sepia and black 30
268 $1 rosine, sepia and black 75
265/8 .. .. *Set of* 4 1·25

Designs:—20 c. Dickens and Scene from *Pickwick Papers*; 35 Dickens and Scene from *Oliver Twist*; $1 Dickens and Scene fro *David Copperfield*.

92 Carib Indian and War Canoe

93 "The Small Passion" (detail) (Dürer)

(Des J.W. Litho Questa)

1970 (19 Aug)–**75.** *Horiz designs as T* **92**. *Multicoloure Toned paper. W* w **12** (*sideways**). *P* 14.

269 ½ c. Type **92** 10 5
270 1 c. Columbus and *Nina* 30 7
271 2 c. Sir Thomas Warner's emblem and *Concepcion* .. .. 40 1·2
a. Whiter paper (20.10.75) .. .. 1·50 3·2
272 3 c. Viscount Hood and H.M.S. *Barfleur* .. 40 1·0
w. Wmk Crown to right of CA .. .. 2·75 2·7
273 4 c. Sir George Rodney and H.M.S. *Formidable* .. .. 40 1·2
274 5 c. Nelson and H.M.S. *Boreas* 50 4
275 6 c. William IV and H.M.S. *Pegasus* .. 50 1·5
276 10 c. "Blackbeard" and pirate ketch .. 65 2
277 15 c. Captain Collingwood and H.M.S. *Pelican* .. .. 3·50 1·0
278 20 c. Nelson and H.M.S. *Victory* .. .. 1·25 4
279 25 c. *Solent I* (paddle-steamer) .. .. 1·25 4
280 35 c. George V (when Prince George) and H.M.S. *Canada* (screw corvette) .. 1·75 8
281 50 c. H.M.S. *Renown* (battle cruiser) .. 5·00 3·2
282 75 c. *Federal Maple* (freighter) .. .. 7·00 5·5
283 $1 *Sol Quest* (yacht) and class emblem 7·00 2·0
284 $2.50, H.M.S. *London* (destroyer) .. 7·00 7·5
285 $5 *Pathfinder* (tug) .. .. .. 7·00 7·5
269/85 .. .. *Set of* 17 38·00 32·0

*The normal sideways watermark shows Crown to left of C *as seen from the back of the stamp.*

See also Nos. 323/34 and 426

(Des G. Drummond. Recess and litho D.L.R.)

1970 (28 Oct). *Christmas. T* **93** *and similar vert design. W* w **12** *P* 13½ × 14.

286 **93** 3 c. black and turquoise-blue 10 1
287 – 10 c. dull purple and pink 10 1
288 **93** 35 c. black and rose-red 30 1
289 – 50 c. black and lilac 45 5
286/9 .. .. *Set of* 4 80 6

Design:—10 c., 50 c. "Adoration of the Magi" (detail) (Dürer).

94 4th King's Own Regt, 1759

95 Market Woman casting Vote

(Des P. W. Kingsland. Litho Questa)

1970 (14 Dec). *Military Uniforms (1st series). T* **94** *and simila vert designs. Multicoloured. W* w **12.** *P* 14 × 13½.

290 ½ c. Type **94** 10
291 10 c. 4th West India Regiment, 1804 50
292 20 c. 60th Regiment, The Royal American, 1809 .. .. 1·00
293 35 c. 93rd Regiment, Sutherland Highlanders, 1826–34 .. .. 1·40 1
294 75 c. 3rd West India Regiment, 1851 .. .. 2·25 2·5
290/4 .. .. *Set of* 5 4·75 2·5
MS295 128 × 146 mm. Nos. 290/4 . .. .. 7·50 11·0

See also Nos. 303/8, 313/18, 353/8 and 380/5.

(Des Sylvia Goaman. Photo Harrison)

1971 (1 Feb). *20th Anniversary of Adult Suffrage. T* **95** *and similar vert designs.* W w **12** *(sideways). P* 14½ × 14.

No.	Description	Mint	Used
296	5 c. brown	10	10
297	20 c. deep olive	10	10
298	35 c. reddish purple	10	10
299	50 c. ultramarine	15	30
296/9	*Set of* 4	30	40

People voting:—20 c. Executive; 35 c. Housewife; 50 c. Artisan.

96 "The Last Supper"

97 "Madonna and Child" (detail, Veronese)

(Des Jennifer Toombs. Litho Questa)

1971 (7 Apr). *Easter. Works by Dürer. T* **96** *and similar vert designs.* W w **12.** *P* 14 × 13½.

No.	Description	Mint	Used
300	5 c. black, grey and scarlet	10	10
301	35 c. black, grey and bluish violet	10	10
302	75 c. black, grey and gold	20	30
300/2	*Set of* 3	30	35

Designs:—35 c. The Crucifixion; 75 c. The Resurrection.

(Des J. W. Litho Questa)

1971 (12 July). *Military Uniforms (2nd series). Multicoloured designs as T* **94.** W w **12.** *P* 13½.

No.	Description	Mint	Used
303	½ c. Private, 12th Regiment, The Suffolk (1704)	10	10
	w. Wmk inverted	50·00	
304	10 c. Grenadier, 38th Regiment, South Staffs (1751)	35	15
305	20 c. Light Company, 5th Regiment, Royal Northumberland Fusiliers (1778)	65	20
306	35 c. Private, 48th Regiment, The Northamptonshire (1793)	1·10	25
307	75 c. Private, 15th Regiment, East Yorks (1805)	2·25	4·00
	w. Wmk inverted	3·25	
303/7	*Set of* 5	4·00	4·25
MS308	127×144 mm. Nos. 303/7	5·50	6·50

(Des Jennifer Toombs. Litho Questa)

1971 (4 Oct). *Christmas. T* **97** *and similar vert design. Multicoloured.* W w **12.** *P* 13½.

No.	Description	Mint	Used
309	3 c. Type **97**	10	10
310	5 c. "Adoration of the Shepherds" (detail, Veronese)	10	10
311	35 c. Type **97**	25	10
312	50 c. As 5 c.	40	30
309/12	*Set of* 4	70	40

(Des J.W. Litho Questa)

1972 (1 July). *Military Uniforms (3rd series). Multicoloured designs as T* **94.** W w **12** *(sideways). P* 14 × 13½.

No.	Description	Mint	Used
313	½ c. Battalion Company Officer, 25th Foot, 1815	10	10
314	10 c. Sergeant, 14th Foot, 1837	85	10
315	20 c. Private, 67th Foot, 1853	1·60	15
316	35 c. Officer, Royal Artillery, 1854	1·90	20
317	75 c. Private, 29th Foot, 1870	2·25	3·75
313/17	*Set of* 5	6·00	3·75
MS318	125 × 141 mm. Nos. 313/17	7·00	8·50

98 Reticulated Cowrie-Helmet

(Des J.W. Litho Questa)

1972 (1 Aug). *Shells. T* **98** *and similar horiz designs. Multicoloured.* W w **12** *(sideways). P* 14½.

No.	Description	Mint	Used
319	3 c. Type **98**	50	10
320	5 c. Measled Cowrie	50	10
321	35 c. West Indian Fighting Conch	1·40	15
322	50 c. Hawk-wing Conch	1·60	2·75
319/22	*Set of* 4	3·50	2·75

1972 (2 Nov)–**74.** *As No. 269 etc., but* W w **12** *(upright) and whiter paper.*

No.	Description	Mint	Used
323	½ c. Type **92**	20	40
324	1 c. Columbus and *Nina* (2.1.74)	30	80
325	3 c. Viscount Hood and H.M.S. *Barfleur* (2.1.74)	35	70
326	4 c. Sir George Rodney and H.M.S. *Formidable* (2.1.74)	35	1·50
327	5 c. Nelson and H.M.S. *Boreas* (2.1.74)	50	40
328	6 c. William IV and H.M.S. *Pegasus* (2.1.74)	50	2·25
329	10 c. "Blackbeard" and pirate ketch (2.1.74)	55	60
330	15 c. Collingwood and H.M.S. *Pelican*	7·50	90
	w. Wmk inverted	65·00	
331	75 c. *Federal Maple* (freighter)	7·50	3·00
332	$1 *Sol Quest* (yacht) and class emblem	3·00	1·75
333	$2.50, H.M.S. *London* (destroyer) (25.2.74)	2·75	6·50
334	$5 *Pathfinder* (tug)	4·00	11·00
323/34	*Set of* 12	25·00	26·00

See also No. 426.

99 St. John's Cathedral, Side View

(Des J.W. Litho Format)

1972 (6 Nov). *Christmas and 125th Anniversary of St. John's Cathedral. T* **99** *and similar horiz designs. Multicoloured.* W w **12.** *P* 14.

No.	Description	Mint	Used
335	35 c. Type **99**	20	10
336	50 c. Cathedral interior	25	25
337	75 c. St. John's Cathedral	30	60
335/7	*Set of* 3	65	80
MS338	165 × 102 mm. Nos. 335/7. P 15	65	1·00

100 Floral Pattern

(Des (from photograph by D. Groves) and photo Harrison)

1972 (20 Nov). *Royal Silver Wedding. Multicoloured; background colour given.* W w **12.** *P* 14 × 14½.

No.	Description	Mint	Used
339 **100**	20 c. bright blue	15	15
340	35 c. turquoise-blue	15	15
	w. Wmk inverted	13·00	

101 Batsman and Map

(Des G. Vasarhelyi. Litho Questa)

1972 (15 Dec). *50th Anniv of Rising Sun Cricket Club. T* **101** *and similar horiz designs. Multicoloured.* W w **12.** *P* 13½.

No.	Description	Mint	Used
341	5 c. Type **101**	55	15
	w. Wmk inverted	3·50	
342	35 c. Batsman and wicket-keeper	1·25	40
343	$1 Club badge	2·25	3·00
341/3	*Set of* 3	3·50	3·25
MS344	88×130 mm. Nos. 341/3	4·50	7·50
	w. Wmk inverted	60·00	

102 Yacht and Map

103 "Episcopal Coat of Arms"

(Des M. and G. Shamir. Litho Format)

1972 (29 Dec). *Sailing Week and Inauguration of Tourist Office, New York. T* **102** *and similar square designs. Multicoloured.* W w **12.** *P* 14½.

No.	Description	Mint	Used
345	35 c. Type **102**	15	10
346	50 c. Yachts	20	15
347	75 c. St. John's G.P.O.	25	25
348	$1 Statue of Liberty	25	25
345/8	*Set of* 4	75	65
MS349	100 × 94 mm. Nos. 346, 348	75	1·25

(Des PAD Studio. Litho Format)

1973 (16 Apr). *Easter. T* **103** *and similar vert designs showing stained-glass windows from St. John's Cathedral. Multicoloured.* W w **12** *(sideways*). P* 13½.

No.	Description	Mint	Used
350	5 c. Type **103**	10	10
351	35 c. "The Crucifixion"	15	10
352	75 c. "Arms of 1st Bishop of Antigua"	25	30
	w. Wmk Crown to right of CA	12·00	
350/2	*Set of* 3	40	35

*The normal sideways watermark shows Crown to left of CA on the 75 c., and to right of CA on the others, *as seen from the back of the stamp.*

(Des J.W. Litho Questa)

1973 (1 July). *Military Uniforms (4th series). Multicoloured designs as T* **94.** W w **12** *(sideways*). P* 13½.

No.	Description	Mint	Used
353	½ c. Private, Zacharia Tiffin's Regiment of Foot, 1701	10	10
354	10 c. Private, 63rd Regiment of Foot, 1759	40	10
355	20 c. Light Company Officer, 35th Regiment of Foot, 1828	60	15
	w. Wmk Crown to right of CA	7·50	
356	35 c. Private, 2nd West India Regiment, 1853	85	15
357	75 c. Sergeant, 49th Regiment, 1858	1·50	1·25
353/7	*Set of* 5	3·00	1·50
MS358	127×145 mm. Nos. 353/7	3·75	3·25

*The normal sideways watermark shows Crown to right of CA on the 35 and 75 c., and to left of CA on the others, *as seen from the back of the stamp.*

104 Butterfly Costumes

(Des G. Vasarhelyi. Litho Format)

1973 (30 July). *Carnival. T* **104** *and similar horiz designs. Multicoloured. P* 13½.

No.	Description	Mint	Used
359	5 c. Type **104**	10	10
360	20 c. Carnival street scene	15	10
361	35 c. Carnival troupe	20	10
362	75 c. Carnival Queen	30	30
359/62	*Set of* 4	65	35
MS363	134 × 95 mm. Nos. 359/62	65	1·00

105 "Virgin of the Milk Porridge" (Gerard David)

106 Princess Anne and Captain Mark Phillips

(Des G. Vasarhelyi. Litho Format)

1973 (15 Oct). *Christmas. T* **105** *and similar vert designs. Multicoloured. P* 14½.

No.	Description	Mint	Used
364	3 c. Type **105**	10	10
365	5 c. "Adoration of the Magi" (Stomer)	10	10
366	20 c. "The Granducal Madonna" (Raphael)	15	10
367	35 c. "Nativity with God the Father and Holy Ghost" (Battista)	20	10
368	$1 "Madonna and Child" (Murillo)	40	60
364/8	*Set of* 5	75	70
MS369	130× 128 mm. Nos. 364/8	1·10	1·75

(Des G. Drummond. Litho Format)

1973 (14 Nov). *Royal Wedding. T* **106** *and similar horiz design. P* 13½.

No.	Description	Mint	Used
370 **106**	35 c. multicoloured	10	10
371 –	$2 multicoloured	25	25
MS372	78 × 100 mm. Nos. 370/1	50	40

The $2 is as T **106** but has a different border.

Nos. 370/1 were each issued in small sheets of five stamps and one stamp-size label.

HONEYMOON VISIT

DECEMBER 16th 1973

(107)

1973 (15 Dec). *Honeymoon Visit of Princess Anne and Captain Phillips. Nos. 370/***MS***372 optd with T* **107** *by lithography.**

No.	Description	Mint	Used
373 **106**	35 c. multicoloured	15	10
	a. Typo opt	95	95
374 –	$2 multicoloured	30	30
	a. Typo opt	2·75	2·75
MS375	78 × 100 mm. Nos. 373/4	55	55
	a. Typo opt	8·50	12·00

*The litho overprints can be distinguished from the typo by the latter being less clear, less intense, and showing through on the reverse.

108 Coats of Arms of Antigua and University

(Des PAD Studio. Litho D.L.R.)

1974 (18 Feb). *25th Anniv of University of West Indies. T* **108** *and similar horiz designs. Multicoloured. W* w **12.** *P* 13.
376 5 c. Type **108** 10 10
377 20 c. Extra-mural art 15 10
378 35 c. Antigua campus 20 10
379 75 c. Antigua chancellor 25 35
376/9 . . . . *Set of* 4 55 40

(Des J.W. Litho Questa)

1974 (1 May). *Military Uniforms (5th series). Multicoloured designs as T* **94.** *W* w **12** *(sideways*). P* 13½.
380 ½ c. Officer, 59th Foot, 1797 . . . . . . 10 10
381 10 c. Gunner, Royal Artillery, 1800 . . . . 45 10
 a. Error. Wmk T **55** of Malawi . . . . 60·00
382 20 c. Private, 1st West India Regiment, 1830 70 10
383 35 c. Officer, 92nd Foot, 1843 . . . . . . 85 10
384 75 c. Private, 23rd Foot, 1846 . . . . . . 1·25 2·00
380/4 . . . . *Set of* 5 3·00 2·00
MS385 127 × 145 mm. Nos. 380/4 . . . . . . 3·00 2·50

*The normal sideways watermark shows Crown to right of CA on the 20 c., and to left of CA on the others, *as seen from the back of the stamp.*

109 English Postman, Mailcoach and Westland Dragonfly Helicopter

110 Traditional Player

(Des G. Vasarhelyi. Litho Format)

1974 (15 July). *Centenary of Universal Postal Union. T* **109** *and similar horiz designs. Multicoloured. P* 14½.
386 ½ c. Type **109** 10 10
387 1 c. Bellman, mail steamer *Orinoco* and satellite 10 10
388 2 c. Train guard, post-bus and hydrofoil . . 10 10
389 5 c. Swiss messenger, Wells Fargo coach and Concorde 60 30
390 20 c. Postilion, Japanese postmen and carrier pigeon 35 10
391 35 c. Antiguan postman, Sikorsky S-88 flying boat and tracking station . . 45 15
392 $1 Medieval courier, American express train and Boeing 747-100 . . . . 1·75 1·60
386/92 . . . . *Set of* 7 3·00 2·00
MS393 141×164 mm. Nos. 386/92 plus label. P 13 . . . . 3·50 2·50

On the ½ c. "English" is spelt "Enlish", and on the 2 c. "Postal" is spelt "Fostal".

(Des C. Abbott. Litho Questa)

1974 (1 Aug). *Antiguan Steel Bands. T* **110** *and similar designs. W* w **12** *(sideways on 5 c., 75 c. and* **MS**398*). P* 13.
394 5 c. rose-red, carmine and black 10 10
395 20 c. brown-ochre, chestnut and black 10 10
396 35 c. light sage-green, blue-green and black . . 10 10
397 75 c. dull blue, dull ultramarine and black . . 20 50
394/7 . . . . *Set of* 4 30 60
MS398 115 × 108 mm. Nos. 394/7 . . . . . . 35 65

Designs: *Horiz*—20 c. Traditional band; 35 c. Modern band. *Vert*—75 c. Modern player.

111 Footballers

EARTHQUAKE
RELIEF
(112)

(Des G. Vasarhelyi. Litho Format)

1974 (23 Sept). *World Cup Football Championships. T* **111** *and similar vert designs showing footballers. P* 14½.
399 **111** 5 c. multicoloured 10 10
400 – 35 c. multicoloured 15 10
401 – 75 c. multicoloured 30 30
402 – $1 multicoloured 35 40
399/402 . . . . *Set of* 4 70 70
MS403 135 × 130 mm. Nos. 399/402 plus two labels. P 13 . . . . 85 90

Nos. 399/402 were each issued in small sheets of five stamps and one stamp-size label.

1974 (16 Oct). *Earthquake Relief Fund. Nos.* 400/2 *and* 397 *optd with T* **112**, *No.* 397 *surch also.*
404 35 c. multicoloured 20 10
405 75 c. multicoloured 30 25
406 $1 multicoloured 40 30
407 $5 on 75 c. dull blue, dull ultram & black 1·25 2·00
404/7 . . . . *Set of* 4 2·00 2·40

113 Churchill as Schoolboy and School College Building, Harrow

114 "Madonna of the Trees" (Bellini)

(Des V. Whiteley. Litho Format)

1974 (20 Oct). *Birth Centenary of Sir Winston Churchill. T* **113** *and similar horiz designs. Multicoloured. P* 14½.
408 5 c. Type **113** 15 10
409 35 c. Churchill and St. Paul's Cathedral . . 20 10
410 75 c. Coat of arms and catafalque 25 55
411 $1 Churchill, "reward" notice and South African escape route 40 90
408/11 . . . . *Set of* 4 90 1·50
MS412 107×82 mm. Nos. 408/11. P 13 . . . . 90 1·50

(Des M. Shamir. Litho Format)

1974 (18 Nov). *Christmas. T* **114** *and similar vert designs showing "Madonna and Child" by the artists given. Multicoloured. P* 14½.
413 ½ c. Type **114** 10 10
414 1 c. Raphael 10 10
415 2 c. Van der Weyden 10 10
416 3 c. Giorgione 10 10
417 5 c. Mantegna 10 10
418 20 c. Vivarini 20 10
419 35 c. Montagna 30 10
420 75 c. Lorenzo Costa 55 85
413/20 . . . . *Set of* 8 1·25 1·25
MS421 139 × 126 mm. Nos. 417/20. P 13 . . . . 95 1·40

$10
(115)

116 Carib War Canoe, English Harbour, 1300

1975 (14 Jan). *Nos.* 331 *and* 390/2 *surch as T* **115**.
422 50 c. on 20 c. multicoloured . . . . . . 1·25 1·75
423 $2.50, on 35 c. multicoloured . . . . 3·00 5·00
424 $5 on $1 multicoloured . . . . . . 5·00 7·00
425 $10 on 75 c. multicoloured . . . . . . 4·00 7·50
422/5 . . . . *Set of* 4 12·00 19·00

1975 (21 Jan). *As No.* 334, *but W* w **14** *(sideways).*
426 $5 *Pathfinder* (tug) . . . . 3·75 10·00

(Des G. Drummond. Litho Format)

1975 (17 Mar). *Nelson's Dockyard. T* **116** *and similar horiz designs. Multicoloured. P* 14½.
427 5 c. Type **116** 20 10
428 15 c. Ship of the line, English Harbour, 1770 80 10
429 35 c. H.M.S. *Boreas* at anchor, and Lord Nelson, 1787 . . . . 1·25 15
430 50 c. Yachts during "Sailing Week", 1974 . . 1·25 1·25
431 $1 Yacht Anchorage, Old Dockyard, 1970 . . 1·50 2·00
427/31 . . . . *Set of* 5 4·50 3·25
MS432 130 × 134 mm. As Nos. 427/31, but in larger format, 43 × 28 mm. P 13½ . . . . . . 3·25 2·00

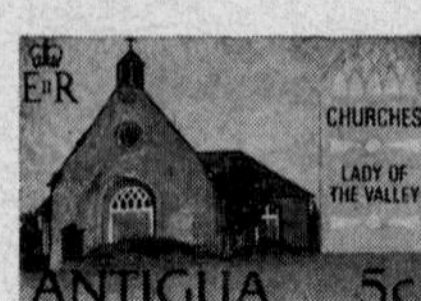

117 Lady of the Valley Church

(Des R. Vigurs. Litho Format)

1975 (19 May). *Antiguan Churches. T* **117** *and similar horiz designs. Multicoloured. P* 14½.
433 5 c. Type **117** 10 10
434 20 c. Gilbert Memorial 10 10
435 35 c. Grace Hill Moravian 15 10
436 50 c. St. Phillips 20 20
437 $1 Ebenezer Methodist 35 50
433/7 . . . . *Set of* 5 65 75
MS438 91 × 101 mm. Nos. 435/7. P 13 . . . . 65 1·25

118 Map of 1721 and Sextant of 1640

(Des PAD Studio. Litho Questa)

1975 (21 July). *Maps of Antigua. T* **118** *and similar horiz designs. Multicoloured. W* w **14** *(sideways). P* 14.
439 5 c. Type **118** 30 15
440 20 c. Map of 1775 and galleon 55 15
441 35 c. Maps of 1775 and 1955 . . . . . . 70 15
442 $1 1973 maps of Antigua and English Harbour . . . . 1·40 2·00
439/42 . . . . *Set of* 4 2·75 2·25
MS443 130 × 89 mm. Nos. 439/42 . . . . . . 3·00 2·25

119 Scout Bugler

(Des G. Vasarhelyi. Litho Questa)

1975 (26 Aug). *World Scout Jamboree, Norway. T* **119** *and similar horiz designs. Multicoloured. P* 14.
444 15 c. Type **119** 25 15
445 20 c. Scouts in camp 30 15
446 35 c. "Lord Baden-Powell" (D. Jagger) . . 50 20
447 $2 Scout dancers from Dahomey . . . . 1·50 2·00
444/7 . . . . *Set of* 4 2·25 2·25
MS448 145 × 107 mm. Nos. 444/7 . . . . . . 3·25 3·50

120 *Eurema elathea*

121 "Madonna and Child" (Correggio)

(Des. G. Vasarhelyi. Litho Questa)

1975 (30 Oct). *Butterflies. T* **120** *and similar horiz designs. Multicoloured. P* 14.
449 ½ c. Type **120** 10 10
450 1 c. *Danaus plexippus* 10 10
451 2 c. *Phoebis philea* 10 10
452 5 c. *Hypolimnas misippus* 20 10
453 20 c. *Eurema proterpia* 75 60
454 35 c. *Battus polydamas* . . . . 1·40 90
455 $2 *Cynthia cardui* . . . . 4·00 7·50
449/55 . . . . *Set of* 7 6·00 8·50
MS456 147×94 mm. Nos 452/5 . . . . . . 6·00 9·50

No. 452 is incorrectly captioned "Marpesia petreus thetys".

(Des G. Vasarhelyi. Litho Questa)

1975 (17 Nov). *Christmas. T* **121** *and similar vert designs showing "Madonna and Child". Multicoloured. P* 14.
457 ½ c. Type **121** 10 10
458 1 c. El Greco 10 10
459 2 c. Dürer 10 10
460 3 c. Antonello 10 10
461 5 c. Bellini 10 10
462 10 c. Dürer *(different)* 10 10
463 35 c. Bellini *(different)* 40 10
464 $2 Dürer *(different)* . . . . 1·00 1·00
457/64 . . . . *Set of* 8 1·50 1·10
MS465 138 × 119 mm. Nos. 461/4 . . . . . . 1·50 1·60

122 Vivian Richards

123 Antillean Crested Hummingbird

(Des G. Vasarhelyi. Litho Format)

75 (15 Dec). *World Cup Cricket Winners. T* **122** *and similar multicoloured designs. P* 13½.

6	5 c. Type **122**	1·25	20
7	35 c. Andy Roberts	2·25	60
8	$2 West Indies team (*horiz*)	4·25	8·00
6/8	*Set of* 3	7·00	8·00

(Des G. Vasarhelyi. Litho Format)

76 (19 Jan)–78. *Various multicoloured designs as T* **123**. *P* 13½ ($2.50, $5 *and* $10) *or* 14½ (*others*). A. *Without imprint* (19.1.76).

9A	½ c. Type **123**	20	50
70A	1 c. Imperial Amazon	30	50
71A	2 c. Zenaida Dove	30	50
72A	3 c. Loggerhead Kingbird	30	60
73A	4 c. Red-necked Pigeon	30	60
74A	5 c. Rufous-throated Solitaire	1·40	10
75A	6 c. Orchid Tree	30	60
76A	10 c. Bougainvillea	30	10
77A	15 c. Geiger Tree	35	10
78A	20 c. Flamboyant	35	35
79A	25 c. Hibiscus	40	15
80A	35 c. Flame of the Wood	40	40
81A	50 c. Cannon at Fort James	55	60
82A	75 c. Premier's Office	60	75
83A	$1 Potworks Dam	75	90
84A	$2.50, Irrigation Scheme, Diamond Estate (44×28 *mm*)	1·50	3·50
85A	$5 Government House (44×28 *mm*)	3·00	5·50
86A	$10 Coolidge Airport (44×28 *mm*)	3·50	6·50
9A/86A	*Set of* 18	13·00	20·00

B. *With imprint date at foot* (1978)

69B	½ c. Type **123**	50	90
70B	1 c. Imperial Amazon	1·25	90
71B	2 c. Zenaida Dove	1·25	90
72B	3 c. Loggerhead Kingbird	1·25	90
73B	4 c. Red-necked Pigeon	1·40	90
74B	5 c. Rufous-throated Solitaire	1·75	45
75B	6 c. Orchid Tree	30	1·00
76B	10 c. Bougainvillea	30	30
77B	15 c. Geiger Tree	30	30
78B	20 c. Flamboyant	30	75
79B	25 c. Hibiscus	35	50
80B	35 c. Flame of the Wood	35	50
81B	50 c. Cannon at Fort James	50	70
82B	75 c. Premier's Office	55	80
83B	$1 Potworks Dam	75	90
84B	$2.50 Irrigation Scheme, Diamond Estate (44×28 *mm*)	3·00	6·00
85B	$5 Government House (44×28 *mm*)	2·00	6·50
86B	$10 Coolidge Airport (44×28 *mm*)	8·50	9·50
69B/86B	*Set of* 18	22·00	29·00

Nos. 469A, 472B, 473A, 474B, 475A/B, 476A/B, 477A, 478B, 79A/B, 480B, 481A/B, 482A/B, 483A, 484A/B, 485A/B and 86A/B exist imperforate from stock dispersed by the liquidator f Format International Security Printers Ltd.

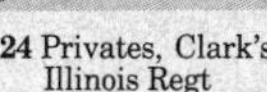

124 Privates, Clark's Illinois Regt

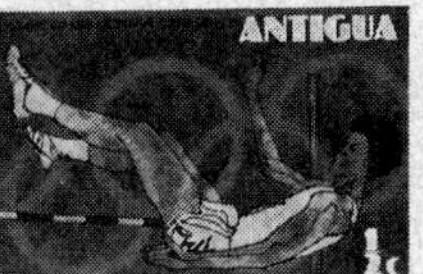

125 High Jump

(Des J.W. Litho Format)

976 (17 Mar). *Bicentenary of American Revolution. T* **124** *and similar vert designs. Multicoloured. P* 14½.

87	½ c. Type **124**	10	10
88	1 c. Riflemen, Pennsylvania Militia	10	10
89	2 c. Powder horn	10	10
	a. Imperf (pair)	£160	
90	5 c. Water bottle	10	10
91	35 c. American flags	50	10
92	$1 *Montgomery* (American brig)	1·25	40
93	$5 *Ranger* (privateer sloop)	2·50	2·75
487/93	*Set of* 7	4·00	3·00
MS494	71×84 mm. $2.50 Congress flag. P 13	1·25	1·75

(Des J.W. Litho Format)

976 (17 July). *Olympic Games, Montreal. T* **125** *and similar horiz designs. P* 14½.

95	½ c. orange-brown, bistre-yellow and black	10	10
96	1 c. light reddish violet, bright blue & black	10	10
97	2 c. light green and black	10	10
98	15 c. bright blue and black	15	10
99	30 c. olive-brown, yellow-ochre and black	20	15
00	$1 red-orange, Venetian red and black	40	40
01	$2 rosine and black	60	80
95/501	*Set of* 7	1·25	1·40
MS502	88×138 mm. Nos. 498/501. P 13½	1·75	2·25

Designs:—1 c. Boxing; 2 c. Pole vault; 15 c. Swimming; 30 c. Running; $1 Cycling; $2 Shot put.

126 Water Skiing

(Des J.W. Litho Questa)

1976 (26 Aug). *Water Sports. T* **126** *and similar horiz designs. Multicoloured. P* 14.

503	½ c. Type **126**	10	10
504	1 c. Sailing	10	10
505	2 c. Snorkeling	10	10
506	20 c. Deep sea fishing	15	10
507	50 c. Scuba diving	35	35
508	$2 Swimming	1·00	1·25
503/8	*Set of* 6	1·40	1·60
MS509	89 × 114 mm. Nos. 506/8	1·40	1·75

127 French Angelfish

128 The Annunciation

(Des G. Drummond. Litho Questa)

1976 (4 Oct). *Fishes. T* **127** *and similar horiz designs. Multicoloured. W w* **14** (*sideways*). *P* 13½.

510	15 c. Type **127**	50	15
511	30 c. Yellow-finned Grouper	75	30
512	50 c. Yellow-tailed Snapper	95	50
513	90 c. Shy Hamlet	1·25	80
510/13	*Set of* 4	3·00	1·60

(Des J.W. Litho Walsall)

1976 (15 Nov). *Christmas. T* **128** *and similar vert designs. Multicoloured. P* 13½.

514	8 c. Type **128**	10	10
515	10 c. The Holy Family	10	10
516	15 c. The Magi	10	10
517	50 c. The Shepherds	20	25
518	$1 Epiphany scene	30	50
514/18	*Set of* 5	60	75

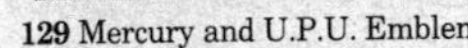

129 Mercury and U.P.U. Emblem

130 Royal Family

(Des BG Studio. Litho Questa)

1976 (28 Dec). *Special Events,* 1976. *T* **129** *and similar horiz designs. Multicoloured. P* 14.

519	½ c. Type **129**	10	10
520	1 c. Alfred Nobel	10	10
521	10 c. Space satellite	30	10
522	50 c. Viv Richards and Andy Roberts	3·50	1·75
523	$1 Bell and telephones	1·00	2·00
524	$2 Yacht *Freelance*	2·25	4·00
519/24	*Set of* 6	6·50	7·00
MS525	127 × 101 mm. Nos. 521/4	7·50	11·00

Events:—½ c. 25th Anniv of U.N. Postal Administration; 1 c. 75th Anniv of Nobel Prize; 10 c. "Viking" Space Mission; 50 c. Cricketing achievements; $1 Telephone Centenary; $2 "Operation Sail", U.S. Bicentennial.

(Des J. W. Litho Questa (Nos. 526/31); Manufactured by Walsall (Nos. 532/3))

1977 (7 Feb–26 Sept). *Silver Jubilee. T* **130** *and similar vert designs. Multicoloured.* (*a*) *Sheet stamps. P* 14 (7 Feb).

526	10 c. Type **130**	10	10
527	30 c. Royal Visit, 1966	10	10
528	50 c. The Queen enthroned	15	15
529	90 c. The Queen after Coronation	15	25
530	$2.50, Queen and Prince Charles	30	55
526/30	*Set of* 5	60	95
MS531	116×78 mm. $5 Queen and Prince Philip	65	85
	a. Error. Imperf	£350	

(*b*) *Booklet stamps. Roul* 5 × *imperf* (50 c.) *or imperf* ($5).* *Self-adhesive* (26 Sept)

532	50 c. Design as No. 529 (24 × 42 *mm*)	35	60
	a. Booklet pane of 6	1·75	
533	$5 Design as stamp from No. **MS**531 (24 × 42 *mm*)	2·00	3·50
	a. Booklet pane of 1	2·00	

*No. 532 was separated by various combinations of rotary knife (giving a straight edge) and roulette. No. 533 exists only with straight edges.

Stamps as Nos. 526/30 but perforated 11½ × 12, come from sheets of 5 stamps and 1 label. These were not placed on sale by the Antigua Post Office.

131 Making Camp

132 Carnival Costume

(Des J.W. Litho Questa)

1977 (23 May). *Caribbean Scout Jamboree, Jamaica. T* **131** *and similar horiz designs. Multicoloured. P* 14.

534	½ c. Type **131**	10	10
535	1 c. Hiking	10	10
536	2 c. Rock-climbing	10	10
537	10 c. Cutting logs	15	10
538	30 c. Map and sign reading	40	10
539	50 c. First aid	65	25
540	$2 Rafting	1·75	2·25
534/40	*Set of* 7	2·75	2·50
MS541	127 × 114 mm. Nos. 538/40	3·75	3·75

1977. *Coil Stamps. As Nos.* 257/9, *but W w* **14** (*inverted on* 10 *c.*). *P* 14½×14.

541*a* **89**	5 c. blue	5·00	
541*b*	10 c. emerald	—	50
541*c*	25 c. crimson	9·00	

(Des C. Abbott. Litho Walsall)

1977 (18 July). *21st Anniv of Carnival. T* **132** *and similar vert designs. Multicoloured. P* 14.

542	10 c. Type **132**	10	10
543	30 c. Carnival Queen	20	10
544	50 c. Butterfly costume	25	15
545	90 c. Queen of the band	35	25
546	$1 Calypso King and Queen	35	30
542/6	*Set of* 5	1·10	70
MS547	140×120 mm. Nos. 542/6	1·10	1·60

ROYAL VISIT
28th OCTOBER 1977

(**133**)

134 "Virgin and Child Enthroned" (Tura)

1977 (17 Oct). *Royal Visit. Nos.* 526/531 *optd with T* **133**. *P* 14.

548	10 c. Type **130**	10	10
549	30 c. Royal Visit, 1966	10	10
550	50 c. The Queen enthroned	15	10
551	90 c. The Queen after Coronation	25	20
552	$2.50, Queen and Prince Charles	45	35
548/52	*Set of* 5	80	65
MS553	116 × 78 mm. $5 Queen and Prince Philip	80	1·00
	a. Opt double	50·00	

Nos. 548/52 also exist perf 11½×12 (*Price for set of* 5 80*p mint or used*) from additional sheetlets of five stamps and one label.

(Des M. Shamir. Litho Questa)

1977 (21 Nov). *Christmas. T* **134** *and similar vert designs showing "Virgin and Child" by the artists given. Multicoloured. P* 14.

554	½ c. Type **134**	10	10
555	1 c. Crivelli	10	10
556	2 c. Lotto	10	10
557	8 c. Pontormo	15	10
558	10 c. Tura (*different*)	15	10
559	25 c. Lotto (*different*)	30	10
560	$2 Crivelli (*different*)	85	60
554/60	*Set of* 7	1·50	75
MS561	144 × 118 mm. Nos. 557/60	1·50	2·25

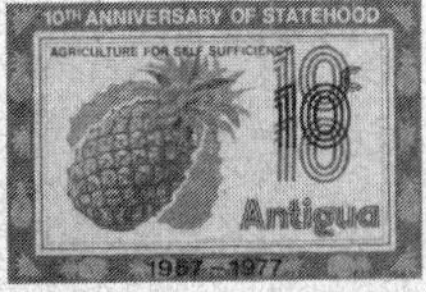

135 Pineapple

(Des and litho J.W.)

1977 (29 Dec). *Tenth Anniv of Statehood. T* **135** *and similar horiz designs. Multicoloured. P* 13.

562	10 c. Type **135**	10	10
563	15 c. State flag	10	10
564	50 c. Police band	2·00	80
565	90 c. Premier V. C. Bird	55	80
566	$2 State Coat of Arms	90	1·40
562/6	*Set of* 5	3·25	2·75
MS567	126 × 99 mm. Nos. 563/6. P 14	3·25	2·75

136 Wright Glider III, 1902

(Des PAD Studio. Litho Questa)

1978 (23 Mar). *75th Anniv of Powered Flight. T* **136** *and similar multicoloured designs. P* 14.
568 ½ c. Type **136** 10 10
569 1 c. Wright Flyer I, 1903 .. .. .. 10 10
570 2 c. Launch system and engine 10 10
571 10 c. Orville Wright (*vert*) 20 10
572 50 c. Wright Flyer III, 1905 .. .. .. 50 15
573 90 c. Wilbur Wright (*vert*) 75 30
574 $2 Wright Type B, 1910 .. .. .. 1·00 80
568/74 .. .. *Set of* 7 2·25 1·25
MS575 90×75 mm. $2.50, Wright Flyer I on launch system .. .. 1·25 2·50

137 Sunfish Regatta

(Des G. Drummond. Litho Format)

1978 (27 Apr). *Sailing Week. T* **137** *and similar horiz designs. Multicoloured. P* 15.
576 10 c. Type **137** 20 10
577 50 c. Fishing and work boat race 35 20
578 90 c. Curtain Bluff race 60 35
579 $2 Power boat rally .. .. 1·10 1·25
576/9 .. .. *Set of* 4 2·00 1·75
MS580 110 × 77 mm. $2.50, Guadeloupe–Antigua race .. .. 1·50 1·75
Nos. 576/9 exist imperforate from stock dispersed by the liquidator of Format International Security Printers Ltd.

138 Queen Elizabeth and Prince Philip

139 Glass Coach

(Des J.W. Litho Questa (Nos. 581/6); Manufactured by Walsall (Nos. 587/9))

1978 (2 June). *25th Anniv of Coronation. Multicoloured. (a) Sheet stamps. Vert designs as T* **138**. *P* 14.
581 10 c. Type **138** 10 10
582 30 c. Crowning 10 10
583 50 c. Coronation procession 15 10
584 90 c. Queen seated in St. Edward's Chair .. 20 15
585 $2.50, Queen wearing Imperial State Crown 40 40
581/5 .. .. *Set of* 5 65 65
MS586 114 × 104 mm. $5 Queen and Prince Philip 80 80

(b) Booklet stamps. Horiz design as T **139** *showing State Coaches. Imperf* ($5) *or roul* 5 × *imperf**. *Self-adhesive.*
587 25 c. Type **139** 15 30
a. Booklet pane. Nos. 587/8 × 3 .. .. 1·25
588 50 c. Irish State Coach 25 50
589 $5 Coronation Coach .. .. .. 1·75 3·00
a. Booklet pane of 1 .. .. .. 1·75
587/9 .. .. *Set of* 3 2·00 3·50
Nos. 581/5 also exist perf 12 (*Price for set of* 5 65*p mint or used*) from additional sheetlets of three stamps and one label. These stamps have changed background colours.
*Nos. 587/8 were separated by various combinations of rotary-knife (giving a straight edge) and roulette. No. 589 exists only with straight edges.

140 Player running with Ball

141 Petrea

(Des BG Studio. Litho Format)

1978 (17 Aug). *World Cup Football Championship, Argentina. T* **140** *and similar vert designs. Multicoloured. P* 14½.
590 10 c. Type **140** 15 10
591 15 c. Players in front of goal 15 10
592 $3 Referee and player .. .. .. 2·00 1·75
590/2 .. .. *Set of* 3 2·00 1·75
MS593 126 × 88 mm. 25 c. Player crouching with ball; 30 c. Players heading ball; 50 c. Players running with ball; $2 Goalkeeper diving. (*All horiz*) .. .. 3·00 2·50
Nos. 590/2 were each printed in small sheets of 6 including 1 *se-tenant* stamp-size label.
Nos. 590/2 exist imperforate from stock dispersed by the liquidator of Format International Security Printers Ltd.

(Des G. Drummond. Litho Questa)

1978 (5 Oct). *Flowers. T* **141** *and similar vert designs. Multicoloured. P* 14.
594 25 c. Type **141** 25 10
595 50 c. Sunflower 35 20
596 90 c. Frangipani 60 30
597 $2 Passion Flower .. .. 1·25 1·10
594/7 .. .. *Set of* 4 2·25 1·40
MS598 118 × 85 mm. $2.50, Hibiscus .. .. 1·40 1·60

142 "St Ildefonso receiving the Chasuble from the Virgin" (Rubens)

143 1d. Stamp of 1863

(Des BG Studio. Litho Questa)

1978 (30 Oct). *Christmas Paintings. T* **142** *and similar horiz designs. Multicoloured. P* 14.
599 8 c. Type **142** 10 10
600 25 c. "The Flight of St. Barbara" (Rubens) .. 20 10
601 $2 "Madonna and Child, with St. Joseph, John the Baptist and Donor" (Sebastiano del Piombo*) 65 55
599/601 .. .. *Set of* 3 80 60
MS602 170 × 113 mm. $4 "The Annunciation" (Rubens) .. .. 1·50 1·75
*The work is incorrectly attributed to Rubens on the stamp.

(Des G. Vasarhelyi. Litho Questa)

1979 (12 Feb). *Death Centenary of Sir Rowland Hill. T* **143** *and similar vert designs. Multicoloured. P* 14.
603 25 c. Type **143** 10 10
604 50 c. Penny Black 20 15
605 $1 Stage-coach and woman posting letter, *circa* 1840 .. .. 30 20
606 $2 Modern mail transport .. .. .. 1·10 60
603/6 .. .. *Set of* 4 1·50 85
MS607 108 × 82 mm. $2.50, Sir Rowland Hill .. 80 90
Nos. 603/6 also exist perf 12 (*Price for set of* 4 £1.75 *mint or used*) from additional sheetlets of five stamps and one label.

144 "The Deposition from the Cross" (painting)

145 Toy Yacht and Child's Hand

(Des BG Studio. Litho Questa)

1979 (15 Mar). *Easter. Works by Dürer. T* **144** *and similar vert designs. P* 14.
608 10 c. multicoloured 10 10
609 50 c. multicoloured 35 20
610 $4 black, magenta and greenish yellow .. 1·25 90
608/10 .. .. *Set of* 3 1·50 1·00
MS611 114 × 99 mm. $2.50, multicoloured .. 80 80
Designs:—50 c., $2.50, "Christ on the Cross—The Passion" (wood engravings) (*both different*); $4 "Man of Sorrows with Hands Raised" (wood engraving).

(Des M. Rubin. Litho Questa)

1979 (9 Apr). *International Year of the Child. T* **145** *and similar vert designs showing toys and hands of children of different races. Multicoloured. P* 14.
612 25 c. Type **145** 10 10
613 50 c. Rocket 25 15
614 90 c. Car 40 25
615 $2 Train .. .. 1·00 90
612/15 .. .. *Set of* 4 1·60 1·25
MS616 80 × 112 mm. $5 Aeroplane .. .. 1·10 1·10

146 Yellow Jack

147 Cook's Birthplace, Marton

(Des P. Powell. Litho Questa)

1979 (14 May). *Fishes. T* **146** *and similar horiz designs. Multi-coloured. P* 14½ × 14.
617 30 c. Type **146** 40 1
618 50 c. Blue-finned Tuna 50 2
619 90 c. Sailfish 75 4
620 $3 Wahoo .. .. 2·25 1·7
617/20 .. .. *Set of* 4 3·50 2·2
MS621 122×75 mm. $2.50, Great Barracuda .. 1·50 1·4

(Des J.W. Litho Questa)

1979 (2 July). *Death Bicentenary of Captain Cook. T* **147** *and similar vert designs. Multicoloured. P* 14.
622 25 c. Type **147** 55 2
623 50 c. H.M.S. *Endeavour* 75 6
624 90 c. Marine chronometer 75 8
625 $3 Landing at Botany Bay .. .. .. 1·60 2·7
622/5 .. .. *Set of* 4 3·25 4·0
MS626 110 × 85 mm. $2.50, H.M.S. *Resolution* .. 2·25 2·0

148 The Holy Family

149 Javelin Throwing

(Des J.W. Litho Questa)

1979 (1 Oct). *Christmas. T* **148** *and similar vert designs. Multi-coloured. P* 14.
627 8 c. Type **148** 10
628 25 c. Virgin and Child on Ass 15
629 50 c. Shepherd and star 30 3
630 $4 Wise Men with gifts .. .. .. 1·10 2·2
627/30 .. .. *Set of* 4 1·50 2·5
MS631 113 × 94 mm. $3 Angel with trumpet. P 12 1·00 1·5

(Des Design Images Inc. Litho Questa)

1980 (18 Feb). *Olympic Games, Moscow. T* **149** *and similar multi-coloured designs. P* 14.
632 10 c. Type **149** 20 1
633 25 c. Running 25 1
634 $1 Pole vaulting 60 5
635 $2 Hurdling .. .. 90 1·5
632/5 .. .. *Set of* 4 1·75 2·0
MS636 127 × 96 mm. $3 Boxing (*horiz*) 80 9

LONDON 1980

150 Mickey Mouse and Aeroplane

(**151**)

(Litho Format)

1980 (24 Mar). *International Year of the Child* (1979). *Walt Disney Cartoon Characters. T* **150** *and similar multicoloured designs showing characters and transport. P* 11.
637 ½ c. Type **150** 10 1
638 1 c. Donald Duck driving car 10 1
639 2 c. Goofy driving taxi 10 1
640 3 c. Mickey Mouse on motorcycle with Minnie Mouse in sidecar 10 1
641 4 c. Huey, Dewey and Louie riding cycle .. 10 1
642 5 c. Grandma Duck, chickens and pickup truck 10 1
643 10 c. Mickey Mouse driving jeep (*vert*) .. 10 1
644 $1 Chip and Dale in sailing boat .. .. 1·75 2·0
645 $4 Donald Duck riding toy train (*vert*) .. 3·75 6·0
637/45 .. .. *Set of* 9 5·50 7·5
MS646 101 × 127 mm. $2.50, Goofy flying biplane. P 14 × 13½ .. .. 4·50 3·2
See also Nos. 671/80.

1980 (6 May). *"London 1980" International Stamp Exhibition. Nos. 603/6 optd with T* **151**. *P* 12.
647 25 c. Type **143** 20 1
648 50 c. Penny Black 30 3
649 $1 Stage-coach and woman posting letter, *circa* 1840 .. .. 55 6
650 $2 Modern mail transport .. .. .. 2·50 2·7
647/50 .. .. *Set of* 4 3·25 3·5

152 "David" (statue, Donatello)

153 Rotary International 75th Anniversary Emblem and Headquarters, U.S.A.

(Des J.W. Litho Questa)

980 (23 June). *Famous Works of Art. T* **152** *and similar multi-coloured designs. P* 13½.

No.	Description	Mint	Used
51	10 c. Type **152**	10	10
52	30 c. "The Birth of Venus" (painting, Sandro Botticelli) (*horiz*)	30	15
53	50 c. "Reclining Couple" (sarcophagus), Cerveteri (*horiz*)	45	40
54	90 c. "The Garden of Earthly Delights" (painting, Hieronymus Bosch) (*horiz*)	65	65
55	$1 "Portinari Altarpiece" (painting, Hugo van der Goes) (*horiz*)	75	75
56	$4 "Eleanora of Toledo and her Son Giovanni de'Medici" (painting, Agnolo Bronzino)	2·25	3·00
51/6	*Set of* 6	4·00	4·50
IS657	99 × 124 mm. $5 "The Holy Family" (painting, Rembrandt)	2·50	2·25

(Des G. Vasarhelyi. Litho Questa)

980 (21 July). *75th Anniv of Rotary International. T* **153** *and similar horiz designs. Multicoloured. P* 14.

No.	Description	Mint	Used
58	30 c. Type **153**	30	30
59	50 c. Rotary anniversary emblem and Antigua Rotary Club banner	40	50
60	90 c. Map of Antigua and Rotary emblem	60	70
61	$3 Paul P. Harris (founder) and Rotary emblem	2·00	3·25
58/61	*Set of* 4	3·00	4·25
IS662	102 × 78 mm. $5 Antiguan flags and Rotary emblems	1·25	2·00

154 Queen Elizabeth the Queen Mother

155 Ringed Kingfisher

(Des G. Vasarhelyi. Litho Questa)

980 (4 Aug). *80th Birthday of Queen Elizabeth the Queen Mother. P* 14.

No.	Description	Mint	Used
63	**154** 10 c. multicoloured	20	10
64	$2.50, multicoloured	1·10	1·75
MS665	68 × 90 mm. **154** $3 multicoloured. P 12	1·25	2·00

(Des Jennifer Toombs. Litho Questa)

980 (3 Nov). *Birds. T* **155** *and similar vert designs. Multi-coloured. P* 14.

No.	Description	Mint	Used
66	10 c. Type **155**	60	25
67	30 c. Plain Pigeon	90	50
68	$1 Green-throated Carib	1·50	1·50
69	$2 Black-necked Stilt	2·00	3·25
66/9	*Set of* 4	4·50	5·00
MS670	73 × 73 mm. $2.50, Roseate Tern	5·50	4·50

(Litho Format)

980 (23 Dec). *Christmas. Scenes from Walt Disney's Cartoon Film "Sleeping Beauty". Horiz designs as T* **150**. *P* 11.

No.	Description	Mint	Used
71	½ c. multicoloured	10	10
72	1 c. multicoloured	10	10
73	2 c. multicoloured	10	10
74	4 c. multicoloured	10	10
75	8 c. multicoloured	10	10
76	10 c. multicoloured	15	10
77	25 c. multicoloured	20	20
78	$2 multicoloured	2·25	2·25
79	$2.50, multicoloured	2·50	2·50
71/9	*Set of* 9	4·75	4·75
MS680	126 × 101 mm. $4 multicoloured (*vert*) P 13½ × 14	5·00	3·25

156 Diesel Locomotive No. 15

(Des G. Drummond. Litho Questa)

1981 (12 Jan). *Sugar Cane Railway Locomotives. T* **156** *and similar horiz designs. Multicoloured. P* 14.

No.	Description	Mint	Used
681	25 c. Type **156**	15	15
682	50 c. Narrow-gauge steam locomotive	30	30
683	90 c. Diesel locomotives Nos. 1 and 10	55	60
684	$3 Steam locomotive hauling sugar cane	2·00	2·25
681/4	*Set of* 4	2·75	3·00
MS685	82 × 111 mm. $2.50, Antigua sugar factory, railway yard and sheds	1·75	1·75

"INDEPENDENCE 1981"

(157)

158 "Pipes of Pan"

1981 (31 Mar). *Independence. Optd with T* **157**. *A. On Nos.* 475A, 478A, 480A *and* 484A/6A.

No.	Description	Mint	Used
686A	6 c. Orchid Tree	60	60
688A	20 c. Flamboyant	60	60
690A	35 c. Flame of the Wood	1·25	1·25
694A	$2.50, Irrigation Scheme, Diamond Estate	3·00	4·00
695A	$5 Government House	5·00	7·50
696A	$10 Coolidge Airport	7·50	11·00
686A/96A	*Set of* 6	15·00	22·00

B. *On Nos.* 475B/6B *and* 478B/86B

No.	Description	Mint	Used
686B	6 c. Orchid Tree	10	10
687B	10 c. Bougainvillea	10	10
688B	20 c. Flamboyant	10	10
689B	25 c. Hibiscus	15	15
690B	35 c. Flame of the Wood	20	20
691B	50 c. Cannon at Fort James	35	35
692B	75 c. Premier's Office	40	40
693B	$1 Potworks Dam	55	55
694B	$2.50, Irrigation Scheme, Diamond Estate	1·25	1·25
695B	$5 Government House	2·50	2·50
696B	$10 Coolidge Airport	3·50	5·00
686B/96B	*Set of* 11	8·00	9·50

(Des J.W. Litho Questa)

1981 (5 May). *Birth Centenary of Picasso. T* **158** *and similar vert designs. Multicoloured. P* 14.

No.	Description	Mint	Used
697	10 c. Type **158**	10	10
698	50 c. "Seated Harlequin"	30	30
699	90 c. "Paulo as Harlequin"	55	55
700	$4 "Mother and Child"	2·50	2·50
697/700	*Set of* 4	3·00	3·00
MS701	115 × 140 mm. $5 "Three Musicians" (detail)	2·25	2·75

159 Prince Charles and Lady Diana Spencer

160 Prince of Wales at Investiture, 1969

(Des J.W. Litho Questa)

1981 (23 June). *Royal Wedding* (1*st issue*). *T* **159** *and similar vert designs. Multicoloured. P* 14.

No.	Description	Mint	Used
702	25 c. Type **159**	10	10
703	50 c. Glamis Castle	10	10
704	$4 Prince Charles skiing	80	80
702/4	*Set of* 3	80	80
MS705	96 × 82 mm. $5 Glass Coach	80	80

Nos. 702/4 also exist perforated 12 (*Price for set of* 3 80*p mint or used*) from additional sheetlets of five stamps and one label. These stamps have changed background colours.

(Manufactured by Walsall)

1981 (23 June). *Royal Wedding* (2*nd issue*). *T* **160** *and similar vert designs. Multicoloured* ($5) *or black and flesh* (*others*). *Self-adhesive. Roul* 5×*imperf**.

No.	Description	Mint	Used
706	25 c. Type **160**	15	25
	a. Booklet pane. Nos. 706/11	1·50	
707	25 c. Prince Charles as baby, 1948	15	25
708	$1 Prince Charles at R.A.F. College, Cranwell, 1971	25	50
709	$1 Prince Charles attending Hill House School, 1956	25	50
710	$2 Prince Charles and Lady Diana Spencer	50	75
711	$2 Prince Charles at Trinity College, 1967	50	75
712	$5 Prince Charles and Lady Diana (*different*)	1·00	1·50
	a. Booklet pane of 1	1·00	
706/12	*Set of* 7	2·50	4·00

*The 25 c. to $2 values were each separated by various combinations of rotary knife (giving a straight edge) and roulette. The $5 value exists only with straight edges.

Nos. 706/12 were only issued in $11.50 stamp booklets.

161 Irene Joshua (founder)

162 Antigua and Barbuda Coat of Arms

(Des M. Diamond. Litho Format)

1981 (28 Oct). *50th Anniv of Antigua Girl Guide Movement. T* **161** *and similar horiz designs. Multicoloured. P* 14½.

No.	Description	Mint	Used
713	10 c. Type **161**	15	10
714	50 c. Campfire sing-song	45	35
715	90 c. Sailing	75	65
716	$2.50, Animal tending	1·75	2·00
713/16	*Set of* 4	2·75	2·75
MS717	110 × 85 mm. $5 Raising the flag	5·50	3·50

INDEPENDENT

Nos. 718/22 and 733 onwards are inscribed "ANTIGUA & BARBUDA".

(Des E. Henry. Litho Format)

1981 (1 Nov). *Independence. T* **162** *and similar multicoloured designs. P* 14½.

No.	Description	Mint	Used
718	10 c. Type **162**	20	10
719	50 c. Pineapple, Antigua flag and map	45	20
720	90 c. Prime Minister Vere Bird	55	55
721	$2.50, St. John's Cathedral (38×25 *mm*)	1·50	2·50
718/21	*Set of* 4	2·40	3·00
MS722	105×79 mm. $5 Map of Antigua and Barbuda (42×42 *mm*)	3·75	2·75

163 "Holy Night" (Jacques Stella)

164 Swimming

(Des Clover Mill. Litho Format)

1981 (16 Nov). *Christmas. Paintings. T* **163** *and similar vert designs. Multicoloured. P* 14½.

No.	Description	Mint	Used
723	8 c. Type **163**	15	10
724	30 c. "Mary with Child" (Julius Schnorr von Carolfeld)	40	15
725	$1 "Virgin and Child" (Alonso Cano)	80	90
726	$3 "Virgin and Child" (Lorenzo di Credi)	1·40	3·75
723/6	*Set of* 4	2·50	4·25
MS727	77 × 111 mm. $5 "Holy Family" (Pieter von Avon)	2·50	4·50

(Des M. Diamond. Litho Format)

1981 (1 Dec). *International Year for Disabled Persons. Sport for the Disabled. T* **164** *and similar horiz designs. Multicoloured. P* 15.

No.	Description	Mint	Used
728	10 c. Type **164**	10	10
729	50 c. Discus throwing	20	30
730	90 c. Archery	40	55
731	$2 Baseball	1·25	1·40
728/31	*Set of* 4	1·75	2·10
MS732	108 × 84 mm. $4 Basketball	5·00	2·75

165 Scene from Football Match

166 Airbus Industrie A300

(Des Clover Mill. Litho Questa)

1982 (15 Apr). *World Cup Football Championship, Spain. T* **165** *and similar horiz designs showing scenes from different matches. P* 14.

No.	Description	Mint	Used
733	10 c. multicoloured	20	10
734	50 c. multicoloured	50	35
735	90 c. multicoloured	80	70
736	$4 multicoloured	3·50	3·50
733/6	*Set of* 4	4·50	4·25
MS737	75 × 92 mm. $5 multicoloured	7·00	9·00

Nos. 733/6 also exist perforated 12 (*Price for set of* 4, £4.50 *mint or used*) from additional sheetlets of five stamps and one label. These stamps have changed inscription colours.

(Des Clover Mill. Litho Format)

1982 (17 June). *Coolidge International Airport. T* **166** *and similar multicoloured designs. P* 14½.
738 10 c. Type **166** 10 10
739 50 c. Hawker Siddeley H.S. 748 .. .. 30 30
740 90 c. De Havilland D.H.C.6 Twin Otter .. 60 60
741 $2.50, Britten Norman Islander .. 1·75 1·75
738/41 .. .. *Set of* 4 2·50 2·50
MS742 99×73 mm. $5 Boeing 747-100 (*horiz*) 3·25 4·00

167 Cordia

(Des G. Drummond. Litho Questa)

1982 (28 June). *Death Centenary of Charles Darwin. Fauna and Flora. T* **167** *and similar multicoloured designs. P* 15.
743 10 c. Type **167**.. .. .. 15 10
744 50 c. Small Indian Mongoose (*horiz*) .. 45 40
745 90 c. Corallita.. .. .. 75 75
746 $3 Mexican Bulldog Bat (*horiz*) .. 2·00 3·25
743/6 .. .. *Set of* 4 3·00 4·00
MS747 107×85 mm. $5 Caribbean Monk Seal 6·50 8·00

168 Queen's House, Greenwich **169** Princess of Wales

(Des PAD Studio. Litho Questa)

1982 (1 July). *21st Birthday of Princess of Wales. T* **168/9** *and similar vert design. Multicoloured. P* 14½ × 14.
748 90 c. Type **168** 45 45
749 $1 Prince and Princess of Wales 50 50
750 $4 Princess Diana (*different*) .. .. 2·00 2·00
748/50 .. .. *Set of* 3 2·75 2·75
MS751 102 × 75 mm. $5 Type **169** .. .. 2·75 2·50
Nos. 748/50 also exist in sheetlets of 5 stamps and 1 label.

170 Boy Scouts decorating Streets for Independence Parade

ROYAL BABY
21.6.82
(**171**)

(Des J.W. Litho Questa)

1982 (15 July). *75th Anniv of Boy Scout Movement. T* **170** *and similar horiz designs. Multicoloured. P* 14.
752 10 c. Type **170** 20 10
753 50 c. Boy Scout giving helping hand during street parade 50 40
754 90 c. Boy Scouts attending Princess Margaret at Independence Ceremony 85 75
755 $2.20, Cub Scout giving directions to tourists 1·75 2·75
752/5 .. .. *Set of* 4 3·00 3·50
MS756 102 × 72 mm. $5 Lord Baden-Powell .. 7·50 7·00

1982 (30 Aug). *Birth of Prince William of Wales. Nos.* 748/51 *optd with T* **171**.
757 90 c. Type **168** 45 45
758 $1 Prince and Princess of Wales 50 50
759 $4 Princess Diana (*different*) .. .. 2·00 1·50
757/9 .. .. *Set of* 3 2·75 2·25
MS760 102 × 75 mm. $5 Type **169** .. 2·40 2·50
Nos. 757/9 also exist in sheetlets of 5 stamps and 1 label.

172 Roosevelt in 1940

(Des PAD Studio. Litho Format)

1982 (20 Sept). *Birth Centenary of Franklin D. Roosevelt (Nos.* 761, 763, 765/6 *and* **MS**767) *and 250th Birth Anniv of George Washington (others). T* **172** *and similar multicoloured designs. P* 15.
761 10 c. Type **172** 20 10
762 25 c. Washington as blacksmith 45 15
763 45 c. Churchill, Roosevelt and Stalin at Yalta Conference .. .. 1·00 40
764 60 c. Washington crossing the Delaware (*vert*) 1·00 40
765 $1 "Roosevelt Special" train (*vert*) .. 1·25 90
766 $3 Portrait of Roosevelt (*vert*) .. .. 1·40 2·40
761/6 .. .. *Set of* 6 4·75 3·75
MS767 92 × 87 mm. $4 Roosevelt and Wife .. 2·00 1·75
MS768 92 × 87 mm. $4 Portrait of Washington (*vert*) .. .. 2·00 1·75

173 "Annunciation"

(Des Design Images. Litho Questa)

1982 (Nov). *Christmas. Religious Paintings by Raphael. T* **173** *and similar horiz designs. Multicoloured. P* 14 × 13½.
769 10 c. Type **173** 10 10
770 30 c. "Adoration of the Magi" 15 15
771 $1 "Presentation at the Temple" 50 50
772 $4 "Coronation of the Virgin" .. .. 2·10 2·25
769/72 .. .. *Set of* 4 2·50 2·75
MS773 95 × 124 mm. $5 "Marriage of the Virgin" 2·75 2·50

174 Tritons and Dolphins **175** Pineapple Produce

(Des Design Images. Litho Format)

1983 (28 Jan). *500th Birth Anniv of Raphael. Details from "Galatea" Fresco. T* **174** *and similar multicoloured designs. P* 14½.
774 45 c. Type **174** 20 25
775 50 c. Sea Nymph carried off by Triton .. 25 30
776 60 c. Winged angel steering Dolphins (*horiz*) 30 35
777 $4 Cupids shooting arrows (*horiz*) .. 1·90 2·00
774/7 .. .. *Set of* 4 2·40 2·50
MS778 101 × 125 mm. $5 Galatea pulled along by Dolphins .. .. 2·50 2·75

(Des Artists International. Litho Questa)

1983 (14 Mar). *Commonwealth Day. T* **175** *and similar horiz designs. Multicoloured. P* 14.
779 25 c. Type **175** 15 15
780 45 c. Carnival 20 25
781 60 c. Tourism 30 35
782 $3 Airport .. .. 1·00 1·50
779/82 .. .. *Set of* 4 1·50 2·00

176 T.V. Satellite Coverage of Royal Wedding

(Des PAD Studio. Litho Questa)

1983 (5 Apr). *World Communications Year. T* **176** *and similar horiz designs. Multicoloured. P* 14.
783 15 c. Type **176** 40 20
784 50 c. Police communications .. .. 2·25 1·50
785 60 c. House-to-train telephone call .. .. 2·25 1·50
786 $3 Satellite earth station with planets Jupiter and Saturn .. .. .. 4·75 5·00
783/6 .. .. *Set of* 4 8·50 7·50
MS787 100 × 90 mm. $5 "Comsat" satellite over West Indies .. .. 2·75 3·25

177 Bottle-nosed Dolphin

(Des D. Miller. Litho Format)

1983 (9 May). *Whales. T* **177** *and similar horiz designs. Multi coloured. P* 14½.
788 15 c. Type **177**.. .. .. 85 2
789 50 c. Fin Whale .. .. 1·75 1·2
790 60 c. Bowhead Whale.. .. .. .. 2·00 1·2
791 $3 Spectacled Porpoise .. .. .. 3·75 4·2
788/91 .. .. *Set of* 4 7·50 6·2
MS792 122×101 mm. $5 Narwhal .. .. 8·50 6·0
Nos. 788/92 exist imperforate from stock dispersed by th liquidator of Format International Security Printers Ltd.

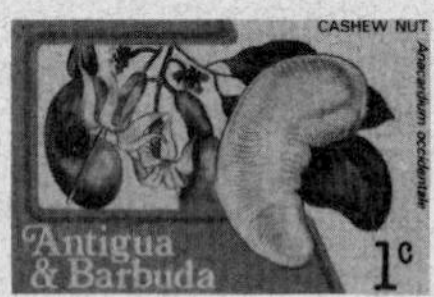

178 Cashew Nut

(Des J.W. Litho Questa)

1983 (11 July)–**85.** *Fruits and Flowers. T* **178** *and simila horiz designs. Multicoloured. P* 14.
793 1 c. Type **178** 15 5
a. Perf 12 (3.85) 20 5
794 2 c. Passion Fruit 15 5
a. Perf 12 (3.85) 20 5
795 3 c. Mango 15 5
a. Perf 12 (3.85) 20 5
796 5 c. Grapefruit 20 3
a. Perf 12 (3.85) 30 3
797 10 c. Pawpaw 40 2
a. Perf 12 (3.85) 30 2
798 15 c. Breadfruit 50 2
a. Perf 12 (3.85) 50 2
799 20 c. Coconut 50 2
a. Perf 12 (3.85) 60 2
800 25 c. Oleander 55 3
a. Perf 12 (3.85) 60 2
801 30 c. Banana 60 4
a. Perf 12 (3.85) 75 3
802 40 c. Pineapple 70 4
a. Perf 12 (3.85) 75 3
803 45 c. Cordia 80 5
a. Perf 12 (3.85) 85 4
804 50 c. Cassia 90 6
a. Perf 12 (3.85) .. .. .. 1·25 5
805 60 c. Poui .. .. 1·50 1·0
a. Perf 12 (3.85) .. .. .. 1·25 1·1
806 $1 Frangipani .. .. 2·25 1·7
a. Perf 12 (3.85) .. .. .. 2·25 1·2
807 $2 Flamboyant .. .. 3·75 3·7
a. Perf 12 (12.85) .. .. .. 3·25 3·7
808 $2.50, Lemon .. .. 4·50 5·5
a. Perf 12 (12.85) .. .. .. 3·75 4·5
809 $5 Lignum Vitae .. .. .. 7·00 10·0
a. Perf 12 (12.85) .. .. .. 6·00 10·0
810 $10 National flag and coat of arms .. 11·00 15·0
a. Perf 12 (3.85) .. .. .. 9·50 15·0
793/810 .. .. *Set of* 18 32·00 38·0

179 Dornier Do X Flying Boat

(Des W. Wright. Litho Format)

1983 (15 Aug). *Bicentenary of Manned Flight. T* **179** *and simila horiz designs. Multicoloured. P* 14½.
811 30 c. Type **179** 75 3
812 50 c. Supermarine S6B seaplane 90 6
813 60 c. Curtiss F-9C Sparrowhawk biplane and airship U.S.S. *Akron* .. .. 1·00 8
814 $4 Hot-air balloon *Pro Juventute* .. 3·00 5·0
811/14 .. .. *Set of* 4 5·00 6·0
MS815 80×105 mm. $5 Airship LZ-127 *Graf Zeppelin* .. .. 2·00 3·2

180 "Sibyls and Angels" (detail) (Raphael)

(Des W. Wright. Litho Format)

1983 (4 Oct). *Christmas. 500th Birth Anniv of Raphael. T* **180** *an similar designs. P* 13½.
816 10 c. multicoloured 30 2
817 30 c. multicoloured 65 3
818 $1 multicoloured .. .. 1·50 1·2
819 $4 multicoloured .. .. 4·00 5·0
816/19 .. .. *Set of* 4 5·75 6·25
MS820 101 × 131 mm. $5 multicoloured.. .. 1·50 2·25
Designs: *Horiz*—10 c. to $4 Different details from "Sibyls an Angels". *Vert*—$5 "The Vision of Ezekiel".

181 John Wesley (founder)

182 Discus

(Des M. Diamond. Litho Questa)

983 (7 Nov). *Bicentenary of Methodist Church* (1984). *T* **181** *and similar vert designs. Multicoloured. P* 14.

21	15 c. Type **181** . .	25	15
22	50 c. Nathaniel Gilbert (founder in Antigua)	70	50
23	60 c. St. John Methodist Church steeple . .	75	65
24	$3 Ebenezer Methodist Church, St. John's . .	2·00	4·00
21/4	. . *Set of* 4	3·25	4·75

(Des Artists International. Litho Format)

984 (9 Jan). *Olympic Games, Los Angeles. T* **182** *and similar vert designs. Multicoloured. P* 14½.

25	25 c. Type **182** . .	20	15
26	50 c. Gymnastics . .	35	30
27	90 c. Hurdling . .	65	70
28	$3 Cycling . .	2·25	3·50
25/8	. . *Set of* 4	3·00	4·25
IS829	82 × 67 mm. $5 Volleyball . .	2·75	3·00

183 *Booker Vanguard* (freighter)

184 Chenille

(Des Artists International. Litho Format)

984 (14 June). *Ships. T* **183** *and similar multicoloured designs. P* 15.

30	45 c. Type **183** . .	1·00	55
31	50 c. S.S. *Canberra* (liner) . .	1·25	80
32	60 c. Sailing boats . .	1·50	1·00
33	$4 *Fairwind* (cargo liner) . .	3·00	7·00
30/3	. . *Set of* 4	6·00	8·50
IS834	107×80 mm. $5 Eighteenth-century British man-of-war (*vert*) . .	1·75	3·50

Nos. 830/3 exist imperforate from stock dispersed by the quidator of Format International Security Printers Ltd.

(Des J.W. Litho Format)

984 (19 June). *Universal Postal Union Congress, Hamburg. T* **184** *and similar vert designs showing flowers. Multicoloured. P* 15.

35	15 c. Type **184** . .	40	15
36	50 c. Shell Flower . .	1·00	70
37	60 c. Anthurium . .	1·10	1·10
38	$3 Angels Trumpet . .	4·00	6·50
35/8	. . *Set of* 4	6·00	7·50
IS839	100 × 75 mm. $5 Crown of Thorns . .	1·50	3·25

Nos. 835/9 exist imperforate from stock dispersed by the iquidator of Format International Security Printers Ltd.

$2

$2 $2

(185) (186)

984 (25 June). (*a*) *Nos.* 702/5 *surch with T* **185**

40	$2 on 25 c. Type **159** . .	3·00	3·00
41	$2 on 50 c. Glamis Castle . .	3·00	3·00
42	$2 on $4 Prince Charles skiing . .	3·00	3·00
40/2	. . *Set of* 3	8·00	8·00
IS843	96 × 82 mm. $2 on $5 Glass Coach . .	4·00	4·00

(*b*) *Nos.* 748/51 *surch with T* **186**

44	$2 on 90 c. Type **168** (Gold)* . .	2·40	2·25
45	$2 on $1 Prince and Princess of Wales (Gold)* . .	2·40	2·25
46	$2 on $4 Princess Diana (*different*) (Gold)*	2·40	2·25
44/6	. . *Set of* 3	6·50	6·00
IS847	102 × 75 mm. $2 on $5 Type **169** (Gold)	4·00	4·00

(*c*) *Nos.* 757/60 *surch with T* **186**

848	$2 on 90 c. Type **168** (Gold)* . .	2·40	2·25
849	$2 on $1 Prince and Princess of Wales (Gold)* . .	2·40	2·25
850	$2 on $4 Princess Diana (*different*) (Gold)*	2·40	2·25
848/50	. . *Set of* 3	6·50	6·00
MS851	102 × 75 mm. $2 on $5 Type **169** (Gold)	4·00	4·00

(*d*) *Nos.* 779/82 *surch as T* **185**

852	$2 on 25 c. Type **175** . .	2·00	1·25
853	$2 on 45 c. Carnival . .	2·00	1·25
854	$2 on 60 c. Tourism . .	2·00	1·25
855	$2 on $3 Airport . .	2·00	1·25
852/5	. . *Set of* 4	7·00	4·50

*Nos. 844/6 and 848/50 also exist with similar surcharges in gold or silver on the sheetlets of five stamps and 1 label (*price for set of* 3 *as Nos.* 844/6, £6 *mint or used*) (*price for set of* 3 *as Nos.* 848/50, £6 *mint or used*).

187 Abraham Lincoln

188 View of Moravian Mission

(Des Liane Fried. Litho Questa)

1984 (18 July). *Presidents of the United States of America. T* **187** *and similar vert designs. Multicoloured. P* 14.

856	10 c. Type **187** . .	15	10
857	20 c. Harry Truman . .	20	15
858	30 c. Dwight Eisenhower . .	30	25
859	40 c. Ronald Reagan . .	50	30
860	90 c. Gettysburg Address, 1863 . .	90	75
861	$1.10, Formation of N.A.T.O., 1949 . .	1·25	1·25
862	$1.50, Eisenhower during Second World War	1·60	1·75
863	$2 Reagan and Caribbean Basin Initiative	1·75	2·00
856/63	. . *Set of* 8	6·00	6·00

(Des and litho Questa)

1984 (1 Aug). *150th Anniv of Abolition of Slavery. T* **188** *and similar horiz designs. Multicoloured. P* 14.

864	40 c. Type **188** . .	80	50
865	50 c. Antigua Courthouse, 1823 . .	90	65
866	60 c. Planting sugar-cane, Monks Hill . .	95	75
867	$3 Boiling house, Delaps' estate . .	4·00	4·75
864/7	. . *Set of* 4	6·00	6·00
MS868	95 × 70 mm. $5 Loading sugar, Willoughby Bay . .	6·50	4·75

189 Rufous-sided Towhee

190 Grass-skiing

(Des Jennifer Toombs. Litho Format)

1984 (15 Aug). *Songbirds. T* **189** *and similar vert designs. Multicoloured. P* 15.

869	40 c. Type **189** . .	1·25	85
870	50 c. Parula Warbler . .	1·40	1·10
871	60 c. House Wren . .	1·50	1·50
872	$2 Ruby-crowned Kinglet . .	2·00	3·75
873	$3 Common Flicker . .	2·75	5·00
869/73	. . *Set of* 5	8·00	11·00
MS874	76 × 76 mm. $5 Yellow-breasted Chat . .	3·00	6·00

(Des Bonny Redecker. Litho Questa)

1984 (21 Sept). *"Ausipex" International Stamp Exhibition, Melbourne. Australian Sports. T* **190** *and similar vert designs. Multicoloured. P* 14½.

875	$1 Type **190** . .	1·50	1·50
876	$5 Australian Football . .	4·25	5·50
MS877	108 × 78 mm. $5 Boomerang-throwing . .	3·00	4·00

191 "The Virgin and Infant with Angels and Cherubs" (Correggio)

192 "The Blue Dancers" (Degas)

(Litho Format)

1984 (4 Oct). *450th Death Anniv of Correggio (painter). T* **191** *and similar vert designs. Multicoloured. P* 15.

878	25 c. Type **191** . .	40	20
879	60 c. "The Four Saints" . .	80	50
880	90 c. "St. Catherine" . .	1·10	90
881	$3 "The Campori Madonna" . .	2·75	4·25
878/81	. . *Set of* 4	4·50	5·25
MS882	90 × 60 mm. $5 "St. John the Baptist" . .	2·00	2·75

(Litho Format)

1984 (4 Oct). *150th Birth Anniv of Edgar Degas (painter). T* **192** *and similar multicoloured designs. P* 15.

883	15 c. Type **192** . .	35	15
884	50 c. "The Pink Dancers" . .	80	60
885	70 c. "Two Dancers" . .	1·10	85
886	$4 "Dancers at the Bar" . .	3·00	4·75
883/6	. . *Set of* 4	4·75	5·75
MS887	90 × 60 mm. $5 "The Folk Dancers" (40 × 27 *mm*) . .	2·00	2·75

193 Sir Winston Churchill

194 Donald Duck fishing

(Des J. Iskowitz. Litho Format)

1984 (19 Nov). *Famous People. T* **193** *and similar multicoloured designs. P* 15.

888	60 c. Type **193** . .	1·10	1·50
889	60 c. Mahatma Gandhi . .	1·10	1·50
890	60 c. John F. Kennedy . .	1·10	1·50
891	60 c. Mao Tse-tung . .	1·10	1·50
892	$1 Churchill with General De Gaulle, Paris, 1944 (*horiz*) . .	1·25	1·75
893	$1 Gandhi leaving London by train, 1931 (*horiz*) . .	1·25	1·75
894	$1 Kennedy with Chancellor Adenauer and Mayor Brandt, Berlin, 1963 (*horiz*) . .	1·25	1·75
895	$1 Mao Tse-tung with Lin Piao, Peking, 1969 (*horiz*) . .	1·25	1·75
888/95	. . *Set of* 8	8·50	11·50
MS896	114×80 mm. $5 Flags of Great Britain, India, the United States and China . .	9·00	4·50

Nos. 890 and 893 exist imperforate from stock dispersed by the liquidator of Format International Security Printers Ltd.

(Litho Format)

1984 (26 Nov). *Christmas. 50th Birthday of Donald Duck. T* **194** *and similar multicoloured designs showing Walt Disney cartoon characters. P* 11.

897	1 c. Type **194** . .	10	10
898	2 c. Donald Duck lying on beach . .	10	10
899	3 c. Donald Duck and nephews with fishing rods and fishes . .	10	10
900	4 c. Donald Duck and nephews in boat . .	10	10
901	5 c. Wearing diving masks . .	10	10
902	10 c. In deckchairs reading books . .	10	10
903	$1 With toy shark's fin . .	2·00	1·25
904	$2 In sailing boat . .	3·00	3·00
905	$5 Attempting to propel boat . .	5·00	6·00
897/905	. . *Set of* 9	9·50	9·50
MS906	Two sheets, each 125×100 mm. (a) $5 Nephews with crayon and paintbrushes (*horiz*). P 14×13½. (b) $5 Donald Duck in deckchair. P 13½×14 . . *Set of* 2 *sheets*	9·00	13·00

No. 904 was printed in sheetlets of 8 stamps.

Nos. 899/900 and 904 exist imperforate from stock dispersed by the liquidator of Format International Security Printers Ltd.

195 Torch from Statue in Madison Square Park, 1885

(Des J. Iskowitz. Litho Format)

1985 (7 Jan). *Centenary of the Statue of Liberty* (1986) (*1st issue*). *T* **195** *and similar multicoloured designs. P* 15.

907	25 c. Type **195** . .	20	20
908	30 c. Statue of Liberty and scaffolding ("Restoration and Renewal") (*vert*) . .	20	20
909	50 c. Frederic Bartholdi (sculptor) supervising construction, 1876 . .	30	30
910	90 c. Close-up of Statue . .	55	55
911	$1 Statue and cadet ship ("Operation Sail", 1976) (*vert*) . .	90	90
912	$3 Dedication ceremony, 1886 . .	1·75	2·00
907/12	. . *Set of* 6	3·50	3·75
MS913	110×80 mm. $5 Port of New York . .	3·75	3·75

See also Nos. 1110/19.

196 Arawak Pot Sherd and Indians making Clay Utensils

(Des N. Waldman. Litho Format)

1985 (21 Jan). *Native American Artefacts. T* **196** *and similar designs. Multicoloured. P* 15.

914 15 c. Type **196**. 15 10
915 50 c. Arawak body design and Arawak Indians tattooing 30 40
916 60 c. Head of the god "Yocahu" and Indians harvesting manioc 40 50
917 $3 Carib war club and Carib Indians going into battle . . . . 1·75 2·50
914/17 . . . . *Set of* 4 2·40 3·25
MS918 97 × 68 mm. $5 Taino Indians worshipping stone idol . . . . 2·00 2·50

197 Triumph 2hp "Jap", 1903

(Des BG Studio. Litho Questa)

1985 (7 Mar). *Centenary of the Motorcycle. T* **197** *and similar horiz designs. Multicoloured. P* 14.

919 10 c. Type **197**. 65 15
920 30 c. Indian "Arrow", 1949 . . . . 1·10 40
921 60 c. BMW "R100RS", 1976 . . . . 1·60 1·25
922 $4 Harley-Davidson "Model II", 1916 . . 5·50 7·00
919/22 . . . . *Set of* 4 8·00 8·00
MS923 90 × 93 mm. $5 Laverda "Jota", 1975 . . 5·50 6·50

198 Slavonian Grebe

(Litho Questa)

1985 (25 Mar). *Birth Bicentenary of John J. Audubon (ornithologist) (1st issue). T* **198** *and similar multicoloured designs showing original paintings. P* 14.

924 90 c. Type **198**. . . . . 1·75 1·25
925 $1 British Storm Petrel . . . . 2·00 1·25
926 $1.50, Great Blue Heron . . . . 2·50 3·25
927 $3 Double-crested Cormorant . . . . . . 3·75 6·00
924/7 . . . . *Set of* 4 9·00 10·50
MS928 103 × 72 mm. $5 White-tailed Tropic Bird (*vert*) . . . . 7·00 5·50

Nos. 924/7 were each issued in sheetlets of five stamps and one stamp-size label, which appears in the centre of the bottom row.

See also Nos. 990/4.

199 *Anaea cyanea*

(Des R. Sauber. Litho Questa)

1985 (16 Apr). *Butterflies. T* **199** *and similar horiz designs. Multicoloured. P* 14.

929 25 c. Type **199** . . . . 1·00 30
930 60 c. *Leodonta dysoni* . . . . 2·25 1·25
931 90 c. *Junea doraete* . . . . 2·75 1·50
932 $4 *Prepona pylene* . . . . 7·50 10·50
929/32 . . . . *Set of* 4 12·00 12·00
MS933 132×105 mm. $5 *Caerois gerdtrudtus* . . 4·50 6·00

200 Cessna 172D Skyhawk

201 Maimonides

(Des A. DiLorenzo. Litho Questa)

1985 (30 Apr). *40th Anniv of International Civil Aviation Organization. T.* **200** *and similar horiz designs. Multicoloured. P* 14.

934 30 c. Type **200** . . . . 1·25 30
935 90 c. Fokker D.VII . . . . 2·75 1·25
936 $1.50, SPAD VII . . . . 3·75 3·25
937 $3 Boeing 747-100 . . . . 5·50 7·50
934/7 . . . . *Set of* 4 12·00 11·00
MS938 97×83 mm. $5 De Havilland D.H.C.6 Twin Otter . . . . 4·50 6·00

(Des and litho Questa)

1985 (17 June). *850th Birth Anniv of Maimonides (physician, philosopher and scholar). P* 14.

939 **201** $2 bright green . . . . 4·00 3·25
MS940 70 × 84 mm. **201** $5 reddish brown . . 7·00 4·50

No. 939 was printed in sheetlets of 6 stamps.

202 Young Farmers with Produce

203 The Queen Mother attending Church

(Des Susan David. Litho Questa)

1985 (1 July). *International Youth Year. T* **202** *and similar horiz designs. Multicoloured. P* 14.

941 25 c. Type **202**. 20 20
942 50 c. Hotel management trainees 30 40
943 60 c. Girls with goat and boys with football ("Environment") 40 60
944 $3 Windsurfing ("Leisure") . . . . . . 1·75 3·00
941/4 . . . . *Set of* 4 2·40 3·75
MS945 102 × 72 mm. $5 Young people with Antiguan flags . . . . 2·75 3·25

(Des J.W. Litho Questa)

1985 (10 July). *Life and Times of Queen Elizabeth the Queen Mother. T* **203** *and similar vert designs. Multicoloured. P* 14.

946 $1 Type **203** 45 60
947 $1.50, Watching children playing in London garden 60 85
948 $2.50, The Queen Mother in 1979 . . . . 90 1·40
946/8 . . . . *Set of* 3 1·75 2·50
MS949 56 × 85 mm. $5 With Prince Edward at Royal Wedding, 1981 . . . . 3·00 3·00

Stamps as Nos. 946/8, but with face values of 90 c., $1 and $3, exist from additional sheetlets of 5 plus a label issued 13 January 1986. These also have changed background colours and are perforated 12×12½ (*price for set of 3 stamps £2 mint*).

204 Magnificent Frigate Bird

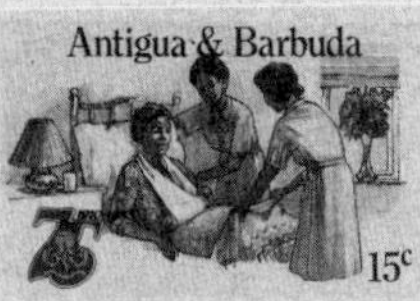

205 Girl Guides Nursing

(Des Mary Walters. Litho Questa)

1985 (1 Aug). *Marine Life. T* **204** *and similar vert designs. Multicoloured. P* 14.

950 15 c. Type **204** . . . . 1·00 30
951 45 c. Brain Coral . . . . 2·00 95
952 60 c. Cushion Star . . . . 2·25 1·75
953 $3 Spotted Moray . . . . 7·00 9·00
950/3 . . . . *Set of* 4 11·00 11·00
MS954 110×80 mm. $5 Elkhorn Coral . . . . 8·00 7·00

(Des Y. Berry. Litho Questa)

1985 (22 Aug). *75th Anniv of Girl Guide Movement. T* **205** *and similar horiz designs. Multicoloured. P* 14.

955 15 c. Type **205**. 75 20
956 45 c. Open-air Girl Guide meeting . . . . 1·40 60
957 60 c. Lord and Lady Baden-Powell . . . . 1·75 90
958 $3 Girl Guides gathering flowers. . . . 4·25 4·50
955/8 . . . . *Set of* 4 7·50 5·75
MS959 67 × 96 mm. $5 Barn Swallow (Nature study) . . . . 6·00 7·00

206 Bass Trombone

207 Flags of Great Britain and Antigua

(Des Susan David. Litho Questa)

1985 (26 Aug). *300th Birth Anniv of Johann Sebastian Bach (composer). T* **206** *and similar vert designs. P* 14.

960 25 c. multicoloured . . . . 1·40 55
961 50 c. multicoloured . . . . 1·75 1·10
962 $1 multicoloured . . . . 3·25 1·75
963 $3 multicoloured . . . . 6·00 7·00
960/3 . . . . *Set of* 4 11·00 9·50
MS964 104 × 73 mm. $5 black and brownish grey . . . . 4·50 4·75

Designs:—50 c. English horn; $1 Violino piccolo; $3 Bass rackett; $5 Johann Sebastian Bach.

(Des Mary Walters. Litho Format)

1985 (24 Oct). *Royal Visit. T* **207** *and similar multicolour designs. P* 14½.

965 60 c. Type **207**. . . . . 1·00
966 $1 Queen Elizabeth II (*vert*) . . . . 1·50 1·
967 $4 Royal Yacht *Britannia* . . . . . . 3·25 6·
965/7 . . . . *Set of* 3 5·25 7·
MS968 110 × 83 mm. $5 Map of Antigua . . 3·00 3·

(Des Walt Disney Productions. Litho Questa)

1985 (4 Nov). *150th Birth Anniv of Mark Twain (author). Hor designs as T* **118** *of Anguilla showing Walt Disney carto characters in scenes from "Roughing It". Multicoloure P* 14 × 13½.

969 25 c. Donald Duck and Mickey Mouse meeting Indians 50
970 50 c. Mickey Mouse, Donald Duck and Goofy canoeing 75
971 $1.10, Goofy as Pony Express rider . . 1·25 1·
972 $1.50, Donald Duck and Goofy hunting buffalo . . . . 1·75 2·
973 $2 Mickey Mouse and silver mine . . 2·50 3·
969/73 . . . . *Set of* 5 6·00 7·
MS974 127 × 101 mm. $5 Mickey Mouse driving stagecoach . . . . 7·50 7·

(Des Walt Disney Productions. Litho Questa)

1985 (11 Nov). *Birth Bicentenaries of Grimm Brothers (fol lorists). Horiz designs as T* **119** *of Anguilla showing W Disney cartoon characters in scenes from "Spindle, Shuttle a Needle". Multicoloured. P* 14 × 13½.

975 30 c. The Prince (Mickey Mouse) searches for a bride 80
   a. Error. Wmk w **16** . . . . . . 95·00
976 60 c. The Prince finds the Orphan Girl (Minnie Mouse) . . . . 1·10
977 70 c. The Spindle finds the Prince . . . . 1·40
978 $1 The Needle tidies the Girl's House . . 1·90 1·
979 $3 The Prince proposes . . . . 4·00 5·
975/9 . . . . *Set of* 5 8·50 8·
MS980 125 × 101 mm. $5 The Orphan Girl and spinning wheel on Prince's horse . . . . 7·50 7·

208 Benjamin Franklin and U.N. (New York) 1953 U.P.U. 5 c. Stamp

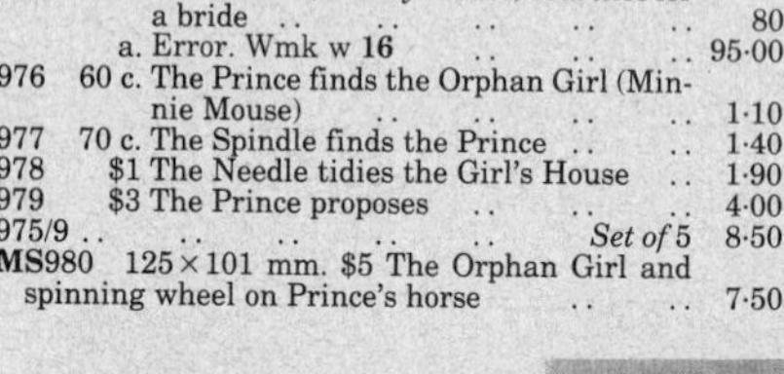

209 "Madonna and Child" (De Landi)

(Litho Walsall)

1985 (18 Nov). *40th Anniv of United Nations Organizatio T* **208** *and similar multicoloured designs showing Unit Nations (New York) stamps. P* 13½ × 14.

981 40 c. Type **208**. . . . . 1·00
982 $1 George Washington Carver (agricultural chemist) and 1982 Nature Conservation 28 c. stamp . . . . . . 2·00 2·
983 $3 Charles Lindbergh (aviator) and 1978 I.C.A.O. 25 c. stamp . . . . . . 4·25 6·
981/3 . . . . *Set of* 3 6·50 8·
MS984 101 × 77 mm. $5 Marc Chagall (artist) (*vert*). P 14 × 13½ . . . . 6·00 4·

(Des Mary Walters. Litho Format)

1985 (30 Dec). *Christmas. Religious Paintings. T* **209** *a similar vert designs. Multicoloured. P* 15.

985 10 c. Type **209**. 30
986 25 c. "Madonna and Child" (Berlinghiero) 55
987 60 c. "The Nativity" (Fra Angelico). . . . 70
988 $4 "Presentation in the Temple" (Giovanni di Paolo) . . . . 1·75 4·
985/8 . . . . *Set of* 4 3·00 4·
MS989 113 × 81 mm. $5 "The Nativity" (Antoniazzo Romano) . . . . 3·00 3·

No. **MS**989 exists imperforate from stock dispersed by th liquidator of Format International Security Printers Ltd.

(Litho Questa)

1986 (6 Jan). *Birth Bicentenary of John J. Audubon (ornitho ogist) (2nd issue). Horiz designs as T* **198** *showing origin paintings. Multicoloured. P* 12.

990 60 c. Mallard . . . . 2·00 1·
991 90 c. North American Black Duck . . . . 2·50 2·
992 $1.50, Pintail . . . . 3·25 4·
993 $3 American Wigeon . . . . 4·50 6·
990/3 . . . . *Set of* 4 11·00 13·
MS994 102 × 73 mm. $5 American Eider. P 14 . . 7·00 5·

Nos. 990/3 were issued in sheetlets of 5 as Nos. 924/7.

210 Football, Boots and Trophy

211 Tug

(Des M. Donk. Litho Questa)

86 (17 Mar). *World Cup Football Championship, Mexico. T* **210** *and similar multicoloured designs. P* 14.
5 30 c. Type **210** . . . . 1·00 40
6 60 c. Goalkeeper (*vert*) . . 1·50 85
7 $1 Referee blowing whistle (*vert*) . . 2·00 1·60
8 $4 Ball in net . . 5·50 7·50
5/8 . . *Set of* 4 9·00 9·25
S999 87 × 76 mm. $5 Two players competing for ball . . 8·50 7·50

(Des W. Hanson. Litho Questa)

86 (24 Mar). *Appearance of Halley's Comet* (*1st issue*). *Horiz designs as T* **123** *of Anguilla. Multicoloured. P* 14.
00 5 c. Edmond Halley and Old Greenwich Observatory . . 30 15
01 10 c. Messerschmitt Me 163B Komet (fighter aircraft), 1944 . . 30 15
02 60 c. Montezuma (Aztec Emperor) and Comet in 1517 (from "Historias de las Indias de Neuva Espana") . . 1·50 70
03 $4 Pocahontas saving Capt. John Smith and Comet in 1607 . . 4·50 5·00
00/3 . . *Set of* 4 6·00 5·50
S1004 101 × 70 mm. $5 Halley's Comet over English Harbour, Antigua . . 3·50 3·75
See also Nos. 1047/51.

(Litho Questa)

86 (21 Apr). *60th Birthday of Queen Elizabeth II. Vert designs as T* **125** *of Anguilla. P* 14.
05 60 c. black and yellow . . 30 35
06 $1 multicoloured . . 50 55
07 $4 multicoloured . . 1·40 1·90
05/7 . . *Set of* 3 2·00 2·50
S1008 120 × 85 mm. $5 black and grey-brown . . 2·00 3·00
Designs:—60 c. Wedding photograph, 1947; $1 Queen at rooping the Colour; $4 In Scotland; $5 Queen Mary and rincess Elizabeth, 1927.

(Des A. DiLorenzo. Litho Questa)

86 (15 May). *Local Boats. T* **211** *and similar vert designs. Multicoloured. P* 14.
09 30 c. Type **211** . . 25 20
10 60 c. Game fishing boat . . 45 35
11 $1 Yacht . . 75 60
12 $4 Lugger with auxiliary sail . . 2·50 3·25
09/12 . . *Set of* 4 3·50 4·00
S1013 108 × 78 mm. $5 Boats under construction . . 3·00 4·00

212 "Hiawatha" Express

213 Prince Andrew and Miss Sarah Ferguson

(Des W. Wright. Litho Format)

86 (22 May). *"Ameripex '86" International Stamp Exhibition, Chicago. Famous American Trains. T* **212** *and similar horiz designs. Multicoloured. P* 15.
14 25 c. Type **212** . . 1·00 40
15 50 c. "Grand Canyon" express . . 1·25 75
16 $1 "Powhattan Arrow" express . . 1·50 1·75
17 $3 "Empire State" express . . 3·00 6·00
14/17 . . *Set of* 4 6·00 8·00
S1018 116×87 mm. $5 Southern Pacific "Daylight" express . . 4·50 9·50
Nos. 1015/16 exist imperforate from stock dispersed by the liquidator of Format International Security Printers Ltd.

(Des and litho Questa)

86 (1 July). *Royal Wedding. T* **213** *and similar vert designs. Multicoloured. P* 14.
19 45 c. Type **213** . . 35 35
20 60 c. Prince Andrew . . 40 45
21 $4 Prince Andrew with Prince Philip . . 2·00 3·00
19/21 . . *Set of* 3 2·50 3·50
S1022 88 × 88 mm. $5 Prince Andrew and Miss Sarah Ferguson (*different*) . . 4·00 4·50

214 Fly-specked Cerith

215 *Nymphaea ampla* (Water Lily)

(Des L. Birmingham. Litho Format)

86 (6 Aug). *Sea Shells. T* **214** *and similar multicoloured designs. P* 15.
23 15 c. Type **214** . . 75 50
24 45 c. Smooth Scotch Bonnet . . 1·75 1·25
25 60 c. West Indian Crown Conch . . 2·00 2·00
26 $3 Ciboney Murex . . 6·50 10·00
23/6 . . *Set of* 4 10·00 12·50
S1027 109×75 mm. $5 Colourful Atlantic Moon (*horiz*) . . 7·50 8·50

(Des Mary Walters. Litho Format)

1986 (25 Aug). *Flowers. T* **215** *and similar horiz designs. Multicoloured. P* 15.
1028 10 c. Type **215** . . 20 15
1029 15 c. Queen of the Night . . 20 15
1030 50 c. Cup of Gold . . 55 55
1031 60 c. Beach Morning Glory . . 70 70
1032 70 c. Golden Trumpet . . 80 80
1033 $1 Air Plant . . 90 1·10
1034 $3 Purple Wreath . . 1·75 3·00
1035 $4 Zephyr Lily . . 2·00 3·75
1028/35 . . *Set of* 8 6·50 9·00
MS1036 Two sheets, each 102 × 72 mm. (a) $4 Dozakie. (b) $5 Four O'Clock Flower *Set of* 2 *sheets* 5·00 7·50

WINNERS
Argentina 3
W.Germany 2

(216)

217 *Hygrocybe occidentalis* var. *scarletina*

1986 (15 Sept). *World Cup Football Championship Winners, Mexico. Nos.* 995/9 *optd as T* **216** *in gold.*
1037 30 c. Type **210** . . 65 40
1038 60 c. Goalkeeper (*vert*) . . 1·00 75
1039 $1 Referee blowing whistle (*vert*) . . 1·40 1·10
1040 $4 Ball in net . . 4·50 4·50
1037/40 . . *Set of* 4 6·75 6·00
MS1041 87 × 76 mm. $5 Two players competing for ball . . 4·00 4·00
The overprint on the horizontal designs is in two lines.

(Litho Format)

1986 (15 Sept). *Mushrooms. T* **217** *and similar vert designs. Multicoloured. P* 15.
1042 10 c. Type **217** . . 30 20
1043 50 c. *Trogia buccinalis* . . 70 55
1044 $1 *Collybia subpruinosa* . . 1·25 1·00
1045 $4 *Leucocoprinus brebissonii* . . 3·00 4·00
1042/5 . . *Set of* 4 4·75 5·25
MS1046 102 × 82 mm $5 *Pyrrhoglossum pyrrhum* 12·00 11·00
An unissued 3$ and examples of No. 1045 with the face value shown as "4$" exist from stock dispersed by the liquidator of Format International Security Printers Ltd.

(218)

219 Auburn "Speedster" (1933)

1986 (15 Oct). *Appearance of Halley's Comet* (*2nd issue*). *Nos.* 1000/4 *optd with T* **218** (*in silver on* $5).
1047 5 c. Edmond Halley and Old Greenwich Observatory . . 15 10
1048 10 c. Messerschmitt Me 163B Komet (fighter aircraft), 1944 . . 20 10
1049 60 c. Montezuma (Aztec Emperor) and Comet in 1517 (from "Historias de las Indias de Neuva Espana") . . 1·00 65
1050 $4 Pocahontas saving Capt. John Smith and Comet in 1607 . . 4·50 4·00
1047/50 . . *Set of* 4 5·25 4·25
MS1051 101×70 mm. $5 Halley's Comet over English Harbour, Antigua . . 5·50 6·50

(Des J. Martin. Litho Questa)

1986 (20 Oct). *Centenary of First Benz Motor Car. T* **219** *and similar horiz designs. Multicoloured. P* 14.
1052 10 c. Type **219** . . 15 10
1053 15 c. Mercury "Sable" (1986) . . 20 10
1054 50 c. Cadillac (1959) . . 55 30
1055 60 c. Studebaker (1950) . . 70 45
1056 70 c. Lagonda "V-12" (1939) . . 80 55
1057 $1 Adler "Standard" (1930) . . 1·10 75
1058 $3 DKW (1956) . . 2·50 2·50
1059 $4 Mercedes "500K" (1936) . . 3·00 3·00
1052/9 . . *Set of* 8 8·00 7·00
MS1060 Two sheets, each 99 × 70 mm. (a) $5 Daimler (1896). (b) $5 Mercedes "Knight" (1921) *Set of* 2 *sheets* 7·00 6·50

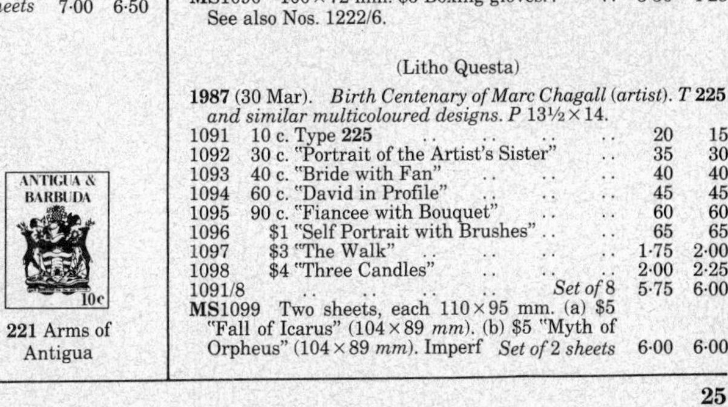

220 Young Mickey Mouse playing Santa Claus

221 Arms of Antigua

(Des Walt Disney Co. Litho Format)

1986 (4 Nov). *Christmas. T* **220** *and similar horiz designs showing Walt Disney cartoon characters as babies. Multicoloured. P* 11.
1061 25 c. Type **220** . . 45 35
1062 30 c. Mickey and Minnie Mouse building snowman . . 50 40
1063 40 c. Aunt Matilda and Goofy baking . . 55 45
1064 60 c. Goofy and Pluto . . 80 85
1065 70 c. Pluto, Donald and Daisy Duck carol singing . . 95 1·00
1066 $1.50, Donald Duck, Mickey Mouse and Pluto stringing popcorn . . 1·60 2·50
1067 $3 Grandma Duck and Minnie Mouse . . 3·00 4·50
1068 $4 Donald Duck and Pete . . 3·25 4·50
1061/8 . . *Set of* 8 10·00 13·00
MS1069 Two sheets, each 127 × 102 mm. P 14 × 13½. (a) $5 Goofy, Donald Duck and Minnie Mouse playing reindeer. (b) $5 Mickey Mouse, Donald and Daisy Duck playing with toys. *Set of* 2 *sheets* 11·00 12·00

1986 (25 Nov). *Coil stamps. T* **221** *and similar vert design. Litho. P* 14.
1070 10 c. new blue . . 50 50
1071 25 c. orange-vermilion . . 75 75
Design:—25 c. Flag of Antigua.

222 *Canada I* (1981)

223 Bridled Burrfish

(Des J. Iskowitz. Litho Format)

1987 (5 Feb). *America's Cup Yachting Championship. T* **222** *and similar multicoloured designs. P* 15.
1072 30 c. Type **222** . . 30 20
1073 60 c. *Gretel II* (1970) . . 45 50
1074 $1 *Sceptre* (1958) . . 85 1·00
1075 $3 *Vigilant* (1893) . . 2·25 3·00
1072/5 . . *Set of* 4 3·50 4·25
MS1076 113 × 84 mm. $5 *Australia II* defeating *Liberty* (1983) (*horiz*) . . 4·00 5·00

(Des G. Drummond. Litho Questa)

1987 (23 Feb). *Marine Life. T* **223** *and similar horiz designs. Multicoloured. P* 14.
1077 15 c. Type **223** . . 1·50 30
1078 30 c. Common Noddy . . 2·75 60
1079 40 c. Nassau Grouper . . 2·00 70
1080 50 c. Laughing Gull . . 4·00 1·50
1081 60 c. French Angelfish . . 2·75 1·50
1082 $1 Porkfish . . 2·75 1·75
1083 $2 Royal Tern . . 5·50 5·00
1084 $3 Sooty Tern . . 6·00 6·00
1077/84 . . *Set of* 8 24·00 15·00
MS1085 Two sheets, each 120 × 94 mm. (a) $5 Banded Butterflyfish. (b) $5 Brown Booby *Set of* 2 *sheets* 15·00 14·00
Nos. 1078, 1080 and 1083/5 are without the World Wildlife Fund logo shown on Type **223**.

224 Handball

225 "The Profile"

(Litho Questa)

1987 (23 Mar). *Olympic Games, Seoul* (1988) (*1st issue*). *T* **224** *and similar horiz designs. Multicoloured. P* 14.
1086 10 c. Type **224** . . 30 10
1087 60 c. Fencing . . 55 35
1088 $1 Gymnastics . . 75 75
1089 $3 Football . . 2·00 3·00
1086/9 . . *Set of* 4 3·25 3·75
MS1090 100 × 72 mm. $5 Boxing gloves . . 3·50 4·25
See also Nos. 1222/6.

(Litho Questa)

1987 (30 Mar). *Birth Centenary of Marc Chagall* (*artist*). *T* **225** *and similar multicoloured designs. P* 13½ × 14.
1091 10 c. Type **225** . . 20 15
1092 30 c. "Portrait of the Artist's Sister" . . 35 30
1093 40 c. "Bride with Fan" . . 40 40
1094 60 c. "David in Profile" . . 45 45
1095 90 c. "Fiancee with Bouquet" . . 60 60
1096 $1 "Self Portrait with Brushes" . . 65 65
1097 $3 "The Walk" . . 1·75 2·00
1098 $4 "Three Candles" . . 2·00 2·25
1091/8 . . *Set of* 8 5·75 6·00
MS1099 Two sheets, each 110 × 95 mm. (a) $5 "Fall of Icarus" (104 × 89 *mm*). (b) $5 "Myth of Orpheus" (104 × 89 *mm*). Imperf *Set of* 2 *sheets* 6·00 6·00

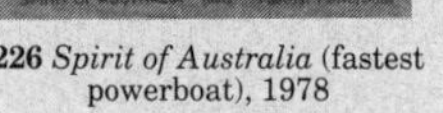

226 *Spirit of Australia* (fastest powerboat), 1978 **227** Lee Iacocca at Unveiling of Restored Statue

(Des W. Wright. Litho Format)

1987 (9 Apr). *Milestones of Transportation. T* **226** *and similar horiz designs. Multicoloured. P* 15.

1100 10 c. Type **226** 40 30
1101 15 c. Werner von Siemen's electric locomotive, 1879 .. .. .. 60 40
1102 30 c. U.S.S. *Triton* (first submerged circumnavigation), 1960 .. .. .. 60 45
1103 50 c. Trevithick's steam carriage (first passenger-carrying vehicle), 1801 70 60
1104 60 c. U.S.S. *New Jersey* (battleship), 1942 80 70
1105 70 c. Draisaine bicycle, 1818 .. .. 80 80
1106 90 c. *United States* (liner) (holder of Blue Riband), 1952 .. .. .. 1·00 1·00
1107 $1.50, Cierva C.4 (first autogyro), 1923 1·40 2·00
1108 $2 Curtiss NC-4 flying boat (first transatlantic flight), 1919 .. 1·50 2·25
1109 $3 *Queen Elizabeth 2* (liner), 1969 .. 2·50 3·00
1100/9 .. .. *Set of* 10 9·00 10·50

(Litho Questa)

1987 (23 Apr). *Centenary of Statue of Liberty* (1986) (*2nd issue*). *T* **227** *and similar multicoloured designs. P* 14.

1110 15 c. Type **227** 15 15
1111 30 c. Statue at sunset (side view) 20 20
1112 45 c. Aerial view of head 30 30
1113 50 c. Lee Iacocca and torch 35 35
1114 60 c. Workmen inside head of Statue (*horiz*) 35 35
1115 90 c. Restoration work (*horiz*) 50 50
1116 $1 Head of Statue 55 55
1117 $2 Statue at sunset (front view) .. .. 1·00 1·25
1118 $3 Inspecting restoration work (*horiz*) .. 1·25 1·75
1119 $5 Statue at night .. .. .. 2·00 3·00
1110/19 .. .. *Set of* 10 6·00 7·50

228 Grace Kelly **229** Scouts around Camp Fire and Red Kangaroo

(Des Lynda Bruscheni. Litho Questa)

1987 (11 May). *Entertainers. T* **228** *and similar vert designs. Multicoloured. P* 14.

1120 15 c. Type **228** 90 40
1121 30 c. Marilyn Monroe .. .. 1·75 65
1122 45 c. Orson Welles 90 60
1123 50 c. Judy Garland 90 65
1124 60 c. John Lennon .. .. 2·25 1·10
1125 $1 Rock Hudson .. .. 1·40 1·10
1126 $2 John Wayne .. .. 2·25 2·00
1127 $3 Elvis Presley .. .. 6·00 3·50
1120/7 .. .. *Set of* 8 14·50 9·00

(Litho Format)

1987 (25 May). *16th World Scout Jamboree, Australia. T* **229** *and similar horiz designs. Multicoloured. P* 15.

1128 10 c. Type **229** 50 20
1129 60 c. Scouts canoeing and Blue-winged Kookaburra .. .. 1·25 70
1130 $1 Scouts on assault course and Ring-tailed Rock Wallaby .. .. .. 1·25 85
1131 $3 Field kitchen and Koala .. .. 2·00 4·00
1128/31 .. .. *Set of* 4 4·50 5·25
MS1132 103×78 mm. $5 Flags of Antigua, Australia and Scout Movement .. .. .. 2·75 3·25

230 Whistling Frog **(231)**

(Des B. Bundock. Litho Questa)

1987 (15 June). *"Capex '87" International Stamp Exhibition, Toronto. Reptiles and Amphibians. T* **230** *and similar horiz designs. Multicoloured. P* 14.

1133 30 c. Type **230** 35 20
1134 60 c. Croaking Lizard 45 40
1135 $1 Antiguan Anole 70 60
1136 $3 Red-footed Tortoise .. .. .. 1·75 2·50
1133/6 .. .. *Set of* 4 3·00 3·25
MS1137 106×76 mm. $5 Ground Lizard .. 2·25 2·75

1987 (9 Sept). *10th Death Anniv of Elvis Presley (entertainer). No.* 1127 *optd with T* **231**.

1138 $3 Elvis Presley .. .. 4·75 3·50

232 House of Burgesses, Virginia ("Freedom of Speech") **233** "Madonna and Child" (Bernardo Daddi)

(Des and litho Questa)

1987 (16 Nov). *Bicentenary of U.S. Constitution. T* **232** *and similar multicoloured designs. P* 14.

1139 15 c. Type **232** 10 10
1140 45 c. State Seal, Connecticut 20 25
1141 60 c. State Seal, Delaware 25 35
1142 $4 Gouverneur Morris (Pennsylvania delegate) (*vert*) .. .. 1·75 2·25
1139/42 .. .. *Set of* 4 2·10 2·75
MS1143 105×75 mm. $5 Roger Sherman (Connecticut delegate) (*vert*) .. .. .. 2·25 2·75

Nos. 1139/42 were each issued in sheetlets of five stamps and one stamp-size label, which appears in the centre of the bottom row.

(Litho Questa)

1987 (1 Dec). *Christmas. Religious Paintings. T* **233** *and similar vert designs. Multicoloured. P* 14.

1144 45 c. Type **233** 30 15
1145 60 c. "St. Joseph" (detail, "The Nativity" (Sano di Pietro)) 40 30
1146 $1 "Virgin Mary" (detail, "The Nativity" (Sano di Pietro)) 60 55
1147 $4 "Music-making Angel" (Melozzo da Forli) .. .. 2·00 3·00
1144/7 .. .. *Set of* 4 3·00 3·50
MS1148 99×70 mm. $5 "The Flight into Egypt" (Sano di Pietro) .. .. 2·25 2·75

234 Wedding Photograph, 1947 **235** Great Blue Heron

(Des and litho Questa)

1988 (8 Feb). *Royal Ruby Wedding. T* **234** *and similar vert designs. P* 14.

1149 25 c. deep brown, black and bright new blue 15 15
1150 60 c. multicoloured 30 40
1151 $2 deep brown, black and light green .. 90 1·10
1152 $3 multicoloured .. .. 1·40 1·60
1149/52 .. .. *Set of* 4 2·50 3·00
MS1153 102×77 mm. $5 multicoloured .. .. 2·25 2·75

Designs:—60 c. Queen Elizabeth II; $2 Princess Elizabeth and Prince Philip with Prince Charles at his christening, 1948; $3 Queen Elizabeth (from photo by Tim Graham), 1980; $5 Royal Family, 1952.

(Des W. Wright. Litho Questa)

1988 (1 Mar). *Birds of Antigua. T* **235** *and similar multicoloured designs. P* 14.

1154 10 c. Type **235** 35 30
1155 15 c. Ringed Kingfisher (*horiz*) 35 30
1156 50 c. Bananaquit (*horiz*) 70 50
1157 60 c. Purple Gallinule (*horiz*) 70 50
1158 70 c. Blue-hooded Euphonia (*horiz*) .. 80 55
1159 $1 Brown-throated Conure ("Caribbean Parakeet") .. .. 1·00 75
1160 $3 Troupial (*horiz*) .. .. .. 2·50 3·25
1161 $4 Purple-throated Carib (*horiz*) .. 2·50 3·25
1154/61 .. .. *Set of* 8 8·00 8·50
MS1162 Two sheets, each 115×86 mm. (a) $5 Greater Flamingo. (b) $5 Brown Pelican *Set of* 2 *sheets* 4·50 5·50

236 First Aid at Daycare Centre, Antigua

(Des G. Vasarhelyi. Litho Format)

1988 (10 Mar). *Salvation Army's Community Service. T* **23**[illegible] *and similar horiz designs. Multicoloured. P* 14×13½.

1163 25 c. Type **236** 65
1164 30 c. Giving penicillin injection, Indonesia 65
1165 40 c. Children at daycare centre, Bolivia .. 75
1166 45 c. Rehabilitation of the handicapped, India 75
1167 50 c. Training blind man, Kenya .. .. 90 1·[illegible]
1168 60 c. Weighing baby, Ghana .. .. 90 1·[illegible]
1169 $1 Training typist, Zambia .. .. 1·40 1·[illegible]
1170 $2 Emergency food kitchen, Sri Lanka .. 2·00 3·[illegible]
1163/70 .. .. *Set of* 8 7·00 8·[illegible]
MS1171 152×83 mm. $5 General Eva Burrows 3·75 4·[illegible]

237 Columbus' Second Fleet, 1493 **238** "Bust of Christ"

(Des I. MacLaury. Litho Questa)

1988 (16 Mar–16 May). *500th Anniv of Discovery of Ameri*[illegible] *by Columbus* (1992) (*1st issue*). *T* **237** *and similar hor*[illegible] *designs. Multicoloured. P* 14.

1172 10 c. Type **237** 50
1173 30 c. Painos Indian village and fleet (16.5) 50
1174 45 c. *Santa Mariagalante* (flagship) and Painos village (16.5) 60
1175 60 c. Painos Indians offering Columbus fruit and vegetables (16.5) 60
1176 90 c. Painos Indian and Columbus with Scarlet Macaw .. .. .. 1·00
1177 $1 Columbus landing on island .. .. 1·00 1·[illegible]
1178 $3 Spanish soldier and fleet .. .. 2·00 2·[illegible]
1179 $4 Fleet under sail (16.5) .. .. 2·25 2·[illegible]
1172/9 .. .. *Set of* 8 7·50 8·[illegible]
MS1180 Two sheets, each 110×80 mm. (a) $5 Queen Isabella's cross. (b) $5 Gold coin of Ferdinand and Isabella (16.5) *Set of* 2 *sheets* 6·50 7·[illegible]

See also Nos. 1267/71, 1360/8, 1503/11, 1654/60 and 1670/1.

(Litho Questa)

1988 (11 Apr). *500th Birth Anniv of Titian. T* **238** *and simil*[illegible] *vert designs showing paintings. Multicoloured. P* 13½×14.

1181 30 c. Type **238** 25
1182 40 c. "Scourging of Christ" 30
1183 45 c. "Madonna in Glory with Saints" .. 30
1184 50 c. "The Averoldi Polyptych" (detail) .. 35
1185 $1 "Christ Crowned with Thorns" .. 55
1186 $2 "Christ Mocked" .. .. .. 90 1·[illegible]
1187 $3 "Christ and Simon of Cyrene" .. 1·50 1·[illegible]
1188 $4 "Crucifixion with Virgin and Saints" 1·75 2·[illegible]
1181/8 .. .. *Set of* 8 5·50 6·[illegible]
MS1189 Two sheets, each 110×95 mm. (a) $5 "Ecce Homo" (detail). (b) $5 "Noli me Tangere" (detail) *Set of* 2 *sheets* 6·50 8·[illegible]

239 Two Yachts rounding Buoy

(Des G. Drummond. Litho Format)

1988 (18 Apr). *Sailing Week. T* **239** *and similar horiz design*[illegible] *Multicoloured. P* 15.

1190 30 c. Type **239** 20
1191 60 c. Three yachts 35
1192 $1 British yacht under way 50
1193 $3 Three yachts (*different*) .. .. 1·10 2·[illegible]
1190/3 .. .. *Set of* 4 2·00 3·[illegible]
MS1194 103×92 mm. $5 Two yachts .. .. 1·75 3·[illegible]

240 Mickey Mouse and Diver with Porpoise **(241)**

(Des Walt Disney Co. Litho Questa)

8 (3 May). *Disney EPCOT Centre, Orlando, Florida. T* **240** *nd similar multicoloured designs showing cartoon characters nd exhibits. P* 14×13½ *(horiz) or* 13½×14 *(vert).*

5 1 c. Type **240** 10 10
6 2 c. Goofy and Mickey Mouse with futuristic car (*vert*) 10 10
7 3 c. Mickey Mouse and Goofy as Atlas (*vert*) 10 10
8 4 c. Mickey Mouse and *Edaphosaurus* (prehistoric reptile) 10 10
9 5 c. Mickey Mouse at Journey into Imagination exhibit 10 10
0 10 c. Mickey Mouse collecting vegetables (*vert*) 10 10
1 25 c. Type **240** 25 25
2 30 c. As 2 c. 25 25
3 40 c. As 3 c. 30 30
4 60 c. As 4 c. 50 50
5 70 c. As 5 c. 60 60
6 $1.50, As 10 c. .. .. 1·25 1·25
7 $3 Goofy and Mickey Mouse with robot (*vert*) .. .. 2·00 2·00
8 $4 Mickey Mouse and Clarabelle at Horizons exhibit .. .. 2·25 2·25
5/1208 .. .. *Set of* 14 7·00 7·00
1209 Two sheets, each 125×99 mm. (a) $5 Mickey Mouse and monorail (*vert*). (b) $5 Mickey Mouse flying over EPCOT Centre *Set of 2 sheets* 6·00 6·50

38 (9 May). *Stamp Exhibitions. Nos.* 1083/5 *optd as T* **241** *showing various emblems.*
10 $2 Royal Tern (optd T **241**, Prague) .. 1·75 1·75
11 $3 Sooty Tern (optd "INDEPENDENCE 40", Israel) .. .. 2·25 2·25
S1212 Two sheets, each 120×94 mm. (a) $5 Banded Butterflyfish (optd "OLYMPHILEX 88", Seoul). (b) $5 Brown Booby (optd FINLANDIA 88", Helsinki) *Set of 2 sheets* 5·50 6·00

242 Jacaranda

243 Gymnastics

(Des Mary Walters. Litho Questa)

38 (16 May). *Flowering Trees. T* **242** *and similar vert designs. Multicoloured. P* 14.
13 10 c. Type **242** 20 15
14 30 c. Cordia 25 20
15 50 c. Orchid Tree 40 40
16 90 c. Flamboyant 50 50
17 $1 African Tulip Tree 55 55
18 $2 Potato Tree .. .. 1·10 1·25
19 $3 Crepe Myrtle .. .. 1·40 1·75
20 $4 Pitch Apple .. .. 1·75 2·50
13/20 .. .. *Set of* 8 5·50 6·50
S1221 Two sheets, each 106×76 mm. (a) $5 Cassia. (b) $5 Chinaberry *Set of 2 sheets* 5·00 6·00

(Des J. Martin. Litho Questa)

88 (10 June). *Olympic Games, Seoul (2nd issue). T* **243** *and similar multicoloured designs. P* 14.
22 40 c. Type **243** 20 25
23 60 c. Weightlifting 25 30
24 $1 Water polo (*horiz*) 45 50
25 $3 Boxing (*horiz*) .. .. 1·40 2·00
22/5 .. .. *Set of* 4 2·10 2·75
S1226 114×80 mm. $5 Runner with Olympic torch .. .. 2·00 3·00

244 *Danaus plexippus*

(Des S. Heimann. Litho Questa)

88 (29 Aug)–**90**. *Caribbean Butterflies. T* **244** *and similar horiz designs. Multicoloured. P* 14.
27 1 c. Type **144** 20 20
28 2 c. *Greta diaphanus* 30 30
29 3 c. *Calisto archebates* 30 30
30 5 c. *Hamadryas feronia* 40 40
31 10 c. *Mestra dorcas* 50 30
32 15 c. *Hypolimnas misippus* 60 30
33 20 c. *Dione juno* 70 30
34 25 c. *Heliconius charithonia* 70 30
35 30 c. *Eurema pyro* 70 30
36 40 c. *Papilio androgeus* 75 30
37 45 c. *Anteos maerula* 75 30
38 50 c. *Aphrissa orbis* 90 45
39 60 c. *Astraptes xagua* .. .. 1·00 60
40 $1 *Heliopetes arsalte* .. .. 1·50 1·00
41 $2 *Polites baracoa* .. .. 2·50 3·25
42 $2.50, *Phocides pigmalion* .. .. .. 3·00 3·75
43 $5 *Prepona amphitoe* .. .. 4·50 5·50
44 $10 *Oarisma nanus* .. .. 7·00 8·00
44*a* $20 *Parides lycimenes* (19.2.90) .. .. 13·00 15·00
27/44*a* .. .. *Set of* 19 35·00 35·00

245 President Kennedy and Family

246 Minnie Mouse carol singing

(Des J. Iskowitz. Litho Questa)

1988 (23 Nov). *25th Death Anniv of John F. Kennedy (American statesman). T* **245** *and similar horiz designs, each showing different inset portrait. Multicoloured. P* 14.
1245 1 c. Type **245** 10 10
1246 2 c. Kennedy commanding *PT109* 10 10
1247 3 c. Funeral cortege 10 10
1248 4 c. In motorcade, Mexico City 10 10
1249 30 c. As 1 c. 25 15
1250 60 c. As 4 c. 35 30
1251 $1 As 3 c. 60 60
1252 $4 As 2 c. .. .. 1·75 2·50
1245/52 .. .. *Set of* 8 2·75 3·25
MS1253 105 × 75 mm. $5 Kennedy taking presidential oath of office .. .. .. 2·50 3·25

(Des Walt Disney Co. Litho Questa)

1988 (1 Dec). *Christmas. "Mickey's Christmas Chorale". T* **246** *and similar multicoloured designs showing Walt Disney cartoon characters. P* 13½ × 14.
1254 10 c. Type **246** 30 30
1255 25 c. Pluto 45 45
1256 30 c. Mickey Mouse playing ukelele 45 45
1257 70 c. Donald Duck and nephew 80 80
1258 $1 Mordie and Ferdie carol singing .. 80 1·00
a. Sheetlet. Nos. 1258/65 .. .. .. 5·75
1259 $1 Goofy carol singing .. .. .. 80 1·00
1260 $1 Chip n'Dale sliding off roof .. .. 80 1·00
1261 $1 Two of Donald Duck's nephews at window .. .. 80 1·00
1262 $1 As 10 c. .. .. 80 1·00
1263 $1 As 25 c. .. .. 80 1·00
1264 $1 As 30 c. .. .. 80 1·00
1265 $1 As 70 c. .. .. 80 1·00
1254/65 .. .. *Set of* 12 7·50 9·00
MS1266 Two sheets, each 127 × 102 mm. (a) $7 Donald Duck playing trumpet and Mickey and Minnie Mouse in carriage. P 13½ × 14. (b) $7 Mickey Mouse and friends singing carols on roller skates (*horiz*). P 14 × 13½ *Set of 2 sheets* 8·50 8·50

Nos. 1258/65 were printed together, *se-tenant* as a composite design, in sheetlets of eight.

247 Arawak Warriors

248 De Havilland Comet 4 Airliner

(Des D. Miller. Litho Questa)

1989 (16 May). *500th Anniv of Discovery of America by Columbus (1992) (2nd issue). Pre-Columbian Arawak Society. T* **247** *and similar vert designs. Multicoloured. P* 14.
1267 $1.50, Type **247** .. .. 1·00 1·25
a. Horiz strip of 4. Nos. 1267/70 .. .. 3·50
1268 $1.50, Whip dancers .. .. 1·00 1·25
1269 $1.50, Whip dancers and chief with pineapple .. .. 1·00 1·25
1270 $1.50, Family and camp fire .. .. .. 1·00 1·25
1267/70 .. .. *Set of* 4 3·50 4·50
MS1271 71 × 84 mm. $6 Arawak chief .. 2·50 3·00

Nos. 1267/70 were printed together, *se-tenant*, in horizontal strips of 4 throughout the sheet, each strip forming a composite design.

(Des W. Wright. Litho Questa)

1989 (29 May). *50th Anniv of First Jet Flight. T* **248** *and similar horiz designs. Multicoloured. P* 14.
1272 10 c. Type **248** 35 35
1273 30 c. Messerschmitt Me 262 fighter 55 45
1274 40 c. Boeing 707 airliner 60 45
1275 60 c. Canadair CL-13 Sabre ("F-86 Sabre") fighter 75 55
1276 $1 Lockheed F-104 Starfighter .. .. 1·00 90
1277 $2 Douglas DC-10 airliner .. .. .. 2·00 2·25
1278 $3 Boeing 747-300/400 airliner .. .. 2·50 2·75
1279 $4 McDonnell Douglas F-4 Phantom II fighter .. .. 2·50 2·75
1272/9 .. .. *Set of* 8 9·00 9·50
MS1280 Two sheets, each 114×83 mm. (a) $7 Grumman F-14A Tomcat fighter. (b) $7 Concorde airliner .. .. *Set of 2 sheets* 8·00 9·50

249 *Festivale*

(Des W. Wright. Litho Questa)

1989 (20 June). *Caribbean Cruise Ships. T* **249** *and similar horiz designs. Multicoloured. P* 14.
1281 25 c. Type **249** 55 30
1282 45 c. *Southward* 80 30
1283 50 c. *Sagafjord* 80 30
1284 60 c. *Daphne* 80 50
1285 75 c. *Cunard Countess* 90 70
1286 90 c. *Song of America* .. .. 1·00 90
1287 $3 *Island Princess* .. .. 2·50 3·50
1288 $4 *Galileo* .. .. 2·50 3·50
1281/8 .. .. *Set of* 8 9·00 9·00
MS1289 (a) 113 × 87 mm. $6 *Norway*. (b) 111 × 82 mm. $6 *Oceanic* *Set of 2 sheets* 6·50 8·00

250 "Fish swimming by Duck half-submerged in Stream"

(Litho Questa)

1989 (1 July). *Japanese Art. Paintings by Hiroshige. T* **250** *and similar horiz designs. Multicoloured. P* 14 × 13½.
1290 25 c. Type **250** 55 30
1291 45 c. "Crane and Wave" 65 40
1292 50 c. "Sparrows and Morning Glories" .. 70 40
1293 60 c. "Crested Blackbird and Flowering Cherry" 80 50
1294 $1 "Great Knot sitting among Water Grass" .. .. 1·00 70
1295 $2 "Goose on a Bank of Water" .. .. 2·00 2·00
1296 $3 "Black Paradise Flycatcher and Blossoms" .. .. 2·50 2·50
1297 $4 "Sleepy Owl perched on a Pine Branch" .. .. 2·50 2·50
1290/7 .. .. *Set of* 8 9·50 8·50
MS1298 Two sheets, each 102 × 75 mm. (a) $5 "Bullfinch flying near a Clematis Branch". (b) $5 "Titmouse on a Cherry Branch" *Set of 2 sheets* 7·50 7·50

Nos. 1290/7 were each printed in sheetlets of 10 containing two horizontal strips of 5 stamps separated by printed labels commemorating Emperor Hirohito.

251 Mickey and Minnie Mouse in Helicopter over River Seine

(Des Walt Disney Company. Litho Questa)

1989 (7 July). *"Philexfrance 89" International Stamp Exhibition, Paris. T* **251** *and similar multicoloured designs showing Walt Disney cartoon characters in Paris. P* 14 × 13½.
1299 1 c. Type **251** 10 10
1300 2 c. Goofy and Mickey Mouse passing Arc de Triomphe 10 10
1301 3 c. Mickey Mouse painting picture of Notre Dame 10 10
1302 4 c. Mickey and Minnie Mouse with Pluto leaving Metro station 10 10
1303 5 c. Minnie Mouse as model in fashion show 10 10
1304 10 c. Daisy Duck, Minnie Mouse and Clarabelle as Folies Bergere dancers 10 10
1305 $5 Mickey and Minnie Mouse shopping in street market .. .. 4·75 5·50
1306 $6 Mickey and Minnie Mouse, Jose Carioca and Donald Duck at pavement cafe .. .. 4·75 5·50
1299/1306 .. .. *Set of* 8 9·00 10·00
MS1307 Two sheets, each 127 × 101 mm. (a) $5 Mickey and Minnie Mouse in hot air balloon. P 14 × 13½. (b) $5 Mickey Mouse at Pompidou Centre cafe (*vert*). P 13½ × 14 *Set of 2 sheets* 9·00 10·00

MINIMUM PRICE

The minimum price quote is 10p which represents a handling charge rather than a basis for valuing common stamps. For further notes about prices see introductory pages.

252 Goalkeeper

253 *Mycena pura*

(Des D. Bruckner. Litho B.D.T.)

1989 (21 Aug). *World Cup Football Championship, Italy* (1990). *T* **252** *and similar multicoloured designs. P* 14.
1308 15 c. Type **252** 65 15
1309 25 c. Goalkeeper moving towards ball .. 75 15
1310 $1 Goalkeeper reaching for ball .. 1·50 1·25
1311 $4 Goalkeeper saving goal .. .. 3·00 4·25
1308/11 .. .. *Set of* 4 5·50 5·25
MS1312 Two sheets, each 75 × 105 mm. (a) $5 Three players competing for ball (*horiz*). (b) $5 Ball and players' legs (*horiz*) *Set of* 2 *sheets* 6·50 7·50

(Litho Questa)

1989 (12 Oct). *Fungi. T* **253** *and similar multicoloured designs. P* 14.
1313 10 c. Type **253** 50 40
1314 25 c. *Psathyrella tuberculata* (*vert*) .. 75 40
1315 50 c. *Psilocybe cubensis* .. .. .. 1·00 60
1316 60 c. *Leptonia caeruleocapitata* (*vert*) .. 1·00 70
1317 75 c. *Xeromphalina tenuipes* (*vert*) .. 1·25 90
1318 $1 *Chlorophyllum molybdites* (*vert*) .. 1·40 1·10
1319 $3 *Marasmius haematocephalus* .. 2·75 3·25
1320 $4 *Cantharellus cinnabarinus* .. .. 2·75 3·25
1313/20 .. .. *Set of* 8 10·00 9·50
MS1321 Two sheets, each 88×62 mm. (a) $6 *Leucopaxillus gracillimus* (*vert*). (b) $6 *Volvariella volvacea* .. .. *Set of* 2 *sheets* 12·00 13·00

254 Desmarest's Hutia

255 Goofy and Old Printing Press

(Des J. Barbaris. Litho B.D.T.)

1989 (19 Oct). *Local Fauna. T* **254** *and similar multicoloured designs. P* 14.
1322 25 c. Type **254** 60 45
1323 45 c. Caribbean Monk Seal .. .. 1·50 80
1324 60 c. Mustache Bat (*vert*) .. .. 1·00 85
1325 $4 American Manatee (*vert*) .. .. 3·00 4·50
1322/5 .. .. *Set of* 4 5·50 6·00
MS1326 113×87 mm. $5 West Indies Giant Rice Rat .. .. 6·00 7·00

(Des Walt Disney Co. Litho Questa)

1989 (2 Nov). *"American Philately". T* **255** *and similar multicoloured designs, each showing Walt Disney cartoon characters with stamps and the logo of the American Philatelic Society. P* 13½×14.
1327 1 c. Type **255** 10 10
1328 2 c. Donald Duck cancelling first day cover for Mickey Mouse 10 10
1329 3 c. Donald Duck's nephews reading recruiting poster for Pony Express riders 10 10
1330 4 c. Morty and Ferdie as early radio broadcasters 10 10
1331 5 c. Donald Duck and water buffalo watching television 10 10
1332 10 c. Donald Duck with stamp album .. 10 10
1333 $4 Daisy Duck with computer system .. 3·50 4·00
1334 $6 Donald's nephews with stereo radio, trumpet and guitar .. .. .. 4·50 5·00
1327/34 .. .. *Set of* 8 7·50 8·50
MS1335 Two sheets, each 127×102 mm. (a) $5 Donald's nephews donating stamps to charity. P 13½×14. (b) $5 Minnie Mouse flying mailplane upside down (*horiz*). P 14×13½ Set of 2 *sheets* 10·00 11·00

256 Mickey Mouse and Donald Duck with Camden and Amboy Locomotive *John Bull*, 1831

(Des Walt Disney Co. Litho Questa)

1989 (17 Nov). *"World Stamp Expo '89" International Stamp Exhibition, Washington* (1*st issue*). *T* **256** *and similar multicoloured designs showing Walt Disney cartoon characters and locomotives. P* 14×13½.
1336 25 c. Type **256** 50 50
1337 45 c. Mickey Mouse and friends with *Atlantic*, 1832 .. .. .. 60 50
1338 50 c. Mickey Mouse and Goofy with *William Crooks*, 1861 .. .. 60 50
1339 60 c. Mickey Mouse and Goofy with *Minnetonka*, 1869 .. .. .. 70 65
1340 $1 Chip n'Dale with *Thatcher Perkins*, 1863 .. .. 75 75
1341 $2 Mickey and Minnie Mouse with *Pioneer*, 1848 .. .. .. 1·50 2·00
1342 $3 Mickey Mouse and Donald Duck with cog railway locomotive *Peppersass*, 1869 .. .. 1·75 2·50
1343 $4 Mickey Mouse with Huey, Dewey and Louie aboard N.Y. World's Fair *Gimbels Flyer*, 1939 .. .. .. 2·00 2·50
1336/43 .. .. *Set of* 8 7·50 9·00
MS1344 Two sheets, each 127×101 mm. (a) $6 Mickey Mouse and locomotive *Thomas Jefferson*, 1835 (*vert*). P 13½×14. (b) $6 Mickey Mouse and friends at Central Pacific "Golden Spike" ceremony, 1869. P 14×13½ .. *Set of* 2 *sheets* 7·50 8·50

257 Smithsonian Institution, Washington

258 Launch of "Apollo 11"

(Des Design Element. Litho Questa)

1989 (17 Nov). *"World Stamp Expo '89" International Stamp Exhibition, Washington* (2*nd issue*). *Sheet* 78×61 *mm. P* 14.
MS1345 **257** $4 multicoloured .. .. .. 1·75 2·25

(Des J. Iskowitz. Litho B.D.T.)

1989 (24 Nov). *20th Anniv of First Manned Landing on Moon. T* **258** *and similar multicoloured designs. P* 14.
1346 10 c. Type **258** 30 20
1347 45 c. Aldrin on Moon 70 30
1348 $1 Module *Eagle* over Moon (*horiz*) .. 1·25 1·00
1349 $4 Recovery of "Apollo 11" crew after splashdown (*horiz*) .. .. .. 2·75 3·75
1346/9 .. .. *Set of* 4 4·50 4·75
MS1350 107×77 mm. $5 Astronaut Neil Armstrong .. .. 3·50 4·00

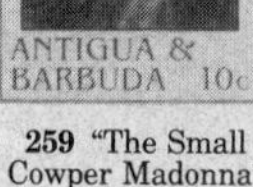

259 "The Small Cowper Madonna" (Raphael)

260 Star-eyed Hermit Crab

(Litho Questa)

1989 (11 Dec). *Christmas. Paintings by Raphael and Giotto. T* **259** *and similar vert designs. Multicoloured. P* 14.
1351 10 c. Type **259** 10 10
1352 25 c. "Madonna of the Goldfinch" (Raphael) 20 15
1353 30 c. "The Alba Madonna" (Raphael) .. 20 15
1354 50 c. Saint (detail, "Bologna Altarpiece") (Giotto) 40 30
1355 60 c. Angel (detail, "Bologna Altarpiece") (Giotto) 45 35
1356 70 c. Angel slaying serpent (detail, "Bologna Altarpiece") (Giotto) .. 50 40
1357 $4 Evangelist (detail, "Bologna Altarpiece") (Giotto) .. .. .. 2·50 3·00
1358 $5 "Madonna of Foligno" (detail) (Raphael) .. .. 3·00 3·75
1351/8 .. .. *Set of* 8 6·50 7·50
MS1359 Two sheets, each 71×96 mm. (a) $5 "The Marriage of the Virgin" (detail) (Raphael). (b) $5 Madonna and Child (detail, "Bologna Altarpiece") (Giotto) .. .. *Set of* 2 *sheets* 7·00 8·50

(Des Mary Walters. Litho Questa)

1990 (26 Mar). *500th Anniv of Discovery of America by Columbus* (1992) (3*rd issue*). *New World Natural History – Marine Life. T* **260** *and similar vert designs. Multicoloured. P* 14.
1360 10 c. Type **260** 15 15
1361 20 c. Spiny Lobster 20 20
1362 25 c. Magnificent Banded Fanworm .. 25 25
1363 45 c. Cannonball Jellyfish 40 40
1364 60 c. Red-spiny Sea Star 60 60
1365 $2 Peppermint Shrimp .. .. .. 1·50 2·00
1366 $3 Coral Crab .. .. 1·75 2·25
1367 $4 Branching Fire Coral .. .. 2·25 2·50
1360/7 .. .. *Set of* 8 6·25 7·50
MS1368 Two sheets, each 100×69 mm. (a) $5 Common Sea Fan. (b) $5 Portuguese Man-of-war *Set of* 2 *sheets* 7·00 8·00

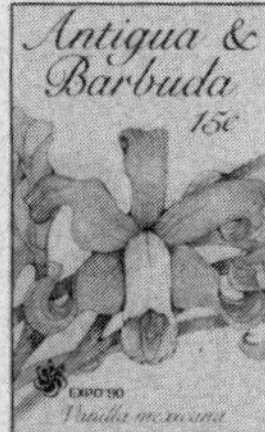

261 *Vanilla mexicana*

262 Queen Victoria and Queen Elizabeth II

(Des Mary Walters. Litho Questa)

1990 (17 Apr). *"EXPO 90" International Garden and Green Exhibition, Osaka. Orchids. T* **261** *and similar vert desig Multicoloured. P* 14.
1369 15 c. Type **261** 50
1370 45 c. *Epidendrum ibaguense* 70
1371 50 c. *Epidendrum secundum* 75
1372 60 c. *Maxillaria conferta* 80
1373 $1 *Oncidium altissimum* .. .. 1·10
1374 $2 *Spiranthes lanceolata* .. .. 1·75 2
1375 $3 *Tonopsis utricularioides* .. .. 2·25 2
1376 $5 *Epidendrum nocturnum* .. .. 3·25 3
1369/76 .. .. *Set of* 8 10·00 10
MS1377 Two sheets, each 102×70 mm. (a) $5 *Octomeria graminifolia*. (b) $5 *Rodriguezia lanceolata* .. .. .. *Set of* 2 *sheets* 5·50 7

(Des M. Pollard. Litho B.D.T)

1990 (3 May). *150th Anniv of the Penny Black. T* **262** *a similar horiz designs. P* 14½×14.
1378 **262** 45 c. blue-green 60
1379 – 60 c. magenta 70
1380 – $5 ultramarine .. .. .. 3·25 4
1378/80 .. .. *Set of* 3 4·00 4
MS1381 102×80 mm. **262** $6 blackish purple 3·75 4
Designs:—60 c, $5 As Type **262**, but with differ backgrounds.

263 *Britannia* (mail paddle-steamer), 1840

(Des M. Pollard. Litho B.D.T.)

1990 (3 May). *"Stamp World London 90" International Sta Exhibition. T* **263** *and similar horiz designs. P* 13½.
1382 50 c. deep grey-green and scarlet-vermilion 65
1383 75 c. purple-brown and scarlet-vermilion 85
1384 $4 deep ultramarine & scarlet-vermilion 3·25 4
1382/4 .. .. *Set of* 3 4·25 5
MS1385 104×81 mm. $6 brownish black and scarlet-vermilion .. .. 3·25 4
Designs:—75 c. Travelling Post Office sorting van, 1892; Short S.23 Empire "C" Class flying boat *Centaurus*, 1938; Post Office underground railway, London, 1927.

264 Flamefish

265 "Voyager 2" passing Saturn

(Des G. Drummond. Litho Questa)

1990 (21 May). *Reef Fishes. T* **264** *and similar horiz desig Multicoloured. P* 14.
1386 10 c. Type **264** 45
1387 15 c. Coney 55
1388 50 c. Long-spined Squirrelfish 80
1389 60 c. Sergeant Major 80
1390 $1 Yellow-tailed Snapper .. .. 1·10
1391 $2 Rock Beauty .. .. 2·00 2
1392 $3 Spanish Hogfish .. .. .. 2·50 3
1393 $4 Striped Parrotfish .. .. .. 2·50 3
1386/93 .. .. *Set of* 8 9·50 10
MS1394 Two sheets, each 99×70 mm. (a) $5 Black-barred Soldierfish. (b) $5 Four-eyed Butterflyfish .. .. .. *Set of* 2 *sheets* 7·50 9

(Des K. Gromell. Litho B.D.T)

1990 (11 June). *Achievements in Space. T* **265** *and simi square designs. Multicoloured. P* 14.
1395 45 c. Type **265** 50
a. Sheetlet. Nos. 1395/1414 .. .. 9·00
1396 45 c. "Pioneer 11" photographing Saturn 50
1397 45 c. Astronaut in transporter 50
1398 45 c. Space shuttle *Columbia* 50
1399 45 c. "Apollo 10" command module on parachutes 50
1400 45 c. "Skylab" space station 50
1401 45 c. Astronaut Edward White in space .. 50
1402 45 c. "Apollo" spacecraft on joint mission .. 50
1403 45 c. "Soyuz" spacecraft on joint mission .. 50
1404 45 c. "Mariner 1" passing Venus 50
1405 45 c. "Gemini 4" capsule 50
1406 45 c. "Sputnik 1" 50
1407 45 c. Hubble space telescope 50

08 45 c. North American X-15 .. .. .. 50 50
09 45 c. Bell XS-1 airplane 50 50
10 45 c. "Apollo 17" astronaut and lunar rock formation 50 50
11 45 c. Lunar Rover 50 50
12 45 c. "Apollo 14" lunar module 50 50
13 45 c. Astronaut Buzz Aldrin on Moon .. 50 50
14 45 c. Soviet "Lunokhod" lunar vehicle .. 50 50
95/1414 .. .. .. *Set of* 20 9·00 9·00
Nos. 1395/1414 were printed together, *se-tenant*, in sheetlets 20 forming a composite design.

266 Queen Mother in Evening Dress

267 Mickey Mouse as Animator

(Des D. Miller. Litho Questa)

90 (27 Aug). *90th Birthday of Queen Elizabeth the Queen Mother. T* **266** *and similar vert designs showing recent photographs of the Queen Mother. P* 14.
15 15 c. multicoloured 30 15
16 35 c. multicoloured 40 25
17 75 c. multicoloured 70 70
18 $3 multicoloured .. .. .. 2·25 3·00
15/18 .. .. *Set of* 4 3·25 3·50
S1419 67×98 mm. $6 multicoloured .. .. 3·75 4·50

(Des Walt Disney Co. Litho Questa)

90 (3 Sept). *Mickey Mouse in Hollywood. T* **267** *and similar horiz designs showing Walt Disney cartoon characters. Multicoloured. P* 14×13½.
20 25 c. Type **267** 35 25
21 45 c. Minnie Mouse learning lines while being dressed 50 25
22 50 c. Mickey Mouse with clapper board .. 60 30
23 60 c. Daisy Duck making-up Mickey Mouse 65 35
24 $1 Clarabelle Cow as Cleopatra .. 90 70
25 $2 Mickey Mouse directing Goofy and Donald Duck .. .. .. 1·60 2·00
26 $3 Mickey Mouse directing Goofy as birdman .. .. .. 2·25 2·50
27 $4 Donald Duck and Mickey Mouse editing film .. .. .. 2·25 2·50
20/7 .. .. *Set of* 8 8·00 8·00
S1428 Two sheets, each 132×95 mm. (a) $5 Minnie Mouse, Daisy Duck and Clarabelle as musical stars. (b) $5 Mickey Mouse on set as director .. .. *Set of 2 sheets* 6·00 7·00

268 Men's 20 Kilometres Walk

269 Huey and Dewey asleep (*Christmas Stories*)

(Des B. Grout. Litho Questa)

90 (1 Oct). *Olympic Games, Barcelona* (1992) (*1st issue*). *T* **268** *and similar vert designs. Multicoloured. P* 14.
29 50 c. Type **268** 55 30
30 75 c. Triple jump 70 65
31 $1 Men's 10,000 metres 90 85
32 $5 Javelin .. .. 3·00 4·25
29/32 .. .. *Set of* 4 4·75 5·50
S1433 100×70 mm. $6 Athlete lighting Olympic flame at Los Angeles Olympics .. 4·25 6·00
See also Nos. 1553/61 and 1609/17.

(Des Walt Disney Co. Litho Questa)

90 (15 Oct). *International Literacy Year. T* **269** *and similar vert designs showing Walt Disney cartoon characters illustrating works by Charles Dickens. Multicoloured. P* 13½×14.
34 15 c. Type **269** 25 25
35 45 c. Donald Duck as Poor Jo looking at grave (*Bleak House*) 45 45
36 50 c. Dewey as Oliver asking for more (*Oliver Twist*) 50 50
37 60 c. Daisy Duck as The Marchioness (*Old Curiosity Shop*) 55 55
38 $1 Little Nell giving nosegay to her grandfather (*Little Nell*) 85 85
39 $2 Scrooge McDuck as Mr. Pickwick (*Pickwick Papers*) .. .. .. 1·50 2·00
40 $3 Minnie Mouse as Florence and Mickey Mouse as Paul (*Dombey and Son*) .. 2·00 2·50
41 $5 Minnie Mouse as Jenny Wren (*Our Mutual Friend*) .. .. .. 2·75 3·25
34/41 .. .. *Set of* 8 8·00 9·00
S1442 Two sheets, each 126×102 mm. (a) $6 Artful Dodger picking pocket (*Oliver Twist*). (b) $6 Unexpected arrivals at Mr. Peggoty's (*David Copperfield*) .. .. .. *Set of 2 sheets* 8·00 9·00

Winners
West Germany 1
Argentina 0

(**270**)

271 Pearly-eyed Thrasher

1990 (11 Nov). *World Cup Football Championship Winners, Italy. Nos.* 1308/12 *optd as T* **270** *by Questa.*
1443 15 c. Type **252** 55 20
1444 25 c. Goalkeeper moving towards ball .. 55 20
1445 $1 Goalkeeper reaching for ball .. 1·40 1·40
1446 $4 Goalkeeper saving goal .. .. 3·25 4·50
1443/6 .. .. *Set of* 4 5·25 5·50
MS1447 Two sheets, each 75×105 mm. (a) $5 Three players competing for ball (*horiz*). (b) $5 Ball and players' legs (*horiz*) .. *Set of 2 sheets* 8·00 9·50
The overprint on No. **MS**1447 is larger and thicker, 31×13 mm.

(Des Jennifer Toombs. Litho B.D.T.)

1990 (19 Nov). *Birds. T* **271** *and similar horiz designs. Multicoloured. P* 14.
1448 10 c. Type **271** 30 30
1449 25 c. Purple-throated Carib 35 35
1450 50 c. Yellowthroat 40 40
1451 60 c. American Kestrel 70 70
1452 $1 Yellow-bellied Sapsucker 80 80
1453 $2 Purple Gallinule .. .. .. 1·75 2·00
1454 $3 Yellow-crowned Night Heron .. 2·10 2·50
1455 $4 Blue-hooded Euphonia .. .. 2·10 2·50
1448/55 .. .. *Set of* 8 7·75 8·50
MS1456 Two sheets, each 76×60 mm. (a) $6 Brown Pelican. (b) $6 Magnificent Frigate Bird *Set of 2 sheets* 12·00 14·00

272 "Madonna and Child with Saints" (detail, Sebastiano del Piombo)

(Litho Questa)

1990 (10 Dec). *Christmas. Paintings by Renaissance Masters. T* **272** *and similar multicoloured designs. P* 14×13½ (*horiz*) *or* 13½×14 (*vert*).
1457 25 c. Type **272** 25 20
1458 30 c. "Virgin and Child with Angels" (detail, Grünewald) (*vert*) 30 20
1459 40 c. "The Holy Family and a Shepherd" (detail, Titian) 40 25
1460 60 c. "Virgin and Child" (detail, Lippi) (*vert*) 50 35
1461 $1 "Jesus, St. John and Two Angels" (Rubens) 70 60
1462 $2 "Adoration of the Shepherds" (detail, Vincenzo Catena) .. .. .. 1·40 1·60
1463 $4 "Adoration of the Magi" (detail, Giorgione) .. .. 2·50 3·00
1464 $5 "Virgin and Child adored by Warrior" (detail, Vincenzo Catena) .. .. 2·50 3·00
1457/64 .. .. *Set of* 8 7·75 8·25
MS1465 Two sheets, each 71×101 mm. (a) $6 "Allegory of the Blessings of Jacob" (detail, Rubens) (*vert*). (b) $6 "Adoration of the Magi" (detail, Fra Angelico) (*vert*) .. *Set of 2 sheets* 3·00 4·00

273 "Rape of the Daughters of Leucippus" (detail)

(Litho Questa)

1991 (21 Jan). *350th Death Anniv of Rubens. T* **273** *and similar horiz designs. Multicoloured. P* 14×13½.
1466 25 c. Type **273** 45 30
1467 45 c. "Bacchanal" (detail) 65 45
1468 50 c. "Rape of the Sabine Women" (detail) 70 50
1469 60 c. "Battle of the Amazons" (detail) .. 75 65
1470 $1 "Rape of the Sabine Women" (different detail) .. .. 1·00 1·00
1471 $2 "Bacchanal" (different detail) .. 1·50 1·75
1472 $3 "Rape of the Sabine Women" (different detail) .. .. 2·00 2·50
1473 $4 "Bacchanal" (different detail) .. 2·50 2·75
1466/73 .. .. *Set of* 8 8·50 9·00
MS1474 Two sheets, each 101×71 mm. (a) $6 "Rape of Hippodameia" (detail). (b) $6 "Battle of the Amazons" (different detail) .. *Set of 2 sheets* 6·50 7·50

274 U.S. Troops cross into Germany, 1944

(Des W. Wright. Litho B.D.T.)

1991 (11 Mar). *50th Anniv of Second World War. T* **274** *and similar horiz designs. Multicoloured. P* 14.
1475 10 c. Type **274** 30 30
1476 15 c. Axis surrender in North Africa, 1943 35 25
1477 25 c. U.S. tanks invade Kwalajalein, 1944 40 40
1478 45 c. Roosevelt and Churchill meet at Casablanca, 1943 .. .. .. 70 50
1479 50 c. Marshal Badoglio, Prime Minister of Italian anti-fascist government, 1943 60 50
1480 $1 Lord Mountbatten, Supreme Allied Commander South-east Asia, 1943 .. 1·00 85
1481 $2 Greek victory at Koritza, 1940 .. 1·75 2·00
1482 $4 Anglo-Soviet mutual assistance pact, 1941 .. .. 2·50 2·75
1483 $5 Operation Torch landings, 1942 .. 2·50 2·75
1475/83 .. .. *Set of* 9 9·00 9·50
MS1484 Two sheets, each 108×80 mm. (a) $6 Japanese attack Pearl Harbor, 1941. (b) $6 U.S.A.A.F. daylight raid on Schweinfurt, 1943 *Set of 2 sheets* 5·50 6·50

275 Locomotive *Prince Regent*, Middleton Colliery, 1812

(Des W. Hanson Studio. Litho Walsall)

1991 (18 Mar). *Cog Railways. T* **275** *and similar multicoloured designs. P* 14.
1485 25 c. Type **275** 60 30
1486 30 c. Snowdon Mountain Railway .. 60 35
1487 40 c. First railcar at Hell Gate, Manitou & Pike's Peak Railway, U.S.A. .. 65 45
1488 60 c. P.N.K.A. rack railway, Java .. 85 65
1489 $1 Green Mountain Railway, Maine, 1883 .. .. 1·25 1·00
1490 $2 Rack locomotive *Pike's Peak*, 1891 .. 2·00 2·50
1491 $4 Vitznau-Rigi Railway, Switzerland, and Mt Rigi hotel local post stamp .. 3·25 3·50
1492 $5 Leopoldina Railway, Brazil .. .. 3·25 3·50
1485/92 .. .. *Set of* 8 11·00 11·00
MS1493 Two sheets, each 100×70 mm. (a) $6 Electric towing locomotives, Panama Canal. (b) $6 Gornergracht Railway, Switzerland (*vert*) *Set of 2 sheets* 11·00 12·00

276 *Heliconius charithonia*

(Des T. Pedersen. Litho B.D.T.)

1991 (15 Apr). *Butterflies. T* **276** *and similar multicoloured designs. P* 14.
1494 10 c. Type **276** 45 40
1495 35 c. *Marpesia petreus* 75 50
1496 50 c. *Anartia amathea* 80 60
1497 75 c. *Siproeta stelenes* .. .. .. 1·10 85
1498 $1 *Battus polydamas* .. .. .. 1·25 95
1499 $2 *Historis odius* .. .. .. 2·00 2·50
1500 $4 *Hypolimnas misippus* .. .. 3·25 3·50
1501 $5 *Hamadryas feronia* .. .. .. 3·25 3·50
1494/1501 .. .. .. *Set of* 8 11·50 11·50
MS1502 Two sheets. (a) 73×100 mm. $6 *Vanessa cardui* caterpillar (*vert*). (b) 100×73 mm. $6 *Danaus plexippus* caterpillar (*vert*) *Set of 2 sheets* 12·00 14·00

277 Hanno the Phoenician, 450 B.C.

278 "Camille Roulin" (Van Gogh)

(Des T. Agans. Litho Questa)

1991 (22 Apr). *500th Anniv of Discovery of America by Columbus (1992) (4th issue). History of Exploration. T* **277** *and similar designs. P* 14.
1503 10 c. multicoloured 30 30
1504 15 c. multicoloured 40 40
1505 45 c. multicoloured 70 50
1506 60 c. multicoloured 75 60
1507 $1 multicoloured .. .. 1·00 75
1508 $2 multicoloured .. .. 1·75 2·00
1509 $4 multicoloured .. .. 2·75 3·00
1510 $5 multicoloured .. .. 2·75 3·00
1503/10 .. .. *Set of* 8 9·00 9·50
MS1511 Two sheets, each 106×76 mm. (a) $6 black and Indian red. (b) $6 black and Indian red *Set of* 2 *sheets* 7·00 8·00

Designs: *Horiz*—15 c. Pytheas the Greek, 325 B.C.; 45 c. Erik the Red discovering Greenland, 985 A.D.; 60 c. Leif Eriksson reaching Vinland, 1000 A.D.; $1 Scylax the Greek in the Indian Ocean, 518 A.D.; $2 Marco Polo sailing to the Orient, 1259 A.D.; $4 Ship of Queen Hatshepsut of Egypt, 1493 B.C.; $5 St. Brendan's coracle, 500 A.D. *Vert*—$6 (No. **MS**1511a) Engraving of Columbus as Admiral; $6 (No. **MS**1511b) Engraving of Columbus bare-headed

(Litho Walsall)

1991 (13 May). *Death Centenary of Vincent van Gogh (artist) (1990). T* **278** *and similar multicoloured designs. P* $13^1/_2$.
1512 5 c. Type **278** 20 20
1513 10 c. "Armand Roulin" 20 20
1514 15 c. "Young Peasant Woman with Straw Hat sitting in the Wheat" 30 30
1515 25 c. "Adeline Ravoux" 40 30
1516 30 c. "The Schoolboy" 40 40
1517 40 c. "Doctor Gachet" 45 40
1518 50 c. "Portrait of a Man" 55 40
1519 75 c. "Two Children" 75 60
1520 $2 "The Postman Joseph Roulin" .. 1·75 2·00
1521 $3 "The Seated Zouave" .. .. .. 2·25 2·50
1522 $4 "L'Arlésienne" .. .. 2·75 3·00
1523 $5 "Self-Portrait, November/December 1888" .. .. 3·00 3·25
1512/23 .. .. *Set of* 12 11·50 12·00
MS1524 Three sheets, each 102×76 mm. (a) $5 "Farmhouse in Provence" (*horiz*). (b) $5 "Flowering Garden" (*horiz*). (c) $6 "The Bridge at Trinquetaille" (*horiz*). Imperf .. *Set of* 3 *sheets* 11·00 12·00

279 Mickey Mouse as Champion Sumo Wrestler

(Des Walt Disney Co. Litho Questa)

1991 (20 June). *"Phila Nippon '91" International Stamp Exhibition, Tokyo. T* **279** *and similar multicoloured designs showing Walt Disney cartoon characters participating in martial arts. P* $13^1/_2 \times 14$ (*vert*) *or* $14 \times 13^1/_2$ (*horiz*).
1525 10 c. Type **279** 30 20
1526 15 c. Goofy using the tonfa (*horiz*) .. 40 25
1527 45 c. Donald Duck as a Ninja (*horiz*) .. 70 50
1528 60 c. Mickey armed for Kung fu 85 65
1529 $1 Goofy with Kendo sword .. .. 1·25 1·25
1530 $2 Mickey and Donald demonstrating Aikido (*horiz*) .. .. .. 1·75 2·00
1531 $4 Mickey and Donald in Judo bout (*horiz*) .. .. 2·75 3·00
1532 $5 Mickey performing Yabusame (mounted archery) .. .. .. 3·00 3·25
1525/32 .. .. *Set of* 8 10·00 10·00
MS1533 Two sheets, each 127×102 mm. (a) $6 Mickey delivering Karate kick (*horiz*). (b) $6 Mickey demonstrating Tamashiwara *Set of* 2 *sheets* 9·00 10·00

280 Queen Elizabeth and Prince Philip in 1976

281 Daisy Duck teeing-off

(Des D. Miller. Litho Walsall)

1991 (8 July). *65th Birthday of Queen Elizabeth II. T* **280** *and similar horiz designs. Multicoloured. P* 14.
1534 15 c. Type **280** 15 10
1535 20 c. The Queen and Prince Philip in Portugal, 1985 .. .. .. 15 10
1536 $2 Queen Elizabeth II .. .. .. 1·25 1·50
1537 $4 The Queen and Prince Philip at Ascot, 1986 .. .. 2·50 2·75
1534/7 .. .. *Set of* 4 3·50 4·00
MS1538 68×90 mm. $4 The Queen at National Theatre, 1986, and Prince Philip .. .. 3·00 4·00

(Des D. Miller. Litho Walsall)

1991 (8 July). *10th Wedding Anniv of Prince and Princess of Wales. Horiz designs as T* **280.** *Multicoloured. P* 14.
1539 10 c. Prince and Princess of Wales at party, 1986 .. .. 20 10
1540 40 c. Separate portraits of Prince, Princess and sons 40 25
1541 $1 Prince Henry and Prince William .. 80 70
1542 $5 Princess Diana in Australia and Prince Charles in Hungary .. .. 3·25 3·75
1539/42 .. .. *Set of* 4 4·25 4·25
MS1543 68×90 mm. $4 Prince Charles in Hackney and Princess and sons in Majorca, 1987 3·50 4·50

(Des Walt Disney Co. Litho Questa)

1991 (7 Aug). *Golf. T* **281** *and similar multicoloured designs showing Walt Disney cartoon characters. P* $13^1/_2 \times 14$.
1544 10 c. Type **281** 40 40
1545 15 c. Goofy playing ball from under trees 50 40
1546 45 c. Mickey Mouse playing deflected shot 80 50
1547 60 c. Mickey hacking divot out of fairway 1·00 65
1548 $1 Donald Duck playing ball out of pond 1·25 1·10
1549 $2 Minnie Mouse hitting ball over pond 2·25 2·50
1550 $4 Donald in a bunker .. .. .. 3·00 3·25
1551 $5 Goofy trying snooker shot into hole 3·00 3·25
1544/51 .. .. *Set of* 8 11·00 11·00
MS1552 Two sheets, each 127×102 mm. (a) $6 Grandma Duck in senior tournament. P $13^1/_2 \times 14$. (b) $6 Mickey and Minnie Mouse on course (*horiz*). P $14 \times 13^1/_2$ .. *Set of* 2 *sheets* 9·00 12·00

282 Moose receiving Gold Medal

283 Presidents De Gaulle and Kennedy, 1961

(Des Archie Comic Publications Inc. Litho Questa)

1991 (19 Aug). *50th Anniv of Archie Comics, and Olympic Games, Barcelona (1992) (2nd issue). T* **282** *and similar multicoloured designs. P* $14 \times 13^1/_2$ (*vert*) *or* $13^1/_2 \times 14$ (*horiz*).
1553 10 c. Type **282** 30 30
1554 25 c. Archie playing polo on a motorcycle (*horiz*) 40 30
1555 40 c. Archie and Betty at fencing class .. 70 45
1556 60 c. Archie joining girls' volleyball team .. 80 65
1557 $1 Archie with tennis ball in his mouth 1·00 1·00
1558 $2 Archie running marathon .. .. 2·00 2·25
1559 $4 Archie judging women's gymnastics (*horiz*) .. .. 3·50 3·75
1560 $5 Archie watching the cheer-leaders .. 3·50 3·75
1553/60 .. .. *Set of* 8 11·00 11·00
MS1561 Two sheets, each 128×102 mm. (a) $6 Archie heading football. (b) $6 Archie catching baseball (*horiz*) .. .. *Set of* 2 *sheets* 9·00 10·00

(Des. J. Iskowitz. Litho Questa)

1991 (11 Sept). *Birth Centenary of Charles de Gaulle (French statesman). T* **283** *and similar multicoloured designs. P* 14.
1562 10 c. Type **283** 40 30
1563 15 c. General De Gaulle with Pres. Roosevelt, 1945 (*vert*) 40 30
1564 45 c. Pres. De Gaulle with Chancellor Adenauer, 1962 (*vert*) 70 40
1565 60 c. De Gaulle at Arc de Triomphe, Liberation of Paris, 1944 (*vert*) .. 80 65
1566 $1 General De Gaulle crossing the Rhine, 1945 .. .. 1·00 1·00
1567 $2 General De Gaulle in Algiers, 1944 1·75 2·00
1568 $4 Presidents De Gaulle and Eisenhower, 1960 .. .. 2·75 3·00
1569 $5 De Gaulle returning from Germany, 1968 (*vert*) .. .. .. 3·00 3·25
1562/9 .. .. *Set of* 8 9·75 9·75
MS1570 Two sheets. (a) 76×106 mm. $6 De Gaulle with crowd. (b) 106×76 mm. $6 De Gaulle and Churchill at Casablanca, 1943 *Set of* 2 *sheets* 9·00 10·00

284 Parliament Building and Map

(Litho Questa)

1991 (28 Oct). *10th Anniv of Independence. T* **284** *and simil horiz design. P* 14.
1571 **284** 10 c. multicoloured 40
MS1572 87×97 mm. $6 Old Post Office, St. Johns, and stamps of 1862 and 1981 (50×37 *mm*) .. .. 4·75 6·

285 Germans celebrating Reunification

(Des L. Fried (Nos. 1573, 1576, 1580, **MS**1583a), W. Hans Studio (Nos. 1574, 1577, 1581, **MS**1583b), J. Iskowitz (N 1575, 1582) or W. Wright (others). Litho Questa)

1991 (9 Dec). *Anniversaries and Events. T* **285** *and simi multicoloured designs. P* 14.
1573 25 c. Type **285** 30
1574 75 c. Cubs erecting tent 50
1575 $1.50, *Don Giovanni* and Mozart .. 1·75 1
1576 $2 Chariot driver and Gate at night .. 1·10 1
1577 $2 Lord Baden-Powell and members of 3rd Antigua Methodist cub pack (*vert*) 1·25 1
1578 $2 Lilienthal's signature and glider *Flugzeug Nr.* 5 .. .. .. 2·25 2
1579 $2.50, Driver in Class P36 steam locomotive (*vert*) .. .. .. 2·25 2
1580 $3 Statues from podium .. .. 1·75 1
1581 $3.50, Cubs and camp fire .. .. 1·90 1
1582 $4 St. Peter's Cathedral, Salzburg .. 2·75 2
1573/82 .. .. *Set of* 10 14·00 14
MS1583 Two sheets. (a) 100×72 mm. $4 Detail of chariot and helmet; (b) 89×117 mm. $5 Antiguan flag and Jamboree emblem (*vert*) *Set of* 2 *sheets* 6·00 7

Anniversaries and Events:—Nos. 1573, 1576, 15 **MS**1583a, Bicentenary of Brandenburg Gate, Germany; N 1574, 1577, 1581, **MS**1583b, 17th World Scout Jambor Korea; Nos. 1575, 1582, Death bicentenary of Mozart; No. 15 Centenary of Otto Lilienthal's gliding experiments; No. 15 Centenary of Trans–Siberian Railway.

286 *Nimitz* Class Carrier and *Ticonderoga* Class Cruiser

287 "The Annunciation" (Fra Angelico)

(Des L. Birmingham. Litho Questa)

1991 (9 Dec). *50th Anniv of Japanese Attack on Pearl Harb T* **286** *and similar horiz designs. Multicoloured, P* $14^1/_2$.
1585 $1 Type **286** .. .. 1·00 1
a. Sheetlet. Nos. 1585/94 .. .. 9·00
1586 $1 Tourist launch .. .. .. 1·00 1
1587 $1 U.S.S. *Arizona* memorial .. .. 1·00 1
1588 $1 Wreaths on water and aircraft .. 1·00 1
1589 $1 White Tern .. .. 1·00 1
1590 $1 Mitsubishi A6M Zero-Sen fighters over Pearl City .. .. 1·00 1
1591 $1 Mitsubishi A6M Zero-Sen fighters attacking .. .. 1·00 1
1592 $1 Battleship Row in flames .. .. 1·00 1
1593 $1 U.S.S. *Nevada* (battleship) underway 1·00 1
1594 $1 Mitsubishi A6M Zero-Sen fighters returning to carriers .. .. .. 1·00 1
1585/94 .. .. *Set of* 10 9·00 9

Nos. 1585/94 were printed together, *se-tenant*, in sheetlets 10 with the stamps arranged in two horizontal strips o separated by a gutter showing the wreck of U.S.S. *Arizona*.

(Litho Walsall)

1991 (12 Dec). *Christmas. Religious Paintings by Angelico. T* **287** *and similar vert designs. Multicoloured. P*
1595 10 c. Type **287** 20
1596 30 c. "Nativity" 35
1597 40 c. "Adoration of the Magi" 40
1598 60 c. "Presentation in the Temple" .. 55
1599 $1 "Circumcision" 75
1600 $3 "Flight into Egypt" .. .. .. 2·25
1601 $4 "Massacre of the Innocents" .. 2·50
1602 $5 "Christ teaching in the Temple" .. 2·50
1595/1602 .. .. .. *Set of* 8 8·50
MS1603 Two sheets, each 102×127 mm. (a) $6 "Adoration of the Magi" (Cook Tondo). (b) $6 "Adoration of the Magi" (*different*). P 14 *Set of* 2 *sheets* 8·50 1(

ALTERED CATALOGUE NUMBERS

Any Catalogue numbers altered from the la edition are shown as a list in the introducto pages.

288 Queen Elizabeth II and Bird Sanctuary

289 Mickey Mouse awarding Swimming Gold Medal to Mermaid

(Des D. Miller. Litho Questa)

92 (27 Feb). *40th Anniv of Queen Elizabeth II's Accession. T* **288** *and similar horiz designs. Multicoloured. P* 14.

)4 10 c. Type **288** 40 30
)5 30 c. Nelson's Dockyard 50 30
)6 $1 Ruins on Shirley Heights 80 70
)7 $5 Beach and palm trees .. .. .. 2·50 3·50
)4/7 .. .. *Set of* 4 3·75 4·25
S1608 Two sheets, each 75×98 mm. (a) $6 Beach. (b) $6 Hillside foliage .. *Set of* 2 *sheets* 7·00 8·00

(Des Walt Disney Co. Litho B.D.T.)

92 (16 Mar). *Olympic Games, Barcelona (3rd issue). T* **289** *and similar multicoloured designs showing Walt Disney cartoon characters. P* 13.

09 10 c. Type **289** 20 20
10 15 c. Huey, Dewey and Louie with kayak .. 25 25
11 30 c. Donald Duck and Uncle Scrooge in yacht 35 35
12 50 c. Donald and horse playing water polo .. 50 50
13 $1 Big Pete weightlifting 80 80
14 $2 Donald and Goofy fencing .. .. 1·40 1·40
15 $4 Mickey and Donald playing volleyball 2·50 2·50
16 $5 Goofy vaulting .. .. 2·50 2·50
09/16 .. .. *Set of* 8 7·75 7·75
S1617 Four sheets, each 123×98 mm. (a) $6 Mickey playing football. (b) $6 Mickey playing basketball (*horiz*). (c) $6 Minnie Mouse on uneven parallel bars (*horiz*). (d) $6 Mickey, Goofy and Donald judging gymnastics (*horiz*) *Set of* 4 *sheets* 14·00 15·00

290 Pteranodon

291 "Supper at Emmaus" (Caravaggio)

(Des R. Frank. Litho Walsall)

92 (6 Apr). *Prehistoric Animals. T* **290** *and similar multicoloured designs. P* 14.

18 10 c. Type **290** 40 30
19 15 c. Brachiosaurus 45 30
20 30 c. Tyrannosaurus Rex 55 35
21 50 c. Parasaurolophus 65 50
22 $1 Deinonychus (*horiz*) .. .. .. 1·00 1·00
23 $2 Triceratops (*horiz*) .. .. .. 1·75 1·75
24 $4 Protoceratops hatching (*horiz*) .. 2·25 2·50
25 $5 Stegosaurus (*horiz*) .. .. .. 2·25 2·50
18/25 .. .. *Set of* 8 8·50 8·25
S1626 Two sheets, each 100×70 mm. (a) $6 Apatosaurus (*horiz*). (b) $6 Allosaurus (*horiz*) *Set of* 2 *sheets* 8·50 9·50

(Litho Questa)

92 (15 Apr). *Easter. Religious Paintings. T* **291** *and similar multicoloured designs. P* 14×13½.

27 10 c. Type **291** 25 25
28 15 c. "The Vision of St. Peter" (Zurbarán) 35 25
29 30 c. "Christ driving the Money-changers from the Temple" (Tiepolo) 55 40
30 40 c. "Martyrdom of St. Bartholomew" (detail) (Ribera) 65 50
31 $1 "Christ driving the Money-changers from the Temple" (detail) (Tiepolo) .. 1·00 1·00
32 $2 "Crucifixion" (detail) (Altdorfer) .. 2·00 2·25
33 $4 "The Deposition" (detail) (Fra Angelico) .. .. 3·00 3·25
34 $5 "The Deposition" (different detail) (Fra Angelico) .. .. 3·00 3·25
27/34 .. .. *Set of* 8 9·75 10·00
S1635 Two sheets. (a) 102×71 mm. $6 "The Last Supper" (detail) (Masip). P 14×13½. (b) 71×102 mm. $6 "Crucifixion" (detail) (*vert*) (Altdorfer). P 13½×14 .. *Set of* 2 *sheets* 9·50 11·00

292 "The Miracle at the Well" (Alonso Cano)

293 *Amanita caesarea*

(Litho B.D.T.)

1992 (11 May). *"Granada '92" International Stamp Exhibition, Spain. Spanish Paintings. T* **292** *and similar multicoloured designs. P* 13×13½ (*vert*) *or* 13½×13 (*horiz*).

1636 10 c. Type **292** 30 30
1637 15 c. "The Poet Luis de Goingora y Argote" (Velázquez) 40 30
1638 30 c. "The Painter Francisco Goya" (Vincente López Portana) 55 40
1639 40 c. "María de las Nieves Michaela Fourdinier" (Luis Paret y Alcázar) .. 65 50
1640 $1 "Carlos III eating before his Court" (Alcázar) (*horiz*) .. .. .. 1·00 1·00
1641 $2 "Rain Shower in Granada" (Antonio Munoz Degrain) (*horiz*) .. .. 1·50 1·75
1642 $4 "Sarah Bernhardt" (Santiago Rusinol i Prats) .. .. 2·50 2·75
1643 $5 "The Hermitage Garden" (Joaquim Mir Trinxet) .. .. 2·75 3·00
1636/43 .. .. *Set of* 8 8·75 9·00
MS1644 Two sheets, each 120×95 mm. (a) $6 "The Ascent of Monsieur Bouclé's Montgolfier Balloon in the Gardens of Aranjuez" (Antonio Carnicero) (112×87 *mm*). (b) $6 "Olympus: Battle with the Giants" (Francisco Bayeu y Subías) (112×87 *mm*). Imperf .. *Set of* 2 *sheets* 10·00 11·00

(Litho Walsall)

1992 (18 May). *Fungi. T* **293** *and similar vert designs. Multicoloured. P* 14.

1645 10 c. Type **293** 50 40
1646 15 c. *Collybia fusipes* 60 40
1647 30 c. *Boletus aereus* 80 40
1648 40 c. *Laccaria amethystina* 90 50
1649 $1 *Russula virescens* .. .. 1·50 1·25
1650 $2 *Tricholoma equestre* ("*Tricholoma auratum*") .. .. 2·25 2·50
1651 $4 *Calocybe gambosa* .. .. 3·25 3·50
1652 $5 *Lentinus tigrinus* ("*Panus tigrinus*") 3·25 3·50
1645/52 .. .. *Set of* 8 11·50 11·00
MS1653 Two sheets, each 100×70 mm. (a) $6 *Clavariadelphus truncatus*. (b) $6 *Auricularia auricula-judae* .. .. .. *Set of* 2 *sheets* 11·00 12·00

294 Memorial Cross and Huts, San Salvador

(Des R. Jung. Litho Questa)

1992 (25 May). *500th Anniv of Discovery of America by Columbus (5th issue). World Columbian Stamp "Expo '92", Chicago. T* **294** *and similar horiz designs. Multicoloured. P* 14.

1654 15 c. Type **294** 20 20
1655 30 c. Martin Pinzon with telescope 35 25
1656 40 c. Christopher Columbus 45 35
1657 $1 *Pinta* .. .. 1·00 1·00
1658 $2 *Nina* .. .. 1·60 1·75
1659 $4 *Santa Maria* .. .. 2·50 2·75
1654/9 .. .. *Set of* 6 5·50 5·75
MS1660 Two sheets, each 108×76 mm. (a) $6 Ship and map of West Indies. (b) $6 Sea monster *Set of* 2 *sheets* 8·50 9·50

297 Ts'ai Lun and Paper

298 Elvis looking Pensive

299 Madison Square Gardens

1492 CHRISTOPHER COLUMBUS 1992

Antigua and Barbuda 10c

ANTIGUA & BARBUDA $1

295 Antillean Crested Hummingbird and Wild Plantain

296 Columbus meeting Amerindians

(Des J. Papeo. Litho Walsall)

1992 (10 Aug). *"Genova '92" International Thematic Stamp Exhibition. Hummingbirds and Plants. T* **295** *and similar horiz designs. Multicoloured. P* 14.

1661 10 c. Type **295** 20 20
1662 25 c. Green Mango and Parrot's Plantain 30 30
1663 45 c. Purple-throated Carib and Lobster Claws 45 45
1664 60 c. Antillean Mango and Coral Plant .. 55 55
1665 $1 Vervain Hummingbird and Cardinal's Guard 85 85
1666 $2 Rufous-breasted Hermit and Heliconia .. .. 1·50 1·50
1667 $4 Blue-headed Hummingbird and Red Ginger .. .. 2·75 2·75
1668 $5 Green-throated Carib and Ornamental Banana .. .. 3·00 3·00
1661/8 .. .. *Set of* 8 8·50 8·50
MS1669 Two sheets, each 100×70 mm. (a) $6 Bee Hummingbird and Jungle Flame. (b) $6 Western Streamertail and Bignonia *Set of* 2 *sheets* 9·50 11·00

(Des F. Paul ($1), J. Esquino ($2). Litho Questa)

1992 (24 Aug). *500th Anniv of Discovery of America by Columbus (6th issue). Organization of East Caribbean States. T* **296** *and similar vert design. Multicoloured. P* 14½.

1670 $1 Type **296** 65 65
1671 $2 Ships approaching island .. .. 1·25 1·25

(Des L. Fried. Litho Questa)

1992 (19 Oct). *Inventors and Inventions. T* **297** *and similar horiz designs. Multicoloured. P* 14.

1672 10 c. Type **297** 15 15
1673 25 c. Igor Sikorsky and *Bolshoi Baltiskii* (first four-engined airplane) .. 40 40
1674 30 c. Alexander Graham Bell and early telephone 45 45
1675 40 c. Johannes Gutenberg and early printing press 45 45
1676 60 c. James Watt and stationary steam engine .. .. 1·00 1·00
1677 $1 Anton van Leeuwenhoek and early microscope .. .. 1·10 1·10
1678 $4 Louis Braille and hands reading braille .. .. 3·00 3·00
1679 $5 Galileo and telescope .. .. .. 3·25 3·25
1672/9 .. .. *Set of* 8 9·00 9·00
MS1680 Two sheets, each 100×73 mm. (a) $6 Edison and Latimer's phonograph. (b) $6 Fulton's steamboat .. .. *Set of* 2 *sheets* 9·50 11·00

(Des J. Iskowitz. Litho Questa)

1992 (26 Oct). *15th Death Anniv of Elvis Presley. T* **298** *and similar vert designs. Multicoloured. P* 14.

1681 $1 Type **298** 95 95
a. Sheetlet. Nos. 1681/9 .. .. .. 7·50
1682 $1 Wearing black and yellow striped shirt 95 95
1683 $1 Singing into microphone 95 95
1684 $1 Wearing wide-brimmed hat 95 95
1685 $1 With microphone in right hand .. 95 95
1686 $1 In Army uniform 95 95
1687 $1 Wearing pink shirt 95 95
1688 $1 In yellow shirt 95 95
1689 $1 In jacket and bow tie 95 95
1681/9 .. .. *Set of* 9 7·50 7·50

Nos. 1681/9 were printed together, *se-tenant*, in sheetlets of 9.

(Des Kerri Schiff. Litho Questa)

1992 (28 Oct). *Postage Stamp Mega Event, New York. Sheet* 100×70 *mm. P* 14.

MS1690 **299** $6 multicoloured .. .. .. 4·25 5·50

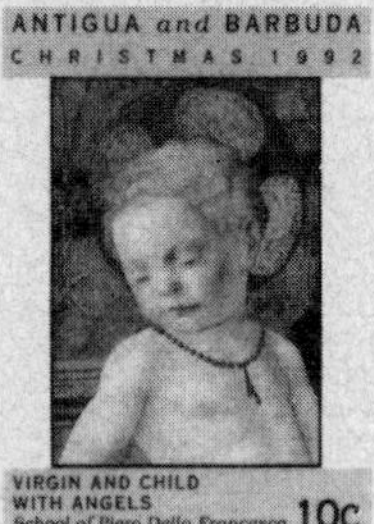

300 "Virgin and Child with Angels" (detail) (School of Piero della Francesca)

301 Russian Cosmonauts

(Litho Questa)

1992 (16 Nov). *Christmas. T* **300** *and similar vert designs showing details of the Holy Child from various paintings. Multicoloured. P* 13½.

1691 10 c. Type **300** 15 15
1692 25 c. "Madonna degli Alberelli" (Giovanni Bellini) 20 15
1693 30 c. "Madonna and Child with St. Anthony Abbot and St. Sigismund" (Neroccio) 30 20
1694 40 c. "Madonna and the Grand Duke" (Raphael) 40 30
1695 60 c. "The Nativity" (Georges de la Tour) 60 60
1696 $1 "Holy Family" (Jacob Jordaens) .. 85 85
1697 $4 "Madonna and Child Enthroned" (Magaritone) .. .. 3·00 3·25
1698 $5 "Madonna and Child on a Curved Throne" (Byzantine school) .. .. 3·25 3·50
1691/8 .. .. *Set of* 8 8·00 8·00
MS1699 Two sheets, each 76×102 mm. (a) $6 "Madonna and Child" (Domenco Ghirlando). (b) $6 "The Holy Family" (Pontormo) *Set of* 2 *sheets* 9·50 11·00

(Des W. Wright and L. Fried (Nos. 1700, 1711, **MS**1714a), W. Wright and W. Hanson (Nos. 1701, 1713, **MS**1714b), W. Wright (others). Litho Questa)

1992 (14 Dec). *Anniversaries and Events. T* **301** *and similar multicoloured designs. P* 14.

1700 10 c. Type **301** 40 40
1701 40 c. Airship LZ-127 *Graf Zeppelin*, 1929 70 55
1702 45 c. Bishop Daniel Davis 50 40
1703 75 c. Konrad Adenauer making speech .. 65 65
1704 $1 Bus Mosbacher and *Weatherly* (yacht) 1·00 1·00
1705 $1.50, Rain forest .. .. .. 1·10 1·10
1706 $2 Tiger .. .. 3·00 3·00
1707 $2 National flag, plant and emblem (*horiz*) .. .. 1·75 1·75
1708 $2 Members of Community Players company (*horiz*) .. .. .. 1·75 1·75
1709 $2.25, Women carrying pots .. .. 1·75 1·75
1710 $3 Lions Club emblem .. .. .. 2·00 2·00
1711 $4 Chinese rocket on launch tower .. 2·00 2·00
1712 $4 West German and N.A.T.O. flags .. 2·00 2·00
1713 $6 Hugo Eckener (airship pioneer) .. 3·00 3·00
1700/13 .. .. *Set of* 14 19·00 19·00
MS1714 Four sheets, each 100×71 mm. (a) $6 Projected European space station. (b) $6 Airship LZ-129 *Hindenburg*, 1936. (c) $6 Brandenburg Gate on German flag. (d) $6 *Danaus plexippus* (butterfly) .. .. .. *Set of* 4 *sheets* 17·00 18·00

Anniversaries and Events:—Nos. 1700, 1711, **MS**1714a, International Space Year; Nos. 1701, 1713, **MS**1714b, 75th death anniv of Count Ferdinand von Zeppelin; No. 1702, 150th anniv of Anglican Diocese of North-eastern Caribbean and Aruba; Nos. 1703, 1712, **MS**1714c, 25th death anniv of Konrad Adenauer (German statesman); No. 1704, Americas Cup Yachting Championship; Nos. 1705/6, **MS**1714d, Earth Summit '92, Rio; No. 1707, 50th anniv of Inter-American Institute for Agricultural Co-operation; No. 1708, 40th anniv of Cultural Development; No. 1709, United Nations World Health Organization Projects; No. 1710, 75th anniv of International Association of Lions Clubs.

302 Boy Hiker resting

303 Goofy playing Golf

(Litho Questa)

1993 (6 Jan). *Hummel Figurines. T* **302** *and similar vert designs. Multicoloured. P* 14.

1715 15 c. Type **302** 15 15
1716 30 c. Girl sitting on fence 25 25
1717 40 c. Boy hunter 35 35
1718 50 c. Boy with umbrella 45 45
1719 $1 Hikers at signpost 75 75
1720 $2 Boy hiker with pack and stick .. 1·40 1·40
1721 $4 Girl with young child and goat .. 2·50 2·50
1722 $5 Boy whistling .. .. .. 2·75 2·75
1715/22 .. .. *Set of* 8 7·50 7·50
MS1723 Two sheets, each 97×122 mm. (a) $1.50 ×4, As Nos. 1715/18. (b) $1.50×4, As Nos. 1719/22 .. .. .. *Set of* 2 *sheets* 12·00 13·00

(Des Euro-Disney, Paris. Litho Questa)

1993 (22 Feb). *Opening of Euro-Disney Resort, Paris. T* **303** *and similar multicoloured designs. P* 14×13½.

1724 10 c. Type **303** 40 30
1725 25 c. Chip and Dale at Davy Crockett's Campground 50 30
1726 30 c. Donald Duck at the Cheyenne Hotel 50 35
1727 40 c. Goofy at the Santa Fe Hotel .. 55 35
1728 $1 Mickey and Minnie Mouse at the New York Hotel 90 80
1729 $2 Mickey, Minnie and Goofy in car .. 1·60 1·75
1730 $4 Goofy at Pirates of the Caribbean .. 2·75 3·25
1731 $5 Donald at Adventureland .. .. 2·75 3·25
1724/31 .. .. *Set of* 8 9·00 9·25
MS1732 Four sheets, each 127×102 mm. (a) $6 Mickey in bellboy outfit. P 14×13½. (b) $6 Mickey on star (*vert*). P 13½×14. (c) $6 Mickey on opening poster (*vert*). P 13½×14. (d) $6 Mickey and balloons on opening poster (*vert*). P 13½×14 .. .. .. *Set of* 4 *sheets* 14·00 15·00

304 Cardinal's Guard

305 "The Destiny of Marie de' Medici" (upper detail) (Rubens)

(Des Dot Barlowe. Litho Questa)

1993 (15 Mar). *Flowers. T* **304** *and similar vert designs. Multicoloured. P* 14.

1733 15 c. Type **304** 35 30
1734 25 c. Giant Granadilla 40 30
1735 30 c. Spider Flower 40 35
1736 40 c. Gold Vine 45 35
1737 $1 Frangipani 80 80
1738 $2 Bougainvillea .. .. 1·40 1·40
1739 $4 Yellow Oleander .. .. .. 2·50 2·50
1740 $5 Spicy Jatropha .. .. .. 2·50 2·50
1733/40 .. .. *Set of* 8 8·00 7·75
MS1741 Two sheets, each 100×70 mm. (a) $6 Bird Lime Tree. (b) $6 Fairy Lily *Set of* 2 *sheets* 8·00 9·00

(Litho Walsall)

1993 (22 Mar). *Bicentenary of the Louvre, Paris. Paintings by Peter Paul Rubens. T* **305** *and similar vert designs. Multicoloured. P* 12.

1742 $1 Type **305** 60 60
a. Sheetlet. Nos. 1742/9 .. .. 4·25
1743 $1 "The Birth of Marie de' Medici" .. 60 60
1744 $1 "The Education of Marie de' Medici" 60 60
1745 $1 "The Destiny of Marie de' Medici" (lower detail) 60 60
1746 $1 "Henry VI receiving the Portrait of Marie" 60 60
1747 $1 "The Meeting of the King and Marie at Lyons" 60 60
1748 $1 "The Marriage by Proxy" 60 60
1749 $1 "The Birth of Louis XIII" 60 60
1750 $1 "The Capture of Juliers" 60 60
a. Sheetlet. Nos. 1750/7 .. .. 4·25
1751 $1 "The Exchange of the Princesses" .. 60 60
1752 $1 "The Regency" 60 60
1753 $1 "The Majority of Louis XIII" 60 60
1754 $1 "The Flight from Blois" 60 60
1755 $1 "The Treaty of Angoulême" 60 60
1756 $1 "The Peace of Angers" 60 60
1757 $1 "The Reconciliation of Louis and Marie de' Medici" 60 60
1742/57 .. .. *Set of* 16 8·50 8·50
MS1758 70×100 mm. $6 "Helene Fourment with a Coach" (52×85 *mm*). P 14½ .. .. 5·00 6·00

Nos. 1742/9 and 1750/7 depict details from "The Story of Marie de' Medici" and were each printed together, *se-tenant*, in sheetlets of 8 stamps and one centre label.

306 St. Lucia Amazon

(Des D. Burkhardt. Litho Questa)

1993 (5 Apr). *Endangered Species. T* **306** *and similar horiz designs. Multicoloured. P* 14.

1759 $1 Type **306** 70 70
a. Sheetlet. Nos. 1759/70 .. .. 7·50
1760 $1 Cahow 70 70
1761 $1 Swallow-tailed Kite 70 70
1762 $1 Everglade Kite 70 70
1763 $1 Imperial Amazon 70 70
1764 $1 Humpback Whale 70 70
1765 $1 Plain Pigeon 70 70
1766 $1 St. Vincent Amazon 70 70
1767 $1 Puerto Rican Amazon 70 70
1768 $1 Leatherback Turtle 70 70
1769 $1 American Crocodile 70
1770 $1 Hawksbill Turtle 70
1759/70 .. .. *Set of* 12 7·50 7·
MS1771 Two sheets, each 100×70 mm. (a) $6 As No. 1764. (b) $6 West Indian manatee *Set of* 2 *sheets* 7·00 8·

Nos.1759/70 were printed together, *se-tenant*, in sheetlets 12 with the background forming a composite design.

307 Queen Elizabeth II at Coronation (photograph by Cecil Beaton)

308 Princess Margaret and Antony Armstrong-Jones

(Des Kerri Schiff. Litho Questa)

1993 (2 June). *40th Anniv of Coronation* (1*st issue*). *T* **307** *ar similar vert designs. P* 13½×14.

1772 30 c. multicoloured 50
a. Sheetlet. Nos. 1772/5×2 .. .. 8·00
1773 40 c. multicoloured 60
1774 $2 indigo and black .. .. .. 1·50 1·
1775 $4 multicoloured .. .. .. 1·90 2·
1772/5 .. .. *Set of* 4 4·00 4·
MS1776 70×100 mm. $6 multicoloured. P 14 4·25 4·

Designs:—40 c. Queen Elizabeth the Queen Mother's Crow 1937; $2 Procession of heralds; $4 Queen Elizabeth II and Prin Edward. (28½×42½ *mm*)—$6 "Queen Elizabeth II" (deta (Dennis Fildes).

Nos. 1772/5 were printed together in sheetlets of 8, containi two *se-tenant* blocks of 4.

(Litho Questa)

1993 (2 June). *40th Anniv of Coronation* (2*nd issue*). *T* **308** *ar similar vert designs. P* 13½×14.

1777/1808 $1×32 either grey and black or mult 18·00 20·

Nos. 1777/1808 were printed in four *se-tenant* sheetlets of (3×3) containing eight stamps and one bottom centre label, ea sheetlet showing views from a decade of the reign.

309 Edward Stanley Gibbons and Catalogue of 1865

310 Paul Gascoigne

(Des Kerri Schiff (Nos. 1809/14), D. Keren (No. **MS**1815). Lit Questa)

1993 (14 June). *Famous Professional Philatelists* (1*st serie T* **309** *and similar horiz designs. P* 14.

1809 $1.50, agate, black and green .. .. 1·10 1·
1810 $1.50, multicoloured .. .. .. 1·10 1·
1811 $1.50, multicoloured .. .. .. 1·10 1·
1812 $1.50, multicoloured .. .. .. 1·10 1·
1813 $1.50, multicoloured .. .. .. 1·10 1·
1814 $1.50, multicoloured .. .. .. 1·10 1·
1809/14 .. .. *Set of* 6 6·00 6·
MS1815 98×69 mm. $3 black; $3 black .. 4·50 4·

Designs:—No. 1810, Theodore Champion and France 1849 1 stamp; No. 1811, J. Walter Scott and U.S.A. 1918 24 c. "Invert Jenny" error; No. 1812, Hugo Michel and Bavaria 1849 1 stamp; No. 1813, Alberto and Giulio Bolaffi with Sardinia 18 5 c. stamp; No. 1814, Richard Borek and Brunswick 1865 1 stamp; No. **MS**1815, Front pages of *Mekeel's Weekly Stan News* in 1891 (misdated 1890) and 1993.

See also No. 1957.

(Des Rosemary DeFiglio. Litho Questa)

1993 (30 July). *World Cup Football Championship, U.S.A.* (*issue*). *T* **310** *and similar vert designs showing Engli players. Multicoloured. P* 14.

1816 $2 Type **310** .. .. 1·40 1·
1817 $2 David Platt .. .. 1·40 1·
1818 $2 Martin Peters .. .. 1·40 1·
1819 $2 John Barnes .. .. 1·40 1·
1820 $2 Gary Lineker .. .. 1·40 1·
1821 $2 Geoff Hurst .. .. 1·40 1·
1822 $2 Bobby Charlton .. .. .. 1·40 1·
1823 $2 Bryan Robson .. .. 1·40 1·
1824 $2 Bobby Moore .. .. 1·40 1·
1825 $2 Nobby Stiles .. .. 1·40 1·
1826 $2 Gordon Banks .. .. 1·40 1·
1827 $2 Peter Shilton .. .. 1·40 1·
1816/27 .. .. *Set of* 12 15·00 15·
MS1828 Two sheets, each 135×109 mm. (a) $6 Bobby Moore holding World Cup. (b) $6 Gary Lineker and Bobby Robson .. *Set of* 2 *sheets* 9·00 10·

See also Nos. 2039/45.

311 Grand Inspector W. Heath

312 Hugo Eckener and Dr. W. Beckers with Airship LZ-127 *Graf Zeppelin* over Lake George, New York

s Kerri Schiff (Nos. 1830, 1837, 1840, 1844, **MS**1847b and **MS**1847e). Litho Questa)

3 (16 Aug). *Anniversaries and Events. T* **311** *and similar designs. Deep blue-green and black (No.* **MS**1847c) *or multicoloured (others). P* 14.

9 10 c. Type **311** 30 30
30 15 c. Rodnina and Oulanov (U.S.S.R.) (pairs figure skating) (*horiz*) .. 30 30
31 30 c. Present Masonic Hall, St. John's (*horiz*) 50 50
32 30 c. Willy Brandt with Helmut Schmidt and George Leber (*horiz*) 30 30
33 30 c. "Cat and Bird" (Picasso) (*horiz*) .. 40 40
34 40 c. Previous Masonic Hall, St. John's (*horiz*) 50 50
35 40 c. "Fish on a Newspaper" (Picasso) (*horiz*) 40 40
36 40 c. Early astronomical equipment .. 40 40
37 40 c. Prince Naruhito and engagement photographs (*horiz*) 40 40
38 60 c. Grand Inspector J. Jeffery 60 60
39 $1 "Woman Combing her Hair" (W. Slewinski) (*horiz*) 70 70
40 $3 Masako Owada and engagement photographs (*horiz*) .. .. 1·75 1·75
41 $3 "Artist's Wife with Cat" (Konrad Kryzanowski) (*horiz*) .. .. .. 1·75 1·75
42 $4 Willy Brandt and protest march (*horiz*) .. .. 2·25 2·40
43 $4 Galaxy .. .. 2·25 2·40
44 $5 Alberto Tomba (Italy) (giant slalom) (*horiz*) .. .. 2·25 2·40
45 $5 "Dying Bull" (Picasso) (*horiz*) .. 2·25 2·40
46 $5 Pres. Clinton and family (*horiz*) .. 2·25 2·40
9/46 .. .. *Set of* 18 18·00 18·00

1847 Seven sheets. (a) 106×75 mm. $5 Copernicus. (b) 106×75 mm. $6 Womens' 1500 metre speed skating medallists (*horiz*). (c) 06×75 mm. $6 Willy Brandt at Warsaw Ghetto Memorial (*horiz*). (d) 106×75 mm. $6 "Woman with a Dog" (detail) (Picasso) (*horiz*). (e) 106×75 mm. $6 Masako Owada. (f) 70×100 mm. $6 "General Confusion" (S. I. Witkiewicz). (g) 06×75 mm. $6 Pres. Clinton taking the Oath 42½×57 *mm*) .. .. .. *Set of* 7 *sheets* 22·00 23·00

Anniversaries and Events:—Nos. 1829, 1831, 1834, 1838, th anniv of St. John's Masonic Lodge No. 492; Nos. 1830, 4, **MS**1847b, Winter Olympic Games '94, Lillehammer; Nos. 2, 1842, **MS**1847c, 80th birth anniv of Willy Brandt rman politician); Nos. 1833, 1835, 1845, **MS**1847d, 20th th anniv of Picasso (artist); Nos.1836, 1843, **MS**1847a, 450th th anniv of Copernicus (astronomer); Nos. 1837, 1840, 1847e, Marriage of Crown Prince Naruhito of Japan; Nos. 9, 1841, **MS**1847f, "Polska '93" International Stamp hibition, Poznań; Nos. 1846, **MS**1847g, Inauguration of U.S. sident William Clinton.

(Des W. Hanson. Litho Questa)

3 (16 Aug–11 Oct). *Aviation Anniversaries. T* **312** *and similar multicoloured designs. P* 14.

8 30 c. Type **312** 55 55
9 40 c. Chicago World's Fair from *Graf Zeppelin* 65 65
0 40 c. Gloster Whittle E28/39, 1941 (11 Oct) 65 65
1 40 c. George Washington writing balloon mail letter (*vert*) (11 Oct) 65 65
2 $4 Pres. Wilson and Curtiss JN-4 "Jenny" (11 Oct) .. .. .. 3·00 3·00
3 $5 Airship LZ-129 *Hindenburg* over Ebbets Field baseball stadium, 1937 3·00 3·00
4 $5 Gloster Meteor in dogfight (11 Oct) 3·00 3·00
8/54 .. .. *Set of* 7 10·50 10·50

1855 Three sheets. (a) 86×105 mm. $6 Hugo Eckener (*vert*). (b) 105×86 mm. $6 Consolidated PBY-5 Catalina flying boat (57×42½ *mm*). (c) 05×86 mm. $6 Alexander Hamilton, Washington and John Jay watching Blanchard's balloon, 1793 (*horiz*) .. .. *Set of* 3 *sheets* 12·00 13·00

Anniversaries:—Nos. 1848/9, 1853, **MS**1855a, 125th birth niv of Hugo Eckener (airship commander); Nos. 1850, 1854, 1855b, 75th anniv of Royal Air Force; Nos. 1851/2, 1855c, Bicent of First Airmail Flight.

313 Lincoln Continental

(Des W. Hanson. Litho Questa)

1993 (11 Oct). *Centenaries of Henry Ford's First Petrol Engine (Nos. 1856, 1858,* **MS**1860a) *and Karl Benz's First Four-wheeled Car (others). T* **313** *and similar horiz designs. Multicoloured. P* 14.

1856 30 c. Type **313** 60 60
1857 40 c. Mercedes racing car, 1914 .. .. 65 65
1858 $4 Ford "GT40", 1966 .. .. .. 3·25 3·25
1859 $5 Mercedes Benz "gull-wing" coupe, 1954 .. .. 3·25 3·25
1856/9 .. .. *Set of* 4 7·00 7·00

MS1860 Two sheets. (a) 114×87 mm. $6 Ford's Mustang emblem. (b) 87×114 mm. $6 Germany 1936 12 pf. Benz and U.S.A. 1968 12 c. Ford stamps .. .. *Set of* 2 *sheets* 8·50 9·00

314 *The Musical Farmer*, 1932

(Des Rosemary DeFiglio. Litho Questa)

1993 (25 Oct). *Mickey Mouse Film Posters. T* **314** *and similar vert designs. Multicoloured. P* 13½×14.

1861 10 c. Type **314** 40 30
1862 15 c. *Little Whirlwind*, 1941 .. .. 45 35
1863 30 c. *Pluto's Dream House*, 1940 .. .. 55 40
1864 40 c. *Gulliver Mickey*, 1934 .. .. 55 40
1865 50 c. *Alpine Climbers*, 1936 .. .. 55 45
1866 $1 *Mr. Mouse Takes a Trip*, 1940 .. 90 80
1867 $2 *The Nifty Nineties*, 1941 .. .. 1·50 1·75
1868 $4 *Mickey Down Under*, 1948 .. .. 2·25 2·75
1869 $5 *The Pointer*, 1939 .. .. .. 2·25 2·75
1861/9 .. .. *Set of* 9 8·50 9·00

MS1870 Two sheets, each 125×105 mm. (a) $6 *The Simple Things*, 1953. (b) $6 *The Prince and the Pauper*, 1990 .. .. *Set of* 2 *sheets* 8·50 9·00

315 Marie and Fritz with Christmas Tree

(Des Alvin White Studio. Litho Questa)

1993 (8 Nov). *Christmas. Mickey's Nutcracker. T* **315** *and similar multicoloured designs showing Walt Disney cartoon characters in scenes from* The Nutcracker. *P* 14×13½.

1871 10 c. Type **315** 40 30
1872 15 c. Marie receives Nutcracker from Godfather Drosselmeir 40 30
1873 20 c. Fritz breaks Nutcracker 45 30
1874 30 c. Nutcracker with sword 50 30
1875 40 c. Nutcracker and Marie in the snow .. 55 30
1876 50 c. Marie and the Prince meet Sugar Plum Fairy 60 40
1877 60 c. Marie and Prince in Crystal Hall .. 60 50
1878 $3 Huey, Dewey and Louie as Cossack dancers .. .. 2·25 2·50
1879 $6 Mother Ginger and her puppets .. 3·50 4·00
1871/9 .. .. *Set of* 9 8·25 8·00

MS1880 Two sheets, each 127×102 mm. (a) $6 Marie and Prince in sleigh. P 14×13½. (b) $6 The Prince in sword fight (*vert*). P 13½×14 *Set of* 2 *sheets* 8·50 9·00

316 "Hannah and Samuel" (Rembrandt)

(Des Kerri Schiff. Litho Questa)

1993 (22 Nov). *Famous Paintings by Rembrandt and Matisse. T* **316** *and similar vert designs. Multicoloured. P* 13½×14.

1881 15 c. Type **316** 30 30
1882 15 c. "Guitarist" (Matisse) 30 30
1883 30 c. "The Jewish Bride" (Rembrandt) .. 40 30
1884 40 c. "Jacob wrestling with the Angel" (Rembrandt) 50 30
1885 60 c. "Interior with a Goldfish Bowl" (Matisse) 70 50
1886 $1 "Mlle Yvonne Landsberg" (Matisse) 1·00 80
1887 $4 "The Toboggan" (Matisse) .. .. 2·75 3·25
1888 $5 "Moses with the Tablets of the Law" (Rembrandt) .. .. .. 2·75 3·25
1881/8 .. .. *Set of* 8 8·00 8·00

MS1889 Two sheets. (a) 124×99 mm. $6 "The Blinding of Samson by the Philistines" (detail) (Rembrandt). (b) 99×124 mm. $6 "The Three Sisters" (detail) (Matisse) .. *Set of* 2 *sheets* 8·50 9·00

317 Hong Kong 1981 $1 Golden Threadfin Bream Stamp and Fishing Boats, Shau Kei Wan

(Des W. Hanson. Litho Questa)

1994 (18 Feb). *"Hong Kong '94" International Stamp Exhibition (1st issue). T* **317** *and similar horiz design. Multicoloured. P* 14.

1890 40 c. Type **317** 35 45
a. Horiz pair. Nos. 1890/1 .. .. 70 90
1891 40 c. Antigua 1990 $2 Rock Beauty stamp and fishing boats, Shau Kei Wan .. 35 45

Nos. 1890/1 were printed together, *se-tenant*, in horizontal pairs throughout the sheet with the centre part of each pair forming a composite design.

318 Terracotta Warriors

(Des Kerri Schiff. Litho Questa)

1994 (18 Feb). *"Hong Kong '94" International Stamp Exhibition (2nd issue). Qin Dynasty Terracotta Figures. T* **318** *and similar horiz designs. Multicoloured. P* 14.

1892 40 c. Type **318** 40 40
a. Sheetlet. Nos. 1892/7 .. .. 2·25
1893 40 c. Cavalryman and horse 40 40
1894 40 c. Warriors in armour 40 40
1895 40 c. Painted bronze chariot and team .. 40 40
1896 40 c. Pekingese dog 40 40
1897 40 c. Warriors with horses 40 40
1892/7 .. .. *Set of* 6 2·25 2·25

Nos. 1892/7 were printed together, *se-tenant*, in sheetlets of 6.

319 Mickey Mouse in Junk

320 Sumatran Rhinoceros lying down

(Litho Questa)

1994 (18 Feb). *"Hong Kong '94" International Stamp Exhibition (3rd issue). T* **319** *and similar multicoloured designs showing Walt Disney cartoon characters. P* 13½×14.

1898 10 c. Type **319** 30 30
1899 15 c. Minnie Mouse as mandarin 35 35
1900 30 c. Donald and Daisy Duck on house boat 45 45
1901 50 c. Mickey holding bird in cage .. 60 60
1902 $1 Pluto and ornamental dog 90 90
1903 $2 Minnie and Daisy celebrating Bun Festival .. .. 1·50 1·75
1904 $4 Goofy making noodles .. .. 2·50 2·75
1905 $5 Goofy pulling Mickey in rickshaw .. 2·50 2·75
1898/1905 .. .. *Set of* 8 8·00 9·00

MS1906 Two sheets, each 133×109 mm. (a) $5 Mickey and Donald on harbour ferry (*horiz*). (b) $5 Mickey in traditional dragon dance (*horiz*). P 14×13½. .. .. .. *Set of* 2 *sheets* 5·50 6·00

(Litho Questa)

1994 (1 Mar). *Centenary of Sierra Club (environmental protection society)* (1992). *Endangered Species. T* **320** *and similar multicoloured designs. P* 14.

1907 $1.50, Type **320** .. .. .. 1·00 1·00
a. Sheetlet. Nos. 1907/14 .. .. 7·00
1908 $1.50, Sumatran Rhinoceros feeding .. 1·00 1·00
1909 $1.50, Ring-tailed Lemur on ground .. 1·00 1·00
1910 $1.50, Ring-tailed Lemur on branch .. 1·00 1·00
1911 $1.50, Red-fronted Brown Lemur on branch .. .. 1·00 1·00
1912 $1.50, Head of Red-fronted Brown Lemur 1·00 1·00
1913 $1.50, Head of Red-fronted Brown Lemur in front of trunk .. .. .. 1·00 1·00
1914 $1.50, Sierra Club Centennial emblem (black, buff and deep blue-green) .. 80 80
a. Sheetlet. Nos. 1914/21 .. .. 7·00
1915 $1.50, Head of Bactrian Camel .. 1·00 1·00
1916 $1.50, Bactrian Camel .. .. .. 1·00 1·00
1917 $1.50, African Elephant drinking .. 1·00 1·00
1918 $1.50, Head of African Elephant .. 1·00 1·00
1919 $1.50, Leopard sitting upright .. .. 1·00 1·00
1920 $1.50, Leopard in grass (emblem at right) 1·00 1·00
1921 $1.50, Leopard in grass (emblem at left) 1·00 1·00
1907/21 .. .. *Set of* 15 13·50 13·50
MS1922 Four sheets. (a) 100×70 mm. $1.50, Sumatran Rhinoceros (*horiz*). (b) 70×100 mm. $1.50, Ring-tailed Lemur (*horiz*). (c) 70×100 mm. $1.50, Bactrian Camel (*horiz*). (d) 100×70 mm. $1.50, African Elephant (*horiz*) *Set of* 4 *sheets* 4·50 5·00

Nos. 1907/14 and 1914/21 were printed together, *se-tenant*, in sheetlets of 8 with each sheetlet containing No. 1914 at bottom right.

321 West Highland White Terrier

322 *Spiranthes lanceolata*

(Des Jennifer Toombs. Litho Questa)

1994 (5 Apr). *Dogs of the World. Chinese New Year ("Year of the Dog"). T* **321** *and similar horiz designs. Multicoloured. P* 14×14½.

1923 50 c. Type **321** 40 40
a. Sheetlet. Nos. 1923/34 .. .. 4·25
1924 50 c. Beagle 40 40
1925 50 c. Scottish Terrier 40 40
1926 50 c. Pekingese 40 40
1927 50 c. Dachshund 40 40
1928 50 c. Yorkshire Terrier 40 40
1929 50 c. Pomeranian 40 40
1930 50 c. Poodle 40 40
1931 50 c. Shetland Sheepdog 40 40
1932 50 c. Pug 40 40
1933 50 c. Shih Tzu 40 40
1934 50 c. Chihuahua 40 40
1935 75 c. Mastiff 45 45
a. Sheetlet. Nos. 1935/46 .. .. 4·75
1936 75 c. Border Collie 45 45
1937 75 c. Samoyed 45 45
1938 75 c. Airedale Terrier 45 45
1939 75 c. English Setter 45 45
1940 75 c. Rough Collie 45 45
1941 75 c. Newfoundland 45 45
1942 75 c. Weimarana 45 45
1943 75 c. English Springer Spaniel 45 45
1944 75 c. Dalmatian 45 45
1945 75 c. Boxer 45 45
1946 75 c. Old English Sheepdog 45 45
1923/46 .. .. *Set of* 24 9·00 9·00
MS1947 Two sheets, each 93×58 mm. (a) $6 Welsh Corgi. (b) $6 Labrador Retriever *Set of* 2 *sheets* 8·00 8·50

Nos. 1923/34 and 1935/46 were printed together, *se-tenant*, in sheetlets of 12.

(Litho Questa)

1994 (11 Apr). *Orchids. T* **322** *and similar vert designs. Multicoloured. P* 14.

1948 10 c. Type **322** 30 30
1949 20 c. *Ionopsis utricularioides* 40 40
1950 30 c. *Tetramicra canaliculata* 50 50
1951 50 c. *Oncidium picturatum* 65 65
1952 $1 *Epidendrum difforme* 90 90
1953 $2 *Epidendrum ciliare* .. .. 1·50 1·75
1954 $4 *Epidendrum ibaguense* .. .. 2·50 2·75
1955 $5 *Epidendrum nocturnum* .. .. 2·50 2·75
1948/55 .. .. *Set of* 8 8·25 9·00
MS1956 Two sheets, each 100×73 mm. (a) $6 *Rodriguezia lanceolata*. (b) $6 *Encyclia cochleata* *Set of* 2 *sheets* 8·00 8·50

323 Hermann E. Sieger, Germany 1931 1 m. Zeppelin Stamp and Airship LZ-127 *Graf Zeppelin*

324 *Danaus plezippus*

(Litho Questa)

1994 (6 June). *Famous Professional Philatelists* (2*nd series*). *P* 14.

1957 **323** $1.50, multicoloured 90 90

(Des B. Hargreaves. Litho Questa)

1994 (27 June). *Butterflies. T* **324** *and similar vert designs. Multicoloured. P* 14.

1958 10 c. Type **324** 30 30
1959 15 c. *Appias drusilla* 35 35
1960 30 c. *Eurema lisa* 50 50
1961 40 c. *Anaea troglodyta* 60 60
1962 $1 *Urbanus proteus* 90 90
1963 $2 *Junonia evarete* .. .. .. 1·50 1·75
1964 $4 *Battus polydamas* .. .. .. 2·50 2·75
1965 $5 *Heliconius charitonia* .. .. 2·50 2·75
1958/65 .. .. *Set of* 8 8·25 9·00
MS1966 Two sheets, each 102×72 mm. (a) $6 *Phoebis sennae*. (b) $6 *Hemiargus hanno* *Set of* 2 *sheets* 7·00 7·50

No. 1959 is inscribed "Appisa drusilla" and No. 1965 "Heliconius charitonius", both in error.

325 Bottlenose Dolphin

326 Edwin Aldrin (astronaut)

(Des J. Genzo. Litho Questa)

1994 (21 July). *Marine Life. T* **325** *and similar multicoloured designs. P* 14.

1967 50 c. Type **325** 45 45
a. Sheetlet. Nos. 1967/75 .. .. 3·50
1968 50 c. Killer Whale 45 45
1969 50 c. Spinner Dolphin 45 45
1970 50 c. Oceanic Sunfish 45 45
1971 50 c. Caribbean Reef Shark and Short Fin Pilot Whale 45 45
1972 50 c. Copper-banded Butterflyfish .. 45 45
1973 50 c. Mosaic Moray 45 45
1974 50 c. Clown Triggerfish 45 45
1975 50 c. Red Lobster 45 45
1967/75 .. .. *Set of* 9 3·50 3·50
MS1976 Two sheets, each 106×76 mm. (a) $6 Seahorse. (b) $6 Swordfish ("Blue Marlin") (*horiz*) .. .. .. *Set of* 2 *sheets* 7·00 7·50

Nos. 1967/75 were printed together, *se-tenant*, in sheetlets of 9.

(Des W. Hanson. Litho Questa)

1994 (4 Aug). *25th Anniv of First Moon Landing. T* **326** *and similar horiz designs. Multicoloured. P* 14.

1977 $1.50, Type **326** .. .. .. 1·25 1·25
a. Sheetlet. Nos. 1977/82 .. .. 7·00
1978 $1.50, First lunar footprint .. .. 1·25 1·25
1979 $1.50, Neil Armstrong (astronaut) .. 1·25 1·25
1980 $1.50, Aldrin stepping onto Moon .. 1·25 1·25
1981 $1.50, Aldrin and equipment .. .. 1·25 1·25
1982 $1.50, Aldrin and U.S.A. flag .. .. 1·25 1·25
1983 $1.50, Aldrin at Tranquility Base .. 1·25 1·25
a. Sheetlet. Nos. 1983/8 .. .. 7·00
1984 $1.50, Moon plaque .. .. .. 1·25 1·25
1985 $1.50, *Eagle* leaving Moon .. .. 1·25 1·25
1986 $1.50, Command module in lunar orbit .. 1·25 1·25
1987 $1.50, First day cover of U.S.A. 1969 10 c. First Man on Moon stamp
1988 $1.50, Pres. Nixon and astronauts .. 1·25 1·25
1977/88 .. .. *Set of* 12 13·50 13·50
MS1989 72×102 mm. $6 Armstrong and Aldrin with postal official .. .. 3·25 4·00

Nos. 1977/82 and 1983/8 were printed together, *se-tenant*, in sheetlets of 6.

327 Edwin Moses (U.S.A.) (400 metres hurdles), 1984

(Des Kerri Schiff. Litho Questa)

1994 (4 Aug). *Centenary of International Olympic Committ Gold Medal Winners. T* **327** *and similar horiz desig Multicoloured. P* 14.

1990 50 c. Type **327** 30
1991 $1.50, Steffi Graf (Germany) (tennis), 1988 .. .. 1·10 1
MS1992 79×110 mm. $6 Johann Olav Koss (Norway) (500, 1500 and 10,000 metre speed skating), 1994 .. .. 3·00 3

328 Antiguan Family

(Litho Questa)

1994 (4 Aug). *International Year of the Family. P* 14.

1993 **328** 90 c. multicoloured 40

329 Mike Atherton (England) and Wisden Trophy

(Des A. Melville-Brown. Litho Questa)

1994 (4 Aug). *Centenary of First English Cricket Tour to West Indies* (1995). *T* **329** *and similar multicoloured desig P* 14.

1994 35 c. Type **329** 40
1995 75 c. Viv Richards (West Indies) (*vert*) .. 70
1996 $1.20, Richie Richardson (West Indies) and Wisden Trophy .. .. .. 1·00 1
1994/6 .. .. *Set of* 3 1·90 1
MS1997 80×100 mm. $3 English team, 1895 (black and grey-brown) .. .. .. 1·90 1

330 Entrance Bridge, Songgwangsa Temple

(Des Kerri Schiff. Litho Questa (Nos. 1998, 2007/9), B.D.T. (N 1999/2006))

1994 (4 Aug). *"Philakorea '94" International Sta Exhibition, Seoul. T* **330** *and similar multicoloured desig P* 13½ (*Nos.* 1999/2006) *or* 14 (*others*).

1998 40 c. Type **330** 30
1999 75 c. Long-necked bottle 50
a. Sheetlet. Nos. 1999/2006 .. .. 3·50
2000 75 c. Punch'ong ware jar with floral decoration 50
2001 75 c. Punch'ong ware jar with blue dragon pattern 50
2002 75 c. Ewer in shape of bamboo shoot .. 50
2003 75 c. Punch'ong ware green jar 50
2004 75 c. Pear-shaped bottle 50
2005 75 c. Porcelain jar with brown dragon pattern 50
2006 75 c. Porcelain jar with floral pattern .. 50
2007 90 c. Song-op Folk Village, Cheju .. 50
2008 $3 Port Sogwipo .. .. .. 1·75 2
1998/2008 .. .. .. *Set of* 11 6·00 6
MS2009 104×71 mm. $4 Ox herder playing flute (*vert*) .. .. 2·40 2

Nos. 1999/2006, each 24×47 mm, were printed togeth *se-tenant*, in sheetlets of 8.

331 Short S.25 Sunderland Flying Boat

332 Travis Tritt

(Des J. Batchelor. Litho Questa)

94 (4 Aug). 50*th Anniv of D-Day. T* **331** *and similar horiz designs. Multicoloured. P* 14.
10 40 c. Type **331** 40 30
11 $2 Lockheed P-38 Lightning fighters attacking train .. .. 1·40 1·60
12 $3 Martin B-26 Marauder bombers .. 1·90 2·00
10/12 .. .. *Set of* 3 3·25 3·50
S2013 108×78 mm. $6 Hawker Typhoon ighter bomber .. .. 3·00 3·50

(Des J. Iskowitz. Litho Questa)

94 (18 Aug). *Stars of Country and Western Music. T* **332** *and similar multicoloured designs. P* 14.
14 75 c. Type **332** 40 40
a. Sheetlet. Nos. 2014/21 .. 3·00
15 75 c. Dwight Yoakam .. 40 40
16 75 c. Billy Ray Cyrus .. 40 40
17 75 c. Alan Jackson .. 40 40
18 75 c. Garth Brooks .. 40 40
19 75 c. Vince Gill .. 40 40
20 75 c. Clint Black .. 40 40
21 75 c. Eddie Rabbit .. 40 40
22 75 c. Patsy Cline .. 40 40
a. Sheetlet. Nos. 2022/9 .. 3·00
23 75 c. Tanya Tucker .. 40 40
24 75 c. Dolly Parton .. 40 40
25 75 c. Anne Murray .. 40 40
26 75 c. Tammy Wynette .. 40 40
27 75 c. Loretta Lynn .. 40 40
28 75 c. Reba McEntire .. 40 40
29 75 c. Skeeter Davis .. 40 40
30 75 c. Hank Snow .. 40 40
a. Sheetlet. Nos. 2030/7 .. 3·00
31 75 c. Gene Autry .. 40 40
32 75 c. Jimmie Rodgers .. 40 40
33 75 c. Ernest Tubb .. 40 40
34 75 c. Eddy Arnold .. 40 40
35 75 c. Willie Nelson .. 40 40
36 75 c. Johnny Cash .. 40 40
37 75 c. George Jones .. 40 40
14/37 .. *Set of* 24 9·00 9·00
S2038 Three sheets. (a) 100×70 mm. $6 Hank Williams Jr. (b) 100×70 mm. $6 Hank Williams Sr. (c) 70×100 mm. $6 Kitty Wells (*horiz*) *Set of* 3 *sheets* 11·00 12·00
Nos. 2014/21, 2022/9 and 2030/7 were printed together, *-tenant*, in sheetlets of 8.

333 Hugo Sanchez (Mexico)

(Litho B.D.T.)

94 (19 Sept). *World Cup Football Championship, U.S.A. 2nd issue). T* **333** *and similar multicoloured designs. P* 14.
39 15 c. Type **333** .. 40 30
40 35 c. Jürgen Klinsmann (Germany) .. 60 30
41 65 c. Antiguan player .. 80 55
42 $1.20, Cobi Jones (U.S.A.) .. 1·25 1·25
43 $4 Roberto Baggio (Italy) .. 2·50 2·75
44 $5 Bwalya Kalusha (Zambia) .. 2·50 2·75
39/44 .. *Set of* 6 7·25 7·25
S2045 Two sheets. (a) 72×105 mm. $6 Maldive Islands player (*vert*). (b) 107×78 mm. $6 World Cup trophy (*vert*) .. *Set of* 2 *sheets* 7·50 8·00
No. 2040 is inscribed "Klinsman" in error.

334 Sir Shridath Ramphal

(Litho Questa)

94 (26 Sept). *First Recipients of Order of the Caribbean Community. T* **334** *and similar horiz designs. Multicoloured. P* 14.
46 65 c. Type **334** .. 50 40
47 90 c. William Demas .. 65 60
48 $1.20, Derek Walcott .. 85 90
46/8 .. *Set of* 3 1·75 1·75

335 Pair of Magnificent Frigate Birds

336 "Virgin and Child by the Fireside" (Robert Campin)

(Des Tracy Pedersen. Litho Questa)

1994 (12 Dec). *Birds. T* **335** *and similar multicoloured designs. P* 14.
2049 10 c. Type **335** .. 30 30
2050 15 c. Bridled Quail Dove .. 35 35
2051 30 c. Magnificent Frigate Bird chick hatching .. 55 55
2052 40 c. Purple-throated Carib (*vert*) .. 55 55
2053 $1 Male Magnificent Frigate Bird in courtship display (*vert*) .. 90 90
2054 $1 Broad-winged Hawk (*vert*) .. 90 90
2055 $3 Young Magnificent Frigate Bird .. 2·00 2·50
2056 $4 Yellow Warbler .. 2·00 2·50
2049/56 .. *Set of* 8 6·75 7·75
MS2057 Two sheets. (a) 70×100 mm. $6 Female Magnificent Frigate Bird (*vert*). (b) 100×70 mm. $6 Black-billed Whistling Duck ducklings *Set of* 2 *sheets* 6·50 7·00
Nos. 2049, 2051, 2053 and 2055 also show the W.W.F. Panda emblem.

(Litho Questa)

1994 (12 Dec). *Christmas. Religious Paintings. T* **336** *and similar vert designs. Multicoloured. P* $13^{1/2}$×14.
2058 15 c. Type **336** .. 30 20
2059 35 c. "The Reading Madonna" (Giorgione) 45 25
2060 40 c. "Madonna and Child" (Giovanni Bellini) .. 50 30
2061 45 c. "The Litta Madonna" (Da Vinci) .. 50 30
2062 65 c. "The Virgin and Child under the Apple Tree" (Lucas Cranach the Elder) .. 65 40
2063 75 c. "Madonna and Child" (Master of the Female Half-lengths) .. 75 50
2064 $1.20, "An Allegory of the Church" (Alessandro Allori) .. 1·00 1·00
2065 $5 "Madonna and Child wreathed with Flowers" (Jacob Jordaens) .. 2·50 3·00
2058/65 .. *Set of* 8 6·00 5·50
MS2066 Two sheets. (a) 123×88 mm. $6 "Madonna and Child with Commissioners" (detail) "Palma Vecchio). (b) 88×123 mm. $6 "The Virgin Enthroned with Child" (detail) (Bohemian master) .. *Set of* 2 *sheets* 7·00 7·50

337 Magnificent Frigate Bird

338 Head of Pachycephalosaurus

(Des W. Wright. Litho China Security Ptg Ltd, Hong Kong)

1995 (6 Feb). *Birds. T* **337** *and similar vert designs. Multicoloured. P* 15×14.
2067 15 c. Type **337** .. 10 10
2068 25 c. Blue-hooded Euphonia .. 10 10
2069 35 c. Eastern Meadowlark .. 15 20
2070 40 c. Red-billed Tropic Bird .. 15 20
2071 45 c. Greater Flamingo .. 20 25
2072 60 c. Yellow-faced Grassquit .. 25 30
2073 65 c. Yellow-billed Cuckoo .. 30 35
2074 70 c. Purple-throated Carib .. 30 35
2075 75 c. Bananaquit .. 35 40
2076 90 c. Painted Bunting .. 40 45
2077 $1.20, Red-legged Honeycreeper .. 50 55
2078 $2 Northern Jacana .. 85 90
2079 $5 Greater Antillean Bullfinch .. 2·10 2·25
2080 $10 Caribbean Elaenia .. 4·25 4·50
2081 $20 Brown Trembler .. 8·75 9·00
2067/81 .. *Set of* 15 18·00 19·00

(Des B. Regal. Litho Questa)

1995 (15 May). *Prehistoric Animals. T* **338** *and similar multicoloured designs. P* 14.
2082 15 c. Type **338** .. 10 10
2083 20 c. Head of Afrovenator .. 10 10
2084 65 c. Centrosaurus .. 30 35
2085 75 c. Kronosaurus (*horiz*) .. 35 40
a. Sheetlet. Nos. 2085/96 .. 4·25
2086 75 c. Ichthyosaurus (*horiz*) .. 35 40
2087 75 c. Plesiosaurus (*horiz*) .. 35 40
2088 75 c. Archelon (*horiz*) .. 35 40
2089 75 c. Pair of Tyrannosaurus (*horiz*) .. 35 40
2090 75 c. Tyrannosaurus (*horiz*) .. 35 40
2091 75 c. Parasaurolophus (*horiz*) .. 35 40
2092 75 c. Pair of Parasaurolophus (*horiz*) .. 35 40
2093 75 c. Oviraptor (*horiz*) .. 35 40
2094 75 c. Protoceratops with eggs (*horiz*) .. 35 40
2095 75 c. Pteranodon and Protoceratops (*horiz*) 35 40
2096 75 c. Pair of Protoceratops (*horiz*) .. 35 40
2097 90 c. Pentaceratops drinking .. 40 45
2098 $1.20, Head of Tarbosaurus .. 50 55
2099 $5 Head of Styracosaurus .. 2·10 2·25
2082/99 .. *Set of* 18 7·75 8·00
MS2100 Two sheets, each 101×70 mm. (a) $6 Head of Corythosaurus (*horiz*). (b) $6 Head of Carnotaurus (*horiz*) .. *Set of* 2 *sheets* 5·50 5·75
Nos. 2085/96 were printed together, *se-tenant*, in sheetlets of 12.

339 Al Oerter (U.S.A.) (discus – 1956, 1960, 1964, 1968)

(Des R. Sauber. Litho B.D.T.)

1995 (6 June). *Olympic Games, Atlanta* (1996). *Previous Gold Medal Winners (1st issue). T* **339** *and similar multicoloured designs. P* 14.
2101 15 c. Type **339** .. 10 10
2102 20 c. Greg Louganis (U.S.A.) (diving – 1984, 1988) .. 10 10
2103 65 c. Naim Suleymanoglu (Turkey) (weightlifting – 1988) .. 30 35
2104 90 c. Louise Ritter (U.S.A.) (high jump – 1988) .. 40 45
2105 $1.20, Nadia Comaneci (Rumania) (gymnastics – 1976) .. 50 55
2106 $5 Olga Bondarenko (Russia) (10,000 metres – 1988) .. 2·10 2·25
2101/6 .. *Set of* 6 3·00 3·25
MS2107 Two sheets, each 106×76 mm. (a) $6 United States crew (eight-oared shell — 1964). (b) $6 Lutz Hessilch (Germany) (cycling — 1988) (*vert*) .. *Set of* 2 *sheets* 5·00 5·25
No. 2106 is inscribed "BOLDARENKO" in error.
See also Nos. 2302/23.

340 Map of Berlin showing Russian Advance

341 Signatures and Earl of Halifax

(Des W. Wright. Litho Questa)

1995 (20 July). 50*th Anniv of End of Second World War in Europe. T* **340** *and similar multicoloured designs. P* 14.
2108 $1.20, Type **340** .. 50 55
a. Sheetlet. Nos. 2108/15 .. 4·00
2109 $1.20, Russian tank and infantry .. 50 55
2110 $1.20, Street fighting in Berlin .. 50 55
2111 $1.20, German tank exploding .. 50 55
2112 $1.20, Russian air raid .. 50 55
2113 $1.20, German troops surrendering .. 50 55
2114 $1.20, Hoisting the Soviet flag on the Reichstag .. 50 55
2115 $1.20, Captured German standards .. 50 55
2108/15 .. *Set of* 8 4·00 4·25
MS2116 104×74 mm. $6 Gen. Konev (*vert*) .. 2·50 2·75
Nos. 2108/15 were printed together, *se-tenant*, in sheetlets of 8 with the stamps arranged in two horizontal strips of 4 separated by a gutter showing a German soldier in the ruins of Berlin.

(Des L. Fried. Litho Questa)

1995 (20 July). 50*th Anniv of United Nations. T* **341** *and similar vert designs. Multicoloured. P* 14.
2117 75 c. Type **341** .. 35 40
a. Horiz strip of 3. Nos. 2117/19 .. 1·25
2118 90 c. Virginia Gildersleeve .. 40 45
2119 $1.20, Harold Stassen .. 50 55
2117/19 .. *Set of* 3 1·25 1·40
MS2120 100×70 mm. $6 Pres. Franklin D. Roosevelt .. 2·50 2·75
Nos. 2117/19 were printed together in sheets of 9 (3×3) containing three *se-tenant* horizontal strips, each forming a composite design.

342 Woman buying Produce from Market

343 Beach and Rotary Emblem

(Des L. Fried. Litho Questa)

1995 (20 July). 50*th Anniv of Food and Agriculture Organization. T* **342** *and similar vert designs. Multicoloured. P* 14.
2121 75 c. Type **342** .. 35 40
a. Horiz strip of 3. Nos. 2121/3 .. 1·25
2122 90 c. Women shopping .. 40 45
2123 $1.20, Women talking .. 50 55
2121/3 .. *Set of* 3 1·25 1·40
MS2124 100×70 mm. $6 Tractor .. 2·50 2·75
Nos. 2121/3 were printed together in sheets of 9 (3×3) containing three *se-tenant* horizontal strips, each forming a composite design.

(Litho Questa)

1995 (20 July). *90th Anniv of Rotary International. T* **343** *and similar vert design. Multicoloured. P* 14.
2125 $5 Type **343** .. .. 2·10 2·25
MS2126 74×104 mm. $6 National flag and emblem .. .. 2·50 2·75

344 Queen Elizabeth the Queen Mother

(Litho Questa)

1995 (20 July). *95th Birthday of Queen Elizabeth the Queen Mother. T* **344** *and similar vert designs. P* $13^{1}/_{2}$×14.
2127 $1.50, orange-brown, pale brown and black 65 70
a. Sheetlet. Nos. 2127/30×2 .. .. 5·25
2128 $1.50, multicoloured 65 70
2129 $1.50, multicoloured 65 70
2130 $1.50, multicoloured 65 70
2127/30 .. .. *Set of* 4 2·50 2·75
MS2131 102×127 mm. $6 multicoloured .. 2·50 2·75
Designs:—No. 2127, Queen Elizabeth the Queen Mother (pastel drawing); No. 2128, Type **344**; No. 2129, At desk (oil painting); No. 2130, Wearing green dress; No. **MS**2131, Wearing blue dress
Nos. 2128/30 were printed together in sheetlets of 8, containing two *se-tenant* horizontal strips of 4.

(Des J. Batchelor. Litho Questa)

1995 (20 July). *50th Anniv of End of Second World War in the Pacific. Horiz designs as T* **340**. *Multicoloured. P* 14.
2132 $1.20, Gen. Chiang Kai-shek and Chinese guerrillas 50 55
a. Sheetlet. Nos. 2132/7 .. .. .. 3·00
2133 $1.20, Gen. Douglas MacArthur and beach landing 50 55
2134 $1.20, Gen. Claire Chennault and U.S. fighter aircraft 50 55
2135 $1.20, Brig. Orde Wingate and supply drop 50 55
2136 $1.20, Gen. Joseph Stilwell and U.S. supply plane 50 55
2137 $1.20, Field-Marshal Bill Slim and loading cow into plane 50 55
2132/7 .. .. *Set of* 6 3·00 3·25
MS2138 108×76 mm. $3 Admiral Nimitz and aircraft carrier .. .. 1·25 1·40
Nos. 2132/7 were printed together, *se-tenant*, in sheetlets of 6 with the stamps arranged in two horizontal strips of 3 separated by a gutter showing Japanese soldiers surrendering.

345 Family ("Caring")

346 Purple-throated Carib

1995 (31 July). *Tourism. Sheet 95×72 mm, containing T* **345** *and similar horiz designs. Multicoloured. Litho. P* 14.
MS2139 $2 Type **345**; $2 Market trader ("Marketing"); $2 Workers and housewife ("Working"); $2 Leisure pursuits ("Enjoying Life") .. .. 3·25 3·50

(Des Tracy Pedersen. Litho Questa)

1995 (31 Aug). *Birds. T* **346** *and similar vert designs. Multicoloured. P* 14.
2140 75 c. Type **346** 35 40
a. Sheetlet. Nos. 2140/51 .. .. 4·25
2141 75 c. Antillean Crested Hummingbird .. 35 40
2142 75 c. Bananaquit 35 40
2143 75 c. Mangrove Cuckoo 35 40
2144 75 c. Troupial 35 40
2145 75 c. Green-throated Carib 35 40
2146 75 c. Yellow Warbler 35 40
2147 75 c. Blue-hooded Euphonia 35 40
2148 75 c. Scaly-breasted Thrasher 35 40
2149 75 c. Burrowing Owl 35 40
2150 75 c. Carib Grackle 35 40
2151 75 c. Adelaide's Warbler 35 40
2152 75 c. Ring-necked Duck 35 40
a. Sheetlet. Nos. 2152/63 .. .. 4·25
2153 75 c. Ruddy Duck 35 40
2154 75 c. Green-winged Teal 35 40
2155 75 c. Wood Duck 35 40
2156 75 c. Hooded Merganser 35 40
2157 75 c. Lesser Scaup 35 40
2158 75 c. Black-billed Whistling Duck ("West Indian Tree Duck") 35 40
2159 75 c. Fulvous Whistling Duck 35 40
2160 75 c. Bahama Pintail 35 40
2161 75 c. Shoveler 35 40
2162 75 c. Masked Duck 35 40
2163 75 c. American Wigeon 35 40
2140/63 .. .. *Set of* 24 8·50 9·50
MS2164 Two sheets, each 104×74 mm. (a) $6 Head of Purple Gallinule. (b) $6 Heads of Blue-winged Teals .. .. *Set of 2 sheets* 5·00 5·25
Nos. 2140/51 and 2152/63 were printed together, *se-tenant*, in sheetlets of 12 with the background forming a composite design.

347 Original Church, 1845

348 Mining Bees

(Litho Questa)

1995 (4 Sept). *150th Anniv of Greenbay Moravian Church. T* **347** *and similar vert designs. Multicoloured. P* 14.
2165 20 c. Type **347** 10 10
2166 60 c. Church in 1967 .. .. .. 25 30
2167 75 c. Present church 35 40
2168 90 c. Revd. John Buckley (first minister of African descent) 40 45
2169 $1.20, Bishop John Ephraim Knight (longest-serving minister) 50 55
2170 $2 As 75 c. 85 90
2165/70 .. .. *Set of* 6 2·40 2·50
MS2171 110×81 mm. $6 Front of present church 2·50 2·75

(Des Y. Lee. Litho Questa)

1995 (7 Sept). *Bees. T* **348** *and similar horiz designs. Multicoloured. P* 14.
2172 90 c. Type **348** 40 45
2173 $1.20, Solitary Bee 50 55
2174 $1.65, Leaf-cutter Bee 85 90
2175 $1.75, Honey Bees 85 90
2172/5 .. .. *Set of* 4 2·10 2·25
MS2176 110×80 mm. $6 Solitary Mining Bee 2·50 2·75

349 Narcissus **350** Somali

(Des Y. Lee. Litho Questa)

1995 (7 Sept). *Flowers. T* **349** *and similar vert designs. Multicoloured. P* 14.
2177 75 c. Type **349** 35 40
a. Sheetlet. Nos. 2177/88 .. .. 4·25
2178 75 c. Camellia 35 40
2179 75 c. Iris 35 40
2180 75 c. Tulip 35 40
2181 75 c. Poppy 35 40
2182 75 c. Peony 35 40
2183 75 c. Magnolia 35 40
2184 75 c. Oriental Lily 35 40
2185 75 c. Rose 35 40
2186 75 c. Pansy 35 40
2187 75 c. Hydrangea 35 40
2188 75 c. Azaleas 35 40
2177/88 .. .. *Set of* 12 4·25 4·75
MS2189 80×110 mm. $6 Calla Lily .. .. 2·50 2·75
Nos. 2177/88 were printed together, *se-tenant*, in sheetlets of 12.
No. 2186 is inscribed "Pansie" in error.

(Des Y. Lee. Litho Questa)

1995 (7 Sept). *Cats. T* **350** *and similar multicoloured designs. P* 14.
2190 45 c. Type **350** 20 25
a. Sheetlet. Nos. 2190/201 .. .. 2·40
2191 45 c. Persian and butterflies 20 25
2192 45 c. Devon Rex 20 25
2193 45 c. Turkish Angora 20 25
2194 45 c. Himalayan 20 25
2195 45 c. Maine Coon 20 25
2196 45 c. Ginger non-pedigree 20 25
2197 45 c. American Wirehair 20 25
2198 45 c. British Shorthair 20 25
2199 45 c. American Curl 20 25
2200 45 c. Black non-pedigree and butterfly .. 20 25
2201 45 c. Birman 20 25
2190/2201 .. .. .. *Set of* 12 2·40 3·00
MS2202 104×74 mm. $6 Siberian kitten (*vert*) 2·50 2·75
Nos. 2190/2201 were printed together, *se-tenant*, in sheetlets of 12, with the backgrounds forming a composite design.

351 The Explorer Tent

1995 (5 Oct). *18th World Scout Jamboree, Netherlands. Ten[ts] T* **351** *and similar multicoloured designs. Litho. P* 14.
2203 $1.20, Type **351** 50
a. Horiz strip of 3. Nos. 2203/5 .. .. 2·50
2204 $1.20, Camper tent 50
2205 $1.20, Wall tent 50
2206 $1.20, Trail tarp 50
a. Horiz strip of 3. Nos. 2206/8 .. .. 2·50
2207 $1.20, Miner's tent 50
2208 $1.20, Voyager tent 50
2203/8 .. .. *Set of* 6 3·00 3·[illegible]
MS2209 Two sheets, each 76×106 mm. (a) $6 Scout and camp fire. (b) $6 Scout with back pack (*vert*) .. .. *Set of 2 sheets* 5·50 5·[illegible]
Nos. 2203/5 and 2206/8 were printed together, *se-tenant*, [in] horizontal strips of 3 in sheets of 9.

352 Trans-Gabon Diesel-electric Train

(Des B. Regal. Litho Questa)

1995 (23 Oct). *Trains of the World. T* **352** *and simil[ar] multicoloured designs. P* 14.
2210 35 c. Type **352** 15
2211 65 c. Canadian Pacific diesel-electric locomotive 30
2212 75 c. Santa Fe Railway diesel-electric locomotive, U.S.A. 35
2213 90 c. High Speed Train, Great Britain .. 40
2214 $1.20, TGV express train, France .. 50
2215 $1.20, Diesel-electric locomotive, Australia 50
a. Sheetlet. Nos. 2215/23 .. .. 4·50
2216 $1.20 Pendolino "ETR 450" electric train, Italy 50
2217 $1.20, Diesel-electric locomotive, Thailand 50
2218 $1.20, Pennsylvania Railroad Type K4 steam locomotive, U.S.A. 50
2219 $1.20, Beyer-Garratt steam locomotive, East African Railways 50
2220 $1.20 Natal Govt steam locomotive .. 50
2221 $1.20, Rail gun, American Civil War .. 50
2222 $1.20, Locomotive *Lion* (red livery), Great Britain 50
2223 $1.20, William Hedley's *Puffing Billy* (green livery), Great Britain .. 50
2224 $6 Amtrak high speed diesel locomotive, U.S.A. .. .. 2·50 2·[illegible]
2210/24 .. .. *Set of* 15 8·50 8·[illegible]
MS2225 Two sheets, each 110×80 mm. (a) $6 Locomotive *Iron Rooster*, China (*vert*). (b) $6 "Indian-Pacific" diesel-electric locomotive, Australia (*vert*)
Set of 2 sheets 5·00 5·[illegible]
Nos. 2215/23 were printed together, *se-tenant*, in sheetlets [of] 9.

353 Dag Hammarskjöld (1961 Peace)

(Des B. Regal. Litho Walsall)

1995 (8 Nov). *Centenary of Nobel Prize Trust Fund. T* **353** *a[nd] similar multicoloured designs. P* 14.
2226 $1 Type **353** 45
a. Sheetlet. Nos. 2226/34 .. .. 4·00
2227 $1 Georg Wittig (1979 Chemistry) .. 45
2228 $1 Wilhelm Ostwald (1909 Chemistry) .. 45
2229 $1 Robert Koch (1905 Medicine) .. 45
2230 $1 Karl Ziegler (1963 Chemistry) .. 45
2231 $1 Alexander Fleming (1945 Medicine) .. 45
2232 $1 Hermann Staudinger (1953 Chemistry) 45
2233 $1 Manfred Eigen (1967 Chemistry) .. 45
2234 $1 Arno Penzias (1978 Physics) 45
2235 $1 Shmuel Agnon (1966 Literature) .. 45
a. Sheetlet. Nos. 2235/43 .. .. 4·00
2236 $1 Rudyard Kipling (1907 Literature) .. 45
2237 $1 Aleksandr Solzhenitsyn (1970 Literature) 45
2238 $1 Jack Steinberger (1988 Physics) .. 45
2239 $1 Andrei Sakharov (1975 Peace) .. 45

0 $1 Otto Stern (1943 Physics) 45 50
1 $1 John Steinbeck (1962 Literature) .. 45 50
2 $1 Nadine Gordimer (1991 Literature) .. 45 50
3 $1 William Faulkner (1949 Literature) .. 45 50
6/43 .. .. *Set of* 18 8·00 9·00
2244 Two sheets, each 100×70 mm. (a) $6
lie Wiesel (1986 Peace) (*vert*). (b) $6 The Dalai
ama (1989 Peace) (*vert*) .. *Set of* 2 *sheets* 5·00 5·25
Nos. 2226/34 and 2235/43 were printed together, *se-tenant*, in
etlets of 9.

354 Elvis Presley

355 John Lennon and Signature

95 (8 Dec). *60th Birth Anniv of Elvis Presley. T* **354** *and similar vert designs. Multicoloured. Litho. P* $13^1/_2$×14.
45 $1 Type **354** 45 50
a. Sheetlet. Nos. 2245/53 .. .. 4·00
46 $1 Holding microphone in right hand .. 45 50
47 $1 In blue shirt and with neck of guitar 45 50
48 $1 Wearing blue shirt and smiling .. 45 50
49 $1 On wedding day 45 50
50 $1 In army uniform 45 50
51 $1 Wearing red shirt 45 50
52 $1 Wearing white shirt 45 50
53 $1 In white shirt with microphone .. 45 50
45/53 .. .. *Set of* 9 4·00 4·50
2254 101×71 mm. $6 "Ghost" image of Elvis
amongst the stars .. .. 2·50 2·75
Nos. 2245/54 were printed together, *se-tenant*, in sheetlets of

(Litho Questa)

95 (8 Dec). *15th Death Anniv of John Lennon (entertainer). T* **355** *and similar vert designs. Multicoloured. P* 14.
55 45 c. Type **355** 50 40
56 50 c. In beard and spectacles 50 50
57 65 c. Wearing sunglasses 55 55
58 75 c. In cap with heart badge 65 65
55/8 .. .. *Set of* 4 2·00 1·90
2259 103×73 mm. $6 As 75 c. .. .. 5·50 6·50
Nos. 2255/8 were each issued in numbered sheets of 16 which
ve enlarged illustrated left-hand margins.

"Hurricane Relief"

(356)

357 "Rest on the Flight into Egypt" (Paolo Veronese)

95 (14 Dec). *Hurricane Relief. Nos.* 2203/9 *optd as T* **356**.
60 $1.20, Type **351** 50 55
a. Horiz strip of 3. Nos. 2260/2 .. .. 1·50
61 $1.20, Camper tent 50 55
62 $1.20, Wall tent 50 55
63 $1.20, Trail tarp 50 55
a. Horiz strip of 3. Nos. 2263/5 .. .. 1·50
64 $1.20, Miner's tent 50 55
65 $1.20, Voyager tent 50 55
60/5 .. .. *Set of* 6 3·00 3·25
2266 Two sheets, each 76×106 mm. (a) $6
Scout and camp fire. (b) $6 Scout with back pack
vert) .. .. .. *Set of* 2 *sheets* 5·00 5·25
The overprints on No. **MS**2266 are larger, $12^1/_2$×5 mm or
$12^1/_2$ mm on the vertical design.

(Litho Questa)

95 (18 Dec). *Christmas. Religious Paintings. T* **357** *and similar vert designs. Multicoloured. P* $13^1/_2$×14.
67 15 c. Type **357** 10 15
68 35 c. "Madonna and Child" (Van Dyck) .. 15 20
69 65 c. "Sacred Conversation Piece" (Veronese) 30 35
70 75 c. "Vision of St. Anthony" (Van Dyck) 35 40
71 90 c. "Virgin and Child" (Van Eyck) .. 40 45
72 $6 "The Immaculate Conception" (Giovanni Tiepolo) .. .. .. 2·50 2·75
67/72 .. .. *Set of* 6 3·75 4·00
2273 Two sheets. (a) 101×127 mm. $5 "Christ
appearing to his Mother" (detail) (Van der
Weyden). (b) 127×101 mm. $6 "The Infant Jesus
and the Young St. John" (Murillo) *Set of* 2 *sheets* 4·75 5·00

358 *Hygrophoropsis aurantiaca*

359 H.M.S. *Resolution* (Cook)

(Des D. Burkhart. Litho Questa)

1996 (22 Apr). *Fungi. T* **358** *and similar vert designs. Multicoloured. P* 14.
2274 75 c. Type **358** 35 40
a. Horiz strip of 4. Nos. 2274/7 .. 1·40
2275 75 c. *Hygrophorus bakerensis* 35 40
2276 75 c. *Hygrophorus conicus* 35 40
2277 75 c. *Hygrophorus miniatus* (*Hygrocybe miniata*) 35 40
2278 75 c. *Suillus brevipes* 35 40
a. Horiz strip of 4. Nos. 2278/81 .. 1·40
2279 75 c. *Suillus luteus* 35 40
2280 75 c. *Suillus granulatus* 35 40
2281 75 c. *Suillus caerulescens* 35 40
2274/81 .. .. *Set of* 8 2·75 3·00
MS2282 Two sheets, each 105×75 mm. (a) $6 *Conocybe filaris*. (b) $6 *Hygrocybe flavescens* *Set of* 2 *sheets* 5·00 5·25
Nos. 2274/7 and 2278/81 were each printed together in sheetlets of 12 containing three horizontal *se-tenant* strips.

(Litho B.D.T.)

1996 (25 Apr). *Sailing Ships. T* **359** *and similar horiz designs. Multicoloured. P* 14.
2283 15 c. Type **359** 10 10
2284 25 c. *Mayflower* (Pilgrim Fathers) .. 10 15
2285 45 c. *Santa Maria* (Columbus) 20 25
2286 75 c. *Aemilia* (Dutch galleon) 35 40
2287 75 c. *Sovereign of the Seas* (English galleon) 35 40
2288 90 c. H.M.S. *Victory* (ship of the line, 1765) 40 45
2289 $1.20, As No. 2286 .. .. .. 50 55
a. Sheetlet. Nos. 2289/94 .. .. 3·00
2290 $1.20, As No. 2287 .. .. .. 50 55
2291 $1.20, *Royal Louis* (French galleon) .. 50 55
2292 $1.20, H.M.S. *Royal George* (ship of the line) 50 55
2293 $1.20, *Le Protecteur* (French frigate) .. 50 55
2294 $1.20, As No. 2288 .. .. .. 50 55
2295 $1.50, As No. 2285 .. .. .. 65 70
a. Sheetlet. Nos. 2295/2300 .. .. 4·00
2296 $1.50, *Vitoria* (Magellan) 65 70
2297 $1.50, *Golden Hind* (Drake) 65 70
2298 $1.50, As No. 2284 .. .. .. 65 70
2299 $1.50, *Griffin* (La Salle) 65 70
2300 $1.50, Type **359** 65 70
2283/2300 .. .. .. *Set of* 18 8·50 8·75
MS2301 (a) 102×72 mm. $6 U.S.S. *Constitution* (frigate); (b) 98×67 mm. $6 *Grande Hermine* (Cartier) .. .. *Set of* 2 *sheets* 5·50 5·75
Nos. 2289/94 and 2295/2300 were each printed together, *se-tenant*, in sheetlets of 6.

360 Florence Griffith Joyner (U.S.A.) (Gold – track, 1988)

361 Black Skimmer

(Des R. Martin. Litho Questa)

1996 (6 May). *Olympic Games, Atlanta. Previous Medal Winners (2nd issue). T* **360** *and similar multicoloured designs. P* 14.
2302 65 c. Type **360** 30 35
2303 75 c. Olympic Stadium, Seoul (1988) (*horiz*) 35 40
2304 90 c. Allison Jolly and Lynne Jewell (U.S.A.) (Gold – yachting, 1988) (*horiz*) 40 45
2305 90 c. Wolfgang Nordwig (Germany) (Gold – pole vaulting, 1972) 40 45
a. Sheetlet. Nos. 2305/13 .. .. 3·50
2306 90 c. Shirley Strong (Great Britain) (Silver – 100 metres hurdles, 1984) .. 40 45
2307 90 c. Sergei Bubka (Russia) (Gold – pole vault, 1988) 40 45
2308 90 c. Filbert Bayi (Tanzania) (Silver – 3000 metres steeplechase, 1980) 40 45
2309 90 c. Victor Saneyev (Russia) (Gold – triple jump, 1968, 1972, 1976) 40 45
2310 90 c. Silke Renk (Germany) (Gold – javelin, 1992) 40 45
2311 90 c. Daley Thompson (Great Britain) (Gold – decathlon, 1980, 1984) 40 45
2312 90 c. Robert Richards (U.S.A.) (Gold – pole vault, 1952, 1956) 40 45
2313 90 c. Parry O'Brien (U.S.A.) (Gold – shot put, 1952, 1956) 40 45
2314 90 c. Ingrid Kramer (Germany) (Gold – Women's platform diving, 1960) .. 40 45
a. Sheetlet. Nos. 2314/22 .. .. 3·50
2315 90 c. Kelly McCormick (U.S.A.) (Silver – Women's springboard diving, 1984) .. 40 45
2316 90 c. Gary Tobian (U.S.A.) (Gold – Men's springboard diving, 1960) 40 45
2317 90 c. Greg Louganis (U.S.A.) (Gold – Men's diving, 1984 and 1988) 40 45
2318 90 c. Michelle Mitchell (U.S.A.) (Silver – Women's platform diving, 1984 and 1988) 40 45
2319 90 c. Zhou Jihong (China) (Gold – Women's platform diving, 1984) 40 45
2320 90 c. Wendy Wyland (U.S.A.) (Bronze – Women's platform diving, 1984) .. 40 45
2321 90 c. Xu Yanmei (China) (Gold – Women's platform diving, 1988) 40 45
2322 90 c. Fu Mingxia (China) (Gold – Women's platform diving, 1992) 40 45
2323 $1.20, 2000 metre tandem cycle race (*horiz*) 50 55
2302/23 .. .. *Set of* 21 8·25 9·25
MS2324 Two sheets, each 106×76 mm. (a) $5 Bill Toomey (U.S.A.) (Gold – decathlon, 1968) (*horiz*). (b) $6 Mark Lenzi (U.S.A.) (Gold – Men's springboard diving, 1992) .. *Set of* 2 *sheets* 4·50 4·75
Nos. 2305/13 and 2314/22 were each printed together, *se-tenant*, in sheetlets of 9, with the backgrounds forming composite designs.

1996 (13 May). *Sea Birds. T* **361** *and similar horiz designs. Multicoloured. Litho. P* 14.
2325 75 c. Type **361** 35 40
a. Vert strip of 4. Nos. 2325/8 .. 1·40
2326 75 c. Black-capped Petrel 35 40
2327 75 c. Sooty Tern 35 40
2328 75 c. Royal Tern 35 40
2329 75 c. Pomarine Skua ("Pomarine Jaegger") 35 40
a. Vert strip of 4. Nos. 2329/32 .. 1·40
2330 75 c. White-tailed Tropic Bird 35 40
2331 75 c. Northern Gannet 35 40
2332 75 c. Laughing Gull 35 40
2325/32 .. .. *Set of* 8 2·75 3·25
MS2333 Two sheets, each 105×75 mm. (a) $5 Great Frigate Bird. (b) $6 Brown Pelican *Set of* 2 *sheets* 4·50 4·75
Nos. 2325/8 and 2329/32 were each printed together, *se-tenant*, in vertical strips of 4 throughout sheets of 12.

362 Mickey and Goofy on Elephant (*Around the World in Eighty Days*)

(Litho Questa)

1996 (6 June). *Novels of Jules Verne. T* **362** *and similar horiz designs showing Walt Disney cartoon characters in scenes from the books. Multicoloured. P* 14×$13^1/_2$.
2334 1 c. Type **362** 10 10
2335 2 c. Mickey, Donald and Goofy entering cave (*A Journey to the Centre of the Earth*) 10 10
2336 5 c. Mickey and Minnie driving postcart (*Michel Strogoff*) 10 10
2337 10 c. Mickey, Donald and Goofy in space rocket (*From the Earth to the Moon*) 10 10
2338 15 c. Mickey and Goofy in balloon (*Five Weeks in a Balloon*) 10 10
2339 20 c. Mickey and Goofy in China (*Around the World in Eighty Days*) 10 10
2340 $1 Mickey, Goofy and Pluto on island (*The Mysterious Island*) 45 50
2341 $2 Mickey, Pluto, Goofy and Donald on Moon (*From the Earth to the Moon*) 85 90
2342 $3 Mickey being lifted by bird (*Captain Grant's Children*) .. .. .. 1·25 1·40
2343 $5 Mickey with seal and squid (*Twenty Thousand Leagues Under the Sea*) .. 2·10 2·25
2334/43 .. .. *Set of* 10 5·25 5·50
MS2344 Two sheets, each 124×99 mm. (a) $6 Mickey on *Nautilus* (*Twenty Thousand Leagues Under the Sea*). (b) $6 Mickey and Donald on raft (*A Journey to the Centre of the Earth*) *Set of* 2 *sheets* 5·00 5·25

363 Bruce Lee

364 Queen Elizabeth II

1996 (13 June). "CHINA '96" *9th Asian International Stamp Exhibition, Peking. Bruce Lee (actor). T* **363** *and similar vert designs. Multicoloured. Litho P* 14.
2345 75 c. Type **363** 35 40
a. Sheetlet. Nos. 2345/53 .. .. 3·00
2346 75 c. Bruce Lee in white shirt and red tie 35 40
2347 75 c. In plaid jacket and tie 35 40
2348 75 c. In mask and uniform 35 40
2349 75 c. Bare-chested 35 40
2350 75 c. In mandarin jacket 35 40
2351 75 c. In brown jumper 35 40
2352 75 c. In fawn shirt 35 40
2353 75 c. Shouting 35 40
2345/53 .. .. *Set of* 9 3·00 3·50
MS2354 76×106 mm. $5 Bruce Lee .. .. 2·10 2·25
Nos 2345/53 were printed together, *se-tenant*, in numbered sheetlets of 9 with enlarged illustrated left-hand margin.

(Litho Questa)

1996 (17 July). *70th Birthday of Queen Elizabeth II. T* **364** *and similar vert designs. Multicoloured. P* 13½×14.
2355 $2 Type **364** 85 90
a. Strip of 3. Nos. 2355/7 .. .. 2·50
2356 $2 With bouquet 85 90
2357 $2 In garter robes 85 90
2355/7 .. .. *Set of* 3 2·50 2·75
MS2358 96×111 mm. $6 Wearing white dress 2·50 2·75
Nos. 2355/7 were printed together, *se-tenant*, in horizontal and vertical strips of 3 throughout sheets of 9.

365 Ancient Egyptian Cavalryman

366 Girl in Red Sari

1996 (24 July). *Cavalry through the Ages. T* **365** *and similar multicoloured designs. Litho. P* 14.
2359 60 c. Type **365** 25 30
a. Block of 4. Nos. 2359/62 .. .. 1·00
2360 60 c. 13th-century English knight .. 25 30
2361 60 c. 16th-century Spanish lancer .. 25 30
2362 60 c. 18th-century Chinese cavalryman .. 25 30
2359/62 .. .. *Set of* 4 1·00 1·25
MS2363 100×70 mm. $6 19th-century French cuirassier (*vert*) .. .. 2·50 2·75
Nos. 2359/62 were printed together, *se-tenant*, in blocks of four within sheets of 16.

(Litho Questa)

1996 (30 July). *50th Anniv of U.N.I.C.E.F. T* **366** *and similar vert designs. Multicoloured . P* 14.
2364 75 c. Type **366** 35 40
2365 90 c. South American mother and child .. 40 45
2366 $1.20, Nurse with child 50 55
2364/6 .. .. *Set of* 3 1·25 1·40
MS2367 114×74 mm. $6 Chinese child .. 2·50 2·75

367 Tomb of Zachariah and *Verbascum sinuatum*

368 Kate Smith

(Des Jennifer Toombs. Litho Questa)

1996 (30 July). *3000th Anniv of Jerusalem. T* **367** *and similar vert designs. Multicoloured. P* 14½.
2368 75 c. Type **367** 35 40
2369 90 c. Pool of Siloam and *Hyacinthus orientalis* 40 45
2370 $1.20, Hurva Synagogue and *Ranunculus asiaticus* 50 55
2368/70 .. .. *Set of* 3 1·25 1·40
MS2371 66×80 mm. $6 Model of Herod's Temple and *Cercis siliquastrum* .. .. .. 2·75 3·00

(Des J. Iskowitz. Litho Questa)

1996 (30 July). *Centenary of Radio. Entertainers. T* **368** *and similar vert designs. P* 13½.
2372 65 c. Type **368** 30 35
2373 75 c. Dinah Shore 35 40
2374 90 c. Rudy Vallee 40 45
2375 $1.20 Bing Crosby 50 55
2372/5 .. .. *Set of* 4 1·50 1·60
MS2376 72×104 mm. $6 Jo Stafford (28×42 *mm*). P 14 .. .. 2·50 2·75

369 "Madonna Enthroned"

370 Robert Preston (*The Music Man*)

(Litho Questa)

1996 (25 Nov). *Christmas. Religious Paintings by Filippo Lippi. T* **369** *and similar vert designs. Multicoloured. P* 13½×14.
2377 60 c. Type **369** 25 30
2378 90 c. "Adoration of the Child and Saints" 40 45
2379 $1 "The Annunciation" 45 50
2380 $1.20 "Birth of the Virgin" 50 55
2381 $1.60, "Adoration of the Child" .. 70 75
2382 $1.75, "Madonna and Child" 70 75
2377/82 .. .. *Set of* 6 3·00 3·25
MS2383 Two sheets, each 76×106 mm. (a) $6 "Madonna and Child" (*different*). (b) $6 "The Circumcision" .. .. .. *Set of 2 sheets* 5·00 5·25

(Des J. Iskowitz. Litho Questa)

1997 (17 Feb). *Broadway Musical Stars. T* **370** *and similar vert designs. Multicoloured. P* 13½×14.
2384 $1 Type **370** 45 50
a. Sheetlet. Nos. 2384/92 .. .. 4·00
2385 $1 Michael Crawford (*Phantom of the Opera*) 45 50
2386 $1 Zero Mostel (*Fiddler on the Roof*) .. 45 50
2387 $1 Patti Lupone (*Evita*) 45 50
2388 $1 Raul Julia (*Threepenny Opera*) .. 45 50
2389 $1 Mary Martin (*South Pacific*) 45 50
2390 $1 Carol Channing (*Hello Dolly*) .. 45 50
2391 $1 Yul Brynner (*The King and I*) .. 45 50
2392 $1 Julie Andrews (*My Fair Lady*) .. 45 50
2384/92 .. .. *Set of* 9 4·00 4·50
MS2393 106×76 mm. $6 Mickey Rooney (*Sugar Babies*) .. .. 2·50 2·75
Nos. 2384/92 were printed together, *se-tenant*, in sheetlets of 9 with the backgrounds forming a composite design.

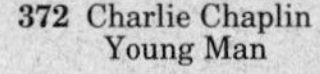

372 Charlie Chaplin as Young Man

373 *Charaxes porthos*

(Des J. Iskowitz. Litho Questa)

1997 (24 Feb). *20th Death Anniv of Charlie Chaplin (film star). T* **372** *and similar vert designs. Multicoloured. P* 13½×14.
2404 $1 Type **372** 45 50
a. Sheetlet. Nos. 2404/12 .. .. 4·25
2405 $1 Pulling face 45 50
2406 $1 Looking over shoulder 45 50
2407 $1 In cap 45 50
2408 $1 In front of star 45 50
2409 $1 In *The Great Dictator* 45 50
2410 $1 With movie camera and megaphone .. 45 50
2411 $1 Standing in front of camera lens .. 45 50
2412 $1 Putting on make-up 45 50
2404/12 .. .. *Set of* 9 4·25 4·50
MS2413 76×106 mm. $6 Charlie Chaplin .. 2·50 2·75
Nos. 2404/12 were printed together, *se-tenant*, in sheetlets of 9 with the backgrounds forming a composite design.

(Des T. Wood. Litho Questa)

1997 (10 Mar). *Butterflies. T* **373** *and similar multicoloured designs. P* 14.
2414 90 c. Type **373** 40 45
2415 $1.10, *Charaxes protoclea protoclea* .. 50 55
a. Sheetlet. Nos. 2415/23 .. .. 4·50
2416 $1.10, *Byblia ilithyia* 50 55
2417 $1.10, Black-headed Bush Shrike ("Tchagra") (bird) 50 55
2418 $1.10, *Charaxes nobilis* 50 55
2419 $1.10, *Pseudacraea boisduvali trimeni* 50 55
2420 $1.10, *Charaxes smaragdalis* 50 55
2421 $1.10, *Charaxes lasti* 50 55
2422 $1.10, *Pseudacrea poggei* 50 55
2423 $1.10, *Graphium colonna* 50 55
2424 $1.10, Carmine Bee Eater (bird) .. 50 55
a. Sheetlet. Nos. 2424/32 .. .. 4·50
2425 $1.10, *Pseudacraea eurytus* 50 55
2426 $1.10, *Hypolimnas monteironis* .. 50 55
2427 $1.10, *Charaxes anticlea* 50 55
2428 $1.10, *Graphium leonidas* 50 55
2429 $1.10, *Graphium illyris* 50 55
2430 $1.10, *Nephronia argia* 50 55
2431 $1.10, *Graphium policenes* 50 5
2432 $1.10, *Papilio dardanus* 50 5
2433 $1.20, *Aethiopana honorius* 50 5
2434 $1.60, *Charaxes hadrianus* 70 7
2435 $1.75, *Precis westermanni* 85 9
2414/35 .. .. *Set of* 22 11·50 12·5
MS2436 Three sheets, each 106×76 mm. (a) $6 *Charaxes lactitinctus* (*horiz*). (b) $6 *Eupheadra neophron*. (c) $6 *Euxanthe tiberius* (*horiz*) *Set of 3 sheets* 7·50 7·5
Nos. 2415/23 and 2424/32 were each printed togethe *se-tenant*, in sheetlets of 9 with the backgrounds formir composite designs.
No. 2430 is inscribed "Nepheronia argia" in error.

374 Convent of the Companions of Jesus, Morelia, Mexico

(Des M. Freedman and Dena Rubin. Litho Questa)

1997 (10 Apr). *50th Anniv of U.N.E.S.C.O. T* **374** *and simil multicoloured designs. P* 14×13½ (*horiz*) *or* 13½×14 (*vert*).
2437 60 c. Type **374** 25 3
2438 90 c. Fortress at San Lorenzo, Panama (*vert*) 40 4
2439 $1 Canaima National Park, Venezuela (*vert*) 45 5
2440 $1.10, Aerial view of church with tower, Guanajuato, Mexico (*vert*) 50 5
a. Sheetlet. Nos. 2440/7 and central label 4·00
2441 $1.10, Church facade, Guanajuato, Mexico (*vert*) 50 5
2442 $1.10, Aerial view of churches with domes, Guanajuato, Mexico (*vert*) .. 50 5
2443 $1.10, Jesuit Missions of the Chiquitos, Bolivia (*vert*) 50 5
2444 $1.10, Huascaran National Park, Peru (*vert*) 50 5
2445 $1.10, Jesuit Missions of La Santisima, Paraguay (*vert*) 50 5
2446 $1.10, Cartagena, Colombia (*vert*) .. 50 5
2447 $1.10, Fortification, Havana, Cuba (*vert*) 50 5
2448 $1.20, As No. 2444 (*vert*) 50 5
2449 $1.60, Church of San Francisco, Guatemala (*vert*) 70 7
2450 $1.65, Tikal National Park, Guatemala 70 7
a. Sheetlet. Nos. 2450/4 and label .. 3·50
2451 $1.65, Rio Platano Reserve, Honduras 70 7
2452 $1.65, Ruins of Copan, Honduras .. 70 7
2453 $1.65, Antigua ruins, Guatemala .. 70 7
2454 $1.65, Teotihuacan, Mexico 70 7
2455 $1.75, Santo Domingo, Dominican Republic (*vert*) 70 7
2437/55 .. .. *Set of* 19 9·75 10·(
MS2456 Two sheets, each 127×102 mm. (a) $6 Tikal National Park, Guatemala. (b) $6 Teotihuacan pyramid, Mexico .. *Set of 2 sheets* 5·00 5·2
Nos. 2440/7 and 2450/4 were each printed, *se-tenant*, sheetlets of 8 and 5 with a label.
No. 2446 is inscribed "Columbia" in error.

375 Red Bishop

376 Child's Face and U.N.E.S.C.O. Emblem

1997 (24 Apr). *Endangered Species. T* **375** *and similar v designs. Multicoloured. Litho. P* 14.
2457 $1.20, Type **375** 50
a. Sheetlet. Nos. 2457/62 .. .. 3·00
2458 $1.20, Yellow Baboon 50
2459 $1.20, Superb Starling 50
2460 $1.20, Ratel 50
2461 $1.20, Hunting Dog 50
2462 $1.20, Serval 50
2463 $1.65, Okapi 70
a. Sheetlet. Nos. 2463/8 .. .. 4·00
2464 $1.65, Giant Forest Squirrel 70
2465 $1.65, Lesser Masked Weaver 70
2466 $1.65, Small-spotted Genet 70
2467 $1.65, Yellow-billed Stork 70
2468 $1.65, Red-headed Agama 70
2457/68 .. .. *Set of* 12 7·00 7·
MS2469 Three sheets, each 106×76 mm. (a) $6 South African Crowned Crane. (b) $6 Bat-eared Fox. (c) $6 Malachite Kingfisher *Set of 3 sheets* 7·50 7
Nos. 2457/62 and 2463/8 were each printed togeth *se-tenant*, in sheetlets of 6 with the backgrounds formi composite designs.

(Litho Questa)

97 (12 June). *10th Anniv of Chernobyl Nuclear Disaster. T* **376** *and similar vert design. Multicoloured. P* 13½.
70 $1.65, Type **376** 70 75
71 $2 As Type **376**, but inscribed "CHABAD'S CHILDREN OF CHERNOBYL" at foot 85 90

377 Paul Harris and James Grant

(Des J. Iskowitz, Litho Questa)

997 (12 June). *50th Death Anniv of Paul Harris (founder of Rotary International). T* **377** *and similar horiz design. Multicoloured. P* 14.
472 $1.75, Type **377** 70 75
IS2473 78×107 mm. $6 Group study exchange, New Zealand 2·50 2·75

378 Queen Elizabeth II

(Litho Questa)

997 (12 June). *Golden Wedding of Queen Elizabeth and Prince Philip. T* **378** *and similar horiz designs. Multicoloured. P* 14.
474 $1 Type **378** 45 50
a. Sheetlet. Nos. 2474/9 2·75
475 $1 Royal coat of arms 45 50
476 $1 Queen Elizabeth and Prince Philip at reception 45 50
477 $1 Queen Elizabeth and Prince Philip in landau 45 50
478 $1 Balmoral 45 50
479 $1 Prince Philip 45 50
474/9 *Set of* 6 2·75 3·00
IS2480 100×71 mm. $6 Queen Elizabeth with Prince Philip in naval uniform 2·50 2·75
Nos. 2474/9 were printed together, *se-tenant*, in sheetlets of 6.

379 Kaiser Wilhelm I and Heinrich von Stephan

380 The Ugly Sisters and their Mother

(Des J. Iskowitz. Litho Questa)

997 (12 June). *"Pacific '97" International Stamp Exhibition, San Francisco. Death Centenary of Heinrich von Stephan (founder of the U.P.U.). T* **379** *and similar horiz designs. P* 14.
481 $1.75, dull blue 70 75
a. Sheetlet. Nos. 2481/3 2·10
482 $1.75, chestnut 70 75
483 $1.75, deep magenta 70 75
481/3 *Set of* 3 2·10 2·25
IS2484 82×119 mm. $6 black and violet 2·50 2·75
Designs: No. 2481, Type **379**; No. 2482, Von Stephan and lercury; No. 2483, Carrier pigeon and loft; No. **MS**2484, Von tephan and 15th-century Basle messenger.
Nos. 2481/3 were printed together, *se-tenant*, in sheetlets of 3 ith enlarged right-hand margin.

(Des R. Sauber. Litho Questa)

997 (12 June). *175th Anniv of Brothers Grimm's Third Collection of Fairy Tales. Cinderella. T* **380** *and similar vert designs. Multicoloured. P* 13½×14.
485 $1.75, Type **380** 70 75
a. Sheetlet. Nos. 2485/7 2·10
486 $1.75, Cinderella and her Fairy Godmother 70 75
487 $1.75, Cinderella and the Prince 70 75
485/7 *Set of* 3 2·10 2·25
IS2488 124×96 mm. $6 Cinderella trying on slipper 2·50 2·75
Nos. 2485/7 were printed together, *se-tenant*, in sheetlets of 3 with illustrated margins.

381 *Marasmius rotula*

382 *Odontoglossum cervantesii*

(Des D. Burkhart, Litho Questa)

1997 (12 Aug). *Fungi. T* **381** *and similar horiz designs. Multicoloured. P* 14.
2489 45 c. Type **381** 20 25
2490 65 c. *Cantharellus cibarius* 30 35
2491 70 c. *Lepiota cristata* 30 35
2492 90 c. *Auricularia mesenterica* 40 45
2493 $1 *Pholiota alnicola* 45 50
2494 $1.65, *Leccinum aurantiacum* 70 75
2495 $1.75, *Entoloma serrulatum* 70 75
a. Sheetlet. Nos. 2495/2500 4·00
2496 $1.75, *Panaeolus sphinctrinus* 70 75
2497 $1.75, *Volvariella bombycina* 70 75
2498 $1.75, *Conocybe percincta* 70 75
2499 $1.75, *Pluteus cervinus* 70 75
2500 $1.75, *Russula foetens* 70 75
2489/2500 *Set of* 12 6·50 7·00
MS2501 Two sheets, each 106×76 mm. (a) $6 *Amanita cothurnata*. (b) $6 *Panellus serotinus* *Set of* 2 *sheets* 5·00 5·25
Nos. 2495/2500 were printed together, *se-tenant*, in sheetlets of 6.

(Des T. Wood. Litho Questa)

1997 (19 Aug). *Orchids of the World. T* **382** *and similar vert designs. Multicoloured. P* 14.
2502 45 c. Type **382** 20 25
2503 65 c. *Phalaenopsis* Medford Star 30 35
2504 75 c. *Vanda* Motes Resplendent 35 40
2505 90 c. *Odontonia* Debutante 40 45
2506 $1 *Iwanagaara* Apple Blossom 45 50
2507 $1.65, *Cattleya* Sophia Martin 70 75
a. Sheetlet. Nos. 2507/14 5·50
2508 $1.65, Dogface Butterfly 70 75
2509 $1.65, *Laeliocattleya* Mini Purple 70 75
2510 $1.65, *Cymbidium* Showgirl 70 75
2511 $1.65, *Brassolaeliocattleya* Dorothy Bertsch 70 75
2512 $1.65, *Disa blackii* 70 75
2513 $1.65, *Paphiopedilum leeanum* 70 75
2514 $1.65, *Paphiopedilum macranthum* 70 75
2515 $1.65, *Brassocattleya* Angel Lace 70 75
a. Sheetlet. Nos. 2515/22 5·50
2516 $1.65, *Saphrolae liocattleya* Precious Stones 70 75
2517 $1.65, Orange Theope Butterfly 70 75
2518 $1.65, *Promenaea xanthina* 70 75
2519 $1.65, *Lycasle macrobulbon* 70 75
2520 $1.65, *Amestella philippinensis* 70 75
2521 $1.65, *Masdevallia* Machu Picchu 70 75
2522 $1.65, *Phalaenopsis* Zuma Urchin 70 75
2523 $2 *Dendrobium victoria-reginae* 85 90
2502/23 *Set of* 22 13·50 14·50
MS2524 Two sheets, each 76×106 mm. (a) $6 *Miltonia* Seine. (b) $6 *Paphiopedilum gratrixanum* *Set of* 2 *sheets* 5·50 5·75
Nos. 2507/14 and 2515/22 were each printed together, *se-tenant*, in sheetlets of 8 with the backgrounds forming composite designs.

383 Maradonna holding World Cup Trophy, 1986

(Litho Questa)

1997 (16 Oct). *World Cup Football Championship, France (1998). T* **383** *and multicoloured designs. P* 14×13½.
2525 60 c. multicoloured 25 30
2526 75 c. agate 35 40
2527 90 c. multicoloured 40 45
2528 $1 agate 45 50
a. Sheetlet. Nos. 2528/35 and central label 3·50
2529 $1 agate 45 50
2530 $1 agate 45 50
2531 $1 grey-black 45 50
2532 $1 agate 45 50
2533 $1 agate 45 50
2534 $1 agate 45 50
2535 $1 agate 45 50
2536 $1.20, multicoloured 50 55
2537 $1.65, multicoloured 70 75
2538 $1.75, multicoloured 70 75
2525/38 *Set of* 14 6·25 7·25
MS2539 Two sheets, each 102×127 mm. $6 multicoloured. P 13½×14. (b) $6 multicoloured. P 14×13½ *Set of* 2 *sheets* 5·00 5·25
Designs: *Horiz*—No. 2526, Fritzwalter, West Germany, 1954; No. 2527, Zoff, Italy, 1982; No. 2536, Moore, England, 1966; No. 2537, Alberto, Brazil, 1970; No. 2538, Matthaus, West Germany, 1990; No. **MS**2539(b), West German players celebrating, 1990. *Vert*—No. 2528, Ademir, Brazil, 1950; No. 2529, Eusebio, Portugal, 1966; No. 2530, Fontaine, France, 1958; No. 2531, Schillaci, Italy, 1990; No. 2532, Leonidas, Brazil, 1938; No. 2533, Stabile, Argentina, 1930; No. 2534, Nejedly, Czechoslovakia, 1934; No. 2535, Muller, West Germany, 1970; No. **MS**2539(a), Bebto, Brazil.
Nos. 2528/35 were printed together, *se-tenant*, in sheetlets of 8 stamps and a central label.

384 Scottish Fold Kitten

(Des R. Martin. Litho Questa)

1997 (27 Oct). *Cats and Dogs. T* **384** *and similar multicoloured designs. P* 14.
2540 $1.65, Type **384** 70 75
a. Sheetlet. Nos. 2540/5 4·00
2541 $1.65, Japanese Bobtail 70 75
2542 $1.65, Tabby Manx 70 75
2543 $1.65, Bicolor American Shorthair 70 75
2544 $1.65, Sorrel Abyssinian 70 75
2545 $1.65, Himalayan Blue Point 70 75
2546 $1.65, Dachshund 70 75
a. Sheetlet. Nos. 2546/51 4·00
2547 $1.65, Staffordshire Terrier 70 75
2548 $1.65, Shar-pei 70 75
2549 $1.65, Beagle 70 75
2550 $1.65, Norfolk Terrier 70 75
2551 $1.65, Golden Retriever 70 75
2540/51 *Set of* 12 8·00 8·50
MS2552 Two sheets, each 107×77 mm. (a) $6 Red Tabby (*vert*). (b) $6 Siberian Husky (*vert*) *Set of* 2 *sheets* 5·00 5·25
Nos. 2540/5 and 2546/51 were each printed together, *se-tenant*, in sheetlets of 6.

385 Original Drawing by Richard Trevithick, 1803

1997 (10 Nov). *Railway Locomotives of the World. T* **385** *and similar horiz designs. Each blackish brown. Litho. P* 14.
2553 $1.65, Type **385** 70 75
a. Sheetlet. Nos. 2553/8 4·00
2554 $1.65, William Hedley's *Puffing Billy*, (1813–14) 70 75
2555 $1.65, Crampton locomotive of French Nord Railway, 1858 70 75
2556 $1.65, Lawrence Machine Shop locomotive, U.S.A., 1860 70 75
2557 $1.65, Natchez and Hamburg Railway steam locomotive *Mississippi*, U.S.A., 1834 70 75
2558 $1.65, Bury "Coppernob" locomotive, Furness Railway, 1846 70 75
2559 $1.65, David Joy's *Jenny Lind*, 1847 70 75
a. Sheetlet. Nos. 2559/64 4·00
2560 $1.65, Schenectady Atlantic locomotive, U.S.A., 1899 70 75
2561 $1.65, Kitson Class 1800 tank locomotive, Japan, 1881 70 75
2562 $1.65, Pennsylvania Railroad express freight 70 75
2563 $1.65, Karl Golsdorf's 4 cylinder locomotive, Austria 70 75
2564 $1.65, Series "E" locomotive, Russia, 1930 70 75
2553/64 *Set of* 12 8·00 8·50
MS2565 Two sheets, each 72×100 mm. (a) $6 George Stephenson "Patentee" type locomotive, 1843. (b) $6 Brunel's trestle bridge over River Lynher, Cornwall *Set of* 2 *sheets* 5·00 5·25
Nos. 2553/8 and 2559/64 were each printed together, *se-tenant*, in sheetlets of 6.
No. 2554 is dated "1860" in error.

386 "The Angel leaving Tobias and his Family" (Rembrandt)

387 Diana, Princess of Wales

(Litho B.D.T.)

1997 (2 Dec). *Christmas. Religious Paintings. T* **386** *and similar multicoloured designs. P* 14.

2566 15 c. Type **386** 10 10
2567 25 c. "The Resurrection" (Martin Knoller) 10 15
2568 60 c. "Astronomy" (Raphael) 25 30
2569 75 c. "Music-making Angel" (Melozzo da Forli) 35 40
2570 90 c. "Amor" (Parmigianino) 40 45
2571 $1.20, "Madonna and Child with Saints" (Rosso Fiorentino) 50 55
2566/71 .. .. *Set of* 6 1·60 2·10
MS2572 Two sheets, each 105×96 mm. (a) $6 "The Wedding of Tobias" (Gianantonio and Francesco Guardi) (*horiz*). (b) $6 "The Portinari Altarpiece" (Hugo van der Goes) (*horiz*) *Set of* 2 *sheets* 5·00 5·25

(Litho Questa)

1998 (19 Jan). *Diana, Princess of Wales Commemoration. T* **387** *and similar vert designs. Multicoloured (except Nos.* 2574, 2581/2 *and* **MS**2585b). *P* 14.

2573 $1.65, Type **387** 70 75
a. Sheetlet. Nos. 2573/8 .. .. .. 4·00
2574 $1.65, Wearing hoop earrings (rose-carm and black) 70 75
2575 $1.65, Carrying bouquet 70 75
2576 $1.65, Wearing floral hat 70 75
2577 $1.65, With Prince Harry 70 75
2578 $1.65, Wearing white jacket 70 75
2579 $1.65, In kitchen 70 75
a. Sheetlet. Nos. 2579/84 .. .. 4·00
2580 $1.65, Wearing black and white dress .. 70 75
2581 $1.65, Wearing hat (orge-brown & black) 70 75
2582 $1.65, Wearing floral print dress (lake-brown and black) 70 75
2583 $1.65, Dancing with John Travolta .. 70 75
2584 $1.65, Wearing white hat and jacket .. 70 75
2573/84 .. .. *Set of* 12 8·00 8·50
MS2585 Two sheets, each 70×100 mm. (a) $6 Wearing red jumper. (b) $6 Wearing black dress for papal audience (lake-brown and black) *Set of* 2 *sheets* 5·00 5·25

Nos. 2573/8 and 2579/84 were each printed together, *se-tenant*, in sheetlets of 6.

388 Yellow Damselfish

(Litho B.D.T.)

1998 (19 Feb). *Fishes. T* **388** *and similar horiz designs. Multicoloured. P* 14.

2586 75 c. Type **388** 35 40
2587 90 c. Barred Hamlet 40 45
2588 $1 Yellow-tailed Damselfish ("Jewelfish") 45 50
2589 $1.20, Blue-headed Wrasse 50 55
2590 $1.50, Queen Angelfish 65 70
2591 $1.65, Jackknife-fish 70 75
a. Sheetlet. Nos. 2591/6 .. .. 4·00
2592 $1.65, Spot-finned Hogfish 70 75
2593 $1.65, Sergeant Major 70 75
2594 $1.65, Neon Goby 70 75
2595 $1.65, Jawfish 70 75
2596 $1.65, Flamefish 70 75
2597 $1.65, Rock Beauty 70 75
a. Sheetlet. Nos. 2597/602 .. .. 4·00
2598 $1.65, Yellow-tailed Snapper 70 75
2599 $1.65, Creole Wrasse 70 75
2600 $1.65, Slender Filefish 70 75
2601 $1.65, Long-spined Squirrelfish .. 70 75
2602 $1.65, Royal Gramma ("Fairy Basslet") 70 75
2603 $1.75, Queen Triggerfish 75 80
2586/2603 .. .. .. *Set of* 18 11·50 12·00
MS2604 Two sheets, each 80×110 mm. (a) $6 Porkfish. (b) $6 Black-capped Basslet *Set of* 2 *sheets* 5·25 5·50

Nos. 2591/6 and 2597/2602 were each printed together, *se-tenant*, in sheetlets of 6 with the backgrounds forming composite designs.

389 First Church and Manse, 1822–40

390 Europa Point Lighthouse, Gibraltar

(Litho B.D.T.)

1998 (16 Mar). *175th Anniv of Cedar Hall Moravian Church. T* **389** *and similar horiz designs. Multicoloured. P* 14.

2605 20 c. Type **389** 15 20
2606 45 c. Cedar Hall School, 1840 .. .. 20 25
2607 75 c. Hugh A. King, minister 1945–53 .. 35 40
2608 90 c. Present Church building 40 45
2609 $1.20, Water tank, 1822 .. .. 50 55
2610 $2 Former Manse, demolished 1978 .. 85 90
2605/10 .. .. *Set of* 6 2·40 2·50
MS2611 100×70 mm. $6 Present church building (*different*) (50×37 *mm*) .. .. 2·50 2·75

(Des M. Friedman. Litho Questa)

1998 (20 Apr). *Lighthouses of the World. T* **390** *and similar multicoloured designs. P* 14.

2612 45 c. Type **390** 20 25
2613 65 c. Tierra del Fuego, Argentina (*horiz*) 30 35
2614 75 c. Point Loma, California, U.S.A. (*horiz*) 35 40
2615 90 c. Groenpoint, Cape Town, South Africa 40 45
2616 $1 Youghal, Cork, Ireland 45 50
2617 $1.20, Launceston, Tasmania, Australia 50 55
2618 $1.65, Point Abino, Ontario, Canada (*horiz*) 70 75
2619 $1.75, Great Inagua, Bahamas .. 75 80
2612/19 .. .. *Set of* 8 3·50 4·00
MS2620 99×70 mm. $6 Cape Hatteras, North Carolina, U.S.A. .. .. 2·50 2·75

No. 2613 is inscribed "Terra Del Fuego" in error.

391 Pooh and Tigger (January)

392 Miss Nellie Robinson (founder)

(Des Walt Disney Co. Litho)

1998 (11 May). *Through the Year with Winnie the Pooh. T* **391** *and similar vert designs. Multicoloured. P* 13½×14.

2621 $1 Type **391** 45 50
a. Sheetlet. Nos. 2621/6 .. .. 2·75
2622 $1 Pooh and Piglet indoors (February) .. 45 50
2623 $1 Piglet hang-gliding with scarf (March) 45 50
2624 $1 Tigger, Pooh and Piglet on pond (April) 45 50
2625 $1 Kanga and Roo with posy of flowers (May) 45 50
2626 $1 Pooh on balloon and Owl (June) .. 45 50
2627 $1 Pooh, Eeyore, Tigger and Piglet gazing at stars (July) 45 50
a. Sheetlet. Nos. 2627/32 .. .. 2·75
2628 $1 Pooh and Piglet by stream (August) .. 45 50
2629 $1 Christopher Robin going to school (September) 45 50
2630 $1 Eeyore in fallen leaves (October) .. 45 50
2631 $1 Pooh and Rabbit gathering pumpkins (November) 45 50
2632 $1 Pooh and Piglet skiing (December) .. 45 50
2621/32 .. .. *Set of* 12 5·25 5·75
MS2633 Four sheets, each 126×101 mm. (a) $6 Pooh, Rabbit and Piglet with blanket (Spring). (b) $6 Pooh by pond (Summer). (c) $6 Pooh sweeping fallen leaves (Autumn). (d) $6 Pooh and Eeyore on ice (Winter) .. *Set of* 4 *sheets* 8·75 9·00

Nos. 2621/6 and 2627/32 were each printed together, *se-tenant*, in sheetlets of 6.

(Des M. Friedman. Litho B.D.T.)

1998 (23 July). *Centenary of Thomas Oliver Robinson Memorial School. T* **392** *and similar designs. P* 14.

2634 20 c. brown-olive and black 10 15
2635 45 c. multicoloured 20 25
2636 65 c. brown-olive and black 30 35
2637 75 c. multicoloured 35 40
2638 90 c. multicoloured 40 45
2639 $1.20, red-brown, brown-olive and black 50 55
2634/9 .. .. *Set of* 6 1·75 2·10
MS2640 106×76 mm. $6 olive-brown .. .. 2·50 2·75

Designs: *Horiz*—45 c. School photo, 1985; 65 c. Former school building, 1930–49: 75 c. Children with Mrs. Natalie Hurst (present headmistress): $1.20, Present school building, 1950. *Vert*—90 c. Miss Ina Loving (former teacher); $6 Miss Nellie Robinson (*different*).

393 Spotted Eagle Ray

(Des. B. Steadman (Nos. 2641/65 and **MS**2678a), R. Martin (others). Litho Questa)

1998 (17 Aug). *International Year of the Ocean. T* **393** *and similar horiz designs. Multicoloured. P* 14.

2641/65 40 c. ×25 Type **393**; Manta Ray: Hawksbill Turtle; Jellyfish; Queen Angelfish; Octopus; Emperor Angelfish; Regal Angelfish; Porkfish; Racoon Butterflyfish; Alantic Barracuda; Sea Horse; Nautilus; Trumpet Fish; White Tip Shark; Sunken Spanish galleon; Black Tip Shark; Long-nosed Butterflyfish; Green Moray Eel; Captain Nemo; Treasure chest; Hammerhead Shark; Divers; Lion Fish; Clown Fish
a. Sheetlet. Nos. 2641/65 .. .. 3·75

2666/77 75 c. ×12 Maroon-tailed Conure; Cocoi Heron; Common Tern; Rainbow Lorikeet; Saddleback Butterfly Fish; Goatfish and Cat Shark; Blue Shark and Stingray; Majestic Snapper; Nassau Grouper; Black-cap Gramma and Blue Tang; Stingrays; Stingrays and Giant Starfish
a. Sheetlet. Nos. 2666/77 .. .. 4·25
2641/77 .. .. *Set of* 37 8·00 8·2
MS2678 Two sheets. (a) 68×98 mm. $6 Humpback Whale. (b) 98×68 mm. $6 Fiddler Ray .. .. *Set of* 2 *sheets* 5·00 5·2

Nos. 2641/65 and 2666/77 were each printed togethe *se-tenant*, in sheetlets of 25 or 12, with the backgrounds formin composite designs.

394 *Savannah* (paddle-steamer)

395 Flags of Antigua and CARICOM

(Des L. Schwinger. Litho Questa)

1998 (18 Aug). *Ships of the World. T* **394** *and simila multicoloured designs. P* 14½.

2679 $1.75, Type **394** 75 8
a. Sheetlet. Nos. 2679/81 .. .. 2·25
2680 $1.75, Viking longship 75 8
2681 $1.75, Greek galley 75 8
2682 $1.75, Sailing clipper 75 8
a. Sheetlet. Nos. 2682/4 .. .. .. 2·25
2683 $1.75, Dhow 75 8
2684 $1.75, Fishing catboat 75 8
2679/84 .. .. *Set of* 6 4·50 4·7
MS2685 Three sheets, each 100×70 mm. (a) $6 13th-century English warship (41×22 *mm*). (b) $6 Sailing dory (22×41 *mm*). (c) $6 Baltimore clipper (41×22 *mm*). P 14 .. *Set of* 3 *sheets* 7·50 7·7

Nos. 2679/81 and 2682/4 were printed together, *se-tenant*, i sheetlets of 3 with enlarged illustrated left-hand margins.

(Des R. Sauber. Litho Cartor)

1998 (20 Aug). *25th Anniv of Caribbean Community. P* 13½.

2686 **395** $1 multicoloured 45 5

STAMP BOOKLETS

1968 (2 Oct). *Blue cover. Stitched.*

SB1 $1.20, booklet containing 5 c., 10 c. and 15 c. (Nos. 185, 187, 188) in blocks of 4 .. .. 8·5

1977 (26 Sept). *Silver Jubilee. Blue, silver and sepia cove 165×82 mm, showing the Royal Family. Stitched.*

SB2 $8 booklet containing pane of 6 (No. 532a) and pane of 1 (No. 533a) .. .. 3·2

1978 (2 June). *25th Anniv of Coronation. Multicoloured cove 165×92 mm, showing Coronation Coach. Stitched.*

SB3 $7.25, booklet containing pane of 6 (No. 587a) and pane of 1 (No. 589a) .. .. 2·7

1981 (23 June). *Royal Wedding. Multicoloured cover, 165×9 mm, showing Prince Charles and Lady Diana Spencer o front and Prince Charles on back. Stitched.*

SB4 $11.50, booklet containing pane of 6 (No. 706a) and pane of 1 (No. 712a) .. .. .. 2·5

BARBUDA

DEPENDENCY OF ANTIGUA

PRICES FOR STAMPS ON COVER TO 1945	
Nos. 1/11	*from* × 5

BARBUDA

(1)

1922 (13 July). *Stamps of Leeward Islands optd with T* **1**. *All Die II. Chalk-surfaced paper (3d. to 5s.).*

(a) Wmk Mult Script CA

No.	Type	Description	Unused	Used
1	**11**	½d. deep green	1·00	8·00
2		1d. bright scarlet	1·00	8·00
		x. Wmk reversed	£450	
3	**10**	2d. slate-grey	1·00	7·00
		x. Wmk reversed	55·00	
4	**11**	2½d. bright blue	1·00	7·50
		w. Wmk inverted	25·00	75·00
5		6d. dull and bright purple	1·75	16·00
6	**10**	2s. purple and blue/*blue*	12·00	48·00
7		3s. bright green and violet	30·00	75·00
8		4s. black and red (R.)	40·00	75·00

(b) Wmk Mult Crown CA

No.	Type	Description	Unused	Used
9	**10**	3d. purple/*pale yellow*	1·00	9·00
10	**12**	1s. black/*emerald* (R.)	1·50	8·00
11		5s. green and red/*pale yellow*	65·00	£130
1/11		*Set of* 11	£130	£325
1/11 Optd "Specimen"		*Set of* 11	£225	

Examples of all values are known showing a forged Barbuda postmark of "JU 1 23".

Stocks of the overprinted stamps were exhausted by October 1925 and issues of Antigua were then used in Barbuda until 1968.

The following issues of Barbuda were also valid for use in Antigua.

(New Currency. 100 cents = 1 Eastern Caribbean dollar)

2 Map of Barbuda

3 Greater Amberjack

(Des R. Granger Barrett. Litho Format)

1968 (19 Nov)–**70**. *Designs as T* **2/3**. *P* 14.

No.	Description	Unused	Used
12	½ c. brown, black and pink	20	30
13	1 c. orange, black and flesh	30	10
14	2 c. blackish brown, rose-red and rose	30	10
15	3 c. blackish brown, orange-yellow and lemon	30	10
16	4 c. black, bright green and apple-green	30	30
17	5 c. blue-green, black and pale blue-green	30	10
18	6 c. black, bright purple and pale lilac	40	10
19	10 c. black, ultramarine and cobalt	30	10
20	15 c. black, blue-green and turquoise-green	30	55
20*a*	20 c. multicoloured (22.7.70)	1·50	2·00
21	25 c. multicoloured (5.2.69)	60	25
22	35 c. multicoloured (5.2.69)	60	25
23	50 c. multicoloured (5.2.69)	60	55
24	75 c. multicoloured (5.2.69)	70	80
25	$1 multicoloured (6.3.69)	85	2·00
26	$2.50, multicoloured (6.3.69)	1·50	5·00
27	$5 multicoloured (6.3.69)	3·75	7·50
12/27	*Set of* 17	11·50	17·00

Designs:—½ to 15 c. Type **2**. *Horiz as T* **3**—20 c. Great Barracuda; 35 c. French Angelfish; 50 c. Porkfish; 75 c. Princess Parrotfish; $1, Long-spined Squirrelfish; $2.50, Bigeye; $5, Blue Chromis.

10 Sprinting and Aztec Sun-stone

14 "The Ascension" (Orcagna)

(Des R. Granger Barrett. Litho Format)

1968 (20 Dec). *Olympic Games, Mexico. T* **10** *and similar horiz designs. Multicoloured. P* 14.

No.	Description	Unused	Used
28	25 c. Type **10**	35	25
29	35 c. High-jumping and Aztec statue	40	25
30	75 c. Yachting and Aztec lion mask	55	45
28/30	*Set of* 3	1·10	85
MS31	85 × 76 mm. $1 Football and engraved plate	1·60	3·25

(Des R. Granger Barret. Litho Format)

1969 (24 Mar). *Easter Commemoration. P* 14.

No.	Type	Description	Unused	Used
32	**14**	25 c. black and light blue	15	45
33		35 c. black and deep carmine	15	50
34		75 c. black and bluish lilac	15	55
32/4		*Set of* 3	40	1·40

15 Scout Enrolment Ceremony

18 "Sistine Madonna" (Raphael)

(Des R. Granger Barrett. Litho Format)

1969 (7 Aug). *3rd Caribbean Scout Jamboree. T* **15** *and similar horiz designs. Multicoloured. P* 14.

No.	Description	Unused	Used
35	25 c. Type **15**	45	55
36	35 c. Scouts around camp fire	60	65
37	75 c. Sea Scouts rowing boat	75	85
35/7	*Set of* 3	1·60	1·90

(Des. R. Granger Barrett. Litho Format)

1969 (20 Oct). *Christmas. P* 14.

No.	Type	Description	Unused	Used
38	**18**	½ c. multicoloured	10	10
39		25 c. multicoloured	10	15
40		35 c. multicoloured	10	20
41		75 c. multicoloured	20	35
38/41		*Set of* 4	30	60

19 William I (1066–87)

20c

(**20**)

(Des R. Granger Barrett. Litho Format (Nos. 42/9) or Questa (others))

1970–71. *English Monarchs. T* **19** *and similar vert designs. Multicoloured. P* 14½ × 14.

No.	Description	Unused	Used
42	35 c. Type **19** (16.2.70)	30	15
43	35 c. William II (2.3.70)	10	15
44	35 c. Henry I (16.3.70)	10	15
45	35 c. Stephen (1.4.70)	10	15
46	35 c. Henry II (15.4.70)	10	15
47	35 c. Richard I (1.5.70)	10	15
48	35 c. John (15.5.70)	10	15
49	35 c. Henry III (1.6.70)	10	15
50	35 c. Edward I (15.6.70)	10	15
51	35 c. Edward II (1.7.70)	10	15
52	35 c. Edward III (15.7.70)	10	15
53	35 c. Richard II (1.8.70)	10	15
54	35 c. Henry IV (15.8.70	10	15
55	35 c. Henry V (1.9.70)	10	15
56	35 c. Henry VI (15.9.70)	10	15
57	35 c. Edward IV (1.10.70)	10	15
58	35 c. Edward V (15.10.70)	10	15
59	35 c. Richard III (2.11.70)	10	15
60	35 c. Henry VII (16.11.70)	10	15
61	35 c. Henry VIII (1.12.70)	10	15
62	35 c. Edward VI (15.12.70)	10	15
63	35 c. Lady Jane Grey (2.1.71)	10	15
64	35 c. Mary I (15.1.71)	10	15
65	35 c. Elizabeth I (1.2.71)	10	15
66	35 c. James I (15.2.71)	10	15
67	35 c. Charles I (1.3.71)	10	15
68	35 c. Charles II (15.3.71)	10	15
69	35 c. James II (1.4.71)	10	15
70	35 c. William III (15.4.71)	10	15
71	35 c. Mary II (1.5.71)	10	15
72	35 c. Anne (15.5.71)	15	15
73	35 c. George I (1.6.71)	15	15
74	35 c. George II (15.6.71)	15	15
75	35 c. George III (1.7.71)	15	15
76	35 c. George IV (15.7.71)	15	15
77	35 c. William IV (2.8.71)	15	60
78	35 c. Victoria (16.8.71)	15	60
42/78	*Set of* 37	3·75	6·00

See also Nos. 710/15.

1970 (26 Feb). *No.* 12 *surch with T* **20**.

No.	Type	Description	Unused	Used
79	**2**	20 c. on ½ c. brown, black and pink	10	20
		a. Surch inverted	50·00	
		b. Surch double	50·00	

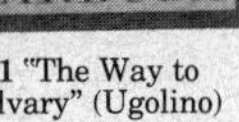

21 "The Way to Calvary" (Ugolino)

22 Oliver is introduced to Fagin (*Oliver Twist*)

(Des R. Granger Barrett. Litho Questa)

1970 (16 Mar). *Easter Paintings. T* **21** *and similar vert designs. Multicoloured P* 14.

No.	Description	Unused	Used
80	25 c. Type **21**	15	30
	a. Horiz strip of 3. Nos. 80/2	40	
81	35 c. "The Deposition from the Cross" (Ugolino)	15	30
82	75 c. Crucifix (The Master of St. Francis)	15	35
80/2	*Set of* 3	40	85

Nos. 80/2 were printed together, *se-tenant*, in horizontal strips of 3 throughout the sheet.

(Des R. Granger Barrett. Litho Questa)

1970 (10 July). *Death Centenary of Charles Dickens. T* **22** *and similar horiz design. Multicoloured. P* 14.

No.	Description	Unused	Used
83	20 c. Type **22**	10	15
84	75 c. Dickens and Scene from *The Old Curiosity Shop*	20	40

23 "Madonna of the Meadow" (Bellini)

24 Nurse with Patient in Wheelchair

(Des R. Granger Barrett. Litho Questa)

1970 (15 Oct). *Christmas. T* **23** *and similar horiz designs. Multicoloured. P* 14.

No.	Description	Unused	Used
85	20 c. Type **23**	10	25
86	50 c. "Madonna, Child and Angels" (from Wilton diptych)	15	30
87	75 c. "The Nativity" (della Francesca)	15	35
85/7	*Set of* 3	30	80

(Des R. Granger Barrett. Litho Questa)

1970 (21 Dec). *Centenary of British Red Cross. T* **24** *and similar multicoloured designs. P* 14.

No.	Description	Unused	Used
88	20 c. Type **24**	15	30
89	35 c. Nurse giving patient magazines (*horiz*)	20	40
90	75 c. Nurse and mother weighing baby (*horiz*)	25	70
88/90	*Set of* 3	55	1·25

25 Angel with Vases

26 Martello Tower

(Des R. Granger Barrett. Litho Questa)

1971 (7 Apr). *Easter. Details of the "Mond" Crucifixion by Raphael. T* **25** *and similar vert designs. Multicoloured. P* 14.

No.	Description	Unused	Used
91	35 c. Type **25**	15	75
	a. Horiz strip of 3. Nos. 91/3	40	
92	50 c. Christ crucified	15	85
93	75 c. Angel with vase	15	90
91/3	*Set of* 3	40	2·25

Nos. 91/3 were issued horizontally *se-tenant* within the sheet.

(Des R. Granger Barrett. Litho Questa)

1971 (10 May). *Tourism. T* **26** *and similar horiz designs. Multicoloured. P* 14.

No.	Description	Unused	Used
94	20 c. Type **26**	15	25
95	25 c. Sailing boats	25	30
96	50 c. Hotel bungalows	25	35
97	75 c. Government House and Mystery Stone	25	40
94/7	*Set of* 4	80	1·10

27 "The Granducal Madonna" (Raphael)

B
A
R
B
U
D
A

(**28**)

(Des R. Granger Barrett. Litho Questa)

1971 (4 Oct). *Christmas. T* **27** *and similar vert designs. Multicoloured. P* 14.

No.	Description	Unused	Used
98	½ c. Type **27**	10	10
99	35 c. "The Ansidei Madonna" (Raphael)	10	20
100	50 c. "The Madonna and Child" (Botticelli)	15	25
101	75 c. "The Madonna of the Trees" (Bellini)	15	30
98/101	*Set of* 4	35	65

The contract with the agency for the distribution of Barbuda stamps was cancelled by the Antiguan Government on 15 August 1971 but the above issue was duly authorised. Four stamps (20, 35, 50 and 70 c.) were prepared to commemorate the 500th anniversary of the birth of Albrecht Dürer but their issue was not authorised.

Barbuda ceased to have separate stamps issues in 1972 but again had stamps of her own on 14 November 1973 with the following issue.

1973 (14 Nov). *Royal Wedding. Nos.* 370/1 *of Antigua optd with T* **28**.

102 35 c. multicoloured .. .. 4·50 2·75
a. Opt inverted £100
103 $2 multicoloured .. .. 1·50 1·50
a. Opt inverted £120

No. **MS**372 of Antigua also exists with this overprint, but was not placed on sale at post offices. Examples of this sheet are known with "Specimen" overprint (*Price* £120).

BARBUDA (29) — B A R B U D A (30) — B A R B U D A (30*a*) — B A R B U D A (31)

1973 (26 Nov)–**74**. *T* **92** *etc. of Antigua optd with T* **29**.

(*a*) *On Nos.* 270 *etc. W w* **12** (*sideways*)

104 1 c. Columbus and *Nina* 15 30
105 2 c. Sir Thomas Warner's emblem and *Concepcion* 25 30
106 4 c. Sir George Rodney and H.M.S. *Formidable* 30 30
107 5 c. Nelson and H.M.S. *Boreas* 40 40
108 6 c. William IV and H.M.S. *Pegasus*.. .. 40 40
109 10 c. "Blackbeard" and pirate ketch 45 45
110 20 c. Nelson and H.M.S. *Victory* 55 60
111 25 c. *Solent I* (paddle-steamer) 55 60
112 35 c. George V (when Prince George) and H.M.S. *Canada* (screw corvette) .. 55 70
113 50 c. H.M.S. *Renown* (battle cruiser) .. 55 70
114 75 c. *Federal Maple* (freighter) 55 70
115 $2.50, H.M.S. *London* (destroyer) (18.2.74) 1·25 1·50

(*b*) *On Nos.* 323 *etc. W w* **12** (*upright*). *White paper*

116 ½ c. Type **92** (11.12.73) 15 20
117 3 c. Viscount Hood and H.M.S. *Barfleur* (11.12.73) 25 25
w. Wmk inverted .. .. 35·00
118 15 c. Captain Collingwood and H.M.S. *Pelican* (11.12.73) 45 50
119 $1 *Sol Quest* (yacht) and class emblem (11.12.73) 55 70
120 $2.50, H.M.S. *London* (destroyer) (18.2.74) 9·00 12·00
121 $5 *Pathfinder* (tug) (26.11.73) .. .. 1·10 2·50
104/21 .. .. *Set of* 18 15·00 20·00

1973 (26 Nov). *Commemorative stamps of Antigua optd.*

(*a*) *Nos.* 353, 355 *and* 357/8 *optd with T* **30**

122 ½ c. Private, Zacharia Tiffin's Regt of Foot, 1701 .. .. 10 10
123 20 c. Light Company Officer, 35th Regt of Foot, 1828 .. .. 15 10
aw. Wmk Crown to right of CA .. .. 7·00
b. Optd with T **30*a*** 60 70
bw. Wmk Crown to right of CA .. .. 6·00
124 75 c. Sergeant, 49th Regt, 1858 .. .. 40 15
122/4 .. .. *Set of* 3 55 25
MS125 127×145 mm. Nos. 353/7 of Antigua .. 2·00 3·50

(*b*) *Nos* 360/3 *optd with T* **31**, *in red*

126 20 c. Carnival street scene 10 10
127 35 c. Carnival troupe 10 10
a. Opt inverted .. .. 30·00
128 75 c. Carnival Queen 20 25
126/8 .. .. *Set of* 3 30 40
MS129 134×95 mm. Nos. 359/62 of Antigua .. 1·25 2·25
a. Albino opt .. ..
b. Opt double £275

Type **30*a*** is a local overprint, applied by typography.

B A R B U D A (32) — BARBUDA (33) — B A R B U D A (34) — B A R B U D A (35)

1973 (11 Dec). *Christmas. Nos.* 364/9 *of Antigua optd with T* **32**.

130 3 c. Type **105** (Sil.) 10 10
a. Opt inverted .. .. 24·00
b. "BABRUDA" (R.4/2) .. .. .. 5·50 5·50
131 5 c. "Adoration of the Magi" (Stomer) (Sil.) 10 10
a. "BABRUDA" (R.4/2) .. .. .. 7·00 7·00
132 20 c. "Granducal Madonna" (Raphael) (Sil.) .. 10 10
a. "BABRUDA" (R.4/2) .. .. .. 9·00 9·00
133 35 c. "Nativity with God the Father and Holy Ghost" (Battista) (R.) 15 15
134 $1 "Madonna and Child" (Murillo) (R.) .. 30 30
a. Opt inverted .. .. 45·00
130/4 .. .. *Set of* 5 60 60
MS135 130 × 128 mm. Nos. 130/4 (Sil.) .. 3·25 10·00

1973 (15 Dec). *Honeymoon Visit of Princess Anne and Capt. Phillips. Nos.* 373/5 *of Antigua further optd with T* **33**.

136 35 c. multicoloured 30 20
a. Type **33** double, one albino .. .. 65·00
b. Optd on Antigua No. 373a .. ..
137 $2 multicoloured 70 60
a. Type **33** double, one albino .. .. † —
b. Optd on Antigua No. 374a .. ..
MS138 78×100 mm. Nos. 136/7 .. .. 5·00 7·50

1974 (18 Feb). *25th Anniv of University of West Indies. Nos.* 376/9 *of Antigua optd with T* **34**.

139 5 c. Coat of arms 10 10
a. Opt double, one albino .. .. † —
140 20 c. Extra-mural art 10 10
141 35 c. Antigua campus 15 15
a. Opt double .. ..
142 75 c. Antigua Chancellor 15 15
139/42 .. .. *Set of* 4 30 30

No. 139a has only been seen used on first day cover. It shows the "normal" impression misplaced and very faint

1974 (1 May). *Military Uniforms. Nos.* 380/4 *of Antigua optd with T* **35**.

143 ½ c. Officer, 59th Foot, 1797 .. .. .. 10 10
144 10 c. Gunner, Royal Artillery, 1800 .. .. 10 10
a. Horiz pair, left-hand stamp without opt £130
145 20 c. Private, 1st West India Regt, 1830 .. 20 10
a. Horiz pair, left-hand stamp without opt £130
146 35 c. Officer, 92nd Foot, 1843 .. .. .. 25 10
a. Opt inverted .. .. 50·00
147 75 c. Private, 23rd Foot, 1846.. .. .. 45 25
a. Horiz pair, left-hand stamp without opt
143/7 .. .. *Set of* 5 90 45

Nos. 144a, 145a and 147a come from sheets on which the overprint was so misplaced as to miss the first vertical row completely. Other stamps in these sheets show the overprint at left instead of right.

No. **MS**385 of Antigua also exists with this overprint, but was not placed on sale at post offices.

BARBUDA 13 JULY 1922 (36) — BARBUDA 15 SEPT. 1874 G.P.U. (37 "General Postal Union") — BARBUDA (38)

1974 (15 July). *Centenary of Universal Postal Union* (*1st issue*). *Nos.* 386/92 *of Antigua optd with T* **36** (*Nos.* 148, 150, 152, 154, 156, 158 *and* 160) *or T* **37** (*others*), *in red.*

148 ½ c. English postman, mailcoach and Westland Dragonfly helicopter .. 10 10
149 ½ c. English postman, mailcoach and Westland Dragonfly helicopter .. 10 10
150 1 c. Bellman, mail steamer *Orinoco* and satellite 10 10
151 1 c. Bellman, mail steamer *Orinoco* and satellite 10 10
152 2 c. Train guard, post-bus and hydrofoil .. 20 15
153 2 c. Train guard, post-bus and hydrofoil .. 20 15
154 5 c. Swiss messenger, Wells Fargo coach and Concorde 50 15
155 5 c. Swiss messenger, Wells Fargo coach and Concorde 50 15
156 20 c. Postilion, Japanese postmen and carrier pigeon 40 70
157 20 c. Postilion, Japanese postmen and carrier pigeon 40 70
158 35 c. Antiguan postman, Sikorsky S-38 flying boat and tracking station .. 80 1·50
159 35 c. Antiguan postman, Sikorsky S-38 flying boat and tracking station .. 80 1·50
160 $1 Medieval courier, American express train and Boeing 747-100 .. .. 2·25 4·00
161 $1 Medieval courier, American express train and Boeing 747-100 .. .. 2·25 4·00
148/61 .. .. *Set of* 14 7·50 12·00
MS162 141×164 mm. No. **MS**393 of Antigua overprinted with T **38**, in red .. .. 3·50 6·00
a. Albino opt .. ..

Nos. 148/9, 150/1, 152/3, 154/5, 156/7, 158/9 and 160/1 were each printed together, *se-tenant*, in horizontal pairs throughout the sheet.

See also Nos. 177/80.

1974 (14 Aug). *Antiguan Steel Bands. Nos.* 394/8 *of Antigua optd with T* **38**.

163 5 c. rose-red, carmine and black 10 10
164 20 c. brown-ochre, chestnut and black 10 10
165 35 c. light sage-green, blue-green and black .. 10 10
166 75 c. dull blue, dull ultramarine and black .. 20 20
163/6 .. .. *Set of* 4 35 35
MS167 115×108 mm. Nos. 163/6 .. .. 65 80

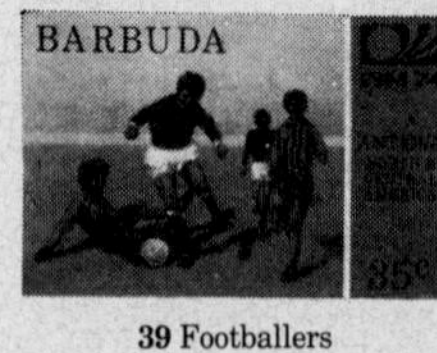

39 Footballers

B A R B U D A (40)

(Des G. Drummond. Litho Format)

1974 (2 Sept). *World Cup Football Championships* (*1st issue*). *Various horiz designs as T* **39** *each showing footballers in action. P* 14.

168 **39** 35 c. multicoloured 10 10
169 $1.20, multicoloured 25 35
170 $2.50, multicoloured 35 50
168/70 .. .. *Set of* 3 60 75
MS171 70 × 128 mm. Nos. 168/70 .. .. 85 90

Nos. 168/71 exist imperforate from stock dispersed by the liquidator of Format International Security Printers Ltd.

1974 (23 Sept). *World Cup Football Championships* (*2nd issue*). *Nos.* 399/403 *of Antigua optd with T* **40**.

172 5 c. multicoloured 10 10
173 35 c. multicoloured 10 10
174 75 c. multicoloured 15 15
175 $1 multicoloured 20 25
172/5 .. .. *Set of* 4 35 45
MS176 135×130 mm. Nos. 172/5 .. .. 75 1·50

41 Ship Letter of 1833 — 42 Greater Amberjack

(Des G. Drummond. Litho Format)

1974 (30 Sept). *Centenary of Universal Postal Union* (*2nd issue*). *T* **41** *and similar vert designs. Multicoloured. P* 13½.

177 35 c. Type **41** 10 10
178 $1.20, Stamps and postmark of 1922 .. 30 50
179 $2.50, Britten Norman Islander mailplane over map of Barbuda 55 75
177/9 .. .. *Set of* 3 75 1·25
MS180 128×97 mm. Nos. 177/9 .. .. 1·00 2·00

Nos. 177/80 exist imperforate from stock dispersed by the liquidator of Format International Security Printers Ltd.

(Des G. Drummond. Litho Format)

1974 (15 Oct)–**75**. *Multicoloured designs as T* **42**. *P* 14×14½ (½ *c. to* 3 *c.,* 25 *c.*), 14½×14 (4 *c. to* 20 *c.,* 35 *c.*), 14 (50 *c. to* $1) *or* 13½ (*others*).

181 ½ c. Oleander, Rose Bay (6.1.75) 10 40
182 1 c. Blue Petrea (6.1.75) 15 40
183 2 c. Poinsettia (6.1.75) 15 40
184 3 c. Cassia tree (6.1.75) 15 40
185 4 c. Type **42** .. .. 1·40 40
186 5 c. Holy Trinity School 15 15
187 6 c. Snorkeling 15 30
188 10 c. Pilgrim Holiness Church 15 20
189 15 c. New Cottage Hospital 15 20
190 20 c. Post Office and Treasury 15 20
191 25 c. Island jetty and boats 30 30
192 35 c. Martello Tower 30 30
193 50 c. Warden's House (6.1.75) 30 30
194 75 c. Britten Norman Islander aircraft .. 75 1·00
195 $1 Tortoise (6.1.75) 70 80
196 $2.50, Spiny lobster (6.1.75) .. .. 80 1·75
197 $5 Magnificent Frigate Bird (6.1.75) .. 4·00 2·50
a. Perf 14×14½ (24.7.75)* .. .. 12·00 22·00
197*b* $10 Hibiscus (19.9.75) .. .. .. 2·50 4·50
181/97*b* .. .. *Set of* 18 11·00 13·00

*See footnote below Nos. 227/8.

The 50 c. to $1 are larger, 39 × 25 mm; the $2.50 and $5 are 45 × 29 mm; the $10 is 34 × 48 mm and the ½ c. to 3c. 25 c. and $10 are vert designs.

1974 (15 Oct). *Birth Centenary of Sir Winston Churchill* (*1st issue*). *Nos.* 408/12 *of Antigua optd with T* **38** *in red.*

198 5 c. Churchill as schoolboy, and school college building, Harrow 15 10
a. Opt inverted .. .. 60·00
199 35 c. Churchill and St. Paul's Cathedral .. 25 15
200 75 c. Coat of arms and catafalque 40 45
201 $1 Churchill, "reward" notice and South African escape route 75 70
a. Opt inverted .. .. 60·00
198/201 .. .. *Set of* 4 1·40 1·25
MS202 107 × 82 mm. Nos. 198/201 .. .. 6·00 13·00

43 Churchill making Broadcast — BARBUDA (44)

(Des G. Drummond. Litho Questa)

1974 (20 Nov). *Birth Centenary of Sir Winston Churchill* (*2nd issue*). *T* **43** *and similar horiz designs. Multicoloured. P* 13½ × 14.

203 5 c. Type **43** 10 10
204 35 c. Churchill and Chartwell 10 10
205 75 c. Churchill painting 20 20
206 $1 Churchill making "V" sign 25 30
203/6 .. .. *Set of* 4 55 60
MS207 146×95 mm. Nos. 203/6 .. .. 75 2·50

1974 (25 Nov). *Christmas. Nos.* 413/21 *of Antigua optd with T* **33**.

208 ½ c. Bellini 10 10
a. Opt inverted .. .. 45·00
209 1 c. Raphael 10 10
210 2 c. Van der Weyden 10 10
211 3 c. Giorgione 10 10
212 5 c. Mantegna 10 10
213 20 c. Vivarini 10 10
214 35 c. Montagna 15 15
215 75 c. Lorenzo Costa 30 30
208/15 .. .. *Set of* 8 60 60
MS216 139 × 126 mm. Nos. 208/15 .. .. 80 1·40

1975 (17 Mar). *Nelson's Dockyard. Nos.* 427/32 *of Antigua optd with T* **44**.

217 5 c. Carib war canoe, English Harbour, 1300 15 15
218 15 c. Ship of the line, English Harbour, 1770 40 25
219 35 c. H.M.S. *Boreas* at anchor, and Lord Nelson, 1787 .. .. 55 35
220 50 c. Yachts during "Sailing Week", 1974 .. 65 50
221 $1 Yacht Anchorage, Old Dockyard, 1970 .. 65 80
217/21 .. .. *Set of* 5 2·10 1·75
MS222 130 × 134 mm. As Nos. 217/21, but in larger format; 43 × 28 mm .. .. 1·75 2·75

45 Battle of the Saints, 1782

(Des G. Vasarhelyi. Litho Format)

75 (30 May). *Sea Battles. T* **45** *and similar horiz designs howing scenes from the Battle of the Saints,* 1782. *Multicoloured.* 13½.
3 35 c. Type **45** 75 65
4 50 c. H.M.S. *Ramillies* 75 75
5 75 c. Ships firing broadsides 90 90
6 95 c. Sailors fleeing burning ship .. .. 1·00 1·25
3/6 .. .. *Set of* 4 3·00 3·25

(46)

75 (24 July). *"Apollo-Soyuz" Space Project. No.* 197a *optd with T* **46** *and similar ("Soyuz") opt.*
7 $5 Magnificent Frigate Bird ("Apollo") .. 4·00 7·50
a. *Se-tenant* strip of 3. Nos. 227/8 and 197a 18·00
8 $5 Magnificent Frigate Bird ("Soyuz") .. 4·00 7·50
Nos. 227/8 were issued together *se-tenant* in sheets of 25 (5 × 5), th the "Apollo" opts in the first and third vertical rows and the oyuz" opts in the second and fourth vertical rows, the fifth rtical row comprising five unoverprinted stamps (No. 197a).

30TH ANNIVERSARY
UNITED NATIONS
1945 — 1975

47 Officer, 65th Foot, 1763 (48)

(Des G. Drummond. Litho Questa)

75 (17 Sept). *Military Uniforms. T* **47** *and similar vert designs. Multicoloured. P* 13½.
29 35 c. Type **47** 75 75
30 50 c. Grenadier, 27th Foot, 1701–10 .. .. 90 90
31 75 c. Officer, 21st Foot, 1793–6 .. .. 1·00 1·00
32 95 c. Officer, Royal Regt of Artillery, 1800 .. 1·25 1·25
9/32 .. .. *Set of* 4 3·50 3·50

75 (24 Oct). 30*th Anniv of United Nations. Nos.* 203/6 *optd with T* **48**.
33 5 c. Churchill making broadcast 10 10
34 35 c. Churchill and Chartwell 10 15
35 75 c. Churchill painting 15 20
36 $1 Churchill making "V" sign 20 30
33/6 .. .. *Set of* 4 40 60

BARBUDA (49) BARBUDA (50)

75 (17 Nov). *Christmas. Nos.* 457/65 *of Antigua optd with T* **49**.
37 ½ c. Correggio 10 10
38 1 c. El Greco 10 10
39 2 c. Dürer 10 10
40 3 c. Antonello 10 10
41 5 c. Bellini 10 10
42 10 c. Dürer 10 10
43 25 c. Bellini 15 20
44 $2 Dürer .. .. 60 1·00
37/44 .. .. *Set of* 8 95 1·50
MS245 138 × 119 mm. Nos. 241/4 .. .. .. 1·10 2·25

75 (15 Dec). *World Cup Cricket Winners. Nos.* 466/8 *of Antigua optd with T* **50**.
46 5 c. Vivian Richards .. .. 90 1·00
47 35 c. Andy Roberts .. .. 1·75 2·00
48 $2 West Indies team .. .. .. 3·25 4·25
46/8 .. .. *Set of* 3 5·50 6·50

51 "Surrender of Cornwallis at Yorktown" (Trumbull)

(Des G. Vasarhelyi. Litho Format)

976 (8 Mar). *Bicentenary of American Revolution. T* **51** *and similar horiz designs. Multicoloured. P* 13½ × 13.
49 15 c. } Type **51** .. 10 15
50 15 c. } .. 10 15
51 15 c. } .. 10 15
252 35 c. } "The Battle of Princeton" .. 10 15
253 35 c. } .. 10 15
254 35 c. } .. 10 15
255 $1 } "Surrender of General Burgoyne at Saratoga" (W. Mercer) .. 15 25
256 $1 } .. 15 25
257 $1 } .. 15 25
258 $2 } "The Declaration of Independence" (Trumbull) .. 25 40
259 $2 } .. 25 40
260 $2 } .. 25 40
249/60 .. .. *Set of* 12 1·50 2·50
MS261 140 × 70 mm. Nos. 249/54 and 255/60 (*two sheets*) .. .. 2·25 9·00
The three designs of each value were printed horizontally *se-tenant* within the sheet to form the composite designs listed. Type **51** shows the left-hand stamp of the 15 c. design.

52 Bananaquits

(Des G. Drummond. Litho Format)

1976 (30 June). *Birds. T* **52** *and similar horiz designs. Multicoloured. P* 13½.
262 35 c. Type **52** .. .. 1·00 50
263 50 c. Blue-hooded Euphonia .. .. .. 1·25 60
264 75 c. Royal Tern .. .. 1·25 80
265 95 c. Killdeer .. .. 1·75 85
266 $1.25, Common Cowbird .. .. .. 1·75 1·00
267 $2 Purple Gallinule .. .. 2·00 1·25
262/7 .. .. *Set of* 6 8·00 4·50

1976 (12 Aug). *Royal Visit to the U.S.A. As Nos.* 249/60 *but redrawn and inscr at top* "H.M. QUEEN ELIZABETH ROYAL VISIT 6TH JULY 1976 H.R.H. DUKE OF EDINBURGH".
268 15 c. } As Type **51** .. 10 15
269 15 c. } .. 10 15
270 15 c. } .. 10 15
271 35 c. } As Nos. 252/4 .. 10 20
272 35 c. } .. 10 20
273 35 c. } .. 10 20
274 $1 } As Nos. 255/7 .. 15 50
275 $1 } .. 15 50
276 $1 } .. 15 50
277 $2 } As Nos. 258/60 .. 25 70
278 $2 } .. 25 70
279 $2 } .. 25 70
268/79 .. .. *Set of* 12 1·50 4·25
MS280 143 × 81 mm. Nos. 268/73 and 274/9 (*two sheets*) .. .. 2·50 9·00
The three designs of each value were printed horizontally *se-tenant*, imperf between.

BARBUDA (53) BARBUDA (54)

1976 (2 Dec). *Christmas. Nos.* 514/18 *of Antigua optd with T* **53**.
281 8 c. The Annunciation 10 10
282 10 c. The Holy Family 10 10
283 15 c. The Magi 10 10
284 50 c. The Shepherds 15 15
285 $1 Epiphany scene 25 30
281/5 .. .. *Set of* 5 45 55

1976 (28 Dec). *Olympic Games, Montreal. Nos.* 495/502 *of Antigua optd with T* **54**.
286 ½ c. High-jump 10 10
287 1 c. Boxing 10 10
288 2 c. Pole-vault 10 10
289 15 c. Swimming 10 10
290 30 c. Running 10 10
291 $1 Cycling 20 20
292 $2 Shot put 35 35
286/92 .. .. *Set of* 7 60 60
MS293 88 × 138 mm. Nos. 289/92 .. .. 1·75 2·40

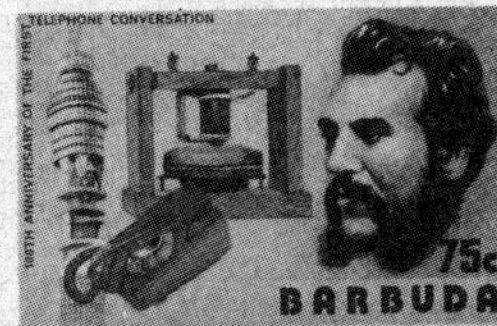

55 Post Office Tower, Telephones and Alexander Graham Bell

(Des G. Vasarhelyi. Litho Format)

1977 (31 Jan). *Telephone Centenary* (1976). *T* **55** *and similar horiz designs. Multicoloured. P* 13½.
294 75 c. Type **55** 15 35
295 $1.25, Dish aerial and television 20 55
296 $2 Globe and satellites 30 75
294/6 .. .. *Set of* 3 60 1·50
MS297 96 × 144 mm. Nos. 294/6. P 15 .. .. 70 2·00

56 St. Margaret's Church, Westminster

1977 (7 Feb). *Silver Jubilee* (1*st issue*). *T* **56** *and similar horiz designs. Multicoloured. Litho. P* 13½ × 13.
298 75 c. Type **56** 10 15
299 75 c. Entrance, Westminster Abbey 10 15
300 75 c. Westminster Abbey 10 15
301 $1.25, Household Cavalry 15 20
302 $1.25, Coronation Coach 15 20
303 $1.25, Team of Horses 15 20
298/303 .. .. *Set of* 6 65 90
MS304 148×83 mm. As Nos. 298/303, but with silver borders. P 15 .. .. 75 1·50
Nos. 298/300 and 301/3 were printed horizontally *se-tenant*, forming composite designs.
See also Nos. 323/30 and 375/8.

1977 (4 Apr). *Nos.* 469A/86A *of Antigua optd with T* **54**.
305 ½ c. Antillean Crested Hummingbird .. 20 20
306 1 c. Imperial Amazon 30 20
307 2 c. Zenaida Dove 30 20
308 3 c. Loggerhead Kingbird 30 20
309 4 c. Red-necked Pigeon 30 20
310 5 c. Rufous-throated Solitaire 30 20
311 6 c. Orchid Tree 30 20
312 10 c. Bougainvillea 30 20
313 15 c. Geiger Tree 30 25
314 20 c. Flamboyant 30 25
315 25 c. Hibiscus 30 25
316 35 c. Flame of the Wood 35 30
317 50 c. Cannon at Fort James 40 40
318 75 c. Premier's Office 40 40
319 $1 Potworks Dam 50 60
320 $2.50, Irrigation scheme .. .. .. 1·25 1·60
321 $5 Government House .. .. .. 2·25 3·25
322 $10 Coolidge Airport .. .. .. 4·00 7·50
305/22 .. .. *Set of* 18 11·00 15·00

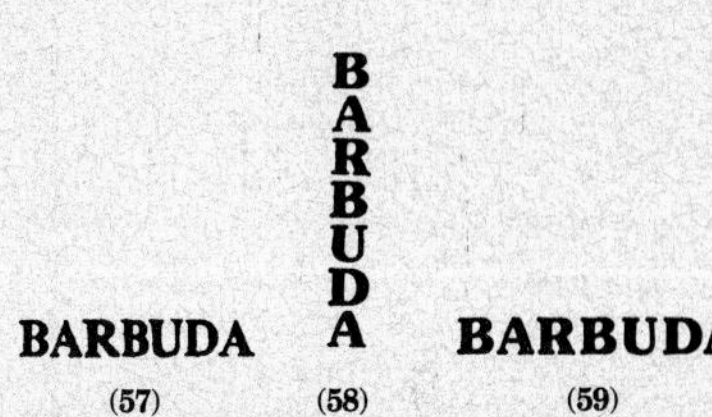

(57) (58) (59)

1977 (4 Apr–20 Dec). *Silver Jubilee* (2*nd issue*).

(*a*) *Sheet stamps. Nos.* 526/31 *of Antigua optd with T* **57**
323 10 c. Royal Family 10 15
a. Opt double .. .. 45·00
324 30 c. Royal Visit, 1966 .. .. .. 15 20
325 50 c. Queen enthroned 20 30
326 90 c. Queen after Coronation 25 40
327 $2.50, Queen and Prince Charles .. .. 75 1·25
323/7 .. .. *Set of* 5 1·25 2·10
MS328 116×78 mm. $5 Queen Elizabeth and Prince Philip .. .. 80 1·25
a. Error. Imperf £600
b. Opt albino .. .. 25·00
c. Opt double

(*b*) *Booklet stamps. Nos.* 532/3 *of Antigua optd with T* **58** *in silver* (50 c.) *or T* **59** *in gold* ($5) (20 Dec)
329 50 c. Queen after Coronation 40 70
a. Booklet pane of 6 .. .. .. 2·25
330 $5 The Queen and Prince Philip .. .. 5·50 13·00
a. Booklet pane of 1 .. .. .. 5·50

BARBUDA (60)

61 Royal Yacht *Britannia*

1977 (13 June). *Caribbean Scout Jamboree, Jamaica. Nos.* 534/41 *of Antigua optd with T* **60**.
331 ½ c. Making camp 10 10
332 1 c. Hiking 10 10
333 2 c. Rock-climbing 10 10
334 10 c. Cutting logs 10 10
335 30 c. Map and sign reading 40 40
336 50 c. First aid 55 65
337 $2 Rafting .. .. 1·50 2·25
331/37 .. .. *Set of* 7 2·25 3·00
MS338 127 × 114 mm. Nos. 335/7 .. .. 3·25 4·00

1977 (12 Aug). 21*st Anniv of Carnival. Nos.* 542/7 *of Antigua optd with T* **60**.
339 10 c. Carnival costume 10 10
340 30 c. Carnival Queen 10 10
341 50 c. Butterfly costume 15 20
342 90 c. Queen of the band 20 30
343 $1 Calypso King and Queen 25 40
339/43 .. .. *Set of* 5 65 90
MS344 140 × 120 mm. Nos. 339/43 .. .. 1·00 1·75

(Des G. Drummond. Litho Format)

1977 (27 Oct). *Royal Visit* (1*st issue*). *T* **61** *and similar horiz designs. Multicoloured. P* 14½.
345 50 c. Type **61** 10 15
346 $1.50, Jubilee emblem 25 35
347 $2.50, Union Jack and flag of Antigua .. 35 55
345/7 .. .. *Set of* 3 60 95
MS348 77 × 124 mm. Nos. 345/7 .. .. 85 2·25

BARBUDA (**62**)   **BARBUDA** (**63**)   **64** Airship LZ-1

1977 (28 Nov–20 Dec). *Royal Visit* (*2nd issue*). *Nos.* 548/53 *of Antigua optd*. A. *With T* **57**. *P* 14 (28 Nov).
349A 10 c. Royal Family .. 10 10
350A 30 c. Royal Visit, 1966 .. 15 20
351A 50 c. Queen enthroned .. 20 25
352A 90 c. Queen after Coronation .. 25 40
353A $2.50, Queen and Prince Charles .. 50 1·25
349A/53A .. *Set of* 5 1·00 2·00
MS354A 116×78 mm. $5 Queen and Prince Philip .. 1·75 4·00

B. *With T* **62**. *P* 11½×12 (20 Dec)
349B 10 c. Royal Family .. 10 10
a. Blue opt .. 35 35
350B 30 c. Royal Visit, 1966 .. 15 15
a. Blue opt .. 90 95
351B 50 c. Queen enthroned .. 20 20
a. Blue opt .. 2·75 1·90
352B 90 c. Queen after Coronation .. 30 30
a. Blue opt .. 5·00 3·50
353B $2.50, Queen and Prince Charles .. 60 80
a. Blue opt .. 11·00 9·50
349B/53B .. *Set of* 5 1·10 1·40
Nos. 349B/53B were each printed in small sheets of 6 including one *se-tenant* stamp-size label.

1977 (28 Nov). *Christmas. Nos.* 554/61 *of Antigua optd with T* **63**. *"Virgin and Child" paintings by the artists given.*
355 ½ c. Tura .. 10 10
356 1 c. Crivelli .. 10 10
357 2 c. Lotto .. 10 10
358 8 c. Pontormo .. 10 10
359 10 c. Tura .. 10 10
360 25 c. Lotto .. 15 10
361 $2 Crivelli .. 45 45
355/61 .. *Set of* 7 70 65
MS362 144 × 118 mm. Nos. 358/61 .. 1·00 1·75

(Des I. Oliver. Litho Format)

1977 (29 Dec). *Special Events*, 1977. *T* **64** *and similar horiz designs. Multicoloured. P* 14.
363 75 c. Type **64** .. 30 30
a. Nos. 363/6 in *se-tenant* block .. 1·10
364 75 c. German battleship and naval airship L-31 .. 30 30
365 75 c. Airship LZ-127 *Graf Zeppelin* in hangar .. 30 30
366 75 c. Gondola of military airship .. 30 30
367 95 c. "Sputnik 1" .. 35 35
a. Nos. 367/70 in *se-tenant* block .. 1·25
368 95 c. "Vostok" .. 35 35
369 95 c. "Voskhod" .. 35 35
370 95 c. Space walk .. 35 35
371 $1.25, Fuelling for flight .. 40 45
a. Nos. 371/4 in *se-tenant* block .. 1·40
372 $1.25, Leaving New York .. 40 45
373 $1.25, Ryan NYP Special *Spirit of St. Louis* .. 40 45
374 $1.25, Welcome in France .. 40 45
375 $2 Lion of England .. 50 70
a. Nos. 375/8 in *se-tenant* block .. 1·75
376 $2 Unicorn of Scotland .. 50 70
377 $2 Yale of Beaufort .. 50 70
378 $2 Falcon of Plantagenets .. 50 70
379 $5 } "Daniel in the Lion's Den" (Rubens) .. 50 1·25
380 $5 .. 50 1·25
381 $5 .. 50 1·25
382 $5 .. 50 1·25
a. Nos. 379/82 in *se-tenant* block .. 1·75
363/82 .. *Set of* 20 6·00 11·00
MS383 132 × 156 mm. Nos. 363/82 .. 6·00 17·00
Events:—75 c. 75th Anniv of Navigable Airships; 95 c. 20th Anniv of U.S.S.R. Space Programme; $1.25, 50th Anniv of Lindbergh's Transatlantic Flight; $2 Silver Jubilee of Queen Elizabeth II; $5 400th Birth Anniv of Rubens.
Nos. 363/66, 367/70, 371/74, 375/78 and 379/82 were printed in *se-tenant* blocks of four within the sheet.
Nos. 363/83 exist imperforate from stock dispersed by the liquidator of Format International Security Printers Ltd.

BARBUDA (**65**)   **66** "Pieta" (sculpture) (detail)

1978 (15 Feb). *Tenth Anniv of Statehood. Nos.* 562/7 *of Antigua optd with T* **65**.
384 10 c. Pineapple .. 10 10
385 15 c. State flag .. 15 10
386 50 c. Police band .. 1·25 70
387 90 c. Premier V. C. Bird .. 20 40
388 $2 State Coat of Arms .. 40 80
384/8 .. *Set of* 5 1·75 1·75
MS389 126 × 99 mm. Nos. 385/88. P 14 .. 5·50 3·50

(Des G. Vasarhelyi. Litho Format)

1978 (23 Mar). *Easter. Works by Michelangelo. T* **66** *and similar horiz designs. Multicoloured. P* 13½ × 14.
390 75 c. Type **66** .. 15 15
391 95 c. "The Holy Family" (painting) .. 20 20
392 $1.25, "Libyan Sibyl" from Sistine Chapel Rome .. 25 25
393 $2 "The Flood" from Sistine Chapel .. 30 35
390/3 .. *Set of* 4 75 85
MS394 117 × 85 mm. Nos. 390/3 .. 1·60 2·00
Nos. 390/4 exist imperforate from stock dispersed by the liquidator of Format International Security Printers Ltd.

BARBUDA (**67**)   **68** St. Edward's Crown

1978 (28 Mar). *75th Anniv of Powered Flight. Nos.* 568/75 *of Antigua optd with T* **67**.
395 ½ c. Wright Glider III, 1902 .. 10 10
396 1 c. Wright Flyer I, 1903 .. 10 10
397 2 c. Launch system and engine .. 10 10
398 10 c. Orville Wright .. 10 10
399 50 c. Wright Flyer III, 1905 .. 25 15
400 90 c. Wilbur Wright .. 35 15
401 $2 Wright Type B, 1910 .. 60 45
395/401 .. *Set of* 7 1·25 75
MS402 90×75 mm. $2.50, Wright Flyer I on launch system .. 1·50 2·25

1978 (22 May). *Sailing Week. Nos.* 576/80 *of Antigua optd with T* **67**.
403 10 c. Sunfish regatta .. 20 10
404 50 c. Fishing and work boat race .. 40 25
405 90 c. Curtain Bluff race .. 55 35
406 $2 Power boat rally .. 85 75
403/6 .. *Set of* 4 1·75 1·25
MS407 110 × 77 mm. $2.50, Guadeloupe–Antigua race .. 1·25 1·60
a. Albino opt .. † —

(Des J. Cooter. Litho Format)

1978 (2 June). *25th Anniv of Coronation* (*1st issue*). *T* **68** *and similar vert designs. Multicoloured. P* 15.
408 75 c. Type **68** .. 15 15
409 75 c. Imperial State Crown .. 15 15
410 $1.50, Queen Mary's Crown .. 20 25
411 $1.50, Queen Mother's Crown .. 20 25
412 $2.50, Queen Consort's Crown .. 35 45
413 $2.50, Queen Victoria's Crown .. 35 45
408/413 .. *Set of* 6 1·10 1·50
MS414 123 × 117 mm. Nos. 408/13. P 14½ .. 1·10 1·75
The two designs for each value were issued as two *se-tenant* pairs, together with 2 labels, in small sheets of 6.
Examples of the 75 c. and $2.50 values in separate miniature sheets of four exist from stock dispersed by the liquidator of Format International Security Printers Ltd, as do imperforate examples of No. **MS**414.

1978 (2 June–12 Oct). *25th Anniv of Coronation* (*2nd issue*).
(*a*) *Sheet stamps. Nos.* 581/6 *of Antigua optd with T* **67**. *P* 14 (2.6)
415 10 c. Queen Elizabeth and Prince Philip .. 10 10
416 30 c. Crowning .. 10 10
417 50 c. Coronation procession .. 10 15
418 90 c. Queen seated in St. Edward's Chair .. 15 20
a. Opt triple .. 85·00
419 $2.50, Queen wearing Imperial State Crown 30 60
415/19 .. *Set of* 5 60 1·00
MS420 114 × 103 mm. $5 Queen and Prince Philip (17.7) .. 1·00 1·50
a. Albino opt .. £250

(*b*) *Booklet stamps. Horiz designs as Nos.* 587/9 *of Antigua but additionally inscr* "BARBUDA". *Multicoloured. Roul* 5 × *imperf**. *Self-adhesive* (12.10)
421 25 c. Glass Coach .. 30 70
a. Booklet pane. Nos. 421/2 × 3 .. 1·60
422 50 c. Irish State Coach .. 30 70
423 $5 Coronation Coach .. 1·00 2·25
a. Booklet pane of 1 .. 1·00
421/3 .. *Set of* 3 1·75 3·25
*The 25 and 50 c. values were separated by various combinations of rotary knife (giving a straight edge) and roulette. The $5 value exists only with straight edges.
Nos. 415/19 also exist perf 12 (*Price for set of* 5 55*p mint or used*) from additional sheetlets of three stamps and one label, issued 12 October 1978. These stamps have different background colours from Nos. 415/19.

1978 (12 Sept). *World Cup Football Championship, Argentina. Nos.* 590/3 *of Antigua optd with T* **67**.
424 10 c. Player running with ball .. 10 10
425 15 c. Players in front of goal .. 10 10
426 $3 Referee and player .. 1·00 1·25
424/6 .. *Set of* 3 1·00 1·25
MS427 126 × 88 mm. 25 c. Player crouching with ball; 30 c. Players heading ball; 50 c. Players running with ball; $2 Goalkeeper diving .. 80 90

BARBUDA (**69**)   **70** Black-barred Soldierfish

1978 (20 Nov). *Flowers. Nos.* 594/8 *of Antigua optd with T* **69**.
428 25 c. Petrea .. 20 30
429 50 c. Sunflower .. 30 50
430 90 c. Frangipani .. 50 60
431 $2 Passion Flower .. 75 1·25
428/31 .. *Set of* 4 1·60 2·40
MS432 118 × 85 mm. $2.50, Hibiscus .. 1·50 2·00

1978 (20 Nov). *Christmas. Paintings. Nos.* 599/602 *optd with T* [cut off] *in silver.*
433 8 c. "St. Ildefonso receiving the Chasuble from the Virgin" .. 10
434 25 c. "The Flight of St. Barbara" .. 15
435 $2 "Madonna and Child, with St. Joseph, John the Baptist and Donor" .. 60 1·
433/5 .. *Set of* 3 75 1·
MS436 170 × 113 mm. $4 "The Annunciation" .. 1·75 2·

(Litho Format)

1978 (20 Nov). *Flora and Fauna. T* **70** *and similar horiz desig*[ns]*. Multicoloured. P* 14½.
437 25 c. Type **70** .. 1·25 1·
438 50 c. *Cynthia cardui* (butterfly) .. 2·00 2·
439 75 c. Dwarf Poinciana .. 1·50 2·
440 95 c. *Heliconius charithonia* (butterfly) .. 2·00 2
441 $1.25, Bougainvillea .. 1·50 2·
437/41 .. *Set of* 5 7·50 10·

71 Footballers and World Cup   **72** Sir Rowland Hill

(Des J. Cooter. Litho Format)

1978 (29 Dec). *Anniversaries and Events. T* **71** *and similar mul*[ti]*coloured designs. P* 14.
442 75 c. Type **71** .. 30
443 95 c. Wright brothers and Flyer I (*horiz*) .. 40
444 $1.25, Balloon *Double Eagle II* and map of Atlantic (*horiz*) .. 50
445 $2 Prince Philip paying homage to the newly crowned Queen .. 60
442/5 .. *Set of* 4 1·60 2·
MS446 122×90 mm. Nos. 442/5. Imperf .. 5·00 6·
Events:—75 c. Argentina—Winners of World Cup Footb[all] Championship; 95 c. 75th anniversary of powered flight; $1.25 [Trans]Atlantic crossing by balloon; $2 25th anniversary of Coronation.

(Des J. Cooter. Litho Format)

1979 (4 Apr). *Death Centenary of Sir Rowland Hill* (*1st issu*[e]). *T* **72** *and similar multicoloured designs. P* 14.
447 75 c. Type **72** .. 25
448 95 c. Mail coach, 1840 (*horiz*) .. 25
449 $1.25, London's first pillar box, 1855 (*horiz*) 30
450 $2 Mail leaving St. Martin's Le Grand Post Office, London .. 45
447/50 .. *Set of* 4 1·10 2
MS451 129 × 104 mm. Nos. 447/50 Imperf .. 1·75 2
Nos. 447/50 were each printed in small sheets of 4 including [one] *se-tenant* stamp-size label.

BARBUDA (**73**)   **74** Passengers alighting from Boeing 747-200

1979 (4 Apr). *Death Centenary of Sir Rowland Hill* (*2nd issu*[e]). *Nos.* 603/7 *of Antigua optd with T* **73** *in black* (*No.* **MS**456) [*in*] *blue* (*others*). *P* 14.
452 25 c. Antigua 1863 1d. stamp .. 15
453 50 c. Penny Black stamp .. 20
454 $1 Stage-coach and woman posting letter, *circa* 1840 .. 35
455 $2 Modern mail transport .. 80
452/5 .. *Set of* 4 1·40 1·
MS456 108 × 82 mm. $2.50, Sir Rowland Hill .. 75
Nos. 452/5 also exist perf 12 (*Price for set of* 4 £1.75 *mint or use*[d]) from additional sheetlets of four stamps and one label, issued December 1979.

1979 (12 Apr). *Easter. Works by Dürer. Nos.* 608/11 *of Antig*[ua] *optd with T* **67**.
457 10 c. multicoloured .. 10
458 50 c. multicoloured .. 20
459 $4 black, magenta and greenish yellow .. 90 1·
457/9 .. *Set of* 3 1·00 1·
MS460 114 × 99 mm. $2.50, multicoloured .. 55

(Litho Format)

1979 (24 May). *35th Anniv of International Civil Aviati*[on] *Organisation. T* **74** *and similar horiz designs. Multicoloure*[d]*. P* 13½×14.
461 75 c. Type **74** .. 25
a. Block of 4. Nos. 461/3 plus label .. 65
462 95 c. Air traffic control .. 25
463 $1.25, Ground crew-man directing Douglas DC-8 on runway .. 25
461/3 .. *Set of* 3 65 1·
Nos. 461/3 were either printed in separate sheets, or togeth[er] with a stamp-size label, *se-tenant*, in blocks of 4, each block divi[ded] in the sheet by margins.

1979 (24 May). *International Year of the Child* (*1st issue*). *N*[os.] 612/16 *of Antigua optd with T* **67**.
464 25 c. Yacht .. 20
465 50 c. Rocket .. 30
466 90 c. Car .. 40
467 $2 Train .. 80
464/7 .. *Set of* 4 1·50 1·
MS468 80 × 112 mm. $5 Aeroplane .. 1·10 1·

BARBUDA (75) BARBUDA (76)

79 (1 Aug). *Fishes. Nos.* 617/21 *of Antigua optd with T* **75**.
) 30 c. Yellow Jack 20 15
) 50 c. Blue-finned Tuna 30 20
1 90 c. Sailfish 40 30
2 $3 Wahoo .. .. 1·10 1·10
9/72 .. .. *Set of* 4 1·75 1·60
S473 122×75 mm. $2.50, Great Barracuda overprinted with T **73**) .. .. .. 1·00 1·25
a. Albino opt ..

79 (1 Aug). *Death Bicentenary of Captain Cook. Nos.* 622/6 *of Antigua optd with T* **76**.
4 25 c. Cook's Birthplace, Marton 30 30
5 50 c. H.M.S. *Endeavour* 85 45
6 90 c. Marine chronometer 90 60
7 $3 Landing at Botany Bay .. .. .. 1·75 1·50
4/7 .. .. *Set of* 4 3·50 2·50
S478 110 × 85 mm. $2.50, H.M.S. *Resolution* (overprinted with T **82**) .. .. .. 1·25 1·50
a. Albino opt

77 "Virgin with the Pear" BARBUDA (**78**)

(Des G. Vasarhelyi. Litho Format)

79 (24 Sept). *International Year of the Child (2nd issue). Details of Paintings by Dürer, showing the infant Jesus. T* **77** *and similar vert designs. Multicoloured. P* 14 × 13½.
9 25 c. Type **77** 15 15
0 50 c. "Virgin with the Pink" 25 25
1 75 c. "Virgin with the Pear" (*different*) .. 30 30
2 $1.25, "Nativity" 40 40
79/82 .. .. .. *Set of* 4 1·00 1·00
S483 86 × 118 mm. Nos. 479/82 .. .. .. 1·00 1·75

79 (21 Nov). *Christmas. Nos.* 627/31 *of Antigua optd with T* **78**.
4 8 c. The Holy Family 10 10
5 25 c. Virgin and Child on Ass 15 10
6 50 c. Shepherd and star 25 15
7 $4 Wise Men with gifts 85 80
84/7 .. .. .. *Set of* 4 1·10 1·00
S488 113 × 94 mm. $3 Angel with trumpet .. 80 1·10

80 (18 Mar). *Olympic Games, Moscow. Nos.* 632/6 *of Antigua optd with T* **67**.
89 10 c. Javelin throwing 10 10
90 25 c. Running 10 10
91 $1 Pole vaulting 30 20
92 $2 Hurdling 55 40
89/92 .. .. .. *Set of* 4 90 65
IS493 127 × 96 mm. $3 Boxing .. .. .. 70 1·10

LONDON 1980 (**79**)

80 "Apollo 11" Crew Badge

980 (6 May). *"London 1980" International Stamp Exhibition. As Nos.* 452/5 *optd with T* **79** *in blue. P* 12.
94 25 c. Antigua 1863 1d. stamp 35 20
95 50 c. Penny Black stamp 45 40
96 $1 Mail coach and woman posting letter, *circa* 1840 .. .. 85 65
97 $2 Modern mail transport .. .. .. 2·75 1·50
94/7 .. .. .. *Set of* 4 4·00 2·50

(Litho Format)

980 (21 May). *10th Anniv of Moon Landing. T* **80** *and similar horiz designs. Multicoloured. P* 13½ × 14.
98 75 c. Type **80** 30 25
99 95 c. Plaque left on Moon 35 30
00 $1.25, Rejoining mother ship 45 50
01 $2 Lunar Module 70 75
98/501 .. .. .. *Set of* 4 1·60 1·60
IS502 118 × 84 mm. Nos. 498/501 .. .. 1·75 2·50

81 American Wigeon

(Litho Questa)

1980 (16 June). *Birds. Multicoloured designs as T* **81**. *P* 14.
503 1 c. Type **81** 70 70
504 2 c. Snowy Plover 70 70
505 4 c. Rose-breasted Grosbeak 75 70
506 6 c. Mangrove Cuckoo 75 70
507 10 c. Adelaide's Warbler 75 70
508 15 c. Scaly-breasted Thrasher 80 70
509 20 c. Yellow-crowned Night Heron 80 70
510 25 c. Bridled Quail Dove 80 70
511 35 c. Carib Grackle 85 70
512 50 c. Pintail 90 55
513 75 c. Black-whiskered Vireo .. .. .. 1·00 55
514 $1 Blue-winged Teal .. .. .. 1·25 80
515 $1.50, Green-throated Carib (*vert*) .. .. 1·50 80
516 $2 Red-necked Pigeon (*vert*) .. .. 2·25 1·25
517 $2.50, Wied's Crested Flycatcher (*vert*) .. 2·75 1·50
518 $5 Yellow-bellied Sapsucker (*vert*) .. .. 3·50 2·50
519 $7.50, Caribbean Elaenia (*vert*) .. .. 4·50 5·00
520 $10 Great Egret (*vert*) .. .. .. 5·00 5·00
503/20 .. .. .. *Set of* 18 26·00 22·00

1980 (29 July). *Famous Works of Art. Nos.* 651/7 *of Antigua optd with T* **67**.
521 10 c. "David" (statue, Donatello) 10 10
522 30 c. "The Birth of Venus" (painting, Sandro Botticelli) 15 15
523 50 c. "Reclining Couple" (sarcophagus), Cerveteri 20 20
524 90 c. "The Garden of Earthly Delights" (painting, Hieronymus Bosch) 25 25
525 $1 "Portinari Altarpiece" (painting, Hugo van der Goes) 25 25
526 $4 "Eleanora of Toledo and her Son Giovanni de' Medici" (painting, Agnolo Bronzino) 80 80
521/6 .. .. .. *Set of* 6 1·50 1·50
MS527 99 × 124 mm. $5 "The Holy Family" (painting, Rembrandt) .. .. .. 1·50 1·75

1980 (8 Sept). *75th Anniv of Rotary International. Nos.* 658/62 *of Antigua optd with T* **67**.
528 30 c. Rotary anniversary emblem and headquarters, U.S.A. 15 15
529 50 c. Rotary anniversary emblem and Antigua Rotary Club banner 20 20
530 90 c. Map of Antigua and Rotary emblem .. 25 25
531 $3 Paul P. Harris (founder) and Rotary emblem 65 65
528/31 .. .. .. *Set of* 4 1·10 1·10
MS532 102 × 77 mm. $5 Antigua flags and Rotary emblems .. .. 1·50 2·25

BARBUDA (**82**) BARBUDA (**83**)

1980 (6 Oct). *80th Birthday of Queen Elizabeth the Queen Mother. Nos.* 663/5 *of Antigua optd with T* **82**.
533 10 c. multicoloured 50 15
a. Opt inverted .. .. .. 38·00
b. Opt double .. .. .. 30·00
534 $2.50, multicoloured .. .. .. 1·50 1·50
MS535 68 × 88 mm. $3 multicoloured .. .. 2·00 1·75

1980 (8 Dec). *Birds. Nos.* 666/70 *of Antigua optd with T* **83**.
536 10 c. Ringed Kingfisher .. .. .. 1·50 75
537 30 c. Plain Pigeon .. .. .. 2·00 1·00
538 $1 Green-throated Carib .. .. .. 3·25 2·25
539 $2 Black-necked Stilt .. .. .. 3·75 4·25
536/9 .. .. .. *Set of* 4 9·50 7·50
MS540 73 × 73 mm. $2.50, Roseate Tern .. .. 3·75 2·75

1981 (26 Jan). *Sugar Cane Railway Locomotives. Nos.* 681/5 *of Antigua optd with T* **67**.
541 25 c. Diesel Locomotive No. 15 .. .. 1·00 25
542 50 c. Narrow-gauge steam locomotive .. 1·25 35
543 90 c. Diesel locomotives Nos. 1 and 10 .. 1·75 45
544 $3 Steam locomotive hauling sugar cane .. 3·25 1·40
541/4 .. .. .. *Set of* 4 6·50 2·25
MS545 82 × 111 mm. $2.50, Antigua sugar factory, railway yard and sheds .. .. .. 1·50 1·75

84 Florence Nightingale

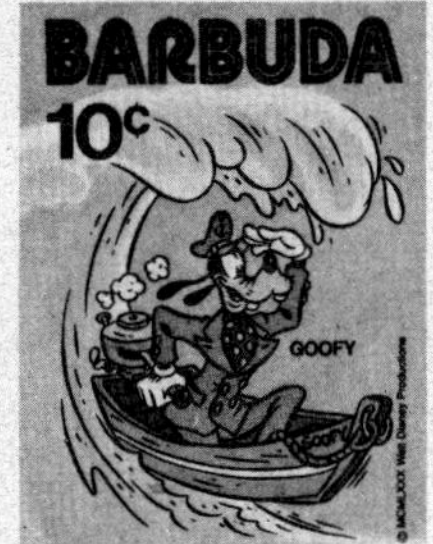

85 Goofy in Motor-boat

(Litho Format)

1981 (9 Mar). *Famous Women. T* **84** *and similar vert designs. P* 14 × 13½.
546 50 c. multicoloured 15 30
547 90 c. multicoloured 40 55
548 $1 multicoloured 35 60
549 $4 black, yellow-brown and rose-lilac .. 50 1·75
546/9 .. .. .. *Set of* 4 1·25 2·75
Designs:—90 c. Marie Curie; $1 Amy Johnson; $4 Eleanor Roosevelt.
Nos. 546/9 exist imperforate from stock dispersed by the liquidator of Format International Security Printers Ltd.

(Litho Format)

1981 (15 May). *Walt Disney Cartoon Characters. T* **85** *and similar vert designs showing characters afloat. Multicoloured. P* 13½.
550 10 c. Type **85** 55 15
551 20 c. Donald Duck reversing car into sea .. 65 20
552 25 c. Mickey Mouse asking tug-boat to take on more than it can handle 80 30
553 30 c. Porpoise turning the tables on Goofy .. 80 35
554 35 c. Goofy in sailing boat 80 35
555 40 c. Mickey Mouse and boat being lifted out of water by fish 90 40
556 75 c. Donald Duck fishing for flying-fish with butterfly net .. .. 1·00 60
557 $1 Minnie Mouse in brightly decorated sailing boat .. .. 1·10 80
558 $2 Chip and Dale on floating ship-in-bottle 1·75 1·40
550/8 .. .. .. *Set of* 9 7·50 4·00
MS559 127 × 101 mm. $2.50, Donald Duck .. 4·00 3·00

BARBUDA (**86**)

1981 (9 June). *Birth Centenary of Picasso. Nos.* 697/701 *of Antigua optd with T* **86**.
560 10 c. "Pipes of Pan" 10 10
561 50 c. "Seated Harlequin" 25 25
562 90 c. "Paulo as Harlequin" 45 45
563 $4 "Mother and Child" .. .. .. 1·60 1·60
560/3 .. .. .. *Set of* 4 2·10 2·10
MS564 115 × 140 mm. $5 "Three Musicians" (detail) .. .. 2·25 2·25

87 Buckingham Palace **88**

(Des G. Drummond. Litho Format)

1981 (27 July). *Royal Wedding (1st issue). Buildings. T* **87/8** *and similar horiz designs. Each bicoloured**. *P* 11 × 11½.
565 $1 Type **87** 25 40
566 $1 Type **88** 25 40
a. Sheetlet. Nos. 565/70 .. .. 2·00
b. Booklet pane. Nos. 565/6 × 2 in imperf between horiz pairs .. .. .. 2·00
567 $1.50 } Caernarvon Castle 30 50
568 $1.50 } 30 50
b. Booklet pane. Nos. 567/8 × 2 in imperf between horiz pairs .. .. .. 2·25
569 $4 } Highgrove House 55 90
570 $4 } 55 90
b. Booklet pane. Nos. 569/70 × 2 in imperf between horiz pairs .. .. .. 3·50
565/70 .. .. .. *Set of* 6 2·00 3·25
MS571 75 × 90 mm. $5 black and olive-yellow (St. Paul's Cathedral—26 × 32 *mm*). P 11½ × 11 .. 80 1·25
*Nos. 565/70 each exist printed in black with three different background colours, rose-pink, turquoise-green and lavender.
No. 566b was printed only in black and rose-pink. No. 568b black and turquoise-green and No. 570b black and lavender.
Nos. 565/70 were printed together, *se-tenant*, in sheetlets of 6, the two versions of each value forming a composite design.
Nos. 565/70 exist imperforate from stock dispersed by the liquidator of Format International Security Printers Ltd.

1981 (14 Aug). *Royal Wedding (2nd issue). Nos.* 702/5 *of Antigua optd with T* **86**.
572 25 c. Prince Charles and Lady Diana Spencer 15 15
573 50 c. Glamis Castle 25 25
a. Opt double .. .. .. 25·00
574 $4 Prince Charles skiing .. .. .. 75 1·00
a. Error. Optd on unissued Uganda 20s. showing Prince Charles at Balmoral 60·00
ab. Opt double .. .. ..
572/4 .. .. .. *Set of* 3 1·10 1·25
MS575 95×85 mm. $5 Glass Coach 90 90
Nos. 572/4 exist perforated 12 (*Price for set of* 3 £1.10 *mint or used*) from additional sheetlets of five stamps and one label. These stamps have changed background colours. One sheetlet of the 25 c. is known with the overprint inverted.

89 "Integration and Travel"

(Litho Format)

1981 (14 Sept). *International Year for Disabled Persons (1st issue). T* **89** *and similar horiz designs. P* 14.
576 50 c. multicoloured 30 20
577 90 c. black, red-orange and blue-green .. 35 30
578 $1 black, light blue and bright green .. 40 35
579 $4 black, yellow-ochre and orange-brown .. 60 1·25
576/9 .. .. .. *Set of* 4 1·50 1·90
Designs:—90 c. Braille and sign language; $1 "Helping hands"; $4 "Mobility aids for disabled".
No. 576 exists imperforate from stock dispersed by the liquidator of Format International Security Printers Ltd.
See also Nos. 603/7.

BARBUDA (**90**)

1981 (12 Oct). *Royal Wedding (3rd issue). Nos.* 706/12 *of Antigua optd with T* **90** *in silver.*
580 25 c. Prince of Wales at Investiture, 1969 .. 35 55
a. Booklet pane. Nos. 580/5 .. .. 2·50
581 25 c. Prince Charles as baby, 1948 .. .. 35 55
582 $1 Prince Charles at R.A.F. College, Cranwell, 1971 .. .. 40 60
583 $1 Prince Charles attending Hill House School, 1956 .. .. 40 60

584	$2 Prince Charles and Lady Diana Spencer	65	80
585	$2 Prince Charles at Trinity College, 1967	65	80
586	$5 Prince Charles and Lady Diana.. ..	2·50	3·50
	a. Booklet pane of 1..	2·50	
580/6	.. .. *Set of* 7	5·00	6·50

1981 (1 Nov). *Independence. Nos.* 686B/96B *of Antigua additionally optd with T* **86**.

587	6 c. Orchid Tree	50	15
588	10 c. Bougainvillea	55	15
589	20 c. Flamboyant	70	20
590	25 c. Hibiscus	80	25
591	35 c. Flame of the Wood	90	30
592	50 c. Cannon at Fort James	1·10	45
593	75 c. Premier's Office	1·25	75
594	$1 Potworks Dam	1·50	80
595	$2.50, Irrigation scheme, Diamond Estate	2·50	2·75
596	$5 Government House	2·75	3·75
597	$10 Coolidge International Airport	4·50	6·00
587/97	*Set of* 11	15·00	14·00

BARBUDA (91) BARBUDA (92)

1981 (14 Dec). *50th Anniv of Antigua Girl Guide Movement. Nos.* 713/17 *of Antigua optd with T* **83** (*No.* **MS**602) *or T* **91** (*others*).

598	10 c. Irene Joshua (founder)	55	10
599	50 c. Campfire sing-song	1·25	30
600	90 c. Sailing	1·75	45
601	$2.50, Animal tending	3·00	1·40
598/601	*Set of* 4	6·00	2·00
MS602	110 × 85 mm. $5 Raising the flag	3·50	3·50

1981 (14 Dec). *International Year for Disabled Persons (2nd issue). Nos.* 728/32 *of Antigua optd with T* **83** (*No.* **MS**607) *or T* **91** (*others*).

603	10 c. Swimming	20	15
604	50 c. Discus throwing	30	25
605	90 c. Archery	70	45
606	$2 Baseball	1·75	1·50
603/6	*Set of* 4	2·75	2·10
MS607	108 × 84 mm. $4 Basketball	2·75	2·25

1981 (22 Dec). *Christmas. Paintings. Nos.* 723/7 *of Antigua optd with T* **92**.

608	8 c. "Holy Night" (Jacques Stella)	10	10
609	30 c. "Mary with Child" (Julius Schnorr von Carolfeld)	20	20
610	$1 "Virgin and Child" (Alonso Cano) (S.)	40	40
611	$3 "Virgin and Child" (Lorenzo di Credi)	1·10	1·10
608/11	*Set of* 4	1·60	1·60
MS612	77 × 111 mm. $5 "Holy Family" (Pieter von Avon)	1·75	2·25

Celebrating the Royal Birth
BARBUDA $1

93 Princess of Wales

S. Atlantic Fund + 5oc. (94)

(Des G. Drummond. Litho Format)

1982 (21 June). *Birth of Prince William of Wales (1st issue). T* **93** *and similar vert portraits. W w* **15**. *P* 14.

613	$1 multicoloured	50	50
	w. Wmk inverted	60	
614	$2.50, multicoloured	90	1·10
	a. Reddish violet (top inscr) omitted	£180	
	w. Wmk inverted	1·10	
615	$5 multicoloured	2·00	2·25
	w. Wmk inverted	2·40	
613/15	*Set of* 3	3·00	3·50
MS616	88×108 mm. $4 multicoloured. No wmk	2·00	2·10

Nos. 613/15 were issued in sheets of 10 stamps with 2 undenominated black prints, in positions 9 and 13, and 9 blank labels. These sheets exist in two different formats, with all stamps upright or with 6 stamps and one black print inverted.

1982 (28 June). *South Atlantic Fund. Nos.* 580/6 *surch as T* **94**.

617	25 c. +50 c. Prince of Wales at Investiture, 1969	20	20
	a. Booklet pane. Nos. 617/22	2·50	
	b. Surch double	20·00	
618	25 c. +50 c. Prince Charles as baby, 1948	20	20
	b. Surch double	20·00	
619	$1 +50 c. Prince Charles at R.A.F. College, Cranwell, 1971	45	45
	b. Surch double	20·00	
620	$1 +50 c. Prince Charles attending Hill House School, 1956	45	45
	b. Surch double	20·00	
621	$2 +50 c. Prince Charles and Lady Diana Spencer	75	75
	b. Surch double	20·00	
622	$2 +50 c. Prince Charles at Trinity College, 1967	75	75
	b. Surch double	20·00	
623	$5 +50 c. Prince Charles and Lady Diana	2·00	2·00
	a. Booklet pane of 1	2·00	
	b. Surch double	£150	
617/23	*Set of* 7	4·00	4·00

(Des G. Drummond. Litho Format)

1982 (1 July). *21st Birthday of Princess of Wales (1st issue). As Nos.* 613/16 *but inscribed* "Twenty First Birthday Greetings to H.R.H. The Princess of Wales". *W w* **15**. *P* 14.

624	$1 multicoloured	75	45
	w. Wmk inverted	80	
625	$2.50, multicoloured	1·40	1·25
	w. Wmk inverted	1·60	
626	$5 multicoloured	2·75	2·40
	w. Wmk inverted	3·00	
624/6	*Set of* 3	4·50	3·75
MS627	88×108 mm. $4 multicoloured. No wmk	2·75	2·25

See note beneath Nos. 613/16

BARBUDA MAIL (95) **BARBUDA MAIL** (96)

1982 (30 Aug). *21st Birthday of Princess of Wales (2nd issue). Nos.* 748/51 *of Antigua optd as T* **95**, *in silver* (*No.* 629) *or black* (*others*).

628	90 c. Queen's House, Greenwich	65	45
629	$1 Prince and Princess of Wales	75	50
630	$4 Princess of Wales	1·60	1·50
628/30	*Set of* 3	2·75	2·25
MS631	102 × 75 mm. $5 Princess of Wales (*different*)	1·75	2·00

The overprint on No. **MS**631 measures 18 × 6 mm.

Nos. 628/30 also exist from additional sheetlets of 5 stamps and 1 label overprinted with a larger overprint, 18 × 6 mm long (*price for set of 3 £3 mint or used*). On the $1 and $4 values the second line of overprint aligns to left.

1982 (12 Oct). *Birth of Prince William of Wales (2nd issue). Nos.* 757/60 *of Antigua further optd with T* **95**, *in silver* ($1, $4) *or black* (*others*).

632	90 c. Queen's House, Greenwich	55	45
633	$1 Prince and Princess of Wales	60	50
634	$4 Princess of Wales	2·25	2·00
632/4	*Set of* 3	3·00	2·75
MS635	102 × 75 mm. $5 Princess of Wales (*different*)	2·75	2·50

The overprint on No. **MS**635 measures 18 × 6 mm.

1982 (6 Dec). *Birth Centenary of Franklin D. Roosevelt* (*Nos.* 636, 638, 640/2) *and 250th Birth Anniv of George Washington* (*others*). *Nos.* 761/8 *of Antigua optd as T* **95** (*second line ranged left on No.* **MS**642).

636	10 c. Roosevelt in 1940	10	10
637	25 c. Washington as blacksmith	15	15
638	45 c. Churchill, Roosevelt and Stalin at Yalta conference	35	25
639	60 c. Washington crossing the Delaware	20	25
640	$1 "Roosevelt Special" train	50	40
641	$3 Portrait of Roosevelt	60	90
636/41	*Set of* 6	1·60	1·75
MS642	92 × 87 mm. $4 Roosevelt and wife	1·00	1·75
MS643	92 × 87 mm. $4 Portrait of Washington	1·00	1·75

1982 (6 Dec). *Christmas. Religious Paintings by Raphael. Nos.* 769/73 *of Antigua optd with T* **96**.

644	10 c. "Annunciation"	10	10
645	30 c. "Adoration of the Magi"	15	15
646	$1 "Presentation at the Temple"	40	40
647	$4 "Coronation of the Virgin"	1·25	1·25
644/7	*Set of* 4	1·75	1·75
MS648	95 × 124 mm. $5 "Marriage of the Virgin"	1·50	2·50

1983 (14 Mar). *500th Birth Anniv of Raphael. Details from "Galatea" Fresco. Nos.* 774/8 *of Antigua optd as T* **95** (45, 50 *c. and larger* (18 × 6 *mm*) *on* **MS**653) *or T* **96** (*others*).

649	45 c. Tritons and Dolphins	20	20
650	50 c. Sea Nymph carried off by Triton	25	25
651	60 c. Winged angel steering Dolphins (*horiz*)	30	30
652	$4 Cupids shooting arrows (*horiz*)	1·25	1·25
649/52	*Set of* 4	1·75	1·75
MS653	101 × 126 mm. $5 Galatea pulled along by Dolphins	1·50	2·25

1983 (14 Mar). *Commonwealth Day. Nos.* 779/82 *of Antigua optd as T* **96**.

654	25 c. Pineapple produce	55	70
655	45 c. Carnival	80	90
656	60 c. Tourism	1·25	1·60
657	$3 Airport	2·75	4·00
654/7	*Set of* 4	4·75	6·50

1983 (12 Apr). *World Communications Year. Nos.* 783/7 *of Antigua optd as T* **96** (*Nos.* 658/61) *or as T* **95** *with second line ranged left* (*No.* **MS**662).

658	15 c. T.V. satellite coverage of Royal Wedding	55	25
659	50 c. Police communications	1·75	90
660	60 c. House-to-train telephone call	1·75	90
661	$3 Satellite earth station with planets Jupiter and Saturn	3·50	2·50
658/61	*Set of* 4	6·75	4·00
MS662	100×90 mm. $5 "Comsat" satellite over West Indies	2·75	3·00
	a. Albino opt	30·00	

200th Anniversary of Man's First Flight 21 November 1983
Barbuda $1

97 Vincenzo Lunardi's Balloon Flight, London, 1785

45c (98)

(Des G. Drummond. Litho)

1983 (13 June). *Bicentenary of Manned Flight (1st issue). T* **9**[…] *and similar vert designs. Multicoloured. P* 14.

663	$1 Type **97**	25	3
664	$1.50, Montgolfier brothers' balloon flight, Paris, 1783	40	5
665	$2.50, Blanchard and Jeffries' Cross-Channel balloon flight, 1785	60	9
663/5	*Set of* 3	1·10	1·6
MS666	111×111 mm. $5 Maiden flight of Airship LZ-127 *Graf Zeppelin*, 1928	2·00	2·7

See also Nos. 672/6.

1983 (4 July). *Whales. Nos.* 788/92 *of Antigua optd as T* **95** (*No*[…] 667/70) *or larger*, 17 × $5\frac{1}{2}$ *mm* (*No.* **MS**671), *each with th*[…] *second line ranged left.*

667	15 c. Bottle-nosed Dolphin	1·25	
668	50 c. Fin Whale	4·00	1·
669	60 c. Bowhead Whale	4·50	1·
670	$3 Spectacled Porpoise	5·50	4·
667/70	*Set of* 4	14·00	7·
MS671	122 × 101 mm. $5 Narwhal	3·75	4·

1983 (12 Sept). *Bicentenary of Manned Flight (2nd issue). No*[…] 811/15 *of Antigua optd as T* **96**.

672	30 c. Dornier Do-X flying boat	85	3
673	50 c. Supermarine S6B seaplane	1·10	6
674	60 c. Curtiss F-9C Sparrowhawk biplane and airship U.S.S. *Akron*	1·25	7
675	$4 Hot-air balloon *Pro Juventute*	4·50	4·0
672/5	*Set of* 4	7·00	5·0
MS676	80×105 mm. $5 Airship LZ-127 *Graf Zeppelin*	3·75	4·2

1983 (21 Oct). *Nos.* 565/70 *surch as T* **98**. *P* 11 × $11\frac{1}{2}$.

677	45 c. on $1 Type **87**	35	5
	a. Sheetlet. Nos. 677/82	1·90	
	b. Perf $14\frac{1}{2}$	1·25	2·5
	ba. Sheetlet. Nos. 677b/82b	6·50	
	bb. Error. 50 c. on $1	4·50	
	bc. Surch omitted	35·00	
678	45 c. on $1 Type **88**	35	5
	b. Perf $14\frac{1}{2}$	1·25	2·5
	bb. Error. 50 c. on $1	4·50	
	bc. Surch omitted	35·00	
679	50 c. on $1.50, Caernarvon Castle (left)	35	5
	b. Perf $14\frac{1}{2}$	1·25	2·5
	bb. Error. 45 c. on $1.50	4·50	
	bc. Surch omitted	35·00	
680	50 c. on $1.50, Caernarvon Castle (right)	35	5
	b. Perf $14\frac{1}{2}$	1·25	2·5
	bb. Error. 45 c. on $1.50	4·50	
	bc. Surch omitted	35·00	
681	60 c. on $4 Highgrove House (left)	35	6
	b. Perf $14\frac{1}{2}$	1·25	2·5
	bc. Surch omitted	35·00	
682	60 c. on $4 Highgrove House (right)	35	6
	b. Perf $14\frac{1}{2}$	1·25	2·5
	bc. Surch omitted	35·00	
677/82	*Set of* 6	1·90	3·0

Nos. 677bb, 678bb, 679bb and 680bb occur on the 14[…] perforated sheetlets with rose-pink background.

Examples of No. 677a, and also of the errors, imperforate exis[…] from stock dispersed by the liquidator of Format Internationa[…] Security Printers Ltd.

1983 (28 Oct). *Nos.* 793/810 *of Antigua optd with T* **96**.

683	1 c. Cashew Nut	10	1
684	2 c. Passion Fruit	15	1
685	3 c. Mango	15	1
686	5 c. Grapefruit	15	1
687	10 c. Pawpaw	20	1
688	15 c. Breadfruit	40	1
689	20 c. Coconut	50	1
690	25 c. Oleander	50	1
691	30 c. Banana	55	2
692	40 c. Pineapple	65	2
693	45 c. Cordia	70	3
694	50 c. Cassia	80	3
695	60 c. Poui	80	3
696	$1 Frangipani	1·10	5
697	$2 Flamboyant	2·00	1·2
698	$2.50, Lemon	2·25	1·7
699	$5 Lignum Vitae	3·50	2·7
700	$10 National flag and coat of arms	5·50	5·5
683/700	*Set of* 18	18·00	12·0

EDWARD VII 1901 – 1910 $1

BARBUDA MAIL (99)

100 Edward VII

1983 (28 Oct). *Christmas. 500th Birth Anniv of Raphael. N*[…] 816/20 *of Antigua optd with T* **99** *or slightly smaller* (29 × 4 *m*[…] (**MS**705).

701	10 c. multicoloured	10	
702	30 c. multicoloured	15	
703	$1 multicoloured	40	
704	$4 multicoloured	1·25	1·
701/4	*Set of* 4	1·60	2·
MS705	101 × 131 mm. $5 multicoloured	1·75	2·

1983 (14 Dec). *Bicentenary of Methodist Church* (1984). *No*[…] 821/4 *of Antigua optd with T* **95** (*in silver on* 15 *c. and* 50 *c.*[…]

706	15 c. John Wesley (founder)	25	1
707	50 c. Nathaniel Gilbert (founder in Antigua)	40	2
708	60 c. St. John Methodist Church steeple	40	3
709	$3 Ebenezer Methodist Church, St. John's	90	1·2
706/9	*Set of* 4	1·75	1·7

(Des G. Drummond. Litho Format)

84 (14 Feb). *Members of British Royal Family. T* **100** *and similar vert portraits. Multicoloured. P* 14½.
.0 $1 Type **100** .. .. 50 1·10
.1 $1 George V .. .. 50 1·10
.2 $1 George VI .. .. 50 1·10
.3 $1 Elizabeth II .. .. 50 1·10
.4 $1 Charles, Prince of Wales .. .. 50 1·10
.5 $1 Prince William .. .. 50 1·10
.0/15 .. .. *Set of* 6 2·75 6·00

84 (26 Apr). *Olympic Games, Los Angeles (1st issue). Nos.* 825/9 *of Antigua optd as T* **99** *(23 × 3 mm in size on Nos.* 716/19).
.6 25 c. Discus 15 20
.7 50 c. Gymnastics 35 40
.8 90 c. Hurdling 50 60
.9 $3 Cycling .. .. 1·25 1·50
.6/19 .. .. *Set of* 4 2·00 2·40
S720 82 × 67 mm. $5 Volleyball .. .. 2·75 3·25

84 (12 July). *Ships. Nos.* 830/4 *of Antigua optd with T* **95** (**MS725**) *or T* **99** *(others).*
21 45 c. *Booker Vanguard* (freighter) .. 1·50 45
22 50 c. *Canberra* (liner) .. .. .. 1·50 50
23 60 c. Sailing boats .. .. 1·75 60
24 $4 *Fairwind* (cargo liner) .. .. 4·25 2·75
21/4 .. .. *Set of* 4 8·00 3·75
S725 107×80 mm. $5 Eighteen-century British man-of-war (*vert*) .. .. .. 4·50 4·25

84 (12 July). *Universal Postal Union Congress, Hamburg. Nos.* 835/9 *of Antigua optd with T* **95**.
26 15 c. Chenille 30 15
27 50 c. Shell Flower 50 40
28 60 c. Anthurium 60 50
29 $3 Angels Trumpet .. .. 1·25 1·50
26/9 .. .. *Set of* 4 2·40 2·25
S730 100 × 75 mm. $5 Crown of Thorns .. 2·00 2·50

101 Olympic Stadium, Athens, 1896

BARBUDA MAIL

(102)

(Litho Format)

84 (27 July). *Olympic Games, Los Angeles (2nd issue). T* **101** *and similar horiz designs. Multicoloured. P* 13½.
31 $1.50, Type **101** .. .. 80 1·10
32 $2.50, Olympic stadium, Los Angeles, 1984 1·25 1·75
33 $5 Athlete carrying Olympic torch .. .. 2·25 2·75
31/3 .. .. *Set of* 3 3·75 5·00
S734 121 × 95 mm. No. 733. P 15 .. .. 1·75 3·00

984 (1 Oct). *Presidents of the United States of America. Nos.* 856/63 *of Antigua optd with T* **95** *(in silver on* 10, 90 *c.,* $1.10 *and* $1.50).
35 10 c. Abraham Lincoln 10 10
36 20 c. Harry Truman 15 15
37 30 c. Dwight Eisenhower 20 25
38 40 c. Ronald Reagan 25 30
39 90 c. Gettysburg Address, 1863 .. .. 50 55
40 $1.10, Formation of N.A.T.O., 1949 .. .. 60 65
41 $1.50, Eisenhower during Second World War 80 85
42 $2 Reagan and Caribbean Basin Initiative 1·00 1·25
35/42 .. .. *Set of* 8 3·25 3·75

984 (1 Oct). 150*th Anniv of Abolition of Slavery. Nos.* 864/8 *of Antigua optd with T* **96** *(Nos.* 743/6) *or as T* **95**, *but* 18 × 6½ *mm (No.* **MS747**).
43 40 c. View of Moravian Mission 30 30
44 50 c. Antigua Courthouse, 1823 .. .. 40 40
45 60 c. Planting sugar-cane, Monks Hill .. 45 45
46 $3 Boiling house, Delaps' Estate .. .. 1·90 1·90
'43/6 .. .. *Set of* 4 2·75 2·75
MS747 95 × 70 mm. $5 Loading sugar, Willoughby Bay .. .. 2·50 3·00

984 (21 Nov). *Songbirds. Nos.* 869/74 *of Antigua optd with T* **95** *or larger* (18 × 7 *mm*) *(No.* **MS753**).
'48 40 c. Rufous-sided Towhee .. .. .. 1·25 45
'49 50 c. Parula Warbler .. .. 1·40 50
'50 60 c. House Wren .. .. 1·50 55
'51 $2 Ruby-crowned Kinglet .. .. .. 2·75 1·50
'52 $3 Common Flicker .. .. 3·25 2·25
'48/52 .. .. *Set of* 5 9·00 4·75
MS753 76 × 76 mm. $5 Yellow-breasted Chat .. 4·00 4·50

984 (21 Nov). 450*th Death Anniv of Correggio (painter). Nos.* 878/82 *of Antigua optd with T* **95** *or larger* (18 × 7 *mm*) *No.* **MS758**), *all in silver.*
'54 25 c. "The Virgin and Infant with Angels and Cherubs" 15 20
'55 60 c. "The Four Saints" 40 45
'56 90 c. "St. Catherine" 60 65
'57 $3 "The Campori Madonna" .. .. 1·75 2·25
'54/7 .. .. *Set of* 4 2·50 3·25
MS758 90 × 60 mm. $5 "St. John the Baptist" .. 2·75 3·75

984 (30 Nov). *"Ausipex" International Stamp Exhibition, Melbourne. Australian Sports. Nos.* 875/7 *of Antigua optd with T* **95** *or larger* (18 × 7 *mm*) *(No.* **MS761**).
'59 $1 Grass-skiing 70 75
60 $5 Australian Football .. .. .. 3·00 3·75
MS761 108 × 78 mm. $5 Boomerang-throwing 3·00 3·75

1984 (30 Nov). 150*th Birth Anniv of Edgar Degas (painter). Nos.* 883/7 *of Antigua optd with T* **95** *(Nos.* 762/5) *or T* **99** *(No.* **MS766**), *all in silver.*
762 15 c. "The Blue Dancers" 10 10
763 50 c. "The Pink Dancers" 30 40
764 70 c. "Two Dancers" 45 55
765 $4 "Dancers at the Bar" .. .. .. 2·40 3·50
762/5 .. .. *Set of* 4 3·00 4·00
MS766 90 × 60 mm. $5 "The Folk Dancers" (40 × 27 *mm*) .. .. 2·75 3·25

1985 (18 Feb). *Famous People. Nos.* 888/96 *of Antigua optd with T* **102** *(horizontally on Nos.* 771/5).
767 60 c. Winston Churchill .. .. .. 2·00 80
768 60 c. Mahatma Gandhi .. .. .. 2·00 80
769 60 c. John F. Kennedy .. .. .. 2·00 80
770 60 c. Mao Tse-tung .. .. 2·00 80
771 $1 Churchill with General De Gaulle, Paris, 1944 (*horiz*) .. .. .. 2·25 1·00
772 $1 Gandhi leaving London by train, 1931 (*horiz*) .. .. 2·25 1·00
773 $1 Kennedy with Chancellor Adenauer and Mayor Brandt, Berlin, 1963 (*horiz*) 2·25 1·00
774 $1 Mao Tse-tung with Lin Piao, Peking, 1969 (*horiz*) .. .. 2·25 1·00
767/74 .. .. *Set of* 8 15·00 6·50
MS775 114×80 mm. $5 Flags of Great Britain, India, the United States and China .. .. 3·50 3·75

103 Lady Elizabeth Bowes-Lyon, 1907, and Camellias

104 Roseate Tern

(Des G. Drummond. Litho Format)

1985 (26 Feb). *Life and Times of Queen Elizabeth the Queen Mother (1st issue). T* **103** *and similar vert designs. Multicoloured. P* 14 × 14½.
776 15 c. Type **103** 10 10
777 45 c. Duchess of York, 1926, and "Elizabeth of Glamis" roses 20 25
778 50 c. The Queen Mother after the Coronation, 1937 .. .. 20 25
779 60 c. In Garter robes, 1971, and Dog Roses .. 20 30
780 90 c. Attending Royal Variety show, 1967, and red Hibiscus 30 45
781 $2 The Queen Mother in 1982, and blue Plumbago .. .. 60 1·10
782 $3 Receiving 82nd birthday gifts from children, and Morning Glory .. .. 90 1·60
776/82 .. .. *Set of* 7 2·25 3·50
See also Nos. 826/9.

(Des G. Drummond. Litho Format)

1985 (4 Apr). *Birth Bicentenary of John J. Audubon (ornithologist) (1st issue). T* **104** *and similar vert designs showing original paintings. Multicoloured. P* 14.
783 45 c. Type **104** 25 30
784 50 c. Mangrove Cuckoo 25 30
785 60 c. Yellow-crowned Night Heron 30 40
786 $5 Brown Pelican .. .. 2·25 3·50
783/6 .. .. *Set of* 4 2·75 4·00
See also Nos. 794/8 and 914/17.

1985 (10 May). *Centenary of the Statue of Liberty* (1986) *(1st issue). Nos.* 907/13 *of Antigua optd horizontally with T* **102**.
787 25 c. Torch from Statue in Madison Square Park, 1885 .. .. 20 20
788 30 c. Statue of Liberty and scaffolding ("Restoration and Renewal") (*vert*) 20 20
789 50 c. Frederic Bartholdi (sculptor) supervising construction, 1876 .. .. 30 30
790 90 c. Close-up of Statue 55 55
791 $1 Statue and sailing ship ("Operation Sail", 1976) (*vert*) 60 60
792 $3 Dedication ceremony, 1886 (*vert*) .. 1·75 1·75
787/92 .. .. *Set of* 6 3·00 3·00
MS793 110×80 mm. $5 Port of New York .. 2·75 3·00
See also Nos. 987/96.

BARBUDA MAIL
(105)

BARBUDA MAIL
(106)

4TH AUG 1900–1985
(107)

1985 (18 July). *Birth Bicentenary of John J. Audubon (ornithologist) (2nd issue). Nos.* 924/8 *of Antigua optd with T* **105**.
794 90 c. Slavonian Grebe .. .. .. 4·00 3·50
795 $1 British Storm Petrel .. .. .. 4·25 3·75
796 $1.50, Great Blue Heron .. .. .. 5·00 4·25
797 $3 Double-crested Cormorant .. .. 8·00 6·50
794/7 .. .. *Set of* 4 19·00 16·00
MS798 103×72 mm. $5 White-tailed Tropic Bird (*vert*) .. .. 15·00 9·00

1985 (18 July). *Butterflies. Nos.* 929/33 *of Antigua optd with T* **106**.
799 25 c. *Anaea cyanea* .. .. 2·50 1·00
800 60 c. *Leodonta dysoni* .. .. .. 4·00 1·75
801 90 c. *Junea doraete* .. .. 5·00 2·25
802 $4 *Prepona pylene* .. .. 10·00 10·00
799/802 .. .. *Set of* 4 19·00 13·50
MS803 132×105 mm. $5 *Caerois gerdtrudtus* .. 15·00 8·50

1985 (2 Aug). *Centenary of the Motorcycle. Nos.* 919/23 *of Antigua optd with T* **106**.
804 10 c. Triumph 2hp "Jap", 1903 .. .. 40 10
805 30 c. Indian "Arrow", 1949 .. .. .. 70 20
806 60 c. BMW "R100RS", 1976 .. .. .. 1·10 40
807 $4 Harley-Davidson "Model II", 1916 .. 3·50 2·75
804/7 .. .. *Set of* 4 5·25 3·00
MS808 90×93 mm. $5 Laverda "Jota", 1975 .. 4·00 4·00

1985 (2 Aug). 85*th Birthday of Queen Elizabeth the Queen Mother. Nos.* 776/82 *optd with T* **107**.
809 15 c. Type **103** 60 30
a. Red (frame, flowers, etc) omitted .. 32·00
810 45 c. Duchess of York, 1926, and "Elizabeth of Glamis" roses 90 50
811 50 c. The Queen Mother after the Coronation, 1937 .. .. 90 50
812 60 c. In Garter robes, 1971, and Dog Roses .. 1·00 80
813 90 c. Attending Royal Variety show, 1967, and red Hibiscus .. .. .. 1·10 1·10
814 $2 The Queen Mother in 1982, and blue Plumbago .. .. 1·40 2·75
815 $3 Receiving 82nd birthday gifts from children, and Morning Glory .. .. 1·50 3·00
809/15 .. .. *Set of* 7 6·50 8·00
The 45 c. exists with the yellow omitted from stock dispersed by the liquidator of Format International Security Printers Ltd.

1985 (30 Aug). *Native American Artefacts. Nos.* 914/18 *of Antigua optd horizontally with T* **102**.
816 15 c. Arawak pot sherd and Indians making clay utensils 15 10
817 50 c. Arawak body design and Arawak Indians tattooing 30 30
818 60 c. Head of the god "Yocahu" and Indians harvesting manioc 40 40
819 $3 Carib war club and Carib Indians going into battle .. .. 1·60 1·75
816/19 .. .. *Set of* 4 2·25 2·25
MS820 97×68 mm. $5 Taino Indians worshipping stone idol .. .. 2·50 3·50

1985 (30 Aug). 40*th Anniv of International Civil Aviation Organization. Nos.* 934/8 *of Antigua optd with T* **106**.
821 30 c. Cessna 172D Skyhawk 80 50
822 90 c. Fokker D.VII .. .. 1·50 1·00
823 $1.50, SPAD VII .. .. 2·25 3·00
824 $3 Boeing 747 .. .. 3·50 4·25
821/4 .. .. *Set of* 4 7·25 8·00
MS825 97×83 mm. De Havilland D.H.C.6 Twin Otter .. .. 3·25 3·50

1985 (8 Nov). *Life and Times of Queen Elizabeth the Queen Mother (2nd issue). Nos.* 946/9 *of Antigua optd with T* **95** *(in silver on Nos.* 826/7 *and* **MS829**).
826 $1 The Queen Mother attending church .. 2·50 2·50
827 $1.50, Watching children playing in London garden .. .. 3·00 3·00
828 $2.50, The Queen Mother in 1979 .. .. 3·50 3·50
826/8 .. .. *Set of* 3 8·00 8·00
MS829 56×85 mm. $5 With Prince Edward at Royal Wedding, 1981 .. .. .. 7·00 7·50
Nos. 826/7 also exist with black and No. 828 with silver overprints (*Price for set of* 3 £50 *mint*).
The stamps from the sheetlets mentioned beneath Antigua No. **MS949** also exist overprinted with Type **95**.

1985 (25 Nov). 850*th Birth Anniv of Maimonides (physician, philosopher and scholar). Nos.* 939/40 *of Antigua optd with T* **95**.
830 $2 bright green .. .. 4·50 3·75
MS831 70×84 mm. $5 reddish brown .. .. 4·25 4·25

1985 (25 Nov). *Marine Life. Nos.* 950/4 *of Antigua optd with T* **95** *(in silver on* 15 *c. and* $3).
832 15 c. Magnificent Frigate Bird .. .. 3·00 75
833 45 c. Brain Coral .. .. 3·00 70
834 60 c. Cushion Star .. .. 3·00 90
835 $3 Spotted Moray .. .. 6·50 4·25
832/5 .. .. *Set of* 4 14·00 6·00
MS836 110×80 mm. $5 Elkhorn Coral .. .. 8·00 5·00

1986 (17 Feb). *International Youth Year. Nos.* 941/5 *of Antigua optd with T* **95**.
837 25 c. Young farmers with produce 15 15
838 50 c. Hotel management trainees 25 30
839 60 c. Girls with goat and boys with football ("Environment") 30 35
840 $3 Windsurfing ("Leisure") .. .. 1·50 1·60
837/40 .. .. *Set of* 4 2·00 2·10
MS841 102×72 mm. $5 Young people with Antiguan flags .. .. 2·75 3·25

1986 (17 Feb). *Royal Visit. Nos.* 965/8 *of Antigua optd with T* **106**.
842 60 c. Flags of Great Britain and Antigua .. 1·25 35
843 $1 Queen Elizabeth II (*vert*) .. .. 1·40 55
844 $4 Royal Yacht *Britannia* .. .. .. 3·75 2·10
842/4 .. .. *Set of* 3 5·75 2·75
MS845 110×83 mm. $5 Map of Antigua .. 4·00 3·50

1986 (10 Mar). *75th Anniv of Girl Guide Movement. Nos.* 955/9 *of Antigua optd with T* **95**.
846 15 c. Girl Guides nursing .. .. .. 1·25 80
847 45 c. Open-air Girl Guide meeting .. .. 2·50 1·75
848 60 c. Lord and Lady Baden-Powell .. .. 2·75 2·50
849 $3 Girl Guides gathering flowers .. .. 7·00 8·50
846/9 .. .. *Set of* 4 12·00 12·00
MS850 67×96 mm. $5 Barn Swallow (Nature study) .. .. 17·00 17·00

1986 (10 Mar). *300th Birth Anniv of Johann Sebastian Bach (composer). Nos.* 960/4 *of Antigua optd with T* **95**.
851 25 c. multicoloured .. .. 1·75 70
852 50 c. multicoloured .. .. 2·25 1·40
853 $1 multicoloured .. .. 3·00 2·00
854 $3 multiciloured .. .. 6·00 8·00
851/4 .. .. *Set of* 4 11·50 11·00
MS855 104×73 mm. $5 black and brownish grey 15·00 12·00

1986 (4 Apr). *Christmas. Religious Paintings. Nos.* 985/9 *of Antigua optd with T* **106**.
856 10 c. "Madonna and Child" (De Landi) .. 40 20
857 25 c. "Madonna and Child" (Berlinghiero) .. 80 50
858 60 c. "The Nativity" (Fra Angelico) .. .. 1·50 1·00
859 $4 "Presentation in the Temple" (Giovanni di Paolo) .. .. 4·00 6·50
856/9 .. .. *Set of* 4 6·00 7·50
MS860 113×81 mm. $5 "The Nativity" (Antoniazzo Romano) .. .. 4·25 5·50

108 Queen Elizabeth II meeting Members of Legislature

(Litho Format)

1986 (21 Apr). *60th Birthday of Queen Elizabeth II (1st issue). T* **108** *and similar horiz designs. Multicoloured. P* 15.
861 $1 Type **108** .. .. 50 1·00
862 $2 Queen with Headmistress of Liberta School .. .. 60 1·10
863 $2.50, Queen greeted by Governor-General of Antigua .. .. 60 1·25
861/3 .. .. *Set of* 3 1·50 3·00
MS864 95×75 mm. $5 Queen Elizabeth in 1928 and 1986 (33×27 *mm*). P 13½×14 .. .. 5·00 7·00
See also Nos. 872/5.

109 Halley's Comet over Barbuda Beach

(Des and litho Format)

1986 (10 July). *Appearance of Halley's Comet (1st issue). T* **109** *and similar multicoloured designs. P* 15.
865 $1 Type **109** .. .. 80 1·25
866 $2.50, Early telescope and dish aerial (*vert*) .. 1·50 2·25
867 $5 Comet and World map .. .. .. 2·50 3·75
865/7 .. .. *Set of* 3 4·25 6·50
See also Nos. 886/90.

1986 (12 Aug). *40th Anniv of United Nations Organization. Nos.* 981/4 *of Antigua optd with T* **96** *(Nos.* 868/70) *or T* **95** *(No.* **MS**871).
868 40 c. Benjamin Franklin and U.N. (New York) 1953 U.P.U. 5 c. stamp .. .. 1·50 1·00
869 $1 George Washington Carver (agricultural chemist) and 1982 Nature Conservation 28 c. stamp .. .. .. 2·25 2·25
870 $3 Charles Lindbergh (aviator) and 1978 I.C.A.O. 25 c. stamp .. .. .. 4·00 5·00
868/70 .. .. *Set of* 3 7·00 7·50
MS871 101×77 mm. $5 Marc Chagall (artist) (*vert*) .. .. 11·00 12·00

1986 (12 Aug). *60th Birthday of Queen Elizabeth II (2nd issue). Nos.* 1005/8 *of Antigua optd with T* **95** *in black (No.* **MS**875) *or silver (others)*
872 60 c. black and yellow .. .. .. 1·50 1·25
873 $1 multicoloured .. .. 2·00 1·75
874 $4 multicoloured .. .. 3·75 4·25
872/4 .. .. *Set of* 3 6·50 6·50
MS875 120×85 mm. $5 black and grey-brown .. 6·50 8·00

1986 (28 Aug). *World Cup Football Championship, Mexico. Nos.* 995/9 *of Antigua optd with T* **96** (30 *c*., $4) *or T* **95** *(others).*
876 30 c. Football, boots and trophy .. .. 2·00 1·00
877 60 c. Goalkeeper (*vert*) .. .. .. 3·00 2·00
878 $1 Referee blowing whistle (*vert*) .. .. 3·25 2·25
879 $4 Ball in net .. .. 7·50 7·00
876/9 .. .. *Set of* 4 14·00 11·00
MS880 87×76 mm. $5 Two players competing for ball .. .. 16·00 13·00

1986 (28 Aug). *"Ameripex '86" International Stamp Exhibition, Chicago. Famous American Trains. Nos.* 1014/18 *of Antigua optd with T* **106**.
881 25 c. "Hiawatha" express .. .. .. 2·00 1·50
882 50 c. "Grand Canyon" express .. .. 2·75 2·25
883 $1 "Powhattan Arrow" express .. .. 3·50 3·00
884 $3 "Empire State" express .. .. 6·00 6·50
881/4 .. .. *Set of* 4 13·00 12·00
MS885 116×87 mm $5 Southern Pacific "Daylight" express .. .. 7·00 8·50

1986 (22 Sept). *Appearance of Halley's Comet (2nd issue). Nos.* 1000/4 *of Antigua optd with T* **96** *(Nos.* 886/9) *or T* **95** (**MS**890).
886 5 c. Edmond Halley and Old Greenwich Observatory 75 55
887 10 c. Messerschmitt Me 163B Komet (fighter aircraft), 1944 .. .. 75 55
888 60 c. Montezuma (Aztec Emperor) and Comet in 1517 (from "Historias de las Indias de Neuva Espana") .. .. 2·50 2·00
889 $4 Pocahontas saving Capt. John Smith and Comet in 1607 .. .. .. 7·50 7·00
886/9 .. .. *Set of* 4 10·50 9·00
MS890 101×70 mm. $5 Halley's Comet over English Harbour, Antigua .. .. .. 4·75 4·75

1986 (22 Sept). *Royal Wedding. Nos.* 1019/22 *of Antigua optd with T* **95** *in silver.*
891 45 c. Prince Andrew and Miss Sarah Ferguson 75 50
892 60 c. Prince Andrew 90 65
893 $4 Prince Andrew with Prince Philip .. 3·50 4·00
891/3 .. .. *Set of* 3 4·75 4·75
MS894 88×88 mm. $5 Prince Andrew and Miss Sarah Ferguson (*different*) .. .. .. 6·00 7·00

1986 (10 Nov). *Sea Shells. Nos.* 1023/7 *of Antigua optd with T* **106** *(in silver on* 15 *c. to* $3).
895 15 c. Fly-specked Cerith .. .. .. 2·50 1·75
896 45 c. Smooth Scotch Bonnet .. .. 2·75 2·25
897 60 c. West Indian Crown Conch .. .. 3·50 2·75
898 $3 Ciboney Murex .. .. .. 8·00 9·50
895/8 .. .. *Set of* 4 15·00 14·50
MS899 109×75 mm. $5 Colourful Atlantic Moon (*horiz*) .. .. 18·00 18·00

1986 (10 Nov). *Flowers. Nos.* 1028/36 *of Antigua optd with T* **106**.
900 10 c. *Nymphaea ampla* (water lily) 20 20
901 15 c. Queen of the Night 30 30
902 50 c. Cup of Gold 50 65
903 60 c. Beach Morning Glory 55 70
904 70 c. Golden Trumpet 70 85
905 $1 Air Plant 85 90
906 $3 Purple Wreath .. .. 2·25 2·75
907 $4 Zephyr Lily .. .. 2·75 3·25
900/7 .. .. *Set of* 8 7·50 8·75
MS908 Two sheets, each 102×72 mm. (a) $4 Dozakie. (b) $5 Four O'Clock Flower *Set of* 2 *sheets* 18·00 20·00

1986 (28 Nov). *Mushrooms. Nos.* 1042/6 *of Antigua optd with T* **106**.
909 10 c. *Hygrocybe occidentalis* var. *scarletina* . 90 50
910 50 c. *Trogia buccinalis* .. .. .. 3·25 1·75
911 $1 *Collybia subpruinosa* .. .. .. 4·75 2·75
912 $4 *Leucocoprinus brebissonii* .. .. 9·50 8·00
909/12 .. .. *Set of* 4 16·00 11·50
MS913 102×82 mm. $5 *Pyrrhoglossum pyrrhum* 20·00 13·00

1986 (Dec). *Birth Bicentenary of John J. Audubon (ornithologist) (3rd issue). Nos.* 990/3 *of Antigua optd with T* **96** *(in silver on* 60, 90 *c.).*
914 60 c. Mallard .. .. 3·00 1·75
915 90 c. North American Black Duck .. .. 3·75 2·25
916 $1.50, Pintail .. .. 5·00 4·75
917 $3 American Wigeon .. .. .. 8·00 8·50
914/17 .. .. *Set of* 4 18·00 15·00

1987 (12 Jan). *Local Boats. Nos.* 1009/13 *of Antigua optd with T* **95**.
918 30 c. Tugboat 60 50
919 60 c. Game fishing boat 80 80
920 $1 Yacht .. .. 1·25 1·25
921 $4 Lugger with auxiliary sail .. .. 3·25 4·00
918/21 .. .. *Set of* 4 5·50 6·00
MS922 108×78 mm. $5 Boats under construction 15·00 15·00

1987 (12 Jan). *Centenary of First Benz Motor Car. Nos.* 1052/60 *of Antigua optd with T* **95** *(No.* **MS**931) *or T* **96** *(others).*
923 10 c. Auburn "Speedster" (1933) 45 30
924 15 c. Mercury "Sable" (1986) 55 40
925 50 c. Cadillac (1959) .. .. 1·10 60
926 60 c. Studebaker (1950) .. .. .. 1·10 70
927 70 c. Lagonda "V-12" (1939) .. .. .. 1·25 1·00
928 $1 Adler "Standard" (1930) .. .. 1·50 1·00
929 $3 DKW (1956) .. .. 2·75 2·75
930 $4 Mercedes "500K" (1936) .. .. 2·75 2·75
923/30 .. .. *Set of* 8 10·50 8·50
MS931 Two sheets, each 99×70 mm. (a) $5 Daimler (1896). (b) $5 Mercedes "Knight" (1921) *Set of* 2 *sheets* 12·00 12·00

1987 (10 Mar). *World Cup Football Championship Winners, Mexico. Nos.* 1037/40 *of Antigua optd with T* **95** (60 *c*., $1) *or T* **96** (30 *c*., $4).
932 30 c. Football, boots and trophy .. .. 1·10 70
933 60 c. Goalkeeper (*vert*) .. .. .. 1·50 1·00
934 $1 Referee blowing whistle (*vert*) .. .. 2·00 1·75
935 $4 Ball in net .. .. 4·75 5·00
932/5 .. .. *Set of* 4 8·50 7·50

1987 (23 Apr). *America's Cup Yachting Championship. Nos* 1072/6 *of Antigua optd horizontally as T* **102**.
936 30 c. *Canada I* (1981) 20 3
937 60 c. *Gretel II* (1970) 35 5
938 $1 *Sceptre* (1958) 60 8
939 $3 *Vigilant* (1893) .. .. 1·75 2·5
936/9 .. .. *Set of* 4 2·75 3·7
MS940 113×84 mm. $5 *Australia II* defeating *Liberty* (1983) (*horiz*) .. .. 3·75 4·2

1987 (1 July). *Marine Life. Nos.* 1077/85 *of Antigua optd wit T* **95** *(No.* **MS**949) *or T* **96** *(others).*
941 15 c. Bridled Burrfish .. .. .. 3·25 7
942 30 c. Common Noddy .. .. 3·50 8
943 40 c. Nassau Grouper .. .. .. 3·50 9
944 50 c. Laughing Gull .. .. 5·00 1·5
945 60 c. French Angelfish .. .. .. 5·00 1·5
946 $1 Porkfish .. .. 5·00 1·7
947 $2 Royal Tern .. .. 11·00 5·0
948 $3 Sooty Tern .. .. 11·00 6·0
941/8 .. .. *Set of* 8 40·00 16·0
MS949 Two sheets, each 120×94 mm. (a) $5 Banded Butterflyfish. (b) $5 Brown Booby *Set of* 2 *sheets* 15·00 13·0

1987 (28 July). *Milestones of Transportation. Nos.* 1100/9 *Antigua optd with T* **106**.
950 10 c. *Spirit of Australia* (fastest powerboat), 1978 .. .. 1·00 6
951 15 c. Werner von Siemen's electric locomotive, 1879 .. .. .. 1·50 8
952 30 c. U.S.S. *Triton* (first submerged circumnavigation), 1960 .. .. .. 1·75 9
953 50 c. Trevithick's steam carriage (first passenger-carrying vehicle), 1801 .. 2·00 1·2
954 60 c. U.S.S. *New Jersey* (battleship), 1942 2·25 1·2
955 70 c. Draisine bicycle, 1818 .. .. 2·25 1·4
956 90 c. *United States* (liner) (holder of Blue Riband), 1952 .. .. 2·25 1·5
957 $1.50, Cierva C.4 (first autogyro), 1923 2·50 2·5
958 $2 Curtiss NC-4 (first translantic flight), 1919 .. .. 3·50 3·5
959 $3 *Queen Elizabeth 2* (liner), 1969 .. 4·25 4·2
950/9 .. .. *Set of* 10 21·00 16·0

110 Shore Crab

(Litho Format)

1987 (15 Sept). *Marine Life. T* **110** *and similar multicoloure designs. P* 15.
960 5 c. Type **110** 10 2
961 10 c. Sea Cucumber 15 2
962 15 c. Stop-light Parrotfish 15 2
963 25 c. Banded Coral Shrimp 15 2
964 35 c. Spotted Drum 15 2
965 60 c. Thorny Starfish 25 4
966 75 c. Atlantic Trumpet Triton 35 6
967 90 c. Feather Star and Yellow Beaker Sponge 40 6
968 $1 Blue Gorgonian (*vert*) 45 6
969 $1.25, Slender Filefish (*vert*) 55 8
970 $5 Barred Hamlet (*vert*) .. .. 1·25 4·0
971 $7.50 Royal Gramma ("Fairy Basslet") (*vert*) .. .. 1·75 5·5
972 $10 Fire Coral and Banded Butterflyfish (*vert*) .. .. 2·25 6·5
960/72 .. .. *Set of* 13 7·00 18·0

1987 (12 Oct). *Olympic Games, Seoul* (1988). *Nos.* 1086/90 *Antigua optd with T* **95** *(No.* **MS**977) *or T* **96** *in silver (others*
973 10 c. Handball 65
974 60 c. Fencing 90
975 $1 Gymnastics .. .. 1·25 1·
976 $3 Football .. .. 2·50 3·
973/6 .. .. *Set of* 4 4·75 5·
MS977 100×72 mm. $5 Boxing gloves .. .. 3·75 4·

1987 (12 Oct). *Birth Centenary of Marc Chagall (artist). No* 1091/9 *of Antigua optd as T* **95** *(in silver on Nos.* 983, **MS**986b
978 10 c. "The Profile" 10
979 30 c. "Portrait of the Artist's Sister" .. 15
980 40 c. "Bride with Fan" 20
981 60 c. "David in Profile" 25
982 90 c. "Fiancee with Bouquet" 40
983 $1 "Self Portrait with Brushes" 45
984 $3 "The Walk" .. .. 1·40 1·
985 $4 "Three Candles" .. .. .. 1·75 2·
978/85 .. .. *Set of* 8 4·25 5·
MS986 Two sheets, each 110×95 mm. (a) $5 "Fall of Icarus" (104×89 *mm*). (b) $5 "Myth of Orpheus" (104×89 *mm*) *Set of* 2 *sheets* 4·50 5·

1987 (5 Nov). *Centenary of Statue of Liberty* (1986) *(2nd issue Nos* 1110/19 *of Antigua optd with T* **95** (15, 30, 45, 50 *c*., $1, $ $5) *or T* **96** (60, 90 *c*., $3), *in black* (50 *c*., $3) *or silver (others*
987 15 c. Lee Iacocca at unveiling of restored Statue 10 1
988 30 c. Statue at sunset (side view) 15 1
989 45 c. Aerial view of head 20 2
990 50 c. Lee Iacocca and torch 25 3
991 60 c. Workmen inside head of Statue (*horiz*) 25 3
992 90 c. Restoration work (*horiz*) 40 5
993 $1 Head of Statue 45 5
994 $2 Statue at Sunset (front view) .. .. 90 1·4
995 $3 Inspecting restoration work (*horiz*) .. 1·40 2·0
996 $5 Statue at night .. .. 2·25 3·0
987/96 .. .. *Set of* 10 5·75 7·7

7 (5 Nov). *Entertainers. Nos.* 1120/7 *of Antigua optd with* 95 (*in silver on* $3).
7 15 c. Grace Kelly 80 50
8 30 c. Marilyn Monroe .. .. .. 1·75 1·00
9 45 c. Orson Welles 90 75
0 50 c. Judy Garland 95 85
1 60 c. John Lennon .. .. 2·75 1·75
2 $1 Rock Hudson .. .. 1·75 1·50
3 $2 John Wayne .. .. 2·75 2·75
4 $3 Elvis Presley .. .. 6·00 5·00
/1004 .. .. *Set of* 8 16·00 13·00

7 (5 Nov). *"Capex '87" International Stamp Exhibition, Toronto. Reptiles and Amphibians. Nos.* 1133/7 *of Antigua optd with T* 95 (*No.* **MS**1009) *or T* 96 (*others*).
5 30 c. Whistling Frog .. .. .. 1·75 85
6 60 c. Croaking Lizard .. .. .. 2·25 1·25
7 $1 Antiguan Anole .. .. .. 2·50 1·40
8 $3 Red-footed Tortoise .. .. .. 6·00 7·00
5/8 .. .. *Set of* 4 11·00 9·50
1009 106×76 mm. $5 Ground Lizard .. 11·00 8·00

88 (12 Jan). *Christmas. Religious Paintings. Nos.* 1144/8 *of Antigua optd with T* 95.
10 45 c. "Madonna and Child" (Bernardo Daddi) 60 25
11 60 c. "St. Joseph" (detail, "The Nativity" (Sano di Pietro)) 75 45
12 $1 "Virgin Mary" (detail, "The Nativity" (Sano di Pietro)) .. .. .. 1·00 85
13 $4 "Music-making Angel" (Melozzo da Forli) .. .. 3·00 4·25
10/13 .. .. *Set of* 4 4·75 5·25
S1014 99×70 mm. $5 "The Flight into Egypt" (Sano di Pietro) .. .. 5·50 5·50

88 (25 Mar). *Salvation Army's Community Service. Nos.* 163/71 *of Antigua optd with T* **106**.
15 25 c. First aid at daycare centre, Antigua .. 80 80
16 30 c. Giving penicillin injection, Indonesia 80 80
17 40 c. Children at daycare centre, Bolivia .. 85 85
18 45 c. Rehabilitation of the handicapped, India 85 85
19 50 c. Training blind man, Kenya .. .. 1·25 1·25
20 60 c. Weighing baby, Ghana .. .. 1·25 1·25
21 $1 Training typist, Zambia .. .. 1·75 1·75
22 $2 Emergency food kitchen, Sri Lanka .. 2·25 2·75
15/22 .. .. *Set of* 8 8·75 9·25
S1023 152×83 mm. $5 General Eva Burrows 12·00 14·00

88 (6 May). *Bicentenary of U.S. Constitution. Nos.* 1139/43 *of Antigua optd with T* 95 ($4, $5) *or T* 96 (*others*), *all in silver.*
24 15 c. House of Burgesses, Virginia ("Freedom of Speech") 10 10
25 45 c. State Seal, Connecticut 20 25
26 60 c. State Seal, Delaware 25 35
27 $4 Gouverneur Morris (Pennsylvania delegate) (*vert*) .. .. .. 1·75 3·00
24/7 .. .. *Set of* 4 2·10 3·25
S1028 105×75 mm. $5 Roger Sherman (Connecticut delegate) (*vert*) .. .. 2·75 3·25

88 (4 July). *Royal Ruby Wedding. Nos.* 1149/53 *of Antigua optd with T* 95.
29 25 c. deep brown, black and bright new blue 60 30
30 60 c. multicoloured .. .. .. 1·00 65
31 $2 deep brown, black and light green .. 2·25 2·25
32 $3 multicoloured .. .. .. 2·50 2·75
a. Opt triple .. .. † —
29/32 .. .. *Set of* 4 5·75 5·50
S1033 102×77 mm. $5 multicoloured .. 6·00 5·50
The only known example of No. 1032a is used, uncancelled, on ver from the Philatelic Bureau.

88 (4 July). *Birds of Antigua. Nos.* 1154/62 *of Antigua optd with T* 95 (10 c., $1, $5) *or T* 96 (*others*).
34 10 c. Great Blue Heron .. .. .. 1·50 80
35 15 c. Ringed Kingfisher (*horiz*) .. .. 1·75 80
36 50 c. Bananaquit (*horiz*) .. .. .. 2·50 1·50
37 60 c. Purple Gallinule (*horiz*) .. .. 2·50 1·50
38 70 c. Blue-hooded Euphonia (*horiz*) .. 2·75 2·00
39 $1 Brown-throated Conure ("Caribbean Parakeet") .. .. 3·00 2·00
40 $3 Troupial (*horiz*) .. .. .. 4·50 5·00
41 $4 Purple-throated Carib (*horiz*) .. 4·50 5·00
34/41 .. .. *Set of* 8 21·00 17·00
S1042 Two sheets, each 115×86 mm. (a) $5 Greater Flamingo. (b) $5 Brown Pelican *Set of* 2 *sheets* 14·00 9·50

88 (25 July–8 Dec). 500*th Anniv of Discovery of America by Columbus* (1992) (1*st issue*). *Nos.* 1172/80 *of Antigua optd with T* 96 (*Nos.* 1043/50) *or T* 95 (*No.* **MS**1051).
43 10 c. Columbus' second fleet, 1493 .. 75 75
44 30 c. Painos Indian village and fleet .. 1·00 80
45 45 c. *Santa Mariagalante* (flagship) and Painos village .. .. 1·40 80
46 60 c. Painos Indians offering Columbus fruit and vegetables .. .. .. 1·00 85
47 90 c. Painos Indian and Columbus with Scarlet Macaw .. .. 2·00 1·25
48 $1 Columbus landing on island .. .. 2·00 1·25
49 $3 Spanish soldier and fleet .. .. 2·75 3·00
50 $4 Fleet under sail .. .. .. 2·75 3·25
43/50 .. .. *Set of* 8 12·50 11·00
S1051 Two sheets, each 110×80 nn. (a) $5 Queen Isabella's cross. (b) $5 Gold coin of Ferdinand and Isabella (8 Dec) *Set of* 2 *sheets* 8·00 9·00
See also Nos. 1112/16, 1177/85, 1285/93, 1374/80 and 1381/2.

1988 (25 July). 500*th Birth Anniv of Titian. Nos.* 1181/9 *of Antigua optd with T* **96** (*Nos.* 1052/9) *or T* **95** (*No.* **MS**1060), *all in silver.*
1052 30 c. "Bust of Christ" 15 15
1053 40 c. "Scourging of Christ" 20 25
1054 45 c. "Madonna in Glory with Saints" .. 20 25
1055 50 c. "The Averoldi Polyptych" (detail) .. 25 30
1056 $1 "Christ Crowned with Thorns" .. 45 50
1057 $2 "Christ Mocked" .. .. .. 90 1·10
1058 $3 "Christ and Simon of Cyrene" .. 1·40 1·75
1059 $4 "Crucifixion with Virgin and Saints" 1·75 2·25
1052/9 .. .. *Set of* 8 4·75 6·00
MS1060 Two sheets, each 110×95 mm. (a) $5 "Ecce Homo" (detail). (b) $5 "Noli me Tangere" (detail) *Set of* 2 *sheets* 4·50 5·50

1988 (25 Aug). 16*th World Scout Jamboree, Australia. Nos.* 1128/32 *of Antigua optd with T* **95** (*No.* **MS**1064) *or T* **96** (*others*).
1061 10 c. Scouts around camp fire and Red Kangaroo 75 60
1062 60 c. Scouts canoeing and Blue-winged Kookaburra .. .. 2·00 95
1063 $1 Scouts on assault course and Ring-tailed Rock Wallaby .. .. 1·75 1·25
1064 $3 Field kitchen and Koala .. .. 3·50 4·50
1061/4 .. .. *Set of* 4 7·25 6·50
MS1065 103 × 78 mm. $5 Flags of Antigua, Australia and Scout Movement .. .. 2·50 3·25

1988 (25 Aug–8 Dec). *Sailing Week. Nos.* 1190/4 *of Antigua optd with T* **95** (*No.* **MS**1070) *or T* **96** (*others*).
1066 30 c. Two yachts rounding buoy 20 20
1067 60 c. Three yachts 45 55
1068 $1 British yacht under way 70 85
1069 $3 Three yachts (*different*) .. .. 1·60 2·25
1066/9 .. .. *Set of* 4 2·75 3·50
MS1070 103 × 92 mm. $5 Two yachts (8 Dec) 2·50 3·25

1988 (16 Sept). *Flowering Trees. Nos.* 1213/21 *of Antigua optd with T* **95**.
1071 10 c. Jacaranda 10 10
1072 30 c. Cordia 15 15
1073 50 c. Orchid Tree 20 25
1074 90 c. Flamboyant 40 45
1075 $1 African Tulip Tree 45 50
1076 $2 Potato Tree .. .. 80 1·25
1077 $3 Crepe Myrtle .. .. .. 1·25 1·75
1078 $4 Pitch Apple .. .. 1·60 2·25
1071/8 .. .. *Set of* 8 4·50 6·00
MS1079 Two sheets, each 106 × 76 mm. (a) $5 Cassia. (b) $5 Chinaberry .. *Set of* 2 *sheets* 4·25 5·00

1988 (16 Sept). *Olympic Games, Seoul. Nos.* 1222/6 *of Antigua optd with T* **95** (*Nos.* 1080/1, **MS**1084) *or T* **96** (*Nos.* 1082/3).
1080 40 c. Gymnastics 40 30
1081 60 c. Weightlifting 50 35
1082 $1 Water polo (*horiz*) 70 70
1083 $3 Boxing (*horiz*) .. .. .. 1·50 2·00
1080/3 .. .. *Set of* 4 2·75 3·00
MS1084 114 × 80 mm. $5 Runner with Olympic torch .. .. 2·10 2·40

BARBUDA MAIL
(111)

1988 (8 Dec)–**90**. *Caribbean Butterflies. Nos.* 1227/44*a of Antigua optd with T* **96** (*Nos.* 1085/1102) *or T* **111** (*No.* 1102*a*).
1085 1 c. *Danaus plexippus* 30 60
1086 2 c. *Greta diaphanus* 30 60
1087 3 c. *Calisto archebates* 40 60
1088 5 c. *Hamadryas feronia* 40 60
1089 10 c. *Mestra dorcas* 50 50
1090 15 c. *Hypolimnas misippus* 60 40
1091 20 c. *Dione juno* 70 50
1092 25 c. *Heliconius charithonia* 75 50
1093 30 c. *Eurema pyro* 85 50
1094 40 c. *Papilio androgeus* 90 50
1095 45 c. *Anteos maerula* 90 50
1096 50 c. *Aphrissa orbis* .. .. .. 1·10 75
1097 60 c. *Astraptes xagua* .. .. .. 1·10 60
1098 $1 *Heliopetes arsalte* .. .. .. 1·40 1·00
1099 $2 *Polites baracoa* .. .. .. 3·00 3·50
1100 $2.50 *Phocides pigmalion* .. .. 3·25 4·00
1101 $5 *Prepona amphitoe* .. .. .. 4·50 5·50
1102 $10 *Oarisma nanus* .. .. .. 7·50 8·50
1102a $20 *Parides lycimenes* (4.5.90) .. .. 12·00 13·00
1085/102a .. .. .. *Set of* 19 35·00 38·00

BARBUDA MAIL
(112)

BARBUDA
MAIL
(113)

1989 (28 Apr). 25*th Death Anniv of John F. Kennedy* (*American statesman*). *Nos.* 1245/53 *of Antigua optd with T* **96** (*Nos.* 1103/10) *or T* **112** (*No.* **MS**1111).
1103 1 c. President Kennedy and family .. 10 10
1104 2 c. Kennedy commanding *PT109* .. 10 10
1105 3 c. Funeral cortege 10 10
1106 4 c. In motorcade, Mexico City 10 10
1107 30 c. As 1 c. 60 30
1108 60 c. As 4 c. 80 55
1109 $1 As 3 c. 95 90
1110 $4 As 2 c. .. .. 3·25 4·50
1103/10 .. .. *Set of* 8 5·50 5·75
MS1111 105 × 75 mm. $5 Kennedy taking presidential oath of office .. .. .. 3·25 4·00

1989 (24 May). 500*th Anniv of Discovery of America by Columbus* (1992) (2*nd issue*). *Pre-Columbian Arawak Society. Nos.* 1267/71 *of Antigua optd with T* **113**.
1112 $1.50, Arawak warriors .. .. .. 1·50 2·00
a. Horiz strip of 4. Nos. 1112/15 .. 5·50
1113 $1.50, Whip dancers .. .. .. 1·50 2·00
1114 $1.50, Whip dancers and chief with pineapple .. .. 1·50 2·00
1115 $1.50, Family and camp fire .. .. 1·50 2·00
1112/15 .. .. *Set of* 4 5·50 7·00
MS1116 71 × 84 mm. $6 Arawak chief .. 3·25 4·00

1989 (29 June). 50*th Anniv of First Jet Flight. Nos.* 1272/80 *of Antigua optd with T* **111**.
1117 10 c. Hawker Siddeley Comet 4 airliner .. 1·00 85
1118 30 c. Messerschmitt Me 262 fighter .. 1·40 90
1119 40 c. Boeing 707 airliner .. .. .. 1·60 90
1120 60 c. Canadair CL-13 Sabre ("F-86 Sabre") fighter .. .. 1·75 1·00
1121 $1 Lockheed F-104 Starfighter .. .. 2·00 1·25
1122 $2 Douglas DC-10 airliner .. .. 3·25 3·50
1123 $3 Boeing 747-300/400 airliner .. .. 3·75 4·00
1124 $4 McDonnell Douglas F-4 Phantom II fighter .. .. 3·75 4·00
1117/24 .. .. *Set of* 8 17·00 15·00
MS1125 Two sheets, each 114×83 mm. (a) $7 Grumman F-14 Tomcat fighter. (b) $7 Concorde airliner .. .. *Set of* 2 *sheets* 19·00 17·00

BARBUDA
MAIL
(114)

BARBUDA
MAIL
(115)

1989 (18 Sept). *Caribbean Cruise Ships. Nos.* 1281/9 *of Antigua optd as T* **114**, *but with lines spaced* (*No.* **MS**1134b), *or with T* **111** (*others*).
1126 25 c. *Festivale* 60 60
1127 45 c. *Southward* 80 60
1128 50 c. *Sagafjord* 90 70
1129 60 c. *Daphne* .. .. 1·00 80
1130 75 c. *Cunard Countess* .. .. .. 1·10 1·40
1131 90 c. *Song of America* .. .. .. 1·25 1·40
1132 $3 *Island Princess* .. .. .. 3·25 4·25
1133 $4 *Galileo* .. .. 3·25 4·25
1126/33 .. .. *Set of* 8 11·00 12·50
MS1134 (a) 113×87 mm. $6 *Norway*. (b) 111×82 mm. $6 *Oceanic*.. .. .. *Set of* 2 *sheets* 20·00 21·00

1989 (14 Dec). *Japanese Art. Paintings by Hiroshige. Nos.* 1290/8 *of Antigua optd with T* **114**.
1135 25 c. "Fish swimming by Duck half-submerged in Stream" 80 55
1136 45 c. "Crane and Wave" .. .. .. 1·25 60
1137 50 c. "Sparrows and Morning Glories" .. 1·40 80
1138 60 c. "Crested Blackbird and Flowering Cherry" .. .. 1·50 85
1139 $1 "Great Knot sitting among Water Grass" .. .. 1·75 1·25
1140 $2 "Goose on a Bank of Water" .. .. 2·50 2·75
1141 $3 "Black Paradise Flycatcher and Blossoms" .. .. 2·75 3·00
1142 $4 "Sleepy Owl perched on a Pine Branch" .. .. 3·00 3·00
1135/42 .. .. *Set of* 8 13·50 11·50
MS1143 Two sheets, each 102×75 mm. (a) $5 "Bullfinch flying near a Clematis Branch". (b) $5 "Titmouse on a Cherry Branch" .. *Set of* 2 *sheets* 18·00 17·00

1989 (20 Dec). *World Cup Football Championship, Italy* (1990). *Nos.* 1308/12 *of Antigua optd with T* **115**.
1144 15 c. Goalkeeper 60 40
1145 25 c. Goalkeeper moving towards ball .. 70 40
1146 $1 Goalkeeper reaching for ball .. .. 1·25 1·25
1147 $4 Goalkeeper saving goal .. .. 3·25 4·00
1144/7 .. .. *Set of* 4 5·25 5·50
MS1148 Two sheets, each 75×105 mm. (a) $5 Three players competing for ball (*horiz*). (b) $5 Ball and players' legs (*horiz*) .. *Set of* 2 *sheets* 15·00 16·00

1989 (20 Dec). *Christmas. Paintings by Raphael and Giotto. Nos.* 1351/9 *of Antigua optd with T* **114**.
1149 10 c. "The Small Cowper Madonna" (Raphael) 10 10
1150 25 c. "Madonna of the Goldfinch" (Raphael) 10 15
1151 30 c. "The Alba Madonna" (Raphael) .. 15 20
1152 50 c. Saint (detail, "Bologna Altarpiece") (Giotto) 25 30
1153 60 c. Angel (detail, "Bologna Altarpiece") (Giotto) 30 45
1154 70 c. Angel slaying serpent (detail, "Bologna Altarpiece") (Giotto) .. 35 50
1155 $4 Evangelist (detail, "Bologna Altarpiece") (Giotto) .. .. 1·90 2·50
1156 $5 "Madonna of Foligno" (Raphael) .. 2·40 3·00
1149/56 .. .. *Set of* 8 5·00 6·50
MS1157 Two sheets, each 71×96 mm. (a) $5 "The Marriage of the Virgin" (detail) (Raphael). (b) $5 Madonna and Child (detail, "Bologna Altarpiece") (Giotto) .. *Set of* 2 *sheets* 10·00 11·00

1990 (21 Feb). *Fungi. Nos.* 1313/21 *of Antigua optd with T* **111**.
1158 10 c. *Mycena pura* .. .. 1·00 55
1159 25 c. *Psathyrella tuberculata* (*vert*) .. 1·25 55
1160 50 c. *Psilocybe cubensis* .. .. .. 1·75 90
1161 60 c. *Leptonia caeruleocapitata* (*vert*) .. 2·00 1·00
1162 75 c. *Xeromphalina tenuipes* (*vert*) .. 2·00 1·40
1163 $1 *Chlorophyllum molybdites* (*vert*) .. 2·00 1·40
1164 $3 *Marasmius haematocephalus* .. .. 4·00 4·25
1165 $4 *Cantharellus cinnabarinus* .. .. 4·00 4·50
1158/65 .. .. *Set of* 8 16·00 13·00
MS1166 Two sheets, each 88×62 mm. (a) $6 *Leucopaxillus gracillimus* (*vert*). (b) $6 *Volvariella volvacea* .. .. *Set of* 2 *sheets* 25·00 20·00

BARBUDA MAIL

(116)

1990 (30 Mar). *Local Fauna. Nos.* 1322/6 *of Antigua optd with T* **116** *(vertically on* 60 c., $4).
1167 25 c. Desmarest's Hutia 40 35
1168 45 c. Caribbean Monk Seal 85 70
1169 60 c. Mustache Bat (*vert*) 90 80
1170 $4 American Manatee (*vert*) .. .. 2·75 4·00
1167/70 .. .. *Set of* 4 4·50 5·25
MS1171 113×87 mm. $5 West Indies Giant Rice Rat .. .. 8·00 9·50

1990 (30 Mar). *20th Anniv of First Manned Landing on Moon. Nos.* 1346/50 *of Antigua optd with T* **116** *(vertically on* 10, 45 *c. and* $5).
1172 10 c. Launch of "Apollo 11" 75 55
1173 45 c. Aldrin on Moon .. .. .. 1·50 70
1174 $1 Module *Eagle* over Moon (*horiz*) .. 2·25 1·75
1175 $4 Recovery of "Apollo 11" crew after splashdown (*horiz*) .. .. 5·00 6·50
1172/5 .. .. *Set of* 4 8·50 8·50
MS1176 107×77 mm. $5 Astronaut Neil Armstrong .. .. 8·50 10·00

1990 (6 June). *500th Anniv of Discovery of America by Columbus* (1992) *(3rd issue). New World Natural History – Marine Life. Nos.* 1360/8 *of Antigua optd as T* **114**, *but with lines spaced.*
1177 10 c. Star-eyed Hermit Crab 55 50
1178 20 c. Spiny Lobster 75 60
1179 25 c. Magnificent Banded Fanworm .. 75 60
1180 45 c. Cannonball Jellyfish .. .. 1·00 60
1181 60 c. Red-spiny Sea Star .. .. .. 1·25 75
1182 $2 Peppermint Shrimp .. .. .. 2·25 2·50
1183 $3 Coral Crab .. .. 2·50 3·00
1184 $4 Branching Fire Coral .. .. 2·50 3·00
1177/84 .. .. *Set of* 8 10·50 10·50
MS1185 Two sheets, each 101×69 mm. (a) $5 Common Sea Fan. (b) $5 Portuguese Man-of-war *Set of* 2 *sheets* 13·00 13·00

1990 (12 July). *"EXPO 90" International Garden and Greenery Exhibition, Osaka. Orchids. Nos.* 1369/77 *of Antigua optd as T* **114**, *but with lines spaced.*
1186 15 c. *Vanilla mexicana* .. .. .. 1·25 70
1187 45 c. *Epidendrum ibaguense* .. .. 1·75 70
1188 50 c. *Epidendrum secundum* .. .. 1·75 80
1189 60 c. *Maxillaria conferta* .. .. .. 2·00 1·10
1190 $1 *Onicidium altissimum* .. .. 2·25 1·75
1191 $2 *Spiranthes lanceolata* .. .. 3·75 4·00
1192 $3 *Tonopsis utricularioides* .. .. 4·50 5·00
1193 $5 *Epidendrum nocturnum* .. .. 5·50 6·50
1186/93 .. .. *Set of* 8 21·00 18·00
MS1194 Two sheets, each 101×69 mm. (a) $6 *Octomeria graminifolia.* (b) $6 *Rodriguezia lanceolata* .. .. .. *Set of* 2 *sheets* 13·00 13·00

1990 (14 Aug). *Reef Fishes. Nos.* 1386/94 *of Antigua optd with T* **111**.
1195 10 c. Flamefish 50 50
1196 15 c. Coney 65 55
1197 50 c. Long-spined Squirrelfish .. .. 1·00 85
1198 60 c. Sergeant Major .. .. .. 1·25 1·00
1199 $1 Yellow-tailed Snapper .. .. 1·75 1·75
1200 $2 Rock Beauty .. .. .. 2·75 3·25
1201 $3 Spanish Hogfish .. .. .. 3·00 3·50
1202 $4 Striped Parrotfish .. .. .. 3·00 3·50
1195/1202 .. .. .. *Set of* 8 12·50 13·50
MS1203 Two sheets, each 99×70 mm. (a) $5 Black-barred Soldierfish. (b) $5 Four-eyed Butterflyfish .. .. .. *Set of* 2 *sheets* 20·00 20·00

$5.00

1st Anniversary
Hurricane Hugo
16th September, 1989-1990

═

(117)

1990 (17 Sept). *First Anniv of Hurricane Hugo. Nos.* 971/2 *surch as T* **117**.
1204 $5 on $7.50, Fairy Basslet (*vert*) .. 5·00 5·50
1205 $7.50 on $10 Fire Coral and Butterfly Fish (*vert*) .. .. 6·00 6·50

1990 (12 Oct). *90th Birthday of Queen Elizabeth the Queen Mother. Nos.* 1415/19 *of Antigua optd as T* **114**, *but with lines spaced.*
1206 15 c. multicoloured 90 55
1207 35 c. multicoloured .. .. .. 1·40 65
1208 75 c. multicoloured .. .. .. 2·25 1·50
1209 $3 multicoloured .. .. .. 5·00 4·50
1206/9 .. .. *Set of* 4 8·50 6·50
MS1210 67×98 mm $6 multicoloured .. .. 12·00 12·00

NEW INFORMATION

The editor is always interested to correspond with people who have new information that will improve or correct the Catalogue.

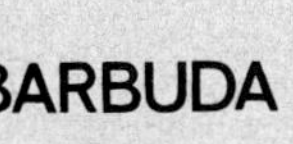

BARBUDA
MAIL

(118)

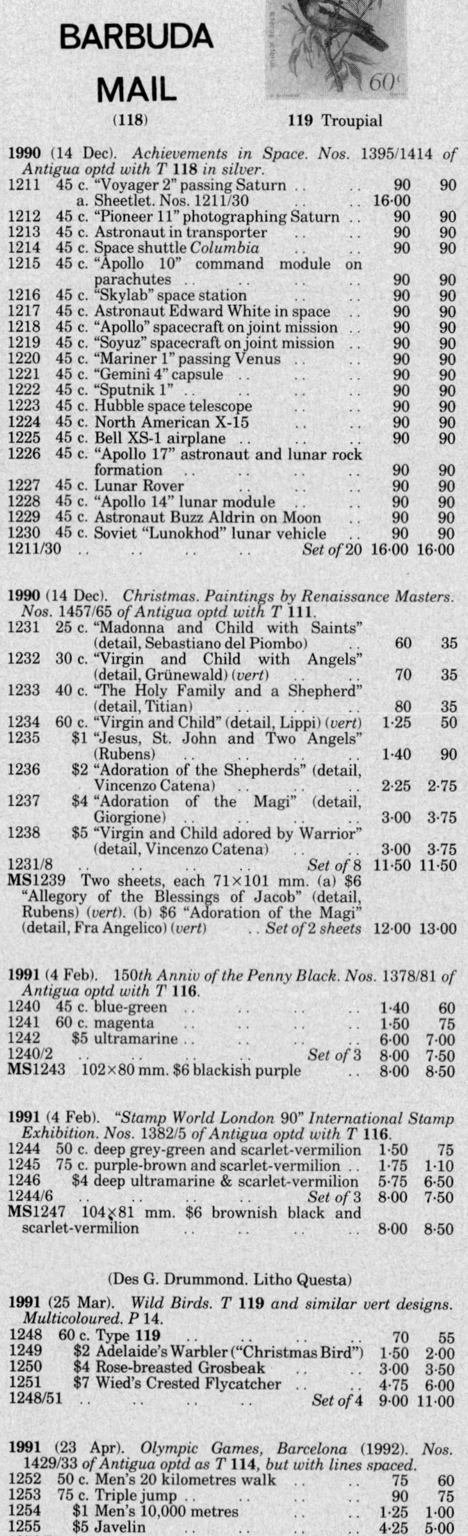

119 Troupial

1990 (14 Dec). *Achievements in Space. Nos.* 1395/1414 *of Antigua optd with T* **118** *in silver.*
1211 45 c. "Voyager 2" passing Saturn 90 90
a. Sheetlet. Nos. 1211/30 .. .. 16·00
1212 45 c. "Pioneer 11" photographing Saturn .. 90 90
1213 45 c. Astronaut in transporter 90 90
1214 45 c. Space shuttle *Columbia* 90 90
1215 45 c. "Apollo 10" command module on parachutes 90 90
1216 45 c. "Skylab" space station 90 90
1217 45 c. Astronaut Edward White in space .. 90 90
1218 45 c. "Apollo" spacecraft on joint mission .. 90 90
1219 45 c. "Soyuz" spacecraft on joint mission .. 90 90
1220 45 c. "Mariner 1" passing Venus 90 90
1221 45 c. "Gemini 4" capsule 90 90
1222 45 c. "Sputnik 1" 90 90
1223 45 c. Hubble space telescope 90 90
1224 45 c. North American X-15 .. .. 90 90
1225 45 c. Bell XS-1 airplane 90 90
1226 45 c. "Apollo 17" astronaut and lunar rock formation 90 90
1227 45 c. Lunar Rover 90 90
1228 45 c. "Apollo 14" lunar module 90 90
1229 45 c. Astronaut Buzz Aldrin on Moon .. 90 90
1230 45 c. Soviet "Lunokhod" lunar vehicle .. 90 90
1211/30 .. .. *Set of* 20 16·00 16·00

1990 (14 Dec). *Christmas. Paintings by Renaissance Masters. Nos.* 1457/65 *of Antigua optd with T* **111**.
1231 25 c. "Madonna and Child with Saints" (detail, Sebastiano del Piombo) .. 60 35
1232 30 c. "Virgin and Child with Angels" (detail, Grünewald) (*vert*) 70 35
1233 40 c. "The Holy Family and a Shepherd" (detail, Titian) 80 35
1234 60 c. "Virgin and Child" (detail, Lippi) (*vert*) 1·25 50
1235 $1 "Jesus, St. John and Two Angels" (Rubens) .. .. 1·40 90
1236 $2 "Adoration of the Shepherds" (detail, Vincenzo Catena) .. .. .. 2·25 2·75
1237 $4 "Adoration of the Magi" (detail, Giorgione) .. .. 3·00 3·75
1238 $5 "Virgin and Child adored by Warrior" (detail, Vincenzo Catena) .. .. 3·00 3·75
1231/8 .. .. *Set of* 8 11·50 11·50
MS1239 Two sheets, each 71×101 mm. (a) $6 "Allegory of the Blessings of Jacob" (detail, Rubens) (*vert*). (b) $6 "Adoration of the Magi" (detail, Fra Angelico) (*vert*) .. *Set of* 2 *sheets* 12·00 13·00

1991 (4 Feb). *150th Anniv of the Penny Black. Nos.* 1378/81 *of Antigua optd with T* **116**.
1240 45 c. blue-green .. .. 1·40 60
1241 60 c. magenta .. .. 1·50 75
1242 $5 ultramarine .. .. 6·00 7·00
1240/2 .. .. *Set of* 3 8·00 7·50
MS1243 102×80 mm. $6 blackish purple .. 8·00 8·50

1991 (4 Feb). *"Stamp World London 90" International Stamp Exhibition. Nos.* 1382/5 *of Antigua optd with T* **116**.
1244 50 c. deep grey-green and scarlet-vermilion 1·50 75
1245 75 c. purple-brown and scarlet-vermilion .. 1·75 1·10
1246 $4 deep ultramarine & scarlet-vermilion 5·75 6·50
1244/6 .. .. *Set of* 3 8·00 7·50
MS1247 104×81 mm. $6 brownish black and scarlet-vermilion .. .. .. 8·00 8·50

(Des G. Drummond. Litho Questa)

1991 (25 Mar). *Wild Birds. T* **119** *and similar vert designs. Multicoloured. P* 14.
1248 60 c. Type **119** 70 55
1249 $2 Adelaide's Warbler ("Christmas Bird") 1·50 2·00
1250 $4 Rose-breasted Grosbeak .. .. 3·00 3·50
1251 $7 Wied's Crested Flycatcher .. .. 4·75 6·00
1248/51 .. .. *Set of* 4 9·00 11·00

1991 (23 Apr). *Olympic Games, Barcelona* (1992). *Nos.* 1429/33 *of Antigua optd as T* **114**, *but with lines spaced.*
1252 50 c. Men's 20 kilometres walk 75 60
1253 75 c. Triple jump 90 75
1254 $1 Men's 10,000 metres .. .. 1·25 1·00
1255 $5 Javelin .. .. 4·25 5·00
1252/5 .. .. *Set of* 4 6·50 6·50
MS1256 100 × 70 mm. $6 Athlete lighting Olympic flame at Los Angeles Olympics .. 7·00 8·00

1991 (23 Apr). *Birds. Nos.* 1448/56 *of Antigua optd with T* **116** *diagonally.*
1257 10 c. Pearly-eyed Thrasher 80 70
1258 25 c. Purple-throated Carib .. .. 1·40 80
1259 50 c. Yellowthroat .. .. .. 1·75 1·00
1260 60 c. American Kestrel .. .. .. 1·75 1·10
1261 $1 Yellow-bellied Sapsucker .. .. 2·25 1·50
1262 $2 Purple Gallinule .. .. .. 3·25 3·50
1263 $3 Yellow-crowned Night Heron .. 3·50 4·00
1264 $4 Blue-hooded Euphonia .. .. 3·50 4·00
1257/64 .. .. *Set of* 8 16·00 15·00
MS1265 Two sheets, each 76×60 mm. (a) $6 Brown Pelican. (b) $6 Magnificent Frigate Bird *Set of* 2 *sheets* 16·00 16·00

1991 (21 June). *350th Death Anniv of Rubens. Nos.* 1466/74 *o Antigua optd with T* **111**.
1266 25 c. "Rape of the Daughters of Leucippus" (detail) 60 5
1267 45 c. "Bacchanal" (detail) 80 6
1268 50 c. "Rape of the Sabine Women" (detail) 90 7
1269 60 c. "Battle of the Amazons" (detail) .. 95 8
1270 $1 "Rape of the Sabine Women" (different detail) .. .. 1·50 1·2
1271 $2 "Bacchanal" (different detail) .. 2·50 2·5
1272 $3 "Rape of the Sabine Women" (different detail) .. .. 2·75 3·0
1273 $4 "Bacchanal" (different detail) .. 2·75 3·C
1266/73 .. .. *Set of* 8 11·50 11·C
MS1274 Two sheets, each 101 × 71 mm. (a) $6 "Rape of Hippodameia" (detail). (b) $6 "Battle of the Amazons" (different detail) *Set of* 2 *sheets* 12·00 13·C

1991 (25 July). *50th Anniv of Second World War. Nos.* 1475/8 *of Antigua optd diagonally with T* **116**.
1275 10 c. U.S. troops cross into Germany, 1944 80 7
1276 15 c. Axis surrender in North Africa, 1943 1·10 8
1277 25 c. U.S. tanks invade Kwalajalein, 1944 1·50 1·0
1278 45 c. Roosevelt and Churchill meet at Casablanca, 1943 .. .. .. 2·00 1·5
1279 50 c. Marshall Badoglio, Prime Minister of Italian anti-fascist government, 1943 1·50 1·5
1280 $1 Lord Mountbatten, Supreme Allied Commander South-east Asia, 1943 .. 2·75 2·2
1281 $2 Greek victory at Koritza, 1940 .. 3·75 4·0
1282 $4 Anglo-Soviet mutual assistance pact, 1941 .. .. 5·00 5·5
1283 $5 Operation Torch landings, 1942 .. 5·00 5·5
1275/83 .. .. *Set of* 9 21·00 21·0
MS1284 Two sheets, each 108×80 mm. (a) $6 Japanese attack on Pearl Harbor, 1941. (b) $6 U.S.A.A.F. daylight raid on Schweinfurt, 1943 *Set of* 2 *sheets* 21·00 21·0

1991 (26 Aug). *500th Anniv of Discovery of America b Columbus* (1992) *(4th issue). History of Exploration. No* 1503/11 *of Antigua optd with T* **111**.
1285 10 c. multicoloured 55 5
1286 15 c. multicoloured 70 6
1287 45 c. multicoloured 85 7
1288 60 c. multicoloured .. .. .. 1·00 1·0
1289 $1 multicoloured .. .. .. 1·40 1·4
1290 $2 multicoloured .. .. .. 2·25 2·5
1291 $4 multicoloured .. .. .. 3·50 4·0
1292 $5 multicoloured .. .. .. 3·75 4·0
1285/92 .. .. *Set of* 8 12·50 13·5
MS1293 Two sheets, each 106×76 mm. (a) $6 black and Indian red. (b) $6 black and Indian red *Set of* 2 *sheets* 15·00 15·0

1991 (18 Oct). *Butterflies. Nos.* 1494/502 *of Antigua optd wit T* **116** *diagonally.*
1294 10 c. *Heliconius charithonia* 90 8
1295 35 c. *Marpesia petreus* .. .. .. 1·40 1·
1296 50 c. *Anartia amathea* .. .. .. 1·75 1·4
1297 75 c. *Siproeta stelenes* .. .. .. 2·00 1·6
1298 $1 *Battus polydamas* .. .. .. 2·25 1·7
1299 $2 *Historis odius* .. .. .. 3·00 3·2
1300 $4 *Hypolimnas misippus* .. .. 4·50 5·0
1301 $5 *Hamadryas feronia* .. .. .. 4·50 5·0
1294/1301 .. .. .. *Set of* 8 18·00 18·0
MS1302 Two sheets. (a) 73×100 mm. $6 *Vanessa cardui* caterpillar (*vert*). (b) 100×73 mm. $6 *Danaus plexippus* caterpillar (*vert*) *Set of* 2 *sheets* 18·00 18·0

BARBUDA
MAIL

(120)

1991 (18 Nov). *65th Birthday of Queen Elizabeth II. No* 1534/8 *of Antigua optd with T* **120**.
1303 15 c. Queen Elizabeth and Prince Philip in 1976 .. .. 80 6
1304 20 c. The Queen and Prince Philip in Portugal, 1985 .. .. .. 80 6
1305 $2 Queen Elizabeth II .. .. .. 2·00 2·C
1306 $4 The Queen and Prince Philip at Ascot, 1986 .. .. 3·50 4·C
1303/6 .. .. *Set of* 4 6·50 6·5
MS1307 68×90 mm. $4 The Queen at National Theatre, 1986, and Prince Philip .. .. 6·50 7·C

1991 (18 Nov). *10th Wedding Anniv of Prince and Princess Wales. Nos.* 1539/43 *of Antigua optd with T* **120**.
1308 10 c. Prince and Princess of Wales at party, 1986 .. .. 60 6
1309 40 c. Separate portraits of Prince, Princess and sons .. .. 1·00 6
1310 $1 Prince Henry and Prince William .. 1·40 1·2
1311 $5 Princess Diana in Australia and Prince Charles in Hungary .. .. 4·50 5·C
1308/11 .. .. *Set of* 4 6·75 6·5
MS1312 68×90 mm. $4 Prince Charles in Hackney and Princess and sons in Majorca, 1987 6·50 7·C

1991 (24 Dec). *Christmas. Religious Paintings by Fr Angelico. Nos.* 1595/602 *of Antigua optd with T* **120**.
1313 10 c. "The Annunciation" 50 4
1314 30 c. "Nativity" 70 4
1315 40 c. "Adoration of the Magi" 70 4
1316 60 c. "Presentation in the Temple" .. 90 5
1317 $1 "Circumcision" .. .. .. 1·25 8
1318 $3 "Flight into Egypt" .. .. .. 3·00 3·5
1319 $4 "Massacre of the Innocents" .. .. 3·25 3·7
1320 $5 "Christ teaching in the Temple" .. 3·50 4·0
1313/20 .. .. *Set of* 8 12·50 12·5

1992 (20 Feb). *Death Centenary of Vincent van Gogh (artist) (1990). Nos.* 1512/24 *of Antigua optd with T* **120**.
1321 5 c. "Camille Roulin" 40 40
1322 10 c. "Armand Roulin" 50 50
1323 15 c. "Young Peasant Woman with Straw Hat sitting in the Wheat" 60 60
1324 25 c. "Adeline Ravoux" 70 70
1325 30 c. "The Schoolboy" 70 70
1326 40 c. "Doctor Gachet" 75 75
1327 50 c. "Portrait of a Man" 75 75
1328 75 c. "Two Children" .. .. .. 1·10 1·10
1329 $2 "The Postman Joseph Roulin" .. 2·50 2·75
1330 $3 "The Seated Zouave" .. .. 2·75 3·00
1331 $4 "L'Arlésienne" .. .. .. 3·00 3·25
1332 $5 "Self-Portrait, November/December 1888" .. .. 3·25 3·50
1321/32 .. .. *Set of* 12 15·00 16·00
MS1333 Three sheets, each 102×76 mm. (a) $5 "Farmhouse in Provence" (*horiz*). (b) $5 "Flowering Garden" (*horiz*). (c) $6 "The Bridge at Trinquetaille" (*horiz*). Imperf .. *Set of* 3 *sheets* 15·00 16·00

1992 (7 Apr). *Birth Centenary of Charles de Gaulle (French statesman). Nos.* 1562/70 *of Antigua optd with T* **111** (10 *c.*, $1, $2, $4, $6) *or T* **114** (*others*).
1334 10 c. Presidents De Gaulle and Kennedy, 1961 .. .. 70 60
1335 15 c. General De Gaulle with Pres. Roosevelt, 1945 (*vert*) 75 65
1336 45 c. Pres. De Gaulle with Chancellor Adenauer, 1962 (*vert*) .. 1·10 75
1337 60 c. De Gaulle at Arc de Triomphe, Liberation of Paris, 1944 (*vert*) .. 1·40 1·00
1338 $1 General De Gaulle crossing the Rhine, 1945 .. .. 1·75 1·50
1339 $2 General De Gaulle in Algiers, 1944 2·75 3·00
1340 $4 Presidents De Gaulle and Eisenhower, 1960 .. .. 3·75 4·00
1341 $5 De Gaulle returning from Germany, 1968 (*vert*) .. .. .. 3·75 4·00
1334/41 .. .. *Set of* 8 14·50 14·00
MS1342 Two sheets, (a) 76×106 mm. $6 De Gaulle with crowd. (b) 106×76 mm. $6 De Gaulle and Churchill at Casablanca, 1943 *Set of* 2 *sheets* 15·00 15·00

1992 (16 Apr). *Easter. Religious Paintings. Nos.* 1627/35 *of Antigua optd with T* **111**.
1343 10 c. "Supper at Emmaus" (Caravaggio) .. 50 45
1344 15 c. "The Vision of St. Peter" (Zurbarán) 60 50
1345 30 c. "Christ driving the Money-changers from the Temple" (Tiepolo) 75 55
1346 40 c. "Martyrdom of St. Bartholomew" (detail) (Ribera) 80 60
1347 $1 "Christ driving the Money-changers from the Temple" (detail) (Tiepolo) .. 1·50 1·25
1348 $2 "Crucifixion" (detail) (Altdorfer) .. 2·50 3·00
1349 $4 "The Deposition" (detail) (Fra Angelico) .. .. 3·75 4·00
1350 $5 "The Deposition" (different detail) (Fra Angelico) .. .. .. 3·75 4·00
1343/50 .. .. *Set of* 8 12·50 13·00
MS1351 Two sheets. (a) 102×71 mm. $6 "The Last Supper" (detail) (Masip). (b) 71×102 mm. $6 "Crucifixion" (detail) (*vert*) (Altdorfer) *Set of* 2 *sheets* 12·50 13·00

1992 (19 June). *Anniversaries and Events. Nos.* 1573/83 *of Antigua optd as T* **114**, *but with lines spaced (Nos.* 1358 *and* **MS**1362b) *or with T* **111** (*others*).
1352 25 c. Germans celebrating Reunification .. 60 60
1353 75 c. Cubs erecting tent .. .. 1·25 1·25
1354 $1.50, *Don Giovanni* and Mozart .. 2·25 2·25
1355 $2 Chariot driver and Gate at night .. 2·25 2·25
1356 $2 Lord Baden-Powell and members of the 3rd Antigua Methodist cub pack (*vert*) .. .. 2·25 2·25
1357 $2 Lilienthal's signature and glider *Flugzeug Nr.* 5 .. .. .. 2·25 2·25
1358 $2.50, Driver in Class P36 steam locomotive (*vert*) .. .. .. 2·50 2·50
1359 $3 Statues from podium .. .. 2·50 2·50
1360 $3.50, Cubs and camp fire .. .. 3·00 3·00
1361 $4 St. Peter's Cathedral, Salzburg .. 3·00 3·00
1352/61 .. .. *Set of* 10 20·00 20·00
MS1362 Two sheets. (a) 100×72 mm. $4 Detail of chariot and helmet. (b) 89×117 mm. $5 Antiguan flag and Jamboree emblem (*vert*) *Set of* 2 *sheets* 11·00 12·00

1992 (12 Aug). 50*th Anniv of Japanese Attack on Pearl Harbor. Nos.* 1585/94 *of Antigua optd as T* **114**, *but with lines spaced.*
1364 $1 *Nimitz* class carrier and *Ticonderoga* class cruiser .. .. 1·75 1·75
a. Sheetlet. Nos. 1364/73 .. .. 16·00
1365 $1 Tourist launch .. .. .. 1·75 1·75
1366 $1 U.S.S. *Arizona* memorial .. .. 1·75 1·75
1367 $1 Wreaths on water and aircraft .. 1·75 1·75
1368 $1 White Tern .. .. .. 1·75 1·75
1369 $1 Mitsubishi A6M Zero-Sen fighters over Pearl City .. .. 1·75 1·75
1370 $1 Mitsubishi A6M Zero-Sen fighters attacking .. .. 1·75 1·75
1371 $1 Battleship Row in flames .. .. 1·75 1·75
1372 $1 U.S.S. *Nevada* (battleship) underway 1·75 1·75
1373 $1 Mitsubishi A6M Zero-Sen fighters returning to carriers .. .. .. 1·75 1·75
1364/73 .. .. *Set of* 10 16·00 16·00

1992 (12 Oct). 500*th Anniv of Discovery of America by Columbus (5th issue). World Columbian Stamp "Expo '92", Chicago. Nos.* 1654/60 *of Antigua optd with T* **111**.
1374 15 c. Memorial cross and huts, San Salvador 50 50
1375 30 c. Martin Pinzon with telescope .. 60 60
1376 40 c. Christopher Columbus 70 70
1377 $1 *Pinta* .. .. 2·25 2·00
1378 $2 *Nina* .. .. 3·00 3·00
1379 $4 *Santa Maria* .. .. .. 4·00 4·25
1374/9 .. .. *Set of* 6 10·00 10·00
MS1380 Two sheets, each 108×76 mm. (a) $6 Ship and map of West Indies. (b) $6 Sea monster *Set of* 2 *sheets* 13·00 14·00

1992 (12 Oct). 500*th Anniv of Discovery of America by Columbus (6th issue). Organization of East Caribbean States. Nos.* 1670/1 *of Antigua optd with T* **111**.
1381 $1 Columbus meeting Amerindians .. 1·50 1·50
1382 $2 Ships approaching island .. .. 3·00 3·00

1992 (29 Oct). *Postage Stamp Mega Event, New York. No.* **MS**1690 *of Antigua optd with T* **111**.
MS1383 $6 multicoloured .. .. .. 5·50 6·50

1992 (3 Nov). 40*th Anniv of Queen Elizabeth II's Accession. Nos.* 1604/8 *of Antigua optd with T* **111**.
1384 10 c. Queen Elizabeth II and bird sanctuary 90 70
1385 30 c. Nelson's Dockyard .. .. 1·50 85
1386 $1 Ruins on Shirley Heights .. .. 2·25 2·00
1387 $5 Beach and palm trees .. .. 5·50 6·50
1384/7 .. .. *Set of* 4 9·00 9·00
MS1388 Two sheets, each 75×98 mm. (a) $6 Beach. (b) $6 Hillside foliage .. *Set of* 2 *sheets* 15·00 16·00

1992 (8 Dec). *Prehistoric Animals. Nos.* 1618/26 *of Antigua optd with T* **120** (*sideways on Nos.* 1391/2 *and* **MS**1397).
1389 10 c. Pteranodon 90 90
1390 15 c. Brachiosaurus .. .. .. 1·00 1·00
1391 30 c. Tyrannosaurus Rex .. .. 1·25 1·25
1392 50 c. Parasaurolophus .. .. .. 1·50 1·50
1393 $1 Deinonychus (*horiz*) .. .. 2·00 2·00
1394 $2 Triceratops (*horiz*) .. .. .. 3·00 3·00
1395 $4 Protoceratops hatching (*horiz*) .. 3·75 3·75
1396 $5 Stegosaurus (*horiz*) .. .. .. 3·75 3·75
1389/96 .. .. *Set of* 8 15·00 15·00
MS1397 Two sheets, each 100×70 mm. (a) $6 Apatosaurus (*horiz*). (b) $6 Allosaurus (*horiz*) *Set of* 2 *sheets* 17·00 17·00

1992 (8 Dec). *Christmas. Nos.* 1691/9 *of Antigua optd with T* **111**.
1398 10 c. "Virgin and Child with Angels" (School of Piero della Francesca) .. 60 55
1399 25 c. "Madonna Degli Alberelli" (Giovanni Bellini) 85 55
1400 30 c. "Madonna and Child with St. Anthony Abbot and St. Sigismund" (Neroccio) 90 55
1401 40 c. "Madonna and the Grand Duke" (Raphael) .. .. 1·00 55
1402 60 c. "The Nativity" (George de la Tour) .. 1·40 70
1403 $1 "Holy Family" (Jacob Jordaens) .. 2·00 1·40
1404 $4 "Madonna and Child Enthroned" (Magaritone) .. .. 5·00 5·50
1405 $5 "Madonna and Child on a Curved Throne" (Byzantine school) .. .. 5·00 5·50
1398/405 .. .. *Set of* 8 15·00 13·50
MS1406 Two sheets, each 76×102 mm. (a) $6 "Madonna and Child" (Domenco Ghirlando). (b) $6 "The Holy Family" (Pontormo) *Set of* 2 *sheets* 15·00 15·00

1993 (25 Jan). *Fungi. Nos.* 1645/53 *of Antigua optd with T* **120**.
1407 10 c. *Amanita caesarea* .. .. .. 1·00 1·00
1408 15 c. *Collybia fusipes* .. .. .. 1·25 1·25
1409 30 c. *Boletus aereus* .. .. .. 1·50 1·50
1410 40 c. *Laccaria amethystina* .. .. 1·50 1·50
1411 $1 *Russula virescens* .. .. .. 2·00 2·00
1412 $2 *Tricholoma equestre* ("*Tricholoma auratum*") .. .. 3·00 3·00
1413 $4 *Calocybe gambosa* .. .. .. 3·75 3·75
1414 $5 *Lentinus tigrinus* ("*Panus tigrinus*") 3·75 3·75
1407/14 .. .. *Set of* 8 16·00 16·00
MS1415 Two sheets, each 100×70 mm. (a) $6 *Clavariadelphus truncatus*. (b) $6 *Auricularia auricula-judae* .. .. *Set of* 2 *sheets* 16·00 16·00

1993 (22 Mar). *"Granada '92" International Stamp Exhibition, Spain. Spanish Paintings. Nos.* 1636/44 *of Antigua optd diagonally with T* **116**.
1416 10 c. "The Miracle at the Well" (Alonzo Cano) 60 60
1417 15 c. "The Poet Luis de Goingora y Argote" (Velázquez) 75 75
1418 30 c. "The Painter Francisco Goya" (Vincente López Portana) .. .. 1·00 1·00
1419 40 c. "Maria de las Nieves Michaela Fourdinier" (Luis Paret y Alcázar) .. 1·00 1·00
1420 $1 "Carlos III eating before his Court" (Alcázar) (*horiz*) .. .. .. 2·00 2·00
1421 $2 "Rain Shower in Granada" (Antonio Munoz Degrain) (*horiz*) .. .. 3·00 3·00
1422 $4 "Sarah Bernhardt" (Santiago Ruisnol i Prats) .. .. 4·50 4·50
1423 $5 "The Hermitage Garden" (Joaquim Mir Trinxet) .. .. .. 4·50 4·50
1416/23 .. .. *Set of* 8 15·00 15·00
MS1424 Two sheets, each 120×95 mm. (a) $6 "The Ascent of Monsieur Boucle's Montgolfier Balloon in the Gardens of Aranjuez" (Antonio Carnicero) (112×87 *mm*). (b) $6 "Olympus: Battle with the Giants" (Francisco Bayeu y Subias) (112×87 *mm*). Imperf .. *Set of* 2 *sheets* 13·00 14·00

1993 (10 May). *"Genova '92" International Thematic Stamp Exhibition. Hummingbirds and Plants. Nos.* 1661/9 *of Antigua optd with T* **120**.
1425 10 c. Antillean Crested Hummingbird and Wild Plantain 75 75
1426 25 c. Green Mango and Parrot's Plantain 1·00 1·00
1427 45 c. Purple-throated Carib and Lobster Claws .. .. 1·25 1·25
1428 60 c. Antillean Mango and Coral Plant .. 1·50 1·50
1429 $1 Vervain Hummingbird and Cardinal's Guard .. .. 1·75 1·75
1430 $2 Rufous-breasted Hermit and Heliconia .. .. 2·50 2·50
1431 $4 Blue-headed Hummingbird and Red Ginger .. .. 3·50 3·50
1432 $5 Green-throated Carib and Ornamental Banana .. .. .. 3·50 3·50
1425/32 .. .. *Set of* 8 14·00 14·00
MS1433 Two sheets, each 100×70 mm. (a) $6 Bee Hummingbird and Jungle Flame. (b) $6 Western Streamertail and Bignonia *Set of* 2 *sheets* 12·00 14·00

1993 (29 June). *Inventors and Inventions. Nos.* 1672/80 *of Antigua optd with T* **111**.
1434 10 c. Ts'ai Lun and paper 25 25
1435 25 c. Igor Sikorsky and *Bolshoi Baltiskii* (first four-engined airplane) .. 60 60
1436 30 c. Alexander Graham Bell and early telephone 60 60
1437 40 c. Johannes Gutenberg and early printing press 60 60
1438 60 c. James Watt and stationary steam engine .. .. 1·50 1·25
1439 $1 Anton van Leeuwenhoek and early microscope .. .. 1·50 1·50
1440 $4 Louis Braille and hands reading braille .. .. 3·50 3·75
1441 $5 Galileo and telescope .. .. 3·50 3·75
1434/41 .. .. *Set of* 8 11·00 11·00
MS1442 Two sheets, each 100×71 mm. (a) $6 Edison and Latimer's phonograph. (b) $6 Fulton's steamboat .. .. *Set of* 2 *sheets* 11·00 12·00

1993 (16 Aug). *Anniversaries and Events. Nos.* 1700/14 *of Antigua optd with T* **111** (*Nos.* 1450/1) *or as T* **114**, *but with lines spaced (others).*
1443 10 c. Russian cosmonauts 60 60
1444 40 c. Airship LZ-127 *Graf Zeppelin*, 1929 1·00 1·00
1445 45 c. Bishop Daniel Davis 50 50
1446 75 c. Konrad Adenauer making speech .. 70 70
1447 $1 Bus Mosbacher and *Weatherly* (yacht) 1·25 1·25
1448 $1.50, Rain Forest .. .. .. 1·50 1·50
1449 $2 Tiger .. .. 3·50 3·50
1450 $2 National flag, plant and emblem (*horiz*) .. .. 1·75 1·75
1451 $2 Members of Community Players company (*horiz*) .. .. .. 1·75 1·75
1452 $2.25, Women carrying pots .. .. 1·75 1·75
1453 $3 Lions Club emblem .. .. 2·75 2·75
1454 $4 Chinese rocket on launch tower .. 3·00 3·00
1455 $4 West German and N.A.T.O. flags .. 3·00 3·00
1456 $6 Hugo Eckener (airship pioneer) .. 4·50 4·50
1443/56 .. .. *Set of* 14 25·00 25·00
MS1457 Four sheets, each 100×71 mm. (a) $6 Projected European space station. (b) $6 Airship LZ-129 *Hindenburg*, 1936. (c) $6 Brandenburg Gate on German flag. (d) $6 *Danaus plexippus* (butterfly) .. .. .. *Set of* 4 *sheets* 23·00 23·00

1993 (21 Sept). *Flowers. Nos.* 1733/41 *of Antigua optd with T* **114**, *but with lines spaced (Nos.* 1458/65) *or T* **111** (*No.* **MS**1466).
1458 15 c. Cardinal's Guard 85 85
1459 25 c. Giant Granadilla .. .. .. 1·10 1·10
1460 30 c. Spider Flower .. .. .. 1·25 1·25
1461 40 c. Gold Vine .. .. .. 1·40 1·40
1462 $1 Frangipani .. .. 2·00 2·00
1463 $2 Bougainvillea .. .. .. 2·75 2·75
1464 $4 Yellow Oleander .. .. .. 3·75 3·75
1465 $5 Spicy Jatropha .. .. .. 3·75 3·75
1458/65 .. .. *Set of* 8 15·00 15·00
MS1466 Two sheets, each 100×70 mm. (a) $6 Bird Lime Tree. (b) $6 Fairy Lily *Set of* 2 *sheets* 15·00 15·00

WORLD BIRDWATCH
9-10 OCTOBER 1993

(121)

1993 (9 Oct). *World Bird Watch. Nos.* 1248/51 *optd as T* **121** (*horiz opt on* $2, $4).
1467 60 c. Type **119** .. .. 2·25 1·75
1468 $2 Adelaide's Warbler .. .. .. 4·00 4·00
1469 $4 Rose-breasted Grosbeak .. .. 5·50 6·00
1470 $7 Wied's Crested Flycatcher .. .. 7·00 8·50
1467/70 .. .. *Set of* 4 17·00 18·00

1993 (11 Nov). *Endangered Species. Nos.* 1759/71 *of Antigua optd with T* **111**.
1471 $1 St. Lucia Amazon .. .. .. 1·75 1·75
a. Sheetlet. Nos. 1471/82 .. .. 19·00
1472 $1 Cahow .. .. 1·75 1·75
1473 $1 Swallow-tailed Kite .. .. .. 1·75 1·75
1474 $1 Everglade Kite .. .. .. 1·75 1·75
1475 $1 Imperial Amazon .. .. .. 1·75 1·75
1476 $1 Humpback Whale .. .. .. 1·75 1·75
1477 $1 Plain Pigeon .. .. 1·75 1·75
1478 $1 St. Vincent Amazon .. .. .. 1·75 1·75
1479 $1 Puerto Rican Amazon .. .. 1·75 1·75
1480 $1 Leatherback Turtle .. .. .. 1·75 1·75
1481 $1 American Crocodile .. .. .. 1·75 1·75
1482 $1 Hawksbill Turtle .. .. .. 1·75 1·75
1471/82 .. .. *Set of* 12 19·00 19·00
MS1483 Two sheets, each 100×70 mm. (a) $6 As No. 1476. (b) $6 West Indian Manatee *Set of* 2 *sheets* 17·00 17·00

1994 (6 Jan). *Bicentenary of the Louvre, Paris. Paintings by Peter Paul Rubens. Nos.* 1742/9 *and* **MS**1758 *of Antigua optd with T* **120**.
1484 $1 "The Destiny of Marie de Medici" (upper detail) .. .. 1·40 1·40
a. Sheetlet. Nos. 1484/91 .. .. 10·00
1485 $1 "The Birth of Marie de Medici" .. 1·40 1·40
1486 $1 "The Education of Marie de Medici" .. 1·40 1·40
1487 $1 "The Destiny of Marie de Medici" (lower detail) .. .. 1·40 1·40
1488 $1 "Henry VI receiving the Portrait of Marie" .. .. 1·40 1·40
1489 $1 "The Meeting of the King and Marie de Medici" .. .. 1·40 1·40
1490 $1 "The Marriage by Proxy" .. .. 1·40 1·40
1491 $1 "The Birth of Louis XIII" .. .. 1·40 1·40
1484/91 .. .. *Set of* 8 10·00 10·00
MS1492 70×100 mm. $6 "Helene Fourment with a Coach" (52×85 *mm*) .. .. .. 8·00 8·50

1994 (3 Mar). *World Cup Football Championship* 1994, *U.S.A.* (*1st issue*). *Nos.* 1816/28 *of Antigua optd with T* **114**, *but with lines spaced* (*Nos.* 1493/1504) *or T* **111** (*No.* **MS**1505).

1493 $2 Paul Gascoigne .. .. 2·25 2·25
1494 $2 David Platt .. .. 2·25 2·25
1495 $2 Martin Peters .. .. 2·25 2·25
1496 $2 John Barnes .. .. 2·25 2·25
1497 $2 Gary Lineker .. .. 2·25 2·25
1498 $2 Geoff Hurst .. .. 2·25 2·25
1499 $2 Bobby Charlton .. .. 2·25 2·25
1500 $2 Bryan Robson .. .. 2·25 2·25
1501 $2 Bobby Moore .. .. 2·25 2·25
1502 $2 Nobby Stiles .. .. 2·25 2·25
1503 $2 Gordon Banks .. .. 2·25 2·25
1504 $2 Peter Shilton .. .. 2·25 2·25
1493/1504 .. .. .. *Set of* 12 24·00 24·00
MS1505 Two sheets, each 135×109 mm. (a) $6 Bobby Moore holding World Cup. (b) $6 Gary Lineker and Bobby Robson .. *Set of* 2 *sheets* 13·00 13·00
See also Nos. 1573/9.

1994 (21 Apr). *Anniversaries and Events. Nos.* 1829/38, 1840 *and* 1842/7 *of Antigua optd with T* **111**.

1506 10 c. Grand Inspector W. Heath 45 45
1507 15 c. Rodnina and Oulanov (U.S.S.R.) (pairs figure skating) (*horiz*) .. 50 50
1508 30 c. Present Masonic Hall, St. John's (*horiz*) 70 70
1509 30 c. Willy Brandt with Helmut Schmidt and George Leber (*horiz*) 70 70
1510 30 c. "Cat and Bird" (Picasso) (*horiz*) .. 70 70
1511 40 c. Previous Masonic Hall, St. John's (*horiz*) 70 70
1512 40 c. "Fish on a Newspaper" (Picasso) (*horiz*) 70 70
1513 40 c. Early astronomical equipment .. 70 70
1514 40 c. Prince Naruhito and engagement photographs (*horiz*) 70 70
1515 60 c. Grand Inspector J. Jeffery 75 75
1516 $3 Masako Owada and engagement photographs (*horiz*) .. .. .. 2·00 2·00
1517 $4 Willy Brandt and protest march (*horiz*) .. .. 2·75 2·75
1518 $4 Galaxy .. .. 2·75 2·75
1519 $5 Alberto Tomba (Italy) (giant slalom) (*horiz*) .. .. 2·75 2·75
1520 $5 "Dying Bull" (Picasso) (*horiz*) .. 2·75 2·75
1521 $5 Pres. Clinton and family (*horiz*) .. 2·75 2·75
1506/21 .. .. *Set of* 16 20·00 20·00
MS1522 Six sheets. (a) 106×75 mm. $5 Copernicus. (b) 106×75 mm. $6 Womens' 1500 metre speed skating medallists (*horiz*). (c) 106×75 mm. $6 Willy Brandt at Warsaw Ghetto Memorial (*horiz*). (d) 106×75 mm. $6 "Woman with a Dog" (detail) (Picasso) (*horiz*). (e) 106×75 mm. $6 Masako Owada. (f) 106×75 mm. $6 Pres. Clinton taking the Oath (42½×57 *mm*) *Set of* 6 *sheets* 24·00 25·00

1994 (15 June). *Aviation Anniversaries. Nos.* 1848/55 *of Antigua optd with T* **111** (*vertically reading down on No.* 1526).

1523 30 c. Hugo Eckener and Dr. W. Beckers with Airship LZ-127 *Graf Zeppelin* over Lake George, New York .. 90 90
1524 40 c. Chicago World's Fair from *Graf Zeppelin* 90 90
1525 40 c. Gloster Whittle E28/39, 1941 .. 90 90
1526 40 c. George Washington writing balloon mail letter (*vert*) 90 90
1527 $4 Pres. Wilson and Curtiss JN-4 "Jenny" .. .. 3·75 3·75
1528 $5 Airship LZ-129 *Hindenburg* over Ebbets Field baseball stadium, 1937 3·75 3·75
1529 $5 Gloster Meteor in dogfight .. .. 3·75 3·75
1523/9 .. .. *Set of* 7 13·50 13·50
MS1530 Three sheets. (a) 86×105 mm. $6 Hugo Eckener (*vert*). (b) 105×86 mm. $6 Consolidated Catalina PBY-5 flying boat (57×42½ *mm*). (c) 105×86 mm. $6 Alexander Hamilton, Washington and John Jay watching Blanchard's balloon, 1793 (*horiz*) .. .. *Set of* 3 *sheets* 16·00 17·00

1994 (15 June). *Centenaries of Henry Ford's First Petrol Engine* (*Nos.* 1531, 1533, **MS**1535a) *and Karl Benz's First Four-wheeled Car* (*others*). *Nos.* 1856/60 *of Antigua optd with T* **111**.

1531 30 c. Lincoln Continental 85 85
1532 40 c. Mercedes racing car, 1914 .. .. 90 90
1533 $4 Ford "GT40", 1966 .. .. .. 3·75 3·75
1534 $5 Mercedes Benz "gull-wing" coupe, 1954 .. .. 3·75 3·75
1531/4 .. .. *Set of* 4 8·25 8·25
MS1535 Two sheets. (a) 114×87 mm. $6 Ford's Mustang emblem. (b) 87×114 mm. $6 Germany 1936 12pf. Benz and U.S.A. 1968 12 c. Ford stamps .. .. *Set of* 2 *sheets* 11·00 12·00

1994 (18 Aug). *Famous Paintings by Rembrandt and Matisse. Nos.* 1881/9 *of Antigua optd with T* **111**.

1536 15 c. "Hannah and Samuel" (Rembrandt) 60 60
1537 15 c. "Guitarist" (Matisse) 60 60
1538 30 c. "The Jewish Bride" (Rembrandt) .. 90 90
1539 40 c. "Jacob wrestling with the Angel" (Rembrandt) 90 90
1540 60 c. "Interior with a Goldfish Bowl" (Matisse) .. .. .. 1·10 1·10
1541 $1 "Mlle. Yvonne Landsberg" (Matisse) 1·40 1·40
1542 $4 "The Toboggan" (Matisse) .. .. 3·75 3·75
1543 $5 "Moses with the Tablets of the Law" (Rembrandt) .. .. .. 3·75 3·75
1536/43 .. .. *Set of* 8 11·50 11·50
MS1544 Two sheets. (a) 124×99 mm. $6 "The Blinding of Samson by the Philistines" (detail) (Rembrandt). (b) 99×124 mm. $6 "The Three Sisters" (detail) (Matisse) .. *Set of* 2 *sheets* 11·00 12·00

1994 (21 Sept). *"Polska '93" International Stamp Exhibition, Poznań. Nos.* 1839, 1841 *and* **MS**1847f *of Antigua optd with T* **114**, *but with lines spaced* (*sideways on* $1, $3).

1545 $1 "Woman Combing her Hair" (W. Slewinski) (*horiz*) .. .. .. 1·75 1·75
1546 $3 "Artist's Wife with Cat" (Konrad Kryzanowski) (*horiz*) .. .. 3·50 3·50
MS1547 70×100 mm. $6 "General Confusion" (S. I. Witkiewicz) .. .. 6·00 7·00

1994 (21 Sept). *Orchids. Nos.* 1948/56 *of Antigua optd with T* **114**, *but with lines spaced* (*Nos.* 1548/55) *or T* **111** (*No.* **MS**1556).

1548 10 c. *Spiranthes lanceolata* 75 75
1549 20 c. *Ionopsis utricularioides* .. .. 1·00 1·00
1550 30 c. *Tetramicra canaliculata* .. .. 1·25 1·25
1551 50 c. *Oncidium picturatum* .. .. 1·50 1·50
1552 $1 *Epidendrum difforme* .. .. 2·00 2·00
1553 $2 *Epidendrum ciliare* .. .. .. 3·00 3·00
1554 $4 *Epidendrum ibaguense* .. .. 4·50 4·50
1555 $5 *Epidendrum nocturnum* .. .. 4·50 4·50
1548/55 .. .. *Set of* 8 17·00 17·00
MS1556 Two sheets, each 100×73 mm. (a) $6 *Rodriguezia lanceolata*. (b) $6 *Encyclia cochleata* *Set of* 2 *sheets* 17·00 17·00

1994 (3 Nov). *Centenary of Sierra Club* (*environmental protection society*) (1992). *Endangered Species. Nos.* 1907/22 *of Antigua optd with T* **114**, *but lines spaced* (*Nos.* 1557/71) *or T* **111** (*No.* **MS**1572).

1557 $1.50, Sumatran Rhinoceros lying down 2·00 2·00
a. Sheetlet. Nos. 1557/64 .. .. 13·50
1558 $1.50, Sumatran Rhinoceros feeding .. 2·00 2·00
1559 $1.50, Ring-tailed Lemur on ground .. 2·00 2·00
1560 $1.50, Ring-tailed Lemur on branch .. 2·00 2·00
1561 $1.50, Red-fronted Brown Lemur on branch .. .. 2·00 2·00
1562 $1.50, Head of Red-fronted Brown Lemur 2·00 2·00
1563 $1.50, Head of Red-fronted Brown Lemur in front of trunk .. .. .. 2·00 2·00
1564 $1.50, Sierra Club Centennial emblem .. 1·25 1·25
a. Sheetlet. Nos. 1564/71 .. .. 13·50
1565 $1.50, Head of Bactrian Camel .. .. 2·00 2·00
1566 $1.50, Bactrian Camel .. .. .. 2·00 2·00
1567 $1.50, African Elephant drinking .. 2·00 2·00
1568 $1.50, Head of African Elephant .. 2·00 2·00
1569 $1.50, Leopard sitting upright .. .. 2·00 2·00
1570 $1.50, Leopard in grass (emblem at right) 2·00 2·00
1571 $1.50, Leopard in grass (emblem at left) 2·00 2·00
1557/71 .. .. *Set of* 15 27·00 27·00
MS1572 Four sheets. (a) 100×70 mm. $1.50, Sumatran Rhinoceros (*horiz*). (b) 70×100 mm. $1.50, Ring-tailed Lemur (*horiz*). (c) 70×100 mm. $1.50, Bactrian Camel (*horiz*). (d) 100×70 mm. $1.50, African Elephant (*horiz*) *Set of* 4 *sheets* 5·00 6·00

1995 (12 Jan). *World Cup Football Championship, U.S.A.* (*2nd issue*). *Nos.* 2039/45 *of Antigua optd with T* **116** *diagonally in silver.*

1573 15 c. Hugo Sanchez (Mexico) 60 60
1574 35 c. Jürgen Klinsmann (Germany) .. 90 90
1575 65 c. Antiguan player .. .. .. 1·25 1·25
1576 $1.20, Cobi Jones (U.S.A.) .. .. 1·75 1·75
1577 $4 Roberto Baggio (Italy) .. .. 3·50 3·50
1578 $5 Bwalya Kalusha (Zambia) .. .. 3·50 3·50
1573/8 .. .. *Set of* 6 10·50 10·50
MS1579 Two sheets. (a) 72×105 mm. $6 Maldive Islands player (*vert*). (b) 107×78 mm. $6 World Cup trophy (*vert*) .. .. *Set of* 2 *sheets* 9·50 11·00

1995 (12 Jan). *Christmas. Religious Paintings. Nos.* 2058/66 *of Antigua optd with T* **111**.

1580 15 c. "Virgin and Child by the Fireside" (Robert Campin) 50 35
1581 35 c. "The Reading Madonna" (Giorgione) 65 40
1582 40 c. "Madonna and Child" (Giovanni Bellini) 65 40
1583 45 c. "The Litta Madonna" (Da Vinci) .. 65 45
1584 65 c. "The Virgin and Child under the Apple Tree" (Lucas Cranach the Elder) 90 90
1585 75 c. "Madonna and Child" (Master of the Female Half-lengths) .. .. 1·00 1·00
1586 $1.20, "An Allegory of the Church" (Alessandro Allori) .. .. .. 1·60 2·00
1587 $5 "Madonna and Child wreathed with Flowers" (Jacob Jordaens) .. .. 3·75 4·50
1580/7 .. .. *Set of* 8 8·75 9·00
MS1588 Two sheets. (a) 123×88 mm. $6 "Madonna and Child with Commissioners" (detail) (Palma Vecchio). (b) 88×123 mm. $6 "The Virgin Enthroned with Child" (detail) (Bohemian master) .. .. *Set of* 2 *sheets* 9·50 11·00

1995 (24 Feb). *"Hong Kong '94" International Stamp Exhibition* (*1st issue*). *Nos.* 1890/1 *of Antigua optd with T* **111**.

1589 40 c. Hong Kong 1981 $1 Fish stamp and fishing boats, Shau Kei Wan .. 80 80
a. Horiz pair. Nos. 1589/90 .. .. 1·60 1·60
1590 40 c. Antigua 1990 $2 Reef Fish stamp and fishing boats, Shau Kei Wan .. 80 80

1995 (24 Feb). *"Hong Kong '94" International Stamp Exhibition* (*2nd issue*). *Nos.* 1892/7 *of Antigua optd with T* **111**.

1591 40 c. Terracotta warriors 30 30
a. Sheetlet. Nos. 1591/6 .. .. 1·60
1592 40 c. Cavalryman and horse 30 30
1593 40 c. Warriors in armour 30 30
1594 40 c. Painted bronze chariot and team .. 30 30
1595 40 c. Pekingese dog 30 30
1596 40 c. Warriors with horses 30 30
1591/6 .. .. *Set of* 6 1·60 1·60

1995 (24 Feb). *Centenary of International Olympic Committee. Nos.* 1990/2 *of Antigua optd with T* **114**, *but with lines spaced.*

1597 50 c. Edwin Moses (U.S.A.) (400 metres hurdles), 1984 .. .. .. 75 75
1598 $1.50, Steffi Graf (Germany) (tennis), 1988 .. .. 3·00 3·00
MS1599 79×110 mm. $6 Johann Olav Koss (Norway) (500, 1500 and 10,000 metre speed skating), 1994 .. .. 4·50 5·00

1995 (4 Apr). *Dogs of the World. Chinese New Year* ("*Year of the Dog*"). *Nos.* 1923/47 *of Antigua optd with T* **111**.

1600 50 c. West Highland White Terrier .. 50 50
a. Sheetlet. Nos. 1600/11 .. .. 5·50
1601 50 c. Beagle 50 50
1602 50 c. Scottish Terrier 50 50
1603 50 c. Pekingese 50 50
1604 50 c. Dachshund 50 50
1605 50 c. Yorkshire Terrier 50 50
1606 50 c. Pomeranian 50 50
1607 50 c. Poodle 50 50
1608 50 c. Shetland Sheepdog 50 50
1609 50 c. Pug 50 50
1610 50 c. Shih Tzu 50 50
1611 50 c. Chihuahua 50 50
1612 50 c. Mastiff 50 50
a. Sheetlet. Nos. 1612/23 .. .. 5·50
1613 50 c. Border Collie 50 50
1614 50 c. Samoyed 50 50
1615 50 c. Airedale Terrier 50 50
1616 50 c. English Setter 50 50
1617 50 c. Rough Collie 50 50
1618 50 c. Newfoundland 50 50
1619 50 c. Weimarana 50 50
1620 50 c. English Springer Spaniel 50 50
1621 50 c. Dalmatian 50 50
1622 50 c. Boxer 50 50
1623 50 c. Old English Sheepdog 50 50
1600/23 .. .. *Set of* 24 11·00 11·00
MS1624 Two sheets, each 93×58 mm. (a) $6 Welsh Corgi. (b) $6 Labrador Retriever *Set of* 2 *sheets* 12·00 12·00

1995 (18 May). *Centenary of First English Cricket Tour to the West Indies* (1995). *Nos.* 1994/7 *of Antigua optd with T* **114**, *but with lines spaced.*

1625 35 c. Mike Atherton (England) and Wisden Trophy 60 45
1626 75 c. Viv Richards (West Indies) (*vert*) .. 1·25 1·25
1627 $1.20, Richie Richardson (West Indies) and Wisden Trophy .. .. .. 1·50 1·75
1625/7 .. .. *Set of* 3 3·00 3·00
MS1628 80×100 mm. $3 English team, 1895 (black and grey-brown) .. .. .. 3·25 3·75

1995 (18 May–12 July). *"Philakorea '94" International Stamp Exhibition* (*1st issue*). *Nos.* 1998/2009 *of Antigua optd with T* **114**, *but with lines spaced* (*Nos.* 1629 *and* 1638/40) *or T* **111** (*others*).

1629 40 c. Entrance bridge, Songgwangsa Temple (12 July) 60 60
1630 75 c. Long-necked Bottle 90 90
a. Sheetlet. Nos. 1630/7 .. .. 6·50
1631 75 c. Punch'ong ware jar with floral decoration 90 90
1632 75 c. Punch'ong ware jar with blue dragon pattern 90 90
1633 75 c. Ewer in shape of bamboo shoot .. 90 90
1634 75 c. Punch'ong ware green jar 90 90
1635 75 c. Pear-shaped bottle 90 90
1636 75 c. Porcelain jar with brown dragon pattern 90 90
1637 75 c. Porcelain jar with floral pattern .. 90 90
1638 90 c. Song-op Folk Village, Cheju (12 July) 90 90
1639 $3 Port Sogwipo (12 July) .. .. 2·50 2·50
1629/39 .. .. *Set of* 11 9·00 9·00
MS1640 104×71 mm. $4 Ox herder playing flute (*vert*) .. .. 2·50 3·00

1995 (18 May). *First Recipients of Order of the Caribbean Community. Nos.* 2046/8 *of Antigua optd with T* **111**.

1641 65 c. Sir Shridath Ramphal 45 50
1642 90 c. William Demas 55 60
1643 $1.20, Derek Walcott 75 85
1641/3 .. .. *Set of* 3 1·60 1·75

1995 (12 July–29 Sept). *25th Anniv of First Moon Landing. Nos.* 1977/89 *of Antigua optd with T* **114**, *but with lines spaced* (*vertically reading upward on Nos.* 1644/55).

1644 $1.50, Edwin Aldrin (astronaut) .. 1·50 1·50
a. Sheetlet. Nos. 1644/49 .. .. 8·00
1645 $1.50, First lunar footprint .. .. 1·50 1·50
1646 $1.50, Neil Armstrong (astronaut) .. 1·50 1·50
1647 $1.50, Aldrin stepping onto Moon .. 1·50 1·50
1648 $1.50, Aldrin and equipment .. .. 1·50 1·50
1649 $1.50, Aldrin and U.S.A. flag .. .. 1·50 1·50
1650 $1.50, Aldrin at Tranquility Base .. 1·50 1·50
a. Sheetlet. Nos. 1650/55 .. .. 8·00
1651 $1.50, Moon plaque .. .. .. 1·50 1·50
1652 $1.50, *Eagle* leaving Moon .. .. 1·50 1·50
1653 $1.50, Command module in lunar orbit .. 1·50 1·50
1654 $1.50, First day cover of U.S.A. 1969 10 c. First Man on Moon stamp .. .. 1·50 1·50
1655 $1.50, Pres. Nixon and astronauts .. 1·50 1·50
1644/55 .. .. *Set of* 12 16·00 16·00
MS1656 72×102 mm. $6 Armstrong and Aldrin with postal official (29 Sept) .. .. 6·50 7·00

1995 (12 July). *International Year of the Family. No.* 1993 *of Antigua optd with T* **114**, *but with lines spaced.*

1657 90 c. Antiguan family 80 80

995 (29 Sept). *50th Anniv of D-Day. Nos.* 2010/13 *of Antigua optd as T* **113**, *but with lines spaced.*
558 40 c. Short S.25 Sunderland flying boat .. 80 65
559 $2 Lockheed P-38 Lightning fighters attacking train .. .. .. 2·50 2·50
560 $3 Martin B-26 Marauder bombers .. 2·75 3·00
558/60 .. .. *Set of* 3 5·50 5·50
IS1661 108×78 mm. $6 Hawker Typhoon fighter bomber .. .. 6·00 7·00

122 Queen Elizabeth the Queen Mother (90th birthday)

(Des G. Vasarhelyi. Litho B.D.T.)

995 (13–27 Nov). *Anniversaries. T* **122** *and similar multi-coloured designs. P* 13.
662 $7.50, Type **122** (20 Nov) .. .. 6·50 6·50
663 $8 German bombers over St. Paul's Cathedral, London (*horiz*) (50th anniv of end of Second World War) .. .. 7·00 7·00
664 $8 New York skyline with U.N. and national flags (*horiz*) (50th anniv of United Nations) (27 Nov) .. .. 6·50 6·50
662/4 .. .. *Set of* 3 18·00 18·00

HURRICANE RELIEF
+ $1
(**123**)

BARBUDA
MAIL
(**124**)

995 (13–27 Nov). *Hurricane Relief. Nos.* 1662/4 *surch with T* **123** *in silver.*
665 $7.50 + $1 Type **122** (90th birthday) (20 Nov) .. .. 5·00 5·50
666 $8 + $1 German bombers over St. Paul's Cathedral, London (*horiz*) (50th anniv of end of Second World War) .. .. 5·00 5·50
667 $8 + $1 New York skyline with U.N. and national flags (*horiz*) (50th anniv of United Nations) (27 Nov) .. .. 5·00 5·50
665/7 .. .. *Set of* 3 13·50 15·00

996 (22 Jan). *Marine Life. Nos.* 1967/76 *of Antigua optd as T* **114**, *but with lines spaced.*
668 50 c. Bottlenose Dolphin 50 50
a. Sheetlet. Nos. 1668/76 .. .. 4·00
669 50 c. Killer Whale 50 50
670 50 c. Spinner Dolphin 50 50
671 50 c. Oceanic Sunfish 50 50
672 50 c. Caribbean Reef Shark and Short Fin Pilot Whale 50 50
673 50 c. Copper-banded Butterflyfish .. 50 50
674 50 c. Mosaic Moray 50 50
675 50 c. Clown Triggerfish 50 50
676 50 c. Red Lobster 50 50
668/76 .. .. *Set of* 9 4·00 4·00
IS1677 Two sheets, each 106×76 mm. (a) $6 Seahorse. (b) $6 Swordfish ("Blue Marlin") (*horiz*) .. .. *Set of* 2 *sheets* 9·00 10·00

996 (22 Jan). *Christmas. Religious Paintings. Nos.* 2267/73 *of Antigua optd with T* **111**.
678 15 c. "Rest on the Flight into Egypt" (Paolo Veronese) 40 30
679 35 c. "Madonna and Child" (Van Dyck) .. 50 35
680 65 c. "Sacred Conversation Piece" (Veronese) 70 55
681 75 c. "Vision of St. Anthony" (Van Dyck) 80 60
682 90 c. "Virgin and Child" (Van Eyck) .. 90 75
683 $6 "The Immaculate Conception" (Giovanni Tiepolo) .. .. .. 3·75 4·50
678/83 .. .. *Set of* 5 6·25 6·25
IS1684 Two sheets. (a) 101×127 mm. $5 "Christ appearing to his Mother" (detail) (Van der Weyden). (b) 127×101 mm. $6 "The Infant Jesus and the Young St. John" (Murillo) *Set of* 2 *sheets* 8·50 10·00

996 (14 Feb). *Stars of Country and Western Music. Nos.* 2014/38 *of Antigua optd with T* **114**, *but with lines spaced.*
685 75 c. Travis Tritt 50 50
a. Sheetlet. Nos. 1685/92 .. .. 3·50
686 75 c. Dwight Yoakam 50 50
687 75 c. Billy Ray Cyrus 50 50
688 75 c. Alan Jackson 50 50
689 75 c. Garth Brooks 50 50
690 75 c. Vince Gill 50 50
691 75 c. Clint Black 50 50
692 75 c. Eddie Rabbit 50 50
693 75 c. Patsy Cline 50 50
a. Sheetlet. Nos. 1693/1700 .. .. 3·50
694 75 c. Tanya Tucker 50 50
695 75 c. Dolly Parton 50 50
696 75 c. Anne Murray 50 50
697 75 c. Tammy Wynette 50 50
698 75 c. Loretta Lynn 50 50
1699 75 c. Reba McEntire 50 50
1700 75 c. Skeeter Davis 50 50
1701 75 c. Hank Snow 50 50
a. Sheetlet. Nos. 1701/8 .. .. 3·50
1702 75 c. Gene Autry 50 50
1703 75 c. Jimmie Rodgers 50 50
1704 75 c. Ernest Tubb 50 50
1705 75 c. Eddy Arnold 50 50
1706 75 c. Willie Nelson 50 50
1707 75 c. Johnny Cash 50 50
1708 75 c. George Jones 50 50
1685/1708 .. .. .. *Set of* 24 11·00 11·00
MS1709 Three sheets. (a) 100×70 mm. $6 Hank Williams Jr. (b) 100×70 mm. $6 Hank Williams Sr. (c) 70×100 mm. $6 Kitty Wells (*horiz*) *Set of* 3 *sheets* 12·00 12·00

1996 (14 Feb). *Birds. Nos.* 2067/81 *of Antigua optd with T* **124**.
1710 15 c. Magnificent Frigate Bird 10 10
1711 25 c. Blue-hooded Euphonia 10 10
1712 35 c. Eastern Meadowlark 15 20
1713 40 c. Red-billed Tropic Bird 15 20
1714 45 c. Greater Flamingo 20 25
1715 60 c. Yellow-faced Grassquit 25 30
1716 65 c. Yellow-billed Cuckoo 30 35
1717 70 c. Purple-throated Carib 30 35
1718 75 c. Bananaquit 35 40
1719 90 c. Painted Bunting 40 45
1720 $1.20, Red-legged Honeycreeper .. 50 55
1721 $2 Northern Jacana 80 90
1722 $5 Greater Antillean Bullfinch .. 2·10 2·25
1723 $10 Caribbean Elaenia .. .. .. 4·25 4·50
1724 $20 Brown Trembler .. .. .. 8·75 9·00
1710/24 .. .. *Set of* 15 18·00 19·00

1996 (2 Apr). *Birds. Nos.* 2050, 2052, 2054 *and* 2056/7 *of Antigua optd with T* **111**.
1725 15 c. Bridled Quail Dove 40 30
1726 40 c. Purple-throated Carib (*vert*) .. 60 40
1727 $1 Broad-winged Hawk (*vert*) .. .. 1·25 1·00
1728 $4 Yellow Warbler .. .. .. 2·50 3·00
1725/8 .. .. *Set of* 4 4·25 4·25
MS1729 Two sheets. (a) 70×100 mm. $6 Female Magnificent Frigate Bird (*vert*). (b) 100×70 mm. $6 Black-billed Whistling Duck ducklings *Set of* 2 *sheets* 8·50 8·50

1996 (13 June). *Prehistoric Animals. Nos.* 2082/100 *of Antigua optd with T* **114**, *but with lines spaced (Nos.* 1730/2 *and* 1745/7) *or T* **111** *(others).*
1730 15 c. Head of Pachycephalosaurus .. 30 30
1731 20 c. Head of Afrovenator 30 30
1732 65 c. Centrosaurus 45 45
1733 75 c. Kronosaurus (*horiz*) 50 50
a. Sheetlet. Nos. 1733/44 .. .. 5·50
1734 75 c. Ichthyosaurus (*horiz*) 50 50
1735 75 c. Plesiosaurus (*horiz*) 50 50
1736 75 c. Archelon (*horiz*) 50 50
1737 75 c. Pair of Tyrannosaurus (*horiz*) .. 50 50
1738 75 c. Tyrannosaurus (*horiz*) 50 50
1739 75 c. Parasaurolophus (*horiz*) 50 50
1740 75 c. Pair of Parasaurolophus (*horiz*) .. 50 50
1741 75 c. Oviraptor (*horiz*) 50 50
1742 75 c. Protoceratops with eggs (*horiz*) .. 50 50
1743 75 c. Pteranodon and Protoceratops (*horiz*) 50 50
1744 75 c. Pair of Protoceratops (*horiz*) .. 50 50
1745 90 c. Pentaceratops drinking 60 60
1746 $1.20, Head of Tarbosaurus 75 75
1747 $5 Head of Styracosaurus .. .. 2·75 2·75
1730/47 .. .. *Set of* 18 10·00 10·00
MS1748 Two sheets, each 101×70 mm. (a) $6 Head of Corythosaurus (*horiz*) (b) $6 Head of Carnotaurus (*horiz*) .. .. *Set of* 2 *sheets* 8·50 9·00

1996 (16 July). *Olympic Games, Atlanta. Previous Gold Medal Winners. Nos.* 2101/7 *of Antigua optd diagonally with T* **116**.
1749 15 c. Al Oerter (U.S.A.) (discus – 1956, 1960, 1964, 1968) 25 25
1750 20 c. Greg Louganis (U.S.A.) (diving – 1984, 1988) 25 25
1751 65 c. Naim Suleymanoglu (Turkey) (weightlifting – 1988) 55 55
1752 90 c. Louise Ritter (U.S.A.) (high jump – 1988) 70 70
1753 $1.20, Nadia Comaneci (Rumania) (gymnastics – 1976) 85 85
1754 $5 Olga Boldarenko (Russia) (10,000 metres – 1988) .. .. .. 2·50 3·00
1749/54 .. .. *Set of* 6 4·50 5·00
MS1755 Two sheets, 106×76 mm. (a) $6 United States crew (eight-oared shell – 1964). (b) $6 Lutz Hessilch (Germany) (cycling – 1988) (*vert*). *Set of* 2 *sheets* 7·50 8·00

1996 (10 Sept). *18th World Scout Jamboree, Netherlands. Tents. Nos.* 2203/9 *of Antigua optd with T* **116** *diagonally.*
1756 $1.20, The Explorer Tent .. .. 1·00 1·00
a. Horiz strip of 3. Nos. 1756/8 .. 2·75
1757 $1.20, Camper tent .. .. .. 1·00 1·00
1758 $1.20, Wall tent .. .. .. 1·00 1·00
1759 $1.20, Trail tent .. .. .. 1·00 1·00
a. Horiz strip of 3. Nos. 1759/61 .. 2·75
1760 $1.20, Miner's tent .. .. .. 1·00 1·00
1761 $1.20, Voyager tent .. .. .. 1·00 1·00
1756/61 .. .. *Set of* 6 5·50 5·50
MS1762 Two sheets, each 76×106 mm. (a) $6 Scout and camp fire. (b) $6 Scout with back pack (*vert*) .. .. *Set of* 2 *sheets* 7·50 8·00

1996 (25 Oct). *Centenary of Nobel Prize Trust Fund. Nos.* 2226/44 *of Antigua optd with T* **120**.
1763 $1 Dag Hammarskjold (1961 Peace) .. 60 60
a. Sheetlet. Nos. 1763/71 .. .. 4·75
1764 $1 Georg Wittig (1979 Chemistry) .. 60 60
1765 $1 Wilhelm Ostwold (1909 Chemistry) .. 60 60
1766 $1 Robert Koch (1905 Medicine) .. 60 60
1767 $1 Karl Ziegler (1963 Chemistry) .. 60 60
1768 $1 Alexander Fleming (1945 Medicine) .. 60 60
1769 $1 Hermann Staudinger (1953 Chemistry) 60 60
1770 $1 Manfred Eigen (1967 Chemistry) .. 60 60
1771 $1 Arno Penzias (1978 Physics) 60 60
1772 $1 Shumal Agnon (1966 Literature) .. 60 60
a. Sheetlet. Nos. 1772/80 .. .. 4·75
1773 $1 Rudyard Kipling (1907 Literature) .. 60 60
1774 $1 Aleksandr Solzhenitsyn (1970 Literature) 60 60
1775 $1 Jack Steinburger (1988 Physics) .. 60 60
1776 $1 Andrei Sakharov (1975 Peace) .. 60 60
1777 $1 Otto Stern (1943 Physics) 60 60
1778 $1 John Steinbeck (1962 Literature) .. 60 60
1779 $1 Nadine Gordimer (1991 Literature) .. 60 60
1780 $1 William Faulkner (1949 Literature) .. 60 60
1763/80 .. .. *Set of* 18 9·50 9·50
MS1781 Two sheets, each 100×70 mm. (a) $6 Elie Wiesel (1986 Peace) (*vert*). (b) $6 Dalai Lama (1989 Peace) (*vert*) .. *Set of* 2 *sheets* 8·00 8·50

1996 (14 Nov). *70th Birthday of Queen Elizabeth II. Nos.* 2355/8 *of Antigua optd with T* **111**.
1782 $2 Queen Elizabeth II in blue dress .. 1·10 1·10
a. Strip of 3. Nos. 1782/4 .. .. 3·00
1783 $2 With bouquet .. .. 1·10 1·10
1784 $2 In Garter robes .. .. .. 1·10 1·10
1782/4 .. .. *Set of* 3 3·00 3·00
MS1785 96×111 mm. $6 Wearing white dress 3·50 3·75

1997 (28 Jan). *Christmas. Religious Paintings by Filippo Lippi. Nos.* 2377/83 *of Antigua optd with T* **111**.
1786 60 c. "Madonna Enthroned" 35 35
1787 90 c. "Adoration of the Child and Saints" .. 55 55
1788 $1 "The Annunciation" 60 60
1789 $1.20, "Birth of the Virgin" 75 75
1790 $1.60, "Adoration of the Child" .. 90 90
1791 $1.75, "Madonna and Child" .. .. 1·00 1·00
1786/91 .. .. *Set of* 6 3·75 3·75
MS1792 Two sheets, each 76×106 mm. (a) $6 "Madonna and Child" (*different*). (b) $6 "The Circumcision" .. .. .. *Set of* 2 *sheets* 5·50 5·75

1997 (24 Feb). *50th Anniv of Food and Agriculture Organization. Nos.* 2121/4 *of Antigua optd with T* **114**, *but with lines spaced.*
1793 75 c. Woman buying produce from market 50 50
a. Horiz strip of 3. Nos. 1793/5 .. 1·60
1794 90 c. Women shopping 60 60
1795 $1.20, Women talking 70 70
1793/5 .. .. *Set of* 3 1·75 1·90
MS1796 100×70 mm. $6 Tractor .. .. 3·25 3·50

1997 (24 Feb). *90th Anniv of Rotary International* (1995). *Nos.* 2125/6 *of Antigua optd with T* **114**, *but with lines spaced.*
1797 $5 Beach and rotary emblem .. .. 2·75 3·00
MS1798 74×104 mm. $6 National flag and emblem .. .. 3·25 3·50

1997 (4 Apr). *50th Anniv of End of Second World War in Europe and the Pacific. Nos.* 2108/16 *and* 2132/8 *of Antigua optd with T* **114** *but with lines spaced (No.* **MS**1813b) *or with T* **111** *(others).*
1799 $1.20, Map of Berlin showing Russian advance 55 60
a. Sheetlet. Nos. 1799/1806 .. .. 4·25
1800 $1.20, Russian tank and infantry .. 55 60
1801 $1.20, Street fighting in Berlin 55 60
1802 $1.20, German tank exploding 55 60
1803 $1.20, Russian air raid 55 60
1804 $1.20, German troops surrendering .. 55 60
1805 $1.20, Hoisting the Soviet flag on the Reichstag 55 60
1806 $1.20, Captured German standards .. 55 60
1807 $1.20, Gen. Chiang Kai-shek and Chinese guerrillas 55 60
a. Sheetlet. Nos. 1807/12 .. .. 4·25
1808 $1.20, Gen. Douglas MacArthur and beach landing 55 60
1809 $1.20, Gen. Claire Chennault and U.S. fighter aircraft 55 60
1810 $1.20, Brig. Orde Wingate and supply drop 55 60
1811 $1.20, Gen. Joseph Stilwell and U.S. supply plane 55 60
1812 $1.20, Field-Marshal Bill Slim and loading cow onto plane 55 60
1799/1812 .. .. *Set of* 14 8·50 8·75
MS1813 Two sheets, each 100×70 mm. (a) $3 Admiral Nimitz and aircraft carrier. (b) $6 Gen. Konev (*vert*) .. .. .. *Set of* 2 *sheets* 4·25 4·50

1997 (25 Apr). *95th Birthday of Queen Elizabeth the Queen Mother. Nos.* 2127/31 *of Antigua optd with T* **111**.
1814 $1.50, orange-brown, pale brown and black 70 75
a. Sheetlet. Nos. 1814/17×2 .. .. 5·50
1815 $1.50, multicoloured 70 75
1816 $1.50, multicoloured 70 75
1817 $1.50, multicoloured 70 75
1814/17 .. .. *Set of* 4 2·75 3·00
MS1818 102×27 mm. $6 multicoloured .. 2·75 3·00

1997 (25 Apr). *50th Anniv of United Nations. Nos.* 2117/20 *optd with T* **114** *but with lines spaced.*
1819 75 c. Signatures and Earl of Halifax .. 35 40
a. Horiz strip of 3. Nos. 1819/21 .. 1·25
1820 90 c. Virginia Gildersleeve 40 45
1821 $1.20, Harold Stassen 55 60
1819/21 .. .. *Set of* 3 1·25 1·40
MS1822 100×70 mm. $6 Pres. Franklin D. Roosevelt .. .. 3·25 3·50

1997 (30 May). *Trains of the World. Nos.* 2210/25 *of Antigua optd with T* **114**, *but with lines spaced* (*No.* **MS**1838) *or with T* **111** (*others*).
1823 35 c. Trans-Gabon diesel-electric train .. 15 20
1824 65 c. Canadian Pacific diesel-electric train 30 35
1825 75 c. Santa Fe Railway diesel-electric locomotive, U.S.A. 35 40
1826 90 c. High Speed Train, Great Britain .. 40 45
1827 $1.20, TGV express train, France .. 55 60
1828 $1.20, Diesel-electric locomotive, Australia 55 60
a. Sheetlet. Nos. 1828/36 .. .. 5·00
1829 $1.20 Pendolino "ETR 450" electric train, Italy 55 60
1830 $1.20, Diesel-electric locomotive, Thailand 55 60
1831 $1.20, Pennsylvania Railroad steam locomotive, U.S.A. 55 60
1832 $1.20, Beyer-Garratt steam locomotive, East African Railways 55 60
1833 $1.20, Natal Govt steam locomotive .. 55 60
1834 $1.20, Rail gun, American Civil War .. 55 60
1835 $1.20, Locomotive *Lion* (red livery), Great Britain 55 60
1836 $1.20, William Hedley's *Puffing Billy* (green livery), Great Britain .. 55 60
1837 $6 Amtrak high-speed diesel locomotive, U.S.A. .. .. 2·75 3·00
1823/37 .. .. *Set of* 15 9·50 10·50
MS1838 Two sheets, each 110×80 mm. (a) $6 Locomotive *Iron Rooster*, China (*vert*). (b) $6 "Indian-Pacific" diesel-electric locomotive, Australia (*vert*) *Set of* 2 *sheets* 5·50 5·75

Golden Wedding of H.M. Queen Elizabeth II and H.R.H. Prince Phillip 1947 - 1997

(125)

1997 (25 July). *Golden Wedding of Queen Elizabeth II and Prince Philip* (1*st issue*). *Nos.* 1662/3 *optd with T* **125** *in gold.*
1839 $7.50, Type **122** .. .. 3·50 3·75
1840 $8 German bombers over St. Paul's Cathedral, London (*horiz*) .. .. 3·75 4·00

1997 (16 Sept). *Fungi. Nos.* 2274/82 *of Antigua optd with T* **114**, *but with lines spaced.*
1841 75 c. *Hygrophoropsis aurantiaca* 35 40
a. Horiz strip of 4. Nos. 1841/4 .. 1·40
1842 75 c. *Hygrophorus bakerensis* 35 40
1843 75 c. *Hygrophorus conicus* 35 40
1844 75 c. *Hygrophorus miniatus* (*Hygrocybe miniata*) 35 40
1845 75 c. *Suillus brevipes* 35 40
a. Horiz strip of 4. Nos. 1845/8 .. 1·40
1846 75 c. *Suillus luteus* 35 40
1847 75 c. *Suillus granulatus* 35 40
1848 75 c. *Suillus caerulescens* 35 40
1841/8 .. .. *Set of* 8 2·75 3·25
MS1849 Two sheets, each 106×76 mm. (a) $6 *Conocybe filaris*. (b) $6 *Hygrocybe flavescens* *Set of* 2 *sheets* 5·50 5·75

1997 (16 Sept). *Birds. Nos.* 2140/64 *of Antigua optd with T* **114** *with lines spaced* (*Nos.* 1850/73) *or T* **111** (*No.* **MS**1874).
1850 75 c. Purple-throated Carib 35 40
a. Sheetlet. Nos. 1850/61 .. .. 4·25
1851 75 c. Antillean Crested Hummingbird .. 35 40
1852 75 c. Bananaquit 35 40
1853 75 c. Mangrove Cuckoo 35 40
1854 75 c. Troupial 35 40
1855 75 c. Green-throated Carib 35 40
1856 75 c. Yellow Warbler 35 40
1857 75 c. Blue-hooded Euphonia 35 40
1858 75 c. Scaly-breasted Thrasher 35 40
1859 75 c. Burrowing Owl 35 40
1860 75 c. Carib Grackle 35 40
1861 75 c. Adelaide's Warbler 35 40
1862 75 c. Ring-necked Duck 35 40
a. Sheetlet. Nos. 1862/73 .. .. 4·25
1863 75 c. Ruddy Duck 35 40
1864 75 c. Green-winged Teal 35 40
1865 75 c. Wood Duck 35 40
1866 75 c. Hooded Merganser 35 40
1867 75 c. Lesser Scaup 35 40
1868 75 c. Black-billed Whistling Duck .. 35 40
1869 75 c. Fulvous Whistling Duck 35 40
1870 75 c. Bahama Pintail 35 40
1871 75 c. Shoveler 35 40
1872 75 c. Masked Duck 35 40
1873 75 c. American Wigeon 35 40
1850/73 .. .. *Set of* 24 8·50 9·50
MS1874 Two sheets, each 104×74 mm. (a) $6 Head of Purple Gallinule. (b) $6 Heads of Blue-winged Teals .. .. *Set of* 2 *sheets* 5·50 5·75

1997 (3 Nov). *Sailing Ships. Nos.* 2283/301 *of Antigua optd with T* **116** *diagonally.*
1875 15 c. H.M.S. *Resolution* (Cook) 10 10
1876 25 c. *Mayflower* (Pilgrim Fathers) .. 10 15
1877 45 c. *Santa Maria* (Columbus) 20 25
1878 75 c. *Aemilia* (Dutch galleon) 35 40
1879 75 c. *Soverign of the Seas* (English galleon) 35 40
1880 90 c. H.M.S. *Victory* (ship of the line, 1765) 40 45
1881 $1.20, As No. 1878 .. .. .. 55 60
a. Sheetlet. Nos. 1881/6 .. .. 3·25
1882 $1.20, As No. 1879 .. .. .. 55 60
1883 $1.20, *Royal Louis* (French galleon) .. 55 60
1884 $1.20, H.M.S. *Royal George* (ship of the line) 55 60
1885 $1.20, *Le Protecteur* (French frigate) .. 55 60
1886 $1.20, As No. 1880 .. .. .. 55 60
1887 $1.50, As No. 1877 .. .. .. 70 75
a. Sheetlet. Nos. 1887/92 .. .. 4·25
1888 $1.50, *Vitoria* (Magellan) 70 75
1889 $1.50, *Golden Hind* (Drake) 70 75
1890 $1.50, As No. 1876 .. .. .. 70 75
1891 $1.50, *Griffin* (La Salle) 70 75
1892 $1.50, As No. 1875 .. .. .. 70 75
1875/92 .. .. *Set of* 18 9·00 9·25
MS1893 (a) 102×72 mm. $6 U.S.S. *Constitution* (frigate). (b) 98×67 mm. $6 *Grande Hermine* (Cartier) .. .. .. *Set of* 2 *sheets* 5·50 5·75

1997 (3 Nov). *Golden Wedding of Queen Elizabeth and Prince Philip* (2*nd issue*). *Nos.* 2474/80 *of Antigua optd with T* **111**.
1894 $1 Queen Elizabeth II 45 50
a. Sheetlet. Nos. 1894/9 .. .. 2·75
1895 $1 Royal coat of arms 45 50
1896 $1 Queen Elizabeth and Prince Philip at reception 45 50
1897 $1 Queen Elizabeth and Prince Philip in landau 45 50
1898 $1 Balmoral 45 50
1899 $1 Prince Philip 45 50
1894/9 .. .. *Set of* 6 2·75 3·00
MS1900 100×71 mm. $6 Queen Elizabeth with Prince Philip in naval uniform .. .. 2·75 3·00

1997 (24 Dec). *Christmas. Religious Paintings. Nos.* 2566/72 *of Antigua optd with T* **116** *diagonally.*
1901 15 c. "The Angel leaving Tobias and his Family" (Rembrandt) 10 10
1902 25 c. "The Resurrection" (Martin Knoller) 10 15
1903 60 c. "Astronomy" (Raphael) 25 30
1904 75 c. "Music-making Angel" (Melozzo da Forli) 35 40
1905 90 c. "Amor" (Parmigianino) 40 45
1906 $1.20, "Madonna and Child with Saints" (Rosso Fiorentino) 50 55
1901/6 .. .. *Set of* 6 1·60 1·75
MS1907 Two sheets, each 105×96 mm. (a) $6 "The Wedding of Tobias" (Gianantonio and Francesco Guardi) (*horiz*). (b) $6 "The Portinari Altarpiece" (Hugo van der Goes) (*horiz*) *Set of* 2 *sheets* 5·00 5·25

1998 (16 Feb). *Sea Birds. Nos.* 2325/33 *of Antigua optd with T* **111**.
1908 75 c. Black Skimmer 35 40
a. Vert strip of 4. Nos. 1908/11 .. 1·40
1909 75 c. Black-capped Petrel 35 40
1910 75 c. Sooty Tern 35 40
1911 75 c. Royal Tern 35 40
1912 75 c. Pomarine Skua ("Pomarine Jaegger") 35 40
a. Vert strip of 4. Nos. 1912/15 .. 1·40
1913 75 c. White-tailed Tropic Bird 35 40
1914 75 c. Northern Gannet 35 40
1915 75 c. Laughing Gull 35 40
1908/15 .. .. *Set of* 8 2·75 3·00
MS1916 Two sheets, each 105×75 mm. (a) $5 Great Frigate Bird. (b) $6 Brown Pelican *Set of* 2 *sheets* 4·75 5·00

STAMP BOOKLETS

1977 (20 Dec). *Silver Jubilee. No.* SB2 *of Antigua with cover optd* "BARBUDA".
SB1 $8 booklet containing pane of 6 (No. 329a) and pane of 1 (No. 330a) .. .. 7·00

1978 (12 Oct). 25th *Anniv of Coronation. No.* SB3 *of Antigua with cover optd* "BARBUDA".
SB2 $7.25, booklet containing pane of 6 (No. 421a) and pane of 1 (No. 423a) .. .. 2·50

1981 (27 July). *Royal Wedding* (1*st issue*). *Cover printed in grey*, 98×63 *mm, showing crown, bells and inscription. Stitched.*
SB3 $26 booklet containing panes of four (Nos. 566b, 568b, 570b) .. .. 7·00
The panes in this booklet each consist of two imperforate-between horizontal pairs.

1981 (12 Oct). *Royal Wedding* (3*rd issue*). *No.* SB4 *of Antigua with cover optd* "BARBUDA" *in silver.*
SB4 $11.50, booklet containing pane of 6 (No. 580a) and pane of 1 (No. 586a) .. .. 5·00

1982 (28 June). *South Atlantic Fund. No.* SB4 *with contents surcharged.*
SB5 $15 booklet containing pane of 6 (No. 617a) and pane of 1 (No. 623a) .. .. 4·75

REDONDA

DEPENDENCY OF ANTIGUA

Appendix

The following stamps were issued in anticipation of commercia and tourist development, philatelic mail being handled by a burea in Antigua. Since at the present time the island is uninhabited, w do not list or stock these items. It is understood that the stamps ar valid for the prepayment of postage in Antigua. Miniature sheet imperforate stamps etc., are excluded from this section.

1979

Antigua 1976 *definitive issue optd* "REDONDA". 3, 5, 10, 25, 35, 5 75 *c.*, $1, $2.50, $5, $10.
Antigua Coronation Anniversary issue optd "REDONDA". 10, 3 50, 90 *c.*, $2.50.
Antigua World Cup Football Championship issue opt "REDONDA". 10, 15 *c.*, $3.
Death Centenary of Sir Rowland Hill. 50, 90 *c.*, $2.50, $3.
International Year of the Child. 25, 50 *c.*, $1, $2.
Christmas. Paintings. 8, 50, 90 *c.*, $3.

1980

Marine Life. 8, 25, 50 *c.*, $4.
75*th Anniv of Rotary International.* 25, 50 *c.*, $1, $2.
Birds of Redonda. 8, 10, 15, 25, 30, 50 *c.*, $1, $2, $5.
Olympic Medal Winners, Lake Placid and Moscow. 8, 25, 50 *c.*, $3
80*th Birthday of Queen Elizabeth the Queen Mother.* 10 *c.*, $2.50.
Christmas. Paintings. 8, 25, 50 *c.*, $4.

1981

Royal Wedding. 25, 55 *c.*, $4.
Christmas. Walt Disney Cartoon Characters. ½, 1, 2, 3, 4, 5, 10 *c* $2.50, $3.
World Cup Football Championship, Spain (1982). 30 *c.* × 50 *c.* × 2, $1 × 2, $2 × 2.

1982

Boy Scout Anniversaries. 8, 25, 50 *c.*, $3, $5.
Butterflies. 8, 30, 50 *c.*, $2.
21*st Birthday of Princess of Wales.* $2, $4.
Birth of Prince William of Wales. Optd on 21*st Birthday of Prince of Wales issue.* $2, $4.
Christmas. Walt Disney's "One Hundred and One Dalmatians". ½ 1, 2, 3, 4, 5, 10 *c.*, $2.50, $3.

1983

Easter. 500*th Birth Anniv of Raphael.* 10, 50, 90 *c.*, $4.
Bicentenary of Manned Flight. 10, 50, 90 *c.*, $2.50.
Christmas. Walt Disney Cartoon Characters. "Deck the Halls". ½ 1, 2, 3, 4, 5, 10 *c.*, $2.50, $3.

1984

Easter. Walt Disney Cartoon Characters. ½, 1, 2, 3, 4, 5, 10 *c.*, $ $4.
Olympic Games, Los Angeles. 10, 50, 90 *c.*, $2.50.
Christmas. 50*th Birthday of Donald Duck.* 45, 60, 90 *c.*, $2, $4.

1985

Birth Bicentenary of John J. Audubon (ornithologist) (1*st issue* 60, 90 *c.*, $1, $3.
Life and Times of Queen Elizabeth the Queen Mother. $1, $1.5 $2.50.
Royal Visit. 45 *c.*, $1, $4.
150*th Birth Anniv of Mark Twain (author).* 25, 50 *c.*, $1.50, $
Birth Bicentenaries of Grimm Brothers (folklorists). Walt Disne Cartoon Characters. 30, 60, 70 *c.*, $4.

1986

Birth Bicentenary of John J. Audubon (ornithologist) (2*nd issue* 90 *c.*, $1, $1.50, $3.
Appearance of Halley's Comet. 5, 15, 55 *c.*, $4.
Centenary of Statue of Liberty (1*st issue*). 20, 25, 30 *c.*, $4.
60*th Birthday of Queen Elizabeth II.* 50, 60 *c.*, $4.
Royal Wedding. 60 *c.*, $1, $4.
Christmas (1*st issue*). *Disney characters in Hans Anderse Stories.* 30, 60, 70 *c.*, $4.
Christmas (2*nd issue*). *"Wind in the Willows" (Kenneth Gra hame).* 25, 50 *c.*, $1.50, $3.

1987

"Capex '87" International Stamp Exhibition, Toronto. Disne characters illustrating Art of Animation. 25, 30, 50, 60, 70 *c.* $1.50, $3, $4.
Birth Centenary of Marc Chagall (artist). 10, 30, 40, 60, 90 *c.*, $ $3, $4.
Centenary of Statue of Liberty (2*nd issue*). 10, 15, 25, 30, 40, 6 70, 90 *c.*, $1, $2, $3, $4.
250*th Death Anniv of Sir Isaac Newton (scientist).* 20 *c.*, $2.50.
750*th Anniv of Berlin.* $1, $4.
Bicentenary of U.S. Constitution. 30 *c.*, $3.
16*th World Scout Jamboree, Australia.* 10 *c.*, $4.

1988

500*th Anniv of Discovery of America by Columbus* (1992) (1*s issue*). 15, 30, 45, 60, 90 *c.*, $1, $2, $3.
"Finlandia '88" International Stamp Exhibition, Helsinki. Dis ney characters in Finnish scenes. 1, 2, 3, 4, 5, 6 *c.*, $5, $6.
Olympic Games, Seoul. 25, 60 *c.*, $1.25, $3.
500*th Birth Anniv of Titian.* 10, 25, 40, 70, 90 *c.*, $2, $3, $4.

1989

20*th Anniv of First Manned Landing on Moon. Disne characters on Moon.* ½, 1, 2, 3, 4, 5 *c.*, $5, $6.
500*th Anniv of Discovery of America by Columbus* (1992) (2*n issue*). *Pre-Columbian Societies.* 15, 45, 45, 50 *c.*, $2, $2, $ $3.
Christmas. Disney characters and Cars of 1950*'s.* 25, 35, 4 60 *c.*, $1, $2, $3, $4.

1990

Christmas. Disney characters and Hollywood Cars. 25, 35, 40 60 *c.*, $1, $2, $4, $5.

1991

Nobel Prize Winners. 5, 15, 25, 40, 50 *c.*, $1, $2, $4.

Ascension

DEPENDENCY OF ST. HELENA

Ascension, first occupied in 1815, was retained as a Royal avy establishment from 1816 until 20 October 1922 when it came a dependency of St. Helena by Letters Patent.

Under Post Office regulations of 1850 (ratings) and 1854 fficers) mail from men of the Royal Navy serving abroad had e postage prepaid in Great Britain stamps, supplies of which ere issued to each ship. Great Britain stamps used on scension before 1860 may have been provided by the naval ficer in charge of the postal service.

The British G.P.O. assumed responsibility for such matters in 860, but failed to send any stamps to the island until January 867.

Until about 1880 naval mail, which made up most early rrespondence, did not have the stamps cancelled until arrival England. The prices quoted for Nos. Z1/3 and Z6 are for amples on cover showing the Great Britain stamps cancelled arrival and an Ascension postmark struck elsewhere on the ont of the envelope.

The use of British stamps ceased in December 1922.

The following postmarks were used on Great Britain stamps om Ascension:

Z 1 Z 2

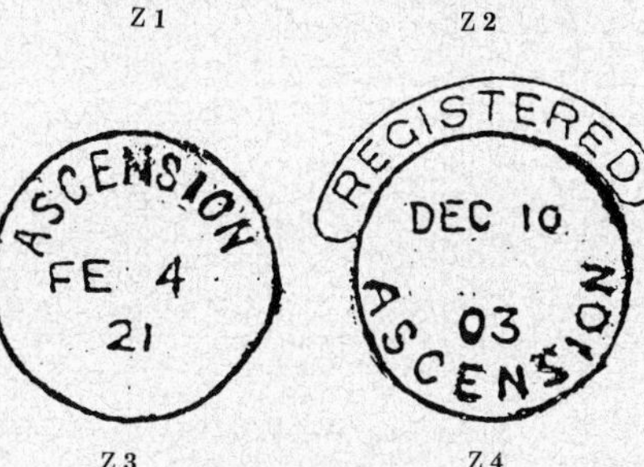

Z 3 Z 4

Z 5

ostmark Type	Approx Period of Use	Diameter	Index Letter
Z 1	1862	20 mm	A
Z 2	1864–1872	20 mm	A
	1872–1878	21½ mm	A
	1879–1889	19½ mm	A
	1891–1894	21½ mm	C
	1894–1902	22 mm	A
	1903–1907	20½ mm	A
	1908–1920	21 mm	A or none
	1909–1920	23 mm	C sideways (1909), none (1910–11), B (1911–20)
Z 3	1920–1922	24 mm	none
Z 4	1897–1903 Registered	23 mm	none
Z 5	1900–1902 Registered	28 mm	C
	1903–1904 Registered	29 mm	A

Postmark Type Z 1 appears in the G.P.O. proof book for 1858, ut the first recorded use is 3 November 1862.

Forged postmarks exist. Those found most frequently are enuine postmarks of the post-1922 period with earlier date ugs fraudulently inserted, namely a 20 mm postmark as Type 2 (because of the shape of the "O" in "ASCENSION" this is ften known as the Square O postmark) and a 24 mm postmark s Type Z 3 but with the index letter A.

tamps of GREAT BRITAIN *cancelled with Types* Z **2/5**. *Prices quoted for Nos.* Z 1/6 *are for complete covers.*

ine-engraved issues.

1	1d. red-brown (1855)	£3000
2	1d. rose-red (1864–79)	*From* £1400
	Plate Nos. 71, 74, 76, 78, 83, 85, 96, 100, 102, 103, 104, 122, 134, 168, 154, 155, 157, 160, 168, 178	

urface-printed issues (1856–1883).

2a	6d. lilac (1856)	
3	6d. lilac (1865) (Plate No. 5)	£3000
4	1s. green (1865) (Plate No. 4)	
5	1s. green (1867) (Plate No. 7)	
6	6d. grey (1874) (Plate Nos. 15, 16)	£2250
6a	6d. on 6d. lilac (1883)	
7	1d. lilac (1881) (16 dots)	30·00

1887–92.

Z 8	½d. vermilion	45·00
Z 9	1½d. purple and green	£180
Z10	2d. green and carmine	95·00
Z11	2½d. purple/*blue*	42·00
Z12	3d. purple/*yellow*	£170
Z13	4d. green and brown	£140
Z14	4½d. green and carmine	£375
Z15	5d. dull purple and blue	£140
Z16	6d. purple/*rose-red*	£120
Z17	9d. purple and blue	£325
Z17a	10d. dull purple and carmine	£400
Z18	1s. green	£325

1900.

Z19	½d. blue-green	45·00
Z20	1s. green and carmine	£350

King Edward VII issues (1902–1911).

Z21	½d. green	29·00
Z22	1d. red	17·00
Z23	1½d. purple and green	95·00
Z24	2d. green and carmine	70·00
Z25	2½d. blue	65·00
Z26	3d. purple/*yellow*	95·00
Z27	4d. green and brown	£300
Z28	4d. orange (1909)	£110
Z29	5d. purple and ultramarine	£110
Z30	6d. purple	£100
Z31	7d. grey-black (1910)	£225
Z32	9d. purple and ultramarine (1910)	£180
Z32a	10d. dull purple and scarlet	£225
Z33	1s. green and carmine	70·00
Z33a	2s. 6d. dull reddish purple (1911)	£550
Z34	5s. carmine	£800
Z35	10s. ultramarine	£1200
Z35a	£1 green	£2500

1911–12. *T* **98/9** *of Great Britain.*

Z36	½d. green (Die A)	60·00
Z37	½d. yellow-green (Die B)	29·00
Z38	1d. scarlet (Die B)	45·00

1912. *T* **101/2** *of Great Britain.*

Z38a	½d. green	45·00
Z38b	1d. scarlet	45·00

1912–22.

Z39	½d. green (1913)	27·00
Z40	1d. scarlet	17·00
Z41	1½d. red-brown	38·00
Z42	2d. orange (Die I)	32·00
Z42a	2d. orange (Die II) (1921)	£250
Z43	2½d. blue	42·00
Z44	3d. violet	55·00
Z45	4d. grey-green (1913)	75·00
Z46	5d. brown (1913)	75·00
Z47	6d. purple (1913)	65·00
Z47a	7d. green (1913)	£250
Z47b	8d. black/*yellow* (1913)	£275
Z48	9d. agate (1913)	£200
Z49	9d. olive-green (1922)	£500
Z50	10d. turquoise-blue (1913)	£200
Z51	1s. bistre (1913)	£100
Z52	2s. 6d. brown (1918)	£750
Z53	5s. rose-red (1919)	£1000

Supplies of some values do not appear to have been sent to the island and known examples originate from maritime or, in the case of high values, philatelic mail.

PRICES FOR STAMPS ON COVER TO 1945	
Nos. 1/34	*from* × 5
Nos. 35/7	*from* × 10
Nos. 38/47	*from* × 6

ASCENSION

(1)

Line through "P" of "POSTAGE" (R. 3/6)

1922 (2 Nov). *Stamps of St. Helena, showing Government House or the Wharf, optd with T* **1** *by D.L.R.*

(*a*) *Wmk Mult Script CA*

1	½d. black and green	3·75	11·00
	w. Wmk reversed	£325	
2	1d. green	3·75	11·00
3	1½d. rose-scarlet	14·00	48·00
4	2d. black and grey	13·00	12·00
	a. Line through "P" of "POSTAGE"	£170	£170
5	3d. bright blue	12·00	15·00
6	8d. black and dull purple	25·00	45·00
7	2s. black and blue/*blue*	80·00	£120
8	3s. black and violet	£120	£160

(*b*) *Wmk Mult Crown CA*

9	1s. black/*green* (R.)	27·00	45·00
1/9	*Set of* 9	£250	£400
1/9 Optd "Specimen"	*Set of* 9	£600	

Nos. 1, 4 and 6/8 are on special printings which were not issued without overprint.

Examples of all values are known showing a forged Ascension postmark dated "MY 24 23".

PLATE FLAWS ON THE 1924–33 ISSUE. Many constant plate varieties exist on both the vignette and duty plates of this issue.

The three major varieties are illustrated and listed below with prices for mint examples. Fine used stamps showing these flaws are worth a considerable premium over the mint prices quoted.

This issue utilised the same vignette plate as the St. Helena 1922–36 set so that these flaws occur there also.

2 Badge of St. Helena

Broken mainmast. Occurs on R.2/1 of all values.

Torn flag. Occurs on R.4/6 of all values except the 5d. Retouched on sheets of ½d. and 1d. printed after 1927.

Cleft rock. Occurs on R.5/1 of all values.

Broken scroll. Occurs on R. 1/4 of 1½d. only

(Typo D.L.R.)

1924 (20 Aug)–**33**. *Wmk Mult Script CA. Chalk-surfaced paper. P* 14.

10	**2**	½d. grey-black and black	3·00	11·00
		a. Broken mainmast	50·00	
		b. Torn flag	70·00	
		c. Cleft rock	45·00	
11		1d. grey-black and deep blue-green	4·75	6·50
		a. Broken mainmast	60·00	
		b. Torn flag	70·00	
		c. Cleft rock	50·00	
11d		1d. grey-black & brt blue-green (1933)	75·00	£325
		da. Broken mainmast	£300	
		dc. Cleft rock	£275	
12		1½d. rose-red	7·00	26·00
		a. Broken mainmast	70·00	
		b. Torn flag	70·00	
		c. Cleft rock	60·00	
		d. Broken scroll	75·00	
13		2d. grey-black and grey	10·00	5·50
		a. Broken mainmast	75·00	
		b. Torn flag	85·00	
		c. Cleft rock	70·00	
14		3d. blue	7·00	11·00
		a. Broken mainmast	70·00	
		b. Torn flag	70·00	
		c. Cleft rock	60·00	
15		4d. grey-black and black/*yellow*	45·00	75·00
		a. Broken mainmast	£170	
		b. Torn flag	£170	
		c. Cleft rock	£150	
15d		5d. purple and olive-green (8.27)	10·00	20·00
		da. Broken mainmast	£110	
		dc. Cleft rock	95·00	
16		6d. grey-black and bright purple	48·00	80·00
		a. Broken mainmast	£225	
		b. Torn flag	£225	
		c. Cleft rock	£190	

17 2 8d. grey-black and bright violet .. 13·00 40·00
a. Broken mainmast .. £110
b. Torn flag .. £110
c. Cleft rock .. 90·00
18 1s. grey-black and brown .. 19·00 45·00
a. Broken mainmast .. £140
b. Torn flag .. £140
c. Cleft rock .. £120
19 2s. grey-black and blue/*blue* .. 55·00 85·00
a. Broken mainmast .. £250
b. Torn flag .. £250
c. Cleft rock .. £200
20 3s. grey-black and black/*blue* .. 80·00 85·00
a. Broken mainmast .. £350
b. Torn flag .. £350
c. Cleft rock .. £325
10/20 .. *Set of* 12 £250 £425
10/20 Optd "Specimen" .. *Set of* 12 £500

3 Georgetown

4 Ascension Island

(Des and recess D.L.R.)

1934 (2 July). *T* **3/4** *and similar designs. Wmk Mult Script CA. P* 14.
21 3 ½d. black and violet .. 90 80
22 4 1d. black and emerald .. 1·75 1·25
23 – 1½d. black and scarlet .. 1·75 2·25
24 4 2d. black and orange .. 1·75 2·50
25 – 3d. black and ultramarine .. 1·75 1·50
26 – 5d. black and blue .. 2·25 3·25
27 4 8d. black and sepia .. 4·25 4·75
28 – 1s. black and carmine .. 18·00 6·50
29 4 2s. 6d. black and bright purple .. 35·00 32·00
30 – 5s. black and brown .. 45·00 55·00
21/30 .. *Set of* 10 95·00 £100
21/30 Perf "Specimen" .. *Set of* 10 £250
Designs: *Horiz*—1½d. The Pier; 3d. Long Beach; 5d. Three Sisters; 1s. Sooty Tern and Wideawake Fair; 5s. Green Mountain.

1935 (6 May). *Silver Jubilee. As Nos.* 91/4 *of Antigua, but ptd by Waterlow. P* 11 × 12.
31 1½d. deep blue and scarlet .. 3·50 6·50
l. Kite and horizontal log .. 90·00
32 2d. ultramarine and grey .. 11·00 22·00
l. Kite and horizontal log .. £170
33 5d. green and indigo .. 17·00 24·00
k. Kite and vertical log .. £200
l. Kite and horizontal log .. £250
34 1s. slate and purple .. 23·00 27·00
l. Kite and horizontal log .. £300
31/4 .. *Set of* 4 48·00 70·00
31/4 Perf "Specimen" .. *Set of* 4 £160
For illustrations of plate varieties see Catalogue Introduction.

1937 (19 May). *Coronation. As Nos.* 95/7 *of Antigua, but printed by D.L.R. P* 14.
35 1d. green .. 50 50
36 2d. orange .. 1·00 40
37 3d. bright blue .. 1·00 50
35/7 .. *Set of* 3 2·25 1·25
35/7 Perf "Specimen" .. *Set of* 3 £130

10 The Pier

Long centre bar to "E" in "GEORGETOWN" (R. 2/3)

"Davit" flaw (R. 5/1) (all ptgs of 1½d. and 2s. 6d.)

(Recess D.L.R.)

1938 (12 May)–**53**. *Horiz designs as King George V issue, but modified and with portrait of King George VI as in T* **10**. *Wmk Mult Script CA. P* 13½.
38 3 ½d. black and violet .. 3·50 1·25
a. Long centre bar to E .. 80·00
b. Perf 13. *Black and bluish violet* (17.5.44) .. 70 1·75
ba. Long centre bar to E .. 32·00
39 – 1d. black and green .. 40·00 7·50
39*a* – 1d. black and yellow-orange (8.7.40) .. 14·00 9·00
b. Perf 13 (5.42) .. 45 60
c. Perf 14 (17.2.49) .. 70 16·00
39*d* – 1d. black and green, *p* 13 (1.6.49) .. 45 40
40 10 1½d. black and vermilion .. 3·50 1·40
a. Davit flaw .. £140
b. Perf 13 (17.5.44) .. 85 80
ba. Davit flaw .. 70·00
c. Perf 14 (17.2.49) .. 2·25 13·00
ca. Davit flaw .. £120
40*d* 1½d. black and rose-carmine, *p* 14 (1.6.49) 55 80
da. Davit flaw .. 65·00
db. *Black and carmine* .. 7·00 5·00
dba. Davit flaw .. £170
e. Perf 13 (25.2.53) .. 45 6·00
ea. Davit flaw .. 60·00
41 – 2d. black and red-orange .. 3·50 1·00
a. Perf 13 (17.5.44) .. 80 40
b. Perf 14 (17.2.49) .. 2·25 35·00
41*c* – 2d. black and scarlet, *p* 14 (1.6.49) .. 75 75
42 – 3d. black and ultramarine .. £100 26·00
42*a* – 3d. black and grey (8.7.40) .. 16·00 90
b. Perf 13 (17.5.44) .. 70 80
42*c* – 4d. black and ultramarine (8.7.40) .. 13·00 3·25
d. Perf 13 (17.5.44) .. 4·50 3·00
43 – 6d. black and blue .. 9·00 1·25
a. Perf 13 (17.5.44) .. 9·00 4·50
44 3 1s. black and sepia .. 14·00 1·50
a. Perf 13 (17.5.44) .. 4·75 2·00
45 10 2s. 6d. black and deep carmine .. 40·00 7·50
a. Frame printed double, once albino £2250
b. Davit flaw .. £500 £225
c. Perf 13 (17.5.44) .. 35·00 32·00
ca. Davit flaw .. £450
46 – 5s. black and yellow-brown .. £110 7·50
a. Perf 13 (17.5.44) .. 48·00 26·00
47 – 10s. black and bright purple .. £110 42·00
a. Perf 13 (17.5.44) .. 65·00 55·00
38/47a .. *Set of* 16 £275 90·00
38/47 Perf "Specimen" .. *Set of* 13 £475
Designs: *Horiz*—1d. (Nos. 39/c), 2d., 4d. Green Mountain; 1d. (No. 39*d*), 6d., 10s. Three Sisters; 3d., 5s. Long Beach.

1946 (21 Oct). *Victory. As Nos.* 110/11 *of Antigua.*
48 2d. red-orange .. 40 50
49 4d. blue .. 40 30
48/9 Perf "Specimen" .. *Set of* 2 £140

1948 (20 Oct). *Royal Silver Wedding. As Nos.* 112/13 *of Antigua.*
50 3d. black .. 50 30
51 10s. bright purple .. 45·00 40·00

1949 (10 Oct). *75th Anniv of Universal Postal Union. As Nos.* 114/17 *of Antigua.*
52 3d. carmine .. 1·40 1·00
53 4d. deep blue .. 3·50 1·10
54 6d. olive .. 3·75 2·50
55 1s. blue-black .. 3·75 1·50
52/5 .. *Set of* 4 11·00 5·50

1953 (2 June). *Coronation. As No.* 120 *of Antigua.*
56 3d. black and grey-black .. 1·00 1·50

15 Water Catchment

(Recess B.W.)

1956 (19 Nov). *T* **15** *and similar horiz designs. Wmk Mult Script CA. P* 13.
57 ½d. black and brown .. 10 30
58 1d. black and magenta .. 1·75 60
59 1½d. black and orange .. 30 60
60 2d. black and carmine-red .. 1·25 50
61 2½d. black and orange-brown .. 85 80
62 3d. black and blue .. 2·75 1·00
63 4d. black and deep turquoise-green .. 1·25 1·40
64 6d. black and indigo .. 1·25 90
65 7d. black and deep olive .. 1·00 1·00
66 1s. black and vermilion .. 1·00 90
67 2s. 6d. black and deep dull purple .. 27·00 6·50
68 5s. black and blue-green .. 35·00 17·00
69 10s. black and purple .. 48·00 35·00
57/69 .. *Set of* 13 £110 60·00
Designs:—1d. Map of Ascension; 1½d. View of Georgetown; 2d. Map showing cable network; 2½d. Mountain road; 3d. White-tailed Tropic Bird; 4d. Yellow-finned Tuna; 6d. Rollers on the seashore; 7d. Young turtles; 1s. Land Crab; 2s. 6d. Sooty Tern; 5s. Perfect Crater; 10s. View of Ascension from North-west.

28 Brown Booby

42 Satellite Station

(Des after photos by N. P. Ashmole. Photo Harrison)

1963 (23 May). *T* **28** *and similar horiz designs. W w* **12**. *P* 14×14½.
70 1d. black, lemon and new blue .. 90 3[illegible]
71 1½d. black, cobalt and ochre .. 1·25 6[illegible]
a. Cobalt omitted .. 75·00
72 2d. black, grey and bright blue .. 1·25 3[illegible]
73 3d. black, magenta and turquoise-blue .. 1·25 3[illegible]
74 4½d. black, bistre-brown and new blue .. 1·25 3[illegible]
w. Wmk inverted .. £180
75 6d. bistre, black and yellow-green .. 1·25 3[illegible]
76 7d. black, brown and reddish violet .. 1·25 3[illegible]
77 10d. black, greenish yellow and blue-green 1·25 3[illegible]
78 1s. multicoloured .. 1·25 3[illegible]
79 1s. 6d. multicoloured .. 4·50 1·7[illegible]
80 2s. 6d. multicoloured .. 6·00 7·0[illegible]
81 5s. multicoloured .. 7·00 6·0[illegible]
82 10s. multicoloured .. 13·00 7·0[illegible]
83 £1 multicoloured .. 20·00 9·0[illegible]
70/83 .. *Set of* 14 55·00 30·0[illegible]
Designs:—1½d. White-capped Noddy; 2d. White Tern; 3d. Re[illegible] billed Tropic Bird; 4½d. Common Noddy; 6d. Sooty Tern; 7[illegible] Ascension Frigate Bird; 10d. Blue-faced Booby; 1s. White-taile[illegible] Tropic Bird; 1s. 6d. Red-billed Tropic Bird; 2s. 6d. Madeiran Storr[illegible] Petrel; 5s. Red-footed Booby (brown phase); 10s. Ascension Frigat[illegible] Birds; £1 Red-footed Booby (white phase).

1963 (4 June). *Freedom from Hunger. As No.* 146 *of Antigua*
84 1s. 6d. carmine .. 1·40 4[illegible]

1963 (2 Sept). *Red Cross Centenary. As Nos.* 147/8 *of Antigua.*
85 3d. red and black .. 3·50 1·[illegible]
86 1s. 6d. red and blue .. 7·50 2·[illegible]

1965 (17 May). *I.T.U. Centenary. As Nos.* 166/7 *of Antigua.*
87 3d. magenta and bluish violet .. 1·00 5[illegible]
88 6d. turquoise-blue and light chestnut .. 1·25 5[illegible]

1965 (25 Oct). *International Co-operation Year. As Nos.* 168/9 *o[illegible] Antigua.*
89 1d. reddish purple and turquoise-green .. 50 5[illegible]
90 6d. deep bluish green and lavender .. 1·00 7[illegible]

1966 (24 Jan). *Churchill Commemoration. As Nos.* 170/3 *[illegible] Antigua.*
91 1d. new blue .. 50 6[illegible]
92 3d. deep green .. 2·75 1·2[illegible]
93 6d. brown .. 3·50 1·5[illegible]
94 1s. 6d. bluish violet .. 4·50 2·0[illegible]
91/4 .. *Set of* 4 10·00 4·7[illegible]

1966 (1 July). *World Cup Football Championships. As Nos.* 176[illegible] *of Antigua.*
95 3d. violet, yellow-green, lake and yell-brn .. 1·25 [illegible]
96 6d. chocolate, blue-green, lake & yellow-brn 1·50 [illegible]

1966 (20 Sept). *Inauguration of W.H.O. Headquarters, Geneva. A[illegible] Nos.* 178/9 *of Antigua.*
97 3d. black, yellow-green and light blue .. 1·75 [illegible]
98 1s. 6d. black, light purple and yellow-brown 4·25 1·[illegible]

(Des V. Whiteley. Photo Harrison)

1966 (7 Nov). *Opening of Apollo Communications Satellite Eart[illegible] Station. W w* **12**. *(sideways). P* 14 × 14½.
99 42 4d. black and reddish violet .. 15 1[illegible]
100 8d. black and deep bluish green .. 15 2[illegible]
101 1s. 3d. black and olive-brown .. 20 2[illegible]
102 2s. 6d. black and turquoise-blue .. 25 3[illegible]
99/102 .. *Set of* 4 65 8[illegible]

43 B.B.C. Emblem

44 Human Rights Emble[illegible] and Chain Links

(Des B.B.C. staff. Photo, Queen's head and emblem die-stampe[illegible] Harrison)

1966 (1 Dec). *Opening of B.B.C. Relay Station. W w* **12**. *P* 14½[illegible]
103 43 1d. gold and ultramarine .. 10 1[illegible]
104 3d. gold and myrtle-green .. 15 2[illegible]
w. Wmk inverted .. 75 1·2[illegible]
105 6d. gold and reddish violet .. 15 2[illegible]
106 1s. 6d. gold and red .. 15 2[illegible]
103/6 .. *Set of* 4 50 7[illegible]

7 (1 Jan). *20th Anniv of U.N.E.S.C.O. As Nos.* 196/8 *of ntigua.*

3d. slate-violet, red, yellow and orange .. 2·50 1·25
6d. orange-yellow, violet and deep olive .. 3·75 1·50
1s. 6d. black, bright purple and orange .. 6·00 2·00
'9 .. .. *Set of* 3 11·00 4·25

(Des and litho Harrison)

8 (8 July). *Human Rights Year. W* w **12** (*sideways**). 14½×14.

44 6d. light orange, red and black 25 25
1s. 6d. light grey-blue, red and black .. 35 35
2s. 6d. light green, red and black .. 40 40
w. Wmk Crown to right of CA .. £200
/12 .. .. *Set of* 3 90 90

The normal sideways watermark shows Crown to left of CA, *een from the back of the stamp.*

45 Black Durgon ("Ascension Black-Fish") **46** H.M.S. *Rattlesnake*

(Des M. Farrar Bell. Litho D.L.R.)

8 (23 Oct). *Fishes* (1*st series*). *T* **45** *and similar horiz lesigns. W* w **12** (*sideways**). *P* 13.

3 4d. black, slate and turquoise-blue .. 40 35
4 8d. multicoloured 50 60
w. Wmk Crown to right of CA £180
5 1s. 9d. multicoloured 60 70
6 2s. 3d. multicoloured 70 75
3/16 .. .. *Set of* 4 2·00 2·25

Designs:—8d. Scribbled Filefish ("Leather-jacket"); 1s. 9d. llow-finned Tuna; 2s. 3d. Short-finned Mako.

*The normal sideways watermark shows Crown to left of CA, *seen from the back of the stamp.*

See also Nos. 117/20 and 126/9.

(Des M. Farrar Bell. Litho D.L.R.)

9 (3 Mar). *Fishes* (2*nd series*). *Horiz designs as T* **45**. *Multi- oloured. W* w **12** (*sideways*). *P* 13.

7 4d. Sailfish .. .. 1·00 90
8 6d. White Seabream ("Old Wife") .. .. 1·25 1·25
9 1s. 6d. Yellowtail .. .. 2·00 2·25
2s. 11d. Rock Hind ("Jack") .. .. 3·00 2·75
/20 .. .. *Set of* 4 6·50 6·50

(Des L. Curtis. Photo Harrison)

9 (1 Oct). *Royal Naval Crests* (1*st series*). *T* **46** *and similar ert designs. W* w **12** (*sideways**). *P* 14×14½.

1 4d. multicoloured 70 25
2 9d. multicoloured 90 25
3 1s. 9d. deep blue, pale blue and gold .. 1·40 35
4 2s. 3d. multicoloured .. .. .. 1·60 45
/4 .. .. *Set of* 4 4·25 1·10
125 165×105 mm. Nos. 121/4. P 14½ .. 7·50 11·00
w. Wmk Crown to right of CA £450

Designs:—9d. H.M.S. *Weston*; 1s. 9d. H.M.S. *Undaunted*; 3d. H.M.S. *Eagle*.

*The normal sideways watermark shows Crown to left of CA, *seen from the back of the stamp.*

See also Nos. 130/4, 149/53, 154/8 and 166/70.

(Des M. Farrar Bell. Litho D.L.R.)

70 (6 Apr). *Fishes* (3*rd series*). *Horiz designs as T* **45**. *Multicoloured. W* w **12** (*sideways**). *P* 14.

6 4d. Wahoo .. .. 4·50 2·50
7 9d. Ascension Jack ("Coalfish") .. .. 5·00 2·50
w. Wmk Crown to right of CA .. .. 5·00 1·75
8 1s. 9d. Pompano Dolphin .. .. .. 5·50 3·25
9 2s. 3d. Squirrelfish ("Soldier") .. .. 5·50 3·25
w. Wmk Crown to right of CA .. .. 5·00 2·50
6/9 .. .. *Set of* 4 18·00 10·50

*The normal sideways watermark shows Crown to left of CA, *seen from the back of the stamp.*

(Des L. Curtis. Photo D.L.R.)

70 (7 Sept). *Royal Naval Crests* (2*nd series*). *Designs as T* **46**. *Multicoloured. W* w **12.** *P* 12½.

0 4d. H.M.S. *Penelope* .. .. 1·75 85
1 9d. H.M.S. *Carlisle* .. .. 2·25 1·25
2 1s. 6d. H.M.S. *Amphion* .. .. .. 2·75 1·75
3 2s. 6d. H.M.S. *Magpie* .. .. .. 3·25 1·75
0/3 .. .. *Set of* 4 9·00 5·00
S134 153 × 96 mm. Nos. 130/3 .. .. .. 14·00 12·00

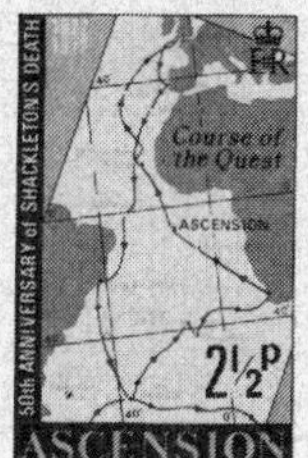

50 Early Chinese Rocket **51** Course of the *Quest*

(Des V. Whiteley. Litho Format)

1971 (15 Feb). *Decimal Currency. The Evolution of Space Travel. T* **50** *and similar multicoloured designs. W* w **12** (*sideways on horiz designs*). *P* 14.

135 ½p. Type **50** 15 20
136 1p. Medieval Arab Astronomers 20 20
137 1½p. Tycho Brahe's Observatory, Quadrant and Supernova 30 30
138 2p. Galileo, Moon and Telescope 40 30
139 2½p. Isaac Newton, Instruments and Apple .. 1·00 70
140 3½p. Harrison's Chronometer and Ship .. 1·75 70
141 4½p. Space Rocket taking-off .. .. .. 1·25 60
142 5p. World's Largest Telescope, Palomar .. 1·00 60
143 7½p. World's largest Radio Telescope, Jodrell Bank .. .. 4·00 1·40
144 10p. Mariner VII and Mars .. .. .. 3·50 1·75
145 12½p. Sputnik II and Space Dog, Laika .. 6·00 2·00
146 25p. Walking in Space .. .. .. 7·00 2·25
147 50p. Apollo XI Crew on Moon .. .. 6·00 2·50
148 £1 Future Space Research Station .. .. 6·00 4·50
135/48 .. .. *Set of* 14 35·00 16·00

The ½p., 1p., 4½p. and 25p. are vertical, and the remainder are horizontal.

(Des L. Curtis. Photo D.L.R.)

1971 (15 Nov). *Royal Naval Crests* (3*rd series*). *Designs as T* **46**. *Multicoloured. W* w **12.** *P* 13.

149 2p. H.M.S. *Phoenix* .. .. 1·50 30
150 4p. H.M.S. *Milford* .. .. 1·75 55
151 9p. H.M.S. *Pelican* .. .. 2·25 80
152 15p. H.M.S. *Oberon* .. .. 2·50 1·00
149/52 .. .. *Set of* 4 7·00 2·40
MS153 151×104 mm. Nos. 149/52 .. .. 8·00 15·00

(Des L. Curtis. Litho Questa)

1972 (29 May). *Royal Naval Crests* (4*th series*). *Multicoloured designs as T* **46**. *W* w **12** (*sideways**). *P* 14.

154 1½p. H.M.S. *Lowestoft* 60 50
155 3p. H.M.S. *Auckland* 65 75
156 6p. H.M.S. *Nigeria* .. .. 70 1·25
157 17½p. H.M.S. *Bermuda* .. .. .. 1·50 2·50
154/7 .. .. *Set of* 4 3·00 4·50
MS158 157×93 mm. Nos. 154/7 .. .. 3·00 7·50
w. Wmk Crown to right of CA £200

*The normal sideways watermark shows Crown to left of CA, *as seen from the back of the stamp.*

(Des J. Cooter. Litho Questa)

1972 (2 Aug). *50th Anniv of Shackleton's Death. T* **51** *and similar multicoloured designs. W* w **12** (*sideways on* 4 *and* 7½*p.*). *P* 14.

159 2½p. Type **51** 55 60
160 4p. Shackleton and *Quest* (*horiz*) 60 70
161 7½p. Shackleton's cabin and *Quest* (*horiz*) .. 65 75
162 11p. Shackleton's statue and memorial .. 75 1·00
159/62 .. .. *Set of* 4 2·25 2·75
MS163 139 × 114 mm. Nos. 159/62 (wmk sideways) 2·25 6·00

52 Land Crab and Short-finned Mako

(Des (from photograph by D. Groves) and photo Harrison)

1972 (20 Nov). *Royal Silver Wedding. Multicoloured; background colour given. W* w **12.** *P* 14 × 14½.

164 **52** 2p. bright bluish violet 15 10
165 16p. rose-carmine 35 30

(Des L. Curtis. Litho J.W.)

1973 (28 May). *Royal Naval Crests* (5*th series*). *Multicoloured designs as T* **46**. *W* w **12** (*sideways**). *P* 14.

166 2p. H.M.S. *Birmingham* .. .. .. 2·50 1·00
167 4p. H.M.S. *Cardiff* .. .. 3·00 1·00
168 9p. H.M.S. *Penzance* .. .. 4·00 1·25
169 13p. H.M.S. *Rochester* .. .. 4·50 1·50
w. Wmk Crown to right of CA .. .. 7·00
166/9 .. .. *Set of* 4 12·50 4·25
MS170 109×152 mm. Nos. 166/9 .. .. 28·00 10·00

*The normal sideways watermark shows Crown to left of CA on 2, 4, 13p. and **MS**170, or Crown to right of CA on 9p., *as seen from the back of the stamp.*

53 Green Turtle

(Des V. Whiteley Studio. Litho Enschedé)

1973 (28 Aug). *Turtles. T* **53** *and similar triangular designs. Multicoloured. W* w **12.** *P* 13½.

171 4p. Type **53** .. .. 3·75 1·25
172 9p. Loggerhead turtle .. .. 4·00 1·50
173 12p. Hawksbill turtle .. .. 4·25 1·75
171/3 .. .. *Set of* 3 11·00 4·00

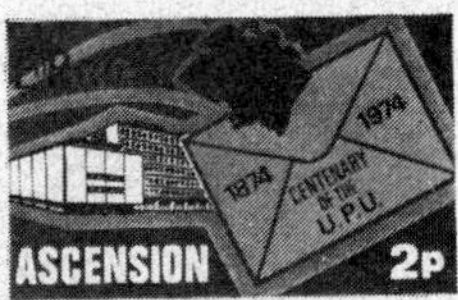

54 Sergeant, R.M. Light Infantry, 1900 **55** Letter and H.Q., Berne

(Des G. Drummond from paintings by C. Stadden. Litho Walsall)

1973 (31 Oct). *50th Anniv of Departure of Royal Marines from Ascension. T* **54** *and similar vert designs. Multicoloured. W* w **12** (*sideways**). *P* 14.

174 2p. Type **54** .. .. 2·00 1·25
175 6p. R.M. Private, 1816 .. .. .. 3·00 1·75
176 12p. R.M. Light Infantry Officer, 1880 .. 3·50 2·25
w. Wmk Crown to right of CA .. .. 24·00
177 20p. R.M. Artillery Colour Sergeant, 1910 4·00 2·50
174/7 .. .. *Set of* 4 11·00 7·00

*The normal sideways watermark shows Crown to left of CA, *as seen from the back of the stamp.*

1973 (14 Nov). *Royal Wedding. As Nos.* 165/6 *of Anguilla. Centre multicoloured. W* w **12** (*sideways*). *P* 13½.

178 2p. ochre 15 10
179 18p. dull blue-green 25 15

(Des PAD Studio. Litho Questa)

1974 (27 Mar). *Centenary of U.P.U. T* **55** *and similar horiz design. Multicoloured. W* w **12.** *P* 14½ × 14.

180 2p. Type **55** 25 30
181 9p. Hermes and U.P.U. monument 40 45

56 Churchill as a Boy, and Birthplace, Blenheim Palace

(Des J.W. Litho Questa)

1974 (30 Nov). *Birth Centenary of Sir Winston Churchill. T* **56** *and similar horiz design. Multicoloured. No wmk. P* 14.

182 5p. Type **56** 25 35
183 25p. Churchill as statesman, and U.N. Building 40 75
MS184 93 × 87 mm. Nos. 182/3 .. .. 1·25 2·50

57 "Skylab 3" and Photograph of Ascension

(Des PAD Studio. Litho Questa)

1975 (20 Mar). *Space Satellites. T* **57** *and similar horiz design. Multicoloured. W* w **12** (*sideways*). *P* 14.

185 2p. Type **57** 30 30
186 18p. "Skylab 4" command module and photograph 35 40

The date "11.1.73" given on the 2p. is incorrect, "Skylab 3" was launched in July 1973 and returned to Earth in September 1973.

The date on the 18p. is also incorrect. The photograph was taken on 6 January 1974, three days later than the date given in the caption.

58 U.S.A.F. Lockheed C-141A Starlifter

APOLLO-SOYUZ LINK 1975

(59)

(Des R. Granger Barrett. Litho Questa)

1975 (19 June). *Wideawake Airfield. T* **58** *and similar horiz designs. Multicoloured. W* w **12** (*sideways**). *P* 13½.

187 2p. Type **58** .. .. 1·75 65
188 5p. R.A.F. Lockheed C-130 Hercules .. 2·00 85
189 9p. Vickers Super VC-10 .. .. .. 2·25 1·40
190 24p. U.S.A.F. Lockheed C-5A Galaxy .. 4·00 3·00
w. Wmk Crown to right of CA .. ..
187/90 .. .. *Set of* 4 9·00 5·50
MS191 144×99 mm. Nos 187/90 .. .. 17·00 22·00

*The normal sideways watermark shows Crown to left of CA, *as seen from the back of the stamp.*

1975 (18 Aug). *"Apollo–Soyuz" Space Link. Nos.* 141 *and* 145/6 *optd with T* **59**.
192 4½p. Space rocket taking-off 15 15
193 12½p. Sputnik II and Space Dog, Laika .. 20 20
194 25p. Walking in Space 30 35
192/4 .. .. *Set of* 3 60 65

60 Arrival of Royal Navy, 1815

(Des J.W. from paintings by Isobel McManus. Litho Walsall)

1975 (22 Oct). *160th Anniv of Occupation. T* **60** *and similar horiz designs. Multicoloured. W* w **14** (*sideways**). *P* 14.
195 2p. Type **60** 30 25
w. Wmk Crown to right of CA £100
196 5p. Water Supply, Dampiers Drip .. 40 40
197 9p. First landing, 1815 .. .. .. 45 60
198 15p. The garden on Green Mountain .. 60 85
195/8 .. .. *Set of* 4 1·60 1·90
*The normal sideways watermark shows Crown to left of CA, *as seen from the back of the stamp.*

61 Yellow Canary

62 Boatswain Bird Island Sanctuary

(Des J.W. Litho Questa)

1976 (26 Apr). *Birds. Multicoloured designs as T* **61** *and T* **62**. *W* w **14** (*sideways on horiz designs**). *P* 13½ (£2) *or* 14 (*others*).
199 1p. Type **61** .. .. 40 1·25
200 2p. White Tern (*vert*) .. .. .. 45 1·25
w. Wmk inverted £170
201 3p. Common Waxbill .. .. .. 45 1·25
202 4p. White-capped Noddy (*vert*) .. .. 50 1·25
203 5p. Common Noddy .. .. .. 70 1·50
204 6p. Common Mynah .. .. .. 70 1·50
205 7p. Madeiran Storm Petrel (*vert*) .. .. 70 1·50
206 8p. Sooty Tern .. .. 70 1·50
w. Wmk Crown to right of CA £140
207 9p. Blue-faced Booby (*vert*) .. .. 70 1·50
208 10p. Red-footed Booby .. .. .. 70 1·50
209 15p. Bare-throated Francolin (*vert*) .. .. 1·25 1·75
210 18p. Brown Booby (*vert*) .. .. .. 1·25 1·75
211 25p. Red-billed Tropic Bird .. .. 1·40 1·75
212 50p. White-tailed Tropic Bird .. .. 2·25 2·50
213 £1 Ascension Frigate Bird (*vert*) .. .. 2·75 3·25
214 £2 Type **62** .. .. 5·50 7·50
199/214 .. .. *Set of* 16 18·00 29·00
*The normal sideways watermark shows Crown to left of CA, *as seen from the back of the stamp.*

63 G.B. Penny Red with Ascension Postmark

(Des C. Abbott. Litho J.W.)

1976 (4 May). *Festival of Stamps, London. T* **63** *and similar designs. W* w **14** (*sideways on* 5 *and* 25*p.*). *P* 13½.
215 5p. rose-red, black and cinnamon 20 15
216 9p. green, black and greenish stone 30 20
217 25p. multicoloured 50 45
215/17 .. .. *Set of* 3 90 70
MS218 133×121 mm. No. 217 with St. Helena 318 and Tristan da Cunha 206 (wmk sideways*). P 13 .. .. 1·50 2·00
w. Wmk Crown to left of CA £325
Designs: *Vert*—9p. ½d. stamp of 1922. *Horiz*—25p. *Southampton Castle* (liner).
*The normal sideways watermark shows Crown to right of CA, *as seen from the back of the stamp.*
No. **MS**218 was postally valid on each island to the value of 25p.

64 U.S. Base, Ascension

65 Visit of Prince Philip, 1957

(Des V. Whiteley Studio. Litho J.W.)

1976 (4 July). *Bicentenary of American Revolution. T* **64** *and similar horiz designs. Multicoloured. W* w **14** (*sideways*). *P* 13.
219 8p. Type **64** 75 40
220 9p. NASA Station at Devils Ashpit 75 45
221 25p. "Viking" landing on Mars .. .. 1·25 80
219/21 .. .. *Set of* 3 2·50 1·50

(Des J. Cooter. Litho Walsall)

1977 (7 Feb). *Silver Jubilee. T* **65** *and similar horiz designs. Multicoloured. W* w **14** (*sideways on* 12 *and* 25*p.*). *P* 13½.
222 8p. Type **65** 15 15
w. Wmk inverted £120
223 12p. Coronation Coach leaving Buckingham Palace 20 20
224 25p. Coronation Coach 35 40
222/4 .. .. *Set of* 3 60 65

66 Tunnel carrying Water Pipe

67 Mars Bay Location, 1877

(Des G. Drummond. Litho Harrison)

1977 (27 June). *Water Supplies. T* **66** *and similar multicoloured designs. W* w **14** (*sideways on* 12 *and* 25*p.*). *P* 14.
225 3p. Type **66** 15 15
226 5p. Breakneck Valley wells 20 20
227 12p. Break tank (*horiz*) 35 35
228 25p. Water catchment (*horiz*) 55 65
225/8 .. .. *Set of* 4 1·10 1·25

(Des J.W. Litho Questa)

1977 (3 Oct). *Centenary of Visit of Professor Gill (astronomer). T* **67** *and similar horiz designs. Multicoloured. W* w **14** (*sideways*). *P* 13½.
229 3p. Type **67** 15 20
230 8p. Instrument sites, Mars Bay 20 25
231 12p. Sir David and Lady Gill 30 40
232 25p. Maps of Ascension 60 70
229/32 .. .. *Set of* 4 1·10 1·40

68 Lion of England

69 Queen Elizabeth II

(Des C. Abbott. Litho Questa)

1978 (2 June). *25th Anniv of Coronation. T* **68/9** *and similar vert design. P* 15.
233 **68** 25p. yellow, sepia and silver 35 50
a. Sheetlet. Nos. 233/5 × 2 .. .. 1·75
234 **69** 25p. multicoloured 35 50
235 – 25p. yellow, sepia and silver 35 50
233/5 .. .. *Set of* 3 95 1·40
Design:—No. 235, Green Turtle.
Nos. 233/5 were printed together in small sheets of 6, containing two *se-tenant* strips of 3 with horizontal gutter margin between.

PRICES OF SETS

Set prices are given for many issues, generally those containing three stamps or more. Definitive sets include one of each value or major colour change, but do not cover different perforations, die types or minor shades. Where a choice is possible the set prices are based on the cheapest versions of the stamps included in the listings.

70 Flank of Sisters, Sisters' Red Hill and East Crater

71 *"The Resolution"* (H. Roberts)

(Des J.W. Litho Questa)

1978 (4 Sept). *Volcanic Rock Formations of Ascension. T* **70** *a*
similar horiz designs. Multicoloured. W w **14**. *P* 14½.
236 3p. Type **70** 15
a. Horiz strip of 5. Nos. 236/40 .. .. 1·10
237 5p. Holland's Crater (Hollow Tooth) .. 20
238 12p. Street Crater, Lower Valley Crater and Bear's Back 25
239 15p. Butt Crater, Weather Post and Green Mountain 30
240 25p. Flank of Sisters, Thistle Hill and Two Boats Village 35
236/40 .. .. *Set of* 5 1·10 1·
MS241 185 × 100 mm. Nos. 236/40, each × 2 .. 2·00 5·
a. Blue ("Ascension Island") omitted .. £3750
Nos. 236/40 were printed together, *se-tenant*, in horizontal stri
of 5 throughout the sheet forming a composite design.

(Des and litho (25p. also embossed) Walsall)

1979 (19 Feb*). *Bicentenary of Captain Cook's Voyages,* 1768–
T **71** *and similar vert designs. Multicoloured. P* 11.
242 3p. Type **71** 40
243 8p. Chronometer 40
244 12p. Green Turtle 45
245 25p. Flaxman/Wedgwood medallion of Captain Cook 55
242/5 .. .. *Set of* 4 1·60 1·
*This is the local date of issue; the stamps were released
London on 8 January.

72 St. Mary's Church, Georgetown

73 Landing Cable, Comfortless Cove

(Des Walsall. Litho Format)

1979 (24 May). *Ascension Day. T* **72** *and similar vert desig*
Multicoloured. W w **14**. *P* 14.
246 8p. Type **72** 15
247 12p. Map of Ascension 20
248 50p. "The Ascension" (painting by Rembrandt) 55
246/8 .. .. *Set of* 3 80 1·

(Des G. Vasarhelyi. Litho Walsall)

1979 (15 Sept). *80th Anniv of Eastern Telegraph Compan*
Arrival on Ascension. T **73** *and similar designs. W* w
(*inverted on* 12*p. or sideways on others**). *P* 14.
249 3p. black and carmine 15
250 8p. black and yellowish green 20
251 12p. black and yellow 25
252 15p. black and bright violet 25
w. Wmk Crown to right of CA .. .. 38·00
253 25p. black and orange-brown 35
249/53 .. .. *Set of* 5 1·10 1
Designs: *Horiz*—8p. C.S. *Anglia*; 15p. C.S. *Seine*; 25p Ca
and Wireless earth station. *Vert*—12p. Map of Atlantic ca
network.
*The normal sideways watermark shows Crown to left of C
as seen from the back of the stamp.

74 1938 6d. Stamp

(Des BG Studio. Litho Questa)

1979 (12 Dec). *Death Centenary of Sir Rowland Hill. T* **74** *a*
similar designs. W w **14** (*sideways on* 3 *and* 8*p.*). *P* 14.
254 3p. black, new blue & deep turquoise-blue 15
255 8p. black, blue-green and light green .. 15
256 12p. black, bright blue and turquoise-blue 20
w. Wmk inverted .. .. 80·00
257 50p. black, brownish grey and red .. 60
254/7 .. .. *Set of* 4 1·00 1·
Designs: *Horiz*—8p. 1956 5s. definitive stamp. *Vert*—12
1924 3s. stamp; 50p. Sir Rowland Hill.

75 *Anogramma ascensionis* **76** 17th-century Bottle Post

(Des J. Cooter. Litho Format)

30 (18 Feb). *Ferns and Grasses. T* **75** *and similar multicoloured designs.* W w **14** (*sideways on* 12 *to* 24*p.*). *P* 14½ × 14 (3 *to* 8*p.*) *or* 14 × 14½ (12 *to* 24*p.*).
8 3p. Type **75** 10 10
9 6p. *Xiphopteris ascensionense* 15 15
0 8p. *Sporobolus caespitosus* 15 15
1 12p. *Sporobolus durus* (*vert*) 15 25
2 18p. *Dryopteris ascensionis* (*vert*) 20 35
a. Brown (thorns) omitted £120
3 24p. *Marattia purpurascens* (*vert*) 30 50
8/63 .. .. *Set of* 6 90 1·25

(Des L. Curtis. Litho Format)

80 (1 May). *"London 1980" International Stamp Exhibition. T* **76** *and similar horiz designs. Multicoloured.* W w **14** (*sideways*). *P* 13½.
4 8p. Type **76** 15 20
5 12p. 19th-century chance calling ship .. 20 25
6 15p. *Garth Castle* (regular mail service from 1863) 20 30
7 50p. *St. Helena* (mail services, 1980) .. 60 90
4/7 .. .. *Set of* 4 1·00 1·50
S268 102×154 mm. Nos. 264/7 .. .. 1·00 2·40

77 Queen Elizabeth the Queen Mother **78** Lubbock's Yellowtail

(Des Harrison. Litho Questa)

30 (11 Aug)*. *80th Birthday of Queen Elizabeth the Queen Mother.* W w **14** (*sideways*). *P* 14.
9 **77** 15p. multicoloured 40 40
*This was the local release date. The Crown Agents placed stocks sale in London on 4 August.

(Des G. Drummond. Litho Enschedé)

80 (15 Sept). *Fishes. T* **78** *and similar horiz designs. Multicoloured.* W w **14** (*sideways**). *P* 13×13½.
0 3p. Type **78** 30 15
1 10p. Resplendent Angelfish 45 25
2 25p. Bicoloured Butterflyfish 75 50
w. Wmk Crown to right of CA .. .. 1·00
3 40p. Marmalade Razorfish .. .. .. 1·00 65
w. Wmk Crown to right of CA .. .. 1·50
0/3 .. .. *Set of* 4 2·25 1·40
*The normal sideways watermark shows Crown to left of CA, *seen from the back of the stamp.*

79 H.M.S. *Tortoise*

(Des D. Bowen. Litho Rosenbaum Bros, Vienna)

80 (17 Nov). *150th Anniv of Royal Geographical Society. T* **79** *and similar multicoloured designs.* W w **14** (*sideways**). *P* 14 (60*p.*) *or* 13½ (*others*).
4 10p. Type **79** 35 40
w. Wmk Crown to left of CA 85
5 15p. "Wideawake Fair" 45 45
w. Wmk Crown to left of CA .. .. 1·25
6 60p. Mid-Atlantic Ridge (38×48 *mm*) .. 80 1·25
w. Wmk Crown to left of CA .. .. 2·75
4/6 .. .. *Set of* 3 1·40 2·00
*The normal sideways watermark shows Crown to right of A, *as seen from the back of the stamp.*

80 Green Mountain Farm, 1881

(Des C. Abbott. Litho Format)

81 (15 Feb). *Green Mountain Farm. T* **80** *and similar horiz designs. Multicoloured.* W w **14** (*sideways*). *P* 13½ × 14.
7 12p. Type **80** 15 35
8 15p. Two Boats, 1881 .. .. 20 40
9 20p. Green Mountain and Two Boats, 1981 .. 25 50
0 30p. Green Mountain Farm, 1981 .. .. 35 70
7/80 .. .. *Set of* 4 85 1·75

81 Cable and Wireless Earth Station

(Des G. Vasarhelyi and Walsall. Litho Walsall)

1981 (27 Apr). *"Space Shuttle" Mission and Opening of 2nd Earth Station.* W w **14** (*sideways*). *P* 14.
281 **81** 15p. black, bright blue and pale blue .. 30 35

82 Poinsettia

83 Solanum

(Des J. Cooter. Litho J.W.)

1981 (11 May)–**82**. *Flowers. Designs as T* **82** (1 *to* 40*p*) *or vert as T* **83** (50*p. to* £2). *Multicoloured.* W w **14** (*sideways* on* 1, 2, 4, 5, 8, 15, 20, 40, 50*p.*, £1 *and* £2). *P* 13½. A. *Without imprint date.*
282A 1p. Type **82** 70 70
283A 2p. Clustered Wax Flower 80 75
284A 3p. Kolanchoe (*vert*) 80 75
285A 4p. Yellow Pops 80 75
286A 5p. Camels Foot Creeper 80 75
287A 8p. White Oleander 80 80
288A 10p. Ascension Lily (*vert*) .. .. .. 1·40 1·25
289A 12p. Coral Plant (*vert*) .. .. .. 1·50 85
290A 15p. Yellow Allamanda .. .. 1·25 85
291A 20p. Ascension Euphorbia .. .. .. 1·25 1·00
w. Wmk Crown to left of CA .. .. 2·00
292A 30p. Flame of the Forest (*vert*) .. .. 1·25 1·25
293A 40p. Bougainvillea "King Leopold" .. .. 1·25 2·00
294A 50p. Type **83** .. .. 1·25 2·50
295A £1 Ladies Petticoat .. .. 2·00 4·00
296A £2 Red Hibiscus .. .. 3·75 5·50
282A/96A .. .. *Set of* 15 17·00 21·00

B. *With imprint date* ("1982") (27.8.82)
283B 2p. Clustered Wax Flower 50 75
284B 3p. Kolanchoe 50 75
288B 10p. Ascension Lily 45 75
290B 15p. Yellow Allamanda 50 75
291B 20p. Ascension Euphorbia .. .. .. 1·00 75
295B £1 Ladies Petticoat .. .. 2·00 2·75
w. Wmk Crown to left of CA .. .. 12·00
283B/95B .. .. *Set of* 6 4·50 6·00
*The normal sideways watermark shows Crown to right of CA, *as seen from the back of the stamp.*
Nos. 283B/95B had the imprint dates printed on the stamps by typography.

84 Map by Maxwell, 1793

(Des L. Curtis. Litho Walsall)

1981 (22 May). *Early Maps of Ascension. T* **84** *and similar horiz designs.* W w **14** (*sideways*). *P* 14 × 14½.
297 10p. black, gold and pale blue 25 35
298 12p. black, gold and apple-green 25 35
299 15p. black, gold and stone 25 35
300 40p. black, gold and pale greenish yellow .. 55 70
297/300 .. .. *Set of* 4 1·10 1·60
MS301 79 × 64 mm. 5p. × 4, multicoloured .. 60 75
Designs:—12p. Maxwell, 1793 (*different*); 15p. Ekeberg and Chapman, 1811; 40p. Campbell, 1819; miniature sheet, Linschoten, 1599.
Stamps from No. **MS**301 form a composite design.

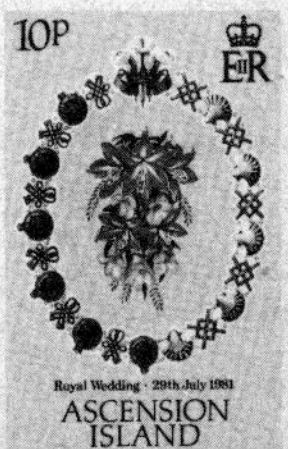

85 Wedding Bouquet from Ascension **86** Prince Charles and Lady Diana Spencer

(Des J.W. Litho Questa)

1981 (22 July). *Royal Wedding. T* **85/6** *and similar vert design. Multicoloured.* W w **14**. *P* 14.
302 10p. Type **85** 15 15
303 15p. Prince Charles in Fleet Air Arm flying kit 25 25
304 50p. Type **86** 65 75
302/4 .. .. *Set of* 3 95 1·00

87 "Interest" **88** Scout crossing Rope Bridge

(Des BG Studio. Litho Questa)

1981 (14 Sept). *25th Anniv of Duke of Edinburgh Award Scheme. T* **87** *and similar vert designs. Multicoloured.* W w **14**. *P* 14.
305 5p. Type **87** 15 15
306 10p. "Physical activities" 15 15
307 15p. "Service" 20 20
308 40p. Duke of Edinburgh 45 45
w. Wmk inverted .. .. 24·00
305/8 .. .. *Set of* 4 85 85

(Des A. Theobald. Litho Format)

1982 (22 Feb). *75th Anniv of Boy Scout Movement. T* **88** *and similar designs.* W w **14** (*sideways*). *P* 14.
309 10p. black, bright blue and azure 15 35
310 15p. black, orange-brown and greenish yellow 20 50
311 25p. black, bright mauve and pale mauve .. 30 60
312 40p. black, rosine and pale orange 50 85
309/12 .. .. *Set of* 4 1·00 2·10
MS313 121 × 121 mm. 10p., 15p., 25p., 40p. As Nos. 309/12 (*each diamond*, 40 × 40 *mm*). P 14½ 1·25 2·50
Designs:—15p. 1st Ascension Scout Group flag; 25p. Scouts learning to use radio; 40p. Lord Baden-Powell.
Stamps from No. **MS**313 have an overall design showing a flag printed on the reverse beneath the gum.

89 Charles Darwin

(Des L. Curtis. Litho Questa)

1982 (19 Apr). *150th Anniv of Charles Darwin's Voyage. T* **89** *and similar horiz designs. Multicoloured.* W w **14** (*sideways*). *P* 14.
314 10p. Type **89** 25 40
315 12p. Darwin's pistols 30 50
316 15p. Rock Crab 35 55
317 40p. H.M.S. *Beagle* 75 95
314/17 .. .. *Set of* 4 1·50 2·25

90 Fairey Swordfish Torpedo Bomber

(Des A. Theobald. Litho Walsall)

1982 (15 June). *40th Anniv of Wideawake Airfield. T* **90** *and similar horiz designs. Multicoloured.* W w **14** (*sideways*). *P* 14.
318 5p. Type **90** .. .. 1·00 35
319 10p. North American B-25C Mitchell .. 1·25 40
320 15p. Boeing EC-135N Aria .. .. .. 1·50 55
321 50p. Lockheed C-130 Hercules .. .. 2·25 1·10
318/21 .. .. *Set of* 4 5·50 2·25

91 Ascension Coat of Arms   **92** Formal Portrait

(Des Jennifer Toombs. Litho Questa)

1982 (1 July). *21st Birthday of Princess of Wales. T* **91/2** *and similar vert designs. Multicoloured. W* w **14.** *P* 14 × 14½.

322 12p. Type **91** 25 25
323 15p. Lady Diana Spencer in Music Room, Buckingham Palace 25 25
324 25p. Bride and Earl Spencer leaving Clarence House 40 40
325 50p. Type **92** 75 75
322/5 .. .. *Set of* 4 1·50 1·50

1st PARTICIPATION
COMMONWEALTH GAMES 1982

(**93**)

94 Bush House, London

1982 (29 Oct). *Commonwealth Games, Brisbane. Nos.* 290B/1B *optd with T* **93**.

326 15p. Yellow Allamanda 30 40
327 20p. Ascension Euphorbia 40 45

(Des A. Theobald. Litho Questa)

1982 (1 Dec). *Christmas. 50th Anniv of B.B.C. External Broadcasting. T* **94** *and similar horiz designs. Multicoloured. W* w **14** (*sideways**). *P* 14.

328 5p. Type **94** 15 20
329 10p. Atlantic relay station 15 30
330 25p. Lord Reith, first director-general .. 30 60
  w. Wmk Crown to right of CA .. .. 4·50
331 40p. King George V making his first Christmas broadcast, 1932 .. .. 45 75
328/31 .. .. *Set of* 4 95 1·60

*The normal sideways watermark shows Crown to left of CA, *as seen from the back of the stamp.*

95 *Marasmius thwaitesii* ("*Marasmius echinosphaerus*")   **96** Aerial View of Georgetown

(Des Harrison. Litho Questa)

1983 (1 Mar). *Fungi. T* **95** *and similar vert designs. Multicoloured. W* w **14**. *P* 14.

332 7p. Type **95** 55 30
333 12p. *Chlorophyllum molybdites* 75 45
334 15p. *Leucocoprinus cepaestripes* 90 50
335 20p. *Lycoperdon marginatum* .. .. .. 1·10 65
336 50p. *Marasmiellus distantifolius* .. .. 1·75 1·25
332/6 .. .. *Set of* 5 4·50 2·75

(Des Jennifer Toombs. Litho Format)

1983 (12 May). *Island Views (1st series). T* **96** *and similar horiz designs. Multicoloured. W* w **14** (*sideways**). *P* 14×13½.

337 12p. Type **96** 20 25
338 15p. Green Mountain farm 20 25
  w. Wmk Crown to right of CA .. ..
339 20p. Boatswain Bird Island 35 40
340 60p. Telemetry Hill by night 70 80
337/40 .. .. *Set of* 4 1·25 1·50

*The normal sideways watermark shows Crown to left of CA, *as seen from the back of the stamp.*
See also Nos. 367/70

97 Westland Wessex 5 Helicopter of No. 845 Naval Air Squadron

(Des D. Hartley-Marjoram. Litho Questa)

1983 (1 Aug). *Bicentenary of Manned Flight. British Military Aircraft. T* **97** *and similar horiz designs. Multicoloured. W* w **14** (*sideways*). *P* 13½.

341 12p. Type **97** 85 65
342 15p. Avro Vulcan B.2 of No. 44 Squadron 95 75
343 20p. Hawker Siddeley H.S.801 Nimrod M.R. 2P of No. 120 Squadron .. .. 1·10 85
344 60p. Handley Page H.P.80 Victor K2 of No. 55 Squadron .. .. 2·00 2·00
341/4 .. .. *Set of* 4 4·50 3·75

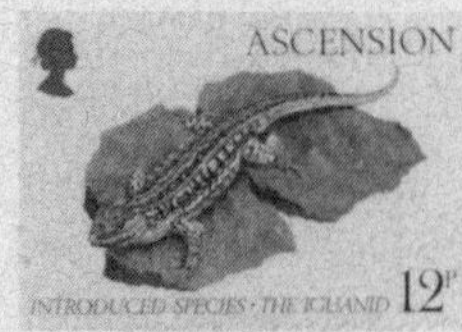

98 Iguanid

(Des D. Nockles. Litho Questa)

1983 (20 Sept). *Introduced Species. T* **98** *and similar horiz designs. Multicoloured. W* w **14** (*sideways*). *P* 14.

345 12p. Type **98** 30 30
346 15p. Rabbit 35 35
347 20p. Cat 45 45
348 60p. Donkey .. .. 1·40 1·40
345/8 .. .. *Set of* 4 2·25 2·25

99 Speckled Tellin (*Tellina listeri*)   **100** 1922 1½d. Stamp

(Des G. Wilby. Litho Format)

1983 (28 Nov). *Sea Shells. T* **99** *and similar horiz designs. Multicoloured. W* w **14** (*sideways*). *P* 14½ × 14.

349 7p. Type **99** 20 20
350 12p. Lion's Paw Scallop (*Lyropecten nodosa*) 30 30
351 15p. Lurid Cowrie (*Cypraea lurida oceanica*) 30 35
352 20p. Ascension Nerite (*Nerita ascensionis*) 40 45
353 50p. Miniature Melo (*Micromelo undatus*) 75 1·10
349/53 .. .. *Set of* 5 1·75 2·25

(Des C. Abbott. Litho Questa)

1984 (3 Jan). *150th Anniv of St. Helena as a British Colony. T* **100** *and similar vert designs showing stamps of the 1922 issue overprinted on St. Helena. Multicoloured. W* w **14**. *P* 14.

354 12p. Type **100** 30 45
355 15p. 1922 2d. stamp 35 50
356 20p. 1922 8d. stamp 40 55
357 60p. 1922 1s. stamp .. .. 90 1·40
354/7 .. .. *Set of* 4 1·75 2·50

101 Prince Andrew   **102** Naval Semaphore

(Des L. Curtis. Litho Questa)

1984 (10 Apr). *Visit of Prince Andrew. Sheet,* 124 × 90 *mm, containing vert designs as T* **101**. *W* w **14** . *P* 14½ × 14.

MS358 12p. Type **101**; 70p. Prince Andrew in naval uniform .. .. 1·40 1·60

(Des D. Hartley-Marjoram. Litho Questa)

1984 (28 May). *250th Anniv of "Lloyd's List" (newspaper). T* **102** *and similar vert designs. Multicoloured. W* w **14**. *P* 14½ × 14.

359 12p. Type **102** 40 30
360 15p. *Southampton Castle* (liner) 45 35
361 20p. Pier Head 55 45
362 70p. *Dane* (screw steamer) .. .. .. 1·60 1·50
359/62 .. .. *Set of* 4 2·75 2·40

NEW INFORMATION

The editor is always interested to correspond with people who have new information that will improve or correct the Catalogue.

103 Penny Coin and Yellow-finned Tuna   **104** Bermuda Cypress

(Des G. Drummond. Litho Questa)

1984 (26 July). *New Coinage. T* **103** *and similar horiz designs Multicoloured. W* w **14** (*sideways*). *P* 14.

363 12p. Type **103** 65 3
364 15p. Twopenny coin and donkey 75 4
365 20p. Fifty pence coin and Green Turtle .. 90 5
366 70p. Pound coin and Sooty Tern .. .. 2·25 1·7
363/6 .. .. *Set of* 4 4·00 2·7

(Des Jennifer Toombs. Litho B.D.T.)

1984 (26 Oct). *Island Views (2nd series). Horiz designs as T* **96** *Multicoloured. W* w **14** (*sideways*). *P* 13½.

367 12p. The Devil's Riding-school 30 3
368 15p. St. Mary's Church 35 3
369 20p. Two Boats Village 45 4
370 70p. Ascension from the sea .. .. .. 1·10 1·5
367/70 .. .. *Set of* 4 2·00 2·4

(Des N. Shewring. Litho Questa)

1985 (8 Mar). *Trees. T* **104** *and similar vert designs. Multicoloured. W* w **14**. *P* 14½.

371 7p. Type **104** 55 2
372 12p. Norfolk Island Pine 65 3
373 15p. Screwpine 75 3
374 20p. Eucalyptus 90 4
375 65p. Spore Tree .. .. 2·25 1·4
371/5 .. .. *Set of* 5 4·50 2·4

105 The Queen Mother with Prince Andrew at Silver Jubilee Service   **106** 32 Pdr. Smooth Bore Muzzle-loader, *c* 1820, and Royal Marine Artillery Hat Plate, *c* 1816

(Des A. Theobald (75p.), C. Abbott (others). Litho Questa)

1985 (7 June). *Life and Times of Queen Elizabeth the Queen Mother. T* **105** *and similar vert designs. Multicoloured W* w **16**. *P* 14½×14.

376 12p. With the Duke of York at Balmoral, 1924 .. .. 25 3
  w. Wmk inverted .. .. .. 15·00
377 15p. Type **105** 25 4
  w. Wmk inverted .. .. .. 1·50
378 20p. The Queen Mother at Ascot 30 5
  w. Wmk inverted .. .. .. 24·00
379 70p. With Prince Henry at his christening (from photo by Lord Snowdon) .. 80 1·7
376/9 .. .. *Set of* 4 1·40 2·7
MS380 91×73 mm. 75p. Visiting the *Queen Elizabeth 2* at Southampton, 1968. Wmk sideways .. .. 1·10 1·6

(Des W. Fenton. Litho Walsall)

1985 (19 July). *Guns on Ascension Island. T* **106** *and similar horiz designs. Multicoloured. W* w **14** (*sideways*). *P* 14×14½

381 12p. Type **106** 70 9
382 15p. 7 inch rifled muzzle-loader, *c* 1866, and Royal Cypher on barrel .. .. .. 80 1·0
383 20p. 7 pdr. rifled muzzle-loader, *c* 1877, and Royal Artillery badge .. .. .. 90 1·2
384 70p. 5·5 inch gun, 1941, and crest from H.M.S. *Hood* .. .. 2·50 3·5
381/4 .. .. *Set of* 4 4·50 6·0

107 Guide Flag   **108** *Clerodendrum fragrans*

(Des N. Shewring. Litho Questa)

1985 (4 Oct). *75th Anniv of Girl Guide Movement and International Youth Year. T* **107** *and similar vert designs. Multicoloured. W* w **14**. *P* 14½ × 14.

385 12p. Type **107** 75 6
  w. Wmk inverted .. .. .. 5·00
386 15p. Practising first aid 85 7
  w. Wmk inverted .. .. .. 5·00
387 20p. Camping 95 8
388 70p. Lady Baden-Powell .. .. .. 2·75 2·0
385/8 .. .. *Set of* 4 4·75 3·7

(Des Josephine Martin. Litho Questa)

85 (6 Dec). *Wild Flowers. T* **108** *and similar vert designs. Multicoloured.* W w **16**. P 14.
9 12p. Type **108** 45 75
0 15p. Shell Ginger 55 90
1 20p. Cape Daisy 65 90
2 70p. Ginger Lily .. .. 2·00 2·50
9/92 .. .. *Set of* 4 3·25 4·50

109 Newton's Reflector Telescope **110** Princess Elizabeth in 1926

(Des D. Hartley. Litho B.D.T.)

86 (7 Mar). *Appearance of Halley's Comet. T* **109** *and similar vert designs. Multicoloured.* W w **16**. P 14.
3 12p. Type **109** .. .. 75 1·10
4 15p. Edmond Halley and Old Greenwich Observatory .. .. 85 1·25
5 20p. Short's Gregorian telescope and comet, 1759 .. .. 95 1·25
6 70p. Ascension satellite tracking station and ICE spacecraft .. .. 2·75 3·50
3/6 .. .. *Set of* 4 4·50 6·00

(Des A. Theobald. Litho Format)

86 (21 Apr). *60th Birthday of Queen Elizabeth II. T* **110** *and similar vert designs. Multicoloured.* W w **16**. P 14×14½.
7 7p. Type **110** 15 25
8 15p. Queen making Christmas broadcast, 1952 .. .. 20 40
9 20p. At Garter ceremony, Windsor Castle, 1983 .. .. 25 50
0 35p. In Auckland, New Zealand, 1981 .. 35 80
1 £1 At Crown Agents' Head Office, London, 1983 .. .. 1·00 2·25
7/401 .. .. *Set of* 5 1·75 3·75

111 1975 Space Satellites 2p. Stamp **112** Prince Andrew and Miss Sarah Ferguson

(Des L. Curtis. Litho Walsall)

86 (22 May). *"Ameripex '86" International Stamp Exhibition, Chicago. T* **111** *and similar horiz designs showing previous Ascension stamps. Multicoloured.* W w **16** (*sideways**). P 14×14½.
2 12p. Type **111** 40 60
3 15p. 1980 "London 1980" International Stamp Exhibition 50p. 45 70
4 20p. 1976 Bicentenary of American Revolution 8p. 55 90
w. Wmk Crown to right of CA .. .. 50·00
5 70p. 1982 40th Anniv of Wideawake Airfield 10p. .. .. 1·25 2·00
2/5 .. .. *Set of* 4 2·40 3·75
S406 60×75 mm. 75p. Statue of Liberty .. 2·00 2·75

*The normal sideways watermark shows Crown to left of CA, *seen from the back of the stamp.*

(Des D. Miller. Litho Questa)

86 (23 July). *Royal Wedding. T* **112** *and similar square design. Multicoloured.* W w **16**. P 14.
7 15p. Type **112** 25 35
8 35p. Prince Andrew aboard H.M.S. *Brazen* .. 50 75

113 H.M.S. *Ganymede* (*c* 1811)

(Des E. Nisbet. Litho Questa)

86 (14 Oct). *Ships of the Royal Navy. T* **113** *and similar horiz designs. Multicoloured.* W w **16** (*sideways**) P 14½.
9 1p. Type **113** .. .. 55 1·25
0 2p. H.M.S. *Kangaroo* (*c* 1811) .. .. 60 1·25
w. Wmk Crown to right of CA
1 4p. H.M.S. *Trinculo* (*c* 1811) .. .. 60 1·25
2 5p. H.M.S. *Daring* (*c* 1811) .. .. 60 1·25
3 9p. H.M.S. *Thais* (*c* 1811) .. .. 70 1·25
4 10p. H.M.S. *Pheasant* (1819) .. .. 70 1·25
5 15p. H.M.S. *Myrmidon* (1819) .. .. 80 1·50
416 18p. H.M.S. *Atholl* (1825) .. .. 90 1·50
417 20p. H.M.S. *Medina* (1830) .. .. 90 1·50
418 25p. H.M.S. *Saracen* (1840) .. .. 1·00 1·75
419 30p. H.M.S. *Hydra* (*c* 1845) .. .. 1·00 1·75
420 50p. H.M.S. *Sealark* (1849) .. .. 1·25 2·25
421 70p. H.M.S. *Rattlesnake* (1868) .. .. 1·75 2·75
422 £1 H.M.S. *Penelope* (1889) .. .. 2·40 3·50
423 £2 H.M.S. *Monarch* (1897) .. .. 5·00 6·50
409/23 .. .. *Set of* 15 17·00 27·00

*The normal sideways watermark shows Crown to left of CA, *as seen from the back of the stamp.*

114 Cape Gooseberry **115** Ignition of Rocket Motors

(Des R. Gorringe. Litho Walsall)

1987 (29 Jan). *Edible Bush Fruits. T* **114** *and similar horiz designs. Multicoloured.* W w **16** (*sideways*). P 14.
424 12p. Type **114** 65 90
425 15p. Prickly Pear .. .. 75 1·00
426 20p. Guava .. .. 85 1·10
427 70p. Loquat .. .. 2·00 2·75
424/7 .. .. *Set of* 4 3·75 5·25

(Des D. Hartley. Litho Questa)

1987 (30 Mar). *25th Anniv of First American Manned Earth Orbit. T* **115** *and similar vert designs. Multicoloured.* W w **16**. P 14.
428 15p. Type **115** 55 75
429 18p. Lift-off 60 80
430 25p. Re-entry 75 95
431 £1 Splashdown .. .. 2·50 3·25
428/31 .. .. *Set of* 4 4·00 5·25
MS432 92×78 mm. 70p. "Friendship 7" capsule 1·75 2·00

116 Captains in Full Dress raising Red Ensign **117** *Cynthia cardui*

(Des C. Collins. Litho Format)

1987 (29 June). *19th-century Uniforms (1st series). Royal Navy, 1815–20. T* **116** *and similar vert designs. Multicoloured.* W w **16**. P 14.
433 25p. Type **116** 60 60
a. Horiz strip of 5. Nos. 433/7 .. .. 2·75
434 25p. Surgeon and seamen 60 60
435 25p. Seaman with water-carrying donkey .. 60 60
436 25p. Midshipman and gun 60 60
437 25p. Commander in undress uniform surveying 60 60
433/7 .. .. *Set of* 5 2·75 2·75

Nos. 433/7 were printed together, *se-tenant*, in horizontal strips of five throughout the sheet.
See also Nos. 478/82.

(Des I. Loe. Litho Questa)

1987 (10 Aug). *Insects (1st series). Butterflies. T* **117** *and similar horiz designs. Multicoloured.* W w **16** (*sideways*). P 14×14½.
438 15p. Type **117** 65 65
439 18p. *Danaus chrysippus* 70 75
440 25p. *Hypolimnas misippus* 85 85
441 £1 *Lampides boeticus* .. .. 2·25 2·50
438/41 .. .. *Set of* 4 4·00 4·25

See also Nos. 452/5 and 483/6.

40TH WEDDING ANNIVERSARY

118 Male Ascension Frigate Birds (**119**)

(Des N. Arlott. Litho B.D.T.)

1987 (8 Oct). *Sea Birds (1st series). T* **118** *and similar vert designs. Multicoloured.* W w **16**. P 14.
442 25p. Type **118** .. .. 1·50 1·75
a. Horiz strip of 5. Nos. 442/6 .. 6·50
443 25p. Juvenile Ascension Frigate Bird, Brown Booby and Blue-faced Boobies 1·50 1·75
444 25p. Male Ascension Frigate Bird and Blue-faced Boobies .. .. 1·50 1·75
445 25p. Female Ascension Frigate Bird .. 1·50 1·75
446 25p. Adult male feeding juvenile Ascension Frigate Bird .. .. 1·50 1·75
442/6 .. .. *Set of* 5 6·50 8·00

Nos. 442/6 were printed together, *se-tenant*, in horizontal strips of five throughout the sheet, forming a composite design.
See also Nos. 469/73.

1987 (9 Dec). *Royal Ruby Wedding. Nos.* 397/401 *optd with T* **119** *in silver.*
447 7p. Type **110** 15 15
448 15p. Queen making Christmas broadcast, 1952 .. .. 25 30
449 20p. At Garter ceremony, Windsor Castle, 1983 .. .. 30 40
a. Opt double .. .. 75·00
450 35p. In Auckland, New Zealand, 1981 .. 50 60
451 £1 At Crown Agents' Head Office, London, 1983 .. .. 1·25 1·40
447/51 .. .. *Set of* 5 2·25 2·50

(Des I. Loe. Litho Questa)

1988 (18 Jan). *Insects (2nd series). Horiz designs as T* **117**. *Multicoloured.* W w **16** (*sideways*). P 14×14½.
452 15p. *Gryllus bimaculatus* (field cricket) .. 50 50
453 18p. *Ruspolia differeus* (bush cricket) .. 55 55
454 25p. *Chilomenus lunata* (ladybird) .. 70 70
455 £1 *Diachrysia orichalcea* (moth) .. 2·25 2·25
452/5 .. .. *Set of* 4 3·50 3·50

120 Bate's Memorial, St. Mary's Church

(Des S. Noon. Litho Questa)

1988 (14 Apr). *150th Death Anniv of Captain William Bate (garrison commander, 1828–38). T* **120** *and similar horiz designs. Multicoloured.* W w **16** (*sideways*). P 14.
456 9p. Type **120** 35 35
457 15p. Commodore's Cottage 45 45
458 18p. North East Cottage 50 50
459 25p. Map of Ascension 70 70
460 70p. Captain Bate and marines .. 1·75 1·75
456/60 .. .. *Set of* 5 3·25 3·25

121 H.M.S. *Resolution* (ship of the line), 1667

(Des E. Nisbet. Litho Questa)

1988 (23 June). *Bicentenary of Australian Settlement. Ships of the Royal Navy. T* **121** *and similar diamond-shaped designs. Multicoloured.* W w **16** (*sideways**). P 14.
461 9p. Type **121** 65 35
w. Wmk Crown to left of CA .. .. 60·00
462 18p. H.M.S. *Resolution* (Captain Cook), 1772 .. .. 90 55
w. Wmk Crown to left of CA .. .. 60·00
463 25p. H.M.S. *Resolution* (battleship), 1892 1·25 75
464 65p. H.M.S. *Resolution* (battleship), 1916 2·25 1·50
461/4 .. .. *Set of* 4 4·50 2·75

*The normal sideways watermark shows Crown to right of CA, *as seen from the back of the stamp positioned with the Royal cypher in the top left corner.*

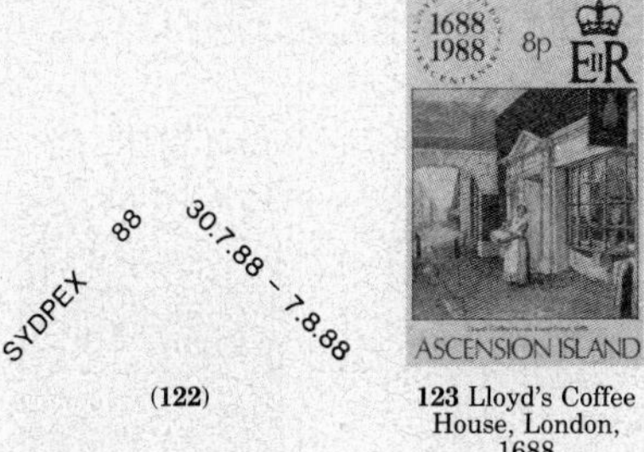

(**122**) **123** Lloyd's Coffee House, London, 1688

1988 (30 July). *"Sydpex '88" National Stamp Exhibition, Sydney. Nos.* 461/4 *optd with T* **122**.
465 9p Type **121** 40 25
466 18p H.M.S. *Resolution* (Captain Cook), 1772 .. .. 60 40
467 25p H.M.S. *Resolution* (battleship), 1892 .. 75 55
468 65p H.M.S. *Resolution* (battleship), 1916 .. 1·60 1·40
465/8 .. .. *Set of* 4 3·00 2·40

(Des N. Arlott. Litho Questa)

1988 (15 Aug). *Sea Birds (2nd series). Sooty Tern. Vert designs as T* **118.** *Multicoloured.* W w **16.** *P* 14.

469 25p. Pair displaying .. .. 1·00 1·00
 a. Horiz strip of 5. Nos. 469/73 .. 4·50
470 25p. Turning egg .. .. 1·00 1·00
471 25p. Incubating egg .. .. 1·00 1·00
472 25p. Feeding chick .. .. 1·00 1·00
473 25p. Immature Sooty Tern .. .. .. 1·00 1·00
469/73 .. .. *Set of* 5 4·50 4·50

Nos. 469/73 were printed together, *se-tenant*, in horizontal strips of five throughout the sheet, forming a composite design of a nesting colony.

(Des E. Nisbet and D. Miller (8p., 25p.), D. Miller (others). Litho Questa)

1988 (17 Oct). *300th Anniv of Lloyd's of London. T* **123** *and similar multicoloured designs.* W w **14** (*sideways on* 18, 25*p.*). *P* 14.

474 8p. Type **123** 25 35
475 18p. *Alert IV* (cable ship) (*horiz*) 65 70
476 25p. Satellite recovery in space (*horiz*) .. 80 90
477 65p. *Good Hope Castle* (cargo liner) on fire off Ascension, 1973 .. .. 1·75 2·00
474/7 .. .. *Set of* 4 3·00 3·50

(Des C. Collins. Litho B.D.T.)

1988 (21 Nov). *19th-century Uniforms (2nd series). Royal Marines,* 1821–34. *Vert designs as T* **116**. *Multicoloured.* W w **14.** *P* 14.

478 25p. Marines landing on Ascension, 1821 .. 1·10 1·60
 a. Horiz strip of 5. Nos. 478/82 .. 5·00
479 25p. Officer and Marine at semaphore station, 1829 .. .. 1·10 1·60
480 25p. Sergeant and Marine at Octagonal Tank, 1831 .. .. 1·10 1·60
481 25p. Officers at water pipe tunnel, 1833 .. 1·10 1·60
482 25p. Officer supervising construction of barracks, 1834 .. .. .. 1·10 1·60
478/82 .. .. *Set of* 5 5·00 7·00

Nos. 478/82 were printed together, *se-tenant,* in horizontal strips of five throughout the sheet.

(Des I. Loe. Litho Questa)

1989 (16 Jan). *Insects (3rd series). Horiz designs as T* **117**. *Multicoloured.* W w **16** (*sideways*). *P* 14×14½.

483 15p. *Trichoptilus wahlbergi* (moth) .. 75 50
484 18p. *Lucilia sericata* (fly) 80 55
485 25p. *Alceis ornatus* (weevil) .. .. 1·10 70
486 £1 *Polistes fuscatus* (wasp) .. .. 3·00 2·40
483/6 .. .. *Set of* 4 5·00 3·75

124 Two Land Crabs

125 1949 75th Anniversary of U. P. U. 1s. Stamp

(Des Doreen McGuiness. Litho Questa)

1989 (17 Apr). *Ascension Land Crabs* (Gecarcinus lagostoma). *T* **124** *and similar vert designs. Multicoloured.* W w **16**. *P* 14.

487 15p. Type **124** 40 45
488 18p. Crab with claws raised 45 50
489 25p. Crab on rock 60 70
490 £1 Crab in surf .. .. 2·25 2·50
487/90 .. .. *Set of* 4 3·25 3·75
MS491 98 × 101 mm. Nos. 487/90 .. .. 3·50 3·75

(Des D. Miller. Litho Walsall)

1989 (7 July). *"Philexfrance 89" International Stamp Exhibition, Paris, and "World Stamp Expo '89", Washington (1st issue). Sheet* 104×86 *mm.* W w **16**. *P* 14×13½.

MS492 **125** 75p. multicoloured .. .. .. 1·50 1·75

See also Nos. 498/503.

126 "Apollo 7" Tracking Station, Ascension

127 *Queen Elizabeth 2* (liner) and U.S.S. *John F. Kennedy* (aircraft carrier) in New York Harbour

(Des A. Theobald (£1), D. Miller (others). Litho Questa)

1989 (20 July). *20th Anniv of First Manned Landing on Moon. T* **126** *and similar multicoloured designs.* W w **16** (*sideways on* 18, 25*p*). *P* 14 × 13½ (15, 70*p.*) *or* 14 (*others*).

493 15p. Type **126** 65 45
494 18p. Launch of "Apollo 7" (30 × 30 *mm*) .. 70 50
495 25p. "Apollo 7" emblem (30 × 30 *mm*) .. 90 70
496 70p. "Apollo 7" jettisoning expended Saturn rocket .. .. 1·75 1·75
493/6 .. .. *Set of* 4 3·50 3·00
MS497 101 × 83 mm. £1 Diagram of "Apollo 11" mission. P 14 × 13½. .. .. .. 2·00 2·10

(Des D. Miller. Litho Walsall)

1989 (21 Aug). *"Philexfrance 89" International Stamp Exhibition, Paris, and "World Stamp Expo '89", Washington (2nd issue). T* **127** *and similar vert designs showing Statue of Liberty and Centenary celebrations. Multicoloured.* W w **14.** *P* 14×13½.

498 15p. Type **127** 35 35
 a. Sheetlet. Nos. 498/503 .. .. 1·90
499 15p. Cleaning Statue 35 35
500 15p. Statue of Liberty 35 35
501 15p. Crown of Statue 35 35
502 15p. Warships and New York skyline .. 35 35
503 15p. *Jean de Vienne* (French destroyer) and skyscrapers 35 35
498/503 .. .. *Set of* 6 1·90 1·90

Nos. 498/503 were printed, *se-tenant*, in sheetlets of 6.

128 Devil's Ashpit Tracking Station

(Des D. Miller. Litho Questa)

1989 (30 Sept). *Closure of Devil's Ashpit Tracking Station, Ascension. T* **128** *and similar horiz design. Multicoloured.* W w **16** (*sideways*). *P* 14.

504 18p. Type **128** 80 50
 a. Sheetlet. Nos. 504/5, each × 5 .. 7·00
505 25p. Launch of shuttle *Atlantis* 80 55

Nos. 504/5 were issued in sheetlets of ten containing vertical strips of five of each design, separated by a central inscribed gutter.

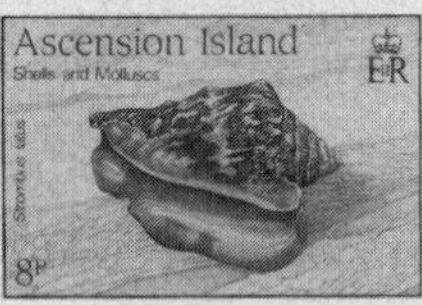

129 Bubonian Conch (*Strombus latus*)

130 Donkeys

(Des I. Loe. Litho Questa)

1989 (2 Nov). *Sea Shells. T* **129** *and similar horiz designs. Multicoloured.* W w **16** (*sideways*). *P* 14.

506 8p. Type **129** 40 30
507 18p. Giant Tun (*Tonna galea*) 70 50
508 25p. Doris Harp (*Harpa doris*) 90 65
509 £1 Atlantic Trumpet Triton (*Charonia variegata*) .. .. 2·75 2·50
506/9 .. .. *Set of* 4 4·25 3·50

(Des G. Drummond, adapted N. Harvey. Litho Walsall)

1989 (17 Nov). *Ascension Wildlife. T* **130** *and similar vert design. Multicoloured.* W w **16** (*sideways*). *P* 14.

510 18p. Type **130** 35 40
 a. Booklet pane. No. 510×6 .. .. 2·10
511 25p. Green Turtle 50 55
 a. Booklet pane. No. 511×4 .. .. 2·00

Nos. 510/11 were only issued in £1 stamp booklets and come with either the left or right-hand side imperforate.

131 Seaman's Pistol, Hat and Cutlass

132 Pair of Ascension Frigate Birds with Young

(Des C. Collins. Litho Questa)

1990 (12 Feb). *Royal Navy Equipment,* 1815-20. *T* **131** *and similar vert designs. Multicoloured.* W w **16**. *P* 14.

512 25p. Type **131** 65 65
 a. Horiz strip of 5. Nos. 512/16 .. 3·00
513 25p. Midshipman's belt plate, button, sword and hat 65 65
514 25p. Surgeon's hat, sword and instrument chest 65 65
515 25p. Captain's hat, telescope and sword 65 6
516 25p. Admiral's epaulette, megaphone, hat and pocket 65 6
512/16 .. .. *Set of* 5 3·00 3·

Nos. 512/16 were printed together, *se-tenant*, in horizont strips of 5 throughout the sheet.

See also Nos. 541/5.

(Des W. Oliver. Litho Questa)

1990 (5 Mar). *Ascension Frigate Bird. T* **132** *and similar ve designs. Multicoloured.* W w **14**. *P* 14½×14.

517 9p. Type **132** .. .. 1·25 1·
518 10p. Fledgeling .. .. 1·25 1·
519 11p. Adult male in flight .. .. 1·25 1·
520 15p. Female and immature birds in flight 1·40 1·
517/20 .. .. *Set of* 4 4·75 3·

133 Penny Black and Twopence Blue

(Des D. Miller. Litho Walsall)

1990 (3 May). *"Stamp World London 90" International Stam Exhibition, London. T* **133** *and similar horiz design. Multicoloured.* W w **14** (*sideways*). *P* 14.

521 9p. Type **133** 50 3
522 18p. Ascension postmarks used on G.B. stamps 70 5
523 25p. Unloading mail at Wideawake Airfield 95 7
524 £1 Mail van and Main Post Office .. 2·25 2·
521/4 .. .. *Set of* 4 4·00 3·5

134 "Queen Elizabeth, 1940" (Sir Gerald Kelly)

135 King George VI and Queen Elizabeth with Bren-gun Carrier

(Des D. Miller. Litho Questa)

1990 (4 Aug). *90th Birthday of Queen Elizabeth the Quee Mother.* W w **16**. *P* 14×15 (25*p.*) *or* 14½ (£1).

525 **134** 25p. multicoloured 75
526 **135** £1 black and deep lilac .. .. 2·25 2·

136 "Madonna and Child" (sculpture, Dino Felici)

137 *Garth Castle* (mail steamer), 1910

(Des D. Miller. Litho B.D.T.)

1990 (24 Oct). *Christmas. Works of Art. T* **136** *and similar ve designs. Multicoloured.* W w **14**. *P* 13½.

527 8p. Type **136** 70
528 18p. "Madonna and Child" (anon) .. .. 1·25 1·
529 25p. "Madonna and Child with St. John" (Johann Gebhard) .. .. .. 1·75 1·
530 65p. "Madonna and Child" (Giacomo Gritti) 3·00 3·
527/30 .. .. *Set of* 4 6·00 6·

(Des L. Curtis. Litho Walsall)

1990 (27 Nov). *Maiden Voyage of* St. Helena II. *T* **137** *an similar horiz designs. Multicoloured.* W w **14** (*sideways P* 14×14½.

531 9p. Type **137** 90
532 18p. *St. Helena I* during Falkland Islands campaign, 1982 .. .. .. 1·25 1·
533 25p. Launch of *St. Helena II* .. .. 1·75 1·
534 70p. Duke of York launching *St. Helena II* 3·00 3·
531/4 .. .. *Set of* 4 6·25 6·
MS535 100×100 mm. £1 *St. Helena II* and outline map of Ascension .. .. .. 3·50 5·

No. **MS**535 also contains two imperforate designs of simil stamps from St. Helena and Tristan da Cunha without fa values.

BRITISH FOR 175 YEARS

(138)

139 Queen Elizabeth II at Trooping the Colour

91 (5 Feb). *175th Anniv of Occupation. Nos.* 418, 420 *and* 422 *optd with T* **138** *in silver by Cartor.*

6 25p. H.M.S. *Saracen* (1840) . . . . 1·50 1·75
7 50p. H.M.S. *Sealark* (1849) . . . . 2·00 2·25
8 £1 H.M.S. *Penelope* (1889) . . . . 3·00 3·75
6/8 . . . . *Set of* 3 6·00 7·00

(Des D. Miller. Litho Questa)

91 (18 June). *65th Birthday of Queen Elizabeth II and 70th Birthday of Prince Philip. T* **139** *and similar vert design. Multicoloured. W w* **16** *(sideways). P* 14½ × 14.

9 25p. Type **139** . . . . 90 1·25
a. Horiz pair. Nos. 539/40 separated by label . . . . 1·75 2·50
0 25p. Prince Philip in naval uniform . . 90 1·25

Nos. 539/40 were printed together, *se-tenant*, in sheetlets of 10 × 5) with designs alternating and the vertical rows separated inscribed labels.

(Des C. Collins. Litho Questa)

91 (1 Aug). *Royal Marines Equipment,* 1821–44. *Vert designs as T* **131**. *Multicoloured. W w* **14**. *P* 14.

1 25p. Officer's shako, epaulettes, belt plate and button . . . . 1·10 1·40
a. Horiz strip of 5. Nos. 541/5 . . . . 5·00
2 25p. Officer's cap, sword, epaulettes and belt plate . . . . 1·10 1·40
3 25p. Drum major's shako and staff . . 1·10 1·40
4 25p. Sergeant's shako, chevrons, belt plate and canteen . . . . 1·10 1·40
5 25p. Drummer's shako and side-drum . . 1·10 1·40
1/5 . . . . *Set of* 5 5·00 6·00

Nos. 541/5 were printed together, *se-tenant*, in horizontal rips of 5 throughout the sheet.

140 B.B.C. World Service Relay Station

(Des D. Miller. Litho Questa)

91 (17 Sept). *25th Anniv of B.B.C. Atlantic Relay Station. T* **140** *and similar multicoloured designs. W w* **16** *(sideways on 15, 18p.). P* 14½.

6 15p. Type **140** . . . . 90 1·00
7 18p. Transmitters at English Bay . . 1·00 1·10
8 25p. Satellite receiving station (*vert*) . . 1·25 1·40
9 70p. Antenna support tower (*vert*) . . 2·50 3·00
6/9 . . . . *Set of* 4 5·00 6·00

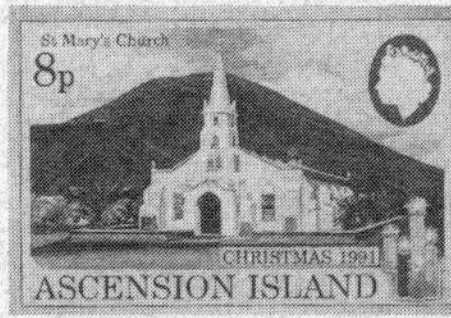

141 St. Mary's Church

(Des D. Miller. Litho Questa)

91 (1 Oct). *Christmas. Ascension Churches. T* **141** *and similar horiz designs. Multicoloured. W w* **16** *(sideways). P* 14.

0 8p. Type **141** 55 55
1 18p. Interior of St. Mary's Church . . 1·00 1·00
2 25p. Our Lady of Ascension Grotto . . 1·25 1·25
3 65p. Interior of Our Lady of Ascension Grotto . . . . 2·75 3·75
0/3 . . . . *Set of* 4 5·00 6·00

142 Black Durgon ("Blackfish")

(Des G. Drummond. Litho Walsall)

91 (10 Dec). *Fishes. T* **142** *and similar horiz designs. Multicoloured. W w* **14** *(sideways). P* 14.

4 1p. Type **142** 40 60
5 2p. Sergeant Major ("Five Finger") . . 50 60
6 4p. Resplendent Angelfish 60 70
7 5p. Derbio ("Silver Fish") 60 70

558 9p. Spotted Scorpionfish ("Gurnard") . . 70 80
559 10p. St Helena Parrotfish ("Blue Dad") . . 70 80
560 15p. St. Helena Butterflyfish ("Cunning Fish") . . . . 90 1·00
561 18p. Rock Hind ("Grouper") . . . . 1·00 1·00
562 20p. Spotted Moray . . . . . . 1·00 1·25
563 25p. Squirrelfish ("Hardback Soldierfish") . . 1·00 1·25
564 30p. Blue Marlin . . . . 1·25 1·40
565 50p. Wahoo . . . . 1·75 2·00
566 70p. Yellow-finned Tuna . . . . . . 2·25 2·75
567 £1 Blue Shark . . . . 2·75 3·50
568 £2.50, Bottlenose Dolphin . . . . 6·00 7·00
554/68 . . . . *Set of* 15 19·00 23·00

143 Holland's Crater

(Des D. Miller. Litho Questa (70p.), Walsall (others))

1992 (6 Feb). *40th Anniv of Queen Elizabeth II's Accession. T* **143** *and similar horiz designs. W w* **14** *(sideways). P* 14.

569 9p. Type **143** 30 30
570 15p. Green Mountain 50 50
571 18p. Boatswain Bird Island 60 60
572 25p. Three portraits of Queen Elizabeth . . 80 80
573 70p. Queen Elizabeth II . . . . . . 2·00 2·00
569/73 . . . . *Set of* 5 3·75 3·75

The portraits shown on the 25p. are repeated from the three lower values of the set.

144 Compass Rose and *Eye of the Wind* (cadet brig)

145 Control Tower, Wideawake Airfield

(Des R. Watton. Litho Walsall)

1992 (18 Feb). *500th Anniv of Discovery of America by Columbus and Re-enactment Voyages. T* **144** *and similar horiz designs. Multicoloured. W w* **14** *(sideways). P* 13½×14.

574 9p. Type **144** 75 70
575 18p. Map of re-enactment voyages and *Soren Larsen* (cadet brigantine) . . 1·25 1·00
576 25p. *Santa Maria, Pinta* and *Nina* . . 1·50 1·25
577 70p. Columbus and *Santa Maria* . . 2·75 2·75
574/7 . . . . *Set of* 4 5·75 5·25

(Des N. Shewring. Litho Questa)

1992 (5 May). *50th Anniv of Wideawake Airfield. T* **145** *and similar square designs. Multicoloured. W w* **14** *(sideways). P* 14.

578 15p. Type **145** 65 65
579 18p. Nose hangar 70 70
580 25p. Site preparation by U.S. Army engineers 90 90
581 70p. Laying fuel pipeline . . . . . . 2·25 2·25
578/81 . . . . *Set of* 4 4·00 4·00

146 Hawker Siddeley H.S.801 Nimrod

147 "Christmas in Great Britain and Ascension"

(Des N. Shewring. Litho Questa)

1992 (12 June). *10th Anniv of Liberation of Falkland Islands. Aircraft. T* **146** *and similar square designs. Multicoloured. W w* **14** *(sideways). P* 14.

582 15p. Type **146** . . . . 1·00 1·00
583 18p. Vickers VC-10 landing at Ascension . . 1·10 1·10
584 25p. Westland Wessex HU Mk 5 helicopter lifting supplies . . . . . . 1·40 1·25
585 65p. Avro Vulcan B.2 over Ascension . . 2·75 3·00
582/5 . . . . *Set of* 4 5·50 5·50

MS586 116×116 mm. 15p. + 3p. Type **146**; 18p. + 4p. As No. 583; 25p. + 5p. As No. 584; 65p. + 13p. As No. 585 . . . . 4·75 6·00

The premiums on No. **MS**586 were for the S.S.A.F.A.

(Adapted G. Vasarhelyi. Litho Walsall)

1992 (13 Oct). *Christmas. Children's Paintings. T* **147** *and similar horiz designs. Multicoloured. W w* **16** *(sideways). P* 14.

587 8p. Type **147** 60 50
588 18p. "Santa Claus riding turtle" . . 1·00 80
589 25p. "Nativity" . . . . 1·25 1·10
590 65p. "Nativity with rabbit" . . . . 2·75 3·25
587/90 . . . . *Set of* 4 5·00 5·00

148 Male Canary singing

149 Sopwith Snipe

(Des N. Arlott. Litho Questa)

1993 (12 Jan). *Yellow Canary. T* **148** *and similar vert designs. Multicoloured. W w* **14**. *P* 14½×14.

591 15p. Type **148** 75 60
592 18p. Adult male and female 85 70
593 25p. Young birds calling for food 95 90
594 70p. Adults and young birds on the wing . . 2·50 3·00
591/4 . . . . *Set of* 4 4·50 4·75

(Des A. Theobald. Litho Questa)

1993 (1 Apr). *75th Anniv of Royal Air Force. T* **149** *and similar horiz designs. Multicoloured. W w* **14** *(sideways). P* 14.

595 20p. Type **149** . . . . 1·00 75
596 25p. Supermarine Southampton . . . . 1·10 85
597 30p. Avro Type 652 Anson . . . . 1·25 95
598 70p. Vickers-Armstrong Wellington . . 2·25 2·50
595/8 . . . . *Set of* 4 5·00 4·50

MS599 110×77 mm. 25p. Westland Lysander; 25p. Armstrong-Whitworth Meteor ("Gloster Meteor"); 25p. De Havilland D.H.106 Comet; 25p. Hawker Siddeley H.S.801 Nimrod . . 2·40 3·50

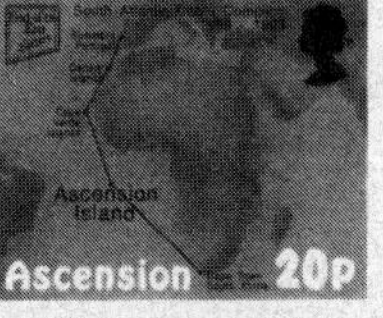

150 Map of South Atlantic Cable

151 Lanatana Camara

(Des D. Miller. Litho Questa)

1993 (8 June). *25th Anniv of South Atlantic Cable Company. T* **150** *and similar horiz designs. Multicoloured. W w* **16** *(sideways). P* 14½.

600 20p. Type **150** 80 80
601 25p. *Vercors* laying cable 90 90
602 30p. Map of Ascension . . . . . . 1·00 1·00
603 70p. *Vercors* (cable ship) off Ascension . . 2·25 2·25
600/3 . . . . *Set of* 4 4·50 4·50

(Des N. Shewring. Litho Questa)

1993 (3 Aug). *Local Flowers. T* **151** *and similar horiz designs. Multicoloured. W w* **16** *(sideways). P* 14×14½.

604 20p. Type **151** 80 70
605 25p. Moonflower 90 75
606 30p. Hibiscus . . . . 1·00 85
607 70p. Frangipani . . . . 2·25 2·00
604/7 . . . . *Set of* 4 4·50 3·75

152 Posting Christmas Card to Ascension

153 Ichthyosaurus

(Des N. Shewring. Litho Walsall)

1993 (19 Oct). *Christmas. T* **152** *and similar vert designs. Multicoloured. W w* **14**. *P* 14½×14.

608 12p. Type **152** 45 35
609 20p. Loading mail onto R.A.F. Lockheed L-1011 TriStar at Brize Norton . . 75 55
610 25p. Tristar over South Atlantic 85 65
611 30p. Unloading mail at Wideawake Airfield 1·10 75
612 65p. Receiving card and Georgetown Post Office . . . . 1·60 1·60
608/12 . . . . *Set of* 5 4·25 3·50

MS613 161×76 mm. Nos. 608/12 . . . . 5·50 4·50

(Des N. Shewring. Litho B.D.T.)

1994 (25 Jan). *Prehistoric Aquatic Reptiles. T* **153** *and similar vert designs. Multicoloured. W w* **14**. *P* 14.

614 12p. Type **153** 55 55
615 20p. Metriorhynchus 75 75
616 25p. Mosasaurus 80 80
617 30p. Elasmosaurus 90 90
618 65p. Plesiosaurus . . . . 1·75 2·00
614/18 . . . . *Set of* 5 4·25 4·50

NEW INFORMATION

The editor is always interested to correspond with people who have new information that will improve or correct the Catalogue.

(154)

155 Young Green Turtles heading towards Sea

1994 (18 Feb). *"Hong Kong '94" International Stamp Exhibition. Nos.* 614/18 *optd with T* **154**.
619 12p. Type **153** 65 70
620 20p. Metriorhynchus 85 90
621 25p. Mosasaurus .. .. 90 1·00
622 30p. Elasmosaurus .. .. .. 1·00 1·10
623 65p. Plesiosaurus .. .. 1·90 2·25
619/23 .. .. *Set of* 5 4·75 5·50

(Des A. Robinson. Litho Questa)

1994 (22 Mar). *Green Turtles. T* **155** *and similar horiz designs. Multicoloured. W* w 14 (*sideways*). *P* 14.
624 20p. Type **155** .. .. 1·10 80
625 25p. Turtle digging nest .. .. .. 1·25 90
626 30p. Turtle leaving sea .. .. .. 1·40 1·10
627 65p. Turtle swimming .. .. .. 2·25 2·50
624/7 .. .. *Set of* 4 5·50 4·75
MS628 116×90 mm. 30p. Turtle leaving sea (*different*); 30p. Turtle digging nest (*different*); 30p. Young turtles heading towards sea (*different*); 30p. Young turtle leaving nest .. 6·00 7·00

156 *Yorkshireman* (tug)

(Des R. Watton. Litho Walsall)

1994 (14 June). *Civilian Ships used in Liberation of Falkland Islands,* 1982. *T* **156** *and similar horiz designs. Multicoloured. W* w **16** (*sideways*). *P* 14.
629 20p. Type **156** .. .. 1·10 80
630 25p. *St. Helena I* (minesweeper support ship) .. .. 1·25 90
631 30p. *British Esk* (tanker) .. .. .. 1·40 1·10
632 65p. *Uganda* (hospital ship) .. .. 2·25 2·50
629/32 .. .. *Set of* 4 5·50 4·75

157 Sooty Tern Chick

(Des N. Arlott. Litho Walsall)

1994 (16 Aug). *Sooty Tern. T* **157** *and similar horiz designs. Multicoloured. W* w 14 (*sideways*). *P* 14½.
633 20p. Type **157** 80 90
634 25p. Juvenile bird 85 95
635 30p. Brooding adult .. .. .. 95 1·10
636 65p. Adult male performing courting display 1·75 2·25
633/6 .. .. *Set of* 4 4·00 4·75
MS637 77×58 mm. £1 Flock of Sooty Terns .. 2·50 3·50

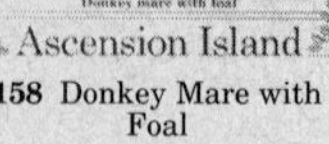

158 Donkey Mare with Foal

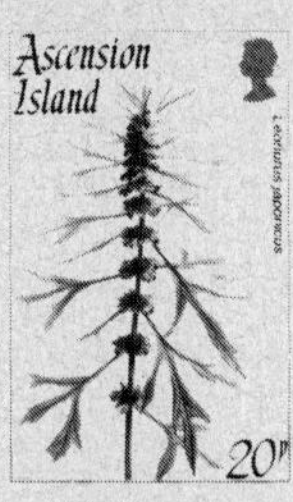

159 *Leonurus japonicus*

(Des Josephine Martin. Litho Questa)

1994 (11 Oct). *Christmas. Donkeys. T* **158** *and similar horiz designs. Multicoloured. W* w **16** (*sideways*). *P* 14½.
638 12p. Type **158** 55 55
639 20p. Juvenile 75 75
640 25p. Foal 80 80
641 30p. Adult and Cattle Egrets 95 95
642 65p. Adult .. .. 1·90 2·50
638/42 .. .. *Set of* 5 4·50 5·00

(Des Jennifer Toombs. Litho Walsall)

1995 (10 Jan). *Flowers. T* **159** *and similar multicoloured designs. W* w **16** (*sideways on horiz designs*). *P* 14.
643 20p. Type **159** .. .. 1·00 85
644 25p. *Catharanthus roseus* (*horiz*) .. .. 1·10 95
645 30p. *Mirabilis jalapa* .. .. .. 1·25 1·10
646 65p. *Asclepias curassavica* (*horiz*) .. 2·25 2·50
643/6 .. .. *Set of* 4 5·00 4·75

160 Two Boats and Green Mountain

(Des S. Noon. Litho Questa)

1995 (7 Mar). *Late* 19*th-century Scenes. T* **160** *and similar horiz designs, each in cinnamon and reddish brown. W* w **16** (*sideways*). *P* 14×14½.
647 12p. Type **160** 50 50
648 20p. Island Stewards' Store 70 70
649 25p. Navy headquarters and barracks .. 80 80
650 30p. Police office .. .. 1·50 1·25
651 65p. Pierhead .. .. 1·75 2·25
647/51 .. .. *Set of* 5 4·75 5·00

161 5.5-inch Coastal Battery

162 Male and Female *Lampides boeticus*

(Des R. Watton. Litho Questa)

1995 (8 May). 50*th Anniv of End of Second World War. T* **161** *and similar multicoloured designs. W* w **16** (*sideways*). *P* 14.
652 20p. Type **161** 75 75
653 25p. Fairey Swordfish aircraft .. .. 1·00 1·00
654 30p. H.M.S. *Dorsetshire* (cruiser) .. .. 1·25 1·25
655 65p. H.M.S. *Devonshire* (cruiser) .. .. 2·25 2·50
652/5 .. .. *Set of* 4 4·75 5·00
MS656 75×85 mm. £1 Reverse of 1939–45 War Medal (*vert*). W w **14** .. .. .. 2·50 3·25

(Des K. McGee. Litho B.D.T.)

1995 (1 Sept). *Butterflies. T* **162** *and similar vert designs. Multicoloured. W* w **16**. *P* 14.
657 20p. Type **162** 80 65
658 25p. *Vanessa cardui* 90 75
659 30p. Male *Hypolimnas misippus* .. .. 1·10 85
660 65p. *Danaus chrysippus* .. .. .. 2·00 1·90
657/60 .. .. *Set of* 4 4·25 3·75
MS661 114×85 mm. £1 *Vanessa atalanta* .. 3·25 3·00
No. **MS**661 includes the "Singapore '95" International Stamp Exhibition logo on the sheet margin.

163 "Santa Claus on Boat" (Phillip Stephens)

(Des B. Dare. Litho Walsall)

1995 (10 Oct). *Christmas. Children's Drawings. T* **163** *and similar horiz designs. Multicoloured. W* w **14** (*sideways*). *P* 14.
662 12p. Type **163** 50 50
663 20p. "Santa sitting on Wall" (Kelly Lemon) 75 75
664 25p. "Santa in Chimney" (Mario Anthony) 80 80
665 30p. "Santa riding Dolphin" (Verena Benjamin) .. .. 90 1·00
666 65p. "Santa in Sleigh over Ascension" (Tom Butler) .. .. 1·75 2·50
662/6 .. .. *Set of* 5 4·25 5·00

164 *Cypraea lurida oceanica*

165 Queen Elizabeth II and St. Mary's Church

(Des I. Loe. Litho B.D.T.)

1996 (10 Jan). *Molluscs. T* **164** *and similar horiz design Multicoloured. W* w **16** (*sideways*). *P* 14.
667 12p. Type **164** 65 6
a. Horiz strip of 4. Nos. 667/70 .. .. 4·00
668 25p. *Cypraea spurca sanctaehelenae* .. 1·00 1·0
669 30p. *Harpa doris* .. .. 1·00 1·0
670 65p. *Umbraculum umbraculum* .. .. 1·75 1·7
667/70 .. .. *Set of* 4 4·00 4·0
Nos. 667/70 were printed together, *se-tenant*, in horizonta strips of 4 throughout the sheet with the backgrounds forming composite design.

(Des D. Miller. Litho B.D.T.)

1996 (22 Apr). 70*th Birthday of Queen Elizabeth II. T* **165** *an similar vert designs. W* w **16**. *P* 13½.
671 20p. Type **165** 55 5
672 25p. The Residency 60 6
673 30p. The Roman Catholic Grotto 70 7
674 65p. The Exiles' Club .. .. .. 1·75 1·7
671/4 .. .. *Set of* 4 3·25 3·2

166 American Army Jeep

167 Madeiran Storm Petrel

(Des B. Dare. Litho Walsall)

1996 (8 June). *"CAPEX '96" International Stamp Exhibitio Toronto. Island Transport. T* **166** *and similar horiz design Multicoloured. W* w **16** (*sideways*). *P* 14.
675 20p. Type **166** 65 6
676 25p. Citroen 7.5hp two-seater car, 1924 .. 70 7
677 30p. Austin ten tourer car, 1930 .. .. 80 8
678 65p. Series 1 Land Rover .. .. .. 1·75 1·7
675/8 .. .. *Set of* 4 3·50 3·5

(Des N. Arlott. Litho Walsall)

1996 (12 Aug). *Birds and their Young. T* **167** *and similar ve designs. Multicoloured. W* w **14**. *P* 13½×13.
679 1p. Type **167** 10 1
680 2p. Red-billed Tropic Bird 10 1
681 4p. Common Mynah 10 1
682 5p. House Sparrow 10 1
683 7p. Common Waxbill 15 2
684 10p. White Tern 20 2
685 12p. Bare-throated Francolin 25 3
686 15p. Common Noddy 30 3
687 20p. Yellow Canary 40 4
688 25p. Lesser Noddy 50 5
689 30p. Red-footed Booby 60 6
690 40p. White-tailed Tropic Bird 80 8
691 65p. Brown Booby .. .. .. 1·25 1·4
692 £1 Blue-faced Booby .. .. .. 2·00 2·1
693 £2 Sooty Tern .. .. 4·00 4·2
694 £3 Ascension Frigate Bird .. .. 6·00 6·2
679/94 .. .. *Set of* 16 16·00 17·0
For 65p. and £1 (with "1997" imprint date) used in miniatu sheets see Nos. **MS**708 and **MS**718.
For 15p. and 35p. in designs of 7p and 20p, but 20×24 m from booklets see Nos. 726/7.

168 Pylons

12p
ASCENSION ISLAND

169 Santa Claus on Dish Aerial

(Des D. Miller. Litho Walsall)

1996 (9 Sept). 30*th Anniv of B.B.C. Atlantic Relay Statio T* **168** *and similar horiz designs. Multicoloured. W* w (*sideways*). *P* 14×14½.
695 20p. Type **168** 65
696 25p. Pylons (*different*) 70
697 30p. Pylons and station buildings .. 80
698 65p. Dish aerial, pylon and beach .. 1·75 1·
695/8 .. .. *Set of* 4 3·50 3·

(Des B. Dare. Litho Questa)

1996 (23 Sept). *Christmas. T* **169** *and similar horiz desig showing Santa Claus. Multicoloured. W* w **14** (*sideways P* 14×14½.
699 12p. Type **169** 35
700 20p. Playing golf 65 6
701 25p. In deck chair 65 6
702 30p. On top of aircraft 75 7
703 65p. On funnel of *St. Helena II* (mail ship) 1·75 2·0
699/703 .. .. *Set of* 5 3·75 4·0

170 Date Palm

171 Red Ensign and *Maersk Ascension* (tanker)

(Des R. Watton. Litho Walsall)

1997 (7 Jan). *"HONG KONG '97" International Stamp Exhibition. Trees. T* **170** *and similar vert designs. Multicoloured.* W w **14**. *P* 14½×14.
704 20p. Type **170** 55 55
705 25p. Mauritius Hemp 65 65
706 30p. Norfolk Island Pine 75 75
707 65p. Dwarf Palm .. .. 1·50 1·60
704/7 .. .. *Set of* 4 3·00 3·25

(Des D. Miller. Litho Questa)

1997 (3 Feb). *"HONG KONG '97" International Stamp Exhibition. Sheet* 130×90 *mm containing design as No.* 691. *Multicoloured.* W w **14**. *P* 14.
MS708 65p. Brown Booby .. .. 1·50 1·50

(Des A. Theobald. Litho Walsall)

1997 (1 Apr). *Flags. T* **171** *and similar vert designs. Multicoloured.* W w **14**. *P* 14½.
709 12p. Type **171** 45 45
710 25p. R.A.F. flag and Tristar airliner .. 75 75
711 30p. N.A.S.A. emblem amd Space Shuttle *Atlantis* landing 85 85
712 65p. White Ensign and H.M.S. *Northumberland* (frigate) .. .. 1·60 1·60
709/12 .. .. *Set of* 4 3·25 3·25

172 *Solanum sodomaeum*

173 Queen Elizabeth II

(Des I. Loe. Litho Questa)

1997 (2 June). *Wild Herbs. T* **172** *and similar horiz designs. Multicoloured.* W w **14** (*sideways*). *P* 14½.
713 30p. Type **172** .. .. 90 1·00
a. Horiz strip of 5. Nos. 713/17 .. .. 4·00
714 30p. *Ageratum conyzoides* .. .. .. 90 1·00
715 30p. *Leonurus sibiricus* .. .. .. 90 1·00
716 30p. *Cerastium vulgatum* .. .. .. 90 1·00
717 30p. *Commelina diffusa* .. .. .. 90 1·00
713/17 .. .. *Set of* 5 4·00 4·50
Nos. 713/17 were printed together, *se-tenant*, in horizontal strips of 5 with the backgrounds forming a composite design.

(Des. D. Miller. Litho Questa)

1997 (20 June). *Return of Hong Kong to China. Sheet* 130×90 *mm containing design as No.* 692, *but with "1997" imprint date.* W w **14** (*inverted*). *P* 13½×13.
MS718 £1 Blue-faced Booby .. .. .. 2·00 2·10

(Des N. Shewring (No. **MS**725), D. Miller (others). Litho Questa (No. **MS**725), B.D.T. (others))

1997 (10 July). *Golden Wedding of Queen Elizabeth and Prince Philip. T* **173** *and similar vert designs. Multicoloured.* W w **16**. *P* 13½.
719 20p. Type **173** 65 65
a. Horiz pair. Nos. 719/20 .. .. .. 1·25 1·25
720 20p. Prince Philip on horseback 65 65
721 25p. Queen Elizabeth with polo pony .. 75 75
a. Horiz pair. Nos. 721/2 .. .. .. 1·50 1·50
722 25p. Prince Philip in Montserrat 75 75
723 30p. Queen Elizabeth and Prince Philip .. 80 80
a. Horiz pair. Nos. 723/4 .. .. .. 1·60 1·60
724 30p. Prince William and Prince Harry on horseback 80 80
719/24 .. .. *Set of* 6 4·00 4·00
MS725 110×70 mm. $1.50, Queen Elizabeth and Prince Philip in landau (*horiz*). W w **14** (sideways). P 14×14½ .. .. 3·50 3·50
Nos. 719/20, 721/2 and 723/4 were each printed together, *se-tenant*, in horizontal pairs throughout the sheets with the backgrounds forming composite designs.

(Des N. Arlott. Litho Walsall)

1997 (1 Sept). *Birds and their Young. Designs as Nos.* 683 *and* 687, *but smaller, size* 20×24 *mm.* W w **14** (*sideways*). *P* 14.
726 15p. Common Waxbill 30 35
a. Booklet pane. Nos. 726/7, each ×2 .. 2·00
727 35p. Yellow Canary 70 75
Nos. 726/7 were only issued in £1 stamp booklets with the vertical edges of the booklet pane imperforate so that they exist imperforate at left or right.

174 Black Marlin

175 Interior of St. Mary's Church

(Des R. Watton. Litho Walsall)

1997 (3 Sept). *Gamefish. T* **174** *and similar horiz designs. Multicoloured.* W w **16** (*sideways*). *P* 14×14½.
728 12p. Type **174** 40 40
729 20p. Atlantic Sailfish 65 65
730 25p. Swordfish 75 75
731 30p. Wahoo 85 85
732 £1 Yellowfin Tuna .. .. 2·25 2·25
728/32 .. .. *Set of* 5 4·50 4·50

(Des G. Vasarhelyi. Litho Walsall)

1997 (1 Oct). *Christmas. T* **175** *and similar vert designs.* W w **16**. *P* 14.
733 15p. Type **175** 35 40
734 35p. Falklands memorial window showing Virgin and Child 75 80
735 40p. Falklands memorial window showing Archangel 85 95
736 50p. Pair of stained glass windows .. 1·10 1·25
733/6 .. .. *Set of* 4 2·75 3·00

176 *Cactoblastis cactorum* (caterpillar and moth)

177 Diana, Princess of Wales, 1985

(Des I. Loe. Litho B.D.T.)

1998 (10 Feb). *Biological Control using Insects. T* **176** *and similar vert designs.* W w **14**. *P* 14.
737 15p. Type **176** 40 40
738 35p. *Teleonemia scrupulosa* (lace-bug) .. 80 80
739 40p. *Neltumius arizonensis* (beetle) .. 90 90
740 50p. *Algarobius prosopis* (beetle) .. .. 1·25 1·25
737/40 .. .. *Set of* 4 3·00 3·00

(Des D. Miller. Litho Questa)

1998 (31 Mar). *Diana, Princess of Wales Commemoration. Sheet,* 145×70 *mm, containing T* **177** *and similar vert designs. Multicoloured.* W w **14** (*sideways*). *P* 14½×14.
MS741 35p. Type **177**; 35p. Wearing yellow blouse, 1992; 35p. Wearing grey jacket, 1984; 35p. Carrying bouquets (*sold at* £1.40 + 20p. *charity premium*) .. .. 3·75 3·75

178 Fairey Fawn

179 Barn Swallow

(Des A. Theobald. Litho Questa)

1998 (1 Apr). *80th Anniv of Royal Air Force. T* **178** *and similar horiz designs. Multicoloured.* W w **16** (*sideways*). *P* 14.
742 15p. Type **178** 50 50
743 35p. Vickers Vernon .. .. 1·00 1·00
744 40p. Supermarine Spitfire F.22 .. .. 1·25 1·25
745 50p. Bristol Britannia C.2 .. .. .. 1·40 1·40
742/5 .. .. *Set of* 4 3·75 3·75
MS746 110×77 mm. 50p. Blackburn Kangaroo; 50p. S.E.5a; 50p. Curtiss Kittyhawk III; 50p. Boeing Fortress II .. .. 4·75 4·75

(Des N. Arlott. Litho Walsall)

1998 (15 June). *Migratory Birds. T* **179** *and similar vert designs. Multicoloured.* W w **14**. *P* 14.
747 15p. Type **179** 45 45
748 25p. House Martin 70 75
749 35p. Cattle Egret 90 95
750 40p. Common Swift .. .. 1·00 1·10
751 50p. Allen's Gallinule .. .. 1·10 1·25
747/51 .. .. *Set of* 4 3·75 4·00

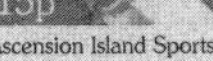

180 Cricket

181 Children in Nativity Play

(Des S. Noon. Litho Walsall)

1998 (17 Aug). *Sporting Activities. T* **180** *and similar vert designs. Multicoloured.* W w **14**. *P* 14.
752 15p. Type **180** 55 50
753 35p. Golf .. .. 1·00 90
754 40p. Football .. .. 1·00 95
755 50p. Shooting .. .. 1·10 1·25
752/5 .. .. *Set of* 4 3·25 3·25

(Des N. Shewring. Litho Questa)

1998 (1 Oct). *Christmas. T* **181** *and similar horiz designs. Multicoloured.* W w **14** (*sideways*). P 14.
756 15p. Type **181** 45 40
757 35p. Santa Claus arriving on Ascension .. 1·00 1·00
758 40p. Santa Claus on carnival float .. 1·10 1·10
759 50p. Carol singers .. .. 1·10 1·25
756/9 .. .. *Set of* 4 3·25 3·25

STAMP BOOKLETS

1963 (23 May). *Buff cover. Stitched.*
SB1 10s.6d. booklet containing 1d., 1½d., 2d., 3d., 6d. and 1s. 6d. (Nos. 70/3, 75, 79), each in block of 4 70·00

1971 (15 Feb). *White cover. Stitched.*
SB2 44p. booklet containing ½p., 1p., 1½p., 2p., 2½p. and 3½p. (Nos 135/40), each in block of 4 17·00
a. "5/71" imprint on back cover .. .. 30·00

1981 (9 Nov)–**84**. *Printed cover,* 104×58 *mm, showing Ascension landscape.*
SB3 £1.20, booklet containing 2p., 3p., 10p. and 15p. (Nos. 283A/4A, 288A, 290A), each in block of 4 (black and pink cover stapled at left) .. 12·00
a. Black and lemon cover stapled at right (4.84) 10·00

1982 (15 June). *Blue, red and brown cover,* 101×60 *mm, showingWorld War II aircraft. A. Cover stapled at left and inscriptions printed in brown. B. Cover stapled at right and inscriptions printed in blue.*
SB4 60p. booklet containing 5p. and 10p. (Nos. 318/19), each in block of 4 (inscr in brown. Stapled at left) .. .. 6·00
a. Inscr in blue. Stapled at right .. .. 6·00

1989 (17 Nov). *Blackish olive and deep brown cover,* 54×41 *mm, showing turtle and outline map of Ascension. Panes attached by selvedge.*
SB5 £1 booklet containing pane of 6 (No. 510a) .. 2·75
SB6 £1 booklet containing pane of 4 (No. 511a) .. 2·75

1989 (17 Nov). *As Nos.* SB5/6, *but with "Expo 89" logo printed on cover in black.*
SB7 £1 booklet containing pane of 6 (No. 510a) .. 4·75
SB8 £1 booklet containing pane of 4 (No. 511a) .. 4·75

1997 (1 Sept). *Cover as Nos.* SB5/6. *Pane attached by selvedge.*
SB9 £1 booklet containing pane of 4 (No. 726a) .. 2·00

POSTAGE DUE STAMPS

D 1 Outline Map of Ascension

(Des L. Curtis. Litho Questa)

1986 (9 June). W w **16**. *P* 14½×14.
D1 D 1 1p. deep brown and cinnamon 10 10
D2 2p. deep brown and bright orange .. 10 10
D3 5p. deep brown and orange-vermilion .. 10 10
D4 7p. black and bright reddish violet .. 15 20
D5 10p. black and violet-blue 20 25
D6 25p. black and pale emerald 50 55
D1/6 .. .. *Set of* 6 1·10 1·25

Australia

The Australian colonies of New South Wales, Queensland, South Australia, Tasmania, Victoria and Western Australia produced their own issues before federation in 1901. Stamps inscribed for the individual states continued in use after federation until the end of December 1912.

NEW SOUTH WALES

PRICES FOR STAMPS ON COVER

Nos. 1/83	*from* ×2
Nos. 84/110	*from* ×3
No. 110*b*	*from* ×10
Nos. 111/13	*from* × 2
No. 114	—
Nos. 115/24	*from* × 2
Nos. 125/6	—
Nos. 127/53	*from* × 2
Nos. 154/70	*from* × 3
Nos. 171/2	—
No. 173	*from* × 2
Nos. 174/81	—
Nos. 186/202	*from* × 2
Nos. 203/6	*from* × 10
Nos. 207/21	*from* × 5
Nos. 222/39	*from* × 6
Nos. 240/1	*from* × 2
Nos. 241*a*/3	*from* × 10
Nos. 244/52	—
Nos. 253/73	*from* × 10
Nos. 274/80	—
Nos. 281/4	*from* × 15
Nos. 285/7	*from* × 10
Nos. 287*c*/*d*	*from* × 2
Nos. 288/97	*from* × 10
Nos. 298/312	*from* × 12
Nos. 313/28	*from* × 10
No. 329	—
Nos. 330/45	*from* × 12
No. 346	—
Nos. 347/60	*from* × 12
No. O1	—
Nos. O2/12	*from* × 4
Nos. O13/18	—
Nos. O19/34	*from* × 20
Nos. O35/8	—
Nos. O39/47	*from* × 40
Nos. O48/53	—
Nos. O54/8	*from* × 20
No. O59	—
Nos. D1/7	*from* × 50
Nos. D8/10	—
Nos. D11/15	*from* × 50

EMBOSSED LETTER SHEETS AND ENVELOPES. From 1 November 1838 the Sydney G.P.O. supplied envelopes and letter sheets pre-stamped with an albino embossing, as illustrated, at $1^1/_2$d. each or 1s. 3d. per dozen. From January 1841 the price was reduced to 1s. per dozen and later the public were able to present their own stationery for embossing. The circular design measures approximately 29 mm in diameter and examples are known on laid or wove paper of varying colours. Embossing continued until 1 May 1852 after which the Post Office refused to carry mail which was not franked with postage stamps. The die was used for reprints in 1870 and 1898 before it was destroyed later the same year.

A

PRINTERS. The early issues of New South Wales were printed on a press supervised by the Inspector of Stamps. On 1 January 1857 this responsibility passed to the Government printer who produced all subsequent issues, *unless otherwise stated*.

SPECIMEN OVERPRINTS. Those listed are from U.P.U. distributions between 1892 and 1903. Further "Specimen" overprints exist, but these were used for other purposes. From 1891 examples of some of these Specimens, together with cancelled stamps, were sold to collectors by the N.S.W. Post Office.

NEW SOUTH WALES USED IN NEW CALEDONIA. From October 1859 mail for Europe from New Caledonia was routed via Sydney and franked with New South Wales stamps in combination with local issues. Such N.S.W. stamps were cancelled on arrival in Sydney.

1

2

(Eng Robert Clayton, Sydney)

1850 (1 Jan). *T* **1.** *Plate I. No clouds.* (*a*) *Soft yellowish paper.*

1	1d. crimson-lake	£4250	£450
2	1d. carmine	£4000	£400
3	1d. reddish rose	£3750	£375
4	1d. brownish red	£4000	£400
	(*b*) *Hard bluish paper*		
5	1d. pale red	£3750	£375
6	1d. dull lake	£4000	£400

1850 (Aug). *T* **2.** *Plate I, re-engraved by H. C. Jervis, commonly termed Plate II. With clouds.* (*a*) *Hard toned white to yellowish paper.*

7	1d. vermilion	£2500	£300
8	1d. dull carmine	£2500	£300
	a. No trees on hill (R.2/2)	£4500	£475
	b. Hill unshaded (R.2/3)	£4500	£475
	c. Without clouds (R.3/5)	£4500	£475
	(*b*) *Hard greyish or bluish paper*		
9	1d. crimson-lake	£2500	£300
10	1d. gooseberry-red	£3000	£450
11	1d. dull carmine	£2250	£275
12	1d. brownish red	£2250	£275
	a. No trees on hill (R.2/2)	£4500	£475
	b. Hill unshaded (R.2/3)	£4500	£475
	c. Without clouds (R.3/5)	£4500	£475
	(*c*) *Laid paper*		
13	1d. carmine	£4000	£475
14	1d. vermilion	£4500	£450
	a. No trees on hill (R.2/2)	—	£800
	b. Hill unshaded (R.2/3)	—	£800
	c. Without clouds (R.3/5)	—	£800

The varieties quoted with the letters "a", "b", "c" of course exist in each shade; the prices quoted are for the commonest shade, and the same applies to the following portions of this list.

Nos. 1/14 were printed in sheets of 25 (5×5).

LAID PAPER. Nos. 13/14, 34/5, 38 and 43*d*/*e* can be found showing parts of the papermaker's watermark (T. H. SAUNDERS 1847 in double-lined capitals and the figure of Britannia seated in an oval beneath a crown).

3

4

A (Pl I)

Illustrations A, B, C, and D are sketches of the lower part of the inner circular frame, showing the characteristic variations of each plate.

(Eng John Carmichael)

1850 (1 Jan). *Plate I. Vertical-lined background. T* **3.**

	(*a*) *Early impressions, full details of clouds, etc.*		
15	2d. greyish blue	£4500	£375
16	2d. deep blue	—	£425
	a. Double lines on bale (R.2/7)	—	£650
	(*b*) *Intermediate impressions*		
16*b*	2d. greyish blue	£3000	£275
16*c*	2d. deep blue	£3250	£325
	(*c*) *Later impressions, clouds, etc., mostly gone, T* 4		
17	2d. blue	£2250	£150
18	2d. dull blue	£1800	£140
	(*d*) *Stamps in the lower row partially retouched* (end Jan).		
19	2d. blue	£3000	£275
20	2d. greyish blue	£2750	£225

5

B (Pl II)

C (Pl III)

(Plate entirely re-engraved by H. C. Jervis)

1850 (Apr). *T* **5.** *Plate II. Horizontal-lined background. Bale on left side supporting the seated figure, dated. Dot in centre of the star in each corner.* (*a*) *Early impressions.*

21	2d. indigo	£3500	£275
22	2d. lilac-blue	—	£1000
23	2d. grey-blue	£3500	£225
24	2d. bright blue	£3500	£225
	a. Fan as in Pl III, but with shading outside (R.1/1)	—	£375
	b. Fan as in Pl III, but without shading, and inner circle intersects the fan (R.1/2)	—	£375
	c. Pick and shovel omitted (R.1/10)	—	£375
	d. "CREVIT" omitted (R.2/1)	—	£600
	e. No whip (R.1/4, 1/8, 2/8)	—	£300
	(*b*) *Worn impressions*		
25	2d. dull blue	£1800	£130
26	2d. Prussian blue	£1900	£17
	a. Fan as in Pl III, but with shading outside (R.1/1)	—	£30
	b. Fan as in Pl III, but without shading, and inner circle intersects the fan (R.1/2)	—	£30
	c. Pick and shovel omitted (R.1/10)	—	£30
	d. "CREVIT" omitted (R.2/1)	—	£40
	e. No whip (R.1/4, 1/8, 2/8)	£2500	£22
	(*c*) *Bottom row retouched with dots and dashes in lower spandrels* (Aug)		
27	2d. Prussian blue	£2750	£225
28	2d. dull blue	£2500	£15
	a. No whip (R.2/8)	—	£25
	b. "CREVIT" omitted (R.2/1)	—	£37

(Plate re-engraved a second time by H.C. Jervis)

1850 (Sept). *Plate III. Bale not dated and single-lined, excep on No.* 30c *which is doubled-lined. No dots in stars.*

29	2d. ultramarine	£2250	£16
30	2d. deep blue	£2250	£16
	a. No whip (R.2/3, 2/7)	—	£25
	b. Fan with 6 segments (R. 2/8)	—	£37
	c. Double lines on bale (R. 1/7, 1/10, 1/12)	—	£22

(Plate re-engraved a third time by H. C. Jervis)

1851 (Jan). *Plate IV. Double-lined bale, and circle in centre of eac star.* (*a*) *Hard bluish grey wove paper.*

31	2d. ultramarine	£2750	£16
32	2d. Prussian blue	£2250	£13
33	2d. bright blue	£2500	£15
	a. Hill not shaded (R.1/12)	—	£22
	b. Fan with 6 segments (R.2/8)	—	£22
	c. No clouds (R.2/10)	—	£22
	d. Retouch (R.2/1)	—	£30
	e. No waves (R.1/9, 2/5)	—	£19
	(*b*) *Stout yellowish vertically laid paper*		
34	2d. ultramarine	£2750	£17
35	2d. Prussian blue	£3000	£18
	a. Hill not shaded (R.1/12)	—	£25
	b. Fan with 6 segments (R.2/8)	—	£25
	c. No clouds (R.2/10)	—	£25
	d. Retouch (R.2/1)	—	£32
	e. No waves (R.1/9, 2/5)	—	£20
	f. "PENOE" (R.1/10, 2/12)	—	£25

The retouch, Nos. 33d and 35d., occurs outside the left margir line on R.2/1.

6

D (Pl V)

7

(Plate re-engraved a fourth time by H. C. Jervis)

1851 (Apr). *T* **6.** *Plate V. Pearl in fan.* (*a*) *Hard greyish wove pape*

36	2d. ultramarine	£2500	£14
37	2d. dull blue	£2500	£14
	a. Pick and shovel omitted (R.2/5)	—	£25
	b. Fan with 6 segments (R.2/8)	—	£25
	(*b*) *Stout yellowish vertically laid paper*		
38	2d. dull ultramarine	£3750	£30
	a. Pick and shovel omitted (R.2/5)	—	£42
	b. Fan with 6 segments (R.2/8)	—	£42

Nos. 15/38 were printed in sheets of 24 (12×2), although th existence of an inter-panneau *tête-bêche* pair from Plate indicates that the printer applied two impressions of the plate t each sheet of paper. The two panes were normally separate before issue. The original plate I was re-cut four times to forı Plates II to V. An interesting variety occurs on R.1/9-11 and 2/ in all five plates. It consists of ten loops of the engine-turning o each side of the design instead of the normal nine loops.

(Eng H. C. Jervis)

1850. *T* **7.** (*a*) *Soft yellowish wove paper.*

39	3d. yellow-green	£3000	£2
40	3d. myrtle-green	£10000	£10
41	3d. emerald-green	£3500	£27
	a. No whip (R.4/3–4)	—	£37
	b. "SIGIIIUM" for "SIGILLUM" (R.5/3)	—	£45
	(*b*) *Bluish to grey wove paper*		
42	3d. yellow-green	£2500	£2
43	3d. emerald-green	£3000	£2
	b. No whip (R.4/3–4)	—	£3
	c. "SIGIIIUM" for "SIGILLUM" (R.5/3)	—	£37
	(*c*) *Yellowish to bluish laid paper*		
43*d*	3d. bright green	£5500	£5
43*e*	3d. yellowish green	£5000	£4
	f. No whip (R.4/3–4)	—	£6
	g. "SIGIIIUM" for "SIGILLUM" (R.5/3)	—	£75

Nos. 39/43*e* were printed in sheets of 25 (5×5).

A used example of No. 42 is known printed double, one albir

8

9

(Des A. W. Manning from sketch by W. T. Levine; eng on steel John Carmichael, Sydney)

1851 (18 Dec)–**52.** *Imperf.* (*a*) *Thick yellowish paper*

44	**8**	1d. carmine	£1800	£1
		a. No leaves right of "SOUTH" (R.1/7, 3/1)	—	£3
		b. Two leaves right of "SOUTH" (R.2/5)	—	£4
		c. "WALE" (R.1/9)	—	£4

(*b*) *Bluish medium wove paper* (1852)

8 1d. carmine £1000 £120
1d. scarlet £1000 £120
1d. vermilion £900 £100
1d. brick-red £900 £100
a. No leaves right of "SOUTH" (R.1/7, 3/1) — £225
b. Two leaves right of "SOUTH" (R.2/5) — £300
c. "WALE" (R.1/9) .. .. .. — £300

(*c*) *Thick vertically laid bluish paper* (1852?)

8 1d. orange-brown £3000 £350
1d. claret £3000 £375
a. No leaves right of "SOUTH" (R.1/7, 3/1) — £550
b. Two leaves right of "SOUTH" ((R.2/5) — £650
c. "WALE" (R.1/9) .. .. .. — £650

Jos. 44/50 were printed in sheets of 50 (10×5).

(Eng on steel by John Carmichael)

1 (24 July). *Plate I. Imperf.* (*a*) *Thick yellowish wove paper*
8 2d. ultramarine .. .. £800 80·00

(*b*) *Fine impressions, blue to greyish medium paper*

8 2d. ultramarine .. .. £750 30·00
2d. chalky blue .. .. £650 30·00
2d. dark blue .. .. £650 30·00
2d. greyish blue .. .. £650 30·00

(*c*) *Worn plate, blue to greyish medium paper*

8 2d. ultramarine .. .. £450 30·00
2d. Prussian blue .. .. £450 30·00

(*d*) *Worn plate, blue wove medium paper*

8 2d. ultramarine .. .. £350 30·00
2d. Prussian blue .. .. £325 30·00

Jos. 51/9 were printed in sheets of 50 (10×5).

(Plate II eng H. C. Jervis)

3 (Oct). *Plate II. Stars in corners. Imperf.*

(*a*) *Bluish medium to thick wove paper*

9 2d. deep ultramarine £1000 £110
2d. indigo .. .. £1100 80·00
a. "WAEES" (R.3/3) .. .. .. — £375

(*b*) *Worn plate, hard blue wove paper*

9 2d. deep Prussian blue £1000 £100
a. "WAEES" (R.3/3) .. .. .. — £375

'os. 60/2 were printed in sheets of 50 (10×5).

5 (Sept). *Plate III, being Plate I* (*T* 8) *re-engraved by H. C. ervis. Background of crossed lines. Imperf.*

(*a*) *Medium bluish wove paper*

2d. Prussian blue .. .. £475 55·00
a. "WALES" partly covered with wavy lines (R.1/3) .. .. .. — £190

(*b*) *Stout white wove paper*

2d. Prussian blue .. .. £475 55·00
a. "WALES" partly covered with wavy lines (R.1/3) .. .. .. — £190

os. 63/4 were printed in sheets of 50 (10×5).

(Eng John Carmichael)

2 (3 Dec). *Imperf.* (*a*) *Medium greyish blue wove paper*

8 3d. deep green £1600 £200
3d. green £1300 £140
3d. dull yellow-green £1200 £100
a. "WAEES" with centre bar of first "E" missing (R.4/7) .. .. .. — £350

(*b*) *Thick blue wove paper*

8 3d. emerald-green £1600 £200
3d. blue-green £1600 £200
a. "WAEES" with centre bar of first "E" missing (R.4/7) .. .. .. — £550

'os. 65/71 were printed in sheets of 50 (10×5).

2 (Apr). *Fine background. Imperf.*

(*a*) *Medium white wove paper*

8 6d. vandyke-brown .. .. — £900
a. "WALLS" (R.2/3) .. .. .. — £1500

(*b*) *Medium bluish grey wove paper*

8 6d. vandyke-brown £1700 £250
6d. yellow-brown £1800 £275
6d. chocolate-brown £1700 £250
6d. grey-brown £1600 £250
a. "WALLS" (R.2/3) .. .. .. — £500

xamples of the 6d. in vandyke-brown on thick yellowish er are proofs.

3 (June). *Plate I re-engraved by H. C. Jervis. Coarse ackground. Imperf.*

6d. brown £1800 £300
6d. grey-brown £1700 £300

'os. 72/6 and 77/8 were printed in sheets of 25 (5×5).

(Eng H. C. Jervis)

3 (May). *Medium bluish paper. Imperf.*

8d. dull yellow £3500 £600
8d. orange-yellow £3500 £600
8d. orange £3750 £650
a. No bow at back of head (R.1/9) .. — £1300
b. No leaves right of "SOUTH" (R.3/1) .. — £1300
c. No lines in spandrel (R.2/2, 3/2, 4/2) .. — £800

'os. 79/81 were issued in sheets of 50 (10×5).

10 13 14

NOTE. All watermarked stamps from No. 82 to No. 172 have double-lined figures, as T **10**.

1854 (Feb). *Wmk* "1", *T* **10**. *Yellowish wove paper. Imperf.*

82 8 1d. red-orange .. .. £170 17·00
83 1d. orange-vermilion .. .. .. £170 17·00
a. No leaves right of "SOUTH" (R. 1/7, 3/1) £350 85·00
b. Two leaves right of "SOUTH" (R.2/5) .. £475 £120
c. "WALE" (R.1/9) £475 £120

Nos. 82/3 were printed in sheets of 50 (10×5).

1854 (Jan). *Plate III. Wmk "2". Imperf.*

84 2d. ultramarine .. .. £110 10·00
85 2d. Prussian blue .. .. £110 10·00
86 2d. chalky blue .. .. £110 8·00
a. "WALES" partly covered by wavy lines (R.1/3) .. .. £425 50·00

Nos. 84/6 were printed in sheets of 50 (10×5).

1854 (Mar). *Wmk "3". Imperf.*

87 8 3d. yellow-green .. .. £200 27·00
a. "WAEES" with centre bar of first "E" missing (R. 4/7) .. .. .. — £120
b. Error. Wmk "2" £3000 £1500

No. 87 was printed in sheets of 50 (10×5).

(Eng John Carmichael)

1856 (1 Jan). *For Registered Letters. T* **13.** *No wmk. Imperf. Soft medium yellowish paper.*

88 (6d.) vermilion and Prussian blue £700 £150
a. Frame printed on back £2500 £2000
89 (6d.) salmon and indigo £700 £170
90 (6d.) orange and Prussian blue £700 £200
91 (6d.) orange and indigo £700 £180

1859 (Apr)–**60.** *Hard medium bluish wove paper, with manufacturer's wmk in sans-serif, double-lined capitals across sheet and only showing portions of letters on a few stamps in a sheet.*

(*a*) *Imperf.*

92 (6d.) orange and Prussian blue £800 £150

(*b*) *P* 12 (2.60)

93 (6d.) orange and Prussian blue .. .. £350 45·00
94 (6d.) orange and indigo .. .. .. £325 50·00

1860 (Feb)–**62.** *Coarse yellowish wove paper having the manufacturer's wmk in Roman capitals.* (*a*) *P* 12.

95 (6d.) rose-red and Prussian blue .. .. £250 35·00
96 (6d.) rose-red and indigo .. .. .. £325 80·00
97 (6d.) salmon and indigo .. .. ..

(*b*) *P* 13 (1862)

98 (6d.) rose-red and Prussian blue .. .. £250 50·00

1863 (May). *Yellowish wove paper. Wmk "6". P* 13.

99 (6d.) rose-red and Prussian blue .. .. 95·00 16·00
100 (6d.) rose-red and indigo .. .. .. £150 20·00
101 (6d.) rose-red and pale blue .. .. 75·00 15·00
a. Double impression of frame .. .. — £500

(T **14**/**21** and **24** printed by the New South Wales Govt Ptg Dept from plates engraved by Perkins, Bacon & Co)

Two plates of the 2d. and 6d. were used. On Plate II of the 2d. the stamps are wider apart and more regularly spaced than on Plate I.

1856 (6 Apr). *Wmk "1". Imperf.*

102 14 1d. orange-vermilion .. .. .. £150 22·00
a. Error. Wmk "2" .. .. ..
103 1d. carmine-vermilion .. .. .. £150 22·00
104 1d. orange-red .. .. £150 22·00
a. Printed on both sides £1400 £1400

1856 (7 Jan)–**58.** *Plate I. Wmk "2". Imperf.*

105 14 2d. deep turquoise-blue .. .. .. £140 8·00
106 2d. ultramarine .. .. £130 8·00
107 2d. blue .. .. £130 8·00
a. Major retouch (1858) £1800 £450
b. Error. Wmk "1" .. .. .. — £4000
c. Wmk "5" (3.57) .. .. .. £450 60·00
d. Error. Wmk "8" .. .. ..
108 2d. pale blue .. .. £130 8·00

The 2d. Plate I was retouched, on a total of ten positions, several times.

No. 107c comes from a printing made when supplies of the "2" paper were unavailable.

1859 (3 Aug). *Lithographic transfer of Plate I.*

110 14 2d. pale blue .. .. — £750
a. Retouched .. .. — £2500

1860 (Jan). *Plate II. Recess. Stamps printed wider apart and with a white patch between the "A" of "WALES" and the back of the Queen's head.*

110*b* 14 2d. blue .. .. £500 50·00

No. 110*b* was principally issued to post offices in Queensland.

1856 (10 Oct). *Wmk "3". Imperf.*

111 14 3d. yellow-green .. .. £800 80·00
112 3d. bluish green .. .. £850 80·00
113 3d. dull green .. .. £850 80·00
a. Error, Wmk "2" .. .. .. — £3000

In the 3d. the value is in block letters on a white ground.

PRICES OF SETS

Set prices are given for many issues, generally those containing three stamps or more. Definitive sets include one of each value or major colour change, but do not cover different perforations, die types or minor shades. Where a choice is possible the set prices are based on the cheapest versions of the stamps included in the listings.

15 17

19 21

(6d. and 1s. des E. H. Corbould after sketches by T. W. Levinge)

1855 (1 Dec). *Wmk "5". Imperf.*

114 15 5d. dull green £1000 £550

1854 (1 Feb)–**59.** *Wmk "6". Imperf.*

115 17 6d. deep slate .. .. £500 32·00
a. Wmk sideways .. .. .. † £750
116 6d. greenish grey .. .. £400 32·00
117 6d. slate-green .. .. £400 32·00
a. Printed both sides .. ..
118 6d. bluish grey .. .. £450 55·00
119 6d. fawn .. .. £500 95·00
a. Wmk "8" (15.8.59) £1600 £110
120 6d. grey .. .. £450 55·00
121 6d. olive-grey .. .. £450 32·00
122 6d. greyish brown .. .. £450 32·00
a. Wmk "8" (15.8.59) £1600 £110
ab. Wmk sideways .. .. .. — £350

Nos. 119a and 122a come from a printing made when supplies of the "6" paper were unavailable.

1855 (1 Dec). *Wmk "8". Imperf.*

125 19 8d. golden yellow £4000 £850
126 8d. dull yellow-orange £3500 £800

1854 (Feb)–**57.** *Wmk "12". Imperf.*

127 21 1s. rosy vermilion .. .. .. £750 65·00
a. Wmk "8" (20.6.57) £2000 £180
128 1s. pale red .. .. £750 65·00
129 1s. brownish red .. .. £800 75·00

No. 127a comes from a printing made when supplies of the "12" paper were unavailable.

1860 (14 Feb)–**63.** *Wmk double-lined figure of value. P* 12.

131 14 1d. orange-red .. .. £170 16·00
ab Imperf between (pair) .. ..
b. Double impression .. .. ..
132 1d. scarlet .. .. £100 16·00
133 2d. pale blue (Pl I) £500 £140
a. Retouched .. .. — £1300
134 2d. greenish blue (Pl II) .. .. .. 90·00 10·00
136 2d. Prussian blue (Pl II) .. .. .. 90·00 10·00
a. Error. Wmk "1" .. .. .. — £2750
b. Retouched (*shades*) .. .. .. — £400
137 2d. Prussian blue (Pl I) (3.61) .. .. £110 11·00
138 2d. dull blue (Pl I) .. .. .. £100 10·00
139 3d. yellow-green (1860) .. .. .. £1000 55·00
140 3d. blue-green .. .. £550 42·00
141 15 5d. dull green (1863) .. .. .. £100 35·00
142 5d. yellowish green (1863) .. .. £100 35·00
143 17 6d. grey-brown .. .. £275 45·00
144 6d. olive-brown .. .. £275 55·00
145 6d. greenish grey .. .. £350 45·00
146 6d. fawn .. .. £325 65·00
147 6d. mauve .. .. £300 35·00
148 6d. violet .. .. £275 16·00
a. Imperf between (pair) .. .. ..
149 19 8d. lemon-yellow .. .. — £1400
150 8d. orange £2250 £650
151 8d. red-orange £2250 £650
152 21 1s. brownish red .. .. £450 48·00
153 1s. rose-carmine .. .. £450 48·00
a. Imperf between (pair) .. .. ..

No. 133 was made by perforating a small remaining stock of No. 108. Nos. 137/8 were printed from the original plate after its return from London, where it had been repaired.

1862–72. *Wmk double-lined figure of value.* (*a*) *P* 13.

154 14 1d. scarlet (1862) .. .. .. 55·00 8·00
155 1d. dull red .. .. 55·00 8·00
156 3d. blue-green (12.62) .. .. .. 45·00 11·00
157 3d. yellow-green .. .. 50·00 8·50
a. Wmk "6" (7.72) .. .. .. £100 12·00
158 3d. dull green .. .. 50·00 8·00
a. Wmk "6" (7.72) .. .. .. £100 15·00
160 15 5d. bluish green (12.63) .. .. .. 40·00 15·00
161 5d. bright yellow-green (8.65) .. .. 70·00 30·00
162 5d. sea-green (1866) .. .. .. 42·00 17·00
162*a* 5d. dark bluish green (11.70) .. .. 30·00 17·00
163 17 6d. reddish purple (Pl I) (7.62) .. .. 80·00 5·50
164 6d. mauve .. .. 80·00 5·50
165 6d. purple (Pl II) (1864) .. .. .. 55·00 4·50
a. Wmk "5" (7.66) .. .. .. £350 25·00
b. Wmk "12" (12.66 and 1868) .. .. £275 20·00
166 6d. violet .. .. 55·00 6·00
167 6d. aniline mauve £900 £120
167*a* 19 8d. red-orange .. .. £140 55·00
167*b* 8d. yellow-orange .. .. £150 40·00
167*c* 8d. bright yellow .. .. £140 40·00
168 21 1s. rose-carmine .. .. 70·00 7·50
169 1s. carmine .. .. 70·00 8·00
170 1s. crimson-lake .. .. 70·00 8·00

(*b*) *Perf compound* 12×13

171 14 1d. scarlet .. .. — £1700
172 2d. dull blue (1.62) £2000 £180

Nos. 157a, 158a and 165a/b come from printings made when supplies of paper with the correct face value were unavailable.

23

1864 (June). *W* **23.** *P* 13.
173 **14** 1d. pale red . . . . 40·00 14·00

24 25

(Des E. H. Corbould, R.I.)

1861–88. *W* **25.** *Various perfs.*
174 **24** 5s. dull violet, *p* 12 (1861) £1000 £325
a. Perf 13 (1861) . . . . . . £160 28·00
175 5s. royal purple, *p* 13 (1872) . . . . £275 45·00
176 5s. deep rose-lilac, *p* 13 (1875) . . . . 95·00 28·00
177 5s. deep purple, *p* 13 (1880) . . . . £150 40·00
a. Perf 10 (1882) . . . . . . £150 45·00
178 5s. rose-lilac, *p* 10 (1883) . . . . £110 40·00
179 5s. purple, *p* 12 (1885) . . . . — 45·00
a. Perf 10 × 12 (1885) . . . . . . — £120
180 5s. reddish purple, *p* 10 (1886) . . . . £110 40·00
a. Perf 12 × 10 (1887) . . . . . . £225 45·00
181 5s. rose-lilac, *p* 11 (1888) . . . . — £120

This value was replaced by Nos. 261, etc. in 1888 but reissued in 1897, *see* Nos. 297*c*/*e*.

26 28 29

(Printed by De La Rue & Co, Ltd, London and perf at Somerset House, London)

1862–65. *Surfaced paper. P* 14. (i) *W* **23.**
186 **26** 1d. dull red (Pl I) (4.64) . . . . 85·00 32·00

(ii) *No wmk*
187 **26** 1d. dull red (Pl II) (1.65) . . . . 65·00 30·00
188 **28** 2d. pale blue (3.62) . . . . . . 70·00 30·00

(Printed from the De La Rue plates in the Colony)

1862 (12 Apr). *Wmk double-lined* "**2**". *P* 13.
189 **28** 2d. blue . . . . 50·00 7·00
a. Perf 12 . . . . £130 30·00
b. Perf 12 × 13 . . . . . . £400

1864–65. *W* **23.** *P* 13.
190 **26** 1d. dark red-brown (Pl I) . . . . 80·00 16·00
191 1d. brownish red (Pl II) . . . . . . 20·00 1·50
a. Imperf between (horiz pair) . . † £500
192 1d. brick-red (Pl II) . . . . . . 20·00 1·50
a. Highly surfaced paper (1865) . . £200
194 **28** 2d. pale blue . . . . £120 3·50

Plates I and II were made from the same die; they can only be distinguished by the colour or by the marginal inscription.

1865–66. *Thin wove paper. No wmk. P* 13.
195 **26** 1d. brick-red . . . . 95·00 16·00
196 1d. brownish red . . . . 95·00 16·00
197 **28** 2d. pale blue . . . . 45·00 3·00

1863–69. *W* **29.** *P* 13.
198 **26** 1d. pale red (3.69) . . . . . . 80·00 12·00
199 **28** 2d. pale blue . . . . 9·50 50
a. Perf 12 . . . .
200 2d. cobalt-blue . . . . 9·50 50
201 2d. Prussian blue . . . . 22·00 3·50

1862 (Sept). *Wmk double-lined* "**5**". *P* 13.
202 **28** 2d. dull blue . . . . 60·00 8·50

32 34

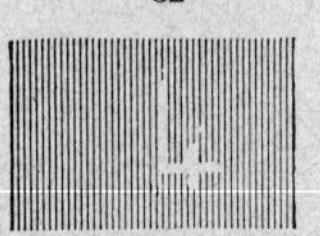

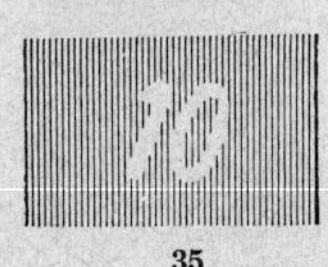

33 35

1867 (Sept)–**93.** *W* **33** *and* **35.**
203 **32** 4d. red-brown, *p* 13 . . . . . . 40·00 3·00
204 4d. pale red-brown, *p* 13 . . . . 40·00 3·00
205 **34** 10d. lilac, *p* 13 (Optd S. £25) . . . . 12·00 3·00
a. Imperf between (pair) £450
206 10d. lilac, *p* 11 (1893) . . . . . . 13·00 3·00
a. Perf 10 . . . . 15·00 4·50
b. Perf 10 and 11, compound . . . . 20·00 7·50
c. Perf 12 × 11 . . . . . . £110 15·00

36 37 38

NINEPENCE
(39)

From 1871 to 1903 the 9d. is formed from the 10d. by a *black* surch. (T **39**), 15 mm long on Nos. 219 to 220h, and 13½ mm long on subsequent issues.

1871–1902. *W* **36.**
207 **26** 1d. dull red, *p* 13 (8.71) . . . . 5·00 20
a. Imperf vert (horiz pair) . . . .
208 1d. salmon, *p* 13 (1878) . . . . 5·00 20
a. Perf 10 (6.80) . . . . . . £250 30·00
b. Perf 10×13 (6.80) . . . . . . 50·00 5·00
ba. Perf 13×10 . . . . . . 16·00 20
c. *Scarlet.* Perf 10 (6.80) . . . . — £180
209 **28** 2d. Prussian-blue, *p* 13 (11.71) . . . . 7·00 20
a. Perf 11×12, comb (11.84) . . . . £250 40·00
b. Imperf vert (horiz pair) . . . . — £500
210 2d. pale blue, *p* 13 (1876) . . . . 7·00 20
aa. "TWO PENCE" double impression at right . . . . — 30·00
a. Perf 10 (6.80) . . . . . . £250 22·00
b. Perf 10×13 (6.80) . . . . . . £100 15·00
ba. Perf 13×10 . . . . . . 7·00 20
c. Surfaced paper. Perf 13 . . . .
211 **14** 3d. yellow-green, *p* 13 (3.74) . . . . 18·00 2·40
a. Perf 10 (6.80) . . . . . . 65·00 5·50
b. Perf 11 (1902) £150 £100
c. Perf 12 (5.85) . . . . . . — £150
d. Perf 10×12 (5.85) . . . . . . £150 32·00
e. Perf 11×12 (1902) . . . . . . £120 32·00
212 3d bright green, *p* 10 (6.80) . . . . £120 11·00
a. Perf 13×10 (6.80) . . . . . . £110 15·00
b. Perf 13 . . . .
213 **32** 4d. pale red-brown, *p* 13 (8.77) . . . . 55·00 6·00
214 4d. red-brown, *p* 13 . . . . . . 55·00 6·00
a. Perf 10 (6.80) . . . . . . £180 50·00
b. Perf 10×13 (6.80) . . . . . . £100 20·00
ba. Perf 13×10 . . . . . . 75·00 3·50
215 **15** 5d. bluish green, *p* 10 (8.84) . . . . 15·00 8·00
a. Perf 12 (5.85) £250 £100
b. Perf 10×13 . . . . . .
c. Perf 10×12 (5.85) . . . . . . £120 40·00
216 **37** 6d. bright mauve, *p* 13 (1.72) . . . . 40·00 1·00
a. Imperf between (horiz pair) . . . . — £500
217 6d. pale lilac, *p* 13 (1878) . . . . 42·00 1·00
a. Perf 10 (6.80) . . . . . . £180 12·00
b. Perf 10×13 (6.80) . . . . . . 80·00 15·00
ba. Perf 13×10 . . . . . . 55·00 1·00
c. Imperf between (horiz pair). Perf 13×10 . . . . — £500
218 **19** 8d. yellow, *p* 13 (3.77) . . . . £100 17·00
a. Perf 10 (6.80) . . . . . . £250 24·00
b. Perf 13×10 (6.80) . . . . . . £170 22·00
219 **34** 9d. on 10d. pale red-brown, *p* 13 (8.71) 20·00 4·50
220 9d. on 10d. red-brown, *p* 13 (1878) (optd S. £25) . . . . 20·00 6·00
a. Perf 10 (6.80) . . . . . . 12·00 4·50
b. Perf 12 (5.85) . . . . . . 12·00 4·50
c. Perf 11 (12.85) . . . . . . 26·00 7·00
d. Perf 12×10 (5.85) £250 £160
e. Perf 10×11 or 11×10 (12.85) . . 42·00 9·00
f. Perf 12×11 (12.85) . . . . . . 14·00 5·00
g. Perf 12×11, comb (1.84) . . . . 14·00 5·50
h. In black and blue. Perf 11 (12.85) . . £110
221 **38** 1s. black, *p* 13 (4.76) . . . . . . 80·00 2·50
a. Perf 10 (6.80) . . . . . . £200 12·00
b. Perf 10×13 (6.80) . . . . . . £240 15·00
ba. Perf 13×10 . . . . . . £170 4·50
c. Perf 11 . . . .
d. Imperf between (horiz pair) . . . . — £750

Collectors should note that the classification of perforations is that adopted by the Royal Philatelic Society, London. "Perf 12" denotes the perforation formerly called "11½, 12" and "perf 13" that formerly called "12½, 13".

40 41

1882 (Apr)–**97.** *W* **40.**
222 **26** 1d. salmon, *p* 10 . . . . . . 11·00
a. Perf 13 . . . .
b. Perf 13×10 . . . . . . 30·00 1
223 1d. orange *to* scarlet, *p* 13 . . . . £800 £
a. Perf 10 . . . . 8·00
ab. Imperf between (horiz pair) . .
b. Perf 10×13 . . . . . . £120 6
c. Perf 10×12 (4.85) £250 65
d. Perf 10×11 (12.85) . . . . £450 £
e. Perf 12×11 (12.85) . . . . — £
f. Perf 11×12, comb (1.84) . . . . 5·50
h. Perf 11 (12.85) . . . . . . — £
224 **28** 2d. pale blue, *p* 13 . . . . . . £450 90
a. Perf 10 . . . . 13·00
b. Perf 10×13 or 13×10 . . . . 65·00 2
225 2d. Prussian blue, *p* 10 . . . . 23·00
a. Perf 10×13 . . . . . . £100 30
b. Perf 12 (4.85) . . . . . . — £
c. Perf 11 (12.85) . . . . . . — £
d. Perf 12×11 (12.85) . . . . £400 £
e. Perf 10×12 (4.85) £225 65
ea. Perf 12×10 . . . . . . £400 £
f. Perf 10×11 or 11×10 (12.85) . . £450 £
g. Perf 11×12, comb (1.84) . . . . 12·00
226 **14** 3d. yellow-green, *p* 10 (1886) . . . . 6·00
a. Wmk sideways . . . . . .
b. Perf 10×12 . . . . . . £160 30
ba. Perf 12×10 . . . . . . £120 15
c. Perf 11 . . . . 5·00
ca. Imperf between (horiz pair) . . £150
d. Perf 11×12 or 12×11 . . . . 5·00
e. Perf 12 . . . . 9·00 1
g. Imperf (pair) £120
227 3d. bluish green, *p* 10 . . . . 5·00
a. Wmk sideways . . . . . . 50·00 10
b. Perf 11 . . . . 5·00
c. Perf 10×11 . . . . . . 15·00 1
ca. Perf 11×10 . . . . . . £100 30
d. Perf 12×11 . . . . . . 5·00 1
e. Perf 10×12 or 12×10 . . . . 30·00 3
228 3d. emerald-green, *p* 10 (1893) . . 55·00 7
a. Wmk sideways . . . . . . — 15
b. Perf 10×11 . . . . . . 55·00 3
ba. Perf 11×10 . . . . . . £120 35
c. Perf 10×12 . . . . . . 50·00 3
ca. Perf 12×10 . . . . . . 75·00 5
d. Perf 12×11 . . . . . . — 10
229 **32** 4d. red-brown, *p* 10 . . . . . . 40·00 3
a. Perf 10×12 (4.85) . . . . — £
b. Perf 11×12, comb (1.84) . . . . 48·00 1
230 4d. dark brown, *p* 10 . . . . 40·00 3
a. Perf 12 (4.85) . . . . . . £250 £
b. Perf 10×12 (4.85) £200 60
ba. Perf 12×10 . . . . . . £300 £
c. Perf 11×12, comb (1.84) . . . . 28·00 1
231 **15** 5d. dull grn, *p* 10 (1890) (Optd S. £25) 13·00
b. Perf 12×10 (4.85) . . . . 80·00 3
232 5d. bright green, *p* 10 . . . . 35·00 4
b. Perf 10×11 (12.85) . . . . 42·00 4
ba. Perf 11×10 . . . . . . 48·00 6
c. Perf 10×12 (4.85) £150 30
ca. Perf 12×10 . . . . . . £100 70
233 5d. blue-green, *p* 10 . . . . . . 9·00
a. Perf (4.85) . . . . . . 12·00
ab. Wmk sideways . . . . . . 50·00
b. Perf 11 (12.85) . . . . . . 9·00
c. Perf 10×11 (12.85) . . . . 26·00 1
d. Perf 11×12 or 12×11 (12.85) . . 7·00
da. Wmk sideways (*p* 11×12) . . . . — 20
e. Imperf (pair) £200
234 **37** 6d. pale lilac, *p* 10 . . . . . . 40·00 1
a. Perf 10×13 or 13×10 . . . . — £
b. Perf 10×12 or 12×10 (4.85) . . 42·00 1
235 6d. mauve, *p* 10 . . . . . . 40·00 1
a. Perf 12 (4.85) . . . . . . 80·00 10
b. Perf 11 (12.85) . . . . . . 80·00 8
c. Perf 10×12 (4.85) . . . . 50·00 8
ca. Perf 12×10 . . . . . . 40·00 2
cb. Imperf between (horiz pair) . . — £
d. Perf 11×12 (12.85) . . . . 80·00 12
da. Perf 12×11 . . . . . . 40·00 1
e. Perf 11×10 (12.85) . . . . 55·00 2
236 **19** 8d. yellow, *p* 10 (1883) £100 15
a. Perf 12 (4.85) £170 27
b. Perf 11 (12.85) £100 17
c. Perf 10×12 (4.85) £130 3
ca. Perf 12×10 . . . . . . £100 25
236*d* **34** 9d. on 10d. red-brown, *p* 11×12 (1897) (Optd S. £25) . . . . . . 8·00 4
da. Perf 12 . . . . 11·00 6
db. Perf 11 . . . . 11·00 6
dc. Surch double, *p* 11 . . . . £140 £
236*e* 10d. violet, *p* 11×12 (1897) (Optd S. £25) 12·00 3
ea. Perf 12×11½ . . . . . . 12·00 3
eb. Perf 12 . . . . 15·00 4
ec. Perf 11 . . . . 20·00 5
237 **38** 1s. black, *p* 10 . . . . . . 65·00 2
a. Perf 11 (12.85) £200 9
b. Perf 10×12 . . . . . .
c. Perf 10×13 . . . . . .
ca. Perf 13×10 . . . . . . £200 20
d. Perf 11×12, comb (1.84) . . . . 65·00 2

1886–87. *W* **41.**
238 **26** 1d. scarlet, *p* 10 . . . . . . 11·00
a. Perf 11 × 12, comb . . . . 3·75
239 **28** 2d. deep blue, *p* 10 . . . . . . 35·00
a. Perf 11 × 12, comb . . . . 12·00
b. Imperf . . . . . .

1891 (July). *Wmk* "10" *as W* **35.** *P* 10.
240 **14** 3d. green (Optd S. £25) . . . . 12·00 80
241 3d. dark green . . . . . . 5·00 17

NEW INFORMATION

The editor is always interested to correspond w people who have new information that improve or correct the Catalogue.

42

43

)TE. The spacing between the Crown and "NSW" is 1 mm in
‹2, as against 2 mm in T **40**.

)3–8. *W* **42**.
1*a* **14** 3d. yellow-green, *p* 11 .. .. 7·00 90
b. Perf 12 .. .. 6·00 90
ba. Imperf between (horiz pair) ..
c. Perf 11×12 or 12×11 .. .. 6·00 90
2 3d. dull green, *p* 12 .. .. .. 21·00 1·75
a. Perf 11×12 or 12×11 .. .. 8·00 1·00
b. Perf 11 .. ..
3 **15** 5d. dark blue-green, *p* 11×12 *or* 12×11 6·00 90
a. Wmk sideways .. .. .. 17·00 5·00
b. Perf 11 .. .. 14·00 90
ba. Wmk sideways .. .. ..
c. Perf 12 .. .. 21·00 3·50
ca. Wmk sideways .. .. .. 32·00 10·00
d. Imperf (pair) £130

35–86. *W* **41** (*sideways*). (i). *Optd* "POSTAGE", *in black*.
4 **43** 5s. green and lilac, *p* 13 .. ..
a. Perf 10 .. ..
b. Perf 12 × 10 .. .. .. £325 80·00
5 10s. claret and lilac, *p* 13 .. ..
a. Perf 12 .. .. £450 £140
6 £1 claret and lilac, *p* 13 (1886) .. — £2250
a. Perf 12 .. .. £2250

(ii) *Overprinted in blue*

7 **43** 10s. claret and mauve, *p* 10 (Optd S. £60) £600 £170
a. Perf 12 .. .. £160 50·00
b. Perf 12 × 11 .. .. ..
8 £1 claret and rose-lilac, *p* 12 × 10 .. £2500 £1100

44

)4. *Optd* "POSTAGE" *in blue. W* **44** (*sideways*).
9 **43** 10s. claret and mauve, *p* 10 .. .. £275 £110
9*a* 10s. claret and violet, *p* 12 .. .. £160 42·00
b. Perf 11 .. .. £250 80·00
c. Perf 12 × 11 .. .. .. £180 50·00
0 10s. aniline crimson & violet, *p* 12 × 11 £160 48·00
a. Perf 12 .. .. £250 80·00
0*b* £1 claret and violet, *p* 12 × 11 ..

)3–04. *Optd* "POSTAGE" *in blue. Chalk-surfaced paper. W* **44** (*sideways*).
)*c* **43** 10s. aniline crimson & violet, *p* 12 × 11
1 10s. rosine and violet, *p* 12 (1904) .. £150 75·00
a. Perf 11 .. .. £200 85·00
b. Perf 12 × 11 .. .. .. £150 45·00
2 10s. claret and violet, *p* 12 × 11 (1904) .. £225 85·00

5 View of Sydney

46 Emu

47 Captain Cook

3 Queen Victoria
ıd Arms of Colony

49 Superb Lyrebird

50 Eastern Grey Kangaroo

51 Map of Australia

52 Capt. Arthur Phillip, first Governor and Lord Carrington, Governor in 1888

(Des M. Tannenberg (1d., 6d.), Miss Devine (2d., 8d.), H. Barraclough (4d.), Govt Ptg Office (1s.), C. Turner (5s.), Mrs. F. Stoddard (20s.). Eng W. Bell).

1888 (1 May)–**89**. *Centenary of New South Wales.* (*a*) *W* **40**. *P* 11 × 12.
253 **45** 1d. lilac (9.7.88) .. .. 3·75 10
a. Perf 12 × 11½ .. .. .. 17·00 90
b. Perf 12 .. .. 5·00 10
c. Imperf (pair) .. ..
d. Mauve .. .. 3·75 10
da. Imperf between (pair) .. ..
db. Perf 12×11½ .. .. .. 6·00 25
dc. Perf 12 .. .. 5·50 25
254 **46** 2d. Prussian blue (1.9.88) .. .. 4·25 10
a. Imperf (pair) £100
b. Imperf between (pair) £375
c. Perf 12 × 11½ .. .. .. 8·00 10
d. Perf 12 .. .. 6·00 10
e. Chalky blue .. .. 4·25 10
ea. Perf 12 × 11½ .. .. ..
eb. Perf 12 .. .. 5·50 25
255 **47** 4d. purple-brown (8.10.88) .. .. 11·00 3·00
a. Perf 12 × 11½ .. .. .. 30·00 7·50
b. Perf 12 .. .. 26·00 3·25
c. Perf 11 .. .. £300 90·00
d. Red-brown .. .. 10·00 3·00
da. Perf 12 × 11½ .. .. .. 13·00 2·75
db. Perf 12 .. .. 13·00 2·75
e. Orange-brown, p 12 × 11½ .. .. 14·00 2·75
f. Yellow-brown, p 12 × 11½ .. .. 13·00 3·00
256 **48** 6d. carmine (26.11.88) .. .. 20·00 3·50
a. Perf 12 × 11½ .. .. .. 25·00 4·00
b. Perf 12 .. .. 21·00 8·50
257 **49** 8d. lilac-rose (17.1.89) .. .. 15·00 2·00
a. Perf 12 × 11½ .. .. .. 38·00 10·00
b. Perf 12 .. .. 15·00 2·25
c. Magenta .. .. 75·00 9·00
ca. Perf 12 × 11½ .. .. .. 15·00 2·25
cb. Perf 12 .. .. 15·00 2·75
258 **50** 1s. maroon (21.2.89) .. .. .. 16·00 90
a. Perf 12 × 11½ .. .. .. 18·00 90
b. Perf 12 .. .. 22·00 90
c. Violet-brown .. .. 16·00 90
ca. Imperf (pair) £550
cb. Perf 12 × 11½ .. .. .. 38·00 1·25
cc. Perf 12 .. .. 38·00 90

(*b*) *W* **41**. *P* 11 × 12

259 **45** 1d. lilac (1888) .. .. .. 14·00
a. Mauve .. .. 12·00 85
260 **46** 2d. Prussian blue (1888) .. .. 45·00 3·00

(*c*) *W* **25**. *P* 10

261 **51** 5s. deep purple (13.3.89) .. .. £180 45·00
a. Deep violet .. .. £180 45·00
262 **52** 20s. cobalt-blue £225 £110
253/8 Optd "Specimen" .. .. *Set of* 6 £150

Nos. 255c and 261/2 are line perforated, the remainder are comb.

A postal forgery exists of the 2d. on unwatermarked paper and perforated 11.

53

54

1890. *W* **53** (*5s.*) *or* **54** (*20s.*). *P* 10.
263 **51** 5s. lilac .. .. £120 27·00
a. Perf 11 .. .. £160 38·00
ab. Imperf between (horiz pair) ..
b. Perf 12 .. .. £225 42·00
c. Perf 10 × 11 or 11 × 10 .. .. £160 27·00
d. Mauve .. .. £160 27·00
da. Perf 11 .. .. £160 38·00
264 **52** 20s. cobalt-blue £300 £130
a. Perf 11 .. .. £225 75·00
b. Perf 11 × 10 .. ..
c. Ultramarine, p 11 .. .. .. £180 75·00
ca. Perf 12 .. .. £225 £130
cb. Perf 11 × 12 or 12 × 11 .. .. £160 75·00
263/4 Optd "Specimen" .. .. *Set of* 2 £180

55 Allegorical figure of Australia

Halfpenny

(**56**)

SEVEN-PENCE

HALFPENNY

(**57**)

1890 (22 Dec). *W* **40**.
281 **55** 2½d. ultramarine, *p* 11 × 12 *comb* (Optd S. £25) .. .. 2·50 40
a. Perf 12 × 11½, comb .. .. 45·00
b. Perf 12, comb .. .. .. 7·00 40

1891 (5 Jan). *Surch as T* **56** *and* **57**. *W* **40**.
282 **26** ½d. on 1d. grey, *p* 11×12 *comb* .. 3·00 3·00
a. Surch omitted .. .. ..
b. Surch double £200
283 **37** 7½d. on 6d. brown, *p* 10 .. .. 5·50 2·75
a. Perf 11 .. .. 5·00 2·75
b. Perf 12 .. .. 6·00 3·25
c. Perf 11×12 or 12×11 .. .. 5·50 3·25
d. Perf 10×12 .. .. .. 6·00 3·25
284 **38** 12½d. on 1s. red, *p* 10 .. .. 12·00 7·50
a. "HALFPENCE" omitted ..
b. Perf 11 .. .. 13·00 7·50
c. Perf 11×12, comb .. .. 12·00 7·00
d. Perf 12×11½, comb .. .. 10·00 7·00
e. Perf 12, comb .. .. .. 15·00 7·00
282/4 Optd "Specimen" .. .. *Set of* 3 70·00

58

Type I. Narrow "H" in "HALF"

1892 (21 Mar)–**99**. *Type I. W* **40**.
285 **58** ½d. grey, *p* 10 .. .. .. 17·00 45
a. Perf 11 .. .. 60·00 5·00
b. Perf 10×12 .. .. .. 55·00 7·50
c. Perf 11×12 (Optd S. £20) .. .. 2·00 10
d. Perf 12 .. .. 2·25 10
286 ½d. slate, *p* 11×12 (1897) .. .. 2·00 10
a. Perf 12×11½ .. .. .. 2·00 10
b. Perf 12 .. .. 2·00 10
c. Imperf between (horiz pair). Perf 11×12 .. .. £400
287 ½d. bluish green, *p* 11×12 (1899) .. 2·50 10
a. Perf 12×11½ .. .. .. 1·50 10
b. Perf 12 .. .. 1·50 10

The perforations 11×12, 12×11½, 12, are from comb machines.

The die for Type **58** was constructed from an electro taken from the die of the De La Rue 1d., Type **26**, with "ONE" replaced by "HALF" and two "½" plugs added to the bottom corners. These alterations proved to be less hard-wearing than the remainder of the die and defects were visible by the 1905 plate of No. 330. It seems likely that repairs were undertaken before printing from the next plate in late 1907 which produced stamps as Type II.

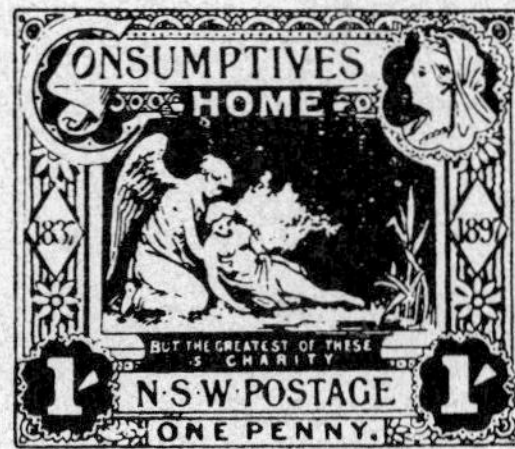

58a

58b

(Des C. Turner. Litho Govt Printing Office, Sydney)

1897. *Diamond Jubilee and Hospital Charity. T* **58a** *and* **58b**. *W* **40**. *P* 12×11 (*1d.*) *or* 11 (*2½d.*).
287*c* **58a** 1d. (1s.) green and brown (22.6) .. 40·00 40·00
287*d* **58b** 2½d. (2s. 6d.), gold, carmine & bl (28.6) £150 £150
287*c/d* Optd "Specimen" .. .. *Set of* 2 £200

These stamps, sold at 1s. and 2s. 6d. respectively, paid postage of 1d. and 2½d. only, the difference being given to a Consumptives' Home.

59

60

61

Dies of the 1d.

Die I

Die II

1d. Die I. The first pearl on the crown on the left side is merged into the arch, the shading under the fleur-de-lis is indistinct, the "S" of "WALES" is open.

Die II. The first pearl is circular, the vertical shading under the fleur-de-lis clear, the "S" of "WALES" not so open.

Dies of the 2½d.

Die I

Die II

2½d. Die I. There are 12 radiating lines in the star on the Queen's breast.

Die II. There are 16 radiating lines in the star and the eye is nearly full of colour.

Des D. Souter (2d., 2½d.). Eng W. Amor)

1897 (22 June)–**99**. *W* **40** (*sideways on* 2½d.). *P* 12×11 (2½d.) *or* 11×12 (*others*).

288 **59** 1d. carmine (Die I) .. .. .. 1·75 10
 a. Perf 12×11½ .. .. .. 2·00 10
289 1d. scarlet (Die I) .. .. .. 1·75 10
 a. Perf 12×11½ .. .. .. 4·50 40
 b. Perf 12 .. .. .. 4·50 50
 ba. Imperf horiz (vert pair) ..
290 1d. rose-carmine (Die II) (11.97) .. 1·75 10
 a. Perf 12×11½ .. .. .. 1·50 10
 b. Perf 12 .. .. .. 1·50 10
 c. Imperf between (pair) £400
291 1d. salmon-red (Die II) (*p* 12×11½) .. 1·75 10
 a. Perf 12 .. .. .. 3·25 30
292 **60** 2d. deep dull blue .. .. .. 2·25 10
 a. Perf 12×11½ .. .. .. 2·25 10
 b. Perf 12 .. .. .. 5·00 10
293 2d. cobalt-blue .. .. .. 3·25 10
 a. Perf 12×11½ .. .. .. 2·75 10
 b. Perf 12 .. .. .. 3·25 10
294 2d. ultramarine (1.12.97) .. .. 2·75 10
 a. Perf 12×11½ .. .. .. 2·25 10
 b. Perf 12 .. .. .. 2·25 10
 c. Imperf between (pair) ..
295 **61** 2½d. purple (Die I) .. .. .. 6·00 1·25
 a. Perf 11½×12 .. .. .. 7·00 80
 b. Perf 11 .. .. .. 7·00 1·75
296 2½d. deep violet (Die II) (11.97) .. 4·25 80
 a. Perf 11½×12 .. .. .. 7·00 1·25
 b. Perf 12 .. .. .. 4·00 1·25
297 2½d. Prussian blue (17.1.99) .. .. 6·00 1·25
 a. Perf 11½×12 .. .. .. 4·00 1·00
 b. Perf 12 .. .. .. 3·25 1·00
288, 292, 294/5 Optd "Specimen" *Set of* 4 60·00

The perforations 11 × 12, 12 × 11½ and 12 are from comb machines, the perforation 11 is from a single-line machine.

1897. *Reissue of T* **24**. *W* **25**. *P* 11.

297*c* 5s. reddish purple (*shades*) .. .. 32·00 12·00
 ca. Imperf between (horiz pair) .. £2750
 d. Perf 12 .. .. .. 42·00 20·00
 e. Perf 11×12 or 12×11 .. .. 35·00 19·00

1898–99. *W* 40. *P* 11 × 12.

297*f* **48** 6d. emerald-green (Optd S. £20) .. 30·00 9·00
 fa. Perf 12 × 11½ .. .. .. 22·00 8·00
 fb. Perf 12 .. .. .. 22·00 8·00
297*g* 6d. orange-yellow (1899) .. .. 14·00 3·25
 ga. Perf 12 × 11½ .. .. .. 13·00 2·75
 gb. Perf 12 .. .. .. 23·00 4·50
 gc. Yellow, p 12 × 11½ .. .. .. 14·00 1·50

1899(Oct). *Chalk-surfaced paper. W* **40** (*sideways on* 2½d.). *P* 12 × 11½ *or* 11½ × 12 (2½d.), *comb*.

298 **58** ½d. blue-green (Type I) .. .. 1·00 10
 a. Imperf (pair) .. .. 65·00 75·00
299 **59** 1d. carmine (Die II) .. .. .. 1·50 10
 a. Imperf horiz (vert pair) £200
300 1d. scarlet (Die II) .. .. .. 1·00 10
301 1d. salmon-red (Die II) .. .. 1·50 10
 a. Imperf (pair) .. .. 65·00 75·00
302 **60** 2d. cobalt-blue .. .. .. 1·75 10
 a. Imperf (pair) .. .. 65·00
303 **61** 2½d. Prussian blue (Die II) .. .. 2·75 70
 a. Imperf (pair) .. .. 80·00
303*b* **47** 4d. red-brown .. .. .. 9·50 3·25
 c. Imperf (pair) £200
304 4d. orange-brown .. .. .. 9·50 3·25
305 **48** 6d. deep orange .. .. .. 11·00 90
 a. Imperf (pair) £150
306 6d. orange-yellow .. .. .. 11·00 90
307 6d. emerald-green .. .. .. 75·00 22·00
 a. Imperf (pair) £190
308 **49** 8d. magenta .. .. .. 18·00 3·25
309 **34** 9d. on 10d. dull brown .. .. 8·00 4·00
 a. Surcharge double .. .. 90·00 £110
 b. Without surcharge .. .. 80·00
310 10d. violet .. .. .. 12·00 3·50
311 **50** 1s. maroon .. .. .. 18·00 1·00
312 1s. purple-brown .. .. .. 18·00 1·50
 a. Imperf (pair) £180

62 Superb Lyrebird

63

1902–03. *Chalk-surfaced paper. W* **42** (*sideways on* 2½d.). *P* 12×11½ *or* 11½×12 (2½d.), *comb*.

313 **58** ½d. blue-green (Type I) .. .. 3·50 10
 a. Perf 12×11 .. .. .. 3·50
314 **59** 1d. carmine (Die II) .. .. .. 1·75 10
315 **60** 2d. cobalt-blue .. .. .. 2·50 10
316 **61** 2½d. dark blue (Die II) .. .. 5·00 10
317 **47** 4d. orange-brown .. .. .. 24·00 4·00
318 **48** 6d. yellow-orange .. .. .. 18·00 1·00
319 6d. orange .. .. .. 17·00 1·00
320 6d. orange-buff .. .. .. 20·00 1·00
321 **49** 8d. magenta .. .. .. 16·00 2·50
322 **34** 9d. on 10d. brownish orange .. 8·00 3·50
323 10d. violet .. .. .. 18·00 3·50
324 **50** 1s. maroon .. .. .. 20·00 80
325 1s. purple-brown .. .. .. 22·00 80
326 **62** 2s. 6d. green (1903) (Optd S. £35) .. 42·00 18·00

(Typo Victoria Govt Printer, Melbourne)

1903 (18 July). *Wmk double-lined V over Crown. W* w **10**.

327 **63** 9d. brown & ultram, *p* 12¼ × 12½, *comb* (Optd S. £27) .. .. 10·00 1·75
328 9d. brown & dp blue, *p* 12¼ × 12½, *comb* .. .. .. 10·00 1·75
329 9d. brown and blue, *p* 11 .. .. £450 £275

Type II. Broad "H" in "HALF"

66

1905 (Oct)–**10**. *Chalk-surfaced paper. W* **66** (*sideways on* 2½d.). *P* 12×11½ *or* 11½×12 (2½d.) *comb, unless otherwise stated.*

330 **58** ½d. blue-green (Type I) .. .. 1·75 10
 a. Perf 11½×11 .. ..
 b. Type II (1908) .. .. 1·25 10
 ba. Perf 11½×11 .. .. 1·75
332 **59** 1d. rose-carmine (Die II) .. .. 1·25 10
 a. Double impression £225
 b. Perf 11½×11 .. .. 1·75
333 **60** 2d. deep ultramarine .. .. 1·75 10
 b. Perf 11½×11 .. .. 2·00
333*d* 2d. milky blue (1910) .. .. 1·75 10
 da. Perf 11 .. .. .. 45·00
 db. Perf 11½×11 .. ..
334 **61** 2½d Prussian blue (Die II) .. .. 2·75 80
335 **47** 4d. orange-brown .. .. .. 9·50 3·25
336 4d. red-brown .. .. .. 11·00 3·25
337 **48** 6d. dull yellow .. .. .. 13·00 1·25
 a. Perf 11½×11 .. .. 21·00
338 6d. orange-yellow .. .. .. 13·00 1·25
 a. Perf 11×11½ .. .. 27·00
339 6d. deep orange .. .. .. 11·00 1·25
 a. Perf 11 .. .. .. £160
339*b* 6d. orange-buff .. .. .. 11·00 1·25
 c. Perf 11½×11 .. .. 17·00 2·75
340 **49** 8d. magenta .. .. .. 18·00 3·50
341 8d. lilac-rose .. .. .. 18·00 3·75
342 **34** 10d. violet .. .. .. 14·00 3·50
 a. Perf 11½×11 .. .. 13·00 3·25
 b. Perf 11 .. .. .. 13·00 3·25
343 **50** 1s. maroon .. .. .. 16·00 1·25
344 1s. purple-brown (1908) .. .. 20·00 1·25
345 **62** 2s. 6d. blue-green .. .. .. 42·00 18·00
 a. Perf 11½×11 .. .. 27·00 16·00
 b. Perf 11 .. .. .. 30·00 20·00

67

1905 (Dec). *Chalk-surfaced paper. W* **67**. *P* 11.

346 **52** 20s. cobalt-blue .. .. .. £150 65·00
 a. Perf 12 .. .. .. £170 75·00
 b. Perf 11 × 12 or 12 × 11 .. .. £140 60·00

(Typo Victoria Govt Printer, Melbourne)

1906 (Sept). *Wmk double-lined* "A" *and Crown, W* w **11**. *P* 12 × 12½, *comb*.

347 **63** 9d. brown and ultramarine .. .. 6·50 1·10
 a. Perf 11 .. .. .. 50·00 42·00
348 9d. yellow-brown and ultramarine .. 6·50 90

1907 (July). *W* w **11** (*sideways on* 2½d.). *P* 12×11½ 11½×12 (2½d.), *comb, unless otherwise stated.*

349 **58** ½d. blue-green (Type I) .. .. 3·25
351 **59** 1d. dull rose (Die II) .. .. 3·00
352 **60** 2d. cobalt-blue .. .. .. 3·25
353 **61** 2½d. Prussian blue (Die II) .. .. 42·00
354 **47** 4d. orange-brown .. .. .. 10·00 4
355 **48** 6d. orange-buff .. .. .. 26·00 5
356 6d. dull yellow .. .. .. 24·00 5
357 **49** 8d. magenta .. .. .. 18·00 4
358 **34** 10d. violet, *p* 11 .. .. .. 18·00
359 **50** 1s. purple-brown .. .. .. 22·00 3
 a. Perf 11 .. ..
360 **62** 2s. 6d. blue-green .. .. .. 45·00 25

STAMP BOOKLETS

There are very few surviving examples of Nos. SB1/4. Listin are provided for those believed to have been issued with pri quoted for those known to still exist.

1904 (May)–**09**. *Black on red cover with map of Australia front and picture of one of six different State G.P.O's on ba Stapled.*

SB1 £1 booklet containing two hundred and forty 1d. in four blocks of 30 and two blocks of 60 ..
 a. Red on pink cover (1909) .. ..
 b. Blue on pink cover .. .. ..

1904 (May). *Black on grey cover as No.* SB1. *Stapled.*

SB2 £1 booklet containing one hundred and twenty 2d. in four blocks of 30 .. .. ..

1910 (May). *Black on cream cover inscribed* "COMMO WEALTH OF AUSTRALIA/POSTMASTER-GENERAI DEPARTMENT". *Stapled.*

SB3 2s. booklet containing eleven ½d. (No. 331), either in block of 6 plus block of 5 or block of 11, and eighteen 1d. (No. 332), either in three blocks of 6 or block of 6 plus 1 block of 12 .. .. £20

Unsold stock of No. SB3 was uprated with one additional ½ in May 1911.

1911 (Aug). *Red on pink cover as No.* SB3. *Stapled.*

SB4 2s. booklet containing twelve ½d. (No. 331), either in two blocks of 6 or block of 12, and eighteen 1d. (No. 332) either in three blocks of 6 or 1 block of 6 plus block of 12 .. .. £15

OFFICIAL STAMPS

O S (O 1) O S (O 2) O S (O 3)

The space between the letters is normally 7 mm as illustrat except on the 5d. and 8d. (11–11½ mm), 5s. (12 mm) and 20s. (mm). Later printings of the 3d., W **40**, are 5½ mm, and these listed. Varieties in the settings are known on the 1d. (8 and mm), 2d. (8½ mm) and 3d. (9 mm).

Varieties of Type O 1 exist with "O" sideways.

Nos. O1/35 *overprinted with Type* O 1

1879. *Wmk double-lined* "6". *P* 13.

O1 **14** 3d. dull green .. .. — £4

1879 (Oct)–**85**. *W* **36**. *P* 13.

O 2 **26** 1d. salmon .. .. .. 10·00 2
 a. Perf 10 (5.81) £180 30
 b. Perf 13×10 (1881) .. .. 20·00 3
O 3 **28** 2d. blue .. .. .. 14·00 1
 a. Perf 10 (7.81) £225 32
 b. Perf 10×13 (1881) .. .. 40·00 20
 ba. Perf 13×10 .. .. 22·00 2
 d. Perf 11×12 (11.84?) .. .. — £2
O 4 **14** 3d. dull green (R.) (12.79) £400 £2
O 5 3d. dull green (3.80) £250 45
 a. Perf 10 (1881) £140 40
 b. Yellow-green. Perf 10 (10.81) .. £140 25
 ba. Perf 13×10 (1881) £140 25
 bb. Perf 12 (4.85) £200 50
 bc. Perf 10×12 or 12×10 (4.85) .. £200 50
O 6 **32** 4d. red-brown £160 7
 a. Perf 10 (1881) .. .. — £1
 b. Perf 10×13 (1881) £200 90
 ba. Perf 13×10 .. .. £150 11
O 7 **15** 5d. green, *p* 10 (8.84) .. .. 18·00 12
O 8 **37** 6d. pale lilac £225 6
 a. Perf 10 (1881) £350 40
 b. Perf 13×10 (1881) £160 40
O 9 **19** 8d. yellow (R.) (12.79) .. .. — £1
O10 8d. yellow (1880) .. .. — 15
 a. Perf 10 (1881) £275 75
O11 **34** 9d. on 10d. brown, *p* 10 (30.5.80) (Optd S £60) £350
O12 **38** 1s. black (R.) £225 7
 a. Perf 10 (1881) .. .. — 16
 b. Perf 10×13 (1881) .. .. — 25
 ba. Perf 13×10 .. .. — 10

Other stamps are known with red overprint but their status is doubt.

1880–88. *Wmk* "5/-", *W* **25**. (*a*) *P* 13.

O13 **24** 5s. deep purple (15.2.80) £425 90
 a. Royal purple .. .. — £3
 b. Deep rose-lilac £425 90

(*b*) *P* 10

O14 **24** 5s. deep purple (9.82) £425 £1
 a. Opt double .. .. † £1
 b. Rose-lilac (1883) £300 £1

(*c*) *P* 10 × 12

O15 **24** 5s. purple (10.86) .. ..

(*d*) *P* 12 × 10

O16 **24** 5s. reddish purple (1886) £425 £1

(*e*) *P* 12
17 **24** 5s. purple . . . . † £500

(*f*) *P* 11
18 **24** 5s. rose-lilac (1888) . . . . £170 80·00

380 (31 May). *Wmk* "10". *W* **35**. *P* 13.
18*a* **34** 10d. lilac (Optd S. £60) . . . . £130 80·00
ab. Perf 10 and 11, compound . . £200 £180
ac. Perf 10 . . . . £200
ad. Opt double, one albino (*p* 10) . .

382–85. *W* **40**. *P* 10.
19 **26** 1d. salmon . . . . 9·50 2·00
a. Perf 13×10 . . . . — £130
20 1d. orange *to* scarlet . . . . . . 8·00 1·50
a. Perf 10×13 . . . . — £130
b. Perf 11×12, comb (1.84) . . . . 5·50 1·40
c. Perf 10×12 or 12×10 (4.85) . . — £110
d. Perf 12×11 (12.85) . . . .
21 **28** 2d. blue . . . . 7·00 1·00
a. Perf 10×13 or 13×10 . . . . £190 75·00
c. Perf 11×12, comb (1.84) . . . . 6·00 1·00
d. Ditto. Opt double . . . . . . — £150
e. Perf 12×11 (12.85) . . . .
22 **14** 3d. yellow-green (7 *mm*) . . . . 7·00 3·50
a. Perf 12 (4.85) . . . . . . £120 80·00
b. Perf 12×10 (4.85) . . . .
c. Perf 12×11 . . . . . .
23 3d. bluish green (7 *mm*) . . . . 7·00 3·50
a. Perf 12 (4.85) . . . . . . £120 80·00
b. Perf 12×10 (4.85) . . . .
c. Perf 10×11 (12.85) . . . .
24 3d. yellow-green (5½ *mm*) . . . . 7·00 3·50
a. Wmk sideways . . . . . . 35·00 20·00
b. Perf 10×12 or 12×10 (4.85) . . 6·00 3·50
c. Perf 10×11 or 11×10 (12.85) . .
25 3d. bluish green (5½ *mm*) (Optd S. £35) 7·00 3·50
a. Perf 10×12 or 12×10 (4.85) . . 6·00 3·50
c. Perf 10×11 or 11×10 (12.85) . . 5·00 3·50
26 **32** 4d. red-brown . . . . . . 30·00 4·00
a. Perf 11×12, comb (1.84) . . . . 12·00 3·00
b. Perf 10×12 (4.85) . . . . — 70·00
27 4d. dark brown . . . . 15·00 3·00
a. Perf 11×12, comb (1.84) . . . . 12·00 3·00
b. Perf 12 (4.85) £200 £150
c. Perf 10×12 (4.85) . . . . £200 90·00
28 **15** 5d. dull green (Optd S. £35) . . . . 12·00 10·00
a. Perf 12×10 (4.85) . . . .
29 5d. blue-green . . . . 13·00 11·00
a. Perf 12 (4.85) £100
b. Perf 10×11 . . . . . . 13·00 11·00
30 **37** 6d. pale lilac . . . . . . 18·00 5·00
a. Perf 11 (12.85) . . . . . . 19·00 4·50
31 6d. mauve . . . . 18·00 5·00
a. Perf 12 (4.85) . . . . . . — 45·00
b. Perf 10×12 or 12×10 (4.85) . . 20·00 4·50
d. Perf 11×10 (12.85) . . . . 18·00 5·00
e. Perf 12×11 (12.85) . . . . 55·00 15·00
32 **19** 8d. yellow . . . . 20·00 10·00
a. Perf 12 (4.85) . . . . . . £130 38·00
b. Perf 10×12 or 12×10 (4.85) . . 20·00 9·00
d. Perf 11 (12.85) . . . . . . 22·00 10·00
da. Opt double . . . .
db. Opt treble . . . . . . † —
33 **38** 1s. black (R.) . . . . . . 25·00 6·00
a. Perf 10×13 . . . . . . — 55·00
b. Perf 11×12, comb (1.84) . . . . 25·00 6·00
c. Ditto. Opt double . . . . . . — £200

886–87. *W* **41**. *P* 10.
34 **26** 1d. scarlet . . . . 25·00 3·50
35 **28** 2d. deep blue . . . . . .
a. Perf 11 × 12 . . . .

887–89. *Nos. 247/8 overprinted in black.* (*a*) *With Type* O **1**.
36 **43** 10s. claret and mauve, *p* 12 . . . . — £800

(*b*) *With Type* O **2** (April 1889)
37 **43** 10s. claret & mauve, *p* 12 (Optd S. £80) £1200 £600
a. Perf 10 . . . . £2250 £1300

(*c*) *With Type* O **3** (Jan 1887)
38 **43** £1 claret and rose-lilac, *p* 12×10 . . £4000 £3000

Only nine examples of No. O38 are recorded, three of which are mint. One of the used stamps, in the Royal Collection, shows overprint Type O **3** double.

888 (17 July)–**90.** *Optd as Type* O **1**. (*a*) *W* **40**. *P* 11 × 12.
39 **45** 1d. lilac . . . . 2·00 15
a. Perf 12 . . . . 2·00 15
b. Mauve . . . . 2·00 15
ba. Perf 12 . . . . 2·00 15
40 **46** 2d. Prussian blue (15.10.88) . . . . 3·75 15
a. Perf 12 . . . . 3·75 15
41 **47** 4d. purple-brown (10.10.89) . . . . 9·00 2·50
a. Perf 12 . . . . 12·00 2·75
b. Perf 11 . . . . . .
c. Red-brown . . . . . . 9·00 2·50
ca. Opt double . . . . . . † —
cb. Perf 12 . . . . 12·00 2·75
42 **48** 6d. carmine (16.1.89) . . . . . . 8·50 3·50
a. Perf 12 . . . . 11·00 3·50
43 **49** 8d. lilac-rose (1890) . . . . . . 16·00 8·50
a. Perf 12 . . . . 20·00 11·00
44 **50** 1s. maroon (9.1.90) . . . . . . 15·00 3·00
a. Perf 12 . . . . 15·00 3·00
b. Purple-brown . . . . . . 15·00 3·00
ba. Opt double . . . .
bb. Perf 12 . . . . 15·00 3·00
39/44 Optd "Specimen" . . . . *Set of* 6 £200

(*b*) *W* **41**. *P* 11 × 12 (1889)
O45 **45** 1d. mauve . . . . . .
O46 **46** 2d. blue . . . . . .

(*c*) *W* **25**. *P* 10
O47 **51** 5s. deep purple (R.) (9.1.90) £600 £500
O48 **52** 20s. cobalt-blue (10.3.90) £1600 £800

1890 (Feb)–**91.** *Optd as Type* O **1**. *W* **53** (5*s.*) *or* **54** (20*s.*) *P* 10.
O49 **51** 5s. lilac £300 £120
a. Mauve . . . . £160 70·00
b. Dull lilac, p 12 . . . . . . £450 £130
O50 **52** 20s. cobalt-blue (3.91) £1600 £600
O49/50 Optd "Specimen" . . . . *Set of* 2 £200

1891 (Jan). *Optd as Type* O **1**. *W* **40**.

(*a*) *On No.* 281. *P* 11×12
O54 **55** 2½d. ultramarine . . . . . . 7·00 3·00

(*b*) *On Nos.* 282/4
O55 **26** ½d. on 1d. grey, *p* 11×12 . . . . 50·00 45·00
O56 **37** 7½d. on 6d. brown, *p* 10 . . . . 35·00 30·00
O57 **38** 12½d. on 1s. red, *p* 11×12 . . . . 60·00 55·00

1892 (May). *No.* 285 *optd as Type* O **1**. *P* 10
O58 **58** ½d. grey . . . . 8·00 12·00
a. Perf 11×12 . . . . . . 6·00 8·00
b. Perf 12 . . . . 7·50 8·50
c. Perf 12×11½ . . . . . . 11·00
O54/8 Optd "Specimen" . . . . *Set of* 5 £160

Official stamps were withdrawn from the government departments on 31 December 1894.

POSTAGE DUE STAMPS

D 1

(Dies eng by A. Collingridge. Typo Govt Printing Office, Sydney)

1891 (1 Jan)–**92.** *W* **40**. *P* 10.
D 1 **D 1** ½d. green (21.1.92) . . . . . . 3·00 2·25
D 2 1d. green . . . . 4·50 90
a. Perf 11 . . . . 4·75 90
b. Perf 12 . . . . 13·00 2·50
c. Perf 12 × 10 . . . . . . 16·00 1·75
d. Perf 10 × 11 . . . . . . 7·50 1·25
e. Perf 11 × 12 or 12 × 11 . . . . 5·00 90
D 3 2d. green . . . . 6·50 1·00
a. Perf 11 . . . . 6·50 1·00
b. Perf 12 . . . . — 8·00
c. Perf 12×10 . . . . . . 15·00 3·00
d. Perf 10×11 . . . . . . 8·00 1·50
e. Perf 11×12 or 12×11 . . . . 7·00 1·00
f. Wmk sideways . . . . . . 13·00 5·00
D 4 3d. green . . . . 11·00 2·75
a. Perf 10 × 11 . . . . . . 11·00 2·75
D 5 4d. green . . . . 8·50 80
a. Perf 11 . . . . 9·50 80
b. Perf 10 × 11 . . . . . . 8·50 80
D 6 6d. green . . . . 17·00 2·00
D 7 8d. green . . . . 60·00 9·00
D 8 5s. green . . . . £120 30·00
a. Perf 11 . . . . £200 75·00
b. Perf 11 × 12 . . . . . . — £250
D 9 10s. green (early 1891) . . . . £225 45·00
a. Perf 12 × 10 . . . . . . £180 80·00
D10 20s. green (early 1891) . . . . £300 80·00
a. Perf 12 . . . . £300
b. Perf 12 × 10 . . . . . . £225 £100
D1/10 Optd "Specimen" . . . . *Set of* 10 £180

1900. *Chalk-surfaced paper. W* **40**. *P* 11.
D11 **D 1** ½d. emerald-green . . . . . .
D12 1d. emerald-green . . . . . . 4·25 2·00
a. Perf 12 . . . . 11·00 3·50
b. Perf 11 × 12 or 12 × 11 . . . . 4·25 1·25
D13 2d. emerald-green . . . . . . 8·00 2·75
a. Perf 12 . . . . — 12·00
b. Perf 11 × 12 or 12 × 11 . . . . 7·00 2·50
D14 3d. emerald-green, *p* 11 × 12 or 12 × 11 15·00 4·50
D15 4d. emerald-green . . . . . . 9·00 3·00

New South Wales became part of the Commonwealth of Australia on 1 January 1901.

QUEENSLAND

The area which later became Queensland was previously part of New South Wales known as the Moreton Bay District. The first post office, at Brisbane, was opened in 1834 and the use of New South Wales stamps from the District became compulsory from 1 May 1854.

Queensland was proclaimed a separate colony on 10 December 1859, but continued to use New South Wales issues until 1 November 1860.

Post Offices opened in the Moreton Bay District before 10 December 1859, and using New South Wales stamps, were

Office	*Opened*	*Numeral Cancellation*
Brisbane	1834	95
Burnett's Inn (*became* Goodes Inn)	1850	108
Callandoon	1850	74
Condamine	1856	151
Dalby	1854	133
Drayton	1846	85
Gayndah	1850	86
Gladstone	1854	131
Goode's Inn	1858	108
Ipswich	1846	87
Maryborough	1849	96
Rockhampton	1858	201
Surat	1852	110
Taroom	1856	152
Toowoomba	1858	214
Warwick	1848	81

ALTERED CATALOGUE NUMBERS

Any Catalogue numbers altered from the last edition are shown as a list in the introductory pages.

PRICES FOR STAMPS ON COVER

Nos. 1/3	*from* × 2
Nos. 4/56	*from* × 3
Nos. 57/8	—
Nos. 59/73	*from* × 4
Nos. 74/82	*from* × 2
Nos. 83/109	*from* × 3
Nos. 110/13	*from* × 2
Nos. 116/17	*from* × 3
Nos. 118/27	—
Nos. 128/50	*from* × 4
Nos. 151/65	—
Nos. 166/78	*from* × 10
Nos. 179/83	*from* × 4
Nos. 184/206	*from* × 15
No. 207	—
Nos. 208/54	*from* × 15
Nos. 256/62c	*from* × 10
Nos. 264*a*/*b*	*from* × 2
Nos. 265/6	*from* × 20
Nos. 270/4	—
Nos. 281/5	*from* × 10
Nos. 286/308	*from* × 12
Nos. 309/13	—
Nos. F1/37	—

1

2 Large Star

3 Small Star

(Dies eng W. Humphrys. Recess P.B.)

1860 (1 Nov). *W* **2**. *Imperf.*
1 **1** 1d. carmine-rose £2750 £800
2 2d. blue £5500 £1500
3 6d. green £4000 £800

1860 (Nov). *W* **2**. *Clean-cut perf* 14–15½.
4 **1** 1d. carmine-rose (1.11) £1200 £250
5 2d. blue (1.11) £500 £100
a. Imperf between (pair) . . . .
6 6d. green (15.11) . . . . . . £550 60·00

1860–61. *W* **3**. *Clean-cut perf* 14–15½.
7 **1** 2d. blue £500 £100
a. Imperf between (horiz pair) . . . . — £900
8 3d. brown (15.4.61) . . . . . . £275 55·00
a. Re-entry . . . . — £200
b. Retouch (R. 2/8) . . . . . . — £200
9 6d. green . . . . £550 60·00
10 1s. violet (15.11.60) . . . . . . £500 75·00
11 "REGISTERED" (6d.) olive-yellow (1.61) £350 70·00
a. Imperf between (pair) £2750

The perforation of the 3d. is that known as "intermediate between clean-cut and rough".

The 3d. re-entry which occurs on one stamp in the second row, shows doubling of the left-hand arabesque and the retouch has redrawn spandrel dots under "EN" of "PENCE", a single dot in the centre of the circle under "E" and the bottom outer frame liner closer to the spandrel's frame line.

1861 (July (?)). *W* **3**. *Clean-cut perf* 14.
12 **1** 1d. carmine-rose . . . . . . £100 40·00
13 2d. blue . . . . £275 50·00

1861 (Sept). *W* **3**. *Rough perf* 14–15½.
14 **1** 1d. carmine-rose . . . . . . 75·00 28·00
15 2d. blue . . . . 95·00 28·00
a. Imperf between (horiz pair) £1800
16 3d. brown . . . . 50·00 30·00
a. Imperf vert (horiz pair) £1800
b. Re-entry £200 £110
c. Retouch (R. 2/8) . . . . . . — £110
17 6d. deep green . . . . . . £110 27·00
18 6d. yellow-green . . . . . . £200 27·00
19 1s. violet . . . . £350 80·00
20 "REGISTERED" (6d.) orange-yellow 50·00 35·00

(Printed and perforated in Brisbane)

1862–67. *Thick toned paper. No wmk.* (*a*) *P* 13 (1862–63).
21 **1** 1d. Indian red (16.12.62) . . . . £250 60·00
22 1d. orange-vermilion (2.63) . . . . 60·00 12·00
a. Imperf (pair) . . . . . . — £550
b. Imperf between (pair) . . . .
23 2d. pale blue (16.12.62) . . . . 80·00 27·00
24 2d. blue . . . . 40·00 9·00
a. Imperf (pair) . . . . . . — £550
b. Imperf between (horiz pair) . . . . — £900
c. Imperf between (vert pair) £1200
25 3d. brown . . . . 55·00 30·00
a. Re-entry . . . . — £110
b. Retouch (R. 2/8) . . . . . . — £110
26 6d. apple-green (17.4.63) . . . . 90·00 15·00
27 6d. yellow-green . . . . . . 80·00 12·00
a. Imperf between (horiz pair) . . . . — £1000
28 6d. pale bluish green . . . . £130 27·00
a. Imperf (pair) . . . . . . — £550
29 1s. grey (14.7.63) (H/S S. £40) . . . . £130 22·00
a. Imperf between (horiz pair) . . . . — £1100
b. Imperf between (vert pair) . . . .

The top or bottom row of perforation was sometimes omitted from the sheet, resulting in stamps perforated on three sides only.

(b) P 12½×13 (1863–67)

No.	Type	Description	Unused	Used
30	1	1d. orange-vermilion	60·00	27·00
31		2d. blue	50·00	20·00
32		3d. brown	65·00	25·00
		a. Re-entry	—	95·00
		b. Retouch (R. 2/8)	—	95·00
33		6d. apple-green	85·00	27·00
34		6d. yellow-green	85·00	27·00
34*a*		6d. pale bluish green		
35		1s. grey	£170	32·00
		a. Imperf between (horiz pair)		

The previously listed stamps perforated 13 round holes come from the same perforating machine as Nos. 21/9 after the pins had been replaced. The holes vary from rough to clean-cut.

1864–65. *W* 3. *(a) P* 13.

No.	Type	Description	Unused	Used
44	1	1d. orange-vermilion (1.65)	65·00	20·00
		a. Imperf between (horiz pair)	£450	
45		2d. pale blue (1.65)	55·00	16·00
46		2d. deep blue	55·00	16·00
		a. Imperf between (vert pair)	£900	
		b. Bisected (1d.) (on cover)	†	£1900
47		6d. yellow-green (1.65)	£120	22·00
48		6d. deep green	£140	22·00
49		"REGISTERED" (6d.) orge-yell (21.6.64)	70·00	30·00
		a. Double printed	£750	
		b. Imperf		

(b) P 12½ × 13

No.	Type	Description	Unused	Used
50	1	1d. orange-vermilion	95·00	40·00
50*a*		2d. deep blue	£120	40·00

1866 (24 Jan). *Wmk "QUEENSLAND/POSTAGE—POSTAGE/STAMPS—STAMPS" in three lines in script capitals with double wavy lines above and below the wmk and single wavy lines with projecting sprays between each line of words. There are ornaments ("fleurons") between "POSTAGE" "POSTAGE" and between "STAMPS" "STAMPS". Single stamps only show a portion of one or two letters of this wmk. (a) P* 13.

No.	Type	Description	Unused	Used
51	1	1d. orange-vermilion	£130	27·00
52		2d. blue	50·00	17·00

(b) P 12½ × 13

No.	Type	Description	Unused	Used
52*a*	1	1d. orange-vermilion	£160	40·00
52*b*		2d. blue	£160	40·00

1866 (24 Sept). *Lithographed on thick paper. No wmk. P* 13.

No.	Type	Description	Unused	Used
53	1	4d. slate (H/S S. £40)	£150	20·00
		a. Re-entry	—	85·00
		b. Retouch (R. 2/8)	—	85·00
55		4d. lilac	£100	16·00
		a. Re-entry	—	75·00
		b. Retouch (R. 2/8)	—	75·00
56		4d. reddish lilac	£100	16·00
		a. Re-entry	—	75·00
		b. Retouch (R. 2/8)	—	75·00
57		5s. bright rose (H/S S. £45)	£275	80·00
58		5s. pale rose	£200	55·00
		a. Imperf between (vert pair)	—	£800

The 4d. is from a transfer taken from the 3d. plate and the 5s. was taken from the 1s. plate, the final "s" being added. The alteration in the values was made by hand on the stone, and there are many varieties, such as tall and short letters in "FOUR PENCE", some of the letters of "FOUR" smudged out, and differences in the position of the two words.

4

1868–74. *Wmk small truncated Star, W* 4 *on each stamp, and the word "QUEENSLAND" in single-lined Roman capitals four times in each sheet. (a) P* 13.

No.	Type	Description	Unused	Used
59	1	1d. orange-vermilion (18.1.71)	45·00	4·50
60		2d. pale blue	45·00	4·50
61		2d. blue (3.4.68)	40·00	2·75
62		2d. bright blue	50·00	2·75
63		2d. greenish blue	85·00	2·50
64		2d. dark blue	45·00	2·50
		a. Imperf		
65		3d. olive-green (27.2.71)	80·00	6·00
		a. Re-entry	—	35·00
		b. Retouch (R. 2/8)	—	35·00
66		3d. greenish grey	95·00	5·50
		a. Re-entry	—	32·00
		b. Retouch (R. 2/8)	—	32·00
67		3d. brown	80·00	5·50
		a. Re-entry	—	32·00
		b. Retouch (R. 2/8)	—	32·00
68		6d. yellow-green (10.11.71)	£140	7·00
69		6d. green	£130	10·00
70		6d. deep green	£170	17·00
71		1s. greenish grey (13.11.72)	£350	35·00
72		1s. brownish grey	£350	35·00
73		1s. mauve (19.2.74)	£225	22·00
59, 61, 65, 69, 73, H/S "Specimen"		*Set of* 5	£180	

(b) P 12 (about Feb 1874)

No.	Type	Description	Unused	Used
74	1	1d. orange-vermilion	£275	24·00
75		2d. blue	£600	35·00
76		3d. greenish grey	—	£150
		a. Re-entry		
		b. Retouch (R. 2.8)		
77		3d. brown	£325	£150
		a. Re-entry		
		b. Retouch (R. 2/8)		
78		6d. green	£850	40·00
79		1s. mauve	£375	40·00

(c) P 13 × 12

No.	Type	Description	Unused	Used
80	1	1d. orange-vermilion	—	£170
81		2d. blue	£850	40·00
82		3d. greenish grey	—	£275

Reprints were made in 1895 of all five values on the paper of the regular issue, and perforated 13; the colours are:—1d. orange and orange-brown, 2d. dull blue and bright blue, 3d. deep brown, 6d. yellow-green, 1s. red-violet and dull violet. The "Registered" was also reprinted with these on the same paper, but perforated 12. One sheet of the 2d. reprint is known to have had the perforations missing between the fourth and fifth vertical rows.

5

6

(4d., litho. Other values recess)

1868–78. *Wmk Crown and Q, W* 5. *(a) P* 13 (1868–75).

No.	Type	Description	Unused	Used
83	1	1d. orange-vermilion (10.11.68)	50·00	4·50
		a. Imperf (pair)	£180	
84		1d. pale rose-red (4.11.74)	48·00	8·50
85		1d. deep rose-red	95·00	9·00
86		2d. pale blue (4.11.74)	48·00	1·75
87		2d. deep blue (20.11.68)	38·00	4·50
		a. Imperf (pair)	£300	
		b. Imperf between (vert pair)		
88		3d. brown (11.6.75)	70·00	12·00
		a. Re-entry	—	55·00
		b. Retouch (R. 2/8)	—	55·00
89		4d. yellow (1.1.75) (H/S S. £60)	£750	42·00
90		6d. deep green (9.4.69)	£120	9·00
91		6d. yellow-green	£100	6·50
92		6d. pale apple-green (1.1.75)	£130	9·00
		a. Imperf (pair)	£300	
93		1s. mauve	£150	29·00

(b) P 12 (1876–78)

No.	Type	Description	Unused	Used
94	1	1d. deep orange-vermilion	38·00	5·00
95		1d. pale orange-vermilion	40·00	5·00
		a. Imperf between (vert pair)		
96		1d. rose-red	45·00	10·00
97		1d. flesh	60·00	10·00
98		2d. pale blue	80·00	15·00
99		2d. bright blue	25·00	1·00
100		2d. deep blue	28·00	1·50
101		3d. brown	60·00	9·00
		a. Re-entry	—	45·00
		b. Retouch (R. 2/8)	—	45·00
102		4d. yellow	£600	25·00
103		4d. buff	£600	20·00
104		6d. deep green	£140	7·00
105		6d. green	£130	4·25
106		6d. yellow-green	£140	4·50
107		6d. apple-green	£140	7·00
108		1s. mauve	45·00	9·00
109		1s. purple	£140	5·00
		a. Imperf between (pair)		

(c) P 13 × 12 *or* 12 × 13

No.	Type	Description	Unused	Used
110	1	1d. orange-vermilion	—	£150
110*a*		1d. rose-red		
111		2d. deep blue	£1100	£250
112		4d. yellow	—	£300
113		6d. deep green	—	£300

(d) P 12½ × 13

No.	Type	Description	Unused	Used
114	1	1d. orange-vermilion	—	£350
115		2d. deep blue	—	£350
115*a*		6d. yellow-green		

(e) P 12½

No.	Type	Description	Unused	Used
115*b*	1	2d. deep blue		

Reprints exist from 1895 of the 1d., 2d., 3d., 6d. and 1s. on thicker paper, Wmk W 6, and in different shades from the originals.

1879. *No wmk. P* 12.

No.	Type	Description	Unused	Used
116	1	6d. pale emerald-green	£170	26·00
		a. Imperf between (horiz pair)	—	£600
117		1s. mauve (*fiscal-cancel* £5)	£100	48·00

No. 117 has a very indistinct lilac *burelé* band at back.

Nos. 116/17 can be found showing portions of a papermaker's watermark, either T. H. Saunders & Co or A. Pirie & Sons.

1881. *Lithographed from transfers from the 1s. die. Wmk Crown and Q, W* 6. *P* 12.

No.	Type	Description	Unused	Used
118	1	2s. pale blue (6 Apr)	65·00	22·00
119		2s. blue (*fiscal-cancel* £3)	65·00	22·00
		a. Imperf vert (horiz pair)		
120		2s. deep blue (*fiscal-cancel* £3)	75·00	22·00
121		2s. 6d. dull scarlet (28 Aug)	£110	42·00
122		2s. 6d. bright scarlet (*fiscal-cancel* £3)	£130	42·00
123		5s. pale yellow-ochre (28 Aug)	£150	60·00
124		5s. yellow-ochre (*fiscal-cancel* £4)	£150	60·00
125		10s. reddish brown (Mar)	£350	£110
		a. Imperf	£375	
126		10s. bistre-brown	£350	£110
127		20s. rose (*fiscal-cancel* £6)	£700	£130

Of the 2s. and 20s. stamps there are five types of each, and of the other values ten types of each.

Beware of fiscally used copies that have been cleaned and provided with forged postmarks.

7

Die I

Die II

Dies I and II often occur in the same sheet.

Die I. The white horizontal inner line of the triangle in the upper right-hand corner merges into the outer white line of the oval above the "L".

Die II. The same line is short and does not touch the inner oval.

1879–80. *Typo. P* 12. *(a) Wmk Crown and Q, W* 5.

No.	Type	Description	Unused	Used
128	7	1d. reddish brown (Die I) (15.5.79)	65·00	15·0
		a. Die II	£100	15·0
		ab. "QOEENSLAND"	£850	£15
129		1d. orange-brown (Die I)	£100	15·0
130		2d. blue (Die I) (10.4.79)	55·00	10·0
		a. "PENGE" (R. 12/6)	£650	£11
		b. "QUEENSbAND" (R. 5/6)	—	£11
		c. "QU" joined	—	£11
131		4d. orange-yellow (6.6.79)	£300	35·0

(b) No wmk, with lilac burelé band on back

No.	Type	Description	Unused	Used
132	7	1d. reddish brown (Die I) (21.10.79)	£275	35·0
		a. Die II	£300	65·0
		ab. "QOEENSLAND"	—	£140
133		2d. blue (Die I) (21.10.79)	£350	17·0
		a. "PENGE" (R. 12/6)	£3250	£60
		b. "QUEENSbAND" (R. 5/6)		

(c) Wmk Crown and Q, W 6

No.	Type	Description	Unused	Used
134	7	1d. reddish brown (Die I) (31.10.79)	35·00	5·0
		a. Imperf between (pair)	—	£30
		b. Die II	45·00	5·0
		ba. "QOEENSLAND"	£200	40·0
		bb. Imperf between (pair)	—	£30
135		1d. dull orange (Die I)	17·00	3·0
		a. Die II	20·00	3·0
		ab. "QOEENSLAND"	55·00	20·0
136		1d. scarlet (Die I) (7.3.81)	14·00	1·7
		a. Die II	16·00	2·2
		ab. "QOEENSLAND"	80·00	24·0
137		2d. blue (Die I) (10.4.79)	27·00	1·0
		a. "PENGE"	£120	40·0
		b. "QUEENSbAND"	£120	40·0
		c. Die II	29·00	3·0
138		2d. grey-blue (Die I)	27·00	1·0
		a. "PENGE"	£120	40·0
		b. "QUEENSbAND"	£120	40·0
		c. Die II	29·00	3·0
139		2d. bright blue (Die I)	30·00	1·0
		a. "PENGE"	£130	40·0
		b. "QUEENSbAND"	£130	40·0
		c. Imperf between (pair)	£450	
		d. Die II	32·00	3·0
140		2d. deep blue (Die I)	32·00	1·0
		a. "PENGE"	£140	40·0
		b. "QUEENSbAND"	£140	40·0
		c. Die II	26·00	4·5
141		4d. orange-yellow	£100	10·0
		a. Imperf between (pair)		
142		6d. deep green	60·00	4·5
		a. Imperf between (pair)		
143		6d. yellow-green	65·00	4·5
144		1s. deep violet (3.80)	55·00	4·5
145		1s. pale lilac	48·00	5·5

The variety "QO" is No. 48 in the first arrangement, and No. 4 in a later arrangement on the sheets.

All these values have been seen imperf and unused, but we hav no evidence that any of them were used in this condition.

The above were printed in sheets of 120, from plates made up 30 groups of four electrotypes. There are four different types in eac group, and two such groups of four are known of the 1d. and 2d thus giving eight varieties of these two values. There was som resetting of the first plate of the 1d., and there are several plates the 2d.; the value in the first plate of the latter value is in thinn letters, and in the last plate three types in each group of four hav the "TW" of "TWO" joined, the letters of "PENCE" are larger ar therefore much closer together, and in one type the "O" of "TW is oval, that letter being circular in the other types.

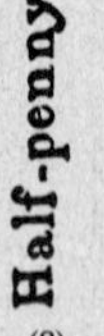

(8)

9

10

1880 (21 Feb). *Surch with T* 8.

No.	Type	Description	Unused	Used
151	7	½d. on 1d. (No. 134) (Die I)	£160	90·0
		a. Die II	£425	£35
		ab. "QOEENSLAND"	£850	£70

Examples with "Half-penny" reading downwards are forge surcharges.

(Eng H. Bourne. Recess Govt Printing Office, Brisbane fror plates made by B.W.)

1882 (13 Apr)–**95.** *P* 12. *(a) W* 5 *(twice sideways). Thin pape*

No.	Type	Description	Unused	Used
152	9	2s. bright blue (14.4.82)	60·00	17·0
153		2s. 6d. vermilion (12.7.82)	50·00	20·0
154		5s. rose	45·00	22·0
155		10s. brown (12.7.82)	95·00	40·0
156		£1 deep green (30.5.83)	£225	£12
		a. Re-entry (R.1/2)	—	£18
		b. Retouch (R.6/4)	—	£18
152, 154/6 H/S "Specimen"		*Set of* 4	£150	

(b) W 10. *Thick paper* (10.11.86)

No.	Type	Description	Unused	Used
157	9	2s. bright blue	60·00	30·(
158		2s. 6d. vermilion	38·00	22·(
159		5s. rose	35·00	30·(

60 9 10s. brown .. .. 95·00 45·00
61 £1 deep green .. .. £170 60·00
a. Re-entry (R.1/2) .. .. — £100
b. Retouch (R.6/4) .. .. — £100

(*c*) *W* **6** (*twice sideways*). *Thin paper* (1895)

62 9 2s. 6d. vermilion .. .. 40·00 30·00
63 5s. rose .. .. 45·00 20·00
64 10s. brown .. .. £180 50·00
65 £1 deep green .. .. £180 60·00
a. Re-entry (R.1/2) .. .. — £100
b. Retouch (R.6/4) .. .. — £100

The re-entry on the £1 shows as a double bottom frame line nd the retouch occurs alongside the bottom right numeral.

See also Nos. 270/1, 272/4 and 309/12.

11

12

In T **12** the shading lines do not extend entirely across, as in T **11**, hus leaving a white line down the front of the throat and point of he bust.

882 (1 Aug)–**91.** *W* **6**. (*a*) *P* 12.

66 11 1d. pale vermilion-red (23.11.82) .. 3·50 30
a. Double impression .. ..
67 1d. deep vermilion-red .. .. .. 3·50 30
68 2d. blue .. .. 4·75 30
a. Imperf between (horiz pair) ..
69 4d. pale yellow (18.4.83) .. .. .. 13·00 2·00
a. "PENGE" for "PENCE" (R. 8/1) .. £130 45·00
b. "EN" joined in "PENCE" (R. 4/6) .. 90·00 30·00
c. Imperf (11.91) .. .. ..
70 6d. green (6.11.82) .. .. .. 9·00 1·00
71 1s. violet (6.2.83) .. .. .. 20·00 2·25
72 1s. lilac .. .. 11·00 2·00
73 1s. deep mauve .. .. 11·00 1·75
74 1s. pale mauve .. .. 12·00 1·75
a. Imperf .. .. † —

(*b*) *P* 9½×12 (1884)

76 11 1d. pale red .. .. 65·00 23·00
77 2d. blue .. .. £200 38·00
78 1s. mauve .. .. £110 28·00

The above were printed from plates made up of groups of four lectrotypes as previously. In the 1d. the words of value are ollowed by a full stop. There are four types of the 4d., 6d., and 1s., ight types of the 1d., and twelve types of the 2d.

No. 169c is from a sheet used at Roma post office and comes ancelled with the "46" numeral postmark.

887 (5 May)–**89.** *W* **6**. (*a*) *P* 12.

79 12 1d. vermilion-red .. .. 3·00 30
80 2d. blue .. .. 5·50 30
a. Oval white flaw on Queen's head behind diadem (R. 12/5) .. .. 25·00 7·50
81 2s. deep brown (12.3.89) .. .. .. 55·00 27·00
82 2s. pale brown .. .. 50·00 25·00

(*b*) *P* 9½×12

83 12 2d. blue .. .. £180 35·00

These are from new plates; four types of each value grouped as efore. The 1d. is without stop. In all values No. 2 in each group of our has the "L" and "A" of "QUEENSLAND" joined at the foot, and No. 3 of the 2d. has "P" of word "PENCE" with a long downstroke.

The 2d. is known bisected and used as a 1d. value.

13

14

890–94. *W* **6** (*sideways on* ½*d.*). *P* 12½, 13 (*comb machine*).

84 13 ½d. pale green .. .. 3·00 50
85 ½d. deep green .. .. 3·00 50
86 ½d. deep blue-green .. .. .. 3·25 50
87 12 1d. vermilion-red .. .. 2·50 15
a. Imperf .. .. 28·00 28·00
b. Oval broken by tip of bust (R.10/3) 20·00 5·00
c. Double impression .. .. † £190
88 2d. blue (old plate) .. .. .. 4·00 15
89 2d. pale blue (old plate) .. .. .. 3·75 15
90 2d. pale blue (retouched plate) .. .. 3·50 30
a. "FWO" for "TWO" (R.8/7) .. .. — 20·00
91 14 2½d. carmine .. .. 10·00 70
92 12 3d. brown .. .. 8·50 1·60
93 11 4d. yellow .. .. 13·00 1·50
a. "PENGE" for "PENCE" (R.8/1) .. 60·00 22·00
b. "EN" joined in "PENCE" (R.4/6) .. 45·00 16·00
94 4d. orange .. .. 16·00 1·50
a. "PENGE" for "PENCE" (R.8/1) .. 70·00 22·00
b. "EN" joined in "PENCE" (R.4/6) .. 50·00 16·00
95 4d. lemon .. .. 20·00 1·75
a. "PENGE" for "PENCE" (R.8/1) .. 80·00 28·00
b. "EN" joined in "PENCE" (R.4/6) .. 60·00 20·00
96 6d. green .. .. 10·00 1·25
97 12 2s. red-brown .. .. 38·00 10·00
98 2s. pale brown .. .. 42·00 12·00

This issue is perforated by a new vertical comb machine, gauging about 12¾ × 12¾. The 3d. is from a plate similar to those of the ast issue, No. 2 in each group of four types having "L" and "A" oined at the foot. The ½d. and 2½d. are likewise in groups of four ypes, but the differences are very minute. In the retouched plate of he 2d. the letters "L" and "A" no longer touch in No. 2 of each group and the "P" in No. 3 is normal.

1895. A. *Thick paper. W* **10**. (*a*) *P* 12½, 13.

202 12 1d. vermilion-red (16.1.95) .. .. 2·75 15
a. Oval broken by tip of bust (R. 10/3) 25·00 5·00
203 1d. red-orange .. .. 2·75 15
a. Oval broken by tip of bust (R. 10/3) 25·00 5·00
204 2d. blue (retouched plate) (16.1.95) .. 3·25 20
a. "FWO" for "TWO" (R. 8/7) .. — 20·00

(*b*) *P* 12

205 11 1s. mauve (8.95) .. .. .. 12·00 3·25

B. *Unwmkd paper; with blue burelé band at back. P* 12½, 13

206 12 1d. vermilion-red (19.2.95) .. .. 2·00 15
a. Oval broken by tip of bust (R. 10/3) 20·00 5·00
b. "PE" of "PENNY" omitted (R. 1/2) £110 75·00
206*c* 1d. red-orange .. .. 2·00 15

C. *Thin paper. Crown and Q faintly impressed. P* 12½, 13

207 12 2d. blue (retouched plate) (6.95) .. 10·00
a. "FWO" for "TWO" (R. 8/7) .. 80·00

15

16

17

18

1895–96. A. *W* **6** (*sideways on* ½*d.*). (*a*) *P* 12½, 13.

208 15 ½d. green (11.5.95) .. .. .. 1·00 60
a. Double impression .. .. ..
209 ½d. deep green .. .. 1·00 60
a. Printed both sides .. .. 75·00
210 16 1d. orange-red (28.2.95) .. .. 2·50 20
211 1d. pale red .. .. 2·25 20
212 2d. blue (19.6.95) .. .. .. 4·50 35
213 17 2½d. carmine (8.95) .. .. .. 10·00 3·25
214 2½d. rose .. .. 11·00 3·25
215 18 5d. purple-brown (10.95) .. .. 14·00 3·25

(*b*) *P* 12

217 16 1d. red (8.95) .. .. 30·00 10·00
218 2d. blue (8.95) .. .. 30·00 14·00

B. *Thick paper. W* **10** (*sideways*) (*part only on each stamp*).

(*a*) *P* 12½, 13

219 15 ½d. green (6.8.95) .. .. .. 1·50 60
220 ½d. deep green .. .. 1·50 60

(*b*) *P* 12

221 15 ½d. green .. .. 12·00
222 ½d. deep green .. .. 12·00

C. *No wmk; with blue burelé band at back.* (*a*) *P* 12½, 13

223 15 ½d. green (1.8.95) .. .. .. 1·50 70
a. Without *burelé* band .. .. 40·00
224 ½d. deep green .. .. 1·50

(*b*) *P* 12

225 15 ½d. green .. .. 15·00
a. Without *burelé* band .. .. 50·00

Nos. 223a and 225a are from the margins of the sheet.

D. *Thin paper, with Crown and Q faintly impressed. P* 12½, 13

227 15 ½d. green .. .. 1·40 70
228 16 1d. orange-red .. .. 3·00 40

19

1896. *W* **6**. *P* 12½, 13.

229 19 1d. vermilion .. .. 9·00 40

Used examples of a 6d. green as Type **19** (figures in lower corners only) are known, mostly with readable 1902 postmarks dates. It is believed that this 6d. was prepared, but not officially issued (*Price* £1700 *used*).

20

21

22

23

24

25

Die I

Die II

Two Dies of 4d.:

Die I. Serif of horizontal bar on lower right 4d. is clear of vertical frame line.

Die II. Serif joins vertical frame line.

1897–1908. *Figures in all corners. W* **6** (*sideways on* ½*d.*). *P* 12½, 13.

231 20 ½d. deep green .. .. 3·50 3·00
a. Perf 12 .. .. — 90·00
232 21 1d. orange-vermilion .. .. .. 1·75 15
233 1d. vermilion .. .. 1·75 15
a. Perf 12 (1903) .. .. .. 2·75 70
234 2d. blue (1902) .. .. 1·75 15
a. Cracked plate .. .. .. 55·00 20·00
b. Perf 12 (1903) .. .. .. — 5·00
235 2d. deep blue .. .. 1·75 15
a. Cracked plate .. .. .. 55·00 20·00
236 22 2½d. rose (10.98) .. .. .. 16·00 11·00
237 2½d. purple/*blue* (20.1.99) .. .. 8·50 85
238 2½d. brown-purple/*blue* .. .. 8·50 85
239 2½d. slate/*blue* (5.08) .. .. .. 11·00 2·75
240 21 3d. brown (10.98) .. .. .. 10·00 1·00
241 3d. deep brown .. .. 8·00 1·00
242 3d. reddish brown (1906) .. .. 8·00 1·00
243 3d. grey-brown (1907) .. .. .. 9·50 1·00
244 4d. yellow (Die I) (10.98) .. .. 8·00 1·25
a. Die II .. .. 18·00 2·00
245 4d. yellow-buff (Die I) .. .. .. 8·00 1·25
a. Die II .. .. 18·00 2·00
246 23 5d. purple-brown .. .. .. 7·50 1·00
247 5d. dull brown (1906) .. .. .. 8·50 1·75
248 5d. black-brown (1907) .. .. .. 9·50 2·00
249 21 6d. green (1.4.98) .. .. .. 7·00 1·50
250 6d. yellow-green .. .. .. 6·00 1·50
251 24 1s. pale mauve (1.7.99) .. .. 13·00 1·50
252 1s. dull mauve .. .. 13·00 1·50
253 1s. bright mauve .. .. .. 15·00 2·50
254 25 2s. turquoise-green .. .. .. 30·00 11·00

The 1d. perf 12×9½ was not an authorised issue.

The cracked plate variety on the 2d. developed during 1901 and shows as a white break on the Queen's head and neck. The electro was later replaced.

1897–8. *W* **6** (*a*) *Zigzag roulette in black.* (*b*) *The same but plain.* (*c*) *Roulette* (*a*) *and also* (*b*). (*d*) *Roulette* (*b*) *and perf* 12½, 13. (*e*) *Roulette* (*a*) *and perf* 12½, 13. (*f*) *Compound of* (*a*), (*b*), *and perf* 12½, 13.

256 21 1d. vermilion (*a*) .. .. .. 8·00 6·50
257 1d. vermilion (*b*) .. .. .. 3·50 3·00
258 1d. vermilion (*c*) .. .. .. 8·00 10·00
259 1d. vermilion (*d*) .. .. .. 5·00 4·00
260 1d. vermilion (*e*) .. .. .. 65·00 80·00
261 1d. vermilion (*f*) .. .. .. 80·00 80·00

26

27

(Des M. Kellar)

1899–1906. *W* **6**. *P* 12½, 13.

262 26 ½d. deep green .. .. 1·50 50
a. Grey-green .. .. .. 1·50 50
b. Green (*p* 12) (1903) .. .. 2·00 60
c. Pale green (1906) .. .. 1·50 50

Stamps of T **26** without wmk, are proofs.

(Des F. Elliott)

1900 (19 June). *Charity. T* **27** *and horiz design showing Queen Victoria in medallion inscr* "PATRIOTIC FUND 1900". *W* **6**. *P* 12.

264*a* 1d. (6d.) claret £100 £100
264*b* 2d. (1s.) violet £250 £250

These stamps, sold at 6d. and 1s. respectively, paid postage of 1d. and 2d. only, the difference being contributed to a Patriotic Fund.

28

QUEENSLAND
A

QUEENSLAND
B

TWO TYPES OF "QUEENSLAND". Three different duty plates, each 120 (12 × 10), were produced for Type **28**. The first contained country inscriptions as Type A and was only used for Nos. 265/6. The second duty plate used for Nos. 265/6 and 282/5 contained 117 examples as Type A and 3 as Type B occurring on R. 1/6, R. 2/6 and R. 3/6. The third plate, also used for Nos. 265/6 and 282/5, had all inscriptions as Type B.

(Typo Victoria Govt Printer, Melbourne)

1903 (4 July)–**05.** *W w* **10.** *P* 12½.
265 **28** 9d. brown and ultramarine (A) .. .. 11·00 2·25
266 9d. brown and ultramarine (B) (1905) .. 11·00 2·25

1903 (Oct). *As Nos.* 162 *and* 165. *W* **6** (*twice sideways*). *P* 12½, 13 (*irregular line*).
270 **9** 2s. 6d. vermilion .. .. 60·00 32·00
271 £1 deep green £900 £500
a. Re-entry (R.1/2) .. .. .. — £750
b. Retouch (R.6/4) .. .. .. — £750

(Litho Govt Ptg Office, Brisbane, from transfers of the recess plates)

1905 (Nov)–**06.** *W* **6** (*twice sideways*).
(*a*) *P* 12½, 13 (*irregular line*)
272 **9** £1 deep green £350 £100
a. Re-entry (R.1/2) .. .. .. — £160
b. Retouch (R.6/4) .. .. .. — £160
(*b*) *P* 12
273 **9** 5s. rose (7.06) .. .. .. 65·00 65·00
274 £1 deep green (7.06) .. .. .. £250 90·00
a. Re-entry (R.1/2) £375 £150
b. Retouch (R.6/4) £375 £150

30

32

Redrawn types of T **21**

T **30.** The head is redrawn, the top of the crown is higher and touches the frame, as do also the back of the chignon and the point of the bust. The forehead is filled in with lines of shading, and the figures in the corners appear to have been redrawn also.

T **32.** The forehead is plain (white instead of shaded), and though the top of the crown is made higher, it does not touch the frame; but the point of the bust and the chignon still touch The figure in the right lower corner does not touch the line below, and has not the battered appearance of that in the first redrawn type. The stamps are very clearly printed, the lines of shading being distinct.

1906 (Sept). *W* **6.** *P* 12½, 13 (*comb*).
281 **30** 2d. dull blue (*shades*) .. .. .. 6·00 2·50

(Typo Victoria Govt Printer, Melbourne)

1906 (Sept)–**10.** *Wmk Crown and double-lined A, W w* **11.**
(*a*) *P* 12 × 12½.
282 **28** 9d. brown and ultramarine (A) .. 24·00 3·25
283 9d. brown and ultramarine (B) .. 12·00 3·00
283*a* 9d. pale brown and blue (A) .. ..
284 9d. pale brown and blue (B) .. 12·00 3·25
(*b*) *P* 11 (1910)
285 **28** 9d. brown and blue (B) .. .. .. — £200

33

1907–11. *W* **33.** (*a*) *P* 12½, 13 (*comb*).
286 **26** ½d. deep green .. .. 1·50 40
287 ½d. deep blue-green .. .. .. 1·50 40
288 **21** 1d. vermilion .. .. 2·00 15
a. Imperf (pair) £160
289 **30** 2d. dull blue .. .. 2·50 15
289*a* 2d. bright blue (3.08) .. .. .. 10·00 2·50
290 **32** 2d. bright blue (4.08) .. .. .. 2·50 15
291 **21** 3d. pale brown (8.08) .. .. .. 11·00 90
292 3d. bistre-brown .. .. .. 11·00 1·00
293 4d. yellow (Die I) .. .. .. 10·00 1·75
a. Die II .. .. 22·00 3·00
294 4d. grey-black (Die I) (4.09) .. .. 13·00 1·60
a. Die II .. .. 27·00 3·50
295 **23** 5d. dull brown .. .. 7·50 2·25
295*a* 5d. sepia (12.09) .. .. .. 12·00 2·75
296 **21** 6d. yellow-green .. .. .. 8·50 1·50
297 6d. bright green .. .. .. 10·00 1·75
298 **24** 1s. violet (1908) .. .. .. 11·00 1·60
299 1s. bright mauve .. .. .. 12·00 1·50
300 **25** 2s. turquoise-green (8.08) .. .. 30·00 10·00

Stamps of this issue also exist with the irregular line perforation 12½, 13. This was used when the comb perforation was under repair.

(*b*) *P* 13×11 *to* 12½ (May 1911)
301 **26** ½d. deep green .. .. 5·00 1·50
302 **21** 1d. vermilion .. .. 6·00 80
303 **32** 2d. blue .. .. 7·50 2·50
304 **21** 3d. bistre-brown .. .. .. 13·00 4·50
305 4d. grey-black .. .. .. 30·00 11·00
306 **23** 5d. dull brown .. .. .. 20·00 11·00
307 **21** 6d. yellow-green .. .. .. 20·00 11·00
308 **23** 1s. violet .. .. 35·00 13·00

The perforation (*b*) is from a machine introduced to help cope with the demands caused by the introduction of penny postage. The three rows at top (or bottom) of the sheet show varieties gauging 13 × 11½, 13 × 11, and 13 × 12 respectively, these are obtainable in strips of three showing the three variations.

(Litho Govt Ptg Office, Brisbane)

1907 (Oct)–**12.** *W* **33** (*twice sideways*). *P* 12½, 13 (*irregular line*).
309 **9** 2s. 6d. vermilion .. .. .. 40·00 28·00
a. Dull orange (1910) .. .. .. 55·00 48·00
b. Reddish orange (1912) £150 £180
310 5s. rose (12.07) .. .. 45·00 30·00
a. Deep rose (1910) .. .. .. 55·00 45·00
b. Carmine-red (1912) £150 £225
311 10s. blackish brown .. .. .. £100 40·00
a. Sepia (1912) £300
312 £1 bluish green .. .. £170 80·00
a. Re-entry (R. 1/2) .. .. .. — £130
b. Retouch (R. 6/4) .. .. .. — £130
c. Deep bluish green (1910) £375 £250
ca. Re-entry (R. 1/2) .. .. .. — £350
cb. Retouch (R. 6/4) .. .. .. — £350
d. Yellow-green (1912) £700
da. Re-entry (R. 1/2) .. .. ..
db. Retouch (R. 6/4) .. .. ..

The 1912 printings are on thinner, whiter paper.

The lithographic stone used for Nos. 272/4 and 309/12 took the full sheet of 30 so the varieties on the £1 recess-printed version also appear on the stamps printed by lithography.

1911. *W* **33.** *Perf irregular compound,* 10½ *to* 12½.
313 **21** 1d. vermilion £350 £190

This was from another converted machine, formerly used for perforating Railway stamps. The perforation was very unsatisfactory and only one or two sheets were sold.

STAMP BOOKLETS

There are very few surviving examples of Nos. SB1/4. Listings are provided for those believed to have been issued with prices quoted for those known to still exist.

1904 (1 Jan)–**09.** *Black on red cover as No.* SB1 *of New South Wales. Stapled.*
SB1 £1 booklet containing two hundred and forty 1d. in four blocks of 30 and two blocks of 60 ..
a. Red on pink cover (1909) .. .. ..
b. Blue on pink cover £6000

1904 (1 Jan). *Black on grey cover as No.* SB1. *Stapled.*
SB2 £1 booklet containing one hundred and twenty 2d. in four blocks of 30 .. ..

1910 (May). *Black on cream cover as No.* SB3 *of New South Wales. Stapled.*
SB3 2s. booklet containing eleven ½d. (No. 301), either in block of 6 plus block of 5 or block of 11, and eighteen 1d. (No. 302), either in three blocks of 6 or block of 6 plus block of 12 .. ..

Unsold stock of No. SB3 was uprated with one additional ½d. in May 1911.

1911 (Aug). *Red on pink cover as No.* SB3. *Stapled.*
SB4 2s. booklet containing twelve ½d. (No. 301), either in two blocks of 6 or block of 12, and eighteen 1d. (No. 302), either in three blocks of 6 or block of 6 plus block of 12 .. .. .. £1500
a. Red on white £1500

POSTAL FISCALS

Authorised for use from 1 January 1880 until 1 July 1892

CANCELLATIONS. Beware of stamps which have had pen-cancellations cleaned off and then had faked postmarks applied. Used prices quoted are for postally used examples between the above dates.

F 1

F 2

1866–68. A. *No wmk. P* 13.
F 1 F 1 1d. blue .. .. 25·00 7·00
F 2 6d. deep violet .. .. .. 25·00 30·00
F 3 1s. blue-green .. .. .. 30·00 9·00
F 4 2s. brown .. .. 85·00 42·00
F 5 2s. 6d. dull red .. .. .. 85·00 30·00
F 6 5s. yellow .. .. £200 60·00
F 6*a* 6s. light brown .. .. ..
F 7 10s. green £350 £100
F 8 20s. rose £425 £150

B. *Wmk* F **2.** *P* 13
F 9 F 1 1d. blue .. .. 15·00 20·00
F10 6d. deep violet .. .. .. 25·00 30·00
F11 6d. blue .. .. 25·00 14·00
F12 1s. blue-green .. .. .. 30·00 14·00
F13 2s. brown .. .. 85·00 30·00
F13*a* 5s. yellow .. .. £200 65·00
F14 10s. green £350 £100
F15 20s. rose £425 £150

COVER PRICES

Cover factors are quoted at the beginning of each country for most issues to 1945. An explanation of the system can be found on page x. The factors quoted do not, however, apply to philatelic covers.

F 3

F 3*a*

1871–2. *P* 12 *or* 13. A. *Wmk Large Crown and Q, Wmk* F 3*a*
F16 F 3 1d. mauve .. .. 10·00 5·0
F17 6d. red-brown .. .. .. 20·00 10·0
F18 1s. green .. .. 30·00 12·0
F19 2s. blue .. .. 40·00 10·0
F20 2s. 6d. brick-red .. .. .. 60·00 25·0
F21 5s. orange-brown .. .. .. £100 25·0
F22 10s. brown .. .. £200 75·0
F23 20s. rose £350 £12

B. *No wmk. Blue burelé band at back*
F24 F 3 1d. mauve .. .. 14·00 6·5
F25 6d. red-brown .. .. .. 20·00 10·0
F26 6d. mauve .. .. 60·00 30·0
F27 1s. green .. .. 30·00 12·0
F28 2s. blue .. .. 45·00 50·0
F29 2s. 6d. vermilion .. .. .. 85·00 35·0
F30 5s. yellow-brown .. .. .. £120 40·0
F31 10s. brown .. .. £225 90·0
F32 20s. rose £350 £11

F 4

F 5

1878–9. A. *No wmk. Lilac burelé band at back. P* 12.
F33 F 4 1d. violet .. .. 40·00 12·0

B. *Wmk Crown and Q, W* **5.** *P* 12
F34 F 4 1d. violet .. .. 15·00 8·0

Stamps as Type F 5 were not issued until 1 July 1892. The existence of postal cancellations on such issues was unauthorised.

Queensland became part of the Commonwealth of Australia on 1 January 1901.

SOUTH AUSTRALIA

PRICES FOR STAMPS ON COVER

Nos. 1/3	*from* × 3
No. 4	†
Nos. 5/12	*from* × 2
Nos. 13/18	*from* × 3
Nos. 19/43	*from* × 4
Nos. 44/9*b*	—
Nos. 50/110	*from* × 3
No. 111	—
Nos. 112/34	*from* × 6
Nos. 135/45	*from* × 3
Nos. 146/66	*from* × 5
Nos. 167/70*a*	*from* × 10
Nos. 171/2*a*	—
Nos. 173/94*a*	*from* × 12
Nos. 195/208	—
Nos. 229/31	*from* × 12
No. 232	—
Nos. 233/42	*from* × 12
Nos. 268/75	*from* × 30
Nos. 276/9	—
Nos. 280/8	*from* × 30
Nos. 289/92	—
Nos. 293/304	*from* × 15
No. 305	—
Nos. O1/13	—
Nos. O14/36	*from* × 20
Nos. O37/42	*from* × 5
Nos. O43/4	*from* × 50
Nos. O45/7	—
Nos. O48/52	*from* × 30
No. O53	—
Nos. O54/85	*from* × 50
Nos. O86/7	—

SPECIMEN OVERPRINTS. Those listed are from U.P.U. distributions between 1889 and 1895. Further "Specimen" overprints exist, but these were used for other purposes.

1

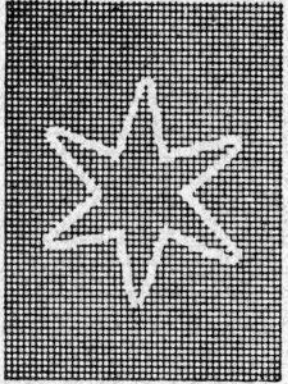

2 Large Star

(Eng Wm Humphrys. Recess P.B.)

855. *Printed in London.* W **2.** *Imperf.*
1 1d. dark green (26.10.55) £2500 £350
2d. rose-carmine (*shades*) (1.1.55) .. £550 80·00
6d. deep blue (26.10.55) £2000 £150

Prepared and sent to the Colony, but not issued
1 1s. violet £4750

A printing of 500,000 of these 1s. stamps was made and elivered, but as the colour was liable to be confused with that of ne 6d. stamp, the stock was destroyed on 5 June 1857.

OTE. Proofs of the 1d. and 6d. without wmk exist, and these are ound with forged star watermarks added, and are sometimes ffered as originals.
For reprints of the above and later issues, see note after No. 194.

856–58. *Printed by Govt Ptr, Adelaide, from Perkins, Bacon plates.* W **2.** *Imperf.*
5 1 1d. deep yellow-green (15.6.58) .. £5000 £400
6 1d. yellow-green (11.10.58) .. .. — £475
7 2d. orange-red (23.4.56) .. .. — 75·00
8 2d. blood-red (14.11.56) .. .. £1200 60·00
a. Printed on both sides .. .. — £800
9 2d. red (*shades*) (29.10.57) .. £650 40·00
a. Printed on both sides .. .. — £600
0 6d. slate-blue (7.57) £2000 £150
1 1s. red-orange (8.7.57) .. .. — £400
2 1s. orange (11.6.58) £3750 £325

858–59. W **2.** *Rouletted. (This first rouletted issue has the same colours as the local imperf issue).*
3 1 1d. yellow-green (8.1.59) .. .. £475 45·00
4 1d. light yellow-green (18.3.59).. .. £475 50·00
a. Imperf between (pair)
5 2d. red (17.2.59).. .. .. £110 18·00
a. Printed on both sides .. .. — £600
7 6d. slate-blue (12.12.58).. .. £375 25·00
8 1s. orange (18.3.59) .. .. £800 35·00
a. Printed on both sides .. .. — £1000

3

4

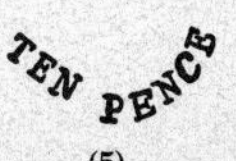

(5)

860–69. *Second rouletted issue, printed (with the exception of No. 24) in colours only found rouletted or perforated. Surch with* T **5** *(Nos. 35/7).* W **2.**
9 1 1d. bright yellow-green (22.4.61) .. 45·00 25·00
0 1d. dull blue-green (17.12.63) .. 42·00 23·00
1 1d. sage-green .. .. .. 55·00 27·00
2 1d. pale sage-green (27.5.65) .. 45·00
3 1d. deep green (1864) .. .. £225 65·00
4 1d. deep yellow-green (1869) .. 90·00
4*a* 2d. pale red .. .. .. 65·00 4·00
b. Printed on both sides .. .. — £375
5 2d. pale vermilion (3.2.63) .. 50·00 4·00
6 2d. bright vermilion (19.8.64) .. 42·00 2·75
a. Imperf between (horiz pair).. £700 £300
7 3 4d. dull violet (24.1.67) .. 60·00 17·00
8 1 6d. violet-blue (19.3.60) .. £140 6·00
9 6d. greenish blue (11.2.63) .. 70·00 4·00
0 6d. dull ultramarine (25.4.64) .. 65·00 4·00
a. Imperf between (horiz pair).. — £300
1 6d. violet-ultramarine (11.4.68).. £150 6·00
2 6d. dull blue (26.8.65) .. £100 6·50
a. Imperf between (pair) .. — £600
3 6d. Prussian blue (7.9.69) .. £550 50·00
3*a* 6d. indigo .. .. .. — 55·00
4 4 9d. grey-lilac (24.12.60) .. 55·00 9·00
a. Imperf between (horiz pair).. — £1000
5 10d. on 9d. orange-red (B.) (20.7.66) £130 24·00
6 10d. on 9d. yellow (B.) (29.7.67) £160 20·00
7 10d. on 9d. yellow (Blk.) (14.8.69) £1200 30·00
a. Surch inverted at the top .. — £2500
b. Printed on both sides .. — £800
c. Roul × perf 10 .. .. † —
8 1 1s. yellow (25.10.61) .. £450 28·00
a. Imperf between (vert pair) .. — £1200
9 1s. grey-brown (10.4.63).. .. £150 16·00
0 1s. dark grey-brown (26.5.63) .. £130 16·00
1 1s. chestnut (25.8.63) .. .. £150 11·00
2 1s. lake-brown (27.3.65).. .. £110 12·00
a. Imperf between (horiz pair).. — £400
3 3 2s. rose-carmine (24.1.67) .. £160 25·00
a. Imperf between (vert pair) .. — £750

868–71. *Remainders of old stock subsequently perforated by the 11½–12½ machine.*

(a) Imperf stamps. P 11½–12½
4 1 2d. pale vermilion (Feb 1868) .. — £900
5 2d. vermilion (18.3.68) .. .. — £1000

(b) Rouletted stamps. P 11½–12½
46 1 1d. bright green (9.11.69) .. .. — £450
47 2d. pale vermilion (15.8.68) .. .. — £400
48 6d. Prussian blue (8.11.69) .. .. — £200
aa. Horiz pair perf all round, roul between
48*a* 6d. indigo .. .. — £300
49 4 9d. grey-lilac (29.3.71) £1500 £160
a. Perf × roulette .. .. .. — £180
49*b* 1 1s. lake-brown (23.5.70).. .. ..

1867–70. W **2.** *P* 11½–12½ × *roulette.*
50 1 1d. pale bright green (2.11.67) .. .. £150 18·00
51 1d. bright green (1868) .. .. £130 18·00
52 1d. grey-green (26.1.70) .. .. £150 20·00
a. Imperf between (horiz pair) .. ..
53 1d. blue-green (29.11.67) .. .. £190 30·00
54 3 4d. dull violet (July 1868) £1400 £130
55 4d. dull purple (1869) .. .. — 90·00
56 1 6d. bright pale blue (29.5.67) .. .. £450 19·00
57 6d. Prussian blue (30.7.67) .. .. £400 19·00
a. Printed on both sides .. ..
58 6d. indigo (1.8.69) .. .. £500 24·00
59 4 10d. on 9d. yellow (B.) (2.2.69) .. £600 30·00
a. Printed on both sides .. .. — £550
60 1 1s. chestnut (April 1868) .. .. £250 15·00
61 1s. lake-brown (3.3.69) .. .. £250 15·00

NOTE. The stamps perf 11½, 12½, or compound of the two, are here combined in one list, as both perforations are on the one machine, and all the varieties *may* be found in each sheet of stamps. This method of classifying the perforations by the machines is by far the most simple and convenient.

(6) 7 (=Victoria W **19**)

1868–79. *Surch with* T **6** *(Nos. 66/8).* W **2.** *P* 11½–12½.
62 1 1d. pale bright green (8.2.68) .. .. £150 18·00
63 1d. grey-green (18.2.68) .. .. £120 40·00
64 1d. dark green (20.3.68) .. .. 60·00 17·00
a. Printed on both sides .. ..
65 1d. deep yellow-green (28.6.72) .. 55·00 18·00
a. Imperf between (horiz pair) .. † £500
66 3 3d. on 4d. Prussian blue (Blk.) (7.2.71) — £700
67 3d. on 4d. sky-blue (Blk.) (12.8.70) .. £275 10·00
a. Imperf .. ..
b. Rouletted .. .. .. — £500
68 3d. on 4d. deep ultramarine (Blk.) (9.72) 70·00 8·00
a. Surch double (10.9.74) .. — £3250
b. Additional surch on back .. — £2500
c. Surch omitted (26.4.74) .. £14000 £8000
70 4d. dull purple (1.2.68) .. .. 60·00 15·00
a. Imperf between (horiz pair) ..
71 4d. dull violet (1868) .. .. 55·00 8·00
72 1 6d. bright pale blue (23.2.68) .. £300 11·00
73 6d. Prussian blue (29.9.69) .. 90·00 6·00
a. Perf 11½×imperf (horiz pair) .. † £500
74 6d. indigo (1869) .. .. £120 17·00
75 4 9d. claret (7.72) .. .. £100 8·00
76 9d. bright mauve (1.11.72) .. £100 8·00
a. Printed on both sides .. .. — £300
77 9d. red-purple (15.1.74) .. .. 65·00 8·00
78 10d. on 9d. yellow (B.) (15.8.68) .. £1000 24·00
a. Wmk Crown and S A (W **10**) (1868) — £750
79 10d. on 9d. yellow (Blk.) (13.9.69) .. £200 27·00
80 1 1s. lake-brown (9.68) .. .. £150 11·00
81 1s. chestnut (8.10.72) .. .. £110 16·00
82 1s. dark red-brown .. .. 90·00 11·00
83 1s. red-brown (6.1.69) .. .. £100 11·00
84 3 2s. pale rose-pink (10.10.69) .. £950 £150
85 2s. deep rose-pink (8.69) .. .. — £100
86 2s. crimson-carmine (16.10.69) .. 80·00 18·00
87 2s. carmine (1869) .. .. 70·00 10·00
a. Printed on both sides .. .. — £300

No. 78a was a trial printing made to test the perforating machine on the new D.L.R. paper.

1870–71. W **2.** *P* 10.
88 1 1d. grey-green (6.70) .. .. £120 15·00
89 1d. pale bright green (9.8.70) .. £120 15·00
90 1d. bright green (1871) .. .. £100 15·00
91 3 3d. on 4d. dull ultramarine (R.) (6.8.70) £325 60·00
92 3d. on 4d. pale ultram (Blk.) (14.2.71) £250 14·00
93 3d. on 4d. ultramarine (Blk.) (14.8.71) £100 17·00
93*a* 3d. on 4d. Prussian blue (Blk.) (16.12.71)
94 4d. dull lilac (1870) .. .. £110 10·00
95 4d. dull purple (1871) .. .. £100 10·00
96 1 6d. bright blue (19.6.70).. .. £180 17·00
97 6d. indigo (11.10.71) .. .. £225 16·00
98 1s. chestnut (4.1.71) .. .. £150 19·00

1870–73. W **2.** *P* 10 × 11½–12½, 11½–12½ × 10, *or compound.*
99 1 1d. pale bright green (11.10.70) .. £140 14·00
a. Printed on both sides ..
100 1d. grey-green .. .. .. £130 15·00
101 1d. deep green (19.6.71) .. .. 75·00 10·00
102 3 3d. on 4d. pale ultram (Blk.) (9.11.70) .. £180 35·00
103 4d. dull lilac (11.5.72) .. .. — 20·00
104 4d. slate-lilac (5.3.73) .. .. £120 18·00
105 1 6d. Prussian blue (2.3.70) .. .. £140 8·00
106 6d. bright Prussian blue (26.10.70) .. £150 10·00
107 4 10d. on 9d. yellow (Blk.) (1.70) .. £110 17·00
108 1 1s. chestnut (17.6.71) .. .. £200 32·00
109 3 2s. rose-pink (24.4.71) .. .. — £170
110 2s. carmine (2.3.72) .. .. £130 25·00

1871 (17 July). W **7.** *P* 10.
111 3 4d. dull lilac £1500 £200
a. Printed on both sides

8 Broad Star

8 PENCE

(9)

1876–1900. W **8.** *Surch with* T **9** *(Nos. 118/21). (a) P* 11½–12½.
112 3 3d. on 4d. ultramarine (1.6.79).. .. 60·00 15·00
a. Surch double .. .. .. — £1000
113 4d. violet-slate (15.3.79) .. .. £100 11·00
114 4d. plum (16.4.80) .. .. 50·00 6·00
115 4d. deep mauve (8.6.82) .. .. 50·00 5·00
116 1 6d. indigo (2.12.76) .. .. £100 4·50
a. Imperf between (horiz pair) ..
117 6d. Prussian blue (7.78) .. .. 65·00 4·00
118 4 8d. on 9d. brown-orange (7.76).. .. 60·00 5·00
119 8d. on 9d. burnt umber (1880) .. .. 65·00 5·00
120 8d. on 9d. brown (9.3.80) .. .. 65·00 5·00
a. Imperf between (vert pair) £400
121 8d. on 9d. grey-brown (10.5.81).. .. 60·00 6·50
a. Surch double .. .. .. — £350
122 9d. purple (9.3.80) .. .. 45·00 7·00
a. Printed on both sides .. .. — £200
123 9d. rose-lilac (21.8.80) .. .. 15·00 3·00
124 9d. rose-lilac (*large holes*) (26.5.00) 10·00 3·25
125 1 1s. red-brown (3.11.77).. .. 48·00 2·75
a. Imperf between (horiz pair) .. — £250
126 1s. reddish lake-brown (1880) .. 45·00 3·00
127 1s. lake-brown (9.1.83).. .. 50·00 2·75
128 1s. Vandyke brown (1891) .. 60·00 8·00
129 1s. dull brown (1891) .. .. 40·00 2·75
130 1s. chocolate (*large holes*) (6.5.97) 24·00 3·00
a. Imperf vert (horiz pair) .. £200
131 1s. sepia (*large holes*) (22.5.00).. 24·00 3·00
a. Imperf between (vert pair) .. £150
132 3 2s. carmine (15.2.77) .. .. 35·00 4·50
a. Imperf between (horiz pair) .. — £425
b. Imperf (pair) .. .. ..
133 2s. rose-carmine (1885) .. .. 38·00 6·50
134 2s. rose-carmine (*large holes*) (6.12.98).. 30·00 6·00

The perforation with larger, clean-cut holes resulted from the fitting of new pins to the machine.

(b) P 10
135 1 6d. Prussian blue (11.11.79) .. .. 90·00 12·00
136 6d. bright blue (1879) .. .. £110 11·00
136*a* 1s. reddish lake-brown £225

(c) P 10 × 11½–12½, 11½–12½ × 10, *or compound*
137 3 4d. violet-slate (21.5.79) .. .. £100 10·00
138 4d. dull purple (4.10.79) .. .. 38·00 2·00
139 1 6d. Prussian blue (29.12.77) .. .. 55·00 2·50
140 6d. bright blue .. .. .. 75·00 5·50
141 6d. bright ultramarine .. .. 40·00 1·75
142 1s. reddish lake-brown (9.2.85) .. 80·00 9·00
143 1s. dull brown (29.6.86) .. .. £100 10·00
144 3 2s. carmine (27.12.77) .. .. 55·00 5·50
145 2s. rose-carmine (1887) .. .. 50·00 5·00
a. Imperf between (horiz pair) .. — £400

10

11

12

1901–2. *Wmk Crown SA (wide),* W **10.** *P* 11½–12½ *(large holes).*
146 4 9d. claret (1.2.02) .. .. 15·00 14·00
147 1 1s. dark brown (12.6.01) .. .. 20·00 10·00
148 1s. dark reddish brown (1902).. .. 22·00 11·00
a. Imperf between (vert pair).. ..
149 1s. red-brown (aniline) (18.7.02) .. 20·00 12·00
150 3 2s. crimson (29.8.01) .. .. 28·00 13·00
151 2s. carmine .. .. .. 22·00 9·00

(Plates and electrotypes by D.L.R. Printed in Adelaide)

1868–76. W **10.** *(a) Rouletted.*
152 12 2d. deep brick-red (8.68) .. .. 50·00 3·25
153 2d. pale orange-red (5.10.68) .. 48·00 2·75
a. Printed on both sides .. .. — £225
b. Imperf between (horiz pair) .. — £275

(b) P 11½–12½
154 11 1d. blue-green (10.1.75) .. .. 70·00 11·00
155 12 2d. pale orange-red (5.5.69) £850 £190

(c) P 11½–12½ × *roulette*
156 12 2d. pale orange-red (20.8.69) .. .. — £120

(d) P 10 × *roulette*
157 12 2d. pale orange-red (7.5.70) .. .. £200 24·00

(e) P 10
158 11 1d. blue-green (4.75) .. .. 25·00 4·25
159 12 2d. brick-red (4.70) .. .. 12·00 35
160 2d. orange-red (1.7.70) .. .. 9·00 30
a. Printed on both sides .. .. — £170

(f) P 10 × 11½–12½, 11½–12½ × 10, *or compound*
161 11 1d. blue-green (27.8.75) .. .. 48·00 14·00
162 12 2d. brick-red (19.1.71) .. .. £400 6·00
163 2d. orange-red (3.2.71) .. .. £100 8·50
a. Imperf (8.76) £750

1869. *Wmk Large Star, W* **2.** *(a) Rouletted.*
164 **12** 2d. orange-red (13.3.69) . . . . 50·00 11·00

(b) P 11½–12½ × roulette
165 **12** 2d. orange-red (1.8.69) . . . . . . — 90·00

(c) P 11½–12½
165*a* **12** 2d. orange-red (7.69) . . . . . . — £800

1871 (15 July). *Wmk V and Crown, W* **7.** *P* 10.
166 **12** 2d. brick-red . . . . 48·00 14·00

HALF-
PENNY

13 (14)

1876–1904. *Wmk Crown SA (close), W* **13.** *(a) P* 10 (1876–85)
167 **11** 1d. blue-green (9.2.76) . . . . 6·50 20
a. Yellowish green (11.78) . . . . 8·00 20
b. Deep green (11.79) . . . . 8·00 20
ba. Imperf between (horiz pair) . .
bb. Printed double . . . . . . † —
168 **12** 2d. orange-red (8.76) . . . . 7·00 10
a. Dull brick-red (21.5.77) . . . . 7·00 10
b. Blood-red (31.10.79) . . . . £200 3·00
c. Pale red (4.85) . . . . 7·00 10

(b) P 10×11½–12½, 11½–12½×10 or compound (1877–80)
169 **11** 1d. deep green (11.2.80) . . . . 20·00 2·25
a. Blue-green (2.3.80) . . . . 10·00 1·90
170 **12** 2d. orange-red (4.9.77) . . . . £120 3·00
a. Dull brick-red (6.80) . . . . £120 3·00

(c) P 11½–12½ (1877–84)
171 **11** 1d. blue-green (2.84) . . . . — £110
172 **12** 2d. orange-red (14.9.77) . . . . — £110
a. Blood-red (1.4.80) . . . . — £110

(d) P 15 (1893)
173 **11** 1d. green (8.5.93) . . . . 4·50 20
174 **12** 2d. pale orange (9.2.93) . . . . 8·50 10
a. Orange-red . . . . 8·00 10
b. Imperf between (vert pair) . . £170

(e) P 13 (1895–1903)
175 **11** 1d. pale green (11.1.95) . . . . 4·50 20
a. Green . . . . 4·50 20
b. Imperf between (vert pair) . .
176 1d. rosine (8.8.99) . . . . 2·75 10
a. Scarlet (23.12.03) . . . . 3·25 10
b. Deep red . . . . 3·00 10
177 **12** 2d. pale orange (19.1.95) . . . . 4·25 10
a. Orange-red (9.5.95) . . . . 4·75 10
178 2d. bright violet (10.10.99) . . . . 2·50 10

(f) P 12×11½ (comb) (1904)
179 **11** 1d. rosine (2.2.04) . . . . 6·00 10
a. Scarlet (25.7.04) . . . . 4·50 10
180 **12** 2d. bright violet (11.10.04) . . . . 3·50 10

Examples of the 1d. pale green with thicker lettering come from a worn plate.

1882 (1 Jan). *No.* 167 *surch with T* **14.**
181 **11** ½d. on 1d. blue-green . . . . 11·00 3·25

15

16

17 18

1883–99. *W* **13** *(sideways on ½d.). (a) P* 10 (1883–95)
182 **15** ½d. chocolate (1.3.83) . . . . 2·75 50
a. Imperf between (horiz pair) . .
b. Red-brown (4.4.89) . . . . 2·50 45
c. Brown (1895) . . . . 2·50 45
183 **16** 3d. sage-green (12.86) (Optd S. £25) . . 8·50 1·10
a. Olive-green (6.6.90) . . . . 8·00 1·50
b. Deep green (12.4.93) . . . . 6·50 90
184 **17** 4d. pale violet (3.90) (Optd S. £30) . . 8·00 1·25
a. Aniline violet (3.1.93) . . . . 9·50 1·50
185 **18** 6d. pale blue (4.87) (Optd S. £25) . . 7·50 1·40
a. Blue (5.5.87) . . . . 9·00 60

(b) P 10×11½–12½, 11½–12½×10 or compound (1891)
186 **15** ½d. red-brown (25.9.91) . . . . 4·25 1·50
a. Imperf between (horiz pair) . . 80·00

(c) P 11½–12½ (1890)
187 **15** ½d. red-brown (12.10.90) . . . . 6·50 1·25

(d) P 15 (1893–94)
188 **15** ½d. pale brown (1.93) . . . . 2·75 50
a. Deep brown . . . . 2·75 50
b. Imperf between (horiz pair) . . 80·00
c. Perf 12½ between (pair) . . £120 28·00
189 **17** 4d. purple (1.1.94) . . . . 14·00 2·00
a. Slate-violet . . . . 14·00 1·75
190 **18** 6d. blue (20.11.93) . . . . 23·00 3·50

(e) P 13 (1895–99)
191 **15** ½d. pale brown (9.95) . . . . 2·50 30
a. Deep brown (19.3.97) . . . . 2·50 30
192 **16** 3d. pale olive-green (26.7.97) . . 7·00 90
a. Deep olive-green (27.11.99) . . 5·00 90
193 **17** 4d. violet (21.1.96) . . . . 6·00 40
194 **18** 6d. pale blue (3.96) . . . . 7·00 65
a. Blue . . . . 7·00 65

REPRINTS. In 1884, and in later years, reprints on paper wmkd Crown SA, W **10**, were made of Nos. 1, 2, 3, 4, 12, 13, 14, 15, 19, 24, 27, 28, 32, 33, 34, 35, 36, 37, 38, 40, 43, 44, 49*a*, 53, 65, 67, 67 with surcharge in red, 70, 71, 72, 73, 78, 79, 81, 83, 86, 90, 118, 119, 120, 121, 122, 155, 158, 159, 164, 181, 182. They are overprinted "REPRINT".

In 1889 examples of the reprints for Nos. 1/3, 12, 15, 19, 27, 32/8, 44, 67, 67 surcharged in red, 70/1, 73, 83, 86, 118, 121/2, 158/9, 164 and 181/2, together with No. 141 overprinted "Specimen", were supplied to the U.P.U. for distribution.

19 (20) (21)

(Plates and electrotypes by D.L.R. Printed in Adelaide)

1886 (20 Dec)–**96.** *T* **19** *(inscr "POSTAGE & REVENUE").* *W* **13.** *Parts of two or more wmks, on each stamp, sometimes sideways. P* 10.
195 2s. 6d. mauve . . . . 30·00 8·00
a. Perf 11½–12½. *Dull violet* . . 27·00 6·00
bb. Bright aniline violet . . 28·00 7·00
196 5s. rose-pink . . . . 48·00 12·00
a. Perf 11½–12½ . . . . 35·00 12·00
ab. Rose-carmine . . . . 35·00 14·00
197 10s. green . . . . £110 35·00
a. Perf 11½–12½ . . . . 80·00 35·00
198 15s. brownish yellow £275
a. Perf 11½–12½ £300 £120
199 £1 blue . . . . £200 90·00
a. Perf 11½–12½ . . . . £150 80·00
200 £2 Venetian red £475 £200
a. Perf 11½–12½ £475 £200
201 50s. dull pink £700 £250
a. Perf 11½–12½ £700
202 £3 sage green £750 £250
a. Perf 11½–12½ £750 £250
203 £4 lemon £950
a. Perf 11½–12½ £850
204 £5 grey £1600
a. Perf 11½–12½ £1700
205 £5 brown (*p* 11½–12½) (1896) . . £1700 £600
206 £10 bronze £2500 £700
a. Perf 11½–12½ £1800 £700
207 £15 silver £4500
a. Perf 11½–12½ £4500
208 £20 claret £5000
a. Perf 11½–12½ £5000
195/208 Optd "Specimen" . . *Set of* 14 £400

Variations exist in the length of the words and shape of the letters of the value inscription.

The 2s. 6d. dull violet, 5s. rose-pink, 10s., £1 and £5 brown exist perf 11½–12½ with either large or small holes; the 2s. 6d. aniline, 5s. rose-carmine, 15s., £2 and 50s. with large holes only and the remainder only with small holes.

Stamps perforated 11½–12½ small holes, are, generally speaking, rather rarer than those with the 1895 (large holes) gauge.

Stamps perf 10 were issued on 20 Dec 1886. Stamps perf 11½–12½ (small holes) are known with earliest dates covering the period from June 1890 to Feb 1896. Earliest dates of stamps with large holes range from July 1896 to May 1902.

1891 (1 Jan)–**93.** *T* **17/18** *surch with T* **20/1.** *W* **13.** *(a) P* 10
229 **17** 2½d. on 4d. pale grn (Br.) (Optd S. £25) 7·50 2·50
a. Fraction bar omitted . . . . 90·00 75·00
b. Deep green . . . . 8·00 1·75
ba. Fraction bar omitted . . . . 90·00 70·00
bb. "2" and "½" closer together . . 20·00 18·00
bc. Imperf between (horiz pair) . .
bd. Imperf between (vert pair) . . — £400
230 **18** 5d. on 6d. pale brn (C.) (Optd S. £25) 16·00 4·00
a. Deep brown . . . . 16·00 3·75
b. No stop after "5D" . . £150

(b) P 10×11½–12½ or 11½–12½×10
231 **17** 2½d. on 4d. pale green (Br.) . . 15·00 3·00
a. Deep green . . . . 15·00 3·00

(c) P 11½–12½
232 **17** 2½d. on 4d. deep green . . 28·00 45·00

(d) P 15
233 **17** 2½d. on 4d. green (14.10.93) . . 12·00 2·50
a. Fraction bar omitted . . . .
b. "2" and "½d." closer together . . 40·00 22·00

22 Red Kangaroo

23

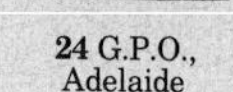

24 G.P.O., Adelaide

(Des M. Tannenberg, plates by D.L.R.)

1894 (1 Mar)–**1906.** *W* **13.** *(a) P* 15
234 **22** 2½d. violet-blue . . . . 14·00 2·0
235 **23** 5d. brown-purple . . . . 14·00 2·2
234/5 Optd "Specimen" . . *Set of* 2 50·00

(b) P 13
236 **22** 2½d. violet-blue (11.2.95) . . . . 12·00
237 2½d. indigo (25.3.98) . . . . 4·50
238 **23** 5d. brown-purple (1.96) . . . . 6·50
a. Purple . . . . 6·50

(c) P 12×11½ (comb)
239 **22** 2½d. indigo (4.7.06) . . . . 7·00
240 **23** 5d. dull purple (1.05) . . . . 8·00

(Typo D.L.R.)

1899 (27 Dec)–**1905.** *W* **13.** *(a) P* 13
241 **24** ½d. yellow-green . . . . 1·50

(b) P 12×11½ (comb)
242 **24** ½d. yellow-green (7.05) . . . . 1·50

25

The measurements given indicate the length of the value inscription in the bottom label. The dates are those of the earliest known postmarks.

1902–04. *As T* **19**, *but top tablet as T* **25** *(thin "POSTAGE")* *W* **13.** *(a) P 11½–12½.*
268 3d. olive-green (18½ mm) (1.8.02) . . 3·50 1·0
269 4d. red-orange (17 mm) (29.11.02) . . 5·00 1·5
270 6d. blue-green (16–16½ mm) (29.11.02) . . 6·00 1·5
271 8d. ultramarine (19 mm) (25.4.02) . . 7·50 3·5
272 8d. ultramarine (16½ mm) (22.3.04) . . 7·50 3·5
a. "EIGNT" (R. 2/9) £800 £110
273 9d. rosy lake (19.9.02) . . . . 8·00 2·2
a. Imperf between (vert pair) . . £275
b. Imperf between (horiz pair) . .
274 10d. dull yellow (29.11.02) . . . . 11·00 4·5
275 1s. brown (18.8.02) . . . . 11·00 2·2
a. Imperf between (horiz pair) . .
b. Imperf between (vert pair) . . £450
c. "POSTAGE" and value in red-brown 45·00 20·0
276 2s. 6d. pale violet (19.9.02) . . . . 28·00 11·0
a. Bright violet (2.2.03) . . . . 22·00 7·0
277 5s. rose (17.10.02) . . . . 55·00 40·0
278 10s. green (1.11.02) . . . . £100 60·0
279 £1 blue (1.11.02) £225 £12

(b) P 12
280 3d. olive-green (20 mm) (15.4.04) . . 6·00 1·5
a. "POSTAGE" omitted; value below "AUSTRALIA" £350
281 4d. orange-red (17½–18 mm) (18.2.03) . . 6·50 1·5
282 6d. blue-green (15 mm) (14.11.03) . . 16·00 3·2
283 9d. rosy lake (2.12.03) . . . . 29·00 4·5

PRINTER. Stamp printing in Adelaide ceased in 1909 when the printer, J. B. Cooke, was appointed head of the Commonwealth Stamp Printing Branch in Melbourne. From March 1909 further printings of current South Australia stamps were made in Melbourne.

26

V X

In Type X the letters in the bottom line are slightly larger than in Type V, especially the "A", "S" and "P".

Y Z

In Type Z the letters "S" and "G" are more open than in Type Y. Nos. 196/*a* and 277 are similar to Type Y with all letters thic[k] and regular and the last "S" has the top curve rounded instead o[f] being slightly flattened.

1904–11. *As T* **19**, *but top tablet as T* **26** *(thick "POSTAGE")* *W* **13.** *P* 12.
284 6d. blue-green (27.4.04) . . . . 7·50 1·7
a. Imperf between (vert pair) . .
285 8d. bright ultramarine (4.7.05) . . 7·00 3·2
a. Value closer (15¼ mm) . . 18·00
b. Dull ultramarine (2.4.08) . . 9·00 2·7
ba. Ditto. Value closer (15¼ mm) . . 25·00
286 9d. rosy lake (17–17¼ mm) (18.7.04) . . 8·00 2·2
a. Value 16½–16¾ mm (2.06) . . 17·00 4·0
b. Brown-lake. Perf 12½ small holes (6.6.11) 13·00
287 10d. dull yellow (8.07) . . . . 14·00 7·0
a. Imperf between (horiz pair) . . £325 £25
b. Imperf between (vert pair) . . £300
288 1s. brown (12.4.04) . . . . 12·00 1·7
a. Imperf between (vert pair) . . £200
b. Imperf between (horiz pair) . . £275
289 2s. 6d. bright violet (V.) (14.7.05) . . 40·00 8·5
a. Dull violet (X) (8.06) . . 40·00 8·5
290 5s. rose-scarlet (Y) (8.04) . . 40·00 26·0
a. Scarlet (Z) (8.06) . . 40·00 26·0
b. Pale rose. Perf 12½ (small holes) (Z) (7.10) 55·00 30·0
291 10s. green (26.8.08) £100 £13
292 £1 blue (29.12.04) £150 £10
a. Perf 12½ (small holes) (7.10) . . £130 80·0

The "value closer" variety on the 8d. occurs six times in the shee[t] of 60. The value normally measures 16½ mm but in the variety is 15¼ mm.

The 9d., 5s. and £1, perf 12½ (small holes), are late printing[s] made in 1910–11 to use up the Crown SA paper.

No. 286*b* has the value as Type C of the 9d. on Crown over A paper.

27

)05–11. *W* **27.** *P* 12 × 11½ (*new comb machine*).

)3	**24**	½d. pale green (4.07)	3·00	65
		a. Yellow-green	3·00	65
)4	**11**	1d. rosine (2.12.05)	3·00	10
		a. Scarlet (4.11)	2·75	20
)5	**12**	2d. bright violet (2.2.06)	4·50	10
		aa. Imperf three sides (horiz pair) ..		
		a. Mauve (4.08)	3·50	10
)6	**22**	2½d. indigo-blue (14.9.10)	8·50	2·00
)7	**23**	5d. brown-purple (11.3.08)	8·50	2·00

No. 295aa is perforated at foot.

Three types of the 9d., perf 12½, distinguishable by the distance etween "NINE" and "PENCE".

A. Distance 1¾ mm. B. Distance 2¼ mm. C. Distance 2½ mm.

906–12. *T* **19** ("POSTAGE" *thick as T* **26**). *W* **27.** *P* 12 *or* 12½ (*small holes*).

98	3d. sage-green (19 mm) (26.6.06)	5·50	1·50
	a. Imperf between (horiz pair)	†	£550
	b. Perf 12½. *Sage-green* (17 mm) (9.12.09)	4·75	1·50
	c. Perf 12½. *Deep olive* (20 mm) (7.10) ..	24·00	5·00
	d. Perf 12½. *Yellow-olive* (14 mm) (16.12.11)	10·00	4·50
	da. Perf 12½. *Bright olive-green* (19–19¾ mm) (5.12)	9·50	5·00
	e. Perf 11 (17 mm) (10.7.11)	£200	£180
99	4d. orange-red (10.9.06)	8·00	1·25
	a. Orange	8·00	1·10
	b. Perf 12½. *Orange* (27.10.09)	6·50	1·90
00	6d. blue-green (1.9.06)	8·00	1·50
	a. Perf 12½ (21.4.10)	6·50	2·00
	ab. Perf 12½. Imperf between (vert pair) ..	£325	£300
01	8d. bright ultramarine (*p* 12½) (8.09) ..	10·00	5·50
	a. Value closer (8.09)	35·00	24·00
02	9d. brown-lake (3.2.06)	10·00	1·50
	a. Imperf between (vert pair)	£275	
	aa. Imperf between (horiz pair)	£275	
	b. Deep lake (9.5.08)	28·00	3·50
	c. Perf 12½. *Lake* (A) (5.9.09)	11·00	3·00
	d. Perf 12½. *Lake* (B) (7.09)	14·00	3·00
	e. Perf 12½. *Brown-lake* (C)	17·00	5·00
	ea. Perf 12½. *Deep lake*. Thin paper (C) ..	16·00	3·00
	f. Perf 11 (1909)	—	£250
03	1s. brown (30.5.06)	12·00	2·75
	a. Imperf between (horiz pair)	£275	
	b. Perf 12½ (10.3.10)	10·00	2·50
04	2s. 6d. bright violet (X) (10.6.09)	35·00	6·00
	a. Perf 12½. *Pale violet* (X) (6.10)	35·00	8·00
	ab. Perf 12½. *Deep purple* (X) (5.11.12) ..	38·00	15·00
05	5s. bright rose (*p* 12½) (Z) (24.4.11). . ..	55·00	

The "value closer" variety of the 8d. occurred 11 times in the heet of 60 in the later printing only. On No. 301 the value measres 16½ mm while on No. 301a it is 15¼ mm.

The 1s. brown, perf compound of 11½ and 12½, formerly isted is now omitted, as it must have been perforated by the 12 nachine, which in places varied from 11½ to 13. The 4d. has ilso been reported with a similar perforation.

STAMP BOOKLETS

There are very few surviving examples of Nos. SB1/4. Listings re provided for those believed to have been issued with prices uoted for those known to still exist.

904 (1 Jan)–**09.** *Black on red cover as No.* SB1 *of New South Wales. Stapled.*

B1 £1 booklet containing two hundred and forty 1d. in four blocks of 30 and two blocks of 60 ..
a. Red on pink cover (1909) .. .. ..
b. Blue on pink cover £6000

904 (1 Jan). *Black on grey cover as No.* SB1. *Stapled.*

B2 £1 booklet containing one hundred and twenty 2d. in four blocks of 30 .. ..

910 (May). *Black on cream cover as No.* SB3 *of New South Wales. Stapled.*

B3 2s. booklet containing eleven ½d. (No. 262A), either in block of 6 plus block of 5 or block of 11, and eighteen 1d. (No. 264A), either in three blocks of 6 or block of 6 plus block of 12 ..

Unsold stock of No. SB3 was uprated with one additional ½d. May 1911.

911 (Aug). *Red on pink cover as No.* SB3. *Stapled.*

B4 2s. booklet containing twelve ½d. (No. 262A), either in two blocks of 6 or block of 12, and eighteen 1d. (No. 264A), either in three blocks of 6 or block of 6 plus block of 12 .. .. £1500

OFFICIAL STAMPS

A. Departmentals

Following suspected abuses involving stamps supplied for official se it was decided by the South Australian authorities that such upplies were to be overprinted with a letter, or letters, indicating he department of the administration to which the stamps had been nvoiced.

The system was introduced on 1 April 1868 using overprints truck in red. Later in the same year the colour of the overprints vas amended to blue, and, during the latter months of 1869, to lack.

In 1874 the Postmaster-General recommended that this somevhat cumbersome system be replaced by a general series of "O.S." verprints with the result that the separate accounting for the)epartmentals ceased on 30 June of that year. Existing stocks ontinued to be used, however, and it is believed that much of the residue was passed to the Government Printer to pay postage on copies of the *Government Gazette*.

We are now able to provide a check list of these most interesting issues based on the definitive work, *The Departmental Stamps of South Australia* by A. R. Butler, FRPSL, RDP, published by the Royal Philatelic Society, London in 1978.

No attempt has been made to assign the various overprints to the catalogue numbers of the basic stamps, but each is clearly identified by both watermark and perforation. The colours are similar to those of the contemporary postage stamps, but there can be shade variations. Errors of overprint are recorded in footnotes, but not errors occurring on the basic stamps used.

Most departmental overprints are considered to be scarce to rare in used condition, with unused examples, used multiples and covers being regarded as considerable rarities.

Forgeries of a few items do exist, but most can be readily identified by comparison with genuine examples. A number of forged overprints on stamps not used for the genuine issues also occur.

A. (Architect)

Optd in red with stop. *W* **2.** 2d. (*roul*), 4d. (*p* 11½–12½), 6d. (*roul*), 1s. (*roul*)
Optd in red without stop. *W* **2.** *Roul.* 1d., 6d., 1s.
Optd in black. (*a*) *W* **2.** 4d. (*p* 11½–12½), 4d. (*p* 10), 4d. (*p* 10 × 11½–12½), 6d. (*p* 11½–12½), 2s. (*roul*)
(*b*) *W* **10.** 2d. D.L.R. (*roul*), 2d. D.L.R. (*p* 10)

A.G. (Attorney-General)

Optd in red. *W* **2.** *Roul.* 1d., 2d., 6d., 1s.
Optd in blue. (*a*) *W* **2.** *Roul.* 6d.
(*b*) *W* **10.** *Roul.* 2d. D.L.R.
Optd in black. (*a*) *W* **2.** 1d. (*p* 11½–12½ × *roul*), 4d. (*p* 11½–12½), 4d. (*p* 10), 6d. (*p* 11½–12½ × *roul*), 6d. (*p* 11½–12½), 1s. (*p* 11½–12½ × *roul*), 1s. (*p* 10)
(*b*) *W* **10.** 2d. D.L.R. (*roul*), 2d. D.L.R. (*p* 10)

A.O. (Audit Office)

Optd in red. *W* **2.** 2d. (*roul*), 4d. (*p* 11½–12½), 6d. (*roul*)
Optd in blue. (*a*) *W* **2.** *P* 11½–12½. 1d., 6d.
(*b*) *W* **10.** *Roul.* 2d. D.L.R.
Optd in black. (*a*) *W* **2.** 1d. (*p* 11½–12½), 1d. (*p* 10), 1d. (*p* 10 × 11½–12), 2d. D.L.R. (*roul*), 4d. (*p* 11½–12½), 4d. (*p* 10), 4d. (*p* 10 × 11½–12½), 6d. (*roul*), 6d. (*p* 11½–12½), 1s. (*p* 10), 1s. (*p* 11½–12½ × *roul*)
(*b*) *W* **7.** *P* 10. 4d.
(*c*) *W* **10.** 2d. D.L.R. (*roul*), 2d. D.L.R. (*p* 10)

B.D. (Barracks Department)

Optd in red. *W* **2.** *Roul.* 2d., 6d., 1s.

B.G. (Botanic Garden)

Optd in black. (*a*) *W* **2.** 1d. (*p* 11½–12½ × *roul*), 1d. (*p* 11½–12½), 1d. (*p* 10), 1d. (*p* 10 × 11½–12½), 2d. D.L.R. (*roul*), 6d. (*roul*), 6d. (*p* 11½–12½ × *roul*), 6d. (*p* 11½–12½), 6d. (*p* 10), 1s. (*p* 11½–12½ × *roul*), 1s. (*p* 11½–12½), 1s. (*p* 10 × 11½–12½)
(*b*) *W* **7.** *P* 10. 2d. D.L.R.
(*c*) *W* **10.** 2d. D.L.R. (*roul*), 2d. D.L.R. (*p* 10)

B.M. (Bench of Magistrates)

Optd in red. *W* **2.** *Roul.* 2d.
Optd in black. *W* **10.** *Roul.* 2d. D.L.R.

C. (Customs)

Optd in red. *W* **2.** 1d. (*roul*), 2d. (*roul*), 4d. (*p* 11½–12½), 6d. (*roul*), 1s. (*roul*)
Optd in blue. (*a*) *W* **2.** *Roul.* 1d., 4d., 6d., 1s., 2s.
(*b*) *W* **10.** *Roul.* 2d. D.L.R.
Optd in black. (*a*) *W* **2.** 1d. (*roul*), 1d. (*p* 10), 1d. (*p* 10 × 11½–12½), 2d. D.L.R. (*p* 10 × 11½–12½), 4d. (*p* 11½–12½), 4d. (*p* 10), 4d. (*p* 10 × 11½–12½), 6d. (*roul*), 6d. (*p* 11½–12½), 6d. (*p* 10), 1s. (*p* 11½–12½ × *roul*), 1s. (*p* 11½–12½), 2s. (*roul*)
(*b*) *W* **7.** *P* 10. 2d. D.L.R.
(*c*) *W* **10.** 2d. D.L.R. (*roul*), 2d. D.L.R. (*p* 10 × *roul*), 2d. D.L.R. (*p* 10), 2d. D.L.R. (*p* 10 × 11½–12½)

The 2d. (*W* **10.** *Roul*) with black overprint is known showing the error "G" for "C".

C.D. (Convict Department)

Optd in red. *W* **2.** 2d. (*roul*), 4d. (*p* 11½–12½), 6d. (*roul*), 1s. (*roul*)
Optd in black. (*a*) *W* **2.** 1d. (*p* 11½–12½ × *roul*), 2d. D.L.R. (*roul*), 2d. D.L.R. (*p* 11½–12½), 2d. D.L.R. (*p* 11½–12½ × *roul*), 4d. (*p* 11½–12½), 6d. (*p* 11½–12½ × *roul*), 1s. (*p* 11½–12½ × *roul*)
(*b*) *W* **10.** *Roul.* 2d. D.L.R.

C.L. (Crown Lands)

Optd in red. *W* **2.** 2d. (*roul*), 4d. (*p* 11½–12½), 6d. (*roul*), 1s. (*roul*)
Optd in blue. (*a*) *W* **2.** *Roul.* 4d., 6d.
(*b*) *W* **10.** *Roul.* 2d. D.L.R.
Optd in black. (*a*) *W* **2.** 2d. D.L.R. (*roul*), 4d. (*p* 11½–12½), 4d. (*p* 10), 4d. (*p* 10 × 11½–12½), 6d. (*roul*), 6d. (*p* 11½–12½), 1s. (*p* 11½–12½ × *roul*), 1s. (*p* 11½–12½), 2s. (*roul*), 2s. (*p* 11½–12½)
(*b*) *W* **7.** *P* 10. 2d. D.L.R., 4d.
(*c*) *W* **10.** 2d. D.L.R. (*roul*), 2d. D.L.R. (*p* 10), 2d. D.L.R. (*p* 10 × 11½–12½)

The 2s. (*W* **2.** *P* 11½–12½) with black overprint is known showing the stop omitted after "L".

C.O. (Commissariat Office)

Optd in red. *W* **2.** 2d. (*roul*), 4d. (*p* 11½–12½), 6d. (*roul*), 1s. (*roul*)
Optd in black. (*a*) *W* **2.** 4d. (*p* 11½–12½), 4d. (*p* 10), 4d. (*p* 10 × 11½–12½), 6d. (*p* 11½–12½), 1s. (*p* 11½–12½), 2s. (*p* 11½–12½)
(*b*) *W* **10.** 2d. D.L.R. (*roul*), 2d. D.L.R. (*p* 10)

The 2s. (*W* **2.** *P* 11½–12½) with black overprint is known showing the stop omitted after "O".

C.P. (Commissioner of Police)

Optd in red. *W* **2.** 2d. (*roul*), 4d. (*p* 11½–12½), 6d. (*roul*)

C.S. (Chief Secretary)

Optd in red. *W* **2.** 2d. (*roul*), 4d. (*p* 11½–12½), 6d. (*roul*), 1s. (*roul*)
Optd in blue. (*a*) *W* **2.** *Roul.* 4d., 6d.
(*b*) *W* **10.** *Roul.* 2d. D.L.R.
Optd in black. (*a*) *W* **2.** 2d. D.L.R. (*roul*), 4d. (*roul*), 4d. (*p* 11½–12½ × *roul*), 4d. (*p* 11½–12½), 4d. (*p* 10), 4d. (*p* 10 × 11½–12½), 6d. (*p* 11½–12½ × *roul*), 6d. (*p* 11½–12½), 6d. (*p* 10), 6d. (*p* 10 × 11½–12½), 1s. (*p* 11½–12½ × *roul*), 1s. (*p* 11½–12½), 1s. (*p* 10), 1s. (*p* 10 × 11½–12½), 2s. (*p* 10 × 11½–12½)
(*b*) *W* **7.** *P* 10. 4d.
(*c*) *W* **10.** 2d. D.L.R. (*roul*), 2d. D.L.R. (*p* 10)

C.Sgn. (Colonial Surgeon)

Optd in red. *W* **2.** 2d. (*roul*), 4d. (*p* 11½–12½), 6d. (*roul*)
Optd in black. (*a*) *W* **2.** 2d. D.L.R. (*roul*), 4d. (*p* 11½–12½), 4d. (*p* 10), 4d. (*p* 10 × 11½–12½), 6d. (*roul*), 6d. (*p* 11½–12½), 1s. (*p* 11½–12½ × *roul*)
(*b*) *W* **10.** 2d. D.L.R. (*roul*), 2d. D.L.R. (*p* 11½–12½ × *roul*), 2d. D.L.R. (*p* 10)

Two types of overprint exist on the 2d. D.L.R. (*W* **10.** *Roul*), the second type having block capitals instead of the serifed type used for the other values.

D.B. (Destitute Board)

Optd in red. *W* **2.** 1d. (*roul*), 2d. (*roul*), 4d. (*p* 11½–12½), 6d. (*roul*), 1s. (*roul*)
Optd in blue. (*a*) *W* **2.** *Roul.* 2d. D.L.R., 6d.
(*b*) *W* **10.** *Roul.* 2d. D.L.R.
Optd in black. (*a*) *W* **2.** 1d. (*p* 11½–12½), 4d. (*p* 11½–12½), 4d. (*p* 10), 6d. (*p* 10 × 11½–12½), 1s. (*p* 10)
(*b*) *W* **10.** 2d. D.L.R. (*roul*), 2d. D.L.R. (*p* 10), 2d. D.L.R. (*p* 10 × 11½–12½)

The 2d. D.L.R. (*W* **10.** *P* 10) with black overprint is known showing the stop omitted after "D".

D.R. (Deeds Registration)

Optd in red. *W* **2.** *Roul*, 2d., 6d.

E. (Engineer)

Optd in red. *W* **2.** 2d. (*roul*), 4d. (*p* 11½–12½), 6d. (*roul*), 1s. (*roul*)
Optd in blue. (*a*) *W* **2.** *Roul.* 1s.
(*b*) *W* **10.** *Roul.* 2d. D.L.R.
Optd in black. (*a*) *W* **2.** 4d. (*p* 11½–12½ × *roul*), 4d. (*p* 11½–12½), 4d. (*p* 10), 4d. (*p* 10 × 11½–12½), 6d. (*p* 11½–12½), 6d. (*p* 10 × 11½–12½), 1s. (*p* 11½–12½ × *roul*), 1s. (*p* 11½–12½), 1s. (*p* 10 × 11½–12½), 2s. (*p* 10 × 11½–12½)
(*b*) *W* **7.** *P* 10. 4d.
(*c*) *W* **10.** 2d. D.L.R. (*roul*), 2d. D.L.R. (*p* 10)

E.B. (Education Board)

Optd in red. *W* **2.** 2d. (*roul*), 4d. (*p* 11½–12½), 6d. (*roul*)
Optd in blue. (*a*) *W* **2.** *Roul.* 4d., 6d.
(*b*) *W* **10.** *Roul.* 2d. D.L.R.
Optd in black. (*a*) *W* **2.** 2d. D.L.R. (*roul*), 4d. (*roul*), 4d. (*p* 11½–12½), 4d. (*p* 10), 4d. (*p* 10 × 11½–12½), 6d. (*p* 11½–12½ × *roul*), 6d. (*p* 11½–12½)
(*b*) *W* **7.** *P* 10. 2d. D.L.R.
(*c*) *W* **10.** 2d. D.L.R. (*roul*), 2d. D.L.R. (*p* 10), 2d. D.L.R. (*p* 10 × 11½–12½)

G.F. (Gold Fields)

Optd in black. (*a*) *W* **2.** *Roul.* 6d.
(*b*) *W* **10.** 2d. D.L.R. (*p* 10 × *roul*), 2d. D.L.R. (*p* 10)

G.P. (Government Printer)

Optd in red. *W* **2.** *Roul.* 1d., 2d., 6d., 1s.
Optd in blue. (*a*) *W* **2.** *Roul.* 1d., 6d., 1s., 2s.
(*b*) *W* **10.** *Roul.* 2d. D.L.R.
Optd in black. (*a*) *W* **2.** 1d. (*roul*), 1d. (*p* 11½–12½ × *roul*), 1d. (*p* 11½–12½), 1d. (*p* 10), 1d. (*p* 10 × 11½–12½), 6d. (*p* 11½–12½ × *roul*), 1s. (*p* 10), 1s. (*p* 10 × 11½–12½), 2s. (*roul*), 2s. (*p* 11½–12½), 2s. (*p* 10 × 11½–12½)
(*b*) *W* **10.** 2d. D.L.R. (*roul*), 2d. D.L.R. (*p* 10)

The 1d. (*W* **2.** *Roul*) with red overprint is known showing "C.P." instead of "G.P.".

G.S. (Government Storekeeper)

Optd in red. *W* **2.** *Roul.* 2d., 6d., 1s.

G.T. (Goolwa Tramway)

Optd in red. *W* **2.** 1d. (*roul*), 2d. (*roul*), 4d. (*p* 11½–12½), 6d. (*roul*), 1s. (*roul*)
Optd in black. (*a*) *W* **2.** 2d. D.L.R. (*roul*), 4d. (*p* 11½–12½)
(*b*) *W* **10.** 2d. D.L.R. (*roul*), 2d. D.L.R. (*p* 10)

The 2d. and 6d. (both *W* **2.** *Roul*) with red overprint are known showing the stop omitted after "T". The 1s. (*W* **2.** *Roul*) with red overprint is known showing "C.T." instead of "G.T.".

H. (Hospitals)

Optd in black. (*a*) *W* **7.** *P* 10. 2d. D.L.R.
(*b*) *W* **10.** 2d. D.L.R. (*p* 10), 2d. D.L.R. (*p* 10 × 11½–12½)

H.A. (House of Assembly)

Optd in red. *W* **2.** 1d. (*roul*), 2d. (*roul*), 4d. (*p* 11½–12½), 6d. (*roul*), 1s. (*roul*)
Optd in black. (*a*) *W* **2.** 1d. (*p* 11½–12½), 1d. (*p* 10), 1d. (*p* 10 × 11½–12½), 4d. (*p* 11½–12½), 4d. (*p* 10), 6d. (*roul*), 6d. (*p* 11½–12½), 1s. (*p* 11½–12½ × *roul*), 1s. (*p* 11½–12½)
(*b*) *W* **10.** 2d. D.L.R. (*roul*), 2d. D.L.R. (*p* 10)

I.A. (Immigration Agent)

Optd in red. *W* **2.** 1d. (*roul*), 2d. (*roul*), 4d. (*p* 11½–12½), 6d. (*roul*)

I.E. (Intestate Estates)

Optd in black. W **10.** *P* 10. 2d. D.L.R.

I.S. (Inspector of Sheep)

Optd in red. *W* **2.** *Roul.* 2d., 6d.
Optd in blue. *W* **2.** *P* 11½–12½. 6d.
Optd in black. (*a*) *W* **2.** 2d. D.L.R. (*roul*), 6d. (*p* 11½–12½ × *roul*)
(*b*) *W* **10.** 2d. D.L.R. (*roul*), 2d. D.L.R. (*p* 10)

L.A. (Lunatic Asylum)

Optd in red. *W* **2.** 1d. (*roul*), 2d. (*roul*), 4d. (*p* 11½–12½), 6d. (*roul*), 1s. (*roul*)
Optd in black. (*a*) *W* **2.** 4d. (*p* 11½–12½), 4d. (*p* 10), 4d. (*p* 10 × 11½–12½), 6d. (*p* 11½–12½ × *roul*), 6d. (*p* 11½–12½), 1s. (*p* 11½–12½), 2s. (*roul*)
(*b*) *W* **10.** 2d. D.L.R. (*roul*), 2d. D.L.R. (*p* 10)

L.C. (Legislative Council)

Optd in red. *W* **2.** *Roul.* 2d., 6d.
Optd in black. (*a*) *W* **2.** *Roul.* 6d.
(*b*) *W* **10.** 2d. D.L.R. (*roul*), 2d. D.L.R. (*p* 10 × *roul*)
The 2d. and 6d. (both *W* **2.** *Roul*) with red overprint are known showing the stop omitted after "C".

L.L. (Legislative Librarian)

Optd in red. *W* **2.** 2d. (*roul*), 4d. (*p* 11½–12½), 6d. (*roul*)
Optd in black. (*a*) *W* **2.** *P* 11½–12½. 6d.
(*b*) *W* **10.** *P* 10. 2d. D.L.R.
The 2d. and 6d. (both *W* **2.** *Roul*) with red overprint are known showing the stop omitted from between the two letters.

L.T. (Land Titles)

Optd in red. *W* **2.** 2d. (*roul*), 4d. (*p* 11½–12½), 6d. (*roul*), 1s. (*roul*)
Optd in blue. *W* **10.** *Roul.* 2d. D.L.R.
Optd in black. (*a*) *W* **2.** 4d. (*p* 11½–12½), 4d. (*p* 10), 4d. (*p* 10 × 11½–12½), 6d. (*p* 11½–12½ × *roul*), 6d. (*p* 11½–12½), 6d. (*p* 10), 6d. (*p* 10 × 11½–12½)
(*b*) *W* **7.** *P* 10. 2d. D.L.R.
(*c*) *W* **10.** 2d. D.L.R. (*roul*), 2d. D.L.R. (*p* 10)
The 2d. and 6d. (both *W* **2.** *Roul*) with red overprint are known showing the stop omitted after "T".

M. (Military)

Optd in red. *W* **2.** *Roul.* 2d., 6d., 1s.
Optd in black. *W* **2.** 6d. (*p* 11½–12½ × *roul*), 1s. (*p* 11½–12½ × *roul*), 2s. (*roul*)

M.B. (Marine Board)

Optd in red. *W* **2.** 1d. (*roul*), 2d. (*roul*), 4d. (*roul*), 4d. (*p* 11½–12½), 6d. (*roul*), 1s. (*roul*)
Optd in black. (*a*) *W* **2.** 1d. (*roul*), 1d. (*p* 11½–12½), 2d. D.L.R. (*roul*), 4d. (*p* 11½–12½ × *roul*), 4d. (*p* 11½–12½), 4d. (*p* 10), 4d. (*p* 10 × 11½–12½), 6d. (*roul*), 6d. (*p* 11½–12½), 6d. (*p* 10), 6d. (*p* 10 × 11½–12½), 1s. (*p* 11½–12½ × *roul*), 1s. (*p* 11½–12½), 1s. (*p* 10), 1s. (*p* 10 × 11½–12½)
(*b*) *W* **7.** *P* 10. 2d. D.L.R., 4d.
(*c*) *W* **10.** 2d. D.L.R. (*roul*), 2d. D.L.R. (*p* 10)

M.R. (Manager of Railways)

Optd in red. *W* **2.** *Roul.* 2d., 6d.
Optd in black. (*a*) *W* **2.** 1d. (*p* 11½–12½), 1d. (*p* 10), 2d. D.L.R. (*roul*), 4d. (*roul*), 4d. (*p* 11½–12½), 6d. (*roul*), 6d. (*p* 11½–12½ × *roul*), 6d. (*p* 11½–12½), 10d. on 9d. (*roul*), 1s. (*roul*), 1s. (*p* 11½–12½ × *roul*), 2s. (*p* 11½–12½), 2s. (*p* 10 × 11½–12½)
(*b*) *W* **10.** 2d. D.L.R. (*roul*), 2d. D.L.R. (*p* 10), 2d. D.L.R. (*p* 10 × 11½–12½)

M.R.G. (Main Roads Gambierton)

Optd in red without stops. *W* **2.** *Roul.* 2d., 6d.
Optd in blue without stops. *W* **10.** *Roul.* 2d. D.L.R.
Optd in black without stops. *W* **10.** 2d. D.L.R. (*roul*), 2d. D.L.R. (*p* 10)
Optd in black with stops. *W* **10.** 2d. D.L.R. (*roul*), 2d. D.L.R. (*p* 10)
The 2d. D.L.R. (*W* **10.** *P* 10) with black overprint is known showing the stops omitted after "M" and "R".

N.T. (Northern Territory)

Optd in black. (*a*) *W* **2.** *P* 11½–12½. 1d., 3d. on 4d., 4d., 6d., 1s.
(*b*) *W* **10.** 2d. D.L.R. (*roul*), 2d. D.L.R. (*p* 10)

O.A. (Official Assignee)

Optd in red. *W* **2.** 2d. (*roul*), 4d. (*p* 11½–12½)
Optd in blue. *W* **10.** *Roul.* 2d. D.L.R.
Optd in black. (*a*) *W* **2.** 4d. (*p* 11½–12½), 4d. (*p* 10)
(*b*) *W* **7.** *P* 10. 2d. D.L.R.
(*c*) *W* **10.** 2d. D.L.R. (*roul*), 2d. D.L.R. (*p* 10 × *roul*), 2d. D.L.R. (*p* 10)

P. (Police)

Optd in blue. (*a*) *W* **2.** *Roul.* 6d.
(*b*) *W* **10.** *Roul.* 2d. D.L.R.
Optd in black. (*a*) *W* **2.** 6d. (*p* 11½–12½ × *roul*), 6d. (*p* 11½–12½), 6d. (*p* 10)
(*b*) *W* **7.** *P* 10. 2d. D.L.R.
(*c*) *W* **10.** 2d. D.L.R. (*roul*), 2d. D.L.R. (*p* 11½–12½), 2d. D.L.R. (*p* 11½–12½ × *roul*), 2d. D.L.R. (*p* 10 × *roul*), 2d. D.L.R. (*p* 10), 2d. D.L.R. (*p* 10 × 11½–12½)

P.A. (Protector of Aborigines)

Optd in red. *W* **2.** *Roul.* 2d., 6d.
Optd in black. (*a*) *W* **2.** *Roul.* 2d. D.L.R., 6d.
(*b*) *W* **10.** 2d. D.L.R. (*roul*), 2d. D.L.R. (*p* 10)

P.O. (Post Office)

Optd in red. *W* **2.** *Roul.* 1d., 2d., 6d., 1s.
Optd in blue. *W* **2.** *Roul.* 2d., 2d. D.L.R.
Optd in black. (*a*) *W* **2.** 1d. (*p* 10 × 11½–12½), 2d. D.L.R. (*roul*), 4d. (*p* 11½–12½), 6d. (*roul*), 6d. (*p* 11½–12½), 1s. (*p* 11½–12½ × *roul*), 1s. (*p* 11½–12½), 1s. (*p* 10), 1s. (*p* 10 × 11½–12½)
(*b*) *W* **10.** 2d. D.L.R. (*roul*), 2d. D.L.R. (*p* 10 × *roul*), 2d. D.L.R. (*p* 10)
The 6d. (*W* **2.** *Roul*) with red overprint is known showing the stop omitted after "O", but with two stops after "P".

P.S. (Private Secretary)

Optd in red. *W* **2.** 1d. (*roul*), 2d. (*roul*), 4d. (*p* 11½–12½), 6d. (*roul*), 1s. (*roul*)
Optd in black. (*a*) *W* **2.** 1d. (*p* 11½–12½ × *roul*), 1d. (*p* 11½–12½), 1d. (*p* 10), 3d. (*in black*) on 4d. (*p* 11½–12½), 3d. (*in red*) on 4d. (*p* 10), 3d. (*in black*) on 4d. (*p* 10), 4d. (*p* 11½–12½), 4d. (*p* 10), 4d. (*p* 10 × 11½–12½), 6d. (*roul*), 6d. (*p* 11½–12½ × *roul*), 6d. (*p* 11½–12½), 6d. (*p* 10), 9d. (*roul*), 9d. (*p* 11½–12½), 10d. on 9d. (*p* 10 × 11½–12½), 1s. (*p* 11½–12½ × *roul*), 2s. (*p* 11½–12½)
(*b*) *W* **7.** *P* 10. 2d. D.L.R.
(*c*) *W* **10.** 2d. D.L.R. (*roul*), 2d. D.L.R. (*p* 10)

P.W. (Public Works)

Optd in red without stop after "W". *W* **2.** *Roul.* 2d., 6d., 1s.
Optd in black. (*a*) *W* **2.** 2d. D.L.R. (*roul*), 4d. (*p* 10), 6d. (*roul*), 6d. (*p* 11½–12½), 1s. (*p* 11½–12½ × *roul*)
(*b*) *W* **10.** 2d. D.L.R. (*roul*), 2d. D.L.R. (*p* 10)

R.B. (Road Board)

Optd in red. *W* **2.** 1d. (*roul*), 2d. (*roul*), 4d. (*p* 11½–12½), 6d. (*roul*), 1s. (*roul*)
Optd in blue without stops. *W* **10.** *Roul.* 2d. D.L.R.
Optd in black. (*a*) *W* **2.** 1d. (*p* 11½–12½ × *roul*), 1d. (*p* 10), 4d. (*p* 10), 2s. (*roul*)
(*b*) *W* **7.** *P* 10. 2d. D.L.R.
(*c*) *W* **10.** 2d. D.L.R. (*roul*), 2d. D.L.R. (*p* 10)
The 6d. (*W* **2.** *Roul*) with red overprint is known showing the stop omitted after "B".

R.G. (Registrar-General)

Optd in red. *W* **2.** *Roul.* 2d., 6d., 1s.
Optd in blue. (*a*) *W* **2.** *P* 11½–12½ × *roul.* 6d.
(*b*) *W* **10.** 2d. D.L.R. (*roul*), 2d. D.L.R. (*p* 11½–12½ × *roul*)
Optd in black. (*a*) *W* **2.** 2d. D.L.R. (*roul*), 6d. (*p* 10), 6d. (*p* 10 × 11½–12½), 1s. (*p* 11½–12½ × *roul*), 1s. (*p* 10)
(*b*) *W* **7.** *P* 10. 2d. D.L.R.
(*c*) *W* **10.** 2d. D.L.R. (*roul*), 2d. D.L.R. (*p* 10 × *roul*), 2d. D.L.R. (*p* 10), 2d. D.L.R. (*p* 10 × 11½–12½)

S. (Sheriff)

Optd in red. *W* **2.** *Roul.* 2d., 6d.
Optd in blue. (*a*) *W* **2.** *P* 11½–12½ × *roul.* 6d.
(*b*) *W* **10.** *Roul.* 2d. D.L.R.
Optd in black. (*a*) *W* **2.** 4d. (*p* 11½–12½), 4d. (*p* 10), 6d. (*roul*), 6d. (*p* 11½–12½), 6d. (*p* 10)
(*b*) *W* **10.** 2d. D.L.R. (*roul*), 2d. D.L.R. (*p* 10 × *roul*), 2d. D.L.R. (*p* 10), 2d. D.L.R. (*p* 10 × 11½–12½)

S.C. (Supreme Court)

Optd in red. *W* **2.** *Roul.* 2d., 6d.
Optd in black. *W* **10.** *P* 10. 2d. D.L.R.

S.G. (Surveyor-General)

Optd in red. *W* **2.** 2d. (*roul*), 4d. (*p* 11½–12½), 6d. (*roul*)
Optd in blue. (*a*) *W* **2.** *Roul.* 4d.
(*b*) *W* **10.** *Roul.* 2d. D.L.R.
Optd in black. (*a*) *W* **2.** 2d. D.L.R. (*roul*), 4d. (*p* 11½–12½), 4d. (*p* 10), 4d. (*p* 10 × 11½–12½), 6d. (*p* 11½–12½ × *roul*), 6d. (*p* 11½–12½), 6d. (*p* 10), 6d. (*p* 10 × 11½–12½)
(*b*) *W* **7.** *P* 10. 2d. D.L.R.
(*c*) *W* **10.** 2d. D.L.R. (*roul*), 2d. D.L.R. (*p* 10 × *roul*), 2d. D.L.R. (*p* 10)

S.M. (Stipendiary Magistrate)

Optd in red. *W* **2.** 1d. (*roul*), 2d. (*roul*), 4d. (*roul*), 4d. (*p* 11½–12½), 6d. (*roul*), 1s. (*roul*)
Optd in blue. (*a*) *W* **2.** *Roul.* 2d., 4d., 6d.
(*b*) *W* **10.** *Roul.* 2d. D.L.R.
Optd in black. (*a*) *W* **2.** 1d. (*p* 11½–12½), 1d. (*p* 10), 2d. D.L.R. (*roul*), 4d. (*roul*), 4d. (*p* 11½–12½ × *roul*), 4d. (*p* 11½–12½), 4d. (*p* 10), 4d. (*p* 10 × 11½–12½), 6d. (*p* 11½–12½ × *roul*), 6d. (*p* 11½–12½), 6d. (*p* 10), 6d. (*p* 10 × 11½–12½), 1s. (*p* 11½–12½ × *roul*)
(*b*) *W* **7.** *P* 10. 2d. D.L.R.
(*c*) *W* **10.** 2d. D.L.R. (*roul*), 2d. D.L.R. (*p* 10 × *roul*), 2d. D.L.R. (*p* 10), 2d. D.L.R. (*p* 10 × 11½–12½)
The 2d. and 4d. (both *W* **2.** *Roul*) with red overprint are known showing the stop omitted after "M".

S.T. (Superintendent of Telegraphs)

Optd in red. *W* **2.** *Roul.* 2d., 6d.
Optd in blue. *W* **10.** 2d. D.L.R. (*roul*), 2d. D.L.R. (*p* 11½–12½)
Optd in black. (*a*) *W* **2.** *Roul.* 2d. D.L.R., 6d.
(*b*) *W* **7.** *P* 10. 2d. D.L.R.
(*c*) *W* **10.** 2d. D.L.R. (*roul*), 2d. D.L.R. (*p* 10 × *roul*), 2d. D.L.R. (*p* 10)
The 2d. and 6d. (both *W* **2.** *Roul*) with red overprint (2d., 6d.) or black overprint (6d.) are known showing the stop omitted after "T".

T. (Treasury)

Optd in red. *W* **2.** 1d. (*roul*), 2d. (*roul*), 4d. (*p* 11½–12½ × *roul*), 6d. (*roul*), 1s. (*roul*)
Optd in blue. (*a*) *W* **2.** *Roul.* 1d., 4d., 6d., 2s.
(*b*) *W* **10.** *Roul.* 2d. D.L.R.
Optd in black. (*a*) *W* **2.** 1d. (*p* 10), 2d. D.L.R. (*roul*), 4d. (*roul*), 4d. (*p* 11½–12½), 6d. (*roul*), 6d. (*p* 11½–12½), 1s. (*p* 11½–12½ × *roul*), 1s. (*p* 10 × 11½–12½), 2s. (*roul*), 2s. (*p* 11½–12½), 2s. (*p* 10 × 11½–12½)
(*b*) *W* **7.** *P* 10. 2d. D.L.R.
(*c*) *W* **10.** 2d. D.L.R. (*roul*), 2d. D.L.R. (*p* 10)

T.R. (Titles Registration)

Optd in black. (*a*) *W* **2.** 4d. (*p* 11½–12½), 4d. (*p* 10 × 11½–12½), 6d. (*p* 11½–12½), 6d. (*p* 10 × 11½–12½), 1s. (*p* 11½–12½), 1s. (*p* 10 × 11½–12½)
(*b*) *W* **10.** *P* 10. 2d. D.L.R.

V. (Volunteers)

Optd in red. *W* **2.** *Roul.* 2d., 6d., 1s.
Optd in black. (*a*) *W* **2.** *Roul.* 6d.
(*b*) *W* **7.** *P* 10. 2d. D.L.R.
(*c*) *W* **10.** 2d. D.L.R. (*roul*), 2d. D.L.R. (*p* 10 × *roul*), 2d. D.L.R. (*p* 10)
The 2d. (*W* **10.** *P* 10 × *roul*) overprinted in black is only known showing the stop omitted after "V".

VA. (Valuator of Runs)

Optd in black without stop after "V". (*a*) *W* **2.** *P* 10. 4d.
(*b*) *W* **10.** *P* 10. 2d. D.L.R.

VN. (Vaccination)

Optd in black without stop after "V". *W* **2.** *P* 10. 4d.

W. (Waterworks)

Optd in red. *W* **2.** *Roul.* 2d.
Optd in black. (*a*) *W* **2.** *P* 11½–12½. 6d., 2s.
(*b*) *W* **10.** 2d. D.L.R. (*roul*), 2d. D.L.R. (*p* 10)
The 2d. (*W* **2.** *Roul*) with red overprint is known showing th[e] stop omitted after "W".

B. General

O.S. (O 1) **O.S.** (O 2)

1874–77. *Optd with Type* O **1.** *W* **2.** (*a*) *P* 10.

No.	Type	Description	Unused	Used
O 1	3	4d. dull purple (18.2.74)	£1000	£27
		(*b*) *P* 11½–12½ × 10.		
O 2	1	1d. green (2.1.74)	—	£10
O 3	3	4d. dull violet (12.2.75)	55·00	5·0
O 4	1	6d. Prussian blue (20.10.75)	65·00	8·0
O 4*a*	3	2s. rose-pink		
O 5		2s. carmine (3.12.76)	—	90·0
		(*c*) *P* 11½–12½		
O 6	1	1d. deep yellow-green (30.1.74)	£1000	16·0
		a. Printed on both sides	—	£40
O 7	3	3d. on 4d. ultramarine (26.6.77)	£1200	£47
		a. No stop after "S"	—	£80
O 8		4d. dull violet (13.7.74)	45·00	6·0
		a. No stop after "S"	—	30·0
O 9	1	6d. bright blue (31.8.75)	70·00	11·0
		a. "O.S." double	—	65·0
O10		6d. Prussian blue (27.3.74)	60·00	6·0
		a. No stop after "S"	—	35·0
O11	4	9d. red-purple (22.3.76)	£600	£25
		a. No stop after "S"	£1000	£45
O12	1	1s. red-brown (5.8.74)	60·00	6·0
		a. "O.S." double	—	70·0
		b. No stop after "S"	£120	35·0
O13	3	2s. crimson-carmine (13.7.75)	95·00	14·0
		a. No stop after "S"	—	60·0
		b. No stops	—	75·0
		c. Stops at top of letters		

1876–85. *Optd with Type* O **1.** *W* **8.** (*a*) *P* 10.

No.	Type	Description	Unused	Used
O14	1	6d. bright blue (1879)	65·00	9·5
		(*b*) *P* 10 × 11½–12½, 11½–12½ × 10, *or compound*		
O15	3	4d. violet-slate (24.1.78)	65·00	6·5
O16		4d. plum (29.11.81)	38·00	2·7
O17		4d. deep mauve	26·00	2·5
		a. No stop after "S"	£100	24·0
		b. No stop after "O"		
		c. "O.S." double		
		d. "O.S." inverted	—	£10
O18	1	6d. bright blue (1877)	45·00	4·2
		a. "O.S." inverted		
		b. No stop after "O"		
O19		6d. bright ultramarine (27.3.85)	40·00	4·0
		a. "O.S." inverted		
		b. "O.S." double		
		c. "O.S." double, one inverted	—	£22
		d. No stop after "S"	—	35·0
		e. No stops after "O" & "S"		
O20		1s. red-brown (27.3.83)	40·00	6·0
		a. "O.S." inverted		
		b. No stop after "O"		
		c. No stop after "S"	—	35·0
O21	3	2s. carmine (16.3.81)	80·00	7·5
		a. "O.S." inverted	—	£13
		b. No stop after "S"	—	50·0
		(*c*) *P* 11½–12½		
O22	3	3d. on 4d. ultramarine	£1200	
O23		4d. violet-slate (14.3.76)	£120	6·5
O24		4d. deep mauve (19.8.79)	45·00	2·7
		a. "O.S." inverted		
		b. "O.S." double, one inverted		
		c. No stop after "S"	—	25·0
O25	1	6d. Prussian blue (6.77)	50·00	5·0
		a. "O.S." double	—	55·0
		b. "O.S." inverted		
O26	4	8d. on 9d. brown (9.11.76)	£900	£37
		a. "O.S." double	£1400	
		b. "O" only	—	£6
O26*c*		9d. purple	£2250	
O27	1	1s. red-brown (12.2.78)	32·00	8·
		a. "O.S." inverted	£190	90·
		b. No stop after "S"	£160	38·
O28		1s. lake-brown (8.11.83)	30·00	3·5
O29	3	2s. rose-carmine (12.8.85)	80·00	8·
		a. "O.S." double	—	80·0
		b. "O.S." inverted	—	85·0
		c. No stop after "S"	—	35·0

1891–1903. *Optd with Type* O **2.** (*a*) *W* **8.** *P* 11½–12½.

No.	Type	Description	Unused	Used
O30	1	1s. lake-brown (18.4.91)	32·00	10·0
O31		1s. Vandyke brown	40·00	7·0
O32		1s. dull brown (2.7.96)	30·00	4·7
		a. No stop after "S"	—	50·0
O33		1s. sepia (*large holes*) (4.1.02)	27·00	4·5
		a. "O.S." double		
		b. No stop after "S"		
O34	3	2s. carmine (26.6.00)	75·00	11·0
		a. No stop after "S"		
		(*b*) *W* **8.** *P* 10 × 11½–12½		
O35	3	2s. rose-carmine (9.11.95)	60·00	9·0
		a. No stop after "S"	£110	
		b. "O.S." double		
		(*c*) *W* **10.** *P* 11½–12½		
O36	1	1s. dull brown (1902)	35·00	5·5

74–76. *Optd with Type* O 1. W **10.** (*a*) *P* 10.
7 11 1d. blue-green (30.9.75) .. .. 70·00 15·00
a. "O.S." inverted .. .. ..
b. No stop after "S" .. .. ..
8 12 2d. orange-red (18.2.74) .. .. 12·00 65
a. No stop after "S" .. .. .. — 20·00
b. "O.S." double .. .. ..

(*b*) *P* 10 × 11½–12½, 11½–12½ × 10, *or compound*
9 11 1d. blue-green (16.9.75) .. ..
a. No stop after "S" .. .. ..
0 12 2d. orange-red (27.9.76) .. .. — 4·75

(*c*) *P* 11½–12½
1 11 1d. blue-green (13.8.75) .. .. — 14·00
a. "O.S." inverted .. .. ..
b. No stop after "S" .. .. ..
2 12 2d. orange-red (20.5.74) .. .. — 80·00

76–80. *Optd with Type* O 1. W **13.** (*a*) *P* 10
3 11 1d. blue-green (2.10.76) .. .. 10·00 40
a. "O.S." inverted .. .. .. — 35·00
b. "O.S." double .. .. .. 45·00 30·00
c. "O.S." double, one inverted ..
d. No stops .. .. .. — 20·00
e. No stop after "O" .. .. ..
f. No stop after "S" .. .. .. — 10·00
g. Deep green .. .. .. 11·00 40
ga. "O.S." double .. .. .. — 32·00
44 12 2d. orange-red (21.9.77) .. .. 7·50 40
a. "O.S." inverted .. .. .. — 18·00
b. "O.S." double .. .. .. 55·00 27·00
c. "O.S." double, one inverted ..
d. "O.S." double, both inverted .. — 85·00
e. No stops .. .. .. — 40·00
f. No stop after "O" .. .. .. — 14·00
g. No stop after "S" .. .. ..
h. Dull brick-red .. .. .. 25·00 65

(*b*) *P* 10×11½–12½, 11½–12½×10 *or compound*
45 11 1d. deep green (14.8.80) .. .. — 18·00
a. "O.S." double .. .. ..
46 12 2d. orange-red (6.4.78) .. .. 45·00 6·00
a. "O.S." inverted .. .. .. — 85·00
b. No stop after "S" .. .. .. — 40·00

(*c*) *P* 11½–12½
47 12 2d. orange-red (15.7.80) .. .. — 60·00

382 (20 Feb). *No.* 181 *optd with Type* O 1.
48 11 ½d. on 1d. blue-green .. .. 55·00 14·00
a. "O.S." inverted .. .. ..

388 (15 Nov)–**91.** *Nos.* 184 *and* 185*a optd with Type* O 1. *P* 10.
49 17 4d. pale violet (24.1.91) .. .. 50·00 3·75
50 18 6d. blue .. .. .. 15·00 1·25
a. "O.S." double .. .. ..
b. No stop after "S" .. .. ..

891. *Nos.* 229*b and* 231*a*/2 *optd with Type* O 1. (*a*) *P* 10
51 17 2½d. on 4d. deep green (Br.) (1 Aug) 45·00 6·50
a. "2" and "½" closer together — 42·00
b. "O.S." inverted .. .. ..
c. "O.S." double .. .. ..
d. "O.S." omitted (in vert pair with normal) .. .. ..
e. No stop after "S" .. .. ..

(*b*) *P* 10×11½–12½ *or* 11½–12½×10
52 17 2½d. on 4d. deep green (Br.) (1 Oct) .. 50·00 9·50

(*c*) *P* 11½–12½
53 17 2½d. on 4d. deep green (Br.) (1 June) £100 50·00

891–96. *Optd with Type* O 2. W **13.** (*a*) *P* 10
54 11 1d. deep green (22.4.91) .. .. 10·00 1·40
a. "O.S." double .. .. .. 45·00 27·00
b. "O.S." double, one inverted ..
c. No stop after "S" .. .. .. 32·00 8·00
d. Blackish blue opt .. .. .. £200 4·00
55 12 2d. orange-red (22.4.91) .. .. 10·00 30
a. "O.S." double .. .. ..
b. "O.S." double, both inverted ..
c. No stop after "S" .. .. .. — 9·00

(*b*) *P* 15
56 11 1d. green (8.9.94) .. .. 8·50 40
a. "O.S." double .. .. ..
b. No stop after "S" .. .. ..
57 12 2d. orange-red (16.6.94) .. .. 8·50 25
a. "O.S." double .. .. .. — 21·00
b. "O.S." inverted .. .. .. — 15·00

(*c*) *P* 13
58 11 1d. green (20.5.95) .. .. 13·00 40
a. No stop after "S" .. .. 48·00 8·00
59 12 2d. orange-red (11.2.96) .. .. 11·00 30
a. "O.S." double .. .. .. 75·00
b. No stop after "S" .. .. .. 45·00 8·00

891–99. *Optd with Type* O 2. W **13** (*sideways on* ½*d.*). (*a*) *P* 10
60 15 ½d. brown (2.5.94) .. .. 9·00 3·50
a. No stop after "S" .. .. 32·00 20·00
61 17 4d. pale violet (13.2.91) .. .. 50·00 2·75
a. "O.S." double .. .. ..
b. "S." omitted .. .. .. — 48·00
c. No stop after "S" .. .. ..
d. Aniline violet (31.8.93) .. .. 50·00 2·50
da. "O.S." double .. .. ..
dc. No stop after "S" .. .. ..
62 18 6d. blue (4.4.93) .. .. 16·00 1·75
a. No stop after "S" .. .. ..
b. Blackish blue opt .. .. ..

(*b*) *P* 10×11½–12½
63 15 ½d. brown (26.3.95) .. .. 9·50 3·75

(*c*) *P* 11½–12½
64 15 ½d. red-brown (13.6.91) .. .. 22·00 4·75

(*d*) *P* 15
O65 15 ½d. pale brown (8.6.95) .. .. 13·00 4·00
O66 17 4d. slate-violet (4.4.95) .. .. 50·00 2·75
a. "O.S." double .. .. .. £150 27·00
O67 18 6d. blue (20.9.93) .. .. 15·00 1·25

(*e*) *P* 13
O68 15 ½d. deep brown (17.5.98) .. .. 8·50 4·00
a. Opt triple, twice sideways .. £150
O69 17 4d. violet (12.96) .. .. .. 50·00 2·25
a. "O.S." double .. .. .. £120 28·00
b. No stop after "S" .. .. .. £120 20·00
O70 18 6d. blue (13.9.99) .. .. .. 20·00 1·50
a. No stop after "S" .. .. .. 70·00 50·00

1891–95. *Nos.* 229*b*, 230*a and* 231*a optd with Type* O 2. (*a*) *P* 10
O71 17 2½d. on 4d. deep green (Br.) (18.8.94) 32·00 4·50
a. Fraction bar omitted .. ..
b. "2" and "½" closer together .. 75·00 20·00
c. "O.S." inverted £130
d. No stop after "S" .. .. — 30·00
O72 18 5d. on 6d. deep brown (C.) (2.12.91) 38·00 12·00
a. No stop after "5D" £170
b. No stop after "S" .. .. 95·00 32·00

(*b*) *P* 10×11½–12½
O73 17 2½d. on 4d. deep green (Br.) (17.9.95) — 38·00
a. "O.S." double .. .. ..

1897–1901. *Nos.* 235/6 *and* 238*a optd with Type* O 2. (*a*) *P* 15
O74 23 5d. brown-purple (29.3.01) .. .. 55·00 6·00

(*b*) *P* 13
O75 22 2½d. violet-blue (5.7.97) .. .. 42·00 4·00
a. No stop after "S" .. .. — 25·00
O76 23 5d. purple (29.9.01) .. .. .. 55·00 7·50
a. No stop after "S" .. .. ..

O. S.

(O 3)

1899–1901. *Optd with Type* O 3. W **13.** *P* 13.
O80 24 ½d. yellow-green (12.2.00) .. .. 8·50 4·25
a. "O.S." inverted .. .. 48·00
b. No stop after "S" .. .. 32·00
O81 11 1d. rosine (22.9.99) .. .. 9·00 85
a. "O.S." inverted .. .. 42·00 30·00
b. "O.S." double .. .. ..
c. No stop after "S" .. .. 38·00 14·00
O82 12 2d. bright violet (1.6.00) .. .. 9·00 50
a. "O.S." inverted .. .. 38·00 20·00
b. "O.S." double .. .. ..
c. No stop after "S" .. .. 27·00
O83 22 2½d. indigo (2.10.01) .. .. 55·00 13·00
a. "O.S." inverted .. .. — 55·00
b. No stop after "S" £140
O84 17 4d. violet (18.11.00) .. .. 48·00 2·25
a. "O.S." inverted £160
b. No stop after "S" £120
O85 18 6d. blue (8.10.00) .. .. 15·00 1·60
a. No stop after "S" .. .. 50·00

1891 (May). *Optd as Type* O 3 *but wider.* W **13.** *P* 10.
O86 19 2s. 6d. pale violet £2000 £1600
O87 5s. pale rose £2000 £1600

Only one sheet (60) of each of these stamps was printed.

The use of stamps overprinted "O S" was made invalid by the Posts and Telegraph Act of 1 November 1902.

South Australia became part of the Commonwealth of Australia on 1 January 1901.

TASMANIA

PRICES FOR STAMPS ON COVER

Nos. 1/4	*from* × 2
Nos. 5/12	*from* × 3
Nos. 14/23	*from* × 2
No. 24	—
Nos. 25/56	*from* × 3
Nos. 57/77	*from* × 6
Nos. 78/9	—
Nos. 80/90	*from* × 3
No. 91	—
Nos. 92/109	*from* × 3
No. 110	—
Nos. 111/23	*from* × 3
Nos. 124/6	—
Nos. 127/34	*from* × 4
Nos. 135/55	*from* × 3
Nos. 156/8	*from* × 20
Nos. 159/66	*from* × 10
Nos. 167/9	*from* × 15
Nos. 170/4	*from* × 6
Nos. 216/22	*from* × 15
Nos. 223/5	—
Nos. 226/7	*from* × 15
Nos. 229/36	*from* × 20
Nos. 237/57	*from* × 10
No. 258	—
Nos. 259/62	*from* × 10
Nos. F1/25	—
Nos. F26/9	*from* × 15
Nos. F30/9	—

SPECIMEN OVERPRINTS. Those listed are from U.P.U. distributions between 1892 and 1904. Further "Specimen" overprints exist, but these were used for other purposes.

1

2

3

(Eng C. W. Coard. Recess H. and C. Best at the *Courier* newspaper, Hobart)

1853 (1 Nov). *No wmk. Imperf. Twenty-four varieties in four rows of six each.*

(*a*) *Medium soft yellowish paper with all lines clear and distinct*
1 1 1d. pale blue £3250 £800
2 1d. blue £3250 £800

(*b*) *Thin hard white paper with lines of the engraving blurred and worn*
3 1 1d. pale blue £3000 £700
4 1d. blue £3000 £700

1853–55. *No wmk. Imperf. In each plate there are twenty-four varieties in four rows of six each.*

(*a*) *Plate I. Finely engraved. All lines in network and background thin, clear, and well defined.* (1853)

(i) *First state of the plate, brilliant colours*
5 2 4d. bright red-orange £2250 £600
a. Double impression .. .. ..
6 4d. bright brownish orange .. .. — £750

(ii) *Second state of plate, with blurred lines and worn condition of the central background*
7 2 4d. red-orange £2000 £375
8 4d. orange £1800 £350
9 4d. pale orange .. .. — £350

(*b*) *Plate II. Coarse engraving, lines in network and background thicker and blurred* (1855)
10 2 4d. orange £2000 £375
a. Double print, one albino .. ..
11 4d. dull orange £2000 £325
12 4d. yellowish orange £2000 £325

In the 4d. Plate I, the outer frame-line is thin all round. In Plate II it is, by comparison with other parts, thicker in the lower left angle.

The 4d. is known on vertically laid paper from proof sheets. Examples from Plate I have the lines close together and those from Plate II wide apart (*Price £5000 unused*).

In 1879 reprints were made of the 1d. in blue and the 4d., Plate I, in brownish yellow, on thin, tough, white wove paper, and perforated 11½. In 1887, a reprint from the other plate of the 4d. was made in reddish brown and in black, and in 1889 of the 1d. in blue and in black, and of the 4d. (both plates) in yellow and in black on white card, imperforate. As these three plates were defaced after the stamps had been superseded, all these reprints show two, or three thick strokes across the Queen's head.

All three plates were destroyed in July 1950.

(Eng. W. Humphrys, after water-colour sketch by E. Corbould. Recess P.B.)

1855 (17 Aug–16 Sept). *Wmk Large Star, W* w **1.** *Imperf.*
14 3 1d. carmine (16.9) £4000 £700
15 2d. deep green (16.9) £1800 £500
16 2d. green (16.9) £1800 £450
17 4d. deep blue .. .. £1200 85·00
18 4d. blue .. .. £1200 95·00

Proofs of the 1d. and 4d. on thick paper, *without watermark*, are sometimes offered as the issued stamps.

(Recess H. and C. Best, Hobart, from P.B. plates)

1856 (Apr)–**57.** *No wmk. Imperf.* (*a*) *Thin white paper.*
19 3 1d. pale brick-red (4.56) £4000 £550
20 2d. dull emerald-green (1.57) £5000 £700
21 4d. deep blue (5.57) .. .. .. £600 85·00
22 4d. blue (5.57) .. .. £500 85·00
23 4d. pale blue (5.57) .. .. .. — £120

(*b*) *Pelure paper*
24 3 1d. deep red-brown (11.56) £3000 £600

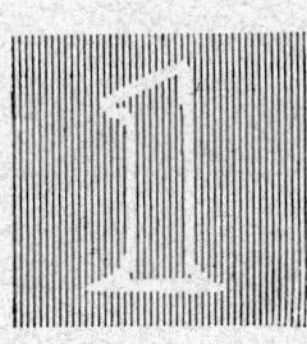
4

7

8

(Recess H. Best (August 1857–May 1859), J. Davies (August 1859–March 1862), J. Birchall (March 1863), M. Hood (October 1863–April 1864), Govt Printer (from July 1864), all from P.B. plates)

1857 (Aug)–**69.** *Wmk double-lined numerals "1", "2" or "4" as* W **4** *on appropriate value. Imperf.*
25 3 1d. deep red-brown .. .. .. £400 21·00
26 1d. pale red-brown .. .. .. £275 16·00
27 1d. brick-red (1863) .. .. .. £140 15·00
28 1d. dull vermilion (1865) .. .. 80·00 15·00
29 1d. carmine (1867) .. .. .. 80·00 15·00
a. Double print .. .. .. — £120
b. Error. Wmkd "2" (1869) .. ..
30 2d. dull emerald-green .. .. .. — 60·00
31 2d. green .. .. — 27·00
a. Double print .. .. .. — £150
32 2d. yellow-green .. .. .. £200 55·00
33 2d. deep green (1858) .. .. .. £170 30·00
34 2d. slate-green (1860) .. .. .. £120 45·00
35 4d. deep blue .. .. — 70·00
a. Double print .. .. .. — £150
36 4d. pale blue .. .. £100 11·00

37 3 4d. blue .. .. £100 15·00
a. Double print .. .. — £150
38 4d. bright blue .. .. £100 15·00
a. Printed on both sides .. .. .. † —
b. Double print .. .. — £120
39 4d. cobalt-blue .. .. — 55·00

Printings before July 1864 were all carried out at the *Courier* printing works which changed hands several times during this period.

CANCELLATIONS. Beware of early Tasmanian stamps with pen-cancellations cleaned off and faked postmarks applied.

(Recess P.B.)

1858 (Jan). *Wmk double-lined numerals "6" or "12" as W* **4**. *Imperf.*
40 7 6d. dull lilac .. .. £600 65·00
41 8 1s. vermilion (*shades*) .. .. .. £500 65·00

Examples of the 6d. lilac on paper watermarked Large Star exist from a proof sheet. These are always creased (*Price* £650 *unused*).

(Recess J. Davies (March 1860), J. Birchall (April 1863), Govt Printer (from February 1865), all from P.B. plates)

1860 (Mar)–**67**. *Wmk double-lined "6" as W* **4**. *Imperf.*
44 7 6d. dull slate-grey .. .. .. £225 50·00
45 6d. grey .. .. — 55·00
46 6d. grey-violet (4.63) .. .. .. £130 50·00
a. Double print .. .. — £200
47 6d. dull cobalt (2.65) .. .. .. £350 75·00
48 6d. slate-violet (2.65) .. .. .. £250 45·00
49 6d. reddish mauve (4.67) £550 £150

In 1871 reprints were made of the 6d. (in mauve) and the 1s. on white wove paper, and perforated 11½. They are found with or without "REPRINT". In 1889 they were again reprinted on white card, imperforate. These later impressions are also found overprinted "REPRINT" and perforated 11½.

PERFORATED ISSUES. From 1 October 1857 the Tasmania Post Office only supplied purchasers requiring five or more complete sheets of stamps. The public obtained their requirements, at face value, from licensed stamp vendors, who obtained their stocks at a discount from the Post Office.

From 1863 onwards a number of the stamp vendors applied their own roulettes or perforations. The Hobart firm of J. Walch & Sons achieved this so successfully that they were given an official contract in July 1869 to perforate sheets for the Post Office. The Government did not obtain a perforating machine until late in 1871.

1863–71. *Double-lined numeral watermarks. Various unofficial roulettes and perforations.*

(*a*) *By. J. Walch & Sons, Hobart*

(i) *Roulette about* 8, *often imperf × roul* (1863–68)
50 3 1d. brick-red .. .. — £150
51 1d. carmine £300 £100
52 2d. yellow-green .. .. — £400
53 2d. slate-green .. ..
54 4d. pale blue .. .. — £140
55 7 6d. dull lilac .. .. — £170
56 8 1s. vermilion .. .. — £500

(ii) *P* 10 (1864–69)
57 3 1d. brick-red .. .. 45·00 19·00
58 1d. dull vermilion .. .. 45·00 19·00
a. Double print .. .. † —
59 1d. carmine .. .. 42·00 19·00
60 2d. yellow-green .. .. £225 70·00
61 2d. slate-green £275 £120
62 4d. pale blue .. .. 90·00 9·50
63 4d. blue .. .. 90·00 9·50
a. Double print .. .. — £110
64 7 6d. grey-violet .. .. £150 13·00
65 6d. dull cobalt .. .. £200 50·00
66 6d. slate-violet .. .. — 18·00
67 6d. reddish mauve .. .. £300 60·00
68 8 1s. vermilion .. .. 95·00 19·00
a. Imperf vert (horiz pair) .. ..

(iii) *P* 12 (1865–71—*from July 1869 under contract to the Post Office*)
69 3 1d. dull vermilion .. .. 45·00
a. Double print .. .. † —
70 1d. carmine .. .. 35·00 6·50
a. Error. Wmkd "2" (*pen cancel* £75) .. — £1000
71 2d. yellow-green .. .. £110 38·00
72 4d. deep blue .. .. 70·00 11·00
73 4d. blue .. .. 70·00 13·00
74 4d. cobalt-blue .. .. — 28·00
75 7 6d. slate-violet .. .. £120 18·00
a. Imperf between (vert pair) .. ..
76 6d. reddish mauve .. .. 75·00 32·00
a. Imperf between (vert or horiz pair) ..
77 8 1s. vermilion .. .. £100 28·00
a. Double print .. .. — £150
b. Imperf between (horiz pair) .. ..

(iv) *Perf compound* 10 × 12 (1865–69)
78 3 1d. carmine £1300
79 4d. blue .. .. — £900

(*b*) *P* 12½ *by R. Harris, Launceston* (1864–68)
80 3 1d. brick-red .. .. 50·00 23·00
81 1d. dull vermilion .. .. 48·00 17·00
82 1d. carmine .. .. 27·00 7·00
83 2d. yellow-green .. .. £225 80·00
84 2d. slate-green £200 £100
85 4d. blue .. .. £130 35·00
86 4d. bright blue .. .. £130 35·00
87 7 6d. dull cobalt .. .. £250 70·00
88 6d. slate-violet .. .. £170 40·00
89 6d. reddish mauve .. .. £350 90·00
90 8 1s. vermilion .. .. £200 75·00

(*c*) *Imperf × oblique roulette* 11½ *at Oatlands* (1866)
91 3 4d. blue .. .. — £375

(*d*) *Oblique roulette* 10–10½, *possibly at Deloraine* (1867)
92 3 1d. brick-red .. .. — £325
93 1d. carmine £900 £275
94 2d. yellow-green .. .. — £425
95 4d. bright blue .. .. — £375
96 7 6d. grey-violet .. .. — £600

(*e*) *Oblique roulette* 14–15, *probably at Cleveland* (1867–69)
97 3 1d. brick-red .. .. — £375
98 1d. dull vermilion .. .. — £375
99 1d. carmine .. .. — £375
100 2d. yellow-green .. .. — £425
101 4d. pale blue .. .. — £325
102 7 6d. grey-violet .. .. — £600
103 8 1s. vermilion .. .. — £750

(*f*) *Pin-perf* 5½ *to* 9½ *at Longford* (1867)
104 3 1d. carmine .. .. £300 70·00
105 2d. yellow-green .. ..
106 4d. bright blue .. .. — £160
107 7 6d. grey-violet .. .. — £150
108 6d. reddish mauve .. .. — £425
109 8 1s. vermilion .. ..

(*g*) *Pin-perf* 12 *at Oatlands* (1867)
110 3 4d. blue .. ..

(*h*) *Pin-perf* 13½ *to* 14½ (1867)
111 3 1d. brick-red .. .. — £190
112 1d. dull vermilion .. .. — £190
113 1d. carmine .. ..
114 2d. yellow-green .. .. — £275
115 4d. pale blue .. .. — £160
116 7 6d. grey-violet .. .. — £375
117 8 1s. vermilion .. ..

(*j*) *Serrated perf* 19 *at Hobart* (1868–69)
118 3 1d. carmine (*pen-cancel* £9) £225 £100
119 2d. yellow-green .. .. — £200
120 4d. deep blue .. .. £550 95·00
121 4d. cobalt-blue .. .. — 95·00
122 7 6d. slate-violet .. .. — £375
123 8 1s. vermilion .. ..

(*k*) *Roul* 4½, *possibly at Macquarie River* (1868)
124 3 4d. blue .. ..
125 7 6d. reddish mauve .. ..
126 8 1s. vermilion .. ..

An example of the 1d. carmine is known perforated 10 on three sides and serrated 19 on the fourth.

For stamps perforated 11½ or 12 by the Post Office see Nos. 134*a*/43.

11

12

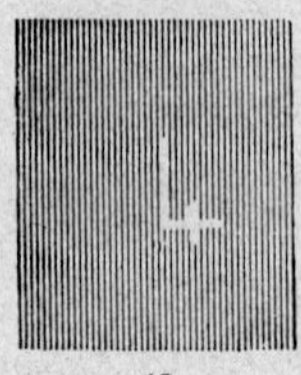
13

14

(Typo Govt Printer, Hobart, from plates made by D.L.R.)

1870 (1 Nov)–**71**. *Wmk single-lined numerals W* **12** (*2d.*), **13** (*1d., 4d.*) *or* **14** (*1d., 10d.*). (*a*) *P* 12 *by J. Walch & Sons.*
127 11 1d. rose-red (*wmk* "10") .. .. 28·00 8·50
a. Imperf (pair) £275 £275
b. *Deep rose-red* .. .. 48·00 6·50
128 1d. rose-red (*wmk* "4") (3.71) .. .. 45·00 8·50
a. Imperf (pair) .. .. — £225
129 2d. yellow-green .. .. 48·00 4·50
a. Imperf (pair) .. ..
b. *Blue-green* .. .. 50·00 4·50
130 4d. blue £700 £400
131 10d. black .. .. 23·00 17·00
a. Imperf (pair) £160

(*b*) *P* 11½ *by the Post Office* (1871)
132 11 1d. rose-red (*wmk* "10") £900
133 2d. yellow-green .. .. 85·00 6·50
a. *Blue-green* .. .. 42·00 3·25
ab. Double print .. ..
134 10d. black .. .. 26·00 17·00

The above were printed on paper obtained from New South Wales.

See also Nos. 144/55, 156/8, 159/66, 170/4, 226/7, 242 and 255/6.

(Recess P.B.)

1871. *Wmk double-lined numeral "6". P* 11½ *by the Post Office.*
134*a* 7 1s. vermilion .. ..

(Recess Govt Printer, Hobart)

1871–91. *Double-lined numeral watermarks as W* **4**. *Perforated by the Post Office.* (*a*) *P* 11½.
135 7 6d. dull lilac .. .. 70·00 19·00
136 6d. lilac .. .. 65·00 19·00
a. Imperf between (pair) .. .. .. — £475
137 6d. deep slate-lilac (3.75) .. .. 65·00 19·00
a. Imperf (pair) .. .. — £450
138 6d. bright violet (5.78) .. .. .. 65·00 28·00
a. Double print .. .. — £110
b. Imperf between (horiz pair) £750
139 6d. dull reddish lilac (10.79) .. .. 70·00 38·00
140 8 1s. brown-red (1.73) .. .. .. 85·00 38·
a. Imperf between (horiz pair) .. ..
141 1s. orange-red (3.75) .. .. .. 75·00 38·
141*a* 1s. orange (5.78) .. ..

(*b*) *P* 12
142 7 6d. reddish purple (1884) .. .. 80·00 18·
a. Imperf between (horiz pair) £425
143 6d. dull claret (7.91) .. .. .. 24·00 12·

The perforation machine used on Nos. 142/3 was previous[ly] owned by J. Walch and Sons and passed to the ownership of th[e] Government in 1884. It may have been used to perforate lef[t] over sheets of previous printings.

15

16

(Typo Govt Printer, Hobart, from plates made by D.L.R.)

1871 (25 Mar)–**78**. *W* **15**. (*a*) *P* 11½.
144 11 1d. rose (5.71) .. .. 4·00
a. Imperf (pair) (*pen cancel* £30) ..
b. *Bright rose* .. .. 4·00
c. *Carmine* .. .. 5·50
d. *Pink* .. .. 5·50 1·
e. *Vermilion* (4.75) .. .. .. £200 65·
145 2d. deep green (11.72) .. .. .. 17·00
a. *Blue-green* .. .. 25·00
b. *Yellow-green* (12.75) .. .. .. £110 1·
146 3d. pale red-brown .. .. .. 40·00 3·
a. Imperf (pair) £160
b. *Deep red-brown* .. .. .. 40·00 3·
ba. Imperf between (pair) .. ..
c. *Purple-brown* (1.78) .. .. .. 40·00 3·
ca. Imperf (pair) .. .. — £3
d. *Brownish purple* .. .. .. 40·00 3·
147 4d. pale yellow (8.8.76) .. .. .. 40·00 12·
a. *Ochre* (7.78) .. .. 50·00 9·
b. *Buff* .. .. 45·00 9·
148 9d. blue (2.10.71) .. .. .. 16·00 5·
a. Imperf (pair) £160
b. Double print .. .. ..
149 5s. purple (*pen cancel* £3.75) .. .. £140 40·
a. Imperf (pair) .. .. ..
b. *Mauve* .. .. £120 40·

(*b*) *P* 12
150 11 1d. rose .. .. 60·00 5·
a. *Carmine* .. .. 65·00 7·
151 2d. green .. .. £400 95·
a. Imperf (pair) .. .. — £2
152 3d. red-brown .. .. 60·00 14·
a. *Deep red-brown* .. .. .. 60·00 14·
153 4d. buff .. .. £225 15·
154 9d. pale blue .. .. 28·00
155 5s. purple £250
a. *Mauve* £160

(Typo D.L.R.)

1878 (28 Oct). *W* **16**. *P* 14.
156 11 1d. carmine .. .. 2·75
a. *Rose-carmine* .. .. 2·75
b. *Scarlet* .. .. 2·75
157 2d. pale green .. .. 3·00
a. *Green* .. .. 3·00
158 8d. dull purple-brown .. .. .. 14·00 4·

(Typo Govt Printer, Hobart (some printings of 1d. in 1891 b[y] *Mercury* Press) from plates made by Victoria Govt Printe[r], Melbourne (½d.) or D.L.R. (others))

1880 (Apr)–**91**. *W* **16** (*sideways on* 1*d.*). (*a*) *P* 11½.
159 11 ½d. orange (8.3.89) .. .. .. 2·25 1·
a. *Deep orange* .. .. .. 2·25 1·
160 1d. dull red (14.2.89) .. .. .. 3·75 1·
a. *Vermilion-red* .. .. .. 3·00 1·
161 3d. red-brown .. .. 12·00 2·
a. Imperf (pair) £120
162 4d. deep yellow (1.83) .. .. .. 29·00 11·
a. *Chrome-yellow* .. .. .. 29·00 12·
b. *Olive-yellow* .. .. .. 95·00 22·
c. *Buff* .. .. 28·00 9·

(*b*) *P* 12
163 11 ½d. orange .. .. 2·00 2·
a. *Deep orange* .. .. .. 1·90 2·
ab. Wmk sideways .. .. ..
164 1d. pink (1891) .. .. 16·00 2·
a. Imperf (pair) £130 £1
b. *Rosine* .. .. 7·00 1·
c. *Dull rosine* .. .. 9·00 3·
ca. Imperf (pair) £100
165 3d. red-brown .. .. 8·00 3·
a. Imperf between (horiz pair) £500
166 4d. deep yellow .. .. 50·00 12·
a. *Chrome-yellow* .. .. .. 70·00 12·
ab. Printed both sides £275

SPECIMEN AND PRESENTATION REPRINTS OF TYP[E] 11. In 1871 the 1d., 2d., 3d., 4d. blue, 9d., 10d. and 5s. wer[e] reprinted on soft white wove paper to be followed, in 1879, by th[e] 4d. yellow and 8d. on rough white wove. Both these reprinting[s] were perforated 11½. In 1886 it was decided to overpri[nt] remaining stocks with the word "REPRINT".

In 1889 Tasmania commenced sending sample stamps to th[e] U.P.U. in Berne and a further printing of the 4d. blue was mad[e] imperforate, on white card. This, together with the 5s. in mauv[e] on white card, both perforated 11½ and overprinted "RE[-] PRINT", were included in presentation sets supplied to membe[rs] of the states' legislatures in 1901.

Ialfpenny d. 2½ d. 2½

(17) (18) (2¼ mm between "d", and "2") (19) (3½ mm between "d" and "2")

389 (1 Jan). *No. 156b surch locally with T* **17**.
67 **11** ½d. on 1d. scarlet .. .. 8·00 9·00
a. "al" in "Half" printed sideways (R. 1/2) £700 £475

No. 167a occurred in a second printing and was later corrected. A reprint on white card, perforated 11½ or imperforate, overprinted "REPRINT" was produced in 1901.

391 (1 Jan–June). *Surch locally. W* **16**. (a) *With T* **18**. *P* 11½.
68 **11** 2½d. on 9d. pale blue .. .. .. 7·00 3·25
a. Surch double, one inverted .. £250 £275
b. Deep blue (May) .. .. .. 7·50 3·75

(b) *With T* **19**. *P* 12
69 **11** 2½d. on 9d. pale blue (June) .. .. 5·00 3·00
a. Blue surch.. .. ..

A reprint, using a third setting, perforated 11½ and overprinted "REPRINT" was produced in 1901.

(Typo Govt Printer, Hobart)

891 (Apr–Aug). *W* **15**. (a) *P* 11½.
70 **11** ½d. orange .. .. 22·00 7·50
a. Brown-orange .. .. .. 17·00 7·00
71 1d. rosine .. .. 14·00 4·50

(b) *P* 12
72 **11** ½d. orange .. .. 16·00 11·00
a. Imperf (pair) .. .. .. 85·00
73 1d. dull rosine .. .. 18·00 8·50
a. Rosine .. .. 30·00 12·00
74 4d. bistre (Aug).. .. .. .. 15·00 7·50

20

21

21*a*

(Typo D.L.R.)

892 (12 Feb)–**99**. *W* **16**. *P* 14.
16 **20** ½d. orange and mauve (11.92) .. 1·25 50
17 **21** 2½d. purple .. .. 2·50 1·00
18 **20** 5d. pale blue and brown .. .. 4·50 1·60
19 6d. violet and black (11.92) .. .. 5·50 2·00
20 **21a** 10d. purple-lake & deep green (30.1.99) 9·00 7·00
21 **20** 1s. rose and green (11.92) .. .. 6·00 1·75
22 2s. 6d. brown and blue (11.92) .. 22·00 9·00
23 5s. lilac and red (3.2.97) .. .. 38·00 18·00
24 10s. mauve and brown (11.92) .. 75·00 50·00
25 £1 green and yellow (2.97) £225 £150
16/25 .. .. *Set of* 10 £350 £200
16/25 Optd "Specimen" .. .. *Set of* 10 £250

See also Nos. 243 and 257/8.

(Typo Govt Printer, Hobart)

896. *W* **16**. *P* 12.
26 **11** 4d. pale bistre .. .. 12·00 5·50
27 9d. pale blue .. .. 8·00 2·25
a. Blue.. .. .. 8·50 3·25

22 Lake Marion

23 Mount Wellington

24 Hobart

25 Tasman's Arch

26 Spring River, Port Davey

27 Russell Falls

28 Mount Gould, Lake St. Clair

29 Dilston Falls

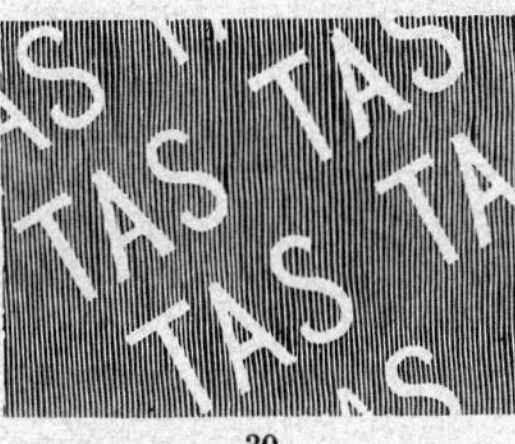

30

(Eng. L. Phillips. Recess D.L.R.)

1899 (Dec)–**1900**. *W* **30**. *P* 14.
229 **22** ½d. deep green (31.3.00) .. .. 7·00 3·50
230 **23** 1d. bright lake (13.12.99)* .. .. 4·50 80
231 **24** 2d. deep violet (15.12.99)* .. .. 9·00 80
232 **25** 2½d. indigo (1900) .. .. .. 10·00 3·75
233 **26** 3d. sepia (1900) .. .. .. 8·00 2·75
234 **27** 4d. deep orange-buff (1900) .. .. 14·00 2·75
235 **28** 5d. bright blue (31.3.00) .. .. 14·00 6·50
236 **29** 6d. lake (31.3.00) .. .. .. 18·00 10·00
229/36 .. .. *Set of* 8 75·00 28·00
229/36 Optd "Specimen" .. .. *Set of* 8 £225

*Earliest known postmark dates.
See also Nos. 237/9, 240/1, 245/8, 249/54, 259 and 261/2.

DIFFERENCES BETWEEN LITHOGRAPHED AND TYPOGRAPHED PRINTINGS OF TYPES 22/9

Lithographed	Typographed
General appearance fine.	*Comparatively crude and coarse appearance.*
½d. All "V over Crown" wmk.	All "Crown over A" wmk.
1d. The shading on the path on the right bank of the river consists of very fine dots. In printings from worn stones the dots hardly show.	The shading on the path is coarser, consisting of large dots and small patches of colour.
The shading on the white mountain is fine (or almost absent in many stamps).	The shading on the mountain is coarse, and clearly defined.
2d. Three rows of windows in large building on shore, at extreme left, against inner frame.	Two rows of windows.
3d. Clouds very white.	Clouds dark.
Stars in corner ornaments have long points.	Stars have short points.
Shading of corner ornaments is defined by a coloured outer line.	Shading of ornaments terminates against white background.
4d. Lithographed only.	—
6d. No coloured dots at base of waterfall.	Coloured dots at base of waterfall.
Outer frame of value tablets is formed by outer line of design.	Thick line of colour between value tablets and outer line.
	Small break in inner frame below second "A" of "TASMANIA".

(Litho, using transfers from D.L.R. plates, Victoria Government Printing Office, Melbourne)

1902 (Jan)–**04**. *Wmk V over Crown, W w* **10** (*sideways on* ½*d.,* 2*d.*). *P* 12½.
237 **22** ½d. green (2.03) .. .. .. 1·25 85
a. Wmk upright .. .. ..
b. Perf 11 .. .. 3·25 2·50
c. Perf comp of 12½ and 11 .. .. 50·00 35·00
d. Perf comp of 12½ and 12 .. ..
238 **23** 1d. carmine-red .. .. .. 5·50 85
239 **24** 2d. deep reddish violet .. .. 4·00 30
a. Perf 11 .. .. 4·00 2·00
b. Perf comp of 12½ and 11 .. .. 55·00 35·00
c. Wmk upright (2.04) .. ..
d. Deep rose-lilac (4.05) .. .. 7·00 10
da. Perf 11 .. .. 6·00 75
db. Perf comp of 12½ and 11 .. ..
237 and 239 Optd "Specimen" .. *Set of* 2 85·00

As the V and Crown paper was originally prepared for stamps of smaller size, portions of two or more watermarks appear on each stamp.

We only list the main groups of shades in this and the following issues. There are variations of shade in all values, particularly in the 2d. where there is a wide range, also in the 1d. in some issues.

(Typo, using electrotyped plates, Victoria Govt Ptg Office, Melbourne)

1902 (Oct)–**04**. *Wmk V over Crown, W w* **10**. *P* 12½.
240 **23** 1d. pale red (*wmk sideways*) .. .. 8·00 90
a. Perf 11 .. .. 22·00 1·00
b. Perf comp of 12½ and 11 .. .. £150 35·00
c. Wmk upright (1.03) .. .. 22·00 5·00
ca. Perf 11 .. .. 27·00 6·00
d. Rose-red (*wmk upright*) (4.03) (Optd S. £40) .. .. 4·00 75
da. Perf 11 .. .. 15·00 75
db. Perf comp of 12½ and 11 .. .. £150 35·00
241 **23** 1d. scarlet (*wmk upright*) (9.03) .. 3·00 30
a. Perf 11 .. .. 4·25 50
b. Perf comp of 12½ and 11 .. ..
c. Rose-scarlet (1904) .. .. 2·50 40
ca. Perf 11 .. .. 3·00 50
cb. Perf comp of 12½ and 11 .. .. 50·00 15·00

The 1d. scarlet of September 1903 was from new electrotyped plates which show less intense shading.

(Typo Victoria Govt Ptg Office, Melbourne)

1903–05. *Wmk V over Crown, W w* **10**. *P* 12½.
242 **11** 9d. blue (1905) .. .. .. 8·00 3·00
a. Perf 11 .. .. 8·00 4·25
b. Perf comp of 12½ and 11 .. .. — £375
c. Wmk sideways .. .. .. 55·00 20·00
d. Pale blue .. .. 9·50 4·00
e. Bright blue .. .. 9·50 4·50
f. Ultramarine £350
g. Indigo £130
243 **20** 1s. rose and green .. .. .. 11·00 3·00
a. Perf 11 .. .. 30·00
242/3 Optd "Specimen" .. .. *Set of* 2 £100

1½d. ONE PENNY

(31) (32)

1904 (29 Dec). *No.* 218 *surch with T* **31**.
244 **20** 1½d. on 5d. pale blue & brn (Optd S. £28) 1·25 60

Stamps with inverted surcharge or without surcharge *se-tenant* with stamps with normal surcharge were obtained irregularly and were not issued for postal use.

PRINTER. The Victoria Govt Ptg Office became the Commonwealth Stamp Printing Branch in March 1909.

(Litho, using transfers from D.L.R. plates, Victoria Govt Ptg Office, Melbourne)

1905 (Sept)–**12**. *Wmk Crown over A, W w* **11** (*sideways on horiz stamps*). *P* 12½.
245 **24** 2d. deep purple .. .. .. 4·00 15
a. Perf 11 .. .. 11·00 20
b. Perf comp of 12½ and 11 .. 17·00 3·00
c. Perf comp of 12½ and 12 .. — 45·00
d. Perf comp of 11 and 12 .. .. 90·00
e. Slate-lilac (1906) .. .. 4·50
ea. Perf 11 .. .. 17·00 25
eb. Perf comp of 12½ and 11 .. ..
ed. Perf comp of 11 and 12 .. ..
f. Reddish lilac (1907) .. .. 11·00 75
fa. Perf 11 .. ..
fb. Perf comp of 12½ and 11 .. ..
246 **26** 3d. brown (5.06) .. .. .. 8·50 2·00
a. Perf 11 .. .. 12·00 4·25
b. Perf comp of 12½ and 11 .. 60·00
247 **27** 4d. pale yellow-brown (3.07) .. 12·00 3·00
a. Perf 11 .. .. 16·00 3·50
b. Orange-buff (5.09) .. .. 12·00 3·00
ba. Perf 11 .. .. 16·00 3·25
bb. Perf comp of 12½ and 11 .. £160
c. Brown-ochre (*wmk sideways*). Perf 11 (6.11) .. .. 24·00 26·00
d. Orange-yellow (3.12) .. .. 15·00 12·00
da. Perf 11 .. .. 25·00 18·00
db. Perf comp of 12½ and 11 .. ..
248 **29** 6d. lake (7.08) .. .. .. 38·00 4·25
a. Perf 11 .. .. 45·00 4·50
b. Perf comp of 12½ and 11 .. £130

Stamps with perf compound of 12½ and 12 or 11 and 12 are found on sheets which were sent from Melbourne incompletely perforated along the outside edge of the pane or sheet. The missing perforations were applied in Hobart using a line machine measuring 12 (11.8 is the exact gauge). This perforation can only occur on one side of a stamp.

(Typo, using electrotyped plates, Victoria Govt Ptg Office, Melbourne)

1905 (Aug)–**11**. *Wmk Crown over A, W w* **11** (*sideways on horiz designs*). *P* 12½.
249 **22** ½d. yellow-green (10.12.08) .. .. 1·25 20
a. Perf 11 .. .. 1·25 20
b. Perf comp of 12½ and 11 .. .. 25·00 5·00
c. Perf comp of 11 and 12 .. .. 65·00
d. Wmk upright (1909) .. .. 5·50 1·75
da. Perf 11 .. ..
250 **23** 1d. rose-red .. .. 1·50 10
a. Perf 11 .. .. 2·75 10
b. Perf comp of 12½ and 11 .. 3·75 1·50
c. Perf comp of 12½ and 12 .. 40·00 5·50
d. Perf comp of 11 and 12 .. .. 45·00 20·00
e. Wmk sideways (1908) .. .. 5·50 75
ea. Perf 11 .. ..
f. Imperf (pair) £140
250*g* 1d. carmine-red (3.10) .. .. 3·25 45
ga. Perf 11 .. .. 5·50 50
gb. Perf comp of 12½ and 11 .. 8·00 4·00
gc. Perf comp of 12½ and 12 .. 40·00
gd. Perf comp of 11 and 12 .. .. 45·00
ge. Imperf (pair) £140
h. Carmine-vermilion (1911) .. 8·50 2·50
ha. Perf 11 .. .. 9·50 2·50
hb. Perf comp of 12½ and 11 .. ..
hc. Perf comp of 12½ and 12 .. ..
hd. Perf comp of 11 and 12 .. ..
251 **24** 2d. plum (8.07) .. .. .. 4·25 10
a. Wmk upright .. .. .. 8·50 90
b. Perf 11 .. .. 2·50 10
ba. Wmk upright (12.07) .. .. 8·50 90
c. Perf comp of 12½ and 11 .. 20·00 6·00
d. Perf comp of 12½ and 12 .. £110 45·00
e. Perf comp of 11 and 12 .. .. 70·00 38·00
f. Bright reddish violet (1910) .. 3·00 80
fa. Perf 11 .. .. 3·25 50
fb. Perf comp of 12½ and 11 .. ..

253 **26** 3d. brown (3.09) .. 6·50 2·50
a. Wmk upright
b. Perf 11 .. 12·00 3·00
c. Perf comp of 12½ and 11 .. £130
254 **29** 6d. carmine-lake (12.10) .. 16·00 16·00
a. Perf 11 .. 20·00 20·00
b. Perf comp of 12½ and 11 .. £180
c. *Dull carmine-red* (3.11) .. 22·00 20·00
ca. Wmk upright .. 27·00
cb. Perf 11 .. 23·00 20·00
cc. Perf comp of 12½ and 11 .. £150

The note after No. 248 re perfs compound with perf 12 also applies here.

Nos. 250/f were printed from the same plates as Nos. 241/cb. Nos. 250g/hd are from a further pair of new plates and the images are sharper.

(Typo Victoria Govt Printing Office, Melbourne)

1906–13. *Wmk Crown over A*, W w **11**. *P* 12½.
255 **11** 8d. purple-brown (1907) .. 17·00 4·75
a. Perf 11 .. 15·00 3·50
256 9d. blue (1907) .. 7·00 2·75
a. Perf 11 .. 7·00 2·75
b. Perf comp of 12½ and 11 (1909) .. 55·00
c. Perf comp of 12½ and 12 (1909) .. £110
d. Perf comp of 11 and 12 .. £190
257 **20** 1s. rose and green (1907) .. 12·00 2·75
a. Perf 11 (1907) .. 16·00 8·00
b. Perf comp of 12½ and 11 .. 22·00
c. Perf comp of 12½ and 12 .. 65·00
258 10s. mauve and brown (1906) .. £110 £100
a. Perf 11 .. £170
b. Perf comp of 12½ and 12 .. £170

The note after No. 248 *re* perfs compound with perf 12, also applies here.

(Typo, using stereotyped plates, Commonwealth Stamp Ptg Branch, Melbourne)

1911 (Jan). *Wmk Crown over A*, W w **11** (*sideways*). *P* 12½.
259 **24** 2d. bright violet .. 4·50 1·40
a. Wmk upright .. 15·00 2·50
b. Perf 11 .. 4·75 1·50
c. Perf comp of 12½ and 11 .. 50·00 15·00
d. Perf comp of 12½ and 12 .. £150

Stamps from this stereotyped plate differ from No. 251 in the width of the design (33 to 33¾ mm, against just over 32 mm), in the taller, bolder letters of "TASMANIA", in the slope of the mountain in the left background, which is clearly outlined in white, and in the outer vertical frame-line at left, which appears "wavy". Compare Nos. 260, etc, which are always from this plate.

1912 (Oct) *No.* 259 *surch with T* **32**. *P* 12½.
260 **24** 1d. on 2d. bright violet (R.) .. 90 30
a. Perf 11 .. 1·50 40
b. Perf comp of 12½ and 11 .. 85·00 85·00

(Typo, using electrotyped plates, Commonwealth Stamp Ptg Branch, Melbourne)

1912 (Dec). *Thin paper, white gum (as Victoria*, 1912). W w **11** (*sideways on 3d.*). *P* 12½.
261 **23** 1d. carmine-vermilion .. 16·00 5·00
a. Perf 11 .. 16·00 5·00
b. Perf comp of 12½ and 11 ..
262 **26** 3d. brown .. 40·00 45·00

STAMP BOOKLETS

There are very few surviving examples of Nos. SB1/4. Listings are provided for those believed to have been issued with prices quoted for those known to still exist.

1904 (1 Jan)–**09.** *Black on red cover as No.* SB1 *of New South Wales. Stapled.*
SB1 £1 booklet containing two hundred and forty 1d. in twelve blocks of 20 (5×4) ..
a. Red on pink cover (1909) ..
b. Blue on pink cover ..

1904 (1 Jan). *Black on grey cover as No.* SB1. *Stapled.*
SB2 £1 booklet containing one hundred and twenty 2d. in four blocks of 30 ..

1910 (May). *Black on white cover as No.* SB3 *of New South Wales. Stapled.*
SB3 2s. booklet containing eleven ½d. (No. 249), either in block of 6 plus block of 5 or block of 11, and eighteen 1d. (No. 250), either in three blocks of 6 or block of 6 plus block of 12 .. £2000

Unsold stock No. SB3 was uprated with one additional ½d. in May 1911.

1911 (Aug). *Red on pink cover as No.* SB3. *Stapled.*
SB4 2s. booklet containing twelve ½d. (No. 249), either in two blocks of 6 or block of 12, and eighteen 1d. (No. 250), either in three blocks of 6 or block of 6 plus block of 12 .. £1500

POSTAL FISCAL STAMPS

VALIDITY. Nos. F1/29 were authorised for postal purposes on 1 November 1882.

CLEANED STAMPS. Beware of postal fiscal stamps with pen-cancellations removed.

F 1

F 2

F 3

F 4

(Recess Alfred Bock, Hobart)

1863–80. *Wmk double-lined* "1", W **4**. (*a*) *Imperf.*
F 1 **F 1** 3d. green (1.65) .. 60·00 40·00
F 2 **F 2** 2s. 6d. carmine (11.63) .. 65·00 40·00
F 3 2s. 6d. lake (5.80) ..
F 4 **F 3** 5s. brown (1.64) .. £160 £130
F 5 5s. sage-green (1880) .. 65·00 48·00
F 6 **F 4** 10s. orange (1.64) .. £225 £130
F 7 10s. salmon (5.80) .. £160 £130

(*b*) *P* 10
F 8 **F 1** 3d. green .. 38·00 20·00
F 9 **F 2** 2s. 6d. carmine .. 40·00
F10 **F 3** 5s. brown .. 60·00
F11 **F 4** 10s. orange .. 40·00

(*c*) *P* 12
F12 **F 1** 3d. green .. 40·00 24·00
F13 **F 2** 2s. 6d. carmine .. 40·00 32·00
F14 **F 3** 5s. brown .. 70·00
F15 5s. sage-green .. 29·00 24·00
F16 **F 4** 10s. orange .. 40·00 32·00
F17 10s. salmon .. 30·00 24·00

(*d*) *P* 12½
F18 **F 1** 3d. green .. 70·00
F19 **F 2** 2s. 6d. carmine .. 70·00
F20 **F 3** 5s. brown .. 90·00
F21 **F 4** 10s. orange-brown .. 60·00

(*e*) *P* 11½
F22 **F 1** 3d. green ..
F23 **F 2** 2s. 6d. lake .. 38·00 30·00
F24 **F 3** 5s. sage-green .. 30·00 20·00
F25 **F 4** 10s. salmon .. 50·00 38·00

See also No. F30.

In 1879, the 3d., 2s. 6d., 5s. (brown), and 10s. (orange) were reprinted on thin, tough, white paper, and are found with or without "REPRINT". In 1889 another reprint was made on white card, imperforate and perforated 12. These are also found with or without "REPRINT".

F 5 Duck-billed Platypus

REVENUE

(F 6)

(Typo D.L.R.)

1880 (19 Apr). W **16** (*sideways*). *P* 14.
F26 **F 5** 1d. slate .. 10·00 3·50
F27 3d. chestnut .. 10·00 2·75
F28 6d. mauve .. 60·00 2·00
F29 1s. rose-pink .. 70·00 5·00
a. Perf comp of 14 and 11 ..

All values are known imperf, but not used.

Reprints are known of the 1d. in *deep blue* and the 6d. in lilac. The former is on yellowish white, the latter on white card. Both values also exist on wove paper, perf 12, with the word "REPRINT".

1888 (Aug). W **16**. *P* 12.
F30 **F 2** 2s. 6d. lake .. 15·00 11·00
a. Imperf between (horiz pair) .. £450

1900 (15 Nov). *Optd with Type* **F 6**. (*a*) *On Types* **F 2** *and* **F 4**.
F31 **F 2** 2s. 6d. carmine (No. F13) ..
a. "REVFNUE" ..
F32 2s. 6d. lake (No. F30) .. £160
a. "REVFNUE" .. £250
b. Opt inverted .. £350
c. Imperf .. £170
F33 **F 4** 10s. salmon (No. F17) ..
a. "REVFNUE" ..

(*b*) *On Nos.* F27 *and* F29
F34 **F 5** 3d. chestnut .. 15·00 15·00
a. Double opt, one vertical .. 75·00 £100
F35 1s. rose-pink ..

(*c*) *On stamps as Nos.* F26/9, *but typo locally.* W **16**. *P* 12
F36 **F 5** 1d. blue .. 18·00
a. Imperf between (horiz pair) .. £300
b. "REVENUE" inverted .. £100
c. "REVENUE" double .. £160
d. *Pale blue* .. 18·00
F37 6d. mauve .. 50·00
a. Double print .. £200
F38 1s. pink .. 75·00

(*d*) *On No.* 225
F39 **20** £1 green and yellow .. £150 £130
a. Opt double, one vertical .. £275 £275

It was not intended that stamps overprinted with Type **F 6** should be used for postal purposes, but an ambiguity in regulations permitted such usage until all postal fiscal stamps were invalidated on 30 November 1900.

Printings of some of the above with different watermarks together with a 2d. as Nos. F36/8, did not appear until after the stamps had become invalid for postal purposes.

Tasmania became part of the Commonwealth of Australia on 1 January 1901.

VICTORIA

PRICES FOR STAMPS ON COVER

Nos. 1/17	*from* × 2
Nos. 18/22	*from* × 4
Nos. 23/4	*from* × 2
No. 25	*from* × 3
Nos. 26/32	*from* × 2
No. 33	*from* × 6
No. 34	*from* × 8
Nos. 35/9	*from* × 4
No. 40	*from* × 3
Nos. 41/53	*from* × 2
No. 54	*from* × 3
No. 55	—
No. 56	*from* × 4
Nos. 57/72	*from* × 2
No. 73	*from* × 3
Nos. 74/80	*from* × 2
No. 81	*from* × 3
Nos. 82/7	*from* × 4
Nos. 88/200	*from* × 3
Nos. 201/6	*from* × 5
Nos. 207/8	*from* × 10
Nos. 209/14	*from* × 5
Nos. 215/19	—
Nos. 220/6	*from* × 20
Nos. 227/33	—
Nos. 234/7	*from* × 20
Nos. 238/52	—
Nos. 253/6	*from* × 20
No. 257	*from* × 10
No. 258	*from* × 20
No. 259	*from* × 10
Nos. 260/4	—
Nos. 265/6	*from* × 20
Nos. 267/73	*from* × 10
Nos. 274/91	—
Nos. 292/304	*from* × 10
Nos. 305/9	*from* × 5
Nos. 310/23	*from* × 10
Nos. 324/8	—
No. 329	*from* × 12
Nos. 330/50	*from* × 8
Nos. 351/2	—
Nos. 353/4	*from* × 4
No. 355	*from* × 10
Nos. 356/73	*from* × 15
Nos. 374/5	*from* × 3
Nos. 376/98	*from* × 10
Nos. 399/400	—
Nos. 401/6	*from* × 10
Nos. 407/15	—
Nos. 416/30	*from* × 10
Nos. 431/2	—
Nos. 433/43	*from* × 4
Nos. 444/53	—
Nos. 454/5	*from* × 10
Nos. 456/63	*from* × 6
No. 464	—
Nos. D1/8	*from* × 30
Nos. D9/10	—
Nos. D11/37	*from* × 30

SPECIMEN OVERPRINTS. Those listed are from U.P.U. distributions in 1892 and 1897. Further "Specimen" overprints exist, but these were used for other purposes.

During the expansion of the Australian settlements in the fourth decade of the nineteenth century the growing population of the Port Phillip District in the south of New South Wales led to a movement for its creation as a separate colony. This aspiration received the approval of the British Government in 1849, but the colony of Victoria, as it was to be called, was not to be created until 1 July 1851.

In the meantime the New South Wales Legislative Council voted for the introduction of postal reforms, including the use of postage stamps, from 1 January 1850, and this act was also to apply to the Port Phillip District where stamps inscribed "VICTORIA" would predate the creation of that colony by eighteen months.

Until the end of 1859 the stamps of Victoria, with the exception of Nos. 40 and 73, were produced by local contractors working under the supervision of the colonial administration.

HAM PRINTINGS. The first contractor was Thomas Ham of Melbourne. He was responsible for the initial printings of the "Half-Length" 1d., 2d. and 3d., together with the replacement "Queen on Throne" 2d. The first printings were produced from small sheets of 30 (5×6) laid down directly from the engraved die which showed a single example of each value. Subsequent printings, of which No. 4*a* was the first, were in sheets of 120 (two panes of 60) laid down using intermediate stones of various sizes. Impressions from the first printings were fine and clear, but the quality deteriorated when intermediate stones were used.

1 Queen Victoria ("Half Length")

(Lithographed by Thomas Ham, Melbourne)

1850 (3 Jan)–**53**. *Imperf.*

1d. Thin line at top

2d. Fine border and background

3d. White area to left of orb

(*a*) *Original state of dies: 1d. (tops of letters of* "VICTORIA" *reach to top of stamp); 2d. (fine border and background); 3d. (thicker white outline around left of orb, central band of orb does not protrude at left). No frame-lines on dies.*

1 1 1d. orange-vermilion £7500 £1500
a. Orange-brown .. .. .. † £750
b. Dull chocolate-brown (shades) £3500 £850
2 2d. lilac-mauve (*shades*) (Stone A) £2250 £400
3 2d. brown-lilac (*shades*) (Stone B) £2250 £250
a. Grey-lilac .. .. .. — £250
4 3d. bright blue (*shades*) £1800 £300
a. Blue (shades) £1800 £170
ab. Retouched (between Queen's head and right border) (No. 11 in transfer-group) (8 varieties) .. .. .. — £275
ac. Retouched (under "V") (No. 10 in transfer group) .. .. .. — £275

With the exception of No. 4*a* the above were printed from small stones of 30 (5×6) laid down directly from the engraved die which showed a single example of each value. There were two stones of the 2d. and one for each of the other values. No. 4*a* is the second printing of the 3d. for which the sheet size was increased to 120, the printing stone being constructed from an intermediate stone of 15 (5×3).

1d. Thick line at top

2d. Coarse background

3d. White area small and band protruding to left of orb

(*b*) *Second state of dies: 1d. (more colour over top of letters of* "VICTORIA"*); 2d. (fine border as (a) but with coarse background); 3d. (thinner white outline around left of orb, central band of orb protrudes at left).*

5 1 1d. red-brown (*shades*) (2.50) £2750 £300
a. Pale dull red-brown £2000 £300
6 2d. grey-lilac (*shades*) (1.50) £1100 £100
a. Dull grey £1100 £110
7 3d. blue (*shades*) (6.51) £1000 £110
a. Retouched (22 varieties) .. *from* £1600 £225

Printed in sheets of 120 (10×12) with the printing stones constructed from intermediate stones of 30 (5×6) for the 1d. and 2d. or 10 (5×2) for the 3d. It is believed that the use of the smaller intermediate stone for the latter resulted in the many retouches.

Frame-lines added

(*c*) *Third state of dies: As in (b) but with frame-lines added, very close up, on all four sides.*

8 1 1d. dull orange-vermilion (11.50) £1300 £400
a. Dull red (shades) £1000 £120
9 1d. deep red-brown (5.51) .. .. .. — £450
a. Brownish red (shades) £650 £110
b. Dull rose (shades) £650 £110
10 2d. grey (*shades*) (8.50) £850 £130
a. Olive-grey (shades) £1000 £130
11 3d. blue (*shades*) (12.52) .. .. .. £400 50·00
a. Deep blue (shades) .. .. .. £500 50·00
b. Pale greenish blue (shades) £650 £100

Printed in sheets of 120 (12×10) produced from intermediate stones of 30 (6×5) for No. 8 and 12 (6×2) for the others.

White veil

(*d*) *As (c) but altered to give, for the 1d. and 3d., the so-called "white veils", and for the 2d., the effect of vertical drapes to the veil.*

12 1 1d. reddish brown (6.51) £700 £100
a. Bright pinky red (shades) £450 £100
13 2d. drab (1.51) £1000 £110
a. Grey-drab £1000 £110
b. Lilac-drab .. .. .. — £110
c. Red-lilac .. .. .. — £500
d. Void lower left corner .. .. —£1800
14 3d. blue (*shades*) (1.53) .. .. .. £400 45·00
a. Deep blue (shades) .. .. .. £400 45·00
b. Greenish blue (shades) .. .. £500 50·00
c. Retouched (9 varieties) £750 £120

Printed in sheets of 120 (12×10) produced from intermediate stones of 12 (6×2) on which the details of the veil were amended as described above.

The "void corner" error occurred on the printing stone. It is believed that only four examples still exist.

2d. Coarse border and background

(*e*) *Fourth state of 2d. die only: Coarse border and background. Veil details as in original die.*

15 1 2d. red-lilac (*shades*) (5.50) £600 £180
a. Lilac £600 £180
b. Grey .. .. .. — £275
c. Dull brownish lilac £400 £100
d. Retouched lower label—value omitted *from* —£1800
e. Other retouches (17 varieties) *from* £1000 £225

Printed in sheets of 120 (12×10) produced from an intermediate stone of 30 (6×5).

(*f*) *2d. as (e), but with veils altered to give effect of vertical drapes.*

16 1 2d. lilac-grey (1.51) £750 £110
a. Deep grey £850 £110
b. Brown-lilac (shades) .. .. £600 60·00
17 2d. cinnamon (*shades*) (2.51) .. .. £500 95·00
a. Drab (shades) .. .. .. £550 60·00
b. Pale dull brown (shades) .. .. £650 70·00
c. Greenish grey .. .. .. £500 60·00
d. Olive-drab (shades) £600 £120
e. Buff .. .. .. † £130

Printed in sheets of 120 (12×10) produced from two successive intermediate stones of 30 (6×5) on which the details of the veils were amended as described above.

This was the final printing of the 2d. "Half Length" as the die for this value had been damaged. A replacement 2d. design was ordered from Thomas Ham.

For the later printings of the 1d. and 3d. in this design see Nos. 23/4, 26/31, 48/9 and 78/9.

2 Queen on Throne

3

(Recess-printed by Thomas Ham)

1852 (27 Dec). *Imperf.*

18 2 2d. reddish brown .. .. .. £160 22·00
a. Chestnut .. .. .. — £110
b. Purple-brown .. .. .. £225 22·00

Printed in sheets of 50 (10×5) from a hand-engraved plate of the same size. Each stamp in the sheet had individual corner letters made-up of various combinations, none of which contained the letter "J".

Reprints were made in 1891 using the original plate, on paper wmk V over Crown, both imperf and perf 12½.

For later printings of this design see Nos. 19/22 and 36/9.

CAMPBELL & CO PRINTINGS. In May 1853 the Victoria postal authorities placed an order for 1d. and 6d. stamps in the "Queen on Throne" design with Perkins, Bacon in London. These would not arrive for some time, however, and supplies of Ham's printings were rapidly becoming exhausted. Local tenders were, therefore, solicited for further supplies of the 1d. and 3d. "Half Lengths" and the 2d. "Queen on Throne". That received from J. S. Campbell & Co was accepted. The stamps were produced by lithography, using transfers from either the "Half Length" engraved die or the 2d. "Queen on Throne" engraved plate of 50. Stamps from the Campbell & Co printings can be distinguished from later printings in lithography by the good quality paper used.

(Lithographed by J. S. Campbell & Co, Melbourne, using transfers taken from Ham's engraved plate)

1854 (Jan–July). *Good quality white or toned paper. Imperf.*

(*a*) *Clear impressions with details around back of throne generally complete*

19 2 2d. brownish purple .. .. .. £170 22·00
a. Grey-brown .. .. .. £250 22·00
b. Purple-black .. .. .. — 22·00
c. Dull lilac-brown (toned paper only) .. £300 40·00

(*b*) *Poor impressions with details around back of throne not fully defined*

20 2 2d. violet-black (2.54) .. .. .. £250 22·00
a. Grey-black .. .. .. £350 24·00
b. Grey-lilac .. .. .. £250 24·00
c. Dull brown (on toned) .. .. £250 24·00
ca. Substituted transfer (in pair) .. .. —£2000

(*c*) *Weak impressions with background generally white without details. Toned paper only*

21 2 2d. grey-purple (7.54) .. .. .. £130 20·00
a. Purple-black .. .. .. £130 20·00

(*d*) *Printings using an intermediate stone. Impression flat and blurred. Background details usually complete. Toned paper only*

22 2 2d. grey-drab (*shades*) (5.54) .. .. £225 19·00
a. Black .. .. .. — £100

Nos. 19/21 were produced using transfers taken directly from the original Ham engraved plate. It is believed that the different strengths of the impressions were caused by the amount of pressure exerted when the tranfers were taken. The stamps were printed in sheets of 100 (2 panes 10×5). On one stone a block of four at bottom left, lettered "FL GM" over "QV RW", was damaged and the stone was repaired by using a block of four substituted transfers. These were lettered "VZ WA" over "FL GM". No. 20ca covers any one of these substituted transfers in pair with normal. As horizontal pairs these are lettered "WA HN" or "GM SX" and as vertical "VZ" over "VZ" or "WA" over "WA".

For No. 22 an intermediate stone was used to produce a printing stone of 300 (6 panes 10×5). The insertion of a further stage into the process caused the blurred appearance of stamps from this printing. No. 22*a* is believed to come from proof sheets issued to post offices for normal use. Examples are usually cancelled with Barred Oval 108 and Barred Numerals 1 and 2.

(Lithographed by J. S. Campbell & Co, Melbourne)

1854 (Feb–June). *Good quality wove paper. Imperf.*

23 1 1d. orange-red (*shades*) £450 £110
a. Rose £2000 £275
24 3d. blue (*shades*) (6.54) .. .. £475 32·00
a. Retouch under "C" of "VICTORIA" .. — £120

The 1d. was produced in sheets of 192 (two panes of 96 (12×8)) and the 3d. in sheets of 320 (two panes of 160 (18×9)). Both printing stones were constructed from transfers taken from intermediate stones of 24 (6×4). The spacing between stamps is far wider than on the Ham printings. The 3d. panes of 160 were constructed using six complete transfers of 24 and three of 6 with the final impression in the bottom two rows removed.

The 1d. Campbell printings have the frame lines almost completely absent due to lack of pressure when taking transfers.

The 3d. retouch, No. 24a, occurs on R.3/5 of the intermediate stone.

CAMPBELL AND FERGUSSON PRINTINGS. Increased postal rates in early 1854 led to a requirement for a 1s. value and in April a contract for this stamp was awarded to Campbell and Fergusson (the new corporate style of J. S. Campbell & Co). Further contracts to print the 1d. and 3d. "Half Lengths" and the 2d. "Queen on Throne" followed. All were produced by lithography with the two "Half Lengths" using transfers from the original engraved die and the 2d. "Queen on Throne" transfers from Ham's original engraved plate.

All Campbell and Fergusson printings were on paper of a poorer quality than that used for the earlier contract.

(Lithographed by Campbell & Fergusson)

1854 (6 July). *Poorer quality paper. Imperf.*

25 3 1s. blue (*shades*) .. .. .. £650 22·00
a. Greenish blue .. .. .. £750 22·00
b. Indigo-blue .. .. .. — £110

No. 25 was produced in sheets of 100 (8×12 with an additional stamp appearing at the end of Rows 6 to 9). The printing stones used each contained four such sheets. They were constructed from an intermediate stone of 40 (8×5) taken from a single engraved die. Each pane of 100 showed two complete transfers of 40, one of 20 and one of a vertical strip of 4.

For this stamp rouletted or perforated see Nos. 54 and 81.

(Lithographed by Campbell & Fergusson)

1854 (July)–**57**. *Poorer quality paper. Imperf.*

26 1 1d. brown (*shades*) .. .. .. £450 95·00
a. Brick-red (shades) .. .. £600 75·00
b. Dull red (shades) .. .. £650 75·00
27 1d. orange-brown (*shades*) (8.55) .. £400 £100
a. Dull rose-red (shades) .. .. £400 60·00
b. Bright rose-pink £500 £100
c. Retouched (6 varieties) £1400 £400

28 1 1d. pink (*shades*) (2.55) .. .. £375 32·00
a. Rose (*shades*) .. .. £375 32·00
b. Lilac-rose (*shades*) .. .. .. £400 32·00
c. Dull brown-red (*shades*) .. .. — £110
d. Retouched (8 varieties) £750 £325
29 3d. bright blue (*shades*) (7.57) .. .. £425 50·00
a. Greenish blue (*shades*) .. .. £375 40·00
b. Retouch under "C" of "VICTORIA" .. — 95·00
30 3d. Prussian blue (*shades*) (11.56) .. £500 70·00
a. Milky blue £750 £110
b. Retouch under "C" of "VICTORIA" .. — £225
31 3d. steel-blue (*shades*) (*heavier impression*) (5.55) .. .. — 42·00
a. Greenish blue (*shades*) .. .. £350 30·00
b. Blue (*shades*) .. .. £350 30·00
c. Deep blue (*shades*) .. .. .. £350 30·00
d. Indigo (*shades*) .. .. .. — 38·00

The 1d. was produced in sheets of 400 (2 panes 20×10) constructed from transfers originating from the J. S. Campbell & Co intermediate stone. Each pane contained six complete tranfers of 24, three of 12, two of 8 and one of 4.

The 3d. was produced in sheets of 320 (2 panes of 160) (No. 29), 200 (No. 30) or 400 (2 panes of 200) (No. 31.) The stone for No. 29 was constructed from transfers taken from the J. S. Campbell intermediate stone with the retouch on R.3/5 still present. The panes of 160 contained six transfers of 24 and three of 6 with the last impression in both rows 8 and 9 removed. Quality of impression is generally poor. The stone for No. 30, once again taken from the Campbell intermediate stone, was laid down in the same combination of transfers as the 1d. value. Impressions from it were, however, so poor that transfers from a new intermediate stone were used for No. 31. Impressions from this stone, on which the panes of 200 were in a similar layout to the 1d., were much further apart than those on the stones used to produce Nos. 29/30.

The Campbell and Fergusson printings of the "Half Lengths" are listed in the order in which they were printed.

CALVERT PRINTINGS. Contracts for the provision of other values required by the postal rate changes in 1853 were placed with Samuel Calvert of Melbourne who used typography as the printing process. Calvert continued to print, and later roulette, stamps for the Victoria Post Office until March 1858 when it was discovered that he had placed some of the stock in pawn.

4

5

6

(Typographed from woodblocks by Samuel Calvert)

1854 (1 Sept)–**55.** *Imperf.*
32 4 6d. reddish brown (13.9.54) .. .. £225 25·00
a. Dull orange .. .. £180 18·00
b. Orange-yellow .. .. £180 19·00
33 5 6d. ("TOO LATE") lilac and green (1.1.55) £650 £130
34 6 1s. ("REGISTERED") rose-pink and blue (1.12.54) £800 £100
35 4 2s. dull bluish green/*pale yellow* £1100 £130

No. 33 was provided to pay the additional fee on letters posted after the normal closure of the mails. This service was only available in the larger towns; examples are usually postmarked Castlemaine, Geelong or Melbourne. The service was withdrawn on 30 June 1857 and remaining stocks of the "TOO LATE" stamps were used for normal postal purposes.

No. 34 was issued to pay the registration fee and was so used until 5 January 1858 after which remaining stocks were used for normal postage.

These four values were produced from individually-engraved boxwood woodblocks. The 6d. was in sheets of 100 printed by two impressions from two plates of 25. The 2s. was in sheets of 50 from a single plate of 25. The bicoloured "TOO LATE" and "REGISTERED" stamps are unusual in that Calvert used a common woodblock "key" plate of 25 for both values combined with "duty" plates made up from metal stereos. Both values were originally in sheets of 50, but the "REGISTERED" later appeared in sheets of 100 for which a second "key" plate of 25 was utilised.

For these stamps roulettted or perforated see Nos. 53, 55/8, 60/1 and 82.

(Lithographed by Campbell & Fergusson)

1855 (Mar)–**56.** *Poorer quality paper. Imperf.*

(*a*) *Printings from stones which were not over-used; background around top of throne generally full and detail good*
36 2 2d. lilac (*shades*) (7.55) .. .. .. £140 19·00
a. Purple (*shades*) .. .. .. £140 19·00
b. "TVO" for "TWO" £2500 £600

(*b*) *Early printings from stones which were over-used. Similar characteristics to those above, though detail is not quite so full. Distinctive shades.*
37 2 2d. brown .. .. — 70·00
a. Brown-purple .. .. .. £170 22·00
b. Warm purple .. .. — 22·00
c. Rose-lilac .. .. — 22·00
d. Substituted transfer (pair) .. .. — £600

(*c*) *Later printings from the same stones used for No. 37 when in a worn condition. Impressions heavy, coarse and overcoloured; details blurred; generally white background around top of throne.*
38 2 2d. dull lilac-mauve (1856) .. .. £170 22·00
a. Dull mauve .. .. £170 22·00
b. Grey-violet .. .. — 22·00
c. Red-lilac .. .. — 24·00
d. Substituted transfer (pair) .. .. — £600

(*d*) *Printings from a stone giving blotchy and unpleasing results, with poor definition. Mainly shows in extra colour patches found on most stamps.*
39 2 2d. dull purple (7.55) .. .. .. — 40·00
a. Dull grey-lilac .. .. .. £180 40·00
b. On thick card paper .. .. .. — £500

The Campbell and Fergusson 2d. "Queen on Throne" printings were in sheets of 200 (4 panes 10 × 5) constructed from transfers taken from the original Ham engraved plate.

Four separate stones were used. On Stone A a creased transfer running through R.4/8, 4/9 and 5/8 caused the "TVO" variety on the stamp from the bottom row of one pane. On Stone C the impression in the first vertical row of one pane were found to be so faulty that they were replaced by substituted transfers taken from elsewhere on the sheet causing abnormal horizontal pairs lettered "UY BF", "TX MQ", "DI WA", "SW GM" and "CH RW". The vertical pairs from the substituted transfers are lettered "UY" over "TX" and "DI" over "SW".

7 Queen on Throne

8 "Emblems"

(Recess Perkins, Bacon & Co, London)

1856 (23 Oct). *Wmk Large Star, W* w **1**. *Imperf.*
40 7 1d. yellow-green .. .. £120 19·00

Supplies of this stamp, and the accompanying 6d. which was only issued rouletted (see No. 73), arrived in the colony at the end of 1854, but the 1d. was not placed on sale until almost two years later.

No. 40 was reprinted from the original plate in 1891. Examples, in either dull yellow-green or bright blue-green, are imperforate and on V over Crown watermarked paper.

(Typographed from electrotypes by Calvert)

1857 (26 Jan–6 Sept). *Imperf.* (*a*) *Wmk Large Star, W* w **1**
41 8 1d. yellow-green (18 Feb) .. .. .. 95·00 13·00
a. Deep green .. .. £110 26·00
b. Printed on both sides .. .. .. † £700
42 4d. vermilion .. .. £250 10·00
a. Brown-vermilion .. .. .. £225 9·00
b. Printed on both sides .. .. .. † £700
43 4d. dull red (20 July) .. .. .. £160 7·50
44 4d. dull rose (6 Sept) .. .. .. £225 7·50

(*b*) *No wmk. Good quality medium wove paper*
45 8 2d. pale lilac (25 May) .. .. .. £170 10·00
a. Grey-lilac .. .. £170 10·00

Nos. 41/5 were produced in sheets of 120, arranged as four panes of 30 (6×5) (1d. and 4d.) or twelve panes of 10 (2×5) (2d.), using electrotypes taken from a single engraved die of each value. The setting of the 4d. was re-arranged before the printing of Nos. 43/4.

Only two examples of No. 41b and No. 42b have been recorded.

For this printing roulettted or perforated see Nos. 46/7, 50/2, 59, 74 and 77.

ROULETTES AND PERFORATIONS. In August 1857 a rouletting machine was provided at the G.P.O., Melbourne, to enable the counter clerks to separate stamp stocks before sale to the public. This machine produced roulettes of 7½–9 in one direction across six rows at a time. There was also a single wheel device which gauged 7–7½. Both were in use between the earliest known date of 12 August and the end of 1857.

Calvert was granted a separate contract in October 1857 to roulette the stamps he printed, but only Nos. 57/61 had been produced when it was found, in April 1858, that he had pawned a quantity of the sheets. His contracts were terminated and his successor, F. W. Robinson, used a roulette machine of a different gauge before switching to a gauge 12 perforating machine in January 1859.

1857 (12 Aug–Sept). *Rouletted 7–9 by counter clerks at G.P.O., Melbourne.*
46 8 1d. yellow-green (No. 41) .. .. .. £300 65·00
47 2d. pale lilac (No. 45) .. .. .. — £225
a. Grey-lilac .. .. — £225
48 1 3d. blue (*shades*) (No. 24) .. .. .. — £180
a. Retouch under "C" of "VICTORIA" ..
49 3d. bright blue (*shades*) (No. 29) .. .. — £190
a. Greenish blue (*shades*) £1000 £170
b. Retouch under "C" of "VICTORIA" ..
50 8 4d. vermilion (No. 42) .. .. .. — £100
51 4d. dull red (No. 43) .. .. .. — 38·00
52 4d. dull rose (No. 44) (Sept) .. .. — 26·00
53 4 6d. reddish brown (No. 32) .. .. — 42·00
a. Dull orange .. .. — 35·00
b. Orange-yellow .. .. .. — 42·00
54 3 1s. blue (*shades*) (No. 25) .. .. .. — 80·00
a. Greenish blue .. .. — 80·00
55 6 1s. ("REGISTERED") rose-pink and blue (No. 34) £3500 £180
56 4 2s. dull bluish green/*pale yellow* (No. 35) £3500 £350

With the exception of the 1s., Nos. 54/a, these stamps are normally found rouletted on one or two sides only.

1857 (Oct). *Rouletted by Calvert.* (*a*) *Rouletted 7–9 on all four sides and with finer points than No. 53b*
57 4 6d. orange-yellow (No. 32*b*) .. .. — 55·00

(*b*) *Serpentine roulette 10–10½*
58 4 6d. orange-yellow (No. 32*b*) .. .. — 60·00

(*c*) *Serrated 18–19*
59 8 2d. grey-lilac (No. 45*a*) £500 £350
60 4 6d. orange-yellow (No. 32*b*) .. .. — 60·00

(*d*) *Compound of serrated 18–19 and serpentine 10–10½*
61 4 6d. orange-yellow (No. 32*b*) .. .. — 60·00

No. 59 was not covered by the contract given to Calvert, but it is believed to be a test run for the rouletting machine. No. 61 always shows serrated 18–19 on three sides and the serpentine roulette at the top or bottom of the stamp.

(Typo from electrotypes by Calvert)

1858 (14 Jan–Apr). *No wmk. Good quality white wove paper.*

(*a*) *Rouletted 7–9 on all four sides*
62 8 1d. pale emerald .. .. £300 15·00
a. Emerald-green .. .. £300 15·00
63 4d. rose-pink (18 Jan) .. .. .. £200 6·00
a. Bright rose .. .. £200 6·00
b. Reddish pink .. .. — 11·00
c. Imperf horiz (vert pair) .. .. † £40

(*b*) *Imperf* (Apr)
64 8 1d. pale emerald .. .. £190 11·00
a. Emerald-green .. .. — 14·00
65 4d. rose-pink .. .. £250 23·00
a. Bright rose .. .. — 23·00
b. Reddish pink .. .. — 30·00

Nos. 62/5 were produced in sheets of 120, arranged as four panes of 30 (6×5).

The Royal Collection contains a used horizontal pair of the 4d. showing the vertical roulettes omitted.

The majority of Nos. 64/5 were issued in April after Calvert's contracts had been terminated, although there is some evidence that imperforate sheets of the 4d., at least, were issued earlier.

For the 1d. of this issue perforated see No. 75.

ROBINSON PRINTINGS. Calvert's contracts were cancelled in April 1858 and the work was then placed with F. W. Robinson, who had unsuccessfully tendered in 1856. The same electrotypes were used, but a perforating machine was introduced from January 1859. Robinson continued to print and perforate stamps under contract until the end of 1859 when the Victoria Post Office purchased his equipment to set up a Stamp Printing Branch and appointed him Printer of Postage Stamps.

(Typo from electrotypes by Robinson)

1858 (May–Dec). (*a*) *Imperf.* (i) *Coarse quality wove paper.*
66 8 4d. dull rose (*oily ink*) .. .. .. — 60·00

(ii) *Smooth vertically-laid paper*
67 8 4d. dull rose (*oily ink*) .. .. .. — 23·00
a. Dull rose-red .. .. — 23·00
68 4d. dull rose-red (*normal ink*) (20 May) .. £400 15·00

(*b*) *Rouletted 5½–6½.* (i) *Smooth laid paper*
69 8 2d. brown-lilac (*shades*) (*horiz laid*) (June) £120 5·50
a. Vert laid paper (21 Sept) .. .. £200 9·50
70 2d. violet (*horiz laid*) (27 Nov) .. .. £150 5·50
a. Dull violet .. .. £180 18·00
71 4d. pale dull rose (*vert laid*) (1 June) .. £150 3·75
a. Horiz laid paper .. .. .. † £800
b. Dull rose-red .. .. £120 3·75
c. Rose-red .. .. £120 3·50
ca. Serrated 19 .. .. † £350

(ii) *Good quality wove paper*
72 8 1d. yellow-green (24 Dec) .. .. .. £275 23·00

Nos. 66/72 were produced in sheets of 120, arranged as four panes of 30 (6 × 5).

For stamps of this issue perforated see Nos. 76 and 80.

(Recess Perkins, Bacon & Co, London)

1858 (1 Nov). *Wmk Large Star, W* w **1**. *Rouletted* 5½–6½.
73 7 6d. bright blue .. .. £120 12·00
a. Light blue .. .. £160 24·00

No. 73 was received from London at the same time as the 1d., No. 40, but was kept in store until November 1858 when the stock was rouletted by Robinson. When issued the gum was in a poor state.

Imperforate examples exist from Perkins, Bacon remainders.

Imperforate reprints, in shades of indigo, were made from the original plate in 1891 on V over Crown watermarked paper.

1859 (Jan–May). *P 12 by Robinson.*
74 8 1d. yellow-green (No. 41) .. .. .. — £275
75 1d. emerald-green (No. 64*a*) .. .. — £275
a. Imperf between (horiz pair) .. ..
76 1d. yellow-green (as No. 72) (11 Jan) .. £160 12·00
a. Imperf horiz (vert pair) .. .. — £300
b. Thin, glazed ("Bordeaux") paper .. † £150
77 2d. pale lilac (No. 45) .. .. .. — £225
a. Grey-lilac .. .. — £225
78 1 3d. blue (*shades*) (No. 24) (2 Feb) .. £750 £110
a. Retouch under "C" of "VICTORIA" .. — £250
79 3d. greenish blue (*shades*) (No. 29*a*) .. † £350
a. Retouch under "C" of "VICTORIA" .. † £1000
80 8 4d. dull rose-red (No. 68) .. .. — £300
81 3 1s. blue (*shades*) (No. 25) (4 Feb)) .. £130 15·00
a. Greenish blue .. .. £150 12·00
b. Indigo-blue .. .. — 30·00
82 4 2s. dull bluish green/*pale yellow* (No. 35) (May) .. .. £250 30·00

The 1s. was reprinted in 1891 using transfers taken from the original die. These reprints were on V over Crown watermarked paper and perforated 12½.

For perforated 6d. black and 2s. blue both as Type 4 see Nos 102 and 129/30.

(Typo from electrotypes by Robinson)

1859 (17 Feb–23 Dec). *P* 12. (*a*) *Good quality wove paper*
83 8 4d. dull rose .. .. £150 3·00
a. Roul 5½–6½ .. .. † £800

(*b*) *Poorer quality wove paper*
84 8 1d. dull green (July) .. .. .. £120 7·50
a. Green (11 Nov) .. .. .. £120 7·50
85 4d. rose-carmine (16 July) .. .. £150 5·00
a. Rose-pink (*thick paper*) (30 Nov) .. — 9·00

(*c*) *Horizontally laid paper with the lines wide apart*
86 8 1d. dull green (18 July) .. ..
a. Laid lines close together .. .. — 15·00
b. Green (*shades*) (Oct) .. .. .. £130 9·50
87 4d. rose-pink (*shades*) (23 Dec) .. .. £120 7·50
a. Laid lines close together .. .. — 10·00

STAMP PRINTING BRANCH. On 1 January 1860 F. W. Robinson was appointed Printer of Postage Stamps and his equipment purchased by the Post Office to establish the Stamp Printing Branch. All later Victoria issues were printed by the Branch which became part of the Victoria Government Printing Office in December 1885. In 1909 the Commonwealth Stamp Printing Office under J. B. Cooke was established in Melbourne and produced stamps for both the states and Commonwealth until 1918.

9

10

11

(Des and eng F. Grosse. Typo from electrotypes)

860 (31 Jan)–**66.** *P* 12. (*a*) *No wmk*
8 9 3d. deep blue (*horiz laid paper*) .. .. £300 24·00
a. Light blue .. ..
9 4d. rose-pink (*thin glazed Bordeaux paper*) (21.4.60) .. .. — 8·00
a. Rose .. .. £275 13·00
ab. Thick coarse paper (7.60) .. .. £275 8·00

(*b*) *On paper made by T. H. Saunders of London wmkd with the appropriate value in words as* W **10**
0 9 3d. pale blue (1.61) .. .. .. £120 7·00
a. Bright blue (10.61) .. .. .. £120 8·00
b. Blue (4.63) .. .. .. £130 6·00
c. Deep blue (4.64) .. .. .. £130 6·00
d. "TRREE" for "THREE" in wmk ..
1 3d. maroon (13.2.66) .. .. .. £100 25·00
a. Perf 13 .. .. .. £120 28·00
2 4d. rose-pink (1.8.60) .. .. .. — 5·50
a. Rose-red .. .. .. 80·00 3·25
b. Rose-carmine .. .. .. — 8·00
c. Dull rose .. .. .. 80·00 3·25
d. Printed on "FIVE SHILLINGS" diagonal wmk paper (11.9.62) .. .. £1500 20·00
3 6d. orange (25.10.60) £3000 £200
4 6d. black (20.8.61) .. .. .. £110 5·50
a. Grey-black .. .. .. £110 5·50

(*c*) *On paper made by De La Rue wmkd with the appropriate value as a single-lined numeral as* W **11**
5 9 4d. dull rose-pink (9.10.62) .. .. 90·00 5·00
a. Dull rose .. .. .. 95·00 5·50
b. Rose-red .. .. .. — 5·00
c. Roul 8 (28.7.63) .. .. .. — £250
d. Imperf (31.7.63) .. .. .. — 60·00
e. Perf 13×12 .. .. ..

All three values were produced in sheets of 120, initially as our panes of 30 (6×5). Printings of the 3d. from 1864 were in a hanged format of six panes of 20 (4×5).

The "TRREE" watermark error comes from early printings of No. 90 on R. 10/7.

Two examples of the 4d. on Saunders paper are known isected in 1863, but such use was unauthorised.

Nos. 95c/e were issued during July and August 1863 when the ormal perforating machine had broken down.

Reprints, from new plates, were made of the 3d. and 4d. in 891 on "V over Crown" paper and perforated 12½.

860 (Apr)–**63.** *P* 12. (*a*) *No wmk*
96 8 1d. bright green (*horiz laid paper*) ..
97 1d. bright green (*thin, glazed Bordeaux paper*) (25.5.60) .. .. .. — 22·00

(*b*) *On paper made by T. H. Saunders of London wmkd with the appropriate value in words as* W **10**
98 8 1d. pale yellowish green (8.7.60) .. .. 65·00 4·50
a. Yellow-green .. .. .. 75·00 4·75
b. Error. Wmkd "FOUR PENCE" .. † —
99 2d. brown-lilac (7.7.61) .. .. .. — 17·00
00 2d. bluish slate (8.61) .. .. .. £100 4·75
a. Greyish lilac (9.61) .. .. .. £110 4·75
b. Slate-grey (1.62) .. .. .. — 4·75
c. Printed on "THREE PENCE" wmkd paper. *Pale slate* (27.12.62) .. .. £110 10·00
ca. Bluish grey (2.63) .. .. .. £120 12·00

(*c*) *On paper made by De La Rue wmkd single-lined* "2", W **11**
01 8 2d. dull reddish lilac (24.4.63) .. .. £160 5·50
a. Grey-lilac (10.63) .. .. .. £150 12·00
ab. Error. Wmkd "6" .. .. .. † £4000
b. Grey-violet (11.63) .. .. .. £100 9·00
c. Slate (12.63) .. .. .. £150 18·00

The only confirmed example of No. 98b is in the Royal Collection. There have been unconfirmed reports of the xistence of another.

861 (22 June). *On paper made by T. H. Saunders of London wmkd* "SIX PENCE" *as* W **10.** *P* 12.
02 4 6d. black .. .. £160 38·00

No. 102 was produced as an emergency measure after the ecision had been taken to change the colour of the current 6d. rom orange (No. 93) to black (No. 94). During the changeover he old Calvert "woodblock" plates were pressed into service to rovide two month's supply.

MINIMUM PRICE

The minimum price quote is 10p which represents a handling charge rather than a basis for valuing common stamps. For further notes about prices see introductory pages.

12

13

(Des, eng and electrotyped De Gruchy & Leigh, Melbourne. Typo)

1861 (1 Oct)–**64.** *P* 12. (*a*) *On paper made by T. H. Saunders of London wmkd* "ONE PENNY" *as* W **10**
103 12 1d. pale green .. .. 75·00 6·50
a. Olive-green .. .. — 7·00

(*b*) *On paper made by De La Rue wmkd single-lined* "1" *as* W **11**
104 12 1d. olive-green (1.2.63) .. .. .. 60·00 6·00
a. Pale green (9.63) .. .. .. 60·00 5·00
b. Apple-green (4.64) .. .. .. 60·00 5·00

(*c*) *On paper supplied to Tasmania by Perkins, Bacon and wmkd double-lined* "1", W **4** *of Tasmania*
105 12 1d. yellow-green (10.12.63) .. .. £110 7·50
a. Dull green .. .. .. — 7·50
b. Imperf between (pair) .. .. † —

All printings were in sheets of 120 containing four panes of 30 (6×5).

Reprints from new plates were made in 1891 on paper watermarked "V over Crown" and perforated 12½.

(Frame die eng F. Grosse. Typo from electrotypes)

1862 (26 Apr)–**64.** *Centre vignette cut from T* **9** *with a new frame as T* **13.**

(*a*) *On paper made by T. H. Saunders of London wmkd* "SIX PENCE" *as* W **10.** *P* 12
106 13 6d. grey .. .. 80·00 5·00
a. Grey-black .. .. .. 80·00 6·50
b. Jet-black .. .. .. 85·00 7·50

(*b*) *On paper made by De La Rue wmkd with single-lined* "6" *as* W **11**
107 13 6d. grey (*p* 12) (18.6.63) .. .. 70·00 4·50
a. Jet-black .. .. .. — 5·50
b. Grey-black .. .. .. 70·00 4·75
c. Perf 13. *Jet-black* .. .. 80·00 5·00
ca. Grey-black .. .. .. 80·00 5·50

Printings before August 1863 were in sheets of 120 containing four panes of 30 (6×5). For subsequent printings of No. 107 the format was changed to six panes of 20 (4×5).

Reprints from new plates were made in 1891 on paper watermarked "V over Crown" and perforated 12½.

SINGLE-LINED NUMERAL WATERMARK PAPERS. The first consignment of this paper, showing watermarks as W **11**, arrived in Victoria during October 1862. Five further consignments followed, all but the last supplied by De La Rue.

The complexity of the scheme for different watermarks for each value, together with the time required to obtain further supplies from Great Britain, resulted in the emergency use of paper obtained from Tasmania and of the wrong numeral watermark on certain printings.

The final order for this paper was placed, in error with the firm of T. H. Saunders of London. Although the actual watermarks are the same (the dandy rolls were the property of the Victoria Government and supplied to each firm in turn) there are considerable differences between the two types of paper. That manufactured by Saunders is of a more even quality and is smoother, thicker, less brittle and less white than the De La Rue type.

De La Rue supplied white paper watermarked "1", "2", "4", "6" and "8", blue paper watermarked "1" and green paper watermarked "2".

The Saunders consignment of October 1865 contained white paper watermarked "1", "4" and "6", blue paper watermarked "1", green paper watermarked "2" and pink paper watermarked "10".

It is helpful for comparison purposes to note that all white paper watermarked "2" or "8" can only be De La Rue and all pink paper watermarked "10" can only be Saunders.

14

15

16

17

18

(Des and eng F. Grosse. Typo from electrotypes)

1863–74. *"Laureated" series.*

(*a*) *On paper made by De La Rue wmkd with the appropriate value in single-lined numerals as* W **11**
108 14 1d. pale green (*p* 12) (9.9.64) .. .. 75·00 7·00
a. Perf 12½×12 (9.64) .. ..
b. Perf 13 (10.10.64) .. .. 70·00 3·50
c. Bluish green (*p* 13) (12.64) .. .. 65·00 2·75
ca. Printed double .. .. .. † £550
d. Green (*p* 12) (7.65) .. .. 70·00 3·00
da. Perf 13 .. .. .. 65·00 3·50
e. Deep green (*p* 12) (12.65) .. .. 85·00 3·00
ea. Perf 13 .. .. .. — 3·00
eb. Perf 12×13 .. .. .. — 6·00
f. Bright yellow-green (*p* 13) (1.67) .. — 15·00
109 14 2d. violet (*p* 12) (1.4.64) .. .. 65·00 5·50
a. Dull violet (*p* 12) (10.64) .. .. 70·00 5·50
ab. Perf 12½×12 .. .. ..
ac. Perf 12½ .. ..
ad. Perf 13 .. .. .. 70·00 4·25
b. Dull lilac (*p* 13) (4.65) .. .. 55·00 4·00
ba. Perf 12 (7.66) .. .. .. — 7·00
bb. Perf 12×13 (7.66) .. .. — 8·50
c. Reddish mauve (*p* 13) (11.65) .. 60·00 4·00
d. Rose-lilac (*p* 13) (1.66) .. .. 55·00 5·50
da. Perf 12×13 or 13×12 (2.66) .. .. 55·00 5·50
e. Grey (*p* 12) (7.66) .. .. 85·00 7·00
ea. Perf 13 .. .. .. 55·00 3·00
110 4d. deep rose (*p* 12) (11.9.63) .. .. £110 3·50
a. Printed double .. .. .. † £500
b. Rose-pink (*p* 12) (9.63) .. .. 85·00 2·50
c. Pink (*p* 12) (7.5.64) .. .. 85·00 2·50
ca. Error. Wmkd single-lined "8" .. † £2000
cb. Perf 12½×12 (9.64) .. ..
d. Dull rose (*p* 13) (10.64) .. .. 75·00 2·50
e. Dull rose-red (*p* 13) (2.65) .. .. 75·00 2·50
ea. Perf 12 (8.65) .. .. .. £120 75·00
111 16 6d. blue (*p* 12) (13.2.66) .. .. 35·00 4·50
a. Perf 13 .. .. .. 35·00 2·75
b. Perf 12×13 .. .. .. 32·00 2·00
112 14 8d. orange (*p* 13) (22.2.65) .. .. £300 50·00
113 17 1s. blue/*blue* (*p* 13) (10.4.65) .. .. £100 3·50
a. Perf 12×13 (4.66) .. .. £100 3·50
ab. Imperf between (vert pair) .. .. † £1200
b. Bright blue/blue (*p* 13) (6.67) .. 85·00 3·00
c. Indigo-blue/blue (*p* 13) (3.68) .. — 2·75
d. Dull blue/blue (*p* 12) (6.74) .. .. — 3·50

(*b*) *Emergency printings on Perkins, Bacon paper borrowed from Tasmania wmkd double-lined* "4" *as* W **4** *of Tasmania*
114 14 4d. deep rose (*p* 12) (7.1.64) .. .. £110 3·75
a. Pale rose (*p* 12) .. .. .. — 3·25
b. Dull reddish rose (*p* 13) (11.8.65) .. £110 3·50
ba. Perf 12 .. .. .. — 3·75
bb. Perf 12×13 .. .. .. — 11·00
c. Red (*p* 13) (4.12.65) .. .. £120 3·50

(*c*) *Emergency printings on De La Rue paper as* W **11**, *but showing incorrect single-lined numeral. P* 13
115 14 1d. brt yellow-grn (*wmkd* "8") (27.12.66) £120 11·00
116 1d. brt yellow-green (*wmkd* "6") (6.67) — 17·00
117 2d. grey (*wmkd* "8") (18.1.67) .. .. £110 5·00
118 15 3d. lilac (*wmkd* "8") (29.9.66) .. .. £110 22·00
119 16 10d. grey (*wmkd* "8") (21.10.65) .. £450 £100
a. Grey-black £450 £100

(*d*) *On paper made by T. H. Saunders wmkd with the appropriate value in single-lined numerals as* W **11**
120 14 1d. deep yellow-green (*p* 12×13) (1.66) £120 6·50
a. Perf 13 (3.66) .. .. 65·00 3·00
b. Perf 12 (7.66) .. .. — 7·50
121 4d. rose-red (*p* 13) (12.12.65) .. .. 75·00 3·00
a. Perf 12×13 or 13×12 (2.66) .. £110 5·50
b. Perf 12 (4.66) .. .. .. — 4·75
122 16 6d. blue (*p* 13) (28.5.66) .. .. 30·00 1·50
a. Perf 12 .. .. .. 35·00 3·50
b. Perf 12×13 .. .. .. 30·00 1·75
ba. Imperf between (horiz pair) .. † £600
123 10d. dull purple/*pink* (*p* 13) (22.3.66) .. 85·00 5·00
a. Perf 12×13 .. .. .. £120 5·50
b. Blackish brown/pink (*p* 13) (12.69) 90·00 5·50
c. Purple-brown/pink (*p* 13) (11.70) ..
124 17 1s. bright blue/*blue* (*p* 13) (5.12.70) .. 55·00 2·50
a. Pale dull blue/blue (*p* 12) (1.73) £120 3·25
ab. Perf 13 .. .. .. — 7·00
b. Indigo-blue/blue (*p* 12) (9.73) — 5·00
ba. Perf 13 .. .. .. 55·00 3·25

(*e*) *Emergency printings on Saunders paper as* W **11**, *but showing incorrect single-lined numeral. P* 13
125 14 1d. brt yellow-green (*wmkd* "4") (6.3.67) 85·00 8·50
126 1d. brt yellow-green (*wmkd* "6") (6.67) £120 15·00
127 2d. grey (*wmkd* "4") (21.2.67) .. 80·00 5·00
128 2d. grey (*wmkd* "6") (13.5.67) .. £130 6·00

The 1d., 2d., 4d. and 8d. were originally produced in sheets of 120 containing eight panes of 15 (3×5). The 3d. and 6d. were in sheets of 120 (12×10) and the 1d. (from February 1866), 2d. (from July 1866) and 4d. (from April 1866) subsequently changed to this format. The 10d. was in sheets of 120 containing twenty panes of 6 (2×3). The 1s. was originally in sheets of 60 containing three panes of 20 (4×5), but this changed to 120 (12×10) in April 1866.

Only single examples are thought to exist of Nos. 110a, 110ca, 113ab, and 122ba and two of No. 108ca.

For later emergency printings on these papers see Nos.153/66.

(Typo from composite woodblock and electrotype plate)

1864 (22 Nov)–**80.** (*a*) *On De La Rue paper wmkd single-lined* "2" *as* W **11**
129 4 2s. light blue/*green* (*p* 13) (22.11.64) .. £150 5·50
a. Dark blue/green (*p* 12) (9.65) .. £170 9·00
ab. Perf 13 (6.66) .. .. £150 5·50
b. Blue/green (*p* 13) (6.68) .. £140 4·75
c. Greenish blue/green (*p* 13) (7.73) .. £140 4·75
ca. Perf 12 .. .. .. £160 6·00
d. Deep greenish blue/green (*p* 12½) .. £140 4·75

(*b*) *On Saunders paper wmkd single-lined* "2" *as* W **11**
130 4 2s. dark blue/*green* (*p* 13) (23.11.67) .. £160 6·00
a. Blue/green (*p* 13) (10.71) .. £160 4·75
ab. Perf 12 (8.74) .. .. £180 6·00
c. Deep greenish blue/green (*p* 12½) (7.80) £140 4·75

Nos. 129/30 were produced in sheets of 30 containing two panes of 15 (3×5). The plate contained eighteen of the original woodblock impressions and twelve electrotypes taken from them.

19

20

V OVER CROWN WATERMARKS. The changeover from the numeral watermarks to a general type to be used for all values was first suggested at the end of 1865, but the first supplies did not reach Melbourne until April 1867. Five different versions were used before the V over Crown watermark was superseded by the Commonwealth type in 1905. The five versions are listed as follows:

Type **19** De La Rue paper supplied 1867 to 1882. Shows four points at the top of the crown with the left and right ornaments diamond-shaped
Type **33** De La Rue paper supplied 1882 to 1895. No points at the top of the crown with the left and right ornaments oval-shaped
Type **82** Waterlow paper supplied 1896 to 1899. Wide base to crown
Type **85** Waterlow paper used for postal issues 1899 to 1905. Wide top to crown
Type **104** James Spicer and Sons paper used for postal issues August and September 1912. Narrow crown

(Typo from electrotypes)

1867–81. *Wmk V over Crown, W* **19**. (*a*) *P* 13
131 **14** 1d. bright yellow-green (10.8.67) .. 65·00 2·50
a. Bright olive-green (1.69) .. .. 95·00 14·00
b. Yellow-green (4.69) .. .. 65·00 2·10
c. Dull green (3.70) .. .. .. 65·00 2·10
d. Pale green (10.70) .. .. .. 60·00 2·10
e. Grass-green (1871) .. .. 60·00 2·40
f. Bluish green (*shades*) (7.72) .. 60·00 2·40
g. Green (*shades*) (9.72) .. .. 60·00 2·25
132 2d. slate-grey (*shades*) (26.8.67) .. 70·00 3·50
a. Grey-lilac (29.1.68) .. .. 70·00 4·75
b. Lilac (26.8.68) .. .. .. 50·00 3·25
c. Dull mauve (*shades*) (10.68) .. 50·00 3·25
d. Lilac-grey (1.69) .. .. .. — 3·50
e. Lilac-rose (2.69) .. .. .. 55·00 3·00
f. Mauve (4.69) .. .. .. 70·00 3·25
g. Red-lilac (5.69) .. .. .. 55·00 3·00
h. Dull lilac (6.69) .. .. .. 55·00 2·50
i. Silver-grey (9.69) .. .. .. £110 7·00
133 **15** 3d. lilac (28.8.67) .. .. .. £200 26·00
a. Grey-lilac (6.68) .. .. .. £225 28·00
134 3d. yellow-orange (12.6.69) .. .. 22·00 3·00
a. Dull orange (6.70) .. .. .. 20·00 1·90
b. Orange (3.73) .. .. .. — 2·25
c. Bright orange (3.73) .. .. 25·00 2·50
d. Orange-brown (*glazed paper*) (10.78) 25·00 5·50
135 **14** 4d. dull rose (28.11.67) .. .. 75·00 5·00
a. Wmk sideways .. .. .. † 60·00
b. Aniline red (*shades*) (21.4.69) .. — 6·50
c. Rose-pink (11.69) .. .. .. — 5·00
d. Rose (*shades*) (8.71) .. .. 70·00 3·00
e. Dull rose (*glazed paper*) (5.3.79) .. 70·00 3·00
f. Dull rose-red (*glazed paper*) (11.79) — 3·00
g. Bright lilac-rose (*aniline*) (*glazed paper*) (2.80) .. .. .. 75·00 3·75
h. Rosine (*aniline*) (*glazed paper*) (9.80) £200 5·00
136 **16** 6d. deep blue (15.1.68) .. .. — 3·00
a. Blue (21.12.68) .. .. .. 20·00 1·25
b. Indigo-blue (10.69) .. .. .. 20·00 1·25
c. Prussian blue (9.72) .. .. .. 19·00 1·25
d. Indigo (4.73) .. .. .. 20·00 1·40
e. Dull blue (*worn plate*) (3.74) .. — 1·25
f. Dull ultramarine (2.12.75) .. .. 27·00 1·25
g. Light Prussian blue (12.75) .. 40·00 1·25
h. Dull violet-blue (7.77) .. .. — 6·00
i. Blue (*glazed paper*) (6.78) .. .. 29·00 1·25
j. Dull milky-blue (*glazed paper*) (9.79) 27·00 1·25
k. Prussian blue (*glazed paper*) (4.80) — 1·25
l. Light blue (*glazed paper*) (4.81) .. 29·00 1·25
m. Deep blue (*glazed paper*) (10.81) .. 27·00 1·25
137 **14** 8d. lilac-brown/*pink* (24.1.77) .. 75·00 5·50
a. Purple-brown/pink (2.78) .. .. 75·00 5·50
b. Chocolate/pink (8.78) .. .. 80·00 5·00
ba. Compound perf 13×12 .. .. † £325
c. Red-brown/pink (12.78) .. .. 75·00 5·00
138 **17** 1s. light blue/*blue* (11.5.75) .. .. £100 7·00
139 **18** 5s. blue/*yellow* (26.12.67) £1600 £300
a. Wmk reversed .. .. .. — £500
140 5s. indigo-blue and carmine (I) (8.10.68) £200 18·00
a. Blue and carmine (4.69) .. .. £170 13·00
b. Pale bright blue and carmine (*glazed paper*) (24.7.77) .. .. .. — 17·00
c. Grey-blue and carmine (*glazed paper*) (4.78) .. .. .. £160 15·00
d. Wmk sideways. *Deep lavender-blue and carmine* (*glazed paper*) (4.6.80) £160 15·00
141 5s. bright blue and red (II) (*glazed paper*) (12.5.81) .. .. £140 13·00
a. Indigo-blue and red (*glazed paper*) — 17·00

(*b*) *P* 12
142 **14** 1d. pale green (10.71) .. .. .. 70·00 2·40
a. Grass-green (1871) .. .. .. 60·00 2·40
b. Bluish green (*shades*) (7.72) .. — 2·40
c. Green (*shades*) (9.72) .. .. 60·00 2·25
143 **15** 3d. dull orange (5.72) .. .. 20·00 2·00
a. Orange (3.73) .. .. .. — 2·10
b. Bright orange (3.73) .. .. — 2·50
c. Dull orange-yellow (*glazed paper*) (12.80) .. ..
144 **14** 4d. rose (*shades*) (8.71) .. .. 70·00 3·00
a. Compound perf 12×13 .. .. — £325
b. Dull rose (*glazed paper*) (3.79) .. — 3·00
c. Dull rose-red (*glazed paper*) (11.79) .. — 3·00
d. Bright lilac-rose (*aniline*) (*glazed paper*) (2.80) .. .. .. — 6·50
e. Rosine (*aniline*) (*glazed paper*) (9.80) 80·00 4·75
145 **16** 6d. deep blue (2.2.72) .. .. ..
a. Prussian blue (9.72) .. .. 21·00 1·25
b. Indigo (4.73) .. .. .. 27·00 1·75
c. Dull blue (*worn plate*) (3.74) .. ..
d. Blue (*glazed paper*) (6.78) .. .. — 1·25
e. Dull milky-blue (*glazed paper*) (9.79) — 1·25
f. Light blue (*glazed paper*) (4.81) .. — 2·40
146 **14** 8d. red-brn/*pink* (*glazed paper*) (11.80) .. 75·00 5·50
147 **17** 1s. light blue/*blue* (5.75) .. .. — 6·50
148 **18** 5s. bright blue and red (II) (*glazed paper*) (5.81) .. .. £130 13·00
a. Indigo-blue and red .. .. £225 17·00

(*c*) *P* 12½
149 **15** 3d. dull orange-yellow (*glazed paper*) (12.80) .. .. 27·00 3·00
150 **14** 4d. rosine (*aniline*) (*glazed paper*) (9.80)
151 **16** 6d. Prussian blue (*glazed paper*) (4.80) ..
a. Light blue (*glazed paper*) (4.81) ..
b. Deep blue (*glazed paper*) (10.81) .. 27·00 1·50
152 **14** 8d. lilac-brown/*pink* (8.77) .. .. 75·00 5·50
a. Red-brown/pink (*glazed paper*) (11.80) † —

The same electrotypes as the previous issues were used for this series with the exception of the 5s. which was a new value. The 1d., 2d., 3d., 4d., 6d. and 1s. plates were arranged to print sheets of 120 (12×10) and the 8d. conformed to this when reintroduced in 1877. New plates for the 1d. (1868), 2d.(1869) and 6d. (1875) were constructed by Robinson's successor, J. P. Atkinson, using the improved facilities then available.

Atkinson was also responsible for the printing of the 5s. value. The original printings in blue on yellow paper were produced in sheets of 25, or possibly 50, using a vertical strip of five electrotypes. Due to its size the 5s. did not exactly fit the watermarked paper and, to avoid a preprinted sheet number, a proportion of the printing was made on the back of the paper creating the reversed watermark variety, No. 139a. These varieties occur in the first printing only as Atkinson created a plate of 25 for the second printing in March 1868. Printings of the 5s. bicoloured to April 1880 were made from electrotypes taken from the monocoloured plate. These showed a blue line beneath the crown (Type I). In early 1881 this plate was found to be too worn for further use and a new die was made from which a plate of 100 was constructed. Stamps from this plate are without the blue line beneath the crown (Type II).

PERFORATIONS. Various perforating machines were in use during this period. The use of line machines gauging 12 ceased around 1883. Of the line machines gauging 13 two were converted to comb types in 1873 and were eventually replaced by the 12½ gauge line and comb machines first used in 1876.

(Typo from electrotypes)

1867–70. *Emergency printings on various papers due to shortages of V over Crown paper. P* 13.

(*a*) *Perkins, Bacon paper borrowed from Tasmania. Wmkd double-lined numerals as W* 4 *of Tasmania*
153 **14** 1d. pale yellowish green (*wmkd* "1") (24.9.67) .. .. 65·00 3·50
a. Deep yellow-green (10.67) .. .. 65·00 3·50
154 1d. pale yellow-green (*wmkd* "4") (27.5.68) £1300 80·00
155 2d. grey-lilac (*wmkd* "4") (3.2.68) .. £110 4·25
a. Slate (4.68) .. .. .. £110 3·50
b. Mauve (7.68) .. .. .. — 4·50
156 2d. mauve (*wmkd* "1") (30.6.68) .. £110 5·50
157 **15** 3d. grey-lilac (*wmkd* "1") (8.68) .. £150 35·00
158 **14** 4d. dull rose-red (*wmkd* "4") (5.68) .. £110 5·00
159 **16** 6d. blue (*wmkd* "4") (20.6.68) .. £150 13·00
a. Indigo-blue .. .. .. — 15·00
160 6d. blue (*wmkd* "1") (28.7.68) .. 55·00 4·25
161 6d. dull blue (*wmkd* "2") (1870) .. † £2250

(*b*) *Saunders paper. Wmkd in words as W* **10**
162 **14** 1d. pale yellow-green (wmkd "SIX PENCE") (23.3.68) .. .. £375 17·00
163 2d. slate-grey (*wmkd* "SIX PENCE") (6.68) .. .. .. † £2500
164 **16** 6d. blue (*wmkd* "SIX PENCE") (20.5.68) £250 13·00
a. Indigo-blue .. .. .. — 17·00
165 6d. dull blue (*wmkd* "THREE PENCE") (6.12.69) .. .. .. £130 6·00
a. Deep blue .. .. .. — 7·00
166 6d. dull blue (*wmkd* "FOUR PENCE") (21.5.70) .. .. .. £250 23·00
a. Deep blue .. .. .. — 24·00

(*c*) *V over Crown, W* **19**, *coloured paper*
167 **14** 2d. mauve/*lilac* (7.68) .. .. 65·00 6·50
a. Lilac/lilac .. .. .. 65·00 6·00

(*d*) *Saunders single-lined numeral "4" as W* **11**
168 **16** 6d. dull blue (21.5.70) .. .. † £1600

The supply of paper was so short during 1868 that many odds and ends were utilised. Nos. 161 (five known), 163 (one known) and 168 (ten known) are the rarest of these emergency printings.

(Printed in Melbourne from a double electrotyped plate of 240 supplied by D.L.R.)

1870 (28 Jan)–**73.** *Wmk V over Crown, W* **19**.
169 **20** 2d. brown-lilac (*p* 13) .. .. 60·00 1·50
a. Dull lilac-mauve (9.70) .. .. 50·00 1·00
b. Mauve (*worn plate*) (3.73) .. .. 50·00 1·25
170 2d. dull lilac-mauve (*p* 12) (28.7.71) .. 55·00 1·50
a. Mauve (*worn plate*) (3.73) .. .. 55·00 1·00

9 9

NINEPENCE

(**21**)

1871 (22 Apr). *No.* 123*c surch with T* **21** *in blue.*
171 **16** 9d. on 10d. purple-brown/*pink* .. £300 10·00
a. Blackish brown/pink .. .. £400 12·00
b. Surch double .. .. .. † £800

22 23 24

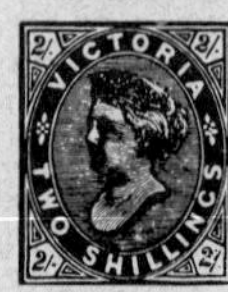

25 26 27

(Des and eng W. Bell. Typo from electrotyped plates)

1873 (25 Mar)–**74.** *Saunders paper wmkd single-lined "10" as W* **11**.
172 **25** 9d. pale brown/*pink* (*p* 13) .. .. 65·00 8·0
a. Red-brown/pink (7.74) .. .. 60·00 8·5
173 9d. pale brown/*pink* (*p* 12) .. .. 70·00 12·0

½ ½

HALF

(**28**)

1873 (25 June). *No.* 131*g surch with T* **28** *in red.*
174 **14** ½d. on 1d. green (*p* 13) .. .. .. 45·00 12·0
a. Grass-green .. .. .. 48·00 12·0
b. Short "1" at right (R. 1/3) .. .. — 70·0
175 ½d. on 1d. green (*p* 12) .. .. .. 60·00 14·0
a. Grass-green .. .. .. 60·00 14·0
b. Short "1" at right (R. 1/3) .. .. — 75·0

Die I

Die II

Two Dies of 2d.:
Die I. Single-lined outer oval
Die II. Double-lined outer oval

(Des and eng W. Bell. Typo from electrotyped plates)

1873–87. *Wmk V over Crown, W* **19**, (*sideways on* ½*d.*).

(*a*) *P* 13
176 **22** ½d. rose-red (10.2.74) .. .. .. 7·00 70
a. Lilac-rose (1874) .. .. .. 7·50 90
b. Rosine (*shades*) (*glazed paper*) (12.80) .. .. 6·00 70
c. Pale red (*glazed paper*) (1882) .. 7·00 60
d. Mixed perf 13 and 12 .. .. † £250
177 **23** 1d. dull bluish green (14.12.75) .. 16·00 85
a. Green (*shades*) (1877) .. .. 16·00 80
b. Yellow-green (*glazed paper*) (1878) 16·00 65
178 **24** 2d. deep lilac-mauve (I) (1.10.73) .. 22·00 55
a. Dull violet-mauve .. .. .. 22·00 55
b. Dull mauve .. .. .. 22·00 55
c. Pale mauve (*worn plate*) (*glazed paper*) (1.79) .. .. .. 23·00 7
d. Mixed perf 13 and 12 .. .. £130 £10
179 2d. lilac-mauve (II) (*glazed paper*) (17.12.78) .. .. 20·00 55
a. Grey-mauve (1.80) .. .. .. — 60
b. Pale mauve (6.80) .. .. .. 28·00 60
c. Vert pair, lower stamp imperf horiz † £120
180 **26** 1s. indigo-blue/*blue* (16.8.76) .. .. 50·00 3·0
a. Deep blue/blue (7.77) .. .. 55·00 3·0
b. Pale blue/blue (3.80) .. .. 60·00 3·0
c. Bright blue/blue (9.80) .. .. 65·00 7·5
d. Bright blue/blue (*glazed paper*) (21.11.83) .. .. 65·00 5·0
e. Pale blue/blue (*glazed paper*) (7.84)
f. Mixed perf 13 and 12 .. .. † —

(*b*) *P* 12
181 **22** ½d. rose-red (1874) .. .. .. 7·50 1·0
a. Lilac-rose (1874) .. .. .. 7·00 1·0
b. Rosine (*shades*) (*glazed paper*) (12.80) 7·00 80
c. Pale red (*glazed paper*) (1882) .. 7·00 85
182 **23** 1d. dull bluish green (1875) .. .. 17·00 1·25
a. Green (*shades*) (1877) .. .. 16·00 5·0
b. Yellow-green (*glazed paper*) (1878) — 2·5
183 **24** 2d. deep lilac-mauve (I) (1873) .. — 2·25
a. Dull violet-mauve .. .. .. — 2·0
b. Dull mauve .. .. .. 25·00 80
c. Pale mauve (*worn plate*) (*glazed paper*) (1879) .. .. .. — 1·0
184 2d. lilac-mauve (II) (*glazed paper*) (1878) 26·00 65
a. Grey-mauve (*glazed paper*) (1880) .. — 70
b. Pale mauve (*glazed paper*) (1880) .. — 1·75
185 **25** 9d. lilac-brown/*pink* (1.12.75) .. .. £100 12·0
186 **26** 1s. deep blue/*blue* (1880) .. .. — 7·5
a. Bright blue/blue (1880) .. .. — 7·5

(*c*) *P* 12½
187 **22** ½d. rosine (*shades*) (*glazed paper*) (1880)
a. Pale red (*glazed paper*) (1882) ..
188 **23** 1d. yellow-green (*glazed paper*) (1880)
189 **24** 2d. grey-mauve (II) (*glazed paper*) (1880)
a. Pale mauve (1880) .. .. ..
190 **27** 2s. deep blue/*green* (*glazed paper*) (8.7.81) .. .. £120 18·0
a. Light blue/green (*glazed paper*) (4.83)
ab. Wmk sideways .. .. .. £130 22·0
b. Ultramarine/green (*glazed paper*) (6.84) .. .. — 28·0
ba. Wmk sideways .. .. .. — 48·0

8d 8d

EIGHTPENCE

(**29**)

1876 (1 July). *No.* 185 *surch with T* **29**.
191 **25** 8d. on 9d. lilac-brown/*pink* .. .. £160 15·0
a. "F.IGHTPENCE" .. .. .. — £18

No. 191a was caused by a broken "E" and it occurred once in each sheet of 120.

77 (24 Jan). *Saunders paper wmkd* "10" *as* W **11**.

2	**14**	8d. lilac-brown/*pink* (*p* 13)	—	£500
		a. Purple-brown/pink (2.78)	£100	8·00
		b. Chocolate/pink (8.78)	†	£600
		c. Red-brown/pink (8.79)	85·00	5·00
3		8d. red-brown/*pink* (*p* 12) (8.79)	—	9·00
4		8d. red-brown/*pink* (*p* 12½) (8.79)	—	50·00

Nos. 192/4 occur amongst the V over Crown printings, the two es of pink paper having become mixed.

78. *Emergency printings on coloured papers wmkd V over Crown,* W **19**, (*sideways on* ½*d.*). *P* 13.

5	**22**	½d. rose-red/*pink* (1.3.78)	23·00	11·00
6	**23**	1d. yellow-green/*yellow* (5.3.78)	75·00	12·00
7		1d. yellow-green/*drab* (5.4.78)	£100	42·00
8	**24**	2d. dull violet-mauve/*lilac* (21.2.78)	—	£400
9		2d. dull violet-mauve/*green* (23.2.78)	£130	12·00
0		2d. dull violet-mauve/*brown* (21.3.78)	£120	12·00

There was a shortage of white V over Crown, W **19**, termarked paper in the early months of 1878 and various oured papers were used for printings of the ½d., 1d. and 2d. lues until fresh stocks of white paper were received.

30

31

32

(Des and eng C. Naish. Typo from electrotyped plates)

80 (3 Nov)–**84**. *Wmk V over Crown,* W **19**.

1	**30**	1d. green (*p* 12½) (2.84)	90·00	8·00
2	**31**	2d. sepia (*p* 12½)	20·00	55
		a. Sepia-brown (2.81)	18·00	55
		b. Brown (aniline) (5.81)	21·00	55
		c. Dull black-brown (10.81)	—	55
		d. Dull grey-brown (3.82)	17·00	55
3		2d. sepia (*p* 13)		
		a. Mixed perf 13 and 12	†	£250
4		2d. sepia (*p* 12)	—	40·00
		a. Sepia-brown (2.81)	—	40·00
		b. Brown (aniline) (5.81)	—	40·00
5		2d. mauve (*worn plate*) (*p* 12½) (2.84)	—	6·00
6	**32**	4d. rose-carmine (*p* 12½) (10.81)	50·00	5·00
		a. Rosine (7.82)	50·00	4·50

Nos. 201 and 205 are subsequent printings of stamps first oduced on watermark W **33**.

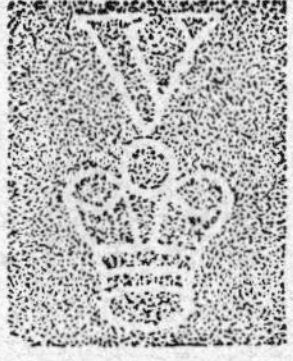

33

882–84. *Wmk V over Crown,* W **33**, (*sideways on* ½*d.*). *P* 12½.

07	**22**	½d. rosine (3.83)	9·00	1·75
		a. Perf 12	—	15·00
08	**23**	1d. yellow-green (9.82)	16·00	1·50
		a. Perf 12		
09	**30**	1d. yellow-green (29.10.83)	16·00	1·25
		a. Green (1.84)	14·00	1·25
		b. Pale green (5.84)	14·00	1·25
10	**31**	2d. dull grey-brown (15.8.82)	18·00	75
		a. Chocolate (3.83)	18·00	75
		ab. Perf 12	—	19·00
11		2d. mauve (20.12.83)	10·00	40
		a. Worn plate (2.84)	11·00	40
		b. Perf 12	†	£250
		c. Mixed perf 12 and 12½	†	£250
12	**15**	3d. yellow-orange (13.4.83)	28·00	6·00
		a. Dull brownish orange	32·00	7·50
13	**32**	4d. rose-red (3.83)	42·00	5·50
14	**16**	6d. dull violet-blue (10.11.82)	20·00	1·25
		a. Indigo-blue (11.83)	20·00	1·25
		b. Light ultramarine (8.84)	20·00	1·40

Reprints were made in 1891 of the "Laureated" 1d., 2d., 3d. (in ellow), 4d., 6d., 8d. (in orange-yellow), 10d. (in greenish slate) nd 5s. (in blue and red), of the Bell ½d., 1d., 2d. (Die II), 9d. and s. and of the Naish 2d. (in brown), 4d. (in pale red) and 2s. With he exception of the Bell 9d., which was watermarked W **19**, all ere watermarked W **33** and perforated 12½. Some were from ew plates.

HE POST OFFICE ACT OF 1883. Following official concern s to the number of different series of adhesive stamps, both scal and postal, used in Victoria it was decided that the system hould be unified to the extent that the postage stamps, Stamp Statute fiscals and Stamp Duty fiscals should be replaced by a ingle series valid for all three purposes. As the Stamp Duty eries contained the largest number of values it was adopted as he basis of the new range.

The regulations for the changeover were detailed in the Post Office Act of 1883 which came into force on 1 January 1884. rom that date all existing Stamp Statute (first produced in 871) and Stamp Duty (first produced in 1879) issues became alid for postal purposes, and the previous postage stamps could e used for fiscal fees.

Until matters could be organised printings of some of the xisting postage values continued and these will be found ncluded in the listings above.

Printing of the Stamp Statute series was discontinued in early 884.

The existing Stamp Duty range was initially supplemented by ostage stamps overprinted "STAMP DUTY" for those values here the available fiscal design was considered to be too large to be easily used on mail. These overprints were replaced by smaller designs inscribed "STAMP DUTY".

Stamp Statute and Stamp Duty values which became valid for postal purposes on 1 January 1884 have previously been listed in this catalogue as Postal Fiscals. Under the circumstances this distinction appears somewhat arbitary and all such stamps are now shown in the main listing. Used prices quoted are for examples with postal cancellations. In some instances prices are also provided for fiscally used and these are marked "F.C.".

34

35

36

37

(Des and dies eng J. Turner (3d., 2s. 6d.), W. Bell (others). Typo from electrotypes)

1884 (1 Jan)*. *Stamp Statute series. Vert designs as T* **34/6**, *and others showing Queen Victoria, and T* **37**. *P* 13.

(*a*) *Wmk single-lined numerals according to face value, as* W **11**, (*sideways*). *Paper manufactured by T. H. Saunders unless otherwise stated*

215	1s. blue/*blue*	42·00	16·00
	a. Perf 12	55·00	22·00
216	2s. blue/*green* (*D.L.R. paper*)	60·00	45·00
	a. Perf 12	60·00	45·00
217	2s. deep blue/*green*	60·00	
	a. Perf 12	—	45·00
	b. Wmk upright		
218	10s. brown-olive/*pink*		
219	10s. red-brown/*pink*	£500	£100
	a. Wmk upright. Perf 12		
	(*b*) *Wmk V over Crown,* W **19**, (*sideways*). *P* 13		
220	1d. pale green	16·00	16·00
	a. Green (*wmk upright*) (*p* 12½)	42·00	35·00
221	3d. mauve	£110	75·00
222	4d. rose	£100	55·00
223	6d. blue	48·00	16·00
	a. Ultramarine	42·00	11·00
	ab. Perf 12	48·00	14·00
224	1s. blue/*blue*	42·00	16·00
	a. Perf 12	48·00	19·00
	b. Ultramarine/blue (*p* 12½)	—	27·00
	ba. Perf 12	—	22·00
	c. Deep blue/blue (*p* 12½)	42·00	16·00
	ca. Perf 12	—	16·00
225	2s. blue/*green*	55·00	38·00
	a. Perf 12	55·00	
	b. Deep blue/blue-green (*glazed paper*)	55·00	42·00
	ba. Perf 12	55·00	48·00
226	2s. 6d. orange	—	50·00
	a. Perf 12		
	b. Yellow (*glazed paper*)	£110	
	ba. Perf 12	£110	55·00
	c. Orange-yellow (*glazed paper*) (*p* 12½)	—	60·00
	ca. Perf 12		
227	5s. blue/*yellow*	£130	42·00
	a. Perf 12	£140	
	b. Wmk upright		
	ba. Perf 12		
	c. Ultram/lemon (*glazed paper*) (*p* 12½)	£130	42·00
	ca. Wmk upright		
228	10s. brown/*pink*	£500	£100
	a. Purple-brown/pink	£500	£100
	ab. Perf 12		
229	£1 slate-violet/*yellow*	£275	85·00
	a. Wmk upright		
	b. Mauve/yellow		
	ba. Perf 12	£275	85·00
	bb. Perf 12½	£275	85·00
230	£5 black and yellow-green	£2000	£425
	a. Perf 12		
	b. Wmk upright. Perf 12½	£2000	£425
	(*c*) *Wmk V over Crown,* W **33**, (*sideways*)		
231	1d. yellowish green (*p* 12½)	28·00	28·00
232	2s. 6d. pale orange-yellow (*p* 12)	£110	50·00
233	£5 black & yellow-grn (*wmk upright*) (*p* 12)	—	£425

½d

HALF

(38)

1884 (1 Jan)*. *No.* 220 *surch with T* **38** *in red.*

234	½d. on 1d. pale green	35·00	30·00

* The dates quoted are those on which the stamps became valid for postal purposes. The ½d., 1d., 4d., 6d., 1s., 5s. and £1 were issued for fiscal purposes on 26 April 1871. The 10s. was added to the series in June 1871, the £5 in September 1871, the 2s. 6d. in July 1876 and the 3d. in October 1879.

All values of the Stamp Statue series were reprinted in 1891 on paper watermarked W **19** (5s., 10s., £1) or W **33** (others). The £5 was pulled from the original plate, but the others were produced from new electrotypes taken from the original dies.

39

40

41

42

43

44

45

46

47

48

49

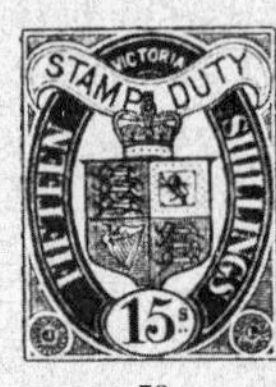

50

51

52

53

54

55

56

57

58

59

60

61

(Des H. Samson and F. Oxenbould (T 39), C. Jackson and L. Lang (all others except T 40). Dies eng C. Jackson, J. Turner, J. Whipple, A. Williams and other employees of Sands & MacDougall. T 40 die eng C. Naish)

1884 (1 Jan*)–**96**. *Existing Stamp Duty series.*

(*a*) *Litho. Wmk V over Crown, W* **19**, (*sideways*). *P* 13

No.	Type	Description	Unused	Used
235	**39**	1d. blue-green	42·00	8·50
		a. Perf 12	42·00	8·50
		b. Perf 12½		
236	**43**	1s. 6d. rosine	£120	17·00
		a. Perf 12	—	24·00
		b. Perf 12½		
237	**45**	3s. purple/*blue*	£300	26·00
		a. Perf 12	—	35·00
		b. Perf 12½		
238	**46**	4s. orange-red	70·00	16·00
		a. Perf 12	70·00	16·00
		b. Perf 12½		
239	**48**	6s. apple-green	£200	24·00
		a. Perf 12½		
240	**49**	10s. brown/*rose* (*glazed paper*)	£300	55·00
		a. Perf 12		
		b. Perf 12½		
		c. Wmk upright		
		cb. Perf 12½		
241	**50**	15s. mauve	£800	£120
242	**51**	£1 red-orange	£350	60·00
		a. Perf 12½	£350	
243	**52**	£1 5s. dull rose (*wmk upright*)	£750	£130
244	**53**	£1 10s. deep grey-olive	£800	90·00
		a. Wmk upright	—	£130
245	–	35s. grey-violet (*wmk upright*) (F.C. £150)	£3000	
246	**54**	£2 blue	—	80·00
247	**55**	45s. dull brown-lilac	£1400	£100
248	**56**	£5 rose-red (*wmk upright*)	£1100	£225
249	**57**	£6 blue/*pk* (*wmk upright*) (*glazed paper*)	—	£475
250	**58**	£7 violet/*blue* (*wmk upright*)	—	£475
251	**59**	£8 brownish red/*yellow* (*wmk upright*) (*glazed paper*)	—	£600
252	**60**	£9 yellow-green/*green* (*wmk upright*) (*glazed paper*) (F.C. £100)	—	£600

(*b*) *Typo from electrotypes*

(i) *Wmk V over Crown, W* **19**, (*sideways*). *P* 13

No.	Type	Description	Unused	Used
253	**39**	1d. yellowish green	28·00	8·00
		a. Perf 12	28·00	8·50
		b. Perf 12½		
254	**40**	1d. pale bistre	8·00	1·25
		a. Perf 12	8·00	2·25
		b. Perf 12½		
255	**41**	6d. dull blue	35·00	5·50
		a. Perf 12	40·00	13·00
		b. Perf 12½		
256	**42**	1s. deep blue/*blue*	55·00	4·50
		a. Perf 12	55·00	5·50
		b. Perf 12½		
		c. Brt blue/blue (*glazed paper*) (*p* 12½)	55·00	5·00
		ca. Perf 12	—	5·50
		d. Ultramarine/blue (*glazed paper*) (*p* 12½) (11.84)	90·00	5·50
257		1s. chalky blue/*lemon* (*glazed paper*) (*p* 12½) (3.3.85)	75·00	22·00
258	**44**	2s. deep blue/*green* (*glazed paper*)	£100	13·00
		a. Perf 12	—	15·00
		b. Perf 12½	—	17·00
		c. Indigo/green	80·00	17·00
		ca. Perf 12	£120	18·00
		cb. Perf 12½		
259	**45**	3s. mar/*bl* (*glazed paper*) (*p* 12½) (8.8.84)	£160	24·00
260	**47**	5s. claret/*yellow* (*glazed paper*)	50·00	4·50
		a. Perf 12	60·00	10·00
		b. Perf 12½		
		c. Pale claret/yellow (*p* 12½)	50·00	10·00
		ca. Perf 12	70·00	10·00
		d. Reddish purple/lemon (*p* 12½) (6.87)	45·00	11·00
		e. Brown-red/yellow (*p* 12½) (5.93)	75·00	22·00
261	**49**	10s. chocolate/*rose* (*glazed paper*)	—	55·00
		a. Perf 12		
		b. Perf 12½		
		c. Wmk upright		
262	**51**	£1 yellow-orange/*yellow* (*p* 12)	£550	75·00
		a. Orange/yellow (*p* 12½) (8.84)	£500	55·00
		b. Reddish orange/yellow (*p* 12½) (9.88)	£325	55·00
263	**54**	£2 deep blue (*p* 12)	—	85·00
264	**61**	£10 dull mauve (*p* 12)		
		a. Deep red-lilac (*p* 12)	£1500	95·00

(ii) *Wmk V over Crown, W* **33**, (*sideways*). *P* 12½

No.	Type	Description	Unused	Used
265	**40**	1d. ochre	16·00	2·50
		a. Perf 12	16·00	2·50
266	**41**	6d. ultramarine	50·00	4·50
		a. Perf 12	50·00	4·50
267	**43**	1s. 6d. pink (1.85)	£130	25·00
		a. Bright rose-carmine (4.86)	£150	23·00
268	**45**	3s. drab (20.10.85)	75·00	16·00
		a. Olive-drab (1.93)	70·00	16·00
269	**46**	4s. red-orange (5.86)	80·00	12·00
		a. Yellow-orange (12.94)		
		ab. Wmk upright	£100	9·00
270	**47**	5s. rosine (8.5.96)	75·00	19·00
271	**48**	6s. pea-green (12.11.91)	£110	35·00
		a. Apple-green (*wmk upright*) (3.96)	£180	35·00
272	**49**	10s. dull bluish green (10.85)	£150	30·00
		a. Grey-green (5.86)	£110	27·00
273	**50**	15s. purple-brown (12.85)	£550	75·00
		a. Brown (*wmk upright*) (5.95)	£550	80·00
274	**52**	£1 5s. pink (*wmk upright*) (6.8.90)	£850	80·00
275	**53**	£1 10s. pale olive (6.88)	£600	70·00
276	**54**	£2 bright blue	—	75·00
		a. Blue (7.88)	£750	75·00
277	**55**	45s. lilac (15.8.90)	£2000	90·00
278	**56**	£5 rose-pink (*p* 12)	—	£200
		a. Pink (*p* 12½)	—	£325
279	**61**	£10 mauve (3.84)	£1700	90·00
		a. Lilac (6.85)	—	£100

*This is the date on which the stamps became valid for postal use. The 1d., 6d., 1s., 1s.6d., 2s., 3s., 4s., 5s., 10s., 15s., £1, £1 10s., £2, £5 and £10 were issued for fiscal purposes on 18 December 1879 with the £1 5s., 35s., 45s., £6 and £9 added to the range later the same month and the 6s., £7 and £8 in January 1880.

Used prices for the £1 5s., £1 10s., £2 (No. 276*a*), 45s. and £10 watermarked W **33** are for examples from the cancelled-to-order sets sold to collectors by the Victoria postal authorities between September 1900 and 30 June 1902.

Similar Stamp Duty designs were prepared for 7s., 8s., 9s., 11s., 12s., 13s., 14s., 16s., 17s., 18s., and 19s., but were never issued.

The two different 1d. designs were reprinted in 1891 on W **33** paper.

For these designs with later watermarks see Nos. 345/50 and 369/71.

62

(Des C. Jackson and L. Lang. Dies eng C. Jackson)

1884 (1 Jan*)–**1900**. *High value Stamp Duty series.*

(*a*) *Recess-printed direct from the die*

(i) *Wmk V over Crown, W* **19**, (*sideways*). *P* 12½

No.	Type	Description	Unused	Used
280	**62**	£25 yellow-green (F.C. £55)		
		a. Wmk upright		
		b. Perf 13		
		c. Deep green (F.C. £55)		
		ca. Wmk upright		
281		£50 bright mauve (F.C. £85)		
		a. Wmk upright		
		b. Perf 13		
282		£100 crimson-lake (F.C. £110)		
		a. Wmk upright		
		b. Perf 13		

(ii) *Wmk V over Crown, W* **33**, (*sideways*). *P* 12½

No.	Type	Description	Unused	Used
283	**62**	£25 yellow-green		
		a. Perf 12		
		b. Deep green (1.85) (F.C. £55)	—	£375
		c. Bright blue-green (10.90) (F.C. £55)		
		ca. Wmk upright		
284		£50 dull lilac-mauve (*wmk upright*) (F.C.£85)		
		a. Black-violet (10.90) (F.C. £65)	—	£375
		ab. Wmk upright		
285	**62**	£100 crimson (F.C. £120)		
		a. Wmk upright		
		b. Perf 12 (F.C. £120)		
		c. Aniline crimson (*wmk upright*) (2.85) (F.C. £120)	—	£45
		d. Scarlet-red (*wmk upright*) (5.95)	—	£35

(*b*) *Litho. Wmk V over Crown, W* **33**, (*sideways*). *P* 12½

No.	Type	Description	Unused	Used
286	**62**	£25 dull yellowish green (1.86) (F.C. £45)		
		a. Wmk upright (11.87)		
		b. Dull blue-green (9.88) (F.C. £45)		
		ba. Wmk upright		
287		£50 dull purple (1.86) (F.C. £60)		
		a. Wmk upright		
		b. Bright violet (11.89) (F.C. £60)		
		ba. Wmk upright		
288		£100 rosine (1.86) (F.C. £95)		
		a. Wmk upright		

(*c*) *Typo from electrotyped plates. Wmk V over Crown, W* **33**. *P* 12½

No.	Type	Description	Unused	Used
289	**62**	£25 dull blue-green (12.97)	—	90·0
290		£50 bright mauve (10.97)	—	£14
291		£100 pink-red (10.1900)	—	£19

*This is the date on which the stamps became valid for posta use. All three values were issued for fiscal purposes o 18 December 1879.

Used prices for Nos. 283*b*, 284*a*, 285*c*/*d* and 289/91 are fc examples from the cancelled-to-order sets described beneath N 279*a*. "F.C." indicates that the price quoted is for a stamp wit a fiscal cancellation.

For the £25 and £50 with watermark W **82** see Nos. 351/2.

63

(Des and die eng C. Naish. Typo from electrotyped plates)

1884 (23 Apr)–**92**. *New design inscr* "STAMP DUTY". *Wmk over Crown, W* **33** (*sideways*). *P* 12½.

No.	Type	Description	Unused	Used
292	**63**	2s. 6d. brown-orange	85·00	12·C
		a. Yellow (8.85)	80·00	11·C
		b. Lemon-yellow (2.92)	80·00	11·C

For this design on later watermarks see Nos. 344 and 368.

64

65

66

67

68

(Des and dies eng C. Naish. Typo from electrotyped plates)

1885 (1 Jan)–**95**. *New designs inscr* "STAMP DUTY". *P* 12½

(*a*) *W* **19**

No.	Type	Description	Unused	Used
293	**68**	8d. rose/*pink*	20·00	5·5
		a. Rose-red/pink (2.88)	22·00	5·5
294	**66**	1s. deep dull blue/*lemon* (11.85)	50·00	7·C
		a. Dull blue/yellow (6.86)	50·00	7·5
295	**68**	2s. olive/*bluish green* (12.85)	38·00	3·C

(*b*) *W* **33**

No.	Type	Description	Unused	Used
296	**64**	½d. pale rosine	6·50	6
		a. Deep rosine (7.85)	7·50	1·C
		b. Salmon (9.85)	8·00	1·2
297	**65**	1d. yellowish green (1.85)	7·50	5
		a. Dull pea-green (2.85)	12·00	1·7
298	**66**	2d. lilac	6·00	3
		a. Mauve (1886)	6·00	3
		b. Rosy-mauve (1886)	7·50	5
299	**65**	3d. yellowish brown	9·00	9
		a. Pale ochre (9.86)	8·50	9
		b. Bistre-yellow (9.92)	9·00	9
300	**67**	4d. magenta	35·00	3·C
		a. Bright mauve-rose (12.86)	38·00	3·5
		b. Error. Lilac (12.86)	£2250	£40
301	**65**	6d. chalky blue (1.85)	48·00	2·5
		a. Bright blue (3.85)	30·00	2·
		b. Cobalt (7.85)	30·00	2·
302	**68**	8d. bright scarlet/*pink* (3.95)	30·00	8·C
303		2s. olive-green/*pale green* (1.90)	25·00	3·7
304		2s. apple-green (12.8.95)	25·00	32·C
		a. Blue-green (29.10.95)	18·00	6·0

The plates for the 1d., 6d., 1s. and 2s. were derived from th dies of the 2d. (1s.), 3d. (1d. and 6d.) and 8d. (2s.). In eac instance lead moulds of six impressions were taken from th original die and the face values altered by hand creating si slightly different versions.

Two states of the 2d. die exist with the second showing a brea in the top frame line near the righthand corner. This damage die was used for seven impressions on Plate 1 and all 120 c Plate 2.

No. 300b occured during the December 1886 printing of th 4d. when about fifty sheets were printed in the colour of the 2 mistake. The sheets were issued to Melbourne post offices ıd used examples are known postmarked between December 1886 and 4 March 1887. Nine unused are also lieved to exist.

Reprints of the ½d., 1d., 2d., 4d., 6d. and 1s. values were made 1891 from the existing plates. The 1s. was watermarked W **19** ıd the remainder W **33**.

For some of these values used with later watermarks see Nos. 6, 343, 360, 368 and X362.

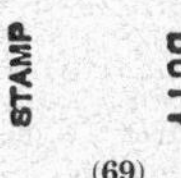

(69)

85 (Feb–Nov). *Optd with T* **69**. *P* 12½. (*a*) *W* **19**

5 **15** 3d. dull orge-yell (*glazed paper*) (B.) (Nov) — £130
6 **26** 1s. pale blue/*blue* (*glazed paper*) (*p* 13) 95·00 20·00
a. Deep blue/blue — 22·00
b. Blue opt (F.C. £14) £1200 £600
7 **27** 2s. ultramarine/*grn* (*glazed paper*) (Mar) 85·00 18·00
a. Wmk sideways 95·00 20·00

(*b*) *W* **33**

8 **15** 3d. yellow-orange (B.) (Nov) 60·00 22·00
a. Dull brownish orange (B.) 65·00 24·00
9 **32** 4d. rose-red (B.) (Nov) 55·00 23·00

Unauthorised reprints of the 4d. and 1s., both with blue erprints and watermarked W **33**, were made during 1895–96. ıe 4d. reprint, which is in pale red, also exists without the erprint.

70 71 72

73 74 75

76 77 78

79 80

Des S. Reading (1d. (No. 313), M. Tannenberg (2½d., 5d.), C. Naish (1s. 6d.), P. Astley (others). Dies eng C. Naish (2d., 4d. (both existing dies with lines added behind Queen's head) and 1s. 6d.), S. Reading (originally as an employee of Fergusson & Mitchell) (others). Typo from electrotyped plates)

1886 (26 July)–**96**. *W* **33** (*sideways on* ½*d.*, 1*s.*, £5, £7 *to* £9). *P* 12½.

310 **70** ½d. lilac-grey (28.8.86) 18·00 3·00
a. Grey-black — 35·00
311 ½d. pink (15.2.87) 6·00 30
a. Rosine (*aniline*) (1889) 4·75 30
b. Rose-red (1891) 4·50 30
c. Vermilion (1896) 4·75 35
312 **71** 1d. green 5·25 40
a. Yellow-green (1887) 5·25 40
313 **72** 1d. dull chestnut (1.1.90) 4·50 30
a. Deep red-brown (1890) 4·50 40
b. Orange-brown (1890) 4·50 30
c. Brown-red (1890) 4·50 30
d. Yellow-brown (1891) 4·50 30
e. Bright yellow-orange (1893) 50·00 12·00
f. Brownish orange (1894) 3·50 30
314 **73** 2d. pale lilac (17.12.86) 4·75 20
a. Pale mauve (1887) 5·50 20
b. Deep lilac (1888, 1892) 4·50 20
c. Purple (1894) 3·25 25
d. Violet (1895) 3·25 20
e. Imperf — £700
315 **74** 2½d. red-brown/*lemon* (1.1.91) 12·00 1·75
a. Brown-red/yellow (1892) 8·00 80
b. Red/yellow (1893) 6·00 70
316 **75** 4d. rose-red (1.4.87) 11·00 1·00
a. Red (1893) 5·75 90
317 **76** 5d. purple-brown (1.1.91) 8·50 85
a. Pale reddish brown (1893) 6·50 80
318 **77** 6d. bright ultramarine (27.8.86) 11·00 80
a. Pale ultramarine (1887) 9·50 50
b. Dull blue (1891) 8·50 50
319 **25** 9d. apple-green (18.10.92) 20·00 9·00
320 9d. carmine-rose (15.10.95) 22·00 5·00
a. Rosine (*aniline*) (1896) 24·00 5·50
321 **78** 1s. dull purple-brown (14.3.87) 35·00 2·00
a. Lake (1890) 27·00 1·75
b. Carmine-lake (1892) 15·00 1·00
c. Brownish red (1896) 16·00 1·60
322 **79** 1s. 6d. pale blue (9.88) £120 65·00
323 1s. 6d. orange (19.9.89) 15·00 4·50
a. Red-orange (1893) 15·00 5·00
324 **80** £5 pale blue and maroon (7.2.88)† £1000 80·00
325 £6 yellow and pale blue (1.10.87)† £1200 £100
326 £7 rosine and black (17.10.89)† £1400 £120
327 £8 mauve & brown-orange (2.8.90)† £1500 £150
328 £9 apple-green and rosine (21.8.88)† £1800 £160

†The used prices provided for these stamps are for cancelled-to-order examples.

Unauthorised reprints of the ½d. lilac-grey and 1s. 6d. pale blue were made in 1894–95 on W **33** paper and perforated 12½. These differ in shade from the originals and have rougher perforations. It should be noted that the original printing of No. 322 does not occur with inverted watermark, but the reprint does.

A single example of No. 314e is known postmarked "737" (Foster). A second, postmarked "249" (Mortlake), was reported in 1892. It is known that an imperforate sheet was sold at Mortlake P.O. in 1890. Other examples are believed to be clandestine.

A £10 value as Type **80** was prepared, but not issued.

1891 (17 June). *W* **19**. *P* 12½.

329 **72** 1d. orange-brown/*pink* 4·50 1·75

No. 329 was an emergency printing during a shortage of white W **33** paper.

81

82

(Die eng A. Williams (1½d.). Typo from electrotyped plates)

1896 (11 June)–**99**. *W* **82** (*sideways on* ½*d.*, 1½*d.*, 1*s.*, 2*s.* 6*d. to* 15*s.*). *P* 12½.

330 **70** ½d. light scarlet (1.7.96) 3·00 15
a. Carmine-rose (1897) 3·25 15
b. Dp carmine-red (*coarse impression*) (1899) — 1·25
c. Wmk upright † —
331 ½d. emerald (1.8.99) 7·50 1·25
332 **72** 1d. brown-red (13.6.96) 4·25 10
a. Brownish orange (1897) 4·25 10
333 **81** 1½d. apple-green (7.10.97) 4·00 1·50
334 **73** 2d. violet 4·50 10
a. Wmk sideways † —
335 **74** 2½d. blue (1.8.99) 7·50 3·75
336 **65** 3d. ochre (11.96) 7·00 55
a. Buff (1898) 6·50 50
337 **75** 4d. red (6.97) 8·50 90
338 **76** 5d. red-brown (7.97) 13·00 95
339 **77** 6d. dull blue (9.96) 10·00 55
340 **25** 9d. rosine (8.96) 24·00 3·00
a. Rose-carmine (1898) — 3·00
b. Dull rose (1898) 20·00 3·00
341 **78** 1s. brownish red (3.97) 11·00 1·75
342 **79** 1s. 6d. brown-orange (8.98) 27·00 9·00
343 **68** 2s. blue-green (4.97) 24·00 6·00
344 **63** 2s. 6d. yellow (9.96) 90·00 12·00
a. Wmk upright (1898) £100 12·00
345 **45** 3s. olive-drab (12.96) 55·00 17·00
a. Wmk upright (1898) 55·00 16·00
346 **46** 4s. orange (9.97) 80·00 7·00
347 **47** 5s. rosine (2.97) 80·00 8·00
a. Rose-carmine (1897) 80·00 8·00
b. Wmk upright. *Rosine* (1899) 80·00 8·50
348 **48** 6s. pale yellow-green (4.99)† 80·00 23·00
349 **49** 10s. grey-green (4.97) £100 16·00
a. Blue-green (1898) £100 16·00
350 **50** 15s. brown (4.97)† £325 40·00
351 **62** £25 dull bluish green (1897)† — £100
352 £50 dull purple (1897)† — £130

†The used prices provided for these stamps are for cancelled-to-order examples.

83 84

(Des M. Tannenberg. Dies eng A. Mitchelhill. Typo from electrotyped plates)

1897 (22 Oct). *Hospital Charity Fund. W* **82** (*sideways*). *P* 12½.

353 **83** 1d. (1s.) blue 18·00 18·00
354 **84** 2½d. (2s. 6d) red-brown 85·00 70·00
353/4 Optd "Specimen" *Set of* 2 £140

These stamps were sold at 1s. and 2s. 6d., but only had postal validity for 1d. and 2½d. with the difference going to the Fund.

1899 (1 Aug). *W* **33** (*sideways*). *P* 12½.

355 **81** 1½d. brown-red/*yellow* 3·00 1·75

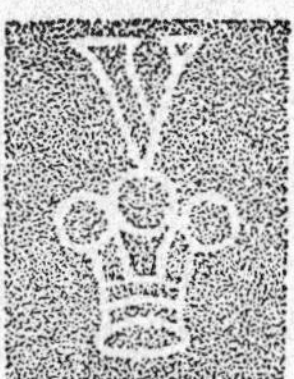

85

1899 (1 Aug)–**1901**. *W* **85** (*sideways on* ½*d.*, 1*s. and* 2*s.* 6*d. to* 10*s.*). *P* 12½.

356 **70** ½d. emerald (12.99) 4·75 40
a. Deep blue-green 5·00 40
b. Wmk upright
357 **72** 1d. rose-red 4·50 15
a. Rosine (1900) 4·25 10
358 1d. olive (6.6.01) 5·00 4·00
359 **73** 2d. violet 6·00 10
a. Wmk sideways † —
360 **74** 2½d. blue (10.99) 7·00 1·50
361 **65** 3d. bistre-yellow (9.99) 7·00 90
362 3d. slate-green (20.6.01) 21·00 7·00
363 **75** 4d. rose-red (12.99) 4·75 95
364 **76** 5d. red-brown (10.99) 9·00 95
365 **77** 6d. dull ultramarine (1.00) 7·00 65
366 **25** 9d. rose-red (9.99) 11·00 1·75
367 **78** 1s. brown-red (5.00) 12·00 1·75
368 **79** 1s. 6d. orange (2.00) 14·00 6·00
369 **68** 2s. blue-green (6.00) 17·00 5·50
370 **63** 2s. 6d. yellow (1.00) £300 13·00
371 **45** 3s. pale olive (4.00)† £130 18·00
372 **47** 5s. rose-red (4.00) £100 18·00
373 **49** 10s. green (3.00)† £130 19·00

†The used prices provided for these stamps are for cancelled-to-order examples.

From 1 July 1901 stamps inscribed "STAMP DUTY" could only be used for fiscal purposes.

86 Victoria Cross

87 Australian Troops in South Africa

(Des Sands and MacDougall (1d.), J. Sutherland (2d.). Dies eng S. Reading. Typo from electrotyped plates)

1900 (22 May). *Empire Patriotic Fund. W* **85** (*sideways*). *P* 12½.

374 **86** 1d. (1s.) olive-brown 55·00 35·00
375 **87** 2d. (2s.) emerald-green £110 £110

These stamps were sold at 1s. and 2s., but only had postal validity for 1d. and 2d. with the difference going to the Fund.

FEDERATION. The six Australian colonies were federated as the Commonwealth of Australia on 1 January 1901. Under the terms of the Post and Telegraph Act their postal services were amalgamated on 1 March 1901, but other clauses to safeguard the financial position of the individual States provided them with a large degree of independence until 13 October 1910 when issues of each state could be used throughout Australia. Postage stamps for the Commonwealth of Australia did not appear until January 1913.

It was agreed in 1901 that stamp printing should be centralised at Melbourne under J. B. Cooke of South Australia who was appointed Commonwealth Stamp Printer. By 1909 the Commonwealth Stamp Printing Branch in Melbourne was producing stamps for Papua, South Australia, Tasmania and Western Australia in addition to those of Victoria.

On federation it was decided to separate postal and fiscal stamp issues so Victoria needed urgent replacements for the current Stamp Duty series which reverted to fiscal use only on 30 June 1901.

1901 (29 Jan). *Re-use of previous designs without* "POSTAGE" *inscr. W* **82** (2*s.*) *or W* **85** (*others*) (*sideways on* ½*d.*). *P* 12×12½.

376 **22** ½d. bluish green 2·00 85
a. "VICTCRIA" (R. 7/19) 35·00 25·00
377 **31** 2d. reddish violet 5·50 75
378 **15** 3d. dull orange 15·00 1·25
379 **32** 4d. bistre-yellow 25·00 12·00
380 **16** 6d. emerald 9·00 5·50
381 **26** 1s. yellow 35·00 30·00
382 **27** 2s. blue/*pink* 42·00 15·00
383 **18** 5s. pale red and deep blue 45·00 30·00

88

89

90

91 92 93 94 95 96 97 98 99 100 101 102

I II III

Three die states of ½d.:

I. Outer vertical line of colour to left of "V" continuous except for a break opposite the top of "V". Triangles either end of "VICTORIA" are more or less solid colour.
II. Die re-engraved. Three breaks in outer line of colour left of "V". White lines added to left triangle.
III. Die re-engraved. As II, but equivalent triangle at right also contains white lines.

I

II

III

I and II

III

Three die states of 1d.:

I. Thick lines fill top of oval above Queen's head.
II. Die re-engraved. Lines thinner, showing white space between.
III. Die re-engraved. As II, but with bottom left value table recut to show full point separated from both "1" and the circular frame.

Two die states of 2d.:

I. Frame line complete at top right corner. Bottom right corner comes to a point.
II. Break in right frame line just below the top corner. Bottom right corner is blunted.

Two types of 1s.:

A. "POSTAGE" 6 mm long (produced by a hand punch applied twice to each impression on the previous 1s. electrotyped plate. Slight variations in position occur).
B. "POSTAGE" 7 mm long (produced from new electrotyped plates incorporating the "POSTAGE" inscriptions).

(Eng S. Reading after photo by W. Stuart (£1, £2))

1901 (29 Jan)–**10.** *Previous issues with* "POSTAGE" *added and new designs* (£1, £2). *W* **85** (*sideways on ½d., 1½d.,* £1, £2).

(a) P 12×12½

No.	Type	Description	Unused	Used
384	**88**	½d. blue-green (I) (26.6.01)	1·90	20
		a. Wmk upright (1903)	1·90	20
		b. Die state II (6.04)	3·25	20
		ba. Wmk upright	3·50	5·50
385	**89**	1d. rose (I)	3·00	15
		a. Dull red (12.02)	2·50	15
		ab. Wmk sideways	†	—
		b. Die state II (4.01)	1·50	15
		ba. Dull red (12.02)	1·25	15
		c. Die state II. *Pale rose-red* (4.05)	3·00	70
		ca. Wmk sideways	50·00	50·00
386	**90**	1½d. maroon/*yellow* (9.7.01)	6·50	3·00
		a. Wmk upright. *Brn-red/yell* (9.01)	2·10	55
		b. Dull red-brown/yellow (1906)	2·10	55
		ba. On yellow-buff back (1908)	2·75	1·00
387	**91**	2d. lilac (I) (26.6.01)	6·00	30
		a. Die state II	20·00	1·50
		b. Reddish violet (1902)	6·00	30
		ba. Die state II	20·00	1·50
		c. Bright purple (II) (1905)	7·00	30
		d. Rosy mauve (II) (1905)		
388	**92**	2½d. dull blue	6·00	35
		a. Deep blue (1902)	6·00	35
389	**93**	3d. dull orange-brown (5.7.01)	7·50	80
		a. Chestnut (1901)	6·50	55
		b. Yellowish brown (1903)	6·50	55
		ba. Wmk sideways	11·00	15·00
390	**94**	4d. bistre-yellow (26.6.01)	5·50	55
		a. Brownish bistre (1905)	8·50	70
391	**95**	5d. reddish brown	7·50	40
		a. Purple-brown (1903)	6·50	40
392	**96**	6d. emerald (5.7.01)	12·00	80
		a. Dull green (1904)	14·00	85
393	**97**	9d. dull rose-red (5.7.01)	12·00	1·75
		a. Wmk sideways (1901)	18·00	3·50
		b. Pale red (1901)	12·00	1·25
		c. Dull brownish red (1905)	15·00	2·00
394	**98**	1s. yellow-orange (A) (5.7.01)	14·00	1·75
		a. Yellow (1902)	16·00	1·75
		b. Type B (4.03)	16·00	3·00
		ba. Orange (1904)	14·00	2·50
		bb. Wmk sideways (1905)	24·00	6·00
395	**99**	2s. blue/*rose* (5.7.01)	22·00	2·00

(b) P 12½

No.	Type	Description	Unused	Used
396	**88**	½d. blue-green (III) (6.05)	7·50	50
397	**92**	2½d. dull blue (1901)	£250	£250
398	**100**	5s. rose-red and pale blue (5.7.01)	65·00	12·00
		a. Scarlet and deep blue (12.01)	70·00	10·00
		b. Rosine and blue (12.04)	70·00	10·00
399	**101**	£1 carmine-rose (18.11.01)	£225	£100
400	**102**	£2 deep blue (2.6.02)	£500	£250

(c) P 11

No.	Type	Description	Unused	Used
401	**88**	½d. blue-green (I) (9.02)	5·00	1·75
		a. Wmk upright (1903)	3·25	50
		b. Die state II (6.04)	4·00	50
		c. Die state III (6.05)	5·00	75
402	**89**	1d. dull red (I) (12.02)	55·00	40·00
		a. Die state II	45·00	18·00
		ab. Pale red (*aniline*) (3.03)	5·00	1·50
		ac. Pale rose (*aniline*) (1904)	25·00	3·50
		b. Die state III. *Pale rose-red* (7.05)	45·00	25·00
403	**90**	1½d. dull red-brown/*yellow* (1910)	40·00	40·00
404	**91**	2d. bright purple (II) (1905)	£500	£180
		a. Rosy mauve (II) (1905)	†	—
405	**93**	3d. yellowish brown (1903)	5·50	4·00
		a. Wmk sideways	15·00	20·00
406	**96**	6d. emerald (2.03)	12·00	15·00
		a. Dull green (1905)	£325	£160
407	**101**	£1 rose (5.05)	£275	£130
408	**102**	£2 deep blue (1905)	£850	£750

(d) Compound or mixed perf 12½ *and* 11

No.	Type	Description	Unused	Used
409	**88**	½d. blue-green (I) (1901)	22·00	7·00
		a. Wmk upright (1903)	—	7·00
		b. Die state II (1904)	20·00	16·00
		ba. Wmk upright	35·00	
410	**89**	1d. dull red (I) (1902)	—	£180
		a. Die state II	£350	£140
411	**90**	1½d. maroon/*yellow* (1903)	£500	£200
412	**91**	2d. reddish violet (I) (1903)	†	£300
413	**93**	3d. dull orange-brown (1902)	—	£450
414	**96**	6d. emerald (1903)	†	£400
415	**100**	5s. rosine and blue (12.04)	£800	

Examples of the 1d. Die state II perforated 12½ exist with two black lines printed across the face of the stamp. These were prepared in connection with stamp-vending machine trials.

1905–13. *Wmk Crown over A, W* w **11** (*sideways on ½d.,* £1, £2).

(a) P 12×12½

No.	Type	Description	Unused	Used
416	**88**	½d. blue-green (*shades*) (III) (21.10.05)	1·60	15
		a. Wmk upright. Thin, ready gummed paper (6.12)	3·50	3·50
417	**89**	1d. rose-red (III) (16.7.05)	1·25	
		a. Pale rose (1907)	1·25	
		b. Rose-carmine (1911)	3·50	
		ba. Wmk sideways	10·00	4·
		c. Thin, ready gummed paper (10.12)	4·50	1·
418	**91**	2d. dull mauve (II) (13.9.05)	6·00	
		a. Lilac (1906)	6·00	
		b. Reddish violet (1907)	6·00	
		c. Bright mauve (1910)	4·75	
		ca. Thin, ready gummed paper (8.12)	26·00	4·
419	**92**	2½d. blue (10.08)	3·00	
		a. Indigo (1909)	5·00	
420	**93**	3d. orange-brown (11.11.05)	7·00	
		a. Yellow-orange (1908)	8·00	
		b. Dull orange-buff (1909)	8·00	
		c. Ochre (1912)	8·00	3·
421	**94**	4d. yellow-bistre (15.1.06)	7·00	
		a. Olive-bistre (1908)	7·00	
		b. Yellow-olive (1912)	7·00	3·
422	**95**	5d. chocolate (14.8.06)	7·00	1·
		a. Dull reddish brown (1908)	7·00	1·
		ab. Thin, ready gummed paper (19.10.12)	13·00	7·
423	**96**	6d. dull green (25.10.05)	12·00	
		a. Dull yellow-green (1907)	12·00	
		b. Emerald (1909)	12·00	1·
		c. Yellowish green (1911)	12·00	1·
		d. Emerald. Thin, ready gummed paper (11.12)	18·00	10·
424	**97**	9d. brown-red (11.12.05)	13·00	1·
		a. Orange-brown (1906)	13·00	1·
		b. Red-brown (1908)	13·00	1·
		c. Pale dull rose (1909)	14·00	2·
		d. Rose-carmine (1910)	9·50	1·
425	**98**	1s. orange (B) (13.2.06)	8·00	2·
		a. Yellow-orange (1906)	11·00	2·
		b. Yellow (1908)	13·00	2·
		ba. Thin, ready gummed paper (11.12)	28·00	18·
		c. Pale orange. Thin, ready gummed paper (1913)	28·00	18·

(b) P 12½

No.	Type	Description	Unused	Used
426	**88**	½d. blue-green (*shades*) (III) (1905)	2·25	
		a. Wmk upright (1909)	12·00	2·
		b. Thin, ready gummed paper (1912)	5·00	
		ba. Wmk upright	3·50	3·
427	**89**	1d. rose-red (III) (1905)	2·25	
		a. Rose-carmine (1911)	5·00	1·
428	**92**	2½d. indigo (1909)	9·00	1·
429	**96**	6d. yellowish green (1911)	17·00	5·
430	**100**	5s. rose-red and ultramarine (12.07)	70·00	13·
		a. Rose-red and blue (1911)	80·00	13·
		ab. Wmk sideways	80·00	16·
431	**101**	£1 salmon (12.2.07)	£225	£1
		a. Dull rose (1910)	£225	£1
		ab. Wmk upright (1911)	£275	£1
432	**102**	£2 dull blue (18.7.06)	£500	£2

(c) P 11

No.	Type	Description	Unused	Used
433	**88**	½d. blue-green (*shades*) (III) (1905)	1·60	
		a. Wmk upright. Thin, ready gummed paper (1912)	15·00	15·
434	**89**	1d. rose-red (III) (1905)	3·50	
		a. Pale rose (1907)	3·50	
		b. Rose-carmine (1911)	7·00	3·
		ba. Wmk sideways	10·00	4·
		c. Thin, ready gummed paper (10.12)	7·50	4·
435	**91**	2d. lilac (II) (1906)	†	£1
		a. Reddish violet (1907)	65·00	15·
		b. Bright mauve (1910)	25·00	8·
436	**92**	2½d. blue (1908)	60·00	8·
		a. Indigo (1909)	10·00	5·
437	**93**	3d. orange-brown (1905)	10·00	7·
		a. Yellow-orange (1908)	†	£1
		b. Dull orange-buff (1909)	15·00	15·
		c. Ochre (1912)	8·00	4·
438	**94**	4d. yellow-bistre (1906)	9·00	15·
		a. Olive-bistre (1909)		
		b. Yellow-olive (1912)	8·50	11·
439	**95**	5d. chocolate (1906)	†	£4
		a. Dull reddish brown (1908)	†	£4
440	**96**	6d. emerald (1909)	10·00	14·
		a. Yellowish green (1911)	15·00	18·
441	**97**	9d. rose-carmine (1910)	†	£3
442	**98**	1s. yellow-orange (B) (1906)	†	£1
		a. Orange (1910)	£375	
443	**100**	5s. rose-red and ultramarine (12.07)	70·00	9·
444	**101**	£1 salmon (12.2.07)	£275	£1
445	**102**	£2 dull blue (1.07)	£650	£3

(d) Compound or mixed perfs 12½ *and* 11

No.	Type	Description	Unused	Used
446	**88**	½d. blue-green (*shades*) (III) (1905)	17·00	16·
		a. Wmk upright. Thin, ready gummed paper (1912)	£110	80·
447	**89**	1d. rose-red (III) (1905)	32·00	32·
		a. Pale rose (1907)	—	40·
		b. Rose-carmine (1911)	—	40·
448	**91**	2d. reddish violet (II) (1907)	£350	£2
449	**93**	3d. orange-brown (1905)	†	£2
		a. Ochre (1912)	£250	
450	**94**	4d. bistre (1908)	†	£2
451	**96**	6d. emerald (1909)	—	£3
		a. Yellowish green (1911)	†	£2
452	**97**	9d. orange-brown (1906)	†	£4
		a. Red-brown (1908)	†	£4
453	**98**	1s. yellow-orange (1906)	£600	

(e) Rotary comb perf 11½×12¼

No.	Type	Description	Unused	Used
454	**89**	1d. pale rose (III) (2.10)	6·50	1·
		a. Rose-carmine (1911)		
		ab. Thin, ready gummed paper (7.12)	3·25	2·
		b. Rose-red. Thin, ready gummed paper (10.12)	3·25	2·
455	**91**	2d. lilac (II) (1910)	8·50	1·

The original Crown over A watermark paper used by Victori[a] was of medium thickness and had toned gum applied aft[er] printing. Stocks of this paper lasted until 1912 when furth[er] supplies were ordered from a new papermakers, Cowan an[d] Sons. This paper was much thinner and was supplied with whi[te] gum already applied. The first delivery arrived in June 1912 an[d] a second in September of the same year.

The rotary comb perforating gauging 11½×12¼ was transferred from South Australia in 1909 when J. B. Cook moved to Melbourne.

Examples of the 1d. perforated 12½ or 11 exist with two black nes across the face of the stamp. These were prepared in nnection with stamp-vending machine trials.

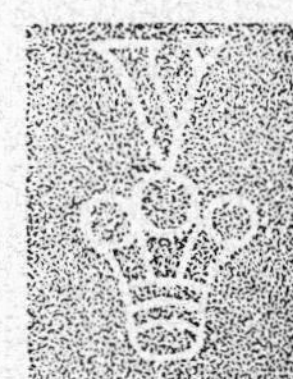

ONE PENNY

(103) 104

912 (29 June). *No. 455 surch with T* **103** *in red.*
56 **91** 1d. on 2d. lilac (II) 70 45

912 (Aug–Sept). *W* **104**. (a) *P* 12×12½
57 **89** 1d. rose-carmine (III) .. .. .. 2·75 2·00
a. Wmk sideways .. .. .. 50·00
58 **91** 2d. reddish violet (II) (Sept) .. .. 3·00 2·75
a. Lilac .. .. 5·50 4·00
59 **97** 9d. rose-carmine .. .. .. 15·00 11·00

(b) *P* 12½
60 **88** ½d. bluish green (III) .. .. .. 3·00 3·00

(c) *P* 11
61 **88** ½d. bluish green (III) .. .. .. 20·00 20·00
62 **89** 1d. rose-carmine (III) .. .. .. 28·00 12·00
63 **97** 9d. rose-carmine .. .. .. 20·00 16·00

(d) *Compound or mixed perfs* 12½ *and* 11
64 **97** 9d. rose-carmine .. .. .. † £425

Nos. 457/64 were emergency printings caused by the non-rrival of stocks of the Cowan thin, ready gummed Crown over watermarked paper. Paper watermarked W **104** had been ntroduced in 1911 and was normally used for Victoria fiscal tamps. This watermark can be easily distinguished from the revious W **85** by its narrow crown.

STAMP BOOKLETS

There are very few surviving examples of Nos. SB1/4. Listings re provided for those believed to have been issued with prices uoted for those known to still exist.

904 (Mar)–09. *Black on red cover as No.* SB1 *of New South Wales. Stapled.*
B1 £1 booklet containing two hundred and forty 1d. in four blocks of 30 and two blocks of 60 ..
a. Red on pink cover (1909) £6000
b. Blue on pink cover £5000

904 (Mar). *Black on grey cover as No.* SB1. *Stapled.*
B2 £1 booklet containing one hundred and twenty 2d. in four blocks of 30 .. ..

910 (May). *Black on white cover as No.* SB3 *of New South Wales. Stapled.*
B3 2s. booklet containing eleven ½d. (No. 426, either in block of 6 plus block of 5 or block of 11, and eighteen 1d. (No. 427), either in three blocks of 6 or block of 6 plus block of 12 .. .. £2000
a. Black on pale green cover £2000

Unsold stock of No. SB3 was uprated with one additional ½d. n May 1911.

911 (Aug). *Red on pink cover as No.* SB3. *Stapled.*
B4 2s. booklet containing twelve ½d. (No. 426), either in two blocks of 6 or block of 12, and eighteen 1d. (No. 427), either in three blocks of 6 or block of 6 plus block of 12 .. .. £1500

POSTAGE DUE STAMPS

D 1

Dies eng A. Williams (values) and J. McWilliams (frame). Typo)

890 (12 Oct)–94. *Wmk V over Crown, W* **33**. *P* 12×12½.
1 **D 1** ½d. dull blue and brown-lake (24.12.90) 3·00 2·00
a. Dull blue and deep claret .. 2·75 3·50
2 1d. dull blue and brown-lake .. 4·50 1·40
a. Dull blue and brownish red (1.93) 6·00 1·10
3 2d. dull blue and brown-lake .. 7·50 1·10
a. Dull blue and brownish red (3.93) 8·00 90
4 4d. dull blue and brown-lake .. 9·00 2·00
a. Dull blue and pale claret (5.94) .. 11·00 6·00
5 5d. dull blue and brown-lake .. 8·50 2·00
6 6d. dull blue and brown-lake .. 9·50 1·75
7 10d. dull blue and brown-lake .. 70·00 38·00
8 1s. dull blue and brown-lake .. 48·00 6·50
9 2s. dull blue and brown-lake .. £110 48·00
10 5s. dull blue and brown-lake .. £160 90·00
1/10 .. .. .. *Set of* 10 £375 £160
1a/10 Optd "Specimen" .. .. *Set of* 10 £300

A used example of the 6d. showing compound perforation of 2×12½ and 11 exists in the Royal Collection.

895 (17 Jan)–96. *Colours changed. Wmk V over Crown, W* **33**. *P* 12×12½.
11 **D 1** ½d. rosine and bluish green .. .. 3·00 1·60
a. Pale scarlet and yellow-green (3.96) 3·50 1·50
12 1d. rosine and bluish green .. .. 2·75 50
a. Pale scarlet and yellow-green (3.96) 3·00 60
D13 **D 1** 2d. rosine and bluish green .. .. 4·25 60
a. Pale scarlet and yellow-green (3.96) 4·75 70
D14 4d. rosine and bluish green .. .. 8·00 1·50
a. Pale scarlet and yellow-green (3.96) 9·50 1·00
D15 5d. rosine and bluish green .. .. 7·50 6·00
a. Pale scarlet and yellow-green (3.96) 8·50 4·25
D16 6d. rosine and bluish green .. .. 8·00 3·00
D17 10d. rosine and bluish green .. .. 14·00 10·00
D18 1s. rosine and bluish green .. .. 10·00 3·25
D19 2s. pale red & yellowish green (28.3.95) 60·00 20·00
D20 5s. pale red & yellowish green (28.3.95) £100 40·00
D11/20 .. .. *Set of* 10 £180 75·00

1897 (July)–**99**. *Wmk V over Crown. W* **82**. *P* 12×12½.
D21 **D 1** 1d. pale scarlet and yellow-green .. 4·25 80
a. Dull red and bluish green (8.99) 6·00 75
D22 2d. pale scarlet and yellow-green .. 6·00 80
a. Dull red and bluish green (6.99) 7·00 75
D23 4d. pale scarlet and yellow-green .. 9·00 2·25
a. Dull red and bluish green (8.99) 13·00 1·10
D24 5d. pale scarlet and yellow-green .. 9·00 2·50
D25 6d. pale scarlet and yellow-green .. 7·50 2·75
D21/5 .. .. *Set of* 5 32·00 7·00

1900 (June)–**04**. *Wmk V over Crown, W* **85**. *P* 12×12½.
D26 **D 1** ½d. rose-red and pale green .. .. 4·50 3·50
a. Pale red and deep green (8.01) .. 3·25 3·00
b. Scarlet and deep green (1.03) .. — 22·00
c. Aniline rosine and green (6.04) .. 5·00 6·00
D27 1d. rose-red and pale green .. .. 5·00 75
a. Pale red and deep green (9.01) .. 4·50 35
b. Scarlet and deep green (2.02) .. 5·50 50
c. Aniline rosine and green (9.03) .. 5·00 85
D28 2d. rose-red and pale green (7.00) .. 6·00 75
a. Pale red and deep green (9.01) .. 6·50 70
b. Scarlet and deep green (2.02) .. 6·50 50
c. Aniline rosine and green (9.03) .. 6·50 85
D29 4d. rose-red and pale green (5.01) .. 13·00 3·75
a. Pale red and deep green (9.01) .. 12·00 1·40
b. Scarlet and deep green (6.03) .. 12·00 2·00
c. Aniline rosine and green (6.04) .. 13·00 2·50
D30 5d. scarlet and deep green (1.03) .. 10·00 4·50
D31 1s. scarlet and deep green (3.02) .. 16·00 4·75
D32 2s. scarlet and deep green (1.03) .. £110 65·00
D33 5s. scarlet and deep green (1.03) .. £130 65·00
D26/33 .. .. *Set of* 8 £250 £130

1905 (Dec)–**09**. *Wmk Crown over A, W* w **11**. *P* 12×12½.
D34 **D 1** ½d. aniline rosine and pale green (1.06) 7·00 7·00
a. Scarlet & pale yellow-green (7.07) 3·75 3·75
b. Dull scarlet and pea-green (3.09) 5·50 4·00
ba. Compound perf 12×12½ and 11 £130 90·00
D35 1d. aniline rosine and pale green .. 35·00 4·75
a. Scarlet & pale yellow-green (5.06) 5·00 1·25
b. Dull scarlet and pea-green (1.07) 8·00 1·00
D36 2d. aniline scarlet & dp yell-grn (5.06) 6·50 1·40
a. Dull scarlet and pea-green (11.07) 8·00 1·00
D37 4d. dull scarlet and pea-green (1908) 18·00 6·50
D34/7 .. .. *Set of* 4 30·00 11·00

A printing of the 5d. in dull scarlet and pea-green on this paper was prepared in 1907–08, but not put into use. A few examples have survived, either mint or cancelled-to-order from presentation sets (*Price* £1000 *mint*, £750 *cancelled-to-order*).

WESTERN AUSTRALIA

PRICES FOR STAMPS ON COVER

Nos. 1/6	*from* × 6
Nos. 15/32	*from* × 4
Nos. 33/46	*from* × 5
Nos. 49/51	*from* × 6
Nos. 52/62	*from* × 10
Nos. 63/*a*	*from* × 8
No. 67	*from* × 6
Nos. 68/92*a*	*from* × 10
Nos. 94/102	*from* × 40
Nos. 103/5	*from* × 8
Nos. 107/10*a*	*from* × 12
Nos. 111*a*/*b*	—
Nos. 112/16	*from* × 25
Nos. 117/25	*from* × 10
Nos. 126/8	—
Nos. 129/34	*from* × 8
Nos. 135/6	—
Nos. 138/48	*from* × 12
Nos. 151/63	*from* × 5
Nos. 168/9	*from* × 20
Nos. 170/1	*from* × 4
Nos. 172/3	*from* × 40
Nos. F11/22	*from* × 10
Nos. T1/2	—

SPECIMEN OVERPRINTS. Those listed are from U.P.U. distributions between 1889 and 1892. Further "Specimen" overprints exist, but those were used for other purposes.

1

2

3

4

GUM. The 1854 issues are hardly ever seen with gum and so the unused prices quoted are for examples without gum.

(Eng W. Humphrys. Recess P.B.)

1854 (1 Aug). *W* **4** (*sideways*). (a) *Imperf.*
1 **1** 1d. black £800 £180

(b) *Rouletted* 7½ *to* 14 *and compound*
2 **1** 1d. black £1200 £350

In addition to the supplies received from London a further printing, using the original plate and watermarked paper from Perkins, Bacon, was made in the colony before the date of issue.

The 1d. is also known pin-perforated.

(Litho H. Samson (later A. Hillman), Government Lithographer)

1854 (1 Aug)–**55**. *W* **4** (*sideways*). (a) *Imperf.*
3 **2** 4d. pale blue £225 £150
a. Blue £225 £150
b. Deep dull blue £1200 £600
c. Slate-blue (1855) £1300 £700
4 **3** 1s. salmon .. .. — £1500
a. Deep red-brown £850 £425
b. Grey-brown (1.55) £450 £325
c. Pale brown (10.55) £325 £275

(b) *Rouletted* 7½ *to* 14 *and compound*
5 **2** 4d. pale blue £1100 £400
a. Blue .. .. — £400
b. Slate-blue (1855) .. .. .. — £1100
6 **3** 1s. grey-brown (1.55) £1400 £650
a. Pale brown (10.55) £1400 £650

The 1s. is also known pin-perforated.

The 4d. value was prepared from the Perkins, Bacon 1d. plate. A block of 60 (5 × 12) was taken as a transfer from this plate, the frames painted out and then individually replaced by transfers taken from a single impression master plate of the frame. Four transfers were then taken from this completed intermediate stone to construct the printing stone of 240 impressions. This first printing stone was used by H. Samson to print the initial supplies in July 1854.

The intermediate stone had carried several transfer errors, the most prominent of which was the "T" of "POSTAGE" sliced at foot, which appeared on four positions of the printing stone.

3d. "T" of "POSTAGE" shaved off to a point at foot (R.7/5, 7/10, 7/15, 7/20) £700 £500

The original printing stone also contained three scarce creased transfers, whose exact positions in the sheet have yet to be established. These were corrected during the first printing.

3e. Top of letters of "AUSTRALIA" cut off so that they are barely 1 mm high .. .. — £6000
f. "PEICE" instead of "PENCE" .. .. — £6000
g. "CE" of "Pence" close together .. .. — £8000

Further supplies were required in January 1855 and A. Hillman, Samson's successor, found, after printing three further sheets from the first printing stone, that two of the impressions on the intermediate stone were defective giving one inverted and one tilted frame. A second printing stone was then prepared on which the four positions of the inverted frame were individually corrected.

3h. Frame inverted (R.8/1, 8/6, 8/11, 8/16) .. † £60000
i. Tilted border (R.7/4, 7/9, 7/14, 7/19) £800 £550

None of the creased transfers from the first printing stone appear on the second, which exhibits its own range of similar varieties.

3j. "WEST" in squeezed-down letters and "F" of "FOUR" with pointed foot (R.2/17) £850 £600
k. "ESTERN" in squeezed-down letters and "U" of "FOUR" squeezed-up (R.3/17) £1400 £1000
l. Small "S" in "POSTAGE" (R.4/17) £850 £600
m. "EN" of "PENCE" shorter (R.6/4) £750 £550
n. "N" of "PENCE" tilted to right with thin first downstroke (R.6/16) £750 £550
o. Swan and water above "ENCE" damaged (R.6/20) £750 £550
p. "F" of "FOUR" slanting to left (R.7/17) £750 £550
q. "WESTERN" in squeezed-down letters only 1½ mm high (R.8/17) £900 £650
r. "P" of "PENCE" with small head (R.9/15) .. £750 £550
s. "RALIA" in squeezed-down letters only 1½ mm high (R.9/16) £850 £600
t. "PE" of "PENCE" close together (R.10/15) .. £750 £550
u. "N" of "PENCE" narrow (R.10/16) £750 £550
v. Part of right cross-stroke and down-stroke of "T" of "POSTAGE" cut off (R.11/15) £750 £550
w. "A" in "POSTAGE" with thin right limb (R.11/16) £750 £550

For the third printing in October 1855 the impressions showing the inverted frame were replaced on the printing stone with fresh individual transfers of the frame. On two of the positions traces of the original frame transfer remained visible.

3x. Coloured line above "AGE" of "POSTAGE" (R.8/6) £750 £550
y. No outer line above "GE" of "POSTAGE" and coloured line under "FOU" of "FOUR" (R.8/11) £800 £600

The same stone was used for a further printing in December 1855 and it is believed that the slate-blue shade occurred from one of the 1855 printings.

The above varieties, with the exception of Nos. 3e/g, also occur on the rouletted stamps.

The 1s. value was produced in much the same way, based on a transfer from the Perkins, Bacon 1d. plate.

5

(Litho A. Hillman, Government Lithographer)

1857 (7 Aug)–**59.** *W* **4** *(sideways). (a) Imperf.*

No.	Type	Description	Unused	Used
15	5	2d. brown-black/*red* (26.2.58)	£1700	£500
		a. Printed both sides	£1900	£800
16		2d. brown-black/*Indian red* (26.2.58)	—	£800
		a. Printed both sides	£1700	£850
17		6d. golden bronze	£3500	£1400
18		6d. black-bronze	£1900	£600
19		6d. grey-black (1859)	£2000	£500
		(b) Rouletted 7½ to 14 and compound		
20	5	2d. brown-black/*red*	£2500	£1000
		a. Printed both sides		
21		2d. brown-black/*Indian red*	—	£1200
22		6d. black-bronze	£2250	£750
23		6d. grey-black	—	£800

The 2d. and 6d. are known pin-perforated.

Prices quoted for Nos. 15/23 are for "cut-square" examples. Collectors are warned against "cut-round" copies with corners added.

(Recess in the colony from P.B. plates)

1860 (11 Aug)–**64.** *W* **4** *(sideways). (a) Imperf.*

No.	Type	Description	Unused	Used
24	1	2d. pale orange	70·00	55·00
25		2d. orange-vermilion	65·00	50·00
		a. Wmk upright		
25*b*		2d. deep vermilion	£225	£300
26		4d. blue (21.6.64)	£190	£1400
		a. Wmk upright	£225	
27		4d. deep blue	£190	£1500
28		6d. sage-green (27.7.61)	£1100	£400
28*a*		6d. deep sage-green	—	£500
		(b) Rouletted 7½ to 14		
29	1	2d. pale orange	£325	£140
30		2d. orange-vermilion	£400	£150
31		4d. deep blue	£1800	
32		6d. sage-green	£1300	£400

(Recess P.B.)

1861. *W* **4** *(sideways). (a) Intermediate perf* 14–16.

No.	Type	Description	Unused	Used
33	1	1d. rose	£275	85·00
34		2d. blue	£120	38·00
35		4d. vermilion	£475	£1200
36		6d. purple-brown	£300	60·00
37		1s. yellow-green	£400	£100
		(b) P 14 at Somerset House		
38	1	1d. rose	£150	42·00
39		2d. blue	65·00	27·00
40		4d. vermilion	£140	£120
		(c) Perf clean-cut 14–16		
41	1	2d. blue	60·00	24·00
		a. Imperf between (pair)		
42		6d. purple-brown	£180	35·00
43		1s. yellow-green	£300	50·00
		(d) P 14–16 very rough (July)		
44	1	1d. rose-carmine	£170	29·00
45		6d. purple/*blued*	£600	£120
46		1s. deep green	£900	£190

Perkins, Bacon experienced considerable problems with their perforating machine during the production of these stamps.

The initial printing showed intermediate perforation 14–16. Further supplies were then sent, in late December 1860, to Somerset House to be perforated on their comb 14 machine. The Inland Revenue Board were only able to process the three lower values, although the 6d. purple-brown and 1s. yellow-green are known from this perforation overprinted "SPECIMEN".

The Perkins, Bacon machine was repaired the following month and the 6d., 1s. and a further supply of the 2d. were perforated on it to give a clean-cut 14–16 gauge.

A final printing was produced in July 1861, but by this time the machine had deteriorated so that it produced a very rough 14–16.

(Recess D.L.R. from P.B. plates)

1863 (16 Dec)–**64.** *No wmk. P* 13.

No.	Type	Description	Unused	Used
49	1	1d. carmine-rose	45·00	3·50
50		1d. lake	45·00	3·50
51		6d. deep lilac (15.4.64)	90·00	35·00
51*a*		6d. dull violet (15.4.64)	£130	40·00

Both values exist on thin and on thick papers, the former being the scarcer.

Both grades of paper show a marginal sheet watermark, "T H SAUNDERS 1860" in double-lined large and small capitals, but parts of this watermark rarely occur on the stamps.

(Recess D.L.R. from P.B. plates)

1864 (27 Dec)–**79.** *Wmk Crown CC (sideways on* 1d.*). P* 12½.

No.	Type	Description	Unused	Used
52	1	1d. bistre	48·00	2·75
53		1d. yellow-ochre (16.10.74)	60·00	6·00
54		2d. chrome-yellow (18.1.65)	48·00	90
55		2d. yellow	48·00	90
		a. Wmk sideways (5.79)	—	15·00
		b. Error. Mauve (1879)	£5000	£3750
56		4d. carmine (18.1.65)	55·00	4·00
		a. Doubly printed	£5000	
57		6d. violet (18.1.65)	65·00	6·00
		a. Doubly printed	†	£7000
		b. Wmk sideways	—	£150
58		6d. indigo-violet	£250	28·00
59		6d. lilac (1872)	£120	6·00
60		6d. mauve (12.5.75)	£110	6·00
61		1s. bright green (18.1.65) (H/S S. £85)	90·00	12·00
62		1s. sage-green (10.68)	£225	23·00

Beware of fakes of No. 55b made by altering the value tablet of No. 60.

7

ONE PENNY

(8)

(Typo D.L.R.)

1871 (29 Oct)–**73.** *Wmk Crown CC (sideways). P* 14.

No.	Type	Description	Unused	Used
63	7	3d. pale brown (H/S S. £75)	30·00	4·00
		a. Cinnamon (1873)	30·00	3·50

1874 (10 Dec). *No.* 55 *surch with T* **8** *by Govt Printer.*

No.	Type	Description	Unused	Used
67	1	1d. on 2d. yellow (G.)	£160	45·00
		a. Pair, one without surch		
		b. Surch triple	†	£1800
		c. "O" of "ONE" omitted		

Forged surcharges of T **8** are known on stamps wmk Crown CC perf 14, and on Crown CA, perf 12 and 14.

(Recess D.L.R. from P.B. plates)

1876–81. *Wmk Crown CC (sideways). P* 14.

No.	Type	Description	Unused	Used
68	1	1d. ochre	45·00	1·50
69		1d. bistre (1878)	65·00	2·75
70		1d. yellow-ochre (1879)	48·00	80
71		2d. chrome-yellow	45·00	50
		a. Wmk upright (1877)	65·00	1·25
74		4d. carmine (1881)	£300	75·00
75		6d. lilac (1877)	85·00	3·25
		a. Wmk upright (1879)	£450	15·00
75*b*		6d. reddish lilac (1879)	85·00	5·50

(Recess D.L.R. from P.B. plates)

1882 (Mar)–**85.** *Wmk Crown CA (sideways). (a) P* 14.

No.	Type	Description	Unused	Used
76	1	1d. yellow-ochre	16·00	50
77		2d. chrome-yellow	20·00	50
		a. Wmk upright	†	—
78		4d. carmine (8.82)	80·00	6·50
		a. Wmk upright (1885)	—	25·00
79		6d. reddish lilac (1882)	70·00	3·00
80		6d. lilac (1884) (H/S S. £75)	70·00	4·00
		(b) P 12 × 14		
81	1	1d. yellow-ochre (2.83)	£1000	£150
		(c) P 12		
82	1	1d. yellow-ochre (2.83)	60·00	1·90
83		2d. chrome-yellow (6.83)	75·00	1·90
		a. Imperf between (pair)		
84		4d. carmine (5.83)	£120	25·00
85		6d. lilac (6.83)	£200	25·00

(Typo D.L.R.)

1882 (July)–**95.** *Wmk Crown CA (sideways). P* 14.

No.	Type	Description	Unused	Used
86	7	3d. pale brown	13·00	1·50
87		3d. red-brown (12.95)	8·50	1·00

The 3d. stamps in other colours, watermark Crown CA and perforated 12, are colour trials dating from 1883.

½ (9) **1d.** (10) **1d.** (11)

1884 (19 Feb). *Surch with T* **9**, *in red, by Govt Printer.*

No.	Type	Description	Unused	Used
89	1	½ on 1d. yellow-ochre (No. 76)	14·00	18·00
		a. Thin bar	70·00	85·00
90		½ on 1d. yellow-ochre (No. 82)	9·00	14·00

Inverted or double surcharges are forgeries made in London about 1886.

The "Thin bar" varieties occur on R12/3, R12/8, R12/13 and R12/18, and show the bar only 0.2 mm thick.

1885 (May). *Nos.* 63/*a surch, in green, by Govt Printer.*

No.	Description	Unused	Used
	(a) Thick "1" with slanting top, T **10** (Horizontal Rows 1/5)		
91	1d. on 3d. pale brown	48·00	10·00
	a. Cinnamon	38·00	8·00
	b. Vert pair. Nos. 91/2	£140	
	(b) Thin "1" with straight top, T **11** (Horizontal Row 6)		
92	1d. on 3d. pale brown	£110	20·00
	a. Cinnamon	85·00	21·00

12

13

14

15

(Typo D.L.R.)

1885 (May)–**93.** *Wmk Crown CA (sideways). P* 14.

No.	Type	Description	Unused	Used
94	12	½d. yellow-green	3·25	30
94*a*		½d. green	3·25	30
95	13	1d. carmine (2.90)	13·00	10
96	14	2d. bluish grey (6.90)	18·00	40
96*a*		2d. grey	17·00	40
97	15	2½d. deep blue (1.5.92)	8·00	3
97*a*		2½d. blue	7·50	3
98		4d. chestnut (7.90)	7·50	4
99		5d. bistre (1.5.92)	8·00	2·5
100		6d. bright violet (1.93)	14·00	1·0
101		1s. pale olive-green (4.90)	22·00	3·0
102		1s. olive-green	17·00	3·0
94, 96*a*, 97*a*/99, 101 Optd/H/S "Specimen"		*Set of* 6	£225	

(Recess D.L.R. from P.B. plates)

1888 (Mar–Apr). *Wmk Crown CA (sideways). P* 14.

No.	Type	Description	Unused	Used
103	1	1d. carmine-pink	13·00	1·7
104		2d. grey	35·00	1·0
105		4d. red-brown (April)	70·00	18·0
103/5 H/S "Specimen"		*Set of* 3	£150	

ONE PENNY (16) **Half-penny** (17)

1893 (Feb). *Surch with T* **16**, *in green, by Govt Printer.*

No.	Type	Description	Unused	Used
107	7	1d. on 3d. pale brown (No. 63)	11·00	2·7
108		1d. on 3d. cinnamon (No. 63*a*)	11·00	3·0
		a. Double surcharge	£500	
109		1d. on 3d. pale brown (No. 86)	32·00	4·2

1895 (21 Nov). *Surch with T* **17** *by Govt Printer. (a) In green.*

No.	Type	Description	Unused	Used
110	7	½d. on 3d. pale brown (No. 63)	7·50	18·0
110*a*		½d. on 3d. cinnamon (No. 63*a*)	5·50	17·0
		b. Surcharge double	£350	
		(b) In red and in green		
111*a*	7	½d. on 3d. cinnamon (No. 63*a*)	70·00	£15
111*b*		½d. on 3d. red-brown (No. 87)	50·00	90·0

Green was the adopted surcharge colour but a trial had earlie been made in red on stamps watermarked Crown CC. As the proved unsatisfactory they were given another surcharge in greer The trial stamps were inadvertently issued and, to prevent specu lation, a further printing of the duplicated surcharge was made, bu on both papers, Crown CC (No. 111*a*) and Crown CA (No. 111*b*).

18

19

20

21

(Typo D.L.R.)

1898 (Dec)–**1907.** *Wmk W Crown A, W* **18.** *P* 14.

No.	Type	Description	Unused	Used
112	13	1d. carmine	4·00	1
113	14	2d. bright yellow (1.99)	10·00	1·2
114	19	2½d. blue (1.01)	7·00	3
115	20	6d. bright violet (10.06)	18·00	5
116	21	1s. olive-green (4.07)	22·00	3·5

22

23

24

25

26

27

28

29

30

31

32

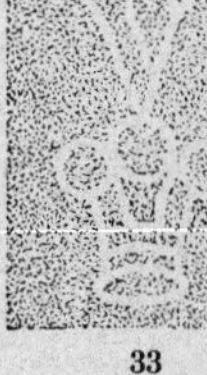

33

ypo Victoria Govt Printer, Melbourne, Commonwealth Stamp Ptg Branch from March, 1909)

02 (Oct)–**12.** *Wmk V and Crown, W* **33** (*sideways on horiz designs*).

(*a*) *P* 12½ *or* 12½ × 12 (*horiz*), 12 × 12½ (*vert*)

.7 **22** 1d. carmine-rose (1.03) .. .. .. 9·00 10
a. Wmk upright (10.02) .. .. 12·00 30
.8 **23** 2d. yellow (4.1.03) .. .. .. 8·50 1·25
a. Wmk upright (12.7.04) .. .. — 1·50
.9 **24** 4d. chestnut (4.03) .. .. .. 8·50 90
a. Wmk upright £160
:0 **15** 5d. bistre (4.9.05) .. .. .. 70·00 42·00
:1 **25** 8d. apple-green (3.03) .. .. .. 18·00 2·50
:2 **26** 9d. yellow-orange (5.03).. .. .. 27·00 4·75
a. Wmk upright (11.03) .. .. 38·00 14·00
:3 **27** 10d. red (3.03) .. .. 30·00 4·50
:4 **28** 2s. bright red/*yellow* .. .. .. 75·00 15·00
a. Wmk sideways .. .. .. £150 16·00
b. Orange/yellow (7.06) .. .. 40·00 8·50
c. Brown-red/yellow (5.11) .. .. 40·00 8·50
:5 **29** 2s. 6d. deep blue/*rose* .. .. .. 40·00 8·00
:6 **30** 5s. emerald-green .. .. .. 60·00 19·00
:7 **31** 10s. deep mauve .. .. £140 55·00
a. Bright purple (1910).. .. .. £160 80·00
:8 **32** £1 orange-brown (1.11.02) £275 £150
a. Orange (10.7.09) £550 £250

(*b*) *P* 11

29 **22** 1d. carmine-rose .. .. .. 80·00 10·00
a. Wmk upright .. .. ..
30 **23** 2d. yellow .. .. £110 12·00
a. Wmk upright .. .. ..
31 **24** 4d. chestnut £400 £120
32 **15** 5d. bistre .. .. 45·00 26·00
33 **26** 9d. yellow-orange .. .. .. 60·00 48·00
34 **28** 2s. bright red/*yellow* .. .. .. £120 70·00
a. Orange/yellow £225 £110

(*c*) *Perf compound of* 12½ *or* 12 *and* 11

35 **22** 1d. carmine-rose £350 £160
36 **23** 2d. yellow £425 £200
37 **24** 4d. chestnut .. ..

Type **22** is similar to Type **13** but larger.

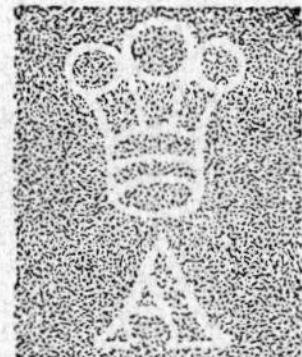

34

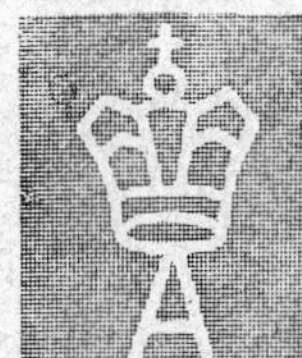

35

905–12. *Wmk Crown and A, W* **34** (*sideways*).

(*a*) *P* 12½ *or* 12½ × 12 (*horiz*), 12 × 12½ (*vert*)

38 **12** ½d. green (6.10) .. .. .. 3·75 2·75
39 **22** 1d. rose-pink (10.05) .. .. .. 6·00 20
a. Wmk upright (1.06) .. .. 5·50 20
b. Carmine (1909) .. .. .. 7·50 30
c. Carmine-red (1912) .. .. 8·50 4·00
40 **23** 2d. yellow (15.11.05) .. .. .. 5·00 1·25
a. Wmk upright (4.10) .. ..
41 **7** 3d. brown (2.06) .. .. .. 11·00 50
42 **24** 4d. bistre-brown (12.06) .. .. 11·00 3·00
a. Pale chestnut (1908) .. .. 11·00 2·50
b. Bright brown-red (14.10.10) .. 8·50 80
43 **15** 5d. pale olive-bistre (8.05) .. .. 12·00 2·75
a. Olive-green (1.09) .. .. .. 12·00 2·75
b. Pale greenish yellow (5.12) .. 55·00 55·00
44 **25** 8d. apple-green (22.4.12) .. .. 17·00 28·00
45 **26** 9d. orange (11.5.06) .. .. .. 22·00 3·50
a. Red-orange (6.10) .. .. .. 32·00 3·50
b. Wmk upright (7.12) .. .. 38·00 24·00
46 **27** 10d. rose-orange (16.2.10) .. .. 22·00 12·00
48 **30** 5s. emerald-grn (*wmk upright*) (9.07) 65·00 50·00

(*b*) *P* 11

50 **12** ½d. green .. ..
51 **22** 1d. rose-pink .. .. .. 20·00 5·00
a. Carmine-red .. .. .. 20·00 4·00
b. Wmk upright .. .. .. 20·00 8·50
52 **23** 2d. yellow .. .. 18·00 8·00
53 **7** 3d. brown .. .. 14·00 2·00
54 **24** 4d. yellow-brown £425 £120
a. Pale chestnut .. .. ..
55 **15** 5d. pale olive-bistre .. .. .. 28·00 10·00
a. Olive-green .. .. .. 16·00 10·00
57 **26** 9d. orange .. .. 75·00 80·00
a. Red-orange .. .. .. — 65·00
b. Wmk upright (1912) .. .. † £275

(*c*) *Perf compound of* 12½ *or* 12 *and* 11

61 **22** 1d. rose-pink (*wmk upright*) .. £200 £100
62 **23** 2d. yellow .. .. £170 90·00
63 **7** 3d. brown £250 £150
64 **26** 9d. red-orange .. ..

912 (Mar). *Wmk Crown and A* (*sideways*). *W* **35.** *P* 11½ × 12.

.68 **20** 6d. bright violet .. .. .. 10·00 3·25
.69 **21** 1s. sage-green .. .. 25·00 4·75
a. Perf 12½ (single line) .. .. — £150

912 (7 Aug). *W* **34** (*sideways*). *Thin paper and white gum* (*as Victoria*).

70 **7** 3d. brown (*p* 12½) .. .. .. 42·00 42·00
a. Wmk upright .. .. .. 42·00 42·00
71 3d. brown (*p* 11) .. .. ..
a. Wmk upright .. .. ..

ONE PENNY

(36)

1912 (6 Nov). *Nos.* 140 *and* 162 *surch with T* **36** *in Melbourne.*

(*a*) *P* 12½ *or* 12 × 12½

172 **23** 1d. on 2d. yellow 80 30
a. Wmk upright .. .. .. 2·00 2·00

(*b*) *Perf compound of* 12½ *and* 11

173 **23** 1d. on 2d. yellow £300

STAMP BOOKLETS

There are very few surviving examples of Nos. SB1/4. Listings are provided for those believed to have been issued with prices quoted for those known to still exist.

1904 (1 Jan)–**09.** *Black on red cover as No.* SB1 *of New South Wales. Stapled.*

SB1 £1 booklet containing two hundred and forty 1d. in four blocks of 30 and two blocks of 60 ..
a. Red on pink cover (1909) £6000
b. Blue on pink cover .. ..

1904 (1 Jan). *Black on grey cover as No.* SB1. *Stapled.*

SB2 £1 booklet containing one hundred and twenty 2d. in four blocks of 30 .. ..

1910 (May). *Black on white cover as No.* SB3 *of New South Wales. Stapled.*

SB3 2s. booklet containing eleven ½d. (No. 138), either in block of 6 plus block of 5 or block of 11, and eighteen 1d. (No. 139) either in three blocks of 6 or block of 6 plus block of 12 .. .. £2000

Unsold stock of No. SB3 was uprated with one additional ½d. in May 1911.

1911 (Aug). *Red on pink cover as No.* SB3. *Stapled.*

SB4 2s. booklet containing twelve ½d. (No. 138), either in two blocks of 6 or block of 12, and eighteen 1d. (No. 139), either in three blocks of 6 or block of 6 plus block of 12 .. .. £1500

POSTAL FISCAL STAMPS

By the Post and Telegraph Act of 5 September 1893 the current issue of fiscal stamps up to and including the 1s. value, Nos. F11/15, was authorised for postal use.

These stamps had been initially supplied, for fiscal purposes, in February 1882 and had been preceded by a series of "I R" surcharges and overprints on postage stamps which were in use for a period of about six months. Examples of these 1881–82 provisionals can be found postally used under the terms of the 1893 Act but, as they had not been current for fiscal purposes for over eleven years, we no longer list them.

F 3

(Typo D.L.R.)

1893 (5 Sept). *Definitive fiscal stamps of Feb* 1882. *Wmk CA over Crown. P* 14.

F11 **F 3** 1d. dull purple .. .. 8·50 1·00
F12 2d. dull purple .. .. 85·00 32·00
F13 3d. dull purple .. .. 32·00 1·75
F14 6d. dull purple .. .. 35·00 3·00
F15 – 1s. dull purple .. .. 65·00 4·75

The 1s. value is as Type F **3** but with rectangular outer frame and circular frame surrounding swan.

Higher values in this series were not validated by the Act for postal use.

Two varieties of watermark exist on these stamps. Initial supplies showed an indistinct watermark with the base of the "A" 4 mm wide. From 1896 the paper used showed a clearer watermark on which the base of the "A" was 5 mm wide.

1897. *Wmk W Crown A, W* **18.** *P* 14.

F19 **F 3** 1d. dull purple .. .. 5·00 1·00
F20 3d. dull purple .. .. 24·00 1·75
F21 6d. dull purple .. .. 24·00 1·75
F22 – 1s. dull purple .. .. 60·00 7·50

TELEGRAPH STAMPS USED FOR POSTAGE

The 1d. Telegraph stamps were authorised for postal purposes from 25 October 1886.

T 1

1886 (25 Oct). *Wmk Crown CC.*

T1 **T 1** 1d. bistre (*p* 12½) .. .. .. 22·00 2·50
T2 1d. bistre (*p* 14) .. .. .. 24·00 4·00

Copies of a similar 6d. value are known postally used, but such use was unauthorised.

OFFICIAL STAMPS

Stamps of the various issues from 1854–85 are found with a circular hole punched out, the earlier size being about 3 mm. in diameter and the later 4 mm. These were used on official correspondence by the Commissariat and Convict Department, branches of the Imperial administration separate from the colonial government. This system of punching ceased by 1886. Subsequently many stamps between Nos. 94 and 148 may be found punctured, "PWD", "WA" or "OS".

Western Australia became part of the Commonwealth of Australia on 1 January 1901.

COMMONWEALTH OF AUSTRALIA

On 1 March 1901 control of the postal service passed to the federal administration although it was not until 13 October 1910 that the issues of the various states became valid for use throughout Australia. Postal rates were standardised on 1 May 1911.

The first national postage due stamps appeared in July 1902, but it was not until January 1913 that postage stamps inscribed "AUSTRALIA" were issued.

PRICES FOR STAMPS ON COVER TO 1945	
Nos. 1/19	*from* × 4
Nos. 20/3	*from* × 2
Nos. 24/30	*from* × 4
Nos. 35/47*f*	*from* × 3
Nos. 51/5*a*	*from* × 4
Nos. 55*b*/75	*from* × 3
Nos. 76/84	*from* × 4
Nos. 85/104	*from* × 3
Nos. 105/6	*from* × 4
Nos. 107/15	*from* × 3
No. 116	*from* × 5
Nos. 117/20	*from* × 4
Nos. 121/39*a*	*from* × 2
Nos. 140/*a*	*from* × 5
Nos. 141/4	*from* × 3
No. 146	*from* × 6
Nos. 147/53	*from* × 3
Nos. 153*a*/*b*	*from* × 2
Nos. 154/63	*from* × 3
Nos. 164/211	*from* × 2
Nos. D1/118	*from* × 8
Nos. O123/36	*from* × 5

PRINTERS. Except where otherwise stated, all Commonwealth stamps to No. 581 were printed under Government authority at Melbourne. Until 1918 there were two establishments (both of the Treasury Dept)—the Note Printing Branch and the Stamp Printing Branch. The former printed T **3** and **4**.

In 1918 the Stamp Printing Branch was closed and all stamps were printed by the Note Printing Branch. In 1926 control was transferred from the Treasury to the Commonwealth Bank of Australia, and on 14 January 1960 the branch was attached to the newly established Reserve Bank of Australia.

Until 1942 stamps bore in the sheet margin the initials or names of successive managers and from 1942 to March 1952 the imprint "Printed by the Authority of the Government of the Commonwealth of Australia". After November 1952 (or Nos. D129/31 for Postage Dues) imprints were discontinued.

SPECIMEN OVERPRINTS. These come from Specimen sets, first produced in 1913. In these sets the lower values were cancelled-to-order, but stamps with a face value of 7s. 6d. or 75 c. were overprinted "Specimen" in different types. These overprints are listed as they could be purchased from the Australian Post Office.

It is, however, believed that examples of No. 112 overprinted "Specimen" were distributed by the U.P.U. in 1929. Supplies of the 1902 and 1902–04 postage due stamps overprinted "Specimen" were supplied to the U.P.U. by some of the states.

The sale of the cancelled-to-order sets ceased after 1966, but high value "Specimen" overprints were retained until the end of 1994 to support philatelic funds.

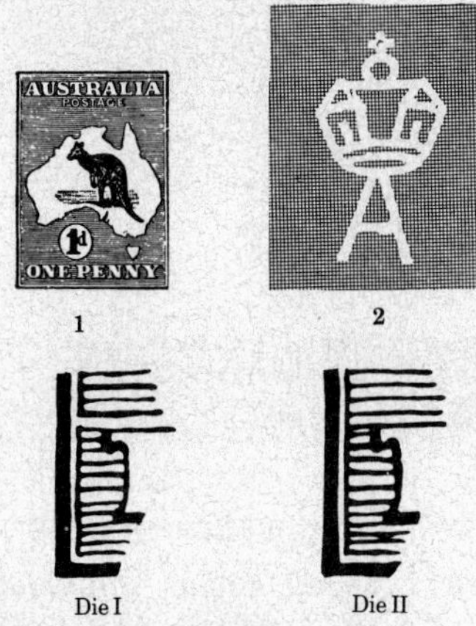

1 2

Die I Die II

Dies of Type 1 (mono-coloured values only):—

Die I. Break in inner frame line at lower left level with top of words of value.

Die II. Die repaired showing no break.

Die I was only used for the ½d., 1d., 2d. and 3d. Several plates ere produced for each except the 3d. When the second plate of the 1. was being prepared the damage became aggravated after aking 105 out of the 120 units when the die was returned for epair. This gave rise to the *se-tenant* pairs showing the two states f the die.

Die II was used until 1945 and deteriorated progressively with amage to the frame lines and rounding of the corners.

Specialists recognise seven states of this die, but we only list the wo most major of the later versions.

Die IIA. This state is as Die II, but, in addition, shows a break n the inner left-hand frame line, 9 mm from the top of the lesign (occurs on 1d., 2d. and 6d.).

Die IIB. As Die IIA, but now also showing break in outer rame line above "ST", and (not illustrated) an incomplete corner o the inner frame line at top right (occurs on 3d., 6d., 9d., 1s. nd £1 (No. 75)).

(Des B. Young. Eng S. Reading. Typo J. B. Cooke)

913 (2 Jan)–**14.** *W* **2**. *P* 12.
1 **1** ½d. green (Die I) (16.1.13) .. .. 6·00 2·75
a. Printed on the gummed side .. £1000
bw. Wmk inverted .. 20·00 8·00
c. Wmk sideways .. † £3000
2 1d. red (Die I) .. 8·50 85
a. Wmk sideways .. £550 £100
b. Carmine .. 8·50 85
cw. Wmk inverted .. 18·00 2·75
d. Die II. *Red* (16.1.13) .. 9·00 85
da. Wmk sideways .. £600 £110
db. Carmine .. 8·50 85
dw. Wmk inverted .. 18·00 2·75
e. Die IIA. *Red* (4.14) .. 14·00 95
eb. Carmine .. 14·00 95
ew. Wmk inverted .. 25·00 2·75
3 2d. grey (Die I) (15.1.13) .. 28·00 4·50
w. Wmk inverted .. 50·00 10·00
4 2½d. indigo (Die II) (27.1.13) .. 29·00 12·00
5 3d. olive (Die I) (1.2.13) .. 48·00 7·50
a. Imperf three sides (horiz pair) .. £11000
b. In pair with Die II .. £425 £160
c. Yellow-olive .. 48·00 9·00
ca. In pair with Die II .. £425 £160
dw. Wmk inverted .. 60·00 17·00
e. Die II. *Olive* .. £160 50·00
ea. Yellow-olive .. £160 50·00
ew. Wmk inverted .. £200 70·00
6 4d. orange (Die II) (15.2.13) .. 50·00 22·00
a. Orange-yellow .. £170 48·00
8 5d. chestnut (Die II) (18.1.13) .. 40·00 32·00
9 6d. ultramarine (Die II) (18.1.13) .. 48·00 20·00
a. Retouched "E" .. £1500 £500
b. Die IIA (substituted cliché) (11.13) £1000 £350
w. Wmk inverted .. 90·00 45·00
10 9d. violet (Die II) (1.2.13) .. 45·00 22·00
11 1s. emerald (Die II) (25.1.13) .. 45·00 15·00
a. Blue-green .. 50·00 15·00
w. Wmk inverted .. £100 45·00
12 2s. brown (Die II) (30.1.13) .. £160 65·00
13 5s. grey and yellow (Die II) (20.3.13) £250 £140
14 10s. grey and pink (Die II) (20.3.13) .. £600 £450
15 £1 brown & ultram (Die II) (20.3.13) £1100 £1000
16 £2 black and rose (Die II) (8.4.13) .. £2250 £1600
1/16 .. *Set of* 15 £4250 £3000
14/16 Optd "Specimen" .. *Set of* 3 £600

Three examples, all used, are known of No. 1c.

The 3d. was printed from two plates, one of which contained 105 stamps as Die I and 15 as Die II. The other plate contained Die I stamps only.

No. 5a. shows the stamp perforated at foot only. Examples are known from the top or bottom rows of different sheets.

No. 9a shows a badly distorted second "E" in "PENCE", which is unmistakable. It occurs on the Upper plate right pane R. 10/6 and was replaced by a substitute cliché in Type IIA (No. 9b) in the November 1913 printing.

See also Nos. 24/30 (*W* **5**), 35/45*b* (*W* **6**), 73/5 (*W* **6**, new colours), 107/14 (*W* **7**), 132/8 (*W* **15**), 212 (2s. re-engraved).

3

4 Laughing Kookaburra

(Des R. A. Harrison. Eng and recess T. S. Harrison)

1913 (8 Dec)–**14.** *No wmk. P* 11.
17 **3** 1d. red .. 2·50 4·50
a. Imperf between (horiz pair) .. £1700
b. Imperf horiz (vert pair) .. £1300
c. Pale rose-red .. 7·00 10·00
ca. Imperf between (vert pair) .. £1500
cb. Imperf between (horiz pair) .. £1900
19 **4** 6d. claret (26.8.14) .. 70·00 38·00

All printings from Plate 1 of the 1d. were in the shade of No. 17*c*. This plate shows many retouches.

5

5*a*

1d. Die II

1d. Die II. The flaw distinguishing the so-called Die II, a white upward spur to the right of the base of the "1" in the left value tablet, is now known to be due to a defective roller-die. It occurred on all stamps in the second and third vertical rows of upper left plate right pane. Each of the twenty defective impressions differs slightly; a typical example is illustrated above.

(Dies eng P.B. Typo J. B. Cooke until May 1918, then T. S. Harrison)

1914 (17 July)–**20.** *W* **5**. *P* 14¼×14 (*comb*).
20 **5a** ½d. bright green (22.2.15) .. 3·75 80
a. Perf 14¼ (line) (12.15) ..
b. Green (1916) .. 3·75 80
c. Yellow-green (1916) .. 22·00 10·00
d. Thin "1" in fraction at right (Pl 5 rt pane R. 8/1) .. £2500 £1000
w. Wmk inverted .. 10·00 4·00
21 1d. carmine-red (*shades*) (Die I) (*p* 14¼ (line)) ..
a. Die II ..
bw. Wmk inverted .. † —
c. Perf 14¼×14 (comb) (8.14) .. 7·00 50
ca. Rusted cliché (Pl 2 rt pane R. 6/4 and 5) (9.16) .. £5000 £300
cb. Substituted cliché (Pl 2 rt pane R. 6/5) (2.18) .. £800 50·00
cc. Pale carmine (shades) .. 10·00 50
cd. Rose-red (1917) .. 11·00 2·50
ce. Carmine-pink (1918) .. 80·00 7·00
cf. Carmine (aniline) (1920) .. 16·00 3·25
cw. Wmk inverted .. 12·00 2·00
d. Die II. *Carmine-red (shades)* .. £300 6·00
db. Substituted cliché (Pl 2 right pane R. 6/4) (2.18) .. £800 50·00
dc. Pale carmine (shades) .. £300 7·00
dw. Wmk inverted .. £400 12·00
22 4d. orange (6.1.15) .. 27·00 2·50
a. Yellow-orange (1915) .. 27·00 3·25
b. Pale orange-yellow (1916) .. 60·00 11·00
c. Lemon-yellow (1916) .. 90·00 14·00
d. Dull orange (1920) .. 42·00 3·25
e. Line through "FOUR PENCE" (Pl 2 right pane R. 2/6) (*all shades*) *From* £300 90·00
w. Wmk inverted .. 45·00 12·00
23 5d. brown (*p* 14¼ (line)) (22.2.15) .. 25·00 4·00
aw. Wmk inverted ..
b. Perf 14¼×14 (comb) (8.17) .. 18·00 1·60
ba. Yellow-brown (1920) .. 25·00 2·25
bw. Wmk inverted .. 45·00 15·00

The variety No. 20d was caused by the engraving of a new fraction in a defective electro in 1918.

No. 21ca was caused by rusting on two positions of the steel plate 2 and shows as white patches on the back of the King's neck and on, and besides, the top of the right frame (right pane R. 6/4) and on the left frame, wattles, head and ears of kangaroo (right pane R. 6/5). These were noticed in December 1916 when the damaged impressions were removed and replaced by a pair of copper electros (Die II for R. 6/4 and Die I for R. 6/5), showing rounded corners and some frame damage, the former also showing a white spot under tail of emu. In time the tops of the crown quickly wore away.

Most of Nos. 20/3 were perforated 14 by a comb machine (exact gauge 14.25×14), but printings of the ½d. in December 1915, of the 1d. in July and August 1914 and of the 5d. until June 1917 were perforated by a line machine measuring 14.2.

See also Nos. 47/fa (*W* **5**, rough paper), 51/5*a* (*W* **6a**), 55/*ba* (1d. Die III), 56/66*b* and 76/81 (*W* **5**, new colours), 82 (*W* **6a**), 83/4 (no wmk), 85/104 (*W* **7**), 124/31 (*W* **15**).

(Typo J. B. Cooke)

1915 (15 Jan–Aug). *W* **5**. *P* 12.
24 **1** 2d. grey (Die I) .. 50·00 10·00
w. Wmk inverted .. † £375
25 2½d. indigo (Die II) (July) .. 50·00 27·00
26 6d. ultramarine (Die II) (April) .. £130 22·00
a. Bright blue .. £170 48·00
b. Die IIA. *Ultramarine* (substituted cliché) (Upper plate rt pane R. 10/6) £1000 £300
ba. Bright blue .. £1300 £375
w. Wmk inverted .. † £950
27 **1** 9d. violet (Die II) (9 July) .. £130 32·00
w. Wmk inverted .. £550 £180
28 1s. blue-green (Die II) (Aug) .. £140 23·00
29 2s. brown (Die II) (April) .. £425 90·00
30 5s. grey and yellow (Die II) (12 Feb) .. £500 £250
a. Yellow portion doubly printed .. £5500 £1500
w. Wmk inverted .. £600 £300
24/30 .. *Set of* 7 £1300 £400

The watermark in this issue is often misplaced as the paper was made for the portrait stamps.

6

6*a*

Nos. 38ca and 73a (Upper plate lt pane R. 1/6)

(Typo J. B. Cooke (to May 1918), T. S. Harrison to February 1926), A. J. Mullett (to June 1927) and thereafter J. Ash)

1915 (12 Oct)–**28.** *W* **6** (*narrow Crown*). *P* 12.
35 **1** 2d. grey (Die I) (11.15) .. 25·00 5·50
a. In pair with Die IIA (1917)* .. £850 £375
bw. Wmk inverted .. 35·00 8·00
c. Silver-grey (shiny paper) (3.18) .. 26·00 6·50
d. Die II. *Silver-grey* (shiny paper) (3.18) .. 35·00 9·00
da. Grey (1920) .. 38·00 9·00
36 2½d. deep blue (Die II) (9.17) .. 22·00 9·50
aw. Wmk inverted .. 50·00 20·00
b. Deep indigo (1920) .. 26·00 8·00
ba. "1" of fraction omitted (Lower plate left pane R. 6/3) .. £9500 £3500
37 3d. yellow-olive (Die I) .. 27·00 3·50
a. In pair with Die II .. £200 80·00
b. Olive-green (1917) .. 30·00 3·50
ba. In pair with Die II .. £200 80·00
cw. Wmk inverted .. 38·00 7·00
d. Die II. *Yellow-olive* .. 80·00 27·00
da. Olive-green .. 80·00 27·00
dw. Wmk inverted .. £110 40·00
e. Die IIB. *Light olive* (1.23) .. 35·00 10·00
38 6d. ultramarine (Die II) (15.12.15) .. 50·00 6·00
a. Die IIA (substituted cliché) (Upper plate rt pane R. 10/6) .. £850 £200
b. Dull blue (6.18) .. 65·00 9·00
ba. Die IIA (substituted cliché) .. £950 £250
cw. Wmk inverted .. 75·00 15·00
d. Die IIB. *Brt ultramarine* (23.7.21) 55·00 6·00
da. Leg of kangaroo broken .. £2250 £450
dw. Wmk inverted .. — 40·00
39 9d. violet (Die II) (29.7.16) .. 38·00 6·00
aw. Wmk inverted .. 60·00 15·00
b. Die IIB. *Violet* (16.4.19) .. 35·00 6·00
bw. Wmk inverted .. 50·00 14·00
40 1s. blue-green (Die II) (6.16) .. 35·00 3·00
aw. Wmk inverted .. 60·00 15·00
b. Die IIB (9.12.20) .. 35·00 3·00
ba. Wmk sideways (12.27) .. 60·00 £100
bw. Wmk inverted .. 55·00 14·00
41 2s. brown (Die II) (6.16) .. £150 11·00
a. Imperf three sides (horiz pair) .. £14000
b. Red-brown (aniline) .. £425 75·00
w. Wmk inverted .. £225 75·00
42 5s. grey and yellow (Die II) (4.18) .. £180 75·00
a. Grey and orange (1920) .. £190 80·00
b. Grey and deep yellow .. £180 75·00
ba. Wmk sideways .. † £5000
c. Grey and pale yellow (1928) .. £180 75·00
w. Wmk inverted .. £250 £120
43 10s. grey and pink (Die II) (5.2.17) .. £400 £190
a. Grey and bright aniline pink (10.18) £350 £150
ab. Wmk sideways .. £7000 £3500
aw. Wmk inverted .. £550 £225
b. Grey and pale aniline pink (1928) £425 £170
44 £1 chocolate & dull blue (Die II) (7.16) £1300 £700
a. Chestnut and bright blue (6.17) .. £1400 £750
ab. Wmk sideways .. £10000 £4500
aw. Wmk inverted .. £1700 £900
b. Bistre-brown and bright blue (7.19) £1300 £700
45 £2 black and rose (Die II) (12.19) .. £2250 £1300
a. Grey and crimson (1921) .. £2000 £1200
b. Purple-black and pale rose (6.24) £1800 £1100
35/45*b* .. *Set of* 11 £3500 £1800
43/5 Optd "Specimen" .. *Set of* 3 £500

*The Die IIA of No. 35a is a substituted cliché introduced to replace a cracked plate which occurred on R. 10/1 of the Upper plate left pane. The Die IIA characteristics are more pronounced in this cliché than on the sheet stamps from this die. The break at left, for instance, extends to the outer, in addition to the inner, frame line.

One plate of the 3d. contained mixed Die I and Die II stamps as described.

All values were printed by both Cooke and Harrison, and the 9d., 1s. and 5s. were also printed by Mullett and Ash.

1916 (14 Dec)–**18.** *Rough, unsurfaced paper, locally gummed. W* **5**. *P* 14.

47 **5a** 1d. scarlet (Die I) .. .. 18·00 2·00
 a. Deep red (1917) .. .. 18·00 2·00
 b. Rose-red (1918) .. .. 28·00 2·50
 ba. Substituted cliché (Pl 2 rt pane R. 6/5) £750 55·00
 c. Rosine (1918) .. .. 90·00 12·00
 ca. Substituted cliché (Pl 2 rt pane R. 6/5) £1200 £140
 dw. Wmk inverted .. .. 28·00 3·50
 e. Die II. *Rose-red* (1918) .. .. .. £275 20·00
 ea. Substituted cliché (Pl 2 rt pane R. 6/4) £750 55·00
 f. Die II. *Rosine* (1918) .. .. .. £375 55·00
 fa. Substituted cliché (Pl 2 rt pane R. 6/4) £1200 £140
 fw. Wmk inverted .. ..

All examples of the 5d. on this paper were perforated "OS" and will be found listed as No. O60.

(Typo J. B. Cooke to May 1918 thereafter T. S. Harrison)

1918 (4 Jan)–**20.** *W* **6a** (*Mult*). *P* 14.

51 **5a** ½d. green (*shades*) .. .. .. 5·00 2·00
 a. Thin 1 in fraction at right (Pl 5 rt pane R. 8/1) .. .. .. £100 50·00
 b. Wmk sideways .. .. .. † £3000
 w. Wmk inverted .. .. .. 15·00 9·00
52 1d. carmine-pink (Die I) (23.1.18) .. £100 55·00
 a. Deep red (1918) £850 £275
 w. Wmk inverted .. .. .. † £1000
53 1d. carmine (10.12.19) .. .. .. 35·00 6·00
 aw. Wmk inverted £200 £100
 b. Deep red (*aniline*) (1920) .. .. £180 55·00
54 1½d. black-brown (30.1.19) .. .. 5·00 2·25
 a. Very thin paper (2.19) .. .. 25·00 13·00
 w. Wmk inverted .. .. .. 18·00 7·00
55 1½d. red-brown (4.19) .. .. .. 12·00 1·50
 a. Chocolate (1920) .. .. .. 11·00 1·50
 w. Wmk inverted .. .. .. 28·00 8·00

No. 51 was printed by Cooke and Harrison, Nos. 52/*a* by Cooke only and Nos. 53/55*a* by Harrison only. Nos. 52/*a* have rather yellowish gum, that of No. 53 being pure white.

1d. Die III

1d. Die III. In 1918 a printing (in sheets of 120) was made on paper originally prepared for printing War Savings Stamps, with watermark T **5**. A special plate was made for this printing, differing in detail from those previously used. The shading round the head is even; the solid background of the words "ONE PENNY" is bounded at each end by a white vertical line; and there is a horizontal white line cutting the vertical shading lines at left on the King's neck.

(Typo J. B. Cooke)

1918 (15 July). *Printed from a new Die III plate on white unsurfaced paper, locally gummed. W* **5**. *P* 14.

55*b* **5a** 1d. rose-red .. .. 55·00 28·00
 ba. *Rose-carmine* .. .. .. 55·00 30·00
 bw. Wmk inverted .. .. .. 75·00 35·00

(Typo T. S. Harrison or A. J. Mullett (1s. 4d. from March 1926))

1918 (9 Nov)–**23.** *W* **5**. *P* 14.

56 **5a** ½d. orange (9.11.23) .. .. .. 2·50 2·50
 w. Wmk inverted .. .. .. 5·00 5·00
57 1d. violet (*shades*) (12.2.22) .. .. 7·00 1·25
 a. Imperf three sides (horiz pair) .. £8500
 b. Red-violet .. .. 8·00 2·00
58 1½d. black-brown .. .. .. 8·50 80
 w. Wmk inverted .. .. .. 12·00 3·00
59 1½d. deep red-brown (4.19) .. .. 6·50 40
 a. Chocolate (1920) .. .. .. 6·50 45
 w. Wmk inverted .. .. .. 14·00 4·00
60 1½d. bright red-brown (20.1.22) .. 12·00 3·25
61 1½d. green (7.3.23) .. .. .. 4·00 55
 a. Rough unsurfaced paper .. .. £110 45·00
 w. Wmk inverted .. .. .. † £850
62 2d. brown-orange (4.10.20) .. .. 15·00 70
 a. Dull orange (1921) .. .. .. 18·00 70
 w. Wmk inverted .. .. .. † £850
63 2d. bright rose-scarlet (19.1.22) .. 9·00 90
 a. Dull rose-scarlet .. .. .. 9·00 90
 w. Wmk inverted £1200
64 4d. violet (21.6.21) .. .. .. 13·00 14·00
 a. Line through "FOUR PENCE" (Pl 2 rt pane R. 2/6) £6000 £2250
 b. "FOUR PENCE" in thinner letters (Pl 2 rt pane R. 2/6) £400 £225
65 4d. ultramarine (*shades*) (23.3.22) .. 48·00 7·00
 a. "FOUR PENCE" in thinner letters (Pl 2 rt pane R. 2/6) £400 £150
 b. Pale milky blue .. .. .. 70·00 11·00
 w. Wmk inverted .. .. .. 65·00 35·00
66 1s. 4d. pale blue (2.12.20) .. .. 60·00 22·00
 a. Dull greenish blue .. .. .. 65·00 22·00
 b. Deep turquoise (1922) £850 £350
56/66 .. .. *Set of* 11 £160 45·00

In addition to a number of mint pairs from two sheets purchased at Gumeracha, South Australia, with the bottom row imperforate on three sides, a single used example of No. 57 imperforate on three sides is known.

No. 61a was printed on a small residue of paper which had been employed for Nos. 47/ea.

The 4d. ultramarine was originally printed from the Cooke plates but the plates were worn in mid-1923 and Harrison prepared a new pair of plates. Stamps from these plates can only be distinguished by the minor flaws which are peculiar to them.

The variety of Nos. 64 and 65 with "FOUR PENCE" thinner, was caused by the correction of the line through "FOUR PENCE" flaw early in the printing of No. 64.

(Typo T. S. Harrison (to February 1926), A. J. Mullett (to June 1927), thereafter J. Ash)

1923 (6 Dec)–**24.** *W* **6**. *P* 12.

73 **1** 6d. chestnut (Die IIB) .. .. .. 24·00 1·50
 a. Leg of kangaroo broken (Upper plate lt pane R. 1/6) .. .. 75·00 95·00
 w. Wmk inverted .. .. .. † £1000
74 2s. maroon (Die II) (1.5.24) .. .. 50·00 23·00
 w. Wmk inverted .. .. .. £120 65·00
75 £1 grey (Die IIB) (1.5.24) (Optd S. £75) £400 £225

The 6d. and 2s. were printed by all three printers, but the £1 only by Harrison.

No. 73a was corrected during the Ash printing.

(Typo T. S. Harrison (to February 1926), thereafter A. J. Mullett)

1924 (1 May–18 Aug). *P* 14. (*a*) *W* **5**.

76 **5a** 1d. sage-green .. .. 3·00 65
 w. Wmk inverted .. .. .. 11·00 5·00
77 1½d. scarlet (*shades*) .. .. .. 2·25 30
 a. Very thin paper .. .. .. 40·00 17·00
 b. "HALEPENCE" (Pl 22 left pane R. 4/4) .. .. 35·00 17·00
 c "RAL" of "AUSTRALIA" thin (Pl 22 left pane R. 5/4) .. .. .. 35·00 17·00
 d. Curved "1" and thin fraction at left (Pl 24 rt pane R. 7/5) .. .. 35·00 17·00
 w. Wmk inverted .. .. .. 30·00 9·00
78 2d. red-brown .. .. 20·00 6·50
 a. Bright red-brown .. .. .. 26·00 7·50
 w. Wmk inverted .. .. .. † £1000
79 3d. dull ultramarine .. .. .. 24·00 1·50
 a. Imperf three sides (horiz pair) .. £6000
80 4d. olive-yellow .. .. 28·00 4·50
 a. Olive-green .. .. 28·00 4·75
 w. Wmk inverted .. .. .. † £750
81 4½d. violet .. .. 23·00 2·75

(*b*) *W* **6a**

82 **5a** 1d. sage-green (20 May) .. .. 8·00 8·00
 w. Wmk inverted .. .. .. † £700

(*c*) *No wmk*

83 **5a** 1d. sage-green (18 August) .. .. 5·50 9·00
84 1½d. scarlet (14 August) .. .. .. 11·00 9·50
76/84 .. .. *Set of* 9 £110 35·00

Nos. 78/*a* and 82/4 were printed by Harrison only but the remainder were printed by both Harrison and Mullett.

In the semi-transparent paper of Nos. 54a and 77a the watermark is almost indistinguishable.

Nos. 77b, 77c and 77d are typical examples of retouching of which there are many others in these issues. In No. 77c the letters "RAL" differ markedly from the normal. There is a white stroke cutting the oval frame-line above the "L", and the right-hand outer line of the Crown does not cut the white frame-line above the "A".

7

I

II

New Dies

1d. For differences see note above No. 20.

1½d. From new steel plates made from a new die. Nos. 87*a* and 96*a* are the Ash printings, the ink of which is shiny.

2d. Die I. Height of frame 25.6 mm. Left-hand frame-line thick and uneven behind Kangaroo. Pearls in Crown vary in size.
Die II. Height of frame 25.6 mm. Left-hand frame-line thin and even. Pearls in Crown are all the same size.
Die III. Height 25.1 mm; lettering and figures of value bolder than Die I.

3d. Die II has bolder letters and figures than Die I, as illustrated above.

5d. Die II has a bolder figure "5" with flat top compared with Die I of the earlier issues.

(Typo A. J. Mullett or J. Ash (from June 1927))

1926–30. *W* **7**. (*a*) *P* 14.

85 **5a** ½d. orange (10.3.27) .. .. .. 7·00 7·50
 w. Wmk inverted .. .. .. 25·00 25·00
86 1d. sage-green (23.10.26) .. .. 3·25 75
 w. Wmk inverted .. .. .. 11·00 3·50
87 1½d. scarlet (5.11.26) .. .. .. 7·50 1·50
 a. Golden scarlet (1927) .. .. 11·00 2·00
 w. Wmk inverted .. .. .. 14·00 4·25
89 2d. red-brown (Die I) (17.8.27) .. 28·00 30·00
90 3d. dull ultramarine (12.26) .. .. 23·00 4·50
 w. Wmk inverted .. .. .. † £850
91 4d. yellow-olive (17.1.28) .. .. 48·00 29·00
92 4½d. violet (26.10.27) .. .. .. 18·00 3·75
93 1s. 4d. pale greenish blue (6.9.27) .. 90·00 75·00
 w. Wmk inverted .. .. .. † £850
85/93 .. .. *Set of* 8 £200 £130

(*b*) *P* 13½×12½

94 **5a** ½d. orange (21.11.28) .. .. .. 2·25 1·2
95 1d. sage-green (Die I) (23.12.26) .. 2·25
 aw. Wmk inverted .. .. .. 10·00 4·5
 b. Die II (6.28) .. .. .. 50·00 80·0
 bw. Wmk inverted £180
96 1½d. scarlet (14.1.27) .. .. .. 2·25
 a. Golden scarlet (1927) .. .. 2·25
 w. Wmk inverted .. .. .. 6·00 2·5
97 1½d. red-brown (16.9.30) .. .. 5·50 5·5
98 2d. red-brown (Die II) (28.4.28) .. 8·00 8·0
99 2d. golden scarlet (Die II) (2.8.30) .. 11·00 1·4
 a. Die III (9.9.30) .. .. .. 9·00
 ab. No wmk £600 £70
 ac. *Tête-bêche* (pair) £30000
 aw. Wmk inverted (*from booklets*) .. 9·00 1·4
100 3d. dull ultramarine (Die I) (28.2.28) 45·00 4·7
 aw. Wmk inverted £100 £12
 b. Die II. *Deep ultramarine* (28.9.29) 23·00 1·4
 bw. Wmk inverted .. .. .. † £7
102 4d. yellow-olive (19.4.29) .. .. 23·00 2·7
 w. Wmk inverted .. .. .. † £7
103 4½d. violet (11.28) .. .. .. 48·00 22·0
103*a* 5d. orange-brown (Die II) (27.8.30) 23·00 5·5
104 1s. 4d. turquoise (30.9.28) .. .. 80·00 25·0
 w. Wmk inverted .. .. .. † £100
94/104 .. .. *Set of* 11 £190 60·0

Owing to defective manufacture, part of a sheet of the 2d. (Di III), discovered in July 1931, escaped unwatermarked; while th watermark in other parts of the same sheet was faint or norma

Only one example of No. 99ac is known.

8 Parliament House, Canberra

9 "DH66" Biplane and Pastoral Scene

(Des R. A. Harrison. Die eng J. A. C. Harrison (Waterl London). Plates and printing by A. J. Mullett)

1927 (9 May). *Opening of Parliament House, Canberra. wmk. P* 11.

105 **8** 1½d. brownish lake 50
 a. Imperf between (vert pair) £2250
 b. Imperf between (horiz pair) £3250 £32

(Eng H. W. Bell. Recess J. Ash)

1928 (29 Oct). *4th National Stamp Exhibition, Melbourne. T* **4**. *No wmk. P* 11.

106 3d. blue .. .. 4·25 4·
 a. Pane of four with margins £130 £2
 ab. Imperf (pane of four) £18000

No. 106a comes from special sheets of 60 stamps divided into blocks of 4 (5 × 3) and separated by wide gutters perforated dov the middle, printed and sold at the Exhibition.

(Typo J. Ash)

1929 (Feb)–**30.** *W* **7**. *P* 12.

107 **1** 6d. chestnut (Die IIB) (25.9.29) .. 23·00 4·
108 9d. violet (Die IIB) .. .. .. 30·00 13·
109 1s. blue-green (Die IIB) (12.6.29) .. 35·00 5·
 w. Wmk inverted .. .. .. † £10
110 2s. maroon (Die II) (3.29) .. .. 45·00 15·
111 5s. grey and yellow (Die II) (30.11.29) £190 80·
112 10s. grey and pink (Die II) £275 £4
114 £2 black and rose (Die II) (11.30) .. £1900 £4
107/14 .. .. *Set of* 7 £2250 £8
112/14 Optd "Specimen" .. .. *Set of* 2 £325

(Des R. A. Harrison and H. Herbert. Eng A. Taylor. Recess J. A

1929 (20 May). *Air. No wmk. P* 11.

115 **9** 3d. green (*shades*) .. .. 10·00 3·

Variations of up to ¾ mm in the design size of No. 115 are d to paper shrinkage on the printings produced by the "we process. The last printing, in 1935, was printed by the "dr method.

10 Black Swan

11 "Capt. Charles Sturt" (J. H. Crossland)

(Des G. Pitt Morrison. Eng F. D. Manley. Recess J. Ash)

1929 (28 Sept). *Centenary of Western Australia. No wmk. P*

116 **10** 1½d. dull scarlet .. .. 1·25 1·
 a. Re-entry ("T" of "AUSTRALIA" clearly double) (Pl 2 R. 7/4) .. 55·00 60·

(Des R. A. Harrison. Eng F. D. Manley. Recess J. Ash)

1930 (2 June). *Centenary of Exploration of River Murray by Ca Sturt. No wmk. P* 11.

117 **11** 1½d. scarlet .. .. 1·00
118 3d. blue .. .. 4·00 6·

No. 117 with manuscript surcharge of "2d. paid P M L H was issued by the Postmaster of Lord Howe Island during shortage of 2d. stamps between 23 August and 17 October 19 A few copies of the 1½d. value No. 96*a* were also endors These provisionals are not recognized by the Australian post authorities. (*Price £500 un. or us., either stamp*).

(12)

13 Fokker F.VIIa/3m *Southern Cross* above Hemispheres

930 (31 July–2 Aug). *T* **5a** *surch as T* **12**. *W* **7**. *P* 13½×12½.
19 2d. on 1½d. golden scarlet .. .. .. 1·25 50
20 5d. on 4½d. violet (2 Aug) .. .. 7·50 8·00

No. 120 is from a redrawn die in which the words "FOURPENCE ALFPENNY" are noticeably thicker than in the original die and e figure "4" has square instead of tapering serifs.

Stamps from the redrawn die without the surcharge were rinted, but not issued thus. Some stamps, *cancelled to order*, were ncluded in sets supplied by the post office. A few mint copies, which scaped, the cancellation were found and some may have been sed postally (*Price* £2000 *unused*, £45 *used c.t.o.*).

(Des and eng F. D. Manley. Recess John Ash)

931 (19 Mar). *Kingsford Smith's Flights. No wmk. P* 11.

(*a*) *Postage.*
21 **13** 2d. rose-red 75 75
22 3d. blue .. .. 4·50 4·50

(*b*) *Air. Inscr* "AIR MAIL SERVICE" *at sides*
23 **13** 6d. violet .. .. 9·00 11·00
a. Re-entry ("FO" and "LD" double) (Pl 1 R. 5/5) .. .. 55·00 70·00
21/3 .. .. *Set of* 3 13·00 14·50

15

17 Superb Lyrebird

(Typo John Ash)

931–36. *W* **15**. (*a*) *P* 13½×12½.
24 **5a** ½d. orange (2.33) .. .. .. 4·75 5·50
25 1d. green (Die I) (10.31) .. .. 1·75 10
w. Wmk inverted .. .. .. 9·00 3·00
x. Wmk reversed .. .. .. £100 40·00
y. Wmk inverted and reversed .. £150 60·00
26 1½d. red-brown (10.36) .. .. 6·00 9·00
27 2d. golden scarlet (Die III) (18.12.31) 1·75 10
w. Wmk inverted (*from booklets*) .. 2·25 50
28 3d. ultramarine (Die II) (30.9.32) .. 18·00 90
w. Wmk inverted £900
29 4d. yellow-olive (2.33) .. .. 18·00 1·00
w. Wmk inverted .. .. .. † £850
30 5d. orange-brown (Die II) (25.2.32) .. 15·00 15
w. Wmk inverted .. .. .. † £650
31 1s. 4d. turquoise (18.8.32) .. .. 60·00 3·50
w. Wmk inverted .. .. .. † £800
24/31 .. .. *Set of* 8 £110 16·00

(*b*) *P* 12
32 **1** 6d. chestnut (Die IIB) (20.4.32) .. 22·00 25·00
33 9d. violet (Die IIB) (20.4.32) .. .. 26·00 1·00
34 2s. maroon (Die II) (6.8.35) .. .. 5·00 45
35 5s. grey and yellow (Die II) (12.32) .. £110 12·00
36 10s. grey and pink (Die II) (31.7.32) .. £250 £100
37 £1 grey (Die IIB) (11.35) £425 £150
38 £2 black and rose (Die II) (6.34) .. £1600 £325
32/138 .. .. .. *Set of* 7 £2250 £550
36/138 Optd "Specimen" .. .. *Set of* 3 85·00

Stamps as No. 127, but without watermark and perforated 11, re forgeries made in 1932 to defraud the P.O.

For re-engraved type of No. 134, see No. 212.

(Des and eng F. D. Manley. Recess John Ash)

931 (4 Nov). *Air Stamp. As T* **13** *but inscr* "AIR MAIL SERVICE" *in bottom tablet. No wmk. P* 11.
39 6d. sepia .. .. 16·00 12·00

931 (17 Nov). *Air. No. 139 optd with Type* O **4**.
39*a* 6d. sepia .. .. 35·00 48·00

This stamp was not restricted to official use but was on general ale to the public.

(Des and eng F. D. Manley. Recess John Ash)

932 (15 Feb). *No wmk. P* 11.
40 **17** 1s. green .. .. 42·00 1·50
a. Yellow-green .. .. 48·00 2·50

18 Sydney Harbour Bridge

19 Laughing Kookaburra

(Des and eng F. D. Manley. Printed John Ash)

1932 (14 Mar). *Opening of Sydney Harbour Bridge.* (*a*) *Recess. No wmk. P* 11.
141 **18** 2d. scarlet .. .. 2·25 2·50
142 3d. blue .. .. 4·25 7·00
143 5s. blue-green £375 £180

(*b*) *Typo. W* **15**. *P* 10½.
144 **18** 2d. scarlet .. .. 2·00 1·40
141/4 .. .. *Set of* 4 £375 £180

Stamps as No. 144 without wmk and perf 11 are forgeries made in 1932 to defraud the P.O.

(Des F. D. Manley. Die eng E. Broad. Typo John Ash)

1932 (1 June). *W* **15**. *P* 13½×12½.
146 **19** 6d. red-brown .. .. 25·00 55
w. Wmk inverted .. .. † £750

20 Melbourne and R. Yarra

21 Merino Ram

(Des and eng F. D. Manley. Recess John Ash)

1934 (2 July). *Centenary of Victoria. W* **15**.

			I. *P* 10½.		II. *P* 11½.	
147	**20**	2d. orange-vermilion ..	2·50	1·75	4·50	1·50
148		3d. blue ..	6·00	5·50	7·50	8·00
149		1s. black ..	45·00	19·00	45·00	20·00
147/9		.. *Set of* 3	48·00	24·00	50·00	27·00

Stamps were originally issued perforated 10½, but the gauge was subsequently changed to 11½ in August 1934 due to difficulties in separating stamps in the first perforation.

(Des and eng F. D. Manley. Recess John Ash)

1934 (1 Nov). *Death Centenary of Capt. John Macarthur. W* **15**. *P* 11½.
150 **21** 2d. carmine-red (A) .. .. .. 4·00 1·50
150*a* 2d. carmine-red (B) .. .. .. 25·00 3·00
151 3d. blue .. .. 10·00 8·50
152 9d. bright purple .. .. .. 38·00 40·00
150/2 .. .. *Set of* 3 48·00 45·00

Type A of the 2d. shows shading on the hill in the background varying from light to dark (as illustrated). Type B has the shading almost uniformly dark.

22 Hermes

23 Cenotaph, Whitehall

(Des F. D. Manley. Eng E. Broad and F. D. Manley. Recess John Ash until April 1940; W. C. G. McCracken thereafter)

1934 (1 Dec)–**48.** (*a*) *No wmk. P* 11.
153 **22** 1s. 6d. dull purple .. .. .. 32·00 1·00

(*b*) *W* **15**. *Chalk-surfaced paper. P* 13½×14
153*a* **22** 1s. 6d dull purple (22.10.37) .. .. 12·00 45
b. Thin rough ordinary paper (12.2.48) .. .. 4·75 1·25

(Des B. Cottier; adapted and eng F. D. Manley. Recess John Ash)

1935 (18 Mar). *20th Anniv of Gallipoli Landing. W* **15**. *P* 13½×12½ *or* 11 (1s.).
154 **23** 2d. scarlet 80 30
155 1s. black (*chalk-surfaced*) .. .. 48·00 38·00
a. Perf 13½×12½ £1500

24 King George V on "Anzac"

25 Amphitrite and Telephone Cable

(Des and eng F. D. Manley. Recess John Ash)

1935 (2 May). *Silver Jubilee. Chalk-surfaced paper. W* **15** (*sideways*). *P* 11½.
156 **24** 2d. scarlet .. .. 1·50 30
157 3d. blue .. .. 7·00 7·50
158 2s. bright violet .. .. 45·00 40·00
156/8 .. .. *Set of* 3 48·00 42·00

(Des and eng F. D. Manley. Recess John Ash)

1936 (1 Apr). *Opening of Submarine Telephone Link to Tasmania. W* **15**. *P* 11½.
159 **25** 2d. scarlet 75 50
160 3d. blue .. .. 2·75 2·75

26 Site of Adelaide, 1836; Old Gum Tree, Glenelg; King William St., Adelaide

(Des and eng F. D. Manley. Recess John Ash)

1936 (3 Aug). *Centenary of South Australia. W* **15**. *P* 11½.
161 **26** 2d. carmine .. .. 1·25 40
162 3d. blue .. .. 4·00 3·50
163 1s. green .. .. 10·00 8·50
161/3 .. .. *Set of* 3 14·00 11·00

27 Wallaroo

28 Queen Elizabeth

28*a*

29

30 King George VI 30*a*

31 King George VI

32 Koala

33 Merino Ram

34 Laughing Kookaburra

35 Platypus

36 Superb Lyrebird

38 Queen Elizabeth

39 King George VI

40 King George VI and Queen Elizabeth

Dies of 3d.:

Die I Die Ia Die II

Die I. The letters "TA" of "POSTAGE" at right are joined by a white flaw; the outline of the chin consists of separate strokes.

No. 168*a* is a preliminary printing made with unsuitable ink and may be detected by the absence of finer details; the King's face appears whitish and the wattles are blank. The greater part of this printing was distributed to the Press with advance notices of the issue.

Die Ia. As Die I, but "T" and "A" have been clearly separated by individual retouches made on the plates.

Die II. A completely new die. "T" and "A" are separate and a continuous line has been added to the chin. The outline of the cheek extends to about 1 mm above the lobe of the King's right ear.

Die III. Differs from Dies I and II in the King's left eyebrow which is shaded downwards from left to right instead of from right to left.

Line to Kangaroo's ear (Rt pane R. 6/8)

Medal flaw
(Right pane R. 2/5)

(Des R. A. Harrison (T **28/30**), F. D. Manley (T **27**, **31/6**), H. Barr (T **38/9**), H. Barr and F. D. Manley (T **40**). Eng F. D. Manley and T. C Duffell (T **34**), T. C Duffell (revised lettering for T **28***a*, **30***a*), F. D. Manley (others). All recess with John Ash, W. C. G. McCracken or "By Authority ..." imprints)

1937–49. *W* **15** (*sideways on 5d., 9d., 5s. and 10s.*). *Chalk-surfaced paper* (*3d.* (*No.* 168), *5s., 10s., £1*).

(*a*) *P* 13½ × 14 (*vert designs*) *or* 14 × 13½ (*horiz*)

164 **27** ½d. orange (3.10.38) .. .. .. 2·50 45
165 **28** 1d. emerald-green (10.5.37) 40 10
166 **29** 1½d. maroon (20.4.38) .. .. 9·00 3·00
167 **30** 2d. scarlet (10.5.37) 40 10
168 **31** 3d. blue (Die I) (2.8.37) .. .. 60·00 9·50
a. "White wattles" (from 1st ptg) .. £120 70·00
b. Die Ia .. .. £140 6·50
c. Die II (3.38) .. .. .. 60·00 3·50
ca. *Bright blue* (*ordinary thin paper*) (20.12.38) .. .. .. 60·00 2·50
170 **32** 4d. green (1.2.38) .. .. .. 14·00 85
171 **33** 5d. purple (1.12.38) .. .. 2·00 60
172 **34** 6d. purple-brown (2.8.37) .. .. 23·00 90
173 **35** 9d. chocolate (1.9.38) .. .. 5·00 90
174 **36** 1s. grey-green (2.8.37) .. .. 48·00 1·90
175 **31** 1s. 4d. pale magenta (3.10.38) .. 1·50 1·50
a. Deep magenta (1943) .. .. 3·25 2·00

(*b*) *P* 13½

176 **38** 5s. claret (1.4.38) .. .. .. 14·00 1·25
a. Thin rough ordinary paper (4.2.48) .. .. .. 5·00 2·00
177 **39** 10s. dull purple (1.4.38) (Optd S. £30) 38·00 12·00
a. Thin rough ordinary paper (11.48) .. .. .. 48·00 28·00
178 **40** £1 bl-slate (1.11.38) (Optd S. £400) 65·00 30·00
a. Thin rough ordinary paper (4.4.49) .. .. .. 75·00 60·00
164/78 .. .. *Set of* 14 £250 48·00

(*c*) *P* 15×14 (*vert designs*) *or* 14×15 (*horiz*) (*1d. and 2d. redrawn with background evenly shaded and lettering strengthened*)

179 **27** ½d. orange (28.1.42) 55 10
a. Line to kangaroo's ear .. 12·00
b. Coil pair (1942) .. .. 15·00 17·00
ba. Coil block of four .. £250
180 **28***a* 1d. emerald-green (1.8.38) .. .. 2·50 10
181 1d. maroon (10.12.41) .. .. 1·25 10
a. Coil pair (1942) .. .. 12·00 16·00
182 **29** 1½d. maroon (21.11.41) .. .. 4·00 7·50
183 1½d. emerald-green (10.12.41) .. 1·00 70
184 **30***a* 2d. scarlet (11.7.38) .. .. 2·50 10
a. Coil pair (10.41) £325 £375
b. Medal flaw .. .. 90·00
w. Wmk inverted (*from booklets*) .. 4·00 50
185 2d. bright purple (10.12.41) .. 50 80
a. Coil pair (1942) .. .. 42·00 48·00
b. Medal flaw .. .. 35·00
w. Wmk inverted (*from coils*) .. 65·00 24·00
186 **31** 3d. bright blue (Die III) (11.40) .. 45·00 2·25
187 3d. purple-brown (Die III) (10.12.41) 30 10
188 **32** 4d. green (10.42) .. .. 1·00 10
w. Wmk inverted .. .. † £550
189 **33** 5d. purple (1.46) .. .. 45 1·50
190 **34** 6d. red-brown (6.42) .. .. 2·00 10
a. Purple-brown (1944) .. .. 1·75 10
191 **35** 9d. chocolate (8.43) .. .. 1·00 20
192 **36** 1s. grey-green (3.41) .. .. 1·00 10
w. Wmk inverted £500 £250
179/92 .. .. .. *Set of* 14 55·00 11·00

For unwmkd issue, see Nos. 228/30*d*.

Thin paper. Nos. 176a, 177a, 178a. In these varieties the watermark is more clearly visible on the back and the design is much less sharp. On early printings of No. 176a the paper appears tinted.

SPECIAL COIL PERFORATION. This special perforation of large and small holes on the narrow sides of the stamps was introduced after 1939 for stamps issued in coils and was intended to facilitate separation. Where they exist they are listed as "Coil pairs".

The following with "special coil" perforation were placed on sale in *sheets*: Nos. 179, 205, 222*a* (1952), 228, 230, 237, 262 (1953), 309, 311, and 314. These are listed as "Coil blocks of four".

Coils with "normal" perforations also exist for Nos. 180 and 184.

41 "Governor Phillip at Sydney Cove" (J. Allcot)

"Tail" flaw
(Left pane R. 7/1)

(Des and eng E. Broad and F. D. Manley. Recess J. Ash)

1937 (1 Oct). *150th Anniv of Foundation of New South Wales. W* **15**. *P* 13½ × 14.

193 **41** 2d. scarlet .. .. 2·25 15
a. "Tail" flaw .. .. .. £225 50·00
194 3d. bright blue .. .. .. 7·50 2·75
195 9d. purple .. .. .. 15·00 9·50
193/5 .. .. *Set of* 3 22·00 11·00

42 A.I.F. and Nurse

(Des and eng F. D. Manley from drawing by Virgil Reilly. Recess W. C. G. McCracken)

1940 (15 July). *Australian Imperial Forces. W* **15** (*sideways*). *P* 14 × 13½.

196 **42** 1d. green .. .. .. 1·75 1·25
197 2d. scarlet .. .. .. 1·75 50
198 3d. blue .. .. .. 12·00 7·50
199 6d. brown-purple .. .. .. 22·00 13·00
196/9 .. .. .. *Set of* 4 35·00 20·00

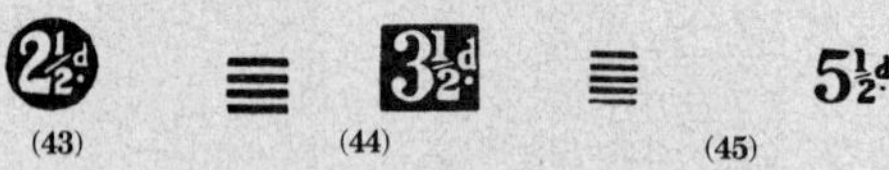

(**43**) (**44**) (**45**)

(Opts designed by F. D. Manley)

1941 (10 Dec). *Nos.* 184, 186 *and* 171 *surch with T* **43/5**.

200 **40***b* 2½d. on 2d. scarlet (V.) 60 40
a. Pair, one without surcharge .. £3500
b. Medal flaw .. .. 90·00
201 **31** 3½d. on 3d. bright blue (Y. on Black) 75 1·50
202 **33** 5½d. on 5d. purple (V.) .. .. 3·50 4·00
200/2 .. .. .. *Set of* 3 4·25 5·50

Nos 200/2 were prepared in connection with the imposition of a ½d. "war tax" increase on most postage rates.

One sheet of the 2½d on 2d. was discovered showing the surcharge omitted on R.1/4 and R.1/5.

46 Queen Elizabeth **46***a*

47 King George VI

48 King George VI

49 King George VI

50 Emu

(Des F. D. Manley. Eng F. D. Manley and T. C. Duffell (T **46/***a*) or F. D. Manley (others))

1942–48. *Recess. W* **15**. *P* 15×14.

203 **46** 1d. brown-purple (2.1.43) 50 10
a. Coil pair (1944) .. .. 18·00 22·00
204 **46***a* 1½d. green (1.12.42) 40 10
205 **47** 2d. bright purple (4.12.44) 55 50
b. Coil pair (4.48) .. .. 85·00 90·00
ba. Coil block of four .. £800
206 **48** 2½d. scarlet (7.1.42) 30 10
a. Imperf (pair)* £2500
w. Wmk inverted (*from booklets*) .. 3·75 30
207 **49** 3½d. bright blue (3.42) 40 2
a. Deep blue 50 2
208 **50** 5½d. slate-blue (12.2.42) 65 1
203/8 .. .. *Set of* 6 2·50 7

*No. 206a comes in horizontal pair with the right-hand stam completely imperforate and the left-hand stamp imperforate a right only.

Coils with normal perforations exist for 1d.

For stamps as Nos. 204/5 but without watermark see Nos 229/30.

The following items are understood to have been the subject of unauthorised leakages from the Commonwealth Note and Stamp Printing Branch and are therefore not listed by us.

It is certain that none of this material was distributed to post offices for issue to the public.

Imperforate all round. 1d. Princess Elizabeth; 1½d. Queen; 2½d. King; 4d. Koala; 6d. Kookaburra; 9d. Platypus; 1s. Lyrebird (small) (also imperf three sides); 1s. 6d. Air Mail (Type **22**); 2½d Mitchell; 2½d. Newcastle (also imperf three sides or imperf vertically).

Also 2½d. Peace, unwatermarked; 2½d. King, *tête-bêche*; 3½d. Newcastle, in dull ultramarine; 2½d. King on "toned" paper.

52 Duke and Duchess of Gloucester

(Des F. D. Manley. Eng F. D. Manley and T. C. Duffell. Reces

1945 (19 Feb). *Arrival of Duke and Duchess of Gloucester Australia. W* **15**. *P* 14½.

209 **52** 2½d. lake 10
210 3½d. ultramarine 15
211 5½d. indigo 20
209/11 .. .. *Set of* 3 40 1·

A

B

1945 (24 Dec). *Kangaroo type, as No.* 134, *but re-engraved a B. W* **15**. *P* 12.

212 **1** 2s. maroon .. .. 3·50 4·2
w. Wmk inverted .. .. .. † £95

No. 134 has two background lines between the value circle an "TWO SHILLINGS"; No. 212 has only one line in this positior There are also differences in the shape of the letters.

53 Star and Wreath

56 Sir Thomas Mitchell and Queensland

(Des F. D. Manley (2½d.), F. D. Manley and G. Lissenden (3½d. G. Lissenden (5½d.). Eng F. D. Manley. Recess)

1946 (18 Feb). *Victory Commemoration. T* **53** *and similar design W* **15** (*sideways on 5½d.*). *P* 14½.

213 2½d. scarlet 10
214 3½d. blue 25 7
215 5½d. green 30 5
213/15 .. .. .. *Set of* 3 60 1·2

Designs: *Horiz*—3½d. Flag and dove. *Vert*—5½d. Angel.

For these designs re-issued in 1995 with face values i decimal currency see Nos. 1542/4.

(Des F. D. Manley. Eng F. D. Manley and T. C. Duffell. Recess

1946 (14 Oct). *Centenary of Mitchell's Exploration of Centra Queensland. W* **15**. *P* 14½.

216 **56** 2½d. scarlet 10
217 3½d. blue 25
218 1s. grey-olive 30
216/18 .. .. .. *Set of* 3 60 1·

57 Lt. John Shortland R.N.

58 Steel Foundry

59 Coal Carrier Cran

(Des and eng G. Lissenden (5½d.), F. D. Manley (others Recess)

1947 (8 Sept). *150th Anniv of City of Newcastle, New Sou Wales. W* **15** (*sideways on 3½d.*). *P* 14½ *or* 15×14 (*2½d.*).

219 **57** 2½d. lake 10
220 **58** 3½d. blue 35
221 **59** 5½d. green 35
219/21 .. .. .. *Set of* 3 70 1·

60 Queen Elizabeth II when Princess

(Des R. A. Harrison. Eng. F. D. Manley. Recess)

47 (20 Nov)–**52.** *Marriage of Princess Elizabeth. P* 14×15.

(*a*) *W* **15** (*sideways*)

2 **60** 1d. purple 15 10

(*b*) *No wmk*

2*a* **60** 1d. purple (8.48) 10 10
b. Coil pair (1.50) .. .. .. 2·25 4·50
c. Coil block of four (9.52) .. .. 4·50

61 Hereford Bull **61*a*** Hermes and Globe

62 Aboriginal Art **62*a*** Commonwealth Coat of Arms

es G. Sellheim (T **62**), F. D. Manley (others). Eng G. Lissenden T **62**), F. D. Manley (1s. 3d., 1s. 6d., 5s.), F. D. Manley and R. J. Becker (10s., £1, £2). Recess)

48 (16 Feb)–**56.** (*a*) *W* **15** (*sideways*). *P* 14½

3 **61** 1s. 3d. brown-purple .. .. .. 1·75 95
3*a* **61*a*** 1s. 6d. blackish brown (1.9.49) .. 90 10
4 **62** 2s. chocolate .. .. .. 2·00 10

(*b*) *W* **15**. *P* 14½×13½

4*a* **62*a*** 5s. claret (11.4.49) .. .. .. 3·25 20
ab. Thin paper (1951) .. .. 27·00 10·00
4*b* 10s. purple (3.10.49) .. .. 17·00 70
4*c* £1 blue (28.11.49) .. .. 35·00 3·50
4*d* £2 green (16.1.50) .. .. .. £110 14·00
4*b/d* Optd "Specimen" .. .. *Set of* 3 £150

(*c*) *No wmk. P* 14½

4*e* **61*a*** 1s. 6d. blackish brown (6.12.56) .. 16·00 1·50
4*f* **62** 2s. chocolate (21.7.56) .. .. 16·00 60
3/4*f* .. .. *Set of* 9 £180 19·00

No. 224ab is an emergency printing on white Harrison paper stead of the toned paper used for No. 224*a*.

William J. Farrer **64** F. von Mueller **65** Boy Scout

(Des and eng F. D. Manley. Recess)

48 (12 July). *William J. Farrer (wheat research) Commemoration. W* **15**. *P* 15×14.
5 **63** 2½d. scarlet 10 10

(Des and eng F. D. Manley. Recess)

48 (13 Sept). *Sir Ferdinand von Mueller (botanist) Commemoration. W* **15**. *P* 15×14.
6 **64** 2½d. lake 10 10

(Des and eng F. D. Manley. Recess)

48 (15 Nov). *Pan-Pacific Scout Jamboree, Wonga Park. W* **15** (*sideways*). *P* 14 × 15.
7 **65** 2½d. lake 10 10
See also No. 254.

Sky retouch (normally unshaded near hill) (Rt pane R. 6/8) (No. 228a retouched in 1951)

"Green mist" retouch. A large area to the left of the bird's feathers is recut (upper plate left pane R. 9/3)

1948–56. *No wmk. P* 15×14 *or* 14×15 (9*d.*).

228 **27** ½d. orange (15.9.49) 20 10
a. Line to kangaroo's ear .. 8·00
b. Sky retouch .. .. 20·00
c. Coil pair (1950) .. .. 75 2·25
ca. Line to kangaroo's ear .. 28·00
cb. Sky retouch (in pair) .. £100
d. Coil block of four (1953) .. 2·50
229 **46*a*** 1½d. green (17.8.49) .. .. 1·25 85
230 **47** 2d. bright purple (1.49) 80 80
aa. Coil pair .. .. 3·00 5·50
230*a* **32** 4d. green (18.8.56) .. .. 2·00 70
230*b* **34** 6d. purple-brown (18.8.56) .. 4·75 60
230*c* **35** 9d. chocolate (13.12.56) .. .. 22·00 2·75
230*d* **36** 1s. grey green (13.12.56) .. .. 5·00 90
da. "Green mist" retouch .. £600
228/30*d* .. .. *Set of* 7 32·00 6·00

66 "Henry Lawson" (Sir Lionel Lindsay) **67** Mounted Postman and Convair CV 240 Aircraft

(Des F. D. Manley. Eng. E. R. M. Jones. Recess)

1949 (17 June). *Henry Lawson (poet) Commemoration. P* 15×14.
231 **66** 2½d. maroon 15 10

(Des Sir Daryl Lindsay and F. D. Manley. Eng F. D. Manley. Recess)

1949 (10 Oct). *75th Anniv of Founding of U.P.U. P* 15 × 14.
232 **67** 3½d. ultramarine 30 40

68 John, Lord Forrest of Bunbury **69** Queen Elizabeth **70** King George VI

(Des and eng F. D. Manley. Recess)

1949 (28 Nov). *John, Lord Forrest of Bunbury (explorer and politician) Commemoration. W* **15**. *P* 15×14.
233 **68** 2½d. lake 15 10

(Des and eng F. D. Manley. Recess)

1950 (12 Apr)–**53.** *P* 15×14. (*a*) *W* **15**

234 **70** 2½d. scarlet (12.4.50) 10 10
235 3d. scarlet (28.2.51) 15 10
aa. Coil pair (4.51) .. .. 17·00 19·00

(*b*) *No wmk*

236 **69** 1½d. green (19.6.50) 15 10
237 2d. yellow-green (28.3.51) 15 10
a. Coil pair .. .. .. 5·00 7·50
b. Coil block of four (8.53) .. .. 10·00
237*c* **70** 2½d. purple-brown (23.5.51) 15 15
237*d* 3d. grey-green (14.11.51) 15 10
da. Coil pair (12.51) .. .. 24·00 30·00
234/7*d* .. .. *Set of* 6 80 40

On 14 October 1951 No. 235 was placed on sale in sheets of 144 originally intended for use in stamp booklets. These sheets contain 3 panes of 48 (16×3) with horizontal gutter margin between.

71 Aborigine **72** **73** Reproductions of First Stamps of New South Wales and Victoria

(Des and eng F. D. Manley. Recess)

1950 (14 Aug). *W* **15**. *P* 15×14.
238 **71** 8½d. brown 15 45
For T **71** in a larger size, see Nos. 253/*b*.

(Des and eng G. Lissenden (T **72**), E. R. M. Jones (T **73**). Recess)

1950 (27 Sept). *Centenary of First Adhesive Postage Stamps in Australia. P* 15×14.
239 **72** 2½d. maroon 15 10
a. Horiz pair. Nos. 239/40 .. .. 30 55
240 **73** 2½d. maroon 15 10
Nos. 239/40 were printed alternately in vertical columns throughout the sheet.

74 Sir Edmund Barton **75** Sir Henry Parkes

76 "Opening First Federal Parliament" (T. Roberts) **77** Federal Parliament House, Canberra

(Des and eng F. D. Manley. Recess)

1951 (1 May). *50th Anniv of Commonwealth of Australia. P* 15×14.
241 **74** 3d. lake 30 10
a. Horiz pair. Nos. 241/2 .. .. 1·75 2·25
242 **75** 3d. lake 30 10
243 **76** 5½d. blue .. .. 20 2·00
244 **77** 1s. 6d. purple-brown 35 50
241/4 .. .. *Set of* 4 2·00 2·50
Nos. 241/2 are printed alternately in vertical columns throughout the sheet.

78 E. H. Hargraves **79** C. J. Latrobe

(Des and eng F. D. Manley. Recess)

1951 (2 July). *Centenaries of Discovery of Gold in Australia and of Responsible Government in Victoria. P* 15×14.
245 **78** 3d. maroon 30 10
a. Horiz pair. Nos. 245/6 .. .. 70 95
246 **79** 3d. maroon 30 10
Nos. 245/6 were printed alternately in vertical columns throughout the sheet.

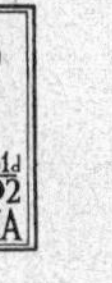

80 **81** **82** King George VI

(Des and eng F. D. Manley. Recess)

1951–52. *W* **15** (*sideways on* 1s. 0½*d.*). *P* 14½ (1*s.* 0½*d.*) *or* 15×14 (*others*).
247 **80** 3½d. brown-purple (28.11.51) 10 10
a. Imperf between (horiz pair) .. £5500
248 4½d. scarlet (20.2.52) 15 70
249 6½d. brown (20.2.52) 15 60
250 6½d. emerald-green (9.4.52) 10 15
251 **81** 7½d. blue (31.10.51) 15 45
a. Imperf three sides (vert pr) .. £7500
252 **82** 1s. 0½d. indigo (19.3.52) 35 30
247/52 .. .. *Set of* 6 90 2·00
No. 251a occurs on the left-hand vertical row of one sheet.

(Des and eng F. D. Manley. Recess.)

1952 (19 Mar)–**65.** *P* 14½. (*a*) *W* **15** (*sideways**)
253 2s. 6d. deep brown .. .. .. 1·50 35
aw. Wmk Crown to left of C of A .. † £700

(*b*) *No wmk*

253*b* 2s. 6d. deep brown (30.1.57) .. .. 5·00 45
ba. Sepia (10.65) .. .. .. 12·00 12·00

Design:—2s. 6d. As T **71** but larger (21×25½ *mm*).

*The normal sideways watermark on No. 253 shows Crown to right of C of A, *as seen from the back of the stamp*.

No. 253*ba* was an emergency printing and can easily be distinguished from No. 253*b* as it is on white Harrison paper, No. 253*b* being on toned paper.

(Des and eng F. D. Manley. Recess)

1952 (19 Nov). *Pan-Pacific Scout Jamboree, Greystanes. As T* **65**, *but inscr* "1952–53". *W* **15** (*sideways*). *P* 14 × 15.
254 3½d. brown-lake 10 10

83 Butter

84 Wheat

85 Beef

(Des P.O. artists; adapted G. Lissenden. Typo)

1953 (11 Feb). *Food Production. P* 14½.

255	**83**	3d. emerald	30	10
		a. Strip of 3. Nos. 255/7	2·00	
256	**84**	3d. emerald	30	10
257	**85**	3d. emerald	30	10
258	**83**	3½d. scarlet	30	10
		a. Strip of 3. Nos. 258/60	2·00	
259	**84**	3½d. scarlet	30	10
260	**85**	3½d. scarlet	30	10
255/60		*Set of* 6	3·75	40

The three designs in each denomination appear in rotation, both horizontally and vertically, throughout the sheet.

86 Queen Elizabeth II

87 Queen Elizabeth II

(Des F. D. Manley from photograph by Dorothy Wilding Ltd. Eng D. Cameron. Recess)

1953–56. *P* 15×14. (*a*) *No wmk.*

261	**86**	1d. purple (19.8.53)	15	10
261*a*		2½d. blue (23.6.54)	20	10
262		3d. deep green (17.6.53)	20	10
		aa. Coil pair	5·00	7·50
		ab. Coil block of four (9.53)	13·00	
262*a*		3½d. brown-red (2.7.56)	1·75	20
262*b*		6½d. orange (9.56)	2·25	1·25
		(*b*) *W* **15**		
263	**86**	3½d. brown-red (21.4.53)	20	10
263*a*		6½d. orange (23.6.54)	1·50	10
261/3*a*		*Set of* 7	5·50	1·50

(Des and eng F. D. Manley. Recess)

1953 (25 May). *Coronation. P* 15 × 14.

264	**87**	3½d. scarlet	35	10
265		7½d. violet	75	1·10
266		2s. dull bluish green	2·50	1·10
264/6		*Set of* 3	3·25	2·00

88 Young Farmers and Calf

(Des P.O. artist; adapted P. E. Morriss. Eng E. R. M. Jones. Recess)

1953 (3 Sept). *25th Anniv of Australian Young Farmers' Clubs. P* 14½.

267	**88**	3½d. red-brown and deep green	10	10

89 Lt.-Gov. D. Collins

90 Lt.-Gov. W. Paterson

91 Sullivan Cove, Hobart, 1804

(Des E. R. M. Jones, eng D. Cameron (T **89/90**); des and eng G. Lissenden (T **91**). Recess)

1953 (23 Sept). *150th Anniv of Settlement in Tasmania. P* 15 × 14.

268	**89**	3½d. brown-purple	30	10
		a. Horiz pair. Nos. 268/9	80	1·25
269	**90**	3½d. brown-purple	30	10
270	**91**	2s. green	1·50	2·75
268/70		*Set of* 3	2·10	2·75

Nos. 268/9 were printed alternately in vertical columns throughout the sheet.

NEW INFORMATION

The editor is always interested to correspond with people who have new information that will improve or correct the Catalogue.

92 Stamp of 1853

(Des R. L. Beck; eng G. Lissenden. Recess)

1953 (11 Nov). *Tasmanian Postage Stamp Centenary. P* 14½.

271	**92**	3d. rose-red	10	30

93 Queen Elizabeth II and Duke of Edinburgh

94 Queen Elizabeth II

Re-entry (lower plate left pane R. 8/2)

(Des and eng F. D. Manley; border and lettering on 7½d. des by R. M. Warner. Recess)

1954 (2 Feb). *Royal Visit. P* 14.

272	**93**	3½d. scarlet	20	10
		a. Re-entry	38·00	13·00
273	**94**	7½d. purple	35	1·25
274	**93**	2s. dull bluish green	85	65
272/4		*Set of* 3	1·25	1·75

95 "Telegraphic Communications"

96 Red Cross and Globe

(Des R. M. Warner. Eng P. E. Morriss. Recess)

1954 (7 Apr). *Australian Telegraph System Centenary. P* 14.

275	**95**	3½d. brown-red	10	10

(Des B. Stewart. Eng P. E. Morriss. Design recess; cross typo)

1954 (9 June). *40th Anniv of Australian Red Cross Society. P* 14½.

276	**96**	3½d. ultramarine and scarlet	10	10

97 Mute Swan

98 Locomotives of 1854 and 1954

(Des R. L. Beck. Eng G. Lissenden. Recess)

1954 (2 Aug). *Western Australian Postage Stamp Centenary. P* 14½.

277	**97**	3½d. black	20	10

(Des R. M. Warner. Eng G. Lissenden. Recess)

1954 (13 Sept). *Australian Railways Centenary. P* 14.

278	**98**	3½d. purple-brown	30	10

99 Territory Badge

100 Olympic Games Symbol

101 Rotary Symbol, Globe and Flags

(Des F. D. Manley. Eng G. Lissenden. Recess)

1954 (17 Nov). *Australian Antarctic Research. P* 14½ × 13½.

279	**99**	3½d. grey-black	15	

(Des R. L. Beck. Eng P. E. Morriss. Recess)

1954 (1 Dec)–**55.** *Olympic Games Propaganda. P* 14.

280	**100**	2s. deep bright blue	70	8
280*a*		2s. deep bluish green (30.11.55)	1·75	1·5

(Des and eng D. Cameron. Recess)

1955 (23 Feb). *50th Anniv of Rotary International. P* 14 × 14½

281	**101**	3½d. carmine	10	

101*a* Queen Elizabeth II

101*b* Queen Elizabeth II

102 Queen Elizabeth

(Des F. D. Manley from bas-relief by W. L. Bowles. Eng Cameron (7½d.), G. Lissenden (others). Recess)

1955 (9 Mar)–**57.** *P* 15×14 (*T* **101***a/b*) *or* **14½** (*T* **102**).

		(*a*) *W* **15** (*sideways*)		
282	**102**	1s. 0½d. deep blue	2·00	
		(*b*) *No wmk*		
282*a*	**101***a*	4d. lake (13.3.57)	20	
		ab. Booklet pane of 6	7·50	
282*b*	**101***b*	7½d. violet (13.11.57)	60	1·
		ba. Double print	£1800	
282*c*	**101***a*	10d. deep grey-blue (6.3.57)	60	
282*d*	**102**	1s. 7d red-brown (13.3.57)	2·00	
282/*d*		*Set of* 5	4·75	2·

No. 282ab has the outer edges of the pane imperfora producing single stamps with one or two adjacent sid imperforate.

103 American Memorial, Canberra

104 Cobb & Co. Coach (from dry-print by Sir Lionel Lindsay)

(Des R. L. Beck (head by F. D. Manley). Eng F. D. Manley. Rece

1955 (4 May). *Australian–American Friendship. P* 14 × 14½.

283	**103**	3½d. violet-blue	10	

(Design adapted and eng by F. D. Manley. Recess)

1955 (6 July). *Mail-coach Pioneers Commemoration. P* 14½ ×

284	**104**	3½d. blackish brown	25	
285		2s. reddish brown	75	1

105 Y.M.C.A. Emblem and Map of the World

106 Florence Nightingal and Young Nurse

(Des E. Thake. Eng P. E. Morriss. Design recess; emblem typo

1955 (10 Aug). *World Centenary of Y.M.C.A. P* 14½ × 14.

286	**105**	3½d. deep bluish green and red	10	
		a. Red (emblem) omitted	£6500	

(Des and eng F.D. Manley. Recess)

1955 (21 Sept). *Nursing Profession Commem. P* 14×14½.

287	**106**	3½d. reddish violet	10	

107 Queen Victoria

108 Badges of New South Wales, Victoria and Tasmania

(Des and eng D. Cameron. Recess)

55 (17 Oct). *Centenary of First South Australian Postage Stamps. P* 14½.
3 **107** 3½d. green 10 10

(Des and eng F. D. Manley. Recess)

56 (26 Sept). *Centenary of Responsible Government in New South Wales, Victoria and Tasmania. P* 14½ × 14.
) **108** 3½d. brown-lake 10 10

109 Arms of Melbourne

110 Olympic Torch and Symbol

11 Collins Street, Melbourne **112** Melbourne across R. Yarra

es P. E. Morriss; eng F. D. Manley (4d.). Des and eng F. D. Manley (7½d.). Recess. Des and photo Harrison from photographs by M. Murphy and sketches by L. Coles (1s.). Des and photo Courvoisier from photographs by M. Murphy (2s.))

56 (31 Oct). *Olympic Games, Melbourne. P* 14½ (4d.), 4 × 14½ (7½d., 1s.) *or* 11½ (2s.).
) **109** 4d. carmine-red 25 10
110 7½d. deep bright blue . . . . 50 1·25
2 **111** 1s. multicoloured 50 30
3 **112** 2s. multicoloured . . . . 70 1·25
0/3 . . . . *Set of* 4 1·75 2·50

115 South Australia Coat of Arms

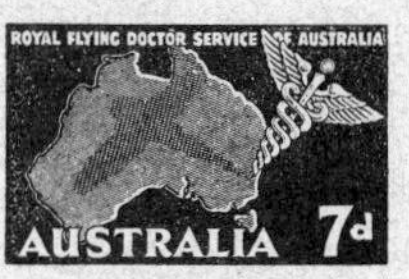

116 Map of Australia and Caduceus

(Des and eng P. E. Morriss. Recess)

57 (17 Apr). *Centenary of Responsible Government in South Australia. P* 14½.
6 **115** 4d. red-brown 10 10

(Des J. E. Lyle; adapted B. Stewart. Eng D. Cameron. Recess)

57 (21 Aug). *Flying Doctor Service. P* 14½ × 14.
7 **116** 7d. ultramarine 15 10

117 "The Spirit of Christmas"

Re-entry (upper plate left pane R. 10/1)

es and eng D. Cameron from a painting by Sir Joshua Reynolds. Recess)

57 (6 Nov). *Christmas. P* 14½ × 14.
3 **117** 3½d. scarlet 10 20
a. Re-entry . . . . 9·00 9·00
9 4d. purple 10 10

118 Lockheed L.1049 Super Constellation Airliner

(Des and eng P. E. Morriss. Recess)

1958 (6 Jan). *Inauguration of Australian "Round the World" Air Service. P* 14½ × 14.
301 **118** 2s. deep blue . . . . 60 1·00

119 Hall of Memory, Sailor and Airman

120 Sir Charles Kingsford Smith and Fokker F.VIIa/3m *Southern Cross*

(Des and eng G. Lissenden. Recess)

1958 (10 Feb). *T* **119** *and similar horiz design. P* 14½ × 14.
302 **119** 5½d. brown-red 40 30
a. Horiz pair. Nos. 302/3 . . . . 80 5·50
303 – 5½d. brown-red 40 30

No. 303 shows a soldier and service-woman respectively in place of the sailor and airman. Nos. 302/3 are printed alternately in vertical columns throughout the sheet.

(Des J. E. Lyle. Eng F. D. Manley. Recess)

1958 (27 Aug). *30th Anniv of First Air Crossing of the Tasman Sea. P* 14 × 14½.
304 **120** 8d. deep ultramarine 60 95

121 Silver Mine, Broken Hill

122 The Nativity

(Des R. H. Evans; adapted and eng F. D. Manley. Recess)

1958 (10 Sept). *75th Anniv of Founding of Broken Hill. P* 14½ × 14.
305 **121** 4d. chocolate 30 10

(Des D. Cameron. Eng P. E. Morriss. Recess)

1958 (5 Nov). *Christmas. P* 14½ × 15.
306 **122** 3½d. deep scarlet 20 10
307 4d. deep violet 20 10

123

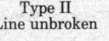

124

126

127

128

129

Queen Elizabeth II

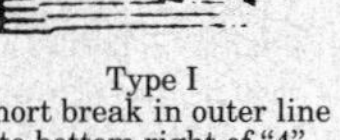

Type I
Short break in outer line to bottom right of "4"

Type II
Line unbroken

Type A
Four short lines inside "5"

Type B
Five short lines inside "5"

(Des G. Lissenden from photographs by Baron Studios. Eng F. D. Manley (2d.), D. Cameron (3d.). P. E. Morriss (others). Recess)

1959–63. *P* 14×15 (*horiz*) *or* 15×14 (*vert*).
308 **123** 1d. deep slate-purple (2.2.59) . . 10 10
a. Deep slate-lilac (1961) . . 85 20
309 **124** 2d. brown (21.3.62) 50 15
a. Coil pair (1962) . . . . 4·00 4·25
b. Coil block of four (1963) . . 8·00
311 **126** 3d. blue-green (20.5.59) 15 10
a. Coil pair (8.59) . . . . 4·00 4·75
b. Coil block of four (8.59) . . 10·00
312 **127** 3½d. deep green (18.3.59) 15 15
313 **128** 4d. carmine-lake (Type I) (2.2.59) . . 1·75 10
a. Carmine-red . . . . 1·75 10
ab. Booklet pane of 6 (18.3.59) . . 19·00
b. Type II . . . . . . 1·75 10
ba. Carmine-red . . . . . . 1·75 10
314 **129** 5d. deep blue (Type A or B) (1.10.59) 90 10
a. Vert *se-tenant* pair (A and B) . . 1·75 2·50
b. Coil pair (18.7.60) . . . . 8·00 10·00
c. Coil block of four (7.61) . . 35·00
d. Booklet pane of 6 (23.3.60) . . 10·00
308/14 . . . . *Set of* 6 3·00 30

No. 313. Produced in printer's sheets, of 640 split into sheets of 160 for issue. Type I occurs on the two upper sheets from the printers' sheet and on ten positions from the left pane of the lower right sheet. Type II occurs on all stamps from the lower sheets except for ten positions from the left pane of lower right sheet.

No. 314. Both types occur in alternate horizontal rows in the sheet (Type A in Row 1, Type B in Row 2, and so on), and their value is identical. Booklet pane No. 314d contains two Type A and four Type B.

Nos. 309a/b, 311a/b and 314b/c have horizontal coil perforations as described after No. 191.

Nos. 313ab and 314d have the outer edges of the panes imperforate, producing stamps with one or two adjacent sides imperforate.

Printings of the 2d. (from March 1965) and of the 3d. (from April 1965), both including coils, were on Helecon paper.

131 Numbat

137 Christmas Bells

142 Aboriginal Stockman

(Des Eileen Mayo (6d., 8d., 9d., 11d., 1s., 1s. 2d.), B. Stewart (5s.), Margaret Stones (others). Eng P. Morriss (11d.), F. D. Manley (1s.), B. Stewart (others). Recess)

1959–64. *T* **131, 137, 142** *and similar designs. W* **15** (5s.), *no wmk* (*others*). *P* 14 × 15 (1s. 2d.), 15 × 14 (6d. *to* 1s.), 14½ × 14 (5s.) *or* 14½ (*others*).
316 6d. brown (30.9.60) . . . . 2·00 10
317 8d. red-brown (11.5.60) 75 10
a. Pale red-brown (9.61) 75 10
318 9d. deep sepia (21.10.59) . . . . 1·75 45
319 11d. deep blue (3.5.61) . . . . 1·25 15
320 1s. deep green (9.9.59) . . . . 4·00 40
321 1s. 2d. deep purple (21.3.62) . . . . 1·25 15
322 1s. 6d. crimson/*yellow* (3.2.60) . . . . 2·50 80
323 2s. grey-blue (8.4.59) . . . . 1·25 10
324 2s. 3d. green/*maize* (9.9.59) . . . . 1·75 10
324*a* 2s. 3d. yellow-green (28.10.64) . . . . 6·00 1·50
325 2s. 5d. brown/*yellow* (16.3.60) . . . . 7·00 55
326 3s. scarlet (15.7.59) . . . . 2·00 10
327 5s. red-brown (26.7.61) . . . . 20·00 85
a. White paper. *Brown-red* (17.6.64) . . £100 7·00
316/327 . . . . . . *Set of* 13 48·00 4·50

Designs: (*As T* **131**) *Vert*—8d. Tiger Cat; 9d. Eastern Grey Kangaroos; 11d. Common Rabbit-Bandicoot; 1s. Platypus. *Horiz*—1s. 2d. Thylacine. (*As T* **137**) *Vert*—2s. Flannel Flower; 2s. 3d. Wattle; 2s. 5d. Banksia; 3s. Waratah.

No. 327 is on toned paper. No. 327a was a late printing on the white paper referred to in the note below No. 360.

An experimental printing of the 11d. was made on Helecon paper in December 1963. See note below No. 362.

All printings of the 8d., 11d., 1s. 2d. and 2s. 3d. (No. 324*a*) were on Helecon paper from April 1965.

NEW INFORMATION

The editor is always interested to correspond with people who have new information that will improve or correct the Catalogue.

143 Postmaster Isaac Nichols boarding the brig *Experiment*

144 Parliament House, Brisbane, and Arms of Queensland

(Des R. Shackel; adapted and eng F. D. Manley. Recess)

1959 (22 Apr). *150th Anniv of the Australian Post Office. P* 14½ × 14.
331 **143** 4d. slate 15 10

(Des and eng G. Lissenden. Recess and typo)

1959 (5 June). *Centenary of Self-Government in Queensland. P* 14 × 14½.
332 **144** 4d. lilac and green 10 10

145 "The Approach of the Magi"

146 Girl Guide and Lord Baden-Powell

(Des and eng F. D. Manley. Recess)

1959 (4 Nov). *Christmas. P* 15 × 14.
333 **145** 5d. deep reddish violet 10 10

(Des and eng B. Stewart. Recess)

1960 (18 Aug). *50th Anniv of Girl Guide Movement. P* 14½×14.
334 **146** 5d. deep ultramarine 30 15

147 "The Overlanders" (Sir Daryl Lindsay)

148 "Archer" and Melbourne Cup

Two types:

I Mane rough II Mane smooth

Type II occurs on Pane A, Row 2 Nos. 8 and 9, Row 4 Nos. 1 to 12, Row 5 Nos. 10 to 12, and on Pane C, Row 4 Nos. 5 to 12, Row 5 Nos. 1 to 9, and Rows 6 to 10 inclusive; the stamps in Row 4 Nos. 5 to 12 and Row 5 Nos. 1 to 9 are considered to be of an intermediate type with the mane as in Type II but the ear and rein being as in Type I. All the rest are Type I.

(Adapted and eng P. E. Morriss. Recess)

1960 (21 Sept). *Centenary of Northern Territory Exploration. P* 15 × 14½.
335 **147** 5d. magenta (I) 30 15
a. Type II .. .. 1·75 55

(Des F. D. Manley. Eng G. Lissenden. Recess)

1960 (12 Oct). *100th Melbourne Cup Race Commemoration. P* 14½.
336 **148** 5d. sepia 20 10

149 Queen Victoria

150 Open Bible and Candle

(Des F. D. Manley. Eng B. Stewart. Recess)

1960 (2 Nov). *Centenary of First Queensland Postage Stamp. P* 14½ × 15.
337 **149** 5d. deep myrtle-green 25 10

(Des K. McKay. Adapted and eng B. Stewart. Recess)

1960 (9 Nov). *Christmas. P* 15 × 14½.
338 **150** 5d. carmine-red 10 10

151 Colombo Plan Bureau Emblem

152 Melba (after bust by Sir Bertram Mackennal)

(Des and eng G. Lissenden. Recess)

1961 (30 June). *Colombo Plan. P* 14×14½.
339 **151** 1s. red-brown 10 10
No. 339 was issued on Helecon paper in April 1965. See note after No. 362.

(Des and eng B. Stewart. Recess)

1961 (20 Sept). *Birth Centenary of Dame Nellie Melba (singer). P* 14½×15.
340 **152** 5d. blue 30 15

153 Open Prayer Book and Text

(Des G. Lissenden. Eng P. E. Morriss. Recess)

1961 (8 Nov). *Christmas. P* 14½ × 14.
341 **153** 5d. brown 10 10

154 J. M. Stuart

155 Flynn's Grave and Nursing Sister

(Des W. Jardine. Eng P. E. Morriss. Recess)

1962 (25 July). *Centenary of Stuart's Crossing of Australia from South to North. P* 14½ × 15.
342 **154** 5d. brown-red 15 10

(Des F. D. Manley. Photo)

1962 (5 Sept). *50th Anniv of Australian Inland Mission. P* 13½.
343 **155** 5d. multicoloured 30 15
a. Red omitted .. .. .. † £500
The note below No. 372b also applies to No. 343a.

156 "Woman"

157 "Madonna and Child"

(Des D. Dundas. Eng G. Lissenden. Recess)

1962 (26 Sept). *"Associated Country Women of the World" Conference, Melbourne. P* 14 × 14½.
344 **156** 5d. deep green 10 10

(Des and eng G. Lissenden. Recess)

1962 (17 Oct). *Christmas. P* 14½.
345 **157** 5d. violet 15 10

158 Perth and Kangaroo Paw (plant)

159 Arms of Perth and Running Track

(Des R. M. Warner (5d.), G. Hamori (2s. 3d.). Photo Harrison

1962 (1 Nov). *Seventh British Empire and Commonwe Games, Perth. P* 14 *(5d.) or* 14½ × 14 *(2s. 3d.).*
346 **158** 5d. multicoloured 40
a. Red omitted £850
347 **159** 2s. 3d. black, red, blue and green .. 3·25 2

160 Queen Elizabeth II.

161 Queen Elizabeth II and Duke of Edinburgh

(Des and eng after portraits by Anthony Buckley, P. E. Mor (5d.), B. Stewart (2s. 3d.). Recess)

1963 (18 Feb). *Royal Visit. P* 14½.
348 **160** 5d. deep green 35
349 **161** 2s. 3d. brown-lake .. .. .. 2·00 3

162 Arms of Canberra and W. B. Griffin (architect)

163 Centenary Emblem

(Des and eng B. Stewart. Recess)

1963 (8 Mar). *50th Anniv of Canberra. P* 14½ × 14.
350 **162** 5d. deep green 15

(Des G. Hamori. Photo)

1963 (8 May). *Red Cross Centenary. P* 13½ × 13.
351 **163** 5d. red, grey-brown and blue 30

164 Blaxland, Lawson and Wentworth on Mt. York

(Des T. Alban. Eng P. E. Morriss. Recess)

1963 (28 May). *150th Anniv of First Crossing of Blue Mounta P* 14½ × 14.
352 **164** 5d. ultramarine 15

165 "Export"

166 Queen Elizabeth II

(Des and eng B. Stewart. Recess)

1963 (28 Aug). *Export Campaign. P* 14½×14.
353 **165** 5d. red 10

(Des and eng P. E. Morriss from photograph by Anthony Buck Recess)

1963 (9 Oct)–**65.** *P* 15×14.
354 **166** 5d. deep green 65
a. Booklet pane of 6 (17.6.64) .. 21·00
b. Imperf between (horiz pair) (31.7.64) 1·75 2
354*c* 5d. red (30.6.65) 55
ca. Coil pair .. .. 18·00 23
cb. Booklet pane of 6 .. .. .. 21·00

The 5d. deep green exists from both sheets and booklets Helecon paper produced in error.

The 5d. red was issued with or without Helecon added to ink. All coil and booklet printings included Helecon in the except for a small printing produced in error. Examples of sheet and booklet printings with Helecon ink have been fo on Helecon *paper*.

Nos. 354a and 354cb have the outer edges of the pa imperforate producing single stamps with one or two adjac sides imperforate.

PRICES OF SETS

Set prices are given for many issues, genera those containing three stamps or more. Definiti sets include one of each value or major colo change, but do not cover different perforatio die types or minor shades. Where a choice possible the set prices are based on the cheap versions of the stamps included in the listings

No. 354b comes from sheets of uncut booklet panes containing 88 stamps (16×18) with wide margins intersecting the sheet orizontally below each third row, alternate rows of stamps nperforate between vertically and the outer left, right and ottom margins imperforate. This means that in each sheet iere are 126 pairs of stamps imperf between vertically, plus a umber with wide imperforate margins attached, as shown in ie illustration.
A 5d. in a similar design, printed in blue and brown with ertical edges imperforate, was prepared, but not issued.

167 Tasman and *Heemskerk*

168 Dampier and *Roebuck*

Des W. Jardine. Eng B. Stewart (4s.), P. E. Morriss (others). Recess)

963–65. *T* **167/8** *and similar designs. No wmk* (4s.) *or W* **15** *(others), (sideways on* 5s., £1). *P* 14 *or* 14½ (5s., £1, £2).
55 4s. ultramarine (9.10.63) . . . . . . 3·75 55
56 5s. red-brown (25.11.64) . . . . . . 5·00 1·00
57 7s. 6d. olive (26.8.64) . . . . . . 19·00 16·00
58 10s. brown-purple (26.2.64) . . . . . . 35·00 4·50
a. White paper. *Deep brown-purple* (14.1.65) 35·00 7·50
59 £1 deep reddish violet (26.2.64) . . . . 35·00 15·00
a. White paper. *Deep bluish violet* (16.11.64) 48·00 24·00
60 £2 sepia (26.8.64) . . . . . . 75·00 75·00
55/360 . . . . . . *Set of* 6 £150 £100
57/60 Optd "Specimen" . . . . *Set of* 4 £450

Designs: *As T* **167**—7s. 6d. Captain Cook; 10s. Flinders and *nvestigator*. *As T* **168**—£1 Bass and whaleboat; £2 Admiral ing and *Mermaid* (survey cutter).
Nos. 358 and 359 were printed on a toned paper but all the ther values are on white paper, the 4s. being on rather thicker aper.

173 "Peace on Earth . . ."

174 "Commonwealth Cable"

(Des R. M. Warner. Eng B. Stewart. Recess)

963 (25 Oct). *Christmas. P* 14½.
61 **173** 5d. greenish blue 10 10

(Des P. E. Morriss. Photo)

963 (3 Dec). *Opening of COMPAC (Trans-Pacific Telephone Cable). Chalk-surfaced paper. P* 13½.
62 **174** 2s. 3d. red, blue, black and pale blue . . 2·00 3·50

IELECON (PHOSPHOR) STAMPS. "Helecon", a chemical ubstance of the zinc sulphide group, has been incorporated in tamps in two different ways, either in the ink with which the tamps are printed, or included in the surface coating of the tamp paper.
Owing to the difficulty of identification without the use of a J.V. lamp we do not list the helecon stamps separately but vhen in stock can supply them after testing under the lamp.
The first stamp to be issued on helecon was the 11d. Bandicoot No. 319) from an experimental printing of four million released o the public in December 1963. The next printing, on ordinary paper, was released in September 1964. The experimental printing was coarse, showing a lot of white dots and the colour is slate-blue, differing from both the ordinary and the later helecon paper.
Further Helecon printings followed from March 1965. Almost all issues from No. 378 onwards were on Helecon paper or paper coated with Derby Luminescence.

175 Yellow-tailed Thornbill

176 Black-backed Magpie

(Des Betty Temple-Watts. Photo)

1964 (11 Mar)–**65.** *Birds. T* **175/6** *and similar designs. Chalk-surfaced paper. P* 13½.
363 6d. brown, yellow, blk & bluish grn (19.8.64) 80 25
a. Brown, yellow, black & emer-grn (6.65) 2·50 2·00
364 9d. black, grey and pale green . . . . 1·00 2·75
365 1s. 6d. pink, grey, dull purple and black . . 75 1·40
366 2s. yellow, black and pink (21.4.65) . . 1·75 50
367 2s. 5d. deep royal blue, light violet-blue, yellow-orange, grey and black . . 2·50 3·50
a. Ordinary paper. *Deep blue, light blue, orange-brown, blue-grey and black* (8.65) 20·00 12·00
368 2s. 6d. black, red, grey and green (21.4.65) 5·00 3·25
a. Red omitted (white breast) £1400
369 3s. black, red, buff & yellow-green (21.4.65) 5·00 1·75
363/9 . . . . *Set of* 7 15·00 12·00

Designs: *Vert*—1s. 6d. Galah; 2s. Golden Whistler; 2s. 5d. Blue Wren; 3s. Straw-necked Ibis. *Horiz*—2s. 6d. Scarlet Robin.
No. 367*a* is from a printing on unsurfaced Wiggins Teape paper, the rest of the set being on chalk-surfaced Harrison paper. Apart from the differences in shade, the inscriptions, particularly "BLUE WREN", stand out very much more clearly on No. 367a. Although two colours are apparent in both stamps, the grey and black were printed from one cylinder.
The 6d. (No. 363) and 2s. 5d were only issued on ordinary paper. The 9d. and 1s. 6d. exist on ordinary or Helecon paper. The 6d. (No. 363*a*), 1s., 2s. 6d. and 3s. were issued on Helecon paper only.

182 Bleriot XI Aircraft (type flown by M. Guillaux, 1914)

Re-entry (upper right plate, R. 4/4)

(Des K. McKay. Adapted and eng P. E. Morriss. Recess)

1964 (1 July). *50th Anniv of First Australian Airmail Flight. P* 14½ × 14.
370 **182** 5d. olive-green 40 10
a. Re-entry . . . . £180 90·00
371 2s. 3d. scarlet . . . . 3·50 2·50

183 Child looking at Nativity Scene

184 "Simpson and his Donkey"

(Des P. E. Morriss and J. Mason. Photo)

1964 (21 Oct). *Christmas. Chalk-surfaced paper. P* 13½.
372 **183** 5d. red, blue, buff and black 10 10
a. Red omitted . . . . . . † £550
b. Black omitted £700

The red ink is soluble and can be removed by bleaching and it is therefore advisable to obtain a certificate from a recognised expert committee before purchasing No. 372a. The used price quoted is for an example on cover.

(Des C. Andrew (after statue, Shrine of Remembrance, Melbourne). Eng E. R. M. Jones. Recess)

1965 (14 Apr). *50th Anniv of Gallipoli Landing. P* 14 × 14½.
373 **184** 5d. drab 65 10
374 8d. blue . . . . 1·00 2·50
375 2s. 3d. reddish purple . . . . . . 1·75 2·50
373/5 . . . . *Set of* 3 3·00 4·50

185 "Telecommunications"

186 Sir Winston Churchill

(Des J. McMahon and G. Hamori. Photo)

1965 (10 May). *I.T.U. Centenary. Chalk-surfaced paper. P* 13½.
376 **185** 5d. black, brown, orange-brown & blue 40 10
a. Black (value and pylon) omitted . . £900

(Des P. E. Morriss from photo by Karsh. Photo)

1965 (24 May). *Churchill Commemoration. Chalk-surfaced paper. P* 13½.
377 **186** 5d. black, pale grey, grey and light blue 15 10
a. Pale grey (facial shading) omitted £900

No. 377a occurred on stamps from the bottom row of one sheet.
Two used examples are known showing the grey ("AUSTRALIA") omitted.
No. 377 exists on ordinary or Helecon paper in approximately equal quantities.

HELECON PAPER. All stamps from No. 378 were on Helecon paper, *unless otherwise stated.*

187 General Monash

188 Hargrave and "Multiplane" Seaplane (1902)

(Des O. Foulkes and W. Walters. Photo)

1965 (23 June). *Birth Centenary of General Sir John Monash (engineer and soldier). P* 13½.
378 **187** 5d. multicoloured 15 10

(Des G. Hamori. Photo)

1965 (4 Aug). *50th Death Anniv of Lawrence Hargrave (aviation pioneer). P* 13½.
379 **188** 5d. purple-brown, blk, yell-ochre & pur 15 10
a. Purple (value) omitted £225

189 I.C.Y. Emblem

190 "Nativity Scene"

(Des H. Fallu from U.N. theme. Photo)

1965 (1 Sept). *International Co-operation Year. P* 13½.
380 **189** 2s. 3d. emerald and light blue . . 90 2·00

(Des J. Mason. Photo)

1965 (20 Oct). *Christmas. P* 13½.
381 **190** 5d. multicoloured 15 10
a. Gold omitted £900
b. Blue omitted £500

No. 381a comes from the bottom row of a sheet in which the gold is completely omitted, the background appearing as black with "CHRISTMAS 1965" and "AUSTRALIA" omitted. The row above had the black missing from the lower two-fifths of the stamp.

(New Currency. 100 cents = 1 dollar)

191 Queen Elizabeth II

192 Blue-faced Honeyeater

193 White-tailed Dascyllus ("Humbug Fish")

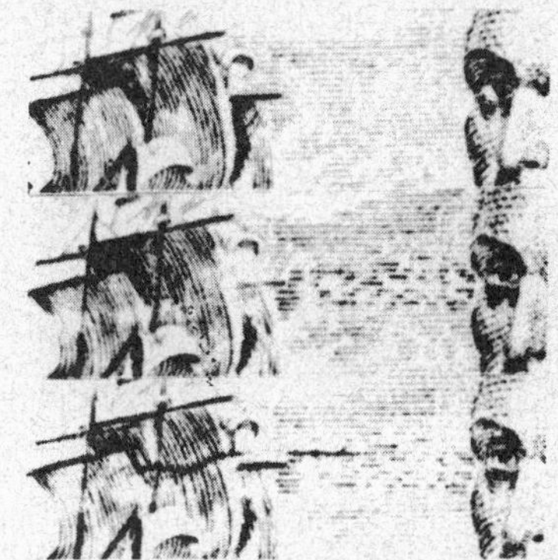

Nos. 401 (top), 401a (centre) and 401b (bottom). No. 401b shows the final form of the variety with a plate crack visible in sky and across sail (Lower sheet left pane. R. 10/1)

(Des Betty Temple-Watts (6 c. (No. 387), 13 c., 24 c.), Eileen Mayo (7 c. (No. 388) to 10 c.). Recess (T **191**, 40 c. to $4). Photo (others))

1966 (14 Feb)–**73**. *Decimal currency. T* **191/3** *and similar designs, some reused from previous issues. P* 15×14 (*T* **191**), 14 (*40 c., 75 c., $1*), 14½ (*50 c., $2, $4*) *or* 13½ (*others*).

382	**191**	1 c. deep red-brown	25	10
383		2 c. olive-green	70	10
384		3 c. slate-green	70	10
385		4 c. red	20	10
		a. Booklet pane. Five stamps plus one printed label	22·00	
386	**175**	5 c. brown, yellow, black & emer-grn	25	10
		a. Brown (plumage) omitted ..	£1000	
		b. Brown, yellow, blk & bl-grn (1.67)	25	20
386*c*	**191**	5 c. deep blue (29.9.67)	70	10
		ca. Booklet pane. Five stamps plus one printed label	8·00	
		cb. Imperf in horiz strip of 3* ..	£1300	
387	**192**	6 c. olive-yellow, blk, blue & pale grey	80	45
		aa. Blue (eye markings) omitted ..	£250	
387*a*	**191**	6 c. orange (28.9.70)	55	10
388	**193**	7 c. black, grey, salmon and brown ..	85	10
388*a*	**191**	7 c. purple (1.10.71)	1·10	10
389	–	8 c. red, yell, bl-grn & blackish green	85	30
390	–	9 c. brown-red, purple-brown, black and light yellow-olive	85	15
391	–	10 c. orange, blackish brown, pale turquoise-blue and olive-brown ..	85	10
392	–	13 c. red, black, grey & light turq-green	2·25	25
		a. Red omitted	£1000	
		b. Grey (plumage and legs) omitted	£800	
393	–	15 c. rose-carmine, black, grey and light bluish green	2·00	80
		a. Rose-carmine omitted	£2250	
394	–	20 c. yellow, black and pink	4·00	15
		a. Yellow (plumage) omitted ..	£900	
395	–	24 c. ultramarine, yellow, blk & lt brn	90	95
396	–	25 c. black, red, grey and green ..	4·50	30
		a. Red omitted	£1200	
397	–	30 c. black, red, buff & lt yellow-green	16·00	65
		a. Red omitted	£1000	
398	**167**	40 c. ultramarine	6·50	10
399	**168**	50 c. red-brown	8·00	10
400	–	75 c. olive	1·00	1·00
401	–	$1 brown-purple (*shades*)	2·25	15
		a. Recut lines in sky	48·00	
		b. Recut lines and plate crack ..	65·00	
		c. Perf 15×14† (9.73) ..	£100	22·00
402	–	$2 deep reddish violet	7·50	50
403	–	$4 sepia	6·50	6·50
382/403		.. .. *Set of* 25	60·00	10·00
400/3		Optd "Specimen" .. .. *Set of* 4	90·00	

Designs: *Vert* (*as T* **193**)—8 c. Copper-banded Butterflyfish ("Coral Fish"); 9 c. Hermit Crab; 10 c. Orange Clownfish ("Anemone Fish"). (*As T* **192**)—13 c. Red-necked Avocet; 15 c. Galah; 20 c. Golden Whistler; 30 c. Straw-necked Ibis. *Horiz* (*as T* **192**)—24 c. Azure Kingfisher; 25 c. Scarlet Robin. *As T* **167**—75 c. Captain Cook; $1 Flinders and *Investigator*. *As T* **168**—$2 Bass and whaleboat; $4 Admiral King and *Mermaid* (survey cutter).

*This shows two stamps imperforate all round and one imperforate at left only.

†The note below No. 553 also applies to No. 401c, its exact gauge being 14.8×14.1. No. 401 is 14.25×13.95.

Nos. 385a and 386ca have the outer edges of the pane imperforate producing single stamps with one or two adjacent sides imperforate.

No. 385 was normally printed in Helecon ink. Early in 1967 experimental printings on different kinds of paper coated with Helecon or Derby Luminescents phosphor were put on sale. These cannot be distinguished by the naked eye.

199 Queen Elizabeth II

200 "Saving Life"

1966 (14 Feb)–**67**. *Coil stamps. Photo. P* 15×*imperf.*

404	**199**	3 c. black, light brown and green ..	30	60
405		4 c. black, light brown & lt vermilion	35	20
405*a*		5 c. black, lt brown & new bl (1.10.67)	40	10
404/5*a*		.. .. *Set of* 3	95	80

(Des L. Mason. Photo)

1966 (6 July). *75th Anniv of Royal Life Saving Society. P* 13½.

406	**200**	4 c. black, bright blue and blue ..	15	10

201 "Adoration of the Shepherds"

202 *Eendracht*

(Des L. Stirling, after medieval engraving. Photo)

1966 (19 Oct). *Christmas. P* 13½.

407	**201**	4 c. black and yellow-olive	10	10
		a. Value omitted	£2000	

No. 407a was caused by a shift of the yellow-olive which covered the white face value.

(Des F. Eidlitz. Photo)

1966 (24 Oct). *350th Anniv of Dirk Hartog's Landing in Australia. P* 13½.

408	**202**	4 c. multicoloured	10	10
		a. Red (sphere) omitted	£1600	

203 Open Bible

204 Ancient Keys and Modern Lock

(Des L. Stirling. Photo)

1967 (7 Mar). *150th Anniv of British and Foreign Bible Society in Australia. P* 13½.

409	**203**	4 c. multicoloured	10	10

(Des G. Andrews. Photo)

1967 (5 Apr). *150th Anniv of Australian Banking. P* 13½.

410	**204**	4 c. black, light blue and emerald ..	10	10

205 Lions Badge and 50 Stars

206 Y.W.C.A. Emblem

(Des M. Ripper. Photo)

1967 (7 June). *50th Anniv of Lions International. P* 13½.

411	**205**	4 c. black, gold and blue	10	10

(Des H. Williamson. Photo)

1967 (21 Aug). *World Y.M.C.A. Council Meeting, Monash University, Melbourne. P* 13½.

412	**206**	4 c. dp blue, ultramarine, lt pur & lt bl	10	10

207 Anatomical Figures

5c

(**208**)

(Des R. Ingpen. Photo)

1967 (20 Sept). *Fifth World Gynaecology and Obstetrics Congress, Sydney. P* 13½.

413	**207**	4 c. black, blue and light reddish violet	10	10

1967 (29 Sept). *No.* 385 *surch with T* **208**.

414	**191**	5 c. on 4 c. red	45	10
		a. Booklet pane. Five stamps plus one printed label	2·25	

No. 414 was only issued in 50 c. or $1 booklets with the outer edges of the pane imperforate so all stamps have one or two adjacent sides imperforate. It only exists printed in Helecon ink.

209 Christmas Bells and Gothic Arches

210 Religious Symbols

(Des M. Ripper (5 c.), Erica McGilchrist (25 c.). Photo)

1967. *Christmas. P* 13½.

415	**209**	5 c. multicoloured (18.10.67) ..	20	10
		a. Imperf three sides (vert pair) ..	£4250	
416	**210**	25 c. multicoloured (27.11.67) ..	1·40	2·00

No. 415a show the stamps perforated at left only.

MINIMUM PRICE

The minimum price quote is 10p which represents a handling charge rather than a basis for valuing common stamps. For further notes about prices see introductory pages.

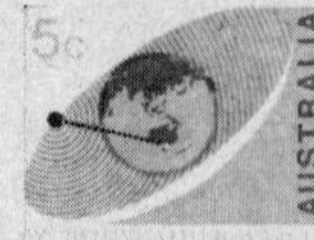

211 Satellite in Orbit

212 World Weather Map

(Des J. Mason. Photo)

1968 (20 Mar). *World Weather Watch. P* 13½.

417	**211**	5 c. orange-brown, pl blue, blk & ochre	30	10
418	**212**	20 c. orange-brown, blue and black ..	1·40	3·25
		a. White (radio waves) omitted ..	£650	
		b. Orange-brown (triangle) omitted	£1600	

213 Radar Antenna

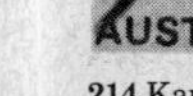

214 Kangaroo Paw (Western Australia)

(Des R. Ingpen. Photo)

1968 (20 Mar). *World Telecommunications via Intelsat II. P* 13½.

419	**213**	25 c. greenish blue, black & lt blue-green	1·75	3·00

(Des Nell Wilson (6c., 30 c.); R. and P. Warner (13 c., 25 c.); Dorothy Thornhill (15 c., 20 c.). Photo)

1968 (10 July)–**71**. *State Floral Emblems. T* **214** *and similar vert designs. Multicoloured. P* 13½.

420	6 c. Type **214**	55	80
421	13 c. Pink Heath (Victoria)	65	50
422	15 c. Tasmanian Blue Gum (Tasmania) ..	90	20
423	20 c. Sturt's Desert Pea (South Australia) ..	3·00	50
424	25 c. Cooktown Orchid (Queensland) ..	2·50	50
425	30 c. Waratah (New South Wales) (Type I)	80	10
	a. Green (leaves) omitted .. .	£1000	
	b. Type II (29.6.71)	4·75	1·50
420/5	.. .. *Set of* 6	7·50	2·25

The 30 c. was reprinted in 1971 from new cylinders so that Type II shows greater areas of white in the pink tones of the petals.

220 Soil Sample Analysis

(Des R. Ingpen. Photo)

1968 (6 Aug). *International Soil Science Congress and World Medical Association Assembly. T* **220** *and similar horiz design. P* 13½.

426	**220**	5 c. orange-brn, stone, greenish bl & blk	10	1
		a. Nos. 426/7 *se-tenant* with gutter margin between	14·00	16·0
427	–	5 c. greenish blue, dull ol-yell, rose & blk	10	1

Design:—No. 427, Rubber-gloved hands, syringe and head of Hippocrates.

The above were printed in sheets of 100 containing a pane of 5 of each design.

The major shades formerly listed have been deleted as there is a range of intermediate shades.

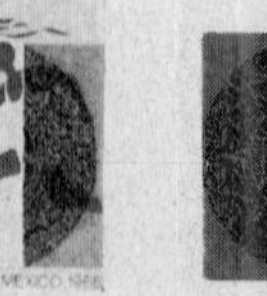

222 Athlete carrying Torch, and Sunstone Symbol

223 Sunstone Symbol and Mexican Flag

(Des H. Williamson. Photo)

1968 (2 Oct). *Olympic Games, Mexico City. P* 13½.

428	**222**	5 c. multicoloured	30	1
429	**223**	25 c. multicoloured	60	1·5

224 Houses and Dollar Signs **225** Church Window and View of Bethlehem

(Des Erica McGilchrist. Photo)

968 (16 Oct). *Building and Savings Societies Congress. P* 13½.
0 **224** 5 c. multicoloured 10 40

(Des G. Hamori. Photo)

968 (23 Oct). *Christmas. P* 13½.
31 **225** 5 c. multicoloured 10 10
a. Green window (gold omitted) .. £475
b. Red (inscr) omitted £750

226 Edgeworth David (geologist)

es Note Ptg Branch (Nos. 432, 434), A. Cook (others). Recess, background litho)

68 (6 Nov). *Famous Australians* (1*st series*). *T* **226** *and similar vert portraits. P* 15 × 14.
2 5 c. myrtle-green/*pale green* 45 20
a. Booklet pane. Five stamps plus one printed label .. .. 2·50
3 5 c. black/*pale blue* 45 20
a. Booklet pane. Five stamps plus one printed label .. .. 2·50
4 5 c. blackish brown/*pale buff*.. .. .. 45 20
a. Booklet pane. Five stamps plus one printed label .. .. 2·50
5 5 c. deep violet/*pale lilac* 45 20
a. Booklet pane. Five stamps plus one printed label .. .. 2·50
32/5 . .. . *Set of* 4 1·60 70

Designs:—No. 432, Type **226**; No. 433, A. B. Paterson (poet); No. 34, Albert Namatjira (artist); No. 435, Caroline Chisholm (social orker).

Nos. 432/5 were only issued in $1 booklets with the outer dges of the pane imperforate so all stamps have one or two djacent sides imperforate.

See also Nos. 446/9, 479/82, 505/8, 537/40, 590/5, 602/7 and 37/40.

230 Macquarie Lighthouse **231** Pioneers and Modern Building, Darwin

(Des and eng Note Ptg Branch. Recess; background litho)

968 (27 Nov). 150*th Anniv of Macquarie Lighthouse. P* 14½ × 13½.
36 **230** 5 c. black and pale yellow 20 50

Used examples are known with the pale yellow background olour omitted.

(Des Marietta Lyon. Photo)

969 (5 Feb). *Centenary of Northern Territory Settlement. P* 13½.
37 **231** 5 c. blackish brown, yellow-olive and yellow-ochre 10 10

232 Melbourne Harbour **233** Concentric Circles (symbolising Management, Labour and Government)

(Des J. Mason. Photo)

969 (26 Feb). *Sixth Biennial Conference of International Association of Ports and Harbours, Melbourne. P* 13½.
38 **232** 5 c. multicoloured 15 10

(Des G. Hamori. Photo.)

1969 (4 June). 50*th Anniv of International Labour Organisation. P* 13½.
439 **233** 5 c. multicoloured 15 10
a. Gold (middle circle) omitted .. £950

234 Sugar Cane **238** "The Nativity" (stained-glass window) **240** Edmund Barton

(Des R. Ingpen. Photo)

1969 (17 Sept). *Primary Industries. T* **234** *and similar vert designs. Multicoloured. P* 13½.
440 7 c. Type **234** .. .. 80 1·50
441 15 c. Timber .. .. 1·75 3·50
a. Black ("Australia" and value) omitted .. £950
442 20 c. Wheat 65 80
443 25 c. Wool .. .. 1·25 2·00
440/3 .. .. *Set of* 4 4·00 7·00

(Des G. Hamori (5 c.), J. Coburn (25 c.). Photo)

1969 (15 Oct). *Christmas. T* **238** *and similar multicoloured designs. P* 13½.
444 5 c. Type **238**.. .. .. .. 25 10
a. Magenta (robe) omitted £600
b. Yellow omitted £450
445 25 c. "Tree of Life", Christ in Crib and Christmas Star (abstract) .. .. 1·25 2·00

(Des from drawings by J. Santry. Recess, background litho)

1969 (22 Oct). *Famous Australians* (2*nd series*). *Prime Ministers. T* **240** *and similar vert designs each black on pale green. P* 15 × 14.
446 5 c. Type **240** 50 20
a. Booklet pane. Five stamps plus one printed label .. .. .. 2·75
447 5 c. Alfred Deakin 50 20
a. Booklet pane. Five stamps plus one printed label .. .. .. 2·75
448 5 c. J. C. Watson 50 20
a. Booklet pane. Five stamps plus one printed label .. .. .. 2·75
449 5 c. G. H. Reid 50 20
a. Booklet pane. Five stamps plus one printed label .. .. .. 2·75
446/9 .. .. *Set of* 4 1·75 70

Nos. 446/9 were only issued in $1 booklets with the outer edges of the pane imperforate so all stamps have one or two adjacent sides imperforate.

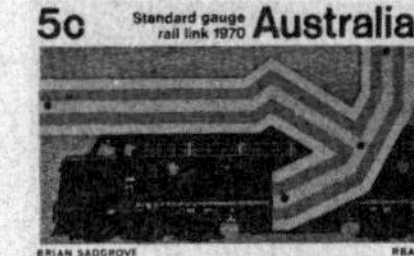

244 Capt. Ross Smith's Vickers Vimy, 1919 **247** Symbolic Track and Diesel Locomotive

(Des E. Thake. Photo)

1969 (12 Nov). 50*th Anniv of First England–Australia Flight. T* **244** *and similar horiz designs. P* 13½.
450 5 c. olive-green, pale blue, black and red .. 15 10
a. Strip of 3. Nos. 450/2 .. .. 1·50
451 5 c. black, red and olive-green 15 10
452 5 c. olive-green, black, pale blue and red .. 15 10
450/2 .. .. *Set of* 3 1·50 25

Designs:—No. 450, Type **244**; No. 451, Lt. H. Fysh and Lt. P. McGinness on 1919 survey with Ford car; No. 452, Capt. Wrigley and Sgt. Murphy in Royal Aircraft Factory B.E.2E taking off to meet the Smiths.

The three designs appear *se-tenant*, both horizontally and vertically, throughout the sheet.

(Des B. Sadgrove. Photo)

1970 (11 Feb). *Sydney–Perth Standard Gauge Railway Link. P* 13½.
453 **247** 5 c. multicoloured 15 10

248 Australian Pavilion, Osaka **251** Australian Flag

(Des J. Copeland (5 c.), A. Leydin (20 c.). Photo)

1970 (16 Mar). *World Fair, Osaka. T* **248** *and similar horiz design. P* 13½.
454 5 c. multicoloured 15 10
455 20 c. orange-red and black 35 65

Design:—20 c. "Southern Cross" and "from the Country of the South with warm feelings" (message).

(Des P.O. Artists (5 c.), J. Mason (30 c.). Photo)

1970 (31 Mar). *Royal Visit. T* **251** *and similar horiz design. P* 13½.
456 5 c. black and deep ochre 35 15
457 30 c. multicoloured .. .. 1·00 2·25

Design:—5 c. Queen Elizabeth II and Prince Philip.

252 Lucerne Plant, Bull and Sun **253** Captain Cook and H.M.S. *Endeavour*

(Des R. Ingpen. Photo)

1970 (13 Apr). *Eleventh International Grasslands Congress, Queensland. P* 13½.
458 **252** 5 c. multicoloured 10 40

(Des R. Ingpen and "Team" (T. Keneally, A. Leydin, J. R. Smith). Photo)

1970 (20 Apr). *Bicentenary of Captain Cook's Discovery of Australia's East Coast. T* **253** *and similar multicoloured designs. P* 13½.
459 5 c. Type **253** 50 10
a. Strip of 5. Nos. 459/63 .. .. 2·25
460 5 c. Sextant and H.M.S. *Endeavour* 50 10
461 5 c. Landing at Botany Bay 50 10
462 5 c. Charting and exploring 50 10
463 5 c. Claiming possession 50 10
464 30 c. Captain Cook, H.M.S. *Endeavour*, sextant, aborigines and kangaroo (63 × 30 *mm*) .. .. 1·75 2·50
459/64 .. .. *Set of* 6 3·50 2·75
MS465 157 × 129 mm. Nos. 459/64. Imperf .. 9·00 9·00

The 5 c. stamps were issued horizontally *se-tenant* within the sheet, to form a composite design in the order listed.

50,000 miniature sheets were made available by the Post Office to the organisers of the Australian National Philatelic Exhibition which overprinted them in the white margin at each side of the 30 c. stamp with "Souvenir Sheet AUSTRALIAN NATIONAL PHILATELIC EXHIBITION" at left and "ANPEX 1970 SYDNEY 27 APRIL–1 MAY" at right in light red-brown and they were also serially numbered. These were put on sale at the exhibition on the basis of one sheet to each visitor paying 30 c. for admission. Although still valid for postage, since the stamps themselves had not been defaced, these sheets were not sold at post offices.

Subsequently further supplies were purchased and similarly overprinted and numbered by a private firm without the authority of the Post Office and ANPEX took successful legal action to stop their further sale to the public. This firm also had the unoverprinted sheets rouletted in colour between the stamps whilst further supplies of the normal sheets were overprinted with reproductions of old coins and others with an inscription commemorating the opening of Melbourne Airport on 1st July 1970, but all these are private productions. Further private productions have been reported.

259 Sturt's Desert Rose

AUSTRALIA AUSTRALIA
I. II.

Two types of 2 c.

I. "AUSTRALIA" thin: "2c" thin; flower name lightly printed.

II. Redrawn. "AUSTRALIA" thicker; "2c" much more heavily printed; flower name thicker and bolder.

(Des Note Ptg Branch. Photo)

1970–75. *Coil Stamps. Vert designs as T* **259**. *Multicoloured White fluorescent paper* (10 c.). *Perf* 15 × *imperf*.
465*a* 2 c. Type **259** (I) (1.10.71) 40 20
ab. White fluorescent paper (6.73) .. 40
b. Type II (white fluorescent paper) (11.73) 65 35
466 4 c. Type **259** (27.4.70) .. .. 70 1·25
467 5 c. Golden Wattle (27.4.70) 20 10
a. White fluorescent paper (6.73) .. 20
468 6 c. Type **259** (28.9.70) .. .. 1·25 1·00
a. Green (leaves) omitted £350
468*b* 7 c. Sturt's Desert Pea (1.10.71) 40 40
ba. Black (berries, "7 c." and inscr) omitted
bb. Buff (shadows on flowers) omitted .. £200
bc. Buff and green (leaves) omitted .. 75·00
bd. White fluorescent paper (10.73) .. 40
468*d* 10 c. As 7 c. (15.1.75) 40 40
465*a*/8*d* .. .. *Set of* 6 3·00 3·00

Nos. 465*a*/8*d* have horizontal coil perforations described after No. 191.

Examples of No. 468bb also show the green colour displaced downwards.

For notes on white fluorescent paper see after No. 504.

264 Snowy Mountains Scheme

265 Rising Flames

(Des L. Mason (7 c.), R. Ingpen (8 c., 9 c.), B. Sadgrove (10 c.). Photo)

1970 (31 Aug). *National Development (1st series). T* **264** *and similar horiz designs. Multicoloured. P* 13½.

469 7 c. Type **264**. 30 80
470 8 c. Ord River Scheme 15 15
471 9 c. Bauxite to aluminium 15 15
472 10 c. Oil and Natural Gas 40 10
469/72 . . . . *Set of* 4 90 1·10

See also Nos. 541/4.

(Des G. Hamori. Photo)

1970 (2 Oct). *16th Commonwealth Parliamentary Association Conference, Canberra. P* 13½.

473 **265** 6 c. multicoloured 10 10

266 Milk Analysis and Dairy Herd

267 "The Nativity"

(Des R. Honisett. Photo)

1970 (7 Oct). *18th International Dairy Congress, Sydney. P* 13½.

474 **266** 6 c. multicoloured 10 10

(Des W. Beasley. Photo)

1970 (14 Oct). *Christmas. P* 13½.

475 **267** 6 c. multicoloured 10 10

268 U.N. "Plant" and Dove of Peace

269 Boeing 707 and Avro 504

(Des Monad Design and Visual Graphics. Photo)

1970 (19 Oct). *25th Anniv of United Nations. P* 13½.

476 **268** 6 c. multicoloured 15 10

(Des G. Hamori. Photo)

1970 (2 Nov). *50th Anniv of QANTAS Airline. T* **269** *and similar horiz design. Multicoloured. P* 13½.

477 6 c. Type **269** 30 10
478 30 c. Avro 504 and Boeing 707 . . . . 95 1·50

270 The Duigan Brothers (Pioneer Aviators)

271 "Theatre"

(Des A. Cook (No. 480), T. Adams (No. 482), Note Ptg Branch (others). Recess (background litho))

1970 (16 Nov). *Famous Australians (3rd series). T* **270** *and similar vert designs. P* 15 × 14.

479 6 c. blue 85 20
  a. Booklet pane. Five stamps plus one printed label . . . . . . 4·00
480 6 c. black/*cinnamon* 85 20
  a. Booklet pane. Five stamps plus one printed label . . . . . . 4·00
481 6 c. purple/*pale pink* 85 20
  a. Booklet pane. Five stamps plus one printed label . . . . . . 4·00
482 6 c. brown-lake/*flesh* 85 20
  a. Booklet pane. Five stamps plus one printed label . . . . . . 4·00
479/82 . . . . *Set of* 4 3·00 75

Designs:—No. 479 Type **270**; No. 480 Lachlan Macquarie (Governor of N.S.W.); No. 481 Adam Lindsay Gordon (poet); No. 482 E.J. Eyre (explorer).

Nos. 479/82 were only issued in 60 c. or $1.20 booklets with the outer edges of the pane imperforate so all stamps have one or two adjacent sides imperforate.

(Des D. Annand. Photo)

1971 (6 Jan). *"Australia-Asia". 28th International Congress of Orientalists, Canberra. T* **271** *and similar horiz designs. Multicoloured. P* 13½.

483 7 c. Type **271** 45 60
484 15 c. "Music" . . . . 70 1·00
485 20 c. "Sea Craft" 65 90
483/5 . . . . *Set of* 3 1·60 2·25

272 The Southern Cross

273 Market "Graph

(Des R. Beck. Photo)

1971 (21 Apr). *Centenary of Australian Natives' Association. P* 13½.

486 **272** 6 c. black, vermilion and bright blue . . 10 10

(Des Monad Design and Visual Graphics Photo)

1971 (5 May). *Centenary of Sydney Stock Exchange. P* 13½.

487 **273** 6 c. multicoloured 10 10

274 Rotary Emblem

275 Dassault Mirage Jets and De Havilland D.H.9A Biplane

(Des H. Williamson. Photo)

1971 (17 May). *50th Anniv of Rotary International in Australia. P* 13½.

488 **274** 6 c. multicoloured 15 10

(Des R. Honisett. Photo)

1971 (9 June). *50th Anniv of R.A.A.F. P* 13½.

489 **275** 6 c. multicoloured 20 10
  a. Black (face value and inscr) omitted £1200

276 Draught-horse, Cat and Dog

277 Bark Painting

(Des R. Ingpen. Photo)

1971 (5 July). *Animals. T* **276** *and similar vert designs. Multicoloured. P* 13½.

490 6 c. Type **276** 20 10
491 12 c. Vet and lamb ("Animal Science") . . 45 35
492 18 c. Red Kangaroo ("Fauna Conservation") . . 80 55
493 24 c. Guide-dog ("Animals Aid to Man") . . 1·00 1·40
490/3 . . . . *Set of* 4 2·25 2·25

The 6 c. commemorated the Centenary of the Australian R.S.P.C.A., and the others were short-term definitives.

(Des J. Mason. Photo)

1971 (29 Sept)–**74**. *Aboriginal Art. T* **277** *and similar multicoloured designs. P* 13½.

494 20 c. Type **277** 20 20
  a. White fluorescent paper (12.73) . . 70
495 25 c. Body decoration 20 50
  a. Black (face value and "AUSTRALIA") omitted £700
  b. White fluorescent paper (11.73) . . 70
496 30 c. Cave painting (*vert*) 30 20
  a. White fluorescent paper (12.73) . . 1·00
497 35 c. Grave posts (*vert*) 30 15
  a. White fluorescent paper (10.74) . . 75
494/7 . . . . *Set of* 4 90 95

The 35 c. exists with both PVA gum and gum arabic.

278 The Three Kings and the Star

279 Andrew Fisher

(Des J. Lee. Photo)

1971 (13 Oct). *Christmas. Colours of star and colour o "AUSTRALIA" given. P* 13½.

498 **278** 7 c. royal blue, pl mauve & pl lake-brn 70 1
  a. Block of 7. Nos. 498/504 . . . . 25·00
  b. White fluorescent paper 90
  ba. Block of 7. Nos. 498b/504b . . 29·00
499 7 c. pale mauve, pl lake-brown & white 70 1
  b. White fluorescent paper 90
500 7 c. pale mauve, white and black . . 4·50 8
  b. White fluorescent paper . . . . 5·50
501 7 c. black, green and black 70 1
  b. White fluorescent paper 90
502 7 c. lilac, green and lilac 70 1
  b. White fluorescent paper 90
503 7 c. black, pale lake-brown and white 70 1
  b. White fluorescent paper 90
504 7 c. royal blue, pale mauve and green 20·00 2·2
  b. White fluorescent paper . . . . 22·00
498/504 . . . . *Set of* 7 25·00 3·5

Nos. 498/504, which also exist on fluorescent paper, were issue in sheets having two panes of 50 stamps. Each half pane had it stamps arranged thus:—

498	499	500	499	498
503	502	501	502	503
504	501	500	501	504
503	502	501	502	503
498	499	500	499	498

FLUORESCENT VERY WHITE CHALK-SURFACEI PAPER. As an experiment 10% of the above issue was printe on very white paper which fluoresces back and front under a ultraviolet lamp; it also has a strong coating of chalk on th surface. Late in 1972 this paper began to be introduced mor generally and a number of stamps exist on both types. Th normal Helecon paper does not fluoresce under the lamp bu does react to the chalky test to a lesser degree.

(Des J. Santry. Recess (off-white backgrounds Litho))

1972 (8 Mar). *Famous Australians (4th series). Prim Ministers. T* **279** *and similar vert designs. P* 15×14.

505 7 c. ultramarine (Type **279**) 30 2
  a. Booklet pane. Five stamps plus one printed label . . . . . . 1·75
506 7 c. ultramarine. (W. M. Hughes) . . 30 2
  a. Booklet pane. Five stamps plus one printed label . . . . . . 1·75
507 7 c. red (Joseph Cook) 30 2
  a. Booklet pane. Five stamps plus one printed label . . . . . . 1·75
508 7 c. red (S. M. Bruce) 30 2
  a. Booklet pane. Five stamps plus one printed label . . . . . . 1·75
505/8 . . . . *Set of* 4 1·10 7

Nos. 505/8 were only issued in 70 c. or $1.40 booklets with th outer edges of the pane imperforate so all stamps have one o two adjacent sides imperforate.

280 Cameo Brooch

281 Fruit

(Des Val Mason. Photo)

1972 (18 Apr). *50th Anniv of Country Women's Associatior P* 13½.

509 **280** 7 c. multicoloured 20 1

(Des D. Annand. Photo)

1972 (14 June). *Primary Industries. T* **281** *and similar hori designs. Multicoloured. P* 13½.

510 20 c. Type **281** . . . . 1·50 3·0
511 25 c. Rice . . . . 1·50 5·0
512 30 c. Fish . . . . 1·50 2·0
513 35 c. Beef . . . . 3·50 1·0
510/13 . . . . *Set of* 4 7·00 10·0

282 Worker in Wheelchair

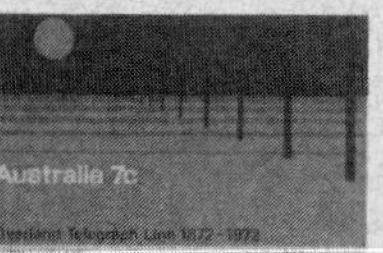

283 Telegraph Line

(Des from photographs by Barbara Ardizzone. Photo)

1972 (2 Aug)–**73.** *Rehabilitation of the Disabled. T* **282** *and similar designs. P* 13½.
514 12 c. yellow-brown and emerald 10 10
a. White fluorescent paper (12.73) .. 10
515 18 c. sage-green and yellow-orange .. 70 35
516 24 c. blue and yellow-brown 15 10
a. White fluorescent paper (7.73) .. 15
514/16 .. .. *Set of* 3 80 50
Designs: *Horiz*—18 c. Patient and teacher. *Vert*—24 c. Boy playing with ball.

(Des J. Copeland. Photo)

1972 (22 Aug). *Centenary of Overland Telegraph Line. P* 13½.
517 **283** 7 c. multicoloured 15 15

284 Athletics **285** Numerals and Computer Circuit

(Des B. Sadgrove. Photo)

1972 (28 Aug). *Olympic Games, Munich. T* **284** *and similar vert designs. Multicoloured. P* 13½.
518 7 c. Type **284** 25 25
519 7 c. Rowing 25 25
520 7 c. Swimming 25 25
521 35 c. Equestrian .. .. 1·50 3·50
518/21 .. .. *Set of* 4 2·00 3·75

(Des G. Andrews. Photo)

1972 (16 Oct). *Tenth International Congress of Accountants, Sydney. P* 13½.
522 **285** 7 c. multicoloured 15 15

286 Australian-built Harvester

(Des R. Ingpen. Photo)

1972 (15 Nov)–**74.** *Pioneer Life. T* **286** *and similar multicoloured designs. P* 13½.
523 5 c. Pioneer family (*vert*) 15 10
a. White fluorescent paper (11.73) .. 15
524 10 c. Water-pump (*vert*) 40 10
a. White fluorescent paper (5.74) .. 70
525 15 c. Type **286** 15 10
a. Black (face value and inscr) omitted £700
b. White fluorescent paper (12.73) .. 40
526 40 c. House 30 60
a. White fluorescent paper (1974) .. 50
527 50 c. Stage-coach 80 20
a. White fluorescent paper (1974) .. 1·25
528 60 c. Morse key (*vert*) .. .. .. 60 1·00
a. White fluorescent paper (1974) .. 60
529 80 c. *Gem* (paddle-steamer) .. .. 60 1·00
a. White fluorescent paper (1974) .. 60
ab. Black (face value and inscr) omitted £600
523/9 .. .. *Set of* 7 2·50 2·50

287 Jesus with Children **288** "Length"

(Des from drawing by Wendy Tamlyn (7 c.), L. Stirling (35 c.). Photo)

1972 (29 Nov). *Christmas. T* **287** *and similar vert design. Multicoloured. White fluorescent paper* (7 c.). *P* 15×14 (7 c.) *or* 13½ (35 c).
530 7 c. Type **287** 30 10
a. Brown-red ("Australia 7c") omitted .. £600
b. Red-brown (inscr) omitted £475
531 35 c. Dove and spectrum motif .. .. 4·00 6·00

(Des Weatherhead & Stitt Pty Ltd. Photo)

1973 (7 Mar). *Metric Conversion. T* **288** *and similar multicoloured designs. White fluorescent paper. P* 15×14 (*No.* 535) *or* 14×15 (*others*).
532 7 c. Type **288** 30 40
533 7 c. "Volume" 30 40
a. Yellow-olive omitted* £700
534 7 c. "Mass" 30 40
535 7 c. "Temperature" (*horiz*) 30 40
532/5 .. .. *Set of* 4 1·10 1·40
*This results in the man's drink and shorts appearing white, and the colour of the stool being the same as the background.

289 Caduceus and Laurel Wreath **290** William Wentworth (statesman and explorer)

(Des H. Williamson. Photo)

1973 (4 Apr). *25th Anniv of W.H.O. White fluorescent paper. P* 15×14.
536 **289** 7 c. multicoloured 30 15

(Des J. Santry. Recess and litho)

1973 (16 May). *Famous Australians* (5*th series*). *T* **290** *and similar vert designs. P* 15×14.
537 7 c. yellow-bistre and black 35 35
a. Block of 4. Nos. 537/40 .. .. .. 1·25
538 7 c. lilac and black 35 35
539 7 c. yellow-bistre and black 35 35
540 7 c. lilac and black 35 35
537/40 .. .. *Set of* 4 1·25 1·25
Designs:—No. 537, Type **290**; No. 538, Isaac Isaacs (first Australian-born Governor-General); No. 539, Mary Gilmore (writer); No. 540, Marcus Clarke (author).
Nos. 537/40 were printed in *se-tenant* blocks of four within the sheet.

291 Shipping **292** Banded Coral Shrimp

(Des J. Copeland. Photo)

1973 (6 June). *National Development* (2*nd series*). *T* **291** *and similar vert designs. Multicoloured. P* 13½.
541 20 c. Type **291** .. .. 2·00 3·25
542 25 c. Iron ore and steel .. .. .. 2·00 3·25
543 30 c. Beef roads .. .. 2·00 3·25
544 35 c. Mapping .. .. 2·50 3·25
541/4 .. .. *Set of* 4 7·50 11·50

(Des Printing Bureau artists (1 to 4 c.), J. Mason (others). Photo)

1973 (11 July)–**74.** *Marine Life and Gemstones. T* **292** *and similar multicoloured designs. White fluorescent paper. P* 14×15 (1 *to* 4 *c.*) *or* 15×14 (*others*).
545 1 c. Type **292** 10 10
a. Black (inscr and face value) omitted £200
b. Yellow-brown omitted £500
546 2 c. Fiddler crab 10 10
547 3 c. Coral crab 10 10
a. Black (inscr and value) omitted .. £500
548 4 c. Mauve stinger 30 55
a. Black (face value and inscr) omitted £450
549 6 c. Chrysoprase (*vert*) 30 10
550 7 c. Agate (*vert*) 30 10
a. Black (value and "agate") omitted 80·00
551 8 c. Opal (*vert*) 30 10
a. Black (face value and inscr) omitted £200
552 9 c. Rhodonite (*vert*) 60 15
552*a* 10 c. Star sapphire (*vert*) (16.10.74) .. 40 10
ab. Black (value, inscr, etc.) omitted .. £150
ac. Turquoise-blue omitted* £100
ad. Printed on the gummed side .. 35·00
545/52*a* .. .. *Set of* 9 2·00 1·25
*The turquoise-blue occurs on the gemstones, and is normally partly covered by the black.
The 1, 3, 7 and 10 c. exist with PVA gum as well as gum arabic.

293 Children at Play **294** John Baptising Jesus

(Des G. Hamori. Photo)

1973 (5 Sept). *50th Anniv of Legacy* (*Welfare Organisation*). *P* 13½.
553 **293** 7 c. cinnamon, deep claret and emerald 30 10

PERFORATIONS. From 1973 to 1975 two different perforating machines were used for some issues, giving gauges of 14½×14 or 15×14 (on horizontal stamps), the exact measurement being 14.4×14.1 or 14.8×14.1. The latter gauge was also used for a reprint of the $1 definitive (No. 401c).

(Des G. Hamori. Photo)

1973 (3 Oct). *Christmas. T* **294** *and similar vert design. Multicoloured. White fluorescent paper. P* 14×14½ (7 *c.*) *or* 13½ (30 *c.*).
554 7 c. Type **294** 35 10
a. Perf 14×15 .. .. 3·50 80
ab. Printed on the gummed side .. 55·00
555 30 c. The Good Shepherd .. .. .. 1·75 2·00

295 Sydney Opera House **296** Wireless Receiver and Speaker

(Des A. Leydin. Photo)

1973 (17 Oct). *Architecture. T* **295** *and similar designs. White fluorescent paper. P* 14½×14 (7, 10 *c.*) *or* 13½ (40, 50 *c.*).
556 7 c. pale turquoise-blue and new blue .. 30 15
a. Perf 15×14 .. .. 3·50 1·60
557 10 c. light ochre and sepia 80 70
558 40 c. black, drab and dull mauve .. .. 1·25 2·00
a. Dull mauve (background) omitted .. £1200
559 50 c. multicoloured .. .. 1·25 2·50
556/9 .. .. *Set of* 4 3·25 4·75
Designs: *Horiz*—10 c. Buchanan's Hotel, Townsville; 40 c. Como House, Melbourne. *Vert*—50 c. St. James' Church, Sydney.

(Des E. Thake. Photo)

1973 (21 Nov). *50th Anniv of Regular Radio Broadcasting. P* 13½.
560 **296** 7 c. lt turquoise-blue, brown-red & blk 15 10

297 Common Wombat **298** "Sergeant of Light Horse" (G. Lambert)

(Des R. Bates. Photo)

1974 (13 Feb)–**76.** *Animals. T* **297** *and similar vert designs. Multicoloured. White fluorescent paper. P* 14×15 (20, 30 *c.*) *or* 13½ (*others*).
561 20 c. Type **297** 35 10
562 25 c. Short-nosed Echidna 75 60
563 30 c. Brush-tailed Possum 50 15
a. Carmine-red (face-value, etc) omitted .. £900
564 75 c. Pygmy Glider .. .. 1·00 85
561/4 .. .. *Set of* 4 2·40 1·50
The 20 c. exists with gum arabic as well as PVA gum.

(Des P.O. artists. Litho Asher & Co, Melbourne ($5, $10). Photo R.B.A. (others))

1974 (24 Apr)–**79.** *Paintings. T* **298** *and similar multicoloured designs. Ordinary paper* ($1, $2, $4). *P* 13½ ($1, $2, $4) *or* 14½ (*others*).
565 $1 Type **298** .. .. 1·00 10
566 $2 "Red Gums of the Far North" (H. Heysen) (*horiz*) .. .. 1·50 25
566*a* $4 "Shearing the Rams" (Tom Roberts) (*horiz*) .. .. .. 3·00 2·25
567 $5 "McMahon's Point" (Sir Arthur Streeton) (14.3.79) .. .. 6·00 2·25
567*a* $10 "Coming South" (Tom Roberts) (19.10.77) .. .. .. 8·50 3·50
565/7*a* .. .. *Set of* 5 18·00 7·50
567/*a*, 778 Optd "Specimen" .. *Set of* 3 9·00
The $1, $2 and $4 exist with PVA gum as well as gum arabic.
Nos. 567/*a* and 778 optd "Specimen" come from a special "Ausipex 84" Presentation Pack issued on 9 February 1983.

299 Supreme Court Judge **300** Rugby Football

(Des T. Thompson. Photo)

1974 (15 May). *150th Anniv of Australia's Third Charter of Justice. White fluorescent paper. P* 14×15.
568 **299** 7 c. multicoloured 20 10

(Des A. Leydin from drawings by D. O'Brien. Photo)

1974 (24 July). *Non-Olympic Sports. T* **300** *and similar multicoloured designs. White fluorescent paper. P* 15×14 (*Nos.* 569/70) *or* 14×15 (*others*).
569 7 c. Type **300** 40 40
570 7 c. Bowls 40 40
571 7 c. Australian football (*vert*) 40 40
572 7 c. Cricket (*vert*) 40 40
573 7 c. Golf (*vert*) 40 40
574 7 c. Surfing (*vert*) 40 40
575 7 c. Tennis (*vert*) 40 40
569/75 .. .. *Set of* 7 2·50 2·50

301 "Transport of Mails"

302 Letter "A" and W. C. Wentworth (co-founder)

(Des J. Copeland. Photo)

1974 (9 Oct). *Centenary of Universal Postal Union. T* **301** *and similar vert design. Multicoloured. White fluorescent paper. P* 15×14 (7 *c.*) *or* 13½ (30 *c.*).

576 7 c. Type **301**.. .. .. 40 20
a. Perf 14½×14 .. .. 60 30
577 30 c. Three-part version of Type **301** .. 85 1·90

Most examples of the 7 c. are on PVA gum; the 30c was on gum arabic.

(Des I. Dalton. Typo and litho)

1974 (9 Oct). *150th Anniv of First Independent Newspaper, "The Australian". White fluorescent paper. P* 14×15.

578 **302** 7 c. black/*light cinnamon* 30 30
a. Perf 14×14½ .. .. .. 1·25 50

=
9c
(**303**)

304 "The Adoration of the Magi"

1974 (16 Oct). *No.* 551 *surch with T* **303**, *in red.*

579 9 c. on 8 c. Opal 15 15

(Des, recess and litho R.B.A.)

1974 (13 Nov). *Christmas. Woodcuts by Dürer. T* **304** *and similar vert design. White fluorescent paper. P* 14×15.

580 10 c. black/*cream* 25 10
581 35 c. black/*cream* .. .. 80 1·00

Design:—35 c. "The Flight into Egypt".

PROCESS. All the following issues to No. 772 were printed in photogravure, *except where otherwise stated.*

PAPER. The following issues were on white fluorescent paper unless otherwise stated. The gum used changed from gum arabic to PVA.

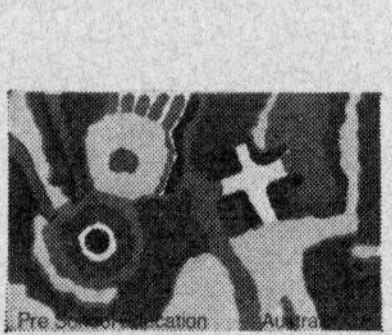

305 "Pre-School Education"

306 "Road Safety"

(Des Vivienne Binns (5 c.), Erica McGilchrist (11 c.), E. Tanner (15 c.), J. Meldrum (60 c.))

1974 (20 Nov). *Education in Australia. T* **305** *and similar multi-coloured designs. P* 13½.

582 5 c. Type **305**.. .. .. 25 40
583 11 c. "Correspondence Schools" 25 25
584 15 c. "Science Education" 40 40
585 60 c. "Advanced Education" (*vert*) .. .. 75 2·00
582/5 .. .. *Set of* 4 1·50 2·75

(Des G. Andrews)

1975 (29 Jan). *Environment Dangers. T* **306** *and similar horiz designs. Multicoloured. P* 14×14½ (*No.* 586) *or* 14½×14 (*others*).

586 10 c. Type **306** 50 50
a. Printed on the gummed side .. 30·00
587 10 c. "Pollution" 50 50
a. Perf 15×14 .. .. 7·50 3·50
588 10 c. "Bush Fires" 50 50
a. Perf 15×14 .. .. 1·40 1·10
586/8 .. .. *Set of* 3 1·40 1·40

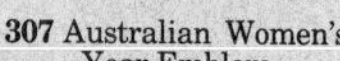

307 Australian Women's Year Emblem

308 J. H. Scullin

(Des Leonora Howlett)

1975 (12 Mar). *International Women's Year. P* 14×15.

589 **307** 10 c. dp violet-blue, green & bluish violet 20 15

This stamp exists with either PVA gum or gum arabic.

(Des B. Dunlop)

1975 (26 Mar). *Famous Australians* (6*th series*). *Prime Ministers. T* **308** *and similar vert designs. Multicoloured. P* 14 × 15.

590 10 c. Type **308** 25 35
591 10 c. J. A. Lyons 25 35
a. Printed on the gummed side .. 70·00
592 10 c. Earle Page 25 35
593 10 c. Arthur Fadden 25 35
594 10 c. John Curtin 25 35
595 10 c. J. B. Chifley 25 35
590/5 .. .. *Set of* 6 1·40 1·90

Nos. 590/5 exist with either PVA gum or gum arabic.

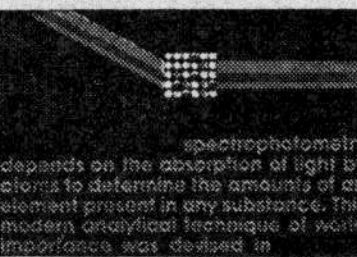

309 Atomic Absorption Spectrophotometry

310 Logo of Australian Postal Commission

(Des Weatherhead & Stitt)

1975 (14 May). *Scientific Development. T* **309** *and similar horiz designs. Multicoloured. P* 13½.

596 11 c. Type **309** 60 40
597 24 c. Radio astronomy.. .. .. 1·40 1·90
598 33 c. Immunology .. .. 1·50 2·50
599 48 c. Oceanography .. .. 2·00 2·75
596/9 .. .. *Set of* 4 5·00 6·75

(Des P. Huveneers)

1975 (1 July). *Inauguration of Australian Postal and Telecommunications Commissions. T* **310** *and similar horiz design. P* 14½×14.

600 10 c. black, rosine and pale grey 25 10
a. Pair. Nos. 600/1 .. .. 1·10 1·40
b. Perf 15×14 .. .. 25 10
ba. Pair. Nos. 600b/1b .. .. .. 1·25 1·50
601 10 c. black, orange-yellow and pale grey .. 25 10
b. Perf 15×14 .. .. 25 10

Design:—No. 601, Logo of Australian Telecommunications Commission.

Nos. 600/1 were printed together, *se-tenant* in horizontal and vertical pairs throughout the sheet.

311 Edith Cowan

312 *Helichrysum thomsonii*

313 "Tambaran" House and Sydney Opera House

(Des D. and J. O'Brien)

1975 (6 Aug). *Famous Australians* (7*th series*). *Australian Women. T* **311** *and similar vert designs. Multicoloured. P* 14×14½.

602 10 c. Type **311** 35 55
a. Perf 14×15 .. .. 35 65
ab. Printed on the gummed side .. 70·00
603 10 c. Louisa Lawson 35 55
a. Perf 14×15 .. .. 60 55
604 10 c. Ethel Richardson 35 55
a. Perf 14×15 .. .. 60 55
605 10 c. Catherine Spence 35 55
a. Perf 14×15 .. .. 45 55
606 10 c. Constance Stone 50 55
a. Perf 14×15 .. .. 35 55
607 10 c. Truganini 35 55
a. Perf 14×15 .. .. 40 55
602/7 .. .. *Set of* 6 2·00 3·00

No. 604 is inscribed with the *nom de plume* "Henry Handel Richardson".

(Des F. Knight)

1975 (27 Aug). *Wild Flowers. T* **312** *and similar multicoloured design. P* 15×14 (18 *c.*) *or* 14×15 (45 *c.*).

608 18 c. Type **312**.. .. .. 25 10
a. Black omitted .. .. 30·00
b. Grey (stem, etc) omitted £100
609 45 c. *Callistemon teretifolius* (*horiz*).. .. 50 10
a. Black (face value and inscr) omitted .. £500
b. Yellow-green (twigs) omitted £140

The 18 c. exists with both PVA gum and gum arabic.

(Des D. Annand (18 c.) or G. Hamori (25 c.))

1975 (16 Sept). *Papua New Guinea Independence. T* **313** *and similar horiz design. Multicoloured. P* 13½.

610 18 c. Type **313** 20 10
611 25 c. "Freedom" (bird in flight) .. .. .. 50 1·25

314 Epiphany Scene

315 Australian Coat of Arms

(Des D. O'Brien (15 c.) or J. Milne (45 c.))

1975 (29 Oct). *Christmas. T* **314** *and similar horiz design P* 14×15 (15 *c.*) *or* 13½ (45 *c.*).

612 15 c. multicoloured 25 1
613 45 c. reddish violet, greenish blue and silver 75 2·4

Design:—45 c. "Shining Star".

I II

Two types of No. 614:
I. Emu's legs without toes.
II. Emu showing toes.
Other minor differences also occur.

(Des J. Spatchurst)

1976 (5 Jan). *75th Anniv of Nationhood. P* 15×14.

614 **315** 18 c. multicoloured (I) .. .. .. 40 2(
a. Buff (supporters) omitted .. £400
b. Gold (shield and star) omitted .. £225
c. Type II 75 30
cb. Gold (shield and star) omitted .. £650

316 Telephone-user, *circa* 1878

317 John Oxley

(Des R. Ingpen)

1976 (10 Mar). *Telephone Centenary. P* 13½.

615 **316** 18 c. multicoloured 20 1

(Des B. Dunlop)

1976 (9 June). *19th Century Explorers. T* **317** *and similar hori designs. Multicoloured. P* 13½.

616 18 c. Type **317** 35 4
617 18 c. Hume and Hovell .. .. 35 4(
618 18 c. John Forrest .. .. 35 4(
619 18 c. Ernest Giles .. .. 35 4(
620 18 c. William Gosse .. .. 35 4(
621 18 c. Peter Warburton.. .. .. 35 4(
616/21 .. .. *Set of* 6 1·90 2·2

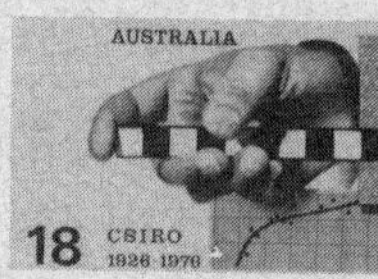

318 Measuring Stick, Graph and Computer Tape

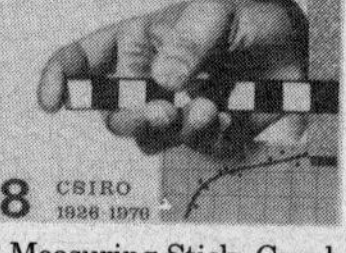

319 Football

(Des R. Ingpen)

1976 (15 June). *50th Anniv of Commonwealth Scientific anc Industrial Research Organisation. P* 15×14.

622 **318** 18 c. multicoloured 20 1

(Des A. Leydin)

1976 (14 July). *Olympic Games, Montreal. T* **319** *and similar multicoloured designs. P* 13½.

623 18 c. Type **319** .. .. 35 2(
624 18 c. Gymnastics (*vert*) .. .. 35 2(
625 25 c. Diving (*vert*) .. .. 60 8(
626 40 c. Cycling .. .. 90 1·0(
623/6 .. .. *Set of* 4 2·00 2·0(

The 25 c. exists with gum arabic as well as PVA gum.

320 Richmond Bridge, Tasmania

321 Blamire Young (designer of first Australian stamp)

(Des O. Borchert)

976 (23 Aug). *Australian Scenes. T* **320** *and similar designs. Multicoloured. P* 14×15 (50 *c.*) *or* 15×14 (*others*).
27 5 c. Type **320** 20 10
28 25 c. Broken Bay, N.S.W. 55 20
29 35 c. Wittenoom Gorge, W.A. 45 20
30 50 c. Mt. Buffalo, Victoria (*vert*) 90 30
31 70 c. Barrier Reef .. .. 1·25 1·25
32 85 c. Ayers Rock, N.T. .. .. 1·25 1·75
27/32 .. .. *Set of* 6 4·25 3·50

(Des R. Honisett)

976 (27 Sept). *National Stamp Week. P* 13½.
33 **321** 18 c. multicoloured 15 15
IS634 101 × 112 mm. No. 633 × 4 .. .. 75 2·00
MS634 contains one stamp coloured as No. 633; the others, howing the different colour separations used in the printing, are ach differently coloured.
The miniature sheet exists with "AUSTRALIAN STAMP ROMOTION COUNCIL" overprinted in red on the margin from privately produced booklet.

322 "Virgin and Child" (detail, Simone Cantarini)

323 John Gould

(Des C. Medlycott (15 c.), Wendy Tamlyn (45 c.))

976 (1 Nov). *Christmas. T* **322** *and similar horiz design. P* 15×14 (15 *c.*) *or* 13½ (45 *c.*).
35 15 c. bright magenta and light azure 25 10
36 45 c. multicoloured 70 90
Design:—45 c. Toy koala bear and decorations.

(Des B. Weatherhead)

976 (10 Nov). *Famous Australians* (8*th series*). *T* **323** *and similar horiz designs. Multicoloured. P* 15×14.
37 18 c. Type **323** 35 45
38 18 c. Thomas Laby 35 45
a. Red-brown ("AUSTRALIA" etc.) omitted £450
39 18 c. Sir Baldwin Spencer 85 45
40 18 c. Griffith Taylor 35 45
37/40 .. .. *Set of* 4 1·25 1·60

324 "Music"

325 Queen Elizabeth II

977 (19 Jan). *Performing Arts. T* **324** *and similar vert designs. Multicoloured. P* 14×15.
41 20 c. Type **324** 25 25
42 30 c. Drama 40 35
43 40 c. Dance 55 40
a. Black (inscr and face value) omitted £1500
44 60 c. Opera .. .. 1·25 1·75
41/4 .. .. *Set of* 4 2·25 2·50

Des P.O. Artists. Litho Govt Printer, Sydney (2% of supplies) or by Norman J. Field, Melbourne)

977 (2 Feb). *Silver Jubilee. T* **325** *and similar vert design. Multicoloured. P* 14×15.
45 18 c. Type **325** 20 10
46 45 c. The Queen and Prince Philip 50 80

326 Fielder and Wicket Keeper

327 Parliament House

(Des B. Weatherhead)

977 (9 Mar). *Australia–England Test Cricket Centenary. T* **326** *and similar vert designs. Multicoloured. P* 13½.
47 18 c. Type **326** 55 55
a. Horiz strip of 5. Nos. 647/51 .. .. 2·50
ab. Black (face value, inscr, etc) omitted
48 18 c. Umpire, batsman and scoreboard .. 55 55
49 18 c. Fielders 55 55
50 18 c. Batsman and umpire 55 55
651 18 c. Bowler and fielder 55 55
652 45 c. Batsman awaiting delivery .. .. 1·00 1·50
647/52 .. .. *Set of* 6 3·25 3·75
Nos. 647/51 were printed together, *se-tenant*, in horizontal strips of 5 throughout the sheet, forming a composite design.
No. 647ab shows the black completely omitted from No. 647, but traces of it remain at the top of the other designs. The error occurs on the bottom row of a sheet.

(Des R.B.A.)

1977 (13 Apr). 50*th Anniv of Opening of Parliament House, Canberra. P* 15×14.
653 **327** 18 c. multicoloured 15 10
a. Yellow (foreground) omitted .. £1000

328 Trade Unions Workers

329 Surfing Santa

(Des D. Lanyon; adapted B. Sadgrove)

1977 (9 May). 50*th Anniv of Australian Council of Trade Unions. P* 13½.
654 **328** 18 c. multicoloured 15 10

(Des R. Roberts (15 c.), J. O'Brien (45 c.))

1977 (31 Oct). *Christmas. T* **329** *and similar vert design. Multicoloured. P* 14×15 (15 *c.*) *or* 13½ (45 *c.*).
655 15 c. Type **329** 25 10
656 45 c. Madonna and Child .. .. .. 75 1·25

330 National Flag

331 Harry Hawker and Sopwith Atlantic

(Des Cato Hibberd Design)

1978 (26 Jan). *Australia Day. P* 13½.
657 **330** 18 c. multicoloured 20 15

(Litho Asher and Co, Melbourne)

1978 (19 Apr). *Early Australian Aviators. T* **331** *and similar horiz designs. Multicoloured. P* 15½.
658 18 c. Type **331** 40 45
a. Imperf (horiz pair) £550
659 18 c. Bert Hinkler and Avro Type 581 Avian 40 45
a. Imperf (horiz pair) £600
660 18 c. Sir Charles Kingsford Smith and Fokker F311a/3m *Southern Cross* .. 40 45
a. Imperf (pair) £110
661 18 c. Charles Ulm and Fokker F311a/3m *Southern Cross* 40 45
658/61 .. .. *Set of* 4 1·50 1·60
MS662 100×112 mm.. Nos. 660/1×2. Imperf 75 1·75
Forgeries of No. **MS**662 have been reported. These can be detected, under strong magnification, by the lack of magenta screen on the blue panel at right and by the presence of magenta dots in the yellow background to No. 661.

332 Piper PA-31 Navajo landing at Station Airstrip

333 Illawarra Flame Tree

1978 (15 May). 50*th Anniv of Royal Flying Doctor Service. P* 13½.
663 **332** 18 c. multicoloured 20 15

(Des D. Rose)

1978 (1 June). *Trees. T* **333** *and similar vert designs. Multicoloured. P* 14×15 (18 *c.*) *or* 13½ (*others*).
664 18 c. Type **333** 20 15
665 25 c. Ghost Gum .. .. 35 1·10
666 40 c. Grass Tree .. .. 45 1·75
667 45 c. Cootamundra Wattle 45 70
664/7 .. .. *Set of* 4 1·25 3·25

NEW INFORMATION

The editor is always interested to correspond with people who have new information that will improve or correct the Catalogue.

334 Sturt's Desert Rose and Map

335 Hooded Plover

(Des D. Pitt. Litho Asher and Co, Melbourne)

1978 (19 June). *Establishment of State Government for the Northern Territory. P* 15½.
668 **334** 18 c. multicoloured 20 15

(Des Kay Breeden-Williams. Photo)

1978 (3 July)–**80**. *Birds* (1*st series*). *Multicoloured designs as T* **335**. *P* 15×14 (20 *c.* (*both*)), 14×15 (22 *c.*) *or* 13½ (*others*).
669 1 c. Spotted-sided Finch (17.9.79) 10 20
670 2 c. Crimson Finch (17.9.79) 10 20
671 5 c. Type **335** (17.7.78) 40 10
a. Grey-brown (bird's back) omitted .. £300
672 15 c. Forest Kingfisher (*vert*) (17.9.79) .. 20 20
673 20 c. Australian Dabchick ("Little Grebe") .. 70 10
a. Yellow (beak and eye) omitted .. £170
674 20 c. Eastern Yellow Robin (17.9.79) 20 10
675 22 c. White-tailed Kingfisher (22 × 29 *mm*) (31.3.80) 30 10
676 25 c. Masked Plover (17.7.78) 90 35
677 30 c. Oystercatcher (17.7.78) .. .. .. 1·00 25
678 40 c. Variegated Wren (*vert*) (17.9.79) .. 30 45
679 50 c. Flame Robin (*vert*) (17.9.79) 40 50
680 55 c. Comb-crested Jacana ("Lotus-bird") .. 85 60
669/80 .. .. *Set of* 12 4·75 2·75
See also Nos. 734/40.

336 1928 3d. "National Stamp Exhibition" Commemorative

337 "The Madonna and Child" (after van Eyck)

(Des Cato Hibberd Design. Litho Asher and Co, Melbourne)

1978 (25 Sept). *National Stamp Week.* 50*th Anniv of National Stamp Exhibition, Melbourne. P* 15½.
694 **336** 20 c. multicoloured 15 15
MS695 78 × 113 mm. No. 694 × 4 .. .. 75 1·75

(Litho Asher and Co, Melbourne)

1978 (3 Oct–1 Nov). *Christmas. Paintings. T* **337** *and similar vert designs. Multicoloured. P* 14½.
696 15 c. Type **337** (1.11) 30 10
697 25 c. "The Virgin and Child" (Marmion) .. 45 55
698 55 c. "The Holy Family" (del Vaga) (1.11) .. 70 90
696/8 .. .. *Set of* 3 1·25 1·40

338 "Tulloch"

339 Raising the Flag, Sydney Cove, 26 January 1788

(Des B. Clinton)

1978 (18 Oct). *Race-horses. T* **338** *and similar multicoloured designs. P* 15×14 (20 *c.*) *or* 13½ (*others*).
699 20 c. Type **338** 35 10
700 35 c. "Bernborough" (*vert*) 60 85
701 50 c. "Phar Lap" (*vert*) .. .. 85 1·25
702 55 c. "Peter Pan" .. .. 90 1·10
699/702 .. .. *Set of* 4 2·40 3·00

(Des B. Clinton. Litho Asher and Co, Melbourne)

1979 (26 Jan). *Australia Day. P* 15½.
703 **339** 20 c. multicoloured 15 15
a. Yellow omitted .. .. ..

340 *Canberra* (paddle-steamer)

341 Port Campbell, Victoria

(Des O. Borchert)

1979 (14 Feb). *Ferries and Murray River Steamers. T* **340** *and similar horiz designs. Multicoloured. P* 15×14 (20 c.) *or* 13½ (*others*).

704	20 c. Type **340**	35	10
705	35 c. *Lady Denman*	60	1·00
706	50 c. *Murray River Queen* (paddle-steamer)	80	1·40
707	55 c. *Curl Curl* (hydrofoil)	90	1·25
704/7	.. .. *Set of* 4	2·40	3·25

(Des M. Robinson. Litho Asher and Co. Melbourne)

1979 (9 Apr). *National Parks. T* **341** *and similar multicoloured designs. P* 15½.

708	20 c. Type **341**	25	25
	a. Horiz strip of 5. Nos. 708/12	1·10	
709	20 c. Uluru, Northern Territory	25	25
710	20 c. Royal, New South Wales	25	25
711	20 c. Flinders Ranges, South Australia ..	25	25
712	20 c. Nambung, Western Australia	25	25
713	20 c. Girraween, Queensland (*vert*)	25	25
	a. Horiz pair. Nos. 713/14	50	50
	ab. Imperf (horiz pair)*	£650	
714	20 c. Mount Field, Tasmania (*vert*)	25	25
708/14	.. .. *Set of* 7	1·40	1·40

Nos. 708/14 were printed together, *se-tenant*; Nos. 708/12 in horizontal strips of 5 and Nos. 713/14 in horizontal pairs, throughout separate sheets.

*The imperforate error, No. 713ab, involves the two right-hand vertical columns of the sheet only, the left-hand stamp having vertical perforations at left.

342 "Double Fairlie" Type Locomotive, Western Australia

343 Symbolic Swan

(Des R. Honisett)

1979 (16 May). *Steam Railways. T* **342** *and similar horiz designs. Multicoloured. P* 14×15 (20 c.) *or* 13½ (*others*).

715	20 c. Type **342**	30	10
716	35 c. Locomotive, Puffing Billy Line, Victoria	60	70
717	50 c. Locomotive, Pichi Richi Line, South Australia	70	1·50
718	55 c. Locomotive, Zig Zag Railway, New South Wales	80	1·40
715/18	.. .. *Set of* 4	2·25	3·25

(Des B. Weatherhead)

1979 (6 June). *150th Anniv of Western Australia. P* 13½.

719	**343** 20 c. multicoloured	15	15

344 Children playing on Slide

345 Letters and Parcels

(Des Wendy Tamlyn. Litho Asher and Co, Melbourne)

1979 (13 Aug). *International Year of the Child. P* 13½ × 13.

720	**344** 20 c. multicoloured	15	10

(Des A. Collins. Litho Asher and Co, Melbourne)

1979 (24 Sept–1 Nov). *Christmas. T* **345** *and similar vert designs. Multicoloured. P* 13 × 13½.

721	15 c. Christ's Nativity (Eastern European icon) (1.11.79)	15	10
722	25 c. Type **345**	25	50
723	55 c. "Madonna and Child" (Buglioni) (1.11.79)	40	75
721/3	.. .. *Set of* 3	70	1·25

346 Fly-fishing

347 Matthew Flinders

(Des B. Clinton)

1979 (24 Oct). *Fishing. T* **346** *and similar vert designs. P* 14×15 (20 c.) *or* 13½ (*others*).

724	20 c. multicoloured	20	10
725	35 c. black, deep grey-blue and violet-blue ..	35	70
726	50 c. multicoloured	40	90
727	55 c. multicoloured	45	85
724/7	.. .. *Set of* 4	1·25	2·25

Designs:—35 c. Spinning; 50 c. Deep sea game-fishing; 55 c. Surf-fishing.

(Des B. Weatherhead. Litho Asher and Co, Melbourne)

1980 (23 Jan). *Australia Day. P* 13½ × 13.

728	**347** 20 c. multicoloured	20	10

348 Dingo

349 Queen Elizabeth II

(Des Marg Towt. Litho Asher and Co, Melbourne)

1980 (20 Feb). *Dogs. T* **348** *and similar horiz designs. Multicoloured. P* 13½ × 13.

729	20 c. Type **348**	35	10
730	25 c. Border Collie	35	50
731	35 c. Australian Terrier	50	90
732	50 c. Australian Cattle Dog	1·10	1·75
733	55 c. Australian Kelpie	1·00	1·40
729/33	.. .. *Set of* 5	3·00	4·25

(Des Kay Breeden-Williams. Litho Asher and Co, Melbourne)

1980 (31 Mar)–**82**. *Birds* (2*nd series*). *Multicoloured designs as T* **335**. *P* 12½.

734	10 c. Golden-shouldered Parrot (*vert*) (1.7.80)	40	10
	a. Perf 14½×14 (1982)	1·50	55
734*b*	18 c. Spotted Catbird (*vert*) (17.11.80) ..	70	1·25
735	28 c. Australian Bee Eater ("Rainbow Bird") (*vert*)	50	20
736	35 c. Regent Bowerbird (*vert*) (1.7.80) ..	35	10
737	45 c. Masked Wood Swallow (1.7.80) ..	40	10
	a. Perf 14×14½ (1982)	2·00	90
738	60 c. Australian King Parrot (*vert*) ..	50	15
739	80 c. Rainbow Pitta (1.7.80)	1·00	75
740	$1 Black-backed Magpie (*vert*) (1.7.80) ..	1·00	10
734/40	.. .. *Set of* 8	4·25	2·25

Designs of Nos. 734/40 measure 22 × 29 mm (vert) or 29 × 22 mm (horiz).

(Des B. Weatherhead. Litho Asher and Co, Melbourne)

1980 (21 Apr). *Queen Elizabeth II's Birthday. P* 13 × 13½.

741	**349** 22 c. multicoloured	30	20

350 "Once a jolly Swagman camp'd by a Billabong"

351 High Court Buildings

(Des R. Roberts. Litho Asher and Co, Melbourne)

1980 (7 May). *Folklore. Scenes and Verses from the Folksong "Waltzing Matilda". T* **350** *and similar vert designs. Multicoloured. P* 13 × 13½.

742	22 c. Type **350**	30	10
	a. Horiz strip of 5. Nos. 742/6	1·40	
743	22 c. "And he sang as he shoved that Jumbuck in his Tuckerbag"	30	10
744	22 c. "Up rode the Squatter, mounted on his Thoroughbred"	30	10
745	22 c. "Down came the Troopers one, two, three"	30	10
746	22 c. "And his Ghost may be heard as you pass by that Billabong"	30	10
742/6	.. .. *Set of* 5	1·40	45

Nos. 742/6 were printed together, *se-tenant*, in horizontal strips of 5 throughout the sheet, forming a composite design.

(Des Cato Hibberd Design. Litho Asher and Co, Melbourne)

1980 (19 May). *Opening of High Court Building, Canberra. P* 13 × 13½.

747	**351** 22 c. multicoloured	20	20

352 Salvation Army

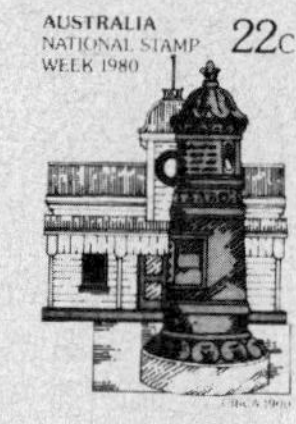

353 Postbox, *circa* 1900

(Des J. Spatchurst. Litho Asher and Co, Melbourne)

1980 (11 Aug). *Community Welfare. T* **352** *and similar mult coloured designs. P* 13½ × 13 (*Nos.* 748, 751) *or* 13 × 13

(*others*).

748	22 c. Type **352**	40	4
749	22 c. St. Vincent de Paul Society (*vert*) ..	40	4
750	22 c. Meals on Wheels (*vert*)	40	4
751	22 c. "Life. Be in it"	40	4
748/51	.. .. *Set of* 4	1·40	1·4

(Des B. Weatherhead. Litho Asher and Co, Melbourne)

1980 (29 Sept). *National Stamp Week. T* **353** *and similar ve designs showing postal history, circa* 1900. *Multicoloure P* 13 × 13½.

752	22 c. Type **353**..	30	1
	a. Horiz strip of 5. Nos. 752/6	1·40	
753	22 c. Postman (facing left)	30	1
754	22 c. Mail van..	30	1
755	22 c. Postman and postbox	30	1
756	22 c. Postman (facing right)	30	1
752/6	.. .. *Set of* 5	1·40	4
MS757	95×130 mm. Nos. 752, 754 and 756 ..	1·10	1·4
	a. Error. Imperf		

Nos. 752/6 were printed together, *se-tenant*, in horizontal stri of 5 throughout the sheet.

Stamps from No. **MS**757 have different backgrounds to th stamps from normal sheets.

354 "Holy Family" (painting, Prospero Fontana)

355 Commonwealth Aircraft Factory CA-6 Wackett, 1941

(Des B. Weatherhead. Litho Asher and Co, Melbourne)

1980 (1 Oct–3 Nov). *Christmas. Works of Art. T* **354** *and simil vert designs. Multicoloured. P* 13 × 13½.

758	15 c. "The Virgin Enthroned" (detail of painting by Justin O'Brien) (3.11) ..	15	1
759	28 c. Type **354**	25	4
760	60 c. "Madonna and Child" (sculpture by School of M. Zuern) (3.11)	50	1·1
758/60	.. .. *Set of* 3	80	1·4

(Des O. Borchert. Litho Victorian Government Printer, Melbourr (22 c.), Asher and Co, Melbourne (others))

1980 (19 Nov). *Aircraft. T* **355** *and similar horiz designs. Mult coloured. P* 13½ × 14 (22 *c.*) *or* 13½ × 13 (*others*).

761	22 c. Type **355**	35	1
762	40 c. Commonwealth Aircraft Factory CA-25 Winjeel, 1955	70	9
763	45 c. Commonwealth Aircraft Factory CA-13 Boomerang, 1944	70	1·0
764	60 c. Government Aircraft Factory N22B Nomad, 1975	80	1·6
761/4	.. .. *Set of* 4	2·25	3·2

356 Flag in shape of Australia

357 Caricature of Darby Munro (jockey)

(Des B. Weatherhead. Litho Asher and Co, Melbourne)

1981 (21 Jan). *Australia Day. P* 13½ × 13.

765	**356** 22 c. multicoloured	20	2

(Des T. Rafty. Litho Cambec Press, Melbourne)

1981 (18 Feb). *Sports Personalities. T* **357** *and similar vert design showing caricatures. Multicoloured. P* 14 × 13½.

766	22 c. Type **357**	30	1
767	35 c. Victor Trumper (cricketer)	65	8
768	55 c. Sir Norman Brookes (tennis player) ..	85	1·2
769	60 c. Walter Lindrum (billiards player) ..	90	1·5
766/9	.. .. *Set of* 4	2·40	3·2

358 1931 Kingsford Smith's Flights 6d. Commemorative

359 Apex Emblem and Map of Australia

(Des Cato Hibberd Design. Litho Asher and Co, Melbourne)

81 (25 Mar). *50th Anniv of Official Australia–U.K. Airmail Service. T* **358** *and similar horiz design showing* 1931 *Kingsford Smith's Flights* 6*d. commemorative. P* 13 × 13½ (22 *c.*) *or* 13½ × 13 (60 *c.*).
) 22 c. blackish lilac, rosine and bright blue . . 20 10
1 60 c. blackish lilac, rosine and ultramarine . . 60 90

(Des P. Clark)

81 (6 Apr). *50th Anniv of Apex (young men's service club). P* 13½.
2 **359** 22 c. multicoloured 20 20

SHER AND CO. From April 1981 this firm was known as Leigh-ardon Ltd, Melbourne.

360 Queen's Personal Standard for Australia

361 "Licence Inspected"

(Litho Leigh-Mardon Ltd, Melbourne)

81 (21 Apr). *Queen Elizabeth II's Birthday. P* 13½ × 13.
3 **360** 22 c. multicoloured 20 20

(Des B. Weatherhead. Litho Leigh-Mardon Ltd, Melbourne)

81 (20 May). *Gold Rush Era. Sketches by S. T. Gill. T* **361** *and similar vert designs. Multicoloured. P* 13 × 13½.
4 22 c. Type **361** 20 25
5 22 c. "Puddling" 20 25
6 22 c. "Quality of washing stuff" 20 25
7 22 c. "On route to deposit gold" 20 25
74/7 . . . . *Set of* 4 70 90

362 "On the Wallaby Track" (Fred McCubbin)

(Litho Leigh-Mardon Ltd, Melbourne)

81 (17 June)–**84**. *Paintings. T* **362** *and similar horiz design. Multicoloured. P* 15 × 14½.
8 $2 Type **362** . . . . 1·50 30
9 $5 "A Holiday at Mentone, 1888" (Charles Conder) (4.4.84) (Optd S. £2·75) . . . . 4·75 1·25

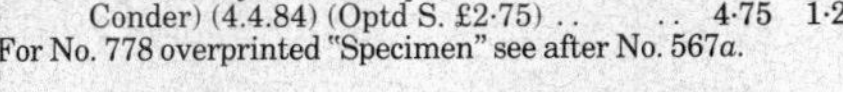
For No. 778 overprinted "Specimen" see after No. 567*a*.

363 Thylacine

363*a* Blue Mountain Tree-Frog

363*b* *Papilio ulysses* (butterfly)

PRINTINGS OF THE 24 C. VALUE. (Nos. 788, 788b). Original printings of this stamp were produced by a combination of printing processes. The centre design was first printed in photogravure by the Note Printing Branch, Reserve Bank of Australia, and then the half-printed sheets were transferred to Leigh-Mardon Ltd for the inscriptions and face value to be added in lithography.

Further supplies of this value were required in late 1981, but these were printed by Leigh-Mardon Ltd entirely in lithography.

The work of the two printers can be identified by the usual differences exhibited by the processes concerned; the lithography version tending to be darker in appearance with much sharper outlines.

Other specific differences are as follows:

On the *photogravure* version the front legs show a diagonal pattern of screening dots which are replaced by vertical and horizontal lines on the *litho* stamp.

The animal's eye is highlighted on the *photogravure* stamp.

The fourth and sixth bands on the animal's back are much longer on the *litho* version.

The end of the right-hand twig is pointed on the *photogravure* and blunt on the *litho*.

Photogravure Centre

Lithography Centre

(Des C. McCubbin (4, 10, 20, 27 c. (No. 791), 30 c. (No. 792*a*), 35, 45, 60, 80 c., $1), F. Knight (5, 24, 25, 30 c. (No. 792), 50, 55 c.) or Beverley Bruen (others). Photo Note Ptg Branch, Reserve Bank of Australia and litho Leigh-Mardon (24 c. (No. 788)), litho Leigh-Mardon (3, 5, 15, 24 c. (No. 788b), 25, 27 c. (both), 30 c. (both), 40, 50, 55, 65, 75, 90 c.), Cambec Press (others))

1981 (19 July)–**83.** *Wildlife. Multicoloured designs as T* **363** (5, 24, 25, 30, 50, 55 *c.*), *T* **363*a*** (1, 3, 5, 27 (*No.* 790), 40, 65, 70, 75, 85, 90, 95 *c.*) *or vert as T* **363*b*** (*others*). *P* 13½ (1, 4, 10, 20, 24, 35, 45, 60, 70, 80, 85, 95 *c.*, $1), 14½×14 (27 *c.* (*No.* 791), 30 *c.* (*No.* 792*a*)) *or* 12½ (*others*).

781 1 c. Lace Monitor (2.2.83) 10 20
782 3 c. Corroboree Frog (19.4.82) 10 10
a. Perf 14×14½ (1983) 40 30
783 4 c. *Euschemon rafflesio* ("Regent Skipper") (butterfly) (*vert*) (15.6.83) . . 55 55
784 5 c. Queensland Hairy-nosed Wombat (*vert*) (15.7.81) 10 10
a. Perf 14½×14 (12.83) . . . . 1·25 30
785 10 c. *Ornithoptera priamus* ("Cairns Birdwing") (butterfly) (*vert*) (15.6.83) . . 60 10
786 15 c. Eastern Snake-necked Tortoise (16.6.82) 40 30
a. Perf 14×14½ (12.83) . . . . 1·25 50
787 20 c. *Graphium macleayanus* ("MacLeay's Swallow Tail") (butterfly) (*vert*) (15.6.83) 80 35
788 24 c. Type **363** (centre photo, inscr litho) . . 45 10
a. Imperf (pair) £200
b. Centre and inscr litho (12.81) . . 65 75
789 25 c. Common Rabbit-Bandicoot (*vert*) (15.7.81) 35 30
a. Perf 14×14½ (1982) 90 75
790 27 c. Type **363*a*** (19.4.82) 45 20
a. Perf 14×14½ (1983) 65 20
791 27 c. Type **363*b*** (15.6.83) 90 30
a. Imperf (pair) £400
792 30 c. Bridle Nail-tailed Wallaby (*vert*) (15.7.81) 55 15
792*a* 30 c. *Pseudalmenus chlorinda* ("Chlorinda Hairstreak") (butterfly) (*vert*) (24.10.83) . . . . 1·00 20
793 35 c. *Danaus hamata* ("Blue Tiger") (butterfly) (*vert*) (15.6.83) . . 1·00 30
794 40 c. Smooth Knob-tailed Gecko (16.6.82) . . 45 30
a. Perf 14×14½ (12.83) . . . . 2·50 75
795 45 c. *Cressida cressida* ("Big Greasy") (butterfly) (*vert*) (15.6.83) . . 1·00 30
796 50 c. Leadbeater's Possum (15.7.81) . . 50 10
a. Perf 14×14½ (1983) . . . . 1·50 40
797 55 c. Stick-nest Rat (*vert*) (15.7.81) . . 50 30
798 60 c. *Delias aganippe* ("Wood White") (butterfly) (*vert*) (15.6.83) . . 1·10 30
799 65 c. Yellow-faced Whip Snake (19.4.82) . . 80 30
a. Perf 14×14½ (1983) . . . . 1·50 1·00
800 70 c. Crucifix Toad (2.2.83) . . . . 65 1·00
801 75 c. Eastern Water Dragon (19.4.82) . . 1·25 40
a. Perf 14×14½ (12.83) . . . . 1·75 1·25
802 80 c. *Ogyris amaryllis* ("Amaryllis Azure") (butterfly) (*vert*) (15.6.83) . . 1·40 1·25
803 85 c. Centralian Blue-tongued Lizard (2.2.83) . . . . 1·10 1·25
804 90 c. Freshwater Crocodile (16.6.82) . . 1·60 1·25
805 95 c. Thorny Devil (2.2.83) . . . . 1·00 1·60
806 $1 *Tisiphone abeona* ("Sword-grass Brown") (butterfly) (*vert*) (15.6.83) . . 1·40 30
781/806 . . . . . . *Set of* 27 18·00 10·00

A late printing of No. 781, issued July 1987, is on thicker paper with a creamier appearance.

364 Prince Charles and Lady Diana Spencer

365 *Cortinarius cinnabarinus*

(Des B. Clinton. Litho Leigh-Mardon Ltd, Melbourne)

1981 (29 July). *Royal Wedding. P* 13½ × 13.
821 **364** 24 c. multicoloured 20 10
822 60 c. multicoloured . . . . . . 55 1·00

(Des Celia Rosser. Litho Leigh-Mardon Ltd, Melbourne)

1981 (19 Aug). *Australian Fungi. T* **365** *and similar vert designs. Multicoloured. P* 13 × 13½.
823 24 c. Type **365** 35 10
824 35 c. *Coprinus comatus* 60 90
825 55 c. *Armillaria luteobubalina* . . . . 80 1·25
826 60 c. *Cortinarius austrovenetus* . . . . 90 1·40
823/6 . . . . *Set of* 4 2·40 3·25

366 Disabled People playing Basketball

367 "Christmas Bush for His Adorning"

(Des J. Spatchurst. Litho Cambec Press, Melbourne)

1981 (16 Sept). *International Year for Disabled Persons. P* 14 × 13½.
827 **366** 24 c. multicoloured 20 20

(Des F. Beck. Litho Leigh-Mardon Ltd, Melbourne)

1981 (28 Sept–2 Nov). *Christmas. Scenes and Verses from Carols by W. James and J. Wheeler. T* **367** *and similar vert designs. Multicoloured. P* 13 × 13½.
828 18 c. Type **367** (2 Nov) 25 10
829 30 c. "The Silver Stars are in the Sky" . . 35 25
830 60 c. "Noeltime" (2 Nov) 60 70
828/30 . . . . *Set of* 3 1·10 90

368 Globe depicting Australia

369 Ocean Racing Yacht

(Des B. Weatherhead. Litho Leigh-Mardon Ltd, Melbourne)

1981 (30 Sept). *Commonwealth Heads of Government Meeting, Melbourne. P* 13 × 13½.
831 **368** 24 c. black, pale blue and gold 20 10
832 60 c. black, pale blue and silver 65 75

(Des R. Fletcher. Litho Leigh-Mardon Ltd, Melbourne)

1981 (14 Oct). *Yachts. T* **369** *and similar vert designs. Multicoloured. P* 13 × 13½.
833 24 c. Type **369** 35 10
834 35 c. "Sharpie" 50 50
835 55 c. "12 Metre" 75 85
836 60 c. "Sabot" . . . . 1·00 1·00
833/6 . . . . *Set of* 4 2·40 2·25

370 Aborigine, Governor Phillip (founder of N.S.W., 1788) and Post World War II Migrant

371 Humpback Whale

(Des B. Clinton. Litho Cambec Press, Melbourne)

1982 (20 Jan). *Australia Day. "Three Great Waves of Migration". P* 13½ × 14.
837 **370** 24 c. multicoloured 35 25

(Des R. and Katrina Ingpen. Litho Cambec Press, Melbourne)

1982 (17 Feb). *Whales. T* **371** *and similar multicoloured designs. P* 13½ × 14 (24, 60 *c.*) *or* 14 × 13½ (*others*).
838 24 c. Sperm Whale 40 10
839 35 c. Black Right Whale (*vert*) 60 70
840 55 c. Blue Whale (*vert*) .. .. .. 1·10 1·75
841 60 c. Type **371** (new blue background) .. 1·25 1·75
a. Solid greenish blue background .. £250 £160
838/41 .. .. *Set of* 4 3·00 3·75

No. 841a comes from a small trial printing, some sheets of which were included amongst normal stock by mistake. The correct version of the 60 c. value shows the new blue background streaked with white at top left. On No. 841a the background is in greenish blue and is without the white streaks.

372 Queen Elizabeth II

373 "Marjorie Atherton"

(Des R. Honisett. Litho Cambec Press, Melbourne)

1982 (21 Apr). *Queen Elizabeth II's Birthday. P* 14 × 13½.
842 **372** 27 c. multicoloured 35 15

(Des Betty Conabere. Litho Leigh-Mardon Ltd, Melbourne)

1982 (19 May). *Roses. T* **373** *and similar vert designs. Multicoloured. P* 13 × 13½.
843 27 c. Type **373** 40 15
844 40 c. "Imp" 75 75
845 65 c. "Minnie Watson" .. .. .. 1·25 2·00
846 75 c. "Satellite" .. .. 1·25 1·60
843/6 .. .. *Set of* 4 3·25 4·00

374 Radio Announcer and 1930-style Microphone

375 Forbes Post Office

(Des Cato Hibberd Design. Litho Leigh-Mardon Ltd, Melbourne)

1982 (16 June). *50th Anniv of ABC (Australian Broadcasting Commission). T* **374** *and similar horiz design. Multicoloured. P* 13½ × 13.
847 27 c. Type **374** 40 45
a. Pair. Nos. 847/8 .. .. 80 90
848 27 c. ABC logo 40 45

Nos. 847/8 were printed together, *se-tenant*, in horizontal and vertical pairs throughout the sheet.

(Des F. Beck. Litho Cambec Press, Melbourne)

1982 (4 Aug). *Historic Australian Post Offices. T* **375** *and similar multicoloured designs. P* 14 × 13½ (*vert*) *or* 13½ × 14 (*horiz*).
849 27 c. Type **375** 40 40
850 27 c. Flemington Post Office 40 40
851 27 c. Rockhampton Post Office 40 40
852 27 c. Kingston S.E. Post Office (*horiz*) .. 40 40
853 27 c. York Post Office (*horiz*) 40 40
854 27 c. Launceston Post Office 40 40
855 27 c. Old Post and Telegraph Station, Alice Springs (*horiz*) 40 40
849/55 .. .. *Set of* 7 2·50 2·50

376 Early Australian Christmas Card

377 Boxing

(Des B. Weatherhead. Litho Leigh-Mardon Ltd, Melbourne)

1982 (15 Sept–1 Nov). *Christmas. T* **376** *and similar multicoloured designs. P* 14½.
856 21 c. Bushman's Hotel, with Cobb's coach arriving (*horiz*) (1.11.82) 30 10
857 35 c. Type **376** 50 60
858 75 c. Little girl offering Christmas pudding to swagman (1.11.82) .. .. .. 75 1·40
856/8 .. .. *Set of* 3 1·40 1·90

(Des R. Carnielye. Litho Leigh-Mardon Ltd, Melbourne)

1982 (22 Sept). *Commonwealth Games, Brisbane. T* **377** *and similar horiz designs. P* 14½.
859 27 c. stone, lemon and bright carmine .. 30 20
860 27 c. lemon, stone and emerald 30 20
861 27 c. stone, lemon and yellow-brown 30 20
862 75 c. multicoloured 90 90
859/62 .. .. *Set of* 4 1·60 1·40
MS863 130 × 95 mm. Nos. 859/61. P 13½ × 13 .. 1·25 1·60

Designs:—No. 859, Type **377**; No. 860, Archery; No. 861, Weight-lifting; No. 862, Pole-vaulting.

378 Sydney Harbour Bridge 5s. Stamp of 1932

379 "Yirawala" Bark Painting

(Des Cato Hibberd Design. Litho Cambec Press, Melbourne)

1982 (27 Sept). *National Stamp Week. P* 13½ × 14.
864 **378** 27 c. multicoloured 35 30

(Des Australia Post Graphic Design Section. Litho Leigh-Mardon Ltd, Melbourne)

1982 (12 Oct). *Opening of Australian National Gallery. P* 14½.
865 **379** 27 c. multicoloured 30 25

380 Mimi Spirits Dancing

381 *Eucalyptus calophylla* "Rosea"

(Des D. Milaybuma (27 c.), L. Nabardayal (40 c.), J. Galareya (65 c.), D. Nguleingulei-Murrumurru (75 c.). Litho Cambec Press, Melbourne)

1982 (17 Nov). *Aboriginal Culture. Music and Dance. T* **380** *and similar horiz designs depicting Aboriginal Bark Paintings of Mimi Spirits. P* 13½ × 14.
866 27 c. multicoloured 25 10
867 40 c. multicoloured 40 70
868 65 c. multicoloured .. .. 60 1·25
869 75 c. multicoloured .. .. 65 1·25
866/9 .. .. *Set of* 4 1·75 3·00

(Des Elizabeth Conabere. Photo Enschedé)

1982 (17 Nov). *Eucalyptus Flowers. T* **381** *and similar horiz designs. Multicoloured. P* 12½×13½.
870 1 c. Type **381** 10 30
a. Booklet pane. Nos. 870/1 and 874 each × 2 1·00
b. Booklet pane. Nos. 870/1 each × 2, 872/3 and 874 × 3 .. .. 2·50
871 2 c. *Eucalyptus casia* 10 30
872 3 c. *Eucalyptus ficifolia* .. .. .. 90 1·40
873 10 c. *Eucalyptus globulus* .. .. .. 90 1·40
874 27 c. *Eucalyptus forrestiana* 30 40
870/4 .. .. *Set of* 5 2·00 3·50

Nos. 870/4 only exist from 60 c. (pane No. 870a) and $1 (pane No. 870b) stamp booklets and the stamps have one or two adjacent sides imperforate. They were printed on Harrison paper which gives a bluish white reaction under U.V. light.

382 Shand Mason Steam Fire Engine, 1891

383 H.M.S. *Sirius*

(Des A. Puckett. Litho Cambec Press, Melbourne)

1983 (12 Jan). *Historic Fire Engines. T* **382** *and similar horiz designs. Multicoloured. P* 13½ × 14.
875 27 c. Type **382** 40 10
876 40 c. Hotchkiss fire engine, 1914 .. .. 60 75
877 65 c. Ahrens-Fox PS2 fire engine, 1929 .. 1·00 1·50
878 75 c. Merryweather manual fire appliance, 1851 .. .. 1·00 1·40
875/8 .. .. *Set of* 4 2·75 3·25

(Des J. Spatchurst. Litho Leigh-Mardon Ltd, Melbourne)

1983 (26 Jan). *Australia Day. T* **383** *and similar horiz design. Multicoloured. P* 14½.
879 27 c. Type **383** 40 50
a. Pair. Nos. 879/80 .. .. .. 80 1·00
ab. Printed on the gummed side .. £150
880 27 c. H.M.S. *Supply* 40 50

Nos. 879/80 were printed together, *se-tenant*, in horizontal and vertical pairs throughout the sheet.

384 Stylised Kangaroo and Kiwi

385 Equality and Dignity

(Des G. Emery. Litho Cambec Press, Melbourne)

1983 (2 Feb). *Closer Economic Relationship Agreement with New Zealand. P* 14 × 13½.
881 **384** 27 c. multicoloured 30 3

(Des G. Emery. Litho Leigh-Mardon Ltd, Melbourne)

1983 (9 Mar). *Commonwealth Day. T* **385** *and similar vert designs. Multicoloured. P* 14½.
882 27 c. Type **385** 20 2
883 27 c. Liberty and Freedom 20 2
884 27 c. Social Justice and Co-operation 20 2
885 75 c. Peace and Harmony .. .. .. 50 1·5
882/5 .. .. *Set of* 4 1·00 2·0

386 R.Y. *Britannia* passing Sydney Opera House

387 "Postal and Telecommunications Services"

(Des J. Richards. Litho Leigh-Mardon Ltd, Melbourne)

1983 (20 Apr). *Queen Elizabeth II's Birthday. P* 14½.
886 **386** 27 c. multicoloured 45 3

(Des B. Sadgrove. Litho Cambec Press, Melbourne)

1983 (18 May). *World Communications Year. P* 13 × 13½.
887 **387** 27 c. multicoloured 30 3

388 Badge of the Order of St. John

389 Jaycee Members and Badge

(Des T. McCauley. Litho Cambec Press, Melbourne)

1983 (8 June). *Centenary of St. John Ambulance in Australia. P* 14 × 13½.
888 **388** 27 c. black and deep turquoise-blue .. 35 3

(Des B. Clinton. Litho Cambec Press, Melbourne)

1983 (8 June). *50th Anniv of Australian Jaycees. P* 13½ × 14.
889 **389** 27 c. multicoloured 30 3

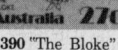

390 "The Bloke"

391 Nativity Scene

(Des B. Clinton. Litho Leigh-Mardon Ltd, Melbourne)

1983 (3 Aug). *Folklore. "The Sentimental Bloke" (humorous poem by C. J. Dennis). T* **390** *and similar vert designs. Multicoloured. P* 14½.
890 27 c. Type **390** 40 5
a. Horiz strip of 5. Nos. 890/4 .. .. 1·75
891 27 c. "Doreen—The Intro" 40 5
892 27 c. "The Stror' at Coot" 40 5
893 27 c. "Hitched" 40 5
894 27 c. "The Mooch o'Life" 40 5
890/4 .. .. *Set of* 5 1·75 2·2

Nos. 890/4 were printed together, *se-tenant*, in horizontal strips of 5 throughout the sheet.

(Des Holly Alvarez (24 c.), Deanne Head (35 c.), Justine Jacobi (85 c.). Litho Cambec Press, Melbourne)

1983 (14 Sept–2 Nov). *Christmas. Children's Paintings. T* **391** *and similar horiz designs. Multicoloured. P* 13½ × 14.
895 24 c. Type **391** (2 November) 20 1
896 35 c. Kookaburra 35 4
897 85 c. Father Christmas in sleigh over beach (2 November) .. .. 90 1·4
895/7 .. .. *Set of* 3 1·25 1·7

392 Sir Paul Edmund de Strzelecki **393** Cook Family Cottage, Melbourne

(Des Dianne Quinn. Litho Leigh-Mardon Ltd, Melbourne)

1983 (26 Sept). *Explorers of Australia. T* **392** *and similar vert designs. Multicoloured. P* 14½.
898 30 c. Type **392** 35 40
899 30 c. Ludwig Leichardt 35 40
900 30 c. William John Wills and Robert O'Hara Burke 35 40
901 30 c. Alexander Forrest 35 40
898/901 .. .. *Set of* 4 1·25 1·40

(Des J. Quinn. Litho Cambec Press, Melbourne)

1984 (26 Jan). *Australia Day. P* 13½ × 14.
902 **393** 30 c. black and stone 30 35

MACHINE LABELS. From 22 February 1984 gummed labels in the above design, ranging in value from 1 c. to $9.99, were available from seven automatic machines. The postcode at the top of the label indicates the location of the machine from which it was issued; 2000, Sydney; 2601, Canberra; 3000, Melbourne; 4000, Brisbane; 5000, Adelaide, 5790 Darwin (from 29 July 1985); 6000, Perth (until 2 November 1998), 7000 Hobart. Labels without code numbers appeared on 24 June 1985.

These were replaced by a further series, with a background pattern of kangaroos, on 22 October 1985. These exist with the same code numbers as before or without code.

On 25 August 1986 a further series, with a background pattern of platypuses, was issued. The design was again changed on 2 September 1987 to show Echidnas. During this issue the postcode for Darwin changed from 5790 to 0800. These were followed by Ringtail Possums on 28 September 1988, Frill-necked Lizards on 1 September 1989, Koalas on 3 September 1990, Emus on 2 January 1992 and the Waratah (flower) on 8 September 1994.

An overall pattern of geometric shapes, streamers and springs was introduced on 6 June 1996.

As the number of machines increased rapidly only those situated at the State, or Capital Territory, General Post Offices showed a postcode. Other machines eventually showed a code, letter followed by numbers at bottom left. Later machines had a top label value of either $10 or $20.

394 Charles Ulm, Avro Type 618 Ten *Faith in Australia* and Trans-Tasman Cover

(Des G. Beck and J. Quinn. Litho Cambec Press, Melbourne)

1984 (22 Feb). *50th Anniv of First Official Airmail Flights, New Zealand–Australia and Australia–Papua New Guinea. T* **394** *and similar horiz design. Multicoloured. P* 13½.
903 45 c. Type **394** .. .. 1·00 1·25
a. Horiz pair. Nos. 903/4 .. .. 2·00 2·50
904 45 c. As Type **394** but showing flown cover to Papua New Guinea .. .. 1·00 1·25

Nos. 903/4 were printed together, *se-tenant*, in horizontal pairs throughout the sheet.

395 Thomson "Steamer", 1898 **396** Queen Elizabeth II

(Des A. Puckett. Litho Leigh-Mardon Ltd, Melbourne)

1984 (14 Mar). *Veteran and Vintage Cars. T* **395** *and similar horiz designs. Multicoloured. P* 14½.
905 30 c. Type **395** 50 60
a. Vert strip of 5. Nos. 905/9 .. .. .. 2·25
906 30 c. Tarrant, 1906 .. .. 50 60
907 30 c. Gordon & Co "Australian Six", 1919 .. 50 60
908 30 c. Summit, 1923 .. .. 50 60
909 30 c. Chic, 1924 .. .. 50 60
905/9 .. .. *Set of* 5 2·25 2·75

Nos. 905/9 were printed together, *se-tenant*, in vertical strips of 5 throughout the sheet.

(Des B. Weatherhead. Litho Leigh-Mardon Ltd, Melbourne)

1984 (18 Apr). *Queen Elizabeth II's Birthday. P* 14½.
910 **396** 30 c. multicoloured 30 35
a. Dull mauve (background) omitted £400

397 *Cutty Sark* **398** Freestyle

(Des J. Earl and J. Quinn. Litho Cambec Press, Melbourne)

1984 (23 May). *Clipper Ships. T* **397** *and similar multicoloured designs. P* 14 × 13½ (30 c., 85 c.) *or* 13½ × 14 (*others*).
911 30 c. Type **397** 40 25
912 45 c. *Orient* (*horiz*) 70 80
913 75 c. *Sobraon* (*horiz*) .. .. 1·25 1·75
914 85 c. *Thermopylae* .. .. 1·25 1·50
911/14 .. .. *Set of* 4 3·25 3·75

(Des B. Clinton. Litho Leigh-Mardon Ltd, Melbourne)

1984 (6 June). *Skiing. T* **398** *and similar multicoloured designs. P* 14½.
915 30 c. Type **398** 40 45
916 30 c. Downhill racer 40 45
917 30 c. Slalom (*horiz*) 40 45
918 30 c. Nordic (*horiz*) 40 45
915/18 .. .. *Set of* 4 1·50 1·75

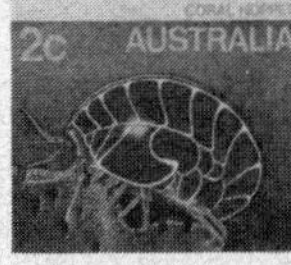

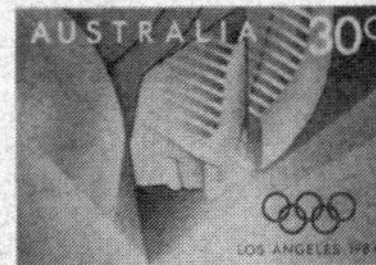

399 Coral Hopper **400** Before the Event

(Des G. Ryan and R. Fletcher (2, 25, 30, 50, 55, 85 c.) or G. Ryan (others). Litho Leigh-Mardon Ltd, Melbourne (30, 33 c.) or Cambec Press, Melbourne (others))

1984 (18 June)–**86**. *Marine Life. T* **399** *and similar horiz designs. Multicoloured. P* 14×14½ (30 c., 33 c.) *or* 13½ (*others*).
919 2 c. Type **399** 10 20
920 3 c. Jimble (11.6.86) 20 20
921 5 c. Tasselled Frogfish ("Anglerfish") (12.6.85) 15 10
922 10 c. Rough Stonefish (11.6.86) 20 10
923 20 c. Red Handfish (12.6.85) 65 30
924 25 c. Orange-lipped Cowrie 45 40
925 30 c. Choat's Wrasse 45 40
926 33 c. Leafy Seadragon (20.3.85) 60 10
927 40 c. Red Velvetfish (12.6.85) 85 60
928 45 c. Textile or Cloth of Gold Cone (11.6.86) 80 50
929 50 c. Clown Surgeonfish 80 50
930 55 c. Bennett's Nudibranch 80 50
a. New blue ("BENNETT'S NUDI-BRANCH") omitted .. .. .. † —
931 60 c. Zebra Lionfish (11.6.86) 90 70
932 65 c. Banded Stingray (11.6.86) 90 70
933 70 c. Southern Blue-ringed Octopus (11.6.86) 90 65
934 80 c. Pineconefish ("Pineapple Fish") (12.6.85) .. .. 1·25 70
935 85 c. Royal Angelfish 90 70
936 90 c. Crab-eyed Goby (12.6.85) .. .. 1·60 75
937 $1 Crown of Thorns Starfish (11.6.86) (Optd S. 50p.) .. .. .. 1·50 80
919/37 .. .. *Set of* 19 12·50 8·00

No. 930a only exists used on maximum card.

Used examples have been reported of both the 33 c. and $1 with the face value and inscriptions omitted. The colours involved were dull orange on the 33 c. and mauve on the $1.

(Des O. Schmidinger and Christine Stead. Litho Cambec Press, Melbourne)

1984 (25 July). *Olympic Games, Los Angeles. T* **400** *and similar multicoloured designs. P* 14 × 13½ (*No.* 943) *or* 13½ × 14 (*others*).
941 30 c. Type **400** 35 35
942 30 c. During the event 35 35
943 30 c. After the event (*vert*) 35 35
941/3 .. .. *Set of* 3 95 95

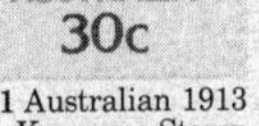

401 Australian 1913 1d. Kangaroo Stamp **402** "Angel" (stained-glass window, St. Francis' Church, Melbourne)

(Des Ken Cato Design Studio. Litho Cambec Press, Melbourne)

1984 (22 Aug–21 Sept). *"Ausipex" International Stamp Exhibition, Melbourne. T* **401** *and similar vert designs. Multicoloured. P* 14½.
944 30 c. Type **401** 35 30
MS945 126 × 175 mm. 30 c. × 7, Victoria 1850 3d. "Half Length"; New South Wales 1850 1d. "Sydney View"; Tasmania 1853 1d.; South Australia 1855 1d.; Western Australia 1854 1d. "Black Swan"; Queensland 1860 6d.; Type **401** (21 Sept) .. .. 3·50 4·50

On No. **MS**945 the emblem and inscription on the sheet margin are embossed.

(Des Ken Cato Design Studio. Litho Cambec Press, Melbourne)

1984 (17 Sept–31 Oct). *Christmas. Stained-glass Windows. T* **402** *and similar vert designs. Multicoloured. P* 14 × 13½.
946 24 c. "Angel and Child" (Holy Trinity Church, Sydney) (31.10.84) 25 20
947 30 c. "Veiled Virgin and Child" (St. Mary's Catholic Church, Geelong) (31.10.84) .. 35 20
948 40 c. Type **402** 50 60
949 50 c. "Three Kings" (St. Mary's Cathedral, Sydney) (31.10.84) 65 80
950 85 c. "Madonna and Child" (St. Bartholomew's Church, Norwood) (31.10.84) .. .. 80 1·25
946/50 .. .. *Set of* 5 2·25 2·75

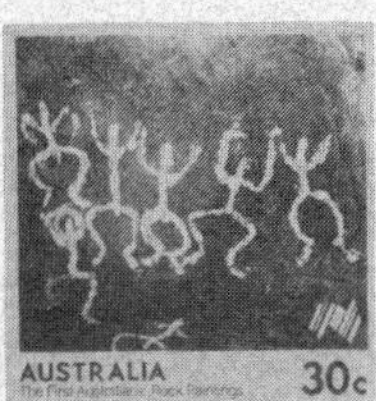

403 "Stick Figures" (Cobar Region) **404** Yellow-tufted Honeyeater

(Des Elizabeth Innes. Litho Leigh-Mardon Ltd, Melbourne)

1984 (7 Nov). *Bicentenary of Australian Settlement* (1988) (1*st issue*). *The First Australians. T* **403** *and similar square designs showing aborigine rock paintings. Multicoloured. P* 14½.
951 30 c. Type **403** 35 45
952 30 c. "Bunjil" (large figure), Grampians .. 35 45
953 30 c. "Quikans" (tall figures), Cape York .. 35 45
954 30 c. "Wandjina Spirit and Baby Snakes" (Gibb River) 35 45
955 30 c. "Rock Python" (Gibb River) 35 45
956 30 c. "Silver Barramundi" (fish) (Kakadu National Park) 35 45
957 30 c. Bicentenary emblem 35 45
958 85 c. "Rock Possum" (Kakadu National Park) 80 1·40
951/8 .. .. *Set of* 8 3·00 4·00

See also Nos. 972/6, 993/6, 1002/7, 1019/22, 1059/63, 1064/6, 1077/81, 1090/2, 1105/9, 1110, 1137/41, 1145/8 and 1149.

(Des. G. Emery. Litho Leigh-Mardon Ltd, Melbourne

1984 (19 Nov). *150th Anniv of Victoria. T* **404** *and similar vert design. Multicoloured. P* 14½.
959 30 c. Type **404** 40 65
a. Pair. Nos. 959/60 .. .. 80 1·25
960 30 c. Leadbeater's Possum 40 65

Nos. 959/60 were printed together, *se-tenant*, in horizontal and vertical pairs throughout the sheet.

405 "Musgrave Ranges" (Sir Sidney Nolan) **406** Young People of Different Races, and Sun

(Des Sue Titcher. Litho Leigh-Mardon Ltd, Melbourne)

1985 (25 Jan). *Australia Day. Birth Centenary of Dorothea Mackellar (author of poem "My Country"). T* **405** *and similar horiz design. Multicoloured. P* 14½.
961 30 c. Type **405** 45 70
a. *Tête-bêche* (vert pair) .. .. .. 1·50 2·25
b. Vert pair. Nos. 961/2 .. .. .. 90 1·40
962 30 c. "The Walls of China" (Russell Drysdale) . 45 70
a. *Tête-bêche* (vert pair) .. .. .. 1·50 2·25

Nos. 961/2 were printed together, *se-tenant*, within the sheet of 100 (2 panes 50 (5×10)). In each pane No. 961 occurs in horizontal rows 1, 4, 5, 8 and 9, and No. 962 in rows 2, 3, 6, 7 and 10. Horizontal rows 3/4 and 7/8 are inverted forming *tête-bêche* pairs of the same design in addition to the vertical *se-tenant* pairs containing both designs.

(Des Derryn Vogelnest. Litho Cambec Press, Melbourne)

1985 (13 Feb). *International Youth Year. P* 14 × 13½.
963 **406** 30 c. multicoloured 40 30

407 Royal Victorian Volunteer Artillery

408 District Nurse of early 1900's

(Des Pam Andrews. Litho Leigh-Mardon Ltd, Melbourne)

1985 (25 Feb). *19th-Century Australian Military Uniforms. T* **407** *and similar vert designs. Multicoloured. P* 14½.
964 33 c. Type **407** 60 65
a. Horiz strip of 5. Nos. 964/8 .. .. 2·75
965 33 c. Western Australian Pinjarrah Cavalry .. 60 65
966 33 c. New South Wales Lancers 60 65
967 33 c. New South Wales Contingent to the Sudan 60 65
968 33 c. Victorian Mounted Rifles 60 65
964/8 .. .. *Set of* 5 2·75 3·00
Nos. 964/8 were printed together, *se-tenant*, in horizontal strips of 5 throughout the sheet.

(Des Wendy Tamlyn. Litho Leigh-Mardon Ltd, Melbourne)

1985 (13 Mar). *Centenary of District Nursing Services. P* 14½.
969 **408** 33 c. multicoloured 45 35

409 Sulphur-crested Cockatoos

(Des R. Bevers. Litho Leigh-Mardon Ltd, Melbourne)

1985 (13 Mar). *Multicoloured, background colour given. P* 14½×*imperf.*
970 **409** 1 c. flesh .. .. 1·50 2·25
a. Booklet pane. Nos. 970, and 971×3 2·75
971 33 c. pale turquoise-green 45 55
Nos. 970/1 only exist from $1 stamp booklets. As stamps from these booklets have their outer edges imperforate, the end example of No. 971 is only perforated along one side.

410 Abel Tasman and Journal Entry

411 Sovereign's Badge of Order of Australia

(Des G. Emery. Litho Cambec Press, Melbourne)

1985 (10 Apr). *Bicentenary of Australian Settlement* (1988) (*2nd issue*). *Navigators. T* **410** *and similar square designs. Multicoloured. P* 13.
972 33 c. Type **410** 60 35
973 33 c. Dirk Hartog's *Eendracht* (detail, Aert Anthonisz) 60 35
974 33 c. "William Dampier" (detail, T. Murray) 60 35
975 90 c. Globe and hand with extract from Dampier's journal .. .. 1·40 1·75
972/5 .. .. *Set of* 4 2·75 2·50
MS976 150×115 mm. As Nos. 972/5, but with cream-coloured margins .. .. 3·25 4·25

(Des Elizabeth Innes. Litho Cambec Press, Melbourne)

1985 (22 Apr). *Queen Elizabeth II's Birthday. P* 14×13½.
977 **411** 33 c. multicoloured 40 30

412 Tree, and Soil running through Hourglass ("Soil")

413 *Elves and Fairies* (Annie Rentoul and Ida Rentoul Outhwaite)

(Des L. Whaite and G. Jorgensen. Litho Cambec Press, Melbourne)

1985 (15 May). *Conservation. T* **412** *and similar vert designs. Multicoloured. P* 14×13½.
978 33 c. Type **412** 45 20
979 50 c. Washing on line and smog ("air") .. 80 85
980 80 c. Tap and flower ("water") .. .. 1·25 1·50
981 90 c. Chain encircling flames ("energy") .. 1·40 2·00
978/81 .. .. *Set of* 4 3·50 4·00

(Des P. Leuver. Litho Leigh-Mardon Ltd, Melbourne)

1985 (17 July). *Classic Australian Children's Books. T* **413** *and similar vert designs. Multicoloured. P* 14½.
982 33 c. Type **413** 50 65
a. Horiz strip of 5. Nos. 982/6 .. .. 2·25
983 33 c. *The Magic Pudding* (Norman Lindsay) 50 65
984 33 c. *Ginger Meggs* (James Charles Bancks) 50 65
985 33 c. *Blinky Bill* (Dorothy Wall) 50 65
986 33 c. *Snugglepot and Cuddlepie* (May Gibbs) 50 65
982/6 .. .. *Set of* 5 2·25 3·00
Nos. 982/6 were printed together, *se-tenant*, in horizontal strips of 5 throughout the sheet.

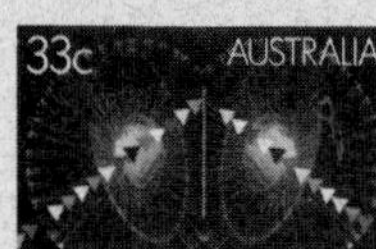

414 Dish Aerials

415 Angel in Sailing Ship

(Des J. Ostoja-Kotkowski. Litho Leigh-Mardon Ltd, Melbourne)

1985 (18 Sept). *Electronic Mail Service. P* 14½.
987 **414** 33 c. multicoloured 35 30

(Des S. Hartshorne. Litho Leigh-Mardon Ltd, Melbourne)

1985 (18 Sept–1 Nov). *Christmas. T* **415** *and similar horiz designs. Multicoloured. P* 14½.
988 27 c. Angel with holly wings (1.11) 35 15
989 33 c. Angel with bells (1.11) 40 15
990 45 c. Type **415** 60 50
991 55 c. Angel with star (1.11) 75 80
992 90 c. Angel with Christmas tree bauble (1.11) .. .. 1·40 1·50
988/92 .. .. *Set of* 5 3·25 2·75

416 Astrolabe (*Batavia*, 1629)

417 Aboriginal Wandjina Spirit, Map of Australia and Egg

(Des G. Emery. Litho Cambec Press, Melbourne)

1985 (2 Oct). *Bicentenary of Australian Settlement* (1988) (*3rd issue*). *Relics from Early Shipwrecks. T* **416** *and similar square designs. Multicoloured. P* 13.
993 33 c. Type **416** 40 15
994 50 c. German beardman jug (*Vergulde Draeck*, 1656) 80 90
995 90 c. Wooden bobbins (*Batavia*, 1629) and encrusted scissors (*Zeewijk*, 1727) .. 1·75 2·25
996 $1 Silver and brass buckle (*Zeewijk*, 1727) 1·75 2·25
993/6 .. .. *Set of* 4 4·25 5·00

(Des R. Meeks. Litho Leigh-Mardon Ltd, Melbourne)

1986 (24 Jan). *Australia Day. P* 14½.
997 **417** 33 c. multicoloured 40 30

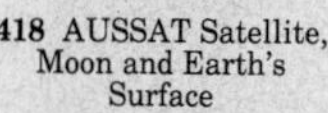

418 AUSSAT Satellite, Moon and Earth's Surface

419 H.M.S. *Buffalo*

(Des O. Schmidinger and Christine Stead. Litho Leigh-Mardon Ltd, Melbourne)

1986 (24 Jan). *AUSSAT National Communications Satellite System. T* **418** *and similar vert design. Multicoloured. P* 14½.
998 33 c. Type **418** 50 15
999 80 c. AUSSAT satellite in orbit .. .. 1·50 2·25

(Des I. Kidd. Litho Cambec Press, Melbourne)

1986 (12 Feb). *150th Anniv of South Australia. T* **419** *an[d] similar horiz design. Multicoloured. P* 13½×14.
1000 33 c. Type **419** 70 9
a. Pair. Nos. 1000/1 .. .. .. 1·40 1·7
1001 33 c. "City Sign" sculpture (Otto Hajek), Adelaide 70 9
Nos. 1000/1 were printed together, *se-tenant*, in horizontal ar[d] vertical pairs throughout the sheet, the background of eac[h] horizontal pair showing an extract from the colony's Lette[rs] Patent of 1836.

420 *Banksia serrata*

421 Radio Telescope, Parkes, and Diagram of Comet's Orbit

(Des Sue Titcher. Litho Cambec Press, Melbourne)

1986 (12 Mar). *Bicentenary of Australian Settlement* (198[8]) (*4th issue*). *Cook's Voyage to New Holland. T* **420** *and simil[ar] horiz designs. Multicoloured. P* 13.
1002 33 c. Type **420** 60
1003 33 c. *Hibiscus meraukensis* 60
1004 50 c. *Dillenia alata* .. .. 90 1·1
1005 80 c. *Correa reflexa* .. .. 1·60 2·5
1006 90 c. "Joseph Banks" (botanist) (Reynolds) and Banks with Dr. Solander .. 2·00 2·(
1007 90 c. "Sydney Parkinson" (self-portrait) and Parkinson drawing .. .. 2·00 2·(
1002/7 .. .. *Set of* 6 7·00 7·5

(Des J. Passmore. Litho Cambec Press, Melbourne)

1986 (9 Apr). *Appearance of Halley's Comet. P* 14×13½.
1008 **421** 33 c. multicoloured 50

422 Queen Elizabeth II

423 Brumbies (wild horses)

(Des Fay Plamka. Litho Leigh-Mardon Ltd, Melbourne)

1986 (21 Apr). *60th Birthday of Queen Elizabeth II. P* 14½.
1009 **422** 33 c. multicoloured 45 3

(Des R. Ingpen. Litho Leigh-Mardon Ltd, Melbourne)

1986 (21 May). *Australian Horses. T* **423** *and similar hor[iz] designs. Multicoloured. P* 14½.
1010 33 c. Type **423** 60 1
1011 80 c. Mustering .. .. 1·50 2·(
1012 90 c. Show-jumping .. .. 1·75 2·2
1013 $1 Child on pony .. .. 2·00 2·2
1010/13 .. .. *Set of* 4 5·25 6·(

424 "The Old Shearer stands"

425 "King George III" (A. Ramsay) and Convicts

(Des R. Ingpen. Litho Leigh-Mardon Ltd, Melbourne)

1986 (21 July). *Folklore. Scenes and Verses from the Folkson[g] "Click go the Shears". T* **424** *and similar vert design[s]. Multicoloured. P* 14½.
1014 33 c. Type **424** 70 7
a. Horiz strip of 5. Nos. 1014/18 .. 3·25
1015 33 c. "The ringer looks around" 70 7
1016 33 c. "The boss of the board" 70 7
1017 33 c. "The tar-boy is there" 70 7
1018 33 c. "Shearing is all over" 70 7
1014/18 .. .. *Set of* 5 3·25 3·5
Nos. 1014/18 were printed together, *se-tenant*, in horizonta[l] strips of 5 throughout the sheet, forming a composite design.

(Des D. Lancashire. Litho Cambec Press, Melbourne)

986 (6 Aug). *Bicentenary of Australian Settlement* (1988) (*5th issue*). *Convict Settlement in New South Wales. T* **425** *and similar horiz designs. Multicoloured. P* 13.

019 33 c. Type **425** 80 50
020 33 c. "Lord Sydney" (Gilbert Stuart) and convicts 80 50
021 33 c. "Captain Arthur Phillip" (F. Wheatley) and ship 80 50
022 $1 "Captain John Hunter" (W. B. Bennett) and aborigines .. .. .. 3·25 4·25
019/22 .. .. *Set of* 4 5·00 5·25

426 Red Kangaroo

427 Royal Bluebell

428 Pink Enamel Orchid

(Des D. Higgins. Litho Leigh-Mardon Ltd, Melbourne)

986 (13 Aug). *Australian Wildlife (1st series). T* **426** *and similar vert designs. Multicoloured. P* 14½×14.

023 36 c. Type **426** 55 70
a. Horiz strip of 5. Nos. 1023/7 .. .. 2·50
024 36 c. Emu 55 70
025 36 c. Koala 55 70
026 36 c. Laughing Kookaburra 55 70
027 36 c. Platypus 55 70
023/7 .. .. *Set of* 5 2·50 3·25

Nos. 1023/7 were printed together, *se-tenant*, in horizontal strips of 5 throughout the sheet.

For 37 c. values see Nos. 1072/6.

(Des Betty Conabere. Litho Mercury-Walch Pty, Hobart)

1996 (25 Aug). *Alpine Wildflowers. T* **427** *and similar vert designs. Multicoloured. Roul.*

028 3 c. Type **427** 35 35
a. Booklet pane. Nos. 1028, 1029 and 1031×2 .. .. 2·50
b. Booklet pane. Nos. 1028, 1030 and 1031×2 .. .. 2·50
029 5 c. Alpine Marsh Marigold .. .. 1·60 2·50
030 25 c. Mount Buffalo Sunray .. .. 1·60 2·50
031 36 c. Silver Snow Daisy 45 30
028/31 .. .. *Set of* 4 3·50 5·00

Nos. 1028/31 only exist from 80 c. (pane No. 1028a) and $1 pane No. 1028b) stamp booklets. The outer edges of the booklet panes are imperforate.

Des O. Schmidinger and Christine Stead. Litho Leigh-Mardon Ltd, Melbourne)

1986 (18 Sept). *Native Australian Orchids. T* **428** *and similar vert designs. Multicoloured. P* 14½.

1032 36 c. Type **428** 70 20
1033 55 c. *Dendrobium nindii* .. .. .. 1·25 1·00
1034 90 c. Duck Orchid .. .. 2·00 2·00
1035 $1 Queen of Sheba Orchid .. .. 2·00 2·00
1032/5 .. .. *Set of* 4 5·50 4·75

429 *Australia II* crossing Finishing Line

430 Dove with Olive Branch and Sun

(Des J. Passmore and G. Rowan. Litho Cambec Press, Melbourne)

1986 (26 Sept). *Australian Victory in America's Cup*, 1983. *T* **429** *and similar vert designs. Multicoloured. P* 14×13½.

1036 36 c. Type **429** 75 75
1037 36 c. Boxing kangaroo flag of winning syndicate 75 75
a. Grey (inscr and face value) omitted .. £130
1038 36 c. America's Cup trophy 75 75
a. Grey (inscr and face value) omitted .. £130
1036/8 .. .. *Set of* 3 2·00 2·00

(Des K. Cato. Litho Cambec Press, Melbourne)

1986 (22 Oct). *International Peace Year. P* 14×13½.

1039 **430** 36 c. multicoloured 65 40

Examples with the gutter margin overprinted to commemorate the Papal visit in November 1986 were not produced by the Australian Post Office.

431 Mary and Joseph

432 Australian Flag on Printed Circuit Board

(Des B. Clinton. Litho Leigh-Mardon Ltd, Melbourne)

1986 (3 Nov–Dec). *Christmas. T* **431** *and similar multicoloured designs showing scenes from children's nativity play. P* 14½.

1040 30 c. Type **431** 40 30
a. Perf 14×13½ (12.86) 75 75
1041 36 c. Three Wise Men leaving gifts .. 50 45
1042 60 c. Angels (*horiz*) .. .. .. 90 1·50
1040/2 .. .. *Set of* 3 1·60 2·00

MS1043 147×70 mm. 30 c. Three angels and shepherd (*horiz*); 30 c. Kneeling shepherds (*horiz*); 30 c. Mary, Joseph and three angels; 30 c. Innkeeper and two angels; 30 c. Three Wise Men (*horiz*) .. .. 2·75 3·00

No. 1040a was printed by Cambec Press after stocks of the original printing by Leigh-Mardon Ltd ran short. It is believed that this Cambec Press printing was distributed in New South Wales, Tasmania, Victoria and Western Australia.

(Des J. Passmore. Litho CPE Australia Ltd, Melbourne)

1987 (23 Jan). *Australia Day. T* **432** *and similar horiz design. Multicoloured. P* 13½×14.

1044 36 c. Type **432** 55 35
1045 36 c. "Australian Made" Campaign logos .. 55 35

433 Aerial View of Yacht

434 Grapes and Melons

(Des O. Schmidinger and Christine Stead. Litho Leigh-Mardon Ltd, Melbourne)

1987 (28 Jan). *America's Cup Yachting Championship. T* **433** *and similar vert designs. Multicoloured. P* 14½.

1046 36 c. Type **433** 40 20
1047 55 c. Two yachts tacking .. .. .. 90 1·00
1048 90 c. Two yachts turning .. .. .. 1·40 2·00
1049 $1 Two yachts under full sail .. .. 1·50 1·75
1046/9 .. .. *Set of* 4 3·75 4·50

(Des Susan Tilley. Litho CPE Australia Ltd, Melbourne)

1987 (11 Feb). *Australian Fruit. T* **434** *and similar vert designs. Multicoloured. P* 14×13½.

1050 36 c. Type **434** 40 20
1051 65 c. Tropical and sub-tropical fruits .. 1·00 1·25
1052 90 c. Citrus fruit, apples and pears .. 1·40 1·90
1053 $1 Stone and berry fruits .. .. 1·40 1·60
1050/3 .. .. *Set of* 4 3·75 4·50

435 Livestock

436 Queen Elizabeth in Australia, 1986

(Des D. Lancashire. Litho CPE Australia Ltd, Melbourne)

1987 (10 Apr). *Agricultural Shows. T* **435** *and similar vert designs. Multicoloured. P* 14×13½.

1054 36 c. Type **435** 60 20
1055 65 c. Produce .. .. 1·25 1·75
1056 90 c. Sideshows .. .. 1·75 2·40
1057 $1 Competitions .. .. 1·90 2·40
1054/7 .. .. *Set of* 4 5·00 6·00

(Des Janet Boschen. Litho CPE Australia Ltd, Melbourne)

1987 (21 Apr). *Queen Elizabeth II's Birthday. P* 13½×14.

1058 **436** 36 c. multicoloured 55 50

437 Convicts on Quay

438 "At the Station"

(Des Sue Passmore. Litho CPE Australia Ltd, Melbourne)

1987 (13 May). *Bicentenary of Australian Settlement* (1988) (*6th issue*). *Departure of the First Fleet. T* **437** *and similar square designs. Multicoloured. P* 13.

1059 36 c. Type **437** 80 90
a. Horiz strip of 5. Nos. 1059/63 .. 3·50
1060 36 c. Royal Marines officer and wife .. 80 90
1061 36 c. Sailors loading supplies 80 90
1062 36 c. Officers being ferried to ships .. 80 90
1063 36 c. Fleet in English Channel 80 90
1059/63 .. .. *Set of* 5 3·50 4·00

Nos. 1059/63 were printed together, *se-tenant*, in horizontal strips of 5 throughout the sheet.

See also Nos. 1064/6, 1077/81, 1090/2 and 1105/9.

(Des Sue Passmore. Litho CPE Australia Ltd, Melbourne)

1987 (3 June). *Bicentenary of Australian Settlement* (1988) (*7th issue*). *First Fleet at Tenerife. Square designs as T* **437**. *Multicoloured. P* 13.

1064 36 c. Ferrying supplies, Santa Cruz .. 80 90
a. Horiz pair. Nos. 1064/5 .. .. 1·60 1·75
1065 36 c. Canary Islands fishermen and departing fleet 80 90
1066 $1 Fleet arriving at Tenerife (Optd S. 50p) .. .. 2·00 2·00
1064/6 .. .. *Set of* 3 3·25 3·50

Nos. 1064/5 were printed together, *se-tenant*, in horizontal pairs throughout the sheet, forming a composite design.

(Des C. Lee. Litho CPE Australia Ltd, Melbourne)

1987 (24 June). *Folklore. Scenes and Verses from Poem "The Man from Snowy River". T* **438** *and similar vert designs. Multicoloured. P* 14×13½.

1067 36 c. Type **438** 70 90
a. Horiz strip of 5. Nos. 1067/71 .. 3·25
1068 36 c. "Mountain bred" 70 90
1069 36 c. "That terrible descent" 70 90
1070 36 c. "At their heels" 70 90
1071 36 c. "Brought them back" 70 90
1067/71 .. .. *Set of* 5 3·25 4·00

Nos. 1067/71 were printed together, *se-tenant*, in horizontal strips of five throughout the sheet, forming a composite background design of mountain scenery.

(Des D. Higgins. Litho Leigh-Mardon Ltd, Melbourne)

1987 (1 July). *Australian Wildlife (2nd series). Vert designs as T* **426**. *Multicoloured. P* 14½×14.

1072 37 c. Common Brushtail Possum 55 65
a. Horiz strip of 5. Nos. 1072/6 .. 2·50
ab. Pale orange (top panel) omitted .. £1500
1073 37 c. Sulphur-crested Cockatoo 55 65
1074 37 c. Common Wombat 55 65
1075 37 c. Crimson Rosella 55 65
1076 37 c. Echidna 55 65
1072/6 .. .. *Set of* 5 2·50 3·00

Nos. 1072/6 were printed together, *se-tenant*, in horizontal strips of 5 throughout the sheet.

(Des Sue Passmore. Litho CPE Australia Ltd, Melbourne)

1987 (6 Aug). *Bicentenary of Australian Settlement* (1988) (*8th issue*). *First Fleet at Rio de Janeiro. Square designs as T* **437**. *Multicoloured. P* 13.

1077 37 c. Sperm Whale and fleet 80 85
a. Horiz strip of 5. Nos. 1077/81 .. 3·50
1078 37 c. Brazilian coast 80 85
1079 37 c. British officers in market 80 85
1080 37 c. Religious procession 80 85
1081 37 c. Fleet leaving Rio 80 85
1077/81 .. .. *Set of* 5 3·50 3·75

Nos. 1077/81 were printed together, *se-tenant*, in horizontal strips of 5, forming a composite design.

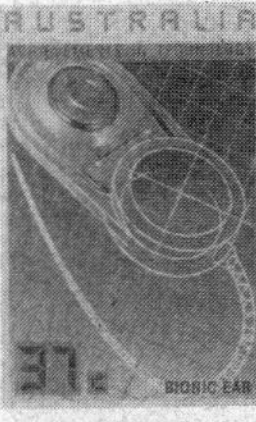

439 Bionic Ear

440 Catching Crayfish

(Des. O. Schmidinger and Christine Stead. Litho Leigh-Mardon Ltd, Melbourne)

1987 (19 Aug). *Australian Achievements in Technology. T* **439** *and similar vert designs. Multicoloured. P* 14½.

1082 37 c. Type **439** 40 35
1083 53 c. Microchips 75 60
1084 63 c. Robotics 85 70
1085 68 c. Ceramics 95 75
1082/5 .. .. *Set of* 4 2·75 2·25

(Des Elizabeth Honey. Litho Leigh-Mardon Ltd, Melbourne)

1987 (16 Sept). *"Aussie Kids". T* **440** *and similar horiz designs. Multicoloured. P* 14½.
1086 37 c. Type **440** 40 35
1087 55 c. Playing cat's cradle .. .. .. 1·00 75
1088 90 c. Young football supporters .. .. 1·40 1·25
1089 $1 Children with kangaroo (Optd S. 50p) .. .. 1·60 1·25
1086/9 .. .. *Set of* 4 4·00 3·25

(Des Sue Passmore. Litho CPE Australia Ltd, Melbourne)

1987 (13 Oct). *Bicentenary of Australian Settlement* (1988) *(9th issue). First Fleet at Cape of Good Hope. Square designs as T* **437**. *Multicoloured. P* 13.
1090 37 c. Marine checking list of livestock .. 75 90
a. Horiz pair. Nos. 1090/1 .. .. 1·50 1·75
1091 37 c. Loading livestock 75 90
1092 $1 First Fleet at Cape Town (Optd S. 50p) .. .. 1·75 2·00
1090/2 .. .. *Set of* 3 3·00 3·50
Nos. 1090/1 were printed together, *se-tenant*, in horizontal and vertical pairs throughout the sheet, the former showing a composite design.

441 Detail of Spearthrower, Western Australia

442 Grandmother and Granddaughters with Candles

(Des J. Passmore. Litho Leigh-Mardon Ltd, Melbourne)

1987 (13 Oct). *Aboriginal Crafts. T* **441** *and similar horiz designs. Multicoloured. P* 15½×*imperf.*
1093 3 c. Type **441** .. .. 1·00 1·50
a. Booklet pane. Nos. 1093 and 1095, each × 2 .. .. 3·75
1094 15 c. Shield pattern, New South Wales .. 3·75 4·75
a. Booklet pane. Nos. 1094, 1096 × 3 and 1097 × 2 .. .. 7·50
1095 37 c. Basket weave, Queensland .. .. 1·00 1·50
1096 37 c. Bowl design, Central Australia .. 90 1·25
1097 37 c. Belt pattern, Northern Territory .. 1·00 1·50
1093/7 .. .. *Set of* 5 7·00 9·50
Nos. 1093/7 only exist from 80 c. (pane No. 1093a) and $2 (pane No. 1094a) stamp booklets. The vertical edges of the booklet panes are imperforate.

(Des B. Clinton. Litho Leigh-Mardon Ltd, Melbourne (30 c.) or CPE Australia Ltd, Melbourne (37 c., 63 c.))

1987 (2 Nov). *Christmas. T* **442** *and similar multicoloured designs showing carol singing by candlelight. P* 14½ (30 c.) *or* 13½ × 14 (37 c., 63 c.).
1098 30 c. Type **442** 55 55
a. Horiz strip of 5. Nos. 1098/102 .. 2·50
1099 30 c. Father and daughters.. .. .. 55 55
1100 30 c. Four children 55 55
1101 30 c. Family 55 55
1102 30 c. Six teenagers 55 55
1103 37 c. Choir (*horiz*) 55 40
1104 63 c. Father and two children (*horiz*) .. 1·00 1·00
1098/104 .. .. *Set of* 7 3·75 3·75
Nos. 1098/1102 were printed together, *se-tenant*, in horizontal strips of five throughout the sheet.

(Des Sue Passmore. Litho CPE Australia Ltd, Melbourne)

1988 (26 Jan). *Bicentenary of Australian Settlement (10th issue). Arrival of First Fleet. Square designs as T* **437**. *Multicoloured. P* 13.
1105 37 c. Aborigines watching arrival of Fleet, Botany Bay 80 85
a. Horiz strip of 5. Nos. 1105/9 .. 3·50
1106 37 c. Aborigine family and anchored ships 80 85
1107 37 c. Fleet arriving at Sydney Cove .. 80 85
1108 37 c. Ship's boat 80 85
1109 37 c. Raising the flag, Sydney Cove, 26 January 1788 .. .. 80 85
1105/9 .. .. *Set of* 5 3·50 3·75
Nos. 1105/9 were printed together, *se-tenant*, in horizontal strips of five throughout the sheet, forming a composite design.

443 Koala with Stockman's Hat and Eagle dressed as Uncle Sam

444 "Religion" (A. Horner)

(Des R. Harvey. Litho CPE Australia Ltd, Melbourne)

1988 (26 Jan). *Bicentenary of Australian Settlement (11th issue). Joint issue with U.S.A. P* 13.
1110 **443** 37 c. multicoloured 60 35

NEW PRINTINGS. From the beginning of 1990 new printings of definitive stamps were identified by small koala or kangaroo symbols printed on the vertical sheet margins alongside alternate rows. One koala represented the first printing, two koalas the second and so on. The kangaroo symbol was used once four koalas had been reached.

(Litho Leigh-Mardon Ltd, Melbourne (4, 5, 20, 25, 30, 37, 39, 40, 50, 53, 70, 80, 90 c., $1) or CPE Australia Ltd, Melbourne (others))

1988 (17 Feb)–**95**. *"Living Together". T* **444** *and similar square designs showing cartoons. Multicoloured (except 30 c.). P* 14.
1111 1 c. Type **444** (16.3.88) 50 30
1112 2 c. "Industry" (P. Nicholson) (16.3.88) .. 50 30
1113 3 c. "Local Government" (A. Collette) (16.3.88) 50 30
1114 4 c. "Trade Unions" (Liz Honey) .. 10 10
1115 5 c. "Parliament" (Bronwyn Halls) (16.3.88) 50 30
1116 10 c. "Transport" (Meg Williams) .. 30 30
1117 15 c. "Sport" (G. Cook) 40 40
1118 20 c. "Commerce" (M. Atcherson) .. 70 30
1119 25 c. "Housing" (C. Smith) 45 30
a. Perf 14½ (14.9.95) .. .. .. 1·50 1·50
1120 30 c. "Welfare" (R. Tandberg) (black and pale rose-lilac) (16.3.88) 55 40
1121 37 c. "Postal Services" (P. Viska) .. 60 50
a. Booklet pane. No. 1121×10 (1.7.88) 6·00
1121*b* 39 c. "Tourism" (J. Spooner) (28.9.88) .. 60 50
ba. Booklet pane. No. 1121*b*×10 .. 7·00
1122 40 c. "Recreation" (R. Harvey) (16.3.88) .. 70 40
1123 45 c. "Health" (Jenny Coopes) 70 50
1124 50 c. "Mining" (G. Haddon) 70 50
1125 53 c. "Primary Industry" (S. Leahy) .. 1·75 1·00
1126 55 c. "Education" (Victoria Roberts) (16.3.88) .. .. 1·50 55
1127 60 c. "Armed Forces" (B. Green) (16.3.88) 1·50 70
1128 63 c. "Police" (J. Russell) (16.3.88) .. 2·00 85
1129 65 c. "Telecommunications" (B. Petty) (16.3.88) .. .. 1·50 75
1130 68 c. "The Media" (A. Langoulant) (16.3.88) 2·00 1·50
1131 70 c. "Science and Technology" (J. Hook) 1·75 1·00
1132 75 c. "Visual Arts" (G. Dazeley) (16.3.88) 1·00 1·00
1133 80 c. "Performing Arts" (A. Stitt) .. 1·25 1·00
1134 90 c. "Banking" (S. Billington) .. .. 1·50 90
1135 95 c. "Law" (C. Aslanis) (16.3.88) .. 1·00 1·00
1136 $1 "Rescue and Emergency" (M. Leunig) (Optd S. 50p.) .. .. .. 1·10 90
1111/36 .. .. *Set of* 27 23·00 14·00
Although Leigh-Mardon printed the 37 c. and 39 c. sheet stamps, and some of the 37 c. booklets, Nos. 1121a and 1121ba were produced by CPE with the upper and lower edges of the panes imperforate, so that stamps from them exist imperforate at top or bottom. These panes also show margins at both right and left.
Early in 1989 Leigh-Mardon Ltd, whose works were situated at Moorabbin, took over C.P.E Australia Ltd of Scoresby. Printings of the 45, 55, 60, 75, 80, 95 c. and $1 were made at both printing works.
No. 1119a comes from part of the 4 koala printing.

445 "Government House, Sydney, 1790" (George Raper)

446 Queen Elizabeth II (from photo by Tim Graham)

(Des J. Passmore. Litho CPE Australia Ltd, Melbourne)

1988 (13 Apr). *Bicentenary of Australian Settlement (12th issue). "The Early Years, 1788–1809". T* **445** *and similar square designs showing paintings. Multicoloured. P* 13.
1137 37 c. Type **445** 75 75
a. Horiz strip of 5. Nos. 1137/41 .. 1·25
1138 37 c. "Government Farm, Parramatta, 1791" ("The Port Jackson Painter") .. 75 75
1139 37 c. "Parramatta Road, 1796" (attr Thomas Watling) 75 75
1140 37 c. "View of Sydney Cove, c. 1800" (detail) (Edward Dayes) 75 75
1141 37 c. "Sydney Hospital, 1803", (detail) (George William Evans) 75 75
1137/41 .. .. *Set of* 5 3·25 3·25
Nos. 1137/41 were printed together, *se-tenant*, in horizontal strips of 5 throughout the sheet, each strip forming a composite background design from the painting, "View of Sydney from the East Side of the Cove, *c.* 1808" by John Eyre.

(Des Sandra Baker. Litho Leigh-Mardon Ltd, Melbourne)

1988 (21 Apr). *Queen Elizabeth II's Birthday. P* 14½.
1142 **446** 37 c. multicoloured 50 40

447 Expo '88 Logo

448 New Parliament House

(Des G. Emery. Litho CPE Australia Ltd, Melbourne)

1988 (29 Apr). *"Expo '88" World Fair, Brisbane. P* 13.
1143 **447** 37 c. multicoloured 50 4

(Des B. Sadgrove. Litho Leigh-Mardon Ltd, Melbourne)

1988 (9 May). *Opening of New Parliament House, Canberr P* 14½.
1144 **448** 37 c. multicoloured 50 4

449 Early Settler and Sailing Clipper

450 Kiwi and Koala at Campfire

(Des G. Emery. Litho CPE Australia Ltd, Melbourne)

1988 (21 June). *Bicentenary of Australian Settlement (13t issue). T* **449** *and similar square designs. Multicoloured. P* 1
1145 37 c. Type **449** .. .. 75 1·0
a. Pair. Nos. 1145/6 .. .. .. 1·50 2·0
1146 37 c. Queen Elizabeth II with British and Australian Parliament Buildings .. 75 1·0
1147 $1 W. G. Grace (cricketer) and tennis racquet .. .. 1·50 2·2
a. Pair. Nos. 1147/8 .. .. .. 3·00 4·5
1148 $1 Shakespeare, John Lennon (entertainer) and Sydney Opera House .. 1·50 2·2
1145/8 .. .. *Set of* 4 4·00 6·0
Nos. 1145/6 and 1147/8 were printed together, *se-tenant*, i horizontal and vertical pairs throughout the sheets, eac horizontal pair showing a background design of the Australia flag.
Stamps in similar designs were also issued by Great Britain

(Des R. Harvey. Litho Leigh-Mardon Ltd, Melbourne)

1988 (21 June). *Bicentenary of Australian Settlement (14t issue). P* 14½.
1149 **450** 37 c. multicoloured 65 40
A stamp in a similar design was also issued by New Zealand

451 "Bush Potato Country" (Turkey Tolsen Tjupurrula and David Corby Tjapaltjarri)

452 Basketball

(Des Janet Boschen. Litho CPE Australia Ltd, Melbourne)

1988 (1 Aug). *Art of the Desert. Aboriginal Paintings fron Central Australia. T* **451** *and similar square designs Multicoloured. P* 13.
1150 37 c. Type **451** 40 4
1151 55 c. "Courtship Rejected" (Limpi Puntungka Tjapangati) 80 6
1152 90 c. "Medicine Story" (artist unknown) .. 1·00 1·5
1153 $1 "Ancestor Dreaming" (Tim Leura Tjapaltjarri) .. .. 1·25 1·4
1150/3 .. .. *Set of* 4 3·00 3·5

(Des Sue Passmore. Litho Leigh-Mardon Ltd, Melbourne)

1988 (14 Sept). *Olympic Games, Seoul. T* **452** *and similar hori designs. Multicoloured. P* 14½.
1154 37 c. Type **452** 40 4
1155 65 c. Athlete crossing finish line .. .. 80 1·1
1156 $1 Gymnast with hoop .. .. .. 1·25 1·5
1154/6 .. .. *Set of* 3 2·25 2·7

453 Rod and Mace

(Des K. Christos. Litho Leigh-Mardon Ltd, Melbourne)

1988 (19 Sept). *34th Commonwealth Parliamentary Conference, Canberra. P* 14½.
1157 **453** 37 c. multicoloured 50 60

454 Necklace by Peter Tully

(Des K. Christos. Litho Mercury-Walch Pty, Hobart)

988 (28 Sept). *Australian Crafts. T* **454** *and similar horiz designs. Multicoloured. Roul×imperf.*
158 2 c. Type **454** .. .. 3·00 4·00
a. Booklet pane. Nos. 1158 and 1160 × 2 3·50
159 5 c. Vase by Colin Levy .. .. .. 3·00 4·00
a. Booklet pane. Nos. 1159 and 1160 × 5 5·00
160 39 c. Teapot by Frank Bauer 50 35
158/60 .. .. *Set of* 3 6·00 7·50
Nos. 1158/60 only exist from 80 c. (pane No. 1158a) and $2 ane No. 1159a) stamp booklets. The vertical edges of the oklet panes are imperforate.

455 Pinnacles Desert

456 "The Nativity" (Danielle Hush)

(Des K. Christos. Litho CPE Australia Ltd, Melbourne)

988 (17 Oct). *Panorama of Australia. T* **455** *and similar horiz designs. Multicoloured. P* 13.
161 39 c. Type **455** 60 40
162 55 c. Flooded landscape, Arnhem Land .. 85 85
163 65 c. Twelve Apostles, Victoria .. .. 1·10 1·25
164 70 c. Mountain Ash wood .. .. .. 1·25 1·75
161/4 .. .. *Set of* 4 3·50 3·75

Des Sandra Baker. Litho CPE Australia Ltd, Melbourne (32, 39 c.) or Leigh-Mardon Ltd, Melbourne (63 c.))

988 (31 Oct). *Christmas. T* **456** *and similar square designs. Multicoloured. P* 14½ *(63 c.) or* 13 *(others).*
165 32 c. Type **456** 50 35
166 39 c. "Koala as Father Christmas" (Kylie Courtney) 55 40
167 63 c. "Christmas Cockatoo" (Benjamin Stevenson) .. .. 1·10 1·40
165/7 .. .. *Set of* 3 1·90 1·90

PRINTERS. On 1 April 1989 Leigh-Mardon Ltd took over CPE ustralia Ltd. Stamp printing continued at both the Moorabbin original Leigh-Mardon) and Scoresby (ex-CPE) works with ome stamps being printed at one and then perforated at the ther. The Scoresby works closed at the end of 1991.

457 Sir Henry Parkes

458 Bowls

(Des R. Bevers. Litho CPE Australia Ltd, Melbourne)

1989 (25 Jan). *Australia Day. Centenary of Federation Speech by Sir Henry Parkes (N.S.W. Prime Minister). P* 14 × 13½.
168 **457** 39 c. multicoloured 45 40

(Des Sue Passmore (5, 10, 20, 41, 43, 65 c., $1, $1.20), N. Stapleton (75, 80, 85, 90 c.), G. Cook (others). Litho Printset Cambec Pty Ltd (5 c., (No. 1172a), 65 c. (No. 1186a) and ptgs of 1 c. (No. 1169), 3 c., 75 c., 80 c. (No. 1189) and $1 (No. 1192) from 1993) or Leigh-Mardon Ltd, Melbourne (others))

1989 (13 Feb)–94. *Sports. T* **458** *and similar horiz designs. Multicoloured. P* 13½ *(5, 10, 20, 65 c., $1.20) or* 14×14½ *(others).*
1169 1 c. Type **458** 10 10
a. Perf 13½ (4.90) 30 30
1170 2 c. Tenpin-bowling 10 10
a. Perf 13½ (9.89) 10 10
1171 3 c. Australian football 10 10
1172 5 c. Kayaking and canoeing (17.1.90) .. 15 10
a. Perf 14×14½ (3.94) 40 10
1174 10 c. Sailboarding (17.1.90) 15 15
a. Perf 14×14½ (2.92) 45 10
1176 20 c. Tennis (17.1.90) 20 25
a. Perf 14×14½ (7.93) .. .. 1·25 40
1179 39 c. Fishing 35 40
a. Booklet pane. No. 1179×10 .. 8·00
b. Perf 13½ (6.89) .. .. .. 1·00 1·00
ba. Booklet pane. No. 1179b×10 .. 10·00
1180 41 c. Cycling (23.8.89) 40 35
a. Booklet pane. No. 1180×10 .. 6·00
b. Imperf horiz (vert pair) £110
1181 43 c. Skateboarding (27.8.90) 35 40
a. Booklet pane. No. 1181×10 .. 5·50
1184 55 c. Kite-flying 40 45
1186 65 c. Rock-climbing (17.1.90) 70 60
a. Perf 14×14½ (2.92) 50 55
1187 70 c. Cricket 85 80
1188 75 c. Netball (22.8.91) 55 60
1189 80 c. Squash (22.8.91) 60 65
1190 85 c. Diving (22.8.91) .. .. .. 1·75 80
1191 90 c. Soccer (22.8.91) .. .. .. 1·75 80
1192 $1 Fun-run (17.1.90) .. .. .. 1·00 95
a. Perf 13½ (1.91) .. .. .. 3·50 3·00
1193 $1.10, Golf 85 90
1194 $1.20, Hang-gliding (27.8.90) .. .. 1·75 1·10
1169/94 .. .. *Set of* 19 11·00 8·00
1192/4 Optd "Specimen" .. .. *Set of* 3 1·75

The booklet panes have the upper and lower edges imperforate, so that the stamps from them are imperforate at top or bottom, and have margins at both left and right.

No. 1180b occurred in booklet panes affixed to first day covers, but not postmarked. The error only exists unused, no gum.

Nos. 1169a (1 koala ptg), 1170a (all ptgs except the first), 1179b (1st new ptg) and 1192a (1 koala ptg) are Scoresby printings of values originally produced at Moorabbin. Nos. 1174a (2, 3 and 4 koala ptgs) and 1176a (2 and 3 koala) are Moorabbin printings of values originally produced at Scoresby.

No. 1186a (2 koala ptg) was printed by Printset Cambec Pty Ltd. instead of Leigh-Mardon Ltd. There are minor differences in the arrangement of the inscriptions. Further supplies of the 1 c. (No. 1169) (2 koala), 3 c. (3 koala), 75 c. (1, 2 and 3 koala), 80 c. (2 koala) and $1 (No. 1192) (2 koala) were also produced by Printset Cambec from 1993.

No. 1172a (4 koala ptg) was printed by McPherson's as were additional supplies of the 65 c. (No. 1186a) (3 koala) and $1 (No. 1192) (1 kangaroo + 1 koala and 1 kangaroo + 2 koala ptgs).

For self-adhesive versions of Nos. 1180/1 see Nos. 1259/60*a*.

WARNING. The coating on a batch of paper used during 1989-90 was defective so that stamps lose parts of their design if immersed in water.

459 Merino

(Des K. McEwan. Litho CPE Australia Ltd, Melbourne)

1989 (27 Feb). *Sheep in Australia. T* **459** *and similar horiz designs. Multicoloured. P* 13½ × 14.
1195 39 c. Type **459** 70 40
1196 39 c. Poll Dorset 70 40
1197 85 c. Polwarth .. .. 1·40 1·75
1198 $1 Corriedale (Optd S. 70p.) .. .. 1·40 1·40
1195/8 .. .. *Set of* 4 3·75 3·50

460 Adelaide Botanic Garden

(Des J. Passmore. Eng B. Stewart. Litho Leigh-Mardon Ltd and die-stamped Avon Graphics, both of Melbourne ($20), litho CPE Australia Ltd, Melbourne ($2 later by Leigh-Mardon Ltd) and recess Note Ptg Branch, Reserve Bank of Australia (others))

1989 (12 Apr)–90. *Botanic Gardens. T* **460** *and similar horiz designs. Multicoloured. P* 14 *($2 to $10) or* 14½×14 *($20).*
1199 $2 Nooroo, New South Wales (13.9.89) 1·50 80
a. Perf 13½ .. .. 4·00 1·40
1200 $5 Mawarra, Victoria (13.9.89) .. 4·25 1·25
a. Perf 13½ .. .. 3·75 2·50
1201 $10 Type **460** .. .. 7·50 2·00
1201*a* $20 "A View of the Artist's House and Garden in Mills Plains, Van Diemen's Land" (John Glover) (15.8.90) .. 15·00 11·00
1199/1201*a* .. .. *Set of* 4 25·00 13·50
1199a/1201*a* Optd "Specimen" .. *Set of* 4 14·00

461 "Queen Elizabeth II" (sculpture, John Dowie)

462 Arrival of Immigrant Ship, 1830's

(Des Sandra Baker. Litho Leigh-Mardon Ltd, Melbourne)

1989 (21 Apr). *Queen Elizabeth II's Birthday. P* 14½.
1202 **461** 39 c. multicoloured 55 50

(Des D. Lancashire. Litho Leigh-Mardon Ltd, Melbourne)

1989 (10 May). *Colonial Development (1st issue). Pastoral Era 1810–1850. T* **462** *and similar square designs. Multicoloured. P* 14½.
1203 39 c. Type **462** 55 55
a. Horiz strip of 5. Nos. 1203/7 .. 2·50
1204 39 c. Pioneer cottage and wool dray .. 55 55
1205 39 c. Squatter's homestead 55 55
1206 39 c. Shepherd with flock (from Joseph Lycett's "Views of Australia") .. 55 55
1207 39 c. Explorer in desert (after watercolour by Edward Frome) 55 55
1203/7 .. .. *Set of* 5 2·50 2·50

Nos. 1203/7 were printed together, *se-tenant*, in horizontal strips of five throughout the sheet.

See also Nos 1254/8 and 1264/8.

463 Gladys Moncrieff and Roy Rene

464 "Impression" (Tom Roberts)

(Des Sue Passmore. Litho Leigh-Mardon Ltd, Melbourne)

1989 (12 July). *Australian Stage and Screen Personalities. T* **463** *and similar vert designs. Multicoloured. P* 14½.
1208 39 c. Type **463** 45 40
a. Perf 14 × 13½ .. .. .. 7·50 7·50
1209 85 c. Charles Chauvel and Chips Rafferty 1·25 1·40
1210 $1 Nellie Stewart and J. C. Williamson .. 1·25 1·10
1211 $1.10, Lottie Lyell and Raymond Longford .. .. 1·25 1·25
1208/11 .. .. *Set of* 4 3·75 3·75
1210/11 Optd "Specimen" .. .. *Set of* 2 1·40

No. 1208a was from a small first printing produced at the Scoresby (ex C.P.E.) plant and used in presentation packs or on first day covers. The rest of the 39 c. printing was perforated at the Moorabbin works.

(Des K. Christos. Litho Leigh-Mardon Ltd, Melbourne)

1989 (23 Aug). *Australian Impressionist Paintings. T* **464** *and similar multicoloured designs. P* 14 × 13½ *(No. 1214) or* 13½ × 14 *(others).*
1212 41 c. Type **464** 55 50
1213 41 c. "Impression for Golden Summer" (Sir Arthur Streeton) 55 50
1214 41 c. "All on a Summer's Day" (Charles Conder) (*vert*) 55 50
1215 41 c. "Petit Déjeuner" (Frederick McCubbin) 55 50
1212/15 .. .. *Set of* 4 2·00 1·75

465 Freeways

(Des Sally Newell and Carolyn Limonta. Litho Leigh-Mardon Ltd, Melbourne)

1989 (1 Sept). *The Urban Environment. T* **465** *and similar horiz designs. P* 15½×*imperf.*
1216 41 c. black, maroon and blue-green .. 65 90
a. Booklet pane. Nos. 1216×2, 1217×3 and 1218×2 .. .. 4·00
1217 41 c. black, maroon and magenta .. 65 90
1218 41 c. black, maroon and bright blue .. 65 90
1216/18 .. .. *Set of* 3 1·75 2·40

Designs:—No. 1217, City buildings, Melbourne; No. 1218, Commuter train at platform.

Nos. 1216/18 only exist from $3 stamp booklets in which the vertical edges of the pane are imperforate.

466 Hikers outside Youth Hostel

467 Horse Tram, Adelaide, 1878

(Des Priscilla Cutter. Litho Leigh-Mardon Ltd, Melbourne)

1989 (13 Sept). *50th Anniv of Australian Youth Hostels. P* 14½.
1219 **466** 41 c. multicoloured 55 50

(Des I. McKellar. Litho Leigh-Mardon Ltd, Melbourne)

1989 (11 Oct). *Historic Trams. T* **467** *and similar horiz designs. Multicoloured. P* 13½×14.
1220 41 c. Type **467** 60 60
1221 41 c. Steam tram, Sydney, 1884 .. .. 60 60
1222 41 c. Cable tram, Melbourne, 1886 .. 60 60
a. Perf 14½ .. .. 1·00 1·00
ab. Booklet pane. No. 1222a×10 .. 10·00
1223 41 c. Double-deck electric tram, Hobart, 1893 .. .. 60 60
1224 41 c. Combination electric tram, Brisbane, 1901 .. .. 60 60
1220/4 .. .. *Set of* 5 2·75 2·75

The upper and lower edges of booklet pane No. 1222ab are imperforate. It was printed and perforated at the Moorabbin plant.

468 "Annunciation" (15th-century Book of Hours)

469 Radio Waves and Globe

(Des Lynette Brown. Litho Leigh-Mardon Ltd, Melbourne)

1989 (1 Nov). *Christmas. Illuminated Manuscripts. T* **468** *and similar vert designs. Multicoloured. P* 14×13½ (36 *c.*) *or* 14½ (*others*).

1225 36 c. Type **468** 40 40
a. Booklet pane. No. 1225×10 .. .. 4·00
1226 41 c. "Annunciation to the Shepherds" (Wharncliffe Book of Hours, c. 1475) 50 45
1227 80 c. "Adoration of the Magi" (15th-century Parisian Book of Hours) .. .. 1·25 1·40
1225/7 .. .. *Set of* 3 1·90 2·00

The vertical sides of booklet pane No. 1225a are imperforate.

(Des B. Sadgrove. Litho Leigh-Mardon Ltd, Melbourne)

1989 (1 Nov). *50th Anniv of Radio Australia. P* 14×13½.

1228 **469** 41 c. multicoloured 55 50

470 Golden Wattle

471 Australian Wildflowers

(Des Celia Rosser. Litho Leigh-Mardon Ltd, Melbourne)

1990 (17 Jan). *Australia Day. P* 14½.

1229 **470** 41 c. multicoloured 55 50

(Des Beverley Graham and G. Rogers. Litho Leigh-Mardon Ltd, Melbourne)

1990 (7 Feb–3 Sept). *Greetings Stamps. P* 14×13½ (41 *c.*) *or* 14½ (43 *c.*).

1230 **471** 41 c. multicoloured 45 45
a. Booklet pane. No. 1230×10 .. 5·50
b. Perf 14½ (May) .. .. .. 1·00 1·00
ba. Booklet pane. No. 1230b×10 .. 10·00
1231 43 c. multicoloured (3 Sept) 35 40
a. Booklet pane. No. 1231×10 .. 4·00

The upper and lower edges of the booklet panes are imperforate.

No. 1230b is a Moorabbin (1 koala) printing which only exists from booklets. The remainder were printed at the Scoresby works.

472 Dr. Constance Stone (first Australian woman doctor), Modern Doctor and Nurses

473 Greater Glider

(Des Priscilla Cutter. Litho Leigh-Mardon Ltd, Melbourne)

1990 (7 Feb). *Centenary of Women in Medical Practice. P* 14½.

1232 **472** 41 c. multicoloured 50 45

(Des D. Higgins. Litho Leigh-Mardon Ltd, Melbourne)

1990 (21 Feb). *Animals of the High Country. T* **473** *and similar vert designs. Multicoloured. P* 14×13½.

1233 41 c. Type **473** 60 45
1234 65 c. Tiger Cat ("Spotted-tailed Quoll") 90 85
1235 70 c. Mountain Pygmy-possum .. 95 90
1236 80 c. Brush-tailed Rock-wallaby .. 1·10 1·00
1233/6 .. .. *Set of* 4 3·25 2·75

PRICES OF SETS

Set prices are given for many issues, generally those containing three stamps or more. Definitive sets include one of each value or major colour change, but do not cover different perforations, die types or minor shades. Where a choice is possible the set prices are based on the cheapest versions of the stamps included in the listings.

474 "Stop Smoking"

475 Soldiers from Two World Wars

(Des A. Stitt. Litho Leigh-Mardon Ltd, Melbourne)

1990 (14 Mar). *Community Health. T* **474** *and similar vert designs. Multicoloured. P* 14×13½.

1237 41 c. Type **474** 55 55
1238 41 c. "Drinking and driving don't mix" .. 55 55
1239 41 c. "No junk food, please" 55 55
1240 41 c. "Guess who's just had a checkup?" 55 55
1237/40 .. .. *Set of* 4 2·00 2·00

(Des O. Schmidinger and Christine Stead. Litho Leigh-Mardon Ltd, Melbourne)

1990 (12 Apr). *"The Anzac Tradition". T* **475** *and similar vert designs. Multicoloured. P* 14½.

1241 41 c. Type **475** 50 40
1242 41 c. Fighter pilots and munitions worker 50 40
1243 65 c. Veterans and Anzac Day parade .. 85 90
1244 $1 Casualty evacuation, Vietnam, and disabled veteran .. .. .. 1·25 1·40
1245 $1.10, Letters from home and returning troopships .. .. 1·40 1·50
1241/5 .. .. *Set of* 5 4·00 4·25
1244/5 Optd "Specimen" .. .. *Set of* 2 1·10

476 Queen at Australian Ballet Performance, London, 1988

477 New South Wales 1861 5s. Stamp

(Des Lynette Brown. Litho Leigh-Mardon Ltd, Melbourne)

1990 (19 Apr). *Queen Elizabeth II's Birthday. P* 14½.

1246 **476** 41 c. multicoloured 65 45

(Des J. Passmore. Litho Leigh-Mardon Ltd, Melbourne)

1990 (1 May). *150th Anniv of the Penny Black. T* **477** *and similar horiz designs showing stamps. Multicoloured. P* 13½×14.

1247 41 c. Type **477** 60 75
a. Block of 6. Nos. 1247/52 .. .. 3·25
1248 41 c. South Australia 1855 unissued 1s. .. 60 75
1249 41 c. Tasmania 1853 4d. 60 75
1250 41 c. Victoria 1867 5s. 60 75
1251 41 c. Queensland 1897 unissued 6d. .. 60 75
1252 41 c. Western Australia 1855 4d. with inverted frame 60 75
1247/52 .. .. *Set of* 6 3·25 4·00
MS1253 122×85 mm. Nos. 1247/52 .. 3·25 4·00

Nos. 1247/52 were printed together, *se-tenant*, throughout the sheet of 100 (two panes 5×10). The first and fifth vertical rows contained Nos. 1247 and 1250 alternately, the second and fourth rows Nos. 1248 and 1251, and the third row Nos. 1249 and 1252.

No. **MS**1253 also exists overprinted with the "Stamp World London 90" logo for sale at this international stamp exhibition.

478 Gold Miners on way to Diggings

479 Glaciology Research

(Des B. Weatherhead. Litho Leigh-Mardon Ltd, Melbourne)

1990 (16 May). *Colonial Development (2nd issue). Gold Fever. T* **478** *and similar square designs. Multicoloured. P* 13.

1254 41 c. Type **478** 60 60
a. Horiz strip of 5. Nos. 1254/8 .. .. 2·75
1255 41 c. Mining camp 60 60
1256 41 c. Panning and washing for gold .. 60 60
1257 41 c. Gold Commissioner's tent 60 60
1258 41 c. Moving gold under escort 60 60
1254/8 .. .. *Set of* 5 2·75 2·75

Nos. 1254/8 were printed together, *se-tenant*, in horizontal strips of 5 throughout the sheet.

1990 (16 May)–**91**. *As Nos.* 1180/1, *but self-adhesive. P* 11½

(*a*) *Typo Pemara Labels, Victoria*

1259 41 c. Cycling .. .. 65 1·0
1260 43 c. Skateboarding (27.8.90) 75 8

(*b*) *Litho Printset-Cambec Pty Ltd, Melbourne*

1260*a* 43 c. Skateboarding (26.6.91) .. .. 1·25 1·5

Nos. 1259/60*a* were only available in rolls of 100, No. 1260 also initially in rolls of 200, from major post offices or as strips of three from philatelic counters, each stamp, with die-cut perforations, being separate on the imperforate backing strip.

No. 1260*a* can be identified by its screened colours: on No. 1260 these are solid. The lithography printing also shows a kangaroo on the reverse and is on plain, rather than waxed backing paper.

Due to the type of adhesive used examples should be retained on piece.

(Des Janet Boschen and Yu. Artsimenev. Litho Leigh-Mardon Ltd, Melbourne)

1990 (13 June). *Australian-Soviet Scientific Co-operation in Antarctica. T* **479** *and similar horiz design. Multicoloured. P* 14½.

1261 41 c. Type **479** 55 4
1262 $1.10, Krill (marine biology research) (Optd S. 55p) .. .. .. 1·40 1·5
MS1263 85 × 65 mm. Nos. 1261/2 .. .. 1·90 1·9

Stamps in similar designs were also issued by Russia.

Examples of No. **MS**1263 imperforate originate from the Russian postal archives.

No. **MS**1263 also exists overprinted with the "New Zealand 1990" logo for sale at this international stamp exhibition in Auckland.

480 Auctioning Building Plots

481 "Salmon Gums" (Robert Juniper)

(Des B. Clinton. Litho Leigh-Mardon Ltd, Melbourne)

1990 (12 July). *Colonial Development (3rd series). Boomtime. T* **480** *and similar square designs. Multicoloured. P* 13.

1264 41 c. Type **480** 55 55
a. Horiz strip of 5. Nos. 1264/8 .. .. 2·50
1265 41 c. Colonial mansion 55 55
1266 41 c. Stock exchange 55 55
1267 41 c. Fashionable society 55 55
1268 41 c. Factories 55 55
1264/8 .. .. *Set of* 5 2·50 2·5

Nos. 1264/8 were printed together, *se-tenant*, in horizontal strips of 5 throughout the sheet.

(Des Sandra Baker. Litho Leigh-Mardon Ltd, Melbourne)

1990 (3 Sept). *"Heidelberg and Heritage" Art Exhibition. T* **481** *and similar vert design. Multicoloured. Imperf* × *p* 14½.

1269 28 c. Type **481** .. .. 1·75 2·2
a. Booklet pane. Nos. 1269 and 1270 × 4 3·00
b. Imperf × p 15½ .. .. .. 3·75 4·7
ba. Booklet pane. Nos. 1269b and 1270a × 4 .. .. 6·00
1270 43 c. "The Blue Dress" (Brian Dunlop) .. 35 4
a. Imperf × p 15½ 85 8

Nos. 1269/70 only exist from $2 stamp booklets in which the horizontal edges of the pane are imperforate.

482 "Adelaide Town Hall" (Edmund Gouldsmith)

483 Laughing Kookaburras and Gifts

(Des Janet Boschen. Litho Leigh-Mardon Ltd, Melbourne)

1990 (31 Oct). *150th Anniv of Local Government. P* 14½.

1271 **482** 43 c. multicoloured 65 5

(Des Marg Towt. Litho Leigh-Mardon Ltd, Melbourne)

1990 (31 Oct). *Christmas. T* **483** *and similar multicoloured designs. P* 14½.

1272 38 c. Type **483** 50 4
a. Booklet pane. No. 1272 × 10 .. 5·50
1273 43 c. Baby Jesus with Koalas and Wallaby (*vert*) 50 4
1274 80 c. Possum on Christmas tree .. 1·50 1·2
1272/4 .. .. *Set of* 3 2·25 1·9

The upper and lower edges of booklet pane No. 1272a are imperforate, producing stamps imperforate top or bottom, and there are margins at left and right.

484 National Flag

485 Black-necked Stork

(Des Dianne Cook. Litho Leigh-Mardon Ltd, Melbourne)

)1 (10 Jan). *Australia Day. 90th Anniv of Australian Flag. T* **484** *and similar horiz designs. P* 14½.
75 43 c. deep ultramarine, brt scarlet & grey . . 50 40
76 90 c. multicoloured . . . . 1·10 1·25
77 $1 multicoloured . . . . 1·25 1·40
78 $1.20, brt scarlet, dp ultramarine & grey 1·60 1·75
75/8 . . . . *Set of* 4 4·00 4·25
Designs:—90 c. Royal Australian Navy ensign; $1 Royal ıstralian Air Force standard; $1.20, Australian merchant ırine ensign.

(Des P. Margocsy. Litho Leigh-Mardon Ltd, Melbourne)

91 (14 Feb). *Waterbirds. T* **485** *and similar multicoloured designs. P* 14½.
79 43 c. Type **485** 75 40
80 43 c. Black Swan (*horiz*) 75 40
81 85 c. Cereopsis Goose ("Cape Barren Goose") . . . . 1·75 2·25
82 $1 Chestnut-breasted Teal (*horiz*) (Optd S. 55p) . . . . 1·90 1·75
79/82 . . . . *Set of* 4 4·75 4·25

486 Recruitment Poster (Women's Services)

487 Queen Elizabeth at Royal Albert Hall, London

(Des Dianne Cook. Litho Leigh-Mardon Ltd, Melbourne)

91 (14 Mar). *Anzac Day. 50th Anniversaries. T* **486** *and similar horiz designs. P* 14½.
83 43 c. multicoloured 60 40
84 43 c. black, brown-olive & pale grey-brown 60 40
85 $1.20, multicoloured (Optd S. 55p) . . 2·25 2·00
83/5 . . . . *Set of* 3 3·00 2·50
Designs:—43 c. (No. 1284) Patrol (Defence of Tobruk); $1.20, '-P Day Canberra" (Harold Abbot) (Australian War emorial).

(Des R. Bulach. Litho Leigh-Mardon Ltd, Melbourne)

91 (11 Apr). *Queen Elizabeth II's Birthday. P* 14½.
86 **487** 43 c. multicoloured 80 50

488 *Tectocoris diophthalmus* (bug)

489 "Bondi" (Max Dupain)

(Des D. Nelson. Litho Leigh-Mardon Ltd, Melbourne)

91 (11 Apr). *Insects. T* **488** *and similar horiz designs. Multicoloured. P* 14½.
87 43 c. Type **488** 75 45
88 43 c. *Cizara ardeniae* (hawk moth) . . 75 45
89 80 c. *Petasida ephippigera* (grasshopper) 2·00 2·00
90 $1 *Castiarina producta* (beetle) . . 2·00 1·50
87/90 . . . . *Set of* 4 5·00 4·00

(Des Janet Boschen. Litho Leigh-Mardon Ltd, Melbourne)

91 (13 May). *150 Years of Photography in Australia. T* **489** *and similar vert designs. P* 14½.
291 43 c. black, chestnut and deep ultramarine 75 65
  a. Horiz pair. Nos. 1291/2 . . . . 1·50 1·25
292 43 c. black, turquoise-green and chestnut 75 65
293 70 c. black, yellow-green and chestnut . . 1·25 1·10
294 $1.20, black, light brown and deep blue-green (Optd S. 55p) . . . . 1·75 1·50
291/4 . . . . *Set of* 4 4·00 3·50
Designs:—No. 1292, "Gears for the Mining Industry, Vickers ıwolt, Melbourne" (Wolfgang Sievers); No. 1293, "The Wheel Youth" (Harold Cazneaux); No. 1294, "Teacup Ballet" (Olive otton).
Nos. 1291/2 were printed together, *se-tenant*, in horizontal airs throughout the sheet.

490 Singing Group

491 Puppy

(Des O. Schmidinger and Christine Stead. Litho Leigh-Mardon Ltd, Melbourne)

1991 (13 June). *Australian Radio Broadcasting. T* **490** *and similar vert designs showing listeners and scenes from radio programmes. Multicoloured. P* 14½.
1295 43 c. Type **490** 60 45
1296 43 c. "Blue Hills" serial 60 45
1297 85 c. "The Quiz Kids" . . . . . . 1·25 1·25
1298 $1 "The Argonauts' Club" children's programme (Optd S. 55p.) . . . . 1·50 1·40
1295/8 . . . . *Set of* 4 3·50 3·25

(Des Betina Ogden. Litho Leigh-Mardon Ltd, Melbourne)

1991 (25 July). *Domestic Pets. T* **491** *and similar vert designs. Multicoloured. P* 14½.
1299 43 c. Type **491** 70 45
1300 43 c. Kitten 70 45
1301 70 c. Pony . . . . 1·40 1·10
1302 $1 Sulphur-crested Cockatoo . . . . 1·90 1·40
1299/1302 . . . . *Set of* 4 4·25 3·00

492 George Vancouver (1791) and Edward Eyre (1841)

493 *Seven Little Australians* (Ethel Turner)

(Des D. Lancashire. Litho Leigh-Mardon Ltd, Melbourne)

1991 (25 Sept). *Exploration of Western Australia. P* 14½.
1303 **492** $1.05, multicoloured . . . . . . 1·00 1·10
MS1304 100 × 65 mm. No. 1303 . . . . 1·25 1·40
No. **MS**1304 also exists overprinted with the "Philanippon '91" logo for sale at this international stamp exhibition in Tokyo.

(Des Dianne Cook. Litho Leigh-Mardon Ltd, Melbourne)

1991 (10 Oct). *Australian Writers of the 1890s. T* **493** *and similar multicoloured designs. P* 14½.
1305 43 c. Type **493** 50 45
1306 75 c. *On Our Selection* (Steele Rudd) . . 80 75
1307 $1 "Clancy of the Overflow" (poem, A. B. Paterson) (*vert*) . . . . . . 1·10 95
1308 $1.20, "The Drover's Wife" (short story, Henry Lawson) (*vert*) (Optd S. 55p) 1·25 1·40
1305/8 . . . . *Set of* 4 3·25 3·25

494 Shepherd

495 Parma Wallaby

(Des Sue Passmore. Litho Leigh-Mardon Ltd, Melbourne)

1991 (1 Nov). *Christmas. T* **494** *and similar horiz designs. Multicoloured. P* 14½.
1309 38 c. Type **494** 40 40
  a. Booklet pane. No. 1309 × 20 . . 9·00
1310 43 c. Infant Jesus 45 45
1311 90 c. Wise Man . . . . 1·50 1·25
1309/11 . . . . *Set of* 3 2·10 1·90
The vertical edges of booklet pane No. 1309a are imperforate, producing stamps imperforate at right or left, and there are margins at top and bottom.
Variations in the shades of all three values were caused by changes in the production method during printing.

(Des Betina Ogden. Litho Leigh-Mardon Ltd, Melbourne)

1992 (2 Jan). *Threatened Species. T* **495** *and similar horiz designs. Multicoloured. P* 14 × 14½.
1312 45 c. Type **495** 65 60
  a. Block of 6. Nos. 1312/17 . . . . 3·50
1313 45 c. Ghost Bat 65 60
1314 45 c. Long-tailed Dunnart 65 60
1315 45 c. Little Pygmy-possum 65 60
1316 45 c. Dusky Hopping-mouse 65 60
1317 45 c. Squirrel Glider 65 60
1312/17 . . . . *Set of* 6 3·50 3·25
Nos. 1312/17 were printed together, *se-tenant*, throughout the sheet of 100, giving fifteen blocks of 6 (3 × 2) and 10 single stamps.
For self-adhesive versions of these designs see Nos. 1321/32.

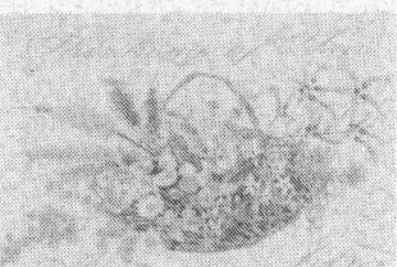

496 Basket of Wild Flowers

(Des Priscilla Cutter. Litho Leigh-Mardon Ltd, Melbourne)

1992 (2 Jan). *Greetings Stamp. P* 14½.
1318 **496** 45 c. multicoloured 40 45
  a. Booklet pane. No. 1318×10 . . 4·50
The upper and lower edges of booklet pane No. 1318a are imperforate, producing stamps imperforate at top or bottom, and there are margins at left and right.

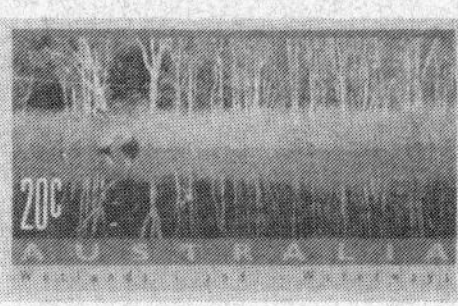

497 Noosa River, Queensland

(Des Sue Passmore. Litho Leigh-Mardon Ltd, Melbourne)

1992 (2 Jan)–**94**. *Wetlands and Waterways. T* **497** *and similar horiz design. P* 14½×*imperf.*
1319 20 c. Type **497** . . . . 1·75 2·00
  a. Booklet pane. Nos. 1319 and 1320×4 3·00
  b. Perf 14×imperf (3.94) . . . . 2·50 3·50
  ba. Booklet pane. Nos. 1319b and 1320b×4 . . . . 3·75
1320 45 c. Lake Eildon, Victoria 40 45
  b. Perf 14×imperf (3.94) 40 45
Nos. 1319/20 only exist from $2 stamp booklets in which the vertical edges of the pane are imperforate.
Nos. 1319b/ba and 1320b (2 koala ptg) were printed by McPherson's Ptg Group.

1992 (2 Jan–24 Dec). *As Nos.* 1312/17, *but self-adhesive.*
(*a*) *Typo Pemara Labels, Victoria. Phosphorised paper. P* 11
1321 45 c. Type **495** 60 70
  a. Black (inscr, etc) omitted £130
1322 45 c. Squirrel Glider 60 70
  a. Black (inscr, etc) omitted £130
1323 45 c. Dusky Hopping-mouse 60 70
  a. Black (inscr, etc) omitted £130
1324 45 c. Little Pygmy-possum 60 70
  a. Black (inscr, etc) omitted £130
1325 45 c. Long-tailed Dunnart 60 70
  a. Black (inscr, etc) omitted £130
1326 45 c. Ghost Bat 60 70
  a. Black (inscr, etc) omitted £130
1321/6 . . . . *Set of* 6 3·25 3·75
(*b*) *Litho Printset Cambec Pty Ltd. Phosphorised paper. P* 11½
1327 45 c. Type **495** 60 70
  p. Broad phosphor band at right . . 1·75 1·75
  pa. Booklet pane. Nos. 1327p×2, 1328p/9p and 1330p/2p×2 . . . . 13·50
  q. Horiz phosphor bands at top, bottom and on animal (22.4.92) . . . . 1·75 1·75
  qa. Booklet pane. Nos. 1327q×2, 1328q/9q and 1330q/2q×2 . . . . 13·50
  qb. Booklet pane. As No. 1327qa, but imperf £300
1328 45 c. Squirrel Glider 60 70
  p. Broad phosphor band at right . . 1·40 1·75
  pa. Sheetlet of 5. Nos. 1328p/32p . . 6·50
  q. Horiz phosphor bands at top, bottom and on animal (22.4.92) . . . . 1·40 1·75
  qa. Sheetlet of 5. Nos. 1328q/32q (24.12.92) . . . . 6·50
1329 45 c. Dusky Hopping-mouse 60 70
  p. Broad phosphor band at right . . 1·40 1·75
  q. Horiz phosphor bands at top, bottom and on animal (22.4.92) . . . . 1·40 1·75
1330 45 c. Little Pygmy-possum 60 70
  p. Broad phosphor band at right . . 1·40 1·75
  q. Horiz phosphor bands at top, bottom and on animal (22.4.92) . . . . 1·40 1·75
1331 45 c. Long-tailed Dunnart 60 70
  p. Broad phosphor band at right . . 1·40 1·75
  q. Horiz phosphor bands at top, bottom and on animal (22.4.92) . . . . 1·40 1·75
1332 45 c. Ghost Bat 60 70
  p. Broad phosphor band at right . . 1·40 1·75
  q. Horiz phosphor bands at top, bottom and on animal (22.4.92) . . . . 1·40 1·75
1327/32 . . . . *Set of* 6 3·25 3·75
1327p/32p . . . . *Set of* 6 8·00 9·50
1327q/32q . . . . *Set of* 6 8·00 9·50
Nos. 1321/6 were only available in rolls of 100 with Nos. 1327/32 in rolls of 100 or 200, each stamp, with die-cut perforations, being separate on the imperforate backing strip.
Nos. 1321a/6a also show a horizontal red line across the stamp which normally occurs on the reverse. Examples are reported to have been purchased from Buxton, N.S.W., post office.
The booklet panes Nos. 1327pa and 1327qa are arranged as a block of eight and a separate vertical pair with backing card forming the booklet cover. Stamps from these panes and the sheetlet of 5, Nos. 1328pa and 1328qa, differ from the coil printing by retaining the surplus self-adhesive paper around the stamps.
Booklet pane No. 1327pa and sheetlet No. 1328pa have a broad phosphor band, which shows pink under U.V. light, over the right-hand half of each design. Nos. 1327qa and 1328pa show this phosphor as horizontal bands at the top and bottom of each design and also have the animal overprinted in phosphor ink.
No. 1328pa also exists overprinted with the "World Columbian Stamp Expo '92" logo for sale at this international stamp exhibition in Chicago.

498 *Young Endeavour* (cadet brigantine)   499 Bombing of Darwin

(Des Sue Passmore. Litho Leigh-Mardon Ltd, Melbourne)

1992 (15 Jan). *Australia Day and 500th Anniv of Discovery of America by Columbus* (No. **MS**1337). *Sailing Ships. T* **498** *and similar multicoloured designs. P* 14½.
1333 45 c. Type **498** 80 50
1334 45 c. *Britannia* (yacht) (*vert*) 80 50
1335 $1.05, *Akarana* (cutter) (*vert*) .. .. 1·75 2·00
1336 $1.20, *John Louis* (pearling lugger) (Optd. S. 55p) .. .. 2·00 1·75
1333/6 .. .. *Set of* 4 4·75 4·25
MS1337 147×64 mm. Nos. 1333/6 .. .. 4·75 4·75
No. **MS**1337 also exists overprinted with either the "World Columbian Stamp Expo '92" or "Genova '92" logos for sale at these international stamp exhibitions in Chicago or Genoa.

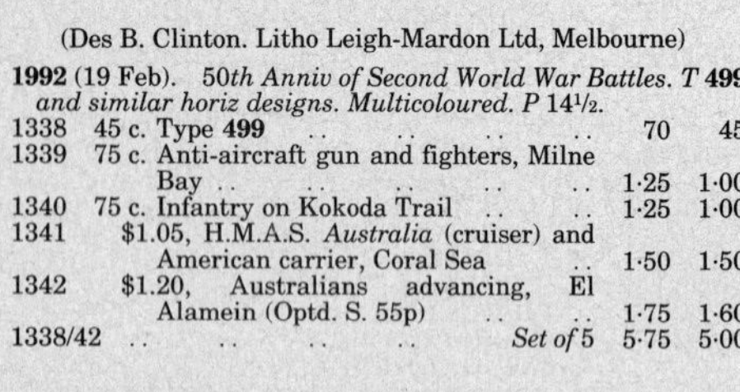

(Des B. Clinton. Litho Leigh-Mardon Ltd, Melbourne)

1992 (19 Feb). *50th Anniv of Second World War Battles. T* **499** *and similar horiz designs. Multicoloured. P* 14½.
1338 45 c. Type **499** 70 45
1339 75 c. Anti-aircraft gun and fighters, Milne Bay .. .. 1·25 1·00
1340 75 c. Infantry on Kokoda Trail .. .. 1·25 1·00
1341 $1.05, H.M.A.S. *Australia* (cruiser) and American carrier, Coral Sea .. 1·50 1·50
1342 $1.20, Australians advancing, El Alamein (Optd. S. 55p) .. .. 1·75 1·60
1338/42 .. .. *Set of* 5 5·75 5·00

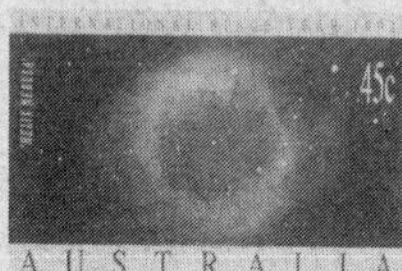

500 Helix Nebula   501 Hunter Valley, New South Wales

(Des Sandra Harman. Litho Leigh-Mardon Ltd, Melbourne)

1992 (19 Mar). *International Space Year. T* **500** *and similar horiz designs. Multicoloured. P* 14½.
1343 45 c. Type **500** 60 45
1344 $1.05, The Pleiades .. .. 1·50 1·25
1345 $1.20, Spiral Galaxy, NGC 2997 (Optd. S. 55p) .. .. 1·75 1·50
1343/5 .. .. *Set of* 3 3·50 3·00
MS1346 133×70 mm. Nos. 1343/5 .. .. 4·00 4·50
No. **MS**1346 also exists overprinted with the "World Columbian Stamp Expo '92" logo for sale at this international stamp exhibition in Chicago.

(Des P. Blizzard-Allen. Litho McPherson's Ptg Group, Mulgrave)

1992 (9 Apr). *Vineyard Regions. T* **501** *and similar horiz designs. Multicoloured. P* 14×14½.
1347 45 c. Type **501** 60 50
1348 45 c. North-east Victoria 60 50
1349 45 c. Barossa Valley, South Australia .. 60 50
1350 45 c. Coonawarra, South Australia .. 60 50
1351 45 c. Margaret River, Western Australia 60 50
1347/51 .. .. *Set of* 5 2·75 2·25

502 3½d. Stamp of 1953   503 Salt Action

(Des Lynette Brown. Litho McPherson's Ptg Group, Mulgrave)

1992 (9 Apr). *Queen Elizabeth II's Birthday. P* 14×14½.
1352 **502** 45 c. multicoloured 70 50

(Des J. Wolseley. Litho McPherson's Ptg Group, Mulgrave)

1992 (11 June). *Land Conservation. T* **503** *and similar vert designs. Multicoloured. P* 14½×14.
1353 45 c. Type **503** 85 85
a. Horiz strip of 5. Nos. 1353/7 .. 3·75
1354 45 c. Farm planning 85 85
1355 45 c. Erosion control 85 85
1356 45 c. Tree planting 85 85
1357 45 c. Dune care 85 85
1353/7 .. .. *Set of* 5 3·75 3·75
Nos. 1353/7 were printed together, *se-tenant*, in horizontal strips of 5 throughout the sheet.

504 Cycling   505 Echidna

(Des G. Emery. Litho Leigh-Mardon Ltd, Melbourne)

1992 (2 July). *Olympic Games and Paralympic Games* (*No.* 1359), *Barcelona. T* **504** *and similar horiz designs. Multicoloured. P* 14½.
1358 45 c. Type **504** 60 45
1359 $1.20, High jumping .. .. 1·50 1·60
1360 $1.20, Weightlifting .. .. 1·50 1·60
1358/60 .. .. *Set of* 3 3·25 3·25
1359/60 Optd "Specimen" .. .. *Set of* 2 1·10

(Des Marg Towt (30, 85 c., $1.35), Betina Ogden (35, 50, 60, 95 c.), S. Morrell (others). Litho McPherson's Ptg Group, Mulgrave)

1992 (13 Aug)–**98.** *Australian Wildlife* (1*st series*). *T* **505** *and similar horiz designs. Multicoloured. P* 14×14½.
1361 30 c. Saltwater Crocodile (10.3.94) .. 25 20
1362 35 c. Type **505** 25 20
1363 40 c. Platypus (12.8.93) 30 25
1364 50 c. Koala 40 35
1365 60 c. Common Bushtail Possum 45 40
1366 70 c. Laughing Kookaburra ("70 c" and "AUSTRALIA" in orange) (12.8.93) 80 85
a. "70 c" and "AUSTRALIA" in orange-brown (3.96) .. .. 1·50 1·75
1367 85 c. Australian Pelican (10.3.94) .. 65 70
1368 90 c. Eastern Grey Kangaroo ("90 c" and "AUSTRALIA" in orange) (12.8.93) 1·00 85
a. "90 c." and "AUSTRALIA" in orange-brown (4.98) 80 85
1369 95 c. Common Wombat 75 80
1370 $1.20, Major Mitchell's Cockatoo ("$1.20" and "AUSTRALIA" in orge) (12.8.93) 90 95
a. "$1.20" and "AUSTRALIA" in orange-brown (12.98) 90 95
1371 $1.35, Emu (10.3.94) .. .. .. 1·00 1·10
1361/71 .. .. *Set of* 11 6·00 5·50
No. 1366a is from the 3 koala or 1 kangaroo + 1 koala printings, No. 1368a from the 2 koala printing, and No. 1370a from the 1 kangaroo printing.

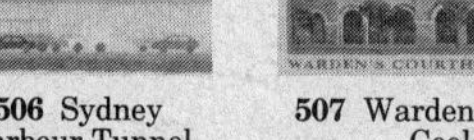

506 Sydney Harbour Tunnel (value at left)   507 Warden's Courthouse, Coolgardie

(Des Sandra Harman. Litho Leigh-Mardon Ltd, Melbourne)

1992 (28 Aug). *Opening of Sydney Harbour Tunnel. T* **506** *and similar vert design. Multicoloured. P* 14½.
1375 45 c. Type **506** .. .. 2·50 2·50
a. Horiz pair. Nos. 1375/6 .. .. 5·00 5·00
b. Perf 15½ .. .. 1·75 1·75
ba. Horiz pair. Nos. 1375b/6b .. .. 3·50 3·50
1376 45 c. Sydney Harbour Tunnel (value at right) .. .. 2·50 2·50
b. Perf 15½ .. .. 1·75 1·75
Nos. 1375/6 were printed together, *se-tenant*, in horizontal pairs throughout the sheet, each pair forming a composite design.

(Des Janet Boschen. Litho Printset Cambec Pty Ltd)

1992 (17 Sept). *Centenary of Discovery of Gold at Coolgardie and Kalgoorlie. T* **507** *and similar horiz designs. Multicoloured. P* 14×14½.
1377 45 c. Type **507** 60 45
1378 45 c. Post Office, Kalgoorlie 60 45
1379 $1.05, York Hotel, Kalgoorlie .. .. 1·50 1·60
1380 $1.20, Town Hall, Kalgoorlie .. .. 1·75 1·90
1377/80 .. .. *Set of* 4 4·00 4·00

508 Bowler of 1892   509 Children's Nativity Play

(Des Janet Boschen and M. Sofilas. Litho Leigh-Mardon Ltd, Melbourne)

1992 (15 Oct). *Centenary of Sheffield Shield Cricket Tournament. T* **508** *and similar vert design. Multicoloured. P* 14½.
1381 45 c. Type **508** 85 50
1382 $1.20, Batsman and wicket-keeper .. 1·90 2·00

(Des C. Smith. Litho McPherson's Ptg Group, Mulgrave)

1992 (30 Oct). *Christmas. T* **509** *and similar horiz desig Multicoloured. P* 14×14½.
1383 40 c. Type **509** 55
a. Booklet pane. No. 1383×20 .. 9·00
1384 45 c. Child waking on Christmas Day .. 60
1385 $1 Children carol singing .. .. 1·90 1·
1383/5 .. .. *Set of* 3 2·75 2·
The vertical edges of booklet pane No. 1383a are imperfora and there are margins at top and bottom.

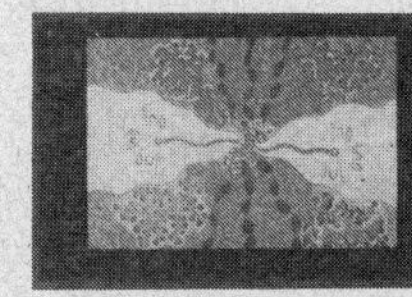

510 "Ghost Gum, Central Australia" (Namatjira)   511 "Wild Onion Dreaming" (Pauline Nakamarra Woods)

(Des Janet Boschen. Litho McPherson's Ptg Group, Mulgrav

1993 (14 Jan). *Australia Day. Paintings by Albert Namatji T* **510** *and similar horiz design. Multicoloured. P* 14×14½.
1386 45 c. Type **510** .. .. 75 1·
a. Pair. Nos. 1386/7 .. .. .. 1·50 2·
1387 45 c. "Across the Plain to Mount Giles" .. 75 1·
Nos. 1386/7 were printed together, *se-tenant*, in horizon and vertical pairs throughout the sheet.

(Des C. Atkinson. Litho Printset Cambec Pty Ltd)

1993 (4 Feb). *"Dreamings". Paintings by Aboriginal Artis T* **511** *and similar multicoloured designs. P* 14×14½ (*hor or* 14½×14 (*vert*).
1388 45 c. Type **511** 60
1389 75 c. "Yam Plants" (Jack Wunuwun) (*vert*) 1·10
1390 85 c. "Goose Egg Hunt" (George Milpurrurru) (*vert*) .. .. .. 1·25 1·
1391 $1 "Kalumpiwarra-Ngulalintji" (Rover Thomas) .. .. 1·40 1·
1388/91 .. .. *Set of* 4 4·00 3·

512 Uluru (Ayers Rock) National Park   513 Queen Elizabeth II on Royal Visit, 199

(Des Lynette Brown. Litho McPherson's Ptg Group, Mulgrav

1993 (4 Mar). *World Heritage Sites* (1*st series*). *T* **512** *a similar horiz designs. Multicoloured. P* 14½×14.
1392 45 c. Type **512** 70
1393 85 c. Rain forest, Fraser Island .. .. 1·75 1·
1394 95 c. Beach, Shark Bay .. .. .. 1·75 1·
1395 $2 Waterfall, Kakadu .. .. .. 2·00 1·
1392/5 .. .. *Set of* 4 5·50 5·
See also Nos. 1582/5.

(Des Dianne Cook. Litho Printset Cambec Pty Ltd)

1993 (7 Apr). *Queen Elizabeth II's Birthday. P* 14½×14.
1396 **513** 45 c. multicoloured 60

514 H.M.A.S. *Sydney* (cruiser, launched 1934) in Action   515 "Work in the Home"

(Des R. Shardlow and Sue Passmore. Litho McPherson's P Group, Mulgrave)

1993 (7 Apr). *Second World War Naval Vessels. T* **514** *a similar horiz designs. Multicoloured. P* 14×14½.
1397 45 c. Type **514** 80
1398 85 c. H.M.A.S. *Bathurst* (minesweeper) .. 1·60 1·
1399 $1.05, H.M.A.S. *Arunta* (destroyer) .. 1·75 2·
1400 $1.20, *Centaur* (hospital ship) and tug (Optd S. £2) .. .. 2·00 2·
1397/1400 .. .. *Set of* 4 5·50 5·

(Des G. Hogg. Litho McPherson's Ptg Group, Mulgrave)

1993 (7 May). *Working Life in the 1890s. T* **515** *and simil vert designs. Multicoloured. P* 14½×14.
1401 45 c. Type **515** 55
1402 45 c. "Work in the Cities" 55
1403 $1 "Work in the Country" .. .. .. 1·10 1·
1404 $1.20, Trade Union banner .. .. .. 1·50 1·
1401/4 .. .. *Set of* 4 3·25 3·

516 "Centenary Special", Tasmania, 1971

)es Sue Passmore and J. Richards. Litho Prinset Cambec Pty Ltd)

993 (1 June). *Australian Trains. T* **516** *and similar horiz designs. (a) Phosphorised paper. P* 14×14½.

405 45 c. Type **516** 65 70
a. Block of 6. Nos. 1405/10 .. .. 3·50
406 45 c. "Spirit of Progress", Victoria .. 65 70
407 45 c. "Western Endeavour", Western Australia, 1970 .. .. 65 70
408 45 c. "Silver City Comet", New South Wales 65 70
409 45 c. Cairns–Kuranda tourist train, Queensland 65 70
410 45 c. "The Ghan", Northern Territory .. 65 70
405/10 .. .. *Set of* 6 3·50 3·75

(b) Self-adhesive. Phosphor frame. P 11½

411 45 c. Type **516** .. .. 85 1·00
a. Booklet pane. Nos. 1411/12×2, 1413, 1414/15×2 and 1416 .. .. 7·50
412 45 c. "Spirit of Progress", Victoria .. 85 1·00
413 45 c. "Western Endeavour", Western Australia, 1970 .. .. 85 1·00
414 45 c. "Silver City Comet", New South Wales 85 1·00
415 45 c. Cairns–Kuranda tourist train, Queensland .. .. 85 1·00
416 45 c. "The Ghan", Northern Territory .. 85 1·00
411/16 .. .. *Set of* 6 4·50 5·50

Nos. 1405/10 were printed together, *se-tenant*, in sheets of 100 2 panes of 50 5×10) each pane providing five blocks of 6 and wenty single stamps.

Nos. 1411/16 occur either in rolls of 100, on which the surplus elf-adhesive paper around each stamp was removed, or in $4.50 ooklets, containing No. 1411a, on which the surplus paper was etained.

The phosphor on both rolls and booklets, which shows pink nder U.V. light, extends from the frame onto sections of the entre design.

:OUNTER-PRINTED LABELS. Since 1960 the Australian 'ost Office used a number of different franking machines at post ffice counters issuing "POSTAGE PAID" labels. On 21 June 993 a further type of self-adhesive label was introduced which ncoporated Threatened Species designs as Nos. 1312/17 with he machine-printed face value and code. Possible face values of hese labels ranged from 45 c. to $9,999.99. This was ubsequently restricted to a top value of $99.00.

The labels were initially available at the National Philatelic 'entre, Melbourne showing code "NPCI" and were subsequently vailable from Canberra Parliament House post office ("ACT 3" and "CPH1") and Royal Exchange, Sydney ("RX1").

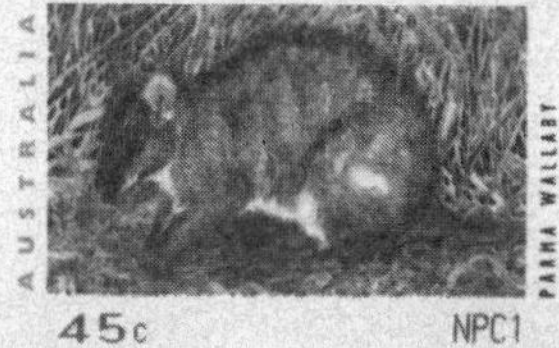

517 "Black Cockatoo Feather" (Fiona Foley)

518 Conference Emblem

Des Lynette Brown. Litho McPherson's Ptg Group, Mulgrave)

993 (1 July). *International Year of Indigenous Peoples. Aboriginal Art. T* **517** *and similar multicoloured designs. P* 14½×14 *(vert) or* 14×14½ *(horiz).*

417 45 c. Type **517** 55 45
418 75 c. "Ngarrgooroon Country" (Hector Jandany) *(horiz)* .. .. 1·10 1·25
419 $1 "Ngak Ngak" (Ginger Riley Munduwalawala) *(horiz)* .. .. .. 1·25 1·40
420 $1.05, "Untitled" (Robert Cole) (Optd S. £2) .. .. 1·50 1·75
417/20 .. .. *Set of* 4 4·00 4·25

(Des Dianne Cook. Litho Leigh-Mardon Ltd, Melbourne)

993 (2 Sept). *Inter-Parliamentary Union Conference and 50th Anniv of Women in Federal Parliament. T* **518** *and similar square design. Multicoloured. P* 14½.

421 45 c. Type **518** .. .. 1·00 1·25
a. Pair. Nos. 1421/2 .. .. .. 2·00 2·50
422 45 c. Dame Enid Lyons and Senator Dorothy Tangney .. .. 1·00 1·25

Nos. 1421/2 were printed together, *se-tenant*, in sheets of 25 5×5) with a block of nine examples of No. 1422 (R. 2/2-4, 3/2-4, 4/2-4) surrounded by sixteen examples of No. 1421 (R. 1/1-5, 2/1, 2/5, 3/1, 3/5, 4/1, 4/5, 5/1-5).

These stamps also exist in reverse format showing No. 1421 as he centre block of nine. Such panes were prepared for inclusion n the Eminent Women portfolio which was jointly produced by Note Printing Australia and Australia Post. Examples from the ortfolio were numbered in red or black with unnumbered panes lso available by mail order.

519 Ornithocheirus **520** "Goodwill"

(Des P. Trusler and Sue Passmore)

1993 (1 Oct). *Prehistoric Animals. T* **519** *and similar multicoloured designs. (a) Litho McPherson's Ptg Group, Mulgrave. Phosphorised paper. P* 14×14½ *(Nos.* 1423, 1427*) or* 14½×14 *(Nos.* 1424/6, 1428*).*

1423 45 c. Type **519** 60 50
1424 45 c. Leaellynasaura (25×30 *mm*) 60 50
1425 45 c. Timimus (26×33 *mm*) 60 50
1426 45 c. Allosaurus (26×33 *mm*) 60 50
1427 75 c. Muttaburrasaurus (30×50 *mm*) .. 1·00 90
1428 $1.05, Minmi (50×30 *mm*) .. .. .. 1·50 1·50
1423/8 .. .. *Set of* 6 4·50 4·00
MS1429 166×73 mm. Nos. 1423/8. P 14½ .. 5·50 6·50

(b) Litho Printset Cambec Pty Ltd. Self-adhesive. Phosphor background. P 11½.

1430 45 c. Type **519** 65 75
a. Booklet pane. Nos. 1430/1, each × 5 6·00
1431 45 c. Leaellynasaura (25×30 *mm*) 65 75

No. **MS**1429 exists overprinted with the logos of "Bangkok '93" or Sydney Stamp and Coin Fair, 1993, for sale at these exhibitions.

Nos. 1430/1 occur either in rolls of 100 and 200, on which the surplus self-adhesive paper around each stamp was removed, or in $4.50 booklets, containing No. 1430a, on which the surplus paper was retained.

The phosphor on both rolls and booklets, which shows pink under U.V. light, covers much of the background of each design.

(Des Sandra Harman. Litho McPherson's Ptg Group, Mulgrave)

1993 (1 Nov). *Christmas. T* **520** *and similar vert designs. Multicoloured. P* 14½×14.

1432 40 c. Type **520** 50 45
a. Booklet pane. No. 1432×20 .. .. 8·50
1433 45 c. "Joy" 55 45
1434 $1 "Peace" .. .. 1·90 1·60
1432/4 .. .. *Set of* 3 2·75 2·25

The horizontal edges of booklet pane No. 1432a are imperforate and there are margins at right and left.

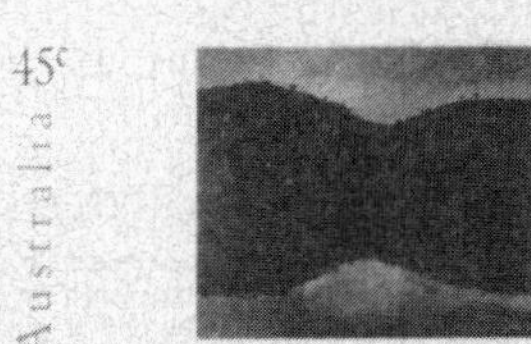

521 "Shoalhaven River Bank – Dawn" (Arthur Boyd)

(Des Lynette Brown. Litho McPherson's Ptg Group, Mulgrave)

1994 (13 Jan). *Australia Day. Landscape Paintings. T* **521** *and similar multicoloured designs. P* 14×14½ *($2) or* 14½×14 *(others).*

1435 45 c. Type **521** 60 45
1436 85 c. "Wimmera" (Sir Sidney Nolan) .. 1·40 1·40
1437 $1.05, "Lagoon, Wimmera" (Nolan) .. 1·60 1·60
1438 $2 "White Cockatoos with Flame Trees" (Boyd) *(vert)* .. .. 2·50 2·50
1435/8 .. .. *Set of* 4 5·50 5·50

522 Teaching Lifesaving Techniques **523** Rose

(Des O. Schmidinger, Christine Stead and Lynette Brown. Litho Printset Cambec Pty Ltd)

1994 (20 Jan). *Centenary of Organised Life Saving in Australia. T* **522** *and similar horiz designs. Multicoloured.*

(a) Phosphorised paper. P 14×14½.

1439 45 c. Type **522** 60 45
1440 45 c. Lifeguard on watch 60 45
1441 95 c. Lifeguard team .. .. 1·25 1·40
1442 $1.20, Lifeguards on surf boards .. 1·60 1·75
1439/42 .. .. *Set of* 4 3·75 3·75

(b) Self-adhesive. Phosphor frame. P 11½.

1443 45 c. Type **522** .. .. 65 1·00
a. Booklet pane. Nos. 1443/4, each × 5 6·00
1444 45 c. Lifeguard on watch .. .. 65 1·00

Nos. 1443/4 occur either in rolls of 100, on which the surplus self-adhesive paper around each stamp was removed, or in $4.50 booklets containing No. 1443a, on which the surplus paper was retained.

The phosphor on the rolls and booklets, which shows pink under U.V. light, extends onto the left or right corner of the centre designs.

(Des Sandra Harman. Litho McPherson's Ptg Group, Mulgrave)

1994 (3 Feb). *Greetings Stamps. Flower photographs by Lariane Fonseca. T* **523** *and similar vert designs. Multicoloured. P* 14½×14.

1445 45 c. Type **523** 40 45
1446 45 c. Tulips 40 45
a. Horiz pair. Nos. 1446/7 .. .. .. 80 90
b. Booklet pane. Nos. 1446/7 each × 5 4·50
1447 45 c. Poppies 40 45
1445/7 .. .. *Set of* 3 1·10 1·25

Nos. 1446/7 were printed together, *se-tenant*, in horizontal pairs throughout the sheet.

The vertical edges of booklet pane No. 1446b are imperforate, producing stamps imperforate at left (No. 1446) or right (No. 1447), and there are margins at top and bottom.

524 Bridge and National Flags **525** "Queen Elizabeth II" (Sir William Dargie)

(Des W. Crossett and Sue Passmore. Litho McPherson's Ptg Group, Mulgrave)

1994 (8 Apr). *Opening of Friendship Bridge between Thailand and Laos. P* 14½×14.

1448 **524** 95 c. multicoloured .. .. 1·25 1·40

(Des Sue Passmore. Litho Leigh-Mardon Ltd, Melbourne)

1994 (8 Apr). *Queen Elizabeth II's Birthday. P* 14½.

1449 **525** 45 c. multicoloured 70 70

526 "Family in Field" (Bobbie-Lea Blackmore) **527** Suffragettes

(Des Lynette Brown. Litho Leigh-Mardon Ltd, Melbourne)

1994 (14 Apr). *International Year of the Family. Children's Paintings. T* **526** *and similar horiz designs. Multicoloured. P* 14½.

1450 45 c. Type **526** 55 45
1451 75 c. "Family on Beach" (Kathryn Teoh) 1·00 1·10
1452 $1 "Family around Fire" (Maree McCarthy) .. .. 1·25 1·50
1450/2 .. .. *Set of* 3 2·50 2·75

Two types of inscr on Nos. 1453/5:
Type I. "KANGAROO" 9 mm long with spaces between letters.
Type II. "KANGAROO" 7 mm long without spaces between letters.

(Des Janet Boschen)

1994 (12 May)–**97**. *Australian Wildlife (2nd series). Horiz designs as T* **505**. *Multicoloured. (a) Litho Leigh-Mardon Ltd, Melbourne (Nos.* 1453/8*) or SNP Cambec (Nos.* 1453b/8b, 1453c/8c*). Phosphorised paper. P* 14×14½.

1453 45 c. Kangaroo (pale orange inscr) (I) .. 60 50
a. Block of 6. Nos. 1453/8 .. .. 3·25
b. Type II. Orange-brown inscr (1.96) 90 90
ba. Block of 6. Nos. 1453b/8b .. .. 4·75
c. Type II. Pale orange inscr (8.97) .. 90 90
ca. Block of 6. Nos. 1453c/5c and 1456/8 4·25
1454 45 c. Female kangaroo with young (pale orange inscr) (I) 60 50
b. Type II. Orange-brown inscr (1.96) 90 90
c. Type II. Pale orange inscr (8.97) .. 90 90
1455 45 c. Two kangaroos (pale orange inscr) (I) 60 50
b. Type II. Orange-brown inscr (1.96) 90 90
c. Type II. Pale orange inscr (8.97) .. 90 90
1456 45 c. Family of koalas on branch (pale orange inscr) 60 50
b. Orange-brown inscr (1.96) 90 90
1457 45 c. Koala on ground (pale orange inscr) 60 50
b. Orange-brown inscr (1.96) 90 90
1458 45 c. Koala asleep in tree (pale orange inscr) 60 50
b. Orange-brown inscr (1.96) 90 90
1453/8 .. .. *Set of* 6 3·25 3·00

(b) Litho Printset Cambec Pty Ltd. Self-adhesive. Phosphor frame. P 11½

1459 45 c. Kangaroo 60 70
a. Booklet pane. Nos. 1459/60×2, 1461, 1462/3×2 and 1464 .. .. 5·50
ab. Imperf pane .. ..
b. Sheetlet of 5. Nos. 1459 and 1461/4 (15.2.95) .. .. 4·50
1460 45 c. Female kangaroo with young 60 70
1461 45 c. Two kangaroos 60 70
1462 45 c. Family of koalas on branch 60 70
1463 45 c. Koala on ground 60 70
1464 45 c. Koala asleep in tree 60 70
1459/64 .. .. *Set of* 6 3·25 3·75

(c) *Typo Pemara Labels, Victoria. Self-adhesive. Phosphor frame. P* 11½.

1464*a* 45 c. Kangaroo (5.95) .. .. .. 5·50 5·50
ap. Phosphorised mesh (9.95) 80 90
1464*b* 45 c. Female kangaroo with young (5.95) 5·50 5·50
bp. Phosphorised mesh (9.95) 80 90
1464*c* 45 c. Two kangaroos (5.95) .. .. 5·50 5·50
cp. Phosphorised mesh (9.95) 80 90
1464*d* 45 c. Family of koalas on branch (5.95) 5·50 5·50
dp. Phosphorised mesh (9.95) 80 90
1464*e* 45 c. Koala on ground (5.95) .. .. 5·50 5·50
ep. Phosphorised mesh (9.95) 80 90
1464*f* 45 c. Koala asleep in tree (5.95) .. 5·50 5·50
fp. Phosphorised mesh (9.95) 80 90
1464*a/f* .. .. *Set of* 6 30·00 30·00
1464ap/fp .. .. .. *Set of* 6 4·25 4·75

Nos. 1453/8 were printed together, *se-tenant*, in sheets of 100 (2 panes of 50 5×10) each pane providing five blocks of 6 and twenty single stamps. They also exist as a *se-tenant* sheetlet of 6 with inscribed margins produced for sale at "Philakorea '94" Stamp Exhibition, Seoul.

The colour of the "AUSTRALIA" inscription and face value is repeated on a horizontal band at the foot of each design.

Nos. 1453b/8b are from the 2 koala printing and Nos. 1453c/5c from the 3 koala printing. Both show "1996" smaller than on the original printing.

Nos. 1459/64 occur either in rolls of 100, rolls of 200, booklets of 10 or sheetlets of 5. On all rolls the surplus self-adhesive paper around each stamp was removed, but this was retained on booklet pane No. 1459a and sheetlet No. 1459b.

The phosphor on Nos. 1459/64 and Nos. 1464*a/f*, which shows pink under U.V. light, extends from bars at top and bottom onto sections of the centre designs. On Nos. 1464ap/fp, which come from the 3 koala, 4 koala, 1 kangaroo and 1 kangaroo + 2 koala printings, the phosphor extends over the same area; but is broken up by a mesh pattern into small squares or diamonds.

The Pemara printings were produced in rolls only.

Counter-printed labels, as described beneath No. 1416, in designs as Nos. 1453/64, but 40×28 mm, were issued on 17 November 1994. Possible face values for these labels ranged from 45 c. to $100. Machines issuing the labels were located at National Philatelic Centre, Melbourne ("NPC"), Canberra Parliament House post office ("CPH"), Royal Exchange ("REX") and Haymarket ("HAYMKT") post offices, Sydney, and at the General Post Offices in Adelaide ("ADEL GPO"), Brisbane ("BRIS GPO"), Melbourne ("MELB GPO"), Perth ("PERTH GPO") (from 26 June 1995) and Bathurst Street, Hobart ("BTH ST HBT") (from 16 October 1995). Exhibition labels were issued at "AEROPEX 94", "AUSTRAPEX 95", "SINGAPORE 95", "SYDNEY 95", "CAPEX 96" and "HONG KONG 97".

Very similar labels were produced from experimental "Weigh & Pay" machines used in the Perth area from May 1996 onwards. Those from Perth itself are inscribed "GPO PERTH" or "PERTH GPO", but labels from other post offices are without inscription.

For Nos. 1453b, 1454b and 1455b in miniature sheet for "CHINA '96" see No. **MS**1638.

(Des Maire Smith. Litho McPherson's Ptg Group, Mulgrave)

1994 (9 June). *Centenary of Women's Emancipation in South Australia. P* 14×14½.
1465 **527** 45 c. multicoloured 60 60

528 Bunyip from Aboriginal Legend

529 "Robert Menzies" (Sir Ivor Hele)

(Des J. Morrison (No. 1466), D. Lancashire (No. 1467), R. Brooks (No. 1468), Marg Towt (No. 1470). Litho Leigh-Mardon Ltd, Melbourne)

1994 (14 July). *The Bunyip (mythological monster). T* **528** *and similar square designs. Multicoloured. P* 14½.
1466 45 c. Type **528** 60 60
a. Pair. Nos. 1466/7 .. .. .. 1·10 1·10
1467 45 c. Nature spirit bunyip 60 60
1468 90 c. "The Bunyip of Berkeley's Creek" (book illustration) .. .. 1·50 1·50
1469 $1.35, Bunyip as natural history .. 1·90 1·90
1466/9 .. .. *Set of* 4 4·00 4·00

Nos. 1466/7 were printed together, *se-tenant*, in horizontal or vertical pairs throughout the sheet.

(Des FHA Design. Litho McPherson's Ptg Group, Mulgrave)

1994 (11 Aug). *Wartime Prime Ministers. T* **529** *and similar horiz designs. Multicoloured. P* 14×14½.
1470 45 c. Type **529** 85 85
a. Horiz strip of 5. Nos. 1470/4 .. 3·75
1471 45 c. "Arthur Fadden" (William Dargie) .. 85 85
1472 45 c. "John Curtin" (Anthony Dattilo-Rubbo) 85 85
1473 45 c. "Francis Forde" (Joshua Smith) .. 85 85
1474 45 c. "Joseph Chifley" (A. D. Colquhoun) .. 85 85
1470/4 .. .. *Set of* 5 3·75 3·75

Nos. 1470/4 were printed together, *se-tenant*, in horizontal strips of 5 throughout the sheet.

NEW INFORMATION

The editor is always interested to correspond with people who have new information that will improve or correct the Catalogue.

530 Lawrence Hargrave and Box Kites

531 Scarlet Macaw

(Des Janet Boschen. Eng C. Slania. Recess Royal Swedish Stamp Ptg Office, Stockholm)

1994 (29 Aug). *Aviation Pioneers. T* **530** *and similar vert designs. P* 12½.
1475 45 c. red-brown, blackish olive & cinnamon 70 45
1476 45 c. red-brown, deep carmine and lavender 70 45
1477 $1.35, red-brown, dp violet & greenish bl 2·25 2·50
1478 $1.80, red-brown, slate-green & sage-grn 2·50 2·75
1475/8 .. .. *Set of* 4 5·50 5·50

Designs:—No. 1475, Type **530**; No. 1476, Ross and Keith Smith with Vickers Vimy (first England-Australia flight); No. 1477, Ivor McIntyre, Stanley Goble and Fairey IIID seaplane (first aerial circumnavigation of Australia); No. 1478, Freda Thompson and De Havilland Moth Major *Christopher Robin* (first Australian woman to fly solo from England to Australia).

No. 1475 also exists as a pane of 25 numbered in red or black from a limited issue Hargrave portfolio.

Two types of phosphor on self-adhesive Type **531**;
Type I. Leaf below second tail feather covered by phosphor
Type II. Leaf without phosphor

(Des G. Cook)

1994 (28 Sept). *Australian Zoos. Endangered Species. T* **531** *and similar multicoloured designs. (a) Litho McPherson's Ptg Group, Mulgrave. Phosphorised paper. P* 14×14½ (*No.* 1479) *or* 14½×14 (*others*).
1479 45 c. Type **531** 65 55
1480 45 c. Cheetah (25×30 *mm*) 65 55
1481 45 c. Orang-Utan (26×37 *mm*) 65 55
1482 45 c. Fijian Crested Iguana (26×37 *mm*) 65 55
1483 $1 Asian Elephants (49×28 *mm*) .. 1·75 1·60
1479/83 .. .. *Set of* 5 4·00 3·50
MS1484 166×73 mm. Nos. 1479/83. P 14½ .. 4·00 4·50

(*b*) *Litho Printset Cambec Pty Ltd. Self-adhesive. Phosphor frame. P* 11½
1485 45 c. Type **531** (I) .. .. 1·50 1·50
a. Type II .. .. 1·50 1·50
b. Booklet pane. Nos. 1485×4, 1485a×2 and 1486×4 .. .. 12·00
1486 45 c. Cheetah .. .. 1·50 1·50

No. **MS**1484 exists overprinted with the logos of the Sydney Stamp and Coin Fair, Brisbane Stamp and Coin Fair, "Stampshow Melbourne '94" or "Swanpex '94" (including one with overprint inverted) for sale at these Australian exhibitions.

Nos. 1485/6 occur in $4.50 booklets, containing No. 1485b.

The phosphor on the booklets, which shows pink under U.V. light, appears as an irregular frame to each design.

532 "Madonna and Child" (detail, "The Adoration of the Magi") (Giovanni Toscani)

533 Yachts outside Sydney Harbour

(Des Lisa Christenson. Litho McPherson's Ptg Group, Mulgrave)

1994 (31 Oct). *Christmas. T* **532** *and similar designs showing "The Adoration of the Magi" by Giovanni Toscani. Multicoloured. P* 14½×14 (40 *c.*, $1.80) *or* 14×14½ (45 *c.*, $1).
1487 40 c. Type **532** 60 40
a. Booklet pane. No. 1487×20 .. 8·50
1488 45 c. "Wise Man and Horse" (detail) (*horiz*) 60 45
1489 $1 "Wise Man and St. Joseph" (detail) (*horiz*) .. .. 1·50 1·40
1490 $1.80, Complete painting (49×29 *mm*) 2·00 2·50
1487/90 .. .. *Set of* 4 4·25 4·25

The vertical edges of booklet pane No. 1487a are imperforate and there are margins at top and bottom.

(Des J. Spatchurst)

1994 (31 Oct). *50th Sydney to Hobart Yacht Race. T* **533** *and similar horiz design. (a) Litho Leigh-Mardon Ltd, Melbourne. Phosphorised paper. P* 14½.
1491 45 c. Type **533** 50 55
a. Pair. Nos. 1491/2 .. .. .. 1·00 1·10
1492 45 c. Yachts passing Tasmania coastline 50 55

(*b*) *Litho Printset Cambec Pty Ltd. Self-adhesive. Phosphor frame. P* 11½.
1493 45 c. Type **533** (31×20 *mm*) 65 70
1494 45 c. Yachts passing Tasmania coastline (31×20 *mm*) 65 70

Nos. 1491/2 were printed together, *se-tenant*, in horizontal and vertical pairs throughout the sheet.

Nos. 1493/4 occur in rolls of 100. The phosphor, which shows pink under U.V. light, appears as an irregular frame to each design.

534 Symbolic Kangaroo

535 "Back Verandah" (Russell Drysdale)

(Des Sandra Harman and J. Passmore. Typo (gold die-stampe[d]) Pemara Labels)

1994 (2 Nov)–**96**. *Self-adhesive. Automatic Cash Machin[e] Stamps. Phosphorised paper. P* 16½.
1495 **534** 45 c. gold, emerald and dull blue-green 50 5
a. Pane of 20. Nos. 1495/1502 .. 9·00
ab. Pane of 20. Nos. 1495/7, 1498a, 1499/1501 and 1502a (11.4.96) 9·00
1496 45 c. gold, emerald and cobalt .. 50 5
1497 45 c. gold, emerald and bright lilac .. 50 5
1498 45 c. gold, emerald and apple-green (grey-brown dots in background) 50 5
a. Emerald dots in background (11.4.96) 50 5
1499 45 c. gold, emerald & pale yellow-green 50 5
1500 45 c. gold, emerald and pink 50 5
1501 45 c. gold, emerald and rose 50 5
1502 45 c. gold, emerald and yellow-ochre (grey-brown dots in background) 50 5
a. Emerald dots in background (11.4.96) 50 5
1495/1502 .. .. .. *Set of* 8 4·00 4·0

Nos. 1495/1502 were issued in panes of 20 from automat[ic] cash machines at Advance Bank branches in Australian Capit[al] Territory, New South Wales and Queensland, and from t[he] National Philatelic Centre, Melbourne. The stamps wer[e] arranged, *tête-bêche*, in horizontal rows of 3 or 4 with the pan[e] containing two examples of Nos. 1495, 1497, 1499 and 1501 an[d] three of Nos. 1496, 1498, 1500 and 1502. As originally issued th[e] backing paper carried advertising for the Advance Bank. [A] second version advertising Postpak packaging was introduce[d] on 11 April 1996 and contained Nos. 1495/7, 1498a, 1499/150[1] and 1502a.

St. George Bank took over Advance Bank on 1 April 1998 an[d] the sale of Nos. 1495/1502 through automatic cash machine[s] was discontinued from 11 September 1998.

(Des Allnutt Graphics. Litho Leigh-Mardon Ltd, Melbourne)

1995 (12 Jan). *Australia Day. Paintings. T* **535** *and simil[ar] horiz designs. Multicoloured. P* 15×14½.
1503 45 c. Type **535** 50 4
1504 45 c. "Skull Springs Country" (Guy Grey-Smith) 50 4
1505 $1.05, "Outcamp" (Robert Juniper) .. 1·40 1·
1506 $1.20, "Kite Flying" (Ian Fairweather) 1·50 1·
1503/6 .. .. *Set of* 4 3·50 3·

536 Red Heart and Rose

537 *Endeavour* Replica at Sea

(Des Kim Roberts. Litho Printset Cambec Pty Ltd, (gold di[e]-stamped Avon Graphics))

1995 (30 Jan). *St. Valentine's Day. T* **536** *and similar ve[rt] designs. Multicoloured. P* 14½×14.
1507 45 c. Type **536** 45 5
a. Horiz strip of 5. Nos. 1507/8×2 and 1509 .. .. 2·10
1508 45 c. Gold and red heart with rose .. 45 5
1509 45 c. Gold heart and roses 45 5
1507/9 .. .. *Set of* 3 1·25 1·

Nos. 1507/9 were printed together, *se-tenant*, in horizont[al] strips of 5 throughout the sheet each containing two examples [of] Nos. 1507/8 and one of No. 1509.

(Des Michelle Gauci. Litho McPherson's Ptg Group, Mulgrave)

1995 (9 Feb). *Completion of* Endeavour *Replica. T* **537** *an[d] similar horiz design. Multicoloured. (a) Sheet stamps,* 38×[2?] *mm. P* 14×14½.
1510 45 c. Type **537** 75 7
a. Pair. Nos. 1510/11 .. .. .. 1·50 1·5
1511 45 c. "Captain Cook's Endeavour" (detail) (Oswald Brett) 75 7

(*b*) *Booklet stamps,* 44×26 *mm. P* 14×*imperf*
1512 20 c. Type **537** .. .. 1·00 1·2
a. Booklet pane. Nos. 1512 and 1513×4 2·50
1513 45 c. As No. 1511 .. .. .. 45 5

Nos. 1510/11 are printed together, *se-tenant*, in horizontal an[d] vertical pairs throughout the sheet.

The 20 c. value was only available from $2 stamp booklet[s]. The vertical edges of pane No. 1512a are imperforate and the[re] are margins at top and bottom.

538 Coalport Plate and Bracket Clock, Old Government House, Parramatta

es Janet Boschen. Recess Note Ptg Branch, Reserve Bank of Australia)

95 (16 Mar). *50th Anniv of Australian National Trusts. T* **538** *and similar horiz designs. P* 14×14½.

14 45 c. deep violet-blue and purple-brown .. 45 45
a. Pair. Nos. 1514/15 .. .. 90 90
15 45 c. deep blue-green and purple-brown .. 45 45
16 $1 brown-red and royal blue .. .. 1·00 95
17 $2 blackish olive and royal blue .. 1·90 1·90
14/17 .. .. *Set of* 4 3·50 3·75

Designs:—No. 1515, Steiner doll and Italian-style chair, ers House, Adelaide; No. 1516, "Advance Australia" teapot d parian-ware statuette, Victoria; No. 1517, Silver bowl and na urn, Old Observatory, Perth.

Nos. 1514/15 were printed together, *se-tenant*, in horizontal d vertical pairs throughout the sheet.

539 Light Opal

es Sue Passmore. Litho Printset Cambec Pty Ltd (exelgrams by Avon Graphics))

995 (5 Apr). *Opals. T* **539** *and similar horiz design. Multicoloured. P* 14½×14.

518 $1.20, Type **539** .. .. 1·75 1·25
519 $2.50, Black opal .. .. 3·25 3·25

The opals depicted on Nos. 1518/19 are produced as exelgrams olographic printing on an ultra thin plastic film) embossed to the stamps.

540 Queen Elizabeth II at Gala Concert, 1992

541 Sir Edward Dunlop and P.O.W. Association Badge

es Nuttshell Graphics. Litho Leigh-Mardon Ltd, Melbourne)

95 (20 Apr). *Queen Elizabeth II's Birthday. P* 14½.

520 **540** 45 c. multicoloured 65 75

wo types of phosphor on Nos. 1527/8:
Type I. Phosphor at right ends level with hat or cap (coils)
Type II. Phosphor at right extends to the ear (No. 1527a) or shoulder (No. 1528a) (booklets)

(Des Sue Passmore)

95 (20 Apr). *Australian Second World War Heroes (1st series). T* **541** *and similar vert designs. Multicoloured. (a) Litho McPherson's Ptg Group, Mulgrave. Phosphorised paper. P* 14½×14.

521 45 c. Type **541** 60 60
a. Block of 4. Nos. 1521/4 .. .. 2·25
522 45 c. Mrs. Jessie Vasey and War Widows' Guild badge 60 60
523 45 c. Sgt. Tom Derrick and Victoria Cross 60 60
524 45 c. Flt. Sgt. Rawdon Middleton and Victoria Cross 60 60
521/4 .. .. *Set of* 4 2·25 2·25

(*b*) *Litho Printset Cambec Pty Ltd. Self-adhesive. Designs* 21×32½ *mm. Phosphor frame. P* 11½

525 45 c. Type **541** (I) 60 70
a. Booklet pane. Nos. 1525×4 and 1526, 1527a/8a, each × 2 .. .. .. 6·50
526 45 c. Mrs. Jessie Vasey and War Widows' Guild badge 70 90
527 45 c. Sgt. Tom Derrick and Victoria Cross (I) 70 90
a. Type II .. .. 90 1·00
528 45 c. Flt. Sgt. Rawdon Middleton and Victoria Cross (I) 70 90
a. Type II .. .. 90 1·00
525/8 .. .. *Set of* 4 2·40 3·00

Nos. 1521/4 were printed together, *se-tenant*, in sheets of 100 2 panes of 50 10×5) each pane providing ten blocks of 4 and ten ngle stamps.

Nos. 1525/8 occur either in rolls of 100, on which the surplus self-adhesive paper around each stamp was removed, or in $4.50 booklets, containing No. 1525a, on which the surplus paper was retained.

The phosphor, which shows pink under U.V. light, covers the designs, with the exception of the portraits and emblems, and the backing paper on both the booklets and the rolls.

See also Nos. 1545/8

542 Children and Globe of Flags

543 *The Story of the Kelly Gang*

(Des FHA Design. Litho McPherson's Ptg Group, Mulgrave)

1995 (11 May). *50th Anniv of United Nations. P* 14×14½.

1529 **542** 45 c. multicoloured 75 75

No. 1529 was printed in sheets with *se-tenant* 10×26 *mm* labels. In rows 1, 3, 5, 7 and 9 these labels occur on the right of each stamp and commemorate either the 50th anniversary or the F.A.O. alternately. On rows 2, 4, 6, 8 and 10 the labels occur on the left of each stamp and are inscribed for either U.N.E.S.C.O. or U.N.I.C.E.F.

(Des J. Spatchurst)

1995 (8 June). *Centenary of Cinema. T* **543** *and similar vert designs showing scenes from films. Multicoloured. (a) Litho McPherson's Ptg Group, Mulgrave. Phosphorised paper. P* 14½×14.

1530 45 c. Type **543** 60 60
a. Horiz strip of 5. Nos. 1530/4 .. 2·75
1531 45 c. *On Our Selection* 60 60
1532 45 c. *Jedda* 60 60
1533 45 c. *Picnic at Hanging Rock* 60 60
1534 45 c. *Strictly Ballroom* 60 60
1530/4 .. .. *Set of* 5 2·75 2·75

(*b*) *Litho Printset Cambec Pty Ltd. Self-adhesive. Designs* 19×30½ *mm. Phosphor frame. P* 11½.

1535 45 c. Type **543** 60 60
a. Booklet pane. Nos. 1535/9 each × 2 5·50
1536 45 c. *On Our Selection* 60 60
1537 45 c. *Jedda* 60 60
1538 45 c. *Picnic at Hanging Rock* 60 60
1539 45 c. *Strictly Ballroom* 60 60
1535/9 .. .. *Set of* 5 2·75 2·75

Nos. 1530/4 were printed together, *se-tenant*, in horizontal strips of 5 throughout the sheet.

Nos. 1535/9 occur either in rolls of 100, on which the surplus self-adhesive paper around each stamp was removed, or in $4.50 booklets, containing No. 1535a, on which the surplus paper was retained.

544 Man in Wheelchair flying Kite

545 Koala with Cub

(Des Tracie Grimwood. Litho McPherson's Ptg Group, Mulgrave)

1995 (13 July). *People with Disabilities. T* **544** *and similar vert design. Multicoloured. P* 14½×14.

1540 45 c. Type **544** 65 65
a. Horiz pair. Nos. 1540/1 .. .. 1·25 1·25
1541 45 c. Blind woman playing violin .. 65 65

Nos. 1540/1 were printed together, *se-tenant*, in horizontal pairs throughout the sheet.

(Adapted L. Dolan. Recess Note Ptg Branch, Reserve Bank of Australia)

1995 (10 Aug). *50th Anniv of Peace in the Pacific. Designs as 1946 Victory Commemoration (Nos. 213/15) redrawn with new face values. P* 14×14½ *(horiz) or* 14½×14 *(vert).*

1542 **53** 45 c. scarlet 75 60
1543 – 45 c. green 75 60
1544 – $1.50, blue .. .. 1·90 2·25
1542/4 .. .. *Set of* 3 3·00 3·00

Designs: *Vert*—No. 1543, Angel. *Horiz*—No. 1544, Flag and dove.

(Des Sue Passmore. Litho McPherson's Ptg Group, Mulgrave)

1995 (10 Aug). *Australian Second World War Heroes (2nd series). Vert designs as T* **541**. *Multicoloured. P* 14½×14.

1545 45 c. Sister Ellen Savage and George Medal 60 60
a. Block of 4. Nos. 1545/8 .. .. 2·25
1546 45 c. Chief Petty Officer Percy Collins and Distinguished Service Medal and Bar 60 60
1547 45 c. Lt-Comm. Leon Goldsworthy and George Cross 60 60
1548 45 c. Warrant Officer Len Waters and R.A.A.F. wings 60 60
1545/8 .. .. *Set of* 4 2·25 2·25

Nos. 1545/8 were printed together, *se-tenant*, in sheets of 100 (2 panes of 50 10×5) each pane providing ten blocks of 4 and ten single stamps.

PRINTERS. Leigh-Mardon Ltd ceased printing Australian stamps in May 1995. On 10 July 1995 Singapore National Printer Pty Ltd took over Printset Cambec and the firm was then known as SNP Cambec.

(Des Xu Yanbo and Lisa Christensen. Litho SNP Cambec (Nos. 1549/50) or Postage Stamp Ptg Works, Peking (No. **MS**1551))

1995 (1 Sept). *Australia–China Joint Issue. Endangered Species. T* **545** *and similar horiz design. Multicoloured. P* 14½×14.

1549 45 c. Type **545** 70 90
a. Pair. Nos. 1549/50 .. .. .. 1·40 1·75
1550 45 c. Giant Panda with cubs 70 90
MS1551 Two sheets, each 106×70 mm. (a) No. 1549. (b) No. 1550. P 11×11½ .. *Set of* 2 *sheets* 1·60 1·60

Nos. 1549/50 were printed together, *se-tenant*, in horizontal and vertical pairs throughout the sheet.

No. **MS**1551a also exists overprinted "AUSTRALIAN STAMP EXHIBITION" and No. **MS**1551b "INTERNATIONAL STAMP & COIN EXPO BEIJING" for sale at these exhibitions in China.

546 Father Joseph Slattery, Thomas Lyle and Walter Filmer (Radiology)

547 Flatback Turtle

(Des O. Schmidinger, Christine Stead and Melinda Whitechurch. Litho McPherson's Ptg Group, Mulgrave)

1995 (7 Sept). *Medical Scientists. T* **546** *and similar multicoloured designs. P* 14×14½ *(horiz) or* 14½×14 *(vert).*

1552 45 c. Type **546** 60 70
a. Pair. Nos. 1552/3 .. .. .. 1·10 1·40
1553 45 c. Dame Jean Macnamara and Sir Macfarlane Burnet (viruses) .. 60 70
1554 45 c. Fred Hollows (ophthalmology) (*vert*) 60 60
1555 $2.50, Sir Howard Florey (antibiotics) (*vert*) .. .. 3·75 4·50
1552/5 .. .. *Set of* 4 5·00 6·00

Nos. 1552/3 were printed together, *se-tenant*, in horizontal and vertical pairs throughout the sheet.

It was intended that 45 c. gutter blocks for philatelic sale would be produced in special sheets, but these were withdrawn just prior to issue when it was found that the gutter pairs contained two examples of the same design, instead of one of each.

No. 1555 also exists as a pane of 10 numbered in red or black from a limited issue Howard Florey portfolio.

Two types of phosphor on self-adhesive Type **547**:
Type I. Outcrop at bottom left completely covered by phosphor (coils).
Type II. Only part of outcrop covered by phosphor (booklets)

(Des G. Ryan. Litho SNP Cambec)

1995 (3 Oct). *Marine Life. T* **547** *and similar horiz designs. (a) Phosphorised paper. P* 14×14½.

1556 45 c. Type **547** 55 55
a. Vert pair. Nos. 1556/7 .. .. 1·10 1·10
1557 45 c. Flame Angelfish and Nudibranch .. 55 55
1558 45 c. Potato Grouper ("Potato Cod") and Hump-headed Wrasse ("Maori Wrasse") 55 55
a. Vert pair. Nos. 1558/9 .. .. 1·10 1·10
1559 45 c. Giant Trevally 55 55
1560 45 c. Black Marlin 55 55
a. Vert pair. Nos. 1560/1 .. .. 1·10 1·10
1561 45 c. Mako and Tiger Sharks 55 55
1556/61 .. .. *Set of* 6 3·00 3·00
MS1562 166×73 mm. As Nos. 1556/61, but without lighter frame .. .. .. 3·00 3·00

(*b*) *Self-adhesive. Phosphor frame on three sides. P* 11½

1563 45 c. Type **547** (I) 50 65
a. Type II 50 65
ab. Booklet pane Nos. 1563a/6, each × 2, and Nos. 1567/8 .. .. .. 4·25
1564 45 c. Flame Angelfish and Nudibranch .. 50 65
1565 45 c. Potato Cod and Maori Wrasse .. 50 65
1566 45 c. Giant Trevally 50 65
1567 45 c. Black Marlin 50 65
1568 45 c. Mako and Tiger Sharks 50 65
1563/8 .. .. *Set of* 6 2·75 3·50

Nos. 1556/7, 1558/9 and 1560/1 were printed together, *se-tenant*, in vertical pairs throughout the sheets. Parts of No. **MS**1562 are printed in luminescent ink.

No. **MS**1562 also exists overprinted with the logos of the Adelaide Stamp and Collectables Fair, Sydney Centrepoint 95 National Stamp Exhibition, Brisbane Stamp Show, Melbourne Stamp and Coin Fair and "Swanpex WA", Perth, for sale at these Australian exhibitions.

Nos. 1563/8 occur either in rolls of 100, on which the surplus self-adhesive paper around each stamp was removed, or in $4.50 booklets, containing No. 1563ab, on which the surplus paper was retained.

The phosphor on both rolls and booklets shows pink under U.V. light.

MINIMUM PRICE

The minimum price quote is 10p which represents a handling charge rather than a basis for valuing common stamps. For further notes about prices see introductory pages.

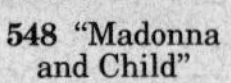

548 "Madonna and Child" **549** "West Australian Banksia" (Margaret Preston)

(Des Dianne Cook. Litho SNP Cambec)

1995 (1 Nov). *Christmas. Stained-glass Windows from Our Lady Help of Christians Church, Melbourne. T* **548** *and similar vert designs. (a) Phosphorised paper. P* 14½×14.
1569 40 c. Type **548** 45 45
1570 45 c. "Angel carrying the Gloria banner" 45 45
1571 $1 "Rejoicing Angels" .. .. .. 1·10 1·50
1569/71 .. .. *Set of* 3 1·75 2·25

(*b*) *Self-adhesive. Phosphor frame. P* 11½
1572 40 c. Type **548** 50 45
a. Booklet pane. No. 1572×20 .. 8·50

No. 1572, on which the phosphor shows pink under U.V. light, was only issued in $8 booklets, on which the surplus self-adhesive paper was retained.

(Des Susan Horvath. Litho McPherson's Ptg Group, Mulgrave)

1996 (16 Jan). *Australia Day. Paintings. T* **549** *and similar multicoloured designs. P* 14×14½ (*vert*) *or* 14½×14 (*horiz*).
1573 45 c. Type **549** 60 45
1574 85 c. "The Babe is Wise" (Lina Bryans) .. 1·40 1·25
1575 $1 "The Bridge in Curve" (Grace Cossington Smith) (*horiz*) .. .. 1·50 1·25
1576 $1.20, "Beach Umbrellas" (Vida Lahey) (*horiz*) .. .. 1·75 1·50
1573/6 .. .. *Set of* 4 4·75 4·00

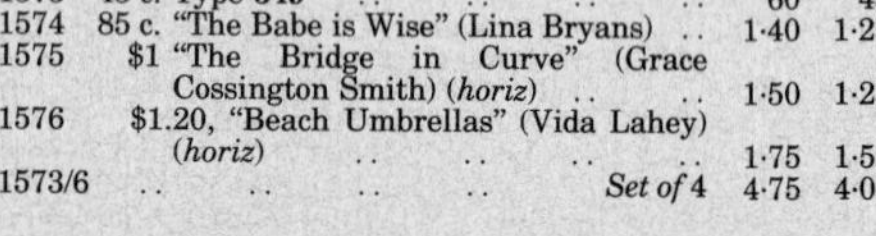

550 Gold Heart and Rose

551 Bristol Type 156 Beaufighter and Curtiss P-40E Kittyhawk I

(Des Kim Roberts and Sandra Harman. Litho SNP Cambec (gold die-stamped Avon Graphics))

1996 (30 Jan). *St. Valentine's Day. P* 14×14½.
1577 **550** 45 c. multicoloured 50 50

(Des Melinda Whitechurch and N. Clifford. Litho SNP Cambec)

1996 (26 Feb). *Military Aviation. T* **551** *and similar horiz designs. Multicoloured. P* 14×14½.
1578 45 c. Type **551** 75 90
a. Block of 4. Nos. 1578/81 .. .. 2·75
1579 45 c. Hawker Sea Fury and Fairey Firefly 75 90
1580 45 c. Bell Kiowa helicopters 75 90
1581 45 c. Government Aircraft Factory Hornets 75 90
1578/81 .. .. *Set of* 4 2·75 3·25

Nos. 1578/81 were printed together, *se-tenant*, in different combinations throughout the pane of 25, giving four blocks of 4 and nine single stamps.

552 Tasmanian Wilderness

553 Australian Spotted Cuscus

(Des Dianne Cook. Litho SNP Cambec)

1996 (14 Mar). *World Heritage Sites (2nd series). T* **552** *and similar horiz designs. Multicoloured. P* 14½×14.
1582 45 c. Type **552** 50 45
1583 75 c. Willandra Lakes 90 90
1584 95 c. Naracoorte Fossil Cave .. .. 1·25 1·25
1585 $1 Lord Howe Island .. .. .. 1·50 1·60
1582/5 .. .. *Set of* 4 3·75 3·75

(Des Rosemary Ganf and Josephine Mure. Litho SNP Cambec)

1996 (22 Mar). *Australia–Indonesia Joint Issue. T* **553** *and similar vert design. Multicoloured. P* 14½×14.
1586 45 c. Type **553** 70 70
a. Horiz pair. Nos. 1586/7 .. .. 1·40 1·40
1587 45 c. Indonesian Bear Cuscus 70 70
MS1588 106×70 mm. Nos. 1586/7 .. .. 1·40 1·40

Nos. 1586/7 were printed together, *se-tenant*, in horizontal pairs throughout the sheet.

No. **MS**1588 also exists overprinted "WORLD PHILATELIC YOUTH EXHIBITION PAMERAN FILATELI REMAJA DUNIA INDONESIA '96" and emblem for sale at this exhibition.

554 Head of Queen Elizabeth II

555 North Melbourne Players

(Des Pendulum Design. Recess and litho Note Ptg Branch, Reserve Bank of Australia and SNP Cambec)

1996 (11 Apr). *Queen Elizabeth II's Birthday. P* 14×14½.
1589 **554** 45 c. multicoloured 55 55

Numbered gutter strips of ten, overprinted to commemorate the 30th anniversary of decimal currency in Australia, come from a limited issue Queen Elizabeth II portfolio.

(Des Rankin Bevers Design and B. Clinton. Litho SNP Cambec)

1996 (23 Apr). *Centenary of Australian Football League. T* **555** *and similar vert designs each showing players from a different team. Multicoloured. (a) Phosphorised paper. P* 14½×14.
1590 45 c. Type **555** 60 65
a. Sheetlet. Nos. 1590/1605 .. 8·75
1591 45 c. Brisbane (red and yellow shirt) .. 60 65
1592 45 c. Sydney (red and white shirt) .. 60 65
1593 45 c. Carlton (black shirt with white emblem) 60 65
1594 45 c. Adelaide (black, red and yellow shirt) 60 65
1595 45 c. Fitzroy (yellow, red and blue shirt) 60 65
1596 45 c. Richmond (black shirt with yellow diagonal stripe) 60 65
1597 45 c. St. Kilda (red, white and black shirt) 60 65
1598 45 c. Melbourne (black shirt with red top) 60 65
1599 45 c. Collingwood (black and white vertical striped shirt) 60 65
1600 45 c. Fremantle (green, red, white and blue shirt) 60 65
1601 45 c. Footscray (blue, white and red shirt) 60 65
1602 45 c. West Coast (deep blue shirt with yellow stripes) 60 65
1603 45 c. Essendon (black shirt with red stripe) 60 65
1604 45 c. Geelong (black and white horizontal striped shirt) 60 65
1605 45 c. Hawthorn (black and yellow vertical striped shirt) 60 65
1590/1605 .. .. .. *Set of* 16 8·75 9·50

(*b*) *Self-adhesive. Phosphor frame at top and left. P* 11½.
1606 45 c. Type **555** 70 75
a. Booklet pane. No. 1606×10 .. 6·00
1607 45 c. Brisbane 70 75
a. Booklet pane. No. 1607×10 .. 6·00
1608 45 c. Sydney 70 75
a. Booklet pane. No. 1608×10 .. 6·00
1609 45 c. Carlton 70 75
a. Booklet pane. No. 1609×10 .. 6·00
1610 45 c. Adelaide 70 75
a. Booklet pane. No. 1610×10 .. 6·00
1611 45 c. Fitzroy 70 75
a. Booklet pane. No. 1611×10 .. 6·00
1612 45 c. Richmond 70 75
a. Booklet pane. No. 1612×10 .. 6·00
1613 45 c. St. Kilda 70 75
a. Booklet pane. No. 1613×10 .. 6·00
1614 45 c. Melbourne 70 75
a. Booklet pane. No. 1614×10 .. 6·00
1615 45 c. Collingwood 70 75
a. Booklet pane. No. 1615×10 .. 6·00
1616 45 c. Fremantle 70 75
a. Booklet pane. No. 1616×10 .. 6·00
1617 45 c. Footscray 70 75
a. Booklet pane. No. 1617×10 .. 6·00
1618 45 c. West Coast 70 75
a. Booklet pane. No. 1618×10 .. 6·00
1619 45 c. Essendon 70 75
a. Booklet pane. No. 1619×10 .. 6·00
1620 45 c. Geelong 70 75
a. Booklet pane. No. 1620×10 .. 6·00
1621 45 c. Hawthorn 70 75
a. Booklet pane. No. 1621×10 .. 6·00
1606/21 .. .. *Set of* 16 10·00 10·50

Nos. 1590/1605 were printed together, *se-tenant*, in sheetlets of 16.

Nos. 1606/21 were only available in $4.50 booklets. The phosphor shows pink under U.V. light.

556 Leadbeater's Possum

557 Edwin Flack (800 and 1500 metres gold medal winner, 1896)

(Des Rankin Bevers Design)

1996 (9 May)–**98**. *Fauna and Flora. T* **556** *and simil multicoloured designs.*

(*a*) *Litho McPherson's Ptg Group, Mulgrave* (5 *c.*, 10 *c.*, $2, $5) *SNP Cambec* (*others*) (*gold on* $10 *die-stamped Av Graphics*). *Phosphorised paper. P* 14½×14 ($10) *or* 14×14 (*others*).
1622 5 c. Type **556** 10
1623 10 c. Powerful Owl 10
1624 20 c. Saltwater Crocodile (10.4.97) .. 15
1625 25 c. Northern Dwarf Tree Frog (10.4.97) 20
1626 45 c. Comb-crested Jacana (2.6.97) .. 35
a. Block of 4. Nos. 1626/9 .. .. 1·40
1627 45 c. Little Kingfisher (2.6.97) 35
1628 45 c. Brolga (2.6.97) 35
1629 45 c. Black-necked Stork ("Jabiru") (2.6.97) 35
1630 $1 *Cressida cressida* (butterfly) (10.4.97) 75
1631 $2 Blackwood Wattle .. .. .. 1·50 1·
1632 $5 Soft Tree Fern and Mountain Ash (30×50 *mm*) .. .. .. 3·75 4·
1633 $10 Kakadu Wetlands (50×30 *mm*) (10.4.97) .. .. 8·75 9·
1622/33 .. .. *Set of* 12 17·50 18·
MS1633*a* 106×70 mm. No. 1633 (10.4.97) .. 8·75 9·

Nos. 1626/9 were printed together, *se-tenant*, in sheets of providing ten blocks of 4 and ten single stamps.

No. **MS**1633*a* was issued in connection with the forthcomi "Australia 99" International Stamp Exhibition. It also exis overprinted with either the "Pacific '97" (San Francisco) "Italia '98" (Milan) logos for sale at these international stan exhibitions.

A further miniature sheet containing Nos. 1628/9 was sold the "International Stamp and Coin Exposition Shanghai 97" a from philatelic outlets.

(*b*) *Self-adhesive. Litho SNP Cambec* (*Nos.* 1634/7) *or Pemar* (*Nos.* 1634d/7d). *Phosphor frame. P* 11½
1634 45 c. Comb-crested Jacana (2.6.97) .. 35
a. Booklet pane. Nos. 1634 and 1636, each × 3, and Nos. 1635 and 1637, each × 2 .. .. 3·50
b. Sheetlet. Nos. 1634 × 2 and 1635/7 1·75
c. Booklet pane. Nos. 1634/7, each × 5 (1.9.98) .. .. 7·50
d. Perf 12½×13 (13.11.97) 35
1635 45 c. Little Kingfisher (2.6.97) 35
d. Perf 12½×13 (13.11.97) 35
1636 45 c. Brolga (2.6.97) 35
d. Perf 12½×13 (13.11.97) 35
1637 45 c. Black-necked Stork (2.6.97) .. 35
d. Perf 12½×13 (13.11.97) 35
1634/7 .. .. *Set of* 4 1·40 1·

Nos. 1634/7 and 1634d/7d were printed in rolls of 100 or 2 (Nos. 1634/7 only) with the surplus paper around each stan removed. Nos. 1634/7 also come in $4.50 and $9 booklets, a also sheetlets of 5, all of which have the surplus paper in plac

The phosphor shows orange-pink under U.V. light a appears as a broken frame around each stamp.

(Des Janet Boschen. Litho McPherson's Ptg Group, Mulgrave

1996 (18 May). *"CHINA '96" 9th Asian International Stan Exhibition, Peking. Sheet* 120×65 *mm, containing No* 1453b, 1454b *and* 1455b. *Multicoloured. P* 14×14½.
MS1638 45 c. Kangaroo; 45 c. Female kangaroo with young; 45 c. Two kangaroos .. .. 1·75 1·

(Des Pendulum Design. Eng L. Dolan. Recess and litho Note P Branch, Reserve Bank of Australia and SNP Cambec)

1996 (6 June). *Centennial Olympic Games and 10th Par lympic Games, Atlanta. T* **557** *and similar horiz design Multicoloured. P* 14×14½.
1639 45 c. Type **557** 70
a. Pair. Nos. 1639/40 .. .. .. 1·40 1·
1640 45 c. Fanny Durack (100 metres freestyle swimming gold medal winner, 1912) 70
1641 $1.05, Wheelchair athletes .. .. 1·60 1·
1639/41 .. .. *Set of* 3 2·75 2·

Nos. 1639/40 were printed together, *se-tenant*, in horizont and vertical pairs throughout the sheet.

558 *Animalia* (Graeme Base)

559 American Bald Eagle, Kangaroo and Olympic Flame

(Des Pendulum Design. Litho SNP Cambec)

1996 (4 July). *50th Anniv of Children's Book Council Awar T* **558** *and similar horiz designs taken from book covers.*

(*a*) *Phosphorised paper. P* 14×14½.
1642 45 c. Type **558** 60
a. Block of 4. Nos. 1642/5 .. .. 2·25
1643 45 c. *Greetings from Sandy Beach* (Bob Graham) 60
1644 45 c. *Who Sank the Boat?* (Pamela Allen) 60
1645 45 c. *John Brown, Rose and the Midnight Cat* (Jenny Wagner, illustrated by Ron Brooks) 60
1642/5 .. .. *Set of* 4 2·25 2·

(*b*) *Self-adhesive. Phosphor frame. P* 11½
1646 45 c. Type **558** 60
a. Booklet pane. Nos. 1646×4 and 1647/9 each × 2 .. .. .. 5·50
1647 45 c. *Greetings from Sandy Beach* (Bob Graham) 60
1648 45 c. *Who Sank the Boat?* (Pamela Allen) 60
1649 45 c. *John Brown, Rose and the Midnight Cat* (Jenny Wagner, illustrated by Ron Brooks) 60
1649/9 .. .. *Set of* 4 2·25 2·

Nos. 1642/5 were printed together, *se-tenant*, in sheets of 50 (2 panes of 25 5×5) providing ten blocks of 4 and ten single stamps.
Nos. 1646/9 occur either in rolls of 100, on which the surplus self-adhesive paper around each stamp was removed, or in $4.50 booklets, containing No. 1646a, on which the surplus paper was retained.
The phosphor on both rolls and booklets shows pink under U.V. light.

(Des C. Ellett. Litho SNP Cambec (gold die-stamped Avon Graphics))

1996 (22 July). *Passing of Olympic Flag to Sydney*. *P* 14×14½.
1650 559 45 c. multicoloured 55 50

560 Margaret Windeyer

561 Pearl

(Des Mad House Design. Litho Canberra Press)

1996 (8 Aug). *Centenary of the National Council of Women*. *T* **560** *and similar vert design*. *P* 14½×14.
1651 45 c. deep reddish purple and lemon .. 50 50
1652 $1 blue and lemon .. .. .. 1·25 1·25
Design:—$1 Rose Scott.

(Des Janet Boschen. Litho SNP Cambec (exelgram (45c.) and hologram ($1.20) Avon Graphics))

1996 (5 Sept). *Pearls and Diamonds*. *T* **561** *and similar horiz designs*. *Multicoloured*. *P* 14½×14.
1653 45 c. Type **561** 60 50
1654 $1.20, Diamond .. .. .. 1·40 1·50
The pearl on the 45 c. is shown as an exelgram (holographic printing on ultra thin plastic film) and the diamond on the $1.20 as a hologram, each embossed on to the stamp.

562 Silhouettes of Female Dancer and Musician on Rural Landscape

563 Ginger Cats

(Des A. Ashton. Litho McPherson's Ptg Group, Mulgrave)

1996 (12 Sept). *50th Anniv of Arts Councils*. *T* **562** *and similar horiz design*. *Multicoloured*. *P* 14×*imperf*.
1655 20 c. Type **562** .. .. .. 60 1·00
a. Booklet pane. Nos. 1655 and 1656×4 2·00
1656 45 c. Silhouettes of musician and male dancer on landscape 35 40
Nos. 1655/6 only exist from $2 stamp booklets in which the vertical edges of the pane are imperforate.

(Des Dianne Cooke. Litho SNP Cambec)

1996 (1 Oct). *Australian Pets*. *T* **563** *and similar multicoloured designs*. (*a*) *Phosphorised paper*. *P* 14×14½ (*Nos*. 1659, 1662) *or* 14½×14 (*others*).
1657 45 c. Type **563** 60 60
a. Pair. Nos. 1657/8 .. .. .. 1·10 1·10
1658 45 c. Blue Heeler dogs 60 60
1659 45 c. Cockatoo (30×25 *mm*) 60 60
1660 45 c. Duck with ducklings (25×30 *mm*) .. 60 60
a. Horiz pair. Nos. 1660/1 .. .. 1·10 1·10
1661 45 c. Dog and cat (25×30 *mm*) 60 60
1662 45 c. Ponies (30×50 *mm*) 60 60
1657/62 .. .. *Set of* 6 3·25 3·50
MS1663 166×73 mm. Nos. 1657/62. P 14½ .. 3·25 3·50
(*b*) *Self-adhesive*. *Phosphor band*. *P* 11½
1664 45 c. Type **563** 60 75
a. Booklet pane. Nos. 1664×4 and 1665×6 .. .. 5·50
1665 45 c. Blue Heeler dogs 60 75
Nos. 1657/8 and 1660/1 were each printed together, *se-tenant*, either in vertical and horizontal pairs (Nos. 1657/8) or in horizontal pairs (Nos. 1660/1) throughout the sheets.
Nos. 1664/5 were printed either in rolls of 100 on which the surplus self-adhesive paper around each stamp was removed, or in $4.50 booklets containing No. 1664a, on which the surplus paper was retained.
The phosphor on both rolls and booklets shows orange-pink under U.V. light and appears as a bar at the top and on the cats for No. 1664 and as a L-shaped frame for No. 1665.
No. MS1163 also exists overprinted with the logos of the ASDA Centrepoint '96 Sydney, St. Peter's Stamp and Coin Fair, Melbourne '96", "TAIPEI '96", Queensland Stamp and Coin Expo, Stamp Show '96 Claremont and "HONG KONG '97" for sale at these exhibitions.

564 Ferdinand von Mueller

565 Willem de Vlamingh

(Des J. Sellitto and D. Blyth. Litho State Ptg Wks, Berlin)

1996 (9 Oct). *Australia–Germany Joint Issue*. *Death Centenary of Ferdinand von Mueller (botanist)*. *P* 14.
1666 564 $1.20, multicoloured .. .. 1·25 1·40

(Des A. Donato. Litho McPherson's Ptg Group, Mulgrave)

1996 (1 Nov). *300th Anniv of the Visit of Willem de Vlamingh to Western Australia*. *P* 14×14½.
1667 565 45 c. multicoloured 75 75
a. Horiz pair. No. 1667 and No. 433 of Christmas Island .. 1·50 1·50
No. 1667 and No. 433 of Christmas Island were printed together, *se-tenant*, in horizontal pairs throughout the sheet.

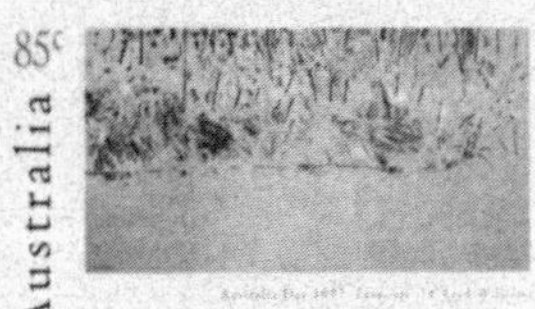

566 Madonna and Child

567 "Landscape '74" (Fred Williams)

(Des Vivienne Goodman. Litho SNP Cambec)

1996 (1 Nov). *Christmas*. *T* **566** *and similar vert designs*. *Multicoloured*. (*a*) *Phosphorised paper*. *P* 14½×14.
1668 40 c. Type **566** 55 45
1669 45 c. Wise man with gift 55 50
1670 $1 Shepherd boy with lamb .. .. 1·25 1·40
1668/70 .. .. *Set of* 3 2·10 2·10
(*b*) *Self-adhesive*. *Phosphor on inscr panel and central figures*. *P* 11½
1671 40 c. Type **566** 50 45
a. Booklet pane. No. 1671×20 .. 9·00
No. 1671, on which the phosphor shows pink under U.V. light was only issued in $8 booklets, on which the surplus self-adhesive paper was retained.

(Des Karina Weston. Litho McPherson's Ptg Group, Mulgrave)

1997 (16 Jan). *Australia Day*. *Contemporary Paintings*. *T* **567** *and similar horiz designs*. *Multicoloured*. *P* 14½×14.
1672 85 c. Type **567** .. .. .. 1·10 1·10
1673 90 c. "The Balcony 2" (Brett Whiteley) .. 1·10 1·10
1674 $1.20, "Fire Haze at Gerringong" (Lloyd Rees) .. .. 1·40 1·40
1672/4 .. .. *Set of* 3 3·25 3·25

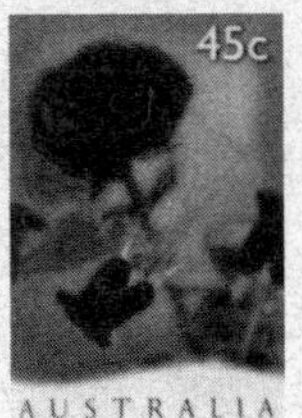

568 Sir Donald Bradman

569 Red Roses

(Des Sophie Byass. Litho SNP Cambec)

1997 (23 Jan). *Australian Legends* (*1st series*). *Sir Donald Bradman (cricketer)*. *T* **568** *and similar square design*. *Multicoloured*. *P* 14½.
1675 45 c. Type **568** 55 55
a. Horiz pair. Nos. 1675/6 .. .. 1·10 1·10
1676 45 c. Bradman playing stroke 55 55
Nos. 1675/6 were printed together, *se-tenant*, in horizontal pairs throughout the sheet of 10.
See also Nos. 1731/54 and 1838/41.

(Des Kate Linton. Litho SNP Cambec)

1997 (29 Jan). *St. Valentine's Day*. (*a*) *Phosphorized paper*. *P* 14½×14.
1677 569 45 c. multicoloured 50 50
(*b*) *Self-adhesive*. *Phosphor on inscr panel and background*. *P* 11½
1678 569 45 c. multicoloured 70 75
a. Booklet pane. No. 1678×10 .. 6·00
No. 1678, on which the phosphor shows pink under U.V. light, was only issued in $4.50 booklets on which the surplus self-adhesive paper was retained.

570 Ford Coupe Utility, 1934

571 May Wirth and Horse

(Des Sandra Harmon. Litho SNP Cambec)

1997 (27 Feb). *Classic Cars*. *T* **570** *and similar horiz designs*. *Multicoloured*. (*a*) *Phosphorised paper*. *P* 14×14½.
1679 45 c. Type **570** 55 60
a. Block of 4. Nos. 1679/82 .. .. 2·00
b. Booklet pane. No. 1679×4 with margins all round .. .. 2·00
1680 45 c. GMH Holden 48-215 (FX), 1948 .. 55 60
a. Booklet pane. No. 1680×4 with margins all round .. .. 2·00
1681 45 c. Austin Lancer, 1958 .. .. 55 60
a. Booklet pane. No. 1681×4 with margins all round .. .. 2·00
1682 45 c. Chrysler Valiant "R" Series, 1962 .. 55 60
a. Booklet pane. No. 1682×4 with margins all round .. .. 2·00
1679/82 .. .. *Set of* 4 2·00 2·25
(*b*) *Self-adhesive*. *Designs* 32½×21 *mm*. *Phosphor frames*. *P* 11½
1683 45 c. Type **570** 55 60
a. Booklet pane. Nos. 1683, 1685 each × 2 and 1684, 1686 each × 3 .. 5·00
1684 45 c. GMH Holden 48-215 (FX), 1948 .. 55 60
1685 45 c. Austin Lancer, 1958 .. .. 55 60
1686 45 c. Chrysler Valiant "R" Series, 1962 .. 55 60
1683/6 .. .. *Set of* 4 2·00 2·25
Nos. 1679/82 were printed together, *se-tenant*, in sheets of 50 (2 panes 5×5) each sheet providing ten blocks of 4 and ten single stamps.
Nos. 1683/6, occur either in rolls of 100, on which the surplus self-adhesive paper was removed, or in $4.50 booklets, containing No. 1683a, on which the surplus paper was retained. The phosphor on both rolls and booklets shows pink under U.V. light.

(Des Cathleen Bryant. Litho McPherson's Ptg Group, Mulgrave)

1997 (13 Mar). *150th Anniv of the Circus in Australia*. *T* **571** *and similar vert designs*. *Multicoloured*. *P* 14½×14.
1687 45 c. Type **571** 50 55
a. Block of 4. Nos. 1687/90 .. .. 1·75
1688 45 c. Con Colleano on tightrope 50 55
1689 45 c. Clowns 50 55
1690 45 c. Acrobats 50 55
1687/90 .. .. *Set of* 4 1·75 2·00
Nos. 1687/90 were printed together, *se-tenant*, in sheets of 50 (2 panes of 5×5), each sheet providing ten blocks of 4 and ten single stamps.

572 Royal Wedding 1d. Stamp of 1947

573 Hand holding Globe and Lions Emblem

(Des Cozzolino Ellett. Recess Note Ptg Branch, Reserve Bank of Australia)

1997 (17 Apr). *Queen Elizabeth II's Birthday*. *P* 14×14½.
1691 572 45 c. blackish purple 50 50

(Des Cozzolino Ellett. Recess Note Ptg Branch, Reserve Bank of Australia)

1997 (17 Apr). *50th Anniv of First Australian Lions Club*. *P* 14½×14.
1692 573 45 c. brt blue, chestnut & blackish pur 50 50

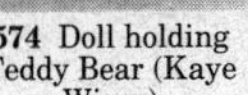

574 Doll holding Teddy Bear (Kaye Wiggs)

575 Police Rescue Helicopter

(Des Cathleen Bryant. Litho McPherson's Ptg Group, Mulgrave)

1997 (8 May). *Dolls and Teddy Bears*. *T* **574** *and similar vert designs*. *Multicoloured*. *P* 14½×14.
1693 45 c. Type **574** 45 50
a. Horiz strip of 5. Nos. 1693/7 .. 2·00
1694 45 c. Teddy bear standing (Jennifer Laing) 45 50

1695 45 c. Doll wearing white dress with teddy bear (Susie McMahon) 45 50
1696 45 c. Doll in brown dress and bonnet (Lynda Jacobson) 45 50
1697 45 c. Teddy bear sitting (Helen Williams) 45 50
1693/7 .. .. *Set of* 5 2·00 2·00

Nos. 1693/7 were printed together in sheets of 10, containing two *se-tenant* strips of 5. Sheets exist overprinted for the 1997 Brisbane Stamp and Coin Expo.

(Des B. Sadgrove. Litho McPherson's Ptg Group, Mulgrave)

1997 (10 July). *Emergency Services. T* **575** *and similar horiz designs. Multicoloured. P* 14×14½.
1698 45 c. Type **575** 40 45
a. Horiz pair. Nos. 1698/9 .. .. 80 90
1699 45 c. Emergency Service volunteers carrying victim 40 45
1700 $1.05, Fire service at fire 90 95
1701 $1.20, Loading casualty into ambulance 1·00 1·10
1698/1701 .. .. .. *Set of* 4 2·75 3·00

Nos. 1698/9 were printed together, *se-tenant*, in horizontal pairs throughout the sheet.

Numbered gutter strips of ten of No. 1701, overprinted "Emergency Services", come from a limited issue portfolio.

576 George Peppin Jnr (breeder) and Merino Sheep

577 Dumbi the Owl

(Des C. Shurey. Litho SNP Cambec)

1997 (7 Aug). *Bicentenary of Arrival of Merino Sheep in Australia. T* **576** *and similar horiz design. Multicoloured. P* 14×14½.
1702 45 c. Type **576** 40 45
a. Horiz pair. Nos. 1702/3 .. .. 80 90
1703 45 c. Pepe chair, cloth and wool logo .. 40 45

Nos. 1702/3 were printed together, *se-tenant*, as horizontal pairs in sheets of 10.

(Des Melinda Coombes. Litho SNP Cambec)

1997 (21 Aug). *"The Dreaming". Cartoons from Aboriginal Stories. T* **577** *and similar square designs. Multicoloured. P* 14½.
1704 45 c. Type **577** 40 45
1705 $1 The Two Willy-Willies 90 95
1706 $1.20, How Brolga became a Bird .. 1·00 1·10
1707 $1.80, Tuggan-Tuggan .. .. .. 1·50 1·60
1704/7 .. .. *Set of* 4 3·75 4·00

578 *Rhoetosaurus brownei*

579 Spotted-tailed Quoll

(Des P. Schouten. Litho SNP Cambec)

1997 (4 Sept). *Prehistoric Animals. T* **578** *and similar vert designs. Multicoloured. P* 14½×14.
1708 45 c. Type **578** 40 45
a. Horiz strip of 5. Nos. 1708/12 .. 2·00
1709 45 c. *Mcnamaraspis kaprios* 40 45
1710 45 c. *Ninjemys oweni* 40 45
1711 45 c. *Paracylotosaurus davidi* 40 45
1712 45 c. *Woolungasaurus glendowerensis* .. 40 45
1708/12 .. .. *Set of* 5 2·00 2·25

Nos. 1708/12 were printed together, *se-tenant*, as horizontal strips of five in sheets of 10.

(Des P. Gouldthorpe. Litho SNP Cambec)

1997 (1 Oct). *Nocturnal Animals. T* **579** *and similar multicoloured designs.*

(*a*) *Phosphorised paper. P* 14×14½ (*Nos.* 1715/17) *or* 14½×14 (*others*)
1713 45 c. Type **579** 50 50
a. Pair. Nos. 1713/14 .. .. .. 1·00 1·00
1714 45 c. Barking Owl 50 50
1715 45 c. Platypus (30×25 *mm*) 50 50
a. Horiz strip of 3. Nos. 1715/17 .. 1·40
1716 45 c. Brown Antechinus (30×25 *mm*) .. 50 50
1717 45 c. Dingo (30×25 *mm*) 50 50
1718 45 c. Yellow-bellied Glider (50×30 *mm*) .. 50 50
1713/18 .. .. *Set of* 6 2·75 2·75
MS1719 166×73 mm. Nos. 1713/18. P 14½ .. 2·75 2·75

(*b*) *Self-adhesive. Phosphor frame. P* 11½
1720 45 c. Type **579** (25×32 *mm*) 55 65
a. Vert pair. Nos. 1720/1 .. .. 1·10
b. Booklet pane. Nos. 1720/1, each ×5 5·00
1721 45 c. Barking Owl (25×32 *mm*) 55 65

Nos. 1713/14 were printed together, *se-tenant*, in horizontal or vertical pairs and Nos. 1715/17 in horizontal strips of three throughout the sheets.

No. **MS**1719 shows a spider and web printed in green phosphor, visible under U.V. light, across much of the sheet.

Nos. 1720/1, on which the phosphor frame appears pink under U.V. light, were printed either in rolls of 100 on which the surplus self-adhesive paper around each stamp was removed or in $4.50 booklets containing No. 1720b on which the surplus paper was retained.

580 Woman

581 Two Angels

(Des Lynda Warner. Litho SNP Cambec)

1997 (27 Oct). *Breast Cancer Awareness Campaign. P* 14×14½.
1722 **580** 45 c. multicoloured 40 45

(Des Cathleen Bryant. Litho SNP Cambec)

1997 (3 Nov). *Christmas. Children's Nativity Play. T* **581** *and similar horiz designs. Multicoloured.*

(*a*) *Phosphorised paper. P* 14×14½
1723 40 c. Type **581** 35 40
1724 45 c. Mary 40 45
1725 $1 Three Kings 90 95
1723/5 .. .. *Set of* 3 1·60 1·75

(*b*) *Self-adhesive. Phosphor frame at right and foot. P* 11½
1726 40 c. Type **581** 35 40
a. Booklet pane. No. 1726×20 .. 7·00

No. 1726, on which the phosphor shows pink under U.V. light, was only issued in $8 booklets on which the surplus self-adhesive paper was retained.

582 *"Flying Cloud"* (clipper) (J. Scott)

583 Betty Cuthbert (1956)

(Des B. Sadgrove. Litho McPherson's Ptg Group, Mulgrave)

1998 (15 Jan). *Ship Paintings. T* **582** *and similar square designs. Multicoloured. P* 14½×14.
1727 45 c. Type **582** 40 45
1728 85 c. *"Marco Polo"* (full-rigged ship) (T. Robertson) 75 80
1729 $1 *"Chusan"* (steamship) (C. Gregory) .. 90 95
1730 $1.20, *"Heather Belle"* (clipper) .. 1·00 1·10
1727/30 .. .. *Set of* 4 3·00 3·25

No. 1727 was reissued on 17 June 1998 in sheets of 10 (2×5) with inscribed margins publicising "Australia 99" International Stamp Exhibition, Melbourne.

(Des Sophie Byass. Litho SNP Cambec)

1998 (21 Jan). *Australian Legends (2nd series). Olympic Gold Medal Winners. T* **583** *and similar horiz designs.*

(*a*) *Phosphorised paper. P* 14×14½.
1731 45 c. Type **583** 45 50
a. Sheetlet. Nos. 1731/42 .. .. 4·75
1732 45 c. Betty Cuthbert running 45 50
1733 45 c. Herb Elliot (1960) 45 50
1734 45 c. Herb Elliot running 45 50
1735 45 c. Dawn Fraser (1956, 1960 and 1964) 45 50
1736 45 c. Dawn Fraser swimming 45 50
1737 45 c. Marjorie Jackson (1952) 45 50
1738 45 c. Marjorie Jackson running 45 50
1739 45 c. Murray Rose (1956) 45 50
1740 45 c. Murray Rose swimming 45 50
1741 45 c. Shirley Strickland (1952 and 1956) 45 50
1742 45 c. Shirley Strickland hurdling .. 45 50
1731/42 .. .. .. *Set of* 12 4·75 5·50

(*b*) *Self-adhesive. Two vertical phosphor bands. P* 11½
1743 45 c. Type **583** 45 50
b. Booklet pane. Nos. 1743/54 .. 4·75
1744 45 c. Betty Cuthbert running 45 50
1745 45 c. Herb Elliot 45 50
1746 45 c. Herb Elliot running 45 50
1747 45 c. Dawn Fraser 45 50
1748 45 c. Dawn Fraser swimming 45 50
1749 45 c. Marjorie Jackson 45 50
1750 45 c. Marjorie Jackson running 45 50
1751 45 c. Murray Rose 45 50
1752 45 c. Murray Rose swimming 45 50
1753 45 c. Shirley Strickland 45 50
1754 45 c. Shirley Strickland hurdling .. 45 50
1743/54 .. .. .. *Set of* 12 4·75 5·50

Nos. 1731/42 were printed together, *se-tenant*, in sheetlets of 12.

Nos. 1743/54, on which the phosphor bands appear pink under U.V. light, were printed in $5.40 stamp booklets containing No. 1743b on which the surplus paper around each stamp was retained.

NEW INFORMATION

The editor is always interested to correspond with people who have new information that will improve or correct the Catalogue.

584 Champagne Rose

585 Queen Elizabeth II

(Des Cathleen Bryant. Litho SNP Cambec)

1998 (12 Feb). *Greetings Stamp.* (*a*) *P* 14½×14.
1755 **584** 45 c. multicoloured 40 4

(*b*) *Self-adhesive. Phosphor band. P* 11½
1756 **584** 45 c. multicoloured 50 4
a. Booklet pane. No. 1756×10 .. 4·50

No. 1756 was only issued in $4.50 booklets on which th surplus self-adhesive paper was retained.

The phosphor, which shows pink under U.V. light, cover most of the row of roses to the left of the design.

(Des Hannah Richardson. Litho McPherson's Ptg Group Mulgrave)

1998 (9 Apr). *Queen Elizabeth II's Birthday. P* 14×14½.
1757 **585** 45 c. multicoloured 40 4

586 Sea Hawk (helicopter) landing on Frigate

587 Sheep Shearer and Sheep

(Des Sandra Harman. Litho McPherson's Ptg Group, Mulgrave

1998 (9 Apr). *50th Anniv of Royal Australian Navy Fleet A Arm. P* 14×14½.
1758 **586** 45 c. multicoloured 40 4

(Des C. Shurey. Litho SNP Cambec)

1998 (21 Apr). *Farming. T* **587** *and similar horiz design Multicoloured.* (*a*) *Phosphorised paper. P* 14×14½.
1759 45 c. Type **587** 45 4
a. Horiz strip of 5. Nos. 1759/63 .. 2·10
1760 45 c. Barley and silo 45 4
1761 45 c. Farmers herding beef cattle .. 45 4
1762 45 c. Sugar cane harvesting 45 4
1763 45 c. Two dairy cows 45 4
1759/63 .. .. .. *Set of* 5 2·10 2·1

(*b*) *Self-adhesive. Phosphor band. P* 11½.
1764 45 c. Type **587** 55 5
a. Booklet pane. Nos. 1764/8, each × 2 4·50
1765 45 c. Barley and silo 55 5
1766 45 c. Farmers herding beef cattle .. 55 5
1767 45 c. Sugar cane harvesting 55 5
1768 45 c. Two dairy cows 55 5
1764/8 .. .. *Set of* 5 2·40 2·4

Nos. 1759/63 were printed together, *se-tenant*, in horizonta strips of 5 throughout the sheet.

On Nos. 1764/8 the phosphor, which shows pink under U. V light, appears as a horizontal band at the top with an irregula extension to the foot of each design. They were printed in $4.5 stamp booklets containing No. 1764a on which the surplu paper around each stamp was retained.

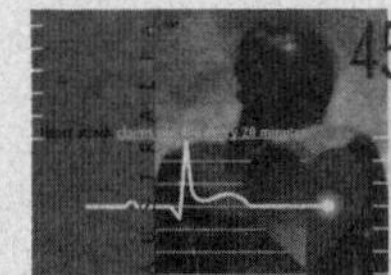

588 Cardiograph Trace and Heart

589 Johnny O'Keefe ("The Wild One", 1958)

(Des Lynda Warner. Litho SNP Cambec)

1998 (4 May). *Heart Disease Awareness. P* 14×14½.
1769 **588** 45 c. multicoloured 40 4

(Des Cozzolino Ellett. Litho SNP Cambec)

1998 (26 May). *Australian Rock and Roll. T* **589** *and simila horiz designs. Multicoloured.* (*a*) *Phosphorised pape P* 14×14½.
1770 45 c. Type **589** 35 4
a. Sheetlet. Nos. 1770/81 .. .. 4·00
1771 45 c. Col Joye ("Oh Yeah Uh Huh", 1959) 35 4
1772 45 c. Little Pattie ("He's My Blonde Headed Stompie Wompie Real Gone Surfer Boy", 1963) 35 4
1773 45 c. Normie Rowe ("Shakin all Over", 1965) 35 4
1774 45 c. Easybeats ("She's so Fine", 1965) .. 35 4
1775 45 c. Russell Morris ("The Real Thing", 1969) 35 4
1776 45 c. Masters Apprentices ("Turn Up Your Radio", 1970) 35 4
1777 45 c. Daddy Cool ("Eagle Rock", 1971) .. 35 4
1778 45 c. Billy Thorpe and the Aztecs ("Most People I know think I'm Crazy", 1972) 35 4
1779 45 c. Skyhooks ("Horror Movie", 1974) .. 35 4
1780 45 c. AC/DC ("It's a Long Way to the Top", 1975) 35 4

'81 45 c. Sherbet ("Howzat", 1976) 35 40
'70/81 . . . . . . Set of 12 4·00 4·25

(b) *Self-adhesive. One side phosphor band. P 11½.*

'82 45 c. Sherbet ("Howzat", 1976) 35 40
a. Horiz strip of 12. Nos. 1782/93 . . 4·00
'83 45 c. AC/DC ("It's a Long Way to the Top", 1975) 35 40
'84 45 c. Skyhooks ("Horror Movie", 1974) . . 35 40
'85 45 c. Billy Thorpe and the Aztecs ("Most People I Know Think I'm Crazy", 1972) 35 40
'86 45 c. Daddy Cool ("Eagle Rock", 1971) . . 35 40
'87 45 c. The Masters Apprentices ("Turn Up Your Radio", 1970) 35 40
'88 45 c. Russell Morris ("The Real Thing", 1969) 35 40
'89 45 c. Easybeats ("She's So Fine", 1965) . . 35 40
'90 45 c. Normie Rowe ("Shakin all Over", 1965) 35 40
'91 45 c. Little Pattie ("He's My Blonde Headed Stompie Wompie Real Gone Surfer Boy", 1963) 35 40
'92 45 c. Col Joye ("Oh Yeah Uh Huh", 1959) 35 40
'93 45 c. Type **589** 35 40
'82/93 . . . . . . Set of 12 4·00 4·25

Nos. 1770/81 were printed together, *se-tenant*, in sheetlets of 2.

Nos. 1782/93, on which the phosphor appears pale purple ıder U.V. light, shows the band alternating at left or right. hey were issued in rolls of 100 on which the surplus paper ound each stamp was removed.

590 Helmeted Honeyeater (Yellow-tufted Honeyeater subspecies)

591 French Horn and Cello Players

)es K. Stead and Melinda Coombes. Litho McPherson's Ptg Group, Mulgrave)

)98 (25 June). *Endangered Species. Birds. T* **590** *and similar horiz designs. Multicoloured. Ordinary paper (Nos. 1794/5). P 14×14½.*

'94 5 c. Type **590** 20 20
a. Horiz pair. Nos. 1794/5 . . . . 40 40
'95 5 c. Orange-bellied Parrot 20 20
'96 45 c. Red-tailed Black-Cockatoo 45 45
a. Horiz pair. Nos. 1796/7 . . . . 90 90
'97 45 c. Gouldian Finch 45 45
'94/7 . . . . . . Set of 4 1·25 1·25

Nos. 1794/5 and 1796/7 were each printed together, *se-tenant*, horizontal pairs throughout the sheets.

(Des Michelle Gauci. Litho SNP Cambec)

)98 (16 July). *Youth Arts, Australia. T* **591** *and similar horiz design. Multicoloured. P 14×14½.*

'98 45 c. Type **591** 40 40
a. Horiz pair. Nos. 1798/9 . . . . 80 80
'99 45 c. Dancers 40 40

Nos. 1798/9 were printed together, *se-tenant*, in horizontal airs throughout the sheet.

592 *Phalaenopsis rosenstromii*

593 Flying Angel with Teapot (cartoon by Michael Leunig)

(Des Clare Kaegi and Cathleen Cram. Litho SNP Cambec)

998 (6 Aug). *Australia–Singapore Joint Issue. Orchids. T* **592** *and similar vert designs. Multicoloured. P 14½×14.*

800 45 c. Type **592** 45 40
801 85 c. *Arundina graminifolia* 80 80
802 $1 *Grammatophyllum speciosum* . . 90 90
803 $1.20, *Dendrobium phalaenopsis* . . 1·10 1·25
800/3 . . . . . . Set of 4 3·00 3·00
1S1804 138×72 mm. Nos. 1800/3 . . . . 3·00 3·00

(Des Sandra Harman. Litho SNP Cambec)

998 (13 Aug). *"The Teapot of Truth" (cartoons by Michael Leunig). T* **593** *and similar horiz designs. Multicoloured. P 14×14½.*

805 45 c. Type **593** 35 40
a. Booklet pane. No. 1805×4 with margins all round . . . . 1·40
806 45 c. Two birds in heart-shaped tree . . 35 40
a. Booklet pane. No. 1806×4 with margins all round . . . . 1·40
807 45 c Pouring tea 35 40
a. Booklet pane. No. 1807×4 with margins all round . . . . 1·40
808 $1 Mother and child (29×24 *mm*) . . 75 80
a. Booklet pane. No. 1808×2 with margins all round . . . . 1·50
809 $1.20, Cat with smiling face (29×24 *mm*) 90 95
a. Booklet pane. No. 1809×2 and stamp-size label with margins all round . . 1·75
805/9 . . . . . . Set of 5 2·50 2·75

Nos. 1805/9 were only issued in $9.95 stamp booklets.

594 Red Lacewing

595 Flinders' Telescope and Map of Tasmania

(Des C. Shurey. Litho SNP Cambec)

1998 (3 Sept). *Butterflies. T* **594** *and similar vert designs. Multicoloured. Phosphorised paper. (a) P 14½×14.*

1810 45 c. Type **594** 35 40
a. Horiz strip of 5. Nos. 1810/14 . . 1·75
1811 45 c. Dull Oakblue 35 40
1812 45 c. Meadow Argus 35 40
1813 45 c. Ulysses Butterfly 35 40
1814 45 c. Common Red-eye 35 40
1810/14 . . . . . . Set of 5 1·75 1·90

(b) *Self-adhesive. P 11½.*

1815 45 c. Type **594** 35 40
a. Vert strip of 5. Nos. 1815/19 . . 1·75
1816 45 c. Dull Oakblue 35 40
1817 45 c. Meadow Argus 35 40
1818 45 c. Ulysses Butterfly 35 40
1819 45 c. Common Red-eye 35 40
1815/19 . . . . . . Set of 5 1·75 1·90

Nos. 1810/14 were printed together, *se-tenant*, as horizontal strips of five in sheets of 10.

Nos. 1815/19 come, *se-tenant*, in strips of 5 or rolls of 100 with the surplus self-adhesive paper around each stamp removed.

(Des Lynda Warner. Litho McPherson's Ptg Group, Mulgrave)

1998 (10 Sept). *Bicentenary of the Circumnavigation of Tasmania by George Bass and Matthew Flinders. T* **595** *and similar vert design. Multicoloured. P 14½×14.*

1820 45 c. Type **595** 35 40
a. Vert pair. Nos. 1820/1 . . . . 70 80
1821 45 c. Sextant and letter from Bass . . 35 40

Nos. 1820/1 were printed together, *se-tenant*, in vertical pairs throughout the sheet.

596 Weedy Seadragon

597 Rose of Freedom

(Des W. Rankin. Litho SNP Cambec)

1998 (1 Oct). *International Year of the Ocean. T* **596** *and similar multicoloured designs.*

(a) *Phosphorised paper. P 14×14½ (Nos. 1825/6) or 14½×14 (others)*

1822 45 c. Type **596** 35 40
a. Horiz pair. Nos. 1822/3 . . . . 70 80
1823 45 c. Bottlenose Dolphin 35 40
1824 45 c. Fiery Squid (24×29 *mm*) 35 40
1825 45 c. Manta Ray (29×24 *mm*) 35 40
1826 45 c. White Pointer Shark (29×49 *mm*) . . 35 40
1827 45 c. Southern Right Whale (49×29 *mm*) 35 40
1822/7 . . . . . . Set of 6 2·10 2·40
MS1828 166×73 mm. Nos. 1822/7. P 14½ . . 2·10 2·40

(b) *Self-adhesive. Phosphor frame. P 11½*

1829 45 c. Type **596** (24×36 *mm*) 35 40
a. Vert pair. Nos. 1829/30 70
b. Booklet pane. Nos. 1829/30, each × 5 3·50
1830 45 c. Bottlenose Dolphin (24×36 *mm*) . . 35 40

Nos. 1822/3 were printed together, *se-tenant*, in horizontal or vertical pairs throughout the sheet.

Nos. 1829/30, on which the phosphor frame appears pink under U.V. light, were printed either in rolls of 100 on which the surplus self-adhesive paper around each stamp was removed or in $4.50 booklets containing No. 1828b on which the surplus paper was retained.

(Des Lynda Warner. Litho SNP Cambec)

1998 (22 Oct). *50th Anniv of Universal Declaration of Human Rights. P 14½×14.*

1831 **597** 45 c. multicoloured 35 40

598 Three Kings

(Des Sophie Byass and K. Done. Litho SNP Cambec)

1998 (2 Nov). *Christmas. T* **598** *and similar horiz designs. Multicoloured. (a) Phosphorised paper. P 14×14½.*

1832 40 c. Type **598** 30 35
1833 45 c. Nativity scene 35 40
1834 $1 Mary and Joseph 75 80
1832/4 . . . . . . Set of 3 1·40 1·50

(b) *Self-adhesive. Phosphor frame. P 11½.*

1835 40 c. Type **598** 30 35
a. Booklet pane. No. 1835×20 . . 6·00

On Nos. 1832/4 the yellow parts of the designs are printed in fluorescent ink.

No. 1835 was only issued in $8 booklets on which the surplus self-adhesive paper was retained.

SNP AUSPRINT. SNP Cambec was renamed SNP Ausprint in January 1999.

599 Australian Coat of Arms

600 Arthur Boyd

(Des B. Sadgrove. Litho SNP Ausprint)

1999 (14 Jan). *50th Anniv of Australian Citizenship.*

(a) *Phosphorised paper. P 14×14½.*

1836 **599** 45 c. multicoloured 35 40

(b) *Self-adhesive. Phosphor frame around central oval. P 11½*

1837 **599** 45 c. multicoloured 35 40

No. 1837, on which the phosphor shows pink under U.V. light, was printed in rolls of 100 on which the surplus self-adhesive paper around each stamp was removed.

(Des Lisa Christensen. Litho SNP Ausprint)

1999 (22 Jan). *Australian Legends (3rd series). Arthur Boyd (painter). T* **600** *and similar horiz design. Multicoloured.*

(a) *Phosphorised paper. P 14×14½*

1838 45 c. Type **600** 35 40
a. Horiz pair. Nos. 1838/9 70
1839 45 c. "Nebuchadnezzer on fire falling over Waterfall" (Arthur Boyd) 35 40

(b) *Self-adhesive. Two phosphor bands over inscr panels. P 11½*

1840 45 c. Type **600** 35 40
a. Booklet pane. Nos. 1840/1, each × 5 3·50
1841 45 c. "Nebuchadnezzer on fire falling over Waterfall" (Arthur Boyd) 35 40

Nos. 1838/9 were printed together, *se-tenant*, in horizontal pairs throughout the sheet.

Nos. 1840/1, on which the phosphor shows pink under U.V. light, were only issued in $4.50 booklets on which the surplus self-adhesive paper was retained.

Index to Australian Stamp Designs from 1942

The following index is intended to facilitate the identification of all Australian stamps from 1942 onwards. Portrait stamps are usually listed under surnames only, views under the name of the town or city and other issues under the main subject or a prominent word and date chosen from the inscription. Simple abbreviations have occasionally been resorted to and when the same design or subject appears on more than one stamp, only the first of each series is indicated.

Index to Australian Stamp Designs from 1942—*Continued*

STAMP BOOKLETS

Illustrations of booklet covers are reduced to ½ size, *unless otherwise stated.*

All booklets from 1913 to 1949 were stapled.

1913 (17 Jan). *Red on pink cover* (SB1) *or blue on pink cover with map of Australia on front and picture of State G.P.O. on back* (SB2)

SB1 2s. booklet containing twelve ½d. and eighteen 1d. (Nos. 1/2) in blocks of 6 .. .. .. £1000
SB2 £1 booklet containing two hundred and forty 1d. (No. 2) in blocks of 30 .. .. .. £5000

1914 (6 Oct)–**18.** *Red on pink cover* (*Nos.* SB2*a*/3), *black on red cover* (*No.* SB4) *or blue on pink cover with map of Australia on front and picture of State G.P.O. on back* (*No.* SB5).

SB2*a* 2s. booklet containing twelve ½d. and eighteen 1d. (Nos. 1, 21c) in blocks of 6 .. .. £1500
SB3 2s. booklet containing twelve ½d. and eighteen 1d. (Nos. 20, 21c) in blocks of 6 (1915) .. £1500
SB4 2s. booklet containing twenty-four 1d. (No. 21c) in blocks of 6 (10.5.17) £1800
a. Black on green cover £1800
b. Red on green cover £1800
SB5 £1 booklet containing two hundred and forty 1d. (No. 21c) in blocks of 30 .. .. .. £5000
a. Back cover without G.P.O. picture (1918) ..

Records show that a £1 booklet containing one hundred and twenty 2d. stamps was issued in very limited quantities during 1914. No examples are known to have survived.

1919 (Jan–Apr). *Black on pink* (*Nos.* SB6/7) *or black on green* (*Nos.* SB8/9c) *covers.*

SB6 2s. 3d. booklet containing eighteen 1½d. (No. 58) in blocks of 6 .. .. £1300
a. Black on green cover £1300
SB7 2s. 3d. booklet containing eighteen 1½d. (No. 54) in blocks of 6 .. .. £1300
a. Black on green cover £1300
SB8 2s. 3d. booklet containing eighteen 1½d. (No. 59) in blocks of 6 (Apr) £1300
a. Black on pink cover £1300
SB9 2s. 3d. booklet containing eighteen 1½d. (No. 55) in blocks of 6 (Apr) £1300
a. Black on pink cover .. .. ..
b. Black on blue cover £1300
SB9*c* £1 booklet containing one hundred and sixty 1½d. (No. 55) in blocks of 20 (Apr) £5000

1920 (Dec)–**22.** *Black on blue* (*Nos.* SB10, SB12), *black on white* (*No.* SB11) *or black on brown* (*No.* SB14) *covers.*

SB10 2s. booklet containing twelve 2d. (No. 62) in blocks of 6 .. .. £1500
a. Black on pink cover £1500
b. Black on orange cover (3.22) £2000
SB11 2s. booklet containing twelve 2d. (No. 63) in blocks of 6 (3.22) £1500
a. Black on orange cover (7.22) £2000
b. Black on pink cover £1500
c. Brown on buff cover £1500
d. Black on pink cover £1500
SB12 £1 booklet containing one hundred and twenty 2d. (No. 62) in blocks of 15 (1.21) .. £5000
a. Black on pink cover .. .. ..
SB13 £1 booklet containing ninety 2d. and fifteen 4d. (Nos. 63, 65) in blocks of 15 (3.22) .. ..
SB14 £1 booklet containing one hundred and twenty 2d. (No. 63) in blocks of 15 (8.22) £2000

1923 (Oct)–**24.** *Black on rose* (*No.* SB15), *or green on pale green* (*Nos.* SB16/18) *covers.*

SB15 2s. 3d. booklet containing eighteen 1½d. (No. 61) in blocks of 6 .. .. £1200
a. Black on pale green cover £1200
b. Green on pale green cover £1200
SB16 2s. 3d. booklet containing eighteen 1½d. (No. 77) in blocks of 6 (5.24) £1200
SB17 £1 booklet containing one hundred and sixty 1½d. (No. 61) in blocks of 20 (3.24) .. £4000
SB18 £1 booklet containing one hundred and sixty 1½d. (No. 77) in blocks of 20 (5.24) .. £4000

1927 (Jan–June). *Green on pale green covers.*

SB19 2s. 3d. booklet containing eighteen 1½d. (No. 87) in blocks of 6 .. .. £750
SB20 2s. 3d. booklet containing eighteen 1½d. (No. 96) in blocks of 6 .. .. £750
SB21 £1 booklet containing one hundred and sixty 1½d. (No. 96) in blocks of 20 (June) .. £3750

1927 (9 May). *Opening of Parliament House, Canberra. Green on pale green cover with picture of H. M. S.* Renown *on back* (2s.).

SB22 2s. booklet containing sixteen 1½d. (No. 105) in blocks of 8 .. .. 80·00
SB22*a* 10s. booklet containing eighty 1½d. (No. 105) in blocks of 8 .. ..

Surviving examples of No. SB22*a* are without front cover and have a blank back cover.

1928 (Nov). *Green on pale green cover.*

SB23 2s. 3d. booklet containing eighteen 1½d. (No. 96a or 96w) in blocks of 6 .. .. .. £325

1930 (July)–**35.** *Air. Black on blue cover inscr* "AIR MAIL. SAVES TIME"

SB24 3s. booklet containing twelve 3d. (No. 115) in blocks of 4 plus two panes of air mail labels £650
a. Cover inscr "USE THE AIR MAIL" (5.35) .. £1200
b. Black on pale green cover inscr "USE THE AIR MAIL" (5.35) £900

1930 (9 Sept)–**33.** *Green on pale green covers inscr* "USE THE AIR MAIL" *on the back* (2s)

SB25 2s. booklet containing twelve 2d. (No. 99a or 99aw) in blocks of 6 .. .. .. £300
SB25*a* 2s. booklet containing twelve 2d. (No. 127 or 127w) in blocks of 6 (1.32) £275
ab. Cover with parcel rates on back (1933) .. £375
SB26 £1 booklet containing one hundred and twenty 2d. (No. 99) in blocks of 20 .. .. £3750
SB26*a* £1 booklet containing one hundred and twenty 2d. (No. 99a) in blocks of 20 .. .. £3750

1934 (June). *Black on cream cover inscr* "Address your mail fully..." *on front.*

SB26*b* 2s. booklet containing twelve 2d. (No. 127 or 127w) in blocks of 6 .. .. .. £375

1935–38. *Black on green cover with Commonwealth Savings Bank advertisement on front inscr* "WHEREVER THERE IS A MONEY ORDER POST OFFICE".

SB26*c* 2s. booklet containing twelve 2d. (No. 127 or 127w) in blocks of 6 .. .. .. £325
ca. Front cover inscr "IN MOST MONEY ORDER OFFICES" (1936) £275
cb. Ditto with waxed interleaves (1938) .. £325

1938 (Dec). *Black on green cover as No.* SB26*c.*

SB27 2s. booklet containing twelve 2d. (No. 184 or 184w) in blocks of 6 .. .. .. £350
a. With waxed interleaves £450
b. Black on buff cover £400

1942 (Aug). *Black on buff cover, size* 73×47½ *mm.*

SB28 2s. 6d. booklet containing twelve 2½d. (No. 206 or 206w) in blocks of 6, upright within the booklet £110
a. With waxed interleaves £200

1949 (Sept). *Black on buff cover, size* 79½×42½ *mm including figure of Hermes.*

SB29 2s. 6d. booklet containing twelve 2½d. (No. 206) in blocks of 6, sideways within the booklet 80·00

All booklets from 1952 to 1972 were stitched and stapled booklets of this period are remakes of defective stitched booklets with new covers. All subsequent booklets have their panes attached by selvedge *unless otherwise stated.*

B 1

1952 (24 June). *Vermilion and deep blue on green cover as Type* B **1**.

SB30 3s. 6d. booklet containing twelve 3½d. (No. 247) in blocks of 6 .. .. 17·00
a. With waxed interleaves .. .. .. 90·00

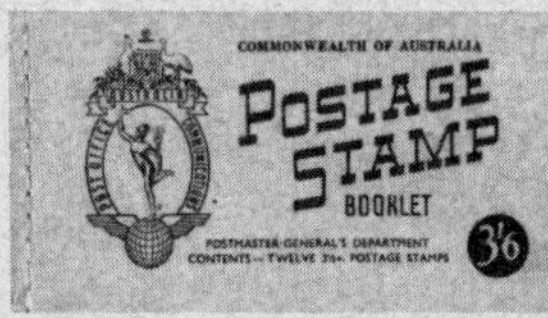

B 1*a*

1953 (8 July)–**56.** *Vermilion and deep blue on green cover as Type* B **1***a.*

SB31 3s. 6d. booklet containing twelve 3½d. (No. 263) in blocks of 6 .. .. 11·00
a. With waxed interleaves .. .. .. 22·00
SB32 3s. 6d. booklet containing twelve 3½d. (No. 262*a*) in blocks of 6 (7.56) .. .. .. 22·00
a. With waxed interleaves .. .. .. 80·00

B 2

1957 (13 Mar)–**59.** *Vermilion and deep blue on green cover as Type* B **2**.

SB33 4s. booklet containing two panes of 6 4d. (Nos. 282ab) .. .. 15·00
a. With waxed interleaves .. .. .. 40·00
SB34 4s. booklet containing two panes of 6 4d. (No. 313ab) (18.3.59) .. .. 38·00
a. With waxed interleaves .. .. .. 75·00

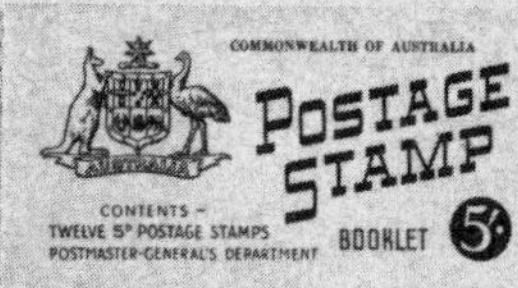

B 3

1960 (23 Mar). *Vermilion and deep blue on green cover as Ty*
B **3**.

SB35 5s. booklet containing two panes of 6 5d. (No. 314d) .. .. 20·
a. With waxed interleaves .. .. .. 42·

B 4

1962 (July)–**65.** *Rose and emerald on green cover as Type* B

SB36 5s. booklet containing two panes of 6 5d. (No. 314d) .. .. 45·
a. With waxed interleaves (1963) £1
SB37 5s. booklet containing two panes of 6 5d. (No. 354a) (17.6.64) .. .. 45·
a. With waxed interleaves £1
SB38 5s. booklet containing two panes of 6 5d. (No. 354cb) (13.7.65) .. .. 50·
a. With waxed interleaves £1

B 5

1966 (14 Feb). *Greenish blue and black on yellow-olive cover*
Type B **5**.

SB39 60 c. booklet containing three panes of 5 4 c. and 1 label (No. 385a) .. .. 60·
a. With waxed interleaves £1

1967 (29 Sept). *Greenish blue and black on yellow-olive cove*
as Type B **5**. (*a*) *Surcharged covers*

SB40 50 c. booklet containing two panes of 5 5 c. on 4 c. and 1 label (No. 414a) .. .. .. 12·
SB41 $1 booklet containing four panes of 5 5 c. on 4 c. and 1 label (No. 414a) .. .. .. 11·
a. Normal cover as Type B **5** .. .. 11·
ab. With waxed interleaves .. .. .. 55·

(*b*) *Normal covers*

SB42 50 c. booklet containing two panes of 5 5 c. and 1 label (No. 386ca) .. .. 15·
SB43 $1 booklet containing four panes of 5 5 c. and 1 label (No. 386ca) .. .. 30·
a. With waxed interleaves .. .. .. 65·

Booklets SB40/1ab were intended as provisional issues un
supplies of the new 5 c. became available in booklet form, but
the event these were put on sale on the same date.

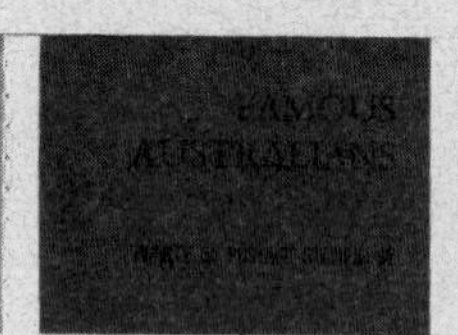

B 6

1968 (6 Nov). *Famous Australians* (1*st series*). *Black, r*
white and blue cover as Type B **6**.

SB44 $1 booklet containing four panes of 5 5 c. and 1 label (Nos 432a, 433a, 434a, 435a) .. .. 10·
a. With waxed interleaves .. .. .. 50·

B 7

1969 (22 Oct). *Famous Australians* (2*nd series*). *Olive-gree*
gold and black cover as Type B **7**.

SB45 $1 booklet containing four panes of 5 5 c. and 1 label (Nos. 446a, 447a, 448a, 449a) .. 11·
a. With waxed interleaves .. .. .. 60·

B 8

0 (16 Nov). *Famous Australians (3rd series). Multicoloured n white covers as Type* B **8**.
46 60 c. booklet containing two panes of 5 6 c. and 1 label (Nos. 479a, 480a) .. .. .. 10·00
47 60 c. booklet containing two panes of 5 6 c. and 1 label (Nos. 481a, 482a) .. .. .. 10·00
48 $1.20 booklet containing four panes of 5 6 c. and 1 label (Nos. 479a, 480a, 481a, 482a) 16·00
a. With waxed interleaves .. .. .. 60·00

72 (8 Mar). *Famous Australians (4th series). Covers in eddish violet (No.* SB49), *yellowish olive (No.* SB50) *or blue No.* SB51), *each with inscr in yellow-brown and black as Type* 3 **7**.
49 70 c. booklet containing two panes of 5 7 c. and 1 label (Nos. 505a, 506a) .. .. .. 3·75
50 70 c. booklet containing two panes of 5 7 c. and 1 label (Nos. 507a, 508a) .. .. .. 3·75
51 $1.40, booklet containing four panes of 5 7 c. and 1 label (Nos. 505a, 506a, 507a, 508a) 6·50
a. With waxed interleaves .. .. .. 50·00

'he Australian Post Office discontinued the general use of mp booklets in May 1973, but from 30 April 1979 tested two mp-vending machines in Brisbane which issued 60 c. and c. folders containing three or four examples of No. 673 taken n sheet stock. These folders were withdrawn on 30 January 31.

)uring 1982 experimental stamp booklet vending machines re under test at the G.P.O.s in Melbourne and Sydney. These chines dispensed a cream card folder, without printing, taining two copies of Nos. 669/70 and 790a. The stamps, from mal sheets, were affixed to the folders by their selvedge. se 60 c. trial folders were replaced by booklets Nos. SB52/3 November 1982.
'rom 1982 all booklets have folded covers with the stamps ached by their selvedge, *unless otherwise stated*.

B 9

2 (17 Nov). *Eucalyptus Flowers. Covers in pale greenish ellow with olive-grey (60 c.) or rose-red ($1) as Type* B **9**.
52 60 c. booklet containing pane of 6 (No. 870a) .. 1·00
53 $1 booklet containing pane of 9 (No. 870b) .. 2·50
Nos. SB52/3 were sold from vending machines.

B 10

5 (13 Mar). *Turquoise-green on white cover as Type* B **10**.
54 $1 booklet containing pane of 4 (No. 970a) .. 2·75
o. SB54 was sold from vending machines.

B 11

1986 (25 Aug). *Alpine Wildflowers. Apple-green (80 c.) or orange-yellow ($1) on white covers as Type* B **11**.
SB55 80 c. booklet containing pane of 4 (No. 1028a) 2·50
SB56 $1 booklet containing pane of 4 (No. 1028b) .. 2·50
Nos. SB55/6 were sold from vending machines.

B 12

1987 (13 Oct). *Aboriginal Crafts. Orange-brown (80 c.) or orange-yellow ($2) on white covers as Type* B **12**.
SB57 80 c. booklet containing pane of 4 (No. 1093a) .. 3·75
SB58 $2 booklet containing pane of 6 (No. 1094a) .. 7·50
Nos. SB57/8 were sold from vending machines
Trial versions of both booklets exist which differ considerably from the main supply. On the trial versions the outside back cover is headed "ABORIGINAL CRAFTS", there is no advertisement on the selvedge of the pane and the bottom stamp in each pane is imperforate at foot.

B 13

1988 (1 July–28 Sept). *Multicoloured covers as Type* B **13**.
SB59 $3.70, booklet containing 37 c. (No. 1121) in block of 10 (printed by Leigh-Mardon Ltd) .. 6·00
SB60 $3.70, booklet containing pane of 10 37 c. (No. 1121a) (printed by CPE Australia Ltd) with upper and lower edges of the pane imperf and margins at left and right .. .. .. 6·00
SB61 $3.90, booklet containing pane of 10 39 c. (No. 1121ba) (28 Sept) .. .. 7·00

B 14

1988 (28 Sept). *Australian Crafts. Orange-yellow (80 c.) or bright purple ($2) on white covers as Type* B **14**.
SB62 80 c. booklet containing pane of 3 (No. 1158a) .. 3·50
SB63 $2 booklet containing pane of 6 (No. 1159a) .. 5·00
Nos. SB62/3 were sold from vending machines.

B 15

1989 (13 Feb). *Multicoloured cover as Type* B **15**.
SB64 $3.90, booklet containing pane of 10 39 c. (No. 1179a) .. .. 8·00
a. Containing pane No. 1179ba .. .. 10·00

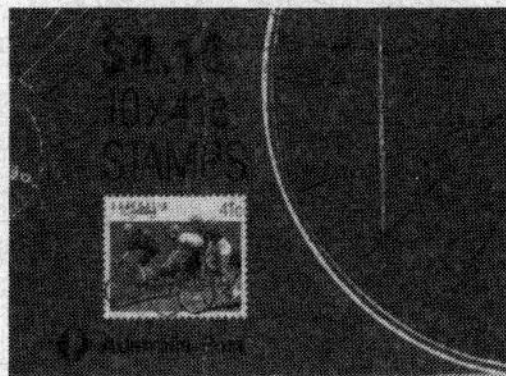

B 16

1989 (23 Aug). *Multicoloured cover as Type* B **16**.
SB65 $4.10, booklet containing pane of 10 41 c. (No. 1180a) .. .. 6·00
No. SB65 also exists overprinted with the "Austamp 90" logo for sale at this exhibition.

B 17

1989 (1 Sept). *Urban Environment. Black and grey-brown on white cover as Type* B **17**.
SB66 $3 booklet containing pane of 7 (No. 1216a) .. 4·00
No. SB66 was sold from vending machines and only contained stamps to a face value of $2.87. A refund of 13 c. could, however, be obtained by returning the empty booklet cover to a post office.
No. SB66 also exists overprinted with the "New Zealand 1990" logo for sale at this exhibition.

B 18
(Illustration reduced. Actual size 132×54 mm)

1989 (11 Oct). *"Stampshow '89" National Stamp Exhibition, Melbourne. Multicoloured cover as Type* B **18**. *Stapled*.
SB67 $8 booklet containing pane of 10 41 c. (No. 1222ab) .. .. 10·00
Booklet No. SB67 also contains a Melbourne Metro travel pass and entrance ticket to "Stampshow '89".

B 19

1989 (1 Nov). *Christmas. Reddish brown on toned cover as Type* B **19**.
SB68 $3.60, booklet containing pane of 10 36 c. (No. 1225a) .. .. 4·00
No. SB68 was also overprinted with the Sydney Stamp and Coin Show, 1989, or "World Stamp Expo", Washington logos for sale at these exhibitions.

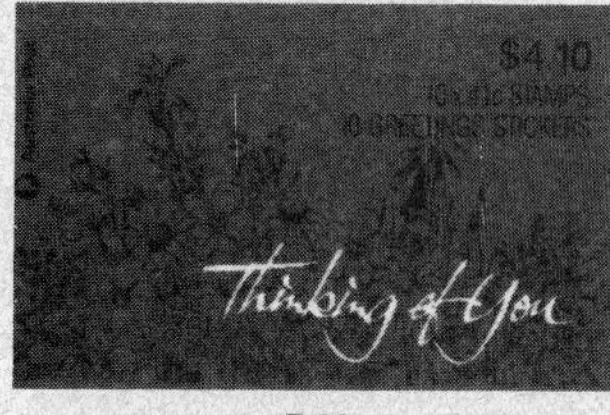

B 20

1990 (7 Feb–May). *Greetings Stamps. Maroon and dull mauve cover as Type* B **20**.
SB69 $4.10, booklet containing pane of 10 41 c. (No. 1230a) and pane of 10 greetings labels .. 5·50
a. Containing pane of 10 (No. 1230ba) and pane of 10 greetings labels (May) .. .. 10·00

For three months from May 1990 a series of provisional booklets was available from a vending machine at Sydney International Airport. These had plain covers, each handstamped with the airport post office's pictorial cancellation, and exist with the following contents:
70 c. (No. 1187) × 5 (lemon cover).
75 c. (No. 1132) × 5 (buff cover).
80 c. (No. 1133) × 5 (buff cover).
$1 (No. 1192) × 5 (buff cover).
$1.10 (No. 1193) × 5 (buff cover).

1990 (27 Aug)–**91**. *Multicoloured cover as Type* B **16**.
SB70 $4.30, booklet containing pane of 10 43 c. (No. 1181a) .. .. 5·50
a. Inscription changed and with additional slotted tab attached at right (2.91) .. 6·50

BARCODES. Barcodes appear on the back cover of booklet No. SB70 and later issues. From 1996 two different barcodes were used on self-adhesive booklets to identify operational from philatelic stock.

1990 (3 Sept). *Greetings Stamps. Maroon, brown-olive and pale olive cover as Type* B **20**.
SB71 $4.30, booklet containing pane of 10 43 c. (No. 1231a) and pane of 10 greetings labels .. 4·00

B 21 "Wild Life is Fun" (David Larwill)

1990 (3 Sept). *"Heidelberg and Heritage" Art Exhibition. Multicoloured cover as Type* B **21**.
SB72 $2 booklet containing pane of 5 (No. 1269a) .. 3·00
a. Containing pane of 5 (No. 1269ba) .. .. 6·00
Nos. SB72/a were sold from vending machines. Both also exist overprinted with the Norpex 91, Newcastle, logo for sale at this exhibition.

B 22 "Parrot unwrapping Parcel"

1990 (31 Oct). *Christmas. Multicoloured cover as Type* B **22**.
SB73 $3.80, booklet containing pane of 10 38 c. (No. 1272a) .. .. 5·50
No. SB73 also exists overprinted with the Sydney Stamp and Coin Show, 1990, logo for sale at this exhibition.

1991 (Jan). *Red-brown and brown-olive cover as Type* B **20**, *but inscr* "8 GREETINGS STICKERS".
SB74 $4.30, booklet containing pane of 10 43 c. (No. 1231a) and 8 self-adhesive greetings labels affixed to the inside back cover .. .. 13·00

B 23

1991 (1 Nov). *Christmas. Multicoloured cover as Type* B **23**.
SB75 $7.60, booklet containing pane of 20 38 c. (No. 1309a) and 20 self-adhesive "Card Only" stickers affixed to the inside back cover .. 9·00

B 24

1992 (2 Jan)–**94**. *Wetlands and Waterways. Multicoloured cover as Type* B **24**.
SB76 $2 booklet containing pane of 5 (No. 1319a) .. 3·00
a. Containing pane No. 1319ba (3.94) .. 3·75
Nos. SB76/a were sold from vending machines. No. SB76 was also overprinted with "N.P.C. Canberra 14–16 March 1992", "World Columbian Stamp Expo '92", Chicago, "Australian Stamp Exhibition 1993", Kaohsiung, and No. S76a with Queensland Stamp and Coin Show 94 logos for sale at these events.

1992 (2 Jan). *"Thinking of You". Orange-yellow, red-orange and grey-black cover as Type* B **20**, *showing wild flowers.*
SB77 $4.50, booklet containing pane of 10 45 c. (No. 1318a) with 8 self-adhesive greetings labels affixed to the inside back cover .. .. 4·50
No. SB77 was also overprinted with "Australian Stamp Exhibition 1993", Taichung, logo for sale at this exhibition.

ALTERED CATALOGUE NUMBERS

Any Catalogue numbers altered from the last edition are shown as a list in the introductory pages.

B 25

1992 (2 Jan)–**94**. *Threatened Species. Multicoloured covers as Type* B **25**. *Self-adhesive.*
SB78 $4.50, booklet containing pane of 10 45 c. (No. 1327pa) (cover showing No. 1329 on front and Olympic draw details on back) .. .. 12·00
a. Containing pane No. 1327qa (cover as Type B **25**, but without Olympic draw flash and with National Philatelic Centre advertisement on back) (22.4.92) .. .. .. 12·00
b. Containing pane No. 1327qa (cover as No. SB78a, but Stamp Collecting Kit advertisement on back) (7.11.92) .. .. .. 12·00
c. Containing pane No. 1327qa (cover as Type B **25**, but showing larger illustration (46×39 *mm*) of Dusky Hopping-mouse instead of stamp) (1.93) .. .. .. 12·00
d. Containing pane No. 1327qa (cover as No. SB78c, but illustration (46×32 *mm*) of Little Pygmy Possum) (7.93) .. .. .. 12·00
e. Containing pane No. 1327qa (cover as No. SB78c, but illustration (46×32 *mm*) of Ghost Bat) (1.94) .. .. 12·00
These booklets can also be identified by the new printing symbols (koalas or kangaroos) which appear in the margin of the pane. No. SB78a shows 1 or 2 koalas, No. SB78b 3 koalas, No. SB78c 4 koalas, No. SB78d 1 kangaroo and No. SB78e 1 kangaroo and 1 koala.
An example of No. SB78e has been reported showing the printing of the stamps omitted.
No. SB78a (1 koala) was also overprinted with "National Stamp Show '92" logo, No. SB78a (2 koalas) with "Kuala Lumpur '92" and No. SB78c with "Australian Stamp Exhibition 1993", Taipeh, logo for sale at these exhibitions.

B 26

1992 (30 Oct). *Christmas. Multicoloured cover as Type* B **26**.
SB79 $8 booklet containing pane of 20 40 c. (No. 1383a) and 20 self-adhesive "Card Only" stickers affixed to the inner cover .. .. 9·00
No. SB79 was also overprinted with "Sydney Stamp and Coin Fair '92" logo for sale at this exhibition.

B 27

1993 (1 June). *Trains of Australia. Multicoloured cover as Type* B **27**. *Self-adhesive.*
SB80 $4.50, booklet containing pane of 10 45 c. (No. 1411a) .. .. 6·00
No. SB80 was also overprinted with "Indopex '93", Surabaya, or "Queensland Stamp and Coin Show" logos for sale at these exhibitions.

B 28

1993 (1 Oct). *Prehistoric Animals. Multicoloured cover as Ty*
B **28**. *Self-adhesive.*
SB81 $4.50, booklet containing pane of 10 45 c. (No. 1430a) .. .. 6·
No. SB81 was also overprinted with the "Sydney Stamp a Coin Show 93" logo for sale at this exhibition.

B 29

1993 (1 Nov). *Christmas. Multicoloured cover as Type* B **29**.
SB82 $8 booklet containing pane of 20 40 c. (No. 1432a) with 20 self-adhesive "Card only" stickers affixed to the inner cover .. .. 8·

B 30 B 31

1994 (20 Jan). *Centenary of Organised Life Saving Australia. Multicoloured cover as Type* B **30**. *Self-adhesive.*
SB83 $4.50, booklet containing pane of 10 45 c. (No. 1443a) .. .. 6·
No. SB83 was also overprinted with the "Newcastle Mi National Exhibition" logo for sale at this event.

1994 (3 Feb). *"Thinking of You". Multicoloured cover as Ty* B **31**.
SB84 $4.50, booklet containing pane of 10 45 c. (No. 1446b) with 8 self-adhesive greetings stickers affixed to the inner cover .. .. .. 4·
No. SB84 was also overprinted with "Melbourne Stamp a Coin Show" or "Canberra Stamp Show 94" logos for sale at the exhibitions.

B 32 B 33

4 (12 May)–**96**. *Australian Wildlife (2nd series). Multicoloured cover as Type* B **32**. *Self-adhesive.*
85 $4.50, booklet containing pane of 10 45 c. (No. 1459a) .. .. 5·50
a. Cover with "BOOKABOUT" advert at foot (1.96) .. .. 5·50
b. Cover with "WIN A TRIP FOR TWO TO THE ATLANTA OLYMPICS" advert at foot (16.3.96) .. .. 5·50

No. SB85a is from the 4 koala, 1 kangaroo + 1 koala, angaroo + 2 koala and 1 kangaroo + 3 koala printings.
No. SB85b is from the 1 kangaroo printing and also exists erprinted "CANBERRA STAMPSHOW 96 16–18 March 96" in gold on the cover.

4 (28 Sept). *Australian Zoos. Endangered Species. Multicoloured cover as Type* B **33**. *Self-adhesive.*
86 $4.50, booklet containing pane of 10 45 c. (No. 1485b) .. .. 12·00

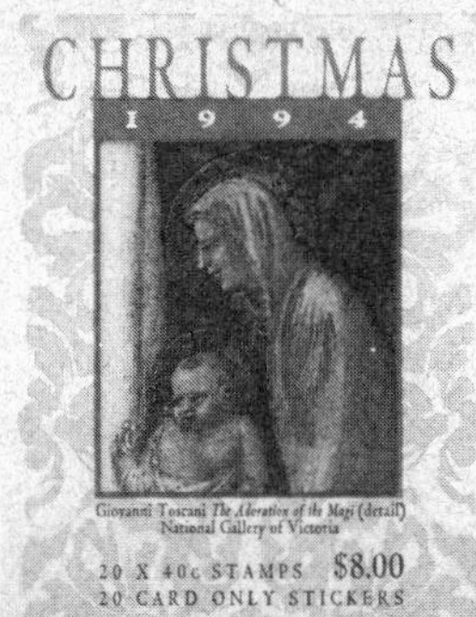

B 34

94 (31 Oct). *Christmas. Multicoloured cover as Type* B **34**.
87 $8 booklet containing pane of 20 40 c. (No. 1487a) and 20 self-adhesive "CARD ONLY" stickers affixed to the inner cover .. .. 8·50

B 35

95 (9 Feb). *Completion of* Endeavour *Replica. Multicoloured cover as Type* B **35**.
88 $2 booklet containing pane of 5 (No. 1512a) .. 2·50

B 36

95 (20 Apr). *Australian Second World War Heroes. Multicoloured cover as Type* B **36**. *Self-adhesive.*
89 $4.50, booklet containing pane of 10 45 c. (No. 1525a) .. .. 6·50

B 37

1995 (8 June). *Centenary of Cinema. Multicoloured cover as Type* B **37**. *Self-adhesive.*
SB90 $4.50, booklet containing pane of 10 45 c. (No. 1535a) .. .. 5·50

No. SB90 was also overprinted with the "Queensland Stamp and Coin Show 1995" logo for sale at this exhibition.

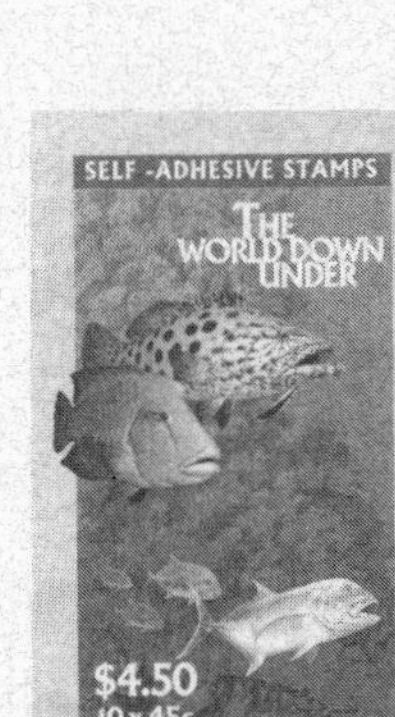

B 38

B 39

1995 (3 Oct). *Marine Life. Multicoloured cover as Type* B **38**. *Self-adhesive.*
SB91 $4.50, booklet containing pane of 10 45 c. (No. 1563ab) .. .. 4·25

1995 (1 Nov). *Christmas. Multicoloured cover as Type* B **39**. *Self-adhesive.*
SB92 $8 booklet containing pane of 20 40 c. (No. 1572a) and 20 self-adhesive "Card Only" labels affixed to the inner cover .. .. 8·50

Booklet No. SB92 shows either an advertisement for B.P. Australia or a selection of Christmas cards available from Australia Post on the back cover.

B 40 North Melbourne

(Des Janet Boschen)

1996 (23 Apr). *Centenary of Australian Football League. Multicoloured covers as Type* B **40** *showing team logos. Self-adhesive.*

SB 93	$4.50, booklet containing pane of ten 45 c. (No. 1606a) (Type B **40**)	6·00
SB 94	$4.50, booklet containing pane of ten 45 c. (No. 1607a) (Brisbane)	6·00
SB 95	$4.50, booklet containing pane of ten 45 c. (No. 1608a) (Sydney)	6·00
SB 96	$4.50, booklet containing pane of ten 45 c. (No. 1609a) (Carlton)	6·00
SB 97	$4.50, booklet containing pane of ten 45 c. (No. 1610a) (Adelaide)	6·00
SB 98	$4.50, booklet containing pane of ten 45 c. (No. 1611a) (Fitzroy)	6·00
SB 99	$4.50, booklet containing pane of ten 45 c. (No. 1612a) (Richmond)	6·00
SB100	$4.50, booklet containing pane of ten 45 c. (No. 1613a) (St. Kilda)	6·00
SB101	$4.50, booklet containing pane of ten 45 c. (No. 1614a) (Melbourne)	6·00
SB102	$4.50, booklet containing pane of ten 45 c. (No. 1615a) (Collingwood)	6·00
SB103	$4.50, booklet containing pane of ten 45 c. (No. 1616a) (Fremantle)	6·00
SB104	$4.50, booklet containing pane of ten 45 c. (No. 1617a) (Footscray)	6·00
SB105	$4.50, booklet containing pane of ten 45 c. (No. 1618a) (West Coast)	6·00
SB106	$4.50, booklet containing pane of ten 45 c. (No. 1619a) (Essendon)	6·00
SB107	$4.50, booklet containing pane of ten 45 c. (No. 1620a) (Geelong)	6·00
SB108	$4.50, booklet containing pane of ten 45 c. (No. 1621a) (Hawthorn)	6·00

No. SB94 also exists overprinted with "Queensland Stamp & Coin Expo 1996" for sale at this event.

B 41

1996 (4 July). *50th Anniv of Children's Book Council Awards. Multicoloured cover as Type* B **41**. *Self-adhesive.*
SB109 $4.50, booklet containing pane of 10 45 c. (No. 1646a) .. .. 5·50

B **42** Silhouettes on Landscape

1996 (12 Sept). *50th Anniv of Arts Councils. Multicoloured cover as Type* B **42**.
SB110 $2 booklet containing pane of 5 (No. 1655a) .. 2·00

B **43** Dog and Cat

1996 (1 Oct). *Australian Pets. Multicoloured cover as Type* B **43**. *Self-adhesive.*
SB111 $4.50, booklet containing pane of 10 45 c. (No. 1664a) .. .. 5·50

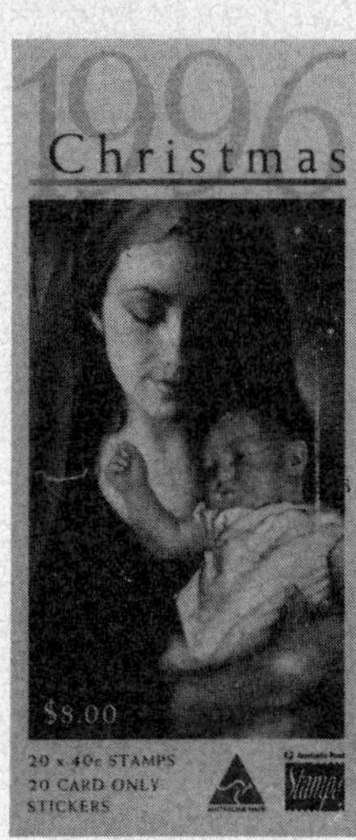

B **44** Madonna and Child

1996 (1 Nov). *Christmas. Multicoloured cover as Type* B **44**. *Self-adhesive.*
SB112 $8 booklet containing pane of 20 40 c. (No 1671a) and 20 self-adhesive "Card Only" labels affixed to the inner cover .. .. 9·00

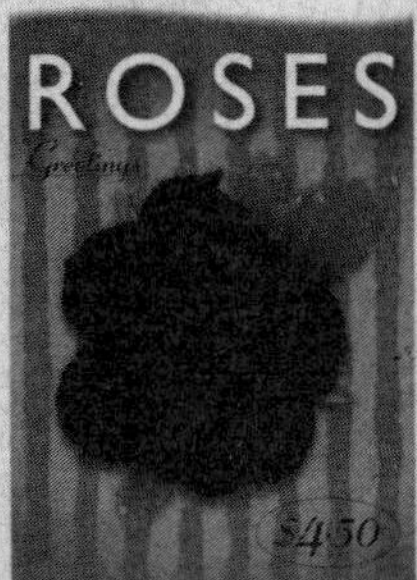

B 45 Rose

1997 (29 Jan). *St. Valentine's Day. Multicoloured cover as Type* B **45**. *Self-adhesive.*
SB113 $4.50, booklet containing pane of 10 45 c. (No. 1678a) and 12 self-adhesive greetings stickers affixed to the inner cover .. .. 6·00

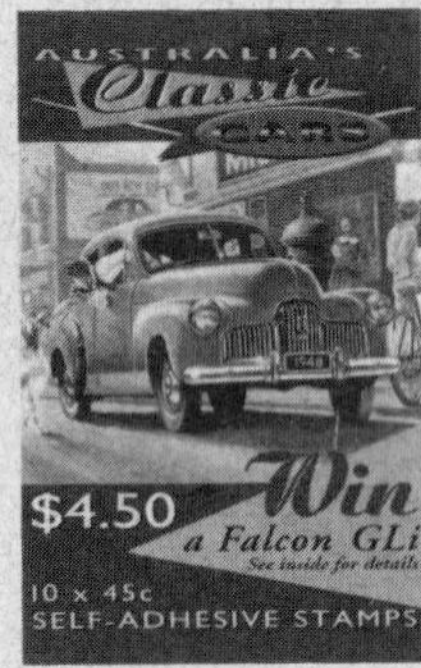

B 46 GMH Holden 48-215 (FX)

1997 (27 Feb). *Classic Cars. Multicoloured cover as Type* B **46**. *Self-adhesive.*
SB114 $4.50, booklet containing pane of 10 45 c. (No. 1683a) .. .. 5·00

B 47 Classic Cars
(*Illustration reduced. Actual size* 155×105 *mm*)

1997 (27 Feb). *Classic Cars Prestige Booklet. Multicoloured cover as Type* B **47**.
SB115 $9.95, booklet containing four panes of 4 45 c. (Nos. 1679b/82a), two pre-paid postcards and 16 self-adhesive labels .. .. .. 10·00

B 48 Wetland Birds

1997 (2 June). *Flora and Fauna. Multicoloured cover as Type* B **48**. *Self-adhesive.*
SB116 $4.50, booklet containing pane of 10 45 c. (No. 1634a) .. .. 3·50

B 49 Barking Owl B 50 Two Angels

1997 (1 Oct). *Nocturnal Animals. Multicoloured cover as Type* B **49**. *Self-adhesive.*
SB117 $4.50, booklet containing pane of 10 45 c. (No. 1720b) .. .. 5·00

1997 (3 Nov). *Christmas. Children's Nativity Play. Multicoloured cover as Type* B **50**. *Self-adhesive.*
SB118 $8 booklet containing pane of 20 40 c. (No. 1726a) and 20 self-adhesive "Card Only" labels affixed to the inner cover .. .. 7·00

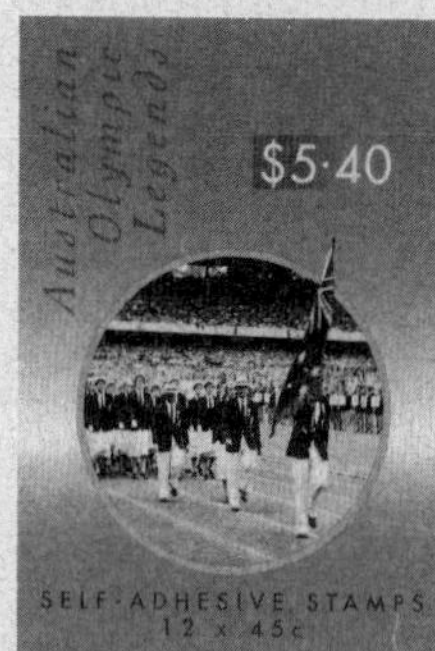

B 51 Australian Athletes

1998 (21 Jan). *Australian Legends (2nd series). Olympic Gold Medal Winners. Multicoloured cover as Type* B **51**. *Self-adhesive.*
SB119 $5.40, booklet containing pane of 12 45 c. (No. 1743b) .. .. 4·75

B 52 Champagne Rose B 53 Brolga

1998 (12 Feb). *Greetings Stamp. Multicoloured cover as Type* B **52**. *Self-adhesive.*
SB120 $4.50, booklet containing pane of 10 45 c. (No. 1756a) and 12 self-adhesive greetings stickers affixed to the inner cover .. .. 4·50

No. SB120 also exists overprinted "Natstamp'98 Canberra 14–16 March 1998" for sale at this exhibition.

1998 (12 Feb). *Wetland Birds. Multicoloured cover as Type* B **53**. *Self-adhesive. Stamps loose within cover.*
SB121 $9 booklet containing 20×45 c. (Nos. 1634d/7d) 10·00

No. SB121 was introduced as a trial product and was available at a number of Post Offices in Victoria and from Philatelic counters.

B 54 Farmhouse and Fields

1998 (21 Apr). *Farming. Multicoloured cover as Type* B **5** *Self-adhesive.*
SB122 $4.50, booklet containing pane of 10 45 c. (No. 1764a) .. .. 4·

B 55 Pouring Tea
(*Illustration reduced. Actual size* 145×103 *mm*)

1998 (13 Aug). *"The Teapot of Truth" Prestige Booklet. Mu coloured cover as Type* B **55**. *Stapled.*
SB123 $9.95, booklet containing three panes of 4 45 c. (Nos. 1805a/7a), panes of 2 $1 and $1.20 (Nos. 1808a/9a), pre-paid postcard and 16 self-adhesive labels 7

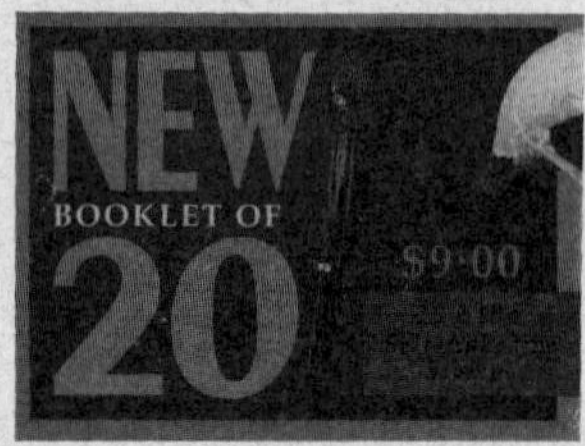

B 56

1998 (1 Sept). *Wetland Birds. Multicoloured cover as T* B **56**. *Self-adhesive.*
SB124 $9 booklet containing pane of 20 45 c. (No. 1634c) .. ..

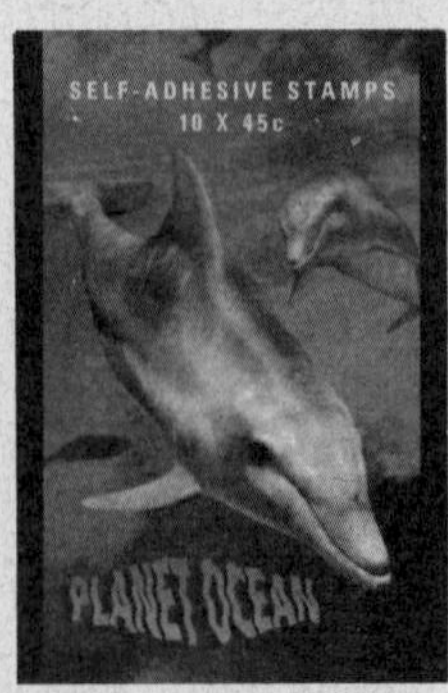

B 57 Bottlenose Dolphin

1998 (1 Oct). *International Year of the Ocean. Multicolou cover as Type* B **57**. *Self-adhesive.*
SB125 $4.50, booklet containing pane of 10 45 c. (No. 1829b) .. ..

COVER PRICES

Cover factors are quoted at the beginning of each country for most issues to 1945. An explanation of the system can be found on page x. The factors quoted do not, however, apply to philatelic covers.

B **58** Christmas Star

98 (2 Nov). *Christmas. Multicoloured cover as Type* B **58**. *Self-adhesive.*
B126 $8 booklet containing pane of 20 40 c. (No. 1835a) and 20 self-adhesive "Card Only" labels affixed to the inner cover .. .. 6·00

B **59**

99 (22 Jan). *Australian Legends (3rd series). Arthur Boyd (painter). Multicoloured cover as Type* B **59**. *Self-adhesive.*
B127 $4.50, booklet containing pane of 10 45 c. (No. 1840a) .. .. 3·50

Military Post Booklets

Issued for the use of Australian Forces in Vietnam.

MB 1

967 (30 May–Sept). *Yellow-green and black on white cover as Type* MB 1. *Pane attached by selvedge.*
MB1 50 c. booklet containing 5 c. (No. 386) in block of 10 .. .. 80·00
a. Containing No. 386*b* (Sept) .. .. 80·00

968 (Mar). *Yellow-green and black on white cover as Type* MB 1. *Pane attached by selvedge.*
MB2 50 c. booklet containing 5 c. (No. 386c) in block of 10 .. .. 55·00

POSTAGE DUE STAMPS

POSTAGE DUE PRINTERS. Nos. D1/62 were typographed at the New South Wales Government Printing Office, Sydney. They were not used in Victoria.

INVERTED WATERMARKS. These occur frequently amongst Nos. D1/62. In some instances examples with inverted watermarks are more common than those showing the watermark upright.

D 1

D 2

D 3

Type D **1** adapted from plates of New South Wales Type D **1**. No letters at foot.

1902 (1 July). *Chalk-surfaced paper. Wmk Type* D **2**.

(a) P 11½, 12

D 1	D 1	½d. emerald-green ..	3·00	3·75
D 2		1d. emerald-green ..	12·00	5·50
D 3		2d. emerald-green ..	28·00	6·50
D 4		3d. emerald-green ..	28·00	18·00
D 5		4d. emerald-green ..	42·00	11·00
D 6		6d. emerald-green ..	55·00	9·00
D 7		8d. emerald-green ..	95·00	70·00
D 8		5s. emerald-green ..	£180	70·00
D1/8		.. *Set of* 8	£400	£170
D1/7 Optd "Specimen"		.. *Set of* 7	£275	

(b) P 11½, 12, *compound with* 11

D 9	D 1	1d. emerald-green ..	£200	£110
D10		2d. emerald-green ..	£250	£110

(c) P 11

D12	D 1	1d. emerald-green ..	£700	£300

The ½d., 6d. and 8d. exist in dull green.

Stamps may be found showing portions of the letters "N S W" at foot.

1902–4. *Type* D **3**, *space at foot filled in. Chalky paper. Wmk Type* D **2**.

(a) P 11½, 12

D13	1d. emerald-green ..	£140	75·00
D14	2d. emerald-green ..	£140	60·00
D15	3d. emerald-green ..	£170	60·00
D17	5d. emerald-green ..	40·00	9·50
D18	10d. emerald-green ..	70·00	17·00
D19	1s. emerald-green ..	55·00	10·00
D20	2s. emerald-green ..	£100	16·00
D21	5s. emerald-green ..	£600	£160

(b) P 11½, 12, *compound with* 11

D22	½d. emerald-green ..	6·00	5·00
D23	1d. emerald-green ..	6·00	2·50
D24	2d. emerald-green ..	20·00	2·75
D25	3d. emerald-green ..	60·00	7·50
D26	4d. emerald-green ..	50·00	8·50
D27	5d. emerald-green ..	50·00	15·00
D28	6d. emerald-green ..	50·00	9·50
D29	8d. emerald-green ..	£120	40·00
D30	10d. emerald-green ..	90·00	18·00
D31	1s. emerald-green ..	85·00	18·00
D32	2s. emerald-green ..	£120	27·00
D33	5s. emerald-green ..	£180	21·00

(c) P 11

D34	½d. emerald-green ..	£190	£130
D35	1d. emerald-green ..	65·00	18·00
D36	2d. emerald-green ..	£100	20·00
D37	3d. emerald-green ..	65·00	26·00
D38	4d. emerald-green ..	£120	35·00
D39	5d. emerald-green ..	£160	20·00
D40	6d. emerald-green ..	85·00	14·00
D41	1s. emerald-green ..	£190	38·00
D42	5s. emerald-green ..	£475	95·00
D43	10s. emerald-green ..	£1600	£1300
D44	20s. emerald-green ..	£3250	£2250
D13/44	.. *Set of* 14	£5000	£3250
D13/44 Optd "Specimen"	.. *Set of* 14	£850	

Most values exist in dull green.

D 4

D 6

1906 (From Jan)–**08.** *Chalky paper. Wmk Type* D **4**.

(a) P 11½, 12, *compound with* 11

D45	D 3	½d. green (1907) ..	9·00	7·00
D46		1d. green ..	12·00	2·25
D47		2d. green ..	28·00	3·50
D48		3d. green ..	£450	£190
D49		4d. green (1907) ..	60·00	20·00
D50		6d. green (1908) ..	£170	20·00
D45/50		.. *Set of* 6	£650	£225

(b) P 11

D51	D 3	1d. dull green ..	£700	£275
D52		4d. dull green ..	£1000	£450

Shades exist.

1907 (From July). *Chalky paper. Wmk Type* w **11** *(see Introduction). P* 11½ × 11.

D53	D 3	½d. dull green ..	20·00	55·00
D54		1d. dull green ..	60·00	27·00
D55		2d. dull green ..	£100	70·00
D56		4d. dull green ..	£160	80·00
D57		6d. dull green ..	£200	£100
D53/7		.. *Set of* 5	£475	£275

1908 (Sept)–**09.** *Stroke after figure of value. Chalky paper. Wmk Type* D **4**.

(a) P 11½ × 11

D58	D 6	1s. dull green (1909) ..	75·00	8·00
D59		5s. dull green ..	£200	48·00

(b) P 11

D60	D 6	2s. dull green (1909) ..	£850	£1200
D61		10s. dull green (1909) ..	£2000	£2250
D62		20s. dull green (1909) ..	£5000	£6000
D58/62		.. *Set of* 5	£7500	£8500

Nos. D61/2 were only issued in New South Wales.

D 7

Die I   Die II

1d.

Die I   Die II

2d.

(Typo J. B. Cooke, Melbourne)

1909 (July)–**1910.** *Type* D **7**. *Wmk Crown over A, Type* w **11**.

(a) P 12×12½ *(comb) or* 12½ *(line)*

D63	½d. rosine and yellow-green ..	13·00	25·00
D64	1d. rosine and yellow-green (I) ..	14·00	4·00
	a. Die II (7.10) ..	16·00	1·50
D65	2d. rosine and yellow-green (I) ..	24·00	3·50
	a. Die II (7.10) ..	18·00	1·50
D66	3d. rosine and yellow-green (1910) ..	24·00	11·00
D67	4d. rosine and yellow-green ..	22·00	4·50
D68	6d. rosine and yellow-green ..	27·00	7·00
D69	1s. rosine and yellow-green ..	30·00	4·00
D70	2s. rosine and yellow-green ..	70·00	13·00
D71	5s. rosine and yellow-green ..	90·00	15·00
D72	10s. rosine and yellow-green ..	£250	£150
D73	£1 rosine and yellow-green ..	£475	£275
D63/73	.. *Set of* 11	£900	£450

(b) P 11

D74	1d. rose and yellow-green (II) ..	£1200	£500
D74*a*	2d. rose and yellow-green (II) ..		
D75	6d. rose and yellow-green ..	£5500	£2750

Only one unused example, without gum, and another pen-cancelled are known of No. D74*a*.

The 1d. of this printing is distinguishable from No. D78 by the colours, the green being very yellow and the rose having less of a carmine tone. The paper is thicker and slightly toned, that of No. D78 being pure white; the gum is thick and yellowish, No. D78 having thin white gum.

All later issues of the 1d. and 2d. are Die II.

(Typo J. B. Cooke and T. S. Harrison (from May 1918))

1912–23. *Type* D **7**. *Thin paper. White gum. W* w **11**. *(a) P* 12½.

D76	½d. scarlet and pale yellow-green (12.12)	22·00	26·00

(b) P 11

D77	½d. rosine and bright apple-green (10.14)	11·00	15·00
	a. Wmk sideways ..	6·00	7·00
D78	1d. rosine and bright apple-green (10.14)	5·00	1·50
	a. Wmk sideways ..	9·00	1·50

(c) P 14

D79	½d. rosine and bright apple-green (1914)	80·00	£100
	a. Carmine and apple-green (Harrison) (1920) ..	9·00	16·00
D80	1d. rosine and bright apple-green (10.14)	55·00	12·00
	a. Scarlet and pale yellow-green (1918)	20·00	3·75
	b. Carmine and apple-green (Harrison) (1919) ..	11·00	3·25
D81	2d. scarlet and pale yellow-green (1918)	17·00	6·00
	a. Carmine and apple-green (Harrison) (1920) ..	18·00	3·50
D82	3d. rosine and apple-green (5.16) ..	70·00	32·00
	a. Wmk sideways ..	£1600	£1000
D83	4d. carmine and apple-green (Harrison) (1918) ..	90·00	55·00
	a. Wmk sideways ..	£475	£325
	b. Carmine and pale yellow-green (Harrison) (26.4.21) ..	65·00	50·00
D85	1s. scarlet and pale yellow-green (7.23)	25·00	12·00
D86	10s. scarlet and pale yellow-green (5.21)	£850	£1100
D87	£1 scarlet and pale yellow-green (5.21)	£700	£900
D76/87	.. *Set of* 8	£1500	£1900

Although printed by Cooke, the three higher values were not issued until some years later.

(Typo T. S. Harrison (to Feb. 1926), A. J. Mullet (to June 1927) ar J. Ash (later))

1919–30. *Type* D **7**. *W* **6**. *(a) P* 14.

D91	½d. carmine and yellow-green (5.23) ..	2·50	4·
D92	1d. carmine and yellow-green (1.3.22) ..	4·00	
D93	1½d. carmine and yellow-green (3.25) ..	1·50	9·
D94	2d. carmine and yellow-green (20.3.22) ..	3·50	1·
D95	3d. carmine and yellow-green (12.11.19) ..	9·50	3·
D96	4d. carmine and yellow-green (13.2.22) .	35·00	12·
D97	6d. carmine and yellow-green (13.2.22) .	26·00	11·

(b) P 11

D98	4d. carmine and yellow-green (9.30) ..	4·00	4
D91/8	.. *Set of* 8	75·00	42

All values perf 14 were printed by Harrison and all except t 4d. by Mullett and Ash. There is a wide variation of shades in th issue.

(Typo J. Ash)

1931–37. *Type* D **7**. *W* **15**. *(a) P* 14.

D100	1d. carmine and yellow-green (10.31) ..	7·00	11·
	a. Imperf between (horiz pair) ..	†	
D102	2d. carmine and yellow-green (19.10.31)	7·00	11·

(b) P 11

D105	½d. carmine and yellow-green (4.34) ..	12·00	14·
D106	1d. carmine and yellow-green (11.32) ..	7·50	1·
D107	2d. carmine and yellow-green (29.9.32)	8·50	
D108	3d. carmine and yellow-green (3.37) ..	70·00	70·
D109	4d. carmine and yellow-green (26.7.34) ..	3·75	2·
D110	6d. carmine and yellow-green (4.36) ..	£300	£2
D111	1s. carmine and yellow-green (8.34) ..	48·00	32·
D105/11	.. *Set of* 7	£375	£3

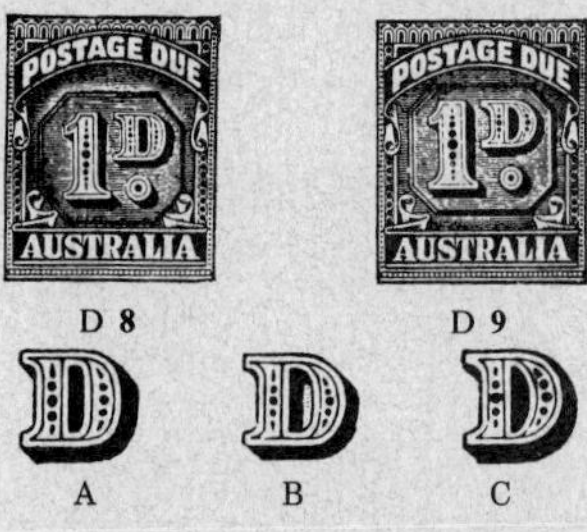

D 8   D 9

A   B   C

The differences are found in the middle of the "D"

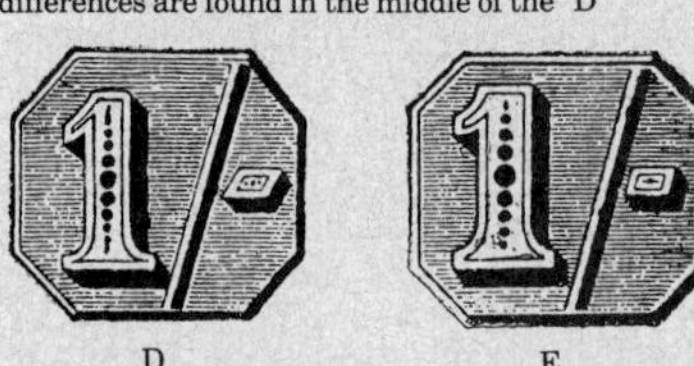

D   E

Type E. Larger "1" with only three background lines abov hyphen more upright.

(Frame recess. Value typo J. Ash)

1938–39. *W* **15**. *P* 14½×14.

D112	D 8	½d. carmine and green (A) (1939) ..	3·75	2·
D113		1d. carmine and green (A) ..	10·00	
D114		2d. carmine and green (A) ..	10·00	1·
D115		3d. carmine and green (B) ..	28·00	13·
D116		4d. carmine and green (A) ..	12·00	
D117		6d. carmine and green (A) ..	70·00	42·
D118		1s. carmine and green (D) ..	55·00	12·
D112/18		.. *Set of* 7	£170	65·

Shades exist.

1946–57. *Redrawn as Type* C *and* E (1s.). *W* **15**. *P* 14½ × 14.

D119	D 9	½d. carmine and green (9.56) ..	85	3·
D120		1d. carmine and green (11.1.47) ..	1·25	
D121		2d. carmine and green (9.46) ..	4·50	1·
D122		3d. carmine and green (25.9.46) ..	6·00	1
D123		4d. carmine and green (11.52) ..	9·00	1·
D124		5d. carmine and green (12.48) ..	12·00	3·
D125		6d. carmine and green (9.47) ..	10·00	1·
D126		7d. carmine and green (26.8.53) ..	4·25	8·
D127		8d. carmine and green (24.4.57) ..	10·00	25·
D128		1s. carmine and green (9.47) ..	18·00	1·
D119/28		.. *Set of* 10	65·00	42·

There are many shades in this issue.

D 10

1953 (26 Aug)–**60.** *W* **15**. *P* 14½ × 14.

D129	D 10	1s. carmine & yellow-grn (17.2.54)	7·50	3·
		a. Carmine and deep green ..	11·00	8·
D130		2s. carmine and yellow-green ..	18·00	12·
		a. Carmine and deep green ..	£170	60·
D131		5s. carmine and green ..	18·00	6·
		a. Carmine and deep green (1960)	12·00	
D129/31		.. *Set of* 3	40·00	19·
D129*a*/31*a*		.. *Set of* 3	£170	60·

A new die was introduced for No. D131*a*. This differs from t original in having a distinct gap between the two arms of the " On No. D131 these two features are joined.

I

II

'ype I. Numeral, "D" ar d stop, generally unoutlined.

'ype II. Clear white line sepai ates numeral, etc. from background.

958–60. *No wmk. P* 14½ × 14.

132 D 9 ½d. carmine and deep green (II) (27.2.58) .. .. 1·60 1·75
133 1d. carmine and deep green (I) (25.2.58) .. .. 3·00 3·50
a. Type II (6.59) .. .. .. 1·00 65
)134 3d. carmine and deep green (II) (25.5.60) .. .. 1·75 2·75
)135 4d. carmine and deep green (I) (27.2.58) .. .. 4·00 9·00
a. Type II (6.59) .. .. .. 3·00 8·50
)136 5d. carmine and deep green (I) (27.2.58) .. .. 13·00 15·00
a. Type II (6.59) .. .. .. 60·00 60·00
)137 6d. carmine and deep green (II) (25.5.60) .. .. 2·75 3·00
)138 8d. carmine and deep green (II) (25.2.58) .. .. 10·00 28·00
)139 10d. carmine and deep green (II) (9.12.59) .. .. 4·50 3·25
)140 D 10 1s. carmine and deep green (8.9.58) 5·00 2·75
a. Deep carmine & deep green (6.59) .. .. 5·50 4·00
)141 2s. deep carmine and deep green (8.3.60) .. .. 22·00 22·00
)132/41 .. .. .. *Set of* 10 55·00 80·00

Nos. D140*a* and D141. Value tablets are re-engraved and have thicker and sharper printed lines than before.

The use of Postage Due stamps ceased on 13 January 1963.

OFFICIAL STAMPS

From 1902 the departments of the Commonwealth government were issued with stamps of the various Australian States perforated "OS" to denote official use. These were replaced in 1913 by Commonwealth of Australia issues with similar perforated initials as listed below.

During the same period the administrations of the Australian States used their own stamps and those of the Commonwealth perforated with other initials for the same purpose. These States issues are outside the scope of this catalogue.

Most shades listed under the postage issues also exist perforated "OS". Only those which are worth more than the basic colours are included below.

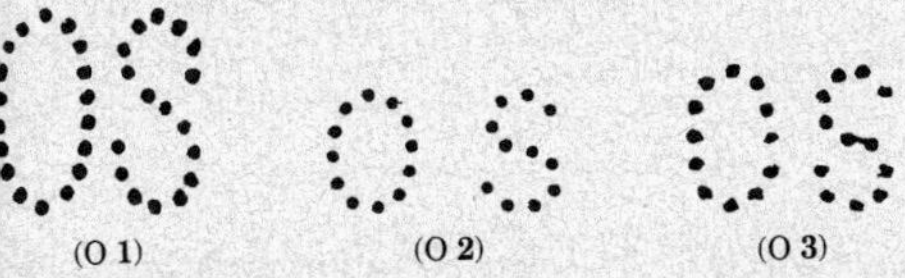
(O 1) (O 2) (O 3)

1913 (Jan–Apr). *Nos.* 1/16 *punctured as Type* O 1. *W* 2. *P* 12.

O1 1 ½d. green (Die I) .. .. 11·00 5·50
w. Wmk inverted .. .. .. † 50·00
O2 1d. red (Die I) .. .. 9·50 1·75
cw. Wmk inverted .. .. .. 50·00 5·00
d. Die II .. .. 14·00 3·00
dw. Wmk inverted .. .. .. 50·00 5·00
O3 2d. grey (Die I) .. .. 23·00 7·00
O4 2½d. indigo (Die II) .. .. .. £140 85·00
O5 3d. olive (Die I) .. .. .. 65·00 28·00
ca. In pair with Die II £475
dw. Wmk inverted .. .. .. 75·00 32·00
e. Die II .. .. £180 50·00
ew. Wmk inverted .. .. .. £225 60·00
O6 4d. orange (Die II) .. .. .. £100 16·00
a. Orange-yellow .. .. .. £160 65·00
O7 5d. chestnut (Die II) .. .. .. 75·00 23·00
O8 6d. ultramarine (Die II) .. .. .. 65·00 13·00
w. Wmk inverted .. .. .. 75·00 35·00
O9 9d. violet (Die II) .. .. .. 70·00 30·00
w. Wmk inverted .. .. .. † £600
O10 1s. emerald (Die II) .. .. .. 95·00 20·00
w. Wmk inverted .. .. .. £130 35·00
O11 2s. brown (Die II) .. .. .. £170 80·00
a. Double print .. .. .. † £1000
O12 5s. grey and yellow £375 £180
O13 10s. grey and pink £1100 £700
O14 £1 brown and ultramarine £1800 £1200
O15 £2 black and rose £3250 £1900
O1/15 .. .. *Set of* 15 £6500 £3750

1914. *Nos.* 1/16 *punctured as Type* O 2. *W* 2. *P* 12.

O16 1 ½d. green (Die I) .. .. 8·00 3·75
w. Wmk inverted .. .. .. † 30·00
O17 1d. red (Die I) .. .. 9·50 3·50
d. Die II .. .. 15·00 2·00
e. Die IIA .. .. 11·00 2·25
O18 2d. grey (Die I) .. .. 38·00 4·50
w. Wmk inverted .. .. .. 48·00 8·00
O19 2½d. indigo (Die II) .. .. .. £120 65·00
O20 3d. olive (Die I) .. .. .. 50·00 5·50
e. Die II .. .. £130 40·00
ew. Wmk inverted .. .. .. £160 50·00
O21 4d. orange (Die II) .. .. .. £110 50·00
a. Orange-yellow .. .. .. £160 70·00
O22 5d. chestnut (Die II) .. .. .. 90·00 32·00
O23 6d. ultramarine (Die II) .. .. .. 60·00 12·00
w. Wmk inverted .. .. .. 75·00 30·00
O24 9d. violet (Die II) .. .. .. 60·00 17·00
O25 1s. emerald (Die II) .. .. .. 60·00 16·00
O26 1 2s. brown (Die II) .. .. .. £150 65·00
O27 5s. grey and yellow £375 £200
O28 10s. grey and pink £1300 £850
O29 £1 brown and ultramarine £2000 £1300
O30 £2 black and rose £3500 £2000
O16/30 .. .. *Set of* 15 £7000 £4000

1915. *Nos.* 24 *and* 26/30 *punctured as Type* O 2. *W* 5. *P* 12.

O31 1 2d. grey (Die I) .. .. 55·00 11·00
O33 6d. ultramarine (Die II) .. .. .. 85·00 15·00
b. Die IIA £750 £170
O34 9d. violet (Die II) .. .. .. £130 48·00
O35 1s. blue-green (Die II) .. .. .. £120 28·00
O36 2s. brown (Die II) .. .. .. £425 70·00
O37 5s. grey and yellow £500 £100
w. Wmk inverted £600 £130

1914–21. *Nos.* 20/3 *punctured as Type* O 2. *W* 5. *P* 14.

O38 5*a* ½d. bright green .. .. .. 8·00 2·00
w. Wmk inverted .. .. .. 12·00 5·00
O39 1d. carmine-red (I) (No. 21c) .. .. 9·00 60
gw. Wmk inverted .. .. .. 14·00 2·00
h. Die II .. .. £250 10·00
O41 4d. orange .. .. 38·00 3·50
a. Yellow-orange .. .. .. 50·00 7·50
b. Pale orange-yellow .. .. .. 80·00 13·00
c. Lemon-yellow .. .. .. £120 38·00
w. Wmk inverted .. .. .. 50·00 15·00
O42 5d. brown .. .. 45·00 3·00
aw. Wmk inverted .. .. .. 75·00 18·00
b. Printed on the gummed side (wmk inverted) £450
c. Perf 14¼×14 (comb) .. .. ..
cw. Wmk inverted .. ..

1915–28. *Nos.* 35/45 *punctured as Type* O 2. *W* 6. *P* 12.

O43 1 2d. grey (Die I) .. .. 15·00 3·25
bw. Wmk inverted .. .. .. 20·00 5·50
d. Die II .. .. 25·00 10·00
O44 2½d. deep blue (Die II) .. .. .. 38·00 7·50
w. Wmk inverted .. .. .. † 20·00
O45 3d. yellow-olive (Die I) .. .. .. 20·00 2·75
cw. Wmk inverted .. .. .. 24·00 6·00
d. Die II .. .. 75·00 38·00
dw. Wmk inverted .. .. .. £100 50·00
e. Die IIB .. .. 20·00 7·50
ew. Wmk inverted .. .. .. 30·00 10·00
O46 6d. ultramarine (Die II) .. .. .. 30·00 3·50
a. Die IIA £450 £110
d. Die IIB .. .. 38·00 7·50
dw. Wmk inverted .. .. .. 50·00 15·00
O47 9d. violet (Die II) .. .. .. 22·00 7·00
b. Die IIB .. .. 22·00 6·00
bw. Wmk inverted .. .. .. † 13·00
O48 1s. blue-green (Die II) .. .. .. 23·00 2·50
aw. Wmk inverted .. .. .. 50·00 13·00
b. Die IIB .. .. 23·00 3·50
O49 2s. brown (Die II) .. .. .. £110 13·00
b. Red-brown (aniline) .. .. .. £225 40·00
w. Wmk inverted .. .. .. £180 60·00
O50 5s. grey and yellow .. .. .. £150 40·00
w. Wmk inverted .. .. .. £225 75·00
O51 10s. grey and pink .. .. .. £250 60·00
w. Wmk inverted .. .. ..
O52 £1 chocolate and dull blue £1400 £900
ab. Wmk sideways. *Chestnut & brt blue* † £4000
aw. Wmk inverted .. .. ..
O53 £2 black and rose £2000 £850
O43/53 .. .. *Set of* 11 £3250 £1600

1916–20. *Nos.* 47/f *and* 5d. *as No.* 23 *punctured as Type* O 2. *W* 5. *Rough paper. P* 14.

O54 5*a* 1d. scarlet (Die I) .. .. .. 16·00 3·00
a. Deep red .. .. 16·00 3·00
b. Rose-red .. .. 16·00 3·00
c. Rosine .. .. 55·00 8·50
dw. Wmk inverted .. .. .. 20·00 4·50
e. Die II. *Rose-red* .. .. .. £200 11·00
f. Die II. *Rosine* .. .. .. £400 38·00
fw. Wmk inverted .. .. ..
O60 5d. bright chestnut (1920) £1200 £100

All examples of the 5d. on this paper were perforated "OS".

1918–20. *Nos.* 51 *and* 53/5 *punctured as Type* O 2. *W* 6*a*. *P* 14.

O61 5*a* ½d. green .. .. 12·00 1·75
w. Wmk inverted .. .. .. 16·00 8·00
O63 1d. carmine (I) .. .. .. 45·00 24·00
O64 1½d. black-brown .. .. .. 15·00 2·25
a. Very thin paper .. .. .. 30·00 11·00
w. Wmk inverted .. .. .. 35·00 8·00
O65 1½d. red-brown .. .. .. 15·00 2·00
w. Wmk inverted .. .. .. 30·00 8·00
O61/5 .. .. *Set of* 4 80·00 27·00

1918–23. *Nos.* 56/9 *and* 61/6 *punctured as Type* O 2. *W* 5. *P* 14.

O66 5*a* ½d. orange .. .. 13·00 7·50
O67 1d. violet .. .. 19·00 7·00
w. Wmk inverted .. .. .. † £1100
O68 1½d. black-brown .. .. .. 19·00 2·25
w. Wmk inverted .. .. .. 30·00 6·00
O69 1½d. deep red-brown .. .. .. 16·00 1·50
w. Wmk inverted .. .. .. 28·00 6·00
O70 1½d. green .. .. 11·00 1·00
O71 2d. brown-orange .. .. .. 12·00 1·25
w. Wmk inverted .. .. .. 26·00 8·00
O72 2d. bright rose-scarlet .. .. .. 12·00 2·75
w. Wmk inverted .. .. .. 25·00 10·00
O73 4d. violet .. .. 32·00 13·00
O74 4d. ultramarine .. .. .. 55·00 9·00
O75 1s. 4d. pale blue .. .. .. 50·00 15·00
b. Deep turquoise £450 £275
O66/75 .. .. *Set of* 10 £200 50·00

1923–24. *Nos.* 73/5 *punctured as Type* O 2. *W* 6. *P* 12.

O76 1 6d. chestnut (Die IIB) .. .. .. 17·00 2·50
O77 2s. maroon (Die II) .. .. .. 55·00 12·00
O78 £1 grey (Die IIB) £475 £275
O76/8 .. .. *Set of* 3 £500 £275

1924. *Nos.* 76/84 *punctured as Type* O 2. *P* 14. (*a*) *W* 5.

O79 5*a* 1d. sage-green .. .. .. 5·50 1·10
O80 1½d. scarlet .. .. 4·75 50
w. Wmk inverted .. .. .. 40·00 10·00
wa. Printed on the gummed side .. £160
O81 2d. red-brown .. .. 20·00 11·00
a. Bright red-brown .. .. .. 35·00 18·00
O82 3d. dull ultramarine .. .. .. 30·00 5·50
O83 4d. olive-yellow .. .. .. 35·00 4·00
O84 4½d. violet .. .. 65·00 12·00
w. Wmk inverted .. .. .. † £750

(*b*) *W* 6*a*

O85 5*a* 1d. sage-green .. .. .. 11·00 12·00

(*c*) *No wmk*

O86 5*a* 1d. sage-green .. .. .. 55·00 50·00
O87 1½d. scarlet .. .. 60·00 50·00
O79/87 .. .. *Set of* 9 £250 £130

1926–30. *Nos.* 85/104 *punctured as Type* O 2. *W* 7. (*a*) *P* 14

O88 5*a* ½d. orange .. .. £140 65·00
O89 1d. sage-green .. .. .. 8·00 50
O90 1½d. scarlet .. .. 15·00 1·60
a. Golden scarlet .. .. .. 17·00 4·00
w. Wmk inverted .. .. .. 16·00 2·50
O92 2d. red-brown (Die I) .. .. .. 95·00 35·00
O93 3d. dull ultramarine .. .. .. 40·00 11·00
w. Wmk inverted .. .. .. 40·00 11·00
O94 4d. yellow-olive .. .. .. £100 35·00
O95 4½d. violet .. .. 90·00 28·00
O96 1s. 4d. pale greenish blue £200 £110
O88/96 .. .. *Set of* 8 £600 £275

(*b*) *P* 13½×12½

O97 5*a* ½d. orange .. .. 2·50 60
O98 1d. sage-green (Die I) .. .. .. 2·50 60
b. Die II .. .. 75·00 90·00
O100 1½d. scarlet .. .. 4·00 80
a. Golden scarlet .. .. .. 3·25 1·00
w. Wmk inverted .. .. .. 5·00 2·50
O102 1½d. red-brown .. .. .. 13·00 3·50
O103 2d. red-brown (Die II) .. .. .. 20·00 11·00
O104 2d. golden scarlet (Die II) .. .. 13·00 2·50
a. Die III .. .. 10·50 1·75
aw. Wmk inverted .. .. .. 17·00 6·50
O106 3d. dull ultramarine (Die I) .. .. 28·00 5·00
aw. Wmk inverted .. .. .. 28·00 12·00
b. Die II. *Deep ultramarine* .. .. 14·00 1·50
bw. Wmk inverted £1200 £750
O108 4d. yellow-olive .. .. .. 18·00 3·50
O109 4½d. violet .. .. 60·00 60·00
O110 5d. orange-brown (Die II) .. .. 38·00 5·00
O111 1s. 4d. turquoise .. .. .. £160 20·00
O97/111 .. .. *Set of* 11 £300 95·00

1927 (9 May). *Opening of Parliament House, Canberra. No.* 105 *punctured as Type* O 3.

O112 8 1½d. brownish lake .. .. .. 13·00 7·50

1928 (29 Oct). *National Stamp Exhibition, Melbourne. No.* 106 *punctured as Type* O 2.

O113 3d. blue .. .. 13·00 9·00

1929–30. *Nos.* 107/14 *punctured as Type* O 2. *W* 7. *P* 12.

O114 1 6d. chestnut (Die IIB) .. .. .. 17·00 2·50
O115 9d. violet (Die IIB) .. .. .. 30·00 5·50
O116 1s. blue-green (Die IIB) .. .. .. 23·00 3·00
O117 2s. maroon (Die II) .. .. .. 60·00 8·00
O118 5s. grey and yellow .. .. .. £160 40·00
O118*a* 10s. grey and pink .. .. ..
O118*b* £2 black and rose £2000

1929 (20 May). *Air. No.* 115 *punctured as Type* O 3.

O119 9 3d. green .. .. 20·00 12·00

1929 (28 Sept). *Centenary of Western Australia. No.* 116 *punctured as Type* O 3.

O120 10 1½d. dull scarlet .. .. .. 13·00 8·00

1930 (2 June). *Centenary of Exploration of River Murray by Capt. Sturt. Nos.* 117/18 *punctured as Type* O 2.

O121 11 1½d. scarlet .. .. 6·50 4·50
O122 3d. blue .. .. 13·00 7·50

OS

(O 4)

1931 (4 May). Nos. 121/2 *optd with Type* O 4.

O123 13 2d. rose-red .. .. 55·00 16·00
O124 3d. blue .. .. £200 32·00

For No. 139 overprinted with Type O 4, see No. 139*a*.

1932 (Feb)–**33.** *Optd as Type* O 4. (*a*) *W* 7. (i) *P* 13½×12½.

O125 5*a* 2d. golden scarlet (Die III) .. .. 8·00 90
a. Opt inverted .. .. .. † £2750
O126 4d. yellow-olive (3.32) .. .. .. 16·00 5·00

(ii) *P* 12

O127 1 6d. chestnut (3.32) .. .. .. 40·00 42·00

(*b*) *W* 15. (i) *P* 13½×12½

O128 5*a* ½d. orange (11.7.32) .. .. .. 4·75 1·50
a. Opt inverted £3250 £1900
O129 1d. green (3.32) .. .. .. 8·25 45
w. Wmk inverted .. .. .. 45·00 25·00
x. Wmk reversed .. .. .. £150 60·00
O130 2d. golden scarlet (Die III) .. .. 6·50 55
a. Opt inverted .. .. .. † £3000
O131 3d. ultramarine (Die II) (2.33) .. .. 7·50 4·00
O132 5d. orange-brown (7.32) .. .. .. 35·00 27·00

(ii) *P* 12

O133 1 6d. chestnut (9.32) .. .. .. 20·00 20·00
a. Opt inverted .. .. .. † £4500

(*c*) *Recess. No wmk. P* 11

O134 18 2d. scarlet (3.32) .. .. .. 5·00 2·00
O135 3d. blue (3.32) .. .. 14·00 7·00
O136 17 1s. green (3.32) .. .. .. 40·00 35·00

Issue of overprinted official stamps ceased in February 1933 and thereafter mail from the federal administration was carried free.

BRITISH COMMONWEALTH OCCUPATION FORCE (JAPAN)

Nos. J1/7 were used by the Australian forces occupying Japan after the Second World War. Initially their military post offices supplied unoverprinted Australian stamps, but it was decided to introduce the overprinted issue to prevent currency speculation.

B.C.O.F.
JAPAN
1946
(1)

B.C.O.F.
JAPAN
1946
(2)

1946 — Wrong fount "6" (left pane R. 9/4)

O.F.O.F. AN — Normal

AN — Narrow "N" (right pane R. 1/8)

1946 (11 Oct)–**48**. *Stamps of Australia optd as T* **1** (*1d., 3d.*) *or T* **2** (*others*) *at Hiroshima Printing Co, Japan.*

J1 **27** ½d. orange (No. 179) .. .. .. 3·00 4·25
a. Wrong fount "6" .. .. .. 60·00 70·00
b. Narrow "N" .. .. .. 60·00 70·00
c. Stop after "JAPAN" (right pane R.5/5) 60·00 70·00
J2 **46** 1d. brown-purple (No. 203) .. .. 2·50 1·75
a. Blue-black overprint .. .. 55·00 95·00
J3 **31** 3d. purple-brown (No. 187) .. .. 2·00 2·00
a. Opt double £400
J4 **34** 6d. purple-brown (No. 189*a*) (8.5.47) .. 15·00 9·00
a. Wrong fount "6" £170 £120
b. Stop after "JAPAN" (right pane R. 5/5) £170 £120
c. Narrow "N" £170 £120
J5 **36** 1s. grey-green (No. 191) (8.5.47) .. 15·00 11·00
a. Wrong fount "6" £180 £140
b. Stop after "JAPAN" (right pane R. 5/5) £180 £140
c. Narrow "N" £180 £140
J6 **1** 2s. maroon (No. 212) (8.5.47) .. .. 42·00 45·00
J7 **38** 5s. claret (No. 176) (8.5.47) £120 £130
a. Thin rough paper (No. 176a) (1948) £120 £140
J1/7 .. .. .. *Set of* 7 £180 £180

The ½d., 1d. and 3d. values were first issued on 11 October 1946, and withdrawn two days later, but were re-issued together with the other values on 8 May 1947.

The following values with T **2** in the colours given were from proof sheets which, however, were used for postage: ½d. (red), 1d. (red or black) and 3d. (gold, red or black). (*Prices for black opts £100, each, and for red or gold from £300 each, all un*)

The use of B.C.O.F. stamps ceased on 12 February 1949.

AUSTRALIAN ANTARCTIC TERRITORY

For use at the Antarctic bases of Casey (opened early 1969: used Wilkes postmark until early 1970), Davis (closed from 1965 until early 1969), Heard Island (seasonal occupation only), Macquarie Island, Mawson and Wilkes (closed January 1969). Stamps of Australia were used from the bases before the introduction of Australian Antarctic Territory issues.

The following are also valid for use in Australia, where they are put on sale for a limited period when first issued.

DATES OF ISSUE. The dates given refer to release dates in Australia. Local release dates are usually later and where known they are given in footnotes.

1 1954 Expedition at Vestfold Hills and Map

(Des. T. Lawrence: adapted by artist of the Printing Branch. Recess)

1957 (27 Mar). *P* 14½.

1 **1** 2s. ultramarine .. .. 1·25 50

Issued Macquarie Island 11.12.57, Davis 6.2.58, Mawson 18.2.58, Wilkes 1.2.59.

2 Members of Shackleton Expedition at South Magnetic Pole, 1909

3 Weazel and Team

1959 (16 Dec). *T* **2** *and designs as T* **3**. *Recess; new values surch typo* (*5d., 8d.*). *P* 14½ (*5d.*), 14½ × 14 (*8d.*) *or* 14 × 14½ (*others*).

2 5d. on 4d. black and sepia 60 15
3 8d. on 7d. black and indigo .. .. .. 4·00 2·25
4 1s. deep green .. .. 3·00 2·00
5 2s. 3d. green .. .. 8·00 4·00
2/5 .. .. *Set of* 4 14·00 7·50

Designs: *Vert*—1s. Dog-team and iceberg; 2s. 3d. Map of Antarctica and Emperor Penguins. Issued Macquarie Island 26.12.59, Davis 30.1.60, Mawson 10.2.60, Wilkes 13.2.60.

6

7 Sir Douglas Mawson (Expedition leader)

1961 (5 July). *Recess. P* 14½.

6 **6** 5d. deep blue .. .. 1·25 20

Issued Macquarie Island 6.12.61, Wilkes 10.1.62, Davis 20.1.62, Mawson 30.1.62.

1961 (18 Oct). 50*th Anniv of* 1911–14 *Australasian Antarctic Expedition. Recess. P* 14½.

7 **7** 5d. myrtle-green 35 20

Issued Macquarie Island 6.12.61, Wilkes 10.1.62, Davis 20.1.62, Mawson 30.1.62.

(New Currency. 100 cents = 1 Australian dollar)

8 Aurora and Camera Dome

9 Bell 47G Trooper Helicopter

(Des J. Mason. Photo)

1966 (28 Sept)–**68**. *Vert designs as T* **8** (*1 c. to 15 c.*) *or horiz as T* **9** (*20 c. to $1*). *Multicoloured. Helecon paper* (*5 c.*). *P* 13½.

8 1 c. Type **8** (*shades*) 70 30
9 2 c. Emperor Penguins (*shades*) .. .. 3·00 80
10 4 c. Ship and iceberg 90 90
11 5 c. Banding Elephant-seals (25.9.68) .. 2·75 1·75
12 7 c. Measuring snow strata 80 80
13 10 c. Wind gauges .. .. .. 1·00 90
14 15 c. Weather balloon .. .. .. 5·00 2·00
15 20 c. Type **9** .. .. 6·00 2·50
16 25 c. Radio operator .. .. .. 3·00 3·00
17 50 c. Ice compression tests .. .. 4·50 5·50
18 $1 Parahelion ("mock sun") .. .. 26·00 14·00
8/18 .. .. *Set of* 11 48·00 29·00

Nos. 13/15 and 17 have parts of the designs printed in bright orange fluorescent ink.

Nos. 8/10 and 12/18 placed on sale locally at Macquarie Island on 11.12.66, Wilkes 9.2.67 and Mawson 16.2.67.

No. 11 issued Macquarie Island 4.12.68, Mawson 13.1.69, Wilkes/Casey 9.2.69 and Davis 20.2.69.

11 Sastrugi (Snow Ridges)

12 Capt. Cook, Sextant and Compass

(Des J. Mason. Photo)

1971 (23 June). *Tenth Anniv of Antarctic Treaty. T* **11** *and similar horiz design. P* 13½.

19 6 c. blue and black .. .. 75 1·00
20 30 c. multicoloured (Pancake ice) .. .. 3·25 6·00

Issued Macquarie Island 23.11.71, Mawson 27.12.71, Davis 13.1.72 and Casey 17.1.72.

(Des J. Mason. Photo)

1972 (13 Sept). *Bicentenary of Cook's Circumnavigation of Antarctica. T* **12** *and similar horiz design. Multicoloured Helecon paper* (*7 c.*). *P* 13½.

21 7 c. Type **12** .. .. 1·25 75
22 35 c. Chart and H.M.S. *Resolution* .. .. 4·75 6·00

Issued Macquarie Island 19.11.72, Mawson 24.12.72, Davis 3.1.73 and Casey 22.1.73.

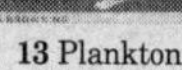

13 Plankton

14 Admiral Byrd (expedition leader), Ford 4-AT-B Trimotor *Floyd Bennett* and Map of South Pole

(Des G. Browning (1, 7, 9, 10, 20 c., $1), R. Honisett (others). Photo)

1973 (5 Aug). *T* **13** *and similar multicoloured designs. Helecon paper. P* 13½.

23 1 c. Type **13** 30 15
24 5 c. Mawson's De Havilland D.H.60G Gipsy Moth, 1931 .. .. .. 70 70
25 7 c. Adélie Penguin .. .. 2·25 70
26 8 c. Rymill's De Havilland D.H.83 Fox Moth, 1934–7 .. .. 75 9
27 9 c. Leopard Seal (*horiz*) 40 9
28 10 c. Killer Whale (*horiz*) .. .. .. 5·50 2·0
a. Buff (overlay on seals) omitted .. £850
29 20 c. Wandering Albatross (*horiz*) .. .. 1·25 1·0
30 25 c. Wilkins's Lockheed X-3903 *San Francisco*, 1928 (*horiz*) .. .. 90 1·0
31 30 c. Ellsworth's Northrop Gamma *Polar Star*, 1935 .. .. 90 1·0
32 35 c. Christensen's Avro Type 581 Avian, 1934 (*horiz*) .. .. 90 1·0
33 50 c. Byrd's Ford 4-AT-B Trimotor *Floyd Bennett*, 1929 .. .. 90 1·0
34 $1 Sperm Whale .. .. 1·25 1·4
23/34 .. .. *Set of* 12 14·00 10·5

The red ink used on the 1 c. and $1 is fluorescent.

Issued Macquarie Island 29.11.73, Mawson 30.12.73, Davis 10.1.74 and Casey 31.1.74.

(Des R. Honisett. Litho Asher and Co, Melbourne)

1979 (20 June). 50*th Anniv of First Flight over South Pole. T* **14** *and similar horiz design. Multicoloured. P* 15½.

35 20 c. Type **14** 30 5
36 55 c. Admiral Byrd, Ford 4-AT-B Trimotor *Floyd Bennett* and Antarctic terrain .. 80 1·5

Issued Macquarie Island 24.10.79, Davis 3.1.80, Mawson 13.1.80 and Casey 9.2.80.

15 *Thala Dan* (supply ship)

16 Sir Douglas Mawson in Antarctic Terrain

(Des R. Honisett, Litho Asher and Co, Melbourne)

1979 (29 Aug)–**81**. *Ships. Multicoloured designs as T* **15**. *P* 13½ × 13 (*horiz*) *or* 13 × 13½ (*vert*).

37 1 c. *Aurora* (*horiz*) (21.5.80) 15 1
38 2 c. *Penola* (Rymill) (9.9.81) 40 1
39 5 c. Type **15** 30 4
40 10 c. H.M.S. *Challenger* (survey ship) (*horiz*) (9.9.81) 50 5
41 15 c. *Morning** (bow view) (whaling ship) (*horiz*) (21.5.80) .. .. .. 2·00 3·0
42 15 c. *Nimrod* (stern view) (Shackleton) (*horiz*) (9.9.81) .. .. 1·40 6
43 20 c. *Discovery II* (supply ship) (*horiz*) .. 1·25 1·5
44 22 c. *Terra Nova* (Scott) (21.5.80) .. .. 90 1·2
45 25 c. *Endurance* (Shackleton) .. .. 60 1·0
46 30 c. *Fram* (Amundsen) (*horiz*) .. .. 60 1·5
47 35 c. *Nella Dan* (supply ship) (*horiz*) (21.5.80) 80 1·5
48 40 c. *Kista Dan* (supply ship) (9.9.81) .. 1·25 1·0
49 45 c. *L'Astrolabe* (D'Urville) (*horiz*) (9.9.81) 70 7
50 50 c. *Norvegia* (supply ship) (*horiz*) (9.9.81) 70 7
51 55 c. *Discovery* (Scott) .. .. .. 85 2·0
52 $1 H.M.S. *Resolution* (Cook) (21.5.80) .. 1·75 2·5
37/52 .. .. *Set of* 16 12·00 16·0

*No. 41 is incorrectly inscribed "S.Y. *Nimrod*".

On No. 46 the S.S. *Fram* is shown flying the Icelandic ensign instead of the Norwegian.

Nos. 37, 41, 44, 47 and 52 issued Macquarie Island 27.10.80, Casey 1.12.80, Mawson 5.12.80 and Davis 11.12.80.

Nos. 38, 40, 42 and 48/50 issued Macquarie Island 21.10.81, Mawson 25.11.81, Davis 11.1.82 and Casey 25.1.82.

Nos. 39, 43, 45/6 and 51 issued Macquarie Island 24.10.79, Davis 3.1.80, Mawson 13.1.80 and Casey 9.2.80.

(Des R. Honisett. Litho Cambec Press, Melbourne)

1982 (5 May). *Birth Centenary of Sir Douglas Mawson* (*Antarctic explorer*). *T* **16** *and similar vert design. Multicoloured. P* 14 × 13½.

53 27 c. Type **16** 35 3
54 75 c. Sir Douglas Mawson and map of Australian Antarctic Territory .. .. 1·25 2·0

Issued Macquarie Island 26.10.82, Casey 16.1.83, Davis 10.2.83 and Mawson 2.3.83.

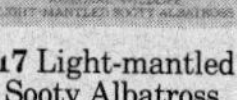

17 Light-mantled Sooty Albatross

18 Antarctic Scientist

(Des R. Honisett. Litho Leigh-Mardon Ltd, Melbourne)

1983 (6 Apr). *Regional Wildlife. T* **17** *and similar vert designs. Multicoloured. P* 14½.

55 27 c. Type **17** 85 9
a. Horiz strip of 5. Nos. 55/9 .. .. 3·75
56 27 c. King Cormorant 85 9
57 27 c. Southern Elephant-Seal 85 9
58 27 c. Royal Penguin 85 9
59 27 c. Dove Prion 85 9
55/9 .. .. *Set of* 5 3·75 4·0

Nos. 55/9 were issued together, *se-tenant*, in horizontal strips of five, forming a composite design.

Issued Macquarie Island 21.10.83, Mawson 9.12.83, Casey 1.1.84 and Davis 2.1.84.

(Des R. Honisett. Litho Leigh-Mardon Ltd, Melbourne)

1983 (7 Sept). *12th Antarctic Treaty Consultative Meeting, Canberra. P* 14½.
60 **18** 27 c. multicoloured 55 55

Issued Macquarie Island 21.10.83, Mawson 9.12.83, Casey ..1.84 and Davis 2.1.84.

19 Prismatic Compass and Lloyd-Creak Dip Circle

20 Dog Team pulling Sledge

(Des R. Fletcher. Litho Leigh-Mardon Ltd, Melbourne)

1984 (16 Jan). *75th Anniv of Magnetic Pole Expedition. T* **19** *and similar horiz design. Multicoloured. P* 14½.
61 30 c. Type **19** 50 50
62 85 c. Aneroid barometer and theodolite .. 1·25 1·50
61/2 ... *Set of* 2 ... (not printed)

Issued Macquarie Island 23.10.84, Mawson 15.11.84, Casey 16.11.84 and Davis 1.2.85.

(Des G. Emery. Litho Leigh-Mardon Ltd (2, 10, 20, 36, 60 c.) or Cambec Press (others), both of Melbourne)

1984 (18 July)–**87**. *Antarctic Scenes. T* **20** *and similar multi-coloured designs. P* 14½ (2 c., 10 c., 20 c., 36 c., 60 c.), 14 × 13½ (45 c., 90 c.) *or* 13½ × 14 (*others*).
63 2 c. Summer afternoon, Mawson Station (11.3.87) 10 30
64 5 c. Type **20** 15 15
65 10 c. Late summer evening, MacRobertson Land (11.3.87) 15 15
66 15 c. Prince Charles Mountains (7.8.85) .. 15 20
67 20 c. Summer morning, Wilkes Land (11.3.87) 15 20
68 25 c. Sea-ice and iceberg 60 60
69 30 c. Mount Coates 25 30
70 33 c. "Iceberg Alley", Mawson (7.8.85) .. 25 30
71 36 c. Early winter evening, Casey Station (11.3.87) 30 35
72 45 c. Brash ice (*vert*) (7.8.85) .. .. .. 70 1·00
73 60 c. Midwinter shadows, Casey Station (11.3.87) 50 55
74 75 c. Coastline .. .. 2·25 2·75
75 85 c. Landing strip .. .. 2·50 3·00
76 90 c. Pancake ice (*vert*) (7.8.85) 75 80
77 $1 Emperor Penguins (7.8.85) (Optd S. 50p) 2·25 1·25
63/77 .. .. *Set of* 15 10·00 10·50

Nos. 63, 65, 67, 71 and 73 issued Macquarie Island 6.10.87, Davis 25.11.87, Mawson 1.1.88 and Casey 13.1.88.

Nos. 64, 68/9 and 74/5 issued Macquarie Island 23.10.84, Mawson 15.11.84, Casey 16.11.84 and Davis 1.2.85.

Nos. 66, 70, 72 and 76/7 issued Heard Island 1.11.85, Casey 31.11.85, Mawson 6.12.85, Macquarie Island 6.12.85 and Davis 11.12.85.

21 Prince Charles Mountains near Mawson Station

22 Hourglass Dolphins and *Nella Dan*

(Des A. McGregor. Litho Cambec Press, Melbourne)

1986 (17 Sept). *25th Anniv of Antarctic Treaty. P* 14 × 13½.
78 **21** 36 c. multicoloured .. .. 1·25 85

Issued Mawson 9.11.86, Davis 15.11.86, Casey 23.11.86 and Macquarie Island 7.12.86.

(Des Trish Hart. Litho CPE Australia Ltd, Melbourne)

1988 (20 July). *Environment, Conservation and Technology. T* **22** *and similar square designs. Multicoloured. P* 13.
79 37 c. Type **22** .. .. 1·10 1·10
a. Horiz strip of 5. Nos. 79/83 .. .. 5·00
80 37 c. Emperor Penguins and Davis Station 1·10 1·10
81 37 c. Crabeater Seal and Hughes 500D helicopters .. .. 1·10 1·10
82 37 c. Adelie Penguins and tracked vehicle 1·10 1·10
83 37 c. Grey-headed Albatross and photo-grapher .. .. 1·10 1·10
79/83 .. .. *Set of* 5 5·00 5·00

Nos. 79/83 were printed together, *se-tenant*, in horizontal strips of five throughout the sheet.

Issued Macquarie Island 29.10.88, Casey 14.12.88, Mawson 21.12.88 and Davis 29.12.88.

23 "Antarctica"

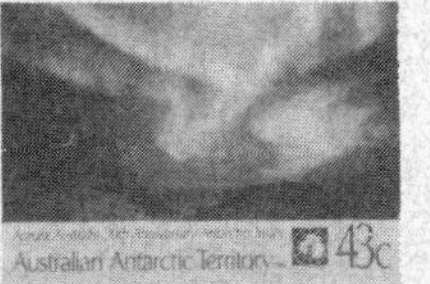

24 Aurora Australis

(Des Janet Boschen. Litho CPE Australia Ltd, Melbourne)

1989 (14 June). *Antarctic Landscape Paintings by Sir Sidney Nolan. T* **23** *and similar vert designs. Multicoloured. P* 14 × 13½.
84 39 c. Type **23** .. .. 1·00 70
85 39 c. "Iceberg Alley" .. .. 1·00 70
86 60 c. "Glacial Flow" .. .. 1·75 1·25
87 80 c. "Frozen Sea" .. .. 2·25 1·40
84/7 .. .. *Set of* 4 5·50 3·50

Issued Casey 28.10.89, Davis 29.10.89, Mawson 17.11 89 and Macquarie Island 24.11.89.

Supplies of Australia Nos. 1261/3 were sent to the Antarctic and were issued at Macquarie Island on 24.11.90, Mawson 10.12.90, Davis 14.12.90 and Casey 19.12.90

(Des Lynette Brown. Litho Leigh-Mardon Ltd, Melbourne)

1991 (20 June). *30th Anniv of Antarctic Treaty* (43 c.) *and Maiden Voyage of* Aurora Australis (*research ship*) ($1.20). *T* **24** *and similar horiz design. Multicoloured. P* 14½.
88 43 c. Type **24** 75 50
89 $1.20, *Aurora Australis* off Heard Island (optd S. 55p.) .. .. 2·75 2·50

Issued Mawson 12.11.91, Casey 22.12.91, Macquarie Island 17.1.92 and Davis 9.2.92.

25 Adélie Penguin and Chick

26 Head of Husky

(Des Janet Boschen. Litho McPherson's Ptg Group, Mulgrave ($1, $1.40, $1.50) or Printset Cambec Pty Ltd (others))

1992 (14 May)–**93**. *Antarctic Wildlife. T* **25** *and similar multicoloured designs. P* 14½×14 ($1.20, $1.50) *or* 14×14½ (*others*).
90 45 c. Type **25** 35 40
91 75 c. Elephant Seal with pup 55 60
92 85 c. Hall's Giant Petrel on nest with fledgeling 65 70
93 95 c. Weddell Seal and pup 75 80
94 $1 Royal Penguin (14.1.93) 75 80
95 $1.20, Emperor Penguins with chicks (*vert*) (Optd. S. 55p) 90 95
96 $1.40, Fur Seal (14.1.93) .. .. 1·10 1·25
97 $1.50, King Penguin (*vert*) (14.1.93) .. 1·10 1·25
90/7 .. .. *Set of* 8 5·75 6·75

Nos. 90/3 and 95 issued Mawson 2.11.92, Davis 11.11.92, Casey 27.11.92 and Macquarie Island 10.12.92.

Nos. 94 and 96/7 issued Mawson 28.10.93, Casey 13.11.93, Davis 2.12.93 and Macquarie Island 19.12.93.

(Des FHA Design. Litho Leigh-Mardon Ltd, Melbourne)

1994 (13 Jan). *Departure of Huskies from Antarctica. T* **26** *and similar multicoloured designs. P* 14½.
104 45 c. Type **26** 60 50
105 75 c. Dogs pulling sledge (*horiz*) .. .. 1·00 1·10
106 85 c. Husky in harness .. .. 1·25 1·40
107 $1.05, Dogs on leads (*horiz*) .. .. .. 1·40 1·50
104/7 .. .. *Set of* 4 3·75 4·00

Issued Casey 31.10.94, Davis 11.11.94, Mawson 14.11.94 and Macquarie Island 4.12.94.

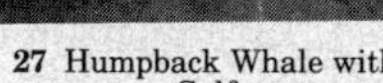

27 Humpback Whale with Calf

28 "Rafting Sea Ice" (Christian Clare Robertson)

(Des D. Nelson. Litho Leigh-Mardon Ltd, Melbourne)

1995 (15 June). *Whales and Dolphins. T* **27** *and similar multicoloured designs. P* 14½.
108 45 c. Type **27** 75 65
109 45 c. Pair of Hourglass Dolphins (*vert*) .. 75 65
a. Horiz pair. Nos. 109/10 .. .. .. 1·50 1·25
110 45 c. Pair of Minke Whales (*vert*) 75 65
111 $1 Killer Whale .. .. 1·50 1·50
108/11 .. .. *Set of* 4 3·25 3·00
MS112 146×64 mm. Nos. 108/11 .. .. .. 3·25 3·00

Nos. 109/10 were printed together, *se-tenant*, in horizontal pairs throughout the sheet, with the background forming a composite design.

Issued Macquarie Island 18.11.95, Casey 5.12.95, Mawson 16.12.95 and Davis 20.12.95.

No. **MS**112 also exists overprinted "Singapore 95 World Stamp Exhibition", "Philately and Collections Fair, Hong Kong '95" or "CAPEX '96 WORLD PHILATELIC EXHIBITION EXPOSITION PHILATELIQUE MONDIALE" for sale at these exhibitions.

(Des Melinda Whitechurch. Litho McPherson's Ptg Group, Mulgrave)

1996 (16 May). *Paintings by Christian Clare Robertson. T* **28** *and similar vert designs. Multicoloured. P* 14½×14.
113 45 c. Type **28** 70 55
a. Horiz pair. Nos. 113/14 .. .. .. 1·40 1·10
114 45 c. "Shadow on the Plateau" 70 55
115 $1 "Ice Cave" .. .. 1·60 1·40
116 $1.20, "Twelve Lake" .. .. 1·75 1·60
113/16 .. .. *Set of* 4 4·25 3·75

Nos. 113/14 were printed together, *se-tenant*, in horizontal pairs throughout the sheet.

Issued Macquarie Island 28.11.96, Mawson 23.12.96, Davis 29.12.96 and Casey 11.1.97.

29 Apple Huts

30 *Aurora Australis* (research ship)

(Des Sophie Byass. Litho McPherson's Ptg Group, Mulgrave)

1997 (15 May). *50th Anniv of Australian National Antarctic Research Expeditions (A.N.A.R.E.). T* **29** *and similar horiz designs. Multicoloured. P* 14×14½.
117 45 c. Type **29** 50 55
a. Pair. Nos. 117/18 .. .. 1·00 1·10
118 45 c. Tuning a radio receiver 50 55
119 95 c. Summer surveying .. .. 90 1·10
120 $1.05, Scientists in cage above sea ice .. 80 85
121 $1.20, Scientists and tents .. .. .. 1·10 1·40
117/21 .. .. *Set of* 5 3·50 4·25

Nos. 117/18 were printed together, *se-tenant*, in horizontal and vertical pairs throughout the sheet.

Issued Macquarie Island 18.11.97, Davis 22.12.97, Mawson 26.12.97 and Casey 7.1.98

(Des Sandra Harman. Litho McPherson's Ptg Group, Mulgrave)

1998 (5 Mar). *Antarctic Transport. T* **30** *and similar multicoloured designs. P* 14×14½ (45 c.) *or* 14½×14 (*others*).
122 45 c. Type **30** 65 65
a. Pair. Nos. 122/3 .. .. 1·25 1·25
123 45 c. Skidoo 65 65
124 $1 Helicopter lifting quad-bike (*vert*) .. 1·40 1·40
125 $2 Hagglunds tractor and trailer (*vert*) .. 2·00 2·00
122/5 .. .. *Set of* 4 4·25 4·25

Nos. 122/5 were printed together, *se-tenant*, in horizontal and vertical pairs throughout the sheet.

CHRISTMAS ISLAND

Formerly a part of the Straits Settlements and then of the Colony of Singapore, Christmas Island was occupied by the Japanese from 31 March, 1942, until September, 1945. It reverted to Singapore after liberation, but subsequently became an Australian territory on 15 October 1958.

Stamps of the STRAITS SETTLEMENTS were used on Christmas Island from 1901 until 1942. Following liberation issues of MALAYA (BRITISH MILITARY ADMINISTRATION) and then SINGAPORE were used from 1946 to 1958.

(Currency. 100 cents = 1 Malayan dollar)

1 Queen Elizabeth II

(Des G. Lissenden. Recess with name and value typo in black. Note Printing Branch, Commonwealth Bank, Melbourne)

1958 (15 Oct). *No wmk. P* 14½.
1 1 2 c. yellow-orange 55 70
2 4 c. brown 60 30
3 5 c. deep mauve 60 30
4 6 c. grey-blue .. .. 1·50 30
5 8 c. black-brown .. .. 3·00 50
6 10 c. violet .. .. 2·00 30
7 12 c. carmine .. .. 3·25 1·75
8 20 c. blue .. .. 2·00 1·75
9 50 c. yellow-green .. .. 3·00 1·75
10 $1 deep bluish green .. .. .. 3·75 1·75
1/10 .. .. *Set of* 10 18·00 8·50

PRINTERS. Nos. 11/32 were printed by the Note Printing Branch, Reserve Bank of Australia, Melbourne. Nos. 33/82 were printed in photogravure by Harrison and Sons, Ltd, London.

2 Map

11 White-tailed Tropic Bird

(Des G. Lissenden (2, 8c.), P. Morriss (4, 5, 10, 20 c.), B. Stewart (others). Recess)

1963 (28 Aug). *T* **2** *and similar designs and T* **11.** *P* 14½ × 14 ($1) *or* 14½ (*others*).
11 2 c. orange 90 55
12 4 c. red-brown 50 20
13 5 c. purple 50 30
14 6 c. indigo 40 50
15 8 c. black .. .. 3·25 60
16 10 c. violet 40 20
17 12 c. brown-red 40 40
18 20 c. blue .. .. 1·00 35
19 50 c. green .. .. 1·50 35
20 $1 yellow .. .. 3·50 60
11/20 .. .. *Set of* 10 11·00 3·50

Designs: *Vert*—4 c. Moonflower; 5 c. Robber Crab; 8 c. Phosphate train; 10 c. Raising phosphate. *Horiz*—6 c. Island scene; 12 c. Flying Fish Cove; 20 c. Loading cantilever; 50 c. Christmas Island Frigate Bird.

I

II

I Thick lettering

II Thinner lettering

1965. *50th Anniversary of Gallipoli Landing. As T* **184** *of Australia, but slightly larger* (22×34½ *mm*) *and colour changed. Photo. P* 13½.
21 10 c. sepia, black and emerald (I) (14.4) .. 45 80
a. Black-brown, black and light emerald (II) (24.4) .. .. 2·00 2·00

(New Currency. 100 cents = 1 Australian dollar)

12 Golden-striped Grouper

13 "Angel" (mosaic)

(Des G. Hamori. Photo)

1968 (6 May)–**70.** *Fishes. T* **12** *and similar horiz designs. Multicoloured. P* 13½.
22 1 c. Type **12** 45 45
23 2 c. Moorish Idol 60 20
24 3 c. Long-nosed Butterflyfish 60 30
25 4 c. Pink-tailed Triggerfish 60 20
a. Deep blue (face value) omitted .. £600
26 5 c. Regal Angelfish 75 20
27 9 c. White-cheeked Surgeonfish .. .. 1·25 40
28 10 c. Lionfish .. .. 1·00 20
28*a* 15 c. Saddle Butterflyfish (14.12.70) .. 10·00 5·50
29 20 c. Ornate Butterflyfish .. .. .. 3·50 55
29*a* 30 c. Giant Ghost Pipefish (14.12.70) .. 10·00 5·50
30 50 c. Clown Surgeonfish .. .. .. 5·00 3·00
31 $1 Meyer's Butterflyfish .. .. .. 5·50 5·00
22/31 .. .. *Set of* 12 35·00 19·00

(Des G. Hamori. Photo)

1969 (10 Nov). *Christmas. P* 13½.
32 **13** 5 c. red, deep blue and gold 20 30

14 "The Ansidei Madonna" (Raphael)

15 "The Adoration of the Shepherds" (ascr to the School of Seville)

(Des Harrison)

1970 (26 Oct). *Christmas. Paintings. T* **14** *and similar vert design. Multicoloured. P* 14 × 14½.
33 3 c. Type **14** 20 15
34 5 c. "The Virgin and Child, St. John the Baptist and an Angel" (Morando) .. 20 15

(Des Harrison)

1971 (4 Oct). *Christmas. T* **15** *and similar vert design. Multicoloured. W* w **12.** *P* 14.
35 6 c. Type **15** 30 50
36 20 c. "The Adoration of the Shepherds" (Reni) 70 1·00

16 H.M.S. *Flying Fish*, 1887

17 Angel of Peace

(Des V. Whiteley)

1972 (7 Feb)–**73.** *Ships. Horiz designs as T* **16.** *Multicoloured. P* 14×13½.
37 1 c. *Eagle* (merchantman), 1714 (5.6.72) .. 25 60
38 2 c. H.M.S. *Redpole* (gunboat), 1890 (5.6.72) 30 70
39 3 c. *Hoi Houw* (freighter), 1959 (5.6.72) .. 30 70
40 4 c. *Pigot* (sailing ship), 1771 (6.2.73) .. 40 75
41 5 c. *Valetta* (cargo-liner), 1968 (6.2.73) .. 40 75
42 6 c. Type **16** 40 75
43 7 c. *Asia* (merchantman), 1805 .. .. 40 75
44 8 c. *Islander* (freighter), 1929–60 .. .. 45 80
45 9 c. H.M.S. *Imperieuse* (armoured cruiser), 1888 (6.2.73) 65 70
46 10 c. H.M.S. *Cerberus* (coast defence turret ship), 1871 (4.6.73) 55 80
47 20 c. *Thomas* (galleon), 1615 .. .. .. 70 90
48 25 c. Royal Navy sail sloop, 1864 (4.6.73) .. 80 1·50
49 30 c. *Cygnet* (flute), 1688 (4.6.73) .. .. 80 1·00
50 35 c. *Triadic* (freighter), 1958 (4.6.73) .. 80 1·00
51 50 c. H.M.S. *Amethyst* (frigate), 1857 (6.2.73) 80 1·50
52 $1 *Royal Mary* (warship), 1643 (5.6.72) .. 1·10 1·75
37/52 .. .. *Set of* 16 8·00 13·50

No. 45 is inscribed "H.M.S. *Imperious*", No. 46 "H.M.S. *Egeria*" and No. 48 "H.M.S. *Gordon*", all in error.

(Des Jennifer Toombs)

1972 (2 Oct). *Christmas. T* **17** *and similar vert design. Multi-coloured. P* 14.
53 3 c. Type **17** 20 4
a. Pair. Nos. 53/4 .. .. 40 8
54 3 c. Angel of Joy 20 4
55 7 c. Type **17** 30 5
a. Pair. Nos. 55/6 .. .. 60 1·0
56 7 c. As No. 54 .. .. 30 5
53/6 .. .. *Set of* 4 90 1·6

Nos. 53/4 and 55/6 have the two designs printed horizontally *se-tenant* within the sheet.

18 Virgin and Child, and Map

19 Mary and Holy Child within Christmas Star

(Des P. Law)

1973 (2 Oct). *Christmas. P* 14 × 13.
57 **18** 7 c. multicoloured 35 3
58 25 c. multicoloured .. .. 1·25 1·2

(Des Jennifer Toombs)

1974 (2 Oct). *Christmas. P* 13 × 14½.
59 **19** 7 c. mauve and grey-black 35 6
60 30 c. light orange, bright yell & grey-blk 1·25 2·5

20 "The Flight into Egypt"

21 Dove of Peace and Star of Bethlehem

(Des Jennifer Toombs)

1975 (2 Oct). *Christmas. P* 14 × 13.
61 **20** 10 c. light greenish yellow, agate and gold 40 3
62 35 c. bright rose, deep blue and gold .. 1·10 1·7

(Des R. Bates)

1976 (2 Oct). *Christmas. P* 13½.
63 **21** 10 c. cerise, lemon and bright mauve .. 20 4
a. Pair. Nos. 63/4 .. .. .. 40 9
64 – 10 c. cerise, lemon and bright mauve .. 20 4
65 **21** 35 c. reddish violet, light greenish blue and light yellow-green 25 5
a. Pair. Nos. 65/6 .. .. .. 50 1·1
66 – 35 c. reddish violet, light greenish blue and light yellow-green 25 5
63/6 .. .. *Set of* 4 80 1·7

Nos. 64 and 66 are "mirror-images" of T **21**, the two designs o[f] each value being printed horizontally *se-tenant* throughout th[e] sheet.

22 William Dampier (explorer)

23 Australian Coat of Arms on Map of Christmas Island

(Des V. Whiteley Studio)

1977 (30 Apr)–**78.** *Famous Visitors. Horiz designs as T* **22** *in black, vermilion and greenish yellow* (45 *c.*) *or multicoloured* (*others*). *P* 14 × 13.
67 1 c. Type **22** 15 7
68 2 c. Capt. de Vlamingh (explorer) (22.2.78) .. 20 7
69 3 c. Vice-Admiral MacLear (22.2.78) .. 30 7
70 4 c. Sir John Murray (oceanographer) (22.2.78) 30 8
71 5 c. Admiral Aldrich (31.5.78) 30 4
72 6 c. Andrew Clunies Ross (first settler) .. 30 6
73 7 c. J. J. Lister (naturalist) (31.5.78) .. 30 4
74 8 c. Admiral of the Fleet Sir William May (1.9.78) 35 7
75 9 c. Henry Ridley (botanist) 40 7
76 10 c. George Clunies Ross (phosphate miner) (1.9.78) 35 5
77 20 c. Capt. Joshua Slocum (yachtsman) (1.9.78) 50 7
78 45 c. Charles Andrews (naturalist) (31.5.78) .. 85 4
79 50 c. Richard Hanitsch (biologist) (31.5.78) .. 95 6
80 75 c. Victor Purcell (scholar) (1.9.78) .. .. 85 1·2
81 $1 Fam Choo Beng (educator) .. .. 85 1·2
82 $2 Sir Harold Spencer-Jones (astronomer) (22.2.78) .. .. 1·00 2·2
67/82 .. .. *Set of* 16 7·00 11·5

(Des Mrs S. Muir. Litho Harrison)

1977 (2 June). *Silver Jubilee. P* 14½ × 13½.
83 **23** 45 c. multicoloured 45 55

24 "A Partridge in a Pear Tree" **25** Abbott's Booby

(Des Jennifer Toombs. Litho Questa)

1977 (20 Oct)–**78**. *Christmas. T* **24** *and similar vert designs depicting the carol "The Twelve Days of Christmas". Multicoloured. P* 14. A. *No wmk.*
84A 10 c. Type **24** 10 20
a. Sheetlet. Nos. 84A/95A .. .. 1·10
85A 10 c. "Two turtle doves" 10 20
86A 10 c. "Three French hens" 10 20
87A 10 c. "Four calling birds" 10 20
88A 10 c. "Five gold rings" 10 20
89A 10 c. "Six geese a-laying" 10 20
90A 10 c. "Seven swans a-swimming" 10 20
91A 10 c. "Eight maids a-milking" 10 20
92A 10 c. "Nine ladies dancing" 10 20
93A 10 c. "Ten lords a-leaping" 10 20
94A 10 c. "Eleven pipers piping" 10 20
95A 10 c. "Twelve drummers drumming" .. 10 20
84A/95A .. .. *Set of* 12 1·10 2·25

B. *W* w **14** (27.1.78)

84B 10 c. Type **24** 25 30
a. Sheetlet. Nos. 84B/95B .. .. 2·75
85B 10 c. "Two turtle doves" 25 30
86B 10 c. "Three French hens" 25 30
87B 10 c. "Four calling birds" 25 30
88B 10 c. "Five gold rings" 25 30
89B 10 c. "Six geese a-laying" 25 30
90B 10 c. "Seven swans a-swimming" 25 30
91B 10 c. "Eight maids a-milking 25 30
92B 10 c. "Nine ladies dancing" 25 30
93B 10 c. "Ten lords a-leaping" 25 30
94B 10 c. "Eleven pipers piping" 25 30
95B 10 c. "Twelve drummers drumming" .. 25 30
84B/95B .. .. *Set of* 12 2·75 3·25

Nos. 84/95 were printed as a *se-tenant* block within a sheetlet 142 × 170 mm.

(Des Jennifer Toombs. Litho Questa)

1978 (21 Apr). *25th Anniv of Coronation. T* **25** *and similar vert designs. P* 15.
96 45 c. black and bright ultramarine 45 75
a. Sheetlet. Nos. 96/8 × 2 .. .. .. 2·50
97 45 c. multicoloured 45 75
98 45 c. black and bright ultramarine 45 75
96/8 .. .. *Set of* 3 1·25 2·00

Designs:—No. 96, White Swan of Bohun; No. 97, Queen Elizabeth II; No. 98, Type **25**.

Nos. 96/8 were printed together in small sheets of 6, containing two *se-tenant* strips of 3 with horizontal gutter margin between.

26 "Christ Child" **27** Chinese Children

(Des Jennifer Toombs. Litho J.W.)

1978 (2 Oct). *Christmas. Scenes from "The Song of Christmas". T* **26** *and similar horiz designs. Multicoloured. P* 14.
99 10 c. Type **26** 15 20
a. Sheetlet. Nos. 99/107 .. .. .. 1·25
100 10 c. "Herald Angels" 15 20
101 10 c. "Redeemer" 15 20
102 10 c. "Israel" 15 20
103 10 c. "Star" 15 20
104 10 c. "Three Wise Men" 15 20
105 10 c. "Manger" 15 20
106 10 c. "All He Stands For" 15 20
107 10 c. "Shepherds Came" 15 20
99/107 .. .. *Set of* 9 1·25 1·60

Nos. 99/107 were printed together, *se-tenant*, in a small sheet of 9.

(Des Jennifer Toombs. Litho Questa)

1979 (20 Apr). *International Year of the Child. T* **27** *and similar vert designs showing children of different races. Multicoloured, colour of inscr given. P* 14.
108 20 c. apple-green (Type **27**) 30 45
a. Horiz strip of 5. Nos. 108/12 .. .. 1·25
109 20 c. turquoise-green (Malay children) .. 30 45
110 20 c. lilac (Indian children) 30 45
111 20 c. rose (European children) 30 45
112 20 c. orange-yellow ("Oranges and Lemons") .. 30 45
108/12 .. .. *Set of* 5 1·25 2·00

Nos. 108/12 were printed together, *se-tenant*, in horizontal strips of 5 throughout the sheet, forming a composite design.

28 1958 2 c. Definitive **29** Wise Men following Star

(Des J.W. Litho Questa)

1979 (27 Aug). *Death Centenary of Sir Rowland Hill. T* **28** *and similar horiz designs showing stamps and Sir Rowland Hill. Multicoloured. P* 13½.
113 20 c. Type **28** 25 40
a. Horiz strip of 5. Nos. 113/17 .. .. 1·10
114 20 c. 1963 2 c. Map definitive 25 40
115 20 c. 1965 50th anniversary of Gallipoli Landing 10 c. commemorative .. 25 40
116 20 c. 1968 4 c. Pink-tailed Triggerfish definitive 25 40
117 20 c. 1969 5 c. Christmas issue 25 40
113/17 .. .. *Set of* 5 1·10 1·75

Nos. 113/17 were printed together, *se-tenant*, in horizontal strips of 5 throughout the sheet.

(Des L. Curtis. Litho Walsall)

1979 (22 Oct). *Christmas. T* **29** *and similar horiz design. Multicoloured. P* 14 × 14½.
118 20 c. Type **29** 20 30
119 55 c. Virgin and Child 45 70

30 9th Green **31** Surveying

(Des R. Granger Barrett. Litho Format)

1980 (12 Feb). *25th Anniv of Christmas Island Golf Club. T* **30** *and similar horiz design. Multicoloured. P* 14½ × 14.
120 20 c. Type **30** 35 50
121 55 c. Clubhouse .. .. 40 1·00

(Des L. Curtis. Litho Walsall)

1980 (6 May). *Phosphate Industry* (1*st issue*). *T* **31** *and similar horiz designs. Multicoloured. P* 14.
122 15 c. Type **31** 15 25
123 22 c. Drilling for samples 20 30
124 40 c. Sample analysis 30 45
125 55 c. Mine planning 40 55
122/5 .. .. *Set of* 4 95 1·40

See also Nos. 126/9, 136/9 and 140/3.

(Des L. Curtis. Litho Walsall)

1980 (14 July). *Phosphate Industry* (2*nd issue*). *Horiz designs as T* **31**. *Multicoloured. P* 14.
126 15 c. Jungle clearing 15 15
127 22 c. Overburden removal 20 20
128 40 c. Open cut mining 30 25
129 55 c. Restoration 35 30
126/9 .. .. *Set of* 4 90 80

32 Angel with Harp **33** *Cryptoblepharus egeriae*

(Des Jennifer Toombs. Litho Walsall)

1980 (6 Oct). *Christmas. T* **32** *and similar vert designs. Multicoloured. P* 13½ × 13.
130 15 c. Type **32** 15 25
a. Sheetlet. Nos. 130/5 .. .. .. 1·10
131 15 c. Angel with wounded soldier 15 25
132 22 c. Virgin and Child 15 30
133 22 c. Kneeling couple 15 30
134 60 c. Angel with harp (*different*) 35 45
135 60 c. Angel with children 35 45
130/5 .. .. *Set of* 6 1·10 1·75

Nos. 130/5 were printed together in small sheets of 6, containing two *se-tenant* strips of 3 (Nos. 130, 132, 134 and 131, 133, 135) with horizontal gutter margin between.

(Des L. Curtis. Litho Walsall)

1981 (9 Feb). *Phosphate Industry* (3*rd issue*). *Horiz designs as T* **31**. *Multicoloured. P* 14.
136 22 c. Screening and stockpiling 20 20
137 28 c. Train loading 25 25
138 40 c. Railing 40 40
139 60 c. Drying 55 55
136/9 .. .. *Set of* 4 1·25 1·25

(Des L. Curtis. Litho Walsall)

1981 (4 May). *Phosphate Industry* (4*th issue*). *Horiz designs as T* **31**. *Multicoloured. P* 14.
140 22 c. Crushing 30 20
141 28 c. Conveying 40 25
142 40 c. Bulk storage 60 40
143 60 c. *Consolidated Venture* (bulk carrier) loading 70 55
140/3 .. .. *Set of* 4 1·75 1·25

(Des L. Curtis. Litho Walsall)

1981 (10 Aug). *Reptiles. T* **33** *and similar horiz designs. Multicoloured. P* 13.
144 24 c. Type **33** 25 25
145 30 c. *Emoia nativitata* 30 30
146 40 c. *Lepidodactylus listeri* 45 45
147 60 c. *Cyrtodactylus sp. nov.* 65 65
144/7 .. .. *Set of* 4 1·50 1·50

34 Scene from Carol "Away in a Manger" **35** Eastern Reef Heron

(Des Jennifer Toombs. Litho Questa)

1981 (19 Oct). *Christmas. T* **34** *and similar horiz designs showing scenes from carol "Away in a Manger". P* 14½ × 14.
148 18 c. silver, deep blue and turquoise-blue .. 35 50
a. Sheetlet. Nos. 148/51 .. .. .. 1·50
149 24 c. multicoloured 40 55
150 40 c. multicoloured 45 65
151 60 c. multicoloured 50 75
148/51 .. .. *Set of* 4 1·50 2·25

Nos. 148/51 were printed together, *se-tenant*, in sheetlets of 4.

(Des N. Arlott. Litho Questa)

1982 (8 Mar)–**83**. *Birds. Multicoloured designs as T* **35**. *P* 14.
152 1 c. Type **35** 70 30
153 2 c. Common Noddy 70 30
154 3 c. White-bellied Swiftlet (14.6.82) 70 70
155 4 c. Christmas Island Imperial Pigeon (14.6.82) 70 70
156 5 c. Christmas Island White Eye (21.2.83) .. 80 70
157 10 c. Island Thrush (14.6.82) 70 70
158 25 c. Red-tailed Tropic Bird .. .. .. 1·25 60
159 30 c. Emerald Dove (21.2.83) 80 70
160 40 c. Brown Booby (23.8.82) 80 55
161 50 c. Red-footed Booby (23.8.82) 80 55
162 65 c. Christmas Island Frigate Bird (23.8.82) .. 80 55
163 75 c. White-tailed Tropic Bird (23.8.82) .. 90 65
164 80 c. Australian Kestrel (*vert*) (21.2.83) .. 1·25 1·75
165 $1 Indonesian Hawk Owl (*vert*) (21.2.83) .. 2·50 2·00
166 $2 Australian Goshawk (*vert*) (14.6.82) .. 1·75 4·00
167 $4 Abbott's Booby (*vert*) .. .. .. 3·00 3·25
152/67 .. .. *Set of* 16 16·00 16·00

36 Joseph **37** "Mirror" Dinghy and Club House

(Des Jennifer Toombs. Litho and embossed Walsall)

1982 (18 Oct). *Christmas. Origami Paper Sculptures. T* **36** *and similar vert designs. Multicoloured. P* 14½ × 14.
168 27 c. Type **36** 30 30
a. Horiz strip of 3. Nos. 168/70 .. .. 1·25
169 50 c. Angel 45 45
170 75 c. Mary and baby Jesus 65 65
168/70 .. .. *Set of* 3 1·25 1·25

Nos. 168/70 were printed together, *se-tenant*, in horiz strips of 3 throughout the sheet.

(Des L. McCombie. Litho Format)

1983 (2 May). *25th Anniv of Christmas Island Boat Club. T* **37** *and similar multicoloured designs. P* 14 × 14½ (27, 35 c.) *or* 14½ × 14 (*others*).
171 27 c. Type **37** 30 35
172 35 c. Ocean-going yachts 35 40
173 50 c. Fishing launch and cargo ship (*horiz*) .. 40 50
174 75 c. Dinghy-racing and cantilever (*horiz*) .. 60 70
171/4 .. .. *Set of* 4 1·50 1·75

38 Maps of Christmas Island and Australia, Eastern Grey Kangaroo and White-tailed Tropic Bird **39** Candle and Holly

(Des A. Theobald. Litho Questa)

1983 (1 Oct). *25th Anniv of Christmas Island as an Australian Territory. T* **38** *and similar horiz designs. Multicoloured. P* 14.
175 24 c. Type **38** 40 25
176 30 c. Christmas Island and Australian flag 45 45
177 85 c. Maps of Christmas Island and Australia, with Boeing 727 . . . . 1·25 1·25
175/7 . . . . *Set of* 3 1·90 1·75

(Des J.W. Litho Walsall)

1983 (31 Oct). *Christmas. Candles. T* **39** *and similar vert designs. Multicoloured. P* 13.
178 24 c. Type **39** 20 20
179 30 c. Six gold candles 30 40
180 85 c. Candles . . . . 70 1·00
178/80 . . . . *Set of* 3 1·10 1·40

40 Feeding on Leaf

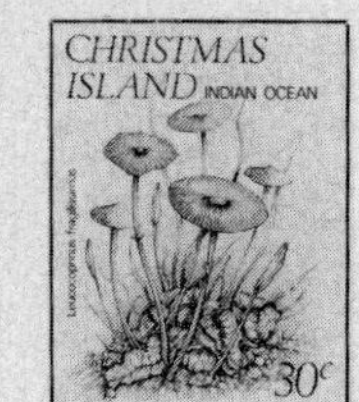

41 *Leucocoprinus fragilissimus*

(Des L. Curtis. Litho Questa)

1984 (20 Feb). *Red Land Crab. T* **40** *and similar horiz designs showing various aspects of crab's life. Multicoloured. P* 14 × 14½.
181 30 c. Type **40** 30 30
182 40 c. Migration 40 40
183 55 c. Development stages 50 50
184 85 c. Adult female and young 70 70
181/4 . . . . *Set of* 4 1·75 1·75

(Des I. Loe. Litho Format)

1984 (30 Apr). *Fungi. T* **41** *and similar vert designs. Multicoloured. P* 14 × 14½.
185 30 c. Type **41** 65 55
186 40 c. *Microporus xanthopus* 75 70
187 45 c. *Hydropus anthidepas* ("*Trogia anthidepas*") 85 80
188 55 c. *Haddowia longipes* 85 90
189 85 c. *Phillipsia domingensis* . . . . 1·10 1·25
185/9 . . . . *Set of* 5 3·75 3·75

42 Run-out

43 Arrival of Father Christmas

(Des A. Theobald. Litho J.W.)

1984 (23 July). *25th Anniversary of Cricket on Christmas Island. T* **42** *and similar horiz designs. Multicoloured. P* 14.
190 30 c. Type **42** 75 85
191 40 c. Bowled-out . . . . 85 1·10
192 55 c. Batsman in action . . . . . . 1·10 1·50
193 85 c. Fielder diving for catch . . . . 1·25 1·75
190/3 . . . . *Set of* 4 3·50 4·75

(Des D. Slater. Litho B.D.T.)

1984 (21 Sept). *Christmas and "Ausipex" International Stamp Exhibition, Melbourne. Sheet* 100 × 100 *mm containing T* **43** *and similar horiz designs. Multicoloured. P* 13½.
MS194 30 c. Type **43**; 55 c. Distribution of presents; 85 c. Departure of Father Christmas . . . . 2·25 2·25
No. **MS**194 also contains three labels horizontally *se-tenant* with the stamps and forming composite designs with them.

44 Robber Crab

45 "Once in Royal David's City"

(Des L. Curtis. Litho Walsall)

1985 (30 Jan). *Crabs* (1*st series*). *T* **44** *and similar horiz designs. Multicoloured. P* 13 × 13½.
195 30 c. Type **44** . . . . 1·00 70
196 40 c. Horn-eyed Ghost Crab . . . . 1·10 1·10
197 55 c. Purple Hermit Crab . . . . 1·50 1·60
198 85 c. Little Nipper . . . . . . 2·25 2·50
195/8 . . . . *Set of* 4 5·50 5·50
See also Nos. 199/202 and 203/6.

(Des L. Curtis. Litho Walsall)

1985 (29 Apr). *Crabs* (2*nd series*). *Horiz designs as T* **44**. *Multicoloured. P* 13 × 13½.
199 33 c. Blue Crab . . . . 1·00 55
200 45 c. Tawny Hermit Crab . . . . . . 1·10 1·10
201 60 c. Red Nipper . . . . 1·60 1·75
202 90 c. Smooth-handed Ghost Crab . . . . 2·25 2·50
199/202 . . . . *Set of* 4 5·50 5·50

(Des L. Curtis. Litho Walsall)

1985 (22 July). *Crabs* (3*rd series*). *Horiz designs as T* **44**. *Multicoloured. P* 13 × 13½.
203 33 c. Red Crab . . . . 1·10 60
204 45 c. Mottled Crab . . . . 1·50 1·40
205 60 c. Rock Hopper Crab . . . . . . 2·25 2·50
206 90 c. Yellow Nipper . . . . 2·75 3·50
203/6 . . . . *Set of* 4 7·00 7·25

(Des Jennifer Toombs. Litho Harrison)

1985 (28 Oct). *Christmas. Carols. T* **45** *and similar vert designs. Multicoloured. P* 14 × 14½.
207 27 c. Type **45** . . . . 1·00 1·25
a. Horiz strip of 5. Nos. 207/11 . . . . 6·00
208 33 c. "While Shepherds Watched Their Flocks by Night" . . . . . . 1·10 1·40
209 45 c. "Away in a Manger" . . . . . . 1·40 1·60
210 60 c. "We Three Kings of Orient Are" . . 1·50 1·75
211 90 c. "Hark the Herald Angels Sing" . . 1·60 1·90
207/11 . . . . *Set of* 5 6·00 7·00
Nos. 207/11 were printed together, *se-tenant* in horizontal strips of 5 throughout the sheet.

46 Halley's Comet over Christmas Island

47 Ridley's Orchid

(Des L. Curtis. Litho Format)

1986 (30 Apr). *Appearance of Halley's Comet. T* **46** *and similar horiz designs. Multicoloured. P* 14.
212 33 c. Type **46** 65 80
213 45 c. Edmond Halley . . . . 80 1·10
214 60 c. Comet and *Consolidated Venture* (bulk carrier) loading phosphate . . . . 1·00 2·25
215 90 c. Comet over Flying Fish Cove . . 1·50 2·50
212/15 . . . . *Set of* 4 3·50 6·00

(Des I. Loe. Litho Format)

1986 (30 June). *Native Flowers. T* **47** *and similar vert designs. Multicoloured. P* 14.
216 33 c. Type **47** 70 55
217 45 c. Hanging Flower 65 85
218 60 c. Hoya . . . . 75 1·50
219 90 c. Sea Hibiscus . . . . 90 2·00
216/19 . . . . *Set of* 4 2·75 4·50

(Des D. Miller. Litho Walsall)

1986 (23 July). *Royal Wedding. Square designs as T* **112** *of Ascension. Multicoloured. P* 14½ × 14.
220 33 c. Prince Andrew and Miss Sarah Ferguson 45 50
221 90 c. Prince Andrew piloting helicopter, Digby, Canada, 1985 . . . . . . 95 1·75

48 Father Christmas and Reindeer in Speed Boat

(Des G. Vasarhelyi. Litho Walsall)

1986 (30 Sept). *Christmas. T* **48** *and similar horiz designs. Multicoloured. P* 13 × 13½.
222 30 c. Type **48** 75 50
223 36 c. Father Christmas and reindeer on beach 85 60
224 55 c. Father Christmas fishing . . . . 1·50 1·50
225 70 c. Playing golf . . . . 2·00 2·50
226 $1 Sleeping in hammock . . . . . . 2·25 3·25
222/6 . . . . *Set of* 5 6·50 7·50

49 H.M.S. *Flying Fish* and Outline Map of Christmas Island

(Des L. Curtis. Litho Format)

1987 (21 Jan). *Centenary of Visits by H.M.S. "Flying Fish" and H.M.S. "Egeria". T* **49** *and similar horiz design. Multicoloured. P* 14½.
227 36 c. Type **49** 80 75
228 90 c. H.M.S. *Egeria* and outline map . . 1·60 3·00

50 Blind Snake

51 Children watching Father Christmas in Sleigh

(Des G. Drummond. Litho Questa)

1987 (25 Mar)–**89**. *Wildlife. T* **50** *and similar horiz designs. Multicoloured. P* 14.
229 1 c. Type **50** 40 80
a. Sheetlet of 16. Nos. 229/37 and 238/44 (1.3.88) . . . . 28·00
230 2 c. Blue-tailed Skink 40 80
231 3 c. Insectivorous Bat (24.6.87) 80 80
232 5 c. Grasshopper (1.3.88) 80 80
233 10 c. Christmas Island Fruit Bat (24.6.87) 80 80
234 25 c. Gecko 80 90
235 30 c. *Mantis religiosa* (mantid) (1.3.88) . . 1·00 90
236 36 c. Indonesian Hawk Owl (24.6.87) . . 2·75 1·60
237 40 c. Bull-mouth Helmet (*Cypraecassis rufa*) (26.8.87) . . . . 1·50 85
237*a* 41 c. Nudibranch (*Phidiana* sp) (1.9.89) . . 1·00 70
238 50 c. Textile or Cloth of Gold Cone (*Conus textile*) (26.8.87) . . . . . . 1·40 1·00
239 65 c. Brittle Stars (26.8.87) . . . . 1·10 1·00
240 75 c. Regal Angelfish (26.8.87) . . . . 1·10 1·00
241 90 c. *Appias paulina* (butterfly) (1.3.88) . . 3·50 2·50
242 $1 *Hypolimnas misippus* (butterfly) (1.3.88) . . . . 3·50 2·50
243 $2 Shrew (*Crocidura attenuata trichura*) (24.6.87) . . . . 3·50 5·50
244 $5 Green Turtle . . . . 4·50 6·50
229/44 . . . . *Set of* 17 26·00 26·00
No. 229a was originally only available from a presentation pack, but was, subsequently, sold separately by the Christmas Island Post Office. Stamps from it show "1988" imprint date. Examples from the ordinary sheets are without imprint date.

(Des D. Miller. Litho CPE Australia Ltd, Melbourne)

1987 (7 Oct). *Christmas. Sheet*, 165 × 65 *mm, containing T* **51** *and similar multicoloured designs. P* 13½.
MS245 30 c. Type **51**; 37 c. Father Christmas distributing gifts (48×22 *mm*); 90 c. Children with presents (48×22 *mm*); $1 Singing carols 4·00 4·00
a. Imperf between 37 c. and 90 c. . .
The stamps within No. **MS**245 form a composite design of a beach scene.

(Des Sue Passmore. Litho CPE Australia Ltd, Melbourne)

1988 (26 Jan). *Bicentenary of Australian Settlement. Arrival of First Fleet. Square designs as Nos.* 1105/9 *of Australia, but each inscribed* "CHRISTMAS ISLAND Indian Ocean" *and* "AUSTRALIA BICENTENARY".
246 37 c. Aborigines watching arrival of Fleet, Botany Bay . . . . 1·40 1·60
a. Horiz strip of 5. Nos. 246/50 . . . . 6·25
247 37 c. Aboriginal family and anchored ships . . 1·40 1·60
248 37 c. Fleet arriving at Sydney Cove . . . . 1·40 1·60
249 37 c. Ship's boat . . . . 1·40 1·60
250 37 c. Raising the flag, Sydney Cove, 26 January 1788 . . . . 1·40 1·60
246/50 . . . . *Set of* 5 6·25 7·25
Nos. 246/50 were printed together, *se-tenant*, in horizontal strips of five throughout the sheet, forming a composite design.

52 Captain William May

53 Pony and Trap, 1910

(Des Josephine Martin. Litho Questa)

1988 (8 June). *Centenary of British Annexation. T* **52** *and similar vert designs. Multicoloured. P* 14½×14.
251 37 c. Type **52** 35 40
252 53 c. Annexation ceremony 50 55
253 95 c. H.M.S. *Imperieuse* (armoured cruiser) firing salute 90 95
254 $1.50, Building commemorative cairn . . 1·40 1·50
251/4 . . . . *Set of* 4 2·75 3·00

(Des L. Curtis. Litho Walsall)

1988 (24 Aug). *Centenary of Permanent Settlement. T* **53** *and similar horiz designs. Multicoloured. P* 14×14½.
255 37 c. Type **53** 50 40
256 55 c. Phosphate mining, 1910 . . . . 75 55
257 70 c. Steam locomotive, 1914 . . . . 1·10 85
258 $1 Arrival of first aircraft, 1957 . . . . 1·50 1·25
255/8 . . . . *Set of* 4 3·50 2·75

54 Beach Toys

55 Food on Table ("Good Harvesting")

(Des N. Shewring. Litho Format)

988 (15 Nov). *Christmas. Toys and Gifts. T* **54** *and similar vert designs. Multicoloured. P* 14.

59	32 c. Type **54**	40	35
60	39 c. Flippers, snorkel and mask	50	40
61	90 c. Model soldier, doll and soft toys	1·10	1·10
62	$1 Models of racing car, lorry and jet air-craft	1·25	1·25
59/62	*Set of* 4	3·00	2·75

(Des D. Miller. Litho Questa)

989 (31 Jan). *Chinese New Year. T* **55** *and similar horiz designs. Multicoloured. P* 14 × 14½.

63	39 c. Type **55**	45	40
64	70 c. Decorations ("Prosperity")	80	70
65	90 c. Chinese girls ("Good Fortune")	1·10	90
66	$1 Lion dance ("Progress Every Year")	1·25	1·00
63/6	*Set of* 4	3·25	2·75

56 Sir John Murray

57 Four Children

(Des S. Noon. Litho Walsall)

1989 (16 Mar). *75th Death Anniv of Sir John Murray (oceanographer). T* **56** *and similar horiz designs. Multicoloured. P* 14 × 14½.

267	39 c. Type **56**	50	50
268	80 c. Map of Christmas Island showing Murray Hill	1·25	95
269	$1 Oceanographic equipment	1·50	1·25
270	$1.10, H.M.S. *Challenger* (survey ship), 1872	1·75	1·50
267/70	*Set of* 4	4·50	3·75

(Des C. Burke. Litho Questa)

1989 (31 May). *Malay Hari Raya Festival. T* **57** *and similar vert designs. Multicoloured. P* 14.

271	39 c. Type **57**	55	50
272	55 c. Man playing tambourine	80	70
273	80 c. Girl in festival costume	1·25	1·00
274	$1.10, Christmas Island Mosque	1·60	1·40
271/4	*Set of* 4	3·75	3·25

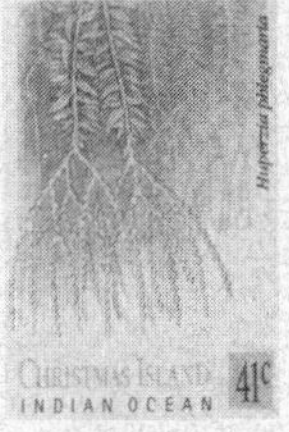

58 *Huperzia phlegmaria*

59 Virgin Mary and Star

(Des Kerrie Rockett. Litho Walsall)

1989 (16 Aug). *Ferns. T* **58** *and similar vert designs. Multicoloured. P* 14.

275	41 c. Type **58**	75	60
276	65 c. *Asplenium polydon*	1·10	85
277	80 c. Common Bracken	1·40	1·00
278	$1.10, Birds-nest Fern	1·60	1·40
275/8	*Set of* 4	4·25	3·50

(Des G. Maynard. Litho Leigh-Mardon Ltd, Melbourne)

1989 (4 Oct). *Christmas. T* **59** *and similar vert designs. Multicoloured. P* 14½.

279	36 c. Type **59**	60	40
280	41 c. Christ Child in manger	60	45
281	80 c. Shepherds and Star	1·40	80
282	$1.10, Three Wise Men following Star	1·50	1·10
279/82	*Set of* 4	3·50	2·50

COVER PRICES

Cover factors are quoted at the beginning of each country for most issues to 1945. An explanation of the system can be found on page x. The factors quoted do not, however, apply to philatelic covers.

(60)

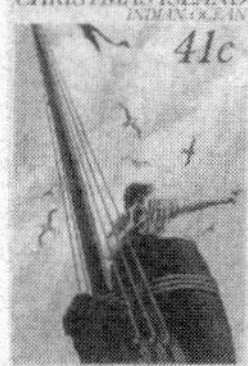

61 First Sighting, 1615

1989 (18 Oct). *"Melbourne Stampshow '89". No. 237a and as No. 242, but with imprint date, optd with T* **60**.

283	41 c. Nudibranch (*Phidiana* sp)	60	45
284	$1 *Hypolimnas misippus*	1·40	1·00

(Des R. Honisett. Litho Note Ptg Branch, Reserve Bank of Australia)

1990 (31 Jan). *375th Anniv of Discovery of Christmas Island. T* **61** *and similar vert design. Multicoloured. P* 14×15.

285	41 c. Type **61**	1·00	50
286	$1.10, Second sighting and naming, 1643	2·00	1·40

62 Miniature Tractor pulling Phosphate

63 Male Abbott's Booby

(Des C. Lee. Litho Leigh-Mardon Ltd, Melbourne)

1990 (18 Apr–22 Aug). *Christmas Island Transport. T* **62** *and similar multicoloured designs. P* 13½×14 (*horiz*) *or* 14×13½ (*vert*).

287	1 c. Type **62**	15	20
288	2 c. Phosphate train (22 Aug)	40	40
289	3 c. Diesel railcar No. 8802 (*vert*)	20	20
290	5 c. Loading Road train (22 Aug)	40	40
291	10 c. Trishaw (*vert*)	30	30
292	15 c. Terex truck (22 Aug)	65	65
293	25 c. Articulated bus	30	30
294	30 c. Cable passenger carriage (*vert*)	30	35
295	40 c. Passenger barge (*vert*)	35	40
296	50 c. Kolek (outrigger canoe)	55	55
297	65 c. Flying Doctor aircraft and ambulance (22 Aug)	3·00	1·50
298	75 c. Commercial van (22 Aug)	1·50	1·50
299	90 c. Vintage lorry (22 Aug)	1·75	1·75
300	$1 Water tanker (22 Aug)	1·75	1·75
301	$2 Traction engine (22 Aug)	3·25	3·25
302	$5 Steam locomotive No. 1	4·50	4·75
287/302	*Set of* 16	17·00	17·00

(Des N. Shewring. Litho Questa)

1990 (6 June). *Abbott's Booby. T* **63** *and similar vert designs. Multicoloured. P* 13½×14.

303	10 c. Type **63**	85	30
304	20 c. Juvenile male	1·40	50
305	29 c. Female with egg	1·60	55
306	41 c. Pair with chick	2·25	70
303/6	*Set of* 4	5·50	1·90
MS307	122×68 mm. 41 c. Male with wings spread; 41 c. Male on branch; 41 c. Female with fledgling. P 14½	2·50	2·25

The three stamps within No. **MS**307 form a composite design and are without the W.W.F. logo.

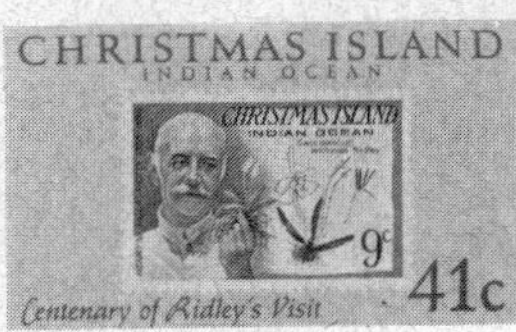

64 1977 Famous Visitors 9 c. Stamp

(Des Elizabeth Innes. Litho Leigh-Mardon Ltd, Melbourne)

1990 (11 July). *Centenary of Henry Ridley's Visit. T* **64** *and similar multicoloured design. P* 15×14½ (41 *c.*) *or* 14½×15 (75 *c.*).

308	41 c. Type **64**	55	65
309	75 c. Ridley (botanist) in rainforest (*vert*)	85	1·75

1990 (24 Aug). *"New Zealand 1990" International Stamp Exhibition, Auckland. No.* **MS**307 *optd* "NZ 1990 WORLD STAMP EXHIBITION AUCKLAND, NEW ZEALAND, 24 AUGUST – 2 SEPTEMBER 1990" *in purple on the sheet margins.*

MS310	122×68 mm. 41 c. Male with wings spread; 41 c. Male on branch; 41 c. Female with fledgling	3·25	3·50
	a. Error. Imperf	£1000	

65 *Corymborkus veratrifolia*

66 *Islander* (freighter), 1898

(Litho Leigh-Mardon Ltd, Melbourne)

1990 (3 Oct). *Christmas. Flowers. T* **65** *and similar horiz designs. Multicoloured. P* 14½.

311	38 c. Type **65**	1·00	60
312	43 c. *Hoya aldrichii*	1·10	65
313	80 c. *Quisqualis indica*	2·00	2·50
314	$1.20, *Barringtonia racemosa*	2·50	3·00
311/14	*Set of* 4	6·00	6·00

1990 (6 Dec). *"Birdpex '90" Stamp Exhibition, Christchurch. No.* **MS**307 *optd* "BIRDPEX '90 NATIONAL PHILATELIC EXHIBITION UNIVERSITY OF CANTERBURY CHRISTCHURCH NZ 6–9 DEC 1990 IN CONJUNCTION WITH THE 20th INTERNATIONAL ORNITHOLOGICAL CONGRESS" *in green on the sheet margins.*

MS315	122×68 mm. 41 c. Male with wings spread; 41 c. Male on branch; 41 c. Female with fledgling	4·00	4·50

(Des C. Lee. Litho Leigh-Mardon Ltd, Melbourne)

1991 (13 Feb). *Centenary of First Phosphate Mining Lease. T* **66** *and similar vert designs. Multicoloured. P* 14½.

316	43 c. Type **66**	90	90
	a. Horiz strip of 5. Nos. 316/20	6·00	
317	43 c. Miners loading tipper wagons, 1908	90	90
318	85 c. Shay steam locomotive No. 4, 1925	1·25	1·25
319	$1.20, Extracting phosphate, 1951	1·60	1·60
320	$1.70, Land reclamation, 1990	1·90	1·90
316/20	*Set of* 5	6·00	6·00

Nos. 316/20 were printed together, *se-tenant*, in horizontal strips of 5 throughout the sheet, the background forming a composite forest design.

67 Teaching Children Road Safety

68 Map of Christmas Island, 1991

(Des R. Honisett. Litho Leigh-Mardon Ltd, Melbourne)

1991 (17 Apr). *Christmas Island Police Force. T* **67** *and similar horiz designs. Multicoloured. P* 14½.

321	43 c. Type **67**	1·25	60
322	43 c. Traffic control	1·25	60
323	90 c. Airport customs	2·00	1·75
324	$1.20, Police launch *Fregata Andrews* towing rescued boat	2·75	2·50
321/4	*Set of* 4	6·50	5·00
MS325	135×88 mm. Nos. 321/4	6·50	5·00

(Des D. Miller. Litho Questa)

1991 (19 June). *Maps of Christmas Island. T* **68** *and similar vert designs. Multicoloured. P* 14×13½.

326	43 c. Type **68**	85	65
327	75 c. Goos Atlas, 1666	1·50	1·10
328	$1.10, De Manevillette, 1745	2·25	1·60
329	$1.20, Comberford, 1667	2·25	1·90
326/9	*Set of* 4	6·00	4·75

69 *Bruguiera gymnorrhiza*

70 "Family round Christmas Tree", (S'ng Yen Luiw)

(Des Jane Moore. Litho Leigh-Mardon Ltd, Melbourne)

1991 (21 Aug). *Local Trees. T* **69** *and similar horiz designs. Multicoloured. P* 14.

330	43 c. Type **69**	75	65
331	70 c. *Syzygium operculatum*	1·25	1·00
332	85 c. *Ficus microcarpa*	1·50	1·25
333	$1.20, *Arenga listeri*	1·75	1·60
330/3	*Set of* 4	4·75	4·00

(Des Liz Innes. Litho Leigh-Mardon Ltd, Melbourne)

1991 (2 Oct). *Christmas. Children's Paintings. T* **70** *and similar horiz designs. Multicoloured. P* 14½.
334 38 c. Type **70** 65 55
a. Horiz strip of 5. Nos 334/8 .. .. 3·00
335 38 c. "Opening Presents" (Liew Ann Nee) 65 55
336 38 c. "Beach Party" (Foo Pang Chuan) .. 65 55
337 38 c. "Christmas Walk" (Too Lai Peng) .. 65 55
338 38 c. "Santa Claus and Christmas Tree" (Jesamine Wheeler) 65 55
339 43 c. "Santa Claus fishing" (Ho Puay Ha) .. 70 60
340 $1 "Santa Claus in Boat" (Ng Hooi Hua) 1·50 1·25
341 $1.20, "Santa Claus surfing" (Yani Kawi) 1·75 1·50
334/41 .. .. *Set of* 8 6·50 5·50
Nos. 334/8 were printed together, *se-tenant*, in horizontal strips of 5 throughout the sheet.

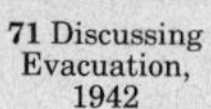

71 Discussing Evacuation, 1942

72 Snake's-head Cowrie (*Cypraea caputserpentis*)

(Des C. Lee. Litho Leigh-Mardon Ltd, Melbourne)

1992 (19 Feb). *50th Anniv of Partial Evacuation. T* **71** *and similar vert designs. Multicoloured. P* 14½.
342 45 c. Type **71** 80 80
343 45 c. Families waiting to embark 80 80
344 $1.05, Ferrying evacuees to *Islander* .. 2·25 2·25
345 $1.20, Departure of *Islander* (freighter) .. 2·50 2·50
342/5 .. .. *Set of* 4 5·75 5·75

(Des G. Ryan. Litho Leigh-Mardon Ltd, Melbourne)

1992 (15 Apr–19 Aug). *Shells. T* **72** *and similar vert designs. Multicoloured. P* 14½.
346 5 c. Tiger Cowrie (*Cypraea tigris*) (19 Aug) 40 40
347 10 c. Type **72** 50 50
348 15 c. Scorpion Conch (*Lambis scorpius*) (19 Aug) 65 50
349 20 c. Royal Oak Scallop (*Cryptopecten pallium*) 75 50
350 25 c. Striped Engina (*Engina mendicaria*) (19 Aug) 75 50
351 30 c. Prickly Pacific Drupe (*Drupa ricinus*) 90 50
352 40 c. Reticulate Distorsio (*Distorsio recticulata*) (19 Aug) 90 55
353 45 c. Tapestry Turban (*Turbo petholatus*) 1·25 60
354 50 c. Beautiful Goblet (*Pollia puchra*) (19 Aug) .. .. 1·25 55
355 60 c. Captain Cone (*Conus capitaneus*) .. 1·50 65
356 70 c. Lajonkaire's Turban (*Turbo lajonkairii*) (19 Aug) .. .. .. 1·50 75
357 80 c. Chiragra Spider Conch (*Lambis chiragra chiragra*) .. .. .. 1·75 85
358 90 c. Common Delphina (*Angaria delphinus*) (19 Aug) .. .. .. 1·75 1·10
359 $1 Ceramic Vase (*Vasum ceramicum*) .. 1·75 1·25
360 $2 Pacific Partridge Tun (*Tonna perdix*) 2·00 2·10
361 $5 Strawberry Drupe (*Drupa rubusidaeus*) (19 Aug) .. .. .. 5·00 5·25
346/61 .. .. .. *Set of* 16 20·00 14·00

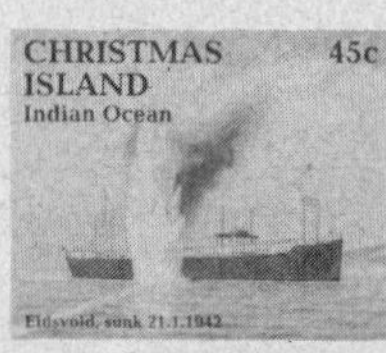

73 Torpedoing of *Eidsvold*

(74)

(Des R. Watton. Litho Enschedé)

1992 (17 June). *50th Anniv of Sinkings of* Eidsvold *and* Nissa Maru. *T* **73** *and similar horiz designs. Multicoloured. P* 14×13½.
362 45 c. Type **73** .. .. 1·25 75
363 80 c. *Eidsvold* sinking .. .. .. 2·00 1·75
364 $1.05, *Nissa Maru* under attack .. .. 2·50 2·75
365 $1.20, *Nissa Maru* beached .. .. 2·50 3·00
362/5 .. .. *Set of* 4 7·50 7·50

1992 (1 Sept). *"Kuala Lumpur '92" International Philatelic Exhibition. No. 361 optd with T* **74** *in red.*
366 $5 Strawberry Drupe (*Drupa rubusidaeus*) 8·50 7·00

75 Jungle

76 Abbott's Booby

(Des Jane Moore and Elizabeth Innes. Litho Leigh-Mardon Ltd, Melbourne)

1992 (7 Oct). *Christmas. T* **75** *and similar vert designs. Multicoloured. P* 14½.
367 40 c. Type **75** .. .. 90 1·00
a. Horiz strip of 5. Nos. 367/71 .. .. 5·50
368 40 c. Seabirds over rock .. .. .. 90 1·00
369 45 c. Brown Boobies on headland .. .. 90 1·00
370 $1.05, Seabirds and cliffs .. .. 1·60 1·75
371 $1.20, Cliffs .. .. .. 1·60 1·75
367/71 .. .. *Set of* 5 5·50 6·00
Nos. 367/71 were printed together, *se-tenant*, in horizontal strips of 5 throughout the sheet, each strip forming a composite coastal design.

On 2 March 1993 responsibility for the Christmas Island postal service passed from the territorial administration to Australia Post. In consequence Nos. 372/7 and all subsequent issues are valid for postal purposes in both Christmas Island and Australia.

(Des D. Nelson and Janet Boschen. Litho McPherson's Ptg Group, Mulgrave)

1993 (4 Mar). *Seabirds. T* **76** *and similar vert designs. Multicoloured. P* 14½×14.
372 45 c. Type **76** 60 80
a. Horiz strip of 5. Nos. 372/6 .. .. 2·75
373 45 c. Christmas Island Frigate Bird .. 60 80
374 45 c. Common Noddy 60 80
375 45 c. White-tailed Tropic Bird ("Golden Bosunbird") 60 80
376 45 c. Brown Booby 60 80
372/6 .. .. *Set of* 5 2·75 3·50
MS377 140×70 mm. Nos. 372/6 .. .. 2·75 3·50
Nos. 372/6 were printed together, *se-tenant*, in horizontal strips of 5 throughout the sheet, forming a composite design.
No. **MS**377 also exists overprinted with the "Indopex '93" or "Taipei '93" logos for sale at these stamp exhibitions in Surabaya, Indonesia, and Taiwan.

77 Dolly Beach

78 Turtle on Beach

(Des Jane Moore and Janet Boschen. Litho McPherson's Ptg Group, Mulgrave)

1993 (1 June). *Scenic Views of Christmas Island. T* **77** *and similar horiz designs. Multicoloured. P* 14×14½.
378 85 c. Type **77** .. .. 1·25 1·50
379 95 c. Blow Holes .. .. 1·50 1·75
380 $1.05, Merrial Beach .. .. .. 1·60 1·90
381 $1.20, Rainforest .. .. .. 1·75 2·00
378/81 .. .. *Set of* 4 5·50 6·50

(Des B. Wood and Sandra Harman. Litho McPherson's Ptg Group, Mulgrave)

1993 (2 Sept). *Christmas. T* **78** *and similar vert designs. Multicoloured. P* 14½×14.
382 40 c. Type **78** 80 50
383 45 c. Crabs and wave 80 50
384 $1 Christmas Island Frigate Bird and rainforest .. .. 2·00 2·50
382/4 .. .. *Set of* 3 3·25 3·25

79 Map of Christmas Island

80 Pekingese

(Des Betina Ogden. Litho McPherson's Ptg Group, Mulgrave)

1993 (1 Dec). *350th Anniv of Naming of Christmas Island. P* 14×14½.
385 **79** $2 multicoloured .. .. .. 3·00 3·25

(Des Yen Lau. Litho McPherson's Ptg Group, Mulgrave)

1994 (20 Jan). *Chinese New Year ("Year of the Dog"). T* **80** *and similar horiz design. P* 14×14½.
386 45 c. Type **80** .. .. 1·00 1·25
a. Pair. Nos. 386/7 .. .. .. 2·00 2·50
387 45 c. Mickey (Christmas Island dog) .. 1·00 1·25
MS388 106×70 mm. Nos. 386/7 .. .. 2·00 2·50
Nos. 386/7 were printed together, *se-tenant*, in horizontal or vertical pairs throughout the sheet.
No. **MS**388 also exists overprinted with "Melbourne Stamp & Coin Show 11–13 February 1994", "Hong Kong '94 Stamp Exhibition", "Canberra Stamp Show 94" or "Queensland Stamp and Coin Show 94" logos for sale at these exhibitions.

81 Shay Locomotive No. 4

82 *Brachypeza archytas*

(Des J. Richards. Litho McPherson's Ptg Group, Mulgrave)

1994 (19 May). *Steam Locomotives. T* **81** *and similar horiz designs. Multicoloured. P* 14×14½.
389 85 c. Type **81** .. .. 1·50 1·75
390 95 c. Locomotive No. 9 .. .. .. 1·50 1·75
391 $1.20, Locomotive No. 1 .. .. 1·75 2·25
389/91 .. .. *Set of* 3 4·25 5·25

(Des Celia Rosser. Litho McPherson's Ptg Group, Mulgrave)

1994 (16 Aug). *Orchids. T* **82** *and similar vert designs. Multicoloured. P* 14½×14.
392 45 c. Type **82** .. .. 1·00 1·10
a. Horiz strip of 5. Nos. 392/6 .. .. 4·50
393 45 c. *Thelasis capitata* .. .. .. 1·00 1·10
394 45 c. *Corymborkis veratrifolia* .. .. 1·00 1·10
395 45 c. *Flickingeria nativitatis* .. .. 1·00 1·10
396 45 c. *Dendrobium crumenatum* .. .. 1·00 1·10
392/6 .. .. *Set of* 5 4·50 5·00
Nos. 392/6 were printed together, *se-tenant*, in horizontal strips of 5 throughout the sheet.

83 Angel blowing Trumpet

84 Pig

(Des Tracie Grimwood. Litho McPherson's Ptg Group, Mulgrave)

1994 (8 Sept). *Christmas. T* **83** *and similar horiz designs. Multicoloured. P* 14×14½.
397 40 c. Type **83** 80 50
398 45 c. Wise Man holding gift 80 50
399 80 c. Star over Bethlehem .. .. 1·75 2·50
397/9 .. .. *Set of* 3 3·00 3·25

(Des J. Chan. Litho McPherson's Ptg Group, Mulgrave)

1995 (12 Jan). *Chinese New Year ("Year of the Pig"). T* **84** *and similar horiz design showing a different pig. P* 14×14½.
400 45 c. multicoloured 75 50
401 85 c. multicoloured .. .. .. 1·25 1·60
MS402 106×71 mm. Nos. 400/1 .. .. 1·75 2·25
No. **MS**402 also exists overprinted with "Melbourne Stamp & Coin Show 10–12 February 1995" logo for sale at this exhibition.

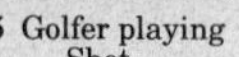

85 Golfer playing Shot

86 Father Christmas with Map on Christmas Island Frigate Bird

(Des N. Buchanan. Litho McPherson's Ptg Group, Mulgrave)

1995 (11 May). *40th Anniv of Christmas Island Golf Course. P* 14×14½.
403 **85** $2.50, multicoloured .. .. .. 3·50 3·75

(Des B. Wood and Sophie Newman. Litho McPherson's Ptg Group, Mulgrave)

1995 (14 Sept). *Christmas. T* **86** *and similar horiz designs. Multicoloured. P* 14×14½.
404 40 c. Type **86** 80 50
405 45 c. Father Christmas distributing presents 80 50
406 80 c. Father Christmas waving goodbye .. 1·75 2·50
404/6 .. .. *Set of* 3 3·00 3·25

COVER PRICES

Cover factors are quoted at the beginning of each country for most issues to 1945. An explanation of the system can be found on page x. The factors quoted do not, however, apply to philatelic covers.

87 De Havilland D.H.98 Mosquito on Reconnaissance Mission

88 Lemon-peel Angelfish

(Des B. Sadgrove. Recess and litho Note Ptg Branch, Reserve Bank of Australia)

1995 (12 Oct). *50th Anniv of End of Second World War. T* **87** *and similar horiz design, each black, stone and vermilion. P* 14×14½.

407	45 c. Type **87**	80	80
	a. Pair. Nos. 407/8	1·60	1·60
408	45 c. H.M.S. *Rother* (frigate)	80	80

Nos. 407/8 were printed together, *se-tenant*, in horizontal and vertical pairs throughout the sheet.

(Des Lisa Christensen (85 c., 95 c., $1.20), Josephine Mure (others). Litho SNP Cambec (75 c., $1) or McPherson's Ptg Group, Mulgrave (others))

1995 (12 Oct)–**97.** *Marine Life. T* **88** *and similar horiz designs. Multicoloured. P* 14×14½.

412	20 c. Pink-tailed Triggerfish (18.4.96)	15	20
413	30 c. Japanese Inflator-filefish ("Longnose Filefish") (18.4.96)	25	30
414	45 c. Princess Anthias (18.4.96)	30	35
415	75 c. Type **88**	55	60
416	85 c. Moon Wrasse (17.7.97)	65	70
417	90 c. Spotted Boxfish (18.4.96)	70	75
418	95 c. Moorish Idol (17.7.97)	75	80
419	$1 Emperor Angelfish	75	80
420	$1.20, Glass-eyed Snapper ("Glass Bigeye") (17.7.97)	1·00	1·10
412/20	*Set of* 9	4·50	5·00

89 Rat with Drum

90 Christmas Island White Eye

(Des L. Chiang. Litho SNP Cambec (gold die-stamped Avon Graphics))

1996 (9 Jan). *Chinese New Year ("Year of the Rat"). T* **89** *and similar horiz design. Multicoloured. P* 14×14½.

425	45 c. Type **89**	75	75
	a. Pair. Nos. 425/6	1·50	1·50
426	45 c. Rat with tambourine	75	75
MS427	106×70 mm. Nos. 425/6	1·50	1·50

Nos. 425/6 were printed together, *se-tenant*, in horizontal and vertical pairs throughout the sheet.

No. **MS**427 also exists overprinted with the logo of the Melbourne Stamp and Coin Fair for sale at this Australian exhibition.

(Des T. Pridham and Susan Horvath. Litho McPherson's Ptg Group, Mulgrave)

1996 (11 July). *Christmas Island Land Birds. T* **90** *and similar vert design. Multicoloured. P* 14½×14.

428	45 c. Type **90**	75	50
429	85 c. Christmas Island Hawk Owl	1·75	2·00

91 Three Ships approaching Island

92 Ox facing Right

(Des P. Gifford. Litho McPherson's Ptg Group, Mulgrave)

1996 (12 Sept). *Christmas. "I saw Three Ships" (carol). T* **91** *and similar square designs. Multicoloured. P* 14½.

430	40 c. Type **91**	65	50
431	45 c. Madonna and Child with ships at anchor	65	50
432	80 c. Ships leaving	1·50	1·75
430/2	*Set of* 3	2·50	2·50

(Des A. Donato. Litho McPherson's Ptg Group, Mulgrave)

1996 (1 Nov). *300th Anniv of Willem de Vlamingh's Discovery of Christmas Island. As No.* 1667 *of Australia. P* 14×14½.

433	45 c. multicoloured	75	75

Nos. 433 and No. 1667 of Australia were printed together, *se-tenant*, in horizontal pairs throughout the sheet which are listed as No. 1667a of Australia.

(Des L. Chiang. Litho SNP Cambec (gold die-stamped Avon Graphics))

1997 (6 Jan). *Chinese New Year ("Year of the Ox"). T* **92** *and similar horiz design. Multicoloured. P* 14×14½.

434	45 c. Type **92**	70	80
	a. Pair. Nos. 434/5	1·40	1·60
435	45 c. Ox facing left	70	80
MS436	106×70 mm. Nos. 434/5	1·40	1·60

Nos. 434/5 were printed together, *se-tenant*, in horizontal and vertical pairs throughout the sheet.

93 Father Christmas reading Letter

94 Tiger

(Des A. Hopgood. Litho McPherson's Ptg Group, Mulgrave)

1997 (11 Sept). *Christmas. T* **93** *and similar horiz designs. Multicoloured. P* 14×14½.

437	40 c. Type **93**	55	45
438	45 c. Father Christmas carving wooden boat	55	45
439	80 c. Father Christmas in sleigh	1·10	1·40
437/9	*Set of* 3	2·00	2·10

(Des L. Chiang. Litho SNP Cambec)

1998 (5 Jan). *Chinese New Year ("Year of the Tiger"). T* **94** *and similar horiz design. Multicoloured. P* 14×14½.

440	45 c. Type **94**	55	65
	a. Pair. Nos. 440/1	1·10	1·25
441	45 c. Tiger with head facing left	55	65
MS442	106×70 mm. Nos. 440/1	1·10	1·25

Nos. 440/1 were printed together, *se-tenant*, in horizontal and vertical pairs throughout the sheet.

95 Christmas Island Frigate Bird

96 Orchid Tree

(Des Lisa Christensen. Litho SNP Cambec)

1998 (12 Mar). *Marine Life. T* **95** *and similar horiz designs. Multicoloured. P* 14×14½.

443	5 c. Type **95**	15	20
	a. Sheetlet. Nos. 443/62	4·50	
444	5 c. Four Ambon Chromis	15	20
445	5 c. Three Ambon Chromis	15	20
446	5 c. One Pink Anemonefish	15	20
447	5 c. Three Pink Anemonefish	15	20
448	10 c. Eastern Reef Egret	20	25
449	10 c. Whitelined Cod	20	25
450	10 c. Pyramid Butterflyfish	20	25
451	10 c. Dusky Parrotfish	20	25
452	10 c. Spotted Garden Eel	20	25
453	25 c. Sooty Tern	25	30
454	25 c. Stripe-tailed Damselfish ("Scissortail Sergeant")	25	30
455	25 c. Thicklip Wrasse	25	30
456	25 c. Blackaxil Chromis	25	30
457	25 c. Orange Anthias	25	30
458	45 c. Brown Booby	35	40
459	45 c. Green Turtle	35	40
460	45 c. Pink Anemonefish	35	40
461	45 c. Blue Sea Star	35	40
462	45 c. Kunie's Chromodoris	35	40
443/62	*Set of* 20	4·50	5·00

Nos. 443/62 were printed together, *se-tenant*, in sheetlets of 20 with the backgrounds forming a composite design.

(Des Clare Kaegi. Litho McPherson's Ptg Group, Mulgrave)

1998 (3 Sept). *Christmas. Flowering Trees. T* **96** *and similar vert designs. Multicoloured. P* 14½×14.

463	40 c. Type **96**	40	35
464	80 c. Flame Tree	80	90
465	95 c. Sea Hibiscus	90	95
463/5	*Set of* 3	1·90	2·00

COVER PRICES

Cover factors are quoted at the beginning of each country for most issues to 1945. An explanation of the system can be found on page x. The factors quoted do not, however, apply to philatelic covers.

97 Leaping Rabbit

(Des L. Chiang. Litho SNP Ausprint)

1999 (14 Jan). *Chinese New Year ("Year of the Rabbit"). T* **97** *and similar horiz design. Multicoloured. P* 14×14½.

466	45 c. Type **97**	35	40
	a. Pair. Nos. 466/7	70	
467	45 c. Rabbit with pestle and mortar	35	40
MS468	106×70 mm. Nos. 466/7	70	75

Nos. 466/7 were printed together, *se-tenant*, in horizontal and vertical pairs throughout the sheet.

STAMP BOOKLETS

Between mid-1995 and 25 June 1996 the Christmas Island Postmaster produced stamp booklets utilising card from surplus Presentation Packs. These booklets contained blocks of ten 45 c. stamps from whichever issue was currently available.

1996 (26 June). *Black on red cover,* 95×150 *mm, inscr* "CHRISTMAS ISLAND POST OFFICE STAMP BOOKLET", *often with Christmas Island postmark on front. Stapled.*

SB1	$4.50, booklet containing 45 c. (No. 414) in block of 10	£150
	a. Containing 45 c. (No. 353)	£550

All examples of No. SB1a are postmarked 23 June 1996.

COCOS (KEELING) ISLANDS

The Cocos (Keeling) Islands, which had been settled by the Clunies Ross family in the 1820s, were annexed by Great Britain in 1857. In 1878 the group was attached to Ceylon, but was transferred to the Straits Settlements on 7 February 1886. During the Second World War the islands were under British military control exercised from Ceylon. At the end of hostilities administration from Singapore was continued until the islands were transferred to Australia on 23 November 1955.

The stamps of the STRAITS SETTLEMENTS were used by a postal agency operating on Cocos (Keeling) Islands from 1 April 1933 until 1 March 1937. The postal agency reopened on 2 September 1952 and used the stamps of SINGAPORE until the islands were transferred to Australia in 1955. From 1955 until 1963 stamps of AUSTRALIA were in use.
Nos. 1/31 were also valid for use in Australia.

PRINTERS. All the following stamps to No. 31 were printed by the Note Printing Branch, Reserve Bank of Australia, Melbourne.

1 Copra Industry

2 "Super Constellation"

(Des K. McKay and E. Jones (5d.), E. Jones (others). Eng E. Jones. Recess)

1963 (11 June). *T* **1/2** *and similar designs. P* 14½×14 (*5d., 2s. 3d.*) *or* 14½ (*others*).
1 3d. chocolate .. .. 1·25 1·50
2 5d. ultramarine .. .. 1·50 80
3 8d. scarlet .. .. 1·75 2·25
4 1s. green .. .. 1·25 55
5 2s. deep purple .. .. 11·00 3·25
6 2s. 3d. deep green .. .. 35·00 3·25
1/6 .. .. *Set of* 6 48·00 10·50
Designs: *Vert* (*as T* 1)—8d. Map of islands; 2s. Jukong (sailboat). *Horiz* (*as T* 2)—1s. Palms. (*as T* 2)—2s. 3d. White Tern.

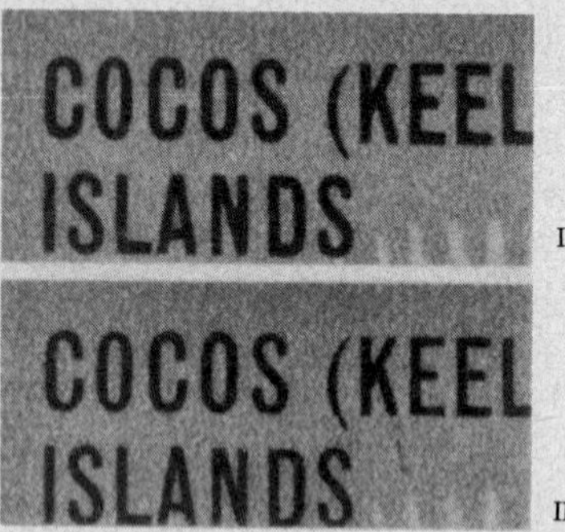

I Thick lettering
II Thinner lettering

1965 (14 Apr). *50th Anniv of Gallipoli Landing. As T* **184** *of Australia, but slightly larger* (22×34½ *mm*) *and colour changed. Photo. P* 13½.
7 5d. sepia, black and emerald (I) 60 45
a. *Black-brown, black and light emerald* (II) 2·50 1·75
No. 7a comes from a second printing, using a new black cylinder, which was available from the end of April.

With the introduction of decimal currency on 14 February 1966, Australian stamps were used in Cocos Islands, until the appearance of the new definitives on 9 July 1969.

(New Currency. 100 cents = 1 Australian dollar)

7 Reef Clam (*Tridacna derasa*)

8 Great Frigate Bird

(Des L. Annois (1 c. to 6 c.), P. Jones (10 c. to $1). Photo)

1969 (9 July). *Decimal Currency. T* **8** *or designs as T* **7**. *Multicoloured. P* 13½.
8 1 c. Lajonkaines Turbo shell (*Turbo lajonkairii*) (*vert*) 30 60
9 2 c. Elongate or Small Giant Clam (*Tridacna maxima*) (*vert*) .. .. 1·00 80
10 3 c. Type **7** 40 20
11 4 c. Floral Blenny (fish) 30 50
a. Salmon-pink omitted £650
12 5 c. *Porites cocosensis* (coral) 35 30
13 6 c. Atrisignis Flyingfish 75 75
14 10 c. Banded Rail .. .. 1·00 70
15 15 c. Java Sparrow .. .. 1·00 30
16 20 c. Red-tailed Tropic Bird .. .. 1·00 30
17 30 c. Sooty Tern .. .. 1·00 30
18 50 c. Eastern Reef Heron (*vert*) .. .. 1·00 30
19 $1 Type **8** .. .. 3·00 1·00
8/19 .. .. *Set of* 12 10·00 5·50

9 *Dragon*, 1609

10 Map of Cocos (Keeling) Islands Union Flag, Stars and Trees

(Des R. Honisett. Photo)

1976 (29 Mar). *Ships. Multicoloured designs as T* **9**. *P* 13½.
20 1 c. Type **9** 30 40
21 2 c. H.M.S. *Juno*, 1857 .. .. .. 30 40
22 5 c. H.M.S. *Beagle*, 1836 .. .. .. 30 40
23 10 c. H.M.A.S. *Sydney*, 1914 .. .. .. 35 40
24 15 c. S.M.S. *Emden*, 1914 .. .. .. 1·00 55
25 20 c. *Ayesha*, 1907 .. .. 1·00 65
26 25 c. T.S.S. *Islander*, 1927 .. .. .. 1·00 1·00
27 30 c. M.V. *Cheshire*, 1951 .. .. .. 1·00 1·00
28 35 c. Jukong (sailboat) .. .. .. 1·00 1·00
29 40 c. C.S. *Scotia*, 1900 .. .. 1·00 1·00
30 50 c. R.M.S. *Orontes*, 1929 .. .. .. 1·40 1·10
31 $1 Royal Yacht *Gothic*, 1954 .. .. 2·00 1·40
20/31 .. .. *Set of* 12 9·50 8·50
The 2 c. to 20 c., 35 c. and 40 c. are horizontal designs.

(Des Marg Towt. Litho Asher and Co, Melbourne)

1979 (3 Sept). *Inauguration of Independent Postal Service* (20 *c.*) *and Establishment of First Statutory Council* (50 *c.*). *T* **10** *and similar horiz design. Multicoloured. P* 15½ × 15.
32 20 c. Type **10** 25 30
33 50 c. Council seal and jukong (sailboat) .. 35 50

11 Forceps Fish

12 "Peace on Earth"

(Des Marg Towt. Litho Asher and Co, Melbourne)

1979 (3 Sept)–**80**. *Fishes. Horiz designs as T* **11**. *Multicoloured. P* 13½ × 13 (22 *c.*, 28 *c.*, 60 *c.*) *or* 15½ × 15 (*others*).
34 1 c. Type **11** 30 80
35 2 c. Ornate Butterflyfish (19.11.79) 30 30
36 5 c. Barbier 50 90
37 10 c. Meyer's Butterflyfish (18.2.80) 30 55
38 15 c. Pink Wrasse (19.11.79) 30 30
39 20 c. Clark's Anemonefish (19.11.79) 45 30
39*a* 22 c. Undulate Triggerfish (1.7.80) 45 30
40 25 c. Red-breasted Wrasse (18.2.80) 45 60
40*a* 28 c. Guineafowl Wrasse (1.7.80) 35 35
41 30 c. Madagascar Butterflyfish (19.11.79) .. 65 45
42 35 c. Cocos-Keeling Angelfish .. .. .. 65 1·40
43 40 c. Coral Hogfish (19.11.79) 70 60
44 50 c. Clown Wrasse (19.11.79) 85 75
45 55 c. Yellow-tailed Tamarin (18.2.80) .. .. 75 1·00
45*a* 60 c. Greasy Grouper (1.7.80) 75 75
46 $1 Palette Surgeonfish .. .. .. 1·75 3·50
47 $2 Melon Butterflyfish (18.2.80) .. .. 2·00 3·50
34/47 .. .. *Set of* 17 10·00 14·50

(Des D. Pitt. Litho Asher & Co, Melbourne)

1979 (22 Oct). *Christmas. T* **12** *and similar multicoloured design. P* 15 × 15½ (25 *c.*) *or* 15½ × 15 (55 *c.*).
48 25 c. Type **12** 25 35
49 55 c. "Goodwill Toward Men" (*horiz*) 40 55

13 Star, Map of Cocos (Keeling) Islands and Island Landscape

14 "Administered by the British Government, 1857"

(Des P. Arnold. Litho Asher and Co, Melbourne)

1980 (22 Oct). *Christmas. T* **13** *and similar horiz designs. Multicoloured. P* 13.
50 15 c. Type **13** 10 10
51 28 c. Map and Wise Men following star .. 15 15
52 60 c. Map and Nativity scene 40 40
50/2 .. .. *Set of* 3 60 60

(Des Sue Wilson. Litho Asher and Co, Melbourne)

1980 (24 Nov). *25th Anniv of Cocos (Keeling) Islands as an Australian Territory. T* **14** *and similar horiz designs. Multicoloured. P* 13½ × 13.
53 22 c. Type **14** 15 15
a. Horiz strip of 5. Nos. 53/7 70
54 22 c. "Administered by the Government of Ceylon, 1878, 1942–6" 15 15
55 22 c. "Administered by the Straits Settlements, 1886" 15
56 22 c. "Administered by the Colony of Singapore, 1946" 15
57 22 c. "Administered by the Australian Government, 1955" 15
53/7 .. .. *Set of* 5 70
Nos. 53/7 were printed together, *se-tenant*, in horizontal strips 5 throughout the sheet, forming a composite design.

15 *Eye of the Wind* and Map of Cocos (Keeling) Islands

16 Aerial View of Animal Quarantine Station

(Des Sue Wilson. Litho Asher and Co, Melbourne)

1980 (18 Dec). *"Operation Drake" (round the world expeditio and 400th Anniv of Sir Francis Drake's Circumnavigation of th World. T* **15** *and similar multicoloured designs. P* 13.
58 22 c. Type **15** 25
59 28 c. Map showing voyage routes (*horiz*) .. 25
60 35 c. Sir Francis Drake and *Golden Hind* .. 25
61 60 c. Prince Charles and *Eye of the Wind* (brigantine) 45
58/61 .. .. *Set of* 4 1·10

(Des Cato Hibberd Design. Litho Leigh-Mardon Ltd, Melbourne

1981 (12 May). *Opening of Animal Quarantine Station. T* **16** *an similar horiz designs. Multicoloured. P* 13½ × 13.
62 22 c. Type **16** 15
63 45 c. Unloading livestock 30
64 60 c. Livestock in pen 35
62/4 .. .. *Set of* 3 70

17 Consolidated "Catalina" *Guba II* Flying Boat

18 Prince Charles and Lady Diana Spencer

(Des R. Honisett. Litho Leigh-Mardon Ltd, Melbourne)

1981 (23 June). *Aircraft. T* **17** *and similar horiz designs. Mult coloured. P* 13½ × 13.
65 22 c. Type **17** 25
a. Horiz strip of 5. Nos. 65/9 .. .. 1·10
66 22 c. Consolidated "Liberator" and Avro "Lancastrian" 25
67 22 c. Douglas "DC4 (Skymaster)" and Lockheed "Constellation" 25
68 22 c. Lockheed "Electra" 25
69 22 c. Boeing "727" airliners 25
65/9 .. .. *Set of* 5 1·10
Nos. 65/9 were printed together, *se-tenant*, in horizontal strips 5 throughout the sheet.

(Des B. Clinton. Litho Leigh-Mardon Ltd, Melbourne)

1981 (29 July). *Royal Wedding. P* 13½ × 13.
70 **18** 24 c. multicoloured 30
71 60 c. multicoloured 50

19 "Angels we have heard on High"

20 *Pachyseris speciosa* and *Heliofungia actiniformis* (corals

(Des B. Weatherhead. Litho Leigh-Mardon Ltd, Melbourne)

1981 (22 Oct). *Christmas. Scenes and Lines from Carol "Angel we have heard on High". T* **19** *and similar horiz designs. Multi coloured. P* 13½ × 13.
72 18 c. Type **19** 10
73 30 c. "Shepherds why this Jubilee?" 20
74 60 c. "Come to Bethlehem and see Him" .. 35
72/4 .. .. *Set of* 3 60

(Des B. Weatherhead. Litho Leigh-Mardon Ltd, Melbourne)

1981 (28 Dec). *150th Anniv of Charles Darwin's Voyage. T* **2** *and similar horiz designs. Multicoloured. P* 13½ × 13.
75 24 c. Type **20** 35
76 45 c. Charles Darwin in 1853 and *Pavona cactus* (coral) 55
77 60 c. H.M.S. *Beagle*, 1832, and *Lobophyllia hemprichii* (coral) 70
75/7 .. .. *Set of* 3 1·40
MS78 130 × 95 mm. 24 c. Cross-section of West Island; 24 c. Cross-section of Home Island .. 75

21 Queen Victoria　　**22** Lord Baden-Powell

(Des B. Weatherhead. Litho Cambec Press, Melbourne)

982 (31 Mar). *125th Anniv of Annexation of Cocos (Keeling) Islands to British Empire. T* **21** *and similar horiz designs. Multicoloured. P* 13½ × 14.

9	24 c. Type **21**	20	15
0	45 c. Union flag	35	25
1	60 c. Capt. S. Fremantle (annexation visit, 1857)	40	35
9/81	*Set of* 3	85	65

(Des B. Clinton. Litho Cambec Press, Melbourne)

1982 (21 July). *75th Anniv of Boy Scout Movement. T* **22** *and similar multicoloured design. P* 13½ × 14 (27 *c.*) *or* 14 × 13½ (75 *c.*).

2	27 c. Type **22**	30	25
3	75 c. "75" and map of Cocos (Keeling) Islands (*vert*)	1·10	1·50

23 *Precis villida*　　**24** "Call His Name Immanuel"

(Des B. Hargreaves. Litho Harrison)

1982 (6 Sept)–**83**. *Butterflies and Moths. T* **23** *and similar multicoloured designs. P* 14.

84	1 c. Type **23**	1·00	60
85	2 c. *Cephonodes picus* (*horiz*) (6.1.83)	40	40
86	5 c. *Macroglossum corythus* (*horiz*)	1·50	70
87	10 c. *Chasmina candida* (6.1.83)	40	40
88	20 c. *Nagia linteola* (*horiz*) (6.4.83)	40	65
89	25 c. *Eublemma rivula* (1.7.83)	40	75
90	30 c. *Eurrhyparodes tricoloralis* (6.4.83)	40	65
91	35 c. *Hippotion boerhaviae* (*horiz*)	1·50	75
92	40 c. *Euploea core* (6.4.83)	40	80
93	45 c. *Psara hipponalis* (*horiz*) (6.4.83)	50	80
94	50 c. *Danaus chrysippus* (*horiz*) (1.7.83)	60	1·25
95	55 c. *Hypolimnas misippus* (6.1.83)	60	70
96	60 c. *Spodoptera litura* (1.7.83)	65	1·75
97	$1 *Achaea janata*	2·75	2·75
98	$2 *Panacra velox* (*horiz*) (1.7.83)	2·00	2·75
99	$3 *Utetheisa pulchelloides* (*horiz*) (6.1.83)	2·75	2·75
84/99	*Set of* 16	14·50	17·00

(Des G. Hamori. Litho Cambec Press, Melbourne)

1982 (25 Oct). *Christmas. T* **24** *and similar horiz designs. Multicoloured. P* 13½ × 14.

100	21 c. Type **24**	25	20
101	35 c. "I bring you good tidings"	40	35
102	75 c. "Arise and flee into Egypt"	1·00	1·00
100/2	*Set of* 3	1·50	1·40

25 "God will look after us" (*Matt.* 1:20)　　**26** Hari Raya Celebrations

(Des R. Roberts. Litho Cambec Press, Melbourne)

1983 (25 Oct). *Christmas. Extracts from the New Testament. T* **25** *and similar vert designs. Multicoloured. P* 14 × 13½.

103	24 c. Type **25**	30	40
	a. Horiz strip of 5. Nos. 103/7	1·40	
104	24 c. "Our baby King, Jesus" (*Matthew* 2:2)	30	40
105	24 c. "Your Saviour is born" (*Luke* 2:11)	30	40
106	24 c. "Wise men followed the Star" (*Matthew* 2:9–10)	30	40
107	24 c. "And worship the Lord" (*Matthew* 2:11)	30	40
103/7	*Set of* 5	1·40	1·75

Nos. 103/7 were printed together, *se-tenant*, in horizontal strips of 5 throughout the sheet.

(Des Marg Towt. Litho Cambec Press, Melbourne)

1984 (24 Jan). *Cocos-Malay Culture.* (*1st series*). *Festivals. T* **26** *and similar vert designs. Multicoloured. P* 13½ × 13.

108	45 c. Type **26**	45	35
109	75 c. Melenggok dancing	65	50
110	85 c. Cocos-Malay wedding	75	55
108/10	*Set of* 3	1·75	1·25

See also Nos. 126/8.

27 Unpacking Barrel　　**28** Captain William Keeling

(Des R. Honisett. Litho Cambec Press, Melbourne)

1984 (20 Apr). *75th Anniv of Cocos Barrel Mail. T* **27** *and similar horiz designs. Multicoloured. P* 13½ × 14.

111	35 c. Type **27**	40	25
112	55 c. Jukong awaiting mail ship	75	50
113	70 c. P. & O. mail ship *Morea*	85	55
111/13	*Set of* 3	1·75	1·10
MS114	125 × 95 mm. $1 Retrieving barrel	90	1·25

(Des B. Clinton. Litho Cambec Press, Melbourne)

1984 (10 July). *375th Anniv of Discovery of Cocos (Keeling) Islands. T* **28** *and similar vert designs. Multicoloured. P* 14.

115	30 c. Type **28**	60	40
116	65 c. Keeling's ship *Hector*	1·25	90
117	95 c. Mariner's astrolabe	1·50	1·25
118	$1. 10, Map *circa* 1666	1·60	1·50
115/18	*Set of* 4	4·50	3·50

29 Malay Settlement, Home Island　　**30** "Rainbow" Fish

(Des E. Roberts. Litho Cambec Press, Melbourne)

1984 (21 Sept). *"Ausipex" International Stamp Exhibition, Melbourne. T* **29** *and similar horiz designs. Multicoloured. P* 13½ × 14.

119	45 c. Type **29**	75	50
120	55 c. Airstrip, West Island	85	60
MS121	130 × 95 mm. $2 Jukongs (native craft) racing	2·75	2·50

(Des R. Roberts. Litho Cambec Press, Melbourne)

1984 (31 Oct). *Christmas. T* **30** *and similar horiz designs. Multicoloured. P* 13½ × 14.

122	24 c. Type **30**	50	50
123	35 c. "Rainbow" butterfly	1·10	1·25
124	55 c. "Rainbow" bird	1·25	1·60
122/4	*Set of* 3	2·50	3·00

31 Cocos Islanders　　**32** Jukong building

(Des B. Weatherhead. Litho Cambec Press, Melbourne)

1984 (30 Nov). *Integration of Cocos (Keeling) Islands with Australia. Sheet* 90 × 52 *mm. containing T* **31** *and similar horiz design. Multicoloured. P* 13½ × 14.

MS125	30 c. Type **31**; 30 c. Australian flag on island	1·50	1·25

(Des Marg Towt. Litho Cambec Press, Melbourne)

1985 (30 Jan). *Cocos-Malay Culture (2nd series). Handicrafts. T* **32** *and similar vert designs. Multicoloured. P* 14 × 13½.

126	30 c. Type **32**	75	35
127	45 c. Blacksmithing	1·00	55
128	55 c. Woodcarving	1·25	65
126/8	*Set of* 3	2·75	1·40

33 C.S. *Scotia*　　**34** Red-footed Booby

(Des B. Clinton. Litho Cambec Press, Melbourne)

1985 (24 Apr). *Cable-laying Ships. T* **33** *and similar horiz designs. Multicoloured. P* 13½ × 14.

129	33 c. Type **33**	1·25	40
130	65 c. C.S. *Anglia*	2·00	1·60
131	80 c. C.S. *Patrol*	2·25	2·25
129/31	*Set of* 3	5·00	3·75

(Des Marg Towt. Litho Cambec Press, Melbourne)

1985 (17 July). *Birds of Cocos (Keeling) Islands. T* **34** *and similar multicoloured designs. P* 13½.

132	33 c. Type **34**	1·75	1·75
	a. Block of 3. Nos. 132/4	5·50	
	ab. Imperf vert (block of 3)	£600	
133	60 c. Rufous Night Heron (juvenile) (*horiz*)	2·00	2·00
134	$1 Banded Rail (*horiz*)	2·25	2·25
132/4	*Set of* 3	5·50	5·50

Nos. 132/4 were printed together, *se-tenant*, in blocks of 3 throughout the sheet, each block forming a composite design.

35 Mantled Top (*Trochus maculatus*)　　**36** Night Sky and Palm Trees

(Des G. Ryan. Litho Cambec Press, Melbourne)

1985 (18 Sept)–**86**. *Shells and Molluscs. T* **35** *and similar horiz designs. Multicoloured. P* 13½ × 14.

135	1 c. Type **35**	45	60
136	2 c. Rang's Nerite (*Smaragdia rangiana*) (29.1.86)	55	65
137	3 c. Jewel Box (*Chama* sp) (29.1.86)	60	70
138	4 c. Money Cowrie (*Cypraea moneta*) (30.7.86)	60	70
139	5 c. Purple Pacific Drupe (*Drupa morum*)	60	70
140	10 c. Soldier Cone (*Conus miles*) (29.1.86)	70	75
141	15 c. Marlin-spike Auger (*Terebra maculata*) (30.4.86)	1·25	1·00
142	20 c. Pacific Strawberry Cockle (*Fragum fragum*) (30.4.86)	1·25	1·10
143	30 c. Lajonkaire's Turban (*Turbo lajonkairii*) (30.4.86)	1·25	1·25
144	33 c. Reticulate Mitre (*Scabricola fissurata*)	1·40	1·25
145	40 c. Common Spider Conch (*Lambis lambis*) (30.4.86)	1·40	1·40
146	50 c. Fluted Giant Clam or Scaled Tridacna (*Tridacna squamosa*) (30.7.86)	1·40	1·50
147	60 c. Minstrel Cowrie (*Cypraea histrio*) (30.7.86)	1·75	2·00
148	$1 Varicose Nudibranch (*Phyllidia varicosa*)	2·75	3·00
149	$2 Tesselated Nudibranch (*Halgerda tessellata*) (30.7.86)	3·50	4·00
150	$3 *Haminoea cymballum* (29.1.86)	4·25	4·75
135/50	*Set of* 16	21·00	23·00

(Des D. Goodwin. Litho Cambec Press, Melbourne)

1985 (30 Oct). *Christmas. Sheet* 121 × 88 *mm, containing T* **36** *and similar horiz designs. P* 13½ × 14.

MS151	27 c. × 4 multicoloured	2·00	2·75

The stamps within **MS**151 show a composite design of the night sky seen through a grove of palm trees. The position of the face value on the four stamps varies. Type **36** shows the top left design. The top right stamp shows the face value at bottom right, the bottom left at top left and the bottom right at top right.

37 Charles Darwin, *c* 1840　　**38** Coconut Palm and Holly Sprigs

(Des B. Clinton. Litho Cambec Press, Melbourne)

1986 (1 Apr). *150th Anniv of Charles Darwin's Visit. T* **37** *and similar vert designs. Multicoloured. P* 14 × 13½.

152	33 c. Type **37**	70	50
153	60 c. Map of H.M.S. *Beagle*'s route Australia to Cocos Islands	1·25	2·00
154	$1 H.M.S. *Beagle*	1·75	2·50
152/4	*Set of* 3	3·25	4·50

(Des S. Hartshorne. Litho Cambec Press, Melbourne)

1986 (29 Oct). *Christmas. T* **38** *and similar horiz designs. Multicoloured. P* 13½ × 14.

155	30 c. Type **38**	60	50
156	90 c. Nautilus shell and Christmas tree bauble	2·00	2·50
157	$1 Tropical fish and bell	2·00	2·50
155/7	*Set of* 3	4·25	5·00

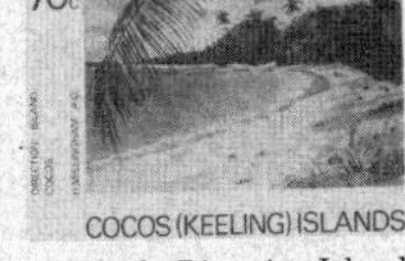

39 Jukong　　**40** Beach, Direction Island

(Des J. Earl. Litho Cambec Press, Melbourne)

1987 (28 Jan). *Sailing Craft. T* **39** *and similar horiz designs. Multicoloured. P* 13½ × 14.

158 36 c. Type **39** . . . . . . 1·10 1·25
 a. Horiz strip of 4. Nos. 158/61 . . 4·00
159 36 c. Ocean racing yachts . . . . 1·10 1·25
160 36 c. *Sarimanok* (replica of early dhow) . . 1·10 1·25
161 36 c. *Ayesha* (schooner) . . . . 1·10 1·25
158/61 . . . . . . *Set of* 4 4·00 4·50

Nos. 158/61 were printed together, *se-tenant*, in horizontal strips of 5 throughout the sheet, each strip forming a composite background design.

(Des H. Missingham and R. Fletcher. Litho CPE Australia Ltd, Melbourne)

1987 (8 Apr). *Cocos Islands Scenes. T* **40** *and similar horiz designs. Multicoloured. P* 13½ × 14.

162 70 c. Type **40** . . . . . . 1·40 1·40
163 90 c. Palm forest, West Island . . . . 1·75 2·00
164 $1 Golf course . . . . . . 2·75 3·00
162/4 . . . . . . *Set of* 3 5·50 5·75

41 Radio Transmitter and Palm Trees at Sunset **42** Batik Printing

(Des R. Fletcher. Litho CPE Australia Ltd, Melbourne)

1987 (29 July). *Communications. T* **41** *and similar horiz designs. Multicoloured. P* 13½ × 14.

165 70 c. Type **41** . . . . . . 1·25 1·50
166 75 c. Air liner at terminal . . . . 1·50 1·75
167 90 c. "Intelsat 5" satellite . . . . 1·75 2·25
168 $1 Airmail letter and globe . . . . 2·00 2·25
165/8 . . . . . . *Set of* 4 6·00 7·00

(Des B. Clinton. Litho CPE Australia Ltd, Melbourne)

1987 (16 Sept). *Cocos (Keeling) Islands Malay Industries. T* **42** *and similar horiz designs. Multicoloured. P* 13½ × 14.

169 45 c. Type **42** . . . . . . 1·25 1·50
170 65 c. Jukong building . . . . 1·75 2·00
171 75 c. Copra production . . . . 2·00 2·25
169/71 . . . . . . *Set of* 3 4·50 5·25

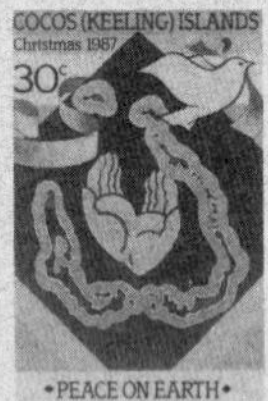

43 Hands releasing Peace Dove and Map of Islands **44** Coconut Flower

(Des Marg Towt. Litho CPE Australia Ltd, Melbourne)

1987 (28 Oct). *Christmas. T* **43** *and similar vert designs. Multicoloured. P* 14 × 13½.

172 30 c. Type **43** 40 40
173 90 c. Local children at Christmas party . . 1·25 1·90
174 $1 Island family and Christmas star . . 1·50 1·90
172/4 . . . . . . *Set of* 3 2·75 3·75

(Des Sue Passmore. Litho CPE Australia Ltd, Melbourne)

1988 (26 Jan). *Bicentenary of Australian Settlement. Arrival of First Fleet. Square designs as Nos.* 1105/9 *of Australia but each inscribed* "COCOS (KEELING) ISLANDS" *and* "AUSTRALIA BICENTENARY".

175 37 c. Aborigines watching arrival of Fleet, Botany Bay . . . . . . 1·50 1·75
 a. Horiz strip of 5. Nos. 175/9 . . 6·75
176 37 c. Aboriginal family and anchored ships . . . . . . 1·50 1·75
177 37 c. Fleet arriving at Sydney Cove . . . . 1·50 1·75
178 37 c. Ship's boat . . . . . . 1·50 1·75
179 37 c. Raising the flag, Sydney Cove, 26 January 1788 . . . . . . 1·50 1·75
175/9 . . . . . . *Set of* 5 6·75 8·00

Nos. 175/9 were printed together, *se-tenant*, in horizontal strips of five throughout the sheet, forming a composite design.

(Des Celia Rosser. Litho CPE Australia Ltd, Melbourne)

1988 (13 Apr). *Life Cycle of the Coconut. T* **44** *and similar vert designs. Multicoloured. P* 14 × 13½.

180 37 c. Type **44** 50 40
181 65 c. Immature nuts . . . . . . 75 1·00
182 90 c. Coconut palm and mature nuts . . 1·10 1·75
183 $1 Seedlings . . . . . . 1·25 1·75
180/3 . . . . . . *Set of* 4 3·25 4·50
MS184 102 × 91 mm. Nos. 180/3 . . . . 4·00 4·50

MINIMUM PRICE

The minimum price quote is 10p which represents a handling charge rather than a basis for valuing common stamps. For further notes about prices see introductory pages.

45 Copra 3d. Stamp of 1963 **46** *Pisonia grandis*

(Des R. Fletcher. Recess and litho Note Printing Branch, Reserve Bank of Australia, Melbourne)

1988 (15 June). *25th Anniv of First Cocos (Keeling) Islands Stamps. T* **45** *and similar vert designs, each showing stamp from* 1963 *definitive set. P* 15 × 14.

185 37 c. chocolate, black and azure . . . . 1·25 85
186 55 c. green, black and pale drab . . . . 1·75 1·50
187 65 c. ultramarine, black and pale grey-lilac 1·90 2·00
188 70 c. scarlet, black and bluish grey . . 1·90 2·00
189 90 c. deep purple, black and greenish grey . . 2·25 2·25
190 $1 deep green, black and light brown . . 2·25 2·25
185/90 . . . . . . *Set of* 6 10·00 9·75

Designs:—55 c. Palms 1s.; 65 c. "Super Constellation" 5d.; 70 c. Map 8d.; 90 c. Jukong (sailboat) 2s.; $1 White Tern 2s. 3d.

(Des R. Fletcher. Litho CPE Australia Ltd, Melbourne)

1988 (29 July)–**89**. *Flora. T* **46** *and similar vert designs. Multicoloured. P* 14 × 13½.

191 1 c. Type **46** 30 50
192 2 c. *Cocos nucifera* (18.1.89) 40 60
193 5 c. *Morinda citrifolia* 65 70
194 10 c. *Cordia subcordata* (18.1.89) 70 70
195 30 c. *Argusia argentea* (18.1.89) . . . . 1·00 90
196 37 c. *Calophyllum inophyllum* . . . . 1·00 1·00
197 40 c. *Barringtonia asiatica* (19.4.89) . . 1·00 1·25
198 50 c. *Caesalpinia bonduc* (19.4.89) . . 1·25 1·50
199 90 c. *Terminalia catappa* (19.4.89) . . 1·75 2·25
200 $1 *Pemphis acidula* (19.4.89) . . 1·75 2·25
201 $2 *Scaevola sericea* (18.1.89) . . 2·50 2·50
202 $3 *Hibiscus tiliaceus* . . . . 3·50 3·75
191/202 . . . . . . *Set of* 12 14·00 16·00

(Des R. Fletcher. Litho CPE Australia Ltd, Melbourne)

1988 (30 July). *"Sydpex '88" National Stamp Exhibition, Sydney. Sheet* 70 × 85 *mm. Multicoloured. P* 14 × 13½.

MS203 $3 As No. 202 . . . . . . 4·25 4·75

47 Beach at Sunset **48** Capt. P. G. Taylor

(Des T. Bland. Litho CPE Australia Ltd, Melbourne)

1988 (12 Oct). *Christmas. P* 13½ × 14.

204 **47** 32 c. multicoloured 80 50
205 90 c. multicoloured . . . . 1·75 2·50
206 $1 multicoloured . . . . 2·00 2·50
204/6 . . . . . . *Set of* 3 4·00 5·00

(Des B. Clinton. Litho CPE Australia Ltd, Melbourne)

1989 (19 July). *50th Anniv of First Indian Ocean Aerial Survey. T* **48** *and similar vert designs. P* 14 × 13½.

207 40 c. multicoloured 80 65
208 70 c. multicoloured . . . . 1·75 2·00
209 $1 multicoloured . . . . 2·00 2·25
210 $1.10, deep ultramarine, pale lilac & black 2·25 2·50
207/10 . . . . . . *Set of* 4 6·00 6·50

Designs:—70 c. Consolidated Catalina "PBY2" *Guba II* and crew; $1 *Guba II* over Direction Island; $1.10, Unissued Australia 5s. stamp commemorating flight.

49 Jukong and Star **50** H.M.A.S. *Sydney* (cruiser)

(Des T. Bland. Litho Leigh-Mardon Ltd, Melbourne)

1989 (18 Oct). *Christmas. P* 14 × 13½.

211 **49** 35 c. multicoloured 75 50
212 80 c. multicoloured . . . . 2·25 2·50
213 $1.10, multicoloured . . . . 2·25 2·50
211/13 . . . . . . *Set of* 3 4·75 5·00

(Des PCS Studios. Litho Leigh-Mardon Ltd, Melbourne)

1989 (9 Nov). *75th Anniv of Destruction of German Cruiser* Emden. *T* **50** *and similar horiz designs. Multicoloured. P* 13½ × 14.

214 40 c. Type **50** . . . . . . 1·75 1·75
 a. Horiz strip of 4, Nos. 214/17, with central label . . . . . . 7·50
215 70 c. *Emden* (German cruiser) . . . . 2·00 2·00
216 $1 *Emden's* steam launch . . . . 2·25 2·25
217 $1.10, H.M.A.S. *Sydney*, (1914) and crest 2·25 2·25
214/17 . . . . . . *Set of* 4 7·50 7·50
MS218 145 × 90 mm. Nos. 214/17 . . . . 7·50 7·50

Nos. 214/17 were printed together, *se-tenant*, in horizontal strips of four stamps and one label throughout the sheet.

51 Xanthid Crab **52** Captain Keeling and *Hector*, 1609

(Des Jill Ruse. Litho Leigh-Mardon Ltd, Melbourne)

1990 (31 May). *Cocos Islands Crabs. T* **51** *and similar multicoloured designs. P* 14½.

219 45 c. Type **51** . . . . . . 1·50 75
220 75 c. Ghost Crab . . . . . . 2·00 2·00
221 $1 Red-backed Mud Crab . . . . 2·25 2·25
222 $1.30, Coconut Crab (*vert*) . . . . 2·50 3·00
219/22 . . . . . . *Set of* 4 7·50 7·25

(Des Elizabeth and R. Innes. Litho Note Ptg Branch, Reserve Bank of Australia)

1990 (24 Aug). *Navigators of the Pacific. T* **52** *and similar horiz designs. P* 14½.

223 45 c. dull mauve . . . . . . 2·00 85
224 75 c. dull mauve and pale azure . . . . 2·25 2·50
225 $1 dull mauve and pale stone . . . . 2·75 3·00
226 $1.30, dull mauve and pale buff . . . . 3·50 4·25
223/6 . . . . . . *Set of* 4 9·50 9·50
MS227 120 × 95 mm. As Nos. 223/6, but imperf 7·50 8·50

Designs—75 c. Captain Fitzroy and H.M.S. *Beagle*, 1836; $1 Captain Belcher and H.M.S. *Samarang*, 1846; $1.30, Captain Fremantle and H.M.S. *Juno*, 1857.

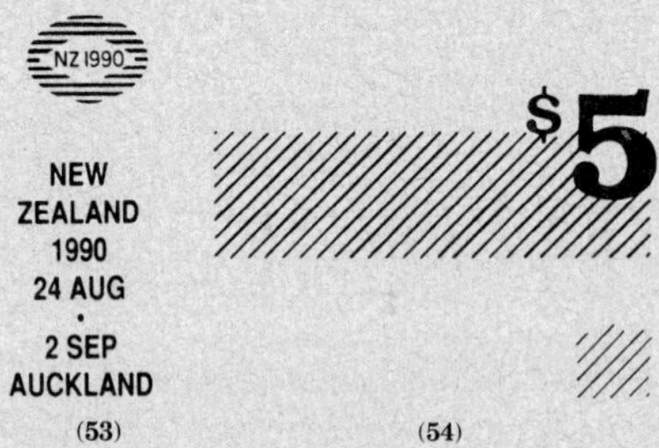

(**53**) (**54**)

(Des Elizabeth Innes (No. **MS**229). Litho Western Australian Govt Ptg Division, Perth)

1990 (3 Sept). *"New Zealand 1990" International Stamp Exhibition, Auckland. No.* 188 *optd with T* **53** *in red and miniature sheet containing designs as Nos.* 194, 199 *and* 201.

228 70 c. scarlet, black and bluish grey . . 2·25 2·75
MS229 127 × 90 mm. As Nos. 194, 199 and 201, but self-adhesive. Roul 9 . . . . 4·00 3·50

Nos. 228/9 were available at the Exhibition from 24 August 1990, but were not sold locally until 3 September.

1990 (11 Dec). *No.* 187 *surch with T* **54** *in deep ultramarine by Western Australian Govt Ptg Division, Perth.*

230 $5 on 65 c. ultram, black & pale grey-lilac 17·00 15·00

55 Cocos Atoll from West and Star

(Des Stylegraphics, Perth. Litho Scott Four-Colour Print, Perth)

1990 (12 Dec). *Christmas. T* **55** *and similar square designs. Multicoloured. Roul* 5.

231 40 c. Type **55** 70 80
 a. Booklet pane. No. 231 × 4 and No. 232 × 2 plus 6 labels . . . . 10·00
 b. Booklet pane. No. 231 × 10 plus 2 labels 15·00
232 70 c. Cocos atoll from south . . . . 1·50 2·25
233 $1.30, Cocos atoll from east . . . . 2·50 2·75
231/3 . . . . . . *Set of* 3 4·25 5·25

Booklet panes Nos. 231a/b have the upper and lower edges imperforate, producing stamps imperforate at top or bottom, and there are margins at left and right.

MAINLAND POSTAGE PAID

(56)

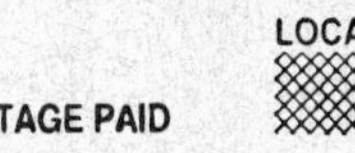

LOCAL

POSTAGE PAID

(57)

1990 (12 Dec)–**91.** *Nos.* 140/1, 143 *and* 146/7 *surch by Western Australian Govt Ptg Division.*

(*a*) *With T* **56** *in blue*

234 (43 c.) on 10 c. Soldier Cone (*Conus miles*) 25·00 3·50

(*b*) *No.* 234 *with additional cross-hatching overprinted on the original face value in blue*

235 (43 c.) on 10 c. Soldier Cone (*Conus miles*) (7.3.91) .. .. 1·40 1·75

(*c*) *As T* **57** *with original face value obliterated*

236 (1 c.) on 30 c. Lajonkaire's Turban (*Turbo lajonkairii*) (Type **57**) (B.) (21.1.91) 1·50 2·00
237 70 c. on 60 c. Minstrel Cowrie (*Cypraea histrio*) ("ZONE 1") (7.3.91) .. 1·50 2·25
238 80 c. on 50 c. Fluted Giant Clam or Scaled Tridacna (*Tridacna squamosa* ("ZONE 2") (7.3.91) .. .. .. 1·75 3·00
239 $1.20 on 15 c. Marlin-spike Auger (*Terebra maculata*) ("ZONE 5") (7.3.91) .. .. 2·00 3·25
234/9 .. .. *Set of* 6 30·00 14·00

58 Beaded Sea Star

59 Cocos Islands

(Des Jill Ruse. Litho Leigh-Mardon Ltd, Melbourne)

1991 (28 Feb). *Starfish and Sea Urchins. T* **58** *and similar horiz designs. Multicoloured. P* 14½.

240 45 c. Type **58** .. .. 1·00 65
241 75 c. Feather Star .. .. 1·90 2·00
242 $1 Slate Pencil Urchin .. .. 2·00 2·25
243 $1.30, Globose Sea Urchin .. .. .. 2·50 3·00
240/3 .. .. *Set of* 4 6·75 7·25

(Des P. Cunningham. Litho Leigh-Mardon Ltd, Melbourne)

1991 (16 Apr). *Malay Hari Raya Festival. T* **59** *and similar horiz designs. Multicoloured. P* 14½.

244 45 c. Type **59** .. .. 1·00 65
245 75 c. Island house .. .. 1·75 2·00
246 $1.30, Islands scene .. .. 2·50 3·00
244/6 .. .. *Set of* 3 4·75 5·00

60 Child praying

61 *Lybia tessellata*

(Des R. Honisett. Litho Leigh-Mardon Ltd, Melbourne)

1991 (6 Nov). *Christmas. T* **60** *and similar vert designs. Multicoloured. P* 15½.

247 38 c. Type **60** 80 55
248 43 c. Child dreaming of Christmas Day .. 85 60
249 $1 Child singing .. .. 2·00 2·25
250 $1.20, Child fascinated by decorations .. 2·50 3·25
247/50 .. .. *Set of* 4 5·50 6·00
MS251 118×74 mm. 38 c., 43 c., $1, $1.20, Local children's choir .. .. 5·00 5·50

The four values in No. **MS**251 form a composite design.

(Des Jane Moore. Litho Leigh-Mardon Ltd, Melbourne)

1992 (28 Feb–11 Aug). *Crustaceans. T* **61** *and similar multicoloured designs. P* 14½.

252 5 c. Type **61** 40 40
253 10 c. *Pilodius areolatus* (11 Aug) 45 45
254 20 c. *Trizopagurus strigatus* 70 70
255 30 c. *Lophozozymus pulchellus* (11 Aug) .. 1·00 1·00
256 40 c. *Thalamitoides quadridens* .. .. 1·00 1·00
257 45 c. *Calcinus elegans* (*vert*) .. .. 1·00 1·00
258 50 c. *Clibarius humilis* (11 Aug) .. .. 1·25 1·25
259 60 c. *Trapezia rufopunctata* (*vert*) .. .. 1·50 1·50
260 80 c. *Pylopaguropsis magnimanus* (*vert*) (11 Aug) .. .. 1·75 1·75
261 $1 *Trapezia ferruginea* (*vert*) (11 Aug) .. 1·75 1·75
262 $2 *Trapezia guttata* (*vert*) (11 Aug) .. 3·00 3·50
263 $3 *Trapezia cymodoce* (*vert*) .. .. 3·50 3·75
252/63 .. .. *Set of* 12 15·00 16·00

OMNIBUS ISSUES

Details, together with prices for complete sets, of the various Omnibus issues from the 1935 Silver Jubilee series to date are included in a special section following Zimbabwe at the end of Volume 2.

62 *Santa Maria*

63 Banded Rail searching for Food

(Des Philatelic Studios, Melbourne. Litho Leigh-Mardon Ltd, Melbourne)

1992 (22 May). *500th Anniv of Discovery of America by Columbus. P* 14½.

264 **62** $1.05, multicoloured .. .. .. 2·25 2·50

(Des G. Drummond. Litho Questa)

1992 (11 June). *Endangered Species. Banded Rail. T* **63** *and similar horiz designs. Multicoloured. P* 14.

265 10 c. Type **63** 50 60
a. Strip of 4. Nos. 265/8 .. .. 2·50
266 15 c. Banded Rail with chick 65 75
267 30 c. Two Rails drinking 80 90
268 45 c. Rail and nest .. .. .. 90 1·10
265/8 .. .. .. *Set of* 4 2·50 3·00
MS269 165×78 mm. 45 c. Two Rails by pool; 85 c. Chick hatching; $1.20, Head of Rail .. .. 3·75 4·25

Nos. 265/8 were printed together, *se-tenant*, in horizontal or vertical strips of 4 throughout the sheet.

64 R.A.F. Spitfires on Island Airstrip

65 Waves breaking on Reef

(Des Philatelic Studios, Melbourne. Litho Leigh-Mardon Ltd, Melbourne)

1992 (13 Oct). *50th Anniv of Second World War. T* **64** *and similar horiz designs. Multicoloured. P* 14½.

270 45 c. Type **64** .. .. 1·50 80
271 85 c. Japanese aircraft bombing Kampong 2·25 2·50
272 $1.20, R.A.F. Sunderland (flying boat) 2·75 3·50
270/2 .. .. *Set of* 3 6·00 6·00

(Des Philatelic Studios, Melbourne. Litho Leigh-Mardon Ltd, Melbourne)

1992 (11 Nov). *Christmas. T* **65** *and similar vert designs. Multicoloured. P* 14½.

273 40 c. Type **65** 80 60
274 80 c. Direction Island .. .. .. 2·00 2·50
275 $1 Moorish Idols (fish) and coral .. 2·00 2·50
273/5 .. .. *Set of* 3 4·25 5·00

66 *Lobophyllia hemprichii*

67 Plastic 5 r. Token

(Litho Leigh-Mardon Ltd, Melbourne)

1993 (28 Jan). *Corals. T* **66** *and similar vert designs. Multicoloured. P* 14½.

276 45 c. Type **66** 75 55
277 85 c. *Pocillopora eydouxi* .. .. .. 1·25 1·75
278 $1.05, *Fungia scutaria* .. .. .. 1·75 2·00
279 $1.20, *Sarcophyton* sp .. .. .. 1·75 2·25
276/9 .. .. *Set of* 4 5·00 6·00

(Des Sandra Harman. Litho Leigh-Mardon Ltd, Melbourne)

1993 (30 Mar). *Early Cocos (Keeling) Islands Currency. T* **67** *and similar vert designs. Multicoloured. P* 14½.

280 45 c. Type **67** 75 55
281 85 c. 1968 1 r. plastic token .. .. 1·25 1·75
282 $1.05, 1977 150 r. commemorative gold coin .. .. 1·75 2·00
283 $1.20, 1910 plastic token .. .. 1·75 2·25
280/3 .. .. *Set of* 4 5·00 6·00

68 Primary School Pupil

69 Lifeboat and Crippled Yacht

(Des Philatelic Studios. Litho Leigh-Mardon Ltd, Melbourne)

1993 (1 June). *Education. T* **68** *and similar vert designs. Multicoloured. P* 14½.

284 5 c. Type **68** 30 50
285 45 c. Secondary school pupil 75 50
286 85 c. Learning traditional crafts .. .. 1·50 1·75
287 $1.05, Learning office skills .. .. 1·75 2·25
288 $1.20, Seaman training .. .. .. 2·25 2·75
284/8 .. .. *Set of* 5 6·00 7·00

(Des Philatelic Studios. Litho Leigh-Mardon Ltd, Melbourne)

1993 (17 Aug). *Air-Sea Rescue. T* **69** *and similar horiz designs. Multicoloured. P* 14½.

289 45 c. Type **69** .. .. 1·25 75
290 85 c. *Westwind Seascan* (aircraft) .. .. 2·25 2·50
291 $1.05, *R.J. Hawke* (ferry) .. .. 2·50 3·25
289/91 .. .. *Set of* 3 5·50 6·00
MS292 135×61 mm. Nos. 289/91 .. .. 5·50 6·50

70 Peace Doves

71 Rectangle Triggerfish and Coral

(Des Philatelic Studios. Litho Leigh-Mardon Ltd, Melbourne)

1993 (26 Oct). *Christmas. P* 14½.

293 **70** 40 c. multicoloured 80 60
294 80 c. multicoloured .. .. .. 2·00 2·50
295 $1 multicoloured .. .. .. 2·00 2·50
293/5 .. .. *Set of* 3 4·25 5·00

On 1 January 1994 responsibility for the Cocos (Keeling) Islands postal service passed from the territorial administration to Australia Post. In consequence Nos. 296/315 and all subsequent issues are valid for postal purposes in both Cocos (Keeling) Islands and Australia.

(Des Sue Passmore. Litho McPherson's Ptg Group, Mulgrave)

1994 (17 Feb). *Transfer of Postal Service to Australia Post. T* **71** *and similar vert designs. Multicoloured. P* 14½×14.

296 5 c. Type **71** 25 30
a. Sheetlet. Nos. 296/315 .. .. 6·00
297 5 c. Three Rectangle Triggerfish and map section 25 30
298 5 c. Two Rectangle Triggerfish and map section 25 30
299 5 c. Two Rectangle Triggerfish, map section and red coral 25 30
300 5 c. Rectangle Triggerfish with red and brown corals 25 30
301 10 c. Green Turtles on beach 25 30
302 10 c. Two Green Turtles 25 30
303 10 c. Crowd of young Green Turtles .. 25 30
304 10 c. Green Turtle and map section .. 25 30
305 10 c. Green Turtle, Pyramid Butterflyfish and map section 25 30
306 20 c. Three Pyramid Butterflyfish and map section 40 45
307 20 c. Pyramid Butterflyfish with brown coral 40 45
308 20 c. Two Pyramid Butterflyfish and coral 40 45
309 20 c. Three Pyramid Butterflyfish and coral 40 45
310 20 c. Coral, Pyramid Butterflyfish and map section 40 45
311 45 c. Jukongs with map of airport .. 50 55
a. Horiz strip of 5. Nos. 311/15 .. 2·25
312 45 c. Two jukongs with red or blue sails and map section 50 55
313 45 c. Jukong in shallows 50 55
314 45 c. Two jukongs with red or yellow sails and map section 50 55
315 45 c. Two jukongs, one with blue jib, and map section 50 55
296/315 .. .. *Set of* 20 6·00 7·00

Nos. 296/315 were printed together, *se-tenant*, in sheetlets of 20 with inscriptions on the sheet margins and the backgrounds forming a composite map. Nos. 311/15 were also avaliable printed together, *se-tenant*, in horizontal strips of 5 in sheets of 100.

72 Prabu Abjasa Puppet

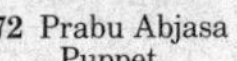

73 Angel playing Harp

(Des Josephine Muré. Litho McPherson's Ptg Group, Mulgrave)

1994 (16 June). *Shadow Puppets. T* **72** *and similar vert designs. Multicoloured. P* 14½×14.

316 45 c. Type **72** 65 50
317 90 c. Prabu Pandu .. .. 1·25 1·50
318 $1 Judistra .. .. 1·40 1·50
319 $1.35, Abimanju .. .. 1·50 2·00
316/19 .. .. *Set of* 4 4·25 5·00

(Des Tracie Grimwood. Litho McPherson's Ptg Group, Mulgrave)

1994 (31 Oct). *Seasonal Festivals. T* **73** *and similar horiz designs. Multicoloured. P* 14×14½.

320	40 c. Type **73**	50	50
321	45 c. Wise Man holding gift	55	50
322	80 c. Mosque at night	1·00	1·75
320/2	*Set of* 3	1·90	2·50

74 White-tailed Tropic Bird and Blue-faced Booby

75 Yellow Crazy Ant

(Des Lisa Christensen and B. Wood. Litho McPherson's Ptg Group, Mulgrave)

1995 (16 Mar). *Sea-birds of North Keeling Island. T* **74** *and similar horiz design. Multicoloured. P* 14×14½.

323	45 c. Type **74**	60	45
324	85 c. Great Frigate Bird and White Tern	1·00	1·50
MS325	106×70 mm. Nos. 323/4	1·60	2·00

No. **MS**325 also exists overprinted with the "JAKARTA 95" logo for sale at this exhibition.

(Des Sue Maddern. Litho McPherson's Ptg Group, Mulgrave)

1995 (13 July). *Insects. T* **75** *and similar vert designs. Multicoloured. P* 14½×14.

326	45 c. Type **75**	70	80
	a. Horiz strip of 5. Nos. 326/30	3·25	
327	45 c. Aedes Mosquito	70	80
328	45 c. Hawk Moth	70	80
329	45 c. Scarab Beetle	70	80
330	45 c. Lauxaniid Fly	70	80
331	$1.20, Common Eggfly (butterfly)	1·25	1·50
326/31	*Set of* 6	4·00	5·00

Nos. 326/30 were printed together, *se-tenant*, in horizontal strips of 5 throughout the sheet, with the backgrounds forming a composite design.

76 Saddle Butterflyfish

77 Members of Malay Community

(Des M. Baker and Sandra Harman (5 c., 75 c., 90 c., $1, $1.20), M. Baker and Dianne Cook (70 c., 95 c., $5), M. Baker and Sophie Byass (others). Litho SNP Cambec (40 c., 80 c., $1.05) or McPherson's Ptg Group, Mulgrave (others))

1995 (1 Nov)–**98**. *Marine Life. T* **76** *and similar horiz designs. Multicoloured. P* 14×14½.

332	5 c. Redspot Wrasse (14.8.97)	10	10
333	30 c. Blue-throated Triggerfish ("Gilded Triggerfish") (15.8.96)	25	30
334	40 c. Type **76**	30	35
335	45 c. Arc-eyed Hawkfish (15.8.96)	35	40
335*a*	70 c. Crowned Squirrelfish (13.8.98)	55	60
336	75 c. Orangespine Unicornfish (14.8.97)	55	60
337	80 c. Blue Tang	60	65
338	85 c. Juvenile Twin-spotted Wrasse ("Humphead Wrasse") (15.8.96)	65	70
339	90 c. Threadfin Butterflyfish (14.8.97)	70	75
339*a*	95 c. Sixstripe Wrasse (13.8.98)	75	80
340	$1 Bluestripe Snapper (14.8.97)	75	80
341	$1.05, Longnosed Butterflyfish	80	85
342	$1.20, Freckled Hawkfish (14.8.97)	90	95
343	$2 Powder-blue Surgeonfish (15.8.96)	1·50	1·60
343*a*	$5 Goldback Anthias (13.8.98)	3·75	4·00
332/43*a*	*Set of* 15	12·50	13·00

(Des Melinda Whitechurch and Jacqui Young. Litho McPherson's Ptg Group, Mulgrave)

1996 (19 Feb). *Hari Raya Puasa Festival. T* **77** *and similar square designs. Multicoloured. P* 14½.

344	45 c. Type **77**	55	50
345	75 c. Beating drums	1·00	1·25
346	85 c. Preparing festival meal	1·10	1·50
344/6	*Set of* 3	2·40	3·00

78 Black Rhinoceros with Calf

79 Dancers and Tambourine

(Des Kerry Argent and Lisa Christensen. Litho Canberra Press)

1996 (13 June). *Cocos Quarantine Station. T* **78** *and similar vert designs. Multicoloured. P* 14½×14.

347	45 c. Type **78**	70	70
348	50 c. Alpacas	70	75
349	$1.05, Boran cattle	1·25	1·50
350	$1.20, Ostrich with chicks	1·50	1·75
347/50	*Set of* 4	3·75	4·25

(Des MYD Graphic. Litho SNP Cambec)

1997 (6 Jan). *Hari Raya Puasa Festival. T* **79** *and similar square designs. Multicoloured. P* 14½.

351	45 c. Type **79**	55	50
352	75 c. Girl clapping and sailing dinghies	90	1·25
353	85 c. Dancers on beach and food	1·00	1·25
351/3	*Set of* 3	2·25	2·75

80 "Wrapped Present" (Lazina Brian)

(Adapted Dianne Cook. Litho SNP Cambec)

1998 (22 Jan). *Hari Raya Puasa Festival. T* **80** *and similar vert designs showing paintings by children. Multicoloured. P* 14½×14.

354	45 c. Type **80**	40	45
	a. Horiz strip of 5. Nos. 354/8	2·00	
355	45 c. "Mosque" (Azran Jim)	40	45
356	45 c. "Cocos Malay Woman" (Kate Gossage)	40	45
357	45 c. "Yacht" (Matt Harber)	40	45
358	45 c. "People dancing" (Rakin Chongkin)	40	45
354/8	*Set of* 5	2·00	2·25

Nos. 354/8 were printed together, *se-tenant*, in horizontal strips of five throughout the sheet.

STAMP BOOKLETS

COCOS (KEELING) ISLANDS
INDIAN OCEAN

PHILATELIC BUREAU

B 1 Prison Island

1990 (12 Dec). *Christmas. Multicoloured cover as Type* B **1**. *Panes attached by selvedge.*

SB1	$3 booklet containing *se-tenant* pane of 6 (No. 231a)	10·00
SB2	$4 booklet containing pane of 10 (No. 231b)	15·00

OFFICIAL STAMP

OFFICIAL PAID MAINLAND

(O 1)

1991 (25 Jan). *No. 182 surch with Type* O 1 *in deep violet-blue.*

O1	(43 c.) on 90 c. Coconut palm and mature nuts	† 90·00

No. O1 was only sold to the public cancelled-to-order and not in unused condition.

NORFOLK ISLAND

Norfolk Island, first settled in 1788 from New South Wales, ·as transferred to Tasmania on 29 September 1844. It became a ·parate settlement on 1 November 1856 under the control of ·e Governor of New South Wales. The island was declared an ·ustralian Territory in 1913. Unlike the other External ·erritories it retains an independent postal administration.

The stamps of TASMANIA were used on Norfolk Island from mid-1854 until May 1855, such use being identified by the "72" numeral cancellation. From 1877 the stamps of NEW SOUTH WALES were in regular use, being replaced by issues for AUSTRALIA from 1913 to 1947.

·RINTERS. Nos. 1 to 42 were printed at the Note Printing Branch ·eserve Bank of Australia (until 14 Jan 1960, known as the Note ·rinting Branch, Commonwealth Bank) by recess. See note at the ·eginning of Australia *re* imprints.

1 Ball Bay

(Des and eng F. Manley)

·947 (10 June)–**59.** *Toned paper. P* 14.

1	1	½d. orange	35	60
		a. White paper (11.56)	1·50	4·50
2		1d. bright violet	50	60
		a. White paper (8.57)	6·50	16·00
3		1½d. emerald-green	50	70
		a. White paper (11.56)	10·00	23·00
4		2d. reddish violet	55	40
		a. White paper (11.56)	£100	£130
5		2½d. scarlet	80	30
6		3d. chestnut	70	70
6a		3d. emerald-green (*white paper*) (6.7.59)	16·00	6·50
7		4d. claret	1·00	40
8		5½d. indigo	70	30
9		6d. purple-brown	70	30
0		9d. magenta	1·25	40
1		1s. grey-green	70	40
2		2s. yellow-bistre	1·50	1·00
2a		2s. deep blue (*white paper*) (6.7.59)	24·00	7·00
/12a		*Set of* 14	45·00	17·00

Stamps of T 1, perf 11, or in different colours, perf 11, are ·rinter's waste which leaked from the Note Ptg Branch. They ·ere never distributed to post offices for sale to the public.

2 Warder's Tower 3 Airfield

Des B. Stewart, eng. G. Lissenden (3½d.), D. Cameron (7½d.). Des and eng D. Cameron (6½d.), P. Morriss (8½d., 10d.) or G. Lissenden (5s.))

·953 (10 June). *T* **2/3** *and similar designs. P* 14½ × 15 (*vert*) *or* 15 × 14½ (*horiz*).

·3	3½d. brown-lake	1·50	90
·4	6½d. deep green	2·50	2·75
·5	7½d. deep blue	2·00	3·00
·6	8½d. chocolate	2·25	4·25
·7	10d. reddish violet	1·50	75
·8	5s. sepia	45·00	10·00
·3/18	*Set of* 6	50·00	19·00

Designs: *Horiz* (*as T* 3)—7½d. Old Stores (Crankmill); 5s. ·loody Bridge. *Vert* (*as T* 2)—8½d. Barracks entrance; 10d. Salt ·ouse.

8 Norfolk Island Seal and Pitcairners Landing

·wo types of 2s.:

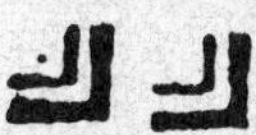

Type I Type II

Alternate stamps on each horizontal row are with or without a ·lot in bottom right corner.

(Des and eng F. Manley)

1956 (8 June). *Centenary of Landing of Pitcairn Islanders on Norfolk Island. P* 15×14½.

·19	8	3d. deep bluish green	1·50	40
·20		2s. violet (I)	2·00	75
		a. Type II	2·00	75
		b. Deep violet (I)	3·50	2·25
		ba. Type II	3·50	2·25

(9) (10) (11)

1958 (1 July). *Nos.* 15/16 *surch with T* **9/10**.

21	7d. on 7½d. deep blue	1·00	1·00
22	8d. on 8½d. chocolate	1·00	1·00

1959 (7 Dec). 150*th Anniv of Australian Post Office. No.* 331 *of Australia surch with T* **11**.

23	5d. on 4d. slate (R.)	35	30

12 *Hibiscus insularis*

14 White Tern

16 Red Hibiscus

17 Queen Elizabeth II and Cereus

21 Rose Apple

22 Red-tailed Tropic Bird

(Des G. Lissenden, eng P. Morriss (5s.). Des and eng G. Lissenden (10s.), P. Morriss (others). Recess and typo (2s. 8d.), recess (others))

1960–62. *T* **12, 14, 16/17, 21/2** *and similar designs. P* 14½ *or* 14½×14 (10s.).

24	1d. bluish green (23.5.60)	15	10
25	2d. rose and myrtle-green (23.5.60)	20	10
26	3d. green (1.5.61)	70	15
27	5d. bright purple (20.6.60)	55	20
28	8d. red (20.6.60)	80	50
29	9d. ultramarine (23.5.60)	80	45
30	10d. brown and reddish violet (as No. 17) (27.2.61)	2·75	1·25
31	1s. 1d. carmine-red (16.10.61)	80	35
32	2s. sepia (1.5.61)	6·00	90
33	2s. 5d. deep violet (5.2.62)	1·00	40
34	2s. 8d. cinnamon and deep green (9.4.62)	2·75	55
35	5s. sepia and deep green (as No. 18) (27.2.61)	6·50	75
36	10s. emerald-green (14.8.61) (Optd S. £48)	50·00	26·00
24/36	*Set of* 13	65·00	28·00

Designs: *Vert* (*as T* **12**)—2d. *Lagunaria patersonii*; 5d. Lantana. (*As T* **21**); 1s. 1d. Fringed Hibiscus; 2s. 5d. Passion-flower. (*As T* **14**)—2s. Solander's Petrel.

Nos. 30 and 35 are redrawn.

The Specimen overprint on No. 36 is from sets sold by the Australian Post Office.

For Nos. 25 and 28 with face values in decimal currency see Nos. 600/1.

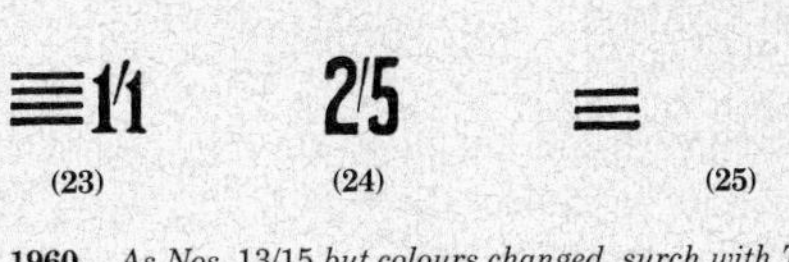

(23) (24) (25)

1960. *As Nos.* 13/15 *but colours changed, surch with T* **23/5**.

37	1s. 1d. on 3½d. deep ultramarine (26.9.60)	3·50	2·50
38	2s. 5d. on 6½d. bluish green (26.9.60)	4·00	1·50
39	2s. 8d. on 7½d. sepia (29.8.60)	10·00	4·75
37/9	*Set of* 3	16·00	8·00

26 Queen Elizabeth II and Map

27 Open Bible and Candle

(Des and eng P. Morriss.)

1960 (24 Oct). *Introduction of Local Government. P* 14.

40	**26**	2s. 8d. reddish purple	16·00	9·50

(Des K. McKay. Adapted and eng B. Stewart. Recess)

1960 (21 Nov). *Christmas. P* 15×14½.

41	**27**	5d. bright purple	80	50

28 Open Prayer Book and Text

29 Stripey (*Atypichthys latus*)

(Des G. Lissenden. Eng P. Morriss. Recess)

1961 (20 Nov). *Christmas. P* 14½×14.

42	**28**	5d. slate-blue	30	40

PRINTERS. All the following issues to No. 233 were printed in photogravure by Harrison and Sons, Ltd, London, *except where otherwise stated.*

1962–63. *Fishes. Horiz designs as T* **29.** *P* 14½×14.

43	6d. sepia, yellow & dp bluish green (16.7.62)	75	25
44	11d. red-orange, brown and blue (25.2.63)	2·00	80
45	1s. blue, pink and yellow-olive (17.9.62)	75	25
46	1s. 3d. blue, red-brown and green (15.7.63)	2·00	1·75
47	1s. 6d. sepia, violet and light blue (6.5.63)	2·75	80
48	2s. 3d. dp blue, red & greenish yell (23.9.63)	5·00	80
43/8	*Set of* 6	12·00	4·25

Designs:—11d. Gold-mouthed Emperor (*Lethrinus chrysostomus*); 1s. Surge Wrasse ("Po'ov"); 1s. 3d. Seachub ("Dreamfish"); 1s. 6d. Giant Grouper (*Promicrops lanceolatus*); 2s. 3d. White Trevally (*Carangidae*).

30 "Madonna and Child"

31 "Peace on Earth..."

(Des and eng G. Lissenden. Recess Note Ptg Branch, Reserve Bank of Australia)

1962 (19 Nov). *Christmas. P* 14½.

49	**30**	5d. ultramarine	45	70

(Des R. Warner. Eng B. Stewart. Recess Note Ptg Branch, Reserve Bank of Australia)

1963 (11 Nov). *Christmas. P* 14½.

50	**31**	5d. red	40	60

32 Overlooking Kingston

33 Norfolk Pine

1964 (24 Feb–28 Sept). *Views. Horiz designs as T* **32.** *Multicoloured. P* 14½×14.

51	5d. Type **32**	75	40
52	8d. Kingston	1·00	1·00
53	9d. The Arches (Bumboras) (11.5)	2·25	30
54	10d. Slaughter Bay (28.9)	2·25	30
51/4	*Set of* 4	5·50	1·75

(Photo Note Ptg Branch, Reserve Bank of Australia, Melbourne)

1964 (1 July). 50*th Anniv of Norfolk Island as Australian Territory. P* 13½.

55	**33**	5d. black, red and orange	40	15
56		8d. black, red and grey-green	40	80

34 Child looking at Nativity Scene

35 Nativity Scene

(Des P. Morriss and J. Mason. Photo Note Ptg Branch, Reserve Bank of Australia)

1964 (9 Nov). *Christmas. P* 13½.

57	**34**	5d. green, blue, buff and violet	30	40

1965 (14 Apr). 50*th Anniv of Gallipoli Landing. As T* **22** *of Nauru. P* 13½.

58	5d. sepia, black and emerald	15	10

(Des J. Mason. Photo Note Ptg Branch, Reserve Bank of Australia)

1965 (25 Oct). *Christmas. Helecon paper. P* 13½.

59	**35**	5d. multicoloured	15	10

(New Currency. 100 cents = 1 Australian dollar)

38 *Hibiscus insularis*

39 Headstone Bridge

1966 (14 Feb). *Decimal currency. Various stamps surch in black on silver tablets, which vary slightly in size, obliterating old value as in T* **38**. *Surch typo.*

No.	Type	Description	Unused	Used
60	**38**	1 c. on 1d. bluish green (*value tablet* 4×5 *mm*)	20	10
		a. Value tablet larger, 5½×5½ mm	40	30
61	–	2 c. on 2d. rose & myrtle-green (No. 25)	20	10
62	**14**	3 c. on 3d. green	50	30
		a. Silver tablet omitted	£250	
63	–	4 c. on 5d. bright purple (No. 27)	25	10
64	**16**	5 c. on 8d. red	30	10
65	–	10 c. on 10d. brown & reddish vio (No. 30)	60	15
66	–	15 c. on 1s. 1d. carmine-red (No. 31)	45	30
67	–	20 c. on 2s. sepia (No. 32)	3·50	2·75
68	–	25 c. on 2s. 5d. deep violet (No. 33)	1·50	40
69	**21**	30 c. on 2s. 8d. cinnamon and deep green	1·00	50
70	–	50 c. on 5s. sepia and deep green (No. 35)	3·50	75
71	**22**	$1 on 10s. emerald-green (*value tablet* 7×6½ *mm*)	2·75	2·00
		a. Value tablet smaller, 6½×4 mm	2·75	2·00
60/71		*Set of* 12	13·00	6·50

1966 (27 June). *Horiz designs as T* **39**. *Multicoloured. P* 14½ × 14.

No.	Description	Unused	Used
72	7 c. Type **39**	40	15
73	9 c. Cemetery Road	40	15

41 St. Barnabas' Chapel (interior)

42 St. Barnabas' Chapel (exterior)

1966 (23 Aug). *Centenary of Melanesian Mission. P* 14 × 14½.

No.	Type	Description	Unused	Used
74	**41**	4 c. multicoloured	10	10
75	**42**	25 c. multicoloured	20	20

43 Star over Philip Island

44 H.M.S. *Resolution*, 1774

(Des B. G. W. McCoy)

1966 (24 Oct). *Christmas. P* 14½.

No.	Type	Description	Unused	Used
76	**43**	4 c. multicoloured	10	10

(Des V. Whiteley)

1967 (17 Apr)–**68**. *T* **44** *and similar horiz designs showing ships. Multicoloured. P* 14×14½.

No.	Description	Unused	Used
77	1 c. Type **44**	10	10
78	2 c. *La Boussole* and *L'Astrolabe*, 1788	15	10
79	3 c. H.M.S. *Supply*, 1788	15	10
80	4 c. H.M.S. *Sirius*, 1790	30	10
81	5 c. *Norfolk* (cutter), 1798 (14.8.67)	20	10
82	7 c. H.M.S. *Mermaid* (survey cutter), 1825 (14.8.67)	20	10
83	9 c. *Lady Franklin*, 1853 (14.8.67)	20	10
84	10 c. *Morayshire*, 1856 (14.8.67)	20	30
85	15 c. *Southern Cross*, 1866 (18.3.68)	45	30
86	20 c. *Pitcairn*, 1891 (18.3.68)	60	40
87	25 c. *Black Billy* (Norfolk Island whaleboat), 1895 (18.3.68)	1·50	75
88	30 c. *Iris* (cable ship), 1907 (18.6.68)	1·50	2·00
89	50 c. *Resolution*, 1926 (18.6.68)	4·00	3·25
90	$1 *Morinda*, 1931 (18.6.68)	5·50	3·25
77/90	*Set of* 14	13·50	9·50

45 Lions Badge and 50 Stars

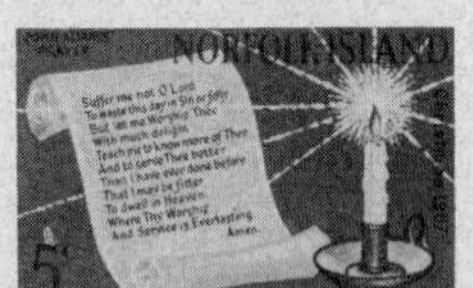

46 Prayer of John Adams and Candle

(Des M. Ripper. Photo Note Ptg Branch, Reserve Bank of Australia)

1967 (7 June). *50th Anniv of Lions International. P* 13½.

No.	Type	Description	Unused	Used
91	**45**	4 c. black, bluish green and olive-yellow	10	10

(Des B. G. W. McCoy)

1967 (16 Oct). *Christmas. P* 14.

No.	Type	Description	Unused	Used
92	**46**	5 c. black, light yellow-olive and red	10	10

47 Queen Elizabeth II

(Photo Note Ptg Branch, Reserve Bank of Australia)

1968 (5 Aug)–**71**. *Coil stamps. P* 15×*imperf.*

No.	Type	Description	Unused	Used
93	**47**	3 c. black, light brown and vermilion	10	10
94		4 c. black, light brown and blue-green	10	10
95		5 c. black, light brown and deep violet	10	10
95*a*		6 c. black, lt brown & lake-brn (25.8.71)	30	45
93/5*a*		*Set of* 4	45	55

59 Avro Type 691 Lancastrian and Douglas DC-4 Aircraft

60 Bethlehem Star and Flowers

(Des Harrison)

1968 (25 Sept). *21st Anniv of QANTAS Air Service, Sydney–Norfolk Island. P* 14.

No.	Type	Description	Unused	Used
96	**59**	5 c. bluish black, carmine-red & lt blue	15	10
97		7 c. blackish brown, carmine-red & turq	15	10

(Des Betty Laing)

1968 (24 Oct). *Christmas. P* 14×14½.

No.	Type	Description	Unused	Used
98	**60**	5 c. multicoloured	10	10

61 Captain Cook, Quadrant and Chart of Pacific Ocean

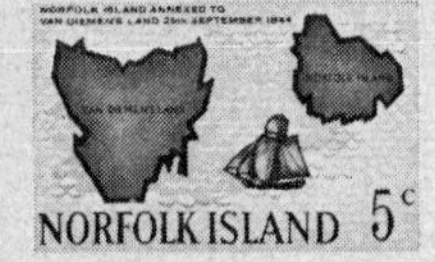

62 Van Diemen's Land, Norfolk Island and Sailing Cutter

(Des V. Whiteley from sketch by J. Cowap)

1969 (3 June). *Captain Cook Bicentenary* (1*st issue*). *Observation of the transit of Venus across the Sun, from Tahiti. P* 14.

No.	Type	Description	Unused	Used
99	**61**	10 c. multicoloured	10	10

See also Nos. 118/19, 129, 152/5, 200/2 and 213/14.

(Des Mrs. A. Bathie and Mrs. M. J. McCoy)

1969 (29 Sept). *125th Anniv of the Annexation of Norfolk Island to Van Diemen's Land. P* 14 × 14½.

No.	Type	Description	Unused	Used
100	**62**	5 c. multicoloured	10	10
101		30 c. multicoloured	50	70
		a. Inscr "VAN DIFMEN'S LAND" (R. 8/5)	11·00	

63 "The Nativity" (carved mother-of-pearl plaque)

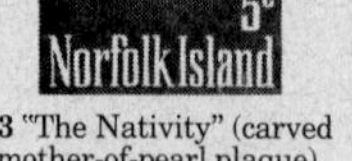

64 New Zealand Grey Flyeater

(Des J. Cowap)

1969 (27 Oct). *Christmas. P* 14½ × 14.

No.	Type	Description	Unused	Used
102	**63**	5 c. multicoloured	10	10

(Des G. Mathews)

1970–71. *Birds. T* **64** *and similar multicoloured designs. Chalk-surfaced paper. P* 14.

No.	Description	Unused	Used
103	1 c. Scarlet Robins (22.7.70)	30	10
104	2 c. Golden Whistler (24.2.71)	30	20
105	3 c. Type **64** (25.2.70)	30	10
106	4 c. Long-tailed Koels (25.2.70)	60	10
107	5 c. Red-fronted Parakeet (24.2.71)	1·50	45
108	7 c. Long-tailed Triller (22.7.70)	45	10
109	9 c. Island Thrush (25.2.70)	70	10
110	10 c. Boobook Owl (22.7.70)	1·75	1·25
111	15 c. Norfolk Island Pigeon (24.2.71)	1·50	65
112	20 c. White-chested White Eye (16.6.71)	7·00	3·25
113	25 c. New Zealand Parrots (22.7.70)	2·50	40
	a. Error. Glazed, ordinary paper	£350	
114	30 c. Collared Grey Fantail (16.6.71)	7·00	1·75
115	45 c. Norfolk Island Starlings (25.2.70)	3·00	80
116	50 c. Crimson Rosella (24.2.71)	3·50	1·75
117	$1 Sacred Kingfisher (16.6.71)	10·00	10·00
103/17	*Set of* 15	35·00	18·00

Nos. 105, 106, 109, 112, 114, 115 and 117 are horizontal, and the remainder vertical designs.

It is believed that only one sheet of No. 113a was issued.

65 Capt. Cook and Map of Australia

66 First Christmas Service, 1788

(Des R. Bates)

1970 (29 Apr). *Captain Cook Bicentenary* (2*nd issue*). *Discovery o Australia's East Coast. T* **65** *and similar horiz design. Multi coloured. P* 14.

No.	Description	Unused	Used
118	5 c. Type **65**	15	1
119	10 c. H.M.S. *Endeavour* and aborigine	40	1

(Des R. Bates)

1970 (15 Oct). *Christmas. P* 14.

No.	Type	Description	Unused	Used
120	**66**	5 c. multicoloured	10	1

67 Bishop Patteson and Martyrdom of St. Stephen

68 Rose Window, St. Barnabas Chapel, Kingston

(Des R. Bates)

1971 (20 Sept). *Death Centenary of Bishop Patteson. T* **67** *an similar horiz designs. Multicoloured. P* 14 × 14½.

No.	Description	Unused	Used
121	6 c. Type **67**	10	2
	a. Pair. Nos. 121/2	15	4
122	6 c. Bible, Martyrdom of St. Stephen and knotted palm-frond	10	2
123	10 c. Bishop Patteson and stained-glass	10	2
	a. Pair. Nos. 123/4	20	4
124	10 c. Cross and Bishop's Arms	10	2
121/4	*Set of* 4	30	7

Nos. 121/2 and 123/4 were printed in *se-tenant* pairs throughou the sheet.

(Des G. Hitch. Photo Heraclio Fournier, Spain)

1971 (25 Oct). *Christmas. P* 14 × 13½.

No.	Type	Description	Unused	Used
125	**68**	6 c. multicoloured	10	1

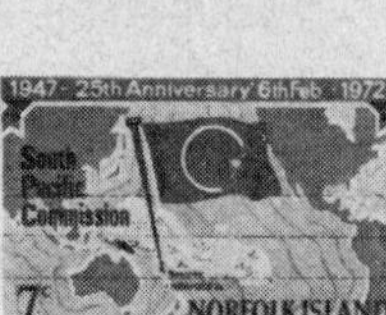

69 Map and Flag

70 "St. Mark" (stained-glass window, All Saints, Norfolk Is

(Des G. Hitch)

1972 (7 Feb). *25th Anniv of South Pacific Commission P* 14 × 14½.

No.	Type	Description	Unused	Used
126	**69**	7 c. multicoloured	15	2

(Des Mrs. M. J. McCoy)

1972 (16 Oct). *Christmas. P* 14.

No.	Type	Description	Unused	Used
127	**70**	7 c. multicoloured	10	1

71 Cross and Pines. (stained-glass window, All Saints Church)

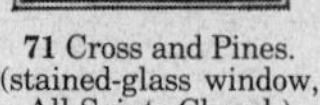

72 H.M.S. *Resolution* in the Antarctic

(Des Harrison)

1972 (20 Nov). *Centenary of First Pitcairner-built Church. P* 14

No.	Type	Description	Unused	Used
128	**71**	12 c. multicoloured	10	
		a. Purple (background to dates) omitted	£550	

No. 128a occurred on the top row of one sheet.

(Des G. Hitch)

973 (17 Jan). *Captain Cook Bicentenary* (3*rd issue*). *Crossing of the Antarctic Circle. P* 14.

9	**72**	35 c. multicoloured	3·00	2·25

73 Child and Christmas Tree

74 Protestant Clergyman's Quarters

(Des B. G. W. McCoy (T **73**), R. Westwood (35 c.))

973 (22 Oct). *Christmas. T* **73** *and similar vert design. Multicoloured. P* 14.

30	7 c. Type **73**	20	10
31	12 c. Type **73**	25	10
32	35 c. Fir trees and star	70	80
30/2	.. .. *Set of* 3	1·00	90

(Des G. Hitch)

973 (19 Nov)–**75.** *Historic Buildings. T* **74** *and similar horiz designs. Multicoloured. P* 14 × 14½.

33	1 c. Type **74**	10	10
34	2 c. Royal Engineers' Office (1.5.74)	10	10
35	3 c. Double Quarters for Free Overseers (19.2.75)	25	30
36	4 c. Guard House (12.7.74)	20	20
37	5 c. Entrance to Pentagonal Gaol	25	15
38	7 c. Pentagonal Gaol (1.5.74)	35	35
39	8 c. Prisoners' Barracks (19.2.75)	1·25	1·50
40	10 c. Officers' Quarters, New Military Barracks	50	55
41	12 c. New Military Barracks (1.5.74)	50	30
42	14 c. Beach Stores (12.7.74)	60	70
43	15 c. The Magazine (19.2.75)	1·25	50
44	20 c. Entrance, Old Military Barracks (12.7.74)	70	90
45	25 c. Old Military Barracks (19.2.75)	1·25	1·00
46	30 c. Old Stores (Crankmill) (1.5.74)	70	60
47	50 c. Commissariat Stores	70	2·00
48	$1 Government House (12.7.74)	1·50	4·00
33/48	.. .. *Set of* 16	9·00	11·00

75 Royal Couple and Map

(Des Harrison)

974 (8 Feb). *Royal Visit. P* 14 × 14½.

49	**75**	7 c. multicoloured	40	15
50		25 c. multicoloured	1·25	75

76 Chichester's De Havilland D.H.60G Gipsy Moth Seaplane *Madame Elijah*

(Des B. G. W. McCoy. Litho State Bank Note Printing Works, Helsinki)

1974 (28 Mar). *First Aircraft Landing on Norfolk Island. P* 14.

151	**76**	14 c. multicoloured	1·00	70

77 "Captain Cook" (engraving by J. Basire)

78 Nativity Scene (pearl-shell pew carving)

(Des C. I. Buffett. Litho Questa)

1974 (8 Oct). *Captain Cook Bicentenary* (4*th issue*). *Discovery of Norfolk Is. T* **77** *and similar vert designs. Multicoloured. P* 14.

152	7 c. Type **77**	1·00	75
153	10 c. "H.M.S. *Resolution*" (H. Roberts) ..	2·00	1·75
154	14 c. Norfolk Island Pine	1·75	2·25
155	25 c. "Norfolk Island flax" (G. Raper)	2·00	3·00
152/5	.. .. *Set of* 4	6·00	7·00

(Des G. Hitch)

1974 (18 Oct). *Christmas. P* 14½.

156	**78**	7 c. multicoloured	15	10
157		30 c. multicoloured	60	75

79 Norfolk Pine

(Manufactured by Walsall)

1974 (16 Dec). *Centenary of Universal Postal Union. T* **79** *and similar "island"-shaped designs. Multicoloured. Imperf* (*backing-paper roul* 20). *Self-adhesive.*

158	10 c. Type **79**	25	40
159	15 c. Offshore islands	35	45
160	35 c. Crimson Rosella and Sacred Kingfisher	60	75
161	40 c. Pacific map	60	90
158/61	.. .. *Set of* 4	1·60	2·25
MS162	106 × 101 mm. Map of Norfolk Is. cut-to-shape with reduced-size replicas of Nos. 158/61	20·00	27·00

80 H.M.S. *Mermaid* (survey cutter)

(Manufactured by Walsall)

1975 (18 Aug). 150*th Anniv of Second Settlement. T* **80** *and similar "island"-shaped design. Multicoloured. Imperf* (*backing-paper roul* 20). *Self-adhesive.*

163	10 c. Type **80**	40	75
164	35 c. Kingston, 1835 (from painting by T. Seller)	60	1·00

81 Star on Norfolk Island Pine

82 Memorial Cross

(Des Harrison)

1975 (6 Oct). *Christmas. P* 14.

165	**81**	10 c. multicoloured	15	10
166		15 c. multicoloured	20	10
167		35 c. multicoloured	30	35
165/7		.. .. *Set of* 3	60	45

(Des Harrison)

1975 (24 Nov). *Centenary of St. Barnabas Chapel. T* **82** *and similar horiz design. Multicoloured. P* 14.

168	30 c. Type **82**	20	15
169	60 c. Laying foundation stone and Chapel in 1975	40	40

83 Launching of *Resolution*

84 Whaleship *Charles W. Morgan*

(Des Harrison)

1975 (1 Dec). 50*th Anniv of Launching of Schooner "Resolution". T* **83** *and similar horiz design. Multicoloured. P* 14.

170	25 c. Type **83**	25	40
171	45 c. *Resolution* at sea	40	70

(Des Harrison)

1976 (5 July). *Bicentenary of American Revolution. T* **84** *and similar horiz designs. Multicoloured. P* 14.

172	18 c. Type **84**	30	30
173	25 c. Thanksgiving Service	40	30
174	40 c. Boeing B-17 Flying Fortress over Norfolk Is	75	65
175	45 c. California Quail	1·00	85
172/5	.. .. *Set of* 4	2·25	1·90

85 Swallow-tailed Tern and Sun

86 *Vanessa ita*

(Des Harrison)

1976 (4 Oct). *Christmas. P* 14.

176	**85**	18 c. multicoloured	30	15
177		25 c. multicoloured	55	20
178		45 c. multicoloured	90	50
176/8		.. .. *Set of* 3	1·60	75

(Des B. Hargreaves)

1976 (17 Nov)–**77.** *Butterflies and Moths. T* **86** *and similar horiz designs. Multicoloured. P* 14.

179	1 c. Type **86**	10	40
180	2 c. *Utetheisa pulchelloides* (moth) (22.2.77)	10	40
181	3 c. *Agathia asterias* (moth) (5.7.77) ..	10	20
182	4 c. *Cynthia kershawi* (5.7.77)	10	25
183	5 c. *Leucania loreyimima* (moth)	15	30
184	10 c. *Hypolimnas bolina*	30	35
185	15 c. *Pyrrhorachis pyrrhogona* (moth) (22.2.77)	30	30
186	16 c. *Austrocarea iocephala* (moth) ..	30	30
187	17 c. *Pseudocoremia christiani* (moth) (10.5.77)	35	30
188	18 c. *Cleora idiocrossa* (moth)	35	30
189	19 c. *Simplicia caeneusalis* (moth) (10.5.77)	35	30
190	20 c. *Austrocidaria ralstonae* (moth) (10.5.77)	40	30
191	30 c. *Hippotion scrofa* (moth) (22.2.77) ..	50	40
192	40 c. *Papilio amynthor* (*ilioneus*) (10.5.77)	55	40
193	50 c. *Tiracola plagiata* (moth) (22.2.77) ..	70	60
194	$1 *Precis villida*	75	75
195	$2 *Cepora perimale* (5.7.77)	1·25	1·40
179/95	.. .. *Set of* 17	5·75	6·50

87 Queen's View, Kingston

(Des Harrison)

1977 (10 June). *Silver Jubilee. P* 14.

196	**87**	25 c. multicoloured	35	30

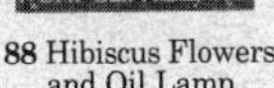

88 Hibiscus Flowers and Oil Lamp

89 Captain Cook (from a portrait by Nathaniel Dance)

(Des Marguerite M. J. McCoy)

1977 (4 Oct). *Christmas. P* 14 × 14½.

197	**88**	18 c. multicoloured	15	10
198		25 c. multicoloured	15	10
199		45 c. multicoloured	30	35
197/9		.. .. *Set of* 3	55	50

(Des Harrison)

1978 (18 Jan). *Captain Cook Bicentenary* (5*th issue*). *Discovery of Hawaii. T* **89** *and similar horiz designs. Multicoloured. P* 14½.

200	18 c. Type **89**	30	20
201	25 c. Discovery of Northern Hawaiian islands	40	30
202	80 c. British flag against island background ..	90	70
200/2	.. .. *Set of* 3	1·40	1·10

90 Guide Flag and Globe

(Manufactured by Walsall)

1978 (22 Feb). *50th Anniv of Girl Guides. T* **90** *and similar "island"-shaped designs. Multicoloured. Imperf (backing paper roul 20). Self-adhesive.*
203 18 c. Type **90** 25 30
204 25 c. Emblem and scarf badge 30 40
a. Horiz roul omitted (vert pair) ..
205 35 c. Emblem and Queen Elizabeth .. 45 60
a. Horiz roul omitted (vert pair) ..
206 45 c. Emblem and Lady Baden-Powell .. 55 70
203/6 .. .. *Set of* 4 1·40 1·75
Nos. 204a and 205a each come from sheets of 20 on which all the horizontal roulettes were omitted.

91 St. Edward's Crown

(Des Harrison)

1978 (29 June). *25th Anniv of Coronation. T* **91** *and similar horiz design. Multicoloured. P* 14½.
207 25 c. Type **91** 15 15
208 70 c. Coronation regalia 40 45

92 View of Duncombe Bay with Scout at Camp Fire

(Des S. Jensen. Manufactured by Walsall)

1978 (22 Aug). *50th Anniv of Boy Scouts. T* **92** *and similar "island"-shaped designs. Multicoloured. Imperf (backing paper roul 20). Self-adhesive.*
209 20 c. Type **92** 30 45
210 25 c. View from Kingston and emblem .. 35 55
211 35 c. View of Anson Bay and Link Badge .. 50 90
212 45 c. Sunset scene and Lord Baden-Powell .. 55 95
209/12 .. .. *Set of* 4 1·50 2·50

93 Chart showing Route of Arctic Voyage

94 Poinsettia and Bible

(Des G. Hitch)

1978 (29 Aug). *Captain Cook Bicentenary (6th issue). Northernmost Voyages. T* **93** *and similar horiz design. Multicoloured. P* 14½.
213 25 c. Type **93** 30 30
214 90 c. "H.M.S. *Resolution* and H.M.S. *Discovery* in Pack Ice" (painting by Webber) 80 80

(Des Marie L. McCoy)

1978 (3 Oct). *Christmas. T* **94** *and similar vert designs. Multicoloured. P* 14½ × 14.
215 20 c. Type **94** 15 10
216 30 c. Native Oak and Bible 20 15
217 55 c. Hibiscus and Bible 30 30
215/17 .. .. *Set of* 3 60 50

95 Cook and Village of Staithes near Marton

(Des Harrison)

1978 (27 Oct). *250th Birth Anniv of Captain Cook. T* **95** *and similar horiz design. Multicoloured. P* 14½.
218 20 c. Type **95** 30 25
219 80 c. Cook and Whitby Harbour .. .. 70 1·25

MINIMUM PRICE

The minimum price quote is 10p which represents a handling charge rather than a basis for valuing common stamps. For further notes about prices see introductory pages.

96 H.M.S. *Resolution*

97 Assembly Building

(Des G. Hitch)

1979 (14 Feb). *Death Bicentenary of Captain Cook. T* **96** *and similar horiz designs. Multicoloured. P* 14.
220 20 c. Type **96** 30 30
a. Pair. Nos. 220/1 .. .. 60 60
221 20 c. Cook (statue) 30 30
222 40 c. Cook's death 40 50
a. Pair. Nos. 222/3 .. .. 80 1·00
223 40 c. Cook's death (*different*) 40 50
220/23 .. .. *Set of* 4 1·25 1·60
The 20 c. designs depict the *Resolution* and Cook's statue on a map showing the last voyage. The 40 c. designs show Cook's death from an aquatint by John Clevely.
Nos. 220/1 and 222/3 were each printed together, *se-tenant*, in horizontal pairs throughout the sheets, forming composite designs.

1979 (10 Aug). *First Norfolk Island Legislative Assembly. P* 14½ × 14.
224 **97** $1 multicoloured 50 50

98 Tasmania 1853 1d. Stamp and Sir Rowland Hill

1979 (27 Aug). *Death Centenary of Sir Rowland Hill. T* **98** *and similar horiz designs showing stamps and Sir Rowland Hill. P* 14 × 14½.
225 20 c. new blue and sepia 20 10
226 30 c. brown-red and olive-grey 25 15
227 55 c. violet and indigo 40 30
225/7 .. .. *Set of* 3 75 50
MS228 142 × 91 mm. No. 227. P 14 .. .. 55 1·25
Designs:—30 c. Penny Red; 55 c. 1d. "Ball Bay".

99 I.Y.C. Emblem and Map of Pacific showing Norfolk Island as Pine Tree

(Des Claire Walters. Litho Asher and Co, Melbourne)

1979 (25 Sept). *International Year of the Child. P* 15.
229 **99** 80 c. multicoloured 40 45

100 Emily Bay

101 Lions International Emblem

1979 (5 Nov).* *Christmas. T* **100** *and similar horiz designs showing different aspects of Emily Bay. P* 12½ × 13.
230 15 c. multicoloured 15 15
a. Horiz strip of 3. Nos. 230/2 40
231 20 c. multicoloured 15 15
232 30 c. multicoloured 15 15
230/2 .. .. *Set of* 3 40 40
MS233 152 × 83 mm. Nos. 230/2. P 14 × 14½ .. 1·00 1·60
Nos. 230/2 were printed together, *se-tenant*, in horizontal strips of 3 throughout the sheet, forming a composite design.
*Although released by the Crown Agents in London on 2 October the stamps were not released locally until 5 November.

(Des Norfolk Island Lions Club. Litho Asher and Co, Melbourne)

1980 (25 Jan). *Lions Convention. P* 15.
234 **101** 50 c. multicoloured 35 30

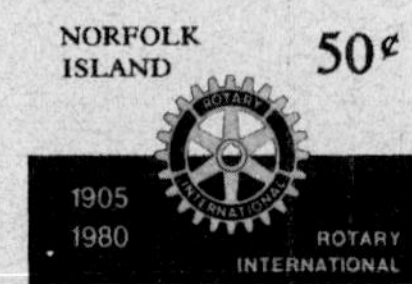

102 Rotary International Emblem

(Des E. Lenthall. Litho Asher and Co, Melbourne)

1980 (21 Feb). *75th Anniv of Rotary International. P* 15.
235 **102** 50 c. multicoloured 35 3
a. Black (face value and "NORFOLK ISLAND") omitted .. .. ..

103 De Havilland D.H.60G Gipsy Moth Seaplane *Madame Elijah*

(Des G. Hitch and B. G. W. McCoy. Litho Harrison)

1980 (25 Mar)–**81.** *Airplanes. Horiz designs as T* **10**
Multicoloured. P 14½×14.
236 1 c. Hawker Siddeley H.S.748 (3.3.81) .. 15 2
237 2 c. Type **103** 15 2
238 3 c. Curtiss P.40E Kittyhawk I 15 2
239 4 c. Chance Vought F4U-1 Corsair (19.8.80) 15 3
240 5 c. Grumman TBF Avenger (19.8.80) .. 15 3
241 15 c. Douglas SBD-5 Dauntless (19.8.80) .. 30 3
242 20 c. Cessna 172D Skyhawk 30 3
243 25 c. Lockheed 414 Hudson (3.3.81) .. 30 3
244 30 c. Lockheed PV-1 Ventura (13.1.81) .. 40 9
245 40 c. Avro Type 685 York (3.3.81) .. 50 5
246 50 c. Douglas DC-3 (13.1.81) 65 6
247 60 c. Avro Type 691 Lancastrian (13.1.81) 75 7
248 80 c. Douglas DC-4 (13.1.81) 95 9
249 $1 Beech 200 Super King Air (3.3.81) .. 1·25 9
250 $2 Fokker F.27 Friendship (19.8.80) .. 2·50 2·2
251 $5 Lockheed C-130 Hercules .. .. 6·00 2·0
236/51 .. .. *Set of* 16 13·00 10·0

104 Queen Elizabeth the Queen Mother

(Des K. Williams. Litho Harrison)

1980 (4 Aug). *80th Birthday of Queen Elizabeth the Queen Mothe*
P 14.
252 **104** 22 c. multicoloured 20 2
253 60 c. multicoloured 35 4

105 Red-tailed Tropic Birds

(Des K. Williams. Litho Harrison)

1980 (28 Oct). *Christmas. Birds. T* **105** *and similar horiz design*
Multicoloured. P 14 × 14½.
254 15 c. Type **105** 30 2
a. Horiz strip of 3. Nos. 254/6 80
255 22 c. White Terns 30 2
256 35 c. White-capped Noddys 30 2
257 60 c. White Terns (*different*) 40 4
254/7 .. .. *Set of* 4 1·10 1·1
Nos. 254/6 were printed together, *se-tenant*, in horizontal stri
of 3 throughout the sheet.

106 *Morayshire* and View of Norfolk Island

107 Wedding Bouquet fro
Norfolk Island

(Des Jennifer Toombs. Litho Harrison)

1981 (5 June). *125th Anniv of Pitcairn Islanders' Migration*
Norfolk Island. T **106** *and similar horiz designs. Multicoloure*
P 14½.
258 5 c. Type **106** 15 1
259 35 c. Islanders arriving ashore 40 3
260 60 c. View of new settlement 60 4
258/60 .. .. *Set of* 3 1·00 8
MS261 183 × 127 mm. Nos. 258/60 .. .. 1·50 2·0

(Des J.W. Litho Harrison)

81 (22 July). *Royal Wedding. T* **107** *and similar vert designs. Multicoloured. P* 14.
2 35 c. Type **107** 15 15
3 55 c. Prince Charles at horse trials 25 25
4 60 c. Prince Charles and Lady Diana Spencer 25 35
2/4 .. .. *Set of* 3 60 65

8 Uniting Church in Australia **109** Pair of White-chested White Eyes

(Des K. Williams. Litho Harrison)

81 (15 Sept). *Christmas. Churches. T* **108** *and similar horiz designs. Multicoloured. P* 14½ × 14.
5 18 c. Type **108** 15 10
6 24 c. Seventh Day Adventist Church 15 15
7 30 c. Church of the Sacred Heart 20 20
8 $1 St. Barnabas Chapel 50 70
5/8 .. .. *Set of* 4 90 1·00

(Des P. Slater. Litho Questa)

81 (10 Nov). *White-chested White Eye ("Silvereye"). T* **109** *and similar horiz designs. Multicoloured. P* 14 × 14½.
9 35 c. Type **109** 35 40
a. Horiz strip of 5. Nos. 269/73 .. .. 1·50
0 35 c. Bird on nest 35 40
1 35 c. Bird with egg 35 40
2 35 c. Parents with chicks 35 40
3 35 c. Fledgelings 35 40
9/73 .. .. *Set of* 5 1·50 2·00
Nos. 269/73 were printed together, *se-tenant*, in horizontal strips 5 throughout the sheet.

110 Aerial View of Philip Island

(Des local artist. Litho Harrison)

82 (12 Jan). *Philip and Nepean Islands. T* **110** *and similar horiz designs. Multicoloured. P* 14 × 13½.
'4 24 c. Type **110** 25 25
a. Horiz strip of 5. Nos. 274/8 .. .. 1·10
'5 24 c. Close-up view of Philip Island landscape 25 25
'6 24 c. Gecko (*Phyllodactylus guentheri*), Philip Island 25 25
'7 24 c. Sooty Tern (*Sterna fuscata*), Philip Island 25 25
'8 24 c. Philip Island Hibiscus (*Hibiscus insularis*) 25 25
'9 35 c. Aerial view of Nepean Island 30 30
a. Horiz strip of 5. Nos. 279/83 .. .. 1·25
30 35 c. Close-up view of Nepean Island landscape 30 30
31 35 c. Gecko (*Phyllodactylus guentheri*), Nepean Island 30 30
32 35 c. Blue-faced Boobies (*Sula dactylatra*), Nepean Island 30 30
33 35 c. *Carpobrotus glaucescens* (flower), Nepean Island 30 30
'4/83 .. .. *Set of* 10 2·25 2·25
The five designs of each value were printed together, *se-tenant*, horizontal strips of 5 throughout the sheet.

111 Sperm Whale

(Des Jennifer Toombs. Litho Harrison)

982 (23 Feb). *Whales. T* **111** *and similar horiz designs. P* 14½.
34 24 c. multicoloured 45 35
35 55 c. multicoloured 85 95
36 80 c. black, mauve and stone .. .. .. 1·10 2·00
34/6 .. .. *Set of* 3 2·25 3·00
Designs:—55 c. Black Right Whale; 80 c. Humpback Whale.

112 *Diocet*, Wrecked 20 April 1873

(Litho Harrison)

1982 (18 May–27 July). *Shipwrecks. T* **112** *and similar horiz designs. Multicoloured. P* 14½ × 14.
287 24 c. H.M.S. *Sirius*, wrecked 19 March 1790 (27 July) 50 50
288 27 c. Type **112** 50 50
289 35 c. *Friendship*, wrecked 17 May 1835 (27 July) 90 80
290 40 c. *Mary Hamilton*, wrecked 6 May 1873 .. 90 1·25
291 55 c. *Fairlie*, wrecked 14 February 1840 (27 July) .. .. 1·25 1·25
292 65 c. *Warrigal*, wrecked 18 March 1918 .. 1·25 1·75
287/92 .. .. *Set of* 6 4·75 5·50

C-KURITY PAPER. The following issues up to No. 342 were all printed on this type of security paper, *unless otherwise stated.* It shows a pattern of blue fluorescent markings, resembling rosettes, on the reverse beneath the gum.

113 R.N.Z.A.F. Lockheed 414 Hudson dropping Christmas Supplies, 1942 **114** 50th (Queen's Own) Regiment

(Des A. Theobald. Litho Walsall)

1982 (7 Sept). *Christmas. 40th Anniv of first Supply-plane Landings on Norfolk Island (Christmas Day 1942). T* **113** *and similar horiz designs. Multicoloured. P* 14.
293 27 c. Type **113** 55 35
294 40 c. Lockheed 414 Hudson landing Christmas supplies, 1942 .. .. 75 65
295 75 c. Christmas, 1942 .. .. 90 1·40
293/5 .. .. *Set of* 3 2·00 2·25

(Des W. Fenton. Litho Questa)

1982 (9 Nov). *Military Uniforms. T* **114** *and similar vert designs. Multicoloured. P* 14½ × 14.
296 27 c. Type **114** 30 35
297 40 c. 58th (Rutlandshire) Regiment 40 75
298 55 c. 80th (Staffordshire Volunteers) Battalion Company 50 95
299 65 c. 11th (North Devonshire) Regiment .. 60 1·25
296/9 .. .. *Set of* 4 1·60 3·00

115 *Panaeolus papilionaceus* **116** Beech 18 Aircraft

(Des Jane Thatcher. Litho Enschedé)

1983 (29 Mar). *Fungi. T* **115** *and similar vert designs. Multicoloured. P* 13½ × 13.
300 27 c. Type **115** 45 35
301 40 c. *Coprinus domesticus* 70 50
302 55 c. *Marasmius niveus* 95 70
303 65 c. *Cymatoderma elegans* var *lamellatum* 1·25 85
300/3 .. .. *Set of* 4 3·00 2·25

(Des Walsall. Litho Format)

1983 (12 July). *Bicentenary of Manned Flight. T* **116** *and similar horiz designs. Multicoloured. P* 14½ × 14.
304 10 c. Type **116** 15 15
305 27 c. Fokker F.28 Fellowship 25 35
306 45 c. French military Douglas C-54 .. .. 40 60
307 75 c. Sikorsky S-61N helicopter 60 95
304/7 .. .. *Set of* 4 1·25 1·90
MS308 105×100 mm. Nos. 304/7 .. .. 1·75 2·75

117 St. Matthew **118** Cable Ship *Chantik*

(Des McCombie-Skinner Studio. Litho Format)

1983 (13 Sept). *Christmas. 150th Birth Anniv of Sir Edward Burne-Jones. T* **117** *and similar vert designs showing stained-glass windows from St. Barnabas Chapel, Norfolk Island. Multicoloured. P* 14.
309 5 c. Type **117** 10 10
310 24 c. St. Mark 20 30
311 30 c. Jesus Christ 25 40
312 45 c. St. Luke 35 55
313 85 c. St. John .. .. 55 1·10
309/13 .. .. *Set of* 5 1·25 2·25

(Des G. Drummond. Litho Format)

1983 (15 Nov). *World Communications Year. ANZCAN Cable. T* **118** *and similar horiz designs. Multicoloured. Ordinary paper. P* 14½ × 14.
314 30 c. Type **118** 30 40
315 45 c. *Chantik* during in-shore operations .. 40 55
316 75 c. Cable ship *Mercury* 55 95
317 85 c. Diagram of cable route .. .. .. 55 1·10
314/17 .. .. *Set of* 4 1·60 2·75

119 Popwood **120** Morwong

(Des I. Loe. Litho B.D.T.)

1984 (10 Jan–27 Mar). *Flowers. T* **119** *and similar vert designs. Multicoloured. P* 14.
318 1 c. Type **119** (27.3) 30 70
319 2 c. Strand Morning Glory 40 70
320 3 c. Native Phreatia 45 70
321 4 c. Philip Island Wisteria (27.3) 45 70
322 5 c. Norfolk Island Palm (27.3) 45 70
323 10 c. Evergreen 50 70
324 15 c. Bastard Oak (27.3) 60 70
325 20 c. Devil's Guts 60 70
326 25 c. White Oak 70 80
327 30 c. Ti (27.3) 70 90
328 35 c. Philip Island Hibiscus (27.3) 70 90
329 40 c. Native Wisteria .. .. 80 1·25
330 50 c. Native Jasmine .. .. 1·25 1·25
331 $1 Norfolk Island Hibiscus (27.3) .. .. 1·25 1·75
332 $3 Native Oberonia (27.3) .. .. .. 2·75 4·00
333 $5 Norfolk Island Pine .. .. .. 3·75 4·50
318/33 .. .. *Set of* 16 14·00 19·00

(Des Marg Towt. Litho Cambec Press, Melbourne)

1984 (17 Apr). *Reef Fishes. T* **120** *and similar horiz designs. Multicoloured. Ordinary paper. P* 13½ × 14.
334 30 c. Type **120** 40 45
335 45 c. Black-spotted Goatfish (*Pseudopeneus signatus*) 60 65
336 75 c. Surgeonfish (*Acanthuridae*) .. .. 1·00 1·10
337 85 c. Three-striped Butterflyfish (*Chaeton ancinetus*) .. .. 1·25 1·40
334/7 .. .. *Set of* 4 2·75 3·25

121 Owl with Eggs **122** 1953 7½d. and 1974 Cook Bicent 10 c. Stamps

(Des P. Slater. Litho Questa)

1984 (17 July). *Boobook Owl. T* **121** *and similar vert designs. Multicoloured. P* 14.
338 30 c. Type **121** 65 60
a. Horiz strip of 5. Nos. 338/42 .. .. 3·00
339 30 c. Fledgeling 65 60
340 30 c. Young owl on stump 65 60
341 30 c. Adult on branch 65 60
342 30 c. Owl in flight 65 60
338/42 .. .. *Set of* 5 3·00 2·75
Nos. 338/42 were printed together, *se-tenant*, in horizontal strips of 5 throughout the sheet.

(Des D. Miller. Litho Harrison)

1984 (18 Sept). *"Ausipex" International Stamp Exhibition, Melbourne. T* **122** *and similar horiz designs. Multicoloured. W w* **14** *(sideways). P* 14.
343 30 c. Type **122** 30 35
344 45 c. John Buffett commemorative postal stationery envelope 50 75
345 75 c. Design from Presentation Pack for 1982 Military Uniforms issue .. .. .. 90 1·75
343/5 .. .. *Set of* 3 1·50 2·50
MS346 151 × 93 mm. Nos. 343/5. P 14½ .. .. 4·00 4·50

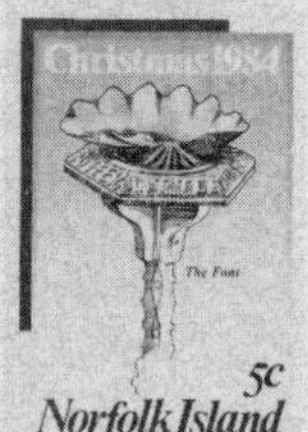

123 Font, Kingston Methodist Church **124** The Revd. Nobbs teaching Pitcairn Islanders

(Des R. Murphy. Litho Questa)

1984 (9 Oct). *Christmas. Centenary of Methodist Church on Norfolk Island. T* **123** *and similar vert designs. Multicoloured. W w* **14**. *P* 14.
347 5 c. Type **123** 10 10
348 24 c. Church service in Old Barracks, Kingston, late 1800's 25 40
349 30 c. The Revd. & Mrs. A. H. Phelps and sailing ship 35 45
350 45 c. The Revd. A. H. Phelps and First Congregational Church, Chester, U.S.A. . . 40 65
351 85 c. Interior of Kingston Methodist Church . . 80 1·40
347/51 . . . . *Set of* 5 1·60 2·50

(Des D. Hopkins. Litho B.D.T.)

1984 (6 Nov). *Death Centenary of the Revd. George Hunn Nobbs (leader of Pitcairn community). T* **124** *and similar vert designs. Multicoloured. W w* **14**. *P* 14 × 15.
352 30 c. Type **124** 30 45
353 45 c. The Revd. Nobbs with sick islander . . 45 65
354 75 c. Baptising baby . . . . 75 1·10
355 85 c. Presented to Queen Victoria, 1852 . . 80 1·40
352/5 . . . . *Set of* 4 2·10 3·25

125 *Fanny Fisher* **126** The Queen Mother (from photo by Norman Parkinson)

(Des D. Hopkins. Litho Cambec Press, Melbourne)

1985 (19 Feb). *19th-Century Whaling Ships (1st series). T* **125** *and similar horiz designs. Multicoloured. P* 13½ × 14.
356 5 c. Type **125** 40 25
357 33 c. *Costa Rica Packet* . . . . . . 1·00 55
358 50 c. *Splendid* . . . . 1·50 1·25
359 90 c. *Onward* . . . . 1·90 2·00
356/9 . . . . *Set of* 4 4·25 3·50
See also Nos. 360/3.

(Des D. Hopkins. Litho Cambec Press, Melbourne)

1985 (30 Apr). *19th-Century Whaling Ships (2nd series). Horiz designs as T* **125**. *Multicoloured. P* 13½ × 14.
360 15 c. *Waterwitch* 70 70
361 20 c. *Canton* 80 80
362 60 c. *Aladdin* . . . . 1·50 2·00
363 80 c. *California* . . . . 1·75 2·50
360/3 . . . . *Set of* 4 4·25 5·50

(Des A. Theobald ($1), C. Abbott (others). Litho Questa)

1985 (6 June). *Life and Times of Queen Elizabeth the Queen Mother. T* **126** *and similar vert designs. Multicoloured. W w* **16**. *P* 14½ × 14.
364 5 c. The Queen Mother (from photo by Dorothy Wilding) 10 10
365 33 c. With Princess Anne at Trooping the Colour 25 25
366 50 c. Type **126** 40 55
367 90 c. With Prince Henry at his christening (from photo by Lord Snowdon) . . 60 1·00
364/7 . . . . *Set of* 4 1·25 1·75
MS368 91 × 73 mm. $1 With Princess Anne at Ascot Races. Wmk sideways . . . . 1·10 1·25

127 "Swimming" **128** Prize-winning Cow and Owner

(Des from children's paintings. Litho Cambec Press, Melbourne)

1985 (9 July). *International Youth Year. T* **127** *and similar horiz design. Multicoloured. P* 13½ × 14.
369 33 c. Type **127** 40 40
370 50 c. "A Walk in the Country" 70 85

(Des Flett Henderson & Arnold. Litho Cambec Press, Melbourne)

1985 (10 Sept). *125th Anniv of Royal Norfolk Island Agricultural and Horticultural Show. T* **128** *and similar horiz design. Multicoloured. P* 13½ × 14.
371 80 c. Type **128** 75 80
372 90 c. Show exhibits 85 90
MS373 132 × 85 mm. Nos. 371/2 . . . . . . 1·75 2·50

129 Shepherds with Flock **130** Long-spined Sea Urchin

(Des R. Murphy. Litho Cambec Press, Melbourne)

1985 (3 Oct). *Christmas. T* **129** *and similar vert designs. Multicoloured. P* 13½.
374 27 c. Type **129** 50 30
375 33 c. Mary and Joseph with donkey 60 40
376 50 c. The Three Wise Men . . . . . . 1·10 65
377 90 c. The Nativity . . . . 1·50 1·25
374/7 . . . . *Set of* 4 3·25 2·25

(Des L. Curtis. Litho Cambec Press, Melbourne)

1986 (14 Jan). *Marine Life. T* **130** *and similar horiz designs. Multicoloured. P* 13½ × 14.
378 5 c. Type **130** 10 10
379 33 c. Blue Starfish 30 35
380 55 c. Southern Eagle Ray 50 85
381 75 c. Snowflake Moray . . . . . . 70 1·25
378/81 . . . . *Set of* 4 1·40 2·25
MS382 100 × 95 mm. Nos. 378/81 . . . . . . 3·00 3·75

131 *Giotto* Spacecraft **132** Isaac Robinson (U.S. Consul 1887–1908)

(Des G. Revell. Litho Leigh-Mardon Ltd, Melbourne)

1986 (11 Mar). *Appearance of Halley's Comet. T* **131** *and similar vert design. Multicoloured. P* 14½ × 15.
383 $1 Type **131** . . . . 75 1·50
a. Horiz pair. Nos. 383/4 . . . . . . 1·50 3·00
384 $1 Halley's Comet . . . . 75 1·50
Nos. 383/4 were printed together, *se-tenant*, in horizontal pairs throughout the sheet, each pair forming a composite design.

(Des G. Revell. Litho Cambec Press, Melbourne)

1986 (22 May). *"Ameripex '86" International Stamp Exhibition, Chicago. T* **132** *and similar multicoloured designs. P* 13½.
385 33 c. Type **132** 40 35
386 50 c. Ford "Model T" (first vehicle on island) (*horiz*) 60 50
387 80 c. Statue of Liberty 65 80
385/7 . . . . *Set of* 3 1·50 1·50
MS388 125 × 100 mm. Nos. 385/7 . . . . . . 2·00 2·25
No. 387 also commemorates the Centenary of the Statue of Liberty.

133 Princess Elizabeth and Dog **134** Stylized Dove and Norfolk Island

(Des Allison Ryves. Litho Cambec Press, Melbourne)

1986 (12 June). *60th Birthday of Queen Elizabeth II. T* **133** *and similar vert designs. Multicoloured. P* 13½.
389 5 c. Type **133** 10 10
390 33 c. Queen Elizabeth II 40 35
391 80 c. Opening Norfolk Island Golf Club . . 1·25 1·40
392 90 c. With Duke of Edinburgh in carriage . . 1·25 1·60
389/92 . . . . *Set of* 4 2·75 3·00

(Des Lyn Studham. Litho Cambec Press, Melbourne)

1986 (23 Sept). *Christmas. P* 13½ × 14.
393 **134** 30 c. multicoloured 25 3
394 40 c. multicoloured 35 4
395 $1 multicoloured . . . . . . 1·00 1·5
393/5 . . . . *Set of* 3 1·40 2·0

135 British Convicts, 1787 **136** Stone Tools

(Des Josephine Martin. Litho Cambec Press, Melbourne)

1986 (14 Oct–16 Dec). *Bicentenary of Norfolk Island Settleme*[nt] *(1988) (1st issue). Governor Phillip's Commission. T* **135** *an*[d] *similar vert designs. Multicoloured. P* 14 × 13½.
396 36 c. Type **135** 80
397 55 c. Judge passing sentence of transportation . . . . 1·50
398 90 c. Governor Phillip meeting Home Secretary (inscr "Home Society") . . 2·50 3·
399 90 c. As No. 398, but correctly inscr "Home Secretary" (16.12) . . . . . . 2·25 3·
400 $1 Captain Arthur Phillip . . . . . . 2·50 2·
396/400 . . . . *Set of* 5 8·50 9·
See also Nos. 401/4, 421/4, 433/5, 436/7 and 438/43.

(Des B. Clinton. Litho Cambec Press, Melbourne)

1986 (16 Dec). *Bicentenary of Norfolk Island Settlement* (198[8]) *(2nd issue). Pre-European Occupation. T* **136** *and similar ho*[riz] *designs. Multicoloured. P* 13½.
401 36 c. Type **136** 65
402 36 c. Bananas and taro 65
403 36 c. Polynesian outrigger canoe 65
404 36 c. Maori chief 65
401/4 . . . . *Set of* 4 2·40 2·

137 Philip Island from Point Ross **138** Male Red-fronted Parakeet

(Des C. Abbott. Litho CPE Australia Ltd, Melbourne)

1987 (17 Feb)–**88**. *Norfolk Island Scenes. T* **137** *and simi*[lar] *square designs. Multicoloured. P* 13½.
405 1 c. Cockpit Creek Bridge (17.5.88) . . 50
406 2 c. Cemetery Bay Beach (17.5.88) . . 50
407 3 c. Island guesthouse (17.5.88) 50
408 5 c. Type **137** 30
409 15 c. Cattle in pasture (27.7.87) . . . . 80 1·
410 30 c. Rock fishing (7.4.87) 30 1
411 37 c. Old Pitcairner-style house (27.7.87) . . 1·40 1
412 40 c. Shopping centre (7.4.87) . . . . 35 1·
413 50 c. Emily Bay 45 1
414 60 c. Bloody Bridge (27.7.87) . . . . 2·00 2
415 80 c. Pitcairner-style shop (7.4.87) . . . . 1·75 2
416 90 c. Government House . . . . . . 1·25 2
417 $1 Melanesian Memorial Chapel . . . . 1·00 1
418 $2 Convict Settlement, Kingston (7.4.87) . . 1·75 3
419 $3 Ball Bay (27.7.87) . . . . . . 5·00 6
420 $5 Northern cliffs (17.5.88) . . . . 7·00 8
405/20 . . . . *Set of* 16 22·00 32

(Des Josephine Martin. Litho CPE Australia Ltd, Melbourn[e])

1987 (13 May). *Bicentenary of Norfolk Island Settlement* (198[8]) *(3rd issue). The First Fleet. Vert designs as T* **135**. *Mu*[lti]*coloured. P* 14 × 13½.
421 5 c. Loading supplies, Deptford 50
422 55 c. Fleet leaving Spithead . . . . . . 1·75 2·
a. Horiz pair. Nos. 422/3 . . . . . . 3·50 4·
423 55 c. H.M.S. *Sirius* leaving Spithead . . 1·75 2
424 $1 Female convicts below decks . . . . 2·25 3
421/4 . . . . *Set of* 4 5·50 7
Nos. 422/3 were printed together, *se-tenant*, in horizon[tal] pairs throughout the sheet, forming a composite design.

(Des P. Slater. Litho CPE Australia Ltd, Melbourne)

1987 (16 Sept). *Red-fronted Parakeet ("Green Parrot"). T* **1**[38] *and similar vert designs. Multicoloured. P* 14 × 13½.
425 5 c. Type **138** . . . . 2·00 1·
a. Horiz strip of 4. Nos. 425/8 . . . . 11·00
426 15 c. Adult with fledgeling and egg . . . . 2·50 2·
427 36 c. Young parakeets . . . . . . 3·50 3
428 55 c. Female parakeet . . . . . . 4·50 3
425/8 . . . . *Set of* 4 11·00 10
Nos. 425/8 were printed together, *se-tenant*, in horizon[tal] strips of four throughout the sheet.

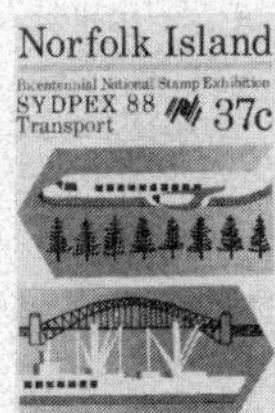

139 Christmas Tree and Restored Garrison Barracks **140** Airliner, Container Ship and Sydney Harbour Bridge

)es T. Bland and Alison Ryves. Litho CPE Australia Ltd, Melbourne)

987 (13 Oct). *Christmas. T* **139** *and similar horiz designs. Multicoloured. P* 13½ × 14.
29 30 c. Type **139** 30 30
30 42 c. Children opening presents . . 45 55
31 58 c. Father Christmas with children . . 60 1·00
32 63 c. Children's party . . . . 70 1·25
29/32 . . . . . . *Set of* 4 1·90 2·75

Des Josephine Martin. Litho CPE Australia Ltd, Melbourne)

987 (8 Dec). *Bicentenary of Norfolk Island Settlement* (1988) (4th issue). *Visit of La Perouse* (navigator). *Vert designs as T* 135. *Multicoloured. P* 14 × 13½.
33 37 c. La Perouse with King Louis XVI . . 95 55
34 90 c. *L'Astrolabe* and *La Boussole* off Norfolk Island . . . . . . 2·75 3·00
35 $1 *L'Astrolabe* wrecked in Solomon Islands 2·75 3·00
33/5 . . . . . . *Set of* 3 5·75 6·00

Des Josephine Martin. Litho CPE Australia Ltd, Melbourne)

988 (25 Jan). *Bicentenary of Norfolk Island Settlement* (5th issue). *Arrival of First Fleet at Sydney. Vert designs as T* **135**. *Multicoloured. P* 14 × 13½.
36 37 c. Ship's cutter approaching Port Jackson 1·25 75
37 $1 Landing at Sydney Cove . . . . 2·75 3·25

Des Josephine Martin. Litho CPE Australia Ltd, Melbourne)

988 (4 Mar). *Bicentenary of Norfolk Island Settlement* (6th issue). *Foundation of First Settlement. Vert designs as T* **135**. *Multicoloured. P* 14 × 13½.
38 5 c. Lt. Philip Gidley King 20 50
39 37 c. Raising the flag, March 1788 . . . . 85 75
40 55 c. King exploring . . . . . . 1·75 1·50
41 70 c. Landing at Sydney Bay, Norfolk Island 2·00 2·50
42 90 c. H.M.S. *Supply* (brig) . . . . 2·25 2·75
43 $1 Sydney Bay settlement, 1788 . . . . 2·25 2·75
38/43 . . . . . . *Set of* 6 8·50 9·75

(Des Janet Boschen. Litho CPE Australia Ltd, Melbourne)

988 (30 July). *"Sydpex '88" National Stamp Exhibition, Sydney. T* **140** *and similar multicoloured designs. P* 14 × 13½ (*vert*) *or* 13½ × 14 (*horiz*).
44 37 c. Type **140** . . . . 95 1·10
45 37 c. Exhibition label under magnifying glass (*horiz*) . . . . . . 95 1·10
46 37 c. Telephone and dish aerial . . . . 95 1·10
44/6 . . . . . . *Set of* 3 2·50 3·00
1S447 118 × 84 mm. Nos. 444/6 . . . . 3·50 4·25
In No. **MS**447 the horizontal design is perforated 14 at foot nd 13½ on the other three sides.

141 Flowers and Decorations **142** Pier Store and Boat Shed

(Des Sue Pearson. Litho CPE Australia Ltd, Melbourne)

988 (27 Sept). *Christmas. T* **141** *and similar vert designs. Multicoloured. P* 14 × 13½.
48 30 c. Type **141** 50 40
49 42 c. Flowers 70 70
50 58 c. Fishes and beach 85 95
51 63 c. Norfolk Island . . . . . . 95 1·25
48/51 . . . . . . *Set of* 4 2·75 3·00

(Des R. Murphy. Litho CPE Australia Ltd, Melbourne)

988 (6 Dec). *Restored Buildings from the Convict Era. T* **142** *and similar horiz designs. Multicoloured. P* 13½ × 14.
52 39 c. Type **142** 45 40
53 55 c. Royal Engineers Building 60 60
54 90 c. Old Military Barracks . . . . 1·00 1·50
55 $1 Commissariat Store and New Military Barracks . . . . . . 1·10 1·50
52/5 . . . . . . *Set of* 4 2·75 3·50

ALTERED CATALOGUE NUMBERS

Any Catalogue numbers altered from the last edition are shown as a list in the introductory pages.

143 *Lamprima aenea* **144** H.M.S. *Bounty* off Tasmania

(Des T. Nolan. Litho CPE Australia Ltd, Melbourne)

1989 (14 Feb). *Endemic Insects. T* **143** *and similar horiz designs. Multicoloured. P* 13½ × 14.
456 39 c. Type **143** 65 40
457 55 c. *Insulascirtus nythos* 90 75
458 90 c. *Caedicia araucariae* . . . . . . 1·40 2·00
459 $1 *Thrincophora aridela* . . . . 1·60 2·00
456/9 . . . . . . *Set of* 4 4·00 4·75

(Des C. Abbott. Litho CPE Australia Ltd, Melbourne (Nos. 460/3), B.D.T. (No. **MS**464))

1989 (28 Apr). *Bicentenary of the Mutiny on the* Bounty. *T* **144** *and similar horiz designs. Multicoloured. P* 13½.
460 5 c. Type **144** 60 60
461 39 c. Mutineers and Polynesian women, Pitcairn Island . . . . . . 1·75 1·25
462 55 c. Lake Windermere, Cumbria (Christian's home county) . . . . 2·25 2·25
463 $1.10, "Mutineers casting Bligh adrift" (Robert Dodd) . . . . . . 3·50 4·50
460/3 . . . . . . *Set of* 4 7·25 7·75
MS464 110 × 85 mm. 39 c. No. 461; 90 c. Isle of Man 1989 Mutiny 35p., No. 414; $1 Pitcairn Islands 1989 Settlement Bicent 90 c., No. 345. P 14 . . . . 5·00 7·00

145 Norfolk Island Flag **146** Red Cross

(Des R. Fletcher. Litho CPE Australia Ltd, Melbourne)

1989 (10 Aug). *10th Anniv of Internal Self-Government. T* **145** *and similar vert designs. Multicoloured. P* 14 × 13½.
465 41 c. Type **145** 90 55
466 55 c. Old ballot box 95 65
467 $1 Norfolk Island Act, 1979 . . . . 1·75 2·00
468 $1.10, Island crest . . . . . . 1·75 2·75
465/8 . . . . . . *Set of* 4 4·75 5·50

(Des E. Lenthall. Litho CPE Australia Ltd, Melbourne)

1989 (25 Sept). *75th Anniv of Red Cross on Norfolk Island. P* 13½.
469 **146** $1 bright rose-red and ultramarine . . 3·00 3·00

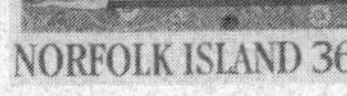

147 "Gethsemane" **148** John Royle (first announcer)

(Des Sue Pearson. Litho CPE Australia Ltd, Melbourne)

1989 (9 Oct). *Christmas. T* **147** *and similar horiz designs showing opening lines of hymns and local scenes. Multicoloured. P* 13½ × 14.
470 36 c. Type **147** 90 40
471 60 c. "In the Sweet Bye and Bye" . . . . 1·75 2·00
472 75 c. "Let the Lower Lights Be Burning" . . 2·25 2·75
473 80 c. "The Beautiful Stream" . . . . 2·25 3·00
470/3 . . . . . . *Set of* 4 6·50 7·25

(Des Philatelic Studios. Litho Leigh-Mardon Ltd, Melbourne)

1989 (21 Nov). *50th Anniv of Radio Australia. T* **148** *and similar vert designs each showing Kingston buildings. Multicoloured. P* 14 × 13½.
474 41 c. Type **148** 95 55
475 65 c. Radio waves linking Australia and Norfolk Island . . . . . . 1·75 2·25
476 $1.10, Anniversary kookaburra logo . . 2·75 3·75
474/6 . . . . . . *Set of* 3 5·00 6·00

149 H.M.S. *Bounty* on fire, Pitcairn Island, 1790 **150** H.M.S. *Sirius* striking Reef

(Des G. Hitch. Litho Leigh-Mardon Ltd, Melbourne)

1990 (23 Jan). *History of the Norfolk Islanders* (1st series). *Settlement on Pitcairn Island. T* **149** *and similar vert design. Multicoloured. P* 14½.
477 70 c. Type **149** . . . . 2·50 2·50
478 $1.10, Arms of Norfolk Island . . . . 2·75 3·00
See also Nos. 503/4 and 516/17.

(Des Maree Edmiston. Litho Leigh-Mardon Ltd, Melbourne)

1990 (19 Mar). *Bicentenary of Wreck of H.M.S.* Sirius. *T* **150** *and similar horiz designs. Multicoloured. P* 13½.
479 41 c. Type **150** . . . . 1·75 2·00
a. Horiz pair. Nos. 479/80 . . . . 3·50 4·00
480 41 c. H.M.S. *Sirius* failing to clear bay . . 1·75 2·00
481 65 c. Divers at work on wreck . . . . 2·50 3·00
482 $1 Recovered artifacts and chart of site 2·75 3·25
479/82 . . . . . . *Set of* 4 8·00 9·25
Nos. 479/80 were printed together, *se-tenant*, in horizontal pairs throughout the sheet, each pair forming a composite design.

151 Unloading Lighter, Kingston **152** *Ile de Lumiere* (freighter)

(Des Philatelic Studios. Litho Leigh-Mardon Ltd, Melbourne)

1990 (17 July)–**91**. *Ships. T* **151** *and horiz designs as T* **152**. *P* 14 × 14½ (5, 10 *c.*) *or* 14½ (*others*).
483 **151** 5 c. purple-brown 20 30
484 10 c. ochre 20 30
485 – 45 c. multicoloured (19.2.91) 80 60
486 – 50 c. multicoloured (19.2.91) . . . . 90 1·00
487 – 65 c. multicoloured (19.2.91) . . . . 1·00 1·25
488 **152** 70 c. multicoloured . . . . . . 90 1·00
489 – 75 c. multicoloured (13.8.91) . . . . 1·50 1·75
490 – 80 c. multicoloured (13.8.91) . . . . 1·50 2·00
491 – 90 c. multicoloured (13.8.91) . . . . 1·50 2·00
492 – $1 multicoloured (13.8.91) . . . . 1·50 1·75
493 – $2 multicoloured . . . . . . 2·25 3·00
494 – $5 multicoloured (19.2.91) . . . . 5·00 7·00
483/94 . . . . . . *Set of* 12 15·00 20·00
Designs: *Horiz* (*as T* **152**)—45 c. *La Dunkerquoise* (French patrol vessel); 50 c. *Dmitri Mendeleev* (Russian research vessel); 65 c. *Pacific Rover* (tanker); 75 c. *Norfolk Trader* (freighter); 80 c. *Roseville* (transport); 90 c. *Kalia* (container ship); $1 *Bounty* (replica); $2 H.M.A.S. *Success* (supply ship); $5 H.M.A.S. *Whyalla* (patrol vessel).

153 Santa on House Roof **154** William Charles Wentworth

(Des G. Hitch, adapted Philatelic Studios. Litho Leigh-Mardon Ltd, Melbourne)

1990 (25 Sept). *Christmas. T* **153** *and similar multicoloured designs. P* 14½.
499 38 c. Type **153** 75 45
500 43 c. Santa at Kingston Post Office 80 50
501 65 c. Santa over Sydney Bay, Kingston (*horiz*) . . . . 1·75 2·25
502 85 c. Santa on Officers' Quarters (*horiz*) . . 2·00 2·75
499/502 . . . . . . *Set of* 4 4·75 5·50

(Des G. Hitch. Litho Leigh-Mardon Ltd, Melbourne)

1990 (11 Oct). *History of the Norfolk Islanders* (2nd series). *The First Generation. T* **154** *and similar vert design. P* 14½.
503 70 c. reddish brown and pale cinnamon . . 1·25 1·50
504 $1.20, reddish brown and pale cinnamon 2·00 2·50
Designs:—$1.20, Thursday October Christian.

155 Adult Robin and Chicks in Nest

156 Map of Norfolk Island

(Des E. Monks. Litho Leigh-Mardon Ltd, Melbourne)

1990 (3 Dec). *"Birdpex '90" Stamp Exhibition, Christchurch, New Zealand. Scarlet Robin. T* **155** *and similar vert designs. Multicoloured. P* 14½.
505 65 c. Type **155** .. .. 1·00 1·25
506 $1 Hen on branch .. .. 1·50 1·75
507 $1.20, Cock on branch .. .. 1·60 2·00
505/7 .. .. *Set of* 3 3·75 4·50
MS508 70×90 mm. $1 Hen; $1 Cock and hen .. 3·75 4·25

(Des Philatelic Studios. Litho Leigh-Mardon Ltd, Melbourne)

1991 (9 Apr). *Ham Radio Network. T* **156** *and similar vert designs. Multicoloured. P* 14½.
509 43 c. Type **156** .. .. 1·25 70
510 $1 Globe showing Norfolk Island .. 2·75 3·00
511 $1.20, Map of South-west Pacific .. 2·75 4·00
509/11 .. .. *Set of* 3 6·00 7·00

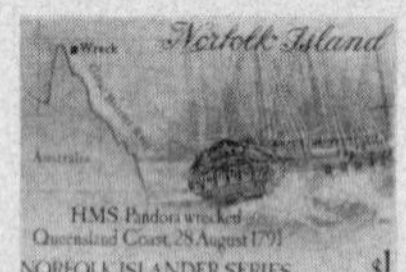

157 Display in *Sirius* Museum

158 H.M.S. *Pandora* wrecked on Great Barrier Reef (1791)

(Des Philatelic Studios. Litho Leigh-Mardon Ltd, Melbourne)

1991 (16 May). *Norfolk Island Museums. T* **157** *and similar multicoloured designs. P* 14½
512 43 c. Type **157** 90 50
513 70 c. 19th-century sitting room, House Museum (*horiz*) .. .. .. 1·75 2·00
514 $1 Carronade, *Sirius* Museum (*horiz*) .. 2·50 2·75
515 $1.20, Reconstructed jug and beaker, Archaeological Museum .. .. 2·50 3·25
512/15 .. .. *Set of* 4 7·00 7·75

(Des Philatelic Studios. Litho Leigh-Mardon, Melbourne)

1991 (2 July). *History of the Norfolk Islanders* (3rd series). *Search for the* Bounty. *T* **158** *and similar horiz design. Multicoloured. P* 13½×14.
516 $1 Type **158** .. .. 2·75 2·50
517 $1.20, H.M.S. *Pandora* leaving bay .. 2·75 3·00

NORFOLK ISLAND 43c
50th ANNIVERSARY—WAR IN THE PACIFIC

159 Hibiscus and Island Scene

160 Tank and Soldier in Jungle

(Des Philatelic Studios. Litho Leigh-Mardon Ltd, Melbourne)

1991 (23 Sept). *Christmas. P* 14½.
518 **159** 38 c. multicoloured 90 45
519 43 c. multicoloured .. .. 1·00 55
520 65 c. multicoloured .. .. 1·50 2·00
521 85 c. multicoloured .. .. 1·75 2·50
518/21 .. .. *Set of* 4 4·75 5·00

(Des Philatelic Studios. Litho Leigh-Mardon Ltd, Melbourne)

1991 (9 Dec). *50th Anniv of Outbreak of Pacific War. T* **160** *and similar horiz designs. Multicoloured. P* 14½.
522 43 c. Type **160** .. .. 1·00 55
523 70 c. Boeing B-17 Flying Fortress on jungle airstrip .. .. 2·00 2·50
524 $1 Warships .. .. 2·50 3·25
522/4 .. .. *Set of* 3 5·00 5·75

161 Coat of Arms

162 Deployment Map

(Des Philatelic Studios. Litho Leigh-Mardon Ltd, Melbourne)

1992 (11 Feb). *500th Anniv of Discovery of America by Columbus. T* **161** *and similar vert designs. Multicoloured. P* 14½.
525 45 c. Type **161** 85 55
526 $1.05, *Santa Maria* .. .. 2·00 2·75
527 $1.20, Columbus and globe .. .. .. 2·50 3·25
525/7 .. .. *Set of* 3 4·75 6·00

(Des Philatelic Studios. Litho Leigh-Mardon Ltd, Melbourne)

1992 (4 May). *50th Anniv of Battle of the Coral Sea. T* **162** *and similar vert designs. Multicoloured. P* 14½.
528 45 c. Type **162** .. .. 1·00 50
529 70 c. H.M.A.S. *Australia* (cruiser) .. .. 1·75 2·25
530 $1.05, U.S.S. *Yorktown* (aircraft carrier) 2·50 3·25
528/30 .. .. *Set of* 3 4·75 5·50

(Des Philatelic Studios. Litho Leigh-Mardon Ltd, Melbourne)

1992 (4 May). *50th Anniv of Battle of Midway. Vert designs as T* **162**. *Multicoloured. P* 14½.
531 45 c. Battle area .. .. 1·00 50
532 70 c. Consolidated PBY-5 Catalina flying boat over task force .. .. 1·75 2·25
533 $1.05, Douglas SBD Dauntless dive bomber and burning Japanese aircraft carrier .. .. 2·50 3·25
531/3 .. .. *Set of* 3 4·75 5·50

(Des Philatelic Studios. Litho Leigh-Mardon Ltd, Melbourne)

1992 (6 Aug). *50th Anniv of Battle of Guadalcanal. Multicoloured designs as T* **162**, *but horiz. P* 14½.
534 45 c. American troops landing .. .. .. 1·00 50
535 70 c. Machine-gun crew .. .. 1·75 2·25
536 $1.05, Map of Pacific with Japanese and American flags .. .. 2·50 3·25
534/6 .. .. *Set of* 3 4·75 5·50

163 Norfolk Pines above Ball Bay

164 Boat Shed and Flaghouses, Kingston

(Des Philatelic Studios. Litho Leigh-Mardon Ltd, Melbourne)

1992 (29 Oct). *Christmas. T* **163** *and similar vert designs. Multicoloured. P* 14½.
537 40 c. Type **163** 70 40
538 45 c. Headstone Creek 75 45
539 75 c. South side of Ball Bay .. .. .. 1·50 2·25
540 $1.20, Rocky Point Reserve .. .. .. 2·00 3·00
537/40 .. .. *Set of* 4 4·50 5·50

(Des Philatelic Studios. Litho Leigh-Mardon Ltd, Melbourne)

1993 (23 Feb). *Tourism. Historic Kingston. T* **164** *and similar horiz designs. Multicoloured. P* 14½.
541 45 c. Type **164** .. .. 80 1·00
a. Horiz strip of 5. Nos. 541/5 .. .. 3·50
542 45 c. Old Military Barracks .. .. .. 80 1·00
543 45 c. All Saints Church .. .. .. 80 1·00
544 45 c. Officers' Quarters .. .. .. 80 1·00
545 45 c. Quality Row .. .. 80 1·00
541/5 .. .. *Set of* 5 3·50 4·50
Nos. 541/5 were printed together, *se-tenant*, in horizontal strips of 5 forming a composite design.

165 Fire Engine

166 Blue Sea Lizard (*Glaucus atlanticus*)

(Des Philatelic Studios, Melbourne. Litho Leigh-Mardon Ltd, Melbourne)

1993 (18 May). *Emergency Services. T* **165** *and similar horiz designs. Multicoloured. P* 14½.
546 45 c. Type **165** .. .. 1·00 60
547 70 c. Cliff rescue squad .. .. .. 1·10 1·75
548 75 c. Ambulance .. .. 1·40 1·90
549 $1.20, Police car .. .. 2·50 3·00
546/9 .. .. *Set of* 4 5·50 6·50

(Des Philatelic Studios. Litho Leigh-Mardon Ltd, Melbourne)

1993 (7 July). *Nudibranchs. T* **166** *and similar horiz designs. Multicoloured. P* 14½.
550 45 c. Type **166** 80 55
551 45 c. Ocellate Nudibranch (*Phyllidia ocellata*) 80 55
552 75 c. *Bornella* sp .. .. 1·50 1·75
553 85 c. *Glossodoris rubroannolata* .. .. 1·75 2·25
554 95 c. *Halgerda willeyi* .. .. 2·00 2·50
555 $1.05, *Ceratosoma amoena* .. .. .. 2·00 3·00
550/5 .. .. *Set of* 6 8·00 9·50

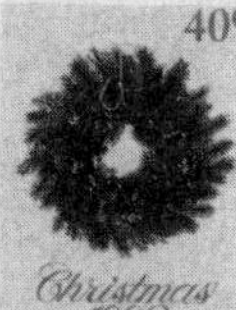

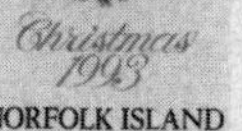

167 Christmas Wreath

168 Maori Stone Clubs

(Des Philatelic Studios. Litho Leigh-Mardon Ltd, Melbourne)

1993 (28 Oct). *Christmas. P* 14½.
556 **167** 40 c. multicoloured 60 45
557 45 c. multicoloured 60 45
558 75 c. multicoloured .. .. 1·00 1·5
559 $1.20, multicoloured .. .. 1·90 2·5
556/9 .. .. *Set of* 4 3·75 4·5

(Des Philatelic Studios. Litho Leigh-Mardon Ltd, Melbourne)

1993 (28 Oct). *Bicentenary of Contact with New Zealand. T* **168** *and similar vert design. Multicoloured. P* 14½.
560 70 c. Type **168** .. .. 1·25 1·5
561 $1.20, First Maori map of New Zealand, 1793 .. .. 2·00 2·50

169 Alvaro de Saavedra, Route Map and *Florida*

170 Sooty Tern

(Des G. Hitch and Philatelic Consultative Services. Lith Leigh-Mardon Ltd, Melbourne)

1994 (8 Feb–26 July). *Pacific Explorers. T* **169** *and simila multicoloured designs. P* 14½.
562 5 c. Vasco Nunez de Balboa, map and *Barbara* (3 May) 40 4
563 10 c. Ferdinand Magellan, map and *Vitoria* (3 May) 40 4
564 20 c. Juan Sebastian del Cano, map and *Vitoria* (3 May) 50 5
565 50 c. Type **169** 75 7
566 70 c. Ruy Lopez de Villalobos, map and *San Juan* .. .. 1·00 1·0
567 75 c. Miguel Lopez de Legaspi, map and *San Lesmes* .. .. 1·00 1·0
568 80 c. Sir Francis Drake, map and *Golden Hind* (26 July) .. .. 1·25 1·2
569 85 c. Alvaro de Mendana, map and *Santiago* (26 July) .. .. 1·25 1·2
570 90 c. Pedro Fernandes de Quiros, map and *San Pedro y Pablo* (26 July) .. .. 1·25 1·2
571 $1 Luis Baez de Torres, map and *San Pedrico* (26 July) .. .. .. 1·40 1·4
572 $2 Abel Tasman, map and *Heemskerk* .. 2·00 2·2
573 $5 William Dampier, map and *Cygnet* (3 May) .. .. 4·25 5·0
562/73 .. .. *Set of* 12 14·00 15·0
MS574 100×80 mm. $1.20, *Golden Hind* (Drake) (32×52 *mm*). P 13 .. .. 1·00 1·1

(Des Philatelic Studios. Litho Leigh-Mardon Ltd, Melbourne)

1994 (17 Aug). *Sea Birds. T* **170** *and similar vert design Multicoloured. P* 14½.
575 45 c. Type **170** .. .. 95 1·0
a. Horiz strip of 5. Nos. 575/9 .. .. 4·25
576 45 c. Red-tailed Tropic Bird .. .. .. 95 1·0
577 45 c. Australian Gannet .. .. .. 95 1·0
578 45 c. Wedge-tailed Shearwater .. .. 95 1·0
579 45 c. Blue-faced Booby .. .. .. 95 1·0
575/9 .. .. *Set of* 5 4·25 4·5
Nos. 575/9 were printed together, *se-tenant*, in horizont strips of 5 throughout the sheet with the backgrounds forming composite design.

171 House and Star

172 Chevrolet, 1926

(Des Olive Gregory. Litho Walsall)

94 (27 Oct). *Christmas. T* **171** *and similar vert designs. Multicoloured. Roul* 9×*imperf**. *Self-adhesive.*
0 45 c. Type **171** 80 55
1 75 c. Figures from stained-glass windows 1·50 2·00
2 $1.20, Rainbow and full-rigged sailing ship 2·50 3·00
0/2 . . . . *Set of* 3 4·25 5·00

*Nos. 580/2 were separated horizontally by roulette and rtically by rotary knife cuts which produce straight edges with o teeth between stamps.

(Litho McPherson's Ptg Group, Mulgrave)

95 (7 Feb). *Vintage Motor Vehicles. T* **172** *and similar horiz designs. Multicoloured. P* 14×14½.
3 45 c. Type **172** 75 55
4 75 c. Ford Model "A", 1928 . . . . 1·25 1·75
5 $1.05, Ford Model "A A/C", 1929 . . 1·60 2·00
6 $1.20, Ford Model "A", 1930 . . . . 1·75 2·25
3/6 . . . . *Set of* 4 4·75 6·00

173 Tail Flukes of Humpback Whale

174 Dot-and-Dash Butterflyfish

)es Mary Butterfield. Litho McPherson's Ptg Group, Mulgrave)

995 (11 May). *Humpback Whale Conservation. T* **173** *and similar multicoloured designs. P* 14½×14 ($1.05) *or* 14×14½ (*others*).
87 45 c. Type **173** . . . . 1·00 55
88 75 c. Mother and calf . . . . . . 1·50 2·00
89 $1.05, Whale breaching (*vert*) . . 1·75 2·50
87/9 . . . . *Set of* 3 3·75 4·50
IS590 107×84 mm. $1.20, Humpback Whale (29×49 *mm*). P 14×14½ . . . . . . 1·60 2·00

(Des Mary Butterfield. Litho Leigh-Mardon Ltd, Melbourne)

995 (15 June). *Butterflyfishes. T* **174** *and similar square designs. Multicoloured. P* 14×14½.
91 5 c. Type **174** 30 50
92 45 c. Blue-spotted Butterflyfish (*Chaetodon plebeius*) 85 50
93 $1.20, Three-belted Butterflyfish (*Chaetodon tricinatus*) . . . . 2·25 2·75
94 $1.50, Thread-finned Butterflyfish (*Chaetodon auriga*) . . . . 2·50 3·00
91/4 . . . . *Set of* 4 5·50 6·00

995 (19 July). *"JAKARTA '95" Stamp Exhibition, Indonesia. No.* **MS**590 *optd* "Selamat Hari Merdeka" *and emblem on sheet margin in gold.*
IS595 107×84 mm. $1.20, Humpback Whale 1·60 2·00

175 International 4×4 Refueller, 1942

176 Servicing Fighter

(Des G. Douran. Litho Southern Colour Print, Dunedin)

995 (8 Aug). *Second World War Vehicles. T* **175** *and similar horiz designs. Multicoloured. P* 14×14½.
96 5 c. Type **175** 30 40
97 45 c. Ford Sedan, 1942 . . . . . . 75 45
98 $1.20, Ford 3 ton tipper, 1942 . . 2·00 2·50
99 $2 D8 caterpillar with scraper . . 3·00 3·50
96/9 . . . . *Set of* 4 5·50 6·25

(Litho Photopress International, Norfolk Island)

995 (1 Sept). *Flower designs as 1960 issues, but with face values in decimal currency. Roul* 7.
)0 5 c. bright rose & dp blue-green (as No. 25) 10 10
a. Booklet pane. No. 600×18 . . . . 1·40
)1 5 c. bright rose-red (as No. 28) . . 10 10
a. Booklet pane. No. 601×18 . . . . 1·40

Nos. 600/1 were only issued in $1.80 stamp booklets ntaining panes of 18 (two blocks of 9 separated by a horizontal itter and with margins all round).

The original printing of Nos. 600a/1a had black inscriptions eneath each pane. These were subsequently changed to deep ue-green (No. 600a) or bright rose-red (No. 601a)

(Des Mary Butterfield (Nos. 602/5). Litho and die-stamped ($10) or litho (others) Southern Colour Print, Dunedin)

1995 (18 Sept). *50th Anniv of End of Second World War in the Pacific. T* **176** *and similar multicoloured designs. P* 12.
602 5 c. Type **176** 40 50
603 45 c. Sgt. Tom Derrick, V.C. (*vert*) . . 70 45
604 75 c. Gen. Douglas MacArthur (*vert*) . . 1·25 1·50
605 $1.05, Girls celebrating victory . . 1·75 2·00
606 $10 Pacific War medals (50×30 *mm*) . . 16·00 18·00
602/6 . . . . *Set of* 5 18·00 20·00

The $10 also includes the "Singapore '95" International stamp exhibition logo.

177 Peace Dove and Anniversary Emblem

178 Skink on Bank

(Des Mary Butterfield. Litho SNP Cambec)

1995 (7 Nov). *Christmas. 50th Anniv of United Nations. T* **177** *and similar vert designs, each including U.N. anniversary emblem. P* 14½×14.
607 45 c. gold and new blue 60 45
608 75 c. gold and bright violet . . . . 1·00 1·25
609 $1.05, gold and bright rose-red . . 1·40 2·00
610 $1.20, gold and light green . . . . 1·60 2·25
607/10 . . . . *Set of* 3 4·25 5·50

Designs:—75 c. Star of Bethlehem; $1.05, Symbolic candles on cake; $1.20, Olive branch.

(Des Doreen McGuiness. Litho Questa)

1996 (6 Feb). *Endangered Species. Skinks and Geckos. T* **178** *and similar horiz designs. Multicoloured. P* 14½×15.
611 5 c. Type **178** 40 45
a. Strip of 4. Nos. 611/14 . . . . 2·00
612 5 c. Gecko on branch 40 45
613 45 c. Skink facing right 70 75
614 45 c. Gecko on flower 70 75
611/14 . . . . *Set of* 4 2·00 2·25

Nos. 611/14 were printed together, *se-tenant*, in horizontal and vertical strips of 4 throughout sheets of 16.

179 Sopwith Pup Biplane and Emblem

(Des B. McCoy and B. Klemke. Litho Southern Colour Print, Dunedin)

1996 (22 Apr). *75th Anniv of Royal Australian Air Force. T* **179** *and similar vert designs showing aircraft. Multicoloured. P* 14.
615 45 c. Type **179** 60 60
616 45 c. Wirraway fighter 60 60
617 75 c. F-111C jet fighter . . . . . . 1·00 1·40
618 85 c. F/A-18 Hornet jet fighter . . . . 1·10 1·50
615/18 . . . . *Set of* 4 3·00 3·50

180 Rat

(Des G. Douran. Litho Southern Colour Print, Dunedin)

1996 (18 May). *Chinese New Year ("Year of the Rat"). Sheet* 100×75 *mm. P* 12.
MS619 **180** $1 black, rosine and brown-ochre 1·25 1·60
a. With "CHINA '96" 9th Asian International Stamp Exhibition logo on bottom margin . . . . . . 1·25 1·60

181 *Naticarlus oncus*

182 Shopping

(Des Mary Butterfield. Litho Southern Colour Print, Dunedin)

1996 (2 July). *Shells. T* **181** *and similar square designs. Multicoloured. P* 14.
620 45 c. Type **181** 70 85
621 45 c. *Janthina janthina* 70 85
622 45 c. *Cypraea caputserpentis* 70 85
623 45 c. *Argonauta nodosa* 70 85
620/3 . . . . *Set of* 4 2·50 3·00

(Des G. Douran. Litho Southern Colour Print, Dunedin)

1996 (17 Sept). *Tourism. T* **182** *and similar horiz designs. Multicoloured. P* 13½×14.
624 45 c. Type **182** 50 50
625 75 c. Celebrating Bounty Day . . . . 1·00 1·00
626 $2.50, Horse riding . . . . . . 3·75 4·25
627 $3.70, Unloading lighter . . . . 4·50 5·25
624/7 . . . . *Set of* 4 8·75 10·00

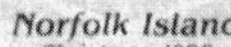

183 The Nativity

184 Coat of Arms

(Des Mary Duke. Litho Questa)

1996 (5 Nov). *Christmas. T* **183** *and similar vert designs. Multicoloured. P* 14½.
628 45 c. Type **183** 50 50
629 45 c. Star and boat sheds 50 50
630 75 c. Star, bungalow and ox . . . . 90 1·50
631 85 c. Star, fruit, flowers and ox . . . . 1·10 1·75
628/31 . . . . *Set of* 4 2·75 3·75

(Litho Photopress International, Norfolk Island)

1997 (22 Jan). *T* **184** *and similar vert design. Roul* 7.
632 **184** 5 c. turquoise-blue and pale lemon . . 20 30
a. Booklet pane of 10 with margins all round . . . . 1·75
633 – 5 c. orange-brown 20 30
a. Booklet pane of 10 with margins all round . . . . 1·75

Design:—No. 633, Great Seal of Norfolk Island.

Nos. 632/3 were only issued in $2 stamp booklets.

185 Calf

186 *Cepora perimale*

(Des G. Douran. Litho Southern Colour Print, Dunedin)

1997 (11 Feb). *Beef Cattle. Sheet* 67×67 *mm. P* 13½×13.
MS634 **185** $1.20, multicoloured . . . . 1·40 1·75

1997 (12 Feb). *"HONG KONG '97" International Stamp Exhibition. As No.* **MS**634, *but with exhibition emblem on sheet margin.*
MS635 67×67 mm. **185** $1.20, multicoloured 1·40 1·60

(Des Tracey Yager. Litho and gold die-stamped Southern Colour Print, Dunedin)

1997 (28 Mar). *Butterflies. T* **186** *and similar horiz designs. Multicoloured. P* 14½.
636 75 c. Type **186** . . . . 1·00 85
637 90 c. *Danaus chrysippus* . . . . . . 1·25 1·50
638 $1 *Danaus hamata* . . . . . . 1·40 1·50
639 $1.20, *Danaus plexippus* . . . . 1·50 2·00
636/9 . . . . *Set of* 4 4·50 5·25

187 Dusky Dolphins

(Des Mary Butterfield. Litho Southern Colour Print, Dunedin)

1997 (29 May). *Dolphins. T* **187** *and similar horiz designs. Multicoloured. P* 14.
640 45 c. Type **187** 60 50
641 75 c. Common dolphin and calf . . . . 80 1·00
MS642 106×80 mm. $1.05, Dolphin . . . . 1·10 1·25

1997 (29 May). *"Pacific '97" International Stamp Exhibition, San Francisco. As No.* **MS**642, *but with exhibition emblem on sheet margin.*
MS643 106×80 mm. $1.05, Dolphin . . . . 1·10 1·25

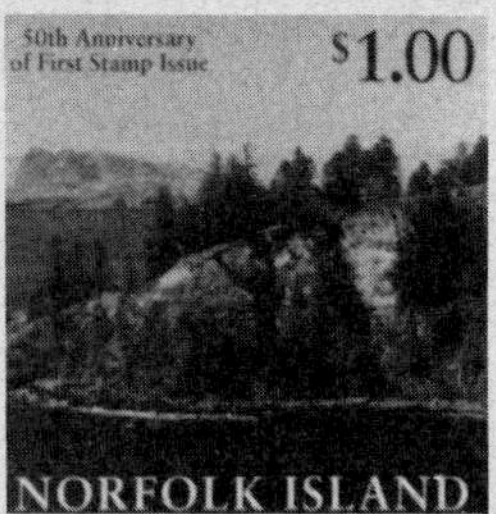

188 Ball Bay, Norfolk Island

(Litho Southern Colour Print, Dunedin)

1997 (30 June). *50th Anniv of Norfolk Island Stamps. T* **188** *and similar multicoloured designs. P* 12.
644 $1 Type **188** . . . . 1·50 2·00
a. Horiz pair. Nos. 644/5 . . . . . . 3·50 4·25
645 $1.50, 1947 2d. stamp . . . . . . 2·00 2·25
646 $8 Ball Bay and 1947 2s. yellow-bistre stamp (90×45 *mm*) . . . . . . 10·00 12·00
644/6 . . . . *Set of* 3 12·00 14·50
Nos. 644/5 were printed together, *se-tenant*, in horizontal pairs with the backgrounds forming a composite design.

(Des N. Shewring (No. **MS**651), D. Miller (others). Litho Questa)

1997 (12 Aug). *Golden Wedding of Queen Elizabeth and Prince Philip. Multicoloured designs as T* **173** *of Ascension. P* 14½×14.
647 20 c. Queen Elizabeth 30 40
a. Horiz pair. Nos. 647/8 . . . . 60 80
648 25 c. Prince Philip in carriage-driving trials 30 40
649 25 c. Prince Philip 30 40
a. Horiz pair. Nos. 649/50 . . . . 90 1·00
650 50 c. Queen in phaeton at Trooping the Colour 60 60
647/50 . . . . *Set of* 4 1·40 1·60
MS651 110×70 mm. $1.50, Queen Elizabeth and Prince Philip in landau (*horiz*). P 14×14½ . . 1·75 1·90
Nos. 647/8 and 649/50 were each printed together, *se-tenant*, in horizontal pairs throughout the sheets with the backgrounds forming composite designs.

189 Royal Yacht *Britannia* leaving Hong Kong

190 Christmas Tree

1997 (16 Sept). *Return of Hong Kong to China. Sheet* 126×91 *mm. Litho. P* 14.
MS652 **189** 45 c. multicoloured 40 45
No. **MS**652 is inscribed "Brittania" in error

(Des Sue Wickison. Litho Southern Colour Print, Dunedin)

1997 (4 Nov). *Annual Festivals. T* **190** *and similar vert designs. Multicoloured. P* 13½.
653 45 c. Type **190** 50 45
654 75 c. Fireworks (New Year's Eve) . . . . 80 1·00
655 $1.20, Rose (Valentine's Day) . . . . 1·25 1·50
653/5 . . . . *Set of* 3 2·25 2·75

191 Oriental Pearl T.V. Tower, Shanghai

192 Tiger Mask

(Litho Questa)

1997 (18 Nov). *"Shanghai '97" International Stamp and Coin Exhibition, Shanghai. Sheet* 103×138 *mm. P* 14½.
MS656 **191** 45 c. multicoloured 40 45

(Des Ren Yu. Litho Southern Colour Print, Dunedin)

1998 (12 Feb). *Chinese New Year ("Year of the Tiger"). Sheet* 75×95 *mm. P* 12.
MS657 **192** 45 c. multicoloured 40 45

193 "Pepper"

194 Entrance to Pentagonal Gaol

(Des Mary Butterfield. Litho Southern Colour Print, Dunedin)

1998 (26 Feb). *Cats. T* **193** *and similar vert designs. Multicoloured. P* 14½.
658 45 c. Type **193** 55 50
659 45 c. "Tabitha" at window 55 50
660 75 c. "Midnight" 75 90
661 $1.20, "Rainbow" with flower pot . . 1·10 1·40
658/61 . . . . *Set of* 4 2·75 3·00

(Des B. Hilder. Litho Photopress International, Norfolk Island)

1998 (27 Feb). *T* **194** *and similar horiz design. Roul* 7.
662 **194** 5 c. black and azure 10 15
a. Booklet pane of 10 with margins all round . . . . 1·00
663 – 5 c. black and turquoise-green . . 10 15
a. Booklet pane of 10 with margins all round . . . . 1·00
Design:—No. 663, Ruined First Settlement cottage.
Nos. 662/3 were only issued in $2 stamp booklets.

(Des D. Miller. Litho Questa)

1998 (28 Apr). *Diana, Princess of Wales Commemoration. Vert designs as T* **177** *of Ascension. Multicoloured. P* 14½×14.
664 45 c. Princess Diana with bouquet, 1991 . . 40 40
MS665 145×70 mm. 45 c. Wearing blue and white dress, 1989; 45 c. Wearing pearl earrings, 1990; 45 c. No. 664; 45 c. Wearing striped dress (*sold at* $1.80 + 45 c. *charity premium*) . . 1·40 1·50

195 Tweed Trousers

196 Hammer Throwing

(Des Mary Butterfield. Litho Questa)

1998 (5 May–29 June). *Reef Fishes. T* **195** *and similar multicoloured designs. P* 14½.
666 10 c. Type **195** 10 15
667 20 c. Conspicuous Angelfish (29 June) . . 15 20
668 30 c. Moon Wrasse 25 30
669 45 c. Wide-striped Clownfish (29 June) . . 35 40
670 50 c. Raccoon Butterflyfish 40 45
671 70 c. Artooti (juvenile) (29 June) 55 60
672 75 c. Splendid Hawkfish 55 60
673 85 c. Scorpion Fish (29 June) 65 70
674 90 c. Orange Fairy Basslet 70 75
675 $1 Sweetlips (29 June) 75 80
676 $3 Moorish Idol (29 June) . . . . . . 2·25 2·40
677 $4 Gold-ribbon Soapfish . . . . . . 2·25 2·40
666/77 . . . . *Set of* 12 8·75 9·75
MS678 110×85 mm. $1.20, Shark (29×39 *mm*). P 14×14½ 90 95
Nos. 672 and 675 are incorrectly inscribed "Splendid Hawkefish" and "Sweetlip".

(Des Tracey Yager. Litho Southern Colour Print, Dunedin)

1998 (23 July). *16th Commonwealth Games, Kuala Lumpur. T* **196** *and similar designs. P* 14½.
679 75 c. orange-vermilion and black 75 80
680 95 c. bluish violet and black . . . . 90 1·00
681 $1.05, deep mauve and black . . . . 95 1·10
679/81 . . . . *Set of* 3 2·40 2·50
MS682 80×100 mm. 85 c. brt blue-green & black 90 95
Designs: *Horiz*—95 c. Trap shooting. *Vert*—85 c. Flag bearer; $1.05, Lawn bowls.

197 *Norfolk* (sloop)

(Des Mary Butterfield. Litho Cartor)

1998 (24 Sept). *Bicentenary of the Circumnavigation of Tasmania by George Bass and Matthew Flinders. P* 13.
683 **197** 45 c. multicoloured 40 4
MS684 101×69 mm. **197** $1.20, multicoloured 90 9

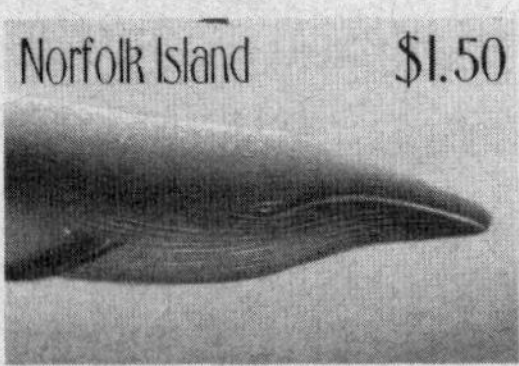

198 Blue Whale

(Des Mary Butterfield. Litho Questa)

1998 (23 Oct). *Whales of the Southern Oceans (joint issue wit. Namibia and South Africa). Sheet* 103×70 *mm. P* 13½×14.
MS685 **198** $1.50, multicoloured . . . . 1·10 1·2

199 "Peace on Earth"

(Des Mary Butterfield. Litho Cartor)

1998 (10 Nov). *Christmas. T* **199** *and similar horiz design Multicoloured. P* 13×13½.
686 45 c. Type **199** 35 4
687 75 c. "Joy to the World" . . . . . . 55 (
688 $1.05, "A Season of Love" 80 8
689 $1.20, "Light of the World" 90 9
686/9 . . . . *Set of* 4 2·50 2·

STAMP BOOKLETS

A $4.10 booklet containing No. 465 in block of ten was epared in 1989, but not issued.

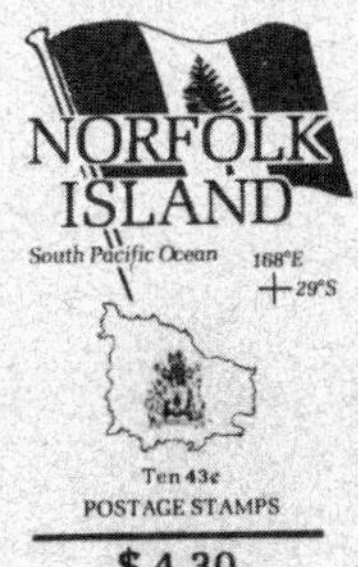

B 1

991 (9 Apr). *Ham Radio Network. Emerald on cinnamon cover as Type* B **1**. *Stamps attached by selvedge.*
B1 $4.30, booklet containing 43 c. (No. 509) in block of 10 .. .. 8·00

B 2

991 (Dec). *Ships. Emerald on bluish grey* (*No.* SB2) *or cinnamon* (*No.* SB3) *covers as Type* B **2**. *Stamps attached by selvedge.*
B2 $4.50, booklet containing 45 c. (No. 485) in block of 10 .. .. 6·50
B3 $7 booklet containing 70 c. (No. 488) in block of 10 7·00

B 3

993 (23 Feb). *Tourism. Emerald on white cover as Type* B **3**. *Stamps attached by selvedge.*
B4 $4.50, booklet containing five different 45 c. (Nos. 541/5) in block of 10 .. .. 7·00

993 (20 Aug). *Nudibranchs. Emerald on white cover as Type* B **3** *showing illustration of No.* 550. *Stamps attached by selvedge.*
B5 $4.50, booklet containing 45 c. (No. 550) in block of 10 .. .. 6·50

994 (17 Aug). *Sea Birds. Emerald on white cover as Type* B **3**, *but showing illustration of No.* 577. *Stamps attached by selvedge.*
B6 $4.50, booklet containing horiz gutter strip of ten 45 c. (No. 575a×2) .. .. 6·00

B 4
(*Illustration reduced. Actual size* 95×130 *mm*)

995 (1 Sept). *Flowers. Rose and blue green cover as Type* B **4**. *Stamps attached by selvedge.*
B7 $1.80, booklet containing two different panes of eighteen 5 c. (Nos. 600a/1a) .. .. 2·75

No. SB7 also exists with either the "Singapore '95" ternational Stamp Exhibition or Australian Stamp Dealers' ssociation logos shown on the front cover at bottom left.

B **5**
(*Illustration reduced. Actual size,* 170×80 *mm*)

1997 (22 Jan). *Multicoloured cover as Type* B **5**. *Stamps attached by selvedge.*
SB8 $2 booklet containing four panes of ten 5 c. (Nos 632a/3a, each × 2) .. .. 6·00

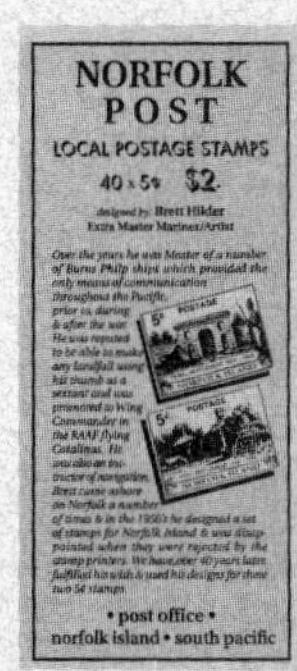

B **6**
(*Illustration reduced. Actual size* 87×177 *mm*)

1998 (27 Feb). *Black and turquoise-green cover as Type* B **6**. *Stamps attached by selvedge.*
SB9 $2 booklet containing four panes of ten 5 c. (Nos. 662a/3a, each × 2) .. .. 1·50

Baghdad
see Iraq

Bahamas

The British Post Office at Nassau was established during the early days of the West Indies packet system, and was certainly operating by 1733. The first known local postmark dates from 1802.

The crowned-circle handstamp No. CC1 was issued in 1846 and was generally replaced, for the public mails, by various stamps of Great Britain in 1858.

Local mail deliveries were rudimentary until 1859 when Nos. 1/2 were issued by the colonial authorities for interisland mails. Examples used for this purpose are usually cancelled in manuscript or with a "27" postmark. The "local" 1d. stamp became valid for overseas mails in May, 1860, when the colonial authorities took over this service from the British G.P.O.

For illustrations of the handstamp and postmark types see BRITISH POST OFFICES ABROAD notes, following GREAT BRITAIN.

NASSAU

CROWNED-CIRCLE HANDSTAMPS

CC1 CC **2** BAHAMAS (Nassau) (18.5.1846) (R.)
Price on cover £1800

No. CC1 was later struck in black and used as an Offical Paid mark between July 1899 and September 1935. Handstamps as Types CC 1 and CC 3 (only three known) struck in black were used for the same purpose from 1933 until 1953; but it is believed that these were never employed during the pre-stamp period. *Price on cover from* £50.

Stamps of GREAT BRITAIN *cancelled* "A 05" *as Type* **2**.

1858 *to* **1860.**

Z1	1d. rose-red (1857), *perf* 14 ..	£1600
Z2	2d. blue (1858) (Plate Nos. 7, 8)	£1300
Z3	4d. rose (1857)	£450
Z4	6d. lilac (1856)	£350
Z5	1s. green (1856)	£2250

PRICES FOR STAMPS ON COVER TO 1945

Nos. 1/2	—
Nos. 3/6	*from* × 6
No. 7	—
Nos. 8/19*a*	*from* × 6
Nos. 20/5	*from* × 10
Nos. 26/31	*from* × 4
No. 33	*from* × 20
Nos. 35/44*a*	*from* × 5
No. 45	*from* × 20
Nos. 47/57	*from* × 4
Nos. 58/89	*from* × 2
Nos. 90/130	*from* × 3
Nos. 131/2	*from* × 10
Nos. 141/5	*from* × 4
Nos. 146/8	*from* × 6
Nos. 149/57	*from* × 3
Nos. 158/60	*from* × 4
No. 161	*from* × 8
Nos. 162/75	*from* × 5
Nos. S1/3	*from* × 20

CROWN COLONY

1

2

3

(Eng and recess P.B.)

1859 (10 June). *No wmk. Imperf. (a) Thick paper.*

No.	Type	Description	Unused	Used
1	1	1d. reddish lake	£4500	£2250
		a. Brown-lake	£4500	£2250
		(b) Thin paper		
2	1	1d. dull lake	50·00	£1500

The handmade paper used for Nos. 1/*a* varies in thickness. Prices quoted for these stamps are for examples on thick paper. Unused remainders in brown-lake on thinner paper are worth about £250.

Collectors are warned against false postmarks upon the remainder stamps of 1d., imperf, on thin paper.

1860 (Oct). *No wmk. Clean-cut perf* 14 *to* 16.

No.	Type	Description	Unused	Used
3	1	1d. lake	£2500	£650

1861 (June)–**62.** *No wmk. (a) Rough perf* 14 *to* 16

No.	Type	Description	Unused	Used
4	1	1d. lake	£750	£300
5	2	4d. dull rose (Dec, 1861)	£1400	£375
		a. Imperf between (pair)	£20000	
6		6d. grey-lilac (Dec, 1861)	£2750	£450
		a. Pale dull lilac	£2750	£475

(b) P 11 *to* 12½ (1862)

No.	Type	Description	Unused	Used
7	1	1d. lake	£2000	

No. 7 was a perforation trial on a new machine at Perkins, Bacon. It was not sent out to the Colony and is also known part perforated.

(Recess D.L.R.)

1862. *No wmk.* (a) P* 11½, 12.

No.	Type	Description	Unused	Used
8	1	1d. carmine-lake	£850	£170
9		1d. lake	£950	£180
10	2	4d. dull rose	£3250	£400
11		6d. lavender-grey	£5500	£400
		(b) P 11½, 12, compound with 11		
12	1	1d. carmine-lake	£1900	£850
13		1d. lake	£1900	£850
14	2	4d. dull rose	£12000	£1800
15		6d. lavender-grey	£13000	£1800
		(c) P 13		
16	1	1d. lake	£750	£160
17		1d. brown-lake	£700	£130
18	2	4d. dull rose	£2500	£375
19		6d. lavender-grey	£3000	£425
		a. Lilac	£2500	£500

*Stamps exist with part of papermaker's sheet wmk ("T. H. SAUNDERS" and date).

1863–77. *Wmk Crown CC (a) P* 12½

No.	Type	Description	Unused	Used
20	1	1d. brown-lake	90·00	55·00
		w. Wmk inverted		
		x. Wmk reversed		
21		1d. carmine-lake	£100	60·00
		w. Wmk inverted	£140	
		x. Wmk reversed	£110	60·00
22		1d. carmine-lake (aniline)	£100	60·00
		w. Wmk inverted	£150	
		x. Wmk reversed		
23		1d. rose-red	60·00	40·00
		w. Wmk inverted	£100	
		x. Wmk reversed	60·00	40·00
24		1d. red	60·00	40·00
		w. Wmk inverted		
		x. Wmk reversed		
		y. Wmk inverted and reversed	£150	
25		1d. vermilion	65·00	40·00
		w. Wmk inverted	£100	
		x. Wmk reversed	65·00	40·00
26	2	4d. dull rose	—	60·00
		w. Wmk inverted	—	£150
		x. Wmk reversed	£375	60·00
27		4d. bright rose	£250	60·00
		w. Wmk inverted	—	£150
		x. Wmk reversed		
28		4d. brownish rose	—	80·00
		w. Wmk inverted		
		x. Wmk reversed	£400	80·00
29		6d. rose-lilac	£5500	£1800
		w. Wmk inverted	£5500	
30		6d. lilac (*shades*)	£325	60·00
		w. Wmk inverted		
		x. Wmk reversed		
31		6d. deep violet	£160	60·00
		w. Wmk inverted	—	£100
		x. Wmk reversed	£180	65·00
32		6d. violet (aniline)	£250	90·00
		(b) P 14		
33	1	1d. scarlet-vermilion (1877)	40·00	15·00
		x. Wmk reversed	40·00	20·00
34		1d. scarlet (or scarlet-vermilion) (aniline)	£1000	
		x. Wmk reversed		
35	2	4d. bright rose (1876)	£350	40·00
		w. Wmk inverted		
36		4d. dull rose	£1500	40·00
		w. Wmk inverted		
37		4d. rose-lake	£375	40·00

No. 29 is believed to be the shade of the first printing only and should not be confused with other lilac shades of the 6d.

No. 34 is not known postally used, although manuscript fiscal cancellations on this shade do exist.

(Typo D.L.R.)

1863–80. *Wmk Crown CC. (a) P* 12½.

No.	Type	Description	Unused	Used
38	3	1s. green (1865)	£2500	£300
		(b) P 14		
39	3	1s. dark green	£100	35·00
		aw. Wmk inverted		
39*b*		1s. green (*thick paper*) (1880)	7·50	7·00
		bw. Wmk inverted	—	£150

1882 (Mar). *Wmk Crown CA. (a) P* 12.

No.	Type	Description	Unused	Used
40	1	1d. scarlet-vermilion	45·00	12·00
		x. Wmk reversed		
41	2	4d. rose	£550	45·00
		(b) P 14		
42	1	1d. scarlet-vermilion	£375	55·00
		x. Wmk reversed		
43	2	4d. rose	£750	60·00
		x. Wmk reversed		

1882 (Mar)–**98.** *Wmk Crown CA. P* 14.

No.	Type	Description	Unused	Used
44	3	1s. green	30·00	14·00
44*a*		1s. blue-green (1898)	35·00	21·00

FOURPENCE
(4)

5

1883. *No.* 30 *surch with T* **4**.

No.	Type	Description	Unused	Used
45	2	4d. on 6d. deep violet	£550	£40
		a. Surch inverted	£7500	£450
		x. Wmk reversed	£550	£40

Type **4** was applied by handstamp and occurs in vario positions.

Caution is needed in buying Nos. 45 and 45a.

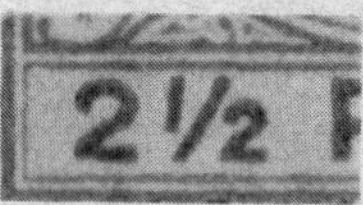

Sloping "2" (R. 10/6)

Malformed "E"

(Typo D.L.R.)

1884–90. *Wmk Crown CA. P* 14.

No.	Type	Description	Unused	Used
47	5	1d. pale rose	50·00	11·0
48		1d. carmine-rose	6·00	2·0
49		1d. bright carmine (aniline)	2·75	6·5
50		2½d. dull blue (1888)	55·00	17·0
51		2½d. blue	40·00	7·5
		a. Sloping "2"	£400	£12
52		2½d. ultramarine	9·00	2·0
		a. Sloping "2"	£130	70·0
		w. Wmk inverted	£130	70·0
53		4d. deep yellow	9·00	4·0
54		6d. mauve (1890)	4·50	26·0
		a. Malformed "E" (R. 6/6)	£160	£32
56		5s. sage-green	65·00	75·0
57		£1 Venetian red	£275	£22
47/57		*Set of* 6	£325	£30
50 & 54 Optd "Specimen"		*Set of* 2	£130	

Examples of Nos. 54/7 are known showing a forged Baham postmark dated "AU 29 94".

6 Queen's Staircase, Nassau

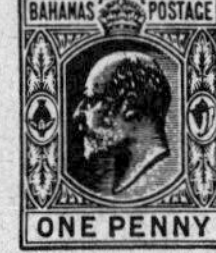

7

8

(Recess D.L.R.)

1901 (23 Sept)–**03.** *Wmk Crown CC. P* 14.

No.	Type	Description	Unused	Used
58	6	1d. black and red	6·00	2·7
		w. Wmk inverted	75·00	
59		5d. black and orange (1.03)	8·00	45·0
		y. Wmk inverted and reversed	75·00	£12
60		2s. black and blue (1.03)	25·00	48·0
61		3s. black and green (1.03)	29·00	55·0
		w. Wmk inverted		
		y. Wmk inverted and reversed	£100	£11
58/61		*Set of* 4	60·00	£13
58/61 Optd "Specimen"		*Set of* 4	£120	

For stamps in this design, but with Mult Crown CA or Mu Script CA watermarks see Nos 75/80 and 111/14.

(Typo D.L.R.)

1902 (18 Dec)–**10.** *Wmk Crown CA. P* 14.

No.	Type	Description	Unused	Used
62	7	1d. carmine	1·50	2·
63		2½d. ultramarine	6·50	1·
64		4d. orange	14·00	48·
65		4d. deep yellow (3.10)	18·00	60·
66		6d. brown	3·50	16·
		a. Malformed "E" (R.6/6)	£130	£1
67		1s. grey-black and carmine	18·00	48·
68		1s. brownish grey and carmine (6.07)	19·00	48·
69		5s. dull purple and blue	55·00	75·
70		£1 green and black	£250	£3
62/70		*Set of* 7	£300	£4
62/70 Optd "Specimen"		*Set of* 7	£250	

Examples of most values are known showing a forged Nassa postmark dated "2 MAR 10".

1906 (Apr)–**11.** *Wmk Mult Crown CA. P* 14.

No.	Type	Description	Unused	Used
71	7	½d. pale green (5.06) (Optd S. £50)	4·50	2·0
72		1d. carmine-rose	22·00	1·
73		2½d. ultramarine (4.07)	22·00	25·0
		w. Wmk inverted	90·00	90·0
74		6d. bistre-brown (8.11)	17·00	48·0
		a. Malformed "E" (R. 6/6)	£275	£47
71/4		*Set of* 4	60·00	70·0

1911 (Feb)–**19.** *Wmk Mult Crown CA. P* 14.

No.	Type	Description	Unused	Used
75	6	1d. black and red	14·00	2·
		a. Grey-black and scarlet (1916)	4·00	2·
		b. Grey-black & deep carmine-red (1919)	4·75	4·
76		3d. purple/*yellow* (*thin paper*) (18.5.17)	3·75	20·
		a. Reddish purple/buff (*thick paper*) (1.19)	4·50	4·
77		3d. black and brown (23.3.19)	1·50	2·
		w. Wmk inverted		
78		5d. black and mauve (18.5.17)	2·75	5·
79		2s. black and blue (11.16)	26·00	45·
		w. Wmk inverted		
80		3s. black and green (8.17)	48·00	50·
		w. Wmk inverted	£110	£1
		y. Wmk inverted and reversed	£110	£1
75/80		*Set of* 6	75·00	£1
76/8 Optd "Specimen"		*Set of* 3	£100	

(Typo D.L.R.)

12–19. *Wmk Mult Crown CA. Chalk-surfaced paper* (1s. *to* £1). *P* 14.
8 ½d. green .. .. 80 6·50
a. *Yellow-green* .. .. 2·25 8·50
1d. carmine (aniline) .. .. 2·75 30
a. *Deep rose* .. .. 7·00 2·00
b. *Rose* .. .. 11·00 2·25
w. Wmk inverted .. .. — 60·00
2d. grey (1919) .. .. 2·25 3·00
2½d. ultramarine .. .. 4·50 17·00
a. *Deep dull blue* .. .. 14·00 27·00
4d. orange-yellow .. .. 5·50 18·00
a. *Yellow* .. .. 2·25 11·00
6d. bistre-brown .. .. 1·75 4·00
a. Malformed "E" (R. 6/6) .. .. 75·00 £100
1s. grey-black and carmine .. .. 1·75 8·50
a. *Jet-black and carmine* .. .. 14·00 22·00
5s. dull purple and blue .. .. 38·00 60·00
a. *Pale dull purple and deep blue* .. 50·00 65·00
£1 dull green and black £150 £275
a. *Green and black* £190 £300
/9 .. .. .. *Set of* 9 £170 £350
/9 Optd "Specimen" .. *Set of* 9 £325

1.1.17. (9) WAR TAX (10)

17 (18 May). *No. 75b optd with T* 9 *in red by D.L.R.*
6 1d. grey-black and deep carmine-red (Optd S. £60) .. .. .. 40 1·60
a. Long stroke to "7" (R.4/6) .. .. 40·00 75·00
It was originally intended to issue No. 90 on 1 January 1917, t the stamps were not received in the Bahamas until May. alf the proceeds from their sale were donated to the British ed Cross Society.

18 (21 Feb–10 July). *Nos.* 75/6, 81/2 *and* 87 *optd at Nassau with T* 10.
8 ½d. green .. .. 8·50 35·00
a. Opt double £1300 £1300
b. Opt inverted £1400
1d. carmine (aniline) 80 50
a. Opt double £1400 £1400
b. Opt inverted £1400 £1400
w. Wmk inverted £150
x. Wmk reversed £150
6 1d. black and red (10 July) .. .. 3·50 3·25
a. Opt double, one inverted £800
b. Opt double £1600 £1700
c. Opt inverted £1400 £1500
x. Wmk reversed .. .. ..
3d. purple/*yellow* (*thin paper*) .. .. 2·25 2·25
a. Opt double £1300 £1400
b. Opt inverted £1000 £1100
8 1s. grey-black and carmine .. .. 85·00 £120
a. Opt double £3000
/5 .. .. .. *Set of* 5 90·00 £140
No. 93 was only on sale for ten days.

WAR TAX (11) WAR TAX (12) WAR CHARITY 3.6.18. (13)

18 (1 June–20 July). *Optd by D.L.R. in London with T* 11 *or* 12 (3*d*).
8 ½d. green .. .. 1·50 1·60
w. Wmk inverted .. .. ..
x. Wmk reversed .. .. ..
1d. carmine 55 35
a. Wmk sideways £350
w. Wmk inverted £200
y. Wmk inverted and reversed £200
6 3d. purple/*yellow* (20 July) .. .. 50 1·50
w. Wmk inverted .. .. .. 70·00
8 1s. grey-black and carmine (R.) .. 7·50 2·75
/9 .. .. .. *Set of* 4 9·00 5·50
/9 Optd "Specimen" .. *Set of* 4 £130

919 (21 Mar). *No. 77 optd with T* 12 *by D.L.R.*
0 6 3d. black and brown (Optd S. £45) .. 45 4·00
a. "C" and "A" missing from wmk .. £1000
w. Wmk inverted .. .. .. 50·00
No. 100a shows the "C" omitted from one impression and the " missing from the next one to the right (as seen from the ont of the stamp). The "C" is badly distorted in the second atermark.

919 (1 Jan). *No. 75b optd with T* 13 *by D.L.R.*
1 6 1d. grey-black and deep carmine-red (R.) (Optd S. £50) .. .. .. 30 2·50
a. Opt double £1400
w. Wmk inverted .. .. .. 50·00
x. Wmk reversed .. .. .. 50·00
y. Wmk inverted and reversed .. .. 75·00
The date is that originally fixed for the issue of the stamp. The ar 1918 was also the bicentenary of the appointment of the first oyal governor.

WAR TAX (14) WAR TAX (15)

1919 (14 July). (*a*) *Optd with T* 14 *by D.L.R.*
102 8 ½d. green (R.) .. .. 30 1·25
103 1d. carmine .. .. 1·00 1·50
104 1s. grey-black and carmine (R.) .. 10·00 26·00

(*b*) *No. 77 optd with T* 15
105 6 3d. black and brown .. .. .. 55 6·00
w. Wmk inverted .. .. .. 50·00
x. Wmk reversed .. .. .. 50·00
y. Wmk inverted and reversed .. .. 50·00
102/5 .. .. .. *Set of* 4 10·50 32·00
102/5 Optd "Specimen" .. *Set of* 4 £120

16

17 Great Seal of the Bahamas.

(Recess D.L.R.)

1920 (1 Mar). *Peace Celebration. Wmk Mult Crown CA* (*sideways**). *P* 14.
106 16 ½d. green .. .. 1·00 4·50
x. Wmk sideways reversed £250 £250
107 1d. carmine .. .. 2·75 90
x. Wmk sideways reversed £300
y. Wmk Crown to right of CA and reversed .. .. ..
108 2d. slate-grey .. .. 2·75 7·00
a. "C" of "CA" missing from wmk .. £750
109 3d. deep brown .. .. 2·75 9·00
w. Wmk Crown to right of CA ..
110 1s. deep myrtle-green .. .. 11·00 32·00
a. Substituted crown in wmk .. £500
x. Wmk sideways reversed £350
106/10 .. .. .. *Set of* 5 18·00 48·00
106/10 Optd "Specimen" .. *Set of* 5 £150
*The normal sideways watermark shows Crown to left of CA, *as seen from the back of the stamp.*
For illustration of the substituted watermark crown see Catalogue Introduction.

1921 (29 Mar)–29. *Wmk Script CA. P* 14.
111 6 1d. grey and rose-red .. .. .. 80 1·00
112 5d. black and purple (8.29) .. .. 3·75 35·00
113 2s. black and blue (11.22) .. .. 15·00 22·00
114 3s. black and green (9.24) .. .. 38·00 60·00
111/14 .. .. .. *Set of* 4 50·00 £110
111/14 Optd/Perf "Specimen" .. *Set of* 4 £160

F PENN

Elongated "E" (left pane R. 9/6)

1921 (8 Sept)–37. *Wmk Mult Script CA. Chalk-surfaced paper* (3*d.*, 1*s.*, 5*s.*, £1). *P* 14.
115 8 ½d. green (1924) 45 40
a. Elongated "E" .. .. .. 24·00
116 1d. carmine .. .. 1·00 15
117 1½d. brown-red (1934) .. .. .. 2·00 1·00
118 2d. grey (1927) .. .. 95 2·75
119 2½d. ultramarine (1922) .. .. .. 80 2·75
120 3d. purple/*pale yellow* (1931) .. .. 5·50 16·00
a. *Purple/orange-yellow* (1937) .. .. 5·50 15·00
121 4d. orange-yellow (1924) .. .. 1·00 5·00
122 6d. bistre-brown (1922) .. .. .. 70 1·25
a. Malformed "E" (R.6/6) .. .. 70·00 £100
123 1s. black and carmine (1926) .. .. 2·50 5·50
124 5s dull purple and blue (1924) .. .. 30·00 55·00
125 £1 green and black (1926) £160 £300
115/25 .. .. .. *Set of* 11 £180 £350
115/25 Optd/Perf "Specimen" .. *Set of* 11 £375

(Recess B. W.)

1930 (2 Jan). *Tercentenary of Colony. Wmk Mult Script CA. P* 12.
126 17 1d. black and scarlet .. .. .. 2·00 2·75
127 3d. black and deep brown .. .. 3·75 14·00
128 5d. black and deep purple .. .. 3·75 14·00
129 2s. black and deep blue .. .. 18·00 42·00
130 3s. black and green .. .. .. 40·00 75·00
126/30 .. .. .. *Set of* 5 60·00 £130
126/30 Perf "Specimen" .. *Set of* 5 £150

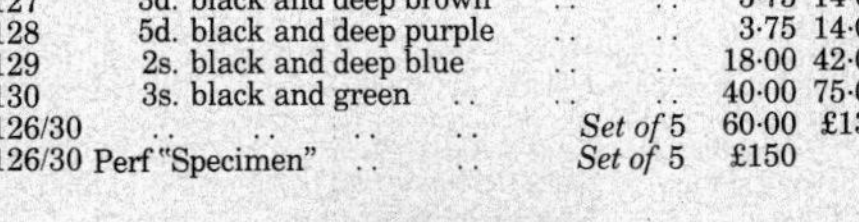

18

(Recess B.W.)

1931 (14 July)–46. *Wmk Mult Script CA. P* 12.
131 18 2s. slate-purple and deep ultramarine .. 20·00 24·00
a. *Slate-purple and indigo* (9.42) .. 60·00 38·00
b. *Brownish black and indigo* (13.4.43) 5·50 2·50
c. *Brownish black and steel-blue* (6.44) 9·00 1·25
132 3s. slate-purple and myrtle-green .. 28·00 24·00
a. *Brownish black and green* (13.4.43) 6·50 2·00
b. *Brownish blk & myrtle-grn* (1.10.46) 5·00 2·00
131/2 Perf "Specimen" .. *Set of* 2 70·00
Most of the stamps from the September 1942 printing (No. 131*a* and further stocks of the 3s. similar to No. 132) were used for the 1942 "LANDFALL" overprints

1935 (6 May). *Silver Jubilee. As Nos.* 91/4 *of Antigua. P* 13½ × 14.
141 1½d. deep blue and carmine.. .. .. 1·00 2·25
h. Dot by flagstaff.. .. .. .. 70·00
i. Dash by turret .. .. 95·00
142 2½d. brown and deep blue .. .. .. 4·50 7·00
f. Diagonal line by turret £100
g. Dot to left of chapel £130
143 6d. light blue and olive-green .. .. 7·00 10·00
g. Dot to left of chapel £170
144 1s. slate and purple .. .. .. 7·00 8·00
h. Dot by flagstaff.. .. .. .. £180
141/4 .. .. .. *Set of* 4 17·00 24·00
141/4 Perf "Specimen" .. *Set of* 4 90·00
For illustrations of plate varieties see Catalogue Introduction.

19 Greater Flamingos in flight

20 King George VI

(Recess Waterlow)

1935 (22 May). *Wmk Mult Script CA. P* 12½.
145 19 8d. ultramarine and scarlet .. .. 5·50 2·75
145 Perf "Specimen".. .. .. .. 42·00

1937 (12 May). *Coronation. As Nos.* 95/7 *of Antigua, but printed by D.L.R. P* 14.
146 ½d. green 15 15
147 1½d. yellow-brown 30 75
148 2½d. bright blue 50 75
146/8 .. .. .. *Set of* 3 85 1·50
146/8 Perf "Specimen" .. *Set of* 3 60·00

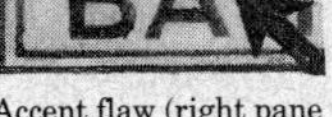

Accent flaw (right pane R. 1/5) (1938 ptg only)

Short "T" in "TWO" (right pane R. 3/6) (Retouched on No. 152*c*, although bottom of letter is still pointed)

(Typo D.L.R.)

1938 (11 Mar)–52. *Wmk Mult Script CA. Chalk-surfaced paper* (1*s. to* £1). *P* 14.
149 20 ½d. green 15 90
a. Elongated "E" .. .. .. 38·00
b. Accent flaw .. .. .. 45·00
c. *Bluish green* (11.9.42) .. .. 1·75 1·25
ca. Elongated "E" .. .. .. 85·00
d. *Myrtle-green* (11.12.46) .. .. 5·50 5·00
da. Elongated "E" £150
149*e* ½d. brown-purple (18.2.52) .. .. 85 2·50
ea. Error. Crown missing £3250
eb. Error. St. Edward's Crown .. £1900
ec. Elongated "E" .. .. .. 75·00
150 1d. carmine .. .. 8·50 4·75
150*a* 1d. olive-grey (17.9.41) .. .. 3·25 3·25
ab. Pale slate (11.9.42) 50 50
151 1½d. red-brown (19.4.38) .. .. 1·25 1·00
a. *Pale red-brown* (19.4.48) .. .. 4·25 2·25
152 2d. pale slate (19.4.38) .. .. 18·00 6·00
a. Short "T" £375
152*b* 2d. scarlet (17.9.41) 75 55
ba. Short "T" .. .. .. 85·00
bb. "TWO PENCE" printed double .. † £4500
bc. Dull rose-red (19.4.48) .. .. 2·50 2·50
152*c* 2d. green (1.5.51) 90 80
153 2½d. ultramarine .. .. .. 3·25 2·00
153*a* 2½d. violet (1.7.43) .. .. .. 1·25 70
ab. "2½ PENNY" printed double .. £2500
154 3d. violet (19.4.38) .. .. .. 16·00 4·00
154*a* 3d. blue (4.43) 60 90
ab. Bright ultramarine (19.4.48) .. 4·00 4·00
154*b* 3d. scarlet (1.2.52) .. .. .. 50 3·00
154*c* 10d. yellow-orange (18.11.46) .. .. 2·00 20
155 1s. grey-black and carmine (*thick paper*) (15.9.38) .. .. 15·00 5·00
a. *Brownish grey and scarlet* (4.42) £250 48·00
b. Ordinary paper. *Black and carmine* (9.42) .. .. 15·00 6·00
c. Ordinary paper. *Grey-black and bright crimson* (6.3.44) .. 8·00 50
d. *Pale brownish grey and crimson* (19.4.48) .. .. .. 8·50 90
156 5s. lilac & blue (*thick paper*) (19.4.38) £170 £100
a. *Reddish lilac and blue* (4.42) .. £950 £375
b. Ordinary paper. *Purple & bl* (9.42) 26·00 13·00
c. Ordinary paper. *Dull mauve and deep blue* (11.46) .. .. 70·00 30·00
d. *Brown-purple & dp brt bl* (19.4.48) 26·00 8·50
e. *Red-purple & dp bright blue* (8.51) 23·00 11·00

157 20 £1 deep grey-green and black (*thick paper*) (15.9.38) £250 £140
a. Ordinary paper. *Blue-green and black* (13.4.43) .. .. .. 60·00 45·00
b. Ordinary paper. *Grey-green and black* (3.44) .. .. .. 90·00 60·00
149/57a .. .. *Set of* 17 £130 70·00
149/57 Perf "Specimen" .. .. *Set of* 14 £425

Nos. 149/50*a* exist in coils, constructed from normal sheets.

No. 149eb occurs on a row in the watermark in which the crowns and letters "CA" alternate.

The thick chalk-surfaced paper, used for the initial printing of the 1s., 5s. and £1, was usually toned and had streaky gum. The April 1942 printing for the 1s. and 5s., which was mostly used for the "LANDFALL" overprints, was on thin, white chalk-surfaced paper with clear gum. Printings of the three values between September 1942 and November 1946 were on a thick, smooth, opaque ordinary paper.

21 Sea Garden, Nassau

22 Fort Charlotte

23 Greater Flamingos in Flight

3d.

(24)

(Recess Waterlow)

1938 (1 July). *Wmk Mult Script CA. P* 12½.
158 21 4d. light blue and red-orange .. .. 1·00 80
159 22 6d. olive-green and light blue 60 80
160 23 8d. ultramarine and scarlet .. .. 5·00 2·00
158/60 .. .. *Set of* 3 6·00 3·25
158/60 Perf "Specimen" .. .. *Set of* 3 £100

1940 (28 Nov). *No.* 153 *surcharged with T* **24** *by* The Nassau Guardian.
161 20 3d. on 2½d. blue 65 40

1492
LANDFALL
OF
COLUMBUS
1942

(25)

"RENCE" flaw (Right pane R. 9/3. Later corrected so that it does not occur on No. 154*a*)

1942 (12 Oct). 450*th Anniv of Landing of Columbus in New World. Optd as T* **25** *by* The Nassau Guardian.
162 20 ½d. bluish green 30 60
a. Elongated "E" .. .. .. 38·00
b. Opt double £250
163 1d. pale slate 30 60
164 1½d. red-brown 40 60
165 2d. scarlet 30 65
a. Short "T" .. .. .. 65·00
166 2½d. ultramarine 30 65
167 3d. ultramarine 30 65
a. "RENCE" flaw .. .. .. 85·00
168 21 4d. light blue and red-orange 40 90
a. "COIUMBUS" (R. 5/2) £600 £600
169 22 6d. olive-green and light blue .. .. 40 1·75
a. "COIUMBUS" (R. 5/2) £600 £650
170 23 8d. ultramarine and scarlet 90 70
a. "COIUMBUS" (R. 5/2) £4500 £2000
171 20 1s. brownish grey and scarlet .. 4·50 3·25
a. Ordinary paper. *Black and carmine* 4·25 3·25
b. Ordinary paper. *Grey-black and bright crimson* .. .. .. 8·50 5·50
172 18 2s. slate-purple and indigo .. .. 15·00 16·00
a. Brownish black and indigo .. 8·00 10·00
b. Brownish black and steel-blue .. 20·00 20·00
c. Stop after "COLUMBUS" (R. 2/12) £1300
173 3s. slate-purple and myrtle-green .. 5·00 6·50
a. Brownish black and green .. 40·00 32·00
b. Stop after "COLUMBUS" (R. 2/12) £750
174 20 5s. reddish lilac and blue .. .. 27·00 13·00
a. Ordinary paper. *Purple and blue* .. 18·00 12·00
175 £1 deep grey-green & blk (*thick paper*) 60·00 48·00
a. Ordinary paper. *Grey-green & black* 30·00 25·00
162/75 .. .. *Set of* 14 60·00 55·00
162/75 Perf "Specimen" .. .. *Set of* 14 £400

These stamps replaced the definitive series for a period of six months. Initially stocks of existing printings were used, but when further supplies were required for overprinting a number of new printings were produced, some of which, including the new colour of the 3d., did not appear without overprint until much later.

1946 (11 Nov). *Victory. As Nos.* 110/11 *of Antigua.*
176 1½d. brown 10 30
177 3d. blue 10 30
176/7 Perf "Specimen" .. .. *Set of* 2 55·00

NEW INFORMATION

The editor is always interested to correspond with people who have new information that will improve or correct the Catalogue.

26 Infant Welfare Clinic

(Recess C.B.N.)

1948 (11 Oct). *Tercentenary of Settlement of Island of Eleuthera. T* **26** *and similar horiz designs. P* 12.
178 ½d. orange 30 70
179 1d. sage-green 30 35
180 1½d. yellow 30 80
181 2d. scarlet 30 40
182 2½d. brown-lake 45 75
183 3d. ultramarine 65 85
184 4d. black 60 70
185 6d. emerald-green .. .. 1·75 80
186 8d. violet 60 70
187 10d. carmine 60 35
188 1s. sepia 90 50
189 2s. magenta .. .. 4·00 8·50
190 3s. blue .. .. 7·50 8·50
191 5s. mauve .. .. 7·50 4·50
192 10s. grey .. .. 9·50 9·00
193 £1 vermilion .. .. 11·00 14·00
178/93 .. .. *Set of* 16 40·00 45·00

Designs:—1d. Agriculture (combine harvester); 1½d. Sisal; 2d. Straw work; 2½d. Dairy farm; 3d. Fishing fleet; 4d. Island settlement; 6d. Tuna fishing; 8d. Paradise Beach; 10d. Modern hotels; 1s. Yacht racing; 2s. Water sports (skiing); 3s. Shipbuilding; 5s. Transportation; 10s. Salt production; £1, Parliament Buildings.

1948 (1 Dec). *Royal Silver Wedding. As Nos.* 112/13 *of Antigua.*
194 1½d. red-brown 20 25
195 £1 slate-green .. .. 32·00 32·00

1949 (10 Oct). 75*th Anniv of Universal Postal Union. As Nos.* 114/17 *of Antigua.*
196 2½d. violet 35 40
197 3d. deep blue .. .. 2·00 2·00
198 6d. greenish blue .. .. 55 2·00
199 1s. carmine 55 75
196/9 .. .. *Set of* 4 3·00 4·75

1953 (3 June). *Coronation. As No.* 120 *of Antigua.*
200 6d. black and pale blue 40 35

42 Infant Welfare Clinic

43 Queen Elizabeth II

(Recess B.W.)

1954 (1 Jan)–**63**. *Designs previously used for King George VI issue, but with portrait of Queen Elizabeth II as in T* **42**, *and commemorative inscr omitted. Wmk Mult Script CA. P* 11 × 11½.
201 ½d. black and red-orange .. .. 10 1·25
202 1d. olive-green and brown 10 10
203 1½d. blue and black 15 40
204 2d. yellow-brown and myrtle-green .. 15 15
a. Yellow-brn & dp myrtle-grn (23.1.62) 5·00 6·00
205 3d. black and carmine-red 55 65
206 4d. turquoise-green & deep reddish purple 30 30
a. Turq-blue & dp reddish pur (23.1.62) 9·00 10·00
207 5d. red-brown and deep bright blue .. 1·40 2·25
208 6d. light blue and black .. .. 1·25 10
w. Wmk inverted .. .. .. — £500
209 8d. black and reddish lilac 70 40
a. Black and deep reddish lilac (21.11.56) 1·60 1·60
210 10d. black and ultramarine 30 10
a. Black and deep ultramarine (8.1.63) 6·00 2·75
211 1s. ultramarine and olive-brown .. 70 10
a. Ultramarine & dp ol-sepia (19.2.58) 2·00 30
212 2s. orange-brown and black .. 2·00 70
a. Chestnut and black (19.2.58) .. 10·00 1·50
213 2s. 6d. black and deep blue .. .. 3·50 2·00
214 5s. bright emerald and orange .. .. 18·00 75
a. Brt emerald & reddish orange (14.1.59) 42·00 5·00
215 10s. black and slate-black .. .. 20·00 2·00
216 £1 slate-black and violet .. .. 20·00 6·00
201/16 .. .. *Set of* 16 60·00 15·00

Designs:—1d. Agriculture (combine harvester); 1½d. Island settlement; 2d. Straw work; 3d. Fishing fleet; 4d. Water sports (skiing); 5d. Dairy farm; 6d. Transportation; 8d. Paradise Beach; 10d. Modern hotels; 1s. Yacht racing; 2s. Sisal; 2s. 6d. Shipbuilding; 5s. Tuna fishing; 10s. Salt production; £1 Parliament Buildings.

Nos. 201/2, 205, 208 and 211 exist in coils, constructed from normal sheets.

See also No. 246.

(Recess Waterlow)

1959 (10 June). *Centenary of First Bahamas Postage Stamp. W* w 12. *P* 13½.
217 43 1d. black and scarlet 35 20
218 2d. black and blue-green 35 80
219 6d. black and blue 45 30
220 10d. black and chocolate 50 90
217/20 .. .. *Set of* 4 1·50 2·00

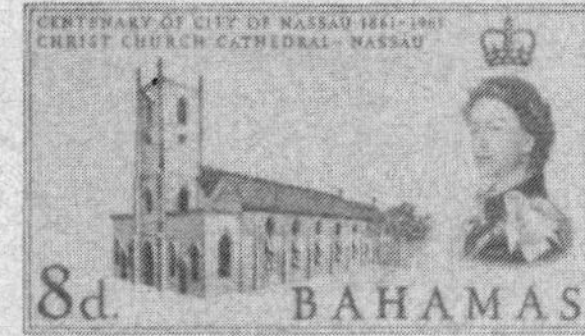

44 Christ Church Cathedral

(Photo Enschedé)

1962 (30 Jan). *Nassau Centenary. T* **44** *and similar horiz desig*[ns.] *P* 14 × 13.
221 8d. green 45
222 10d. bluish violet 45

Design:—10d. Nassau Public Library.

1963 (4 June). *Freedom from Hunger. As No.* 146 *of Antigu*[a.]
223 8d. sepia 40
a. Name and value omitted £900

BAHAMAS TALKS
1962

(46)

NEW CONSTITUTION
1964

(47)

1963 (15 July). *Bahamas Talks*, 1962. *Nos.* 209/10 *optd w*[ith] *T* **46**.
224 8d. black and reddish lilac 40
225 10d. black and deep ultramarine 50

1963 (2 Sept). *Red Cross Centenary. As Nos.* 147/8 *of Antigua.*
226 1d. red and black 50
227 10d. red and blue .. .. 1·75 2·

SELF GOVERNMENT

1964 (7 Jan). *New Constitution. As Nos.* 201/16 *but W* w **12**, *op*[td] *with T* **47**, *by* B.W.
228 ½d. black and red-orange 15
229 1d. olive-green and brown 15
230 1½d. blue and black 70
231 2d. yellow-brown and deep myrtle-green .. 15
232 3d. black and carmine-red .. .. 1·25
233 4d. turquoise-blue and deep reddish purple 40
234 5d. red-brown and deep bright blue .. 40 1·
235 6d. light blue and black .. .. 1·50
236 8d. black and reddish lilac 70
237 10d. black and deep ultramarine .. 30
238 1s. ultramarine and olive-brown .. 1·00
239 2s. chestnut and black .. .. 1·50 1
240 2s. 6d. black and deep blue .. .. 2·50 2
241 5s. bright emerald and orange .. 6·00 3
242 10s. black and slate black .. .. 6·00 5·
243 £1 slate-black and violet .. .. 8·50 17·
228/243 .. .. .. *Set of* 16 26·00 32·

1964 (23 April). 400*th Birth Anniv of William Shakespeare. No.* 164 *of Antigua.*
244 6d. turquoise 10
w. Wmk inverted .. .. .. 48·00

(48)

1964 (1 Oct). *Olympic Games, Tokyo. As No.* 211 *but W* w [12] *surch with T* **48**.
245 8d. on 1s. ultramarine and olive-brown 45

1964 (6 Oct). *As No.* 204*a*, *but wmk* w **12**.
246 2d. yellow-brown and deep myrtle-green .. 45

49 Colony's Badge

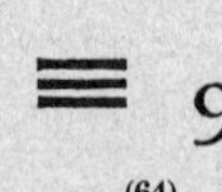

(64)

(Queen's portrait by Anthony Buckley. Litho and recess (portr[ait] and "BAHAMAS") B.W.)

1965 (7 Jan–14 Sept). *Horiz designs as T* **49**. *W* w **12**. *P* 13½.
247 ½d. multicoloured 15
248 1d. slate, light blue and orange 30
249 1½d. rose-red, green and brown 15 1
250 2d. slate, green and turquoise-blue .. 15
251 3d. red, light blue and purple .. .. 1·25
252 4d. green, blue and orange-brown .. 1·75 1
253 6d. dull green, light blue and rose .. 30
254 8d. reddish purple, light blue & bronze-green 50
255 10d. orange-brown, green and violet .. 25
256 1s. red, yellow, turquoise-blue & deep emer 50
a. Red, yellow, dull blue & emer (14.9.65) 30
257 2s. brown, light blue and emerald .. 1·00 1
258 2s. 6d. yellow-olive, blue and carmine .. 2·25 3
259 5s. orange-brown, ultramarine and green .. 2·25 1

60 10s. rose, blue and chocolate .. .. 14·00 3·00
61 £1 chestnut, blue and rose-red .. .. 14·00 8·00
47/261 .. .. *Set of* 15 35·00 19·00

Designs:—1d. Out Island regatta; 1½d. Hospital; 2d. High :hool; 3d. Greater Flamingo; 4d. R.M.S. *Queen Elizabeth*; 6d.)evelopment"; 8d. Yachting; 10d. Public square; 1s. Sea arden; 2s. Old cannons at Fort Charlotte; 2s. 6d. Sikorsky S-38 ying boat, 1929, and Boeing 707 airliner; 5s. Williamson film roject, 1914, and Undersea Post Office, 1939; 10s. Queen or ink Conch; £1, Columbus's flagship.

Nos. 247/8, 251, 253 and 256 exist in coils, constructed from ormal sheets.

)65 (17 May). *I.T.U Centenary. As Nos.* 166/7 *of Antigua.*
52 1d. light emerald and orange 15 10
w. Wmk inverted .. .. .. 50·00
53 2s. purple and yellow-olive 65 45
w. Wmk inverted .. .. .. 16·00

)65 (12 July). *No.* 254 *surch with T* **64**.
54 9d. on 8d. reddish purple, light blue and bronze-green 30 15

)65 (25 Oct). *International Co-operation Year. As Nos.* 168/9 *of Antigua.*
55 ½d. reddish purple and turquoise-green .. 10 85
56 1s. deep bluish green and lavender 30 40

)66 (24 Jan). *Churchill Commemoration. As Nos.* 170/3 *of Antigua.*
57 ½d. new blue 10 40
w. Wmk inverted .. .. .. 28·00
58 2d. deep green 30 30
59 10d. brown 65 85
70 1s. bluish violet .. .. 75 1·40
67/70 .. .. *Set of* 4 1·60 2·75

)66 (4 Feb). *Royal Visit. As Nos.* 174/5 *of Antigua, but inscr* "to the Caribbean" *omitted.*
71 6d. black and ultramarine 90 50
72 1s. black and magenta .. .. .. 1·60 1·25

(New Currency. 100 cents = 1 Bahamas dollar)

(65) (66)

)66 (25 May). *Decimal Currency. Nos.* 247/61 *variously surch as T* **65/6**, *by* B.W.
73 1 c. on ½d. multicoloured 10 30
74 2 c. on 1d. slate, light blue and orange .. 60 30
75 3 c. on 2d. slate, green and turquoise-blue .. 10 10
76 4 c. on 3d. red, light blue and purple .. 85 10
77 5 c. on 4d. green, blue and orange-brown .. 70 2·50
a. Surch omitted (vert strip of 10) £2250
78 8 c. on 6d. dull green, light blue and rose .. 20 20
79 10 c. on 8d. reddish purple, light blue and bronze-green 30 75
80 11 c. on 1½d. rose-red, green and brown .. 15 30
81 12 c. on 10d. orange-brown, green and violet 15 10
82 15 c. on 1s. multicoloured 25 10
83 22 c. on 2s. brown, light blue and emerald .. 60 80
84 50 c. on 2s. 6d. yellow-olive, blue and carmine 90 1·40
85 $1 on 5s. orange-brown, ultram & green .. 1·50 1·50
86 $2 on 10s. rose, blue and chocolate .. .. 6·50 4·25
87 $3 on £1 chestnut, blue and rose-red .. 6·50 4·25
73/287 .. .. *Set of* 15 17·00 15·00

The above were made on new printings some of which vary ightly in shade and in No. 273 the shield appears as vermilion and reen instead of carmine and blue-green due to a different combi-ation of the printing colours.

No. 277a. One sheet exists and the stamp can be distinguished om No. 252 when in a vertical strip of ten as these were printed in heets of 100 whereas No. 252 was printed in sheets of 60 (six rows f ten across).

)66 (1 July). *World Cup Football Championships. As Nos.* 176/7 *of Antigua.*
88 8 c. violet, yellow-green, lake & yell-brown 25 15
89 15 c. chocolate, blue-green, lake & yell-brown 30 25

)66 (20 Sept). *Inauguration of W.H.O. Headquarters, Geneva. As Nos.* 178/9 *of Antigua.*
90 11 c. black, yellow-green and light blue .. 40 40
91 15 c. black, light purple and yellow-brown .. 45 50

1966 (1 Dec). 20*th Anniv of U.N.E.S.C.O. As Nos.* 196/8 *of Antigua.*
92 3 c. slate-violet, red, yellow and orange .. 10 10
93 15 c. orange-yellow, violet and deep olive .. 25 35
94 $1 black, bright purple and orange .. 1·00 2·50
92/4 .. .. *Set of* 3 1·25 2·75

67 *Oceanic*

68 Conch Shell

(Portrait by Anthony Buckley. Litho and recess (portrait, "BAHAMAS" and value), B.W.)

1967 (25 May)–**71**. *T* **67/8** *or designs as Nos.* 247/51, 253/9 *and* 261 *but values in decimal currency and colours changed. Toned paper. W* w **12**. *P* 13½.
295 1 c. multicoloured (as ½d.) .. .. .. 10 2·00
a. Whiter paper (1970) .. .. .. 45 3·25
296 2 c. slate, light blue & deep emerald (as 1d.) 20 60
a. Whiter paper (1970) .. .. .. 1·40 3·50
297 3 c. slate, green and violet (as 2d.) 10 10
a. Whiter paper (1970) .. .. .. 55·00 5·00
298 4 c. red, light blue and ultramarine (as 3d.) 4·25 50
a. Whiter paper (9.70*) .. .. .. 12·00 18·00
299 5 c. black, greenish blue and purple .. 75 2·00
a. Whiter paper (1970) .. .. .. 1·50 4·50
300 8 c. dull green, light blue and sepia (as 6d.) 25 10
a. Whiter paper (1970) .. .. .. £170 17·00
301 10 c. reddish pur, greenish bl & carm (as 8d.) 30 70
a. Whiter paper (1970) .. .. .. 1·00 2·75
302 11 c. rose-red, green and blue (as 1½d.) .. 25 80
a. Whiter paper (1970) .. .. .. 80 2·25
303 12 c. orange-brown, green and olive (as 10d.) 25 10
a. Whiter paper (4.71) .. .. .. 12·00 26·00
304 15 c. red, yellow, turquoise-bl & carm (as 1s.) 55 10
a. Whiter paper (1970) .. .. .. £170 22·00
305 22 c. brown, new blue and rose-red (as 2s.) .. 70 65
a. Whiter paper (1970) .. .. .. 2·00 5·00
306 50 c. yellow-olive, new bl & emer (as 2s. 6d.) 2·00 75
a. Whiter paper (1970) .. .. .. 2·25 3·75
307 $1 orange-brown, ultram & slate-pur (as 5s.) 2·00 60
a. Whiter paper (4.71) .. .. .. 19·00 48·00
308 $2 multicoloured .. .. 10·00 3·00
a. Whiter paper (4.71) .. .. .. 30·00 55·00
309 $3 chestnut, new blue and purple (as £1) 3·75 2·00
a. Whiter paper (4.71) .. .. .. 30·00 55·00
295/309 .. .. *Set of* 15 22·00 12·00
295a/309a .. .. *Set of* 15 (whiter paper) £450 £250

*This is the earliest known date recorded in the Bahamas.

The 3 c. has the value at right instead of at left as on No. 250.

The 1970–71 printings on whiter paper were released as needed, the 12 c., $1, $2 and $3 only a week or two before the issue was with-drawn. Due to the marked difference in paper and the use of some new plates there are marked differences in shade in nearly all values.

69 Bahamas Crest

(Des R. Granger Barrett. Photo Enschedé)

1967 (1 Sept). *Diamond Jubilee of World Scouting. T* **69** *and similar horiz design. Multicoloured. W* w **12** (*sideways**). *P* 14×13.
310 3 c. Type **69** 35 15
w. Wmk Crown to left of CA .. .. 13·00
311 15 c. Scout badge 40 15

*The normal sideways watermark shows Crown to right of CA, *as seen from the back of the stamp.*

71 Globe and Emblem **74** Golf

(Des R. Granger Barrett, Litho D.L.R)

1968 (13 May). *Human Rights Year. T* **71** *and similar horiz designs. Multicoloured. W* w **12** (*sideways**). *P* 14×13½.
312 3 c. Type **71** 10 10
313 12 c. Scales of Justice and emblem 20 10
314 $1 Bahamas Crest and emblem 70 80
312/14 .. .. *Set of* 3 90 85

*The normal sideways watermark shows Crown to right of CA on the 12 c. and Crown to left of CA on the others, *each when seen from the back of the stamp.*

(Litho B.W.)

1968 (20 Aug). *Tourism. T* **74** *and similar vert designs. Multi-coloured. P* 13.
315 5 c. Type **74** .. .. 1·75 1·25
316 11 c. Yachting .. .. 1·25 40
317 15 c. Horse-racing .. .. 1·75 45
318 50 c. Water-skiing .. .. 2·50 5·50
315/18 .. .. *Set of* 4 6·50 7·00

ALTERED CATALOGUE NUMBERS

Any Catalogue numbers altered from the last edition are shown as a list in the introductory pages.

78 Racing Yacht and Olympic Monument

(Photo Harrison)

1968 (29 Sept). *Olympic Games, Mexico City. T* **78** *and similar horiz designs. No wmk. P* 14½ × 13½.
319 5 c. red-brown, orange-yellow & blue-green 30 40
320 11 c. multicoloured 40 25
321 50 c. multicoloured .. .. 80 1·40
322 $1 olive-grey, greenish blue and violet .. 2·25 3·50
319/22 .. .. *Set of* 4 3·25 5·00

Designs:—11 c. Long-jumping and Olympic Monument; 50 c. Running and Olympic Monument; $1, Type **78**.

It is understood that the above were released by the Philatelic Agency in the U.S.A. on 1st September.

81 Legislative Building

(Des J. Cooter, Litho Format)

1968 (1 Nov). 14*th Commonwealth Parliamentary Conference. T* **81** *and similar multicoloured designs. P* 14.
323 3 c. Type **81** 10 20
324 10 c. Bahamas Mace and Westminster Clock-Tower (*vert*) 15 25
325 12 c. Local straw market (*vert*) 15 25
326 15 c. Horse-drawn Surrey 20 30
323/6 .. .. *Set of* 4 55 90

85 Obverse and reverse of $100 Gold Coin

(Recess D.L.R.)

1968 (2 Dec). *Gold Coins commemorating the first General Elec-tion under the New Constitution. T* **85** *and similar "boomerang" shaped designs. P* 13½.
327 3 c. red/*gold* 40 25
328 12 c. blue-green/*gold* 60 50
329 15 c. dull purple/*gold* 70 60
330 $1 black/*gold* .. .. 1·75 2·50
327/30 .. .. *Set of* 4 3·00 3·50

Designs:—12 c. Obverse and reverse of $50 gold coin; 15 c. Obverse and reverse of $20 gold coin; $1, Obverse and reverse of $10 gold coin.

89 First Flight Postcard of 1919

90 Sikorsky S-38 Flying Boat of 1929

(Des V. Whiteley. Litho Format)

1969 (30 Jan). 50*th Anniv of Bahamas Airmail Service. P* 14.
331 **89** 12 c. multicoloured 50 50
332 **90** 15 c. multicoloured .. .. .. 60 1·25

91 Game-fishing Boats

92 "The Adoration of the Shepherds" (Louis le Nain)

(Des J. Cooter. Litho Format)

1969 (26 Aug). *Tourism. One Millionth Visitor to Bahamas. T* **91** *and similar horiz designs. Multicoloured. W* w **12** (*sideways*). *P* 14½.

333 3 c. Type **91** 25 10
334 11 c. Paradise Beach 35 15
335 12 c. "Sunfish" sailing boats 35 15
336 15 c. Rawson Square and Parade 45 25
333/6 .. .. *Set of* 4 1·25 60
MS337 130 × 96 mm. Nos. 333/6 .. .. .. 2·50 3·00

(Des G. Drummond. Litho D.L.R.)

1969 (15 Oct). *Christmas. T* **92** *and similar vert designs. W* w **12**. *P* 12.

338 3 c. Type **92** 10 10
339 11 c. "The Adoration of the Shepherds" (Poussin) 15 15
340 12 c. "The Adoration of the Kings" (Gerard David) 15 20
341 15 c. "The Adoration of the Kings" (Vincenzo Foppa) 20 40
338/41 .. .. *Set of* 4 55 75

93 Badge of Girl Guides

(Des Mrs. R. Sands. Litho Harrison)

1970 (23 Feb). *Girl Guides Diamond Jubilee. T* **93** *and similar designs. Multicoloured. W* w **12**. *P* 14½.

342 3 c. Type **93** 30 10
w. Wmk inverted .. .. ..
343 12 c. Badge of Brownies 45 20
344 15 c. Badge of Rangers 50 35
w. Wmk inverted .. .. ..
342/4 .. .. *Set of* 3 1·10 55

94 U.P.U. Headquarters and Emblem

(Des L. Curtis, Litho J.W.)

1970 (20 May). *New U.P.U. Headquarters Building. W* w **12** (*sideways*). *P* 14.

345 **94** 3 c. multicoloured 10 10
346 15 c. multicoloured 20 30

95 Coach and Globe

(Des G. Drummond. Litho B.W.)

1970 (14 July). *"Goodwill Caravan". T* **95** *and similar horiz designs. Multicoloured. W* w **12** (*sideways**). *P* 13½×13.

347 3 c. Type **95** 75 15
w. Wmk Crown to right of CA .. ..
348 11 c. Diesel train and globe .. .. .. 2·00 30
349 12 c. *Canberra* (liner), yacht and globe .. 2·00 40
w. Wmk Crown to right of CA .. .. 3·50
350 15 c. B.A.C. One Eleven airliner and globe 2·00 1·25
347/50 .. .. *Set of* 4 6·00 1·90
MS351 165×125 mm. Nos. 347/50 .. .. 9·50 15·00

*The normal sideways watermark shows Crown to left of CA, *as seen from the back of the stamp.*

96 Nurse, Patients and Greater Flamingo

97 "The Nativity" (detail, Pittoni)

(Photo Harrison)

1970 (1 Sept). *Centenary of British Red Cross. T* **96** *and similar horiz design. Multicoloured. W* w **12** (*sideways**). *P* 14½.

352 3 c. Type **96** .. .. 1·00 50
a. Gold ("EIIR", etc) omitted £275
w. Wmk Crown to right of CA .. ..
353 15 c. Hospital and Blue Marlin .. .. 1·00 1·50

*The normal sideways watermark shows Crown to left of CA, *as seen from back of the stamp.*

(Des G. Drummond. Litho D.L.R.)

1970 (3 Nov). *Christmas. T* **97** *and similar vert designs. Multicoloured. W* w **12**. *P* 13.

354 3 c. Type **97** 15 10
355 11 c. "The Holy Family" (detail, Anton Raphael Mengs) 20 20
356 12 c. "The Adoration of the Shepherds" (detail, Giorgione) 20 20
357 15 c. "The Adoration of the Shepherds" (detail, School of Seville) 30 55
354/7 .. .. *Set of* 4 75 95
MS358 114 × 140 mm. Nos. 354/7 plus two labels 1·40 3·00

98 International Airport

(Des Mrs. W. Wasile. Litho Format)

1971 (27 Apr–1 Sept). *Multicoloured designs as T* **98**. *W* w **12** (*sideways on $1 to $3*). *P* 14½×14 (*1 to 50 c.*) *or* 14×14½ (*$1 to $3*).

359 1 c. Type **98** 10 30
360 2 c. Breadfruit 15 35
361 3 c. Straw market 15 30
362 4 c. Hawksbill turtle .. .. 1·75 7·00
363 5 c. Nassau Grouper 60 60
364 6 c. As 4 c. (21.9.71) .. .. 45 1·25
365 7 c. Hibiscus (21.9.71) .. .. 2·00 3·25
366 8 c. Yellow Elder .. .. 60 1·50
367 10 c. Bahamian sponge boat 55 30
368 11 c. Greater Flamingos .. .. 2·50 2·25
w. Wmk inverted .. .. 11·00
369 12 c. As 7 c. .. .. 2·00 3·00
370 15 c. Bonefish 40 55
w. Wmk inverted .. .. ..
371 18 c. Royal Poinciana (21.9.71) 65 65
w. Wmk inverted .. .. ..
372 22 c. As 18 c. .. .. 2·75 11·00
373 50 c. Post Office, Nassau .. .. 1·40 2·25
374 $1 Pineapple (*vert*) .. .. 5·50 3·00
375 $2 Crawfish (*vert*) .. .. 4·00 6·00
376 $3 Junkanoo (*vert*) .. .. 4·50 10·00
359/76 .. .. *Set of* 18 26·00 48·00

See also Nos. 395/400, 460/73 and 518/25.

99 Snowflake

(Litho (15 c. additionally die-stamped in gold) Walsall)

1971 (19 Oct). *Christmas. T* **99** *and similar horiz designs. W* w **12**. *P* 14 × 14½.

377 3 c. deep reddish purple, orange and gold 10 10
378 11 c. light ultramarine and gold 20 15
w. Wmk inverted .. .. .. 1·00
379 15 c. multicoloured 20 20
380 18 c. bluish green, royal blue and gold .. 25 25
377/80 .. .. *Set of* 4 65 60
MS381 126×95 mm. Nos. 377/80. P 15 .. 1·25 1·50

Designs:—11 c. "Peace on Earth" (doves); 15 c. Arms of Bahamas and holly; 18 c. Starlit lagoon.

100 High jumping

(Des J. W. Litho B.W.)

1972 (11 July). *Olympic Games, Munich. T* **100** *and similar horiz designs. Multicoloured. W* w **12**. *P* 13½.

382 10 c. Type **100** 35 60
383 11 c. Cycling .. .. 1·50 75
384 15 c. Running 60 75
385 18 c. Sailing .. .. 95 1·25
382/5 .. .. *Set of* 4 3·00 3·00
MS386 127 × 95 mm. Nos. 382/5 .. .. .. 3·00 3·00

101 Shepherd

102 Northerly Bahama Islands

(Des Jennifer Toombs. Litho (15 c. additionally embossed) J.W.)

1972 (3 Oct). *Christmas. T* **101** *and similar vert designs. Mul- coloured. W* w **12** (*sideways on* 6 *and* 20 *c.*) *P* 14.

387 3 c. Type **101** 10
388 6 c. Bells 10
389 15 c. Holly and Cross 15
390 20 c. Poinsettia 25
387/90 .. .. *Set of* 4 50
MS391 108 × 140 mm. Nos. 387/90 (wmk sideways) 80 1·

(Des M. Shamir. Litho Format)

1972 (1 Nov). *Tourism Year of the Americas. She 133 × 105 mm, containing T* **102** *and similar vert designs. P* 15

MS392 11, 15, 18 and 50 c. multicoloured .. 2·50 3·

The four designs are printed horizontally *se-tenant* in **MS**39 forming a composite map design of the Bahamas.

103 Mace and Galleon

(Des (from photograph by D. Groves) and photo Harrison)

1972 (13 Nov). *Royal Silver Wedding. Multicoloured; backgrou colour given. W* w **12**. *P* 14 × 14½.

393 **103** 11 c. rose 15
w. Wmk inverted .. .. .. 55·00
394 18 c. bluish violet 15
w. Wmk inverted .. .. .. 1·75

1972 (23 Nov)–**73**. *As Nos.* 363, 366 *and* 373/6 *but W* w *sideways* on* 5 *to* 50 *c. and upright on* $1 *to* $3.

395 5 c. Nassau Grouper .. .. 8·00 2·
396 8 c. Yellow Elder (25.7.73) .. .. .. 2·75 2·
397 50 c. Post Office, Nassau (25.7.73) .. .. 2·00 2·
w. Wmk Crown to left of CA .. .. 3·50
398 $1 Pineapple (25.7.73) .. .. .. 3·00 4·
399 $2 Crawfish (25.7.73) .. .. .. 3·00 6·
400 $3 Junkanoo (1973) .. .. .. 3·00 14·
395/400 .. .. *Set of* 6 20·00 28·

*The normal sideways watermark shows Crown to right CA, *as seen from the back of the stamp.*

Nos. 401/9 vacant.

104 Weather Satellite

(Des C. Abbott. Litho Questa)

1973 (3 Apr). *I.M.O./W.M.O. Centenary. T* **104** *and similar ho design. Multicoloured. W* w **12**. *P* 14.

410 15 c. Type **104** 50
411 18 c. Weather radar 60

INDEPENDENT

105 C. A. Bain (national hero)

106 "The Virgin in Prayer" (Sassoferrato)

(Des PAD Studio. Litho Questa)

1973 (10 July–1 Aug). *Independence. T* **105** *and similar v designs. Multicoloured. W* w **12** (*sideways*). *P* 14½ × 14.

412 3 c. Type **105** 10
413 11 c. Coat of arms 15
414 15 c. Bahamas flag 20
415 $1 Governor-General, M. B. Butler (1 Aug) 65 1·
412/15 .. .. *Set of* 4 1·00 1·
MS416 86 × 121 mm. Nos. 412/15 (1 Aug) .. 1·50 1·

(Des C. Abbott. Litho Format)

73 (16 Oct). *Christmas. T* **106** *and similar vert designs. Multicoloured.* W w **12** (*sideways**). P 14.

7	3 c. Type **106** ..	10	10
8	11 c. "Virgin and Child with St. John" (Filippino Lippi)	15	15
9	15 c. "A Choir of Angels" (Simon Marmion) ..	15	15
0	18 c. "The Two Trinities" (Murillo) ..	25	25
7/20	*Set of* 4	60	55
S421	120×99 mm. Nos. 417/20	90	1·40
	w. Wmk Crown to right of CA ..	2·75	

*The normal sideways watermark shows Crown to left of CA, *seen from the back of the stamp.*

107 "Agriculture and Sciences"

(Des C. Abbott. Litho Questa)

974 (5 Feb). *25th Anniv of University of West Indies. T* **107** *and similar horiz design. Multicoloured.* W w **12**. P 13½.

22	15 c. Type **107** ..	20	25
23	18 c. "Arts, Engineering and General Studies"	25	30

108 U.P.U. Monument, Berne

(Des P. Powell. Litho Questa)

974 (23 Apr). *Centenary of Universal Postal Union. Designs as T* **108** *showing different arrangements of the U.P.U. Monument.* W w **12** (*upright on* 3 c., 14 c. *and* **MS**428; *sideways on others*). P 14.

No.	Type	Description		
24	**108**	3 c. multicoloured ..	10	10
25	–	13 c. multicoloured (*vert*)	20	25
26	–	14 c. multicoloured	20	30
27	–	18 c. multicoloured (*vert*)	25	35
24/7		*Set of* 4	65	90
MS428		128×95 mm. Nos. 424/7	80	1·60
		w. Wmk inverted	£150	

109 Roseate Spoonbills

(Des G. Drummond. Litho Questa)

974 (10 Sept). *15th Anniv of Bahamas National Trust. T* **109** *and similar horiz designs. Multicoloured.* W w **12** (*sideways*). P 13½.

29	13 c. Type **109** ..	1·40	85
30	14 c. White-crowned Pigeon ..	1·40	75
31	21 c. White-tailed Tropic Birds	1·75	1·25
32	36 c. Cuban Amazon ..	2·25	3·75
29/32	*Set of* 4	6·00	6·00
MS433	123 × 120 mm. Nos. 429/32	7·50	10·00

110 "The Holy Family" (Jacques de Stella)

(Des J. W. Litho Enschedé)

1974 (29 Oct). *Christmas. T* **110** *and similar horiz designs. Multicoloured.* W w **12** (*sideways*). P 13 × 13½.

434	8 c. Type **110** ..	10	10
435	10 c. "Madonna and Child" (16th-cent Brescian School) ..	15	15
436	12 c. "Virgin and Child with St. John the Baptist and St. Catherine" (Previtali) ..	15	15
437	21 c. "Virgin and Child with Angels" (Previtali) ..	25	30
434/7	*Set of* 4	60	60
MS438	126 × 105 mm. Nos. 434/7	80	1·40

111 *Anteos maerula*

(Des PAD Studio. Litho D.L.R.)

1975 (4 Feb). *Butterflies. T* **111** *and similar horiz designs. Multicoloured.* W w **12**. P 14 × 13½.

439	3 c. Type **111** ..	25	15
440	14 c. *Eurema nicippe*	80	50
441	18 c. *Papilio andraemon*	95	65
442	21 c. *Euptoieta hegesia*	1·10	85
	w. Wmk inverted	42·00	
439/42	*Set of* 4	2·75	2·00
MS443	119×94 mm. Nos. 439/42	7·50	6·50

112 Sheep Husbandry

113 Rowena Rand (evangelist)

(Des Daphne Padden. Litho Questa)

1975 (27 May). *Economic Diversification. T* **112** *and similar multicoloured designs.* P 14.

444	3 c. Type **112** ..	10	10
445	14 c. Electric-reel fishing (*vert*)	20	15
446	18 c. Farming ..	25	20
447	21 c. Oil Refinery (*vert*)	45	35
444/7	*Set of* 4	90	65
MS448	127 × 94 mm. Nos. 444/7 ..	90	1·50

(Des Jennifer Toombs. Litho Questa)

1975 (22 July). *International Women's Year. T* **113** *and similar vert design.* W w **14**. P 14.

449	14 c. bistre-brown, lt turquoise-blue & ultram	20	40
450	18 c. lemon, bright yellow-green and sepia ..	25	45

Design:—18 c. I.W.Y. symbol and Harvest symbol.

114 "Adoration of the Shepherds" (Perugino)

(Des Jennifer Toombs. Litho J.W.)

1975 (2 Dec). *Christmas. T* **114** *and similar horiz design. Multicoloured.* W w **14** (*sideways*). P 13.

451	3 c. Type **114** ..	15	50
452	8 c. "Adoration of the Magi" (Ghirlandaio) ..	20	10
453	18 c. As 8 c. ..	55	80
454	21 c. Type **114** ..	60	85
451/4	*Set of* 4	1·40	2·00
MS455	142 × 107 mm. Nos. 451/4. P 13½	2·25	3·50

115 Telephones, 1876 and 1976

(Des G. Vasarhelyi. Litho D.L.R.)

1976 (23 Mar). *Telephone Centenary. T* **115** *and similar horiz designs. Multicoloured.* W w **14** (*sideways**). P 14.

456	3 c. Type **115**	15	30
	w. Wmk Crown to right of CA ..	2·00	
457	16 c. Radio-telephone link, Deleporte	30	40
	w. Wmk Crown to right of CA ..		
458	21 c. Alexander Graham Bell ..	40	55
	w. Wmk Crown to right of CA ..	55·00	
459	25 c. Satellite ..	50	70
	w. Wmk Crown to right of CA ..	2·50	
456/9	*Set of* 4	1·25	1·75

*The normal sideways watermark shows Crown to left of CA, *as seen from the back of the stamp.*

1976 (30 May)–**79**. *Designs as Nos.* 359/63, 365/7 *and* 373/6 (*some with new face values*). W w **14** (*sideways on* $1 *to* $3). *Ordinary paper.*

460	1 c. Type **98** (1.11.76) ..	1·75	2·50
	a. Chalk-surfaced paper (1979) ..	16·00	17·00
461	2 c. Breadfruit ..	2·00	30
462	3 c. Straw market (1.11.76) ..	2·25	3·00
	a. Chalk-surfaced paper (1979) ..	60	60
463	5 c. Nassau Grouper (1.11.76) ..	3·75	3·50
	a. Chalk-surfaced paper (1979) ..	70	70
464	8 c. Yellow Elder ..	4·50	30
465	10 c. Bahamian sponge boat ..	80	30
466	16 c. As 7 c. (2.11.76) ..	70	35
	a. Chalk-surfaced paper (1979) ..	70	80
	aw. Wmk inverted ..	18·00	
467	21 c. As 2 c. (2.11.76) ..	3·00	1·50
	a. Chalk-surfaced paper (1979) ..	80	1·25
	aw. Wmk inverted ..	18·00	
468	25 c. As 4 c. (2.11.76) ..	90	40
	a. Chalk-surfaced paper (1979) ..	90	2·00
	aw. Wmk inverted ..	18·00	
469	40 c. As 10 c. (2.11.76) ..	3·25	75
470	50 c. Post Office, Nassau ..	1·75	1·75
471	$1 Pineapple ..	2·00	2·50
472	$2 Crawfish (2.5.76) ..	3·00	7·00
	a. Chalk-surfaced paper (1979) ..	18·00	27·00
473	$3 Junkanoo (1.11.76) ..	3·00	9·00
460/73	*Set of* 14	29·00	30·00
460a/72a	*Set of* 7	35·00	45·00

No. 474 vacant.

116 Map of North America

(Des and litho Walsall)

1976 (1 June). *Bicentenary of American Revolution. T* **116** *and similar horiz design. Multicoloured.* W w **14** (*sideways**). P 14.

475	16 c. Type **116**	30	30
476	$1 John Murray, Earl of Dunmore ..	1·50	1·75
MS477	127×100 mm. No. 476×4 ..	6·00	7·50
	w. Wmk Crown to right of CA ..	18·00	

*The normal sideways watermark shows Crown to left of CA, *as seen from the back of the stamp.*

117 Cycling

118 "Virgin and Child" (detail, Lippi)

(Des J.W. Litho Questa)

1976 (13 July). *Olympic Games, Montreal. T* **117** *and similar vert designs.* W w **14**. P 14.

478	8 c. magenta, blue and pale cobalt ..	60	10
479	16 c. orange, brown and pale cobalt ..	35	25
480	25 c. blue, deep magenta and pale cobalt ..	45	45
481	40 c. brown, orange and pale cobalt ..	55	1·25
478/81	*Set of* 4	1·75	1·75
MS482	100 × 126 mm. Nos. 478/81 ..	2·50	2·50

Designs:—16 c. Jumping; 25 c. Sailing; 40 c. Boxing.

(Des G. Drummond. Litho Questa)

1976 (5 Oct). *Christmas. T* **118** *and similar vert designs. Multicoloured.* W w **14**. P 14.

483	3 c. Type **118** ..	10	10
484	21 c. "Adoration of the Shepherds" (School of Seville) ..	20	15
485	25 c. "Adoration of the Kings" (detail, Foppa)	20	20
486	40 c. "Virgin and Child" (detail, Vivarini)	35	40
483/6	*Set of* 4	75	75
MS487	107 × 127 mm. Nos. 483/6 ..	1·00	2·00

119 Queen beneath Cloth of Gold Canopy

(Des G. Vasarhelyi. Litho Cartor)

1977 (7 Feb). *Silver Jubilee. T* **119** *and similar horiz designs. Multicoloured. No wmk.* P 12.

488	8 c. Type **119** ..	10	10
489	16 c. The Crowning ..	15	15
490	21 c. Taking the Oath ..	15	15
491	40 c. Queen with sceptre and orb ..	25	30
488/91	*Set of* 4	60	60
MS492	122 × 90 mm. Nos. 488/91 ..	80	1·25

120 Featherduster

(Des BG Studio. Litho J.W.)

1977 (24 May). *Marine Life. T* **120** *and similar designs. Multi-coloured. W* w **14** *(sideways). P* 13½.
493 3 c. Type **120** 30 15
494 8 c. Porkfish and cave 45 20
495 16 c. Elkhorn Coral 70 40
496 21 c. Soft Coral and sponge 80 55
493/6 .. .. *Set of* 4 2·00 1·10
MS497 119×93 mm. Nos. 493/6. P 14½ .. 2·50 4·00

121 Scouts around Campfire and Home-made Shower

Royal Visit
October 1977
(122)

(Des Harrison. Litho J.W.)

1977 (27 Sept). *Sixth Caribbean Scout Jamboree. T* **121** *and similar horiz design. Multicoloured. W* w **14** *(sideways). P* 13½.
498 16 c. Type **121** 75 30
499 21 c. Boating scenes 85 35
One used example of No. 498 is known with the mauve (face value and inscription) omitted.

1977 (19 Oct). *Royal Visit. As Nos.* 488/92, *but* W w **14** *(sideways*), optd with T* **122**.
500 8 c. Type **119** 15 10
501 16 c. The Crowning 20 15
w. Wmk Crown to right of CA 70
502 21 c. Taking the Oath 25 20
503 40 c. Queen with sceptre and orb 30 40
500/3 .. .. *Set of* 4 80 75
MS504 122×90 mm. Nos. 500/3 .. .. 1·00 2·00
w. Wmk Crown to right of CA .. .. 2·00
*The normal sideways watermark shows Crown to right of CA on 8, 21, 40 c.; to left on 16 c. and miniature sheet; *all as seen from the back of the stamp.*

123 Virgin and Child

124 Public Library, Nassau (Colonial)

(Des and litho J.W.)

1977 (25 Oct). *Christmas. T* **123** *and similar vert designs. Multi-coloured.* W w **14**. *P* 13½.
505 3 c. Type **123** 10 10
506 16 c. The Magi 20 25
507 21 c. Nativity scene 25 40
508 25 c. The Magi and star 30 45
505/8 .. .. *Set of* 4 75 1·10
MS509 136 × 74 mm. Nos. 505/8. P 14 .. .. 75 1·75

(Des G. Drummond. Litho Questa)

1978 (28 Mar). *Architectural Heritage. T* **124** *and similar vert designs.* W w **14**. *P* 14½ × 14.
510 3 c. black and apple-green 10 10
511 8 c. black and pale greenish blue 15 10
512 16 c. black and mauve 20 20
513 18 c. black and salmon-pink 25 30
510/13 .. .. *Set of* 4 60 65
MS514 91×91 mm. Nos. 510/13 .. .. 70 1·60
Designs:—8 c. St. Matthew's Church (Gothic); 16 c. Government House (Colonial); 18 c. Hermitage, Cat Island (Spanish).

125 Sceptre, St. Edward's Crown and Orb

126 Coat of Arms within Wreath and Three Ships

(Des BG Studio. Litho Enschedé)

1978 (27 June). *25th Anniv of Coronation. T* **125** *and similar vert design. Multicoloured.* W w **14**. *P* 14 × 13½.
515 16 c. Type **125** 15 10
516 $1 Queen in Coronation regalia 50 65
MS517 147×96 mm. Nos. 515/16 .. .. 1·25 1·00
w. Wmk inverted .. .. .. 9·00

1978 (June). *As Nos.* 359/76, *but no wmk.*
518 1 c. Type **98** .. .. 65 2·25
519 5 c. Nassau Grouper .. .. .. 1·00 1·00
520 16 c. Hibiscus .. .. 1·25 1·75
521 25 c. Hawksbill Turtle .. .. .. 4·50 1·75
522 50 c. Post Office, Nassau .. .. .. 2·50 3·00
523 $1 Pineapple .. .. 2·50 3·00
524 $2 Crawfish .. .. 4·25 8·00
525 $3 Junkanoo .. .. 4·50 8·00
518/25 .. .. *Set of* 8 19·00 26·00
Nos. 526/31 vacant.

(Des Jennifer Toombs. Litho Questa)

1978 (14 Nov). *Christmas. T* **126** *and similar horiz design.* W w **14** *(sideways). P* 14 × 14½.
532 5 c. gold, bright crimson and bright rose .. 20 10
533 21 c. gold, deep ultramarine and violet-blue .. 55 25
MS534 95 × 95 mm. Nos. 532/3 .. .. 2·75 5·00
Design:—21 c. Three angels with trumpets.

127 Child reaching for Adult

128 Sir Rowland Hill and Penny Black

(Litho J.W.)

1979 (15 May). *International Year of the Child. T* **127** *and similar vert designs. Multicoloured.* W w **14**. *P* 13.
535 5 c. Type **127** 20 15
536 16 c. Boys playing leap-frog 40 45
537 21 c. Girls skipping 50 60
538 25 c. Bricks with I.Y.C. emblem 50 75
535/8 .. .. *Set of* 4 1·40 1·75
MS539 101 × 125 mm. Nos. 535/8. P 14 .. .. 1·40 2·75

(Des J. Cooter. Litho Walsall)

1979 (14 Aug). *Death Centenary of Sir Rowland Hill. T* **128** *and similar horiz designs. Multicoloured.* W w **14** *(sideways). P* 13½ × 14.
540 10 c. Type **128** 30 10
541 21 c. Printing press, 1840 and 6d. stamp of 1862 40 30
542 25 c. Great Britain 6d. stamp of 1856 with "A 05" (Nassau) cancellation and Two-penny blue 40 50
543 40 c. Early mailboat and 1d. stamp of 1859 .. 45 70
540/3 .. .. *Set of* 4 1·40 1·40
MS544 115 × 80 mm. Nos. 540/3 .. .. 2·00 2·50

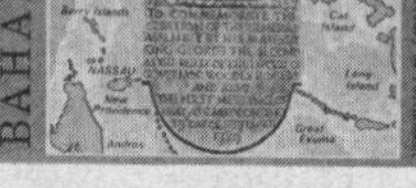

129 Commemorative Plaque and Map of Bahamas

130 Goombay Carnival Headdress

(Des G. Drummond. Litho Secura, Singapore)

1979 (27 Sept). *250th Anniv of Parliament. T* **129** *and similar horiz designs. Multicoloured.* W w **14** *(sideways*). P* 13½.
545 16 c. Type **129** 25 10
w. Wmk Crown to right of CA 35
546 21 c. Parliament Buildings 30 15
w. Wmk Crown to right of CA 40
547 25 c. Legislative Chamber 30 15
w. Wmk Crown to right of CA 45
548 $1 Senate Chamber 80 80
w. Wmk Crown to right of CA .. .. 1·40
545/8 .. .. *Set of* 4 1·50 1·00
MS549 116×89 mm. Nos. 545/8 (wmk upright) 2·50 3·50
w. Wmk inverted .. .. .. 2·50
*The normal sideways watermark shows Crown to left of CA, *as seen from the back of the stamp.*

(Des BG Studio. Litho J.W.)

1979 (6 Nov). *Christmas. T* **130** *and similar vert designs showing Goombay Carnival headdresses.* W w **14**. *P* 13.
550 5 c. multicoloured 10 10
551 10 c. multicoloured 10 10
552 16 c. multicoloured 15 10
553 21 c. multicoloured 20 20
554 25 c. multicoloured 20 20
w. Wmk inverted .. .. .. 2·25
555 40 c. multicoloured 30 35
550/5 .. .. *Set of* 6 90 85
MS556 50×88 mm. Nos. 550/5 (wmk sideways). P 13½ .. .. 2·00 2·75

COVER PRICES

Cover factors are quoted at the beginning of each country for most issues to 1945. An explanation of the system can be found on page x. The factors quoted do not, however, apply to philatelic covers.

131 Landfall of Columbus, 1492

132 Virgin and Child

(Des J.W. Litho Format)

1980 (9 July). *Horiz designs as T* **131**. *Multicoloured.* W w
P 14½.
557 1 c. Type **131** 85 2
558 3 c. Blackbeard the Pirate, 1718 .. .. 30 2
559 5 c. Eleutheran Adventurers (Articles and Orders, 1647) 30
560 10 c. Ceremonial mace 20
w. Wmk inverted .. .. .. †
561 12 c. The Loyalists, 1783–88 (Colonel Andrew Deveaux) 30 1
562 15 c. Slave trading, Vendue House .. 5·50
563 16 c. Wrecking in the 1800's 80
564 18 c. Blockade running (American Civil War) 90 1
565 21 c. Bootlegging, 1919–29 .. .. .. 40 1
566 25 c. Pineapple cultivation 40 1
567 40 c. Sponge clipping 70 1
568 50 c. Tourist development 75 1
569 $1 Modern agriculture .. .. .. 1·10 4
570 $2 Modern air and sea transport .. 4·00 4
571 $3 Banking in the Bahamas (Central Bank) .. .. 1·50 4
572 $5 Independence, 10 July 1973 (Prince of Wales and Prime Minister L. O. Pindling) .. .. .. 1·75 6
557/72 .. .. *Set of* 16 17·00 30
See also Nos. 720/6 for stamps watermarked w **16**.

(Des B. Malone. Litho Walsall)

1980 (28 Oct). *Christmas. Straw-work. T* **132** *and similar v designs. Multicoloured.* W w **14**. *P* 14½ × 14.
573 5 c. Type **132** 10
574 21 c. Three Kings 25
575 25 c. Angel 25
576 $1 Christmas Tree 75
573/6 .. .. *Set of* 4 1·25
MS577 168 × 105 mm. Nos. 573/6 .. .. 1·25 2

133 Disabled Person with Walking-stick

(Des and litho Walsall)

1981 (10 Feb). *International Year for Disabled Persons. T* 1 *and similar horiz design. Multicoloured.* W w **14** *(sideway P* 14½ × 14.
578 5 c. Type **133** 10
579 $1 Disabled person in wheelchair .. .. 1·25 1
MS580 120 × 60 mm. Nos. 578/9 .. .. 1·40 2

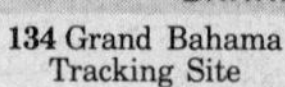

134 Grand Bahama Tracking Site

135 Prince Charles and Lady Diana Spencer

(Litho Enschedé)

1981 (21 Apr). *Space Exploration. T* **134** *and simi multicoloured designs.* W w **14** *(sideways* on 10 and 25 P* 13½.
581 10 c. Type **134** 25
582 20 c. Satellite view of Bahamas *(vert)* .. 55
w. Wmk inverted .. .. .. 20·00
583 25 c. Satellite view of Eleuthera 60
w. Wmk Crown to right of CA .. .. 1·60
584 50 c. Satellite view of Andros and New Providence *(vert)* 85 1
581/4 .. .. *Set of* 4 2·00 2
MS585 115×99 mm. Nos. 581/4 (wmk sideways) 1·60 2
*The normal sideways watermark shows Crown to left of C *as seen from the back of the stamp.*

(Des C. Abbott. Litho Questa)

1981 (22 July). *Royal Wedding. T* **135** *and similar ho design. Multicoloured.* W w **14** *(sideways*). P* 14×14½.
586 30 c. Type **135** .. .. 1·00
587 $2 Prince Charles and Prime Minister Pindling .. .. 1·50 1
MS588 142×120 mm. Nos. 586/7 .. .. 5·00 1
a. Upper stamp in miniature sheet imperf on 3 sides £650
w. Wmk Crown to right of CA .. .. 30·00
*The normal sideways watermark shows Crown to left of C *as seen from the back of the stamp.*
No. **MS**588a shows the upper stamp in the miniature sh perforated at foot only.

136 Bahama Pintail

(Des Walsall. Litho Questa)

1981 (25 Aug). *Wildlife (1st series). Birds. T* **136** *and similar horiz designs. Multicoloured.* W w **14** *(sideways). P* 14.
589 5 c. Type **136** 90 30
590 20 c. Reddish Egret .. .. 1·75 50
591 25 c. Brown Booby .. .. 1·75 55
592 $1 Black-billed Whistling Duck .. .. .. 3·50 5·00
589/92 .. .. *Set of* 4 7·00 5·75
MS593 100 × 74 mm. Nos. 589/92 .. .. .. 8·00 7·50
See also Nos. 626/30, 653/7 and 690/4.

21 23 SEPTEMBER 1981

COMMONWEALTH FINANCE MINISTERS' MEETING

(137)

1981 (21 Sept). *Commonwealth Finance Ministers' Meeting. Nos.* 559/60, 566 *and* 568 *optd with T* **137**.
594 5 c. Eleutheran Adventurers (Articles and Orders, 1647) 15 15
a. Opt inverted .. .. 50·00
595 10 c. Ceremonial mace 20 20
w. Wmk inverted .. .. 6·50
596 25 c. Pineapple cultivation 50 60
597 50 c. Tourist development .. .. .. 85 1·50
594/7 .. .. *Set of* 4 1·50 2·25

138 Poultry

139 Father Christmas

(Des L. McCombie. Litho J.W.)

1981 (16 Oct). *World Food Day. T* **138** *and similar horiz designs. Multicoloured.* W w **14** *(sideways). P* 13.
598 5 c. Type **138** 10 10
599 20 c. Sheep 30 35
600 30 c. Lobsters 40 50
601 50 c. Pigs .. .. 75 1·50
598/601 .. .. *Set of* 4 1·40 2·25
MS602 115 × 63 mm. Nos. 598/601. P 14 .. 1·50 3·25

(Des local artists. Litho Format)

1981 (24 Nov). *Christmas. T* **139** *and similar vert designs. Multicoloured.* W w **14**. *P* 13½ × 14.
603 5 c. Type **139** 35 60
a. Sheetlet of 9. Nos. 603/11 .. .. 4·00
604 5 c. Mother and child 35 60
605 5 c. St. Nicholas, Holland 35 60
606 25 c. Lussibruden, Sweden 50 85
607 25 c. Mother and child *(different)* 50 85
608 25 c. King Wenceslas, Czechoslovakia .. 50 85
609 30 c. Mother with child on knee 50 85
610 30 c. Mother carrying child 50 85
611 $1 Christkindl Angel, Germany .. .. 1·00 1·50
603/11 .. .. *Set of* 9 4·00 6·75
Nos. 603/11 were printed together, *se-tenant*, in a sheetlet of 9.

140 Robert Koch

141 Male Flamingo (*Phoenicopterus ruber*)

(Des A. Theobald. Litho Harrison)

1982 (3 Feb). *Centenary of Discovery of Tubercle Bacillus by Robert Koch. T* **140** *and similar horiz designs.* W w **14** *(sideways). P* 14.
612 5 c. black, red-brown and rose-lilac 70 40
613 16 c. black, drab and dull orange .. .. 1·25 50
614 21 c. multicoloured .. .. 1·40 55
615 $1 multicoloured .. .. 3·00 6·50
612/15 .. .. *Set of* 4 5·75 7·25
MS616 94 × 97 mm. Nos. 612/15. P 14½ .. 6·00 7·50
Designs:—16 c. Stylised infected person; 21 c. Early and modern microscopes; $1 Mantoux test.

(Des N. Arlott. Litho Questa)

1982 (28 Apr). *Greater Flamingos. T* **141** *and similar vert designs. Multicoloured.* W w **14**. *P* 14 × 13½.
617 25 c. Type **141** .. .. 1·40 1·00
a. Horiz strip of 5. Nos. 617/21 .. .. 6·00
618 25 c. Female .. .. 1·40 1·00
619 25 c. Female with nestling .. .. .. 1·40 1·00
620 25 c. Juvenile .. .. 1·40 1·00
621 25 c. Immature bird .. .. 1·40 1·00
617/21 .. .. *Set of* 5 6·00 4·50
Nos. 617/21 were printed together, *se-tenant*, in horizontal strips of 5 throughout the sheet, forming a composite design.

142 Lady Diana Spencer at Ascot, June 1981

143 House of Assembly Plaque

(Des C. Abbott. Litho Format)

1982 (1 July). *21st Birthday of Princess of Wales. T* **142** *and similar vert designs. Multicoloured.* W w **14**. *P* 13½ × 14 (16 c., $1) *or* 13½ *(others)*.
622 16 c. Bahamas coat of arms 20 10
a. Perf 13½ .. .. 1·00 1·25
623 25 c. Type **142** 45 15
624 40 c. Bride and Earl Spencer arriving at St. Paul's 60 20
w. Wmk inverted .. .. 11·00
625 $1 Formal portrait .. .. 1·00 1·25
622/5 .. .. *Set of* 4 2·00 1·40

(Des Walsall. Litho Questa)

1982 (18 Aug). *Wildlife (2nd series). Mammals. Horiz designs as T* **136**. *Multicoloured.* W w **14** *(sideways). P* 14.
626 10 c. Buffy Flower Bat 70 15
627 16 c. Bahaman Hutia 90 25
628 21 c. Common Racoon .. .. 1·10 35
629 $1 Common Dolphin .. .. 2·75 1·75
626/9 .. .. *Set of* 4 5·00 2·25
MS630 115 × 76 mm. Nos. 626/9 .. .. .. 5·00 3·50

(Des and litho Walsall)

1982 (16 Oct). *28th Commonwealth Parliamentary Association Conference. T* **143** *and similar vert designs. Multicoloured.* W w **14**. *P* 14 × 13½.
631 5 c. Type **143** 15 10
632 25 c. Association coat of arms 50 35
633 40 c. Coat of arms 80 60
634 50 c. House of Assembly .. .. 1·10 75
631/4 .. .. *Set of* 4 2·25 1·60

144 Wesley Methodist Church, Baillou Hill Road

(Des Jennifer Toombs. Litho Format)

1982 (3 Nov). *Christmas. Churches. T* **144** *and similar horiz designs. Multicoloured.* W w **14** *(sideways). P* 14.
635 5 c. Type **144** 10 10
636 12 c. Centreville Seventh Day Adventist Church 15 20
637 15 c. The Church of God of Prophecy, East Street 20 30
638 21 c. Bethel Baptist Church, Meeting Street 25 30
639 25 c. St. Francis Xavier Catholic Church, Highbury Park 25 50
640 $1 Holy Cross Anglican Church, Highbury Park .. .. 75 2·75
635/40 .. .. *Set of* 6 1·50 3·75

145 Prime Minister Lynden O. Pindling

(Des Walsall. Litho Questa)

1983 (14 Mar). *Commonwealth Day. T* **145** *and similar horiz designs. Multicoloured.* W w **14** *(sideways). P* 14.
641 5 c. Type **145** 10 10
642 25 c. Bahamian and Commonwealth flags .. 30 40
643 35 c. Map showing position of Bahamas .. 40 50
644 $1 Ocean liner .. .. 1·10 1·40
641/4 .. .. *Set of* 4 1·60 2·10

═ **20c**

(146)

1983 (5 Apr). *Nos.* 562/5 *surch as T* **146**.
645 20 c. on 15 c. Slave trading, Vendue House 50 35
646 31 c. on 21 c. Bootlegging, 1919–29 .. 60 55
w. Wmk inverted .. .. 2·50
647 35 c. on 16 c. Wrecking in the 1800's .. 1·25 60
648 80 c. on 18 c. Blockade running (American Civil War) .. .. 1·50 1·40
w. Wmk inverted .. .. 7·00
645/8 .. .. *Set of* 4 3·50 2·50

147 Customs Officers and Liner

148 Raising the National Flag

(Des Walsall. Litho Harrison)

1983 (31 May). *30th Anniv of Customs Co-operation Council. T* **147** *and similar vert design. Multicoloured.* W w **14**. *P* 13½ × 13.
649 31 c. Type **147** .. .. 1·50 45
650 $1 Customs officers and Lockheed Jet Star 1 airliner .. .. 3·50 2·75

(Des L. Curtis. Litho Questa)

1983 (6 July). *10th Anniv of Independence.* W w **14**. *P* 14.
651 **148** $1 multicoloured .. .. 1·00 1·40
MS652 105 × 65 mm. No. 651. P 12 .. .. 1·00 1·40

(Des F. Solomon, adapted N. Arlott. Litho Harrison)

1983 (24 Aug). *Wildlife (3rd series). Butterflies. Horiz designs as T* **136**. W w **14** *(sideways). P* 14½ × 14.
653 5 c. multicoloured 90 20
654 25 c. multicoloured .. .. 1·60 40
655 31 c. black, bistre-yellow and bright rose-red 1·60 55
656 50 c. multicoloured .. .. 1·75 85
653/6 .. .. *Set of* 4 5·00 1·75
MS657 120 × 80 mm. Nos. 653/6 .. .. .. 5·00 5·00
a. Perf 14 .. .. 4·25 6·00
Designs:—5 c. *Atalopedes carteri*; 25 c. *Ascia monuste*; 31 c. *Phoebis agarithe*; 50 c. *Dryas julia*.
No. **MS**657a was perforated by Questa, the remainder of the issue by Harrison.

149 "Loyalist Dreams"

150 Consolidated PBY-5 Catalina

(Des A. Lowe; adapted C. Abbott. Litho Questa)

1983 (28 Sept). *Bicentenary of Arrival of American Loyalists in the Bahamas. T* **149** *and similar multicoloured designs.* W w **14** *(sideways on* 31 c., 35 c.). *P* 14.
658 5 c. Type **149** 10 10
659 31 c. New Plymouth, Abaco *(horiz)* 45 50
660 35 c. New Plymouth Hotel *(horiz)* 50 70
661 50 c. "Island Hope" 65 90
658/61 .. .. *Set of* 4 1·50 2·00
MS662 111 × 76 mm. Nos. 658/61. Wmk sideways 1·50 2·50

(Des and litho Harrison)

1983 (13 Oct). *Air Bicentenary of Manned Flight. T* **150** *and similar horiz designs. Multicoloured.* W w **14** *(sideways). P* 14.
663 10 c. Type **150** 55 15
664 25 c. Avro Type 688 Tudor IV 75 40
665 31 c. Avro Type 691 Lancastrian 85 45
666 35 c. Consolidated Commodore .. .. 1·00 50
663/6 .. .. *Set of* 4 2·75 1·40
For these stamps without the Manned Flight logo see Nos. 699/702 (W w **14** (sideways)) and 752/3 (W w **16** (sideways)).

151 "Christmas Bells" (Monica Pinder)

152 1861 4d. Stamp

(Des local children, adapted G. Vasarhelyi. Litho Walsall)

1983 (1 Nov). *Christmas. Children's Paintings. T* **151** *and similar multicoloured designs. W w* **14** *(sideways on* 31 c. *and* 50 c.). *P* 14.

667 5 c. Type **151** 10 10
668 20 c. "Flamingo" (Cory Bullard) 25 30
669 25 c. "Yellow Hibiscus with Christmas Candle" (Monique Bailey) 35 40
670 31 c. "Santa goes a Sailing" (Sabrina Seiler) (*horiz*) 40 45
671 35 c. "Silhouette scene with Palm Trees" (James Blake) 45 50
672 50 c. "Silhouette scene with Pelicans" (Erik Russell) (*horiz*) 65 70
667/72 .. .. *Set of* 6 1·90 2·25

(Des D. Miller. Litho Format)

1984 (22 Feb). *125th Anniv of First Bahamas Postage Stamp. T* **152** *and similar vert design. Multicoloured. W w* **14**. *P* 14.

673 5 c. Type **152** 25 10
674 $1 1859 1d. stamp .. .. 1·75 1·50

153 *Trent I* (paddle steamer)

154 Running

(Des L. Curtis. Litho Questa)

1984 (25 Apr). *250th Anniv of "Lloyd's List" (newspaper). T* **153** *and similar vert designs. Multicoloured. W w* **14**. *P* 14½ × 14.

675 5 c. Type **153** 30 10
676 31 c. *Orinoco II* (mailship), 1886 .. .. 80 60
677 35 c. Cruise liners in Nassau harbour .. 90 75
678 50 c. *Oropesa* (container ship) .. .. 1·40 1·60
675/8 .. .. *Set of* 4 3·00 2·75

(Des McCombie Skinner Studio. Litho Questa)

1984 (20 June). *Olympic Games, Los Angeles. T* **154** *and similar horiz designs. W w* **14** *(sideways). P* 14 × 14½.

679 5 c. green, black and gold 15 15
680 25 c. new blue, black and gold 50 50
681 31 c. brown-lake, black and gold 55 60
682 $1 sepia, black and gold .. .. 3·75 4·25
679/82 .. .. *Set of* 4 4·50 5·00
MS683 115 × 80 mm. Nos. 679/82 .. .. 4·50 6·00

Designs:— 25 c. Shot-putting; 31 c. Boxing; $1 Basketball.

155 Bahamas and Caribbean Community Flags

156 Bahama Woodstar

(Des McCombie Skinner Studio. Litho Questa)

1984 (4 July). *5th Conference of Caribbean Community Heads of Government. W w* **14**. *P* 14.

684 **155** 50 c. multicoloured 90 95

(Des N. Arlott. Litho Questa)

1984 (15 Aug). *25th Anniv of National Trust. T* **156** *and similar vert designs. Multicoloured. W w* **14**. *P* 14.

685 31 c. Type **156**.. .. .. 2·75 2·75
a. Horiz strip of 5. Nos. 685/9 .. .. 12·00
686 31 c. Belted Kingfishers, Greater Flamingos and *Eleutherodactylus planirostris* (frog) .. .. 2·75 2·75
687 31 c. Black-necked Stilts, Greater Flamingos and *Phoebis sennae* (butterfly) .. 2·75 2·75
688 31 c. *Urbanus proteus* (butterfly) and *Chelonia mydas* (turtle) .. .. .. 2·75 2·75
689 31 c. Osprey and Greater Flamingos .. 2·75 2·75
685/9 .. .. *Set of* 5 12·00 12·00

Nos. 685/9 were printed together, *se-tenant*, in horizontal strips of 5 throughout the sheet, forming a composite design.

(Des N. Arlott. Litho Questa)

1984 (18 Sept). *Wildlife (4th series). Reptiles and Amphibians. Horiz designs as T* **136**. *W w* **14** *(sideways). P* 14.

690 5 c. Allen's Cay Iguana 30 20
691 25 c. Curly-tailed Lizard 85 60
692 35 c. Greenhouse Frog .. .. .. 1·00 85
693 50 c. Atlantic Green Turtle .. .. 1·60 2·25
690/3 .. .. *Set of* 4 3·25 3·50
MS694 112 × 82 mm. Nos. 690/3 .. .. 4·25 6·50

157 "The Holy Virgin with Jesus and Johannes" (19th-century porcelain plaque after Titian)

158 Brownie Emblem and Queen or Pink Conch

(Des D. Slater. Litho J.W.)

1984 (7 Nov). *Christmas. Religious Paintings. T* **157** *and similar vert designs. Multicoloured, W w* **14**. *P* 13½.

695 5 c. Type **157** 20 10
696 31 c. "Madonna with Child in Tropical Landscape" (aquarelle, Anais Colin) .. 75 60
w. Wmk inverted .. .. 1·00
697 35 c. "The Holy Virgin with the Child" (miniature on ivory, Elena Caula) .. 80 65
695/7 .. .. *Set of* 3 1·60 1·25
MS698 116×76 mm. Nos. 695/7. P 14 .. .. 1·40 3·00

1985 (2 Jan). *Air. As Nos.* 663/6, *but without Manned Flight logo. W w* **14** *(sideways*). P* 14.

699 10 c. Type **150** 70 30
700 25 c. Avro Type 688 Tudor IV 85 40
701 31 c. Avro Type 691 Lancastrian 85 55
w. Wmk Crown to right of CA .. .. 18·00
702 35 c. Consolidated Commodore .. .. 1·25 85
699/702 .. .. *Set of* 4 3·25 1·90

*The normal sideways watermark shows Crown to left of CA, *as seen from the back of the stamp.*

See also Nos. 752/3 for stamps watermarked w **16** (sideways).

(Des Berta Dallen Sands. Litho Walsall)

1985 (22 Feb). *International Youth Year. 75th Anniv of Girl Guide Movement. T* **158** *and similar horiz designs. Multicoloured. W w* **14** *(sideways). P* 14.

703 5 c. Type **158** 50 40
704 25 c. Tents and coconut palm .. .. 1·25 90
705 31 c. Guide salute and Greater Flamingos .. 1·50 90
706 35 c. Ranger emblem and marlin .. .. 1·75 1·40
703/6 .. .. *Set of* 4 4·50 3·25
MS707 95 × 74 mm. Nos. 703/6 .. .. 4·50 5·50

159 Killdeer

160 The Queen Mother at the Christening of Peter Phillips, 1977

(Des Josephine Martin. Litho Walsall)

1985 (24 Apr). *Birth Bicentenary of John J. Audubon (ornithologist). T* **159** *and similar multicoloured designs. W w* **14** *(sideways on* 5 c., $1). *P* 14.

708 5 c. Type **159**.. .. .. .. 1·00 30
709 31 c. Mourning Dove (*vert*) .. .. .. 2·25 55
710 35 c. "Mourning Dove" (John J. Audubon) (*vert*) .. .. 2·25 60
711 $1 "Killdeer" (John J. Audubon) .. .. 3·50 3·25
708/11 .. .. *Set of* 4 8·00 4·25

(Des A. Theobald ($1.25), C. Abbott (others). Litho Questa)

1985 (7 June). *Life and Times of Queen Elizabeth the Queen Mother. T* **160** *and similar vert designs. Multicoloured. W w* **16**. *P* 14½ × 14.

712 5 c. Visiting Auckland, New Zealand, 1927 10 10
713 25 c. Type **160** 40 40
714 35 c. The Queen Mother attending church 55 55
w. Wmk inverted 80
715 50 c. With Prince Henry at his christening (from photo by Lord Snowdon) .. 75 75
712/15 .. .. *Set of* 4 1·60 1·60
MS716 91×73 mm. $1.25, In horse-drawn carriage, Sark. Wmk sideways .. .. 1·75 1·90

161 Ears of Wheat and Emblems

162 Queen Elizabeth II

(Des A. Theobald. Litho Questa)

1985 (26 Aug). *40th Annivs of United Nations and F.A.O. (Food and Agriculture Organization). W w* **16** *(sideways). P* 14.

717 **161** 25 c. multicoloured 85 60

(Des L. Curtis. Litho Walsall)

1985 (16 Oct). *Commonwealth Heads of Government Meeting, Nassau. T* **162** *and similar vert design. Multicoloured. W w* **16** *P* 14½.

718 31 c. Type **162** .. .. 2·00 2·25
w. Wmk inverted .. .. .. 16·00
719 35 c. Bahamas Prime Minister's flag and Commonwealth emblem .. .. 2·00 2·75
w. Wmk inverted .. .. .. 16·00

1985 (6 Nov). *As Nos.* 557/8, 560 *and* 566, *but W w* **16**. *P* 14½.

720 1 c. Type **131** .. .. 1·75 4·00
721 3 c. Blackbeard the Pirate, 1718 .. .. 2·25 4·50
723 10 c. Ceremonial mace .. .. .. 3·00 1·75
726 25 c. Pineapple cultivation .. .. 6·50 6·50
720/6 .. .. *Set of* 4 12·00 15·00

163 "Grandma's Christmas Bouquet" (Alton Roland Lowe)

(Des D. Miller. Litho J.W.)

1985 (12 Nov). *Christmas. Paintings by Alton Roland Lowe. T* **163** *and similar multicoloured designs. W w* **16** *(sideways on* 5, 35 c.). *P* 13 × 13½ (5, 35 c.) *or* 13½ × 13 *(others).*

736 5 c. Type **163**.. .. .. 25 10
737 25 c. "Junkanoo Romeo and Juliet" (*vert*) .. 85 75
738 31 c. "Bunce Gal" (*vert*) .. .. .. 1·10 1·25
739 35 c. "Home for Christmas" .. .. 1·40 1·50
736/9 .. .. *Set of* 4 3·25 3·25
MS740 110×68 mm. Nos. 736/9. Wmk sideways. P 14 .. .. 2·00 3·00

(Des A. Theobald. Litho Harrison)

1986 (21 Apr). *60th Birthday of Queen Elizabeth II. Vert designs as T* **110** *of Ascension. Multicoloured. W w* **16**. *P* 14½×14.

741 10 c. Princess Elizabeth aged one, 1927 .. 15 15
742 25 c. The Coronation, 1953 .. .. 30 30
w. Wmk inverted .. .. ..
743 35 c. Queen making speech at Commonwealth Banquet, Bahamas, 1985 .. 35 40
744 40 c. In Djakova, Yugoslavia, 1972 .. 35 45
w. Wmk inverted .. .. .. 8·00
745 $1 At Crown Agents Head Office, London 1983 .. .. 80 1·40
741/5 .. .. *Set of* 5 1·75 2·40

164 1980 1 c. and 18 c. Definitive Stamps

(Des G. Drummond. Litho Walsall)

1986 (19 May). *"Ameripex '86" International Stamp Exhibition, Chicago. T* **164** *and similar designs. W w* **16** *(sideways on* 5 to 50 c). *P* 14.

746 5 c. multicoloured 40 30
747 25 c. multicoloured .. .. 1·00 50
748 31 c. multicoloured .. .. 1·25 60
749 50 c. multicoloured .. .. 1·75 2·75
750 $1 black, emerald and pale blue .. .. 2·00 3·25
746/50 .. .. *Set of* 5 5·75 6·75
MS751 80×80 mm. No. 750 .. .. .. 3·00 3·50

Designs: *Horiz* (showing Bahamas stamps)—25 c. 1969 50th Anniversary of Bahamas Airmail Service pair; 31 c. 1976 Bicentenary of American Revolution 16 c.; 50 c. 1981 Space Exploration miniature sheet. *Vert*—$1 Statue of Liberty.

Nos. 750/1 also commemorate the Centenary of the Statue of Liberty.

1986 (17 June). *Air. As Nos.* 699/700, *but W w* **16** *(sideways). P* 14.

752 10 c. Type **150** .. .. 1·75 50
753 25 c. Avro Type 688 Tudor IV .. .. 2·00 1·50

(Des D. Miller. Litho Walsall)

986 (23 July). *Royal Wedding. Square designs as T* **112** *of Ascension. Multicoloured.* W w **16**. *P* 14½×14.

56 10 c. Prince Andrew and Miss Sarah Ferguson 20 20
57 $1 Prince Andrew 1·25 2·10

165 Rock Beauty (juvenile)

166 Christ Church Cathedral, Nassau, 1861

(Des Harrison Studio. Litho Questa)

986 (5 Aug)–**90**. *Fishes. T* **165** *and similar horiz designs. Multicoloured.* W w **16**. *P* 14. A. *Without imprint date at foot.*

58A 5 c. Type **165** 75 75
59A 10 c. Stoplight Parrotfish 80 90
60A 15 c. Jackknife-fish 1·50 1·50
61A 20 c. Flamefish 1·25 1·25
62A 25 c. Peppermint Basslet ("Swissguard Basslet") 1·50 1·50
63A 30 c. Spot-finned Butterflyfish 1·10 1·50
64A 35 c. Queen Triggerfish 1·10 1·50
65A 40 c. Four-eyed Butterflyfish 1·50 1·25
66A 45 c. Royal Gramma ("Fairy Basslet") 1·50 1·25
67A 50 c. Queen Angelfish 2·00 2·25
68A 60 c. Blue Chromis 3·50 4·00
69A $1 Spanish Hogfish 3·50 4·00
70A $2 Harlequin Bass 8·00 9·00
771A $3 Black-barred Soldierfish 6·00 7·00
772A $5 Cherub Angelfish ("Pygmy Angelfish") 6·50 8·00
773A $10 Red Hind (2.1.87) 15·00 20·00
758A/73A *Set of* 16 48·00 60·00

B. *With imprint date*

759B 10 c. Stoplight Parrotfish (8.90) 1·00 2·00
762B 25 c. Peppermint Basslet ("Swissguard Basslet") (8.90) 1·00 2·25
765B 40 c. Four-eyed Butterflyfish (15.8.88) 1·10 1·60
766B 45 c. Royal Gramma ("Fairy Basslet") (8.90) 1·60 2·75
767B 50 c. Queen Angelfish (8.90) 1·60 2·75
769B $1 Spanish Hogfish (15.8.88) 2·75 3·00
770B $2 Harlequin Bass (15.8.88) 12·00 9·50
771B $3 Black-barred Soldierfish (8.90) 5·00 11·00
772B $5 Cherub Angelfish ("Pygmy Angelfish") (8.90) 6·50 13·00
759B/72B *Set of* 9 29·00 42·00

Imprint dates: "1988", Nos. 765B, 769B/70B; "1990", Nos. 759B, 762B, 765B/7B, 769B, 771B/2B.

For those designs watermarked w **14** see Nos. 791/9.

(Des L. Curtis. Litho Walsall)

1986 (16 Sept). *125th Annivs of City of Nassau, Diocese and Cathedral. T* **166** *and similar vert design. Multicoloured.* W w **16**. *P* 14½×14.

774 10 c. Type **166**. 20 20
775 40 c. Christ Church Cathedral, 1986 65 80
MS776 75×100 mm. Nos. 774/5 2·25 4·25

167 Man and Boy looking at Crib

168 Great Isaac Lighthouse

(Des Jennifer Toombs. Litho Questa)

1986 (4 Nov). *Christmas. International Peace Year. T* **167** *and similar horiz designs. Multicoloured.* W w **16** (*sideways*). *P* 14.

777 10 c. Type **167**. 35 20
778 40 c. Mary and Joseph journeying to Bethlehem 85 75
779 45 c. Children praying and Star of Bethlehem 95 1·00
780 50 c. Children exchanging gifts 1·00 2·00
777/80 *Set of* 4 2·75 3·50
MS781 95×90 mm. Nos. 777/80 7·00 9·50

(Des A. Lowe, adapted L. Curtis. Litho Walsall)

1987 (31 Mar). *Lighthouses. T* **168** *and similar horiz designs. Multicoloured.* W w **16** (*sideways*). *P* 14×14½.

782 10 c. Type **168**. 1·50 60
783 40 c. Bird Rock Lighthouse 3·50 1·50
784 45 c. Castle Island Lighthouse 3·50 1·50
785 $1 "Hole in the Wall" Lighthouse 5·00 8·50
782/5 *Set of* 4 12·00 11·00

MINIMUM PRICE

The minimum price quote is 10p which represents a handling charge rather than a basis for valuing common stamps. For further notes about prices see introductory pages.

169 Anne Bonney

170 Boeing 737

(Des D. and Jane Hartley. Litho Questa)

1987 (2 June). *Pirates and Privateers of the Caribbean. T* **169** *and similar vert designs. Multicoloured.* W w **16**. *P* 14½.

786 10 c. Type **169**. 1·50 75
787 40 c. Edward Teach ("Blackbeard") 3·50 2·50
788 45 c. Captain Edward England 3·50 2·50
789 50 c. Captain Woodes Rogers 4·00 3·75
786/9 *Set of* 4 11·00 8·50
MS790 75×95 mm. $1.25, Map of Bahamas and colonial coat of arms 6·00 3·50

1987 (25 June). *As Nos.* 758/60 *and* 765/70, *but* W w **14**. *With imprint date. P* 14.

791 5 c. Type **165** 1·00 1·75
792 10 c. Stoplight Parrotfish 1·00 75
793 15 c. Jackknife-fish 1·75 2·25
794 40 c. Four-eyed Butterflyfish 1·75 2·25
795 45 c. Royal Gramma 2·00 2·25
796 50 c. Queen Angelfish 2·00 2·75
797 60 c. Blue Chromis 2·00 4·00
798 $1 Spanish Hogfish 2·25 4·00
799 $2 Harlequin Bass 2·75 6·50
791/9 *Set of* 9 15·00 24·00

Imprint dates: "1987", Nos. 791/9; "1988", No. 792; "1989", No. 791.

(Des A. Theobald. Litho Questa)

1987 (7 July). *Air. Aircraft. T* **170** *and similar horiz designs. Multicoloured.* W w **16**. *P* 14.

800 15 c. Type **170** 1·25 70
801 40 c. Boeing 757-200 2·00 1·25
802 45 c. Airbus Industrie A300B4-200 2·00 1·25
803 50 c. Boeing 747-200 2·00 2·00
800/3 *Set of* 4 6·50 4·75

171 *Norway* (liner) and Catamaran

172 *Cattleyopsis lindenii*

(Des A. Theobald. Litho Questa)

1987 (26 Aug). *Tourist Transport. T* **171** *and similar vert designs. Multicoloured.* W w **16**. *P* 14.

804 40 c. Type **171**. 1·50 1·50
a. Horiz strip of 5. Nos. 804/8 6·50
805 40 c. Liners and speedboat 1·50 1·50
806 40 c. Game fishing boat and cruising yacht 1·50 1·50
807 40 c. Game fishing boat and racing yachts 1·50 1·50
808 40 c. Fishing boat and schooner 1·50 1·50
809 40 c. Hawker Siddeley H.S.748 airliner 1·50 1·50
a. Horiz strip of 5. Nos. 809/13 6·50
810 40 c. Boeing 737 and Boeing 727-200 airliners 1·50 1·50
811 40 c. Beech 200 Super King Air aircraft and radio beacon 1·50 1·50
812 40 c. Aircraft and Nassau control tower 1·50 1·50
813 40 c. Helicopter and parked aircraft 1·50 1·50
804/13 *Set of* 10 13·00 13·00

Nos. 804/8 and 809/13 were each printed together, *se-tenant*, in horizontal strips of 5 throughout the sheets, each strip forming a composite design.

(Des. A. Lowe; adapted L. Curtis. Litho Questa)

1987 (20 Oct). *Christmas. Orchids. T* **172** *and similar horiz designs. Multicoloured.* W w **16** (*sideways*). *P* 14×14½.

814 10 c. Type **172**. 1·00 30
815 40 c. *Encyclia lucayana* 2·25 1·00
816 45 c. *Encyclia hodgeana* 2·25 1·00
817 50 c. *Encyclia lleidae* 2·25 2·25
814/17 *Set of* 4 7·00 4·00
MS818 120×92 mm. Nos. 814/17 7·00 4·00

173 King Ferdinand and Queen Isabella of Spain

174 Whistling Ducks in Flight

(Des L. Curtis. Litho Format)

1988 (24 Feb). *500th Anniv of Discovery of America by Columbus* (1992) (*1st issue*). *T* **173** *and similar vert designs. Multicoloured.* W w **14**. *P* 14×14½.

819 10 c. Type **173**. 75 30
820 40 c. Columbus before Talavera Committee. 1·60 1·60
821 45 c. Lucayan village. 1·75 1·75
822 50 c. Lucayan potters. 1·90 2·25
819/22 *Set of* 4 5·50 5·50
MS823 65×50 mm. $1.50, Map of Antilles, c. 1500. Wmk sideways 5·50 3·75

See also Nos. 844/8, 870/4, 908/12, 933/7 and **MS**946.

(Des W. Oliver. Litho Walsall)

1988 (29 Apr). *Black-billed Whistling Duck. T* **174** *and similar horiz designs. Multicoloured.* W w **14** (*sideways*). *P* 14×14½.

824 5 c. Type **174** 1·90 80
825 10 c. Whistling Duck in reeds 1·90 80
826 20 c. Pair with brood 3·50 1·75
827 45 c. Pair wading 5·50 2·25
824/7 *Set of* 4 11·50 5·00

175 Grantstown Cabin, c. 1820

176 Olympic Flame, High Jumping, Hammer throwing, Basketball and Gymnastics

(Des N. Shewring. Litho B.D.T.)

1988 (9 Aug). *150th Anniv of Abolition of Slavery. T* **175** *and similar horiz design. Multicoloured.* W w **14** (*sideways*). *P* 13½.

828 10 c. Type **175** 50 30
829 40 c. Basket-making, Grantstown 1·25 95

(Des D. Miller. Litho Walsall)

1988 (30 Aug). *Olympic Games, Seoul. T* **176** *and similar horiz designs taken from painting by James Martin. Multicoloured.* W w **16** (*sideways*). *P* 14.

830 10 c. Type **176** 50 20
831 40 c. Athletics, archery, swimming, long jumping, weightlifting and boxing 70 60
832 45 c. Javelin throwing, gymnastics, hurdling and shot put 70 60
833 $1 Athletics, hurdling, gymnastics and cycling 2·50 2·75
830/3 *Set of* 4 4·00 3·75
MS834 113×85 mm. Nos. 830/3. W w **14** (sideways) 2·50 2·75

(Des O. Bell and D. Miller (40 c.), E. Nisbet and D. Miller ($1), D. Miller (others). Litho Format)

1988 (4 Oct). *300th Anniv of Lloyd's of London. Multicoloured designs as T* **123** *of Ascension.* W w **14** (*sideways on* 40, 45 *c.*). *P* 14.

835 10 c. Lloyd's List of 1740 30 15
836 40 c. Freeport Harbour (*horiz*) 1·25 60
837 45 c. Space shuttle over Bahamas (*horiz*) 1·25 60
838 $1 *Yarmouth Castle* (freighter) on fire 2·25 1·90
835/8 *Set of* 4 4·50 3·00

177 "Oh Little Town of Bethlehem"

178 Cuban Emerald

(Des Josephine Martin. Litho Questa)

1988 (21 Nov). *Christmas. Carols. T* **177** *and similar vert designs. Multicoloured.* W w **16**. *P* 14½×14.

839 10 c. Type **177** 35 20
840 40 c. "Little Donkey" 1·00 75
841 45 c. "Silent Night" 1·10 90
842 50 c. "Hark the Herald Angels Sing" 1·25 1·50
839/42 *Set of* 4 3·25 3·00
MS843 88×108 mm. Nos. 839/42. W w **14** 2·25 2·50

(Des A. Lowe (50 c.), L. Curtis (others). Litho Questa)

1989 (25 Jan). *500th Anniv of Discovery of America by Columbus* (1992) (*2nd issue*). *Vert designs as T* **173**. *Multicoloured.* W w **16**. *P* 14½×14.

844 10 c. Columbus drawing chart 1·10 40
845 40 c. Types of caravel 2·50 1·25
846 45 c. Early navigational instruments 2·50 1·25
847 50 c. Arawak artefacts 2·50 2·75
844/7 *Set of* 4 7·75 5·00
MS848 64×64 mm. $1.50, Caravel under construction (from 15th-cent *Nuremburg Chronicles*) 2·25 1·90

(Des N. Shewring. Litho Questa)

1989 (29 Mar). *Hummingbirds. T* **178** *and similar vert designs. Multicoloured. W* w **16**. *P* 14½ × 14.
849 10 c. Type **178** .. .. 1·50 75
850 40 c. Ruby-throated Hummingbird .. 2·75 2·00
851 45 c. Bahama Woodstar .. .. .. 2·75 2·00
852 50 c. Rufous Hummingbird .. .. 3·00 3·00
849/52 .. .. *Set of* 4 9·00 7·00

179 Teaching Water Safety

180 Church of the Nativity, Bethlehem

(Des S. Noon. Litho Questa)

1989 (31 May). *125th Anniv of International Red Cross. T* **179** *and similar horiz design. Multicoloured. W* w **16** *(sideways). P* 14×14½.
853 10 c. Type **179** 75 25
854 $1 Henri Dunant (founder) and Battle of Solferino .. .. 3·00 2·50

(Des A. Theobald ($2), D. Miller (others). Litho Questa)

1989 (20 July). *20th Anniv of First Manned Landing on Moon. Multicoloured designs as T* **126** *of Ascension. W* w **16** *(sideways on* 40, 45 *c.). P* 14×13½ *(*10 *c.,* $1*) or* 14 *(others).*
855 10 c. "Apollo 8" Communications Station, Grand Bahama 35 30
856 40 c. Crew of "Apollo 8" (30×30 *mm*) .. 80 55
857 45 c. "Apollo 8" emblem (30×30 *mm*) .. 80 60
858 $1 The Earth seen from "Apollo 8" .. 1·50 2·75
855/8 .. .. *Set of* 4 3·00 3·75
MS859 100×83 mm. $2 "Apollo 11" astronauts in training, Manned Spacecraft Centre, Houston. P 14×13½ .. .. 2·50 3·50

(Des E. Weishoff. Litho Questa)

1989 (16 Oct). *Christmas. Churches of the Holy Land. T* **180** *and similar vert designs. W* w **14**. *P* 14½×14.
860 10 c. Type **180** 40 20
861 40 c. Basilica of the Annunciation, Nazareth 1·10 60
862 45 c. Tabgha Church, Galilee .. .. 1·10 60
863 $1 Church of the Holy Sepulchre, Jerusalem .. .. 2·25 3·00
860/3 .. .. *Set of* 4 4·25 4·00
MS864 92×109 mm. Nos. 860/3. Wmk sideways 3·50 6·00

181 1974 U.P.U. Centenary 13 c. Stamp and Globe

(Des J. Sayer. Litho Questa)

1989 (17 Nov). *"World Stamp Expo '89" International Stamp Exhibition, Washington. T* **181** *and similar multicoloured designs. W* w **16** *(sideways). P* 14.
865 10 c. Type **181** 60 30
866 40 c. 1970 New U.P.U. Headquarters Building 3 c. and building .. .. 1·25 75
867 45 c. 1986 "Ameripex '86" $1 and Capitol, Washington .. .. .. 1·25 80
868 $1 1949 75th anniversary of U.P.U. 2½d. and Boeing 737 airliner .. .. 4·25 5·50
865/8 .. .. *Set of* 4 6·50 6·50
MS869 107×80 mm. $2 Map showing route of Columbus, 1492 (30×38 *mm*). P 14½ .. .. 8·50 10·00

(Des A. Lowe (50 c.), L. Curtis (others). Litho Questa)

1990 (24 Jan). *500th Anniversary of Discovery of America by Columbus* (1992) *(3rd issue). Vert designs as T* **173**. *Multicoloured. W* w **14**. *P* 14½×14.
870 10 c. Launching caravel .. .. .. 1·25 60
871 40 c. Provisioning ship .. .. .. 2·25 2·00
872 45 c. Shortening sail .. .. .. 2·25 2·00
873 50 c. Lucayan fishermen .. .. .. 2·25 3·00
870/3 .. .. *Set of* 4 7·25 7·00
MS874 70×61 mm. $1.50, Departure of Columbus, 1492 .. .. 5·50 7·00

182 Bahamas Flag, O.A.S. Headquarters and Centenary Logo

(Des O. Bell. Litho Questa)

1990 (14 Mar). *Centenary of Organization of American States. W* w **16** *(sideways). P* 14.
875 **182** 40 c. multicoloured .. .. .. 1·75 1·75

183 Supermarine Spitfire Mk I *Bahamas I*

(Des A. Theobald. Litho Questa)

1990 (3 May). *"Stamp World London 90" International Stamp Exhibition, London. Presentation Fighter Aircraft. Sheet* 107×78 *mm. containing T* **183** *and similar horiz design. Multicoloured. W* w **16** *(sideways). P* 14.
MS876 $1 Type **183**; $1 Hawker Hurricane Mk IIc *Bahamas V* .. .. 6·00 6·00

184 Teacher with Boy

185 Cuban Amazon preening

(Des G. Vasarhelyi. Litho Questa)

1990 (27 June). *International Literacy Year. T* **184** *and similar horiz designs. Multicoloured. W* w **16** *(sideways). P* 14.
877 10 c. Type **184** 75 50
878 40 c. Three boys in class .. .. .. 1·60 1·25
879 50 c. Teacher and children with books .. 1·60 2·25
877/9 .. .. *Set of* 3 3·50 3·50

(Des D. Miller. Litho Questa)

1990 (4 Aug). *90th Birthday of Queen Elizabeth the Queen Mother. Vert designs as T* **134** *(*40 *c.) or* **135** *(*$1.50*) of Ascension. W* w **16**. *P* 14×15 *(*40 *c.) or* 14½ *(*$1.50*).*
880 40 c. multicoloured .. .. .. 1·00 50
881 $1.50, brownish black and ochre .. 2·25 3·00
Designs:—40 c. "Queen Elizabeth, 1938" (Sir Gerald Kelly); $1.50, Queen Elizabeth at garden party, France, 1938.

(Des N. Arlott. Litho Questa)

1990 (26 Sept). *Cuban Amazon (Bahamian Parrot). T* **185** *and similar vert designs. Multicoloured. W* w **14**. *P* 14.
882 10 c. Type **185** .. .. 1·00 55
883 40 c. Pair in flight .. .. 2·00 1·00
884 45 c. Cuban Amazon's head .. .. 2·00 1·00
885 50 c. Perched on branch .. .. .. 2·25 2·50
882/5 .. .. *Set of* 4 6·50 4·50
MS886 73×63 mm. $1.50, Feeding on berries .. 6·00 7·50

186 The Annunciation

187 Green Heron

(Des Jennifer Toombs. Litho B.D.T.)

1990 (5 Nov). *Christmas. T* **186** *and similar vert designs. Multicoloured. W* w **14**. *P* 14×13½.
887 10 c. Type **186** 40 20
888 40 c. The Nativity 90 55
889 45 c. Angel appearing to Shepherds .. 90 65
890 $1 The three Kings .. .. .. 2·50 3·50
887/90 .. .. *Set of* 4 4·25 4·50
MS891 94×110 mm. Nos. 887/90 .. .. 5·50 6·50

(Des N. Arlott. Litho Questa)

1991 (4 Feb–1 July). *Birds. T* **187** *and similar vert designs. Multicoloured. W* w **16** *(sideways).* "1991" *imprint date. P* 14.
892 5 c. Type **187** 70 50
893 10 c. Turkey Vulture 80 60
894 15 c. Osprey .. .. 2·00 70
895 20 c. Clapper Rail .. .. 1·00 70
896 25 c. Royal Tern .. .. 1·25 75
897 30 c. Key West Quail Dove .. .. 1·25 75
898 40 c. Smooth-billed Ani .. .. .. 1·50 55
899 45 c. Burrowing Owl .. .. .. 2·25 80
900 50 c. Hairy Woodpecker .. .. .. 2·00 70
901 55 c. Mangrove Cuckoo .. .. .. 2·00 75
902 60 c. Bahama Mockingbird .. .. 2·00 1·40
903 70 c. Red-winged Blackbird .. .. 2·00 1·50
904 $1 Thick-billed Vireo .. .. .. 2·50 1·50
905 $2 Bahama Yellowthroat .. .. 5·00 4·5
906 $5 Stripe-headed Tanager .. .. 10·00 11·0
907 $10 Greater Antillean Bullfinch (1 July) .. 13·00 15·0
892/907 .. .. *Set of* 16 45·00 38·0
For these designs watermarked w **14** (sideways) see Nos 975/88.

(Des A. Lowe (55 c.), L. Curtis (others). Litho Questa)

1991 (9 Apr). *500th Anniv of Discovery of America by Columbus* (1992) *(4th issue). Vert designs as T* **173**. *Multicoloured. W* w **16**. *P* 14½ × 14.
908 15 c. Columbus navigating by stars .. 1·25 6
909 40 c. Fleet in mid-Atlantic .. .. .. 2·00 1·7
910 55 c. Lucayan family worshipping at night 2·00 2·0
911 60 c. Map of First Voyage .. .. .. 2·50 3·5
908/11 .. .. *Set of* 4 7·00 7·0
MS912 56 × 61 mm. $1.50, *Pinta's* look-out sighting land .. .. 5·25 6·5

(Des D. Miller. Litho Questa)

1991 (17 June). *65th Birthday of Queen Elizabeth II and 70th Birthday of Prince Philip. Vert designs as T* **139** *of Ascension. Multicoloured. W* w **16** *(sideways). P* 14½ × 14.
913 15 c. Prince Philip .. .. 1·00 1·5
a. Horiz pair. Nos. 913/14 separated by label .. .. 2·75 3·5
914 $1 Queen Elizabeth II .. .. .. 1·75 2·0
Nos. 913/14 were printed in the same sheet format as Nos. 539/40 of Ascension.

188 Radar Plot of Hurricane Hugo

189 The Annunciation

(Des A. Theobald. Litho B.D.T)

1991 (28 Aug). *International Decade for Natural Disaster Reduction. T* **188** *and similar horiz designs. Multicoloured. W* w **16** *(sideways). P* 14.
915 15 c. Type **188** 75 30
916 40 c. Diagram of hurricane .. .. 1·25 1·10
917 55 c. Flooding caused by Hurricane David, 1979 .. .. 1·50 1·75
918 60 c. U.S. Dept of Commerce weather reconnaissance Lockheed WP-3D Orion 2·25 3·00
915/18 .. .. *Set of* 4 5·25 5·50

(Des Jennifer Toombs. Litho B.D.T.)

1991 (28 Oct). *Christmas. T* **189** *and similar vert designs. Multicoloured. W* w **14**. *P* 14.
919 15 c. Type **189** 40 25
920 55 c. Mary and Joseph travelling to Bethlehem .. .. 1·00 1·00
921 60 c. Angel appearing to the shepherds .. 1·10 1·40
922 $1 Adoration of the Kings .. .. 2·00 3·25
919/22 .. .. *Set of* 4 4·00 5·50
MS923 92 × 108 mm. Nos. 919/22 .. .. 6·00 7·50

190 First Progressive Liberal Party Cabinet

(Des G. Vasarhelyi. Litho B.D.T.)

1992 (10 Jan). *25th Anniv of Majority Rule. T* **190** *and similar multicoloured designs. W* w **14** *(sideways on* 15 *c. and* 40 *c.). P* 14.
924 15 c. Type **190** 60 40
925 40 c. Signing of Independence Constitution 1·40 1·10
926 55 c. Prince of Wales handing over Constitutional Instrument (*vert*) .. 1·50 1·50
927 60 c. First Bahamian Governor-General, Sir Milo Butler (*vert*) .. .. .. 1·75 2·75
924/7 .. .. *Set of* 4 4·75 5·25

(Des D. Miller. Litho Questa ($1), B.D.T. (others))

1992 (6 Feb). *40th Anniv of Queen Elizabeth II's Accession. Horiz designs as T* **143** *of Ascension. Multicoloured. W* w **14** *(sideways). P* 14.
928 15 c. Queen Elizabeth with bouquet .. 50 30
929 40 c. Queen Elizabeth with flags .. .. 1·00 70
930 55 c. Queen Elizabeth at display .. .. 1·00 90
931 60 c. Three portraits of Queen Elizabeth .. 1·10 1·25
932 $1 Queen Elizabeth II .. .. .. 1·50 2·25
928/32 .. .. *Set of* 5 4·50 4·75

(Des A. Lowe and L. Curtis. Litho Questa)

1992 (17 Mar). *500th Anniv of Discovery of America by Columbus (5th issue). Vert designs as T* **173**. *Multicoloured. W* w **16**. *P* 14½×14.
933 15 c. Lucayans sighting fleet .. .. 1·00 60
934 40 c. *Santa Maria* and dolphins .. .. 1·75 1·50
935 55 c. Lucayan canoes approaching ships .. 1·75 1·75
936 60 c. Columbus giving thanks for landfall 2·25 3·00
933/6 .. .. *Set of* 4 6·00 6·25
MS937 61×57 mm. $1.50, Children at Columbus Monument .. .. 3·50 4·50

191 Templeton, Galbraith and Hansberger Ltd Building

192 Pole Vaulting

(Des O. Bell. Litho Questa)

1992 (22 Apr). *20th Anniv of Templeton Prize for Religion. W w* **16** *(sideways). P* 14½.
938 **191** 55 c. multicoloured .. .. 1·50 1·50

(Des O. Bell. Litho Questa)

1992 (2 June). *Olympic Games, Barcelona. T* **192** *and similar vert designs. Multicoloured. W w* **14**. *P* 14½.
939 15 c. Type **192** 50 35
940 40 c. Javelin 90 90
941 55 c. Hurdling .. .. 1·10 1·25
942 60 c. Basketball .. .. 3·50 3·75
939/42 .. .. *Set of* 4 5·50 5·50
MS943 70×50 mm. $2 Sailing .. .. .. 6·00 7·00

193 Arid Landscape and Starving Child

194 Mary visiting Elizabeth

(Des Jennifer Toombs. Litho Enschedé)

1992 (11 Aug). *International Conference on Nutrition. T* **193** *and similar horiz design. Multicoloured. W w* **14** *(sideways). P* 14½×13½.
944 15 c. Type **193** 75 50
945 55 c. Seedling, cornfield and child .. .. 1·75 2·00

(Des L. Curtis. Litho B.D.T.)

1992 (12 Oct). *500th Anniv of Discovery of America by Columbus (6th issue). Sheet, 65×65 mm, containing vert design as T* **173**. *Multicoloured. W w* **16**. *P* 13½.
MS946 $2 Columbus landing in Bahamas .. 5·50 6·50

(Des Jennifer Toombs. Litho B.D.T.)

1992 (2 Nov). *Christmas. T* **194** *and similar vert designs. Multicoloured. W w* **14**. *P* 14×13½.
947 15 c. Type **194** 40 20
948 55 c. The Nativity .. .. 1·10 1·00
949 60 c. Angel and Shepherds .. .. .. 1·25 1·50
950 70 c. Wise Men and star .. .. .. 1·40 2·50
947/50 .. .. *Set of* 4 3·75 4·75
MS951 95×110 mm. Nos. 947/50 .. .. 5·50 6·50

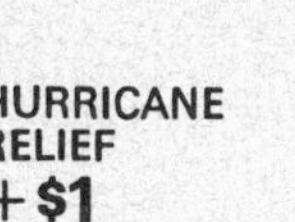

(195)

196 Flags of Bahamas and U.S.A. with Agricultural Worker

1992 (16 Nov). *Hurricane Relief. No.* **MS**876 *showing each stamp surch with T* **195**.
MS952 $1 + $1 Type **183**; $1 + $1 Hawker Hurricane MkIIc *Bahamas V* .. .. .. 8·50 11·00

(Des Lorraine Cox, adapted D. Miller. Litho Questa)

1993 (16 Mar). *50th Anniv of The Contract (U.S.A.–Bahamas farm labour programme). T* **196** *and similar horiz designs, each including national flags. Multicoloured. W w* **16** *(sideways). P* 14×14½.
953 15 c. Type **196** 75 60
954 55 c. Onions .. .. 1·75 1·50
955 60 c. Citrus fruit .. .. 1·75 2·00
956 70 c. Apples .. .. 2·00 2·25
953/6 .. .. *Set of* 4 5·50 5·75

(Des A. Theobald. Litho Questa)

1993 (1 Apr). *75th Anniv of Royal Air Force. Horiz designs as T* **149** *of Ascension. Multicoloured. W w* **14** *(sideways). P* 14.
957 15 c. Westland Wapiti IIA 80 65
958 40 c. Gloster Gladiator I .. .. .. 1·50 1·00
959 55 c. De Havilland D.H.100 Vampire F.3 1·75 1·50
960 70 c. English Electric Lightning F.3 .. 2·00 2·75
957/60 .. .. *Set of* 4 5·50 5·50
MS961 110×77 mm. 60 c. Avro Shackleton M.R.2; 60 c. Fairey Battle; 60 c. Douglas Boston III; 60 c. De Havilland D.H.9a .. .. .. 5·50 6·50

197 1978 Coronation Anniversary Stamps

198 *Lignum vitae* (national tree)

(Des D. Miller. Litho Enschedé)

1993 (2 June). *40th Anniv of Coronation. T* **197** *and similar horiz designs. Multicoloured. W w* **14** *(sideways). P* 13½.
962 15 c. Type **197** 70 50
963 55 c. Two examples of 1953 Coronation stamp .. .. 1·75 1·75
964 60 c. 1977 Silver Jubilee 8 c. and 16 c. stamps .. .. 1·75 2·00
965 70 c. 1977 Silver Jubilee 21 c. and 40 c. stamps .. .. 2·00 2·75
962/5 .. .. *Set of* 4 5·50 6·25

(Des N. Shewring. Litho B.D.T.)

1993 (8 July). *20th Anniv of Independence. T* **198** *and similar vert designs. Multicoloured. W w* **14**. *P* 14.
966 15 c. Type **198** 20 20
967 55 c. Yellow Elder (national flower) .. 90 90
968 60 c. Blue Marlin (national fish) .. .. 1·00 1·25
969 70 c. Greater Flamingo (national bird) .. 1·40 1·90
966/9 .. .. *Set of* 4 3·25 3·75

199 Cordia

200 The Annunciation

(Des D. Miller and A. Lowe. Litho B.D.T.)

1993 (8 Sept). *Environment Protection (1st issue). Wildflowers. T* **199** *and similar vert designs. Multicoloured. W w* **14**. *P* 13½.
970 15 c. Type **199** 50 40
971 55 c. Seaside Morning Glory .. .. .. 1·50 1·25
972 60 c. Poinciana .. .. 1·75 1·75
973 70 c. Spider Lily .. .. 1·75 2·50
970/3 .. .. *Set of* 4 5·00 5·50
See also Nos. 1017/22, 1035/9, 1084/8, 1121/4 and 1149/54

1993 (23 Sept)–**95**. *As Nos. 893/4, 896/8, 901 and 906, but W w* **14** *(sideways). With imprint date. P* 14.
975 10 c. Turkey Vulture 80 70
976 15 c. Osprey (4.95) 70 70
978 25 c. Royal Tern 60 70
979 30 c. Key West Quail Dove .. .. .. 1·00 80
980 40 c. Smooth-billed Ani (31.12.93) .. .. 1·25 1·50
983 55 c. Mangrove Cuckoo .. .. 2·00 80
988 $5 Stripe-headed Tanager .. .. .. 6·50 8·50
975/88 .. .. *Set of* 7 11·50 12·00
Imprint dates: "1993", Nos. 975, 978/80, 983, 988; "1995", Nos. 976, 978, 980, 983, 988.

(Des Jennifer Toombs. Litho B.D.T.)

1993 (1 Nov). *Christmas. T* **200** *and similar vert designs. Multicoloured. W w* **14**. *P* 13½.
990 15 c. Type **200** 55 30
991 55 c. Angel and shepherds .. .. .. 1·75 1·75
992 60 c. Holy family .. .. 1·75 2·00
993 70 c. Three Kings .. .. 2·00 2·50
990/3 .. .. *Set of* 4 5·50 6·00
MS994 86×106 mm. $1 Virgin Mary with Child 4·00 5·50

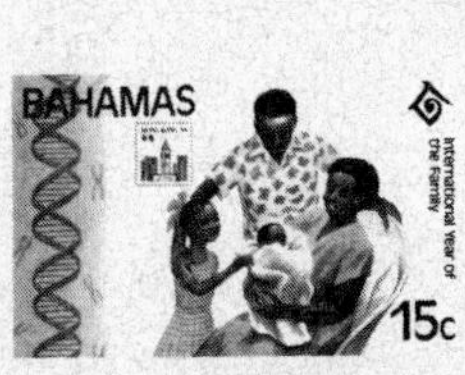
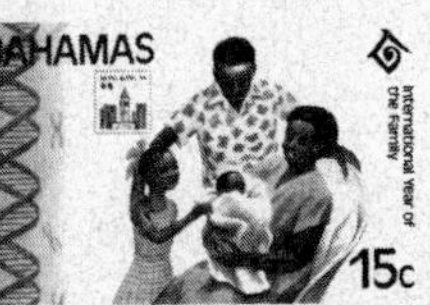

201 Family

202 Flags of Bahamas and Great Britain

(Des Jennifer Toombs. Litho B.D.T.)

1994 (18 Feb). *"Hong Kong '94" International Stamp Exhibition. International Year of the Family. T* **201** *and similar horiz designs. Multicoloured. W w* **16** *(sideways). P* 13½.
995 15 c. Type **201** 50 30
996 55 c. Children doing homework .. .. 1·25 1·25
997 60 c. Grandfather and grandson fishing .. 1·40 1·40
998 70 c. Grandmother teaching grandchildren the Lord's Prayer .. .. 2·00 2·50
995/8 .. .. *Set of* 4 4·75 5·00

(Des D. Miller. Litho B.D.T.)

1994 (7 Mar). *Royal Visit. T* **202** *and similar vert designs. Multicoloured. W w* **14**. *P* 13½.
999 15 c. Type **202** 55 40
1000 55 c. Royal Yacht *Britannia* .. .. .. 1·75 1·25
1001 60 c. Queen Elizabeth II .. .. 1·75 1·75
1002 70 c. Queen Elizabeth and Prince Philip .. 1·75 2·50
999/1002 .. .. *Set of* 4 5·25 5·50

203 Yachts

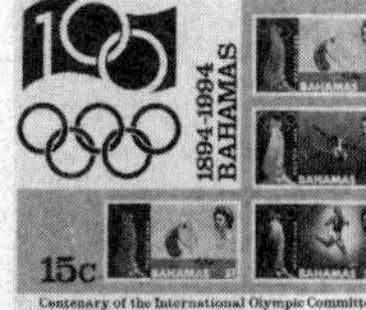

204 Logo and Bahamas 1968 Olympic Games Stamps

(Des D. Miller and A. Lowe. Litho B.D.T.)

1994 (27 Apr). *40th Anniv of National Family Island Regatta. T* **203** *and similar multicoloured designs. W w* **14** *(sideways). P* 13½.
1003 15 c. Type **203** 60 40
1004 55 c. Dinghy racing .. .. 1·40 1·10
1005 60 c. Working boats .. .. 1·50 1·75
1006 70 c. Sailing sloop .. .. 2·00 3·00
1003/6 .. .. *Set of* 4 5·00 5·50
MS1007 76×54 mm. $2 Launching sloop (*vert*). Wmk upright .. .. 5·50 6·50

(Des D. Miller. Litho Enschedé)

1994 (31 May). *Centenary of International Olympic Committee. T* **204** *and similar multicoloured designs. W w* **14** *(sideways on 55 c. and 70 c.). P* 13½.
1008 15 c. Type **204** 80 40
1009 55 c. 1976 Olympic Games stamps (*vert*) 1·75 1·25
1010 60 c. 1984 Olympic Games stamps .. 1·75 2·00
1011 70 c. 1992 Olympic Games stamps (*vert*) 2·25 2·75
1008/11 .. .. *Set of* 4 6·00 5·75

205 Star of Order

206 *Calpodes ethlius* and Canna

(Des D. Miller. Litho Enschedé)

1994 (5 July). *First Recipients of Order of the Caribbean Community. Sheet 90×69 mm. W w* **14**. *P* 13×14.
MS1012 **205** $2 multicoloured .. .. .. 3·75 4·50

(Des R. Watton. Litho Walsall)

1994 (16 Aug). *Butterflies and Flowers. T* **206** *and similar vert designs. Multicoloured. W w* **14**. *P* 14.
1013 15 c. Type **206** .. .. 1·10 55
1014 55 c. *Phoebis sennae* and Cassia .. .. 2·00 1·50
1015 60 c. *Anartia jatrophae* and Passion Flower 2·25 2·25
1016 70 c. *Battus devilliersi* and Calico Flower 2·25 2·75
1013/16 .. .. *Set of* 4 7·00 6·25

207 Spot-finned Hogfish and Spanish Hogfish

208 Angel

(Des A. Robinson. Litho Enschedé)

1994 (13 Sept). *Environment Protection (2nd issue). Marine Life. T* **207** *and similar vert designs. Multicoloured. W w* **14**. *P* 13×14½.
1017 40 c. Type **207** .. .. 90 1·10
a. Horiz strip of 5. Nos. 1017/21 .. 4·00
1018 40 c. Tomate and Long-spined Squirrelfish 90 1·10
1019 40 c. French Angelfish .. .. 90 1·10
1020 40 c. Queen Angelfish .. .. 90 1·10
1021 40 c. Rock Beauty .. .. 90 1·10
1017/21 .. .. *Set of* 5 4·00 5·00
MS1022 57×55 mm. $2 Rock Beauty, Queen Angelfish and windsurfer .. .. .. 4·00 5·00
Nos. 1017/21 were printed together, *se-tenant*, in horizontal strips of 5 throughout the sheet with the backgrounds forming a composite design.

(Des Jennifer Toombs. Litho B.D.T.)

1994 (31 Oct). *Christmas. T* **208** *and similar multicoloured designs.* W w **16** (*sideways*). *P* 14.
1023 15 c. Type **208** 30 30
1024 55 c. Holy Family .. .. 90 1·10
1025 60 c. Shepherds .. .. 1·10 1·40
1026 70 c. Wise Men .. .. 1·25 2·00
1023/6 .. .. *Set of* 4 3·25 4·25
MS1027 73×85 mm. $2 Jesus in manger. Wmk upright .. .. 3·25 4·50

209 Lion and Emblem

210 Kirtland's Warbler on Nest

(Des D. Miller. Litho Enschedé)

1995 (8 Feb). *20th Anniv of the College of the Bahamas. T* **209** *and similar vert design. Multicoloured.* W w **14**. *P* 14×13½.
1028 15 c. Type **209** 30 30
1029 70 c. Queen Elizabeth II and College building .. .. 1·25 1·75

(Des R. Watton. Litho Cartor (Nos. 1030/3) or Questa (No. **MS**1034))

1995 (8 May). *50th Anniv of End of Second World War. Multicoloured designs as T* **161** *of Ascension.* W w **14** (*sideways*). *P* 13½.
1030 15 c. Bahamian infantry drilling 60 40
1031 55 c. Consolidated PBY-5A Catalina flying boat .. .. 1·75 1·25
1032 60 c. Bahamian women in naval operations room .. .. 1·75 1·75
1033 70 c. Consolidated B-24 Liberator bomber 2·00 2·50
1030/3 .. .. *Set of* 4 5·50 5·50
MS1034 75×85 mm. $2 Reverse of 1939–45 War Medal (*vert*). Wmk upright. P 14 .. .. 3·00 4·00

(Des N. Arlott. Litho Cartor)

1995 (7 June). *Environment Protection (3rd issue). Endangered Species. Kirtland's Warbler. T* **210** *and similar vert designs. Multicoloured.* W w **14**. *P* 13½.
1035 15 c. Type **210** 55 60
w. Wmk inverted 55 60
wa. Strip of 4. Nos. 1035/8 .. .. 2·00
1036 15 c. Singing on branch 55 60
w. Wmk inverted 55 60
1037 25 c. Feeding chicks 55 60
w. Wmk inverted 55 60
1038 25 c. Catching insects 55 60
w. Wmk inverted 55 60
1035/8 .. .. *Set of* 4 2·00 2·25
MS1039 73×67 mm. $2 On branch. Wmk sideways. P 13 .. .. 6·00 7·00

Nos. 1035/8 were issued in sheets of 50 of each design and Nos. 1035w/8w in sheets of 16 (4×4) containing horizontal and vertical *se-tenant* strips.

No. **MS**1039 does not show the W.W.F. Panda emblem.

211 Eleuthera Cliffs

(Des D. Miller. Litho Questa)

1995 (18 July). *Tourism. T* **211** *and similar horiz designs. Multicoloured.* W w **16** (*sideways*). *P* 14½.
1040 15 c. Type **211** 55 40
1041 55 c. Clarence Town, Long Island .. .. 1·40 1·25
1042 60 c. Albert Lowe Museum .. .. .. 1·50 1·75
1043 70 c. Yachts .. .. 1·75 2·00
1040/3 .. .. *Set of* 4 4·75 4·75

212 Pigs and Chick

(Des Jennifer Toombs. Litho Cartor)

1995 (5 Sept). *50th Anniv of Food and Agriculture Organization. T* **212** *and similar horiz designs. Multicoloured.* W w **14** (*sideways*). *P* 13½×13.
1044 15 c. Type **212** 50 35
1045 55 c. Seedling and hand holding seed .. 1·25 1·10
1046 60 c. Family with fruit and vegetables .. 1·40 1·60
1047 70 c. Fishes and crustaceans .. .. .. 1·75 2·00
1044/7 .. .. *Set of* 4 4·50 4·50

213 Sikorsky S-55 Helicopter, Sinai, 1957

(Des A. Theobald. Litho B.D.T.)

1995 (24 Oct). *50th Anniv of United Nations. T* **213** *and similar horiz designs. Multicoloured.* W w **16** (*sideways*). *P* 14.
1048 15 c. Type **213** 50 40
1049 55 c. Ferret armoured car, Sinai, 1957 .. 1·25 1·25
1050 60 c. Fokker F.27 Friendship (airliner), Cambodia, 1991–93 .. .. 1·25 1·50
1051 70 c. Lockheed C-130 Hercules (transport) 1·50 2·00
1048/51 .. .. *Set of* 4 4·00 4·75

214 St. Agnes Anglican Church

(Des R. Watton. Litho B.D.T.)

1995 (17 Nov). *Christmas. Churches. T* **214** *and similar horiz designs. Multicoloured.* W w **16** (*sideways*). *P* 14.
1052 15 c. Type **214** 30 25
1053 55 c. Church of God, East Street 90 90
1054 60 c. Sacred Heart Roman Catholic Church 95 1·25
1055 70 c. Salem Union Baptist Church .. 1·10 1·75
1052/5 .. .. *Set of* 4 3·00 3·75

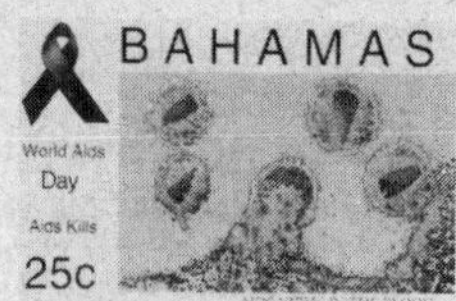

215 Microscopic View of AIDS Virus

(Des N. Shewring. Litho B.D.T.)

1995 (1 Dec). *World AIDS Day. T* **215** *and similar horiz design. Multicoloured.* W w **14** (*sideways*). *P* 14.
1056 25 c. Type **215** 60 50
1057 70 c. Research into AIDS .. .. .. 1·00 1·50

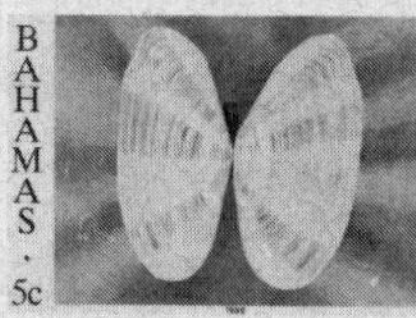

216 Sunrise Tellin

(Des D. Miller. Litho Questa)

1996 (2 Jan–1 July). *Sea Shells. T* **216** *and similar horiz designs. Multicoloured.* "1996" *imprint date.* W w **14** (*sideways*). *P* 14.
1058 5 c. Type **216** 25 30
1059 10 c. Queen Conch 35 30
1060 15 c. Angular Triton 55 40
1061 20 c. True Tulip 70 40
1062 25 c. Reticulated Cowrie-helmet 70 45
1063 30 c. Sand Dollar 80 55
1064 40 c. Lace Short-frond Murex .. .. 1·00 60
1065 45 c. Inflated Sea Biscuit .. .. .. 1·00 60
1066 50 c. West Indian Top Shell .. .. 1·10 70
1067 55 c. Spiny Oyster .. .. 1·25 75
1068 60 c. King Helmet .. .. 1·50 80
1069 70 c. Lion's Paw .. .. 1·60 1·00
1070 $1 Crown Cone .. .. 2·25 1·75
1071 $2 Atlantic Partridge Tun .. .. 3·50 4·00
1072 $5 Wide-mouthed Purpura .. .. 8·00 8·50
1073 $10 Atlantic Trumpet Triton (1 July) .. 14·00 15·00
1058/73 .. .. *Set of* 16 35·00 32·00

For 70 c. in miniature sheet with "1997" imprint date see No. **MS**1097 and for the $1 with inverted watermark and "1997" imprint date No. **MS**1096.

For these designs with watermark w **14** (upright) and "1997" imprint date see Nos. 1098/1113.

217 East Goodwin Lightship with Marconi Apparatus on Mast

218 Swimming

(Des N. Shewring. Litho B.D.T.)

1996 (2 Apr). *Centenary of Radio. T* **217** *and similar horiz designs. Multicoloured.* W w **14** (*sideways*). *P* 13½×14.
1074 15 c. Type **217** 60 45
1075 55 c. Newspaper headline concerning Dr. Crippen .. .. 1·40 1·25
1076 60 c. *Philadelphia* (liner) and first readable transatlantic message .. .. 1·50 1·75
1077 70 c. Guglielmo Marconi and *Elettra* (yacht) .. .. 1·75 2·00
1074/7 .. .. *Set of* 4 4·75 5·00
MS1078 80×47 mm. $2 *Titanic* and *Carpathia* (liners) .. .. 3·75 4·50

(Des S. Noon. Litho B.D.T.)

1996 (25 June). *Centenary of Modern Olympic Games. T* **218** *and similar vert designs. Multicoloured.* W w **16**. *P* 14×13½.
1079 15 c. Type **218** 40 25
1080 55 c. Running 90 90
1081 60 c. Basketball .. .. 1·40 1·60
1082 70 c. Long jumping .. .. 1·40 2·00
1079/82 .. .. *Set of* 4 3·50 4·25
MS1083 73×68 mm. $2 Javelin throwing .. 3·00 4·00

219 Green Anole

220 The Annunciation

(Des Doreen McGuiness. Litho Questa)

1996 (3 Sept). *Environment Protection (4th issue). Reptiles. T* **219** *and similar vert designs. Multicoloured.* W w **16**. *P* 14.
1084 15 c. Type **219** 55 40
1085 55 c. Little Bahama Bank Boa .. .. 1·10 1·00
1086 60 c. Inagua Freshwater Turtle .. .. 1·50 1·75
1087 70 c. Acklins Rock Iguana .. .. .. 1·75 2·25
1084/7 .. .. *Set of* 4 4·50 4·75
MS1088 85×105 mm. Nos. 1084/7 .. .. 4·50 5·50

(Des Jennifer Toombs. Litho B.D.T.)

1996 (4 Nov). *Christmas. T* **220** *and similar vert designs. Multicoloured.* W w **14**. *P* 14.
1089 15 c. Type **220** 40 25
1090 55 c. Joseph and Mary travelling to Bethlehem .. .. 1·00 85
1091 60 c. Shepherds and Angel .. .. .. 1·25 1·50
1092 70 c. Adoration of the Magi .. .. .. 1·40 2·00
1089/92 .. .. *Set of* 4 3·50 4·25
MS1093 70×87 mm. $2 Presentation in the Temple .. .. 2·50 3·25

221 Department of Archives Building

222 Underwater Scene

(Des N. Shewring. Litho Questa)

1996 (9 Dec). *25th Anniv of Archives Department. T* **221** *and similar horiz design showing Archives Building.* W w **16**. *P* 14½×14.
1094 **221** 55 c. multicoloured .. .. .. 1·00 1·00
MS1095 83×54 mm. $2 multicoloured. Wmk sideways. P 14 .. .. 3·50 4·00

(Des D. Miller. Litho Questa)

1997 (3 Feb). *"HONG KONG '97" International Stamp Exhibition. Sheet* 130×90 *mm, containing design as No.* 1070, *but with "1997" imprint date. Multicoloured.* W w **14** (*inverted*). *P* 14.
MS1096 $1 Crown Cone .. .. 1·50 2·00

(Des D. Miller. Litho Walsall)

1997 (20 June). *Return of Hong Kong to China. Sheet 130×90 mm containing design as No. 1069, but with "1997" imprint date.*
MS1097 70 c. Lion's Paw .. .. 1·50 1·75

1997 (1 July–22 Sept). *As Nos.* 1058/73, *but W* w **14** (*upright*). *"1997" imprint date. P* 14.
1098 5 c. Type **216** (22 Sept) 10 10
1099 10 c. Queen Conch (22 Sept) 10 10
1100 15 c. Angular Triton (22 Sept) 20 25
1101 20 c. True Tulip (22 Sept) 25 30
1102 25 c. Reticulated Cowrie-helmet (22 Sept) 30 35
1103 30 c. Sand Dollar (22 Sept) 35 40
1104 40 c. Lace Short-frond Murex (22 Sept) .. 50 55
1105 45 c. Inflated Sea Biscuit (22 Sept) .. 55 60
1106 50 c. West Indian Top Shell (22 Sept) .. 60 65
1107 55 c. Spiny Oyster (22 Sept) 65 70
1108 60 c. King Helmet (22 Sept) 70 75
1109 70 c. Lion's Paw (22 Sept) 85 90
1110 $1 Crown Cone .. .. .. 1·25 1·40
1111 $2 Atlantic Partridge Tun .. .. 2·40 2·50
1112 $5 Wide-mouthed Purpura .. .. 6·00 6·25
1113 $10 Atlantic Trumpet Triton .. .. 12·00 12·50
1098/113 .. .. *Set of* 16 26·00 27·00

(Des N. Shewring (No. **MS**1120), D. Miller (others). Litho Questa (No. **MS**1120) or Cartor (others))

1997 (9 July). *Golden Wedding of Queen Elizabeth and Prince Philip. Multicoloured designs as T* **173** *of Ascension.* W w **14**. *P* 13.
1114 50 c. Queen Elizabeth II in Bonn, 1992 .. 1·00 1·10
a. Horiz pair. Nos. 1114/15 .. .. 2·00 2·10
1115 50 c. Prince Philip and Prince Charles at Trooping the Colour .. .. 1·00 1·10
1116 60 c. Prince Philip .. .. .. 1·10 1·25
a. Horiz pair. Nos. 1116/17 .. .. 2·10 2·50
1117 60 c. Queen at Trooping the Colour .. 1·10 1·25
1118 70 c. Queen Elizabeth and Prince Philip at polo, 1970 .. .. 1·40 1·50
a. Horiz pair. Nos. 1118/19 .. .. 2·75 3·00
1119 70 c. Prince Charles playing polo .. 1·40 1·50
1114/19 .. .. *Set of* 6 6·25 7·00
MS1120 110×70 mm. $2 Queen Elizabeth and Prince Philip in landau (*horiz*). W w **14** (sideways). P 14×14½ .. .. .. 3·50 4·00

Nos. 1114/15, 1116/17 and 1118/19 were each printed together, *se-tenant*, in horizontal pairs throughout the sheets with the backgrounds forming composite designs.

(Des D. Miller. Litho Questa)

1997 (3 Sept). *Environment Protection* (5*th issue*). *International Year of the Reefs. T* **222** *and similar horiz designs showing different children's paintings of underwater scenes.* W w **16** (*sideways*). *P* 14½.
1121 15 c. multicoloured 45 30
1122 55 c. multicoloured .. .. .. 1·10 1·00
1123 60 c. multicoloured .. .. .. 1·25 1·40
1124 70 c. multicoloured .. .. .. 1·50 1·75
1121/4 .. .. *Set of* 4 3·75 4·00

223 Angel

224 Newsletters

(Des Jennifer Toombs. Litho Cartor)

1997 (4 Nov). *Christmas. T* **223** *and similar vert designs. Multicoloured.* W w **14** (*inverted*). *P* 13×13½.
1125 15 c. Type **223** 30 25
1126 55 c. Mary and Baby Jesus 80 70
1127 60 c. Shepherd 90 90
1128 70 c. King .. .. 1·10 1·25
1125/8 .. .. *Set of* 4 2·75 2·75
MS1129 74×94 mm. $2 Baby Jesus wrapped in swaddling-bands. Wmk upright .. .. 3·00 3·50

(Des D. Miller. Litho Questa)

1998 (31 Mar). *Diana, Princess of Wales Commemoration. Vert designs as T* **177** *of Ascension.* W w **16** (*No.* 1130). *P* 14½×14.
1130 15 c. Wearing grey jacket, 1988 .. .. 40 40
MS1131 145×70 mm. 15 c. As No. 1130; 55 c. Wearing striped jacket, 1983; 60 c. In evening dress, 1983; 70 c. Meeting crowds, 1993. W w **14** (sideways) .. .. 2·50 2·75

(Des A. Theobald. Litho Enschedé)

1998 (1 Apr). *80th Anniv of the Royal Air Force. Horiz designs as T* **178** *of Ascension. Multicoloured.* W w **14** (*sideways*). *P* 13½×14.
1132 15 c. Handley Page Hyderabad 40 30
1133 55 c. Hawker Demon 85 80
1134 60 c. Gloster Meteor F.8 .. .. .. 95 95
1135 70 c. Lockheed Neptune MR.1 .. .. 1·25 1·40
1132/5 .. .. *Set of* 4 3·00 3·00
MS1136 110×76 mm. 50 c. Sopwith Camel; 50 c. Short 184 (seaplane); 50 c. Supermarine Spitfire PR.19; 50 c. North American Mitchell III .. 3·00 3·25

(Des D. Miller. Litho Questa)

1998 (15 Apr). *50th Anniv of Organisation of American States. T* **224** *and similar horiz design. Multicoloured.* W w **14** (*sideways*). *P* 13½×14.
1137 15 c. Type **224** 30 30
1138 55 c. Headquarters building and flags, Washington 70 80

225 Start of Declaration and Birds

(Des D. Miller. Litho Questa)

1998 (15 Apr). *50th Anniv of Universal Declaration of Human Rights.* W w **14** (*sideways*). *P* 13½×14.
1139 **225** 55 c. bright blue and black 80 80

226 University Arms and Graduates

(Des D. Miller. Litho Questa)

1998 (15 Apr). *50th Anniv of University of the West Indies.* W w **14** (*sideways*). *P* 13½×14.
1140 **226** 55 c. multicoloured 80 80

227 Supreme Court Building

(Des D. Miller. Litho Cartor)

1998 (9 July). *25th Anniv of Independence. T* **227** *and similar horiz designs. Multicoloured.* W w **14** (*sideways*). *P* 13½.
1141 15 c. Type **227** 30 25
1142 55 c. Nassau Library 75 75
1143 60 c. Government House 80 85
1144 70 c. Gregory Arch .. .. .. 90 1·00
1141/4 .. .. *Set of* 4 2·50 2·50
MS1145 70×55 mm. $2 Island Regatta, George Town .. .. 3·00 3·25

228 Cruise Liner at Night

(Des N. Shewring. Litho Questa)

1998 (1 Aug). *Disney Cruise Line's Castaway Cay Holiday Development. T* **228** *and similar horiz design. Multicoloured.* W w **14** (*sideways*). *P* 14.
1146 55 c. Type **228** 75 80
a. Pair. Nos. 1146/7 .. .. .. 1·50 1·60
b. Booklet pane. Nos. 1146/7, each ×5 with margins all round .. .. 9·00
1147 55 c. Cruise liner by day 75 80

Nos. 1146/7 were printed together, *se-tenant*, in horizontal and vertical pairs throughout the sheet.

229 *Ryndam* (cruise liner)

(Des N. Shewring. Litho Cartor)

1998 (19 Aug). *Holland America Line's Half Moon Cay Holiday Development.* W w **14** (*sideways*). *P* 13½×13.
1148 **229** 55 c. multicoloured 80 80

230 Barrel Pink Rose 231 The Annunciation

(Des D. Miller. Litho B.D.T.)

1998 (8 Sept). *Environment Protection* (6*th issue*). *Roses. T* **230** *and similar horiz designs. Multicoloured.* W w **14** (*sideways*). *P* 14.
1149 55 c. Type **230** 65 70
a. Booklet pane. Nos. 1149/53, each × 2 with margins all round .. .. 6·50
1150 55 c. Yellow Cream 65 70
1151 55 c. Seven Sisters 65 70
1152 55 c. Big Red 65 70
1153 55 c. Island Beauty 65 70
1149/53 .. .. *Set of* 5 3·25 3·50
MS1154 100×70 mm. No. 1153 .. .. 65 70

(Des Jennifer Toombs. Litho Questa)

1998 (10 Nov). *Christmas. T* **231** *and similar horiz designs. Multicoloured.* W w **16** (*sideways*). *P* 14½.
1155 15 c. Type **231** 20 25
1156 55 c. Shepherds 65 70
1157 60 c. Three Kings 70 75
1158 70 c. The Flight into Egypt 85 90
1155/8 .. .. *Set of* 4 2·40 2·50
MS1159 87×67 mm. $2 The Nativity .. .. 2·40 2·50

232 Killer Whale and other Marine Life

(Des B. Dare. Litho Questa)

1998 (24 Nov). *International Year of the Ocean. T* **232** *and similar horiz design. Multicoloured.* W w **14** (*sideways*). *P* 13½×14.
1160 15 c. Type **232** 30 30
1161 55 c. Tropical fish 70 80

233 Timothy Gibson (composer)

(Des D. Miller. Litho Cartor)

1998 (10 Dec). *25th Anniv of "March on Bahamaland" (national anthem).* W w **14** (*sideways*). *P* 13½.
1162 **233** 60 c. multicoloured 70 75

STAMP BOOKLETS

1938. *Black on pink cover with map and* "BAHAMAS ISLES OF JUNE" *on reverse. Stapled.*
SB1 2s. booklet containing twelve 1d. (No. 150) in blocks of 6 and eight 1½d. (No. 151) in folded block of 8 .. .. £5000

1961 (15 Aug). *Brown-purple cover* (3s.) *or green cover* (6s.). *Stitched.*
SB2 3s. booklet containing eight each of 1d. 1½d. and 2d. (Nos. 202/4) in blocks of 4 .. .. 25·00
SB3 6s. booklet containing four each of 4d., 6d. and 8d. (Nos. 206, 208/9) in blocks of 4 .. .. 32·00

1965 (23 Mar). *Pink cover* (3s.) *or green cover* (6s.). *Stapled.*
SB4 3s. booklet containing eight each of 1d., 1½d. and 2d. (Nos. 248/50) in blocks of 4 .. .. 19·00
SB5 6s. booklet containing four each of 4d., 6d. and 8d. (Nos. 252/4) in blocks of 4 .. .. 19·00

PRICES OF SETS

Set prices are given for many issues, generally those containing three stamps or more. Definitive sets include one of each value or major colour change, but do not cover different perforations, die types or minor shades. Where a choice is possible the set prices are based on the cheapest versions of the stamps included in the listings.

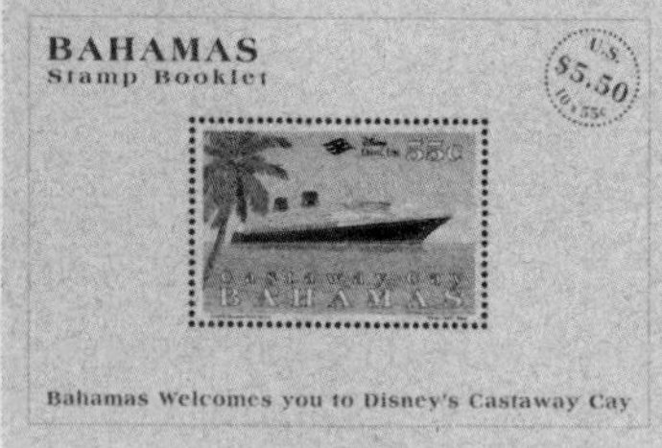

B 1

1998 (1 Aug). *Disney Cruise Line's Castaway Cay Holiday Development. Folded card cover as Type* B 1. *Pane attached by selvedge.*
SB6 $5.50, booklet containing pane No. 1146b .. 9·00

B 2
(Illustration reduced. Actual size 137×70 *mm)*

1998 (8 Sept). *Environment Protection (6th issue). Roses. Folded card cover as Type* B 2. *Pane attached by selvedge.*
SB7 $5.50, booklet containing pane No. 1149a .. 6·50

SPECIAL DELIVERY STAMPS

SPECIAL
DELIVERY
(S 1)

1916 (1 May). *No.* 59 *optd with Type* S 1 *by* The Nassau Guardian.

S1	**6**	5d. black and orange	5·00	30·00
		a. Opt double	£800	£1200
		b. Opt double, one inverted	£950	£1300
		c. Opt inverted	£1300	£1400
		d. Pair, one without opt	£13000	£18000
		x. Wmk reversed		

There were three printings from similar settings of 30, and each sheet had to pass through the press twice. The first printing of 600 was on sale from 1 May 1916 in Canada at Ottawa, Toronto, Westmount (Montreal) and Winnipeg; and under an agreement with the Canadian P.O. were used in combination with Canadian stamps and were cancelled in Canada. The second printing (number unknown) was made about the beginning of December 1916, and the third of 6000, issued probably on 1 March 1917, were on sale only in the Bahamas. These printings caused the revocation, in mid-December 1916, of the agreement by Canada, which no longer accepted the stamps as payment of the special delivery fee and left them to be cancelled in the Bahamas.

It is not possible to identify the printings of the normal stamps without plating both the basic stamp and the overprint, though, in general, the word "SPECIAL" is further to the right in relation to "DELIVERY" in the third printing than in the first or second. Our prices for No. S1 are for the third printing and any stamps which can be positively identified as being from the first or second printings would be worth about eight times as much unused, and any on cover are very rare. All the errors appear to be from the third printing.

SPECIAL
DELIVERY
(S 2)

SPECIAL
DELIVERY
(S 3)

1917 (2 July). *As No.* 59, *but Wmk Mult Crown CA. Optd with Type* S 2 *by D.L.R.*
S2 **6** 5d. black and orange (Optd S. £65) .. 45 4·75

1918. *No.* 78 *optd with Type* S 3 *by D.L.R.*
S3 **6** 5d. black and mauve (R.) (Optd S. £65) .. 30 1·75

Nos. S2/3 were only on sale in the Bahamas.

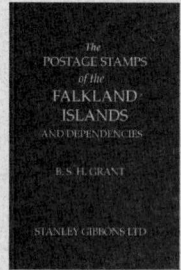

Bahrain

An independent shaikhdom, with an Indian postal administration from 1884. A British postal administration operated from 1 April 1948 to 31 December 1965.

The first, and for 62 years the only, post office in Bahrain opened at the capital, Manama, on 1 August 1884 as a sub-office of the Indian Post Office at Bushire (Iran), both being part of the Bombay Postal Circle.

Unoverprinted postage stamps of India were supplied to the new office, continuing on sale there until 1933. Examples of the lower values can sometimes be found postmarked at Bahrain, but such cancellations on values over 4 a. are decidedly scarce. The occasional Official stamp can also be discovered, possibly used by the office of the Indian Political Agent.

The initial cancellation supplied showed a "B" against a circular background of horizontal lines, this being used in conjunction with a single ring date-stamp without any indication of the year of use.

1884 Cancellation and Date-stamp

This was followed by a squared-circle type, first seen in 1886, which was used into the early years of the 20th century. Its replacement was a single ring date-stamp, succeeded in turn by the first of a considerable number of Indian-style double-circle postmarks, all inscribed "BAHRAIN".

1886 Squared-circle

PRICES FOR STAMPS ON COVER TO 1945

Nos. 1/14	*from* × 5
Nos. 15/19	*from* × 6
Nos. 20/37	*from* × 2
Nos. 38/50	*from* × 6

(Currency. 12 pies = 1 anna; 16 annas = 1 rupee)

BAHRAIN (1) BAHRAIN (2)

Stamps of India overprinted with T 1 or T 2 (rupee values)

1933 (10 Aug–Dec). *King George V. Wmk Mult Star, T* **69**.

No.	Type	Description	Unused	Used
1	**55**	3 p. slate (Dec)	3·00	45
2	**56**	½ a. green	7·50	3·25
		w. Wmk inverted	—	10·00
3	**80**	9 p. deep green	3·75	90
4	**57**	1 a. chocolate	7·00	2·50
		w. Wmk inverted		
5	**82**	1 a. 3 p. mauve	4·00	70
		w. Wmk inverted	4·00	70
6	**70**	2 a. vermilion	10·00	7·50
		w. Wmk inverted	10·00	7·50
7	**62**	3 a. blue	19·00	40·00
8	**83**	3 a. 6 p. ultramarine	3·75	30
		w. Wmk inverted	5·50	30
9	**71**	4 a. sage-green	18·00	40·00
10	**65**	8 a. reddish purple	6·00	30
11	**66**	12 a. claret	7·50	1·00
		w. Wmk inverted	—	20·00
12	**67**	1 r. chocolate and green	16·00	7·50
13		2 r. carmine and orange	32·00	38·00
14		5 r. ultramarine and purple	90·00	£120
		w. Wmk inverted	90·00	£120
1/14		*Set of* 14	£200	£225

The 9 p. exists both offset-litho and typo.

1934–37. *King George V. Wmk Mult Star, T* **69**.

No.	Type	Description	Unused	Used
15	**79**	½ a. green (1935)	4·50	55
		w. Wmk inverted	6·50	55
16	**81**	1 a. chocolate	9·00	40
		w. Wmk inverted	25·00	10·00
17	**59**	2 a. vermilion (1935)	38·00	7·50
17*a*		2 a. vermilion (*small die*) (1937)	48·00	25
18	**62**	3 a. carmine	4·75	40
19	**63**	4 a. sage-green (1935)	3·50	40
15/19		*Set of* 6	95·00	8·50

1938–41. *King George VI.*

No.	Type	Description	Unused	Used
20	**91**	3 p. slate (5.38)	7·50	3·25
21		½ a. red-brown (5.38)	3·75	10
22		9 p. green (5.38)	3·00	3·00
23		1 a. carmine (5.38)	2·50	10
24	**92**	2 a. vermilion (1939)	6·50	1·50
26	–	3 a. yellow-green (1941)	10·00	5·00
27	–	3 a. 6 p. bright blue (7.38)	4·25	3·00
28	–	4 a. brown (1941)	£120	60·00
30	–	8 a. slate-violet (1940)	£140	35·00
31	–	12 a. lake (1940)	£100	45·00
32	**93**	1 r. grey and red-brown (1940)	2·75	1·75
33		2 r. purple and brown (1940)	13·00	2·75
34		5 r. green and blue (1940)	15·00	13·00
35		10 r. purple and claret (1941)	65·00	28·00
36		15 r. brown and green (1941)	45·00	45·00
		w. Wmk inverted	45·00	45·00
37		25 r. slate-violet and purple (1941)	95·00	80·00
20/37		*Set of* 16	£550	£275

1942–45. *King George VI on white background.*

No.	Type	Description	Unused	Used
38	**100*a***	3 p. slate	1·50	60
39		½ a. purple	4·00	90
40		9 p. green	12·00	12·00
41		1 a. carmine	3·50	50
42	**101**	1 a. 3 p. bistre	8·00	13·00
43		1½ a. dull violet	4·75	4·25
44		2 a. vermilion	4·00	1·50
45		3 a. bright violet	14·00	4·00
46		3½ a. bright blue	3·50	13·00
47	**102**	4 a. brown	2·00	1·50
48		6 a. turquoise-green	9·50	9·00
49		8 a. slate-violet	3·25	2·50
50		12 a. lake	5·00	4·00
38/50		*Set of* 13	65·00	60·00

Stamps of Great Britain surcharged

For similar surcharges without the name of the country, see BRITISH POSTAL AGENCIES IN EASTERN ARABIA.

BAHRAIN
1
ANNA
(3)

BAHRAIN
5 RUPEES
(4)

1948 (1 Apr)–**49.** *Surch as T* **3**, **4** *(2 r. and 5 r.) or similar surch with bars at foot (10 r.).*

No.	Type	Description	Unused	Used
51	**128**	½ a. on ½d. pale green	40	85
52		1 a. on 1d. pale scarlet	40	1·25
53		1½ a. on 1½d. pale red-brown	40	1·25
54		2 a. on 2d. pale orange	40	20
55		2½ a. on 2½d. light ultramarine	50	2·25
56		3 a. on 3d. pale violet	40	10
57	**129**	6 a. on 6d. purple	40	10
58	**130**	1 r. on 1s. bistre-brown	1·25	10
59	**131**	2 r. on 2s. 6d. yellow-green	5·00	4·50
60		5 r. on 5s. red	5·50	4·50
60*a*	**132**	10 r. on 10s. ultramarine (4.7.49)	60·00	42·00
51/60*a*		*Set of* 11	65·00	50·00

BAHRAIN
2½
ANNAS
(5)

BAHRAIN
15
RUPEES
(6)

1948 (26 Apr). *Silver Wedding, surch as T* **5** *or* **6**.

No.	Type	Description	Unused	Used
61	**137**	2½ a. on 2½d. ultramarine	75	30
62	**138**	15 r. on £1 blue	40·00	48·00

1948 (29 July). *Olympic Games, surch as T* **5**, *but in one line (6 a.) or two lines (others); the 1 r. also has a square of dots as T* **7**.

No.	Type	Description	Unused	Used
63	**139**	2½ a. on 2½d. ultramarine	55	1·25
		a. Surch double	£750	£1300
64	**140**	3 a. on 3d. violet	55	2·00
65	**141**	6 a. on 6d. bright purple	1·50	2·50
66	**142**	1 r. on 1s. brown	1·50	2·50
63/6		*Set of* 4	3·75	7·50

Fourteen used examples of No. 63a are known, of which twelve were postmarked at Experimental P.O. K-121 (Muharraq), one at F.P.O. 756 (Shaibah) and one apparently cancelled-to-order at Bahrain on 10 October 1949.

BAHRAIN
3 ANNAS

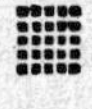

(7)

1949 (10 Oct). *75th Anniv of U.P.U., surch as T* **7**, *in one line (2½ a.) or in two lines (others).*

No.	Type	Description	Unused	Used
67	**143**	2½ a. on 2½d. ultramarine	55	2·00
68	**144**	3 a. on 3d. violet	85	2·75
69	**145**	6 a. on 6d. bright purple	75	3·00
70	**146**	1 r. on 1s. brown	1·60	1·75
67/70		*Set of* 4	3·25	8·50

BAHRAIN
2 RUPEES
(7*a*)

BAHRAIN
2 RUPEES
Type II

BAHRAIN
Extra bar (R. 6/1)

Three Types of 2 r.:

Type I. As Type 7*a* showing "2" level with "RUPEES" and "BAHRAIN" sharp.

Type II. "2" raised. "BAHRAIN" worn. 15 mm between "BAHRAIN" and "2 RUPEES".

Type III. As Type II, but 16 mm between "BAHRAIN" and "2 RUPEES". Value is set more to the left of "BAHRAIN".

1950 (2 Oct)–**55.** *Surch as T* **3** *or* **7*a*** *(rupee values).*

No.	Type	Description	Unused	Used
71	**128**	½ a. on ½d. pale orange (3.5.51)	80	90
72		1 a. on 1d. light ultramarine (3.5.51)	1·75	10
73		1½ a. on 1½d. pale green (3.5.51)	1·75	9·00
74		2 a. on 2d. pale red-brown (3.5.51)	80	30
75		2½ a. on 2½d. pale scarlet (3.5.51)	1·75	9·00
76	**129**	4 a. on 4d. light ultramarine	1·75	1·50
77	**147**	2 r. on 2s. 6d. yellow-green (3.5.51)	21·00	5·50
		a. Surch Type II (1953)	65·00	32·00
		b. Surch Type III (1955)	£700	80·00
		ba. "T" inverted and raised (R.2/1)	£2250	£550
78	**148**	5 r. on 5s. red (3.5.51)	13·00	3·75
		a. Extra bar	£225	
79	**149**	10 r. on 10s. ultramarine (3.5.51)	26·00	7·00
71/79		*Set of* 9	60·00	32·00

1952 (5 Dec)–**54.** *Q.E. II (W* **153**), *surch as T* **3** *(in two lines on 2½ and 6 a.).*

No.	Type	Description	Unused	Used
80	**154**	½ a. on ½d. orange-red (31.8.53)	10	50
		a. Fraction "½" omitted	£110	£140
81		1 a. on 1d. ultramarine (31.8.53)	10	10
82		1½ a. on 1½d. green	10	10
83		2 a. on 2d. red-brown (31.8.53)	20	10
84	**155**	2½ a. on 2½d. carmine-red	20	1·25
85		3 a. on 3d. deep lilac (B.) (18.1.54)	1·00	10
86	**156**	4 a. on 4d. ultramarine (2.11.53)	8·00	20
87	**157**	6 a. on 6d. reddish purple (18.1.54)	3·25	10
88	**160**	12 a. on 1s. 3d. green (2.11.53)	3·00	20
89	**159**	1 r. on 1s. 6d. grey-blue (2.11.53)	3·25	10
80/89		*Set of* 10	17·00	2·00

The word BAHRAIN is in taller letters on the 1½ a., 2½ a., 3 a. and 6 a.

2½ BAHRAIN
ANNAS
(8)

1953 (3 June). *Coronation. Surch as T* **8**, *or similarly.*

No.	Type	Description	Unused	Used
90	**161**	2½ a. on 2½d. carmine-red	1·25	75
91	**162**	4 a. on 4d. ultramarine	2·25	3·25
92	**163**	12 a. on 1s. 3d. deep yellow-green	3·25	3·25
93	**164**	1 r. on 1s. 6d. deep grey-blue	7·50	50
90/3		*Set of* 4	13·00	7·00

BAHRAIN 2 RUPEES

I

BAHRAIN 2 RUPEES

II

BAHRAIN 2 RUPEES

III

(9)

BAHRAIN 5 RUPEES
I

BAHRAIN 5 RUPEES
II

(10)

BAHRAIN 10 RUPEES
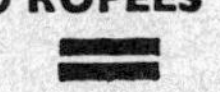
I

BAHRAIN 10 RUPEES
II

(11)

TYPE I (T **9/11**). Type-set surch by Waterlow. Bold thick letters with sharp corners and straight edges.

TYPE II (T **9/11**). Plate-printed surch by Harrison. Thinner letters, rounded corners and rough edges. Bars wider apart.

TYPE III (T **9**). Plate-printed surch by Harrison. Similar to Type II as regards the position of the bars on all 40 stamps of the sheet, but the letters are thinner and with more rounded corners than in II, while the ink of the surcharge is less black.

The general characteristics of Type II of the 2 r. are less pronounced than in the other values, but a distinguishing test is in the relative position of the bars and the "U" of "RUPEES". In Type II (except for the 1st stamp, 5th row) the bars start immediately beneath the left-hand edge of the "U". In Type I they start more to the right.

In the 10 r. the "1" and the "0" are spaced 0.9 mm in Type I and only 0.6 mm in Type II.

1955 (23 Sept)–**60.** *T* **166/8** *(Waterlow ptgs) surch as T* **9/11**.

No.	Type	Description	Unused	Used
94	**166**	2 r. on 2s. 6d. black-brown (Type I)	5·50	1·60
		a. Type II (13.5.58)	11·00	9·00
		b. Type III (No. 536a, D.L.R.) (29.1.60)	25·00	45·00
95	**167**	5 r. on 5s. rose-red (Type I)	11·00	2·75
		a. Type II (19.8.57)	11·00	8·00
96	**168**	10 r. on 10s. ultramarine (Type I)	20·00	2·75
		a. Type II (13.5.58)	50·00	95·00
		ab. Type II. Surch on No. 538a (D.L.R. ptg) (1960)	£100	
94/6		*Set of* 3	32·00	6·25
94*a*/6*a*		*Set of* 3	65·00	£100

1956–7. *Q.E. II (W* **165**), *surch as T* **3** *(in two lines on 6 a.).*

No.	Type	Description	Unused	Used
97	**154**	½ a. on ½d. orange-red (1.57)	10	15
98	**156**	4 a. on 4d. ultramarine (8.6.56)	5·50	17·00
99	**157**	6 a. on 6d. reddish purple (5.12.56)	50	50
100	**160**	12 a. on 1s. 3d. green (2.8.56)	7·50	11·00
101	**159**	1 r. on 1s. 6d. grey-blue (4.3.57)	8·00	10
		a. Surch double		† £1700
97/101		*Set of* 5	19·00	26·00

(New Currency. 100 naye paise = 1 rupee)

BAHRAIN BAHRAIN BAHRAIN

NP 1 NP   NP 3 NP   75 NP

(12)   (13)   (14)

1957 (1 Apr)–**59.** *Q.E. II (W* **165**)*, surch as T* **12** *(1 n.p., 15 n.p., 25 n.p., 40 n.p., and 50 n.p.), T* **14** *(75 n.p.) or T* **13** *(others).*

102	**157**	1 n.p. on 5d. brown		10	10
103	**154**	3 n.p. on ½d. orange-red		30	1·50
104		6 n.p. on 1d. ultramarine		30	1·50
105		9 n.p. on 1½d. green		30	1·50
106		12 n.p. on 2d. light red-brown		30	60
107	**155**	15 n.p. on 2½d. carmine-red (Type I)		30	15
		a. Type II (1959)		1·00	1·75
108		20 n.p. on 3d. deep lilac (B.)		30	10
109	**156**	25 n.p. on 4d. ultramarine		75	1·75
110	**157**	40 n.p. on 6d. reddish purple		40	10
		a. *Deep claret* (1959)		55	10
111	**158**	50 n.p. on 9d. bronze-green		3·75	4·50
112	**160**	75 n.p. on 1s. 3d. green		2·25	50
102/112			*Set of* 11	8·00	10·50

BAHRAIN
15 NP

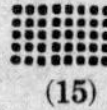

(15)

1957 (1 Aug). *World Scout Jubilee Jamboree. Surch in two lines as T* **15** *(15 n.p.), or in three lines (others).*

113	**170**	15 n.p. on 2½d. carmine-red		25	35
114	**171**	25 n.p. on 4d. ultramarine		30	35
115	**172**	75 n.p. on 1s. 3d. green		40	45
113/15			*Set of* 3	85	1·00

1960 (24 May). *Q.E. II (W* **179**)*, surch as T* **12**.

116	**155**	15 n.p. on 2½d. carmine-red (Type II)	2·25	8·00

16   17
Shaikh Sulman bin Hamed al-Khalifa

(Des M. Farrar Bell. Photo Harrison (T **16**). Des O. C. Meronti. Recess D.L.R. (T **17**))

1960 (1 July). *P 15 × 14 (T* **16**) *or* 13½ × 13 *(T* **17**).

117	**16**	5 n.p. bright blue		10	10
118		15 n.p. red-orange		10	10
119		20 n.p. reddish violet		10	10
120		30 n.p. bistre-brown		10	10
121		40 n.p. grey		15	10
122		50 n.p. emerald-green		15	10
123		75 n.p. chocolate		30	15
124	**17**	1 r. black		1·50	30
125		2 r. rose-red		2·75	1·50
126		5 r. deep blue		4·50	2·25
127		10 r. bronze-green		12·00	3·75
117/127			*Set of* 11	19·00	7·50

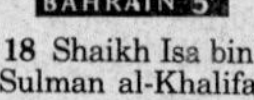

18 Shaikh Isa bin Sulman al-Khalifa

19 Air Terminal, Muharraq

20 Deep Water Harbour

(Des M. Farrar Bell. Photo Harrison (5 to 75 n.p.). Des D. C. Rivett. Recess B.W. (others))

1964 (22 Feb). *P 15 × 14 (T* **18**) *or* 13½ × 13 *(T* **19/20**).

128	**18**	5 n.p. bright blue		10	10
129		15 n.p. orange red		10	10
130	**18**	20 n.p. reddish violet		10	10
131		30 n.p. olive-brown		10	10
132		40 n.p. slate		15	10
133		50 n.p. emerald-green		15	10
134		75 n.p. brown		25	10
135	**19**	1 r. black		5·50	1·25
136		2 r. carmine-red		8·50	1·25
137	**20**	5 r. ultramarine		9·50	8·50
138		10 r. myrtle-green		13·00	8·50
128/138			*Set of* 11	32·00	18·00

LOCAL STAMPS

The following stamps were issued primarily for postage within Bahrain, but apparently also had franking value when used on external mail.

L **1** Shaikh Sulman bin Hamed al-Khalifa L **2**

(Types L **1/2**. Recess D.L.R.)

1953–56. *P* 12 × 12½.

L1	L **1**	½ a. deep green (1.10.56)		3·75	75
L2		1 a. deep blue (1.10.56)		3·75	45
L3		1½ a. carmine (15.2.53)		50	3·50
L1/3			*Set of* 3	7·25	4·25

1957 (16 Oct). *As Nos.* L 1/3 *but values in new currency.*

L4	3 p. deep green		4·25	1·25
L5	6 p. carmine		4·25	1·25
L6	9 p. deep blue		4·25	1·25
L4/6		*Set of* 3	11·50	3·25

1961 (20 Mar). *P* 12 × 12½.

L 7	L **2**	5 p. green		1·00	30
L 8		10 p. carmine-red		1·40	30
L 9		15 p. grey		1·00	25
L10		20 p. blue		1·25	25
L11		30 p. sepia		1·00	25
L12		40 p. ultramarine		1·75	30
L7/12			*Set of* 6	6·75	1·50

STAMP BOOKLETS

1934. *Red and black on tan cover. Mysore Sandal Soap advertisement on front.*

SB1 16 a. booklet containing sixteen 1 a. (No. 16w) in blocks of 4 . . £750

The Bahrain Post Department took over the postal services on 1 January 1966. Later stamp issues will be found in Part 19 (*Middle East*) of the Stanley Gibbons catalogue.

Bangkok
see British Post Office in Siam

Bangladesh

In elections during December 1970 the Awami League party won all but two of the seats in the East Pakistan province and, in consequence, held a majority in the National Assembly. On 1 March 1971 the Federal Government postponed the sitting of the Assembly with the result that unrest spread throughout the eastern province. Pakistan army operations against the dissidents forced the leaders of the League to flee to India from where East Pakistan was proclaimed independent as Bangladesh. In early December the Indian army moved against Pakistan troops in Bangladesh and civilian government was re-established on 22 December 1971.

From 20 December 1971 various Pakistan issues were overprinted by local postmasters, mainly using handstamps. Their use was permitted until 30 April 1973. These are of philatelic interest, but are outside the scope of the catalogue.

(Currency. 100 paisa = 1 rupee)

বাংলাদেশ P.10
POSTAGE REVENUE
Bangla Desh

1 Map of Bangladesh

BANGLADESH
LIBERATED
বাংলাদেশের মুক্তি

(**2**)

(Des B. Mullick. Litho Format)

1971 (29 July). *Vert designs as T* **1**. *P* 14 × 14½.

1	10 p. indigo-blue, red-orange and pale blue		10	10
2	20 p. multicoloured		10	10
3	50 p. multicoloured		10	10
4	1 r. multicoloured		10	10
5	2 r. deep greenish blue, light new blue and rose-magenta		25	35
6	3 r. apple-green, dull yellowish green and greenish blue		30	55
7	5 r. multicoloured		50	90
8	10 r. gold, rose-magenta & deep greenish blue		1·00	1·75
1/8		*Set of* 8	2·00	3·50

Designs:—20 p. "Dacca University Massacre"; 50 p. "75 Million People"; 1 r. Flag of Independence; 2 r. Ballot box; 3 r. Broken chain; 5 r. Shaikh Mujibur Rahman; 10 r. "Support Bangla Desh" and map.

Nos. 1/8 exist imperforate from stock dispersed by the liquidator of Format International Security Printers Ltd.

1971 (20 Dec). *Liberation. Nos.* 1 *and* 7/8 *optd with T* **2**.

9	10 p. indigo-blue, red-orange and pale blue		10	10
10	5 r. multicoloured (O.)		1·50	1·75
11	10 r. gold, rose-magenta & deep greenish blue		2·00	2·50
9/11		*Set of* 3	3·25	3·75

The remaining values of the original issue were also overprinted and placed on sale in Great Britain but were not issued in Bangladesh. (*Price for the complete set £4 un.*)

On 1 February 1972 the Agency placed on sale a further issue in the flag, map and Shaikh Mujibur designs in new colours and new currency (100 paisas = 1 taka). This issue proved to be unacceptable to the Bangladesh authorities who declared them to be invalid for postal purposes, no supplies being sold within Bangladesh. The values comprise 1, 2, 3, 5, 7, 10, 15, 20, 25, 40, 50, 75 p., 1, 2 and 5 t. (*Price for set of* 15 *un.,* £1.)

(New Currency. 100 paisa = 1 taka)

3 "Martyrdom"

4 Flames of Independence

(Des and photo Indian Security Printing Press, Nasik)

1972 (21 Feb). *In Memory of the Martyrs. P* 13.

12	**3**	20 p. dull green and rose-red	30	50

(Des N. Kundu. Photo Indian Security Printing Press, Nasik)

1972 (26 Mar). *First Anniv of Independence. P* 13.

13	**4**	20 p. brown-lake and red		20	10
14		60 p. dull ultramarine and red		25	45
15		75 p. reddish violet and red		30	55
13/15			*Set of* 3	65	1·00

5 Doves of Peace

6 "Homage to Martyrs"

(Litho B.W.)

1972 (16 Dec). *Victory Day. P* 13½.

16	**5**	20 p. multicoloured		15	10
17		60 p. multicoloured		20	55
18		75 p. multicoloured		20	55
16/18			*Set of* 3	50	1·10

(Des K. Mustafa. Litho B.W.)

1973 (25 Mar). *In Memory of the Martyrs. P* 13½.

19	**6**	20 p. multicoloured		15	10
20		60 p. multicoloured		30	40
21		1 t. 35, multicoloured		65	1·75
19/21			*Set of* 3	1·10	2·00

7 Embroidered Quilt

8 Court of Justice

(Litho B.W.)

1973 (30 Apr). *T* **7/8** *and similar designs. P* 14½ × 14 *(50 p., 1 t., 5 t., 10 t.) or* 14 × 14½ *(others).*

22	2 p. black	10	40
23	3 p. blue-green	20	30
	a. Imperf (pair)		

4 5 p. light brown 20 10
5 10 p. slate-black 20 10
6 20 p. yellow-green 50 10
7 25 p. bright reddish mauve .. .. .. 2·75 10
8 50 p. bright purple .. .. 1·50 30
9 60 p. greenish slate 75 50
0 75 p. yellow-orange 80 50
1 90 p. orange-brown 90 70
2 1 t. light violet .. .. 4·00 30
3 2 t. olive-green .. .. 4·00 55
4 5 t. grey-blue .. .. 5·50 1·50
5 10 t. rose .. .. 5·50 3·25
2/35 .. .. *Set of* 14 24·00 7·50

Designs: *As T* **7**—3 p. Jute field; 5 p. Jack fruit; 10 p. Bullocks loughing; 20 p. Rakta jaba (flower); 25 p. Tiger; 60 p. Bamboo rove; 75 p. Plucking tea; 90 p. Handicrafts. *Horiz* (28 × 22 *m*)—50 p. Hilsa (fish). *Horiz as T* **8**—5 t. Fishing boat; 10 t. ixty-dome mosque, Bagerhat. *Vert as T* **8**—2 t. Date tree.

See also Nos. 49/51*a* and 64/75.

9 Flame Emblem

10 Family, Map and Graph

(Des A. Karim. Litho B.W.)

1973 (10 Dec). *5th Anniv of Declaration of Human Rights. P* 13½.
36 **9** 10 p. multicoloured 10 10
37 1 t. 25, multicoloured 20 20

(Des A. Karim. Litho B.W.)

1974 (10 Feb). *First Population Census. P* 13½.
38 **10** 20 p. multicoloured 10 10
39 25 p. multicoloured 10 10
40 75 p. multicoloured 20 20
38/40 .. .. *Set of* 3 30 30

11 Copernicus and Heliocentric System

12 U.N. H.Q. and Bangladesh Flag

(Des K. Mustafa. Litho B.W.)

1974 (22 July). *500th Birth Anniv of Copernicus. P* 13½.
41 **11** 25 p. yellow-orange, bluish violet & blk 10 10
a. Imperf (pair) .. .. 24·00
42 75 p. orange, yellow-green and black .. 25 50

(Des A. Karim. Litho B.W.)

1974 (25 Sept). *Bangladesh's Admission to the U.N. Multicoloured; frame colour given. P* 13½.
43 **12** 25 p. light lilac 10 10
44 1 t. light greenish blue 35 40

13 U.P.U. Emblem

14 Courts of Justice

(Des K. Mustafa. Litho B.W.)

1974 (9 Oct). *Centenary of Universal Postal Union. T* **13** *and similar vert designs. Multicoloured; country name on a yellow background* (*Nos.* 45/6) *or a blue background* (*Nos.* 47/8). *P* 13½.
45 25 p. Type **13** 10 10
46 1 t. 25, Mail runner 20 15
47 1 t. 75, Type **13** 25 25
48 5 t. As 1 t. 25 .. .. 80 1·60
45/8 .. .. *Set of* 4 1·25 1·75

The above exist imperforate in a miniature sheet from a restricted printing.

1974–76. *Nos.* 32/5 *redrawn with revised value inscriptions as T* **14**.
49 1 t. light violet .. .. 1·50 10
50 2 t. olive .. .. 2·00 80
51 5 t. grey-blue (1975) .. .. 5·50 70
51*a* 10 t. rose (1976) .. .. 12·00 8·00
49/51*a* .. .. *Set of* 4 19·00 8·75

15 Royal Bengal Tiger

16 Symbolic Family

(Des and litho B.W.)

1974 (4 Nov). *Wildlife Preservation. T* **15** *and similar vert designs. Multicoloured. P* 13½.
52 25 p. Type **15** 70 10
53 50 p. Tiger whelp .. .. 1·25 70
54 2 t. Tiger in stream .. .. 2·75 3·50
52/4 .. .. *Set of* 3 4·25 3·75

(Des A. Karim. Litho B.W.)

1974 (30 Dec). *World Population Year. "Family Planning for All". T* **16** *and similar multicoloured designs. P* 14.
55 25 p. Type **16** 15 10
56 70 p. Village family 25 50
57 1 t. 25, Heads of family (*horiz*) .. .. 40 1·10
55/7 .. .. *Set of* 3 70 1·50

The Bengali numerals on the 70 p. resemble "90".

17 Radar Antenna

18 Woman's Head

(Des and litho B.W.)

1975 (14 June). *Inauguration of Betbunia Satellite Earth Station. P* 13½.
58 **17** 25 p. black, silver and dull red 10 10
59 1 t. black, silver and ultramarine .. 20 60

(Des A. Karim. Litho Asher & Co, Melbourne)

1975 (31 Dec). *International Women's Year. P* 15.
60 **18** 50 p. multicoloured 10 10
61 2 t. multicoloured 25 85
a. Vert pair, bottom stamp imperf .. 75·00

(Litho Asher & Co., Melbourne)

1976 (15 Jan)–**77**. *As Nos.* 24/31 *and* 49/51*a but redrawn in smaller size and colours changed* (5, 75*p.*). *P* 14½×15 (50 *p.*), 14½ (1 *to* 10 *t.*) *or* 15×14½ (*others*). (*a*) 23×18 *mm* (50 *p.*) *or* 18×23 *mm* (*others*).
64 5 p. deep yellow-green (11.2.76) 20 10
a. Imperf (pair) .. .. .. 10·00
65 10 p. slate-black (28.4.76) 20 10
66 20 p. yellow-green 70 10
a. Imperf (pair) .. .. .. 10·00
67 25 p. bright reddish mauve .. .. 2·25 10
a. Imperf (pair) .. .. .. 10·00
68 50 p. light purple (8.6.76) .. .. 1·75 10
69 60 p. greenish slate (10.11.76) 40 20
70 75 p. yellow-olive (10.11.76) .. .. 1·25 2·00
71 90 p. orange-brown (10.11.76) 40 20

(*b*) 20×32 *mm* (2 *t.*) *or* 32×20 *mm* (*others*)
72 1 t. light violet .. .. .. 2·00 10
73 2 t. olive-green (8.6.76) .. .. 6·00 10
a. Imperf (pair) .. .. .. 35·00
74 5 t. grey-blue (10.11.76) .. .. 3·25 1·75
75 10 t. rose (25.2.77) .. .. .. 8·50 1·75
64/75 .. .. .. *Set of* 12 24·00 6·00

19 Telephones, 1876 and 1976

20 Eye and Nutriments

(Des A. Karim. Litho Asher & Co, Melbourne)

1976 (10 Mar). *Telephone Centenary. T* **19** *and similar vert design. P* 15.
76 2 t. 25, multicoloured 25 20
77 5 t. dull vermilion, apple-green and black .. 55 65

Design:— 5 t. Alexander Graham Bell.

(Des A. Karim. Litho Asher & Co, Melbourne)

1976 (17 Apr). *Prevention of Blindness. P* 15.
78 **20** 30 p. multicoloured 50 10
79 2 t. 25, multicoloured .. .. .. 1·40 2·25

21 Liberty Bell

22 Industry, Science, Agriculture and Education

(Des E. Roberts. Photo Heraclio Fournier)

1976 (29 May). *Bicentenary of American Revolution. T* **21** *and similar horiz designs. Multicoloured. P* 14.
80 30 p. Type **21** 10 10
81 2 t. 25, Statue of Liberty 30 25
82 5 t. *Mayflower* 80 50
83 10 t. Mount Rushmore 80 80
80/3 .. .. *Set of* 4 1·75 1·40
MS84 167 × 95 mm. Nos. 80/3 .. .. .. 2·50 3·00

No. **MS**84 also exists imperforate from a restricted printing.

(Des K. Mustafa. Litho Asher & Co, Melbourne)

1976 (29 July). *25th Anniv of the Colombo Plan. P* 15.
85 **22** 30 p. multicoloured 15 10
86 2 t. 25, multicoloured 35 35

23 Hurdling

24 The Blessing

(Des K. Mustafa. Litho Asher & Co, Melbourne)

1976 (29 Nov). *Olympic Games, Montreal. T* **23** *and similar multicoloured designs. P* 14½.
87 25 p. Type **23** 10 10
88 30 p. Running (*horiz*) 10 10
a. Imperf (pair) .. .. ..
89 1 t. Pole vault 15 10
90 2 t. 25, Swimming (*horiz*) 40 45
91 3 t. 50, Gymnastics .. .. .. 75 1·25
92 5 t. Football .. .. 1·40 2·00
87/92 .. .. *Set of* 6 2·50 3·50

(Des and litho Harrison)

1977 (7–17 Feb). *Silver Jubilee. T* **24** *and similar vert designs. Multicoloured. P* 14 × 14½.
93 30 p. Type **24** 10 10
94 2 t. 25, Queen Elizabeth II 20 25
95 10 t. Queen Elizabeth and Prince Philip .. 70 85
93/5 .. .. *Set of* 3 80 1·00
MS96 114 × 127 mm. Nos. 93/5. P 14½ (17 Feb) 80 1·50

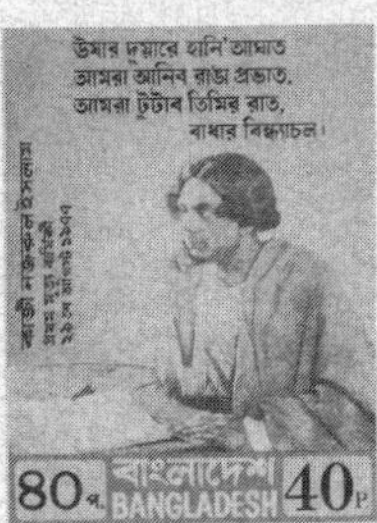

25 Qazi Nazrul Islam (poet)

(Des K. Mustafa. Litho Harrison)

1977 (29 Aug). *Qazi Nazrul Islam Commemoration. T* **25** *and similar design. P* 14.
97 40 p. blue-green and black 10 10
98 2 t. 25, sepia, stone and chestnut 30 30

Design: *Horiz*—2 t. 25, Head and shoulders portrait.

26 Bird with Letter

(Des A. Karim. Litho Harrison)

1977 (29 Sept). *15th Anniv of Asian-Oceanic Postal Union. P* 14.
99 **26** 30 p. light rose, new blue and dull green .. 10 10
100 2 t. 25, light rose, new blue and light grey 20 25

27 Sloth Bear

28 Campfire and Tent

(Des K. Mustafa. Litho Harrison)

1977 (9 Nov). *Animals. T* **27** *and similar multicoloured designs. P* 13.
101 40 p. Type **27** 20 10
102 1 t. Spotted Deer 30 10
103 2 t. 25, Leopard (*horiz*) 85 20
104 3 t. 50, Gaur (*horiz*) 90 35
105 4 t. Indian Elephant (*horiz*) .. .. 1·75 50
106 5 t. Tiger (*horiz*) .. .. 2·00 75
101/6 .. .. *Set of* 6 5·50 1·75
The Bengali numerals on the 40 p. resemble "80", and that on the 4 t. resembles "8".

(Des A. Karim. Litho Harrison)

1978 (22 Jan). *First National Scout Jamboree. T* **28** *and similar designs. P* 13.
107 40 p. red, deep blue and light blue 30 10
108 3 t. 50, carmine, deep blue and green .. 1·25 30
109 5 t. reddish lilac, deep blue and bright green 1·40 45
107/9 .. .. *Set of* 3 2·75 70
Designs: *Horiz*—3 t. 50, Scout stretcher-team. *Vert*—5 t. Scout salute.

29 Michelia champaca

(Des and litho Harrison)

1978 (29 Apr). *Flowers. T* **29** *and similar horiz designs. Multicoloured. P* 14.
110 40 p. Type **29** 30 10
111 1 t. *Cassia fistula* 55 15
112 2 t. 25, *Delonix regia* 85 30
113 3 t. 50, *Nymphaea nouchali* .. .. .. 1·00 60
114 4 t. *Butea monosperma* .. .. 1·10 80
115 5 t. *Anthocephalus indicus* .. .. .. 1·25 85
110/15 .. .. *Set of* 6 4·50 2·40

30 St. Edward's Crown and Sceptres

31 Sir Alan Cobham's De Havilland D.H.50J

(Des and litho Harrison)

1978 (20 May). *25th Anniv of Coronation. T* **30** *and similar vert designs. Multicoloured. P* 14.
116 40 p. Type **30** 10 10
117 3 t. 50, Balcony scene 15 30
118 5 t. Queen Elizabeth and Prince Philip .. 25 50
119 10 t. Coronation portrait by Cecil Beaton .. 45 80
116/19 .. .. *Set of* 4 80 1·50
MS120 89 × 121 mm. Nos. 116/19. P $14\frac{1}{2}$ .. 90 1·50

(Des and litho Harrison)

1978 (15 June). *75th Anniv of Powered Flight. T* **31** *and similar horiz designs. P* 13.
121 40 p. multicoloured 15 10
122 2 t. 25, blackish brown and light new blue .. 50 45
123 3 t. 50, blackish brown and yellow 65 65
124 5 t. multicoloured .. .. 4·00 3·50
121/4 .. .. *Set of* 4 4·75 4·25
Designs:—2 t. 25, Captain Hans Bertram's Junkers W.33 seaplane *Atlantis*; 3 t. 50, Wright brothers' Flyer III; 5 t. Concorde.

32 Fenchuganj Fertilizer Factory

33 Tawaf-E-Ka'aba, Mecca

(Des P. Mandal (5 p.), A. Karim (10 p.), Harrison (30, 50 p., 1 t.). Photo Harrison)

1978 (6 Nov)–**82**. *Designs as T* **32**. *P* $14\frac{1}{2}$.
125 5 p. deep brown (25.3.79) 10 10
126 10 p. turquoise-blue 10 10
127 15 p. orange (1.8.80) 10 10
128 20 p. brown-red (15.12.79) 10 10
129 25 p. grey-blue (1982) 15 10
130 30 p. deep green (10.12.80) .. .. .. 1·25 10
131 40 p. maroon (15.12.79) 30 10
132 50 p. black (1981) .. .. 3·25 1·50
134 80 p. brown (1.8.80) 20 10
136 1 t. reddish violet (6.81) .. .. .. 4·00 10
137 2 t. dull ultramarine (21.10.81) .. .. 50 1·75
125/37 .. .. *Set of* 11 9·00 3·25
Designs: *Horiz*—5 p. Lalbag Fort; 25 p. Jute on a boat; 40 p., 50 p. Baitul Mukarram Mosque; 1 t. Dotara (musical instrument); 2 t. Karnaphuli Dam. *Vert*—15 p. Pineapple; 20 p. Bangladesh gas; 30 p. Banana Tree; 80 p. Mohastan Garh.

(Des A. Karim. Litho J.W.)

1978 (9 Nov). *Holy Pilgrimage to Mecca. T* **33** *and similar multicoloured design. P* 13.
140 40 p. Type **33** 20 10
141 3 t. 50, Pilgrims in Wuquf, Arafat (*horiz*) .. 60 45

34 Jasim Uddin

(Des P. Mandal. Litho J.W.)

1979 (14 Mar). *3rd Death Anniv of Jasim Uddin (poet). P* 14.
142 **34** 40 p. multicoloured 20 40

35 Moulana Abdul Hamid Khan Bhashani

36 Sir Rowland Hill

(Des P. Mandal. Litho Harrison)

1979 (17 Nov). *3rd Death Anniv of Moulana Abdul Hamid Khan Bhashani (national leader). P* $12\frac{1}{2}$.
143 **35** 40 p. multicoloured 40 30

(Des A. Karim. Litho Harrison)

1979 (26 Nov). *Death Centenary of Sir Rowland Hill. T* **36** *and similar designs. P* 14.
144 40 p. turquoise-blue, Venetian red and pale turquoise-blue 10 10
145 3 t. 50, multicoloured 35 30
146 10 t. multicoloured .. .. 80 1·00
144/6 .. .. *Set of* 3 1·10 1·25
MS147 176 × 96 mm. Nos. 144/6 .. .. .. 2·00 2·75
Designs: *Horiz*—3 t. 50, 1971 10 p. definitive stamp and Sir Rowland Hill; 10 t. 1974 1 t. 25, Centenary of U.P.U. commemorative stamp and Sir Rowland Hill.

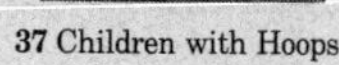

37 Children with Hoops

38 Rotary International Emblem

(Des P. Mandal. Litho Harrison)

1979 (17 Dec). *International Year of the Child. T* **37** *and similar vert designs. Multicoloured. P* 14 × $14\frac{1}{2}$.
148 40 p. Type **37** 10
149 3 t. 50, Child with kite 35
150 5 t. Children playing 50 5
148/50 .. .. *Set of* 3 80 8
MS151 170 × 120 mm. Nos. 148/50. P $14\frac{1}{2}$ .. 1·50 2·7

(Des P. Mandal. Litho Rosenbaum Bros, Vienna)

1980 (23 Feb). *75th Anniv of Rotary International. T* **38** *and similar vert design showing club emblem. P* $13\frac{1}{2}$ × 14.
152 40 p. black, vermilion and bistre-yellow .. 20 1
153 5 t. gold and bright blue 65 4

39 Canal Digging

40 A. K. Fazlul Huq

(Des A. Karim. Litho Rosenbaum Bros, Vienna)

1980 (27 Mar). *Mass Participation in Canal Digging. P* 14 × $13\frac{1}{2}$.
154 **39** 40 p. multicoloured 40 3

(Des P. Mandal. Litho Rosenbaum Bros, Vienna)

1980 (27 Apr). *18th Death Anniv of A. K. Fazlul Huq (national leader). P* $13\frac{1}{2}$ × 14.
155 **40** 40 p. multicoloured 30 30
On the face value the Bengali numerals resemble "80".

41 Early forms of Mail Transport

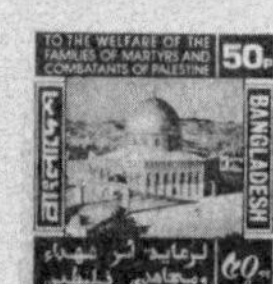

42 Dome of the Rock

(Des A. Karim. Litho Rosenbaum Bros, Vienna)

1980 (5 May). *"London 1980" International Stamp Exhibition. T* **41** *and similar horiz design. Multicoloured. P* 14 × $13\frac{1}{2}$.
156 1 t. Type **41** 15 1
157 10 t. Modern forms of mail transport .. 1·25 8
MS158 140 × 95 mm. Nos. 156/7 .. .. .. 1·40 2·0

(Des A. Karim. Litho Harrison)

1980 (21 Aug). *Palestinian Welfare. P* $14\frac{1}{2}$.
159 **42** 50 p. deep mauve 70 3
A similar stamp in grey, showing a Palestinian guerilla and the Dome of the Rock, printed by the State Printing Works Moscow, was prepared in 1980, but not issued due to errors in the Arabic inscription. Quantities of the stamp were subsequently reported stolen. Examples were also issued by Comilla and Kotbari post offices on 27 September 1992 without authority.

43 Outdoor Class

(Des P. Mandal. Litho Rosenbaum Bros, Vienna)

1980 (23 Aug). *Education. P* $13\frac{1}{2}$ × 14.
160 **43** 50 p. multicoloured 40 30

44 Beach Scene

45 Mecca

(Des A. Karim. Litho Rosenbaum Bros, Vienna)

1980 (27 Sept). *World Tourism Conference, Manila. T* **44** *and similar horiz design showing different beach scene. P* 14.
161 50 p. multicoloured 30 30
a. Horiz pair. Nos. 161/2 .. .. 90 1·00
162 5 t. multicoloured 60 70
MS163 140 × 88 mm. Nos. 161/2 .. .. 90 1·50
Nos. 161/2 were printed together, *se-tenant*, in horizontal pairs throughout the sheet.

(Des A. Karim. Litho Rosenbaum Bros, Vienna)

1980 (11 Nov). *Moslem Year* 1400 A.H. *Commemoration. P* 14×13½.
164 **45** 50 p. multicoloured 20 20

46 Begum Roquiah

47 Spotted Deer and Scout Emblem

(Des A. Karim. Litho Rosenbaum Bros, Vienna)

1980 (9 Dec). *Birth Centenary of Begum Roquiah (campaigner for women's rights). P* 14.
165 **45** 50 p. multicoloured 10 10
166 2 t. multicoloured 35 20

(Des A. Karim. Litho Rosenbaum Bros, Vienna)

1981 (1 Jan). *5th Asia-Pacific/2nd Bangladesh Scout Jamboree. P* 13½×14.
167 **47** 50 p. multicoloured 40 15
168 5 t. multicoloured .. .. 1·25 2·00

2nd.
CENSUS
1981

(48)

49 Queen Elizabeth the Queen Mother

1981 (6 Mar). *Second Population Census. Nos.* 38/40 *optd with T* **48**.
169 **10** 20 p. multicoloured 10 10
170 25 p. multicoloured 10 10
171 75 p. multicoloured 20 30
169/71 .. .. *Set of* 3 30 40

(Des R. Granger Barrett. Litho Rosenbaum Bros, Vienna)

1981 (16 Mar). *80th Birthday of Queen Elizabeth the Queen Mother. P* 13½×14.
172 **49** 1 t. multicoloured 15 15
173 15 t. multicoloured .. .. 1·75 2·50
MS174 95 × 73 mm. Nos. 172/3 .. .. 2·40 2·50

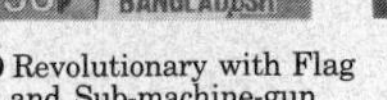

50 Revolutionary with Flag and Sub-machine-gun

51 Bangladesh Village and Farm Scenes

(Des P. Mandal. Litho Rosenbaum Bros, Vienna)

1981 (26 Mar). *Tenth Anniv of Independence. T* **50** *and similar vert design. Multicolourd. P* 13½×14.
175 50 p. Type **50** 15 10
176 2 t. Figures on map symbolising Bangladesh life-style 25 45

(Des A. Karim. Litho Rosenbaum Bros, Vienna)

1981 (1 Sept). *U.N. Conference on Least Developed Countries, Paris. P* 14×13½.
177 **51** 50 p. multicoloured 35 15

52 Kemal Atatürk in Civilian Dress

53 Deaf People using Sign Language

(Des F. Karim and P. Mandal. Litho Rosenbaum Bros, Vienna)

1981 (10 Nov). *Birth Centenary of Kemal Atatürk (Turkish statesman). T* **52** *and similar vert design. Multicoloured. P* 13½×14.
178 50 p. Type **52** 45 30
179 1 t. Kemal Atatürk in uniform 80 80

(Des F. Karim. Litho Ueberreuter, Austria)

1981 (26 Dec). *International Year for Disabled Persons. T* **53** *and similar multicoloured design. P* 13½ × 14 (50 *p.*) *or* 14 × 13½ (2 *t.*).
180 50 p. Type **53** 40 20
181 2 t. Disabled person writing (*horiz*) .. .. 1·25 2·00

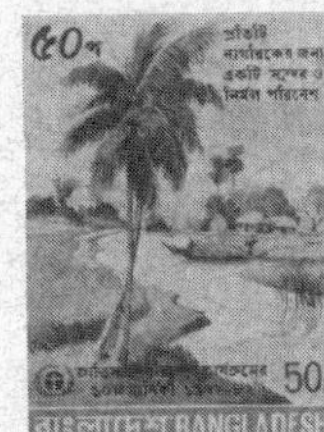

54 Farm Scene and Wheat Ear

55 River Scene

(Des F. Karim. Litho Ueberreuter, Austria)

1981 (31 Dec). *World Food Day. P* 13½ × 14.
182 **54** 50 p. multicoloured 50 80

(Des P. Mandal. Litho Ueberreuter, Vienna)

1982 (22 May). *10th Anniv of Human Environment Conference. P* 13½ × 14.
183 **55** 50 p. multicoloured 50 80

56 Dr. M. Hussain

57 Knotted Rope surrounding Bengali "75"

(Des F. Karim. Litho Ueberreuter, Vienna)

1982 (9 Oct). *First Death Anniv of Dr. Motahar Hussain (educationist). P* 13½.
184 **56** 50 p. multicoloured 50 80

(Des F. Karim and P. Mandal. Litho Ueberreuter, Vienna)

1982 (21 Oct). *75th Anniv of Boy Scout Movement and 125th Birth Anniv of Lord Baden-Powell. T* **57** *and similar multicoloured design. P* 14×13½ (50 *p.*) *or* 13½×14 (2 *t.*).
185 50 p. Type **57** .. .. 1·00 30
186 2 t. Lord Baden-Powell (*vert*) .. .. 3·25 4·50

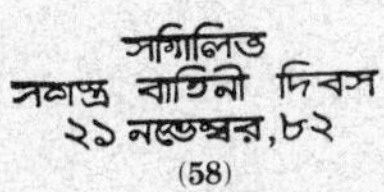

(58)

59 Capt. Mohiuddin Jahangir

1982 (21 Nov). *Armed Forces' Day. No.* 175 *optd with T* **58**.
187 50 p. Type **50** .. .. 2·25 2·25

(Litho Ueberreuter, Vienna)

1982 (16 Dec). *Heroes and Martyrs of the Liberation. T* **59** *and similar horiz designs. Multicoloured: background colours of commemorative plaque given. P* 14×13½.
188 50 p. Type **59** (pale orange) 30 45
a. Horiz strip of 7. Nos. 188/94 .. .. 1·90
189 50 p. Sepoy Hamidur Rahman (apple-green) 30 45
190 50 p. Sepoy Mohammed Mustafa Kamal (dull claret) 30 45
191 50 p. Muhammed Ruhul Amin (bistre-yellow) 30 45
192 50 p. Flt. Lt. M. Matiur Rahman (olive-bistre) 30 45
193 50 p. Lance-Naik Munshi Abdur Rob (chestnut) 30 45
194 50 p. Lance-Naik Nur Mouhammad (bright green) 30 45
188/94 .. .. *Set of* 7 1·90 2·75
Nos. 188/94 were printed together, *se-tenant*, in horizontal strips of 7 throughout the sheet.

60 Metric Scales

61 Dr. Robert Koch

(Des F. Karim. Litho Ueberreuter, Vienna)

1983 (10 Jan). *Introduction of Metric Weights and Measures. T* **60** *and similar multicoloured design. P* 13½×14 (50 *p.*) *or* 14×13½ (2 *t.*).
195 50 p. Type **60** 40 30
196 2 t. Weights, jug and tap measure (*horiz*) .. 1·75 2·50

(Des F. Karim. Litho Ueberreuter, Vienna)

1983 (20 Feb). *Centenary* (1982) *of Robert Koch's Discovery of Tubercle Bacillus. T* **61** *and similar vert design. Multicoloured. P* 13½×14.
197 50 p. Type **61** .. .. 1·00 40
198 1 t. Microscope, slide and X-ray .. .. 2·25 3·25

62 Open Stage Theatre

63 Dr. Muhammed Shahidulla

(Des F. Karim and P. Mandal. Litho Ueberreuter, Vienna)

1983 (14 Mar). *Commonwealth Day. T* **62** *and similar horiz designs. Multicoloured. P* 14.
199 1 t. Type **62** 10 15
200 3 t. Boat race 20 30
201 10 t. Snake dance 50 90
202 15 t. Picking tea .. .. 60 1·50
199/202 .. .. *Set of* 4 1·25 2·50

(Litho Ueberreuter, Vienna)

1983 (10 July). *Dr. Muhammed Shahidulla (Bengali scholar) Commemoration. P* 13½×14.
203 **63** 50 p. multicoloured .. .. 75 1·00

64 Magpie Robin

(Des F. Karim and P. Mandal. Litho Ueberreuter, Vienna)

1983 (17 Aug). *Birds of Bangladesh. T* **64** *and similar multicoloured designs. P* 14×13½ (50 *p.*, 5 *t.*) *or* 13½×14 (2 *t.*, 3 *t.* 75).
204 50 p. Type **64** .. .. 1·25 40
205 2 t. White-brested Kingfisher (*vert*) .. .. 2·25 2·25
206 3 t. 75 Lesser Golden-backed Woodpecker (*vert*) .. .. 3·00 3·00
207 5 t. White-winged Wood Duck .. .. 3·50 3·50
204/7 .. .. *Set of* 4 9·00 8·25
MS208 165×110 mm. Nos. 204/7 (*sold at* 13 *t.*) .. 11·00 14·00

65 *Macrobrachium rosenbergii*

Visit of Queen
Nov. '83

(66)

(Litho Ueberreuter, Vienna)

1983 (31 Oct). *Marine Life. T* **65** *and similar horiz designs. Multicoloured. P* 14×13½.
209 50 p. Type **65** 80 30
210 2 t. White Pomfret .. .. 2·00 1·60
211 3 t. 75, Rohu .. .. 2·50 2·00
212 5 t. Climbing Perch .. .. 3·00 2·75
209/12 .. .. *Set of* 4 7·50 6·00
MS213 119×98 mm. Nos. 209/12. Imperf (*sold at* 13 *t.*) .. .. 5·00 6·00

1983 (14 Nov). *Visit of Queen Elizabeth II. No.* 95 *optd with T* **66** *in red.*
214 10 t. Queen Elizabeth and Prince Philip .. 3·00 4·00
a. Optd "Nov '33" (R. 3/10) .. ..

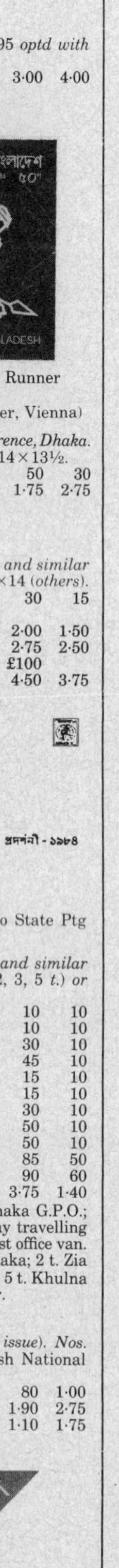

67 Conference Hall, Dhaka

68 Early Mail Runner

(Des M. Begum and M. Shamim. Litho Ueberreuter, Vienna)

1983 (5 Dec). *14th Islamic Foreign Ministers' Conference, Dhaka. T* **67** *and similar horiz design. Multicoloured. P* 14×13½.
215 50 p. Type **67** 50 30
216 5 t. Old Fort, Dhaka .. .. 1·75 2·75

(Litho Ueberreuter, Vienna)

1983 (21 Dec). *World Communications Year. T* **68** *and similar multicoloured designs. P* 14×13½ (10 *t.*) *or* 13½×14 (*others*).
217 50 p. Type **68** 30 15
218 5 t. Sailing ship, steam train and Boeing 707 airliner .. .. 2·00 1·50
219 10 t. Mail runner and dish aerial (*horiz*) .. 2·75 2·50
a. Gold (on dish aerial) omitted .. £100
217/19 .. .. *Set of* 3 4·50 3·75

69 Carrying Mail by Boat

প্রথম বাংলাদেশ জাতীয় ডাকটিকিট প্রদর্শনী-১৯৮৪

(70)

(Des M. Akond, P. Mandal and M. Shamim. Litho State Ptg Wks, Moscow)

1983 (21 Dec)–**86**. *Postal Communications. T* **69** *and similar designs. P* 11½×12½ (5, 25 *p.*), 12×11½ (1, 2, 3, 5 *t.*) *or* 12½×11½ (*others*).
220 5 p. turquoise-blue 10 10
221 10 p. purple 10 10
222 15 p. new blue 30 10
223 20 p. grey-black 45 10
224 25 p. slate 15 10
225 30 p. brown 15 10
226 50 p. light brown 30 10
227 1 t. dull ultramarine 50 10
228 2 t. deep bluish green 50 10
228*a* 3 t. bistre (11.1.86) 85 50
229 5 t. bright purple 90 60
220/9 .. .. *Set of* 11 3·75 1·40

Designs: *Horiz* (22 × 17 *mm*)—10 p. Counter, Dhaka G.P.O.; 15 p. I.W.T.A. Terminal, Dhaka; 20 p. Inside railway travelling post office; 30 p. Emptying pillar box; 50 p. Mobile post office van. (30 × 19 *mm*)—1 t. Kamalapur Railway Station, Dhaka; 2 t. Zia International Airport; 3 t. Sorting mail by machine; 5 t. Khulna G.P.O. *Vert* (17×22 *mm*)—25 p. Delivering a letter.

1984 (1 Feb). *1st National Stamp Exhibition (1st issue). Nos.* 161/2 *optd with T* **70** (5 *t.*) *or* "First Bangladesh National Philatelic Exhibition–1984" (50 *p.*), *both in red.*
230 **44** 50 p. multicoloured .. .. .. 80 1·00
a. Horiz pair. Nos. 230/1 .. .. 1·90 2·75
231 – 5 t. multicoloured .. .. .. 1·10 1·75

71 Girl with Stamp Album

(Des P. Mandal. Litho Harrison)

1984 (12 May). *1st National Stamp Exhibition (2nd issue). T* **71** *and similar triangular design. Multicoloured. P* 14.
232 50 p. Type **71** .. .. 65 1·25
a. Pair. Nos. 232/3 .. .. 1·75 2·75
233 7 t. 50, Boy with stamp album .. .. 1·10 1·60
MS234 98×117 mm. Nos. 232/3 (*sold at* 10 *t.*) .. 3·00 4·00

Nos. 232/3 were printed together, *se-tenant*, in pairs throughout the sheet.

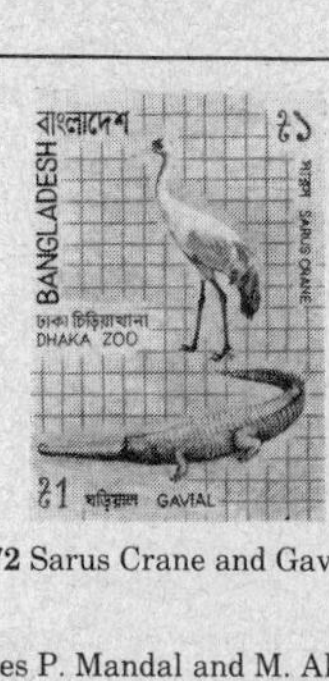

72 Sarus Crane and Gavial

73 Eagle attacking Hen with Chicks

(Des P. Mandal and M. Akond. Litho Ueberreuter, Vienna)

1984 (17 July). *Dhaka Zoo. T* **72** *and similar vert design. Multicoloured. P* 13½×14.
235 1 t. Type **72** .. .. 1·75 85
236 2 t. Common Peafowl and Tiger .. .. 2·50 3·50

(Des K. Mustafa. Litho Harrison)

1984 (3 Dec). *Centenary of Postal Life Insurance. T* **73** *and similar vert design. Multicoloured. P* 14.
237 1 t. Type **73** 50 20
238 5 t. Bangladesh family and postman's hand with insurance cheque .. .. .. 1·50 1·50

খুলনাপেক্স—৮৪

74 Abbasuddin Ahmad

(75)

(Des K. Mustafa. Litho Harrison)

1984 (24 Dec). *Abbasuddin Ahmad (singer) Commemoration. P* 14.
239 **74** 3 t. multicoloured 70 40

1984 (27 Dec). *"Khulnapex-84" Stamp Exhibition. No.* 86 *optd with T* **75**.
240 **22** 2 t. 25, multicoloured 70 60

76 Cycling

(Des M. Shamim. Litho Harrison)

1984 (31 Dec). *Olympic Games, Los Angeles. T* **76** *and similar horiz designs. Multicoloured. P* 14.
241 1 t. Type **76** .. .. 1·25 30
242 5 t. Hockey .. .. 2·50 2·25
243 10 t. Volleyball .. .. 2·75 3·00
241/3 .. .. *Set of* 3 6·00 5·00

77 Farmer with Rice and Sickle

78 Mother and Baby

(Des M. Shamim. Litho Harrison)

1985 (2 Feb). *9th Annual Meeting of Islamic Development Bank, Dhaka. T* **77** *and similar horiz design. Multicoloured. P* 14.
244 1 t. Type **77** 35 15
245 5 t. Citizens of four races .. .. .. 1·25 1·25

(Des M. Akond. Litho Harrison)

1985 (14 Mar). *Child Survival Campaign. T* **78** *and similar vert design. Multicoloured. P* 14.
246 1 t. Type **78** 30 10
247 10 t. Young child and growth graph .. 2·50 2·00

উপজেলা নির্বাচন ১৯৮৫

(79)

1985 (16 May). *Local Elections. Nos.* 110/15 *optd with T* **79**.
248 40 p. Type **29** 10 1
249 1 t. *Cassia fistula* 10 2
250 2 t. 25, *Delonix regia* 15 3
251 3 t. 50, *Nymphaea nouchali* 20 4
252 4 t. *Butea monosperma* 20 4
253 5 t. *Anthocephalus indicus* 30 5
248/53 .. .. *Set of* 6 85 1·9

80 Women working at Traditional Crafts

81 U.N. Building, New York, Peace Doves and Flags

(Des M. Akond. Litho Harrison)

1985 (18 July). *United Nations Decade for Women. T* **80** *an similar vert design. Multicoloured. P* 14.
254 1 t. Type **80** 25 1
255 10 t. Women with microscope, computer terminal and in classroom .. .. .. 1·25 8

(Des M. Akond. Litho Harrison)

1985 (14 Sept). *40th Anniv of United Nations Organization an 11th Anniv of Bangladesh Membership. T* **81** *and similar hori design. Multicoloured. P* 14.
256 1 t. Type **81** 10 1
257 10 t. Map of world and Bangladesh flag .. 80 9

82 Head of Youth, Flowers and Symbols of Commerce and Agriculture

83 Emblem and Seven Doves

(Des M. Shamim. Litho Harrison)

1985 (2 Nov). *International Youth Year. T* **82** *and similar ver design. Multicoloured. P* 14.
258 1 t. Type **82** 10 1
259 5 t. Head of youth, flowers and symbols of industry 40 6

(Des M. Akond. Litho Harrison)

1985 (8 Dec). *1st Summit Meeting of South Asian Associatio for Regional Co-operation, Dhaka. T* **83** *and similar ve design. Multicoloured. P* 14.
260 1 t. Type **83** 10 1
261 5 t. Flags of member nations and lotus blossom 40 6

তৃতীয় বাংলাদেশ জাতীয় জাম্বুরী ১৯৮৫-৮৬

84 Zainul Abedin

(85)

(Des P. Mandal. Litho Harrison)

1985 (28 Dec). *10th Death Anniv of Zainul Abedin (artist). P* 14.
262 **84** 3 t. multicoloured 75 3
a. Red-brown ("BANGLADESH" and face value) omitted

1985 (29 Dec). *3rd National Scout Jamboree. No.* 109 *optd wit T* **85**.
263 5 t. reddish lilac, deep blue and bright green 2·25 1·2

OMNIBUS ISSUES

Details, together with prices for complete sets of the various Omnibus issues from the 193 Silver Jubilee series to date are included in a special section following Zimbabwe at the end o Volume 2.

86 "Fishing Net" (Safiuddin Ahmed)

(Litho Harrison)

1986 (6 Apr). *Bangladesh Paintings. T* **86** *and similar horiz designs. Multicoloured. P* 14.
264 1 t. Type **86** 15 10
265 5 t. "Happy Return" (Quamrul Hassan) .. 40 50
266 10 t. "Levelling the Ploughed Field" (Zainul Abedin) 70 80
264/6 .. .. *Set of* 3 1·10 1·25

87 Two Players competing for Ball **88** General M. A. G. Osmani

(Des K. Mustafa. Litho Harrison)

1986 (29 June). *World Cup Football Championship, Mexico. T* **87** *and similar horiz design. Multicoloured. P* 15 × 14.
267 1 t. Type **87** 50 10
268 10 t. Goalkeeper and ball in net .. .. 2·25 2·50
MS269 105 × 75 mm. 20 t. Four players (60 × 44 *mm*). Imperf. .. .. 4·50 4·50

(Des P. Mandal. Litho Harrison)

1986 (18 Sept). *General M. A. G. Osmani (army commander-in-chief) Commemoration. P* 14.
270 **88** 3 t. multicoloured .. .. 1·00 75

SAARC SEMINAR '86

(**89**) **90** Butterflies and Nuclear Explosion

1986 (3 Dec). *South Asian Association for Regional Co-operation Seminar. No.* 183 *optd with T* **89**.
271 **55** 50 p. multicoloured .. .. 1·75 2·25

(Des M. Shamim. Litho State Ptg Wks, Moscow)

1986 (29 Dec). *International Peace Year. T* **90** *and similar vert designs. Multicoloured. P* 12 × 12½.
272 1 t. Type **90** 50 25
273 10 t. Flowers and ruined buildings .. .. 2·75 3·00
MS274 109 × 80 mm. 20 t. Peace dove and soldier 1·50 2·00

TK. 1.00

CONFERENCE FOR
DEVELOPMENT '87

(**91**)

1987 (12 Jan). *Conference for Development. Nos.* 152/3 *surch or optd as T* **91**.
275 **38** 1 t. on 40 p. black, vermilion & bistre-yell 10 15
a. Surch double .. .. ..
b. Surch triple .. ..
c. Surch sideways .. .. ..
d. Surch inverted .. .. ..
276 – 5 t. gold and bright blue 30 60
a. Opt double .. ..
b. Opt double, one inverted .. ..
c. Opt inverted.. .. .. ..
Stamp booklets containing Nos. 275/6 in strips of three are private productions and were not sold by the Bangladesh Post Office.

92 Demonstrators with Placards **93** Nurse giving Injection

(Des B. Sardar. Litho State Ptg Wks, Moscow)

1987 (21 Feb). *35th Anniv of Bangla Language Movement. T* **92** *and similar horiz design. Multicoloured. P* 12½ × 12.
277 3 t. Type **92** .. .. 1·00 1·50
a. Horiz pair. Nos. 277/8 .. .. .. 2·00 3·00
278 3 t. Martyrs' Memorial .. .. .. 1·00 1·50
Nos. 277/8 were printed together, *se-tenant*, in horizontal pairs throughout the sheet, each pair forming a composite design.

(Litho State Ptg Wks, Moscow)

1987 (7 Apr). *World Health Day. P* 11½ × 12.
279 **93** 1 t. blue-black and deep blue .. .. 1·75 1·50
See also No. 295.

94 Pattern and Bengali Script **95** Jute Shika

(Des M. Akond. Litho State Ptg Wks, Moscow)

1987 (16 Apr). *Bengali New Year. T* **94** *and similar vert design. Multicoloured. P* 12 × 12½.
280 1 t. Type **94** 10 10
281 10 t. Bengali woman 40 60

(Des P. Mandal, K. Mustafa and M. Akond. Photo State Ptg Wks, Moscow)

1987 (18 May). *Export Products. T* **95** *and similar multi-coloured designs. P* 12½ × 12 (5 *t.*) *or* 12 × 12½ (*others*).
282 1 t. Type **95** 10 10
283 5 t. Jute carpet (*horiz*) 30 35
284 10 t. Cane table lamp 45 70
282/4 .. .. *Set of* 3 70 1·00

96 Ustad Ayet Ali Khan and Surbahar **97** Palanquin

(Litho State Ptg Wks, Moscow)

1987 (2 Sept). *20th Death Anniv of Ustad Ayet Ali Khan (musician and composer). P* 12 × 12½.
285 **96** 5 t. multicoloured 55 40

(Litho State Ptg Wks, Moscow)

1987 (24 Oct). *Transport. T* **97** *and similar horiz designs. Multicoloured. P* 12½ × 12.
286 2 t. Type **97** 20 15
287 3 t. Bicycle rickshaw 30 20
288 5 t. River steamer 70 35
289 7 t. Express diesel train .. .. .. 1·40 50
290 10 t. Bullock cart 50 75
286/90 .. .. *Set of* 5 2·75 1·75

98 H. S. Suhrawardy **99** Villagers fleeing from Typhoon

(Des P. Mandal. Litho State Ptg Wks, Moscow)

1987 (5 Dec). *Hossain Shahid Suhrawardy (politician) Commem. P* 12 × 12½.
291 **98** 3 t. multicoloured 20 30

(Des M. Akond. Litho State Ptg Wks, Moscow)

1987 (15 Dec). *International Year of Shelter for the Homeless. T* **99** *and similar horiz design. Multicoloured. P* 12½ × 12.
292 5 t. Type **99** 20 30
a. Horiz pair. Nos. 292/3 .. .. .. 40 60
293 5 t. Villagers and modern houses 20 30
Nos. 292/3 were printed together, *se-tenant*, in horizontal pairs throughout the sheet.

100 President Ershad addressing Parliament

(Des K. Mustafa. Litho State Ptg Wks, Moscow)

1987 (31 Dec). *1st Anniv of Return to Democracy. P* 12½ × 12.
294 **100** 10 t. multicoloured 40 60

(Litho State Ptg Wks, Moscow)

1988 (16 Jan). *World Health Day. Vert design as T* **93**. *P* 11½ × 12.
295 25 p. brown 30 20
Design:—25 p. Oral rehydration.

101 Woman Planting Palm Saplings

(Des K. Mustafa. Litho State Ptg Wks, Moscow)

1988 (26 Jan). *I.F.A.D. Seminar on Agricultural Loans for Rural Women. T* **101** *and similar horiz design. Multicoloured. P* 12½ × 12.
296 3 t. Type **101** 15 20
297 5 t. Village woman milking cow 20 40

102 Basketball

(Litho State Ptg Wks, Moscow)

1988 (20 Sept). *Olympic Games, Seoul. T* **102** *and similar diamond-shaped designs. Multicoloured. P* 11½.
298 5 t. Type **102** 40 30
a. Strip of 5. Nos. 298/302 .. .. 1·75
299 5 t. Weightlifting 40 30
300 5 t. Tennis 40 30
301 5 t. Rifle-shooting 40 30
302 5 t. Boxing 40 30
298/302 .. .. *Set of* 5 1·75 1·40
Nos. 298/302 were printed together, *se-tenant*, in horizontal and vertical strips of five throughout the sheet.

103 Interior of Shait Gumbaz Mosque, Bagerhat **104** Henri Dunant (founder), Red Cross and Crescent

(Litho State Ptg Wks, Moscow)

1988 (9 Oct). *Historical Buildings. T* **103** *and similar horiz designs. Multicoloured. P* 12½×12.

303	1 t. Type **103**	10	10
304	4 t. Paharpur Monastery	10	10
305	5 t. Kantanagar Temple, Dinajpur	10	10
306	10 t. Lalbag Fort, Dhaka	15	15
303/6	*Set of* 4	30	30

(Litho State Ptg Wks, Moscow)

1988 (26 Oct). *125th Anniv of International Red Cross and Red Crescent. T* **104** *and similar vert design. Multicoloured. P* 12 × 12½.

307	5 t. Type **104**	25	25
308	10 t. Red Cross workers with patient	45	45

105 Dr. Qudrat-i-Khuda in Laboratory

106 Wicket-keeper

(Litho State Ptg Wks, Moscow)

1988 (3 Nov). *Dr. Qudrat-i-Khuda (scientist) Commemoration. P* 12 × 12½.

309 **105**	5 t. multicoloured	20	25

(Litho State Ptg Wks, Moscow)

1988 (27 Nov). *Asia Cup Cricket. T* **106** *and similar vert designs. Multicoloured. P* 12 × 12½.

310	1 t. Type **106**	70	90
	a. Horiz strip of 3. Nos. 310/12	2·40	
311	5 t. Batsman	90	1·00
312	10 t. Bowler	1·10	1·40
310/12	*Set of* 3	2·40	3·00

Nos. 310/12 were printed together, *se-tenant,* in horizontal strips of three throughout the sheet.

107 Labourers, Factory and Technician

(Litho State Ptg Wks, Moscow)

1988 (29 Nov). *32nd Meeting of Colombo Plan Consultative Committee, Dhaka. P* 12×12½.

313 **107**	3 t. multicoloured	10	10
314	10 t. multicoloured	40	45

108 Dhaka G.P.O. Building

(Litho State Ptg Wks, Moscow)

1988 (6 Dec). *25th Anniv of Dhaka G.P.O. Building. T* **108** *and similar horiz design. Multicoloured. P* 12.

315	1 t. Type **108**	10	10
316	5 t. Post Office counter	20	25

৫ম জাতীয় রোভার মুট
১৯৮৮-৮৯

(109)

110 Bangladesh Airport

1988 (29 Dec). *5th National Rover Scout Moot. No. 168 optd with T* **109**.

317 **47**	5 t. multicoloured	1·25	1·25
	a. Opt inverted		

(Des K. Mustafa (3, 10 t.), N. Islam (5 t.), M. Akond (20 t.). Litho State Ptg Wks, Moscow)

1989 (1 Jan)–**92**. *Bangladesh Landmarks. T* **110** *and similar designs. P* 12×11½ (3 *t.*), 12×12½ (4, 20 *t.*), 12½×12 (5 *t.*) *or* 11½×12 (10 *t.*).

318	3 t. black and light blue	10	10
318*a*	4 t. steel blue (15.7.92)	15	20
319	5 t. black and orange-brown (31.3.89)	15	20
320	10 t. rosine (1.7.89)	30	35
321	20 t. multicoloured (1.7.89)	65	70
318/21	*Set of* 5	1·25	1·50

Designs: *Vert* (22×33 *mm*)—5 t. Curzon Hall. (19½×31½ *mm*) 10 t. Fertiliser factory, Chittagong. *Horiz* (33×23 *mm*)—4 t. Chittagong port. 20 t. Postal Academy, Rajshahi.

চতুর্থ দ্বিবার্ষিক এশীয়
চারুকলা প্রদর্শনী
বাংলাদেশ ১৯৮৯

(111)

112 Irrigation Methods and Student with Telescope

1989 (1 Mar). *4th Biennial Asian Art Exhibition. No. 266 optd with T* **111**.

322	10 t. "Levelling the Ploughed Field" (Zainul Abedin)	40	45

(Litho State Ptg Wks, Moscow)

1989 (7 Mar). *12th National Science and Technology Week. P* 12×12½.

323 **112**	10 t. multicoloured	40	45

113 Academy Logo

114 Rejoicing Crowds, Paris, 1789

(Litho State Ptg Wks, Moscow)

1989 (13 Mar). *75th Anniv of Police Academy, Sardah. P* 12×12½.

324 **113**	10 t. multicoloured	40	45

(Des K. Mustafa (Nos. **MS**327/8). Litho Harrison)

1989 (12 July). *Bicentenary of French Revolution. T* **114** *and similar horiz design. Multicoloured. P* 14×14½.

325	17 t. Type **114**	70	75
	a. Horiz pair. Nos. 325/6 plus label	1·40	1·50
326	17 t. Storming the Bastille, 1789	70	75
MS327	125×125 mm. 5 t. Men with pickaxes; 10 t. "Liberty guiding the People" (detail) (Delacroix); 10 t. Crowd with cannon. P 14	1·75	2·50
MS328	152×88 mm. 25 t. Storming the Bastille. Imperf	1·75	2·50

Nos. 325/6 were printed in sheets of 30 (6×5) with No. 325 in vertical columns one and four, labels showing the Bicentenary emblem in columns two and five, and No. 326 in columns three and six.

The design of No. **MS**328 incorporates the three scenes featured on No. **MS**327.

115 Sowing and Harvesting

(Litho State Ptg Wks, Moscow)

1989 (10 Aug). *10th Anniv of Asia-Pacific Integrated Rural Development Centre. T* **115** *and similar horiz design. Multicoloured. P* 12½×12.

329	5 t. Type **115**	45	45
	a. Horiz pair. Nos. 329/30	95	95
330	10 t. Rural activities	50	50

Nos. 329/30 were printed together, *se-tenant,* in horizontal pairs throughout the sheet, each pair forming a composite design.

116 Helper and Child playing with Baby

117 U.N. Soldier on Watch

(Litho State Ptg Wks, Moscow)

1989 (22 Aug). *40th Anniv of S.O.S. International Children's Village. T* **116** *and similar horiz design. Multicoloured. P* 12½ × 12.

331	1 t. Type **116**	15	10
332	10 t. Foster mother with children	55	55

(Litho State Ptg Wks, Moscow)

1989 (12 Sept). *1st Anniv of Bangladesh Participation in U.N. Peace-keeping Force. T* **117** *and similar vert design. Multicoloured. P* 12×12½.

333	4 t. Type **117**	50	30
334	10 t. Two soldiers checking positions	1·00	70

118 Festival Emblem

119 State Security Printing Press

(Litho State Ptg Wks, Moscow)

1989 (17 Nov). *2nd Asian Poetry Festival, Dhaka. T* **118** *and similar vert design. P* 12×12½.

335	2 t. brt scarlet, dp carmine & myrtle-green	15	10
336	10 t. multicoloured	60	65

Design:—10 t. Festival emblem and hall.

(Litho State Security Ptg Press, Gazipur)

1989 (7 Dec). *Inauguration of State Security Printing Press, Gazipur. P* 13½.

337 **119**	10 t. multicoloured	65	65

120 Water Lilies and T.V. Emblem

(Litho State Ptg Wks, Moscow (5 t.), State Security Ptg Press, Gazipur (10 t.))

1989 (25 Dec). *25th Anniv of Bangladesh Television. T* **120** *and similar horiz design. Multicoloured. P* 12½×12 (5 *t.*) *or* 13½ (10 *t.*).

338	5 t. Type **120**	30	30
339	10 t. Central emblem and water lilies	65	80

121 Gharial in Shallow Water

122 Symbolic Family

(Des K. Mustafa. Litho Harrison)

1990 (31 Jan). *Endangered Wildlife. Gharial. T* **121** *and similar horiz designs. Multicoloured. P* 14.

340	50 p. Type **121**	80	45
	a. Block of 4. Nos. 340/3	4·50	
341	2 t. Gharial feeding	1·00	60
342	4 t. Gharials basking on sand bank	1·40	70
343	10 t. Two gharials resting	1·75	95
340/3	*Set of* 4	4·50	2·40

Nos. 340/3 were printed together, *se-tenant,* in blocks of four throughout the sheet.

(Litho State Ptg Press, Gazipur)

1990 (10 Feb). *Population Day. P* 13½.

344 **122**	6 t. multicoloured	55	35

123 Justice S.M. Murshed

124 Boy learning Alphabet

(Des P. Mandal. Litho State Ptg Wks, Moscow)

90 (3 Apr). *10th Death Anniv of Justice Syed Mahbub Murshed. P* 12½×12.

45 **123** 5 t. multicoloured	1·25	35

(Litho State Ptg Wks, Moscow)

90 (10 Apr). *International Literacy Year. T* **124** *and similar vert design. Multicoloured. P* 12×12½.

46 6 t. Type **124**	1·00	50
47 10 t. Boy teaching girl to write	1·50	1·00

125 Penny Black with "Stamp World London 90" Exhibition Emblem

126 Goalkeeper and Ball

(Des K. Mustafa. Litho State Security Ptg Press, Gazipur)

990 (6 May). *150th Anniv of the Penny Black. T* **125** *and similar vert design. Multicoloured. P* 13½.

48 7 t. Type **125**	1·50	60
49 10 t. Penny Black, 1983 World Communications Year stamp and Bengali mail runner	1·75	1·00

(Des M. Shamim. Litho State Security Ptg Press, Gazipur)

990 (12 June). *World Cup Football Championship, Italy. T* **126** *and similar horiz designs. Multicoloured. P* 13½.

50 8 t. Type **126**	1·75	90
51 10 t. Footballer with ball	2·00	1·00
IS352 104×79 mm. 25 t. Colosseum, Rome, with football. Imperf	5·00	5·50
a. Country and commemorative inscrs inverted		

On No. **MS**352a "BANGLADESH WORLD CUP FOOTBALL TALY 1990" at the foot of the design is in white with the same scriptions in blue inverted at the top of the miniature sheet.

127 Mango

128 Man gathering Wheat

Des M. Shamim (1, 2t.), N. Islam (3, 4 t.), P. Mandal (5, 10 t). Litho State Ptg Wks, Moscow)

990 (16 July). *Fruit. T* **127** *and similar vert designs. Multicoloured. P* 12×12½.

53 1 t. Type **127**	30	10
54 2 t. Guava	30	10
55 3 t. Water-melon	35	15
56 4 t. Papaya	40	25
57 5 t. Bread fruit	65	50
58 10 t. Carambola	1·25	1·25
53/8 *Set of* 6	3·00	2·00

RINTERS. The following issues were printed in lithography the State Security Printing Press, Gazipur, *unless otherwise ated.*

(Des M. Akond)

990 (3 Sept). *U.N. Conference on Least Developed Countries, Paris. P* 14.

59 **128** 10 t. multicoloured	1·25	90
a. Blue (U.N. emblem and inscr) inverted		

On the evidence of the sheet marginal markings it would ppear that the blue on No. 359a may be printed correctly and e remainder of the colours inverted. Unequal margins at top d bottom of the sheet also cause the country name and face alue, in green, to be displaced.

129 Map of Asia with Stream of Letters

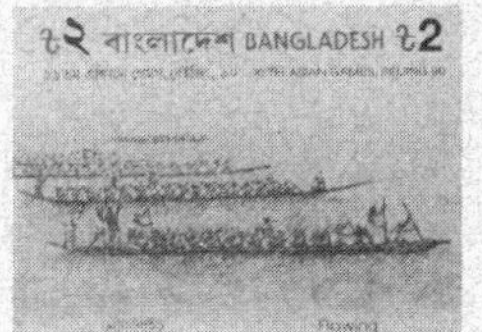

130 Canoe Racing

(Des K. Mustafa)

1990 (10 Sept). *20th Anniv of Asia–Pacific Postal Training Centre. T* **129** *and similar vert design. Multicoloured. P* 13½×14.

360 2 t. Type **129**	75	50
a. Horiz pair. Nos. 360/1	1·50	1·00
361 6 t. Map of Pacific with stream of letters	75	50

Nos. 360/1 were printed together, *se-tenant*, in horizontal pairs throughout the sheet, forming a composite map design.

(Des K. Mustafa)

1990 (22 Sept). *Asian Games, Beijing. T* **130** *and similar horiz designs. Multicoloured. P* 14×13½.

362 2 t. Type **130**	60	10
363 4 t. Kabaddi	75	25
364 8 t. Wrestling	1·25	75
365 10 t. Badminton	2·00	1·50
362/5 *Set of* 4	4·25	2·25

131 Lalan Shah

132 U.N. Logo and "40"

(Des K. Mustafa)

1990 (17 Oct). *1st Death Anniv of Lalan Shah (poet). P* 13½×14.

366 **131** 6 t. multicoloured	1·00	35

(Des M. Akond)

1990 (24 Oct). *40th Anniv of United Nations Development Programme. P* 14×13½.

367 **132** 6 t. multicoloured	80	35

133 Baby

134 *Danaus chrysippus*

(Des M. Akond)

1990 (29 Nov). *Immunization. P* 14½×14.

368 **133** 1 t. emerald	10	10
369 2 t. brown	10	10

(Des M. Shamim)

1990 (3 Dec). *Butterflies. T* **134** *and similar square designs. Multicoloured. P* 13½×12.

370 6 t. Type **134**	1·60	1·60
a. Block of 4. Nos. 370/3	6·00	
ab. Deep blue and chestnut inscr inverted (block of 4)		
371 6 t. *Precis almana*	1·60	1·60
372 10 t. *Ixias pyrene*	1·75	1·75
373 10 t. *Danaus plexippus*	1·75	1·75
370/3 *Set of* 4	6·00	6·00

Nos. 370/3 were printed together, *se-tenant*, in blocks of four throughout the sheet.

On No. 370ab the printing of "BANGLADESH", in deep blue on No. 371 and in chestnut on No. 372, is inverted so that the inscription does not occur on these two designs. The inverted deep blue "BANGLADESH" appears on the left sheet margin of No. 373 and the chestnut on No. 370.

135 Drugs attacking Bangladesh

136 Salimullah Hall

(Des F. Karim (2 t.), M. Akond (4 t.))

1991 (1 Jan). *United Nations Anti-Drugs Decade. T* **135** *and similar horiz design. Multicoloured. P* 14.

374 2 t. Type **135**	1·00	50
375 4 t. "Drug" snake around globe	1·25	1·25

(Des P. Mandal)

1991 (30 Jan). *P* 14½×14.

376 **136** 6 t. slate-blue and greenish yellow	20	25

137 Silhouetted People on Map

138 "Invincible Bangla" (statue)

(Des P. Mandal)

1991 (12 Mar). *Third National Census. P* 14.

382 **137** 4 t. multicoloured	65	60

(Des M. Akond)

1991 (26 Mar). *20th Anniv of Independence. T* **138** *and similar square designs. Multicoloured. P* 13½.

383 4 t. Type **138**	55	65
a. Horiz strip of 5. Nos. 383/7	2·50	
384 4 t. "Freedom Fighter" (statue)	55	65
385 4 t. Mujibnagar Memorial	55	65
386 4 t. Eternal Flame	55	65
387 4 t. National Martyrs' Memorial	55	65
383/7 *Set of* 5	2·50	3·00

Nos. 383/7 were printed together, *se-tenant*, in horizontal strips of five throughout the sheet, with the backgrounds forming a composite design.

139 Pres. Rahman Seated

140 Red Giant Flying Squirrel

(Des P. Mandal. Litho Ueberreuter, Austria)

1991 (30 May). *10th Death Anniv of President Ziaur Rahman. T* **139** *and similar vert design. Multicoloured. P* 13½×14.

388 50 p. Type **139**	20	15
389 2 t. President Rahman's head in circular decoration	65	85
MS390 146 × 75 mm. Nos. 388/9 (*sold at* 10 *t.*)	1·25	1·75

(Des K. Mustafa)

1991 (16 June). *Endangered Species. T* **140** *and similar multicoloured designs. P* 12.

391 2 t. Type **140**	1·00	1·25
a. Vert pair. Nos. 391 and 394	2·10	2·50
392 4 t. Black-faced Monkey (*vert*)	1·00	1·25
a. Horiz pair. Nos. 392/3	2·00	2·50
393 6 t. Great Indian Hornbill (*vert*)	1·00	1·25
394 10 t. Armoured Pangolin	1·10	1·25
391/4 *Set of* 4	3·75	4·50

Nos. 391 and 394, and 392/3 were printed together, *se-tenant*, in vertical (Nos. 391 and 394) or horizontal (Nos. 392/3) pairs throughout separate sheets.

141 Kaikobad

142 Rabindranath Tagore and Temple

(Des K. Mustafa)

1991 (21 July). *40th Death Anniv of Kaikobad (poet). P* 14.

395 **141** 6 t. multicoloured	60	60

(Des A. Karim)

1991 (7 Aug). *50th Death Anniv of Rabindranath Tagore (poet). P* 14.

396 **142** 4 t. multicoloured	70	55

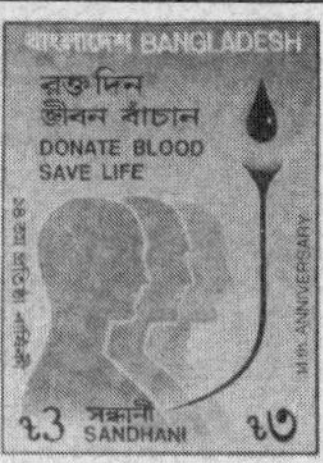
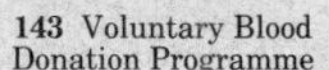
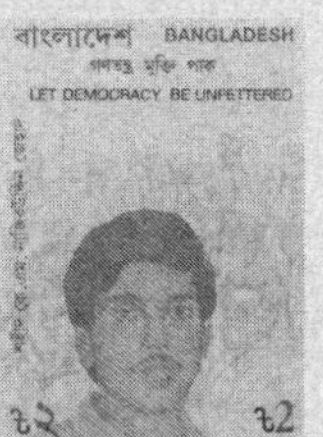

143 Voluntary Blood Donation Programme

144 Shahid Naziruddin and Crowd

(Des P. Mandal)

1991 (19 Sept). *14th Anniv of "Sandhani" (medical students' association). T* 143 *and similar vert design. P* 14.
397 3 t. black and bright carmine 75 50
398 5 t. multicoloured .. .. .. 1·25 1·50
Design:—5 t. Blind man and eye

1991 (10 Oct). *1st Death Anniv of Shahid Naziruddin Jahad (democrat). P* 14.
399 **144** 2 t. black, emerald and cinnamon .. 55 50
a. Emerald ("BANGLADESH" and face value) omitted £100

145 Shaheed Noor Hossain with Slogan on Chest

146 Bronze Stupa

(Des K. Mustafa)

1991 (10 Nov). *4th Death Anniv of Shaheed Noor Hossain (democrat). P* 14.
400 **145** 2 t. multicoloured 45 40

(Des M. Akond)

1991 (26 Nov). *Archaeological Relics from Mainamati. T* **146** *and similar horiz designs. Multicoloured. P* 13½.
401 4 t. Type **146** .. .. 90 1·00
a. Horiz strip of 5. Nos. 401/5 .. .. 4·00
402 4 t. Earthenware and bronze pitchers .. 90 1·00
403 4 t. Remains of Salban Vihara Monastery 90 1·00
404 4 t. Gold coins .. .. 90 1·00
405 4 t. Terracotta plaque .. .. .. 90 1·00
401/5 .. .. *Set of* 5 4·00 4·50
Nos. 401/5 were printed together, *se-tenant*, in horizontal strips of 5 throughout the sheet.

147 Demonstrators

148 Munier Chowdhury

(Des. M. Muniruzzaman)

1991 (6 Dec). *1st Anniv of Mass Uprising. P* 13½.
406 **147** 4 t. multicoloured 65 50

1991 (14 Dec). *20th Anniv of Independence. Martyred Intellectuals (1st series). T* **148** *and similar vert designs. Each grey-black and reddish brown. P* 13½.
407 2 t. Type **148** 30 30
a. Sheetlet. Nos. 407/16 .. .. 2·75
408 2 t. Ghyasuddin Ahmad 30 30
409 2 t. Rashidul Hasan 30 30
410 2 t. Muhammad Anwar Pasha 30 30
411 2 t. Dr. Muhammad Mortaza 30 30
412 2 t. Shahid Saber 30 30
413 2 t. Fazlur Rahman Khan 30 30
414 2 t. Ranada Prasad Saha 30 30
415 2 t. Adhyaksha Joges Chandra Ghose .. 30 30
416 2 t. Santosh Chandra Bhattacharyya .. 30 30
417 2 t. Dr. Gobinda Chandra Deb 30 30
a. Sheetlet. Nos. 417/26 .. .. 2·75
418 2 t. A. Muniruzzaman 30 30
419 2 t. Mufazzal Haider Chaudhury 30 30
420 2 t. Dr. Abdul Alim Choudhury 30 30
421 2 t. Sirajuddin Hossain 30 30
422 2 t. Shahidulla Kaiser 30 30
423 2 t. Altaf Mahmud 30 30
424 2 t. Dr. Jyotirmay Guha Thakurta .. 30 30
425 2 t. Dr. Muhammad Abul Khair 30 30
426 2 t. Dr. Serajul Haque Khan 30 30
427 2 t. Dr. Mohammad Fazle Rabbi 30 30
a. Sheetlet. Nos. 427/36 .. .. 2·75
428 2 t. Mir Abdul Quyyum 30 30
429 2 t. Golam Mostafa 30 30
430 2 t. Dhirendranath Dutta 30 30
431 2 t. S. Mannan 30 30
432 2 t. Nizamuddin Ahmad 30 30
433 2 t. Abul Bashar Chowdhury 30 30
434 2 t. Selina Parveen 30 30
435 2 t. Dr. Abul Kalam Azad 30 30
436 2 t. Saidul Hassan 30 30
407/36 .. .. *Set of* 30 8·00 8·00
Nos. 407/16, 417/26 and 427/36 were printed together, *se-tenant*, in sheetlets of 10, the two horizontal rows in each sheetlet being separated by a row of inscribed labels.
See also Nos. 483/92, 525/40, 568/83, 620/35 and 656/71.

149 *Penaeus monodon*

1991 (31 Dec). *Shrimps. T* **149** *and similar horiz design. Multicoloured. P* 14×13½.
437 6 t. Type **149** .. .. 1·25 1·50
a. Horiz pair. Nos. 437/8 .. .. 2·50 3·00
438 6 t. *Metapenaeus monoceros* .. .. 1·25 1·50
Nos. 437/8 were printed together, *se-tenant*, in horizontal pairs throughout the sheet.

150 Death of Raihan Jaglu

151 Rural and Urban Scenes

(Des M. Muniruzzaman)

1992 (8 Feb). *5th Death Anniv of Shaheed Mirze Abu Raihan Jaglu. P* 14×13½.
439 **150** 2 t. multicoloured 60 50

(Des K. Mustafa (4 t.), A. Karim (10 t.))

1992 (5 June). *World Environment Day. T* **151** *and similar multicoloured design. P* 14.
440 4 t. Type **151** 50 15
441 10 t. World Environment Day logo (*horiz*) 1·25 1·75

152 Nawab Sirajuddaulah

153 Syed Ismail Hossain Sirajee

(Des K. Mustafa)

1992 (2 July). *235th Death Anniv of Nawab Sirajuddaulah of Bengal. P* 13½.
442 **152** 10 t. multicoloured 80 80
a. Emerald ("BANGLADESH" inscr) omitted £100

1992 (17 July). *61st Death Anniv of Syed Ismail Hossain Sirajee. P* 14.
443 **153** 4 t. multicoloured 60 40

154 Couple planting Seedling

(Des M. Huq and M. Muniruzzaman)

1992 (19 July). *Plant Week. T* **154** *and similar multicolour design. P* 14.
444 2 t. Type **154** 85
445 4 t. Birds on tree (*vert*) 85

155 Canoe Racing

(156)

(Des M. Akond, M. Mia and S. Datta)

1992 (25 July). *Olympic Games, Barcelona. T* **155** *and simil horiz designs. Multicoloured. P* 14.
446 4 t. Type **155** .. .. 90 1·
a. Block of 4. Nos. 446/9 .. .. 3·25
447 6 t. Hands holding torch with Olympic rings .. .. 90 1·
448 10 t. Olympic rings and doves .. .. 90 1·
449 10 t. Olympic rings and multiracial handshake .. .. 90 1·
446/9 .. .. *Set of* 4 3·25 3·
Nos. 446/9 were printed together, *se-tenant*, in blocks of fo throughout the sheet of 100 with the two 10 t. values occurri in the first, third, fifth, seventh and ninth horizontal rows.

1992 (18 Aug). *"Banglapex '92", National Philatelic Exhibiti (1st issue). No.* 290 *optd with T* **156.**
450 10 t. Bullock cart .. .. 1·00 1·

157 Masnad-e-Ala Isa Khan

158 Ceremonial Elephant (19th-century ivory carving)

1992 (15 Sept). *393rd Death Anniv of Masnad-e-Ala Isa Kho P* 14.
451 **157** 4 t. multicoloured 60

(Des M. Begum)

1992 (26 Sept). *"Banglapex '92", National Philatelic Exhibiti (2nd issue). T* **158** *and similar horiz design. Multicolour P* 14.
452 10 t. Type **158** .. .. 1·00 1·
a. Horiz pair. Nos. 452/3 plus label .. 2·00 2·
453 10 t. Victorian pillarbox between early and modern postmen .. .. .. 1·00 1·
MS454 145×92 mm. Nos. 452/3 plus label. Imperf (*sold at* 25 *t.*) .. .. .. 2·50 3
Nos. 452/3 were printed together, *se-tenant*, in sheets with 452 in vertical columns one and four, labels showing exhibition emblem in columns two and five, and No. 453 columns three and six.

159 Star Mosque

(Des Md. Jasimuddin)

1992 (29 Oct). *Star Mosque, Dhaka. P* 14½×13½.
455 **159** 10 t. multicoloured 90

160 Meer Nisar Ali Titumeer and Fort

(Des M. Akond)

1992 (19 Nov). *161st Death Anniv of Meer Nisar Ali Titume P* 14½×13½.
456 **160** 10 t. multicoloured 90

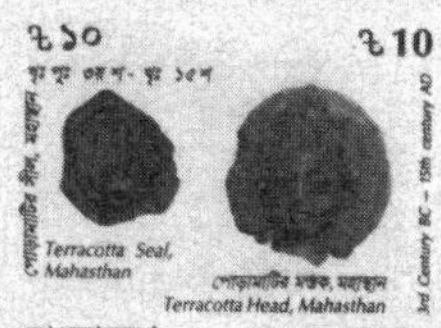

161 Terracotta Head and Seal

(Des M. Akond, M. Begum and M. Mia)

992 (30 Nov). *Archaeological Relics from Mahasthangarh. T* **161** *and similar horiz designs. Multicoloured. P* 14½×13½.
.57 10 t. Type **161** .. .. 1·10 1·25
a. Horiz strip of 4. Nos. 457/60 .. .. 4·00
58 10 t. Terracotta panel showing swan .. 1·10 1·25
59 10 t. Terracotta statue of Surya .. .. 1·10 1·25
.60 10 t. Gupta stone column .. .. .. 1·10 1·25
.57/60 .. .. *Set of* 4 4·00 4·50
Nos. 457/60 were printed together, *se-tenant*, in horizontal trips of 4 throughout the sheet.

162 Young Child and Food 163 National Flags

(Des M. Muniruzzaman)

992 (5 Dec). *International Conference on Nutrition, Rome. P* 14½×13½.
61 **162** 4 t. multicoloured 60 40

(Des N. Islam (6 t.), M. Akond (10 t.))

992 (5 Dec). *7th South Asian Association for Regional Co-operation Summit Conference, Dhaka. T* **163** *and similar vert design. Multicoloured. P* 13½×14½.
62 6 t. Type **163** 60 60
63 10 t. S.A.A.R.C. emblem 80 90

164 Syed Abdus Samad 165 Haji Shariat Ullah

(Des P. Mandal)

993 (2 Feb). *Syed Abdus Samad (footballer) Commemoration. P* 14.
64 **164** 2 t. multicoloured 70 50

(Des M. Rahman)

993 (10 Mar). *Haji Shariat Ullah Commemoration. P* 14½.
65 **165** 2 t. multicoloured 50 40

166 People digging Canal

(Des M. Rahman)

993 (31 Mar). *Irrigation Canals Construction Project. T* **166** *and similar horiz design. Multicoloured. P* 14.
66 2 t. Type **166** 45 55
a. Horiz pair. Nos. 466/7 .. .. 90 1·10
67 2 t. Completed canal and paddy-fields .. 45 55
Nos. 466/7 were printed together, *se-tenant*, in horizontal airs throughout the sheet.

MINIMUM PRICE

he minimum price quote is 10p which represents handling charge rather than a basis for valuing ommon stamps. For further notes about prices see introductory pages.

167 Accident Prevention 168 National Images

(Des A. Hussain (6 t.), N. Islam (10 t.))

1993 (7 Apr). *World Health Day. T* **167** *and similar multicoloured design. P* 14.
468 6 t. Type **167** .. .. 1·25 75
469 10 t. Satellite photograph and symbols of trauma (*vert*) .. .. 1·50 1·75

(Des Md. Shamsuzzoha)

1993 (14 Apr). *1400th Year of Bengali Solar Calendar. P* 14.
470 **168** 2 t. multicoloured 55 40

169 Schoolchildren and Bengali Script 170 Nawab Sir Salimullah and Palace

(Des M. Huq (No. 471), M. Mia (No. 472))

1993 (26 May). *Compulsory Primary Education. T* **169** *and similar multicoloured design. P* 14×14½ *(No. 471) or* 14½×14 *(No. 472).*
471 2 t. Type **169** 40 50
472 2 t. Books and slate (*horiz*) 40 50

(Des S. Shaheen)

1993 (7 June). *122nd Birth Anniv of Nawab Sir Salimullah. P* 14½×14.
473 **170** 4 t. multicoloured 55 40

171 Fish Production

(Des M. Rahman)

1993 (15 Aug). *Fish Fortnight. P* 14½×14.
474 **171** 2 t. multicoloured 30 30

172 Sunderban 173 Exhibition Emblem

(Des M. Mia, M. Rahman and B. Biswas)

1993 (30 Oct). *Natural Beauty of Bangladesh. T* **172** *and similar multicoloured designs. P* 14½×14 *(horiz) or* 14×14½ *(vert).*
475 10 t. Type **172** 60 80
476 10 t. Kuakata beach 60 80
477 10 t. Madhabkunda waterfall (*vert*) .. 60 80
478 10 t. River Piyain, Jaflang (*vert*) 60 80
475/8 .. .. *Set of* 4 2·25 2·75
MS479 174×102 mm. Nos. 475/8. Imperf. (*sold at* 50 *t.*) .. .. 2·75 3·25
No. 476 and the same design in No. **MS**479 also exist with smaller country name and inscr "TOURISM MONTH '93" in English and Bengali. This version was not issued.

(Des Q. Chowdhury)

1993 (2 Nov). *6th Asian Art Biennale. P* 14×14½.
480 **173** 10 t. multicoloured 60 80

174 Foy's Lake 175 Burdwan House

(Des A. Hussain)

1993 (6 Nov). *Tourism Month. P* 14½×14.
481 **174** 10 t. multicoloured 70 80

(Des N. Islam)

1993 (3 Dec). *Foundation Day, Bangla Academy. P* 14×14½.
482 **175** 2 t. deep brown and emerald 20 20

1993 (14 Dec). *Martyred Intellectuals (2nd series). Vert designs as T* **148**. *Each grey-black and reddish brown. P* 14½.
483 2 t. Lt. Cdr. Moazzam Hussain 15 20
a. Sheetlet. Nos. 483/92 .. .. 1·25
484 2 t. Muhammad Habibur Rahman .. 15 20
485 2 t. Khandoker Abu Taleb 15 20
486 2 t. Moshiur Rahman 15 20
487 2 t. Md Abdul Muktadir 15 20
488 2 t. Nutan Chandra Sinha 15 20
489 2 t. Syed Nazmul Haque 15 20
490 2 t. Dr. Mohammed Amin Uddin .. 15 20
491 2 t. Dr. Faizul Mohee 15 20
492 2 t. Sukha Ranjan Somaddar 15 20
483/92 .. .. *Set of* 10 1·25 1·75
Nos. 483/92 were printed together, *se-tenant*, as a sheetlet of 10, the two horizontal rows being separated by a row of inscribed labels.

176 Throwing the Discus

1993 (19 Dec). *6th South Asian Federation Games, Dhaka. T* **176** *and similar multicoloured design. P* 14½×14 *(2 t.) or* 14×14½ *(4 t).*
493 2 t. Type **176** 15 15
a. Rose-lilac, yellow-brown and orange (parts of logo) omitted .. ..
494 4 t. Running (*vert*) 25 25
a. Yellow-brown (part of logo) omitted £100

177 Tomb of Sultan Ghiyasuddin Azam Shah 178 Scouting Activities and Jamboree Emblem

(Des Md. Shamsuzzoha)

1993 (30 Dec). *Muslim Monuments. P* 14½×14.
495 **177** 10 t. multicoloured 60 70

(Des A. Hussain)

1994 (5 Jan). *14th Asian-Pacific and 5th Bangladesh National Scout Jamboree. P* 14×14½.
496 **178** 2 t. multicoloured 30 30

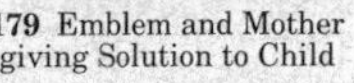

179 Emblem and Mother giving Solution to Child 180 Interior of Chhota Sona Mosque, Nawabgonj

(Des Md. Shamsuzzoha)

1994 (5 Feb). *25th Anniv of Oral Rehydration Solution. P* 14×14½.
497 **179** 2 t. multicoloured 30 30

(Des A. Hussain, M. Huq and M. Rahman)

1994 (30 Mar). *Ancient Mosques. T* **180** *and similar horiz designs. Multicoloured. P* 14½×14.

498 4 t. Type **180** 15 15
499 6 t. Exterior of Chhota Sona Mosque .. 30 40
500 6 t. Exterior of Baba Adam's Mosque, Munshigonj 30 40
498/500 .. .. *Set of* 3 65 85

181 Agricultural Workers and Emblem

182 Priest releasing Peace Doves

(Des R. Hussain and M. Huq)

1994 (11 Apr). *75th Anniv of International Labour Organization. T* **181** *and similar multicoloured design. P* 14½×14 (4 *t.*) *or* 14×14½ (10 *t.*).

501 4 t. Type **181** 15 15
a. Bright blue ("BANGLADESH" inscr) omitted £150
502 10 t. Worker turning cog (*vert*) 60 85

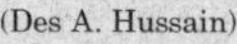

(Des A. Hussain)

1994 (14 Apr). *1500th Year of Bengali Solar Calendar. P* 14×14½.

503 **182** 2 t. multicoloured 15 15

183 Scenes from Baishakhi Festival

184 Family, Globe and Logo

(Des A. Hussain)

1994 (12 May). *Folk Festivals. T* **183** *and similar horiz design. Multicoloured. P* 14½×14.

504 4 t. Type **183** 25 25
505 4 t. Scenes from Nabanna and Paush Parvana Festivals 25 25

(Des M. Huq)

1994 (15 May). *International Year of the Family. P* 14×14½.

506 **184** 10 t. multicoloured .. .. .. 80 1·00

185 People planting Saplings

186 Player kicking Ball

(Des M. Mia and R. Hussain)

1994 (15 June). *Tree Planting Campaign. T* **185** *and similar vert design. Multicoloured. P* 14×14½.

507 4 t. Type **185** 25 15
508 6 t. Hands holding saplings 40 50

(Des M. Shamim)

1994 (17 June). *World Cup Football Championship, U.S.A. T* **186** *and similar vert design. Multicoloured. P* 14½.

509 20 t. Type **186** .. .. 1·50 2·00
a. Horiz strip of 3. Nos. 509/10 and label 3·00
510 20 t. Player heading ball .. .. .. 1·50 2·00

Nos. 509/10 were printed together, *se-tenant*, in sheets of 15 (3×5) with each horizontal row containing one of each design separated by a label showing the championship mascot.

187 Traffic on Bridge

188 Asian Black-headed Oriole

(Des A. Rouf)

1994 (24 July). *Inauguration of Jamuna Multi-purpose Bridge Project. P* 14½×14.

511 **187** 4 t. multicoloured 40 30

(Des A. Hussain)

1994 (31 Aug). *Birds. T* **188** *and similar vert designs. Multicoloured. P* 14×14½.

512 4 t. Type **188** 40 40
513 6 t. Greater Racquet-tailed Drongo (*Dicrurus paradiseus*) 60 80
514 6 t. Indian Tree Pie (*Dendrocitta vagabunda*) 60 80
515 6 t. Red Junglefowl (*Gallus gallus*) .. 60 80
512/15 .. .. *Set of* 4 2·00 2·50
MS516 165×110 mm. Nos. 512/15 (*sold at* 25 t.) 2·00 2·75

189 Dr. Mohammad Ibrahim and Hospital

190 Nawab Faizunnessa Chowdhurani

(Des M. Shamim)

1994 (6 Sept). *5th Death Anniv of Dr. Mohammad Ibrahim (diabetes treatment pioneer). P* 14½×14.

517 **189** 2 t. multicoloured 30 20

(Des M. Rahman)

1994 (23 Sept). *160th Birth Anniv of Nawab Faizunnessa Chowdhurani (social reformer). P* 14×14½.

518 **190** 2 t. multicoloured 20 20

191 Boxing

(Des A. Hussain)

1994 (2 Oct). *Asian Games, Hiroshima, Japan. P* 14½×14.

519 **191** 4 t. multicoloured 50 30

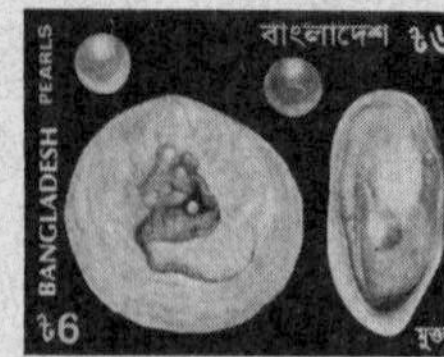

192 Pink and White Pearls with Windowpane Oysters

(Des M. Mia, M. Rahman and Md. Shamsuzzoha)

1994 (30 Oct). *Sea Shells. T* **192** *and similar multicoloured designs. P* 14×14½ (*No.* 523) *or* 14½×14 (*others*).

520 6 t. Type **192** 60 70
521 6 t. Tranquelous Scallop and other shells 60 70
522 6 t. Lister's Conch, Asiatic Arabian Cowrie, Bladder Moon and Woodcock Murex 60 70
523 6 t. Spotted Tun, Spiny Frog Shell, Spiral Melongena and Gibbous Olive .. 60 70
520/3 .. .. *Set of* 4 2·25 2·50

193 Dr. Milon and Demonstrators

194 *Diplazium esculentum*

(Des M. Akond)

1994 (27 Nov). *4th Death Anniv of Dr. Shamsul Alam Kha Milon (medical reformer). P* 14½×14.

524 **193** 2 t. multicoloured 15 1

(Des M. Huq, A. Hussain, M. Mia, A. Moniruzzaman, M Rahman and Md. Shamsuzzoha)

1994 (14 Dec). *Martyred Intellectuals (3rd series). Vert design as T* **148**. *Each grey-black and reddish brown. P* 14×14½.

525 2 t. Dr. Harinath Dey 15
a. Sheetlet. Nos. 525/32 .. .. 1·10
526 2 t. Dr. A. F. Ziaur Rahman 15
527 2 t. Mamun Mahmud 15
528 2 t. Mohsin Ali Dewan 15
529 2 t. Dr. N. A. M. Jahangir 15
530 2 t. Shah Abdul Majid 15
531 2 t. Muhammad Akhter 15
532 2 t. Meherunnesa 15
533 2 t. Dr. Kasiruddin Talukder 15
a. Sheetlet. Nos. 533/40 .. .. 1·10
534 2 t. Fazlul Haque Choudhury 15
535 2 t. Md. Shamsuzzaman 15
536 2 t. A. K. M. Shamsuddin 15
537 2 t. Lt. Mohammad Anwarul Azim .. 15
538 2 t. Nurul Amin Khan 15
539 2 t. Mohammad Sadeque 15
540 2 t. Md. Araz Ali 15
525/40 .. .. *Set of* 16 2·00 2·

Nos. 525/32 and 533/40 were printed together, *se-tenant*, sheetlets of 8, the two horizontal rows in each sheetlet bei separated by a row of inscribed labels.

(Des A. Hussain, N. Islam and Md. Shamsuzzoha)

1994 (24 Dec). *Vegetables. T* **194** *and similar multicolour designs. P* 14½×14 (*No.* 546) *or* 14×14½ (*others*).

541 4 t. Type **194** 30
542 4 t. *Momordica charantia* 30
543 6 t. *Lagenaria siceraria* 50
544 6 t. *Trichosanthes dioica* 50
545 10 t. *Solanum melongena* .. .. .. 80 1·
546 10 t. *Cucurbita maxima* (*horiz*) .. .. 80 1·
541/6 .. .. *Set of* 6 2·75 3·

195 Sonargaon

(Des A. Hussain)

1995 (2 Jan). *20th Anniv of World Tourism Organizati P* 14½.

547 **195** 10 t. multicoloured 65

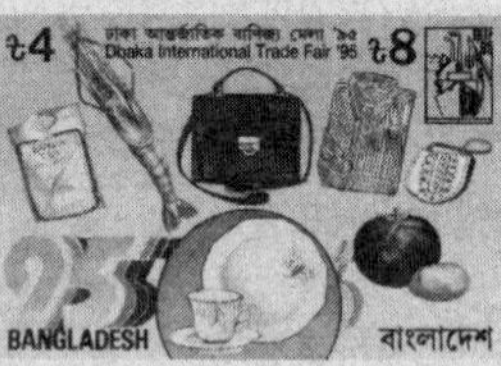

196 Exports

(Des M. Huq)

1995 (7 Jan). *Dhaka International Trade Fair '95. T* **196** *a similar horiz design. Multicoloured. P* 14½.

548 4 t. Type **196** 20
549 6 t. Symbols of industry 45

197 Soldiers of Ramgarh Battalion (1795) and of Bangladesh Rifles (1995)

(Des M. Rahman and Md. Shamsuzzoha)

5 (10 Jan). *Bicentenary of Bangladesh Rifles. T* **197** *and imilar horiz design. Multicoloured. P* 14½.
2 t. Type **197** 15 15
4 t. Riflemen on patrol 25 30

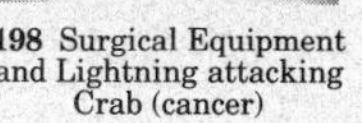

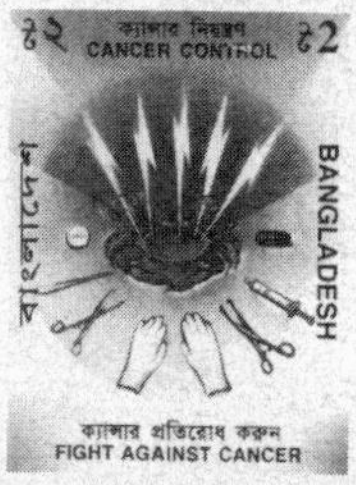

198 Surgical Equipment and Lightning attacking Crab (cancer)

199 Fresh Food and Boy injecting Insulin

(Des M. Rohana)

5 (7 Apr). *Campaign against Cancer. P* 14×14½.
198 2 t. multicoloured 20 20

(Des N. Islam)

5 (28 Feb). *National Diabetes Awareness Day. P* 14.
199 2 t. multicoloured 20 20

রাজশাহীপেক্স-৯৫

200 Munshi Mohammad Meherullah

(201)

(Des M. Huq)

5 (7 June). *Munshi Mohammad Meherullah (Islamic ducator) Commemoration. P* 14×14½
200 2 t. multicoloured 20 20

5 (23 Aug). *"Rajshahipex '95" National Philatelic Exhibition. No. 499 optd with T* **201** *in red.*
6 t. Exterior of Chhota Sona Mosque . . 60 60

202 *Lagerstroemia speciosa*

203 Aspects of Farming

s A. Hussain, Md. Shamsuzzoha, Md. Jasimuddin, M. Muniruzzaman)

5 (9 Oct). *Flowers. T* **202** *and similar multicoloured esigns. P* 14½.
6 t. Type **202** 50 50
6 t. *Bombax ceiba* (*horiz*) 50 50
10 t. *Passiflora incarnata* 75 75
10 t. *Bauhina purpurea* 75 75
10 t. *Canna indica* 75 75
10 t. *Gloriosa superba* 75 75
/61 . . . . *Set of* 6 3·50 3·50

(Des A. Hussain)

5 (16 Oct). *50th Anniv of Food and Agriculture rganization. P* 14×14½.
203 10 t. multicoloured 45 55

2 t. stamp, in a vertical design, commemorating Shaheed andaker Mosharraf Hossain was due for release on 21 ober 1995, but was withdrawn on day of issue although the tructions may not have reached some offices in time to vent sale of these stamps. Some used examples are known.

COVER PRICES

ver factors are quoted at the beginning of each untry for most issues to 1945. An explanation of e system can be found on page x. The factors oted do not, however, apply to philatelic covers.

204 Anniversary Emblem, Peace Dove and U.N. Headquarters

(Des A. Hussain)

1995 (24 Oct). *50th Anniv of United Nations. T* **204** *and similar horiz designs. Multicoloured. P* 14½×14.
563 2 t. Type **204** 15 15
564 10 t. Peace doves circling dates and Globe 65 75
565 10 t. Clasped hands and U.N. Headquarters 65 75
563/5 . . . . *Set of* 3 1·25 1·50

205 Diseased Lungs, Microscope, Family and Map

206 Peace Doves, Emblem and National Flags

(Des A. Hussain)

1995 (29 Oct). *18th Eastern Regional Conference on Tuberculosis, Dhaka. P* 14½×14.
566 **205** 6 t. multicoloured 40 40

(Des A. Hussain)

1995 (8 Dec). *10th Anniv of South Asian Association for Regional Co-operation. P* 14×14½.
567 **206** 2 t. multicoloured 15 15

1995 (14 Dec). *Martyred Intellectuals* (4*th series*). *Vert designs as T* **148**. *Each grey-black and reddish brown. P* 14×14½.
568 2 t. Abdul Ahad 15 15
a. Sheetlet. Nos. 568/75 . . . . 1·10
569 2 t. Lt. Col. Mohammad Qadir 15 15
570 2 t. Mozammel Hoque Chowdhury . . 15 15
571 2 t. Rafiqul Haider Chowdhury 15 15
572 2 t. Dr. Azharul Haque 15 15
573 2 t. A. K. Shamsuddin 15 15
574 2 t. Anudwaipayan Bhattacharjee . . 15 15
575 2 t. Lutfunnahar Helena 15 15
576 2 t. Shaikh Habibur Rahman 15 15
a. Sheetlet. Nos. 576/83 . . . . 1·10
577 2 t. Major Naimul Islam 15 15
578 2 t. Md. Shahidullah 15 15
579 2 t. Ataur Rahman Khan Khadim . . 15 15
580 2 t. A. B. M. Ashraful Islam Bhuiyan . . 15 15
581 2 t. Dr. Md. Sadat Ali 15 15
582 2 t. Sarafat Ali 15 15
583 2 t. M. A. Sayeed 15 15
568/83 . . . . *Set of* 16 2·00 2·00

Nos. 568/75 and 576/83 were printed together, *se-tenant*, in sheetlets of 8, the two horizontal rows in each sheetlet being separated by a row of inscribed labels.

207 Aspects of COMDECA Projects

208 Volleyball Players

(Des Md. Shamsuzzoha)

1995 (18 Dec). *2nd Asia-Pacific Community Development Scout Camp. P* 14×14½.
584 **207** 2 t. multicoloured 15 15

(Des A. Hussain)

1995 (25 Dec). *Centenary of Volleyball. P* 14×14½.
585 **208** 6 t. multicoloured 40 40

209 Man in Punjabi and Lungi

210 Shaheed Amanullah Mohammad Asaduzzaman

(Des M. Huq, A. Hussain, Md. Shamsuzzoha and M. Rahman)

1995 (25 Dec). *Traditional Costumes. T* **209** *and similar multicoloured designs. P* 14½.
586 6 t. Type **209** 40 40
587 6 t. Woman in sari 40 40
588 10 t. Christian bride and groom 65 75
589 10 t. Muslim bride and groom 65 75
590 10 t. Buddhist bride and groom (*horiz*) . . 65 75
591 10 t. Hindu bride and groom (*horiz*) . . 65 75
586/91 . . . . *Set of* 6 3·00 3·50

(Des A. Hussain)

1996 (20 Jan). *27th Death Anniv of Shaheed Amanullah Mohammad Asaduzzaman (student leader). P* 14×14½.
592 **210** 2 t. multicoloured 20 20

211 Bowler and Map

(Des M. Huq, A. Hussain and Md. Shamsuzzoha)

1996 (14 Feb). *World Cup Cricket Championship. T* **211** *and similar multicoloured designs. P* 14½×14 (10 *t.*) *or* 14×14½ (*others*).
593 4 t. Type **211** 45 20
594 6 t. Batsman and wicket keeper 55 40
595 10 t. Match in progress (*horiz*) . . . . 95 1·10
593/5 . . . . *Set of* 3 1·75 1·50

212 Liberation Struggle, 1971

(Des A. Hussain, M. Huq, M. Rahman and Md. Shamsuzzoha)

1996 (26 Mar). *25th Anniv of Independence. T* **212** *and similar horiz designs. Multicoloured. P* 14½.
596 4 t. Type **212** 15 20
597 4 t. National Martyrs Memorial 15 20
598 4 t. Education 15 20
599 4 t. Health 15 20
600 4 t. Communications 15 20
601 4 t. Industry 15 20
596/601 . . . . *Set of* 6 90 1·10

213 Michael Madhusudan Dutt

214 Gymnastics

(Des M. Huq)

1996 (29 June). *Michael Madhusudan Dutt (poet) Commemoration. P* 14×14½.
602 **213** 4 t. multicoloured 15 15

(Des M. Huq, Md. Shamsuzzoha and M. Rahman)

1996 (19 July). *Olympic Games, Atlanta. T* **214** *and similar multicoloured designs. P* 14×14½ (*vert*) *or* 14½×14 (*horiz*).
603 4 t. Type **214** 15 20
604 6 t. Judo 20 25
605 10 t. Athletics (*horiz*) 30 35
606 10 t. High jumping (*horiz*) 30 35
603/6 .. .. *Set of* 4 95 1·25
MS607 165×110 mm. Nos. 603/6. P 14×14½ (*sold at* 40 *t.*) .. .. 1·25 1·40

1996 (29 July). *25th Anniv of Bangladesh Stamps. No.* **MS**234 *optd* "Silver Jubilee Bangladesh Postage Stamps 1971–96" *on sheet margin.*
MS608 98×117 mm. Nos. 232/3 (*sold at* 10 *t.*) 30 35

215 Bangabandhu Sheikh Mujibur Rahman

216 Maulana Mohammad Akrum Khan

(Des M. Rahman)

1996 (15 Aug). *21st Death Anniv of Bangabandhu Sheikh Mujibur Rahman. P* 14×14½.
609 **215** 4 t. multicoloured 20 20

(Des Md. Muniruzzaman)

1996 (18 Aug). *28th Death Anniv of Maulana Mohammad Akrum Khan. P* 14×14½.
610 **216** 4 t. multicoloured 20 20

217 Ustad Alauddin Khan

218 "Kingfisher" (Mayeesha Robbani)

(Des A. Hussain)

1996 (6 Sept). *24th Death Anniv of Ustad Alauddin Khan (musician). P* 14×14½.
611 **217** 4 t. multicoloured 20 20

1996 (9 Oct). *Children's Paintings. T* **218** *and similar multicoloured design. P* 13½×14½ (2 *t.*) *or* 14½×13½ (4 *t.*).
612 2 t. Type **218** 15 10
613 4 t. "River Crossing" (Iffat Panchlais) (*horiz*) 15 20

219 Syed Nazrul Islam

220 Children receiving Medicine

(Des M. Rahman)

1996 (3 Nov). *21st Death Anniv of Jail Martyrs. T* **219** *and similar vert designs. Multicoloured. P* 14×14½.
614 4 t. Type **219** 15 20
a. Block of 4. Nos. 614/17 60
615 4 t. Tajuddin Ahmad 15 20
616 4 t. M. Monsoor Ali 15 20
617 4 t. A. H. M. Quamaruzzaman 15 20
614/17 .. .. *Set of* 4 60 80
Nos. 614/17 were printed together, *se-tenant*, in blocks of four throughout the sheet.

(Des A. Hussain)

1996 (11 Dec). *50th Anniv of U.N.I.C.E.F. T* **220** *and similar vert design. Multicoloured. P* 14×14½.
618 4 t. Type **220** 25 20
619 10 t. Mother and child 45 45

(Des A. Hussain (Nos. 620/1, 625, 632/3), M. Huq (Nos. 622, 624, 627/9, 631) M. Rahman (Nos. 623, 630, 634), T. Hussain (No. 626), N. Islam (No. 635))

1996 (14 Dec). *Martyred Intellectuals (5th series). Vert designs as T* **148**. *Each grey-black and reddish brown. P* 14×14½.
620 2 t. Dr. Jekrul Haque 15 15
a. Sheetlet. Nos. 620/7 .. .. .. 1·10
621 2 t. Munshi Kabiruddin Ahmed 15 15
622 2 t. Md. Abdul Jabbar 15 15
623 2 t. Mohammad Amir 15 15
624 2 t. A. K. M. Shamsul Huq Khan .. 15 15
625 2 t. Dr. Siddique Ahmed 15 15
626 2 t. Dr. Soleman Khan 15 15
627 2 t. S. B. M. Mizanur Rahman 15 15
628 2 t. Aminuddin 15 15
a. Sheetlet. Nos. 628/35 .. .. 1·10
629 2 t. Md. Nazrul Islam 15 15
630 2 t. Zahirul Islam 15 15
631 2 t. A. K. Lutfor Rahman 15 15
632 2 t. Afsar Hossain 15 15
633 2 t. Abul Hashem Mian 15 15
634 2 t. A. T. M. Alamgir 15 15
635 2 t. Baser Ali 15 15
620/35 .. .. *Set of* 16 2·00 2·00
Nos. 620/7 and 628/35 were each printed together, *se-tenant*, in sheetlets of 8, the two horizontal rows in each sheetlet being separated by a row of inscribed labels.

221 Celebrating Crowds

222 Paul P. Harris

(Des Md. Shamsuzzoha)

1996 (16 Dec). *25th Anniv of Victory Day. T* **221** *and similar multicoloured design. P* 14½×14 (4 *t.*) *or* 14×14½ (6 *t.*).
636 4 t. Type **221** 15 20
637 6 t. Soldiers and statue (*vert*) 20 25

(Des M. Huq)

1997 (18 Feb). *50th Death Anniv of Paul Harris (founder of Rotary). P* 14×14½.
638 **222** 4 t. multicoloured 15 20

223 Shaikh Mujibur Rahman making Speech

(Des A. Hussain)

1997 (7 Mar). *25th Anniv of Shaikh Mujibur's Speech of 7 March* (1996). *P* 12½.
639 **223** 4 t. multicoloured 15 20

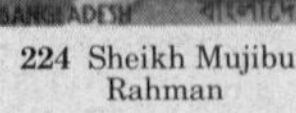

224 Sheikh Mujibur Rahman

225 Sheikh Mujibur Rahman and Crowd with Banners

(Des M. Mozammel)

1997 (17 Mar). *77th Birth Anniv of Sheikh Mujibur Rahman (first President). P* 14×14½.
640 **224** 4 t. multicoloured 30 20

(Des M. Rahman)

1997 (26 Mar). *25th Anniv* (1996) *of Independence. P* 12½.
641 **225** 4 t. multicoloured 15 20

226 Heinrich von Stephan

227 Sheep

(Des A. Hussain)

1997 (8 Apr). *Death Centenary of Heinrich von Stepha (founder of U.P.U.). P* 14×14½.
642 **226** 4 t. multicoloured 15

(Des A. Hussain)

1997 (10 Apr). *Livestock. T* **227** *and similar horiz design Multicoloured. P* 14½×14.
643 4 t. Type **227** 15
644 4 t. Goat 15
645 6 t. Buffalo bull 20
646 6 t. Cow 20
643/6 .. .. *Set of* 4 70

228 "Tilling the Field – 2" (S. Sultan)

1997 (26 June). *Bangladesh Paintings. T* **228** *and simil horiz design. Multicoloured. P* 12½.
647 6 t. Type **228** 20
648 10 t. "Three Women" (Quamrul Hassan) .. 30

229 Trophy, Flag and Cricket Ball

(Des A. Hussain)

1997 (4 Sept). *6th International Cricket Council Trop Championship, Malaysia. P* 12½.
649 **229** 10 t. multicoloured 55

230 Kusumba Mosque, Naogaon

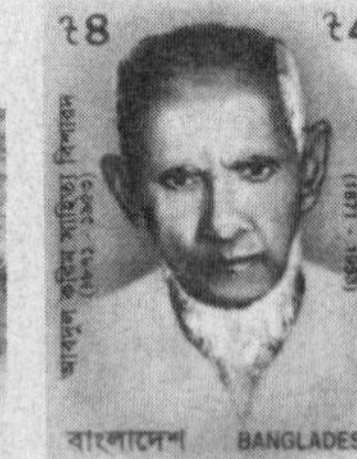

231 Adul Karim Sahitya Vishard

(Des Md. Shamsuzzoha)

1997 (4 Sept). *Historic Mosques. T* **230** *and similar ho designs. Multicoloured. P* 14½×14.
650 4 t. Type **230** 15
651 6 t. Atiya Mosque, Tangail 20
652 10 t. Bagha Mosque, Rajshahi 30
650/2 .. .. *Set of* 3 65

(Des M. Rahman)

1997 (11 Oct). *126th Birth Anniv of Abdul Karim Sah Vishard (scholar). P* 14×14½.
653 **231** 4 t. multicoloured 15

OMNIBUS ISSUES

Details, together with prices for complete se of the various Omnibus issues from the 19 Silver Jubilee series to date are included in special section following Zimbabwe at the end Volume 2.

232 Rover Moot Emblem and Scouts standing on top of World

233 Officers and Flag

(Des M. Rahman)

997 (25 Oct). *9th Asia-Pacific and 7th Bangladesh Rover Moot, Lakkatura. P* 14×14½.
54 **232** 2 t. multicoloured 10 10

(Des Md. Jasimuddin)

997 (21 Nov). *25th Anniv of Armed Forces. P* 14½×14.
55 **233** 2 t. multicoloured 10 10

997 (14 Dec). *Martyred Intellectuals* (6*th series*). *Vert designs as T* **148**. *Each grey-black and reddish brown. P* 14×14½.
56 2 t. Dr. Shamsuddin Ahmed 10 10
a. Sheetlet. Nos. 656/63 60
57 2 t. Mohammad Salimullah 10 10
58 2 t. Mohiuddin Haider 10 10
59 2 t. Abdur Rahin 10 10
60 2 t. Nitya Nanda Paul 10 10
61 2 t. Abdel Jabber 10 10
62 2 t. Dr. Humayun Kabir 10 10
63 2 t. Khaja Nizamuddin Bhuiyan 10 10
64 2 t. Gulam Hossain 10 10
a. Sheetlet. Nos. 664/71 60
65 2 t. Ali Karim 10 10
66 2 t. Md. Moazzem Hossain 10 10
67 2 t. Rafiqul Islam 10 10
68 2 t. M. Nur Husain 10 10
69 2 t. Captain Mahmood Hossain Akonda .. 10 10
70 2 t. Abdul Wahab Talukder 10 10
71 2 t. Dr. Hasimoy Hazra 10 10
56/71 .. .. *Set of* 16 1·10 1·25

Nos. 656/63 and 664/71 were printed together, *se-tenant*, in heetlets of 8, the two horizontal rows in each sheetlet being eparated by a row of inscribed labels.

234 Mohammad Mansooruddin

235 Standard-bearer and Soldiers

(Des P. Mandal)

998 (4 Feb). *Professor Mohammad Mansooruddin (folklorist) Commemoration. P* 14×14½.
72 **234** 4 t. multicoloured 15 20

(Des M. Rahman)

998 (15 Feb). *50th Anniv of East Bengal Regiment. P* 14½×14.
73 **235** 2 t. multicoloured 10 10

236 Bulbul Chowdhury

237 World Cup Trophy

(Des A. Hussain)

998 (17 May). *Bulbul Chowdhury (traditional dancer) Commemoration. P* 14×14½.
74 **236** 4 t. multicoloured 15 20

(Des A. Hussain)

998 (10 June). *World Cup Football Championship, France. T* **237** *and similar vert design. Multicoloured. P* 14×14½.
75 6 t. Type **237** 20 25
76 18 t. Footballer and trophy 60 65

238 Eastern Approach Road, Bangabandhu Bridge

239 Diana, Princess of Wales

(Des Md. Mia and Md. Shamsuzzoha)

1998 (23 June). *Opening of Bangabandhu Bridge. T* **238** *and similar horiz designs. Multicoloured. P* 14½×14.
677 4 t. Type **238** 15 20
678 6 t. Western approach road 20 25
679 8 t. Embankment 30 35
680 10 t. Main span, Bangabandhu Bridge .. 30 35
677/80 .. .. *Set of* 4 95 1·10

(Des Md. Miah and A. Hussain)

1998 (6 June). *Diana, Princess of Wales Commemoration. T* **239** *and similar vert designs. Multicoloured. P* 14.
681 8 t. Type **239** 30 35
a. Horiz strip of 3. Nos. 681/3 .. .. 1·60
682 18 t. Wearing pearl choker 60 65
683 22 t. Wearing pendant necklace 70 75
681/3 .. .. *Set of* 3 1·60 1·75

Nos. 681/3 were printed together, *se-tenant*, in horizontal strips of 3 throughout the sheet.

240 Means of collecting Solar Energy

241 World Habitat Day Emblem and City Scene

(Des A. Hussain)

1998 (24 Sept). *World Solar Energy Programme Summit. P* 14×14½.
684 **240** 10 t. multicoloured 30 35

(Des A. Hussain)

1998 (5 Oct). *World Habitat Day. P* 14×14½.
685 **241** 4 t. multicoloured 15 20
a. Logo at top left in green .. ..

No. 685 normally shows the logo at top left in white.

242 Farmworkers, Sunflower and "20"

243 Batsman

(Des. A. Hussain)

1998 (17 Oct). *20th Anniv of International Fund for Agricultural Development. T* **242** *and similar vert design. Multicoloured. P* 14×14½.
686 6 t. Type **242** 20 25
687 10 t. Farmworker with baskets and harvested crops 30 35

(Des A. Hussain)

1998 (24 Oct). *Wills International Cricket Cup, Dhaka. P* 14×14½.
688 **243** 6 t. multicoloured 20 25

OFFICIAL STAMPS

SERVICE (O 1) SERVICE (O 2) SERVICE (O 3)

1973 (30 Apr). *Nos. 22/7, 29/30, 32 and 34 optd with Type* O **1**.
O 1 **7** 2 p. black (R.) 10 60
O 2 – 3 p. blue-green 10 60
O 3 – 5 p. light brown 20 10
O 4 – 10 p. slate-black (R.) 20 10
O 5 – 20 p. yellow-green .. .. .. 1·25 10
O 6 – 25 p. bright reddish mauve .. .. 3·25 10
O 7 – 60 p. greenish slate (R.) .. .. .. 3·25 1·50
O 8 – 75 p. yellow-orange .. .. .. 1·25 30
O 9 **8** 1 t. light violet .. .. 11·00 4·25
O10 – 5 t. grey-blue .. .. 5·00 7·50
O1/10 .. .. *Set of* 10 23·00 13·50

1974–75. *Nos. 49/51 optd with Type* O **1**.
O11 **14** 1 t. light violet .. .. 4·00 30
O12 – 2 t. olive .. .. 5·00 1·75
O13 – 5 t. grey-blue (1975) .. .. .. 10·00 8·00
O11/13 .. .. *Set of* 3 17·00 9·00

1976. *Nos. 64/70 and 73 optd with Type* O **2** *and Nos. 72 and 74 optd with Type* O **3**.
O14 5 p. deep yellow-green (11.2.76) .. .. 1·00 30
O15 10 p. slate-black (R.) (28.4.76) .. .. 1·50 30
O16 20 p. yellow-green (1.76) .. .. .. 1·75 30
O17 25 p. bright reddish mauve (1.76) .. .. 3·00 30
O18 50 p. light purple (8.6.76) .. .. .. 3·00 30
O19 60 p. greenish slate (R.) (10.11.76) .. .. 30 1·50
O20 75 p. yellow-olive (10.11.76) .. .. .. 30 2·00
O21 1 t. ultramarine (1.76) .. .. .. 2·50 40
O22 2 t. olive-green (8.6.76) .. .. .. 35 1·25
O23 5 t. grey-blue (10.11.76) .. .. .. 30 1·25
O14/23 .. .. *Set of* 10 12·50 7·00

1979–82. *Nos. 125/37 optd with Type* O **1**.
O24 5 p. deep brown .. .. 90 1·25
O25 10 p. turquoise-blue .. .. 90 1·25
O26 15 p. orange (1980) .. .. 1·00 1·50
O27 20 p. brown-red .. .. 80 1·00
O28 25 p. grey-blue (1982) .. .. .. 80 1·75
O29 30 p. deep green .. .. 2·00 1·75
O30 40 p. maroon .. .. 2·00 15
O31 50 p. black (24.9.81) 30 10
O32 80 p. brown 70 15
O33 1 t. reddish violet (24.9.81) 30 10
O34 2 t. dull ultramarine (21.10.81) .. .. 35 1·75
O24/34 .. .. *Set of* 11 9·00 9·50

Service (O 4) সার্ভিস (O 5) সার্ভিস (O 6)

1983 (21 Dec)–**94.** *Nos. 220/9 and 318/a optd as Type* O **4** *in red, diagonally on 1 t. to 5 t.*
O35 5 p. turquoise-blue 10 10
O36 10 p. purple 10 10
O37 15 p. new blue 10 10
O38 20 p. grey-black 10 10
O39 25 p. slate 10 10
O40 30 p. brown 10 10
O41 50 p. light brown (opt horiz) 10 10
a. Opt diagonal (1993) 10 10
O42 1 t. dull ultramarine 75 10
O43 2 t. deep bluish green 75 10
O44 3 t. black and light blue (16.7.94) .. 10 10
O45 4 t. slate-blue (28.6.90) 15 20
O46 5 t. bright purple (27.7.92) 15 20
O35/46 .. .. *Set of* 12 2·00 1·00

1989 (31 Mar)–**92.** *Nos. 227 and 319 optd with Type* O **5**.
O47 1 t. ultramarine (R.) (16.9.92) 10 10
O48 5 t. black and orange-brown (B.) 15 20

1990 (29 Nov). *Nos. 368/9 (Immunization) optd with Type* O **6** *in red.*
O49 **133** 1 t. emerald 10 10
O50 2 t. brown 10 10

1992 (22 Nov). *No. 376 optd as Type* O **6**, *but horiz in red.*
O51 **136** 6 t. slate-blue and greenish yellow .. 20 25

1995 (28 Feb). *No. 553 (National Diabetes Awareness Day) optd as Type* O **6**, *but horiz in red.*
O52 **199** 2 t. multicoloured 15 15

Barbados

Regular mails between Barbados and Great Britain were established at an early date in the island's development and it is believed that the British Mail Packet Agency at Bridgetown was opened in 1688 as part of the considerable expansion of the Packet Service in that year.

From 1 August 1851 the colonial authorities were responsible for the internal post system, but the British G.P.O. did not relinquish control of the overseas post until 1858.

For illustrations of the handstamp types see BRITISH POST OFFICES ABROAD notes, following GREAT BRITAIN.

CROWNED-CIRCLE HANDSTAMPS

CC1 CC 1 BARBADOES (3.10.1849) (R.) *Price on cover* **£425**

Combination covers exist with the local postage paid by a Barbados 1d. stamp and the overseas fee by an example of No. CC1.

During shortages of ½d. stamps in 1893 (17 February to 15 March) and of the ¼d. in 1896 (23 January to 4 May) No. CC1 was utilised, struck in black, on local mail. *Price on cover from* £85.

PRICES FOR STAMPS ON COVER TO 1945

Nos. 1/35	*from* × 5
Nos. 43/63	*from* × 4
Nos. 64/6	*from* × 10
Nos. 67/83	*from* × 5
Nos. 86/8	*from* × 3
Nos. 89/103	*from* × 4
No. 104	*from* × 20
Nos. 105/15	*from* × 4
Nos. 116/24	*from* × 8
Nos. 125/33	*from* × 5
Nos. 135/44	*from* × 4
Nos. 145/52	*from* × 6
No. 153	*from* × 8
Nos. 158/62	*from* × 5
Nos. 163/9	*from* × 3
Nos. 170/96	*from* × 4
Nos. 197/8	*from* × 10
Nos. 199/212	*from* × 6
Nos. 213/39	*from* × 3
No. 240	*from* × 10
Nos. 241/4	*from* × 5
Nos. 245/7	*from* × 6
Nos. 248/56*a*	*from* × 4
Nos. 257/61	*from* × 5
Nos. D1/3	*from* × 25

CROWN COLONY

1 Britannia 2

(Recess Perkins, Bacon & Co)

1852 (15 April)–**55.** *Paper blued. No wmk. Imperf.*

1	**1**	(½d.) yellow-green	—	£550
2		(½d.) deep green	80·00	£300
3		(1d.) blue	28·00	£190
4		(1d.) deep blue	17·00	65·00
4*a*		(2d.) greyish slate	£200	£1100
		b. Bisected (1d.) (on cover) (1854)	†	£5500
5		(4d.) brownish red (1855)	65·00	£250

The bisect, No. 4b, was authorised for use between 4 August and 21 September 1854 during a shortage of 1d. stamps.

Nos. 5*a*/*b* were never sent to Barbados and come from the Perkins Bacon remainders sold in the 1880's.

Apart from the shade, which is distinctly paler, No. 4*a* can be distinguished from No. 5*b* by the smooth even gum, the gum of No. 5*b* being yellow and patchy, giving a mottled appearance to the back of the stamp. No. 5*a* also has the latter gum.

Prepared for use but not issued

5*a*	**1**	(No value), slate-blue (*shades*)	16·00	
5*b*		(No value), deep slate	£200	

1855–58. *White paper. No wmk. Imperf.*

7	**1**	(½d.) yellow-green (1857)	£375	£110
8		(½d.) green (1858)	90·00	£200
9		(1d.) pale blue	65·00	65·00
10		(1d.) deep blue	22·00	55·00

1858 (10 Nov). *No wmk. Imperf.*

11	**2**	6d. pale rose-red	£700	£110
11*a*		6d. deep rose-red	£700	£180
12		1s. brown-black	£250	£110
12*a*		1s. black	£170	70·00

1860. *No wmk.* (*a*) *Pin-perf* 14.

13	**1**	(½d.) yellow-green	£1500	£375
14		(1d.) pale blue	£1500	£150
15		(1d.) deep blue	£1500	£170
		(*b*) *Pin-perf* 12½		
16	**1**	(½d.) yellow-green	£5000	£600
16*a*		(1d.) blue	—	£1200
		(*c*) *Pin-perf* 14 × 12½		
16*b*	**1**	(½d.) yellow-green	—	£5500

Two examples of No. 15 are known bisected and used on separate pieces.

1861. *No wmk. Clean-cut perf* 14 *to* 16.

17	**1**	(½d.) deep green	65·00	7·50
18		(1d.) pale blue	£550	48·00
19		(1d.) blue	£650	48·00
		a. Bisected (½d.) (on cover)	†	£2750

1861–70. *No wmk.* (*a*) *Rough perf* 14 *to* 16

20	**1**	(½d.) deep green	16·00	14·00
21		(½d.) green	11·00	8·50
21*a*		(½d.) blue-green	55·00	75·00
		b. Imperf (pair)	£475	
22		(½d.) grass-green	20·00	14·00
		a. Imperf (pair)	£550	
23		(1d.) blue (1861)	30·00	2·00
		a. Imperf (pair)	£475	
24		(1d.) deep blue	23·00	3·00
		a. Bisected diag (½d.) (on cover) (1863)	†	£1800
25		(4d.) dull rose-red (1861)	65·00	28·00
		a. Imperf (pair)	£650	
26		(4d.) dull brown-red (1865)	85·00	38·00
		a. Imperf (pair)	£900	
27		(4d.) lake-rose (1868)	70·00	50·00
		a. Imperf (pair)	£950	
28		(4d.) dull vermilion (1869)	£170	55·00
		a. Imperf (pair)	£900	
29	**2**	6d. rose-red (1861)	£190	11·00
30		6d. orange-red (1864)	70·00	16·00
31		6d. bright orange-vermilion (1868)	60·00	16·00
32		6d. dull orange-vermilion (1870)	70·00	11·00
		a. Imperf (pair)	£425	
33		6d. orange (1870)	80·00	24·00
34		1s. brown-black (1863)	45·00	4·00
		a. Error. Blue	£12000	
35		1s. black (1866)	40·00	6·00
		a. Imperf between (horiz pair)	£5000	
		(*b*) *Prepared for use, but not issued. P* 11 *to* 12		
36	**1**	(½d.) grass-green	£6500	
37		(1d.) blue	£2000	

The bisect, No. 24a, was authorised for use in April 1863 and November 1866 during shortages of ½d. stamps.

No. 34a was an error on the part of the printer who supplied the first requisition of the 1s. value in the colour of the 1d. The 1s. blue stamps were never placed on sale, but the Barbados Colonial Secretary circulated some samples which were defaced by a manuscript corner-to-corner cross. A number of these samples subsequently had the cross removed.

Nos. 36/7 were never sent to Barbados and come from the Perkins Bacon remainders. It is believed that the imperforate pairs came from the same source.

1870. *Wmk Large Star, Type* w 1. *Rough perf* 14 *to* 16.

43	**1**	(½d.) green	75·00	5·00
		a. Imperf (pair)	£650	
43*b*		(½d.) yellow-green	£100	40·00
44		(1d.) blue	£950	40·00
		a. Blue paper	£2750	80·00
45		(4d.) dull vermilion	£650	75·00
46	**2**	6d. orange-vermilion	£650	50·00
47		1s. black	£225	16·00

1871. *Wmk Small Star, Type* w 2. *Rough perf* 14 *to* 16.

48	**1**	(1d.) blue	85·00	1·25
49		(4d.) dull rose-red	£650	24·00
50	**2**	6d. orange-vermilion	£300	11·00
51		1s. black	£110	7·50

1872. *Wmk Small Star, Type* w 2. (*a*) *Clean-cut perf* 14½ *to* 15½.

52	**1**	(1d.) blue	£180	1·50
		a. Bisected diag (½d.) (on cover)	†	£1600
53	**2**	6d. orange-vermilion	£550	55·00
54		1s. black	£100	6·00
		(*b*) *P* 11 *to* 13 × 14½ *to* 15½		
56	**1**	(½d.) green	£225	25·00
57		(4d.) dull vermilion	£425	80·00

1873. *Wmk Large Star, Type* w 1. (*a*) *Clean-cut perf* 14½ *to* 15½.

58	**1**	(½d.) green	£180	10·00
59		(4d.) dull rose-red	£750	£120
60	**2**	6d. orange-vermilion	£550	50·00
		a. Imperf between (horiz pair)	£4250	
		b. Imperf (pair)	75·00	
61		1s. black	95·00	6·50
		a. Imperf between (horiz pair)	£4500	
		(*b*) *Prepared for use, but not issued. P* 11 *to* 12		
62	**2**	6d. orange-vermilion	£4000	

Only eight mint examples, in two strips of four, are known of No. 62.

Two used singles of No. 60b have been seen.

1873 (June). *Wmk Small Star, Type* w 2 (*sideways* = *two points upwards*). *P* 14.

63	**2**	3d. brown-purple	£325	£110

3

1873 (June). *Wmk Small Star, Type* w 2 (*sideways*). *P* 15½×15.

64	**3**	5s. dull rose (H/S S. £300)	£950	£300

1874 (May). *Wmk Large Star, Type* w 1. (*a*) *Perf* 14.

65	**2**	½d. deep green	20·00	5·00
66		1d. deep blue	60·00	1·50
		(*b*) *Clean-cut perf* 14½ *to* 15½		
66*a*	**2**	1d. deep blue	†	£8000
		b. Imperf (pair)		

(Recess D.L.R.)

1875–80. *Wmk Crown CC* (*sideways* on* 6d., 1s.). (*a*) *P* 12½.

67	**2**	½d. bright green	30·00	2·50
		x. Wmk reversed		
68		4d. deep red	£170	7·50
		w. Wmk inverted	£225	25·00
		x. Wmk reversed	£170	10·00
69		6d. bright yellow (aniline)	£850	75·00
70	**2**	6d. chrome-yellow	£475	65·0
		a. Wmk upright	†	£150
71		1s. violet (aniline)	£400	3·5
		x. Wmk sideways reversed	£400	3·0
		y. Wmk sideways inverted and reversed	—	10·0
		(*b*) *P* 14		
72	**2**	½d. bright green (1876)	7·00	5
		w. Wmk inverted		
		x. Wmk reversed	7·00	7
73		1d. dull blue	40·00	5
		a. Bisected (½d.) (on cover) (1877)	†	£140
		w. Wmk inverted		
		x. Wmk reversed		
74		1d. grey-blue	40·00	3
		a. Wmk sideways	†	£85
		w. Wmk inverted	75·00	20·0
		x. Wmk reversed	50·00	5
		y. Wmk inverted and reversed	—	30·0
75		3d. mauve-lilac (1878)	80·00	4·5
76		4d. red (1878)	80·00	7·0
		x. Wmk reversed		
77		4d. carmine	£130	1·7
		w. Wmk inverted		
		x. Wmk reversed		
78		4d. crimson-lake	£450	2·5
79		6d. chrome-yellow (1876)	90·00	1·0
		w. Wmk Crown to right of CA	—	2·0
		x. Wmk sideways reversed	—	2·0
80		6d. yellow	£275	5·0
		w. Wmk Crown to right of CA		
81		1s. purple (1876)	£100	3·0
		w. Wmk Crown to right of CA	—	3·0
		x. Wmk sideways reversed		
82		1s. violet (aniline)	£2500	32·0
		w. Wmk Crown to right of CA	—	32·0
		x. Wmk sideways reversed		
83		1s. dull mauve	£350	2·2
		a. Bisected (6d.) (on cover) (1.80)	†	£375
		x. Wmk sideways reversed		
		(*c*) *P* 14×12½		
84	**2**	4d. red	£5000	
72/3 (in red), 75/6, 79, 81 (in red) H/S "Specimen"		*Set of* 6	£500	
72/3 (in black) H/S "Specimen"		*Set of* 2	£150	

*The normal sideways watermark shows Crown to left of C *as seen from the back of the stamp.*

Only two examples, both used, of No. 70a have been reporte

Very few examples of No. 84 have been found unused and onl one used specimen is known.

1D. 1D. 1D.

(**3***a*) (**3***b*) (**3***c*)

1878 (28 Mar). *No.* 64 *surch by West Indian Press with T* **3***a* *sideways twice on each stamp and then divided vertically* *11½ to* 13 *perforations. The lower label, showing the origin face value, was removed before use.*

(*a*) *With T* **3***a*. *Large numeral "1", 7 mm high with curved serif, and large letter "D", 2¾ mm high.*

86	**3**	1d. on half 5s. dull rose	£3500	£6
		a. No stop after "D"	£10000	£16
		b. Unsevered pair (both No. 86)	£14000	£18
		c. Ditto, Nos. 86 and 87	—	£35
		ca. Pair without dividing perf	†	£200
		d. Ditto, Nos. 86 and 88	£23000	£55
		(*b*) *With T* **3***b*. *As last, but numeral with straight serif*		
87	**3**	1d. on half 5s. dull rose	£4000	£7
		a. Unsevered pair	†	£25
		(*c*) *With T* **3***c*. *Smaller numeral "1", 6 mm high and smaller "D", 2½ mm high.*		
88	**3**	1d. on half 5s dull rose	£4750	£8
		a. Unsevered pair	£16000	£35

All types of the surcharge are found reading upwards as well downwards, and there are minor varieties of the type.

4

HALF-PENNY (5)

(Typo D.L.R.)

1882 (28 Aug)–**86.** *Wmk Crown CA. P* 14.

89	**4**	½d. dull green (1882)	10·00	1·
		w. Wmk inverted		
90		½d. green	10·00	1
91		1d. rose (1882)	45·00	1·
		a. Bisected (½d.) (on cover)	†	£9
		w. Wmk inverted		
92		1d. carmine	10·00	
93		2½d. ultramarine (1882)	70·00	1
		w. Wmk inverted		
94		2½d. deep blue	75·00	1·
95		3d. deep purple (1885)	85·00	25·
96		3d. reddish purple	3·50	12·
97		4d. grey (1882)	£190	2·
98		4d. pale brown (1885)	6·00	2·
		w. Wmk inverted	—	50·
		x. Wmk reversed		
99		4d. deep brown	4·00	1
100		6d. olive-black (1886)	65·00	32
102		1s. chestnut (1886)	24·00	21
103		5s. bistre (1886)	£140	£1
89/103		*Set of* 9	£450	£2
95/103, except 97, Optd "Specimen"		*Set of* 5	£375	

92 (July). *No. 99 surch with T* **5** *by West Indian Press.*
4 **4** ½d. on 4d. deep brown .. .. .. 1·60 2·75
a. No hyphen .. .. 8·50 16·00
b. Surch double (R. + Bk.) £450 £700
ba. Surch double (R. + Bk.) both without hyphen £1300 £1300
c. Surch double, one albino .. ..
d. Surch "PENNY HALF" .. .. — £200

Nos. 104b/ba come from a sheet with a trial surcharge in red 1ich was subsequently surcharged again in black and put back to stock.

No. 104c is known in a horizontal pair with the left hand amp showing the first two letters of the second impression ked. The right hand stamp shows a complete albino surcharge.

6 Seal of Colony

7

(Typo D.L.R.)

92 (July)–**1903.** *Wmk Crown CA. P* 14.
5 **6** ¼d. slate-grey and carmine (5.5.96) .. 2·00 10
w. Wmk inverted .. .. ..
6 ½d. dull green .. .. 1·50 10
w. Wmk inverted .. .. ..
7 1d. carmine .. .. 3·50 10
8 2d. slate-black and orange (5.99) .. 7·00 65
9 2½d. ultramarine .. .. .. 14·00 20
0 5d. grey-olive .. .. 6·00 4·50
1 6d. mauve and carmine .. .. 9·00 2·00
2 8d. orange and ultramarine .. .. 3·25 18·00
3 10d. dull blue-green and carmine .. 7·00 6·50
4 2s. 6d. blue-black and orange .. 45·00 48·00
w. Wmk inverted .. .. .. 85·00 95·00
5 2s. 6d. violet and green (29.5.03) .. 70·00 £110
5/15 .. .. *Set of* 11 £150 £170
5/15 Optd "Specimen" .. .. *Set of* 11 £170
See also Nos. 135/44 and 163/9.

(Typo D.L.R.)

97 (Dec)–**98.** *Diamond Jubilee. T* **7**. *Wmk Crown CC. P* 14.

(*a*) *White paper*
6 ¼d. grey and carmine .. .. .. 2·50 50
7 ½d. dull green .. .. 2·50 50
8 1d. rose .. .. 2·50 50
9 2½d. ultramarine .. .. 5·50 75
w. Wmk inverted .. .. ..
0 5d. olive-brown .. .. 13·00 13·00
1 6d. mauve and carmine .. .. .. 17·00 18·00
2 8d. orange and ultramarine .. .. 6·50 20·00
3 10d. blue-green and carmine .. .. 45·00 50·00
4 2s. 6d. blue-black and orange .. .. 48·00 50·00
w. Wmk inverted .. .. ..
6/24 .. .. *Set of* 9 £130 £140
6/24 Optd "Specimen" .. .. *Set of* 9 £150

(*b*) *Paper blued*
5 ¼d. grey and carmine .. .. .. 26·00 30·00
6 ½d. dull green .. .. 27·00 30·00
7 1d. carmine .. .. 35·00 40·00
8 2½d. ultramarine .. .. 38·00 45·00
9 5d. olive-brown £225 £250
0 6d. mauve and carmine £130 £140
1 8d. orange and ultramarine £130 £150
2 10d. dull green and carmine £190 £225
3 2s. 6d. blue-black and orange £110 £120

05. *Wmk Mult Crown CA. P* 14.
5 **6** ¼d. slate-grey and carmine .. .. 6·50 2·25
6 ½d. dull green .. .. 11·00 10
7 1d. carmine .. .. 11·00 10
9 2½d. blue .. .. 6·50 15
1 6d. mauve and carmine .. .. 11·00 12·00
2 8d. orange and ultramarine .. .. 32·00 65·00
4 2s. 6d. violet and green .. .. 32·00 75·00
5/144 .. .. *Set of* 7 £100 £140
See also Nos. 163/9.

8 Nelson Monument

(Des Mrs. G. Goodman. Recess D.L.R.)

06 (1 Mar). *Nelson Centenary. Wmk Crown CC. P* 14.
5 **8** ¼d. black and grey .. .. .. 6·00 1·50
w. Wmk inverted .. .. .. 28·00
6 ½d. black and pale green .. .. 8·50 15
w. Wmk inverted .. .. ..
x. Wmk reversed .. .. ..
7 1d. black and red .. .. .. 9·50 15
w. Wmk inverted .. .. .. 28·00
x. Wmk reversed .. .. ..
8 2d. black and yellow .. .. .. 1·75 4·50
9 2½d. black and bright blue .. .. 3·75 1·25
w. Wmk inverted .. .. ..
0 6d. black and mauve .. .. .. 18·00 25·00
1 1s. black and rose .. .. .. 19·00 45·00
5/51 .. .. *Set of* 7 60·00 70·00
5/51 Optd "Specimen" .. .. *Set of* 7 £130

Two sets may be made of the above: one on thick, opaque, creamy ite paper; the other on thin, rather transparent, bluish white per.

See also Nos. 158/62*a*.

9 *Olive Blossom*, 1605

Kingston Relief Fund. 1d.

(10)

(Des Lady Carter. Recess D.L.R.)

1906 (15 Aug). *Tercentenary of Annexation. Wmk Multiple Crown CA (sideways). P* 14.
152 **9** 1d. black, blue and green .. .. 10·00 25
152 Optd "Specimen" .. .. 65·00

1907 (25 Jan–25 Feb). *Kingston Relief Fund. No. 108 surch with T* **10** *by T. E. King & Co., Barbados.*
153 **6** 1d. on 2d. slate-black and orange (R.) .. 1·75 4·25
a. Surch inverted (25.2.07) .. .. 1·50 6·50
b. Surch double £550 £600
c. Surch double, both inverted .. £550
d. Surch *tête-bêche* (pair) £700
e. No stop after "1d." .. .. 32·00 55·00
ea. Do., surch inverted (25.2.07) .. 32·00 65·00
eb. Do., surch double .. .. — £950
f. Vert pair, one normal, one surch double .. .. — £750

The above stamp was sold for 2d. of which 1d. was retained for the postal revenue, and the other 1d. given to a fund for the relief of the sufferers by the earthquake in Jamaica.

An entire printing as No. 153a was created after a sheet of inverted surcharges was found in the initial supply.

1907 (6 July). *Nelson Centenary. Wmk Mult Crown CA. P* 14.
158 **8** ¼d. black and grey .. .. .. 5·00 3·00
161 2d. black and yellow .. .. .. 18·00 23·00
162 2½d. black and bright blue .. .. 10·00 19·00
a. Black and indigo £700 £800
158/62 .. .. *Set of* 3 30·00 40·00

1909 (July)–**10.** *Wmk Mult Crown CA. P* 14.
163 **6** ¼d. brown .. .. 2·50 30
164 ½d. blue-green .. .. 17·00 60
165 1d. red .. .. 7·50 10
166 2d. greyish slate (8.10) .. .. 6·00 9·50
167 2½d. bright blue (1910) .. .. 38·00 5·50
168 6d. dull and bright purple (1910) .. 8·00 14·00
169 1s. black/*green* (8.10) .. .. 8·50 14·00
163/9 .. .. *Set of* 7 80·00 38·00
163, 165/6, 168/9 Optd "Specimen" *Set of* 5 £100

11

12

13

(Typo D.L.R.)

1912 (23 July)–**16.** *Wmk Mult Crown CA. P* 14.
170 **11** ¼d. brown .. .. 1·25 1·50
a. Pale brown (1916) .. .. 65 2·00
aw. Wmk inverted .. .. ..
171 ½d. green .. .. 2·75 10
a. Wmk sideways .. .. .. † —
172 1d. red (13.8.12) .. .. .. 5·50 10
a. Scarlet (1915) .. .. .. 16·00 2·50
173 2d. greyish slate (13.8.12) .. .. 2·00 12·00
174 2½d. bright blue (13.8.12) .. .. 1·25 30
175 **12** 3d. purple/*yellow* (13.8.12) .. .. 1·25 11·00
176 4d. red and black/*yellow* (13.8.12) .. 1·25 15·00
177 6d. purple and dull purple (13.8.12) .. 9·50 11·00
178 **13** 1s. black/*green* (13.8.12) .. .. 7·00 9·00
179 2s. blue and purple/*blue* (13.8.12) .. 38·00 40·00
180 3s. violet and green (13.8.12) .. .. 70·00 80·00
170/80 .. .. *Set of* 11 £120 £160
170/80 Optd "Specimen" .. .. *Set of* 11 £140

14

WAR TAX

(15)

(Recess D.L.R.)

1916 (16 June)–**19.** *Wmk Mult Crown CA. P* 14.
181 **14** ¼d. deep brown 75 40
a. Chestnut-brown (9.17) .. .. 1·50 35
b. Sepia-brown (4.18) .. .. 3·50 2·50
w. Wmk inverted .. .. .. 16·00 16·00
y. Wmk inverted and reversed .. 27·00
182 ½d. green .. .. 1·10 15
a. Deep green (9.17) .. .. 1·40 15
b. Pale green (4.18) .. .. 1·90 80
w. Wmk inverted .. .. .. 22·00
y. Wmk inverted and reversed
183 1d. deep red .. .. 17·00 6·00
a. Bright carmine-red (4.17) .. .. 2·50 15
b. Pale carmine-red (9.17) .. .. 6·00 65
w. Wmk inverted .. .. .. 22·00
x. Wmk reversed .. .. ..
y. Wmk inverted and reversed .. 22·00
184 **14** 2d. grey .. .. 3·50 15·00
a. Grey-black (9.19) .. .. 25·00 60·00
y. Wmk inverted and reversed ..
185 2½d. deep ultramarine .. .. .. 2·50 1·50
a. Royal blue (11.17) .. .. 2·50 1·50
w. Wmk inverted .. .. ..
y. Wmk inverted and reversed .. 27·00 27·00
186 3d. purple/*yellow* (thin paper) .. 1·75 4·50
a. Dp purple/yell (thick paper) (9.19) 28·00 30·00
187 4d. red/*yellow* .. .. .. 70 14·00
188 6d. purple .. .. 2·50 3·50
189 1s. black/*green* .. .. .. 7·00 7·00
190 2s. purple/*blue* .. .. .. 16·00 7·50
y. Wmk inverted and reversed .. 38·00
191 3s. deep violet .. .. .. 45·00 85·00
w. Wmk inverted .. .. ..
y. Wmk inverted and reversed .. ..
181/91 .. .. *Set of* 11 75·00 £120
181/91 Optd "Specimen" .. *Set of* 11 £180

Dates quoted for shades are those of despatch from Great Britain.

Examples of the ½d. and 1d. values can be found perforated either by line or by comb machines.

See also Nos. 199/200*a*.

1917 (10 Oct)–**18.** *War Tax. Optd in London with T* **15**.
197 **11** 1d. bright red (Optd S. £55) 15 15
w. Wmk inverted .. .. ..
198 1d. pale red (*thicker bluish paper*) (4.18) 2·75 40

1918 (18 Feb)–**20.** *Colours changed. Wmk Mult Crown CA. P* 14.
199 **14** 4d. black and red .. .. .. 80 3·50
200 3s. green and deep violet .. .. 16·00 48·00
a. Green and bright violet (1920) .. £180 £250
199/200 Optd "Specimen" .. *Set of* 2 £120

The centres of these are from a new die having no circular border line.

16 Winged Victory from the Louvre.

17 Victory from Victoria Memorial, London

(Recess D.L.R.)

1920 (9 Sept)–**21.** *Victory. P* 14.

(*a*) *Wmk Mult Crown CA (sideways* on T* **17**)
201 **16** ¼d. black and bistre-brown 30 70
a "C" of "CA" missing from wmk .. £200
c. Substituted crown in wmk ..
w. Wmk inverted .. .. ..
x. Wmk reversed .. .. ..
y. Wmk inverted and reversed .. 38·00
202 ½d. black and bright yellow-green .. 90 15
a. "C" of "CA" missing from wmk .. £225
b. "A" of "CA" missing from wmk .. £225
c. Substituted crown in wmk
w. Wmk inverted .. .. ..
x. Wmk reversed .. .. ..
y. Wmk inverted and reversed
203 1d. black and vermilion .. .. 2·75 10
a. "A" of "CA" missing from wmk .. † £250
w. Wmk inverted .. .. .. 32·00
y. Wmk inverted and reversed
204 2d. black and grey .. .. .. 2·00 6·50
a. "C" of "CA" missing from wmk .. £275
205 2½d. indigo and ultramarine .. .. 2·75 10·00
a. "C" of "CA" missing from wmk .. £275
w. Wmk inverted .. .. ..
y. Wmk inverted and reversed .. 75·00
206 3d. black and purple .. .. .. 2·75 5·00
w. Wmk inverted .. .. .. 27·00 27·00
207 4d. black and blue-green .. .. 2·75 5·50
208 6d. black and brown-orange .. .. 3·50 10·00
w. Wmk inverted .. .. .. 48·00
wa. "C" of "CA" missing from wmk .. £750
209 **17** 1s. black and bright green .. .. 9·00 22·00
w. Wmk Crown to left of CA
x. Wmk sideways reversed £100
y. Wmk sideways inverted and reversed .. ..
210 2s. black and brown .. .. .. 21·00 28·00
w. Wmk Crown to left of CA .. 60·00
x. Wmk sideways reversed .. ..
y. Wmk sideways inverted and reversed .. ..
211 3s. black and dull orange .. .. 24·00 35·00
a. "C" of "CA" missing from wmk .. £550
w. Wmk Crown to left of CA .. 60·00
x. Wmk sideways reversed .. ..

(*b*) *Wmk Mult Script CA*
212 **16** 1d. black and vermilion (22.8.21) .. 17·00 30
201/12 .. .. *Set of* 12 80·00 £110
201/12 Optd "Specimen" .. *Set of* 12 £200

*The normal sideways watermark on Nos. 209/11 shows Crown to right of CA, *as seen from the back of the stamp.*

For illustration of the substituted watermark crown see Catalogue Introduction.

18

19

(Recess D.L.R.)

1921 (14 Nov)–**24**. *P* 14. (*a*) *Wmk Mult Crown CA.*
213 **18** 3d. purple/*pale yellow* .. .. .. 2·00 6·00
x. Wmk reversed .. .. ..
214 4d. red/*pale yellow* .. .. .. 1·75 12·00
215 1s. black/*emerald* .. .. .. 4·50 11·00
w. Wmk inverted .. .. ..

(*b*) *Wmk Mult Script CA*
217 **18** ¼d. brown 15 10
x. Wmk reversed .. .. .. 22·00
y. Wmk inverted and reversed .. 27·00
219 ½d. green 80 10
220 1d. red 80 10
aw. Wmk inverted .. .. .. 22·00
ax. Wmk reversed .. .. ..
ay. Wmk inverted and reversed ..
b. Bright rose-carmine .. .. 5·50 1·00
bw. Wmk inverted .. .. .. 20·00
221 2d. grey .. .. 1·60 20
y. Wmk inverted and reversed ..
222 2½d. ultramarine .. .. .. 1·50 5·50
225 6d. reddish purple .. .. .. 3·50 5·50
226 1s. black/*emerald* (18.9.24) .. .. 48·00 75·00
227 2s. purple/*blue* .. .. .. 10·00 19·00
228 3s. deep violet .. .. .. 13·00 45·00
y. Wmk inverted and reversed ..
213/28 .. .. *Set of* 12 75·00 £160
213/28 Optd "Specimen" .. .. *Set of* 12 £160

1925 (1 Apr)–**35**. *Wmk Mult Script CA. P* 14.
229 **19** ¼d. brown 15 10
230 ½d. green 30 10
a. Perf 13½×12½ (2.32) .. .. 6·00 10
231 1d. scarlet 50 10
a. Perf 13½×12½ (2.32) .. .. 5·00 30
231*b* 1½d. orange (1933) .. .. .. 8·50 2·00
ba. Perf 13½×12½ (15.8.32) .. 2·00 1·00
232 2d. grey .. .. 50 2·75
233 2½d. blue 50 80
a. Bright ultramarine (1933) .. 11·00 1·25
ab. Perf 13½×12½ (2.32) .. .. 5·00 2·00
234 3d. purple/*pale yellow* 60 45
a. Reddish purple/yellow (1935) .. 5·50 5·00
235 4d. red/*pale yellow* 75 95
236 6d. purple 75 90
237 1s. black/*emerald* .. .. .. 1·50 5·50
a. Perf 13½×12½ (8.32) .. .. 42·00 22·00
b. Brownish black/bright yellow-green (1934) .. .. 4·50 10·00
238 2s. purple/*blue* .. .. .. 7·00 6·50
238*a* 2s. 6d. carmine/*blue* (1.9.32) .. 22·00 24·00
239 3s. deep violet .. .. .. 11·00 13·00
229/39 .. .. *Set of* 13 42·00 50·00
229/39 Optd/Perf "Specimen" .. *Set of* 13 £170

Nos. 230/1 exist in coils constructed from normal sheets.

20 King Charles I and King George V

21 Badge of the Colony

(Recess B.W.)

1927 (17 Feb). *Tercentenary of Settlement of Barbados. Wmk Mult Script CA. P* 12½.
240 **20** 1d. carmine (Optd S. £40) 75 60

1935 (6 May). *Silver Jubilee. As Nos.* 91/4 *of Antigua, but ptd by Waterlow. P* 11 × 12.
241 1d. deep blue and scarlet 30 20
j. Damaged turret .. .. 70·00
242 1½d. ultramarine and grey .. .. 3·00 5·00
j. Damaged turret £100
243 2½d. brown and deep blue .. .. 2·25 3·25
244 1s. slate and purple .. .. 15·00 16·00
l. Kite and horizontal log £190
241/4 .. .. *Set of* 4 18·00 22·00
241/4 Perf "Specimen" .. .. *Set of* 4 65·00

For illustrations of plate varieties see Catalogue Introduction.

1937 (14 May). *Coronation. As Nos.* 95/7 *of Antigua, but printed by D.L.R. P* 14.
245 1d. scarlet 30 15
246 1½d. yellow-brown 40 45
247 2½d. bright blue 70 45
245/7 .. .. *Set of* 3 1·25 95
245/7 Perf "Specimen" .. .. *Set of* 3 50·00

Recut line (R. 10/6)

Extra frame line (R. 11/9)

Mark on central ornament (R. 1/3, 2/3, 3/3)

Vertical line over horse's head (R. 4/10) (corrected on Dec 1947 ptg)

"Flying mane" (R. 4/1) (corrected on Dec 1947 ptg)

Curved line at top right (R. 7/8)

Cracked plate (extends to top right ornament) (R. 6/10))

(Recess D.L.R.)

1938 (3 Jan)–**47**. *Wmk Mult Script CA. P* 13½×13.
248 **21** ½d. green .. .. 6·00 15
a. Recut line £110
b. Perf 14 (8.42) .. .. .. 70·00 1·25
ba. Recut line £275
248*c* ½d. yellow-bistre (16.10.42) 15 30
ca. "A" of "CA" missing from wmk .. £1100
cb. Recut line .. .. .. 16·00
249 1d. scarlet (1941) .. .. .. £275 4·00
a. Perf 14 (3.1.38) .. .. .. 16·00 10
249*b* 1d. blue-green (1943) .. .. 2·50 80
c. Perf 14 (16.10.42) 15 10
ca. "A" of "CA" missing from wmk .. £1100
250 1½d. orange 15 40
a. "A" of "CA" missing from wmk .. £1100
b. Perf 14 (11.41) .. .. .. 4·75 65
250*c* 2d. claret (3.6.41) .. .. .. 40 1·75
ca. Extra frame line .. .. 27·00
250*d* 2d. carmine (20.9.43) 15 40
da. Extra frame line .. .. 16·00
e. Perf 14 (11.9.44) .. .. .. 15 1·25
ea. Extra frame line .. .. 16·00
251 2½d. ultramarine 50 40
a. Mark on central ornament .. 30·00
b. Blue (17.2.44) .. .. .. 1·10 4·25
ba. "A" of "CA" missing from wmk £1000
bb. Mark on central ornament .. 40·00
252 3d. brown .. .. 20 1·90
a. Vertical line over horse's head .. 70·00
b. Perf 14 (4.41) 20 40
ba. Vertical line over horse's head .. 70·00
252*c* 3d. blue (1.4.47) .. .. .. 20 1·25
ca. Vertical line over horse's head .. 70·00
253 4d. black 20 10
a. Flying mane .. .. .. 75·00
b. Curved line at top right .. .. 65·00
c. Cracked plate .. .. .. 65·00
d. Perf 14 (11.9.44) .. .. .. 20 3·00
da. Flying mane .. .. .. 75·00
db. Curved line at top right .. .. 65·00
dc. Cracked plate .. .. .. 65·00
254 6d. violet 80 10
254*a* 8d. magenta (9.12.46) .. .. .. 55 1·75
255 1s. olive-green .. .. .. 16·00 2·25
a. Deep brown-olive (19.11.45) .. 1·00 10
256 2s. 6d. purple .. .. .. 6·50 1·50
256*a* 5s. indigo (3.6.41) .. .. .. 3·25 5·50
ab. "A" of "CA" missing from wmk .. £1300
248/56*a* .. .. *Set of* 16 32·00 12·00
248/56*a* Perf "Specimen" .. .. *Set of* 16 £180

No. 249a was perforated by two machines, one gauging 13.8×14.1 (1938), the other 14.1 (1939).

Nos. 248/*c* and 249/*c* exist in coils constructed from normal sheets.

Nos. 249*c* and 256*a* both exist showing "A" of "CA" missing from a watermark on the sheet margin.

22 Kings Charles I, George VI, Assembly Chamber and Mace

(Recess D.L.R.)

1939 (27 June). *Tercentenary of General Assembly. Wmk Mult Script CA. P* 13½ × 14.
257 **22** ½d. green .. .. 2·00 30
258 1d. scarlet .. .. 2·00 30
259 1½d. orange .. .. 2·00 60
260 2½d. bright ultramarine .. .. .. 2·00 3·25
261 3d. brown .. .. 2·00 2·25
257/61 .. .. *Set of* 5 9·00 6·00
257/61 Perf "Specimen" .. .. *Set of* 5 £140

NEW INFORMATION

The editor is always interested to correspond with people who have new information that will improve or correct the Catalogue.

Two flags on tug (R. 5/2)

1946 (18 Sept). *Victory. As Nos.* 110/11 *of Antigua.*
262 1½d. red-orange 15
a. Two flags on tug .. .. .. 20·00
263 3d. brown 15
262/3 Perf "Specimen" .. .. *Set of* 2 48·00

ONE
PENNY
(23)

NY PEN

Short "Y" (R. 6/2) Broken "E" (R. 7/4 and 11/4)

(Surch by Barbados Advocate Co)

1947 (21 Apr). *Surch with T* **23**. (*a*) *P* 14.
264 **21** 1d. on 2d. carmine (No. 250e) .. .. 1·00
a. Extra frame line .. .. .. 45·00
b. Short "Y" .. .. .. 45·00
c. Broken "E" .. .. .. 25·00

(*b*) *P* 13½×13
264*d* **21** 1d. on 2d. carmine (No. 250*d*) .. .. 4·50
da. Extra frame line £140
db. Short "Y" £140
dc. Broken "E" .. .. .. 85·00

The relationship of the two words in the surcharge differs each position of the sheet.

1948 (24 Nov). *Royal Silver Wedding. As Nos.* 112/13 *Antigua.*
265 1½d. orange 30
266 5s. indigo .. .. 9·50

1949 (10 Oct). *75th Anniv of Universal Postal Union. As N* 114/17 *of Antigua.*
267 1½d. red-orange 30
268 3d. deep blue .. .. 1·50
269 4d. grey 35
270 1s. olive 35
267/70 .. .. *Set of* 4 2·25

(New Currency. 100 cents = 1 West Indian, later Barbados, dollar)

24 Dover Fort

27 Statue of Nelson

(Recess B.W.)

1950 (1 May). *T* **24**, **27** *and similar designs. Wmk Mult Script* *P* 11 × 11½ (*horiz*), 13½ (*vert*).
271 1 c. indigo 15
272 2 c. emerald-green 15
273 3 c. reddish brown and blue-green 75
274 4 c. carmine 15
275 6 c. light blue 15
276 8 c. bright blue and purple-brown 65
277 12 c. greenish blue and brown-olive 90
278 24 c. scarlet and black 90
279 48 c. violet .. .. 8·00
280 60 c. green and claret .. .. .. 6·00
281 $1.20, carmine and olive-green .. .. 8·50
282 $2.40, black .. .. 15·00
271/282 .. .. *Set of* 12 35·00

Designs: *Horiz*—2 c. Sugar cane breeding; 3 c. Pub buildings; 6 c. Casting net; 8 c. *Frances W. Smith* (schoon 12 c. Four-winged Flyingfish; 24 c. Old Main Guard Garris 60 c. Careenage; $2.40, Seal of Barbados. *Vert*—48 c. Michael's Cathedral; $1.20, Map of Barbados and wireless ma

1951 (16 Feb). *Inauguration of B.W.I. University College. As N* 118/19 *of Antigua.*
283 3 c. brown and blue-green 30
284 12 c. blue-green and brown-olive 55

36 King George VI and Stamp of 1852

(Recess Waterlow)

952 (15 Apr). *Barbados Stamp Centenary. Wmk Mult Script CA. P* 13½.
35 **36** 3 c. green and slate-green 15 40
36 4 c. blue and carmine 15 90
37 12 c. slate-green and bright green .. 15 90
38 24 c. red-brown and brownish black .. 15 40
85/8 .. .. *Set of* 4 55 2·40

37 Harbour Police

(Recess B.W.)

953 (13 Apr)–**61**. *Designs previously used for King George VI issue, but with portrait or cypher* ($2.40) *of Queen Elizabeth II, as in T* **37**. *Wmk Mult Script CA. P* 11×11½ *(horiz) or* 13½ *(vert).*
89 1 c. indigo 10 70
90 2 c. orange and deep turquoise (15.4.54) 15 40
91 3 c. black and emerald (15.4.54) .. .. 1·00 50
92 4 c. black and orange (15.4.54) 20 20
a. Black and reddish orange (18.3.59) 1·75 90
93 5 c. blue and deep carmine-red (4.1.54) .. 90 40
94 6 c. red-brown (15.4.54) 50 40
w. Wmk inverted
95 8 c. black and blue (15.4.54) .. .. 2·00 40
96 12 c. turquoise-blue & brown-olive (15.4.54) 1·00 10
a. Turquoise-grn & brown-olive (18.3.59) 12·00 2·75
b. Turquoise-blue & bronze-grn (13.6.61) 12·00 2·00
97 24 c. rose-red and black (2.3.56) .. 45 10
98 48 c. deep violet (2.3.56) .. .. 5·00 1·00
99 60 c. blue-green and brown-purple (3.4.56) 18·00 5·00
a. Blue-green and pale maroon (17.5.60) 27·00 7·50
00 $1.20, carmine and bronze-green (3.4.56) 19·00 2·50
01 $2.40, black (1.2.57) .. .. 7·50 1·25
89/301 .. .. .. *Set of* 13 50·00 11·50

Designs: *Horiz*—1 c. Dover Fort; 2 c. Sugar cane breeding; 3 c. ublic buildings; 6 c. Casting net; 8 c. *Frances W. Smith* chooner); 12 c. Flying fish; 24 c. Old Main Guard Garrison; 60 c. areenage; $2.40, Seal of Barbados. *Vert*—4 c. Statue of Nelson; 3 c. St. Michael's Cathedral; $1.20, Map of Barbados and ireless mast.
See also Nos. 312/19.

953 (4 June). *Coronation. As No.* 120 *of Antigua.*
2 4 c. black and red-orange 40 10

958 (23 Apr). *Inauguration of British Caribbean Federation. As Nos.* 135/7 *of Antigua.*
03 3 c. deep green 45 20
04 6 c. blue .. .. .. 60 2·00
05 12 c. scarlet 60 30
03/5 .. .. .. *Set of* 3 1·50 2·25

38 Deep Water Harbour, Bridgetown

(Recess B.W.)

961 (6 May). *Opening of Deep Water Harbour, Bridgetown.* W w **12**. *P* 11 × 12.
06 **38** 4 c. black and red-orange 25 40
07 8 c. black and blue 25 50
08 24 c. carmine-red and black 25 50
6/8 .. .. .. *Set of* 3 65 1·25

SELF-GOVERNMENT

39 Scout Badge and Map of Barbados

40 Deep Sea Coral

(Recess B.W.)

62 (9 Mar). *Golden Jubilee of Barbados Boy Scout Association.* W w **12**. *P* 11½ × 11.
9 **39** 4 c. black and orange 40 10
0 12 c. blue and olive-brown 80 15
1 $1.20, carmine and olive-green.. .. 1·25 3·00
9/11 .. .. .. *Set of* 3 2·25 3·00

64 (14 Jan)–**65**. *As Nos.* 289, *etc., but wmk* w **12**.
2 1 c. indigo (6.10.64) .. .. 50 1·50
3 4 c. black and orange 40 50
4 8 c. black and blue (29.6.65) 60 35
5 12 c. turquoise-blue and brown-olive (29.6.65) 90 50
6 24 c. rose-red and black (6.10.64) .. 70 35
7 48 c. deep violet .. .. .. 4·00 2·00
318 60 c. blue-green and brown-purple (6.10.64) .. 12·00 4·00
319 $2.40, black (29.6.65) .. .. 1·75 2·25
312/19 .. .. .. *Set of* 8 19·00 10·50

The above dates are for Crown Agents releases. The 14.1.64 printings were not released in Barbados until April 1964, the 6.10.64 printings until December 1964 and of the stamps released in London on 29 June 1965 the 8 c. and $2.40 were released from about 15 June 1965, but the 12 c. value was never put on sale in Barbados.

1965 (17 May). *I.T.U. Centenary. As Nos.* 166/7 *of Antigua.*
320 2 c. lilac and red 20 40
321 48 c. yellow and grey-brown .. .. 70 1·50

(Des V. Whiteley, from drawings by Mrs. J. Walker. Photo Harrison)

1965 (15 July). *Marine Life. Horiz designs as T* **40**. W w **12** *(upright). P* 14×13½.
322 1 c. black, pink and blue 20 30
323 2 c. olive-brown, yellow and magenta .. 20 15
324 3 c. olive-brown and orange 45 60
325 4 c. deep blue and olive-green 15 10
a. Imperf (pair) £225 £150
w. Wmk inverted .. .. .. — 15·00
326 5 c. sepia, rose and lilac 30 20
327 6 c. multicoloured 45 20
w. Wmk inverted .. .. .. 1·25
328 8 c. multicoloured 25 10
w. Wmk inverted .. .. .. 2·75
329 12 c. multicoloured 35 10
a. Grey printing double .. .. 45·00
w. Wmk inverted
330 15 c. black, greenish yellow and red .. 80 80
331 25 c. ultramarine and yellow-ochre .. 95 75
332 35 c. brown-red and deep green .. .. 1·50 15
w. Wmk inverted
333 50 c. bright blue and apple-green .. .. 2·00 40
334 $1 multicoloured .. .. .. 2·75 1·25
335 $2.50, multicoloured .. .. .. 2·75 1·75
322/35 .. .. .. *Set of* 14 12·00 6·00

Designs:—2 c. Lobster; 3 c. Lined Seahorse; 4 c. Sea Urchin; 5 c. Staghorn Coral; 6 c. Spot-finned Butterflyfish; 8 c. Rough File shell; 12 c. Porcupinefish ("Balloon Fish"); 15 c. Grey Angelfish; 25 c. Brain Coral; 35 c. Brittle Star; 50 c. Four-winged Flyingfish; $1 Queen or Pink Conch shell; $2.50 Fiddler Crab.

The 3 c. value is wrongly inscribed "Hippocanpus", the correct spelling "Hippocampus" was used for subsequent printings, see No. 344.

See also Nos. 342, etc.

1966 (24 Jan). *Churchill Commemoration. As Nos.* 170/3 *of Antigua.*
336 1 c. new blue .. .. .. 10 1·50
w. Wmk inverted .. .. .. 16·00
337 4 c. deep green 30 10
338 25 c. brown 70 50
339 35 c. bluish violet 80 60
336/9 .. .. .. *Set of* 4 1·75 2·40

1966 (4 Feb). *Royal Visit. As Nos.* 174/5 *of Antigua.*
340 3 c. black and ultramarine 50 25
341 35 c. black and magenta .. .. 1·75 80

41 Dolphin

54 Arms of Barbados

1966 (15 Mar)–**69**. *As Nos.* 322/35 *but wmk* w **12** *(sideways*). New value and design (as T* **41**).
342 1 c. black, pink and blue 10 20
w. Wmk Crown to right of CA .. ..
343 2 c. olive-brn, yellow & magenta (16.5.67) 30 80
344 3 c. olive-brown and orange (4.12.67) .. 30 2·00
345 4 c. deep blue and olive-green 50 10
w. Wmk Crown to right of CA .. .. 40·00
346 5 c. sepia, rose and lilac (23.8.66) .. 45 10
347 6 c. multicoloured (31.1.67) 70 10
348 8 c. multicoloured (19.9.67) 75 10
349 12 c. multicoloured (31.1.67) 45 10
350 15 c. black, greenish yellow and red .. 2·25 10
351 25 c. ultramarine and yellow-ochre .. 2·25 40
aw. Wmk Crown to right of CA .. .. 7·00
b. Deep ultram & yellow-ochre (26.9.66) 8·00 2·25
352 35 c. brown-red and deep green (23.8.66) 2·50 65
a. Chestnut and deep green (26.11.68) 6·50 3·00
353 50 c. bright blue and apple-green .. 1·75 2·75
w. Wmk Crown to right of CA .. .. 45·00
354 $1 multicoloured (23.8.66) .. .. 6·00 1·00
355 $2.50, multicoloured (23.8.66) .. .. 7·00 3·00
355*a* $5 multicoloured (9.1.69) .. .. 12·00 7·00
342/55*a* .. .. .. *Set of* 15 32·00 16·00

**The normal sideways watermark shows Crown to left of CA, as seen from the back of the stamp.*

The 3 c. value is correctly inscribed "Hippocampus".

All values except the 50 c. exist with PVA gum as well as gum arabic but the $5 exists with PVA gum only.

The $5 was released by the Crown Agents on 6 January but was not put on sale locally until 9 January.

INDEPENDENT

(Des. V. Whiteley. Photo Harrison)

1966 (2 Dec). *Independence. T* **54** *and similar multicoloured designs. P* 14.
356 4 c. Type **54** 10 10
357 25 c. Hilton Hotel *(horiz)* 15 10
358 35 c. G. Sobers (Test cricketer) .. .. 1·50 55
359 50 c. Pine Hill Dairy *(horiz)* 70 75
356/9 .. .. .. *Set of* 4 2·00 1·40

1967 (6 Jan). *20th Anniv of U.N.E.S.CO. As Nos.* 196/8 *of Antigua.*
360 4 c. slate-violet, red, yellow and orange .. 30 10
361 12 c. orange-yellow, violet and deep olive .. 70 65
362 25 c. black, bright purple and orange.. .. 1·00 1·50
360/2 .. .. .. *Set of* 3 1·75 2·00

58 Policeman and Anchor

62 Governor-General Sir Winston Scott, G.C.M.G.

(Des V. Whiteley. Litho D.L.R.)

1967 (16 Oct). *Centenary of Harbour Police. T* **58** *and similar multicoloured designs. P* 14.
363 4 c. Type **58** 25 10
364 25 c. Policeman with telescope 40 15
365 35 c. *BP1* (police launch) *(horiz)* 45 15
366 50 c. Policeman outside H.Q. .. .. 60 1·25
363/6 .. .. .. *Set of* 4 1·50 1·50

(Des V. Whiteley. Photo Harrison)

1967 (4 Dec). *First Anniv of Independence. T* **62** *and similar multicoloured designs. P* 14½ × 14 (4 c.) *or* 14 × 14½ *(others).*
367 4 c. Type **62** 10 10
368 25 c. Independence Arch *(horiz)* 20 10
369 35 c. Treasury Building *(horiz)* 25 10
370 50 c. Parliament Building *(horiz)* 35 60
367/70 .. .. .. *Set of* 4 75 75

66 U.N. Building, Santiago, Chile

67 Radar Antenna

(Des G. Vasarhelyi. Photo Harrison)

1968 (27 Feb). *20th Anniv of the Economic Commission for Latin America. P* 14½.
371 **66** 15 c. multicoloured 10 10

(Des G. Vasarhelyi. Photo Harrison)

1968 (4 June). *World Meteorological Day. T* **67** *and similar multicoloured designs. P* 14 × 14½ (25 c.) *or* 14½ × 14 *(others).*
372 3 c. Type **67** 10 10
373 25 c. Meteorological Institute *(horiz)* .. 25 10
374 50 c. Harp Gun and coat of arms 30 70
372/4 .. .. .. *Set of* 3 55 80

70 Lady Baden-Powell, and Guide at Camp Fire

(Des V. Whiteley (from local designs). Photo Harrison)

1968 (29 Aug). *50th Anniv of Girl Guiding in Barbados. T* **70** *and similar horiz designs. P* 14.
375 3 c. ultramarine, black and gold 25 50
376 25 c. turquoise-blue, black and gold .. 50 50
377 35 c. orange-yellow, black and gold .. 65 50
375/7 .. .. .. *Set of* 3 1·25 1·40

Designs:—25 c. Lady Baden-Powell and Pax Hill; 35 c. Lady Baden-Powell and Guide badge.

73 Hands breaking Chain, and Human Rights Emblem

(Des V. Whiteley. Litho B.W.)

1968 (10 Dec).* *Human Rights Year. T* **73** *and similar horiz designs. P* 11 × 12.
378 4 c. violet, brown and light green 10 15
379 25 c. black, blue and orange-yellow 10 20
380 35 c. multicoloured 15 20
378/80 .. .. *Set of* 3 20 50

Designs:—25 c. Human Rights emblem and family enchained; 35 c. Shadows of refugees beyond opening fence.

* This was the local release date but the Crown Agents issued the stamps on 29 October.

76 Racehorses in the Paddock

(Des J. Cooter. Litho Format)

1969 (20 Mar).* *Horse-Racing. T* **76** *and similar horiz designs. Multicoloured. P* 14.
381 4 c. Type **76** 20 15
382 25 c. Starting-gate 25 15
383 35 c. On the flat 25 15
384 50 c. Winning post .. .. 35 1·75
381/4 .. .. *Set of* 4 95 2·00
MS385 117 × 85 mm. Nos. 381/4 .. .. 2·00 2·75

*This was the local release date but the Crown Agents issued the stamps on 15 March.

80 Map showing "CARIFTA" Countries **81** "Strength in Unity"

(Des J. Cooter. Photo Harrison)

1969 (6 May). *First Anniv of CARIFTA (Caribbean Free Trade Area). W* w **12** *(sideways on T* **80***). P* 14.
386 **80** 5 c. multicoloured 10 10
387 **81** 12 c. multicoloured 10 10
388 **80** 25 c. multicoloured 10 10
389 **81** 50 c. multicoloured 15 20
386/9 .. .. *Set of* 4 30 30

82 I.L.O. Emblem and "1919-1969".

ONE
CENT
(83)

(Des Sylvia Goaman. Litho Enschedé)

1969 (12 Aug). *50th Anniv of International Labour Organisation. P* 14 × 13.
390 **82** 4 c. black, emerald and turquoise-blue 10 10
391 25 c. black, cerise and brown-red 20 10

Although released by the Crown Agents on 5 August, the above were not put on sale in Barbados until 12 August.

1969 (30 Aug). *No.* 363 *surch with T* **83**.
392 1 c. on 4 c. Type **58** 10 10
a. Surch double .. .. 65·00

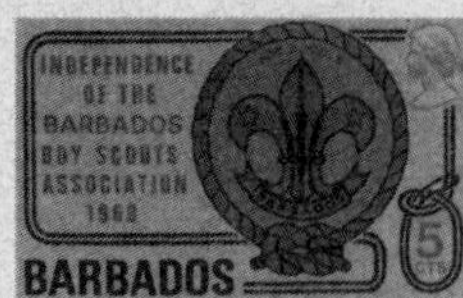

84 National Scout Badge

(Des J. Cooter. Litho Enschedé)

1969 (16 Dec). *Independence of Barbados Boy Scouts Association and 50th Anniv of Barbados Sea Scouts. T* **84** *and similar horiz designs. Multicoloured. P* 13 × 13½.
393 5 c. Type **84** 15 10
394 25 c. Sea Scouts rowing 45 10
395 35 c. Scouts around camp fire 55 10
396 50 c. Scouts and National Scout Headquarters 80 90
393/6 .. .. *Set of* 4 1·75 1·10
MS397 155 × 115 mm. Nos. 393/6 .. .. 11·00 12·00

4 x
(88)

89 Lion at Gun Hill

1970 (11 Mar). *No.* 346 *surch locally with T* **88**.
398 4 c. on 5 c. sepia, rose and lilac 10 10
a. Vert pair, one without surch .. .. 35·00
b. Surch double .. .. 25·00
c. Vert pair, one normal, one surch double 50·00
d. Surch triple .. .. — £100
e. Surch normal on front, inverted on back 12·00
f. Surch omitted on front, inverted on back 16·00

(Des J.W. Photo D.L.R.)

1970 (4 May)–**71**. *Multicoloured designs as T* **89**. *W* w **12** *(sideways on 12 c. to $5). Chalk-surfaced paper. P* 12½.
399 1 c. Type **89** 10 50
a. Glazed, ordinary paper (15.3.71) .. 10 1·00
400 2 c. Trafalgar Fountain 30 60
a. Glazed, ordinary paper (15.3.71) .. 10 1·50
401 3 c. Montefiore Drinking Fountain .. 10 60
a. Glazed, ordinary paper (15.3.71) .. 10 1·50
aw. Wmk inverted .. .. .. 6·50
402 4 c. St. James' Monument 75 15
a. Glazed, ordinary paper (15.3.71) .. 10 10
403 5 c. St. Anne's Fort 10 10
a. Glazed, ordinary paper (15.3.71) .. 10 10
404 6 c. Old Sugar Mill, Morgan Lewis .. 35 2·50
405 8 c. Cenotaph 10 10
a. Glazed, ordinary paper (15.3.71) .. 10 10
406 10 c. South Point Lighthouse .. .. 2·50 50
a. Glazed, ordinary paper (15.3.71) .. 85 15
407 12 c. Barbados Museum *(horiz)* 60 10
a. Glazed, ordinary paper (13.12.71) .. 2·50 30
408 15 c. Sharon Moravian Church *(horiz)* .. 30 15
a. Glazed, ordinary paper (13.12.71) .. 60 30
409 25 c. George Washington House *(horiz)* .. 25 15
a. Glazed, ordinary paper (15.3.71) .. 50 35
410 35 c. Nicholas Abbey *(horiz)* 30 85
a. Glazed, ordinary paper (15.3.71) .. 45 70
411 50 c. Bowmanston Pumping Station *(horiz)* 40 95
a. Glazed, ordinary paper (15.3.71) .. 70 3·00
412 $1 Queen Elizabeth Hospital *(horiz)* .. 70 2·50
a. Glazed, ordinary paper (15.3.71) .. 4·00 8·00
413 $2.50, Modern sugar factory *(horiz)* .. 1·50 4·00
a. Glazed, ordinary paper (13.12.71) .. 26·00 16·00
414 $5 Seawell International Airport *(horiz)* 6·00 11·00
a. Glazed, ordinary paper (15.3.71) .. 11·00 15·00
399/414 .. .. *Set of* 16 12·00 22·00

105 Primary Schoolgirl

(Des V. Whiteley. Litho J.W.)

1970 (26 June). *25th Anniv of United Nations. T* **105** *and similar horiz designs. Multicoloured. W* w **12**. *P* 14.
415 4 c. Type **106** 10 10
416 5 c. Secondary Schoolboy 10 10
417 25 c. Technical Student 35 10
418 50 c. University Buildings .. .. .. 55 1·25
415/18 .. .. *Set of* 4 90 1·40

106 Minnie Root

(Des and litho J.W.)

1970 (24 Aug). *Flowers of Barbados. T* **106** *and similar designs. Multicoloured. W* w **12** *(sideways on horiz designs). P* 14½.
419 1 c. Barbados Easter Lily *(vert)* .. .. 10 1·50
420 5 c. Type **106** 40 10
421 10 c. Eyelash Orchid .. .. .. 1·75 20
422 25 c. Pride of Barbados *(vert)* .. .. 1·25 75
423 35 c. Christmas Hope .. .. .. 1·25 85
419/23 .. .. *Set of* 5 4·25 3·00
MS424 162 × 101 mm. Nos. 419/23. Imperf .. 2·00 5·50

107 "Via Dolorosa" (Window, St. Margaret's Church, St. John) **108** "Sailfish" Craft

(Des Jennifer Toombs. Litho J.W.)

1971 (7 Apr). *Easter. T* **107** *and similar vert design. Multi coloured. W* w **12**. *P* 14.
425 4 c. Type **107** 10 1
426 10 c. "The Resurrection" (Benjamin West) .. 10 1
427 35 c. Type **107** 15 1
428 50 c. As 10 c. .. .. 30 1·2
425/8 .. .. *Set of* 4 45 1·4

(Des and litho Harrison)

1971 (17 Aug). *Tourism. T* **108** *and similar horiz designs. Multi coloured. W* w **12** *(sideways on 5 c. and 25 c.). P* 14.
429 1 c. Type **108** 10 2
w. Wmk inverted 50 4
430 5 c. Tennis 30 1
431 12 c. Horse-riding 40 1
w. Wmk inverted .. .. .. 1·75 1·2
432 25 c. Water-skiing 40 2
433 50 c. Scuba-diving 50 8
w. Wmk inverted 80 8
429/33 .. .. *Set of* 5 1·50 1·2

109 S. J. Prescod (politician) **110** Arms of Barbados

(Des J.W. Litho Questa)

1971 (28 Sept).* *Death Centenary of Samuel Jackman Prescod. W* w **12**. *P* 14.
434 **109** 3 c. multicoloured 10
435 35 c. multicoloured 15

*This is the local date but the Crown Agents released the stamps two days earlier.

(Des G. Drummond. Litho Questa)

1971 (23 Nov). *Fifth Anniv of Independence. T* **110** *and simil horiz design. Multicoloured. W* w **12** *(sideways). P* 14.
436 4 c. Type **110** 20
437 15 c. National flag and map 45
438 25 c. Type **110** 45
439 50 c. As 15 c. 90 1
436/9 .. .. *Set of* 4 1·75 1·

111 Transmitting "Then and Now" **112** Map and Badge

(Des Cable & Wireless Ltd. Litho J.W.)

1972 (28 Mar). *Cable Link Centenary. T* **111** *and similar ho designs. Multicoloured. W* w **12** *(sideways). P* 14.
440 4 c. Type **111** 10
441 10 c. *Stanley Angwin* (cable ship) 15
442 35 c. Barbados Earth Station and "Intelsat 4" 35
443 50 c. Mt. Misery and Tropospheric Scatter Station .. .. 50 1·
440/3 .. .. *Set of* 4 95 1·

(Des Mrs. C. Barrow (50 c.), Major L. Quintyne (others) adapted by G. Drummond. Litho Questa)

1972 (1 Aug). *Diamond Jubilee of Scouts. T* **112** *and simi horiz designs. Multicoloured. W* w **12** *(sideways* on 5 c.). P*
444 5 c. Type **112** 10
w. Wmk Crown to right of CA .. ..
445 15 c. Pioneers of scouting 15
446 25 c. Scouts 30
447 50 c. Flags 50
444/7 .. .. *Set of* 4 90

*The normal sideways watermark shows Crown to left of C *as seen from the back of the stamp.*

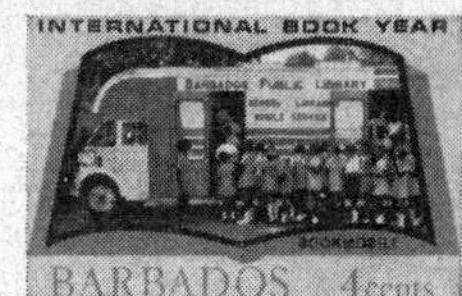

113 Mobile Library

(Des PAD Studio. Litho Harrison)

1972 (31 Oct). *International Book Year. T* **113** *and similar horiz designs. Multicoloured. W* w **12**. *P* 14.

448	4 c. Type **113**	20	10
449	15 c. Visual-aids van	25	10
450	25 c. Public library	30	10
451	$1 Codrington College	1·25	1·50
448/51	*Set of* 4	1·75	1·50

1972 (17 Nov)–**74**. *As Nos.* 402B/14B, *but W* w **12** (*sideways on* 4 *to* 10 *c.; upright on* 12 *c. to* $5).

455	4 c. St. James' Monument	1·50	1·50
456	5 c. St. Anne's Fort	1·25	1·50
457	6 c. Old Sugar Mill, Morgan Lewis	3·75	9·00
458	8 c. Cenotaph	1·50	1·25
459	10 c. South Point Lighthouse (21.1.74)	3·50	6·00
460	12 c. Barbados Museum	2·25	3·50
461	15 c. Sharon Moravian Church	75	1·25
462	25 c. George Washington House	2·75	2·50
463	35 c. Nicholas Abbey	2·50	70
464	50 c. Bowmanston Pumping Station	4·25	1·50
465	$1 Queen Elizabeth Hospital	7·00	2·75
466	$2.50, Modern sugar factory (2.10.73)	4·00	7·00
467	$5 Seawell International Airport (2.10.73)	4·00	5·50
	w. Wmk inverted	6·50	
455/67	*Set of* 13	35·00	38·00

114 Potter's Wheel

(Des PAD Studio. Litho Questa)

1973 (1 Mar). *Pottery in Barbados. T* **114** *and similar horiz designs. Multicoloured. W* w **12**. *P* 14.

468	5 c. Type **114**	10	10
469	15 c. Kilns	20	10
470	25 c. Finished products	25	10
471	$1 Market scene	90	1·10
	w. Wmk inverted	25·00	
468/71	*Set of* 4	1·25	1·25

115 First Flight, 1911

(Des C. Abbott. Litho Enschedé)

1973 (25 July). *Aviation. T* **115** *and similar horiz designs. W* w **12** (*sideways*). *P* 12½ × 12.

472	5 c. multicoloured	30	10
473	15 c. multicoloured	90	10
474	25 c. grey-blue, black and cobalt	1·25	20
475	50 c. multicoloured	2·00	1·90
472/5	*Set of* 4	4·00	2·00

Designs:—15 c. De Havilland D.H.60 Cirrus Moth on first flight to Barbados, 1928; 25 c. Lockheed 14 Super Electra, 1939; 50 c. Vickers Super VC-10 airliner, 1973.

4c.

116 University Chancellor (**117**)

(Des J. W. Litho Enschedé)

1973 (11 Dec). *25th Anniv of University of West Indies. T* **116** *and similar horiz designs. Multicoloured. W* w **12**. *P* 13 × 14.

476	5 c. Type **116**	10	10
	w. Wmk inverted	22·00	
477	25 c. Sherlock Hall	25	15
478	35 c. Cave Hill Campus	30	25
476/8	*Set of* 3	55	40

1974 (30 Apr). *No. 462 surch with T* **117**.

479	4 c. on 25 c. George Washington House	15	15
	a. "4c." omitted	16·00	

No. 479a occurs on R. 10/1, the overprint being applied to sheets consisting of two horizontal panes, 5 × 5. The variety occurs on plate 1A, and shows a clear albino impression of the "4c." on the reverse.

118 Old Sail Boat

(Des J. Cooter. Litho Questa)

1974 (11 June). *Fishing Boats of Barbados. T* **118** *and similar diamond-shaped designs. Multicoloured. W* w **12**. *P* 14.

480	15 c. Type **118**	30	15
481	35 c. Rowing-boat	55	25
482	50 c. Motor fishing-boat	70	70
483	$1 *Calamar* (fishing boat)	1·10	1·40
480/3	*Set of* 4	2·40	2·25
MS484	140 × 140 mm. Nos. 480/3	3·25	3·00

119 *Cattleya Gaskelliana Alba*

(Des PAD Studio. Photo Harrison)

1974 (16 Sept)–**77**. *Orchids. T* **119** *and similar multicoloured designs. W* w **12** (*upright on* 1, 20, 25 *c.*, $1 *and* $10; *sideways* on others*). *P* 14½×14 ($1, $10), 14×14½ ($2.50, $5) *or* 14 (*others*).

485	1 c. Type **119**	15	1·50
486	2 c. *Renanthera storiei*	20	1·50
487	3 c. *Dendrobium* "Rose Marie"	30	1·50
488	4 c. *Epidendrum ibaguense*	1·75	90
	w. Wmk Crown to right of CA	45·00	
489	5 c. *Schomburgkia humboldtii*	35	15
490	8 c. *Oncidium ampliatum*	1·00	90
	w. Wmk Crown to right of CA		
491	10 c. *Arachnis maggie oei*	55	20
492	12 c. *Dendrobium aggregatum*	45	1·75
	w. Wmk Crown to right of CA		
493	15 c. *Paphiopedilum puddle*	45	1·00
	aw. Wmk Crown to right of CA	6·00	
493*b*	20 c. *Spathoglottis* "The Gold" (3.5.77)	4·75	4·75
494	25 c. *Epidendrum ciliare* (Eyelash)	55	60
	w. Wmk inverted		
495	35 c. *Bletia patula*	2·00	1·75
	aw. Wmk Crown to right of CA	2·50	1·75
495*b*	45 c. *Phalaenopsis schilleriana* "Sunset Glow" (3.5.77)	4·75	4·50
496	50 c. As 45 c.	4·50	3·50
	w. Wmk Crown to left of CA	4·50	
497	$1 *Ascocenda* "Red Gem"	5·50	3·25
498	$2.50, *Brassolaeliocattleya* "Nugget"	3·50	5·50
499	$5 *Caularthron bicornutum*	3·50	6·00
500	$10 *Vanda* "Josephine Black"	4·00	13·00
485/500	*Set of* 18	32·00	45·00

The 1 c., 20 c., 25 c., $2.50 and $5 are horiz designs and the remainder are vert.

*The normal sideways watermark shows Crown to right of CA on the 50 c. and to left of CA on the others, *as seen from the back of the stamp.*

See also Nos. 510/24 and 543/51.

120 4d. Stamp of 1882, and U.P.U. Emblem

(Des Harrison. Litho Questa)

1974 (9 Oct). *Centenary of Universal Postal Union. T* **120** *and similar horiz designs. W* w **12** (*sideways**). *P* 14.

501	8 c. magenta, light orange & lt grey-green	10	10
502	35 c. dp rose-red, dull orange & bistre-brown	20	10
503	50 c. ultramarine, cobalt and silver	25	30
504	$1 bright blue, dull brown and grey-black	55	80
	w. Wmk Crown to right of CA	12·00	
501/4	*Set of* 4	1·00	1·10
MS505	126×101 mm. Nos. 501/4	1·50	2·25

Designs:—35 c. Letters encircling the globe; 50 c. U.P.U. emblem and arms of Barbados; $1 Map of Barbados, sailing ship and Boeing 747 airliner.

*The normal sideways watermark shows Crown to left of CA, *as seen from the back of the stamp.*

121 Royal Yacht *Britannia*

(Des Jennifer Toombs. Litho Harrison)

1975 (18 Feb). *Royal Visit. T* **121** *and similar horiz design. Multi-coloured. W* w **12** (*sideways on* 8 *and* 25 *c.*) *P* 14.

506	8 c. Type **121**	55	20
507	25 c. Type **121**	90	30
508	35 c. Sunset and palms	60	35
509	$1 As 35 c.	1·75	2·50
506/9	*Set of* 4	3·50	3·00

1975 (30 Apr)–**79**. *As Nos.* 485/9, 491/3, 494 *and* 495*b*/500 *but W* w **14** (*sideways* on* 1, 25 *c.*, $1 *and* $10).

510	1 c. Type **119**	15	1·00
511	2 c. *Renanthera storiei*	15	1·00
512	3 c. *Dendrobium* "Rose Marie"	15	1·00
513	4 c. *Epidendrum ibaguense*	50	2·50
514	5 c. *Schomburgkia humboldtii* (19.10.77)	35	15
515	10 c. *Arachnis maggie oei* (19.10.77)	35	10
	w. Wmk inverted		
516	12 c. *Dendrobium aggregatum* (19.10.77)	7·50	15
517	15 c. *Paphiopedilum puddle*	70	15
518	25 c. *Epidendrum ciliare* (Eyelash) (27.3.79)	70	10
519	45 c. *Phalaenopsis schilleriana* "Sunset Glow" (25.5.78)	60	15
	w. Wmk inverted		
520	50 c. As 45 c. (23.8.79)	6·50	6·50
521	$1 *Ascocenda* "Red Gem"	8·50	11·00
	w. Wmk Crown to right of CA	17·00	
522	$2.50, *Brassolaeliocattleya* "Nugget"	7·00	3·75
523	$5 *Caularthron bicornutum*	8·50	6·00
524	$10 *Vanda* "Josephine Black"	11·00	11·00
	a. Dull green (stems) omitted	£110	
510/24	*Set of* 15	48·00	40·00

*The normal sideways watermark shows Crown to left of CA, *as seen from the back of the stamp.*

No. 525 vacant.

122 St. Michael's Cathedral **123** Pony Float

(Des R. Granger Barrett. Litho Questa)

1975 (29 July). *150th Anniv of Anglican Diocese. T* **122** *and similar square designs. Multicoloured. W* w **12** (*sideways*). *P* 13½.

526	5 c. Type **122**	10	10
527	15 c. Bishop Coleridge	15	10
528	50 c. All Saints' Church	45	50
529	$1 "Archangel Michael and Satan" (stained-glass window, St. Michael's Cathedral, Bridgetown)	70	80
526/9	*Set of* 4	1·25	1·25
MS530	95 × 96 mm. Nos. 526/9 (wmk upright)	1·40	2·00

(Des R. Granger Barrett. Litho Questa)

1975 (18 Nov). *Crop-over Festival. T* **123** *and similar horiz designs. Multicoloured. W* w **14** (*sideways*). *P* 14.

531	8 c. Type **123**	10	10
532	25 c. Man on stilts	10	10
533	35 c. Maypole dancing	15	10
534	50 c. Cuban dancers	30	45
531/4	*Set of* 4	55	60
MS535	127 × 85 mm. Nos. 531/4	90	1·60

124 Barbados Coat of Arms **125** 17th-Century Sailing Ship

(Des and litho Harrison)

1975 (15 Dec). *Coil Definitives. W* w **12** *P* 15 × 14.

536	**124**	5 c. greenish blue	15	80
537		25 c. bluish violet	25	1·10

For 5 c. in this design, but watermarked W w **14**, see No. 743.

(Des PAD Studio. Litho J.W.)

1975 (17 Dec). *350th Anniv of First Settlement. T* **125** *and similar vert designs. Multicoloured. W* w **14**. *P* 13½.

538	4 c. Type **125**	50	10
539	10 c. Bearded fig tree and fruit	40	15
540	25 c. Ogilvy's 17th-century map	1·00	30
541	$1 Captain John Powell	2·00	5·00
538/41	*Set of* 4	3·50	5·00
MS542	105 × 115 mm. Nos. 538/41. P 14 × 14½	3·50	6·50

1976 (20 Feb). *As Nos.* 485 *etc., but W* w **12** (*sideways on* 1 *c.*, 25 *c.*, $1) *or upright* (*others*).

543	1 c. Type **119**	45	2·75
544	2 c. *Renanthera storiei*	60	2·75
545	3 c. *Dendrobium* "Rose Marie"	65	3·00
546	4 c. *Epidendrum ibaguense*	45	3·50
547	10 c. *Arachnis maggie oei*	85	3·00
548	15 c. *Paphiopedilum puddle*	75	1·25
549	25 c. *Epidendrum ciliare* "Eyelash"	1·50	1·25
550	35 c. *Bletia patula*	2·00	1·75
551	$1 *Ascocenda* "Red Gem"	5·00	5·50
543/51	*Set of* 9	11·00	22·00

Nos. 552/8 vacant.

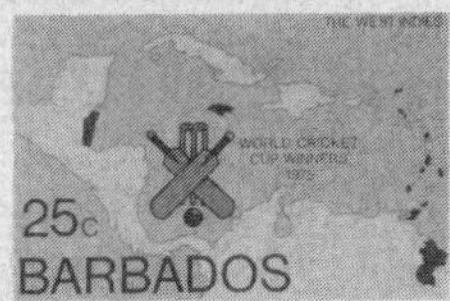

126 Map of the Caribbean

(Des PAD Studio. Litho Questa)

1976 (7 July). *West Indian Victory in World Cricket Cup. T* **126** *and similar design. No wmk. P* 14.

559 25 c. multicoloured .. .. 1·25 1·00
560 45 c. black and magenta .. .. 1·25 2·00

Design: *Vert*—45 c. The Prudential Cup.

127 Flag and Map of S. Carolina

(Des G. Vasarhelyi. Litho Walsall)

1976 (17 Aug). *Bicentenary of American Revolution. T* **127** *and similar horiz designs. Multicoloured.* W w **14** (*sideways*). *P* 13½.

561 15 c. Type **127** 55 15
562 25 c. George Washington and map of Bridgetown 55 15
563 50 c. Independence Declaration .. .. .. 70 1·00
564 $1 Prince Hall .. .. 1·00 3·00
561/4 .. .. *Set of* 4 2·50 3·75

128 Early Postman

(Des Jennifer Toombs. Litho Questa)

1976 (19 Oct). *125th Anniv of Post Office Act. T* **128** *and similar horiz designs. Multicoloured.* W w **14** (*sideways*) *P* 14.

565 8 c. Type **128** 10 10
566 35 c. Modern postman 25 10
567 50 c. Early letter 30 50
568 $1 Delivery van .. .. 50 1·40
565/8 .. .. *Set of* 4 1·00 1·90

129 Coast Guard Launches

(Des PAD Studio. Litho J.W.)

1976 (1 Dec).* *Tenth Anniv of Independence. T* **129** *and similar horiz designs. Multicoloured.* W w **14** (*sideways*). *P* 13 × 13½.

569 5 c. Type **129** 25 10
570 15 c. Reverse of currency note 25 10
571 25 c. National anthem 25 20
572 $1 Independence Day parade .. .. 90 2·25
569/72 .. .. *Set of* 4 1·50 2·25
MS573 90 × 125 mm. Nos. 569/72. P 14 .. .. 1·75 3·00

*This is the local date of issue; the Crown Agents released the stamps a day earlier.

130 Arrival of Coronation Coach at Westminster Abbey

131 Underwater Park

(Des C. Abbott. Litho Walsall)

1977 (7 Feb). *Silver Jubilee. T* **130** *and similar vert designs. Multicoloured* W w **14**. *P* 13½.

574 15 c. Garfield Sobers being knighted, 1975 .. 30 25
575 50 c. Type **130** 30 40
576 $1 Queen entering abbey 30 70
574/6 .. .. *Set of* 3 80 1·25

For the above with different inscription, see Nos. 590/2.

(Des R. Granger Barrett. Litho Questa)

1977 (3 May). *Natural Beauty of Barbados. T* **131** *and similar multicoloured designs.* W w **14** (*sideways on Nos.* 577 *and* 579). *P* 14.

577 5 c. Type **131** 15 10
578 35 c. Royal Palms (*vert*) 30 10
579 50 c. Underwater caves 40 50
580 $1 Stalagmite in Harrison's Cave (*vert*) .. 70 1·10
577/80 .. .. *Set of* 4 1·40 1·60
MS581 138 × 92 mm. Nos. 577/80 (wmk sideways) 2·00 2·75

132 Maces of the House of Commons

133 The Charter Scroll

(Des C. Abbott. Litho J. W.)

1977 (2 Aug). *13th Regional Conference of the Commonwealth Parliamentary Association. T* **132** *and similar designs.* W w **14** (*sideways on* $1). *P* 13½.

582 10 c. pale orange, yellow and lake-brown .. 10 10
583 25 c. apple-green, orange and deep green .. 10 10
584 50 c. multicoloured 20 20
w. Wmk inverted .. .. 12·00
585 $1 pale blue, orange and deep violet-blue 55 75
582/5 .. .. *Set of* 4 80 95

Designs: *Vert*—25 c. Speaker's Chair, 50 c. Senate Chamber. *Horiz*—$1 Sam Lord's Castle.

(Des Walsall. Litho J.W.)

1977 (11 Oct). *350th Anniv of Granting of Charter to Earl of Carlisle. T* **133** *and similar multicoloured designs.* W w **14** (*sideways on* 45 *c. and* $1). *P* 13.

586 12 c. Type **133** 15 10
587 25 c. The earl receiving charter 15 10
588 45 c. The earl and Charles I (*horiz*) 30 35
589 $1 Ligon's map, 1657 (*horiz*) .. .. 50 1·00
586/9 .. .. *Set of* 4 1·00 1·40

(Des C. Abbott. Litho Walsall)

1977 (31 Oct). *Royal Visit. As Nos. 574/6 but inscr at top* "SILVER JUBILEE ROYAL VISIT". W w **14**. *Roul* 5. *Self-adhesive.*

590 15 c. Garfield Sobers being knighted, 1975 30 40
w. Wmk inverted .. .. 12·00
591 50 c. Type **130** 35 60
w. Wmk inverted .. .. 13·00
592 $1 Queen entering abbey .. .. .. 45 1·00
w. Wmk inverted .. .. 6·00
590/2 .. .. *Set of* 3 1·00 1·75

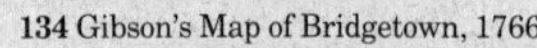

134 Gibson's Map of Bridgetown, 1766

135 Brown Pelican

(Des J. W. Litho Questa)

1978 (1 Mar). *350th Anniv of Founding of Bridgetown. T* **134** *and similar horiz designs.* W w **14** (*sideways*). *P* 14.

593 12 c. multicoloured 15 10
594 25 c. black, light green and gold 20 10
595 45 c. multicoloured 25 15
596 $1 multicoloured 40 60
593/6 .. .. *Set of* 4 90 80

Designs:—25 c. "A Prospect of Bridgetown in Barbados" (engraving by S. Copens, 1695); 45 c. "Trafalgar Square, Bridgetown" (drawing by J. M. Carter, 1835); $1 The Bridges, 1978.

(Des C. Abbott. Litho Questa)

1978 (21 Apr). *25th Anniv of Coronation. T* **135** *and similar vert designs. P* 15.

597 50 c. yellow-olive, black and blue 25 50
a. Sheetlet. Nos. 597/9 × 2 .. .. .. 1·25
598 50 c. multicoloured 25 50
599 50 c. yellow-olive, black and blue 25 50
597/9 .. .. *Set of* 3 65 1·40

Designs:—No. 597, Griffin of Edward III; No. 598, Queen Elizabeth II; No. 599, Type **135**.

Nos. 597/9 were printed together in small sheets of 6 containing two *se-tenant* strips of 3, with horizontal gutter margin between.

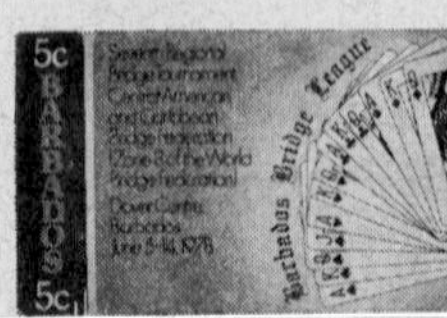

136 Barbados Bridge League Logo

(Des J.W. Litho Questa)

1978 (6 June). *7th Regional Bridge Tournament, Barbados T* **136** *and similar horiz designs. Multicoloured.* W w **14** (*sideways**). *P* 14½.

600 5 c. Type **136** 10 1
601 10 c. Emblem of World Bridge Federation .. 15 1
602 45 c. Central American and Caribbean Bridge Federation emblem 25 1
603 $1 Playing cards on map of Caribbean .. 40 6
600/3 .. .. *Set of* 4 80 7
MS604 134×83 mm. Nos. 600/3 .. .. 1·25 2·5
w. Wmk Crown to right of CA .. .. 45·00

*The normal sideways watermark shows Crown to left of CA, *as seen from the back of the stamp.*

137 Camp Scene

(Des and litho Harrison)

1978 (1 Aug). *Diamond Jubilee of Guiding. T* **137** *and simila diamond-shaped designs. Multicoloured.* W w **14** (*sideways o* 12, 28 *c.*). *P* 13½.

605 12 c. Type **137** 25 1
606 28 c. Community work 40 1
607 50 c. Badge and "60" (*vert*) 55 3
608 $1 Guide badge (*vert*) .. .. .. 75 1·0
605/8 .. .. *Set of* 4 1·75 1·4

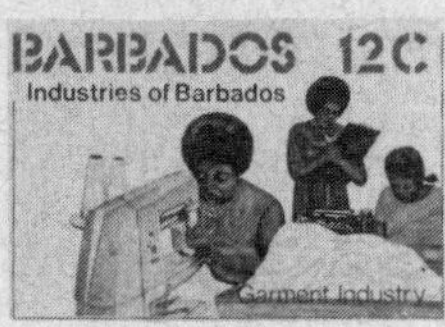

138 Garment Industry

(Des Walsall. Litho Harrison)

1978 (14 Nov). *Industries. T* **138** *and similar multicoloure designs.* W w **14** (*sideways on* 12 *and* 50 *c.*). *P* 14.

609 12 c. Type **138** 15 1
610 28 c. Cooper (*vert*) 25 2
611 45 c. Blacksmith (*vert*) 35
612 50 c. Wrought iron working 40
609/12 .. .. *Set of* 4 1·00 1·7

139 Early Mail Steamer

(Des J. Cooter. Litho J. W.)

1979 (8 Feb). *Ships. T* **139** *and similar horiz designs. Mul coloured.* W w **14** (*sideways*). *P* 13.

613 12 c. Type **139** 35
614 25 c. *Queen Elizabeth 2* in Deep Water Harbour 55
615 50 c. *Ra II* nearing Barbados .. .. 75 1·
616 $1 Early mail steamer (*different*) .. .. 1·00 2·
613/16 .. .. *Set of* 4 2·40 3·

140 1953 1 c. Definitive Stamp

(Des J.W. Litho Format)

1979 (8 May). *Death Centenary of Sir Rowland Hill. T* **140** *a similar multicoloured designs showing stamps.* W w (*sideways* on* 12 *c.*). *P* 14.

617 12 c. Type **140** 15
618 28 c. 1975 350th anniv of first settlement 25 c. commemorative (*vert*) 20
a. Ultramarine (face value) omitted .. £130
619 45 c. Penny Black with Maltese Cross postmark (*vert*) 30
617/19 .. .. *Set of* 3 60
MS620 137×90 mm 50 c. Unissued "Britannia" blue (wmk sideways) 55
w. Wmk Crown to left of CA .. ..

*The normal sideways watermark on No. **MS**620 sho Crown to right of CA, *as seen from the back of the stamp.*

All examples of No. 618 show anniversary spelt "anniverary".

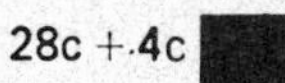

ST. VINCENT
RELIEF
FUND

(141)

142 Grassland Yellow Finch

1979 (29 May). *St. Vincent Relief Fund. No.* 495 *surch with T* **141**.
621 28 c. + 4 c. on 35 c. *Bletia patula* 50 60

(Des J.W. Photo Harrison)

1979 (7 Aug)–**83**. *Birds. Vert designs as T* **142**. *Multicoloured. W w* **14** (*sideways* on* 1, 5, 10, 12, 15, 20, 25, 28, 40, 50, 55, 60, 70 *c. and* $1). *P* 14.
622 1 c. Type **142** 10 70
w. Wmk Crown to right of CA . . 2·00
623 2 c. Grey Kingbird 10 70
624 5 c. Lesser Antillean Bullfinch 10 70
625 8 c. Magnificent Frigate Bird . . . . 10 1·25
w. Wmk inverted . . . . . . 26·00
626 10 c. Cattle Egret (deep slate inscr) . . 10 40
a. Slate-blue inscr 20 40
w. Wmk Crown to right of CA . . 6·00
627 12 c. Green Heron 15 60
627*a* 15 c. Carib Grackle (1.3.82) . . . . 4·50 5·00
628 20 c. Antillean Crested Hummingbird . . 20 55
w. Wmk Crown to right of CA (14.3.83) 20 55
629 25 c. Scaly-breasted Ground Dove . . 20 60
630 28 c. As 15 c. . . . . 75 1·25
631 35 c. Green-throated Carib 30 70
a. Yellow omitted £225
631*b* 40 c. Red-necked Pigeon (1.3.82) . . . . 4·50 5·00
632 45 c. Zenaida Dove 35 70
w. Wmk inverted . . . . . . 10·00
633 50 c. As 40 c. . . . . 55 1·00
633*a* 55 c. American Golden Plover (1.9.81) . . 3·50 3·00
aw. Wmk Crown to right of CA . . 10·00
633*b* 60 c. Bananaquit (1.3.82) . . . . 4·50 6·00
634 70 c. As 60 c. . . . . 55 2·00
635 $1 Caribbean Elaenia . . . . . . 1·00 1·50
636 $2.50, American Redstart . . . . 2·00 5·00
637 $5 Belted Kingfisher . . . . . . 3·25 8·00
w. Wmk inverted . . . . . . 8·00
638 $10 Moorhen . . . . 6·50 14·00
w. Wmk inverted . . . . . . 16·00
622/38 . . . . *Set of* 21 30·00 50·00

*The normal sideways watermark shows Crown to left of CA, *as seen from the back of the stamp.*

No. 626*a* occurred in the initial supply sent to Barbados.

No. 631*a* shows the birds' plumage in blue instead of green and has the background flowers omitted.

143 Gun aboard Landing Craft at Foul Bay

144 Family

(Des G. Vasarhelyi. Litho Format)

1979 (9 Oct). *Space Project Commemorations. T* **143** *and similar multicoloured designs. W w* **14** (*sideways on* 10, 28 *and* 45 *c.*). *P* 14.
639 10 c. Type **143** 15 10
640 12 c. Transporting launcher through Barbados (*vert*) 15 15
641 20 c. Firing of 16" launcher in daylight (*vert*) 15 20
642 28 c. Bath Earth Station and "Intelsat IV A" 15 30
643 45 c. "Intelsat V" over the Caribbean 25 50
644 50 c. "Intelsat IV A" over Atlantic (*vert*) . . 25 60
639/44 . . . . *Set of* 6 1·00 1·60
MS645 118 × 90 mm. $1 Lunar module descending on to Moon (wmk sideways) 65 80

Commemorations:—10 to 20 c. H.A.R.P. Gun experiment: 28 to 50 c. First use of "Intelsat" satellites; $1, 10th anniversary of Moon landing.

(Des R. Granger Barrett. Litho Questa)

1979 (27 Nov). *International Year of the Child. T* **144** *and similar vert designs. Multicoloured. W w* **14**. *P* 14.
646 12 c. Type **144** 10 10
647 28 c. Ring of children and map of Barbados . . 15 15
648 45 c. Child with teacher 20 20
649 50 c. Children playing 20 20
650 $1 Children and kite 35 45
646/50 . . . . *Set of* 5 80 90

ALTERED CATALOGUE NUMBERS

Any Catalogue numbers altered from the last edition are shown as a list in the introductory pages.

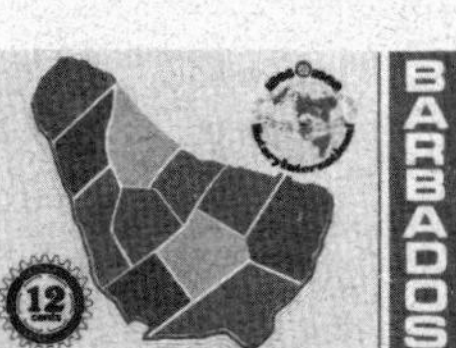

145 Map of Barbados

146 Private, Artillery Company, Barbados Volunteer Force, *circa* 1909

(Des G. Hutchins. Litho Security Printers (M), Malaysia)

1980 (19 Feb). *75th Anniv of Rotary International. T* **145** *and similar horiz designs. Multicoloured. W w* **14** (*sideways*). *P* 13.
651 12 c. Type **145** 15 10
652 28 c. Map of Caribbean 20 15
653 50 c. Rotary anniversary emblem 25 35
654 $1 Paul P. Harris (founder) 40 95
651/4 . . . . *Set of* 4 90 1·40

(Des J.W. Litho Questa)

1980 (8 Apr). *Barbados Regiment. T* **146** *and similar vert designs. Multicoloured. W w* **14**. *P* 14×14½.
655 12 c. Type **146** 25 10
656 35 c. Drum Major, Zouave uniform 35 15
657 50 c. Sovereign's and Regimental colours . . 40 30
w. Wmk inverted . . . . . . 10·00
658 $1 Barbados Regiment Women's Corps . . 55 70
655/8 . . . . *Set of* 4 1·40 1·10

147 Early Postman

148 Yellow-tailed Snapper and other Fishes

(Des. V. Whiteley Studio. Litho Walsall)

1980 (6 May). *"London 1980" International Stamp Exhibition. Two sheets each* 122 × 125 *mm containing T* **147** *or similar vert design. Multicoloured. W w* **14**. *P* 14 × 13½.
MS659 (a) 28 c. × 6, Type **147**. (b) 50 c. × 6, Modern Postwoman and Inspector *Set of* 2 *sheets* 1·40 2·25

The two sheets each contain the stamp in full colour and in five different colour separations.

(Des G. Drummond. Litho Security Printers (M), Malaysia)

1980 (30 Sept). *Underwater Scenery. T* **148** *and similar horiz designs. Multicoloured. W w* **14** (*sideways**). *P* 13½.
660 12 c. Type **148** 20 10
661 28 c. Banded Butterflyfish 35 15
w. Wmk Crown to right of CA . . . . 30·00
662 50 c. Male and female Blue-headed Wrasse and Princess Parrotfish 45 25
663 $1 French Grunt and French Angelfish . . 70 70
w. Wmk Crown to right of CA . . . . 30·00
660/3 . . . . *Set of* 4 1·50 1·00
MS664 136×110 mm. Nos. 660/3 (wmk upright) 2·50 3·25

*The normal sideways watermark shows Crown to left of CA, *as seen from the back of the stamp.*

149 Bathsheba Railway Station

(Des J. W. Litho Questa)

1981 (13 Jan). *Early Transport. T* **149** *and similar horiz designs. Multicoloured. W w* **14** (*sideways*). *P* 14½ × 14.
665 12 c. Type **149** 30 10
666 28 c. Cab stand at The Green 20 15
667 45 c. Animal-drawn tram 30 30
668 70 c. Horse-drawn bus 45 60
669 $1 Railway station in Fairchild Street . . 70 95
665/9 . . . . *Set of* 5 1·75 1·90

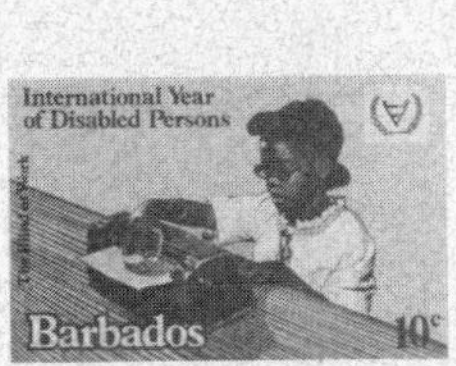

150 "The Blind at Work"

151 Prince Charles dressed for Polo

(Des BG Studio. Litho Walsall)

1981 (19 May). *International Year for Disabled Persons. T* **150** *and similar multicoloured designs. W w* **14** (*sideways on* 10 *c. and* $2.50). *P* 14.
670 10 c. Type **150** 20 10
671 25 c. Sign language (*vert*) 25 15
672 45 c. "Be alert to the white cane" (*vert*) . . 40 25
673 $2.50, Children at play . . . . . . 1·25 3·00
670/3 . . . . *Set of* 4 1·90 3·00

(Des and litho J.W.)

1981 (22 July). *Royal Wedding. T* **151** *and similar vert designs. Multicoloured. W w* **14**. *P* 13½ × 13.
674 28 c. Wedding bouquet from Barbados . . 15 10
675 50 c. Type **151** 20 15
676 $2.50, Prince Charles and Lady Diana Spencer . . . . 55 1·25
674/6 . . . . *Set of* 3 80 1·25

152 Landship Manoeuvre

(153)

(Des C. Abbott. Litho Harrison)

1981 (11 Aug). *Carifesta (Caribbean Festival of Arts), Barbados. T* **152** *and similar vert designs. Multicoloured. W w* **14**. *P* 14½ × 14.
677 15 c. Type **152** 15 15
678 20 c. Yoruba dancers 15 15
679 40 c. Tuk band 20 25
680 55 c. Sculpture of Frank Collymore 25 35
w. Wmk inverted . . . . . . 25·00
681 $1 Harbour scene 50 75
677/81 . . . . *Set of* 5 1·10 1·50

1981 (1 Sept). *Nos.* 630, 632 *and* 634 *surch as T* **153**.
682 15 c. on 28 c. Carib Grackle 30 15
683 40 c. on 45 c. Zenaida Dove 30 35
684 60 c. on 70 c. Bananaquit 30 45
682/4 . . . . *Set of* 3 80 85

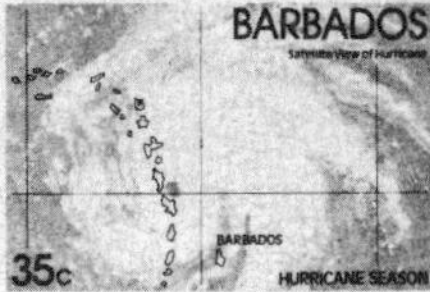

154 Satellite view of Hurricane

(Des A. Theobald. Litho Walsall)

1981 (29 Sept). *Hurricane Season. T* **154** *and similar horiz designs. W w* **14** (*sideways**). *P* 14.
685 35 c. black and blue 35 20
w. Wmk Crown to right of CA . . . . 26·00
686 50 c. multicoloured 45 35
w. Wmk Crown to right of CA . . . . 26·00
687 60 c. multicoloured 70 50
w. Wmk Crown to right of CA . . . . 7·50
688 $1 multicoloured 85 90
685/8 . . . . *Set of* 4 2·10 1·75

Designs:—50 c. Hurricane "Gladys" from "Apollo 7"; 60 c. Police Department on hurricane watch; $1 McDonnell F2H-2P Banshee "hurricane chaser" aircraft.

*The normal sideways watermark shows Crown to left of CA, *as seen from the back of the stamp.*

155 Twin Falls

156 Black Belly Ram

(Des. L. Curtis. Litho Format)

1981 (1 Dec.). *Harrison's Cave. T* **155** *and similar vert designs. Multicoloured. W w* **14**. *P* 14 × 14½.
689 10 c. Type **155** 10 10
690 20 c. Stream in Rotunda Room 20 15
691 55 c. Formations in Rotunda Room 30 50
692 $2.50, Cascade Pool . . . . . . 80 2·25
689/92 . . . . *Set of* 4 1·25 2·75

(Des BG Studio. Litho Format)

1982 (9 Feb). *Black Belly Sheep. T* **156** *and similar horiz designs. Multicoloured. W w* **14** (*sideways*). *P* 14.
693 40 c. Type **156** 20 30
694 50 c. Black Belly ewe 20 35
695 60 c. Ewe with lambs 30 60
696 $1 Ram and ewe, with map of Barbados . . 50 1·50
693/6 . . . . *Set of* 4 1·10 2·50

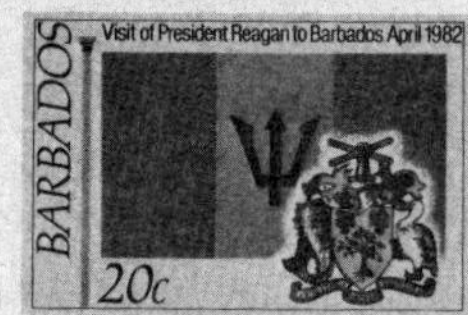

157 Barbados Coat of Arms and Flag

(Des Harrison. Litho Format)

1982 (8 Apr). *President Reagan's Visit. T* **157** *and similar horiz design. Multicoloured. W w* **14** *(sideways). P* 14.
697 20 c. Type **157** .. .. 40 1·25
a. Pair. Nos. 697/8 .. .. 80 2·50
698 20 c. U.S.A. coat of arms and flag .. .. 40 1·25
699 55 c. Type **157** .. .. 50 1·50
a. Pair. Nos. 699/700 .. .. .. 1·00 3·00
700 55 c. As No. 698 .. .. 50 1·50
697/700 .. .. *Set of* 4 1·60 5·00
The two designs of each value were printed together, *se-tenant*, in horizontal and vertical pairs within small sheets of 8 stamps.

158 Lighter

159 Bride and Earl Spencer proceeding up Aisle

(Des J.W. Litho Harrison)

1982 (4 May). *Early Marine Transport. T* **158** *and similar horiz designs. Multicoloured. W w* **14** *(sideways). P* 14½.
701 20 c. Type **158** 20 15
702 35 c. Rowing boat 35 25
703 55 c. Speightstown schooner 50 40
704 $2.50, Inter-colonial schooner .. .. 1·75 2·50
701/4 .. .. *Set of* 4 2·50 3·00

(Des Jennifer Toombs. Litho Questa)

1982 (1 July). *21st Birthday of Princess of Wales. T* **159** *and similar vert designs. Multicoloured W w* **14**. *P* 14½ × 14.
705 20 c. Barbados coat of arms 20 15
706 60 c. Princess at Llanelwedd, October 1981 .. 45 50
707 $1.20, Type **159** .. .. 75 1·10
708 $2.50, Formal portrait .. .. .. 1·25 1·90
705/8 .. .. *Set of* 4 2·40 3·25

160 "To Help other People"

161 Arms of George Washington

(Des G. Drummond. Litho Format)

1982 (7 Sept). *75th Anniv of Boy Scout Movement. T* **160** *and similar multicoloured designs. W w* **14** *(sideways on Nos.* 710/11). *P* 14.
709 15 c. Type **160** 50 10
710 40 c. "I Promise to do my Best" *(horiz)* 80 30
711 55 c. "To do my Duty to God, the Queen and my Country" *(horiz)* 90 65
712 $1 National and Troop flags .. .. 1·40 1·75
709/12 .. .. *Set of* 4 3·25 2·50
MS713 119 × 93 mm. $1.50, The Scout Law .. 4·25 2·75

(Des and litho J.W.)

1982 (2 Nov). *250th Birth Anniv of George Washington. T* **161** *and similar vert designs. Multicoloured. W w* **14**. *P* 13½ × 13.
714 10 c. Type **161** 10 10
715 55 c. Washington House, Barbados 45 45
716 60 c. Washington with troops 50 50
717 $2.50, Washington taking Oath .. .. 1·60 1·60
714/17 .. .. *Set of* 4 2·40 2·40

162 *Agraulis vanillae*

(Des I. Loe. Litho J.W.)

1983 (8 Feb). *Butterflies. T* **162** *and similar horiz designs. Multicoloured. W w* **14** *(sideways). P* 13 × 13½.
718 20 c. Type **162** .. .. 1·00 30
719 40 c. *Danaus plexippus* .. .. .. 1·50 40
720 55 c. *Hypolimnas misippus* .. .. .. 1·50 45
721 $2.50, *Hemiargus hanno* .. .. .. 3·25 2·50
718/21 .. .. *Set of* 4 6·50 3·25

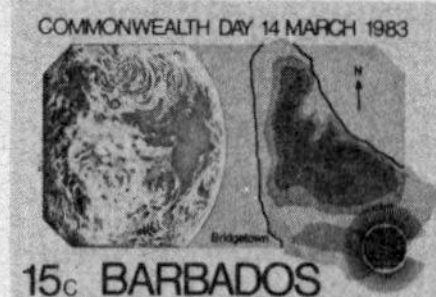

163 Map of Barbados and Satellite View

(Des D. Bowen. Litho J.W.)

1983 (14 Mar). *Commonwealth Day. T* **163** *and similar horiz designs. Multicoloured. W w* **14** *(sideways). P* 13.
722 15 c. Type **163** 20 10
723 40 c. Tourist beach 25 20
724 60 c. Sugar cane harvesting 35 40
725 $1 Cricket match .. .. 1·25 1·10
722/5 .. .. *Set of* 4 1·75 1·60

164 U.S. Navy "M" Class Airship M-20

(Des L. Curtis. Litho Format)

1983 (14 June). *Bicentenary of Manned Flight. T* **164** *and similar horiz designs. Multicoloured. W w* **14** *(sideways). P* 14.
726 20 c. Type **164** 60 15
727 40 c. Douglas DC-3 .. .. 80 40
728 55 c. Vickers Viscount 837 .. .. .. 90 80
729 $1 Lockheed L-1011 TriStar 500 .. .. 1·50 2·50
726/9 .. .. *Set of* 4 3·50 3·50

165 Nash "600", 1941

166 Game in Progress

(Des and litho Harrison)

1983 (9 Aug). *Classic Cars. T* **165** *and similar horiz designs. Multicoloured. W w* **14** *(sideways). P* 14.
730 25 c. Type **165** 60 20
731 45 c. Dodge, 1938 .. .. 75 30
732 75 c. Ford "Model AA", 1930 .. .. .. 95 1·50
733 $2.50, Dodge "Four", 1918 .. .. .. 2·50 4·00
730/3 .. .. *Set of* 4 4·25 5·50

(Des L. Curtis. Litho Questa)

1983 (30 Aug). *Table Tennis World Cup Competition. T* **166** *and similar vert designs. Multicoloured. W w* **14**. *P* 14.
734 20 c. Type **166** 25 20
735 65 c. Map of Barbados 50 55
736 $1 World Table Tennis Cup .. .. .. 75 1·00
734/6 .. .. *Set of* 3 1·40 1·60

167 Angel playing Lute (detail "The Virgin and Child") (Masaccio))

168 Track and Field Events

(Des D. Miller. Litho Questa)

1983 (1 Nov). *Christmas. 50th Anniv of Barbados Museum. T* **167** *and similar multicoloured designs. W w* **14** *(sideways on 45 c., 75 c. and $2.50). P* 14.
737 10 c. multicoloured 30 10
738 25 c. multicoloured 60 20
739 45 c. multicoloured 90 40
740 75 c. black and gold .. .. 1·40 1·60
741 $2.50, multicoloured .. .. 4·50 5·50
737/41 .. .. *Set of* 5 7·00 7·00
MS742 59 × 98 mm. $2 multicoloured .. .. 1·75 2·00
Designs: *Horiz*—45 c. "The Barbados Museum" (Richard Day); 75 c. "St. Ann's Garrison" (W. S. Hedges); $2.50, Needham's Point, Carlisle Bay. *Vert*—25 c., $2 Different details from "The Virgin and Child" (Masaccio).

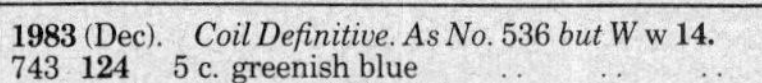

1983 (Dec). *Coil Definitive. As No.* 536 *but W w* **14**.
743 **124** 5 c. greenish blue .. .. 1·25 1·75
No. 743 was also available from sheets.

(Des McCombie Skinner Studio. Litho Walsall)

1984 (28 Mar). *Olympic Games, Los Angeles. T* **168** *and similar horiz designs. W w* **14** *(sideways). P* 14.
745 50 c. bright green, black and olive-sepia .. 60 45
746 65 c. dull orange, black and drab 80 60
747 75 c. greenish blue, black and deep cobalt .. 1·00 85
748 $1 light brown, black and yellow-ochre .. 2·50 1·75
745/8 .. .. *Set of* 4 4·50 3·25
MS749 115 × 97 mm. Nos. 745/8 .. .. .. 6·50 8·00
Designs:—65 c. Shooting; 75 c. Sailing; $1 Cycling.

169 Global Coverage

170 U.P.U. 1943 3d. Stamp and Logo

(Des C. Abbott. Litho Questa)

1984 (25 Apr). *250th Anniv of Lloyd's List (newspaper). T* **169** *and similar vert designs. Multicoloured. W w* **14**. *P* 14½ × 14.
750 45 c. Type **169** 70 40
751 50 c. Bridgetown harbour 80 50
752 75 c. *Philosopher* (full-rigged ship), 1857 .. 1·10 90
753 $1 *Sea Princess* (liner), 1984 .. .. 1·25 1·25
750/3 .. .. *Set of* 4 3·50 2·75

(Des McCombie Skinner Studio. Litho J.W.)

1984 (6 June). *Universal Postal Union Congress, Hamburg. Sheet* 90 × 75 *mm. W w* **14** *(sideways). P* 13½.
MS754 **170** $2 multicoloured .. .. .. 2·50 2·50

171 Local Junior Match

172 Poinsettia

(Des L. Curtis. Litho Walsall)

1984 (8 Aug). *60th Anniv of World Chess Federation. T* **171** *and similar horiz designs. Multicoloured. W w* **14** *(sideways). P* 14½.
755 25 c. Type **171** .. .. 1·25 30
756 45 c. Staunton and 19th-century Knights 1·60 50
757 65 c. Staunton Queen and 18th-century Queen from Macao .. .. 1·75 1·60
758 $2 Staunton and 17th-century Rooks .. 3·50 5·00
755/8 .. .. *Set of* 4 7·25 6·75

(Des I. Loe. Litho Questa)

1984 (24 Oct). *Christmas. Flowers. T* **172** *and similar vert designs. Multicoloured. W w* **14**. *P* 14.
759 50 c. Type **172** .. .. 1·50 80
760 65 c. Snow-on-the-Mountain .. .. .. 1·75 1·50
761 75 c. Christmas Candle .. .. 2·00 3·00
762 $1 Christmas Hope .. .. 2·25 3·50
759/62 .. .. *Set of* 4 6·75 8·00

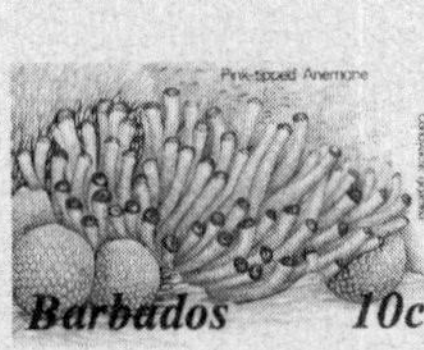

173 Pink-tipped Anemone

174 The Queen Mother at the Docks

(Des I. Loe. Litho Questa)

1985 (26 Feb)–**87**. *Marine Life. T* **173** *and similar horiz designs. Multicoloured. W w* **14** *(sideways). P* 14. *A. Without imprint date at foot.*
763A 1 c. Bristle Worm (7.5.85) .. .. 70 1·25
764A 2 c. Spotted Trunkfish (7.5.85) .. .. 70 1·25
765A 5 c. Coney (9.4.85) .. .. .. 2·25 75
766A 10 c. Type **173** 80 75
767A 20 c. Christmas Tree Worm .. .. 2·00 2·00
768A 25 c. Hermit Crab .. .. 1·50 70
769A 35 c. Animal Flower (9.4.85) .. .. 3·50 75
770A 40 c. Vase Sponge (9.4.85) .. .. 3·50 80
771A 45 c. Spotted Moray (7.5.85) .. .. 1·50 90
772A 50 c. Ghost Crab .. .. 2·50 3·00
773A 65 c. Flamingo Tongue Snail (9.4.85) .. 2·50 1·00
774A 75 c. Sergeant Major (7.5.85) .. .. 2·50 2·00
775A $1 Caribbean Warty Anemone (7.5.85) .. 2·75 1·25

76A $2.50, Green Turtle .. .. 7·00 8·00
77A $5 Rock Beauty (fish) .. .. 8·00 9·00
78A $10 Elkhorn Coral (9.4.85) .. .. .. 8·50 9·00
63A/78A . .. . *Set of* 16 42·00 38·00

B. *With imprint date* ("1987") (15.9.87)

63B 1 c. Bristle Worm .. .. 2·50 3·50
64B 2 c. Spotted Trunkfish .. .. 2·50 3·50
67B 20 c. Christmas Tree Worm .. .. .. 3·50 4·50
72B 50 c. Ghost Crab .. .. 7·00 7·00
74B 75 c. Sergeant Major .. .. 8·00 8·50
76B $2.50, Green Turtle .. .. 12·00 16·00
77B $5 Rock Beauty (fish) .. .. 16·00 20·00
63B/77B .. .. *Set of* 7 45·00 55·00

For these designs watermarked w **16** (sideways) see Nos. 94/809.

(Des A. Theobald ($2), C. Abbott (others). Litho Questa)

985 (7 June). *Life and Times of Queen Elizabeth the Queen Mother. T* **174** *and similar vert designs. Multicoloured.* W w **16**. P 14½ × 14.

79 25 c. In the White Drawing Room, Buckingham Palace, 1930s 15 20
80 65 c. With Lady Diana Spencer at Trooping the Colour, 1981 .. .. 70 50
81 75 c. Type **174**.. .. .. 55 60
82 $1 With Prince Henry at his christening (from photo by Lord Snowdon).. .. .. 70 75
79/82 .. .. *Set of* 4 1·90 1·90
MS783 91×73 mm. $2 In Land Rover opening Syon House Garden Centre. Wmk sideways .. 1·40 1·50

176 Intelsat Satellite orbitting Earth

177 Traffic Policeman

(Des D. Miller. Litho Walsall)

985 (6 Aug). *Birth Bicentenary of John J. Audubon (ornithologist). T* **175** *and similar multicoloured designs showing original paintings.* W w **14** (*sideways on* 45 c.). P 14.

84 45 c. Type **175**.. .. .. 2·00 70
85 65 c. Prairie Warbler (*vert*) .. .. .. 2·25 2·00
86 75 c. Great Blue Heron (*vert*) .. .. .. 2·50 2·75
87 $1 Yellow Warbler (*vert*) .. .. .. 2·75 3·75
84/7 .. .. *Set of* 4 8·50 8·25

175 Peregrine Falcon

(Des L. Curtis. Litho Harrison)

985 (10 Sept). *20th Anniv of Intelsat Satellite System.* W w **14** (*sideways*). P 14.

88 **176** 75 c. multicoloured 75 60

(Des L. Curtis. Litho Format)

985 (19 Nov). *150th Anniv of Royal Barbados Police. T* **177** *and similar multicoloured designs.* W w **16**. P 14.

89 25 c. Type **177**.. .. .. 80 20
90 50 c. Police Band on bandstand .. .. 1·40 80
91 65 c. Dog handler .. .. 2·00 1·40
92 $1 Mounted policeman in ceremonial uniform .. .. 2·25 2·00
89/92 .. .. *Set of* 4 5·75 4·00
MS793 85×60 mm. $2 Police Band on parade (*horiz*). Wmk sideways .. .. .. 2·00 2·75

986 (6 Jan)–**87**. *As Nos.* 763/78 *but* W w **16** (*sideways*). P 14.

A. *Without imprint date at foot*

96A 5 c. Coney 50 50
97A 10 c. Type **173** 50 50
98A 20 c. Christmas Tree Worm 70 75
99A 25 c. Hermit Crab 70 50
00A 35 c. Animal Flower .. .. 1·00 85
03A 50 c. Ghost Crab .. .. 2·00 1·50
07A $2.50, Green Turtle .. .. 3·50 3·50
08A $5 Rock Beauty (fish) .. .. .. 7·00 7·00
09A $10 Elkhorn Coral .. .. 10·00 10·00
96A/809A .. .. .. *Set of* 9 23·00 23·00

B. *With imprint date*

94B 1 c. Bristle Worm (23.7.86) .. .. .. 20 1·00
95B 2 c. Spotted Trunkfish (23.7.86) .. .. 20 1·00
96B 5 c. Coney (15.9.87) .. .. .. 14·00 8·00
97B 10 c. Type **173** (18.8.86) 30 30
98B 20 c. Christmas Tree Worm (18.8.86) 30 40
99B 25 c. Hermit Crab (18.8.86) 40 40
00B 35 c. Animal Flower (15.9.87) .. .. 14·00 8·00
01B 40 c. Vase Sponge (23.7.86) 50 50
02B 45 c. Spotted Moray (23.7.86) 60 50
03B 50 c. Ghost Crab (18.8.86) 60 60
04B 65 c. Flamingo Tongue Snail (18.8.86) .. 65 70
05B 75 c. Sergeant Major (18.8.86) 70 75
06B $1 Caribbean Warty Anemone (18.8.86) .. 85 85

807B $2.50, Green Turtle (18.8.86) .. .. 2·00 3·50
808B $5 Rock Beauty (fish) (18.8.86) .. .. 2·50 5·50
809B $10 Elkhorn Coral (18.8.86) .. .. 4·25 8·00
794B/809B .. .. .. *Set of* 16 38·00 35·00

Imprint dates: "1986", Nos. 794B/5B, 797B/9B, 801B/9B; "1987", Nos. 796B/7B, 799B/802B, 804B, 806B, 809B; "1988", No. 797B.

(Des A. Theobald. Litho Format)

1986 (21 Apr). *60th Birthday of Queen Elizabeth II. Vert designs as T* **110** *of Ascension. Multicoloured.* W w **16**. P 14×14½.

810 25 c. Princess Elizabeth aged two, 1928 .. 15 20
811 50 c. At University College of West Indies, Jamaica, 1953 .. .. 30 40
812 65 c. With Duke of Edinburgh, Barbados, 1985 .. .. 40 50
a. Silver (logo) omitted £300
813 75 c. At banquet in Sao Paulo, Brazil, 1968 .. 45 60
814 $2 At Crown Agents Head Office, London, 1983 .. .. 1·00 1·50
810/14 .. .. *Set of* 5 2·10 3·00

178 Canadair DC-4M2 North Star of Trans-Canada Airlines

(Des L. Curtis. Litho Format)

1986 (2 May). *"Expo '86" World Fair, Vancouver. T* **178** *and similar horiz design. Multicoloured.* W w **16** (*sideways*). P 14.

815 50 c. Type **178** 75 50
816 $2.50, *Lady Nelson* (cargo liner) .. .. 2·00 2·50

(Des D. Miller. Litho Walsall)

1986 (22 May). *"Ameripex '86" International Stamp Exhibition, Chicago. Horiz designs as T* **164** *of Bahamas, showing Barbados stamps (Nos.* 817/20). *Multicoloured.* W w **16** (*sideways*). P 14.

817 45 c. 1976 Bicentenary of American Revolution 25 c.. .. .. 85 35
818 50 c. 1976 Bicentenary of American Revolution 50 c.. .. .. 95 55
819 65 c. 1981 Hurricane Season $1 .. .. 1·10 1·00
820 $1 1982 Visit of President Reagan 55 c. pair.. .. .. 1·25 1·75
817/20 .. .. *Set of* 4 3·75 3·25
MS821 90×80 mm. $2 Statue of Liberty and liner *Queen Elizabeth 2* .. .. .. 5·00 7·50

No. **MS**821 also commemorates the Centenary of the Statue of Liberty.

(Des D. Miller. Litho Walsall)

1986 (23 July). *Royal Wedding. Square designs as T* **112** *of Ascension. Multicoloured.* W w **16**. P 14½×14.

822 45 c. Prince Andrew and Miss Sarah Ferguson 60 35
823 $1 Prince Andrew in Midshipman's uniform .. .. 1·00 75
w. Wmk inverted .. .. 12·00

179 Transporting Electricity Poles, 1923

180 *Alpinia purpurata* and Church Window

(Des A. Theobald. Litho B.D.T.)

1986 (16 Sept). *75th Anniv of Electricity in Barbados. T* **179** *and similar multicoloured designs.* W w **16** (*sideways on* 10, 65 *c.*). P 13½.

824 10 c. Type **179**.. .. .. 15 10
825 25 c. Heathman Ladder, 1935 (*vert*).. .. 25 20
826 65 c. Transport fleet, 1941 .. .. .. 60 60
827 $2 Bucket truck, 1986 (*vert*) .. .. 1·60 2·00
824/7 .. .. *Set of* 4 2·40 2·50

(Des A. Atkinson. Litho Questa)

1986 (28 Oct). *Christmas. T* **180** *and similar vert designs showing flowers and church windows. Multicoloured.* W w **14**. P 14.

828 25 c. Type **180**.. .. .. 20 20
829 50 c. *Anthurium andraeanum* 45 45
830 75 c. *Heliconia rostrata* 70 80
831 $2 *Heliconia x psittacorum* .. .. 1·50 2·50
828/31 .. .. *Set of* 4 2·50 3·50

181 Shot Putting

182 Barn Swallow

(Des G. Vasarhelyi. Litho Format)

1987 (27 Mar). *10th Anniv of Special Olympics. T* **181** *and similar horiz designs. Multicoloured.* W w **14** (*sideways*). P 14.

832 15 c. Type **181**.. .. .. 25 15
833 45 c. Wheelchair racing 45 30
834 65 c. Long jumping 60 65
835 $2 Logo and slogan .. .. 1·25 2·50
832/5 .. .. *Set of* 4 2·25 3·25

(Des P. Broadbent. Litho Walsall)

1987 (12 June). *"Capex '87" International Stamp Exhibition, Toronto. Birds. T* **182** *and similar vert designs. Multicoloured.* W w **16**. P 14.

836 25 c. Type **182** .. .. 1·75 40
w. Wmk inverted .. .. 9·00
837 50 c. Yellow Warbler .. .. 2·00 1·50
838 65 c. Audubon's Shearwater .. .. .. 2·00 2·50
839 75 c. Black-whiskered Vireo .. .. .. 2·25 3·00
840 $1 Scarlet Tanager .. .. 2·50 3·75
836/40 .. .. *Set of* 5 9·50 10·00

183 Sea Scout saluting

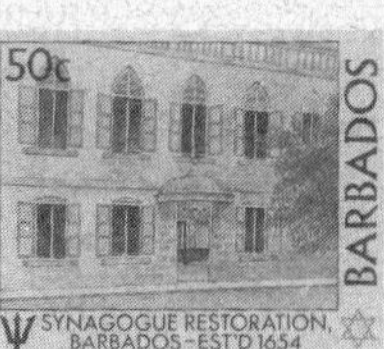

184 Bridgetown Synagogue

(Des L. Curtis. Litho Format)

1987 (24 July). *75th Anniv of Scouting in Barbados. T* **183** *and similar vert designs. Multicoloured.* W w **16**. P 14.

841 10 c. Type **183**.. .. .. 20 10
842 25 c. Scout jamboree 30 20
843 65 c. Scout badges 65 45
844 $2 Scout band .. .. 1·60 1·75
841/4 .. .. *Set of* 4 2·50 2·25

(Des R. Edge. Litho Questa)

1987 (6 Oct). *Restoration of Bridgetown Synagogue. T* **184** *and similar multicoloured designs.* W w **16** (*sideways on* 50, 65 *c.*). P 14×14½ (*horiz*) *or* 14½×14 (*vert*).

845 50 c. Type **184**.. .. .. 1·40 1·40
846 65 c. Interior of Synagogue .. .. .. 1·60 1·60
847 75 c. Ten Commandments (*vert*) .. .. 1·90 1·90
848 $1 Marble laver (*vert*) .. .. .. 2·25 2·75
845/8 .. .. *Set of* 4 6·50 7·00

185 Arms and Colonial Seal

(Des D. Hartley. Litho Walsall)

1987 (24 Nov). *21st Anniv of Independence. T* **185** *and similar multicoloured designs.* W w **16** (*sideways*). P 14×14½.

849 25 c. Type **185**.. .. .. 30 20
850 45 c. Flags of Barbados and Great Britain .. 40 30
851 65 c. Silver dollar and one penny coins .. 70 45
852 $2 Colours of Barbados Regiment .. 1·50 1·40
849/52 .. .. *Set of* 4 2·50 2·10
MS853 94×56 mm. $1.50, Prime Minister E. W. Barrow (*vert*). Wmk upright. P 14½×14 .. 1·00 1·25

186 Herman C. Griffith

186*a*

(Des D. Hartley. Litho Walsall)

1988 (6 June–11 July). *West Indian Cricket. T* **186** *and similar horiz designs, each showing portrait, cricket equipment and early belt buckle. Multicoloured. W* w **14** *(sideways). P* 14.
854 15 c. E. A. (Manny) Martindale .. .. 1·75 50
855 45 c. George Challenor .. .. .. 2·50 75
856 50 c. Type **186** (11.7) .. .. .. 2·75 2·00
a. Error. Portrait as Type **186***a* .. £150
857 75 c. Harold Austin .. .. .. 3·25 3·25
858 $2 Frank Worrell .. .. .. 4·25 8·00
854/8 .. .. *Set of* 5 13·00 13·00

As originally prepared the 50 c., inscribed "Herman C. Griffith", showed the portrait of another Barbadian cricketer, E. Lawson Bartlett, in error. The mistake was noticed two days prior to issue and the 50 c. was delayed until 11 July while supplies showing the correct portrait were printed. The instructions to withdraw the stamps with the Bartlett portrait, No. 856a, failed to reach the Parcel Post Department in time and, it is reported, 101 examples were sold in the normal course of business before the, belated, notification was received.

187 *Kentropyx borckianus*

188 Cycling

(Des Doreen McGuinness. Litho B.D.T.)

1988 (13 June). *Lizards of Barbados. T* **187** *and similar vert designs. Multicoloured. W* w **14**. *P* 14.
859 10 c. Type **187** .. .. 1·00 30
860 50 c. *Hemidactylus mabouia* .. .. 2·25 60
861 65 c. *Anolis extremus* .. .. .. 2·25 1·00
862 $2 *Gymnophthalmus underwoodii* .. 4·50 6·00
859/62 .. .. *Set of* 4 9·00 7·00

(Des A. Edmonston. Litho Walsall)

1988 (2 Aug). *Olympic Games, Seoul. T* **188** *and similar vert designs. Multicoloured. W* w **14**. *P* 14½×14.
863 25 c. Type **188** 50 20
864 45 c. Athletics 50 30
865 75 c. Relay swimming 65 55
866 $2 Yachting .. .. 1·50 1·75
863/6 .. .. *Set of* 4 2·75 2·50
MS867 144×63 mm. Nos. 863/6. W w **16** .. 3·50 3·00

(Des S. Noon and D. Miller (50, 65 c.), D. Miller (others). Litho Questa)

1988 (18 Oct). *300th Anniv of Lloyd's of London. Designs as T* **123** *of Ascension. W* w **14** *(sideways on* 50, 65 *c.). P* 14.
868 40 c. multicoloured 55 30
869 50 c. multicoloured 65 35
870 65 c. multicoloured .. .. .. 1·25 45
871 $2 steel-blue and brown-lake .. .. 2·50 2·00
868/71 .. .. *Set of* 4 4·50 2·75

Designs: *Vert*—40 c. Royal Exchange, 1774; $2 Sinking of *Titanic*, 1912. *Horiz*—50 c. Early sugar mill; 65 c. *Author* (container ship).

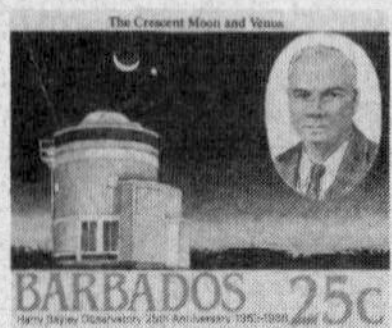

189 Harry Bayley and Observatory

190 L.I.A.T. Hawker Siddeley H.S.748

(Des Josephine Martin. Litho Walsall)

1988 (28 Nov). *25th Anniv of Harry Bayley Observatory. T* **189** *and similar horiz designs. Multicoloured. W* w **16** *(sideways). P* 14×14½.
872 25 c. Type **189** 60 20
873 65 c. Observatory with North Star and Southern Cross constellations .. 1·00 55
874 75 c. Andromeda galaxy .. .. .. 1·25 70
875 $2 Orion constellation .. .. .. 2·75 3·25
872/5 .. .. *Set of* 4 5·00 4·25

(Des A. Theobald. Litho Walsall)

1989 (20 Mar). *50th Anniv of Commercial Aviation in Barbados. T* **190** *and similar horiz designs. Multicoloured. W* w **16** *(sideways). P* 14.
876 25 c. Type **190** .. .. 1·50 30
877 65 c. Pan Am Douglas D.C.8-62 .. .. 2·50 80
878 75 c. British Airways Concorde at Grantley Adams Airport .. .. .. 2·50 90
879 $2 Caribbean Air Cargo Boeing 707-351C 4·00 3·50
876/9 .. .. *Set of* 4 9·50 5·00

MINIMUM PRICE

The minimum price quote is 10p which represents a handling charge rather than a basis for valuing common stamps. For further notes about prices see introductory pages.

191 Assembly Chamber

192 Brown Hare

(Des A. Edmonston. Litho B.D.T.)

1989 (19 July). *350th Anniv of Parliament. T* **191** *and similar square designs. W* w **16**. *P* 13½.
880 25 c. multicoloured 40 20
881 50 c. multicoloured 60 35
882 75 c. deep slate-blue and brownish black .. 1·00 50
883 $2.50, multicoloured .. .. .. 2·50 2·00
880/3 .. .. *Set of* 4 4·00 2·75

Designs:—50 c. The Speaker; 75 c. Parliament Buildings, c. 1882; $2.50, Queen Elizabeth II and Prince Philip in Parliament.

(Des R. Suffolk. Litho Questa)

1989 (1 Aug). *Wildlife Preservation. T* **192** *and similar multicoloured designs. W* w **16** *(sideways on* 50 *c.,* $2). *P* 14×13½ *(vert) or* 13½×14 *(horiz).*
884 10 c. Type **192** 55 20
885 50 c. Red-footed Tortoise (*horiz*) .. .. 1·25 60
886 65 c. Savanna ("Green") Monkey .. .. 1·40 1·10
887 $2 *Bufo marinus* (toad) (*horiz*) .. .. 2·75 4·25
884/7 .. .. *Set of* 4 5·50 5·50
MS888 87×97 mm. $1 Small Indian Mongoose 75 80

(Des A. Edmonston. Litho B.D.T.)

1989 (9 Oct). *35th Commonwealth Parliamentary Conference. Square design as T* **191**. *Multicoloured. W* w **14**. *P* 13½.
MS889 108×69 mm. $1 Barbados Mace .. 75 1·00

193 Bread 'n Cheese

194 Water Skiing

(Des Rosanne Sanders. Litho Questa)

1989 (1 Nov)–**92**. *Wild Plants. T* **193** *and similar vert designs. Multicoloured. W* w **14**. *P* 14½.
890 2 c. Type **193** .. .. 50 1·25
891 5 c. Scarlet Cordia 30 50
892 10 c. Columnar Cactus 30 30
893 20 c. Spiderlily 40 30
894 25 c. Rock Balsam .. .. .. 70 1·00
895 30 c. Hollyhock 50 25
895*a* 35 c. Red Sage (9.6.92) .. .. .. 1·00 1·00
896 45 c. Yellow Shak-shak .. .. .. 85 1·00
897 50 c. Whitewood .. .. 85 1·00
898 55 c. Bluebell 70 55
899 65 c. Prickly Sage .. .. .. 1·00 1·50
900 70 c. Seaside Samphire 80 70
901 80 c. Flat-hand Dildo 90 80
901*a* 90 c. Herringbone (9.6.92) .. .. 1·50 2·00
902 $1.10, Lent Tree .. .. .. 1·25 2·00
903 $2.50, Rodwood .. .. .. 3·75 7·50
904 $5 Cowitch .. .. 6·50 11·00
905 $10 Maypole .. .. 11·00 17·00
890/905 .. .. *Set of* 18 29·00 45·00

Imprint dates: "1989", Nos. 890/5, 896/901, 902/5; "1991", Nos. 891/3, 895*a*, 900, 901*a*, 902.

For similar stamps but watermarked w **16**, see Nos. 921/36.

(Des C. Burke. Litho Harrison)

1989 (17 Nov). *"World Stamp Expo '89" International Stamp Exhibition, Washington. Watersports. T* **194** *and similar vert designs. Multicoloured. W* w **16**. *P* 14.
906 25 c. Type **194** 80 30
907 50 c. Yachting .. .. 1·50 1·00
908 65 c. Scuba diving .. .. .. 1·60 1·60
909 $2.50, Surfing .. .. 4·75 6·50
906/9 .. .. *Set of* 4 7·75 8·50

195 Barbados 1852 1d. Stamp

196 Bugler and Jockeys

(Des D. Miller. Litho B.D.T.)

1990 (3 May). *150th Anniv of the Penny Black and "Stamp World London 90" International Stamp Exhibition. T* **195** *and similar vert designs showing stamps. W* w **14**. *P* 14.
910 25 c. dp bluish green, blk & pale yell-ochre 1·00 30
911 50 c. multicoloured .. .. .. 1·50 1·00
912 65 c. multicoloured .. .. .. 1·60 1·25
913 $2.50, multicoloured .. .. .. 3·75 5·50
910/13 .. .. *Set of* 4 7·00 7·25
MS914 90×86 mm. 50 c. multicoloured; 50 c. multicoloured .. .. 1·75 2·25

Designs:—50 c. 1882 1d. Queen Victoria; 65 c. 1899 2d.; $2.50, 1912 3d.; miniature sheet, 50 c. Great Britain Penny Black, 50 c. Barbados 1906 Nelson Centenary 1s.

(Adapted G. Vasarhelyi. Litho B.D.T.)

1990 (3 May). *Horse Racing. T* **196** *and similar multicoloured designs. W* w **14** *(sideways on* 25, 45 *and* 75 *c.). P* 14.
915 25 c. Type **196** 45 30
916 45 c. Horse and jockey in parade ring .. 70 50
917 75 c. At the finish 90 85
918 $2 Leading in the winner (*vert*) .. .. 2·50 4·00
915/18 .. .. *Set of* 4 4·00 5·00

(Des D. Miller. Litho Questa)

1990 (8 Aug). *90th Birthday of Queen Elizabeth the Queen Mother. Vert designs as T* **134** (75 *c.) or* **135** ($2.50) *of Ascension. W* w **16**. *P* 14×15 (75 *c.) or* 14½ ($2.50).
919 75 c. multicoloured 75 60
920 $2.50, black and bronze-green .. .. 2·25 2·75

Designs:—75 c. Lady Elizabeth Bowes-Lyon, April 1923 (from painting by John Lander); $2.50, Lady Elizabeth Bowes-Lyon on her engagement, January 1923.

1990 (Sept). *As Nos.* 890/4, 896/7, 903/5, *but W* w **16**. "1990" *imprint date. P* 14½.
921 2 c. Type **193** 20 90
922 5 c. Scarlet Cordia .. .. .. 70 1·40
923 10 c. Columnar Cactus .. .. .. 70 1·40
924 20 c. Spiderlily .. .. 90 1·50
925 25 c. Rock Balsam 30 20
927 45 c. Yellow Shak-shak 45 35
928 50 c. Whitewood 50 40
930 65 c. Prickly Sage 60 55
934 $2.50, Rodwood .. .. .. 1·90 4·00
935 $5 Cowitch .. .. 3·25 6·00
936 $10 Maypole .. .. 6·50 9·00
921/36 .. .. *Set of* 11 14·50 23·00

197 *Orthemis ferruginea* (dragonfly)

VISIT OF
HRH THE
PRINCESS ROYAL
OCTOBER 1990
(**198**)

(Des I. Loe. Litho Harrison)

1990 (16 Oct). *Insects. T* **197** *and similar horiz designs. Multicoloured. P* 14.
937 50 c. Type **197** .. .. 1·25 70
938 65 c. *Ligyrus tumulosus* (beetle) .. .. 1·50 1·00
939 75 c. *Neoconocephalus* sp (grasshopper) .. 1·75 1·25
940 $2 *Bostra maxwelli* (stick-insect) .. 3·25 4·25
937/40 .. .. *Set of* 4 7·00 6·50

1990 (21 Nov). *Visit of the Princess Royal. Nos.* 894, 901 *and* 903 *optd with T* **198**.
941 25 c. Rock Balsam 65 20
942 80 c. Flat-hand Dildo .. .. .. 1·40 1·40
943 $2.50, Rodwood .. .. .. 3·50 4·50
941/3 .. .. *Set of* 3 5·00 5·50

199 Star

200 Adult Male Yellow Warbler

(Des D. Miller. Litho B.D.T.)

1990 (4 Dec). *Christmas. T* **199** *and similar vert designs. Multicoloured. W* w **14**. *P* 14.
944 20 c. Type **199** 55 15
945 50 c. Figures from crib 85 50
946 $1 Stained glass window .. .. 1·75 1·25
947 $2 Angel (statue) .. .. .. 2·50 4·00
944/7 .. .. *Set of* 4 5·00 5·50

(Des G. Drummond. Litho B.D.T.)

1991 (4 Mar). *Endangered Species. Yellow Warbler. T* **200** *and similar horiz designs. Multicoloured. W* w **14** *(sideways). P* 14.
948 10 c. Type **200** .. .. 1·10 55
949 20 c. Pair feeding chicks in nest .. .. 1·75 55
950 45 c. Female feeding chicks in nest .. 2·00 60
951 $1 Male with fledgeling .. .. 3·50 4·25
948/51 .. .. *Set of* 4 7·50 5·50

201 Sorting Daily Catch

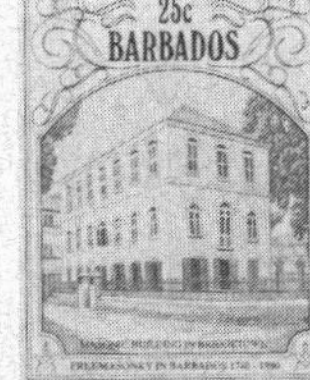

202 Masonic Building, Bridgetown

(Des M. Maynard, adapted G. Vasarhelyi. Litho Cartor)

991 (18 June). *Fishing in Barbados. T* **201** *and similar multicoloured designs. W* w **14** (*sideways on* 50, 75 *c.*). *P* 13½×14 (5 *c.*, $2.50) *or* 14×13½ (*others*).

52 5 c. Type **201** 40 40
53 50 c. Line fishing (*horiz*) .. .. .. 1·50 90
54 75 c. Fish cleaning (*horiz*) .. .. .. 2·00 1·25
55 $2.50, Game fishing .. .. .. 4·00 5·50
52/5 .. .. *Set of* 4 7·00 7·25

(Des N. Shewring. Litho B.D.T.)

991 (17 Sept). 250*th Anniv of Freemasonry in Barbados* (1990). *T* **202** *and similar vert designs. W* w **14**. *P* 14.

56 25 c. multicoloured .. .. .. 1·00 40
57 65 c. multicoloured .. .. .. 1·75 1·00
58 75 c. black, greenish yellow & yellow-brown 1·75 1·00
59 $2.50, multicoloured .. .. .. 4·25 6·00
56/9 .. .. *Set of* 4 8·00 7·50

Designs:—65 c. Compass and Square (masonic symbols); 75 c. oyal Arch Jewel; $2.50, Ceremonial apron, columns and badge.

203 *Battus polydamus*

(Des I. Loe. Litho B.D.T.)

991 (15 Nov). *"Phila Nippon '91" International Stamp Exhibition, Tokyo. Butterflies. T* **203** *and similar multicoloured designs. W* w **16** (*sideways on* 20 *c.*, 65 *c.*). *P* 14.

60 20 c. Type **203** 75 30
61 50 c. *Urbanus proteus* (*vert*) .. .. .. 1·25 65
62 65 c. *Phoebis sennae* .. .. .. 1·40 95
63 $2.50, *Junonia evarete* (*vert*) .. .. 3·50 5·00
60/3 .. .. *Set of* 4 6·25 6·25
MS964 87×86 mm. $4 *Vanessa cardui*. Wmk sideways .. .. 7·50 8·50

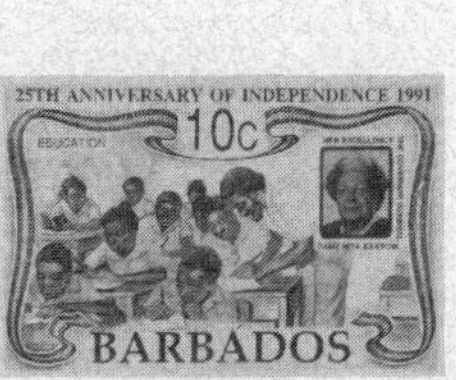

204 School Class

205 Jesus carrying Cross

(Des G. Vasarhelyi. Litho B.D.T.)

991 (20 Nov). 25*th Anniv of Independence. T* **204** *and similar multicoloured designs. W* w **14** (*sideways*). *P* 14.

65 10 c. Type **204** 15 15
66 25 c. Barbados Workers' Union Labour College 25 25
67 65 c. Building a house 60 80
68 75 c. Sugar cane harvesting 70 90
69 $1 Health clinic .. .. 90 1·75
65/9 .. .. *Set of* 5 2·40 3·50
MS970 123 × 97 mm. $2.50, Gordon Greenidge and Desmond Haynes (cricketers) (*vert*). Wmk upright .. .. 5·00 6·00

(Des P. Argent. Litho B.D.T.)

1992 (7 Apr). *Easter. T* **205** *and similar vert designs. Multicoloured. W* w **16**. *P* 14.

971 35 c. Type **205** 70 30
972 70 c. Crucifixion .. .. 1·25 90
973 90 c. Descent from the Cross .. .. 1·40 1·25
974 $3 Risen Christ .. .. 3·75 5·00
971/4 .. .. *Set of* 4 6·50 6·75

206 Cannon Ball

207 *Epidendrum* "Costa Rica"

(Des Jennifer Toombs. Litho Cartor)

1992 (9 June). *Conservation. Flowering Trees. T* **206** *and similar horiz designs. Multicoloured. W* w **14** (*sideways*). *P* 14×13½.

975 10 c. Type **206** 50 30
976 30 c. Golden Shower Tree 90 40
977 80 c. Frangipani .. .. 2·00 2·25
978 $1.10, Flamboyant .. .. .. 2·25 2·25
975/8 .. .. *Set of* 4 5·00 4·75

(Des Annette Robinson. Litho B.D.T.)

1992 (8 Sept). *Orchids. T* **207** *and similar horiz designs. Multicoloured. W* w **14** (*sideways*). *P* 13½×14.

979 55 c. Type **207** 75 55
980 65 c. *Cattleya guttaca* 90 90
981 70 c. *Laeliacattleya* "Splashing Around" .. 90 90
982 $1.40, *Phalaenopsis* "Kathy Saegert" .. 1·40 2·50
979/82 .. .. *Set of* 4 3·50 4·25

208 Mini Moke and Gun Hill Signal Station, St. George

209 Barbados Gooseberry

(Des D. Miller. Litho Questa)

1992 (15 Dec). *Transport and Tourism. T* **208** *and similar horiz designs. Multicoloured. W* w **14** (*sideways*). *P* 14×14½.

983 5 c. Type **208** 40 40
984 35 c. Tour bus and Bathsheba Beach, St. Joseph 85 30
985 90 c. B.W.I.A. McDonnell Douglas MD-83 over Grantley Adams Airport .. 2·25 2·00
986 $2 *Festivale* (liner) and Bridgetown harbour .. .. 3·25 4·00
983/6 .. .. *Set of* 4 6·00 6·00

(Des I. Loe. Litho B.D.T.)

1993 (9 Feb). *Cacti and Succulents. T* **209** *and similar vert designs. Multicoloured. W* w **14**. *P* 14.

987 10 c. Type **209** 45 30
988 35 c. Night-blooming Cereus .. .. 1·00 35
989 $1.40, Aloe .. .. 2·75 3·25
990 $2 Scrunchineel .. .. 3·25 4·00
987/90 .. .. *Set of* 4 6·75 7·00

(Des A. Theobald. Litho Questa)

1993 (1 Apr). 75*th Anniv of Royal Air Force. Horiz designs as T* **149** *of Ascension. Multicoloured. W* w **14** (*sideways*). *P* 14.

991 10 c. Hawker Hunter F.6 .. .. .. 50 30
992 30 c. Handley Page H.P.80 Victor K2 .. 75 35
993 70 c. Hawker Typhoon 1B .. .. .. 1·25 1·25
994 $3 Hawker Hurricane Mk 1 .. .. 3·00 4·00
991/4 .. .. *Set of* 4 5·00 5·50
MS995 110×77 mm. 50 c. Armstrong Whitworth Siskin IIIA; 50 c. Supermarine S6B; 50 c. Supermarine Walrus Mk1; 50 c. Hawker Hart 2·00 2·50

WORLD
ORCHID
CONFERENCE
1993

(**210**)

211 18 pdr Culverin of 1625, Denmark Fort

1993 (1 Apr). 14*th World Orchid Conference, Glasgow. Nos.* 979/82 *optd as T* **210**.

996 55 c. Type **207** .. .. 1·10 1·10
997 65 c. *Cattleya guttaca* .. .. .. 1·25 1·25
998 70 c. *Laeliacattleya* "Splashing Around" .. 1·25 1·25
999 $1.40, *Phalaenopsis* "Kathy Saegert" .. 2·00 2·50
996/9 .. .. *Set of* 4 5·00 5·50

The overprints on the 70 c. and $1.40 are in two lines.

(Des J. Batchelor. Litho Cartor)

1993 (8 June). 17*th-century English Cannon. T* **211** *and similar horiz designs. Multicoloured. W* w **14** (*sideways*). *P* 13.

1000 5 c. Type **211** 30 40
1001 45 c. 6 pdr of 1649–60, St. Ann's Fort .. 85 50
1002 $1 9 pdr demi-culverin of 1691, The Main Guard .. .. 1·75 2·00
1003 $2.50, 32 pdr demi-cannon of 1693–94, Charles Fort .. .. .. 2·75 3·75
1000/3 .. .. *Set of* 4 5·00 6·00

COVER PRICES

Cover factors are quoted at the beginning of each country for most issues to 1945. An explanation of the system can be found on page x. The factors quoted do not, however, apply to philatelic covers.

212 Sailor's Shell-work Valentine and Carved Amerindian

213 Plesiosaurus

(Des D. Miller. Litho B.D.T.)

1993 (14 Sept). 60*th Anniv of Barbados Museum. T* **212** *and similar vert designs. Multicoloured. W* w **14**. *P* 13½.

1004 10 c. Type **212** 35 30
1005 75 c. "Barbados Mulatto Girl" (Agostino Brunias) .. .. 1·25 1·25
1006 90 c. Morris Cup and soldier of West India Regiment, 1858 .. .. .. 1·50 1·60
1007 $1.10, Ogilby's map of Barbados, 1679, and Ashanti gold weights .. .. 1·75 2·25
1004/7 .. .. *Set of* 4 4·25 4·75

(Des N. Shewring. Litho Cartor)

1993 (28 Oct). *Prehistoric Aquatic Reptiles. T* **213** *and similar vert designs. Multicoloured. W* w **14**. *P* 13.

1008 90 c. Type **213** .. .. 1·40 1·60
a. Horiz strip of 5. Nos. 1008/12 .. 6·00
1009 90 c. Ichthyosaurus .. .. .. 1·40 1·60
1010 90 c. Elasmosaurus .. .. .. 1·40 1·60
1011 90 c. Mosasaurus .. .. .. 1·40 1·60
1012 90 c. Archelon .. .. 1·40 1·60
1008/12 .. .. *Set of* 5 6·00 7·00

Nos. 1008/12 were printed together, *se-tenant*, in horizontal strips of 5 throughout the sheet with the background forming a composite design.

214 Cricket

215 Whimbrel

(Des S. Noon. Litho B.D.T.)

1994 (11 Jan). *Sports and Tourism. T* **214** *and similar vert designs. Multicoloured. W* w **16**. *P* 14.

1013 10 c. Type **214** 85 50
1014 35 c. Rally driving .. .. .. 1·00 40
1015 50 c. Golf .. .. 1·75 1·25
1016 70 c. Long distance running .. .. 1·50 1·75
1017 $1.40, Swimming .. .. .. 1·75 2·50
1013/17 .. .. *Set of* 5 6·25 5·75

(Des N. Arlott. Litho B.D.T.)

1994 (18 Feb). *"Hong Kong '94" International Stamp Exhibition. Migratory Birds. T* **215** *and similar horiz designs. Multicoloured. W* w **14** (*sideways*). *P* 14.

1018 10 c. Type **215** 40 40
1019 35 c. American Golden Plover 75 40
1020 70 c. Turnstone .. .. 1·25 1·25
1021 $3 Louisiana Heron ("Tricoloured Heron") .. .. 3·25 4·00
1018/21 .. .. *Set of* 4 5·00 5·50

216 Bathsheba Beach and Logo

217 William Demas

(Des D. Miller. Litho B.D.T.)

1994 (25 Apr). *First United Nations Conference of Small Island Developing States. T* **216** *and similar horiz designs showing scenery. Multicoloured. W* w **16** (*sideways*). *P* 14×15.

1022 10 c. Type **216** 15 15
1023 65 c. Pico Tenneriffe 60 60
1024 90 c. Ragged Point Lighthouse .. .. 1·25 1·25
1025 $2.50, Consett Bay .. .. .. 2·25 3·50
1022/5 .. .. *Set of* 4 3·75 5·00

(Des D. Miller. Litho Cot Printery Ltd)

1994 (4 July). *First Recipients of Order of the Caribbean Community. T* **217** *and similar vert designs. Multicoloured. W* w **14**. *P* 14.

1026 70 c. Type **217** 70 95
1027 70 c. Sir Shridath Ramphal 70 95
1028 70 c. Derek Walcott 70 95
1026/8 .. .. *Set of* 3 1·90 2·50

218 Dutch Flyut, 1695 **219** Private, 2nd West India Regt, 1860

(Des A. Theobald. Litho B.D.T.)

1994 (16 Aug)–**98**. *Ships. T* **218** *and similar horiz designs. Multicoloured.* W w **14** (*sideways*). *P* 14. A. *Without imprint date*

1029A 5 c. Type **218** 40 60
1030A 10 c. *Geestport* (container ship), 1994 .. 40 60
1031A 25 c. H.M.S. *Victory* (ship of the line), 1805 .. .. 15 20
1032A 30 c. *Royal Viking Queen* (liner), 1994 .. 80 40
1033A 35 c. H.M.S. *Barbados* (frigate), 1945 .. 85 45
1034A 45 c. *Faraday* (cable ship), 1924 .. 1·00 55
1035A 50 c. U.S.C.G. *Hamilton* (coastguard cutter), 1974 .. .. 1·00 60
1036A 65 c. H.M.C.S. *Saguenay* (destroyer), 1939 .. .. 1·25 1·00
1037A 70 c. *Inanda* (cargo liner), 1928 .. 1·25 1·00
1038A 80 c. H.M.S. *Rodney* (battleship), 1944 1·25 1·25
1039A 90 c. U.S.S. *John F. Kennedy* (aircraft carrier), 1982 .. .. .. 1·50 1·50
1040A $1.10, *William and John* (immigrant ship), 1627 .. .. 1·75 2·00
1041A $5 U.S.C.G. *Champlain* (coastguard cutter), 1931 .. .. .. 6·00 7·00
1042A $10 *Artist* (full-rigged ship), 1877 .. 6·25 6·50
1029A/42A .. .. *Set of* 14 21·00 21·00

B. *With imprint date*

1029B 5 c. Type **218** (20.1.98) 10 10
1030B 10 c. *Geestport* (container ship), 1994 (20.1.98) 10 10
1031B 25 c. H.M.S. *Victory* (ship of the line), 1805 (20.1.98) 15 20
1032B 30 c. *Royal Viking Queen* (liner), 1994 (20.1.98) 20 25
1033B 35 c. H.M.S. *Barbados* (frigate), 1945 (20.1.98) 20 25
1034B 45 c. *Faraday* (cable ship), 1924 (20.1.98) 30 35
1037B 70 c. *Inanda* (cargo liner), 1928 (20.1.98) 40 45
1039B 90 c. U.S.S. *John F. Kennedy* (aircraft carrier), 1982 (20.1.98) 55 60
1042B $10 *Artist* (full-rigged ship), 1877 (20.1.98) .. .. 6·25 6·50
1029B/42B .. .. *Set of* 9 8·00 8·50

For these designs watermarked W w **16** (sideways) and with imprint date see Nos. 1075/88.

(Des D. Cribbs. Litho Enschedé)

1995 (21 Feb). *Bicentenary of Formation of West India Regiment. T* **219** *and similar vert designs. Multicoloured.* W w **14**. *P* 15×14.

1043 30 c. Type **219** 35 35
1044 50 c. Light Company private, 4th West India Regt, 1795 .. .. 50 55
1045 70 c. Drum Major, 3rd West India Regt, 1860 .. .. 65 85
1046 $1 Privates in undress and working dress, 5th West India Regt, 1815 .. 90 1·25
w. Wmk inverted .. .. 1·00
1047 $1.10, Troops from 1st and 2nd West India Regts in Review Order, 1874 .. 95 1·40
1043/7 .. .. *Set of* 5 3·00 4·00

(Des R. Watton. Litho Cot Printery Ltd)

1995 (8 May). *50th Anniv of End of Second World War. Multicoloured designs as T* **161** *of Ascension.* W w **14** (*sideways*). *P* 14.

1048 10 c. Barbadian Bren gun crew 50 40
1049 35 c. Avro Type 683 Lancaster bomber .. 75 40
1050 55 c. Supermarine Spitfire .. .. .. 1·00 65
1051 $2.50, *Davisian* (cargo liner) .. .. 2·75 3·50
1048/51 .. .. *Set of* 4 4·50 4·50
MS1052 75×85 mm. $2 Reverse of 1939–45 War Medal (*vert*). Wmk upright .. .. .. 1·50 2·25

220 Member of 1st Barbados Combermere Scout Troop, 1912 **221** Blue Beauty

(Des S. Noon. Litho Cot Printery Ltd)

1995 (25 July). *300th Anniv of Combermere School. T* **220** *and similar multicoloured designs.* W w **14** (*sideways on horiz designs*). *P* 14.

1053 5 c. Type **220** 20 30
1054 20 c. Violin and sheet of music 30 30
1055 35 c. Sir Frank Worrell (cricketer) (*vert*) 90 55
1056 $3 Painting by pupil .. .. 2·25 3·50
1053/6 .. .. *Set of* 4 3·25 4·25
MS1057 174×105 mm. Nos. 1053/6 and 90 c. 1981 Carifesta 55 c. stamp. Wmk sideways .. 4·00 4·75
a. All four horiz stamps imperforate ..

(Des A. Theobald. Litho Cot Printery Ltd)

1995 (24 Oct). *50th Anniv of United Nations. Horiz designs as T* **213** *of Bahamas. Multicoloured.* W w **14** (*sideways*). *P* 14.

1058 30 c. Douglas C-124 Globemaster (transport), Korea, 1950–53 .. 60 40
1059 45 c. Royal Navy Sea King helicopter .. 80 50
1060 $1.40, Westland Wessex helicopter, Cyprus, 1964 .. .. 1·25 2·00
1061 $2 Sud Aviation SA 341 Gazelle helicopter, Cyprus, 1964 .. .. 1·50 2·50
1058/61 .. .. *Set of* 4 3·75 4·75

(Des I. Loe. Litho Cot Printery Ltd)

1995 (19 Dec). *Water Lilies. T* **221** *and similar vert designs. Multicoloured.* W w **14** (*inverted*). *P* 14.

1062 10 c. Type **221** 30 30
1063 65 c. White Water Lily 75 60
1064 70 c. Sacred Lotus 75 60
1065 $3 Water Hyacinth .. .. 2·50 3·50
1062/5 .. .. *Set of* 4 3·75 4·50

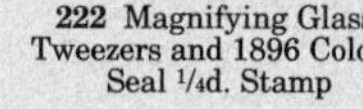

222 Magnifying Glass, Tweezers and 1896 Colony Seal ¼d. Stamp **223** Football

(Des D. Miller. Litho Cot Printery Ltd)

1996 (30 Jan). *Centenary of Barbados Philatelic Society. T* **222** *and similar horiz designs, each showing magnifying glass, tweezers and stamp. Multicoloured.* W w **14** (*sideways*). *P* 14.

1066 10 c. Type **222** 30 30
1067 55 c. 1906 Tercentenary of Annexation 1d. 55 45
1068 $1.10, 1920 Victory 1s. .. .. .. 1·10 1·25
1069 $1.40, 1937 Coronation 2½d. .. .. 1·40 2·00
1066/9 .. .. *Set of* 4 3·00 3·50

(Des S. Noon (Nos. 1070/3), G. Vasarhelyi (No. **MS**1074). Litho Cot Printery Ltd)

1996 (2 Apr). *Centenary of Modern Olympic Games. T* **223** *and similar vert designs. Multicoloured.* W w **14**. *P* 14.

1070 20 c. Type **223** 30 30
1071 30 c. Relay running 35 30
1072 55 c. Basketball 85 60
1073 $3 Rhythmic gymnastics .. .. .. 2·25 3·00
1070/3 .. .. *Set of* 4 3·25 3·75
MS1074 68×89 mm. $2.50, "The Discus Thrower" (Myron). Wmk inverted .. .. 2·00 2·50

1996 (May–1 Sept). *As Nos.* 1029/30 *and* 1032/41, *but* W w **16** (*sideways*) *and with imprint date. P* 14.

1075 5 c. Type **218** 10 15
1076 10 c. *Geestport* (container ship), 1994 .. 10 15
1078 30 c. *Royal Viking Queen* (liner), 1994 (1 Sept) 20 25
1079 35 c. H.M.S. *Barbados* (frigate), 1945 (1 Sept) 20 25
1080 45 c. *Faraday* (cable ship), 1996 (1 Sept) 30 35
1081 50 c. U.S.C.G. *Hamilton* (coastguard cutter), 1974 .. .. 30 35
1082 65 c. H.M.C.S. *Saguenay* (destroyer), 1939 (1 Sept) 40 45
1083 70 c. *Inanda* (cargo liner), 1928 (1 Sept) .. 40 45
1084 80 c. H.M.S. *Rodney* (battleship), 1944 (1 Sept) 50 55
1085 90 c. U.S.S. *John F. Kennedy* (aircraft carrier), 1982 (1 Sept) 55 60
1086 $1.10, *William and John* (immigrant ship), 1627 .. .. 65 70
1087 $5 U.S.C.G. *Champlain* (coastguard cutter), 1931 .. .. .. 3·00 3·25
1075/87 .. .. *Set of* 12 6·00 6·75

Imprint date: "1996", Nos. 1075/6 and 1078/87.

224 Douglas DC-10 of Canadian Airlines

(Des N. Shewring. Litho Cot Printery Ltd)

1996 (7 June). *"CAPEX '96" International Stamp Exhibition, Toronto. Aircraft. T* **224** *and similar horiz designs. Multicoloured.* W w **14** (*sideways*). *P* 14.

1089 10 c. Type **224** 30 20
1090 90 c. Boeing 767 of Air Canada 80 80
1091 $1 Airbus Industrie A320 of Air Canada 85 90
1092 $1.40, Boeing 767 of Canadian Airlines 1·10 1·50
1089/92 .. .. *Set of* 4 2·50 3·00

225 Chattel House

(Des G. Vasarhelyi. Litho Cot Printery Ltd)

1996 (7 June). *Chattel Houses. T* **225** *and similar horiz designs showing different houses.* W w **14** (*sideways*). *P* 14.

1093 35 c. multicoloured 30 25
1094 70 c. multicoloured 55 55
1095 $1.10, multicoloured .. .. 80 1·10
1096 $2 multicoloured .. .. 1·60 2·25
1093/6 .. .. *Set of* 4 3·00 3·75

226 "Going to Church" **227** Doberman Pinscher

(Des Jennifer Toombs. Litho Cot Printery Ltd)

1996 (12 Nov). *Christmas. 50th Anniv of U.N.I.C.E.F. Children's Paintings. T* **226** *and similar horiz designs. Multicoloured.* W w **14** (*sideways*). *P* 14×14½.

1097 10 c. Type **226** 20 15
1098 30 c. "The Tuk Band" 35 25
1099 55 c. "Singing carols" 50 40
1100 $2.50, "Decorated house" .. .. .. 1·75 2·50
1097/1100 .. .. *Set of* 4 2·50 3·00

(Des N. Shewring. Litho Cot Printery Ltd)

1997 (12 Feb). *"HONG KONG '97" International Stamp Exhibition. Dogs. T* **227** *and similar horiz designs. Multicoloured.* W w **14** (*sideways*). *P* 14×14½.

1101 10 c. Type **227** 30 20
1102 30 c. German Shepherd 50 35
1103 90 c. Japanese Akita .. .. 1·10 1·10
1104 $3 Irish Red Setter .. .. 3·00 3·75
1101/4 .. .. *Set of* 4 4·50 4·75

228 Barbados Flag and State Arms  **229** Measled Cowrie

(Des A. Theobald. Litho Cot Printery Ltd)

1997 (9 May). *Visit of President Clinton of U.S.A.. T* **228** *and similar horiz design. Multicoloured.* W w **14** (*sideways*). *P* 14.

1105 35 c. Type **228** 50 65
a. Sheetlet. Nos. 1105/6 each × 4 and 2 labels .. .. 4·25
1106 90 c. American flag and arms 70 80

Nos. 1105/6 were printed together, both horizontally and vertically *se-tenant*, in sheetlets of 8 with the blocks of four separated horizontally by two different stamp-sized illustrated labels.

Sheetlet No. 1105a was re-issued on 29 May 1997 with the bottom margin overprinted with two examples of the "PACIFIC '97" International Stamp Exhibition logo.

(Des N. Shewring. Litho Cot Printery Ltd)

1997 (29 July). *Shells. T* **229** *and similar vert designs. Multicoloured.* W w **14**. *P* 14.

1107 5 c. Type **229** 15 15
1108 35 c. Trumpet Triton 35 25
1109 90 c. Scotch Bonnet 75 75
1110 $2 West Indian Murex .. .. 1·50 2·00
1107/10 .. .. *Set of* 4 2·50 2·75
MS1111 71×76 mm. $2.50, Underwater scene. Wmk inverted .. .. 1·90 2·25

NEW INFORMATION

The editor is always interested to correspond with people who have new information that will improve or correct the Catalogue.

230 Lucas Manuscripts

231 Barbados Cherry

(Des O. Bell. Litho Cot Printery Ltd)

997 (1 Oct). *150th Anniv of the Public Library Service. T* **230** *and similar horiz designs. Multicoloured. W w* **14** *(sideways). P* 14×14½.

112 10 c. Type **230** 15 15
113 30 c. Librarian reading to children .. 30 25
114 70 c. Mobile library van 60 60
115 $3 Man using computer .. .. .. 2·25 3·00
112/15 .. .. *Set of* 4 3·00 3·50

(Des I. Loe. Litho Cot Printery Ltd)

997 (16 Dec). *Local Fruits. T* **231** *and similar horiz designs. Multicoloured. W w* **14** *(sideways). P* 14×14½.

116 35 c. Type **231** 30 25
117 40 c. Sugar Apple 35 30
118 $1.15, Soursop 85 90
119 $1.70, Pawpaw .. .. 1·25 1·50
116/19 .. .. *Set of* 4 2·50 2·75

232 Arms of former British Caribbean Federation

233 Environment Regeneration

(Des B. Dare. Litho Cartor)

998 (27 Apr). *Birth Centenary of Sir Grantley Adams (statesman). Sheet,* 118×74 *mm, containing T* **232** *and similar vert designs. Multicoloured. W w* **14**. *P* 13.

MS1120 $1 Type **232**; $1 Sir Grantley Adams; $1 Flag of former British Caribbean Federation .. 2·10 2·25

(Des D. Miller. Litho Questa)

998 (18 May). *Diana, Princess of Wales Commemoration. Sheet* 145×70 *mm, containing vert designs as T* **177** *of Ascension. Multicoloured. W w* **14** *(sideways). P* 14½×14.

MS1121 $1.15, Wearing blue hat, 1985; $1.15, Wearing red jacket, 1981; $1.15, Wearing tiara, 1987; $1.15, Wearing black jacket, 1993 .. 3·25 3·50

(Des N. Shewring. Litho Cot Printery Ltd)

998 (30 June). *50th Anniv of Organization of American States. T* **233** *and similar horiz designs. Multicoloured. W w* **14** *(sideways). P* 14.

122 15 c. Type **233** 10 10
123 $1 Stilt dancing 60 65
124 $2.50, Judge and figure of Justice .. 1·50 1·60
122/4 .. .. *Set of* 3 2·10 2·25

234 Frank Worrell Hall

235 Catamaran

(Des N. Shewring. Litho Cot Printery Ltd)

1998 (22 July). *50th Anniv of University of West Indies. T* **234** *and similar horiz designs. Multicoloured. W w* **14** *(sideways). P* 14.

1125 40 c. Type **234** 25 30
1126 $1.15, Student graduating 80 85
1127 $1.40, 50th anniversary plaque .. .. 1·10 1·25
1128 $1.75, Quadrangle .. .. 2·50 2·75
1125/8 .. .. *Set of* 4 4·50 5·00

(Des N. Shewring. Litho Cot Printery Ltd)

1998 (1 Dec). *Tourism. T* **235** *and similar multicoloured designs. W w* **14** *(sideways on* 45, 70 *c.). P* 14.

1129 10 c. Type **235** 10 10
1130 45 c. *Jolly Roger* (tourist schooner) (*horiz*) 30 35
1131 70 c. *Atlantis* (submarine) (*horiz*) .. 40 45
1132 $2 *Harbour Master* (ferry) .. .. .. 1·25 1·40
1129/32 .. .. *Set of* 4 2·00 2·25

STAMP BOOKLETS

1906 (Feb).
SB1 2s. ½d. booklet containing twenty-four 1d. (No. 137) in blocks of 6 .. ..

1909. *Black on red cover. Stapled.*
SB1*a* 1s. 6d. booklet containing eighteen 1d. (No. 165) in blocks of 6 .. ..

1913 (June). *Black on red cover. Stapled.*
SB2 2s. booklet containing twelve ½d. and eighteen 1d. (Nos. 171/2) in blocks of 6 .. ..

1916 (16 June). *Black on red cover. Stapled.*
SB3 2s. booklet containing twelve ½d. and eighteen 1d. (Nos. 182/3) in pairs £650

1920 (Sept). *Black on red cover. Stapled.*
SB4 2s. booklet containing twelve ½d. and eighteen 1d. (Nos. 202/3) in pairs .. ..

1932 (12 Nov). *Black on pale green cover. Austin Cars and Post Office Guide advertisements on front. Stapled.*
SB5 2s. booklet containing ½d. and 1d. (Nos. 230a, 231a) each in block of 10 and 1½d. (No. 231ba) in block of 6 .. ..

1933 (4 Dec). *Black on pale green cover. Advocate Co. Ltd. advertisement on front. Stapled.*
SB6 2s. booklet containing ½d. and 1d. (Nos. 230/1) each in block of 10 and 1½d. (No. 231*b*) in block of 6 .. ..

1938 (3 Jan). *Black on light blue cover. Advocate Co. Ltd. advertisement on front. Stapled.*
SB7 2s. booklet containing ½d. and 1d. (Nos. 248, 249a) each in block of 10 and 1½d. (No. 250) in block of 6 .. .. £1300

POSTAGE DUE STAMPS

D 1

D 2

(Typo D.L.R.)

1934 (2 Jan)–**47**. *Wmk Mult Script CA. P* 14.

D1 D 1 ½d. green (10.2.35) .. .. .. 1·00 6·50
D2 1d. black .. .. 1·00 1·00
a. Bisected (½d.) (on cover) .. .. † £750
D3 3d. carmine (13.3.47) .. .. .. 19·00 17·00
D1/3 .. .. *Set of* 3 19·00 22·00
D1/3 Perf "Specimen" .. .. *Set of* 3 65·00

The bisected 1d. was officially authorised for use between March 1934 and February 1935, Some specimens had the value "½d." written across the half stamp in red or black ink (*Price on cover* £850).

(Typo D.L.R.)

1950 (8 Dec)–**53**. *Values in cents. Wmk Mult Script CA. Ordinary paper. P* 14.

D4 D 1 1 c. green .. .. 3·50 16·00
a. Chalk-surfaced paper. *Deep green* (29.11.51) .. .. .. 30 3·00
ab. Error. Crown missing, W **9*a*** .. £275
ac. Error. St. Edward's Crown, W **9*b*** £160
D5 2 c. black .. .. 6·50 9·50
a. Chalk-surfaced paper (20.1.53) .. 40 4·25
ac. Error. St. Edward's Crown, W **9*b*** £275
D6 6 c. carmine .. .. 15·00 16·00
a. Chalk-surfaced paper (20.1.53) .. 1·00 8·50
ab. Error. Crown missing, W **9*a*** .. £160
ac. Error. St. Edward's Crown, W **9*b*** £130
D4/6 .. .. *Set of* 3 22·00 38·00
D4a/6a .. .. *Set of* 3 1·50 14·00

The 1 c. has no dot below "c".

1965 (3 Aug)–**68**. *As Nos.* D4/6 *but wmk* w **12** *(upright). Chalk-surfaced paper.*

D7 D 1 1 c. deep green .. .. .. 30 3·50
a. Missing top serif on "C" (R. 2/4) .. 6·00
b. Green .. .. 1·75 5·50
D8 2 c. black .. .. 30 3·50
D9 6 c. carmine .. .. 50 5·00
a. Carmine-red (14.5.68) .. .. 1·40 9·50
D7/9 .. .. *Set of* 3 1·00 11·00

1974 (4 Feb). *As No.* D9 *but W w* **12** *(sideways). Glazed, ordinary paper. P* 14 × 13½.

D10 D 1 6 c. carmine .. .. 9·00 17·00

1974 (4 Dec). *W w* **12** *(sideways). P* 13.

D12 D 1 2 c. black .. .. 3·75 16·00
D13 6 c. carmine .. .. 3·75 16·00

(Des Jennifer Toombs. Litho Questa)

1976 (12 May)–**85**. *Different floral backgrounds as Type* D **2**. *W w* **14**. *P* 14.

D14 1 c. deep mauve and light pink 30 80
a. Perf 15 × 14 (7.85) 10 10
D15 2 c. ultramarine and light cobalt 30 80
a. Perf 15 × 14 (7.85) 10 10
D16 5 c. reddish brown and yellow 30 90
a. Perf 15 × 14 (7.85) 10 15
D17 10 c. royal blue and light lilac 45 90
a. Perf 15 × 14 (7.85) 15 20
D18 25 c. deep green and bright yellow-green .. 70 1·10
a. Perf 15 × 14 (7.85) 20 30
D19 $1 rose-carmine and rose .. .. .. 75 1·10
D14/19 .. .. *Set of* 6 2·50 5·00
D14a/18a .. .. *Set of* 5 50 70

Barbuda
(*see after* Antigua)

Basutoland
see Lesotho

Batum

Batum, the outlet port on the Black Sea for the Russian Transcaucasian oilfields, was occupied by the Turks on 15 April 1918.

Under the terms of the armistice signed at Mudros on 30 October 1918 the Turks were to withdraw and be replaced by an Allied occupation of Batum, the Baku oilfields and the connecting Transcaucasia Railway. British forces arrived off Batum in early December and the oblast, or district, was declared a British military governorship on 25 December 1918. The Turkish withdrawal was completed five days later.

The provision of a civilian postal service was initially the responsibility of the Batum Town Council. Some form of mail service was in operation by February 1919 with the postage prepaid in cash. Letters are known showing a framed oblong handstamp, in Russian, to this effect. The Town Council was responsible for the production of the first issue, Nos. 1/6, but shortly after these stamps were placed on sale a strike by Council employees against the British military governor led to the postal service being placed under British Army control.

SURCHARGES. Types **2** and **4/8** were all applied by handstamp. Most values from No. 19 onwards are known showing the surcharge inverted, surcharge double or in pairs with surcharge *tête-bêche*.

BRITISH OCCUPATION

(Currency. 100 kopeks = 1 rouble)

PRICES FOR STAMPS ON COVER

Nos. 1/6	*from* × 60
Nos. 7/10	*from* × 15
Nos. 11/18	*from* × 60
Nos. 19/20	*from* × 15
Nos. 21/44	—
Nos. 45/53	*from* × 200

1 Aloe Tree

БАТУМ. ОБ.

Руб 10 Руб

(2)

1919 (4 Apr). *Litho. Imperf.*

No.	Type	Description	Unused	Used
1	1	5 k. green	5·00	6·50
2		10 k. ultramarine	5·00	6·50
3		50 k. yellow	1·75	2·25
4		1 r. chocolate	2·25	2·75
5		3 r. violet	7·50	9·00
6		5 r. brown	8·50	11·00
1/6		*Set of* 6	27·00	35·00

Nos. 1/6 were printed in sheets of 198 (18×11).

1919 (13 Apr). *Russian stamps (Arms types) handstamped with T* **2**.

No.	Description	Unused	Used
7	10 r. on 1 k. orange (*imperf*)	28·00	30·00
8	10 r. on 3 k. carmine-red (*imperf*)	15·00	17·00
9	10 r. on 5 k. brown-lilac (*perf*)	£275	£275
10	10 r. on 10 on 7 k. deep blue (*perf*)	£225	£225

A similar handstamped surcharge, showing the capital letters without serifs, is bogus.

BRITISH
OCCUPATION

(3)

1919 (10 Nov.) *Colours changed and new values. Optd with T* **3**.

No.	Type	Description	Unused	Used
11	1	5 k. yellow-green	7·00	7·00
12		10 k. bright blue	7·00	7·00
13		25 k. orange-yellow	7·00	7·00
14		1 r. pale blue	3·25	6·00
15		2 r. pink	1·00	1·25
16		3 r. bright violet	1·00	1·25
17		5 r. brown	1·25	1·40
		a. "CCUPATION" (R.5/1)	£275	
18		7 r. brownish red	2·75	4·00
11/18		*Set of* 8	27·00	32·00

Nos. 11/18 were printed in sheets of 432 (18×24).

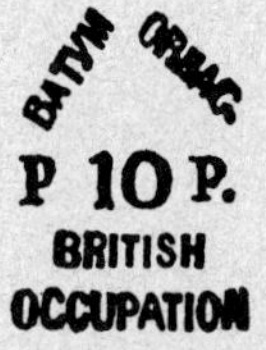

(4)

БАТУМЪ
BRITISH
P. 15 P.
OCCUPATION
ОБЛ.

(5)

1919 (27 Nov)–**20**. *Russian stamps (Arms types) handstamped with T* **4** *or* **5**. *Imperf.*

No.	Description	Unused	Used
19	10 r. on 3 k. carmine-red	11·00	13·00
20	15 r. on 1 k. orange	38·00	38·00
	a. Red surch	30·00	30·00
	b. Violet surch (10.3.20)	40·00	40·00

Nos. 20a/b have the handstamp in soluble ink.

1920 (12 Jan). *Russian stamps (Arms types) handstamped as T* **4**.

No.	Description	Unused	Used
	(*a*) *Imperf*		
21	50 r. on 1 k. orange	£275	£275
22	50 r. on 2 k. yellow-green (R.)	£375	£375
	(*b*) *Perf*		
23	50 r. on 2 k. yellow-green	£375	£375
24	50 r. on 3 k. carmine-red	£850	£850
25	50 r. on 4 k. red	£600	£600
26	50 r. on 5 k. brown-lilac	£350	£350
27	50 r. on 10 k. deep blue (R.)	£950	£950
28	50 r. on 15 k. blue and red-brown	£375	£375

(6)

1920 (30 Jan–21 Feb). *Russian stamps (Arms types) handstamped as T* **6**. (*a*) *Perf*

No.	Description	Unused	Used
29	25 r. on 5 k. brown-lilac (21 Feb)	30·00	30·00
	a. Blue surch	30·00	30·00
30	25 r. on 10 on 7 k. blue (21 Feb)	85·00	85·00
	a. Blue surch	48·00	48·00
31	25 r. on 20 on 14 k. dp carmine & bl (21 Feb)	50·00	50·00
	a. Blue surch	48·00	48·00
32	25 r. on 25 k. deep violet & lt green (21 Feb)	85·00	85·00
	a. Blue surch	70·00	70·00
33	25 r. on 50 k. green and copper-red (21 Feb)	48·00	48·00
	a. Blue surch	50·00	50·00
34	50 r. on 2 k. yellow-green	75·00	75·00
35	50 r. on 3 k. carmine-red	75·00	75·00
36	50 r. on 4 k. red	65·00	65·00
37	50 r. on 5 k. brown-lilac	48·00	48·00
	(*b*) *Imperf*		
38	50 r. on 2 k. yellow-green	£250	£250
39	50 r. on 3 k. carmine-red	£325	£325
40	50 r. on 5 k. brown-lilac	£950	£950

1920 (10 Mar). *Romanov issue, as T* **25** *of Russia, handstamped with T* **6**.

No.	Description	Unused	Used
41	50 r. on 4 k. rose-carmine (B.)	38·00	42·00

РУБ 25 ЛЕЙ

25 РУБ. 25

(7)

R.50R.
BRITISH
OCCUPATION
РУБ.

(8)

1920 (1 Apr). *Nos.* 3, 11 *and* 13 *handstamped with T* **7** (*Nos.* 42/3) *or* **8** (*No.* 44).

No.	Description	Unused	Used
42	25 r. on 5 k. yellow-green	22·00	22·00
	a. Blue surch	24·00	24·00
43	25 r. on 25 k. orange-yellow	17·00	17·00
	a. Blue surch	65·00	65·00
44	50 r. on 50 k. yellow	13·00	13·00
	a. "50" cut	10·00	10·00
	b. Blue surch	70·00	70·00
	ba. "50" cut	£120	£120

Nos. 44a and 44ba show the figures broken by intentional file cuts applied as a protection against forgery. The "5" is cut at the base and on the right side of the loop. The "0" is chipped at top and foot, and has both vertical lines severed.

1920 (19 June). *Colours changed and new values. Optd with T* 3. *Imperf.*

No.	Type	Description	Unused	Used
45	1	1 r. chestnut	60	3·00
		a. "BPITISH"	45·00	
46		2 r. pale blue	70	3·00
		a. "BPITISH"	55·00	
47		3 r. pink	85	3·00
		a. "BPITISH"	55·00	
48		5 r. black-brown	70	3·00
		a. "BPITISH"	55·00	
49		7 r. yellow	70	3·00
		a. "BPITISH"	55·00	
50		10 r. myrtle-green	60	3·00
		a. "BPITISH"	55·00	
51		15 r. violet	90	4·25
		a. "BPITISH"	£110	
52	1	25 r. scarlet	80	3·7
		a. "BPITISH"	£100	
53		50 r. deep blue	1·00	6·(
		a. "BPITISH"	£170	
45/53		*Set of* 9	6·00	29·0

Nos. 45/53 were printed in sheets of 308 (22×14). Th "BPITISH" error occurs on R. 1/19 of the overprint.

POSTCARD STAMPS

When Nos. 7/10 were issued on 13 April 1919 a similar 35 surcharge was applied to stocks of various Russian postcar held by the post office. The majority of these had stam impressions printed directly on to the card, but there were also few cards, originally intended for overseas mail, on which Russ 4 k. stamps had been affixed.

PRICES. Those in the left-hand column are for unus examples on complete postcard; those on the right for use examples off card. Examples used on postcard are worth more

1919 (13 Apr). *Russian stamps handstamped as T* **2**.

No.	Description	Unused	Used
P1	35 k. on 4 k. red (Arms type)	£2750	£325
P2	35 k. on 4 k. carmine-red (Romanov issue)	£7500	£85(

Batum was handed over to the National Republic of Georgi on 7 July 1920.

Bechuanaland
see Botswana

Belize
(*formerly* British Honduras)

BRITISH HONDURAS

It is recorded that the first local post office was established by t inhabitants in 1809, but Belize did not become a regular pack port of call until 1829. A branch office of the British G.P.O. w established in 1857 and the stamps of Great Britain were suppli for use on overseas mail from 1858.

The colonial authorities took over the postal service on 1 Apr 1860, the Great Britain stamps being withdrawn the followir month. There was no inland postal service until 1862.

For illustrations of the handstamp and postmark types s BRITISH POST OFFICES ABROAD notes, following GREA BRITAIN.

BELIZE

CROWNED-CIRCLE HANDSTAMPS

CC1 CC 1*b* BELIZE (R.)(13.11.1841) .. *Price on cover* £40(

Stamps of GREAT BRITAIN *cancelled* "A 06" *as Type* **2**.

1858 *to* **1860**.

Z1	1d. rose-red (1857), *perf* 14	£8
Z2	4d. rose (1857)	£3
Z3	6d. lilac (1856)	£3
Z4	1s. green (1856)	£13

PRICES FOR STAMPS ON COVER TO 1945

Nos. 1/4	*from* × 20
Nos. 5/16	*from* × 25
Nos. 17/22	*from* × 20
Nos. 23/6	*from* × 10
Nos. 27/30	*from* × 15
Nos. 35/42	*from* × 20
Nos. 43/4	*from* × 30
Nos. 49/50	*from* × 25
Nos. 51/69	*from* × 15
Nos. 80/100	*from* × 6
Nos. 101/10	*from* × 5
Nos. 111/20	*from* × 15
Nos. 121/2	*from* × 8
No. 123	*from* × 10
Nos. 124/37	*from* × 6
Nos. 138/42	*from* × 10
Nos. 143/9	*from* × 8
Nos. 150/61	*from* × 5
Nos. D1/3	*from* × 30

CROWN COLONY

1

(Typo D.L.R.)

1865 (1 Dec). *No wmk. P* 14.
1 1 1d. pale blue .. .. 55·00 48·00
a. Imperf between (pair) .. ..
2 1d. blue .. .. 60·00 48·00
3 6d. rose £250 £110
4 1s. green £275 £100
a. In horiz pair with 6d. £16000
b. In vert pair with 1d. £23000

In the first printing all three values were printed in the same sheet separated by horizontal and vertical gutter margins. The sheet comprised two panes of 60 of the 1d. at the top with a pane of 60 of the 1s. at bottom left and another of 6d. at bottom right. Copies of 1d. *se-tenant* with the 6d. are not known. There were two later printings of the 1d. but they were in sheets without the 6d. and 1s.

1872–79. *Wmk Crown CC. (a) P* 12½
5 1 1d. pale blue .. .. 60·00 16·00
y. Wmk inverted and reversed ..
6 1d. deep blue (1874) .. .. .. 65·00 16·00
7 3d. red-brown .. .. £100 65·00
8 3d. chocolate (1874) .. .. .. £120 80·00
9 6d. rose .. .. £190 28·00
9*a* 6d. bright rose-carmine (1874) .. .. £300 38·00
10 1s. green .. .. £300 28·00
10*a* 1s. deep green (1874) .. .. .. £250 20·00
b. Imperf between (horiz pair) .. † £13000
w. Wmk inverted .. ..

(*b*) *P* 14 (1877–79)
11 1 1d. pale blue (1878) .. .. .. 55·00 15·00
12 1d. blue .. .. 50·00 10·00
a. Imperf between (horiz pair) .. £3750
13 3d. chestnut .. .. 95·00 16·00
14 4d. mauve (1879) .. .. .. £140 8·00
x. Wmk reversed .. ..
15 6d. rose (1878) £275 £160
w. Wmk inverted .. .. .. — £250
16 1s. green .. .. £160 11·00
a. Imperf between (pair) .. ..

1882–87. *Wmk Crown CA. P* 14.
17 1 1d. blue (4.84) .. .. 38·00 13·00
18 1d. rose (1884) .. .. 20·00 12·00
a. Bisected (½d.) (on cover) .. ..
19 1d. carmine (1887) .. .. .. 50·00 16·00
20 4d. mauve (7.82) .. .. 70·00 4·75
w. Wmk inverted .. ..
21 6d. yellow (1885) £275 £180
22 1s. grey (1.87) £250 £150
18,22 Optd "Specimen" .. .. *Set of* 2 £200

(New Currency. 100 cents = 1 British Honduras (later Belize) dollar)

2 CENTS (2) TWO (3) 2 CENTS (4)

1888 (1 Jan). *Stamps of* 1872–79 (*wmk Crown CC*), *surch locally as T* 2. (*a*) *P* 12½.
23 1 2 c. on 6d. rose .. .. £150 95·00
24 3 c. on 3d. chocolate £10000 £4750

(*b*) *P* 14
25 1 2 c. on 6d. rose .. .. 85·00 75·00
a. Surch double £1400
b. Bisected (1 c.) (on cover) .. .. † £200
c. Slanting "2" with curved foot .. £950
w. Wmk inverted .. .. .. — £250
26 3 c. on 3d. chestnut .. .. .. 65·00 65·00

There are very dangerous forgeries of these surcharges.

1888. *Stamps of* 1882–87 (*wmk Crown CA*), *surch locally as T* 2, *P* 14.
27 1 2 c. on 1d. rose .. .. 8·50 18·00
a. Surch inverted £1700 £1600
b. Surch double £900 £900
c. Bisected (1 c.) (on cover) .. .. † £180
28 10 c. on 4d. mauve .. .. .. 42·00 15·00
29 20 c. on 6d. yellow .. .. .. 27·00 32·00
30 50 c. on 1s. grey £325 £450
a. Error. "5" for "50" £7500

Various settings were used for the surcharges on Nos. 23/30, the most common of which was of 36 (6 × 6) impressions. For No. 29 this setting was so applied that an albino surcharge occurs in the margin above each stamp in the first horizontal row.

The same setting was subsequently amended, by altering the "2" to "1", to surcharge the 4d. value. As this was in sheets of 30 it was only necessary to alter the values on the bottom five rows of the setting. Albino surcharges once again occur in the top margin of the sheet, but, as the type in the first horizontal row remained unaltered, these read "20 CENTS" rather than the "10 CENTS" on the actual stamps.

1888 (Mar). *No.* 30 *further surch locally with T* 3.
35 1 "TWO" on 50c. on 1s. grey (R.) .. 42·00 80·00
a. Bisected (1 c.) (on cover) .. .. † £200
b. Surch in black £8000 £7000
c. Surch double (R. + Blk.) £8000 £7000

1888 (July)–**91.** *Surch in London as T* 4. *Wmk Crown CA. P* 14.
36 1 1 c. on 1d. dull green (?12.91) .. .. 40 1·25
37 2 c. on 1d. carmine .. .. .. 30 1·50
a. Bisected (1 c.) (on cover) .. .. † 90·00
w. Wmk inverted .. ..
38 3 c. on 3d. red-brown .. .. .. 2·25 1·40
39 6 c. on 3d. ultramarine (?4.91) .. .. 2·25 10·00
40 10 c. on 4d. mauve .. .. .. 5·00 40
a. Surch double £1500
41 20 c. on 6d. yellow (2.89) .. .. 11·00 14·00
42 50 c. on 1s. grey (11.88) .. .. 27·00 70·00
36/42 .. .. *Set of* 7 42·00 85·00
36/42 Optd "Specimen" .. .. *Set of* 7 £350

6 ~~10~~ CENTS (5)

FIVE (6) 15 (7)

1891. *Stamps of* 1888–9 *surch locally. (a) With T* 5 (May).
43 1 6 c. on 10 c. on 4d. mauve (R.) .. .. 80 1·75
a. "6" and bar inverted £375 £375
b. "6" only inverted .. .. .. — £2250
44 6 c. on 10 c. on 3d. mauve (Blk.) .. 60 1·50
a. "6" and bar inverted £2250 £650
b. "6" only inverted .. .. .. † £2250

Of variety (b) only six copies of each can exist, as one of each of these errors came in the first six sheets, and the mistake was then corrected. Of variety (a) more copies exist.

Essays are known with "SIX" in place of "6", both with and without bars (*price* £75 *and* £375 *respectively*). Although not issued we mention them, as three contemporary covers franked with them are known.

(*b*) *With T* 6/7 (23 Oct)
49 1 5 c. on 3 c. on 3d. red-brown .. .. 80 1·40
a. Wide space between "I" and "V" .. 45·00 65·00
b. "FIVE" and bar double £250 £275
50 15 c. on 6 c. on 3d. ultramarine (R.) .. 9·50 22·00
a. Surch double .. .. ..

8

9

10 11

(Typo D.L.R.)

1891 (July)–**1901.** *Wmk Crown CA. P* 14.
51 8 1 c. dull green (4.95) .. .. .. 1·50 90
a. Malformed "S" .. .. .. 90·00 50·00
w. Wmk inverted .. ..
52 2 c. carmine-rose .. .. .. 1·25 10
a. Malformed "S" .. .. .. 85·00 27·00
b. Repaired "S" .. .. .. 70·00 27·00
53 3 c. brown .. .. 4·75 2·25
w. Wmk inverted .. ..
54 5 c. ultramarine (4.95) .. .. .. 12·00 40
a. Malformed "S" .. .. .. £225 50·00
55 11 5 c. grey-black & ultram/*blue* (10.00) .. 13·00 2·00
56 8 6 c. ultramarine .. .. .. 4·75 1·75
57 9 10 c. mauve and green (4.95) .. .. 8·50 8·50
58 10 10 c. dull purple and green (1901) .. 9·00 7·50
59 9 12 c. pale mauve and green .. .. 23·00 7·00
a. Violet and green .. .. 2·50 2·00
60 24 c. yellow and blue .. .. .. 5·50 14·00
a. Orange and blue .. .. .. 29·00 50·00
61 25 c. red-brown and green (4.95) .. .. 50·00 90·00
62 10 50 c. green and carmine (3.98) .. .. 21·00 50·00
63 11 $1 green and carmine (12.99) .. .. 55·00 95·00
64 $2 green and ultramarine (12.99) .. 75·00 £110
65 $5 green and black (12.99) £225 £275
51/65 .. .. *Set of* 15 £425 £600
51/65 Optd "Specimen" .. .. *Set of* 15 £300

For illustrations of Nos. 51a, 52a/b and 54a see above Gambia No. 37.

1899 (1 July). *Optd* "REVENUE" 12 *mm long.*
66 8 5 c. ultramarine .. .. .. 8·00 2·25
a. "BEVENUE" .. .. .. 80·00 85·00
b. Repaired "S" at right £170
c. Opt 11 mm long .. .. .. 17·00 7·00
67 9 10 c. mauve and green .. .. .. 3·00 11·00
a. "BEVENUE" £180 £225
b. "REVENU" £400
c. Opt 11 mm long .. .. .. 18·00 40·00
cb. "REVENU" £425 £475
68 25 c. red-brown and green .. .. 2·75 30·00
a. "BEVENUE" £120 £275
b. "REVE UE" .. .. ..
c. Opt 11 mm long .. .. .. 4·00 48·00
69 1 50 c. on 1s. grey £120 £275
a. "BEVENUE" £2750
c. Opt 11 mm long £200 £375

Two minor varieties, a small "U" and a tall, narrow "U" are found in the word "REVENUE".

The overprint setting of 60 (6 × 10) contained 43 examples of the 12 mm size and 17 of the 11 mm. The smaller size overprints occur on R.8/1, R8/3 to 6 and on all positions in Rows 9 and 10.

The "BEVENUE" error appears on R.6/4 and, it is believed, "REVE UE" comes from R.6/6. Both occur on parts of the printing only. The missing "E" developed during the overprinting and damage to this letter can be observed on at least eight positions in the setting. Examples of No. 67b are now known to exist on both sizes of the overprint.

14

15

(Typo D.L.R.)

1902 (10 Oct)–**04.** *Wmk Crown CA. P* 14.
80 14 1 c. grey-green and green (28.4.04) .. 1·25 20·00
81 2 c. purple and black/*red* (18.3.03) .. 75 25
w. Wmk inverted .. .. .. — 50·00
82 5 c. grey-black and blue/*blue* .. .. 4·50 30
w. Wmk inverted .. ..
83 15 20 c. dull and bright purple (28.4.04) .. 4·25 17·00
80/3 .. .. *Set of* 4 9·75 35·00
80/3 Optd "Specimen" .. .. *Set of* 4 55·00

1904 (Dec)–**07.** *Wmk Mult Crown CA. Ordinary paper* (1, 2 c.) *or chalk-surfaced paper (others). P* 14.
84 14 1 c. grey-green and green (8.05) .. 5·50 6·50
a. Chalk-surfaced paper (1906) .. 65 1·50
85 2 c. purple and black/*red* .. .. 2·75 20
a. Chalk-surfaced paper (1906) .. 65 10
86 5 c. grey-black and blue/*blue* (5.2.06) .. 1·75 20
87 15 10 c. dull purple & emerald-green (20.9.07) 5·00 11·00
89 25 c. dull purple and orange (20.9.07) .. 7·00 40·00
90 50 c. grey-green and carmine (20.9.07) .. 15·00 65·00
91 14 $1 grey-green and carmine (20.9.07) .. 45·00 65·00
92 $2 grey-green and blue (20.9.07) .. 80·00 £140
93 $5 grey-green and black (20.9.07) .. £180 £250
84/93 .. .. *Set of* 9 £300 £500
87/93 Optd "Specimen" .. .. *Set of* 6 £225

Examples of most values are known showing a forged Belize postmark dated "OC 23 09".

1908 (7 Dec)–**11.** *Colours changed. Wmk Mult Crown CA. Chalk-surfaced paper* (25 c.). *P* 14.
95 14 1 c. blue-green (1.7.10) .. .. 8·00 30
96 2 c. carmine .. .. 8·00 10
w. Wmk inverted .. ..
97 5 c. ultramarine (1.6.09) .. .. 1·75 10
100 15 25 c. black/*green* (14.10.11) .. .. 2·75 45·00
95/100 .. .. *Set of* 4 18·00 45·00
95/100 Optd "Specimen" .. .. *Set of* 3 70·00

16

17

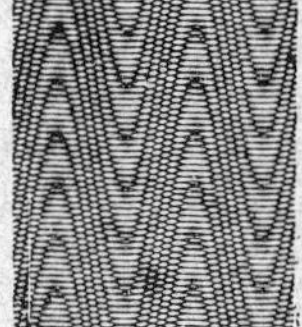
(18)

1913–21. *Wmk Mult Crown CA. Chalk-surfaced paper* (10 c. *to* $5). *P* 14.
101 16 1 c. blue-green .. .. .. 2·50 75
a. Yellow-green (13.3.17) .. .. 4·00 1·60
w. Wmk inverted .. ..
102 2 c. red .. .. 2·00 75
a. Bright scarlet (1915) .. .. 4·00 80
b. Dull scarlet (8.17) .. .. 3·00 1·25
c. Red/bluish .. .. .. 9·00 7·50
w. Wmk inverted .. ..
103 3 c. orange (16.4.17) 40 20
104 5 c. bright blue .. .. .. 2·00 45
105 17 10 c. dull purple and yellow-green .. 2·75 6·50
a. Dull purple and bright green (1917) 10·00 22·00
106 25 c. black/*green* .. .. .. 1·25 11·00
a. On blue-green, olive back (8.17) .. 3·50 10·00
b. On emerald back (1921) .. .. 1·75 25·00
107 50 c. purple and blue/*blue* .. .. 8·00 11·00
108 16 $1 black and carmine .. .. 16·00 35·00
109 $2 purple and green .. .. .. 60·00 70·00
110 $5 purple and black/*red* £190 £225
101/10 .. .. *Set of* 10 £250 £325
101/10 Optd "Specimen" .. .. *Set of* 10 £225

1915–16. *Optd with T* 18, *in violet.*
111 16 1 c. green (30.12.15) .. .. 2·25 15·00
a. Yellow-green (6.6.16) .. .. 30 10·00
112 2 c. scarlet (3.11.15) .. .. .. 2·00 50
113 5 c. bright blue (29.7.15) .. .. 30 4·50
111/13 Optd "Specimen" .. .. *Set of* 3 90·00

These stamps were shipped early in the 1914–18 war, and were thus overprinted, so that if seized by the enemy, they could be distinguished and rendered invalid.

WAR (19) WAR (20)

21

1916 (23 Aug). *No.* 111 *optd locally with T* 19.
114 16 1 c. green 10 50
a. Opt inverted £180 £200

1917. *Nos.* 101 *and* 103 *optd with T* 19.
116 16 1 c. blue-green .. .. 90 2·50
aw. Wmk inverted .. ..
ax. Wmk reversed .. ..
b. Yellow-green .. .. .. 20 1·25
118 3 c. orange .. .. 2·25 3·75
a. Opt double £300

1918. *Nos.* 101 *and* 103 *optd with T* **20**.
119 **16** 1 c. blue-green 10 25
a. *Yellow-green* 3·00 4·00
120 3 c. orange 30 85
y. Wmk inverted and reversed
119/20 Optd "Specimen" *Set of* 2 £100

(Recess D.L.R.)

1921 (28 Apr). *Peace Commemoration. Wmk Mult Crown CA (sideways). P* 14.
121 **21** 2 c. rose-red (Optd S. £45) 2·50 30
a. "C" of "CA" missing from wmk

1921 (26 Nov). *Wmk Mult Script CA. P* 14.
122 **16** 1 c. green (Optd S. £45) 2·75 9·00

1922 (4 Jan). *As T* **21** *but with words* "PEACE" *omitted. Wmk Mult Script CA (sideways). P* 14.
123 4 c. slate (Optd S. £45) 5·00 30

$2 $2 POSTAGE REVENUE BRITISH HONDURAS

22

BELIZE
RELIEF FUND
PLUS
3 CENTS

(23)

(Typo D.L.R.)

1922 (1 Aug)–**33**. *Ordinary paper* (1 *c. to* 5 *c.*) *or chalk-surfaced paper (others). P* 14 (a) *Wmk Mult Crown CA.*
124 **22** 25 c. black/*emerald* 5·50 28·00
125 $5 purple and black/*red* (1.10.24) £170 £190

(b) *Wmk Mult Script CA*

126 **22** 1 c. green (2.1.29) 2·00 5·00
127 2 c. brown (1.3.23) 75 80
128 2 c. rose-carmine (10.12.26) 1·25 80
129 3 c. orange (1933) 10·00 3·50
130 4 c. grey (1.10.29) 2·75 65
131 5 c. ultramarine 1·25 55
a. *Milky blue* (1923) 4·50 3·75
132 10 c. dull purple and sage-green (1.12.22) 1·00 30
133 25 c. black/*emerald* (1.10.24) 1·00 7·50
134 50 c. purple and blue/*blue* (1.11.23) 4·75 14·00
136 $1 black and scarlet (2.1.25) 6·50 22·00
137 $2 yellow-green and bright purple 32·00 75·00
124/37 *Set of* 13 £200 £300
124/37 Optd/Perf "Specimen" *Set of* 13 £250

1932 (2 May). *Belize Relief Fund. Surch as T* **23**. *Wmk Mult Script CA. P* 14.
138 **22** 1 c. + 1 c. green 70 6·50
139 2 c. + 2 c. rose-carmine 75 6·50
140 3 c. + 3 c. orange 85 12·00
141 4 c. + 4 c. grey (R.) 7·00 17·00
142 5 c. + 5 c. ultramarine 6·00 13·00
138/42 *Set of* 5 14·00 50·00
138/42 Perf "Specimen" *Set of* 5 £110

1935 (6 May). *Silver Jubilee. As Nos.* 91/4 *of Antigua, but ptd by B. W. & Co. P* 11 × 12.
143 3 c. ultramarine and grey-black 65 45
a. Extra flagstaff 50·00
b. Short extra flagstaff 55·00
c. Lightning conductor 48·00
d. Flagstaff on right-hand turret 85·00
144 4 c. green and indigo 1·50 2·75
a. Extra flagstaff £180
c. Lightning conductor £130
d. Flagstaff on right-hand turret £180
e. Double flagstaff £180
145 5 c. brown and deep blue 1·50 60
146 25 c. slate and purple 2·50 2·75
a. Extra flagstaff £250
b. Short extra flagstaff £225
c. Lightning conductor £200
d. Flagstaff on right-hand turret £275
e. Double flagstaff £275
143/6 *Set of* 4 5·50 6·00
143/6 Perf "Specimen" *Set of* 4 75·00
For illustrations of plate varieties see Catalogue Introduction.

1937 (12 May). *Coronation. As Nos.* 95/7 *of Antigua, but printed by D.L.R. P* 14.
147 3 c. orange 30 30
148 4 c. grey-black 70 30
149 5 c. bright blue 80 1·10
147/9 *Set of* 3 1·60 1·50
147/9 Perf "Specimen" *Set of* 3 50·00

BRITISH HONDURAS 1c

24 Maya Figures

BRITISH HONDURAS 2 CENTS

25 Chicle Tapping

(Recess B.W.)

1938 (10 Jan)–**47**. *T* **24/5** *and similar designs. Wmk Mult Script CA (sideways on horizontal stamps). P* 11½ × 11 *(horiz designs) or* 11 × 11½ *(vert designs).*
150 1 c. bright magenta and green (14.2.38) 10 1·25
151 2 c. black and scarlet (14.2.38) 20 90
a. Perf 12 (1947) 1·90 90
152 3 c. purple and brown 30 55
153 4 c. black and green 30 70
154 5 c. mauve and dull blue 75 50
155 10 c. green and reddish brown (14.2.38) 75 60
156 15 c. brown and light blue (14.2.38) 2·00 70
157 25 c. blue and green (14.2.38) 2·00 1·25
158 50 c. black and purple (14.2.38) 11·00 3·00
159 $1 scarlet and olive (28.2.38) 20·00 9·00
160 $2 deep blue and maroon (28.2.38) 23·00 16·00
161 $5 scarlet and brown (28.2.38) 23·00 23·00
150/61 *Set of* 12 75·00 50·00
150/61 Perf "Specimen" *Set of* 12 £160
Designs: *Vert*—3 c. Cohune palm; $1 Court House, Belize. $2 Mahogany felling; $5 Arms of Colony. *Horiz*—4 c. Local products; 5 c. Grapefruit; 10 c. Mahogany logs in river; 15 c. Sergeant's Cay; 25 c. Dorey; 50 c. Chicle industry.

1946 (9 Sept). *Victory. As Nos.* 110/11 *of Antigua.*
162 3 c. brown 10 10
163 5 c. blue 10 10
162/3 Perf "Specimen" *Set of* 2 50·00

1948 (1 Oct). *Royal Silver Wedding. As Nos.* 112/13 *of Antigua.*
164 4 c. green 15 50
165 $5 brown 15·00 35·00

St. George's Cay 1798–1948 BRITISH HONDURAS 3c

36 Island of St George's Cay

St. George's Cay 1798–1948 5c BRITISH HONDURAS

37 H.M.S. *Merlin*

(Recess Waterlow)

1949 (10 Jan). *150th Anniv of Battle of St. George's Cay. Wmk Mult Script CA. P* 12½.
166 **36** 1 c. ultramarine and green 10 50
167 3 c. blue and yellow-brown 10 1·00
168 4 c. olive and violet 10 50
169 **37** 5 c. brown and deep blue 70 20
170 10 c. green and red-brown 50 30
171 15 c. emerald and ultramarine 50 30
166/71 *Set of* 6 1·75 2·50

1949 (10 Oct). *75th Anniv of U.P.U. As Nos.* 114/17 *of Antigua.*
172 4 c. blue-green 40 30
173 5 c. deep blue 1·50 30
174 10 c. red-brown 50 2·00
175 25 c. blue 60 50
172/5 *Set of* 4 2·75 2·75

1951 (16 Feb). *Inauguration of B.W.I. University College. As Nos.* 118/19 *of Antigua.*
176 3 c. reddish violet and brown 45 1·00
177 10 c. green and brown 45 30

1953 (2 June). *Coronation. As No.* 120 *of Antigua.*
178 4 c. black and green 40 30

BRITISH HONDURAS SUB UMBRA FLOREO ARMS OF THE COLONY POSTAGE & REVENUE

38 Arms of British Honduras

50c

46 Maya Indian

(Recess Waterlow (until 20.6.1961), then D.L.R.)

1953 (2 Sept)–**62**. *T* **38**, **46** *and similar designs. Wmk Mult Script CA. P* 13½.
179 1 c. green and black 10 40
a. Perf 13½×13 (3.10.61) 20 1·00
180 2 c. yellow-brown and black 20 1·75
a. Perf 14 (18.9.57) 50 10
b. Perf 13½×13 (20.6.61) 10 50
181 3 c. reddish violet and bright purple 30 10
a. Perf 14 (18.9.57) 10 10
b. Perf 13½×13 (20.6.61) 4·00 8·00
ba. *Reddish lilac and pale magenta* (19.1.62) 45 70
182 4 c. brown and green 40 30
183 5 c. deep olive-green and scarlet 10 10
a. Perf 14 (15.5.57) 20 10
ab. D.L.R. ptg (3.10.61) 3·50 6·00
184 10 c. slate and bright blue 10 10
a. Perf 13½×13 (19.1.62) 10 10
185 15 c. green and violet 15 10
186 25 c. bright blue and yellow-brown 6·00 2·00
187 50 c. yellow-brown and reddish purple 6·00 1·75
a. *Pale yellow-brown & pale pur* (22.3.60) 16·00 6·00
188 $1 slate-blue and red-brown 5·50 4·50
189 $2 scarlet and grey 6·50 4·50
190 $5 purple and slate 42·00 17·00
179/90 *Set of* 12 60·00 27·00
Designs: *Horiz*—2 c. Baird's Tapir ("Mountain Cow"); 3 c. Mace and Legislative Council Chamber, 4 c. Pine industry; 5 c. Spiny Lobster; 10 c. Stanley Field Airport; 15 c. Maya frieze; 25 c. *Morpho peleides* (butterfly); $1 Nine-banded Armadillo; $2 Hawksworth Bridge. *Vert*—$5 Mountain Orchid.
Nos. 179/90 were released a day earlier by the Crown Agents in London.
Stamps from the Waterlow printings perforated 13½ × 13 or 14 have a very fine perforation tooth at the *top* of each vertical side. On the De La Rue printings this tooth is at the *bottom*.

VR BRITISH HONDURAS EIIR 1860 POST OFFICE CENTENARY 1960 2c VIEW OF BELIZE FROM FORT GEORGE, 1842

50 "Belize from Fort George, 1842" (C. J. Hullmandel)

VR BRITISH HONDURAS EIIR 1860 POST OFFICE CENTENARY 1960 10c PUBLIC SEALS 1860 AND 1960

51 Public Seals, 1860 and 1960

VR BRITISH HONDURAS EIIR 1860 POST OFFICE CENTENARY 1960 15c TAMARIND TREE, NEWTOWN BARRACKS

52 Tamarind Tree, Newtown Barracks.

(Recess B.W.)

1960 (1 July). *Post Office Centenary. W* w **12**. *P* 11½ × 11.
191 **50** 2 c. green 30 9
192 **51** 10 c. deep carmine 30 1
193 **52** 15 c. blue 35 3
191/3 *Set of* 3 85 1·2

NEW CONSTITUTION
1960

(53)

HURRICANE
HATTIE

(54)

1961 (1 Mar). *New Constitution. Nos.* 180a, 181a *and* 184/5 *optd with T* **53** *by Waterlow.*
194 2 c. yellow-brown and black 25 1
195 3 c. reddish violet and bright purple 30 1
196 10 c. slate and bright blue 30 1
197 15 c. green and violet 30 1
194/7 *Set of* 4 1·00 3

1962 (15 Jan). *Hurricane Hattie Relief Fund. Nos.* 179a, 184a, 18 *and* 187 *optd with T* **54** *by D.L.R.*
198 1 c. green and black 10 5
199 10 c. slate and bright blue 30 1
200 25 c. bright blue and yellow-brown 1·40 7
201 50 c. yellow-brown and reddish purple 50 9
198/201 *Set of* 4 2·00 2·0

BRITISH HONDURAS 1c POSTAGE REVENUE

55 Great Curassow

(Des D. R. Eckelberry. Photo Harrison)

1962 (2 Apr). *Horiz designs on T* **55**. *Multicoloured. W* w 1 *(upright). P* 14 × 14½.
202 1 c. Type **55** 1·50 7
a. Orange-yellow (knob) omitted
w. Wmk inverted
203 2 c. Red-legged Honey-creeper 2·00 1
a. Turquoise-blue (bird's head) omitted £200
204 3 c. Northern Jacana 2·00 1·7
a. Blue-green (legs) omitted £275
205 4 c. Great Kiskadee 3·75 2·2
206 5 c. Scarlet-rumped Tanager 2·00 1
w. Wmk inverted
207 10 c. Scarlet Macaw 2·75 1
a. Blue omitted £250
w. Wmk inverted † –
208 15 c. Slaty-tailed Trogon 1·50 1
w. Wmk inverted 18·00
209 25 c. Red-footed Booby 4·50 3
w. Wmk inverted
210 50 c. Keel-billed Toucan 6·00 3
a. Pale blue (claw and beak) omitted
211 $1 Magnificent Frigate Bird 9·00 7
212 $2 Rufous-tailed Jacamar 13·00 3·0
a. *Shade** 38·00 14·0
w. Wmk inverted 60·00
213 $5 Montezuma Oropendola 25·00 14·0
202/13 *Set of* 12 60·00 21·0
*On No. 212*a*, the bird is myrtle-green and red-brown instead of yellow-green and orange-brown.
See also Nos. 239/45.

1963 (4 June). *Freedom from Hunger. As No.* 146 *of Antigua.*
214 22 c. bluish green 30 1

1963 (2 Sept). *Red Cross Centenary. As Nos.* 147/8 *of Antigua.*
215 4 c. red and black 20 4
216 22 c. red and blue 40 8

SELF-GOVERNMENT

SELF GOVERNMENT
1964

(56)

DEDICATION OF SITE
NEW CAPITAL
9th OCTOBER 1965

(57)

1964. *New Constitution. Nos.* 202, 204/5, 207 *and* 209 *optd with T* **56**.
217 1 c. Type **55** (20.4) 10 2
a. Opt inverted £225
b. Orange-yellow (knob) omitted 80·00
218 3 c. Northern Jacana (20.4) 35 2
219 4 c. Great Kiskadee (3.2) 35 2
220 10 c. Scarlet Macaw (20.4) 35 1
221 25 c. Red-footed Booby (3.2) 55 3
217/21 *Set of* 5 1·50 8

65 (17 May). *I.T.U. Centenary. As Nos. 166/7 of Antigua.*
2 2 c. orange-red and light green 10 10
3 50 c. yellow and light purple 35 25

65 (25 Oct). *International Co-operation Year. As Nos. 168/9 of Antigua.*
4 1 c. reddish purple and turquoise-green .. 10 15
5 22 c. deep bluish green and lavender 20 15

66 (24 Jan). *Churchill Commemoration. As Nos. 170/3 of Antigua.*
6 1 c. new blue 10 10
7 4 c. deep green 15 10
8 22 c. brown 40 10
9 25 c. bluish violet 50 45
6/9 .. .. *Set of* 4 95 60

66 (1 July). *Dedication of New Capital Site. As Nos. 202, 204/5, 207 and 209, but wmk sideways*, optd with T* **57** *by Harrison.*
0 1 c. Type **55** 10 30
a. Orange-yellow (knob) omitted .. 95·00
w. Wmk Crown to right of CA 70
1 3 c. Northern Jacana 35 30
2 4 c. Great Kiskadee 35 30
3 10 c. Scarlet Macaw 35 10
4 25 c. Red-footed Booby 55 35
0/4 .. .. *Set of* 5 1·50 1·25
*The normal sideways watermark shows Crown to left of CA, *s seen from the back of the stamp.*

58 Citrus Grove

(Des V. Whiteley. Photo Harrison)

966 (1 Oct). *Stamp Centenary. T* **58** *and similar horiz designs. Multicoloured. W w* **12**. *P* 14 × 14½.
35 5 c. Type **58** 10 10
36 10 c. Half Moon Cay 10 10
37 22 c. Hidden Valley Falls 10 10
38 25 c. Maya Ruins, Xunantunich 15 30
35/8 .. .. *Set of* 4 30 50

967. *As Nos. 202, etc, but W w* **12** *(sideways).*
39 1 c. Type **55** (16.2) 10 30
40 2 c. Red-legged Honey-creeper (28.11) .. 30 50
41 4 c. Great Kiskadee (16.2) .. .. .. 1·75 85
42 5 c. Scarlet-rumped Tanager (16.2) 40 10
43 10 c. Scarlet Macaw (28.11) 50 10
44 15 c. Slaty-tailed Trogon (28.11) 60 10
45 50 c. Keel-billed Toucan (16.2) .. .. 3·00 3·50
39/45 .. .. *Set of* 7 6·00 4·75
The 15 c. value exists with PVA gum as well as gum arabic.

59 Sailfish

60 *Schomburgkia tibicinis*

(Des R. Granger Barrett. Photo Harrison)

1967 (1 Dec). *International Tourist Year. T* **59** *and similar horiz designs. W w* **12**. *P* 12½.
246 5 c. deep violet-blue, black and light yellow 15 20
247 10 c. brown, black and orange-red 15 10
248 22 c. yellow-orange, black and bright green .. 30 10
249 25 c. lt greenish blue, black & greenish yellow 30 45
246/9 .. .. *Set of* 4 80 75
Designs:—10 c. Red Brocket; 22 c. Jaguar; 25 c. Atlantic Tarpon.

(Des Sylvia Goaman. Photo Harrison)

1968 (16 Apr). *20th Anniv of Economic Commission for Latin America. T* **60** *and similar vert designs showing orchids. Multicoloured. W w* **12** *(sideways). P* 14½×14.
250 5 c. Type **60** 20 15
251 10 c. *Maxillaria tenuifolia* 25 10
252 22 c. *Bletia purpurea* 30 10
253 25 c. *Sobralia macrantha* 40 20
250/3 .. .. *Set of* 4 1·10 40

61 Monument to Belizean Patriots

62 Monument at Site of New Capital

(Des G. Vasarhelyi. Litho B.W.)

1968 (15 July). *Human Rights Year. W w* **12**. *P* 13½.
254 **61** 22 c. multicoloured 15 10
255 **62** 50 c. multicoloured 15 20

63 Spotted Jewfish

(Des J. W. Litho D.L.R.)

1968 (15 Oct). *Wildlife. Horiz designs as T* **63**. *Multicoloured. No wmk. P* 13 × 12½.
256 1 c. Type **63** 20 10
257 2 c. White-lipped Peccary ("Warree") .. 10 10
258 3 c. Misty Grouper 20 10
259 4 c. Collared Anteater 10 60
260 5 c. Bonefish 10 60
261 10 c. Paca ("Gibnut") 15 10
262 15 c. Dolphin 40 20
263 25 c. Kinkajou ("Night Walker") 30 20
264 50 c. Mutton Snapper .. .. 70 1·25
265 $1 Tayra ("Bush Dog") .. .. .. 2·50 1·25
266 $2 Great Barracuda .. .. 2·50 2·00
267 $5 Puma .. .. 13·00 6·50
256/67 .. .. *Set of* 12 18·00 11·50
See also Nos. 276/8 and 338/40

64 *Rhyncholaelia digbyana*

65 Ziricote Tree

(Des Sylvia Goaman. Photo Harrison)

1969 (9 Apr). *Orchids of Belize (1st series). T* **64** *and similar vert designs. Multicoloured. W w* **12** *(sideways). P* 14½ × 14.
268 5 c. Type **64** 50 20
269 10 c. *Cattleya bowringiana* 55 15
270 22 c. *Lycaste cochleatum* 85 15
271 25 c. *Coryanthes speciosum* .. .. .. 1·10 1·10
268/71 .. .. *Set of* 4 2·75 1·40
See also Nos. 287/90.

(Des V. Whiteley. Litho D.L.R.)

1969 (1 Sept). *Indigenous Hardwoods (1st series). T* **65** *and similar vert designs. Multicoloured. W w* **12**. *P* 14.
272 5 c. Type **65** 10 20
273 10 c. Rosewood 10 10
274 22 c. Mayflower 20 10
275 25 c. Mahogany 20 45
272/5 .. .. *Set of* 4 45 70
See also Nos. 291/4, 315/18 and 333/7.

1969–72. *As Nos. 257/8, 261, 267 and new value and design (½ c.), but W w* **12** *(sideways*).*
276 ½ c. Mozambique Mouthbrooder ("Crana") (ultramarine background) (1.9.69) .. 10 10
277 ½ c. Mozambique Mouthbrooder ("Crana") (yellow-olive background) (1.2.71) .. 1·75 1·00
a. Black (inscr and value) omitted .. £200
bw. Wmk Crown to right of CA .. 2·50
277*c* 2 c. White-lipped Peccary (5.5.72) .. 3·25 3·75
277*d* 3 c. Misty Grouper (5.5.72) .. .. 3·25 3·75
277*e* 10 c. Paca (5.5.72) .. .. .. 3·25 3·75
278 $5 Puma (12.5.70) .. .. .. 6·50 12·00
276/8 .. .. *Set of* 6 16·00 22·00
*The normal sideways watermark shows Crown to left of CA, *as seen from the back of the stamp.*

66 "The Virgin and Child" (Bellini

POPULATION
CENSUS 1970

(68

(Des adapted by G. Drummond. Litho Format)

1969 (1 Nov). *Christmas. Paintings. T* **66** *and similar vert design. Multicoloured. W w* **12**. *P* 14× 14½.
279 5 c. Type **66** 10 10
280 15 c. Type **66** 10 10
281 22 c. "The Adoration of the Kings" (Veronese) 10 10
282 25 c. As 22 c. 10 20
279/82 .. .. *Set of* 4 30 30
Although released by the Crown Agents on 1 October this issue was not put on sale locally until 1 November.

1970 (2 Feb). *Population Census. As Nos. 260 and 262/3 but W w* **12** *(sideways) and No. 277e optd with T* **68**.
283 5 c. Bonefish 10 10
284 10 c. Paca 15 10
285 15 c. Dolphin 20 10
286 25 c. Kinkajou 20 15
283/6 .. .. *Set of* 4 55 30

(Des G. Drummond. Litho Format)

1970 (2 Apr). *Orchids of Belize (2nd series). As T* **64**. *Multicoloured. W w* **12**. *P* 14.
287 5 c. Black Orchid 35 15
288 15 c. White Butterfly Orchid 50 10
289 22 c. Swan Orchid 70 10
290 25 c. Butterfly Orchid 70 40
287/90 .. .. *Set of* 4 2·00 60

69 Santa Maria

70 "The Nativity" (A. Hughes).

(Des Jennifer Toombs, Litho Questa)

1970 (7 Sept). *Indigenous Hardwoods (2nd series). T* **69** *and similar vert designs. Multicoloured. W w* **12** *(sideways). P* 14 × 14½.
291 5 c. Type **69** 25 10
292 15 c. Nargusta 35 10
293 22 c. Cedar 40 10
294 25 c. Sapodilla 40 35
291/4 .. .. *Set of* 4 1·25 55

(Des J. Cooter Litho J.W.)

1970 (7 Nov*). *Christmas. T* **70** *and similar vert design. Multicoloured. W w* **12**. *P* 14.
295 ½ c. Type **70** 10 10
296 5 c. "The Mystic Nativity" (Botticelli) .. 10 10
297 10 c. Type **70** 10 10
298 15 c. As 5 c 20 10
299 22 c. Type **70** 25 10
300 50 c. As 5 c. 40 60
295/300 .. .. *Set of* 6 85 70
*These stamps were released by the Crown Agents in London on 2 November.

71 Legislative Assembly House

(Des. G. Drummond. Litho Enschedé)

1971 (30 Jan). *Establishment of New Capital, Belmopan. T* **71** *and similar horiz designs. Multicoloured. W w* **12** *upright* (5 c., 10 c.) *or sideways (others). P* 13 × 13½.
301 5 c. Old Capital, Belize 10 10
302 10 c. Government Plaza 10 10
303 15 c. Type **71** 10 10
304 22 c. Magistrates' Court 15 10
305 25 c. Police H.Q. 15 15
306 50 c. New G.P.O. 25 40
301/6 .. .. *Set of* 6 70 75
The 5 c. and 10 c. are larger, 60 × 22 mm.

72 *Tabebuia chrysantha*

(Des Sylvia Goaman. Litho Questa)

1971 (27 Mar). *Easter. T* **72** *and similar horiz designs showing flowers. Multicoloured. W w* **12** *(sideways). P* 14.
307 ½ c. Type **72** 10 10
308 5 c. *Hymenocallis littoralis* 10 10
309 10 c. *Hippeastrum equestre* 10 10
310 15 c. Type **72** 20 10
311 22 c. As 5 c. 20 10
312 25 c. As 10 c. 20 30
307/12 .. .. *Set of* 6 65 50

RACIAL EQUALITY
YEAR - 1971

(73)

74 Tubroos

1971 (14 June). *Racial Equality Year. As No.* 264, *but W* w **12** *(sideways*) and No. 277e optd with T* **73**.

313	10 c. Paca ..	25	10
314	50 c. Mutton Snapper ..	55	20
	w. Wmk Crown to left of CA ..	6·50	

*The normal sideways watermark shows Crown to left of CA on the 10 c. and to the right on the 50 c., *both as seen from the back of the stamp.*

(Des Jennifer Toombs, Litho Questa)

1971 (16 Aug). *Indigenous Hardwoods (3rd series). T* **74** *and similar vert designs. Multicoloured. W* w **12**. *P* 13½.

315	5 c. Type **74** ..	50	10
	w. Wmk inverted ..	2·00	
316	15 c. Yemeri ..	70	30
317	26 c. Billywebb ..	95	35
318	50 c. Logwood ..	1·75	3·25
315/18	.. *Set of* 4	3·50	3·50
MS319	96×171 mm. Nos. 315/18 ..	3·50	6·50
	a. Silver (Queen's head) omitted ..	£1600	

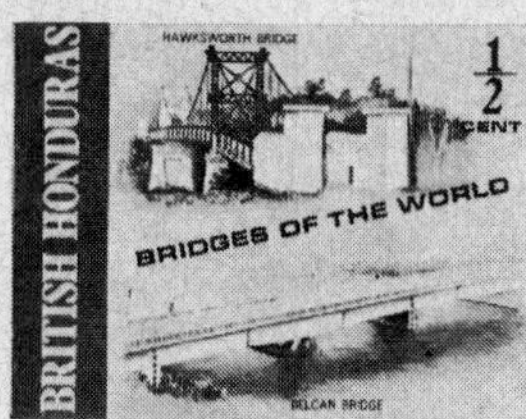

75 Hawksworth and Belcan Bridges

(Des and litho J.W.)

1971 (23 Sept). *Bridges of the World. T* **75** *and similar horiz designs. Multicoloured. W* w **12** *(sideways). P* 13½.

320	½ c. Type **75** ..	10	10
321	5 c. Narrows Bridge, N.Y. and Quebec Bridge	20	10
322	26 c. London Bridge (1871) and reconstructed, Arizona (1971) ..	50	10
323	50 c. Belize Mexican Bridge and Swing Bridge	70	90
320/3	.. *Set of* 4	1·25	1·10

76 *Petrae volubis* **77** Seated Figure

(Des G. Drummond. Litho Format)

1972 (28 Feb). *Easter. T* **76** *and similar vert designs showing wild flowers. Multicoloured. W* w **12**. *P* 14½.

324	6 c. Type **76** ..	15	10
325	15 c. Yemeri ..	35	30
326	26 c. Mayflower ..	50	45
327	50 c. Tiger's Claw ..	80	1·40
324/7	.. *Set of* 4	1·60	2·00

(Des Jennifer Toombs. Litho Questa)

1972 (22 May). *Mayan Artefacts. T* **77** *and similar multicoloured designs. W* w **12** *(sideways except 16 c.). P* 13½ × 13 *(16 c.) or* 13 × 13½ *(others).*

328	3 c. Type **77** ..	15	10
329	6 c. Priest in "dancing" pose ..	20	10
330	16 c. Sun God's head *(horiz)* ..	35	15
331	26 c. Priest and Sun God ..	50	20
332	50 c. Full-front figure ..	1·00	2·75
328/32	.. *Set of* 5	2·00	3·00

Nos. 328/32 are inscribed on the reverse with information about the artefacts depicted.

78 Banak **79** Orchids of Belize

(Des Jennifer Toombs. Litho Questa)

1972 (21 Aug). *Indigenous Hardwoods (4th series). T* **78** *and similar vert designs. Multicoloured. W* w **12** *(sideways). P* 14½.

333	3 c. Type **78** ..	20	10
334	5 c. Quamwood ..	20	10
335	16 c. Waika Chewstick ..	55	15
336	26 c. Mamee-Apple ..	75	25
337	50 c. My Lady ..	1·60	3·25
333/7	.. *Set of* 5	3·00	3·50

1972 (17 Nov). *As Nos.* 258 *and* 260/1, *but W* w **12** *(upright).*

338	3 c. Misty Grouper ..	1·50	2·00
339	5 c. Bonefish ..	1·50	2·00
340	10 c. Paca ..	1·50	2·00
	w. Wmk inverted ..	6·00	
338/40	.. *Set of* 3	4·00	5·50

(Des (from photograph by D. Groves) and photo Harrison)

1972 (20 Nov). *Royal Silver Wedding. Multicoloured; background colour given. W* w **12**. *P* 14 × 14½.

341 **79**	26 c. deep myrtle-green ..	25	10
	w. Wmk inverted ..	45·00	
342	50 c. bright bluish violet ..	40	55
	w. Wmk inverted ..	35·00	

80 Baron Bliss Day

(Des J.W. Litho Questa)

1973 (9 Mar). *Festivals of Belize. T* **80** *and similar horiz designs. Multicoloured. W* w **12**. *P* 14½ × 14.

343	3 c. Type **80** ..	15	10
344	10 c. Labour Day ..	15	10
345	26 c. Carib Settlement Day ..	30	15
346	50 c. Pan American Day ..	50	70
343/6	.. *Set of* 4	1·00	85

BELIZE

British Honduras was renamed Belize on 1 June 1973.

☼BELIZE☼

(81)

1973 (11 June*). *Designs as Nos.* 256/7, 259, 262/7 *and* 277, *but W* w **12** *(upright), and Nos.* 338/40 *optd with T* **81** *in black on silver by D.L.R. P* 13×12½.

347	½ c. Mozambique Mouthbrooder ("Crana")	10	20
348	1 c. Spotted Jewfish ..	10	20
349	2 c. White-lipped Peccary ("Waree") ..	10	20
350	3 c. Misty Grouper ..	10	10
	a. Silver background to opt omitted ..	†	—
351	4 c. Collared Anteater ..	10	20
352	5 c. Bonefish ..	10	20
353	10 c. Paca ("Gibnut") ..	15	15
	a. Black (value etc.) omitted ..	£200	
354	15 c. Dolphin ..	20	20
355	25 c. Kinkajou ("Night Walker") ..	35	35
356	50 c. Mutton Snapper ..	65	75
357	$1 Tayra ("Bush Dog") ..	1·10	1·50
358	$2 Great Barracuda ..	2·00	2·75
359	$5 Puma ..	2·50	4·75
347/59	.. *Set of* 13	6·50	10·50

*This is the local date of issue: the Crown Agents released the stamps on 1 June.

No. 350a shows the silver background to the overprint omitted. Traces of the adhesive used to apply the silver are visible.

1973 (14 Nov). *Royal Wedding. As Nos.* 165/6 *of Anguilla. Centre multicoloured. W* w **12** *(sideways). P* 13½.

360	26 c. light turquoise-blue ..	15	10
361	50 c. ochre ..	15	20

82 Mozambique Mouthbrooder

1974 (1 Jan). *Designs as Nos.* 256/67 *and* 277, *but inscr* "BELIZE" *as in T* **82**. *W* w **12**. *P* 13½.

362	½ c. Type **82** ..	10	20
363	1 c. Spotted Jewfish ..	10	20
364	2 c. White-lipped Peccary ("Waree") ..	10	20
365	3 c. Misty Grouper ..	10	10
366	4 c. Collared Anteater ..	10	20
367	5 c. Bonefish ..	10	20
368	10 c. Paca ("Gibnut") ..	15	15
369	15 c. Dolphin ..	20	20
370	25 c. Kinkajou ("Night Walker") ..	35	35
371	50 c. Mutton Snapper ..	60	70
372	$1 Tayra ("Bush Dog") ..	1·00	1·50
373	$2 Great Barracuda ..	1·50	2·25
374	$5 Puma ..	3·50	5·50
362/74	.. *Set of* 13	7·00	10·50

83 Deer

(Des Mrs. Hosek; adapted PAD Studio, Litho Questa)

1974 (1 May). *Mayan Artefacts (1st series). T* **83** *and similar horiz designs showing pottery motifs. Multicoloured. W* w **12**. *P* 14½.

375	3 c. Type **83** ..	10	10
376	6 c. Jaguar deity ..	10	10
377	16 c. Sea monster ..	15	10
378	26 c. Cormorant ..	25	10
379	50 c. Scarlet macaw ..	40	40
375/9	.. *Set of* 5	85	65

See also Nos. 398/402.

84 *Parides arcas*

(Des J. Cooter from the collection of P.T. Hill. Litho Harrison

1974 (2 Sept)–**76**. *Butterflies. Horiz designs as T* 8 *Multicoloured. W* w **12** *(sideways*). P* 14 (½, 1, 2, 3, 4, 5, 1 26 *c.) or* 14×14½ *(others).*

380	½ c. Type **84** ..	90	2·5
381	1 c. *Evenus regalis* ..	90	1·
382	2 c. *Colobura dirce* ..	1·25	2·0
383	3 c. *Catonephele numilia* ..	1·40	2·0
384	4 c. *Battus belus* ..	1·75	2·5
385	5 c. *Callicore patelina* ..	2·00	2·5
386	10 c. *Diaethria astala* ..	1·50	7
387	15 c. *Nessaea aglaura* ..	4·00	3·0
	w. Wmk Crown to right of CA ..	4·00	
388	16 c. *Prepona pseudojoiceyi* ..	4·00	5·0
389	25 c. *Papilio thoas* ..	4·00	8
	w. Wmk Crown to right of CA ..	42·00	
390	26 c. *Hamadryas arethusa* ..	2·50	4·2
391	50 c. *Panthiades bathildis* ..	2·75	6
392	$1 *Caligo uranus* ..	6·50	4·0
	w. Wmk Crown to right of CA ..	42·00	
393	$2 *Heliconius sapho* ..	4·00	1·2
394	$5 *Eurytides philolaus* ..	4·75	4·0
395	$10 *Philaethria dido* (2.1.75) ..	10·00	4·0
	w. Wmk Crown to left of CA (2.8.76) ..	12·00	9·0
380/95	.. *Set of* 16	48·00	35·0

*The normal sideways watermark shows Crown to right of C on the 16 c. and $10 and to left on the others, *as seen from th back of the stamp.*

See also Nos. 403/13 and 426/33.

85 Churchill when Prime Minister, and Coronation Scene **86** The Actun Balam Vase

(Des J.W. Litho Questa)

1974 (30 Nov). *Birth Centenary of Sir Winston Churchill. T* 8 *and similar horiz design. Multicoloured. W* w **14** *(sideways). P* 1

396	50 c. Type **85** ..	20	2
397	$1 Churchill in stetson, and Williamsburg Liberty Bell ..	30	3

(Des Mrs. Hosek; adapted P. Powell. Litho Questa)

1975 (2 June). *Mayan Artefacts (2nd series). T* **86** *and similar ve designs showing decorated vessels. Multicoloured. W* w **14**. *P* 14

398	3 c. Type **86** ..	10	1
399	6 c. Seated figure ..	10	1
400	16 c. Costumed priest ..	25	1
401	26 c. Head with headdress ..	35	2
402	50 c. Layman and priest ..	45	1·4
398/402	.. *Set of* 5	1·10	1·7

1975–78. *As Nos.* 380, 382/7 *and* 389 *and new value* (35 *c.*), *b* W w **14** *(sideways on* ½, 2, 3, 4, 5, 10 *and* 35 *c.). P* 14 × 14½ (1 25 *c.) or* 14 *(others).*

403	½ c. Type **84** (11.6.75) ..	2·00	7·5
405	2 c. *Colobura dirce* (17.5.77) ..	50	
406	3 c. *Catonephele numulia* (17.5.77) ..	1·25	
407	4 c. *Battus belus* (7.3.77) ..	3·00	
408	5 c. *Callicore patelina* (11.2.77) ..	3·25	
409	10 c. *Diaethria astala* (11.2.77) ..	3·25	
410	15 c. *Nessaea aglaura* (17.5.77) ..	75	
412	25 c. *Papilio thoas* (27.1.78) ..	2·75	4
413	35 c. Type **84** (25.7.77) ..	11·00	4·5
403/13	.. *Set of* 9	25·00	14·0

1975–77. *As Nos.* 387, 389, 391 *and* 394 *but W* w **12** *upright.*

426	15 c. *Nessaea aglaura* (20.10.75) ..	1·00	2·2
428	25 c. *Papilio thoas* (7.3.77) ..	5·00	1·7
429	50 c. *Panthiades bathildis* (7.3.77) ..	5·50	1·7
433	$5 *Eurytides philolaus* (20.10.75) ..	5·50	9·
	w. Wmk inverted ..	38·00	
426/33	.. *Set of* 4	15·00	13·5

87 Musicians

(Des PAD Studio. Litho Harrison)

1975 (17 Nov). *Christmas. T* **87** *and similar multicoloure designs. W* w **12** *(upright on 6 c. 26 c.) or sideways (others P* 14 × 14½ *(horiz) or* 14½ × 14 *(vert).*

435	6 c. Type **87** ..	10	1
436	26 c. Children and "crib" ..	20	1
	w. Wmk inverted ..	5·00	3·0
437	50 c. Dancer and drummers *(vert)* ..	30	4
	a. Imperf (pair) ..	£100	
438	$1 Family and map *(vert)* ..	55	1·4
435/8	.. *Set of* 4	1·00	1·7

88 William Wrigley Jr. and Chicle Tapping

(Des PAD Studio. Litho Questa)

76 (29 Mar). *Bicentenary of American Revolution. T* **88** *and similar horiz designs. Multicoloured.* W w **14** *(sideways). P* 14.
9 10 c. Type **88** 10 10
0 35 c. Charles Lindbergh and *Spirit of St. Louis* 20 40
1 $1 J. L. Stephens (archaeologist) . . . . 50 1·00
9/41 . . . . *Set of* 3 70 1·40

89 Cycling

(Des J.W. Litho Walsall)

76 (17 July). *Olympic Games. Montreal. T* **89** *and similar horiz designs. Multicoloured.* W w **14** *(sideways). P* 14.
2 35 c. Type **89** 15 10
3 45 c. Running 20 15
4 $1 Shooting 35 80
2/4 . . . . *Set of* 3 65 95

20c **5c**

(90) **(91)**

976 (30 Aug). *No.* 390 *surch with T* **90** *by Harrison.*
45 20 c. on 26 c. *Hamadryas arethusa* . . . . 1·50 80

976 (18 Oct). *West Indian Victory in World Cricket Cup. As Nos.* 559/60 *of Barbados.*
46 35 c. Map of the Caribbean 50 50
47 $1 The Prudential Cup . . . . . . 1·10 2·00

976 (2 Dec). *No.* 426 *surch with T* **91** *by the Govt Printery, Belize.*
48 5 c. on 15 c. *Nessaea aglaura*. . . . . . 1·50 2·25

92 Queen and Bishops

(Des R. Granger Barrett. Litho Enschedé)

1977 (7 Feb). *Silver Jubilee. T* **92** *and similar horiz designs. Multicoloured.* W w **14** *(sideways*). P* 13×13½.
449 10 c. Royal Visit, 1975 . . . . . . 10 10
450 35 c. Queen and Rose Window 15 15
w. Wmk Crown to right of CA . . . . 80·00
451 $2 Type **92** 45 90
w. Wmk Crown to right of CA . . . . 42·00
449/51 . . . . *Set of* 3 60 1·00
*The normal sideways watermark shows Crown to left of CA, *as seen from the back of the stamp.*

93 Red-capped Manakin

94 Laboratory Workers

(Des and litho J.W.)

1977 (3 Sept). *Birds (1st series). T* **93** *and similar vert designs. Multicoloured.* W w **14**. *P* 14.
452 8 c. Type **93** 75 40
453 10 c. Hooded Oriole 90 30
454 25 c. Blue-crowned Motmot . . . . . . 1·25 55
455 35 c. Slaty-breasted Tinamou . . . . 1·50 75
456 45 c. Ocellated Turkey . . . . . . 1·75 1·25
457 $1 White Hawk . . . . 3·00 5·00
452/7 . . . . *Set of* 6 8·25 7·50
MS458 110 × 133 mm. Nos. 452/7. . . . 8·25 11·00
See also Nos. 467/73, 488/94 and 561/7.

(Des G. Hutchins. Litho J.W.)

1977 (2 Dec). *75th Anniv of Pan-American Health Organisation. T* **94** *and similar horiz design. Multicoloured.* W w **14** *(sideways). P* 13½.
459 35 c. Type **94** 20 20
460 $1 Mobile medical unit 40 65
MS461 126 × 95 mm. Nos. 459/60. P 13 . . . . 85 1·25

BELIZE DEFENCE FORCE
1ST JANUARY 1978
(95)

1978 (15 Feb). *Establishment of Belize Defence Force. Nos.* 409 *and* 413 *optd with T* **95** *in gold by Govt Printery, Belize.*
462 10 c. *Diaethria astala* 75 75
463 35 c. *Parides arcas* . . . . . . 1·50 1·75

96 White Lion of Mortimer

97 *Russelia sarmentosa*

(Des. C. Abbott. Litho Questa)

1978 (21 Apr). *25th Anniv of Coronation (1st issue). T* **96** *and similar vert designs. P* 15.
464 75 c. bistre, carmine and silver 20 30
a. Sheetlet. Nos. 464/6 × 2. . . . . . 1·10
465 75 c. multicoloured 20 30
466 75 c. bistre, carmine and silver 20 30
464/6 . . . . *Set of* 3 55 80
Designs:—No. 464, Type **96**; No. 465, Queen Elizabeth II; No 466, Jaguar (Maya god of Day and Night).
Nos. 464/6 were printed together in small sheets of 6, containing two *se-tenant* strips of 3 with horizontal gutter margin between.
See also Nos. 495/503.

(Des. J.W. Litho Questa)

1978 (31 July). *Birds (2nd series). Vert designs as T* **93**. *Multicoloured.* W w **14**. *P* 14½.
467 10 c. White-capped Parrot 55 30
468 25 c. Crimson-collared Tanager . . . . 1·00 45
469 35 c. Citreoline Trogon . . . . . . 1·40 55
470 45 c. American Finfoot . . . . . . 1·60 1·75
471 50 c. Muscovy Duck . . . . . . 1·75 2·50
472 $1 King Vulture . . . . 2·50 5·00
467/72 . . . . *Set of* 6 8·00 9·50
MS473 111 × 133 mm. Nos. 467/72 . . . . 8·00 10·00

(Des J. Cooter. Litho Questa)

1978 (16 Oct). *Christmas. Wild Flowers and Ferns. T* **97** *and similar vert designs. Multicoloured.* W w **14**. *P* 14 × 13½.
474 10 c. Type **97** 15 10
475 15 c. *Lygodium polymorphum* 20 15
476 35 c. *Heliconia aurantiaca* 25 20
477 45 c. *Adiantum tetraphyllum* 30 40
478 50 c. *Angelonia ciliaris* 30 50
479 $1 *Thelypteris obliterata* . . . . 50 1·00
474/79 . . . . *Set of* 6 1·50 2·00

98 Fairchild Monoplane of Internal Airmail Service, 1937

(Des D. Bowen. Litho Questa)

1979 (15 Jan). *Centenary of U.P.U. Membership. T* **98** *and similar horiz designs. Multicoloured.* W w **14** *(sideways). P* 13½ × 14.
480 5 c. Type **98** 25 20
481 10 c. *Heron H* (mail boat), 1949 . . . . 25 10
482 35 c. Internal mail service, 1920 (canoe) . . 30 20
483 45 c. Stann Creek Railway mail, 1910 . . 60 55
484 50 c. Mounted mail courier, 1882 . . . . 60 60
485 $2 *Eagle* (mail boat), 1856 . . . . 1·10 2·25
480/5 . . . . *Set of* 6 2·75 3·50

15¢

15c

(99) **(100)**

1979. *No.* 413 *surch. (a) By typography, locally, with T* **99**.
486 15 c. on 35 c. Type **84** (March) . . . . 42·00

(b) By lithography, in Great Britain, with T **100**
487 15 c. on 35 c. Type **84** (June) . . . . 1·50 1·75
w. Wmk Crown to right of CA . . . . 22·00
*The normal sideways watermark shows Crown to left of CA, *as seen from the back of the stamp.*

(Des J.W. Litho Questa)

1979 (16 Apr). *Birds (3rd series). Vert designs as T* **93**. *Multicoloured. P* 14.
488 10 c. Boat-billed Heron 50 20
489 25 c. Grey-necked Wood Rail 75 30
490 35 c. Lineated Woodpecker 85 55
491 45 c. Blue-grey Tanager 90 70
492 50 c. Laughing Falcon. . . . . 90 1·25
493 $1 Long-tailed Hermit . . . . . . 1·40 3·00
488/93 . . . . *Set of* 6 4·75 5·50
MS494 113 × 136 mm. Nos. 488/93 . . . . 4·75 6·00

PRINTER. The following issues to No. 742 were printed in lithography by Lito Nacional, Porto, Portugal.

AVAILABILITY. Certain values of some issues to No. 742 were only available in restricted quantities in Belize.

101 Paslow Building, Belize G.P.O.

(Des A. Medina)

1979 (31 May). *25th Anniv of Coronation (2nd issue). T* **101** *and similar multicoloured designs. P* 14.
495 25 c. Type **101** 80 10
496 50 c. Houses of Parliament . . . . . . 1·25 10
497 75 c. Coronation State Coach . . . . . . 1·75 15
498 $1 Queen on horseback *(vert)* . . . . 2·25 15
499 $2 Prince of Wales *(vert)* . . . . . . 2·75 25
500 $3 Queen and Duke of Edinburgh *(vert)* . . 2·75 25
501 $4 Portrait of Queen *(vert)* . . . . . . 3·00 30
502 $5 St. Edward's Crown *(vert)* . . . . 3·50 30
495/502 . . . . *Set of* 8 16·00 1·40
MS503 Two sheets, both 126 × 95 mm: (a) $5 Princess Anne on horseback at Montreal Olympics *(vert)*, $10 Queen at Montreal Olympics *(vert)*; (b) $15 As Type **101** . . . . . . *Set of* 2 *sheets* 18·00
Nos. 495/502 also exist imperforate from a restricted printing *(price for set of* 8 *£15 mint).*

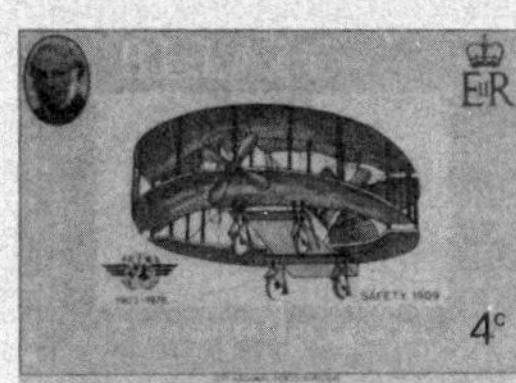

102 Mortimer and Vaughan "Safety" Airplane, 1910

(Des A. Medina)

1979 (30 July). *Death Centenary of Sir Rowland Hill and 60th Anniv of I.C.A.O. (International Civil Aviation Organization, previously International Commission for Air Navigation). T* **102** *and similar horiz designs. Multicoloured. P* 14.
504 4 c. Type **102** 40 10
505 25 c. Boeing 720 . . . . 1·25 20
506 50 c. Concorde . . . . 3·00 30
507 75 c. Handley Page H.P.18 W8b (1922) . . 1·75 30
508 $1 Avro Type F (1912) . . . . . . 1·75 30
509 $1.50, Samuel Cody's biplane (1910) . . 2·50 30
510 $2 A. V. Roe Triplane I (1909) . . . . 2·50 40
511 $3 Santos Dumont's biplane *14 bis* . . 2·50 45
512 $4 Wright Type A . . . . 3·00 65
504/12 . . . . *Set of* 9 16·00 2·75
MS513 Two sheets: (a) 115×95 mm. $5 Dunne D-5 (1910), $5 G.B. 1969 Concorde stamp; (b) 130×95 mm. $10 Boeing 720 *(different)* *Set of* 2 *sheets* 20·00
Nos. 504/12 also exist imperforate from a restricted printing *(price for set of* 9 *£55 mint).*

103 Handball

104 Olympic torch

(Des A. Medina)

1979 (10 Oct). *Olympic Games, Moscow* (1980). *T* **103** *and similar vert designs. Multicoloured. P* 14.

514 25 c. Type **103** 45 10
515 50 c. Weightlifting 65 10
516 75 c. Athletics 90 15
517 $1 Football .. .. 1·25 20
518 $2 Yachting .. .. 1·75 25
519 $3 Swimming .. .. 2·00 30
520 $4 Boxing .. .. 2·50 30
521 $5 Cycling .. .. 4·00 50
514/21 .. .. *Set of* 8 12·00 1·60
MS522 Two sheets: (a) 126 × 92 mm. $5 Athletics (*different*), $10 Boxing (*different*); (b) 92 × 126 mm. $15 As $5 .. .. *Set of* 2 *sheets* 16·00

Nos. 514/21 also exist imperforate from a restricted printing (*price for set of* 8 £55 *mint*).

(Des A. Medina)

1979 (4 Dec). *Winter Olympic Games, Lake Placid* (1980). *T* **104** *and similar vert designs. Multicoloured. P* 14.

523 25 c. Type **104** 20 10
524 50 c. Giant slalom 45 15
525 75 c. Figure-skating 65 15
526 $1 Slalom skiing 80 15
527 $2 Speed-skating .. .. 1·60 20
528 $3 Cross-country skiing .. .. 2·50 30
529 $4 Shooting .. .. 3·00 40
530 $5 Gold, Silver and Bronze medals .. .. 3·50 45
523/30 .. .. *Set of* 8 11·50 1·60
MS531 Two sheets: (a) 127 × 90 mm. $5 Lighting the Olympic Flame, $10 Gold, Silver and Bronze medals (*different*); (b) 90 × 127 mm. $15 Olympic Torch (*different*) .. .. .. *Set of* 2 *sheets* 20·00

Nos. 523/30 also exist imperforate from a restricted printing (*price for set of* 8 £55 *mint*).

105 Measled Cowrie (*Cypraea zebra*)

106 Girl and Flower Arrangement

(Des C. Abbott)

1980 (7 Jan). *Shells. Multicoloured designs as T* **105**. *P* 14.

532 1 c. Type **105** 55 10
533 2 c. Callico Clam (*Macrocallista maculata*) 70 10
534 3 c. Atlantic Turkey Wing (*Arca zebra*) (*vert*) 80 10
535 4 c. Leafy Jewel Box (*Chama macerophylla*) (*vert*) 80 10
536 5 c. Trochlear Latirus (*Latirus cariniferus*) 80 10
537 10 c. Alphabet Cone (*Conus spurius*) (*vert*) 1·00 10
538 15 c. Cabrit's Murex (*Murex cabritii*) (*vert*) 1·40 10
539 20 c. Stiff Pen Shell (*Atrina rigida*) .. 1·50 10
540 25 c. Little Knobbed Scallop (*Chlamys imbricata*) (*vert*) .. .. 1·50 10
541 35 c. Glory of the Atlantic Cone (*Conus granulatus*) .. .. 1·75 10
542 45 c. Sunrise Tellin (*Tellina radiata*) (*vert*) 2·00 10
543 50 c. *Leucozonia nassa leucozonalis* .. 2·00 10
544 85 c. Triangular Typhis (*Tripterotyphis triangularis*) .. .. 3·00 10
545 $1 Queen or Pink Conch (*Strombus gigas*) (*vert*) .. .. 3·25 10
546 $2 Rooster-tail Conch (*Strombus gallus*) (*vert*) .. .. 5·00 30
547 $5 True Tulip (*Fasciolaris tulipa*) .. 7·50 75
548 $10 Star Arene (*Arene cruentata*) .. 9·50 1·25
532/48 .. .. *Set of* 17 38·00 2·50
MS549 Two sheets, each 125×90 mm. (a) Nos. 544 and 547; (b) Nos. 546 and 548 .. .. 24·00 15·00

Imprint dates: "1980", Nos. 532/49; "1981" Nos. 537, 543/5.

(Des A. Medina ($5), C. Mullin (others))

1980 (15 Mar). *International Year of the Child* (1*st issue*). *T* **106** *and similar vert designs. Multicoloured. P* 14.

550 25 c. Type **106** 45 10
551 50 c. Boy holding football 70 10
552 75 c. Boy with butterfly .. .. 1·00 10
553 $1 Girl holding doll .. .. 1·00 10
554 $1.50, Boy carrying basket of fruit .. 1·50 15
555 $2 Boy holding Reticulated Cowrie-Helmet shell .. .. 1·75 20
556 $3 Girl holding posy .. .. 2·25 25
557 $4 Boy and girl wrapped in blanket .. 2·50 30
550/7 .. .. *Set of* 8 10·00 1·00
MS558 130×95 mm. $5 Three children of different races. $5 "Madonna with Cat" (A. Dürer) (*each* 35×53 *mm*). P 13 .. .. 8·00
MS559 111×151 mm. $10 Children and Christmas tree (73×110 *mm*). P 13 .. .. 8·00

Nos. 550/7 also exist imperforate from a restricted printing (*price for set of* 8 £35 *mint*).

See also Nos. 583/91

NEW INFORMATION

The editor is always interested to correspond with people who have new information that will improve or correct the Catalogue.

10¢

(107)

108 Jabiru

1980 (10 Apr*). *No.* 412 *surch with T* **107**.

560 10 c. on 25 c. *Papilio thoas* .. .. .. 75 1·00
a. Surch inverted .. .. 60·00

* Earliest known date of use.

(Des J.W. Litho Questa)

1980 (16 June). *Birds* (4*th series*). *T* **108** *and similar vert designs. Multicoloured. P* 13.

561 10 c. Type **108** .. .. 5·00 2·75
a. Sheetlet. Nos. 561/6 .. .. .. 32·00
562 25 c. Barred Antshrike .. .. 5·50 2·75
563 35 c. Northern Royal Flycatcher .. .. 5·50 2·75
564 45 c. White-necked Puffbird .. .. .. 6·00 3·00
565 50 c. Ornate Hawk-eagle .. .. .. 6·00 3·00
566 $1 Golden-masked Tanager .. .. .. 6·50 3·75
561/6 .. .. *Set of* 6 32·00 16·00
MS567 85×90 mm. $2 Type **108**, $3 As $1 .. 25·00 17·00

Nos. 561/6 were printed together, *se-tenant* in sheetlets of 6 or in "double" sheetlets of 12. Stamps from the "double" sheetlets have a red frame and red imprint at foot.

109 Speed Skating

40c

(110)

1980 (20 Aug). *Medal Winners, Winter Olympic Games, Lake Placid. T* **109** *and similar vert designs. Multicoloured. P* 14.

568 25 c. Type **109** 30 15
569 50 c. Ice hockey 50 15
570 75 c. Figure-skating 60 15
571 $1 Alpine skiing 85 15
572 $1.50, Giant slalom (women) .. .. .. 1·25 25
573 $2 Speed-skating (women) .. .. .. 1·50 30
574 $3 Cross-country skiing .. .. .. 2·25 40
575 $5 Giant slalom .. .. 3·50 55
568/75 .. .. *Set of* 8 9·75 1·90
MS576 Two sheets: (a) 126 × 91 mm. $5 Type **109**; $10 Type **109**; (b) 91 × 126 mm. $10 As 75 c. *Set of* 2 *sheets* 15·00

Nos. 568/75 were each printed in sheets of 30 (6×5) containing stamps in vertical rows 1, 3/4 and 6, and stamp-sized labels in rows 2 and 5.

Nos. 568/75 also exist imperforate from a restricted printing (*price for set of* 8 £55 *mint*).

1980 (3 Oct). "ESPAMER" *International Stamp Exhibition, Madrid. Nos.* 561/6 *optd (Nos.* 577/9) *or surch as T* **110**.

577 10 c. Type **107** .. .. 4·75 2·50
a. Sheetlet. Nos. 577/82 .. .. .. 28·00
578 25 c. Barred Antshrike .. .. 5·00 2·75
579 35 c. Northern Royal Flycatcher .. .. 5·00 2·75
580 40 c. on 45 c. White-necked Puffbird .. .. 5·50 3·00
581 40 c. on 50 c. Ornate Hawk-eagle .. .. 5·50 3·00
582 40 c. on $1 Golden-masked Tanager .. .. 5·50 3·00
577/82 .. .. *Set of* 6 28·00 15·00

111 Witch in Sky

112 Queen Elizabeth The Queen Mother

(Des C. Mullin)

1980 (24 Nov). *International Year of the Child* (2*nd issue*). *Sleeping Beauty. T* **111** *and similar vert designs illustrating the story. P* 14.

583 35 c. multicoloured 90 15
584 40 c. multicoloured .. .. 1·00 15
585 50 c. multicoloured .. .. 1·25 15
586 75 c. multicoloured .. .. 1·40 15
587 $1 multicoloured .. .. 1·50 20
588 $1.50, multicoloured .. .. 2·25 3
589 $3 multicoloured .. .. 3·25 3
590 $4 multicoloured .. .. 3·25 4
583/90 .. .. *Set of* 8 13·50 1·6
MS591 Two sheets: (a) 82 × 110 mm. $8 "Paumgartner Altar-piece" (Dürer); (b) 110 × 82 mm. $5 Marriage ceremony, $5 Sleeping Beauty and Prince on horseback .. .. *Set of* 2 *sheets* 17·00

Nos. 583/90 were printed in a similar sheet format to Nos 568/75.

Nos. 583/90 also exist imperforate from a restricted printing (*price for set of* 8 £55 *mint*).

(Des C. Mullen)

1980 (12 Dec). 80*th Birthday of Queen Elizabeth the Queen Mother. P* 13.

592 **112** $1 multicoloured .. .. 1·25 4
MS593 82 × 110 mm, $5 As Type **112** (41 × 32 *mm*) 9·00 4·0

No. 592 exists imperforate from a restricted printing (*price* £4.5 *mint*).

$1

113 The Annunciation

WIPA 1981

(114)

(Des C. Mullin)

1980 (30 Dec). *Christmas. T* **113** *and similar vert designs. Multicoloured. P* 14.

594 25 c. Type **113** 45 1
595 50 c. Bethlehem 75 1
596 75 c. The Holy Family .. .. 1·00 1
597 $1 The Nativity .. .. 1·10 1
598 $1.50, The flight into Egypt .. .. .. 1·50 1
599 $2 Shepherds following the Star .. .. 1·75 2
600 $3 Virgin, Child and Angel .. .. .. 2·25 2
601 $4 Adoration of the Kings .. .. .. 2·25 3
594/601 .. .. *Set of* 8 10·00 1·0
MS602 Two sheets, each 82 × 111 mm: (a) $5 As $1; (b) $10 As $3 .. .. .. *Set of* 2 *sheets* 13·00

Nos. 594/601 were printed in a similar sheet format to Nos 568/75.

1981 (22 May). *"WIPA" International Stamp Exhibition. Vienna. Nos.* 598 and 601/2b *surch with T* **114**.

603 $1 on $1.50, The flight into Egypt .. .. 2·00 65
604 $2 on $4 Adoration of the Kings .. .. 2·50 1·40
MS605 82 × 111 mm. $2 on $10 Virgin, Child and Angel .. .. 4·25 3·00

115 Paul Harris (founder)

116 Prince of Wales Coat of Arms

1981 (26 May). 75*th Anniv of Rotary International. T* **115** *and similar multicoloured designs. P* 14.

606 25 c. Type **115** 80 25
607 50 c. Emblems of Rotary activities .. .. 1·25 35
608 $1 75th Anniversary emblem .. .. 1·75 65
609 $1·50, Educational scholarship programme (*horiz*) .. .. 2·50 1·00
610 $2 "Project Hippocrates" .. .. .. 3·00 1·40
611 $3 Emblems (*horiz*) .. .. 3·50 2·00
612 $5 Emblem and handshake (*horiz*) .. .. 4·50 3·25
606/12 .. .. *Set of* 7 15·00 8·00
MS613 Two sheets: (a) 95 × 130 mm. $10 As 50 c.; (b) 130 × 95 mm, $5 As $1, $10 As $2 *Set of* 2 *sheets* 26·00

*Nos. 606/13, together with a 75 c. value showing a map, were originally issued on 30 March 1981, but were withdrawn from sale after two hours as there were objections to the colours used on the map. The stamps, without the offending 75 c., were reissued on 26 May. First Day covers carry the later date and there are no reports of examples used before 26 May.

(Des C. Mullin)

1981 (16 July). *Royal Wedding. T* **116** *and similar vert designs. Multicoloured.* (a) *Size* 22 × 38 *mm* (*from sheets of* 27). *P* 13½ × 14.

614 50 c. Type **116** 35 40
a. Horiz pair. Nos. 614/15 .. .. .. 1·10
615 $1 Prince Charles in military uniform .. 70 75
a. Horiz pair. Nos. 615/16 .. .. .. 1·90
616 $1.50, Royal couple .. .. 1·10 1·25

(b) *Size* 25 × 42 *mm with gold borders (sheets of* 6 *stamps and* 3 *labels).* P 13.
617 50 c. Type **116** 35 15
618 $1 As No. 615 . . . . 70 35
619 $1.50, As No. 616 . . . . 1·10 45
614/19 . . . . *Set of* 6 3·75 3·00
MS620 145 × 85 mm. $3 × 3 As Nos 614/16, but 30 × 47 mm. P 14 . . . . 2·50 4·25

Nos. 614/16 were each printed in blocks of 9 (3 × 3), the blocks *se-tenant* within the sheet.

Nos. 614/16 also exist imperforate from a restricted printing (*price for set of* 3 £4 *mint*).

10c

(117)

1981 (22 Aug). *No.* 538 *surch with T* **117**.
621 10 c. on 15 c. Cabrit's Murex (*Murex cabritii*) 2·25 2·25
a. Surch double . . . . † —

For a similar surcharge, but with rectangular obliterating panel see No. 728.

118 Athletics

(Des C. Mullin)

1981 (14 Sept). *History of the Olympic Games. T* **118** *and similar vert designs. Multicoloured.* P 14.
622 85 c. Type **118** . . . . 1·50 20
623 $1 Cycling . . . . 3·00 30
624 $1.50, Boxing . . . . 2·50 30
625 $2 1984 Games–Los Angeles and Sarajevo 3·00 30
626 $3 Baron Pierre de Coubertin . . 3·50 45
627 $5 Olympic Flame . . . . 4·50 60
622/7 . . . . *Set of* 6 16·00 1·75
MS628 Two sheets, each 175 × 123 mm: (a) $5 As $3, $10 As $5 (*each* 35 × 53 *mm*). P 13½; (b) $15 As $2 (45 × 67 *mm*). P 14½. . . *Set of* 2 *sheets* 30·00

The two miniature sheets of No. **MS**628 also exist with the stamps and borders printed in gold from a restricted printing.

INDEPENDENCE

Independence
21 Sept.,1981
$1

(119)

(120)

1981 (21 Sept). *Independence Commemoration* (1*st issue*). *Optd as T* **119** *by Benex Press, Belize City.* (a) *On Nos.* 532/44 *and* 546/9.
629 1 c. Type **119** 50 10
630 2 c. Callico Clam (*Macrocallista maculata*) 50 10
631 3 c. Atlantic Turkey Wing (*Arca zebra*) (*vert*) 60 10
632 4 c. Leafy Jewel Box (*Chama macerophylla*) (*vert*) 60 10
a. Opt inverted . .
633 5 c. Trochlear Latirus (*Latirus cariniferus*) 60 10
634 10 c. Alphabet Cone (*Conus spurius*) (*vert*) 75 10
a. Opt inverted . .
635 15 c. Cabrit's Murex (*Murex cabritii*) (*vert*) 1·25 10
636 20 c. Stiff Pen Shell (*Atrina rigida*) . . 1·40 15
637 25 c. Little Knobbed Scallop (*Chlamys imbricata*) (*vert*) . . 1·50 25
638 35 c. Glory of the Atlantic Cone (*Conus granulatus*) . . 1·50 30
639 45 c. Sunrise Tellin (*Tellina radiata*) (*vert*) 2·00 40
640 50 c. *Leucozonia nassa leucozonalis* . . 2·00 40
641 85 c. Triangular Typhis (*Tripterotyphis triangularis*) . . 3·00 90
a. Opt inverted . .
642 $2 Rooster-tail Conch (*Strombus gallus*) (*vert*) . . 6·00 2·50
643 $5 True Tulip (*Fasciolaris tulipa*) . . 8·00 5·50
a. Opt inverted . . † —
644 $10 Star Arene (*Arene cruentata*) . . 12·00 9·50
629/44 . . . . *Set of* 16 38·00 18·00
MS645 Two sheets, each 126 × 91 mm: (a) Nos. 641 and 643; (b) Nos. 642 and 644 . . *Set of* 2 *sheets* 26·00

On the vertical designs and the miniature sheets the overprint is in roman type.

The 10 c. exists with either "1980" or "1981" imprint date.

Examples of the miniature sheets have been seen showing forged overprints apparently applied by rubber handstamp.

(b) *On Nos.* 606/13
646 25 c. Type **115** (Gold) . . . . 1·00 25
a. Opt double . .
647 50 c. Emblems of Rotary activities . . 1·50 35
648 $1 75th Anniversary emblem . . 1·75 65
649 $1.50, Educational scholarship programme 2·50 1·25
650 $2 "Project Hippocrates" (Gold) . . 3·25 1·60
651 $3 Emblems . . . . 3·75 2·50
652 $5 Emblems and handshake . . 5·00 3·75
646/52 . . . . *Set of* 7 17·00 9·25
MS653 Two sheets: (a) 95 × 130 mm. $10 As 50 c.; (b) 130 × 95 mm. $5 As $1, $10 As $2 (Gold) *Set of* 2 *sheets* 24·00

See also Nos. 657/63.

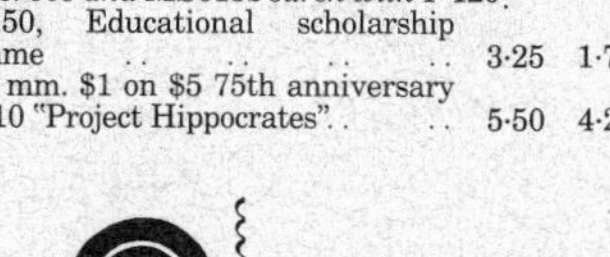

1981 (13 Nov). *"ESPAMER" International Stamp Exhibition, Buenos Aires. Nos.* 609 *and* **MS**613b *surch with T* **120**.
654 $1 on $1.50, Educational scholarship programme . . . . 3·25 1·75
MS655 95 × 130 mm. $1 on $5 75th anniversary emblem, $1 on $10 "Project Hippocrates". . . 5·50 4·25

(121)

1981 (14 Nov). *"Philatelia 81" International Stamp Exhibition, Frankfurt. No.* **MS**549 *surch with T* **121** *in red.*
MS656 Two sheets, each 125 × 90 mm: (a) $1 on 85 c. *Tripterotyphis triangularis*, $1 on $5 *Fasciolaria tulipa*; (b) $1 on $2 *Strombus gallus*. $1 on $10 *Arene cruentata* . . . . *Set of* 2 *sheets* 30·00

122 Black Orchid

123 Uruguayan Footballer

(Des C. Mullin)

1981 (18 Dec)–**82**. *Independence Commemoration* (2*nd issue*) *T* **122** *and similar multicoloured designs.* P 14.
657 10 c. Belize Coat of Arms (*horiz*) (10.2.82) . . 70 10
658 35 c. Map of Belize (10.2.82) . . . . 1·75 30
659 50 c. Type **122** . . . . 5·00 80
660 85 c. Baird's Tapir (*horiz*) . . . . 2·00 1·00
661 $1 Mahogany Tree . . . . 2·00 1·10
662 $2 Keel-billed Toucan (*horiz*) . . 7·00 2·75
657/62 . . . . *Set of* 6 16·00 5·50
MS663 130 × 98 mm. $5 As 10 c. P 14½ (10.2.82) 7·00 4·00

(Des C. Mullin)

1981 (28 Dec). *World Cup Football Championship, Spain* (1*st issue*). *T* **123** *and similar vert designs. Multicoloured.* P 14.
664 10 c. Type **123** . . . . 1·40 20
665 25 c. Italian footballer . . . . 2·25 20
666 50 c. German footballer . . . . 3·00 30
667 $1 Brazilian footballer . . . . 4·00 40
668 $1.50, Argentinian footballer . . 4·50 70
669 $2 English footballer . . . . 5·00 80
664/9 . . . . *Set of* 6 18·00 2·40
MS670 Two sheets: (a) 145 × 115 mm. $2 "SPAIN '82" logo; (b) 155 × 115 mm. $3 Footballer (46 × 76 *mm*) . . . . *Set of* 2 *sheets* 16·00 4·75

See also Nos. 721/7.

124 British 19th-century Warship

(Des C. Mullin)

1982 (15 Mar). *Sailing Ships. T* **124** *and similar horiz designs. Multicoloured.* P 14.
671 10 c. Type **124** . . . . 2·00 35
672 25 c. *Madagascar* (1837) . . . . 3·00 45
673 35 c. Brig *Whitby* (1838) . . . . 3·50 50
674 50 c. *China* (1838) . . . . 4·00 75
675 85 c. *Swiftsure* (1850) . . . . 4·75 1·10
676 $2 *Windsor Castle* (1857) . . . . 7·50 2·00
671/6 . . . . *Set of* 6 22·00 4·75
MS677 110 × 87 mm. $5 Ships in battle . . 22·00 6·50

NEW INFORMATION

The editor is always interested to correspond with people who have new information that will improve or correct the Catalogue.

(125)

126 Princess Diana

1982 (28 Apr). *"ESSEN '82" International Stamp Exhibition, West Germany. Nos.* 662 *and* 669 *surch with T* **125**.
678 $1 on $2 Keel-billed Toucan . . . . 3·75 1·00
679 $1 on $2 English footballer . . . . 3·75 1·00

(Des C. Mullin)

1982 (20 May). 21*st Birthday of Princess of Wales. T* **126** *and similar vert designs showing portrait of Princess of Wales with different backgrounds.* (a) *Size* 22 × 38 *mm (from sheets of* 25). P 13½ × 14.
680 50 c. multicoloured 70 45
a. *Tête-bêche* (pair) . . . . 1·40
681 $1 multicoloured 80 75
a. *Tête-bêche* (pair) . . . . 1·60
682 $1.50, multicoloured . . . . 1·00 1·25
a. *Tête-bêche* (pair) . . . . 2·00

(b) *Size* 25 × 43 *mm (from sheets of* 6 *stamps and* 3 *labels).* P 13
683 50 c. multicoloured 70 30
684 $1 multicoloured 80 50
685 $1.50, multicoloured . . . . 1·00 75
680/5 . . . . *Set of* 6 4·50 3·50
MS686 145 × 85 mm. $3 × 3 As Nos. 680/2, but 30 × 47 mm. P 14 . . . . 2·75 3·00

Stamps as Nos. 680/2, size 30×47 mm and perforated 14, exist from a limited printing. These have gold backgrounds to the central ovals and gold frames. In addition the Queen's head and the centre oval are embossed (*Price per set of* 3 £9 *mint*).

127 Lighting Camp-fire

(Des C. Mullin)

1982 (31 Aug). 125*th Birth Anniv of Lord Baden-Powell. T* **127** *and similar horiz designs. Multicoloured.* P 14.
687 10 c. Type **127** . . . . 1·00 20
688 25 c. Bird watching . . . . 1·75 25
689 35 c. Three scouts, one playing guitar . . 1·75 30
690 50 c. Hiking . . . . 2·00 55
691 85 c. Scouts with flag . . . . 2·50 90
692 $2 Saluting . . . . 3·50 2·25
687/92 . . . . *Set of* 6 11·00 4·00
MS693 Two sheets: each 85 × 115 mm: (a) $2 Scout with flag; (b) $3 Portrait of Lord Baden-Powell . . *Set of* 2 *sheets* 16·00 8·00

128 *Gorgonia ventalina*

(Des C. Mullin)

1982 (20 Sept). *First Anniv of Independence. Marine Life. T* **128** *and similar horiz designs.* P 14.
694 10 c. Type **128** . . . . 1·40 20
695 35 c. *Carpiuis corallinus* . . . . 2·50 20
696 50 c. *Plexaura flexuasa* . . . . 3·00 35
697 85 c. *Candylactis gigantea* . . . . 3·25 50
698 $1 *Stenopus hispidus* . . . . 3·75 70
699 $2 Sergeant Major ("*Abudefduf saxatilis*") 4·50 1·25
694/9 . . . . *Set of* 6 16·00 2·75
MS700 130×98 mm. $5 *Schyllarides aequinocialis*. P 14½ . . . . 20·00 7·00

(129)

1982 (1 Oct). *"BELGICA 82" International Stamp Exhibition, Brussels. Nos* 687/92 *optd as T* **129** *in gold.*
701 10 c. Type **127** . . . . 1·50 30
702 25 c. Bird watching . . . . 2·50 75
703 35 c. Three scouts, one playing guitar . . 2·50 1·00
704 50 c. Hiking . . . . 3·00 1·50
705 85 c. Scouts with flag . . . . 4·50 2·50
706 $2 Saluting . . . . 9·00 6·50
701/6 . . . . *Set of* 6 21·00 11·50

BIRTH OF H.R.H.

PRINCE
WILLIAM ARTHUR
PHILIP LOUIS
21ST JUNE 1982

(130) **131** Scotland v New Zealand

1982 (21 Oct). *Birth of Prince William of Wales (1st issue). Nos.* 680/6 *optd as T* **130** *in silver. (a) Size* 22 × 38 *mm.*
707 50 c. multicoloured 35 35
a. *Tête-bêche* (pair) 70
b. Opt double . . . . 55·00
708 $1 multicoloured 45 50
a. *Tête-bêche* (pair) 90
709 $1.50, multicoloured 65 75
a. *Tête-beche* (pair) . . . . 1·25

(*b*) *Size* 25 × 43 *mm*
710 50 c. multicoloured 35 35
a. Opt double . . . .
711 $1 multicoloured 45 50
712 $1.50, multicoloured 65 75
707/12 . . . . *Set of* 6 2·50 2·75
MS713 145 × 85 mm. $3 × 3 As Nos. 707/9, but 30 × 47 mm. . . . . 3·25 3·50

A similar overprint exists on the stamps from the limited printing described beneath No. **MS**686 (*Price per set of* 3 £4 *mint*).

1982 (25 Oct). *Birth of Prince William of Wales (2nd issue). Nos* 614/20 *optd as T* **130** *in gold (a) Size* 22 × 38 *mm.*
714 50 c. Type **116** . . . . 2·50 1·00
a. Horiz pair. Nos. 714/15 . . . . 7·50
715 $1 Prince Charles in military uniform . . 5·00 2·00
a. Horiz pair. Nos. 715/16 . . . . 12·50
716 $1.50, Royal couple . . . . 7·50 3·00

(*b*) *Size* 25 × 42 *mm*
717 50 c. Type **116** 35 35
718 $1 As No. 715 . . . . 70 70
719 $1.50, As No. 716 . . . . 1·10 1·10
714/9 . . . . *Set of* 6 16·00 7·25
MS720 145 × 85 mm. $3 × 3 As Nos. 714/16 but 30 × 47 mm . . . . 7·00 7·00

No. **MS**720 occurs with two different sizes of overprint. On the normal version the top line of the overprint, "BIRTH OF H.R.H." measures 19½ mm in length. On examples with the larger overprint this measures 22 mm. (*Price for miniature sheet with larger overprint £30 mint*).

(Des Baumann)

1982 (10 Dec). *World Cup Football Championship, Spain (2nd issue). T* **131** *and similar horiz designs. Multicoloured. P* 14.
721 20 c. + 10 c. Type **131** . . . . 1·25 65
722 30 c. + 15 c. Scotland v New Zealand (*different*) 1·25 65
723 40 c. + 20 c. Kuwait v France . . . . 1·50 65
724 60 c. + 30 c. Italy v Brazil . . . . 2·00 85
725 $1 + 50 c. France v Northern Ireland . . 2·50 1·10
726 $1.50 + 75 c. Austria v Chile . . . . 3·00 1·40
721/6 . . . . *Set of* 6 10·50 4·75
MS727 Two sheets: (a) 91 × 137 mm. $1 + 50 c. Germany v Italy (50 × 70 *mm*); (b) 122 × 116 mm. $2 + $1 England v France (50 × 70 *mm*) *Set of* 2 *sheets* 11·00 6·50

10c

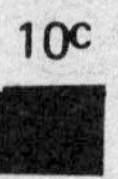

(132) **133** Belize Cathedral

1983 (28 Jan). *No.* 538 *surch with T* **132**.
728 10 c. on 15 c. *Murex cabritii* . . . .

No. 728 differs from the previous provisional, No. 621, in the size of the obliterating panel over the original face value. On No. 621 this measures 4½ × 4½ mm, but No. 728 shows it larger, 7 × 5½ mm.

1983 (7 March). *Visit of Pope John Paul II. P* 13½.
729 **133** 50 c. multicoloured . . . . 2·25 90
MS730 135 × 110 mm. $2.50, Pope John Paul II (30 × 47 *mm*). P 14 . . . . 10·00 4·75

10c

134 Map of Belize (135)

1983 (14 Mar). *Commonwealth Day. T* **134** *and similar multicoloured designs. P* 13.
731 35 c. Type **134** 35 35
732 50 c. "Maya Stella" from Lamanai Indian church (*horiz*) 50 50
733 85 c. Supreme Court Building (*horiz*) . . 60 75
734 $2 University Centre, Belize (*horiz*) . . 1·25 2·00
731/4 . . . . *Set of* 4 2·40 3·25

1983 (15 Apr). *No.* 658 *surch with T* **135**.
735 10 c. on 35 c. Map of Belize . . . .

136 De Lana-Terzi's "Aerial Ship", 1670

(Des C. Mullin)

1983 (16 May). *Bicentenary of Manned Flight. T* **136** *and similar horiz designs. Multicoloured. P* 14.
736 10 c. Type **136** . . . . 1·40 30
737 25 c. De Gusmao's *La Passarola*, 1709 . . 2·00 40
738 50 c. Guyton de Morveau's balloon with oars, 1784 . . . . 2·25 70
739 85 c. Early airship . . . . 2·75 1·10
740 $1 Airship *Clement Bayard* . . . . 3·00 1·50
741 $1.50, Beardmore airship R-34 . . . . 3·25 2·25
736/41 . . . . *Set of* 6 13·00 5·50
MS742 Two sheets: (a) 125×84 mm. $3 Charles Green's balloon *Royal Vauxhall*; (b) 115×128 mm. $3 Montgolfier balloon, 1783 (*vert*) *Set of* 2 *sheets* 13·00 4·50

$1.25

$1.25

(137) (138)

1983 (9 June). *Nos.* 662 *and* 699 *surch with T* **137/8**.
743 $1.25 on $2 Keel-billed Toucan (surch T 137) . . . . 6·00 6·00
a. Surch double . . . . † —
744 $1.25 on $2 Sergeant Major (surch T 138) 6·00 7·00

10C

10C

(139) (140)

1983 (28 Sept). *No.* 541 *surch with T* **139/40**.
745 10 c. on 35 c. Glory of the Atlantic Cone (*Conus granulatus*) (surch T 139) . . 30·00
a. Surch inverted . . . . 38·00
b. Vert pair, lower stamp without "10 c"
c. Surch double . . . .
746 10 c. on 35 c. Glory of the Atlantic Cone (*Conus granulatus*) (surch T 140) . . 27·00
a. Surch triple . . . . 25·00

141 Altun Ha

(Des G. Vasarhelyi. Litho Format)

1983 (14 Nov). *Maya Monuments. T* **141** *and similar horiz designs. Multicoloured. P* 13½ × 14.
747 10 c. Type **141** 10 10
748 15 c. Xunantunich 10 10
749 75 c. Cerros 30 40
750 $2 Lamanai . . . . 70 1·25
747/50 . . . . *Set of* 4 1·00 1·60
MS751 102 × 72 mm. $3 Xunantunich (*different*) 1·00 1·75

Nos. 747/50 exist imperforate from stock dispersed by the liquidator of Format International Security Printers Ltd.

142 Belmopan Earth Station

(Des G. Vasarhelyi. Litho Format)

1983 (28 Nov). *World Communications Year. T* **142** *and similar horiz designs. Multicoloured. P* 14.
752 10 c. Type **142** 30 10
753 15 c. *Telstar* 2 . . . . 40 25
754 75 c. U.P.U. logo . . . . 1·25 1·75
755 $2 M.V. *Heron H* mail service . . 2·75 4·50
752/5 . . . . *Set of* 4 4·25 6·00

Nos. 752/5 exist imperforate from stock dispersed by the liquidator of Format International Security Printers Ltd.

143 Jaguar Cub

(Des G. Vasarhelyi. Litho Format)

1983 (9 Dec). *The Jaguar. T* **143** *and similar horiz designs. Multicoloured. P* 14.
756 5 c. Type **143** 30 30
757 10 c. Adult Jaguar 35 20
758 85 c. Jaguar in river . . . . 1·75 2·25
759 $1 Jaguar on rock . . . . 2·00 2·75
756/9 . . . . *Set of* 4 4·00 5·00
MS760 102 × 72 mm. $3 Jaguar in tree (44 × 28 *mm*). P 13½ × 14 . . . . 2·50 2·50

Nos. 756/9 exist imperforate from stock dispersed by the liquidator of Format International Security Printers Ltd.

144 Pope John Paul II

(Des G. Vasarhelyi. Litho Format)

1983 (22 Dec). *Christmas. T* **144** *and similar designs showing Pope John Paul II at Papal Mass on* 11 *March* 1983 *in Belize. P* 13½ × 14.
761 10 c. multicoloured 25 10
762 15 c. multicoloured 25 10
763 75 c. multicoloured 60 60
764 $2 multicoloured . . . . 1·25 1·40
761/4 . . . . *Set of* 4 2·10 2·00
MS765 102 × 72 mm. $3 multicoloured . . 2·75 3·75

145 Four-eyed Butterflyfish

(Des G. Drummond, Litho Format)

1984 (27 Feb)–**88.** *Marine Life from the Belize Coral Reef. T* **145** *and similar horiz designs. Multicoloured. P* 15.
766 1 c. Type **145** 15 20
767 2 c. Cushion Star 20 30
a. Perf 13½ (7.88) . . . . 3·50 3·50
768 3 c. Flower Coral 25 30
769 4 c. Royal Gramma ("Fairy Basslet") . . 25 30
770 5 c. Spanish Hogfish 30 30
771 6 c. Star-eyed Hermit Crab 30 30
772 10 c. Sea Fans and Fire Sponge 70 40
a. Perf 13½ (7.88) 35 35
773 15 c. Blue-headed Wrasse 80 70
a. Perf 13½ (7.88) 50 60
774 25 c. Blue-striped Grunt . . . . 1·00 80
a. Perf 13½ (7.88) 70 80
775 50 c. Coral Crab . . . . 2·00 1·50
a. Perf 13½ (7.88) . . . . 1·25 1·75
776 60 c. Tube Sponge . . . . 2·00 1·50
a. Perf 13½ (7.88) . . . . 1·25 1·75
777 75 c. Brain Coral . . . . 1·00 1·00
778 $1 Yellow-tailed Snapper . . . . 1·25 1·25
a. Perf 13½ (7.88) . . . . 1·50 2·00

9	$2 Common Lettuce Slug		1·75	1·25
)	$5 Three-spotted Damselfish		2·00	1·75
l	$10 Rock Beauty		3·00	5·00
3/81	.. ..	Set of 16	15·00	15·00

Nos. 766/81 exist imperforate from stock dispersed by the uidator of Format International Security Printers Ltd. Other ues exist perforated 13½, but there is no evidence for their temporary postal use.

Nos. 776 and 778 exist overprinted to commemorate the niversary of Hurricane Hattie. These stamps were not issued, exist from stock dispersed by the liquidator.

VISIT OF THE LORD
ARCHBISHOP OF CANTERBURY
8th–11th MARCH 1984

(146)

34 (8 Mar). *Visit of the Archbishop of Canterbury. Nos. 772A ınd 775A optd with T* **146.**

2	10 c. Sea Fans and Fire Sponge	75	40
3	50 c. Coral Crab	1·50	1·00

147 Shooting

(Des G. Vasarhelyi. Litho Format)

84 (30 Apr). *Olympic Games, Los Angeles, (a) Sheet stamps. T* **147** *and similar horiz designs. Multicoloured. P* 13½ × 14.

4	25 c. Type **147**		30	25
5	75 c. Boxing		70	70
6	$1 Marathon		90	90
7	$2 Cycling		1·75	2·00
4/7	.. ..	Set of 4	3·25	3·50
S788	101 × 72 mm. $3 Statue of Discus-thrower		2·10	2·75

(b) *Booklet stamps. Similar designs to T* **147** *but Royal cypher replaced by Queen's head. P* 14½.

9	5 c. 1896 Marathon		15	30
	a. Booklet pane. No. 789 × 4		55	
0	20 c. Sprinting		25	50
	a. Booklet pane. No. 790 × 4		90	
1	25 c. Shot-putting		25	50
	a. Booklet pane. No. 791 × 4		90	
2	$2 Olympic torch		35	80
	a. Booklet pane. No. 792 × 4		1·25	
9/92	.. ..	Set of 4	90	1·90

148 British Honduras 1866 1s. Stamp

149 Prince Albert

(Des G. Vasarhelyi. Litho Format)

84 (26 Sept). *"Ausipex" International Stamp Exhibition, Melbourne. T* **148** *and similar horiz designs. Multicoloured. P* 14 × 13½ ($2) *or* 15 (*others*).

3	15 c. Type **148**		15	15
4	30 c. Bath mail coach, 1784		25	25
5	65 c. Sir Rowland Hill and Penny Black ..		55	65
6	75 c. British Honduras railway locomotive, 1910		65	75
7	$2 Royal Exhibition Buildings, Melbourne (46 × 28 *mm*)		1·50	2·00
3/7	.. ..	Set of 5	2·75	3·50
S798	103 × 73 mm. $3 Australia 1932 Sydney Harbour Bridge 5s. and British Honduras 1866 1s. stamps (44 × 28 *mm*). P 13½ × 14 ..		1·40	2·00

(Des G. Vasarhelyi. Litho Format)

984 (15 Oct). *500th Anniv of British Royal House of Tudor* (1985). *T* **149** *and similar vert designs showing members of the Royal Family. Multicoloured. P* 14.

9	50 c. Type **149**		25	35
	a. Sheetlet. Nos. 799/800 × 2 ..		90	
0	50 c. Queen Victoria		25	35
1	75 c. King George VI		35	45
	a. Sheetlet. Nos. 801/2 × 2		1·25	
2	75 c. Queen Elizabeth the Queen Mother		35	45
3	$1 Princess of Wales		50	70
	a. Sheetlet. Nos. 803/4 × 2		1·75	
4	$1 Prince of Wales		50	70
99/804	.. ..	Set of 6	2·00	2·75
S805	147 × 97 mm. $1.50, Prince Philip; $1.50, Queen Elizabeth II		1·25	2·00

Nos. 799/804 were only issued in sheetlets of four stamps of one alue, two of each design, with an illustrated vertical gutter argin

150 White-fronted Amazon

151 Effigy Censer, 1450 (Santa Rita Site)

(Des. G. Vasarhelyi. Litho Format)

1984 (1 Nov). *Parrots. T* **150** *and similar multicoloured designs. P* 11.

806	$1 Type **150**		1·50	1·50
	a. Block of 4. Nos. 806/9		5·50	
807	$1 White-capped Parrot (*horiz*)		1·50	1·50
808	$1 Mealy Amazon (*horiz*)		1·50	1·50
809	$1 Red-lored Amazon		1·50	1·50
806/9	.. ..	Set of 4	5·50	5·50
MS810	102 × 73 mm. $3 Scarlet Macaw. P 13½ × 14		3·25	3·75

Nos. 806/9 were issued together, *se-tenant*, in blocks of 4 throughout the sheet, each block forming a composite design.

Nos. 806/9 exist imperforate from stock dispersed by the liquidator of Format International Security Printers Ltd.

(Des G. Vasarhelyi. Litho Format)

1984 (30 Nov). *Maya Artefacts. T* **151** *and similar vert designs. Multicoloured. P* 15.

811	25 c. Type **151**		25	25
812	75 c. Vase, 675 (Actun Chapat)		50	70
813	$1 Tripod Vase, 500 (Santa Rita site) ..		65	90
814	$2 Sun god Kinich Ahau, 600 (Altun Ha site)		1·40	2·25
811/14	.. ..	Set of 4	2·50	3·75

152 Governor-General inspecting Girl Guides

153 White-tailed Kite

(Des R. Granger Barrett. Litho Format)

1985 (15 Mar). *International Youth Year and 75th Anniv of Girl Guide Movement. T* **152** *and similar horiz designs. Multicoloured. P* 15.

815	25 c. Type **152**		30	30
816	50 c. Girl Guides camping		45	45
817	90 c. Checking map on hike		60	65
818	$1.25, Students in laboratory		70	80
819	$2 Lady Baden-Powell (founder) ..		90	1·10
815/19	.. ..	Set of 5	2·75	3·00

(Des G. Vasarhelyi. Litho Format ($1, $5) Questa (others))

1985 (30 May)–**88**. *Birth Bicentenary of John J. Audubon (ornithologist). T* **153** *and similar multicoloured designs showing original paintings. P* 15 ($1) *or* 14 (*others*).

820	10 c. Type **153**		70	40
821	15 c. Ruby-crowned Kinglet (*horiz*) ..		90	40
822	25 c. Painted Bunting		1·25	40
822*a*	60 c. As 25 c. (1988)		8·50	5·50
823	75 c. Belted Kingfisher		1·75	1·40
824	$1 Common Cardinal		1·75	2·25
825	$3 Long-billed Curlew (*horiz*)		3·00	4·00
820/5	.. ..	Set of 7	16·00	13·00
MS826	139 × 99 mm. $5 "John James Audubon" (John Syme). P 13½ × 14		3·25	3·25

154 The Queen Mother with Princess Elizabeth, 1928

INAUGURATION OF
NEW GOVERNMENT –
21st. DECEMBER 1984

(155)

(Des G. Vasarhelyi. Litho Format)

1985 (20 June). *Life and Times of Queen Elizabeth the Queen Mother. T* **154** *and similar multicoloured designs. P* 13½ × 14.

827	10 c. Type **154**		10	10
828	15 c. The Queen Mother, 1980		10	10
829	75 c. Waving to the crowd, 1982		40	40
830	$5 Four generations of Royal Family at Prince William's Christening		1·50	2·75
827/30	.. ..	Set of 4	1·75	3·00
MS831	Two sheets, each 138 × 98 mm. (a) $2 The Queen Mother with Prince Henry (from photo by Lord Snowdon) (38 × 50 *mm*): (b) $5 The Queen Mother, 1984 (38 × 50 *mm*)	Set of 2 sheets	3·75	4·50

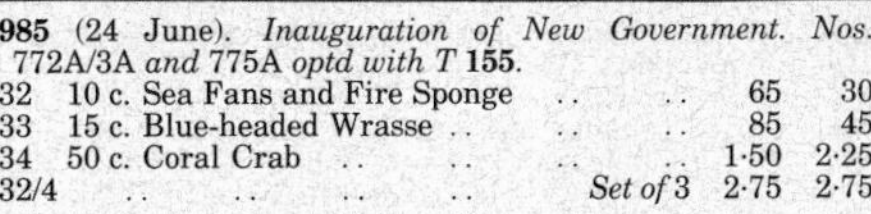

1985 (24 June). *Inauguration of New Government. Nos.* 772A/3A *and* 775A *optd with T* **155**.

832	10 c. Sea Fans and Fire Sponge		65	30
833	15 c. Blue-headed Wrasse		85	45
834	50 c. Coral Crab		1·50	2·25
832/4	.. ..	Set of 3	2·75	2·75

156 British Honduras 1935 Silver Jubilee 25 c. stamp and King George V with Queen Mary in Carriage

(Des Harrison. Litho Format)

1985 (25 July). *50th Anniv of First Commonwealth Omnibus Issue. T* **156** *and similar horiz designs showing British Honduras/Belize stamps. Multicoloured. P* 14.

835	50 c. Type **156**		40	50
	a. Sheetlet. Nos. 835/44		3·50	
836	50 c. 1937 Coronation 3 c., and King George VI and Queen Elizabeth in Coronation robes		40	50
837	50 c. 1946 Victory 3 c., and Victory celebrations		40	50
838	50 c. 1948 Royal Silver Wedding 4 c., and King George VI and Queen Elizabeth at Westminster Abbey service ..		40	50
839	50 c. 1953 Coronation 4 c., and Queen Elizabeth II in Coronation robes ..		40	50
840	50 c. 1966 Churchill 25 c., Sir Winston Churchill and fighter aircraft		40	50
841	50 c. 1972 Royal Silver Wedding 50 c., and 1948 Wedding photograph ..		40	50
842	50 c. 1973 Royal Wedding 50 c., and Princess Anne and Capt. Mark Phillips at their Wedding		40	50
843	50 c. 1977 Silver Jubilee $2, and Queen Elizabeth II during tour		40	50
844	50 c. 1978 25th anniv of Coronation 75 c. and Imperial Crown		40	50
835/44	.. ..	Set of 10	3·50	4·50
MS845	138 × 98 mm. $5 Queen Elizabeth II in Coronation robes (38 × 50 *mm*). P 13½ × 14 ..		4·50	4·50

Nos. 835/44 were printed together, *se-tenant*, in sheetlets of 10.

157 Mounted Postboy and Early Letter to Belize

COMMONWEALTH SUMMIT
CONFERENCE, BAHAMAS
16th–22nd OCTOBER 1985

(158)

(Des G. Drummond. Litho Format)

1985 (1 Aug). *350th Anniv of the British Post Office. T* **157** *and similar horiz designs. Multicoloured. P* 15.

846	10 c. Type **157**		40	15
847	15 c. *Hinchinbrook II* (sailing packet) engaging *Grand Turk* (American privateer)		55	25
848	25 c. *Duke of Marlborough II* (sailing packet)		70	30
849	75 c. *Diana* (packet)		1·25	1·50
850	$1 Falmouth packet ship		1·50	1·75
851	$3 *Conway* (mail paddle-steamer) ..		3·75	4·50
846/51	.. ..	Set of 6	7·25	7·75

A $5 miniature sheet was prepared, but not issued. Examples exist from stock dispersed by the liquidator of Format International Security Printers Ltd.

1985 (5 Sept). *Commonwealth Heads of Government Meeting, Nassau, Bahamas. Nos.* 827/31 *optd with T* **158** *in silver.*

852	10 c. Type **154**		30	30
853	15 c. The Queen Mother, 1980		40	35
854	75 c. Waving to the crowd, 1980		80	80
855	$5 Four generations of Royal Family at Prince William's christening		2·75	3·75
852/5	.. ..	Set of 4	3·75	4·75
MS856	Two sheets, each 138 × 98 mm. (a) $2 The Queen Mother with Prince Henry (from photo by Lord Snowdon) (38 × 50 *mm*): (b) $5 The Queen Mother, 1984 (38 × 50 *mm*)	Set of 2 sheets	4·00	4·50

80TH ANNIVERSARY OF
ROTARY INTERNATIONAL

(159)

160 Royal Standard and Belize Flag

1985 (25 Sept). *80th Anniv of Rotary International. Nos.* 815/19 *optd with T* **159**.
857 25 c. Type **152**. 50 30
858 50 c. Girl Guides camping 80 75
859 90 c. Checking map on hike .. .. .. 1·25 1·60
860 $1.25, Students in laboratory .. .. 1·75 2·25
861 $2 Lady Baden-Powell (founder) .. .. 2·25 2·75
857/61 .. .. *Set of* 5 6·00 7·00

(Des G. Vasarhelyi. Litho Format)

1985 (9 Oct). *Royal Visit. T* **160** *and similar multicoloured designs. P* 15 × 14½.
862 25 c. Type **160**. 55 95
a. Horiz strip of 3. Nos. 862/4 .. .. 4·25
863 75 c. Queen Elizabeth II .. .. .. 1·25 2·00
864 $4 Royal Yacht *Britannia* (81 × 39 *mm*) .. 3·00 3·25
862/4 .. .. *Set of* 3 4·25 5·50
MS865 138 × 98 mm. $5 Queen Elizabeth II (38 × 50 *mm*). P 13½ × 14 .. .. .. 5·50 4·75
Nos. 862/4 were printed together, *se-tenant*, in horizontal strips of 3 within small sheets of 9 stamps.

161 Mountie in Canoe (Canada)

(Des Walt Disney Productions. Litho Format)

1985 (1 Nov). *Christmas. 30th Anniv of Disneyland, U.S.A. T* **161** *and similar vert designs showing dolls from "It's a Small World" exhibition. Multicoloured. P* 11.
866 1 c. Type **161**. 10 10
867 2 c. Indian chief and squaw (U.S.A.) .. 10 10
868 3 c. Incas climbing Andes (South America) 10 10
869 4 c. Africans beating drums (Africa) .. 10 10
870 5 c. Snake-charmer and dancer (India and Far East) 10 10
871 6 c. Boy and girl with donkey (Belize) .. 10 10
872 50 c. Musician and dancer (Balkans) .. 1·00 1·25
873 $1.50, Boys with camel (Egypt and Saudi Arabia) .. .. 2·25 2·75
874 $3 Woman and girls playing with kite (Japan) .. .. 3·25 4·25
866/74 .. .. *Set of* 9 6·00 7·50
MS875 127 × 102 mm. $4 Beefeater and castle (Great Britain). P 13½ × 14 .. .. .. 4·50 5·50

PRE "WORLD CUP FOOTBALL"
MEXICO 1986

(**162**)

163 Indian Costume

1985 (20 Dec). *World Cup Football Championship, Mexico* (1986) (*1st issue*). *Nos.* 835/45 *optd with T* **162**.
876 50 c. Type **156**. 65 65
a. Sheetlet. Nos. 876/85 .. .. .. 6·00
877 50 c. 1937 Coronation 3 c., and King George VI and Queen Elizabeth in Coronation robes 65 65
878 50 c. 1946 Victory 3 c., and Victory celebrations 65 65
879 50 c. 1948 Royal Silver Wedding 4 c., and King George VI and Queen Elizabeth at Westminster Abbey service 65 65
880 50 c. 1953 Coronation 4 c., and Queen Elizabeth II in Coronation robes .. 65 65
881 50 c. 1966 Churchill 25 c., Sir Winston Churchill and fighter aircraft 65 65
882 50 c. 1972 Royal Silver Wedding 50 c., and 1948 Wedding photograph 65 65
883 50 c. 1973 Royal Wedding 50 c., and Princess Anne and Capt. Mark Phillips at their Wedding 65 65
884 50 c. 1977 Silver Jubilee $2, and Queen Elizabeth II during tour 65 65
885 50 c. 1978 25th anniv of Coronation 75 c., and Imperial Crown 65 65
876/85 .. .. *Set of* 10 6·00 6·00
MS886 138 × 98 mm. $5 Queen Elizabeth II in Coronation robes .. .. 4·25 4·25
See also Nos. 936/40.

(Des Jane Clark. Litho Format)

1986 (15 Jan). *Costumes of Belize. T* **163** *and similar vert designs. Multicoloured. P* 15.
887 5 c. Type **163**. 75 30
888 10 c. Maya 80 30
889 15 c. Garifuna. . .. . 1·00 35
890 25 c. Creole .. .. 1·25 35
891 50 c. Chinese .. .. 1·75 1·25
892 75 c. Lebanese .. .. 2·00 2·00
893 $1 European *c* 1900 .. .. .. 2·00 2·50
894 $2 Latin .. .. 2·75 3·75
887/94 .. .. *Set of* 8 11·00 9·75
MS895 139 × 98 mm. $5 Amerindian (38 × 50 *mm*). P 13½ × 14. .. .. .. 6·00 7·50

164 Pope Pius X

165 Princess Elizabeth aged Three

(Des G. Vasarhelyi. Litho Format)

1986 (15 Apr). *Easter. 20th-century Popes. T* **164** *and similar multicoloured designs. P* 11.
896 50 c. Type **164**. . .. . 1·00 1·10
a. Sheetlet. Nos. 896/903 .. .. .. 7·25
897 50 c. Benedict XV .. .. 1·00 1·10
898 50 c. Pius XI .. .. 1·00 1·10
899 50 c. Pius XII .. .. 1·00 1·10
900 50 c. John XXIII .. .. 1·00 1·10
901 50 c. Paul VI .. .. 1·00 1·10
902 50 c. John Paul I .. .. 1·00 1·10
903 50 c. John Paul II .. .. 1·00 1·10
896/903 .. .. *Set of* 8 7·25 8·00
MS904 147 × 92 mm. $4 Pope John Paul II preaching (*vert*). P 13½ × 14 .. .. 8·50 8·50
Nos. 896/903 were printed together, *se-tenant*, in sheetlets of eight stamps and one stamp-size label.

(Des G. Vasarhelyi. Litho Format)

1986 (21 Apr). *60th Birthday of Queen Elizabeth II. T* **165** *and similar vert designs. Multicoloured. P* 14 × 13½.
905 25 c. Type **165**. 15 20
a. Sheetlet. Nos. 905/8, each × 2 .. .. 4·00
906 50 c. Queen wearing Imperial State Crown .. 35 40
907 75 c. At Trooping the Colour 50 55
908 $3 Queen wearing diadem .. .. 1·25 2·25
905/8 .. .. *Set of* 4 2·00 3·00
MS909 147 × 93 mm. $4 Queen Elizabeth II (37 × 50 *mm*). P 13½ × 14 .. .. .. 2·50 3·25
Nos. 905/8 were printed together, *se-tenant*, in sheetlets of eight stamps, two of each value, and one stamp-size label.

166 Halley's Comet and Japanese *Planet A* Spacecraft

(Des G. Vasarhelyi. Litho Format)

1986 (30 Apr). *Appearance of Halley's Comet. T* **166** *and similar multicoloured designs. P* 13½ × 14.
910 10 c. Type **166**. 20 35
a. Sheetlet. Nos. 910/12, each × 3 .. 2·40
911 15 c. Halley's Comet, 1910 .. .. .. 30 50
912 50 c. Comet and European *Giotto* spacecraft 40 60
913 75 c. Belize Weather Bureau 70 80
a. Sheetlet. Nos. 913/15, each × 3 .. 8·50
914 $1 Comet and U.S.A. space telescope .. 95 1·10
915 $2 Edmond Halley .. .. 1·50 1·60
910/15 .. .. *Set of* 6 3·50 4·25
MS916 147 × 93 mm. $4 Computer enhanced photograph of Comet (37 × 50 *mm*) .. .. 5·00 6·00
Nos. 910/12 and 913/15 were each printed together, *se-tenant*, in horizontal and vertical strips of 3, within the two sheetlets of nine.

167 George Washington

(Des G. Vasarhelyi. Litho Format)

1986 (7 May). *United States Presidents. T* **167** *and similar ve[rt] designs. Multicoloured. P* 11.
917 10 c. Type **167**. 35 4
a. Sheetlet. Nos. 917/22 .. .. .. 3·00
918 20 c. John Adams 35 5
919 30 c. Thomas Jefferson 40 6
920 50 c. James Madison 50 6
921 $1.50, James Monroe .. .. .. 80 1·2
922 $2 John Quincy Adams .. .. .. 1·00 1·5
917/22 .. .. *Set of* 6 3·00 4·5
MS923 147 × 93 mm. $4 George Washington (*different*). P 13½ × 14 .. .. 5·00 5·5
Nos. 917/19 and 920/2 were printed together, *se-tenant*, i[n] horizontal strips of 3, separated by three stamp-size labe[ls] within the sheetlet of six stamps.

168 Auguste Bartholdi (sculptor) and Statue's Head

(Des G. Vasarhelyi. Litho Format)

1986 (15 May). *Centenary of Statue of Liberty. T* **168** *an[d] similar multicoloured designs. P* 13½ × 14.
924 25 c. Type **168**. 50
a. Sheetlet. Nos. 924/7, each × 2 .. .. 5·50
925 50 c. Statue's head at U.S. Centennial Celebration, Philadelphia, 1876 .. .. 60 8
926 75 c. Unveiling Ceremony, 1886 .. .. 65 9
927 $3 Statue of Liberty and flags of Belize and U.S.A. .. .. 1·40 2·
924/7 .. .. *Set of* 4 2·75 4·
MS928 147 × 92 mm. $4 Statue of Liberty and New York skyline (37 × 50 *mm*) .. .. .. 3·75 5·
Nos. 924/7 were printed together, *se-tenant*, in sheetlets [of] eight stamps, two of each value, and one stamp-size label.

169 British Honduras 1866 1s. Stamp

(Des G. Vasarhelyi. Litho Format)

1986 (22 May). *"Ameripex" International Stamp Exhibitio[n], Chicago. T* **169** *and similar multicoloured design[s]. P* 13½ × 14.
929 10 c. Type **169**. 40 5
a. Sheetlet. Nos. 929/31, each × 3 .. 4·50
930 15 c. 1981 Royal Wedding $1.50 stamp .. 55 7
931 50 c. U.S.A. 1918 24 c. airmail inverted centre error 75 8
932 75 c. U.S.S. *Constitution* (frigate) .. .. 90 1·1
a. Sheetlet. Nos. 932/4, each × 3 .. .. 9·00
933 $1 Liberty Bell .. .. 1·00 1·4
934 $2 White House .. .. 1·40 1·6
929/34 .. .. *Set of* 6 4·50 5·5
MS935 147 × 93 mm. $4 Capitol, Washington (37 × 50 *mm*) .. .. 3·25 4·0
Nos. 929/31 and 932/4 were each printed together, *se-tenan[t]*, in horizontal and vertical strips of 3, within the two sheetlets [of] nine.
Nos. 929/34 exist imperforate from stock dispersed by th[e] liquidator of Format International Security Printers Ltd.

170 English and Brazilian Players

(Des G. Vasarhelyi. Litho Format)

1986 (16 June) *World Cup Football Championship, Mexi[co] (2nd issue). T* **170** *and similar multicoloured designs. P* 11.
936 25 c. Type **170**. . .. . 1·00 1·2
a. Sheetlet. Nos. 936/9, each × 2 .. .. 13·00
937 50 c. Mexican player and Maya statues .. 1·40 1·6
938 75 c. Two Belizean players .. .. .. 1·75 2·
939 $3 Aztec stone calendar .. .. .. 3·00 3·5
936/9 .. .. *Set of* 4 6·50 7·5
MS940 147 × 92 mm. $4 Flags of competing nations on two footballs (37 × 50 *mm*). P 13½ × 14 .. .. 7·50 8·
Nos. 936/9 were printed together, *se-tenant*, in sheetlets [of] eight stamps, two of each value, and one stamp-size label.
No. 936a exists imperforate from stock dispersed by th[e] liquidator of Format International Security Printers Ltd.

171 Miss Sarah Ferguson

ARGENTINA-
WINNERS 1986

(172)

(Des G. Vasarhelyi. Litho Format)

86 (23 July). *Royal Wedding. T* **171** *and similar multicoloured designs. P* 14½.
1 25 c. Type **171**. . . . 40 40
a. Horiz strip of 3. Nos. 941/3 . . 2·25
2 75 c. Prince Andrew 70 90
3 $3 Prince Andrew and Miss Sarah Ferguson (92×41 *mm*) . . 1·40 2·25
1/3 . . *Set of* 3 2·25 3·25
S944 155×106 mm. $1 Miss Sarah Ferguson (*different*), $3 Prince Andrew (*different*) . . 3·25 5·00
Nos. 941/3 were printed together, *se-tenant*, in horizontal rips of 3 within small sheets of nine stamps.
No. **MS**944 exists imperforate from stock dispersed by the quidator of Format International Security Printers Ltd.

86 (15 Aug). *World Cup Football Championship Winners, Mexico. Nos.* 936/40 *optd with T* **172**.
5 25 c. Type **170**. . . . 1·00 1·00
a. Sheetlet. Nos. 945/8, each×2 . . 13·00
6 50 c. Mexican player and Maya statues . . 1·40 1·40
7 75 c. Two Belizean players . . 1·75 1·75
8 $3 Aztec stone calendar . . 3·00 3·00
5/8 . . *Set of* 4 6·50 6·50
S949 147×92 mm. $4 Flags of competing nations on two footballs (37×50 *mm*) . . 5·00 6·50

(173)

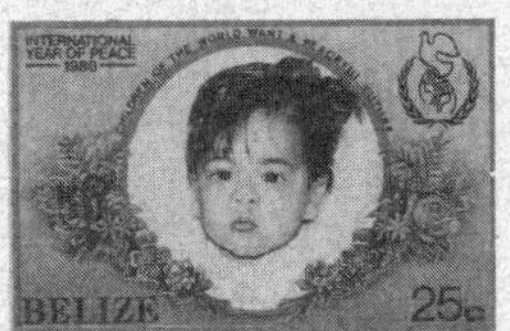

174 Amerindian Girl

86 (28 Aug). *"Stockholmia '86" International Stamp Exhibition, Sweden. Nos.* 929/35 *optd with T* **173**.
0 10 c. Type **169**. . . . 40 50
a. Sheetlet. Nos. 950/2, each×3 . . 4·75
1 15 c. 1981 Royal Wedding $1.50 stamp . . 50 60
2 50 c. U.S.A. 1918 24 c. airmail inverted centre error . . 70 80
3 75 c. U.S.S. *Constitution* . . 90 1·10
a. Sheetlet. Nos. 953/5, each×3 . . 10·50
4 $1 Liberty Bell . . 1·10 1·25
5 $2 White House . . 1·60 1·60
0/5 . . *Set of* 6 4·75 5·25
S956 147×93 mm. $4 Capitol, Washington (37×50 *mm*) . . 4·50 6·00

(Des G. Vasarhelyi. Litho Format)

986 (3 Oct). *International Peace Year. T* **174** *and similar multicoloured designs. P* 13½×14.
7 25 c. Type **174**. . . . 45 60
a. Sheetlet. Nos. 957/60, each×2 . . 7·00
8 50 c. European boy and girl . . 70 85
9 75 c. Japanese girl . . 1·00 1·25
0 $3 Indian boy and European girl . . 1·75 2·25
7/60 . . *Set of* 4 3·50 4·50
S961 132×106 mm. $4 As 25 c. but vert (35×47 *mm*) . . 4·00 5·00
Nos. 957/60 were printed together, *se-tenant*, in sheetlets of ght stamps, two of each value, and one stamp-size label.
No. **MS**961 exists imperforate from stock dispersed by the quidator of Format International Security Printers Ltd.

175 *Amanita lilloi*

176 Jose Carioca

(Des G. Drummond. Litho Format)

986 (30 Oct). *Fungi and Toucans. T* **175** *and similar vert designs. Multicoloured. P* 14×13½.
62 5 c. Type **175** 75 75
a. Sheetlet. Nos. 962, 964, 966 and 969, each×2 . . 11·00
963 10 c. Keel-billed Toucan . . 90 90
a. Sheetlet. Nos. 963, 965 and 967/8, each×2 . . 10·00
964 20 c. *Boletellus cubensis* . . 1·25 1·25
965 25 c. Collared Aracari . . 1·25 1·25
966 75 c. *Psilocybe caerulescens* . . 1·50 1·50
967 $1 Emerald Toucanet . . 1·50 1·50
968 $1.25, Crimson-rumped Toucanet . . 1·50 1·50
969 $2 *Russula puiggarii* . . 2·00 2·00
962/9 . . *Set of* 8 9·50 9·50
Nos. 962, 964, 966 and 969, and Nos. 963, 965 and 967/8, were each printed together, *se-tenant*, in sheetlets of eight stamps, two of each value, and one stamp-size label.
No. 962a exists imperforate from stock dispersed by the liquidator of Format International Security Printers Ltd.

(Des Walt Disney Productions. Litho Format)

1986 (14 Nov). *Christmas. T* **176** *and similar vert designs showing Walt Disney cartoon characters in scenes from "Saludos Amigos". Multicoloured. P* 11.
970 2 c. Type **176** 20 10
a. Sheetlet. Nos. 970/8 . . 7·25
971 3 c. Jose Carioca, Panchito and Donald Duck . . 20 10
972 4 c. Daisy Duck as Rio Carnival dancer . . 20 10
973 5 c. Mickey and Minnie Mouse as musician and dancer . . 20 10
974 6 c. Jose Carioca using umbrella as flute . . 20 10
975 50 c. Donald Duck and Panchito . . 1·00 1·25
976 65 c. Jose Carioca and Donald Duck playing hide and seek . . 1·25 1·50
977 $1.35, Donald Duck playing maracas . . 2·00 3·00
978 $2 Goofy as matador . . 2·75 3·50
970/8 . . *Set of* 9 7·25 8·50
MS979 131×111 mm. $4 Donald Duck. P 13½×14 . . 6·50 8·50
Nos. 970/8 were printed together, *se-tenant*, in sheetlets of nine.

177 Princess Elizabeth in Wedding Dress, 1947

178 *America II*

(Des G. Vasarhelyi. Litho Format)

1987 (7 Oct). *Royal Ruby Wedding. T* **177** *and similar vert designs. Multicoloured. P* 15.
980 25 c. Type **177**. . . . 20 20
981 75 c. Queen and Duke of Edinburgh, 1972 . . 35 40
982 $1 Queen on her 60th birthday . . 40 50
983 $4 In Garter robes . . 1·00 1·50
980/3 . . *Set of* 4 1·75 2·40
MS984 171×112 mm. $6 Queen and Duke of Edinburgh (44×50 *mm*). P 13½×14 . . 5·00 6·50

(Des G. Vasarhelyi. Litho Format)

1987 (21 Oct). *America's Cup Yachting Championship. T* **178** *and similar multicoloured designs. P* 15.
985 25 c. Type **178** 20 25
986 75 c. *Stars and Stripes* . . 35 50
987 $1 *Australia II*, 1983 . . 40 60
988 $4 *White Crusader* . . 1·00 1·60
985/8 . . *Set of* 4 1·75 2·75
MS989 171×112 mm. $6 Sails of *Australia II* (44×50 *mm*). P 13½×14 . . 5·50 7·00

179 "Mother and Child"

180 Black-handed Spider Monkey

(Des G. Vasarhelyi. Litho Format)

1987 (4 Nov). *Wood Carvings by George Gabb. T* **179** *and similar vert designs. Multicoloured. P* 15.
990 25 c. Type **179** 15 25
991 75 c. "Standing Form" . . 35 50
992 $1 "Love-doves" . . 40 60
993 $4 "Depiction of Music" . . 1·10 1·60
990/3 . . *Set of* 4 1·75 2·75
MS994 173×114 mm. $6 "African Heritage" (44×50 *mm*). P 13½×14 . . 3·50 5·00

(Des G. Drummond. Litho Format)

1987 (11 Nov). *Primates. T* **180** *and similar vert designs. Multicoloured. P* 15.
995 25 c. Type **180** 25 20
996 75 c. Black Howler Monkey . . 40 55
997 $1 Spider Monkeys with baby . . 45 65
998 $4 Two Black Howler Monkeys . . 1·10 2·00
995/8 . . *Set of* 4 2·00 3·00
MS999 171×112 mm. $6 Young Spider Monkey (41×48 *mm*). P 13½×14 . . 4·50 6·50

181 Guides on Parade

(Des G. Vasarhelyi. Litho Format)

1987 (25 Nov). *50th Anniv of Girl Guide Movement in Belize. T* **181** *and similar multicoloured designs. P* 15.
1000 25 c. Type **181** 45 20
1001 75 c. Brownie camp . . 80 90
1002 $1 Guide camp . . 1·00 1·25
1003 $4 Olave, Lady Baden-Powell . . 3·00 4·25
1000/3 . . *Set of* 4 4·75 6·00
MS1004 173×114 mm. $6 As $4, but vert (44×50 *mm*). P 13½×14 . . 5·00 6·50

182 Indian Refugee Camp

183 *Laelia euspatha*

(Des G. Vasarhelyi. Litho Format)

1987 (3 Dec). *International Year of Shelter for the Homeless. T* **182** *and similar horiz designs. Multicoloured. P* 15.
1005 25 c. Type **182** 50 25
1006 75 c. Filipino family and slum . . 90 90
1007 $1 Family in Middle East shanty town . . 1·10 1·25
1008 $4 Building modern house in Belize . . 3·00 4·25
1005/8 . . *Set of* 4 5·00 6·00

(Des G. Drummond. Litho Format)

1987 (16 Dec). *Christmas. Orchids. T* **183** *and similar vert designs showing illustrations from Sanders'* Reichenbachia. *Multicoloured. P* 13½×14.
1009 1 c. Type **183** 60 50
a. Sheetlet. Nos. 1009/15, each×2 . . 7·50
1010 2 c. *Cattleya citrina* . . 60 50
1011 3 c. *Masdevallia backhousiana* . . 60 50
1012 4 c. *Cypripedium tautzianum* . . 60 50
1013 5 c. *Trichopilia suavis alba* . . 60 50
1014 6 c. *Odontoglossum hebraicum* . . 60 50
1015 7 c. *Cattleya trianaei schroederiana* . . 60 50
1016 10 c. *Saccolabium giganteum* . . 75 65
a. Sheetlet. Nos. 1016/22, each×2 . . 17·00
1017 30 c. *Cattleya warscewiczii* . . 90 80
1018 50 c. *Chysis bractescens* . . 1·25 1·00
1019 70 c. *Cattleya rochellensis* . . 1·40 1·10
1020 $1 *Laelia elegans schilleriana* . . 1·50 1·10
1021 $1.50, *Laelia anceps percivaliana* . . 1·60 1·40
1022 $3 *Laelia gouldiana* . . 2·25 1·90
1009/22 . . *Set of* 14 12·50 10·50
MS1023 Two sheets, each 171×112 mm. (a) $3 *Odontoglossum roezlii* (40×47 *mm*). (b) $5 *Cattleya dowiana aurea* (40×47 *mm*) *Set of* 2 *sheets* 7·50 10·00
Nos. 1009/1015 and 1016/22 were each printed together, *se-tenant*, in sheetlets of fourteen stamps, containing two of each value and one stamp-size label.
Examples of the $3 value from No. **MS**1023 with the orchid name incorrectly spelt are from stock dispersed by the liquidator of Format International Security Printers Ltd.

184 Christ condemned to Death

185 Basketball

(Des G. Vasarhelyi. Litho Format)

1988 (21 Mar). *Easter. The Stations of the Cross. T* **184** *and similar vert designs. Multicoloured. P* 13½×14.
1024 40 c. Type **184** 35 45
a. Sheetlet. Nos. 1024/37 . . 4·25
1025 40 c. Christ carrying the Cross . . 35 45
1026 40 c. Falling for the first time . . 35 45
1027 40 c. Christ meets Mary . . 35 45
1028 40 c. Simon of Cyrene helping to carry the Cross . . 35 45
1029 40 c. Veronica wiping the face of Christ . . 35 45
1030 40 c. Christ falling a second time . . 35 45

1031 40 c. Consoling the women of Jerusalem 35 45
1032 40 c. Falling for the third time 35 45
1033 40 c. Christ being stripped 35 45
1034 40 c. Christ nailed to the Cross 35 45
1035 40 c. Dying on the Cross 35 45
1036 40 c. Christ taken down from the Cross .. 35 45
1037 40 c. Christ being laid in the sepulchre .. 35 45
1024/37 .. .. *Set of* 14 4·25 5·50

Nos. 1024/37 were printed together, *se-tenant*, in a sheetlet of 14 stamps and one stamp-size label which appears in the central position.

No. 1024a exists imperforate from stock dispersed by the liquidator of Format International Security Printers Ltd.

A $6 miniature sheet was prepared, but not issued. Examples exist from stock dispersed by the liquidator.

(Des J. McDaniel. Litho Questa)

1988 (15 Aug). *Olympic Games, Seoul. T* **185** *and similar vert designs. Multicoloured. P* 14.
1038 10 c. Type **185** 70 30
1039 25 c. Volleyball 75 30
1040 60 c. Table tennis 80 60
1041 75 c. Diving 80 70
1042 $1 Judo 90 85
1043 $2 Hockey .. .. 3·00 3·25
1038/43 .. .. *Set of* 6 6·25 5·50
MS1044 76×106 mm. $3 Gymnastics .. .. 3·00 4·00

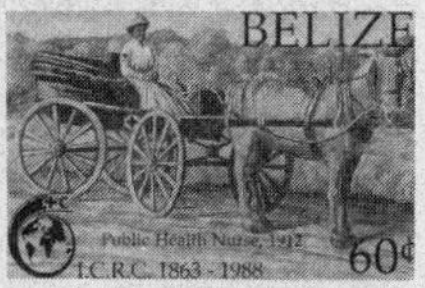

186 Public Health Nurse, c. 1912

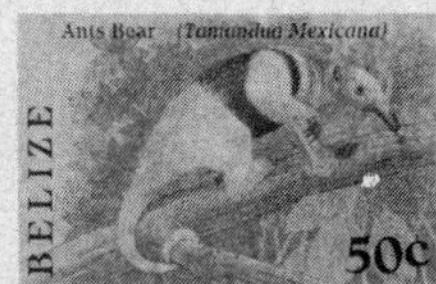

187 Collared Anteater ("Ants Bear")

(Des O. Fernandez. Litho Questa)

1988 (18 Nov). *125th Anniv of International Red Cross. T* **186** *and similar horiz designs. Multicoloured. P* 14.
1045 60 c. Type **186** .. .. 1·50 1·25
1046 75 c. Hospital ship and ambulance launch, 1937 .. .. 1·75 1·50
1047 $1 Ambulance at hospital tent, 1956 .. 2·25 1·75
1048 $2 Auster ambulance plane, 1940 .. 3·00 4·00
1045/8 .. .. *Set of* 4 7·75 7·75

(Des J. Barberis. Litho Questa)

1989 (24 Feb)–**90**. *Small Animals of Belize. T* **187** *and similar multicoloured designs. P* 14. (a) *W w* **16** (*sideways on* 25 *c.*).
1049 10 c. Paca ("Gibnut") (30.6.89) .. .. 1·50 1·50
1049*a* 25 c. Four-eyed Opossum (*vert*) (1.90) .. 1·75 1·75

(*b*) *No wmk*
1050 25 c. Four-eyed Opossum (*vert*) .. .. 1·50 1·50
1051 50 c. Type **187** .. .. 2·00 2·00
1052 60 c. As 10 c. .. .. 2·00 2·00
1053 75 c. Red Brocket .. .. .. 2·00 2·00
1054 $2 Collared Peccary .. .. .. 3·50 4·50
1049/54 .. .. *Set of* 7 13·00 14·00

(Des A. Theobald ($5), D. Miller (others). Litho Questa)

1989 (20 July). *20th Anniv of First Manned Landing on Moon. Multicoloured designs as T* **126** *of Ascension. W w* **16** (*sideways on* 50, 75 *c.*). *P* 14×13½ (25 *c.*, $1) *or* 14 (*others*).
1055 25 c. Docking of "Apollo 9" modules .. 45 25
1056 50 c. "Apollo 9" command service module in space (30×30 *mm*) 65 65
1057 75 c. "Apollo 9" emblem (30×30 *mm*) .. 90 1·00
1058 $1 "Apollo 9" lunar module in space .. 1·25 1·40
1055/8 .. .. *Set of* 4 3·00 3·00
MS1059 83×100 mm. $5 "Apollo 11" command service module undergoing tests. P 14×13½. .. 5·50 6·00

5c

(**188**)

WORLD STAMP EXPO '89
United States Postal Service
Nov. 17 — 20 and
Nov. 24 — Dec. 3, 1989
Washington Convention Center
Washington, DC

(**189**)

1989 (15 Nov). *No.* 771A *surch with T* **188** *by Govt Printer, Belize.*
1060 5 c. on 6 c. Star-eyed Hermit Crab .. 12·00 1·50

1989 (17 Nov). *"World Stamp Expo '89" International Stamp Exhibition, Washington. No.* **MS**1059 *optd with T* **189**.
MS1061 83×100 mm. $5 "Apollo 11" command service module undergoing tests .. .. 5·50 6·50

190 Wesley Church

191 White-winged Tanager and *Catonephele numilia*

(Des Jennifer Toombs. Litho B.D.T.)

1989 (13 Dec). *Christmas. Belize Churches. T* **190** *and similar vert designs. W w* **16**. *P* 13½.
1062 10 c. black, rose-pink and cinnamon .. 20 10
1063 25 c. black, reddish lilac and rose-lilac .. 25 20
1064 60 c. black, pale turquoise-blue and cobalt 50 60
1065 75 c. black, pale blue-green and sage-green 65 80
1066 $1 blk, pale greenish yell & chrome-yell 80 1·10
1062/6 .. .. *Set of* 5 2·25 2·50

Designs:—25 c. Baptist Church; 60 c. St. John's Anglican Cathedral; 75 c. St. Andrew's Presbyterian Church; $1 Holy Redeemer Roman Catholic Cathedral.

(Des I. Loe. Litho Questa)

1990 (1 Mar)–**93**. *Birds and Butterflies. T* **191** *and similar vert designs. Multicoloured. W w* **14**. *P* 14. A. *Without imprint date.*
1067A 5 c. Type **191** 40 40
1068A 10 c. Keel-billed Toucan and *Nessaea aglaura* 60 50
1069A 15 c. Magnificent Frigate Bird and *Eurytides philolaus* 60 30
1070A 25 c. Jabiru and *Heliconius sapho* .. 60 40
1071A 30 c. Great Blue Heron and *Colobura dirce* 60 40
1072A 50 c. Northern Oriole and *Hamadryas arethusia* 70 60
1073A 60 c. Scarlet Macaw and *Evenus regalis* 80 70
1074A 75 c. Red-legged Honeycreeper and *Callicore patelina* 90 75
1075A $1 Spectacled Owl and *Caligo uranus* 1·75 1·25
1076A $2 Green Jay and *Philaethria dido* .. 2·25 3·00
1077A $5 Turkey Vulture and *Battus belus* 4·00 5·00
1078A $10 Osprey and *Papilio thoas* .. .. 8·00 9·00
1067A/78A .. .. .. *Set of* 12 19·00 20·00

B. *With imprint date* ("1993") (5.7.93)
1068B 10 c. Keel-billed Toucan and *Nessaea aglaura* 50 50

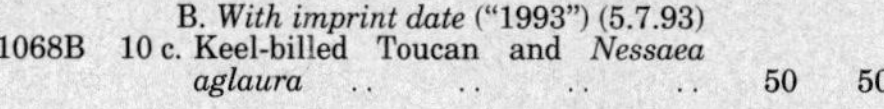

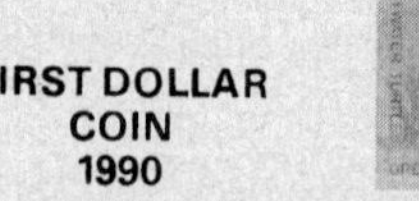

FIRST DOLLAR COIN 1990

(**192**)

193 Green Turtle

1990 (1 Mar). *First Belize Dollar Coin. No.* 1075A *optd with T* **192** *in gold.*
1079 $1 Spectacled Owl and *Caligo uranus* .. 3·50 2·50

(Des G. Drummond. Litho B.D.T.)

1990 (8 Aug). *Turtles. T* **193** *and similar horiz designs. Multicoloured. W w* **14** (*sideways*). *P* 14.
1080 10 c. Type **193** 55 30
1081 25 c. Hawksbill Turtle 85 30
1082 60 c. Saltwater Loggerhead Turtle .. 1·25 1·25
1083 75 c. Freshwater Loggerhead Turtle .. 1·40 1·40
1084 $1 Bocatora Turtle .. .. .. 1·75 1·75
1085 $2 Hicatee Turtle .. .. .. 2·50 4·00
1080/5 .. .. *Set of* 6 7·50 8·00

194 Fairey Battle

195 *Cattleya bowringiana*

(Des A. Theobald. Litho B.D.T)

1990 (15 Sept). *50th Anniv of the Battle of Britain. T* **194** *and similar horiz designs. Multicoloured. W w* **16** (*sideways*). *P* 13½.
1086 10 c. Type **194** 60 40
1087 25 c. Bristol Type 152 Beaufort .. .. 1·10 40
1088 60 c. Bristol Type 142 Blenheim Mk IV .. 1·75 1·75
1089 75 c. Armstrong-Whitworth Whitley .. 1·75 1·75
1090 $1 Vickers-Armstrong Wellington Mk 1c 1·75 1·75
1091 $2 Handley-Page Hampden .. .. 2·25 3·25
1086/91 .. .. *Set of* 6 8·25 8·50

(Des Lynn Chadwick. Litho Questa)

1990 (1 Nov). *Christmas. Orchids. T* **195** *and similar ve designs. Multicoloured. W w* **14**. *P* 14.
1092 25 c. Type **195** 70 2
1093 50 c. *Rhyncholaelia digbyana* .. .. 1·00 5
1094 60 c. *Sobralia macrantha* .. .. 1·25 1·0
1095 75 c. *Chysis bractescens* .. .. .. 1·25 1·0
1096 $1 *Vanilla planifolia* .. .. .. 1·50 1·5
1097 $2 *Epidendrum polyanthum* .. .. 2·25 3·0
1092/7 .. .. *Set of* 6 7·25 6·5

196 Common Iguana

(Des G. Drummond. Litho B.D.T.)

1991 (10 Apr). *Reptiles and Mammals. T* **196** *and similar hor designs. Multicoloured. W w* **14** (*sideways*). *P* 14.
1098 25 c. Type **196** 80 3
1099 50 c. Morelet's Crocodile .. .. 1·25 9
1100 60 c. American Manatee .. .. 1·50 1·5
1101 75 c. Boa Constrictor .. .. .. 1·75 1·7
1102 $1 Baird's Tapir .. .. .. 2·00 2·0
1103 $2 Jaguar .. .. 2·75 3·7
1098/1103 .. .. .. *Set of* 6 9·00 9·0

(Des D. Miller. Litho Questa)

1991 (17 June). *65th Birthday of Queen Elizabeth II and 70 Birthday of Prince Philip. Vert designs as T* **139** *of Ascensio Multicoloured. W w* **16** (*sideways*). *P* 14½×14.
1104 $1 Queen Elizabeth II wearing tiara 1·00 1·2
a. Horiz pair. Nos. 1104/5 separated by label .. .. 2·00 2·5
1105 $1 Prince Philip wearing panama .. 1·00 1·2

Nos. 1104/5 were printed in a similar sheet format to No 539/40 of Ascension

197 Weather Radar

(Des D. Miller. Litho Walsall)

1991 (31 July). *International Decade for Natural Disast Reduction. T* **197** *and similar horiz designs. W w* (*sideways*). *P* 14.
1106 60 c. multicoloured .. .. .. 1·25 1·2
1107 75 c. multicoloured .. .. .. 1·40 1·4
1108 $1 greenish blue and grey-black .. 1·50 1·5
1109 $2 multicoloured .. .. .. 2·25 2·7
1106/9 .. .. *Set of* 4 5·75 6·2

Designs:—75 c. Weather station; $1 Floods in Belize aft Hurricane Hattie, 1961; $2 Satellite image of Hurricane Gilber

198 Thomas Ramos and Demonstration

(Des G. Vasarhelyi. Litho Questa)

1991 (4 Sept). *10th Anniv of Independence. Famous Belizia (1st series). T* **198** *and similar horiz designs. Multicoloure W w* **16** (*sideways*). *P* 14.
1110 25 c. Type **198** 60 3
1111 60 c. Sir Isaiah Morter and palm trees .. 1·25 1·2
1112 75 c. Antonio Soberanis and political meeting .. .. 1·25 1·5
1113 $1 Santiago Ricalde and cutting sugar-cane .. .. 1·50 1·7
1110/13 .. .. *Set of* 4 4·25 4·2

See also Nos. 1126/9 and 1148/51.

199 "Anansi the Spider"

200 *Gongora quinquenervis*

(Des G. Vasarhelyi. Litho B.D.T.)

91 (6 Nov). *Christmas. Folklore. T* **199** *and similar multicoloured designs.* W w **14** (*sideways on horiz designs*). P 14.

14 25 c. Type **199** 70 20
15 50 c. "Jack-o-Lantern" .. .. .. 1·00 55
16 60 c. "Tata Duende" (*vert*) .. .. 1·25 1·25
17 75 c. "Xtabai" .. .. 1·25 1·25
18 $1 "Warrie Massa" (*vert*) .. .. 1·50 1·50
19 $2 "Old Heg" .. .. 2·50 3·50
14/19 .. .. *Set of* 6 7·50 7·50

(Des Lynn Chadwick. Litho B.D.T.)

92 (1 Apr). *Easter. Orchids. T* **200** *and similar vert designs.* W w **14**. P 14×13½.

20 25 c. Type **200** 90 20
21 50 c. *Oncidium sphacelatum* .. .. 1·50 75
22 60 c. *Encyclia bratescens* .. .. 1·75 1·75
23 75 c. *Epidendrum ciliare* .. .. 1·75 1·75
24 $1 *Psygmorchis pusilla* .. .. 2·00 2·00
25 $2 *Galeandra batemanii* .. .. 2·75 4·00
20/5 .. .. *Set of* 6 9·50 9·50

(Des G. Vasarhelyi. Litho Enschedé)

92 (26 Aug). *Famous Belizeans (2nd series). Horiz designs as T* **198**, *but inscr* "EMINENT BELIZEANS" *at top. Multicoloured.* W w **14** (*sideways*). P 13×12½.

26 25 c. Gwendolyn Lizarraga (politician) and High School 55 30
27 60 c. Rafael Fonseca (civil servant) and Government Offices, Belize .. .. 90 1·00
28 75 c. Vivian Seay (health worker) and nurses .. .. 1·10 1·25
29 $1 Samuel Haynes (U.N.I.A. worker) and words of National Anthem .. .. 1·40 1·75
26/9 .. .. *Set of* 4 3·50 3·75

201 Xunantunich and National Assembly

(Des D. Miller. Litho Questa)

92 (1 Oct). *500th Anniv of Discovery of America by Columbus. T* **201** *and similar horiz designs showing Mayan sites and modern buildings. Multicoloured.* W w **16** (*sideways*). P 14.

30 25 c. Type **201** 70 25
31 60 c. Altun Ha and Supreme Court .. 1·00 1·00
32 75 c. Santa Rita and Tower Hill Sugar Factory .. .. 1·25 1·25
33 $5 Lamanai and Citrus Company works 6·00 7·50
30/3 .. .. *Set of* 4 8·00 9·00

202 Hashishi Pampi **203** *Lycaste aromatica*

(Des G. Vasarhelyi. Litho Enschedé)

992 (16 Nov). *Christmas. Folklore. T* **202** *and similar multicoloured designs.* W w **14** (*sideways on* 25, 60 *c.*, $5). P 12½×13 ($1) *or* 13×12½ (*others*).

134 25 c. Type **202** 30 20
135 60 c. Cadejo 60 60
136 $1 La Sucia (*vert*) .. .. .. 90 1·00
137 $5 Sisimito .. .. 4·00 6·00
134/7 .. .. *Set of* 4 5·25 7·00

(Des A. Theobald. Litho Questa)

993 (1 Apr). *75th Anniv of Royal Air Force. Horiz designs as T* **149** *of Ascension. Multicoloured.* W w **14** (*sideways*). P 14.

138 25 c. Sud Aviation SA 330L Puma helicopter 70 40
139 50 c. Hawker Siddeley Harrier GR3 .. 90 65
140 60 c. De Havilland DH98 Mosquito Mk XVIII .. .. 1·10 1·10
141 75 c. Avro Type 683 Lancaster .. .. 1·10 1·10
142 $1 Consolidated Liberator I .. .. 1·25 1·25
143 $3 Short Stirling Mk I .. .. .. 3·00 4·50
138/43 .. .. *Set of* 6 7·25 8·00

(Des Annette Robinson. Litho Walsall)

993 (23 Apr). *14th World Orchid Conference, Glasgow. T* **203** *and similar vert designs. Multicoloured.* W w **16**. P 14½×14.

144 25 c. Type **203** 40 25
145 60 c. *Sobralia decora* 75 80
146 $1 *Maxillaria alba* .. .. .. 1·00 1·10
147 $2 *Brassavola nodosa* .. .. .. 1·75 2·50
144/7 .. .. *Set of* 4 3·50 4·25

(Des G. Vasarhelyi. Litho Questa)

1993 (11 Aug). *Famous Belizeans (3rd series). Horiz designs as T* **198**, *but inscr* "EMINENT BELIZEANS" *at top. Multicoloured.* W w **16** (*sideways*). P 14.

1148 25 c. Herbert Watkin Beaumont, Post Office and postmark 40 25
1149 60 c. Dr. Selvyn Walford Young and score of National Anthem 75 85
1150 75 c. Cleopatra White and health centre 90 1·25
1151 $1 Dr. Karl Heusner and early car .. 1·10 1·40
1148/51 .. .. *Set of* 4 2·75 3·25

204 Boom and Chime Band

(Des Jennifer Toombs. Litho B.D.T.)

1993 (3 Nov). *Christmas. Local Customs. T* **204** *and similar horiz designs. Multicoloured.* W w **14** (*sideways*). P 14.

1152 25 c. Type **204** 30 20
1153 60 c. John Canoe dance 70 70
1154 75 c. Cortez dance 80 80
1155 $2 Maya musical group .. .. 2·00 3·25
1152/5 .. .. *Set of* 4 3·50 4·50

1994 (18 Feb). *"Hong Kong '94" International Stamp Exhibition. No.* 1075A *optd as T* **154** *of Ascension.*

1156 $1 Spectacled Owl and *Caligo uranus* .. 1·40 1·75

(Des D. Miller. Litho Questa)

1994 (22 Feb). *Royal Visit. Vert designs as T* **202** *of Bahamas. Multicoloured.* W w **16**. P 14½.

1157 25 c. Flags of Belize and Great Britain .. 35 20
1158 60 c. Queen Elizabeth II in yellow coat and hat 65 65
1159 75 c. Queen Elizabeth in evening dress .. 85 85
1160 $1 Queen Elizabeth, Prince Philip and Yeomen of the Guard .. .. 1·25 1·40
1157/60 .. .. *Set of* 4 2·75 2·75

205 *Lonchorhina aurita* (bat) (**206**)

(Des N. Arlott. Litho B.D.T.)

1994 (30 May). *Bats. T* **205** *and similar horiz designs. Multicoloured.* W w **16** (*sideways*). P 14.

1161 25 c. Type **205** 35 20
1162 60 c. *Vampyrodes caraccioli* 65 65
1163 75 c. *Noctilio leporinus* 80 80
1164 $2 *Desmodus rotundus* .. .. .. 2·00 3·00
1161/4 .. .. *Set of* 4 3·50 4·25

1994 (18 Aug). *75th Anniv of International Labour Organization. No.* 1074A *surch with T* **206**.

1165 10 c. on 75 c. Red-legged Honey-creeper and *Callicore patelina* 50 50

207 *Cycnoches chlorochilon* **208** Ground Beetle

(Des N. Shewring. Litho B.D.T.)

1994 (7 Nov). *Christmas. Orchids. T* **207** *and similar vert designs. Multicoloured.* W w **16**. P 14×13½.

1166 25 c. Type **207** 35 20
1167 60 c. *Brassavola cucullata* 65 70
1168 75 c. *Sobralia mucronata* 80 90
1169 $1 *Nidema boothii* .. .. .. 1·10 1·25
1166/9 .. .. *Set of* 4 2·50 2·75

(Des I. Loe and D. Miller. Litho B.D.T.)

1995 (11 Jan)–**96**. *Insects. T* **208** *and similar horiz designs. Multicoloured.* W w **14** (*sideways**). P 14. A. *Without imprint date at foot.*

1170A 5 c. Type **208** 30 40
1171A 10 c. Harlequin Beetle 30 40
w. Wmk Crown to right of CA ..
1172A 15 c. Giant Water Bug 40 50
1173A 25 c. Peanut-head Bug 50 20
1174A 30 c. Coconut Weevil 55 25
1175A 50 c. Mantis 70 40
1176A 60 c. Tarantula Wasp 90 50
1177A 75 c. Rhinoceros Beetle .. .. .. 1·00 60
1178A $1 Metallic Wood Borer .. .. 1·40 90
1179A $2 Dobson Fly .. .. .. 3·00 3·50
1180A $5 Click Beetle .. .. .. 5·50 6·00
1181A $10 Long-horned Beetle .. .. 8·50 10·00
1070A/81A .. .. *Set of* 12 21·00 21·00

B. *With imprint date "1996" at bottom right* (10.96)

1170B 5 c. Type **208** 10 10
1171B 10 c. Harlequin Beetle 10 10
1172B 15 c. Giant Water Bug 10 10
1173B 25 c. Peanut-head Bug 15 20
1174B 30 c. Coconut Weevil 15 20
1175B 50 c. Mantis 30 35
1176B 60 c. Tarantula Wasp 35 40
1177B 75 c. Rhinoceros Beetle 45 50
1178B $1 Metallic Wood Borer 60 65
1179B $2 Dobson Fly .. .. .. 1·25 1·40
1180B $5 Click Beetle .. .. .. 3·00 3·25
1181B $10 Long-horned Beetle .. .. 6·00 6·50
1170B/81B .. .. *Set of* 12 13·50 14·00

**The normal sideways watermark shows Crown to left of CA, as seen from the back of the stamp.*

(Des R. Watton. Litho Cartor)

1995 (8 May). *50th Anniv of End of Second World War. Horiz designs as T* **161** *of Ascension.* W w **14** (*sideways*). P 13½.

1182 25 c. War memorial 30 25
1183 60 c. Remembrance Day parade 65 70
1184 75 c. British Honduras forestry unit .. 80 90
1185 $1 Vickers-Armstrong Wellington bomber .. .. 95 1·10
1182/5 .. .. *Set of* 4 2·40 2·75

(**209**) **210** Male and Female Blue Ground Dove

1995 (1 Sept). *"Singapore '95" International Stamp Exhibition. Nos.* 1166/9 *optd with T* **209** *in blue.*

1186 25 c. Type **207** 30 20
1187 60 c. *Brassavola cucullata* 65 80
1188 75 c. *Sobralia mucronata* 80 95
1189 $1 *Nidema boothii* .. .. .. 1·00 1·25
1186/9 .. .. *Set of* 4 2·50 2·75

(Des A. Theobald. Litho B.D.T.)

1995 (24 Oct). *50th Anniv of United Nations. Horiz designs as T* **213** *of Bahamas.* W w **16** (*sideways*). P 14.

1190 25 c. M113-light reconnaisance vehicle .. 25 20
1191 60 c. Sultan armoured command vehicle 60 65
1192 75 c. Leyland-Daf 8×4 drops lorry .. 75 80
1193 $2 Warrior infantry combat vehicle .. 1·50 2·25
1190/3 .. .. *Set of* 4 2·75 3·50

(Des N. Arlott. Litho B.D.T.)

1995 (6 Nov). *Christmas. Doves. T* **210** *and similar vert designs. Multicoloured.* W w **14**. P 14.

1194 25 c. Type **210** 35 20
1195 60 c. White-fronted Doves 70 70
1196 75 c. Pair of Ruddy Ground Doves .. 85 90
1197 $1 White-winged Doves .. .. .. 1·25 1·25
1194/7 .. .. *Set of* 4 2·75 2·75

(**211**) **212** Unloading Banana Train, Commerce Bight Pier

1996 (17 May). *"CHINA '96" 9th Asian International Stamp Exhibition, Peking. Nos.* 1172A, 1174A/5A *and* 1179A *optd with T* **211**.

1198 15 c. Giant Water Bug 15 15
1199 30 c. Coconut Weevil 30 30
1200 50 c. Mantis 45 50
1201 $2 Dobson Fly .. .. .. 1·60 2·00
1198/1201 .. .. *Set of* 4 2·25 2·75

(Des A. Theobald. Litho Cartor)

1996 (7 June). *"CAPEX '96" International Stamp Exhibition, Toronto. Railways. T* **212** *and similar horiz designs. Multicoloured.* W w **14** (*sideways*). *P* 13½×13.

1202 25 c. Type **212** 35 20
1203 60 c. Locomotive No. 1, Stann Creek station 65 55
1204 75 c. Locomotive No. 4 pulling mahogany log train 80 70
1205 $3 L.M.S. No. 5602 *British Honduras* locomotive .. .. 2·50 3·50
1202/5 .. .. *Set of* 4 3·75 4·50

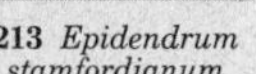

213 *Epidendrum stamfordianum* **214** Red Poll

(Des Lynn Chadwick. Litho Cot Printery Ltd, Barbados)

1996 (6 Nov). *Christmas. Orchids. T* **213** *and similar vert designs. Multicoloured.* W w **14**. *P* 14.

1206 25 c. Type **213** 40 20
1207 60 c. *Oncidium carthagenense* 70 70
1208 75 c. *Oerstedella verrucosa* 80 90
1209 $1 *Coryanthes speciosa* .. .. 1·10 1·25
1206/9 .. .. *Set of* 4 2·75 2·75

(Des G. Vasarhelyi. Litho Cot Printery Ltd, Barbados)

1997 (12 Feb). *"HONG KONG '97" International Stamp Exhibition. Chinese New Year ("Year of the Ox"). T* **214** *and similar horiz designs showing cattle breeds. Multicoloured.* W w **14** (*sideways*). *P* 14.

1210 25 c. Type **214** 30 20
1211 60 c. Brahman 60 70
1212 75 c. Longhorn 70 80
1213 $1 Charbray .. .. 95 1·10
1210/13 .. .. *Set of* 4 2·25 2·50

215 Coral Snake **216** Adult Male Howler Monkey

(Des Doreen McGuiness. Litho Cot Printery, Barbados)

1997 (28 May). *Snakes. T* **215** *and similar vert designs. Multicoloured.* W w **14**. *P* 14.

1214 25 c. Type **215** 25 20
1215 60 c. Green Vine Snake 50 50
1216 75 c. Yellow-jawed Tommygoff 60 60
1217 $1 Speckled Racer 75 80
1214/17 .. .. *Set of* 4 1·90 1·90

(Des N. Shewring. Litho Walsall)

1997 (13 Aug). *Endangered Species. Howler Monkey. T* **216** *and similar vert designs. Multicoloured.* W w **14**. *P* 14.

1218 10 c. Type **216** 15 10
1219 25 c. Female feeding 25 20
1220 60 c. Female with young 55 55
1221 75 c. Juvenile monkey feeding 65 75
1218/21 .. .. *Set of* 4 1·40 1·40

217 *Maxillaria elatior* **218** School Children using the Internet

(Des Lynn Chadwick. Litho B.D.T.)

1997 (21 Nov). *Christmas. Orchids. T* **217** *and similar vert designs. Multicoloured.* W w **16**. *P* 13½.

1222 25 c. Type **217** 25 20
1223 60 c. *Dimerandra emarginata* 50 50
1224 75 c. *Macradenia brassavolae* 60 60
1225 $1 *Ornithocephalus gladiatus* 75 80
1222/5 .. .. *Set of* 4 1·90 1·90

(Des D. Miller. Litho Questa)

1998 (31 Mar). *Diana, Princess of Wales Commemoration. Sheet, 145×70 mm, containing vert designs as T* **177** *of Ascension. Multicoloured.* W w **14** (*sideways*). *P* 14½×14.

MS1226 $1 Wearing floral dress, 1988; $1 In evening dress, 1981; $1 Wearing pearl drop earrings, 1988; $1 Carrying bouquet, 1983 .. 3·00 3·50

(Des N. Shewring. Litho Cartor)

1998 (22 July). *50th Anniv of Organization of American States. T* **218** *and similar horiz design. Multicoloured.* W w **14** (*sideways*). *P* 13.

1227 25 c. Type **218** 25 20
1228 $1 Map of Central America 75 80

219 University Arms **220** Baymen Gun Flats

(Des N. Shewring. Litho Cartor)

1998 (22 July). *50th Anniv of University of West Indies.* W w **14** (*sideways*). *P* 13.

1229 **219** $1 multicoloured 75 75

(Des A. Theobald. Litho Cartor)

1998 (5 Aug). *Bicentenary of Battle of St. George's Cay. T* **220** *and similar multicoloured designs.* W w **14** (*sideways on* 25 *c. to* $2). *P* 13½.

1230 10 c. Boat moored at quayside (*vert*) .. 20 20
 a. Horiz strip of 3. Nos. 1230/2 .. 55
1231 10 c. Three sentries and cannon (*vert*) .. 20 20
1232 10 c. Cannon and rowing boats (*vert*) .. 20 20
1233 25 c. Type **220** 30 20
1234 60 c. Baymen sloops 50 50
1235 75 c. British schooners 55 55
1236 $1 H.M.S. *Merlin* (sloop) 70 70
1237 $2 Spanish flagship .. .. .. 1·25 1·60
1230/7 .. .. *Set of* 8 3·50 3·75

Nos. 1230/2 were printed together, *se-tenant*, in horizontal strips of 3 throughout the sheet, showing a composite view of Belize from Fort George.

221 *Brassia maculata*

(Des Lynn Chadwick. Litho Cot Printery Ltd, Barbados)

1998 (4 Nov). *Christmas. Orchids. T* **221** *and similar vert designs. Multicoloured.* W w **14**. *P* 14½×14.

1238 25 c. Type **221** 15 20
1239 60 c. *Encyclia radiata* 35 40
1240 75 c. *Stanhopea ecornuta* 45 50
1241 $1 *Isochilus carnosiflorus* 60 65
1238/41 .. .. *Set of* 4 1·50 1·75

STAMP BOOKLETS

1920. *Black on pink cover inscr* "British Honduras–100–Tv Cent Stamps". *Stapled.*

SB1 $2 booklet containing one hundred 2 c. (No. 102*b*) in blocks of 10 (5×2) .. ..

1920. *Grey-blue cover inscr* "British Honduras–100–Thr Cent Stamps". *Stapled.*

SB2 $3 booklet containing one hundred 3 c. (No. 103) in blocks of 10 (5×2) .. .. ..

1923. *Black on pink cover inscr* "British Honduras–100–Tv Cent Stamps". *Stapled.*

SB3 $2 booklet containing one hundred 2 c. brown (No. 127) in blocks of 10 (5×2) .. .. ..

1927. *Black on pink cover inscr* "British Honduras–100–Tv Cent Stamps". *Stapled.*

SB4 $2 booklet containing one hundred 2 c. rose-carmine (No. 128) in blocks of 10 (5×2) ..

1984 (30 Apr). *Olympic Games, Los Angeles. Multicolour cover,* 155×102 *mm, showing athlete and chariot. Stitched.*

SB5 $10 booklet containing 5 c., 20 c., 25 c. and $2, each in pane of 4 (Nos. 789a, 790a, 791a, 792a) 3·

POSTAGE DUE STAMPS

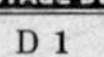

D 1 D 2

(Typo D.L.R.)

1923–64. *Wmk Mult Script CA. Ordinary paper. P* 14.

D1 D 1 1 c. black .. .. 2·00 12·
 a. Chalk-surfaced paper (25.9.56) .. 50 16·
 b. White uncoated paper (9.4.64) .. 14·00 27·
D2 2 c. black .. .. 1·75 7·
 a. Chalk-surfaced paper (25.9.56) .. 50 16·
D3 4 c. black .. .. 1·25 6·
 a. Missing top serif on "C" (R. 6/6) .. 10·00
 b. Chalk-surfaced paper (25.9.56) .. 90 10·
 ba. Missing top serif on "C" (R. 6/6) .. 9·00
 w. Wmk inverted .. .. ..
D1/3 .. .. *Set of* 3 4·50 23·
D1a/3b .. .. *Set of* 3 1·75 38·
D1/3 Optd "Specimen" .. .. *Set of* 3 48·00

The early ordinary paper printings were yellowish and qui distinct from No. D1b.

1965 (3 Aug)–**72.** *As Nos.* D2a *and* D3b, *but Wmk* w (*sideways on* 2 *c.*). *P* 13½×13 (2 *c.*) *or* 13½×14 (4 *c.*)

D4 D 1 2 c. black (10.1.72) .. .. .. 2·50 5·
D5 4 c. black .. .. 75 5·

The missing top serif on "C" variety of R. 6/6 was correcte before No. D5 was printed.

(Des P. Powell. Litho Questa)

1976 (1 July). *Type* D **2** *and similar vert designs, but with differe frames.* W w **14** (*sideways*). *P* 13½ x 14.

D 6 D **2** 1 c. red and dull green 10
D 7 – 2 c. light magenta and bluish violet .. 10
D 8 – 5 c. dull green and orange-brown .. 15 1·
D 9 – 15 c. apple-green and dull vermilion .. 25 1·
D10 – 25 c. orange and olive-green .. .. 40 1·
D6/10 .. .. *Set of* 5 85 4·

CAYES OF BELIZE

A chain of several hundred islands, coral atolls, reefs and san banks stretching along the eastern seaboard of Belize.

Appendix

The following issues for the Cayes of Belize fall outside t criteria for full listing as detailed on page xi.

1984

Marine Life, Map and Views. 1, 2, 5, 10, 15, 25, 75 *c.*, $3, $5
250*th Anniv of* Lloyd's List (*newspaper*). 25, 75 *c.*, $1, $2.
Olympic Games, Los Angeles. 10, 15, 75 *c.*, $2
90*th Anniv of "Caye Service" Local Stamps.* 10, 15, 75 *c.*, $2

1985

Birth Bicentenary of John J. Audubon (*ornithologist*). 25, 75 $1, $3
Shipwrecks. $1 × 4

Issues for the Cayes of Belize were discontinued after Ju 1985. It is reported that remainders, probably the 19 definitive stamps, were later issued to other Belize post offic for postal purposes.

Bermuda

The first internal postal system for Bermuda was organised by Joseph Stockdale, the proprietor of the *Bermuda Gazette*, in 1784. This service competed with that of the colonial post office, set up in 1812, until 1818.

Control of the overseas postal service passed to the British G.P.O. in 1818. The internal delivery system was discontinued between 1821 and 1830. The overseas posts became a colonial responsibility in 1859.

For illustrations of the handstamp types see BRITISH POST OFFICES ABROAD notes, following GREAT BRITAIN.

CROWNED-CIRCLE HANDSTAMPS

CC1 CC1 ST. GEORGES BERMUDA (R.) (1.8.1845) .. .. *Price on cover* £6500

CC2 IRELAND ISLE BERMUDA (R.) (1.8.1845) .. .. *Price on cover* £6500

CC3 HAMILTON BERMUDA (R.) (13.11.1846) .. .. *Price on cover* £3500

For Nos. CC1 and CC3 used as adhesive Postmasters' Stamps see Nos. O7 and O6.

PRICES FOR STAMPS ON COVER TO 1945	
Nos. 1/11	*from* × 5
Nos. 12/17	*from* × 10
Nos. 19/29*a*	*from* × 8
Nos. 30/*a*	*from* × 10
Nos. 31/4	*from* × 4
Nos. 34*a*/55	*from* × 3
Nos. 56/8	*from* × 10
Nos. 59/76	*from* × 4
Nos. 76*a*/93	*from* × 3
Nos. 94/7	*from* × 4
Nos. 98/106	*from* × 3
Nos. 107/15	*from* × 4
Nos. 116/21	*from* × 5
No. 122	*from* × 20

COLONY

O 1

O 2

1848–61. *Postmasters' Stamps. Adhesives prepared and issued by the postmasters at Hamilton and St. Georges. Dated as given in brackets.*

(*a*) *By W. B. Perot at Hamilton*

O1	O 1	1d. black/*bluish grey* (1848)	—	£80000
O2		1d. black/*bluish grey* (1849)	—	£110000
O3		1d. red/*thick white* (1853)	—	£80000
O4		1d. red/*bluish wove* (1854)	—	£250000
O5		1d. red/*bluish wove* (1856)	—	£160000
O6	O 2	(1d.) carmine-red/*bluish laid* (1861) ..	—	£70000

(*b*) *By J. H. Thies at St. Georges*
As Type O 2 *but inscr* "ST. GEORGES"

O7	–	(1d.) carmine-red/*buff* (1860)	†	£60000

Stamps of Type O 1 bear manuscript value and signature, the dates being those shown on the eleven known examples. The stamps are distributed between the dates as follows: 1848 three examples, 1849 two examples, 1853 three examples, 1854 two examples, 1856 one example.

It is believed that the franking value of Nos. O6/7 was 1d., although this is not shown on the actual stamps. Four examples are known of this type used from Hamilton, from March 1861 (and one unused), and five used from St. Georges between July 1860 and January 1863, both issues being cancelled by pen.

Prices shown reflect our estimation of value based on known copies. For instance of the two copies known of No. O4, one is in the Royal collection and the other is on entire.

It is possible that a fourth postmaster's provisional was used by Robert Ward at Hamilton in late 1862 when two examples of Type O 2 on laid paper are known cancelled by blue crayon.

1

2

3

4

5

(Typo D.L.R.)

1865–1903. *Wmk Crown CC.* (*a*) *P* 14.

1	1	1d. rose-red (25.9.65)	85·00	1·25
		w. Wmk inverted	£150	75·00
2		1d. pale rose	£110	6·50
		w. Wmk inverted	£150	75·00
3	2	2d. dull blue (14.3.66)	£225	19·00
		w. Wmk inverted	—	£200
4		2d. bright blue (1875)	£250	13·00
		w. Wmk inverted	—	£200
5	3	3d. yellow-buff (10.3.73)	£450	65·00
		aw. Wmk inverted	£750	£150
		ax. Wmk reversed		
5*b*		3d. orange (1875)	£750	90·00
6	4	6d. dull purple (25.9.65)	£800	75·00
		w. Wmk inverted	—	£500
7		6d. dull mauve (1874)	23·00	12·00
		w. Wmk inverted	85·00	85·00
8	5	1s. green (25.9.65)	£250	45·00
		w. Wmk inverted	£400	£180

(*b*) *Imperf*

9	1	1d. rose-red	£16000	£9000

(*c*) *P* 14×12½

10	3	3d. yellow-buff (1882)	£170	60·00
10*a*	4	6d. bright mauve (1903)	13·00	22·00
		aw. Wmk inverted	£300	
11	5	1s. green (1894)	11·00	£120
		a. Vert strip of 3, two stamps imperf horiz	£12000	
		w. Wmk inverted		

Though manufactured early in 1880, stamps *P* 14 × 12½ were not issued until the dates given above.

THREE PENCE (6)

THREE PENCE (6*a*)

THREE PENCE (7)

One Penny. (8)

1874 (12 Mar–19 May). *Nos. 1 and 8 surch diagonally.*

(*a*) *With T* **6** ("P" *and* "R" *different type*)

12	1	3d. on 1d. rose-red	£10000	
13	5	3d. on 1s. green	£2000	£850

(*b*) *With T* **6*a*** ("P" *same type as* "R")

13*b*	5	3d. on 1s. green	£2000	£800

(*c*) *With T* **7** (19 May)

14	5	3d. on 1s. green	£1200	£650

The 3d. on 1d. was a trial surcharge which was not regularly issued, though a few specimens were postally used before 1879. Nos. 13, 13*b* and 14, being handstamped, are found with double or partial double surcharges.

(Surch by Queen's Printer, Donald McPhee Lee)

1875 (March–May). *Surch with T* **8**.

15	2	1d. on 2d. (No. 4) (23 Apr)	£700	£350
		a. No stop after "Penny"	£9500	£6000
16	3	1d. on 3d. (No. 5) (8 May)	£450	£350
17	5	1d. on 1s. (No. 8) (11 Mar)	£500	£250
		a. Surch inverted	†	£16000
		b. No stop after "Penny"	—	£8500

It is emphasised that the prices quoted for Nos. 12/17 are for fine examples. The many stamps from these provisional issues which are in inferior condition are worth much less.

9

10

11

(Typo D.L.R.)

880 (23 Mar). *Wmk Crown CC. P* 14.
 9 ½d. stone .. .. 2·50 3·75
 w. Wmk inverted .. .. .. 50·00
 y. Wmk inverted and reversed ..
 10 4d. orange-red .. .. .. 16·00 1·75
 w. Wmk inverted .. .. ..
 x. Wmk reversed .. .. ..

(Typo D.L.R.)

83–98. *Wmk Crown CA. P* 14.
 9 ½d. dull green (10.92) .. .. 2·50 2·50
a ½d. deep grey-green (1893) .. .. 2·50 80
 1 1d. dull rose (12.83) .. .. .. £130 3·75
 w. Wmk inverted .. .. .. — £100
 1d. rose-red .. .. .. 75·00 3·00
 w. Wmk inverted .. .. .. — £100
 1d. carmine-rose (1886) .. .. 45·00 70
a 1d. aniline carmine (1889) .. .. 8·50 20
 aw. Wmk inverted .. .. .. £100 50·00
 2 2d. blue (12.86) .. .. .. 50·00 3·50
 2d. aniline purple (7.93) .. .. 11·00 3·75
a 2d. brown-purple (1898) .. .. 3·25 1·50
 11 2½d. deep ultramarine (10.11.84) .. 13·00 2·25
 aw. Wmk inverted .. .. .. £225 75·00
b 2½d. pale ultramarine .. .. .. 5·00 40
 bw. Wmk inverted .. .. .. — 75·00
 3 3d. grey (1.86) .. .. .. 22·00 6·00
 5 1s. yellow-brown (1893) .. .. 15·00 16·00
 ax. Wmk reversed .. .. .. — £350
b 1s. olive-brown .. .. .. 13·00 15·00
 bx. Wmk reversed .. .. ..
/9b .. .. .. *Set of* 7 95·00 25·00
, 26 & 29 Optd "Specimen" .. *Set of* 3 £375

893 PROVISIONAL POSTCARD. Following the reduction the overseas postcard rate to 1d. in 1893 existing stocks of stal stationery postcards, including some from the September 880 issue franked with Nos. 19 and 22, were surcharged "One nny". This surcharge was applied by the *Royal Gazette* press. is generally believed that an individual in the Post Office quired all the examples showing Nos. 19 and 22, but ovisional postcards are known used to Europe and, one ample only, locally. *Price from* £550 *unused*, £1400 *used*.

ONE
FARTHING

(12)

13 Dry Dock

14

901. *As Nos. 29/a but colour changed, surch with T*
) 5 ¼d. on 1s. dull grey (11.1.01) (Optd S. £75) 90 50
a ¼d. on 1s. bluish grey (18.3.01) .. 1·25 85
 ab. "F" in "FARTHING" inserted by handstamp £6000 £7000

Seven examples of No. 30ab are known, five unused (one eing in the Royal Collection) and two used (one on postcard). It would appear that the "F" in position one of an unspecified orizontal row was either weak or missing and an additional npression of the letter was then inserted by a separate andstamp.

(Typo D.L.R.)

1902 (Nov)–**04.** *Wmk Crown CA. P* 14.
1 13 ½d. black and green (12.03) .. .. 9·50 1·25
2 1d. brown and carmine .. .. 8·00 10
3 3d. magenta and sage-green (9.03) .. 2·50 1·75
4 10 4d. orange-brown (18.1.04) .. .. 27·00 48·00
 ax. Wmk reversed £275
1/4 .. .. .. *Set of* 4 42·00 48·00
1/3 Optd "Specimen" .. .. *Set of* 3 £130

906–09. *Wmk Mult Crown CA. P* 14.
4b 13 ¼d. brown and violet (9.08) .. .. 1·50 1·50
5 ½d. black and green (12.06) .. .. 17·00 65
6 1d. brown and carmine (4.06) .. .. 20·00 20
 w. Wmk inverted £275 £180
7 2d. grey and orange (10.07) .. .. 7·50 11·00
8 2½d. brown and ultramarine (12.06) .. 14·00 7·00
9 4d. blue and chocolate (11.09) .. .. 3·00 15·00
4b/9 .. .. .. *Set of* 6 55·00 32·00
4b, 37/9 Optd "Specimen" .. *Set of* 4 £200

908–10. *Wmk Mult Crown CA. P* 14.
1 13 ½d. green (3.09) .. .. .. 11·00 2·50
2 1d. red (5.08) .. .. .. 18·00 10
3 2½d. blue (14.2.10) .. .. .. 12·00 5·75
1/3 .. .. .. *Set of* 3 38·00 7·50
1/3 Optd "Specimen" .. .. *Set of* 3 £180

(Recess D.L.R.)

910–25. *Wmk Mult Crown CA. P* 14.
4 14 ¼d. brown (26.3.12) .. .. .. 1·50 2·50
 a. Pale brown .. .. .. 60 1·50
5 ½d. green (4.6.10) .. .. .. 1·25 25
 a. Deep green (1918) .. .. .. 6·50 90
 w. Wmk inverted .. .. ..
 x. Wmk reversed .. .. .. — £160
 y. Wmk inverted and reversed ..
6 1d. red (I) (15.10.10) .. .. .. 14·00 30
 a. Rose-red .. .. .. 18·00 30
 b. Carmine (12.19) .. .. .. 48·00 8·00
 w. Wmk inverted £325
 x. Wmk reversed .. .. ..
 y. Wmk inverted and reversed £225
7 2d. grey (1.13) .. .. .. 3·00 7·50
 x. Wmk reversed .. .. ..

48 14 2½d. blue (27.3.12) .. .. .. 3·50 60
 w. Wmk inverted .. .. ..
 x. Wmk reversed .. .. .. — £160
 y. Wmk inverted and reversed .. £120 85·00
49 3d. purple/*yellow* (1.13) .. .. 1·75 6·00
49a 4d. red/*yellow* (1.9.19) .. .. 4·75 10·00
50 6d. purple (26.3.12) .. .. .. 15·00 19·00
 a. Pale claret (2.6.24) .. .. 11·00 8·00
51 1s. black/*green* (26.3.12) .. .. 3·75 4·00
 a. Jet black/olive (1925) .. .. 4·50 13·00
44/51 .. .. .. *Set of* 9 40·00 35·00
44/51 Optd "Specimen" .. .. *Set of* 9 £400

Nos. 44 to 51a are comb-perforated 13.8×14 or 14. No. 45 exits also line-perforated 14, probably from the printing dispatched to Bermuda on 13 March 1911.

See also Nos. 76b/87a.

15

HIGH VALUE KEY TYPES. The reign of King Edward VII saw the appearance of the first in a new series of "key type" designs, initially on the issues of Malaya — Straits Settlements and Nyasaland, to be used for high value denominations where a smaller design was felt to be inappropriate. The system was extended during the reign of King George V, using the portrait as Bermuda Type **15**, to cover Bermuda, Ceylon, Leeward Islands, Malaya — Straits Settlements, Malta and Nyasaland. A number of these territories continued to use the key type concept for high value King George VI stamps and one, Leeward Islands, for stamps of Queen Elizabeth II.

In each instance the King George V issues were printed in sheets of 60 (12×5) on various coloured papers. The system utilised a common "head" plate used with individual "duty" plates which printed the territory name and face value.

Two major plate flaws occur on the King George V head plate: the break in scroll on R.1/12 and the broken crown and scroll on R.2/12. Both of these occur in different states, having been repaired and then damaged once again, perhaps on several occasions. Later printings of R. 1/12 show additional damage to the crown and upper scrolls. The prices quoted in the listings are for examples approximately as illustrated.

Break in scroll (R. 1/12)

Broken crown and scroll (R. 2/12)

Break through scroll (R. 1/9. Ptgs from June 1929. Some show attempts at repair)

(Typo D.L.R.)

1918 (1 Apr)–**22.** *Wmk Mult Crown CA. Chalk-surfaced paper. P* 14.
51b 15 2s. purple and blue/*blue* (19.6.20) .. 17·00 48·00
 ba. Break in scroll £180
 bb. Broken crown and scroll £180
 bx. Wmk reversed £1400
52 2s. 6d. black and red/*blue* .. .. 27·00 70·00
 a. Break in scroll £250
52b 4s. black and carmine (19.6.20) .. 60·00 £130
 ba. Break in scroll £275
 bb. Broken crown and scroll £275
53 5s. deep green and deep red/*yellow* .. 50·00 95·00
 a. Break in scroll £350
 c. Green & carmine-red/pale yell (1920) 40·00 80·00
 ca. Break in scroll £300
 cb. Broken crown and scroll £300
 cw. Wmk inverted £250
 cx. Wmk reversed £1600
 cy. Wmk inverted and reversed .. £1600
54 10s. green and carmine/*pale bluish green* £150 £300
 a. Break in scroll £550
 c. Green & red/pale bluish green (1922) £190 £325
 ca. Break in scroll £600
 cb. Broken crown and scroll £600
 w. Wmk inverted .. .. ..
55 £1 purple and black/*red* £350 £550
 a. Break in scroll £800
 b. Broken crown and scroll £900
 c. Break through scroll £1200
 w. Wmk inverted £1500
51b/5 .. .. .. *Set of* 6 £550 £1000
51b/5 Optd "Specimen" .. .. *Set of* 6 £800

Beware of cleaned copies of the 10s. with faked postmarks.

Examples of Nos. 51b/5 are known showing a forged Hamilton double ring postmark dated "22 JAN 13".

See also Nos. 88/93.

WAR TAX (16) **WAR TAX** (17)

1918 (4 May). *Nos. 46 and 46a optd locally with T* **16**.
56 14 1d. red 45 60
 a. Rose-red .. .. 45 1·00

1920 (5 Feb). *No. 46b optd with T* **17**.
58 14 1d. carmine .. .. 75 1·50

The War Tax stamps represented a compulsory levy in addition to normal postal fees until 31 Dec 1920. Subsequently they were valid for ordinary postage.

18

19

(Des by the Governor (Gen. Sir James Willcocks). Typo D.L.R.)

1920 (11 Nov)–**21.** *Tercentenary of Representative Institutions (1st issue). Chalk-surfaced paper (3d. to 1s.). P* 14.

(*a*) *Wmk Mult Crown CA (sideways*)* (19.1.21)
59 18 ¼d. brown .. .. 2·75 14·00
 a. "C" of "CA" missing from wmk .. £325
 b. "A" of "CA" missing from wmk .. £325
 w. Wmk Crown to right of CA .. £120
 x. Wmk sideways reversed £150
60 ½d. green .. .. 2·75 7·50
 w. Wmk Crown to right of CA .. £180
 x. Wmk sideways reversed £150
 y. Wmk sideways inverted and reversed .. .. ..
61 2d. grey .. .. 9·50 28·00
 a. "C" of "CA" missing from wmk .. £475
 w. Wmk Crown to right of CA .. £250
 y. Wmk sideways inverted and reversed .. .. ..
62 3d. dull and deep purple/*pale yellow* .. 8·50 26·00
 w. Wmk Crown to right of CA ..
 x. Wmk sideways reversed .. ..
63 4d. black and red/*pale yellow* .. .. 9·50 26·00
 a. "C" of "CA" missing from wmk .. £750
64 1s. black/*blue-green* .. .. .. 16·00 48·00

(*b*) *Wmk Mult Script CA (sideways)*
65 18 1d. carmine .. .. 2·75 30
66 2½d. bright blue .. .. 8·50 9·50
67 6d. dull and bright purple (19.1.21) .. 21·00 60·00
59/67 .. .. .. *Set of* 9 75·00 £200
59/67 Optd "Specimen" .. .. *Set of* 9 £350

*The normal sideways watermark shows Crown to left of CA *as seen from the back of the stamp.*

(Des H. J. Dale. Recess D.L.R.)

1921 (12 May). *Tercentenary of Representative Institutions (2nd issue). P* 14. (*a*) *Wmk Mult Crown CA (sideways*).*
68 19 2d. slate-grey .. .. 4·50 23·00
 a. "C" of "CA" missing from wmk ..
 w. Wmk Crown to left of CA £325
69 2½d. bright ultramarine .. .. .. 9·00 3·00
 a. "C" of "CA" missing from wmk .. £475
 b. "A" of "CA" missing from wmk .. £475
 x. Wmk sideways reversed .. .. — £275
70 3d. purple/*pale yellow* .. .. .. 4·00 14·00
71 4d. red/*pale yellow* .. .. .. 14·00 18·00
 x. Wmk sideways reversed £180
72 6d. purple .. .. 9·00 40·00
 a. "C" of "CA" missing from wmk .. £600
 b. "A" of "CA" missing from wmk .. £650
 c. Substituted crown in wmk .. .. † —
73 1s. black/*green* .. .. 21·00 48·00

(*b*) *Wmk Mult Script CA (sideways*)*
74 19 ¼d. brown .. .. 80 2·75
 w. Wmk Crown to left of CA .. ..
 x. Wmk sideways reversed .. ..

75 19 ½d. green .. .. 2·75 6·00
w. Wmk Crown left of CA £100 £120
y. Wmk sideways inverted and reversed £200
76 1d. deep carmine .. .. 2·50 35
a. "C" of "CA" missing from wmk ..
68/76 .. .. *Set of* 9 60·00 £140
68/76 Optd "Specimen" .. .. *Set of* 9 £325

*The normal sideways watermark shows Crown to right of CA, *as seen from the back of the stamp.*

For illustration of the substituted watermark crown see Catalogue Introduction.

I II III

Three Types of the 1d.

I. Scroll at top left very weak and figure "1" has pointed serifs.
II. Scroll weak. "1" has square serifs and "1d" is heavy.
III. Redrawn. Scroll is completed by a strong line and "1" is thinner with long square serifs.

I II

Two Types of the 2½d.

I. Short, thick figures, especially of the "1", small "d".
II. Figures taller and thinner, "d" larger.

1922–34. *Wmk Mult Script CA. P* 14.
76*b* 14 ¼d. brown (7.28) .. .. .. 1·25 2·50
77 ½d. green (11.22) 90 15
w. Wmk inverted .. .. ..
x. Wmk reversed .. .. ..
78 1d. scarlet (I) (11.22) .. .. .. 15·00 60
a. Carmine (6.24) .. .. .. 18·00 60
bx Wmk reversed .. .. ..
78*c* 1d. carmine (II) (12.25) .. .. 30·00 4·50
cx. Wmk reversed .. .. ..
d. Scarlet (8.27) .. .. .. 9·00 80
79 1d. scarlet (III) (10.28) .. .. 12·00 30
a. Carmine-lake (1934) .. .. 20·00 1·50
79*b* 1½d. red-brown (27.3.34) .. .. 8·00 35
80 2d. grey (12.23) .. .. .. 1·50 1·50
x. Wmk reversed .. .. .. 55·00
81 2½d. pale sage-green (12.22) .. .. 2·00 1·50
a. Deep sage-green (1924) .. .. 1·50 1·50
aw. Wmk inverted .. .. ..
ax. Wmk reversed .. .. ..
ay. Wmk inverted and reversed ..
82 2½d. ultramarine (I) (1.12.26) .. .. 2·50 50
aw. Wmk inverted .. .. .. 80·00
82*b* 2½d. ultramarine (II) (3.32) .. .. 1·75 50
83 3d. ultramarine (12.24) .. .. 16·00 26·00
w. Wmk inverted £100
84 3d. purple/*yellow* (10.26) .. .. 3·50 1·00
85 4d. red/*yellow* (8.24) .. .. .. 1·75 1·00
x. Wmk reversed .. .. ..
86 6d. purple (8.24) .. .. .. 1·00 80
87 1s. black/*emerald* (10.27) .. .. 4·75 8·50
a. Brownish black/yellow-green (1934) 32·00 48·00
76*b*/87 .. .. *Set of* 12 45·00 40·00
76*b*/87 Optd/Perf "Specimen" .. *Set of* 12 £500

Values to 1s. come perforated either comb (13.8×14) or line (13.75, 14, 13.75×14 or 14×13.75). Nos. 78/*a* and 83 only exist comb-perforated, Nos. 76*b*, 78*c*/9*b*, 81*a*, 82*b* and 87*a* line-perforated and the remainder come in both forms.

Breaks in scrolls at right (R. 1/3. Ptgs of 12s. 6d. from July 1932)

1924–32. *Wmk Mult Script* CA. *Chalk-surfaced paper. P* 14.
88 15 2s. purple and brt blue/*pale blue* (1.9.27) 40·00 65·00
a. Break in scroll £190
b. Broken crown and scroll £190
c. Purple and blue/grey-blue (1931) .. 48·00 70·00
ca. Break in scroll £225
cb. Broken crown and scroll £225
cc. Break through scroll £250
89 2s. 6d. black and carmine/*pale blue* (4.27) 50·00 £100
a. Break in scroll £225
b. Broken crown and scroll £225
c. Black and red/blue to deep blue (6.29) 65·00 £100
ca. Break in scroll £300
cb. Broken crown and scroll £300
cc. Break through scroll £325
(89) *d. Grey-black and pale orange-vermilion/grey-blue* (3.30) £2500 £2500
da. Break in scroll £4000
db. Broken crown and scroll £4000
dc. Break through scroll £4000
e. Black and carmine-red/deep grey-blue (8.30) .. .. 65·00 £100
ea. Break in scroll £300
eb. Broken crown and scroll £300
ec. Break through scroll £325
f. Black & scarlet-vermilion/dp bl (9.31) 70·00 £100
fa. Break in scroll £300
fb. Broken crown and scroll £300
fc. Break through scroll £325
g. Black & brt orge-verm/dp blue (8.32) £2750 £2500
ga. Broken crown and scroll £4250
gb. Break through scroll £4250
92 10s. green and red/*pale emerald* (12.24) £120 £250
b. Broken crown and scroll £450
c. Break through scroll £475
d. Green and red/deep emerald (1931) £120 £250
da. Break in scroll £475
db. Broken crown and scroll £450
dc. Break through scroll £500
93 12s. 6d. grey and orange (8.32) £250 £350
a. Break in scroll £650
b. Broken crown and scroll £700
c. Break through scroll £750
d. Breaks in scrolls at right £750
e. Error. Ordinary paper .. ..
88/93 .. .. *Set of* 4 £425 £700
88/93 Optd/Perf "Specimen" .. *Set of* 4 £500

The true No. 89*d* is the only stamp on grey-blue paper; other deeper orange-vermilion shades exist on different papers.

Beware of fiscally used 2s. 6d. 10s. and 12s. 6d. stamps cleaned and bearing faked postmarks. Large quantities were used for a "head tax" levied on travellers leaving the country.

For 12s. 6d. design inscribed "Revenue" at both sides see No. F1 under POSTAL FISCAL.

1935 (6 May). *Silver Jubilee. As Nos.* 91/4 *of Antigua, but ptd by Waterlow. P* 11×12.
94 1d. deep blue and scarlet 45 55
j. Damaged turret .. .. .. 80·00
m. "Bird" by turret .. .. .. 80·00
95 1½d. ultramarine and grey .. .. .. 70 2·00
m. "Bird" by turret .. .. .. 90·00
96 2½d. brown and deep blue .. .. .. 1·40 90
m. "Bird" by turret £120
97 1s. slate and purple .. .. .. 13·00 22·00
k. Kite and vertical log £140
l. Kite and horizontal log £200
94/7 .. .. *Set of* 4 14·00 23·00
94/7 Perf "Specimen" .. .. *Set of* 4 £160

For illustrations of plate varieties see Catalogue Introduction.

20 Red Hole, Paget

21 South Shore

22 *Lucie* (yacht)

23 Grape Bay, Paget Parish

24 Point House, Warwick Parish

25 Gardener's Cottage, Par-la-Ville, Hamilton

(Recess B.W.)

1936 (14 Apr)–**47.** *Wmk Mult Script CA (sideways on horiz designs). P* 12.
98 20 ½d. bright green 10 10
99 21 1d. black and scarlet 20 20
100 1½d. black and chocolate 90 30
101 22 2d. black and pale blue .. .. .. 4·50 2·00
102 23 2½d. light and deep blue 80 25
103 24 3d. black and scarlet .. .. .. 2·50 90
104 25 6d. carmine-lake and violet 80 10
a. Claret and dull violet (6.47) .. .. 3·00 85
105 23 1s. green .. .. 4·00 7·00
106 20 1s. 6d. brown 50 10
98/106 .. .. *Set of* 9 13·00 9·50
98/106 Perf "Specimen" .. .. *Set of* 9 £250

All are line-perf 11.9, except printings of the 6d. from July 1951 onwards, which are comb-perf 11.9 × 11.75.

1937 (14 May). *Coronation. As Nos.* 95/7 *of Antigua, but printed by D.L.R. P* 14.
107 1d. scarlet 50 50
108 1½d. yellow-brown .. .. 60 1·40
109 2½d. bright blue .. .. 70 1·50
107/9 .. .. *Set of* 3 1·60 3·00
107/9 Perf "Specimen" .. .. *Set of* 3 £110

26 Ships in Hamilton Harbour

27 St. David's Lighthouse

28 White-tailed Tropic Bird, Arms of Bermuda and Native Flower

(Des Miss Higginbotham (T 28). Recess B.W.)

1938 (20 Jan)–**1952.** *T* 22, *T* 23 *(but with portrait of King George VI) and T* 26 *to* 28. *Wmk Mult Script CA. P* 12.
110 26 1d. black and red (*a*) (*b*) 65 20
111 1½d. deep blue and purple-brown (*a*) (*b*) 5·00 1·50
a. Blue and brown (*a*) (3.43) .. 5·50 2·50
b. Lt blue & purple-brn (*a*) (*b*) (9.45) 2·25 35
ba. "A" of "CA" missing from wmk ..
112 22 2d. light blue and sepia (*a*) .. .. 42·00 8·50
112*a* 2d. ultramarine and scarlet (*a*) (*b*) (8.11.40) .. .. 1·50 80
113 23 2½d. light and deep blue (*a*) .. .. 11·00 1·25
113*a* 2½d. lt blue & sepia-black (*a*) (18.12.41) 3·00 1·50
b. Pale blue & sepia-black (*a*) (3.43) 2·75 1·25
c. Bright blue and deep sepia-black (*b*) (23.9.52) .. .. .. 4·50 3·50
114 27 3d. black and rose-red (*a*) .. .. 15·00 1·75
114*a* 3d. black & deep blue (*a*) (*b*) (16.7.41) 1·75 40
114*b* 28 7½d. black, blue & brt grn (*a*) (18.12.41) 6·50 2·00
c. Black, blue & yellow-grn (*a*) (3.43) 4·50 2·25
115 23 1s. green (*a*) (*b*) .. .. .. 2·00 50
a. Bluish green (*b*) (20.6.52) .. .. 6·50 5·50

Perforations. Two different perforating machines were used on the various printings of these stamps: (*a*) the original 11.9 line perforation; (*b*) 11.9 × 11.75 comb perforation, introduced in July 1950. These perforations occur as indicated above.

29 King George VI

Shading omitted from top right scroll (R. 1/1. March 1943 ptgs of 2s. and £1)

Lower right scroll with broken tail (R. 2/10. Line perforated printings only)

Broken top right scroll (R. 5/11. Line perforated ptgs only. A retouched state of the flaw is visible in later ptgs up to March 1943)

Broken lower right scroll (R. 5/12. Occurs on printings made between May 1941 and March 1943)

Gash in chin (R.2/5. Ptgs between May 1941 and March 1943

Missing pearl (R.5/1, Nov 1945 ptg of 5s. only)

(Typo D.L.R.)

38 (20 Jan)–**53.** *T* **29.** *Wmk Mult Crown CA* (£1) *or Mult Script CA* (*others*). *Chalk-surfaced paper. P* 14 (*comb*).

6 2s. deep purple and ultramarine/*grey-blue* £110 10·00
 a. *Deep reddish purple and ultram/grey-blue* (21.11.40)* £250 20·00
 b. Perf 14¼ line. *Deep purple and ultram/grey-blue* (14.11.41)* £300 85·00
 bc. Lower right scroll with broken tail £1000 £425
 bd. Broken top right scroll £900 £375
 be. Broken lower right scroll £900 £375
 bf. Gash in chin £900 £375
 c. Ordinary paper. *Pur & bl /dp bl* (7.6.42) 7·00 1·50
 ce. Broken lower right scroll £190 70·00
 cf. Gash in chin £190 70·00
 d. Ordinary paper. *Purple and deep blue/pale blue* (5.3.43) 11·00 1·50
 db. Shading omitted from top right scroll £800 £425
 de. Broken lower right scroll £500 £275
 df. Gash in chin £500 £275
 e. Perf 13. Ordinary paper. *Dull purple and blue/pale blue* (15.2.50) 17·00 14·00
 f. Perf 13. Ordinary paper. *Reddish purple and blue/pale blue* (10.10.50) 8·50 13·00

17 2s. 6d. black and red/*grey-blue* 70·00 8·00
 a. Perf 14¼ line. *Black and red/grey-blue* (21.2.42)* £475 £110
 ac. Lower right scroll with broken tail £1200 £500
 ad. Broken top right scroll £1100 £425
 ae. Broken lower right scroll £1100 £425
 af. Gash in chin £1100 £425
 b. Ordinary paper. *Black and red/pale blue* (5.3.43) 19·00 6·50
 be. Broken lower right scroll £425 £190
 bf. Gash in chin £425 £190
 c. Perf 13. Ordinary paper. *Black and orange-red/pale blue* (10.10.50) 19·00 11·00
 d. Perf 13. Ordinary paper. *Black and red/pale blue* (18.6.52) 16·00 12·00

18 5s. green and red/*yellow* £140 25·00
 a. *Pale green and red/yellow* (14.3.39)* £275 60·00
 b. Perf 14¼ line. *Dull yellow-green and red/yellow* (5.1.43)* £200 28·00
 bc. Lower right scroll with broken tail £700 £275
 bd. Broken top right scroll £650 £200
 be. Broken lower right scroll £650 £200
 bf. Gash in chin £650 £200
 c. Ordinary paper. *Dull yellow-green and carmine-red/pale yellow* (5.42)* £400 90·00
 ce. Broken lower right scroll £2250 £800
 cf. Gash in chin £2250 £800
 d. Ordinary paper. *Pale bluish green and carmine-red/pale yellow* (5.3.43) £100 50·00
 de. Broken lower right scroll £650 £375
 df. Gash in chin £650 £375
 e. Ordinary paper. *Green and red/pale yellow* (11.45)* 50·00 20·00
 ea. Missing pearl £600
 f. Perf 13. Ordinary paper. *Yellow-green and red/pale yellow* (15.2.50) 21·00 16·00
 g. Perf 13. *Green and scarlet/yellow* (*chalk-surfaced*) (10.10.50) 30·00 30·00

19 10s. green and deep lake/*pale emerald* £450 £275
 a. *Bluish green and deep red/green* (8.39)* £200 £130
 b. Perf 14¼ line. Ordinary paper. *Yellow-green and carmine/green* (1942)* £400 £140
 bc. Lower right scroll with broken tail £1200 £650
 bd. Broken top right scroll £1000 £500
 be. Broken lower right scroll £1000 £500
 bf. Gash in chin £1000 £1000
 c. Ordinary paper. *Yellowish green and deep carmine-red/green* (5.3.43) 80·00 55·00
 ce. Broken lower right scroll £1900
 cf. Gash in chin £1700
 d. Ordinary paper. *Deep green and dull red/green* (*emerald back*) (11.12.46) 85·00 60·00
 e. Perf 13. Ordinary paper. *Green and vermilion/green* (19.9.51) 32·00 40·00
 f. Perf 13. Ordinary paper. *Green and dull red/green* (16.4.53) 32·00 45·00

20 12s. 6d. deep grey and brownish orange £475 £400
 a. *Grey & brownish orge* (*shades*) (11.39)* £180 65·00
 b. *Grey and pale orange* (9.11.40)* 90·00 50·00
 c. Ordinary paper (2.3.44)* £100 60·00
 ce. Broken lower right scroll £1500 £1600
 cf. Gash in chin £1500
 d. Ordinary paper. *Grey & yell*† (17.9.47)* £550 £450
 e. Perf 13. *Grey and pale orange* (*chalk-surfaced*) (10.10.50) 95·00 75·00

21 £1 purple and black/*red* £275 £100
 a. *Pale purple & black/pale red* (13.5.43)* 80·00 60·00
 ab. Shading omitted from top right scroll £1400
 ae. Broken lower right scroll £1000 £800
 af. Gash in chin £1000
 b. *Deep reddish purple and black/pale red* (5.3.43)* 70·00 45·00
 be. Broken lower right scroll £1000
 bf. Gash in chin £1000
 c. Perf 13. *Violet & black/scarlet* (7.12.51) 48·00 75·00
 d. Perf 13. *Brt violet & blk/scar* (10.12.52) £160 £150

10/21*c* *Set of* 16 £250 £150
10/21 Perf "Specimen" *Set of* 16 £1500

Following extensive damage to their printing works on 29 December 1940 much of De La Rue's work was transferred to other firms operating under their supervision. It is understood that Williams Lea & Co produced those new printings ordered for the Bermuda high value stamps during 1941. The first batch of these printings showed the emergency use, by Williams Lea, of a 14¼ line perforating machine (exact gauge 14.15) instead of the comb perforation (exact gauge 13.9 × 13.8).

Dates marked * are those of earliest known use.

In No. 116*c* the coloured surfacing of the paper is mottled with white specks sometimes accompanied by very close horizontal lines. In Nos. 116*d*, 117*b* and 118*c*/*d* the surfacing is the same colour as the back, sometimes applied in widely spaced horizontal lines giving the appearance of laid paper.

†No. 120*d* is the so-called "lemon" shade.

HALF
PENNY

X **X**

(30)

31 Postmaster Perot's Stamp

1940 (20 Dec). *No.* 110 *surch with T* **30** *by* Royal Gazette, *Hamilton.*

222 **26** ½d. on 1d. black and red (*shades*) 40 45

The spacing between "PENNY" and "X" varies from 12½ mm to 14 mm.

1946 (6 Nov). *Victory. As Nos.* 110/11 *of Antigua.*

123 1½d. brown 15 15
124 3d. blue 15 15
123/4 Perf "Specimen" *Set of* 2 75·00

1948 (1 Dec). *Royal Silver Wedding. As Nos.* 112/13 *of Antigua.*

125 1½d. red-brown 30 50
126 £1 carmine 40·00 48·00

(Recess B.W.)

1949 (11 Apr). *Centenary of Postmaster Perot's Stamp. Wmk Mult Script CA. P* 13½.

127 **31** 2½d. blue and brown 15 15
128 3d. black and blue 15 15
129 6d. violet and green 15 15
127/9 *Set of* 3 40 40

1949 (10 Oct). *75th Anniv of Universal Postal Union. As Nos.* 114/17 *of Antigua.*

130 2½d. blue-black 60 75
131 3d. deep blue 1·75 85
132 6d. purple 60 75
133 1s. blue-green 60 75
130/3 *Set of* 4 3·25 2·75

1953 (4 June). *Coronation. As No.* 120 *of Antigia, but ptd by B.W.*

134 1½d. black and blue 60 15

32 Easter Lilies

34 Easter Lily

37 Map of Bermuda

Die I "Sandy's" Die II "Sandys"

(Des C. Deakins (½d., 3d., 1s. 3d., 5s.), J. Berry (1d., 1½d., 2½d., 4d., 1s.). B. Brown (2d., 6d., 8d.), D. Haig (4½d., 9d.), Pamela Braley-Smith (2s. 6d.) and E. C. Leslie (10s.) Recess (except £1, centre typo), B.W.)

1953 (9 Nov)–**62**. *T* **32, 34, 37,** *and similar designs. Wmk Mult Script CA. P* 13½.

135 **32** ½d. olive-green 45 2·25
 a. *Yellow-olive* (19.5.54) 40 60
136 – 1d. black and red 1·25 50
 a. *Black and deep red* (19.5.54) 1·50 40
137 **34** 1½d. green 30 10
138 – 2d. ultramarine and brown-red 50 40
139 – 2½d. rose-red 2·00 50
140 **37** 3d. deep purple (I) 30 10
140*a* 3d. deep purple (II) (2.1.57) 1·00 20
141 – 4d. black and bright blue 30 40
142 – 4½d. emerald 45 1·00
143 – 6d. black and deep turquoise 5·00 60
143*a* – 8d. black and red (16.5.55) 2·50 30
143*b* – 9d. violet (6.1.58) 7·00 2·50
144 – 1s. orange 50 15
145 **37** 1s. 3d. blue (I) 3·50 30
 a. *Greenish blue* (21.9.54) 8·00 1·25
145*b* 1s. 3d. blue (II) (2.1.57) 7·00 50
 bc. *Bright blue* (14.8.62) 11·00 3·50
146 – 2s. brown 4·00 85
147 – 2s. 6d. scarlet 4·50 45
148 – 5s. carmine 19·00 85
149 – 10s. deep ultramarine 13·00 5·00
 a. *Ultramarine* (13.2.57) 42·00 14·00
150 – £1 brown, blue, red, grn & bronze-grn 24·00 21·00
135/150 *Set of* 18 75·00 32·00

Designs: *Horiz*—1d., 4d. Postmaster Perot's stamps; 2d. *Victory II* (racing dinghy); 2½d. Sir George Somers and *Sea Venture*; 4½d., 9d. *Sea Venture* (galleon), coin and Perot stamp; 6d., 8d. White-tailed Tropic Bird; 1s. Early Bermudian coinage; 2s. Arms of St. Georges; 5s. Hog coin; 10s. Obverse and reverse of hog coin; £1 Arms of Bermuda. *Vert*—2s. 6d. Warwick Fort.

Nos. 136, 138 and 143 exist in coils, constructed from normal sheets.

1953 (26 Nov). *Royal Visit. As No.* 143 *but inscr* "ROYAL VISIT 1953" *in top left corner.*

151 6d. black and deep turquoise 30 20

Three Power Talks
December, 1953.

(46)

Three Power Talks
December, 1953.

(46*a*)

First setting (Type **46**). First line 24½ mm long.
Second setting (Type **46***a*). First line 25¼ mm long.

1953 (8 Dec). *Three Power Talks. Nos.* 140 *and* 145 *optd with T* **46**.

152 **37** 3d. deep purple (Type **46**) (B.) 10 10
 a. Optd with Type **46***a* 45 15
153 1s. 3d. blue (Type **46**) (R.) 10 10
 a. Optd with Type **46***a* 1·75 1·75

50TH ANNIVERSARY
U S – BERMUDA
OCEAN RACE 1956

(47)

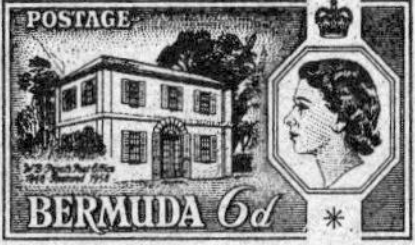

48 Perot's Post Office

1956 (22 June). *50th Anniv of United States–Bermuda Yacht Race. Nos.* 143*a and* 145*a optd with T* **47** *by the Bermuda Press.*

154 8d. black and red (Bk.) 20 40
155 1s. 3d. greenish blue (R.) 20 55

(Des W. Harrington. Recess B.W.)

1959 (1 Jan). *Wmk Mult Script CA. P* 13½.

156 **48** 6d. black and deep mauve 70 15

49 Arms of King James I and Queen Elizabeth II

(Des W. Harrington. Recess; arms litho D.L.R.)

1959 (29 July). *350th Anniv of First Settlement. Arms, red, yellow and blue; frame colours below. W w* **12**. *P* 13.

157 **49** 1½d. grey-blue 25 10
158 3d. drab-grey 30 50
159 4d. reddish purple 35 55
160 8d. slate-violet 35 15
161 9d. olive-green 35 1·25
162 1s. 3d. brown 35 30
157/162 *Set of* 6 1·75 2·50

50 The Old Rectory, St. George's, *circa* 1730

67 *Tsotsi in the Bundu* (Finn class yacht)

(Des W. Harrington. Photo Harrison)

1962 (26 Oct)–**68**. *Horiz designs as T* **50**. *W* w **12** (*upright*). *P* 12½.

163 1d. reddish purple, black and orange 10 45
 w. Wmk inverted † —
164 2d. lilac, indigo, yellow and green 10 15
 a. Lilac omitted £900 £650
 b. Green omitted † £3750
 c. Imperf (pair) £1200
 d. *Pale lilac, indigo, yell & grn* (22.10.68) 85 15
 w. Wmk inverted — £150
165 3d. yellow-brown and light blue 10 10
 a. Yellow-brown omitted £2750
166 4d. red-brown and magenta 20 40

167 5d. grey-blue and rose .. .. .. 1·50 2·50
168 6d. grey-blue, emerald and light blue .. 20 30
w. Wmk inverted .. .. 80·00
169 8d. bright blue, bright green and orange 30 35
170 9d. light blue and brown 25 30
170*a* 10d. violet and ochre (8.2.65) .. .. 8·00 1·00
aw. Wmk inverted .. ..
171 1s. black, emerald, bright blue & orange 20 10
172 1s. 3d. lake, grey and bistre 75 15
173 1s. 6d. violet and ochre .. .. .. 1·75 1·75
174 2s. red-brown and orange .. .. 3·00 1·25
175 2s. 3d. bistre-brown and yellow-green .. 2·00 6·00
176 2s. 6d. bistre-brn, bluish grn & olive-yell 55 50
177 5s. brown-purple and blue-green .. 1·25 1·50
w. Wmk inverted .. .. 60·00
178 10s. magenta, deep bluish green and buff 4·00 5·00
w. Wmk inverted £250 £300
179 £1 black, yellow-olive and yellow-orange 14·00 14·00
163/79 .. .. *Set of* 18 35·00 32·00

Designs:—2d. Church of St. Peter, St. Georges; 3d. Government House, 1892; 4d. The Cathedral, Hamilton, 1894; 5d. H.M. Dockyard, 1811; 6d. Perot's Post Office, 1848; 8d. G.P.O. Hamilton, 1869; 9d. Library, Par-la-Ville; 10d., 1s. 6d. Bermuda cottage, *circa* 1705; 1s. Christ Church, Warwick, 1719; 1s. 3d. City Hall, Hamilton, 1960; 2s. Town of St. George; 2s. 3d. Bermuda house, *circa* 1710; 2s. 6d. Bermuda house, early 18th-century; 5s. Colonial Secretariat, 1833; 10s. Old Post Office, Somerset, 1890; £1 The House of Assembly, 1815.

Three examples of No. 164b are known, all used on piece.

See also Nos. 195/200 and 246a.

1963 (4 June). *Freedom from Hunger. As No.* 146 *of Antigua.*
180 1s. 3d. sepia 80 40

1963 (2 Sept). *Red Cross Centenary. As Nos.* 147/8 *of Antigua.*
181 3d. red and black 75 25
182 1s. 3d. red and blue .. .. 2·00 2·75

(Des V. Whiteley. Photo D.L.R.)

1964 (28 Sept). *Olympic Games, Tokyo.* W w **12**. *P* 14 × 13½.
183 **67** 3d. red, violet and blue 10 10

1965 (17 May). *I.T.U. Centenary. As Nos.* 166/7 *of Antigua.*
184 3d. light blue and emerald 50 25
185 2s. yellow and ultramarine .. .. .. 1·00 1·25

68 Scout Badge and St. Edward's Crown

(Des W. Harrington. Photo Harrison)

1965 (24 July). *50th Anniv of Bermuda Boy Scouts Association.* W w **12**. *P* 12½.
186 **68** 2s. multicoloured 50 50
w. Wmk inverted .. .. .. 35·00

1965 (25 Oct). *International Co-operation Year. As Nos.* 168/9 *of Antigua.*
187 4d. reddish purple and turquoise-green .. 50 20
188 2s. 6d. deep bluish green and lavender .. 1·10 80

1966 (24 Jan). *Churchill Commemoration. As Nos.* 170/3 *of Antigua.*
189 3d. new blue 45 20
190 6d. deep green 70 45
191 10d. brown 90 75
192 1s. 3d. bluish violet .. .. 1·25 2·00
189/92 .. .. *Set of* 4 3·00 3·00

1966 (1 July). *World Cup Football Championships. As Nos.* 176/7 *of Antigua.*
193 10d. violet, yellow-green, lake & yellow-brn .. 50 15
194 2s. 6d. chocolate, blue-grn, lake & yell-brn .. 75 65

1966 (25 Oct)–**69**. *Designs as Nos.* 164, 167 (1*s.* 6*d.*), 169, 170*a*/1 *and* 174 *but* W w **12** (*sideways**).
195 2d. lilac, indigo, yellow and green (20.5.69) 3·75 5·00
196 8d. brt blue, brt green & orange (14.2.67) 50 1·25
197 10d. violet and ochre (1.11.66) 75 60
w. Wmk Crown to right of CA .. .. † —
198 1s. black, emerald, brt bl & orge (14.2.67) 70 1·40
199 1s. 6d. grey-blue and rose (1.11.66) .. 2·75 75
w. Wmk Crown to right of CA .. .. 50·00
200 2s. red-brown and orange .. .. 2·75 2·00
195/200 .. .. *Set of* 6 10·00 10·00

*The normal sideways watermark shows Crown to left of CA, *as seen from the back of the stamp.*

The 2d. value exists with PVA gum only, and the 8d. exists with PVA gum as well as gum arabic.

1966 (1 Dec). *20th Anniv of U.N.E.S.C.O. As Nos.* 196/8 *of Antigua.*
201 4d. slate-violet, red, yellow and orange .. 60 15
202 1s. 3d. orange-yellow, violet and deep olive 1·00 50
203 2s. black, bright purple and orange.. .. 1·25 1·25
201/3 .. .. *Set of* 3 2·50 1·75

NEW INFORMATION

The editor is always interested to correspond with people who have new information that will improve or correct the Catalogue.

69 G.P.O. Building

(Des G. Vasarhelyi. Photo Harrison)

1967 (23 June). *Opening of New General Post Office. Hamilton.* W w **12**. *P* 14½.
204 **69** 3d. multicoloured 10 10
205 1s. multicoloured 10 10
206 1s. 6d. multicoloured 15 20
207 2s. 6d. multicoloured 15 40
204/7 .. .. *Set of* 4 45 65

70 *Mercury* (cable ship) and Chain Links

(Des V. Whiteley. Photo Harrison)

1967 (14 Sept). *Inauguration of Bermuda–Tortola Telephone Service. T* **70** *and similar horiz designs. Multicoloured.* W w **12**. *P* 14½ × 14.
208 3d. Type **70** 15 10
209 1s. Map, telephone and microphone.. .. 20 10
210 1s. 6d. Telecommunications media 25 25
211 2s. 6d. *Mercury* (cable ship) and marine fauna 35 40
208/11 .. .. *Set of* 4 85 70

74 Human Rights Emblem and Doves

(Des M. Farrar Bell. Litho Harrison)

1968 (1 Feb). *Human Rights Year.* W w **12**. *P* 14 × 14½.
212 **74** 3d. indigo, blue and dull green.. .. 10 10
213 1s. yellow-brown, blue and light blue .. 10 10
214 1s. 6d. black, blue and rose 10 10
215 2s. 6d. grey-green, blue and yellow .. 15 15
212/15 .. .. *Set of* 4 30 30

REPRESENTATIVE GOVERNMENT

75 Mace and Queen's Profile

(Des R. Granger Barrett. Photo Harrison)

1968 (1 July). *New Constitution. T* **75** *and similar horiz design.* W w **12**. *P* 14.
216 **75** 3d. multicoloured 10 10
217 1s. multicoloured 10 10
218 – 1s. 6d. greenish yellow, black & turq-bl 10 20
219 – 2s. 6d. lilac, black and orange-yellow .. 15 30
216/19 .. .. *Set of* 4 30 60

Design:—1s. 6d., 2s. 6d. Houses of Parliament and House of Assembly, Bermuda.

77 Football, Athletics and Yachting

(Des V. Whiteley. Photo Harrison)

1968 (24 Sept). *Olympic Games, Mexico.* W w **12**. *P* 12½.
220 **77** 3d. multicoloured 15 10
a. Red-brown ("BERMUDA" and value) omitted £2500
221 1s. multicoloured 25 10
222 1s. 6d. multicoloured 50 25
223 2s. 6d. multicoloured .. .. .. 50 1·10
220/3 .. .. *Set of* 4 1·25 1·40

78 Brownie and Guide

80 Emerald-studded Gold Cross and Seaweed

(Des Harrison. Litho Format)

1969 (17 Feb). *50th Anniv of Bermuda Girl Guides. P* 14.
224 **78** 3d. multicoloured 10 10
225 1s. multicoloured 20 10
226 – 1s. 6d. multicoloured 25 40
227 – 2s. 6d. multicoloured .. .. .. 35 1·10
224/7 .. .. *Set of* 4 80 1·50

Design:—1s. 6d., 2s. 6d. Guides and badge.

(Des K. Giles adapted by V. Whiteley. Photo Harrison)

1969 (29 Sept). *Underwater Treasure. T* **80** *and similar vert design. Multicoloured.* W w **12** (*sideways*). *P* 14½ × 14.
228 4d. Type **80** 20 1
229 1s. 3d. Emerald-studded gold cross and seabed 35 15
230 2s. Type **80** 45 8
231 2s. 6d. As 1s. 3d. .. .. 45 1·5
228/31 .. .. *Set of* 4 1·25 2·25

(New Currency. 100 cents = 1 Bermuda dollar)

1c

(82) Tall "2" (Pl 1A. R.2/2)

1970 (6 Feb). *Decimal Currency. As Nos.* 163, 165/6, 168, 170, 172, 175/9 *and* 195/200 *surch as T* **82**. W w **12** (*sideways* on* 2, 5, 10, 12, 15, 18, 24, 30, 60 *c.*, $1.20 *and* $2.40).
232 1 c. on 1d. reddish purple, black and orange 10 1·5
w. Wmk inverted .. .. .. 75·00 25·0
233 2 c. on 2d. lilac, indigo, yellow and green 10 1
a. Lilac omitted £800
b. Vert pair, one without surch .. £3500
c. Tall "2" .. .. 4·75
dw. Wmk Crown to right of CA .. .. 50·00
e. Wmk upright (No. 164) .. .. 1·00 2·0
ea. Tall "2" .. .. 10·00
f. Wmk upright (No. 164*d*) .. .. 1·10 2·75
fa. Tall "2" .. .. 11·00
234 3 c. on 3d. yellow-brown and light blue .. 10 1
235 4 c. on 4d. red-brown and magenta (Br.) 10 1
236 5 c. on 8d. bright blue, brt green & orange 15 1·5
237 6 c. on 6d. grey-blue, emerald & light blue 15 7
a. Horiz pair, one with albino surch, the other with albino bar .. ..
w. Wmk inverted .. .. .. † £15
238 9 c. on 9d. light blue and brown (Br.) .. 30 1·75
239 10 c. on 10d. violet and ochre 30 25
240 12 c. on 1s. black, emerald, brt blue & orge 30 5
241 15 c. on 1s. 3d. lake, grey and bistre .. 1·50 1·0
242 18 c. on 1s. 6d. grey-blue and rose .. 80 65
243 24 c. on 2s. red-brown and orange .. 85 85
w. Wmk Crown to right of CA .. .. 70·00
244 30 c. on 2s. 6d. bistre-brown, bluish green and olive-yellow .. .. .. 1·00 2·00
245 36 c. on 2s. 3d. bistre-brown & yellow-green 1·75 5·00
246 60 c. on 5s. brown-purple and blue-green 2·25 3·00
a. Surch omitted† £800
247 $1.20, on 10s. mag, dp bluish green & buff 4·00 15·00
248 $2.40, on £1 black, yellow-olive & yell-orge 7·00 19·00
232/48 .. .. *Set of* 17 18·00 48·00

*The normal sideways watermark shows Crown to left of CA, *as seen from the back of the stamp.*

†No. 246a differs from the normal No. 177 by its watermark, which is sideways, and its gum, which is PVA.

83 Spathiphyllum

(Des W. Harrington. Photo D.L.R.)

1970 (6 July)–**75**. *Flowers. Multicoloured designs as T* **83**. W w **12** (*sideways on horiz designs*). *P* 14.
249 1 c. Type **83** 10 20
250 2 c. Bottlebrush 20 25
251 3 c. Oleander (*vert*) 15 10
252 4 c. Bermudiana 15 10
253 5 c. Poinsettia 30 20
254 6 c. Hibiscus 30 30
255 9 c. Cereus 20 45
256 10 c. Bougainvillea (*vert*) 20 15
257 12 c. Jacaranda 80 60

	15 c. Passion-Flower	90	1·40
a	17 c. As 15 c. (2.6.75)	2·75	3·50
	18 c. Coralita	2·25	2·25
a	20 c. As 18 c. (2.6.75)	2·75	3·25
	24 c. Morning Glory	1·50	3·50
a	25 c. As 24 c. (2.6.75)	2·75	4·50
	30 c. Tecoma	1·00	1·25
	36 c. Angel's Trumpet	1·25	2·25
a	40 c. As 36 c. (2.6.75)	2·75	5·00
	60 c. Plumbago	1·75	2·75
a	$1 As 60 c. (2.6.75)	3·25	6·50
	$1.20, Bird of Paradise flower	2·75	3·00
a	$2 As $1.20 (2.6.75)	5·50	8·50
	$2.40, Chalice Cup	5·50	6·00
5a	$3 As $2.40 (2.6.75)	10·00	11·00
/65a	*Set of* 24	45·00	55·00

See also Nos. 303/6 and 340/1.

84 The State House, St. George's

(Des G. Drummond. Litho Questa)

0 (12 Oct). *350th Anniv of Bermuda Parliament. T* **84** *and imilar horiz designs. Multicoloured.* W w **12** (*sideways*). *P* 14.

6	4 c. Type **84**	10	10
7	15 c. The Sessions House, Hamilton	25	15
8	18 c. St. Peter's Church, St George's	25	20
9	24 c. Town Hall, Hamilton	35	45
6/9	*Set of* 4	85	75
S270	131 × 95 mm. Nos. 266/9	1·40	4·25

85 Street Scene, St. George's

(Des G. Drummond. Litho Questa)

71 (8 Feb). *"Keep Bermuda Beautiful". T* **85** *and similar horiz lesigns. Multicoloured.* W w **12** (*sideways*). *P* 14.

1	4 c. Type **85**	20	10
2	15 c. Horseshoe Bay	65	55
3	18 c. Gibb's Hill Lighthouse	1·25	1·75
4	24 c. Hamilton Harbour	1·25	2·25
1/4	*Set of* 4	3·00	4·25

86 Building of the *Deliverance*

(Des E. Amos. Adapted C. Abbott. Litho Questa)

71 (10 May). *Voyage of the "Deliverance". T* **86** *and similar nulticoloured designs.* W w **12** (*sideways on* 4 c. *and* 24 c.). *P* 14.

5	4 c. Type **86**	50	20
6	15 c. *Deliverance* and *Patience* at Jamestown	1·50	1·75
7	18 c. Wreck of the *Sea Venture*	1·75	2·25
8	24 c. *Deliverance* and *Patience* on the high seas	1·90	2·50
5/8	*Set of* 4	5·00	6·00

The 15 c. and 18 c. are vert designs.

87 Green overlooking Ocean View

(Des G. Drummond. Litho D.L.R.)

71 (1 Nov). *Golfing in Bermuda. T* **87** *and similar horiz lesigns. Multicoloured.* W w **12** (*sideways**). *P* 13.

9	4 c. Type **87**	75	10
	w. Wmk Crown to right of CA	80·00	50·00
0	15 c. Golfers at Port Royal	1·50	70
1	18 c. Castle Harbour	1·60	1·00
	w. Wmk Crown to right of CA	3·50	
2	24 c. Belmont	1·75	1·75
9/82	*Set of* 4	5·00	3·00

*The normal sideways watermark shows Crown to left of CA, *seen from the back of the stamp.*

HEATH - NIXON
DECEMBER 1971

(88)

1971 (20 Dec). *Anglo-American Talks. Nos.* 252, 258, 259 *and* 260 *optd with T* **88** *by Format.*

283	4 c. Bermudiana	10	10
284	15 c. Passion Glory	10	20
285	18 c. Coralita	15	65
286	24 c. Morning Glory	20	80
283/6	*Set of* 4	50	1·60

89 Bonefish

(Des Maynard Reece. Litho B.W.)

1972 (21 Aug). *World Fishing Records. T* **89** *and similar horiz designs. Multicoloured.* W w **12**. *P* 13½ × 14.

287	4 c. Type **89**	35	10
288	15 c. Wahoo	40	50
289	18 c. Yellow-finned Tuna	45	65
290	24 c. Greater Amberjack	60	90
287/90	*Set of* 4	1·60	1·90

90 "Admiralty Oar" and Mace

(Des (from photograph by D. Groves) and photo Harrison)

1972 (20 Nov). *Royal Silver Wedding. Multicoloured; background colour given.* W w **12**. *P* 14 × 14½.

291	**90**	4 c. bright bluish violet	15	10
292		15 c. rose-carmine	15	50
		w. Wmk inverted	2·00	

91 Palmetto **92** Bernard Park, Pembroke, 1973

(Des Jennifer Toombs. Litho J.W.)

1973 (3 Sept). *Tree Planting Year. T* **91** *and similar vert designs. Multicoloured.* W w **12** (*sideways*). *P* 14.

293	4 c. Type **91**	30	10
294	15 c. Olivewood Bark	90	75
	a. Brown (Queen's head and value) omitted	£900	
295	18 c. Bermuda Cedar	1·00	1·25
296	24 c. Mahogany	1·10	1·60
293/6	*Set of* 4	3·00	3·25

1973 (21 Nov*). *Royal Wedding. As Nos.* 165/6 *of Anguilla. Centre multicoloured.* W w **12** (*sideways*). *P* 13½.

297	15 c. bright mauve	15	15
298	18 c. steel blue	15	15

*This is the local date of issue. The Crown Agents released the stamps on the 14 November.

(Des J.W. Litho Questa)

1973 (17 Dec). *Lawn Tennis Centenary. T* **92** *and similar horiz designs. Multicoloured.* W w **12**. *P* 14.

299	4 c. Type **92**	30	10
300	15 c. Clermont Court, 1873	60	65
301	18 c. Leamington Spa Court, 1872	70	1·25
302	24 c. Staten Island Courts, 1874	85	2·00
299/302	*Set of* 4	2·25	3·50

1974 (13 June)–**76**. *As Nos.* 253/4, 257 *and* 261, *but* W w **12** (*upright*).

303	5 c. Poinsettia	90	2·50
304	6 c. Hibiscus	9·50	14·00
305	12 c. Jacaranda	1·75	4·50
	w. Wmk inverted	55·00	
306	30 c. Tecoma (11.6.76)	7·00	7·50
303/6	*Set of* 4	17·00	26·00

Nos. 307/19 vacant.

PRICES OF SETS

Set prices are given for many issues, generally those containing three stamps or more. Definitive sets include one of each value or major colour change, but do not cover different perforations, die types or minor shades. Where a choice is possible the set prices are based on the cheapest versions of the stamps included in the listings.

93 Weather Vane, City Hall **94** Jack of Clubs and "good bridge hand"

(Des G. Drummond. Litho Questa)

1974 (24 June). *50th Anniv of Rotary in Bermuda. T* **93** *and similar horiz designs. Multicoloured.* W w **12** (*sideways*). *P* 14.

320	5 c. Type **93**	15	10
321	17 c. St. Peter's Church, St George's	45	35
322	20 c. Somerset Bridge	50	1·50
323	25 c. Map of Bermuda, 1626	60	2·00
320/3	*Set of* 4	1·50	3·50

(Des J.W. Litho Format)

1975 (27 Jan). *World Bridge Championships, Bermuda. T* **94** *and similar vert designs. Multicoloured.* W w **12**. *P* 14.

324	5 c. Type **94**	20	10
325	17 c. Queen of Diamonds and Bermuda Bowl	35	50
326	20 c. King of Hearts and Bermuda Bowl	40	1·75
327	25 c. Ace of Spades and Bermuda Bowl	40	2·25
324/7	*Set of* 4	1·25	4·00

95 Queen Elizabeth II and the Duke of Edinburgh

(Des and photo Harrison)

1975 (17 Feb). *Royal Visit.* W w **14**. *P* 14 × 14½.

328	**95**	17 c. multicoloured	60	65
329		20 c. multicoloured	65	2·10

96 Short S.23 Flying Boat *Cavalier*, 1937

(Des R. Granger Barrett. Litho Questa)

1975 (28 Apr). *50th Anniv of Air-mail Service to Bermuda. T* **96** *and similar horiz designs. Multicoloured.* W w **14** (*sideways*). *P* 14.

330	5 c. Type **96**	40	10
331	17 c. U.S.N. airship *Los Angeles*, 1925	1·25	85
332	20 c. Lockheed L.049 Constellation, 1946	1·40	2·75
333	25 c. Boeing 747-100, 1970	1·50	3·50
330/3	*Set of* 4	4·00	6·50
MS334	128×85 mm. Nos. 330/3	11·00	15·00

97 Supporters of American Army raiding Royal Magazine **98** Launching *Ready* (bathysphere)

(Des J. Cooter. Litho J.W.)

1975 (27 Oct). *Bicentenary of Gunpowder Plot, St George's. T* **97** *and similar horiz designs. Multicoloured.* W w **14** (*sideways**). *P* 13×13½.

335	5 c. Type **97**	20	10
336	17 c. Setting off for raid	40	30
337	20 c. Loading gunpowder aboard American ship	45	1·25
338	25 c. Gunpowder on beach	50	1·40
	w. Wmk Crown to left of CA	60·00	
335/8	*Set of* 4	1·40	2·75
MS339	165×138 mm. Nos. 335/8. P 14 (*sold for* 75 c.)	2·75	6·50

*The normal sideways watermark shows Crown to right of CA, *as seen from the back of the stamp.*

1975 (8 Dec)–**76**. *As Nos.* 250 *and* 254 *but* W w **14** (*sideways*).

340	2 c. Bottlebrush	85	4·00
341	6 c. Hibiscus (11.6.76)	6·00	8·00

Nos. 342/56 vacant.

(Des G. Drummond. Litho Questa)

1976 (29 Mar). *50th Anniv of Bermuda Biological Station. T* **98** *and similar multicoloured designs. W* w **14** (*sideways on* 17 *and* 20 *c.*). *P* 14.

No.	Value	Design	Unused	Used
357	5 c.	Type **98**	30	10
358	17 c.	View from the sea (*horiz*)	60	60
359	20 c.	H.M.S. *Challenger*, 1873 (*horiz*)	65	2·25
360	25 c.	Beebe's bathysphere descent, 1934	70	2·75
357/60		*Set of* 4	2·00	5·00

99 *Christian Radich* (cadet ship)

(Des R. Granger Barrett. Litho J.W.)

1976 (15 June). *Tall Ships Race*, 1976. *T* **99** *and similar horiz designs. Multicoloured. W* w **12** (*sideways*). *P* 13.

No.	Value	Design	Unused	Used
361	5 c.	Type **99**	75	20
362	12 c.	*Juan Sebastian de Elcano* (Spanish cadet schooner)	1·00	2·00
363	17 c.	*Eagle* (U.S. coastguard cadet ship)	1·10	1·75
364	20 c.	*Sir Winston Churchill* (cadet schooner)	1·25	2·50
365	40 c.	*Kruzenshtern* (Russian cadet barque)	1·40	3·25
366	$1	*Cutty Sark* trophy	2·25	8·00
361/6		*Set of* 6	7·00	16·00

100 Silver Trophy and Club Flags

(Des C. Abbott. Litho Questa)

1976 (16 Aug). *75th Anniv of the St. George's v. Somerset Cricket Cup Match. T* **100** *and similar horiz designs. Multicoloured. W* w **14** (*sideways**). *P* 14½×14.

No.	Value	Design	Unused	Used
367	5 c.	Type **100**	35	10
		w. Wmk Crown to right of CA		
368	17 c.	Badge and Pavilion, St. George's Club	60	65
369	20 c.	Badge and Pavilion, Somerset Club	80	2·75
370	25 c.	Somerset playing field	1·25	3·75
367/70		*Set of* 4	2·75	6·50

*The normal sideways watermark shows Crown to left of CA, *as seen from the back of the stamp.*

101 Royal Visit, 1975

102 Stockdale House, St. George's 1784–1812

(Des Harrison. Litho Walsall)

1977 (7 Feb). *Silver Jubilee. T* **101** *and similar vert designs. Multicoloured. W* w **14**. *P* 13½.

No.	Value	Design	Unused	Used
371	5 c.	Type **101**	10	10
		w. Wmk inverted	£110	75·00
372	20 c.	St. Edward's Crown	15	20
373	$1	Queen in Chair of Estate	40	1·25
371/3		*Set of* 3	55	1·40

(Des G. Drummond. Litho J.W.)

1977 (20 June). *Centenary of U.P.U. Membership. T* **102** *and similar horiz designs. Multicoloured. W* w **14** (*sideways*). *P* 13.

No.	Value	Design	Unused	Used
374	5 c.	Type **102**	15	10
375	15 c.	Perot Post Office and stamp	30	50
376	17 c.	St. George's P.O. *circa* 1860	30	50
377	20 c.	Old G.P.O., Hamilton, *circa* 1935	35	60
378	40 c.	New G.P.O., Hamilton, 1967	60	1·10
374/8		*Set of* 5	1·50	2·50

103 17th-Century Ship approaching Castle Island

104 Great Seal of Queen Elizabeth I

(Des R. Granger Barrett. Litho Questa)

1977 (26 Sept). *Piloting. T* **103** *and similar horiz designs. Multicoloured. W* w **14** (*sideways*). *P* 13½.

No.	Value	Design	Unused	Used
379	5 c.	Type **103**	35	10
380	15 c.	Pilot leaving ship, 1795	65	50
381	17 c.	Pilots rowing out to paddle-steamer	75	50
382	20 c.	Pilot gigs and brig *Harvest Queen*	80	2·25
383	40 c.	Modern pilot cutter and R.M.S. *Queen Elizabeth 2*	1·25	3·25
379/83		*Set of* 5	3·50	6·00

(Des BG Studio. Litho Questa)

1978 (28 Aug). *25th Anniv of Coronation. T* **104** *and similar vert designs. Multicoloured. W* w **14**. *P* 14 × 13½.

No.	Value	Design	Unused	Used
384	8 c.	Type **104**	10	10
385	50 c.	Great Seal of Queen Elizabeth II	30	30
386	$1	Queen Elizabeth II	60	75
384/6		*Set of* 3	80	1·00

105 White-tailed Tropic Bird

(Des G. Drummond. Photo Harrison)

1978 (15 Nov)–**83**. *Wildlife. Horiz designs as T* **105**. *Multicoloured. W* w **14** (*sideways* on* 8, 15, 20, 40 *c. and* $1). *P* 14×14½ (4, 5 *c.*, $2, $3, $5) *or* 14 (*others*).

No.	Value	Design	Unused	Used
387	3 c.	Type **105**	1·75	2·00
		aw. Wmk inverted	15·00	
		b. Perf 14×14½ (3.8.83)†	2·75	2·50
388	4 c.	White-eyed Vireo	1·50	2·00
		w. Wmk inverted	55·00	
389	5 c.	Eastern Bluebird	1·25	1·75
		w. Wmk inverted	55·00	30·00
390	7 c.	Whistling Frog (19.2.79)	50	1·50
391	8 c.	Common Cardinal	1·25	55
392	10 c.	Spiny Lobster (19.2.79)	20	10
393	12 c.	Land Crab (19.2.79)	30	70
394	15 c.	Lizard (Skink) (19.2.79)	30	15
395	20 c.	Four-eyed Butterflyfish (12.3.79)	30	30
		w. Wmk Crown to right of CA	1·00	
396	25 c.	Red Hind (12.3.79)	30	20
		a. Greenish blue omitted		
397	30 c.	*Danaus plexippus* (butterfly) (19.2.79)	2·25	2·50
398	40 c.	Rock Beauty (12.3.79)	45	1·50
399	50 c.	Banded Butterflyfish (12.3.79)	55	85
400	$1	Blue Angelfish (12.3.79)	1·25	1·75
		w. Wmk Crown to right of CA	£275	
401	$2	Humpback Whale (12.3.79)	2·00	2·75
402	$3	Green Turtle (19.2.79)	2·75	3·00
403	$5	Cahow	6·50	6·00
387/403		*Set of* 17	21·00	25·00

*The normal sideways watermark shows Crown to left of CA, *as seen from the back of the stamp.*

†Earliest known postmark date.

106 Map by Sir George Somers, 1609

107 Policeman and Policewoman

(Des J. Cooter. Litho Questa)

1979 (14 May). *Antique Maps. T* **106** *and similar multicoloured designs. W* w **14** (*sideways on* 8, 15, 25 *and* 50 *c.*) *P* 14 × 13½ (20 *c.*) *or* 13½ × 14 (*others*).

No.	Value	Design	Unused	Used
404	8 c.	Type **106**	15	10
405	15 c.	Map by John Seller, 1685	20	15
406	20 c.	Map by H. Moll, 1729–40 (*vert*)	25	25
407	25 c.	Map by Desbruslins, 1740	30	30
408	50 c.	Map by Speed, 1626	45	80
404/8		*Set of* 5	1·25	1·40

(Des L. Curtis. Litho Questa)

1979 (26 Nov). *Centenary of Police Force. T* **107** *and similar multicoloured designs. W* w **14** (*sideways on* 20 *and* 25 *c.*). *P* 14.

No.	Value	Design	Unused	Used
409	8 c.	Type **107**	30	10
		w. Wmk inverted	11·00	
410	20 c.	Policeman directing traffic (*horiz*)	55	55
411	25 c.	*Blue Heron* (police launch) (*horiz*)	65	65
412	50 c.	Police car and motorcycle	1·00	1·50
409/12		*Set of* 4	2·25	2·50

108 1848 1d. "Perot" and Penny Black Stamps

(Des J.W. Litho Enschedé)

1980 (25 Feb). *Death Centenary of Sir Rowland Hill* (1979). *T* **10** *and similar horiz designs. Multicoloured. W* w **14** (*sideways*, *P* 13 × 13½.

No.	Value	Design	Unused	Used
413	8 c.	Type **108**	15	1
414	20 c.	1848 1d. "Perot" stamp and Sir Rowland Hill	25	2
415	25 c.	1848 1d. "Perot" stamp and early letter	25	3
416	50 c.	1848 1d. "Perot" stamp and "Paid 1" cancellation	35	7
413/16		*Set of* 4	90	1·2

109 Lockheed L-1011 TriStar 500 Airliner approaching Bermuda

110 Gina Swainson with Rose

(Des R. Granger Barrett. Litho Harrison)

1980 (6 May). *"London* 1980*" International Stamp Exhibition Mail-carrying Transport. T* **109** *and similar horiz design Multicoloured. W* w **14** (*sideways**). *P* 13×13½.

No.	Value	Design	Unused	Used
417	25 c.	Type **109**	30	
418	50 c.	*Orduna I* (liner) in Grassy Bay	45	3
		w. Wmk Crown to right of CA	42·00	
419	$1	*Delta* (screw steamer) at St. George's Harbour	85	1·0
420	$2	*Lord Sidmouth* (sailing packet) in Old Ship Channel, St. George's	1·40	2·0
417/20		*Set of* 4	2·75	3·2

*The normal sideways watermark shows Crown to left of CA *as seen from the back of the stamp.*

(Des Walsall. Litho Questa)

1980 (8 May). *"Miss World* 1979–80*" (Gina Swainson) Commemoration. T* **110** *and similar vert designs. Multicoloured. W* w 1 *P* 14 × 13½.

No.	Value	Design	Unused	Used
421	8 c.	Type **110**	15	
422	20 c.	After crowning ceremony	20	2
423	50 c.	On Peacock Throne at "Welcome Home" party	35	3
424	$1	In Bermuda carriage	70	9
421/4		*Set of* 4	1·25	1·4

111 Queen Elizabeth the Queen Mother

(Des and litho Harrison)

1980 (4 Aug). *80th Birthday of Queen Elizabeth the Queen Mothe* W w **14** (*sideways*). *P* 14.

No.	Type	Value	Unused	Used
425	**111**	25 c. multicoloured	30	7

112 Bermuda from Satellite

113 Kitchen, 18th-century

(Des L. Curtis. Litho Questa)

1980 (24 Sept). *Commonwealth Finance Ministers Meetin T* **112** *and similar horiz designs. Multicoloured. W* w (*sideways**). *P* 14.

No.	Value	Design	Unused	Used
426	8 c.	Type **112**	10	
427	20 c.	"Camden"	20	
428	25 c.	Princess Hotel, Hamilton	20	
		w. Wmk Crown to right of CA	70·00	
429	50 c.	Government House	35	1·
426/9		*Set of* 4	75	2·

*The normal sideways watermark shows Crown to left of C *as seen from the back of the stamp.*

(Des J.W. Litho Questa)

1981 (21 May). *Heritage Week. T* **113** *and similar hor designs. Multicoloured. W* w **14** (*sideways**). *P* 14.

No.	Value	Design	Unused	Used
430	8 c.	Type **113**	15	
		w. Wmk Crown to right of CA	8·00	
431	25 c.	Gathering Easter lilies, 20th-century	40	
432	30 c.	Fishing, 20th-century	50	
433	40 c.	Stone cutting, 19th-century	55	1·
		w. Wmk Crown to right of CA	1·50	
434	50 c.	Onion shipping, 19th-century	75	1·
435	$1	Privateering, 17th-century	1·60	2·
430/5		*Set of* 6	3·50	5·

*The normal sideways watermark shows Crown to left of C *as seen from the back of the stamp.*

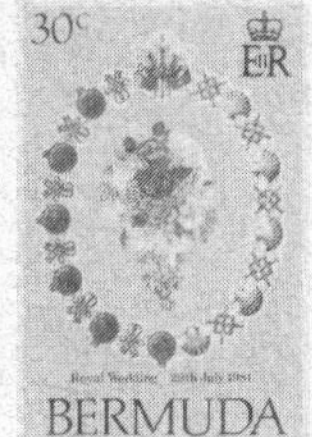

114 Wedding Bouquet from Bermuda   **115** "Service", Hamilton

(Des J.W. Litho Questa)

81 (22 July). *Royal Wedding. T* **114** *and similar vert designs. Multicoloured. W* w **14**. *P* 14.
6 30 c. Type **114** 20 20
7 50 c. Prince Charles as Royal Navy Commander 35 40
8 $1 Prince Charles and Lady Diana Spencer 55 80
6/8 .. .. *Set of* 3 1·00 1·25

(Des L. Curtis. Litho Questa)

81 (28 Sept). *25th Anniv of Duke of Edinburgh Award Scheme. T* **115** *and similar vert designs. Multicoloured. W* w **14**. *P* 14.
9 10 c. Type **115** 15 10
0 25 c. "Outward Bound", Paget Island 20 20
1 30 c. "Expedition", St. David's Island 20 30
2 $1 Duke of Edinburgh .. .. .. 55 1·25
9/42 .. .. *Set of* 4 1·00 1·75

116 Lightbourne's Cone (*Conus lightbourni*)

(Des Walsall. Litho Questa)

82 (22 Apr). *Sea-shells. T* **116** *and similar horiz designs. Multicoloured. W* w **14** (*sideways*). *P* 14.
3 10 c. Type **116** 40 10
4 25 c. Finlay's Frog Shell (*Bursa finlayi*) .. 80 75
5 30 c. Royal Bonnet (*Sconsia striata*) .. 85 85
6 $1 Lightbourne's Murex (*Murex lightbourni*) .. .. 2·25 3·25
3/6 .. .. *Set of* 4 3·75 4·50

117 Regimental Colours and Colour Party   **118** Charles Fort

(Des G. Drummond. Litho Questa)

82 (17 June). *Bermuda Regiment. T* **117** *and similar horiz designs. Multicoloured. W* w **14** (*sideways*). *P* 14.
7 10 c. Type **117** 45 10
8 25 c. Queen's Birthday Parade 90 80
9 30 c. Governor inspecting Guard of Honour .. 1·00 1·40
0 40 c. Beating the Retreat .. .. .. 1·25 1·75
1 50 c. Ceremonial gunners .. .. .. 1·40 2·00
2 $1 Guard of Honour, Royal visit, 1975 .. 2·25 3·50
7/52 .. .. *Set of* 6 6·50 8·50

(Des L. Curtis. Litho Questa)

82 (18 Nov) *Historic Bermuda Forts. T* **118** *and similar multicoloured designs. W* w **14** (*sideways on* 30 c. *and* $1). *P* 14.
3 10 c. Type **118** 20 20
4 25 c. Pembroks Fort 50 85
5 30 c. Southampton Fort (*horiz*) .. .. 60 1·25
6 $1 Smiths Fort and Pagets Fort (*horiz*) .. 1·75 4·25
3/6 .. .. *Set of* 4 2·75 6·00

119 Arms of Sir Edwin Sandys   **120** Early Fitted Dinghy

(Des Harrison. Litho J.W.)

1983 (14 Apr). *Coats of Arms* (1*st series*). *T* **119** *and similar vert designs. Multicoloured. W* w **14**. *P* 13.
457 10 c. Type **119** 45 15
458 25 c. Arms of the Bermuda Company .. .. 1·40 1·00
459 50 c. Arms of William Herbert, Earl of Pembroke .. .. 2·25 3·25
460 $1 Arms of Sir George Somers .. .. 3·00 5·00
457/60 .. .. *Set of* 4 6·50 8·50
See also Nos. 482/5 and 499/502.

(Des L. Curtis. Litho Harrison)

1983 (23 June). *Fitted Dinghies. T* **120** *and similar vert designs. Multicoloured. W* w **14** (*sideways*). *P* 14.
461 12 c. Type **120** 45 15
462 30 c. Modern dinghy inshore 75 75
463 40 c. Early dinghy (*different*) 90 90
464 $1 Modern dinghy with red and white spinnaker .. .. 1·75 3·25
461/4 .. .. *Set of* 4 3·50 4·50

121 Curtiss N-9 Seaplane (first flight over Bermuda)   **122** Joseph Stockdale

(Des A. Theobald. Litho Walsall)

1983 (13 Oct). *Bicentenary of Manned Flight. T* **121** *and similar horiz designs. Multicoloured. W* w **14** (*sideways*). *P* 14.
465 12 c. Type **121** 60 20
466 30 c. Stinson Pilot Radio seaplane (First completed flight between U.S.A. and Bermuda) .. .. 1·25 1·25
467 40 c. Short S.23 flying boat *Cavalier* (First scheduled passenger flight) .. .. 1·50 1·75
468 $1 U.S.N. *Los Angeles* (airship) moored to U.S.S. *Patoka* .. .. 2·50 5·00
465/8 .. .. *Set of* 4 5·25 7·50

(Des L. Curtis. Litho Harrison)

1984 (26 Jan). *Bicentenary of Bermuda's First Newspaper and Postal Service. T* **122** *and similar multicoloured designs. W* w **14** (*sideways** *on* 40 c. *and* $1). *P* 14.
469 12 c. Type **122** 30 15
470 30 c. *The Bermuda Gazette* 60 80
471 40 c. Stockdale's postal service (*horiz*) .. 80 1·10
w. Wmk Crown to right of CA £200
472 $1 *Lady Hammond* (mail boat) (*horiz*) .. 2·50 3·25
469/72 .. .. *Set of* 4 3·75 4·75
*The normal sideways watermark shows Crown to left of CA, *as seen from the back of the stamp.*

123 Sir Thomas Gates and Sir George Somers   **124** Swimming

(Des R. Granger Barrett. Litho Walsall)

1984 (3 May). *375th Anniv of First Settlement. T* **123** *and similar horiz designs. Multicoloured. W* w **14** (*sideways*). *P* 14.
473 12 c. Type **123** 20 15
474 30 c. Jamestown, Virginia .. .. .. 50 1·25
475 40 c. Wreck of *Sea Venture* .. .. .. 90 1·25
476 $1 Fleet leaving Plymouth, Devon .. 2·00 5·00
473/6 .. .. *Set of* 4 3·25 7·00
MS477 130×73 mm. Nos. 474 and 476 .. 3·75 8·50

(Des C. Collins. Litho J.W.)

1984 (19 July). *Olympic Games, Los Angeles. T* **124** *and similar multicoloured designs. W* w **14** (*sideways on* 30 c., $1). *P* 14.
478 12 c. Type **124** 40 15
479 30 c. Track and field events (*horiz*) 70 85
480 40 c. Equestrian competition .. .. .. 1·25 1·25
481 $1 Sailing (*horiz*) .. .. 2·50 5·00
478/81 .. .. *Set of* 4 4·25 6·50

(Des Harrison. Litho J.W.)

1984 (27 Sept). *Coats of Arms* (2*nd series*). *Vert designs as T* **119**. *Multicoloured. W* w **14**. *P* 13.
482 12 c. Arms of Henry Wriothesley, Earl of Southampton 50 15
483 30 c. Arms of Sir Thomas Smith .. .. 1·00 85
w. Wmk inverted .. .. 1·25
484 40 c. Arms of William Cavendish, Earl of Devonshire .. .. 1·25 1·50
485 $1 Town arms of St. George .. .. 2·75 4·00
482/5 .. .. *Set of* 4 5·00 6·00

125 Buttery   **126** Osprey

(Des D. Miller. Litho Walsall)

1985 (24 Jan). *Bermuda Architecture. T* **125** *and similar multicoloured designs. W* w **14** (*inverted on* 12 c., $1.50, *sideways on* 30 c., 40 c.). *P* 13½ × 13 (12 c., $1.50) *or* 13 × 13½ (30 c., 40 c.).
486 12 c. Type **125** 35 15
487 30 c. Limestone rooftops (*horiz*) 80 70
488 40 c. Chimneys (*horiz*) .. .. 95 1·00
489 $1.50, Entrance archway .. .. .. 3·00 3·75
486/9 .. .. *Set of* 4 4·75 5·00

(Des D. Miller. Litho Walsall)

1985 (28 Mar). *Birth Bicentenary of John J. Audubon (ornithologist). T* **126** *and similar multicoloured designs showing original drawings. W* w **14** (*sideways on* 40 c.). *P* 14.
490 12 c. Type **126** .. .. 2·00 65
491 30 c. Yellow-crowned Night Heron .. .. 2·00 95
492 40 c. Great Egret (*horiz*) .. .. 2·25 1·25
493 $1.50, Eastern Bluebird .. .. .. 3·75 5·50
490/3 .. .. *Set of* 4 9·00 7·50

127 The Queen Mother with Grandchildren, 1980   **128** Halley's Comet and Bermuda Archipelago

(Des A. Theobald ($1), C. Abbott (others). Litho Questa)

1985 (7 June). *Life and Times of Queen Elizabeth the Queen Mother. T* **127** *and similar vert designs. Multicoloured. W* w **16**. *P* 14½×14.
494 12 c. Queen Consort, 1937 .. .. .. 25 15
w. Wmk inverted .. .. † —
495 30 c. Type **127** 40 50
w. Wmk inverted .. .. 1·50
496 40 c. At Clarence House on 83rd birthday 50 60
497 $1.50, With Prince Henry at his christening (from photo by Lord Snowdon) .. 2·00 2·75
494/7 .. .. *Set of* 4 2·75 3·50
MS498 91×73 mm. $1 With Prince Charles at 80th birthday celebrations. Wmk sideways .. 2·00 2·25

(Des Harrison. Litho J.W.)

1985 (19 Sept). *Coats of Arms* (3*rd series*). *Vert designs as T* **119**. *Multicoloured. W* w **14**. *P* 13×13½.
499 12 c. Hamilton 75 15
500 30 c. Paget .. .. 1·40 80
501 40 c. Warwick .. .. 1·60 1·40
502 $1.50, City of Hamilton .. .. .. 3·75 4·25
499/502 .. .. *Set of* 4 6·75 6·00

(Des Jennifer Toombs. Litho Walsall)

1985 (21 Nov). *Appearance of Halley's Comet. T* **128** *and similar horiz designs. Multicoloured. W* w **16** (*sideways*). *P* 14×14½.
503 15 c. Type **128** 85 25
504 40 c. Halley's Comet, A.D. 684 (from Nuremberg Chronicles, 1493) .. .. .. 1·60 1·75
505 50 c. "Halley's Comet, 1531" (from Peter Apian woodcut, 1532) .. .. .. 1·90 2·50
506 $1.50, "Halley's Comet, 1759" (Samuel Scott) .. .. 3·50 5·00
503/6 .. .. *Set of* 4 7·00 8·50

129 *Constellation* (schooner), 1943

(Des L. Curtis. Litho Questa)

1986 (16 Jan)–**90**. *Ships Wrecked on Bermuda. T* **129** *and similar horiz designs. Multicoloured. W* w **16** (*sideways**). *P* 14. *A. Without imprint date at foot*
507A 3 c. Type **129** .. .. 70 1·00
508A 5 c. *Early Riser* (pilot boat), 1876 .. 20 20
509A 7 c. *Madiana* (steamer), 1903 (20.3.86) 65 85
510A 10 c. *Curlew* (sail/steamer), 1856 .. 30 30
511A 12 c. *Warwick* (galleon), 1619 .. .. 60 80
w. Wmk Crown to right of CA .. ..

512A 15 c. H.M.S. *Vixen* (gunboat), 1890 (18.9.86) 40 60
512cA 18 c. As 7 c. (22.9.88) .. .. 4·50 2·75
513A 20 c. *San Pedro* (Spanish galleon), 1594 (20.3.86) .. .. 1·10 80
514A 25 c. *Alert* (fishing sloop), 1877 (18.9.86) 60 1·50
515A 40 c. *North Carolina* (barque), 1880 (18.9.86) .. .. 65 1·25
516A 50 c. *Mark Antonie* (Spanish privateer), 1777 (18.9.86) .. .. 1·50 1·75
517A 60 c. *Mary Celestia* (Confederate paddle-steamer), 1864 (20.3.86) .. .. 1·50 1·75
517cA 70 c. *Caesar* (brig), 1818 (27.10.88) .. 5·00 4·50
518A $1 *L'Herminie* (French frigate), 1839 (18.9.86) .. .. 4·00 4·50
519A $1.50, As 70 c. (20.3.86) .. .. 4·50 4·50
520A $2 *Lord Amherst* (transport), 1778 (20.3.86) .. .. 7·00 8·00
521A $3 *Minerva* (sailing ship), 1849 (20.3.86) 7·50 9·00
522A $5 *Caraquet* (cargo liner), 1923 (18.9.86) 6·50 10·00
523A $8 H.M.S. *Pallas* (frigate), 1783 .. 8·00 12·00
507A/23A .. .. .. *Set of* 19 48·00 55·00

B. *With imprint date*

507B 3 c. Type **129** (1.8.90) .. .. .. 1·75 2·25
513B 20 c. *San Pedro* (Spanish galleon), 1594 (1.8.90) .. .. 2·50 2·75
518B $1 *L'Herminie* (French frigate), 1839 (7.89) .. .. 1·50 1·60
520B $2 *Lord Amherst* (transport), 1778 (7.89) 2·50 3·50
521B $3 *Minerva* (sailing ship), 1849 (7.89) .. 4·25 5·50
507B/21B .. .. .. *Set of* 5 11·00 14·50

*The normal sideways watermark shows Crown to left of CA, *as seen from the back of the stamp.*

It is reported that the vessel depicted on the 70 c. is the *Wolf* and not the *Caesar.*

Imprint dates: "1989", Nos. 518B, 520B/1B; "1990", Nos. 507B, 513B.

No. 523A shows "BERMUDA" printed in yellow fluorescent ink as a security marking.

For some of these designs watermarked w **14** (sideways) see Nos. 664/78.

(Des A. Theobald. Litho Harrison)

1986 (21 Apr). *60th Birthday of Queen Elizabeth II. Vert designs as T* **110** *of Ascension. Multicoloured.* W w **16**. P 14½×14.

524 15 c. Princess Elizabeth aged three, 1929 .. 30 30
w. Wmk inverted .. .. .. 17·00
525 40 c. With Earl of Rosebery at Oaks May Meeting, Epsom, 1954 .. .. .. 50 60
526 50 c. With Duke of Edinburgh, Bermuda, 1975 .. .. 65 75
527 60 c. At British Embassy, Paris, 1972 .. 80 90
528 $1.50, At Crown Agents Head Office, London, 1983 .. .. .. 2·00 2·50
524/8 .. .. .. *Set of* 5 3·75 4·50

(Des G. Drummond. Litho Walsall)

1986 (22 May). *"Ameripex '86" International Stamp Exhibition, Chicago. Horiz designs as T* **164** *of Bahamas, showing Bermuda stamps (Nos. 529/32). Multicoloured.* W w **16** (*sideways*). P 14.

529 15 c. 1984 375th Anniv of Settlement miniature sheet.. .. .. .. 85 30
530 40 c. 1973 Lawn Tennis Centenary 24 c. .. 1·50 70
531 50 c. 1983 Bicentenary of Manned Flight 12 c. 1·75 1·00
532 $1 1976 Tall Ships Race 17 c. .. .. 3·00 2·50
529/32 .. .. *Set of* 4 6·25 4·00
MS533 80×80 mm. $1.50, Statue of Liberty and *Monarch of Bermuda* .. .. 5·00 5·00

No. **MS**533 also commemorates the Centenary of the Statue of Liberty.

(130)

1986 (4 Dec). *25th Anniv of World Wildlife Fund. No.* 402 *surch with T* **130** *by J. W. Dunn Printers Ltd, Sutton, Surrey.*

534 90 c. on $3 Green Turtle .. .. .. 2·25 3·25
a. Surch double £100
b. Surch double, one inverted £425
c. "90 c" omitted .. .. ..

131 Train in Front Street, Hamilton, 1940

(Des A. Theobald. Litho Walsall)

1987 (22 Jan). *Transport (1st series). Bermuda Railway. T* **131** *and similar horiz designs. Multicoloured.* W w **16** (*sideways*). P 14.

535 15 c. Type **131**.. .. .. 1·25 25
536 40 c. Train crossing Springfield Trestle .. 1·75 90
537 50 c. "St. George Special" at Bailey's Bay Station .. .. 1·90 1·50
538 $1 50, Boat train at St. George .. .. 3·25 4·00
535/8.. .. .. .. *Set of* 4 7·25 6·00

See also Nos. 557/60, 574/7 and 624/9.

132 "Bermuda Settlers", 1901

(Des L. Curtis. Litho Walsall)

1987 (30 Apr). *Bermuda Paintings (1st series). Works by Winslow Homer. T* **132** *and similar horiz designs. Multicoloured.* W w **16** (*sideways*). P 14×14½.

(*a*) *Sheet stamps (No. 541 with a buff frame).*

539 15 c. Type **132**.. .. .. 60 25
540 30 c. "Bermuda", 1900 .. .. .. 85 45
541 40 c. "Bermuda Landscape", 1901 .. .. 95 55
542 50 c. "Inland Water", 1901 .. .. .. 1·10 70
543 $1.50, "Salt Kettle", 1899 .. .. .. 2·50 2·50
539/43 .. .. .. *Set of* 5 5·50 4·00

(*b*) *Booklet stamps, each with grey frame*

544 40 c. Type **132**.. .. .. 90 1·50
a. Booklet pane. Nos. 544/8, each × 2 .. 8·00
545 40 c. As No. 540 .. .. 90 1·50
546 40 c. As No. 541 .. .. 90 1·50
547 40 c. As No. 542 .. .. 90 1·50
548 40 c. As No. 543 .. .. 90 1·50
544/8 .. .. *Set of* 5 4·00 6·50

See also Nos. 607/10 and 630/3.

133 Sikorsky S-42B Flying Boat *Bermuda Clipper* of Pan Am

(Des A. Theobald. Litho Walsall)

1987 (18 June). *50th Anniv of Inauguration of Bermuda – U.S.A. Air Service. T* **133** *and similar horiz designs. Multicoloured.* W w **16** (*sideways*). P 14.

549 15 c. Type **133** .. .. 1·25 15
550 40 c. Short S.23 flying boat *Cavalier* of Imperial Airways .. .. 2·25 70
551 50 c. *Bermuda Clipper* in flight over signpost 2·50 80
552 $1.50, *Cavalier* on apron and *Bermuda Clipper* in flight .. .. .. 5·00 3·50
549/52 .. .. *Set of* 4 10·00 4·75

134 19th-century Wagon carrying Telephone Poles

135 Mail Wagon, *c.* 1869

(Des L. Curtis. Litho B.D.T.)

1987 (1 Oct). *Centenary of Bermuda Telephone Company. T* **134** *and similar horiz designs. Multicoloured.* W w **16** (*sideways*). P 14×13½.

553 15 c. Type **134**.. .. .. 75 15
554 40 c. Early telephone exchange .. .. 1·40 60
555 50 c. Early and modern telephones .. .. 1·75 70
556 $1.50, Communications satellite orbiting Earth .. .. 2·75 3·50
553/6 .. .. *Set of* 4 6·00 4·50

(Des O. Bell. Litho Questa)

1988 (3 Mar). *Transport (2nd series). Horse-drawn Carts and Wagons. T* **135** *and similar horiz designs. Multicoloured.* W w **16** (*sideways*). P 14.

557 15 c. Type **135**.. .. .. 25 15
558 40 c. Open cart, *c.* 1823 .. .. .. 55 55
559 50 c. Closed cart, *c.* 1823 .. .. .. 65 65
560 $1.50, Two-wheeled wagon, *c.* 1930 .. 2·00 2·50
557/60 .. .. .. *Set of* 4 3·00 3·50

136 "Old Blush"

137 Devonshire Parish Militia, 1812

(Des R. Gorringe. Litho B.D.T.)

1988 (21 Apr). *Old Garden Roses (1st series). T* **136** *ar similar multicoloured designs.* W w **14** (*sideways on hor designs*). P 14×13½ (*vert*) *or* 13½×14 (*horiz*).

561 15 c. Type **136** 45
562 30 c. "Anna Olivier" 60
563 40 c. *Rosa chinensis semperflorens* (*vert*) .. 75
564 50 c. "Archduke Charles" 85
565 $1.50, *Rosa chinensis viridiflora* (*vert*) .. 2·25 2·
561/5 .. .. .. *Set of* 5 4·50 4·

See also Nos. 584/8 and, for these designs with the roy cypher instead of the Queen's head, Nos. 589/98, and 683/6.

(Des D. Miller (18 c.), E. Nisbet and D. Miller (others). Litho Questa)

1988 (13 Oct). *300th Anniv of Lloyd's of London. Mul coloured designs as T* **123** *of Ascension.* W w **16** (*sideways** 50, 60 *c.*). P 14.

566 18 c. Loss of H.M.S. *Lutine* (frigate), 1799
w. Wmk inverted .. .. .. 10·00
567 50 c. *Sentinel* (cable ship) (*horiz*) .. .. 1·00
w. Wmk Crown to right of CA .. .. 15·00
568 60 c. *Bermuda* (liner), Hamilton, 1931 (*horiz*) .. .. 1·10
w. Wmk Crown to right of CA .. .. 12·00
569 $2 Loss of H.M.S. *Valerian* (sloop) in hurricane, 1926 .. .. .. 3·00 3·
566/9 .. .. .. *Set of* 4 5·00 4·

*The normal sideways watermark shows Crown to left of C *as seen from the back of the stamp.*

(Des A. Barbosa. Litho Harrison)

1988 (10 Nov). *Military Uniforms. T* **137** *and similar ve designs. Multicoloured.* W w **14**. P 14½.

570 18 c. Type **137** 75
571 50 c. 71st (Highland) Regiment, 1831-34 .. 1·40
572 60 c. Cameron Highlanders, 1942 .. .. 1·50
573 $2 Troop of horse, 1774 .. .. .. 4·00 4
570/3 .. .. .. *Set of* 4 7·00 6

138 *Corona* (ferry)

139 Morgan's Island

(Des C. Abbott, adapted L. Curtis. Litho Questa)

1989 (16 Feb). *Transport (3rd series). Ferry Services. T* **1** *and similar horiz designs. Multicoloured.* W w **16** (*sideway* P 14.

574 18 c. Type **138** 25
575 50 c. Rowing boat ferry 65
576 60 c. St. George's barge ferry 75
577 $2 *Laconia* .. .. 2·50 2·
574/7 .. .. .. *Set of* 4 3·75 4·

(Des A. Theobald. Litho Questa)

1989 (11 May). *150 Years of Photography. T* **139** *and simi horiz designs. Multicoloured.* W w **14** (*sideways*). P 14×14

578 18 c. Type **139** 45
579 30 c. Front Street, Hamilton 65
580 50 c. Waterfront, Front Street, Hamilton .. 1·00
581 60 c. Crow Lane from Hamilton Harbour .. 1·10 1
582 70 c. Shipbuilding, Hamilton Harbour .. 1·25 1
583 $1 Dockyard .. .. 1·75 2
578/83 .. .. .. *Set of* 6 5·50 6

(Des R. Gorringe. Litho B.D.T.)

1989 (13 July). *Old Garden Roses (2nd series). Multicolou designs as T* **136**. W w **14** (*sideways on* 50, 60 *c. and* $1.5 P 14×13½ (18, 30 *c.*) *or* 13½×14 (*others*).

584 18 c. "Agrippina" (*vert*) 40
585 30 c. "Smith's Parish" (*vert*) 55
586 50 c. "Champney's Pink Cluster" .. .. 90 1·
587 60 c. "Rosette Delizy" .. .. .. 1·00 1·
588 $1.50, *Rosa bracteata* .. .. .. 2·00 3·
584/8 .. .. .. *Set of* 5 4·25 6

For these designs with the royal cypher instead of the Quee head, see Nos. 589/98.

1989 (13 July). *Old Garden Roses (3rd series). Designs as N* 561/5 *and* 584/8, *but with royal cypher at top left instead Queen's head. Multicoloured.* W w **14** (*sideways on hor inverted on vert designs*). P 13½.

589 50 c. As No. 565 (*vert*) .. .. .. 1·40 1
a. Booklet pane. Nos. 589/98 .. .. 12·00
590 50 c. As No. 563 (*vert*) .. .. .. 1·40 1
591 50 c. Type **136** .. .. 1·40 1
592 50 c. As No. 562 .. .. 1·40 1
593 50 c. As No. 564 .. .. 1·40 1
594 50 c. As No. 585 (*vert*) .. .. .. 1·40 1
595 50 c. As No. 584 (*vert*) .. .. .. 1·40 1
596 50 c. As No. 586 .. .. 1·40 1
597 50 c. As No. 587 .. .. 1·40 1
598 50 c. As No. 588 .. .. 1·40 1
589/98 .. .. .. *Set of* 10 12·00 14

Nos. 589/98 were only issued in $5 stamp booklets in wh the pane has margins on three sides.

NEW INFORMATION

The editor is always interested to correspond w people who have new information that w improve or correct the Catalogue.

140 Main Library, Hamilton

141 1865 1d. Rose

(Des O. Bell. Litho B.D.T.)

89 (5 Oct). *150th Anniv of Bermuda Library. T* **140** *and similar horiz designs. Multicoloured.* W w **14** (*sideways*). P $13^1/_2\times14$.

99 18 c. Type **140** 30 25
00 50 c. The Old Rectory, St. George's .. 70 65
01 60 c. Somerset Library, Springfield .. 80 75
02 $2 Cabinet Building, Hamilton .. .. 2·75 2·75
99/602 .. .. *Set of* 4 4·00 4·00

(Des D. Miller. Litho Questa)

89 (3 Nov). *Commonwealth Postal Conference. T* **141** *and similar vert designs. Multicoloured.* W w **16**. P 14.

03 18 c. brownish grey, brown-rose & brt scar 70 25
04 50 c. brownish grey, slate-bl & pale grey-bl 1·25 65
05 60 c. brownish grey, dull purple and purple 1·40 1·00
06 $2 brownish grey, dull green & brt emer 2·75 3·50
03/6 .. .. *Set of* 4 5·50 4·75

Designs:—50 c. 1866 2d. blue; 60 c. 1865 6d purple; $2 1865 s. green.

142 "Fairylands, *c.* 1890" (Ross Turner)

(143)

(Des L. Curtis. Litho B.D.T.)

990 (19 Apr). *Bermuda Paintings (2nd series). T* **142** *and similar horiz designs. Multicoloured.* W w **16** (*sideways*). P $13^1/_2$.

07 18 c. Type **142** 40 25
08 50 c. "Shinebone Alley, *c.* 1953" (Ogden Pleissner) .. .. 85 1·10
09 60 c. "Salt Kettle, 1916" (Prosper Senat) .. 90 1·50
10 $2 "St. George's, 1934" (Jack Bush) .. 2·75 5·00
07/10 .. .. *Set of* 4 4·50 7·00

990 (3 May). *"Stamp World London 90" International Stamp Exhibition, London. Nos. 603/6 optd with T* **143**.

11 18 c. brownish grey, brown-rose & brt scar 75 25
12 50 c. brownish grey, slate-bl & pale grey-bl 1·25 1·25
13 60 c. brownish grey, dull purple and purple 1·40 1·50
14 $2 brownish grey, dull green & brt emer 3·25 5·00
11/14 .. .. *Set of* 4 6·00 7·25

(144)

145 The Halifax and Bermudas Cable Company Office, Hamilton

990 (13 Aug). *Nos.* 511A, 516A *and* 519A *surch as T* **144**.

15 30 c. on 12 c. *Warwick* (galleon), 1619 .. 65 65
16 55 c. on 50 c. *Mark Antonie* (Spanish privateer), 1777 .. .. .. 1·00 1·00
17 80 c. on $1.50 *Caesar* (brig), 1818 .. .. 1·75 3·00
15/17 .. .. *Set of* 3 3·00 4·25

(Des C. Abbott. Litho Harrison)

990 (18 Oct). *Centenary of Cable and Wireless in Bermuda. T* **145** *and similar horiz designs.* P 14.

18 20 c. light brown and black 60 25
19 55 c. light brown and black .. .. 1·75 1·25
20 70 c. multicoloured .. .. 1·75 2·00
21 $2 multicoloured .. .. 4·00 5·00
18/21 .. .. .. *Set of* 4 7·25 7·75

Designs:—55 c. *Westmeath* (cable ship), 1890; 70 c. Wireless transmitter station, St. George's, 1928; $2 *Sir Eric Sharp* (cable ship).

OMNIBUS ISSUES

Details, together with prices for complete sets, of the various Omnibus issues from the 1935 Silver Jubilee series to date are included in a special section following Zimbabwe at the end of Volume 2.

BUSH - MAJOR
16 MARCH 1991

(146)

147 Two-seater Pony Cart, 1805

1991 (16 Mar). *President Bush – Prime Minister Major Talks, Bermuda. Nos.* 618/19 *optd with T* **146** *by Island Press.*

622 **145** 20 c. light brown and black .. .. 1·25 75
623 – 55 c. light brown and black .. .. 2·25 2·75

(Des N. Shering. Litho Walsall)

1991 (21 Mar). *Transport (4th series). Horse-drawn Carriages. T* **147** *and similar horiz designs. Multicoloured.* W w **14** (*sideways*). P $14^1/_2$.

624 20 c. Type **147** 70 30
625 30 c. Varnished rockaway, 1830 .. .. 80 50
626 55 c. Vis-a-Vis victoria, 1895 .. .. 1·40 1·10
627 70 c. Semi-formal phaeton, 1900 .. .. 2·00 2·00
628 80 c. Pony runabout, 1905 .. .. 2·25 2·25
629 $1 Ladies phaeton, 1910 .. .. 2·50 2·50
624/9 .. .. *Set of* 6 8·75 7·75

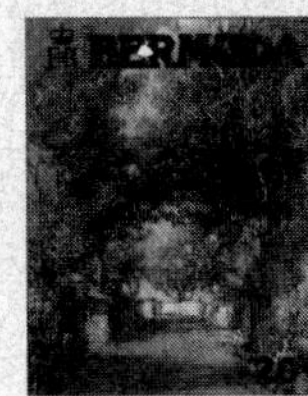

148 "Bermuda, 1916" (Prosper Senat)

149 H.M.S. *Argonaut* (cruiser) in Floating Dock

(Des L. Curtis. Litho Questa)

1991 (16 May). *Bermuda Paintings (3rd series). T* **148** *and similar multicoloured designs.* W w **14** (*sideways on* 55 c., $2). P $13^1/_2\times14$ (20, 70 c.) *or* $14\times13^1/_2$ (55 c., $2).

630 20 c. Type **148** 80 30
631 55 c. "Bermuda Cottage", 1930 (Frank Allison) (*horiz*) .. .. .. 1·75 1·40
632 70 c. "Old Maid's Lane", 1934 (Jack Bush) 2·25 2·75
633 $2 "St. George's", 1953 (Ogden Pleissner) (*horiz*) .. .. .. 4·00 6·00
630/3 .. .. .. *Set of* 4 8·00 9·50

(Des D. Miller. Litho Questa)

1991 (20 June). *65th Birthday of Queen Elizabeth II and 70th Birthday of Prince Philip. Vert designs as T* **139** *of Ascension. Multicoloured.* W w **16** (*sideways*). P $14^1/_2\times14$.

634 55 c. Prince Philip in tropical naval uniform 90 1·25
a. Horiz pair. Nos. 634/5 separated by label .. .. .. 2·00 2·50
635 70 c. Queen Elizabeth II in Bermuda .. 1·10 1·25

Nos. 634/5 were printed together in a similar sheet format to Nos. 539/40 of Ascension.

(Des N. Shewring. Litho Walsall)

1991 (19 Sept). *50th Anniv of Second World War. T* **149** *and similar horiz designs. Multicoloured.* W w **14** (*sideways*). P 14.

636 20 c. Type **149** .. .. 1·25 40
637 55 c. Kindley Airfield .. .. .. 2·00 1·40
638 70 c. Boeing 314A flying boat and map of Atlantic route .. .. .. 2·50 2·75
639 $2 Censored trans-Atlantic mail .. 4·25 6·00
636/9 .. .. .. *Set of* 4 9·00 9·50

(Des D. Miller. Litho Questa ($1), B.D.T. (others))

1992 (6 Feb). *40th Anniv of Queen Elizabeth II's Accession. Horiz designs as T* **143** *of Ascension. Multicoloured.* W w **14** (*sideways*). P 14.

640 20 c. Old fort on beach 50 30
641 30 c. Public gardens 65 55
642 55 c. Cottage garden .. .. .. 1·00 90
643 70 c. Beach and hotels .. .. .. 1·40 1·60
644 $1 Queen Elizabeth II .. .. .. 1·75 2·25
640/4 .. .. .. *Set of* 5 4·75 5·00

150 Rings and Medallion

(Des N. Shewring. Litho Enschedé)

1992 (23 July). *500th Anniv of Discovery of America by Columbus. Spanish Artifacts. T* **150** *and similar horiz designs. Multicoloured.* W w **14** (*sideways*). P $13^1/_2$.

645 25 c. Type **150** 80 35
646 35 c. Ink wells .. .. 1·00 75
647 60 c. Gold ornaments .. .. .. 1·75 2·00
648 75 c. Bishop buttons and crucifix .. .. 2·00 2·75
649 85 c. Earrings and pearl buttons .. .. 2·25 3·00
650 $1 Jug and bowls .. .. .. 2·50 3·25
645/50 .. .. .. *Set of* 6 9·25 11·00

151 "Wreck of *Sea Venture*"

(Des D. Miller. Litho Questa)

1992 (24 Sept). *Stained Glass Windows. T* **151** *and similar horiz designs. Multicoloured.* W w **14** (*sideways*). P $13^1/_2\times14$.

651 25 c. Type **151** 90 40
652 60 c. "Birds in tree" .. .. .. 2·00 2·00
653 75 c. "St. Francis feeding bird" .. .. 2·50 2·75
654 $2 "Shells" .. .. 5·25 6·00
651/4 .. .. *Set of* 4 9·50 10·00

152 German Shepherd

153 Policeman, Cyclist and Liner

(Des Jacqueline Murray-Hall, adapted D. Miller. Litho Enschedé)

1992 (12 Nov). *7th World Congress of Kennel Clubs. T* **152** *and similar multicoloured designs.* W w **14** (*sideways on* 25, 35 c.). P $13^1/_2$.

655 25 c. Type **152** .. .. 1·00 40
656 35 c. Irish Setter .. .. 1·25 70
657 60 c. Whippet (*vert*) .. .. .. 2·00 2·25
658 75 c. Border Terrier (*vert*) .. .. .. 2·00 2·75
659 85 c. Pomeranian (*vert*) .. .. .. 2·25 3·25
660 $1 Schipperke (*vert*) .. .. .. 2·50 3·50
655/60 .. .. .. *Set of* 6 10·00 11·50

1993 (25 Feb). *As Nos.* 510, 512, 513/14, 517 *and* 522/3, *but* W w **14** (*sideways*). *With "1992" imprint date.* P 14.

664 10 c. *Curlew* (sail/steamer), 1856 .. .. 1·00 1·00
665 15 c. H.M.S. *Vixen* (gunboat), 1890 .. 1·50 1·25
667 20 c. *San Pedro* (Spanish galleon), 1594 .. 1·50 1·25
668 25 c. *Alert* (fishing sloop), 1877 .. .. 1·50 60
672 60 c. *Mary Celestia* (Confederate paddle-steamer), 1864 .. .. .. 2·50 1·75
677 $5 *Caraquet* (cargo liner), 1923 .. .. 9·00 9·00
678 $8 H.M.S. *Pallas* (frigate), 1788 .. .. 15·00 16·00
664/78 .. .. .. *Set of* 7 29·00 27·00

No. 678 does not have the fluorescent security marking present on the previous printing, No. 523A.

(Des adapted D. Miller. Litho Questa)

1993 (25 Feb). *Tourism Posters by Adolph Treidler. T* **153** *and similar vert designs. Multicoloured.* W w **14**. P 14.

679 25 c. Type **153** .. .. 1·00 60
680 60 c. Seaside golf course .. .. .. 2·00 2·25
681 75 c. Deserted beach .. .. .. 2·00 2·50
682 $2 Dancers in evening dress and liner .. 4·00 5·50
679/82 .. .. *Set of* 4 8·00 9·75

154 Duchesse de Brabant Rose and Bee

(Des D. Miller. Litho Questa)

1993 (1 Apr). *Garden Roses (4th series).* W w **16** (*sideways*). P 14.

683 **154** 10 c. multicoloured 50 75
a. Booklet pane. Nos. 683×2 and 685×3 with margins all round .. 3·25
b. Pane. No. 683×10 with margins all round .. .. 4·50
684 25 c. multicoloured 30 40
a. Booklet pane. No. 684×5 with margins all round .. .. .. 1·60
685 50 c. multicoloured .. .. .. 80 1·25
686 60 c. multicoloured 75 95
a. Booklet pane. No. 686×5 with margins all round .. .. .. 3·75
683/6 .. .. *Set of* 4 2·10 3·00

The 10 c. was available as a loose pane of 10 and from $2.95 stamp booklets which also contained the 25 c. and 50 c. values. The 25 c. was also issued, together with the 60 c., in $4.25 booklets.

(Des A. Theobald. Litho Questa)

1993 (1 Apr). *75th Anniv of Royal Air Force. Horiz designs as T* **149** *of Ascension. Multicoloured.* W w **14** (*sideways*). P 14.

687 25 c. Consolidated PBY-5 Catalina 75 35
688 60 c. Supermarine Spitfire Mk IX .. .. 1·75 2·00
689 75 c. Bristol Type 156 Beaufighter Mk X .. 1·90 2·25
690 $2 Handley Page Halifax Mk III .. .. 3·50 4·50
687/90 .. .. *Set of* 4 7·00 8·00

155 Hamilton from the Sea

(Des R. Baxter and Sheila Semos (25 c.), N. Shewring and Sheila Semos (others). Litho Questa)

1993 (16 Sept). *Bicentenary of Hamilton. T* **155** *and similar horiz designs. Multicoloured. W* w **14** (*sideways*). *P* $14\frac{1}{2}$.

691 25 c. Type **155** 75 35
692 60 c. Waterfront .. .. 1·75 2·00
693 75 c. Barrel warehouse .. .. 2·00 2·50
694 $2 Sailing ships off Hamilton .. .. .. 4·00 5·00
691/4 .. .. *Set of* 4 7·75 8·75

156 *Queen of Bermuda* (liner) at Hamilton

157 Queen Elizabeth II in Bermuda

(Des adapted D. Miller. Litho B.D.T.)

1994 (20 Jan). *75th Anniv of Furness Line's Bermuda Cruises. T* **156** *and similar multicoloured designs showing Adolph Treidler posters. W* w **16** (*sideways on* 60 c. *and* 75 c.). *P* 15×14 (*vert*) *or* 14×15 (*horiz*).

695 25 c. Type **156** 45 35
696 60 c. *Monarch of Bermuda* entering port (*horiz*) .. .. 1·25 1·60
697 75 c. *Queen of Bermuda* and *Ocean Monarch* (liners) (*horiz*) .. .. 1·40 1·75
698 $2 Passengers on promenade deck at night .. .. 3·50 4·50
695/8 .. .. *Set of* 4 6·00 7·50

The vessel depicted on the 60 c. was incorrectly identified as the *Queen of Bermuda* on the original, 1930s, travel poster.

(Des D. Miller. Litho Enschedé)

1994 (9 Mar). *Royal Visit. T* **157** *and similar vert designs. Multicoloured. W* w **14**. *P* 14.

699 25 c. Type **157** 65 35
700 60 c. Queen Elizabeth and Prince Philip in open carriage .. .. 1·25 1·75
701 75 c. Royal Yacht *Britannia* .. .. .. 2·50 2·75
699/701 .. .. *Set of* 3 4·00 4·25

158 Peach

159 Nurse with Mother and Baby

(Des Christine Phillips-Watlington and D. Miller. Litho Questa)

1994 (14 July)–**96**. *Flowering Fruits. T* **158** *and similar multicoloured designs. W* w **14** (*sideways on horiz designs*). *P* 14. A. *Without imprint date*

702A 5 c. Type **158** 10 10
703A 7 c. Fig 10 10
704A 10 c. Calabash (*vert*) (6.10.94) 10 15
705A 15 c. Natal Plum 20 25
706A 18 c. Locust and Wild Honey (23.3.95) .. 25 30
707A 20 c. Pomegranate 25 30
708A 25 c. Mulberry (*vert*) (6.10.94) 30 35
709A 35 c. Grape (*vert*) (6.10.94) 40 45
710A 55 c. Orange (*vert*) (6.10.94) 65 70
711A 60 c. Surinam Cherry (23.3.95) 70 75
712A 75 c. Loquat (23.3.95) 90 95
713A 90 c. Sugar Apple (23.3.95) .. .. .. 1·10 1·25
714A $1 Prickly Pear (*vert*) (6.10.94) .. .. 1·25 1·40
715A $2 Paw Paw (23.3.95) .. .. 2·40 2·50
716A $3 Bay Grape (23.3.95) .. .. 3·50 3·75
717A $5 Banana (*vert*) (6.10.94) .. .. .. 6·00 6·25
718A $8 Lemon .. .. 10·00 10·50
702A/18A .. .. *Set of* 17 28·00 29·00

B. *Imprint date* ("1996") *at foot* (1.9.96)

706B 18 c. Locust and Wild Honey 25 30

For some of these designs watermarked w **16** (sideways on horiz designs) and with imprint date see Nos. 792/804.

(Des S. Noon. Litho Enschedé)

1994 (15 Sept). *Centenary of Hospital Care. T* **159** *and similar vert designs. Multicoloured. W* w **14**. *P* 15×14.

719 25 c. Type **159** 80 35
720 60 c. Patient on dialysis machine .. .. .. 1·75 1·90
721 75 c. Casualty on emergency trolley .. .. 2·00 2·25
722 $2 Elderly patient in wheelchair with physiotherapists .. .. 4·25 5·00
719/22 .. .. *Set of* 4 8·00 8·50

160 Gombey Dancers

(Des Jennifer Toombs. Litho Enschedé)

1994 (10 Nov). *Cultural Heritage* (1*st series*). *T* **160** *and similar horiz designs. Multicoloured. W* w **14** (*sideways*). *P* 14×15.

723 25 c. Type **160** 55 35
724 60 c. Christmas carol singers .. .. .. 1·10 1·25
725 75 c. Marching band .. .. 1·40 2·00
726 $2 National Dance Group performers .. 3·50 4·75
723/6 .. .. *Set of* 4 6·00 7·50

See also Nos. 731/4.

161 Bermuda 1970 Flower 1 c. Stamps and 1 c. Coin

162 Bermuda Coat of Arms

(Des D. Miller. Litho Enschedé)

1995 (6 Feb). *25th Anniv of Decimal Currency. T* **161** *and similar horiz designs. Multicoloured. W* w **14** (*sideways*). *P* $13\frac{1}{2}$×14.

727 25 c. Type **161** 45 35
728 60 c. 1970 5 c. stamps and coin .. .. .. 1·00 1·25
729 75 c. 1970 10 c. stamps and coin .. .. .. 1·25 1·75
730 $2 1970 25 c. stamps and coin .. .. .. 3·50 4·25
727/30 .. .. *Set of* 4 5·75 7·00

(Des Jennifer Toombs. Litho Enschedé)

1995 (30 May). *Cultural Heritage* (2*nd series*). *Horiz designs as T* **160**. *Multicoloured. W* w **14** (*sideways*). *P* 14×15.

731 25 c. Kite flying 55 35
732 60 c. Majorettes .. .. 1·50 1·50
733 75 c. Portuguese dancers .. .. 1·75 2·00
734 $2 Floral float .. .. 3·75 4·75
731/4 .. .. *Set of* 4 6·75 7·75

(Des Sheila Semas. Litho Enschedé)

1995 (3 Nov). *375th Anniv of Bermuda Parliament. W* w **14**. *P* 14×$13\frac{1}{2}$.

735 **162** 25 c. multicoloured 50 35
736 $1 multicoloured .. .. 1·75 2·25

For design as No. 736, but inscr "Commonwealth Finance Ministers Meeting" see No. 765.

163 U.S. Navy Ordnance Island Submarine Base

164 Triple Jump

(Des R. Watton. Litho Walsall)

1995 (4 Dec). *Military Bases. T* **163** *and similar horiz designs. Multicoloured. W* w **14** (*sideways*). *P* 14.

737 20 c. Type **163** 50 30
738 25 c. Royal Naval Dockyard 60 35
739 60 c. U.S.A.F. Fort Bell and Kindley Field 1·25 1·25
740 75 c. R.A.F. Darrell's Island flying boat base 1·50 1·75
741 90 c. U.S. Navy operating base .. .. .. 1·50 2·25
742 $1 Canadian Forces Communications Station, Daniel's Head .. .. .. 1·60 2·25
737/42 .. .. *Set of* 6 6·25 7·25

(Des S. Noon. Litho B.D.T.)

1996 (21 May). *Olympic Games, Atlanta. T* **164** *and similar vert designs. Multicoloured. W* w **16**. *P* 14.

743 25 c. Type **164** 45 35
744 30 c. Cycling 75 60
745 65 c. Yachting .. .. 1·25 1·60
746 80 c. Show jumping .. .. 1·50 1·90
743/6 .. .. *Set of* 4 3·50 4·00

165 Jetty and Islets, Hamilton

(Des D. Miller. Litho Walsall)

1996 (21 May). *Panoramic Paintings of Hamilton* (*Nos* 747/51) *and St. George's* (*Nos.* 752/6) *by E. J. Holland. T* **165** *and similar horiz designs. Multicoloured. W* w **14** (*sideways*). *P* 14×$14\frac{1}{2}$.

747 60 c. Type **165** 70 75
a. Booklet pane. Nos. 747/56, with margins all round .. .. .. 7·00
748 60 c. End of island and buildings 70 75
749 60 c. Yachts and hotel 70 75
750 60 c. Islet, hotel and cathedral 70 75
751 60 c. Cliff and houses by shore 70 75
752 60 c. Islet and end of main island 70 75
753 60 c. Yacht and houses on hillside 70 75
754 60 c. Yacht and St. George's Hotel on hilltop 70 75
755 60 c. Shoreline and fishing boats 70 75
756 60 c. Entrance to harbour channel 70 75
747/56 .. .. *Set of* 10 7·00 7·25

Nos. 747/56 were only available from $6 stamp booklets containing a pane of 10 (5×2) (No. 747a) showing the Hamilton panorama above that of St. George's.

166 Somerset Express Mail Cart, *c.* 1900

167 Hog Fish Beacon

(Des B. Dare. Litho Enschedé)

1996 (7 June). *"CAPEX '96" International Stamp Exhibition, Toronto. Local Transport. T* **166** *and similar horiz designs. Multicoloured. W* w **14** (*sideways*). *P* $13\frac{1}{2}$×14.

757 25 c. Type **166** 70 35
758 60 c. Victoria carriage and railcar, 1930s .. 1·75 1·75
759 75 c. First bus, 1946 .. .. 1·75 2·00
760 $2 Sightseeing bus, *c.* 1947 .. .. .. 4·00 4·50
757/60 .. .. *Set of* 4 7·50 7·75

(Des N. Shewring. Litho Enschedé)

1996 (15 Aug). *Lighthouses. T* **167** *and similar vert designs. Multicoloured. W* w **14** (*inverted on* $2). *P* 14×$13\frac{1}{2}$.

761 30 c. Type **167** 70 45
762 65 c. Gibbs Hill Lighthouse .. .. .. 1·25 1·25
763 80 c. St. David's Lighthouse .. .. .. 1·75 2·00
764 $2 North Rock Beacon .. .. 3·50 4·50
761/4 .. .. *Set of* 4 6·50 7·50

(Litho Enschedé)

1996 (24 Sept). *Commonwealth Finance Ministers' Meeting. As No.* 736, *but inscr* "Commonwealth Finance Ministers Meeting" *at top and with wider gold frame. W* w **14**. *P* 14×$13\frac{1}{2}$.

765 $1 multicoloured .. .. 1·50 2·00

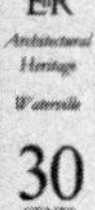

168 Waterville

(Des D. Miller. Litho Walsall)

1996 (28 Nov). *Architectural Heritage. T* **168** *and similar horiz designs. Multicoloured. W* w **16** (*sideways*). *P* 14.

766 30 c. Type **168** 60 45
767 65 c. Bridge House .. .. 1·10 1·25
768 80 c. Fannie Fox's Cottage .. .. 1·40 2·00
769 $2.50, Palmetto House .. .. 3·50 4·50
766/9 .. .. *Set of* 4 6·00 7·50

(Des N. Shewring. Litho Walsall)

997 (12 Feb). *"HONG KONG '97" International Stamp Exhibition. Designs as Nos. 761/4, but incorporating* "HONG KONG '97" *logo and with one value changed.* W w **14**. P 14.
'70 30 c. As Type **167** 60 45
71 65 c. Gibbs Hill Lighthouse .. .. 1·25 1·25
72 80 c. St David's Lighthouse .. .. 1·40 1·50
73 $2.50, North Rock Beacon .. .. 3·75 4·25
70/3 .. .. *Set of* 4 6·25 6·75
The 65 c. and 80 c. also show "c. 1900" added to the inscription t foot.

169 White-tailed Tropic Bird

(Des N. Arlott. Litho B.D.T.)

1997 (17 Apr). *Birds Conservation. T* **169** *and similar multicoloured designs.* W w **16** (*sideways on* 30 c., $2.50). P 14.
'74 30 c. Type **169** 60 45
'75 60 c. White-tailed Tropic Bird and chick (*vert*) .. .. 1·25 1·25
'76 80 c. Cahow and chick (*vert*) .. .. 1·75 2·00
'77 $2.50, Cahow .. .. 4·00 4·50
'74/7 .. .. *Set of* 4 7·00 7·50

170 Queen Elizabeth II with Crowd

171 Father playing with Children

(Des D. Miller. Litho Questa)

1997 (9 Oct). *Golden Wedding of Queen Elizabeth and Prince Philip. T* **170** *and similar horiz design. Multicoloured.* W w **14** (*sideways*). P $14\frac{1}{2}$.
778 30 c. Type **170** 50 40
779 $2 Queen Elizabeth and Prince Philip .. 2·75 3·25
MS780 90×56 mm. Nos. 778/9 .. .. 3·25 3·75

(Litho Questa)

1997 (18 Dec). *Education. T* **171** *and similar horiz designs. Multicoloured.* W w **14** (*sideways*). P 14.
781 30 c. Type **171** 50 40
782 40 c. Teacher and children with map .. 60 55
783 60 c. Boys holding sports trophy 85 90
784 65 c. Pupils outside Berkeley Institute .. 90 1·00
785 80 c. Scientific experiments .. .. 1·25 1·40
786 90 c. New graduates .. .. .. 1·40 1·60
781/6 .. .. *Set of* 6 5·00 5·25

(Des D. Miller. Litho Questa)

1998 (31 Mar). *Diana, Princess of Wales Commemoration. Sheet, 145×70 mm, containing vert designs as T* **177** *of Ascension. Multicoloured.* W w **14** (*sideways*). P $14\frac{1}{2}\times14$.
MS787 30 c. Wearing black hat, 1983; 40 c. Wearing floral dress; 65 c. Wearing blue evening dress, 1996; 80 c. Carrying bouquets, 1993 (*sold at $2.15 + 25 c. charity premium*) .. .. 3·50 4·00

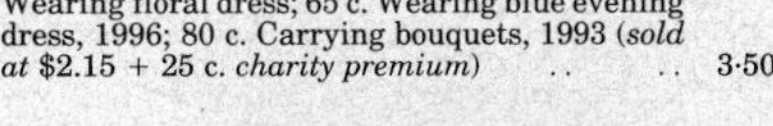

172 "Fox's Cottage, St. David's" (Ethel Tucker)

(Litho Enschedé)

1998 (4 June). *Paintings by Catherine and Ethel Tucker. T* **172** *and similar horiz designs. Multicoloured.* W w **14** (*sideways*). P $13\frac{1}{2}\times14$.
788 30 c. Type **172** 45 40
789 40 c. "East Side, Somerset" 60 60
790 65 c. "Long Bay Road, Somerset" .. .. 1·00 1·10
791 $2 "Flatts Village" .. .. .. 2·75 3·00
788/91 .. .. *Set of* 4 4·25 4·50

1998 (1 Sept). *As Nos. 702/18, but with* W w **16** (*sideways on horiz designs*) *and with imprint date* ("1998"). P 14.
792 5 c. Peach 10 10
795 15 c. Natal Plum 20 25
796 18 c. Locust and Wild Honey 25 30
797 20 c. Pomegranate 25 30
798 25 c. Mulberry (*vert*) 30 35
802 75 c. Loquat 90 95
803 90 c. Sugar Apple .. .. 1·25 1·40
804 $1 Prickly Pear (*vert*) .. .. .. 1·25 1·40
792/804 .. .. *Set of* 8 4·25 4·75

173 Horse and Carriage

(Des J. Semos. Litho Walsall)

1998 (24 Sept). *Hospitality in Bermuda. T* **173** *and similar horiz designs. Multicoloured.* W w **16** (*sideways*). P $14\frac{1}{2}$.
809 25 c. Type **173** 30 35
810 30 c. Golf club desk 35 40
811 65 c. Chambermaid preparing room .. 80 85
812 75 c. Kitchen staff under training .. 90 95
813 80 c. Waiter at beach hotel .. .. 1·00 1·10
814 90 c. Nightclub bar .. .. .. 1·10 1·25
809/14 .. .. *Set of* 6 4·25 4·75

174 *Agave attenuata*

175 "Lizard with Fairy Lights" (Claire Critchley)

(Des Harris and Mitchell Associates. Litho Questa)

1998 (15 Oct). *Centenary of Botanical Gardens. T* **174** *and similar horiz designs.* W w **14** (*sideways*). P 14.
815 30 c. Type **174** 35 40
816 65 c. Bermuda Palmetto Tree 80 85
817 $1 Banyan Tree .. .. 1·25 1·40
818 $2 Cedar Tree .. .. 2·40 2·50
815/18 .. .. *Set of* 4 4·75 5·00

(Litho B.D.T.)

1998 (26 Nov). *Christmas. Children's Paintings. T* **175** *and similar multicoloured design.* W w **14** (*sideways on* 40 c.). P 14.
819 25 c. Type **175** 30 35
820 40 c. "Christmas stairway" (Cameron Rowling) (*horiz*) 50 55

STAMP BOOKLETS

1948 (5 Apr–10 May). *Pink* (No. SB1), *or light blue* (No. SB2) *covers. Stapled.*
SB1 5s. booklet containing six 1d., $1\frac{1}{2}$d., 2d., $2\frac{1}{2}$d. and 3d. (Nos. 110, 111*b*, 112*a*, 113*b*, 114*a*) in blocks of 6 (10 May) £130
SB2 10s. 6d. booklet containing six 3d. and eighteen 6d. (Nos. 114*a*, 104) in blocks of 6 with twelve air mail labels £150

B **1** "Window" Design (*Illustration reduced. Actual size* 125×91 *mm*)

1987 (30 Apr). *Paintings by Winslow Homer. Folded card covers, printed in gold. Pane attached by selvedge.*
SB3 $4 containing booklet pane of 10 40 c. (No. 544a) 8·50

1989 (13 July). *Old Garden Roses. Folded card cover,* 125×91 *mm, as Type* B **1**, *printed in grey. Pane attached by selvedge.*
SB4 $5 containing booklet pane of 10 50 c. (No. 589a) 12·00

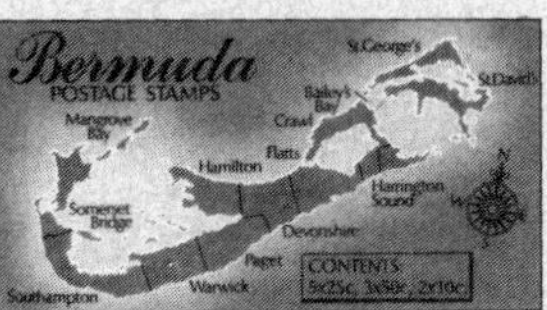

B **2** Map of Bermuda

1993 (1 Apr). *Folded card covers as Type* B **2** *printed in Venetian red, new blue and black. Panes attached by selvedge.*
SB5 $2.95, booklet containing panes Nos. 683a and 684a .. .. 4·75
SB6 $4.25, booklet containing panes Nos. 684a and 686a .. .. 5·25

B **3** Coats of Arms of Hamilton and St. George's

1996 (21 May). *Panoramic Paintings of Hamilton and St. George's. Pane attached by selvedge.*
SB7 $6 booklet containing pane No. 747a .. .. 7·00

EXPRESS LETTER STAMPS

E **1** Queen Elizabeth II

(Des D. Miller. Litho Enschedé)

1996 (7 Nov). W w **14**. P $14\times13\frac{1}{2}$.
E1 E **1** $22 orange and royal blue .. .. 25·00 26·00
No. E1 shows the face value, all other inscriptions, the Crown and much of both the inner and the outer frames printed in yellow fluorescent ink as a security marking.

POSTAL FISCAL

1937 (1 Feb). *As T* **15**, *but inscr* "REVENUE" *at each side. Wmk Mult Script CA. Chalk-surfaced paper.* P 14.
F1 12s. 6d. grey and orange £1000 £1100
a. Break in scroll (R. 1/12) .. £2750
b. Broken crown and scroll (R. 2/12) .. £2750
c. Breaks in scrolls at right (R. 1/3) .. £2750
No. F1 was issued for fiscal purposes towards the end of 1936. Its use as a postage stamp was authorised from 1 February to April 1937. The used price quoted above is for examples postmarked during this period. Later in the same year postmarks with other dates were obtained by favour.
For illustration of No. F1a/c see above Nos. 51*b* and 88.

Botswana

(*formerly* Bechuanaland)

Before the 1880s the only Europeans in the area which became Bechuanaland were scattered hunters and traders, together with the missionaries who were established at Kuruman as early as 1816.

Tribal conflicts in the early years of the decade led to the intervention of Boers from the Transvaal who established the independent republics of Goshen and Stellaland.

STELLALAND

The Boer republic of Stellaland was proclaimed towards the end of 1882. A postal service was organised from the capital, Vryburg, and stamps were ordered from a firm in Cape Town. These were only valid within the republic. Until June 1885 mail to other parts of South Africa was sent through Christiana, in the Transvaal, and was franked with both Stellaland and Transvaal stamps.

No date stamps or obliterators were used by the Stellaland Post Office. Stamps were pen-cancelled with the initials of a postal official and the date.

PRICES FOR STAMPS ON COVER
The issues of Stellaland are very rare on cover.

1 Arms of the Republic

(Litho by Van der Sandt, de Villiers & Co., Cape Town)

1884 (29 Feb). *P* 12.
1 1 1d. red £170 £275
a. Imperf between (horiz pair) £2250
b. Imperf between (vert pair) £2250
2 3d. orange .. .. 20·00 £275
a. Imperf between (horiz pair) £600
b. Imperf between (vert pair) £800
3 4d. olive-grey .. .. 20·00 £300
a. Imperf between (horiz pair) £600
4 6d. lilac-mauve .. .. 20·00 £300
a. Imperf between (horiz pair) £900
b. Imperf between (vert pair) £1200
5 1s. green .. .. 40·00

In 1884 the British Government, following appeals from local chiefs for protection, decided to annex both Goshen and Stellaland. A force under Sir Charles Warren from the Cape reached Vryburg on 7 February 1885 and continued to Mafeking, the principal town of Goshen.

On 30 September 1885 Stellaland and other territory to the south of the Molopo River was constituted the Crown Colony of British Bechuanaland. A protectorate was also proclaimed over a vast tract of land to the north of the Molopo.

Stellaland stamps continued to be used until 2 December 1885 with external mail routed via Barkly West and Kimberley in Griqualand West franked with both Stellaland and Cape of Good Hope stamps. The latter were cancelled on arrival at Barkly West.

1885 (Oct). *Handstamped "Twee" sideways in violet-lake.*
6 1 2d. on 4d. olive-grey £3500

On 2 December 1885 Cape of Good Hope stamps overprinted "British Bechuanaland" were placed on sale at the Vryburg post office.

BRITISH BECHUANALAND

CROWN COLONY

PRICES FOR STAMPS ON COVER

Nos. 1/8	*from* × 12
No. 9	*from* × 80
Nos. 10/21	*from* × 8
Nos. 22/8	*from* × 10
No. 29	*from* × 10
No. 30	*from* × 10
Nos. 31/2	*from* × 12
Nos. 33/7	*from* × 20
Nos. 38/9	*from* × 25

British
Bechuanaland
(1)

BRITISH
BECHUANALAND
(2)

1885 (1 Dec)–**87**. *Stamps of Cape of Good Hope ("Hope" seated) optd with T* 1, *by W. A. Richards & Sons, Cape Town.*

(*a*) *Wmk Crown CC* (*No.* 3) *or Crown CA* (*others*)
1 ½d. grey-black (No. 40*a*) (R.) .. .. 11·00 15·00
a. Opt in lake £3000
b. Opt double (Lake+Black) £600
2 3d. pale claret (No. 43) .. .. .. 32·00 35·00
3 4d. dull blue (No. 30) (12.86?) .. .. 55·00 60·00

(*b*) *Wmk Anchor* (*Cape of Good Hope. Type* **13**)
4 ½d. grey-black (No. 48*a*) (3.87) .. .. 7·00 11·00
a. Error. "ritish" £1700
b. Opt double £2750
5 1d. rose-red (No. 49) .. .. .. 9·00 9·00
a. Error. "ritish" £2250 £1800
b. Opt double .. .. † £1800
6 2d. pale bistre (No. 50) .. .. .. 30·00 8·00
a. Error. "ritish" £4250 £3250
b. Opt double .. .. † £1500
7 6d. reddish purple (No. 52) .. .. 75·00 38·00
8 1s. green (No. 53) (11.86?) £200 £140
a. Error. "ritish" £12000 £9000

Nos. 1/8 were overprinted from settings of 120. The missing "B" errors are believed to have occurred on one position for one of these settings only.

Overprints with stop after "Bechuanaland" are forged.

1887 (1 Nov). *No.* 197 *of Great Britain optd with T* **2**, *by D.L.R.*
9 ½d. vermilion (H/S S. £80) .. .. 1·00 1·25
a. Opt double £2250

3

4

5

(Typo D.L.R.)

1887 (1 Nov). (*a*) *Wmk Orb* (*Great Britain Type* **48**). *P* 14.
10 3 1d. lilac and black .. .. .. 13·00 1·50
11 2d. lilac and black .. .. .. 60·00 1·50
a. Pale dull lilac and black .. .. 38·00 22·00
12 3d. lilac and black .. .. .. 3·25 4·75
a. Pale reddish lilac and black .. 58·00 14·00
13 4d. lilac and black .. .. .. 40·00 2·50
14 6d. lilac and black .. .. .. 50·00 2·50

(*b*) *Wmk Script "V R"* (*sideways, reading up*). *P* 13½
15 4 1s. green and black .. .. .. 28·00 5·00
16 2s. green and black .. .. .. 48·00 35·00
17 2s. 6d. green and black.. .. .. 60·00 42·00
18 5s. green and black .. .. .. 80·00 £140
19 10s. green and black £170 £325

(*c*) *Two Orbs* (*sideways*). *P* 14×13½
20 5 £1 lilac and black £900 £800
21 £5 lilac and black £2750 £1300
10/21 H/S "Specimen" .. .. *Set of* 12 £900

Nos. 10/21 were produced by overprinting a series of "Unappropriated Die" designs originally produced by the Board of Inland Revenue for use as Great Britain fiscal stamps.

Several values are known on blued paper. No. 11*a* is the first printing of the 2d. (on safety paper?) and has a faded appearance.

When purchasing Nos. 20/21 in used condition beware of copies with fiscal cancellations cleaned off and bearing forged postmarks.

For No. 15 surcharged "£5" see No. F2.

1d.
(6)

1s.
(7)

One
Half-
Penny
(8)

1888 (7 Aug). *Nos.* 10/11 *and* 13/15 *surch as T* **6** *or* **7**, *by P. Townshend & Co, Vryburg.*
22 3 1d. on 1d. lilac and black .. .. 7·50 5·50
23 2d. on 2d. lilac and black (R.) .. .. 15·00 2·50
a. Pale dull lilac and black (No. 11*a*) .. 75·00 48·00
b. Curved foot to "2" £200 £150
c. Surch in green .. .. .. † £2500
25 4d. on 4d. lilac and black (R.) £180 £250
26 6d. on 6d. lilac and black .. .. 75·00 10·00
a. Surch in blue .. .. .. † £6000
28 4 1s. on 1s. green and black .. .. £100 65·00

Nos. 23c and 26a are from two sheets of surcharge trials subsequently put into stock and used at Vryburg (2d.) or Mafeking (6d.) during 1888–89.

1888 (Dec). *No.* 12*a surch with T* **8**, *by P. Townshend & Co, Vryburg.*
29 3 ½d. on 3d. pale reddish lilac and black £130 £140
a. Broken "f" in "Half" £4000

No. 29 was produced from a setting of 60 (12×5).

No. 29a shows the letter "f" almost completely missing and occurs on R. 5/11 of the setting. Five examples are known, one being in the Royal Collection.

Errors of spelling on this surcharge are bogus.

British
Bechuanaland.
(9)

British
Bechuanaland.
(10)

BRITISH
BECHUANALAND
(11)

1889 (Jan). *No.* 48*a of Cape of Good Hope* (*wmk Anchor*) *optd with T* **9**, *by P. Townshend & Co, Vryburg.*
30 ½d. grey-black (G.) .. .. .. 3·25 19·00
b. Opt double, one inverted.. .. .. £1000
c. Opt double, one vertical £500
ca. *Se-tenant* with stamp without opt .. £2750
e. "British" omitted.. .. .. .. £2000

No. 30 was produced using a setting of 30 (6×5). No. 30e occurred on R. 5/1 of the setting on some sheets only.

1891 (Nov). *Nos.* 49/50 *of Cape of Good Hope* (*wmk Anchor*), *optd with T* **10**, *reading upwards.*
31 1d. rose-red .. .. 10·00 8·0
a. Horiz pair, one without opt £1900
b. "British" omitted .. .. .. — £110
c. "Bechuanaland" omitted £1100
32 2d. pale bistre .. .. 3·25 2·2
a. No stop after "Bechuanaland" £225 £27
31/2 H/S "Specimen" .. .. *Set of* 2 £130

Nos. 31/2 were produced from separate settings of 120 (12×10). No. 32a occurs on R. 3/3.

See also Nos. 38 and 39.

1891 (1 Dec)–**1904**. *Nos.* 172, 200, 205, 208 *and* 211 *of Great Britain optd with T* **11**, *by D.L.R.*
33 1d. lilac .. .. 6·00 8
34 2d. grey-green and carmine .. .. 4·50 3·2
35 4d. green and purple-brown .. .. 2·50 5
a. Bisected (2d.) (on cover) (11.99) .. † £200
36 6d. purple/*rose-red* .. .. .. 3·00 2·0
37 1s. dull green (7.94) .. .. .. 13·00 16·0
a. Bisected (6d.) (on cover) (12.04) .. † —
33/7 .. .. *Set of* 5 26·00 20·0
33/6 H/S "Specimen" .. .. *Set of* 4 £170

No. 35a was used at Palapye station and No. 37a at Kanye.

1893 (Dec)–**95**. *As Nos.* 31/2, *but T* **10** *reads downwards.*
38 1d. rose-red .. .. 2·25 2·2
a. Pair, one without opt .. .. ..
b. "British" omitted £1000
c. Optd "Bechuanaland. British" £800 £90
d. No dots to "i" of "British" (R. 1/10) .. 80·00 80·0
e. Opt reading up, no dots to "i" of "British" £1300
39 2d. pale bistre (15.3.95) .. .. .. 4·50 2·2
a. Opt double £850 £55
b. "British" omitted £450 £45
c. Optd "Bechuanaland. British" £325 £20
d. No dots to "i" of "British" (R. 1/10) .. £100 £10
e. Opt reading up, no dots to "i" of "British"

A common setting of 120 (12×10) was used for Nos. 38/9. Some sheets of both values were overprinted the wrong way up, resulting in Nos. 38e and 39e.

On 16 November 1895 British Bechuanaland was annexed to the Cape of Good Hope and ceased to have its own stamps, but they remained in use in the Protectorate until superseded in 1897. The Postmaster-General of Cape Colony had assumed control of the Bechuanaland postal service on 1 April 1893 and the Cape, and subsequently the South African, postal authorities continued to be responsible for the postal affairs of the Bechuanaland Protectorate until 1963.

BECHUANALAND PROTECTORATE

PRICES FOR STAMPS ON COVER TO 1945

Nos. 40/51	*from* × 10
Nos. 52/71	*from* × 6
Nos. 72/82	*from* × 5
Nos. 83/98	*from* × 4
Nos. 99/110	*from* × 6
Nos. 111/17	*from* × 10
Nos. 118/28	*from* × 4
Nos. 129/31	*from* × 10
Nos. D1/3	*from* × 50
Nos. D4/6	*from* × 60
No. F1	*from* × 5
No. F2	—
No. F3	*from* × 5

This large area north of the Molopo River was proclaimed a British Protectorate on 30 September 1885 at the request of the native chiefs.

A postal service using runners was inaugurated on 9 August 1888 and Nos. 40 to 55 were issued as a temporary measure with the object of assessing the cost of this service.

Protectorate
(12) 15½ mm

Protectorate
1d
(13)

1888 (7 Aug). *No.* 9 *optd with T* **12** *and Nos.* 10/19 *surch or optd only as T* **13**.
40 – ½d. vermilion (H/S S. £75) .. .. 3·00 22·0
a. "Protectorate" double £300
41 3 1d. on 1d. lilac and black .. .. 6·50 12·0
a. Small figure "1" (R. 5/4, 7/2, 10/2) .. £275 £30
42 2d. on 2d. lilac and black .. .. 19·00 17·0
b. Curved foot to "2" £400 £37
43 3d. on 3d. pale reddish lilac and black .. 95·00 £14
44 4d. on 4d. lilac and black £250 £25
a. Small figure "4" £2500 £250
45 6d. on 6d. lilac and black .. .. 65·00 40·0
46 4 1s. green and black (H/S S. £100) .. 65·00 50·0
a. First "o" omitted £3500 £300
47 2s. green and black £500 £75
a. First "o" omitted £8000
48 2s. 6d. green and black £500 £65
a. First "o" omitted £8000
49 5s. green and black £1100 £170
a. First "o" omitted £10000
50 10s. green and black £3000 £450
a. First "o" omitted £15000

Nos. 40/5 were produced from a basic setting of 120 (12×10) on which a faulty first "o" in "Protectorate" occurred on R.5/12. For Nos. 46/50 the setting was reduced to 84 (12×7) and on many sheets the first "o" on R.5/12 failed to print.

See also Nos. 54/5

1888 (Dec). *No.* 25 *optd with T* **12** *by P. Townshend & Co, Vryburg.*
51 3 4d. on 4d. lilac and black .. .. . 60·00 32·00

Bechuanaland

Protectorate. (14)

Protectorate Fourpence (15)

89 (Jan). *No.* 48*a of Cape of Good Hope* (*wmk Anchor*), *optd with T* **14** *by P. Townshend & Co., Vryburg.*
½d. grey-black (G.) .. .. 2·75 28·00
a. Opt double £425 £550
ab. Ditto, one reading "Protectorate Bechuanaland" £750
b. "Bechuanaland" omitted £750
c. Optd "Protectorate Bechuanaland" .. £375 £450

89 (Aug). *No.* 9 *surch with T* **15** *by P. Townshend & Co., Vryburg.*
4d. on ½d. vermilion (H/S S. £120) .. 16·00 3·25
a. "rpence" omitted (R. 9/2) .. .. † £6000
b. "ourpence" omitted (R. 9/2) £10000
c. Surch (T **15**) inverted .. .. † £4000
cb. Ditto. "ourpence" omitted .. .. † £11000
Examples of No. 53c are postmarked "679" (Tati).

Protectorate (**16**) 15 mm

Protectorate (**17**)

890. *No.* 9 *optd.*
4 **16** ½d. vermilion £120 £130
a. Type **16** inverted .. .. .. 70·00 90·00
b. Type **16** double .. .. .. 85·00 £110
c. Type **16** double and inverted .. £550 £550
d. Optd "Portectorate" inverted .. £2750
w. Wmk inverted .. .. ..
5 **17** ½d. vermilion £140 £200
a. Type **17** double £750
b. Optd "Protectorrte" .. ..
c. Optd "Protectorrte" double .. £12000
These were trial printings made in 1888 which were ıbsequently issued.

In June 1890 the Bechuanaland Protectorate and the Colony of ritish Bechuanaland came under one postal administration and e stamps of British Bechuanaland were used in the Protectorate ntil 1897.

BRITISH BECHUANALAND (18)

BECHUANALAND PROTECTORATE (19)

897. *No.* 61 *of Cape of Good Hope* (*wmk Anchor*), *optd as T* **18**.

(*a*) *Lines* 13 *mm apart, bottom line* 16 *mm long, by Taylor & Marshall, Cape Town*
6 ½d. yellow-green (July?) .. .. .. 2·50 7·00

(*b*) *Lines* 13½ *mm apart, bottom line* 15 *mm long, by P. Townshend & Co, Vryburg*
7 ½d. yellow-green (April) .. .. .. 18·00 60·00
a. Opt double, one albino inverted ..

(*c*) *Lines* 10½ *mm apart, bottom line* 15 *mm long, by W. A. Richards & Sons, Cape Govt Printers*
8 ½d. yellow-green (July?) .. .. .. 8·00 35·00
Although issued only in the Protectorate, the above were resumably overprinted "BRITISH BECHUANALAND" because amps bearing this inscription were in use there at the time.

897 (Oct)–**1902**. *Nos.* 172, 197, 200, 202, 205 *and* 208 *of Great Britain* (*Queen Victoria*) *optd with T* **19** *by D.L.R.*
9 ½d. vermilion .. .. 1·00 1·75
0 ½d. blue-green (25.2.02) .. .. .. 1·40 2·50
1 1d. lilac .. .. 4·00 55
2 2d. grey-green and carmine .. .. 2·50 4·50
3 3d. purple/*yellow* (1898) .. .. .. 5·50 8·50
4 4d. green and purple-brown .. .. 11·00 11·00
5 6d. purple/*rose-red* .. .. .. 21·00 11·00
9/65 .. .. *Set of* 7 42·00 35·00
9/65 Optd/H.S. (No. 60) "Specimen" *Set of* 7 £225

BECHUANALAND PROTECTORATE (20)

BECHUANALAND PROTECTORATE (21)

904 (29 Nov)–**13**. *Nos.* 216, 218/19, 230 *and* 313/14 (*Somerset House ptgs*) *of Great Britain* (*King Edward VII*) *optd with T* **20**, *by D.L.R.*
6 ½d. blue-green (3.06) .. .. .. 1·25 1·25
7 ½d. yellowish green (11.08) .. .. 3·00 3·50
8 1d. scarlet (4.05) (S. £60) .. .. .. 5·50 25
9 2½d. ultramarine .. .. 5·00 5·00
a. Stop after "P" in "PROTECTORATE" £800 £1200
0 1s. deep green and scarlet (10.12) .. 35·00 90·00
1 1s. green and carmine (1913) (S. £80) .. 35·00 90·00
No. 69a occurs on R.5/9 of the lower pane.

912 (Sept). *No.* 342 *of Great Britain* (*King George V, wmk Crown*) *optd with T* **20**.
2 1d. scarlet .. .. 1·00 60
a. No cross on crown .. .. .. — 75·00
b. *Aniline scarlet* (No. 343) .. .. £120 80·00

1913 (July)–**24**. *Stamps of Great Britain* (*King George V*) *optd.*

(*a*) *Nos.* 351, 357, 362, 367, 370/1, 376, 379, 385 *and* 395 (*wmk Simple Cypher, T* **100**) *optd with T* **20**
73 ½d. green (*shades*) .. .. .. 1·25 1·75
74 1d. scarlet (*shades*) (4.15) .. .. 2·75 60
a. *Carmine-red* (1922) .. .. .. 12·00 1·75
75 1½d. red-brown (12.20) .. .. .. 2·25 3·00
76 2d. reddish orange (Die I) .. .. 2·50 3·50
a. *Orange* (Die I) (1921) .. .. .. 11·00 4·50
aw. Wmk inverted .. .. ..
77 2d. orange (Die II) (1924) .. .. 35·00 5·00
78 2½d. cobalt-blue .. .. .. 3·50 16·00
a. *Blue* (1915) .. .. .. 6·00 17·00
79 3d. bluish violet .. .. .. 5·50 12·00
80 4d. grey-green .. .. .. 6·00 14·00
81 6d. reddish purple (*shades*) .. .. 6·50 16·00
a. Opt double, one albino .. ..
82 1s. bistre (S. £75) .. .. .. 9·00 18·00
a. *Bistre-brown* (1923) .. .. .. 20·00 32·00
73/82 .. .. .. *Set of* 9 35·00 75·00

(*b*) *With T* **21**
(i) *Waterlow printings* (*Nos.* 399 *and* 401) (1914–15)
83 2s. 6d. deep sepia-brown (1.15) £100 £200
a. Re-entry (R.2/1) £950 £1300
b. Opt double, one albino £225
84 5s. rose-carmine (1914) £140 £325
a. Opt double, one albino £300
83/4 Optd "Specimen" .. .. *Set of* 2 £275
(ii) *D.L.R. printings* (*Nos.* 407/8 *and* 409) (1916–19)
85 2s. 6d. pale brown (7.16) £100 £200
a. Re-entry (R. 2/1) £1000
86 2s. 6d. sepia (1917) £120 £190
a. Opt treble, two albino .. ..
b. Re-entry (R. 2/1) .. ..
87 5s. bright carmine (8.19) £250 £375
a. Opt double, one albino £350
(iii) *B.W. printings* (*Nos.* 414 *and* 416) (1920–23)
88 2s. 6d. chocolate-brown (7.23) .. .. 80·00 £150
a. Major re-entry (R.1/2) £1900
b. Opt double, one albino .. ..
89 5s. rose-red (7.20) £110 £225
a. Opt treble, two albino £300
b. Opt double, one albino .. ..

1925 (July)–**27**. *Nos.* 418/19, 421, 423/4, 426/*a and* 429 *of Great Britain* (*wmk Block Cypher, T* **111**) *optd with T* **20**.
91 ½d. green (1927) .. .. .. 1·00 1·75
92 1d. scarlet (8.25) .. .. .. 1·50 70
w. Wmk inverted .. .. ..
93 2d. orange (Die II) .. .. .. 1·50 1·00
94 3d. violet (10.26) .. .. .. 4·75 14·00
a. Opt double, one albino £225
w. Wmk inverted £150
95 4d. grey-green (10.26) .. .. 4·75 27·00
a. Printed on the gummed side .. ..
96 6d. reddish purple (*chalk-surfaced paper*) (12.25) .. .. 25·00 45·00
97 6d. purple (*ordinary paper*) (1926) .. 45·00 45·00
98 1s. bistre-brown (10.26) .. .. 9·00 24·00
w. Wmk inverted .. .. — £275
91/8 .. .. .. *Set of* 8 85·00 £140

22 King George V, Baobab Tree and Cattle drinking

23 King George VI, Baobab Tree and Cattle drinking

(Des from photo by Resident Commissioner, Ngamiland, Recess Waterlow)

1932 (12 Dec). *Wmk Mult Script CA. P* 12½.
99 **22** ½d. green .. .. .. 1·00 30
a. Imperf between (horiz pair) £12000
100 1d. scarlet .. .. .. 1·00 25
101 2d. brown .. .. .. 1·00 30
102 3d. ultramarine .. .. .. 1·00 70
103 4d. orange .. .. .. 1·25 4·50
104 6d. purple .. .. .. 2·50 2·25
105 1s. black and olive-green .. .. 3·00 7·00
106 2s. black and orange .. .. 24·00 38·00
107 2s.6d. black and scarlet .. .. 19·00 30·00
108 3s. black and purple .. .. 35·00 42·00
109 5s. black and ultramarine .. .. 48·00 50·00
110 10s. black and brown £100 £110
99/110 .. .. *Set of* 12 £200 £250
99/110 Perf "Specimen" .. .. *Set of* 12 £250

1935 (4 May). *Silver Jubilee. As Nos.* 91/4 *of Antigua but ptd by B.W. P* 11 × 12.
111 1d. deep blue and scarlet .. .. 30 2·00
a. Extra flagstaff £200
b. Short extra flagstaff £200
c. Lightning conductor £200
d. Flagstaff on right-hand turret .. £200
e. Double flagstaff £200
112 2d. ultramarine and grey-black .. 1·00 2·00
a. Extra flagstaff .. .. 90·00
b. Short extra flagstaff .. .. 75·00
c. Lightning conductor .. .. 70·00
113 3d. brown and deep blue .. .. 1·75 2·00
a. Extra flagstaff £130
b. Short extra flagstaff £100
c. Lightning conductor £100
114 6d. slate and purple .. .. 3·50 2·00
a. Extra flagstaff £120
b. Short extra flagstaff .. .. 95·00
c. Lightning conductor £110
111/14 .. .. *Set of* 4 6·00 7·25
111/14 Perf "Specimen" .. *Set of* 4 80·00
For illustrations of plate varieties see Catalogue Introduction.

1937 (12 May). *Coronation. As Nos.* 95/7 *of Antigua, but printed by D.L.R. P* 14.
115 1d. scarlet 45 40
116 2d. yellow-brown 60 80
117 3d. bright blue .. .. .. 60 1·00
115/17 .. .. .. *Set of* 3 1·50 2·00
115/17 Perf "Specimen" .. *Set of* 3 55·00

(Recess Waterlow)

1938 (1 Apr)–**52**. *Wmk Mult Script CA. P* 12½.
118 **23** ½d. green .. .. .. 2·00 2·25
a. *Light yellowish green* (1941) .. 4·00 5·50
b. *Yellowish green* (4.43) .. .. 3·25 3·25
c. *Deep green* (4.49) .. .. 2·00 5·00
119 1d. scarlet 40 40
120 1½d. dull blue .. .. .. 8·50 1·75
a. *Light blue* (4.43) 40 70
121 2d. chocolate-brown 40 40
122 3d. deep ultramarine .. .. 40 1·75
123 4d. orange .. .. .. 1·40 2·50
124 6d. reddish purple .. .. 3·50 3·00
a. *Purple* (1944) .. .. 3·00 2·50
125 1s. black and brown-olive .. .. 3·00 2·75
a. *Grey-black and olive-green* (21.5.52) 11·00 13·00
126 2s.6d. black and scarlet .. .. 14·00 9·50
127 5s. black and deep ultramarine .. 30·00 9·50
a. *Grey-black & dp ultramarine* (10.46) 65·00 35·00
128 10s. black and red-brown .. .. 14·00 17·00
118/28 .. .. .. *Set of* 11 60·00 42·00
118/28 Perf "Specimen" .. *Set of* 11 £170

Bechuanaland (**24**)

24a King George VI and Queen Elizabeth

1945 (3 Dec). *Victory. Stamps of South Africa optd with T* **24**. *Inscr alternately in English and Afrikaans.*
Un. pair / *Used pair* / *Used single*
129 **55** 1d. brown and carmine 50 45 10
130 **56** 2d. slate-blue and violet 50 80 10
131 **57** 3d. deep blue and blue 50 80 10
a. Opt omitted (in vert pair with normal) £6000
129/31 .. .. *Set of* 3 1·40 1·90 25
No. 131a comes from a sheet on which the overprint was displaced downwards so that it is omitted from stamps in the top row and shown on the sheet margin at foot.

(Recess Waterlow)

1947 (17 Feb). *Royal Visit. T* **24a** *and similar designs. Wmk Mult Script CA. P* 12½.
132 1d. scarlet 10 10
133 2d. green 10 10
134 3d. ultramarine 10 10
135 1s. mauve 10 10
132/5 .. .. .. *Set of* 4 35 30
132/5 Perf "Specimen" .. *Set of* 4 80·00
Designs: *Vert*—1d. King George VI. *Horiz*—3d. Princess Elizabeth and Princess Margaret; 1s. The Royal Family.

1948 (1 Dec). *Royal Silver Wedding. As Nos.* 112/13 *of Antigua.*
136 1½d. ultramarine 30 10
137 10s. black .. .. .. 27·00 35·00

1949 (10 Oct). *75th Anniv of Universal Postal Union. As Nos.* 114/17 *of Antigua.*
138 1½d. blue 45 65
139 3d. deep blue .. .. .. 1·25 1·75
140 6d. magenta 90 80
141 1s. olive 95 80
138/41 .. .. .. *Set of* 4 3·25 3·50

1953 (3 June). *Coronation. As No.* 120 *of Antigua.*
142 2d. black and brown 30 30

25 Queen Elizabeth II, Baobab Tree and Cattle drinking

26 Queen Victoria, Queen Elizabeth II and Landscape

(Des from photo by Resident Commissioner, Ngamiland. Recess Waterlow)

1955 (3 Jan)–**58**. *Wmk Mult Script CA. P* 13½ × 14.
143 **25** ½d. green 50 30
144 1d. rose-red 80 10
145 2d. red-brown .. .. .. 1·25 30
146 3d. ultramarine .. .. .. 3·00 70
a. *Bright ultramarine* (16.1.57) .. 7·00 2·75
146*b* 4d. red-orange (1.12.58) .. .. 6·50 7·00
147 4½d. blackish blue .. .. .. 1·50 35
148 6d. purple .. .. .. 1·25 60
149 1s. black and brown-olive .. .. 1·25 80
150 1s. 3d. black and lilac .. .. 13·00 9·50
151 2s. 6d. black and rose-red .. .. 10·00 9·50
152 5s. black and violet-blue .. .. 15·00 6·50
153 10s. black and red-brown .. .. 20·00 15·00
143/53 .. .. .. *Set of* 12 65·00 45·00

(Photo Harrison)

1960 (21 Jan). *75th Anniv of Bechuanaland Protectorate. W* w **12**. *P* 14½ × 14.

154 **26** 1d. sepia and black . . 40 50
155 3d. magenta and black . . 40 30
156 6d. bright blue and black . . 40 50
154/6 . . *Set of* 3 1·10 1·10

(New Currency. 100 cents = 1 rand)

1c (27) — 1c (I) — 1c (II) — 2½c (I) — 2½c (II)

3 (I) — 3 (II) — 3 (III) (3½ c. on 4d.) — 5c (I) — 5c (II) — R1 (I) — R1 (II)

2½c
Spaced "c" (R. 10/3)

1961 (14 Feb–June). *Nos.* 144/6*a and* 148/53 *surch as T* **27** *by South African Govt Printer, Pretoria.*

157 **25** 1 c. on 1d. rose-red (Type I) . . 30 10
a. Type II (6 June) . . 40 10
158 2 c. on 2d. red-brown . . 20 10
159 2½ c. on 2d. red-brown (Type I) . . 30 10
a. Type II (26 July) . . 85 65
b. Vert pair, one without surch . . £2250
160 2½ c. on 3d. bright ultramarine . . 2·00 3·00
a. Spaced "c" (R.10/3) . . 42·00
161 3½ c. on 4d. red-orange (Type I) . . 50 20
a. Type II . . 2·00 3·25
b. Wide surch (I) . . 14·00 21·00
c. Wide surch (II) . . 50·00 65·00
d. Type III (6 June) . . 20 20
162 5 c. on 6d. purple (Type I) . . 65 30
a. Type II (12 May) . . 20 10
163 10 c. on 1s. black and brown-olive . . 20 10
a. Horiz pair, one without surch . . £1500
164 12½ c. on 1s. 3d. black and lilac . . 65 20
165 25 c. on 2s. 6d. black and rose-red . . 2·00 50
166 50 c. on 5s. black and violet-blue . . 3·00 2·00
167 1 r. on 10s. black & red-brown (Type I) £250 90·00
a. Type II (surch at bottom left) (17 Mar) . . 8·50 7·50
b. Type II (surch at foot, either to right or central) (Apr) . . 7·00 2·25
157/67b . . *Set of* 11 14·50 7·50

Nos. 161/c occur from the same printing each sheet containing thirty-three examples of Type I, five of Type I with wide spacing, nineteen of Type II and three of Type II with wide spacing. The wide surcharge measures 9½ mm overall (with "C" spaced 1½ mm from "½") and comes on 8 of the 10 stamps in the last vertical row. The surcharge on the remainder of the sheet varies between 8½ and 9½ mm.

A later printing of the 12½ c. on 1s. 3d. was from a fresh setting of type, but is insufficiently different for separate listing. Later printings of the 10 c. and 25 c. were identical with the originals.

28 African Golden Oriole

39 Bechuana Ox

(Des P. Jones. Photo Harrison)

1961 (2 Oct). *T* **28, 39** *and similar designs. W* w **12**. *P* 14½ × 14 (25, 50 *c.*) *or* 14 × 14½ (*others*).

168 1 c. yellow, red, black and lilac . . 1·25 40
169 2 c. orange, black and yellow-olive . . 1·50 2·25
170 2½ c. carmine, green, black and bistre . . 1·50 10
171 3½ c. yellow, black, sepia and pink . . 1·75 1·25
172 5 c. yellow, blue, black and buff . . 3·00 1·00
173 7½ c. brown, red, black and apple-green . . 1·75 1·75
174 10 c. red, yellow, sepia & turquoise-green . . 1·75 60
175 12½ c. buff, blue, red and grey-black . . 18·00 5·00
176 20 c. yellow-brown and drab . . 80 70
177 25 c. deep brown and lemon . . 1·00 85
178 35 c. deep blue and orange . . 1·00 1·75
179 50 c. sepia and olive . . 1·00 2·25
180 1 r. black and cinnamon . . 3·00 2·50
181 2 r. brown and turquoise-blue . . 18·00 9·00
168/81 . . *Set of* 14 50·00 26·00

Designs: *Vert*—2 c. Hoopoe; 2½ c. Scarlet-chested Sunbird; 3½ c. Yellow-rumped Bishop; 5 c. Swallow-tailed Bee Eater; 7½ c. African Grey Hornbill; 10 c. Red-headed Weaver; 12½ c. Brown-hooded Kingfisher; 20 c. Woman musician; 35 c. Woman grinding maize; 1 r. Lion; 2 r. Police camel patrol. *Horiz*—25 c. Baobab Tree.

1963 (4 June). *Freedom from Hunger. As No.* 146 *of Antigua.*

182 12½ c. bluish green . . 30 15

1963 (2 Sept). *Red Cross Centenary. As Nos.* 147/8 *of Antigua.*

183 2½ c. red and black . . 20 10
184 12½ c. red and blue . . 40 50

1964 (23 April). *400th Birth Anniv of William Shakespeare. As No.* 164 *of Antigua.*

185 12½c. light brown . . 15 15

BECHUANALAND

INTERNAL SELF-GOVERNMENT

42 Map and Gaberones Dam

(Des Mrs. M. Townsend, adapted V. Whiteley. Photo Harrison)

1965 (1 Mar). *New Constitution. W* w **12**. *P* 14½×14.

186 **42** 2½ c. red and gold . . 10 10
w. Wmk inverted . . 14·00 3·75
187 5 c. ultramarine and gold . . 15 40
188 12½ c. brown and gold . . 20 40
189 25 c. green and gold . . 20 55
186/9 . . *Set of* 4 55 1·25

1965 (17 May). *I.T.U. Centenary. As Nos.* 166/7 *of Antigua.*

190 2½ c. red and bistre-yellow . . 20 10
191 12½ c. mauve and brown . . 45 30

1965 (25 Oct). *International Co-operation Year. As Nos.* 168/9 *of Antigua.*

192 1 c. reddish purple and turquoise-green 10 10
193 12½ c. deep bluish green and lavender . . 60 55

1966 (24 Jan). *Churchill Commemoration. As Nos.* 170/3 *of Antigua.*

194 1 c. new blue . . 15 30
195 2½ c. deep green . . 35 10
196 12½ c. brown . . 70 30
197 20 c. bluish violet . . 75 40
194/7 . . *Set of* 4 1·75 90

43 Haslar Smoke Generator

(Des V. Whiteley. Photo Harrison)

1966 (1 June). *Bechuanaland Royal Pioneer Corps. T* **43** *and similar horiz designs. W* w **12**. *P* 14½.

198 2½ c. Prussian blue, red and light emerald . . 20 10
199 5 c. brown and light blue . . 20 20
200 15 c. Prussian blue, rosine and emerald . . 30 25
201 35 c. buff, blackish brown, red and green . . 30 80
198/201 . . *Set of* 4 90 1·25

Designs:—5 c. Bugler; 15 c. Gun-site; 35 c. Regimental cap badge.

BOTSWANA

INDEPENDENCE

Bechuanaland became the independent republic of Botswana, within the Commonwealth, on 30 September 1966.

47 National Assembly Building

(Des R. Granger Barrett. Photo Harrison)

1966 (30 Sept). *Independence. T* **47** *and similar horiz designs. Multicoloured. P* 14½.

202 2½ c. Type **47** . . 15 10
a. Imperf (pair) . . £250
203 5 c. Abattoir, Lobatsi . . 20 10
204 15 c. National Airways Douglas DC-3 . . 65 20
205 35 c. State House, Gaberones . . 40 30
202/5 . . *Set of* 4 1·25 55

REPUBLIC OF BOTSWANA
(51)

52 Golden Oriole

1966 (30 Sept). *Nos.* 168/81 *optd as T* **51**.

206 1 c. yellow, red, black and lilac . . 25 10
207 2 c. orange, black and yellow-olive . . 30 40
208 2½ c. carmine, green, black and bistre . . 30 10
209 3½ c. yellow, black, sepia and pink . . 40 15
a. Yellow, black, sepia and flesh . . 1·25 1·00
210 5 c. yellow, blue, black and buff . . 40 1·0
211 7½ c. brown, red, black and apple-green . . 40 1·2
a. Blue-green omitted
212 10 c. red, yellow, sepia & turquoise-green 60 2
213 12½ c. buff, blue, red and grey-black . . 2·75 2·5
214 20 c. yellow-brown and drab . . 75 1·0
215 25 c. deep brown and lemon . . 75 1·7
216 35 c. deep blue and orange . . 85 2·0
217 50 c. sepia and olive . . 50 7
218 1 r. black and cinnamon . . 75 1·2
219 2 r. brown and turquoise-blue . . 1·25 2·5
206/19 . . *Set of* 14 9·00 13·0

No. 209*a* was a special printing produced to make up quantities. It does not exist without the overprint.

No. 211a shows the background in yellow instead of apple-green, the blue-green overlay being omitted.

(Des D. M. Reid-Henry. Photo Harrison)

1967 (3 Jan). *Birds. Vert designs as T* **52**. *Multicoloured. P* 14×14½.

220 1 c. Type **52** . . 30 1
a. Error. Wmk **105** of Malta . . † £70
221 2 c. Hoopoe . . 40
222 3 c. Groundscraper Thrush . . 55
223 4 c. Cordon-bleu ("Blue Waxbill") . . 55
224 5 c. Secretary Bird . . 55
225 7 c. Yellow-billed Hornbill . . 60 9
226 10 c. Burchell's Gonolek ("Crimson-breasted Shrike") . . 60 1
227 15 c. Malachite Kingfisher . . 8·00 2·7
228 20 c. African Fish Eagle . . 8·00 1·7
229 25 c. Go-away Bird ("Grey Loerie") . . 4·50 1·2
230 35 c. Scimitar-bill . . 7·00 2·0
231 50 c. Comb Duck . . 3·25 2·5
232 1 r. Levaillant's Barbet . . 8·00 3·5
233 2 r. Didric Cuckoo . . 9·50 16·0
220/33 . . *Set of* 14 45·00 28·0

A used copy of the 20 c. has been seen with the pale brown colour missing, resulting in the value (normally shown in white) being omitted.

The 1, 2, 4, 7 and 10 c. values exist with PVA gum as well as gum arabic.

66 Students and University

(Des V. Whiteley. Photo Harrison)

1967 (7 Apr). *First Conferment of University Degrees. P* 14 × 14½.

234 **66** 3 c. sepia, ultramarine & lt orange-yell 10 1
235 7 c. sepia, ultram & lt greenish bl . . 10 1
236 15 c. sepia, ultramarine and rose . . 10 1
237 35 c. sepia, ultramarine and light violet 20 2
234/7 . . *Set of* 4 30 3

67 Bushbuck

(Des G. Vasarhelyi. Photo Harrison)

1967 (2 Oct). *Chobe Game Reserve. T* **67** *and similar horiz designs. Multicoloured. P* 14.

238 3 c. Type **67** . . 10 2
239 7 c. Sable Antelope . . 15 3
240 35 c. Fishing on Chobe River . . 80 1·1
238/40 . . *Set of* 3 90 1·4

70 Arms of Botswana and Human Rights Emblem

(Litho D.L.R.)

1968 (8 Apr). *Human Rights Year. T* **70** *and similar horiz designs showing Arms of Botswana and Human Rights emblem arranged differently. P* 13½ × 13.

241 3 c. multicoloured . . 10
242 15 c. multicoloured . . 25 4
243 25 c. multicoloured . . 25 5
241/3 . . *Set of* 3 50 8

73 Eland and Giraffe Rock Paintings, Tsodilo Hills

75 "Baobab Trees" (Thomas Baines)

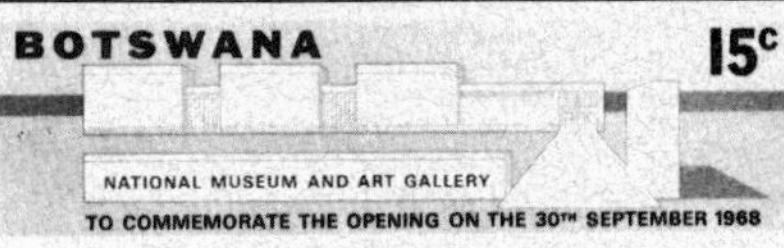

76 National Museum and Art Gallery

(Litho D.L.R.)

968 (30 Sept). *Opening of National Museum and Art Gallery. T* **73/6** *and similar multicoloured design. P* 12½ (7 *c.*), 12½ × 13½ (15 *c.*), *or* 13 × 13½ (*others*).

44	3 c. Type **73**	20	20
45	7 c. Girl wearing ceremonial beads (30 × 48 *mm*)	35	20
46	10 c. Type **75**	35	30
47	15 c. Type **76**	50	1·40
44/7	*Set of* 4	1·25	1·90
IS248	132 × 82 mm. Nos. 244/7. P 13	1·25	2·00

77 African Family, and Star over Village

(Des Mrs M. E. Townsend, adapted J. Cooter. Litho Enschedé)

968 (11 Nov). *Christmas. P* 13 × 14.

249 **77**	1 c. multicoloured	10	10
250	2 c. multicoloured	10	10
251	5 c. multicoloured	10	10
252	25 c. multicoloured	15	50
249/52	*Set of* 4	30	70

78 Scout, Lion and Badge in Frame

(Des D.L.R. Litho Format)

1969 (21 Aug). *22nd World Scout Conference, Helsinki. T* **78** *and similar multicoloured designs. P* 13½.

253	3 c. Type **78**	50	30
254	15 c. Scouts cooking over open fire (*vert*)	75	1·25
255	25 c. Scouts around camp fire	75	1·25
253/5	*Set of* 3	1·75	2·50

81 Woman, Child and Christmas Star   **82** Diamond Treatment Plant, Orapa

(Des A. Vale, adapted V. Whiteley. Litho Harrison)

1969 (6 Nov). *Christmas. P* 14½ × 14.

256 **81**	1 c. pale blue and chocolate	10	10
257	2 c. pale yellow-olive and chocolate	10	10
258	4 c. yellow and chocolate	10	10
259	35 c. chocolate and bluish violet	20	20
256/9	*Set of* 4	30	30
MS260	86 × 128 mm. Nos. 256/9. P 14½ (*shades*)	70	1·10

(Des J.W. Litho Harrison)

1970 (23 Mar). *Developing Botswana. T* **82** *and similar designs. Multicoloured. P* 14½ × 14 (3 *c.*, 7 *c.*) *or* 14 × 14½ (*others*).

261	3 c. Type **82**	70	20
262	7 c. Copper-nickel mining	95	20
263	10 c. Copper-nickel mine, Selebi-Pikwe (*horiz*)	1·25	25
264	35 c. Orapa diamond mine, and diamonds (*horiz*)	2·75	1·60
261/4	*Set of* 4	5·00	2·00

83 Mr. Micawber (*David Copperfield*)

(Des V. Whiteley. Litho Walsall)

1970 (6 July). *Death Centenary of Charles Dickens. T* **83** *and similar horiz designs. Multicoloured. P* 11.

265	3 c. Type **83**	25	10
266	7 c. Scrooge (*A Christmas Carol*)	35	10
267	15 c. Fagin (*Oliver Twist*)	60	40
268	25 c. Bill Sykes (*Oliver Twist*)	90	60
265/8	*Set of* 4	1·90	1·00
MS269	114 × 81 mm. Nos. 265/8	3·25	3·25

84 U.N. Building and Emblem

(Des J. Cooter. Litho Walsall)

1970 (24 Oct). *25th Anniv of United Nations. P* 11.

270 **84**	15 c. bright blue, chestnut and silver	70	30

85 Crocodile

(Des A. Vale. Litho Questa)

1970 (3 Nov). *Christmas. T* **85** *and similar horiz designs. Multicoloured. P* 14.

271	1 c. Type **85**	10	10
272	2 c. Giraffe	10	10
273	7 c. Elephant	15	10
274	25 c. Rhinoceros	60	80
271/4	*Set of* 4	80	95
MS275	128 × 90 mm. Nos. 271/4	1·25	2·50

86 Sorghum

(Des J.W. Litho Questa)

1971 (6 April). *Important Crops. T* **86** *and similar horiz designs. Multicoloured. P* 14.

276	3 c. Type **86**	15	10
277	7 c. Millet	20	10
278	10 c. Maize	20	10
279	35 c. Groundnuts	70	40
276/9	*Set of* 4	1·10	50

87 Map and Head of Cow   **88** King bringing Gift of Gold

(Des A. Vale, adapted L. Curtis. Litho Harrison)

1971 (30 Sept). *Fifth Anniv of Independence. T* **87** *and similar vert designs inscr* "PULA" (*local greeting*). *P* 14½ × 14.

280	3 c. black, brown and apple-green	10	10
281	4 c. black, new blue and pale blue	10	10
282	7 c. black and red-orange	20	15
283	10 c. multicoloured	25	15
284	20 c. multicoloured	80	2·00
280/4	*Set of* 5	1·25	2·25

Designs:—4 c. Map and cogs; 7 c. Map and zebra; 10 c. Map and sorghum stalk crossed by tusk; 20 c. Arms and map of Botswana.

(Des A. Vale. Litho Questa)

1971 (11 Nov). *Christmas. T* **88** *and similar vert designs. Multicoloured. P* 14.

285	2 c. Type **88**	10	10
286	3 c. King bearing frankincense	10	10
287	7 c. King bearing myrrh	10	10
288	20 c. Three Kings behold the star	35	65
285/8	*Set of* 4	40	75
MS289	85 × 128 mm. Nos. 285/8	1·00	2·75

ALTERED CATALOGUE NUMBERS

Any Catalogue numbers altered from the last edition are shown as a list in the introductory pages.

89 Orion   **90** Postmark and Map

(Des R. Granger Barrett. Litho Questa)

1972 (24 Apr). *"Night Sky". T* **89** *and similar vert designs. P* 14.

290	3 c. turquoise-blue, black and red	75	20
291	7 c. dull blue, black and yellow	1·10	60
292	10 c. dull green, black and orange	1·25	85
293	20 c. deep violet-blue, black and blue-green	1·75	2·75
290/3	*Set of* 4	4·25	4·00

Constellations:—7 c. The Scorpion; 10 c. The Centaur; 20 c. The Cross.

(Des M. Bryan. Litho A. & M.)

1972 (21 Aug). *Mafeking-Gubulawayo Runner Post. T* **90** *and similar vert designs. Multicoloured. P* 13½ × 13.

294	3 c. Type **90**	30	10
	a. Imperf (vert pair)	£425	
295	4 c. Bechuanaland stamp and map	30	35
296	7 c. Runners and map	45	50
297	20 c. Mafeking postmark and map	1·10	1·25
294/7	*Set of* 4	2·00	2·00
MS298	84×216 mm. Nos. 294/7 vertically *se-tenant*, forming a composite map design	11·00	15·00

For these designs redrawn smaller with changed inscriptions see Nos. 652/6.

91 Cross, Map and Bells   **92** Thor

(Des M. Bryan. Litho Questa)

1972 (6 Nov). *Christmas. Vert designs each with Cross and Map as T* **91**. *Multicoloured. P* 14.

299	2 c. Type **91**	10	75
300	3 c. Cross, map and candle	10	10
301	7 c. Cross, map and Christmas tree	15	25
302	20 c. Cross, map, star and holly	40	85
299/302	*Set of* 4	60	1·75
MS303	96 × 119 mm. Nos. 299/302	1·25	2·75

(Des Edna Elphick. Litho Questa)

1973 (23 Mar). *I.M.O./W.M.O. Centenary. T* **92** *and similar designs showing Norse myths. Multicoloured. P* 14.

304	3 c. Type **92**	20	10
305	4 c. Sun God's chariot (*horiz*)	25	15
306	7 c. Ymir, the frost giant	30	15
307	20 c. Odin and Sleipnir (*horiz*)	75	70
304/7	*Set of* 4	1·40	1·00

93 Livingstone and River Scene

(Des G. Vasarhelyi. Litho Walsall)

1973 (10 Sept). *Death Centenary of Dr. Livingstone. T* **93** *and similar horiz designs. Multicoloured. P* 13½.

308	3 c. Type **93**	20	10
309	20 c. Livingstone meeting Stanley	90	80

94 Donkey and Foal at Village Trough   **95** Gaborone Campus

(Des M. Bryan. Litho Questa)

1973 (3 Dec). *Christmas. T* **94** *and similar multicoloured designs. P* 14.

310	3 c. Type **94**	10	10
311	4 c. Shepherd and flock (*horiz*)	10	10
312	7 c. Mother and child	10	10
313	20 c. Kgotla meeting (*horiz*)	40	80
310/13	*Set of* 4	55	90

(Des. M. Bryan, adapted P. Powell. Litho Questa)

1974 (8 May). *Tenth Anniv of University of Botswana, Lesotho and Swaziland. T* **95** *and similar horiz designs. Multicoloured. P* 14.

314	3 c. Type **95**	10	10
315	7 c. Kwaluseni Campus	10	10
316	20 c. Roma Campus	15	20
317	35 c. Map and flags of the three countries	20	35
314/17	*Set of* 4	35	55

96 Methods of Mail Transport

(Des. M. Bryan. Litho J.W.)

1974 (29 May). *Centenary of Universal Postal Union. T* **96** *and similar horiz designs. Multicoloured. P* 14.

318	2 c. Type **96**	55	35
319	3 c. Post Office, Palapye, *circa* 1889	55	35
320	7 c. Bechuanaland Police Camel Post, *circa* 1900	95	70
321	20 c. Hawker Siddeley H.S.748 and De Havilland D.H.9 mail planes of 1920 and 1974	2·75	2·50
318/21	*Set of* 4	4·25	3·50

97 Amethyst

98 *Stapelia variegata*

(Des M. Bayliss, adapted PAD Studio. Photo Enschedé)

1974 (1 July). *Botswana Minerals. T* **97** *and similar horiz designs. Multicoloured. P* 14×13.

322	1 c. Type **97**	60	80
323	2 c. Agate—"Botswana Pink"	60	80
324	3 c. Quartz	65	80
325	4 c. Copper nickel	70	60
326	5 c. Moss agate	70	1·00
327	7 c. Agate	80	60
328	10 c. Stilbite	1·60	65
329	15 c. Moshaneng Banded Marble	2·00	3·00
330	20 c. Gem diamonds	4·00	3·25
331	25 c. Chrysotile	5·00	2·50
332	35 c. Jasper	5·00	3·75
333	50 c. Moss quartz	4·50	7·00
334	1 r. Citrine	7·50	10·00
335	2 r. Chalcopyrite	20·00	20·00
322/35	*Set of* 14	48·00	48·00

(Des M. Bryan. Litho Questa)

1974 (4 Nov). *Christmas. T* **98** *and similar vert designs showing flowers. Multicoloured. P* 14.

336	2 c. Type **98**	20	40
337	7 c. *Hibiscus lunarifolius*	50	20
338	15 c. *Ceratotheca triloba*	80	1·50
339	20 c. *Nerine laticoma*	90	1·75
336/9	*Set of* 4	2·25	3·50
MS340	85 × 130 mm. Nos. 336/9	3·50	4·25

99 President Sir Seretse Khama

100 Ostrich

(Des M. Bryan, adapted G. Vasarhelyi. Photo Enschedé)

1975 (24 Mar). *Tenth Anniv of Self-Government. P* 13½×13.

341 **99**	4 c. multicoloured	10	10
342	10 c. multicoloured	15	10
343	20 c. multicoloured	25	25
344	35 c. multicoloured	45	50
341/4	*Set of* 4	85	85
MS345	93×130 mm. Nos. 341/4	1·00	1·50

(Des M. Bryan. Litho Questa)

1975 (23 June). *Rock Paintings, Tsodilo Hills. T* **100** *and similar horiz designs. Multicoloured. P* 14.

346	4 c. Type **100**	80	10
347	10 c. White Rhinoceros	1·40	10
348	25 c. Spotted Hyena	2·75	55
349	35 c. Scorpion	2·75	1·10
346/9	*Set of* 4	7·00	1·60
MS350	150 × 150 mm. Nos. 346/9	11·00	7·50

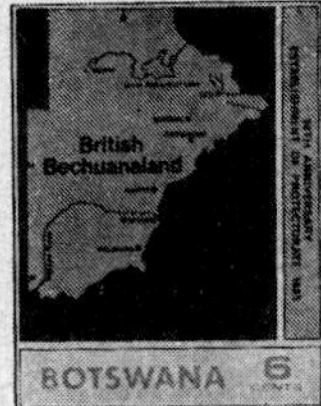

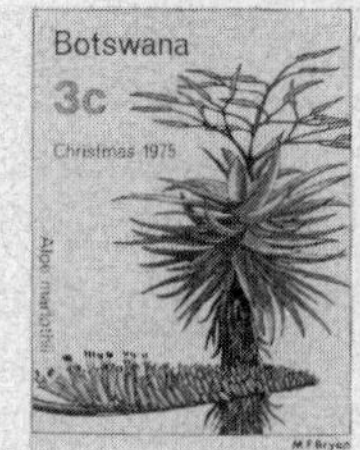

101 Map of British Bechuanaland, 1885

102 *Aloe marlothii*

(Des M. Bryan, adapted G. Vasarhelyi. Litho Harrison)

1975 (13 Oct). *Anniversaries. T* **101** *and similar multicoloured designs. P* 14 × 14½ (25 *c.*) *or* 14½ × 14 (*others*).

351	6 c. Type **101**	30	20
352	10 c. Chief Khama, 1875	40	15
353	25 c. Chiefs Sebele, Bathoen and Khama, 1895 (*horiz*)	80	75
351/3	*Set of* 3	1·40	1·00

Events:—6 c. 90th Anniv of Protectorate; 10 c. Centenary of Khama's Accession; 25 c. 80th Anniv of Chiefs' visit to London.

(Des M. Bryan. Litho Questa)

1975 (3 Nov). *Christmas. T* **102** *and similar vert designs showing aloes. Multicoloured. P* 14½.

354	3 c. Type **102**	30	10
355	10 c. *Aloe lutescens*	75	20
356	15 c. *Aloe zebrina*	1·40	1·75
357	25 c. *Aloe littoralis*	1·60	3·00
354/7	*Set of* 4	3·50	4·50

103 Drum

(Des M. Bryan. Litho Questa)

1976 (1 Mar). *Traditional Musical Instruments. T* **103** *and similar horiz designs. Multicoloured. P* 14.

358	4 c. Type **103**	15	10
359	10 c. Hand Piano	20	10
360	15 c. Segankuru (violin)	25	50
361	25 c. Kudu Signal Horn	30	1·25
358/61	*Set of* 4	80	1·75

104 One Pula Note

(Des M. Bryan from banknotes by D.L.R. Litho Questa)

1976 (28 June). *First National Currency. T* **104** *and similar horiz designs. Multicoloured. P* 14.

362	4 c. Type **104**	15	10
363	10 c. Two pula note	20	10
364	15 c. Five pula note	35	20
365	25 c. Ten pula note	45	45
362/5	*Set of* 4	1·00	70
MS366	163 × 107 mm. Nos. 362/5	1·50	3·25

(New Currency. 100 thebe = 1 pula)

1t (105) (Type I)	1t (105) (Type II)	2t (I)	2t (II)
4t (I)	4t (II)	5t (I)	5t (II)
15t (I)	15t (II)	20t (I)	20t (II)

(Surch in letterpress by Govt Printer, Pretoria (Type I), or in lithography by Enschedé (Type II))

1976 (23 Aug)–**77**. *Nos.* 322/35 *surch as T* **105.**

367	1 t. on 1 c. Type **97** (I)	2·00	70
	a. Type II Surch (15.7.77)	2·50	80
368	2 t. on 2 c. Agate—"Botswana Pink" (I)	2·00	80
	a. Type II Surch (15.7.77)	2·50	80
369	3 t. on 3 c. Quartz (surch at top right) (Gold)	1·50	60
	a. Surch at bottom right (17.10.77)	50·00	
370	4 t. on 4 c. Copper nickel (I)	2·50	40
	a. Type II Surch (15.7.77)	2·75	80
371	5 t. on 5 c. Moss agate (I)	2·50	40
	a. Type II Surch (15.7.77)	2·75	70
372	7 t. on 7 c. Agate (surch at top right)	1·25	2·00
	a. Surch at bottom right (10.10.77)	60·00	
373	10 t. on 10 c. Stilbite	1·25	80
374	15 t. on 15 c. Moshaneng Banded Marble (I) (Gold)	4·25	1·50
	a. Type II Surch (15.7.77)	5·00	1·50
375	20 t. on 20 c. Gem diamonds (I)	7·50	80
	a. Type II Surch (15.7.77)	8·00	1·50
376	25 t. on 25 c. Chrysotile	5·00	1·25
377	35 t. on 35 c. Jasper	4·50	3·50
378	50 t. on 50 c. Moss quartz (surch at top right)	7·00	8·50
	a. Surch at bottom right (17.10.77)	£250	
379	1 p. on 1 r. Citrine (surch at top right)	8·00	9·00
	a. Surch at bottom left (10.10.77)	80·00	
380	2 p. on 2 r. Chalcopyrite (Gold)	11·00	11·00
367/80	*Set of* 14	50·00	38·00
367a/75a	*Set of* 6	21·00	5·50

Nos. 369a, 372a, 378a and 379a come from a second Pretoria printing on a small stock returned from the Crown Agents. By the time the stamps arrived in Pretoria the surcharge type for the 3 t., 7 t., 50 t. and 1 p. had been dispersed and when it was reset the position of the value figures was changed.

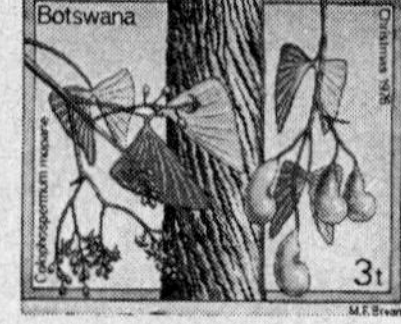

106 Botswanan Cattle

107 *Colophospermum mopane*

(Des M. Bryan. Litho Questa)

1976 (30 Sept). *Tenth Anniv of Independence. T* **106** *and similar multicoloured designs. P* 14.

381	4 t. Type **106**	15	10
382	10 t. Deer, Okavango Delta (*vert*)	30	10
383	15 t. Schools and pupils	40	40
384	25 t. Rural weaving (*vert*)	55	50
385	35 t. Miner (*vert*)	1·25	85
381/5	*Set of* 5	2·40	1·75

Nos. 381/5 were printed on sand-grained paper which has an uneven surface.

(Des M. Bryan. Litho J.W.)

1976 (1 Nov). *Christmas. T* **107** *and similar horiz designs showing trees. Multicoloured. P* 13.

386	3 t. Type **107**	15	10
387	4 t. *Baikiaea plurijuga*	15	10
388	10 t. *Sterculia rogersii*	40	15
389	25 t. *Acacia nilotica*	80	50
390	40 t. *Kigelia africana*	1·25	1·25
386/90	*Set of* 5	2·50	1·75

108 Coronation Coach

(Des M. Bryan, adapted G. Vasarhelyi. Litho Cartor)

1977 (7 Feb). *Silver Jubilee. T* **108** *and similar horiz designs. Multicoloured. P* 12.

391	4 t. Queen and Sir Seretse Khama	10	10
392	25 t. Type **108**	20	15
393	40 t. The Recognition	35	80
391/3	*Set of* 3	60	90

Nos. 391/3 have matt, almost invisible gum.

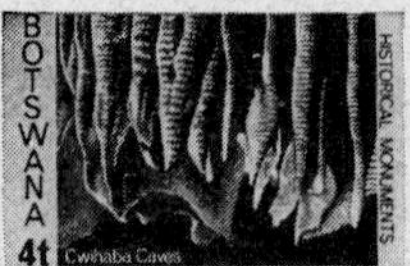

109 African Clawless Otter

110 Cwihaba Caves

(Des M. Bryan. Litho Questa)

1977 (7 June). *Diminishing Species. T* **109** *and similar horiz designs. Multicoloured. P* 14.

394	3 t. Type **109**	2·00	30
395	4 t. Serval	2·00	30
396	10 t. Bat-eared Fox	3·00	40
397	25 t. Temminck's Ground Pangolin	8·00	1·75
398	40 t. Brown Hyena	9·50	5·50
394/8	*Set of* 5	22·00	7·50

(Des M. Bryan. Litho J.W.)

1977 (22 Aug). *Historical Monuments. T* **110** *and similar horiz designs. Multicoloured. P* 14.

399	4 t. Type **110**	25	10
400	5 t. Khama Memorial	25	10
401	15 t. Green's Tree	40	40
402	20 t. Mmajojo Ruins	40	45
403	25 t. Ancient morabaraba board	40	50
404	35 t. Matsieng's footprint	55	60
399/404	*Set of* 6	2·00	2·00
MS405	154 × 105 mm. Nos. 399/404	2·50	3·25

111 *Hypoxis nitida*

112 Little Black Bustard

(Des M. Bryan. Litho Questa)

977 (7 Nov). *Christmas. T* **111** *and similar vert designs showing lilies. Multicoloured. P* 14.

06 3 t. Type **111** 15 10
07 5 t. *Haemanthus magnificus* 15 10
08 10 t. *Boophane disticha* 20 10
09 25 t. *Vellozia retinervis* 40 55
10 40 t. *Ammocharis coranica* .. .. .. 55 1·25
06/10 .. .. *Set of* 5 1·40 1·75

(Des M. Bryan. Photo Harrison)

978 (3 July). *Birds. Vert designs as T* **112**. *Multicoloured. P* 14 × 14½ (1 *to* 20 *t.*) *or* 14 (25*t to* 5 *p.*).

11 1 t. Type **112** .. .. 30 1·25
12 2 t. Marabou Stork .. .. 30 1·25
13 3 t. Green Wood Hoopoe 30 85
14 4 t. Carmine Bee Eater 30 75
15 5 t. African Jacana 30 40
16 7 t. African Paradise Flycatcher .. .. 40 2·00
17 10 t. Bennett's Woodpecker .. .. .. 1·75 60
18 15 t. Red Bishop .. .. 70 2·00
19 20 t. Crowned Plover .. .. .. 1·00 2·00
20 25 t. Giant Kingfisher .. .. .. 70 2·00
421 30 t. White-faced Whistling Duck 70 70
422 35 t. Green Heron .. .. 70 2·75
423 45 t. Black-headed Heron .. .. .. 70 2·25
424 50 t. Spotted Eagle Owl .. .. .. 6·00 4·50
425 1 p. Gabar Goshawk .. .. .. 2·50 4·50
426 2 p. Martial Eagle .. .. .. 3·25 8·00
427 5 p. Saddle-bill Stork .. .. .. 12·00 16·00
411/27 .. .. *Set of* 17 28·00 45·00

113 Tawana making Karos

(Des M. Bryan. Litho Questa)

1978 (11 Sept). *Okavango Delta. T* **113** *and similar horiz designs. Multicoloured. P* 14.

428 4 t. Type **113** 15 10
429 5 t. Tribe localities 15 10
430 15 t. Bushmen collecting roots 35 40
431 20 t. Herero woman milking 40 55
432 25 t. Yei poling "mokoro" (canoe) 50 60
433 35 t. Mbukushu fishing .. .. .. 65 1·50
428/33 .. .. *Set of* 6 2·00 2·75
MS434 150 × 98 mm. Nos. 428/33 .. .. 2·00 3·50

Nos. 428/34 were printed on sand-grained paper which has an uneven surface.

114 *Caralluma lutea*

115 Sip Well

(Des M. Bryan. Litho J.W.)

1978 (6 Nov). *Christmas. Flowers. T* **114** *and similar vert designs. Multicoloured. P* 14.

435 5 t. Type **114** 35 10
436 10 t. *Hoodia lugardii* 50 15
437 15 t. *Ipomoea transvaalensis* 90 55
438 25 t. *Ansellia gigantea* .. .. .. 1·10 70
435/8 .. .. *Set of* 4 2·50 1·40

(Des M. Bryan. Litho Questa)

1979 (30 Mar). *Water Development. T* **115** *and similar vert designs. Multicoloured. P* 14.

439 3 t. Type **115** 10 10
440 5 t. Watering pit 15 10
441 10 t. Hand dug well 15 10
442 25 t. Windmill 30 30
443 40 t. Modern drilling rig 55 55
439/43 .. .. *Set of* 5 1·10 1·00

ALTERED CATALOGUE NUMBERS

Any Catalogue numbers altered from the last edition are shown as a list in the introductory pages.

116 Pottery

117 1885 British Bechuanaland 1d. Stamp and Sir Rowland Hill

(Des M. Bryan. Litho Questa)

1979 (11 June). *Handicrafts. T* **116** *and similar vert designs. Multicoloured. P* 14½ × 14.

444 5 t. Type **116** 10 10
445 10 t. Clay modelling 15 10
446 25 t. Basketry 30 25
447 40 t. Beadwork 50 50
444/7 .. .. *Set of* 4 95 80
MS448 123 × 96 mm. Nos. 444/7 .. .. .. 95 2·25

(Des M. Bryan. Litho Secura, Singapore)

1979 (27 Aug). *Death Centenary of Sir Rowland Hill. T* **117** *and similar horiz designs showing stamps and Sir Rowland Hill. Multicoloured. P* 13½.

449 5 t. Type **117** 20 10
450 25 t. 1932 Bechuanaland Protectorate 2d .. 45 50
451 45 t. 1967 2 c. definitive .. .. .. 55 1·10
449/51 .. .. *Set of* 3 1·10 1·50

118 Children Playing

119 *Ximenia caffra*

(Des K. Mosinyi (5 t.), M. Bryan (10 t.). Litho Questa)

1979 (24 Sept). *International Year of the Child. T* **118** *and similar multicoloured design. P* 14.

452 5 t. Type **118** 20 10
453 10 t. Child playing with doll (*vert*) 30 20

(Des M. Bryan. Litho Questa)

1979 (12 Nov). *Christmas. Fruit. T* **119** *and similar vert designs. Multicoloured. P* 14.

454 5 t. Type **119** 10 10
455 10 t. *Sclerocarya caffra* 20 20
456 15 t. *Hexalobus monopetalus* 35 35
457 25 t. *Ficus soldanella* 45 45
454/7 .. .. *Set of* 4 1·00 1·00

120 Flap-necked Chameleon

121 Rock Breaking

(Des M. Bryan. Litho Security Printers (M), Malaysia)

1980 (3 Mar). *Reptiles. T* **120** *and similar horiz designs. Multicoloured. P* 13½.

458 5 t. Type **120** 40 10
459 10 t. Leopard Tortoise 40 15
460 25 t. Puff Adder .. .. 1·10 65
461 40 t. White-throated Monitor .. .. .. 1·25 2·50
458/61 .. .. *Set of* 4 2·75 3·00

(Des M. Bryan. Litho Secura, Singapore)

1980 (7 July). *Early Mining. T* **121** *and similar horiz designs. Multicoloured. P* 13½.

462 5 t. Type **121** 25 15
463 10 t. Ore hoisting 30 15
464 15 t. Ore transport 70 60
465 20 t. Ore crushing 75 70
466 25 t. Smelting 80 90
467 35 t. Tools and products .. .. .. 1·00 1·40
462/7 .. .. *Set of* 6 3·50 3·50

122 "Chiwele and the Giant"

(Des W. Battiss. Litho Questa)

1980 (8 Sept). *Folktales. T* **122** *and similar multicoloured designs. P* 14 (5 *t.*), 14 × 13½ (45 *t.*) *or* 14½ × 14 (*others*).

468 5 t. Type **122** (35 × 22 *mm*) 10 10
469 10 t. "Kgori is not deceived" (28 × 37 *mm*) .. 15 10
470 30 t. "Nyambi's wife and Crocodile" (28 × 37 *mm*) 45 45
471 45 t. "Clever Hare" (44 × 27 *mm*) 60 60
468/71 .. .. *Set of* 4 1·10 1·10

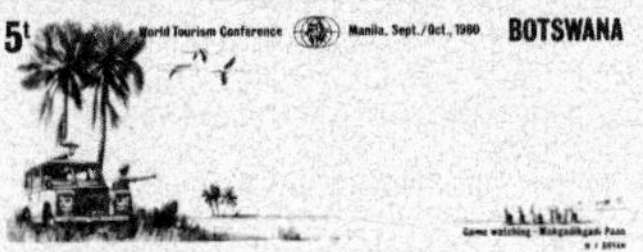

123 Game watching. Makgadikgadi Pans

(Des M. Bryan. Litho Govt Printer, Pretoria)

1980 (6 Oct). *World Tourism Conference, Manila. P* 14.

472 **123** 5 t. multicoloured 45 20

124 *Acacia gerrardii*

125 Heinrich von Stephan with Bechuanaland 1949 3d. and Botswana 1974 3 c. U.P.U. Anniversary Commemoratives

(Des M. Bryan. Litho Govt Printer, Pretoria)

1980 (3 Nov). *Christmas. Flora. T* **124** *and similar vert designs. Multicoloured. P* 14 × 13½.

473 5 t. Type **124** 10 10
474 10 t. *Acacia nilotica* 20 10
475 25 t. *Acacia erubescens* 45 30
476 40 t. *Dichrostachys cinerea* 70 70
473/6 .. .. *Set of* 4 1·25 1·00

(Des M. Bryan. Litho Govt Printer, Pretoria)

1981 (7 Jan). *150th Birth Anniv of Heinrich von Stephan (founder of U.P.U.). T* **125** *and similar horiz design showing Von Stephan and U.P.U. anniversary commemoratives. Multicoloured. P* 14.

477 6 t. Type **125** 75 30
478 20 t. Bechuanaland 1949 6d. and Botswana 1974 7 c. .. .. 1·75 2·25

126 *Anax imperator* (dragonfly)

127 Camphill Community Ramkoromane, Otse

(Des M. Bryan. Litho Govt Printer, Pretoria)

1981 (23 Feb). *Insects. T* **126** *and similar vert designs. Multicoloured. P* 14.

479 6 t. Type **126** 15 10
480 7 t. *Sphodromantis gastrica* (mantid) .. 15 20
481 10 t. *Zonocerus elegans* (grasshopper) .. 20 20
482 20 t. *Kheper nigroaeneus* (beetle) 35 50
483 30 t. *Papilio demodocus* (butterfly) .. 70 70
484 45 t. *Acanthocampa belina* (moth larva) .. 80 1·10
479/84 .. .. *Set of* 6 2·10 2·50
MS485 180×89 mm. Nos. 479/84 .. .. 4·50 7·00

(Des M. Bryan. Litho Govt Printer, Pretoria)

1981 (6 Apr). *International Year for Disabled Persons. T* **127** *and similar horiz designs. Multicoloured. P* 14.

486 6 t. Type **127** 20 10
487 20 t. Resource Centre for the Blind, Mochudi 55 35
488 30 t. Tlamelong Rehabilitation Centre, Tlokweng 75 45
486/8 .. .. *Set of* 3 1·40 80

128 Woman reading Letter

129 Sir Seretse Khama and Building

(Des Petra Rouendaal. Litho Govt Printer, Pretoria)

1981 (8 June). *Literacy Programme. T* **128** *and similar vert designs. Multicoloured. P* 14.

489 6 t. Type **128** 20 10
490 7 t. Man filling in form 20 15
491 20 t. Boy reading newspaper 60 35
492 30 t. Child being taught to read 80 45
489/92 .. .. *Set of* 4 1·60 90

(Des G. Vasarhelyi. Litho Format)

1981 (13 July). *First Death Anniv of President Sir Seretse Khama. T* **129** *and similar horiz designs. Multicoloured. P* 14.

493 6 t. Type **129** 15 10
494 10 t. Seretse Khama and building (*different*) 25 15
495 30 t. Seretse Khama and Botswana flag .. 40 45
496 45 t. Seretse Khama and building (*different*) 55 70
493/6 .. .. *Set of* 4 1·25 1·25

25t
(130)

131 Traditional Ploughing

1981 (1 Sept). *Nos.* 417 *and* 422 *surch as T* **130**.

497 25 t. on 35 t. Green Heron .. .. .. 2·75 2·00
498 30 t. on 10 t. Bennett's Woodpecker .. .. 2·75 2·00

(Des K. Mosinyi. Litho Format)

1981 (21 Sept). *Cattle Industry. T* **131** *and similar horiz designs. Multicoloured. P* 14½.

499 6 t. Type **131** 10 10
500 20 t. Agricultural show 30 50
501 30 t. Botswana Meat Commission 35 60
502 45 t. Vaccine Institute, Botswana .. .. 50 1·00
499/502 .. .. *Set of* 4 1·10 2·00

132 *Nymphaea caerulea*

133 "Cattle Post Scene" (Boitumelo Golaakwena)

(Des M. Bryan. Litho Govt Printer, Pretoria)

1981 (11 Nov). *Christmas. Flowers. T* **132** *and similar vert designs. Multicoloured. P* 14.

503 6 t. Type **132** 20 10
504 10 t. *Nymphoides indica* 25 10
505 25 t. *Nymphaea lotus* 60 90
506 40 t. *Ottelia kunenensis* .. .. .. 80 2·25
503/6 .. .. *Set of* 4 1·60 3·00

(Litho Govt Printer, Pretoria)

1982 (15 Feb). *Children's Art. T* **133** *and similar horiz designs. Multicoloured. P* 14.

507 6 t. Type **133** 40 10
508 10 t. "Kgotla Meeting" (Reginald Klinck) .. 50 15
509 30 t. "Village Water Supply" (Keromemang Matswiri) .. .. 1·75 1·25
510 45 t. "With the Crops" (Kennedy Balemoge) .. 1·75 2·75
507/10 .. .. *Set of* 4 4·00 3·75

134 Common Type

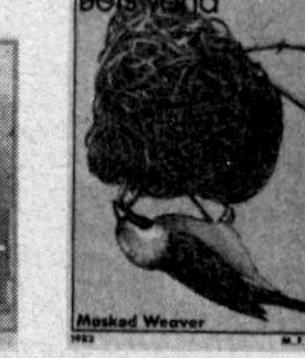

135 African Masked Weaver

(Des K. Mosinyi and V. Moremi. Litho Govt Printer, Pretoria)

1982 (3 May). *Traditional Houses. T* **134** *and similar horiz designs. Multicoloured. P* 14.

511 6 t. Type **134** 40 15
512 10 t. Kgatleng type 50 15
513 30 t. North Eastern type .. .. .. 2·00 1·10
514 45 t. Sarwa type .. .. 2·00 3·00
511/14 .. .. *Set of* 4 4·50 4·00

(Des M. Bryan. Photo Harrison)

1982 (2 Aug). *Birds. T* **135** *and similar multicoloured designs. P* 14×14½ (1 *t. to* 10 *t.*) *or* 14½×14 (*others*).

515 1 t. Type **135** .. .. 80 1·25
516 2 t. Lesser Double-collared Sunbird .. .. 90 1·40
517 3 t. Red-throated Bee Eater .. .. .. 1·00 1·40
518 4 t. Ostrich .. .. 1·00 1·40
519 5 t. Grey-headed Gull .. .. 1·00 1·40
520 6 t. African Pygmy Goose .. .. .. 1·00 40
521 7 t. Cattle Egret .. .. 1·00 15
522 8 t. Lanner Falcon .. .. 2·00 1·25
523 10 t. Yellow-billed Stork .. .. .. 1·00 20
524 15 t. Red-billed Pintail (*horiz*) .. .. 2·50 25
525 20 t. Barn Owl (*horiz*) .. .. 5·00 3·50
526 25 t. Hammerkop (*horiz*) .. .. .. 3·00 70
527 30 t. South African Stilt (*horiz*) .. .. 3·50 90
528 35 t. Blacksmith Plover (*horiz*) .. .. 3·50 80
529 45 t. Senegal Wattled Plover (*horiz*) .. .. 3·50 1·75
530 50 t. Helmet Guineafowl (*horiz*) .. .. 4·50 2·50
531 1 p. Cape Vulture (*horiz*) .. .. .. 8·50 12·00
532 2 p. Augur Buzzard (*horiz*) .. .. .. 10·00 16·00
515/32 .. .. *Set of* 18 48·00 42·00

136 *Coprinus comatus*

137 President Quett Masire

(Des Gillian Condy. Litho Mardon Printers Ltd, Zimbabwe)

1982 (2 Nov). *Christmas. Fungi. T* **136** *and similar vert designs. Multicoloured. P* 14½.

533 7 t. Type **136** .. .. 1·25 15
534 15 t. *Lactarius deliciosus* .. .. .. 2·25 55
535 35 t. *Amanita pantherina* .. .. .. 4·00 1·75
536 50 t. *Boletus edulis* .. .. 4·75 5·25
533/6 .. .. *Set of* 4 11·00 7·00

(Des G. Vasarhelyi. Litho Questa)

1983 (14 Mar). *Commonwealth Day. T* **137** *and similar horiz designs. Multicoloured. P* 14.

537 7 t. Type **137** 10 10
538 15 t. Native dancers 15 20
539 35 t. Melbourne conference centre 45 55
540 45 t. Meeting of Heads of State, Melbourne .. 55 80
537/40 .. .. *Set of* 4 1·00 1·50

138 Wattled Crane

139 Wooden Spoons

(Des Petra Rouendaal (50 t.), Gillian Condy (others). Litho Mardon Printers Ltd, Zimbabwe)

1983 (19 Apr). *Endangered Species. T* **138** *and similar vert designs. Multicoloured. P* 14×14½.

541 7 t. Type **138** .. .. 2·75 55
542 15 t. *Aloe lutescens* .. .. 2·25 80
543 35 t. Roan Antelope .. .. 2·50 3·00
544 50 t. Ivory Palm (*Hyphaene ventricosa*) .. 3·00 5·00
541/4 .. .. *Set of* 4 9·50 8·50

(Des M. Bryan. Litho Mardon Printers Ltd, Zimbabwe)

1983 (20 July). *Traditional Artifacts. T* **139** *and similar vert designs. Multicoloured. P* 14½.

545 7 t. Type **139** 25 10
546 15 t. Personal ornaments 45 30
547 35 t. Ox-hide milk bag 75 65
548 50 t. Decorated knives .. .. 1·00 1·10
545/8 .. .. *Set of* 4 2·25 1·90
MS549 115 × 102 mm. Nos. 545/8 .. .. .. 4·25 5·00

140 *Pantala flavescens*

141 Sorting Diamonds

(Des Beverley Boudreau. Litho Mardon Printers Ltd, Zimbabwe)

1983 (7 Nov). *Christmas. Dragonflies. T* **140** *and similar horiz designs. Multicoloured. P* 14½×14.

550 6 t. Type **140** 70 10
551 15 t. *Anax imperator* .. .. 1·40 50
552 25 t. *Trithemis arteriosa* .. .. .. 1·75 85
553 45 t. *Chlorolestes elegans* .. .. .. 2·25 3·50
550/3 .. .. *Set of* 4 5·50 4·50

(Des M. Kahn. Litho Mardon Printers Ltd, Zimbabwe)

1984 (19 Mar). *Mining Industry. T* **141** *and similar multicoloured designs. P* 14½.

554 7 t. Type **141** .. .. 2·00 50
555 15 t. Lime kiln .. .. 2·00 75
556 35 t. Copper-nickel smelter plant (*vert*) .. 3·25 2·75
557 50 t. Stockpiled coal (*vert*) .. .. .. 3·75 6·00
554/7 .. .. *Set of* 4 10·00 9·00

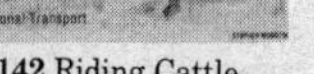

142 Riding Cattle

143 Avro 504 Aircraft

(Des S. Mogotsi. Litho Mardon Printers Ltd, Zimbabwe)

1984 (18 June). *Traditional Transport. T* **142** *and similar hori[z] designs. Multicoloured. P* 14½ × 14.

558 7 t. Type **142** .. .. 20 1[0]
559 25 t. Sledge .. .. 65 5[0]
560 35 t. Wagon .. .. 85 1·2[5]
561 50 t. Two wheeled donkey cart .. .. 1·25 2·7[5]
558/61 .. .. *Set of* 4 2·75 4·2[5]

(Des V. Larsson. Litho Mardon Printers Ltd, Zimbabwe)

1984 (8 Oct). *40th Anniv of International Civil Aviation Organization. T* **143** *and similar horiz designs, each with I.C.A.O emblem. Multicoloured. P* 14½ × 14.

562 7 t. Type **143** .. .. 60 1[5]
563 10 t. Westland Wessex trimotor .. .. 75 2[0]
564 15 t. Junkers Ju 52/3m .. .. .. 1·40 7[5]
565 25 t. De Havilland D.H.89B Dominie .. 2·00 1·5[0]
566 35 t. Douglas DC-3 .. .. 2·25 2·7[5]
567 50 t. Fokker F.27 Friendship .. .. 2·50 4·2[5]
562/7 .. .. *Set of* 6 8·50 8·7[5]

144 *Papilio demodocus*

145 Seswaa (meat dish)

(Des M. Kahn. Litho Mardon Printers Ltd, Zimbabwe)

1984 (5 Nov). *Christmas. Butterflies. T* **144** *and similar horiz designs. Multicoloured. P* 14½ × 14.

568 7 t. Type **144** .. .. 1·75 30
569 25 t. *Byblia anvatara* .. .. .. 3·00 1·50
570 35 t. *Danaus chrysippus* .. .. .. 3·25 2·75
571 50 t. *Graphium taboranus* .. .. .. 4·50 7·00
568/71 .. .. *Set of* 4 11·00 10·50

No. 570 is incorrectly inscribed "Hypolimnas misippus".

(Des K. Mosinyi. Litho Mardon Printers Ltd, Zimbabwe)

1985 (18 Mar). *5th Anniv of Southern African Developmen[t] Co-ordination Conference. Traditional Foods. T* **145** *an[d] similar vert designs. Multicoloured. P* 14½.

572 7 t. Type **145** 25 1
573 15 t. Bogobe (cereal porridge) 45 3
574 25 t. Madila (soured coagulated cows milk) 70 5
575 50 t. Phane (caterpillars) .. .. .. 1·10 1·7
572/5 .. .. *Set of* 4 2·25 2·5
MS576 117×103 mm. Nos. 572/5 .. .. 6·00 8·0

146 1885 British Bechuanaland Overprint on Cape of Good Hope ½d.

147 Bechuanaland Border Police, 1885–95

(Des D. Finlay and J. Hodgson. Litho Mardon Printers Ltd Zimbabwe)

1985 (24 June). *Centenary of First Bechuanaland Stamps T* **146** *and similar designs. P* 14½.

577 7 t. black, grey-black and orange-vermilion 75 2
578 15 t. black, deep brown and greenish yellow 1·25 5
579 25 t. black and bright scarlet .. .. 1·75 8
580 35 t. black, ultramarine and gold .. .. 2·00 2·0
581 50 t. multicoloured .. .. 2·25 3·2
577/81 .. .. *Set of* 5 7·25 6·0

Designs: *Vert*—15 t. 1897 Bechuanaland Protectorate overprint on G.B. 3d.; 25 t. Bechuanaland Protectorate 1932 1d definitive. *Horiz*—35 t. Bechuanaland 1965 Internal Self Government 5 c.; 50 t. Botswana 1966 Independence 2½ c.

(Des V. Larsson. Litho Mardon Printers Ltd, Zimbabwe)

1985 (5 Aug). *Centenary of Botswana Police. T* **147** *and simila[r] horiz designs. Multicoloured. P* 14½×14.

582 7 t. Type **147** .. .. 2·00 5
583 10 t. Bechuanaland Mounted Police, 1895–1902 .. .. 2·25 5
584 25 t. Bechuanaland Protectorate Police, 1903–66 .. .. 3·25 2·0
585 50 t. Botswana Police, from 1966 .. .. 4·50 6·0
582/5 .. .. *Set of* 4 11·00 8·0

MINIMUM PRICE

The minimum price quote is 10p which represents a handling charge rather than a basis for valuing common stamps. For further notes about prices see introductory pages.

148 *Cucumis metuliferus*

149 Mr. Shippard and Chief Gaseitsiwe of the Bangwaketse

Des Audrey Renew. Litho Mardon Printers Ltd, Zimbabwe)

85 (4 Nov). *Christmas. Edible Wild Cucumbers. T* **148** *and similar horiz designs. Multicoloured. P* 14½×14.
6 7 t. Type **148**.. .. .. 75 10
7 15 t. *Acanthosicyos naudinianus* .. .. 1·25 70
8 25 t. *Coccinia sessifolia* .. .. .. 2·00 1·10
9 50 t. *Momordica balsamina* .. .. .. 3·25 5·50
6/9 .. .. *Set of* 4 6·50 6·50

(Des A. Campbell. Litho Mardon Printers Ltd, Zimbabwe)

85 (30 Dec). *Centenary of Declaration of Bechuanaland Protectorate. T* **149** *and similar vert designs. Multicoloured. P* 14×14½.
90 7 t. Type **149**.. .. .. 35 10
91 15 t. Sir Charles Warren and Chief Sechele of the Bakwena 70 45
92 25 t. Revd. Mackenzie and Chief Khama of the Bamangwato .. .. .. 1·25 85
93 50 t. Map showing Protectorate .. .. 2·75 2·75
90/3 .. .. *Set of* 4 4·50 3·75
IS594 130×133 mm. Nos. 590/3 .. .. 7·50 9·00

150 Halley's Comet over Serowe

151 Milk Bag

(Des L. Hutchings. Litho Mardon Printers Ltd, Zimbabwe)

1986 (24 Mar). *Appearance of Halley's Comet. T* **150** *and similar horiz designs. Multicoloured. P* 14½×14.
595 7 t. Type **150**.. .. .. 80 15
596 15 t. Comet over Bobonong at sunset .. 1·50 70
597 35 t. Comet over Gomare at dawn .. .. 2·00 1·50
598 50 t. Comet over Thamaga and Letlhakeng 2·25 3·50
595/8 .. .. *Set of* 4 6·00 5·25

(Des B. Mazebedi. Litho Mardon Printers Ltd, Zimbabwe)

1986 (23 June). *Traditional Milk Containers. T* **151** *and similar vert designs. Multicoloured. P* 14½.
599 8 t. Type **151**.. .. .. 15 10
600 15 t. Clay pot and calabashes 25 30
601 35 t. Wooden milk bucket 50 65
602 50 t. Milk churn .. .. 70 1·10
599/602 .. .. *Set of* 4 1·40 1·90

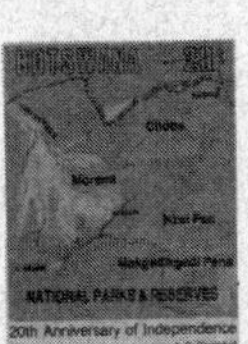
152 Map showing National Parks and Reserves

153 *Ludwigia stogonifera*

(Des K. Bogatsu, A. Campbell, I. Marshall and K. Mosinyi. Litho Govt Printer, Pretoria)

1986 (30 Sept). *20th Anniv of Independence. Sheet* 100×120 *mm, containing T* **152** *and similar vert designs. Multicoloured. P* 14.
MS603 20 t. Type **152**; 20 t. Morupule Power Station; 20 t. Cattle breeding in Kgalagadi; 20 t. National Assembly Building .. .. .. 2·25 1·75

(Des Julia Cairns. Litho Mardon Printers Ltd, Zimbabwe)

1986 (3 Nov). *Christmas. Flowers of Okavango. T* **153** *and similar vert designs. Multicoloured. P* 14×14½.
604 8 t. Type **153**.. .. .. 1·25 10
605 15 t. *Sopubia mannii*.. .. .. .. 2·25 1·10
606 35 t. *Commelina diffusa* .. .. .. 3·50 3·00
607 50 t. *Hibiscus diversifolius* .. .. .. 4·00 8·50
604/7 .. .. *Set of* 4 10·00 11·50

154 Divining

(**155**)

156 Oral Rehydration Therapy

(Des K. Mosinyi. Litho Mardon Printers Ltd, Zimbabwe)

1987 (2 Mar). *Traditional Medicine. T* **154** *and similar horiz designs. Multicoloured. P* 14½×14.
608 8 t. Type **154**.. .. .. 80 10
609 15 t. Lightning prevention .. .. .. 1·50 80
610 35 t. Rain making .. .. 2·25 2·50
611 50 t. Blood letting .. .. 2·75 5·50
608/11 .. .. *Set of* 4 6·50 8·00

1987 (1 Apr). *Nos.* 520, 523 *and* 530 *surch as T* **155**.
612 3 t. on 6 t. African Pygmy Goose .. .. 1·25 60
613 5 t. on 10 t. Yellow-billed Stork .. .. 1·25 60
614 20 t. on 50 t. Helmet Guineafowl (*horiz*) .. 2·75 1·40
612/14 .. .. *Set of* 3 4·75 2·40

(Des A. Nunoo. Litho Govt Printer, Pretoria)

1987 (1 June). *U.N.I.C.E.F. Child Survival Campaign. T* **156** *and similar vert designs. Multicoloured. P* 14.
615 8 t. Type **156**.. .. .. 35 10
616 15 t. Growth monitoring 60 55
617 35 t. Immunization .. .. 1·25 1·75
618 50 t. Breast feeding .. .. 1·50 3·75
615/18 .. .. *Set of* 4 3·25 5·50

157 Cape Fox

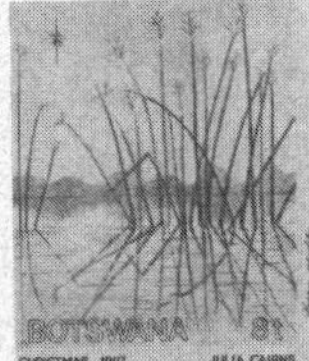

158 *Cyperus articulatus*

(Des P. Huebsch. Photo Harrison)

1987 (3 Aug). *Animals. T* **157** *and similar horiz designs. Multicoloured. P* 14.
619 1 t. Type **157**.. .. .. 10 50
620 2 t. Lechwe 10 50
621 3 t. Zebra 10 50
622 4 t. Duiker 10 70
623 5 t. Banded Mongoose 15 70
624 6 t. Rusty-spotted Genet 15 70
625 8 t. Hedgehog 30 10
626 10 t. Scrub Hare 25 10
627 12 t. Hippopotamus .. .. 1·00 1·75
628 15 t. Suricate 60 15
629 20 t. Caracal 70 65
630 25 t. Steenbok.. .. .. 70 65
631 30 t. Gemsbok.. .. .. 85 50
632 35 t. Square-lipped Rhinoceros .. .. 1·50 40
633 40 t. Mountain Reedbuck .. .. .. 1·10 65
634 50 t. Rock Dassie .. .. 90 1·00
635 1 p. Giraffe .. .. 2·50 2·75
636 2 p. Tsessebe .. .. 2·50 3·50
637 3 p. Side-striped Jackal .. .. .. 3·75 6·50
638 5 p. Hartebeest .. .. 6·00 10·00
619/38 .. .. *Set of* 20 20·00 29·00

(Des Julia Cairns. Litho National Printing & Packaging, Zimbabwe)

1987 (26 Oct). *Christmas. Grasses and Sedges of Okavango. T* **158** *and similar vert designs. Multicoloured. P* 14×14½.
639 8 t. Type **158**.. .. .. 40 10
640 15 t. Broomgrass 60 40
641 30 t. *Cyperus alopurcides* .. .. .. 1·25 75
642 1 p. Bulrush Sedge .. .. 2·50 4·00
639/42 .. .. *Set of* 4 4·25 4·75
MS643 88×99 mm. Nos. 639/42 .. .. 4·25 4·75
a. 30 t. value imperf vert .. .. .. 40·00

159 Planting Seeds with Digging Stick

160 Red Lechwe at Water-hole

(Des K. Mosinyi. Litho National Printing & Packaging, Zimbabwe)

1988 (14 Mar). *Early Cultivation. T* **159** *and similar horiz designs. Multicoloured. P* 14½×14.
644 8 t. Type **159**.. .. .. 40 10
645 15 t. Using iron hoe 60 35
646 35 t. Wooden ox-drawn plough .. .. 1·00 1·00
647 50 t. Villagers using lesotlas .. .. .. 1·40 2·00
644/7 .. .. *Set of* 4 3·00 3·00

(Des P. Augustinus. Litho National Printing & Packaging, Zimbabwe)

1988 (6 June). *Red Lechwe. T* **160** *and similar horiz designs. Multicoloured. P* 14½×14.
648 10 t. Type **160** 65 15
649 15 t. Red Lechwe and early morning sun .. 1·25 65
650 35 t. Female and calf .. .. .. 2·00 1·75
651 75 t. Herd on the move .. .. .. 3·25 5·00
648/51 .. .. *Set of* 4 6·50 6·75

COVER PRICES

Cover factors are quoted at the beginning of each country for most issues to 1945. An explanation of the system can be found on page x. The factors quoted do not, however, apply to philatelic covers.

161 Gubulawayo Postmark and Route Southwards to Tati

162 Pope John Paul II and Outline Map of Botswana

(Des M. Bryan, adapted Lucy Phalayagae. Litho National Printing & Packaging, Zimbabwe)

1988 (22 Aug). *Centenary of Mafeking-Gubalawayo Runner Post. Designs as Nos.* 294/8, *but redrawn smaller with changed inscription as in T* **161**. *Multicoloured. P* 14½.
652 10 t. Type **161** 35 10
653 15 t. Bechuanaland 1888 6d. on 6d. stamp and route from Tati southwards .. 55 30
654 30 t. Runners and twin routes south from Shoshong 95 75
655 60 t. Mafeking postmark and routes to Bechuanaland and Transvaal .. .. 1·60 2·75
652/5 .. .. *Set of* 4 3·00 3·50
MS656 81×151 mm. Nos. 652/5 vertically *se-tenant*, forming a composite map design .. 5·50 6·50

(Des P. Lodoen. Litho National Printing & Packaging, Zimbabwe)

1988 (13 Sept). *Visit of Pope John Paul II. T* **162** *and similar vert designs. Multicoloured. P* 14×14½.
657 10 t. Type **162** 70 10
658 15 t. Pope John Paul II 90 30
659 30 t. Pope giving blessing and outline map 1·40 70
660 80 t. Pope John Paul II (*different*) .. .. 2·00 2·75
657/60 .. .. *Set of* 4 4·50 3·50

163 National Museum and Art Gallery

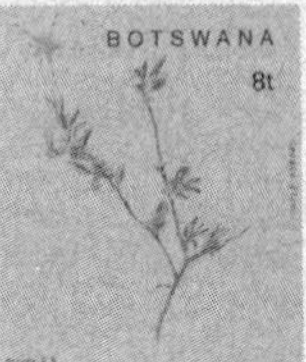

164 *Grewia flava*

(Des G. Mattsson and T. Sandberg (8 t.), A. Campbell (15 t.), K. Bogatsu (30 t.), T. Sandberg (60 t.). Litho National Printing & Packaging, Zimbabwe)

1988 (30 Sept). *20th Anniv of National Museum and Art Gallery, Gaborone. T* **163** *and similar vert designs. Multicoloured. P* 14½.
661 8 t. Type **163** 15 10
662 15 t. Pottery 20 25
663 30 t. Blacksmith's buffalo bellows 35 40
664 60 t. Children and mobile museum van .. 70 1·00
661/4 .. .. *Set of* 4 1·25 1·60

(Des Verena Blomberg-Ermatinger. Litho National Printing & Packaging, Zimbabwe)

1988 (31 Oct). *Flowering Plants of South-eastern Botswana. T* **164** *and similar vert designs. Multicoloured. P* 14×14½.
665 8 t. Type **164** 20 10
666 15 t. *Cienfuegosia digitata* 30 25
667 40 t. *Solanum seaforthianum* 60 55
668 75 t. *Carissa bispinosa* .. .. .. 1·00 1·40
665/8 .. .. *Set of* 4 1·90 2·00

165 Basket Granary

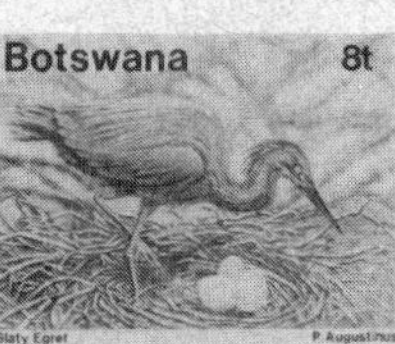

166 Female Red-throated Heron with Eggs

(Des K. Mosinyi. Litho National Printing & Packaging, Zimbabwe)

1989 (13 Mar). *Traditional Grain Storage. T* **165** *and similar vert designs. Multicoloured. P* 14 × 14½.
669 8 t. Type **165** 30 10
670 15 t. Large letlole granary 60 40
671 30 t. Pot granary .. .. 1·00 60
672 60 t. Two types of serala .. .. .. 1·75 2·25
669/72 .. .. *Set of* 4 3·25 3·00
The use of different paper stocks led to a wide range of shades in this issue.

(Des P. Augustinus. Litho Harrison)

1989 (5 July). *Red-throated Heron ("Slaty Egret"). T* **166** *and similar horiz designs. Multicoloured. P* 15×14.
673 8 t. Type **166** 45 15
674 15 t. Chicks in nest 65 40
675 30 t. Red-throated Heron in flight 90 75
676 60 t. Pair building nest .. .. .. 1·40 1·60
673/6 .. .. *Set of* 4 3·00 2·50
MS677 119×89 mm. Nos. 673/6 .. .. 3·00 2·75

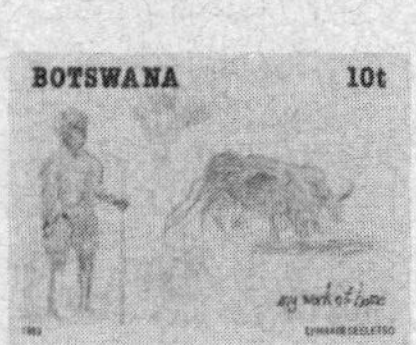

167 "My Work at Home" (Ephraim Seeletso)

168 *Eulophia angolensis*

(Litho Govt Printer, Pretoria)

1989 (4 Sept). *Children's Paintings. T* **167** *and similar multicoloured designs. P* 14.

678 10 t. Type **167** 35 10
679 15 t. "My Favourite Game" (hopscotch) (Neelma Bhatia) (*vert*) 50 35
680 30 t. "My Favourite Toy" (clay animals) (Thabo Habana) 75 70
681 1 p. "My School Day" (Thabo Olesitse) .. 2·00 3·25
678/81 .. .. *Set of* 4 3·25 4·00

(Des Julia Cairns. Litho Govt Printer, Pretoria)

1989 (30 Oct). *Christmas. Orchids. T* **168** *and similar vert designs. Multicoloured. P* 14.

682 8 t. Type **168** 60 10
683 15 t. *Eulophia hereroensis* .. .. .. 1·10 50
684 30 t. *Eulophia speciosa* .. .. .. 1·60 1·00
685 60 t. *Eulophia petersii* .. .. .. 2·25 4·50
682/5 .. .. *Set of* 4 5·00 5·50

169 Bechuanaland 1965 New Constitution 25 c. Stamp (25th anniv of Self Government)

10t

(170)

(Des K. Mosinyi. Litho National Printing & Packaging, Zimbabwe)

1990 (5 Mar). *Anniversaries. T* **169** *and similar horiz designs. P* 14½.

686 8 t. multicoloured 60 15
687 15 t. multicoloured 75 50
688 30 t. multicoloured .. .. .. 1·60 1·40
689 60 t. black, new blue and yellow-ochre .. 2·25 3·50
686/9 .. .. *Set of* 4 4·75 5·00

Designs:—15 t. Casting vote in ballot box (25th anniv of First Elections); 30 t. Outline map and flags of Southern African Development Coordination Conference countries (10th anniv); 60 t. Penny Black (150th anniv of first postage stamp).

1990 (27 Apr). *Nos.* 619, 624 *and* 627 *surch as T* **170**.

690 10 t. on 1 t. Type **157** 45 20
a. Surch double .. .. † —
691 20 t. on 6 t. Rusty-spotted Genet 60 70
692 50 t. on 12 t. Hippopotamus .. .. 1·75 2·50
690/2 .. .. *Set of* 3 2·50 3·00

171 Telephone Engineer

172 Young Children

(Des M. Kahn. Litho National Printing & Packaging, Zimbabwe)

1990 (3 May). *"Stamp World London 90" International Stamp Exhibition. T* **171** *and similar vert designs. Multicoloured. P* 14½.

693 8 t. Type **171** 35 10
694 15 t. Transmission pylon 65 40
695 30 t. Public telephone .. .. .. 1·00 75
696 2 p. Testing circuit board .. .. .. 3·00 5·00
693/6 .. .. *Set of* 4 4·50 5·50

(Des K. Mosinyi. Litho National Printing & Packaging, Zimbabwe)

1990 (1 Aug). *Traditional Dress. T* **172** *and similar vert designs. Multicoloured. P* 14½.

697 8 t. Type **172** 35 10
698 15 t. Young woman 65 40
699 30 t. Adult man .. .. 1·00 70
700 2 p. Adult woman .. .. 3·00 5·00
697/700 .. .. *Set of* 4 4·50 5·50
MS701 104×150 mm. Nos. 697/700 .. .. 4·50 6·00
a. 30 t. and 2 p. imperf vert .. ..

173 *Acacia nigrescens*

174 Children running in front of Car

(Des Gillian Condy. Litho National Printing & Packaging, Zimbabwe)

1990 (30 Oct). *Christmas. Flowering Trees. T* **173** *and similar vert designs. Multicoloured. P* 14×14½.

702 8 t. Type **173** 40 10
703 15 t. *Peltophorum africanum* 75 30
704 30 t. *Burkea africana* .. .. .. 1·25 65
705 2 p. *Pterocarpus angolensis* .. .. 2·75 4·50
702/5 .. .. *Set of* 4 4·75 5·00

(Des B. Heman-Ackah. Litho National Printing & Packaging, Zimbabwe)

1990 (7 Dec). *First National Road Safety Day. T* **174** *and similar horiz designs. Multicoloured. P* 14½.

706 8 t. Type **174** .. .. 1·00 25
707 15 t. Careless overtaking .. .. .. 1·50 85
708 30 t. Cattle on road .. .. .. 2·00 2·25
706/8 .. .. *Set of* 3 4·00 3·00

175 Cattle

176 Children

(Des B. Mazebedi. Litho Questa)

1991 (4 Mar). *Rock Paintings. T* **175** *and similar horiz designs. Multicoloured. P* 14.

709 8 t. Type **175** 75 30
710 15 t. Cattle, drying frames and tree .. 1·25 75
711 30 t. Animal hides .. .. 1·75 1·25
712 2 p. Family herding cattle .. .. 3·50 5·00
709/12 .. .. *Set of* 4 6·50 6·50

Nos. 709/12 were printed on sand-grained paper which has an uneven surface.

(Des H. Methorst. Litho National Printing & Packaging, Zimbabwe)

1991 (3 June). *National Census. T* **176** *and similar vert designs. Multicoloured. P* 14.

713 8 t. Type **176** 40 10
a. Perf 14½ .. .. 3·50 10
714 15 t. Village .. .. 2·50 60
a. Perf 14½ 75 55
715 30 t. School 85 75
a. Perf 14½ 85 75
716 2 p. Hospital .. .. 2·75 5·00
a. Perf 14½ .. .. 2·75 5·00
713/16 .. .. *Set of* 4 6·00 5·75

177 Tourists viewing Elephants

178 *Harpagophytum procumbens*

(Des P. Lodoen. Litho Govt Printer, Pretoria)

1991 (30 Sept). *African Tourism Year. Okavango Delta. T* **177** *and similar multicoloured designs. P* 14 (2 *p.*) *or* 14×14½ (*others*).

717 8 t. Type **177** .. .. 1·10 50
718 15 t. Crocodiles basking on river bank .. 1·50 70
719 35 t. African Fish Eagles and De Havilland D.H.C.7 Dash Seven aircraft .. 2·75 1·75
720 2 p. Okavango wildlife (26×44 *mm*) .. 4·50 6·00
717/20 .. .. *Set of* 4 9·00 8·00

(Des Gillian Condy. Litho Govt Printer, Pretoria)

1991 (4 Nov). *Christmas. Seed Pods. T* **178** *and similar vert designs. Multicoloured. P* 14.

721 8 t. Type **178** 60 10
722 15 t. *Tylosema esculentum* 90 40
723 30 t. *Abrus precatorius* .. .. .. 1·50 70
724 2 p. *Kigelia africana* .. .. .. 3·50 5·00
721/4 .. .. *Set of* 4 6·00 5·50

1992 (9 Mar). *Nos.* 621, 624 *and* 627 *surch as T* **170**.

725 8 t. on 12 t. Hippopotamus 90 40
726 10 t. on 12 t. Hippopotamus 90 40
727 25 t. on 6 t. Rusty-spotted Genet .. 1·25 1·25
728 40 t. on 3 t. Zebra .. .. .. 2·00 2·50
725/8 .. .. *Set of* 4 4·50 4·00

179 *Cacosternum boettgeri*

180 Air-conditioned Carriages

(Des Julia Cairns. Litho Govt Printer, Pretoria)

1992 (23 Mar). *Climbing Frogs. T* **179** *and similar multicoloured designs. P* 14.

729 8 t. Type **179** 45 20
730 10 t. *Hyperolius marmoratus angolensis* (*vert*) 45 20
731 40 t. *Bufo fenoulheti* .. .. .. 1·40 1·25
732 1 p. *Hyperolius* sp (*vert*) .. .. .. 2·00 3·50
729/32 .. .. *Set of* 4 3·75 4·75

(Des P. Lodoen. Litho Harrison)

1992 (29 June). *Deluxe Railway Service. T* **180** *and similar multicoloured designs. P* 14.

733 10 t. Type **180** 75 30
734 25 t. Diesel locomotive No. BD001 (*vert*) .. 1·25 70
735 40 t. Carriage interior (*vert*) .. .. 1·75 1·00
736 2 p. Diesel locomotive No. BD028 .. 3·50 5·00
733/6 .. .. *Set of* 4 6·50 6·25
MS737 127×127 mm. Nos. 733/6 .. .. 7·00 8·00

181 Cheetah

182 Boxing

(Des Judith Penny. Photo Harrison)

1992 (3 Aug). *Animals. T* **181** *and similar horiz designs. Multicoloured. P* 14½×14.

738 1 t. Type **181** 20 50
739 2 t. Spring Hare 20 50
740 4 t. Blackfooted Cat 30 50
741 5 t. Striped Mouse 30 50
742 10 t. Oribi 30 10
743 12 t. Pangolin 45 60
744 15 t. Aardwolf 45 30
745 20 t. Warthog 45 30
746 25 t. Ground Squirrel 45 20
747 35 t. Honey Badger 50 30
748 40 t. Common Mole Rat 50 30
749 45 t. Wild Dog 50 30
750 50 t. Water Mongoose 60 35
751 80 t. Klipspringer .. .. 90 1·00
752 1 p. Lesser Bushbaby .. .. .. 1·00 1·00
753 2 p. Bushveld Elephant Shrew .. .. 1·75 2·00
754 5 p. Zorilla .. .. 3·50 4·25
755 10 p. Vervet Monkey .. .. .. 5·50 7·00
738/55 .. .. *Set of* 18 16·00 18·00

(Litho Harrison)

1992 (7 Aug). *Olympic Games, Barcelona. T* **182** *and similar vert designs. Multicoloured. P* 14×15.

756 10 t. Type **182** 30 10
757 50 t. Running 65 50
758 1 p. Boxing (*different*) .. .. .. 1·10 1·60
759 2 p. Running (*different*) .. .. .. 1·75 2·75
756/9 .. .. *Set of* 4 3·50 4·50
MS760 87×117 mm. Nos. 756/9 .. .. 4·00 5·00

183 *Adiantum incisum*

184 Helping Blind Person (Lions Club International)

(Des Gillian Condy. Litho National Printing & Packaging, Zimbabwe)

1992 (23 Nov). *Christmas. Ferns. T* **183** *and similar vert designs. Multicoloured. P* 14½.

761 10 t. Type **183** 30 10
762 25 t. *Actiniopteris radiata* 55 35
763 40 t. *Ceratopteris cornuta* 70 55
764 1 p. 50, *Pellaea calomelanos* .. .. 2·25 4·00
761/4 .. .. *Set of* 4 3·50 4·50

(Des Ann Nilsson. Litho National Printing & Packaging, Zimbabwe)

1993 (29 Mar). *Charitable Organizations in Botswana. T* **184** *and similar multicoloured designs. P* 14.

765 10 t. Type **184** 35 10
766 15 t. Nurse carrying child (Red Cross Society) (*horiz*) 45 25

67 25 t. Woman watering seedling (Ecumenical Decade) 55 40
68 35 t. Deaf children (Round Table) (*horiz*) .. 70 80
69 40 t. Crowd of people (Rotary International) 80 1·10
70 50 t. Hands at prayer (Botswana Christian Council) (*horiz*) .. .. 95 1·50
65/70 .. .. *Set of* 6 3·50 3·50

185 Bechuanaland Railways Class "6" Locomotive No. 1

186 Long-crested Eagle

(Des P. Lodoen. Litho Harrison)

993 (24 May). *Railway Centenary. T* **185** *and similar horiz designs. Multicoloured. P* 15×14.
71 10 t. Type **185** 50 20
72 40 t. Class "19" locomotive No. 317 .. 90 60
73 50 t. Class "12" locomotive No. 256 .. 95 70
74 1 p. 50, Class "7" locomotive No. 71 .. 1·40 2·75
71/4 .. .. *Set of* 4 3·25 3·75
1S775 190×100 mm. Nos. 771/4 .. .. 3·25 4·25

Des J. Leath. Litho National Printing & Packaging, Zimbabwe)

993 (30 Aug). *Endangered Eagles. T* **186** *and similar vert designs. Multicoloured. P* 14½.
76 10 t. Type **186** 45 20
77 25 t. Short-toed Eagle 80 60
78 50 t. Bateleur .. .. 1·25 1·50
79 1 p. 50, Secretary Bird .. .. .. 2·50 3·75
76/9 .. .. *Set of* 4 4·50 5·50

187 *Aloe zebrina*

188 Boy with String Puppet

Des Gillian Condy. Litho National Printing & Packaging, Zimbabwe)

1993 (25 Oct). *Christmas. Flora. T* **187** *and similar vert designs. Multicoloured. P* 14×14½.
780 12 t. Type **187** 25 10
781 25 t. *Croton megalobotrys* 40 25
782 50 t. *Boophane disticha* 65 70
783 1 p. *Euphoria davyi* .. .. 1·10 2·00
780/3 .. .. *Set of* 4 2·25 2·75

(Des K. Mosinyi. Litho National Printing & Packaging, Zimbabwe)

1994 (28 Mar). *Traditional Toys. T* **188** *and similar horiz designs. Multicoloured. P* 14½.
784 10 t. Type **188** 15 10
785 40 t. Boys with clay cattle 35 30
786 50 t. Boy with spinner 40 50
787 1 p. Girls playing in make-believe houses 90 1·60
784/7 .. .. *Set of* 4 1·60 2·25

189 Interior of Control Tower, Gaborone Airport

10t

(190)

(Des M. McArthur. Litho National Printing & Packaging, Zimbabwe)

1994 (30 June). *50th Anniv of International Civil Aviation Organization. T* **189** *and similar multicoloured designs. P* 14½.
788 10 t. Type **189** 20 10
789 25 t. Crash tender 35 25
790 40 t. Loading supplies onto airliner (*vert*) .. 50 60
791 50 t. Control tower, Gaborone (*vert*) .. 60 1·25
788/91 .. .. *Set of* 4 1·50 2·00

1994 (1 Aug). *No.* 743 *surch with T* **190** *by Govt Printer, Pretoria.*
792 10 t. on 12 t. Pangolin .. .. 1·00 40

MINIMUM PRICE

The minimum price quote is 10p which represents a handling charge rather than a basis for valuing common stamps. For further notes about prices see introductory pages.

191 Lesser Flamingos at Sua Pan

192 *Ziziphus mucronata*

(Des P. Lodoen. Litho National Printing & Packaging, Zimbabwe)

1994 (26 Sept). *Environment Protection. Makgadikgadi Pans. T* **191** *and similar multicoloured designs. P* 14×14½ (*vert*) *or* 14½×14 (*horiz*).
793 10 t. Type **191** 40 20
794 35 t. Baobab trees (*horiz*) 50 30
795 50 t. Zebra and palm trees 65 70
796 2 p. Map of area (*horiz*) .. .. .. 1·75 2·75
793/6 .. .. *Set of* 4 3·00 3·50

(Des Gillian Condy. Litho National Printing & Packaging, Zimbabwe)

1994 (24 Oct). *Christmas. Edible Fruits. T* **192** *and similar vert designs. Multicoloured. P* 14×14½.
797 10 t. Type **192** 20 10
798 25 t. *Strychnos cocculoides* 30 25
799 40 t. *Bauhinia petersiana* 50 50
800 50 t. *Schinziphyton rautoneii* 60 70
797/800 .. .. *Set of* 4 1·40 1·40

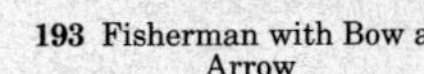

193 Fisherman with Bow and Arrow

194 Boys watering Horses (F.A.O.)

(Des B. Mazebedi. Litho National Printing & Packaging, Zimbabwe)

1995 (3 Apr). *Traditional Fishing. T* **193** *and similar horiz designs. Multicoloured. P* 14½.
801 15 t. Type **193** 20 15
802 40 t. Men in canoe and boy with fishing rod 35 30
803 65 t. Fisherman with net 50 60
804 80 t. Fisherman with basket fish trap .. 65 1·25
801/4 .. .. *Set of* 4 1·50 2·10

(Des M. McArthur. Litho National Printing & Packaging Zimbabwe)

1995 (16 Oct). *50th Anniv of United Nations. T* **194** *and similar vert designs. Multicoloured. P* 14½.
805 20 t. Type **194** 20 10
806 50 t. Schoolchildren queuing for soup (W.F.P.) 35 30
807 80 t. Letters and postman delivering to village (U.N.D.P.) 60 80
808 1 p. Weighing baby (U.N.I.C.E.F.) .. 70 1·00
805/8 .. .. *Set of* 4 1·60 2·00

195 Brown Hyena

196 *Adenia glauca*

(Des Judith Penny. Litho Questa)

1995 (6 Nov). *Endangered Species. Brown Hyena. T* **195** *and similar horiz designs. Multicoloured. P* 14½.
809 20 t. Type **195** 40 50
a. Strip of 4. Nos. 809/12 .. .. .. 2·25
810 50 t. Pair of Hyenas 55 65
811 80 t. Hyena stealing ostrich eggs 70 85
812 1 p. Adult Hyena and cubs 75 90
809/12 .. .. *Set of* 4 2·25 2·50

In addition to separate sheets of 50 Nos. 809/12 were also available in sheets of 16 (4×4) with the stamps arranged *se-tenant* both horizontally and vertically.

(Des Gillian Condy. Litho National Printing & Packaging, Zimbabwe)

1995 (27 Nov). *Christmas. Plants. T* **196** *and similar vert designs. Multicoloured. P* 14.
813 20 t. Type **196** 20 10
814 50 t. *Pterodiscus ngamicus* 40 30
815 80 t. *Sesamothamnus lugardii* 65 80
816 1 p. *Fockea multiflora* .. .. 75 1·00
813/16 .. .. *Set of* 4 1·75 2·00

(197)

20t

Different "2" (R. 7/5, 8/5, 9/5)

1996 (12 Feb). *Nos.* 738/40 *surch as T* **197**.
817 20 t. on 2 t. Spring Hare 20 20
a. Different "2" .. .. 2·50
818 30 t. on 1 t. Type **181** 25 25
819 70 t. on 4 t. Blackfooted Cat 50 70
817/19 .. .. *Set of* 3 85 1·00

198 Spears

(Des B. Mazebedi. Litho National Printing & Packaging, Zimbabwe)

1996 (25 Mar). *Traditional Weapons. T* **198** *and similar horiz designs. Multicoloured. P* 14½×14.
820 20 t. Type **198** 15 10
821 50 t. Axes 30 30
822 80 t. Shield and knobkerries 45 60
823 1 p. Knives and sheaths 50 75
820/3 .. .. *Set of* 4 1·25 1·60

199 Child with Basic Radio

200 Olympic Flame, Rings and Wreath

(Des P. Lodoen. Litho National Printing & Packaging, Zimbabwe)

1996 (3 June). *Centenary of Radio. T* **199** *and similar vert designs. Multicoloured. P* 14×14½.
824 20 t. Type **199** 20 10
825 50 t. Radio Botswana's mobile transmitter 35 30
826 80 t. Police radio control 50 65
827 1 p. Listening to radio 65 90
824/7 .. .. *Set of* 4 1·50 1·75

(Des R. Andersson. Litho Govt Printer, Pretoria)

1996 (19 July). *Centenary of Modern Olympic Games. T* **200** *and similar vert designs. Multicoloured. P* 14.
828 20 t. Type **200** 20 10
829 50 t. Pierre de Coubertin (founder of modern Olympics) 35 30
830 80 t. Map of Botswana with flags and athletes 50 70
831 1 p. Ruins of ancient stadium at Olympia 60 90
828/31 .. .. *Set of* 4 1·50 1·75

201 Family Planning Class (Botswana Family Welfare Association)

202 *Adansonia digitata* Leaf and Blossom

(Des K. Mosinyi. Litho National Printing and Packaging, Zimbabwe)

1996 (23 Sept). *Local Charities. T* **201** *and similar vert designs. Multicoloured. P* 14½.
832 20 t. Type **201** 15 10
833 30 t. Blind workers (Pudulogong Rehabilitation Centre) 15 15
834 50 t. Collecting seeds (Forestry Association of Botswana) 25 30
835 70 t. Secretarial class (Y.W.C.A.) 35 50
836 80 t. Children's day centre (Botswana Council of Women) 40 60
837 1 p. Children's village, Tlokweng (S.O.S. Children's village) 50 70
832/7 .. .. *Set of* 6 1·60 2·00

(Des Gillian Condy. Litho National Printing and Packaging, Zimbabwe)

1996 (4 Nov). *Christmas. T* **202** *and similar vert designs showing parts of life cycle for* Adansonia digitata. *Multicoloured. P* 14.
838 20 t. Type **202** 15 10
839 50 t. Fruit 30 25
840 80 t. Tree in leaf 45 55
841 1 p. Tree with bare branches 50 70
838/41 .. .. *Set of* 4 1·25 1·40

203 Tati Hotel

204 Steam Locomotive, Bechuanaland Railway, 1897

(Des M. Smith. Litho National Printing and Packaging, Zimbabwe)

1997 (21 Apr). *Francistown Centenary. T* **203** *and similar horiz designs. Multicoloured. P* 14½×14.
842 20 t. Type **203** 15 10
843 50 t. Railway Station 30 25
844 80 t. Company Manager's House 40 50
845 1 p. Monarch Mine 50 75
842/5 .. .. *Set of* 4 1·25 1·40

(Des P. Lodoen. Litho National Printing and Packaging, Zimbabwe)

1997 (12 July). *Railway Centenary. T* **204** *and similar vert designs. Multicoloured. P* 14×14½.
846 35 t. Type **204** 20 15
847 50 t. Elephants crossing railway line .. 30 25
848 80 t. First locomotive in Bechuanaland, 1897 .. .. 40 40
849 1 p. Beyer-Garratt type steam locomotive No. 352 .. .. 50 55
850 2 p. Diesel locomotive No. BD339 .. 80 1·00
851 2 p. 50, Fantuzzi container stacker .. 90 1·25
846/51 .. .. *Set of* 6 2·75 3·25

205 Pel's Fishing Owl

206 *Combretum zeyheri*

(Des Helena Schüssel. Litho Enschedé)

1997 (4 Aug). *Birds. T* **205** *and similar multicoloured designs. P* 13½×13 *(vert) or* 13×13½ *(horiz).*
852 5 t. Type **205** 10 10
853 10 t. Gymnogene (*horiz*) 10 10
854 15 t. Meyer's Parrot 10 10
855 20 t. Harlequin Quail (*horiz*) 10 10
856 25 t. Marico Sunbird (*horiz*) 10 10
857 30 t. Kurrichane Thrush (*horiz*) 10 10
858 40 t. Redheaded Finch 10 10
859 50 t. Buffalo Weaver 15 20
860 60 t. Sacred Ibis (*horiz*) 15 20
861 70 t. Cape Shoveler (*horiz*) 20 25
862 80 t. Greater Honeyguide (*horiz*) 20 25
863 1 p. Woodland Kingfisher (*horiz*) 25 30
864 1 p. 25, Purple Heron 25 30
865 1 p. 50, Yellow-billed Oxpecker (*horiz*) .. 25 30
866 2 p. Shaft-tailed Whydah 55 60
867 2 p. 50, White Stork 55 60
868 5 p. Sparrowhawk .. .. .. 1·40 1·50
869 10 p. Spotted Crake .. .. .. 2·75 3·00
852/69 .. .. *Set of* 18 7·25 7·50
No. 861 is inscribed "Shoveller" in error.

(Des N. Shewring (No. **MS**876), D. Miller (others). Litho Questa (No. **MS**876), Cartor (others))

1997 (22 Sept). *Golden Wedding of Queen Elizabeth and Prince Philip. Multicoloured designs as T* **173** *of Ascension.* W w **14**. *P* 13.
870 35 t. Prince Philip with carriage 20 20
a. Horiz pair. Nos. 870/1 .. .. 40 40
871 35 t. Queen Elizabeth with binoculars .. 20 20
872 2 p. Queen Elizabeth with horse team .. 90 1·00
a. Horiz pair. Nos. 872/3 .. .. 1·75 2·00
873 2 p. Prince Philip and horse .. .. 90 1·00
874 2 p. 50, Queen Elizabeth and Prince Philip 1·10 1·25
a. Horiz pair. Nos. 874/5 .. .. 2·10 2·50
875 2 p. 50, Princess Anne and Prince Edward 1·10 1·25
870/5 .. .. *Set of* 6 4·00 4·50
MS876 110×70 mm. 10 p. Queen Elizabeth and Prince Philip in landau (*horiz*). Wmk sideways. P 14×14½ .. .. 4·00 4·50
Nos. 870/1, 872/3 and 874/5 were each printed together, *se-tenant*, in horizontal pairs throughout the sheets.

(Des Gillian Condy. Litho National Printing and Packaging, Zimbabwe)

1997 (10 Nov). *Christmas. Plants. T* **206** *and similar vert designs. Multicoloured. P* 14.
877 35 t. Type **206** 20 10
878 1 p. *Combretum apiculatum* 50 35
879 2 p. *Combretum molle* 90 90
880 2 p. 50, *Combretum imberbe* .. .. 1·00 1·25
877/80 .. .. *Set of* 4 2·40 2·40

207 Baobab Trees

208 "Village Life" (tapestry)

(Des A. Campbell. Litho National Printing and Packaging, Zimbabwe)

1998 (23 Mar). *Tourism. T* **207** *and similar multicoloured designs. P* 14½.
881 35 t. Type **207** 25 15
882 1 p. Crocodile 40 35
883 2 p. Stalactites (*vert*) 75 80
884 2 p. 50, Tourists and rock paintings (*vert*) 90 1·00
881/4 .. .. *Set of* 4 2·10 2·10

(Des D. Miller. Litho Cartor)

1998 (1 June). *Diana, Princess of Wales Commemoration. Vert designs as T* **177** *of Ascension. Multicoloured.* W w **14**. *P* 13.
885 35 t. Princess Diana, 1990 .. .. 25 15
886 1 p. In green hat, 1992 .. .. .. 40 35
887 2 p. In white blouse, 1993 .. .. 75 80
888 2 p. 50, With crowd, Cambridge, 1993 .. 90 1·00
885/8 .. .. *Set of* 4 2·10 2·10
MS889 145×70 mm. As Nos. 885/8, but each with a face value of 2 p. 50 .. .. 3·75 4·00

(Des M. McArthur. Litho Enschedé)

1998 (28 Sept). *Botswana Weavers. T* **208** *and similar multicoloured designs. P* 14×13½.
890 35 t. Type **208** 10 15
891 55 t. Weaver dyeing threads 15 20
892 1 p. "African wildlife" (tapestry) 25 30
893 2 p. Weaver at loom 55 60
890/3 .. .. *Set of* 4 1·00 1·25
MS894 68×58 mm. 2 p. 50, "Elephants" (tapestry) (*horiz*). P 13½×14 .. .. .. 65 70

209 *Ficus ingens*

(Des Gillian Condy. Litho Oriental Press, Bahrain)

1998 (30 Nov). *Christmas. Plants. T* **209** *and similar vert designs. Multicoloured. P* 13×13½.
895 35 t. Type **209** 10 10
896 55 t. *Ficus pygmaea* 15 20
897 1 p. *Ficus abutilifolia* 25 30
898 2 p. 50, *Ficus sycomorus* 65 70
895/8 .. .. *Set of* 4 1·10 1·25

STAMP BOOKLETS

B 1

1989 (1 Dec)–**92.** *Covers as Type* B **1** *printed in blue on coloured card, each showing different stamp and postal logo. Stapled.*
SB1 20 t. booklet containing 2 t. (No. 620) in block of 10 (white cover) 50
SB2 40 t. booklet containing 2 t. (No. 620) in block of 20 (white cover) 75
SB3 50 t. booklet containing 5 t. (No. 623) in block of 10 (claret cover) 80
SB4 80 t. booklet containing 8 t. (No. 625) in block of 10 (grey cover) .. .. 1·10
a. Containing 8 t. on 12 t. (No. 725) (1992) ..
SB5 1 p. booklet containing 5 t. (No. 623) in block of 20 (claret cover) .. .. 1·25
SB6 1 p. booklet containing 10 t. (No. 626) in block of 10 (cinnamon cover) .. .. .. 1·25
a. Containing 10 t. on 1 t. (No. 690) (1990) ..
b. Containing 10 t. on 12 t. (No. 726) (1992)
SB7 1 p. 50, booklet containing 15 t. (No. 628) in block of 10 (pink cover) .. .. .. 2·00
SB8 1 p. 60, booklet containing 8 t. (No. 625) in block of 20 (grey cover) .. .. 2·00
a. Containing 8 t. on 12 t. (No. 725) (1992) ..
SB9 2 p. booklet containing 10 t. (No. 626) in block of 20 (cinnamon cover) .. .. .. 2·25
a. Containing 10 t. on 1 t. (No. 690) (1990) ..
b. Containing 10 t. on 12 t. (No. 726) (1992)
SB10 2 p. booklet containing 20 t. (No. 629) in block of 10 (pale blue cover) .. .. .. 2·25
a. Containing 20 t. on 6 t. (No. 691) (1990) ..
SB11 3 p. booklet containing 15 t. (No. 628) in block of 20 (pink cover) .. .. 3·25
SB12 3 p. booklet containing 30 t. (No. 631) in block of 10 (lemon cover) .. .. 3·25
SB13 4 p. booklet containing 20 t. (No. 629) in block of 20 (pale blue cover) .. .. .. 3·75
SB14 4 p. booklet containing 40 t. (No. 633) in block of 10 (pale green cover) .. .. .. 3·75
a. Containing 40 t. on 3 t. (No. 728) (1992) ..
b. Error. Containing 50 t. on 12 t. (No. 692) (1990) .. ..
SB15 6 p. booklet containing 30 t. (No. 631) in block of 20 (lemon cover) .. .. 5·50
SB16 8 p. booklet containing 40 t. (No. 633) in block of 20 (pale green cover) .. .. .. 7·00
a. Containing 40 t. on 3 t. (No. 728) (1992) ..
The booklets of twenty are larger, 81×69 mm.
No. SB14b, which was produced in error, has the face value of the booklet amended in manuscript.

B 2

1993 (4 Oct)–**94.** *Covers as Type* B **2** *printed in black on coloured card, each showing different stamp with postal logo. Stapled.*
SB17 1 p. booklet containing 10 t. (No. 742) in strip of 10 (yellow cover) 75
a. Containing 10 t. on 12 t. (No. 792) (1994) 75
SB18 1 p. 20, booklet containing 12 t. (No. 743) in strip of 10 (pale orange cover) 90
SB19 1 p. 50, booklet containing 15 t. (No. 744) in strip of 10 (orange cover) .. .. 1·10
SB20 2 p. booklet containing 10 t. (No. 742) in block of 20 (yellow cover) .. .. 1·40
a. Containing 10 t. on 12 t. (No. 792) (1994) 1·40
SB21 2 p. booklet containing 20 t. (No. 745) in strip of 10 (white cover) .. .. 1·40
SB22 2 p. 40, booklet containing 12 t. (No. 743) in block of 20 (pale orange cover) .. .. 1·75
SB23 2 p. 50, booklet containing 25 t. (No. 746) in strip of 10 (pink cover) .. .. .. 1·75
SB24 3 p. booklet containing 15 t. (No. 744) in block of 20 (orange cover) .. .. 1·90
SB25 3 p. 50, booklet containing 35 t. (No. 747) in strip of 10 (green cover) .. .. .. 2·00
SB26 4 p. booklet containing 20 t. (No. 745) in block of 20 (white cover) .. .. 2·50
SB27 4 p. booklet containing 40 t. (No. 748) in strip of 10 (blue cover) .. .. 2·50
SB28 4 p. 50, booklet containing 45 t. (No. 749) in strip of 10 (pale rose-lilac cover) .. .. 2·75
SB29 5 p. booklet containing 25 t. (No. 746) in block of 20 (pink cover) .. .. 3·00
SB30 5 p. booklet containing 50 t. (No. 750) in strip of 10 (grey cover) .. .. 3·00
SB31 7 p. booklet containing 35 t. (No. 747) in block of 20 (green cover) .. .. 3·75
SB32 8 p. booklet containing 40 t. (No. 748) in block of 20 (blue cover) .. .. 4·00
SB33 9 p. booklet containing 45 t. (No. 749) in block of 20 (pale rose-lilac cover) .. .. 4·50
SB34 10 p. booklet containing 50 t. (No. 750) in block of 20 (grey cover) .. .. 5·00
The booklets of twenty are larger, 75×80 mm.

996. *Covers as Nos.* SB17 *and* SB21 *cut down to* 75×40 *mm. Stamps attached by selvedge.*

B35	1 p. booklet containing 5 t. and 15 t. (Nos. 741 and 744) each in strip of 5 (yellow cover) ..	
B36	1 p. booklet containing 20 t. (No. 809) in strip of 5 (white cover)	

Nos. SB35/6 were issued from machines at Gaborone and rancistown Main Post Offices. They were subsequently eplaced by booklets with plain white covers containing 1 p. orth of current stamps attached by the selvedges.

POSTAGE DUE STAMPS

BECHUANALAND PROTECTORATE

(D 1)

BECHUANALAND PROTECTORATE

(D 2)

1926 (Jan). *Nos.* D9/10 *and* D13 *of Great Britain, optd with Types* D **1** *or* D **2** (2*d.*).

D1	½d. emerald (No. D10)	3·25	60·00
D2	1d. carmine (No. D9)	3·25	45·00
D3	2d. agate (No. D13)	6·00	80·00
D1/3	.. .. *Set of* 3	11·00	£160

D 3

2d Normal

2d Large "d" (R. 9/6, 10/6)

Serif on "d" (R.1/6)

(Typo D.L.R.)

1932 (12 Dec)–**58.** *Wmk Mult Script CA. Ordinary paper. P* 14.

D4	D **3**	½d. sage-green	6·00	30·00
D5		1d. carmine	6·50	8·50
		a. Chalk-surfaced paper (27.11.58) ..	1·00	12·00
D6		2d. violet	8·00	35·00
		a. Large "d"	80·00	
		b. Chalk-surfaced paper (27.11.58) ..	1·50	17·00
		ba. Large "d"	20·00	
		bb. Serif on "d"	25·00	
D4/6b		.. .. *Set of* 3	7·75	50·00
D4/6 Perf "Specimen"		.. .. *Set of* 3	65·00	

No. D6a first occurred on the 1947 printing.

1c 1c

I (Small) II (Large)

1961 (14 Feb). *Surch as T* **27**. *Chalk-surfaced paper* (*Nos.* D7/8).

D7	D **3**	1 c. on 1d. (Type I)	25	50
		a. Type II (Apr)	15	1·75
		ab. Double surch	£150	
		ac. Ordinary paper	16·00	50·00
D8		2 c. on 2d. (Type I)	25	1·50
		a. Large "d"	6·00	
		b. Serif on "d"	8·00	
		c. Type II	15	2·00
		ca. Large "d"	4·50	
		cb. Serif on "d"	6·00	
		d. Ordinary paper. Type II	80·00	90·00
		da. Large "d"	£300	
D9		5 c. on ½d.	20	60
D7/9		.. .. *Set of* 3	45	2·40

1961 (15 Nov). *As Type* D **3** *but values in cents. Chalk-surfaced paper. Wmk Mult Script CA. P* 14.

D10	1 c. carmine	15	1·50
D11	2 c. violet	15	1·50
D12	5 c. green	30	1·75
D10/12	.. .. *Set of* 3	55	4·25

REPUBLIC OF
BOTSWANA

(D 4)

D 5 African Elephant

D 6 Common Zebra

1967 (1 Mar). *Nos.* D10/12 *optd with Type* D **4**.

D13	1 c. carmine	15	2·25
D14	2 c. violet	15	2·50
D15	5 c. green	20	2·50
D13/15	.. .. *Set of* 3	45	6·50

(Des and litho B.W.)

1971 (9 June). *P* 13½.

D16	D **5**	1 c. carmine	1·10	3·25
D17		2 c. bluish violet	1·40	3·50
D18		6 c. sepia	2·50	5·50
D19		14 c. blue-green	2·75	7·50
D16/19		.. .. *Set of* 4	7·00	18·00

(Des M. Bryan. Litho Govt Printer, Pretoria)

1977 (18 Apr)–**84**. *P* 12½.

D20	D **6**	1 t. black and vermilion (1978) ..	50	2·50
		a. Black and bright orange (1980) ..	90	2·50
		b. Perf 14 (1982?) ..	55	2·00
D21		2 t. black and emerald	40	2·75
		a. Perf 14 (5.8.81*)	60	2·25
D22		4 t. black and red	40	2·75
		a. Perf 14 (28.9.81*)	60	2·25
D23		10 t. black and deep ultramarine ..	40	2·75
		a. Perf 14 (7.3.84)	60	2·25
D24		16 t. black and chestnut	65	3·25
		a. Perf 14 (7.3.84)	75	2·75
D20/24		.. .. *Set of* 5	2·10	12·50
D20b/24a		.. .. *Set of* 5	2·75	10·00

* First supplies of Nos. D20b, D21a and D22a were sent to Botswana in June 1981. The dates quoted for the 2 t. and 4 t. are earliest known dates of use. Early use of the 1 t. has yet to be identified.

Nos. D20b/4a are on white paper. A subsequent printing in September 1988 was on poorer grade paper. Stamps perforated 14 measure 24 mm across from perforation to perforation.

Type I

Type II

Two Types of Nos. D25/9 (Zimbabwe ptgs):—

Type I. Grass sparse. No shading dots on zebra. Zebra's right ear has right edge missing.

Type II. Grass thicker. Shading dots on zebra. Right ear almost complete.

(Litho National Printing & Packaging, Zimbabwe)

1989 (1 Apr)–**96.** *P* 14½.

D25	D **6**	1 t. black and reddish orange (I) ..	20	50
		a. Type II. Perf 14 (1993) ..	10	10
		ab. Perf 14½ (1996)	10	10
D26		2 t. black and emerald (I)	20	50
		a. Type II. Perf 14 (1993) ..	10	10
		ab. Perf 14½ (1996)	10	10
D27		4 t. black and bright scarlet (I) ..	20	50
		a. Type II. Perf 14 (1993) ..	10	10
		ab. Perf 14½ (1996)	10	10
D28		10 t. black and deep ultramarine (I)	25	50
		a. Type II. Perf 14 (1993) ..	10	10
		ab. Perf 14½ (1996)	10	10
D29		16 t. black and reddish brown (I) ..	35	80
		a. Type II. Perf 14 (1993) ..	10	10
		ab. Perf 14½ (1996)	10	10
D25/9		.. .. *Set of* 5	1·10	2·50
D25a/9a		.. .. *Set of* 5	25	25

Nos. D25a/9a measure 26 mm across from perforation to perforation.

POSTAL FISCAL STAMPS

The following stamps issued for fiscal purposes were each allowed to be used for postal purposes for a short time. No. F2 was used by the public because the word "POSTAGE" had not been obliterated and No. F3 because the overprint did not include the words "Revenue only" as did the contemporary fiscal overprints for Basutoland and Swaziland.

Bechuanaland

Protectorate	£5	Bechuanaland Protectorate.
(F 1)	(F 2)	(F 3)

1910 (July). *No.* 266a *of Transvaal, optd with Type* F **1** *by Transvaal Govt Ptg Wks, Pretoria.*
F1 6d. black and brown-orange (Bl-Blk) .. £150 £300

No. F1 was supplied to Assistant Commissioners in January 1907 for revenue purposes. The "POSTAGE" inscription was not obliterated, however, and the stamp is known postally used for a period of a year from July 1910.

1918. *No.* 15 *surch with Type* F **2** *at top.*
F2 4 £5 on 1s. green and black £9000

1922. *No.* 4b *of South Africa optd with Type* F **3**, *in varying positions.*
F3 1d. scarlet .. .. 42·00 £130
a. Opt double, one albino £140

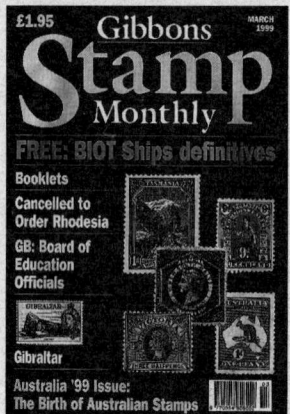

British Antarctic Territory

or use at the following bases:
Adelaide Island (Graham Land) (*closed* 1977)
Argentine Islands ("Faraday" *from* 1981), (Graham Land) (*closed* 8 *February* 1996 *and transferred to Ukraine*)
Brabant Island (Graham Land) (*opened* 1984, *closed* 1985)
Deception Island (South Shetlands) (*closed* December 1967, *opened* 4 December 1968, *closed* 23 February 1969)
Halley Bay (Coats Land)
Hope Bay (Graham Land) (*closed* 12 February 1964)
Port Lockroy (Graham Land) (*opened* 21 November 1996)
Rothera Point (Graham Land) (*opened* 1977)
Signy Island (South Orkneys)
Stonington Island (Graham Land) (*closed* February 1975)

1 M.V. *Kista Dan*

(Des B.W. (No. 15*a*), M. Goaman (others). Recess B.W.)

963 (1 Feb)–**69**. *Horiz designs as T* **1**, *W w* **12**. *P* 11 × 11½.
1 ½d. deep blue . . 75 1·40
2 1d. brown . . 1·00 80
3 1½d. orange-red and brown-purple . . 1·00 1·00
4 2d. purple . . 1·25 80
5 2½d. myrtle-green . . 2·50 70
6 3d. deep blue . . 3·50 80
7 4d. sepia . . 2·50 1·25
8 6d. olive and deep ultramarine . . 4·25 1·75
9 9d. olive-green . . 3·50 1·50
0 1s. deep turquoise-blue . . 3·75 70
1 2s. deep violet and orange-sepia . . 18·00 6·00
2 2s. 6d. blue . . 17·00 6·50
3 5s. red-orange and rose-red . . 20·00 12·00
4 10s. deep ultramarine and emerald . . 45·00 25·00
5 £1 black and light blue . . 55·00 48·00
5*a* £1 red and brownish black (1.12.69) . . £150 £120
/15*a* . . *Set of* 16 £300 £200
Designs:—1d. Manhauling; 1½d. Muskeg (tractor); 2d. kiing; 2½d. De Havilland D.H.C.2 Beaver (aircraft); 3d. R.R.S. *ohn Biscoe II*; 4d. Camp scene; 6d. H.M.S. *Protector*; 9d. ledging; 1s. De Havilland D.H.C.3 Otter (aircraft); 2s. Huskies; s. 6d. Westland Whirlwind helicopter; 5s. Snocat (tractor); 10s. .R.S. *Shackleton*; £1 (No. 15) Antarctic map; £1 (No. 15*a*) .M.S. *Endurance*.

966 (24 Jan). *Churchill Commemoration. As Nos.* 170/3 *of Antigua.*
6 ½d. new blue . . 80 3·25
7 1d. deep green . . 3·00 3·25
8 1s. brown . . 21·00 6·50
9 2s. bluish violet . . 24·00 7·00
6/19 . . *Set of* 4 45·00 18·00

17 Lemaire Channel and Icebergs

(Des R. Granger Barrett. Litho Format)

1969 (6 Feb). *25th Anniv of Continuous Scientific Work. T* **17** *and similar horiz designs. W w* **12** (*sideways*). *P* 14.
20 3½d. black, pale blue and ultramarine . . 4·00 3·00
21 6d. multicoloured . . 3·50 2·50
22 1s. black, pale blue and vermilion . . 3·50 2·00
23 2s. black, orange and turquoise-blue . . 3·75 3·00
20/3 . . *Set of* 4 13·00 9·50
Designs:—6d. Radio Sonde balloon; 1s. Muskeg pulling tent equipment; 2s. Surveyors with theodolite.

≡ ½P

(18)

19 Setting up Camp

1971 (15 Feb). *Decimal Currency. As Nos.* 1/14, *but glazed paper, colours changed and surch as T* **18**.
24 ½p. on ½d. blue . . 60 2·75
25 1p. on 1d. pale brown . . 1·00 75
26 1½p. on 1½d. red and pale brown-purple . . 1·25 50
27 2p. on 2d. bright purple . . 1·25 30
28 2½p. on 2½d. green . . 2·25 1·25
29 3p. on 3d. blue . . 2·50 55
w. Wmk inverted . . 60·00
30 4p. on 4d. bistre-brown . . 2·25 55
31 5p. on 6d. olive and ultramarine . . 4·25 3·00
32 6p. on 9d. dull green . . 14·00 7·00
33 7½p. on 1s. turquoise-blue . . 15·00 7·50
34 10p. on 2s. violet and orange-sepia . . 18·00 13·00
w. Wmk inverted . . £550
35 15p. on 2s. 6d. pale blue . . 18·00 14·00
36 25p. on 5s. orange and pale rose-red . . 24·00 16·00
37 50p. on 10s. ultramarine and emerald . . 42·00 30·00
w. Wmk inverted . . £120
24/37 . . *Set of* 14 £130 85·00

(Des M. Goaman. Recess and litho Enschedé)

1971 (23 June). *10th Anniv of Antarctic Treaty. Vert designs each including Antarctic Map and Queen Elizabeth, as T* **19**. *Multicoloured. W w* **12** (*sideways*). *P* 14 × 13.
38 1½p. Type **19** . . 6·00 5·50
39 4p. Snow Petrels . . 16·00 8·00
40 5p. Weddell Seals . . 9·50 8·00
41 10p. Adelie Penguins . . 22·00 9·00
38/41 . . *Set of* 4 48·00 27·00

20 Kerguelen Fur Seals and Emperor Penguins

21 James Cook and H.M.S. *Resolution*

(Des (from photograph by D. Groves) and photo Harrison)

1972 (13 Dec*). *Royal Silver Wedding. Multicoloured; background colour given. W w* **12**. *P* 14 × 14½.
42 **20** 5p. red-brown . . 3·00 3·00
w. Wmk inverted . . 18·00
43 10p. brown-olive . . 3·00 3·00
w. Wmk inverted . . £160
*This is the local release date; they were issued by the Crown Agents on 20 November.

(Des J.W. Litho Questa)

1973 (14 Feb). *T* **21** *and similar vert designs. Multicoloured. W w* **12** (*sideways*). *P* 14 × 14½.
44 ½p. Type **21** (*shades*) . . 1·25 2·00
45 1p. Thaddeus von Bellingshausen and *Vostok* . . 2·50 3·25
46 1½p. James Weddell and *Jane* . . 11·00 4·50
47 2p. John Biscoe and *Tula* . . 2·00 1·75
48 2½p. J. S. C. Dumont d'Urville and *L'Astrolabe* . . 1·50 1·75
49 3p. James Clark Ross and H.M.S. *Erebus* . . 95 1·75
50 4p. C. A. Larsen and *Jason* . . 95 1·75
51 5p. Adrien de Gerlache and *Belgica* . . 1·00 1·75
52 6p. Otto Nordenskjöld and *Antarctic* . . 1·25 1·75
53 7½p. W. S. Bruce and *Scotia* . . 1·50 2·25
54 10p. Jean-Baptiste Charcot and *Pourquoi Pas?* . . 2·75 3·00
55 15p. Ernest Shackleton and *Endurance* . . 5·50 4·00
56 25p. Hubert Wilkins and Lockheed Vega *San Francisco* . . 2·75 4·00
57 50p. Lincoln Ellsworth and Northrop Gamma *Polar Star* . . 2·50 4·50
58 £1 John Rymill and *Penola* . . 3·00 8·00
44/58 . . *Set of* 15 35·00 42·00
The 25 and 50p. show aircraft; the rest show ships.
See also Nos. 64/78.

1973 (23 Dec*). *Royal Wedding. As Nos.* 165/6 *of Anguilla. Centre multicoloured. W w* **12** (*sideways*). *P* 13½.
59 5p. ochre . . 40 20
60 15p. light turquoise-blue . . 70 30
*This is the local date of issue: the Crown Agents released the stamps on 14 November.

22 Churchill and Churchill Peninsula, B.A.T.

(Des G. Vasarhelyi. Litho Format)

1974 (10 Dec*). *Birth Centenary of Sir Winston Churchill. T* **22** *and similar horiz design. Multicoloured. W w* **12** (*sideways on* 5p). *P* 14.
61 5p. Type **22** . . 1·75 1·75
62 15p. Churchill and *Trepassey* ("Operation Tabarin", 1943) . . 2·25 2·25
MS63 114 × 88 mm. Nos. 61/2. Wmk upright . . 13·00 10·00
*This is the local date of issue: the Crown Agents released the stamps on 30 November.

1975 (11 June)–**81**. *As Nos.* 44/58 *but W w* **14**. *Ordinary paper* (½, 2, 2½, 3, 5, 10, 15, 25, 50*p*.) *or chalk-surfaced paper* (1, 1½, 4, 6, 7½*p*., £1). *P* 12 (4, 6, 7½*p*.) *or* 14 × 14½ (*others*).
64 ½p. Type **21** . . 2·75 3·00
a. Chalk-surfaced paper (14.3.78) . . 75 2·25
65 1p. Thaddeus von Bellingshausen and *Vostok* (14.3.78) . . 60 2·00
a. Ordinary paper (11.12.79) . . 80 2·75
66 1½p. James Weddell and *Jane* (14.3.78) . . 60 1·50
a. Ordinary paper (11.12.79) . . 80 2·75
67 2p. John Biscoe and *Tula* (11.12.79) . . 1·50 2·25
68 2½p. J. S. C. Dumont d'Urville and *L'Astrolabe* (11.12.79) . . 1·50 2·25
69 3p. James Clark Ross and H.M.S. *Erebus* (11.12.79) . . 2·50 2·50
70 4p. C. A. Larsen and *Jason* (5.12.80) . . 55 2·75
71 5p. Adrien de Gerlache and *Belgica* (11.12.79) . . 2·75 3·25
72 6p. Otto Nordenskjöld and *Antarctic* (5.12.80) . . 80 2·75
73 7½p. W. S. Bruce and *Scotia* (5.12.80) . . 1·25 3·25
74 10p. Jean-Baptiste Charcot and *Pourquoi Pas?* (11.12.79) . . 1·75 3·00
a. Perf 12. Chalk-surfaced paper (25.11.81) 85 2·75
75 15p. Ernest Shackleton and *Endurance* (11.12.79) . . 1·25 1·50
a. Perf 12. Chalk-surfaced paper (25.11.81) 85 2·75
76 25p. Hubert Wilkins and Lockheed Vega *San Francisco* (11.12.79) . . 1·25 1·50
a. Perf 12. Chalk-surfaced paper (25.11.81) 85 3·00
77 50p. Lincoln Ellsworth and Northrop Gamma *Polar Star* (11.12.79) . . 1·25 2·75
aw. Wmk inverted . . 18·00
b. Perf 12. Chalk-surfaced paper (5.12.80) 85 2·75
78 £1 John Rymill and *Penola* (14.3.78) . . 3·25 2·00
a. Perf 12 (5.12.80) . . 1·50 4·00
aw. Wmk inverted . . £450
64a/78a . . *Set of* 15 16·00 32·00

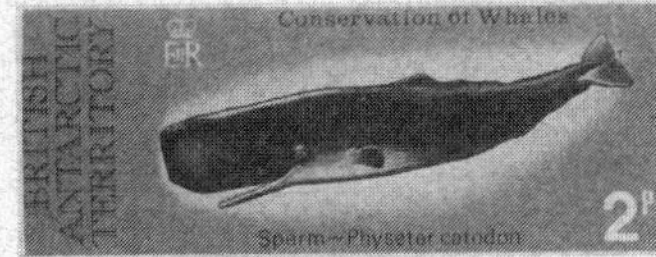

23 Sperm Whale

(Des J. Cooter. Litho Questa)

1977 (4 Jan). *Whale Conservation. T* **23** *and similar horiz designs. W w* **14** (*sideways*). *P* 13½.
79 2p. brownish black, slate and bright blue . . 6·00 3·50
80 8p. grey, brownish black and rosine . . 7·00 4·00
81 11p. multicoloured . . 7·50 4·00
82 25p. grey-blue, brownish blk & lt blue-green 8·50 5·00
79/82 . . *Set of* 4 26·00 15·00
Designs:—8p. Fin Whale; 11p. Humpback Whale; 25p. Blue Whale.

24 The Queen before Taking the Oath

25 Emperor Penguin

(Des J.W. Litho Questa)

1977 (7 Feb). *Silver Jubilee. T* **24** *and similar horiz designs. Multicoloured. W w* **14** (*sideways**). *P* 13½.
83 6p. Prince Philip's visit, 1956/7 . . 70 30
84 11p. Coronation Oath . . 80 40
w. Wmk Crown to right of CA . . 8·00 10·00
85 33p. Type **24** . . 1·25 50
w. Wmk Crown to right of CA . . £150
83/5 . . *Set of* 3 2·50 1·10
*The normal sideways watermark shows Crown to left of CA, *as seen from the back of the stamp.*

(Des C. Abbott. Litho Questa)

1978 (2 June). *25th Anniv of Coronation. T* **25** *and similar vert designs. P* 15.
86 25p. green, deep bluish green and silver . . 80 1·00
a. Sheetlet Nos. 86/8 × 2 . . 4·50
87 25p. multicoloured . . 80 1·00
88 25p. green, deep bluish green and silver . . 80 1·00
86/8 . . *Set of* 3 2·25 2·75
Designs:— No. 86. Black Bull of Clarence; No. 87, Queen Elizabeth II; No. 88, Type **25**.
Nos. 86/8 were printed together in small sheets of 6, containing two *se-tenant* strips of 3 with a horizontal gutter margin between.

26 Macaroni Penguins

(Des G. Drummond. Litho Walsall)

1979 (14 Jan). *Penguins. T* **26** *and similar horiz designs. Multicoloured. W w* **14** (*sideways**). *P* 13½.
89 3p. Type **26** . . 11·00 11·00
w. Wmk Crown to right of CA . . £325
90 8p. Gentoo penguins . . 3·00 3·00
91 11p. Adelie penguins . . 3·50 3·50
92 25p. Emperor penguins . . 4·50 4·50
89/92 . . *Set of* 4 20·00 20·00
*The normal sideways watermark shows Crown to left of CA, *as seen from the back of the stamp.*

27 Sir John Barrow and *Tula*

(Des A. Theobald. Litho Secura, Singapore)

1980 (14 Dec*). *150th Anniv of Royal Geographical Society. Former Presidents. T* **27** *and similar horiz designs. Multicoloured. W* w **14** *(sideways†). P* 13½.

93 3p. Type **27** 20 15
94 7p. Sir Clement Markham and *Discovery* 25 25
w. Wmk Crown to right of CA .. .. 5·50
95 11p. Lord Curzon and whaleboat *James Caird* 30 30
w. Wmk Crown to right of CA .. .. 4·00
96 15p. Sir William Goodenough 35 35
97 22p. Sir James Wordie 50 55
w. Wmk Crown to right of CA .. .. 75·00
98 30p. Sir Raymond Priestley 60 65
93/8 .. .. *Set of* 6 2·00 2·00

*This is the local date of issue; the Crown Agents released the stamps on 1 December.

†The normal sideways watermark shows Crown to left of CA, *as seen from the back of the stamp.*

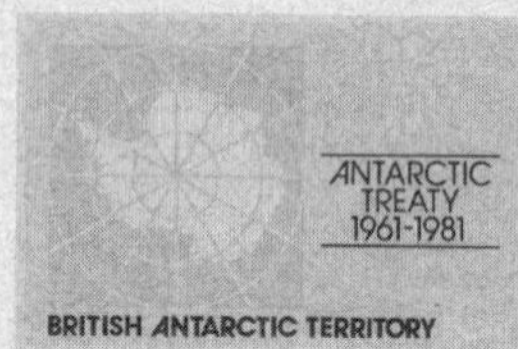

28 Map of Antarctic

(Des Walsall. Litho Questa)

1981 (1 Dec). *20th Anniv of Antarctic Treaty. T* **28** *and similar horiz designs. W* w **14** *(sideways*). P* 13½×14.

99 10p. black, new blue and azure 40 80
w. Wmk Crown to right of CA £190
100 13p. black, new blue and apple-green .. 45 90
101 25p. black, new blue and mauve .. .. 55 1·00
102 26p. black, brown-ochre and rose-red .. 55 1·00
99/102 .. .. *Set of* 4 1·75 3·25

Designs:—13p. Conservation research ("scientific co-operation"); 25p. Satellite image mapping ("technical co-operation"); 26p Global geophysics ("scientific co-operation").

*The normal sideways watermark shows Crown to left of CA, *as seen from the back of the stamp.*

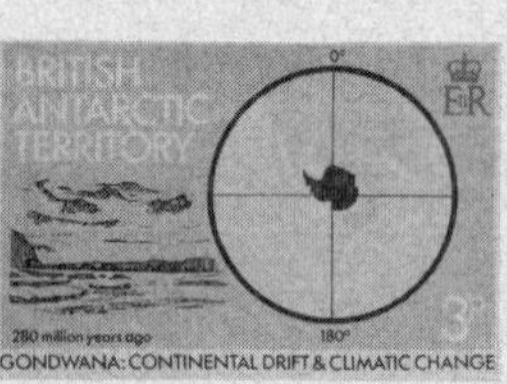

29 Map of Gondwana showing position of Continents 280 million years ago, and Contemporary Landscape Scene

30 British Antarctic Territory Coat of Arms

(Des C. Abbott. Litho Walsall)

1982 (8 Mar). *Gondwana—Continental Drift and Climatic Change. T* **29** *and similar horiz designs depicting maps of Gondwana showing position of continents, and contemporary landscape scenes. Multicoloured. W* w **14** *(sideways). P* 13½ × 14.

103 3p. Type **29** 25 40
104 6p. 260 million years ago 30 50
105 10p. 230 million years ago 35 60
106 13p. 175 million years ago 45 70
107 25p. 50 million years ago 55 75
108 26p. Present day 55 75
a. Gold (royal cypher) omitted .. ..
103/8 .. .. *Set of* 6 2·25 3·25

(Des Jennifer Toombs. Litho Questa)

1982 (1 July). *21st Birthday of Princess of Wales. T* **30** *and similar vert designs. Multicoloured. W* w **14**. *P* 14½ × 14.

109 5p. Type **30** 20 20
110 17p. Princess of Wales (detail of painting by Bryan Organ) 45 50
111 37p. Wedding ceremony 70 80
112 50p. Formal portrait .. .. 1·10 1·10
109/12 .. .. *Set of* 4 2·25 2·40

31 Leopard Seal

(Des R. Granger Barrett. Litho Walsall)

1983 (3 Jan). *10th Anniv (1982) of Antarctic Seal Conservation Convention. T* **31** *and similar horiz designs. Multicoloured. W* w **14** *(sideways). P* 11.

113 5p. Type **31** 45 35
114 10p. Weddell Seals 50 40
115 13p. Southern Elephant Seals 55 45
116 17p. Kerguelen Fur Seals 65 55
117 25p. Ross Seal.. .. .. 75 65
118 34p. Crabeater Seals 95 85
113/18 .. .. *Set of* 6 3·50 3·00

32 De Havilland D.H.C.6 Twin Otter 200/300

(Des Harrison. Litho Questa)

1983 (20 Dec). *Bicentenary of Manned Flight. T* **32** *and similar horiz designs. Multicoloured. W* w **14** *(sideways). P* 14.

119 5p. Type **32** 25 30
120 13p. De Havilland D.H.C.3 Otter 40 45
121 17p. Consolidated PBY-5A Canso 55 60
122 50p. Lockheed Vega *San Francisco* .. 1·10 1·25
119/22 .. .. *Set of* 4 2·10 2·40

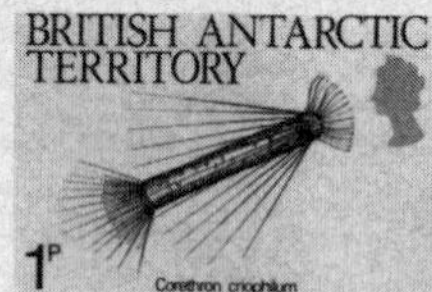

33 *Corethron criophilum*

(Des I. Loe. Litho Walsall)

1984 (15 Mar). *Marine Life. T* **33** *and similar horiz designs. Multicoloured. W* w **14** *(sideways*). P* 14.

123 1p. Type **33** .. .. 60 1·40
124 2p. *Desmonema gaudichaudi* .. .. 65 1·40
125 3p. *Tomopteris carpenteri* .. .. 65 1·40
126 4p. *Pareuchaeta antarctica* .. .. 70 1·50
127 5p. *Antarctomysis maxima* .. .. 70 1·50
128 6p. *Antarcturus signiensis* .. .. 70 1·50
129 7p. *Serolis cornuta* .. .. .. 70 1·50
130 8p. *Parathemisto gaudichaudii* .. .. 70 1·50
131 9p. *Bovallia gigantea* .. .. .. 70 1·50
132 10p. *Euphausia superba* .. .. .. 70 1·50
133 15p. *Colossendeis australis* .. .. 70 1·75
134 20p. *Todarodes sagittatus* .. .. .. 75 1·75
w. Wmk Crown to right of CA .. 75·00
135 25p. Antarctic Rockcod ("*Notothenia neglecta*") .. .. 80 1·75
136 50p. Black-finned Icefish ("*Chaenocephalus aceratus*") .. .. 1·25 2·00
137 £1 Crabeater Seal .. .. 1·75 2·50
138 £3 Antarctic marine food chain .. .. 5·00 6·50
123/38 .. .. *Set of* 16 15·00 28·00

*The normal sideways watermark shows Crown to left of CA on 1, 3, 4, 6, 7, 8, 9, 10, 20p. and to right on 2, 5, 15, 25, 50p., £1, £3, *all as seen from the back of the stamp.*

34 M.Y. *Penola* in Stella Creek

35 Robert McCormick and McCormick's Skua

(Des A. Theobald. Litho Questa)

1985 (23 Mar). *50th Anniv of British Graham Land Expedition. T* **34** *and similar horiz designs. Multicoloured. W* w **14** *(sideways). P* 14½.

139 7p. Type **34** 40 75
140 22p. Northern Base, Winter Island .. 70 1·40
141 27p. De Havilland D.H.83 Fox Moth at Southern Base, Barry Island .. 80 1·60
142 54p. Dog team near Ablation Point, George VI Sound .. .. 1·50 2·25
139/42 .. .. *Set of* 4 3·00 5·50

(Des I. Strange. Litho Questa)

1985 (4 Nov). *Early Naturalists. T* **35** *and similar vert designs. Multicoloured. W* w **14**. *P* 14½×14.

143 7p. Type **35** .. .. 1·25 1·50
144 22p. Sir Joseph Dalton Hooker and *Deschampsia antarctica* .. .. 1·75 2·75
145 27p. Jean René C. Quoy and Hourglass Dolphin .. .. 1·90 2·75
146 54p. James Weddell and Weddell Seal .. 2·75 4·00
143/6 .. .. *Set of* 4 7·00 10·00

NEW INFORMATION

The editor is always interested to correspond with people who have new information that will improve or correct the Catalogue.

36 Dr. Edmond Halley

37 Snow Crystal

(Des A. Theobald. Litho Questa)

1986 (6 Jan). *Appearance of Halley's Comet. T* **36** *and simila vert designs. Multicoloured. W* w **14**. *P* 14.

147 7p. Type **36** .. .. 1·00 1·2
148 22p. Halley Station, Antarctica .. .. 1·75 2·2
149 27p. "Halley's Comet, 1531" (from Peter Apian woodcut, 1532) .. .. .. 2·00 2·5
150 54p. *Giotto* spacecraft .. .. .. 3·50 4·5
147/50 .. .. *Set of* 4 7·50 9·5

(Des C. Abbott. Litho Questa)

1986 (6 Dec). *50th Anniv of International Glaciological Societ T* **37** *and similar vert designs showing snow crystals. W* w **1** *P* 14½.

151 10p. cobalt and deep ultramarine 60
152 24p. pale turquoise-green & dp bluish green 90 1·
153 29p. mauve and deep mauve.. .. .. 1·00 1·
154 58p. violet-blue and bright violet .. .. 1·40 2·
151/4 .. .. *Set of* 4 3·50 5·

38 Captain Scott, 1904

39 I.G.Y. Logo

(Des A. Theobald. Litho Questa)

1987 (19 Mar). *75th Anniv of Captain Scott's Arrival at Sou Pole. T* **38** *and similar horiz designs. Multicoloured. W* w **1** *(sideways). P* 14×14½.

155 10p. Type **38** 85
156 24p. Hut Point and *Discovery*, Ross Island, 1902–4 .. .. 1·40 2·
157 29p. Cape Evans Hut, 1911–13 .. .. 1·75 2·
158 58p. Scott's Expedition at South Pole, 1912.. 2·25 3·
155/8 .. .. *Set of* 4 5·50 7·

(Des L. Curtis. Litho Questa)

1987 (25 Dec). *30th Anniv of International Geophysical Yea T* **39** *and similar vert designs. W* w **16**. *P* 14½×14.

159 10p. black and pale green 30 7
160 24p. multicoloured .. .. 60 1·4
161 29p. multicoloured .. .. 75 1·7
162 58p. multicoloured .. .. 1·40 2·5
159/62 .. .. *Set of* 4 2·75 5·7

Designs:—24p. Port Lockroy; 29p. Argentine Islands; 58p Halley Bay.

40 Aurora over South Ice Plateau Station

41 *Xanthoria elegans*

(Des D. Hartley. Litho Questa)

1988 (19 Mar). *30th Anniv of Commonwealth Trans-Antarcti Expedition. T* **40** *and similar vert designs. Multicoloured W* w **16**. *P* 14.

163 10p. Type **40** 30 5
164 24p. "Otter" aircraft at Theron Mountains .. 60 9
165 29p. Seismic ice-depth sounding .. .. 70 1·1
166 58p. "Sno-cat" over crevasse.. .. .. 1·25 1·7
163/6 .. .. *Set of* 4 2·50 3·7

(Des I. Loe. Litho Walsall)

1989 (25 Mar). *Lichens. T* **41** *and similar horiz designs Multicoloured. W* w **14** *(sideways). P* 14.

167 10p Type **41** 90 90
168 24p *Usnea aurantiaco-atra* .. .. 1·60 1·60
169 29p *Cladonia chlorophaea* .. .. 1·75 1·75
170 58p *Umbilicaria antarctica* .. .. 2·50 3·00
167/70 .. .. *Set of* 4 6·00 6·50

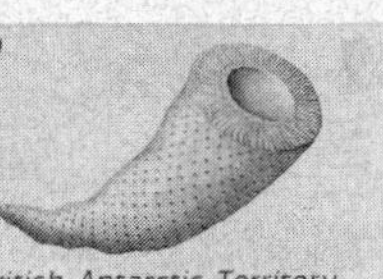

42 *Monocyathus* (archaeocyath)

43 Late Cretaceous Forest and Southern Beech Fossil

(Des I. Loe. Litho Questa)

) (2 Apr). *Fossils. T* **42** *and similar horiz designs.* *ulticoloured.* W w **16** (*sideways*). P 14.

1p. Type **42** 50 80
2p. *Lingulella* (brachiopod) 50 80
3p. *Triplagnoslus* (trilobite) 60 80
4p. *Lyriaspis* (trilobite) 60 80
5p. *Glossopteris* leaf (gymnosperm) .. 60 80
6p. *Gonatosorus* (fern) 70 90
7p. *Belemnopsis aucklandica* (belemnite) 70 90
8p. *Sanmartinoceras africanum insignicostatum* (ammonite) 70 90
9p. *Pinna antarctica* (mussel) 80 90
10p. *Aucellina andina* (mussel) 80 90
20p. *Pterotrigonia malagninoi* (mussel) .. 1·25 1·60
25p. *Anchura* sp. (conch shell) .. .. 1·25 1·60
50p. *Ainoceras zinsmeisteri* (ammonite) .. 1·75 2·75
£1 *Gunnarites antarcticus* (ammonite) .. 3·50 4·25
£3 *Hoploparia* (crayfish) .. .. .. 7·00 8·00
85 .. .. *Set of* 15 19·00 24·00

(Des D. Miller. Litho Questa)

0 (25 Dec*). *90th Birthday of Queen Elizabeth the Queen* *Iother. Vert designs as T* **134** *(26p.) or* **135** *(£1) of Ascension.* *V* w **16**. *P* 14×15 (26p.) or $14^1/_2$ (£1).

26p. multicoloured .. .. 1·75 2·25
£1 brownish black and olive-bistre .. 3·75 4·25

Designs:—26p. Wedding of Prince Albert and Lady Elizabeth ·wes-Lyon, 1923; £1 The Royal Family, 1940.

*This is the local date of issue, the Crown Agents released the ·mps on 4 August.

(Des N. Shewring. Litho Questa)

1 (27 Mar). *Age of the Dinosaurs. T* **43** *and similar horiz* *esigns. Multicoloured.* W w **14** (*sideways*). P 14×$13^1/_2$.

12p. Type **43** .. .. 1·25 1·25
26p. Hypsilophodont dinosaurs and skull .. 2·00 2·00
31p. Frilled Sharks and tooth .. .. 2·25 2·25
62p. Mosasaur, Plesiosaur, and Mosasaur vertebra .. .. 3·50 3·50
/91 .. .. *Set of* 4 8·00 8·00

44 Launching Meteorological Balloon, Halley IV Station

45 Researching Dry Valley

(Des O. Bell. Litho Questa)

1 (30 Mar). *Discovery of Antarctic Ozone Hole. T* **44** *and* *imilar horiz designs. Multicoloured.* W w **16** (*sideways*). 14×$13^1/_2$.

12p. Type **44** 90 90
26p. Measuring ozone with Dobson spectrophotometer .. .. 1·60 1·60
31p. Satellite map showing ozone hole .. 1·75 1·75
62p. Lockheed ER-2 aircraft and graph of chlorine monoxide and ozone levels 3·00 3·00
2/5 .. .. *Set of* 4 6·50 6·50

(Des O. Bell. Litho Questa)

91 (2 Dec*). *30th Anniv of Antarctic Treaty. T* **45** *and* *similar vert designs.* W w **14**. *P* $13^1/_2$×14 (31p.) *or* $14^1/_2$×14 (*others*).

6 12p. multicoloured 90 90
7 26p. multicoloured .. .. .. 1·60 1·60
3 31p. black and blue-green .. .. 1·75 1·75
9 62p. multicoloured .. .. .. 3·00 3·00
6/9 .. .. *Set of* 4 6·50 6·50

Designs:—26p. Relief map of ice sheet; 31p. BIOMASS logo; p. Ross Seal.

*This is the local date of issue, the Crown Agents released the ·mps on 24 June.

46 "H.M.S. *Erebus* and H.M.S. *Terror* in the Antarctic" (J. Carmichael)

(Des R. Watton. Litho Walsall)

1991 (10 Dec). *Maiden Voyage of* James Clark Ross *(research ship). T* **46** *and similar horiz designs. Multicoloured.* W w **14** (*sideways*). *P* $14^1/_2$.

200 12p. Type **46** 90 90
201 26p. Launch of *James Clark Ross* .. 1·60 1·60
202 31p. *James Clark Ross* in Antarctica .. 1·75 1·75
203 62p. Scientific research .. .. .. 3·00 3·00
200/3 .. .. *Set of* 4 6·50 6·50

1991 (24 Dec). *Birth Bicentenary of Michael Faraday (scientist). Nos.* 200/3 *additionally inscr* "200th Anniversary M. Faraday 1791–1867" *in blue.*

204 12p. Type **46** 90 90
205 26p. Launch of *James Clark Ross* .. 1·60 1·60
206 31p. *James Clark Ross* in Antarctica .. 1·75 1·75
207 62p. Scientific research .. .. .. 3·00 3·00
204/7 .. .. *Set of* 4 6·50 6·50

47 Ross Seals

(Des A. Robinson. Litho B.D.T.)

1992 (10 Dec*). *Endangered Species. Seals and Penguins. T* **47** *and similar horiz designs. Multicoloured.* W w **14** (*sideways*). *P* $13^1/_2$.

208 4p. Type **47** 60 60
209 5p. Adelie Penguins 60 60
210 7p. Weddell Seal with pup 65 65
211 29p. Emperor Penguins with chicks .. 1·75 1·75
212 34p. Crabeater Seals with pup .. .. 1·75 1·75
213 68p. Chinstrap Penguins with young .. 2·25 2·25
208/13 .. .. *Set of* 6 7·00 7·00

*This is the local date of issue, the Crown Agents released the stamps in London, and at the "Genova 92" International Thematic Stamp Exhibition, on 20 October.

Nos. 212/13 do not carry the W.W.F. Panda emblem.

48 Sun Pillar at Faraday

49 *Fitzroy* (mail and supply ship)

(Des N. Shewring. Litho Questa)

1992 (22 Dec). *Lower Atmospheric Phenomena. T* **48** *and similar horiz designs. Multicoloured.* W w **14** (*sideways*). *P* $14^1/_2$.

214 14p. Type **48** 80 70
215 29p. Halo over iceberg .. .. .. 1·40 1·00
216 34p. Lee Wave Cloud .. .. .. 1·75 1·25
217 68p. Nacreous Clouds .. .. .. 2·75 2·00
214/17 .. .. *Set of* 4 6·00 4·50

(Des R. Watton. Litho Walsall)

1993 (13 Dec). *Antarctic Ships. T* **49** *and simlar horiz designs. Multicoloured.* W w **14** (*sideways*). *P* 14.

218 1p. Type **49** 10 10
219 2p. *William Scoresby* (research ship) .. 10 10
220 3p. *Eagle* (sealer) 10 10
221 4p. *Trepassey* (supply ship) 10 10
222 5p. *John Biscoe I* (research ship) .. 10 10
223 10p. *Norsel* (supply ship) 20 25
224 20p. H.M.S. *Protector* (ice patrol ship) .. 40 45
225 30p. *Oluf Sven* (supply ship) 60 65
226 50p. *John Biscoe II* and *Shackleton* (research ships) .. .. .. 1·00 1·10
227 £1 *Tottan* (supply ship) .. .. .. 2·00 2·10
228 £3 *Perla Dan* (supply ship) .. .. 6·00 6·25
229 £5 H.M.S. *Endurance I* (ice patrol ship) 10·00 10·50
218/29 .. .. *Set of* 12 20·00 21·00

For miniature sheets containing the 50p or £1 ("1997" imprint date) see Nos. **MS**274/5.

1994 (19 Mar*). *"Hong Kong '94" International Stamp Exhibition. Nos.* 240/5 *optd as T* **154** *of Ascension.*

230 15p. Type **51** 85 90
231 24p. De Havilland D.H.C.2 Turbo Beaver III aircraft .. .. 1·25 1·50
232 31p. De Havilland D.H.C.3 Otter aircraft and dog team .. .. .. 1·50 1·60
233 36p. De Havilland D.H.C.6 Twin Otter 200/300 aircraft and dog team .. 1·60 1·75
234 62p. De Havilland D.H.C.7 Dash Seven aircraft over landing strip, Rothera Point .. .. 2·25 2·75
235 72p. De Havilland D.H.C.7 Dash Seven aircraft on runway .. .. .. 2·25 2·75
230/5 .. .. *Set of* 6 8·75 10·00

*This is the local release date, the Crown Agents released the stamps in London and at the Exhibition on 18 February.

COVER PRICES

Cover factors are quoted at the beginning of each country for most issues to 1945. An explanation of the system can be found on page x. The factors quoted do not, however, apply to philatelic covers.

50 Bransfield House Post Office, Port Lockroy

(Des R. Watton. Litho Walsall)

1994 (19 Mar). *50th Anniv of Operation Tabarin. T* **50** *and similar horiz designs. Multicoloured.* W w **16** (*sideways*). *P* 14×$14^1/_2$.

236 15p. Type **50** 65 65
237 31p. Survey team, Hope Bay .. .. 1·10 1·10
238 36p. Dog team, Hope Bay .. .. .. 1·40 1·40
239 72p. *Fitzroy* (supply ship) and H.M.S. *William Scoresby* (minesweeper) .. 2·25 2·50
236/9 .. .. *Set of* 4 4·75 5·00

51 Huskies and Sledge

(Des D. Miller. Litho Walsall)

1994 (21 Mar). *Forms of Transportation. T* **51** *and similar horiz designs. Multicoloured.* W w **14** (*sideways*). *P* $14^1/_2$.

240 15p. Type **51** 60 70
241 24p. De Havilland D.H.C.2 Turbo Beaver III aircraft 80 90
242 31p. De Havilland D.H.C.3 Otter aircraft and dog team .. .. .. 90 1·00
243 36p. De Havilland D.H.C.6 Twin Otter 200/300 aircraft and dog team .. 1·00 1·25
244 62p. De Havilland D.H.C.7 Dash Seven aircraft over landing strip, Rothera Point .. .. 1·90 2·50
245 72p. De Havilland D.H.C.7 Dash Seven aircraft on runway .. .. .. 2·00 2·75
240/5 .. .. *Set of* 6 6·50 8·00

52 Capt. James Cook and H.M.S. *Resolution*

(Des R. Watton. Litho Questa)

1994 (23 Nov). *Antarctic Heritage Fund. T* **52** *and similar horiz designs. Multicoloured.* W w **16** (*sideways*). *P* $14^1/_2$×14.

246 17p. + 3p. Type **52** .. .. .. 1·50 1·40
247 35p. + 15p. Sir James Clark Ross with H.M.S. *Erebus* and H.M.S. *Terror* 1·75 1·60
248 40p. + 10p. Capt. Robert Falcon Scott and interior of hut .. .. .. 1·75 1·60
249 76p. + 4p. Sir Ernest Shackleton and H.M.S. *Endurance* .. .. .. 2·50 2·25
246/9 .. .. *Set of* 4 6·75 6·25

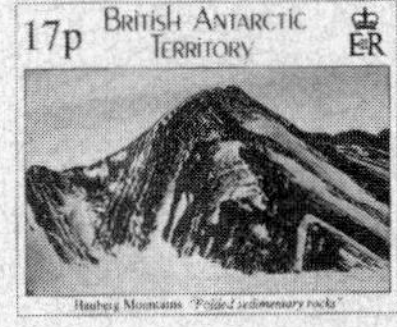

53 Pair of Crabeater Seals

54 Hauberg Mountains

(Des A. Robinson. Litho Questa)

1994 (29 Nov). *Antarctic Food Chain. T* **53** *and similar horiz designs. Multicoloured.* W w **14**. *P* 14×$14^1/_2$.

250 35p. Type **53** .. .. 95 1·25
a. Sheetlet. Nos. 250/5 .. .. .. 5·25
251 35p. Blue Whale .. .. 95 1·25
252 35p. Wandering Albatross .. .. .. 95 1·25
253 35p. Mackerel Icefish .. .. .. 95 1·25
254 35p. Krill .. .. 95 1·25
255 35p. Seven Star Flying Squid (*Martialia hyadesi*) .. .. 95 1·25
250/5 .. .. *Set of* 6 5·25 6·50

Nos. 250/5 were printed together, *se-tenant*, in sheetlets of 6.

(Des N. Shewring. Litho Walsall)

1995 (28 Nov). *Geological Structures. T* **54** *and similar horiz designs. Multicoloured.* W w **14** (*sideways*). *P* 14×$14^1/_2$.

256 17p. Type **54** 65 60
257 35p. Arrowsmith Peninsula .. .. 1·25 1·10
258 40p. Colbert Mountains .. .. .. 1·50 1·40
259 76p. Succession Cliffs .. .. .. 2·25 2·25
256/9 .. .. *Set of* 4 5·00 4·75

55 World Map showing Member Countries

(Des R. Watton. Litho Walsall)

1996 (23 Mar). *24th Meeting of Scientific Committee on Antarctic Research, Cambridge. T* **55** *and similar horiz designs. Multicoloured. W w* **16** *(sideways). P* 14.

260	17p. Type **55**	65	60
261	35p. Scientist analysing ice samples ..	1·25	1·10
262	40p. Releasing balloon	1·50	1·40
263	76p. Antarctic research ship catching marine life	2·25	2·00
260/3	.. .. .. *Set of* 4	5·00	4·50
MS264	100×90 mm. £1 S.C.A.R. logo. Wmk inverted	3·50	3·00

56 Killer Whales

57 Chinstrap Penguins sledging

(Des Dafila Scott. Litho Questa)

1996 (25 Nov). *Whales. T* **56** *and similar horiz designs. Multicoloured. W w* **14** *(sideways). P* 14.

265	17p. Type **56**	70	60
266	35p. Sperm Whales	1·25	1·10
267	40p. Minke Whales	1·50	1·40
268	76p. Blue Whale and calf	2·25	2·00
265/8	.. .. .. *Set of* 4	5·00	4·50
MS269	105×82 mm. £1 Humpback Whale ..	2·50	2·75

(Des D. Miller. Litho Walsall)

1996 (25 Nov). *70th Birthday of Queen Elizabeth II. Vert designs as T* **165** *of Ascension, each incorporating a different photograph of the Queen. Multicoloured. W w* **16**. *P* 14½.

270	17p. At premiere of *Chaplin*, Leicester Square, 1992	50	60
271	35p. At Buckingham Palace dinner, 1991	95	1·10
272	40p. In Aberdeen, 1993	1·25	1·40
273	76p. At Royal Military School of Music, 1990	1·75	2·00
270/3	.. .. .. *Set of* 4	4·00	4·50

(Des D. Miller. Litho Questa)

1997 (3 Feb). *"HONG KONG '97" International Stamp Exhibition. Sheet* 130×90 *mm, containing design as No.* 226. *Multicoloured. W w* **14**. *P* 14.

MS274	50p. *John Biscoe II* and *Shackleton* (research ships)	1·40	1·40

(Des R. Watton. Litho Walsall)

1997 (20 June). *Return of Hong Kong to China. Sheet* 130×90 *mm containing design as No.* 227, *but with* "1997" *imprint date.*

MS275	£1 *Tottan*	2·75	3·00

(Des R. Watton. Litho Questa)

1997 (22 Dec). *Christmas. T* **57** *and similar vert designs. Multicoloured. W w* **16**. *P* 14½×14.

276	17p. Type **57**	60	65
277	35p. Emperor Penguins carol singing ..	1·10	1·25
278	40p. Adelié Penguins throwing snowballs	1·40	1·50
279	76p. Gentoo Penguins ice-skating ..	2·00	2·25
276/9	.. .. .. *Set of* 4	4·50	5·00

(Des D. Miller. Litho Questa)

1998 (17 Mar). *Diana, Princess of Wales Commemoration. Sheet,* 145×70 *mm, containing vert designs as T* **177** *of Ascension. Multicoloured. W w* **14** *(sideways). P* 14½×14.

MS280	35p. Wearing sunglasses; 35p. Wearing round-necked white blouse, 1993; 35p. Wearing white blouse and jacket, 1990; 35p. Wearing green jacket, 1992 (*sold at* £1.40 + 20p. *charity premium*)	3·75	3·75

58 Chart of South Shetland Islands (Swedish South Polar Expedition, 1902–03)

59 Antarctic Explorer, 1843

(Des N. Shewring. Litho Walsall)

1998 (19 Mar). *History of Mapping in Antarctica. T* **58** *and similar vert designs. Multicoloured. W w* **14**. *P* 14.

281	16p. Type **58**	55	65
282	30p. Map of Antarctic Peninsula (1949) ..	80	90
283	35p. Map of Antarctic Peninsula (1964) ..	1·00	1·10
284	40p. Map of Antarctic Peninsula from Landsat (1981)	1·10	1·25
285	65p. Map of Antarctic Peninsula from satellite (1995)	1·50	1·75
281/5	.. .. .. *Set of* 5	4·50	5·00

(Des V. Ambrus. Litho Walsall)

1998 (27 Nov). *Antarctic Clothing. T* **59** *and similar vert designs. Multicoloured. W w* **14**. *P* 14½×14.

286	30p. Type **59**	60	65
287	35p. Explorer with dog, 1900	70	75
288	40p. Surveyor, 1943	80	85
289	65p. Scientist with penguins, 1998 ..	1·25	1·40
286/9	.. .. .. *Set of* 4	3·25	3·50

60 Snowy Sheathbill

(Des A. Robinson. Litho Walsall)

1998 (30 Nov). *Antarctic Birds. T* **60** *and similar horiz designs. Multicoloured. W w* **14** *(sideways). P* 14.

290	1p. Type **60**	10	10
291	2p. Dove Prion ("Antarctic Prion") ..	10	10
292	5p. Adelié Penguin	10	10
293	10p. Emperor Penguin	20	25
294	20p. Swallow-tailed Tern ("Antarctic Tern")	40	45
295	30p. Black-bellied Storm Petrel	60	65
296	35p. Antarctic Fulmar	70	75
297	40p. Blue-eyed Shag	80	85
298	50p. McCormick's Skua	1·00	1·10
299	£1 Southern Black-backed Gull ("Kelp Gull")	2·00	2·10
300	£3 Wilson's Storm Petrel	6·00	6·25
301	£5 Brown Skua	10·00	10·50
290/301	.. .. .. *Set of* 12	21·00	22·00

British Central Africa *see* Nyasaland Protectorate

see Nyasaland Protectorate

British Columbia and Vancouver Island *see* Canada

British East Africa *see* Kenya, Uganda and Tanganyika

British Forces in Egypt *see* Egypt

British Guiana *see* Guyana

British Honduras *see* Belize

British Indian Ocean Territory

This Crown Colony was created on 8 November 1965 when it omprised the Chagos Archipelago, previously administered by lauritius, together with the islands of Aldabra, Farquhar and esroches, previously administered by Seychelles.

(Currency. 100 cents=1 rupee)

B.I.O.T.

(1)

968 (17 Jan). *As Nos.* 196/200, 202/4 *and* 206/12 *of Seychelles, optd with T* **1**. *W* w **12** (*sideways* on* 5, 10, 15, 20, 25, 50, 75 *c. and* 10 *r.*).

1	5 c. multicoloured	75	40
	a. No stop after "I"	7·00	10·00
	b. No stop after "O"	4·75	8·00
	w. Wmk Crown to right of CA	26·00	
2	10 c. multicoloured	10	15
	a. No stop after "I"	8·00	11·00
	b. No stop after "O"	5·50	8·50
3	15 c. multicoloured	10	15
	a. No stop after "I"	8·00	11·00
	b. No stop after "O"	5·50	8·50
4	20 c. multicoloured	15	15
	a. No stop after "I"	8·00	11·00
	b. No stop after "O"	5·50	8·50
5	25 c. multicoloured	15	15
	a. No stop after "I"	8·50	12·00
	b. No stop after "O"	5·50	9·00
6	40 c. multicoloured	20	20
	a. No stop after "I"	12·00	16·00
	b. No stop after "O"	7·50	10·00
7	45 c. multicoloured	20	30
	a. No stop after "I"	12·00	16·00
	b. No stop after "B"	12·00	16·00
	c. No stop after "O"	12·00	16·00
8	50 c. multicoloured	20	30
	a. No stop after "I"	12·00	16·00
	b. No stop after "O"	7·00	9·50
9	75 c. multicoloured	20	35
10	1 r. multicoloured	40	35
	a. No stop after "I"	12·00	16·00
	b. No stop after "O"	7·00	9·50
11	1 r. 50, multicoloured	1·75	1·50
	a. No stop after "I"	24·00	27·00
	b. No stop after "O"	13·00	17·00
12	2 r. 25, multicoloured	3·00	3·75
	a. No stop after "I"	60·00	65·00
	b. No stop after "O"	28·00	35·00
13	3 r. 50, multicoloured	3·00	4·50
	a. No stop after "I"	60·00	65·00
	b. No stop after "O"	28·00	35·00
14	5 r. multicoloured	6·50	7·50
	a. No stop after "I"	80·00	85·00
	b. No stop after "O"	40·00	45·00
15	10 r. multicoloured	17·00	20·00
	a. No stop after "B"	£110	£120
	b. No stop after "I"	£110	£120
	c. No stop after "O"	70·00	80·00
1/15	*Set of* 15	30·00	35·00

*The normal sideways watermark shows Crown to left of CA, *as seen from the back of the stamp.*

These were issued by the Crown Agents on 15 January but owing to shipping delays they were not put on sale locally until 17 January.

The positions of the "no stop" varieties are as follows:

After "I": R. 2/4 on horiz stamps except 45 c. where it occurs on R. 3/3, and R. 8/5 on vert stamps except 10 r. where it occurs on R. 4/3.

After "O": R. 3/2 and 5/1 on vert stamps, R. 2/1 and 4/4 on horiz stamps (only occurs on R. 2/1 for 45 c.), and R. 2/7 and 5/9 on 10 r. value.

After "B": R. 10/4 (45 c.) or R. 1/8 (10 r.).

As sheets of all values from 5 c. to 50 c. are known with all stops in place the no stop varieties either developed during printing or their omission was discovered and replacements inserted.

2 Lascar

(Des G. Drummond, based on drawings by Mrs. W. Veevers-Carter. Litho D.L.R.)

1968 (23 Oct)–**70**. *Marine Life. Multicoloured designs as T* **2**. *White paper (Nos.* 20*a*, 23*a*, 24*a*) *or cream paper (others). W* w **12** (*sideways on horiz, inverted on vert designs*). *P* 14.

16	5 c. Type **2**	30	1·50
17	10 c. Smooth Hammerhead (*vert*)	30	1·25
18	15 c. Tiger Shark	30	1·50
19	20 c. Spotted Eagle Ray ("Bat Ray")	30	1·00
20	25 c. Yellow-finned Butterflyfish and Ear-spotted Angelfish (*vert*)	80	1·00
20*a*	30 c. Robber Crab (7.12.70)	3·50	2·75
21	40 c. Blue-finned Trevally ("Caranx")	40	40
22	45 c. Crocodile Needlefish ("Garfish") (*vert*)	2·25	2·50
23	50 c. Pickhandle Barracuda	45	30
23*a*	60 c. Spotted Pebble Crab (7.12.70)	3·50	3·25
24	75 c. Indian Ocean Steep-headed Parrotfish	2·50	2·75
24*a*	85 c. Rainbow Runner ("Dorade") (7.12.70)	6·00	3·50
25	1 r. Giant Hermit Crab	1·50	35
26	1 r. 50, Parrotfish ("Humphead")	2·50	2·50
27	2 r. 25, Yellow-edged Lyretail and Areolate Grouper ("Rock Cod")	8·00	8·50
28	3 r. 50, Black Marlin	4·00	3·75
29	5 r. black, blue-green and greenish blue (Whale Shark) (*vert*)	9·00	8·00
30	10 r. Lionfish	9·00	8·00
	a. Imperf (pair)	£550	
16/30	*Set of* 18	48·00	48·00

See also No. 52.

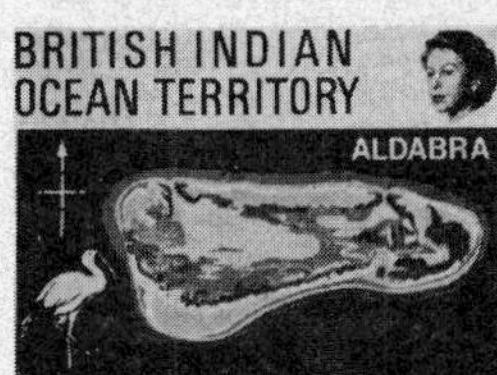

3 Sacred Ibis and Aldabra Coral Atoll

(Des and litho D.L.R.)

1969 (10 July). *Coral Atolls. W* w **12** (*sideways*). *P* 13½ × 13.

31	**3**	2 r. 25, multicoloured	1·75	70

4 Outrigger Canoe

(Des Mrs. M. Hayward adapted by V. Whiteley. Litho D.L.R.)

1969 (15 Dec.) *Ships of the Islands. T* **4** *and similar horiz designs. Multicoloured. W* w **12** (*sideways*). *P* 13½ × 14.

32	45 c. Type **4**	65	75
33	75 c. Pirogue	65	80
34	1 r. M. V. *Nordvaer*	70	90
35	1 r. 50, *Isle of Farquhar*	80	1·00
32/5	*Set of* 4	2·50	3·00

5 Giant Land Tortoise

(Des G. Drummond. Litho Format)

1971 (1 Feb). *Aldabra Nature Reserve. T* **5** *and similar horiz designs. Multicoloured. W* w **12** (*sideways*). *P* 13½.

36	45 c. Type **5**	2·50	2·25
37	75 c. Aldabra Lily	3·00	2·50
38	1 r. Aldabra Tree Snail (*Rhachis aldabrae*)	3·50	2·75
39	1 r. 50, Western Reef Herons	12·00	9·00
36/9	*Set of* 4	19·00	15·00

6 Arms of Royal Society and White-throated Rail

(Des V. Whiteley. Litho J.W.)

1971 (30 June). *Opening of Royal Society Research Station on Aldabra. W* w **12** (*sideways*). *P* 13½.

40	**6**	3 r. 50, multicoloured	15·00	8·50

7 Staghorn Coral

(Des V. Whiteley. Litho A. & M.)

1972 (1 Mar). *Coral. T* **7** *and similar horiz designs. Multicoloured. W* w **12** (*sideways**). *P* 13½.

41	40 c. Type **7**	3·50	3·50
	w. Wmk Crown to left of CA	14·00	
42	60 c. Brain coral	4·00	4·00
	w. Wmk Crown to left of CA	9·00	
43	1 r. Mushroom coral	4·00	4·00
	w. Wmk Crown to left of CA	5·00	
44	1 r. 75, Organ Pipe coral	5·00	6·00
	w. Wmk Crown to left of CA	12·00	
41/4	*Set of* 4	15·00	16·00

*The normal sideways watermark shows Crown to right of CA, *as seen from the back of the stamp.*

On some sheets of No. 43 the inks have been applied in a different order, resulting in an almost total absence of blue.

8 White-throated Rail and Sacred Ibis

9 "Christ on the Cross"

(Des (from photograph by D. Groves) and photo Harrison)

1972 (20 Nov). *Royal Silver Wedding. Multicoloured; background colour given. W* w **12.** *P* 14 × 14½.

45	**8**	95 c. deep dull green	75	40
		a. Silver (frame and inscr) ptd double	£450	
		b. Slate-green	2·00	2·00
46		1 r. 50, bright bluish violet	75	40

(Des Jennifer Toombs. Litho Questa)

1973 (9 Apr). *Easter. T* **9** *and similar vert design showing illustrations from 17th-century Ethiopian manuscript. Multicoloured. W* w **12** (*sideways*). *P* 14.

47	45 c. Type **9**	25	40
48	75 c. Joseph and Nicodemus burying Jesus	35	55
49	1 r. Type **9**	35	60
50	1 r. 50. As 75 c.	40	70
47/50	*Set of* 4	1·25	2·00
MS51	126 × 110 mm. Nos. 47/50	1·50	4·00

1973 (2 Oct). *As No.* 16 *but white paper and wmk upright.*
52 5 c. Type **2** .. .. 1·00 4·00
No. 52 differs in shade from No. 16 because of the change of paper.

10 Upsidedown Jellyfish **11** M.V. *Nordvaer*

(Des G. Drummond. Litho Walsall)

1973 (12 Nov). *Wildlife* (1*st series*). *T* **10** *and similar vert designs. Multicoloured. W* w **12** (*sideways**). *P* 14.
53 50 c. Type **10** .. .. 3·50 3·00
54 1 r. *Hypolimnas misippus* and *Belenois aldabrensis* (butterflies) .. .. 4·00 3·00
55 1 r. 50, *Nephila madagascariensis* (spider) 4·25 3·00
w. Wmk Crown to right of CA .. .. 6·50
53/5 .. .. *Set of* 3 10·50 8·00
*The normal sideways watermark shows Crown to left of CA, *as seen from the back of the stamp.*
See also Nos. 58/61, 77/80 and 86/9.

(Des C. Abbott. Litho Walsall)

1974 (14 July). *Fifth Anniv of "Nordvaer" Travelling Post Office. T* **11** *and similar vert design. Multicoloured. W* w **12** (*sideways*). *P* 14.
56 85 c. Type **11** 85 75
57 2 r. 50, *Nordvaer* off shore .. .. .. 1·40 1·25

12 Red-cloud Auger (*Terebra nebulosa*) and Subulate Auger (*Terebra subulata*)

(Des PAD Studio. Litho J.W.)

1974 (12 Nov). *Wildlife* (2*nd series*). *T* **12** *and similar horiz designs showing shells. Multicoloured. W* w **12**. *P* 13½ × 14.
58 45 c. Type **12** .. .. 2·25 1·00
59 75 c. Great Green Turbo (*Turbo marmoratus*) 2·50 1·25
60 1 r. Strawberry Drupe (*Drupa rubusidaeus*) 2·75 1·50
61 1 r. 50, Bull-mouth Helmet (*Cypraecassis rufa*) .. .. 3·00 1·75
58/61 .. .. *Set of* 4 9·50 5·00

13 Aldabra Drongo **14** *Grewia salicifolia*

(Des R. Granger Barrett. Litho Questa)

1975 (28 Feb). *Birds. Multicoloured designs as T* **13**. *W* w **12** (*sideways* on horiz designs*). *P* 14.
62 5 c. Type **13** .. .. 1·25 2·75
63 10 c. Black Coucal .. .. 1·25 2·75
64 20 c. Mascarene Fody .. .. 1·25 2·75
w. Wmk inverted .. .. 90·00
65 25 c. White Tern .. .. 1·25 2·75
66 30 c. Crested Tern .. .. 1·25 2·75
67 40 c. Brown Booby .. .. 1·25 2·75
68 50 c. Common Noddy (*horiz*) .. .. 1·25 3·00
69 60 c. Grey Heron .. .. 1·25 3·00
70 65 c. Blue-faced Booby (*horiz*) .. .. 1·25 3·00
71 95 c. Madagascar White Eye (*horiz*) .. 1·25 3·00
w. Wmk Crown to right of CA .. .. 60·00
72 1 r. Green Heron (*horiz*) .. .. .. 1·25 3·00
73 1 r. 75, Lesser Frigate Bird (*horiz*) .. 2·00 4·75
74 3 r. 50, White-tailed Tropic Bird (*horiz*) 2·75 4·75
75 5 r. Souimanga Sunbird (*horiz*) .. .. 4·00 5·00
76 10 r. Madagascar Turtle Dove (*horiz*) .. 8·00 9·00
62/76 .. .. *Set of* 15 27·00 48·00
*The normal sideways watermark shows Crown to left of CA, *as seen from the back of the stamp.*

(Des Sylvia Goaman. Litho Questa)

1975 (10 July). *Wildlife* (3*rd series*). *T* **14** *and similar vert designs showing seashore plants. Multicoloured. W* w **12** (*sideways*). *P* 14.
77 50 c. Type **14** .. .. 60 1·25
78 65 c. *Cassia aldabrensis* .. .. .. 65 1·40
79 1 r. *Hypoestes aldabrensis* .. .. .. 80 1·50
80 1 r. 60, *Euphorbia pyrifolia* .. .. 1·10 1·60
77/80 .. .. *Set of* 4 2·75 5·25

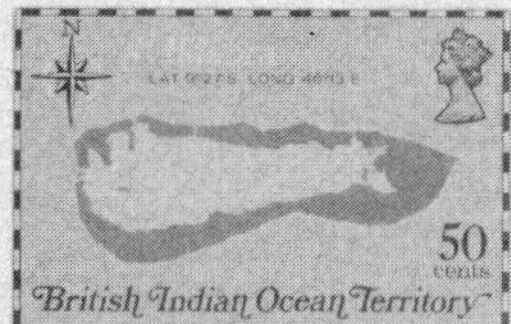

15 Map of Aldabra

(Des L. Curtis. Litho Questa)

1975 (8 Nov). 10*th Anniv of Territory. Maps. T* **15** *and similar horiz designs. Multicoloured. W* w **12**. *P* 13½.
81 50 c. Type **15** 70 65
82 1 r. Desroches 85 85
83 1 r. 50, Farquhar .. .. 95 1·00
84 2 r. Diego Garcia .. .. 1·00 1·25
81/4 .. .. *Set of* 4 3·25 3·25
MS85 147 × 147 mm. Nos. 81/4 (wmk sideways) 7·00 13·00

16 *Utetheisa pulchella* (moth)

(Des PAD Studio. Litho Questa)

1976 (22 Mar). *Wildlife* (4*th series*). *T* **16** *and similar horiz designs. Multicoloured. W* w **12** (*sideways*). *P* 13½.
86 65 c. Type **16** .. .. 60 1·10
87 1 r. 20, *Dysdercus fasciatus* (bug) .. .. 75 1·25
88 1 r. 50, *Sphex torridus* (wasp) .. .. 80 1·40
89 2 r. *Oryctes rhinoceros* (beetle) .. .. 85 1·40
86/9 .. .. *Set of* 4 2·75 4·50

When the Seychelles achieved independence on 29 June 1976 the islands of Aldabra, Farquhar and Desroches reverted to its administration so that British Indian Ocean Territory from that date consisted of the Chagos Archipelago, an island group, the largest of whose five main atolls is Diego Garcia. The indigenous population was resettled on Mauritius and Diego Garcia was developed as a U.S. Navy base while remaining under British administration.

Nos. 62/76 were withdrawn in August 1979 and, until May 1990, base personnel used British and American forces mail facilities routed via the Philippines and San Francisco. From 1987 British mails were routed via Singapore. The growing number of civilian workers eventually led to the re-introduction of a public postal service in May 1990 using stamps with face values in sterling.

(New Currency. Sterling)

17 White-tailed Tropic Bird **18** 1974 Wildlife 1 r. 50 Stamp

(Des N. Arlott. Litho Questa)

1990 (3 May). *Birds. T* **17** *and similar vert designs. Multicoloured. W* w **16** (*sideways*). *P* 14.
90 15p. Type **17** .. .. 1·10 1·50
91 20p. Madagascar Turtle Dove .. .. 1·25 1·60
92 24p. Great Frigate Bird .. .. .. 1·40 1·75
93 30p. Green Heron .. .. 1·50 2·00
94 34p. Great Sand Plover .. .. .. 1·60 2·00
95 41p. Crab Plover .. .. 1·75 2·25
96 45p. Crested Tern .. .. 2·00 2·25
97 54p. Lesser Crested Tern .. .. .. 2·25 2·50
98 62p. White Tern .. .. 2·25 2·50
99 71p. Red-footed Booby .. .. .. 2·25 3·00
100 80p. Common Mynah .. .. .. 2·50 3·25
101 £1 Madagascar Red Fody .. .. .. 2·50 3·50
90/101 .. .. *Set of* 12 20·00 25·00

(Des D. Miller. Litho Walsall)

1990 (3 May). *"Stamp World London 90" International Stamp Exhibition. T* **18** *and similar horiz designs showing stamps. Multicoloured. W* w **14** (*sideways*). *P* 14.
102 15p. Type **18** .. .. 2·25 2·25
103 20p. 1976 Wildlife 2 r. .. .. .. 2·50 2·50
104 34p. 1975 Diego Garcia map 2 r. .. .. 4·00 4·00
105 54p. 1969 *Nordvaer* 1 r. .. .. .. 5·75 5·75
102/5 .. .. *Set of* 4 13·00 13·00

(Des D. Miller. Litho Questa)

1990 (4 Aug). 90*th Birthday of Queen Elizabeth the Queen Mother. Vert designs as T* **134** (24*p.*) *or* **135** (£1) *of Ascension. W* w **16**. *P* 14×15 (24*p.*) *or* 14½ (£1).
106 24p. multicoloured .. .. 3·00 3·50
107 £1 brownish black and purple-brown .. 5·00 5·50
Designs:—24p. Lady Elizabeth Bowes-Lyon, 1923; £1 Queen Elizabeth and her daughters, 1940.

19 Territory Flag **20** Postman emptying Pillar Box

(Des D. Miller. Litho Questa)

1990 (8 Nov). 25*th Anniv of British Indian Ocean Territory T* **19** *and similar vert designs. Multicoloured. W* w **14** *P* 14×13½.
108 20p. Type **19** .. .. 4·00 4·50
109 24p. Coat of arms .. .. 4·00 4·50
MS110 63×99 mm. £1 Map of Chagos Archipelago .. .. 9·50 11·00

(Des O. Bell. Litho Walsall)

1991 (3 June). *British Indian Ocean Territory Administration. T* **20** *and similar horiz designs. Multicoloured. W* w **14** (*sideways*). *P* 14.
111 20p. Type **20** .. .. 2·00 2·50
112 24p. Commissioner inspecting guard of Royal Marines .. .. .. 2·25 2·50
113 34p. Policemen outside station .. .. 4·00 4·50
114 54p. Customs officers boarding yacht .. 5·50 6·00
111/14 .. .. *Set of* 4 12·50 14·00

21 *Experiment* (E.I.C. survey brig), 1786

(Des E. Nisbet. Litho Walsall)

1991 (8 Nov). *Visiting Ships. T* **21** *and similar horiz designs. Multicoloured. W* w **14** (*sideways*). *P* 14.
115 20p. Type **21** .. .. 2·75 3·00
116 24p. *Pickering* (American brig), 1819 .. 3·00 3·25
117 34p. *Emden* (German cruiser), 1914 .. 4·00 4·25
118 54p. H.M.S. *Edinburgh* (destroyer), 1988 5·00 5·50
115/18 .. .. *Set of* 4 13·50 14·50

(Des D. Miller. Litho Questa (54p.), Walsall (others))

1992 (6 Feb). 40*th Anniv of Queen Elizabeth II's Accession. Horiz designs as T* **143** *of Ascension. Multicoloured. W* w **14** (*sideways*). *P* 14.
119 15p. Catholic chapel, Diego Garcia .. 1·00 1·25
120 20p. Planter's house, Diego Garcia .. 1·10 1·40
121 24p. Railway tracks on wharf, Diego Garcia 1·75 1·75
122 34p. Three portraits of Queen Elizabeth .. 1·75 1·90
123 54p. Queen Elizabeth II .. .. .. 2·00 2·40
119/23 .. .. *Set of* 5 7·00 8·00

22 R.A.F. Consolidated PBY-5 Catalina (flying boat) **23** "The Mystical Marriage of St. Catherine" (Correggio)

(Des A. Theobald. Litho Walsall)

1992 (23 Oct). *Visiting Aircraft. T* **22** *and similar horiz designs. Multicoloured. W* w **16** (*sideways*). *P* 14.
124 20p. Type **22** .. .. 2·00 2·50
125 24p. R.A.F. Hawker Siddeley H.S.801 Nimrod M.R.2 (maritime reconnaissance aircraft) .. .. .. 2·25 2·50
126 34p. Lockheed P-3 Orion (transport aircraft) 2·75 3·25
127 54p. U.S.A.A.F. Boeing B-52 Stratofortress (heavy bomber) .. .. .. 3·50 4·50
124/7 .. .. *Set of* 4 9·50 11·50

(Des D. Miller. Litho Walsall)

1992 (27 Nov). *Christmas. Religious Paintings. T* **23** *and similar vert designs. Multicoloured. W* w **16**. *P* 14½×14.
128 5p. Type **23** 70 80
129 24p. "Madonna" (anon) .. .. .. 1·50 1·60
130 34p. "Madonna" (anon) (*different*) .. .. 1·75 2·25
131 54p. "The Birth of Jesus" (Kaspar Jele) .. 2·50 3·50
128/31 .. .. *Set of* 4 5·75 7·50

24 Coconut Crab and Rock

25 *Stachytarpheta urticifolia*

(Des G. Vasarhelyi. Litho Questa)

93 (5 Mar). *Endangered Species. Coconut Crab. T* **24** *and similar horiz designs. Multicoloured.* W w **16** (*sideways*). *P* 14.
2 10p. Type **24** .. .. 1·25 1·25
3 10p. Crab on beach .. .. .. 1·25 1·25
4 10p. Two crabs .. .. 1·25 1·25
5 15p. Crab climbing coconut tree .. .. 1·50 1·50
2/5 .. .. *Set of* 4 4·75 4·75

(Des A. Theobald. Litho Questa)

93 (1 Apr). *75th Anniv of Royal Air Force. Horiz designs as T* **149** *of Ascension. Multicoloured.* W w **14** (*sideways*). *P* 14.
6 20p. Vickers Virginia Mk X .. .. 1·25 1·50
7 24p. Bristol Bulldog IIA .. .. .. 1·40 1·50
8 34p. Short S.25 Sunderland Mk III .. 1·75 2·00
9 54p. Bristol Type 142 Blenheim Mk IV .. 2·75 3·25
6/9 .. .. *Set of* 4 6·50 7·50
S140 110×77 mm. 20p. Douglas DC-3 Dakota; 20p. Gloster G.41 Javelin; 20p. Blackburn Beverley C1; 20p. Vickers VC-10 .. .. 6·00 7·00

(Des N. Shewring. Litho Questa)

93 (22 Nov). *Christmas. Flowers. T* **25** *and similar vert designs. Multicoloured.* W w **14**. *P* 14½.
1 20p. Type **25** .. .. 1·25 1·25
2 24p. *Ipomea pes-caprae* .. .. .. 1·25 1·25
3 34p. *Sida pusilla* .. .. 1·50 2·00
4 54p. *Catharanthus roseus* .. .. .. 2·50 3·00
1/4 .. .. *Set of* 4 6·00 6·75

94 (18 Feb). *"Hong Kong '94" International Stamp Exhibition. Nos.* 92 *and* 101 *optd as T* **154** *of Ascension.*
5 24p. Great Frigate Bird .. .. .. 1·25 1·50
6 £1 Madagascar Red Fody .. .. .. 3·00 4·00

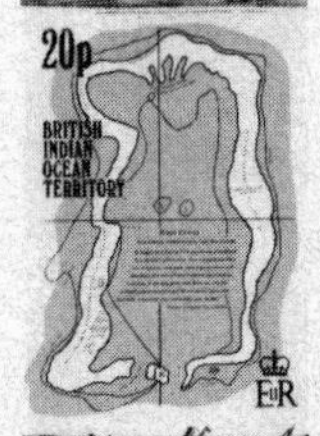

26 Forrest's Map of Diego Garcia, 1778

27 *Junonia villida*

(Des D. Miller. Litho Questa)

94 (1 June). *18th-century Maps. T* **26** *and similar vert designs. Each black and cobalt.* W w **14**. *P* 14½.
47 20p. Type **26** .. .. 90 1·40
a. Horiz strip of 5. Nos. 147/51 .. .. 5·50
48 24p. Blair's plan of Diego Garcia harbour, 1786–87 .. .. 1·00 1·50
49 34p. Blair's chart of Chagos Archipelago, 1786–87 .. .. 1·10 1·60
50 44p. Plan of part of Diego Garcia, 1774 .. 1·40 1·75
51 54p. Fontaine's plan of Diego Garcia, 1770 1·60 1·90
47/51 .. .. *Set of* 5 5·50 7·25
Nos. 147/51 were printed together, *se-tenant*, in horizontal strips of 5 throughout the sheet.

(Des I. Loe. Litho Walsall)

94 (16 Aug). *Butterflies. T* **27** *and similar vert designs. Multicoloured.* W w **16**. *P* 14½×14.
52 24p. Type **27** .. .. 1·50 1·50
53 30p. *Petrelaea dana* .. .. .. 2·00 2·25
54 56p. *Hypolimnas misippus* .. .. .. 3·00 3·75
52/4 .. .. *Set of* 3 6·00 6·75

28 Short-tailed Nurse Sharks

(Des N. Shewring. Litho Walsall)

994 (1 Nov). *Sharks. T* **28** *and similar horiz designs. Multicoloured.* W w **14** (*sideways*). *P* 14.
55 15p. Type **28** 30 35
56 20p. Silver-tipped Sharks 40 45
57 24p. Black-finned Reef Shark 50 55
58 30p. Oceanic White-tipped Sharks 60 65
159 35p. Black-tipped Shark 70 75
160 41p. Smooth Hammerhead 80 85
161 46p. Sickle-finned Lemon Shark 90 95
162 55p. White-tipped Reef Shark .. .. 1·10 1·25
163 65p. Tiger Sharks .. .. 1·25 1·40
164 74p. Indian Sand Tiger .. .. .. 1·50 1·60
165 80p. Great Hammerhead .. .. .. 1·60 1·75
166 £1 Great White Shark .. .. .. 2·00 2·10
155/66 .. .. *Set of* 12 11·50 12·50
For miniature sheets containing the 65p. or 74p. (with "1997" imprint date) see Nos. **MS**193/4.

(Des R. Watton. Litho Walsall (Nos. 167/70) or Questa (No. **MS**171))

1995 (8 May). *50th Anniv of End of Second World War. Multicoloured designs as T* **161** *of Ascension.* W w **14** (*sideways*). *P* 14.
167 20p. Military cemetery .. .. .. 1·25 1·50
168 24p. Rusty 6-inch naval gun at Cannon Point .. .. 1·40 1·50
169 30p. Short S.25 Sunderland flying boat .. 1·75 1·90
170 56p. H.M.I.S. *Clive* (sloop) .. .. 2·75 3·25
167/70 .. .. *Set of* 4 6·50 7·25
MS171 75×85 mm. £1 Reverse of 1939–45 War Medal (*vert*). Wmk upright .. .. .. 2·50 3·00

29 Dolphin (fish)

30 *Terebra crenulata*

(Des K. McGee. Litho B.D.T.)

1995 (6 Oct). *Gamefish. T* **29** *and similar horiz designs. Multicoloured.* W w **16** (*sideways*). *P* 14.
172 20p. Type **29** .. .. 1·00 1·25
173 24p. Sailfish .. .. 1·10 1·25
174 30p. Wahoo .. .. 1·75 1·90
175 56p. Striped Marlin .. .. .. 2·75 3·25
172/5 .. .. *Set of* 4 6·00 7·00

(Des G. Drummond. Litho Walsall)

1996 (8 Jan). *Sea Shells. T* **30** *and similar horiz designs. Multicoloured.* W w **14** (*sideways*). *P* 14½.
176 20p. Type **30** .. .. 1·00 1·25
177 24p. *Bursa bufonia* .. .. .. 1·10 1·25
178 30p. *Nassarius papillosus* .. .. .. 1·75 1·90
179 56p. *Lopha cristagalli* .. .. .. 2·75 3·25
176/9 .. .. *Set of* 4 6·00 7·00

(Des D. Miller. Litho Walsall)

1996 (22 Apr). *70th Birthday of Queen Elizabeth II. Vert designs as T* **165** *of Ascension, each incorporating a different photograph of the Queen. Multicoloured.* W w **16**. *P* 14½.
180 20p. View of lagoon from south 60 80
181 24p. Manager's House, Peros Banhos .. 65 80
182 30p. Wireless Hut, Peros Banhos .. .. 80 1·25
183 56p. Sunset .. .. 1·25 1·75
180/3 .. .. *Set of* 4 3·00 4·25
MS184 64×66 mm. £1 Queen Elizabeth II .. 2·50 3·25

31 Loggerhead Turtle

32 Commissioner's Representative (naval officer)

(Des O. Bell. Litho Questa)

1996 (2 Sept). *Turtles. T* **31** *and similar horiz designs. Multicoloured.* W w **14** (*sideways*). *P* 14×14½.
185 20p. Type **31** 80 90
186 24p. Leatherback Turtle 85 90
187 30p. Hawksbill Turtle .. .. .. 1·25 1·50
188 56p. Green Turtle .. .. 1·75 2·00
185/8 .. .. *Set of* 4 4·25 4·75

(Des R. Watton. Litho Questa)

1996 (16 Dec). *Uniforms. T* **32** *and similar vert designs. Multicoloured.* W w **14**. *P* 14.
189 20p. Type **32** .. .. 90 1·00
190 24p. Royal Marine officer .. .. .. 95 1·00
191 30p. Royal Marine in battledress .. .. 1·40 1·60
192 56p. Police officers .. .. .. 2·00 2·25
189/92 .. .. *Set of* 4 4·75 5·25

(Des D. Miller. Litho Questa)

1997 (3 Feb). *"HONG KONG '97" International Stamp Exhibition. Sheet 130×90 mm, containing design as No.* 163. *Multicoloured.* W w **14**. *P* 14.
MS193 65p. Tiger Sharks .. .. .. 2·00 2·50

(Des N. Shewring. Litho Walsall)

1997 (20 June). *Return of Hong Kong to China. Sheet 130×90 mm containing design as No. 164, but with "1997" imprint date.*
MS194 74p. Indian Sand Tiger .. .. 2·00 2·50

(Des N. Shewring (No. **MS**201), D. Miller (others). Litho Questa)

1997 (10 July). *Golden Wedding of Queen Elizabeth and Prince Philip. Multicoloured designs as T* **173** *of Ascension.* W w **14**. *P* 14½.
195 20p. Queen Elizabeth at Bristol, 1994 .. 70 90
a. Horiz pair. Nos. 195/6 .. .. 1·40 1·75
196 20p. Prince Philip competing in Royal Windsor Horse Show, 1996 .. .. 70 90
197 24p. Queen Elizabeth in phaeton, Trooping the Colour, 1987 .. .. .. 70 90
a. Horiz pair. Nos. 197/8 .. .. 1·40 1·75
198 24p. Prince Philip 70 90
199 30p. Queen Elizabeth and Prince Philip with Land Rover .. .. 80 1·00
a. Horiz pair. Nos. 199/200 .. .. 1·60 2·00
200 30p. Queen Elizabeth at Balmoral .. 80 1·00
195/200 .. .. *Set of* 6 4·00 5·00
MS201 110×71 mm. £1.50, Queen Elizabeth and Prince Philip in landau (*horiz*). Wmk sideways. P 14×14½ .. .. 3·75 4·50
Nos. 195/6, 197/8 and 199/200 were each printed together, *se-tenant*, in horizontal pairs throughout the sheets with the backgrounds forming composite designs.

33 H.M.S. *Richmond* (frigate) and H.M.S. *Beaver* (frigate)

(Litho Questa)

1997 (1 Dec). *Exercise Ocean Wave. T* **33** *and similar horiz designs. Multicoloured.* W w **14** (*sideways*). *P* 14×14½.
202 24p. Type **33** 70 80
a. Sheetlet. Nos. 202/13 .. .. 7·50
203 24p. H.M.S. *Illustrious* (aircraft carrier) launching aircraft 70 80
204 24p. H.M.S. *Beaver* 70 80
205 24p. R.Y. *Britannia*, R.F.A. *Sir Percival* and H.M.S. *Beaver* 70 80
206 24p. R.Y. *Britannia* 70 80
207 24p. H.M.S. *Richmond*, H.M.S. *Beaver* and H.M.S. *Gloucester* (destroyer) .. 70 80
208 24p. H.M.S. *Richmond* 70 80
209 24p. Aerial view of H.M.S. *Illustrious* .. 70 80
210 24p. H.M.S. *Gloucester* 70 80
211 24p. H.M.S. *Trenchant* (submarine) and R.F.A. *Diligence* 70 80
212 24p. R.F.A. *Fort George* replenishing H.M.S. *Illustrious* and H.M.S. *Gloucester* .. 70 80
213 24p. Aerial view of H.M.S. *Richmond*, H.M.S. *Beaver* and H.M.S. *Gloucester* 70 80
202/13 .. .. *Set of* 12 7·50 8·50
Nos. 202/13 were printed together, *se-tenant*, in sheetlets of 12.
No. 210 is inscribed "HMS Sheffield" in error.

(Des D. Miller. Litho Questa)

1998 (31 Mar). *Diana, Princess of Wales Commemoration. Sheet, 145×70 mm, containing vert designs as T* **177** *of Ascension. Multicoloured.* W w **14** (*sideways*). *P* 14½×14.
MS214 26p. Wearing patterned jacket, 1993; 26p. Wearing heart-shaped earrings, 1988; 34p. Wearing cream jacket, 1993; 60p. Wearing blue blouse, 1982 (*sold at £1.46 + 20p. charity premium*) .. .. 3·25 3·50

(Des A. Theobald. Litho Questa)

1998 (1 Apr). *80th Anniv of the Royal Air Force. Horiz designs as T* **178** *of Ascension. Multicoloured.* W w **16** (*sideways*). *P* 14.
215 26p. Blackburn Iris 75 80
216 34p. Gloster Gamecock .. .. .. 90 1·00
217 60p. North American Sabre F.4 .. .. 1·75 2·00
218 80p. Avro Lincoln .. .. 2·25 2·50
215/18 .. .. *Set of* 4 5·00 5·50
MS219 110×77 mm. 34p. Sopwith Baby (seaplane); 34p. Martinsyde Elephant; 34p. De Havilland Tiger Moth; 34p. North American Mustang III .. .. 2·75 3·25

34 Bryde's Whale

(Des N. Shewring. Litho Walsall)

1998 (7 Dec). *International Year of the Ocean. T* **34** *and similar horiz designs.* W w **14** (*sideways*). *P* 13½×14.
220 26p. Type **34** 50 55
221 26p. Striped Dolphin 50 55
222 34p. Pilot Whale 70 75
223 34p. Spinner Dolphin 70 75
220/3 .. .. *Set of* 4 2·40 2·50

British Levant

The term "British Levant" is used by stamp collectors to describe the issues made by various British Post Offices within the former Turkish Empire.

Arrangements for the first such service were included amongst the terms of a commercial treaty between the two countries in 1832, but the system did not start operations until September 1857 when a post office for civilian use was opened in Constantinople, replacing the Army Post Office which had existed there since June 1854.

Eventually the number of British Post Offices grew to five:

Beyrout (Beirut, Lebanon). Opened 1873, closed 30 September 1914.

Constantinople (Istanbul). Opened 1 September 1857, closed 30 September 1914, re-opened 4 February 1919, finally closed 27 September 1923.

Salonica (Thessalonika, Greece). Opened 1 May 1900, closed October 1914. The city was captured by Greek troops on 7 November 1912 and incorporated into Greece by the Treaty of London (July 1913).

Smyrna (Izmir). Opened 1872, closed 30 September 1914, re-opened 1 March 1919, finally closed September 1922. Between 15 May 1919 and 8 September 1922 the city was under Greek occupation.

Stamboul (a sub-office of Constantinople). Opened 1 April 1884, closed 25 August 1896, re-opened 10 February 1908, finally closed 30 September 1914.

Stamps from the two British Post Offices in Egypt, still technically part of the Turkish Empire, are listed under EGYPT.

A. BRITISH POST OFFICES IN TURKISH EMPIRE, 1857–1914

For illustrations of the postmark types see BRITISH POST OFFICES ABROAD notes, following GREAT BRITAIN.

From 1 August 1885 letter and registered charges were prepaid with surcharged stamps (No. 1 onwards). Until 14 August 1905 postcards and parcels continued to be franked with unoverprinted Great Britain stamps. Only a limited range of values were stocked for this purpose and these are listed. Other values exist with Levant postmarks, but these stamps did not originate from the local post offices.

After 15 August 1905 the post offices were supplied with Great Britain stamps overprinted "LEVANT". Subsequent examples of unoverprinted stamps with Levant postmarks are omitted from the listing. The use of such stamps during 1919–22 at Constantinople and Smyrna is, however, covered by a later note.

BEYROUT (BEIRUT)

Between 1873 and 1876 much of the mail from the British Post Office in Beyrout sent to European addresses was forwarded through the French or Italian Post Offices at Alexandria. Such covers show Great Britain stamps used in combination with those of French or Italian P.O's in the Turkish Empire.

Stamps of GREAT BRITAIN *cancelled* "G 06" *or circular postmark as in Types* **8**, **18** *or* **20**.

1873.

No.	Description		Price
Z 1	½d. rose-red (1870–79)	*From*	30·00
	Plate Nos. 12, 13, 14, 19, 20.		
Z 2	1d. rose-red (1864–79)	*From*	13·00
	Plate Nos. 107, 118, 130, 140, 145, 148, 155, 157, 162, 167, 177, 179, 180, 184, 185, 186, 187, 195, 198, 200, 203, 204, 211, 213, 215, 218, 220, 222.		
Z 3	1½d. lake-red (1870–74) (Plate 3)		£200
Z 4	2d. blue (1858–69)	*From*	18·00
	Plate Nos. 13, 14, 15.		
Z 5	2½d. rosy mauve (1875) (*blued paper*)		70·00
	Plate No. 1.		
Z 6	2½d. rosy mauve (1875–76)	*From*	30·00
	Plate Nos. 1, 2, 3.		
Z 7	2½d. rosy mauve (1876–79)	*From*	25·00
	Plate Nos. 3, 4, 5, 6, 7, 8, 9, 10, 11, 12, 13, 14, 15, 16, 17.		
Z 8	2½d. blue (1880)	*From*	15·00
	Plate Nos. 17, 18, 19, 20.		
Z 9	2½d. blue (1881)	*From*	10·00
	Plate Nos. 21, 22, 23.		
Z10	3d. rose (1867–73) (Plate No. 10)		
Z11	3d. rose (1873–76)		32·00
	Plate Nos. 12, 15, 16, 18, 19, 20.		
Z12	3d. rose (1881) (Plate Nos. 20, 21)		
Z13	4d. vermilion (1865–73)	*From*	32·00
	Plate Nos. 11, 12, 13, 14.		
Z14	4d. vermilion (1876) (Plate No. 15)		£180
Z15	4d. sage-green (1877)		£120
	Plate Nos. 15, 16.		
Z16	4d. grey-brown (1880) *wmk* Large Garter (Plate No. 17)		
Z17	4d. grey-brown (1880) *wmk* Crown		42·00
	Plate Nos. 17, 18.		
Z18	6d. mauve (1870) (Plate Nos. 8, 9)		
Z19	6d. buff (1872–73)	*From*	80·00
	Plate Nos. 11, 12.		
Z20	6d. chestnut (1872) (Plate No. 11)		38·00
Z21	6d. grey (1873) (Plate No. 12)		
Z22	6d. grey (1874–80)	*From*	28·00
	Plate Nos. 13, 14, 15, 16, 17.		
Z23	8d. orange (1876)		£300
Z24	10d. red-brown (1867)		£160
Z25	1s. green (1867–73)		25·00
	Plate Nos. 6, 7.		
Z26	1s. green (1873–77)	*From*	35·00
	Plate Nos. 8, 9, 10, 12, 13.		
Z27	1s. orange-brown (1880) (Plate No. 13)		
Z28	1s. orange-brown (1881)		50·00
	Plate Nos. 13, 14.		
Z29	2s. blue (1867)		£140
Z30	5s. rose (1867) (Plate Nos. 1, 2)	*From*	£600

1880.

No.	Description		Price
Z31	½d. deep green		9·00
Z32	½d. pale green		10·00
Z33	1d. Venetian red		11·00
Z34	1½d. Venetian red		£140
Z35	2d. pale rose		42·00
Z36	2d. deep rose		42·00
Z37	5d. indigo		70·00

1881.

No.	Description		Price
Z38	1d. lilac (14 *dots*)		
Z39	1d. lilac (16 *dots*)		5·50

1884.

No.	Description		Price
Z40	½d. slate-blue		11·00
Z41	1½d. lilac		60·00
Z42	2d. lilac		60·00
Z43	2½d. lilac		11·00
Z44	4d. dull green		£150
Z45	5d. dull green		£100
Z46	1s. dull green		£200

1887–92.

No.	Description		Price
Z47	½d. vermilion		5·50
Z54	6d. purple/*rose-red*		18·00
Z55	1s. dull green		£100

1900.

No.	Description		Price
Z56	½d. blue-green		8·50
Z57	1s. green and carmine		£130

1902–04. *De La Rue ptgs.*

No.	Description		Price
Z58	½d. blue-green		4·50
Z59	½d. yellowish green		5·00
Z60	1d. scarlet		4·00
Z64	1s. dull green and carmine		26·00

CONSTANTINOPLE

Stamps of GREAT BRITAIN *cancelled* "C" *or circular postmark as in Types* **1**, **10**, **18** *or* **19**.

1857.

No.	Description		Price
Z 68	½d. rose-red (1870–79)	*From*	21·00
	Plate Nos. 5, 6, 10, 11, 12, 13, 14, 15, 20.		
Z 69	1d. red-brown (1854), Die I, *wmk* Small Crown, *perf* 16		
Z 70	1d. red-brown (1855), Die II, *wmk* Small Crown, *perf* 14		
Z 71	1d. red-brown, (1855), Die II, *wmk* Large Crown, *perf* 14		17·00
Z 72	1d. rose-red (1857)		6·50
Z 73	1d. rose-red (1861) Alphabet IV		
Z 74	1d. rose-red (1864–79)	*From*	6·50
	Plate Nos. 71, 72, 73, 74, 76, 78, 79, 80, 81, 83, 85, 87, 89, 90, 92, 93, 94, 95, 96, 97, 99, 101, 102, 105, 106, 108, 109, 110, 113, 116, 118, 119, 120, 121, 122, 123, 124, 125, 127, 129, 130, 131, 134, 135, 136, 137, 138, 140, 141, 143, 144, 145, 146, 147, 148, 149, 150, 151, 152, 155, 156, 157, 158, 159, 160, 161, 162, 163, 164, 166, 167, 170, 171, 172, 173, 174, 175, 176, 177, 178, 179, 180, 181, 183, 184, 186, 187, 188, 189, 190, 191, 192, 193, 194, 195, 196, 197, 198, 200, 201, 203, 204, 205, 206, 207, 208, 210, 212, 214, 215, 216, 220, 222, 224.		
Z 75	1½d. rose-red (1870) (Plate 1)		£180
Z 76	2d. blue (1855), *wmk* Large Crown, *perf* 14. (Plate Nos. 5, 6)		
Z 77	2d. blue (1858–69)	*From*	9·50
	Plate Nos. 7, 8, 9, 12, 13, 14, 15.		
Z 78	2½d. rosy mauve (1875–76) (*blued paper*) (Plate Nos. 1, 2)	*From*	50·00
Z 79	2½d. rosy mauve (1875–76)	*From*	27·00
	Plate Nos. 1, 2, 3.		
Z 80	2½d. rosy mauve (*Error of Lettering*)		
Z 81	2½d. rosy mauve (1876–79)	*From*	23·00
	Plate Nos. 3 to 17.		
Z 82	2½d. blue (1880–81)	*From*	11·00
	Plate Nos. 17, 18, 19, 20.		
Z 83	2½d. blue (1881) (Plate Nos. 21, 22, 23)		7·50
Z 84	3d. carmine-rose (1862) (Plate No. 2)		£110
Z 85	3d. rose (1865) (Plate No. 4)		65·00
Z 86	3d. rose (1867–73) (Plate Nos. 4 to 10)		65·00
Z 87	3d. rose (1873–76)		20·00
	Plates, 11, 12, 15, 16, 17, 18, 19.		
Z 88	3d. rose (1881) (Plate No. 21)		
Z 89	3d. on 3d. lilac (1883) (Plate No. 21)		
Z 90	4d. rose (1857)		40·00
	a. *Rose-carmine*		
Z 91	4d. red (1862) (Plate Nos. 3, 4)	*From*	35·00
Z 92	4d. vermilion (1865–73)	*From*	26·00
	Plate Nos. 7 to 14.		
Z 93	4d. vermilion (1876) (Plate No. 15)		£150
Z 94	4d. sage-green (1877)		90·00
	Plate Nos. 15, 16.		
Z 95	4d. grey-brown (1880) *wmk* Large Garter (Plate No. 17)		
Z 96	4d. grey-brown (1880) *wmk* Crown (Plate Nos. 17, 18)	*From*	28·00
Z 97	6d. lilac (1856)		50·00
Z 98	6d. lilac (1862) (Plate Nos. 3, 4)	*From*	35·00
Z 99	6d. lilac (1865–67)		32·00
	Plate Nos. 5, 6.		
Z100	6d. lilac (1867) (Plate No. 6)		40·00
Z101	6d. violet (1867–70)	*From*	32·00
	Plate Nos. 6, 8, 9.		
Z102	6d. buff (1872–73)		48·00
	Plate Nos. 11, 12.		
Z103	6d. chestnut (1872) (Plate No. 11)		28·00
Z104	6d. grey (1873) (Plate No. 12)		75·00
Z105	6d. grey (1874–76)	*From*	22·00
	Plate Nos. 13, 14, 15, 16.		
Z106	6d. grey (1881–82) (Plate Nos. 17, 18)		22·00
Z107	6d. on 6d. lilac (1883)		65·00
	a. Dots slanting (Letters MI or SJ)		£110
Z108	8d. orange (1876)		£2
Z109	10d. red-brown (1867), *wmk* Emblems		£120
Z110	10d. red-brown (1867)		£1
Z111	1s. green (1856)		£1
Z112	1s. green (1862)		60·
Z113	1s. green (1862) ("K" *variety*)		
Z114	1s. green (1862) (*thick paper*)		
Z115	1s. green (1865) (Plate No. 4)		60·
Z116	1s. green (1867–73)	*From*	12·
	Plate Nos. 4, 5, 6, 7.		
Z117	1s. green (1873–77)	*From*	26·
	Plate Nos. 8, 9, 10, 11, 12, 13.		
Z118	1s. orange-brown (1880) (Plate No. 13)		£1
Z119	1s. orange-brown (1881)	*From*	42·
	Plate Nos. 13, 14.		
Z120	2s. blue (1867)		85·
Z121	5s. rose (1867–74)	*From*	£2
	Plate Nos. 1, 2.		
Z122	5s. rose (1882) (*white paper*)		£8
Z123	5s. rose (1882) (*blued paper*)		£10

1880.

No.	Description		Price
Z124	½d. deep green		5·
Z125	½d. pale green		6·
Z126	1d. Venetian red		4·
Z127	2d. pale rose		35·
Z128	2d. deep rose		35·
Z129	5d. indigo		

1881.

No.	Description		Price
Z130	1d. lilac (14 *dots*)		
Z131	1d. lilac (16 *dots*)		2·

1883–84.

No.	Description		Price
Z132	½d. slate-blue		6·
Z133	1½d. lilac		
Z134	2d. lilac		50·
Z135	2½d. lilac		7·
Z136	3d. lilac		
Z137	4d. dull green		
Z138	5d. dull green		90·
Z139	6d. dull green		
Z140	9d. dull green		
Z141	1s. dull green		£1
Z142	2s. 6d. lilac (*blued paper*)		£5
Z143	2s. 6d. lilac (*white paper*)		80·
Z144	5s. rose (*blued paper*)		
Z145	5s. rose (*white paper*)		

1887–92.

No.	Description		Price
Z146	½d. vermilion		2·5
Z154	6d. purple/*rose-red*		10·
Z157	1s. dull green		70·

1900.

No.	Description		Price
Z158	½d. blue-green		4·
Z159	1s. green and carmine		£1

1902–04. *De La Rue ptgs.*

No.	Description		Price
Z160	½d. blue-green		3·
Z161	½d. yellowish green		3·
Z162	1d. scarlet		2·
Z169	6d. purple		11·
Z172	1s. green and carmine		16·
Z173	2s. 6d. lilac		
Z174	5s. carmine		

POSTAL FISCALS

No.	Description		Price
Z175	1d. purple (*wmk Anchor*) (1868)		
Z176	1d. purple (*wmk Orb*) (1881)		£6

SALONICA

Stamps of GREAT BRITAIN *cancelled with circular postmark as Type* **18** *or double-circle datestamp.*

1900.

No.	Description		Price
Z202	½d. vermilion (1887)		14·
Z203	½d. blue-green (1900)		16·
Z204	1d. lilac (1881)		16·
Z205	6d. purple/*red* (1887)		20·
Z206	1s. green and carmine (1900)		£1
Z207	5s. rose (*white paper*) (1883)		£6

1902.

No.	Description		Price
Z208	½d. blue-green		20·
Z209	½d. yellow-green		14·
Z209*a*	1d. scarlet		14·
Z209*c*	1s. green and carmine		35·

SMYRNA (IZMIR)

Stamps of GREAT BRITAIN *cancelled* "F 87" *or circular postma[rk] as in Type* **8**, **16** *or* **18**.

1872.

No.	Description		Price
Z210	½d. rose-red (1870–79)	*From*	24
	Plates 11, 12, 13, 14, 15.		
Z211	1d. rose-red (1864–79)	*From*	10
	Plate Nos. 120, 124, 134, 137, 138, 139, 140, 142, 143, 145, 146, 148, 149, 150, 151, 152, 153, 155, 156, 157, 158, 159, 160, 161, 162, 163, 164, 166, 167, 168, 169, 170, 171, 172, 173, 174, 175, 176, 177, 178, 183, 184, 185, 186, 187, 188, 191, 193, 195, 196, 198, 200, 201, 204, 210, 212, 215, 217, 218.		
Z212	1½d. lake-red (1870–74) (Plate Nos. 1, 3)	*From*	£2
Z213	2d. blue (1858) *wmk* Large Crown, *perf* 16		
Z214	2d. blue (1858–69)	*From*	14·
	Plate Nos. 13, 14, 15.		
Z215	2½d. rosy mauve (1875) (*blued paper*)		55·
	Plate No. 1.		
Z216	2½d. rosy mauve (1875–76)	*From*	26·
	Plate Nos. 1, 2, 3.		
Z217	2½d. rosy mauve (*Error of lettering*)		
Z218	2½d. rosy mauve (1876–79)	*From*	22·
	Plate Nos. 3, 4, 5, 6, 7, 8, 9, 10, 11, 12, 13, 14, 15, 16, 17.		
Z219	2½d. blue (1880)	*From*	11·
	Plate Nos. 17, 18, 19, 20.		

20 2½d. blue (1881) . . .. 9·00
Plate Nos. 21, 22, 23.
21 3d. rose (1867–73) .. .. 28·00
Plate Nos. 5, 7, 9, 10.
22 3d. rose (1873–76) (Plate No. 14) .. ..
23 4d. vermilion (1865–73) .. .. .. 26·00
Plate Nos. 12, 13, 14.
24 4d. vermilion (1876) (Plate No. 15) £150
25 4d. sage-green (1877) .. .. 90·00
Plate Nos. 15, 16.
26 4d. grey-brown (1880) *wmk* Large Garter (Plate No. 17)
27 4d. grey-brown (1880) *wmk* Crown (Plate Nos. 17, 18) .. .. *From* 28·00
28 6d. buff (1872–73) .. .. .. *From* 70·00
Plate Nos. 11, 12.
29 6d. chestnut (1872) (Plate No. 11) .. ..
30 6d. grey (1873) (Plate No. 12) .. .. .. 75·00
31 6d. grey (1874–80) .. .. .. *From* 25·00
Plate Nos. 13, 14, 15, 16, 17.
32 6d. grey (1881–82) (Plate Nos. 17, 18) .. .. 50·00
33 6d. on 6d. lilac (1883) .. .. 75·00
34 8d. orange (1876) .. ..
35 9d. straw (1867) £190
36 10d. red-brown (1867) £130
37 1s. green (1867–73) (Plate Nos. 6, 7) .. ..
38 1s. green (1873–77) .. .. .. *From* 28·00
Plate Nos. 8, 9, 10, 11, 12, 13.
39 1s. orange-brown (1880) (Plate No. 13) .. £160
40 1s. orange-brown (1881) (Plate Nos. 13, 14) .. 42·00
41 5s. rose (1867–74) (Plate No. 2) .. ..

80.
42 ½d. deep green .. .. 6·50
43 ½d. pale green .. .. 7·50
44 1d. Venetian red .. .. 9·50
45 1½d. Venetian red .. .. 70·00
46 2d. pale rose .. .. 32·00
47 2d. deep rose .. .. 32·00
48 5d. indigo .. .. 50·00

81.
49 1d. lilac (16 *dots*) .. .. 4·25

84.
50 ½d. slate-blue .. .. 9·00
51 2d. lilac .. .. 60·00
52 2½d. lilac .. .. 10·00
53 4d. dull green .. ..
54 5d. dull green £100
55 1s. dull green £190

87.
56 ½d. vermilion .. .. 4·75
63 6d. purple/*rose-red* .. .. .. 16·00
64 1s. dull green £100

00.
65 ½d. blue-green .. .. 7·00
66 1s. green and carmine .. ..

02–04. *De La Rue ptgs.*
67 ½d. blue-green .. .. 4·25
68 ½d. yellowish green .. .. .. 4·75
69 1d. scarlet .. .. 3·75
76 6d. purple .. .. 12·00
79 1s. green and carmine .. .. .. 21·00
80 2s. 6d. purple .. ..
81 5s. carmine .. ..

STAMBOUL (CONSTANTINOPLE)

amps *of* GREAT BRITAIN *cancelled* "S" *as Type* **10**, *or circular postmarks inscribed either* "BRITISH POST OFFICE CONSTANTINOPLE S" *or* "BRITISH POST OFFICE STAMBOUL" *as Type* **18**.

84.
96 ½d. slate-blue .. .. 17·00
97 1d. lilac .. .. 8·00
98 2d. lilac .. ..
99 2½d. lilac .. .. 11·00
00 5d. dull green £100

887–92.
306 ½d. vermilion .. .. 8·00
314 6d. purple/*rose-red* .. .. .. 25·00
317 1s. dull green .. ..

The "S" cancellation was in use from 1885 to 1891 and the "Stamoul" mark from 1892 to 1896, when the office was closed, and from s reopening in 1908 to 1914. The "CONSTANTINOPLE S" handamp was normally used as a back stamp, but can be found cancelng stamps in the period 1885 to 1892.

PRICES FOR STAMPS ON COVER	
Nos. 1/3a	*from* × 8
Nos. 4/6a	*from* × 5
Nos. 7/40	*from* × 3
Nos. L1/10	*from* × 6
Nos. L11/17	*from* × 3

I. TURKISH CURRENCY

(40 paras = 1 piastre)

Following the depreciation of the Turkish piastre against sterng in 1884 it was decided to issue stamps surcharged in Turkish urrency to avoid speculation. During the early period unsurharged stamps of Great Britain remained on sale from the British ost Offices at the current rate of exchange until replaced by LEVANT" overprints.

0 PARAS (1) 4 PIASTRES (2) 12 PIASTRES (3)

RINTERS. Nos. 1/24 were surcharged or overprinted by De La ue, *unless otherwise stated.*

Stamps of Great Britain (Queen Victoria) surch as T 1 to 3

1885 (1 Aug)–**88.**
1 **64** 40 pa. on 2½d. lilac .. .. .. 85·00 1·00
2 **62** 80 pa. on 5d. green .. .. .. £180 9·50
3 **58** 12 pi. on 2s. 6d. lilac/*bluish* £275 £200
a. On white paper (4.88) .. .. 40·00 22·00

1887 (June)–**96.**
4 **74** 40 pa. on 2½d. purple/*blue* .. .. 1·75 10
a. Surch double £1900 £2500
5 **78** 80 pa. on 5d. purple and blue (7.90) .. 11·00 25
a. Small "0" in "80" .. .. £140 85·00
w. Wmk inverted .. .. .. † £500
6 **81** 4 pi. on 10d. dull purple & carm (10.10.96) 35·00 8·00
a. Dull purple and deep bright carmine 35·00 11·00
b. Large, wide "4" (R. 1/2, 1/4) .. £110 55·00

No. 5a first appeared on the June 1895 printing when the size of the surcharge plate was increased from 60 to 120. On the Victorian stamp the variety comes on R. 4/1 and 4/7. The same setting was used for the first printing of the Edward VII surcharge, but here the sheet size was further increased to 240 so that No. 9a occurs on R. 4/1, 4/7, 14/1 and 14/7.

1893 (25 Feb). *Roughly handstamped at Constantinople, as T* **1**.
7 **71** 40 pa. on ½d. vermilion £425 £100

This provisional was in use for five days only at the Constantinople and Stamboul offices. As fraudulent copies were made with the original handstamp, and can be found "used" on piece cancelled by fraudulent use of the usual canceller, this stamp should only be purchased from undoubted sources.

The handstamp became damaged during use so that by 1 March the top of the "S" was broken. Used examples dated 25 or 26 February showing the broken "S" *must* be fraudulent. It is also known with genuine handstamp inverted (*Price* £800 *unused*, £300 *used*).

1902–5. *Stamps of King Edward VII surch as T* **1** *to* **3**.
8 **86** 40 pa. on 2½d. ultramarine (3.02) .. 9·00 10
a. Pale ultramarine .. .. 9·50 10
ab. Surch double .. .. .. † £2000
9 **89** 80 pa. on 5d. dull purple & ultram (5.6.02) 3·25 2·00
a. Small "0" in "80" £180 £190
10 **92** 4 pi. on 10d. dull purple & carm (6.9.02) 8·50 4·00
a. No cross on crown .. .. 90·00 90·00
b. Chalk-surfaced paper .. .. 6·00 8·50
ba. Chalk-surfaced paper. No cross on crown .. .. .. 85·00 £100
11 **94** 12 pi. on 2s. 6d. lilac (29.8.03) .. 32·00 35·00
a. Chalk-surfaced paper. *Pale dull pur* 70·00 75·00
b. Chalk-surfaced paper. *Dull purple* 35·00 35·00
12 **95** 24 pi. on 5s. bright carmine (15.8.05) .. 32·00 40·00
8/12 .. .. *Set of* 5 75·00 70·00
9/11 Optd "Specimen" .. .. *Set of* 3 £150

No. 9a only occurs on the first printing of 80 pa. on 5d.

1 PIASTRE
(4)

1905–08. *Surch in* "PIASTRES" *instead of* "PARAS" *as T* **4** and **2**.
13 **86** 1 pi. on 2½d. ultramarine (17.4.06) .. 8·00 10
a. Surch double .. .. .. † £1300
14 **89** 2 pi. on 5d. dull purple & ultram (11.11.05) 19·00 2·50
a. Chalk-surfaced paper (1.08) .. 16·00 1·75
ab. Slate-purple and ultramarine .. 20·00 6·50

1 Piastre (5) 1 PIASTRE 10 PARAS (6)

1906 (2 July). *Issued at Beyrout. No.* L4 *surch with T* **5** *by American Press, Beyrout.*
15 **85** 1 pi. on 2d. grey-green and carmine .. £1300 £600

1909 (16 Nov–Dec.) *Stamps of King Edward VII surch as T* **1** (30 *pa.*), **6**, *and* **2** (5 *pi*). *Ordinary paper* (*No.* 19) *or chalk-surfaced paper* (*others*).
16 **84** 30 pa. on 1½d. pale dull purple and green 8·00 1·25
a. Surch double, one albino ..
17 **87** 1 pi. 10 pa. on 3d. dull purple/*orange-yell* 11·00 26·00
18 **88** 1 pi. 30 pa. on 4d. green & chocolate-brn 5·00 15·00
19 1 pi. 30 pa. on 4d. pale orange (16.12.09) 14·00 38·00
20 **83** 2 pi. 20 pa. on 6d. dull purple .. .. 15·00 48·00
21 **93** 5 pi. on 1s. dull grn & carm (Optd S. £60) 3·75 7·50
16/21 .. .. *Set of* 6 50·00 £120

1¾ PIASTRE (7) 4 Normal "4" 4 Pointed "4"

1910 (24 Jan). *Stamps of King Edward VII surch as T* **7**. *Chalk-surfaced paper* (*Nos.* 22 *and* 24).
22 **87** 1¼ pi. on 3d. dull purple/*orange-yellow* .. 40 1·00
23 **88** 1¾ pi. on 4d. pale orange 40 60
a. Orange-red .. .. .. 4·50 5·50
b. Thin, pointed "4" in fraction .. 5·50 26·00
24 **83** 2½ pi. on 6d. dull purple 90 65
22/4 .. .. *Set of* 3 1·50 2·00

No. 23b occurs in the first and seventh vertical rows of the sheet. The variety also occurs on No. 38, but not on No. 38b.

1 PIASTRE (8) 1 PIASTRE (9)

TYPE DIFFERENCES. In T 4 the letters are tall and narrow and the space enclosed by the upper part of the "A" is small.

In T 8 the opening of the "A" is similar but the letters are shorter and broader, the "P" and the "E" being particularly noticeable.

In T 9 the letters are short and broad, but the "A" is thin and open.

1911–13. *Stamps of King Edward VII, Harrison or Somerset House ptgs, surch at Somerset House.*

(*a*) *Surch with T* **4** (20 July)
25 **86** 1 pi. on 2½d. bright blue (*perf* 14) .. 11·00 6·00
a. Surch double, one albino .. £200
26 1 pi. on 2½d. bright blue (*perf* 15×14) (14.10.11) 8·00 2·25
a. Dull blue .. .. .. 7·50 1·60

(*b*) *Surch with T* **8**
27 **86** 1 pi. on 2½d. bright blue (*perf* 15×14) (3.12) .. .. 10·00 2·00
a. Dull blue .. .. .. 17·00 3·25

(*c*) *Surch with T* **9** (7.12)
28 **86** 1 pi. on 2½d. bright blue (*perf* 15×14) 55·00 45
a. Dull blue .. .. .. 55·00 45

(*d*) *Surch with T* **1** *to* **3** (1911–13)
29 **84** 30 pa. on 1½d. reddish purple and bright green (22.8.11) .. .. .. 4·25 55
a. Slate-purple and green .. .. 8·00 2·25
b. Surch double, one albino .. 50·00
30 **89** 2 pi. on 5d. dull reddish purple and bright blue (13.5.12) .. .. 6·50 1·50
a. Deep dull reddish purple and bright blue .. .. .. 7·50 2·00
31 **92** 4 pi. on 10d. dull purple & scar (26.6.12) 23·00 9·00
a. Dull reddish purple & aniline pink £150 70·00
b. Dull reddish purple and carmine 9·50 11·00
c. No cross on crown .. ..
32 **93** 5 pi. on 1s. green and carmine (1913) .. 19·00 5·00
a. Surch double, one albino .. £200
33 **94** 12 pi. on 2s. 6d. dull reddish pur (3.2.12) 50·00 32·00
a. Dull greyish purple .. .. 50·00 32·00
34 **95** 24 pi. on 5s. carmine (1913) .. .. 55·00 75·00
a. Surch double, one albino £225
29/34 .. .. *Set of* 6 £130 £110

1913 (Apr)–**14.** *Stamps of King George V, wmk Royal Cypher, surch as T* **1** (30 *pa.*), **9** (1 *pi.*), **7** *or* **2** (4 *and* 5 *pi.*).
35 **105** 30 pa. on 1½d. red-brown (4.13) .. 3·00 11·00
a. Surch double, one albino .. £100
36 **104** 1 pi. on 2½d. cobalt-blue (6.13) .. 3·00 10
a. Bright blue .. .. .. 1·50 15
37 **106** 1¼ pi. on 3d. dull reddish violet (9.13) .. 3·00 4·25
a. Violet .. .. .. 3·50 5·50
b. Surch double, one albino .. £300
38 1¾ pi. on 4d. deep grey-green (7.13) .. 3·00 6·00
a. Thin, pointed "4" in fraction .. 45·00 80·00
b. Grey-green .. .. .. 2·50 5·00
39 **108** 4 pi. on 10d. turquoise-blue (12.13) .. 6·00 14·00
40 5 pi. on 1s. bistre-brown (1.14) .. 32·00 48·00
35/40 .. .. *Set of* 6 42·00 75·00

II. BRITISH CURRENCY

Stamps overprinted "LEVANT" were for use on parcels, with the ½d. and 1d. principally used for printed paper and post cards. They replaced unoverprinted Great Britain stamps, Nos. Z58/64, Z160/74, Z208/9c and Z267/81, which had previously been used for these purposes.

From October 1907 the three lowest values were also used for certain other amended postal rates until Nos. 16/21 were introduced.

LEVANT
(L 1)

1905 (15 Aug)–**12.** *Stamps of King Edward VII optd with Type* L **1**.

(*a*) *De La Rue ptgs*
L 1 **83** ½d. pale yellowish green .. .. 5·50 15
a. Yellowish green .. .. 5·50 15
L 2 1d. scarlet .. .. .. 3·75 15
a. Bright scarlet .. .. 3·75 90
L 3 **84** 1½d. dull purple and green .. 4·50 1·50
a. Chalk-surfaced paper. *Pale dull purple and green* .. .. 11·00 2·00
L 4 **85** 2d. grey-green and carmine-red .. 3·00 18·00
a. Chalk-surfaced paper. *Pale grey-green and carmine-red* .. 2·00 6·00
ab. Dull blue-green and carmine .. 3·00 7·00
L 5 **86** 2½d. ultramarine .. .. 7·50 18·00
L 6 **87** 3d. dull purple/*orange-yellow* .. 5·50 11·00
L 7 **88** 4d. green and grey-brown .. .. 7·00 25·00
a. Green and chocolate-brown .. 13·00 27·00
L 8 **89** 5d. dull purple and ultramarine .. 14·00 25·00
L 9 **83** 6d. pale dull purple .. .. 11·00 25·00
L10 **93** 1s. dull green and carmine .. 30·00 40·00
a. Chalk-surfaced paper .. .. 30·00 40·00
L1/10 .. .. .. *Set of* 10 80·00 £140

(*b*) *Harrison ptgs optd at Somerset House*
L11 **83** ½d. dull yellow-green (*p.* 14) (2.12) .. 17·00 14·00
a. Dull green .. .. .. 17·00 14·00
b. Deep dull green .. .. 20·00 15·00

On 28 December 1909 all values, except for the ½d. and 1d. were withdrawn from sale. A further consignment of the 2d, No. L 4*ab*, probably ordered in error was, however, received, and, as there was no requirement for this value, sold mainly to collectors. Subsequently dated cancellations on the withdrawn values are philatelic, being worth only a fraction of the used prices quoted.

Distorted "N" (R. 2/10, 12/10)

1911–13. *Stamps of King George V optd with Type* L 1 *at Somerset House. (a) Die A. Wmk Crown.*

No.	Type	Description		Unused	Used
L12	98	½d. green (No. 322) (12.9.11)	..	40	90
		a. Distorted "N" ..	.. ..	17·00	
L13	99	1d. carmine-red (No. 327) (1.1.12)	..	40	3·75
		a. No cross on crown ..	..	£150	
		b. Opt double, one albino	..	£100	
		c. Distorted "N" ..	.. ..	17·00	
		(b) Redrawn types. Wmk Crown			
L14	101	½d. green (No. 339) (19.3.12)	..	25	10
		a. Yellow-green ..	.. ..	70	15
		b. Distorted "N" ..	.. ..	13·00	
L15	102	1d. bright scarlet (No. 341) (24.2.12)		25	85
		a. Scarlet (No. 342)	.. ..	1·50	85
		b. Opt triple, two albino ..	..	40·00	
		c. Distorted "N" ..	.. ..	13·00	
		(c) New types. Wmk Royal Cypher (7.13)			
L16	105	½d. green (No. 351)	.. ..	15	30
		a. Yellow-green ..	.. ..	30	90
		b. Distorted "N" ..	.. ..	11·00	
L17	104	1d. scarlet (No. 357)	.. ..	15	3·25
		a. Vermilion	.. ..	4·75	7·00
		b. Distorted "N" ..	.. ..	11·00	

Similar overprints were issued when the British Post Offices reopened in 1919, and are listed below.

B. BRITISH POST OFFICES IN CONSTANTINOPLE AND SMYRNA, 1919–1923

CONSTANTINOPLE

Following the occupation of Constantinople by Allied forces a British Military Post Office was opened for civilian use on 4 February 1919. During the period of its existence stamps of Great Britain with face values to 10s. were available and such use can be identified by the following cancellations:

"FIELD POST OFFICE H12" (4 February 1919 to 18 March 1919)

"ARMY POST OFFICE Y" (20 March 1919 to May 1920)

"ARMY POST OFFICE S.X.3" (April 1919 to August 1920)

"BRITISH A.P.O. CONSTANTINOPLE" (5 July 1919 to 1 Sept 1920).

Of these four marks the first two types were also used for military mail.

The office reverted to civilian control in July 1920, Nos. 41/50 and L18/24 being intended for its use.

Z 1

Z 2

Z 3 Z 4

1919–20. *Used at the Army Post Office. Stamps of* GREAT BRITAIN *cancelled with Types* Z 1, Z 2, Z 3, Z 4.

No.	Description	Used
Z176	½d. green ..	2·00
Z177	1d. scarlet ..	2·00
Z178	1½d. brown ..	3·25
Z179	2d. orange (Die I) ..	2·50
Z180	2½d. blue ..	4·00
Z181	4d. grey-green	8·50
Z182	6d. purple ..	4·50
Z183	9d. agate ..	22·00
Z184	1s. bistre ..	5·50
Z185	2s. 6d. brown	32·00
Z186	5s. rose-red	50·00
Z187	10s. dull grey-blue ..	90·00

1920–21. *Used at the Civilian Post Office. Stamps of* GREAT BRITAIN *cancelled with Type* **18** *or double-circle datestamp.*

No.	Description	Used
Z188	½d. green ..	2·00
Z189	1d. scarlet ..	2·00
Z190	1½d. brown ..	3·25
Z191	2d. orange (Die I)	2·50
Z192	2½d. blue ..	4·00
Z193	3d. violet ..	6·50
Z194	4d. grey-green	8·50
Z195	5d. brown ..	13·00
Z196	6d. purple ..	4·50
Z197	10d. turquoise-blue ..	22·00
Z198	1s. bistre ..	5·50
Z199	2s. 6d. brown	32·00
Z200	5s. rose-red	50·00
Z201	10s. dull grey-blue ..	90·00

PRICES FOR STAMPS ON COVER

Nos. 41/50 *from* × 2
Nos. L18/24 *from* × 5

Stamps of Great Britain surch at Somerset House

I. TURKISH CURRENCY

1½ PIASTRES (10)   15 PIASTRES (11)

18¾

Short hyphen bar (R. 4/12, 14/12.)

1921 (Aug). *Stamps of King George V, wmk Royal Cypher, surch as T* **1** *(30 pa.),* **10** *and* **11** *(15 and 18¾ pi.).*

No.	Type	Description	Unused	Used
41	105	30 pa. on ½d. green ..	40	8·00
		a. Yellow-green ..	2·25	10·00
42	104	1½ pi. on 1d. bright scarlet	1·00	30
		a. Vermilion	3·75	2·25
		b. Scarlet-vermilion	3·50	2·50
43		3¾ pi. on 2½d. blue	1·00	25
		a. Dull Prussian blue	18·00	2·50
44	106	4½ pi. on 3d. violet	1·50	3·25
		a. Bluish violet	2·25	3·00
45	107	7½ pi. on 5d. brown ..	30	10
		a. Yellow-brown ..	1·50	20
46	108	15 pi. on 10d. turquoise-blue ..	55	15
47		18¾ pi. on 1s. bistre-brown	3·75	3·75
		a. Short hyphen bar	50·00	
		b. Olive-bistre ..	4·50	4·50
		ba. Short hyphen bar	60·00	

45 PIASTRES (12)   45

Joined figures (second stamp in each horiz row)

1921. *Stamps of King George V (Bradbury, Wilkinson printing) surch as T* **12**.

No.	Type	Description	Unused	Used
48	109	45 pi. on 2s. 6d. chocolate-brown	20·00	42·00
		a. Joined figures ..	30·00	60·00
		b. Olive-brown ..	48·00	60·00
		ba. Joined figures ..	65·00	80·00
49		90 pi. on 5s. rose-red ..	25·00	30·00
		a. Surch double, one albino	£225	
50		180 pi. on 10s. dull grey-blue ..	45·00	40·00
		a. Surch double, one albino	£225	
41/50		.. .. .. *Set of* 10	85·00	£110
47/50 Optd "Specimen"		.. .. *Set of* 4	£250	

II. BRITISH CURRENCY

1921. *Stamps of King George V optd as Type* L 1.

No.	Type	Description	Unused	Used
L18	106	2d. reddish orange (Die I)	1·25	24·00
		a. Bright orange	2·00	24·00
L19		3d. bluish violet	7·50	10·00
L20		4d. grey-green ..	4·50	13·00
L21	107	5d. yellow-brown	9·00	26·00
L22		6d. dull purple (*chalk-surfaced paper*)	22·00	38·00
		a. Reddish purple	22·00	8·50
L23	108	1s. bistre-brown (Optd S. £65)	11·00	7·50
		a. Olive-bistre	11·00	7·50
L24	109	2s. 6d. chocolate-brown (Optd S. £130)	35·00	80·00
		a. Olive-brown	65·00	£120
L18/24		.. .. .. *Set of* 7	80·00	£150

On No. L24 the letters of the overprint are shorter, being only 3 mm high.

Nos. 41/50 and L18/24 were used at the Constantinople office only.

SMYRNA

When the office re-opened on 1 March 1919 existing stocks of surcharged or overprinted issues were utilised until they were exhausted in mid-1920. During this period examples of Nos. 24, 29*a*, 30*a*, 33*b*/7, 39/40, L4*b*, L14/17 are known with commercial postmarks. These stamps were supplemented and finally replaced in mid-1920 by ordinary stamps of Great Britain.

Stamps of GREAT BRITAIN *cancelled with circular postmark as Type* **18** *or with "REGISTERED" oval.*

No.	Description	Used
Z282	½d. green ..	2·50
Z283	1d. scarlet ..	2·50
Z284	1½d. brown ..	3·50
Z285	2d. orange (Die I) ..	3·00
Z286	2d. orange (Die II) ..	25·00
Z287	2½d. blue ..	5·00
Z288	2½d. dull Prussian blue	
Z289	4d. grey-green	11·00
Z290	6d. purple ..	8·00
Z291	10d. turquoise-blue ..	29·00
Z292	1s. bistre ..	8·50
Z293	2s. 6d. brown	60·00
Z294	5s. rose-red	85·00
Z295	10s. dull grey-blue ..	£130

MINIMUM PRICE

The minimum price quote is 10p which represents a handling charge rather than a basis for valuing common stamps. For further notes about prices see introductory pages.

C. BRITISH FIELD OFFICE IN SALONICA

These overprints were originally prepared for use by a civili post office to be set up on Mt Athos, Northern Greece. When t project was abandoned they were placed on sale at the Army Fi Office in Salonica.

PRICES FOR STAMPS ON COVER

Nos. S1/8 *from* × 10

Levant (S 1)

1916 (end Feb–9 Mar). *Stamps of Gt. Britain, optd with Type by Army Printing Office, Salonica.*

No.	Type	Description	Unused	Used
S 1	105	½d. green ..	30·00	£
		a. Opt double ..	£1800	£22
		b. Vert pair, one without opt ..	£900	£12
S 2	104	1d. scarlet ..	30·00	£
		a. Opt double ..	£1200	£15
S 3	106	2d. reddish orange (Die I)	£120	£3
S 4		3d. bluish violet	90·00	£3
		a. Opt double ..		
S 5		4d. grey-green ..	£120	£3
S 6	107	6d. reddish pur (*chalk-surfaced paper*)	70·00	£2
		a. Vert pair, one without opt	£1000	£14
S 7	108	9d. agate ..	£275	£5
		a. Opt double ..	£8000	£65
S 8		1s. bistre-brown ..	£225	£4
S1/8		.. .. .. *Set of* 8	£850	£2(

There are numerous forgeries of this overprint.

All values can be found with an additional albino overpri inverted on the gummed side.

British New Guinea *see* Papua New Guinea

British Occupation of Irac *see* Iraq

British Occupation of Italian Colonies

PRICES FOR STAMPS ON COVER TO 1945

Nos. M1/21 *from* × 4
Nos. MD1/5 *from* × 10
Nos. S1/9 *from* × 4

The above prices refer to covers from the territorie concerned, not examples used in Great Britain.

MIDDLE EAST FORCES

For use in territory occupied by British Forces in Eritr (1942), Italian Somaliland (from 13 April 1942), Cyrena (1943), Tripolitania (1943), and some of the Dodecanese Islan (1945).

PRICES. Our prices for used stamps with "M.E.F." overprints a for specimens with identifiable postmarks of the territories which they were issued. These stamps were also used in the Unit Kingdom with official sanction, from the summer of 1950 onwar and with U.K. postmarks are worth about 25 per cent less.

PRINTERS. Considerable research has been undertaken discover the origins of Nos. M1/10. It is now suggested that N M1/5, previously assigned to Harrison and Sons, were produc by the Army Printing Services, Cairo, and that the small printing, Nos. M6/10, previously identified as the work of t Army Printing Services, Cairo, was from an unidentified print within the Middle East Forces area.

M.E.F. M.E.F.

(M 1) (M 2)

…pt. 14 mm long. Regular lettering and upright oblong stops.

Opt. 13½ mm long. Regular lettering and square stops.

M.E.F.

(M 2*a*)

Opt. 13½ mm long. Rough lettering and round stops.

(Illustrations twice actual size)

M.E.F.

Sliced "M"
(R.6/10)

…42 (2 Mar). *Stamps of Great Britain optd. W* **127**. *P* 15 × 14.

(a) With Type M 1

…1 **128** 1d. scarlet (No. 463) .. .. 60 1·25
a. Sliced "M" .. .. .. 45·00
…2 2d. orange (No. 465) .. .. 30 2·25
a. Sliced "M" .. .. .. 30·00
…3 2½d. ultramarine (No. 466) 30 45
a. Sliced "M" .. .. .. 30·00
…4 3d. violet (No. 467) 30 10
a. Opt double .. .. .. — £2000
…5 **129** 5d. brown 30 15
a. Sliced "M" .. .. .. 30·00

(b) With Type M 2

…6 **128** 1d. scarlet (No. 463) .. .. 50·00 11·00
a. Optd. with Type M 2*a* .. 40·00 8·50
b. Nos. M6/*a se-tenant* vert .. £170 70·00
…7 2d. orange (No. 465) .. .. 55·00 70·00
a. Optd with Type M 2*a* .. 48·00 60·00
b. Nos. M7/*a se-tenant* vert .. £225 £180
…8 2½d. ultramarine (No. 466) .. 30·00 7·00
a. Optd with Type M 2*a* .. 28·00 5·50
b. Nos. M8/*a se-tenant* vert .. £130 50·00
…9 3d. violet (No. 467) .. .. 85·00 26·00
a. Optd with Type M 2*a* .. 75·00 24·00
b. Nos. M9/*a se-tenant* vert .. £325 £130
…10 **129** 5d. brown .. .. .. £325 85·00
a. Optd with Type M 2*a* .. £300 75·00
b. Nos. M10/*a se-tenant* vert.. £1000 £550

See note after No. M21.

Nos. M6/10 were issued in panes of 60 (6 × 10), rows 2, 3, and 7 …eing overprinted with Type M 2 and the other seven rows with …ype M 2*a*.

M.E.F.

(M 3)

Optd 13½ mm long. Regular lettering and upright oblong stops.

(Illustration twice actual size)

…943 (1 Jan)–**1947**. *Stamps of Great Britain optd with Type* M 3 *by Harrison & Sons. W* **127**, *P* 15 × 14 *(1d. to 1s.); W* **133**, *P* 14 *(others).*

…11 **128** 1d. pale scarlet (No. 486) .. .. 1·50 10
…12 2d. pale orange (No. 488) .. .. 1·50 90
…13 2½d. light ultramarine (No. 489) .. 45 10
…14 3d. pale violet (No. 490) .. .. 1·50 10
…15 **129** 5d. brown .. .. .. 2·25 10
…16 6d. purple 40 10
…17 **130** 9d. deep olive-green 85 10
…18 1s. bistre-brown 50 10
…19 **131** 2s. 6d. yellow-green .. .. 7·00 50
…20 5s. red (1947) .. .. .. 11·00 17·00
…21 **132** 10s. ultramarine (1947) .. .. 14·00 10·00
…111/21 .. .. .. *Set of* 11 35·00 26·00
…118/21 Optd "Specimen" .. *Set of* 4 £500

The overprint on No. M15 should not be confused with the other …verprints on the 5d. value. It can be distinguished from No. M5 by …he ½ mm difference in length; and from No. M10 by the more …ntense colour, thicker lettering and larger stops.

POSTAGE DUE STAMPS

M.E.F.

(MD 1)

…942. *Postage Due stamps of Great Britain Nos.* D27/30 *and* D33 *optd with Type* MD 1, *in blue-black.*

…D1 D 1 ½d. emerald .. .. .. 30 7·50
…D2 1d. carmine .. .. .. 30 1·50
…D3 2d. agate .. .. .. 1·25 1·00
…D4 3d. violet .. .. .. 50 4·25
…D5 1s. deep blue (Optd S. £150) .. 3·25 9·50
…D1/5 .. .. .. *Set of* 5 5·00 21·00

CYRENAICA

In June 1949 the British authorities recognised the leader of the Senussi, Amir Mohammed Idris Al-Senussi, as Amir of Cyrenaica with autonomy in internal affairs.

(Currency. 10 millièmes = 1 piastre, 100 piastres = 1 Egyptian pound)

24 Mounted Warrior **25**

(Recess Waterlow)

1950 (16 Jan). *P* 12½.

136 **24** 1 m brown .. .. 55 1·75
137 2 m. carmine .. .. 70 1·50
138 3 m. orange-yellow .. .. .. 70 1·50
139 4 m. blue-green .. .. .. 1·25 2·50
140 5 m. grey-black 60 70
141 8 m. orange 75 65
142 10 m. violet 75 65
143 12 m. scarlet 75 65
144 20 m. blue 75 60
145 **25** 50 m. ultramarine and purple-brown .. 2·25 3·00
146 100 m. carmine and black .. .. 6·00 9·00
147 200 m. violet and deep blue .. .. 11·00 25·00
148 500 m. orange-yellow and green .. 42·00 65·00
136/148 .. .. .. *Set of* 13 60·00 £100

POSTAGE DUE STAMPS

D 26

(Recess Waterlow)

1950 (16 Jan). *P* 12½

D149 **D 26** 2 m. brown .. .. 45·00 90·00
D150 4 m. blue-green .. .. .. 45·00 90·00
D151 8 m. scarlet .. .. 45·00 90·00
D152 10 m. orange .. .. 45·00 90·00
D153 20 m. orange-yellow .. .. .. 45·00 90·00
D154 40 m. blue .. .. 45·00 90·00
D155 100 m. grey-brown .. .. .. 45·00 90·00
D149/155 .. .. .. *Set of* 7 £275 £550

On 24 December 1951 Cyrenaica united with Tripolitania, Fezzan and Ghadames to form the independent Kingdom of Libya, whose issues are listed in Part 13 *(Africa since Independence F—M)* of this catalogue.

ERITREA

From early 1950 examples of Nos. E1/32 exist precancelled in manuscript by a black or blue horizontal line for use by British troops on concession rate mail.

BRITISH MILITARY ADMINISTRATION

(Currency. 100 cents = 1 shilling)

B. M. A. ERITREA

10 CENTS

(E 1)

B. M. A. ERITREA

5 SHILLINGS

(E 2)

SH. 50 SH .50

Normal Misplaced Stop

1948–9. *Stamps of Great Britain surch as Types* E 1 *or* E 2.

E 1 **128** 5 c. on ½d. pale green 50 65
E 2 10 c. on 1d. pale scarlet .. .. .. 65 2·00
E 3 20 c. on 2d. pale orange .. .. .. 45 2·25
E 4 25 c. on 2½d. light ultramarine 40 60
E 5 30 c. on 3d. pale violet .. .. .. 1·25 4·00
E 6 **129** 40 c. on 5d. brown .. .. .. 30 4·00
E 7 50 c. on 6d. purple 30 60
E 7*a* **130** 65 c. on 8d. bright carmine (1.2.49) .. 7·00 2·00
E 8 75 c. on 9d. deep olive-green 50 75
E 9 1 s. on 1s. bistre-brown 50 50
E10 **131** 2 s. 50 c. on 2s. 6d. yellow-green .. 6·50 10·00
a. Misplaced stop (R. 4/7) .. .. 80·00 £110
E11 5 s. on 5s. red .. .. .. 6·50 16·00
E12 **132** 10 s. on 10s. ultramarine .. .. 18·00 21·00
E1/12 .. .. *Set of* 13 38·00 55·00

BRITISH ADMINISTRATION

1950 (6 Feb). *As Nos.* E1/12, *but surch* "B.A. ERITREA" *and new values instead of* "B.M.A." *etc.*

E13 **128** 5 c. on ½d. pale green .. .. .. 50 6·00
E14 10 c. on 1d. pale scarlet .. .. .. 30 2·75
E15 20 c. on 2d. pale orange 30 70
E16 25 c. on 2½d. light ultramarine 30 60
E17 **128** 30 c. on 3d. pale violet .. .. .. 30 1·00
E18 **129** 40 c. on 5d. brown 40 90
E19 50 c. on 6d. purple 30 20
E20 **130** 65 c. on 8d. bright carmine .. .. 40 1·00
E21 75 c. on 9d. deep olive-green 30 25
E22 1 s. on 1s. bistre-brown 30 15
E23 **131** 2 s. 50 c. on 2s. 6d. yellow-green .. 3·50 4·50
E24 5 s. on 5s. red .. .. 6·00 9·00
E25 **132** 10 s. on 10s. ultramarine .. .. 48·00 48·00
E13/25 .. .. *Set of* 13 55·00 65·00

1951 (28 May*). *Nos.* 503/4, 506/7 *and* 509/11 *of Great Britain surch* "B.A. ERITREA" *and new values.*

E26 **128** 5 c. on ½d. pale orange 30 60
E27 10 c. on 1d. light ultramarine 30 60
E28 20 c. on 2d. pale red-brown 30 30
E29 25 c. on 2½d. pale scarlet 30 30
E30 **147** 2 s. 50 c. on 2s. 6d. yellow-green .. 6·00 17·00
E31 **148** 5 s. on 5s. red .. .. .. 18·00 17·00
E32 10 s. on 10s. ultramarine .. .. 19·00 17·00
E26/32 .. .. *Set of* 7 40·00 48·00

*This is the local release date. The stamps were placed on sale in London on 3 May.

POSTAGE DUE STAMPS

B. M. A. ERITREA

10 CENTS

(ED 1)

1948. *Postage Due stamps of Great Britain Nos.* D27/30 *and* D33 *surch as Type* ED 1.

ED1 D 1 5 c. on ½d. emerald .. .. .. 9·00 18·00
ED2 10 c. on 1d. carmine .. .. .. 8·00 19·00
a. No stop after "B" .. .. 95·00
ED3 20 c. on 2d. agate .. .. .. 7·00 14·00
a. No stop after "A" .. .. 60·00
b. No stop after "B" (R. 1/9) .. £110
ED4 30 c. on 3d. violet .. .. .. 8·00 13·00
ED5 1 s. on 1s. deep blue .. .. .. 15·00 24·00
ED1/5.. .. .. .. *Set of* 5 42·00 80·00

1950 (6 Feb). *As Nos.* ED1/5, *but surch* "B.A. ERITREA" *and new values instead of* "B.M.A." *etc.*

ED6 D 1 5 c. on ½d. emerald .. .. 11·00 35·00
ED7 10 c. on 1d. carmine .. .. 9·00 15·00
a. "C" of "CENTS" omitted .. £1400
ab. "C" omitted and vertical oblong for "E" of "CENTS" £2500
ED8 20 c. on 2d. agate .. .. .. 9·50 13·00
ED9 30 c. on 3d. violet .. .. .. 9·50 13·00
w. Wmk sideways-inverted* ..
ED10 1 s. on 1s. deep blue .. .. 15·00 22·00
a. Stop after "A" omitted (R. 2/13) £275
ED6/10 .. .. *Set of* 5 48·00 90·00

No. ED7a, and probably No. ED7ab, occurred on R.7/20, but the error was quickly corrected.

*No. ED9w shows the Crowns pointing to the left, *as seen from the back of the stamp.*

Stamps of Ethiopia were used in Eritrea after 15 September 1952 following federation with Ethiopia.

SOMALIA

BRITISH OCCUPATION

E.A.F.

(S 1. "East Africa Forces")

1943 (15 Jan)–**46**. *Stamps of Great Britain optd with Type* S 1, *in blue.*

S1 **128** 1d. pale scarlet 60 40
S2 2d. pale orange .. .. .. 1·50 1·25
S3 2½d. light ultramarine .. .. 30 3·50
S4 3d. pale violet 50 15
S5 **129** 5d. brown 50 40
S6 6d. purple 30 90
S7 **130** 9d. deep olive-green .. .. 60 2·25
S8 1s. bistre-brown .. .. .. 1·25 15
S9 **131** 2s. 6d. yellow-green (1946) .. 6·00 6·50
S1/9 .. .. .. *Set of* 9 10·50 14·00
S8/9 Optd "Specimen" .. *Set of* 2 £250

The note *re* used prices above Type M 1 of Middle East Forces also applies to the above issue.

BRITISH MILITARY ADMINISTRATION

(Currency. 100 cents = 1 shilling)

1948 (27 May). *Stamps of Great Britain surch* "B.M.A./SOMALIA" *and new values, as Types* E 1 *and* E 2 *of Eritrea.*

S10 **128** 5 c. on ½d. pale green .. .. 50 1·25
S11 15 c. on 1½d. pale red-brown .. .. 80 10·00
S12 20 c. on 2d. pale orange .. .. 1·50 3·25
S13 25 c. on 2½d. light ultramarine .. 1·00 4·00
S14 30 c. on 3d. pale violet .. .. 2·00 9·00
S15 **129** 40 c. on 5d. brown 40 20
S16 50 c. on 6d. purple .. .. .. 40 2·00
S17 **130** 75 c. on 9d. deep olive-green .. 2·00 14·00
S18 1 s. on 1s. bistre-brown .. .. 1·25 20
S19 **131** 2 s. 50 c. on 2s. 6d. yellow-green .. 3·25 22·00
a. Misplaced stop (R. 4/7) .. 80·00 £200
S20 5 s. on 5s. red .. .. .. 8·00 29·00
S10/20 .. .. .. *Set of* 11 19·00 85·00

For illustration of No. S19a, see previous column above No. E1 of Eritrea.

BRITISH ADMINISTRATION

1950 (2 Jan). *As Nos.* S10/20, *but surch* "B.A./SOMALIA" *and new values, instead of* "B.M.A." *etc.*

S21 **128** 5 c. on ½d. pale green .. .. 20 2·25
S22 15 c. on 1½d. pale red-brown .. 60 13·00
S23 20 c. on 2d. pale orange .. .. 60 3·50
S24 25 c. on 2½d. light ultramarine .. 40 4·50
S25 30 c. on 3d. pale violet .. .. 1·00 3·00
S26 **129** 40 c. on 5d. brown 55 85
S27 50 c. on 6d. purple .. .. .. 40 1·00
S28 **130** 75 c. on 9d. deep olive-green .. 1·00 5·50
S29 1 s. on 1s. bistre-brown .. .. 60 1·50

No.	Type	Description	Unused	Used
S30	131	2 s. 50 c. on 2s. 6d. yellow-green	4·00	22·00
S31		5 s. on 5s. red	8·50	27·00
S21/31		*Set of* 11	16·00	75·00

Somalia reverted to Italian Administration on 1 April 1950 later becoming independent. Later issues will be found listed in Part 8 (*Italy and Switzerland*) of this catalogue.

TRIPOLITANIA

BRITISH MILITARY ADMINISTRATION

(Currency. 100 centesimi = 1 Military Administration lira)

4 M.A.L. 4 M.A.L.

Normal — Misaligned surcharge (R.8/8, 18/8)

1948 (1 July). *Stamps of Great Britain surch* "B.M.A./TRIPOLITANIA" *and new values, as Types* E 1 *and* E 2 *of Eritrea, but expressed in M(ilitary) A(dministration) L(ire).*

No.	Type	Description	Unused	Used
T 1	128	1 l. on ½d. pale green	30	80
T 2		2 l. on 1d. pale scarlet	20	15
T 3		3 l. on 1½d. pale red-brown	20	50
		a. Misaligned surch	20·00	
T 4		4 l. on 2d. pale orange	25	50
		a. Misaligned surch	23·00	
T 5		5 l. on 2½d. light ultramarine	30	20
T 6		6 l. on 3d. pale violet	20	40
T 7	129	10 l. on 5d. brown	20	15
T 8		12 l. on 6d. purple	30	20
T 9	130	18 l. on 9d. deep olive-green	50	65
T10		24 l. on 1s. bistre-brown	50	65
T11	131	60 l. on 2s. 6d. yellow-green	2·00	6·00
T12		120 l. on 5s. red	11·00	15·00
T13	132	240 l. on 10s. ultramarine	19·00	80·00
T1/13		*Set of* 13	32·00	95·00

BRITISH ADMINISTRATION

1950 (6 Feb). *As Nos.* T1/13, *but surch.* "B.A. TRIPOLITANIA" *and new values, instead of* "B.M.A." *etc.*

No.	Type	Description	Unused	Used
T14	128	1 l. on ½d. pale green	90	8·50
T15		2 l. on 1d. pale scarlet	1·00	40
T16		3 l. on 1½d. pale red-brown	35	8·00
		a. Misaligned surch	30·00	
T17		4 l. on 2d. pale orange	25	4·50
		a. Misaligned surch	23·00	
T18		5 l. on 2½d. light ultramarine	25	70
T19		6 l. on 3d. pale violet	90	2·25
T20	129	10 l. on 5d. brown	30	2·75
T21		12 l. on 6d. purple	75	50
T22	130	18 l. on 9d. deep olive-green	75	1·60
T23		24 l. on 1s. bistre-brown	75	3·50
T24	131	60 l. on 2s. 6d. yellow-green	4·25	11·00
T25		120 l. on 5s. red	17·00	21·00
T26	132	240 l. on 10s. ultramarine	23·00	45·00
T14/26		*Set of* 13	45·00	95·00

1951 (3 May). *Nos.* 503/7 *and* 509/11 *of Great Britain surch* "B.A. TRIPOLITANIA" *and new values.*

No.	Type	Description	Unused	Used
T27	128	1 l. on ½d. pale orange	20	3·50
T28		2 l. on 1d. light ultramarine	20	90
T29		3 l. on 1½d. pale green	30	6·50
T30		4 l. on 2d. pale red-brown	20	1·25
T31		5 l. on 2½d. pale scarlet	30	6·50
T32	147	60 l. on 2s. 6d. yellow-green	3·50	17·00
T33	148	120 l. on 5s. red	7·50	21·00
T34	149	240 l. on 10s. ultramarine	26·00	35·00
T27/34		*Set of* 8	35·00	80·00

POSTAGE DUE STAMPS

1948. *Postage Due stamps of Great Britain Nos.* D27/30 *and* D33 *surch.* "B.M.A./TRIPOLITANIA" *and new values, as Type* ED 1 *of Eritrea, but expressed in M(ilitary) A(dministration) L(ire).*

No.	Type	Description	Unused	Used
TD1	D 1	1 l. on ½d. emerald	4·50	38·00
		a. No stop after "A"	60·00	
TD2		2 l. on 1d. carmine	2·50	28·00
		a. No stop after "A"	42·00	
		b. No stop after "M" (R.1/17)	80·00	
TD3		4 l. on 2d. agate	7·00	24·00
		a. No stop after "A"	£120	
		b. No stop after "M"	£150	
TD4		6 l. on 3d. violet	7·50	20·00
TD5		24 l. on 1s. deep blue	28·00	90·00
TD1/5		*Set of* 5	45·00	£180

1950 (6 Feb). *As Nos.* TD1/5, *but surch* "B.A. TRIPOLITANIA" *and new values, instead of* "B.M.A." *etc.*

No.	Type	Description	Unused	Used
TD 6	D 1	1 l. on ½d. emerald	9·50	65·00
		a. No stop after "B"	£110	
TD 7		2 l. on 1d. carmine	2·50	25·00
		a. No stop after "B"	65·00	
TD 8		4 l. on 2d. agate	2·75	28·00
		a. No stop after "B"	70·00	
TD 9		6 l. on 3d. violet	17·00	60·00
		a. No stop after "B"	£160	
		w. Wmk sideways-inverted*		
TD10		24 l. on 1s. deep blue	40·00	£120
		a. No stop after "A"	£300	
		b. No stop after "B"	£300	
TD6/10		*Set of* 5	65·00	£275

*No. TD9w shows the Crowns pointing to the left, *as seen from the back of the stamp.*

Tripolitania became part of the independent kingdom of Libya on 24 December 1951.

British P.Os in Crete

BRITISH ADMINISTRATION OF CANDIA PROVINCE (HERAKLEION)

Crete, formerly part of the Turkish Empire, was made autonomous, under Turkish suzerainty, in November 1898 with British, French, Italian and Russian troops stationed in separate zones to keep the peace.

Overseas mail franked with Nos. B1/5 was forwarded through the Austrian post office at Canea, being additionally franked with stamps of the Austro-Hungarian Post Offices in the Turkish Empire.

(Currency. 40 paras = 1 piastre)

PRICES FOR STAMPS ON COVER	
No. B1	*from* × 10
Nos. B2/5	—

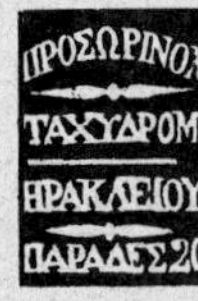

B 1

B 2

1898 (25 Nov). *Handstruck locally. Imperf.*

No.	Type	Description	Unused	Used
B1	B 1	20 pa. bright violet	£425	£225

1898 (3 Dec). *Litho by M. Grundmann, Athens. P* 11½.

No.	Type	Description	Unused	Used
B2	B 2	10 pa. blue	8·00	15·00
		a. Imperf (pair)	£250	
B3		20 pa. green	11·00	13·00
		a. Imperf (pair)	£250	

1899. *P* 11½.

No.	Type	Description	Unused	Used
B4	B 2	10 pa. brown	8·00	22·00
		a. Imperf (pair)	£250	
B5		20 pa. rose	16·00	15·00
		a. Imperf (pair)	£250	

The British postal service closed at the end of 1899.

British P.O. in Siam

(Bangkok)

An overseas postal service for foreign residents was operated by the British Consulate at Bangkok from 1858. Mail was despatched by steamer to Singapore and from 1876 onwards was increasingly franked with Straits Settlements stamps. These were initially cancelled on arrival at Singapore, but later an oval postmark inscribed "BRITISH CONSULATE BANGKOK" was used. In 1883 a circular "BANGKOK" datestamp was introduced for use with Nos. 1/23. Both cancellations can also be found used on Hong Kong stamps between 1881 and 1885.

(Currency. 100 cents = 1 Straits dollar)

Stamps of Straits Settlements (see Malaysia) cancelled with oval postmark inscribed "BRITISH CONSULATE BANGKOK" *around Royal Arms.*

1877 *to* **1882.** *Wmk Crown CC (Nos.* 11/15, 33 *and* 35*).*

Z1	2 c. brown	£325
Z2	4 c. rose	£325
Z3	6 c. dull lilac	£375
Z4	8 c. orange-yellow	£325
Z5	10 c. on 30 c. claret (thin "0") (No. 33)	£1000
Z6	10 c. on 30 c. claret (thick "10") (No. 34)	£1000
Z7	10 c. on 30 c. claret (thin "1", thick "0".) (No. 35)	£1000
Z8	12 c. blue	£425

Subsequent Straits Settlements values to 8 c. watermarked Crown CA are known used at Bangkok in 1883 and 1884. During this period the stamps overprinted "B" were on sale at the British Post Office.

PRICES FOR STAMPS ON COVER

The issues of the British Post Offices in Siam are worth from × 100 the prices quoted for used stamps when on cover.

B

(1)

1882 (May)–**85.** *Stamps of Straits Settlements optd with T* **1.**

(*a*) *On No.* 9 *of* 1867

No.	Description	Unused	Used
1	32 c. on 2 a. yellow (1885)	£35000	

(*b*) *On Nos.* 11/13, 14*a*, 15/17 *and* 19 *of* 1867–72 *and Nos.* 48/9 *of* 1882. *Wmk Crown CC*

No.	Description	Unused	Used
2	2 c. brown	£2500	£1400
3	4 c. rose	£2000	£1100
	a. Opt double	—	£7500
4	5 c. purple-brown	£250	£275
5	6 c. lilac	£160	£110
6	8 c. orange	£1700	£200
7	10 c. slate	£300	£150
8	12 c. blue	£900	£475
9	24 c. green	£700	£150
10	30 c. claret	£30000	£20000
11	96 c. grey	£4500	£2500

(*c*) *On Nos.* 59/60 *of April* 1883

No.	Description	Unused	Used
12	2 c. on 32 c. pale red (*Wide* "S")	£1900	£225
13	2 c. on 32 c. pale red (*Wide* "E")	£2250	£250

(*d*) *On Nos.* 50/3 *of* 1882 *and Nos.* 63/7 *of* 1883–84. *Wm Crown CA*

No.	Description	Unused	Used
14	2 c. brown	£450	£32
15	2 c. pale rose (1883)	55·00	45·0
	a. Opt inverted	—	£950
	b. Opt double	£2750	£275
	c. Opt treble	£10000	
16	4 c. rose (1883)	£500	£30
17	4 c. pale brown (1883)	75·00	70·0
	a. Opt double	£3500	
	b. Broken oval	£900	£90
18	5 c. blue (1884)	£225	£16
19	6 c. lilac (1884)	£160	£11
20	8 c. orange (1883)	£140	65·0
	a. Opt inverted	£17000	£1000
21	10 c. slate (1883)	£150	85·0
22	12 c. brown-purple (1883)	£275	£15
23	24 c. yellow-green (1884?)	£4000	£250

The prices quoted for the overprint double errors, Nos. 3a, 15 and 17a, are for stamps showing two clear impressions of th overprint. Examples showing partial doubling, on these an other values, are worth a small premium over the price quote for normal stamps.

No. 17b shows the edge of the central oval broken above th "O" of "POSTAGE". It occurs on R. 10/5 of the lower right pan

The use of these stamps ceased on 30 June 1885. Siam joine the Universal Postal Union on 1 July 1885.

British Postal Agencies in Eastern Arabia

Certain Arab States in Eastern Arabia, whilst remaining ind pendent, had British postal administrations.

Bahrain and Kuwait (from 1948) and Qatar (from 1957) us British stamps overprinted and surcharged in local currency. Al Dhabi (from 1964) and Trucial States (from 1961 and used only Dubai) had definitive issues made under the auspices of the Briti Agencies.

In addition, British stamps were surcharged with value only f use in Muscat and certain other states. They were formerly list under Muscat as they were first put on sale there, but in view their more extended use, the list has been transferred he retaining the same numbering.

The stamps were used in Muscat from 1 April 1948 to 29 Ap 1966; in Dubai from 1 April 1948 to 6 January 1961; in Qatar: Do from August 1950, Umm Said from February 1956, to 31 Mar 1957; and in Abu Dhabi from 30 March 1963 (Das Island fro December 1960) to 29 March 1964.

Nos. 21/2 were placed on sale in Kuwait Post Offices in Ap and May 1951 and from February to November 1953 due shortages of stamps with "KUWAIT" overprint. Isolat examples of other values can be found commercially used fro Bahrain or Kuwait.

(Currency. 12 pies = 1 anna; 16 annas = 1 rupee)

Stamps of Great Britain surcharged

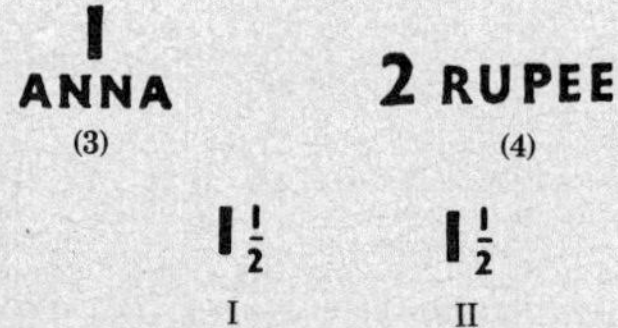

(3) (4)

I II

Two types of 1½ a. surcharge:

I. "1" 3¼ mm high and aligns with top of "2" in "½" (Rows 1 to 10).

II. "1" 3½ mm high with foot of figure below top of "2" (Rows 11 to 20).

1948 (1 Apr). *Surch with T* **3** (½ *a. to* 1 *r.*) *or* **4** (2 *r.*).

No.	Type	Description	Unused	Used
16	128	½ a. on ½d. pale green	1·75	5·
17		1 a. on 1d. pale scarlet	1·75	
18		1½ a. on 1½d. pale red-brown (I)	4·00	
		a. Type II	4·00	
		b. Vert pair. Nos. 18/a	25·00	
19		2 a. on 2d. pale orange	1·50	
20		2½ a. on 2½d. light ultramarine	2·00	4·
21		3 a. on 3d. pale violet	2·00	
22	129	6 a. on 6d. purple	2·00	
23	130	1 r. on 1s. bistre-brown	3·00	
24	131	2 r. on 2s. 6d. yellow-green	7·00	26·
16/24		*Set of* 9	23·00	35·

One example of No. 22 is known with the surcharge alm completely omitted from position R. 20/2 in the sheet.

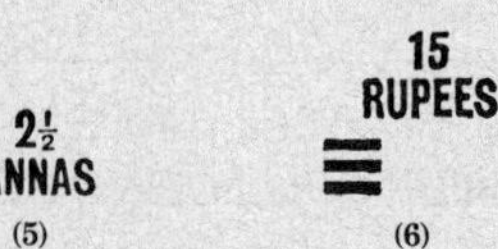

(5) (6)

1948 (26 Apr). *Royal Silver Wedding. Nos.* 493/4 *surch with T* **5** *or* **6**.

No.	Type	Description	Unused	Used
25	137	2½ a. on 2½d. ultramarine	1·25	
26	138	15 r. on £1 blue	23·00	35·

8 (29 July). *Olympic Games. Nos. 495/8 surch with new values* "ANNAS" *or* "1 RUPEE", *as T 5/6, but in one line on 2½ a.* ert) *or 6 a. and 1 r. (horiz) and grills obliterating former values* all except 2½ a.

139	2½ a. on 2½d. ultramarine	.. ..	35	1·75
140	3 a. on 3d. violet	.. ..	45	1·75
141	6 a. on 6d. bright purple	.. ..	45	1·75
142	1 r. on 1s. brown	.. ..	1·25	2·00
	a. Surch double	.. ..	£650	
30 ..	.. ..	*Set of 4*	2·25	6·50

9 (10 Oct). *75th Anniv of Universal Postal Union. Nos. 499/* 02 *surch with new values in* "ANNAS" *or* "1 RUPEE" *as T 3/4,* ut *all in one line, with grills obliterating former values.*

143	2½ a. on 2½d. ultramarine	.. ..	60	2·25
144	3 a. on 3d. violet	.. ..	60	2·25
145	6 a. on 6d. bright purple	.. ..	60	1·75
146	1 r. on 1s. brown	.. ..	3·00	2·50
4 ..	.. ..	*Set of 4*	4·25	8·00

2 RUPEES (6a)   2 RUPEES (6b)

pe 6a. "2" and "RUPEES" level and in line with lower of the two bars.
pe 6b. "2" raised in relation to "RUPEES" and whole surcharge below the lower bar.

0 (2 Oct)–55. *Nos. 503/8 surch as T* **3** *and No.* 509 *with* T 6a.

128	½ a. on ½d. pale orange (3.5.51)	..	30	8·00
	1 a. on 1d. light ultramarine (3.5.51)	..	30	5·50
	1½ a. on 1½d. pale green (I) (3.5.51)	..	3·50	19·00
	a. Type II	.. ..	3·50	19·00
	b. Vert pair. Nos. 37/a	.. ..	30·00	
	2 a. on 2d. pale red-brown (3.5.51)	..	30	7·00
	2½ a. on 2½d. pale scarlet (3.5.51)	..	30	15·00
129	4 a. on 4d. light ultramarine	..	30	2·50
147	2 r. on 2s. 6d. yellow-green (3.5.51)	..	22·00	6·00
	a. Surch with Type 6b (1955)	..	£120	65·00
41	.. ..	*Set of 7*	24·00	55·00

52 (5 Dec)–54. *Stamps of Queen Elizabeth II wmk Tudor* Crown, *surch as T* **3** *(in one line on 2½ and 6 a.).*

154	½ a. on ½d. orange-red (31.8.53)	..	10	1·50
	1 a. on 1d. ultramarine (31.8.53)	..	10	1·50
	1½ a. on 1½d. green	.. ..	10	50
	2 a. on 2d. red-brown (31.8.53)	..	10	10
155	2½ a. on 2½d. carmine-red	.. ..	10	10
	3 a. on 3d. deep lilac (B.) (18.1.54)	..	20	30
156	4 a. on 4d. ultramarine (2.11.53)	..	55	3·00
157	6 a. on 6d. reddish purple (18.1.54)	..	35	10
160	12 a. on 1s. 3d. green (2.11.53)	..	2·00	30
159	1 r. on 1s. 6d. grey-blue (2.11.53)	..	2·00	10
51 ..	.. ..	*Set of 10*	5·00	6·50

53 (10 June). *Coronation. Nos. 532/5 surch with new values.*

161	2½ a. on 2½d. carmine-red	.. ..	1·75	95
162	4 a. on 4d. ultramarine	.. ..	1·75	95
163	12 a. on 1s. 3d. deep yellow-green	..	3·25	95
164	1 r. on 1s. 6d. deep grey-blue	..	4·50	45
5 ..	.. ..	*Set of 4*	10·00	3·00

2 RUPEES I

2 RUPEES II

2 RUPEES III

(7)

5 RUPEES I

5 RUPEES II

(8)

Types of surcharges

rupees.
pe I. On *Waterlow ptg*. Top of "R" level with top of "2" and other letters of "RUPEES". Bars 7 mm long.
pe II. On *Waterlow ptg* by Harrison: "R" dropped out of alignment with "2" and other letters of "RUPEES". Bars 6½ mm long.
pe III. On *De La Rue ptg* by Harrison. Top of "R" below level of top of "2". Bars 7–7¼ mm long and with left sides aligned with "S".

rupees.
pe I. On *Waterlow ptg* by Harrison. Ends of letters square and sharp. There were two printings made in March and May 1957.
pe II. On *De La Rue ptg* by Harrison. Type is thicker and ends of letters are relatively rounded.

For differences between Waterlow and De La Rue printings of basic stamps see notes in Great Britain after No. 539.

55–60. *T* **166/7** *(Waterlow ptgs) (W* **165**, *St. Edward's Crown)* surch *with T* **7/8**.

166	2 r. on 2s. 6d. black-brown (Type I) (23.9.55)	.. ..	3·25	70
	a. Type II (2.57)	.. ..	6·00	3·00
	b. Type III (No. 536a D.L.R.) (6.60)	..	20·00	48·00

57 167	5 r. on 5s. rose-red (Type I) (1.3.57)	..	9·00	2·00
	a. Wide surcharge	.. .. ..	£250	£200
	b. Type II (No. 537a D.L.R.) (27.1.60)		20·00	48·00

No. 57a ("5" and "R" spaced 2¼ mm instead of 1¼ mm) occurred on R. 8/4 of the first surcharging of No. 57 only.

1956–57. *Stamps of Queen Elizabeth II, W* **165**, *St. Edward's Crown, surch as T* **3** *(in one line on 2½ and 6 a.).*

58 154	1 a. on 1d. ultramarine (4.3.57)	..	35	50
58*a*	1½ a. on 1½d. green (1956)	..	£3500	£600
59	2 a. on 2d. red-brown (8.6.56)	..	70	1·75
60 155	2½ a. on 2½d. carmine-red (8.6.56)	..	80	3·00
61	3 a. on 3d. deep lilac (B.) (3.2.57)	..	1·00	5·50
62 156	4 a. on 4d. ultramarine (9.12.56)	..	5·00	14·00
63 157	6 a. on 6d. red-purple (10.2.57)	..	1·10	6·00
64 159	1 r. on 1s. 6d. grey-blue (2.8.56)	..	3·25	15
58/64 (*ex* 58*a*)	.. ..	*Set of 7*	11·00	28·00

No. 58*a* came from a few sheets of the St. Edward's Crown watermark included, in error, with a printing of No. 44. Most examples were used in Dubai, but two are known from Muscat and a pair on a cover from Bahrain. A single mint example also exists.

(New Currency. 100 naye paise = 1 rupee)

NP 1 NP (9)   3 NP NP (10)   75 NP (11)

1957 (1 Apr)–**59.** *Value in naye paise. Stamps of Queen Elizabeth II, W* **165**, *St. Edward's Crown, surch as T* **9** (1, 15, 25, 40, 50 *n.p.*), **11** (75 *n.p.*) *or* **10** (*others*).

65 157	1 n.p. on 5d. brown	.. ..	10	50
66 154	3 n.p. on ½d. orange-red	.. ..	20	1·75
67	6 n.p. on 1d. ultramarine	.. ..	20	1·75
68	9 n.p. on 1½d. green	.. ..	20	75
69	12 n.p. on 2d. light red-brown	.. ..	30	1·00
70 155	15 n.p. on 2½d. carmine-red (Type I)	..	30	10
	a. Type II (4.59)	.. ..	30	3·25
71	20 n.p. on 3d. deep lilac (B.)	.. ..	20	10
72 156	25 n.p. on 4d. ultramarine	.. ..	70	2·75
73 157	40 n.p. on 6d. reddish purple	.. ..	30	10
	a. Deep claret (3.59)	.. ..	35	10
74 158	50 n.p. on 9d. bronze-green	.. ..	1·25	2·50
75 160	75 n.p. on 1s. 3d. green	.. ..	2·00	35
65/75 ..	.. ..	*Set of 11*	5·00	10·50

15 NP

(12)

1957 (1 Aug). *World Scout Jubilee Jamboree. Nos. 557/9 surch in one line as T* **12** *(15 n.p.), or in two lines (others).*

76	15 n.p. on 2½d. carmine-red	.. ..	25	85
77	25 n.p. on 4d. ultramarine	.. ..	30	85
78	75 n.p. on 1s. 3d. green	.. ..	35	85
76/8	.. ..	*Set of 3*	80	2·25

1960 (26 Apr)–**61.** *Stamps of Queen Elizabeth II, W* **179**, *Mult Crown, surch as T* **9** (1, 15, 30, 40, 50 *n.p.*), **11** (75 *n.p.*), **3** (1 *r.*), **7** (2 *r.*, 5 *r.*) *or* **10** (*others*).

79 157	1 n.p. on 5d. brown (30.8.60)	.. ..	10	20
80 154	3 n.p. on ½d. orange-red (21.6.60)	..	55	80
81	5 n.p. on 1d. ultramarine (8.4.61)	..	80	55
82	6 n.p. on 1d. ultramarine (21.6.60)	..	1·25	90
83	10 n.p. on 1½d. green (8.4.61)	..	50	1·00
84	12 n.p. on 2d. light red-brown (21.6.60)		2·00	2·50
85 155	15 n.p. on 2½d. carmine-red (Type II)	..	25	10
86	20 n.p. on 3d. deep lilac (B.) (28.9.60)	..	25	10
87 156	30 n.p. on 4½d. chestnut (8.4.61)	..	40	40
88 157	40 n.p. on 6d. deep claret (28.9.60)	..	45	10
89 158	50 n.p. on 9d. bronze-green (8.4.61)	..	1·00	1·25
90 160	75 n.p. on 1s. 3d. green (8.4.61)	..	2·25	90
91 159	1 r. on 1s. 6d. grey-blue (8.4.61)	..	13·00	2·25
92 166	2 r. on 2s. 6d. black-brown (No. 595) (8.4.61)	.. .. ..	7·00	24·00
93 167	5 r. on 5s. rose-red (No. 596) (8.4.61)		16·00	38·00
79/93 ..	.. ..	*Set of 15*	42·00	65·00

British Solomon Islands
see Solomon Islands

British Somaliland
see Somaliland Protectorate

British South Africa Company
see Rhodesia

British Virgin Islands

CROWN COLONY

Apart from the 1951 Legislative Council issue, the word "BRITISH" did not appear regularly on the stamps until 1968 when it was introduced to avoid confusion with the nearby Virgin Islands of the United States (the former Danish West Indies).

Most mail from the early years of the islands' history was sent via the Danish island of St. Thomas.

It is not known exactly when the first post office, or agency, was established on Tortola, but an entry in a G.P.O. account book suggest that it was operating by 1787 and the earliest letter postmarked "TORTOLA" dates from June of that year. The stamps of Great Britain were used from 1858 to May 1860, when the colonial authorities assumed responsibility for the overseas mails from the British G.P.O.

For illustrations of the handstamp and postmark types see BRITISH POST OFFICES ABROAD notes, following GREAT BRITAIN.

TORTOLA

CROWNED-CIRCLE HANDSTAMPS

CC1	CC 1	TORTOLA (R.) (15.12.1842) *Price on cover*	£4000
CC2	CC 5	TORTOLA (R.) (21.6.1854) *Price on cover*	£7000

No. CC2 is known used as an Official Paid mark during the years 1900 to 1918. *Price on cover* £1200.

Stamps of GREAT BRITAIN *cancelled* "A 13" *as Type* **2**.

1858 *to* **1860.**

Z1	1d. rose-red (1857), *perf* 14	£3000
Z2	4d. rose (1857)	£2750
Z3	6d. lilac (1856)	£1100
Z4	1s. green (1856)	

PRICES FOR STAMPS ON COVER TO 1945

Nos. 1/7	*from* × 15
Nos. 8/22	*from* × 12
Nos. 24/31	*from* × 8
Nos. 32/41	*from* × 10
No. 42	*from* × 20
Nos. 43/50	*from* × 6
Nos. 54/77	*from* × 5
Nos. 78/81	*from* × 6
Nos. 82/101	*from* × 3
Nos. 103/6	*from* × 4
Nos. 107/9	*from* × 6
Nos. 110/21	*from* × 2

1   St. Ursula   2

(Litho Nissen & Parker from original dies by Waterlow)

1866 (Dec). *No wmk. P* 12 (*a*) *White wove paper.*

1 1	1d. green	.. ..	45·00	60·00
2	1d. deep green	.. ..	50·00	65·00
3 2	6d. rose	.. ..	90·00	£110
4	6d. deep rose	.. ..	£130	£140
	a. Large "V" in "VIRGIN"	.. ..	£375	£475

(*b*) *Toned paper*

5 1	1d. green	.. ..	45·00	60·00
	a. Perf 15 × 12	.. .. ..	£4250	£5500
6	1d. deep green	.. .. ..	£100	£120
7 2	6d. rose-red	.. .. ..	60·00	90·00
	a. Large "V" in "VIRGIN" (R. 2/1)	..	£275	£375

The above were printed in sheets of 25.

6d. stamps showing part of the papermaker's watermark ("A. Cowan & Sons Extra Superfine A. C. & S.") are worth 50% more.

Beware of fakes of No. 5a made from perf 12 stamps.

3   4

Normal Variety

1s. Long-tailed "S" in "ISLANDS" (R. 3/1)

(Litho Nissen and Parker from original dies by Waterlow)

1867–70. *No wmk. P* 15. 1s. *with double-lined frame.*

(a) White wove paper

8 **1** 1d. yellow-green (1868) . . . . 80·00 80·00
9 1d. blue-green (1870) . . . . 65·00 70·00
10 **2** 6d. pale rose £475 £475
11 **4** 1s. black and rose-carmine £225 £300
a. Long-tailed "S" £600 £650

(b) Toned paper

12 **1** 1d. yellow-green (1868) . . . . . . 85·00 80·00
13 **2** 6d. dull rose (1868) £225 £275
14 **4** 1s. black and rose-carmine (*greyish paper*) £225 £300
aa. Long-tailed "S" £600 £650
14*a* 1s. black and rose-carmine £300 £325
b. Long-tailed "S" £650 £700

(c) Pale rose paper

15 **3** 4d. lake-red . . . . 50·00 70·00

(d) Buff paper

16 **3** 4d. lake-red . . . . 40·00 60·00
17 4d. lake-brown . . . . 40·00 60·00

The thin lines of the frame on the 1s. are close together and sometimes merge into one.

The 1d. from the 1868 printing was in sheets of 20 with narrow margins between the stamps. Later printings were in sheets of 12 with wider margins. The 4d. was in sheets of 25; and the remaining two values in sheets of 20.

In Type 4 the figure of the Virgin was printed by typography and the remainder of the design by lithography.

The greyish paper used for Nos. 14 and 20 often shows traces of blue.

1867. *As T* **4**, *but with crimson frames superimposed with bands extending through margins. P* 15.

18 **4** 1s. black and rose-carmine (*white paper*) 48·00 60·00
a. Long-tailed "S" £160 £180
b. Figure of Virgin omitted £60000
19 1s. black and rose-carmine (*toned paper*) 48·00 60·00
a. Long-tailed "S" £160 £180
20 1s. black and rose-carmine (*greyish paper* £700 £850
a. Long-tailed "S" £1600 £1600

1868. *Nos. 11 and 14a with frame lines retouched so as to make them single lines. Margins remain white. P* 15.

21 **4** 1s. black and rose-carmine (*white paper*) £130 £160
aa. Long-tailed "S" £375 £450
21*a* 1s. black and rose-carmine (*toned paper*) £130 £160
b. Long-tailed "S" £375 £450

(Litho D.L.R.)

1878. *Wmk Crown CC (sideways). P* 14.

22 **1** 1d. green . . . . 70·00 85·00
a. Yellow-green £170 £130
ab. Wmk upright . . . . . . 90·00 £120

6 (Die I)

4D

(**7**)

(Typo D.L.R.)

1879–80. *Wmk Crown CC. P* 14.

24 **6** 1d. emerald-green (1880) . . . . 65·00 85·00
25 2½d. red-brown . . . . 90·00 £120

1883 (June)–84. *Wmk Crown CA. P* 14.

26 **6** ½d. yellow-buff . . . . 80·00 80·00
27 ½d. dull green (*shades*) (11.83) . . 3·50 8·00
b. Top left triangle detached . . 90·00
29 1d. pale rose (15.9.83) . . . . 23·00 26·00
a. Deep rose (1884) . . . . 55·00 60·00
31 2½d. ultramarine (9.84) . . . . 2·50 13·00
b. Top left triangle detached . . 90·00
w. Wmk inverted . . . .

For illustration of "top left triangle detached" variety see above No. 21 of Antigua.

(Litho D.L.R.)

1887–89. *Wmk Crown CA. P* 14.

32 **1** 1d. red (5.89) . . . . . . 2·00 7·00
33 1d. rose-red . . . . . . 2·25 7·00
34 1d. rose . . . . 5·00 14·00
35 **3** 4d. chestnut . . . . . . 35·00 65·00
x. Wmk reversed
36 4d. pale chestnut . . . . . . 35·00 65·00
37 4d. brown-red . . . . . . 45·00 70·00
38 **2** 6d. dull violet . . . . . . 13·00 48·00
39 6d. deep violet . . . . . . 12·00 42·00
40 **4** 1s. sepia (2.89) . . . . . . 80·00 £100
41 1s. brown *to* deep brown . . . . 45·00 70·00
34/40 Optd "Specimen" . . . . *Set of* 4 £300

The De La Rue transfers of T 1 to 4 are new transfers and differ from those of Messrs. Nissen and Parker, particularly T 4

1888 (July). *Nos. 18/19 surch with T* **7**, *in violet, in Antigua.*

42 **4** 4d. on 1s. black and rose-carmine (*toned paper*) £110 £150
a. Surch double £6500
b. Surch inverted (in pair with normal) £40000
c. Long-tailed "S" £400 £500
42*d* 4d. on 1s. black and rose-carmine (*white paper*) £140 £180

The special issues for Virgin Islands were superseded on 31 October 1890, by the general issue for Leeward Islands. In 1899, however, a new special issue (given below) appeared; it did not supersede the general issue for Leeward Islands, but was used concurrently, as were all subsequent issues, until 1 July 1956, when the general Leeward Islands stamps were withdrawn.

8 **9** **10**

(Recess D.L.R.)

1899 (Jan). *Wmk Crown CA. P* 14.

43 **8** ½d. yellow-green 75 55
a. Error. "HALFPFNNY" (R. 10/1) . . 80·00 £120
b. Error. "HALΓPENNY" (R. 8/2) . . 80·00 £120
c. Imperf between (horiz pair) . . £7000
44 1d. brick-red . . . . . . 2·25 2·75
45 2½d. ultramarine . . . . . . 12·00 4·00
46 4d. brown . . . . . . 4·00 17·00
a. Error "FOURPENCF" (R.10/3) . . £850 £1200
47 6d. dull violet . . . . . . 4·50 4·50
48 7d. deep green . . . . . . 7·00 8·00
49 1s. brown-yellow . . . . . . 20·00 32·00
50 5s. indigo . . . . . . 65·00 80·00
43/50 . . . . . . *Set of* 8 £100 £130
43/50 Optd "Specimen" . . . . *Set of* 8 £160

Nos. 43a/b and 46a were corrected after the first printing.

(Typo D.L.R.)

1904 (1 June). *Wmk Mult Crown CA. P* 14.

54 **9** ½d. dull purple and green 60 40
55 1d. dull purple and scarlet . . . . 1·50 35
56 **10** 2d. dull purple and ochre . . . . 4·50 4·50
57 **9** 2½d. dull purple and ultramarine . . 1·75 2·00
58 **10** 3d. dull purple and black . . . . 2·75 3·00
59 **9** 6d. dull purple and brown . . . . 2·75 3·00
60 **10** 1s. green and scarlet . . . . 3·25 4·75
61 2s. 6d. green and black . . . . 22·00 48·00
62 **9** 5s. green and blue . . . . 48·00 65·00
54/62 . . . . . . *Set of* 9 75·00 £110
54/62 Optd "Specimen" . . . . *Set of* 9 £140

11 **12**

(Typo D.L.R.)

1913 (Feb)–19. *Die I. Wmk Mult Crown CA. Chalk-surfaced paper (3d. to 5s.). P* 14.

69 **11** ½d. green . . . . . . 1·50 2·75
a. Yellow-green (8.16) . . . . 2·25 9·00
b. Blue-green and deep green (3.19) . . 1·25 4·75
70 1d. deep red . . . . . . 8·00 10·00
a. Deep red and carmine (10.17) . . 2·25 12·00
b. Scarlet (10.17) . . . . 2·25 13·00
c. Carmine-red (3.19) . . . . 45·00 26·00
71 **12** 2d. grey . . . . . . 3·75 19·00
a. Slate-grey . . . . . . 4·00 24·00
72 **11** 2½d. bright blue . . . . . . 4·50 7·00
73 **12** 3d. purple/*yellow* . . . . 2·25 5·00
74 **11** 6d. dull and bright purple . . . . 4·00 7·00
75 **12** 1s. black/*blue-green* . . . . 3·25 7·00
76 2s. 6d. black and red/*blue* . . . . 48·00 48·00
77 **11** 5s. green and red/*yellow* . . . . 32·00 £110
69/77 . . . . . . *Set of* 9 90·00 £190
69/77 Optd "Specimen" . . . . *Set of* 9 £180

Stock of the original printing of the ½d., No. 69, was exhausted by January 1916 and Leeward Islands ½d. stamps were used until the yellow-green printing, No. 69*a*, arrived in August 1916.

WAR STAMP

(**13**)

14

1916 (20 Oct)–19. *Optd with T* **13**.

78 **11** 1d. carmine . . . . . . 1·60 15·00
a. Watermark sideways £900
b. Pale red/bluish . . . . 20 5·50
bw. Wmk inverted . . . . 50·00
by. Wmk inverted and reversed . .
c. Scarlet (1918) . . . . 20 3·25
d. Short opt (right pane R. 10/1) . . 20·00
79 **12** 3d. purple/*yellow* . . . . 85 11·00
a. Purple/lemon . . . . 2·75 8·00
b. Purple/buff-yellow (11.3.19) . . 1·50 16·00
bw. Wmk inverted . . . . 15·00
by. Wmk inverted and reversed . .
c. Short opt (right pane R. 10/1) . . 30·00
78/9 Optd "Specimen" . . . . *Set of* 2 70·00

Nos. 78d and 79c show the overprint 2 mm high instead of 2½ mm.

1921 (18 Nov). *As 1913–19, but Die II and wmk Mult Script CA.*

80 **11** ½d. green . . . . . . 2·00 23·00
w. Wmk inverted . . . .
81 1d. scarlet and deep carmine . . 1·25 18·00
80/1 Optd "Specimen" . . . . *Set of* 2 70·00

(Typo D.L.R.)

1922 (15 June)–29. *P* 14. (*a*) *Wmk Mult Crown CA. Cha[…] surfaced paper.*

82 **14** 3d. purple/*pale yellow* . . . . 65 12·
83 1s. black/*emerald* . . . . 75 12·
84 2s. 6d. black and red/*blue* . . 4·00 9
85 5s. green and red/*pale yellow* . . 30·00 90·
82/5 . . . . . . *Set of* 4 32·00 £1
82/5 Optd "Specimen" . . . . *Set of* 4 90·00

(*b*) *Wmk Mult Script CA. Chalk-surfaced paper* (5*d. to* 5s.

86 **14** ½d. dull green 85 2
87 1d. rose-carmine 60
88 1d. bright violet (1927) . . . . 1·00 3
89 1d. scarlet (1929) . . . . 11·00 13
90 1½d. carmine-red (1927) . . . . 1·50 2·
91 1½d. Venetian red (1928) . . . . 1·75 2
92 2d. grey 60 5
93 2½d. pale bright blue . . . . 1·50 12
94 2½d. dull orange (1.9.23) . . . . 1·25 1
95 2½d. bright blue (1927) . . . . 1·25 3
96 3d. purple/*pale yellow* (1928) . . 2·00 9
97 5d. dull purple and olive . . . . 5·00 45
98 6d. dull and bright purple . . . . 1·25 5
99 1s. black/*emerald* (1928) . . . . 1·25 12
100 2s. 6d. black and red/*blue* (1928) . . 19·00 42
101 5s. green and red/*yellow* (1.9.23) . . 19·00 65
86/101 . . . . . . *Set of* 16 60·00 £2
86/101 Optd/Perf "Specimen" . . *Set of* 16 £275

In the 1½d. stamps the value is in colour on a white grour

1935 (6 May). *Silver Jubilee. As Nos.* 91/4 *of Antigua but prin[…] by Waterlow. P* 11 × 12.

103 1d. deep blue and scarlet . . . . 95 2·
k. Kite and vertical log . . . . 55·00
l. Kite and horizontal log . . . . 55·00
104 1½d. ultramarine and grey . . . . 95 2·
k. Kite and vertical log . . . . 60·00
l. Kite and horizontal log . . . . 60·00
105 2½d. brown and deep blue . . . . 95 2·
k. Kite and vertical log . . . . 65·00
l. Kite and horizontal log . . . . 65·00
106 1s. slate and purple . . . . 5·50 12·
k. Kite and vertical log £130
l. Kite and horizontal log £130
103/6 . . . . . . *Set of* 4 7·50 18·
103/6 Perf "Specimen" . . . . *Set of* 4 85·00

For illustrations of plate varieties see Catalogue Introductio

1937 (12 May). *Coronation. As Nos.* 95/7 *of Antigu[…] P* 11×11½.

107 1d. carmine 20 1
108 1½d. yellow-brown 40 2
109 2½d. blue 45 1
107/9 . . . . . . *Set of* 3 95 4
107/9 Perf "Specimen" . . . . *Set of* 3 55·00

15 King George VI and Badge of Colony

16 Map

(Photo Harrison)

1938 (1 Aug)–47. *Wmk Mult Script CA. Chalk-surfaced pap[…] P* 14.

110 **15** ½d. green . . . . . . 2·25 1·
a. Ordinary paper (10.43) 30
111 1d. scarlet . . . . . . 2·25 1
a. Ordinary paper (10.43) 30
112 1½d. red-brown . . . . . . 3·00 4
a. Ordinary paper (10.43) 65
w. Wmk inverted . . . . † £10
113 2d. grey . . . . . . 4·25 1·
a. Ordinary paper (10.43) 40
114 2½d. ultramarine . . . . . . 3·25 1·
a. Ordinary paper (10.43) . . . . 60 1·
115 3d. orange . . . . . . 5·50
a. Ordinary paper (10.43) 40
116 6d. mauve . . . . . . 3·50
a. Ordinary paper (10.43) . . . . 1·50
117 1s. olive-brown . . . . . . 7·50 2·
a. Ordinary paper (8.42) . . . . 1·50
118 2s. 6d. sepia . . . . . . 23·00 4·
a. Ordinary paper (8.42) . . . . 14·00 3·
119 5s. carmine . . . . . . 45·00 5·
a. Ordinary paper (8.42) . . . . 13·00 4·
120 10s. blue (1.12 47) . . . . 7·00 8
121 £1 black (1.12.47) . . . . 11·00 20
110/21 . . . . . . *Set of* 12 45·00 38
110/21 Perf "Specimen" . . . . *Set of* 12 £225

The ordinary paper, used as a substitute for t[…] chalk-surfaced for printings between 1942 and 1945, is thi[…] smooth and opaque.

1946 (1 Nov). *Victory. As Nos.* 110/11 *of Antigua.*

122 1½d. lake-brown 10
123 3d. orange 10
122/3 Perf "Specimen" . . . . *Set of* 2 55·00

1949 (3 Jan). *Royal Silver Wedding. As Nos.* 112/13 […] *Antigua.*

124 2½d. ultramarine 10
125 £1 black . . . . 12·00 14

1949 (10 Oct). *75th Anniv of U.P.U. As Nos.* 114/17 *of Antigua*

126 2½d. ultramarine 30
127 3d. orange 80 1
128 6d. magenta 50
129 1s. olive 50
126/9 . . . . . . *Set of* 4 1·90 2

(New Currency. 100 cents = 1 B.W.I. dollar)

51. *Inauguration of B.W.I. University College. As Nos.* 118/19 *of Antigua.*
) 3 c. black and brown-red (10.4) 40 60
12 c. black and reddish violet (16.2) .. 40 60

(Recess Waterlow)

51 (2 Apr). *Restoration of Legislative Council. Wmk Mult Script CA. P* 14½ x 14.
2 16 6 c. orange 20 75
3 12 c. purple 20 50
4 24 c. olive 20 50
5 $1.20 carmine 45 75
2/5 .. .. *Set of* 4 95 2·25

17 Sombrero Lighthouse

18 Map of Jost Van Dyke

(Recess D.L.R.)

52 (15 Apr). *T* **17/18** *and similar designs. Wmk Mult Script CA. P* 12½ × 13 (*vert*) *or* 13 × 12½ (*horiz*).
6 1 c. black 40 90
7 2 c. deep green 35 30
8 3 c. black and brown 30 80
9 4 c. carmine-red 35 90
0 5 c. claret and black 90 50
1 8 c. bright blue 35 85
2 12 c. dull violet .. .. 45 1·00
3 24 c. deep brown 35 30
4 60 c. yellow-green and blue .. .. .. 2·50 11·00
5 $1.20, black and bright blue .. .. 3·75 12·00
6 $2.40, yellowish green and red-brown .. 10·00 13·00
7 $4.80, bright blue and carmine .. .. 11·00 14·00
6/47 .. .. *Set of* 12 27·00 50·00
Designs: *Horiz*—3 c. Sheep industry; 4 c. Map of Anegada; 5 c. attle industry; 8 c. Map of Virgin Gorda; 12 c. Map of Tortola; 60 c. ead Man's Chest; $1.20, Sir Francis Drake Channel; $2.40, Road own; $4.80, Map of Virgin Islands. *Vert*—24 c. Badge of the esidency.

53 (2 June). *Coronation. As No.* 120 *of Antigua.*
8 2 c. black and green 30 85

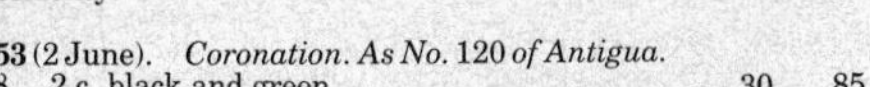

29 Map of Tortola

30 Brown Pelican

(Recess D.L.R.)

56 (1 Nov)–**62**. *Designs as T* **29/30**. *Wmk Mult Script CA. P* 13×12½ (½ *c. to* $1.20) *or* 12×11½ ($2.40 *and* $4.80).
9 ½ c. black and reddish purple 40 20
a. Black and deep reddish purple (19.4.60) 90 2·25
0 1 c. turquoise-blue and slate .. .. 1·50 75
a. Turquoise and slate-violet (26.11.62) 14·00 6·00
1 2 c. vermilion and black 30 10
2 3 c. blue and deep olive 30 30
3 4 c. deep brown and turquoise-green .. 35 30
4 5 c. grey-black 45 10
5 8 c. yellow-orange and deep blue 60 40
6 12 c. ultramarine and rose-red .. .. 2·00 75
7 24 c. myrtle-green and brown-orange .. 1·00 65
8 60 c. indigo and yellow-orange .. .. 8·00 8·00
9 $1.20, deep yellow-green and carmine-red 2·00 7·00
0 $2.40, lemon and deep dull purple .. 32·00 13·00
1 $4.80, blackish brown and turquoise-blue 32·00 13·00
9/61 .. .. *Set of* 13 70·00 40·00
Designs: *Size as T* **29**—1 c. Virgin Islands Sloop; 2 c. Nelthrop ed Poll Bull; 3 c. Road Harbour; 4 c. Mountain travel; 5 c. Badge the Presidency; 8 c. Beach scene; 12 c. *New Idea* (sloop) under nstruction; 24 c. White Cedar tree; 60 c. Skipjack Tuna Bonito"); $1.20, Treasury Square. *Size as T* **30**—$4.80, agnificent Frigate Bird.

(New Currency. 100 cents = 1 U.S. dollar)

(42)

962 (10 Dec). *As Nos.* 149/53 *and* 155/61, *but W w* **12**, *surch in U.S. currency as T* **42** *by D.L.R.*
62 1 c. on ½ c. black and deep reddish purple .. 30 10
63 2 c. on 1 c. turquoise and slate-violet .. 1·50 10
64 3 c. on 2 c. vermilion and black 30 10
65 4 c. on 3 c. black and deep olive 30 10
66 5 c. on 4 c. deep brown and turquoise-green 30 10
67 8 c. on 8 c. yellow-orange and deep blue .. 30 10
68 10 c. on 12 c. ultramarine and rose-red .. 40 10
69 12 c. on 24 c. myrtle-green and brown-orange 30 10
70 25 c. on 60 c. indigo and yellow-orange .. 2·50 45
71 70 c. on $1.20, dp yellow-green & carmine-red 35 45
a. Stop to right of C in surcharge instead of beneath it (in pair with normal) .. .. 9·50 7·50
72 $1.40 on $2.40, lemon and deep dull purple 8·00 3·50
73 $2.80 on $4.80, blackish brown and turquoise-blue .. .. 8·00 3·50
62/73 .. .. *Set of* 12 20·00 7·50
No. 171a occurs on the first stamp on Rows 1 to 10.

963 (4 June). *Freedom from Hunger. As No.* 146 *of Antigua.*
74 25 c. reddish violet 20 10

1963 (2 Sept). *Red Cross Centenary. As Nos.* 147/8 *of Antigua.*
175 2 c. red and black 15 20
176 25 c. red and blue 50 20

1964 (23 Apr). *400th Birth Anniv of William Shakespeare. As No.* 164 *of Antigua.*
177 10 c. bright blue 20 10

43 Skipjack Tuna

44 Map of Tortola

45 Badge of the Colony

(Des and recess D.L.R.)

1964 (2 Nov)–**68**. *Designs as T* **43/5**. *W w* **12**. *P* 11½×12 ($2.80), 13×13½ (70 c., $1, $1.40), *or* 13×12½ (*others*).
178 1 c. blue and olive-green .. .. .. 30 1·25
179 2 c. yellow-olive and rose-red 15 30
180 3 c. sepia and turquoise-blue .. .. 3·00 1·25
181 4 c. black and carmine-red .. .. .. 80 1·25
182 5 c. black and deep bluish green .. .. 65 1·25
183 6 c. black and brown-orange 30 85
184 8 c. black and magenta 30 45
185 10 c. lake and deep lilac .. .. .. 1·25 30
a. Bright lake and reddish lilac (26.11.68) 8·50 2·00
186 12 c. deep bluish green and deep violet-blue 2·00 1·75
187 15 c. yellow-green and grey-black .. .. 35 1·75
188 25 c. green and purple .. .. .. 11·00 1·60
189 70 c. black and yellow-brown .. .. 3·50 4·00
190 $1 yellow-green and chestnut .. .. 3·00 1·50
191 $1.40, light blue and rose .. .. 20·00 8·00
192 $2.80, black and bright purple .. .. 20·00 8·00
178/92 .. .. *Set of* 15 60·00 30·00
Designs: *Horiz as T* **43**—2 c. Soper's Hole; 3 c. Brown Pelican; 4 c. Dead Man's Chest; 5 c. Road Harbour; 6 c. Fallen Jerusalem; 8 c. The Baths, Virgin Gorda; 10 c. Map of Virgin Islands; 12 c. *Youth of Tortola* (Tortola-St. Thomas ferry); 15 c. The Towers, Tortola; 25 c. Beef Island Airfield. *Vert as T* **44**—$1 Virgin Gorda; $1.40, Yachts at anchor.

1965 (17 May). *I.T.U. Centenary. As Nos.* 166/7 *of Antigua.*
193 4 c. yellow and turquoise 20 10
194 25 c. light blue and orange-buff 45 20

1965 (25 Oct). *International Co-operation Year. As Nos.* 168/9 *of Antigua.*
195 1 c. reddish purple and turquoise-green .. 10 15
196 25 c. deep bluish green and lavender 30 15

1966 (24 Jan). *Churchill Commemoration. As Nos.* 170/3 *of Antigua.*
197 1 c. new blue 10 10
198 2 c. deep green 15 10
199 10 c. brown 30 10
200 25 c. bluish violet 60 25
197/200 .. .. *Set of* 4 1·00 40

1966 (22 Feb). *Royal Visit. As Nos.* 174/5 *of Antigua.*
201 4 c. black and ultramarine 40 10
202 70 c. black and magenta .. .. .. 1·40 45

58 *Atrato I* (paddle-steamer), 1866

(Des R. Granger Barrett. Litho B.W.)

1966 (25 Apr). *Stamp Centenary. T* **58** *and similar horiz designs. W w* **12** (*sideways*). *P* 13.
203 5 c. black, red, yellow and emerald 35 10
204 10 c. black, green and rose-red/*cream* 35 10
205 25 c. black, rose-red and blue/*pale green* .. 55 10
206 60 c. black, red and green/*pale blue* .. 1·00 2·25
203/6 .. .. *Set of* 4 2·00 2·25
Design:—10 c. 1d. and 6d. stamps of 1866; 25 c. Air mail transport, Beef Island, and 6d. stamp of 1866; 60 c. Landing mail at Roadtown, 1866 and 1d. stamp of 1866.

50c.

(62)

1966 (15 Sept). *As Nos.* 189 *and* 191/2 *but wmk sideways, surch as T* **62**.
207 50 c. on 70 c. black and yellow-brown .. .. 1·00 90
208 $1.50 on $1.40, light blue and rose .. .. 2·75 2·00
209 $3 on $2.80, black and bright purple .. 2·75 2·75
207/9 .. .. *Set of* 3 6·00 5·00

1966 (1 Dec). *20th Anniv of U.N.E.S.C.O. As Nos.* 196/8 *of Antigua.*
210 2 c. slate-violet, red, yellow and orange .. 10 10
211 12 c. orange-yellow, violet and deep olive .. 20 10
212 60 c. black, bright purple and orange 50 45
210/12 .. .. *Set of* 3 65 60

63 Map of Virgin Islands

(Des G. Vasarhelyi. Photo Harrison)

1967 (18 Apr). *New Constitution. W w* **12**. *P* 14½.
213 **63** 2 c. multicoloured 10 10
214 10 c. multicoloured 15 10
w. Wmk inverted .. .. .. 15·00
215 25 c. multicoloured 15 10
w. Wmk inverted .. .. .. 9·00
216 $1 multicoloured 55 40
213/16 .. .. *Set of* 4 75 55

64 *Mercury* (cable ship) and Bermuda-Tortola Link

(Des G. Drummond, Photo Harrison)

1967 (14 Sept). *Inauguration of Bermuda-Tortola Telephone Service. T* **64** *and similar horiz designs. Multicoloured. W w* **12**. *P* 14½.
217 4 c. Type **64** 20 10
218 10 c. Chalwell Telecommunications Station 20 10
219 50 c. *Mercury* (cable ship) 50 30
217/19 .. .. *Set of* 3 80 40

67 Blue Marlin

(Des V. Whiteley. Photo Enschedé)

1968 (2 Jan). *Game Fishing. T* **67** *and similar horiz designs. W w* **12** (*sideways*). *P* 12½ × 12.
220 2 c. multicoloured 10 55
221 10 c. multicoloured 25 10
222 25 c. black, blue and bright violet 55 10
223 40 c. multicoloured 85 70
220/3 .. .. *Set of* 4 1·60 1·25
Designs—10 c. Cobia; 25 c. Wahoo; 40 c. Fishing launch and map.

1968 INTERNATIONAL YEAR FOR HUMAN RIGHTS

(71)

72 Dr. Martin Luther King, Bible, Sword and Armour Gauntlet

1968 (29 July). *Human Rights Year. Nos.* 185 *and* 188 *optd with T* **71**.
224 10 c. lake and deep lilac 20 10
225 25 c. green and purple 30 40
29 July was the date of issue in the islands. The Crown Agents supplies went on sale in London on 1 July, the local consignment being delayed in transit.

(Des V. Whiteley. Litho Format)

1968 (15 Oct). *Martin Luther King Commemoration. W w* **12** (*sideways*). *P* 14.
226 **72** 4 c. multicoloured 20 20
227 25 c. multicoloured 30 40

73 De Havilland D.H.C.6 Twin Otter 100

(Des R. Granger Barrett. Litho Format)

1968 (16 Dec). *Opening of Beef Island Airport Extension. T* **73** *and similar horiz designs. Multicoloured. P* 14.

228 2 c. Type **73** 15 60
229 10 c. Hawker Siddeley H.S.748 airliner .. 20 10
230 25 c. De Havilland D.H.114 Heron 2 .. 40 10
231 $1 Royal Engineers cap badge .. .. 50 2·00
228/31 .. .. *Set of* 4 1·10 2·50

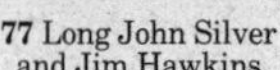

77 Long John Silver and Jim Hawkins **78** Jim Hawkins escaping from the Pirates

(Des Jennifer Toombs. Photo Enschedé)

1969 (18 Mar). *75th Death Anniv of Robert Louis Stevenson. Scenes from* Treasure Island. *T* **77/8** *and similar designs. W* w **12** (*sideways on* 10 *c.*, $1). *P* 13½×13 (4 *c.*, 40 *c.*) *or* 13×13½ (*others*).

232 4 c. indigo, pale yellow and carmine-red .. 25 15
233 10 c. multicoloured 25 10
234 40 c. brown, black and blue 30 30
235 $1 multicoloured .. .. 60 1·40
232/5 .. .. *Set of* 4 1·25 1·75

Designs: *Vert*—40 c. The fight with Israel Hands. *Horiz*—$1 Treasure trove.

82 Yachts in Road Harbour, Tortola

(Des J. Cooter, Litho P.B.)

1969 (20 Oct). *Tourism. T* **82** *and similar multicoloured designs. W* w **12** (*sideways on* 2 *c.*, $1). *P* 12½.

236 2 c. Tourist and Yellow-finned Grouper (fish) (*vert*) 15 50
237 10 c. Type **82** 30 10
238 20 c. Sun-bathing at Virgin Gorda National Park 40 20
239 $1 Tourist and Pipe Organ Cactus at Virgin Gorda (*vert*) .. .. .. 90 1·50
236/9 .. .. *Set of* 4 1·60 2·00

85 Carib Canoe

(Des and litho J.W.)

1970 (16 Feb)–**74**. *Horiz designs as T* **85**. *W* w **12** (*sideways**). *P* 14.

240 ½ c. buff, red-brown and sepia 10 85
241 1 c. new blue, apple-green and chalky blue 15 30
a. Perf 13½ (12.11.74) .. .. .. 1·25 2·00
242 2 c. yellow-orange, red-brown and slate .. 40 1·00
243 3 c. orange-red, cobalt and sepia .. .. 30 1·25
244 4 c. greenish blue, chalky blue & bistre-brn 30 50
w. Wmk Crown to right of CA .. ..
245 5 c. emerald, pink and black 30 10
246 6 c. reddish violet mauve and myrtle-green 40 1·75
247 8 c. apple-green, greenish yellow and sepia 50 2·25
248 10 c. greenish blue, yellow-brown & red-brn 50 15
a. Perf 13½ (12.11.74) .. .. .. 2·50 2·25
249 12 c. yellow, crimson and brown .. .. 65 1·00
a. Perf 13½ (12.11.74) .. .. .. 2·50 3·25
250 15 c. turquoise-green, orange & bistre-brn 6·00 85
a. Perf 13½ (12.11.74) .. .. .. 4·50 3·25
251 25 c. grey-green, steel-blue and plum .. 6·00 1·75
252 50 c. magenta, dull green and purple-brown 4·00 1·50
253 $1 salmon, olive-green and red-brown .. 4·50 4·75
254 $2 buff, slate and grey .. .. .. 8·00 9·00
255 $3 ochre, deep blue and sepia .. .. 5·00 6·50
256 $5 violet and grey .. .. 7·00 9·00
240/56 .. .. *Set of* 17 38·00 38·00

Designs:—1 c. *Santa Maria* (Columbus' flagship); 2 c. *Elizabeth Bonaventure* (Drake's flagship); 3 c. Dutch Buccaneer, *circa* 1660; 4 c. *Thetis*, 1827 (after etching by E. W. Cooke); 5 c. Henry Morgan's ship (17th century); 6 c. H.M.S. *Boreas* (Captain Nelson, 1784); 8 c. H.M.S. *Eclair*, 1804; 10 c. H.M.S. *Formidable*, 1782; 12 c. H.M.S. *Nymph*, 1778; 15 c. *Windsor Castle* (sailing packet) engaging *Jeune Richard* (French brig), 1807; 25 c. H.M.S. *Astrea*, 1808; 50 c. Wreck of R.M.S. *Rhone*, 1867; $1 Tortola sloop; $2 H.M.S. *Frobisher*; $3 *Booker Viking* (cargo liner), 1967; $5 Hydrofoil *Sun Arrow*.

*The normal sideways watermark shows Crown to left of CA, *as seen from the back of the stamp.*

See also Nos. 295/300.

102 *A Tale of Two Cities*

(Des W. G. Brown. Litho D.L.R.)

1970 (4 May). *Death Centenary of Charles Dickens. T* **102** *and similar horiz designs showing original book illustrations. W* w **12** (*sideways*). *P* 14.

257 5 c. black, light rose and grey 10 30
258 10 c. black, light blue and pale green 20 10
259 25 c. black, light green and pale yellow .. 30 40
257/9 .. .. *Set of* 3 55 70

Designs:—10 c. *Oliver Twist*; 25 c. *Great Expectations*.

103 Hospital Visit

(Des R. Granger Barrett. Litho Questa)

1970 (10 Aug). *Centenary of British Red Cross. T* **103** *and similar horiz designs. Multicoloured. W* w **12** (*sideways**). *P* 14.

260 4 c. Type **103** 25 10
261 10 c. First Aid Class 35 10
262 25 c. Red Cross and Coat of Arms 80 55
w. Wmk Crown to right of CA .. .. 38·00
260/2 .. .. *Set of* 3 1·25 70

*The normal sideways watermark shows Crown to left of CA, *as seen from the back of the stamp.*

104 Mary Read **105** Children and "UNICEF"

(Des and litho J.W.)

1970 (16 Nov). *Pirates. T* **104** *and similar vert designs. Multicoloured. W* w **12**. *P* 14 × 14½.

263 ½ c. Type **104** 10 15
264 10 c. George Lowther 35 10
265 30 c. Edward Teach (Blackbeard) 85 25
266 60 c. Henry Morgan .. .. 1·25 1·00
263/6 .. .. *Set of* 4 2·25 1·40

(Des L. Curtis. Litho Format)

1971 (13 Dec). *25th Anniv of UNICEF. W* w **12** (*sideways*). *P* 13½ × 14.

267 **106** 15 c. multicoloured 10 10
268 30 c. multicoloured 20 25

VISIT OF H.R.H. THE PRINCESS MARGARET

1972 1972

(106)

1972 (7 Mar). *Royal Visit of Princess Margaret. Nos.* 244 *and* 251 *optd with T* **106**.

269 4 c. greenish blue, chalky blue & bistre-brn 20 15
270 25 c. grey-green, steel-blue and plum 30 45

107 Seaman of 1800 **108** Sailfish and *Sir Winston Churchill* (cadet schooner)

(Des J.W. Litho Questa)

1972 (17 Mar). *"Interpex" Stamp Exhibition, New York. T* **1**(*and similar vert designs showing Naval Uniforms. Mult*- *coloured. W* w **12** (*sideways**). *P* 13½.

271 ½ c. Type **107** 10
w. Wmk Crown to left of CA .. .. 1·75
272 10 c. Boatswain, 1787–1807 35
273 30 c. Captain, 1795–1812 85
274 60 c. Admiral, 1787–95 .. .. .. 1·50 2·2
271/4 .. .. *Set of* 4 2·50 2·7

*The normal sideways watermark shows Crown to right CA, *as seen from the back of the stamp.*

(Des (from photograph by D. Groves) and photo Harrison)

1972 (24 Nov). *Royal Silver Wedding. Multicoloured; backgrour colour given. W* w **12**. *P* 14 × 14½.

275 **108** 15 c. bright blue 20
276 25 c. turquoise-blue 20
a. Blue omitted* £300
w. Wmk inverted .. .. .. 28·00

*The omission of the blue colour results in the Duke's su appearing sepia instead of deep blue.

109 Blue Marlin

(Des G. Drummond. Litho Questa)

1972 (12 Dec). *Game Fish. T* **109** *and similar horiz designs. Mul coloured. W* w **12**. *P* 13½.

277 ½ c. Type **109** 10
a. Pair. Nos. 277/8 .. .. .. 15 1·
278 ½ c. Wahoo 10
279 15 c. Yellow-finned Tuna ("Allison Tuna") 55
280 25 c. White Marlin 60
281 50 c. Sailfish .. .. 1·25 1·
282 $1 Dolphin .. .. 2·00 2·
277/82 .. .. *Set of* 6 4·00 4·
MS283 194×158 mm. Nos. 277/82 .. .. 8·50 8·

Nos. 277/8 were printed horizontally and vertically *se-tena* within the sheet.

110 J. C. Lettsom **111** Green-throated Carib and Antillean Crested Hummingbird

(Des J. Cooter. Litho Questa)

1973 (9 Mar). *"Interpex 1973" (Quakers). T* **110** *and similar mul coloured designs. W* w **12** (*sideways on* ½ *c. and* 15 *c.*). *P* 13½.

284 ½ c. Type **110** 10
285 10 c. Lettsom House (*horiz*) 15
286 15 c. Dr. W. Thornton 20
287 30 c. Dr. Thornton and Capitol, Washington (*horiz*) 25
288 $1 William Penn (*horiz*) .. .. .. 70 1·
284/8 .. .. *Set of* 5 1·25 1·

(Des G. Drummond. Litho Questa)

1973 (30 June). *First Issue of Coinage. T* **111** *and similar hor designs showing coins and local scenery. Multicoloured. W* w *P* 14.

289 1 c. Type **111** 10
290 5 c. Zenaida Dove 60
291 10 c. Ringed Kingfisher 75
292 25 c. Mangrove Cuckoo 95
293 50 c. Brown Pelican .. .. .. 1·10 1·
294 $1 Magnificent Frigate Bird .. .. 1·40 2·
289/94 .. .. *Set of* 6 4·50 3·

1973 (17 Oct). *As Nos.* 240, 243/5 *and* 248/9, *but W* w *upright.*

295 ½ c. buff, red-brown and sepia .. .. 50 5·
296 3 c. orange-red, cobalt and sepia .. .. 1·25 2·
297 4 c. greenish blue, chalky blue & bistre-brn 1·25 4·
298 5 c. emerald, pink and black .. .. 1·25 2·
299 10 c. greenish blue, yellow-brown & red-brn 1·50 2·
w. Wmk inverted .. .. ..
300 12 c. yellow, dull crimson and light brown 2·00 3·
295/300 .. .. *Set of* 6 7·00 18·

1973 (14 Nov). *Royal Wedding. As Nos.* 165/6 *of Anguilla. Cen multicoloured. W* w **12** (*sideways*). *P* 13½.

301 5 c. brown-ochre 10
302 50 c. light turquoise-blue 20

112 "The Virgin and Child" (Pintoricchio) 113 Crest of the *Canopus* (French)

(Des G. Drummond. Litho Questa)

73 (7 Dec). *Christmas. T* **112** *and similar vert designs Multi coloured.* W w **12**. *P* 14.
3 ½ c. Type **112** 10 10
4 3 c. "Virgin and Child" (Lorenzo di Credi) .. 10 10
5 25 c. "Virgin and Child" (Crivelli) 15 10
6 50 c. "Virgin and Child with St. John" (Luini) 30 40
3/6 .. .. *Set of* 4 50 50

(Des J. Cooter. Litho Questa)

74 (22 Mar). *"Interpex 1974" (Naval Crests). T* **113** *and similar vert designs. Multicoloured.* W w **12**. *P* 14.
7 5 c. Type **113** 20 10
8 18 c. U.S.S. *Saginaw* 35 25
9 25 c. H.M.S. *Rothesay* 40 30
0 50 c. H.M.C.S. *Ottawa* 60 60
7/10 .. .. *Set of* 4 1·40 1·10
S311 196 × 128 mm. Nos. 307/10 .. .. 1·75 3·50

114 Christopher Columbus 115 Atlantic Trumpet Triton (*Charonia variegata*)

(Des J. W. Litho Format)

974 (19 Aug). *Historical Figures. T* **114** *and similar vert designs.* W w **12**. *P* 14.
12 5 c. orange and black 20 10
w. Wmk inverted .. .. .. 2·25
13 10 c. greenish blue and black 30 10
14 25 c. reddish violet and black 35 25
15 40 c. yellow-brown and sepia 60 75
2/15 .. .. *Set of* 4 1·25 1·00
S316 84×119 mm. Nos. 312/15 .. .. 1·25 2·25
Portraits:—10 c. Sir Walter Raleigh; 25 c. Sir Martin obisher; 40 c. Sir Francis Drake.

(Des G. Drummond. Litho Harrison)

974 (30 Sept). *Seashells. T* **115** *and similar horiz designs. Multicoloured.* W w **12**. *P* 13 × 13½.
17 5 c. Type **115** 30 15
a. Wmk T **53** of Lesotho (sideways) .. £140
w. Wmk inverted .. .. .. 70·00
18 18 c. West Indian Murex (*Murex brevifrons*) 60 30
19 25 c. Bleeding Tooth (*Nerita peloranta*) .. 75 35
20 75 c. Virgin Islands Latirus (*Latirus virginensis*) .. .. 1·75 2·00
17/20 .. .. *Set of* 4 3·00 2·50
MS321 146×95 mm. Nos. 317/20 .. .. 3·00 5·50
a. Printed on the gummed side .. £500
w. Wmk inverted .. .. .. 32·00

116 Churchill and St. Mary, Aldermanbury, London 117 H.M.S. *Boreas*

(Des J. W. Litho Questa)

974 (30 Nov). *Birth Centenary of Sir Winston Churchill. T* **116** *and similar horiz design. Multicoloured.* W w **14** *(sideways*).* *P* 14.
22 10 c. Type **116** 15 10
w. Wmk Crown to right of CA .. .. 3·75
23 50 c. St. Mary, Fulton, Missouri 35 50
MS324 141×108 mm. Nos. 322/3 .. .. 80 1·40
*The normal sideways watermark shows Crown to left of CA, as seen from the back of the stamp.

(Des J. Cooter. Litho J. W.)

1975 (14 Mar). *"Interpex 1975" Stamp Exhibition, New York. Ships' Figureheads. T* **117** *and similar vert designs. Multicoloured.* W w **12**. *P* 13.
325 5 c. Type **117** 20 10
326 18 c. *Golden Hind* 50 15
327 40 c. H.M.S. *Superb* 70 25
328 85 c. H.M.S. *Formidable* .. .. .. 1·50 1·50
325/8 .. .. *Set of* 4 2·50 1·75
MS329 192×127 mm. Nos. 325/8 (Wmk inverted). P 14 .. .. 2·50 7·00
w. Wmk upright .. .. .. 80·00

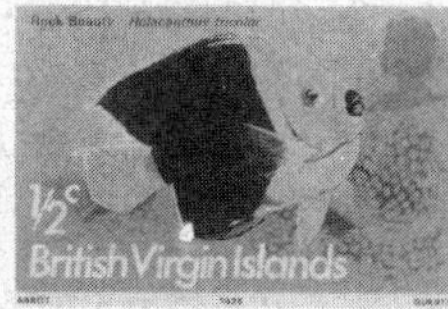

118 Rock Beauty

(Des C. Abbott. Litho Questa)

1975 (16 June–15 Aug). *Fishes. Horiz designs as T* **118**. *Multicoloured.* W w **14** *(sideways*).* *P* 14.
330 ½ c. Type **118** 15 40
w. Wmk Crown to right of CA .. .. 6·00
331 1 c. Long-spined Squirrelfish .. .. 40 1·25
332 3 c. Queen Triggerfish .. .. .. 90 1·25
333 5 c. Blue Angelfish 30 20
334 8 c. Stoplight Parrotfish 30 25
335 10 c. Queen Angelfish 30 25
336 12 c. Nassau Grouper 40 30
337 13 c. Blue Tang 40 30
338 15 c. Sergeant Major 40 35
339 18 c. Spotted Jewfish 70 80
340 20 c. Bluehead Wrasse 60 80
w. Wmk Crown to right of CA .. .. 50·00
341 25 c. Grey Angelfish .. .. .. 1·00 60
342 60 c. Glass-eyed Snapper .. .. .. 1·25 2·25
343 $1 Blue Chromis .. .. 1·75 1·75
w. Wmk Crown to right of CA .. .. 3·50
344 $2.50, French Angelfish .. .. .. 3·50 4·00
345 $3 Queen Parrotfish .. .. .. 4·25 5·00
346 $5 Four-eyed Butterflyfish (15.8) .. 6·00 7·50
330/46 .. .. *Set of* 17 20·00 25·00
*The normal sideways watermark shows Crown to left of CA, *as seen from the back of the stamp.*
Imprint dates: "1975", Nos. 330/46; "1977", Nos. 330, 333/8, 340.
The imprints on all the stamps show the designer's name as "Abbot".

119 St. George's Parish School (First meeting-place, 1950)

(Des R. Granger Barrett. Litho Questa)

1975 (27 Nov). *25th Anniv of Restoration of Legislative Council. T* **119** *and similar horiz designs. Multicoloured.* W w **14** *(sideways).* *P* 14.
347 5 c. Type **119** 10 10
348 25 c. Legislative Council Building 25 10
349 40 c. Mace and gavel 35 15
350 75 c. Commemorative scroll 55 65
347/50 .. .. *Set of* 4 1·10 80

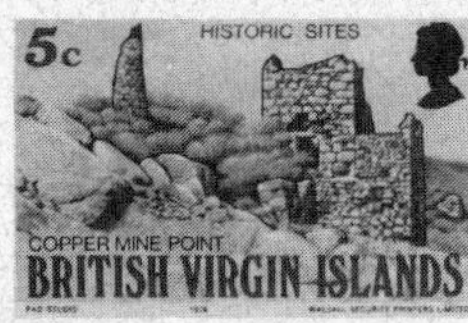

120 Copper Mine Point

(Des PAD Studio. Litho Walsall)

1976 (12 Mar). *Historic Sites. T* **120** *and similar horiz designs. Multicoloured.* W w **14** *(sideways).* *P* 14½.
351 5 c. Type **120** 10 10
352 18 c. Pleasant Valley 20 10
353 50 c. Callwood Distillery 40 30
354 75 c. The Dungeon 60 65
351/4 .. .. *Set of* 4 1·10 1·00

121 Massachusetts Brig *Hazard*

(Des J. W. Litho Questa)

1976 (29 May). *Bicentenary of American Revolution. T* **121** *and similar horiz designs. Multicoloured,* W w **14** *(sideways).* *P* 14.
355 8 c. Type **121** 50 15
356 22 c. American Privateer *Spy* 70 45
357 40 c. *Raleigh* (American frigate) .. .. 1·10 1·00
358 75 c. Frigate *Alliance* and H.M.S. *Trepassy* 1·25 1·90
355/8 .. .. *Set of* 4 3·25 3·25
MS359 114×89 mm. Nos. 355/8 .. .. 5·50 11·00

122 Government House, Tortola 123 Royal Visit, 1966

(Des Walsall. Litho Questa)

1976 (29 Oct). *Fifth Anniv of Friendship Day with U.S. Virgin Is. T* **122** *and similar multicoloured designs.* W w **14** *(sideways on 8 and 75 c.).* *P* 14.
360 8 c. Type **122** 10 10
361 15 c. Government House, St. Croix (*vert*) .. 10 10
362 30 c. Flags (*vert*) 15 10
363 75 c. Government seals 30 40
360/3 .. .. *Set of* 4 50 55

(Des J. Cooter. Litho Walsall)

1977 (7 Feb). *Silver Jubilee. T* **123** *and similar vert designs (inscr "SILVER JUBILEE" at top). Multicoloured.* W w **14**. *P* 13½.
364 8 c. Type **123** 10 10
365 30 c. The Holy Bible 15 15
366 60 c. Presentation of Holy Bible 25 40
364/6 .. .. *Set of* 3 40 50
For stamps with different inscription, see Nos. 371/3.
The imprint at the stamp's foot gives the designer (wrongly) as "Waddington Studio".

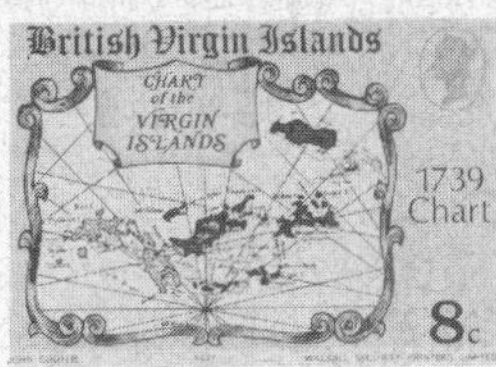

124 Chart of 1739

(Des J. Cooter. Litho Walsall)

1977 (13 June). *18th-Century Maps. T* **124** *and similar horiz designs. Multicoloured.* W w **14**. *P* 13½.
367 8 c. Type **124** 40 10
368 22 c. French Map, 1758 .. .. .. 65 30
369 30 c. Map from English and Danish surveys, 1775 .. .. 80 65
370 75 c. Map of 1779 .. .. 1·25 1·50
367/70 .. .. *Set of* 4 2·75 2·25

1977 (26 Oct). *Royal Visit. Designs as Nos. 364/6 but inscr.* "SILVER JUBILEE ROYAL VISIT" *at top, and face-values changed.*
371 5 c. Type **123** 10 10
372 25 c. The Holy Bible 20 10
373 50 c. Presentation of Holy Bible 35 25
w. Wmk inverted .. .. 5·50
371/3 .. .. *Set of* 3 55 35
The above also differ from Nos. 364/6 in having the silver frame removed and the silver lettering replaced by white. The imprint at foot now has the designer's name correctly given as "J. E. Cooter".

125 Divers checking Equipment 126 Fire Coral

(Des J. W. Litho Rosenbaum Bros, Vienna)

1978 (10 Feb). *Tourism. T* **125** *and similar vert designs. Multicoloured.* W w **14**. *P* 13½.
374 ½ c. Type **125** 10 10
w. Wmk inverted .. .. 8·00
375 5 c. Cup coral on wreck of *Rhone* 20 10
w. Wmk inverted .. .. 1·00
376 8 c. Sponge formation on wreck of *Rhone* 25 10
w. Wmk inverted .. .. 1·00
377 22 c. Cup coral and sponges 60 15
w. Wmk inverted .. .. 1·00
378 30 c. Sponges inside cave 75 20
w. Wmk inverted .. .. 1·25
379 75 c. Marine life .. .. 1·25 85
w. Wmk inverted .. .. 2·00
374/9 .. .. *Set of* 6 2·75 1·25

(Des G. Drummond. Litho Harrison)

1978 (27 Feb). *Corals. T* **126** *and similar horiz designs. Multicoloured. W* w **14** *(sideways). P* 14.
380 8 c. Type **126** 25 15
381 15 c. Staghorn coral 40 30
382 40 c. Brain coral 75 85
383 75 c. Elkhorn coral .. .. 1·50 1·60
380/3 .. .. *Set of* 4 2·50 2·50

127 Iguana

128 Lignum Vitae

(Des Jennifer Toombs. Litho Questa)

1978 (2 June). *25th Anniv of Coronation. T* **127** *and similar vert designs. P* 15.
384 50 c. brown-ochre, green and silver 20 40
a. Sheetlet. Nos. 384/6 × 2 .. .. .. 1·00
385 50 c. multicoloured 20 40
386 50 c. brown-ochre, green and silver 20 40
384/6 .. .. *Set of* 3 55 1·10
Designs:—No. 384, Plantagenet Falcon; No. 385, Queen Elizabeth II; No. 386, Type **127**.

(Des and litho J.W.)

1978 (4 Sept). *Flowering Trees. T* **128** *and similar horiz designs. Multicoloured. W* w **14** *(sideways*). P* 13.
387 8 c. Type **128** 15 10
388 22 c. Ginger Thomas 25 15
389 40 c. Dog Almond 35 20
390 75 c. White Cedar 60 70
387/90 .. .. *Set of* 4 1·25 1·00
MS391 131×95 mm. Nos. 387/90. P 14 .. 1·50 3·00
w. Wmk Crown to left of CA .. .. 60·00
*The normal sideways watermark shows Crown to right of CA, *as seen from the back of the stamp.*

129 *Eurema lisa*

(Des G. Hutchins. Litho Questa)

1978 (4 Dec). *Butterflies. T* **129** *and similar horiz designs. Multicoloured. W* w **14** *(sideways). P* 14.
392 5 c. Type **129** 35 10
393 22 c. *Agraulis vanillae* 85 20
394 30 c. *Heliconius charithonia* .. .. .. 1·10 30
395 75 c. *Hemiargus hanno* .. .. 1·75 1·25
392/5 .. .. *Set of* 4 3·50 1·75
MS396 159×113 mm. No. 392×6 and 393×3 .. 2·50 5·50

130 Spiny Lobster

(Des Picton Print. Litho Harrison)

1979 (10 Feb). *Wildlife Conservation. T* **130** *and similar multicoloured designs. W* w **14** *(sideways on 5 and 22 c.). P* 14.
397 5 c. Type **130** 15 10
398 15 c. Large Iguana (*vert*) 30 10
399 22 c. Hawksbill Turtle 50 15
400 75 c. Black Coral (*vert*) .. .. 1·10 90
397/400 .. .. *Set of* 4 1·90 1·10
MS401 130 × 153 mm. Nos. 397/400 (wmk sideways) .. .. 2·25 3·75

131 Strawberry Cactus

132 West Indian Girl

(Des BG Studio. Litho Format)

1979 (7 May). *Cacti. T* **131** *and similar vert designs. Multicoloured. W* w **14**. *P* 14.
402 ½ c. Type **131** 10 10
403 5 c. Snowy Cactus 15 10
404 13 c. Barrel Cactus 20 20
405 22 c. Tree Cactus 30 35
406 30 c. Prickly Pear 35 40
407 75 c. Dildo Cactus .. .. 60 1·00
402/7 .. .. *Set of* 6 1·40 1·90

(Des R. Granger Barrett. Litho Questa)

1979 (9 July). *International Year of the Child. T* **132** *and similar vert designs. Multicoloured. W* w **14** *(inverted). P* 14½ × 14.
408 5 c. Type **132** 10 10
409 10 c. African boy 10 10
410 13 c. Asian girl 10 10
411 $1 European boy 50 85
408/11 .. .. *Set of* 4 65 1·00
MS412 91 × 114 mm. Nos. 408/11 .. .. .. 70 1·50

133 1956 Road Harbour 3 c. Definitive Stamp

134 Pencil Urchin

(Des J. W. Photo Heraclio Fournier)

1979 (1 Oct). *Death Centenary of Sir Rowland Hill. T* **133** *and similar designs showing stamps. P* 13½.
413 5 c. deep blue, new blue and brown-olive .. 10 10
414 13 c. deep blue and claret 10 10
415 75 c. deep blue and bright purple 45 50
413/15 .. .. *Set of* 3 55 55
MS416 37 × 91 mm. $1 deep blue & carm-red. P 13 70 1·25
Designs: (39 × 27 *mm*)—13 c. 1889 2½d.; 75 c. Great Britain unissued 1910 2d. Tyrian plum. (40 × 28 *mm*)—$1. 1867 1s. "Missing Virgin" error.

(Des BG Studio. Litho Questa)

1979 (17 Dec)–**82**. *Marine Life. Vert designs as T* **134**. *Multicoloured. W* w **14**. *Ordinary paper. P* 14.
417 ½ c. Calcified Algae (1.4.80) .. .. .. 40 1·50
418 1 c. Purple-tipped Sea Anemone (1.4.80) .. 55 1·50
419 3 c. Common Starfish (1.4.80) .. .. 60 1·50
420 5 c. Type **134** 60 80
a. Chalk-surfaced paper (27.8.82) .. 75 60
421 8 c. Atlantic Trumpet Triton (*Charonia variegata*) .. .. 85 1·00
a. Chalk-surfaced paper (27.8.82) .. 1·25 60
422 10 c. Christmas Tree Worms 30 85
423 13 c. Flamingo Tongue (*Cyphoma gibbosus*) (1.4.80) .. .. 1·50 2·25
a. Chalk-surfaced paper (27.8.82) .. 1·50 75
424 15 c. Spider Crab 40 60
a. Chalk-surfaced paper (27.8.82) .. 1·50 55
425 18 c. Sea Squirts (1.4.80) .. .. .. 2·00 2·75
426 20 c. True Tulip (*Fasciolaria tulipa*) 55 85
a. Chalk-surfaced paper (27.8.82) .. 1·25 65
427 25 c. Rooster-tail Conch (*Strombus gallus*) .. 1·25 2·75
w. Wmk inverted
428 30 c. West Indian Fighting Conch (*Strombus pugilis*) (1.4.80) .. .. 1·75 1·25
a. Chalk-surfaced paper (27.8.82) .. 2·00 1·00
429 60 c. Mangrove Crab (1.4.80) .. .. .. 1·75 2·50
430 $1 Coral Polyps (1.4.80) .. .. .. 2·00 3·50
431 $2.50, Peppermint Shrimp .. .. .. 2·50 5·00
432 $3 West Indian Murex (*Murex brevifrons*) 2·50 6·00
433 $5 Carpet Anemone (1.4.80) .. .. .. 3·25 7·50
417/33 .. .. *Set of* 17 20·00 32·00
Imprint dates: "1979", Nos. 420/2, 424, 426/7, 431/2; "1980", Nos. 417/19, 423, 425, 428/30, 433; "1982", Nos. 420a/1a, 423a/4a, 426a, 428a.

135 Rotary Athletics Meeting, Tortola

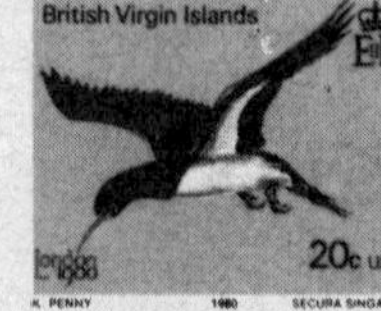

136 Brown Booby

(Des J. W. Litho Enschedé)

1980 (23 Feb). *75th Anniv of Rotary International. T* **135** *and similar horiz designs. Multicoloured. W* w **14** *(sideways). P* 13½ × 14.
434 8 c. Type **135** 10 10
435 22 c. Paul P. Harris (founder) and Rotary emblem 15 10
436 60 c. "Creation of a National Park", Mount Sage, Tortola 40 40
437 $1 Rotary anniversary emblem 70 75
434/7 .. .. *Set of* 4 1·25 1·25
MS438 149 × 148 mm. Nos. 434/7 .. .. 1·25 3·25

(Des K. Penny. Litho Secura, Singapore)

1980 (6 May). *"London 1980" International Stamp Exhibition. Birds. T* **136** *and similar horiz designs. Multicoloured. W* w 1 *(sideways*). P* 13½.
439 20 c. Type **136** 20 2
aw. Wmk Crown to right of CA ..
b. Wmk upright 40 4
bw. Wmk inverted 50 5
440 25 c. Magnificent Frigate Bird 25 2
b. Wmk upright .. .. 1·75 1·7
bw. Wmk inverted .. .. 1·75 1·7
441 50 c. White-tailed Tropic Bird 40 4
b. Wmk upright 65 6
bw. Wmk inverted 80 8
442 75 c. Brown Pelican 55 5
w. Wmk Crown to right of CA .. .. 5·00
439/42 .. .. *Set of* 4 1·25 1·2
MS443 152×130 mm. Nos. 439/42 .. .. 1·25 2·2
w. Wmk Crown to left of CA .. .. 15·00
*The normal sideways watermark shows Crown to left of C on the sheet stamps and to right of CA on the miniature shee *both as seen from the back*. Singles of Nos. 439aw and 442 cannot be identified as the listed variety unless part of the shee margin is attached to distinguish them from stamps originatin in No. **MS**443.

CARIBBEAN
COMMONWEALTH
PARLIAMENTARY
ASSOCIATION
MEETING
TORTOLA 11-19 JULY 1980

(137)

138 Sir Francis Drake

1980 (7 July). *Caribbean Commonwealth Parliamentary Association Meeting, Tortola. Nos. 414/15 optd with T* **137**.
444 13 c. deep blue and claret 15 1
445 75 c. deep blue and bright blue 40 4

(Des Franklin Mint. Litho Questa)

1980 (26 Sept). *Sir Francis Drake Commemoration. T* **138** *and similar vert designs. Multicoloured. W* w **14** *(inverted on 75 c.). P* 14 × 14½.
446 8 c. Type **138** 50 1
447 15 c. Queen Elizabeth I 70 1
448 30 c. Drake receiving knighthood 90 3
449 75 c. *Golden Hind* and coat of arms .. .. 1·75 1·2
446/9 .. .. *Set of* 4 3·50 1·6
MS450 171 × 121 mm. Nos. 446/9. Wmk inverted 3·50 6·0
a. 75 c. value in miniature sheet imperf .. £150
b. 30 c. value in miniature sheet imperf .. £150

139 Jost van Dyke

(Des Jennifer Toombs. Litho Rosenbaum Bros, Vienna)

1980 (1 Dec). *Island Profiles. T* **139** *and similar horiz designs. Multicoloured. W* w **14** *(sideways*). P* 13½.
451 2 c. Type **139** 10 1
w. Wmk Crown to right of CA 10
452 5 c. Peter Island 10 1
w. Wmk Crown to right of CA 10
453 13 c. Virgin Gorda 15 1
w. Wmk Crown to right of CA 20
454 22 c. Anegada 20 1
w. Wmk Crown to right to CA 30
455 30 c. Norman Island 25 1
w. Wmk Crown to right of CA 45
456 $1 Tortola .. .. 70 1·0
w. Wmk Crown to right of CA .. .. 1·10
451/6 .. .. *Set of* 6 1·25 1·
MS457 95×88 mm. No. 456 (wmk upright) .. 85 1·5
a. Error. Imperf £325
b. Gold and black omitted £325
w. Wmk inverted .. .. 1·25
*The normal sideways watermark shows Crown to left of CA *as seen from the back of the stamp.*

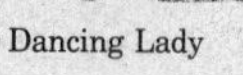

140 Dancing Lady

141 Wedding Bouquet from British Virgin Islands

(Des C. Abbott. Litho Walsall)

81 (3 Mar). *Flowers. T* **140** *and similar vert designs. Multicoloured.* W w **14** (*sideways*). *P* 11.
8 5 c. Type **140** 15 10
9 20 c. Love in the Mist 40 25
) 22 c. *Pitcairnia angustifolia* 40 25
75 c. Dutchman's Pipe.. .. .. 75 1·10
2 $1 Maiden Apple .. .. 90 1·40
8/62 .. .. *Set of* 5 2·40 2·75

(Des J. W. Litho Harrison)

81 (22 July). *Royal Wedding. T* **141** *and similar vert designs. Multicoloured.* W w **14**. *P* 14.
3 10 c. Type **141** 10 10
w. Wmk inverted .. .. 4·00
4 35 c. Prince Charles and Queen Elizabeth the Queen Mother in Garter robes .. 20 15
w. Wmk inverted .. .. 4·00
5 $1.25, Prince Charles and Lady Diana Spencer 60 80
3/5 .. .. *Set of* 3 80 90

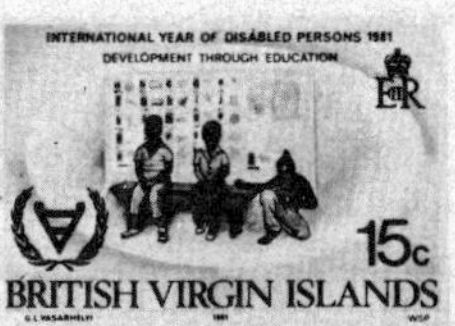

142 Stamp Collecting

143 "Development through Education"

(Des BG Studio. Litho Questa)

81 (10 Oct). *25th Anniv of Duke of Edinburgh Award Scheme. T* **142** *and similar vert designs. Multicoloured.* W w **14**. *P* 14.
66 10 c. Type **142** 10 10
67 15 c. Athletics 10 10
68 50 c. Camping 25 25
69 $1 Duke of Edinburgh 40 45
66/9 .. .. *Set of* 4 65 80

(Des G. Vasarhelyi. Litho Walsall)

981 (19 Oct). *International Year for Disabled Persons. T* **143** *and similar horiz designs. Multicoloured.* W w **14** (*sideways*). *P* 14.
70 15 c. Type **143** 15 15
71 20 c. Fort Charlotte Children's Centre .. 20 20
72 30 c. "Developing cultural awareness" .. 30 30
73 $1 Fort Charlotte Children's Centre (*different*) .. .. 85 1·25
70/3 .. .. *Set of* 4 1·40 1·75

144 Detail from "The Adoration of the Shepherds" (Rubens)

145 Green-throated Caribs and Erythrina

(Des J. W. Litho Questa)

1981 (30 Nov). *Christmas. T* **144** *and similar designs showing details from "The Adoration of the Shepherds" by Rubens.* W w **14**. *P* 14.
474 5 c. multicoloured 15 10
475 15 c. multicoloured 25 10
476 30 c. multicoloured 45 15
477 $1 multicoloured .. .. 1·10 1·10
474/7 .. .. *Set of* 4 1·75 1·25
MS478 117 × 90 mm. 50 c. multicoloured (*horiz*) (wmk sideways) .. .. 1·40 85

(Des Walsall. Litho Format)

1982 (5 Apr). *Hummingbirds. T* **145** *and similar vert designs. Multicoloured.* W w **14**. *P* 14 × 14½.
479 15 c. Type **145** 50 15
480 30 c. Green-throated Carib and Bougainvillea 75 45
481 35 c. Antillean Crested Hummingbirds and *Granadilla passiflora* 85 55
482 $1.25, Antillean Crested Hummingbird and Hibiscus .. .. 2·50 3·00
479/82 .. .. *Set of* 4 4·25 3·75

146 "People caring for People"

147 Princess at Victoria and Albert Museum, November 1981

(Des Harrison. Litho Format)

1982 (3 May). *Tenth Anniv of Lions Club of Tortola. T* **146** *and similar horiz designs. Multicoloured.* W w **14** (*sideways*). *P* 13½ × 14.
483 10 c. Type **146** 25 15
484 20 c. Tortola Headquarters 35 20
485 30 c. "We Serve" 45 30
486 $1.50, "Lions" symbol .. .. 1·25 1·75
483/6 .. .. *Set of* 4 2·10 2·25
MS487 124 × 102 mm. Nos. 483/6 .. .. 3·25 4·75

(Des C. Abbott. Litho Harrison)

1982 (2 July*). *21st Birthday of Princess of Wales. T* **147** *and similar vert designs. Multicoloured.* W w **14**. *P* 14½ × 14.
488 10 c. British Virgin Islands coat of arms .. 15 10
489 35 c. Type **147** 30 25
490 50 c. Bride and groom proceeding into Vestry 45 45
491 $1.50, Formal portrait .. .. 1·10 1·40
488/91 .. .. *Set of* 4 1·75 2·00

*This is the local release date. The Crown Agents released the stamps on 1 July.

148 Douglas DC-3

(Des A. Theobald. Litho Questa)

1982 (10 Sept). *10th Anniv of Air BVI. T* **148** *and similar horiz designs. Multicoloured.* W w **14** (*sideways*). *P* 14.
492 10 c. Type **148** 45 15
493 15 c. Britten Norman Islander 60 20
494 60 c. Hawker Siddeley H.S.748 .. .. 1·25 75
495 75 c. Runway scene .. .. 1·50 90
492/5 .. .. *Set of* 4 3·50 1·75

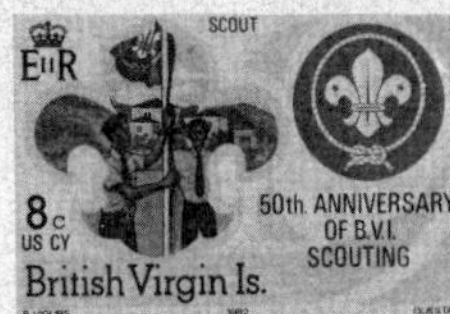

149 Scouts raising Flag

(Des R. Vigurs. Litho Questa)

1982 (18 Nov). *75th Anniv of Boy Scout Movement ($1) and 50th Anniv of Scouting in B.V.I. (others). T* **149** *and similar horiz designs. Multicoloured.* W w **14** (*sideways**). *P* 14.
496 8 c. Type **149** 20 10
497 20 c. Cub Scout 45 25
498 50 c. Sea Scout 60 55
w. Wmk Crown to right of CA .. .. 13·00
499 $1 First camp, Brownsea Island, and portrait of Lord Baden-Powell .. .. 1·00 1·50
w. Wmk Crown to right of CA .. .. 13·00
496/9 .. .. *Set of* 4 2·00 2·25

*The normal sideways watermark shows Crown to left of CA, *as seen from the back of the stamp.*

150 Legislature in Session

151 Florence Nightingale

(Des G. Vasarhelyi. Litho Enschedé)

1983 (10 Mar). *Commonwealth Day. T* **150** *and similar horiz designs. Multicoloured.* W w **14** (*sideways*). *P* 13 × 13½.
500 10 c. Type **150** 10 10
501 30 c. Tourism 25 20
502 35 c. Satellite view of Earth showing Virgin Islands 25 25
503 75 c. B.V.I. and Commonwealth flags .. 70 90
500/3 .. .. *Set of* 4 1·10 1·25

(Des L. Curtis. Litho Questa)

1983 (9 May). *Nursing Week. T* **151** *and similar multicoloured designs.* W w **14** (*sideways on* 60 c. *and* 75 c.). *P* 14.
504 10 c. Type **151** 50 15
505 30 c. Staff nurse and assistant nurse .. 90 45
506 60 c. Public Health nurses testing blood pressure (*horiz*) .. .. .. 1·75 1·25
507 75 c. Peebles Hospital (*horiz*) .. .. 1·90 1·75
504/7 .. .. *Set of* 4 4·50 3·25

152 Frame Construction

(Des R. Burnett. Litho Harrison)

1983 (25 July). *Traditional Boat-building. T* **152** *and similar horiz designs. Multicoloured.* W w **14** (*sideways*). *P* 14.
508 15 c. Type **152** 35 25
509 25 c. Planking 50 45
510 50 c. Launching 80 80
511 $1 Maiden voyage .. .. 1·25 1·75
508/11 .. .. *Set of* 4 2·50 3·00
MS512 127 × 101 mm. Nos. 508/11 .. .. 2·50 3·75

153 Grumman G-21 Goose Amphibian

154 "Madonna and Child with the Infant Baptist"

(Des Walsall. Litho Questa)

1983 (15 Sept). *Bicentenary of Manned Flight. T* **153** *and similar horiz designs. Multicoloured.* W w **14** (*sideways*). *P* 14.
513 10 c. Type **153** 20 15
514 30 c. Riley Turbo Skyliner 45 45
515 60 c. Embraer EMB-110 Bandeirante .. 85 85
516 $1.25, Hawker Siddeley H.S.748 .. .. 1·50 1·60
513/16 .. .. *Set of* 4 2·75 2·75

(Des M. Joyce. Litho Questa)

1983 (7 Nov). *Christmas. 500th Birth Anniv of Raphael. T* **154** *and similar vert designs showing details of different paintings. Multicoloured.* W w **14**. *P* 14½ × 14.
517 8 c. Type **154** 10 10
518 15 c. "La Belle Jardiniére" 20 25
519 50 c. "Madonna Del Granduca" 65 70
520 $1 "The Terranuova Madonna" .. .. 1·25 1·40
517/20 .. .. *Set of* 4 2·00 2·25
MS521 108 × 101 mm. Nos. 517/20 .. .. 2·75 3·75

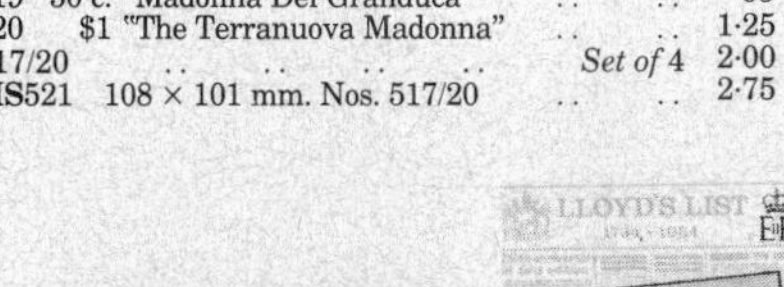

155 Local Tournament

156 Port Purcell

(Des L. Curtis. Litho Questa)

1984 (20 Feb). *60th Anniv of World Chess Federation. T* **155** *and similar multicoloured designs.* W w **14** (*sideways on* 10 c. *and* $1, *inverted on* 35 c.). *P* 14.
522 10 c. Type **155** .. .. 1·00 40
523 35 c. Staunton chess pieces (*vert*) .. .. 2·00 1·50
524 75 c. Karpov's winning position, 1980 Chess Olympiad (*vert*) .. .. .. 3·75 4·25
525 $1 B.V.I. Gold Medal won by Bill Hook at 1980 Chess Olympiad .. .. .. 4·25 5·50
522/5 .. .. *Set of* 4 10·00 10·50

(Des L. Curtis. Litho Questa)

1984 (16 Apr). *250th Anniv of "Lloyd's List" (newspaper). T* **156** *and similar vert designs. Multicoloured.* W w **14**. *P* 14½ × 14.
526 15 c. Type **156** 25 30
527 25 c. Boeing 747-100 .. .. 45 50
528 50 c. Wreck of *Rhone* (mail steamer), 1867 90 95
529 $1 *Booker Viking* (cargo liner) .. .. 1·50 1·60
526/9 .. .. *Set of* 4 2·75 3·00

157 Mail Ship *Boyne*, Boeing 747-100 and U.P.U. Logo

(Des L. Curtis. Litho Walsall)

1984 (16 May). *Universal Postal Union Congress, Hamburg. Sheet* 90 × 69 *mm.* W w **14** (*sideways*). *P* 14.
MS530 **157** $1 pale blue and black .. .. 2·25 2·50

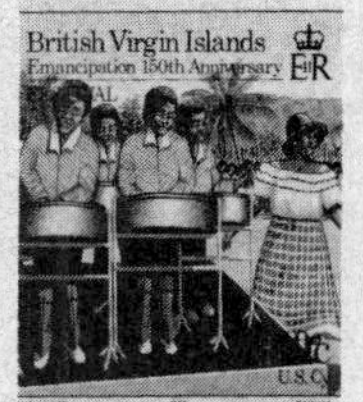

158 Running 159 Steel Band

(Des R. Granger Barrett. Litho Walsall)

1984 (3 July). *Olympic Games, Los Angeles. T* **158** *and similar horiz designs. Multicoloured. W* w **14** *(sideways*). P* 14.

531	15 c. Type **158**	40	40
	a. Pair. Nos. 531/2	80	80
	aw. Wmk Crown to right of CA	6·00	
532	15 c. Runner	40	40
533	20 c. Wind-surfing	45	45
	a. Pair. Nos. 533/4	90	90
534	20 c. Surfer	45	45
535	30 c. Sailing	65	65
	a. Pair. Nos. 535/6	1·25	1·25
536	30 c. Yacht	65	65
531/6	*Set of* 6	2·75	2·75
MS537	97×69 mm. $1 Torch bearer. Wmk upright	1·50	1·90

*The normal sideways watermark shows Crown to left of CA, *as seen from the back of the stamp.*

Nos. 531/2, 533/4 and 535/6 were printed together, *se-tenant*, in horizontal and vertical pairs throughout the sheets.

(Des D. Miller. Litho Format)

1984 (14 Aug). *150th Anniv of Abolition of Slavery. T* **159** *and similar vert designs showing various aspects of Emancipation Festival. Multicoloured. W* w **14**. *P* 14.

538	10 c. Type **159**	30	35
	a. Horiz strip of 5. Nos. 538/42	1·40	
539	10 c. Dancing girls	30	35
540	10 c. Men in traditional costumes	30	35
541	10 c. Girl in traditional costume	30	35
542	10 c. Festival Queen	30	35
543	30 c. Green and yellow dinghies	45	50
	a. Horiz strip of 5. Nos. 543/7	2·00	
544	30 c. Blue and red dinghies	45	50
545	30 c. White and blue dinghies	45	50
546	30 c. Red and yellow dinghies	45	50
547	30 c. Blue and white dinghies	45	50
538/47	*Set of* 10	3·00	3·50

Nos. 538/42 and 543/7 were each printed together, *se-tenant*, in horizontal strips of 5 throughout the sheet, forming composite designs. On Nos. 543/7 the sail colours of the dinghies are described to assist identification.

160 Sloop

(Des R. Burnett. Litho J.W.)

1984 (15 Nov). *Boats. T* **160** *and similar horiz designs. Multicoloured. W* w **14** *(sideways). P* 13 × 13½.

548	10 c. Type **160**	40	20
549	35 c. Fishing boat	1·00	65
550	60 c. Schooner	1·40	1·25
551	75 c. Cargo boat	1·40	1·60
548/51	*Set of* 4	3·75	3·25
MS552	125 × 90 mm. Nos. 548/51. P 14	3·75	4·00

161 One Cent Coin and Aerial View 162 Red-billed Tropic Bird

(Litho Walsall)

1985 (15 Jan). *New Coinage. T* **161** *and similar horiz designs showing coins and local scenery. Multicoloured. W* w **14** *(sideways). P* 14½.

553	1 c. Type **161**	10	10
554	5 c. Five cent coin and boulders on beach	10	10
555	10 c. Ten cent coin and scuba diving	20	20
556	25 c. Twenty-five cent coin and yachts	45	50
557	50 c. Fifty cent coin and jetty	90	1·25
558	$1 One dollar coin and beach at night	1·75	2·25
553/8	*Set of* 6	3·00	4·00
MS559	103 × 156 mm. Nos. 553/8	3·00	6·00

A set of stamps, 55 c. and $1·50 each × 2, showing Michael Jackson the entertainer was prepared in 1985, but was never released for postal use. Samples of the $1.50 values were, however, distributed for publicity purposes and both values exist from stock dispersed by the liquidator of Format International Security Printers Ltd.

(Des N. Arlott. Litho Questa)

1985 (3 July). *Birds of the British Virgin Islands. T* **162** *and similar vert designs. Multicoloured. W* w **14**. "1985" *imprint date. P* 14.

560	1 c. Type **162**	60	1·00
561	2 c. Yellow-crowned Night Heron	60	1·00
562	5 c. Mangrove Cuckoo	70	90
563	8 c. Northern Mockingbird	75	1·25
564	10 c. Grey Kingbird	75	40
565	12 c. Red-necked Pigeon	1·00	55
566	15 c. Least Bittern	1·25	55
567	18 c. Smooth-billed Ani	1·40	1·50
568	20 c. Clapper Rail	1·40	1·00
569	25 c. American Kestrel	1·50	1·50
570	30 c. Pearly-eyed Thrasher	1·50	1·10
571	35 c. Bridled Quail Dove	1·75	1·25
572	40 c. Green Heron	1·75	1·50
573	50 c. Scaly-breasted Ground Dove	2·00	2·25
574	60 c. Little Blue Heron	2·25	3·00
575	$1 Audubon's Shearwater	3·00	3·00
576	$2 Blue-faced Booby	3·50	6·00
577	$3 Cattle Egret	4·75	7·50
578	$5 Zenaida Dove	7·00	11·00
560/78	*Set of* 19	35·00	42·00

For these stamps watermarked w **16** see Nos. 647/60.

IMPERFORATES AND MISSING COLOURS. Various issues between Nos. 579 and 609 exist either imperforate or with colours omitted. Many originate from stock dispersed by the liquidator of Format International Security Printers Ltd. Such items are not listed as there is no evidence that they fulfil the criteria outlined on page xi of this catalogue.

163 The Queen Mother at Festival of Remembrance 164 Seaside Sparrow

(Des Maxine Marsh. Litho Format)

1985 (26 Aug). *Life and Times of Queen Elizabeth the Queen Mother. Various vertical portraits as T* **163**. *Multicoloured. P* 12½. A. *W* w **15** *(sideways)*

579A	10 c. Type **163**	10	20
	a. Horiz pair. Nos. 579A/80A	20	40
580A	10 c. At Victoria Palace Theatre, 1984	10	20
581A	25 c. At the engagement of the Prince of Wales, 1981	15	40
	a. Horiz pair. Nos. 581A/2A	30	80
582A	25 c. Opening Celia Johnson Theatre, 1985	15	40
583A	50 c. The Queen Mother on her 82nd birthday	20	70
	a. Horiz pair. Nos. 583A/4A	40	1·40
584A	50 c. At the Tate Gallery, 1983	20	70
585A	75 c. At the Royal Smithfield Show, 1983	25	1·00
	a. Horiz pair. Nos. 585A/6A	50	2·00
586A	75 c. Unveiling Mountbatten statue, 1983	25	1·00
579A/86A	*Set of* 8	1·25	4·25
MS587A	85×114 mm. $1 At Columbia University; $1 At a Wedding, St. Margaret's Westminster, 1983	85	4·00

B. *No wmk*

579B	10 c. Type **163**	2·50	2·50
	a. Horiz pair. Nos. 579B/80B	5·00	5·00
580B	10 c. At Victoria Palace Theatre, 1984	2·50	2·50
581B	25 c. At the engagement of the Prince of Wales, 1981	2·50	2·50
	a. Horiz pair. Nos. 581B/2B	5·00	5·00
582B	25 c. Opening Celia Johnson Theatre, 1985	2·50	2·50
583B	50 c. The Queen Mother on her 82nd birthday	3·00	3·00
	a. Horiz pair. Nos. 583B/4B	6·00	6·00
584B	50 c. At the Tate Gallery, 1983	3·00	3·00
585B	75 c. At the Royal Smithfield Show, 1983	3·00	3·00
	a. Horiz pair. Nos. 585B/6B	6·00	6·00
586B	75 c. Unveiling Mountbatten statue, 1983	3·00	3·00
579B/86B	*Set of* 8	20·00	20·00

The two designs of each value were issued, *se-tenant*, in horizontal pairs within the sheets.

Each *se-tenant* pair shows a floral pattern across the bottom of the portraits which stops short of the left-hand edge on the left-hand stamp and of the right-hand edge on the right-hand stamp.

Sets of four miniature sheets, containing the two designs of each value, were prepared, but not issued. Examples exist from stock dispersed by the liquidator of Format International Security Printers Ltd.

Designs as Nos. 583/4 and 585/6, but with face values of $2.50×2 and $1×2, also exist in additional miniature sheets from a restricted printing issued 18 December 1985.

(Des R. Vigurs. Litho Format)

1985 (17 Dec). *Birth Bicentenary of John J. Audubon (ornithologist). T* **164** *and similar vert designs showing original paintings. Multicoloured. P* 15.

588	5 c. Type **164**	40	20
589	30 c. Passenger Pigeon	70	70
590	50 c. Yellow-breasted Chat	80	1·75
591	$1 American Kestrel	1·25	2·75
588/91	*Set of* 4	2·75	4·75

MIAMI B.V.I. INAUGURAL FLIGHT

165 S.V. *Flying Cloud* (166)

(Des G. Drummond. Litho Format)

1986 (27 Jan). *Visiting Cruise Ships. T* **165** *and similar hori[z] designs. Multicoloured. W* w **15**. *P* 15.

592	35 c. Type **165**	80	8
	w. Wmk inverted	10·00	
593	50 c. M.V. *Newport Clipper*	1·10	1·5
	w. Wmk inverted	9·00	
594	75 c. M.V. *Cunard Countess*	1·40	2·5
595	$1 M.V. *Sea Goddess*	1·50	3·0
	w. Wmk inverted	17·00	
592/5	*Set of* 4	4·25	7·0

1986 (17 Apr). *Inaugural Flight of Miami–Beef Island Ai[r] Service. Nos.* 581/2 *and* 585/6 *optd with T* **166**. A. *W* w **1[5]** *(sideways)*

596A	25 c. At the engagement of the Prince of Wales, 1981	40	5
	a. Horiz pair. Nos. 596A/7A	80	1·0
597A	25 c. Opening Celia Johnson Theatre, 1985	40	5
598A	75 c. At the Royal Smithfield Show, 1983	1·25	1·5
	a. Horiz pair. Nos. 598A/9A	2·50	3·0
599A	75 c. Unveiling Mountbatten statue, 1983	1·25	1·5
596A/9A	*Set of* 4	3·00	3·5

B. *No wmk*

596B	25 c. At the engagement of the Prince of Wales, 1981	1·75	2·2
	a. Horiz pair. Nos. 596B/7B	3·50	4·5
597B	25 c. Opening Celia Johnson Theatre, 1985	1·75	2·2
598B	75 c. At the Royal Smithfield Show, 1983	1·75	2·2
	a. Horiz pair. Nos. 598B/9B	3·50	4·5
599B	75 c. Unveiling Mountbatten statue, 1983	1·75	2·2
596B/9B	*Set of* 4	6·00	8·0

167 Queen Elizabeth II in 1958

(Des Court House Studio. Litho Format)

1986 (21 Apr). *60th Birthday of Queen Elizabeth II. T* **167** *an[d] similar multicoloured designs. P* 12½.

600	12 c. Type **167**	15	2
601	35 c. At a Maundy Service	20	4
	a. Wmk w **15** (sideways)	2·00	
602	$1.50. Queen Elizabeth	45	1·7
	a. Wmk w **15** (sideways)	3·25	
603	$2 During a visit to Canberra, 1982 (*vert*)	60	2·2
600/3	*Set of* 4	1·25	4·2
MS604	85 × 115 mm $3 Queen with bouquet	4·00	5·5

Examples of the 12 c., 35 c. and $1.50 values with the blue (ribbons and frame) omitted are from stock dispersed by the liquidator of Format International Security Printers Ltd.

Unissued sets of five miniature sheets, each containing one value, come from the same source.

168 Miss Sarah Ferguson 169 Harvesting Sugar Cane

(Des Court House Studio. Litho Format)

1986 (23 July–15 Oct). *Royal Wedding. T* **168** *and similar multicoloured designs. P* 12½.

605	35 c. Type **168**	25	55
	a. Pair. Nos. 605/6	50	1·10
	b. Wmk w **15**	3·00	
	ba. Pair. Nos. 605b/6b	6·00	
606	35 c. Prince Andrew and Miss Sarah Ferguson	25	55
	b. Wmk w **15**	3·00	
607	$1 Prince Andrew in morning dress (*horiz*)	40	1·25
	a. Pair. Nos. 607/8	80	2·50

3 $1 Miss Sarah Ferguson (*different*) (*horiz*) 40 1·25
5/8 .. .. *Set of* 4 1·10 3·25
S609 115×85 mm. $4 Duke and Duchess of York in carriage after wedding (*horiz*) (15.10.86) 3·00 5·50

Nos. 605/6 and 607/8 were each printed together, *se-tenant*, in horizontal and vertical pairs throughout the sheets.

Nos. 605/8 imperforate come from souvenir stamp booklets.

Nos. 605/8 overprinted "Congratulations to T.R.H. The Duke Duchess of York" were not issued.

(Des Toni Lance. Litho Questa)

86 (30 July). *History of Rum Making. T* **169** *and similar horiz designs. Multicoloured. W w* **15**. *P* 14.
0 12 c. Type **169**.. .. .. 80 40
1 40 c. Bringing sugar cane to mill .. .. 1·50 1·25
2 60 c. Rum distillery .. .. 2·00 3·25
3 $1 Delivering barrels of rum to ship .. 3·25 4·00
0/13 .. .. *Set of* 4 6·75 8·00
S614 115×84 mm. $2 Royal Navy rum issue. Wmk sideways .. .. 6·50 8·50

170 C.S. *Sentinel* 171 Statue of Liberty at Sunset

(Des Court House Studio. Litho Format)

986 (28 Oct). *20th Anniv of Cable and Wireless Caribbean Headquarters, Tortola. T* **170** *and similar horiz designs. Multicoloured. W w* **15**. *P* 12½.
5 35 c. Type **170**.. .. .. 60 80
a. Vert pair. Nos. 615/16 .. .. .. 1·10 1·60
6 35 c. C.S. *Retriever* (1961) 60 80
7 60 c. C.S. *Cable Enterprise* (1964) .. .. 1·00 1·50
a. Vert pair. Nos. 617/18 .. .. .. 2·00 3·00
8 60 c. C.S. *Mercury* (1962) .. .. .. 1·00 1·50
9 75 c. C.S. *Recorder* (1955) .. .. .. 1·10 1·75
a. Vert pair. Nos. 619/20 .. .. .. 2·10 3·50
20 75 c. C.S. *Pacific Guardian* (1984) .. .. 1·10 1·75
21 $1 S.S. *Great Eastern* (1860's) .. .. 1·25 2·00
a. Vert pair. Nos. 621/2 .. .. .. 2·50 4·00
22 $1 C.S. *Cable Venture* (1977) .. .. 1·25 2·00
15/22 .. .. *Set of* 8 7·00 11·00
MS623 Four sheets, each 102×131 mm. (a) 40 c. × 2 As 35 c. (b) 50 c. × 2 As 60 c. (c) 80 c. × 2 As 75 c. (d) $1.50 × 2 As $1 .. *Set of* 4 *sheets* 6·00 12·00

The two designs of each value were printed, *se-tenant*, in vertical pairs throughout the sheets.

(Des Court House Studio. Litho Format)

986 (15 Dec). *Centenary of Statue of Liberty. T* **171** *and similar vert views of Statue in separate miniature sheets. Multicoloured. P* 14×13½.
MS624 Nine sheets, each 85×115 mm. 50 c.; 75 c.; 90 c.; $1; $1.25; $1.50; $1.75; $2; $2.50 *Set of* 9 *sheets* 9·00 18·00

172 18th-century Spanish Galleon 173 Outline Map and Flag of Montserrrat

(Des J. Batchelor. Litho Questa)

1987 (15 Apr). *Shipwrecks. T* **172** *and similar horiz designs. Multicoloured. W w* **15**. *P* 14.
625 12 c. Type **172** .. .. 1·50 45
626 35 c. H.M.S. *Astrea* (frigate), 1808 .. 2·75 1·40
627 75 c. *Rhone* (mail steamer), 1867 .. .. 4·25 4·00
628 $1.50 *Captain Rokos* (freighter), 1929 .. 6·00 7·50
625/8 .. .. *Set of* 4 13·00 12·00
MS629 86×65 mm. $1.50, *Volvart*, 1819 .. 13·00 13·00

(Des R. Burnett. Litho Walsall)

1987 (28 May). *11th Meeting of Organization of Eastern Caribbean States. T* **173** *and similar vert designs, each showing outline map and flag. Multicoloured. W w* **16**. *P* 14.
630 10 c. Type **173**.. .. .. 70 60
631 15 c. Grenada 80 60
632 20 c. Dominica 85 65
633 25 c. St. Kitts–Nevis 90 70
634 35 c. St. Vincent and Grenadines .. .. 1·40 1·00
635 50 c. British Virgin Islands .. .. .. 2·00 2·50
636 75 c. Antigua and Barbuda .. .. .. 2·25 3·00
637 $1 St. Lucia.. .. .. 2·75 3·25
630/7 .. .. *Set of* 8 10·50 11·00

174 Spider Lily 175 Early Mail Packet and 1867 1s. Stamp

(Des Jennifer Toombs. Litho Questa)

1987 (20 Aug). *Opening of Botanical Gardens. T* **174** *and similar vert designs. Multicoloured. W w* **16**. *P* 14.
638 12 c. Type **174**.. .. .. 80 35
639 35 c. Barrel Cactus .. .. 1·75 1·00
640 $1 Wild Plantain .. .. 2·75 3·25
641 $1.50, Little Butterfly Orchid .. .. 8·00 8·50
638/41 .. .. *Set of* 4 12·00 12·00
MS642 139×104 mm. $2.50, White Cedar .. 3·75 6·00

1987 (28 Oct). *As Nos.* 564, 566, 568/9, 571, 575 *and* 577 *but W w* **16**. "1987" *imprint date. P* 14.
647 10 c. Grey Kingbird 60 80
649 15 c. Least Bittern 80 80
651 20 c. Clapper Rail 80 70
652 25 c. American Kestrel 90 75
654 35 c. Bridled Quail Dove 90 85
658 $1 Audubon's Shearwater.. .. .. 2·00 3·25
660 $3 Cattle Egret .. .. 6·00 9·50
647/60 .. .. *Set of* 7 11·00 15·00

(Des and litho Walsall)

1987 (17 Dec). *Bicentenary of Postal Services. T* **175** *and similar horiz designs, each including stamp and cancellation. Multicoloured. W w* **16** (*sideways*). *P* 14½.
662 10 c. Type **175**.. .. .. 1·00 55
663 20 c. Map and 1899 1d. .. .. .. 1·50 95
664 35 c. Road Town Post Office and Customs House, 1913, and 1867 4d. .. .. 2·00 1·50
665 $1.50, Piper PA-23 Apache mail plane and 1964 25 c. definitive .. .. .. 6·00 9·00
662/5 .. .. *Set of* 4 9·50 11·00
MS666 70×60 mm. $2.50, Mail ship, 1880's, and 1880 1d. .. .. 6·00 9·00

(Litho Questa)

1988 (11 Aug). *500th Birth Anniv of Titian (artist). Vert designs as T* **238** *of Antigua. Multicoloured. P* 13½×14.
667 10 c. "Salome" 55 55
668 12 c. "Man with the Glove" 60 60
669 20 c. "Fabrizio Salvaresio" 80 80
670 25 c. "Daughter of Roberto Strozzi" .. 90 90
671 40 c. "Pope Julius II" .. .. .. 1·40 2·00
672 50 c. "Bishop Ludovico Beccadelli" .. .. 1·60 2·00
673 60 c. "King Philip II" .. .. .. 1·75 2·50
674 $1 "Empress Isabella of Portugal" .. 2·25 2·75
667/74 .. .. *Set of* 8 9·00 11·00
MS675 Two sheets, each 110×95 mm. (a) $2 "Emperor Charles V at Muhlberg" (detail). (b) $2 "Pope Paul III and his Grandsons" (detail) *Set of* 2 *sheets* 9·50 12·00

176 De Havilland D.H.C.5 over Sir Francis Drake Channel and Staunton Pawn

(Des B. Bundock. Litho Questa)

1988 (25 Aug). *First British Virgin Islands Open Chess Tournament. T* **176** *and similar horiz designs. Multicoloured. P* 14.
676 35 c. Type **176** .. .. 4·00 1·50
677 $1 Jose Capablanca (former World Champion) and Staunton king .. 8·00 8·50
MS678 109×81 mm. $2 Chess match .. 8·00 10·00

177 Hurdling

(Des L. Fried. Litho B.D.T.)

1988 (8 Sept). *Olympic Games, Seoul. T* **177** *and similar horiz designs. Multicoloured. P* 14.
679 12 c. Type **177** 30 25
680 20 c. Windsurfing 45 45
681 75 c. Basketball .. .. 3·00 3·25
682 $1 Tennis .. .. 3·50 3·75
679/82 .. .. *Set of* 4 6·50 7·00
MS683 71 × 102 mm. $2 Athletics .. .. 3·00 4·50

178 Swimmer ("Don't Swim Alone") 179 Princess Alexandra

(Des I. Arbell. Litho Questa)

1988 (26 Sept). *125th Anniv of International Red Cross. T* **178** *and similar designs. P* 14.
684 12 c. black, bright scarlet and cobalt .. 85 40
685 30 c. black, bright scarlet and cobalt .. 1·50 80
686 60 c. black, bright scarlet and cobalt .. 2·75 3·00
687 $1 black, bright scarlet and cobalt .. 3·25 4·00
684/7 .. .. *Set of* 4 7·50 7·50
MS688 68 × 96 mm. 50 c. × 4 black and bright scarlet .. .. 5·00 6·50

Designs: *Horiz*—30 c. Swimmers ("No swimming during electrical storms"); 60 c. Beach picnic ("Don't eat before swimming"); $1 Boat and equipment ("Proper equipment for boating"). *Vert*—50 c. × 4 Recovery position; clearing airway; mouth-to-mouth resuscitation; cardiac massage.

(Litho Questa)

1988 (9 Nov). *Visit of Princess Alexandra. T* **179** *and similar vert designs showing different portraits. P* 14.
689 40 c. multicoloured .. .. 1·75 75
690 $1.50, multicoloured .. .. 3·75 4·75
MS691 102 × 98 mm. $2 multicoloured .. 5·00 6·50

180 Brown Pelican in Flight 181 Anegada Rock Iguana

(Des S. Barlowe. Litho Questa)

1988 (30 Nov). *Wildlife (1st series). Aquatic Birds. T* **180** *and similar multicoloured designs. P* 14.
692 10 c. Type **180** .. .. 1·10 50
693 12 c. Brown Pelican perched on post .. 1·25 55
694 15 c. Brown Pelican .. .. 1·40 1·10
695 35 c. Brown Pelican swallowing fish .. 2·75 3·00
692/5 .. .. *Set of* 4 6·00 4·75
MS696 106×76 mm. $2 Common Shoveler (*horiz*) .. .. 7·50 9·00

No. **MS**696 is without the WWF logo.

(Des S. Barlowe. Litho Questa)

1988 (15 Dec). *Wildlife (2nd series). Endangered Species. T* **181** *and similar multicoloured designs. P* 14.
697 20 c. Type **181** .. .. 1·25 75
698 40 c. Virgin Gorda Dwarf Gecko .. .. 1·50 1·40
699 60 c. Hawksbill Turtle .. .. .. 2·50 3·50
700 $1 Humpback Whale .. .. .. 7·00 8·00
697/700 .. .. *Set of* 4 11·00 12·00
MS701 106 × 77 mm. $2 Trunk Turtle (*vert*) .. 5·00 7·00

182 Yachts at Start 183 "Apollo 11" Emblem

(Des D. Miller. Litho Questa)

1989 (7 Apr). *Spring Regatta. T* **182** *and similar multicoloured designs. P* 14.
702 12 c. Type **182** 45 40
703 40 c. Yacht tacking (*horiz*) .. .. .. 1·00 1·00
704 75 c. Yachts at sunset .. .. .. 1·60 2·50
705 $1 Yachts rounding buoy (*horiz*) .. 2·00 2·75
702/5 .. .. *Set of* 4 4·50 6·00
MS706 83×69 mm. $2 Yacht under full sail .. 4·75 6·00

(Des D. Miller. Litho Questa)

1989 (8 May). *500th Anniv of Discovery of America by Columbus* (1992) (*1st issue*). *Pre-Columbian Arawak Society. Multicoloured designs as T* **247** *of Antigua, but horiz. P* 14.
707 10 c. Arawak in hammock 60 45
708 20 c. Making fire 85 50
709 25 c. Making implements 90 60
710 $1.50, Arawak family .. .. .. 4·25 7·00
707/10 .. .. *Set of* 4 6·00 7·75
MS711 85×70 mm. $2 Religious ceremony .. 6·00 8·00

See also Nos. 741/5, 793/7 and 818/26.

(Des W. Hanson. Litho Questa)

1989 (28 Sept). *20th Anniv of First Manned Landing on Moon. T* **183** *and similar multicoloured designs. P* 14.
712 15 c. Type **183** 90 50
713 30 c. Edwin Aldrin deploying scientific experiments .. .. 1·75 1·00
714 65 c. Aldrin and U.S. flag on Moon .. 2·50 3·50
715 $1 "Apollo 11" capsule after splashdown 3·25 3·75
712/15 .. .. *Set of* 4 7·75 8·00
MS716 102×77 mm. $2 Neil Armstrong (38×50 *mm*). P 13½×14 .. .. .. 5·50 7·50

184 Black Harry and Nathaniel Gilbert preaching to Slaves

185 Player tackling

(Des R. Vigurs. Litho Questa)

1989 (24 Oct). *Bicentenary of Methodist Church in British Virgin Islands. T* **184** *and similar multicoloured designs. P* 14.
717 12 c. Type **184** 75 40
718 25 c. Methodist school exercise book .. 1·00 60
719 35 c. East End Methodist Church, 1810 .. 1·10 75
720 $1.25, Revd. John Wesley (founder of Methodism) and church youth choir .. 3·25 5·00
717/20 .. .. *Set of* 4 5·50 6·00
MS721 100×69 mm. $2 Dr. Thomas Coke .. 4·50 7·00

(Des R. Vigurs. Litho Questa)

1989 (6 Nov). *World Cup Football Championship, Italy,* 1990. *T* **185** *and similar vert designs. Multicoloured. P* 14.
722 5 c. Type **185** 70 70
723 10 c. Player dribbling ball 70 70
724 20 c. Two players chasing ball .. .. 1·25 70
725 $1.75, Goalkeeper diving for ball .. 6·00 7·00
722/5 .. .. *Set of* 4 7·75 8·00
MS726 100×70 mm. $2 British Virgin Islands team captain .. .. 7·00 9·00

186 Princess Alexandra and Sunset House

(Litho Questa)

1990 (3 May). *"Stamp World London 90" International Stamp Exhibition. Royal Visitors. T* **186** *and similar horiz designs. Multicoloured. P* 14.
727 50 c. Type **186** .. .. 1·50 1·75
a. Sheetlet. Nos. 727/30 .. .. 5·50
728 50 c. Princess Margaret and Government House .. .. 1·50 1·75
729 50 c. Hon. Angus Ogilvy and Little Dix Bay Hotel .. .. 1·50 1·75
730 50 c. Princess Diana with Princes William and Harry and Necker Island Resort .. 1·50 1·75
727/30 .. .. *Set of* 4 5·50 6·00
MS731 89×80 mm. $2 Royal Yacht *Britannia* 6·00 6·50
Nos. 727/30 were printed together, *se-tenant*, in sheetlets of four.

187 Audubon's Shearwater

188 Queen Elizabeth the Queen Mother

(Litho Questa)

1990 (15 May). *Birds. T* **187** *and similar multicoloured designs showing birds and eggs. P* 14.
732 5 c. Type **187** 40 60
733 12 c. Red-necked Pigeon 60 40
734 20 c. Moorhen ("Common Gallinule") .. 70 50
735 25 c. Green Heron 75 50
736 40 c. Yellow Warbler .. .. .. 1·25 1·25
737 60 c. Smooth-billed Ani .. .. .. 1·50 2·25
738 $1 Antillean Crested Hummingbird .. 1·75 2·25
739 $1.25, Black-faced Grassquit .. .. 2·00 2·75
732/9 .. .. *Set of* 8 8·00 9·50
MS740 Two sheets, each 98×70 mm. (a) $2 Royal Tern egg (*vert*). (b) $2 Red-billed Tropicbird egg (*vert*) .. .. *Set of 2 sheets* 7·00 7·00

(Des Mary Walters. Litho Questa)

1990 (18 June). *500th Anniv of Discovery of America by Columbus* (1992) (2nd *issue*). *New World Natural History–Fishes. Multicoloured designs as T* **260** *of Antigua, but horiz. P* 14.
741 10 c. Blue Tang 65 50
742 35 c. Glass-eyed Snapper .. .. .. 1·25 70
743 50 c. Slippery Dick .. .. .. 1·75 2·25
744 $1 Porkfish .. .. 2·75 3·00
741/4 .. .. *Set of* 4 5·75 5·75
MS745 100×70 mm. $2 Yellow-tailed Snapper 3·75 4·75

(Litho Questa)

1990 (30 Aug). *90th Birthday of Queen Elizabeth the Queen Mother. T* **188** *and similar vert designs showing recent photographs. P* 14.
746 12 c. multicoloured 35 20
747 25 c. multicoloured 65 45
748 60 c. multicoloured .. .. .. 1·40 2·00
749 $1 multicoloured .. .. .. 1·75 2·25
746/9 .. .. *Set of* 4 3·75 4·50
MS750 75×75 mm. $2 multicoloured .. .. 2·75 2·75

189 Footballers

190 Judo

(Litho Questa)

1990 (10 Dec). *World Cup Football Championship, Italy. T* **189** *and similar vert designs showing footballers. P* 14.
751 12 c. multicoloured 60 35
752 20 c. multicoloured 90 50
753 50 c. multicoloured .. .. .. 1·75 2·00
754 $1.25, multicoloured .. .. .. 2·50 3·00
751/4 .. .. *Set of* 4 5·25 5·25
MS755 91×76 mm. $2 multicoloured .. .. 4·00 4·00

(Litho Questa)

1990 (20 Dec). *Olympic Games, Barcelona* (1992). *T* **190** *and similar horiz designs. Multicoloured. P* 14.
756 12 c. Type **190** 70 35
757 40 c. Yachting .. .. 1·40 1·40
758 60 c. Hurdling .. .. 2·00 2·50
759 $1 Show jumping .. .. .. 2·50 3·00
756/9 .. .. *Set of* 4 6·00 6·50
MS760 78×105 mm. $2 Windsurfing .. .. 3·50 3·50

191 Tree-fern, Sage Mountain National Park

192 Haiti Haiti

(Litho Questa)

1991 (1 Mar). *30th Anniv of National Parks Trust. T* **191** *and similar multicoloured designs. P* 14.
761 10 c. Type **191** 50 50
762 25 c. Coppermine ruins, Virgin Gorda (*horiz*) 75 50
763 35 c. Ruined windmill, Mount Healthy .. 85 60
764 $2 The Baths (rock formation), Virgin Gorda (*horiz*) .. .. 5·50 7·00
761/4 .. .. *Set of* 4 7·00 7·75

(Des Wendy Smith-Griswold. Litho Questa)

1991 (1 May)–**95**. *Flowers. T* **192** *and similar vert designs. Multicoloured. Without imprint date. P* 14.
765 1 c. Type **192** 20 40
766 2 c. Lobster Claw 20 40
767 5 c. Frangipani 20 40
768 10 c. Autograph Tree 60 70
769 12 c. Yellow Allamanda 40 30
770 15 c. Lantana 70 80
771 20 c. Jerusalem Thorn 50 30
772 25 c. Turk's Cap 55 40
773 30 c. Swamp Immortelle 80 80
774 35 c. White Cedar 90 90
775 40 c. Mahoe Tree 75 65
776 45 c. Pinguin .. .. 1·25 1·25
777 50 c. Christmas Orchid .. .. .. 2·00 1·75
a. Perf 12 (8.95) .. .. .. 2·50 2·50
778 70 c. Lignum Vitae .. .. .. 1·10 1·75
779 $1 African Tulip Tree .. .. .. 1·25 1·75
a. Perf 12 (8.95) .. .. .. 2·25 2·50
780 $2 Beach Morning Glory .. .. .. 4·00 6·00
a. Perf 12 (8.95) .. .. .. 5·00 6·00
781 $3 Organ Pipe Cactus .. .. .. 4·00 6·00
a. Perf 12½×11½ (8.95) .. .. 5·00 6·00
782 $5 Tall Ground Orchid .. .. .. 11·00 14·00
783 $10 Ground Orchid (1.5.92) .. .. 14·00 16·00
765/83 .. .. *Set of* 19 40·00 48·00
No. 781a shows a larger hole on every sixth perforation, both vertically and horizontally.
Nos. 777a, 779a and 780a/1a are known to have been sold for postal purposes by the B.V.I. post offices.
For some of these designs watermarked w **14** (sideways) and with imprint date see Nos. 887/901.

193 *Phoebis sennae*

194 *Agaricus bisporus*

(Litho Questa)

1991 (28 June). *Butterflies. T* **193** *and similar multicoloure[d] designs. P* 14.
784 5 c. Type **193** 60 7
785 10 c. *Dryas iulia* 65 7
786 15 c. *Junonia evarete* 80 7
787 20 c. *Dione vanillae* 90 7
788 25 c. *Battus polydamus* .. .. .. 1·00 8
789 30 c. *Eurema lisa* .. .. 1·10 9
790 35 c. *Heliconius charitonius* .. .. 1·25 1·1
791 $1.50, *Siproeta stelenes* .. .. .. 3·50 5·0
784/91 .. .. *Set of* 8 8·75 9·7
MS792 Two sheets. (a) 77×117 mm. $2 *Danaus plexippus* (*horiz*). (b) 117×77 mm. $2 *Biblis hyperia* (*horiz*) .. .. .. *Set of 2 sheets* 13·00 14·0

(Des T. Agans. Litho Questa)

1991 (20 Sept). *500th Anniv of Discovery of America b[y] Columbus* (1992) (3*rd issue*). *History of Exploration. Design[s] as T* **277** *of Antigua. P* 14.
793 12 c. multicoloured 70 4
794 50 c. multicoloured .. .. .. 1·75 1·7
795 75 c. multicoloured .. .. .. 2·25 2·5
796 $1 multicoloured .. .. .. 2·75 3·2
793/6 .. .. *Set of* 4 6·75 7·0
MS797 105×76 mm. $2 black and red-orange .. 4·00 5·5
Designs: *Horiz*—12 c. *Vitoria* in Pacific (Magellan, 1519–21[)]; 50 c. La Salle on the Mississippi, 1682, 75 c. John Cabot landin[g] in Nova Scotia, 1497–98; $1 Cartier discovering the S[t] Lawrence, 1534. *Vert*—$2 *Santa Maria* (woodcut).

(Litho B.D.T.)

1991 (1 Nov). *Death Centenary of Vincent van Gogh (artist[)]* (1990). *Multicoloured designs as T* **278** *of Antigua. P* 13.
798 15 c. "Cottage with Decrepit Barn and Stooping Woman" (*horiz*) 65 4
799 30 c. "Paul Gauguin's Armchair" .. .. 1·10 8
800 75 c. "Breton Women" (*horiz*) .. .. 2·00 2·7
801 $1 "Vase with Red Gladioli" .. .. 2·50 3·2
798/801 .. .. *Set of* 4 5·50 6·5
MS802 103×81 mm. $2 "Dance Hall in Arles" (detail) (*horiz*) .. .. 6·50 8·0

(Litho Walsall)

1991 (12 Dec). *Christmas. Religious Paintings by Quinte[n] Massys. Vert designs as T* **291** *of Antigua. Multicoloured. P* 12.
803 15 c. "The Virgin and Child Enthroned" (detail) 70 2
804 30 c. "The Virgin and Child Enthroned" (different detail) .. .. .. 1·25 5
805 60 c. "Adoration of the Magi" (detail) .. 2·75 3·5
806 $1 "Virgin in Adoration" .. .. .. 3·25 3·7
803/6 .. .. *Set of* 4 7·25 7·2
MS807 Two sheets, each 102×127 mm. (a) $2 "The Virgin standing with Angels"; (b) $2 "The Adoration of the Magi". P 14×14½. *Set of 2 sheets* 9·00 11·0

(Litho Questa)

1992 (15 Jan). *Fungi. T* **194** *and similar multicoloure[d] designs. P* 14.
808 12 c. Type **194** .. .. 1·00 4
809 30 c. *Lentinula edodes* (*horiz*) .. .. 1·60 8
810 45 c. *Hygrocybe acutoconica* .. .. 1·75 1·0
811 $1 *Gymnopilus chrysopellus* (*horiz*) .. 3·50 5·0
808/11 .. .. *Set of* 4 7·00 6·5
MS812 94×68 mm. $2 *Pleurotus ostreatus* (*horiz*) 6·50 8·5

(Des D, Miller. Litho Questa)

1992 (12 Mar). *40th Anniv of Queen Elizabeth II's Accession. Horiz designs as T* **288** *of Antigua. Multicoloured. P* 14.
813 12 c. Little Dix Bay, Virgin Gorda 45 3
814 45 c. Deadchest Bay, Peter Island .. .. 1·10 9
815 60 c. Pond Bay, Virgin Gorda .. .. 1·40 2·0
816 $1 Cane Garden Bay, Tortola .. .. 1·75 2·5
813/16 .. .. *Set of* 4 4·25 5·0
MS817 75×97 mm. $2 Long Bay, Beef Island .. 4·50 5·5

195 Queen Isabella of Spain

196 Basketball

(Des W. Hanson. Litho B.D.T.)

•2 (26 May). *500th Anniv of Discovery of America by* *'olumbus (4th issue). T* **195** *and similar multicoloured* *'esigns. P* 14.

.	10 c. Type **195**	60	60
•	15 c. Fleet of Columbus (*horiz*) ..	80	80
•	20 c. Arms awarded to Columbus	80	80
.	30 c. Landing Monument, Watling Island and Columbus' signature (*horiz*) ..	90	90
:	45 c. Christopher Columbus	1·40	1·40
;	50 c. Landing in New World and Spanish royal standard (*horiz*)	1·40	1·50
ŧ	70 c. Convent at La Rabida	2·25	3·00
5	$1.50, Replica of *Santa Maria* and Caribbean Pavilion, New York World's Fair (*horiz*)	3·50	4·25
3/25	.. .. *Set of* 8	10·50	12·00
3826	Two sheets. (a) 116× 86 mm. $2 Ships of econd voyage at Virgin Gorda (*horiz*). (b) '6×116 mm. $2 De la Cosa's map of New World *'horiz*) .. .. *Set of* 2 *sheets*	8·00	11·00

(Litho Questa)

92 (26 Oct). *Olympic Games, Barcelona. T* **196** *and similar* *'ert designs. Multicoloured. P* 14.

7	15 c. Type **196**	1·25	65
3	30 c. Tennis	1·75	90
9	60 c. Volleyball	2·50	3·00
0	$1 Football	2·75	3·75
7/30	.. .. .. *Set of* 4	7·50	7·50
S831	100×70 mm. $2 Olympic flame ..	6·00	8·00

197 Issuing Social Security Cheque

(Litho Questa)

•93 (14 May). *25th Anniv of Ministerial Government. T* **197** *and similar horiz designs. Multicoloured. P* 14.

2	12 c. Type **197**	30	25
3	15 c. Map of British Virgin Islands ..	55	40
4	45 c. Administration building	70	70
5	$1.30, International currency abbreviations	2·00	3·25
2/5	.. .. *Set of* 4	3·25	4·25

198 Cruising Yacht and Swimmers, The Baths, Virgin Gorda

(Litho Questa)

993 (23 July). *Tourism. T* **198** *and similar multicoloured designs. P* 14.

36	15 c. Type **198**	60	30
37	30 c. Cruising yacht under sail (*vert*) ..	85	60
38	60 c. Scuba diving	1·50	2·00
39	$1 Cruising yacht at anchor and snorklers (*vert*)	1·75	2·25
36/9	.. .. .. *Set of* 4	4·25	4·75
IS840	79×108 mm. $1 *Promenade* (trimaran) (*vert*); $1 Scuba diving (*different*) (*vert*) ..	4·50	5·50

(Des Kerri Schiff. Litho Questa)

993 (27 Aug). *40th Anniv of Coronation. Vert designs as T* **307** *of Antigua. P* 13½×14.

41	12 c. multicoloured	80	1·00
	a. Sheetlet. Nos. 841/4×2 ..	7·50	
42	45 c. multicoloured	1·00	1·25
43	60 c. bluish grey and black	1·10	1·40
44	$1 multicoloured	1·40	1·75
41/4	.. .. .. *Set of* 4	3·75	4·75

Designs:—12 c. Queen Elizabeth II at Coronation (photograph y Cecil Beaton); 45 c. Orb; 60 c. Queen with Prince Philip,)ueen Mother and Princess Margaret, 1953; $1 Queen :lizabeth II on official visit.

Nos. 841/4 were printed in sheetlets of 8, containing two *e-tenant* blocks of 4.

A $2 miniature sheet showing "Queen Elizabeth II" (Sir Ierbert James) was prepared, but not issued in British Virgin slands.

200 Columbus with King Ferdinand and Queen Isabella

(Des G. Vasarhelyi. Litho Questa)

1993 (24 Sept). *500th Anniv of Discovery of Virgin Islands by Columbus. T* **200** *and similar horiz designs. Multicoloured. P* 14.

846	3 c. Type **200**	15	40
847	12 c. Columbus's ship leaving port ..	40	40
848	15 c. Blessing the fleet	45	45
849	25 c. Arms and flag of B.V.I.	60	60
850	30 c. Columbus and *Santa Maria*	70	70
851	45 c. Ships of second voyage	95	95
852	60 c. Columbus in ship's boat	1·50	2·25
853	$1 Landing of Columbus	2·00	2·50
846/53	.. .. .. *Set of* 8	6·00	7·50
MS854	Two sheets, each 120×80 mm. (a) $2 Amerindians sighting fleet. (b) $2 Christopher Columbus and ships .. .. *Set of 2 sheets*	6·00	8·00

201 Library Services Publications

202 Anegada Ground Iguana

1993 (20 Dec). *50th Anniv of Secondary Education and Library Services. T* **201** *and similar multicoloured designs. Litho. P* 14×13½ (*horiz*) *or* 13½×14 (*vert*).

855	5 c. Type **201**	40	50
856	10 c. Secondary school sports	50	50
857	15 c. Stanley Nibbs (school teacher) (*vert*)	60	50
858	20 c. Mobile library	70	50
859	30 c. Dr. Norwell Harrigan (adminstrator and lecturer) (*vert*)	85	60
860	35 c. Children in library	90	65
861	70 c. Commemorative inscription on book	1·75	2·50
862	$1 B.V.I. High School	2·00	2·50
855/62	.. .. .. *Set of* 8	7·00	7·50

(Litho Questa)

1994 (18 Mar). *Endangered Species. Anegada Ground Iguana. T* **202** *and similar vert designs showing iguanas. P* 14.

863	5 c. multicoloured	30	40
864	10 c. multicoloured	30	40
865	15 c. multicoloured	40	40
866	45 c. multicoloured	1·10	1·25
863/6	.. .. .. *Set of* 4	1·90	2·25
MS867	106×77 mm. $2 multicoloured ..	3·00	4·00

No. **MS**867 does not carry the W.W.F. Panda emblem.

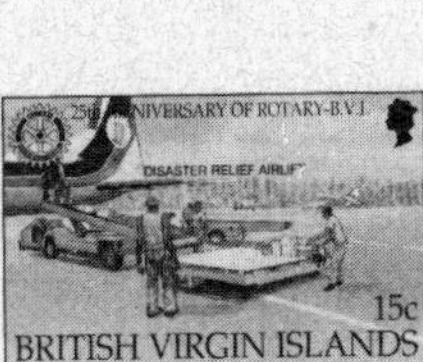

203 Loading Disaster Relief Aircraft

204 Argentina v. Netherlands, 1978

(Litho Questa)

1994 (3 June). *Centenary of Rotary International in B.V.I. T* **203** *and similar horiz designs. Multicoloured. P* 14.

868	15 c. Type **203**	35	35
869	45 c. Training children in marine safety ..	85	85
870	50 c. Donated operating table	90	1·00
871	90 c. Paul Harris (founder) and emblem ..	1·60	2·25
868/71	.. .. .. *Set of* 4	3·25	4·00

(Des W. Hanson. Litho Questa)

1994 (30 Sept). *25th Anniv of First Moon Landing. Horiz designs as T* **326** *of Antigua. Multicoloured. P* 14.

872	50 c. Anniversary logo	1·75	2·00
	a. Sheetlet. Nos. 872/7	9·50	
873	50 c. Lunar landing training vehicle ..	1·75	2·00
874	50 c. Launch of "Apollo 11"	1·75	2·00
875	50 c. Lunar module *Eagle* in flight ..	1·75	2·00
876	50 c. Moon's surface	1·75	2·00
877	50 c. Neil Armstrong (astronaut) taking first step	1·75	2·00
872/7	.. .. .. *Set of* 6	9·50	11·00
MS878	106×76 mm. $2 Signatures and mission logo	5·00	6·00

Nos. 872/7 were printed together, *se-tenant*, in sheetlets of 6.

(Des J. Iskowitz. Litho Questa)

1994 (16 Dec). *World Cup Football Championship, U.S.A. Previous Winners. T* **204** *and similar multicoloured designs. P* 14.

879	15 c. Type **204**	75	40
880	35 c. Italy v. West Germany, 1982 ..	1·25	70
881	50 c. Argentina v. West Germany, 1986 ..	2·00	2·00
882	$1.30, West Germany v. Argentina, 1990	4·00	5·00
879/82	.. .. .. *Set of* 4	7·25	7·25
MS883	74×101 mm. $2 U.S. flag and World Cup trophy (*horiz*)	5·50	6·50

1995 (June). *As Nos.* 768, 770, 773/4, 776/7, 780 *and* 782, *but* W w **14** (*sideways*) *and with* "1995" *imprint date. P* 14.

887	10 c. Autograph Tree	40	60
889	15 c. Lantana	55	35
892	30 c. Swamp Immortelle	70	50
893	35 c. White Cedar	75	55
895	45 c. Pinguin	85	80
896	50 c. Christmas Orchid	1·75	1·75
899	$2 Beach Morning Glory	2·75	4·00
901	$5 Tall Ground Orchid	8·00	10·00
887/901	.. .. *Set of* 8	14·00	17·00

(Des A. Theobald. Litho Questa)

1995 (24 Oct). *50th Anniv of United Nations. Horiz designs as T* **213** *of Bahamas. Multicoloured. W w* **16** (*sideways*). *P* 14.

903	15 c. Peugeot P4 all-purpose field cars ..	45	40
904	30 c. Foden medium road tanker	75	60
905	45 c. SISU all-terrain vehicle	1·00	90
906	$2 Westland Lynx AH7 helicopter ..	3·75	5·00
903/6	.. .. .. *Set of* 4	5·50	6·25

205 Pair of Juvenile Flamingos

206 "Tortola House with Christmas Tree" (Maureen Walters)

(Des N. Arlott. Litho Cartor)

1995 (15 Nov). *Anegada Flamingos Restoration Project. T* **205** *and similar vert designs. Multicoloured. W w* **14**. *P* 13×13½.

907	15 c. Type **205**	60	40
908	20 c. Pair of adults	65	45
909	60 c. Adult feeding	1·25	1·75
910	$1.45, Adult feeding chick	2·25	3·25
907/10	.. .. .. *Set of* 4	4·25	5·25
MS911	80×70 mm. $2 Chicks. P 13	3·25	4·50

(Adapted G. Vasarhelyi. Litho Walsall)

1995 (1 Dec). *Christmas. Children's Paintings. T* **206** *and similar horiz designs. Multicoloured. W w* **16** (*sideways*). *P* 13½×14.

912	12 c. Type **206**	70	30
913	50 c. "Father Christmas in Rowing Boat" (Collin Collins)	1·75	1·40
914	70 c. "Christmas Tree and Gifts" (Clare Wassell)	2·00	2·25
915	$1.30, "Peace Dove" (Nicholas Scott) ..	3·00	3·50
912/15	.. .. .. *Set of* 4	6·75	6·75

207 Seine Fishing

(Des G. Vasarhelyi. Litho Cartor)

1996 (14 Feb). *Island Profiles (1st series). Jost Van Dyke. T* **207** *and similar horiz designs. Multicoloured. W w* **14** (*sideways*). *P* 13½×13.

916	15 c. Type **207**	60	35
917	35 c. Sandy Spit	80	55
918	90 c. Map	2·25	2·50
919	$1.50, Foxy's Regatta	2·75	3·50
916/19	.. .. .. *Set of* 4	5·75	6·25

See also Nos. 1003/7.

(Des D. Miller. Litho Cartor)

1996 (22 Apr). *70th Birthday of Queen Elizabeth II. Vert designs as T* **165** *of Ascension, each incorporating a different photograph of the Queen. Multicoloured. W w* **14**. *P* 13½×14.

920	10 c. Government House, Tortola	20	20
921	30 c. Legislative Council Building	55	55
922	45 c. Liner in Road Harbour	1·00	70
923	$1.50, Map of British Virgin Islands ..	2·75	3·50
920/3	.. .. .. *Set of* 4	4·00	4·50
MS924	63×65 mm. $2 Queen Elizabeth II. P 13×13½	3·00	3·50

208 Hurdling

(Des S. Noon. Litho Cartor)

1996 (22 May). *Centenary of Modern Olympic Games. T* **208** *and similar horiz designs. Multicoloured. W* w **14** (*sideways*). *P* 13.

925	20 c. Type **208**	35	30
926	35 c. Volleyball	60	60
927	50 c. Swimming	90	1·50
928	$1 Yachting	1·75	2·50
925/8	*Set of* 4	3·25	4·50

209 Mercedes-Benz "500 K A", 1934

(Des R. Watton. Litho B.D.T.)

1996 (8 June). *"CAPEX '96" International Stamp Exhibition, Toronto. Early Motor Cars. T* **209** *and similar horiz designs. Multicoloured. W* w **14** (*sideways**). *P* 13½.

929	15 c. Type **209**	30	30
930	40 c. Citröen "12", 1934	70	70
931	60 c. Cadillac "V-8 Sport Phaeton", 1932	1·00	1·50
	w. Wmk Crown to right of CA	2·75	
932	$1.35, Rolls Royce "Phantom II", 1934	2·25	3·00
	w. Wmk Crown to right of CA	2·75	
929/32	*Set of* 4	3·75	5·00
MS933	79×62 mm. $2 Ford "Sport Coupé", 1932	3·00	4·00

*The normal sideways watermark shows Crown to left of CA, *as seen from the back of the stamp.*

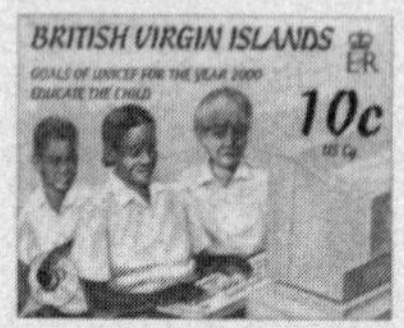

210 Children with Computer

(Des R. Watton. Litho Cot Printery Ltd, Barbados)

1996 (16 Sept). *50th Anniv of U.N.I.C.E.F. T* **210** *and similar horiz designs. Multicoloured. W* w **14** (*sideways*). *P* 14×14½.

934	10 c. Type **210**	30	30
935	15 c. Carnival costume	40	40
936	30 c. Children on Scales of Justice	70	70
937	45 c. Children on beach	1·00	1·00
934/7	*Set of* 4	2·25	2·25

211 Young Rainbows in Art Class

(Des G. Vasarhelyi. Litho Cartor)

1996 (30 Dec). *75th Anniv of Guiding in the British Virgin Islands. T* **211** *and similar horiz designs. Multicoloured. W* w **14** (*sideways*). *P* 13½.

938	10 c. Type **211**	20	20
939	15 c. Brownies serving meals	30	25
940	30 c. Guides around campfire	50	45
941	45 c. Rangers on parade	65	60
942	$2 Lady Baden-Powell	2·75	3·50
938/42	*Set of* 5	4·00	4·50

212 Spanish Mackerel

(Des A. Robinson. Litho Walsall)

1997 (6 Jan). *Game Fishes. T* **212** *and similar horiz designs. Multicoloured. W* w **16** (*sideways*). *P* 14.

943	1 c. Type **212**	10	10
944	10 c. Wahoo	10	15
945	15 c. Great Barracuda	20	25
946	20 c. Tarpon	25	30
947	25 c. Tiger Shark	30	35
948	35 c. Sailfish	40	45
949	40 c. Dolphin	50	55
950	50 c. Black-finned Tuna	60	65
951	60 c. Yellow-finned Tuna	75	80
952	75 c. King Mackerel ("Kingfish")	90	95
953	$1.50, White Marlin	1·75	1·90
954	$1.85, Amberjack	2·25	2·40
955	$2 Atlantic Bonito	2·40	2·50
956	$5 Bonefish	6·00	6·25
957	$10 Blue Marlin	12·00	12·50
943/57	*Set of* 15	28·00	29·00

(Des D. Miller. Litho Questa)

1997 (3 Feb). *"HONG KONG '97" International Stamp Exhibition. Sheet* 130×90 *mm, containing design as No.* 953, *but with* "1997" *imprint date. Multicoloured. W* w **14** (*inverted*). *P* 14.

MS958	$1.50, White Marlin	2·25	2·75

(Des N. Shewring (No. **MS**965), D. Miller (others). Litho Questa (No. **MS**965), Cartor (others))

1997 (10 July). *Golden Wedding of Queen Elizabeth and Prince Philip. Multicoloured designs as T* **173** *of Ascension. W* w **14**. *P* 13.

959	30 c. Prince Philip with horse	60	65
	a. Horiz pair. Nos. 959/60	1·10	1·25
960	30 c. Queen Elizabeth at Windsor, 1989	60	65
961	45 c. Queen in phaeton, Trooping the Colour	80	90
	a. Horiz pair. Nos. 961/2	1·60	1·75
962	45 c. Prince Philip in Scots Guards uniform	80	90
963	70 c. Queen Elizabeth and Prince Philip at the Derby, 1993	1·10	1·25
	a. Horiz pair. Nos. 963/4	2·10	2·50
964	70 c. Prince Charles playing polo, Mexico 1993	1·10	1·25
959/64	*Set of* 6	4·50	5·00
MS965	110×70 mm. $2 Queen Elizabeth and Prince Philip in landau (*horiz*). Wmk sideways. P 14×14½	2·75	3·25

Nos. 959/60, 961/2 and 963/4 were each printed together, *se-tenant*, in horizontal pairs throughout the sheets with the backgrounds forming composite designs.

213 Fiddler Crab

(Des Jennifer Toombs. Litho Cartor)

1997 (11 Sept). *Crabs. T* **213** *and similar horiz designs. Multicoloured. W* w **14** (*sideways*). *P* 13.

966	12 c. Type **213**	30	25
967	15 c. Coral Crab	35	30
968	35 c. Blue Crab	70	60
969	$1 Giant Hermit Crab	1·50	2·00
966/9	*Set of* 4	2·50	2·75
MS970	76×67 mm. $2 Arrow Crab	3·25	3·75

214 *Psychilis macconnelliae*

(Des I. Loe. Litho Cot Printery Ltd, Barbados)

1997 (26 Nov). *Orchids of the World. T* **214** *and similar multicoloured designs. W* w **14** (*sideways*). *P* 14.

971	20 c. Type **214**	50	60
	a. Horiz strip of 4. Nos. 971/4	2·75	
972	50 c. *Tolumnia prionochila*	80	90
973	60 c. *Tetramicra canaliculata*	85	1·00
974	75 c. *Liparis elata*	90	1·10
971/4	*Set of* 4	2·75	3·25
MS975	59×79 mm. $2 *Dendrobium crumenatum* (*vert*). Wmk upright	3·00	3·50

Nos. 971/4 were printed together, *se-tenant*, in horizontal strips of four throughout the sheet.

215 Sir Francis Drake and Signature

(Des E. Nisbet. Litho Questa)

1997 (13 Dec). *420th Anniv of Drake's Circumnavigation of the World. T* **215** *and similar horiz designs. Multicoloured. W* w **14** (*sideways*). *P* 14½.

976	40 c. Type **215**	70	80
	a. Sheetlet. Nos. 976/87	7·50	
977	40 c. Drake's coat of arms	70	80
978	40 c. Queen Elizabeth I and signature	70	80
979	40 c. *Christopher* and *Marigold*	70	80
980	40 c. *Golden Hind*	70	80
981	40 c. *Swan*	70	80
982	40 c. *Cacafuego* (Spanish galleon)	70	80
983	40 c. *Elizabeth*	70	80
984	40 c. *Maria*	70	80
985	40 c. Drake's astrolabe	70	80
986	40 c. *Golden Hind's* figurehead	70	80
987	40 c. Compass rose	70	80
976/87	*Set of* 12	7·50	8·50
MS988	96×76 mm. $2 *Sir Francis Drake* (ketch)	3·00	3·50

Nos. 976/87 were printed together, *se-tenant*, in sheetlets of 12 with the backgrounds forming a composite map of Drake's route.

(Des D. Miller. Litho Questa)

1998 (31 Mar). *Diana, Princess of Wales Commemoration. Sheet,* 145×70 *mm, containing vert designs as T* **177** *of Ascension. Multicoloured. W* w **14** (*sideways*). *P* 14½×14.

MS989	15 c. Wearing pink jacket, 1992; 45 c. Holding child, 1991; 70 c. Laughing, 1991; $1 Wearing high-collared blouse, 1986 (*sold at* $2.30 + 20 c. *charity premium*)	3·50	4·0

(Des A. Theobald. Litho Enschedé)

1998 (1 Apr). *80th Anniv of Royal Air Force. Horiz designs as T* **178** *of Ascension. Multicoloured. W* w **14** (*sideways*). *P* 13½×14.

990	20 c. Fairey IIIF (seaplane)	45	3
991	35 c. Supermarine Scapa (flying boat)	65	5
992	50 c. Westland Sea King H.A.R.3 (helicopter)	90	9
993	$1.50, BAe Harrier GR7	2·25	2·5
990/3	*Set of* 4	3·75	3·7
MS994	110×77 mm. 75 c. Curtiss H.16 (flying boat); 75 c. Curtiss JN-4A; 75 c. Bell Airacobra; 75 c. Boulton-Paul Defiant	4·00	4·2

216 Fingerprint Cyphoma

217 "Carnival Reveller" (Rebecca Peck)

(Des Odile and J. Scheiner. Litho Questa)

1998 (20 May). *Marine Life. T* **216** *and similar horiz designs. Multicoloured. W* w **16** (*sideways*). *P* 14×14½.

995	15 c. Type **216**	40	30
996	30 c. Long-spined Sea Urchin	60	45
997	45 c. Split Crown Feather Duster Worm	80	65
998	$1 Upside Down Jelly	1·50	2·00
995/8	*Set of* 4	3·00	3·00
MS999	77×56 mm. $2 Giant Anemone	3·00	3·25

(Adapted G. Vasarhelyi. Litho Cot Printery, Barbados)

1998 (25 Aug). *Festival. Children's Paintings. T* **217** *and similar multicoloured designs. W* w **14** (*sideways on* $1.30, *inverted on others*). *P* 14.

1000	30 c. Type **217**	35	40
1001	45 c. "Leader of a Troupe" (Jehiah Maduro)	55	60
1002	$1.30, "Steel Pans" (Rebecca McKenzie) (*horiz*)	1·50	1·60
1000/2	*Set of* 3	2·40	2·50

218 Salt Pond

(Des G. Vasarhelyi. Litho Cot Printery Ltd, Barbados)

1998 (28 Oct). *Island Profiles (2nd series). Salt Island. T* **218** *and similar horiz designs. Multicoloured. W* w **14** (*sideways*). *P* 14.

1003	12 c. Type **218**	15	20
1004	30 c. Wreck of *Rhone* (mail steamer)	35	40
1005	70 c. Traditional house	85	90
1006	$1.45, Salt Island from the air	1·75	1·90
1003/6	*Set of* 4	3·00	3·25
MS1007	119×78 mm. $2 Collecting salt	2·40	2·50

219 Business Studies, Woodwork and Technology Students

(Des N. Shewring. Litho Questa)

1998 (14 Dec). *Anniversaries. T* **219** *and similar horiz designs. Multicoloured. W* w **16** (*sideways*). *P* 14.

1008	5 c. Type **219**	10	10
1009	15 c. Comprehensive school band	20	25
1010	30 c. Chapel, Mona Campus, Jamaica	35	40
1011	45 c. Anniversary plaque and University arms	55	60
1012	50 c. Dr. John Coakley Lettsom and map of Little Jost Van Dyke	60	65
1013	$1 The Medical Society of London building and arms	1·25	1·40
1008/13	*Set of* 6	1·75	2·00

Events:—5, 15 c. 30th anniv of Comprehensive Education in B.V.I.; 30, 45 c. 50th anniv of University of West Indies; 50 c., $1 250th anniv of Medical Society of London

STAMP BOOKLETS

31 (22 July). *Royal Wedding. Gold on blue cover, 75×50 mm, showing Royal coat of arms on front and St. Paul's Cathedral on back. Stapled.*

1 $3.50, booklet containing 10 c., 35 c., $1.25 (Nos. 463/5), in pairs .. .. 2·25

No. SB1 was sold at a 10 c. premium above the total face value the stamps it contained.

36 (23 July). *Royal Wedding. Gold* (No. SB2) *or silver* (No. SB3) *on new blue covers. Stapled.*

2 $4.20, booklet (Westminster Abbey cover) containing twelve 35 c. (Nos. 605/6) in blocks of four .. .. 5·50

3 $5.40, booklet (State Coach cover) containing four 35 c. (Nos. 605/6) and four $1 (Nos. 607/8), each in block of four .. .. 5·50

The stamps from No. SB3 are imperforate.

OFFICIAL STAMPS

OFFICIAL

(O 1)

wo varieties of overprint:

Type I. Foot of "OFFICIAL" 15–16 mm from top of design. ght impression with little or no black outline to letters.

Type II. Foot of "OFFICIAL" 20 mm from top of design. Heavy npression with thick black outline to letters.

985 (Feb). *Nos.* 418/19, 420*a*/1*a*, 423*a*/4*a*, 425, 426*a*, 427, 428*a and* 429/33 *optd as Type* O 1 *in silver by Questa.*

1 1 c. Purple-tipped Sea Anemone (I) .. 30 70
a. Opt Type II .. .. 50·00 60·00
2 3 c. Common Starfish (I) 45 70
a. Opt Type II .. .. 55·00 65·00
3 5 c. Type **134** (II) 45 30
4 8 c. Atlantic Trumpet Triton (*Charonia variegata*) (I) 55 30
a. Opt Type II £100
5 13 c. Flamingo Tongue (*Cyphoma gibbosus*) (II) 80 50
6 15 c. Spider Crab (I) 85 70
7 18 c. Sea Squirts (I) .. .. .. 90 1·00
a. Opt Type II £110
8 20 c. True Tulip (*Fasciolaria tulipa*) (I) .. 90 80
9 25 c. Rooster-tail Conch (*Strombus gallus*) (I) .. .. 1·25 1·25
w. Wmk inverted .. .. .. 15·00
10 30 c. West Indian Fighting Conch (*Strombus pugilis*) (I) .. .. 1·40 1·00
a. Optd on No. 428 .. .. .. 7·00 13·00
11 60 c. Mangrove Crab (I) .. .. .. 2·00 2·50
12 $1 Coral Polyps (I) .. .. .. 3·00 3·75
13 $2.50, Peppermint Shrimp (I) .. .. 4·50 9·00
14 $3 West Indian Murex (*Murex brevifrons*) (I) .. .. 5·50 10·00
a. Opt inverted £100 £120
15 $5 Carpet Anemone (I) .. .. .. 7·50 12·00
1/15 .. .. *Set of* 15 27·00 40·00

Examples of the ½ c. and 10 c. overprinted in silver and of all eventeen values overprinted in gold also exist, but were not ssued in British Virgin Islands.

OFFICIAL OFFICIAL

(O 2) (O 3)

986 (10 Feb–Sept). *Nos.* 560/78 *optd with Type* O **2** *by Questa.*

)16 1 c. Type **162** (9.86).. .. .. .. 20 40
)17 2 c. Yellow-crowned Night Heron.. .. 20 40
)18 5 c. Mangrove Cuckoo (9.86) 30 50
)19 8 c. Northern Mockingbird.. .. .. 30 60
)20 10 c. Grey Kingbird (9.86) 40 60
)21 12 c. Red-necked Pigeon 40 40
)22 15 c. Least Bittern (9.86) 40 40
)23 18 c. Smooth-billed Ani 45 60
)24 20 c. Clapper Rail (9.86) 70 70
)25 25 c. American Kestrel (9.86) 70 70
)26 30 c. Pearly-eyed Thrasher (9.86) .. .. 1·00 1·00
)27 35 c. Bridled Quail Dove (9.86) .. .. 1·00 1·00
)28 40 c. Green Heron .. .. 1·00 1·00
)29 50 c. Scaly-breasted Ground Dove .. .. 1·40 1·75
)30 60 c. Little Blue Heron .. .. .. 1·50 2·00
)31 $1 Audubon's Shearwater .. .. .. 2·25 2·50
)32 $2 Blue-faced Booby .. .. .. 2·50 3·50
)33 $3 Cattle Egret .. .. 6·00 7·00
)34 $5 Zenaida Dove (9.86) .. .. .. 6·50 7·50
)16/34 .. .. *Set of* 19 24·00 29·00

991 (Sept). *Nos.* 767/8, 771, 773/9 *and* 781 *optd with Type* O **3**.

)35 5 c. Frangipani 30 40
)36 10 c. Autograph Tree 30 40
)37 20 c. Jerusalem Thorn 35 40
)38 30 c. Swamp Immortelle 50 50
)39 35 c. White Cedar 55 55
)40 40 c. Mahoe Tree 60 60
)41 45 c. Pinguin 70 65
)42 50 c. Christmas Orchid 75 75
)43 70 c. Lignum Vitae .. .. .. 1·00 1·75
)44 $1 African Tulip Tree .. .. .. 1·25 2·00
)45 $3 Organ Pipe Cactus .. .. .. 4·00 5·50
)35/45 .. .. *Set of* 11 9·25 12·00

The same stamps, except for the 30 c., exist overprinted with Type O 2, but such overprints were not placed on sale in British Virgin Islands.

Brunei

Sultan Hashim Jalil-ul-alam Akamudin, 1885–1906

(Currency. 100 cents = 1 Straits, later Malayan and Brunei, dollar)

For many years the status of the 1895 issue remained uncertain to such an extent that the 1906 provisionals on Labuan were taken to be the first issue of Brunei.

The 1895 "Star and Crescent" design stamps were, from their first appearance, considered bogus or, at best, as an issue made purely for philatelic purposes. Research into the background of the events surrounding the set led to the publication, in 1933, of the original agreement between Sultan Hashim and J. C. Robertson dated 20 August 1894 which made clear that the stamps fulfilled a genuine postal purpose. Although Robertson and his partners intended to exploit the philatelic sales for their own benefit the agreement testifies, as does other evidence, to the use of the stamps by the Sultan for his postal service. As Brunei did not, at that time, belong to any local or international postal union the stamps were only valid within the state or on mail to Labuan or Sarawak. Items for further afield required franking with Labuan stamps in addition. Although most covers surviving are addressed to Robertson's associates enough commercial covers and cards exist to show that there was, indeed, a postal service.

PRICES FOR STAMPS ON COVER TO 1945

Nos. 1/10 are rare used on cover.
Nos. 11/22 *from* × 30
Nos. 23/33 *from* × 25
Nos. 34/50 *from* × 10
Nos. 51/9 *from* × 12
Nos. 60/78 *from* × 8

The Sarawak Government maintained a post office at the coal mining centre of Brooketon, and the stamps of SARAWAK were used there from 1893 until the office was handed over to Brunei in February 1907.

1 Star and Local Scene

(Litho in Glasgow)

1895 (22 July). *P* 13–13½.

No.	Type	Description		
1	1	½ c. brown	2·00	18·00
2		1 c. brown-lake	2·50	13·00
3		2 c. black	3·75	13·00
4		3 c. deep blue	3·00	12·00
5		5 c. deep blue-green	6·00	14·00
6		8 c. plum	6·00	23·00
7		10 c. orange-red	7·50	23·00
		a. Imperf (pair)	£1200	
8		25 c. turquoise-green	45·00	65·00
9		50 c. yellow-green	18·00	80·00
10		$1 yellow-olive	20·00	95·00
1/10		*Set of* 10	£100	£325

BRUNEI. (2)

BRUNEI. TWO CENTS. (3)

BRUNEI. 25 CENTS. (4)

Line through "B" (R.5/10)

(Optd by Govt Printer, Singapore)

1906 (1 Oct). *Nos.* 117/26 *of Labuan (see Malaysia), optd with T* 2, *or surch as T* 3 *or* 4 (25 *c.*), *in red. P* 13½ *or* 14 (1 *c.*).

No.	Type	Description		
11		1 c. black and purple	25·00	48·00
		a. Error. Opt in black	£1700	£2500
		b. Line through "B"	£275	
12		2 c. on 3 c. black and sepia	2·00	7·50
		a. "BRUNEI" double	£3750	£2500
		b. "TWO CENTS" double	£9000	
		c. Line through "B"	85·00	
13		2 c. on 8 c. black and vermilion	26·00	75·00
		a. "TWO CENTS" double	£8000	
		b. "TWO CENTS" omitted (in vert pair with normal)	£9000	
		c. Line through "B"	£275	
14		3 c. black and sepia	27·00	75·00
		a. Line through "B"	£275	
15		4 c. on 12 c. black and yellow	2·50	5·00
		a. Line through "B"	90·00	
16		5 c. on 16 c. green and brown	40·00	65·00
		a. Line through "B"	£300	
17		8 c. black and vermilion	8·50	28·00
		a. Line through "B"	£170	
18		10 c. on 16 c. green and brown	6·50	20·00
		a. Line through "B"	£150	
19		25 c. on 16 c. green and brown	95·00	£130
		a. Line through "B"	£550	
20		30 c. on 16 c. green and brown	85·00	£120
		a. Line through "B"	£550	
21		50 c. on 16 c. green and brown	85·00	£120
		a. Line through "B"	£550	
22		$1 on 8 c. black and vermilion	85·00	£120
		a. Line through "B"	£550	
11/22		*Set of* 12	£400	£700

Only one sheet of the 1 c. received the black overprint.

The surcharges were applied in settings of 50. Nos. 13a/b occur from one sheet on which the surcharge from the second impression of the setting was misplaced to give two surcharges on row five and none on row ten.

Examples of all values are known showing a forged Brunei postmark dated "13 JUL".

Sultan Mohamed Jemal-ul-Alam, 1906–1924

PRINTERS. All Brunei stamps from Nos. 23 to 113 were recess-printed by De La Rue.

5 View on Brunei River

1907 (26 Feb)–**10.** *Wmk Mult Crown CA. P* 14.

No.	Type	Description		
23	5	1 c. grey-black and pale green	2·25	10·00
		x. Wmk reversed	15·00	
24		2 c. grey-black and scarlet	2·50	4·50
		x. Wmk reversed	25·00	
25		3 c. grey-black and chocolate	10·00	20·00
		x. Wmk reversed	30·00	
26		4 c. grey-black and mauve	7·50	10·00
		a. Grey-black and reddish purple (1910)	70·00	60·00
		w. Wmk inverted		
		x. Wmk reversed	50·00	
27		5 c. grey-black and blue	50·00	90·00
		x. Wmk reversed	85·00	
28		8 c. grey-black and orange	7·50	23·00
29		10 c. grey-black and deep green	4·50	7·00
30		25 c. pale blue and ochre-brown	30·00	48·00
31		30 c. violet and black	20·00	22·00
32		50 c. green and deep brown	15·00	22·00
33		$1 red and grey	60·00	90·00
23/33		*Set of* 11	£190	£300
23/33 Optd "Specimen"		*Set of* 11	£275	

I

II

I Double plate. Lowest line of shading on water is dotted.
II Single plate. Dotted line of shading removed.

Stamps printed in two colours are as I.

1908 (12 June)–**22.** *Colours changed. Double or single plates. Wmk Mult Crown CA. P* 14.

No.	Type	Description		
34	5	1 c. green (I)	80	2·25
35		1 c. green (II) (1911)	60	1·75
		a. "A" missing from wmk	£200	
		b. "C" missing from wmk	£200	
36		2 c. black and brown (5.4.11)	2·50	1·25
		w. Wmk inverted	40·00	
37		3 c. scarlet (I)	2·50	1·25
38		3 c. scarlet (II) (1916)	65·00	35·00
39		4 c. claret (I)	2·50	75
40		5 c. black and orange	7·00	7·00
41		8 c. blue and indigo-blue (10.08)	7·00	11·00
42		10 c. purple/*yellow* (II) (1912)	1·50	1·25
		a. On pale yellow (1922) (Optd S. £38)	1·25	4·00
		w. Wmk inverted	75·00	
		x. Wmk reversed	50·00	
43		25 c. deep lilac (II) (30.5.12)	3·50	13·00
		a. Deep dull purple (1920)		
44		30 c. purple and orange-yellow (18.3.12)	8·50	12·00
45		50 c. black/*green* (II) (1912)	27·00	65·00
		a. On blue-green (1920)	8·50	32·00
46		$1 black and red/*blue* (18.3.12)	20·00	48·00
47		$5 carmine/*green* (I) (1910)	90·00	£150
48		$25 black/*red* (I) (1910)	£450	£850
34/47		*Set of* 12	£130	£250
34/48 Optd "Specimen"		*Set of* 13	£500	

The used price for No. 48 is for a cancelled-by-favour example, dated before December 1941; there being no actual postal rate for which this value could be used. Examples dated after 1945 are worth much less.

Retouch Normal

MALAYA-
BORNEO
EXHIBITION.
1922.

(6)

RETOUCHES. We list the very distinctive 5 c. Retouch (top le value tablet, 1st row, 8th stamp) but there are others of interes notably in the clouds.

1916. *Colours changed. Single plates. Wmk Mult Crown CA. P* 1

No.	Type	Description		
49	5	5 c. orange	13·00	13·
		a. "5 c." retouch	£325	£3
50		8 c. ultramarine	5·00	22·
49/50 Optd "Specimen"		*Set of* 2	£100	

MALAYA-BORNEO EXHIBITION OVERPRINTS. The were produced from a setting of 30 examples, applied twice to ove print the complete sheet of 60 stamps. Three prominent overpri flaws exist, each occurring on all the stamps in two vertical rows the sheet.

HI EX NE

Short "I" (all stamps in 2nd and 8th vertical rows) Broken "E" (all stamps in 4th and 10th vertical rows) Broken "N" (all stamps in 6th 12th vertical row

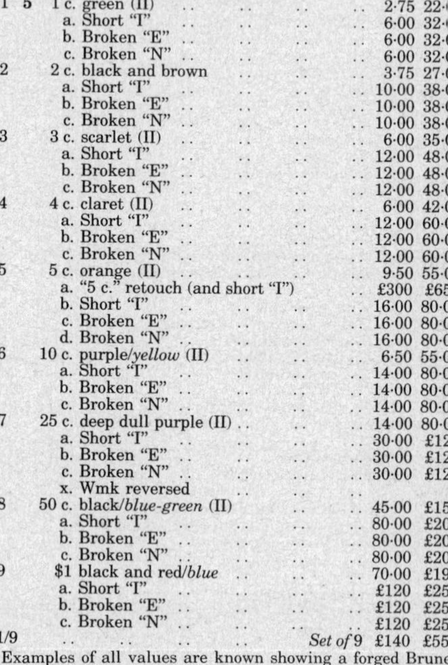

(Optd by Govt Printer, Singapore)

1922 (31 Mar). *Optd with T* **6**, *in black.*

No.	Type	Description		
51	5	1 c. green (II)	2·75	22·
		a. Short "I"	6·00	32·
		b. Broken "E"	6·00	32·
		c. Broken "N"	6·00	32·
52		2 c. black and brown	3·75	27·
		a. Short "I"	10·00	38·
		b. Broken "E"	10·00	38·
		c. Broken "N"	10·00	38·
53		3 c. scarlet (II)	6·00	35·
		a. Short "I"	12·00	48·
		b. Broken "E"	12·00	48·
		c. Broken "N"	12·00	48·
54		4 c. claret (II)	6·00	42·
		a. Short "I"	12·00	60·
		b. Broken "E"	12·00	60·
		c. Broken "N"	12·00	60·
55		5 c. orange (II)	9·50	55·
		a. "5 c." retouch (and short "I")	£300	£65
		b. Short "I"	16·00	80·
		c. Broken "E"	16·00	80·
		d. Broken "N"	16·00	80·
56		10 c. purple/*yellow* (II)	6·50	55·
		a. Short "I"	14·00	80·
		b. Broken "E"	14·00	80·
		c. Broken "N"	14·00	80·
57		25 c. deep dull purple (II)	14·00	80·
		a. Short "I"	30·00	£12
		b. Broken "E"	30·00	£12
		c. Broken "N"	30·00	£12
		x. Wmk reversed		
58		50 c. black/*blue-green* (II)	45·00	£15
		a. Short "I"	80·00	£20
		b. Broken "E"	80·00	£20
		c. Broken "N"	80·00	£20
59		$1 black and red/*blue*	70·00	£19
		a. Short "I"	£120	£25
		b. Broken "E"	£120	£25
		c. Broken "N"	£120	£25
51/9		*Set of* 9	£140	£55

Examples of all values are known showing a forged Brune postmark dated "13 JUL".

Sultan Ahmed Tajudin Akhazul Khairi Wadin, 1924–1950

7 Native houses, Water Village

1924 (Feb)–**37.** *Printed from single plates as Type* II, *excep* 30 *c. and* $1 *as Type* I. *Wmk Mult Script CA. P* 14.

No.	Type	Description		
60	5	1 c. black (9.26)	60	3
61		2 c. brown (3.24)	90	5·0
62		2 c. green (3.33)	60	3
63		3 c. green (3.24)	80	5·5
64		4 c. maroon (3.24)	1·50	7
65		4 c. orange (1929)	1·00	5
66		5 c. orange-yellow* (3.24)	3·75	1·0
		a. "5 c." retouch	£150	£11
67		5 c. grey (1931)	9·00	9·0
		a. "5 c." retouch	£325	£27
68		5 c. chocolate (1933)	7·50	2
		a. "5 c." retouch	£170	50·0
69	7	6 c. intense black** (3.24)	13·00	10·0
		x. Wmk reversed		
70		6 c. scarlet (1931)	3·75	11·0
71	5	8 c. ultramarine (9.27)	6·00	5·0
72		8 c. grey-black (1933)	7·50	5
73		10 c. purple/*yellow* (3.37)	12·00	24·0
74	7	12 c. blue	4·50	9·0
		a. Pale greenish blue (1927)	£130	£20
75	5	25 c. slate-purple (1931)	5·00	11·0
76		30 c. purple and orange-yellow (1931)	8·00	16·0
77		50 c. black/*emerald* (1931)	7·00	15·0
78		$1 black and red/*blue* (1931)	24·00	70·0
60/78		*Set of* 19	£100	£17
60/72, 74/8 Optd/Perf "Specimen"		*Set of* 18	£350	

*For 5 c. orange, see No. 82. No. 66 is a "Wet" printing and No. 8 a "Dry".

**For 6 c. black, see No. 83. Apart from the difference in shad there is a variation in size, No. 69 being 37¾ mm long and No. 8 39 mm.

The 2 c. orange and 3 c. blue-green in Type **5**, and the 6 c. eenish grey, 8 c. red and 15 c. ultramarine in Type **7** were not sued without the Japanese Occupation overprint although overprinted examples exist. It is believed that these 1941 intings were produced and possibly perforated, by other firms Great Britain following bomb damage to the De La Rue works the end of 1940 (*Price for set of* 5, £450 *un*).

During the life of this issue De La Rue changed the method of oduction from a "Wet" to a "Dry" process. Initially the stamps ere printed on ungummed paper which was dampened before ing put on the press. Once the paper had dried, and contracted in e process, the gum was then applied. "Dry" printings, introduced ound 1934, were on pre-gummed paper. The contraction of the Vet" printings was considerable and usually involves a difference between 0.5 mm and 1 mm when compared with the larger "Dry" intings. The following stamps occur from both "Wet" and "Dry" ersions: 1 c., 2 c. green, 4 c. orange, 5 c. chocolate, 6 c. scarlet, 8 c. ey-black, 10 c. and 25 c.

Stamps of this issue can be found either line or comb perforated.

Brunei was occupied by the Japanese Army in January 1942 nd remained under Japanese administration until liberated by e 9th Australian Division in June 1945.

After the cessation of hostilities with the Japanese postal services were re-introduced by the British Military Administration. Post offices under B.M.A. control were opened at Brunei Town and Kuala Belait on 17 December 1945 where B.M.A. overprints on the stamps of NORTH BORNEO and SARAWAK were used until the reappearance of Brunei issues on 2 January 1947.

Redrawn clouds (R. 1/1 of No. 80*ab* only)

1947 (2 Jan)–**51**. *Colours changed and new values. Wmk Mult Script CA. P* 14.

79 **5** 1 c. chocolate .. 50 1·50
 a. "A" of "CA" missing from wmk .. £1100
80 2 c. grey .. 90 2·00
 a. Perf 14½×13½ (25.9.50) .. 1·50 4·25
 ab. Black (27.6.51) .. 2·00 6·00
 ac. Redrawn clouds .. 65·00
81 **7** 3 c. green .. 1·00 3·50
82 **5** 5 c. orange* .. 80 1·25
 a. "5 c." retouch .. 55·00 75·00
 b. Perf 14½×13½ (25.9.50) .. 4·00 12·00
 c. Ditto "5 c." retouch .. £120 £180
83 **7** 6 c. black* .. 1·00 3·25
84 **5** 8 c. scarlet .. 40 70
 a. Perf 13 (25.1.51) .. 55 8·50
85 10 c. violet .. 70 20
 a. Perf 14½×13½ (25.9.50) .. 2·00 4·75
86 15 c. ultramarine .. 50 60
87 25 c. deep claret .. 1·25 70
 a. Perf 14½×13½ (25.1.51) .. 1·50 7·00
88 30 c. black and orange .. 1·00 1·00
 a. Perf 14½×13½ (25.1.51) .. 1·50 11·00
89 50 c. black .. 2·00 55
 a. Perf 13 (25.9.50) .. 1·75 14·00
90 $1 black and scarlet .. 4·50 75
91 $5 green and red-orange (2.2.48) .. 16·00 17·00
92 $10 black and purple (2.2.48) .. 48·00 30·00
79/92 .. *Set of* 14 70·00 55·00
79/92 Perf "Specimen" .. *Set of* 14 £200

*See also Nos. 66 and 69.

The 1, 2, 3, 5, 6, 10 and 25 c. values utilised the plates of the pre-war issue and were line perforated until the introduction of the 14½×13½ comb machine for some values in 1950–51. The 8, 15, 50 c., $1, $5 and $10 were from new plates with the sheets comb perforated. The 30 c. was initially a pre-war plate, but it is believed that a new plate was introduced in 1951.

8 Sultan Ahmed Tajudin and Water Village

1949 (22 Sept). *Sultan's Silver Jubilee. Wmk Mult Script CA. P* 13.

93 **8** 8 c. black and carmine .. 55 70
94 25 c. purple and red-orange .. 55 1·25
95 50 c. black and blue .. 70 1·25
93/5 .. *Set of* 3 1·60 2·75

1949 (10 Oct). *75th Anniv of Universal Postal Union. As Nos.* 114/17 *of Antigua.*

96 8 c. carmine .. 1·25 1·25
97 15 c. deep blue .. 3·00 1·50
98 25 c. magenta .. 1·25 1·50
99 50 c. blue-black .. 1·75 1·25
96/9 .. *Set of* 4 6·50 5·00

Sultan Sir Omar Ali Saifuddin-Wasa'adul Khairi Wadin, 1950–1967

9 Sultan Omar Ali Saifuddin   **10** Native houses, Water Village

1952 (1 Mar)–**58**. *Wmk Mult Script CA. P* 13.

100 **9** 1 c. black .. 10 50
101 2 c. black and orange .. 10 50
102 3 c. black and lake-brown .. 10 30
103 4 c. black and green .. 10 20
104 6 c. black and grey .. 10 10
105 8 c. black and crimson .. 50 60
 a. Black and crimson-lake (15.2.56) .. 4·50 20
106 10 c. black and sepia .. 15 10
107 12 c. black and violet .. 4·00 10
108 15 c. black and pale blue .. 3·25 10
109 25 c. black and purple .. 2·50 10
 a. Black and reddish purple (8.10.53) 4·50 90
110 50 c. black and ultramarine .. 1·50 10
 a. Black and blue (22.6.55) .. 4·00 10
111 **10** $1 black and green .. 1·50 1·10
 a. Black and bronze-green (23.7.58) .. 3·50 2·75
112 $2 black and scarlet .. 4·50 2·25
113 $5 black and maroon .. 12·00 6·00
 a. Black and brown-purple (15.2.56) .. 15·00 5·00
100/13 .. *Set of* 14 27·00 9·25

No. 106 exists in coils constructed from normal sheets.
See also Nos. 118/31 and 202/9.

11 Brunei Mosque and Sultan Omar

(Recess B.W.)

1958 (24 Sept). *Opening of Brunei Mosque. W w* **12**. *P* 13½.

114 **11** 8 c. black and myrtle-green .. 20 65
115 15 c. black and carmine .. 25 15
116 35 c. black and deep lilac .. 30 90
114/16 .. *Set of* 3 65 1·50

12 "Protein Foods"

(Des M. Goaman. Photo Harrison)

1963 (4 June). *Freedom from Hunger. W w* **12**. *P* 14 × 14½.

117 **12** 12 c. sepia .. 2·75 90

1964–72. *As Nos.* 100/13, *but W w* **12**. *Glazed paper* ($2, 5) *or ordinary paper* (*others*).

118 **9** 1 c. black (17.3.64) .. 50 70
 a. Glazed paper. *Grey* (28.11.69) .. 1·10 2·25
 ab. Slate-grey (30.6.72) .. 15 1·75
119 2 c. black and orange (17.3.64) .. 1·50 20
 a. Glazed paper (27.5.70) .. 1·75 10
120 3 c. black and lake-brown (10.11.64) .. 1·50 30
 a. Glazed paper (27.5.70) .. 1·75 10
121 4 c. black and green (12.5.64) .. 30 10
 a. Glazed paper (22.4.70) .. 50 10
 ab. Black and emerald (19.11.71) .. 60 3·25
122 6 c. black and grey (12.5.64) .. 2·00 10
 a. Black (28.11.69) .. 5·50 5·50
 b. Glazed paper (28.11.69) .. 35 30
 ba. Light grey (19.11.71) .. 2·00 3·50
123 8 c. black and crimson-lake (12.5.64) .. 60 10
 a. Glazed paper (27.5.70) .. 75 15
 ab. Black and brown-red (19.11.71) .. 2·25 3·75
124 10 c. black and sepia (12.5.64) .. 50 10
 a. Glazed paper (31.3.70) .. 2·75 10
 ab. Grey and pale brown (coil) (11.10.71) 3·50 3·50
125 12 c. black and violet (12.5.64) .. 1·50 10
 a. Glazed paper (5.11.70) .. 11·00 1·00
126 15 c. black and pale blue (12.5.64) .. 55 10
 a. Glazed paper (28.11.69) .. 65 20
127 25 c. black and purple (12.5.64) .. 5·50 10
 a. Glazed paper (18.5.70) .. 9·50 4·50
 ab. Glazed paper. *Black and reddish violet* (30.4.71) .. 12·00 1·00
128 50 c. black and ultramarine (10.11.64) .. 2·50 10
 a. Black & brt ultramarine (17.3.69) 5·00 75
 b. Glazed paper (5.11.70) .. 10·00 3·00
 ba. Grey and indigo (21.12.71) .. 11·00 3·00
129 **10** $1 black and bronze-green (14.5.68) .. 3·00 5·50
 a. Glazed paper (5.11.70) .. 6·00 5·50
130 $2 black and scarlet (5.11.70) .. 35·00 20·00
131 $5 black and maroon (5.11.70) .. 42·00 30·00
118/29 .. *Set of* 12 17·00 6·00
118a/29a, 130/1 .. *Set of* 14 £100 50·00

Printings of the 6 and 15 c. issued on 28 November 1969 were on both ordinary and glazed paper, the 6 c. on ordinary producing a distinct shade.

No. 124a exists in coils constructed from normal sheets.

13 I.T.U. Emblem

(Des M. Goaman. Litho Enschedé)

1965 (17 May). *I.T.U. Centenary. W w* **12**. *P* 11 × 11½.

132 **13** 4 c. mauve and orange-brown .. 35 10
133 75 c. orange-yellow and light emerald .. 1·00 75

14 I.C.Y. Emblem

(Des V. Whiteley. Litho Harrison)

1965 (25 Oct). *International Co-operation Year. W w* **12**. *P* 14.

134 **14** 4 c. reddish purple and turquoise-green 20 10
135 15 c. deep bluish green and lavender .. 55 35

15 Sir Winston Churchill and St. Paul's Cathedral in Wartime

(Des Jennifer Toombs. Photo Harrison)

1966 (24 Jan). *Churchill Commemoration. W w* **12**. *P* 14.

136 **15** 3 c. black, cerise, gold and new blue .. 30 20
137 10 c. black, cerise, gold and deep green .. 1·50 20
138 15 c. black, cerise, gold and brown .. 1·75 35
139 75 c. black, cerise, gold and bluish violet 4·25 2·25
136/9 .. *Set of* 4 7·00 2·75

16 Footballer's Legs, Ball and Jules Rimet Cup

(Des V. Whiteley. Litho Harrison)

1966 (4 July). *World Cup Football Championships. W w* **12** (*sideways*). *P* 14.

140 **16** 4 c. violet, yellow-green, lake & yell-brn 20 15
141 75 c. chocolate, blue-grn, lake & yell-brn 75 60

17 W.H.O. Building

(Des M. Goaman. Litho Harrison)

1966 (20 Sept). *Inauguration of W.H.O. Headquarters, Geneva. W w* **12** (*sideways*). *P* 14.

142 **17** 12 c. black, yellow-green and light blue 35 40
143 25 c. black, light purple and yellow-brown 55 85

18 "Education"

19 "Science"

20 "Culture"

(Des Jennifer Toombs. Litho Harrison)

1966 (1 Dec). *20th Anniv of U.N.E.S.C.O. W* w **12** (*sideways*). *P* 14.
144 **18** 4 c. slate-violet, red, yellow and orange .. 35 10
145 **19** 15 c. orange-yellow, violet and deep olive .. 75 50
146 **20** 75 c. black, bright purple and orange .. 2·50 5·50
144/6 .. .. *Set of* 3 3·25 5·50

Sultan Sir Hassanal Bolkiah Mu'izzadin Waddaulah, 1967

21 Religious Headquarters Building

(Des and photo Harrison)

1967 (19 Dec). *1400th Anniv of Revelation of the Koran. W* w **12** (*sideways*). *P* 12½.
147 **21** 4 c. multicoloured 10 10
148 10 c. multicoloured 15 10
149 – 25 c. multicoloured 20 30
150 – 50 c. multicoloured .. .. 35 1·50
147/50 .. .. *Set of* 4 70 1·75
Nos. 149/50 are as T **21** but have sprigs of laurel flanking the main design (which has a smaller circle) in place of flagpoles.

22 Sultan of Brunei, Mosque and Flags

(Des V. Whiteley. Photo Enschedé)

1968 (9 July). *Installation of Y.T.M. Seri Paduka Duli Pengiran Temenggong. T* **22** *and similar multicoloured design. P* 14 × 13 (12 c.) *or* 13 × 14 (*others*).
151 4 c. Type **22** 15 30
152 12 c. Sultan of Brunei, Mosque and Flags (*horiz*) 40 75
153 25 c. Type **22** .. .. 50 1·25
151/3 .. .. *Set of* 3 95 2·10

23 Sultan of Brunei **24** Sultan of Brunei

(Des V. Whiteley. Litho D.L.R.)

1968 (15 July). *Sultan's Birthday. W* w **12** (*sideways*). *P* 12.
154 **23** 4 c. multicoloured 10 25
155 12 c. multicoloured 20 50
156 25 c. multicoloured 30 90
154/6 .. .. *Set of* 3 55 1·50

(Des V. Whiteley. Photo Harrison)

1968 (1 Aug). *Coronation of the Sultan of Brunei. W* w **12** (*sideways*). *P* 14½ × 14.
157 **24** 4 c. multicoloured 15 25
158 12 c. multicoloured 25 50
159 25 c. multicoloured 40 75
157/9 .. .. *Set of* 3 70 1·40

25 New Building and Sultan's Portrait

26 New Building and Sultan's Portrait

(Photo Enschedé)

1968 (29 Sept). *Opening of Language and Literature Bureau. W* w **12** (*sideways*). *P* 13½ (10 c.) *or* 12½ × 13½ (*others*).
160 **25** 10 c. multicoloured .. .. 20 1·50
a. Tête-bêche (pair) .. .. 40 3·00
161 **26** 15 c. multicoloured 20 35
162 30 c. multicoloured 45 90
160/2 .. .. *Set of* 3 75 2·50
The above were scheduled for release in 1967, and when finally issued had the year altered by overprinting.

27 Human Rights Emblem and struggling Man **28** Sultan of Brunei and W.H.O. Emblem

(Des V. Whiteley. Litho Harrison)

1968 (16 Dec). *Human Rights Year. W* w **12**. *P* 14.
163 **27** 12 c. black, yellow and green 10 20
164 25 c. black, yellow and blue 15 25
165 75 c. black, yellow and dull purple .. 45 1·75
163/5 .. .. *Set of* 3 65 2·00

(Des V. Whiteley. Litho Format)

1968 (19 Dec). *20th Anniv of World Health Organization. P* 14.
166 **28** 4 c. yellow, black and cobalt 30 30
167 15 c. yellow, black and deep bluish violet .. 55 65
168 25 c. yellow, black and pale yellow-olive .. 65 1·25
166/8 .. .. *Set of* 3 1·40 2·00

29 Deep Sea Oil-Rig, Sultan of Brunei and inset portrait of Pengiran Di-Gadong

(Des adapted by V. Whiteley. Photo Enschedé)

1969 (10 July). *Installation (9th May, 1968) of Pengiran Shahbandar as Y.T.M. Seri Paduka Duli Pengiran Di-Gadong Sahibol Mal. W* w **12**. *P* 14 × 13.
169 **29** 12 c. multicoloured 85 40
170 40 c. multicoloured .. .. 1·25 1·75
171 50 c. multicoloured .. .. 1·25 1·75
169/71 .. .. *Set of* 3 3·00 3·50

30 Aerial View of Parliament Buildings

(Des Harrison. Litho D.L.R.)

1969 (23 Sept). *Opening of Royal Audience Hall and Legislative Council Chamber. P* 15.
172 **30** 12 c. multicoloured 20 25
173 25 c. multicoloured 30 45
174 – 50 c. rose-red and bluish violet .. .. 60 1·50
172/4 .. .. *Set of* 3 1·00 2·00
Design:—50 c. Elevation of new buildings.

32 Youth Centre and Sultan's Portrait

(Des V. Whiteley. Litho D.L.R.)

1969 (20 Dec). *Opening of the New Youth Centre. W* w **12**. *P* 15 × 14½.
175 **32** 6 c. flesh, slate-lilac and black .. .. 20 1·00
176 10 c. olive-yellow, grey-green and blackish brown 25 10
177 30 c. yellow-olive, yellow-brown & black .. 70 1·00
175/7 .. .. *Set of* 3 1·00 1·90

33 Soldier, Sultan and Badge **34** Badge, and Officer in Full-dress Uniform

(Des Maj. M. A. Bowman. Adapted V. Whiteley. Litho Questa)

1971 (3 May). *Tenth Anniv of Royal Brunei Malay Regimen Multicoloured designs, each with Badge and Sultan's portrait T* **33**. *W* w **12** (*sideways on* 15 *and* 75 *c.*). *P* 14½.
178 10 c. Type **33** 70 3
179 15 c. Bell 205 UH-1H Iroquois helicopter (*horiz*) 90 9
180 75 c. *Pahlawan* (patrol boat) (*horiz*) .. 2·75 6·0
178/80 .. .. *Set of* 3 4·00 6·5

(Des Supt. T. Swan. Litho Format)

1971 (14 Aug). *50th Anniv of Royal Brunei Police Force. T* **34** *an similar vert designs. Multicoloured. W* w **12** (*sideways*). *P* 14½
181 10 c. Type **34** 50 3
182 15 c. Badge and Patrol Constable 60 8
183 50 c. Badge and Traffic Constable .. .. 1·75 5·5
181/3 .. .. *Set of* 3 2·50 6·0

35 Perdana Wazir, Sultan of Brunei and view of Water Village

(Des and litho Harrison)

1971 (27 Aug). *Installation of the Yang Teramat Mulia as t Perdana Wazir* (1970). *T* **35** *and similar horiz designs showin different views of Brunei Town. W* w **12**. *P* 14.
184 **35** 15 c. multicoloured 40 5
185 – 25 c. multicoloured .. .. .. 70 1·0
186 – 50 c. multicoloured .. .. .. 1·40 4·5
184/6 .. .. *Set of* 3 2·25 5·5

36 Pottery

(Des C. Abbott. Litho Questa)

1972 (29 Feb). *Opening of Brunei Museum. T* **36** *and simila horiz designs. Multicoloured. W* w **12** (*sideways*). *P* 13½.
187 10 c. Type **36** 30 1
188 12 c. Straw-work 40 2
189 15 c. Leather-work 45 2
190 25 c. Gold-work .. .. 1·25 1·1
191 50 c. Museum Building (58 × 21 *mm*) .. 2·25 3·5
187/91 .. .. *Set of* 5 4·25 4·5

37 Brunei Museum, Queen Elizabeth and Sultan of Brunei

(Des locally. Photo Enschedé)

1972 (29 Feb). *Royal Visit. T* **37** *and similar horiz designs eac with portraits of Queen and Sultan. Multicoloured. W* w **1** (*sideways**). *P* 13×13½.
192 10 c. Type **37** 70 2
193 15 c. Native houses 95 5
w. Wmk Crown to right of CA .. ..
194 25 c. Mosque .. .. 2·00 1·6
195 50 c. Royal Assembly Hall .. .. 3·75 6·5
192/5 .. .. *Set of* 4 6·75 8·0
*The normal sideways watermark shows Crown to left of CA *as seen from the back of the stamp.*

38 Secretariat Building

(Des Harrison. Litho J.W.)

72 (4 Oct). *Renaming of Brunei Town as Bandar Seri Begawan. T* **38** *and similar horiz designs. W* w **12** (*sideways*). *P* 13½.

96		10 c. multicoloured	30	15
97		15 c. green, light yellow and black	35	15
98		25 c. ultramarine, lemon and black	60	50
99		50 c. rosine, pale turquoise-blue and black ..	95	2·00
96/9		.. .. *Set of* 4	2·00	2·50

Views:—15 c. Darul Hana Palace; 25 c. Old Brunei Town; 50 c. own and Water Village.

39 Blackburn Beverley C1 parachuting Supplies

(Des Trident Artists. Litho Questa)

972 (15 Nov). *Opening of R.A.F. Museum, Hendon. T* **39** *and similar horiz design. Multicoloured. W* w **12** (*sideways on* 75 *c.*). *P* 14 × 13½ (25 *c.*) *or* 13½ × 14 (75 *c.*).

00		25 c. Type **39**	1·75	1·25
01		75 c. Blackburn Beverley C1 landing ..	3·25	3·75

1972 (17 Nov)–**74.** *As Nos.* 119/26, *but W* w **12** (*sideways**). *Glazed paper.*

202	**9**	2 c. black and orange (9.5.73)	1·75	6·50
203		3 c. black and lake-brown	1·75	40
204		4 c. black and green	50	1·00
205		6 c. black and grey	2·75	30
206		8 c. black and brown-red (9.5.73) ..	2·25	4·00
207		10 c. black and sepia	80	30
		a. *Black and bistre-brown* (24.7.74) ..	80	3·25
		aw. Wmk Crown to right of CA ..	5·00	
208		12 c. black and violet	1·50	2·25
209		15 c. black and pale blue	1·75	2·25
202/9		.. .. *Set of* 8	11·50	15·00

*The normal sideways watermark shows Crown to left of CA, *as seen from the back of the stamp.*

40 Girl with Traditional Flower-pot, and Boy with Bowl and Pipe

(Des (from photograph by D. Groves) and photo Harrison)

1972 (20 Nov). *Royal Silver Wedding. Multicoloured; background colour given. W* w **12**. *P* 14 × 14½.

210	**40**	12 c. carmine-red	10	10
		w. Wmk inverted	23·00	
211		75 c. deep myrtle-green	20	50

41 Interpol H.Q., Paris

(Des Shamir Bros. Litho Harrison)

1973 (7 Sept). *50th Anniv of Interpol. T* **41** *and similar horiz design. W* w **12** (*inverted on* 50 *c.*). *P* 14 × 14½.

212		25 c. bright green, purple and dull blue-black	1·50	1·25
213		50 c. pale greenish blue, ultramarine & carm	1·50	1·25

The 50 c. shows a different view of the H.Q.

42 Sultan, Princess Anne and Capt. Phillips

(Des PAD Studio. Litho Format)

1973 (14 Nov). *Royal Wedding. W* w **12**. *P* 14.

214	**42**	25 c. multicoloured	15	10
215		50 c. multicoloured	15	25

43 Churchill Painting

44 Sultan Sir Hassanal Bolkiah Mu'izzaddin Waddaulah

(Des C. Abbott. Litho Questa)

1973 (31 Dec). *Opening of Churchill Memorial Building. T* **43** *and similar vert design. Multicoloured. W* w **12** (*sideways*). *P* 14 × 13½.

216		12 c. Type **43**	10	20
217		50 c. Churchill Statue	30	1·40

(Des Staff Artists, Dept of Language and Literature. Photo Harrison)

1974 (15 July*). *Multicoloured; background colour given. W* w **12** (*sideways*†). *P* 13½×14½.

218	**44**	4 c. turquoise-green	20	20
219		5 c. pale blue	20	30
220		6 c. olive	90	1·75
221		10 c. lavender	30	10
222		15 c. light brown	75	10
223		20 c. stone	30	20
		w. Wmk Crown to right of CA ..	1·40	
224		25 c. sage-green	40	15
225		30 c. bright blue	40	15
226		35 c. grey	40	20
227		40 c. bright purple	40	20
228		50 c. cinnamon	40	20
229		75 c. light yellow-green	60	2·50
230		$1 pale salmon	1·50	4·00
231		$2 greenish yellow	2·25	8·50
232		$5 silver	4·50	17·00
233		$10 gold	7·00	28·00
218/33		.. .. *Set of* 16	17·00	55·00

*This was the London release date. The stamps were not put on sale locally until 29 August 1974, but First Day Covers were cancelled with the 15 July date.

†The normal sideways watermark shows Crown to left of CA, *as seen from the back of the stamp.*

See also Nos. 244/59 and 260/2.

45 Aerial View of Airport

(Des Harrison. Litho B.W.)

1974 (18 July). *Inauguration of Brunei International Airport. T* **45** *and similar horiz design. Multicoloured. W* w **12** (*sideways on* 75 *c.*). *P* 14×14½ (50 *c.*) *or* 12½×13 (75 *c.*).

234		50 c. Type **45**	1·25	1·00
235		75 c. Sultan in Army uniform, and airport (48 × 36 *mm*)	1·50	1·50

46 U.P.U. Emblem and Sultan

(Des J.W. Litho Harrison)

1974 (28 Oct). *Centenary of Universal Postal Union. W* w **12** (*sideways*). *P* 14½.

236	**46**	12 c. multicoloured	20	20
237		50 c. multicoloured	40	1·40
238		75 c. multicoloured	50	1·75
236/8		.. .. *Set of* 3	1·00	3·00

47 Sir Winston Churchill

(Des C. Abbott. Litho Questa)

1974 (30 Nov). *Birth Centenary of Sir Winston Churchill. T* **47** *and similar horiz design. Multicoloured. W* w **14** (*sideways*). *P* 14.

239		12 c. Type **47**	25	20
240		75 c. Churchill smoking cigar (profile) ..	45	1·25

A set of four, 12, 20, 25 and 75 c., was prepared during this period to mark the opening of new port facilities at Muara, but these stamps were never issued.

48 Boeing 737 and R.B.A. Crest

(Des PAD Studio. Litho Enschedé)

1975 (14 May). *Inauguration of Royal Brunei Airlines. T* **48** *and similar horiz designs. Multicoloured. No wmk. P* 12½ × 12.

241		12 c. Type **48**	1·00	25
242		35 c. Boeing 737 over Bandar Seri Begawan Mosque	1·75	1·25
243		75 c. Boeing 737 in flight	2·25	2·50
241/3		.. .. *Set of* 3	4·50	3·50

1975 (13 Aug)–**78.** *As Nos.* 218/33, *but W* w **14** (*sideways**).

244	**44**	4 c. turquoise-green	30	1·75
245		5 c. pale blue	30	1·75
246		6 c. olive	2·75	3·50
247		10 c. lavender	30	10
		a. *Pale bluish violet* (19.4.77) ..	30	10
248		15 c. light brown	60	90
249		20 c. stone	60	75
250		25 c. sage-green	70	90
		a. *Grey-olive* (25.5.78)	30	1·00
251		30 c. bright blue	35	1·25
		w. Wmk Crown to right of CA ..	1·25	
252		35 c. grey	45	1·25
253		40 c. bright purple	55	1·50
254		50 c. cinnamon	90	50
		a. Blue omitted†	55·00	
255		75 c. light yellow-green	80	2·75
256		$1 pale salmon	1·50	2·75
		w. Wmk Crown to right of CA ..	2·25	3·50
257		$2 greenish yellow	4·00	8·50
258		$5 silver	5·50	17·00
259		$10 gold	23·00	28·00
244/59		.. .. *Set of* 16	38·00	65·00

*The normal sideways watermark shows Crown to left of CA, *as seen from the back of the stamp.*

†The blue colour on the 50 c. value is only evident in the bluish green stripes of the sash and on several of the medal ribbons.

1976 (12 Apr). *As Nos.* 221 *and* 223/4 *but W* w **12** (*upright*).

260	**44**	10 c. lavender	3·50	1·50
261		20 c. stone	3·50	3·50
262		25 c. sage-green	3·50	5·00
260/2		.. .. *Set of* 3	9·50	9·00

(49)

50 Royal Coat of Arms

(Surchd by Govt Printer, Brunei)

1976 (16 Aug). *No.* 246 *surch with T* **49** *in silver.*

263	**44**	10 c. on 6 c. olive	1·75	80
		a. Surch on No. 220	2·25	1·10

(Des C. Abbott. Litho D.L.R.)

1977 (7 June). *Silver Jubilee. T* **50** *and similar vert designs. Multicoloured. W* w **14**. *P* 13½ × 14.

264		10 c. Type **50**	15	15
265		20 c. Imperial State Crown	20	20
		a. Silver omitted	£200	
266		75 c. Queen Elizabeth (portrait by Annigoni)	45	60
264/6		.. .. *Set of* 3	70	85

51 The Moment of Crowning

52 Royal Crest

(Des J. Cooter. Litho Enschedé)

1978 (2 June). *25th Anniv of Coronation. T* **51** *and similar vert designs. Multicoloured. W* w **14**. *P* 13½ × 13.

267		10 c. Type **51**	15	10
268		20 c. Queen in Coronation regalia ..	20	20
		w. Wmk inverted	75·00	
269		75 c. Queen's departure from Abbey ..	55	80
267/9		.. .. *Set of* 3	80	1·00

(Des local artist; adapted BG Studio. Litho Cartor)

1978 (1 Aug). *10th Anniv of Sultan's Coronation. T* **52** *and similar vert designs. W* w **14** (*inverted*). *P* 12.
270 10 c. black, scarlet and greenish yellow .. 20 10
271 20 c. multicoloured 40 25
272 75 c. multicoloured .. .. 1·10 2·00
270/2 .. .. *Set of* 3 1·50 2·00
MS273 182 × 77 mm. Nos. 270/2 .. .. .. 11·00 15·00
Designs:—20 c. Coronation ceremony; 75 c. Royal Crown.

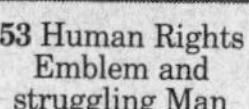

53 Human Rights Emblem and struggling Man

54 Smiling Children

(Des V. Whiteley; adapted L. McCombie. Litho Questa)

1978 (10 Dec). *Human Rights Year. W* w **14**. *P* 14½.
274 **53** 10 c. black, yellow and scarlet 10 10
275 20 c. black, yellow and violet 20 35
276 75 c. black, yellow and bistre .. .. 50 1·75
274/6 .. .. *Set of* 3 70 2·00
Type **53** is similar to the design used for the 1968 Human Rights Year issue.

(Des L. Curtis. Litho Harrison)

1979 (30 June). *International Year of the Child. T* **54** *and similar horiz design. W* w **14** (*sideways*). *P* 14.
277 10 c. multicoloured 20 10
278 $1 black and dull green .. .. .. 1·25 2·50
Design:—$1 I.Y.C. emblem.

55 Earth Satellite Station

56 Hegira Symbol

(Des A. Theobald. Litho Questa)

1979 (23 Sept). *Telisai Earth Satellite Station. T* **55** *and similar horiz designs. Multicoloured. W* w **14** (*sideways*). *P* 14.
279 10 c. Type **55** 20 15
280 20 c. Satellite and antenna 35 35
281 75 c. Television camera, telex machine and telephone .. .. 75 2·25
279/81 .. .. *Set of* 3 1·10 2·50

(Litho Secura, Singapore)

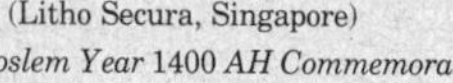

1979 (21 Nov). *Moslem Year 1400 AH Commemoration. W* w **14**. *P* 13 × 13½.
282 **56** 10 c. black, yellow and emerald .. 10 15
283 20 c. black, yellow and light blue .. 15 30
284 75 c. black, yellow and violet .. .. 45 1·75
282/4 .. .. *Set of* 3 60 2·00
MS285 178×200 mm. Nos. 282/4 .. .. 3·50 6·00
w. Wmk inverted .. .. .. 3·50

57 Installation Ceremony

58 Royal Umbrella and Sash

(Des BG Studio. Litho Questa)

1980 (8 Nov). *1st Anniv of Prince Sufri Bolkiah's Installation as First Wazir. T* **57** *and similar vert design. Multicoloured. W* w **14**. *P* 13½.
286 10 c. Type **57** 15 10
287 75 c. Prince Sufri .. .. 85 1·75
Nos. 286/7 have blue borders.

(Des BG Studio. Litho Secura, Singapore)

1980 (6 Dec). *1st Anniv of Prince Jefri Bolkiah's Installation as Second Wazir. Vert designs as T* **57**. *Multicoloured. W* w **14**. *P* 13½.
288 10 c. Installation ceremony 15 10
w. Wmk inverted .. .. 24·00
289 75 c. Prince Jefri .. .. 45 1·75
Nos. 288/9 have green borders.

(Des BG Studio. Litho Security Printers (M), Malaysia)

1981 (18 Jan*). *Royal Regalia* (*1st series*). *T* **58** *and similar multicoloured designs. P* 13½ × 13 (50 c.) *or* 12 × 11½ (*others*).
290 10 c. Type **58** 20 15
291 15 c. Sword and Shield 30 25
292 20 c. Lance and Sheath 40 35
293 30 c. Betel-leaf Container .. .. .. 60 1·00
294 50 c. Coronation Crown (23 × 40 *mm*) .. 1·00 3·75
290/4 .. .. *Set of* 5 2·25 5·00
MS295 98 × 142 mm. Nos. 290/4 .. .. .. 3·50 5·50
*This is the local release date. The Crown Agents released the stamps on 19 January.
See also Nos. 298/303, 314/19 and 320/5.

59 I.T.U. and W.H.O. Emblems

60 Shield and Broadsword

(Litho Security Printers (M), Malaysia)

1981 (17 May). *World Telecommunications and Health Day. P* 13 × 13½.
296 **59** 10 c. black and bright crimson 50 25
297 75 c. black, chalky blue & pale violet-bl 2·25 4·25

(Des BG Studio. Litho Security Printers (M), Malaysia)

1981 (15 July). *Royal Regalia* (*2nd series*). *T* **60** *and similar multicoloured designs. P* 12.
298 10 c. Type **60** 10 10
299 15 c. Blunderbuss and Pouch 20 30
300 20 c. Crossed Lances and Sash 30 30
301 30 c. Sword, Shield and Sash 40 65
302 50 c. Forked Lance .. .. 60 2·00
303 75 c. Royal Drum (29 × 45 *mm*) .. .. 80 3·25
298/303 .. .. *Set of* 6 2·10 6·00

61 Prince Charles as Colonel of the Welsh Guards

62 Fishing

(Des J.W. Litho Format)

1981 (29 July). *Royal Wedding. T* **61** *and similar vert designs. Multicoloured. W* w **14**. *P* 14.
304 10 c. Wedding bouquet from Brunei 15 15
305 $1 Type **61** .. .. 50 1·50
306 $2 Prince Charles and Lady Diana Spencer .. .. 70 2·50
w. Wmk inverted .. .. 40·00
304/6 .. .. *Set of* 3 1·25 3·75

(Des local artist. Litho Secura, Singapore)

1981 (16 Oct). *World Food Day. T* **62** *and similar vert design. Multicoloured. P* 12 × 11½.
307 10 c. Type **62** 50 15
308 $1 Farm produce and machinery .. .. 4·50 6·00

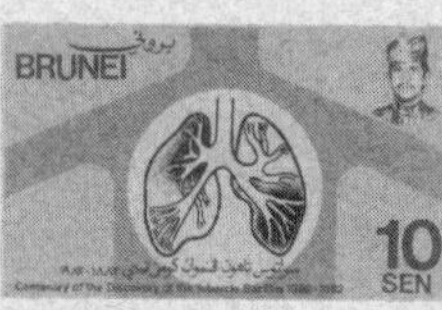

63 Blind Man and Braille Alphabet

64 Drawing of Infected Lungs

(Des local artist. Litho Security Printers (M), Malaysia)

1981 (16 Dec). *International Year for Disabled Persons. T* **63** *and similar vert designs. Multicoloured. W* w **14**. *P* 12.
309 10 c. Type **63** 65 20
w. Wmk inverted .. .. 13·00
310 20 c. Deaf people and sign language .. .. 1·50 80
a. Wmk sideways .. .. 1·75 1·75
311 75 c. Disabled person and wheelchairs .. 3·00 5·50
309/11 .. .. *Set of* 3 4·75 6·00

(Des local artist. Litho Security Printers (M), Malaysia)

1982 (24 May). *Centenary of Robert Koch's Discovery of Tuber[c]*
Bacillus. T **64** *and similar horiz design. Multicoloured. W* w **1**[4]
P 12 (10 *c.*) *or* 13½ (75 *c.*).
312 10 c. Type **64** 50
313 75 c. Magnified tubercle bacillus and microscope .. .. 3·00 4·

(Des PAD Studio. Litho Security Printers (M), Malaysia)

1982 (31 May). *Royal Regalia* (*3rd series*). *Multicoloured desig[ns]*
as T **60**. *W* w **14** (*sideways*). *P* 13½ (75 *c.*) *or* 12 × 11½ (*others*)
314 10 c. Ceremonial Ornament 10
315 15 c. Silver Betel Caddy 20
316 20 c. Traditional Flower-pot 25
317 30 c. Solitary Candle 50
318 50 c. Golden Pipe .. .. 70 2·
319 75 c. Royal Chin Support (28 × 45 *mm*) .. 90 3·
314/19 .. .. *Set of* 6 2·40 5·

(Des BG Studio. Litho Security Printers (M), Malaysia)

1982 (15 July). *Royal Regalia* (*4th series*). *Multicolour[ed]*
designs as T **60**. *W* w **14** (*sideways**). *P* 12 (75 *c.*) *or* 12×11[½]
(*others*).
320 10 c. Royal Mace 25
321 15 c. Ceremonial Shield and Spears 35
322 20 c. Embroidered Ornament 45
323 30 c. Golden-tasselled Cushion .. .. 75 1·
324 50 c. Ceremonial Dagger and Sheath .. 1·25 3·
325 75 c. Religious Mace (28×45 *mm*) .. .. 1·60 4·
w. Wmk Crown to left of CA .. .. 18·00
320/5 .. .. *Set of* 6 4·25 8·
*The normal sideways watermark shows Crown to right [of]
CA, *as seen from the back of the stamp.*

65 Brunei Flag

(Des Siti Zaleha Haji Kaprawi. Litho Secura, Singapore)

1983 (14 Mar). *Commonwealth Day. T* **65** *and similar hor[iz]*
designs. P 13 × 13½.
326 10 c. multicoloured 15
a. Horiz strip of 4. Nos. 326/9 .. .. 1·75
327 20 c. bright blue, black and buff 20
328 75 c. bright blue, black and bright green .. 45
329 $2 bright blue, black and lemon .. .. 1·10 1·
326/9 .. .. *Set of* 4 1·75 3·
Designs:—20 c. Brunei Mosque; 75 c. Machinery; $2 Sultan [of]
Brunei.
Nos. 326/9 were printed together, *se-tenant*, in horizontal strip[s]
of four throughout the sheet.

66 "Postal Service"

67 Football

(Litho Secura, Singapore)

1983 (15 Aug). *World Communications Year. T* **66** *and simila[r]*
horiz designs. P 13½.
330 10 c. multicoloured 15 1
331 75 c. yellow, orange-brown and black .. 60 7
332 $2 multicoloured .. .. 1·75 2·2
330/2 .. .. *Set of* 3 2·25 2·7
Designs:—75 c. "Telephone Service"; $2 "Communications".

(Litho Security Printers (M), Malaysia)

1983 (23 Sept). *Official Opening of the Negara Hassanal Bolkia*
Stadium. T **67** *and similar multicoloured designs. P* 12.
333 10 c. Type **67** 55 1
334 75 c. Athletics .. .. 2·25 1·5
335 $1 View of stadium (44 × 27 *mm*) .. .. 2·75 3·0
333/5 .. .. *Set of* 3 5·00 4·2

68 Fishermen and Crustacea

(Litho Secura, Singapore)

1983 (23 Sept). *Fishery Resources. T* **68** *and similar horiz design[s]*
Multicoloured. P 13½ × 14.
336 10 c. Type **68** 80 1
337 50 c. Fishermen with net .. .. .. 2·00 1·2
338 75 c. Fishing trawler .. .. 2·50 2·2
339 $1 Fishing with hook and tackle .. .. 2·50 2·7
336/9 .. .. *Set of* 4 7·00 5·7

INDEPENDENCE

From No. 349 onwards issues are inscribed "BRUNEI
RUSSALAM".

69 Royal Assembly Hall

es Haji Salleh bin Haji Ibrahim (No. 346), Pengiran Haji Muhammed bin Pengiran Duraman (No. MS348) or Siti Zaleha Haji Kaprawi (others). Litho Cartor)

84 (1 Jan). *Independence. T* **69** *and similar designs. P* 13.
0 10 c. pale stone and bright orange 20 10
1 20 c. flesh and brown-red 30 20
2 35 c. rose-pink and plum 60 60
3 50 c. pale blue and new blue .. .. .. 1·75 1·00
4 75 c. bright yellow-green and emerald .. 1·75 2·00
5 $1 light brownish grey and light brown .. 2·00 2·50
6 $3 multicoloured .. .. .. 5·00 8·00
0/6 .. .. *Set of* 7 10·50 13·00
S347 150 × 120 mm. Nos. 340/6 .. .. .. 9·50 14·00
S348 Two sheets each 150 × 120 mm. containing 4 stamps (34 × 69 *mm.*). (a) 25 c. × 4 grey-black and new blue (Signing of the Brunei Constitution). (b) 25 c. × 4 multicoloured (Signing of Brunei-U.K. Friendship Agreement) .. .. *Set of* 2 *sheets* 1·75 3·25

Designs:—34×25 *mm.* 20 c. Government Secretariat Building; 35 c. New Supreme Court; 50 c. Natural gas well; 75 c. mar Ali Saifuddin Mosque; $1 Sultan's Palace; 68×24 *mm.* $3 runei flag and map of South-East Asia.

70 Natural Forests and Enrichment Planting

(Des Awang Nor Ariffin bin Md. Yassin. Litho Secura, Singapore)

1984 (21 Apr). *Forestry Resources. T* **70** *and similar horiz designs. Multicoloured. P* 13½ × 14.
349 10 c. Type **70** 90 25
350 50 c. Forests and water resources .. .. 2·00 2·25
351 75 c. Recreation forests .. .. .. 2·75 3·50
352 $1 Forests and wildlife .. .. .. 4·00 4·50
349/52 .. .. *Set of* 4 8·75 9·50

71 Sultan Omar Saifuddin 50 c. Stamp of 1952

(Recess and litho D.L.R.)

1984 (22 Oct). *"Philakorea" International Stamp Exhibition, Seoul. T* **71** *and similar vert designs. Multicoloured. P* 13.
353 10 c. Type **71** 60 15
354 75 c. Brunei River view 10 c. stamp of 1907 .. 2·00 2·25
355 $2 Star and view ½ c. stamp of 1895 .. 3·00 5·00
353/5 .. .. *Set of* 3 5·00 6·75
MS356 Three sheets, 117 × 100 mm, each containing one stamp as Nos. 353/5 *Set of* 3 *sheets* 3·75 5·50
a. Line perf 14 at left *Set of* 3 *sheets* 4·50 7·50

The stamps within the miniature sheets were perforated by means of a three-sided comb gauging 13 and completed by a line perforation at left. Normally this line perforation is also 13, but on **MS**356a it measures 14.

72 United Nations Emblem

73 Young People and Brunei Flag

(Des Awang Nor Ariffin bin Md. Yassin (No. 357, 359), Haji Salleh bin Haji Ibrahim (358) or Siti Zaleha Haji Kaprawi (360). Litho Cartor)

1985 (23 Sept). *Admission of Brunei to World Organizations (1st issue). T* **72** *and similar horiz designs. W* w **17** *(sideways*). P* 13.
357 50 c. black, gold and pale greenish blue .. 50 70
358 50 c. multicoloured 50 70
359 50 c. multicoloured 50 70
360 50 c. multicoloured 50 70
357/60 .. .. *Set of* 4 1·75 2·50
MS361 110×151 mm. Nos. 357/60 .. .. 2·00 3·00
w. Wmk reading upwards .. .. 2·00 3·00

Designs:—No. 357, Type **72**; No. 358, Islamic Conference Organization logo; No. 359, Commonwealth logo; No. 360 A.S.E.A.N. emblem.

*The normal sideways version of the watermark shows the words reading downwards.

See also Nos. 383/7.

(Des Siti Zaleha Haji Kaprawi. Litho Security Printers (M), Malaysia)

1985 (17 Oct). *International Youth Year. T* **73** *and similar horiz designs. Multicoloured. P* 12.
362 10 c. Type **73** 80 20
363 75 c. Young people at work .. .. .. 4·00 5·00
364 $1 Young people serving the community .. .. 4·50 5·50
362/4 .. .. *Set of* 3 8·50 9·50

74 Palestinian Emblem

75 Early and Modern Scout Uniforms

(Des Haji Salleh bin Haji Ibrahim. Litho Secura, Singapore)

1985 (29 Nov). *International Palestinian Solidarity Day. P* 12 × 12½.
365 **74** 10 c. multicoloured .. .. .. 1·00 20
366 50 c. multicoloured .. .. .. 3·00 1·50
367 $1 multicoloured .. .. .. 3·75 3·00
365/7 .. .. *Set of* 3 7·00 4·25

(Des Awang Nor Ariffin bin Md. Yassin. Litho Secura, Singapore)

1985 (14 Dec). *National Scout Jamboree. T* **75** *and similar vert designs. Multicoloured. P* 13½.
368 10 c. Type **75** 50 10
369 20 c. Scout on tower signalling with flag .. 80 40
370 $2 Jamboree emblem .. .. .. 2·50 3·25
368/70 .. .. *Set of* 3 3·50 3·25

76 Sultan Sir Hassanal Bolkiah Mu'izzaddin Waddaulah

77

(Des Awang Nor Ariffin bin Md. Yassin. Photo Harrison)

1985 (23 Dec)–**86**. *W* **77**. *P* 13½ × 14½ (10 *to* 75 *c.*) *or* 14 ($1 *to* $10).
371 **76** 10 c. multicoloured 10 10
372 15 c. multicoloured 10 10
373 20 c. multicoloured 15 10
374 25 c. multicoloured 20 15
375 35 c. multicoloured (15.1.86) 25 20
376 40 c. multicoloured (15.1.86) 30 25
377 50 c. multicoloured (15.1.86) 40 35
378 75 c. multicoloured (15.1.86) 55 50
379 $1 multicoloured (23.2.86) 75 70
a. Wmk sideways .. ..
380 $2 multicoloured (23.2.86) .. .. 1·50 1·50
a. Wmk sideways .. ..
381 $5 multicoloured (23.2.86) .. .. 3·75 4·00
a. Wmk sideways .. ..
382 $10 multicoloured (29.3.86) .. .. 7·50 7·75
a. Wmk sideways .. ..
371/82 .. .. .. *Set of* 12 15·00 16·00

Nos. 379/82 are larger, size 32×39 mm.

The sideways watermark printings of the dollar values may date from around 1995.

(Des Awang Nor Ariffin bin Md. Yassin. Litho Cartor)

1986 (30 Apr). *Admission of Brunei to World Organizations (2nd issue). Horiz designs as T* **72**. *W* w **17** *(sideways). P* 13.
383 50 c. black, gold and bright yellow-green .. 40 60
384 50 c. black, gold and bright pinkish mauve .. 40 60
385 50 c. black, gold and orange-red 40 60
386 50 c. black, gold and dull ultramarine .. 40 60
383/6 .. .. *Set of* 4 1·40 2·25
MS387 105 × 155 mm. Nos. 383/6. Wmk upright 1·50 3·00

Designs:—No. 383, World Meteorological Organization emblem; 384, International Telecommunication Union emblem; 385, Universal Postal Union emblem; 386, International Civil Aviation Organization emblem.

78 Soldiers on Assault Course and Bell 205 UH-1H Iroquois Helicopter

79 Tunggul Charok Buritan, Alam Bernaga (Alam Besar), Pisang-Pisang and Sandaran

(Des Awang Nor Ariffin bin Md. Yassin. Litho Secura, Singapore)

1986 (31 May). *25th Anniv of Brunei Armed Forces. T* **78** *and similar horiz designs. Multicoloured. P* 13½.
388 10 c. Type **78** .. .. 2·25 2·25
a. Horiz strip of 4. Nos. 388/91 .. .. 11·00
389 20 c. Operating computer .. .. .. 2·75 2·75
390 50 c. Anti-aircraft missile, MBB-Bolkow Bo 105L helicopter and missile boat .. 3·25 3·25
391 75 c. Army commanders and parade .. 4·00 4·00
388/91 .. .. *Set of* 4 11·00 11·00

Nos. 388/91 were printed together, *se-tenant*, in horizontal strips of 4 throughout the sheet, forming a composite design.

(Des Awang Nor Ariffin bin Md. Yassin. Litho Secura, Singapore)

1986 (15 July). *Royal Ensigns (1st series). T* **79** *and similar vert designs. P* **12**.
392 10 c. black, greenish yellow and red .. 30 10
393 75 c. multicoloured .. .. 1·10 1·10
394 $2 black, greenish yellow and green .. 2·25 2·75
392/4 .. .. *Set of* 3 3·25 3·50

Designs:—75 c. Ula-Ula Besar, Sumbu Layang and Payong Haram; $2 Panji-Panji, Chogan Istiadat (Chogan Di-Raja) and Chogan Ugama.

(Des Awang Nor Ariffin bin Md. Yassin. Litho Secura, Singapore)

1986 (30 Sept). *Royal Ensigns (2nd series). Vert designs as T* **79**. *P* 12.
395 10 c. multicoloured 30 10
396 75 c. black, red and greenish yellow .. 1·10 1·10
397 $2 multicoloured .. .. 2·25 2·75
395/7 .. .. *Set of* 3 3·25 3·50

Designs:—10 c. Dadap, Tunggul Kawan, Ambal, Payong Ubor-Ubor, Sapu-Sapu Ayeng and Rawai Lidah; 75 c. Payong Tinggi and Payong Ubor-Ubor Tiga Ringkat; $2 Lambang Duli Yang Maha Mulia and Mahligai.

80 Stylised Peace Doves

81 Drug Addict in Cage and Syringe (poster by Othman bin Ramboh)

(Des Zainal Abidin Haji Ibrahim. Litho Security Printers (M), Malaysia)

1986 (24 Oct). *International Peace Year. T* **80** *and similar horiz designs. Multicoloured. P* 12.
398 50 c. Type **80** 75 75
399 75 c. Stylised hands and "1986" .. .. 1·00 1·10
400 $1 International Peace Year emblem and arms of Brunei .. .. 1·25 1·50
398/400 .. .. *Set of* 3 2·75 3·00

(Litho Security Printers (M), Malaysia)

1987 (15 Mar). *National Anti-drug Campaign. Children's Posters. T* **81** *and similar vert designs. Multicoloured. P* 12.
401 10 c. Type **81** 80 25
402 75 c. Drug addict and noose (Arman bin Mohd. Zaman) .. .. 2·25 3·00
403 $1 Blindfolded drug addict and noose (Abidin bin Hj. Rashid) .. .. .. 2·75 4·00
401/3 .. .. *Set of* 3 5·25 6·50

82 Cannon ("badil")

83 Map showing Member Countries

(Des Haji Salleh bin Haji Ibrahim. Litho Security Printers (M), Malaysia)

1987 (15 July). *Brassware* (1*st series*). *T* **82** *and similar vert designs. Multicoloured. P* 12.

404 50 c. Type **82** 40 40
405 50 c. Lamp ("pelita") 40 40
406 50 c. Betel container ("langguai") 40 40
407 50 c. Water jug ("kiri") 40 40
404/7 .. .. *Set of* 4 1·60 1·60

See also Nos. 434/7.

(Des Zainal Abidin bin Haji Ibrahim. Litho Security Printers (M), Malaysia)

1987 (8 Aug). *20th Anniv of Association of South East Asian Nations. T* **83** *and similar horiz designs. Multicoloured. P* 14×13½.

408 20 c. Type **83** 35 20
409 50 c. Dates and figures "20" 60 50
410 $1 Flags of member states.. .. .. 1·25 1·25
408/10 .. .. *Set of* 3 2·00 1·75

84 Brunei Citizens

(Des Pengiran Haji Muhammad bin Pengiran Duraman. Litho Secura, Singapore)

1987 (29 Sept). *25th Anniv of Language and Literature Bureau* (1986). *T* **84** *and similar horiz designs. Multicoloured. P* 13×12½.

411 10 c. Type **84** 10 10
a. Horiz strip of 3. Nos. 411/13 .. .. 2·00
412 50 c. Flame emblem and hands holding open book 40 40
413 $2 Scenes of village life .. .. .. 1·50 1·50
411/13 .. .. *Set of* 3 2·00 2·00

Nos. 411/13 were printed together, *se-tenant*, in horizontal strips of three throughout the sheet, each strip forming a composite design taken from a mural.

85 *Artocarpus odoratissima*

(Litho Security Printers (M), Malaysia)

1987 (31 Oct). *Local Fruits* (1*st series*). *T* **85** *and similar horiz designs. Multicoloured. P* 12.

414 50 c. Type **85** 45 55
a. Horiz strip of 4. Nos. 414/17 .. .. 1·60
415 50 c. *Canarium odontophyllum mig*.. .. 45 55
416 50 c. *Litsea garciae* 45 55
417 50 c. *Mangifera foetida lour* 45 55
414/17 .. .. *Set of* 4 1·60 2·00

Nos. 414/17 were printed together, *se-tenant*, in horizontal strips of 4 throughout the sheet.

See also Nos. 421/4, 459/62, 480/2 and 525/8.

86 Modern House

87 Wooden Lathe

(Litho Security Printers (M), Malaysia)

1987 (28 Nov). *International Year of Shelter for the Homeless. T* **86** *and similar horiz designs, each showing modern Brunei housing. P* 13×12½.

418 50 c. multicoloured 40 50
419 75 c. multicoloured 55 65
420 $1 multicoloured 80 90
418/20 .. .. *Set of* 3 1·60 1·90

(Des Awang Nor Ariffin bin Md. Yassin. Litho Security Printers (M), Malaysia)

1988 (30 Jan). *Local Fruits* (2*nd series*). *Horiz designs as T* **85**. *Multicoloured. P* 12.

421 50 c. *Durio spp* 50 50
a. Horiz strip of 4. Nos. 421/4 .. .. 1·75
422 50 c. *Durio oxleyanus*.. .. .. 50 50
423 50 c. *Durio graveolens* (blue background) .. 50 50
424 50 c. *Durio graveolens* (white background) .. 50 50
421/4 .. .. *Set of* 4 1·75 1·75

Nos. 421/4 were printed together, *se-tenant*, in horizontal strips of four throughout the sheet.

(Des Awang Padzil bin Haji Ahmad. Litho Security Printers (M), Malaysia)

1988 (29 Feb). *Opening of Malay Technology Museum. T* **87** *and similar vert designs. Multicoloured. P* 12.

425 10 c. Type **87** 15 10
426 75 c. Crushing sugar cane 55 70
427 $1 Bird scarer 70 85
425/7 .. .. *Set of* 3 1·25 1·50

88 Beragi Bunga Sakah-Sakah dan Bunga Cengkih Cloth

89 Sultan reading Proclamation

(Des Awang Nor Ariffin bin Md. Yassin. Litho Security Printers (M), Malaysia)

1988 (30 Apr). *Handwoven Material* (1*st series*). *T* **88** *and similar horiz designs showing different patterns. Multicoloured. P* 12.

428 10 c. Type **88** 10 10
429 20 c. Jong Sarat cloth 15 15
430 25 c. Si Pugut cloth 20 25
431 40 c. Si Pugut Bunga Berlapis cloth 30 35
432 75 c. Si Lobang Bangsi Bunga Belitang Kipas cloth 55 80
428/32 .. .. *Set of* 5 1·10 1·50
MS433 150×204 mm. Nos. 428/32 .. .. 2·00 2·50

See also Nos. 442/7.

(Des Haji Salleh bin Haji Ibrahim. Litho Security Printers (M), Malaysia)

1988 (30 June). *Brassware* (2*nd series*). *Vert designs as T* **82.** *Multicoloured. P* 12.

434 50 c. Lidded two-handled pot ("periok") .. 40 50
435 50 c. Candlestick ("lampong") 40 50
436 50 c. Shallow circular dish with stand ("gangsa") 40 50
437 50 c. Repousse box with lid ("celapa") .. 40 50
434/7 .. .. *Set of* 4 1·40 1·75

(Des Awang Nor Ariffin bin Md. Yassin. Litho Security Printers (M), Malaysia)

1988 (1 Aug). *20th Anniv of Sultan's Coronation. T* **89** *and similar vert designs. Multicoloured. P* 14 (20, 75 *c.*) *or* 12½×13 ($2).

438 20 c. Type **89** 15 15
439 75 c. Sultan reading from Koran 55 60
440 $2 In Coronation robes (26×63 *mm*) .. 1·50 1·60
438/40 .. .. *Set of* 3 2·10 2·25
MS441 164×125 mm. Nos. 438/40 .. .. 2·10 2·25

In No. **MS**441 the perforations of the stamps are as Nos. 438/40 except for the 75 c. which is perforated 13 at right.

(Des Awang Nor Ariffin bin Md. Yassin. Litho Security Printers (M), Malaysia)

1988 (29 Sept). *Handwoven Material* (2*nd series*). *Horiz designs as T* **88**. *Multicoloured. P* 12.

442 10 c. Beragi cloth 10 10
443 20 c. Bertabur cloth 15 20
444 25 c. Sukma Indra cloth 20 25
445 40 c. Si Pugut Bunga cloth 30 35
446 75 c. Beragi Si Lobang Bangsi Bunga Cendera Kesuma cloth 55 60
442/6 .. .. *Set of* 5 1·25 1·40
MS447 150×204 mm. Nos. 442/6 .. .. 2·00 2·75

90 Malaria-carrying Mosquito

(Litho Cartor)

1988 (17 Dec). *40th Anniv of World Health Organization. T* **90** *and similar vert designs. Multicoloured. P* 14×13½.

448 25 c. Type **90** 60 30
449 35 c. Man with insecticide spray and sample on slide 70 45
450 $2 Microscope and magnified malaria cells 2·25 2·00
448/50 .. .. *Set of* 3 3·25 2·50

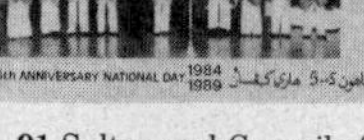

91 Sultan and Council of Ministers

92 Dove escaping from Cage

(Des Awang Nor Ariffin bin Md Yassin. Litho Security Printers (M), Malaysia)

1989 (23 Feb). *5th Anniv of National Day. T* **91** *and simila multicoloured designs. P* 12.

451 20 c. Type **91** 15 1
452 30 c. Guard of honour 20 1
453 60 c. Firework display (27 × 55 *mm*) .. 45 4
454 $2 Congregation in mosque .. .. 1·50 1·7
451/4 .. .. *Set of* 4 2·25 2·2
MS455 164 × 124 mm. Nos. 451/4 .. .. 2·25 2·7

(Des Haji Salleh bin Haji Ibrahim. Litho Secura, Singapore)

1989 (1 Apr). *"Freedom of Palestine". T* **92** *and similar hori designs. Multicoloured. P* 13½.

456 20 c. Type **92** 30 2
457 75 c. Map and Palestinian flag 90 8
458 $1 Dome of the Rock, Jerusalem .. .. 1·10 1·2
456/8 .. .. *Set of* 3 2·10 2·1

(Des Awang Nor Ariffin bin Md. Yassin. Litho Secura Singapore)

1989 (31 Oct). *Local Fruits* (3*rd series*). *Horiz designs as T* **85** *Multicoloured. P* 12.

459 60 c. *Daemonorops fissa* .. .. .. 1·60 1·7
a. Horiz strip of 4. Nos. 459/62 .. 5·50
460 60 c. *Eleiodoxa conferta* .. .. .. 1·60 1·7
461 60 c. *Salacca zalacca* .. .. .. 1·60 1·7
462 60 c. *Calamus ornatus* .. .. .. 1·60 1·7
459/62 .. .. *Set of* 4 5·50 6·0

Nos. 459/62 were printed together, *se-tenant*, in horizonta strips of four throughout the sheet.

93 Oil Pump

(Des Brunei Shell Petroleum Co. Litho Secura, Singapore)

1989 (28 Dec). *60th Anniv of Brunei Oil and Gas Industry T* **93** *and similar horiz designs. Multicoloured. P* 13½.

463 20 c. Type **93** .. .. 1·00 3
464 60 c. Loading tanker .. .. 2·00 2·0
465 90 c. Oil well at sunset .. .. .. 2·25 2·5
466 $1 Pipe laying .. .. 2·50 2·5
467 $2 Oil terminal .. .. 4·50 5·5
463/7 .. .. *Set of* 5 11·00 11·5

94 Museum Building and Exhibits

(Des Awang Padzil bin Haji Ahmad ($1), Mohd Yamin bin Haj Abd. Momin (others). Litho Security Printers (M), Malaysia)

1990 (1 Jan). *25th Anniv of Brunei Museum. T* **94** *and simila horiz designs. Multicoloured. P* 12.

468 30 c. Type **94** .. .. 1·00 6
469 60 c. Official opening, 1965 .. .. 1·75 2·0
470 $1 Brunei Museum .. .. 2·25 2·5
468/70 .. .. *Set of* 3 4·50 4·5

95 Letters from Malay Alphabet

96 Tarsier in Tree

(Des Pengiran Haji Muhammad bin Pengiran Duraman. Litho Security Printers (M), Malaysia)

1990 (15 July). *International Literacy Year. T* **95** *and similar horiz designs. Multicoloured. P* 12.

471 15 c. Type **95** 60 20
472 90 c. English alphabet .. .. 2·25 2·75
473 $1 Literacy Year emblem and letters .. 2·25 3·00
471/3 .. .. *Set of* 3 4·50 5·50

(Des Haji Salleh bin Haji Ibrahim. Litho Security Printers (M), Malaysia)

1990 (29 Sept). *Endangered Species. Western Tarsier. T* **96** *and similar vert designs. Multicoloured. P* 12 (20 *c.*) *or* 12½×13 (*others*).

474 20 c. Western Tarsier on branch .. .. 1·00 35
475 60 c. Western Tarsier feeding .. .. 2·00 2·50
476 90 c. Type **96** .. .. 3·00 3·50
474/6 .. .. *Set of* 3 5·50 5·75

97 Symbolic Family

98 Proboscis Monkey on Ground

(Litho Security Printers (M), Malaysia)

90 (1 Dec). *Worldwide Campaign against AIDS. T* **97** *and similar vert designs. Multicoloured. P* 12½.
7 20 c. Type **97** .. .. 1·00 60
8 30 c. Sources of infection .. .. .. 1·75 1·25
9 90 c. "AIDS" headstone surrounded by skulls 4·50 5·50
7/9 .. .. *Set of* 3 6·50 6·50

(Litho Security Printers (M), Malaysia)

90 (31 Dec). *Local Fruits* (4*th series*). *Horiz designs as T* **85**. *Multicoloured. P* 12.
0 60 c. *Willoughbea* sp. (brown fruit) .. 2·50 2·75
a. Horiz strip of three. Nos. 480/2 .. 6·50
1 60 c. Ripe *Willoughbea* sp. (yellow fruit) .. 2·50 2·75
2 60 c. *Willoughbea angustifolia* .. .. 2·50 2·75
0/2 .. .. *Set of* 3 6·50 7·50
Nos. 480/2 were printed together, *se-tenant*, in horizontal strips of three throughout the sheet.

(Des Haji Salleh bin Haji Ibrahim. Litho Cartor)

91 (30 Mar). *Endangered Species. Proboscis Monkey. T* **98** *and similar vert designs. Multicoloured. P* 13½×14.
3 15 c. Type **98** .. .. 1·25 50
4 20 c. Head of monkey .. .. .. 1·40 60
5 50 c. Monkey sitting on branch .. .. 2·75 3·00
6 60 c. Female monkey with baby climbing tree .. .. 3·00 3·50
3/6 .. .. *Set of* 4 7·75 7·00

99 Junior School Classes

100 Young Brunei Beauty

(Des Awang Nor Ariffin bin Md Yassin. Litho, Secura Singapore)

91 (29 Sept). *Teachers' Day. T* **99** *and similar horiz design. Multicoloured. P* 13½×14.
7 60 c. Type **99** .. .. 2·00 2·25
8 90 c. Secondary school class .. .. 2·25 2·75

es Awang Padzil bin Haji Ahmad. Litho Security Printers (M), Malaysia)

91 (1 Oct). *Fishes. Brunei Beauty. T* **100** *and similar horiz designs. Multicoloured. P* 12½.
9 30 c. Type **100** .. .. 1·50 85
0 60 c. Female fish .. .. 2·50 3·00
1 $1 Male fish .. .. 3·00 3·50
9/91 .. .. *Set of* 3 6·25 6·50

101 Graduate with Family

102 Symbolic Heart and Trace

(Des A. Mansur. Litho Cartor)

991 (30 Nov). *Happy Family Campaign. T* **101** *and similar vert designs. Multicoloured. P* 13.
92 20 c. Type **101** 15 10
93 60 c. Mothers with children 45 50
94 90 c. Family 70 75
92/4 .. .. *Set of* 3 1·25 1·40

(Des Siti Zaleha Haji Kaprawi. Litho Cartor)

992 (7 Apr). *World Health Day. T* **102** *and similar horiz designs showing heart and heartbeat trace. P* 13.
495 20 c. multicoloured 15 10
496 50 c. multicoloured 40 45
497 75 c. multicoloured 55 60
495/7 .. .. *Set of* 3 1·10 1·25
The 75 c. is larger, 48 × 27 mm.

103 Map of Cable System

(Des Awang Nor Ariffin bin Md. Yassin. Litho Security Printers (M), Malaysia)

1992 (28 Apr). *Launching of Singapore–Borneo–Philippines Fibre Optic Submarine Cable System. T* **103** *and similar horiz designs. P* 12.
498 20 c. Type **103** 15 10
499 30 c. Diagram of Brunei connection .. 20 15
500 90 c. Submarine cable 70 75
498/500 .. .. *Set of* 3 1·00 1·10

104 Modern Sculptures

105 "A.S.E.A.N. 25" and Logo

(Des Awang Nor Ariffin bin Md. Yassin. Litho Enschedé)

1992 (30 June). *Visit A.S.E.A.N. Year. T* **104** *and similar horiz designs. Multicoloured. P* 13½×14.
501 20 c. Type **104** 15 20
a. Horiz strip of 3. Nos. 501/3 .. .. 1·25
502 60 c. Traditional martial arts 45 50
503 $1 Modern sculptures (*different*) .. 75 80
501/3 .. .. *Set of* 3 1·25 1·50
Nos. 501/3 were printed together, *se-tenant*, in horizontal strips of 3 throughout the sheet with the backgrounds forming a composite design.

(Des Mohd. Yamin bin Haji Abd. Momin. Litho Questa)

1992 (8 Aug). *25th Anniv of A.S.E.A.N* (*Association of South East Asian Nations*). *T* **105** *and similar vert designs. Multicoloured. P* 14.
504 20 c. Type **105** 85 50
505 60 c. Headquarters building .. .. 2·00 2·50
506 90 c. National landmarks .. .. .. 2·75 3·50
504/6 .. .. *Set of* 3 5·00 6·00

106 Sultan in Procession

107 Crested Wood Partridge

(Des Awang Padzil bin Haji Ahmad. Litho Enschedé)

1992 (5 Oct). *25th Anniv of Sultan's Accession. T* **106** *and similar vert designs. Multicoloured. P* 14×13½.
507 25 c. Type **106** 20 25
a. Horiz strip of 5. Nos. 507/11 .. .. 1·00
508 25 c. Brunei International Airport .. 20 25
509 25 c. Sultan's Palace 20 25
510 25 c. Docks and Brunei University .. 20 25
511 25 c. Mosque 20 25
507/11 .. .. *Set of* 5 1·00 1·10
Nos. 507/11 were printed together, *se-tenant*, in horizontal strips of 5 throughout the sheet, each strip forming a composite design.

(Des Awang Padzil bin Haji Ahmad. Litho Enschedé)

1992 (30 Dec). *Birds* (1*st series*). *T* **107** *and similar vert designs. Multicoloured. P* 14×13½.
512 30 c. Type **107** 65 50
513 60 c. Asiatic Paradise Flycatcher .. .. 1·50 2·00
514 $1 Great Argus Pheasant .. .. 1·75 2·75
512/14 .. .. *Set of* 3 3·50 4·75

(Des Awang Padzil bin Haji Ahmad (60 c.), Kassim bin Haji Ismail (others). Litho Enschedé)

1993 (2 Jan). *Birds* (2*nd series*). *Vert designs as T* **107**. *Multicoloured. P* 14×13½.
515 30 c. Long-tailed Parakeet 75 50
516 60 c. Magpie Robin .. .. .. 1·50 2·00
517 $1 Blue-crowned Hanging Parrot .. 2·25 2·75
515/17 .. .. *Set of* 3 4·00 4·75

(Des Kassim bin Haji Ismail. Litho Enschedé)

1993 (3 May). *Birds* (3*rd series*). *Multicoloured designs as T* **107**. *P* 13½×14 (*horiz*) *or* 14×13½ (*vert*).
518 30 c. Chesnut-breasted Malkoha 90 50
519 60 c. White-rumped Shama .. .. 1·75 2·00
520 $1 Black and Red Broadbill (*vert*) .. 2·50 3·00
518/20 .. .. *Set of* 3 4·75 5·00

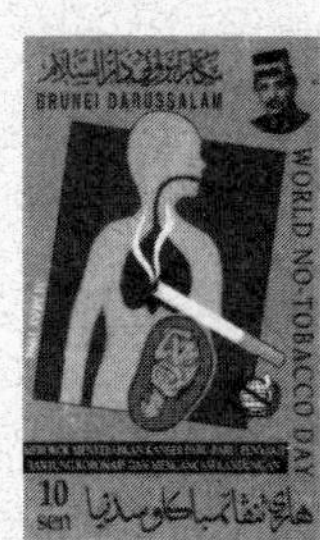

108 National Flag and "10"

109 Cigarette burning Heart and Deformed Baby in Womb

(Des Awang Nor Ariffin bin Md. Yassin. Litho Cartor)

1994 (16 June). *10th Anniv of National Day. T* **108** *and similar vert designs. Multicoloured. P* 13.
521 10 c. Type **108** 10 10
a. Horiz strip of 4. Nos. 521/4 90
522 20 c. Symbolic hands 15 20
523 30 c. Previous National Day symbols .. 20 25
524 60 c. Coat of arms 45 50
521/4 .. .. *Set of* 4 90 1·00
Nos. 521/4 were printed together, *se-tenant*, in horizontal strips of 4 throughout the sheet.

(Des Al bin Haji Abd Rahim. Litho Cartor)

1994 (8 Aug). *Local Fruits* (5*th issue*). *Horiz designs as T* **85**, *but each* 36×26 *mm. Multicoloured. P* 13½.
525 60 c. *Nephelium mutabile* 45 50
526 60 c. *Nephelium xerospermoides* 45 50
527 60 c. *Nephelium spp* 45 50
528 60 c. *Nephelium macrophyllum* 45 50
525/8 .. .. *Set of* 4 1·75 1·90

(Litho Enschedé)

1994 (1 Sept). *World No Tobacco Day. T* **109** *and similar vert designs. Multicoloured. P* 14×13½.
529 10 c. Type **109** 10 10
530 15 c. Symbols of smoking over crowd of people 10 10
531 $2 Globe crushing cigarettes .. .. 1·50 1·60
529/31 .. .. *Set of* 3 1·60 1·75

110 Girl Guide

111 Turbo-prop Airliner on Runway

(Des Awang Nor Ariffin bin Md. Yassin. Litho Enschedé)

1994 (7 Oct). *40th Anniv of Brunei Girl Guides' Association. T* **110** *and similar vert designs. Multicoloured. P* 14×13½.
532 40 c. Type **110** 30 35
a. Horiz strip of 5. Nos. 532/6 .. .. 1·50
533 40 c. Guide receiving award 30 35
534 40 c. Guide reading 30 35
535 40 c. Group of guides 30 35
536 40 c. Guides erecting tent 30 35
532/6 .. .. *Set of* 5 1·50 1·60
Nos. 532/6 were printed together, *se-tenant*, in horizontal strips of 5 throughout the sheet.

(Des Mohd Yamin bin Haji Abd Momin. Litho Cartor)

1994 (18 Nov). *20th Anniv of Royal Brunei Airlines. T* **111** *and similar horiz designs. Multicoloured. P* 13½.
537 10 c. Type **111** 10 10
538 20 c. Jet airliner on runway 15 20
539 $1 Jet airliner in the air 75 80
537/9 .. .. *Set of* 3 1·00 1·10

112 Malay Family

113 Aerial View of City, 1970

(Des Awang Padzil bin Haji Ahmad. Litho Cartor)

1994 (30 Dec). *International Day against Drug Abuse and Trafficking. T* **112** *and similar vert designs. P* 13½×14.
540 20 c. Type **112** 15 20
a. Horiz strip of 3. Nos. 540/2 . . . . 1·25
541 60 c. Chinese family 45 50
542 $1 Doctor, police officers and members of youth organizations 75 80
540/2 . . . . *Set of* 3 1·25 1·50
Nos. 540/2 were printed together, *se-tenant*, in horizontal strips of 3 throughout the sheet, each strip forming a composite design.

(Des Awang Padzil bin Haji Ahmad. Litho Cartor)

1995 (4 Oct). *25th Anniv of Bandar Seri Begawan. T* **113** *and similar horiz designs. Multicoloured. P* 13½.
543 30 c. Type **113** 20 20
544 50 c. City in 1980 . . . . 40 45
545 $1 City in 1990 . . . . 75 80
543/5 . . . . *Set of* 3 1·25 1·40

114 United Nations General Assembly

115 Students in Laboratory

(Des Mohd Yamin bin Haji Abd Momin. Litho Walsall)

1995 (24 Oct). *50th Anniv of United Nations. T* **114** *and similar vert designs. Multicoloured. P* 14½×14.
546 20 c. Type **114** 15 10
547 60 c. Security Council in session 45 50
548 90 c. United Nations Building, New York (27×44 *mm*) 70 75
546/8 . . . . *Set of* 3 1·25 1·40

(Des Mahadi bin Haji Matzain. Litho Cartor)

1995 (28 Oct). *10th Anniv of University of Brunei. T* **115** *and similar vert designs. Multicoloured. P* 13×13½.
549 30 c. Type **115** 20 20
550 50 c. University building 40 45
551 90 c. Sultan visiting University 70 75
549/51 . . . . *Set of* 3 1·25 1·40

116 Police Officers

117 Telephones

(Des Awang Nor Affin bin Md. Yassin. Litho Enschedé)

1996 (10 Feb). *25th Anniv of Royal Brunei Police Force. T* **116** *and similar vert designs. Multicoloured. P* 13½×13.
552 25 c. Type **116** 20 15
553 50 c. Aspects of police work 40 45
554 75 c. Sultan inspecting parade 55 60
552/4 . . . . *Set of* 3 1·10 1·25

(Litho Cartor)

1996 (17 May). *World Telecommunications Day. Children's Paintings. T* **117** *and similar vert designs. Multicoloured. P* 13½.
555 20 c. Type **117** 15 10
556 35 c. Telephone dial and aspects of telecommunications 25 30
557 $1 Globe and aspects of telecommunications 75 80
555/7 . . . . *Set of* 3 1·10 1·25

118 Sultan and Crowd

119 Sultan Hassanal Bolkiah Mu'izzaddin Waddaulah

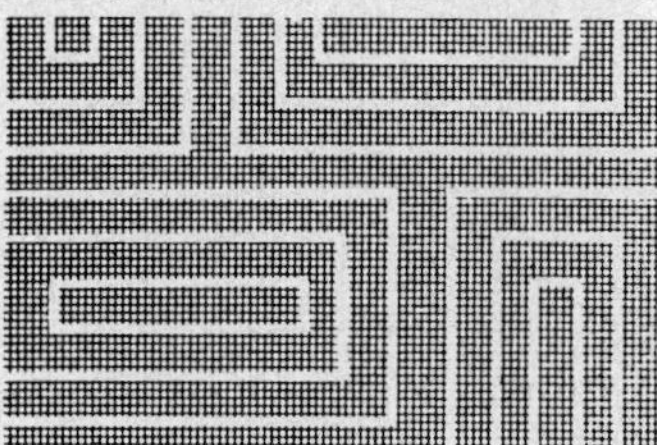

120

(Des Awang Nor Ariffin bin Md. Yassin. Litho Cartor)

1996 (15 July). *50th Birthday of Sultan Hassanal Bolkiah Mu'izzaddin Waddaulah. T* **118** *and similar vert designs. Multicoloured. P* 13×13½.
558 50 c. Type **118** 40 45
559 50 c. Sultan in ceremonial dress 40 45
560 50 c. Sultan receiving dignitaries at mosque 40 45
561 50 c. Sultan with subjects 40 45
558/61 . . . . *Set of* 4 1·60 1·75
MS562 152×100 mm. $1 Sultan in ceremonial dress (*different*). P 13 . . . . 75 80
A larger miniature sheet, 176×128 mm, containing five vertical $50 values was produced in a limited printing for presentation purposes.

(Des A. Robinson. Litho Walsall)

1996 (9 Oct). *T* **119** *and similar vert design. W* **120**. *P* 14×13½.
563 **119** 10 c. multicoloured 10 15
564 15 c. multicoloured 10 15
565 20 c. multicoloured 15 20
566 30 c. multicoloured 20 25
567 50 c. multicoloured 40 45
568 60 c. multicoloured 45 50
569 75 c. multicoloured 55 60
570 90 c. multicoloured 70 75
571 – $1 multicoloured 75 80
572 – $2 multicoloured . . . . . . 1·50 1·60
573 – $5 multicoloured . . . . . . 3·75 4·00
574 – $10 multicoloured . . . . . . 7·50 8·00
563/74 . . . . *Set of* 12 16·00 17·00
Design: (27×39 *mm*)—$1 to $10 Sultan in ceremonial robes.

121 Black-naped Tern

122 *Acanthus ebracteatus*

(Des Siti Zaleha Haji Kaprawi. Litho Enschedé)

1996 (11 Nov). *Birds (4th series). Sea Birds. T* **121** *and similar vert designs. Multicoloured. P* 14×13½.
575 20 c. Type **121** 15 10
576 30 c. Roseate Tern 20 15
577 $1 Bridled Tern 75 80
575/7 . . . . *Set of* 3 1·10 1·25
No. 576 is inscribed "ROSLATE TERN" in error.

(Des J. Lee. Litho Security Printers (M), Malaysia)

1997 (29 May). *Mangrove Flowers. T* **122** *and similar horiz designs. Multicoloured. P* 12.
578 20 c. Type **122** 15 20
579 30 c. *Lumnitzera littorea* 20 25
580 $1 *Nypa fruticans* 75 80
578/80 . . . . *Set of* 3 1·10 1·25

123 *Heterocentrotus mammillatus*

(Des Esther Lee. Litho Southern Colour Print, Dunedin)

1997 (15 Dec). *Marine Life. T* **123** *and similar horiz designs. Multicoloured. P* 12.
581 60 c. Type **123** 45 50
582 60 c. *Linckia laevigata* (starfish) 45 50
583 60 c. *Oxycomanthus bennetti* (plant) 45 50
584 60 c. *Bohadschia argus* (sea slug) 45 50
581/4 . . . . *Set of* 4 1·75 2·00

124 Children and Sign Language

(Des Padzil bin Haj Ahmed. Litho Cartor)

1998 (31 May). *Asian and Pacific Decade of Disabled Person 1993–2002. T* **124** *and similar horiz designs. Multicoloure P* 13×13½.
585 20 c. Type **124** 15 2
586 50 c. Woman typing and firework display 40 4
587 $1 Disabled athletes 75 8
585/7 . . . . *Set of* 3 1·25 1·4

125 Sultan performing Ceremonial Duties

126 A.S.E.A.N. Architecture and Transport

(Des Awang Nor Ariffin bin Md. Yassin. Litho Security Printer (M), Malaysia)

1998 (1 Aug). *30th Anniv of Coronation of Sultan Hassanc Bolkiah Mu'izzaddin Waddaulah. T* **125** *and similar hor designs. Multicoloured. P* 12.
588 60 c. Type **125** 45 5
589 90 c. Sultan on Coronation throne 70 7
590 $1 Coronation parade 75 8
588/90 . . . . *Set of* 3 1·90 2·0
MS591 150×180 mm. Nos. 588/90 . . . . 1·90 2·0

(Des Siti Zaleha Haji Kaprawi. Litho Enschedé)

1998 (8 Aug). *30th Anniv of Association of South-east Asia Nations. T* **126** *and similar vert designs. Multicoloure P* 13½.
592 30 c. Type **126** 20 2
593 30 c. Map of Brunei and city scenes . . 20 2
594 30 c. Flags of member nations 20 2
592/4 . . . . *Set of* 3 60 7

127 Crown Prince at Desk

128 Koran, Civil Servants and Handshake

(Litho Security Printers (M), Malaysia)

1998 (10 Aug). *Proclamation of Prince Al-Muhtadee Billah Crown Prince. T* **127** *and similar vert designs. Multicoloure P* 12.
595 $1 Type **127** 75
596 $2 Crown Prince in military uniform . . 1·50 1·
597 $3 Crown Prince's emblem . . . . . . 2·25 2·
595/7 . . . . *Set of* 3 4·50 4·
MS598 175×153 mm. Nos. 595/7 . . . . 4·50 4·

(Des Awang Nor Ariffin bin Md. Yassin. Litho Cartor)

1998 (29 Sept). *5th Anniv of Civil Service Day. T* **128** *a similar vert designs. Multicoloured. P* 13×13½.
599 30 c. Type **128** 20
600 60 c. Symbols of progress 45
601 90 c. Civil servants at work 70
599/601 . . . . *Set of* 3 1·25 1·

129 Blue-eared Kingfisher

(Des J. Esther Lee. Litho Cartor)

1998 (11 Nov). *Birds (5th series). Kingfishers. T* **129** *and similar vert designs. Multicoloured. P* 13½×13.

602	20 c. Type **129**	15	20
603	30 c. Common Kingfisher	20	25
604	60 c. White-collared Kingfisher	45	50
605	$1 Stork-billed Kingfisher	75	80
602/5	*Set of* 4	1·50	1·75

STAMP BOOKLETS

1976 (23 Feb). *Buff card cover showing Sultan's arms. Stitched.*

SB1 $1 booklet containing four 5 c. and eight 10 c. (Nos. 245, 247) in blocks of 4 .. .. .. 2·50

1986. *Black and bright scarlet printed cover showing Post Office emblem. Stitched.*

SB2 $1 booklet containing four 10 c. and four 15 c. (Nos. 371/2) in blocks of 4 .. .. .. 1·25

JAPANESE OCCUPATION OF BRUNEI

Japanese forces landed in Northern Borneo on 15 December 1941 and the whole of Brunei had been occupied by 6 January 1942.

Brunei, North Borneo, Sarawak and, after a short period, Labuan, were administered as a single territory by the Japanese. Until September–October 1942, previous stamp issues, without overprint, continued to be used in conjunction with existing postmarks. From the Autumn of 1942 onwards unoverprinted stamps of Japan were made available and examples can be found used from the area for much of the remainder of the War. Japanese Occupation issues for Brunei, North Borneo and Sarawak were equally valid throughout the combined territory but not, in practice, equally available.

PRICES FOR STAMPS ON COVER

Nos. J1/16	*from* × 8
Nos. J17/20	—

本日大

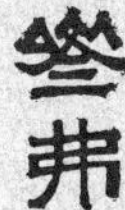

府政国帝本日大 便郵國帝

(1) (2)

("Imperial Japanese Government") ("Imperial Japanese Postal Service $3")

1942 (Oct)–**44.** *Stamps of Brunei handstamped with T* **1** *in violet to blue. Wmk Mult Script CA (except Nos.* J18/19, *Mult Crown CA). P* 14.

J 1	**5**	1 c. black	6·00	23·00
		a. Red opt	48·00	65·00
J 2		2 c. green	48·00	£100
J 3		2 c. orange (1943)	2·75	9·00
J 4		3 c. blue-green	28·00	75·00
J 5		4 c. orange	3·00	13·00
J 6		5 c. chocolate	3·00	13·00
		a. "5 c." retouch	£150	£375
J 7	**7**	6 c. greenish grey (*p* 14×11½) (1944)	50·00	£200
J 8		6 c. scarlet	£550	£550
J 9	**5**	8 c. grey-black	£650	£850
J10	**7**	8 c. red	3·75	12·00
		a. Opt omitted (in pair with normal)	£900	
J11	**5**	10 c. purple/*yellow*	8·50	26·00
J12	**7**	12 c. blue	22·00	26·00
		a. Red opt	£130	£190
J13		15 c. ultramarine (1944)	13·00	26·00
J14	**5**	25 c. slate-purple	23·00	50·00
		a. Red opt	£200	£275
J15		30 c. purple and orange-yellow	90·00	£180
J16		50 c. black/*emerald*	38·00	60·00
		a. Red opt	£225	
J17		$1 black and red/*blue* (1944)	55·00	70·00
		a. Red opt	—	£500
J18		$5 carmine/*green* (1944)	£800	£1600
J19		$25 black/*red* (1944)	£850	£1600

The overprint varies in shade from violet to blue, and being handstamped, exists double, double one inverted and treble.

Nos. J3, J7, J10 and J13 were not issued without the overprint.

1944 (11 May). *No.* J1 *surch with T* **2** *in orange-red.*

J20	**5**	$3 on 1 c. black	£5500	£5000
		a. Surch on No. 60 of Brunei	£6500	

Three separate handstamps were used to apply Type **2**, one for the top line, one for the bottom and the third for the two central characters.

Burma

(Currency. 12 pies = 1 anna; 16 annas = 1 rupee)

Stamps of India were used in Burma from 1854 and, after 1856, individual examples can be identified by the use of the concentric octagonal postmarks of the Bengal Postal Circle of which the following were supplied to Burmese post offices:

Type A
No. B 156
(Rangoon)

Type B
No. B 5
(Akyab)

B5	Akyab	B146	Pegu
B12*	Bassein	B150	Prome
B22	Nga Thine Khyoung	B156*	Rangoon
B56	Amherst	B159	Sandoway
B108	Kyouk Phyoo	B165	Sarawah (*to* 1860)
B111	Meeaday	B165	Henzada (*from* 1861)
B112	Mengyee	B171	Shoay Gyeen
B127	Moulmein	B173	Sittang
B128	Mergui	B179	Thayetmyo
B129	Tavoy	B181	Toungoo
B133	Myanoung	B227	Port Blair
B136	Namayan		

*Exists in black or blue. Remainder in black only.

Akyab, Moulmein and Rangoon used postmarks as both Type A and Type B, Port Blair as Type B only and the remainder as Type A only.

From 1860 various types of duplex cancellations were introduced and Burmese examples can be identified when sufficient of the left-hand portion is visible on the stamp. Such marks were issued for the following offices:

Akyab	Rangoon
Bassein	Rangoon C.R.H.
Mandalay	(Cantonment Receiving House)
Moulmein	Thayetmyo
Port Blair	Toungoo
Prome	

1862 Duplex from
Toungoo

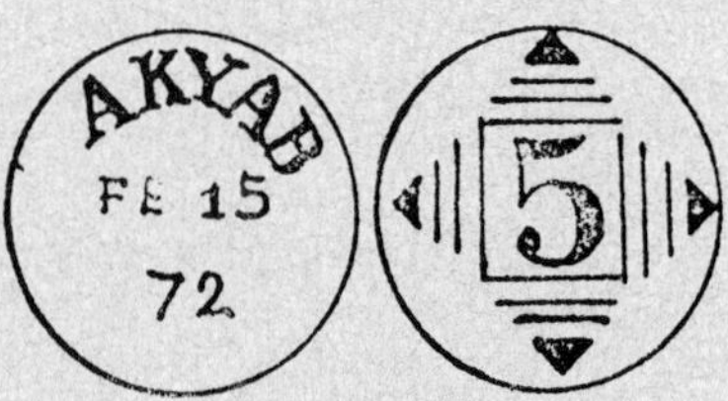

1865 Duplex from
Akyab

During 1875, a further series of duplex marks was introduced in which the right-hand portion of the cancellation included the office code number, prefixed by the letter "R" for Rangoon:

R–1	Rangoon	R–9	Myanoung
R–1/1	Rangoon Cantonment	R–10	Port Blair
R–2	Akyab	1/R–10	Nancowry
R–3	Bassein	R–11	Prome
R–4	Henzada	R–12	Sandoway
R–5	Kyouk Phyoo	R–13	Shwegyeen
R–6	Mandalay	R–14	Tavoy
R–7	Mergui	R–15	Thayetmyo
R–8	Moulmein	R–16	Tounghoo
1/R–8	Amherst		

1875 type from
Rangoon

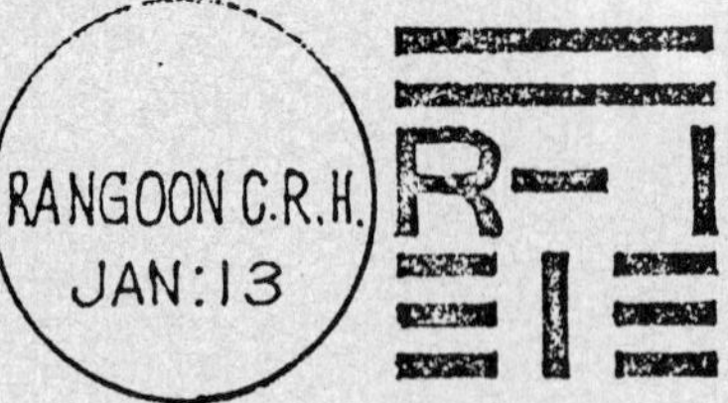

1875 type from Rangoon
Cantonment Receiving House

From 1886 the whole of Burma was united under the Crown and the post offices were supplied with circular date stamps giving the name of the town.

Most Indian stamps, both postage and official, issued during the period were supplied to post offices in Burma. None of the imperforates printed by De La Rue have been seen however, and from the later issues the following have not been recorded with Burma postmarks:

Nos. 39a, 66a, 68, 85a, 92a, 110a/b, 148a, 155a, 165, 192a/c, 195a/b, O15, O38, O40b, O50a/b, O76a, O101a, O102, O103/a, O104/5 and O142.

The value of most India stamps used in Burma coincides proportionately with the used prices quoted for India, but some, especially the provisional surcharges, are extremely rare with Burmese postmarks. Stamps of the face value of 2 r. and above from the reigns of Victoria and Edward VII are more common with telegraph cancellations than with those of the postal service.

PRICES FOR STAMPS ON COVER TO 1945

Nos. 1/18	*from* × 6
Nos. 18a/33	*from* × 4
No. 34	*from* × 5
Nos. 35/50	*from* × 8
Nos. O1/27	*from* × 15

BRITISH ADMINISTRATION

From 1 January 1886 Burma was a province of the Indian Empire but was separated from India and came under direct British administration on 1 April 1937.

BURMA (1) **BURMA** (1a)

1937 (1 Apr). *Stamps of India (King George V inscr* "INDIA POSTAGE") *optd with T* **1** *or* **1a** *(rupee values). W* **69**. *P* 14.

1	3 p. slate	30	10
	w. Wmk inverted	1·00	50
2	½ a. green	50	10
	w. Wmk inverted	1·50	50
3	9 p. deep green	75	10
	w. Wmk inverted	1·00	50
4	1 a. chocolate	40	10
	w. Wmk inverted	1·25	50
5	2 a. vermilion (*small die*)	40	10
6	2½ a. orange	30	10
	w. Wmk inverted	1·25	50
7	3 a. carmine	75	30
	w. Wmk inverted	2·50	1·00
8	3½ a. deep blue	65	10
	aw. Wmk inverted	1·00	20
	b. Dull blue	6·00	6·00
	bw. Wmk inverted	4·25	4·00
9	4 a. sage-green	70	10
	w. Wmk inverted	—	22·00
10	6 a. bistre	60	35
	w. Wmk inverted	—	22·00
11	8 a. reddish purple	1·50	10
12	12 a. claret	2·50	85
	w. Wmk inverted	6·00	1·75
13	1 r. chocolate and green	16·00	2·00
14	2 r. carmine and orange	23·00	9·00
	w. Wmk inverted	35·00	13·00
15	5 r. ultramarine and purple	35·00	15·00
16	10 r. green and scarlet	65·00	50·00
17	15 r. blue and olive (*wmk inverted*)	£200	90·00
18	25 r. orange and blue	£400	£190
	w. Wmk inverted	£475	£250
1/18	*Set of* 18	£700	£325

The opt is at top on all values except the 3 a.

The 1 a. has been seen used from Yenangyaung on 22 Mar 1937.

2 King George VI and "Chinthes"

3 King George VI and "Nagas"

4 Royal Barge

8 King George VI and Peacock

10 Elephants' Heads

Extra trees flaw (R. 11/8)

(Des Maung Kyi (2 a. 6 p.), Maung Hline (3 a.), Maung Ohn P(3 a. 6 p.) and N. K. D. Naigamwalla (8 a.). Litho Security Ptg Press, Nasik)

1938 (15 Nov)–**40**. *T* **2/4**, **8** *and similar designs. W* **10**. *P* 14 (*vert*) *or* 13½ × 13 (*horiz*).

18a	**2**	1 p. red-orange (1.8.40)	3·00	8
19		3 p. bright violet	20	3
20		6 p. bright blue	20	1
21		9 p. yellow-green	1·00	8
22	**3**	1 a. purple-brown	20	1
23		1½ a. turquoise-green	20	6
24		2 a. carmine	45	1
25	**4**	2 a. 6 p. claret	14·00	9
26	–	3 a. dull violet	14·00	1·5
27	–	3 a. 6 p. light blue and blue	1·25	3·7
		a. Extra trees flaw	40·00	
28	**3**	4 a. greenish blue	60	1
29	–	8 a. myrtle-green	5·00	3
30	**8**	1 r. purple and blue	7·50	2
31		2 r. brown and purple	16·00	1·7
32	–	5 r. violet and scarlet	48·00	20·0
33	–	10 r. brown and myrtle	55·00	42·0
18a/33		*Set of* 16	£150	65·0

Designs: *Horiz* (*as T* 4)—3 a. Burma teak; 3 a. 6 p. Burma rice 8 a. River Irrawaddy. *Vert* (*as T* 8)—5 r., 10 r. King George V and "Nats".

The 1 a. exists lithographed and typographed, the latter havin a "Jubilee" line in the sheet margin.

COMMEMORATION
POSTAGE STAMP
6th MAY 1840

(11)

1940 (6 May) *Centenary of First Adhesive Postage Stamps. No. 2 surch with T* **11**.

34	**4**	1 a. on 2 a. 6 p. claret	3·50	1·2

For stamps issued in 1942–45 see under Japanese Occupation.

CHIN HILLS DISTRICT. This area, in the far north-west c the country, remained in British hands when the Japanes overran Burma in May 1942.

During the period July to December 1942 the local official were authorised to produce provisional stamps and the letter "OHMS" are known overprinted by typewriter on Nos. 3, 20 22/4, 28/9 and 31 of Burma or handstamped, in violet, on Nos 25, 27 and 29. The two types can also occur together or in combination with a handstamped "SERVICE".

From early in 1943 ordinary postage stamps of India were use from the Chin Hills post offices of Falam, Haka, Fort White an Tiddim, this expedient continuing until the fall of Falam to th Japanese on 7 November 1943.

The provisional stamps should only be collected on Official cove where dates and the sender's handwriting can be authenticated.

BRITISH MILITARY ADMINISTRATION

MILY ADMN (12) MILY ADMN (13)

1945 (from 16 June). *Nos. 18a to 33 optd with T* **12** (*sma stamps*) *or* **13** (*others*) *by Security Printing Press, Nasik.*

35	**2**	1 p. red-orange	10	1
		a. Opt omitted (in pair with normal)	£1500	
36		3 p. bright violet	10	3
37		6 p. bright blue	10	3
38		9 p. yellow-green	30	3
39	**3**	1 a. purple-brown (16.6)	10	1
40		1½ a. turquoise-green (16.6)	10	1
41		2 a. carmine	10	1
42	**4**	2 a. 6 p. claret	2·00	6
43	–	3 a. dull violet	1·50	2
44	–	3 a. 6 p. light blue and blue	10	7
		a. Extra trees flaw	15·00	
45	**3**	4 a. greenish blue	10	2
46	–	8 a. myrtle-green	10	4

No.	Type	Description	Unused	Used
47	8	1 r. purple and blue	40	50
48		2 r. brown and purple	40	1·00
49	–	5 r. violet and scarlet	40	1·00
50	–	10 r. brown and myrtle	40	1·00
35/50		*Set of* 16	4·75	6·25

Only the typographed version of the 1 a., No. 22, received this overprint.

BRITISH CIVIL ADMINISTRATION

1946 (1 Jan). *As Nos. 19/33, but colours changed.*

No.	Type	Description	Unused	Used
51	2	3 p. brown	10	90
52		6 p. deep violet	10	30
53		9 p. green	15	1·60
54	3	1 a. blue	15	20
55		1½ a. orange	15	10
56		2 a. claret	15	40
57	4	2 a. 6 p. greenish blue	80	3·00
57*a*	–	3 a. blue-violet	6·50	3·00
57*b*	–	3 a. 6 p. black and ultramarine	30	1·25
		ba. Extra trees flaw	27·00	
58	3	4 a. purple	30	30
59	–	8 a. maroon	1·75	1·75
60	8	1 r. violet and maroon	1·00	40
61		2 r. brown and orange	6·00	2·00
62	–	5 r. green and brown	6·00	10·00
63	–	10 r. claret and violet	6·00	16·00
51/63		*Set of* 15	26·00	38·00

No. 54 was printed in typography only.

14 Burman

(Des A. G. I. McGeogh. Litho Nasik)

1946 (2 May). *Victory. T* **14** *and similar vert designs. W* **10** *(sideways). P* 13.

No.	Description	Unused	Used
64	9 p. turquoise-green	20	20
65	1½ a. violet	20	10
66	2 a. carmine	20	10
67	3 a. 6 p. ultramarine	30	20
64/7	*Set of* 4	80	50

Designs:—1½ a. Burmese woman; 2 a. Chinthe; 3 a. 6 p. Elephant.

INTERIM BURMESE GOVERNMENT

ကြားဖြတ် အစိုးရ။ (18 *Trans.* "Interim Government")

ားဖြတ်ကြ အစိုးရ။ (18*a*)

တ်ကြားဖြ အစိုးရ။ (18*b*)

Type **18***a* shows the first character transposed to the end of the top line (R. 6/15).

Type **18***b* shows the last two characters transposed to the front of the top line (R. 14/14).

Some sheets of the 3 p. show both errors corrected by a handstamp as Type **18**.

1947 (1 Oct). *Stamps of* 1946 *optd with T* **18** *(small stamps) or larger opt (others).*

No.	Type	Description	Unused	Used
68	2	3 p. brown	70	70
		a. Opt Type **18***a*	18·00	
		ab. Corrected by handstamp as Type **18**		
		b. Opt Type **18***b*	18·00	
		ba. Corrected by handstamp as Type **18**		
69		6 p. deep violet	10	30
		a. Opt Type **18***a*	9·00	
70		9 p. green	10	30
		a. Opt inverted	19·00	21·00
71	3	1 a. blue	10	30
		a. Vert pair, one with opt omitted		
72		1½ a. orange	90	10
73		2 a. claret	30	15
		a. Horiz pair, one with opt omitted		
		b. Opt Type **18***a*	20·00	
74	4	2 a. 6 p. greenish blue	1·75	95
75	–	3 a. blue-violet	2·50	1·50
76	–	3 a. 6 p. black and ultramarine	45	1·50
		a. Extra trees flaw	24·00	
77	3	4 a. purple	1·75	30
78	–	8 a. maroon	1·75	90
79	8	1 r. violet and maroon	2·50	30
80		2 r. brown and orange	3·25	2·50
81	–	5 r. green and brown	3·25	3·25
82	–	10 r. claret and violet	3·25	3·25
68/82		*Set of* 15	20·00	14·00

The 3 p., 6 p., 2 a., 2 a. 6 p., 3 a. 6 p. and 1 r. are also known with overprint inverted.

OFFICIAL STAMPS

BURMA SERVICE (O 1)

BURMA SERVICE (O 1*a*)

1937 (Apr–June). *Stamps of India (King George V inscr* "INDIA POSTAGE") *optd with Type* O **1** *or* O **1***a (rupee values). W* **69**. *P* 14.

No.	Description	Unused	Used
O 1	3 p. slate	1·00	10
	w. Wmk inverted	—	11·00
O 2	½ a. green	5·50	10
O 3	9 p. deep green	3·25	30
O 4	1 a. chocolate	3·75	10
O 5	2 a. vermilion (*small die*)	6·00	35
	w. Wmk inverted	—	11·00
O 6	2½ a. orange	4·00	1·50
O 7	4 a. sage-green	3·75	10
O 8	6 a. bistre	4·00	5·50
O 9	8 a. reddish purple (1.4.37)	3·00	80
O10	12 a. claret (1.4.37)	3·00	3·00
O11	1 r. chocolate and green (1.4.37)	20·00	3·75
O12	2 r. carmine and orange	40·00	28·00
	w. Wmk inverted	50·00	35·00
O13	5 r. ultramarine and purple	85·00	42·00
O14	10 r. green and scarlet	£250	£110
O1/14	*Set of* 14	£375	£170

For the above issue the stamps were either overprinted "BURMA" and "SERVICE" at one operation or had the two words applied separately. Research has yet to establish if all values exist with both forms of overprinting.

SERVICE (O 2)

SERVICE (O 3)

1939. *Nos. 19/24 and 28 optd with Type* O **2** *(typo) and Nos. 25 and 29/33 optd with Type* O **3** *(litho).*

No.	Type	Description	Unused	Used
O15	2	3 p. bright violet	15	20
O16		6 p. bright blue	15	20
O17		9 p. yellow-green	5·00	1·90
O18	3	1 a. purple-brown	15	15
O19		1½ a. turquoise-green	4·50	1·25
O20		2 a. carmine	1·25	20
O21	4	2 a. 6 p. claret	25·00	9·00
O22	3	4 a. greenish blue	5·50	45
O23	–	8 a. myrtle-green	25·00	3·75
O24	8	1 r. purple and blue	38·00	5·00
O25		2 r. brown and purple	45·00	10·00
O26	–	5 r. violet and scarlet	42·00	28·00
O27	–	10 r. brown and myrtle	£120	38·00
O15/27		*Set of* 13	£275	85·00

Both versions of the 1 a. value exist with this overprint.

1946. *British Civil Administration. Nos. 51/6 and 58 optd with Type* O **2** *(typo) and Nos. 57 and 59/63 optd with Type* O **3** *(litho).*

No.	Type	Description	Unused	Used
O28	2	3 p. brown	80	2·25
O29		6 p. deep violet	80	1·75
O30		9 p. green	20	2·50
O31	3	1 a. blue	20	1·50
O32		1½ a. orange	20	20
O33		2 a. claret	20	1·50
O34	4	2 a. 6 p. greenish blue	1·40	4·00
O35	3	4 a. purple	20	70
O36	–	8 a. maroon	1·50	2·50
O37	8	1 r. violet and maroon	60	2·50
O38		2 r. brown and orange	7·00	32·00
O39	–	5 r. green and brown	9·00	38·00
O40	–	10 r. claret and violet	17·00	48·00
O28/40		*Set of* 13	35·00	£120

1947. *Interim Burmese Government. Nos. O28/40 optd with T* **18** *(small stamps) or larger opt (others).*

No.	Type	Description	Unused	Used
O41	2	3 p. brown	15	40
O42		6 p. deep violet	70	10
O43		9 p. green	1·00	90
O44	3	1 a. blue	1·75	80
O45		1½ a. orange	3·25	20
O46		2 a. claret	1·50	15
O47	4	2 a. 6 p. greenish blue	19·00	7·00
O48	3	4 a. purple	5·50	40
O49	–	8 a. maroon	5·50	3·00
O50	8	1 r. violet and maroon	14·00	2·25
O51		2 r. brown and orange	14·00	17·00
O52	–	5 r. green and brown	14·00	18·00
O53	–	10 r. claret and violet	14·00	28·00
O41/53		*Set of* 13	85·00	70·00

Later stamp issues will be found listed in Part 21 (*South-East Asia*) of this catalogue.

JAPANESE OCCUPATION OF BURMA

PRICES FOR STAMPS ON COVER

Nos. J1/44	—
Nos. J45/72	*from* × 6
Nos. J73/94	*from* × 12
Nos. J95/101	—
Nos. J102/8	*from* × 25

BURMA INDEPENDENCE ARMY ADMINISTRATION

The Burma Independence Army, formed by Aung San in 1941, took control of the Delta area of the Irrawaddy in May 1942. They reopened a postal service in the area and were authorised by the Japanese to overprint local stocks of stamps with the Burmese emblem of a peacock.

Postage and Official stamps with the peacock overprints or handstamps were used for ordinary postal purposes with the probable exception of No. J44.

DISTINGUISHING FEATURES. Type **1**. Body and head of Peacock always clearly outlined by broad uncoloured band. There are four slightly different sub-types of overprint Type **1**.

Type **2**. Peacock with slender neck and more delicately detailed tail. Clear spur on leg at right. Heavy fist-shaped blob of ink below and parallel to beak and neck.

Type **4**. No basic curve. Each feather separately outlined. Straight, short legs.

Type **5**. Much fine detail in wings and tail in clearly printed overprints. Thin, long legs ending in claws which, with the basic arc, enclose clear white spaces in well-printed copies. Blob of colour below beak shows shaded detail and never has the heavy fist-like appearance of this portion in Type **2**.

Two sub-types may be distinguished in Type **5**, the basic arc of one having a chord of 14–15 mm and the other 12½–13 mm.

Type **6**. Similar to Type **5**, but with arc deeply curved and reaching nearly to the top of the wings. Single diagonal line parallel to neck below beak.

Collectors are warned against forgeries of these overprints, often in the wrong colours or on the wrong values.

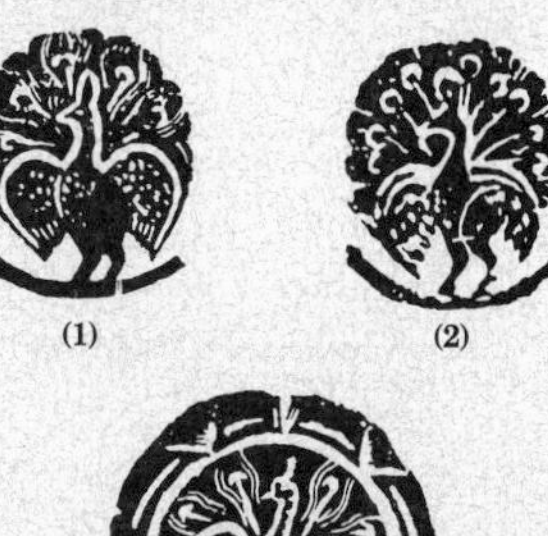

(1) (2)

(3)

1942 (May). *Stamps of Burma overprinted with the national device of a Peacock.*

I. *Overprinted at Myaungmya*

A. *With Type* **1** *in black*

On Postage Stamps of King George V

No.	Type	Description	Unused	Used
J 1		9 p. deep green (No. 3)	£100	
J 2		3½ a. deep blue (No. 8)	48·00	

On Official Stamp of King George V

No.	Type	Description	Unused	Used
J 3		6 a. bistre (No. O8)	70·00	

On Postage Stamps of King George VI

No.	Type	Description	Unused	Used
J 4	2	9 p. yellow-green	£150	
J 5	3	1 a. purple-brown	£475	
J 6		4 a. greenish blue (opt black on red)	£160	
		a. Triple opt, black on double red	£425	

On Official Stamps of King George VI

No.	Type	Description	Unused	Used
J 7	2	3 p. bright violet	20·00	70·00
J 8		6 p. bright blue	15·00	48·00
J 9	3	1 a. purple-brown	14·00	40·00
J 9*a*		1½ a. turquoise-green	£650	
J10		2 a. carmine	22·00	70·00
J11		4 a. greenish blue	20·00	60·00

The overprint on No. J6 was apparently first done in red in error, and then corrected in black. Some stamps have the black overprint so accurately superimposed that the red hardly shows. These are rare.

Nos. J5 and J9 exist with the Peacock overprint on both the typographed and the litho printings of the original stamps.

B. *With Types* **2** *or* **3** *(rupee values), in black*

On Postage Stamps of King George VI

No.	Type	Description	Unused	Used
J12	2	3 p. bright violet	17·00	60·00
J13		6 p. bright blue	45·00	80·00
J14		9 p. yellow-green	17·00	55·00
J15	3	1 a. purple-brown	14·00	48·00
J16		2 a. carmine	16·00	55·00
J17		4 a. greenish blue	32·00	80·00
		a. Opt double		
		b. Opt inverted	£500	
		c. Opt double, one inverted	£350	
		d. Opt double, both inverted	£500	
J18		1 r. purple and blue	£225	
J19		2 r. brown and purple	£140	

The Myaungmya overprints (including No. J44) are usually clearly printed.

(4)

(5)

(6)

Type **5** generally shows the details of the peacock much less clearly and, due to heavy inking, or careless impression, sometimes appears as almost solid colour.

Type **6** was officially applied only to postal stationery. However, the handstamp remained in the possession of a postal official who used it on postage stamps after the war. These stamps are no longer listed.

II. *Handstamped (at Pyapon?) with T* **4**, *in black (so-called experimental type)*

On Postage Stamps of King George VI

No.	Type	Description	Unused	Used
J19*a*	2	6 p. bright blue	£150	
J19*b*	3	1 a. purple-brown	95·00	
J20		2 a. carmine	£100	
J21		4 a. greenish blue	£650	£650

Unused specimens of these stamps are usually in poor condition.

III. *Overprinted at Henzada with T* **5** *in blue, or blue-black*

On Postage Stamps of King George V

No.	Type	Description	Unused	Used
J22		3 p. slate (No. 1)	3·00	17·00
		a. Opt double	10·00	48·00
J23		9 p. deep green (No. 3)	21·00	60·00
		a. Opt double	80·00	
J24		2 a. vermilion (No. 5)	£100	£180

On Postage Stamps of King George VI

J25 **2** 1 p. red-orange £180 £275
J26 3 p. bright violet .. .. 30·00 75·00
J27 6 p. bright blue .. .. 25·00 50·00
a. Opt double £100
b. Clear opt, on back and front .. £275
J28 9 p. yellow-green £650
J29 **3** 1 a. purple-brown .. .. .. 9·00 38·00
a. Opt inverted £400
J30 1½ a. turquoise-green .. .. .. 21·00 65·00
a. Opt omitted (in pair with normal) .. £1400
J31 2 a. carmine .. .. 21·00 65·00
J32 4 a. greenish blue .. .. .. 42·00 95·00
a. Opt double £250
b. Opt inverted £900

On Official Stamps of King George VI

J33 **2** 3 p. bright violet £100 £200
J34 6 p. bright blue £140 £200
J35 **3** 1½ a. turquoise-green £140 £200
J35*a* 2 a. carmine £325 £375
J36 4 a. greenish blue £900

(6*a*)

("Yon Thon" = "Office use")

V. *Official Stamp of King George VI optd at Myaungmya with Type 6a in black*

J44 **7** 8 a. myrtle-green .. .. .. 80·00

No. J44 was probably for official use.

There are two types of T 6*a*, one with base of peacock 8 mm long and the other with base about 5 mm long. The neck and other details also vary. The two types are found *se-tenant* in the sheet.

Stocks of the peacock types were withdrawn when the Japanese Directorate-General took control of the postal services in the Delta in August 1942.

JAPANESE ARMY ADMINISTRATION

7

8 Farmer

1942 (1 June). *Impressed by hand. Thick yellowish paper. P* 12 × 11. *No gum.*

J45 **7** (1 a.) red .. .. 38·00 65·00

This device was the personal seal of Yano Sitza, the Japanese official in charge of the Posts and Telegraphs department of the Japanese Army Administration. It was impressed on paper already perforated by a line machine. Some stamps show part of the papermaker's watermark, either "ABSORBO DUPLICATOR" or "ELEPHANT BRAND", each with an elephant.

Other impressions of this seal on different papers, and showing signs of wear, were not valid for postal purposes.

(Des T. Kato. Typo *Rangoon Gazette* Press)

1942 (15 June). *Value in annas. P* 11 *or* 11 × 11½. *Laid bâtonné paper. No gum.*

J46 **8** 1 a. scarlet .. .. 15·00 15·00

Some stamps show part of the papermaker's watermark, either "ELEPHANT BRAND" or "TITAGHUR SUPERFINE", each with an elephant.

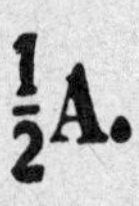

(9)

1R.

(10)

1942 (22 Sept). (*a*) *Nos.* 314/17, 320/2, 325, 327 *and* 396 *of Japan surch as T* **9**/**10**.

J47 **9** ¼ a. on 1 s. chestnut (Rice harvesting) 22·00 26·00
a. Surch inverted .. .. .. 95·00 95·00
b. Surch double, one inverted .. £140
J48 ½ a. on 2 s. bright scarlet (General Nogi) 22·00 26·00
a. Surch inverted .. .. .. 85·00 90·00
b. Surch double, one inverted .. £140
J49 ¾ a. on 3 s. green (Power station) .. 45·00 48·00
a. Surch inverted £110 £110
b. Surch double, one inverted .. — £160
J50 1 a. on 5 s. claret (Admiral Togo) .. 38·00 38·00
a. Surch inverted £140 £140
b. Surch double, one inverted .. £160 £160
c. Surch omitted (in pair with normal) — £190
J51 3 a. on 7 s. green (Diamond Mts) .. 75·00 85·00
a. Surch inverted £140
J52 4 a. on 4 s. emerald (Togo) .. .. 38·00 40·00
a. Surch inverted £140
J53 8 a. on 8 s. violet (Meiji Shrine) .. £140 £140
a. Surch inverted £200 £200
b. Surch double, one inverted .. £325
c. Surch in red £225 £250
d. Red surch inverted £325
e. Surch double (black and red) .. £500
J54 **10** 1 r. on 10 s. deep carmine (Yomei Gate) 15·00 24·00
a. Surch inverted .. .. .. 80·00 90·00
b. Surch double .. .. .. 80·00 £100
c. Surch double (black and red) .. £375
d. Surch omitted (in pair with normal) £180 £180
e. Surch omitted (in pair with inverted surch) £275
J55 **10** 2 r. on 20 s. ultramarine (Mt Fuji) .. 42·00 42·00
a. Surch inverted £110 £110
b. Surch double, one inverted .. £130
c. Surch omitted (in pair with normal black surch) £160 £160
d. Surch in red .. .. .. 40·00 40·00
e. Red surch inverted £110 £110
f. Red surch double £110 £110
g. Surch omitted (in pair with normal red surch) £200 £200
ga. Surch omitted (in pair with double red surch) .. .. ..
h. Surch double (black and red) .. £300
J56 **9** 5 r. on 30 s. turquoise (Torii Shrine) 12·00 27·00
a. Surch inverted .. .. .. 85·00
b. Surch double £110
c. Surch double, one inverted .. £150
d. Surch omitted (in pair with normal surch) £170 £170
e. Surch omitted (in pair with inverted black surch) £250
f. Surch in red .. .. .. 23·00 32·00
fa. Red surch inverted .. .. 90·00 90·00
fb. J56a and J56fa *se-tenant* .. £375 £375
fc. Surch omitted (in pair with normal red surch) £170 £170

(*b*) *No.* 386 *of Japan commemorating the fall of Singapore similarly surch*

J56*g* **9** 4 a. on 4 + 2 s. green and red .. £150 £160
h. Surch omitted (in pair with normal) £500
ha. Surch omitted (in pair with inverted surch) £550
i. Surch inverted £350

(New Currency. 100 cents = 1 rupee)

15C. 15C. 15C.

(11) (12) (13)

1942 (15 Oct). *Previous issues, with "anna" surcharges obliterated, handstamped with new value in cents, as T* **11** *and* **12** (*No. J57 handstamped with new value only*).

(*a*) *On No.* J46

J57 5 c. on 1 a. scarlet .. .. .. 11·00 15·00

(*b*) *On Nos.* J47/53

J58 1 c. on ¼ a. on 1 s. chestnut .. .. 40·00 40·00
a. "1 c." omitted (in pair with normal) .. £500
b. "¼ a." inverted £250
J59 2 c. on ½ a. on 2 s. bright scarlet .. 38·00 38·00
J60 3 c. on ¾ a. on 3 s. green .. .. 42·00 42·00
a. Surch in blue £160
J61 5 c. on 1 a. on 5 s. claret .. .. 65·00 65·00
J62 10 c. on 3 a. on 7 s. green .. .. £100 95·00
J63 15 c. on 4 a. on 4 s. emerald .. .. 28·00 30·00
J64 20 c. on 8 a. on 8 s. violet £325 £275
a. Surch on No. J53c (surch in red) .. £200 £140

The "anna" surcharges were obliterated by any means available, in some cases by a bar or bars, and in others by the butt of a pencil dipped in ink. In the case of the fractional surcharges, the letter "A" and one figure of the fraction, were sometimes barred out, leaving the remainder of the fraction to represent the new value, e.g. the "1" of "½" deleted to create the 2 c. surcharge or the "4" of "¾" to create the 3 c. surcharge.

1942. *Nos.* 314/17, 320/1 *and* 396 *of Japan surcharged in cents only as T* **13**.

J65 1 c. on 1 s. chestnut (Rice harvesting) .. 18·00 20·00
a. Surch inverted £110 £110
J66 2 c. on 2 s. brt scarlet (General Nogi) .. 35·00 32·00
J67 3 c. on 3 s. green (Power station) .. 38·00 38·00
a. Pair, with and without surch .. — £190
b. Surch inverted £120
c. Surch in blue .. .. .. 85·00 95·00
d. Surch in blue inverted £200 £225
J68 5 c. on 5 s. claret (Admiral Togo) .. 40·00 40·00
a. Pair, with and without surch .. £250
b. Surch in violet £130 £150
ba. Surch inverted .. .. .. — £225
J69 10 c. on 7 s. green (Diamond Mts) .. 48·00 50·00
J70 15 c. on 4 s. emerald (Togo) .. .. 14·00 20·00
a. Surch inverted £120 £130
b. Pair, with and without surch .. — £180
J71 20 c. on 8 s. violet (Meiji Shrine) .. £120 85·00
a. Surch double £250

Nos. J67c and J68b were issued for use in the Shan States.

BURMESE GOVERNMENT

On 1 November 1942 the Japanese Army Administration handed over the control of the postal department to the Burmese Government. On 1 August 1943 Burma was declared by the Japanese to be independent.

14 Burma State Crest

15 Farmer

(Des U Tun Tin and Maung Tin from drawing by U Ba Than. Typo Rangoon)

1943 (15 Feb). *P* 11. *No gum.*

J72 **14** 5 c. scarlet .. .. .. 14·00 18·00
a. Imperf .. .. 15·00 19·00
ab. Printed on both sides .. .. 80·00

No. J72 was usually sold affixed to envelopes, particularly those with the embossed 1 a. King George VI stamp, which it covered. Unused specimens off cover are not often seen and blocks are rare.

1943. *Typo. No gum. P* 11½.

J73 **15** 1 c. orange (22 March) .. .. 1·25 3·50
a. Brown-orange .. .. .. 70 3·75
J74 2 c. yellow-green (24 March) .. .. 60 1·00
a. "3" for "2" in face value (R.2/10) .. £150
b. Blue-green .. .. .. 7·00
J75 3 c. light blue (25 March) 80 85
a. On laid paper .. .. .. 18·00 25·00
b. Imperf between (horiz pair) .. — £250
J76 5 c. carmine (small "c") (17 March) .. 13·00 9·00
J77 5 c. carmine (large "C") .. .. 1·50 3·00
a. Imperf (pair) £160
b. "G" for "C" (R.2/6) £170
J78 10 c. grey-brown (25 March) .. .. 3·00 3·25
a. Imperf (pair) £160
b. Imperf between (horiz pair) .. — £250
J79 15 c. magenta (26 March) 30 90
a. Imperf between (vert strip of 3) ..
b. On laid paper .. .. .. 6·00 15·00
c. Inverted "C" in value (R.2/3) .. £120
J80 20 c. grey-lilac (29 March) 30 65
J81 30 c. deep blue-green (29 March) .. 30 70

The 1 c., 2 c. and 3 c. have large "C" in value as illustrated. The 10 c. and higher values have small "c". Nos. J73/81 had the face values inserted individually into the plate used for No. J46 with the original face value removed. There were a number of printings for each value, often showing differences such as missing stops, various founts of figures or "c", etc., in the value tablets.

The face value error, No. J74a, was later corrected.

Some sheets of No. J75a show a sheet watermark of Britannia seated within a crowned oval spread across fifteen stamps in each sheet. Examples showing part of this sheet watermark are rare.

No. J79a shows the horizontal perforations omitted between rows 3/4 and 4/5.

There are marked varieties of shade in this issue.

16 Soldier carving word "Independence"

17 Rejoicing Peasant

18 Boy with National Flag

Normal

Skyline flaw (R. 5/6)

(Des Maung Ba Thit (**16**), Naung Ohn Maung (**17**), and Maung Sc Yi (**18**). Typo State Press, Rangoon)

1943 (1 Aug). *Independence Day.* (*a*) *P* 11.

J82 **16** 1 c. orange .. .. 7·00 12·0
J83 **17** 3 c. light blue .. .. 7·50 13·0
J84 **18** 5 c. carmine .. .. 14·00 8·0
a. Skyline flaw .. .. .. 60·00
J82/4 .. .. *Set of* 3 26·00 30·0

(*b*) *Rouletted*

J85 **16** 1 c. orange .. .. 1·00 1·5
b. Perf×roul .. .. 90·00 90·0
c. Imperf (pair) .. .. .. 45·00 55·0
J86 **17** 3 c. light blue .. .. 1·00 1·5
b. Perf×roul .. .. 85·00 85·0
c. Imperf (pair) .. .. .. 45·00 55·0
J87 **18** 5 c. carmine .. .. 1·00 1·5
a. Horiz roulette omitted (vert pair) ..
b. Perf×roul .. .. 55·00 55·0
c. Imperf (pair) .. .. .. 45·00 55·0
d. Skyline flaw .. .. .. 7·00
J85/7 .. .. *Set of* 3 2·75 4·0

The stamps perf × rouletted may have one, two or three side perforated.

The rouletted stamps often appear to be roughly perforat owing to failure to make clean cuts. These apparent perforation are very small and quite unlike the large, clean holes of the stam perforated 11.

A few imperforate sets, mounted on a special card folder ar cancelled with the commemorative postmark were presented officials. These are rare.

19 Burmese Woman

20 Elephant carrying Log

21 Watch Towe Mandalay

(Litho G. Kolff & Co, Batavia)

1943 (1 Oct). *P* 12½.

J88	**19**	1 c. red-orange	20·00	15·00
J89		2 c. yellow-green	50	2·00
J90		3 c. deep violet	50	2·25
		a. Bright violet	70	2·50
J91	**20**	5 c. carmine	55	60
J92		10 c. blue	65	95
J93		15 c. red-orange	65	2·00
J94		20 c. yellow-green	65	1·75
J95		30 c. olive-brown	65	1·75
J96	**21**	1 r. red-orange	30	2·00
J97		2 r. bright violet	30	2·25
J88/97		.. .. *Set of* 10	22·00	27·00

22 Bullock Cart

23 Shan Woman

ဗမာနိုင်ငံတော်

၂၀ ဆင့်။

(**24** "Burma State" and value)

(Litho G. Kolff & Co, Batavia)

1943 (1 Oct). *Issue for Shan States. P* 12½.

98	**22**	1 c. olive-brown	22·00	28·00
99		2 c. yellow-green	20·00	30·00
100		3 c. bright violet	2·75	10·00
101		5 c. ultramarine	2·00	5·50
102	**23**	10 c. blue	8·00	17·00
103		20 c. carmine	22·00	17·00
104		30 c. olive-brown	14·00	30·00
98/104		.. .. *Set of* 7	80·00	£120

The Shan States, except for the frontier area around Keng Tung which was ceded to Thailand, were placed under the administration of the Burmese Government on 24 December 1943, and these stamps were later overprinted as T **24** for use throughout Burma.

1944 (1 Nov). *Optd as T* **24** (*the lower characters differ for each value*).

J105	**22**	1 c. olive-brown	2·50	6·00
J106		2 c. yellow-green	40	1·50
		a. Opt inverted	£325	£550
J107		3 c. bright violet	1·50	7·00
J108		5 c. ultramarine	80	1·00
J109	**23**	10 c. blue	1·75	2·00
J110		20 c. carmine	40	1·50
J111		30 c. olive-brown	40	1·75
J105/11		.. .. *Set of* 7	7·00	18·00

The British 14th Army recaptured Mandalay on 20 March 1945 and Rangoon on 6 May.

Bushire

BRITISH OCCUPATION

(Currency. 20 chahis = 1 kran; 10 kran = 1 toman)

Bushire, a seaport town of Persia, was occupied by the British on 8 August 1915. The Persian postal authorities resumed control on 18 October 1915. British forces returned to Bushire during 1916, but mail from this period was carried by Indian Army F.P.O. No. 319.

PRICES FOR STAMPS ON COVER

Nos. 1/29 *from* × 5

Types of Iran (Persia) overprinted

57

66

67

68

BUSHIRE
Under British
Occupation.

(1)

1915 (15 Aug). *Nos.* 361/3, 365, 367/70, 372, 374/6 *and* 378/9 *of Iran optd with T* **1** *at the British Residency.*

1	**57**	1 ch. orange and green	28·00	32·00
		a. No stop	75·00	85·00
2		2 ch. sepia and carmine	28·00	26·00
		a. No stop	75·00	75·00
3		3 ch. green and grey	35·00	42·00
		a. No stop	95·00	£120
4		5 ch. carmine and brown	£250	£250
5		6 ch. brown-lake and green	27·00	21·00
		a. No stop	75·00	70·00
6		9 ch. indigo-lilac and brown	28·00	32·00
		a. No stop	85·00	90·00
		b. Opt double		
7		10 ch. brown and carmine	30·00	30·00
		a. No stop	90·00	90·00
8		12 ch. blue and green	38·00	42·00
		a. No stop	£110	£130
9		24 ch. green and purple	55·00	42·00
		a. No stop	£160	£130
10		1 kr. carmine and blue	55·00	26·00
		a. Double overprint	£5000	
		b. No stop	£160	80·00
11		2 kr. claret and green	£170	£120
		a. No stop	£450	£325
12		3 kr. black and lilac	£150	£150
		a. No stop	£400	£400
13		5 kr. blue and red	90·00	80·00
		a. No stop	£275	£250
14		10 kr. rose and bistre-brown	80·00	75·00
		a. No stop	£250	£225

Nos. 1/3 and 5/14 were overprinted in horizontal strips of 10 and No. 4 in horizontal strips of 5. Eight different settings are recognized, with the "No stop" variety occurring on stamp 9 from the four settings with 3 mm between "Under" and "British" and on stamp 10 from one setting where the gap is 2 mm.

1915 (Sept). *Nos.* 426/40 *and* 441 *of Iran optd with T* **1**.

15	**66**	1 ch. deep blue and carmine	£300	£300
16		2 ch. carmine and deep blue	£5000	£5500
17		3 ch. deep green	£375	£400
18		5 ch. vermilion	£3750	£4000
19		6 ch. carmine and green	£3000	£3250
20		9 ch. deep violet and brown	£475	£500
21		10 ch. brown and deep green	£800	£850
22		12 ch. ultramarine	£900	£1000
23		24 ch. sepia and brown	£375	£400
24	**67**	1 kr. black, brown and silver	£350	£375
25		2 kr. carmine, slate and silver	£300	£325
26		3 kr. sepia, dull lilac and silver	£425	£450
27		5 kr. slate, sepia and silver	£400	£425
		a. Opt inverted	—	£9000
28	**68**	1 t. black, violet and gold	£350	£400
29		3 t. red, crimson and gold	£2250	£2500

Nos. 15/29 were overprinted in strips of 5

Examples of overprint Type **1** on Iran No. 414, 1 ch. on 5 ch. (previously No. 30), are now believed to be forged.

Cameroon

I. CAMEROONS EXPEDITIONARY FORCE

Allied operations against the German protectorate of Kamerun commenced in September 1914 and were completed on 18 February 1916. The territory was divided, under an Anglo-French agreement, on 31 March 1916 with the British administering the area in the west along the Nigerian border. League of Nations mandates were issued for the two sections of Cameroon, which were converted into United Nations trusteeships in 1946.

Supplies of Kamerun stamps were found on the German steamer *Professor Woermann* captured at Freetown and these were surcharged, probably in Sierra Leone, and issued by the Cameroons Expeditionary Force at Duala in July 1915.

A French Post Office opened in Duala on 10 November 1915 using stamps of Gabon overprinted "Corps Expeditionnaire Franco-Anglais Cameroun". Although under the overall control of the British combined force commander this office remained part of the French postal system.

PRICES FOR STAMPS ON COVER

The stamps of British Occupation of Cameroons are rare used on cover.

A

B

C. E. F.

1d.

(1)

C. E. F.

1s.

(2)

SETTINGS. Nos. B1/3 were surcharged from a setting of 100 (10×10) with the face value changed for the 1d.

Nos. B4 and B6/9 were surcharged from a common setting of 50 (5×10) with the face value amended.

No. B5 was surcharged from a setting of 10 in a vertical strip repeated across the sheet. The figures of the surcharge on this value are in a different style from the remainder of the pence stamps.

Nos. B10/13 were surcharged from a common setting of 20 (4×5) with the face value amended.

Different fount "d" (R. 1/10, 6/9, 10/10)

"1" with thin serifs (R. 5/1)

Large "3" (R. 3/5, 3/10)

Short "4" (R. 10/2, 10/7)

"s" inverted (R. 3/4)

5s

"s" broken at top (R. 3/1)

1915 (12 July). *Stamps of German Kamerun. Types* A *and* B, *surch as T* **1** (*Nos.* B1/9) *or* **2** (*Nos.* B10/13) *in black or blue.*

B1	A	½d. on 3 pf. (No. K7) (B.)	10·00	23·00
		a. Different fount "d"	90·00	£180
B2		½d. on 5 pf. (No. K21 *wmk lozenges*) (B.)	1·75	8·00
		a. Different fount "d"	24·00	70·00
		b. Surch double	—	£650
		ba. Surch double, one albino	£170	
B3		1d. on 10 pf. (No. K22 *wmk lozenges*) (B.)	1·25	8·00
		a. "1" with thin serifs	12·00	60·00
		b. Surch double	£225	
		ba. Surch double, one albino	85·00	
		c. "1d." only double	£1700	
		d. Surch triple, two albino	£190	
		e. Surch in black	14·00	55·00
		ea. "1" with thin serifs	£140	
		eb. "C.E.F." omitted	£2500	
B4		2d. on 20 pf. (No. K23 *wmk lozenges*)	3·50	17·00
		a. Surch double, one albino	£180	
B5		2½d. on 25 pf. (No. K11)	12·00	35·00
		a. Surch double	£6500	
		ab. Surch double, one albino		
B6		3d. on 30 pf. (No. K12)	12·00	35·00
		a. Large "3"	£650	
		b. Surch triple, two albino	£190	
B7		4d. on 40 pf. (No. K13)	12·00	35·00
		a. Short "4"	£475	£750
		b. Surch triple, two albino	£180	
		c. Surch quadruple, three albino ..	£1500	
B8		6d. on 50 pf. (No. K14)	12·00	35·00
		a. Surch double, one albino	£170	
B9		8d. on 80 pf. (No. K15)	12·00	35·00
B10	B	1s. on 1 m. (No. K16)	£140	£500
		a. "s" inverted	£600	£1800
B11		2s. on 2 m. (No. K17)	£140	£500
		a. "s" inverted	£600	£1800
		b. Surch double, one albino	£1000	
B12		3s. on 3 m. (No. K18)	£140	£500
		a. "s" inverted	£600	£1800
		b. "s" broken at top	£425	
		c. Surch double	£6000	
		ca. Surch double, one albino	£1000	
B13		5s. on 5 m. (No. K25a *wmk lozenges*)	£170	£550
		a. "s" inverted	£700	£1900
		b. "s" broken at top	£475	
B1/13		.. .. *Set of* 13	£600	£2000

Examples of all values exist showing a forged Duala Kamerun postmark dated "11 10 15". Another forged cancel dated "16 11 15" is also known. This can be identified by the lack of a serif on the index letter "b".

The stamps of Nigeria were subsequently used in British Cameroons and the area was administered as part of Nigeria from February 1924.

For issues of Cameroun under French administration see *Part 6 (France)* and for the Cameroun Republic (1960–1995) *Part 12 (Africa since Independence A to E).*

II. CAMEROONS TRUST TERRITORY

Following the independence of the French Trust Territory of Cameroun on 1 January 1960 the United Nations directed that a plebiscite should be held in the British Trust Territory. The northern area voted to join Nigeria, but the southern part of the territory decided to join the Cameroun Republic.

The following issue, although ordered by the Southern Cameroons authorities, was also on sale in Northern Cameroons, until the latter joined Nigeria on 1 June 1961. The stamps therefore can be found with Nigerian postmarks.

CAMEROONS
U.K.T.T.

(1)

1960 (1 Oct)–**61.** *Nos.* 69/71, 72*ca*/*cc and* 73/80 *of Nigeria optd with T* **1**, *in red.*

T 1	**18**	½d. black and orange	10	80
T 2	–	1d. black and bronze-green	10	50
		a. Grey-black and dull bronze-green (19.9.61)	60	1·50
T 3	–	1½d. blue-green	10	20
T 4	**21**	2d. grey (Type B)	10	40
		a. Slate-blue (Type A)	£800	£250
		b. Bluish grey (Type B)	45·00	14·00
		c. Pale grey (Type B) (19.9.61) ..	10	30
T 5	–	3d. black and deep lilac	15	10
T 6	–	4d. black and blue	10	80
T 7	**24**	6d. orange-brown and black (*p* 14) ..	30	10
		a. Perf 13×13½ (19.9.61)	20	1·75
T 8	–	1s. black and maroon	15	10
T 9	**26**	2s. 6d. black and green	1·10	80

T10	–	5s. black and red-orange	1·60	3·50
T11	–	10s. black and red-brown	2·50	5·00
T12	**29**	£1 black and violet	8·50	16·00
T1/12		*Set of* 12	13·00	25·00

Nos. T2 and T4/*b* were overprinted on stamps printed by Waterlows' subsidiary, Imprimerie Belge de Securité.

Nos. T2*a*, T4*c* and T7a were from new printings produced by De La Rue instead of Waterlow.

The above stamps were withdrawn on 30 September 1961, when Southern Cameroons became part of the Cameroun Republic.

III. REPUBLIC OF CAMEROON

COMMONWEALTH MEMBER

1 November 1995

The Republic of Cameroon joined the Commonwealth on 1 November 1995 and issues from that date will be listed below when details and examples are received.

Canada

Separate stamp issues appeared for British Columbia and /ancouver Island, Canada, New Brunswick, Newfoundland, Nova Scotia and Prince Edward Island before these colonies joined the Dominion of Canada.

BRITISH COLUMBIA & VANCOUVER ISLAND

Vancouver Island was organised as a Crown Colony in 1849 nd the mainland territory was proclaimed a separate colony as ritish Columbia, in 1858. The two colonies combined, as British olumbia, on 19 November 1866.

PRICES FOR STAMPS ON COVER

Nos. 2/3	*from* × 6
Nos. 11/12	*from* × 2
Nos. 13/14	*from* × 6
Nos. 21/2	*from* × 10
Nos. 23/7	*from* × 6
Nos. 28/9	*from* × 10
No. 30	—
No. 31	*from* × 10
Nos. 32/3	—

1

(Typo D.L.R.)

860. *No wmk. P* 14.
1 2½d. deep reddish rose £275 £180
2½d. pale reddish rose £275 £180

When Vancouver Island adopted the dollar currency in 1862 he 2½d. was sold at 5 c. From 18 May until 1 November 1865 xamples of Nos. 2/3 were used to prepay mail from Vancouver sland to British Columbia at the price of 15 cents a pair.

From 20 June 1864 to 1 November 1865, the 2½d. was sold in British Columbia for 3d. and was subsequently used for the ame purpose during a shortage of 3d. stamps in 1867.

Imperforate plate proofs exist in pale dull red (*Price* £2500 *un*)

VANCOUVER ISLAND

(New Currency. 100 cents = 1 dollar)

2 3

(Typo D.L.R.)

865 (19 Sept). *Wmk Crown CC. (a) Imperf* (1866)
1 2 5 c. rose £20000 £8000
2 3 10 c. blue £1400 £850

(*b*) *P* 14
3 2 5 c. rose £225 £140
4 3 10 c. blue £200 £140

Medium or poor copies of Nos. 11 and 12 can be supplied at much ower prices, when in stock.

After the two colonies combined Nos. 13/14 were also used in British Columbia.

BRITISH COLUMBIA

4

(Typo D.L.R.)

865 (1 Nov)–67. *Wmk Crown CC. P* 14.
1 4 3d. deep blue .. .. 75·00 60·00
2 3d. pale blue (19.7.67) .. .. 75·00 60·00

British Columbia changed to the dollar currency on 1 January 866. Remaining stocks of No. 21 and the supply of No. 22, when finally arrived, were sold at 12½ c. a pair.

(New Currency. 100 cents = 1 dollar)

TWO CENTS (5) **5.CENTS.5** (6)

868–71. *T* 4 *in various colours. Wmk Crown CC. Surch as T* 5 *or* 6. (*a*) *P* 12½ (3.69)
3 5 c. red (Bk.) £600 £550
4 10 c. lake (B.) £450 £425
5 25 c. yellow (V.) £350 £350
6 50 c. mauve (R.) £425 £375
7 $1 green (G.) £650 £700

(*b*) *P* 14
28 2 c. brown (Bk.) (1.68) .. .. .. 90·00 90·00
29 5 c. pale red (Bk.) (5.69) £120 £120
30 10 c. lake (B.) £650
31 25 c. yellow (V.) (21.7.69) £120 £120
32 50 c. mauve (R.) (23.2.71) £400 £750
33 $1 green (G.) £600

Nos. 30 and 33 were not issued.

British Columbia joined the Dominion of Canada on 20 July 1871.

COLONY OF CANADA

The first British post offices in what was to become the colony of Canada were opened at Quebec, Montreal and Trois Rivières during 1763. These, and subsequent, offices remained part of the British G.P.O. system until 6 April 1851.

The two provinces of Upper Canada (Ontario) and Lower Canada (Quebec) were united in 1840.

For illustration of the handstamp types see BRITISH POST OFFICES ABROAD notes, following GREAT BRITAIN.

NEW CARLISLE, GASPÉ

POSTMASTER'S PROVISIONAL ENVELOPE

1

1851 (7 April).
1 1 3d. black .. ..

Only one example is known, with the impression cancelled by the signature of the postmaster, R. W. Kelly.

QUEBEC

CROWNED-CIRCLE HANDSTAMPS

CC1 CC 1*b* QUEBEC L.C. (R.) (13.1.1842) *Price on cover* £150

PRICES FOR STAMPS ON COVER

Nos. 1/23	*from* × 2
Nos. 25/8	*from* × 3
Nos. 29/43*a*	*from* × 3
Nos. 44/5	*from* × 8

1 American Beaver (Designed by Sir Sandford Fleming)

2 Prince Albert

3

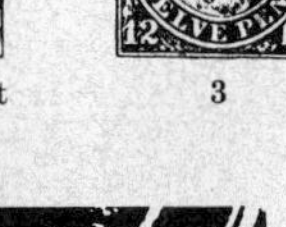

Major re-entry: Line though "EE PEN" (Upper pane R. 5/7)

(T 1/6. Eng and recess Rawdon, Wright, Hatch and Edson, New York)

1851. *Imperf. Laid paper.*
1 1 3d. red (23 April) £11000 £650
1*a* 3d. orange-vermilion £11000 £650
b. Major re-entry .. .. .. — £1600
2 2 6d. slate-violet (15 May) £14000 £900
3 6d. brown-purple £15000 £1200
a. Bisected (3d.) on cover .. .. † £20000
4 3 12d. black (14 June) £60000 £40000

There are several re-entries on the plate of the 3d. in addition to the major re-entry listed. All re-entries occur in this stamp on all papers.

Forgeries of the 3d. are known without the full stop after "PENCE". They also omit the foliage in the corners, as do similar forgeries of the 6d.

4

5

6 Jacques Cartier

1852–57. *Imperf.*

A. *Handmade wove paper, varying in thickness* (1852–56)
5 1 3d. red £1100 £160
a. Bisected (1½d.) on cover (1856) .. † £22000
6 3d. deep red £1200 £160
7 3d. scarlet-vermilion £1500 £170
8 3d. brown-red £1200 £160
a. Bisected (1½d.) on cover (1856) .. † —
b. Major re-entry (*all shades*) *from* £2500 £650
9 2 6d. slate-violet £12000 £950
a. Bisected (3d.) on cover .. .. † £12000
10 6d. greenish grey £12000 £950
11 6d. brownish grey £13000 £1100
12 5 7½d. yellow-green (*shades*) (2.6.57) .. £7000 £1500
13 6 10d. bright blue (1.55) £7000 £1200
14 10d. dull blue £6500 £1100
15 10d. blue *to* deep blue £7000 £1200
a. Major re-entry (*all shades*) *from* — £2000
16 3 12d. black .. .. — £45000

B. *Machine-made medium to thick wove paper of a more even hard texture with more visible mesh. Clearer impressions* (1857)
17 4 ½d. deep rose (1.8.57) £700 £400
18 1 3d. red £1600 £450
a. Bisected (1½d.) on cover .. .. † £20000
b. Major re-entry .. .. .. — £1200
19 2 6d. grey-lilac £14000 £2000
20 6 10d. blue *to* deep blue £7000 £2000
a. Major re-entry £11000 £2500

C. *Thin soft horizontally ribbed paper* (1857)
21 4 ½d. deep rose £5500 £1600
a. Vertically ribbed paper £6000 £2250
22 1 3d. red £3000 £400
a. Major re-entry .. .. .. — £1100

D. *Very thick soft wove paper* (1857)
23 2 6d. reddish purple £14000 £2500
a. Bisected (3d.) on cover .. .. † £18000

Bisected examples of the 3d. value were used to make up the 7½d. Canadian Packet rate to England from May 1856 until the introduction of the 7½d. value on 2 June 1857.

The 7½d. and 10d. values can be found in wide and narrow versions. These differences are due to shrinkage of the paper, which was wetted before printing and then contracted unevenly during drying. The width of these stamps varies between 17 and 18 mm.

The listed major re-entry on the 10d. occurs on R.3/5 and shows strong doubling of the top frame line and the left-hand "8d. stg." with a line through the lower parts of "ANAD" and "ENCE". Smaller re-entries occur on all values.

Examples of the 12d. on wove paper come from a proof sheet used for postal purposes by the postal authorities.

The 3d. is known perforated 14 and also *percé en scie* 13. Both are contemporary, but were unofficial.

1858–59. *P* 11¾. A. *Machine-made medium to thick wove paper with a more even hard texture.*
25 4 ½d. deep rose (12.58) £1700 £600
a. Lilac-rose £1900 £650
26 1 3d. red (1.59) £2500 £300
a. Major re-entry .. .. .. — £1000
27 2 6d. brownish grey (1.59) £6500 £2500
a. Slate-violet £6500 £2250

B. *Thin soft horizontally ribbed paper*
27*b* 4 ½d. deep rose-red .. .. .. — £3250
28 1 3d. red .. .. — £1200
a. Major re-entry .. .. ..

(New Currency. 100 cents = 1 dollar)

7

8 American Beaver

9 Prince Albert

10

11 Jacques Cartier

(Recess A.B.N. Co)

(On 1 May 1858, Messrs. Rawdon, Wright, Hatch and Edson joined with eight other firms to form "The American Bank Note Co" and the "imprint" on sheets of the following stamps has the new title of the firm with "New York" added.)

1859 (1 July). *P* 12.
29 7 1 c. pale rose (to rose-red) .. .. £225 24·00
30 1 c. deep rose (to carmine-rose) .. £300 42·00
a. Imperf (pair) £2500
b. Imperf × perf
31 8 5 c. pale red .. .. .. £250 11·00
32 5 c. deep red .. .. .. £250 11·00
a. Re-entry* (R.3/8) £2500 £450
b. Imperf (pair) £7000
c. Bisected (2½ c.) with 10 c. on cover † £4000
33 9 10 c. black-brown £6000 £1300
a. Bisected (5 c.), on cover .. .. † £5500
33*b* 10 c. deep red-purple £2500 £500
ba. Bisected (5 c.), on cover .. .. † £3750
34 10 c. purple (*shades*) .. .. £750 40·00
a. Bisected (5 c.), on cover .. .. † £3750
35 10 c. brownish purple .. .. £700 40·00
36 10 c. brown (to pale) .. .. £700 40·00
a. Bisected (5 c.), on cover .. .. † £4500
37 10 c. dull violet .. .. .. £750 45·00
38 10 c. bright red-purple .. .. £750 40·00
a. Imperf (pair) £6000
39 10 12½ c. deep yellow-green .. .. £600 38·00
40 12½ c. pale yellow-green .. .. £550 38·00
41 12½ c. blue-green .. .. .. £650 45·00
a. Imperf (pair) £2500
b. Imperf between (vert pair) ..

2 **11** 17 c. deep blue .. .. £700 60·00
a. Imperf (pair) £3000
3 17 c. slate-blue .. .. £850 90·00
3*a* 17 c. indigo .. .. £750 65·00
b. Imperf (pair) £3000

*The price of No. 32a is for the very marked re-entry showing val frame line doubled above "CANADA". Slighter re-entries are orth from £30 upwards in used condition.

As there were numerous P.O. Dept. orders for the 10 c., 12½ c. nd 17 c. and some of these were executed by more than one eparate printing, with no special care to ensure uniformity of olour, there is a wide range of shade, especially in the 10 c., and ome shades recur at intervals after periods during which other hades predominated. The colour-names given in the above list herefore represent groups only.

It has been proved by leading Canadian specialists that the erforations may be an aid to the approximate dating of a articular stamp, the gauge used measuring 11¾ × 11¾ from id-July, 1859 to mid 1863, 12 × 11¾ from March 1863 to mid 865 and 12 × 12 from April 1865 to 1868. Exceptionally in the c. value many sheets were perforated 12 × 12 between May and ctober, 1862, whilst the last printings of the 12½ c. and 17 c. perf 1¾ × 11¾ were in July 1863, the perf 12 × 11¾ starting towards ne end of 1863.

12

(Recess A.B.N. Co)

864 (1 Aug). *P* 12.
4 **12** 2 c. rose-red £400 £140
5 2 c. bright rose £400 £140
a. Imperf (pair) £1600

The Colony of Canada became part of the Dominion of Canada n 1 July 1867.

NEW BRUNSWICK

New Brunswick, previously part of Nova Scotia, became a eparate colony in June 1784.

PRICES FOR STAMPS ON COVER

Nos. 1/4	*from* × 2
Nos. 5/6	*from* × 3
Nos. 7/9	*from* × 10
Nos. 10/12	*from* × 30
No. 13	—
Nos. 14/17	*from* × 2
No. 18	*from* × 5
No. 19	*from* × 100

1 Royal Crown and Heraldic Flowers of the United Kingdom

(Recess P.B.)

851 (5 Sept). *Blue paper. Imperf.*
1 3d. bright red £1600 £325
3d. dull red £1800 £325
a. Bisected (1½d.) (on cover) .. .. † £2750
b 6d. mustard-yellow £6000 £1500
6d. yellow £4500 £800
6d. olive-yellow £4500 £700
a. Bisected (3d.) (on cover) .. .. † £3000
b. Quartered (1½d.) (on cover) .. † £20000
1s. reddish mauve £13000 £4000
1s. dull mauve £14000 £4500
a. Bisected (6d.) (on cover) .. .. † £20000
b. Quartered (3d.) (on cover) .. .. † £20000

Reprints of all three values were made in 1890 on thin, hard, hite paper. The 3d. is bright orange, the 6d. and 1s. violet-black.

Nos. 2a and 4b were to make up the 7½d. rate to Great ritain, introduced on 1 August 1854.

(New Currency. 100 cents = 1 dollar)

2 Locomotive

3

3*a* Charles Connell

4

5

6 Paddle-steamer *Washington*

7 King Edward VII when Prince of Wales

(Recess A.B.N. Co)

1860 (15 May)–**63**. *No wmk. P* 12.
7 **2** 1 c. brown-purple .. .. .. 50·00 38·00
8 1 c. purple .. .. 30·00 30·00
9 1 c. dull claret .. .. 30·00 30·00
a. Imperf vert (horiz pair) £500
10 **3** 2 c. orange (1863) .. .. .. 14·00 14·00
11 2 c. orange-yellow .. .. .. 15·00 14·00
12 2 c. deep orange .. .. .. 18·00 14·00
a. Imperf horiz (vert pair) £450
13 **3*a*** 5 c. brown £4000
14 **4** 5 c. yellow-green .. .. .. 12·00 12·00
15 5 c. deep green .. .. 12·00 12·00
16 5 c. sap-green (deep yellowish green) .. £300 40·00
17 **5** 10 c. red .. .. 35·00 35·00
a. Bisected (5 c.) (on cover) (1860) .. † £600
18 **6** 12½ c. indigo .. .. 50·00 40·00
19 **7** 17 c. black .. .. 32·00 40·00
Beware of forged cancellations.

New Brunswick joined the Dominion of Canada on 1 July 1867 and its stamps were withdrawn in March of the following year.

NEWFOUNDLAND

Newfoundland became a self-governing colony in 1855 and a Dominion in 1917. In 1934 the adverse financial situation led to the suspension of the constitution.

The first local postmaster, at St. John's, was appointed in 1805, the overseas mails being routed via Halifax, Nova Scotia. A regular packet service was established between these two ports in 1840, the British G.P.O. assuming control of the overseas mails at the same time.

The responsibility for the overseas postal service reverted to the colonial administration on 1 July 1851.

For illustrations of the handstamp types see BRITISH POST OFFICES ABROAD notes, following GREAT BRITAIN.

ST. JOHN'S

CROWNED-CIRCLE HANDSTAMPS

CC1 **CC 1a** ST. JOHNS NEWFOUNDLAND (R.) (27.6.1846) .. .. *Price on cover* £900

PRICES FOR STAMPS ON COVER TO 1945

No. 1	*from* × 30
Nos. 2/4	*from* × 3
No. 5	*from* × 20
No. 6	*from* × 10
No. 7	*from* × 3
No. 8	*from* × 30
No. 9	*from* × 8
No. 10	—
No. 11	*from* × 8
No. 12	*from* × 3
Nos. 13/14	*from* × 20
No. 15	—
Nos. 16/19	*from* × 15
No. 20	—
Nos. 21/4*c*	*from* × 15
Nos. 24*d*/*e*	—
No. 25	*from* × 30
No. 26	*from* × 5
No. 27	*from* × 8
No. 28	*from* × 3
Nos. 29/30	*from* × 10
No. 31	*from* × 30
No. 32	*from* × 8
No. 33	*from* × 5
No. 33*a*	—
Nos. 34/9	*from* × 8
Nos. 40/1	*from* × 5
Nos. 42/3	*from* × 30
Nos. 44/8	*from* × 8
No. 49	*from* × 50
Nos. 50/3	*from* × 10
No. 54	*from* × 4
Nos. 55/8*b*	*from* × 10
No. 59	*from* × 100
No. 59*a*	*from* × 10
Nos. 60/1	*from* × 4
Nos. 62/5	*from* × 8
Nos. 65*a*/79	*from* × 3
Nos. 83/90	*from* × 10
Nos. 91/3	*from* × 2
No. 94	*from* × 50
Nos. 95/141	*from* × 3
Nos. 142/3	—
Nos. 144/8*f*	*from* × 2
Nos. 149/62	*from* × 3
No. 163	—
Nos. 164/78	*from* × 2
Nos. 179/90	*from* × 3
No. 191	—
Nos. 192/220	*from* × 2
No. 221	—
Nos. 222/9	*from* × 3
Nos. 230/4	*from* × 2
No. 235	—
Nos. 236/91	*from* × 2
Nos. D1/6	*from* × 10

1

2

4

3

5

Royal Crown and Heraldic flowers of the United Kingdom

(Recess P.B.)

1857 (1 Jan–15 Feb). *No wmk. Thick, machine-made paper with a distinct mesh. Imperf.*
1 **1** 1d. brown-purple .. .. .. 85·00 £140
a. Bisected (½d.) (on cover) .. .. † £12000
2 **2** 2d. scarlet-vermilion (15 Feb) £9000 £4500
3 **3** 3d. yellowish green £700 £400
4 **4** 4d. scarlet-vermilion £6000 £2500
a. Bisected (2d.) (on cover) .. .. † £16000
5 **1** 5d. brown-purple £180 £350
6 **4** 6d. scarlet-vermilion £12000 £3000
7 **5** 6½d. scarlet-vermilion £2250 £2500
8 **4** 8d. scarlet-vermilion £225 £300
a. Bisected (4d.) (on cover) .. .. † £3500
9 **2** 1s. scarlet-vermilion £13000 £4750
a. Bisected (6d.) (on cover) .. .. † £12000

The 6d. and 8d. differ from the 4d. in many details, as does also the 1s. from the 2d.

1860 (15 Aug). *Medium, hand-made paper without mesh. Imperf.*
10 **2** 2d. orange-vermilion £300 £375
11 **3** 3d. green *to* deep green* .. .. 65·00 £150
12 **4** 4d. orange-vermilion £2250 £800
a. Bisected (2d.) (on cover) .. .. † £13000
13 **1** 5d. Venetian red .. .. .. 90·00 £275
14 **4** 6d. orange-vermilion £2750 £600
15 **2** 1s. orange-vermilion £19000 £8000
a. Bisected (6d.) (on cover) .. .. † £40000

*No. 11 includes stamps from the November 1861 printing which are very difficult to distinguish.

The 1s. on horizontally or vertically *laid* paper is now considered to be a proof (*Price* £10000).

Stamps of this and the following issue may be found with part of the paper-maker's watermark "STACEY WISE 1858".

BISECTS. Collectors are warned against buying bisected stamps of these issues without a reliable guarantee.

1861. *New colours. Imperf.* (*a*) *1st printing. Soft, hand-made paper without mesh* (July).
16 **2** 2d. deep rose-lake £190 £500
17 **4** 4d. deep rose-lake £100 £180
a. Bisected (2d.) (on cover) .. ..
18 6d. deep rose-lake £100 £190
a. Bisected (3d.) (on cover) .. .. † £9000
19 **5** 6½d. deep rose-lake £225 £700
20 **2** 1s. deep rose-lake £225 £650
a. Bisected (6d.) (on cover) .. .. † £14000

(*b*) *2nd printing. Hard, hand-made paper without mesh* (Nov)
21 **1** 1d. chocolate-brown £150 £225
a. Red-brown £4000
22 **2** 2d. pale rose-lake £150 £375
23 **4** 4d. pale rose-lake .. .. .. 26·00 90·00
24 **1** 5d. chocolate-brown .. .. .. 55·00 £300
a. Red-brown .. .. .. 45·00 £190
24*b* **4** 6d. pale rose-lake .. .. .. 20·00 £100
24*c* **5** 6½d. pale rose-lake .. .. .. 65·00 £425
24*d* **4** 8d. pale rose-lake .. .. .. 70·00 £475
24*e* **2** 1s. pale rose-lake .. .. .. 35·00 £300

Stamps of the second printing of the pale rose-lake shades have a more transparent look due to the paper being generally thinner, but paper thickness alone is not a sure test for distinguishing the printings.

Beware of buying used specimens of the stamps which are worth much less in unused condition, as many unused stamps have been provided with faked postmarks. A guarantee should be obtained.

(New Currency. 100 cents = 1 dollar)

6 Atlantic Cod

7 Common Seal on Ice-floe

8 Prince Consort

9 Queen Victoria

10 Schooner

11 Queen Victoria

(Recess A.B.N. Co, New York)

1865 (15 Nov)–**71.** *P* 12. (*a*) *Thin yellowish paper.*

No.	Type	Description	Unused	Used
25	**6**	2 c. yellowish green	£100	38·00
		a Bisected (1 c.) (on cover) (1870)	†	£3750
26	**7**	5 c. brown	£450	£170
		a. Bisected (2½ c.) (on cover)		
27	**8**	10 c. black	£250	65·00
		a. Bisected (5 c.) (on cover) (1869)	†	£2750
28	**9**	12 c. red-brown	£400	£150
		a. Bisected (6 c.) (on cover)	†	£2750
29	**10**	13 c. orange-yellow	85·00	60·00
30	**11**	24 c. blue	32·00	32·00

(*b*) *Medium white paper*

No.	Type	Description	Unused	Used
31	**6**	2 c. bluish green (*to* deep) (1870)	65·00	28·00
32	**8**	10 c. black (1871)	£160	35·00
33	**9**	12 c. chestnut (1870)	40·00	40·00
33*a*	**11**	24 c. blue (1870?)	£800	£275

The inland postage rate was reduced to 3 c. on 8 May, 1870. Until the 3 c. value became available examples of No. 25 were bisected to provide 1 c. stamps.

12 King Edward VII when Prince of Wales

14 Queen Victoria

I

II

In Type II the white oval frame line is unbroken by the scroll containing the words "ONE CENT", the letters "N.F." are smaller and closer to the scroll, and there are other minor differences.

(Recess National Bank Note Co, New York)

1868 (Nov). *P* 12.

No.	Type	Description	Unused	Used
34	**12**	1 c. dull purple (I)	48·00	45·00

(Recess A.B.N. Co)

1868 (Nov)–**73**. *P* 12.

No.	Type	Description	Unused	Used
35	**12**	1 c. brown-purple (II) (5.71)	75·00	50·00
36	**14**	3 c. vermilion (7.70)	£250	£100
37		3 c. blue (1.4.73)	£275	18·00
38	**7**	5 c. black	£225	£100
39	**14**	6 c. rose (7.70)	6·50	16·00

1876–79. *Rouletted.*

No.	Type	Description	Unused	Used
40	**12**	1 c. lake-purple (II) (1877)	85·00	38·00
41	**6**	2 c. bluish green (1879)	£120	45·00
42	**14**	3 c. blue (1877)	£250	3·50
43	**7**	5 c. blue	£170	2·75
		a. Imperf (pair)		

15 King Edward VII when Prince of Wales

16 Atlantic Cod

17

18 Common Seal on Ice-floe

(Recess British American Bank Note Co, Montreal)

1880–82. *P* 12.

No.	Type	Description	Unused	Used
44	**15**	1 c. dull grey-brown	24·00	7·50
		a. Dull brown	22·00	7·50
		b. Red-brown	26·00	12·00
46	**16**	2 c. yellow-green (1882)	42·00	20·00
47	**17**	3 c. pale dull blue	60·00	5·00
		a. Bright blue	65·00	2·50
48	**18**	5 c. pale dull blue	£200	7·50

19 Newfoundland Dog

20 Atlantic Brigantine

21 Queen Victoria

(Recess British American Bank Note Co, Montreal)

1887 (15 Feb)–**88.** *New colours and values. P* 12.

No.	Type	Description	Unused	Used
49	**19**	½ c. rose-red	8·00	6·50
50	**15**	1 c. blue-green (1.88)	10·00	5·00
		a. Green	5·50	2·50
		b. Yellow-green	10·00	7·00
51	**16**	2 c. orange-vermilion (1.88)	12·00	4·00
52	**17**	3 c. deep brown (1.88)	55·00	1·00
53	**18**	5 c. deep blue (1.88)	90·00	4·25
54	**20**	10 c. black (1.88)	45·00	48·00
49/54		*Set of* 6	£190	60·00

For reissues of 1880/8 stamps in similar colours, see Nos. 62/5*a*.

(Recess B.A.B.N.)

1890 (Nov). *P* 12.

No.	Type	Description	Unused	Used
55	**21**	3 c. deep slate	24·00	1·00
		a. Imperf (pair)		
56		3 c. slate-grey (*to* grey)	25·00	1·00
		a. Imperf horiz (vert pair)	£400	
57		3 c. slate-violet	29·00	3·25
58		3 c. grey-lilac	29·00	1·00
58*a*		3 c. brown-grey	29·00	5·50
58*b*		3 c. purple-grey	35·00	5·00

There is a very wide range of shades in this stamp, and those given only cover the main groups.

Stamps on pink paper are from a consignment recovered from the sea and which were affected by the salt water.

(Recess British American Bank Note Co, Montreal)

1894 (Aug–Dec). *Changes of colour. P* 12.

No.	Type	Description	Unused	Used
59	**19**	½ c. black (11.94)	8·00	4·00
59*a*	**18**	5 c. bright blue (12.94)	55·00	2·50
60	**14**	6 c. crimson-lake (12.94)	13·00	16·00
61	**9**	12 c. deep brown	45·00	48·00

The 6 c. is printed from the old American Bank Note Company's plates.

1896 (Jan)–**98.** *Reissues. P* 12.

No.	Type	Description	Unused	Used
62	**19**	½ c. orange-vermilion	38·00	48·00
63	**15**	1 c. deep brown	50·00	50·00
63*a*		1 c. deep green (1898)	14·00	7·00
64	**16**	2 c. green	70·00	38·00
65	**17**	3 c. deep blue	60·00	12·00
65*a*		3 c. chocolate-brown	75·00	70·00
62/5*a*		*Set of* 6	£275	£200

The above were *reissued* for postal purposes. The colours were generally brighter than those of the original stamps.

22 Queen Victoria

23 John Cabot

24 Cape Bonavista

25 Caribou hunting

26 Mining

27 Logging

28 Fishing

29 *Matthew* (Cabot)

30 Willow Grouse

31 Group of Grey Seals

32 Salmon-fishing

33 Seal of the Colony

34 Iceberg off St. John's

35 Henry VII

(Des R. O. Smith. Recess A.B.N. Co)

1897 (24 June). *400th Anniv of Discovery of Newfoundlanc and 60th year of Queen Victoria's reign. P* 12.

No.	Type	Description	Unused	Used
66	**22**	1 c. green	2·00	4·0
67	**23**	2 c. bright rose	1·25	2·2
		a. Bisected (1 c.) on cover	†	£25
68	**24**	3 c. bright blue	3·00	5
		a. Bisected (1½ c.) on cover	†	£25
69	**25**	4 c. olive-green	9·00	2·7
70	**26**	5 c. violet	11·00	2·7
71	**27**	6 c. red-brown	8·00	2·7
		a. Bisected (3 c.) on cover	†	£25
72	**28**	8 c. orange	16·00	7·5
73	**29**	10 c. sepia	35·00	5·0
74	**30**	12 c. deep blue	32·00	5·0
75	**31**	15 c. bright scarlet	18·00	15·0
76	**32**	24 c. dull violet-blue	22·00	18·0
77	**33**	30 c. slate-blue	42·00	55·0
78	**34**	35 c. red	60·00	55·0
79	**35**	60 c. black	16·00	11·0
66/79		*Set of* 14	£250	£16

The 60 c. surcharged "TWO–2–CENTS" in three lines is a essay made in December 1918 (*Price* £275).

ONE CENT

(**36**)

ONE CENT

(**37**)

ONE CENT

(**38**)

1897 (19 Oct). *T* **21** *surch with T* **36/8** *by Royal Gazette, S Johns, on stamps of various shades.*

No.	Type	Description	Unused	Used
80	**36**	1 c. on 3 c. grey-purple	40·00	17·(
		a. Surch double, one diagonal	£1100	
		d. Vert pair, one without lower bar and "ONE CENT"	£3500	
81	**37**	1 c. on 3 c. grey-purple	95·00	85·
82	**38**	1 c. on 3 c. grey-purple	£450	£3

Nos. 80/2 occur in the same setting of 50 (10×5) applied twi to each sheet. Type **36** appeared in the first four horizontal row Type **37** on R. 5/1–8 and Type **38** on R. 5/9 and 10.

Trial surcharges in red or red and black were not issue

rice: Type **36** *in red* £750, *in red and black* £750: Type **37** *in* d £2250, *in red and black* £2500: Type **38** *in red* £5000, *in red* d *black* £6000).

These surcharges exist on stamps of various shades, but those brown-grey are clandestine forgeries, having been produced one of the printers at the *Royal Gazette*.

Prince Edward later Duke of Windsor

40 Queen Victoria

41 King Edward VII when Prince of Wales

42 Queen Alexandra when Princess of Wales

43 Queen Mary when Duchess of York

44 King George V when Duke of York

(Recess A.B.N. Co)

97 (4 Dec)–**1918.** *P* 12.

Type	Description		Unused	Used
39	½ c. olive (8.98)	..	2·00	1·25
	a. Imperf (pair)	..	£275	
40	1 c. carmine	..	2·75	2·75
	1 c. blue-green (6.98)	..	6·50	10
	a. Yellow-green	..	6·00	10
	b. Imperf horiz (vert pair)	..	£170	
41	2 c. orange	..	2·75	1·75
	a. Imperf (pair)	..	—	£300
	2 c. scarlet (6.98)	..	12·00	30
	a. Imperf (pair)	..	£225	£225
	b. Imperf between (pair)	..	£300	
42	3 c. orange (6.98)	..	12·00	20
	a. Imperf horiz (vert pair)	..	£275	
	b. Imperf (pair)	..	£225	£225
	c. Red-orange/bluish (6.18)	..	30·00	2·75
43	4 c. violet (21.10.01)	..	22·00	3·75
	a. Imperf (pair)	..	£300	
44	5 c. blue (6.99)	..	35·00	2·75
/90		*Set of* 8	85·00	11·50

No. 88*c* was an emergency war-time printing made by the merican Bank Note Co from the old plate, pending receipt of e then current 3 c. from England.

The imperforate errors of this issue are found used, but only s philatelic "by favour" items. It is possible that No. 86a only xists in this condition.

45 Map of Newfoundland

(Recess A.B.N. Co)

08 (31 Aug). *P* 12.

Type	Description		Unused	Used
45	2 c. lake	..	25·00	60

King James I

47 Arms of Colonisation Co

48 John Guy

49 *Endeavour* (immigrant ship), 1610

50 Cupids

51 Sir Francis Bacon

52 View of Mosquito

53 Logging Camp, Red Indian Lake

54 Paper Mills, Grand Falls

55 King Edward VII

56 King George V

6 c. (A) "Z" in "COLONIZATION" reversed. (B) "Z" correct.

(Litho Whitehead, Morris & Co Ltd)

1910 (15 Aug). (*a*) *P* 12

No.	Type	Description		Unused	Used
95	**46**	1 c. green	..	6·00	2·00
		a. "NFWFOUNDLAND" (Right pane R. 5/1)	..	48·00	75·00
		b. "JAMRS" (Right pane R. 5/2)	..	48·00	75·00
		c. Imperf between (horiz pair)	..	£275	£300
96	**47**	2 c. rose-carmine	..	9·00	1·75
97	**48**	3 c. olive	..	5·00	14·00
98	**49**	4 c. violet	..	12·00	12·00
99	**50**	5 c. bright blue	..	19·00	6·00
100	**51**	6 c. claret (A)	..	45·00	£120
100*a*		6 c. claret (B)	..	18·00	65·00
101	**52**	8 c. bistre-brown	..	48·00	85·00
102	**53**	9 c. olive-green	..	40·00	75·00
103	**54**	10 c. purple-slate	..	55·00	95·00
104	**55**	12 c. pale red-brown	..	55·00	75·00
		a. Imperf (pair)	..	£300	
105	**56**	15 c. black	..	65·00	95·00
95/105			*Set of* 11	£275	£450
		(*b*) *P* 12×14			
106	**46**	1 c. green	..	3·75	6·50
		a. "NFWFOUNDLAND"	..	45·00	90·00
		b. "JAMRS"	..	45·00	90·00
		c. Imperf between (horiz pair)	..	£475	£500
107	**47**	2 c. rose-carmine	..	3·50	35
		a. Imperf between (horiz pair)	..	£450	
108	**50**	5 c. bright blue (*p* 14×12)	..	8·00	2·50
		(*c*) *P* 12×11			
109	**46**	1 c. green	..	1·25	20
		a. Imperf between (horiz pair)	..	£250	
		b. Imperf between (vert pair)	..	£300	
		c. "NFWFOUNDLAND"	..	23·00	42·00
		e. "JAMRS"	..	23·00	42·00
		(*d*) *P* 12×11½			
110	**47**	2 c. rose-carmine	..	£190	£180

(Dies eng Macdonald & Sons. Recess A. Alexander & Sons, Ltd)

1911 (7 Feb). *As T* **51** *to* **56**, *but recess printed. P* 14.

No.	Description		Unused	Used
111	6 c. claret (B)	..	17·00	42·00
112	8 c. yellow-brown	..	48·00	60·00
	a. Imperf between (horiz pair)	..	£400	
	b. Imperf (pair)	..	£300	
113	9 c. sage-green	..	40·00	85·00
	a. Imperf between (horiz pair)	..	£350	
114	10 c. purple-black	..	80·00	£110
	a. Imperf between (horiz pair)	..	£350	
	b. Imperf (pair)	..	£250	
115	12 c. red-brown	..	60·00	60·00
116	15 c. slate-green	..	55·00	£110
111/16		*Set of* 6	£275	£425

The 9 c. and 15 c. exist with papermaker's watermark "E. TOWGOOD FINE".

57 Queen Mary

58 King George V

59 Duke of Windsor when Prince of Wales

60 King George VI when Prince Albert

61 Princess Mary, the Princess Royal

62 Prince Henry Duke of Gloucester

63 Prince George, Duke of Kent

64 Prince John

65 Queen Alexandra

66 Duke of Connaught

67 Seal of Newfoundland

(1 c. to 5 c., 10 c. eng and recess D.L.R.; others eng Macdonald & Co, recess A. Alexander & Sons)

1911 (19 June)–**16.** *Coronation. P* 13½ × 14 (*comb*) (1 *c. to* 5 *c.,* 10 *c.*) *or* 14 (*line*) (*others*).

No.	Type	Description		Unused	Used
117	**57**	1 c. yellow-green	..	5·50	20
		a. Blue-green (1915)	..	6·50	30
118	**58**	2 c. carmine	..	3·00	20
		a. Rose-red (*blurred impression*). Perf 14 (1916)	..	6·50	55
119	**59**	3 c. red-brown	..	17·00	26·00
120	**60**	4 c. purple	..	16·00	25·00
121	**61**	5 c. ultramarine	..	4·75	1·25
122	**62**	6 c. slate-grey	..	10·00	24·00
123	**63**	8 c. aniline blue	..	48·00	75·00
		a. Greenish blue	..	55·00	90·00
124	**64**	9 c. violet-blue	..	14·00	40·00
125	**65**	10 c. deep green	..	26·00	38·00
126	**66**	12 c. plum	..	20·00	38·00
127	**67**	15 c. lake	..	16·00	45·00
117/27			*Set of* 11	£160	£275

The 2 c. rose-red, No. 118*a* is a poor war-time printing by Alexander & Sons.

Although No. 123 has a typical aniline appearance it is believed that the shade results from the thinning of non-aniline ink.

68 Reindeer

FIRST
TRANS-
ATLANTIC
AIR POST
April, 1919.

(69)

(Des J. H. Noonan. Recess D.L.R.)

1919 (2 Jan). *Newfoundland Contingent,* 1914–1918. *P* 14.

No.	Type	Description		Unused	Used
130	**68**	1 c. green (*a*) (*b*)	..	3·00	20
131		2 c. scarlet (*a*) (*b*)	..	2·75	85
		a. Carmine-red (*b*)	..	8·50	45
132		3 c. brown (*a*) (*b*)	..	4·00	20
		a. Red-brown (*b*)	..	5·00	30
133		4 c. mauve (*a*)	..	4·25	60
		a. Purple (*b*)	..	8·50	30
134		5 c. ultramarine (*a*) (*b*)	..	4·50	1·10
135		6 c. slate-grey (*a*)	..	4·50	30·00
136		8 c. bright magenta (*a*)	..	8·00	38·00
137		10 c. deep grey-green (*a*)	..	4·50	3·25
138		12 c. orange (*a*)	..	18·00	45·00
139		15 c. indigo (*a*)	..	15·00	55·00
		a. Prussian blue (*a*)	..	80·00	£140
140		24 c. bistre-brown (*a*)	..	22·00	25·00
141		36 c. sage-green (*a*)	..	12·00	24·00
130/41			*Set of* 12	90·00	£200

Each value bears with "Trail of the Caribou" the name of a different action: 1 c. Suvla Bay; 3 c. Gueudecourt; 4 c. Beaumont Hamel; 6 c. Monchy; 10 c. Steenbeck; 15 c. Langemarck; 24 c. Cambrai; 36 c. Combles; 2 c., 5 c., 8 c., and 12 c. inscribed "Royal Naval Reserve-Ubique".

Perforations. Two perforating heads were used: (*a*) comb 14 × 13.9; (*b*) line 14.1 × 14.1.

1919 (12 Apr). *Air. No.* 132 *optd with T* **69**, *by Robinson & Co Ltd, at the offices of the "Daily News".*

No.	Type	Description		Unused	Used
142	**68**	3 c. brown	..	£15000	£8000

These stamps franked correspondence carried by Lieut. H. Hawker on his Atlantic flight. 18 were damaged and destroyed, 95 used on letters, 11 given as presentation copies, and the remaining 76 were sold in aid of the Marine Disasters Fund.

1919 (19 April). *Nos.* 132 *optd in MS.* "Aerial Atlantic Mail. J.A.R."

No.	Type	Description		Unused	Used
142*a*	**68**	3 c. brown	..	—	£20000

This provisional was made by W. C. Campbell, the Secretary of the Postal Department, and the initials are those of the Postmaster, J. A. Robinson, for use on correspondence intended to be carried on the abortive Morgan-Raynham Trans-Atlantic flight. The mail was eventually delivered by sea.

In addition to the 25 to 30 used examples, one unused, no gum, copy of No. 142*a* is known.

A single example of a similar overprint on the 2 c., No. 131, is known used on cover together with an unoverprinted example of the same value.

Trans-Atlantic
AIR POST,
1919.
ONE DOLLAR.

(70)

THREE
CENTS

(71)

1919 (9 June). *Air. No.* 75 *surch with T* **70** *by Royal Gazette, St. Johns.*

No.	Type	Description		Unused	Used
143	**31**	$1 on 15 c. bright scarlet	..	£110	£110
		a. No comma after "AIR POST"	..	£140	£150
		b. As Var a and no stop after "1919"	..	£350	£350
		c. As Var a and "A" of "AIR" under "a" of "Trans"	..	£350	£350

These stamps were issued for use on the mail carried on the first successful flight across the Atlantic by Capt. J. Alcock and Lieut. A. Brown, and on other projected Trans-Atlantic flights (Alcock flown cover, *Price* £3000).

The surcharge was applied in a setting of which 16 were normal, 7 as No. 143a, 1 as No. 143b and 1 as No. 143c.

1920 (Sept). *Nos. 75 and 77/8 surch as T* **71**, *by Royal Gazette (2 c. with only one bar, at top of stamp).*

A. Bars of surch 10½ mm apart. B. Bars 13½ mm apart.

No.	Type	Description	Unused	Used
144	**33**	2 c. on 30 c. slate-blue (24 Sept)	3·50	15·00
		a. Surch inverted	£425	£450
145	**31**	3 c. on 15 c. bright scarlet (A) (13 Sept)	£140	£140
		a. Surch inverted	£900	
146		3 c. on 15 c. bright scarlet (B) (13 Sept)	12·00	11·00
147	**34**	3 c. on 35 c. red (15 Sept)	5·00	9·00
		a. Surch inverted	£750	
		b. Lower bar omitted	£120	£130
		c. "THREE" omitted	£1100	

Our prices for Nos. 147b and 147c are for stamps with lower bar or "THREE" entirely missing. The bar may be found in all stages of incompleteness and stamps showing broken bar are not of much value.

On the other hand, stamps showing either only the top or bottom of the letters "THREE" are scarce, though not as rare as No. 147c.

The 6 c. T **27** surcharged "THREE CENTS", in red or black, is an essay (*Price* £400). The 2 c. on 30 c. with red surcharge is a colour trial (*Price* £475).

AIR MAIL to Halifax, N.S. 1921.

(72)

1921 (16 Nov). *Air. No. 78 optd with T* **72** *by Royal Gazette.*

I. 2¾ mm between "AIR" and "MAIL"

No.	Type	Description	Unused	Used
148	**34**	35 c. red	90·00	90·00
		a. No stop after "1921"	80·00	80·00
		b. No stop and first "1" of "1921" below "f" of "Halifax"	£180	£180
		c. As No. 148, inverted	£4000	
		d. As No. 148a, inverted	£3750	
		e. As No. 148b, inverted	£8000	

II. 1½ mm between "AIR" and "MAIL"

No.	Type	Description	Unused	Used
148*f*	**34**	35 c. red	£100	£100
		g. No stop after "1921"	£120	£120
		h. No stop and first "1" of "1921" below "f" of "Halifax"	£180	£180
		i. As No. 148f, inverted	£4500	
		k. As No. 148g, inverted	£5500	
		l. As No. 148h, inverted	£8000	

Type **72** was applied as a setting of 25 which contained ten stamps as No. 148a, seven as No. 148, four as No. 148*f*, two as No. 148g, one as No. 148b and one as No. 148h.

73 Twin Hills, Tor's Cove

74 South-West Arm, Trinity

75 Statue of the Fighting Newfoundlander, St. John's

(Recess D.L.R.)

1923 (9 July)–**26**. *T* **73/5** *and similar designs. P* 14 (*comb or line*).

No.	Description	Unused	Used
149	1 c. green	60	10
150	2 c. carmine	60	10
	a. Imperf (pair)	£160	
151	3 c. brown	60	10
152	4 c. deep purple	90	30
153	5 c. ultramarine	1·50	1·50
154	6 c. slate	2·50	7·00
155	8 c. purple	3·00	3·25
156	9 c. slate-green	17·00	28·00
157	10 c. violet	4·25	2·50
	a. Purple	4·75	2·50
158	11 c. sage-green	2·25	15·00
159	12 c. lake	2·50	8·00
160	15 c. Prussian blue	2·50	12·00
161	20 c. chestnut (28.4.24)	4·75	10·00
162	24 c. sepia (22.4.24)	45·00	75·00
149/62	.. .. .. *Set of* 14	75·00	£140

Designs: *Horiz* (*as T* **73**)—6 c. Upper Steadies, Humber River; 11 c. Shell Bird Island; 20 c. Placentia. (*As T* **74**)—8 c. Quidi Vidi, near St. John's; 9 c. Caribou crossing lake; 12 c. Mount Moriah, Bay of Islands. *Vert* (*as T* **75**)—4 c. Humber River, 5 c. Coast at Trinity; 10 c. Humber River Canon; 15 c. Humber River near Little Rapids; 24 c. Topsail Falls.

Perforations. Three perforating heads were used: comb 13.8×14 (all values); line 13.7 and 14, and combinations of these two (for all except 6, 8, 9 and 11 c.).

Air Mail DE PINEDO 1927

(87)

1927 (18 May). *Air. No. 79 optd with T* **87**, *by Robinson & Co, Ltd.*

No.	Type	Description	Unused	Used
163	**35**	60 c. black (R.)	£23000	£7000

For the mail carried by De Pinedo to Europe 300 stamps were overprinted, 230 used on correspondence, 66 presented to De Pinedo, Government Officials, etc., and 4 damaged and destroyed. Stamps without overprint were also used.

NEW INFORMATION

The editor is always interested to correspond with people who have new information that will improve or correct the Catalogue.

88 Newfoundland and Labrador

89 S.S. *Caribou*

90 King George V and Queen Mary

91 Duke of Windsor when Prince of Wales

92 Express Train

93 Newfoundland Hotel, St. John's

94 Heart's Content

95 Cabot Tower, St. John's

96 War Memorial, St. John's

97 G.P.O., St. John's

98 Vickers "Vimy" Aircraft

99 Parliament House, St. John's

100 Grand Falls, Labrador

(Recess D.L.R.)

1928 (3 Jan)–**29**. *Publicity issue. P* 14 (1 *c.*), 13½×13 (2, 3, 5, 6, 10, 20 *c.*), 13×13½ (4 *c.*) (*all comb*), *or* 14–13½* (*line*) (*others*).

No.	Type	Description	Unused	Used
164	**88**	1 c. deep green	2·00	1·00
165	**89**	2 c. carmine	2·50	40
166	**90**	3 c. brown	2·75	1·00
		a. Perf 14–13½ (line)	2·25	1·00
167	**91**	4 c. mauve	5·00	2·25
		a. Rose-purple (1929)	5·50	5·50
168	**92**	5 c. slate-grey	13·00	4·25
		a. Perf 14–13½ (line)	22·00	5·00
169	**93**	6 c. ultramarine	2·25	17·00
		a. Perf 14–13½ (line)	5·50	17·00
170	**94**	8 c. red-brown	2·00	23·00
171	**95**	9 c. deep green	2·00	10·00
172	**96**	10 c. deep violet	10·00	11·00
		a. Perf 14–13½ (line)	6·00	12·00
173	**97**	12 c. carmine-lake	2·00	18·00
174	**95**	14 c. brown-purple	9·00	10·00
		a. Perf 14–13½ (line)	5·00	7·50
175	**98**	15 c. deep blue	2·75	26·00
176	**99**	20 c. grey-black	8·50	9·50
		a. Perf 14–13½ (line)	2·50	6·50
177	**97**	28 c. deep green	27·00	48·00
178	**100**	30 c. sepia	6·00	15·00
164/78 (*cheapest*)		.. .. *Set of* 15	70·00	£170

*Exact gauges for the various perforations are: 14 comb = 14×13.9; 13½×13 comb = 13.5×12.75; 14–13½ line = 14–13.75.

See also Nos. 179/87 and 198/208.

D 1 c. P D 2 c. P

D 3 c. P D 4 c. P

D 5 c. P

D 6 c. P D 10 c. P

D 15 c. P

D 20 c. P

D. De La Rue printing

P. Perkins, Bacon printing

1929 (10 Aug)–**31**. *Perkins, Bacon printing. Former typ*[e] *re-engraved. No wmk. P* 14 (*comb*) (1 *c.*), 13½ (*comb*) (2, 6 *c* 14–13½ (*line*) (20 *c.*) *or* 13½×14 (*comb*) (*others*)*.

No.	Type	Description	Unused	Used
179	**88**	1 c. green (26.9.29)	3·50	2
		a. Perf 14–13½ (line)	3·50	3
		b. Imperf between (vert pair) ..	£130	
		c. Imperf (pair)	£110	
180	**89**	2 c. scarlet	1·50	2
		a. Imperf (pair)	95·00	
		b. Perf 14–13½ (line)	2·50	9
181	**90**	3 c. red-brown	1·00	1
		a. Imperf (pair)	95·00	
182	**91**	4 c. reddish purple (26.8.29) ..	2·75	6
		a. Imperf (pair)	£110	
183	**92**	5 c. deep grey-green (14.9.29) ..	5·50	2·0
184	**93**	6 c. ultramarine (8.11.29)	5·50	10·0
		a. Perf 14–13½ (line)	2·25	11·0
185	**96**	10 c. violet (5.10.29)	3·50	3·0
186	**98**	15 c. blue (1.30)	17·00	75·0
187	**99**	20 c. black (1.1.31)	42·00	40·0
179/87		.. .. *Set of* 9	70·00	£12

*Exact gauges for the various perforations are: 14 comb 14×13.9; 13½ comb = 13.6×13.5; 14–13½ line = 14–13.7 13½×14 comb = 13.6×13.8.

THREE CENTS

(101)

Trans-Atlantic AIR MAIL By B. M. "Columbia" September 1930 Fifty Cents

(102)

(Surch by Messrs D. R. Thistle, St. John's)

1929 (23 Aug). *No. 154 surch with T* **101**.

No.	Description	Unused	Used
188	3 c. on 6 c. slate (R.)	85	4·
	a. Surch inverted	£600	£9
	b. Surch in black	£700	

1930 (25 Sept). *Air. No. 141 surch with T* **102** *by Messrs D. Thistle.*

No.	Type	Description	Unused	Used
191	**68**	50 c. on 36 c. sage-green	£4500	£42

103 Aeroplane and Dog-team

104 Vickers-Vimy Biplane and early Sailing Packet

105 Routes of historic Transatlantic Flights

106

(Des A. B. Perlin. Recess P.B.)

31. *Air. P* 14. (*a*) *Without wmk* (2.1.31)

2	**103**	15 c. chocolate . .	4·00	10·00
		a. Imperf between (horiz or vert pair)	£600	
		b. Imperf (pair)	£375	
3	**104**	50 c. green	26·00	42·00
		a. Imperf between (horiz or vert pair)	£650	£500
		b. Imperf (pair)	£500	
4	**105**	$1 deep blue . .	45·00	85·00
		a. Imperf between (horiz or vert pair)	£600	
		b. Imperf (pair)	£500	
2/4		*Set of* 3	65·00	£120

(*b*) *Wmk W* **106**, (*sideways*) (13.3.31)

5	**103**	15 c. chocolate . .	5·00	15·00
		a. Pair, with and without wmk	30·00	
		b. Imperf between (horiz or vert pair)	£550	
		ba. Ditto, one without wmk (vert pair)	£800	
		c. Imperf (pair)	£375	
		d. Wmk Cross (pair)	85·00	
6	**104**	50 c. green	23·00	60·00
		a. Imperf between (horiz or vert pair)	£600	
		b. Imperf (pair)		
		c. Pair, with and without wmk	£170	
7	**105**	$1 deep blue . .	70·00	£130
		a. Imperf between (horiz or vert pair)	£600	
		b. Imperf horiz (vert pair)	£475	
		c. Pair, with and without wmk	£300	
		d. Imperf (pair)	£400	
5/7		*Set of* 3	85·00	£180

WITH AND WITHOUT WMK" PAIRS listed in the issues from o. 195a onwards must have one stamp *completely* without any ace of watermark.

31 (25 March–July). *Perkins, Bacon printing* (*re-engraved types*). *W* **106** (*sideways on* 1 *c.*, 4 *c.*, 30 *c.*). *P* 13½ (1 *c.*) *or* 13½×14 (*others*), *both comb**.

8	**88**	1 c. green (7.31)	5·00	3·00
		a. Imperf between (horiz pair)	£500	
9	**89**	2 c. scarlet (7.31)	5·50	3·00
		w. Wmk inverted	40·00	
0	**90**	3 c. red-brown (7.31) . .	1·75	1·50
		w. Wmk inverted	40·00	
1	**91**	4 c. reddish purple (7.31)	1·75	70
2	**92**	5 c. deep grey-green (7.31)	7·00	8·50
3	**93**	6 c. ultramarine	10·00	20·00
4	**94**	8 c. chestnut (1.4.31) . .	20·00	26·00
		w. Wmk inverted	55·00	
5	**96**	10 c. violet (1.4.31)	7·00	8·50
6	**98**	15 c. blue (1.7.31)	21·00	48·00
7	**99**	20 c. black (1.7.31)	50·00	13·00
8	**100**	30 c. sepia (1.7.31)	27·00	38·00
8/208		*Set of* 11	£140	£150

*Exact gauges for the two perforations are: 13½ = 13.6×13.5; ½×14 = 13.6×13.8.

107 Atlantic Cod

108 King George V

109 Queen Mary

110 Duke of Windsor when Prince of Wales

111 Caribou

112 Queen Elizabeth II when Princess

113 Atlantic Salmon

114 Newfoundland Dog

115 Harp Seal

116 Cape Race

117 Sealing Fleet

118 Fishing Fleet

(Recess P.B.)

1932 (2 Jan). *W* **106** (*sideways* on vert designs*). *P* 13½ (*comb*).

209	**107**	1 c. green	2·00	20
		a. Imperf (pair)	£100	
		b. Perf 13 (line)	15·00	25·00
		ba. Imperf between (vert pair)	£110	
		w. Wmk top of shield to right	40·00	
210	**108**	2 c. carmine . .	1·50	10
		a. Imperf (pair)	£100	
		c. Perf 13 (line)	10·00	20·00
		w. Wmk top of shield to right	40·00	
211	**109**	3 c. orange-brown	1·50	10
		a. Imperf (pair)	75·00	
		c. Perf 13 (line)	15·00	26·00
		d. Perf 14 (line). Small holes	18·00	20·00
		da. Imperf between (vert pair)	£140	
		w. Wmk top of shield to right	40·00	
212	**110**	4 c. bright violet	5·00	1·75
		w. Wmk top of shield to right		
213	**111**	5 c. maroon . .	2·25	1·00
		a. Imperf (pair)	£150	
		w. Wmk top of shield to right		
214	**112**	6 c. light blue	4·00	13·00
215	**113**	10 c. black-brown	70	40
		a. Imperf (pair)	70·00	
		w. Wmk inverted	10·00	
216	**114**	14 c. black	3·25	4·00
		a. Imperf (pair)	£120	
217	**115**	15 c. claret	1·25	1·75
		a. Imperf (pair)	£130	
		b. Perf 14 (line)	8·00	10·00
218	**116**	20 c. green	1·00	80
		a. Imperf (pair)	£120	
		b. Perf 14 (line)	55·00	50·00
		w. Wmk inverted	20·00	
219	**117**	25 c. slate	2·00	2·00
		a. Imperf (pair)	£130	
		b. Perf 14 (line)	25·00	40·00
		ba. Imperf between (vert pair)	£275	
220	**118**	30 c. ultramarine	26·00	26·00
		a. Imperf (pair)	£325	
		b. Imperf between (vert pair)	£600	
		c. Perf 14 (line)	£225	
209/20		*Set of* 12	45·00	45·00

*The normal sideways watermark shows the top of the shield to left, *as seen from the back of the stamp*.

Nos. 209b, 210c and 211c were only issued in stamp booklets.

For similar stamps in different perforations see Nos. 222/8c and 276/89.

TRANS-ATLANTIC
WEST TO EAST
Per Dornier DO-X
May, 1932.
One Dollar and Fifty Cents

(**119**)

1932 (19 May). *Air. No.* 197 *surch as T* **119**, *by Messrs. D. R. Thistle. P* 14.

221	**105**	$1.50 on $1 deep blue (R.)	£180	£225
		a. Surch inverted	£9500	

120 Queen Mother, when Duchess of York

121 Corner Brook Paper Mills

122 Loading Iron Ore, Bell Island

(Recess P.B.)

1932 (15 Aug)–**38**. *W* **106** (*sideways* on vert designs*). *P* 13½ (*comb*).

222	**107**	1 c. grey	70	10
		a. Imperf (pair)	40·00	
		c. Perf 14 (line)	6·00	8·50
		d. Perf 14 (line). Small holes	15·00	23·00
		e. Pair, with and without wmk	40·00	
		w. Wmk top of shield to right	50·00	

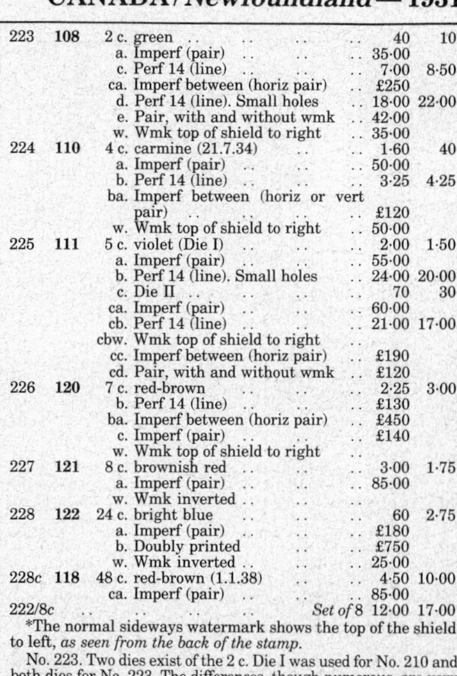

223	**108**	2 c. green	40	10
		a. Imperf (pair)	35·00	
		c. Perf 14 (line)	7·00	8·50
		ca. Imperf between (horiz pair)	£250	
		d. Perf 14 (line). Small holes	18·00	22·00
		e. Pair, with and without wmk	42·00	
		w. Wmk top of shield to right	35·00	
224	**110**	4 c. carmine (21.7.34)	1·60	40
		a. Imperf (pair)	50·00	
		b. Perf 14 (line)	3·25	4·25
		ba. Imperf between (horiz or vert pair)	£120	
		w. Wmk top of shield to right	50·00	
225	**111**	5 c. violet (Die I)	2·00	1·50
		a. Imperf (pair)	55·00	
		b. Perf 14 (line). Small holes	24·00	20·00
		c. Die II	70	30
		ca. Imperf (pair)	60·00	
		cb. Perf 14 (line)	21·00	17·00
		cbw. Wmk top of shield to right		
		cc. Imperf between (horiz pair)	£190	
		cd. Pair, with and without wmk	£120	
226	**120**	7 c. red-brown	2·25	3·00
		b. Perf 14 (line)	£130	
		ba. Imperf between (horiz pair)	£450	
		c. Imperf (pair)	£140	
		w. Wmk top of shield to right		
227	**121**	8 c. brownish red	3·00	1·75
		a. Imperf (pair)	85·00	
		w. Wmk inverted . .		
228	**122**	24 c. bright blue	60	2·75
		a. Imperf (pair)	£180	
		b. Doubly printed	£750	
		w. Wmk inverted . .	25·00	
228*c*	**118**	48 c. red-brown (1.1.38)	4·50	10·00
		ca. Imperf (pair)	85·00	
222/8*c*		*Set of* 8	12·00	17·00

*The normal sideways watermark shows the top of the shield to left, *as seen from the back of the stamp*.

No. 223. Two dies exist of the 2 c. Die I was used for No. 210 and both dies for No. 223. The differences, though numerous, are very slight.

No. 225. There are also two dies of the 5 c., Die I only being used for No. 213 and both dies for the violet stamp. In Die II the antler pointing to the "T" of "POSTAGE" is taller than the one pointing to the "S" and the individual hairs on the underside of the caribou's tail are distinct.

For similar stamps in a slightly larger size and perforated 12½ or 13½ (5 c.) see Nos. 276/89.

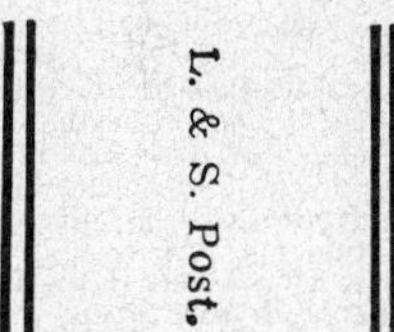

(**123**) "L.&S."—Land and Sea

1933 (9 Feb). *No.* 195 *optd with T* **123** *for ordinary postal use, by Messrs D. R. Thistle. W* **106** (*sideways*). *P* 14.

229	**103**	15 c. chocolate	2·75	8·50
		a. Pair, one without wmk	23·00	
		b. Opt reading up	£1400	
		c. Vertical pair, one without surch	£2250	

124 Put to Flight

125 Land of Heart's Delight

(Des J. Scott. Recess P.B.)

1933 (31 May). *Air. T* **124/5** *and similar horiz designs. W* **106** (*sideways*). *P* 14 (5, 30, 75 *c.*) *or* 11½ (10, 60 *c.*).

230	5 c. red-brown	13·00	15·00
	a. Imperf (pair) . .	£160	
	b. Imperf between (horiz or vert pair)	£900	
231	10 c. orange-yellow	9·00	24·00
	a. Imperf (pair) . .	£130	
232	30 c. light blue	27·00	38·00
	a. Imperf (pair) . .	£375	
233	60 c. green . .	45·00	75·00
	a. Imperf (pair) . .	£425	
234	75 c. yellow-brown . .	45·00	70·00
	a. Imperf (pair) . .	£375	
	b. Imperf between (horiz or vert pair)	£1600	
230/4	*Set of* 5	£110	£200

Designs:—30 c. Spotting the herd; 60 c. News from home; 75 c. Labrador.

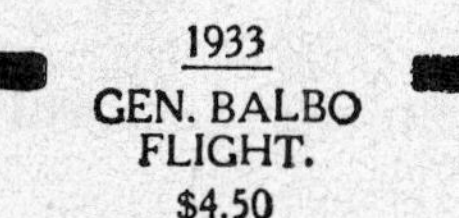

(**129**)

(Surch by Robinson & Co, St. John's)

1933 (24 July). *Air. Balbo Transatlantic Mass Formation Flight. No.* 234 *surch with T* **129.** *W* **106.** *P* 14.

235	$4.50 on 75 c. yellow-brown. .	£250	£300
	a. Surch inverted	£30000	
	b. Surch on 10 c. (No. 231). .	£30000	

No. 235a. When this error was discovered the stamps were ordered to be officially destroyed but four copies which had been torn were recovered and skilfully repaired. In addition four undamaged examples exist and the price quoted is for one of these.

130 Sir Humphrey Gilbert

131 Compton Castle, Devon

132 Gilbert Coat of Arms

(Recess P.B.)

1933 (3 Aug). *350th Anniv of the Annexation by Sir Humphrey Gilbert. T* **130/2** *and similar designs. W* **106** *(sideways* on vert designs). P* 13½ *(comb†).*

236 1 c. slate .. 70 90
a. Imperf (pair) .. 45·00
237 2 c. green .. 1·00 50
a. Imperf (pair) .. 48·00
b. Doubly printed .. £300
238 3 c. chestnut .. 1·75 1·00
239 4 c. carmine .. 80 40
a. Imperf (pair) .. 45·00
240 5 c. violet .. 2·00 70
241 7 c. greenish blue .. 10·00 15·00
a. Perf 14 (line) .. 10·00 35·00
242 8 c. vermilion .. 7·00 11·00
a. Brownish red .. £275
b. Bisected (4 c.) (on cover) .. † £375
243 9 c. ultramarine .. 7·00 9·00
a. Imperf (pair) .. £200
b. Perf 14 (line) .. 40·00 50·00
244 10 c. brown-lake .. 4·00 7·00
a. Imperf (pair) .. £275
b. Perf 14 (line) .. 50·00 55·00
245 14 c. grey-black .. 12·00 30·00
a. Perf 14 (line) .. 17·00 48·00
246 15 c. claret .. 10·00 18·00
w. Wmk top of shield to right .. 7·50 14·00
247 20 c. grey-green .. 13·00 15·00
a. Perf 14 (line) .. 19·00 30·00
w. Wmk inverted .. 40·00
248 24 c. maroon .. 11·00 22·00
a. Imperf (pair) .. £100
b. Perf 14 (line) .. 22·00 35·00
w. Wmk top of shield to right .. 35·00
249 32 c. olive-black .. 7·00 45·00
a. Perf 14 (line) .. 22·00 60·00
w. Wmk top of shield to right .. 20·00
236/49 .. *Set of* 14 65·00 £150

Designs: *Horiz*—4 c. Eton College; 7 c. Gilbert commissioned by Elizabeth I; 8 c. Fleet leaving Plymouth, 1583; 9 c. Arrival at St. John's; 10 c. Annexation, 5 August 1583; 20 c. Map of Newfoundland, 1626. *Vert*—5 c. Anchor token; 14 c. Royal Arms; 15 c. Gilbert in the *Squirrel*; 24 c. Queen Elizabeth I. 32 c. Gilbert's statue at Truro.

*The normal sideways watermark shows the top of the shield to left, *as seen from the back of the stamp.*

†Exact gauges for the two perforations are: 13½ comb = 13.4; 14 line = 13.8.

1935 (6 May). *Silver Jubilee. As Nos.* 91/4 *of Antigua, but ptd by B.W. P* 11 × 12.

250 4 c. rosine .. 1·00 1·75
251 5 c. bright violet .. 1·25 1·75
252 7 c. blue .. 1·50 6·00
253 24 c. olive-green .. 5·00 6·00
250/3 .. *Set of* 4 8·00 14·00
250/3 Perf "Specimen" .. *Set of* 4 £120

1937 (12 May). *Coronation Issue. As Nos.* 95/7 *of Antigua, but name and value uncoloured on coloured background. P* 11×11½.

254 2 c. green .. 1·00 2·25
255 4 c. carmine .. 1·60 2·75
256 5 c. purple .. 3·00 2·75
254/6 .. *Set of* 3 5·00 7·00
254/6 Perf "Specimen" .. *Set of* 3 75·00

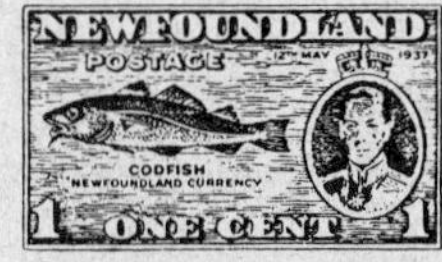

144 Atlantic Cod

Die I

Die II

No. 258. In Die II the shading of the King's face is heavier and dots have been added down the ridge of the nose. The top frame line is thicker and more uniform.

NEW INFORMATION

The editor is always interested to correspond with people who have new information that will improve or correct the Catalogue.

Fish-hook flaw (R. 1/7 or 3/3)

Re-entry to right of design (inscr oval, tree and value) (R.4/8)

Extra chimney (R. 6/5)

(Recess P.B.)

1937 (12 May). *Additional Coronation Issue. T* **144** *and similar horiz designs. W* **106**. *P* 14–13½ *(line)*.*

257 1 c. grey .. 2·00 20
a. Pair, with and without wmk .. 22·00
b. Fish-hook flaw .. 19·00
c. Perf 13 (comb) .. 23·00 42·00
ca. Pair, with and without wmk
cb. Fish-hook flaw .. £170
258 3 c. orange-brown (I) .. 4·00 2·25
a. Pair, with and without wmk .. 55·00
b. Imperf between (horiz or vert pair) .. £350
c. Perf 13 (comb) .. 3·25 2·25
d. Die II .. 3·25 3·00
da. Pair, with and without wmk
db. Imperf between (horiz or vert pair) .. £450
dc. Perf 13 (comb) .. 4·50 2·25
dca. Pair, with and without wmk .. 90·00
259 7 c. bright ultramarine .. 2·00 75
a. Pair, with and without wmk
b. Re-entry at right .. 45·00
c. Perf 13 (comb) .. £250 £325
cb. Re-entry at right .. £1200
260 8 c. scarlet .. 1·75 2·50
a. Pair, with and without wmk .. 55·00
b. Imperf between (horiz or vert pair) .. £550
c. Imperf (pair) .. £275
d. Perf 13 (comb) .. 6·00 7·50
261 10 c. blackish brown .. 3·25 6·00
a. Pair, with and without wmk .. 60·00
b. Perf 13 (comb) .. 3·25 9·50
bw. Wmk inverted .. 75·00
262 14 c. black .. 1·40 2·00
a. Pair, with and without wmk .. 50·00
b. Perf 13 (comb) .. £4500 £2500
263 15 c. claret .. 8·50 4·00
a. Pair, with and without wmk .. 60·00
b. Imperf between (vert pair) .. £375
cw. Wmk inverted .. 75·00
d. Perf 13 (comb) .. 17·00 18·00
da. Pair, with and without wmk .. 95·00
264 20 c. green .. 2·25 5·00
a. Pair, with and without wmk .. £120
b. Imperf between (vert pair) .. £600
c. Extra chimney .. 40·00
dw. Wmk inverted .. 85·00
e. Perf 13 (comb) .. 2·50 7·00
ec. Extra chimney .. 42·00
265 24 c. light blue .. 2·25 2·50
a. Pair, with and without wmk .. £120
b. Imperf between (vert pair) .. £600
c. Perf 13 (comb) .. 20·00 21·00
266 25 c. slate .. 2·75 1·75
a. Pair, with and without wmk .. £110
b. Perf 13 (comb) .. 20·00 38·00
267 48 c. slate-purple .. 8·50 4·50
a. Pair, with and without wmk .. £150
b. Imperf between (vert pair) .. £600
c. Perf 13 (comb) .. 29·00 55·00
257/67 .. *Set of* 11 32·00 28·00

Designs:—3 c. Map of Newfoundland; 7 c. Reindeer; 8 c. Corner Brook paper mills; 10 c. Atlantic Salmon; 14 c. Newfoundland dog; 15 c. Harp Seal; 20 c. Cape Race; 24 c. Bell Island; 25 c. Sealing fleet; 48 c. The Banks fishing fleet.

*The line perforation was produced by two machines measuring respectively 13.7 and 14.1. The comb perforation measures 13.3×13.2.

Four used examples of No. 259c have now been identified on separate covers.

The paper used had the watermarks spaced for smaller format stamps. In consequence the individual watermarks are out of alignment so that stamps from the second vertical row were sometimes without watermark.

155 King George VI

156 Queen Mother

Damaged "A" (R. 5/9)

(Recess P.B.)

1938 (12 May). *T* **155/6** *and similar vert designs. W* **10**[6] *(sideways). P* 13½ *(comb).*

268 2 c. green .. 1·50 5[0]
a. Pair, with and without wmk .. £130
b. Imperf (pair) .. 75·00
269 3 c. carmine .. 1·00 5[0]
a. Perf 14 (line) .. £350 £20[0]
b. Pair, with and without wmk .. £180
c. Imperf (pair) .. 75·00
d. Damaged "A" .. 38·00
270 4 c. light blue .. 1·75 2[0]
a. Pair, with and without wmk .. 85·00
b. Imperf (pair) .. 70·00
w. Wmk inverted .. 65·00
271 7 c. deep ultramarine .. 75 3·7[5]
a. Imperf (pair) .. £100
268/71 .. *Set of* 4 4·50 4·5[0]

Designs:—4 c. Queen Elizabeth II as princess; 7 c. Queen Mary

For similar designs, perf 12½, see Nos. 277/281.

159 King George VI and Queen Elizabeth

(Recess B.W.)

1939 (17 June). *Royal Visit. No wmk. P* 13½.

272 **159** 5 c. deep ultramarine .. 1·50 3

2

▲ CENTS ▲

(160)

1939 (20 Nov). *No.* 272 *surch as T* **160**, *at St. John's.*

273 **159** 2 c. on 5 c. deep ultramarine (Br.) .. 1·75 3
274 4 c. on 5 c. deep ultramarine (C.) .. 90 5

161 Grenfell on the *Strathcona* (after painting by Gribble)

162 Memorial University College

(Recess C.B.N.)

1941 (1 Dec). *50th Anniv of Sir Wilfred Grenfell's Labrad*[or] *Mission. P* 12.

275 **161** 5 c. blue .. 30 5

(Recess Waterlow)

1941–44. *W* **106** *(sideways* on vert designs). P* 12½ *(line).*

276 **107** 1 c. grey .. 20 3
277 **155** 2 c. green .. 30 2
w. Wmk top of shield to right .. 35·00
278 **156** 3 c. carmine .. 30 1
a. Pair, with and without wmk .. 75·00
w. Wmk top of shield to right .. 35·00
279 – 4 c. blue (As No. 270) .. 2·25 2
a. Pair, with and without wmk .. £140
w. Wmk top of shield to right .. 35·00
280 **111** 5 c. violet (Die I) (*p* 13½ *comb*) .. 90·00
a. Perf 12½ (line) (6.42) .. 2·75 3
ab. Pair, with and without wmk .. £120
ac. Printed double .. £300
ad. Imperf vert (horiz pair) .. £325
b. Imperf (pair) .. £120
281 – 7 c. deep ultramarine (As No. 271) .. 6·00 9·0
a. Pair, with and without wmk .. £150
282 **121** 8 c. rose-red .. 1·00 1·7
a. Pair, with and without wmk .. £140
283 **113** 10 c. black-brown .. 1·75 7
284 **114** 14 c. black .. 2·25 5·5
285 **115** 15 c. claret .. 5·50 7·5
286 **116** 20 c. green .. 5·50 5·5
287 **122** 24 c. blue .. 3·25 11·0
w. Wmk top of shield to right .. 55·00

38 **117** 25 c. slate .. .. 6·50 7·50
39 **118** 48 c. red-brown (1944) .. .. 3·00 5·50
76/89 .. .. *Set of* 14 35·00 50·00

*The normal sideways watermark shows the top of the shield left, *as seen from the back of the stamp.*

Nos. 276/89 are redrawn versions of previous designs with ightly larger dimensions; the 5 c. for example, measures mm in width as opposed to the 20.4 mm of the Perkins Bacon intings.

No. 280. For Die I see note relating to No. 225.

(Recess C.B.N.)

43 (1 Jan). *P* 12.
0 **162** 30 c. carmine .. .. .. 1·00 1·40

163 St. John's

TWO
CENTS
(164)

(Recess C.B.N.)

43 (1 June). *Air. P* 12.
1 **163** 7 c. ultramarine 40 65

46 (21 Mar). *No.* 290 *surch locally with T* **164**.
2 **162** 2 c. on 30 c. carmine 30 65

165 Queen Elizabeth II when Princess
166 Cabot off Cape Bonavista

(Recess Waterlow)

47 (21 Apr). *Princess Elizabeth's 21st Birthday. W* **106** (*sideways*). *P* 12½.
3 **165** 4 c. light blue 30 65
a. Imperf vert (horiz pair) £275

(Recess Waterlow)

47 (24 June). *450th Anniv of Cabot's Discovery of Newfoundland. W* **106** (*sideways*). *P* 12½.
4 **166** 5 c. mauve 20 80
a. Imperf between (horiz pair) .. £1200

STAMP BOOKLETS

926. *Black on pink cover with Ayre and Sons advertisement on front. Stapled.*
B1 40 c. booklet containing eight 1 c. and sixteen 2 c. (Nos. 149/50) in blocks of 8 .. .. £1200

B **1**

932 (2 Jan). *Black on buff cover as Type* B **1**. *Stapled.*
B2 40 c. booklet containing four 1 c., twelve 2 c. and four 3 c. (Nos. 209b, 210c, 211c) in blocks of 4 £350
a. Contents as No. SB2, but containing Nos. 209b, 210 and 211c £425
b. Contents as No. SB2, but containing Nos. 222d, 223d and 211d £400

B **2**

932. *Black on cream cover as Type* B **2**. *Stapled.*
B3 40 c. booklet containing four 1 c., twelve 2 c. and four 3 c. (Nos. 222, 223, 211) in blocks of 4 £350

POSTAGE DUE STAMPS

D **1**
D **6**ac

(Litho John Dickinson & Co, Ltd)

1939 (1 May)–**49.** *P* 10.
D1 D **1** 1 c. green .. .. 2·00 8·00
a. Perf 11 (1949) .. .. .. 3·00 9·00
D2 2 c. vermilion .. .. 11·00 7·00
a. Perf 11 × 9 (1946) .. .. .. 11·00 18·00
D3 3 c. ultramarine .. .. .. 4·50 18·00
a. Perf 11 × 9 (1949) .. .. .. 10·00 27·00
b. Perf 9 .. .. £500
D4 4 c. orange .. .. 9·00 16·00
a. Perf 11 × 9 (May 1948) .. .. 11·00 45·00
D5 5 c. brown .. .. 5·50 23·00
D6 10 c. violet .. .. 6·00 16·00
a. Perf 11 (W **106**) (1949) .. .. 22·00 75·00
ab. Ditto. Imperf between (vert pair) .. £650
ac. "POSTAGE LUE" (R 3/3 or 3/8) .. £100 £275
D1/6 .. .. *Set of* 6 38·00 80·00

Newfoundland joined the Dominion of Canada on 31 March 1949.

NOVA SCOTIA

Organised postal services in Nova Scotia date from April 1754 when the first of a series of Deputy Postmasters was appointed, under the authority of the British G.P.O. This arrangement continued until 6 July 1851 when the colony assumed responsibility for its postal affairs.

For illustrations of the handstamp types see BRITISH POST OFFICES ABROAD notes, following GREAT BRITAIN.

AMHERST

CROWNED-CIRCLE HANDSTAMPS

CC1 CC **1** AMHERST. N.S.(R) (25.2.1845) *Price on cover* £1000

ST. MARGARETS BAY

CROWNED-CIRCLE HANDSTAMPS

CC2 CC **1** ST. MARGARETS BAY. N.S.(R) (30.6.1845) *Price on cover* £9000

Nos. CC1/2 were later used during temporary shortages of stamps, struck in red or black.

PRICES FOR STAMPS ON COVER

No. 1	*from* × 5
Nos. 2/4	*from* × 2
Nos. 5/8	*from* × 4
Nos. 9/10	*from* × 10
Nos. 11/13	*from* × 2
Nos. 14/15	—
No. 16	*from* × 4
Nos. 17/19	*from* × 10
Nos. 20/5	*from* × 2
No. 26	*from* × 50
Nos. 27/8	*from* × 4
No. 29	*from* × 10

1
2

Crown and Heraldic Flowers of United Kingdom and Mayflower of Nova Scotia.

(Recess P.B.)

1851 (1 Sept)–**57.** *Bluish paper. Imperf.*
1 **1** 1d. red-brown (12.5.53) £2000 £400
a. Bisected (½d.) (on cover) .. † £50000
2 **2** 3d. deep blue £1000 £160
a. Bisected (1½d.) (on cover) .. † £2250
3 3d. bright blue £900 £110
a. Bisected (1½d.) (on cover) .. † £2250
4 3d. pale blue (1857) £750 £130
a. Bisected (1½d.) (on cover) .. † £2250
5 6d. yellow-green £4000 £400
a. Bisected (3d.) (on cover) .. .. † £3000
6 6d. deep green (1857) £10000 £750
a. Bisected (3d.) (on cover) .. .. † £5000
b. Quartered (1½d.) (on cover) .. † £38000
7 **2** 1s. cold violet £19000 £6000
a. Bisected (6d.) (on cover) .. .. † £42000
b. Quartered (3d.) (on cover) .. † £55000
7*c* 1s. deep purple (1851) £15000 £3750
d. Watermarked £20000 £6000
8 1s. purple (1857) £14000 £2500
a. Bisected (6d.) (on cover) .. .. † £32000

The watermark on No. 7d consists of the whole or part of a letter from the name "P. H. SAUNDERS" (the papermakers).

The stamps formerly catalogued on almost white paper are probably some from which the bluish paper has been discharged.

Reprints of all four values were made in 1890 on thin, hard, white paper. The 1d. is brown, the 3d. blue, the 6d. deep green, and the 1s. violet-black.

The 3d. bisects are usually found used on cover to make up the 7½d. rate.

(New Currency. 100 cents = 1 dollar)

3
4
5

(Recess American Bank Note Co, New York)

1860–63. *P* 12. (*a*) *Yellowish paper.*
9 **3** 1 c. jet black .. .. 3·00 12·00
a. Bisected (½ c.) (on cover) .. † £10000
10 1 c. grey-black .. .. .. 3·00 12·00
11 2 c. grey-purple .. .. .. 11·00 15·00
11*a* 2 c. purple .. .. 17·00 14·00
12 5 c. blue .. .. £300 16·00
13 5 c. deep blue .. .. .. £300 16·00
14 **4** 8½ c. deep green .. .. .. 2·50
15 8½ c. yellow-green .. .. .. 2·50
16 10 c. scarlet .. .. 12·00 23·00
17 **5** 12½ c. black .. .. 26·00 26·00
17*a* 12½ c. greyish black .. .. .. — 26·00

(*b*) *White paper*
18 **3** 1 c. black .. .. 3·00 12·00
a. Imperf vert (horiz pair) £150
19 1 c. grey .. .. 3·00 12·00
20 2 c. dull purple .. .. .. 3·25 14·00
21 2 c. purple .. .. 3·25 14·00
22 2 c. grey-purple .. .. .. 3·25 14·00
a. Bisected (1 c.) (on cover) .. † £4500
23 2 c. slate-purple .. .. .. 3·25 12·00
24 5 c. blue .. .. £325 16·00
25 5 c. deep blue .. .. .. £325 16·00
26 **4** 8½ c. deep green .. .. .. 17·00 40·00
27 10 c. scarlet .. .. 4·00 20·00
28 10 c. vermilion .. .. .. 4·00 20·00
a. Bisected (5 c.) (on cover) .. † £750
29 **5** 12½ c. black .. .. 35·00 30·00

Nova Scotia joined the Dominion of Canada on 1 July 1867.

PRINCE EDWARD ISLAND

Prince Edward Island, previously administered as part of Nova Scotia, became a separate colony in 1769.

PRICES FOR STAMPS ON COVER

Nos. 1/4	*from* × 3
Nos. 5/6	—
Nos. 7/8	*from* × 5
Nos. 9/20	*from* × 6
Nos. 21/6	*from* × 3
Nos. 27/31	*from* × 6
Nos. 32/3	*from* × 50
Nos. 34/7	*from* × 6
Nos. 38/41	*from* × 20
No. 42	*from* × 50
Nos. 43/7	*from* × 5

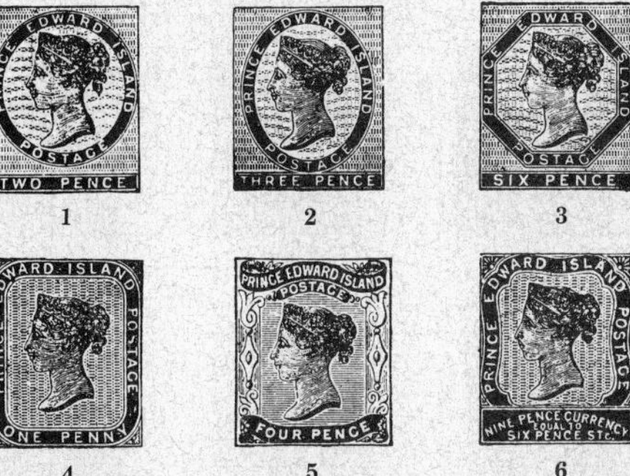

1 2 3
4 5 6

Two Dies of 2d:

Die I. Left-hand frame and circle merge at centre left (all stamps in the sheet of 60 (10×6) except R. 2/5)

Die II. Left-hand frame and circle separate at centre left (R. 2/5). There is also a break in the top frame line.

(Typo Charles Whiting, London)

1861 (1 Jan). *Yellowish toned paper.* (*a*) *P* 9.
1 **1** 2d. rose (I) £250 £120
a. Imperf between (horiz pair) .. . £4250
b. Imperf horiz (vert pair) .. ..
c. Bisected (1d.) (on cover) .. .. † £2750
d. Die II .. ..

2 1 2d. rose-carmine (I) .. £275 £130
a. Die II
3 2 3d. blue .. £475 £225
a. Bisected (1½d.) (on cover) .. † £2750
b. Double print .. £1300
4 3 6d. yellow-green .. £700 £350

(b) Rouletted

5 1 2d. rose (I) .. £2750 £2000

The 2d. and 3d., perf 9, were authorised to be bisected and used for half their normal value.

1862. *Yellowish toned paper. P 11.*

6 4 1d. brown-orange .. 28·00 50·00
7 6 9d. bluish lilac (29.3.62) .. 60·00 45·00
8 9d. dull mauve .. 60·00 45·00

1863–68. *Yellowish toned paper. (a) P 11½–12*

9 4 1d. yellow-orange .. 22·00 27·00
a. Bisected (½d.) (on cover) .. † £1600
b. Imperf between (horiz pair) .. £250
10 1d. orange-buff .. 23·00 27·00
11 1d. yellow .. 24·00 27·00
12 1 2d. rose (I) .. 8·00 8·50
a. Imperf vert (horiz pair)
b. Bisected (1d.) (on cover) .. † £1400
c. Die II .. 75·00 80·00
13 2d. deep rose (I) .. 8·50 11·00
a. Die II .. 80·00 90·00
14 2 3d. blue .. 14·00 14·00
a. Imperf horiz (vert pair)
b. Bisected (1½d.) (on cover)
15 3d. deep blue .. 14·00 12·00
16 5 4d. black (1867) .. 14·00 18·00
a. Imperf vert (horiz pair) .. £200
b. Bisected (2d.) (on cover) .. † £1400
17 3 6d. yellow-green (15.12.66) .. 75·00 65·00
a. Bisected (3d.) (on cover) .. † £2250
18 6d. blue-green (1868) .. 65·00 70·00
19 6 9d. lilac .. 48·00 45·00
20 9d. reddish mauve .. 45·00 45·00
a. Imperf vert (horiz pair) .. £350
b. Bisected (4½d.) (on cover) .. † £1800

(b) Perf compound of 11 and 11½–12

21 4 1d. yellow-orange .. £150 65·00
22 1 2d. rose (I) .. £150 65·00
a. Die II
23 2 3d. blue .. £170 65·00
24 5 4d. black .. £190 £180
25 3 6d. yellow-green .. £170 £180
26 6 9d. reddish mauve .. £180 £180

1870. *Coarse, wove bluish white paper. P 11½–12.*

27 1 2d. rose (I) .. 9·00 10·00
a. Die II .. 85·00 95·00
28 2d. rose-pink (I) .. 5·50 8·00
a. Die II .. 65·00 75·00
b. "TWC" (R. 6/4) .. 65·00 75·00
c. Imperf between (horiz pair) .. £120
29 2 3d. pale blue .. 8·00 9·00
30 3d. blue .. 8·00 9·00
a. Imperf between (horiz pair) .. £275
31 5 4d. black .. 4·00 26·00
a. Imperf between (horiz pair) .. £120
b. Bisected (2d.) (on cover) .. † £1500
c. Perf compound 11 and 11½–12

7

(Recess British-American Bank Note Co., Montreal and Ottawa)

1870 (1 June). *P 12.*

32 7 4½d. (3d. stg), yellow-brown .. 35·00 42·00
33 4½d. (3d. stg), deep brown .. 38·00 45·00

(New Currency. 100 cents = 1 dollar)

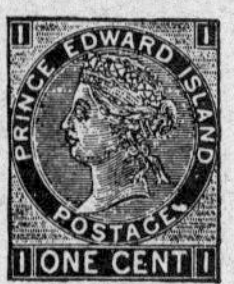

8

9

10

11

12

13

(Typo Charles Whiting, London)

1872 (1 Jan). *(a) P 11½–12.*

34 8 1 c. orange .. 3·50 11·00
35 1 c. yellow-orange .. 3·50 9·00
36 1 c. brown-orange .. 4·00 12·00
37 10 3 c. rose .. 13·00 17·00
a. Stop between "PRINCE. EDWARD" 38·00 45·00
b. Bisected (1½ c.) (on cover)
c. Imperf horiz (vert pair) .. £325

(b) Perf 12 to 12¼, large holes

38 9 2 c. blue .. 10·00 30·00
a. Bisected (1 c.) (on cover)
39 11 4 c. yellow-green .. 4·00 15·00
40 4 c. deep green .. 4·50 13·00
a. Bisected (2 c.) (on cover) .. † £2000
41 12 6 c. black .. 3·50 14·00
a. Bisected (3 c.) (on cover) .. † £950
b. Imperf between (horiz pair) .. £200
c. Imperf vert (horiz pair)
42 13 12 c. reddish mauve .. 3·50 25·00

(c) P 12½–13, smaller holes

43 8 1 c. orange .. 12·00
44 1 c. brown-orange .. 4·00 11·00
45 10 3 c. rose .. 13·00 20·00
a. Stop between "PRINCE. EDWARD" 50·00 65·00
45*b* 12 6 c. black .. — £250

(d) Perf compound of (a) and (c) 11½–12 × 12½–13

46 8 1 c. orange .. 30·00 32·00
47 10 3 c. rose .. 32·00 32·00
a. Stop between "PRINCE. EDWARD" £170 £180

Prince Edward Island joined the Dominion of Canada on 1 July 1873.

DOMINION OF CANADA

On July 1867, Canada, Nova Scotia and New Brunswick were united to form the Dominion of Canada.

The provinces of Manitoba (1870), British Columbia (1871), Prince Edward Island (1873), Alberta (1905), Saskatchewan (1905), and Newfoundland (1949) were subsequently added, as were the Northwest Territories (1870) and Yukon Territory (1898).

PRICES FOR STAMPS ON COVER TO 1945

Nos. 46/66	*from* × 2
Nos. 67/70	*from* × 10
Nos. 71/89	*from* × 3
Nos. 90/100	*from* × 2
Nos. 101/2	*from* × 5
Nos. 103/11	*from* × 3
Nos. 115/20	*from* × 6
Nos. 121/49	*from* × 3
Nos. 150/65	*from* × 2
Nos. 166/72	*from* × 3
Nos. 173/87	*from* × 5
Nos. 188/95	*from* × 2
Nos. 196/215	*from* × 3
Nos. 219/224*b*	*from* × 4
Nos. 225/45	*from* × 2
Nos. 246/55	*from* × 8
Nos. 256/310	*from* × 2
No. 312	*from* × 20
No. 313	*from* × 10
Nos. 315/18	*from* × 2
Nos. 319/28	*from* × 3
Nos. 329/40	*from* × 2
Nos. 341/400	*from* × 1
Nos. R1/11	*from* × 1
Nos. S1/3	*from* × 8
No. S4	*from* × 6
No. S5	*from* × 5
Nos. S6/11	*from* × 3
Nos. S12/14	*from* × 5
Nos. D1/8	*from* × 4
Nos. D9/13	*from* × 5
Nos. D14/24	*from* × 4

13

14

15

Large types

PRINTERS. Nos. 46/120 were recess-printed by the British American Bank Note Co at Ottawa or Montreal.

1868 (1 Apr)–**90.** *As T 13/15 (various frames).*

I. *Ottawa printings. P 12.*

(a) Thin rather transparent crisp paper

46 13 ½ c. black (1.4.68) .. 65·00 50·00
47 14 1 c. red-brown (1.4.68) .. £325 48·00
48 2 c. grass-green (1.4.68) .. £350 38·00
49 3 c. red-brown (1.4.68) .. £600 20·00
50 6 c. blackish brown (1.4.68) .. £850 £150
51 12½ c. bright blue (1.4.68) .. £500 £110
52 15 c. deep reddish purple .. £750 £150

In these first printings the impression is generally blurred and the lines of the background are less clearly defined than in later printings.

(b) Medium to stout wove paper (1868–71)

53 13 ½ c. black .. 45·00 45·00
54 ½ c. grey-black .. 45·00 45·00
a. Imperf between (pair)
b. Watermarked .. £11000 £6000
55 14 1 c. red-brown .. £300 40·00
a. Laid paper .. £6500 £1600
b. Watermarked (1868) .. £1800 £180
56 1 c. deep orange (Jan, 1869) .. £700 80·00
56*a* 1 c. orange-yellow (May (?), 1869) .. £650 60·00
56*b* 1 c. pale orange-yellow .. £750 75·00
ba. Imperf
57 14 2 c. deep green .. £325 27·0
57*a* 2 c. pale emerald-green (1871) .. £400 38·0
ab. Bisected (1 c. with 2 c. to make 3 c. rate) on cover .. † £400
ac. Laid paper .. † £6000
57*d* 2 c. bluish green .. £325 27·0
da. Watermarked (1868) .. £1500 £20
58 3 c. brown-red .. £650 15·0
a. Laid paper .. £6000 £30
b. Watermarked (1868) .. £2250 £16
59 6 c. blackish brown (*to* chocolate) .. £700 35·0
a. Watermarked (1868) .. £3000 £60
59*b* 6 c. yellow-brown (1870) .. £650 35·0
ba. Bisected (3 c.), on cover .. † £200
60 12½ c. bright blue .. £400 35·0
a. Imperf horiz (vert pair) .. † £600
b. Watermarked (1868) .. £1600 £22
60*c* 12½ c. pale dull blue (milky) .. £425 35·0
61 15 c. deep reddish purple .. £450 60·0
61*a* 15 c. pale reddish purple .. £400 60·0
ab. Watermarked (1868) .. — £120
61*b* 15 c. dull violet-grey .. £200 28·0
ba. Watermarked (1868) .. £3000 £50
61*c* 15 c. dull grey-purple .. £300 28·0

The official date of issue was 1 April 1868. Scattered example of most values can be found used in the second half of March.

The watermark on the stout paper stamps consists of th words "E & G BOTHWELL CLUTHA MILLS," in large double lined capitals. Portions of one or two letters only may be foun on these stamps, which occur in the early printings of 1868.

The papers may, in most cases, be easily divided if the stamps ar laid face downwards and carefully compared. The thin hard pape is more or less transparent and shows the design through th stamp; the thicker paper is softer to the feel and more opaque.

The paper of this issue may be still further subdivided in severa values into sets on—(a) *Medium to stout wove.* (b) *Thin, soft, ver white*: and (c) *Thinner and poorer quality, sometimes greyish c yellowish (from* 1878 *to end of issue).*

Of the 2 c. laid paper No. 57ac two examples only are know

II. *Montreal printings. Medium to stout wove paper.*

(a) P 11½×12 or 11¾×12

62 13 ½ c. black (1873) .. 55·00 55·0
63 15 5 c. olive-green (1.10.75) .. £700 65·0
a. Perf 12 .. £3500 £80
64 14 15 c. dull grey-purple (1874) .. £650 £15
65 15 c. lilac-grey (3.77) .. £850 £15
a. Script watermark .. £7000 £180
b. "BOTHWELL" watermark .. † —
66 15 c. slate .. £850 £30

(b) P 12

67 14 15 c. clear deep violet (1879) .. £2250 £50
68 15 c. deep slate (1881) .. £130 27·0
69 15 c. slaty blue (1887) .. £130 27·0
70 15 c. slate-purple (*shades*) (7.88–92) .. 60·00 16·0

No. 63a gauges 12 or above on all four sides.

The watermark on No. 65a is part of "Alex.Pirie & Sons" which appeared as script letters once per sheet in a small batc of the paper used for the 1877 printing. For a description of th sheet watermark on No. 65b see note after No. 61*c*.

Several used examples of the 12½ c. have been reporte perforated 11½×12 or 11¾×12.

The last printing of the 15 c. slate-purple, No. 70, took place a Ottawa.

III. *Ottawa printings. Thinnish paper of poor quality, often toned grey or yellowish. P 12*

71 14 15 c. slate-violet (*shades*) (5.90) .. 60·00 20·0
a. Imperf (pair). *Brown-purple* .. £1000

Examples of No. 71 are generally found with yellowis streaky gum.

21

Small type

1870–91. *As T* **21** *(various frames). Ottawa* (1870–73) *an Montreal printings. P* 12 *(or slightly under).*
Papers (*a*) 1870–80. *Medium to stout wove.*
(*b*) 1870–72. *Thin, soft, very white.*
(*c*) 1878–97. *Thinner and poorer quality.*

72 21 1 c. bright orange (*a, b*) (1870–73) .. £120 20·
a. Thick soft paper (1871) .. £350 £1
73 1 c. orange-yellow (*a*) (1876–79) .. 42·00 1·
74 1 c. pale dull yellow (*a*) (1877–79) .. 27·00
75 1 c. bright yellow (*a, c*) (1878–97) .. 20·00
a. Imperf (pair) (*c*) .. £300
b. Bisected (½ c.) (on *Railway News*) † £300
c. Printed both sides .. £1400
76 1 c. lemon-yellow (*c*) (1880) .. 75·00 15·
77 2 c. dp green (*a, b*) (1872–73 & 1876–78) 70·00 1·
78 2 c. grass-green (*c*) (1878–88) .. 40·00
a. Imperf (pair) (1891–93?) .. £350
b. Bisected (1 c. with 2 c. to make 3 c. rate) on cover .. † £14
79 3 c. Indian red (*a*) (1.70) .. £850 50·
a. Perf 12½ (2.70) .. £4250 £5
80 3 c. pale rose-red (*a*) (9.70) .. £275 8·
81 3 c. deep rose-red (*a, b*) (1870–73) .. £300 8·5
a. Thick soft paper (1.71) .. — £15
82 3 c. dull red (*a, c*) (1876–88) .. 55·00 1·
83 3 c. orange-red (*shades*) (*a, c*) (1876–88) 45·00
84 3 c. rose-carm (*c*) (10.88–4.89) .. £350 11·
85 5 c. olive-green (*a, c*) (2.76–88) .. £200 7·
86 6 c. yellowish brown (*a, b, c*) (1872–73 and 1876–90) .. £180 9·
a. Bisected (3 c.) on cover .. † £16
b. Perf 12×11½ (1873) .. † -
87 10 c. pale lilac-magenta (*a*) (1876–?) .. £450 48·
88 10 c. deep lilac-magenta (*a, c*) (3.76–88) £425 48·
89 10 c. lilac-pink (3.88) .. £225 28·

Nos. 75 and 78 were printed in the same shades during th second Ottawa period.

Examples of paper (*a*) can often be found showing traces ribbing, especially on the 2 c. value.

No. 79a was issued in New Brunswick and Nova Scotia.
One used copy of the 10 c. perf 12½ has been reported.

73–79. *Montreal printings. Medium to stout wove paper. P 11½×12 or 11¾×12.*

0	21	1 c. bright orange	£180	24·00
1		1 c. orange-yellow (1873–79)	£150	9·00
2		1 c. pale dull yellow (1877–79)	£140	14·00
3		1 c. lemon-yellow (1879)	£170	14·00
4		2 c. deep green (1873–78)	£200	16·00
5		3 c. dull red (1875–79)	£200	12·00
6		3 c. orange-red (1873–79)	£200	12·00
7		5 c. olive-green (1.2.76–79)	£375	22·00
8		6 c. yellowish brown (1873–79)	£375	26·00
9		10 c. very pale lilac magenta (1874)	£850	£250
0		10 c. deep lilac-magenta (1876–79)	£550	£170

27

382–97. *Montreal (to March 1889) and Ottawa printings. Thinnish paper of poor quality. P 12.*

)1	27	½ c. black (7.82–97)	7·50	6·00
)2		½ c. grey-black	7·50	6·00
		ab. Imperf (pair) (1891–93?)	£400	
		ac. Imperf between (pair)	£700	

889–97. *Ottawa printings. Thinnish paper of poor quality, often toned grey or yellowish. P 12.*

03	21	2 c. dull sea-green	35·00	70
04		2 c. blue-green (7.89–91)	30·00	90
05		3 c. bright vermilion (4.89–97)	23·00	50
		a. Imperf (pair) (1891–93?)	£300	
06		5 c. brownish grey (5.89)	60·00	1·25
		a. Imperf (pair) (1891–93)	£400	
07		6 c. deep chestnut (10.90)	30·00	7·50
		a. "5 c." re-entry*	£2000	£1300
		b. Imperf (pair) (1891–93?)	£400	
08		6 c. pale chestnut	35·00	7·50
09		10 c. salmon-pink	£225	£110
10		10 c. carmine-pink (4.90)	£150	20·00
		ab. Imperf (pair) (1891–93?)	£450	
11		10 c. brownish red (1894?)	£150	20·00
		ba. Imperf (pair)	£400	

The 1 c. showed no change in the Ottawa printings, so is not ncluded. The 2 c. reverted to its previous grass-green shade in 891.

The 3 c. is known bisected and used as a ⅔ stamp for the 2 c. drop letter" rate at Halifax in 1892.

28 29

(Recess B.A.B.N.)

893 (17 Feb). *P 12.*

15	28	20 c. vermilion	£160	42·00
		a. Imperf (pair)	£1200	
16		50 c. blue	£225	24·00
		a. Imperf (Prussian blue) (pair)	£1200	

893 (1 Aug). *P 12.*

17	29	8 c. pale bluish grey	80·00	3·50
		a. Imperf (pair)	£475	
18		8 c. bluish slate	90·00	3·50
19		8 c. slate-purple	80·00	3·50
20		8 c. blackish purple	70·00	3·50
		a. Imperf (pair)	£500	

PRINTERS. The following stamps to No. 287 were recess-printed by the American Bank Note Co, Ottawa, which in 1923 became the Canadian Bank Note Co.

30

(Des L. Pereira and F. Brownell)

897 (19 June). *Jubilee issue. P 12.*

21	30	½ c. black	48·00	48·00
22		1 c. orange	9·00	4·00
23		1 c. orange-yellow	9·00	4·00
		a. Bisected (½ c.) on cover		† £2500
24		2 c. green	13·00	8·00
25		2 c. deep green	13·00	8·00
26		3 c. carmine	9·50	2·00
27		5 c. slate-blue	35·00	13·00
28		5 c. deep blue	35·00	13·00
29		6 c. brown	85·00	85·00
30		8 c. slate-violet	32·00	29·00
31		10 c. purple	50·00	40·00
32		15 c. slate	85·00	85·00
33		20 c. vermilion	85·00	85·00
34		50 c. pale ultramarine	£120	95·00
35		50 c. bright ultramarine	£120	£100
36		$1 lake	£400	£400
37		$2 deep violet	£700	£350

138	30	$3 bistre	£800	£650
139		$4 violet	£800	£600
140		$5 olive-green	£800	£600
121/40		*Set of* 16	£3500	£2500
133/40		Handstamped "Specimen" *Set of* 7	£1800	

No 123a was used on issues of the *Railway News* of 5, 6 and 8 November 1897 and must be on a large part of the original newspaper with New Glasgow postmark.

31

32

(From photograph by W. & D. Downey, London)

1897–98. *P 12.*

141	31	½ c. grey-black (9.11.97)	5·50	4·00
142		½ c. black	7·00	4·50
		a. Imperf (pair)	£375	
143		1 c. blue-green (12.97)	17·00	70
		a. Imperf (pair)	£375	
144		2 c. violet (12.97)	17·00	1·00
		a. Imperf (pair)	£375	
145		3 c. carmine (1.98)	22·00	40
		a. Imperf (pair)	£700	
146		5 c. deep blue/*bluish* (12.97)	60·00	2·25
		a. Imperf (pair)	£375	
147		6 c. brown (12.97)	55·00	18·00
		a. Imperf (pair)	£700	
148		8 c. orange (12.97)	75·00	6·50
		a. Imperf (pair)	£400	
149		10 c. brownish purple (1.98)	£130	55·00
		a. Imperf (pair)	£425	
141/9		*Set of* 8	£325	75·00

BOOKLET PANES. Most definitive booklets issued from 1900 onwards had either the two horizontal sides or all three outer edges imperforate. Stamps from the panes show one side or two adjacent sides imperforate.

Two types of the 2 c.

Die Ia. Frame consists of four fine lines.
Die Ib. Frame has one thick line between two fine lines.

The die was retouched in 1900 for Plates 11 and 12 producing weak vertical frame lines and then retouched again in 1902 for Plates 15 to 20 resulting in much thicker frame lines. No. 155*b* covers both states of the retouching.

1898–1902. *P 12.*

150	32	½ c. black (9.98)	2·75	95
		a. Imperf (pair)	£375	
151		1 c. blue-green (6.98)	21·00	30
152		1 c. deep green/*toned paper*	21·00	30
		a. Imperf (pair)	£700	
153		2 c. dull purple (Die Ia) (9.98)	22·00	30
		a. Thick paper (6.99)	90·00	10·00
154		2 c. violet (Die Ia)	22·00	30
154*a*		2 c. reddish purple (Die Ia)	35·00	1·00
155		2 c. rose-carmine (Die Ia) (20.8.99)	28·00	30
		a. Imperf (pair)	£300	
155*b*		2 c. rose-carmine (Die Ib) (1900)	35·00	40
		ba. Booklet pane of 6 (11.6.00)	£750	
156		3 c. rose-carmine (6.98)	38·00	70
157		5 c. slate-blue/*bluish*	90·00	1·25
		a. Imperf (pair)	£750	
158		5 c. Prussian blue/*bluish*	95·00	1·25
159		6 c. brown (9.98)	85·00	48·00
		a. Imperf (pair)	£650	
160		7 c. greenish yellow (23.12.02)	50·00	11·00
161		8 c. orange-yellow (10.98)	£110	23·00
162		8 c. brownish orange	£100	23·00
		a. Imperf (pair)	£650	
163		10 c. pale brownish purple (11.98)	£160	13·00
164		10 c. deep brownish purple	£160	13·00
		a. Imperf (pair)	£650	
165		20 c. olive-green (29.12.00)	£300	48·00
150/65		*Set of* 11	£750	£120

The 7 c. and 20 c. also exist imperforate, but unlike the values listed in this condition, they have no gum. (*Price, 7 c. £350, 20 c. £1400 pair, un*).

33

(Des R. Weir Crouch, G. Hahn, A. H. Howard and R. Holmes. Eng C. Skinner. Design recess, colours added by typo)

1898 (7 Dec). *Imperial Penny Postage. Design in black. British possessions in red. Oceans in colours given. P 12.*

166	33	2 c. lavender	29·00	5·50
167		2 c. greenish blue	23·00	5·00
168		2 c. blue	23·00	4·75
		a. Imperf (pair)	£350	

Forgeries of Type **33** are without horizontal lines across the continents and have a forged Montreal postmark of 24.12.98.

1899 (4 Jan). *Provisionals used at Port Hood, Nova Scotia. No. 156 divided vertically and handstamped.*

169	32	"1" in blue, on ⅓ of 3 c.	—	£3500
170		"2" in violet, on ⅔ of 3 c.	—	£3000

Nos. 169/70 were prepared by the local postmaster during a shortage of 2 c. stamps caused by a change in postage rates.

2 CENTS

(34)

35 King Edward VII

1899. *Surch with T* **34**, *by Public Printing Office.*

171	31	2 c. on 3 c. carmine (8 Aug)	11·00	7·00
		a. Surch inverted	£275	
172	32	2 c. on 3 c. rose-carmine (28 July)	16·00	3·50
		a. Surch inverted	£275	

(Des King George V when Prince of Wales and J. A. Tilleard)

1903 (1 July)–**12.** *P 12.*

173	35	1 c. pale green	20·00	30
174		1 c. deep green	18·00	30
175		1 c. green	18·00	30
176		2 c. rose-carmine	18·00	20
		a. Booklet pane of 6	£750	
177		2 c. pale rose-carmine	18·00	20
		a. Imperf (pair) (18.7.09)	28·00	32·00
178		5 c. blue/*bluish*	70·00	2·00
179		5 c. indigo/*bluish*	70·00	2·25
180		7 c. yellow-olive	55·00	2·25
181		7 c. greenish bistre	65·00	2·50
181*a*		7 c. straw (1.12)	£110	35·00
182		10 c. brown-lilac	£110	7·50
183		10 c. pale dull purple	£110	7·50
184		10 c. dull purple	£110	7·50
185		20 c. pale olive-green (27.9.04)	£200	22·00
186		20 c. deep olive-green (H/S S. £75)	£225	22·00
187		50 c. deep violet (19.11.08)	£350	75·00
173/87		*Set of* 7	£700	£100

The 1 c., 5 c., 7 c. and 10 c. exist imperforate but are believed to be proofs. (*Prices per pair*, 1 c. £400, 5 c. £600, 7 c. £400, 10 c. £600).

IMPERFORATE AND PART-PERFORATED SHEETS. Prior to 1946 many Canadian issues exist imperforate, or with other perforation varieties, in the colours of the issued stamps and, usually, with gum. In the years before 1927 such examples are believed to come from imprimatur sheets, removed from the Canadian Post Office archives. From 1927 until 1946 it is known that the printers involved in the production of the various issues submitted several imperforate plate proof sheets of each stamp to the Post Office authorities for approval. Some of these sheets or part sheets were retained for record purposes, but the remainder found their way onto the philatelic market.

Part-perforated sheets also occur from 1927–29 issues.

From 1908 until 1946 we now only list and price such varieties of this type which are known to be genuine errors, sold from post offices. Where other imperforate or similar varieties are known they are recorded in footnotes.

It is possible, and in some cases probable, that some imperforate varieties listed before 1908 may have also been removed from the archives as mentioned above, but it is far harder to be explicit over the status of this earlier material.

36 King George V and Queen Mary when Prince and Princess of Wales

37 Jacques Cartier and Samuel Champlain

(Des Machado)

1908 (16 July). *Quebec Tercentenary T* **36/7** *and similar horiz designs. P 12.*

188	½ c. sepia	3·25	3·00
189	1 c. blue-green	11·00	2·50
190	2 c. carmine	17·00	85
191	5 c. indigo	45·00	16·00
192	7 c. olive-green	50·00	35·00
193	10 c. violet	55·00	45·00
194	15 c. brown-orange	75·00	65·00
195	20 c. dull brown	£100	80·00
188/95	*Set of* 8	£300	£225

Designs:—2 c. King Edward VII and Queen Alexandra; 5 c. Champlain's House in Quebec; 7 c. Generals Montcalm and Wolfe; 10 c. Quebec in 1700; 15 c. Champlain's departure for the West; 20 c. Cartier's arrival before Quebec.

Some values exist on both toned and white papers.

Nos. 188/95 exist imperforate. (*Price £325, un, for each pair*).

WET AND DRY PRINTINGS. Until the end of December 1922 all Canadian stamps were produced by the "wet" method of recess-printing in which the paper was dampened before printing, dried and then gummed.

In late December 1922 the Canadian Bank Note Co. began to use the "dry" process in which the paper was gummed before printing. Late printings of the 3 c. brown were the first stamps to be produced by this method, but the changeover was not completed until January 1926.

"Dry" printings have a sharper appearance and can often be found with a degree of embossing showing on the reverse. Stamps from "wet" printings shrink during drying and are narrower than "dry" examples. In many cases the difference can be as great as 0.5 mm. On some early booklet panes the difference is in the vertical, rather than the horizontal, measurement.

On Nos. 196/215 all values only exist from "wet" printings except the 3 c., 20 c. and 50 c. which come from both types of printing.

44

1911–22. *P* 12.
196 **44** 1 c. yellow-green (22.12.11) .. .. 5·50 20
a. With fine horiz lines across stamp 35·00 8·50
197 1 c. bluish green .. .. .. 5·50 30
a. Booklet pane of 6 (1.5.13) .. .. 50·00
198 1 c. deep bluish green .. .. .. 6·00 30
199 1 c. deep yellow-green .. .. .. 6·00 30
a. Booklet pane of 6 .. .. .. 18·00
200 2 c. rose-red (22.12.11) .. .. .. 4·50 20
201 2 c. deep rose-red .. .. .. 4·75 20
a. Booklet pane of 6 (1.12) .. .. 32·00
202 2 c. pale rose-red .. .. .. 4·50 20
a. With fine horiz lines across stamp 25·00 7·00
203 2 c. carmine .. .. 5·50 20
204 3 c. brown (6.8.18) .. .. .. 6·00 20
205 3 c. deep brown .. .. 5·00 20
a. Booklet pane of 4 + 2 labels (2.22) 50·00
205*b* 5 c. deep blue (17.1.12) .. .. .. 60·00 50
206 5 c. indigo .. .. 85·00 1·75
206*a* 5 c. grey-blue .. .. 75·00 1·25
206*b* 7 c. straw (12.1.12) .. .. .. 75·00 12·00
207 7 c. pale sage-green (1914) .. .. £180 30·00
208 7 c. olive-yellow (1915) .. .. .. 20·00 2·50
209 7 c. yellow-ochre (1916) .. .. .. 20·00 2·50
210 10 c. brownish purple (12.1.12) .. .. 90·00 2·00
211 10 c. reddish purple .. .. .. £100 2·50
212 20 c. olive-green (23.1.12) .. .. 28·00 1·25
213 20 c. olive .. .. 28·00 1·50
214 50 c. grey-black (26.1.12) .. .. £100 8·00
215 50 c. sepia .. .. 48·00 3·25
196/215 .. .. *Set of* 8 £225 9·00

The 20 c. and 50 c. values exist imperforate (*Price* £1100 *un, for each pair*).

1912 (Nov)–**21.** *For use in coil-machines.* (*a*) *P* 12×*imperf.*
216 **44** 1 c. yellow-green (1914) .. .. 3·50 9·00
217 1 c. blue-green .. .. .. 12·00 23·00
a. Two large holes at top and bottom (vert pair) (7.18) .. .. 60·00 75·00
218 2 c. deep rose-red (1914) .. .. 25·00 17·00
218*a* 3 c. brown (1921) .. .. .. 3·50 5·50

No. 217a has two large holes about 3½ mm in diameter in the top and bottom margins. They were for experimental use in a vending machine at Toronto in July 1918 and were only in use for two days.

The 1 c. and 2 c. also exist with two small "V" shaped holes about 9.5 mm apart at top which are gripper marks due to modifications made in vending machines in 1917.

(*b*) *Imperf* × *perf* 8
219 **44** 1 c. yellow-green (9.12) .. .. 12·00 3·00
220 1 c. blue-green .. .. .. 15·00 3·25
a. With fine horiz lines across stamp 55·00
221 2 c. carmine (9.12) .. .. .. 11·00 90
222 2 c. rose-red .. .. 12·00 2·00
223 2 c. scarlet .. .. 32·00 4·75
224 3 c. brown (8.18) .. .. .. 5·00 1·25

(*c*) *P* 8 × *imperf*
224*a* **44** 1 c. blue-green (15.2.13) .. .. 60·00 48·00
224*b* 2 c. carmine (15.2.13) .. .. 60·00 48·00

The stamps imperf × perf 8 were sold in coils over the counter; those perf 8 × imperf were on sale in automatic machines. Varieties showing perf 12 on 2 or 3 adjacent sides and 1 or 2 sides imperf are from booklets, or the margins of sheets.

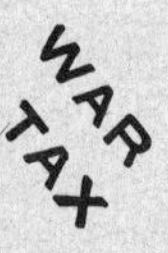

(45)

46

47

1915 (12 Feb). *Optd with T* **45**.
225 **44** 5 c. blue £110 £180
226 20 c. olive-green .. .. .. 55·00 90·00
227 50 c. sepia (R.) £110 £140
225/7 .. .. *Set of* 3 £250 £375

These stamps were intended for tax purposes, but owing to ambiguity in an official circular dated 16 April 1915, it was for a time believed that their use for postal purposes was authorised. The position was clarified by a further circular on 20 May 1916 which made clear that Nos. 225/7 were for fiscal use only.

1915. *P* 12.
228 **46** 1 c. green (15.4.15) .. .. .. 7·50 20
229 2 c. carmine-red (16.4.15) .. .. 9·00 30
230 2 c. rose-carmine .. .. .. 10·00 2·50

PRICES OF SETS

Set prices are given for many issues, generally those containing three stamps or more. Definitive sets include one of each value or major colour change, but do not cover different perforations, die types or minor shades. Where a choice is possible the set prices are based on the cheapest versions of the stamps included in the listings.

Die I

Die II

In Die I there is a long horizontal coloured line under the foot of the "T", and a solid bar of colour runs upwards from the "1" to the "T".

In Die II this solid bar of colour is absent, and there is a short horizontal line under the left side of the "T", with two short vertical dashes and a number of dots under the right-hand side.

1916 (1 Jan). *P* 12.
231 **47** 2 c. + 1 c. rose-red (Die I) .. .. 20·00 90
232 2 c. + 1 c. bright carmine (Die I) .. 20·00 90
233 2 c. + 1 c. scarlet (Die I) .. .. .. 17·00 90

1916 (Feb). *Imperf* × *perf* 8 (*coils*).
234 **47** 2 c. + 1 c. rose-red (Die I) .. .. 48·00 9·50

1916 (July). *P* 12 × 8.
235 **47** 2 c. + 1 c. carmine-red (Die I) .. .. 14·00 45·00
236 2 c. + 1 c. bright rose-red (Die I) .. 14·00 45·00

1916 (Aug). *P* 12.
237 **47** 2 c. + 1 c. carmine-red (Die II) .. .. 85·00 16·00

1916 (Aug). *Colour changed.* (*a*) *P* 12.
238 **47** 2 c. + 1 c. brown (Die I) .. .. .. £180 20·00
239 2 c. + 1 c. yellow-brown (Die II) .. 4·00 20
a. Imperf (pair) £750
240 2 c. + 1 c. deep brown (Die II) .. .. 10·00 20

(*b*) *Imperf* × *perf* 8
241 **47** 2 c. + 1 c. brown (Die I) .. .. .. 90·00 7·50
a. Pair, 241 and 243 .. .. .. £325
243 2 c. + 1 c. deep brown (Die II) .. .. 35·00 3·25

No. 239a, which is a genuine error, should not be confused with ungummed proofs of the Die I stamp, No. 238 (*Price per pair,* £130).

This value also exists p 12×imperf or imperf×p 12, but was not issued with these perforations (*Price, in either instance,* £250, *un, per pair*).

48 Quebec Conference, 1864, from painting "The Fathers of Confederation", by Robert Harris

1917 (15 Sept). *50th Anniv of Confederation. P* 12.
244 **48** 3 c. bistre-brown .. .. .. 16·00 1·25
245 3 c. deep brown .. .. .. 18·00 1·50

No. 244 exists imperforate (*Price per pair,* £250 *un*).

I

II

Die I. Space between top of "N" and oval frame line and space between "CENT" and lower frame line.

Die II. "ONE CENT" appears larger so that "N" touches oval and "CENT" almost touches frame line. There are other differences but this is the most obvious one.

I

II

Die I. The lowest of the three horizontal lines of shading below the medals does not touch the three heavy diagonal lines; three complete white spaces over both "E's" of "THREE"; long centre bar to figures "3". Vertical spandrel lines fine.

Die II. The lowest horizontal line of shading touches the first of the three diagonal lines; two and a half spaces over first "E" and spaces over second "E" partly filled by stem of maple leaf; short centre bar to figures "3". Vertical spandrel lines thick. There are numerous other minor differences.

WET AND DRY PRINTINGS. See notes above No. 196.

On Nos. 246/63 all listed items occur from both "wet" and "dry" printings except Nos. 246aa/ab, 248aa, 256, 259, 260 and 262 which come "wet" only, and Nos. 246a, 248/a, 252/4*a*, 256b and 263 which are "dry" only.

1922–31. *As T* **44**. (*a*) *P* 12.
246 **44** 1 c. chrome-yellow (Die I) (7.6.22) .. 2·50 2
aa. Booklet pane of 4 + 2 labels (7.22) 48·00
ab. Booklet pane of 6 (12.22) .. .. 27·00
a. Die II (1925) .. .. .. 5·50 1
247 2 c. deep green (6.6.22) .. .. .. 2·25 1
aa. Booklet pane of 4 + 2 labels (7.22) 27·00
ab. Booklet pane of 6 (12.22) £250
b. Thin paper (9.24) .. .. .. 2·75 3·7
248 3 c. carmine (Die I) (18.12.23) .. .. 3·75 1
aa. Booklet pane of 4 + 2 labels (12.23) 28·00
a. Die II (11.24) .. .. .. 19·00 3
249 4 c. olive-yellow (7.7.22) .. .. 8·00 3·2
a. Yellow-ochre .. .. .. 8·00 3·2
250 5 c. violet (2.2.22) .. .. .. 5·00 1·0
a. Thin paper (9.24) .. .. .. 5·00 8·0
b. Reddish violet (1925) .. .. 7·00 1·5
251 7 c. red-brown (12.12.24) .. .. 12·00 6·5
a. Thin paper .. .. £130 30·0
252 8 c. blue (1.9.25) .. .. .. 19·00 9·0
253 10 c. blue (20.2.22) .. .. .. 20·00 2·2
254 10 c. bistre-brown (1.8.25) .. .. 18·00 2·0
a. Yellow-brown .. .. .. 18·00 2·0
255 $1 brown-orange (22.7.23) .. .. 50·00 6·0
246/55 .. .. *Set of* 10 £130 27·0

The $1 differs from T **44** in that the value tablets are oval.

Nos. 249/55 exist imperforate (*Prices per un pair* 4 c. *to* 8 c. £850 *each,* 10 c. £900, $1 £1000).

(*b*) *Imperf* × *perf* 8
256 **44** 1 c. chrome-yellow (Die I) (1922) .. 4·00 4·7
a. Imperf horiz (vert pair) (1924) .. £160
b. Die II (1925) .. .. .. 4·50 7·0
c. Do. Imperf horiz (vert pair) (1927) 11·00 27·0
257 2 c. deep green (26.7.22) .. .. 8·00 1·5
b. Imperf horiz (vert pair) (1927) .. 12·00 27·0
258 3 c. carmine (Die I) (9.4.24) .. .. 55·00 8·5
a. Imperf horiz (vert pair) (1924) .. £250
b. Die II (1925) .. .. .. 75·00 19·0
256/8 .. .. *Set of* 3 60·00 13·0

Nos. 256a, 256c, 257b and 258a come from coil printings sold in sheet form. Those issued in 1924 were from "wet" printings and those in 1927 from "dry". A "wet" printing of No. 257b issued in 1924, also exists (*Price* £160 *mint*), but cannot be identified from that issued in 1927 except by the differences between "wet" and "dry" stamps.

(*c*) *Imperf* (*pairs*)
259 **44** 1 c. chrome-yellow (Die I) (6.10.24) .. 50·00 70·0
260 2 c. deep green (6.10.24) .. .. 50·00 70·0
261 3 c. carmine (Die I) (31.12.23)† .. .. 28·00 40·0

(*d*) *P* 12 × *imperf*
262 **44** 2 c. deep green (9.24) .. .. .. 65·00 60·0

(*e*) *P* 12 × 8
263 **44** 3 c. carmine (Die II) (24.6.31) .. .. 2·00 3·0

Nos. 259 to 261 were on sale only at the Philatelic Branch P.O. Dept, Ottawa.

†Earliest known postmark.

2 CENTS

(49)

(50)

1926. *No.* 248 *surch.*

(*a*) *With T* **49**, *by the Govt Printing Bureau*
264 **44** 2 c. on 3 c. carmine (12.10.26) .. .. 38·00 48·0
a. Pair, one without surch £300
b. On Die II £350

(*b*) *With T* **50**, *by the Canadian Bank Note Co*
265 **44** 2 c. on 3 c. carmine (4.11.26) .. .. 14·00 18·0
a. Surch double (partly treble) .. £200

51 Sir J. A. Macdonald

52 "The Fathers of Confederation"

53 Parliament Buildings, Ottawa

54 Sir W. Laurier

55 Canada, Map 1867–1927

1927 (29 June). *60th Anniv of Confederation. P* 12. I. *Commemorative Issue. Inscr* "1867–1927 CANADA CONFEDERATION".
266 **51** 1 c. orange .. .. 2·00 9
267 **52** 2 c. green .. .. 2·00 1
268 **53** 3 c. carmine .. .. 6·50 3·7
269 **54** 5 c. violet .. .. 3·25 3·2
270 **55** 12 c. blue .. .. 20·00 4·5
266/70 .. .. *Set of* 5 30·00 11·0

Nos. 266/70 exist imperforate, imperf×perf or perf×imperf (*Prices from* £60, *un, per pair*).

56 Darcy McGee

57 Sir W. Laurier and Sir J. A. Macdonald

58 R. Baldwin and L. H. Lafontaine

II. *Historical Issue*

271	**56**	5 c. violet	3·00	2·00
272	**57**	12 c. green	14·00	4·00
273	**58**	20 c. carmine	14·00	11·00
271/3		.. .. *Set of* 3	28·00	15·00

Nos. 271/3 exist imperforate, imperf×perf or perf×imperf (*Prices from* £60, *un, per pair*).

59

(Des H. Schwartz)

1928 (21 Sept). *Air. P* 12.

274	**59**	5 c. olive-brown	3·75	2·50

No. 274 exists imperforate, imperf×perf or perf×imperf (*Price per pair*, £130, *un*).

60 King George V

61 Mt Hurd and Indian Totem Poles

62 Quebec Bridge

63 Harvesting with Horses

64 *Bluenose* (fishing schooner)

65 Parliament Buildings, Ottawa

1928–29. (*a*) *P* 12.

275	**60**	1 c. orange (25.10.28)	2·25	40
		a. Booklet pane of 6	18·00	
276		2 c. green (16.10.28)	1·00	10
		a. Booklet pane of 6	18·00	
277		3 c. lake (12.12.28)	14·00	14·00
278		4 c. olive-bistre (16.8.29)	13·00	5·50
279		5 c. violet (12.12.28)	5·50	2·50
		a. Booklet pane of 6 (6.1.29)	90·00	
280		8 c. blue (21.12.28)	7·50	3·50
281	**61**	10 c. green (5.12.28)	7·00	85
282	**62**	12 c. grey-black (8.1.29)	17·00	9·00
283	**63**	20 c. lake (8.1.29)	27·00	9·50
284	**64**	50 c. blue (8.1.29)	£100	35·00
285	**65**	$1 olive-green (8.1.29)	£110	55·00
		a. Brown-olive	£225	95·00
275/85		.. .. *Set of* 11	£250	£120

(*b*) *Imperf* × *perf* 8 (5.11.28)

286	**60**	1 c. orange	13·00	21·00
287		2 c. green	13·00	3·75

Slight differences in the size of many Canadian stamps, due to paper shrinkage, are to be found.

Nos. 275/85 exist imperforate, imperf×perf or perf×imperf (*Prices per unused pair*, 1 c. to 8 c., *from* £60, 10 c. to 20 c., *from* £90, 50 c. and $1, *from* £350). *Tête-bêche* horizontal pairs of the 1 c., 2 c. and 5 c. are also known from uncut booklet sheets (*Prices per pair*, £200, *un*).

PRINTERS. The following stamps to No. 334 were recess-printed by the British American Bank Note Co, Ottawa.

66

67 Parliamentary Library, Ottawa

68 The Old Citadel, Quebec

69 Harvesting with Tractor

70 Acadian Memorial Church and Statue of "Evangeline", Grand Pre, Nova Scotia

71 Mt Edith Cavell, Canadian Rockies

Die I 1 c. Die II Die I 2 c. Die II

1 c. Die I. Three thick coloured lines and one thin between "P" and ornament, at right. Curved line in ball-ornament short.

Die II. Four thick lines. Curved line longer.

2 c. Die I. Three thick coloured lines between "P" and ornament, at left. Short line in ball.

Die II. Four thick lines. Curved line longer.

1930–31. (*a*) *P* 11.

288	**66**	1 c. orange (I) (17.7.30)	1·25	80
289		2 c. green (I) (6.7.30)	1·10	10
		a. Booklet pane of 6 (17.6.30) ..	35·00	
290		4 c. yellow-bistre (5.11.30)	6·00	3·25
291		5 c. violet (18.6.30)	2·50	3·50
292		8 c. blue (13.8.30)	7·00	13·00
293	**67**	10 c. olive-green (15.9.30)	13·00	85
		a. Imperf (pair)	£900	
294	**68**	12 c. grey-black (4.12.30)	11·00	3·75
295	**69**	20 c. red (4.12.30)	22·00	60
296	**70**	50 c. blue (4.12.30)	80·00	17·00
297	**71**	$1 olive-green (4.12.30)	95·00	23·00
288/97		.. .. *Set of* 10	£200	55·00

Nos. 294/7 exist imperforate (*Prices per unused pair*, 12 c. £500, 20 c. £500, 50 c. £600, $1 £650).

(*b*) *Imperf* × *perf* 8½

298	**66**	1 c. orange (I)	10·00	13·00
299		2 c. green (I)	3·75	4·50

Colours changed and new value. (*a*) *P* 11

300	**66**	1 c. green (I) (6.12.30)	1·00	10
		a. Imperf (pair)	£800	
		b. Booklet pane of 6 (21.7.31) ..	25·00	
		c. Booklet pane of 4 + 2 labels (13.11.31)	75·00	
		d. Die II	1·00	10
301		2 c. scarlet (I) (17.11.30)	70	30
		a. Booklet pane of 6 (17.11.30) ..	23·00	
		b. Die II	90	10
302		2 c. deep brown (I) (4.7.31)	1·25	2·75
		a. Booklet pane of 6 (23.7.31) ..	35·00	
		b. Die II	85	10
		ba. Booklet pane of 4 + 2 labels (13.11.31)	£100	
303		3 c. scarlet (13.7.31)	90	10
		a. Booklet pane of 4 + 2 labels ..	35·00	
304		5 c. deep slate-blue (13.11.30)	5·00	20
		a. Dull blue	13·00	50
305		8 c. red-orange (5.11.30)	6·50	4·75
300/5		.. .. *Set of* 6	13·00	4·75

(*b*) *Imperf* × *perf* 8½

306	**66**	1 c. green (I)	6·00	7·00
307		2 c. scarlet (I)	4·50	3·25
308		2 c. deep brown (I) (4.7.31)	9·00	1·25
309		3 c. scarlet (13.7.31)	14·00	1·00
306/9		.. .. *Set of* 4	30·00	11·00

Some low values in the above and subsequent issues have been printed by both Rotary and "Flat plate" processes. The former can be distinguished by the gum, which has a striped appearance.

For 13 c. bright violet, T **68**, see No. 325.

ALTERED CATALOGUE NUMBERS

Any Catalogue numbers altered from the last edition are shown as a list in the introductory pages.

72 Mercury and Western Hemisphere

73 Sir Georges Etienne Cartier

(Des H. Schwartz)

1930 (4 Dec). *Air. P* 11.

310	**72**	5 c. deep brown	15·00	17·00

1931 (30 Sept). *P* 11.

312	**73**	10 c. olive-green	2·75	10

No. 312 exists imperforate (*Price per pair*, £300, *un*).

(**74**) (**75**)

1932 (22 Feb). *Air. No.* 274 *surch with T* **74**.

313	**59**	6 c. on 5 c. olive-brown	2·25	2·00

Examples of this stamp with surcharge inverted, surcharge double, surcharge triple or surcharge omitted in pair with normal are not now believed to have been regularly issued. Such "errors" have also been forged and collectors are warned against forged examples, some of which bear unauthorized markings which purport to be the guarantee of Stanley Gibbons Ltd.

1932 (21 June). *Nos.* 301/*b surch with T* **75**.

314	**66**	3 c. on 2 c. scarlet (I)	1·75	2·25
		a. Die II	1·00	40

76 King George V

77 Duke of Windsor when Prince of Wales

78 Allegory of British Empire

6 6

OTTAWA CONFERENCE
1932

(**79**)

1932 (12 July). *Ottawa Conference. P* 11. (*a*) *Postage stamps.*

315	**76**	3 c. scarlet	70	60
316	**77**	5 c. blue	7·00	3·50
317	**78**	13 c. green	8·50	6·00

(*b*) *Air. No.* 310 *surch with T* **79**

318	**72**	6 c. on 5 c. deep brown (B.)	10·00	12·00
315/18		.. .. *Set of* 4	23·00	20·00

80 King George V

"3" level Die I

"3" raised Die II

1932 (1 Dec)–**33**. (*a*) *P* 11.

319	**80**	1 c. green	60	10
		a. Booklet pane of 6 (28.12.33) ..	15·00	
		b. Booklet pane of 4 + 2 labels (19.9.33)	75·00	
320		2 c. sepia	70	10
		a. Booklet pane of 6 (7.9.33)	15·00	
		b. Booklet pane of 4 + 2 labels (19.9.33)	75·00	
321		3 c. scarlet (Die I)	1·00	10
		a. Booklet pane of 4 + 2 labels (22.8.33)	40·00	
		b. Die II (29.11.32)	85	10
		ba. Booklet pane of 4 + 2 labels (19.9.33)	30·00	
322		4 c. yellow-brown	35·00	7·50
323		5 c. blue	10·00	10
		a. Imperf vert (horiz pair)	£850	
324		8 c. red-orange	22·00	3·50
325	**68**	13 c. bright violet	32·00	2·00
319/25		.. .. *Set of* 7	90·00	12·00

A plate block of four from Plate 1 exists printed in varnish ink.

Nos. 319/25 exist imperforate (*Prices per unused pair*, 1 c. to 8 c. £140, 13 c. £400)

(b) *Imperf × perf* 8½ (1933)

326 **80** 1 c. green .. .. 13·00 2·50
327 2 c. sepia .. .. 19·00 2·00
328 3 c. scarlet (Die II) .. .. 12·00 1·00
326/8 .. .. *Set of* 3 40·00 5·00

81 Parliament Buildings, Ottawa

1933 (18 May). *U.P.U. Congress Preliminary Meeting. P* 11.
329 **81** 5 c. blue .. .. 5·00 2·50
No. 329 exists imperforate (*Price per pair* £425, *un*).

WORLD'S
GRAIN EXHIBITION &
CONFERENCE

REGINA 1933

(82)

1933 (24 July). *World's Grain Exhibition and Conference, Regina. No.* 295 *optd with T* **82** *in blue.*
330 **69** 20 c. red .. .. 16·00 6·50
No. 330 exists imperforate (*Price per pair* £425, *un*).

83 S.S. *Royal William* (after S. Skillett) **84** Jacques Cartier approaching Land

1933 (17 Aug). *Centenary of First Trans-Atlantic Steamboat Crossing. P* 11.
331 **83** 5 c. blue .. .. 8·00 2·75
No. 331 exists imperforate (*Price per pair* £425, *un*).

1934 (1 July). *Fourth Centenary of Discovery of Canada. P* 11.
332 **84** 3 c. blue .. .. 2·00 1·25
No. 332 exists imperforate (*Price per pair* £425, *un*).

85 U.E.L. Statue, Hamilton **86** Seal of New Brunswick

1934 (1 July). *150th Anniv of Arrival of United Empire Loyalists. P* 11.
333 **85** 10 c. olive-green .. .. 8·50 4·50
No. 333 exists imperforate (*Price per pair* £750, *un*).

1934 (16 Aug). *150th Anniv of Province of New Brunswick. P* 11.
334 **86** 2 c. red-brown .. .. 1·50 2·25
No. 334 exists imperforate (*Price per pair* £375, *un*).

PRINTERS. The following stamps were recess-printed (except where otherwise stated) by the Canadian Bank Note Co, Ottawa, until No. 616.

87 Queen Elizabeth II when Princess **89** King George V and Queen Mary

1935 (4 May). *Silver Jubilee. T* **87**, **89** *and similar designs. P* 12.
335 1 c. green 55 40
336 2 c. brown 60 30
337 3 c. carmine-red .. .. 1·75 30
338 5 c. blue .. .. 4·25 4·00
339 10 c. green .. .. 3·25 3·00
340 13 c. blue .. .. 6·50 4·50
335/40 .. .. *Set of* 6 15·00 11·00
Designs: *Vert* (*as T* **87**)—2 c. King George VI when Duke of York; 5 c. King Edward VIII when Prince of Wales. *Horiz* (*as T* **89**)—10 c. Windsor Castle; 13 c. Royal Yacht *Britannia.*
Nos. 335/40 exist imperforate (*Price* £160, *un, for each pair*).

93 King George V **94** Royal Canadian Mounted Policeman

99 Daedalus

1935 (1 June–5 Nov). *T* **93/4**, **99** *and similar designs.* (*a*) *Postage.* (i) *P* 12.
341 **93** 1 c. green 30 10
a. Booklet pane of 6 (19.8.35) .. 22·00
b. Booklet pane of 4+2 labels (22.7.35) .. .. .. 55·00
342 2 c. brown 50 10
a. Booklet pane of 6 (16.11.35) .. 26·00
b. Booklet pane of 4+2 labels (22.7.35) .. .. .. 55·00
343 3 c. scarlet 60 10
a. Booklet pane of 4+2 labels .. 28·00
b. Printed on the gummed side .. £225
344 4 c. yellow .. .. 2·50 90
345 5 c. blue .. .. 1·75 10
a. Imperf vert (horiz pair) £200
346 8 c. orange .. .. 2·50 2·50
347 **94** 10 c. carmine .. .. 5·00 30
348 – 13 c. purple .. .. 4·75 45
349 – 20 c. olive-green .. .. 17·00 70
350 – 50 c. deep violet .. .. 25·00 4·25
351 – $1 bright blue .. .. 40·00 10·00
341/51 .. .. *Set of* 11 90·00 17·00

(ii) *Coil stamps. Imperf × perf* 8
352 **93** 1 c. green (5.11.35) .. .. .. 13·00 3·25
353 2 c. brown (14.10.35) .. .. .. 9·00 3·00
354 3 c. scarlet (20.7.35) .. .. .. 9·00 1·00
352/4 .. .. *Set of* 3 28·00 6·50

(*b*) *Air. P* 12
355 **99** 6 c. red-brown .. .. 2·50 60
a. Imperf vert (horiz pair) £4500
Designs: *Horiz* (*as T* **94**)—13 c. Confederation Conference, Charlottetown, 1864; 20 c. Niagara Falls; 50 c. Parliament Buildings, Victoria, British Columbia; $1 Champlain Monument, Quebec.
Nos. 341/51 (*Prices per pair,* 1 c. *to* 8 c. *each* £95, 10 c. *to* $1 *each* £190, *un.*) and 355 (*Price per pair* £375, *un*) exist imperforate.

100 King George VI and Queen Elizabeth

1937 (10 May). *Coronation. P* 12.
356 **100** 3 c. carmine 85 30
No. 356 exists imperforate (*Price per pair* £400, *un*).

101 King George VI **102** Memorial Chamber Parliament Buildings, Ottawa

107 Fairchild 45-80 Sekani Seaplane over *Distributor* on River Mackenzie

(T **101**. Photograph by Bertram Park)

1937–38. *T* **101/2**, **107** *and similar designs.* (*a*) *Postage.* (i) *P* 12.
357 **101** 1 c. green (1.4.37) .. .. .. 1·50 10
a. Booklet pane of 4 + 2 labels (14.4.37) .. .. .. 28·00
b. Booklet pane of 6 (18.5.37) .. 3·50
358 2 c. brown (1.4.37) .. .. .. 1·75 10
a. Booklet pane of 4 + 2 labels (14.4.37) .. .. .. 50·00
b. Booklet pane of 6 (3.5.38) .. 11·00

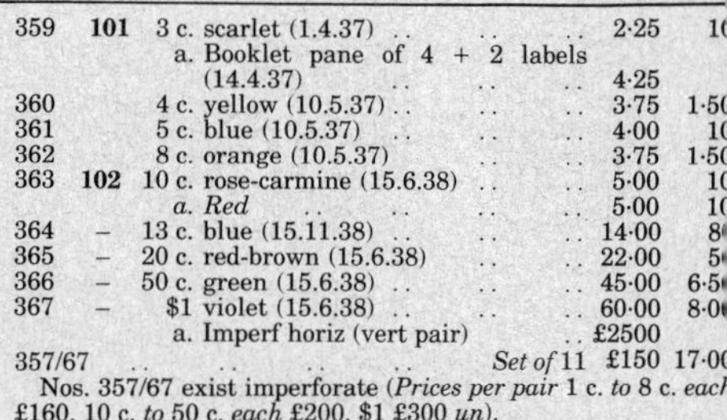

359 **101** 3 c. scarlet (1.4.37) .. .. .. 2·25 10
a. Booklet pane of 4 + 2 labels (14.4.37) .. .. .. 4·25
360 4 c. yellow (10.5.37) .. .. .. 3·75 1·50
361 5 c. blue (10.5.37) .. .. .. 4·00 10
362 8 c. orange (10.5.37) .. .. .. 3·75 1·50
363 **102** 10 c. rose-carmine (15.6.38) .. .. 5·00 10
a. Red .. .. 5·00 10
364 – 13 c. blue (15.11.38) .. .. .. 14·00 80
365 – 20 c. red-brown (15.6.38) .. .. 22·00 50
366 – 50 c. green (15.6.38) .. .. .. 45·00 6·50
367 – $1 violet (15.6.38) .. .. .. 60·00 8·00
a. Imperf horiz (vert pair) .. £2500
357/67 .. .. *Set of* 11 £150 17·00
Nos. 357/67 exist imperforate (*Prices per pair* 1 c. *to* 8 c. *each* £160, 10 c. *to* 50 c. *each* £200, $1 £300 *un*).

(ii) *Coil stamps. Imperf × perf* 8
368 **101** 1 c. green (15.6.37) .. .. .. 3·50 2·00
369 2 c. brown (18.6.37) .. .. .. 3·50 2·25
370 3 c. scarlet (15.4.37) .. .. .. 17·00 60
368/70 .. .. *Set of* 3 22·00 4·25

(*b*) *Air. P* 12
371 **107** 6 c. blue (15.6.38) .. .. .. 9·50 50
Designs: *Horiz* (*as T* **107**)—13 c. Entrance to Halifax Harbour; 20 c. Fort Garry Gate, Winnipeg; 50 c. Entrance, Vancouver Harbour; $1 Chateau de Ramezay, Montreal.
No. 371 exists imperforate (*Price per pair* £325, *un*).

108 Queen Elizabeth II when Princess and Princess Margaret **109** National War Memorial, Ottawa

110 King George VI and Queen Elizabeth

1939 (15 May). *Royal Visit. P* 12.
372 **108** 1 c. black and green .. .. .. 1·75 10
373 **109** 2 c. black and brown 60 40
374 **110** 3 c. black and carmine 60 10
372/4 .. .. *Set of* 3 2·75 50
Nos. 372/4 exist imperforate (*Price* £250, *un, for each pair*).

111 King George VI in Naval uniform **112** King George VI in Military uniform **113** King George VI in Air Force uniform

114 Grain Elevator **116** Parliament Buildings

117 Ram Tank **121** Air Training Camp

1942 (1 July)–**48.** *War Effort. T* **111/14**, **116/17**, **121** *and similar designs.* (*a*) *Postage.* (i) *P* 12.
375 **111** 1 c. green .. .. 1·50 10
a. Booklet pane of 4 + 2 labels (12.9.42) .. .. .. 22·00
b. Booklet pane of 6 (24.11.42) .. 2·50
376 **112** 2 c. brown .. .. 1·75 10
a. Booklet pane of 4 + 2 labels (12.9.42) .. .. .. 26·00
b. Booklet pane of 6 (6.10.42) .. 18·00
377 **113** 3 c. carmine-lake .. .. .. 1·25 60
a. Booklet pane of 4 + 2 labels (20.8.42) .. .. .. 4·25

378 **113** 3 c. purple (30.6.43) 90 10
a. Booklet pane of 4 + 2 labels (28.8.43) .. .. .. 5·50
b. Booklet pane of 6 (24.11.47) .. 11·00
379 **114** 4 c. slate .. .. 5·50 90
380 **112** 4 c. carmine-lake (9.4.43) 70 10
a. Booklet pane of 6 (3.5.43) .. 3·50
381 **111** 5 c. blue .. .. 3·00 10
382 – 8 c. red-brown .. .. 5·50 75
383 **116** 10 c. brown .. .. 5·00 10
384 **117** 13 c. dull green .. .. .. 6·00 6·00
385 14 c. dull green (16.4.43) .. .. 14·00 75
386 – 20 c. chocolate .. .. .. 13·00 15
387 – 50 c. violet .. .. 25·00 2·25
388 – $1 blue .. .. 42·00 4·75
375/88 .. .. *Set of* 14 £110 14·00

Nos. 375/88 exist imperforate (*Prices per pair* 1 c. to 8 c. *each* £180, 10 c. to 20 c. *each* £250, 50 c. and $1 *each* £325, *un*).

(ii) *Coil stamps. Imperf × perf* 8

389 **111** 1 c. green (9.2.43) .. .. .. 1·00 1·50
390 **112** 2 c. brown (24.11.42) .. .. .. 2·25 1·00
391 **113** 3 c. carmine-lake (23.9.42) .. .. 1·75 4·50
392 3 c. purple (19.8.43) .. .. .. 4·75 3·00
393 **112** 4 c. carmine-lake (13.5.43) .. .. 5·50 1·50
389/93 .. .. *Set of* 5 13·00 10·50

(iii) *Booklet stamps. Imperf × perf* 12 (1.9.43)

394 **111** 1 c. green .. .. 3·00 1·00
a. Booklet pane of 3 .. .. .. 9·00
395 **113** 3 c. purple .. .. 3·00 1·25
a. Booklet pane of 3 .. .. .. 9·00
396 **112** 4 c. carmine-lake .. .. .. 3·00 1·50
a. Booklet pane of 3 .. .. .. 9·00
394/6 .. .. *Set of* 3 8·00 3·25

Nos. 394/6 are from booklets in which the stamps are in strips of three, imperforate at top and bottom and right-hand end.

(iv) *Coil stamps. Imperf × perf* 9½

397 **111** 1 c. green (13.7.48) .. .. .. 3·00 4·00
397*a* **112** 2 c. brown (1.10.48) .. .. .. 7·50 19·00
398 **113** 3 c. purple (2.7.48) .. .. .. 4·75 6·00
398*a* **112** 4 c. carmine-lake (22.7.48) .. .. 7·00 3·50
397/8*a* .. .. *Set of* 4 20·00 29·00

(*b*) *Air P* 12

399 **121** 6 c. blue (1.7.42) .. .. .. 14·00 4·00
400 7 c. blue (16.4.43) .. .. .. 2·50 10

Designs: *Horiz* (*as T* **114**)—8 c. Farm scene. (*As T* **117**)—20 c. Launching of corvette H.M.C.S. *La Malbaie*, Sorel; 50 c. Munitions factory; $1 H.M.S. *Cossack* (destroyer).

Nos. 399/400 exist imperforate (*Price* £400, *un, for each pair*).

122 Ontario Farm Scene

129 Alexander Graham Bell and "Fame"

1946 (16 Sept)–**47**. *Peace Re-conversion. T* **122** *and similar horiz designs. P* 12. (*a*) *Postage*.

401 8 c. brown .. .. 1·25 1·50
402 10 c. olive-green .. .. 1·75 10
403 14 c. sepia .. .. 4·00 80
404 20 c. slate .. .. 3·00 10
405 50 c. green .. .. 17·00 2·25
406 $1 purple .. .. 27·00 2·25

(*b*) *Air*

407 7 c. blue .. .. 3·75 10
a. Booklet pane of 4 (24.11.47) .. 9·00
401/7 .. .. *Set of* 7 50·00 6·00

Designs:—7 c. Canada Geese in flight; 10 c. Great Bear Lake; 14 c. St. Maurice River Power Station; 20 c. Combine Harvester; 50 c. Lumbering in British Columbia; $1 *Abegweit* (train ferry), Prince Edward Is.

1947 (3 Mar). *Birth Centenary of Bell* (*inventor of telephone*). *P* 12.

408 **129** 4 c. blue 15 10

130 "Canadian Citizenship".

131 Queen Elizabeth II when Princess

1947 (1 July). *Advent of Canadian Citizenship and Eightieth Anniv of Confederation. P* 12.

409 **130** 4 c. blue 10 10

(From photograph by Dorothy Wilding)

1948 (16 Feb). *Princess Elizabeth's Marriage. P* 12.

410 **131** 4 c. blue 10 10

NEW INFORMATION

The editor is always interested to correspond with people who have new information that will improve or correct the Catalogue.

132 Queen Victoria, Parliament Building, Ottawa, and King George VI

133 Cabot's Ship *Matthew*

1948 (1 Oct). *One Hundred Years of Responsible Government. P* 12.

411 **132** 4 c. grey 10 10

1949 (1 Apr). *Entry of Newfoundland into Canadian Confederation. P* 12.

412 **133** 4 c. green 30 10

134 "Founding of Halifax, 1749" (C. W. Jefferys)

1949 (21 June). *Bicentenary of Halifax, Nova Scotia. P* 12.

413 **134** 4 c. violet 20 10

135 **136** **137**

138 King George VI **139**

(From photographs by Dorothy Wilding)

1949 (15 Nov)–**51**. (i) *P* 12.

414 **135** 1 c. green 10 10
415 **136** 2 c. sepia 40 30
415*a* 2 c. olive-green (25.7.51) 30 10
416 **137** 3 c. purple 30 10
a. Booklet pane of 4+2 labels (12.4.50) 2·25
417 **138** 4 c. carmine-lake 20 10
a. Booklet pane of 6 (5.5.50) .. 27·00
417*b* 4 c. vermilion (2.6.51) 40 10
ba. Booklet pane of 6 .. .. 6·00
418 **139** 5 c. blue .. .. 1·75 10
414/18 .. .. *Set of* 7 3·00 40

(ii) *Imperf × perf* 9½ (*coil stamps*)

419 **135** 1 c. green (18.5.50) .. .. .. 90 1·00
420 **136** 2 c. sepia (18.5.50) .. .. .. 4·50 4·50
420*a* 2 c. olive-green (9.10.51) .. .. 1·75 1·60
421 **137** 3 c. purple (18.5.50) .. .. .. 2·25 2·00
422 **138** 4 c. carmine-lake (20.4.50) .. .. 14·00 7·50
422*a* 4 c. vermilion (27.11.51) .. .. 1·50 2·00
419/22*a* .. .. *Set of* 6 22·00 17·00

(iii) *Imperf × perf* 12 (*booklets*)

422*b* **135** 1 c. green (18.5.50) .. .. .. 50 1·60
ba. Booklet pane of 3 .. .. .. 1·50
423 **137** 3 c. purple (18.5.50) .. .. .. 1·25 85
a. Booklet pane of 3 .. .. .. 3·75
423*b* **138** 4 c. carmine-lake (18.5.50) .. .. 15·00 7·00
ba. Booklet pane of 3 .. .. 45·00
423*c* 4 c. vermilion (25.10.51) .. .. 7·00 7·00
ca. Booklet pane of 3 .. .. 21·00
422*b*/3*c* .. .. *Set of* 4 21·00 14·50

These booklet panes are imperforate at top, bottom and right-hand end.

140 King George VI

141 Oil Wells in Alberta

(From photograph by Dorothy Wilding)

1950 (19 Jan). *As T* **135/9** *but without* "POSTES POSTAGE", *as T* **140**. (i) *P* 12.

424 1 c. green 10 50
425 2 c. sepia 10 60
426 3 c. purple 10 90
427 4 c. carmine-lake 10 20
428 5 c. blue .. .. 30 1·25
424/8 .. .. *Set of* 5 60 3·00

(ii) *Imperf × perf* 9½ (*coil stamps*)

429 1 c. green .. .. 30 1·00
430 3 c. purple .. .. 80 1·50

1950 (1 Mar). *P* 12.

431 **141** 50 c. green .. .. 7·50 1·00

142 Drying Furs

143 Fisherman

1950 (2 Oct). *P* 12.

432 **142** 10 c. brown-purple .. .. .. 1·25 10

1951 (1 Feb). *P* 12.

433 **143** $1 ultramarine .. .. .. 38·00 5·00

144 Sir R. L. Borden

145 W. L. Mackenzie King

1951 (25 June). *Prime Ministers* (*1st issue*). *P* 12.

434 **144** 3 c. blue-green 10 50
435 **145** 4 c. rose-carmine 10 10

See also Nos. 444/5, 475/6 and 483/4.

146 Mail Trains, 1851 and 1951

147 SS. *City of Toronto* and SS. *Prince George*

148 Mail Coach and DC-4M North Star

149 Reproduction of 3d., 1851

1951 (24 Sept). *Canadian Stamp Centenary. P* 12.

436 **146** 4 c. black 35 10
437 **147** 5 c. violet .. .. 65 1·75
438 **148** 7 c. blue .. .. 35 1·00
439 **149** 15 c. scarlet .. .. 1·10 10
436/9 .. .. *Set of* 4 2·25 2·75

150 Queen Elizabeth II when Princess and Duke of Edinburgh

151 Forestry Products

1951 (26 Oct). *Royal Visit. P* 12.

440 **150** 4 c. violet 10 10

(Des A. L. Pollock)

1952 (1 Apr). *P* 12.

441 **151** 20 c. grey .. .. 1·25 10

152 Red Cross Emblem

1952 (26 July). *18th International Red Cross Conference, Toronto. Design recess; cross litho. P* 12.

442 **152** 4 c. scarlet and blue 15 10

153 Canada Goose

154 Pacific Coast Indian House and Totem Pole

(Des E. Hahn)

1952 (3 Nov). *P* 12.
443 **153** 7 c. blue 65 10

1952 (3 Nov). *Prime Ministers (2nd issue). Various portraits as T* **144**. *P* 12.
444 3 c. reddish purple 15 20
445 4 c. orange-red 15 10
Portraits:—3 c. Sir John J. C. Abbott; 4 c. A. Mackenzie.

(Des E. Hahn)

1953 (2 Feb). *P* 12.
446 **154** $1 black . . . . 5·50 20

155 Polar Bear **156** Elk **157** American Bighorn

(Des J. Crosby (2 c.), E. Hahn (others))

1953 (1 Apr). *National Wild Life Week. P* 12.
447 **155** 2 c. blue 10 10
448 **156** 3 c. sepia 10 20
449 **157** 4 c. slate 15 10
447/9 . . . . *Set of* 3 30 30

158 Queen Elizabeth II **159**

(From photograph by Karsh, Ottawa)

1953 (1 May–3 Sept). (*a*) *Sheet stamps. P* 12.
450 **158** 1 c. purple-brown 10 10
451 2 c. green 15 10
452 3 c. carmine 15 15
a. Booklet pane of 4+2 labels (17.7) 1·25
453 4 c. violet 20 10
a. Booklet pane of 6 (6.7) . . . . 3·00
454 5 c. ultramarine 20 10
450/4 . . . . *Set of* 5 70 30

(*b*) *Coil stamps. Imperf* × *perf* 9½
455 **158** 2 c. green (30.7) . . . . 1·75 1·00
456 3 c. carmine (27.7) . . . . 1·75 1·00
457 4 c. violet (3.9) . . . . 1·50 1·00
455/7 . . . . *Set of* 3 4·50 2·75

(*c*) *Booklet stamps. Imperf* × *perf* 12
458 **158** 1 c. purple-brown (12.8) . . . . 2·00 1·50
a. Booklet pane of 3 . . . . 5·50
459 3 c. carmine (17.7) . . . . 2·00 1·50
a. Booklet pane of 3 . . . . 5·50
460 4 c. violet (6.7) . . . . 2·00 1·50
a. Booklet pane of 3 . . . . 5·50
458/60 . . . . *Set of* 3 5·50 4·00

These booklet stamps have top and bottom or top, bottom and right-hand sides imperforate.

(Des E. Hahn)

1953 (1 June). *Coronation. P* 12
461 **159** 4 c. violet 10 10

160 Textile Industry **161** Queen Elizabeth II

(Des A. L. Pollock)

1953 (2 Nov). *P* 12.
462 **160** 50 c. deep bluish green . . . . . . 1·25 10

(From photograph by Dorothy Wilding)

1954–62. (i) *P* 12.
463 **161** 1 c. purple-brown (10.6.54) 10 10
a. Booklet pane. Five stamps plus printed label (1.6.56) . . . . 1·00
p. Two phosphor bands (13.1.62) . . 80 2·75
464 2 c. green (10.6.54) 20 10
a. Pack. Two blocks of 25 (12.61) . . 6·00
p. Two phosphor bands (13.1.62) . . 80 3·00
465 3 c. carmine (10.6.54) 60 10
a. Imperf vert (horiz pair) £1300
p. Two phosphor bands (13.1.62) . . 1·50 3·00
466 4 c. violet (10.6.54) 30 10
a. Booklet pane of 6 (7.7.55) . . 4·25
b. Booklet pane. Five stamps plus printed label (1.6.56) . . . . 1·75
p. One phosphor band (13.1.62) . . 2·00 8·00
467 **161** 5 c. bright blue (1.4.54) 30 10
a. Booklet pane. Five stamps plus printed label (14.7.54) . . . . 2·75
b. Pack. One block of 20 (12.61) . . 5·00
c. Imperf vert (horiz pair) . . . .
p. Two phosphor bands (13.1.62) . . 2·00 8·00
468 6 c. red-orange (10.6.54) . . . . 1·00 30
463/8 . . . . *Set of* 6 2·25 45
463p/7p . . . . *Set of* 5 6·50 22·00

(ii) *Imperf* × *perf* 9½ (*coil stamps*)
469 **161** 2 c. green (9.9.54) 55 75
470 4 c. violet (23.8.54) . . . . . . 55 1·00
471 5 c. bright blue (6.7.54) . . . . . . 1·75 45
469/71 . . . . *Set of* 3 2·50 2·00

No. 467c is from the left side of a sheet and shows perforations between the stamps and the sheet margin.

Nos. 464a and 467b are blocks with the outer edges imperf. These come from "One Dollar Plastic Packages" sold at post offices.

WINNIPEG PHOSPHOR BANDS. In 1962 facer-cancelling machines were introduced in Winnipeg which were activated by phosphor bands on the stamps. Under long or short wave ultra-violet light the phosphor glows and there is also a short after-glow when the lamp is turned off. This should not be confused with the fluorescent bands introduced in Ottawa in 1971.

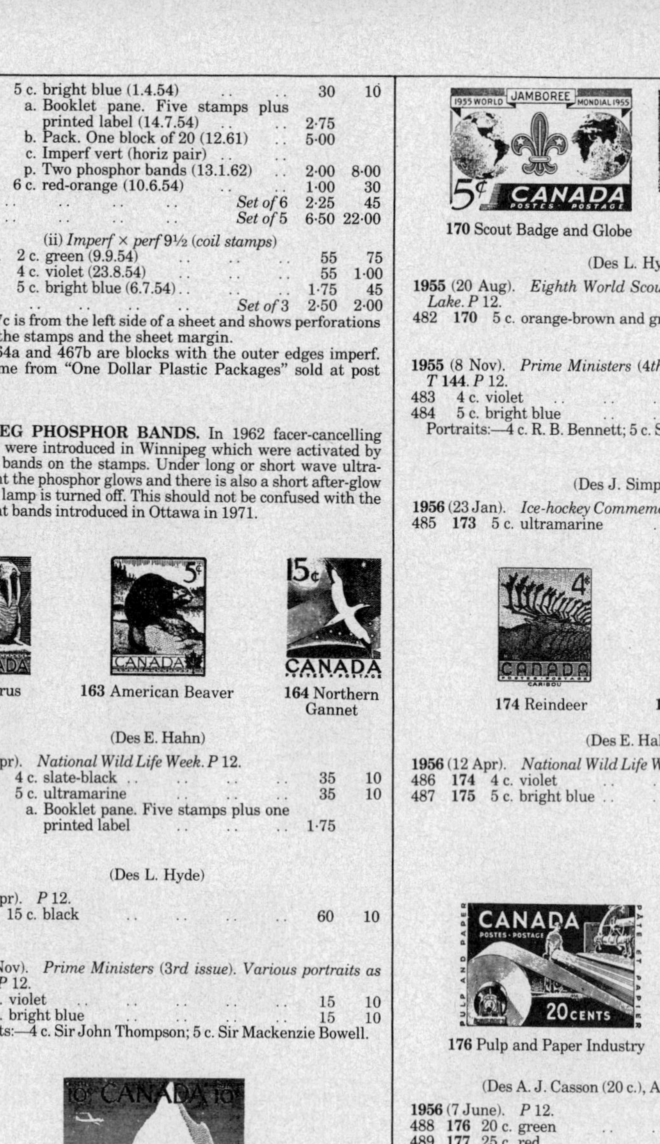

162 Walrus **163** American Beaver **164** Northern Gannet

(Des E. Hahn)

1954 (1 Apr). *National Wild Life Week. P* 12.
472 **162** 4 c. slate-black 35 10
473 **163** 5 c. ultramarine 35 10
a. Booklet pane. Five stamps plus one printed label . . . . . . 1·75

(Des L. Hyde)

1954 (1 Apr). *P* 12.
474 **164** 15 c. black 60 10

1954 (1 Nov). *Prime Ministers (3rd issue). Various portraits as T* **144**. *P* 12.
475 4 c. violet 15 10
476 5 c. bright blue 15 10
Portraits:—4 c. Sir John Thompson; 5 c. Sir Mackenzie Bowell.

165 Eskimo Hunter

(Des H. Beament)

1955 (21 Feb). *P* 12.
477 **165** 10 c. purple-brown 20 10

166 Musk Ox **167** Whooping Cranes

(Des E. Hahn (4 c.), Dr. W. Rowan (5 c.))

1955 (4 Apr). *National Wild Life Week. P* 12.
478 **166** 4 c. violet 30 10
479 **167** 5 c. ultramarine 90 10

168 Dove and Torch **169** Pioneer Settlers

(Des W. Lohse)

1955 (1 June). *Tenth Anniv of International Civil Aviation Organisation. P* 12.
480 **168** 5 c. ultramarine 10 10

(Des L. Hyde)

1955 (30 June). *50th Anniv of Alberta and Saskatchewan Provinces. P* 12.
481 **169** 5 c. ultramarine 15 15

170 Scout Badge and Globe **173** Ice-hockey Players

(Des L. Hyde)

1955 (20 Aug). *Eighth World Scout Jamboree, Niagara-on-the Lake. P* 12.
482 **170** 5 c. orange-brown and green 20 1

1955 (8 Nov). *Prime Ministers (4th issue). Various portraits as T* **144**. *P* 12.
483 4 c. violet 10 2
484 5 c. bright blue 10 1
Portraits:—4 c. R. B. Bennett; 5 c. Sir Charles Tupper.

(Des J. Simpkins)

1956 (23 Jan). *Ice-hockey Commemoration. P* 12.
485 **173** 5 c. ultramarine 15 15

174 Reindeer **175** Mountain Goat

(Des E. Hahn)

1956 (12 Apr). *National Wild Life Week. P* 12.
486 **174** 4 c. violet 20 15
487 **175** 5 c. bright blue 20 10

176 Pulp and Paper Industry **177** Chemical Industry

(Des A. J. Casson (20 c.), A. L. Pollock (25 c.))

1956 (7 June). *P* 12.
488 **176** 20 c. green 40 1
489 **177** 25 c. red 55 1

178

(Des A. Price)

1956 (9 Oct). *Fire Prevention Week. P* 12
490 **178** 5 c. red and black 30 1

179 Fishing **180** Swimming

(Des L. Hyde)

1957 (7 Mar). *Outdoor Recreation. T* **179/180** *and similar horiz designs. P* 12.
491 **179** 5 c. ultramarine 25 10
a. Block of 4. Nos. 491/4 . . . . 1·25
492 **180** 5 c. ultramarine 25 10
493 – 5 c. ultramarine 25 10
494 – 5 c. ultramarine 25 10
491/4 . . . . *Set of* 4 1·25 35

Designs:— No. 493, Hunting. No. 494, Skiing.

No. 491/4 are printed together in sheets of 50 (5 × 10). In the first, second, fourth and fifth vertical rows the four different designs are arranged in *se-tenant* blocks, whilst the central row is made up as follows (reading downwards):—Nos. 491/4, 491/2 (or 493/4), 491/4.

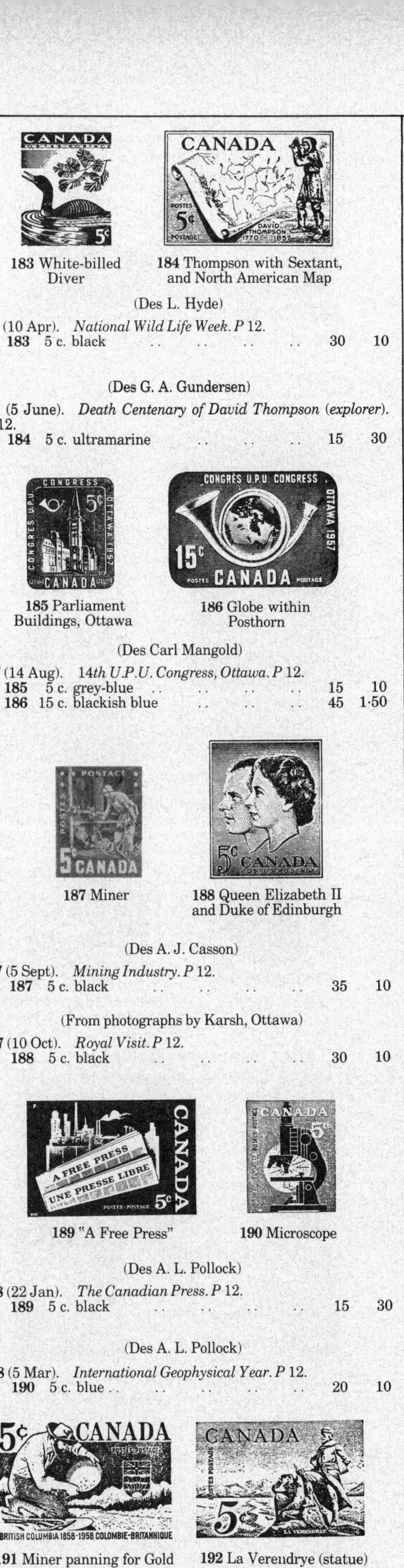

183 White-billed Diver

184 Thompson with Sextant, and North American Map

(Des L. Hyde)

1957 (10 Apr). *National Wild Life Week. P* 12.
495 **183** 5 c. black 30 10

(Des G. A. Gundersen)

1957 (5 June). *Death Centenary of David Thompson (explorer). P* 12.
496 **184** 5 c. ultramarine 15 30

185 Parliament Buildings, Ottawa

186 Globe within Posthorn

(Des Carl Mangold)

1957 (14 Aug). *14th U.P.U. Congress, Ottawa. P* 12.
497 **185** 5 c. grey-blue 15 10
498 **186** 15 c. blackish blue . . . . 45 1·50

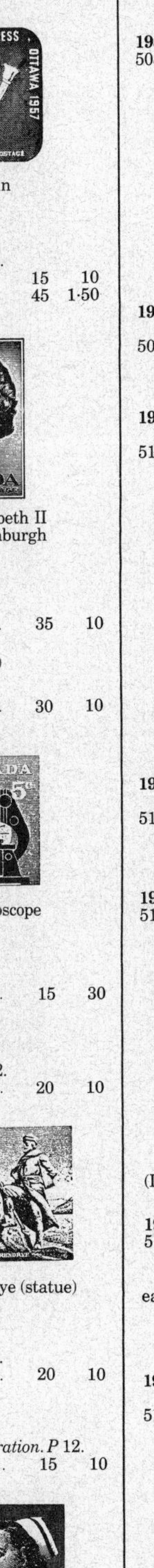

187 Miner

188 Queen Elizabeth II and Duke of Edinburgh

(Des A. J. Casson)

1957 (5 Sept). *Mining Industry. P* 12.
499 **187** 5 c. black 35 10

(From photographs by Karsh, Ottawa)

1957 (10 Oct). *Royal Visit. P* 12.
500 **188** 5 c. black 30 10

189 "A Free Press"

190 Microscope

(Des A. L. Pollock)

1958 (22 Jan). *The Canadian Press. P* 12.
501 **189** 5 c. black 15 30

(Des A. L. Pollock)

1958 (5 Mar). *International Geophysical Year. P* 12.
502 **190** 5 c. blue 20 10

191 Miner panning for Gold

192 La Verendrye (statue)

(Des J. Harman)

1958 (8 May). *Centenary of British Columbia. P* 12.
503 **191** 5 c. deep turquoise-green 20 10

(Des G. Trottier)

1958 (4 June). *La Verendrye (explorer) Commemoration. P* 12.
504 **192** 5 c. ultramarine 15 10

193 Samuel de Champlain and the Heights of Quebec

194 Nurse

(Des G. Trottier)

1958 (26 June). *350th Anniv of Founding of Quebec. P* 12.
505 **193** 5 c. brown-ochre and deep green . . 30 10

(Des G. Trottier)

1958 (30 July). *National Health. P* 12.
506 **194** 5 c. reddish purple 30 10

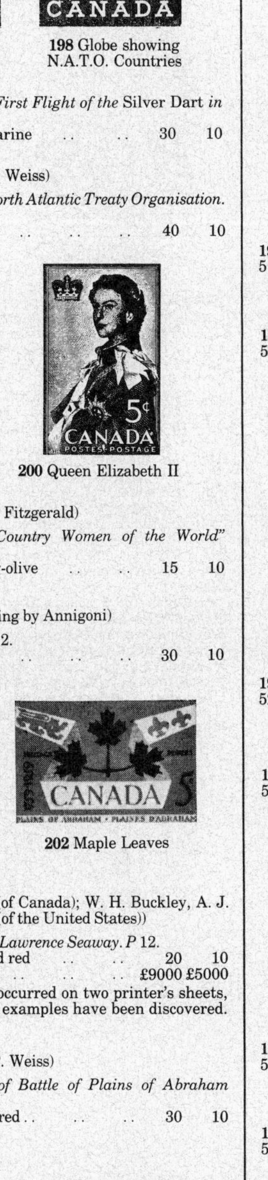

195 "Petroleum 1858–1958"

196 Speaker's Chair and Mace

(Des A. L. Pollock)

1958 (10 Sept). *Centenary of Canadian Oil Industry. P* 12.
507 **195** 5 c. scarlet and olive 30 10

(Des G. Trottier and C. Dair)

1958 (2 Oct). *Bicentenary of First Elected Assembly. P* 12.
508 **196** 5 c. deep slate 30 10

197 John McCurdy's *Silver Dart* Biplane

198 Globe showing N.A.T.O. Countries

1959 (23 Feb). *50th Anniv of First Flight of the* Silver Dart *in Canada. P* 12.
509 **197** 5 c. black and ultramarine 30 10

(Des P. Weiss)

1959 (2 Apr). *Tenth Anniv of North Atlantic Treaty Organisation. P* 12.
510 **198** 5 c. ultramarine 40 10

199

200 Queen Elizabeth II

(Des Helen Fitzgerald)

1959 (13 May). *"Associated Country Women of the World" Commemoration. P* 12.
511 **199** 5 c. black and yellow-olive 15 10

(Des after painting by Annigoni)

1959 (18 June). *Royal Visit. P* 12.
512 **200** 5 c. lake-red 30 10

201 Maple Leaf linked with American Eagle

202 Maple Leaves

(Des A. L. Pollock, G. Trottier (of Canada); W. H. Buckley, A. J. Copeland, E. Metzl (of the United States))

1959 (26 June). *Opening of St. Lawrence Seaway. P* 12.
513 **201** 5 c. ultramarine and red 20 10
a. Centre inverted £9000 £5000

It is believed that No. 513a occurred on two printer's sheets, each of 200 stamps. About 230 examples have been discovered.

(Des P. Weiss)

1959 (10 Sept). *Bicentenary of Battle of Plains of Abraham (Quebec). P* 12.
514 **202** 5 c. deep green and red 30 10

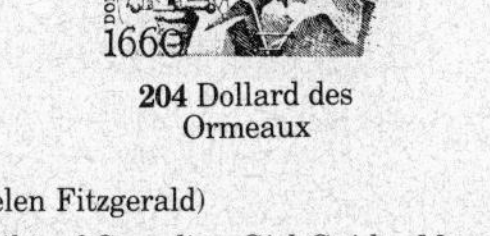

203

204 Dollard des Ormeaux

(Des Helen Fitzgerald)

1960 (20 Apr). *Golden Jubilee of Canadian Girl Guides Movement. P* 12.
515 **203** 5 c. ultramarine and orange-brown . . 20 10

(Des P. Weiss)

1960 (19 May). *Tercentenary of Battle of the Long Sault. P* 12.
516 **204** 5 c. ultramarine and light brown . . 20 10

205 Surveyor, Bulldozer and Compass Rose

206 E. Pauline Johnson

(Des B. J. Reddie)

1961 (8 Feb). *Northern Development. P* 12.
517 **205** 5 c. emerald and red 15 10

(Des B. J. Reddie)

1961 (10 Mar). *Birth Centenary of E. Pauline Johnson (Mohawk poetess). P* 12.
518 **206** 5 c. green and red 15 10

207 Arthur Meighen (statesman)

208 Engineers and Dam

1961 (19 Apr). *Arthur Meighen Commemoration. P* 12.
519 **207** 5 c. ultramarine 15 10

(Des B. J. Reddie)

1961 (28 June). *Tenth Anniv of Colombo Plan. P* 12.
520 **208** 5 c. blue and brown 30 10

209 "Resources for Tomorrow"

210 "Education"

(Des A. L. Pollock)

1961 (12 Oct). *Natural Resources. P* 12.
521 **209** 5 c. blue-green and brown 15 10

(Des Helen Fitzgerald)

1962 (28 Feb). *Education Year. P* 12.
522 **210** 5 c. black and orange-brown 15 10

211 Lord Selkirk and Farmer

212 Talon bestowing Gifts on Married Couple

(Des Phillips-Gutkin Ltd)

1962 (3 May). *150th Anniv of Red River Settlement. P* 12.
523 **211** 5 c. chocolate and green 20 10

(Des P. Weiss)

1962 (13 June). *Jean Talon Commemoration. P* 12.
524 **212** 5 c. blue 20 10

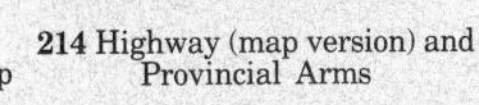

213 Br Columbia & Vancouver Is 2½d. stamp of 1860, and Parliament Buildings, B.C.

214 Highway (map version) and Provincial Arms

(Des Helen Bacon)

1962 (22 Aug). *Centenary of Victoria, B.C. P* 12.
525 **213** 5 c. red and black 30 10

(Des A. L. Pollock)

1962 (31 Aug). *Opening of Trans-Canada Highway. P* 12.
526 **214** 5 c. black and orange-brown 15 10

215 Queen Elizabeth II and Wheat (agriculture) Symbol

216 Sir Casimir Gzowski

(From drawing by Ernst Roch)

1962–64. *Horiz designs as T* **215** *showing Queen Elizabeth II and industry symbols.* (i) *P* 12
527 1 c. chocolate (4.2.63) 10 10
a. Booklet pane. Five stamps plus one printed label (15.5.63) .. .. 3·50
p. Two phosphor bands (15.5.63) .. 15 45
528 2 c. green (2.5.63) 15 10
a. Pack. Two blocks of 25 .. .. 8·50
p. Two phosphor bands (15.5.63) .. 20 45
529 3 c. reddish violet† (2.5.63) 15 10
p. Two phosphor bands (15.5.63) .. 30 70
530 4 c. carmine-red (4.2.63) 15 10
a. Booklet pane. Five stamps plus one printed label (15.5.63) .. .. 3·50
b. Pack. One block of 25 .. .. 4·25
p. One centre phosphor band (*narrow*)* (2.63) .. .. 50 2·75
pa. One centre phosphor band (*wide*) (8.64) 3·75 5·00
pb. One side phosphor band (12.64) .. 40 2·25
531 5 c. ultramarine (3.10.62) 15 10
a. Booklet pane. Five stamps plus one printed label (5.63) .. .. .. 3·00
b. Pack. One block of 20 .. .. 4·75
c. Imperf horiz (vert pair) £2000 £600
p. Two phosphor bands (31.1.63?) .. 35 45
pa. Pack. One block of 20 .. .. 14·00
pb. Imperf (pair) .. ..
527/31 .. .. *Set of* 5 65 15
527p/31p .. .. *Set of* 5 1·25 3·75

(ii) *P* 9½×*imperf* (*coil stamps*)
532 2 c. green (1963) .. .. 6·50 8·00
532*a* 3 c. reddish violet (1964) .. .. 4·75 3·00
533 4 c. carmine-red (15.5.63) .. .. 1·75 3·00
a. Imperf (pair) .. ..
534 5 c. ultramarine (15.5.63) .. .. 4·50 1·00
532/4 .. .. *Set of* 4 16·00 13·50

Symbols:–1 c. Crystals (Mining); 2 c. Tree (Forestry); 3 c. Fish (Fisheries); 4 c. Electricity pylon (Industrial power).

Nos. 528a, 530b, 531b and 531pa are blocks with the outer edges imperf. These come from "One Dollar Plastic Packages" sold at post offices.

†This is a fugitive colour which tends to become reddish on drying. In successive printings the violet colour became more and more reddish as the printer tried to match the shade of each previous printing instead of referring back to the original shade. A deep reddish violet is also known from Plate 3. As there is such a range of shades it is not practical to list them.

*On No. 530p the band is 4 mm wide as against 8 mm on No. 530pa. No. 530pb exists with the band at either left or right side of the stamp, the bands being applied across alternate vertical perforations.

Postal forgeries are known of the 4 c. showing a coarser background and lack of shading on the Queen's face.

(Des P. Weiss)

1963 (5 Mar). *150th Birth Anniv of Sir Casimir Gzowski (engineer). P* 12.
535 **216** 5 c. reddish purple 10 10

217 "Export Trade"

218 Frobisher and barque *Gabriel*

(Des A. L. Pollock)

1963 (14 June). *P* 12.
536 **217** $1 carmine .. .. 4·75 2·00

(Des P. Weiss)

1963 (21 Aug). *Sir Martin Frobisher Commemoration. P* 12.
537 **218** 5 c. ultramarine 20 10

219 Horseman and Map

220 Canada Geese

(Des B. J. Reddie)

1963 (25 Sept). *Bicentenary of Quebec–Trois-Rivieres–Montreal Postal Service. P* 12.
538 **219** 5 c. red-brown and deep green 15 10

(Des A. Short and P. Arthur)

1963 (30 Oct). *P* 12.
539 **220** 15 c. blue .. .. 1·25 10

221 Douglas DC-9 Airliner and Uplands Airport, Ottawa

222 "Peace on Earth"

1964. *P* 12.
540 **221** 7 c. blue (11 Mar) 35 70
540*a* 8 c. blue (18 Nov) 50 40

1964 (8 Apr). *"Peace". Litho and recess. P* 12.
541 **222** 5 c. ochre, blue and turquoise-blue .. 15 10

223 Maple Leaves

1964 (14 May). *"Canadian Unity". P* 12.
542 **223** 5 c. lake-red and light blue 10 10

224 White Trillium and Arms of Ontario

236 Maple Leaf and Arms of Canada

1964–66. *Provincial Emblems. T* **224**, **236** *and similar horiz designs. Recess (No. 555) or litho and recess (others). P* 12.
543 5 c. green, brown and orange (30.6.64) .. 40 20
544 5 c. green, orange-brown and yellow (30.6.64) 40 20
545 5 c. carmine-red, green and bluish violet (3.2.65) 30 20
546 5 c. blue, red and green (3.2.65) 30 20
547 5 c. purple, green and yellow-brown (28.4.65) 30 20
548 5 c. red-brown, deep bluish green and mauve (28.4.65) 30 20
549 5 c. slate-lilac, green and light reddish purple (21.7.65) 50 20
550 5 c. green, yellow and rose-red (19.1.66) .. 30 20
551 5 c. sepia, orange and green (19.1.66) .. 30 20
552 5 c. black, green and red (23.2.66) 30 20
553 5 c. drab, green and yellow (23.3.66) .. 30 20
554 5 c. blue, green and rose-red (23.3.66) .. 30 20
555 5 c. red and blue (30.6.66) 30 20
543/55 .. .. .. *Set of* 13 4·00 2·40

Designs:—No. 543, Type **224;** No. 544, Madonna Lily and Arms of Quebec; No. 545, Purple Violet and Arms of New Brunswick; No. 546, Mayflower and Arms of Nova Scotia; No. 547, Dogwood and Arms of British Columbia; No. 548, Prairie Crocus and Arms of Manitoba; No. 549, Lady's Slipper and Arms of Prince Edward Island; No. 550, Wild Rose and Arms of Alberta; No. 551, Prairie Lily and Arms of Saskatchewan; No. 552, Pitcher Plant and Arms of Newfoundland; No. 553, Mountain Avens and Arms of Northwest Territories; No. 554, Fireweed and Arms of Yukon Territory; No. 555, Type **236**.

8
═
(**237**)

238 Fathers of the Confederation Memorial, Charlottetown

1964 (15 July). *No.* 540 *surch with T* **237**.
556 **221** 8 c. on 7 c. blue 15 15
a. Surch omitted (left-hand stamp of horiz pair) £6000

(Des P. Weiss)

1964 (29 July). *Centenary of Charlottetown Conference. P* 12.
557 **238** 5 c. black 10 10

239 Maple Leaf and Hand with Quill Pen

240 Queen Elizabeth II

(Des P. Weiss)

1964 (9 Sept). *Centenary of Quebec Conference. P* 12.
558 **239** 5 c. light red and chocolate 15 10

(Portrait by Anthony Buckley)

1964 (5 Oct). *Royal Visit. P* 12.
559 **240** 5 c. reddish purple 15 10

241 "Canadian Family"

242 "Co-operation"

1964 (14 Oct). *Christmas. P* 12.
560 **241** 3 c. scarlet 10 10
a. Pack. Two blocks of 25 .. .. 7·00
p. Two phosphor bands .. .. 60 2·25
pa. Pack. Two blocks of 25 .. .. 13·00
561 5 c. ultramarine 10 10
p. Two phosphor bands .. .. 90 2·25

Nos. 560a and 560pa are blocks with the outer edges imperf. These come from "$1.50 Plastic Packages" sold at post offices.

1965 (3 Mar). *International Co-operation Year. P* 12.
562 **242** 5 c. grey-green 35 10

243 Sir W. Grenfell

244 National Flag

1965 (9 June). *Birth Centenary of Sir Wilfred Grenfell (missionary). P* 12.
563 **243** 5 c. deep bluish green 20 10

1965 (30 June). *Inauguration of National Flag. P* 12.
564 **244** 5 c. red and blue 15 10

245 Sir Winston Churchill

246 Peace Tower, Parliament Buildings, Ottawa

(Des P. Weiss from photo by Karsh. Litho)

1965 (12 Aug). *Churchill Commemoration. P* 12.
565 **245** 5 c. purple-brown 15 10

(Des Philips-Gutkin)

1965 (8 Sept). *Inter-Parliamentary Union Conference, Ottawa. P* 12.
566 **246** 5 c. deep green 10 10

247 Parliament Buildings, Ottawa, 1865

248 "Gold, Frankincense and Myrrh"

(Des G. Trottier)

1965 (8 Sept). *Centenary of Proclamation of Ottawa as Capital. P* 12.
567 **247** 5 c. brown 10 10

(Des Helen Fitzgerald)

1965 (13 Oct). *Christmas. P* 12.
568 **248** 3 c. olive-green 10 10
a. Pack. Two blocks of 25 .. .. 5·00
p. Two phosphor bands 10 55
pa. Pack. Two blocks of 25 .. .. 5·50
569 5 c. ultramarine 10 10
p. Two phosphor bands 20 35

Nos. 568a and 568pa are blocks with the outer edges imperf. These come from "$1.50 Plastic Packages" sold at post offices.

249 "Alouette 2" over Canada

250 La Salle

1966 (5 Jan). *Launching of Canadian Satellite, "Alouette 2". P* 12.
570 **249** 5 c. ultramarine 15 10

(Des Brigdens Ltd., Toronto)

966 (13 Apr). *300th Anniv of La Salle's Arrival in Canada*. P 12.
71 **250** 5 c. deep bluish green 15 10

251 Road Signs **252** Canadian Delegation and Houses of Parliament

(Des Helen Fitzgerald)

966 (2 May). *Highway Safety. Invisible gum*. P 12.
72 **251** 5 c. yellow, blue and black 15 10

(Des P. Pederson (Brigdens Ltd))

966 (26 May). *London Conference Centenary*. P 12.
73 **252** 5 c. red-brown 10 10

253 Douglas Point Nuclear Power Station **254** Parliamentary Library, Ottawa

(Des A. L. Pollock)

1966 (27 July). *Peaceful Uses of Atomic Energy*. P 12.
574 **253** 5 c. ultramarine 10 10

(Des Brigdens Ltd)

1966 (8 Sept). *Commonwealth Parliamentary Association Conference, Ottawa*. P 12.
575 **254** 5 c. purple 10 10

255 "Praying Hands", after Dürer **256** Flag and Canada on Globe

(Des G. Holloway)

1966 (12 Oct). *Christmas*. P 12.
576 **255** 3 c. carmine 10 10
a. Pack. Two blocks of 25 .. .. 4·00
p. Two phosphor bands 30 65
pa. Pack. Two blocks of 25 .. .. 6·50
577 5 c. orange 10 10
p. Two phosphor bands 30 95

Nos. 576a and 576pa are blocks with the outer edges imperf. These come from "$1.50 Plastic Packages" sold at post offices.

(Des Brigdens Ltd)

1967 (11 Jan). *Canadian Centennial. Invisible gum*. P 12.
578 **256** 5 c. scarlet and blue 10 10
p. Two phosphor bands .. .. 30 1·00

257 Northern Lights and Dog-team **263** "The Jack Pine" (T. Thomson)

1967 (8 Feb)–**73**. *T* **257, 263** *and similar horiz designs*.

A. *Recess C.B.N.*

(i) *P* 12

579 1 c. brown 10 10
a. Booklet pane. Five stamps plus one printed label (2.67) 50
b. Printed on the gummed side .. £450
p. Two phosphor bands 30 80
pa. Centre phosphor band (12.68) .. 30 70
q. Two fluorescent bands (11.71) .. 30 10
580 2 c. green 10 10
a. Booklet pane. No. 580×4 *se-tenant* with No. 581×4 with gutter margin between (26.10.70) .. .. .. 2·50
p. Two phosphor bands 30 70
pa. Centre phosphor band (12.68) .. 30 70
q. Two fluorescent bands (12.72) .. 40 10
581 3 c. slate-purple 30 10
p. Two phosphor bands 30 90
q. Two fluorescent bands (1972?) ..

582 4 c. red 20 10
a. Booklet pane. Five stamps plus one printed label (2.67) .. .. .. 1·75
b. Pack. One block of 25 (8.2.67) .. 10·00
p. One side phosphor band .. .. 1·60 2·00
pa. Centre phosphor band (3.69) .. 30 70
q. Two fluorescent bands (4.73) .. 40 10
583 5 c. blue 20 10
a. Booklet pane. Five stamps plus one printed label (3.67) .. .. .. 6·50
b. Pack. One block of 20 (2.67) .. 17·00
p. Two phosphor bands 45 65
pa. Pack. One block of 20 (8.2.67) .. 35·00
pb. Centre phosphor band (12.68) .. 30 65
583*c* 6 c. black (2.72) .. .. 1·50 30
ca. Printed on the gummed side .. 9·50
cp. Centre phosphor band .. .. 2·50 2·25
cq. Two fluorescent bands 40 30
584 8 c. purple-brown 35 30
585 10 c. olive-green 30 10
p. Two phosphor bands (9.12.69) .. 1·50 1·75
q. Two fluorescent bands (1.72) .. 75 50
586 15 c. dull purple 30 10
p. Two phosphor bands (9.12.69) .. 2·25 2·75
q. Two fluorescent bands (2.72) .. 1·25 1·00
587 20 c. deep blue 80 10
p. Two phosphor bands (9.12.69) .. 2·25 2·75
588 25 c. myrtle-green .. .. 1·00 10
p. Two phosphor bands (9.12.69) .. 4·75 5·50
589 50 c. cinnamon .. .. 1·75 10
590 $1 scarlet .. .. 2·50 65
579/90 .. .. *Set of* 13 8·50 1·60
579pa/588p .. .. .. *Set of* 10 13·50 16·00

(ii) *Perf* 9½ × *imperf* (*coil stamps*)

591 3 c. slate-purple (3.67) .. .. .. 2·50 2·75
592 4 c. red (3.67) .. .. 2·50 1·75
593 5 c. blue (2.67) .. .. 2·50 1·75

(iii) *Perf* 10×*imperf* (*coil stamps*)

594 6 c. orange-red (1.69) 90 35
a. Imperf (vert pair) £200
595 6 c. black (8.70) 35 30
a. Imperf (vert pair) £600
596 7 c. green (30.6.71) 40 60
a. Imperf (vert pair) £550
597 8 c. black (30.12.71) 40 30
a. Imperf (vert pair) £225
q. Two fluorescent bands 30 30
qa. Imperf (vert pair) £275

B. *Recess B.A.B.N.*

(i) *P* 10 (*sheets* (601/p) *or booklets*)

598 1 c. brown (9.68) .. .. 40 2·00
a. Booklet pane. No. 598 × 5 *se-tenant* with No. 599 × 5 (9.68) .. .. .. 2·50
b. Booklet pane. No. 601 × 4 *se-tenant* with No. 598 plus one printed label (10.68) .. 2·50
599 4 c. red (9.68) .. .. 30 1·00
a. Booklet pane. 25 stamps plus two printed labels .. .. 9·00
600 5 c. blue (9.68) .. .. 30 1·00
a. Booklet pane of 20 .. .. .. 6·50
601 6 c. orange-red (10.68) 45 10
a. Booklet pane. 25 stamps plus two printed labels (1.69) .. .. .. 11·00
p. Two phosphor bands (1.11.68) .. 75 85
602 6 c. black (1.70) .. .. 1·40 95
a. Booklet pane. 25 stamps plus two printed labels .. .. 20·00
603 6 c. black (*re-engraved die*) (8.70) .. 4·25 3·00
a. Booklet pane of 4 .. .. .. 13·00

(ii) *P* 12½×12 (*sheets* (606/10) *or booklets*)

604 1 c. brown (30.6.71) .. .. .. 80 1·40
a. Booklet pane. Nos. 604×4, 605×4 and 609×12 *se-tenant* .. .. .. 14·00
b. Booklet pane. Nos. 604/5 and 609×3 *se-tenant* plus one printed label .. 5·50
c. Booklet pane. Nos. 604×3, 608 and 610×2 *se-tenant* (30.12.71) .. 2·00
d. Booklet pane. Nos. 604×6, 608 and 610×11 *se-tenant* (30.12.71) .. 7·50
e. Booklet pane. Nos. 604×4, 608 and 610×5 *se-tenant* (8.72) .. .. 4·50
q. Two fluorescent bands (30.12.71) .. 40 10
qc. Booklet pane. Nos. 604q×3, 608q and 610q×2 *se-tenant* .. .. .. 2·50
qd. Booklet pane. Nos. 604q×6, 608q and 610q×11 *se-tenant* .. .. .. 7·00
qe. Booklet pane. Nos. 604q×4, 608q and 610q×5 *se-tenant* (8.72) .. .. 4·50
605 3 c. slate-purple (30.6.71) .. .. 3·50 4·25
606 6 c. orange-red (3.69) .. .. .. 1·00 10
p. Two phosphor bands .. .. 1·00 1·25
607 6 c. black (7.1.70) 30 10
a. Booklet pane. 25 stamps plus two printed labels (8.70) .. .. .. 16·00
p. Two phosphor bands .. .. 90 1·50
608 6 c. black (*re-engraved die*) (9.70) .. 80 10
a. Booklet pane of 4 (11.70) .. .. 5·50
p. One centre phosphor band (9.71) .. 1·75 2·50
q. Two fluorescent bands (30.12.71) .. 75 10
609 7 c. myrtle-green (30.6.71) 30 10
p. Two phosphor bands .. .. 60 1·60
610 8 c. slate-black (30.12.71) 30 10
p. Two phosphor bands .. .. 60 1·00
q. Two fluorescent bands (30.12.71) .. 45 15

Designs: (*as T* **257**)—2 c. Totem pole; 3 c. Combine-harvester and oil derrick; 4 c. Ship in lock; 5 c. Harbour scene; 6 c., 7 c. "Transport"; 8 c. (Nos. 597, 610) Library of Parliament. (*as T* **263**)—8 c. (No. 584) "Alaska Highway" (A. Y. Jackson); 15 c. "Bylot Island" (L. Harris); 20 c. "Quebec Ferry" (J. W. Morrice); 25 c. "The Solemn Land" (J. E. H. MacDonald); 50 c. "Summer's Stores" (grain elevators) (J. Ensor); $1 "Oilfield" (near Edmonton) (H. G. Glyde).

No. 581q only exists as a pre-cancel.

Nos. 582b, 583b and 583pa are blocks with the outer edges imperf. These come from "One Dollar Plastic Packages" sold at post offices.

No. 592p comes with the band to the left or right of the stamp, the phosphor having been applied across alternate vertical perforations.

Postal forgeries exist of the 6 c. orange printed in lithography and perforated 12½.

Normal

Re-engraved

When the basic postal rate was changed to 6 c. the C.B.N. lent their die to B.A.B.N. who made a duplicate die from it by transfer. Parts of this proved to be weak, but it was used for Nos. 601/2 and 606/7. B.A.B.N. later re-engraved their die to make fresh plates which were used for Nos. 603 and 608. No. 608 first appeared on sheets from Plate 4.

There are no records of dates of issue of the booklets, packs and coils, but supplies of these were distributed to depots in the months indicated.

IMPERF BETWEEN PAIRS FROM COIL STAMPS. Nos. 594/7 are known in blocks or horizontal pairs imperf between vertically. Coils are supplied to post offices in batches of ten coils held together by roulettes between every fourth stamp so that they can easily be split apart. If two or more unsplit coils are purchased it is possible to obtain blocks or pairs imperf between vertically.

Vertical coil stamps are also known imperf between horizontally or with some stamps apparently completely imperf. These can result from blind perforations identifiable by slight indentations.

WHITE FLUORESCENT PAPER. Different papers with varying degrees of whiteness have been used for Canadian stamps, but during 1968–70 a distinctive very white and highly fluorescent paper was used known as "hybrite"; this fluoresces on the back and front. This paper has also been employed for commemorative issues, some of which exist on more than one type of paper. The white fluorescent papers are recorded in the Stanley Gibbons *Elizabethan Catalogue*.

FLUORESCENT BANDS. During the second half of 1971 new sorting machines were installed in the Ottawa area which were activated by stamps bearing fluorescent bands. These differ from the Winnipeg phosphor bands in that they react green and have no after-glow. To the naked eye the fluorescent bands appear shiny when compared with the remainder of the stamp when looking along its surface. Winnipeg phosphor bands appear matt.

The experiments were successful and what was at first called "Ottawa tagging" has since come into more general use and the Winnipeg phosphor was phased out. However, the substance at first used (known as OP–4) was found to migrate to envelopes, documents, album pages, etc. as well as to adjoining stamps. Late in 1972 this fault was cured by using another substance (called OP–2). The migrating bands were used on early printings of Nos. 604q, 608q and 610q as well as certain stamps referred to in a footnote after No. 692. It is most advisable to use plastic mounts for housing stamps with migrating bands or else clear acetate should be affixed to the album leaves.

269 Canadian Pavilion **270** Allegory of "Womanhood" on Ballot-box

(Des C.B.N.)

1967 (28 Apr). *World Fair, Montreal*. P 12.
611 **269** 5 c. blue and red 10 10

(Des Helen Fitzgerald. Litho)

1967 (24 May). *50th Anniv of Women's Franchise*. P 12.
612 **270** 5 c. reddish purple and black 10 10

271 Queen Elizabeth II and Centennial Emblem **272** Athlete

(Portrait from photo by Anthony Buckley)

1967 (30 June). *Royal Visit*. P 12.
613 **271** 5 c. plum and orange-brown 15 10

(Des Brigdens Ltd)

1967 (19 July). *Fifth Pan-American Games, Winnipeg*. P 12.
614 **272** 5 c. rose-red 10 10

273 "World News" **274** Governor-General Vanier

(Des W. McLauchlan)

1967 (31 Aug). *50th Anniv of the Canadian Press. P* 12.
615 **273** 5 c. blue 10 10

(Des from photo by Karsh)

1967 (15 Sept). *Vanier Commemoration. P* 12.
616 **274** 5 c. black 10 10

PRINTERS. The following were printed either by the Canadian Bank Note Co, Ottawa (C.B.N.) or the British American Bank Note Co, Ottawa (B.A.B.N.), *except where otherwise stated.*

275 People of 1867 and Toronto, 1967 **276** Carol Singers

(Des and recess C.B.N.)

1967 (28 Sept). *Centenary of Toronto as Capital City of Ontario. P* 12.
617 **275** 5 c. myrtle-green and vermilion . . 10 10

(Des and recess B.A.B.N.)

1967 (11 Oct). *Christmas. P* 12.
618 **276** 3 c. scarlet 10 10
a. Pack. Two blocks of 25 . . . . 3·25
p. Two phosphor bands 15 50
pa. Pack. Two blocks of 25 . . . . 3·25
619 5 c. emerald-green 10 10
p. Two phosphor bands 30 50

Nos. 618a and 618pa are blocks with the outer edges imperf. These come from "$1.50 Plastic Packs" sold at post offices.

277 Grey Jays **278** Weather Map and Instruments

(Des M. G. Loates. Litho C.B.N.)

1968 (15 Feb). *Wild Life. P* 12.
620 **277** 5 c. multicoloured 30 10
See also Nos. 638/40.

(Des and litho B.A.B.N.)

1968 (13 Mar). *Bicentenary of First Meteorological Readings. P* 11.
621 **278** 5 c. multicoloured 15 10

279 Narwhal **280** Globe, Maple Leaf and Rain Gauge

(Des J. A. Crosby. Litho B.A.B.N.)

1968 (10 Apr). *Wildlife. P* 11.
622 **279** 5 c. multicoloured 15 10

No. 622 has a background of yellow-green and pale blue but copies are known with the yellow-green apparently missing. This "yellow-green" is produced by an overlay of yellow on the blue but we have not come across any copies where the yellow is completely missing and the wide range of colour variation is due to technical dificulties in maintaining an exact blend of the two colours.

(Des I. von Mosdossy. Litho B.A.B.N.)

1968 (8 May). *International Hydrological Decade. P* 11.
623 **280** 5 c. multicoloured 15 10

IMPERF EDGES. On Nos. 624/54, 657 and 659 (stamps printed by the B.A.B.N. Co.) the outer edges of the sheets were guillotined to remove the imprints for P.O. stock so that single stamps may, therefore, be found with either one, or two adjacent sides imperforate.

281 *Nonsuch* **282** Lacrosse Players

(Recess and photo B.A.B.N.)

1968 (5 June). *300th Anniv of Voyage of the "Nonsuch". P* 10.
624 **281** 5 c. multicoloured 20 10

(Des J. E. Aldridge. Recess and photo B.A.B.N.)

1968 (3 July). *Lacrosse. P* 10.
625 **282** 5 c. black, red and lemon 15 10

283 Front Page of *The Globe*, George Brown and Legislative Building **284** H. Bourassa

(Des N. Sabolotny. Recess and photo B.A.B.N.)

1968 (21 Aug). *150th Birth Anniv of George Brown (politician and journalist). P* 10.
626 **283** 5 c. multicoloured 10 10

(Des, recess and litho C.B.N.)

1968 (4 Sept). *Birth Centenary of Henri Bourassa (journalist and politician). P* 12.
627 **284** 5 c. black, red and pale cream 10 10

285 John McCrae, Battlefield and First Lines of "In Flanders Fields" **286** Armistice Monument, Vimy

(Des I. von Mosdossy. Litho C.B.N.)

1968 (15 Oct). *50th Death Anniv of John McCrae (soldier and poet). P* 12.
628 **285** 5 c. multicoloured 10 10

(Des and recess C.B.N.)

1968 (15 Oct). *50th Anniversary of* 1918 *Armistice. P* 12.
629 **286** 15 c. slate-black 30 40

287 Eskimo Family (carving) **288** "Mother and Child" (carving)

(Designs from Eskimo carvings by Munamee (6 c.) and unknown carver (5 c.). Photo C.B.N.)

1968. *Christmas. P* 12.
630 **287** 5 c. black and new blue (1.11.68) . . 10 10
a. Booklet pane of 10 (15.11.68) . . 2·50
p. One centre phosphor band 10 50
pa. Booklet pane of 10 (15.11.68) . . 3·50
631 **288** 6 c. black and ochre (15.11.68) 10 10
p. Two phosphor bands 20 50

289 Curling **290** Vincent Massey

(Des D. Eales. Recess and photo B.A.B.N.)

1969 (15 Jan). *Curling. P* 10.
632 **289** 6 c. black, new blue and scarlet . . 15 10

(Des I. von Mosdossy. Recess and litho C.B.N.)

1969 (20 Feb). *Vincent Massey, First Canadian-born Governor General. P* 12.
633 **290** 6 c. sepia and yellow-ochre 10 1

291 "Return from the Harvest Field" (Suzor-Côté) **292** Globe and Tools

(Photo C.B.N.)

1969 (14 Mar). *Birth Centenary of Marc Aurèle de Foy Suzor-Côté (painter). P* 12.
634 **291** 50 c. multicoloured . . . . . . 70 2·0

(Des J. Hébert. Recess B.A.B.N.)

1969 (21 May). *50th Anniv of International Labour Organisation P* 12½ × 12.
635 **292** 6 c. bronze-green 10 1

293 Vickers FB-27 Vimy Aircraft over Atlantic Ocean **294** "Sir William Osler" (J. S. Sargent)

(Des R. W. Bradford. Recess and photo B.A.B.N.)

1969 (13 June). *50th Anniv of First Non-stop Transatlantic Flight. P* 12 × 12½.
636 **293** 15 c. chocolate, bright green & pale blue 40 55

(Des, recess and photo B.A.B.N.)

1969 (23 June). *50th Death Anniv of Sir William Osler (physician). P* 12½ × 12.
637 **294** 6 c. deep blue, light blue and chestnut 20 10

295 White-throated Sparrows **298** Flags of Winter and Summer Games

(Des M. G. Loates. Litho C.B.N.)

1969 (23 July). *Birds. T* **295** *and similar multicoloured designs. P* 12.
638 6 c. Type **295** 25 10
639 10 c. Savannah Sparrow (*horiz*) . . . . 50 1·10
640 25 c. Hermit Thrush (*horiz*) . . . . 1·60 2·75
638/40 . . . . . . *Set of* 3 2·10 3·50

(Des C. McDiarmid. Recess and litho C.B.N.)

1969 (15 Aug). *Canadian Games. P* 12.
641 **298** 6 c. emerald, scarlet and blue 10 10

299 Outline of Prince Edward Island showing Charlottetown **300** Sir Isaac Brock and Memorial Column

(Des L. Fitzgerald. Recess and photo B.A.B.N.)

1969 (15 Aug). *Bicentenary of Charlottetown as Capital of Prince Edward Island. P* 12 × 12½.
642 **299** 6 c. yellow-brown, black and blue 20 10

(Des I. von Mosdossy. Recess and litho C.B.N.)

1969 (12 Sept). *Birth Bicentenary of Sir Isaac Brock. P* 12.
643 **300** 6 c. orange, bistre and bistre-brown 10 10

301 Children of the World in Prayer

302 Stephen Butler Leacock, Mask and "Mariposa"

(Des Rapid Grip and Batten Ltd. Litho C.B.N.)

969 (8 Oct). *Christmas. P* 12.
44 **301** 5 c. multicoloured 10 10
a. Booklet pane of 10 .. .. 1·75
p. One centre phosphor band 10 70
pa. Booklet pane of 10 .. .. 2·50
45 6 c. multicoloured 10 10
a. Black (inscr, value and frame omitted £1200
p. Two phosphor bands 20 70

(Des, recess and photo B.A.B.N.)

969 (12 Nov). *Birth Centenary of Stephen Butler Leacock (humorist). P* 12 × 12½.
346 **302** 6 c. multicoloured 10 10

303 Symbolic Cross-roads

304 "Enchanted Owl" (Kenojuak)

(Des K. C. Lochhead. Litho C.B.N.)

1970 (27 Jan). *Centenary of Manitoba. P* 12.
647 **303** 6 c. ultramarine, lemon and vermilion 15 10
p. Two phosphor bands 15 70

(Des N. E. Hallendy and Miss S. Van Raalte. Recess C.B.N.)

1970 (27 Jan). *Centenary of Northwest Territories. P* 12.
648 **304** 6 c. carmine-red and black 10 10

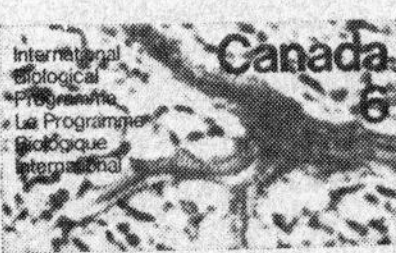

305 Microscopic View of Inside of Leaf

306 Expo 67 Emblem and Stylized Cherry Blossom

(Des I. Charney. Recess and photo B.A.B.N.)

1970 (18 Feb). *International Biological Programme. P* 12 × 12½.
649 **305** 6 c. emerald, orange-yellow & ultram .. 15 10

(Des E. R. C. Bethune. Litho C.B.N.)

1970 (18 Mar). *World Fair, Osaka. T* **306** *and similar horiz designs. Multicoloured; colour of Cherry Blossom given. P* 12.
650 25 c. red .. .. 1·50 2·00
a. Block of 4. Nos. 650/3 .. .. .. 5·50
p. Two phosphor bands .. .. .. 1·50 2·25
pa. Block of 4. Nos. 650p/3p .. .. .. 5·50
651 25 c. violet .. .. 1·50 2·00
p. Two phosphor bands .. .. .. 1·50 2·25
652 25 c. green .. .. 1·50 2·00
p. Two phosphor bands .. .. .. 1·50 2·25
653 25 c. blue .. .. 1·50 2·00
p. Two phosphor bands .. .. .. 1·50 2·25
650/3 .. .. *Set of* 4 5·50 7·00
650p/3p .. .. *Set of* 4 5·50 8·00

Designs:—No. 650, Type **306**; No. 651, Dogwood and stylized cherry blossom; No. 652, White Trillium and stylized cherry blossom; No. 653, White Garden Lily and stylized cherry blossom.

Nos. 650/3 and 650p/3p are printed together in sheets of 50 (5 × 10). In the first, second, fourth and fifth vertical rows the four different designs are arranged in *se-tenant* blocks, whilst the centre row is composed as follows (reading downwards:—650(p)/3(p), 650(p) × 2, 653(p), 651(p), 652(p) and 650(p).

310 Henry Kelsey

311 "Towards Unification"

(Des D. Burton. Recess and photo B.A.B.N.)

1970 (15 Apr). *300th Birth Anniv of Henry Kelsey (explorer). P* 12 × 12½.
654 **310** 6 c. multicoloured 10 10

(Des B. Fisher. Litho B.A.B.N.)

1970 (13 May). *25th Anniv of United Nations. P* 11.
655 **311** 10 c. blue 40 30
p. Two phosphor bands .. .. 60 2·00
656 15 c. magenta and bluish lilac 40 35
p. Two phosphor bands .. .. 70 2·00

312 Louis Riel (Métis leader)

313 Mackenzie's Inscription, Dean Channel

(Des R. Derreth. Photo B.A.B.N.)

1970 (19 June). *Louis Riel Commemoration. P* 12½ × 12.
657 **312** 6 c. greenish blue and vermilion .. 10 10

(Design from Government Archives photo. Recess C.B.N.)

1970 (25 June). *Sir Alexander Mackenzie (explorer). P* 12 × 11½.
658 **313** 6 c. bistre-brown 15 10

314 Sir Oliver Mowat (statesman)

315 "Isles of Spruce" (A. Lismer)

(Des E. Roch. Recess and photo B.A.B.N.)

1970 (12 Aug). *Sir Oliver Mowat Commemoration. P* 12×12½.
659 **314** 6 c. vermilion and black 10 10

(Litho Ashton-Potter)

1970 (18 Sept). *50th Anniv of "Group of Seven" (artists). P* 11.
660 **315** 6 c. multicoloured 10 10

316 "Horse-drawn Sleigh" (D. Niskala)

317 "Christ in Manger" (C. Fortier)

(Des from children's drawings. Litho C.B.N.)

1970 (7 Oct). *Christmas. Horiz designs as T* **316/17**, *showing children's drawings. Multicoloured. P* 12.
661 5 c. Type **316** 50 20
a. Strip of 5. Nos. 661/5 .. .. .. 2·25
p. One centre phosphor band .. .. 90 1·25
pa. Strip of 5. Nos. 661p/5p .. .. .. 4·00
662 5 c. "Stable" and Star of Bethlehem" (L. Wilson) (26 × 21 *mm*) 50 20
p. One centre phosphor band .. .. 90 1·25
663 5 c. "Snowmen" (M. Lecompte) (26 × 21 *mm*) 50 20
p. One centre phosphor band .. .. 90 1·25
664 5 c. "Skiing" (D. Durham) (26 × 21 *mm*) .. 50 20
p. One centre phosphor band .. .. 90 1·25
665 5 c. "Santa Claus" (A. Martin) (26 × 21 *mm*) 50 20
p. One centre phosphor band .. .. 90 1·25
666 6 c. "Santa Claus" (E. Bhattacharya) (26 × 21 *mm*) 50 20
a. Strip of 5. Nos. 666/70 .. .. .. 2·25
p. Two phosphor bands .. .. .. 90 1·25
pa. Strip of 5. Nos. 666p/70p .. .. .. 4·00
667 6 c. "Christ in Manger" (J. McKinney) (26 × 21 *mm*) 50 20
p. Two phosphor bands .. .. .. 90 1·25
668 6 c. "Toy Shop" (N. Whateley) (26 × 21 *mm*) 50 20
p. Two phosphor bands .. .. .. 90 1·25
669 6 c. "Christmas Tree" (J. Pomperleau) (26 × 21 *mm*) 50 20
p. Two phosphor bands .. .. .. 90 1·25
670 6 c. "Church" (J. McMillan) (26 × 21 *mm*) .. 50 20
p. Two phosphor bands .. .. .. 90 1·25
671 10 c. Type **317** 30 30
p. Two phosphor bands .. .. .. 55 1·25
672 15 c. "Trees and Sledge" (J. Dojcak) (35 × 21 mm) 45 60
p. Two phosphor bands .. .. .. 70 1·75
661/72 .. .. *Set of* 12 4·75 2·50
661p/672p .. .. *Set of* 12 8·50 12·50

The designs of the 5 c. and 6 c. were each issued with the various designs *se-tenant* in a diamond shaped arrangement within the sheet. This generally results in *se-tenant* pairs both vert and horiz, but due to the sheet arrangement vert and horiz pairs of the same design exist from the two centre vert and horiz rows.

328 Sir Donald A. Smith

329 "Big Raven" (E. Carr)

(Des Dora de Pédery-Hunt. Litho C.B.N.)

1970 (4 Nov). *150th Birth Anniv of Sir Donald Alexander Smith. P* 12.
673 **328** 6 c. yellow, brown and bronze-green .. 15 10

(Litho C.B.N.)

1971 (12 Feb). *Birth Centenary of Emily Carr (painter). P* 12.
674 **329** 6 c. multicoloured 20 30

330 Laboratory Equipment

331 "The Atom"

(Des R. Webber. Litho B.A.B.N.)

1971 (3 Mar). *50th Anniv of Discovery of Insulin. P* 10½.
675 **330** 6 c. multicoloured 30 30

(Des R. Webber. Litho B.A.B.N.)

1971 (24 Mar). *Birth Centenary of Lord Rutherford (scientist). P* 11.
676 **331** 6 c. yellow, red and deep chocolate 20 20

332 Maple "Keys"

333 Louis Papineau

(Des Alma Duncan. Litho Ashton-Potter)

1971. *"The Maple Leaf in Four Seasons". T* **332** *and similar vert designs. Multicoloured. P* 11.
677 6 c. Type **332** (Spring) (14.4) 20 20
a. Imperf (pair) £600
678 6 c. Green leaves (Summer) (16.6) 20 20
679 7 c. Autumn leaves (3.9) 20 20
a. Grey (inscr and value) omitted £2000
680 7 c. Withered leaves and snow (Winter) (19.11) 20 20
677/80 .. .. *Set of* 4 70 70

(Des L. Marquart. Recess and photo B.A.B.N.)

1971 (7 May). *Death Centenary of Louis-Joseph Papineau (politician). P* 12½ × 12.
681 **333** 6 c. multicoloured 15 20

334 Chart of Coppermine River

335 "People" and Computer Tapes

(Des L. Marquart. Recess and photo B.A.B.N.)

1971 (7 May). *Bicentenary of Samuel Hearne's Expedition to Coppermine River. P* 12×12½.
682 **334** 6 c. red, sepia and pale buff 40 40

(Des H. Kleefeld. Litho C.B.N.)

1971 (1 June). *Centenary of First Canadian Census. P* 11½.
683 **335** 6 c. blue, red and black 30 20

336 Maple Leaves

(Des B. Kramer. Litho C.B.N.)

1971 (1 June). *Radio Canada International. P* 12.
684 **336** 15 c. red, yellow and black .. .. 50 1·25
p. Two phosphor bands .. .. 1·75 3·50

337 "BC"

(Des E. R. C. Bethune. Litho C.B.N.)

1971 (20 July). *Centenary of British Columbia's Entry into the Confederation. P* 12.
685 **337** 7 c. multicoloured 15 10

338 "Indian Encampment on Lake Huron" (Kane)   **339** "Snowflake"

(Des and litho B.A.B.N.)

1971 (11 Aug). *Death Centenary of Paul Kane (painter). P* 12½.

686	**338**	7 c. multicoloured	20	10

(Des Lisl Levinsohn. Recess (6 c., 7 c.) or recess and litho (others) C.B.N.)

1971 (6 Oct). *Christmas. T* **379** *and similar design. P* 12.

687	**339**	6 c. deep blue	10	10
		p. One centre phosphor band	30	60
688		7 c. deep emerald	15	10
		p. Two phosphor bands	40	65
689	–	10 c. silver and cerise	50	1·25
		p. Two phosphor bands	1·00	2·25
690	–	15 c. silver, brown-purple and lavender	65	1·50
		p. Two phosphor bands	1·00	2·75
687/90		.. .. *Set of* 4	1·25	2·75
687p/90p		.. .. *Set of* 4	2·40	5·50

Design:—10 c., 15 c. "Snowflake" design similar to Type **339**, but square (26×26 mm).

340 Pierre Laporte (Quebec Cabinet Minister)   **341** Skaters

(Des G. Gundersen. Recess and litho B.A.B.N.)

1971 (20 Oct). *First Anniv of the Assassination of Pierre Laporte. P* 12½ × 12.

691	**340**	7 c. black/*pale buff*	15	10

(Des Design Workshop, Toronto. Litho C.B.N.)

1972 (1 Mar). *World Figure Skating Championships, Calgary. P* 12.

692	**341**	8 c. purple	15	10

MIGRATING FLUORESCENT BANDS. These are referred to in the notes after No. 610. In the following issues they exist on Nos. 719q/22q, 731q/2q and on early printings only of Nos. 702/6.

342 J. A. MacDonald   **343** Forest, Central Canada

344 Vancouver

Type I

Type II

Two types of 10 c. (No. 702):

Type I. Light impression of green recess colour. Cross-hatching around "Canada" clearly visible (plate 1).

Type II. Green recess colour much more deeply etched. Cross-hatching around "Canada" entirely obscured (plates 2 and 3).

Type I

Type II

Two types of 15 c.:

Type I. Trees on hillside, shown in blue, clearly detailed (plate 1).

Type II. Trees shown in solid colour (plate 2).

Two types of 25 c.:

Type I. Bears' shadows evenly shaded.

Type II. Shadows have a solid central area.

(Des D. Annesley (1 to 10 c. (701)), R. Derreth (others))

1972–77. *Various designs as T* **342/4**.

(*a*) *T* **342** *and similar vert portraits. Recess C.B.N. (1 to 6 c. and last ptgs of 7 and 8 c. (No. 700), B.A.B.N. (7, 8, 10 c. and booklet panes). Two fluorescent bands. P* 12 × 12½ (1 *to* 8 *c.*) *or* 13 (10 *c.*). (17.10.73)

693	1 c. orange	10	10
	a. Booklet pane. Nos. 693×3, 698 and 700×2 (10.4.74)	65	
	b. Booklet pane. Nos. 693×6, 698 and 700×11 (17.1.75)	2·25	
	c. Booklet pane. Nos. 693×2, 694×4 and 701a×4 (1.9.76)	1·50	
	d. Printed on the gummed side ..	£150	
694	2 c. deep green	10	10
695	3 c. agate	10	30
696	4 c. black	10	10
697	5 c. deep magenta	10	10
698	6 c. Indian red	10	10
	a. Printed on the gummed side ..	75·00	
699	7 c. reddish brown (8.4.74)	10	30
700	8 c. dull ultramarine	15	10
	a. Perf 13 (12.76)	1·25	60
701	10 c. brown-lake (1.9.76)	40	10
	a. Perf 12×12½ (booklets)	90	90

(*b*) *T* **343** *and similar vert designs. Recess and photo B.A.B.N. Two fluorescent bands. P* 12½×12 (8.9.72)

702	10 c. dp green, blue-green & yellow-orge (I)	60	10
	a. Type II (7.74)	40	15
	b. Perf 13½ (2.76)	60	10
	p. Two phosphor bands	1·00	2·00
703	15 c. dull ultramarine and orange-brown (I)	90	15
	a. Type II (1975)	2·50	1·25
	b. Perf 13½ (2.76)	60	10
	p. Two phosphor bands	1·75	2·75
704	20 c. pale orange, reddish violet & ultram	75	10
	a. Perf 13½ (30.1.76)	30	10
	p. Two phosphor bands	2·00	3·00
705	25 c. deep ultramarine and pale blue (I) ..	1·00	10
	a. Type II (1975)	6·50	2·50
	b. Perf 13½ (2.76)	90	10
	p. Two phosphor bands	3·00	4·25
706	50 c. blue-green, royal blue and buff ..	45	30
	a. Blue-green, ultramarine and buff (8.74)	65	20
	b. Perf 13½ (2.76)	1·50	10

(*c*) *T* **344** *and similar horiz design. Recess B.A.B.N. and litho Ashton-Potter. No fluorescent bands. P* 11 (17.3.72)

707	$1 multicoloured	4·50	4·50
708	$2 multicoloured	1·50	2·00

(*d*) *T* **344.** *Recess and photo B.A.B.N. Two fluorescent bands. P* 12½ × 12 (24.10.73)

709	$1 multicoloured	2·50	1·00
	a. Perf 13½ (4.77)	85	70

(*e*) *As Nos.* 700/1. *Recess C.B.N. Imperf × perf* 10 (*coil stamps*)

710	8 c. dull ultramarine (10.4.74)	85	20
	a. Imperf (horiz pair)	80·00	
711	10 c. brown-lake (1.9.76)	30	20
	a. Imperf (horiz pair)	£100	

Designs (1 to 7c. show Canadian Prime Ministers):—2 c. W Laurier; 3 c. R. Borden; 4 c. W. L. Mackenzie King; 5 c. R. B Bennett; 6 c. L. B. Pearson; 7 c. Louis St. Laurent; 8 and 10 (Nos. 701/a, 711), Queen Elizabeth II; 15 c. American Bighor sheep; 20 c. Prairie landscape from the air; 25 c. Polar Bear 50 c. Seashore, Eastern Canada; $2 Quebec.

Stamps from booklets exist with one or two adjacent side imperforate.

345 Heart

(Des Joyce Wieland. Recess B.A.B.N.)

1972 (7 Apr). *Heart Disease (World Health Day). P* 12×12½.

719	**345**	8 c. carmine	30	1
		q. Two fluorescent bands	60	2

The chemical used on No. 719q migrates.

346 Frontenac and Fort Saint-Louis, Quebec

(Des L. Marquart. Recess and photo B.A.B.N.)

1972 (17 May). *300th Anniv of Governor Frontenac's Appointmen to New France. P* 12 × 12½.

720	**346**	8 c. brown-red, orange-brn & dp ultram	15	15
		q. Two fluorescent bands	15	15

The chemical used on No. 720q migrates.

347 Plains Indians' Artefacts   **347***a* Buffalo Chase

(Des G. Beaupré. Litho Ashton-Potter (721/2, 725/6 and 729/30) B.A.B.N. (723/4), C.B.N. (727/8))

1972–76. *Canadian Indians. Two fluorescent bands* (*Nos* 723/30 *and* 733/40). *P* 12×12½ (721/2, 725/6), 12 (723/4), 13 (727/30), 12½×12 (731/6) *or* 12½ (737/40).

(*a*) *Horiz designs issued in se-tenant pairs, the first showing Artefacts as T* **347**, *the second showing Scenes from Indian Life as T* **347***a*.

721	8 c. multicoloured (6.7.72)	40	10
	a. Pair. Nos. 721/2	85	1·00
	q. Two fluorescent bands	40	15
	qa. Pair. Nos. 721q/2q	85	1·00
722	8 c. dp brown, yellow & grey-black (6.7.72)	40	10
	q. Two fluorescent bands	40	15
723	8 c. multicoloured (21.2.73)	40	10
	a. Pair. Nos. 723/4	85	1·00
724	8 c. multicoloured (21.2.73)	40	10
725	8 c. multicoloured (16.1.74)	40	10
	a. Pair. Nos. 725/6	85	1·25
726	8 c. dp brown, yellow & grey-black (16.1.74)	40	10
727	8 c. multicoloured (4.4.75)	40	10
	a. Pair. Nos. 727/8	85	1·25
728	8 c. multicoloured (4.4.75)	40	10
729	10 c. multicoloured (17.9.76)	40	20
	a. Pair. Nos. 729/30	85	1·00
730	10 c. light stone and black (17.9.76) ..	40	20

Designs show the following tribes: Nos. 721/2 (T 347/*a*), Plains Indians; 723/4, Algonkians; 725/6, Pacific Coast Indians; 727/8 Subarctic Indians; 729/30, Iroquoians.

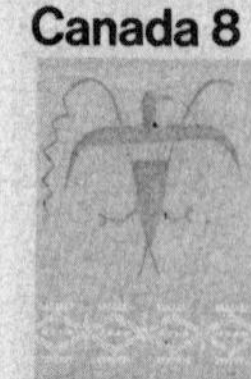

348 Thunderbird and Tribal Pattern   **348***a* Dancer in Ceremonial Costume

(Des G. Beaupré. Recess and photo B.A.B.N. (731/6). Litho and embossed Ashton-Potter (737, 739). Litho Ashton-Potter (738, 740))

(*b*) *Vert designs issued in se-tenant pairs, the first showing Thunderbird and pattern as T* **348**, *the second Costumes as T* **348***a*.

731	8 c. lt yellow-orge, rose-red & blk (4.10.72)	40	15
	a. Pair. Nos. 731/2	85	1·00
	q. Two fluorescent bands	40	15
	qa. Pair. Nos. 731q/2q	85	1·00
732	8 c. multicoloured (4.10.72)	40	15
	q. Two fluorescent bands	40	15
733	8 c. light rose-red, violet & black (28.11.73)	40	10
	a. Pair. Nos. 733/4	85	1·00
734	8 c. turq-green, lake-brn & blk (28.11.73)	40	10

'5 8 c. rose-red and black (22.2.74) 40 10
a. Pair. Nos. 735/6 . . . . . . 85 1·00
'6 8 c. multicoloured (22.2.74) 40 10
'7 8 c. myrtle-green, grey-brn & blk (4.4.75) 40 10
a. Pair. Nos. 737/8 . . . . . . 85 1·25
'8 8 c. multicoloured (4.4.75) 40 10
'9 10 c. olive-bistre, reddish orange and black (17.9.76) 40 20
a. Pair. Nos. 739/40 . . . . . . 85 1·00
.0 10 c. multicoloured (17.9.76) 40 20
.1/40 . . . . . . *Set of* 20 7·50 2·10

Designs show the following tribes: Nos. 731/2 (T **348/a**), Plains ıdians; 733/4, Algonkians; 735/6, Pacific Coast Indians; 737/8, ıbarctic Indians; 739/40, Iroquoians.

The fluorescent bands on Nos. 721q/2q and 731q/2q migrate.

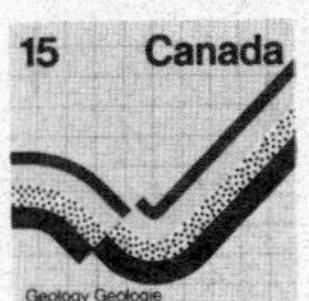

349 Earth's Crust

350 Candles

(Des Gottschalk and Ash Ltd. Litho Ashton-Potter)

972 (2 Aug). *Earth Sciences. T* **349** *and similar square designs. P* 12.

41 15 c. multicoloured . . . . . . 1·40 1·90
a. Block of 4. Nos. 741/4 . . . . 5·00
q. Two fluorescent bands . . . . 1·50 2·00
qa. Block of 4. Nos. 741q/4q . . . . 5·50
42 15 c. pale grey, dull ultramarine and black 1·40 1·90
q. Two fluorescent bands . . . . 1·50 2·00
43 15 c. multicoloured . . . . . . 1·40 1·90
q. Two fluorescent bands . . . . 1·50 2·00
44 15 c. light emerald, red-orange and black 1·40 1·90
q. Two fluorescent bands . . . . 1·50 2·00
'41/4 . . . . . . *Set of* 4 5·00 6·50
'41q/4q . . . . . . *Set of* 4 5·50 7·50

Designs and Events:—No. 741, Photogrammetric surveying 12th Congress of International Society of Photogrammetry); No. 742, "Siegfried" lines (6th Conference of International Cartographic Association); No. 743, Type **349** (24th International Geological Congress); No. 744, Diagram of village at road-intersection (22nd International Geographical Congress).

Nos. 741/4 were issued in sheets of 64, made up of 4 panes of 6, each pane having a marginal commemorative inscription. Within a pane are 4 copies of each design, arranged in *se-tenant* blocks of 4.

(Des R. Webber. Litho Ashton-Potter)

972 (1 Nov). *Christmas. T* **350** *and similar designs. P* 12½ × 12 (6 *and* 8 c.) *or* 11 × 10½ (*others*).

'45 **350** 6 c. multicoloured 15 10
p. One centre phosphor band . . 35 60
q. Two fluorescent bands 20 15
'46 8 c. multicoloured 15 10
p. Two phosphor bands 40 70
q. Two fluorescent bands 25 15
747 – 10 c. multicoloured 50 85
p. Two phosphor bands . . . . 1·25 1·75
q. Two fluorescent bands 60 90
748 – 15 c. multicoloured . . . . . . 60 1·25
p. Two phosphor bands . . . . 1·50 2·50
q. Two fluorescent bands . . . . 90 1·50
745/8 . . . . . . *Set of* 4 1·25 2·00
745p/8p . . . . . . *Set of* 4 3·25 5·00
745q/8q . . . . . . *Set of* 4 1·75 2·40

Designs: *Horiz* (36 × 20 *mm*)—10 c. Candles with fruits and pine boughs; 15 c. Candles with prayer-book, caskets and vase.

351 "The Blacksmith's Shop" (Krieghoff)

352 François de Montmorency-Laval

(Des and litho B.A.B.N. and Saults & Pollard Ltd., Winnipeg)

1972 (29 Nov). *Death Centenary of Cornelius Krieghoff (painter). P* 12½.

749 **351** 8 c. multicoloured 30 15
q. Two fluorescent bands 30 40

FLUORESCENT BANDS. Stamps from No. 750 onwards were issued only with two fluorescent bands, *unless otherwise stated.* Examples are known with the bands omitted in error, but such varieties are outside the scope of the catalogue.

(Des M. Fog and G. Lorange. Litho Ashton-Potter)

1973 (31 Jan). *350th Birth Anniv of Monsignor de Laval (First Bishop of Quebec). P* 11.

750 **352** 8 c. ultramarine, gold and silver . . 20 40

353 Commissioner French and Route of the March West

(Des Dallaire Morin DeVito Inc. Litho Ashton-Potter)

1973 (9 Mar). *Centenary of Royal Canadian Mounted Police. T* **353** *and similar horiz designs. Multicoloured (except* 8 c.). *P* 11.

751 8 c. Type **353** (deep reddish brown, dull orange and orange-vermilion) 35 20
752 10 c. Spectrograph . . . . . . 1·00 1·25
753 15 c. Mounted policeman . . . . 1·75 2·00
751/3 . . . . . . *Set of* 3 2·75 3·00

354 Jeanne Mance

(Des R. Bellemare. Litho Ashton-Potter)

1973 (18 Apr). *300th Death Anniv of Jeanne Mance (nurse). P* 11.

754 **354** 8 c. multicoloured 20 40

355 Joseph Howe

356 "Mist Fantasy" (MacDonald)

(Des A. Fleming. Litho Ashton-Potter)

1973 (16 May). *Death Centenary of Joseph Howe (Nova Scotian politician). P* 11.

755 **355** 8 c. gold and black 20 40

(Des and litho Ashton-Potter)

1973 (8 June). *Birth Centenary of J. E. H. MacDonald (artist). P* 12½.

756 **356** 15 c. multicoloured 30 55

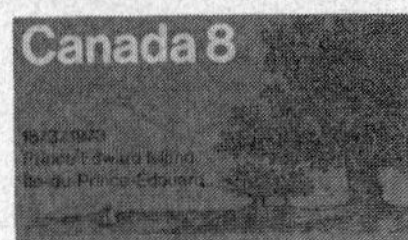

357 Oaks and Harbour

(Des A. Mann. Recess and photo B.A.B.N.)

1973 (22 June). *Centenary of Prince Edward Island's Entry into the Confederation. P* 12.

757 **357** 8 c. pale orange and brown-red . . 20 30

358 Scottish Settlers

359 Queen Elizabeth II

(Des P. Swan. Litho Ashton-Potter)

1973 (20 July). *Bicentennial of Arrival of Scottish Settlers at Pictou, Nova Scotia. P* 12 × 12½.

758 **358** 8 c. multicoloured 25 20

(Des A. Fleming from photograph by Anthony Buckley. Eng G. A. Gundersen. Recess and photo B.A.B.N.)

1973 (2 Aug). *Royal Visit and Commonwealth Heads of Government Meeting, Ottawa. P* 12 × 12½.

759 **359** 8 c. multicoloured 25 20
760 15 c. red, black and bright gold . . 80 1·50
a. Red, black and pale dull gold . . 1·25 1·90

360 Nellie McClung

361 Emblem of 1976 Olympics

(Des S. Mennie. Litho Ashton-Potter)

1973 (29 Aug). *Birth Centenary of Nellie McClung (feminist). P* 10½ × 11.

761 **360** 8 c. multicoloured 20 50

(Des Wallis and Matanovic. Litho Ashton-Potter)

1973 (20 Sept). *Olympic Games, Montreal* (1976) (*1st issue*). *P* 12 × 12½.

762 **361** 8 c. multicoloured 25 15
763 15 c. multicoloured . . . . . . 45 1·25

See also Nos. 768/71, 772/4, 786/9, 798/802, 809/11, 814/16, 829/31, 833/7 and 842/4.

362 Ice-skate

363 Diving

(Des A. Maggs. Litho Ashton-Potter)

1973 (7 Nov). *Christmas. T* **362** *and similar vert designs. Multicoloured. P* 12½ × 12 (6, 8 c.) *or* 11 (*others*).

764 6 c. Type **362** 15 10
765 8 c. Bird decoration 20 10
766 10 c. Santa Claus (20 × 36 *mm*) . . . . 70 1·40
767 15 c. Shepherd (20 × 36 *mm*) . . . . 80 1·75
764/7 . . . . . . *Set of* 4 1·75 3·00

(Des Hunter, Straker, Templeton Ltd. Recess C.B.N.)

1974 (22 Mar). *Olympic Games, Montreal* (1976) (*2nd issue*). *"Summer Activities". T* **363** *and similar vert designs. Each deep blue. P* 12.

768 8 c. Type **363** 25 50
a. Block of 4. Nos. 768/71 90
769 8 c. "Jogging" 25 50
770 8 c. Cycling 25 50
771 8 c. Hiking 25 50
768/71 . . . . . . *Set of* 4 90 1·75

Nos. 768/71 were printed in *se-tenant* blocks of four throughout the sheet. Each design has a second (latent) image—the Canadian Olympic Games symbol—which appears when the stamp is viewed obliquely to the light.

See also Nos. 786/9.

(Des Wallis and Matanovic. Litho Ashton-Potter)

1974 (17 Apr). *Olympic Games, Montreal* (1976) (*3rd issue*). *As T* **361** *but smaller* (20 × 36½ *mm*). *P* 12½.

772 **361** 8 c. + 2 c. multicoloured 25 45
773 10 c. + 5 c. multicoloured . . . . 35 1·00
774 15 c. + 5 c. multicoloured . . . . 40 1·40
772/4 . . . . . . *Set of* 3 90 2·50

364 Winnipeg Signpost, 1872

365 Postmaster and Customer

(Des J. R. MacDonald. Litho and embossed Ashton-Potter)

1974 (3 May). *Winnipeg Centennial. P* 12½ × 12.

775 **364** 8 c. multicoloured 20 15

(Des S. Mennie. Litho Ashton-Potter)

1974 (11 June). *Centenary of Canadian Letter Carrier Delivery Service. T* **365** *and similar horiz designs. Multicoloured. P* 13½.

776 8 c. Type **365** 50 80
a. Block of 6. Nos. 776/81 . . . . 2·75
777 8 c. Postman collecting mail 50 80
778 8 c. Mail handler 50 80
779 8 c. Mail sorters 50 80
780 8 c. Postman making delivery 50 80
781 8 c. Rural delivery by car 50 80
776/81 . . . . . . *Set of* 6 2·75 4·25

Nos. 776/81 were printed in *se-tenant* combinations throughout a sheet of 50, giving 6 blocks of 6 and 14 single stamps.

366 "Canada's Contribution to Agriculture"

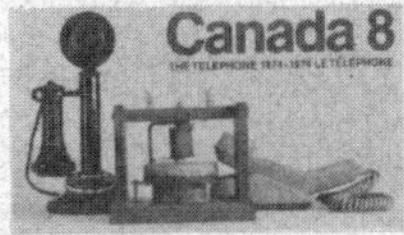

367 Telephone Development

(Des M. Brett, P. Cowley-Brown, and A. McAllister. Litho Ashton-Potter)

1974 (12 July). *"Agricultural Education". Centenary of Ontario Agricultural College. P* 12½ × 12.

782 **366** 8 c. multicoloured 20 20

(Des R. Webber. Litho Ashton-Potter)

1974 (26 July). *Centenary of Invention of Telephone by Alexander Graham Bell. P* 12½.

783 **367** 8 c. multicoloured 20 20

368 Bicycle Wheel

(Des Burns and Cooper. Recess and photo B.A.B.N.)

1974 (7 Aug). *World Cycling Championships, Montreal. P* 12 × 12½.
784 **368** 8 c. black, rosine and silver 20 30

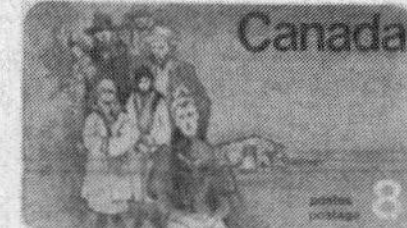

369 Mennonite Settlers

(Des W. Davies. Litho Ashton-Potter)

1974 (28 Aug). *Centenary of Arrival of Mennonites in Manitoba. P* 12½.
785 **369** 8 c. multicoloured 20 20

(Des Hunter, Straker, Templeton Ltd. Recess C.B.N.)

1974 (23 Sept). *Olympic Games, Montreal* (1976) (4*th issue*). *"Winter Activities". Horiz designs as T* **363**, *each rosine. P* 13½ × 13.
786 8 c. Snow-shoeing 50 60
a. Block of 4. Nos. 786/9 . . . . 1·75
ab. Printed on the gummed side (block of four) £650
787 8 c. Skiing 50 60
788 8 c. Skating 50 60
789 8 c. Curling 50 60
786/9 . . . . *Set of* 4 1·75 2·25

370 Mercury, Winged Horses and U.P.U. Emblem

(Des G. Gundersen. Recess and photo B.A.B.N.)

1974 (9 Oct). *Centenary of Universal Postal Union. P* 12 × 12½.
790 **370** 8 c. violet, red-orange and cobalt . . 15 15
791 15 c. red-orange, violet and cobalt . . 50 1·50

371 "The Nativity" (J. P. Lemieux)

372 Marconi and St. John's Harbour, Newfoundland

(Des Wallis and Matanovic. Litho Ashton-Potter)

1974 (1 Nov). *Christmas. T* **371** *and similar horiz designs showing paintings. Multicoloured. P* 13½.
792 6 c. Type **371** 10 10
793 8 c. "Skaters in Hull" (H. Masson) (34 × 31 *mm*) 10 10
794 10 c. "The Ice Cone, Montmorency Falls" (R. C. Todd) 20 75
795 15 c. "Village in the Laurentian Mountains" (C. A. Gagnon) . . . . . . 30 1·10
792/5 . . . . *Set of* 4 60 1·75

(Des J. Boyle. Litho Ashton-Potter)

1974 (15 Nov). *Birth Centenary of Guglielmo Marconi (radio pioneer). P* 13.
796 **372** 8 c. multicoloured 20 20

373 Merritt and Welland Canal

374 Swimming

(Des W. Rueter. Recess (B.A.B.N.) and litho (C.B.N.))

1974 (29 Nov). *William Merritt Commemoration. P* 13 × 13½.
797 **373** 8 c. multicoloured 20 30

(Des Wallis and Matanovic. Litho C.B.N.)

1975 (5 Feb). *Olympic Games, Montreal* (1976) (5*th issue*). *T* **374** *and similar horiz designs. Multicoloured.*
798 8 c. + 2 c. Type **374** 30 50
799 10 c. + 5 c. Rowing 40 90
800 15 c. + 5 c. Sailing . . . . . . 45 1·00
798/800 . . . . *Set of* 3 1·00 2·25

375 "The Sprinter"

376 "Anne of Green Gables" (Lucy Maud Montgomery)

(Des A. R. Fleming. Litho and embossed Ashton-Potter)

1975 (14 Mar). *Olympic Games, Montreal* (1976) (6*th issue*). *T* **375** *and similar multicoloured design showing sculpture by R. T. McKenzie. P* 12½ × 12 ($1) *or* 12 × 12½ ($2).
801 $1 Type **375** . . . . 2·00 2·75
802 $2 "The Diver" (*vert*) . . . . . . 2·75 4·75

(Des P. Swan (No. 803), C. Gagnon (No. 804). Litho Ashton-Potter)

1975 (15 May). *Canadian Writers* (1*st series*). *T* **376** *and similar vert design. Multicoloured. P* 13½.
803 8 c. Type **376** 30 10
a. Pair. Nos. 803/4 . . . . . . 60 80
804 8 c. "Maria Chapdelaine" (Louis Hémon) . . 30 10
Nos. 803/4 were printed horizontally and vertically *se-tenant* throughout the sheet.
See also Nos. 846/7, 940/1 and 1085/6.

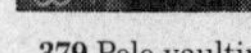

377 Marguerite Bourgeoys (founder of the Order of Notre Dame)

378 S. D. Chown (founder of United Church of Canada)

(Des Design and Communication, Montreal. Litho Ashton-Potter (Nos. 805/6). Des W. Southern. Eng G. Gundersen. Recess and photo B.A.B.N. (Nos. 807/8))

1975 (30 May). *Canadian Celebrities. T* **377/8** *and similar vert designs.*

(*a*) *As T* **377.** *P* 12½ × 12
805 8 c. multicoloured 50 40
806 8 c. multicoloured 50 40

(*b*) *As T* **378.** *P* 12 × 12½
807 8 c. sepia, flesh and light yellow 30 75
a. Pair. Nos. 807/8 . . . . . . 60 2·25
808 8 c. sepia, flesh and light yellow 30 75
805/8 . . . . *Set of* 4 1·40 2·25
Designs:—No. 805, Type **377**; No. 806, Alphonse Desjardins (leader of Credit Union movement); No. 807, Type **378**; No. 808, Dr. J. Cook (first moderator of Presbyterian Church in Canada).
Nos. 807/8 were printed together in the sheet horizontally and vertically *se-tenant*.

379 Pole-vaulting

380 "Untamed" (photo by Walt Petrigo)

(Des P. Swan. Litho Ashton-Potter)

1975 (11 June). *Olympic Games, Montreal* (1976) (7*th issue*). *T* **379** *and similar vert designs. Multicoloured. P* 12 × 12½.
809 20 c. Type **379** 40 50
810 25 c. Marathon-running 55 80
811 50 c. Hurdling . . . . 70 1·25
809/11 . . . . *Set of* 3 1·50 2·25

(Des B. Reilander. Litho C.B.N.)

1975 (3 July). *Centenary of Calgary. P* 12 × 12½.
812 **380** 8 c. multicoloured 20 30

381 I.W.Y. Symbol

382 Fencing

(Des Susan McPhee. Recess and photo B.A.B.N.)

1975 (14 July). *International Women's Year. P* 13.
813 **381** 8 c. lt grey-brown, bistre-yellow & blk 20 3

(Des J. Hill. Litho C.B.N.)

1975 (6 Aug). *Olympic Games, Montreal* (1976) (8*th issue*). *T* 38 *and similar vert designs showing combat sports. Multicoloure P* 13.
814 8 c. + 2 c. Type **382** 30 4
815 10 c. + 5 c. Boxing . . . . . . 35 1·0
816 15 c. + 5 c. Judo . . . . . . 40 1·2
814/16 . . . . *Set of* 3 95 2·4

383 "Justice-Justitia" (statue by W. S. Allward)

384 *William D. Lawrence* (full-rigged ship)

(Des A. Fleming. Litho Ashton-Potter)

1975 (2 Sept). *Centenary of Canadian Supreme Court. P* 12½.
817 **383** 8 c. multicoloured 20 3

(Des T. Bjarnason. Recess and photo B.A.B.N.)

1975 (24 Sept). *Canadian Ships* (1*st series*). *T* **384** *and simila horiz designs showing coastal ships. P* 13.
818 8 c. yellow-brown and black 60 75
a. Block of 4. Nos. 818/21 . . . . . . 2·25
819 8 c. blue-green and black 60 75
820 8 c. yellow-green and black 60 75
821 8 c. yellow-brown and black 60 75
818/21 . . . . *Set of* 4 2·25 2·75
Designs:—No. 819, *Neptune* (steamer). No. 820, *Beaver* (paddle-steamer). No. 821, *Quadra* (steamer).
Nos. 818/21 were printed together, *se-tenant*, in different combinations throughout the sheet, giving ten blocks of 4 and ten single stamps.
See also Nos. 851/4, 902/5 and 931/4.

385 "Santa Claus" (G. Kelly)

386 Text, Badge and Bugle

(Des B. Reilander from children's paintings. Litho Ashton-Potter)

1975 (22 Oct). *Christmas. T* **385** *and similar multicoloure designs. P* 13.
822 6 c. Type **385** 15 1
a. Pair. Nos. 822/3 . . . . . . 30 4
823 6 c. "Skater" (Bill Cawsey) 15 1
824 8 c. "Child" (D. Hébert) 15 1
a. Pair. Nos. 824/5 . . . . . . 30 4
825 8 c. "Family" (L. Caldwell) 15 1
826 10 c. "Gift" (D. Lovely) 30 5
827 15 c. "Trees" (R. Kowalski) (*horiz*) 40 7
822/7 . . . . *Set of* 6 1·10 1·9
Nos. 822/3 and 824/5 were respectively issued together *se-tenan* in an alternate arrangement within the sheet.

(Des R. Kavach. Recess and photo B.A.B.N.)

1975 (10 Nov). 50*th Anniv of Royal Canadian Legion P* 12½ × 13.
828 **386** 8 c. multicoloured 20 2

387 Basketball

(Des J. Hill. Litho Ashton-Potter)

1976 (7 Jan). *Olympic Games, Montreal* (9*th issue*). *T* **387** *and similar vert designs. Multicoloured. P* 13.
829 8 c. + 2 c. Type **387** 50 55
830 10 c. + 5 c. Gymnastics 50 90
831 20 c. + 5 c. Soccer . . . . . . 65 1·25
829/31 . . . . *Set of* 3 1·50 2·40

388 Games Symbol and Snow Crystal

389 "Communications Arts"

(Des R. Harder. Litho Ashton-Potter)

976 (6 Feb). *12th Winter Olympic Games, Innsbruck. P* 12½.
32 **388** 20 c. multicoloured 20 40

(Des R. Webber. Litho C.B.N.)

976 (6 Feb). *Olympic Games, Montreal* (10*th issue*). *T* **389** *and similar vert designs. Multicoloured. P* 12 × 12½.
33 20 c. Type **389** 30 25
34 25 c. "Handicrafts" 55 75
35 50 c. "Performing Arts" .. .. .. 70 1·60
33/5 .. .. *Set of* 3 1·40 2·40

390 Place Ville Marie and Notre-Dame Church

(Des J. and P. Mercier. Recess and photo B.A.B.N.)

976 (12 Mar). *Olympic Games, Montreal* (11*th issue*). *T* **390** *and similar horiz design. Multicoloured. P* 13.
36 $1 Type **390** .. .. 2·00 4·50
37 $2 Olympic Stadium and flags .. .. 2·50 5·50

391 Flower and Urban Sprawl

392 Benjamin Franklin and Map

(Des I. McLeod. Litho Ashton-Potter)

1976 (12 May). *U.N. Conference on Human Settlements* (*HABITAT*), *Vancouver. P* 12 × 12½.
38 **391** 20 c. multicoloured 20 30

(Des B. Reilander. Recess and photo B.A.B.N.)

1976 (1 June). *Bicentenary of American Revolution. P* 13.
39 **392** 10 c. multicoloured 20 35

393 Wing Parade before Mackenzie Building

394 Transfer of Olympic Flame by Satellite

(Des W. Davies. Litho C.B.N.)

1976 (1 June). *Royal Military College Centenary. T* **393** *and similar vert design. Multicoloured. P* 12 × 12½.
840 8 c. Colour party and Memorial Arch .. 15 20
a. Pair. Nos. 840/1 .. .. 30 80
ab. Printed double (pair) .. .. ..
841 8 c. Type **393** 15 20

Nos. 840/1 were printed horizontally and vertically *se-tenant* throughout the sheet.

(Des P. Swan. Litho Ashton-Potter)

1976 (18 June). *Olympic Games, Montreal* (12*th issue*). *T* **394** *and similar horiz designs. Multicoloured. P* 13½.
842 8 c. Type **394** 15 10
843 20 c. Carrying the Olympic flag 40 60
844 25 c. Athletes with medals 40 85
842/4 .. .. *Set of* 3 85 1·40

395 Archer

(Des T. Bjarnason. Litho C.B.N.)

1976 (3 Aug). *Olympiad for the Physically Disabled. P* 12 × 12½.
845 **395** 20 c. multicoloured 20 30

396 "Sam McGee" (Robert W. Service)

397 "Nativity" (F. Mayer)

(Des D. Bierk (No. 846), A. Dumas (No. 847). Litho Ashton-Potter)

1976 (17 Aug). *Canadian Writers* (2*nd series*). *T* **396** *and similar vert design. Multicoloured. P* 13.
846 8 c. Type **396** 15 30
a. Pair. Nos. 846/7 .. .. 30 1·00
847 8 c. "Le Survenant" (Germaine Guèvremont) 15 30

Nos. 846/7 were printed horizontally and vertically *se-tenant* throughout the sheet.

(Des B. Reilander. Litho Ashton-Potter)

1976 (3 Nov). *Christmas. T* **397** *and similar vert designs showing stained-glass windows. Multicoloured. P* 13½.
848 8 c. Type **397** 10 10
849 10 c. "Nativity" (G. Maile & Son) 10 10
850 20 c. "Nativity" (Yvonne Williams) 20 60
848/50 .. .. *Set of* 3 30 60

398 *Northcote* (paddle-steamer)

399 Queen Elizabeth II

(Des T. Bjarnason. Recess and litho C.B.N.)

1976 (19 Nov). *Canadian Ships* (2*nd series*). *T* **398** *and similar horiz designs showing inland vessels. P* 12 × 12½.
851 10 c. ochre, chestnut and black 40 55
a. Block of 4. Nos. 851/4 .. .. .. 1·40
852 10 c. violet-blue and black 40 55
853 10 c. bright blue and black 40 55
854 10 c. apple-green, olive-green and black .. 40 55
851/4 .. .. *Set of* 4 1·40 2·00

Designs:— No. 851, Type **398**; No. 852, *Passport* (paddle-steamer); No. 853, *Chicora* (paddle-steamer); No. 854, *Athabasca* (steamer).

Nos. 851/4 were printed together, *se-tenant*, in different combinations throughout the sheet, giving ten blocks of 4 and ten single stamps.

(Des K. Rodmell from photograph by P. Grugeon. Litho ("25" die-stamped) Ashton-Potter)

1977 (4 Feb). *Silver Jubilee. P* 12½×12.
855 **399** 25 c. multicoloured 30 50
a. Silver (die-stamped "25") omitted £650 £325

400 Bottle Gentian

401 Queen Elizabeth II (bas-relief by J. Huta)

402 Houses of Parliament

403 Trembling Aspen

404 Prairie Town Main Street

405 Fundy National Park

(Des R. Derreth (Nos. 870/4). T. Bjarnason (880/3*a*), R. Bolt (884), B. Laycock and W. Tibbles (884*b*), B. Laycock (884*c*), A. Collier (885), W. Tibbles and G. Weber (No. 885*a*), W. Terry and W. Tibbles (885*b*), L. Marois and W. Tibbles (885*c*), Heather Cooper (others). Eng Y. Baril (880/3*a*))

1977 (1 Mar)–**86.** (*a*) *Vert designs as T* **400** *showing flowers. Multicoloured.* (i) *Recess and litho C.B.N. Sheet stamps. P* 12×12½.
856 1 c. Type **400** (22.4.77) 10 10
a. Printed on the gummed side (pre-cancelled only) £500
857 2 c. Red Columbine (22.4.77) 10 10
a. Printed on the gummed side .. £160
858 3 c. Canada Lily (22.4.77) 10 10
859 4 c. Hepatica (22.4.77) 10 10
a. Printed on the gummed side .. £130
860 5 c. Shooting Star (22.4.77) 10 10
861 10 c. Franklin's Lady's Slipper Orchid (22.4.77) 15 10
a. Perf 13×13½ (5.10.78) 40 30

(ii) *Recess and photo B.A.B.N. Booklet stamps* (1, 2 c.) *or sheet stamps* (*others*). *Chalk-surfaced paper. P* 12×12½ (1, 2 c.) *or* 13×13½ (*others*)
862 1 c. Type **400** (1.11.77) .. .. .. 65 2·50
a. Booklet pane. Nos. 862×2 and 867a×4 .. .. 2·75
b. Perf 13×13½ (from sheets) (16.6.79) 10 10
863 2 c. Red Columbine (1.4.78) 65 90
a. Booklet pane. Nos. 863×4 and 868a×3 plus one printed label .. 3·25
b. Perf 13×13½ (from sheets) (2.8.79) 10 10
864 3 c. Canada Lily (11.4.79) 20 10
864*a* 4 c. Hepatica (3.7.79) 20 10
865 5 c. Shooting Star (24.1.79) 20 10
865*a* 10 c. Franklin's Lady's Slipper Orchid (4.10.79) 60 10
866 12 c. Jewelweed (6.7.78) 15 40
866*a* 15 c. Canada Violet (16.8.79) 15 15

(*b*) *T* **401**. *Recess and photo B.A.B.N. Chalk-surfaced paper. P* 13×13½
867 12 c. black, grey and cobalt (1.3.77) .. 15 10
a. Perf 12×12½ (from booklets) (1.11.77) 70 1·00
868 14 c. black, grey and rose-red (7.3.78) .. 20 10
a. Perf 12×12½ (from booklets) (1.4.78) 50 85
ab. Booklet pane. No. 868a×25, plus two printed labels (13.11.78) .. .. 11·00
869 17 c. black, grey & yellowish green (8.3.79) 50 10
a. Perf 12×12½ (from booklets) (28.3.79) 50 30
ab. Booklet pane. No. 869a×25, plus two printed labels (3.7.79) .. .. 11·00
869*b* 30 c. maroon, grey & reddish pur (11.5.82) 70 70
ba. Maroon, grey and bright mauve (9.83) 1·75 1·10
869*c* 32 c. black, grey and light blue (24.5.83) 45 60
ca. Grey printed double .. .. † —

(*c*) *T* **402**. (i) *Recess C.B.N.* (*Nos.* 872*a*, 873/4) *or B.A.B.N.* (*others*). *Booklet stamps* (*Nos.* 870/1) *or sheet stamps* (*others*). *Chalk-surfaced paper* (1, 5, 12 *c.*). *P* 12×12½ (1, 5 *c.*) *or* 13×13½ (*others*)
870 1 c. indigo (28.3.79) .. .. 1·25 2·75
a. Booklet pane. Nos. 869a×2, 870 and 871×3 .. .. 2·50
871 5 c. deep rose-lilac (28.3.79) 35 40
872 12 c. blue (chalk-surfaced paper) (3.5.77) .. 30 10
a. New blue (ordinary paper) (4.78) .. 50 10
ab. Printed on the gummed side .. £130
873 14 c. scarlet (7.3.78) 15 10
a. Printed on the gummed side .. 18·00
874 17 c. deep green (8.3.79) 30 10
a. Printed on the gummed side .. 19·00

(ii) *Recess C.B.N. Coil stamps. Imperf* × *perf* 10
874*b* 12 c. new blue (3.5.77) 30 30
ba. Imperf (horiz pair) .. .. .. 90·00
874*c* 14 c. scarlet (7.3.78) 60 40
ca. Imperf (horiz pair) .. .. .. 90·00
874*d* 17 c. deep green (8.3.79) 50 20
da. Imperf (horiz pair) £100

(*d*) *Vert designs as T* **403** *showing leaves. Multicoloured. Recess and photo B.A.B.N. Chalk-surfaced paper. P* 13½
875 15 c. Type **403** (8.8.77) 15 10
876 20 c. Douglas Fir (8.8.77) 15 10
877 25 c. Sugar Maple (8.8.77) 15 10
878 30 c. Red Oak (7.3.78) 20 10
879 35 c. White Pine (8.3.79) 25 10

(*e*) *Horiz designs at T* **404** *showing city streets. Multicoloured. P* 13½

(i) *Recess and photo B.A.B.N. Chalk-surfaced paper. No fluorescent bands* (75, 80 *c.*) (6.7.78)
880 50 c. Type **404** .. .. 1·00 90
881 75 c. Eastern city street .. .. .. 85 1·00
882 80 c. Maritimes street 85 90

(ii) *Recess and litho C.B.N.*
883 50 c. Type **404** (13.12.78) 85 60
883*a* 60 c. Ontario city street (11.5.82) 65 50

(*f*) *Horiz designs as T* **405** *showing national parks. Multicoloured. Recess and litho C.B.N. or B.A.B.N.* (*ptgs of Nos.* 884ba, 885*c and* 885*e from* 26 *Sept* 1986). *No.* 884 *with or without fluorescent bands, others only exist without. P* 13½
884 $1 Type **405** (fluorescent bands) (24.1.79) 90 50
a. No fluorescent bands (4.3.81) .. 1·10 55
ab. Black (inscr and value) ptd albino .. £400
884*b* $1 Glacier (*chalk-surfaced paper*) (15.8.84) 85 45
ba. Ordinary paper (12.7.85) .. .. 1·50 80
884*c* $1.50, Waterton Lakes (18.6.82) .. 2·50 2·50

885 $2 Kluane (27.4.79) .. .. .. 1·50 45
a. Silver (inscr and value) omitted .. £250
b. Chalk-surfaced paper (14.12.84) .. 4·00 2·00
885*c* $2 Banff (21.6.85) .. .. .. 3·75 1·25
ca. Bottle-green (inscr and value) omitted £600
885*d* $5 Point Pelee (10.1.83) .. .. .. 5·50 2·25
da. Chalk-surfaced paper (14.12.84) .. 7·00 3·50
885*e* $5 La Mauricie (14.3.86) .. .. 7·00 4·00

The main differences between No. 861a and No. 865*a* are in the background. On No. 865*a* this is toned and has the blurred edges typical of photogravure. No. 861a has a background of solid appearance with the edges clean. The B.A.B.N. version also has stronger lines on the recess part of the design.

No. 883 can be identified from 880 in that the brown printing from the recess plate of the former is deeper and the detail more defined; the registration plate of the car in the foreground can clearly be seen under a glass as "1978". The "hidden date" (1977) occurs alongside the grain elevator door on No. 880. Also the colours from the lithographic plates of No. 883 are much bolder than those from the photogravure cylinders of 880. In addition the paper of No. 883 has a shiny appearance.

No. 884ab shows an uninked impression of the recess-printed part of the design.

Stamps with one or two adjacent sides imperforate come from booklets.

406 Puma

407 "April in Algonquin Park"

(Des R. Bateman. Litho Ashton-Potter)

1977 (30 Mar). *Endangered Wildlife* (*1st series*). *P* 12½.
886 **406** 12 c. multicoloured 20 20
See also Nos. 906, 936/7, 976/7 and 1006/7.

(Litho Ashton-Potter)

1977 (26 May). *Birth Centenary of Tom Thomson (painter). T* **407** *and similar square design. Multicoloured. P* 12.
887 12 c. Type **407** 15 10
a. Pair. Nos. 887/8 .. .. 30 70
888 12 c. "Autumn Birches" 15 10
Nos. 887/8 were printed horizontally and vertically *se-tenant* throughout the sheet.

408 Crown and Lion

409 Peace Bridge, Niagara River

(Des A. Hobbs. Litho (No. 890 also embossed) Ashton-Potter)

1977 (30 June). *Anniversaries. T* **408** *and similar horiz design. Multicoloured. P* 12½.
889 12 c. Type **408** 15 20
890 12 c. Order of Canada 15 20
Events:—No. 889, 25th Anniv of first Canadian-born Governor-General; No. 890, Tenth Anniv of Order of Canada.

(Des R. Harder. Litho Ashton-Potter)

1977 (4 Aug). *50th Anniv of Opening of Peace Bridge. P* 12½.
891 **409** 12 c. multicoloured 15 15

410 Sir Sandford Fleming (engineer)

(Des W. Davies. Recess B.A.B.N.)

1977 (16 Sept). *Famous Canadians. T* **410** *and similar horiz design. P* 13.
892 12 c. grey-blue 20 10
a. Pair. Nos. 892/3 .. .. 40 70
893 12 c. reddish brown 20 10
Design:—No. 892, Joseph E. Bernier (explorer) and *Arctic* (survey ship).
The above were printed together, horizontally and vertically *se-tenant* throughout the sheet.

411 Peace Tower, Parliament Buildings, Ottawa

412 Hunter Braves following Star

(Des S. Ash. Litho Ashton-Potter)

1977 (19 Sept). *23rd Commonwealth Parliamentary Conference. P* 12½.
894 **411** 25 c. multicoloured 20 30

(Des R. G. White. Litho C.B.N.)

1977 (26 Oct). *Christmas. T* **412** *and similar horiz designs depicting Canada's first Christmas carol "Jesous Ahatonhia". Multicoloured. P* 13½ × 13.
895 10 c. Type **412** 10 10
a. Printed on the gummed side .. £200
896 12 c. Angelic choir and the Northern Lights 10 10
a. Imperf (vert pair) £500
897 25 c. Christ Child and chiefs 20 45
895/7 .. .. *Set of* 3 35 45

413 Seal Hunter (soapstone sculpture)

414 Pinky (fishing boat)

(Des R. Derreth. Litho Ashton-Potter)

1977 (18 Nov). *Canadian Eskimos ("Inuits") (1st series). Hunting. T* **413** *and similar horiz designs. Multicoloured. P* 12 × 12½.
898 12 c. Type **413** 25 25
a. Pair. Nos. 898/9 .. .. 50 70
899 12 c. Fishing with spear 25 25
900 12 c. Disguised archer 25 25
a. Pair. Nos. 900/1 .. .. 50 70
901 12 c. Walrus hunting 25 25
898/901 .. .. *Set of* 4 90 90
Nos. 898/9 and 900/1 were each printed together, *se-tenant*, in horizontal and vertical pairs throughout the sheet.
See also Nos. 924/7, 958/61 and 989/92.

(Des T. Bjarnason. Recess and litho C.B.N.)

1977 (18 Nov). *Canadian Ships (3rd series). T* **414** *and similar horiz designs, showing sailing craft. Multicoloured. P* 12 × 12½.
902 12 c. Type **414** 20 30
a. Block of 4. Nos. 902/5 70
ab. Imperf (block of 4) .. ..
903 12 c. *Malahat* (schooner) 20 30
904 12 c. Tern schooner 20 30
905 12 c. Mackinaw boat 20 30
902/5 .. .. *Set of* 4 70 1·10
Nos. 902/5 were printed together, *se-tenant*, in different combinations throughout the sheet, giving ten blocks of 4 and ten single stamps.

415 Peregrine Falcon

416 Pair of 1851 12d. Black Stamps

(Des R. Bateman. Litho Ashton-Potter)

1978 (18 Jan). *Endangered Wildlife (2nd series). P* 12½.
906 **415** 12 c. multicoloured 30 20

(Des C. Brett. Recess and photo B.A.B.N.)

1978 (18 Jan). *"CAPEX 78" International Stamp Exhibition, Toronto (1st issue). P* 13.
907 **416** 12 c. black and brownish grey 10 10
See also Nos. 914/17.

417 Games Emblem

418 "Captain Cook" (Nathaniel Dance)

(Des S. Ash. Litho Ashton-Potter)

1978 (31 Mar). *Commonwealth Games, Edmonton (1st issue). T* **417** *and similar horiz design. Multicoloured. P* 12½.
908 14 c. Type **417** 10 10
909 30 c. Badminton 20 50
See also Nos. 918/21.

(Des W. Rueter. Litho Ashton-Potter)

1978 (26 Apr). *Bicentenary of Cook's Third Voyage. T* **418** *and similar vert design. Multicoloured. P* 13½.
910 14 c. Type **418** 20 20
a. Pair. Nos. 910/11 .. .. 40 70
911 14 c. "Nootka Sound" (J. Webber) 20 20
Nos. 910/11 were printed together, *se-tenant*, in horizontal and vertical pairs throughout the sheet.

419 Hardrock Silver Mine, Cobalt, Ontario

420 Princes' Gate (Exhibition entrance)

(Des W. Davies. Litho Ashton-Potter)

1978 (19 May). *Resource Development. T* **419** *and similar hori[z] design. Multicoloured. P* 12½.
912 14 c. Type **419** 15 2
a. Pair. Nos. 912/13 .. .. 30 7
913 14 c. Giant excavators, Athabasca Tar Sands 15 2
Nos. 912/13 were printed together, *se-tenant*, in horizontal an[d] vertical pairs throughout the sheet.

(Des C. Brett. Eng R. Couture. Recess and photo B.A.B.N.)

1978 (10 June). *"CAPEX 78" International Stamp Exhibition Toronto (2nd issue). Horiz designs as T* **416.** *Two fluorescen[t] bands (none on* $1.25 *from miniature sheet). P* 13.
914 14 c. Prussian blue, pale grey and brownish grey 15 1
915 30 c. deep rose, pale grey and brownish grey 25 3
916 $1.25, slate-violet, pale grey & brnish grey 1·00 1·4
914/16 .. .. *Set of* 3 1·25 1·6
MS917 101 × 76 mm. Nos. 914/16 .. .. 1·50 2·5
Designs:—14 c. Pair of 1855 10d. Cartier stamps; 30 c. Pair o[f] 1857 ½d. deep rose stamps; $1.25, Pair of 1851 6d. Prince Albe[rt] stamps.

(Des S. Ash. Litho Ashton-Potter)

1978 (3 Aug). *Commonwealth Games, Edmonton (2nd issue). Horiz designs as T* **417**. *Multicoloured. P* 12½.
918 14 c. Games stadium 20 2
a. Pair. Nos. 918/19 .. .. 40 7
919 14 c. Running 20 2
920 30 c. Alberta Legislature building 40 5
a. Pair. Nos. 920/1 .. .. 80 1·5
921 30 c. Bowls 40 5
918/21 .. .. *Set of* 4 1·10 1·1
Nos. 918/19 and 920/1 were each printed together, *se-tenant*, i[n] horizontal and vertical pairs throughout the sheet.

(Des T. Dimson, Litho Ashton-Potter)

1978 (16 Aug). *Centenary of National Exhibition. P* 12½.
922 **420** 14 c. multicoloured 15 3

421 Marguerite d'Youville

422 "Madonna of the Flowering Pea" (Cologne School)

(Des A. Dumas. Litho C.B.N.)

1978 (21 Sept). *Marguerite d'Youville (founder of Grey Nuns) Commemoration. P* 13.
923 **421** 14 c. multicoloured 15 3

(Des R. Derreth. Litho Ashton-Potter)

1978 (27 Sept). *Canadian Eskimos ("Inuits") (2nd series). Travel Horiz designs as T* **413.** *Multicoloured. P* 13½.
924 14 c. Woman on foot (painting by Pitseolak) .. 20 1
a. Pair. Nos. 924/5 .. .. 40 6
925 14 c. "Migration" (soapstone sculpture of sailing umiak by Joe Talurinili) 20 1
926 14 c. Aeroplane (stonecut and stencil print by Pudlo) 20 1
a. Pair. Nos. 926/7 .. .. 40 6
927 14 c. Dogteam and dogsled (ivory sculpture by Abraham Kingmeatook) 20 1
924/7 .. .. *Set of* 4 70 5
Nos. 924/5 and 926/7 were each printed together, *se-tenant*, in horizontal and vertical pairs throughout the sheet.

(Des J. Morin. Litho Ashton-Potter)

1978 (20 Oct). *Christmas. Paintings. T* **422** *and similar ver[t] designs. Multicoloured. P* 12½.
928 12 c. Type **422** 10 1
929 14 c. "The Virgin and Child with St. Anthony and Donor" (detail, Hans Memling) .. 10 1
930 30 c. "The Virgin and Child" (Jacopo di Cione) 25 7
928/30 .. .. *Set of* 3 35 8

423 *Chief Justice Robinson* (paddle-steamer)

424 Carnival Revellers

(Des T. Bjarnason. Recess and litho C.B.N.)

1978 (15 Nov). *Canadian Ships (4th series). T* **423** *and similar horiz designs showing ice vessels. Multicoloured. P* 13.
931 14 c. Type **423** 45 65
a. Block of 4. Nos. 931/4 .. .. 1·60
932 14 c. *St. Roch* (steamer) 45 65
933 14 c. *Northern Light* (steamer) 45 65
934 14 c. *Labrador* (steamer) 45 65
931/4 .. .. *Set of* 4 1·60 2·40
Nos. 931/4 were printed together, *se-tenant*, in different combinations throughout the sheet, giving ten block of 4 and ten single stamps.

(Des A. Dumas. Litho Ashton-Potter)

979 (1 Feb). *Quebec Carnival. P* 13.
35 **424** 14 c. multicoloured 20 20

425 Eastern Spiny Soft-shelled Turtle (*Trionyx spinifera*) **426** Knotted Ribbon round Woman's Finger

(Des G. Lowe (17 c.), R. Bateman (35 c.). Litho Ashton-Potter)

979 (10 Apr). *Endangered Wildlife (3rd series). T* **425** *and similar horiz design. Multicoloured. P* 12½.
36 17 c. Type **425** 20 10
37 35 c. Bowhead Whale (*Balaena mysticetus*) . . 90 90

(Des D. Haws. Litho Ashton-Potter)

979 (27 Apr). *Postal Code Publicity. T* **426** *and similar vert design. Multicoloured. P* 13.
38 17 c. Type **426** 20 10
a. Pair. Nos. 938/9 . . . . 40 90
39 17 c. Knotted string round man's finger . . 20 10
Nos. 938/9 were printed together, *se-tenant*, in horizontal and vertical pairs throughout the sheet.

427 Scene from "Fruits of the Earth" by Frederick Philip Grove **428** Charles-Michel de Salaberry (military hero)

Des Rosemary Kilbourne (No. 940), Monique Charbonneau (941). Litho C.B.N.)

979 (3 May). *Canadian Writers (3rd series). T* **427** *and similar horiz design. Multicoloured. P* 13.
40 17 c. Type **427** 15 15
a. Pair. Nos. 940/1 . . . . 30 85
ab. Imperf (vert pair) . . . . . .
41 17 c. Scene from "Le Vaisseau d'Or" by Emile Nelligan 15 15
Nos. 940/1 were printed together, *se-tenant*, in horizontal and vertical pairs throughout the sheet.

(Des T. Dimson. Litho and embossed Ashton-Potter)

979 (11 May). *Famous Canadians. T* **428** *and similar vert design. Multicoloured. P* 13.
42 17 c. Type **428** 25 15
a. Pair. Nos. 942/3 . . . . 50 80
43 17 c. John By (engineer) 25 15
Nos. 942/3 were printed together, *se-tenant*, in horizontal and vertical pairs throughout the sheet.

429 Ontario **430** Paddling Kayak

(Des R. Bellemare. Litho Ashton-Potter)

1979 (15 June). *Canada Day. Flags. Sheet* 128 × 140 *mm containing T* **429** *and similar horiz designs. Multicoloured. P* 13.
MS944 17 c. × 12; Type **429**; Quebec; Nova Scotia; New Brunswick; Manitoba; British Columbia; Prince Edward Island; Saskatchewan; Alberta; Newfoundland; Northwest Territories; Yukon Territory . . . . 3·50 4·50

(Des J. Eby. Litho Ashton-Potter)

1979 (3 July). *Canoe-Kayak Championships. P* 12½.
956 **430** 17 c. multicoloured 15 30

431 Hockey Players **432** Toy Train

(Des J. Eby. Litho Ashton-Potter)

1979 (16 Aug). *Women's Field Hockey Championships, Vancouver. P* 12½.
957 **431** 17 c. black, yellow and emerald 15 30

(Des R. Derreth. Litho Ashton-Potter)

1979 (13 Sept). *Canadian Eskimos ("Inuits") (3rd series). "Shelter" (Nos. 958/9) and "Community" (Nos. 960/1). Horiz designs as T* **413**. *Multicoloured. P* 13.
958 17 c. "Summer Tent" (print by Kiakshuk) . . 15 15
a. Pair. Nos. 958/9 . . . . 30 80
959 17 c. "Five Eskimos building an Igloo" (soapstone sculpture by Abraham) 15 15
960 17 c. "The Dance" (print by Kalvak) 15 15
a. Pair. Nos. 960/1 . . . . 30 80
961 17 c. "Inuit drum dance" (soapstone sculptures by Madeleine Isserkut and Jean Mapsalak) 15 15
958/61 . . . . *Set of* 4 60 55
Nos. 958/9 and 960/1 were each printed together, *se-tenant*, in horizontal and vertical pairs throughout the sheet.

(Des A. Maggs. Litho C.B.N.)

1979 (17 Oct). *Christmas. T* **432** *and similar multicoloured designs showing toys. Fluorescent frame* (35 c.) *or two fluorescent bands (others). P* 13.
962 15 c. Type **432** 10 10
963 17 c. Hobby-horse 10 10
964 35 c. Rag-doll (*vert*) 25 50
962/4 . . . . *Set of* 3 35 50

433 "Child watering Tree of Life" (painting by Marie-Annick Viatour) **434** Canadair CL-215

(Des J. Morin. Litho Ashton-Potter)

1979 (24 Oct). *International Year of the Child. P* 13.
965 **433** 17 c. multicoloured 15 30

(Des R. Bradford and J. Charette. Litho Ashton-Potter)

1979 (15 Nov). *Canadian Aircraft (1st series). Flying Boats. T* **434** *and similar horiz designs. Multicoloured. P* 12½.
966 17 c. Type **434** 20 15
a. Pair. Nos. 966/7 . . . . 40 70
967 17 c. Curtiss HS-2L 20 15
968 35 c. Vickers Vedette 50 55
a. Pair. Nos. 968/9 . . . . 1·00 1·40
969 35 c. Consolidated PBY-5A Canso . . 50 55
966/9 . . . . *Set of* 4 1·25 1·10
Nos. 966/7 and 968/9 were each printed together, *se-tenant*, in horizontal and vertical pairs throughout the sheet.
See also Nos. 996/9, 1026/9 and 1050/3.

435 Map of Arctic Islands **436** Skiing

(Des Gottschalk and Ash Ltd. Litho Ashton-Potter)

1980 (23 Jan). *Centenary of Arctic Islands Acquisition. P* 13.
970 **435** 17 c. multicoloured 15 30

(Des C. Malenfant. Litho C.B.N.)

1980 (23 Jan). *Winter Olympic Games, Lake Placid, U.S.A. P* 13.
971 **436** 35 c. multicoloured 55 75

437 "A Meeting of the School Trustees" (painting by Robert Harris) **438** Canadian Whitefish (*Coregonus canadenis*)

(Des J. Morin. Litho Ashton-Potter)

1980 (6 Mar). *Centenary of Royal Canadian Academy of Arts. T* **437** *and similar horiz designs. Multicoloured. P* 13.
972 17 c. Type **437** 25 15
a. Pair. Nos. 972/3 . . . . 50 50
973 17 c. "Inspiration" (sculpture by Philippe Hébert) 25 15
974 35 c. "Sunrise on the Saguenay" (painting by Lucius O'Brien) 50 35
a. Pair. Nos. 974/5 . . . . 1·00 1·50
975 35 c. Sketch of design for original Parliament Buildings by Thomas Fuller 50 35
972/5 . . . . *Set of* 4 1·40 90
Nos. 972/3 and 974/5 were each printed together, *se-tenant*, in horizontal and vertical pairs throughout the sheet.

(Des M. Dumas (No. 976), R. Bateman (No. 977). Litho Ashton-Potter)

1980 (6 May). *Endangered Wildlife (4th series). T* **438** *and similar horiz design. Multicoloured. P* 12½.
976 17 c. Type **438** 25 15
977 17 c. Prairie Chicken (*Tympanuchus cupido pinnatus*) 25 15

439 Garden Flowers **440** "Helping Hand"

(Des Heather Cooper. Litho Ashton-Potter)

1980 (29 May). *International Flower Show, Montreal. P* 13.
978 **439** 17 c. multicoloured 15 20

(Des R. Harder. Litho and embossed Ashton-Potter)

1980 (29 May). *Rehabilitation. P* 12½.
979 **440** 17 c. gold and ultramarine 15 20

441 Opening Bars of "O Canada" **442** John G. Diefenbaker

(Des F. Peter. Litho Ashton-Potter)

1980 (6 June). *Centenary of "O Canada" (national song). T* **441** *and similar horiz design. Multicoloured. P* 12½.
980 17 c. Type **441** 15 15
a. Pair. Nos. 980/1 . . . . 30 40
981 17 c. Calixa Lavallee (composer), Adolphe-Basile Routhier (original writer) and Robert Stanley Weir (writer of English version) 15 15
Nos. 980/1 were printed together, *se-tenant*, in horizontal and vertical pairs throughout the sheet.

(Des B. Reilander. Eng Y. Baril. Recess C.B.N.)

1980 (20 June). *John G. Diefenbaker (former Prime Minister) Commemoration. P* 13½ × 13.
982 **442** 17 c. deep ultramarine 15 20

443 Emma Albani (singer) **444** Alberta

(Des C. Webster (No. 985), H. Brown (others). Litho Ashton-Potter)

1980 (4 July). *Famous Canadians. T* **443** *and similar multicoloured designs. P* 13.
983 17 c. Type **443** 15 25
a. Pair. Nos. 983/4 . . . . 30 85
984 17 c. Healey Willan (composer) 15 25
985 17 c. Ned Hanlan (oarsman) (*horiz*) . . 15 15
983/5 . . . . *Set of* 3 40 60
Nos. 983/4 were printed together, *se-tenant*, in horizontal and vertical pairs throughout the sheet.

(Des G. Hunter and C. Yaneff. Litho Ashton-Potter)

1980 (27 Aug). *75th Anniv of Alberta and Saskatchewan Provinces. T* **444** *and similar horiz design. Multicoloured. P* 13.
986 17 c. Type **444** 15 15
987 17 c. Saskatchewan 15 15

445 Uraninite Molecular Structure **446** "Christmas Morning" (J. S. Hallam)

(Des J. Charette. Litho C.B.N.)

1980 (3 Sept). *Uranium Resources. P* 13.
988 **445** 35 c. multicoloured 30 30

(Des R. Derreth. Litho C.B.N.)

1980 (25 Sept). *Canadian Eskimos ("Inuits") (4th series). Spirits. Horiz designs as T* **413**. *Multicoloured. P* 13½.
989 17 c. "Return of the Sun" (print by Kenojouak) 20 15
a. Pair. Nos. 989/90 . . . . 40 65
990 17 c. "Sedna" (sculpture by Ashoona Kiawak) 20 15
991 35 c. "Shaman" (print by Simon Tookoome) . . 35 30
a. Pair. Nos. 991/2 . . . . 70 1·25
992 35 c. "Bird Spirit" (sculpture by Doris Hagiolok) 35 30
989/92 . . . . *Set of* 4 1·00 80
Nos. 989/90 and 991/2 were each printed together, *se-tenant*, in horizontal and vertical pairs throughout the sheet.

(Des Yvon Laroche. Litho Ashton-Potter)

1980 (22 Oct). *Christmas. Paintings. T* **446** *and similar vert designs. Multicoloured. P* 12½ × 12.

993 15 c. Type **446** 10 10
994 17 c. "Sleigh Ride" (Frank Hennessy) 15 10
995 35 c. "McGill Cab Stand" (Kathleen Morris) .. 30 1·25
993/5 .. .. *Set of* 3 50 1·25

447 Avro (Canada) CF-100 Canuck Mk 5

(Des R. Bradford and J. Charette. Litho C.B.N.)

1980 (10 Nov). *Canadian Aircraft* (*2nd series*). *T* **447** *and similar horiz designs. Multicoloured. P* 13.

996 17 c. Type **447** 15 15
a. Pair. Nos. 996/7 .. .. 30 60
997 17 c. Avro Type 683 Lancaster 15 15
998 35 c. Curtiss JN-4 Canuck 30 50
a. Pair. Nos. 998/9 .. .. 60 1·25
999 35 c. Hawker Hurricane Mk 1 .. .. 30 50
996/9 .. .. *Set of* 4 80 1·10

Nos. 996/7 and 998/9 were each printed together, *se-tenant*, in horizontal and vertical pairs throughout the sheet.

448 Emmanuel-Persillier Lachapelle **449** Mandora Instrument (18th-century)

(Des J. Morin. Litho Ashton-Potter)

1980 (5 Dec). *Dr. Emmanuel-Persillier Lachapelle* (*founder of Notre-Dame Hospital, Montreal*) *Commemoration. P* 13½.

1000 **448** 17 c. cobalt, chocolate and brown .. 15 15

(Des C. Webster. Litho Ashton-Potter)

1981 (19 Jan). *"The Look of Music" Exhibition, Vancouver. P* 12½.

1001 **449** 17 c. multicoloured 15 15

450 Henrietta Edwards **451** Vancouver Marmot (*Marmota vancouverensis*)

(Des Muriel Wood and D. Goddard. Litho C.B.N.)

1981 (4 Mar). *Feminists. T* **450** *and similar horiz designs. Multicoloured. P* 13.

1002 17 c. Type **450** 20 15
a. Block of 4. Nos. 1002/5 70
1003 17 c. Louise McKinney 20 15
1004 17 c. Idola Saint-Jean 20 15
1005 17 c. Emily Stowe 20 15
1002/5 .. .. *Set of* 4 70 55

Nos. 1002/5 were printed together, *se-tenant*, in different combinations throughout the sheet, giving ten blocks of 4 and ten single stamps.

(Des M. Dumas (17 c.), R. Bateman (35 c.). Litho C.B.N.)

1981 (6 Apr). *Endangered Wildlife* (*5th series*). *T* **451** *and similar horiz design. Multicoloured. P* 13.

1006 17 c. Type **451** 15 10
1007 35 c. American Bison (*Bison bison athabascae*) 35 30

452 Kateri Tekakwitha **453** "Self Portrait" (Frederick H. Varley)

(Des L. Marquart. Litho Ashton-Potter)

1981 (24 Apr). *17th-century Canadian Catholic Women. Statues by Emile Brunet. T* **452** *and similar vert design. P* 12½.

1008 17 c. red-brown and pale grey-olive 15 15
a. Pair. Nos. 1008/9 .. .. 30 40
1009 17 c. steel blue and new blue 15 15

Designs:—No. 1008, Type **452**; No. 1009, Marie de l'Incarnation.

Nos. 1008/9 were printed together, *se-tenant*, in horizontal and vertical pairs throughout the sheet.

(Des P. Fontaine. Litho Ashton-Potter (17 c. (*both*)), B.A.B.N. (35 c.))

1981 (22 May). *Canadian Paintings. T* **453** *and similar multicoloured designs. P* 12½ (17 c. (*both*)) *or* 13 × 13½ (35 c.).

1010 17 c. Type **453** 15 10
1011 17 c. "At Baie Saint-Paul" (Marc-Aurele Fortin) (*horiz*) 15 10
1012 35 c. "Untitled No. 6" (Paul-Emile Borduas) .. 30 30
1010/12 .. .. *Set of* 3 55 45

454 Canada in 1867 **455** Frère Marie-Victorin

(Des R. Bellemare. Litho B.A.B.N.)

1981 (30 June). *Canada Day. Maps showing evolution of Canada from Confederation to present day. T* **454** *and similar horiz designs. Multicoloured. P* 13½.

1013 17 c. Type **454** 15 20
a. Horiz strip of 4. Nos. 1013/16 55
1014 17 c. Canada in 1873 .. .. 15 20
1015 17 c. Canada in 1905 .. .. 15 20
1016 17 c. Canada since 1949 .. .. .. 15 20
1013/16 .. .. *Set of* 4 55 70

Nos. 1013/16 were printed together, *se-tenant*, in horizontal strips of 4 throughout the sheet.

(Des R. Hill. Litho and embossed Ashton-Potter)

1981 (22 July). *Canadian Botanists. T* **455** *and similar vert design. Multicoloured. P* 12½ × 12.

1017 17 c. Type **455** 15 15
a. Pair. Nos. 1017/18 .. .. 30 50
1018 17 c. John Macoun 15 15

Nos. 1017/18 were printed together, *se-tenant*, in horizontal and vertical pairs throughout the sheet.

456 The Montreal Rose **457** Drawing of Niagara-on-the-Lake

(Des J.-P. Beaudin, J. Morin and T. Yakobina. Litho C.B.N.)

1981 (22 July). *Montreal Flower Show. P* 13½.

1019 **456** 17 c. multicoloured 15 20

(Des J. Mardon. Recess and litho B.A.B.N.)

1981 (31 July). *Bicentenary of Niagara-on-the-Lake* (*town*). *P* 13 × 13½.

1020 **457** 17 c. multicoloured 15 20

458 Acadian Community **459** Aaron R. Mosher

(Des N. DeGrâce. Litho Ashton-Potter)

1981 (14 Aug). *Centenary of first Acadia* (*community*) *Convention. P* 13½.

1021 **458** 17 c. multicoloured 15 20

(Des R. Hill. Litho Ashton-Potter)

1981 (8 Sept). *Birth Centenary of Aaron R. Mosher* (*founder of Canadian Labour Congress*). *P* 13½.

1022 **459** 17 c. multicoloured 15 20

NEW INFORMATION

The editor is always interested to correspond with people who have new information that will improve or correct the Catalogue.

460 Christmas Tree, 1781 **461** De Havilland D.H.82C Tiger Moth

(Des Anita Kunz and W. Tibbles. Litho Ashton-Potter)

1981 (16 Nov). *Christmas. Bicentenary of First Illuminated Christmas Tree in Canada. T* **460** *and similar vert designs. Multicoloured. P* 13½.

1023 15 c. Type **460** 20 1
1024 15 c. Christmas Tree, 1881 .. .. .. 20 1
1025 15 c. Christmas Tree, 1981 .. .. .. 20 1
1023/5 .. .. *Set of* 3 55 4

(Des R. Bradford and J. Charette. Litho Ashton-Potter)

1981 (24 Nov). *Canadian Aircraft* (*3rd series*). *T* **461** *and similar horiz designs. Multicoloured. P* 12½.

1026 17 c. Type **461** 20 1
a. Pair. Nos. 1026/7 .. .. .. 40 4
1027 17 c. Canadair CL-41 Tutor 20 1
1028 35 c. Avro (Canada) CF-102 jet airliner .. 35 3
a. Pair. Nos. 1028/9 .. .. .. 70 7
1029 35 c. De Havilland D.H.C.7 Dash Seven .. 35 3
1026/9 .. .. *Set of* 4 1·10 9

The two designs of each value were printed together *se-tenant*, in horizontal and vertical pairs throughout the sheet

462 Canadian Maple Leaf Emblem **463** 1851 3d. Stamp

(Des R. Bellemare, Recess B.A.B.N. (No. 1030*a*),C.B.N. (others))

1981 (29 Dec). *Ordinary paper.* (*a*) *Sheet stamp. P* 13×13½.

1030 **462** A (30 c.), bright scarlet 20 3
a. Carmine-red, chalk-surfaced paper 20 2
b. Printed on the gummed side .. £300

(*b*) *Coil stamp, Imperf×perf* 10

1031 **462** A (30 c.), bright scarlet 40 7
a. Imperf (pair) £250 £14

Nos. 1030/1 were printed before a new first class domestic lette rate had been agreed, "A" representing the face value of the stam later decided at 30 c. Because of U.P.U. regulations these stamp were only intended for use within Canada.

(Recess, or recess and photo (Nos. 1032/*b*), B.A.B.N. (Nos. 1032/5*b* or C.B.N. (Nos. 1036/*a*))

1982 (1 Mar)–**83.** *Designs as Nos.* 1030/1 *but including face values.*

(*a*) *Sheet stamps* (*Nos.* 1032, 1032*b*) *or from booklets* (*Nos.* 1032a, 1032ba). *Chalk-surfaced paper. P* 13×13½

1032 **462** 30 c. verm, slate-blue & azure (11.5.82) 30 4
a. Perf 12 × 12½ (from booklets) (30.6.82) .. .. 70 1·0
ab. Booklet pane. No. 1032a × 20 plus one printed label .. .. .. 15·00
1032*b* 32 c. verm, orge-brn & stone (10.2.83) 45 4
ba. Perf 12 × 12½ (from booklets) (8.4.83) .. .. 60 1·0
bb. Booklet pane. No. 1032ba × 25 plus two printed labels.. .. .. 17·00

(*b*) *Booklet stamps. Ordinary paper. P* 12 × 12½*

1033 **462** 5 c. maroon 10 2
a. Booklet pane. Nos. 1033 × 2, 1034 and 1035 plus two printed labels in bottom row .. .. .. 2·50
ab. Ditto. Printed labels in top row (10.82) .. .. 2·75
b. Chalk-surfaced paper (8.82) .. 40 5
ba. Booklet pane. Nos. 1033b × 2, 1034a and 1035a plus two printed labels in bottom row .. .. 7·50
bb. Ditto. Printed labels in top row (10.82) .. .. 7·50
c. Booklet pane. Nos. 1033 × 2, 1033*d* and 1035*b* plus two printed labels (15.2.83) .. .. 3·00
1033*d* 8 c. indigo (15.2.83) .. .. .. 1·25 1·7
1034 10 c. bottle green .. .. .. 1·25 1·7
a. Chalk-surfaced paper .. .. 3·75 3·7
1035 30 c. carmine-red .. .. .. 1·50 2·0
a. Chalk-surfaced paper .. .. 3·75 3·7
1035*b* 32 c. Indian red (15.2.83) .. .. 1·75 2·2

(*c*) *Coil stamps. Ordinary paper. Imperf×perf* 10

1036 **462** 30 c. bright scarlet (20.5.82)† .. 35 3
a. Imperf (pair) £180
1036*b* 32 c. Indian red (10.2.83) .. .. 1·50 1·5
ba. Imperf (pair) .. .. .. 90·00

*The 30 c. and 32 c. values are perforated on two sides, the other values on three.

†The 30 c. coil stamp was originally intended for release on 11 May, but, due to production difficulties, it was not placed on sale until 20 May; F.D.C.s, however, carry the 11 May postmark.

(Des Gottschalk and Ash Ltd. Litho C.B.N.)

82 (11 Mar–20 May). *"Canada 82" International Philatelic Youth Exhibition, Toronto. Stamps on Stamps. T* **463** *and similar horiz designs. Multicoloured. P* 13½.

37 30 c. Type **463** 30 25
38 30 c. 1908 Centenary of Quebec 15 c. commemorative (20.5.82) 30 25
39 35 c. 1935 10 c. 30 40
40 35 c. 1928 10 c. (20.5.82) 30 40
41 60 c. 1929 50 c. (20.5.82) 60 85
37/41 . . . . *Set of* 5 1·60 2·00
S1042 159 × 108 mm. Nos. 1037/41 (20.5.82) . . 2·25 3·25

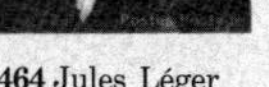

464 Jules Léger

465 Stylised Drawing of Terry Fox

)es P. Fontaine from photograph by M. Bedford. Litho Ashton-Potter)

982 (2 Apr). *Jules Léger (politician) Commemoration. P* 13½.
043 **464** 30 c. multicoloured 20 20

(Des F. Peter. Litho Ashton-Potter)

982 (13 Apr). *Cancer-victim Terry Fox's "Marathon of Hope" (Trans-Canada fund-raising run) Commemoration. Fluorescent frame. P* 12½.
044 **465** 30 c. multicoloured 20 20

466 Stylised Open Book

(Des F. Peter. Litho Ashton-Potter)

982 (16 Apr). *Patriation of Constitution. P* 12 × 12½.
045 **466** 30 c. multicoloured 20 20

467 1880's Male and Female alvationists with Street Scene

468 "The Highway near Kluane Lake" (Yukon Territory) (Jackson)

(Des T. Dimson. Litho C.B.N.)

982 (25 June). *Centenary of the Salvation Army in Canada. P* 13½.
046 **467** 30 c. multicoloured 20 20

(Des J. Morin and P. Sasseville. Litho Ashton-Potter)

1982 (30 June). *Canada Day. Paintings of Canadian Landscapes. Sheet,* 139 × 139 *mm, containing T* **468** *and similar horiz designs. Multicoloured. P* 12½ × 12.
MS1047 30 c. × 12, Type **468**; "Street Scene, Montreal" (Quebec) (Hébert); "Breakwater" (Newfoundland) (Pratt); "Along Great Slave Lake" (Northwest Territories) (Richard); "Till Hill" (Prince Edward Island) (Lamb); "Family and Rainstorm" (Nova Scotia) (Colville); "Brown Shadows" (Saskatchewan) (Knowles); "The Red Brick House" (Ontario) (Milne); "Campus Gates" (New Brunswick) (Bobak); "Prairie Town—Early Morning" (Alberta) (Kerr); "Totems at Ninstints" (British Columbia) (Plaskett); "Doc Snider's House" (Manitoba) (FitzGerald) . . . . 4·25 4·75

469 Regina Legislature Building

470 Finish of Race

(Des Kim Martin and R. Russell. Litho Ashton-Potter)

1982 (3 Aug). *Regina Centenary. P* 13½ × 13.
1048 **469** 30 c. multicoloured 20 20

(Des B. Reilander. Litho Ashton-Potter)

1982 (4 Aug). *Centenary of Royal Canadian Henley Regatta. P* 12½.
1049 **470** 30 c. multicoloured 20 25

471 Fairchild FC-2W1

472 Decoy

(Des R. Bradford. Litho Ashton-Potter)

1982 (5 Oct). *Canadian Aircraft (4th series). Bush Aircraft. T* **471** *and similar horiz designs. Multicoloured. P* 12½.

1050 30 c. Type **471** 35 20
a. Pair. Nos. 1050/1 . . . . . . 70 95
1051 30 c. De Havilland D.H.C.2 Beaver . . 35 20
1052 60 c. Fokker Super Universal 65 85
a. Pair. Nos. 1052/3 . . . . . . 1·25 2·00
1053 60 c. Noorduyn Norseman 65 85
1050/3 . . . . *Set of* 4 1·90 1·90

Nos. 1050/1 and 1052/3 were each printed together, *se-tenant,* in horiz and vert pairs throughout the sheet.

(Des J. P. Beaudin and J. Morin. Litho C.B.N. (Nos. 1054b/ba, 1055b/bc, 1056b, 1057b/ba, 1058b) or Ashton-Potter (others))

1982 (19 Oct)–**87**. *Heritage Artifacts. T* **472** *and similar designs. No fluorescent bands* (1 c. *to* 5 c.). *Chalk-surfaced paper* (25, 42, 50, 72 c.). *P* 12×12½ (37 c. *to* 72 c.) *or* 14×13½ (*others*).

1054 1 c. black, grey-brown and brown . . 10 10
a. Chalk-surfaced paper (4.7.86) . . 10 10
b. Perf 13×13½ (10.1.85) 30 30
ba. Chalk-surfaced paper (6.8.85) . . 1·25 1·00
1055 2 c. black, pale turquoise-blue & dp bl-grn 10 10
a. Chalk-surfaced paper (4.7.86) . . 20 20
b. Perf 13×13½ (10.2.84) 30 30
ba. Imperf (horiz pair) £650
bb. Printed on the gummed side . . 35·00
bc. Ordinary paper (23.1.86) 10 10
1056 3 c. black, dull violet-blue and chalky blue 10 10
a. Chalk-surfaced paper (4.7.86) . . 30 10
b. Perf 13×13½ (10.1.85) 30 40
1057 5 c. black, flesh and chestnut 10 10
a. Chalk-surfaced paper (15.8.86) . . 10 10
b. Perf 13×13½ (*chalk-surfaced paper*) (6.7.84) 20 20
ba. Ordinary paper (1.3.85) 20 30
1058 10 c. black, light blue & dp turquoise-blue 10 10
a. Chalk-surfaced paper (22.8.86) . . 40 40
b. Perf 13×13½ (15.3.85) 60 30
1059 20 c. black, brownish grey and sepia . . 20 10
a. Chalk-surfaced paper (4.7.86) . . 50 50
1060 25 c. multicoloured (6.5.87) 35 10
1061 37 c. grey-black, deep yellow-green and sage-green (8.4.83) 50 40
a. Chalk-surfaced paper (18.5.84) . . 1·00 90
1062 39 c. brownish black, violet-grey and slate-violet (1.8.85) . . . . . . 1·60 70
1063 42 c. multicoloured (6.5.87) 50 15
1064 48 c. blackish brown, red-brown and pale pink (8.4.83) 70 40
a. Chalk-surfaced paper (19.12.83) . . 80 70
1065 50 c. black, dull turq-blue & turq-bl (1.8.85) 1·50 20
1066 55 c. multicoloured (6.5.87) 65 30
1067 64 c. grey-black, black & pale grey (8.4.83) 80 35
a. Chalk-surfaced paper (29.6.84) . . 1·50 1·10
1068 68 c. black, pale brn & reddish brn (1.8.85) 1·60 50
1069 72 c. multicoloured (6.5.87) 85 35
1054/69 . . . . *Set of* 16 8·50 3·00

Designs: *Vert (as T* **472**)—2 c. Fishing spear; 3 c. Stable lantern; 5 c. Bucket; 10 c. Weathercock; 20 c. Skates; 25 c. Butter stamp. *Horiz* (26 × 20 *mm*)—37 c. Plough; 39 c. Settle-bed; 42 c. Linen chest; 48 c. Cradle; 50 c. Sleigh; 55 c. Iron kettle; 64 c. Kitchen stove; 68 c. Spinning wheel; 72 c. Hand-drawn cart.

No. 1058b has a fluorescent frame instead of bands.

475 Mary, Joseph and Baby Jesus

476 Globes forming Symbolic Designs

(Des J. Eby. Litho C.B.N.)

1982 (3 Nov). *Christmas. Nativity Scenes. T* **475** *and similar vert designs. Multicoloured. P* 13.

1080 30 c. Type **475** 20 10
1081 35 c. The Shepherds 25 55
1082 60 c. The Three Wise Men . . . . . . 45 1·10
1080/2 . . . . *Set of* 3 80 1·50

(Des R. Bellemare. Litho Ashton-Potter)

1983 (10 Mar). *World Communications Year. Fluorescent frame. P* 12 × 12½.
1083 **476** 32 c. multicoloured 30 30

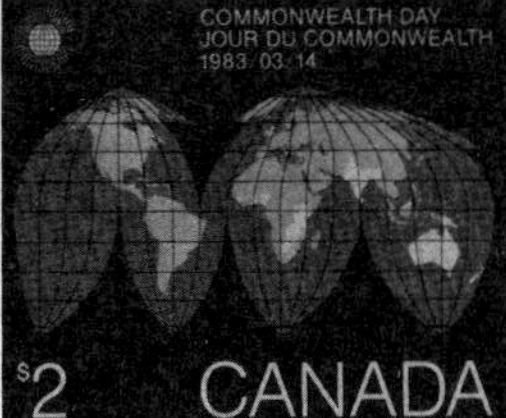

477 Map of World showing Canada

(Des R. Harder. Litho Ashton-Potter)

1983 (14 Mar). *Commonwealth Day. Without fluorescent bands. P* 12½.
1084 **477** $2 multicoloured . . . . . . 2·00 3·00

478 Scene from Novel "Angéline de Montbrun" by Laure Conan (Félicité Angers)

479 St. John Ambulance Badge and "100"

(Des R. Milot (No. 1085), Claire Pratt (No. 1086), adapted W. Tibbles. Litho C.B.N.)

1983 (22 Apr). *Canadian Writers (4th series). T* **478** *and similar horiz design. Multicoloured. P* 13.

1085 32 c. Type **478** 40 75
a. Pair. Nos. 1085/6 . . . . . . 80 1·50
1086 32 c. Woodcut illustrating "Sea-gulls" (poem by E. J. Pratt) 40 75

Nos. 1085/6 were printed together, *se-tenant,* in horizontal and vertical pairs throughout the sheet.

(Des L. Fishauf. Litho Ashton-Potter)

1983 (3 June). *Centenary of St. John Ambulance in Canada. P* 13.
1087 **479** 32 c. brt rose-red, gold & dp chocolate 30 30

480 Victory Pictogram

481 Fort William, Ontario

(Des Krista Huebner, D. Kilvert and P.-Y. Pelletier. Litho C.B.N.)

1983 (28 June). *"Universiade 83" World University Games, Edmonton. P* 13.

1088 **480** 32 c. multicoloured 25 15
a. Printed on the gummed side . . £400
1089 64 c. multicoloured 50 70

(Des R. Harder. Litho Ashton-Potter)

1983 (30 June). *Canada Day. Forts (1st series). T* **481** *and similar horiz designs. Multicoloured. P* 12½ × 13.

1090 32 c. Fort Henry, Ontario (44 × 22 *mm*) . . 55 75
a. Booklet pane. Nos. 1090/9 . . . . 5·00
1091 32 c. Type **481** 55 75
1092 32 c. Fort Rodd Hill, British Columbia . . 55 75
1093 32 c. Fort Wellington, Ontario (28 × 22 *mm*) . . 55 75
1094 32 c. Fort Prince of Wales, Manitoba (28 × 22 *mm*) 55 75
1095 32 c. Halifax Citadel, Nova Scotia (44 × 22 *mm*) 55 75
1096 32 c. Fort Chambly, Quebec 55 75
1097 32 c. Fort No. 1, Point Levis, Quebec . . 55 75
1098 32 c. Coteau-du-Lac Fort, Quebec (28 × 22 *mm*) 55 75
1099 32 c. Fort Beauséjour, New Brunswick (28 × 22 *mm*) 55 75
1090/9 . . . . *Set of* 10 5·00 6·50

Nos. 1090/9 were only available from $3.20 stamp booklets containing the *se-tenant* pane, No. 1090a.

See also Nos. 1163/72.

482 Scouting Poster by Marc Fournier (aged 12)

483 Cross Symbol

(Des F. Dallaire. Litho Ashton-Potter)

1983 (6 July). *75th Anniv of Scouting in Canada and 15th World Scout Jamboree, Alberta. P* 13.
1100 **482** 32 c. multicoloured 30 30

(Des G. Tsetsekas. Recess and photo B.A.B.N.)

1983 (22 July). *6th Assembly of the World Council of Churches, Vancouver. P* 13.
1101 **483** 32 c. blue-green and grey-lilac 30 20

484 Sir Humphrey Gilbert (founder)   **485** "NICKEL" Deposits

(Des R. Hill. Litho C.B.N.)

1983 (3 Aug). *400th Anniv of Newfoundland. P* 13.
1102 **484** 32 c. multicoloured 30 20

(Des J. Capon. Litho ("NICKEL" die-stamped) C.B.N.)

1983 (12 Aug). *Centenary of Discovery of Sudbury Nickel Deposits. P* 13.
1103 **485** 32 c. multicoloured 30 20
a. Silver ("NICKEL") omitted .. £650

486 Josiah Henson and Escaping Slaves   **487** Robert Stephenson's Locomotive *Dorchester*, 1836

(Des T. Kew and J. Hamel. Litho B.A.B.N.)

1983 (16 Sept). *Nineteenth-century Social Reformers. T* **486** *and similar horiz design. Multicoloured. P* 13 × 13½ *(No.* 1104) *or* 13 *(No.* 1105).
1104 32 c. Type **486** 35 25
1105 32 c. Father Antoine Labelle and rural village (32 × 26 *mm*) 35 25

(Des E. Roch. Litho Ashton-Potter)

1983 (3 Oct). *Railway Locomotives* (1*st series*). *T* **487** *and similar horiz designs. Multicoloured. P* 12½×13.
1106 32 c. Type **487** 90 90
a. Pair. Nos. 1106/7 .. .. .. 1·75 1·75
1107 32 c. Locomotive *Toronto*, 1853 .. .. 90 90
1108 37 c. Timothy Hackworth's locomotive *Samson*, 1838 .. .. 90 1·00
1109 64 c. Western Canadian Railway locomotive *Adam Brown*, 1855 .. 1·40 2·00
1106/9 .. .. *Set of* 4 3·75 4·25
Nos. 1106/7 were printed together, *se-tenant*, in horizontal and vertical pairs throughout the sheet.
See also Nos. 1132/6, 1185/8 and 1223/6.

488 School Coat of Arms   **489** City Church

(Des Denise Saulnier. Litho C.B.N.)

1983 (28 Oct). *Centenary of Dalhousie Law School. P* 13.
1110 **488** 32 c. multicoloured 30 30

(Des C. Simard. Litho Ashton-Potter)

1983 (3 Nov). *Christmas. Churches. T* **489** *and similar horiz designs. Multicoloured. P* 13.
1111 32 c. Type **489** 40 10
1112 37 c. Family walking to church 55 70
1113 64 c. Country chapel .. .. 1·25 2·00
1111/13 .. .. *Set of* 3 2·00 2·50

490 Royal Canadian Regiment and British Columbia Regiment

(Des W. Southern and R. Tibbles. Litho C.B.N.)

1983 (10 Nov). *Canadian Army Regiments. T* **490** *and similar vert design. Multicoloured. Fluorescent frame. P* 13.
1114 32 c. Type **490** .. .. 75 1·00
a. Pair. Nos. 1114/15 .. .. .. 1·50 2·00
1115 32 c. Royal Winnipeg Rifles and Royal Canadian Dragoons .. .. .. 75 1·00
Nos. 1114/15 were printed together, *se-tenant*, in horizontal and vertical pairs throughout the sheet.

(Illustration reduced: actual size 112 × 88 mm)

"STICK 'N TICK" POSTAGE LABELS. Prepaid labels in the above design, printed in a combination of red, green and black, were tested by the Canadian Post Office in Winnipeg, Manitoba, between 21 November and 17 December 1983. These self-adhesive labels were sold to the public in kits of 12 or 25, at a saving of 35 c. or $1.11 on the normal postage. They were primarily intended for use on Christmas cards and were only valid on mail posted to Canadian addresses.

The label was affixed to normally addressed envelopes, but the user was then required to mark the postal code on the three lines at the foot. It was hoped that this incentive would increase the use of the postal codes and so speed automatic mail sorting.

The system was extended to seven other cities in 1984. The second version had separate postage paid and Postal Code labels, being available from 5 November until 17 December 1984.

491 Gold Mine in Prospecting Pan   **492** Montreal Symphony Orchestra

(Des K. Hughes. Litho Ashton-Potter)

1984 (15 Mar). *50th Anniv of Yellowknife. P* 13½.
1116 **491** 32 c. multicoloured 30 30

(Des J. Delisle and P. Kohler. Litho Ashton-Potter)

1984 (24 Mar). *50th Anniv of Montreal Symphony Orchestra. P* 12½.
1117 **492** 32 c. multicoloured 35 30

493 Jacques Cartier   **494** *Eagle* (U.S. Coastguard cadet ship)

(Des Y. Paquin, Engraved C. Haley. Recess French Govt Ptg Wks, Perigueux)

1984 (20 Apr). *450th Anniv of Jacques Cartier's Voyage to Canada. P* 13.
1118 **493** 32 c. multicoloured 40 30

(Des O. Schenk. Litho Ashton-Potter)

1984 (18 May). *Tall Ships Visit. Fluorescent frame. P* 12×12½.
1119 **494** 32 c. multicoloured 35 30

495 Service Medal   **496** Oared Galleys

(Des W. Tibbles and C. Webster. Litho Ashton-Potter)

1984 (28 May). *75th Anniv of Canadian Red Cross Society. P* 13½.
1120 **495** 32 c. multicoloured 35 30

(Des P. Dorn. Photo and recess B.A.B.N.)

1984 (18 June). *Bicentenary of New Brunswick. P* 13½.
1121 **496** 32 c. multicoloured 35 30

497 St. Lawrence Seaway

(Des E. Barenscher. Litho C.B.N.)

1984 (26 June). *25th Anniv of St. Lawrence Seaway. Fluorescent frame. P* 13.
1122 **497** 32 c. multicoloured 45 30

498 New Brunswick   **499** Loyalists of 1784

(Des J. Morin and T. Yakobina. Litho C.B.N.)

1984 (29 June). *Canada Day. Paintings by Jean Paul Lemieux. Sheet,* 138 × 122 *mm, containing T* **498** *and similar multi-coloured designs. P* 13.
MS1123 32 c. × 12, Type **498**; British Columbia; Northwest Territories; Quebec; Manitoba; Alberta; Prince Edward Island; Saskatchewan; Nova Scotia (*vert*); Yukon Territory, Newfoundland; Ontario (*vert*) .. .. 6·00 6·5
The captions on the Northwest Territories and Yukon Territory paintings were transposed at the design stage.

(Des W. Davies. Litho B.A.B.N.)

1984 (3 July). *Bicentenary of Arrival of United Empire Loyalists. P* 13 × 13½.
1124 **499** 32 c. multicoloured 30 3

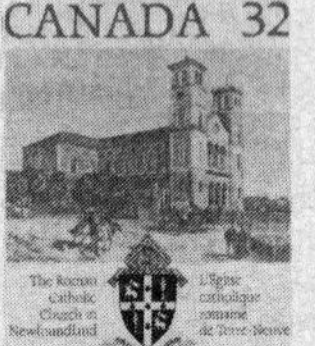

500 St. John's Basilica   **501** Coat of Arms of Pope John Paul II

(Des J. Morin and R. Ethier. Litho C.B.N.)

1984 (17 Aug). *Bicentenary of Roman Catholic Church in Newfoundland. P* 13½.
1125 **500** 32 c. multicoloured 30 2

(Des L. Rivard. Litho Ashton-Potter)

1984 (31 Aug). *Papal Visit. P* 12½.
1126 **501** 32 c. multicoloured 40 2
1127 64 c. multicoloured .. .. .. 85 1·1

502 Louisbourg Lighthouse, 1734

(Des D. Noble and K. Rodmell. Litho Ashton-Potter)

1984 (21 Sept). *Canadian Lighthouses* (1*st series*). *T* **502** *and similar horiz designs. Multicoloured. P* 12½.
1128 32 c. Type **502** .. .. 1·10 1·25
a. Block of 4. Nos. 1128/31 .. .. 4·00
1129 32 c. Fisgard Lighthouse, 1860 .. .. 1·10 1·25
1130 32 c. Ile Verte Lighthouse, 1809 .. .. 1·10 1·25
1131 32 c. Gibraltar Point Lighthouse, 1808 .. 1·10 1·25
1128/31 .. .. *Set of* 4 4·00 4·50
Nos. 1128/31 were printed together, *se-tenant*, in different combinations throughout the sheet, giving ten blocks of 4 and ten single stamps.
See also Nos. 1176/80.

503 Great Western Railway Locomotive, *Scotia*, 1860

(Des E. Roch. Litho Ashton-Potter)

1984 (25 Oct). *Railway Locomotives* (2*nd series*). *T* **503** *and similar horiz designs. Multicoloured. P* 12½×13.
1132 32 c. Type **503** 90 90
a. Pair. Nos. 1132/3 .. .. .. 1·75 1·75
1133 32 c. Northern Pacific Railroad locomotive *Countess of Dufferin*, 1872 .. .. 90 90
1134 37 c. Grand Trunk Railway Class E3 locomotive, 1886 .. .. .. 90 1·40
1135 64 c. Canadian Pacific Class D10a steam locomotive .. .. 1·40 2·00
1132/5 .. .. *Set of* 4 3·75 4·75
MS1136 153×104 mm. As Nos. 1132/5, but with background colour changed from pale green to pale grey-blue .. .. 5·00 6·50
Nos. 1132/3 were issued together, *se-tenant*, in horizontal and vertical pairs throughout the sheet.
No. **MS**1136 commemorates "CANADA 84" National Stamp Exhibition, Montreal.
See also Nos. 1185/8 and 1223/6.

504 "The Annunciation" (Jean Dallaire)

505 Pilots of 1914–18, 1939–45 and 1984

(Des J. Morin and T. Yakobina. Litho Ashton-Potter)

34 (2 Nov). *Christmas. Religious Paintings. T* **504** *and similar oriz designs. Multicoloured. P* 13½.
37 32 c. Type **504** 40 10
38 37 c. "The Three Kings" (Simone Bouchard) .. 55 80
39 64 c. "Snow in Bethlehem" (David Milne) .. 80 1·60
37/9 .. .. *Set of* 3 1·60 2·25

(Des W. Southern and R. Tibbles. Litho Ashton-Potter)

84 (9 Nov). *60th Anniv of Royal Canadian Air Force. Fluorescent frame. P* 12×12½.
40 **505** 32 c. multicoloured 35 30

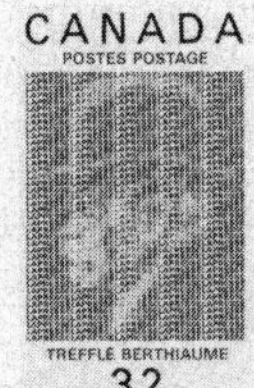

506 Treffle Berthiaume (editor)

507 Heart and Arrow

(Des P.-Y. Pelletier. Litho Ashton-Potter)

84 (16 Nov). *Centenary of* La Presse (*newspaper*). *Fluorescent frame. P* 13×13½.
41 **506** 32 c. agate, vermilion & pale grey-brn 35 30

(Des F. Dallaire. Litho Ashton-Potter)

85 (8 Feb). *International Youth Year. P* 12½.
42 **507** 32 c. multicoloured 30 30

508 Astronaut in Space, and Planet Earth

509 Emily Murphy

(Des L. Holloway. Litho Ashton-Potter)

85 (15 Mar). *Canadian Space Programme. P* 13½.
43 **508** 32 c. multicoloured 40 30

(Des Muriel Wood and R. Tibbles. Litho Ashton-Potter)

85 (17 Apr). *Women's Rights Activists. T* **509** *and similar horiz design. Multicoloured. P* 13½.
44 32 c. Type **509** 40 70
a. Horiz pair. Nos. 1144/5 .. .. 80 1·40
45 32 c. Therese Casgrain 40 70
Nos. 1144/5 were printed together, *se-tenant*, in horizontal irs throughout the sheet.

510 Gabriel Dumont (Métis leader) and Battle of Batoche, 1885

(Des R. Derreth. Litho Ashton-Potter)

85 (6 May). *Centenary of the North-West Rebellion. P* 14×13½.
146 **510** 32 c. blue, carmine and grey .. 30 30

511 Rear View, arliament Building, Ottawa

512 Queen Elizabeth II

512*a* Queen Elizabeth II in 1984 (from photo by Karsh)

(Des R. Bellemare. Eng R. Couture (Nos. 1161/2). Des T. Yakobina and C. Candlish (Nos. 1162*a*/*h*), R. Harder (others))

1985 (21 June)–**98.** *No fluorescent bands* (1 *c. to* 6 *c.*) *or fluorescent frame* (34, 36, 39, 40, 42, 43, 45, 46 *c.*).

(*a*) *T* **511** *and similar horiz designs*

(i) *Booklet stamps. Recess B.A.B.N. Chalk-surfaced paper* (6 *c.* (*No.* 1150*b*), 37 *c.*, 38 *c.*) *or ordinary paper* (*others*). *P* 12½×12.
1147 – 1 c. grey-olive (30.3.87) .. .. 70 1·60
a. Booklet pane. Nos. 1147×2, 1150×2, 1152 and label .. 4·50
b. Chalk-surfaced paper (1.10.87) 50 70
ba. Booklet pane. Nos. 1147b×2, 1150a×2, 1152a and label .. 4·00
bb. Booklet pane. Nos. 1147b, 1150a×2, 1153 and two labels (3.2.88) .. .. .. 2·25
1148 – 2 c. bottle green 20 40
a. Booklet pane. Nos. 1148×3, 1149×2 and 1151 .. .. 2·25
b. Chalk-surfaced paper (18.1.89) 30 40
ba. Booklet pane. Nos. 1148b×3, 1150*b*, 1154 and label .. 1·90
1149 – 5 c. sepia 40 50
1150 – 6 c. chestnut (30.3.87) .. .. 80 1·00
a. Chalk-surfaced paper (1.10.87) 40 30
1150*b* – 6 c. blackish purple (18.1.89) .. 65 95
1151 **511** 34 c. blue-black .. .. .. 1·00 1·50
1152 36 c. reddish purple (30.3.87) .. 2·50 3·00
a. Chalk-surfaced paper (1.10.87) 3·00 3·00
1153 37 c. dull ultramarine (3.2.88) .. 1·00 30
1154 38 c. deep blue (18.1.89) .. .. 75 1·25

(ii) *Litho C.B.N.* (*Nos.* 1155 (*from sheets*), 1156/7*c*), *B.A.B.N.* (*No.* 1155 (*from booklets*)) *or Ashton-Potter* (*Nos.* 1155b, 1156a, 1157a/ba, 1157ca/cb). *Chalk-surfaced paper* (*Nos.* 1155b/ba, 1156, 1156b/bb *and* 1157*c*/cb). *P* 13×13½ (*No.* 1157*c*) *or* 13½×13 (*others*).
1155 **511** 34 c. multicoloured 50 10
a. Booklet pane. No. 1155×25 (1.8.85) .. .. .. 11·50
b. Perf 13½×14 (4.7.86) .. 1·25 1·75
ba. Booklet pane. No. 1155b×25 26·00
1156 36 c. multicoloured (30.3.87) .. 30 30
a. Ordinary paper 30 45
b. Perf 13½×14 .. .. 1·40 1·40
ba. Booklet pane. No. 1156a×10 10·00
bb. Booklet pane. No. 1156a×25 (19.5.87) .. .. .. 22·00
c. Imperf (vert pair) £500
1157 – 37 c. multicoloured (30.12.87) .. 85 10
a. Perf 13½×14 (5.1.88) .. 1·00 1·00
ab. Booklet pane. No. 1157a×10 12·00
ac. Booklet pane. No. 1157a×25 (2.5.88) .. .. .. 15·00
ad. Chalk-surfaced paper (5.1.88) 1·50 1·75
ae. Booklet pane. No. 1157ad×25 27·00
1157*c* – 38 c. multicoloured (29.12.88) .. 35 10
ca. Booklet pane. No. 1157*c*×10 and two labels .. .. 3·50
cb. Booklet pane. No. 1157*c*×25 and two labels .. .. 12·00
cc. Printed on the gummed side 35·00

(iii) *Coil stamps. Recess C.B.N. P* 10×*imperf*
1158 **511** 34 c. purple-brown (1.8.85) . 2·25 2·75
a. Imperf (pair) £100
1159 36 c. carmine-vermilion (19.5.87) .. 90 55
a. Imperf (pair) £150
1160 37 c. deep ultramarine (22.2.88) .. 60 40
a. Imperf (pair) £100
1160*b* 38 c. bottle green (1.2.89) 40 30
ba. Imperf (pair) £200

(*b*) *Recess and photo B.A.B.N. P* 13×13½
1161 **512** 34 c. black and cobalt (12.7.85) .. 45 30
1162 36 c. reddish purple (1.10.87) .. 2·75 1·10

(*c*) *Litho B.A.B.N.* (*Nos.* 1162*a*/*c*), *Ashton-Potter* (*Nos.* 1162bc, 1162ca, 1162*d*/*e*, 1162fa), *C.B.N.* (*Nos.* 1162*f*/*g*) *or Ashton-Potter Canada* (*No.* 1162*h*). *Chalk-surfaced paper* (40 *c. to* 46 *c.*). *P* 13½×13 (*Nos.* 1162*a*, 1162*h*), 13×12½ (*No.* 1162*b*) *or* 13×13½ (*Nos.* 1162*c*, 1162*d*/*g*).
1162*a* **512*a*** 37 c. multicoloured (30.12.87) .. 2·00 10
1162*b* 38 c. multicoloured (29.12.88) .. 35 20
ba. Imperf (horiz pair) £275
bb. Imperf at top and sides (horiz pair) £225
bc. Perf 13×13½. Chalk-surfaced paper 45 65
bd. Booklet pane. No. 1162bc×10 and two labels .. .. 4·50
be. Imperf between (horiz pair) (from pane No. 1162bd) .. £500
1162*c* 39 c. multicoloured (12.1.90) .. 1·00 20
ca. Chalk-surfaced paper .. 1·40 55
cb. Booklet pane. No. 1162ca×10 and two labels .. .. 13·00
cc. Perf 13×12½ (2.90) .. .. 7·00 1·00
1162*d* 40 c. multicoloured (28.12.90) .. 80 20
da. Booklet pane. No. 1162*d*×10 and two labels .. .. 8·00
db. Ordinary paper (24.5.91) .. 85 20
1162*e* 42 c. multicoloured (27.12.91) .. 80 40
ea. Booklet pane. No. 1162*e*×10 8·00
1162*f* 43 c. multicoloured (30.12.92) .. 80 55
fa. Booklet pane. No. 1162*f*×10 .. 8·00
1162*g* 45 c. multicoloured (31.7.95) .. 35 40
ga. Booklet pane. No. 1162*g*×10 3·50
1162*h* 46 c. multicoloured (28.12.98) .. 35 40

Designs:—1 c., 5 c., 6 c. (No. 1150*b*) East Block, Parliament Building; 2 c., 6 c. (No. 1150) West Block, Parliament Building; 37 c. (No. 1157) Front view, Parliament Building; 38 c. (No. 1157*c*) Side view, Parliament Building.

Stamps from booklet panes Nos. 1147a, 1147ba/bb and 1148a/b have one or two adjacent sides imperforate. Stamps from the first and last vertical columns of booklet panes Nos. 1155a, 1155ba, 1156ba/bb, 1157ab/ac, 1157ae, 1157ca/cb, 1162bd, 1162cb, 1162da, 1162ea, 1162fa and 1162ga are imperforate at left or right. Those from the bottom row of No. 1157ac are also imperforate at foot.

Nos. 1157c and 1162*b*/*h* have a slightly larger design image 21×17 mm.

Printings of booklet pane No. 1162fa from booklet No. SB164 were initially by Ashton-Potter. On 7 January 1994 the printer changed to C.B.N. and the booklet cover to Type B **37**. This booklet is listed as No. SB177. There were further printings by C.B.N. before production reverted to Ashton-Potter Canada for supplies released on 27 March 1995.

Nos. 1162*g*/ga were reissued on 6 October 1995 showing a change of printer to Ashton-Potter Canada. There are no listable differences between these stamps and the previous printings.

(Des R. Harder. Litho Ashton-Potter)

1985 (28 June). *Canada Day. Forts* (*2nd series*). *Horiz designs as T* **481.** *Multicoloured. P* 12½×13.
1163 34 c. Lower Fort Garry, Manitoba (44×22 *mm*) 50 60
a. Booklet pane. Nos. 1163/72 .. 4·50
1164 34 c. Fort Anne, Nova Scotia 50 60
1165 34 c. Fort York, Ontario 50 60
1166 34 c. Castle Hill, Newfoundland (28×22 *mm*) 50 60
1167 34 c. Fort Whoop Up, Alberta (28×22 *mm*) 50 60
1168 34 c. Fort Erie, Ontario (44×22 *mm*) .. 50 60
1169 34 c. Fort Walsh, Saskatchewan 50 60
1170 34 c. Fort Lennox, Quebec 50 60
1171 34 c. York Redoubt, Nova Scotia (28×22 *mm*) 50 60
1172 34 c. Fort Frederick, Ontario (28×22 *mm*) 50 60
1163/72 .. .. *Set of* 10 4·50 5·50
Nos. 1163/72 were only available from $3.40 stamp booklets containing the *se-tenant* pane, No. 1163a.

513 Louis Hébert (apothecary)

514 Parliament Buildings and Map of World

515 Guide and Brownie Saluting

(Des C. Malenfant. Litho Ashton-Potter)

1985 (30 Aug). *45th International Pharmaceutical Sciences Congress of Pharmaceutical Federation, Montreal. Fluorescent frame. P* 12½.
1173 **513** 34 c. multicoloured 45 35

(Des E. Barenscher. Litho Ashton-Potter)

1985 (3 Sept). *74th Conference of Inter-Parliamentary Union, Ottawa. P* 13½.
1174 **514** 34 c. multicoloured 45 35

(Des Barbara Griffin. Recess and photo B.A.B.N.)

1985 (12 Sept). *75th Anniv of Girl Guide Movement. Fluorescent frame. P* 13½×13.
1175 **515** 34 c. multicoloured 45 35

516 Sisters Islets Lighthouse

517 Santa Claus in Reindeer-drawn Sleigh

(Des B. Reilander (No. **MS**1180), L. Rivard (others). Litho Ashton-Potter)

1985 (3 Oct). *Canadian Lighthouses* (*2nd series*). *T* **516** *and similar horiz designs. Multicoloured. P* 13½.
1176 34 c. Type **516** .. .. 1·40 1·40
a. Block of 4. Nos. 1176/9 .. .. 5·00
1177 34 c. Pelee Passage Lighthouse .. .. 1·40 1·40
1178 34 c. Haut-fond Prince Lighthouse .. .. 1·40 1·40
1179 34 c. Rose Blanche Lighthouse, Cains Island .. .. 1·40 1·40
1176/9 .. .. *Set of* 4 5·00 5·00
MS1180 109×90 mm. Nos. 1176/9 .. .. 6·00 7·00
Nos. 1176/9 were printed together, *se-tenant*, in different combinations throughout the sheet, giving ten blocks of 4 and ten single stamps.
No. **MS**1180 Publicises "Capex 87" International Stamp Exhibition, Toronto.

(Des Barbara Carroll and C. Yaneff. Litho Ashton-Potter)

1985 (23 Oct). *Christmas. Santa Claus Parade. T* **517** *and similar horiz designs. Multicoloured. P* 13½.
1181 32 c. Canada Post's parade float 70 70
a. Booklet pane. No. 1181×10 .. .. 6·50
1182 34 c. Type **517** 60 15
1183 39 c. Acrobats and horse-drawn carriage .. 70 1·00
1184 68 c. Christmas tree, pudding and goose on float .. .. 1·50 1·60
1181/4 .. .. *Set of* 4 3·25 3·00
No. 1181 was only available from $3.20 stamp booklets, which had the upper and lower edges of the pane imperforate. This value was intended for use on greeting cards posted on or before 31 January 1986, and represented a 2 c. saving of postage. After this date these stamps could be used for any postal purpose in conjunction with other values.

(Des E. Roch. Litho Ashton-Potter)

1985 (7 Nov). *Railway Locomotives* (*3rd series*). *Horiz designs as T* **503**. *Multicoloured. P* 12½×13.
1185 34 c. Grand Trunk Railway Class K2 steam locomotive 80 80
a. Pair. Nos. 1185/6 .. .. 1·60 1·60
1186 34 c. Canadian Pacific Class P2a steam locomotive 80 80
1187 39 c. Canadian Northern Class O10a steam locomotive .. .. 95 1·25
1188 68 c. Canadian Govt Railway Class H4D steam locomotive .. .. 1·60 1·75
1185/8 .. .. *Set of* 4 3·75 4·25
Nos. 1185/6 were printed together, *se-tenant*, in horizontal and vertical pairs throughout the sheet.

518 Naval Personnel of 1910, 1939–45 and 1985

519 "The Old Holton House, Montreal" (James Wilson Morrice)

(Des W. Southern and R. Tibbles. Litho C.B.N.)

1985 (8 Nov). *75th Anniv of Royal Canadian Navy. Fluorescent frame. P* 13½×13.
1189 **518** 34 c. multicoloured 65 55

(Des L. Parent and J. Morin. Litho C.B.N.)

1985 (15 Nov). *125th Anniv of Montreal Museum of Fine Arts. P* 13½.
1190 **519** 34 c. multicoloured 40 35

520 Map of Alberta showing Olympic Sites

(Des P.-Y. Pelletier. Litho Ashton-Potter)

1986 (13 Feb). *Winter Olympic Games, Calgary* (1988) (*1st issue*). *Fluorescent frame. P* 12½×13.
1191 **520** 34 c. multicoloured 40 50
See also Nos. 1216/17, 1236/7, 1258/9 and 1281/4.

521 Canada Pavilion

522 Molly Brant

(Des Debbie Adams. Recess and photo B.A.B.N.)

1986 (7 Mar). *"Expo '86" World Fair, Vancouver* (*1st issue*). *T* **521** *and similar horiz design. Multicoloured. Fluorescent frame. P* 13×13½.
1192 34 c. Type **521** .. .. 1·00 50
1193 39 c. Early telephone, dish aerial and satellite .. .. 1·25 2·00
See also Nos. 1196/7.

(Des Sara Tyson. Litho Ashton-Potter)

1986 (14 Apr). *250th Birth Anniv of Molly Brant* (*Iroquois leader*). *P* 13½.
1194 **522** 34 c. multicoloured 40 40

523 Philippe Aubert de Gaspé and Scene from *Les Anciens Canadiens*

524 Canadian Field Post Office and Cancellation, 1944

(Des P. Fontaine and Y. Paquin. Litho Ashton-Potter)

1986 (14 Apr). *Birth Bicentenary of Philippe Aubert de Gaspé* (*author*). *Fluorescent frame. P* 12½.
1195 **523** 34 c. multicoloured 40 40

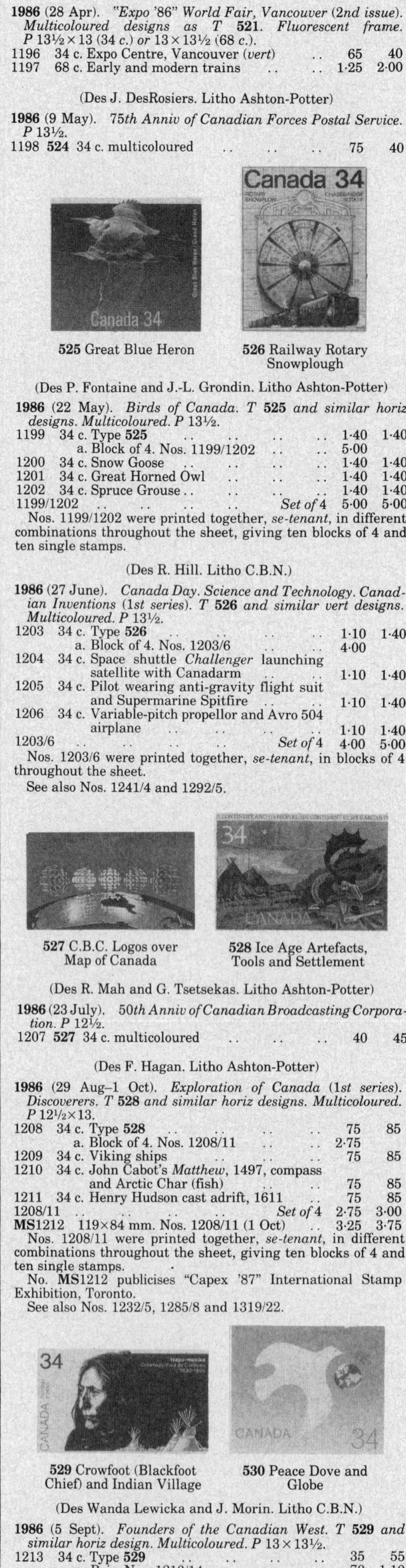

(Des Debbie Adams. Recess and photo B.A.B.N.)

1986 (28 Apr). *"Expo '86" World Fair, Vancouver* (*2nd issue*). *Multicoloured designs as T* **521**. *Fluorescent frame. P* 13½×13 (*34 c.*) *or* 13×13½ (*68 c.*).
1196 34 c. Expo Centre, Vancouver (*vert*) .. 65 40
1197 68 c. Early and modern trains .. .. 1·25 2·00

(Des J. DesRosiers. Litho Ashton-Potter)

1986 (9 May). *75th Anniv of Canadian Forces Postal Service. P* 13½.
1198 **524** 34 c. multicoloured 75 40

525 Great Blue Heron

526 Railway Rotary Snowplough

(Des P. Fontaine and J.-L. Grondin. Litho Ashton-Potter)

1986 (22 May). *Birds of Canada. T* **525** *and similar horiz designs. Multicoloured. P* 13½.
1199 34 c. Type **525** .. .. 1·40 1·40
a. Block of 4. Nos. 1199/1202 .. .. 5·00
1200 34 c. Snow Goose .. .. 1·40 1·40
1201 34 c. Great Horned Owl .. .. .. 1·40 1·40
1202 34 c. Spruce Grouse .. .. 1·40 1·40
1199/1202 .. .. *Set of* 4 5·00 5·00
Nos. 1199/1202 were printed together, *se-tenant*, in different combinations throughout the sheet, giving ten blocks of 4 and ten single stamps.

(Des R. Hill. Litho C.B.N.)

1986 (27 June). *Canada Day. Science and Technology. Canadian Inventions* (*1st series*). *T* **526** *and similar vert designs. Multicoloured. P* 13½.
1203 34 c. Type **526** .. .. 1·10 1·40
a. Block of 4. Nos. 1203/6 .. .. 4·00
1204 34 c. Space shuttle *Challenger* launching satellite with Canadarm .. .. 1·10 1·40
1205 34 c. Pilot wearing anti-gravity flight suit and Supermarine Spitfire .. .. 1·10 1·40
1206 34 c. Variable-pitch propellor and Avro 504 airplane .. .. 1·10 1·40
1203/6 .. .. *Set of* 4 4·00 5·00
Nos. 1203/6 were printed together, *se-tenant*, in blocks of 4 throughout the sheet.
See also Nos. 1241/4 and 1292/5.

527 C.B.C. Logos over Map of Canada

528 Ice Age Artefacts, Tools and Settlement

(Des R. Mah and G. Tsetsekas. Litho Ashton-Potter)

1986 (23 July). *50th Anniv of Canadian Broadcasting Corporation. P* 12½.
1207 **527** 34 c. multicoloured 40 45

(Des F. Hagan. Litho Ashton-Potter)

1986 (29 Aug–1 Oct). *Exploration of Canada* (*1st series*). *Discoverers. T* **528** *and similar horiz designs. Multicoloured. P* 12½×13.
1208 34 c. Type **528** 75 85
a. Block of 4. Nos. 1208/11 .. .. 2·75
1209 34 c. Viking ships 75 85
1210 34 c. John Cabot's *Matthew*, 1497, compass and Arctic Char (fish) 75 85
1211 34 c. Henry Hudson cast adrift, 1611 .. 75 85
1208/11 .. .. *Set of* 4 2·75 3·00
MS1212 119×84 mm. Nos. 1208/11 (1 Oct) .. 3·25 3·75
Nos. 1208/11 were printed together, *se-tenant*, in different combinations throughout the sheet, giving ten blocks of 4 and ten single stamps.
No. **MS**1212 publicises "Capex '87" International Stamp Exhibition, Toronto.
See also Nos. 1232/5, 1285/8 and 1319/22.

529 Crowfoot (Blackfoot Chief) and Indian Village

530 Peace Dove and Globe

(Des Wanda Lewicka and J. Morin. Litho C.B.N.)

1986 (5 Sept). *Founders of the Canadian West. T* **529** *and similar horiz design. Multicoloured. P* 13×13½.
1213 34 c. Type **529** 35 55
a. Pair. Nos. 1213/14 .. .. .. 70 1·10
1214 34 c. James Macleod of the North West Mounted Police and Fort Macleod .. 35 55
Nos. 1213/4 were printed together, *se-tenant*, in horizontal and vertical pairs throughout the sheet.

(Des Carole Jeghers. Litho and embossed Ashton-Potter)

1986 (16 Sept). *International Peace Year. P* 13½.
1215 **530** 34 c. multicoloured 40 45

531 Ice Hockey

532 Angel with Crown

(Des P.-Y. Pelletier. Litho C.B.N.)

1986 (15 Oct). *Winter Olympic Games, Calgary* (1988) (2 *issue*). *T* **531** *and similar vert design. Multicoloure P* 13½×13.
1216 34 c. Type **531** .. .. 1·25 1·
a. Pair. Nos. 1216/17 .. .. .. 2·50 2·
1217 34 c. Biathlon .. .. 1·25 1·
Nos. 1216/17 were printed together, *se-tenant*, in horizon and vertical pairs throughout the sheet.
See also Nos. 1236/7, 1258/9 and 1281/4.

(Des T. Dimson. Litho Ashton-Potter)

1986 (29 Oct). *Christmas. T* **532** *and similar multicolou designs. Fluorescent frame* (*34 to 68 c.*). *P* 13½×*imperf* (29 *or* 12½ (*others*).
1218 29 c. Angel singing carol (36×22 *mm*) .. 65 3
a. Booklet pane. No. 1218×10 .. 6·50
b. Perf 12½ × imperf .. .. .. 5·00 3
ba. Booklet pane. No. 1218b×10 .. 50·00
1219 34 c. Type **532** 60 2
1220 39 c. Angel playing lute .. .. .. 1·00 9
1221 68 c. Angel with ribbon .. .. .. 1·50 2·2
1218/21 .. .. *Set of* 4 3·25 3·2
Nos. 1218/b were only available from $2.90 stamp booklet which had the sides of the pane imperforate. In addition to th design each stamp in the pane included an integral horizonta label showing a bar code. This value was intended for use o greeting cards posted on or before 31 January 1987, an represented a 5 c. saving when used in conjunction with speci postcoded envelopes. These stamps were valid for normal posta purposes after 31 January when used with other values.

533 John Molson with Theatre Royal, Montreal, *Accommodation* (paddle-steamer) and Railway Train

534 Toronto's First Post Office

(Des C. Malenfant. Litho Ashton-Potter)

1986 (4 Nov). *150th Death Anniv of John Molson* (*busines man*). *P* 12½.
1222 **533** 34 c. multicoloured 50

(Des E. Roch. Litho Ashton-Potter)

1986 (21 Nov). *Railway Locomotives* (*4th series*). *Horiz desig as T* **503**, *but size* 60×22 *mm. Multicoloured. P* 12½×13.
1223 34 c. Canadian National Class V-1-a steam locomotive No. 9000 .. .. 1·25 1·
a. Pair. Nos. 1223/4 .. .. .. 2·50 2·
1224 34 c. Canadian Pacific Class T1a diesel locomotive No. 9000 .. .. 1·25 1·
1225 39 c. Canadian National Class U-2-a steam locomotive .. .. 1·40 1·
1226 68 c. Canadian Pacific Class H1c steam locomotive No. 2850 .. .. 2·25 2·
1223/6 .. .. *Set of* 4 5·50 5·
Nos. 1223/4 were issued together, *se-tenant*, in horizontal a vertical pairs throughout the sheet.

(Des J. Mardon (stamps) and B. Reilander (sheet). Recess a litho B.A.B.N.)

1987 (16 Feb–12 June). *"Capex '87" International Sta Exhibition, Toronto. T* **534** *and similar horiz designs showi Post Offices. Fluorescent frame. P* 13×13½.
1227 34 c. Type **534** 60
1228 36 c. Nelson-Miramichi, New Brunswick (12.6) 65
1229 42 c. Saint-Ours, Quebec (12.6) 70
1230 72 c. Battleford, Saskatchewan (12.6) .. 1·00 1·
1227/30 .. .. *Set of* 4 2·75 2·
MS1231 155×92 mm. 36 c. As No. 1227 and Nos. 1228/30, but main inscr in brt green (12.6) .. 2·25 2·

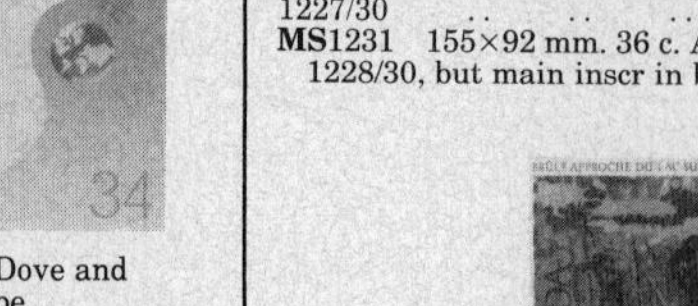

535 Étienne Brûlé exploring Lake Superior

(Des J. Britton and F. Hagan. Litho Ashton-Potter)

1987 (13 Mar). *Exploration of Canada* (*2nd series*). *Pioneers New France. T* **535** *and similar horiz designs. Multicoloure P* 12½×13.
1232 34 c. Type **535** .. .. 85 1·
a. Block of 4. Nos. 1232/5 .. .. 3·00
1233 34 c. Radisson and des Groseilliers with British and French flags .. .. 85 1·

:34 34 c. Jolliet and Father Marquette on the Mississippi .. .. 85 1·00
:35 34 c. Jesuit missionary preaching to Indians .. .. 85 1·00
32/5 .. .. *Set of* 4 3·00 3·50

Nos. 1232/5 were printed together, *se-tenant*, in different mbinations throughout the sheet, giving ten blocks of 4 and n single stamps.

(Des P.-Y. Pelletier. Litho C.B.N.)

87 (3 Apr). *Winter Olympic Games, Calgary* (1988) (*3rd issue*). *Vert designs as T* **531**. *Multicoloured. P* 13½×13.
36 36 c. Speed skating 50 40
37 42 c. Bobsleighing 75 60

536 Volunteer Activities **537** Canadian Coat of Arms

(Des W. Davies. Litho Ashton-Potter)

87 (13 Apr). *National Volunteer Week. P* 12½×13.
38 **536** 36 c. multicoloured 30 35

(Des R. Tibbles. Litho Ashton-Potter)

87 (15 Apr). *5th Anniv of Canadian Charter of Rights and Freedoms. Fluorescent frame. P* 14×13½.
39 **537** 36 c. multicoloured 35 35

538 Steel Girder, Gear Wheel and Microchip **539** R. A. Fessenden (AM Radio)

es L. Holloway, R. Kerr and Nita Wallace. Litho Ashton-Potter)

87 (19 May). *Centenary of Engineering Institute of Canada. P* 12½×13.
40 **538** 36 c. multicoloured 35 40

(Des R. Hill. Litho C.B.N.)

87 (25 June). *Canada Day. Science and Technology. Canadian Inventors* (*2nd series*). *T* **539** *and similar vert designs. Multicoloured. P* 13½.
41 36 c. Type **539** 80 80
a. Block of four. Nos. 1241/4 .. .. 2·75
42 36 c. C. Fenerty (newsprint pulp) 80 80
43 36 c. G.-E. Desbarats and W. Leggo (half-tone engraving) 80 80
44 36 c. F. N. Gisborne (first North American undersea telegraph) 80 80
41/4 .. .. *Set of* 4 2·75 2·75

Nos. 1241/4 were printed together, *se-tenant*, in blocks of four roughout the sheet.

540 *Segwun* **541** Figurehead from *Hamilton*, 1813

(Des D. Champion. Litho C.B.N.)

87 (20 July). *Canadian Steamships. T* **540** *and similar multicoloured design. P* 13.
45 36 c. Type **540** .. .. 1·25 1·75
a. Horiz pair. Nos. 1245/6 .. .. 2·50 3·50
46 36 c. *Princess Marguerite* (52×22 *mm*) .. 1·25 1·75

Nos. 1245/6 were printed together horizontally, *se-tenant*, roughout the sheet of 25, with No. 1245 occurring in columns 3 and 5 and No. 1246 in columns 2 and 4.

(Des L.-A. Rivard. Litho Ashton-Potter)

87 (7 Aug). *Historic Shipwrecks. T* **541** *and similar horiz designs. Multicoloured. P* 13½×13.
47 36 c. Type **541** 70 85
a. Block of four. Nos. 1247/50 .. .. 2·50
48 36 c. Hull of *San Juan*, 1565 .. .. 70 85
49 36 c. Wheel from *Breadalbane*, 1853 .. 70 85
50 36 c. Bell from *Ericsson*, 1892 .. .. 70 85
47/50 .. .. *Set of* 4 2·50 3·00

Nos. 1247/50 were printed together, *se-tenant*, in different mbinations throughout the sheet, giving ten blocks of 4 and ten ngle stamps.

542 Air Canada Boeing 767-200 and Globe **543** Summit Symbol

(Des Debbie Adams and D. Carter. Litho C.B.N.)

1987 (1 Sept). *50th Anniv of Air Canada. P* 13½.
1251 **542** 36 c. multicoloured 55 35

(Des C. Gaudreau. Litho Ashton-Potter)

1987 (2 Sept). *2nd International Francophone Summit, Quebec. Fluorescent frame. P* 13×12½.
1252 **543** 36 c. multicoloured 30 35

544 Commonwealth Symbol **545** Poinsettia

(Des G. Tsetsekas. Litho Ashton-Potter)

1987 (13 Oct). *Commonwealth Heads of Government Meeting, Vancouver. Fluorescent frame. P* 13×12½.
1253 **544** 36 c. multicoloured 35 40

(Des C. Simard. Litho Ashton-Potter)

1987 (2 Nov). *Christmas. Christmas Plants. T* **545** *and similar multicoloured designs. Fluorescent frame. P* 12½×13 (31 *c.*) *or* 13½ (*others*).
1254 31 c. Decorated Christmas tree and presents (36×20 *mm*) 50 35
a. Booklet pane. No. 1254×10 .. 5·00
b. Imperf between (horiz pair) (from booklet) .. ..
1255 36 c. Type **545** 35 40
1256 42 c. Holly wreath 40 45
1257 72 c. Mistletoe and decorated tree .. 65 70
1254/7 .. .. *Set of* 4 1·75 1·75

On No. 1254 the left-hand third of the design area is taken up by a bar code which has fluorescent bands between the bars. This value was only available from $3.10 stamp booklets which had the sides of the pane imperforate. This value was intended for use on greeting cards posted on or before 31 January 1988 and represented a 5 c. saving when used in conjunction with special postcoded envelopes.

(Des P.-Y. Pelletier. Litho C.B.N.)

1987 (13 Nov). *Winter Olympic Games, Calgary* (1988) (*4th issue*). *Vert designs as T* **531**. *Multicoloured. Fluorescent frame. P* 13½×13.
1258 36 c. Cross-country skiing 50 40
a. Pair. Nos. 1258/9 .. .. .. 1·00 80
1259 36 c. Ski-jumping 50 40

Nos. 1258/9 were printed together, *se-tenant*, in horizontal and vertical pairs throughout the sheet.

546 Football, Grey Cup and Spectators

(Des L. Holloway. Litho Ashton-Potter)

1987 (20 Nov). *75th Grey Cup Final* (*Canadian football championship*), *Vancouver. Fluorescent frame. P* 12½.
1260 **546** 36 c. multicoloured 35 40

547 Flying Squirrel

548 Lynx

548a Runnymede Library, Toronto

(Des Gottschalk & Ash International (1 c. to 25 c.), B. Tsang (43 c. to 80 c.), R. Bellemare ($1, $2, $5). Litho Ashton-Potter (1 c. to 80 c.), Recess and litho B.A.B.N. to June 1992, thereafter C.B.N. ($1, $2, $5))

1988 (18 Jan)–**93.** *Canadian Mammals and Architecture. Multicoloured. Fluorescent frame* (10 *c. and* 43 *c. to* 80 *c.*).

(*a*) *Horiz designs as T* **547**. *Chalk-surfaced paper. P* 13×13½
1261 1 c. Type **547** (3.10.88) 10 10
a. Perf 13×12½ (1.92) .. .. 1·25 95
1262 2 c. Porcupine (3.10.88) 10 10
1263 3 c. Muskrat (3.10.88) 10 10
1264 5 c. Varying Hare (3.10.88) 10 10
1265 6 c. Red Fox (3.10.88) 10 10
1266 10 c. Striped Skunk (3.10.88) 10 10
a. Perf 13×12½ (2.91) .. .. 3·50 1·50
b. No fluorescent frame (25.10.91) .. 30 10
1267 25 c. American Beaver (3.10.88) 30 15
a. No fluorescent frame (22.4.92) .. 60 15

(*b*) *Horiz designs as T* **548**. *Chalk-surfaced paper* (45, 46, 57, 61, 63, 78, 80 *c.*) *or ordinary paper* (*others*). *P* 12×12½ (43, 57, 74 *c.*) *or* 14½×14 (*others*)
1268 43 c. Type **548** .. .. 1·40 30
1269 44 c. Walrus (18.1.89) 45 20
a. Perf 12½×13. Chalk-surfaced paper 1·00 55
ab. Booklet pane. No. 1269a×5 and label with margins all round .. .. 5·00
b. Chalk-surfaced paper (9.6.89) .. 2·25 1·25
c. Perf 13½×13. Chalk-surfaced paper (1989) .. .. £130 12·00
1270 45 c. Pronghorn (12.1.90) 35 20
a. Perf 12½×13 .. .. .. 1·75 30
ab. Booklet pane. No. 1270a×5 and label with margins all round .. .. 7·00
b. Perf 13 (6.90) .. .. .. 7·00 50
1270*c* 46 c. Wolverine (28.12.90) 45 30
ca. Perf 13 .. .. 2·00 2·00
cb. Perf 12½×13 .. .. .. 1·25 45
cc. Booklet pane. No. 1270cb×5 and label with margins all round .. 5·00
1271 57 c. Killer Whale .. .. .. 2·00 55
a. Ordinary paper (26.9.88) .. .. 3·25 1·75
1272 59 c. Musk Ox (18.1.89) .. .. .. 1·75 45
a. Chalk-surfaced paper (1.11.89) .. 3·75 2·25
b. Perf 13. Chalk-surfaced paper (1.11.89) .. .. 6·00 3·50
1273 61 c. Wolf (12.1.90) 60 75
a. Perf 13 (7.90) .. .. .. 27·00 1·50
1273*b* 63 c. Harbour Porpoise (28.12.90) .. 65 45
ba. Perf 13 .. .. 4·25 1·25
1274 74 c. Wapiti .. .. 1·60 50
a. Chalk-surfaced paper .. .. £100 5·00
1275 76 c. Brown Bear (18.1.89) 90 50
a. Perf 12½×13. Chalk-surfaced paper 1·75 70
ab. Booklet pane. No. 1275a×5 and label with margins all round .. .. 8·50
b. Chalk-surfaced paper (25.8.89) .. 3·25 2·25
c. Perf 13. Chalk-surfaced paper (1989) 17·00 3·75
1276 78 c. White Whale (12.1.90) 90 55
a. Perf 12½×13 .. .. .. 1·90 70
ab. Booklet pane. No. 1276a×5 and label with margins all round .. .. 9·00
b. Perf 13 (4.90) .. .. .. 18·00 2·50
1276*c* 80 c. Peary Caribou (28.12.90) 80 60
ca. Perf 13 .. .. 2·00 80
cb. Perf 12½×13 .. .. .. 1·50 60
cc. Booklet pane. No. 1276cb×5 and label with margins all round .. 8·00

(*c*) *Horiz designs as T* **548***a*. *Chalk-surfaced paper* ($5) *or ordinary paper* (*others*). *P* 13½
1277 $1 Type **548***a* (brown roof) (5.5.89) .. 1·25 30
a. Chalk-surfaced paper (28.8.92) .. 3·50 1·10
ab. Black (recess inscr) inverted .. £6000
ac. Imperf (pair) £750
ad. Black roof (1993) .. .. .. 10·00 1·25
1278 $2 McAdam Railway Station, New Brunswick (5.5.89) .. .. .. 2·00 50
a. Chalk-surfaced paper (29.7.92) .. 8·50 2·10
ab. Imperf (pair) £600
1279 $5 Bonsecours Market, Montreal (28.5.90) .. .. 4·75 5·00
1261/79 .. .. *Set of* 22 17·00 8·50

The later issues of the mammal series are slightly larger than the original three, measuring 27×21 mm.

Nos. 1269a, 1270a, 1270cb, 1275a, 1276a and 1276cb were only issued in stamp booklets.

Nos. 1277a/ac and 1278a were printed by C.B.N. There was also a printing of the $5 by C.B.N. in September 1992, but this does not differ from the B.A.B.N. version. All C.B.N. printings are on thinner paper, less crisp than the initial printings.

No. 1277ad appears to be from new plates. In addition to the differences in the roof colour it shows a less solid blue background around the building.

For further designs as Type **548***a*, but in a changed format, see Nos. 1479/81.

(Des P.-Y. Pelletier. Litho Ashton-Potter)

1988 (12 Feb). *Winter Olympic Games, Calgary* (*5th issue*). *Vert designs as T* **531**. *Multicoloured. Fluorescent frame. P* 12×12½ (37 *c.*) *or* 12½ (*others*).
1281 37 c. Slalom skiing 65 40
a. Pair. Nos. 1281/2 .. .. .. 1·25 80
1282 37 c. Curling 65 40
1283 43 c. Figure skating 75 45
1284 74 c. Luge .. .. 1·25 70
1281/4 .. .. *Set of* 4 3·00 1·75

Nos. 1281/2 were printed together, *se-tenant*, in horizontal and vertical pairs throughout the sheet.

549 Trade Goods, Blackfoot Encampment and Page from Anthony Henday's Journal

(Des F. Hagan. Litho Ashton-Potter)

1988 (17 Mar). *Exploration of Canada* (3rd *series*). *Explorers of the West. T* **549** *and similar horiz designs. Multicoloured. Fluorescent frame. P* 12½×13.

1285 37 c. Type **549** 65 50
 a. Block of 4. Nos. 1285/8 .. .. 2·40
1286 37 c. *Discovery* and map of George Vancouver's voyage 65 50
1287 37 c. Simon Fraser's expedition portaging canoes 65 50
1288 37 c. John Palliser's surveying equipment and view of prairie 65 50
1285/8 .. .. *Set of* 4 2·40 1·75

Nos. 1285/8 were printed together, *se-tenant*, in different combinations throughout the sheet, giving ten blocks of 4 and ten single stamps.

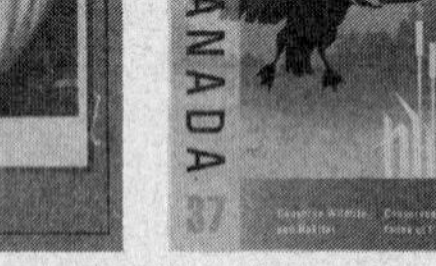

550 "The Young Reader" (Ozias Leduc)

551 Mallard landing on Marsh

(Des P.-Y. Pelletier. Eng G. Prosser. Recess and photo B.A.B.N.)

1988 (20 May). *Canadian Art* (1st *series*). *No fluorescent bands. P* 13×13½.

1289 **550** 50 c. multicoloured 70 70

No. 1289 was issued in sheets of 16 with descriptive texts on the margins.

See also Nos. 1327, 1384, 1421, 1504, 1539, 1589, 1629, 1681, 1721 and 1825.

(Des J. Gault and T. Telmet. Litho C.B.N.)

1988 (1 June). *Wildlife and Habitat Conservation. T* **551** *and similar horiz design. Multicoloured. Fluorescent frame. P* 13 × 13½.

1290 37 c. Type **551** 75 40
 a. Pair. Nos. 1290/1 .. .. .. 1·50 80
1291 37 c. Moose feeding in marsh 75 40

Nos. 1290/1 were printed together, *se-tenant*, in horizontal and vertical pairs throughout the sheet.

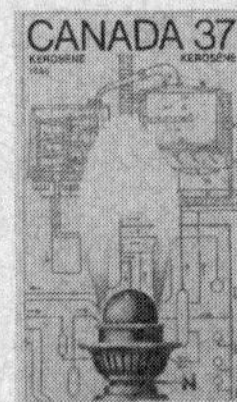

552 Kerosene Lamp and Diagram of Distillation Plant

553 *Papilio brevicauda*

(Des R. Hill. Litho Ashton-Potter)

1988 (17 June). *Canada Day. Science and Technology. Canadian Inventions* (3rd *series*). *T* **552** *and similar vert designs. Multicoloured. Fluorescent frame. P* 12½×13.

1292 37 c. Type **552** 50 60
 a. Block of 4. Nos. 1292/5 .. .. 1·75
1293 37 c. Ears of Marquis wheat 50 60
1294 37 c. Electron microscope and magnified image 50 60
1295 37 c. Patient under "Cobalt 60" cancer therapy 50 60
1292/5 .. .. *Set of* 4 1·75 2·25

Nos. 1292/5 were printed together, *se-tenant*, in blocks of 4 throughout the sheet.

(Des Heather Cooper. Litho Ashton-Potter)

1988 (4 July). *Canadian Butterflies. T* **553** *and similar vert designs. Multicoloured. Fluorescent frame. P* 12×12½.

1296 37 c. Type **553** 70 60
 a. Block of four. Nos. 1296/9 .. .. 2·50
1297 37 c. *Lycaeides idas* 70 60
1298 37 c. *Oeneis macounii* 70 60
1299 37 c. *Papilio glaucus* 70 60
1296/9 .. .. *Set of* 4 2·50 2·25

Nos. 1296/9 were printed together, *se-tenant*, in different combinations throughout the sheet, giving ten blocks of 4 and ten single stamps.

554 St. John's Harbour Entrance and Skyline

555 Club Members working on Forestry Project and Rural Scene

(Des L.-A. Rivard. Litho Ashton-Potter)

1988 (22 July). *Centenary of Incorporation of St. John's, Newfoundland. Fluorescent frame. P* 13½×13.

1300 **554** 37 c. multicoloured 35 40

(Des Debbie Adams. Litho Ashton-Potter)

1988 (5 Aug). 75*th Anniv of* 4-*H Clubs. Fluorescent frame. P* 13½×13.

1301 **555** 37 c. multicoloured 35 40

556 Saint-Maurice Ironworks

557 Tahltan Bear Dog

(Des Michèle Cayer and Hélène Racicot. Eng. Y. Baril. Recess and litho C.B.N.)

1988 (19 Aug). 250*th Anniv of Saint-Maurice Ironworks, Québec. Fluorescent frame. P* 13½.

1302 **556** 37 c. black, pale orange and cinnamon 35 40

(Des Mia Lane and D. Nethercott. Litho Ashton-Potter)

1988 (26 Aug). *Canadian Dogs. T* **557** *and similar horiz designs. Multicoloured. Fluorescent frame. P* 12½×12.

1303 37 c. Type **557** 85 50
 a. Block of 4. Nos. 1303/6 .. .. 3·00
1304 37 c. Nova Scotia Duck Tolling Retriever .. 85 50
1305 37 c. Canadian Eskimo Dog 85 50
1306 37 c. Newfoundland 85 50
1303/6 .. .. *Set of* 4 3·00 1·75

Nos. 1303/6 were printed together, *se-tenant*, in different combinations throughout the sheet, giving ten blocks of 4 and ten single stamps.

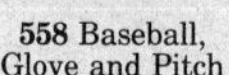

558 Baseball, Glove and Pitch

559 Virgin with Inset of Holy Child

(Des L. Holloway. Litho C.B.N.)

1988 (14 Sept). 150*th Anniv of Baseball in Canada. Fluorescent frame. P* 13½ × 13.

1307 **558** 37 c. multicoloured 35 40

(Des E. Roch and T. Yakobina. Litho Ashton-Potter)

1988 (27 Oct). *Christmas. Icons. T* **559** *and similar multicoloured designs. Fluorescent frame. P* 12½×13 (32 *c.*) *or* 13½ (*others*).

1308 32 c. Holy Family (36×21 *mm*) 35 35
 a. Booklet pane. No. 1308×10 .. .. 3·50
1309 37 c. Type **559** 35 40
1310 43 c. Virgin and Child 40 45
1311 74 c. Virgin and Child (*different*) 70 75
1308/11 .. .. *Set of* 4 1·60 1·75

On No. 1308 the left-hand third of the design area is taken up by a bar code which has fluorescent bands between the bars. This value was only available from $3.20 stamp booklets which had the sides and bottom of the pane imperforate. It was intended for use on greeting cards posted on or before 31 January 1989.

No. 1309 also commemorates the Millenium of Ukrainian Christianity.

560 Bishop Inglis and Nova Scotia Church

561 Frances Ann Hopkins and "Canoe manned by Voyageurs"

(Des S. Slipp and K. Sollows. Litho Ashton-Potter)

1988 (1 Nov). *Bicentenary of Consecration of Charles Inglis* (*first Canadian Anglican bishop*) (1987). *Fluorescent frame. P* 12½ × 12.

1312 **560** 37 c. multicoloured 35 40

(Des D. Nethercott. Litho Ashton-Potter)

1988 (18 Nov). 150*th Birth Anniv of Frances Ann Hopki*
(artist). Fluorescent frame. P 13½ × 13.

1313 **561** 37 c. multicoloured 35 4

562 Angus Walters and *Bluenose* (yacht)

563 Chipewyan Canoe

(Des R. Hill. Litho Ashton-Potter)

1988 (18 Nov). 20*th Death Anniv of Angus Walters (yach*
man). Fluorescent frame. P 13½.

1314 **562** 37 c. multicoloured 35

(Des B. Leduc and L.-A. Rivard. Litho Ashton-Potter)

1989 (1 Feb). *Small Craft of Canada* (1st *series*). *Nati*
Canoes. T **563** *and similar horiz designs. Multicoloure*
Fluorescent frame. P 13½ × 13.

1315 38 c. Type **563** 70
 a. Block of 4. Nos. 1315/18 .. .. 2·50
1316 38 c. Haida canoe 70
1317 38 c. Inuit kayak 70
1318 38 c. Micmac canoe 70
1315/18 .. .. *Set of* 4 2·50 1·

Nos. 1315/18 were printed together, *se-tenant*, throughout th
sheet, giving ten blocks of 4 and ten single stamps.

See also Nos. 1377/80 and 1428/31.

564 Matonabbee and Hearne's Expedition

565 Construction of Victoria Bridge, Montreal and William Notman

(Des F. Hagan. Litho Ashton-Potter)

1989 (22 Mar). *Exploration of Canada* (4*th series*). *Explorers*
the North. T **564** *and similar horiz designs. Multicoloure*
Fluorescent frame. P 12½×13.

1319 38 c. Type **564** 65
 a. Block of 4. Nos. 1319/22 .. .. 2·40
1320 38 c. Relics of Franklin's expedition and White Ensign 65
1321 38 c. Joseph Tyrrell's compass, hammer and fossil 65
1322 38 c. Vilhjalmur Stefansson, camera on tripod and sledge dog team 65
1319/22 .. .. *Set of* 4 2·40 2·

Nos. 1319/22 were printed together, *se-tenant*, in differe
combinations throughout the sheet, giving ten blocks of 4 a
ten single stamps.

(Des J. Morin and T. Yakobina. Litho Ashton-Potter)

1989 (23 June). *Canada Day. "150 Years of Canadi*
Photography". T **565** *and similar horiz designs, each showi*
early photograph and photographer. Multicoloure
P 12½×12.

1323 38 c. Type **565** 50
 a. Block of 4. Nos. 1323/6 .. .. 1·75
1324 38 c. Plains Indian village and W. Hanson Boorne 50
1325 38 c. Horse-drawn sleigh and Alexander Henderson 50
1326 38 c. Quebec street scene and Jules-Ernest Livernois 50
1323/6 .. .. *Set of* 4 1·75 1·

Nos. 1323/6 were printed together, *se-tenant*, in blocks of
throughout the sheet.

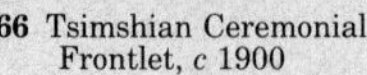

566 Tsimshian Ceremonial Frontlet, *c* 1900

567 Canadian Flag and Forest

(Des P.-Y. Pelletier. Litho and die-stamped Ashton-Potter)

1989 (29 June). *Canadian Art* (2nd *series*). *No fluoresce*
bands. P 12½×13.

1327 **566** 50 c. multicoloured 55

No. 1327 was issued in a similar sheet format to No. 1289

(Des Gottschalk & Ash International, Litho Ashton-Potter)

89 (30 June)–93. *T* **567** *and similar horiz designs. Multicoloured. Fluorescent frame. Self-adhesive. Die-cut.*
28 38 c. Type **567** .. .. 90 1·40
a. Booklet pane. No. 1328×12 .. 10·00
28*b* 39 c. Canadian flag and prairie (8.2.90) .. 1·00 1·50
ba. Booklet pane. No. 1328*b*×12 .. 11·00
28*c* 40 c. Canadian flag and sea (11.1.91) .. 1·00 1·25
ca. Booklet pane. No. 1328*c*×12 .. 11·00
28*d* 42 c. Canadian flag and mountains (28.1.92) .. .. 1·00 1·50
da. Booklet pane. No. 1328*d*×12 .. 11·00
28*e* 43 c. Canadian flag over lake (15.2.93) .. 80 1·10
ea. Booklet pane. No. 1328*e*×12 .. 9·00
28/*e* .. .. *Set of* 5 4·25 6·00

Nos. 1328, 1328*b*, 1328*c*, 1328*d* and 1328*e* were only available om self-adhesive booklets in which the backing card forms the oklet cover.

568 Archibald Lampman **569** *Clavulinopsis fusiformis*

(Des R. Milot. Litho Ashton-Potter)

989 (7 July). *Canadian Poets. T* **568** *and similar horiz design. Multicoloured. Fluorescent frame. P* 13½.
329 38 c. Type **568** 40 45
a. Pair. Nos. 1329/30 .. .. .. 80 90
330 38 c. Louis-Honoré Fréchette 40 45

Nos. 1329/30 were printed together, *se-tenant*, in horizontal nd vertical pairs throughout the sheet.

(Des E. Roch. Litho Ashton-Potter)

989 (4 Aug). *Mushrooms. T* **569** *and similar vert designs. Multicoloured. Fluorescent frame. P* 13½.
331 38 c. Type **569** 70 60
a. Block of 4. Nos. 1331/4 .. .. 2·50
332 38 c. *Boletus mirabilis* 70 60
333 38 c. *Cantharellus cinnabarinus* 70 60
334 38 c. *Morchella esculenta* 70 60
331/4 .. .. *Set of* 4 2·50 2·25

Nos. 1331/4 were printed together, *se-tenant*, in different ombinations throughout the sheet, giving ten blocks of 4 and en single stamps.

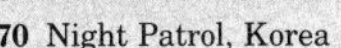

570 Night Patrol, Korea **571** Globe in Box

Des N. Fontaine, J. Gault and T. Telmet. Eng Y. Baril. Recess and litho C.B.N.)

989 (8 Sept). *75th Annivs of Canadian Regiments. T* **570** *and similar horiz design. Multicoloured. Fluorescent frame. P* 13.
335 38 c. Type **570** (Princess Patricia's Canadian Light Infantry) 70 70
a. Vert pair. Nos. 1335/6 .. .. 1·40 1·40
336 38 c. Trench raid, France, 1914-18 (Royal 22e Régiment) 70 70

Nos. 1335/6 were printed together, *se-tenant*, in vertical pairs hroughout the sheet.

(Des L. Holloway and Nita Wallace. Litho Ashton-Potter)

989 (2 Oct). *Canada Export Trade Month. Fluorescent frame. P* 13½×13.
337 **571** 38 c. multicoloured 40 45

572 Film Director **573** "Snow II" (Lawren S. Harris)

Des W. Tibbles from paper sculptures by J. Milne. Litho Ashton-Potter)

989 (4 Oct). *Arts and Entertainment. T* **572** *and similar vert designs. Fluorescent frame. P* 13×13½.
338 38 c. grey-brown, blackish brown and bright reddish violet 40 45
a. Block of 4. Nos. 1338/41 .. .. 1·50
339 38 c. grey-brown, blackish brown & brt grn 40 45
340 38 c. grey-brn, blackish brn & brt magenta 40 45
341 38 c. grey-brown, blackish brown & new bl 40 45
338/41 .. .. *Set of* 4 1·50 1·60

Designs:—No. 1339, Actors; No. 1340, Dancers; No. 1341, Musicians.

Nos. 1338/41 were printed together, *se-tenant*, in different ombinations throughout the sheet, giving ten blocks of 4 and en single stamps.

(Des D. Nethercott and Viviane Warburton. Litho Ashton-Potter)

1989 (26 Oct). *Christmas. Paintings of Winter Landscapes. T* **573** *and similar multicoloured designs. Fluorescent frame. P* 12½×13 (33 *c.*), 13×13½ (38 *c.*) *or* 13½ (*others*).
1342 33 c. "Champ-de-Mars, Winter" (William Brymner) (35×21 *mm*) 80 55
a. Booklet pane. No. 1342×10 .. 8·00
b. Imperf between (horiz pair) (from booklet) .. ..
1343 38 c. "Bend in the Gosselin River" (Marc-Aurèle Suzor-Coté) (21×35 *mm*) .. 40 35
a. Perf 13×12½ .. .. .. 3·00 3·25
ab. Booklet pane. No. 1343a×10 .. 28·00
1344 44 c. Type **573** 45 50
a. Booklet pane. No. 1344×5 plus one printed label .. .. 11·00
1345 76 c. "Ste. Agnès" (A. H. Robinson) .. 80 85
a. Booklet pane. No. 1345×5 plus one printed label .. .. 19·00
1342/5 .. .. *Set of* 4 2·25 2·00

On No. 1342 the left-hand third of the design area is taken up by a bar code which has fluorescent bands between the bars. This value was only available from $3.30 stamp booklets which had the sides and bottom of the pane imperforate. It was intended for use on greeting cards posted on or before 31 January 1990.

No. 1343a was only issued in $3.80 stamp booklets.

Booklet pane No. 1343ab has the outer edges of the pane imperforate while Nos. 1344a and 1345a have the vertical edges imperforate.

574 Canadians listening to Declaration of War, 1939

(Des J.-P. Armanville and P.-Y. Pelletier. Litho C.B.N.)

1989 (10 Nov). *50th Anniv of Second World War (1st issue). T* **574** *and similar horiz designs. Fluorescent frame. P* 13½.
1346 38 c. black, silver and slate-purple .. 55 55
a. Block of 4. Nos. 1346/9 .. .. 2·00
1347 38 c. black, silver and olive-grey 55 55
1348 38 c. black, silver and grey-green .. 55 55
1349 38 c. black, silver and azure 55 55
1346/9 .. .. *Set of* 4 2·00 2·00

Designs:—No. 1347, Army mobilization; No. 1348, British Commonwealth air crew training; No. 1349, North Atlantic convoy.

Nos. 1346/9 were printed together, *se-tenant*, in different combinations throughout the sheet, giving four blocks of 4.

See also Nos. 1409/12, 1456/9, 1521/4, 1576/9, 1621/4 and 1625/8.

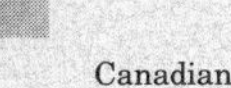

575 Canadian Flag **576**

1989 (28 Dec)–**98**. *No fluorescent bands* (1, 5 *c.*) *or fluorescent frame* (39, 40, 42, 43, 45 *c.*).

(*a*) *Booklet stamps. T* **575** *and similar horiz designs, each showing Canadian flag. Litho Ashton-Potter. Chalk-surfaced paper. P* 13½×14.
1350 **575** 1 c. multicoloured (12.1.90) 20 85
a. Booklet pane. Nos. 1350, 1351×2 and 1352 .. .. 1·40
b. Perf 12½×13 .. .. .. 13·00 15·00
ba. Booklet pane. Nos. 1350b, 1351a×2 and 1352a .. .. 35·00
c. Booklet pane. Nos. 1350×2, 1351 and 1353 (28.12.90) .. .. 2·00
1351 – 5 c. multicoloured (12.1.90) 20 30
a. Perf 12½×13 .. .. .. 6·00 7·00
1352 – 39 c. multicoloured (12.1.90) .. .. 1·50 1·75
a. Perf 12½×13 .. .. .. 13·00 15·00
1353 – 40 c. multicoloured (28.12.90) .. .. 1·75 2·00

(*b*) *Litho (for printers see below). Chalk-surfaced paper. P* 14½ (45 *c.*) *or* 13½×13 (*others*)
1354 **576** 39 c. multicoloured 50 10
a. Booklet pane. No. 1354×10 and two labels .. .. .. 7·00
b. Booklet pane. No. 1354×25 and two labels .. .. .. 17·00
c. Perf 12½×13 (2.90) .. .. 4·00 3·25
1355 – 40 c. multicoloured (28.12.90) 60 10
a. Booklet pane. No. 1355×10 and two labels .. .. .. 8·00
b. Booklet pane. No. 1355×25 and two labels .. .. .. 18·00
1356 – 42 c. multicoloured (27.12.91) 60 15
a. Booklet pane. No. 1356×10 .. 8·00
b. Booklet pane. No. 1356×25 and two labels .. .. .. 16·00
c. Booklet pane. No. 1356×50 and two labels .. .. .. 48·00
1357 – 43 c. multicoloured (30.12.92) 60 60
a. Booklet pane. No. 1357×10 .. 7·50
b. Booklet pane. No. 1357×25 and two labels .. .. .. 17·00
c. Perf 14½ (18.1.94) .. .. 1·25 90
ca. Booklet pane. No. 1357c×10 .. 11·00
cb. Booklet pane. No. 1357c×25 and two labels .. .. .. 26·00
cc. Imperf between (vert pair) .. £500
1358 – 45 c. mult (21×25 *mm*) (31.7.95) .. 60 75
a. Booklet pane. No. 1358×10 .. 6·00
b. Booklet pane. No. 1358×25 and two labels .. .. .. 14·00
c. Perf 13½×13 (6.10.95) 35 40
ca. Booklet pane. No. 1358c×10 .. 3·50
cb. Booklet pane. No. 1358c×25 and two labels .. .. .. 14·00
d. Perf 13×13½ (19×23 *mm*) (2.2.98) 35 40
da. Booklet pane. No. 1358d×10 .. 3·50
db. Booklet pane. No. 1358d×30 (two blocks of 15 (5×3) separated by vertical gutter) .. .. .. 10·50

(*c*) *Coil stamps. Designs as T* **575**, *but different folds in flag. Recess C.B.N. P* 10×*imperf.*
1360 – 39 c. deep purple (8.2.90) 60 75
a. Imperf (pair) .. .. .. 55·00
1361 – 40 c. indigo (28.12.90) 40 45
a. Imperf (pair) £100
1362 – 42 c. scarlet-vermilion (27.12.91) .. 40 45
a. Imperf (pair) .. .. .. 55·00
1363 – 43 c. deep olive (30.12.92) 55 80
a. Imperf (pair) .. .. .. 55·00
1364 – 45 c. bluish green (31.7.95) 35 40
a. Imperf (pair) .. .. .. 55·00

Designs:—40 c. (No. 1355) Canadian flag over forest; 42 c. (No. 1356) Flag over mountains; 43 c. (No. 1357) Flag over prairie; 45 c. (No. 1358) Flag and skyscraper.

Booklet panes Nos. 1350a/b, 1356a/c, 1357ca/cb, 1358a/b, 1358ca/cb and 1358da/db have the vertical edges of the panes imperforate and each shows a margin at foot. Booklet panes Nos. 1354a/b, 1355a/b and 1357a/b are imperforate at top and bottom.

Due to changes in the Canada Post contracts the printing history of Nos. 1354/8 is very complex. Details are provided below with Ashton-Potter Ltd. printings shown as AP, Canadian Bank Note Co as CBN, Leigh-Mardon Ltd as LM and Ashton-Potter Canada Ltd. as APC.

39 c. (No. 1354) CBN (28.12.89), AP (14.2.90)
(No. 1354a/b) AP (28.12.89)
(No. 1354c) AP (2.90)
40 c. (No. 1355) CBN (28.12.90)
(Nos. 1355a/b) AP (28.12.90)
42 c. (Nos. 1356/c) AP (27.12.91)
43 c. (Nos. 1357/b) AP (30.12.92), CBN (14.11.94)
(Nos. 1357c/cb) LM (18.1.94)
45 c. (Nos. 1358/b) LM (31.7.95)
(Nos. 1358c/cb) CBN (6.10.95)
(No. 1358d) CBN (2.2.98), APC (2.2.98)
(No. 1358da) CBN (2.2.98)
(No. 1358db) APC (2.2.98)

The C.B.N. printings of the 45 c. (No. 1358c) show the copyright date on flag changed from "1990" to 1995".

Postal forgeries of Nos. 1359 and 1362 exist showing heavier printing across the foot of the design.

577 Norman Bethune in 1937, and performing Operation, Montreal **578** Maple Leaf Mosaic

(Des Wanda Lewicka, J. Morin and Liu Xiang Ping. Eng Hu Zhenyuan and Yan Bingwu. Recess and litho C.B.N.)

1990 (2 Mar). *Birth Centenary of Dr. Norman Bethune (surgeon). T* **577** *and similar horiz design. Multicoloured. Fluorescent frame. P* 13×13½.
1375 39 c. Type **577** 45 65
a. Pair. Nos. 1375/6 .. .. .. 90 1·25
1376 39 c. Bethune in 1939, and treating wounded Chinese soldiers 45 65

Nos. 1375/6 were printed together, *se-tenant*, in horizontal and vertical pairs throughout the sheet.

(Des B. Leduc and L.-A. Rivard. Litho Ashton-Potter)

1990 (15 Mar). *Small Craft of Canada (2nd series). Early Work Boats. Horiz designs as T* **563**. *Multicoloured. Fluorescent frame. P* 13½×13.
1377 39 c. Fishing dory 50 55
a. Block of 4. Nos. 1377/80 .. .. 1·75
1378 39 c. Logging pointer 50 55
1379 39 c. York boat 50 55
1380 39 c. North canoe 50 55
1377/80 .. .. *Set of* 4 1·75 2·00

Nos. 1377/80 were printed together, *se-tenant*, throughout the sheet, giving ten blocks of 4 and ten single stamps.

(Des F. Peter. Recess and litho C.B.N.)

1990 (5 Apr). *Multiculturalism. P* 13.
1381 **578** 39 c. multicoloured 35 40

579 Mail Van (facing left) **580** Amerindian and Inuit Dolls

(Des J. Morin and A. Rochon. Litho Ashton-Potter)

1990 (3 May). *"Moving the Mail". T* **579** *and similar horiz design. Multicoloured. Fluorescent frame. P* 13½.
1382 39 c. Type **579** 45 55
a. Booklet pane. Nos. 1382/3, each × 4 4·50
b. Booklet pane. Nos. 1382×5, 1383×4 and 3 labels .. .. 9·00
1383 39 c. Mail van (facing right) 45 55

Nos. 1382/3 were only issued in $9.75 stamp booklets.

(Des P.-Y. Pelletier. Litho and die-stamped Ashton-Potter)

1990 (3 May). *Canadian Art* (*3rd series*). *Vert design as T* **550**. *Multicoloured. No fluorescent bands. P* 12½×13.
1384 50 c. "The West Wind" (Tom Thomson) .. 55 65
No. 1384 was issued in a similar sheet format to No. 1289.

(Des Nita Wallace. Litho Ashton-Potter)

1990 (8 June). *Dolls. T* **580** *and similar horiz designs. Multicoloured. Fluorescent frame. P* 12½×12.
1385 39 c. Type **580** 65 60
a. Block of 4. Nos. 1385/8 .. .. 2·40
1386 39 c. 19th-century settlers' dolls 65 60
1387 39 c. Commercial dolls, 1917–36 .. .. 65 60
1388 39 c. Commercial dolls, 1940–60 .. .. 65 60
1385/8 .. .. *Set of* 4 2·40 2·10
Nos. 1385/8 were printed together, *se-tenant*, in different combinations throughout the sheet, giving ten blocks of 4 and ten single stamps.

581 Canadian Flag and Fireworks

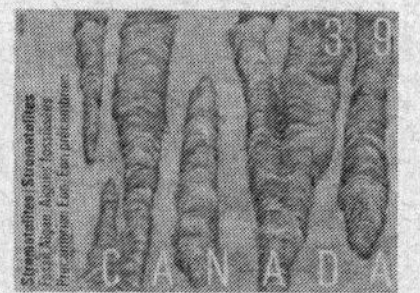

582 *Stromatolites* (fossil algae)

(Des C. Malenfont. Litho Ashton-Potter)

1990 (1 July*). *Canada Day. Fluorescent frame. P* 13×12½
1389 **581** 39 c. multicoloured 45 50
No. 1389 was issued in sheets of 16 with descriptive texts on the coloured margins.
*First day covers of No. 1389 are postmarked 29 June 1990. The stamp was available from two temporary post offices in Ottawa on Sunday 1 July, but was not sold throughout Canada until 3 July.

(Des R. Harder. Eng Y. Baril. Recess and litho C.B.N.)

1990 (12 July). *Prehistoric Canada* (*1st series*). *Primitive Life. T* **582** *and similar horiz designs. Multicoloured. Fluorescent frame. P* 13×13½.
1390 39 c. Type **582** 60 70
a. Block of 4. Nos. 1390/3 .. .. 2·25
1391 39 c. *Opabinia regalis* (soft invertebrate) 60 70
1392 39 c. *Paradoxides davidis* (trilobite) .. 60 70
1393 39 c. *Eurypterus remipes* (sea scorpion) .. 60 70
1390/3 .. .. *Set of* 4 2·25 2·50
Nos. 1390/3 were printed together, *se-tenant*, in different combinations throughout the sheet, giving four blocks of 4 and four single stamps.
See also Nos. 1417/20, 1568/71 and 1613/16.

583 Acadian Forest

584 Clouds and Rainbow

(Des M. and Jan Waddell. Litho Ashton-Potter)

1990 (7 Aug). *Canadian Forests. T* **583** *and similar horiz designs. Multicoloured. Fluorescent frame. P* 12½×13.
1394 39 c. Type **583** 60 70
a. Block of 4. Nos. 1394/7 .. .. 2·25
1395 39 c. Great Lakes–St. Lawrence forest .. 60 70
1396 39 c. Pacific Coast forest 60 70
1397 39 c. Boreal forest 60 70
1394/7 .. .. *Set of* 4 2·25 2·50
Nos. 1394/7 were printed together, *se-tenant*, in different combinations throughout the sheet, giving four blocks of 4 and four single stamps.
Nos. 1394/7 also exist as blocks of four of the same design surrounded by margins. Such blocks were not available from post offices, but could be obtained for $1 each at Petro-Canada filling stations by using a previously-distributed voucher in conjunction with the purchase of 25 litres of petrol. They could also be obtained, at face value, from the Canadian Philatelic Service by post.

(Des D. L'Allier and Dominique Trudeau. Litho Ashton-Potter)

1990 (5 Sept). *150th Anniv of Weather Observing in Canada. Fluorescent frame. P* 12½×13½.
1398 **584** 39 c. multicoloured 40 50
No. 1398 has a break in the lower vertical sides of the fluorescent frame to allow the clouds to run on to the margins.

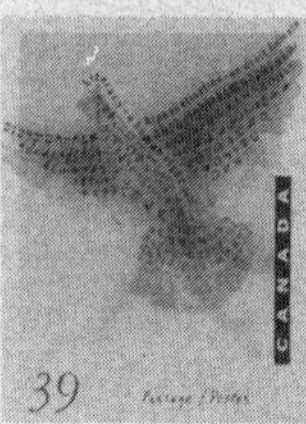

585 "Alphabet" Bird

586 Sasquatch

(Des Debbie Adams. Recess and litho C.B.N.)

1990 (7 Sept). *International Literacy Year. Fluorescent frame. P* 13½×13.
1399 **585** 39 c. multicoloured 40 50

(Des A. Cormack, Deborah Drew-Brook and R. Tibbles. Litho Ashton-Potter)

1990 (1 Oct). *Legendary Creatures. T* **586** *and similar horiz designs. Multicoloured. Fluorescent frame. P* 12½×13½.
1400 39 c. Type **586** 70 70
a. Block of 4. Nos. 1400/3 .. .. 2·50
b. Perf 12½×12 .. .. .. 5·50 5·00
ba. Block of 4. Nos. 1400b/3b .. .. 20·00
1401 39 c. Kraken 70 70
b. Perf 12½×12 .. .. .. 5·50 5·00
1402 39 c. Werewolf 70 70
b. Perf 12½×12 .. .. .. 5·50 5·00
1403 39 c. Ogopogo 70 70
b. Perf 12½×12 .. .. .. 5·50 5·00
1400/3 .. .. *Set of* 4 2·50 2·50
Nos. 1400/3 were printed together, *se-tenant*, in different combinations throughout the sheet, giving ten blocks of four and ten single stamps.
Stamps perforated 12½×12 come from a small percentage of the "non-philatelic" stock without imprints. Examples have also been found on official First Day Covers included in Presentation Packs.

587 Agnes Macphail

588 "Virgin Mary with Christ Child and St. John the Baptist" (Norval Morrisseau)

(Des M. and Jan Waddell. Litho Ashton-Potter)

1990 (9 Oct). *Birth Centenary of Agnes Macphail* (*first woman elected to Parliament*). *Fluorescent frame. P* 13×13½.
1404 **587** 39 c. multicoloured 40 50

(Des C. Malenfant. Litho Ashton-Potter)

1990 (25 Oct). *Christmas. Native Art. T* **588** *and similar designs. Fluorescent frame. P* 12½×13 (34 c.) *or* 13½ (*others*).
1405 34 c. multicoloured (35×21 *mm*) 40 35
a. Booklet pane. No. 1405×10 .. .. 4·00
1406 39 c. multicoloured 40 40
a. Booklet pane. No. 1406×10 .. .. 7·00
1407 45 c. multicoloured 40 45
a. Booklet pane. No. 1407×5 plus one printed label .. .. .. 4·00
1408 78 c. black, bright scarlet and violet-grey 70 75
a. Booklet pane. No. 1408×5 plus one printed label .. .. .. 7·00
1405/8 .. .. *Set of* 4 1·75 1·75
Designs:—34 c. "Rebirth" (Jackson Beardy); 45 c. "Mother and Child" (Inuit sculpture, Cape Dorset); 78 c. "Children of the Raven" (Bill Reid).
On No. 1405 the left-hand third of the design area is taken up by a bar code which has fluorescent bands between the bars. This value was only available from $3.40 stamp booklets which had the sides and bottom of the pane imperforate. It was intended for use on greeting cards posted on or before 31 January 1991.
Booklet panes Nos. 1406a, 1407a and 1408a also have the side and bottom edges imperforate.

(Des J.-P. Armanville and P.-Y. Pelletier. Litho Ashton-Potter)

1990 (9 Nov). *50th Anniv of Second World War* (*2nd issue*). *Horiz designs as T* **574**. *Fluorescent frame. P* 12½×12.
1409 39 c. black, silver and grey-olive 90 90
a. Block of 4. Nos. 1409/12 .. .. 3·25
1410 39 c. black, silver and red-brown 90 90
1411 39 c. black, silver and bistre-brown .. 90 90
1412 39 c. black, silver and dull mauve .. 90 90
1409/12 .. .. *Set of* 4 3·25 3·25
Designs:—No. 1409, Canadian family at home, 1940; No. 1410, Packing parcels for the troops; No. 1411, Harvesting; No. 1412, Testing anti-gravity flying suit.
Nos. 1409/12 were printed together, *se-tenant*, in different combinations throughout the sheet, giving four blocks of 4.

589 Jennie Trout (first woman physician) and Women's Medical College, Kingston

590 Blue Poppies and Butchart Gardens, Victoria

(Des R. Milot. Litho Ashton-Potter)

1991 (15 Mar). *Medical Pioneers. T* **589** *and similar vert designs. Multicoloured. Fluorescent frame. P* 13½.
1413 40 c. Type **589** 90 90
a. Block of 4. Nos. 1413/16 .. .. 3·25
1414 40 c. Wilder Penfield (neurosurgeon) and Montreal Neurological Institute .. 90 90
1415 40 c. Frederick Banting (discoverer of insulin) and University of Toronto medical faculty .. .. .. 90 9(
1416 40 c. Harold Griffith (anesthesiologist) and Queen Elizabeth Hospital, Montreal 90 9(
1413/16 .. .. *Set of* 4 3·25 3·2
Nos. 1413/16 were printed together, *se-tenant*, in differen combinations throughout the sheet, giving ten blocks of 4 an ten single stamps.

(Des R. Harder. Eng L. Bloss. Recess and litho Ashton-Potter)

1991 (5 Apr). *Prehistoric Canada* (*2nd series*). *Primitiv Vertebrates. Horiz designs as T* **582**. *Multicoloured Fluorescent frame. P* 12½×13½.
1417 40 c. Foord's Crossopt (*Eusthenopteron foordi*) (fish fossil) .. .. .. 1·25 1·4
a. Block of 4. Nos. 1417/20 .. .. 4·50
1418 40 c. *Hylonomus lyelli* (land reptile) .. 1·25 1·4
1419 40 c. Fossil Conodonts (fossil teeth) .. 1·25 1·4
1420 40 c. *Archaeopteris halliana* (early tree) .. 1·25 1·4
1417/20 .. .. *Set of* 4 4·50 5·0
Nos. 1417/20 were printed together, *se-tenant*, in differen combinations throughout the sheet, giving four blocks of 4 an four single stamps.

(Des P.-Y. Pelletier. Litho and die-stamped Ashton-Potter)

1991 (7 May). *Canadian Art* (*4th series*). *Vert design as T* **550** *Multicoloured. No fluorescent bands. P* 12½×13.
1421 50 c. "Forest, British Columbia" (Emily Carr) .. .. 90 1·0
No. 1421 was issued in a similar sheet format to No. 1289.

(Des G. Gauci and D. Wyman. Litho Ashton-Potter)

1991 (22 May). *Public Gardens. T* **590** *and similar ver designs. Multicoloured. Fluorescent frame. P* 13×12½.
1422 40 c. Type **590** 55 5
a. Booklet pane. Nos. 1422/6, each × 2 5·50
1423 40 c. Marigolds and International Peace Garden, Boissevain 55 5
1424 40 c. Lilac and Royal Botanical Gardens, Hamilton 55 5
1425 40 c. Roses and Montreal Botanical Gardens 55 5
1426 40 c. Rhododendrons and Halifax Public Gardens 55 5
1422/6 .. .. *Set of* 5 2·50 2·5
Nos. 1422/6 were only available from $4 stamp booklet containing No. 1422a, which is imperforate at top and bottom.

591 Maple Leaf

592 South Nahanni River

(Des Lisa Miller, R. Séguin and J.-P. Veilleux. Litho C.B.N.)

1991 (28 June). *Canada Day. Fluorescent frame. P* 13½×13.
1427 **591** 40 c. multicoloured 50 6
No. 1427 was issued in sheets of 20 with inscribed an decorated margins.

(Des B. Leduc and L.-A. Rivard. Litho Ashton-Potter)

1991 (18 July). *Small Craft of Canada* (*3rd series*). *Hor designs as T* **563**. *Multicoloured. Fluorescent fram P* 13½×13.
1428 40 c. Verchère rowboat 85 9
a. Block of 4. Nos. 1428/31 .. .. 3·00
1429 40 c. Touring kayak 85 9
1430 40 c. Sailing dinghy 85 9
1431 40 c. Cedar strip canoe 85 9
1428/31 .. .. *Set of* 4 3·00 3·2
Nos. 1428/31 were printed together, *se-tenant*, throughout th sheet, giving ten blocks of 4 and ten single stamps.

(Des M. and Jan Waddell. Litho Ashton-Potter)

1991 (20 Aug). *Canadian Rivers* (*1st series*). *T* **592** *and simil vert designs. Multicoloured. Fluorescent frame. P* 13×12½.
1432 40 c. Type **592** 80
a. Booklet pane. Nos. 1432/6, each × 2 with margins all round .. .. 7·50
1433 40 c. Athabasca River 80
1434 40 c. Boundary Waters, Voyageur Waterway 80
1435 40 c. Jacques-Cartier River 80
1436 40 c. Main River 80
1432/6 .. .. *Set of* 5 3·50 4·
Nos. 1432/6 were only issued in $4 stamp booklets.
See also Nos. 1492/6, 1558/62 and 1584/8.

593 "Leaving Europe"

594 Ski Patrol rescuing Climber

(Des J. Gault and T. Telmet. Litho C.B.N.)

91 (29 Aug). *Centenary of Ukrainian Immigration. Panels rom "The Ukrainian Pioneer" by William Kurelek. T* **593** *and similar vert designs. Multicoloured. Fluorescent frame.* P 13½×13.

37 40 c. Type **593** 80 85
a. Block of 4. Nos. 1437/40 .. .. 2·75
38 40 c. "Canadian Winter" 80 85
39 40 c. "Clearing the Land" 80 85
40 40 c. "Harvest" 80 85
37/40 .. .. *Set of* 4 2·75 3·00

Nos. 1437/40 were printed together, *se-tenant*, in different nbinations throughout the sheet, giving four blocks of 4 and r single stamps.

(Des Suzanne Duranceau. Litho C.B.N.)

91 (23 Sept). *Emergency Services. T* **594** *and similar vert designs. Multicoloured. Fluorescent frame. P* 13½.

41 40 c. Type **594** .. .. 1·10 1·10
a. Block of 4. Nos 1441/4 .. .. 4·00
42 40 c. Police at road traffic accident .. 1·10 1·10
43 40 c. Firemen on extending ladder .. 1·10 1·10
44 40 c. Boeing-Vertol CH-147 Chinook rescue helicopter and lifeboat .. .. 1·10 1·10
41/4 .. .. *Set of* 4 4·00 4·00

Nos. 1441/4 were printed together, *se-tenant*, in different mbinations throughout the sheet, giving ten blocks of 4 and n single stamps.

595 "The Witched Canoe"

596 Grant Hall Tower

Des A. Cormack, Deborah Drew-Brook and R. Tibbles. Litho Ashton-Potter)

91 (1 Oct). *Canadian Folktales. T* **595** *and similar vert designs. Multicoloured. Fluorescent frame. P* 13½×12½.

45 40 c. Type **595** 95 95
a. Block of 4. Nos. 1445/8 .. .. 3·50
46 40 c. "The Orphan Boy" 95 95
47 40 c. "Chinook" 95 95
48 40 c. "Buried Treasure" 95 95
45/8 .. .. *Set of* 4 3·50 3·50

Nos. 1445/8 were printed together, *se-tenant*, in different mbinations throughout the sheet, giving ten blocks of 4 and n single stamps.

(Des L. Holloway and R. Kerr. Litho Ashton-Potter)

991 (16 Oct). *150th Anniv of Queen's University, Kingston. Fluorescent frame. P* 13×12½.

49 **596** 40 c. multicoloured .. .. .. 75 1·00
a. Booklet pane. No. 1449×10 plus two printed labels with margins all round .. .. .. 7·50

No. 1449 was only issued in $4 stamp booklets.

597 North American Santa Claus

598 Players jumping for Ball

(Des S. Slipp. Litho Ashton-Potter)

991 (23 Oct). *Christmas. T* **597** *and similar multicoloured designs. Fluorescent frame. P* 12½×13 (35 c.) *or* 13½ (*others*).

450 35 c. British Father Christmas (35×21 *mm*) 70 40
a. Booklet pane. No. 1450×10 .. .. 7·00
451 40 c. Type **597** 70 20
a. Booklet pane. No. 1451×10 .. .. 8·00
452 46 c. French Bonhomme Noel 75 90
a. Booklet pane. No. 1452×5 plus one printed label .. .. 4·00
453 80 c. Dutch Sinterklaas .. .. .. 1·40 2·00
a. Booklet pane. No. 1453×5 plus one printed label .. .. 4·00
450/3 .. .. *Set of* 4 3·25 3·25

On No. 1450 the left-hand third of the design area is taken up y a bar code which has fluorescent bands between the bars. 'his value was only available from $3.50 stamp booklets which ad the edges of the pane imperforate. It was intended for use on reeting cards posted on or before 31 January 1992.

Nos. 1451a, 1452a and 1453a also have the vertical edges of he panes imperforate.

(Des J. Gault, C. Reynolds and T. Telmet. Litho Ashton-Potter)

991 (25 Oct). *Basketball Centenary. T* **598** *and similar vert designs. Multicoloured. Fluorescent frame. P* 13×13½.

454 40 c. Type **598** 90 75
MS1455 155×90 mm. 40 c. Type **598**, but with shorter inscr below face value; 46 c. Player taking shot; 80 c. Player challenging opponent 5·00 5·00

(Des J.-P. Armanville and P.-Y. Pelletier. Litho C.B.N)

1991 (8 Nov). *50th Anniv of Second World War (3rd issue). Horiz designs as T* **574**. *Fluorescent frame. P* 13½.

1456 40 c. black, silver and greenish blue .. 1·10 1·10
a. Block of 4. Nos. 1456/9 .. .. 4·00
1457 40 c. black, silver and brown .. .. 1·10 1·10
1458 40 c. black, silver and lilac .. .. 1·10 1·10
1459 40 c. black, silver and ochre .. .. 1·10 1·10
1456/9 .. .. *Set of* 4 4·00 4·00

Designs:—No. 1456, Women's services, 1941; No. 1457, Armament factory; No. 1458, Cadets and veterans; No. 1459, Defence of Hong Kong.

Nos. 1456/9 were printed together, *se-tenant*, in different combinations throughout the sheet, giving four blocks of 4.

599 Blueberry

600 McIntosh Apple

600a Court House, Yorkton

(Des Tania Craan and D. Noble (1 c. to 25 c.), C. Malenfant (48 c. to 90 c.), R. Bellemare ($1, $2, $5))

1991 (27 Dec)–**96**. *Multicoloured. Chalk-surfaced paper.*

(*a*) *Edible Berries. Litho (for printers see below). T* **599** *and similar horiz designs. No fluorescent frame. P* 13×13½ (5.8.92).

1460 1 c. Type **599** 10 10
1461 2 c. Wild Strawberry 10 10
1462 3 c. Black Crowberry 10 10
1463 5 c. Rose Hip 10 10
1464 6 c. Black Raspberry 10 10
1465 10 c. Kinnikinnick 10 10
a. Imperf (horiz pair) .. .. ..
1466 25 c. Saskatoon Berry 20 25

(*b*) *Fruit and Nut Trees. Litho (for printers see below). T* **600** *and similar horiz designs. Three fluorescent bands* (90 c.) *or fluorescent frame (others). P* 13.

1467 48 c. Type **600** 50 35
a. Perf 14½×14 .. .. .. 1·00 80
ab. Booklet pane. No. 1467a×5 and label 5·00
1468 49 c. Delicious Apple (30.12.92) .. .. 1·00 1·00
a. Booklet pane. No. 1468×5 and label (7.1.94) .. .. 5·50
b. Perf 14½×14 .. .. .. 90 1·25
ba. Booklet pane. No. 1468b×5 and label 4·50
1469 50 c. Snow Apple (25.2.94) .. .. 1·00 1·00
a. Booklet pane. No. 1469×5 and label 5·00
b. Perf 14½×14 (27.3.95) .. .. 1·00 1·50
ba. Booklet pane. No. 1469b×5 and label 5·00
1470 52 c. Gravenstein Apple (31.7.95) .. 50 50
a. Booklet pane. No. 1470×5 and label 2·00
b. Perf 14½×14 (6.10.95) 40 45
ba. Booklet pane. No. 1470b×5 and label 4·00
1471 65 c. Black Walnut 70 50
1472 67 c. Beaked Hazelnut (30.12.92) .. 1·00 1·25
1473 69 c. Shagbark Hickory (25.2.94) .. 1·25 1·25
1474 71 c. American Chestnut (31.7.95) .. 80 1·00
a. Perf 14½×14 (6.10.95) .. .. 2·50 70
1475 84 c. Stanley Plum 90 75
a. Perf 14½×14 .. .. .. 1·40 1·50
ab. Booklet pane. No. 1475a×5 and label 8·00
1476 86 c. Bartlett Pear (30.12.92) .. .. 85 1·00
a. Booklet pane. No. 1476×5 and label (7.1.94) .. .. 7·50
b. Perf 14½×14 .. .. .. 2·50 2·75
ba. Booklet pane. No. 1476b×5 and label 12·00
1477 88 c. Westcot Apricot (25.2.94) .. .. 1·60 1·60
a. Booklet pane. No. 1477×5 and label 8·00
b. Three fluorescent bands (14.11.94) .. 1·60 2·00
ba. Booklet pane. No. 1477b×5 and label 8·00
c. Perf 14½×14. Three fluorescent bands (27.3.95) .. .. .. 1·60 2·00
ca. Booklet pane. No. 1477c×5 and label 8·00
1478 90 c. Elberta Peach (31.7.95) .. .. 80 1·00
a. Booklet pane. No. 1478×5 and label 3·75
b. Perf 14½×14 (6.10.95) 70 75
ba. Booklet pane. No. 1478b×5 and label 3·50

(*c*) *Architecture. Recess and litho Leigh-Mardon Ltd, Melbourne (Nos. 1479/80) or C.B.N. (Nos. 1479a, 1480a, 1481). T* **600a** *and similar horiz designs. P* 14½×14 ($1, $2) *or* 13½×13 ($5)

1479 $1 Type **600a** (21.2.94) 90 95
a. Perf 13½×13 (20.2.95) .. .. 1·50 80
1480 $2 Provincial Normal School, Truro (21.2.94) .. .. 1·90 2·00
a. Perf 13½×13 (20.2.95) .. .. 2·25 1·60
ab. Deep turquoise-blue (recess inscr) omitted £650
ac. Deep turquoise-blue (recess inscr) inverted .. ..
1481 $5 Public Library, Victoria (29.2.96) .. 4·00 4·25
1460/81 .. .. *Set of* 22 16·00 16·00

Nos. 1460/6 were so printed that each horizontal row formed a composite design.

Nos. 1467a, 1468b, 1469b, 1475a, 1476b and 1477c were only issued in stamp booklets.

Booklet panes Nos. 1467ab, 1468a, 1468ba, 1475ab, 1476a, 1476ab, 1477a and 1477ba each have the vertical edges of the pane imperforate and margins at top and bottom.

Due to changes in the Canada Post contracts the printing history of Nos. 1460/80 is very complex. Details are provided below with Ashton-Potter Ltd printings shown as AP, Canadian Bank Note Co as CBN, Leigh-Mardon Ltd as LM and Ashton-Potter Canada Ltd as APC.

1 c. No. 1460 AP (5.8.92), CBN (19.8.94), APC (3.4.95)
2 c. No. 1461 AP (5.8.92), CBN (22.4.94), APC (1.8.95)
3 c. No. 1462 AP (5.8.92), CBN (22.4.94), APC (2.5.97)
5 c. No. 1463 AP (5.8.92), CBN (11.3.94), APC (20.9.95)
6 c. No. 1464 AP (5.8.92), CBN (11.3.94)
10 c. No. 1465 AP (5.8.92), CBN (11.3.94), APC (1.9.95)
25 c. No. 1466 AP (5.8.92), CBN (22.4.94), APC (1.5.96)
48 c. Nos. 1467/ab AP (27.12.91)
49 c. No. 1468 AP (30.12.92), CBN (7.1.94)
No. 1468a CBN (7.1.94)
Nos. 1468b/ba AP (30.12.92)
50 c. No. 1469 CBN (25.2.94), APC (10.4.95)
No. 1469a CBN (25.2.94)
Nos. 1469b/ba APC (27.3.95)
52 c. No. 1470 CBN (31.7.95), APC (6.10.95)
No. 1470a CBN (31.7.95), APC (1997)
Nos. 1470b/ba APC (6.10.95)
65 c. No. 1471 AP (27.12.91)
67 c. No. 1472 AP (30.12.92)
69 c. No. 1473 CBN (25.2.94), APC (10.4.95)
71 c. No. 1474 CBN (31.7.95), APC (6.10.95)
No. 1474a APC (6.10.95)
84 c. Nos. 1475/ab AP (27.12.91)
86 c. No. 1476 AP (30.12.92), CBN (7.1.94)
No. 1476a CBN (7.1.94)
Nos. 1476b/ba AP (30.12.92)
88 c. Nos. 1477/a CBN (25.2.94)
No. 1477b CBN (14.11.94), APC (10.4.95)
No. 1477ba CBN (14.11.94)
Nos. 1477c/ca APC (27.3.95)
90 c. No. 1478 CBN (31.7.95), APC (6.10.95)
No. 1478a CBN (31.7.95), APC (1997)
Nos. 1478b/ba APC (6.10.95)
$1 No. 1479 LM (21.2.94)
No. 1479a CBN (20.2.95)
$2 No. 1480 LM (21.2.294)
No. 1480a CBN (20.2.95)
$5 No. 1481 CBN (29.2.96)

601 Ski Jumping

(Des Gottschalk & Ash International. Litho Ashton-Potter)

1992 (7 Feb). *Winter Olympic Games, Albertville. T* **601** *and similar horiz designs. Multicoloured. Fluorescent frame. P* 12½×13.

1482 42 c. Type **601** 70 70
a. Booklet pane. Nos. 1482/6, each × 2 with margins all round .. .. 6·50
1483 42 c. Figure skating 70 70
1484 42 c. Ice hockey 70 70
1485 42 c. Bobsleighing 70 70
1486 42 c. Alpine skiing 70 70
1482/6 .. .. *Set of* 5 3·25 3·25

Nos. 1482/6 were only available from $4.20 stamp booklets.

602 Ville-Marie in 17th Century

603 Road Bed Construction and Route Map

(Des Suzanne Duranceau and P.-Y. Pelletier. Litho C.B.N.)

1992 (25 Mar). *"CANADA 92" International Youth Stamp Exhibition, Montreal. T* **602** *and similar horiz designs. Multicoloured. Fluorescent frame. P* 13½.

1487 42 c. Type **602** 80 80
a. Pair. Nos. 1487/8 .. .. .. 1·60 1·60
1488 42 c. Modern Montreal 80 80
1489 48 c. Compass rose, snow shoe and crow's nest of Cartier's ship *Grande Hermine* 90 90
1490 84 c. Atlantic map, Aztec "calendar stone" and navigational instrument .. .. 1·75 2·00
1487/90 .. .. *Set of* 4 3·75 4·00
MS1491 181×120 mm. Nos. 1487/90 .. .. 4·25 5·00

Nos. 1487/8 were printed together, *se-tenant*, in horizontal and vertical pairs throughout the sheet.

Nos. MS1491 also exists showing the facsimile signature of Paul Chomedy de Maisonneuve printed at bottom right. These miniature sheets were prepared in connection with "CANADA '92", but were not sold by the Canadian Post Office.

(Des M. and Jan Waddell. Litho Ashton-Potter)

1992 (22 Apr). *Canadian Rivers (2nd series). Multicoloured designs as T* **592**, *but horiz. Fluorescent frame. P* 12½×13.

1492 42 c. Margaree River .. .. .. 80 1·00
a. Booklet pane. Nos. 1492/6, each × 2 7·50
1493 42 c. West (Eliot) River .. .. .. 80 1·00
1494 42 c. Ottawa River .. .. 80 1·00
1495 42 c. Niagara River .. .. 80 1·00
1496 42 c. South Saskatchewan River .. .. 80 1·00
1492/6 .. .. *Set of* 5 3·50 4·50

Nos. 1492/6 were only issued in $4.20 stamp booklets.

Booklet pane No. 1492a has the horizontal edges of the pane imperforate.

(Des J. Charette and Vivian Laliberté. Litho C.B.N.)

1992 (15 May). *50th Anniv of Alaska Highway. Fluorescent frame. P* 13½.
1497 **603** 42 c. multicoloured 70 70

(Des Gottschalk & Ash International. Litho Ashton-Potter)

1992 (15 June). *Olympic Games, Barcelona. Horiz designs as T* **601.** *Multicoloured. Fluorescent frame. P* 12½×13.
1498 42 c. Gymnastics .. .. 90 1·10
a. Booklet pane. Nos. 1498/1502 each × 2 with margins all round .. 8·00
1499 42 c. Athletics .. .. 90 1·10
1500 42 c. Diving .. .. 90 1·10
1501 42 c. Cycling .. .. 90 1·10
1502 42 c. Swimming .. .. 90 1·10
1498/1502 .. .. *Set of* 5 4·00 5·00
Nos. 1482/1502 were only available from $4.20 stamp booklets.

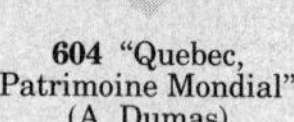

604 "Quebec, Patrimoine Mondial" (A. Dumas) **605** Jerry Potts (scout)

(Des P.-Y. Pelletier. Litho Ashton-Potter)

1992 (29 June). *Canada Day. Paintings. Sheet,* 190 × 256 *mm, containing T* **604** *and similar diamond-shaped designs. Multicoloured. Fluorescent frame. P* 12½.
MS1503 42 c. Type **604**; 42 c. "Christie Passage, Hurst Island, British Columbia" (E. J. Hughes); 42 c. "Toronto, Landmarks of Time" (Ontario) (V. McIndoe); 42 c. "Near the Forks" (Manitoba) (S. Gouthro); 42 c. "Off Cape St. Francis" (Newfoundland) (R. Shepherd); 42 c. "Crowd at City Hall" (New Brunswick) (Molly Bobak); 42 c. "Across the Tracks to Shop" (Alberta) (Janet Mitchell); 42 c. "Cove Scene" (Nova Scotia) (J. Norris); 42 c. "Untitled" (Saskatchewan) (D. Thauberger); 42 c. "Town Life" (Yukon) (T. Harrison); 42 c. "Country Scene" (Prince Edward Island) (Erica Rutherford); 42 c. "Playing on an Igloo" (Northwest Territories) (Agnes Nanogak) .. .. 12·00 12·00

(Des P.-Y. Pelletier. Litho and die-stamped Ashton-Potter)

1992 (29 June). *Canadian Art (5th series). Vert design as T* **550.** *Multicoloured. No fluorescent bands. P* 12½×13.
1504 50 c. "Red Nasturtiums" (David Milne) .. 90 90
No. 1504 was issued in a similar sheet format to No. 1289

(Des A. Cormack, Deborah Cormack and R. Tibbles. Litho Ashton-Potter)

1992 (8 Sept). *Folk Heroes. T* **605** *and similar vert designs. Multicoloured. Fluorescent frame. P* 12½.
1505 42 c. Type **605** .. .. 90 1·00
a. Block of 4. Nos. 1505/8 .. .. 3·25
1506 42 c. Capt. William Jackman and wreck of *Sea Clipper*, 1867 .. .. .. 90 1·00
1507 42 c. Laura Secord (messenger) .. .. 90 1·00
1508 42 c. Jos Montferrand (lumberjack) .. 90 1·00
1505/8 .. .. *Set of* 4 3·25 3·50
Nos. 1505/8 were printed together, *se-tenant*, in different combinations throughout the sheet, giving ten blocks of 4 and ten single stamps.

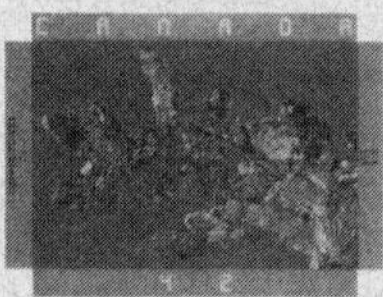

606 Copper **607** Satellite and Photographs from Space

(Des R. Bellamare. Litho Ashton-Potter)

1992 (21 Sept). *150th Anniv of Geological Survey of Canada. Minerals. T* **606** *and similar horiz designs. Multicoloured. Fluorescent frame. P* 12½.
1509 42 c. Type **606** .. .. 1·00 1·10
a. Booklet pane. Nos. 1509/13, each × 2 with margins all round .. .. 9·00
1510 42 c. Sodalite .. .. 1·00 1·10
1511 42 c. Gold .. .. 1·00 1·10
1512 42 c. Galena .. .. 1·00 1·10
1513 42 c. Grossular .. .. 1·00 1·10
1509/13 .. .. *Set of* 5 4·50 5·00
Nos. 1509/13 were only issued in $4.20 stamp booklets.

(Des Debbie Adams. Litho C.B.N.)

1992 (1 Oct). *Canadian Space Programme. T* **607** *and similar horiz design. Multicoloured. Fluorescent frame. P* 13.
1514 42 c. Type **607** .. .. 90 1·00
a. Horiz pair. Nos. 1514/15 .. .. 1·75 2·00
1515 42 c. Space Shuttle over Canada (hologram) (32×26 *mm*) .. .. 90 1·00
a. Hologram omitted £750
Nos. 1514/15 were printed together, *se-tenant*, in horizontal pairs throughout the sheet of 20 with No. 1514 occurring on the first and fourth vertical rows and No. 1515 on the second and third.

608 Babe Siebert, Skates and Stick **609** Companion of the Order of Canada Insignia

(Des L. Holloway and R. Kerr. Litho Ashton-Potter)

1992 (9 Oct). *75th Anniv of National Ice Hockey League. T* **608** *and similar horiz designs. Multicoloured. Fluorescent frame. P* 13×12½.
1516 42 c. Type **608** .. .. 95 1·10
a. Booklet pane. No. 1516×8 plus one printed label with margins all round 6·50
1517 42 c. Claude Provost, Terry Sawchuck and team badges .. .. 95 1·10
a. Booklet pane. No. 1517×8 plus one printed label with margins all round 6·50
1518 42 c. Hockey mask, gloves and modern player .. .. 95 1·10
a. Booklet pane. No. 1518×9 with margins all round .. .. 6·50
1516/18 .. .. *Set of* 3 2·50 3·00
Nos. 1516/18 were only issued in $10.50 stamp booklets.
Booklet pane Nos. 1516a/18a only exist folded between the first and second vertical rows.

(Des Tania Craan. Litho Ashton-Potter)

1992 (21 Oct). *25th Anniv of the Order of Canada and Daniel Roland Michener (former Governor-General) Commemoration. T* **609** *and similar vert design. Multicoloured. Fluorescent frame. P* 12½.
1519 42 c. Type **609** .. .. 90 1·00
a. Pair. Nos. 1519/20 .. .. 1·75 2·00
1520 42 c. Daniel Roland Michener .. .. 90 1·00
Nos. 1519/20 were printed together, *se-tenant*, within the sheet of 25 (5×5) with sixteen examples of No. 1519 (R. 1/1-5, 2/1, 2/5, 3/1, 3/5, 4/1, 4/5, 5/1-5) and nine of No. 1520 (R. 2/2-4, 3/2-4, 4/2-4).

(Des J.-P. Armanville and P.-Y. Pelletier. Litho C.B.N)

1992 (10 Nov). *50th Anniv of Second World War (4th issue). Horiz designs as T* **574.** *Fluorescent frame. P* 13½.
1521 42 c. black, silver and sepia .. .. 90 1·00
a. Block of 4. Nos. 1521/4 .. .. 3·25
1522 42 c. black, silver and dull blue-green .. 90 1·00
1523 42 c. black, silver and brown .. .. 90 1·00
1524 42 c. black, silver and light blue .. .. 90 1·00
1521/4 .. .. *Set of* 4 3·25 3·50
Designs:—No. 1521, Reporters and soldiers, 1942; No. 1522, Consolidated Liberator bombers over Newfoundland; No. 1523, Dieppe raid; No. 1524, U-boat sinking merchant ship.
Nos. 1521/4 were printed together, *se-tenant*, in different combinations throughout the sheet, giving four blocks of 4.

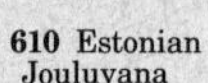

610 Estonian Jouluvana **611** Adelaide Hoodless (women's movement pioneer)

(Des R. MacDonald (37 c.), Anita Kunz (42 c.), J. Bennett (48 c.), S. Ng (84 c.), adapted L. Fishauf and Stephanie Power. Litho Ashton-Potter)

1992 (13 Nov). *Christmas. T* **610** *and similar multicoloured designs. Fluorescent frame. P* 12½×*imperf* (37 c.), 12½ (42 c.) *or* 13½ (*others*).
1525 37 c. North American Santa Claus (35×21 *mm*) 70 70
a. Booklet pane. No. 1525×10 .. 7·00
1526 42 c. Type **610** 40 20
a. Perf 13½ 70 75
ab. Booklet pane. No. 1526a×10 .. 7·00
1527 48 c. Italian La Befana 70 80
a. Booklet pane. No. 1527×5 plus one printed label .. .. .. 4·50
1528 84 c. German Weihnachtsmann .. .. 1·25 1·50
a. Booklet pane. No. 1528×5 plus one printed label .. .. .. 7·00
1525/8 .. .. *Set of* 4 2·75 2·75
On No. 1525 the left-hand third of the design area is taken up by a bar code which has fluorescent bands between the bars.

This value was only available from $3.70 stamp booklets whi[ch] had the vertical edges of the pane imperforate. It was intend[ed] for use on greeting cards posted on or before 31 January 199[3].
No. 1526a was only issued in $4.20 stamp booklets. No[s.] 1526ab, 1527a and 1528a have the vertical edges of the pan[e] imperforate.

(Des Heather Cooper. Litho Ashton-Potter)

1993 (8 Mar). *Prominent Canadian Women. T* **611** *and simil[ar] vert designs. Multicoloured. Fluorescent frame. P* 12½.
1529 43 c. Type **611** 85
a. Block of 4. Nos. 1529/32 .. .. 3·00
1530 43 c. Marie-Josephine Gérin-Lajoie (social reformer) 85
1531 43 c. Pitseolak Ashoona (Inuit artist) .. 85
1532 43 c. Helen Kinnear (lawyer) 85
1529/32 .. .. *Set of* 4 3·00 3·
Nos. 1529/32 were printed together, *se-tenant*, in differe[nt] combinations throughout the sheet, giving ten blocks of 4 a[nd] ten single stamps.

612 Ice Hockey Players with Cup **613** Coverlet, New Brunswick

(Des F. Dallaire and Lise Giguère. Litho C.B.N.)

1993 (16 Apr). *Centenary of Stanley Cup. Fluorescent fram[e]. P* 13½.
1533 **612** 43 c. multicoloured 75

(Des P. Adam. Litho Ashton-Potter)

1993 (30 Apr). *Hand-crafted Textiles. T* **613** *and simila[r] square designs. Multicoloured. Fluorescent frame. P* 13×12½.
1534 43 c. Type **613** 75
a. Booklet pane. Nos. 1534/8, each × 2 7·00
1535 43 c. Pieced quilt, Ontario 75
1536 43 c. Doukhobor bedcover, Saskatchewan 75
1537 43 c. Ceremonial robe, Kwakwaka'wakw 75
1538 43 c. Boutonné coverlet, Quebec 75
1534/8 .. .. *Set of* 5 3·25 4·
Nos. 1534/8 were only available from $4.30 stamp booklets.
Booklet pane No. 1534a has the horizontal edges of the pa[ne] imperforate and margins at both left and right.

(Des P.-Y. Pelletier. Litho and die-stamped Ashton-Potter)

1993 (17 May). *Canadian Art (6th series). Vert design as T* **55**[0]. *Multicoloured. Fluorescent frame. P* 12½×13.
1539 86 c. "The Owl" (Kenojuak Ashevak) .. 1·75 2·
No. 1539 was issued in a similar sheet format to No. 1289.

614 Empress Hotel, Victoria **615** Algonquin Park, Ontario

(Des G. Tsetsekas. Litho Ashton-Potter)

1993 (14 June). *Historic Hotels. T* **614** *and similar hor[iz] designs. Multicoloured. Fluorescent frame. P* 13½.
1540 43 c. Type **614** 60
a. Booklet pane. Nos. 1540/4, each × 2 6·00
1541 43 c. Banff Springs Hotel 60
1542 43 c. Royal York Hotel, Toronto 60
1543 43 c. Le Chateau Frontenac, Quebec .. 60
1544 43 c. Algonquin Hotel, St. Andrews .. 60
1540/4 .. .. *Set of* 5 2·75 3·
Nos. 1540/4 were only issued in $4.30 stamp booklets.
Booklet pane No. 1540a has the horizontal edges of the pa[ne] imperforate and margins at both left and right.

(Des M. and Jan Waddell. Litho C.B.N.)

1993 (30 June). *Canada Day. Provincial and Territorial Par[ks]. T* **615** *and similar horiz designs. Multicoloured. Fluoresce[nt] frame. P* 13.
1545 43 c. Type **615** 70
a. Sheetlet. Nos. 1545/56 .. .. 7·50
1546 43 c. De La Gaspésie Park, Québec .. 70
1547 43 c. Cedar Dunes Park, Prince Edward Island 70
1548 43 c. Cape St. Mary's Seabird Reserve, Newfoundland 70
1549 43 c. Mount Robson Park, British Columbia 70
1550 43 c. Writing-on-Stone Park, Alberta .. 70
1551 43 c. Spruce Woods Park, Manitoba .. 70
1552 43 c. Herschel Island Park, Yukon .. 70
1553 43 c. Cypress Hills Park, Saskatchewan .. 70
1554 43 c. The Rocks Park, New Brunswick .. 70
1555 43 c. Blomidon Park, Nova Scotia .. 70
1556 43 c. Katannilik Park, Northwest Territories 70
1545/56 .. .. *Set of* 12 7·50 8·
Nos. 1545/56 were printed together, *se-tenant*, in sheetlets [of] 12, which come with or without a large illustrated and inscrib[ed] margin at top.

616 Toronto Skyscrapers

617 Taylor's Steam Buggy, 1867

(Des R. Heeney and V. McIndoe. Litho C.B.N.)

993 (6 Aug). *Bicentenary of Toronto. Fluorescent frame. P 13½×13.*

557 **616**	43 c. multicoloured	70	50

(Des M. and Jan Waddell. Litho Ashton-Potter)

993 (10 Aug). *Canadian Rivers (3rd series). Vert designs as T* **592**. *Multicoloured. Fluorescent frame. P 13×12½.*

558	43 c. Fraser River	60	80
	a. Booklet pane. Nos. 1558/62, each × 2	6·00	
559	43 c. Yukon River	60	80
560	43 c. Red River	60	80
561	43 c. St. Lawrence River	60	80
562	43 c. St. John River	60	80
558/62	.. .. *Set of* 5	2·75	3·50

Nos. 1558/62 were only issued in $4.30 stamp booklets.

(Des J. Gault, T. Telmet and C. Wykes. Litho C.B.N.)

993 (23 Aug). *Historic Automobiles (1st series). Sheet, 177×125 mm, containing T* **617** *and similar horiz designs. Multicoloured. Fluorescent frame. P 12½×13.*

IS1563 43 c. Type **617**; 43 c. Russel "Model L" touring car, 1908; 49 c. Ford "Model T" touring car, 1914 (43×22 *mm*); 49 c. Studebaker "Champion Deluxe Starlight" coupe, 1950 (43×22 *mm*); 86 c. McLaughlin-Buick "28-496 special", 1928 (43×22 *mm*); 86 c. Gray-Dort "25 SM" luxury sedan, 1923 (43×22 *mm*) .. .. 6·50 7·00

See also Nos. **MS**1611, **MS**1636 and **MS**1683/4.

618 "The Alberta Homesteader"

619 Polish Swiety Mikolaj

Des Deborah Cormack, A. Cormack and R. Tibbles. Litho Ashton-Potter)

993 (7 Sept). *Folk Songs. T* **618** *and similar horiz designs. Multicoloured. Fluorescent frame. P 12½.*

564	43 c. Type **618**	70	85
	a. Block of 4. Nos. 1564/7	2·50	
565	43 c. "Les Raftmans" (Quebec)	70	85
566	43 c. "I'se the B'y that Builds the Boat" (Newfoundland)	70	85
567	43 c. "Onkwá:ri Tenhanónniahkwe" (Mohawk Indian)	70	85
564/7	.. .. *Set of* 4	2·50	3·00

Nos. 1564/7 were printed together, *se-tenant*, in different combinations throughout the sheet, giving ten blocks of 4 and ten single stamps.

(Des R. Harder. Litho Ashton-Potter)

993 (1 Oct). *Prehistoric Canada (3rd series). Dinosaurs. Horiz designs as T* **582**, *but 40×28 mm. Multicoloured. Fluorescent frame. P 13½.*

568	43 c. Massospondylus	60	60
	a. Block of 4. Nos. 1568/71	2·25	
569	43 c. Stryacosaurus	60	60
570	43 c. Albertosaurus	60	60
571	43 c. Platecarpus	60	60
568/71	.. .. *Set of* 4	2·25	2·25

Nos. 1568/71 were printed together, *se-tenant*, in different combinations throughout the sheet, giving four blocks of 4 and four single stamps.

Des J. Bennett (38 c.), J. Jackson (43 c.), B. Dawson (49 c.), B. Blitt (86 c.), adapted L. Fishauf and Stephanie Power. Litho C.B.N.)

993 (4 Nov). *Christmas. T* **619** *and similar multicoloured designs. Fluorescent frame. P 13×imperf (38 c.) or 13½ (others).*

572	38 c. North American Santa Claus (35×22 *mm*)	70	70
	a. Booklet pane. No. 1572×10 ..	7·00	
573	43 c. Type **619**	50	20
	a. Booklet pane. No. 1573×10 ..	8·00	
	b. Imperf between (horiz pair) ..	£750	
574	49 c. Russian Ded Moroz	70	70
	a. Booklet pane. No. 1574×5 plus one printed label	4·50	
575	86 c. Australian Father Christmas ..	1·10	1·75
	a. Booklet pane. No. 1575×5 plus one printed label	8·00	
572/5	.. .. *Set of* 4	2·75	3·00

On No. 1572 the left-hand third of the design area is taken up by a barcode which has fluorescent bands between the bars. This value was only available from $3.80, stamp booklets which had the vertical edges of the pane imperforate. It was intended for use on greeting cards posted before 31 January 1994.

Nos. 1573a/5a have the vertical edges of the panes imperforate.

No. 1573b appears to originate from the incorrect use of the booklet pane perforation on ordinary sheet stock.

(Des J.-P. Armanville and P.-Y. Pelletier. Litho C.B.N.)

1993 (8 Nov). *50th Anniv of Second World War (5th issue). Horiz designs as T* **574**. *Fluorescent frame. P 13½.*

1576	43 c. black, silver and brown-olive ..	90	90
	a. Block of 4. Nos. 1576/9	3·25	
1577	43 c. black, silver and slate-blue	90	90
1578	43 c. black, silver and dull-violet blue ..	90	90
1579	43 c. black, silver and chestnut	90	90
1576/9	.. .. *Set of* 4	3·25	3·25

Designs:—No. 1576, Loading munitions for Russia, 1943; No. 1577, Loading bombs on Avro Type 683 Lancaster; No. 1578, Escorts attacking U-boat; No. 1579, Infantry advancing, Italy.

Nos. 1576/9 were printed together, *se-tenant*, in different combinations throughout the sheet, giving four blocks of 4.

620 (face value at right)

(Des Tarzan Communication Graphique. Litho Leigh-Mardon Ltd, Melbourne)

1994 (28 Jan). *Greetings stamps. T* **620** *and similar horiz design. Multicoloured. Inscriptions behind face value and "CANADA" show names of family events. Fluorescent outline. Self-adhesive. Die-cut.*

1580	43 c. Type **620**	60	70
	a. Booklet pane. Nos. 1580/1, each × 5, and 35 circular greetings labels ..	5·50	
1581	43 c. As Type **620**, but face value at left ..	60	70

Nos. 1580/1 were only available from $4.50 self-adhesive booklets in which the backing card formed the cover. It was intended that the sender should insert the appropriate greetings label into the circular space on each stamp before use.

For 45 c. values in this design see Nos. 1654/5.

621 Jeanne Sauvé

622 Timothy Eaton, Toronto Store of 1869 and Merchandise

(Des J. Morin and T. Yakobina. Litho C.B.N.)

1994 (8 Mar). *Jeanne Sauvé (former Governor-General) Commemoration. Fluorescent frame. P 12½×13.*

1582 **621**	43 c. multicoloured	60	60

No. 1582 was printed in sheets of 20 (4×5), the horizontal rows containing four stamps, each with a differently-inscribed 6×22½ mm *se-tenant* label. These are at the right of the stamps on rows 1, 3 and 5 and at left on rows 2 and 4.

(Des L. Fishauf. Litho C.B.N.)

1994 (17 Mar). *125th Anniv of T. Eaton Company Ltd (department store group). Fluorescent frame. P 13½×13.*

1583 **622**	43 c. multicoloured	55	75
	a. Booklet pane. No. 1583×10 and 2 labels with margins all round ..	5·50	

No. 1583 was only available from $4.30 stamp booklets.

(Des M. and Jan Waddell. Litho C.B.N.)

1994 (22 Apr). *Canadian Rivers (4th series). Horiz designs as T* **592**. *Multicoloured. Fluorescent frame. P 13½×13.*

1584	43 c. Saguenay River	60	75
	a. Booklet pane. Nos. 1584/8 each × 2	5·50	
1585	43 c. French River	60	75
1586	43 c. Mackenzie River	60	75
1587	43 c. Churchill River	60	75
1588	43 c. Columbia River	60	75
1584/8	.. .. *Set of* 5	2·75	3·25

Nos. 1584/8 were only issued in $4.30 stamp booklets.

Booklet pane No. 1584a has the vertical edges of the pane imperforate.

(Des P.-Y. Pelletier. Litho and die-stamped Leigh-Mardon Ltd, Melbourne)

1994 (6 May). *Canadian Art (7th series). Vert design as T* **550**. *Multicoloured. Fluorescent frame. P 14×14½.*

1589	88 c. "Vera" (detail) (Frederick Varley) ..	1·25	1·60

No. 1589 was issued in a similar sheet format to No. 1289.

623 Lawn Bowls

624 Mother and Baby

(Des D. Coates and R. Roodenburg. Litho and die-stamped Leigh-Mardon Ltd, Melbourne)

1994 (20 May–5 Aug). *15th Commonwealth Games, Victoria. T* **623** *and similar horiz designs. Multicoloured. Fluorescent frame. P 14.*

1590	43 c. Type **623**	40	50
	a. Pair. Nos. 1590/1	80	1·00
1591	43 c. Lacrosse	40	50
1592	43 c. Wheelchair race (5 Aug)	40	50
	a. Pair. Nos. 1592/3	80	1·00
1593	43 c. High jumping (5 Aug)	40	50
1594	50 c. Diving (5 Aug)	45	60
1595	88 c. Cycling (5 Aug)	80	95
1590/5	.. .. *Set of* 6	2·75	3·25

Nos. 1590/1 and 1592/3 were printed together, *se-tenant*, in horizontal and vertical pairs throughout the sheets.

(Des Suzanne Duranceau. Litho Leigh-Mardon Ltd, Melbourne)

1994 (2 June). *International Year of the Family. Sheet 178×134 mm, containing T* **624** *and similar vert designs. Multicoloured. Fluorescent paper. P 14×14½.*

MS1596 43 c. Type **624**; 43 c. Family outing; 43 c. Grandmother and granddaughter; 43 c. Computer class; 43 c. Play group, nurse with patient and female lawyer .. .. .. 3·00 3·50

625 Big Leaf Maple Tree

626 Billy Bishop (fighter ace) and Nieuport 17

(Des D. Noble. Litho C.B.N.)

1994 (30 June). *Canada Day. Maple Trees. T* **625** *and similar horiz designs. Multicoloured. Fluorescent frame. P 13×13½.*

1597	43 c. Type **625**	60	65
	a. Sheetlet. Nos. 1597/1608	6·50	
1598	43 c. Sugar Maple	60	65
1599	43 c. Silver Maple	60	65
1600	43 c. Striped Maple	60	65
1601	43 c. Norway Maple	60	65
1602	43 c. Manitoba Maple	60	65
1603	43 c. Black Maple	60	65
1604	43 c. Douglas Maple	60	65
1605	43 c. Mountain Maple	60	65
1606	43 c. Vine Maple	60	65
1607	43 c. Hedge Maple	60	65
1608	43 c. Red Maple	60	65
1597/1608	.. .. *Set of* 12	6·50	7·00

Nos. 1597/1608 were printed together, *se-tenant*, in sheetlets of 12, which come with or without a large illustrated and inscribed margin at top.

(Des P. Fontaine and B. Leduc. Litho C.B.N.)

1994 (12 Aug). *Birth Centenaries. T* **626** *and similar horiz design. Multicoloured. Fluorescent frame. P 13½.*

1609	43 c. Type **626**	75	80
	a. Pair. Nos. 1609/10	1·50	1·60
1610	43 c. Mary Travers ("La Bolduc") (singer) and musicians	75	80

Nos. 1609/10 were printed together, *se-tenant*, in horizontal and vertical pairs throughout the sheet.

(Des J. Gault, T. Telmet, and C. Wickes. Litho C.B.N.)

1994 (19 Aug). *Historic Automobiles (2nd issue). Sheet 177×125 mm, containing horiz designs as T* **617**. *Multicoloured. Fluorescent frame. P 12½×13.*

MS1611 43 c. Ford "Model F60L-AMB" military ambulance, 1942–43; 43 c. Winnipeg police wagon, 1925; 50 c. Sicard snowblower, 1927 (43×22 *mm*); 50 c. Bickle "Chieftain" fire engine, 1936 (43×22 *mm*); 88 c. St. John Railway Company tramcar No. 40, 1894 (51×22 *mm*); 88 c. Motor Coach Industries "Courier 50 Skyview" coach, 1950 (51×22 *mm*) .. .. 6·00 6·50

No. **MS**1611 was sold in a protective pack.

627 Symbolic Aircraft, Radar Screen and Clouds

628 Carol Singing around Christmas Tree

(Des Gottschalk & Ash International, Katalin Kovats and S. Napoleone. Litho C.B.N.)

1994 (16 Sept). *50th Anniv of International Civil Aviation Organization. Fluorescent frame. P 13.*

1612 **627**	43 c. multicoloured	60	60

(Des R. Harder. Litho C.B.N.)

1994 (26 Sept). *Prehistoric Canada (4th series). Mammals. Multicoloured designs as T* **582**, *but* 40×28 *mm. Fluorescent frame. P* 13½.

1613 43 c. Coryphodon .. .. 90 1·00
a. Block of 4. Nos. 1613/16 .. .. 3·25
1614 43 c. Megacerops .. .. 90 1·00
1615 43 c. Arctodus simus (bear) .. .. 90 1·00
1616 43 c. Mammuthus primigenius (mammoth) 90 1·00
1613/16 .. .. *Set of* 4 3·25 3·50

Nos. 1613/16 were printed together, *se-tenant*, in different combinations throughout the sheet, giving four blocks of 4 and four single stamps.

(Des Nina Berkson, Diti Katona and J. Pylypczak. Litho C.B.N.)

1994 (3 Nov). *Christmas. T* **628** *and similar multicoloured designs. Fluorescent frame. P* 13×*imperf* (*No.* 1617) *or* 13½ (*others*).

1617 (–) c. Carol singer (35×21 *mm*) 70 70
a. Booklet pane. No. 1617×10 .. 7·00
1618 43 c. Type **628** 45 20
a. Booklet pane. No. 1618×10 .. 8·00
1619 50 c. Choir (*vert*) 65 80
a. Booklet pane. No. 1619×5 plus one printed label .. .. .. 4·25
1620 88 c. Couple carol singing in snow (*vert*) .. 1·60 2·00
a. Booklet pane. No. 1620×5 plus one printed label .. .. .. 8·00
1617/20 .. .. *Set of* 4 3·00 3·25

No. 1617 was only available from $3.80 stamp booklets with the vertical edges of the pane imperforate. The stamp is without face value, but was intended for use as a 38 c. on internal greetings cards posted before 31 January 1995. The design shows a barcode at left with fluorescent bands between the bars.

Nos. 1617a/20a have the vertical edges of the panes imperforate.

(Des J.-P. Armanville and P.-Y. Pelletier. Litho C.B.N.)

1994 (7 Nov). *50th Anniv of Second World War* (*6th issue*). *Horiz designs as T* **574**. *Fluorescent frame. P* 13½.

1621 43 c. black, silver and dull green .. 85 85
a. Block of 4. Nos. 1621/4 .. .. 3·00
1622 43 c. black, silver and Venetian red .. 85 85
1623 43 c. black, silver and light blue 85 85
1624 43 c. black, silver and violet-grey .. 85 85
1621/4 .. .. *Set of* 4 3·00 3·00

Designs:—No. 1621, D-Day landings, Normandy; No. 1622, Canadian artillery, Normandy; No. 1623, Hawker Typhoons on patrol; No. 1624, Canadian infantry and disabled German self-propelled gun, Walcheren.

Nos. 1621/4 were printed together, *se-tenant*, in different combinations throughout the sheet, giving four blocks of 4.

(Des J.-P. Armanville and P.-Y. Pelletier. Litho C.B.N.)

1995 (20 Mar). *50th Anniv of Second World War* (*7th issue*). *Horiz designs as T* **574**. *Fluorescent frame. P* 13½.

1625 43 c. black, silver and reddish purple .. 90 90
a. Block of 4. Nos. 1625/8 .. .. 3·25
1626 43 c. black, silver and yellow-brown .. 90 90
1627 43 c. black, silver and dull yellowish green 90 90
1628 43 c. black, silver and light greenish blue 90 90
1625/8 .. .. *Set of* 4 3·25 3·25

Designs:—No. 1625, Returning troopship; No. 1626, Canadian P.O.W's celebrating freedom; No. 1627, Canadian tank liberating Dutch town; No. 1628, Parachute drop in support of Rhine Crossing.

Nos. 1625/8 were printed together, *se-tenant*, in different combinations throughout the sheet, giving four blocks of 4.

(Des P.-Y. Pelletier. Litho and die-stamped C.B.N.)

1995 (21 Apr). *Canadian Art* (*8th series*). *Vert design as T* **550**. *Multicoloured. Fluorescent frame. P* 13×13½.

1629 88 c. "Floraison" (Alfred Pellan) .. .. 1·25 1·60

No. 1629 was issued in a similar sheet format to No. 1289.

629 Flag and Lake

(Des Gottschalk & Ash International. Litho C.B.N.)

1995 (1 May). *30th Anniv of National Flag. Fluorescent frame. P* 13½×13.

1630 **629** (43 c.) multicoloured 50 50

No. 1630 is without any indication of face value, but was sold for 43 c.

PRINTER. Following a change in ownership, and the awarding of a further Canada Post contract, the previous Ashton Potter Ltd was known as Ashton Potter Canada Ltd from 1995.

630 Louisbourg Harbour

(Des R. Harder. Litho Ashton-Potter Canada)

1995 (5 May). *275th Anniv of Fortress of Louisbourg. T* **630** *and similar horiz designs. Multicoloured. "All-over" fluorescent. P* 12½×13.

1631 (43 c.) Type **630** 40 55
a. Booklet pane. Nos. 1631/5 each × 2 with margins all round .. .. 4·00
1632 (43 c.) Barracks (32×29 *mm*) 40 55
1633 (43 c.) King's Bastion (40×29 *mm*) .. 40 55
1634 (43 c.) Site of King's Garden, convent and hospital (56×29 *mm*) 40 55
1635 (43 c.) Site of coastal fortifications .. 40 55
1631/5 .. .. *Set of* 5 2·00 2·50

Nos. 1631/5 are without any indication of face value, but were sold in booklets of 10 for $4.30.

(Des J. Gault, T. Telmet and C. Wykes. Litho C.B.N.)

1995 (26 May). *Historic Automobiles* (*3rd issue*). *Sheet* 177×25 *mm, containing horiz designs as T* **617**. *Multicoloured. Fluorescent frame. P* 12½×13.

MS1636 43 c. Cockshutt "30" farm tractor, 1950; 43 c. Bombardier "Ski-Doo Olympique 335" snowmobile, 1970; 50 c. Bombardier "B-12 CS" multi-passenger snowmobile, 1948 (43×22 *mm*); 50 c. Gotfredson "Model 20" farm truck, 1924 (43×22 *mm*); 88 c. Robin-Nodwell "RN 110" tracked carrier, 1962 (43×22 *mm*); 88 c. Massey-Harris "No. 21" self-propelled combine-harvester, 1942 (43×22 *mm*) .. .. .. 5·00 5·50

No. **MS**1636 was sold in a protective pack.

631 Banff Springs Golf Club, Alberta

(Des P. Adam. Litho Ashton-Potter Canada)

1995 (6 June). *Centenaries of Canadian Amateur Golf Championship and of the Royal Canadian Golf Association. T* **631** *and similar horiz designs. Fluorescent frame. P* 13½×13.

1637 43 c. Type **631** 50 60
a. Booklet pane. Nos. 1637/41 each × 2 4·50
1638 43 c. Riverside Country Club, New Brunswick 50 60
1639 43 c. Glen Abbey Golf Club, Ontario .. 50 60
1640 43 c. Victoria Golf Club, British Columbia 50 60
1641 43 c. Royal Montreal Golf Club, Quebec .. 50 60
1637/41 .. .. *Set of* 5 2·25 2·75

Nos. 1637/41 were only issued in $4.30 stamp booklets.

Booklet pane No. 1637a has the vertical edges of the pane imperforate.

632 "October Gold" (Franklin Carmichael)

633 Academy Building and Ship Plan

(Des A. Leduc. Litho C.B.N.)

1995 (29 June). *Canada Day. 75th Anniv of "Group of Seven" (artists). Three sheets, each* 180×80 *mm, containing T* **632** *and similar square designs. Multicoloured. Fluorescent paper. P* 13.

MS1642 (a) 43 c. Type **632**; 43 c. "From the North Shore, Lake Superior" (Lawren Harris); 43 c. "Evening, Les Eboulements, Quebec" (A. Jackson). (b) 43 c. "Serenity, Lake of the Woods" (Frank Johnston); 43 c. "A September Gale, Georgian Bay" (Arthur Lismer); 43 c. "Falls, Montreal River" (J. E. H. MacDonald); 43 c. "Open Window" (Frederick Varley). (c) 43 c. "Mill Houses" (Alfred Casson); 43 c. "Pembina Valley" (Lionel FitzGerald); 43 c. "The Lumberjack" (Edwin Holgate) .. .. *Set of* 3 *sheets* 6·50 7·50

The three sheets of No. **MS**1642 were sold together in an envelope which also includes a small descriptive booklet.

(Des B. Mackay-Lyons and S. Slipp. Litho C.B.N.)

1995 (29 June). *Centenary of Lunenburg Academy. Fluorescent frame. P* 13.

1643 **633** 43 c. multicoloured 40 45

634 Aspects of Manitoba

635 Monarch Butterfly

(Des T. Gallagher and S. Rosenberg. Litho Ashton-Potte Canada)

1995 (14 July). *125th Anniv of Manitoba as Canadia Province. Fluorescent frame. P* 13½×13.

1644 **634** 43 c. multicoloured 40 4

Two Types of Belted Kingfisher design:

Type I. Inscr "aune migratrice" in error.
Type II. Inscr corrected to "faune migratrice".

(Des Debbie Adams. Litho C.B.N.)

1995 (15 Aug–26 Sept). *Migratory Wildlife. T* **635** *and simila vert designs. Fluorescent paper. P* 13×12½.

1645 45 c. Type **635** 65 7
a. Block of 4. Nos. 1645/6, 1648/9 .. 2·40
b. Block of 4. Nos. 1645, 1647/9 (26 Sept) 2·40
1646 45 c. Belted Kingfisher (I) 65 7
1647 45 c. Belted Kingfisher (II) (26 Sept) .. 65 7
1648 45 c. Pintail 65 7
1649 45 c. Hoary Bat 65 7
1645/9 .. .. *Set of* 5 3·00 3·2

The inscription error on No. 1646 was corrected in a ne printing issued 26 September 1995.

The four different designs were printed together, *se-tenan* throughout the sheet, giving four blocks of 4 and four singl stamps, showing an overall background design of migratio routes.

636 Quebec Railway Bridge

(Des J. Gault, T. Telmet and C. Wykes. Litho Ashton-Potte Canada)

1995 (1 Sept). *20th World Road Congress, Montreal. Bridge. T* **636** *and similar horiz designs. Multicoloured. Fluorescen paper. P* 12½×13.

1650 45 c. Type **636** 90 9
a. Block of 4. Nos. 1650/3 .. .. 3·25
1651 45 c. 401-403-410 Interchange, Mississauga 90 9
1652 45 c. Hartland Bridge, New Brunswick .. 90 9
1653 45 c. Alex Fraser Bridge, British Columbia 90 9
1650/3 .. .. *Set of* 4 3·25 3·2

Nos. 1650/3 were printed together, *se-tenant*, throughout th sheet, giving four blocks of 4 and four single stamps.

Two Types of Background to Nos. 1654/5:

Type I. Inscriptions behind face value and "CANADA" sho names of Canadian Provinces.
Type II. Inscription behind face value and "CANADA" sho names of family events.

(Des Tarzan Communication Graphique. Litho Ashton-Potte Canada (Nos. 1654/5) or Leigh-Mardon Ltd, Melbourne (No 1654b/5b)).

1995 (1 Sept)–**96.** *Greetings stamps. Horiz designs as T* **62** *Multicoloured. Fluorescent outline. Self-adhesive. Die-cut.*

1654 45 c. Face value at right (I) 35 4
a. Booklet pane. Nos. 1654/5, each × 5 3·50
b. Type II (15.1.96) 55 6
ba. Booklet pane. Nos. 1654b and 1655b each × 5 .. .. 5·50
1655 45 c. Face value at left (I) 35 4
b. Type II (15.1.96) 55 6

Nos. 1654/5 were only available from $4.70 self-adhesiv booklets in which the backing card formed the cover. Booklet containing Nos. 1654/5 also include a separate pane of 1 self-adhesive labels which it was intended the sender shoul insert in the circular space on each stamp before use. Booklet containing Nos. 1654b/5b included 35 circular greetings label on the same pane as the stamps.

637 Mountain, Baffin Island, Polar Bear and Caribou

638 Superman

(Des Eskind Waddell. Litho C.B.N.)

95 (15 Sept). *50th Anniv of Arctic Institute of North America. T* **637** *and similar horiz designs. Multicoloured. Fluorescent paper. P* 13×12½.

56 45 c. Type **637** 70 80
a. Booklet pane. Nos. 1656/60, each × 2, with margins all round 6·50
57 45 c. Arctic poppy, Auyuittuq National Park and cargo canoe 70 80
58 45 c. Inuk man and igloo 70 80
59 45 c. Ogilvie Mountains, dog team and ski-equipped airplane 70 80
60 45 c. Inuit children 70 80
56/60 *Set of* 5 3·25 3·50

Nos. 1656/60 were only issued in $4.50 stamp booklets.

(Des L. Fishauf. Litho Ashton-Potter Canada)

95 (2 Oct). *Comic Book Superheroes. T* **638** *and similar vert designs. Multicoloured. Fluorescent frame. P* 13×12½.

61 45 c. Type **638** 50 60
a. Booklet pane. Nos. 1661/5, each × 2, with margins all round 4·75
62 45 c. Johnny Canuck 50 60
63 45 c. Nelvana 50 60
64 45 c. Captain Canuck 50 60
65 45 c. Fleur de Lys 50 60
61/5 *Set of* 5 2·25 2·75

Nos. 1661/5 were only issued in $4.50 stamp booklets.

39 Prime Minister MacKenzie King signing U.N. Charter, 1945

640 "The Nativity"

Des L. Holloway and R. Kerr. Litho and die-stamped C.B.N.)

995 (24 Oct). *50th Anniv of United Nations. Fluorescent frame. P* 13½.

66 **639** 45 c. multicoloured 50 50

No. 1666 was issued in sheets of 10 with a large illustrated nd inscribed margin at top.

)es F. Dallaire. Litho Ashton-Potter Canada (40 c.) or C.B.N. (others))

995 (2 Nov). *Christmas. T* **640** *and similar multicoloured designs showing sculptured capitals from Ste.-Anne-de-Beaupré Basilica designed by Emilé Brunet (Nos. 1668/70). Fluorescent frames. P* 12½×13 *(40 c.) or* 13½ *(others).*

667 40 c. Sprig of holly (35×22 *mm*) 65 65
a. Booklet pane. No. 1667×10 6·50
668 45 c. Type **640** 50 20
a. Booklet pane. No. 1668×10 7·50
669 52 c. "The Annunciation" 75 80
a. Booklet pane. No. 1669×5 plus one printed label 4·25
670 90 c. "The Flight to Egypt" 1·25 1·75
a. Booklet pane. No. 1670×5 plus one printed label 7·50
667/70 *Set of* 4 2·50 3·00

On No. 1667 the left-hand third of the design area is taken up y a barcode which has fluorescent bands between the bars. This alue was only available from $4 stamp booklets which had the ertical edges of the pane imperforate. It was intended for use on reetings cards posted before 31 January 1996.

Nos. 1668a/70a have the vertical edges of the panes nperforate.

641 World Map and Emblem

(Des A. Leduc. Litho Ashton-Potter Canada)

995 (6 Nov). *25th Anniv of La Francophonie and The Agency for Cultural and Technical Co-operation. Fluorescent frame. P* 13×13½.

671 **641** 45 c. multicoloured 50 50

642 Concentration Camp Victims, Uniform and Identity Card

(Des Q30 Design. Litho Ashton-Potter Canada)

995 (9 Nov). *50th Anniv of the End of The Holocaust. Fluorescent paper. P* 12½×13.

672 **642** 45 c. multicoloured 50 50

Horizontal strips of No. 1672 form a continuous design which s carried over onto the vertical sheet margins.

643 American Kestrel

(Des R. Bellemare and P. Leduc. Litho C.B.N.)

1996 (9 Jan). *Birds (1st issue). T* **643** *and similar horiz designs. Multicoloured. Fluorescent frame. P* 13½.

1673 45 c. Type **643** 70 70
a. Horiz strip of 4. Nos. 1673/6 2·50
1674 45 c. Atlantic Puffin 70 70
1675 45 c. Pileated Woodpecker 70 70
1676 45 c. Ruby-throated Hummingbird 70 70
1673/6 *Set of* 4 2·50 2·50

Nos. 1673/6 were printed together, *se-tenant*, in panes of 12 (4×3) containing three examples of No. 1673a. Those panes intended for philatelic sale had inscribed margins so arranged as to produce a diamond-shaped format.

See also Nos. 1717/20 and 1779/82

644 *Louis R. Desmarais* (tanker), Three-dimensional Map and Radar Screen

(Des Q30 Design Inc. Litho C.B.N.)

1996 (15 Feb). *High Technology Industries. T* **644** *and similar horiz designs. Multicoloured. Fluorescent paper. P* 13½.

1677 45 c. Type **644** 65 70
a. Booklet pane. Nos. 1677/80, each × 3 6·75
1678 45 c. Canadair Challenger 601-3R, jet engine and navigational aid 65 70
1679 45 c. Map of North America and eye 65 70
1680 45 c. Genetic engineering experiment and Canola (plant) 65 70
1677/80 *Set of* 4 2·40 2·50

Nos. 1677/80 were only available from $5.40 stamp booklets which had the vertical edges of the pane imperforate.

(Des P.-Y. Pelletier. Litho and die-stamped Ashton-Potter Canada)

1996 (30 Apr). *Canadian Art (9th series). Vert design as T* **550**. *Multicoloured. Fluorescent paper. P* 12½×13.

1681 90 c. "The Spirit of Haida Gwaii" (sculpture) (Bill Reid) 1·40 1·75

No. 1681 was issued in a similar sheet format to No. 1289.

645 "One World, One Hope" (Joe Average)

(Des G. Tsetsekas. Litho Ashton-Potter Canada)

1996 (8 May). *11th International Conference on AIDS, Vancouver. Fluorescent frame. P* 13½.

1682 **645** 45 c. multicoloured 70 70

(Des J. Gault, T. Telmet and C. Wickes. Litho C.B.N.)

1996 (8 June). *Historic Automobiles (4th issue). Sheet* 177×125 *mm, containing horiz designs as T* **617**. *Multicoloured. Fluorescent frame. P* 12½×13.

MS1683 45 c. Still Motor Co. electric van, 1899; 45 c. Waterous Engine Works steam roller, 1914; 52 c. International "D.35" delivery truck, 1938; 52 c. Champion road grader, 1936; 90 c. White "Model WA 122" articulated lorry, 1947 (51×22 *mm*); 90 c. Hayes "HDX 45-115" logging truck, 1975 (51×22 *mm*) 5·00 5·50

No. **MS**1683 also includes the "CAPEX '96" International Stamp Exhibition logo on the sheet margin and was sold in a protective pack.

(Des J. Gault, T. Telmet and C. Wickes. Litho C.B.N.)

1996 (8 June). *"CAPEX '96" International Stamp Exhibition, Toronto. Sheet,* 368×182 *mm, containing horiz designs as Nos.* **MS**1563, **MS**1611, **MS**1636, **MS**1683, *but with different face values, and one new design (45 c.). Fluorescent frame (45 c.). P* 12½×13.

MS1684 5 c. Bombardier "Ski-Doo Olympique 335" snowmobile, 1970; 5 c. Cockshutt "30" farm tractor, 1950; 5 c. Type **617**; 5 c. Ford "Model F160L-AMB" military ambulance, 1942; 5 c. Still Motor Co electric van, 1895; 5 c. International "D.35" delivery truck, 1936; 5 c. Russel "Model L" touring car, 1908; 5 c. Winnipeg police wagon, 1925; 5 c. Waterous Engine Works steam roller, 1914; 5 c. Champion road grader, 1936; 10 c. White "Model WA 122" articulated lorry, 1947 (51×22 *mm*); 10 c. St. John Railway Company tramcar, 1894 (51×22 *mm*); 10 c. Hayes "HDX 45-115" logging truck, 1975 (51×22 *mm*); 10 c. Motor Coach Industries "Courier 50 Skyview" coach, 1950 (51×22 *mm*); 20 c. Ford "Model T" touring car, 1914 (43×22 *mm*); 20 c. McLaughlin-Buick "28-496 special", 1928 (43×22 *mm*); 20 c. Bombardier "B-12 CS" multi-passenger snowmobile, 1948 (43×22 *mm*); 20 c. Robin-Nodwell "RN 110" tracked carrier, 1962 (43×22 *mm*); 20 c. Studebaker "Champion Deluxe Starlight" coupe, 1950 (43×22 *mm*); 20 c. Gray-Dort "25 SM" luxury sedan, 1923 (43×22 *mm*); 20 c. Gotfredson "Model 20" farm truck, 1924 (43×22 *mm*); 20 c. Massey-Harris "No. 21" self-propelled combine-harvester, 1942 (43×22 *mm*); 20 c. Bickle "Chieftain" fire engine, 1936 (43×22 *mm*); 20 c. Sicard snowblower, 1927 (43×22 *mm*); 45 c. Bricklin "SV-1" sports car, 1975 (51×22 *mm*) 6·00 6·50

No. **MS**1684 was sold folded within a special pack at $3.75, a premium of 40 c. over the face value. It was only possible to obtain an unfolded example by purchasing an uncut press sheet, containing three miniature sheets, of which only 25000 were made available. The price quoted for No. **MS**1684 is for a folded example.

646 Skookum Jim Mason and Bonanza Creek

647 Patchwork Quilt Maple Leaf

(Des S. Slipp. Litho and gold die-stamped Ashton-Potter Canada)

1996 (13 June). *Centenary of Yukon Gold Rush. T* **646** *and similar horiz designs. Multicoloured. Fluorescent paper. P* 13½.

1685 45 c. Type **646** 60 60
a. Horiz strip of 5. Nos. 1685/9 2·75
1686 45 c. Prospector and boats on Lake Laberge 60 60
1687 45 c. Superintendent Sam Steele (N.W.M.P.) and U.S.A.–Canada border 60 60
1688 45 c. Dawson saloon 60 60
1689 45 c. Miner with rocker box and sluice 60 60
1685/9 *Set of* 5 2·75 2·75

Nos. 1685/9 were printed together, *se-tenant*, in sheetlets of 10, containing two examples of No. 1685a.

(Des R. Bellemare. Litho Ashton-Potter Canada)

1996 (28 June). *Canada Day. Self-adhesive. Fluorescent frame. Die-cut.*

1690 **647** 45 c. multicoloured 50 50

No. 1690 was printed in sheets of 12 with each stamp separate on the backing paper.

648 Ethel Catherwood (high jump), 1928

649 Indian Totems, City Skyline, Forest and Mountains

(Des M. Koudys. Litho and die-stamped Ashton-Potter Canada)

1996 (8 July). *Canadian Olympic Gold Medal Winners. T* **648** *and similar vert designs. Multicoloured. Fluorescent paper. P* 13×12½.

1691 45 c. Type **648** 55 60
a. Booklet pane. Nos. 1691/5, each × 2 with margins all round 5·00
1692 45 c. Etienne Desmarteau (56lb weight throw), 1904 55 60
1693 45 c. Fanny Rosenfeld (400 metres relay), 1928 55 60
1694 45 c. Gerald Ouellette (small bore rifle, prone), 1956 55 60
1695 45 c. Percy Williams (100 and 200 metres), 1928 55 60
1691/5 *Set of* 5 2·50 2·75

Nos. 1691/5 were only issued in $4.50 stamp booklets.

(Des M. Warburton. Litho Ashton-Potter Canada)

1996 (19 July). *125th Anniv of British Columbia. Fluorescent paper. P* 13×12½.

1696 **649** 45 c. multicoloured 50 50

NEW INFORMATION

The editor is always interested to correspond with people who have new information that will improve or correct the Catalogue.

650 Canadian Heraldic Symbols

651 *L'Arrivee d'un Train en Gare* (1896)

(Des D. Sarty and R. Gaynor. Litho Ashton-Potter Canada)

1996 (19 Aug). *22nd International Congress of Genealogical and Heraldic Sciences, Ottawa. Fluorescent paper. P* $12^1/_2$.
1697 **650** 45 c. multicoloured 50 50

(Des P.-Y. Pelletier. Litho C.B.N.)

1996 (22 Aug). *Centenary of Cinema. Two sheets, each 180×100 mm containing T* **651** *and similar vert designs. Multicoloured. Self-adhesive. Fluorescent paper. Die-cut.*
MS1698 Two sheets. (a) 45 c. Type **651**; 45 c. *Back to God's Country* (1919); 45 c. *Hen Hop!* (1942); 45 c. *Pour la Suite du Monde* (1963); 45 c. *Goin' Down the Road* (1970). (b) 45 c. *Mon Oncle Antoine* (1971); 45 c. *The Apprenticeship of Duddy Kravitz* (1974); 45 c. *Les Ordres* (1974); 45 c. *Les Bons Debarras* (1980); 45 c. *The Grey Fox* (1982) . . . . 6·00 7·00
The two sheets of No. **MS**1698 were sold together in an envelope with a descriptive booklet.

652 Interlocking Jigsaw Pieces and Hands

653 Edouard Montpetit and Montreal University

(Des Debbie Adam. Litho Ashton-Potter Canada)

1996 (9 Sept). *Literacy Campaign. Fluorescent paper.* P $13\times12^1/_2$.
1699 **652** 45 c. + 5 c. multicoloured 60 65
a. Booklet pane. No. 1699×10 with margins all round . . . . 5·50
No. 1699 has one piece of the jigsaw removed by die-cutting and was only issued in $5 stamp booklet

(Des J. Beauchesne. Litho Ashton-Potter Canada)

1996 (26 Sept). *Edouard Montpetit (academic) Commemoration. Fluorescent frame. P* $12\times12^1/_2$.
1700 **653** 45 c. multicoloured 50 50

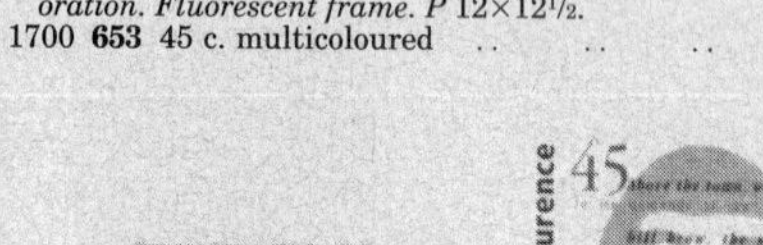

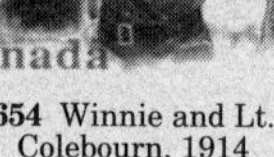

654 Winnie and Lt. Colebourn, 1914

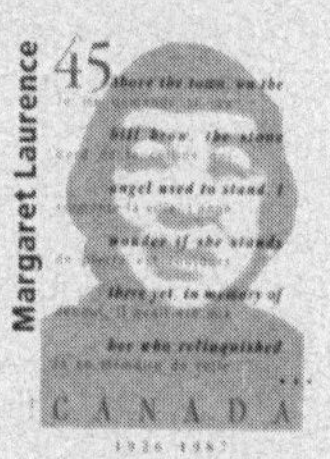

655 Margaret Laurence

(Des Wai Poon. Litho Ashton-Potter Canada)

1996 (1 Oct). *Stamp Collecting Month. Winnie the Pooh. T* **654** *and similar horiz designs. Multicoloured. Fluorescent frame. P* $12^1/_2\times13$.
1701 45 c. Type **654** 60 60
a. Double sheetlet of 16. Nos. 1701/4 each × 4 . . . . . . 8·00
1702 45 c. Christopher Robin Milne and teddy bear, 1925 . . . . 60 60
1703 45 c. Illustration from *Winnie the Pooh*, 1926 . . . . 60 60
1704 45 c. Winnie the Pooh at Walt Disney World, 1996 . . . . 60 60
1701/4 . . . . *Set of* 4 2·25 2·25
MS1705 152×112 mm. Nos. 1701/4 . . . . 2·25 2·75
Nos. 1701/4 were printed together, *se-tenant*, as blocks of 4 in double sheetlets, used as a cover to "The True Story of Winnie the Pooh" booklet.

(Des A. Leduc. Recess and litho C.B.N.)

1996 (10 Oct). *Canadian Authors. T* **655** *and similar vert designs. Fluorescent paper. P* $13^1/_2\times13$.
1706 45 c. multicoloured 60 65
a. Booklet pane. Nos. 1706/10 each × 2 5·25
1707 45 c. black, greenish grey & scarlet-verm 60 65
1708 45 c. multicoloured 60 65
1709 45 c. multicoloured 60 65
1710 45 c. multicoloured 60 65
1706/10 . . . . *Set of* 5 2·75 3·00
Designs:—No. 1706, Type **655**; No. 1707, Donald G. Creighton; No. 1708, Gabrielle Roy; No. 1709, Felix-Antoine Savard; No. 1710, Thomas C. Haliburton.
Nos. 1706/10 were only issued in $4.50 stamp booklets with the horizontal edges of the pane imperforate and margins at left and right.

656 Children tobogganing

657 Head of Ox

(Des T. Harrison (45 c.), Pauline Paquin (52 c.), Joan Bacquie (90 c.). Litho C.B.N. (45 c.) or Ashton-Potter Canada (others))

1996 (1 Nov). *Christmas. 50th Anniv of U.N.I.C.E.F. T* **656** *and similar vert designs. Multicoloured. Fluorescent frame. P* $13^1/_2$ *(45 c.) or* $12^1/_2\times12$ *(others).*
1711 45 c. Type **656** 50 20
a. Booklet pane. No. 1711×10 . . 4·25
1712 52 c. Father Christmas skiing 60 70
a. Perf $13^1/_2$ 60 70
ab. Booklet pane. No. 1712a×5 plus one printed label . . . . . . 2·75
1713 90 c. Couple ice-skating . . . . . . 90 1·25
a. Perf $13^1/_2$ . . . . 90 1·25
ab. Booklet pane. No. 1713a×5 plus one printed label . . . . . . 4·25
1711/13 . . . . *Set of* 3 1·75 1·90
Nos. 1712a and 1713a were only issued in stamp booklets.
Nos. 1711a, 1712ab and 1713ab have the vertical edges of the panes imperforate and margins at top and bottom.

(Des Ivy Li and Liu Xiang-Ping. Litho Ashton-Potter Canada)

1997 (7 Jan). *Chinese New Year ("Year of the Ox"). Fluorescent frame. P* $13\times12^1/_2$.
1714 45 c. multicoloured 85 90
MS1715 155×75 mm*. No. 1714×2 . . . . 2·00 2·50
No. **MS**1715 is an extended fan shape with overall measurements as quoted.
Two examples of No. 1714, taken from the miniature sheet, have been found with the gold ("Canada, 45", etc.) omitted.

1997 (7 Jan). *"HONG KONG '97" International Stamp Exhibition. As No.* **MS**1715, *but with exhibition logo added to the sheet margin in gold. Fluorescent frame. P* $13\times12^1/_2$.
MS1716 155×75 mm. No. 1714×2 . . . . 2·75 3·25

(Des R. Bellemare and P. Leduc. Litho Ashton-Potter, Canada)

1997 (10 Jan). *Birds (2nd series). Horiz designs as T* **643**. *Multicoloured. Fluorescent frame. P* $12^1/_2\times13$.
1717 45 c. Mountain Bluebird 65 65
a. Horiz strip of 4. Nos. 1717/20 . . 2·40
1718 45 c. Western Grebe 65 65
1719 45 c. Northern Gannet 65 65
1720 45 c. Scarlet Tanager 65 65
1717/20 . . . . *Set of* 4 2·40 2·40
Nos. 1717/20 printed together, *se-tenant*, in sheets of 20 (4×5) containing five examples of No. 1717a.

(Des P.-Y. Pelletier. Litho and die-stamped Ashton-Potter, Canada)

1997 (17 Feb). *Canadian Art (10th series). Vert design as T* **550**. *Multicoloured. Fluorescent paper. P* $12^1/_2\times13^1/_2$.
1721 90 c. "York Boat on Lake Winnipeg, 1930" (Walter Phillips) . . . . . . 1·00 1·25
No. 1721 was issued in a similar sheet format to No. 1289

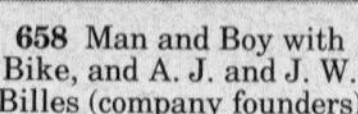

658 Man and Boy with Bike, and A. J. and J. W. Billes (company founders)

659 Abbé Charles-Emile Gadbois

(Des Fuel Design. Litho Ashton-Potter Canada)

1997 (3 Mar). *75th Anniv of Canadian Tire Corporation. Fluorescent frame. P* $13\times13^1/_2$.
1722 **658** 45 c. multicoloured 50 50
No. 1722 was printed in sheets of 12 which were supplied in special envelopes each with a pamphlet on the history of the company.

(Des Marie Lessard. Litho C.B.N.)

1997 (20 Mar). *Abbé Charles-Emile Gadbois (musicologist) Commemoration. Fluorescent frame. P* $13^1/_2\times13$.
1723 **659** 45 c. multicoloured 50 50

660 Blue Poppy

661 Nurse attending Patient

(Des C. Simard. Litho Ashton-Potter Canada)

1997 (4 Apr). *"Quebec in Bloom" International Floral Festiva Fluorescent frame. P* $13\times12^1/_2$.
1724 **660** 45 c. multicoloured 35 4
a. Booklet pane. No. 1724×12 . . 4·25
No. 1724 was only issued in $5.40 booklets. No. 1724a has th horizontal edges of the pane imperforate and margins at left ar right.

(Des Margaret Issenman. Litho Ashton-Potter Canada)

1997 (12 May). *Centenary of Victorian Order of Nurse Fluorescent frame. P* $12^1/_2\times13$.
1725 **661** 45 c. multicoloured 50 5

662 Osgoode Hall and Seal of Law Society

663 Great White Shark

(Des L. Holloway. Litho C.B.N.)

1997 (23 May). *Bicentenary of Law Society of Upper Canad Fluorescent frame. P* $13^1/_2\times13$.
1726 **662** 45 c. multicoloured 50 5

(Des Q30 Design. Litho Ashton-Potter Canada)

1997 (30 May). *Ocean Fishes. T* **663** *and similar horiz design Multicoloured. Fluorescent frame. P* $12^1/_2\times13$.
1727 45 c. Type **663** 60 6
a. Block of 4. Nos. 1727/30 . . . . 2·25
1728 45 c. Pacific Halibut 60 6
1729 45 c. Common Sturgeon 60 6
1730 45 c. Blue-finned Tuna 60 6
1727/30 . . . . *Set of* 4 2·25 2·2
Nos. 1727/30 were printed together, *se-tenant*, throughout th sheet giving four blocks of 4 and four single stamps.

664 Lighthouse and Confederation Bridge

(Des C. Burke and J. Hudson. Litho C.B.N.)

1997 (31 May). *Opening of Confederation Bridge, Northuml erland Strait. T* **664** *and similar horiz design. Multicoloure Fluorescent frame. P* $12^1/_2\times13$.
1731 45 c. Type **664** 65 6
a. Horiz pair. Nos. 1731/2 and centre label . . . . 1·25 1·2
1732 45 c. Confederation Bridge and Great Blue Heron 65 6
Nos. 1731/2 were printed together, horizontally *se-tenant*, i sheets of 20 (4×5) with labels measuring $16\times23^1/_2$ mm betwee vertical rows 1 and 2 and 3 and 4 which link the two designs.

665 Gilles Villeneuve in Ferrari T-3

(Des J. Gault and N. Skinner. Litho C.B.N.)

1997 (12 June). *15th Death Anniv of Gilles Villeneuve (racir car driver). T* **665** *and similar horiz design. Multicoloure Fluorescent frame. P* $12^1/_2\times13$.
1733 45 c. Type **665** 60 6
1734 90 c. Villeneuve in Ferrari T-4 . . . . 1·25 1·2
MS1735 203×115 mm. Nos. 1733/4 each × 4 . . 6·00 6·5
No. **MS**1735 was sold in an illustrated folder.

666 Globe and the *Matthew*

(Des Susan Warr. Litho Ashton-Potter Canada)

997 (24 June). *500th Anniv of John Cabot's Discovery of North America. Fluorescent paper.* P 12½×13.
736 **666** 45 c. multicoloured 50 50

667 Sea to Sky Highway, British Columbia, and Skier

(Des L. Cable. Litho C.B.N.)

997 (30 June). *Scenic Highways (1st series). T* **667** *and similar horiz designs. Multicoloured. Fluorescent frame.* P 12½×13.
.737 45 c. Type **667** 60 60
a. Block of 4. Nos. 1737/40 .. .. 2·25
.738 45 c. Cabot Trail, Nova Scotia, and rug-making 60 60
.739 45 c. Wine route, Ontario, and glasses of wine 60 60
.740 45 c. Highway 34, Saskatchewan, and cowboy 60 60
.737/40 .. .. *Set of* 4 2·25 2·25
Nos. 1737/40 were printed together, *se-tenant*, in sheets of 20 containing four blocks of 4 and four single stamps.
See also Nos. 1810/13.

668 Kettle, Ski-bike, Lounger and Plastic Cases

(Des F. Dallaire. Litho C.B.N.)

1997 (23 July). *20th Congress of International Council of Societies for Industrial Design. Fluorescent frame.* P 12½×13.
1741 **668** 45 c. multicoloured 50 50
No. 1741 was printed in sheets of 24 (4×6), the horizontal rows containing four stamps each with a different 11½×24 mm *se-tenant* label showing examples of Canadian industrial design. These labels are on the right of the stamps in rows 1, 3 and 5 and to the left in rows 2, 4 and 6.

669 Caber Thrower, Bagpiper, Drummer and Highland Dancer

670 Knights of Columbus Emblem

(Des F. Ross. Litho C.B.N.)

1997 (1 Aug). *50th Anniv of Glengarry Highland Games, Ontario. Fluorescent frame.* P 12½×13.
1742 **669** 45 c. multicoloured 50 50

(Des A. Leduc. Litho C.B.N.)

1997 (5 Aug). *Centenary of Knights of Columbus (welfare charity) in Canada. Fluorescent frame.* P 13.
1743 **670** 45 c. multicoloured 50 50

671 Postal and Telephone Workers with P.T.T.I. Emblem

(Des Epicentre. Litho C.B.N.)

1997 (18 Aug). *28th World Congress of Postal, Telegraph and Telephone International Staff Federation, Montreal. Fluorescent frame.* P 13.
1744 **671** 45 c. multicoloured 50 50

672 C.Y.A.P. Logo

(Des K. Fung. Litho C.B.N.)

1997 (25 Aug). *Canada's Year of Asia Pacific. Fluorescent frame.* P 13½.
1745 **672** 45 c. multicoloured 50 50

673 Paul Henderson celebrating Goal

674 Martha Black

(Des C. Vinh. Litho Ashton-Potter Canada)

1997 (20 Sept). *25th Anniv of Canada–U.S.S.R. Ice Hockey Series. T* **673** *and similar horiz design. Multicoloured. Fluorescent frame.* P 12½×13.
1746 45 c. Type **673** 35 40
a. Booklet pane. Nos. 1746/7, each × 5 with margins all round .. .. 3·50
1747 45 c. Canadian team celebrating 35 40
Nos. 1746/7 were only issued in $4.50 stamp booklets with a partial fluorescent frame around each stamp.
Examples of the booklet pane, No. 1746a, exist overprinted "SERIES OF THE CENTURY 97-09-28 Anniversaire 25 Anniversary LA SERIE DU SIECLE" and player Paul Henderson's signature. These come from Collector Gift Sets which also included a sweatshirt, puck and print.

(Des S. Hepburn. Litho C.B.N.)

1997 (26 Sept). *Federal Politicians. T* **674** *and similar vert designs. Multicoloured. Fluorescent frame.* P 13½×13.
1748 45 c. Type **674** 35 40
a. Block of 4. Nos. 1748/51 .. .. 1·40
1749 45 c. Lionel Chevrier 35 40
1750 45 c. Judy LaMarsh 35 40
1751 45 c. Réal Caouette 35 40
1748/51 .. .. *Set of* 4 1·40 1·60
The four different designs were printed together, *se-tenant*, throughout the sheet, giving four blocks of 4 and four single stamps.

675 Vampire and Bat

(Des L. Fishauf, J. Bennett, B. Drawson, T. Hunt, S. Ng. Litho Ashton-Potter Canada)

1997 (1 Oct). *The Supernatural. Centenary of Publication of Bram Stoker's* Dracula. *T* **675** *and similar square designs. Multicoloured. Fluorescent paper.* P 12½×13.
1752 45 c. Type **675** 35 40
a. Block of 4. Nos. 1752/5 .. .. 1·40
1753 45 c. Werewolf 35 40
1754 45 c. Ghost 35 40
1755 45 c. Goblin 35 40
1752/5 .. .. *Set of* 4 1·40 1·60
Nos. 1752/5 were printed together, *se-tenant*, in blocks of 4 throughout the sheet.

676 Grizzly Bear

(Des R.-R. Carmichael and S. Slipp ($1), S. Slipp and B. Townsend ($2), A. Leduc ($8). Eng M. Morck ($2), J. Peral (others). Recess and litho C.B.N.)

1997 (15 Oct)–**98**. *Mammals . T* **676** *and similar horiz designs. Multicoloured.* P 12½×13 ($8) *or* 13½×13 (*others*).
1756 $1 Loon (47×39 *mm*) (27.10.98) 80 85
1757 $2 Polar Bear (47×39 *mm*) (27.10.98) .. 1·60 1·75
1758 $8 Type **676** .. .. 6·50 6·75
1756/8 .. .. *Set of* 3 8·75 9·25
No. 1758 was printed in sheets of 4.

677 "Our Lady of the Rosary" (detail, Holy Rosary Cathedral, Vancouver)

(Des G. Nincheri (45 c.), Ellen Simon (52 c.), C. Wallis (90 c.). Litho Ashton-Potter Canada)

1997 (3 Nov). *Christmas. Stained Glass Windows. T* **677** *and similar horiz designs. Multicoloured. Fluorescent frame.* P 12½×13.
1763 45 c. Type **677** 35 40
a. Perf 12½×imperf 35 40
ab. Booklet pane. No. 1763a×10 .. 3·50
1764 52 c. "Nativity" (detail, Leith United Church, Ontario) 40 45
a. Perf 12½×imperf 40 45
ab. Booklet pane. No. 1764a×5 .. 2·00
1765 90 c. "Life of the Blessed Virgin" (detail, St. Stephen's Ukrainian Catholic Church, Calgary) 75 80
a. Perf 12½×imperf 75 80
ab. Booklet pane. No. 1765a×5 .. 3·75
1736/5 .. .. *Set of* 3 1·50 1·60
Nos. 1763a/5a were only issued in stamp booklets with the vertical edges of the panes imperforate and margins at top and bottom.

678 Livestock and Produce

(Des Heather Lafleur and Shelagh Armstrong. Litho C.B.N.)

1997 (6 Nov). *75th Anniv of Royal Agricultural Winter Fair, Toronto. Fluorescent frame.* P 12½×13.
1766 **678** 45 c. multicoloured 35 40

679 Tiger

680 John Robarts (Ontario, 1961–71)

(Des R. Mah. Litho Ashton-Potter Canada)

1998 (8 Jan). *Chinese New Year ("Year of the Tiger"). Fluorescent frame.* P 13½×12½.
1767 **679** 45 c. multicoloured 35 40
MS1768 130×110 mm. As No. 1767×2. P 13×12½ 70 75
No. **MS**1768 is diamond-shaped with overall measurements as quoted.
As originally issued the miniature sheet was surrounded by a plain gold margin. Examples from the "Lunar New Year" pack issued on 28 January were additionally inscribed with design and printing information on this gold margin at foot.

(Des R. Bellemare. Litho C.B.N.)

1998 (18 Feb). *Canadian Provincial Premiers. T* **680** *and similar horiz designs. Multicoloured. Fluorescent frame.* P 13½.
1769 45 c. Type **680** 35 40
a. Sheetlet. Nos.1769/78 .. .. 3·50
1770 45 c. Jean Lesage (Quebec, 1960–66) .. 35 40
1771 45 c. John McNair (New Brunswick, 1940–52) 35 40
1772 45 c. Tommy Douglas (Saskatchewan, 1944–61) 35 40
1773 45 c. Joseph Smallwood (Newfoundland, 1949–72) 35 40
1774 45 c. Angus MacDonald (Nova Scotia, 1933–40, 1945–54) 35 40
1775 45 c. W. A. C. Bennett (British Columbia, 1960–66) 35 40
1776 45 c. Ernest Manning (Alberta, 1943–68) 35 40
1777 45 c. John Bracken (Manitoba, 1922–43) 35 40
1778 45 c. J. Walter Jones (Prince Edward Island, 1943–53) 35 40
1769/78 .. .. *Set of* 10 3·50 4·00
Nos. 1769/78 were printed together, *se-tenant*, in sheetlets of 10 with illustrated margins.

(Des R. Bellemare and P. Leduc. Litho C.B.N.)

1998 (13 Mar). *Birds* (*3rd series*). *Horiz designs as T* **643**. *Multicoloured. Fluorescent frame. P* 13×13½.
1779 45 c. Hairy Woodpecker 35 40
a. Horiz strip of 4. Nos. 1779/82 .. 1·40
1780 45 c. Great Crested Flycatcher 35 40
1781 45 c. Eastern Screech Owl 35 40
1782 45 c. Gray-crowned Rosy-finch 35 40
1779/82 .. .. *Set of* 4 1·40 1·60
Nos. 1779/82 were printed together, *se-tenant*, in sheets of 20 (4×5) containing five examples of No. 1779a.

681 Maple Leaf **682** Coquihalla Orange Fly

(Des Gottschalk & Ash. Litho Avery Dennison, U.S.A.)

1998 (14 Apr). *Self-adhesive. Automatic Cash Machine Stamp. Fluorescent paper. Die-cut.*
1783 **681** 45 c. multicoloured 35 40
No. 1783 was issued, in sheets of 18 (3×6), from bank automatic cash machines and philatelic centres.
For stamps in this design, but without "POSTAGE POSTES" at top left see Nos. 1836/40.

(Des P. Brunelle. Litho Ashton Potter Canada)

1998 (16 Apr). *Fishing Flies. T* **682** *and similar horiz designs. Multicoloured. Fluorescent frame. P* 12½×13.
1784 45 c. Type **682** 35 40
a. Booklet pane. Nos. 1784/9, each × 2 4·00
1785 45 c. Steelhead Bee 35 40
1786 45 c. Dark Montréal 35 40
1787 45 c. Lady Amherst 35 40
1788 45 c. Coho Blue 35 40
1789 45 c. Cosseboom Special 35 40
1784/9 .. .. *Set of* 6 2·10 2·40
Nos. 1784/9 were only issued in stamp booklets containing pane No. 1784a which incorporates an inscribed margin at left.

683 Mineral and Petroleum Excavation and Pickaxe **684** 1898 2 c. Imperial Penny Postage Stamp and Postmaster General Sir William Mulock

(Des Monique Dufour and Sophie Lafortune. Litho Ashton Potter Canada)

1998 (4 May). *Centenary of Canadian Institute of Mining, Metallurgy and Petroleum. Fluorescent frame. P* 12½.
1790 **683** 45 c. multicoloured 35 40

(Des F. Dallaire. Litho C.B.N.)

1998 (29 May). *Centenary of Imperial Penny Postage. Fluorescent frame. P* 12½×13.
1791 **684** 45 c. multicoloured 35 40
No. 1791 was printed in sheets of 14 stamps with a label showing the Imperial State Crown appearing in the centre of the sheet.

685 Two Sumo Wrestlers **686** St. Peters Canal, Nova Scotia

(Des G. Takeuchi and S. Dittberner. Litho and embossed Ashton Potter Canada)

1998 (5 June). *First Canadian Sumo Basho* (*tournament*), *Vancouver. T* **685** *and similar horiz design. Multicoloured. Fluorescent frame. P* 12½×13.
1792 45 c. Type **685** 35 40
a. Pair. Nos. 1792/3 70
1793 45 c. Sumo wrestler in ceremonial ritual 35 40
MS1794 84×152 mm. Nos. 1792/3 .. .. 70 75
On Nos. 1792/4 the outlines of the wrestlers are embossed.
Nos. 1792/3 were printed together, *se-tenant*, both horizontally and vertically in sheets of 20 (4×5). The horizontal rows include labels, 7×30 mm, either side of each stamp with that on the left inscribed in English and that on the right in Japanese.

(Des V. McIndoe, G. George and D. Martin. Litho Ashton-Potter Canada)

1998 (17 June). *Canadian Canals. T* **686** *and similar vert designs. Multicoloured. Fluorescent frame. P* 12½.
1795 45 c. Type **686** 35 40
a. Booklet pane. Nos. 1795/1804 and ten stamp-size labels .. .. .. 3·50
1796 45 c. St. Ours Canal, Quebec 35 40
1797 45 c. Port Carling Lock, Ontario .. 35 40
1798 45 c. Lock on Rideau Canal, Ontario .. 35 40
1799 45 c. Towers and platform of Peterborough Lift Lock, Trent–Severn Waterway, Ontario 35 40
1800 45 c. Chambly Canal, Quebec 35 40
1801 45 c. Lachine Canal, Quebec 35 40
1802 45 c. Rideau Canal in winter, Ontario .. 35 40
1803 45 c. Boat on Big Chute incline railway, Trent–Severn Waterway, Ontario .. 35 40
1804 45 c. Sault Ste. Marie Canal, Ontario .. 35 40
1795/1804 .. .. .. *Set of* 10 3·50 4·00
Nos. 1795/1804 were only issued in $4.50 stamp booklets with the ten labels in the pane providing a location map for the canals depicted.

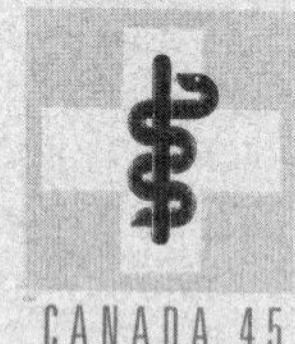

687 Staff of Aesculapius and Cross **688** Policeman of 1873 and Visit to Indian Village

(Des P.-Y. Pelletier. Typo (embossed) and litho Ashton-Potter Canada)

1998 (25 June). *Canadian Health Professionals. Fluorescent paper. P* 12½.
1805 **687** 45 c. multicoloured 35 40

(Des A. Valko and Circle Design. Litho (No. **MS**1808 also embossed) Ashton-Potter Canada)

1998 (3 July). 125*th Anniv of Royal Canadian Mounted Police. T* **688** *and similar horiz design. Multicoloured. Fluorescent frame. P* 12½×13.
1806 45 c. Type **688** 35 40
a. Horiz pair. Nos. 1806/7 with label .. 70
1807 45 c. Policewoman of 1998 and aspects of modern law enforcement 35 40
MS1808 160×102 mm. Nos. 1806/7 .. .. 70 80
Nos. 1806/7 were printed together, *se-tenant*, in pairs both horizontally and vertically, throughout the sheet of 20 (4×5). The horizontal rows include labels, 15×26 mm, on either side of each stamp. There are two label designs, one showing the R.C.M.P. crest and the other the Musical Ride which continues the design shown on the two stamps.
No. **MS**1808 also exists from a limited printing with the facsimile signature of Lieut-Col. G. A. French, the first commissioner, added to the bottom margin.
No. **MS**1808 was also issued overprinted with the logos of "Portugal 98" or "Italia 98" for sale at these International Stamp Exhibitions.

689 William J. Roue (designer) and *Bluenose* (schooner) **690** "Painting" (Jean-Paul Riopelle)

(Des L. Hebert. Litho C.B.N.)

1998 (24 July). *William James Roue* (*naval architect*) *Commemoration. Fluorescent frame. P* 13.
1809 **689** 45 c. multicoloured 35 40

(Des L. Cable. Litho Ashton-Potter Canada)

1998 (28 July). *Scenic Highways* (*2nd series*). *Horiz designs as T* **667**. *Multicoloured. Fluorescent frame. P* 12½×13.
1810 45 c. Dempster Highway, Yukon, and caribou 35 40
a. Block of 4. Nos. 1810/13 .. .. 1·40
1811 45 c. Dinosaur Trail, Alberta, and skeleton 35 40
1812 45 c. River Valley Drive, New Brunswick, and fern 35 40
1813 45 c. Blue Heron Route, Prince Edward Island, and lobster 35 40
1810/13 .. .. *Set of* 4 1·40 1·50
Nos. 1810/13 were printed together, *se-tenant*, in sheets of 20 containing four blocks of 4 and four single stamps.

(Des R. Bellemare. Litho C.B.N.)

1998 (7 Aug). 50*th Anniv of* Refus Global (*manifesto of Th Automatistes group of artists*). *T* **690** *and simil multicoloured designs. Self-adhesive. Fluorescent fram Die-cut.*
1814 45 c. Type **690** 35 4
a. Booklet pane. Nos. 1814/20 .. 2·40
1815 45 c. "La derniĕre campagne de Napoléon" (Fernand Leduc) (37×31½ *mm*) .. 35 4
1816 45 c. "Jet fuligineux sur noir torturé" (Jean-Paul Mousseau) 35 4
1817 45 c. "Le fond du garde-robe" (Pierre Gauvreau) (29½×42 *mm*) 35 4
1818 45 c. "Joie lacustre" (Paul-Émile Borduas) 35 4
1819 45 c. "Seafarers Union" (Marcelle Ferron) (36×34 *mm*) 35 4
1820 45 c. "Le tumulte ã la mâchoire crispée" (Marcel Barbeau) (36×34 *mm*) .. 35 4
1814/20 .. .. *Set of* 7 2·40 2·7
Nos. 1814/20 were only available from $3.15 self-adhesiv booklets in which the backing card formed the cover.

691 Napoléon-Alexandre Comeau (naturalist) **692** Indian Wigwam

(Des Catherine Bradbury and D. Bartsch. Litho C.B.N.)

1998 (15 Aug). *Legendary Canadians. T* **691** *and similar ver designs. Multicoloured. Fluorescent frame. P* 13½.
1821 45 c. Type **691** 35 4
a. Block of 4. Nos. 1821/4 .. .. 1·40
1822 45 c. Phyllis Munday (mountaineer) .. 35 4
1823 45 c. Bill Mason (filmmaker) 35 4
1824 45 c. Harry Red Foster (sports commentator) 35 4
1821/4 .. .. *Set of* 4 1·40 1·5
Nos. 1821/4 were printed together, *se-tenant*, in sheets of 2 containing four blocks of 4 and four single stamps.

(Des P.-Y. Pelletier. Litho and die-stamped Ashton Potte Canada)

1998 (8 Sept). *Canadian Art* (*11th series*). *Vert design as T* **550**. *Multicoloured. Fluorescent frame. P* 12½×13.
1825 90 c. "The Farmer's Family" (Bruno Bobak) 70 75
No. 1825 was issued in a similar sheet format to No. 1289.

(Des C. Gibson and P. Scott. Litho Ashton Potter Canada)

1998 (23 Sept). *Canadian Houses. T* **692** *and similar horiz designs. Multicoloured. Fluorescent frame. P* 12½×13.
1826 45 c. Type **692** 35 40
a. Sheetlet. Nos. 1826/34 .. .. 3·00
1827 45 c. Settler sod hut 35 40
1828 45 c. Maison Saint-Gabriel (17th-cent farmhouse), Quebec 35 40
1829 45 c. Queen Anne style brick house, Ontario 35 40
1830 45 c. Terrace of town houses 35 40
1831 45 c. Prefabricated house 35 40
1832 45 c. Veterans' houses 35 40
1833 45 c. Modern bungalow 35 40
1834 45 c. Healthy House, Toronto 35 40
1826/34 .. .. *Set of* 9 3·00 3·50
Nos. 1826/34 were printed together, *se-tenant*, in sheetlets of 9 with additional side margins carrying design descriptions.

693 University of Ottawa **694** Performing Animals

(Des Harris Design Associates. Litho C.B.N.)

1998 (25 Sept). 150*th Anniv of University of Ottawa. Fluorescent frame. P* 13½.
1835 **693** 45 c. multicoloured 35 40

1998 (30 Sept–28 Dec). *As T* **681**, *but without* "POSTAGE POSTES" *at top left.*
(*a*) *Litho Ashton-Potter Canada. Fluorescent frame. P* 13×13½
1836 **681** 55 c. multicoloured (28 Dec) .. 45 50
a. Booklet pane. No. 1836×5 plus printed label .. .. .. 2·25
1837 73 c. multicoloured (28 Dec) .. 60 65
1838 95 c. multicoloured (28 Dec) .. 75 80
a. Booklet pane. No. 1838×5 plus printed label .. .. .. 3·75

(b) Coil stamp. Litho and die-stamped (gold) Ashton-Potter Canada. Fluorescent frame. P 13
839 **681** 45 c. multicoloured 35 40

(c) Self-adhesive automatic cash machine stamp. Litho Avery Dennison, U.S.A. Fluorescent paper. Die-cut.
840 **681** 46 c. multicoloured (28 Dec) .. 35 40

Booklet panes Nos. 1836a and 1838a have the vertical edges the panes imperforate and margins at top and bottom.

No. 1839 was available in rolls of 100 on which the surplus lf-adhesive paper around each stamp was removed.

No. 1840 was issued in sheets of 18 (3×6), from bank utomatic cash machines and philatelic centres.

)es Monique Dufour, Sophie Lafortune and Paule Thibault. Litho Ashton-Potter Canada)

998 (1 Oct). *Canadian Circus. T* **694** *and similar vert designs, each incorporating a different clown. Multicoloured. Fluorescent frame. P* 13.

851 45 c. Type **694** 35 40
 a. Booklet pane. Nos. 1851/4, each × 3 4·00
852 45 c. Flying trapeze and acrobat on horseback 35 40
853 45 c. Lion tamer 35 40
854 45 c. Acrobats and trapeze artists .. 35 40
851/4 .. .. *Set of* 4 1·40 1·60
MS1855 133×133 mm. Nos. 1851/4 .. .. 1·40 1·60

Nos. 1851/4 only exist from $5.40 booklets in which the upper nd lower edges of the pane are imperforate.

The fluorescent frames on Nos. 1851/4 are broken at various oints where the designs encroach onto the margins.

695 John Peters Humphrey (author of original Declaration draft)

(Des J. Hudson. Litho C.B.N.)

998 (7 Oct). *50th Anniv of Universal of Declaration of Human Rights. Fluorescent frame. P* 13×13½.
856 **695** 45 c. multicoloured 35 40

696 H.M.C.S. *Sackville* (corvette)

(Des T. Hawkins and D. Page. Litho C.B.N.)

1998 (4 Nov). *75th Anniv of Canadian Naval Reserve. T* **696** *and similar horiz design. Multicoloured. Fluorescent frame. P* 12½×13.

1857 45 c. Type **696** 35 40
 a. Pair. Nos. 1857/8 70
1858 45 c. H.M.C.S. *Shawinigan* (coastal defence vessel) 35 40

Nos. 1857/8 were printed together, *se-tenant*, in horizontal and vertical pairs throughout the sheet.

697 Angel blowing Trumpet

(Des Anita Zeppetelli. Litho Ashton Potter Canada)

1998 (6 Nov). *Christmas. Statues of Angels. T* **697** *and similar vert designs. Multicoloured. Fluorescent frame. P* 13 (45 c.) *or* 13×13½ *(others)*.

1859 45 c. Type **697** 35 40
 a. Booklet pane. No. 1859×10 .. 3·50
 b. Perf 13×13½ 35 40
 ba. Booklet pane. No. 1859b×10 .. 3·50
1860 52 c. Adoring Angel 40 45
 b. Perf 13 .. .. 40 45
 ba. Booklet pane. No. 1860b×5 plus one printed label .. .. .. 2·00
1861 90 c. Angel at prayer 70 75
 b. Perf 13 .. .. 70 75
 ba. Booklet pane. No. 1861b×5 plus one printed label .. .. .. 3·50
1859/61 .. .. *Set of* 3 1·40 1·60

Nos. 1859b/61b were only issued in stamp booklets with the outside vertical edges of the panes imperforate and margins at top and bottom.

698 Rabbit

(Des K. Koo and K. Fung. Litho Ashton-Potter Canada)

1999 (8 Jan). *Chinese New Year. ("Year of the Rabbit"). Fluorescent frame. P* 13½.
1862 **698** 46 c. multicoloured 35 40
MS1863 Circular 100 mm diam. **698** 95 c. mult (40×40 *mm*). P 12½×13 .. .. .. 75 80

Index to Canada Stamp Designs from 1942

The following index is intended to facilitate the identification of Canadian issues from 1942. Portrait stamps are usually listed under surnames only, views under the name of the town or city and other issues under the main subject or a prominent word and date chosen from the inscription. Simple abbreviations have occasionally been resorted to and when the same design or subject appears on more than one stamp, only the first of each series is indicated.

Index to Canada Stamp Designs from 1942—*Continued*

Index to Canada Stamp Designs from 1942—*Continued*

STAMP BOOKLETS

Booklet Nos. SB1/60 are stapled, all subsequent booklets have their panes attached by selvedge, *unless otherwise stated.*

All booklets up to and including No. SB41 contain panes consisting of two rows of three (3×2).

B 1

1900 (11 June). *Red on pink cover. Two panes of six 2 c. (No. 155ba).*
SB1 25 c. booklet. Cover as Type B **1** with English text £1700

1903 (1 July). *Red on pink cover. Two panes of six 2 c. (No. 176a).*
SB2 25 c. booklet. Cover as Type B **1** with English text £1800

1912 (Jan)–**16**. *Red on pink cover. Two panes of six 2 c. (No. 201a).*
SB3 25 c. booklet. Cover as Type B **1** with English text 60·00
a. Cover handstamped "NOTICE Change in Postal Rates For New Rates See Postmaster" 60·00
b. French text (4.16) £100
ba. Cover handstamped "AVIS Changement des tarifs Postaux Pour les nouveaux tarifs consulter le maitre de poste" £100

1913 (1 May)–**16**. *Green on pale green cover. Four panes of six 1 c. (No. 197a).*
SB4 25 c. booklet. Cover as Type B **1** with English text £350
a. Containing pane No. 199a .. .. .. 65·00
ab. Cover handstamped "NOTICE Change in Postal Rates For New Rates See Postmaster" 65·00
b. French text (28.4.16) £500
ba. Containing pane No. 199a £130
bb. Cover handstamped "AVIS Changement des tarifs Postaux Pour les nouveaux tarifs consulter le maitre de poste" £275

1922 (Mar). *Black on brown cover. Two panes of four 3 c. and 2 labels (No. 205a).*
SB5 25 c. booklet. Cover as Type B **1** with English text £300
a. French text £600

1922 (July–Dec). *Black on blue cover. Panes of four 1 c., 2 c. and 3 c. (Nos. 246aa, 247aa, 205a) and 2 labels.*
SB6 25 c. booklet. Cover as Type B **1** with English text £300
a. French text (Dec) £475

1922 (Dec). *Black on orange cover. Four panes of six 1 c. (No. 246ab).*
SB7 25 c. booklet. Cover as Type B **1** with English text £100
a. French text £130

1922 (Dec). *Black on green cover. Two panes of six 2 c. (No. 247ab).*
SB8 25 c. booklet. Cover as Type B **1** with English text £600
a. French text £700

1923 (Dec). *Black on blue cover. Panes of four 1 c., 2 c. and 3 c. (Nos. 246aa, 247aa, 248aa) and 2 labels.*
SB9 25 c. booklet. Cover as Type B **1** with English text £200
a. French text £325

1923 (Dec)–**24**. *Black on brown cover. Two panes of four 3 c. (No. 248aa) and 2 labels.*
SB10 25 c. booklet. Cover as Type B **1** with English text £180
a. French text (5.24) £275

B 2

1928 (16 Oct). *Black on green cover. Two panes of six 2 c. (No. 276a).*
SB11 25 c. booklet. Cover as Type B **2** with English text 55·00
a. French text .. .. 75·00

1928 (25 Oct). *Black on orange cover. Four panes of six 1 c. (No. 275a).*
SB12 25 c. booklet. Cover as Type B **2** with English text £100
a. French text £190

1929 (6 June). *Plain manilla cover. Three panes of six 1 c., two panes of six 2 c. and one pane of six 5 c. (Nos. 275a, 276a, 279a).*
SB13 72 c. booklet. Plain cover £300
a. With "Philatelic Div., Fin. Br. P.O. Dept., Ottawa" circular cachet on front cover .. £800
b. With code number in the centre of the circular cachet £900

1930 (17 June). *Black on green cover. Two panes of six 2 c. (No. 289a).*
SB14 25 c. booklet. Cover as Type B **2** with English text 80·00
a. French text £110

1930 (17 Nov). *Black on red cover. Two panes of six 2 c. (No. 301a).*
SB15 25 c. booklet. Cover as Type B **2** with English text 55·00
a. French text .. .. 75·00

1931 (13 July). *Black on red cover. Two panes of four 3 c. (No. 303a) and 2 labels.*
SB16 25 c. booklet. Cover as Type B **2** with English text 80·00
a. French text £110

1931 (21 July). *Black on green cover. Four panes of six 1 c. (No. 300b).*
SB17 25 c. booklet. Cover as Type B **2** with English text £120
a. French text £160

1931 (23 July). *Black on brown cover. Two panes of six 2 c. (No. 302a).*
SB18 25 c. booklet. Cover as Type B **2** with English text 80·00
a. French text £110

1931 (13 Nov). *Black on blue cover. Panes of four 1 c., 2 c. and 3 c. (Nos. 300c, 302ba, 303a) and 2 labels.*
SB19 25 c. booklet. Cover as Type B **2** with English text £250
a. French text £350

1933 (22 Aug–13 Nov). *Black on red cover. Two panes of four 3 c. (No. 321a) and 2 labels.*
SB20 25 c. booklet. Cover as Type B **2** with English text (13 Nov) .. .. 85·00
a. French text (22 Aug) £160

1933 (7 Sept). *Black on brown cover. Two panes of six 2 c. (No. 320a).*
SB21 25 c. booklet. Cover as Type B **2** with English text 60·00
a. French text £100

1933 (19 Sept–5 Dec). *Black on blue cover. Panes of four 1 c., 2 c. and 3 c. (Nos. 319b, 320b, 321ba) and 2 labels.*
SB22 25 c. booklet. Cover as Type B **2** with English text £200
a. French text (5 Dec) £300

1933 (28 Dec)–**34**. *Black on green cover. Four panes of six 1 c. (No. 319a).*
SB23 25 c. booklet. Cover as Type B **2** with English text 85·00
a. French text (26.3.34) £120

B 3

1935 (1 June–8 Aug). *Red on white cover. Two panes of four 3 c. (No. 343a) and 2 labels.*
SB24 25 c. booklet. Cover as Type B **3** with English text (8 Aug) .. .. 55·00
a. French text (1 June) .. .. .. 70·00

1935 (22 July–1 Sept). *Blue on white cover. Panes of four 1 c., 2 c. and 3 c. (Nos. 341b, 342b, 343a) and 2 labels.*
SB25 25 c. booklet. Cover as Type B **3** with English text £140
a. French text (1 Sept) £180

1935 (19 Aug–18 Oct). *Green on white cover. Four panes of six 1 c. (No. 341a).*
SB26 25 c. booklet. Cover as Type B **3** with English text 90·00
a. French text (18 Oct) £130

1935 (16–18 Mar). *Brown on white cover. Two panes of six 2 c. (No. 342a).*
SB27 25 c. booklet. Cover as Type B **3** with English text 70·00
a. French text (18 Mar) £120

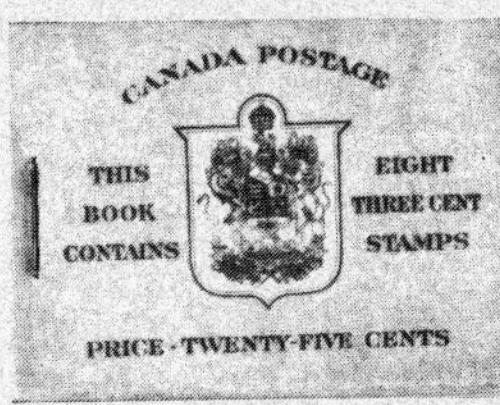

B 4

1937 (14 Apr)–**38**. *Blue and white cover. Panes of four 1 c., 2 c. and 3 c. (Nos. 357a, 358a, 359a) and 2 labels.*
SB28 25 c. booklet. Cover as Type B **3** with English text 85·00
a. French text (4.1.38) .. .. .. 95·00
SB29 25 c. booklet. Cover as Type B **4** with English text 57 mm wide .. .. 70·00
a. English text 63 mm wide .. .. .. 85·00
b. French text 57 mm wide (4.1.38) .. .. 90·00
ba. French text 63 mm wide £140

1937 (23–27 Apr). *Red and white cover. Two panes of four 3 c. (No. 359a) and 2 labels.*
SB30 25 c. booklet. Cover as Type B **3** with English text (27 Apr) .. .. 17·00
a. French text (23 Apr) .. .. .. 26·00
SB31 25 c. booklet. Cover as Type B **4** with English text 57 mm wide (27 Apr) .. .. .. 10·00
a. English text 63 mm wide .. .. .. 28·00
b. French text 57 mm wide (23 Apr) .. 13·00
ba. French text 63 mm wide £130

1937 (18 May)–**38**. *Green and white cover. Four panes of six 1 c. (No. 357b).*
SB32 25 c. booklet. Cover as Type B **3** with English text 27·00
a. French text (14.10.38) .. .. .. 38·00
SB33 25 c. booklet. Cover as Type B **4** with English text 57 mm wide .. .. 16·00
a. English text 63 mm wide .. .. .. 50·00
b. French text 57 mm wide (14.10.38) .. 18·00
ba. French text 63 mm wide £120

1938 (3 May)–**39**. *Brown and white cover. Two panes of six 2 c. (No. 358b).*
SB34 25 c. booklet. Cover as Type B **3** with English text 35·00
a. French text (3.3.39) .. .. .. 45·00
SB35 25 c. booklet. Cover as Type B **4** with English text 57 mm wide .. .. 23·00
a. English text 63 mm wide .. .. .. 55·00
b. French text 57 mm wide .. .. .. 38·00
ba. French text 63 mm wide .. .. .. 80·00

1942 (20–29 Aug) *Red and white cover. Two panes of four 3 c. (No. 377a) and 2 labels.*
SB36 25 c. booklet. Cover as Type B **4** with English text 8·50
a. French text (29 Aug) .. .. .. 12·00

1942 (12–14 Sept). *Violet and white cover. Panes of four 1 c., 2 c. and 3 c. (Nos. 375a, 376a, 377a), each with 2 labels.*
SB37 25 c. booklet. Cover as Type B **4** with English text (14 Sept) .. .. 48·00
a. French text (12 Sept) .. .. .. 90·00

1942 (6 Oct)–**43**. *Brown and white cover. Two panes of six 2 c. (No. 376b).*
SB38 25 c. booklet. Cover as Type B **4** with English text 38·00
a. French text (6.4.43) .. .. .. 65·00

1942 (24 Nov)–**46**. *Green and white cover. Four panes of six 1 c. (No. 375b).*
SB39 25 c. booklet. Cover as Type B **4** with English text 11·00
a. French text (16.2.43) .. .. .. 17·00
b. Bilingual text (8.1.46) .. .. .. 17·00

1943 (3 May)–**46**. *Orange and white cover. One pane of six 4 c. (No. 380a).*
SB40 25 c. booklet. Cover as Type B **4** with English text 4·00
a. French text (12.5.43) .. .. .. 9·00
b. Bilingual text (8.1.46) .. .. .. 13·00

1943 (28 Aug)–**46**. *Purple and white cover. Two panes of four 3 c. (No. 378a) and 2 labels.*
SB41 25 c. booklet. Cover as Type B **4** with English text 10·00
a. French text (7.9.43) .. .. .. 24·00
b. Bilingual text (8.1.46) .. .. .. 18·00

B 5

1943 (1 Sept)–**46**. *Black and white cover. Panes of three 1 c., 3 c. and 4 c. (Nos. 394a, 395a, 396a) (3×1).*
SB42 25 c. booklet. Cover as Type B **5** with English text 26·00
a. French text (18.9.43) .. .. .. 30·00
c. Bilingual text (23.1.46) .. .. .. 28·00

B 6

1947 (24 Nov). *Brown on orange cover. Panes of six 3 c. and 4 c. (3×2) and two panes of four 7 c. (2×2) (Nos. 378b, 380a, 407a).*
SB43 $1 booklet. Cover as Type B **6** with English text 25·00
a. French text .. .. 40·00

1950 (12 Apr–18 May). *Purple and white cover. Two panes of four* 3 c. (*No.* 416a) *and* 2 *labels* (3×2).
SB44 25 c. booklet. Cover as Type B **4** with English text 5·00
a. Bilingual text (18 May) . . . . 5·00

1950 (5–10 May). *Orange and white cover. One pane of six* 4 c. (*No.* 417a) (3×2).
SB45 25 c. booklet. Cover as Type B **4** with English text 28·00
a. Stitched . . . . 60·00
b. Bilingual text (10 May) . . . . . . 30·00

1950 (18 May). *Black and white cover. Panes of three* 1 c., 3 c. *and* 4 c. (*Nos.* 422ba, 423a, 423ba) (3×1).
SB46 25 c. booklet. Cover as Type B **5** with English text 50·00
a. Bilingual text . . . . 55·00

1951 (2 June). *Orange and white cover. One pane of six* 4 c. (*No.* 417ba) (3×2).
SB47 25 c. booklet. Cover as Type B **4** with English text 6·00
a. Stitched . . . . 11·00
b. Bilingual text . . . . 7·50

1951 (25 Oct)–**52.** *Black and white cover. Panes of three* 1 c., 3 c. *and* 4 c. (*Nos.* 422ba, 423a, 423ca) (3×1).
SB48 25 c. booklet. Cover as Type B **5** with English text 26·00
a. Bilingual text (9.7.52) . . . . . . 28·00

1953 (6 July–19 Aug). *Orange cover. One pane of six* 4 c. (*No.* 453a) (3×2).
SB49 25 c. booklet. Cover as Type B **4** with English text 3·50
a. Bilingual text (19 Aug) . . . . . . 4·50

1953 (17 July–20 Oct). *Purple cover. Two panes of four* 3 c. (*No.* 452a) *and* 2 *labels* (3×2).
SB50 25 c. booklet. Cover as Type B **4** with English text 3·75
a. Bilingual text (20 Oct) . . . . . . 8·00

1953 (12 Aug). *Grey cover. Panes of three* 1 c., 3 c. *and* 4 c. (*Nos.* 458a, 459a, 460a) (3×1).
SB51 25 c. booklet. Cover as Type B **5** with English text 16·00
a. Bilingual text . . . . 18·00

All the following booklets are bilingual

1954 (1 Apr–Nov). *Blue cover as Type* B **4**.
SB52 25 c. booklet containing pane of five 5 c. and 1 label (No. 473a) (3×2) . . . . 2·00
a. Stitched (Nov) . . . . 3·25

1954 (14 July–Nov). *Blue cover as Type* B **4**.
SB53 25 c. booklet containing pane of five 5 c. and 1 label (No. 467a) (3×2) . . . . 2·00
a. Stitched (Nov) . . . . 3·25

1955 (7 July). *Violet cover as Type* B **4**.
SB54 25 c. booklet containing pane of six 4 c. (No. 466a) (3×2) . . . . 4·75

B **7**

1956 (1 June). *Red and white cover as Type* B **7**.
SB55 25 c. booklet containing two panes of five 1 c. and five 4 c., each with 1 label (Nos. 463a, 466b) (3×2) . . . . 3·00

1956 (July). *Blue and white cover as Type* B **7**.
SB56 25 c. booklet containing pane of five 5 c. and 1 label (No. 467a) (3×2) . . . . 2·75

B **8**

1963 (May)–**67.** *Blue and white cover as Type* B **7**.
SB57 25 c. booklet containing pane of five 5 c. and 1 label (No. 531a) (2×3) . . . . 3·50
a. Cover Type B **8** (1.67) . . . . . . 30·00

1963 (15 May). *Red and white cover as Type* B **7**.
SB58 25 c. booklet containing two panes of five 1 c. and five 4 c., each with 1 label (Nos. 527a, 530a) (2×3) . . . . 7·00

1967 (Feb). *Red cover as Type* B **8**.
SB59 25 c. booklet containing two panes of five 1 c. and five 4 c., each with 1 label (Nos. 579a, 582a) (2×3) . . . . 2·50

1967 (Mar). *Blue cover as Type* B **8**.
SB60 25 c. booklet containing pane of five 5 c. and 1 label (No. 583a) (2×3) . . . . 7·00

B **9**

1968 (Sept). *Brown and cream cover, 70×48 mm, as Type* B **9**.
SB61 25 c. booklet containing *se-tenant* pane of five 1 c. and five 4 c. (No. 598a) (2×5) . . . . . . 2·50

1968 (Sept). *Red and cream cover as Type* B **9**.
SB62 $1 booklet containing pane of twenty-five 4 c. and 2 labels (No. 599a) (3×9) . . . . 9·00

1968 (Sept). *Blue and cream cover, 82×48 mm, as Type* B **9**.
SB63 $1 booklet containing pane of twenty 5 c. (No. 600a) (2×10) . . . . 6·50

1968 (Oct). *Orange and cream cover, 70×48 mm, as Type* B **9**, *but without border.*
SB64 25 c. booklet containing *se-tenant* pane of one 1 c., four 6 c. and 1 label (No. 598b) (2×3) . . 2·50

B **10** (*Illustration reduced. Actual size* 128×60 *mm*)

1968 (15 Nov). *Christmas. Red and green cover as Type* B **10**.
SB65 $1 booklet containing two panes of ten 5 c. (No. 630a) (5×2) . . . . 6·00
p. Phosphor (No. 630pa) . . . . . . 7·50

Nos. SB65/p exist with left or right opening (i.e. with selvedge at left or right of pane).

1969 (Jan). *Orange-red on cream cover as Type* B **9**, *but without border.*
SB66 $1.50, booklet containing pane of twenty-five 6 c. and 2 labels (No. 601a) (3×9) . . . . 11·00

1969 (8 Oct). *Christmas. Red cover size as Type* B **10**.
SB67 $1 booklet containing two panes of ten 5 c. (No. 644a) (5×2) . . . . 3·75
p. Phosphor (No. 644pa) . . . . . . 6·00

1970 (Jan). *Black on cream cover as Type* B **9**, *but without border.*
SB68 $1.50, booklet containing pane of twenty-five 6 c. and 2 labels (No. 602a) (3×9) . . . . 20·00

1970 (Aug). *Black on cream cover, 70×48 mm, as Type* B **9**, *but without border.*
SB69 25 c. booklet containing pane of four 6 c. (No. 603a) (2×2) . . . . 13·00

1970 (Aug). *Black on cream cover as Type* B **9**, *but without border.*
SB70 $1.50, booklet containing pane of twenty-five 6 c. and 2 labels (No. 607a) (3×9) . . . . 16·00

1970 (26 Oct). *Indigo on cream cover, 70×50 mm. Inscr* "CANADIAN POSTAGE STAMPS...MADE EXPRESSLY FOR OPAL MANUFACTURING CO. LIMITED".
SB71 25 c. booklet containing four 2 c. and four 3 c. (No. 580a) (2×2) with gutter margin between 2·50

No. SB71 was produced by the Canadian Bank Note Co for use in the private stamp-vending machines owned by the Opal Manufacturing Co Ltd, Toronto. To cover the cost of manufacture and installation these booklets were sold at 25 c. each. They were not available from the Canadian Post Office.

1970 (Nov). *Black on cream cover, 70×48 mm, as Type* B **9**, *but without border.*
SB72 25 c. booklet containing pane of four 6 c. (No. 608a) (2×2) . . . . 5·50

1971 (30 June). *Green on cream cover, 70×48 mm, as Type* B **9** *but without border.*
SB73 25 c. booklet containing *se-tenant* pane of one 1 c., one 3 c., three 7 c. and 1 label (No. 604b) (2×3) . . . . 5·5

This exists with or without a black sealing strip inside the cover.

1971 (30 June). *Green and buff cover, 82×47 mm, as Type* B **9** *but without border.*
SB74 $1 booklet containing *se-tenant* pane of four 1 c., four 3 c. and twelve 7 c. (No. 604a) (2×10) 14·0

1971 (Aug). *Booklet No.* SB73 *with label affixed giving the new contents. Sold as an experiment in Toronto for* 50 c.
SB75 50 c. booklet. Contents as No. SB73, but containing two panes . . . . . . 11·00

The experiment was later continued by the use of machines which issued two 25 c. booklets for 50 c.

1971 (30 Dec). *Grey on cream cover, 70×48 mm, as Type* B **9**, *but without border.*
SB76 25 c. booklet containing *se-tenant* pane of three 1 c., one 6 c. and two 8 c. (No. 604c) (2×3) 2·00
q. With fluorescent bands (No. 604qc) . . 4·50

1971 (30 Dec). *Grey on cream cover, 77×48 mm, as Type* B **9**, *but without border.*
SB77 $1 booklet containing *se-tenant* pane of six 1 c., one 6 c. and eleven 8 c. (No. 604d) (2×9) . . 7·50
q. With fluorescent bands (No. 604qd) . . 7·00

B **11**

1972 (Mar). *As No.* SB76, *but with brown on cream illustrated covers as Type* B **11**. *Ten different designs showing Mail Transport:*
(a) Post Office, 1816
(b) Stage Coach, *c* 1820
(c) Paddle Steamer, 1855
(d) Rural postman, *c* 1900
(e) Motor car, 1910
(f) Ford Model "T", 1914
(g) Curtis "JN4", 1918
(h) Mail truck, 1921
(i) Motorcycle, 1923
(j) Horse-drawn mail wagon, 1926

SB78 25 c. booklet. Contents as No. SB76 (*any cover*) 2·00
q. With fluorescent bands . . . . . . 2·50
Set of 10 *different cover designs* . . . . 18·00
Set of 10 *different cover designs (fluorescent bands on stamps)* . . . . . . 22·00

1972 (Aug). *Ten cover designs as No.* SB78, *but in blue on cream.*
SB79 50 c. booklet (*any cover*) containing *se-tenant* pane of one 6 c., four 1 c. and five 8 c. (No. 604e) (2×5) . . . . 4·50
q. With fluorescent bands (No. 604qe) . . 4·50
Set of 10 *different cover designs* . . . . 42·00
Set of 10 *different cover designs (fluorescent bands on stamps)* . . . . . . 42·00

This exists with black or white sealing strip inside the cover.

1974 (10 Apr). *Red on cream covers as Type* B **11**. *Ten different designs showing aircraft:*
(a) Gibson "Twin-plane"
(b) Burgess Dunne seaplane
(c) Nieuport "Scout"
(d) Curtiss "HS-2L"
(e) Junkers "W-34"
(f) Fokker "Super Universal"
(g) "Mosquito"
(h) "Stranraer" flying-boat
(i) "CF-100 Canuck"
(j) "Argus"

SB80 25 c. booklet (*any cover*) containing *se-tenant* pane of three 1 c., one 6 c. and two 8 c. (No. 693a) (3×2) 65
Set of 10 *different cover designs* . . . . 6·00

B **12**

1975 (17 Jan). *Violet on cream cover as Type* B **12**.
SB81 $1 booklet containing *se-tenant* pane of six 1 c., one 6 c. and eleven 8 c. (No. 693b) (9×2) . . 2·25

1976 (1 Sept). *Violet on cream cover. Designs as No.* SB80.
SB82 50 c. booklet (*any cover*) containing *se-tenant* pane of two 1 c., four 2 c. and four 10 c. (No. 693c) (5×2) . . . . 1·50
Set of 10 *different cover designs* . . . . 14·00

1977 (1 Nov). *Brown on cream covers, similar to Type* B **11**, *but vert. Ten different designs showing flowers or trees:*
(a) Bottle Gentian
(b) Western Columbine
(c) Canada Lily
(d) Hepatica
(e) Shooting Star
(f) Lady's Slipper
(g) Trembling Aspen
(h) Douglas Fir
(i) Sugar Maple
(j) Rose, Thistle, Shamrock, Lily and Maple leaf

383 50 c. booklet (*any cover*) containing *se-tenant* pane of two 1 c. and four 12 c. (No. 862a) (3×2) . . . . 2·75
Set of 10 *different cover designs* . . 25·00

78 (17 May). *Green on cream covers. Designs as No.* SB83.
384 50 c. booklet (*any cover*) containing *se-tenant* pane of four 2 c., three 14 c. and 1 label (No. 863a) (4×2) . . . . 3·25
Set of 10 *different cover designs* . . 30·00

B 13

978 (13 Nov). *Black on cream covers as Type* B **13**. *Five different designs showing postcode publicity cartoons*:
(a) Talking post box
(b) Woman throwing letter to man
(c) Running letters
(d) Letter running to post box
(e) Womam with letter and laughing post box
B85 $3.50, booklet (*any cover*) containing pane of twenty-five 14 c. and 2 labels (No. 868ab) (9×3) . . . . 11·00
Set of 5 *different cover designs* . . 50·00

1979 (28 Mar). *Blue on cream covers. Designs as No.* SB83.
SB86 50 c. booklet (*any cover*) containing *se-tenant* pane of one 1 c., three 5 c. and two 17 c. (No. 870a) (3×2) . . . . 2·50
Set of 10 *different cover designs* . . 23·00

1979 (3 July)–**81**. *Violet on cream covers. Designs as No.* SB85.
SB87 $4.25, booklet (*any cover*) containing pane of twenty-five 17 c. and 2 labels (No. 869ab) (9×3) (cover without wavy lines) . . 11·00
Set of 5 *different cover designs* . . 50·00
SB88 $4.25, booklet (*any cover*) containing No. 869ab (horizontal wavy lines across cover) (4.2.81) 12·00
Set of 5 *different cover designs* . . 55·00

B 14

1982 (1 Mar). *Black on cream covers as Type* B **14**. *Ten different designs showing provincial legislature buildings*:
(a) Victoria, British Columbia
(b) Fredericton, New Brunswick
(c) Halifax, Nova Scotia
(d) Charlottetown, Prince Edward Island
(e) Quebec
(f) Edmonton, Alberta
(g) Toronto, Ontario
(h) Regina, Saskatchewan
(i) Winnipeg, Manitoba
(j) St. John's, Newfoundland

SB89 50 c. booklet (*any cover*) containing *se-tenant* pane of two 5 c., one 10 c., one 30 c. and 2 labels (No. 1033a) (3×2) . . . . 2·50
a. Containing pane No. 1033ab . . . . 2·75
b. Containing pane No. 1033ba . . . . 7·50
c. Containing pane No. 1033bb . . . . 7·50
Set of 10 *different cover designs* (*No.* SB89) 22·00

B **15** Parliament Buildings, Ottawa

1982 (30 June). *Black on cream cover as Type* B **15**.
SB90 $6 booklet containing pane of twenty 30 c. and 1 label (No. 1032ab) (7×3) . . . . 15·00

1983 (15 Feb)–**85**. *Indian red on cream covers as Type* B **14**. *Designs as No.* SB89.
SB91 50 c. booklet (*any cover*) containing *se-tenant* pane of two 5 c., one 8 c., one 32 c. and 2 labels (No. 1033c) (3×2) . . . . 3·00
Set of 10 *different cover designs* . . 27·00
a. Indian red on surfaced yellow cover (3.4.85) 3·00
Set of 10 *different cover designs* . . 27·00

1983 (8 Apr). *Indian red on cream cover as Type* B **15**.
SB92 $8 booklet containing pane of twenty-five 32 c. and 2 labels (No. 1032bb) (9×3) . . . . 17·00

1983 (30 June). *Canada Day. Multicoloured cover*, 100×78 *mm, showing location map of various forts.*
SB93 $3.20, booklet containing *se-tenant* pane of ten 32 c. (No. 1090a) (5×2) . . . . 5·00

1984 (15 Feb). *Cover as Type* B **15**, *but additionally inscribed* "1984" *below* "POSTES".
SB94 $8 booklet containing pane of twenty-five 32 c. and 2 labels (No. 1032bb) (9×3) . . . . 21·00

1985 (21 June). *Reddish brown on grey-brown covers similar to Type* B **14**. *Ten different designs showing architectural or ornamental details from Parliament Buildings, Ottawa*:
(a) Clock from Peace Tower
(b) Library entrance
(c) Gargoyle from Peace Tower
(d) Indian mask sculpture
(e) Stone carving at Memorial Chamber entrance
(f) Door to House of Commons
(g) Stone ornament at House of Commons main entrance
(h) Carved head, Senate Chamber
(i) Windows, Centre Block
(j) Window and war memorial, Peace Tower
SB95 50 c. booklet (*any cover*) containing *se-tenant* pane of three 2 c., two 5 c. and one 34 c. (No. 1148a) (2×3) . . . . 2·25
Set of 10 *different cover designs* . . 20·00
a. "R" on bottom left-hand corner of back cover 2·25
Set of 10 *different cover designs* . . 20·00

1985 (28 June). *Canada Day. Black, pale brown and pale grey-brown cover*, 100×78 *mm, showing location map of various forts.*
SB96 $3.40, booklet containing *se-tenant* pane of ten 34 c. (No. 1163a) (5×2) . . . . 4·50

B **16** Parliament Buildings, Ottawa
(*Illustration reduced. Actual size* 120×70 *mm*)

1985 (1 Aug)–**86**. *White on agate cover as Type* B **16**.
SB97 $8.50, booklet containing pane of twenty-five 34 c. (No. 1155a) (5×5) . . . . 11·50
a. Containing pane No. 1155ba (4.7.86) . . 26·00

B **17**
(*Illustration reduced. Actual size* 121×61 *mm*)

1985 (23 Oct). *Christmas. Rosine and emerald cover as Type* B **17**.
SB98 $3.20, booklet containing pane of ten 32 c. (No. 1181a) (5×2) . . . . 6·50

B **18**
(*Illustration reduced. Actual size* 150×72 *mm*)

1986 (29 Oct). *Christmas. Black and brown-red cover as Type* B **18**.
SB99 $2.90, booklet containing pane of ten 29 c. (No. 1218a) (1×10) . . . . 6·50
a. Containing pane No. 1218ba . . . . 50·00

1987 (30 Mar). *Ten cover designs as No.* SB95 *but in blackish olive on grey-brown.*
SB100 50 c. booklet (*any cover*) containing *se-tenant* pane of two 1 c., two 6 c., one 36 c. and 1 label (No. 1147a) (2×3) . . . . 4·50
Set of 10 *different cover designs* . . 40·00
a. Containing pane No. 1147ba (1.10.87) . . 4·00
Set of 10 *different cover designs* . . 35·00

1987 (30 Mar). *Yellow-orange on agate cover similar to Type* B **16**, *but* 48×74 *mm.*
SB101 $3.60, booklet containing pane of ten 36 c. (No. 1156ba) (2×5) . . . . 10·00

1987 (19 May). *Yellow-orange on agate cover as Type* B **16**.
SB102 $9 booklet containing pane of twenty-five 36 c. (No. 1156bb) (5×5) . . . . 22·00

1987 (2 Nov). *Christmas. Christmas Plants. Black and magenta cover as Type* B **18**, *but* 148×80 *mm.*
SB103 $3.10, booklet containing pane of ten 31 c. (No. 1254a) (2×5) . . . . 5·00

B 19

1988 (5 Jan). *White and black on bright green cover as Type* B **19**.
SB104 $3.70, booklet (49×73 *mm*) containing pane of ten 37 c. (No. 1157ab) (2×5) . . . . 12·00
SB105 $9.25, booklet (120×73 *mm*) containing pane of twenty-five 37 c. (No. 1157ae) (5×5) . . 27·00

1988 (15 Jan). *Covers as Type* B **19**, *but inscribed* "LUNCH SAVER".
SB106 $3.70, booklet (49×73 *mm*) containing pane of ten 37 c. (No. 1157ab) (2×5) . . . . 12·00
SB107 $9.25, booklet (120×73 *mm*) containing pane of twenty-five 37 c. (No. 1157ae) (5×5) . . 27·00

1988 (3 Feb). *Deep blue on grey-brown covers as Type* B **14**. *Ten different designs as No.* SB95.
SB108 50 c. booklet (*any cover*) containing *se-tenant* pane of one 1 c., two 6 c., one 37 c. and 2 labels (No. 1147bb) (2×3) . . . . 2·25
Set of 10 *different cover designs* . . 20·00

1988 (27 Oct). *Christmas. Icons. Multicoloured cover as Type* B **18**, *but* 150×80 *mm, showing stamp illustration on the front.*
SB109 $3.20, booklet containing pane of ten 32 c. (No. 1308a) (2×5) . . . . 3·50

B **20** B **21**
(*Illustrations reduced. Actual size* 79×152 *mm*)

1988 (29 Dec)–**89**. *Multicoloured stamps on bright scarlet and violet-blue covers* (*Type* B **20**) *or on scarlet with white inscr* (*Type* B **21**).
SB110 $2.20, booklet containing pane of five 44 c. and 1 label (No. 1269ab) (2×3) (18.1.89) . . 5·00
a. Cover Type B **21** (17.3.89) . . 5·00
SB111 $3.80, booklet containing pane of ten 38 c. and 2 labels (No. 1157ca) (3×4) . . . . 5·00
a. Cover Type B **21** (17.3.89) . . . . 5·00
SB112 $3.80, booklet containing pane of ten 38 c. and 2 labels (No. 1162bd) (3×4) . . . . 4·50
a. Cover Type B **21** (17.3.89) . . . . 4·50
SB113 $3.80, booklet containing pane of five 76 c. and 1 label (No. 1275ab) (2×3) (18.1.89) . . 8·50
a. Cover Type B **21** (17.3.89) . . . . 8·50

SB114 $9.50, booklet containing pane of twenty-five 38 c. and 2 labels (No. 1157cb) (3×9) .. 12·00
a. Cover Type B **21** (17.3.89) .. .. 12·00

Booklet Nos. SB110/14 each exist with either "Lunch Savers" or "Would it be more convenient" advertisement on the reverse.

Booklet Nos. SB110a/14a also exist with "Your "Rush" Connection" advertisement on the reverse.

1989 (18 Jan). *Brown-purple on grey-brown covers as Type* B **14**. *Ten different designs as No.* SB95.

SB115 50 c. booklet (*any cover*) containing *se-tenant* pane of three 2 c., one 6 c., one 38 c. and 1 label (No. 1148ba) (2×3) .. .. 1·90
Set of 10 *different cover designs* .. .. 17·00

B **22**
(*Illustration reduced. Actual size* 85 × 155 *mm*)

1989 (30 June). *Multicoloured cover as Type* B **22**.

SB116 $5 booklet containing pane of twelve self-adhesive 38 c. (No. 1328ea) (6×2) .. 10·00

Two types of cover exist for No. SB116 with one being the mirror image of the other.

1989 (26 Oct). *Christmas. Paintings of Winter Landscapes. Multicoloured covers as Type* B **21**.

SB117 $2.20, booklet containing pane of five 44 c. and 1 label (No. 1344a) (2×3) (*cover* 60×155 *mm*) 11·00
SB118 $3.30, booklet containing pane of ten 33 c. (No. 1342a) (2×5) (80×155 *mm*) .. .. 8·00
SB119 $3.80, booklet containing pane of ten 38 c. (No. 1343ab) (5×2) (80×155 *mm*) .. .. 28·00
SB120 $3.80, booklet containing pane of five 76 c. and 1 label (No. 1345a) (2×3) (60×155 *mm*) .. 19·00

1989 (28 Dec). *Multicoloured covers as Type* B **21**.

SB121 $3.90, booklet containing pane of ten 39 c. and 2 labels (No. 1354a) (4×3) .. .. 7·00
SB122 $9.75, booklet containing pane of twenty-five 39 c. and 2 labels (No. 1354b) (9×3) .. 17·00

B **23** Park Corner, Prince Edward Island

1990 (12 Jan). *Multicoloured cover as Type* B **23**.

SB123 50 c. booklet containing *se-tenant* pane of one 1 c., two 5 c. and one 39 c. (No. 1350a) (2×2) (*p* 13½×14) .. .. .. 1·40
a. Containing pane No. 1350ba (*p* 12½×13) 35·00

1990 (12 Jan). *Multicoloured covers as Type* B **21**.

SB124 $2.25, booklet containing pane of five 45 c. and 1 label (No. 1270ab) (2×3) .. .. 7·00
SB125 $3.90, booklet containing pane of ten 39 c. and 2 labels (No. 1162cb) (3×4) .. .. 13·00
SB126 $3.90, booklet containing pane of five 78 c. and 1 label (No. 1276ab) (2×3) .. .. 9·00

1990 (8 Feb). *Multicoloured cover as Type* B **22** *showing wheatfield*.

SB127 $5 booklet containing pane of twelve self-adhesive 39 c. (No. 1328ba) (2×6) .. 11·00

Two types of cover exist for No. SB127 with one being the mirror image of the other.

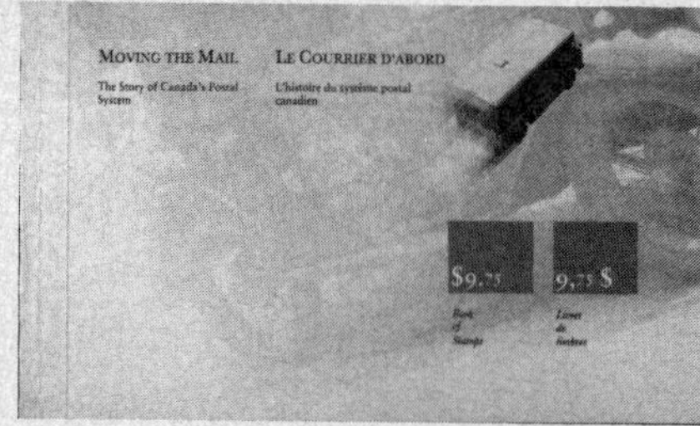

B **24**
(*Illustration reduced. Actual size* 170 × 100 *mm*)

1990 (3 May). *"Moving the Mail". Multicoloured cover as Type* B **24**. *Booklet contains text and illustrations on labels attached to the panes and on interleaving pages. Stitched.*

SB128 $9.75, booklet containing two panes of eight 39 c. (No. 1382a) (2×4) and one pane of nine 39 c. (No. 1382b) (3×4) .. .. .. 18·00

1990 (25 Oct). *Christmas. Native Art. Multicoloured covers as Type* B **21**.

SB129 $2.25, booklet containing pane of five 45 c. (No. 1407a) (2×3) (*cover* 60×155 *mm*) .. .. 4·00
SB130 $3.40, booklet containing pane of ten 34 c. (No. 1405a) (2×5) (80×155 *mm*) .. .. 4·00
SB131 $3.90, booklet containing pane of ten 39 c. (No. 1406a) (2×5) (60×155 *mm*) .. .. 7·00
SB132 $3.90, booklet containing pane of five 78 c. (No. 1408a) (2×3) (60×155 *mm*) .. .. 7·00

1990 (28 Dec). *Multicoloured cover as Type* B **23**, *but showing Point Atkinson, British Columbia.*

SB133 50 c. booklet containing *se-tenant* pane of two 1 c., one 5 c. and one 40 c. (No. 1350c) (2×2) 2·00

The face value of No. SB133 included 3 c. Goods and Service Tax.

1990 (28 Dec). *Covers as Type* B **21** *showing multicoloured stamps on scarlet background with white inscriptions.*

SB134 $2.30, booklet containing pane of five 46 c. and 1 label (No. 1270cc) (2×3) .. .. 5·00
SB135 $4 booklet containing pane of ten 40 c. and 2 labels (No. 1162da) (3×4) .. .. 8·00
SB136 $4 booklet containing pane of five 80 c. and 1 label (No. 1276cc) (2×3) .. .. 8·00
SB137 $4 booklet containing pane of ten 40 c. and 2 labels (No. 1355a) (4×3) .. .. 8·00
SB138 $10 booklet containing pane of twenty-five 40 c. and 2 labels (No. 1355b) (9×3) .. .. 18·00

1991 (11 Jan). *Multicoloured cover as Type* B **22**, *but showing coastal scene.*

SB139 $5.25, booklet containing pane of twelve self-adhesive 40 c. (No. 1328ca) (2×6) .. .. 11·00

Two types of cover exist for No. SB139 with one being the mirror image of the other.

B **25** (*Illustration reduced. Actual size* 80×125 *mm*)

B **26** (*Illustration reduced. Actual size* 64×156 *mm*)

1991 (22 May). *Public Gardens. Multicoloured cover as Type* B **25**.

SB140 $4 booklet containing *se-tenant* pane of ten 40 c. (No. 1422a) (5×2) .. .. 5·50

1991 (20 Aug). *Canadian Rivers (1st series). Multicoloured cover as Type* B **26**.

SB141 $4 booklet containing *se-tenant* pane of ten 40 c. (No. 1432a) (10×1) .. .. 7·50

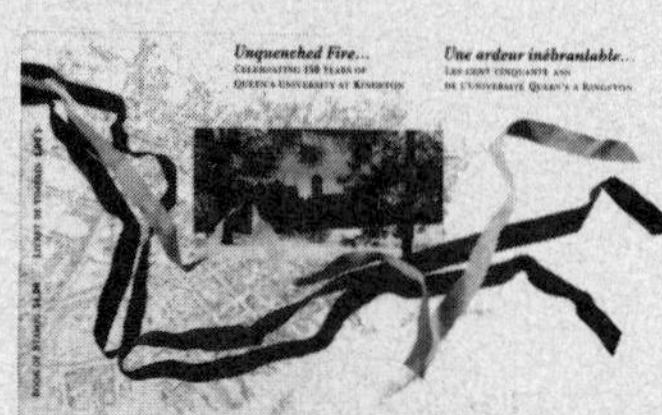

B **27**
(*Illustration reduced. Actual size* 150×81 *mm*)

1991 (16 Oct). 150*th Anniv of Queen's University. Mul coloured cover as Type* B **27**. *Booklet contains text a illustrations on labels attached to the pane and on interleavi pages. Stitched.*

SB142 $4 booklet containing pane of ten 40 c. and 2 labels (No. 1449a) (4×3) .. .. .. 7·

B **28** Christmas Tree B **29**

1991 (23 Oct). *Christmas. Multicoloured covers as Type* B **28**

SB143 $2.30, booklet containing pane of five 46 c. and 1 label (No. 1452a) (2×3) .. .. .. 4·
SB144 $3.50, booklet containing pane of ten 35 c. (No. 1450a) (2×5) (punch bowl and candles cover design, 80×155 mm) .. .. .. 7·
SB145 $4 booklet containing pane of ten 40 c. (No. 1451a) (2×5) (Christmas stocking cover design) .. .. 8·
SB146 $4 booklet containing pane of five 80 c. and 1 label (No. 1453a) (2×3) (Christmas presents cover design) .. .. 8·0

1991 (27 Dec). *Covers as Type* B **29** *showing multicolour stamps on scarlet background with Olympic logo in black.*

SB147 $2.40, booklet containing pane of five 48 c. and 1 label (No. 1467ab) (2×3) .. .. 5·0
SB148 $4.20, booklet containing pane of five 84 c. and 1 label (No. 1475ab) (2×3) .. .. 8·0
SB149 $4.20, booklet containing pane of ten 42 c. (No. 1162ea) (2×5) .. .. 8·0
SB150 $4.20, booklet containing pane of ten 42 c. (No. 1356a) (2×5) .. .. 8·0
SB151 $10.50, booklet containing pane of twenty-five 42 c. and 2 labels (No. 1356b) (3×9) .. 16·0
SB152 $21 booklet containing pane of fifty 42 c. and 2 labels (No. 1356c) (4×13) .. .. 48·0

The cover of booklet No. SB152 is made up of two $10.5 covers rouletted down the centre. It was issued in connectio with a Canada Post special offer of a $1 coupon towards the cos of its purchase.

1992 (28 Jan). *Multicoloured cover as Type* B **22**, *but showin mountain peaks.*

SB153 $5.25, booklet containing pane of twelve self-adhesive 42 c. stamps (No. 1328da) (2×6) 11·0

Two types of cover exist for No. SB153 with one being th mirror image of the other.

B **30** Olympic Flame
(*Illustration reduced. Actual size* 83×151 *mm*)

1992 (7 Feb). *Winter Olympic Games, Albertville. Multi coloured cover as Type* B **30**.

SB154 $4.20, booklet containing *se-tenant* pane of ten 42 c. (No. 1482a) (5×2) .. .. .. 6·5

Two types of cover exist for No. SB154 with one being th mirror image of the other.

1992 (22 Apr). *Canadian Rivers (2nd series). Multicolour vert cover as Type* B **26**.

SB155 $4.20, booklet containing *se-tenant* pane of ten 42 c. (No. 1492a) (5×2) .. .. .. 7·5

1992 (15 June). *Olympic Games, Barcelona. Multicolour cover as Type* B **30**, *but showing Olympic flag.*

SB156 $4.20, booklet containing *se-tenant* pane of ten 42 c. (No. 1498a) (5×2) .. .. .. 8·0

Two types of cover exist for No. SB156 with one being th mirror image of the other.

B 31 Prospecting Equipment
(Illustration reduced. Actual size 90×151 mm)

1992 (21 Sept). *150th Anniv of Geological Survey of Canada. Multicoloured cover as Type* B **31**.
SB157 $4.20, booklet containing *se-tenant* pane of ten 42 c. (No. 1509a) (5×2) .. .. .. 9·00

B 32 Hockey Players
(Illustration reduced. Actual size 171×105 mm)

1992 (9 Oct). *75th Anniv of National Ice Hockey League. Multicoloured cover as Type* B **32**. *Booklet contains text and illustrations on labels attached to the pane and on interleaving pages. Stitched.*
SB158 $10. 50, booklet containing twenty-five 42 c. stamps in two panes of 8 and 1 label and one pane of 9 (Nos. 1516a, 1517a, 1518a) (each 3×3) .. .. 19·00

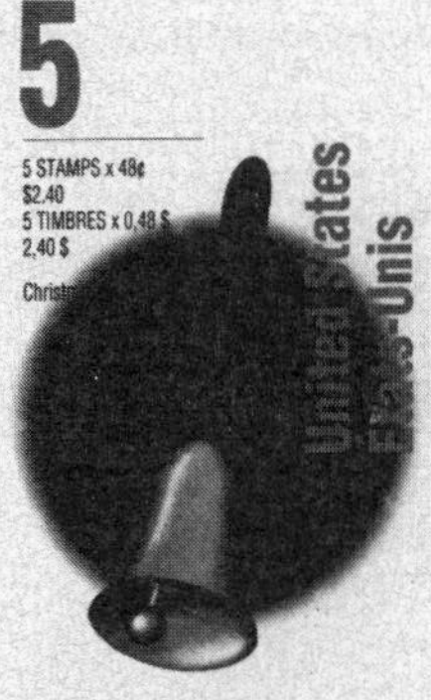

B 33 Hand Bell

1992 (13 Nov). *Christmas. Multicoloured covers as Type* B **33**.
SB159 $2.40, booklet containing pane of five 48 c. and 1 label (No. 1527a) (2×3) .. .. .. 4·50
SB160 $3.70, booklet containing pane of ten 37 c. (No. 1525a) (2×5) (candle and cookies cover design, 80×156 mm) .. .. .. 7·00
SB161 $4.20, booklet containing pane of ten 42 c. (No. 1526ab) (2×5) (hobby horse cover design) 7·00
SB162 $4.20, booklet containing pane of five 84 c. and 1 label (No. 1528a) (2×3) (Christmas tree cover design) .. .. 7·00

1992 (30 Dec). *Multicoloured covers as Type* B **29**, *but without Olympic symbol at top right.*
SB163 $2.45, booklet containing pane of five 49 c. and 1 label (No. 1468ba) (2×3) .. .. 5·50
SB164 $4.30, booklet containing pane of ten 43 c. (No. 1162fa) (2×5) .. .. 8·00
SB165 $4.30, booklet containing pane of ten 43 c. (No. 1357a) (2×5) .. .. 7·50
SB166 $4.30, booklet containing pane of five 86 c. and 1 label (No. 1476ba) (2×3) .. .. 12·00
SB167 $10.75, booklet containing pane of twenty-five 43 c. and 2 labels (No. 1357b) (3×9) .. 17·00

1993 (15 Feb). *Multicoloured cover as Type* B **22**, *but showing lake.*
SB168 $5.25, booklet containing pane of twelve self-adhesive 43 c. stamps (2×6) (No. 1328ea) .. .. 9·00

Two types of cover exist for No. SB168 with one being the mirror image of the other.

B 34 Hand-crafting Techniques *(Illustration reduced. Actual size 81×156 mm)*

B 35 Postcards and Stamps *(Illustration reduced. Actual size 60×155 mm)*

1993 (30 Apr). *Hand-crafted Textiles. Multicoloured cover as Type* B **34**.
SB169 $4.30, booklet containing *se-tenant* pane of ten 43 c. (5×2) (No. 1534a) .. .. .. 7·00

1993 (14 June). *Historic Hotels. Multicoloured cover as Type* B **35**.
SB170 $4.30, booklet containing *se-tenant* pane of ten 43 c. (5×2) (No. 1540a) .. .. .. 6·00

1993 (10 Aug). *Canadian Rivers* (3rd *series*). *Multicoloured vert cover as Type* B **26**.
SB171 $4.30, booklet containing *se-tenant* pane of ten 43 c. (10×1) (No. 1558a) .. .. .. 6·00

B 36 Rabbit and Present

B 37

1993 (4 Nov). *Christmas. Multicoloured covers as Type* B **36**.
SB172 $2.45, booklet containing pane of five 49 c. and 1 label (2×3) (No. 1574a) .. .. .. 4·50
SB173 $3.80, booklet containing pane of ten 38 c. (2×5) (No. 1572a) (wooden puppet cover design, 80×156 mm) .. .. .. 7·00
SB174 $4.30, booklet containing pane of ten 43 c. (2×5) (No. 1573a) (angel cover design) .. 8·00
SB175 $4.30, booklet containing pane of five 86 c. and 1 label (2×3) (No. 1575a) (kangaroo cover design) .. .. 8·00

1994 (7 Jan–14 Nov). *Covers as Type* B **37**, *each showing multicoloured stamps in a continuous pattern on scarlet background.*
SB176 $2.45, booklet containing pane of five 49 c. and 1 label (No. 1468a) (2×3) .. .. 5·50
SB177 $4.30, booklet containing pane of ten 43 c. (No. 1162fa) (2×5) .. .. 7·00
SB178 $4.30, booklet containing pane of ten 43 c. (No. 1357ca) (*p* 14½) (2×5) (18 Jan) .. 6·00
a. Containing pane No. 1357a (*p* 13½×13) (14 Nov) .. .. 6·00
SB179 $4.30, booklet containing pane of five 86 c. (No. 1476a) and 1 label (2×3) .. .. 7·50
SB180 $10.75, booklet containing pane of twenty-five 43 c. and 2 labels (No. 1357cb) (*p* 14½) (3×9) (18 Jan) .. .. 15·00
a. Containing pane No. 1357b (*p* 13½×13) (14 Nov) .. .. 15·00

ALTERED CATALOGUE NUMBERS

Any Catalogue numbers altered from the last edition are shown as a list in the introductory pages.

B 38
(Illustration reduced. Actual size 106×157 mm)

1994 (28 Jan). *Greetings. Multicoloured cover as Type* B **38**.
SB181 $4.50, booklet containing pane of ten self-adhesive 43 c. (No. 1580a) and 35 circular greetings labels .. .. 5·50

1994 (25 Feb)–**95**. *Covers as Type* B **37** *showing multicoloured stamps in a continuous pattern on scarlet backgrounds.*
SB182 $2.50, booklet containing pane of five 50 c. and 1 label (No. 1469a) (*p* 13) (2×3) .. .. 5·00
a. Containing pane No. 1469ba (*p* 14½×14) (27.3.95) .. .. 5·00
SB183 $4.40, booklet containing pane of five 88 c. and 1 label (No. 1477a) (fluorescent frame) (*p* 13) (2×3) .. .. 8·00
a. Containing pane No. 1477ba (three fluorescent bands) (*p* 13) (14.11.94) .. 8·00
b. Containing pane No. 1477ca (three fluorescent bands) (*p* 14½×14) (27.3.95) .. 8·00

B 39 Images of T. Eaton Company Ltd
(Illustration reduced. Actual size 151×101 mm)

1994 (17 Mar). *125th Anniv of T. Eaton Company Ltd. Multicoloured cover as Type* B **39**. *Booklet containing text and illustrations on label attached to the pane and on interleaving pages. Stitched.*
SB184 $4.30, booklet containing ten 43 c. stamps and 2 labels (No. 1583a) (6×2) .. .. 5·50

1994 (22 Apr). *Canadian Rivers* (4*th series*). *Multicoloured vert cover as Type* B **26**.
SB185 $4.30, booklet containing *se-tenant* pane of ten 43 c. (No. 1584a) (2×5) .. .. .. 5·50

B 40 Carol Singer

1994 (3 Nov). *Christmas. Multicoloured covers as Type* B **40**.
SB186 $2.50, booklet containing pane of five 50 c. and 1 label (2×3) (No. 1619a) .. .. .. 4·25
SB187 $3.80, booklet containing pane of ten (38 c.) (2×5) (No. 1617a) (chorister wearing ruff cover design, 80×156 mm) .. .. 7·00
SB188 $4.30, booklet containing pane of ten 43 c. (2×5) (No. 1618a) (pair of singers cover design) 8·00
SB189 $4.40, booklet containing pane of five 88 c. and 1 label (2×3) (No. 1620a) (singer in hat and scarf cover design) .. .. 8·00

B **41** Fortress Gateway (*Illustration reduced. Actual size* 96×157 *mm*)

1995 (5 May). *275th Anniv of Fortress of Louisbourg. Multicoloured cover as Type* B **41**.
SB190 $4.30, booklet containing pane of ten (43 c.) (5×2) (No. 1631a) .. .. .. 4·00

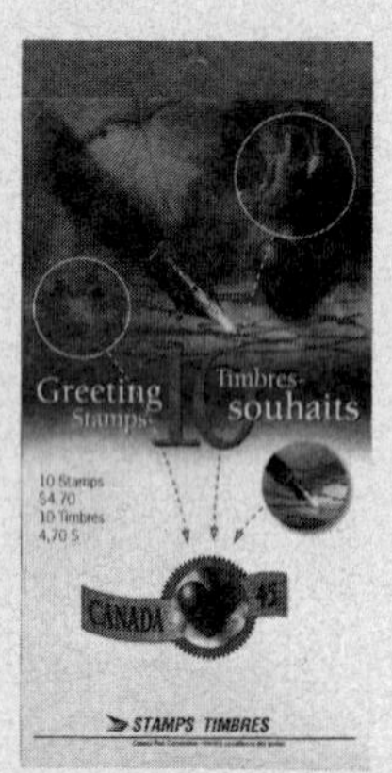

B **42** Player and Bunker (*Illustration reduced. Actual size* 52×156 *mm*)

B **43** Fountain Pen (*Illustration reduced. Actual size* 78×156 *mm*)

1995 (6 June). *Centenaries of Canadian Amateur Golf Championship and of the Royal Canadian Golf Association. Multicoloured cover as Type* B **42**.
SB191 $4.30, booklet containing *se-tenant* pane of ten 43 c. (5×2) (No. 1637a) .. .. .. 4·50

1995 (31 July–6 Oct). *Covers as Type* B **37**, *each showing multicoloured stamps in a continuous pattern on scarlet background.*
SB192 $2.60, booklet containing pane of five 52 c. and 1 label (No. 1470a) (*p* 13) (2×3) .. .. 2·00
a. Containing pane No. 1470ba (*p* 14½×14) (6 Oct) .. .. 4·00
SB193 $4.50, booklet containing pane of ten 45 c. (No. 1162ga) (2×5) .. .. 3·50
SB194 $4.50, booklet containing pane of ten 45 c. (No. 1358a) (*p* 14½) (2×5) .. .. .. 6·00
a. Containing pane No. 1358ca (*p* 13½×13) (6 Oct) .. .. 3·50
SB195 $4.50, booklet containing pane of five 90 c. and 1 label (No. 1478a) (*p* 13) (2×3) .. .. 3·75
a. Containing pane No. 1478ba (*p* 14½×14) (6 Oct) .. .. 3·50
SB196 $11.25, booklet containing pane of twenty-five 45 c. and 2 labels (No. 1358b) (*p* 14½) (3×9) 14·00
a. Containing pane No. 1358cb (*p* 13½×13) (6 Oct) .. .. 14·00

Nos. SB192a, SB194a, SB195a and SB196a, together with a new printing of No. SB193 issued on the same date, show a revised back cover layout including a customer service phone number.

1995 (1 Sept). *Greetings. Multicoloured cover as Type* B **43**.
SB197 $4.70, booklet containing pane of ten self-adhesive 45 c. (No. 1654a) and 15 circular greetings labels .. .. 4·00

B **44** Aspects of Chiropractic Healing (*Illustration reduced. Actual size* 78×156 *mm*)

1995 (15 Sept). *Centenary of Chiropractic Healing in Canada. Multicoloured cover as Type* B **44**.
SB198 $4.70, booklet containing pane of ten self-adhesive 45 c. (No. 1654a) and 15 circular commemorative labels .. .. .. 4·50

1995 (15 Sept). *50th Anniv of Arctic Institute of North America. Multicoloured cover as Type* B **26**, *but showing Inuk woman and Arctic scene.*
SB199 $4.50, booklet containing *se-tenant* pane of ten 45 c. (No. 1656a) (5×2) .. .. .. 6·50

B **45** Superman (*Illustration reduced. Actual size* 105×169 *mm*)

1995 (2 Oct). *Comic Book Superheroes. Multicoloured cover as Type* B **45**.
SB200 $4.50, booklet containing *se-tenant* pane of ten 45 c. (No. 1661a) (5×2) .. .. .. 4·75

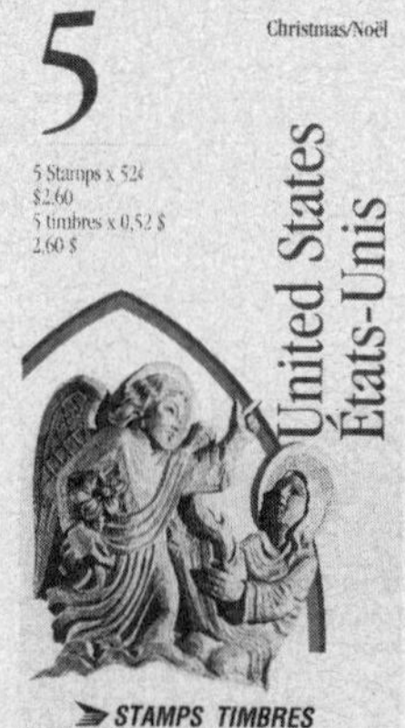

B **46** "The Annunciation"

1995 (2 Nov). *Christmas. Multicoloured covers as Type* B **46**.
SB201 $2.60, booklet containing pane of five 52 c. and 1 label (2×3) (No. 1669a) .. .. .. 4·25
SB202 $4 booklet containing pane of ten 40 c. (2×5) (No. 1667a) (Sprig of holly cover design, 80×156 *mm*) .. .. .. 6·50
SB203 $4.50, booklet containing pane of ten 45 c. (2×5) (No. 1668a) ("The Nativity" cover design) 7·50
SB204 $4.50, booklet containing pane of five 90 c. and 1 label (2×3) (No. 1670a) ("The Flight to Egypt" cover design) .. .. .. 7·50

1996 (15 Jan). *Greetings. Multicoloured cover as Type* B **38**.
SB205 $4.70, booklet containing pane of ten self-adhesive 45 c. (No. 1654ba) and 35 circular greetings labels .. .. 5·50

B **47** Binary Codes and Globe (*Illustration reduced. Actual size* 90×155 *mm*)

1996 (15 Feb). *High Technology Industries. Multicoloured cover as Type* B **47**.
SB206 $5.40, booklet containing pane of twelve 45 c. (No. 1677a) (2×6) .. .. .. 6·75

B **48** Ethel Catherwood (*Illustration reduced. Actual size* 95×155 *mm*)

1996 (8 July). *Canadian Olympic Gold Medal Winners. Multicoloured cover as Type* B **48**.
SB207 $4.50, booklet containing pane of ten 45 c. (No. 1691a) (5×2) .. .. 5·00

B **49** Father reading to Children (*Illustration reduced. Actual size* 95×155 *mm*)

1996 (9 Sept). *Literacy Campaign. Multicoloured cover as Type* B **49**.
SB208 $5 booklet containing pane of ten 45 + 5 c. (5×2) (No. 1699a) .. .. 5·50

PRICES OF SETS

Set prices are given for many issues, generally those containing three stamps or more. Definitive sets include one of each value or major colour change, but do not cover different perforations, die types or minor shades. Where a choice is possible the set prices are based on the cheapest versions of the stamps included in the listings.

B **50** Canadian Authors
(*Illustration reduced.*
Actual size 80×155 *mm*)

96 (10 Oct). *Canadian Authors. Multicoloured cover as Type* B **50**.
209 $4.50, booklet containing pane of ten 45 c. (5×2) (No. 1706a) .. .. 5·25

B **51** Father Christmas

96 (1 Nov). *Christmas. 50th Anniv of U.N.I.C.E.F. Multicoloured covers as Type* B **51**.
B210 $2.60, booklet containing pane of five 52 c. and 1 label (2×3) (No. 1712ab) .. .. .. 2·75
B211 $4.50, booklet containing pane of ten 45 c. (2×5) (No. 1711a) (Child tobogganing design) .. 4·25
B212 $4.50, booklet containing pane of five 90 c. and 1 label (2×3) (No. 1713ab) (Couple ice-skating design) .. .. 4·25

B **52** Blue Poppy

1997 (4 Apr). *"Quebec in Bloom" International Floral Festival. Multicoloured cover as Type* B **52**.
SB213 $5.40, booklet containing pane of twelve 45 c. (6×2) (No. 1724a) .. .. 4·25

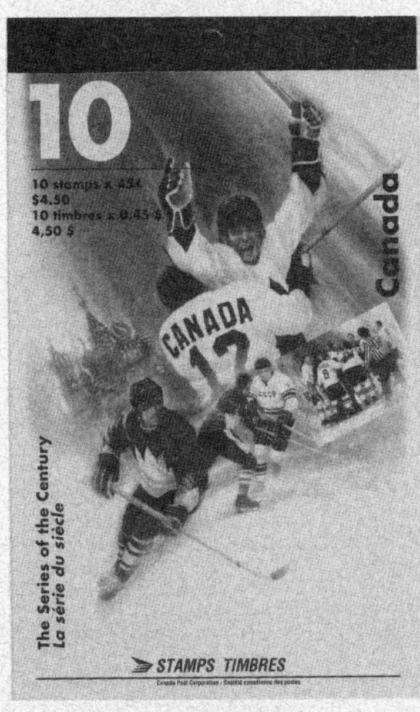

B **53** Paul Henderson celebrating

1997 (20 Sept). *25th Anniv of the Canada–U.S.S.R Ice Hockey Series. Multicoloured cover as Type* B **53**.
SB214 $4.50, booklet containing pane of ten 45 c. (2×5) (No. 1746a) .. .. 3·50

B **54** "The Holy Family"

1997 (3 Nov). *Christmas. Stained Glass Windows. Multicoloured covers as Type* B **54**.
SB215 $2.60, booklet containing pane of five 52 c. (No. 1764ab) .. .. 2·25
SB216 $4.50, booklet containing pane of ten 45 c. (No. 1763ab) (cover showing "Regina SSi Rosarii") 3·75
SB217 $4.50, booklet containing pane of five 90 c. (No. 1765ab) (cover showing "Madonna and Child") .. .. 3·75

1998 (2 Feb). *Covers as Type* B **37**, *each showing multicoloured stamps in a continuous pattern on scarlet background.*
SB218 $4. 50, booklet containing pane of 10 45 c. (5×2) (No. 1358da) .. .. .. 3·50
SB219 $13. 50, booklet containing pane of 30 45 c. (two blocks of 15 (5×3) separated by vertical margin (No. 1358db) .. .. .. 10·50

PRICES OF SETS

Set prices are given for many issues, generally those containing three stamps or more. Definitive sets include one of each value or major colour change, but do not cover different perforations, die types or minor shades. Where a choice is possible the set prices are based on the cheapest versions of the stamps included in the listings.

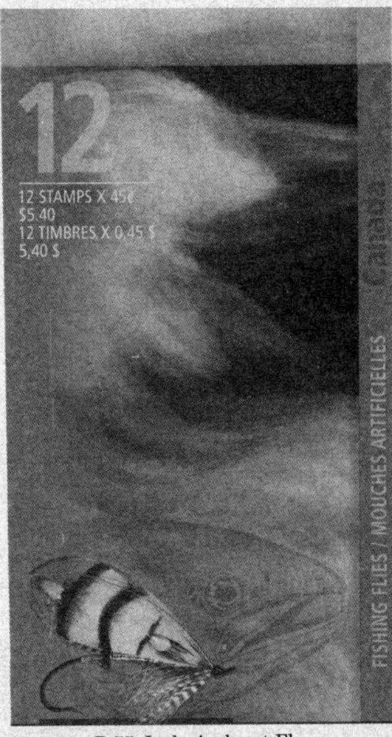

B **55** Lady Amherst Fly

1998 (16 Apr). *Fishing Flies. Multicoloured cover as Type* B **55**.
SB220 $5.40, booklet containing pane of twelve 45 c. (1×12) (No. 1784a) .. .. .. 4·00

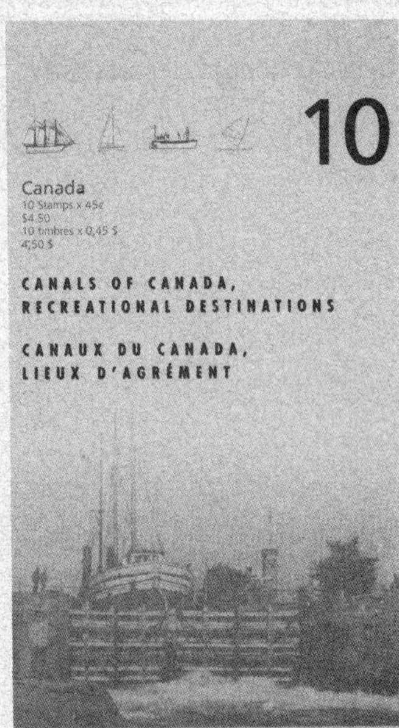

B **56** Ship in Canal Lock

1998 (17 June). *Canadian Canals. Multicoloured cover as Type* B **56**.
SB221 $4.50, booklet containing pane of ten 45 c. and ten labels (No. 1795a) (10×2) .. .. 3·50

B **57** "Joie Lacustre" (Paul-Emile Borduas)
(*Illustration reduced. Actual size* 130×115 *mm*)

1998 (7 Aug). *50th Anniv of* Refus Global (*manifesto of The Automatistes group of artists*). *Multicoloured cover as Type* B **57**.
SB222 $3.15, booklet containing pane of seven self-adhesive 45 c. (No. 1814a) .. .. 2·40

B **58** Circus Scenes and VIA Rail Train
(Illustration reduced. Actual size 182×80 mm)

1998 (1 Oct). *Canadian Circus. Multicoloured cover as Type* B **58**.
SB223 $5.40, booklet containing *se-tenant* pane of twelve 45 c. (No. 1851a) (6×2) .. .. 4·00

B **59** Adoring Angel B **60**

1998 (6 Nov). *Christmas. Statues of Angels. Multicoloured covers as Type* B **59**.
SB224 $2.60, booklet containing pane of five 52 c. and 1 label (2×3) (No. 1860ba) .. .. 2·00
SB225 $4.50, booklet containing pane of ten 45 c. (2×5) (No. 1859a) (*p* 13×13½) (cover showing Angel blowing trumpet) .. .. .. 3·50
a. Containing pane No. 1859ba (*p* 13) .. 3·50
SB226 $4.50, booklet containing pane of five 90 c. and 1 label (2×3) (No. 1861ba) (cover showing Angel at prayer) .. .. 3·50

1998 (28 Dec). *Multicoloured covers as Type* B **60**.
SB227 $4.60, booklet containing pane of ten 46 c. (2×5) (No. 1359a) .. .. .. 3·50
SB228 $13.80, booklet containing pane of 30 self-adhesive 46 c. (3×10) (No. 1366a) (72×102 *mm*) .. .. 12·50

B **61**

1998 (28 Dec). *Multicoloured covers as Type* B **61**.
SB229 $2.75, booklet containing pane of five 55 c. and 1 label (2×3) (No. 1836a) .. .. .. 2·25
SB230 $4.75, booklet containing pane of five 95 c. and 1 label (2×3) (No. 1838a) .. .. .. 3·75

REGISTRATION STAMPS

R 1

ng and recess – printed British-American Bank Note Co, Montreal and Ottawa)

875 (15 Nov)–**92.** *White wove paper. (a) P 12 (or slightly under).*
1 R 1 2 c. orange .. .. 60·00 1·00
2 2 c. orange-red (1889) .. .. .. 70·00 6·00
3 2 c. vermilion .. .. 75·00 7·50
a. Imperf (pair) .. .. .. † —
4 2 c. rose-carmine (1888) .. .. £150 55·00
5 5 c. yellow-green (1878) .. .. £100 1·25
6 5 c. deep green .. .. 80·00 1·00
a. Imperf (pair) £650
7 5 c. blue-green (1888) .. .. .. 90·00 1·25
7a 5 c. dull sea-green (1892) .. .. £130 3·25
8 8 c. bright blue £325 £225
9 8 c. dull blue £300 £200

(b) P 12 × 11½ or 12 × 11¾
10 R 1 2 c. orange .. .. £300 60·00
11 5 c. green (*shades*) £750 £150

SPECIAL DELIVERY STAMPS

RINTERS. The following Special Delivery and Postage Due tamps were recess-printed by the American Bank Note Co (to 928), the British American Bank Note Co (to 1934), and the anadian Bank Note Co (1935 onwards).

S 1

898–1920. *P* 12.
1 S 1 10 c. blue-green (28.6.98) .. .. 80·00 6·50
2 10 c. deep green (12.13) .. .. .. 45·00 5·50
3 10 c. yellowish green (8.20) .. .. 55·00 5·00

The differences between Types I and II (figures "10" with and without shading) formerly illustrated were due to wear of the plate. There was only one die.

S 2

S 3 Mail-carrying, 1867 and 1927

1922 (21 Aug). *P* 12.
4 S 2 20 c. carmine-red .. .. .. 35·00 5·50

No. S4 exists in two slightly different sizes due to the use of "wet" or "dry" printing processes. See note below No. 195.

1927 (29 June). *60th Anniversary of Confederation. P* 12.
5 S 3 20 c. orange .. .. 11·00 10·00

No. S5 exists imperforate, imperf×perf or perf×imperf (*Price, in each instance, £120 per pair, un*).

S 4

1930 (2 Sept). *P* 11.
S6 S 4 20 c. brown-red .. .. 40·00 7·00

1932 (24 Dec). *Type as* S 4, *but inscr* "CENTS" *in place of* "TWENTY CENTS". *P* 11.
S7 20 c. brown-red .. .. 45·00 12·00

No. S7 exists imperforate (*Price per pair £275, un*).

MINIMUM PRICE

The minimum price quote is 10p which represents a handling charge rather than a basis for valuing common stamps. For further notes about prices see introductory pages.

S 5 Allegory of Progress

(Des A. Foringer)

1935 (1 June). *P* 12.
S8 S 5 20 c. scarlet .. .. 3·50 2·50

No. S8 exists imperforate (*Price per pair £325, un*).

S 6 Canadian Coat of Arms

1938–39. *P* 12.
S 9 S 6 10 c. green (1.4.39) .. .. .. 18·00 3·00
S10 20 c. scarlet (15.6.38) .. .. .. 40·00 23·00

Nos. S9/10 exist imperforate (*Price £350, un, for each pair*).

≡10 10≡

(S 7)

1939 (1 Mar). *Surch with Type* **S 7.**
S11 S 6 10 c. on 20 c. scarlet .. .. .. 9·00 8·00

S 8 Coat of Arms and Flags

S 9 Lockheed L.18 Lodestar

1942 (1 July)–**1943.** *War Effort. P 12. (a) Postage.*
S12 S 8 10 c. green .. .. 4·25 30

(b) Air
S13 S 9 16 c. ultramarine .. .. .. 4·00 45
S14 17 c. ultramarine (1.4.43) .. .. 4·00 55

Nos. S12/14 exist imperforate (*Prices per un pair* 10 c. £325, 16 c. £375, 17 c. £375).

S 10 Arms of Canada and Peace Symbols

S 11 Canadair DC-4M North Star

1946 (16 Sept–5 Dec). *P 12. (a) Postage*
S15 S 10 10 c. green .. .. 2·00 30

(b) Air. (i) Circumflex accent in "EXPRÊS"
S16 S 11 17 c. ultramarine .. .. .. 4·00 3·50

(ii) Grave accent in "EXPRÈS"
S17 S 11 17 c. ultramarine (5.12.46) .. .. 5·00 4·00

POSTAGE DUE STAMPS

PRINTERS. See note under "Special Delivery Stamps".

D 1

D 2

1906 (1 July)–**28.** *P* 12.
D1 D 1 1 c. dull violet .. .. 8·00 2·50
D2 1 c. red violet (1916) .. .. .. 10·00 3·25
a. Thin paper (10.24) .. .. .. 15·00 18·00
D3 2 c. dull violet .. .. 17·00 90
D4 2 c. red-violet (1917) .. .. .. 14·00 1·25
a. Thin paper (10.24) .. .. .. 27·00 19·00
D5 4 c. violet (3.7.28) .. .. .. 45·00 50·00
D6 5 c. dull violet .. .. 22·00 2·50
D7 5 c. red-violet (1917) .. .. .. 22·00 2·50
a. Thin paper (10.24) .. .. .. 16·00 24·00
D8 10 c. violet (3.7.28) .. .. .. 32·00 16·00
D1/8 .. .. *Set of* 5 £100 65·00

The 1 c., 2 c. and 5 c. values exist imperforate (*Price* £250 *for each un pair*).

Printings up to October 1924 used the "wet" method, those from mid 1925 onwards the "dry". For details of the differences between these two methods, see above No. 196.

1930–2. *P* 11.
D 9 D 2 1 c. bright violet (14.7.30) .. .. 8·50 10·00
D10 2 c. bright violet (21.8.30) .. .. 7·50 1·60
D11 4 c. bright violet (14.10.30) .. .. 15·00 6·50
D12 5 c. bright violet (12.12.31) .. .. 15·00 25·00
D13 10 c. bright violet (24.8.32) .. .. 65·00 26·00
D9/13 .. .. *Set of* 5 £100 60·00

Nos. D9/11 and D13 exist imperforate, No. D13 also exists imperf×perf (*Price for vertical pair £450, un*).

D 3

D 4

CANADA POSTAGE DUE 1 A PERCEVOIR

D 5

1933–4. *P* 11.
D14 D 3 1 c. violet (5.5.34) .. .. .. 9·00 13·00
D15 2 c. violet (20.12.33) .. .. .. 6·50 4·00
D16 4 c. violet (12.12.33) .. .. .. 11·00 12·00
D17 10 c. violet (20.12.33) .. .. .. 23·00 27·00
D14/17 .. .. *Set of* 4 45·00 50·00

No. D14 exists imperforate (*Price per pair £275, un*).

1935–65. *P* 12.
D18 D 4 1 c. violet (14.10.35) 60 10
D19 2 c. violet (9.9.35) 60 10
D20 3 c. violet (4.65) .. .. 3·50 5·00
D21 4 c. violet (2.7.35) .. .. .. 1·50 10
D22 5 c. violet (12.48) .. .. .. 3·00 65
D23 6 c. violet (1957) .. .. 1·50 3·00
D24 10 c. violet (16.9.35) 60 10
D18/24 .. .. *Set of* 7 10·00 8·00

The 1 c., 2 c., 4 c. and 10 c. exist imperforate (*Price* £140 *for each un pair*).

1967–78. *Litho. P 12½ × 12 (20 c., 24 c., 50 c.) or 12 (others).*

(a) Size 20 × 17½ mm
D25 D 5 1 c. scarlet (3.67) .. .. .. 1·75 3·50
D26 2 c. scarlet (3.67) .. .. .. 1·00 80
D27 3 c. scarlet (3.67) .. .. .. 1·00 4·00
D28 4 c. scarlet (2.67) .. .. .. 2·50 1·25
D29 5 c. scarlet (3.67) .. .. .. 3·75 3·25
D30 6 c. scarlet (2.67) .. .. .. 1·60 3·75
D31 10 c. scarlet (1.67) .. .. .. 2·00 2·50
D25/31 .. .. *Set of* 7 12·00 17·00

(b) Size 19½×16 mm
D32 D 5 1 c. scarlet (12.70) 30 30
a. Perf 12½×12 (11.77) 15 90
D33 2 c. scarlet (1972) .. .. .. 75 2·00
D34 3 c. scarlet (1.74) .. .. .. 2·50 3·00
D35 4 c. scarlet (4.69) 30 40
a. Printed on the gummed side .. £325
b. Perf 12½×12 (11.77) 30 90
D36 5 c. scarlet (2.69) .. .. .. 20·00 35·00
a. Perf 12½×12 (11.77) .. .. 30 1·50
D37 6 c. scarlet (1972) .. .. .. 2·75 3·50
D38 8 c. scarlet (1.69) 30 45
a. Perf 12½×12 (28.6.78) .. .. 75 1·40
D39 10 c. scarlet (4.69) 30 45
a. Perf 12½×12 (9.77) 40 60
D40 12 c. scarlet (1.69) 40 50
a. Perf 12½×12 (9.77) .. .. 80 1·50
D41 16 c. scarlet (1.74) .. .. .. 80 2·75
D42 20 c. scarlet (10.77) .. .. .. 40 1·25
D43 24 c. scarlet (10.77) .. .. .. 40 1·75
D44 50 c. scarlet (10.77) .. .. .. 60 2·25
D32a/44 .. .. *Set of* 13 8·50 18·00

There are no records of dates of issue of the above but supplies were distributed to depots in the months indicated.

Both white and ordinary papers have been used for Nos. D32/41.

The last Postage Due stamps were withdrawn on 30 June 1982.

OFFICIAL STAMPS

Stamps perforated "O H M S" were introduced in May 1923 for use by the Receiver General's department in Ottawa and by the Assistant Receiver Generals' offices in provincial cities. From 1 July 1939 this use was extended to all departments of the federal government and such stamps continued to be produced until replaced by the "O.H.M.S." overprinted issue of 1949.

The perforated initials can appear either upright, inverted or sideways on individual stamps. The prices quoted are for the cheapest version. Stamps perforated with Type O 1 are only priced used. Only isolated examples are known mint and these are very rare.

A number of forged examples of the perforated "O.H.M.S." are known, in particular of Type O 1. Many of these forged perforated initials were applied to stamps which had already been used and this can aid their detection. Genuine examples, postmarked after the perforated initials were applied, often show the cancellation ink bleeding into the holes.

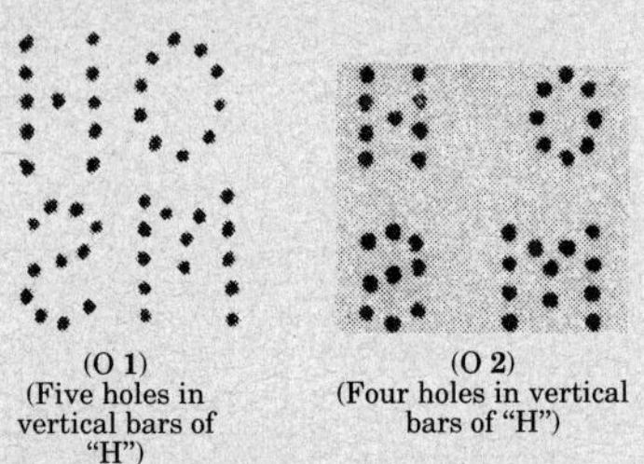

(O 1) (Five holes in vertical bars of "H")

(O 2) (Four holes in vertical bars of "H")

1923 (May). *Nos.* 196/215 *punctured as Type* O **1**.

O1	**44**	1 c. yellow-green	—	20·00
O2		2 c. carmine	—	18·00
O3		3 c. deep brown	—	16·00
O4		5 c. deep blue	—	20·00
O5		7 c. yellow-ochre	—	35·00
O6		10 c. reddish purple	—	35·00
O7		20 c. olive	—	22·00
O8		50 c. sepia	—	35·00
O1/8		*Set of* 8	—	£180

1923 (May). 50*th Anniv of Confederation. No.* 244 *punctured as Type* O **1**.

O9	**48**	3 c. bistre-brown	—	£110

1923 (May)–**31**. *Nos.* 246/55 *and* 263 *punctured as Type* O **1**.

(*a*) *P* 12

O10	**44**	1 c. chrome-yellow (Die I)	—	18·00
		a. Die II (1925)	—	18·00
O11		2 c. deep green	—	13·00
O12		3 c. carmine (Die I) (12.23)	—	13·00
		a. Die II (1924)	—	16·00
O13		4 c. olive-yellow	—	18·00
O14		5 c. violet	—	18·00
		a. Thin paper (1924)	—	22·00
O15		7 c. red-brown (1924)	—	27·00
O16		8 c. blue (1925)	—	32·00
O17		10 c. blue	—	22·00
O18		10 c. bistre-brown (1925)	—	13·00
O19		$1 brown-orange (7.23)	—	55·00
O10/19		*Set of* 10	—	£200

(*b*) *P* 12×8

O20	**44**	3 c. carmine (Die II) (1931)	—	42·00

1927 (29 June). 60*th Anniv of Confederation. Nos.* 266/73 *punctured as Type* O **1**. (*a*) *Commemorative issue.*

O21	**51**	1 c. orange	—	18·00
O22	**52**	2 c. green	—	25·00
O23	**53**	3 c. carmine	—	35·00
O24	**54**	5 c. violet	—	23·00
O25	**55**	12 c. blue	—	£140
O21/5		*Set of* 5	—	£225

(*b*) *Historical issue*

O26	**56**	5 c. violet	—	18·00
O27	**57**	12 c. green	—	£110
O28	**58**	20 c. carmine	—	70·00
O26/8		*Set of* 3	—	£180

1928 (21 Sept). *Air. No.* 274 *punctured as Type* O **1**.

O29	**59**	5 c. olive-brown	—	90·00

1928–29. *Nos.* 275/85 *punctured as Type* O **1**.

O30	**60**	1 c. orange	—	23·00
O31		2 c. green	—	15·00
O32		3 c. lake	—	40·00
O33		4 c. olive-bistre	—	48·00
O34		5 c. violet	—	16·00
O35		8 c. blue	—	45·00
O36	**61**	10 c. green	—	13·00
O37	**62**	12 c. grey-black	—	£120
O38	**63**	20 c. lake	—	38·00
O39	**64**	50 c. blue	—	£110
O40	**65**	$1 olive-green	—	£100
O30/40		*Set of* 11	—	£500

1930–31. *Nos.* 288/97, *and* 300/5 *punctured as Type* O **1**.

O41	**66**	1 c. orange (Die I)	—	23·00
O42		1 c. green (Die I)	—	13·00
		a. Die II	—	11·00
O43		2 c. green (Die I)	—	35·00
O44		2 c. scarlet (Die I)	—	18·00
		a. Die II	—	16·00
O45		2 c. deep brown (Die I)	—	22·00
		a. Die II	—	18·00
O46		3 c. scarlet	—	13·00
O47		4 c. yellow-bistre	—	42·00
O48		5 c. violet	—	29·00
O49		5 c. deep slate-blue	—	23·00
O50		8 c. blue	—	55·00
O51		8 c. red-orange	—	40·00
O52	**67**	10 c. olive-green	—	18·00
O53	**68**	12 c. grey-black	—	75·00
O54	**69**	20 c. red	—	38·00
O55	**70**	50 c. blue	—	55·00
O56	**71**	$1 olive-green	—	£130
O41/56		*Set of* 15	—	£500

1930 (4 Dec). *Air. No.* 310 *punctured as Type* O **1**.

O57	**72**	5 c. deep brown	—	£140

1931 (30 Sept). *No.* 312 *punctured as Type* O **1**.

O58	**73**	10 c. olive-green	—	18·00

1932 (22 Feb). *Air. No.* 313 *punctured as Type* O **1**.

O59	**59**	6 c. on 5 c. olive-brown	—	95·00

1932 (21 June). *Nos.* 314/*a punctured as Type* O **1**.

O60	**66**	3 c. on 2 c. scarlet (Die I)	—	30·00
		a. Die II	—	23·00

1932 (12 July). *Ottawa Conference. Nos.* 315/18 *punctured as Type* O **1**. (*a*) *Postage.*

O61	**76**	3 c. scarlet	—	15·00
O62	**77**	5 c. blue	—	27·00
O63	**78**	13 c. green	—	£160

(*b*) *Air*

O64	**72**	6 c. on 5 c. deep brown	—	£120
O61/4		*Set of* 4	—	£300

1932–33. *Nos.* 319/25 *punctured as Type* O **1**.

O65	**80**	1 c. green	—	13·00
O66		2 c. sepia	—	13·00
O67		3 c. scarlet	—	13·00
O68		4 c. yellow-brown	—	45·00
O69		5 c. blue	—	20·00
O70		8 c. red-orange	—	45·00
O71	**68**	13 c. bright violet	—	45·00
O65/71		*Set of* 7	—	£180

1933 (18 May). *U.P.U. Congress Preliminary Meeting. No.* 329 *punctured as Type* O **1**.

O72	**81**	5 c. blue	—	38·00

1933 (24 July). *World's Grain Exhibition and Conference, Regina. No.* 330 *punctured as Type* O **1**.

O73	**69**	20 c. red	—	45·00

1933 (17 Aug). *Centenary of First Trans-Atlantic Steamboat Crossing. No.* 331 *punctured as Type* O **1**.

O74	**83**	5 c. blue	—	40·00

1934 (1 July). *Fourth Centenary of Discovery of Canada. No.* 332 *punctured as Type* O **1**.

O75	**84**	3 c. blue	—	45·00

1934 (1 July). 150*th Anniv of Arrival of United Empire Loyalists. No.* 333 *punctured as Type* O **1**.

O76	**85**	10 c. olive-green	—	48·00

1934 (16 Aug). 150*th Anniv of Province of New Brunswick. No.* 334 *punctured as Type* O **1**.

O77	**86**	2 c. red-brown	—	60·00

1935 (4 May). *Silver Jubilee. Nos.* 335/40 *punctured as Type* O **1**.

O78	**87**	1 c. green	—	25·00
O79	–	2 c. brown	—	32·00
O80	**89**	3 c. carmine-red	—	40·00
O81	–	5 c. blue	—	38·00
O82	–	10 c. green	—	£110
O83	–	13 c. blue	—	£110
O78/83		*Set of* 6	—	£325

1935. *Nos.* 341/51 *and* 355 *punctured as Type* O **1**. (*a*) *Postage*

O84	**93**	1 c. green	—	15·00
O85		2 c. brown	—	28·00
O86		3 c. scarlet	—	25·00
O87		4 c. yellow	—	45·00
O88		5 c. blue	—	25·00
O89		8 c. orange	—	45·00
O90	**94**	10 c. carmine	—	35·00
O91	–	13 c. purple	—	45·00
O92	–	20 c. olive-green	—	48·00
O93	–	50 c. deep violet	—	35·00
O94	–	$1 bright blue	—	95·00

(*b*) *Air*

O95	**99**	6 c. red-brown	—	75·00
O84/95		*Set of* 12	—	£475

1937 (10 May). *Coronation. No.* 356 *punctured as Type* O **1**.

O96	**100**	3 c. carmine	—	40·00

1937–38. *Nos.* 357/67, 370 *and* 371 *punctured as Type* O **1**.

(*a*) *Postage*

O 97	**101**	1 c. green	—	2·50
O 98		2 c. brown	—	2·75
O 99		3 c. scarlet	—	2·50
O100		4 c. yellow	—	8·00
O101		5 c. blue	—	6·50
O102		8 c. orange	—	13·00
O103	**102**	10 c. rose-carmine	—	20·00
		a. Red	—	23·00
O104	–	13 c. blue	—	28·00
O105	–	20 c. red-brown	—	28·00
O106	–	50 c. green	—	65·00
O107	–	$1 violet	—	95·00
O97/107		*Set of* 11	—	£250

(*b*) *Coil stamp*

O108	**101**	3 c. scarlet	—	65·00

(*c*) *Air*

O109	**107**	6 c. blue	—	28·00

1939 (15 May). *Royal Visit. Nos.* 372/4 *punctured as Type* O **1**.

O110	**108**	1 c. black and green	—	32·00
O111	**109**	2 c. black and brown	—	42·00
O112	**110**	3 c. black and carmine	—	32·00
O110/12		*Set of* 3	—	95·00

1939 (1 July). *Air. No.* 274 *punctured as Type* O **2**.

O113	**59**	5 c. olive-brown	20·00	14·00

1939 (1 July). *Nos.* 347/50 *and* 355 *punctured as Type* O **2**.

(*a*) *Postage*

O114	**94**	10 c. carmine	55·00	38·00
O115	–	13 c. purple	60·00	38·00
O116	–	20 c. olive-green	75·00	48·00
O117	–	50 c. deep violet	60·00	38·00

(*b*) *Air*

O118	**99**	6 c. red-brown	50·00	42·00
O114/18		*Set of* 5	£275	£180

1939 (1 July). *Coronation. No.* 356 *punctured as Type* O **2**.

O119	**100**	3 c. carmine	70·00	45·00

1939 (1 July). *Nos.* 357/67, 369/70 *and* 371 *punctured as Type* O **2**. (*a*) *Postage*

O120	**101**	1 c. green	1·50	10
O121		2 c. brown	2·25	10
O122		3 c. scarlet	2·50	10
O123		4 c. yellow	5·00	2·25
O124		5 c. blue	3·50	20
O125		8 c. orange	13·00	4·25
O126	**102**	10 c. rose-carmine	48·00	3·25
		a. Red	7·00	30
O127	–	13 c. blue	13·00	1·50
O128	–	20 c. red-brown	35·00	2·00
O129	–	50 c. green	40·00	8·00
O130	–	$1 violet	£110	30·00
O120/30		*Set of* 11	£200	42·00

(*b*) *Coil stamps*

O131	**101**	2 c. brown	70·00	45·00
O132		3 c. scarlet	70·00	45·00

(*c*) *Air*

O133	**107**	6 c. blue	3·00	80

1939 (1 July). *Royal Visit. Nos.* 372/4 *punctured as Type* O **2**.

O134	**108**	1 c. black and green	80·00	38·00
O135	**109**	2 c. black and brown	80·00	38·00
O136	**110**	3 c. black and carmine	80·00	38·00
O134/6		*Set of* 3	£225	£100

1942–43. *War Effort. Nos.* 375/88 *and* 399/400 *punctured as Type* O **2**. (*a*) *Postage*

O137	**111**	1 c. green	40	10
O138	**112**	2 c. brown	50	10
O139	**113**	3 c. carmine-lake	1·10	40
O140		3 c. purple	60	10
O141	**114**	4 c. slate	2·75	75
O142	**112**	4 c. carmine-lake	55	10
O143	**111**	5 c. blue	1·25	15
O144	–	8 c. red-brown	7·50	2·00
O145	**116**	10 c. brown	4·50	20
O146	**117**	13 c. dull green	5·50	5·50
O147		14 c. dull green	9·00	85
O148	–	20 c. chocolate	11·00	70
O149	–	50 c. violet	35·00	5·50
O150	–	$1 blue	90·00	25·00

(*b*) *Air*

O151	**121**	6 c. blue	3·50	2·00
O152		7 c. blue	3·00	25
O137/52		*Set of* 16	£160	40·00

1946. *Peace Re-conversion. Nos.* 401/7 *punctured as Type* O **2**.

(*a*) *Postage*

O153	**122**	8 c. brown	9·00	3·50
O154	–	10 c. olive-green	3·00	15
O155	–	14 c. sepia	3·75	65
O156	–	20 c. slate	4·00	50
O157	–	50 c. green	22·00	5·00
O158	–	$1 purple	60·00	15·00

(*b*) *Air*

O159	–	7 c. blue	2·50	40
O153/9		*Set of* 7	95·00	23·00

1949. *Nos.* 415 *and* 416 *punctured as Type* O **2**.

O160	**136**	2 c. sepia	75	75
O161	**137**	3 c. purple	75	75

O.H.M.S.

(O 3)

49. *Nos.* 375/6, 378, 380 *and* 402/7 *optd as Type* O **3** *by typography.*

(a) Postage

62 **111** 1 c. green .. .. 1·75 2·00
a. Missing stop after "S" .. .. £140 45·00
63 **112** 2 c. brown .. .. 12·00 12·00
a. Missing stop after "S" .. .. £140 85·00
64 **113** 3 c. purple .. .. 1·25 1·10
65 **112** 4 c. carmine-lake .. .. .. 2·00 80
66 – 10 c. olive-green .. .. .. 3·75 15
a. Missing stop after "S" .. .. 70·00 35·00
67 – 14 c. sepia .. .. 4·50 1·75
a. Missing stop after "S" .. .. 90·00 45·00
68 – 20 c. slate .. .. 12·00 60
a. Missing stop after "S" .. .. £130 50·00
69 – 50 c. green £160 £120
a. Missing stop after "S" £850 £550
70 – $1 purple .. .. 45·00 45·00
a. Missing stop after "S" £1400

(b) Air

71 – 7 c. blue .. .. 24·00 7·00
a. Missing stop after "S" .. .. £130 60·00
62/71 .. .. *Set of* 10 £225 £140

Forgeries exist of this overprint. Genuine examples are 3×15 mm and show the tops of all letters aligned, as are the ops.

Only a few sheets of the $1 showed the variety, No. O170a.

ISSING STOP VARIETIES. These occur on R. 6/2 of the wer left pane (Nos. O162a, O163a and O176a) or R. 10/2 of the wer left pane (O166a, O167a, O168a, O169a, O170a and 171a). No. O176a also occurs on R. 8/8 of the upper left pane in ldition to R. 6/2 of the lower left pane.

49–50. *Nos.* 414/15, 416/17, 418 *and* 431 *optd as Type* O **3** *by typography.*

172 **135** 1 c. green 85 85
173 **136** 2 c. sepia .. .. 1·75 1·50
174 **137** 3 c. purple .. .. 1·00 70
175 **138** 4 c. carmine-lake .. .. .. 1·50 15
176 **139** 5 c. blue (1949) .. .. .. 2·50 2·00
a. Missing stop after "S" .. .. 80·00 38·00
177 **141** 50 c. green (1950) .. .. .. 32·00 28·00
172/7 .. .. *Set of* 6 35·00 30·00

G (O 4) G (O 5) G (O 6)

Type O **6** differs from Type O **5** in having a thinner ppearance and an upward sloping left serif to the lower arm. It sults from a new plate introduced in 1961/62. Variations in ickness are known in Type O **4** but these are due to wear and ubsequent cleaning of the plate. All are produced by pography. Examples showing the "G" applied by lithography re forgeries.

950 (2 Oct)–52. *Nos.* 402/4, 406/7, 414/18 *and* 431 *optd with Type* O **4** *(1 to 5 c.) or* O **5** *(7 c. to $1). (a) Postage.*

178 **135** 1 c. green 70 10
179 **136** 2 c. sepia .. .. 1·50 1·60
180 2 c. olive-green (11.51) .. .. 1·75 10
181 **137** 3 c. purple .. .. 1·50 10
182 **138** 4 c. carmine-lake .. .. .. 1·50 30
183 4 c. vermilion (1.5.52) .. .. 1·60 10
184 **139** 5 c. blue .. .. 2·50 30
185 – 10 c. olive-green .. .. .. 3·00 10
186 – 14 c. sepia .. .. 11·00 2·25
187 – 20 c. slate .. .. 15·00 20
188 **141** 50 c. green .. .. 10·00 8·00
189 – $1 purple .. .. 60·00 55·00

(b) Air

190 – 7 c. blue .. .. 24·00 12·00
178/90 .. .. *Set of* 13 £120 70·00

950–51. *Nos.* 432/3 *optd with Type* O **5**.

191 **142** 10 c. brown-purple .. .. .. 2·25 10
a. Opt omitted in pair with normal £400 £350
192 **143** $1 ultramarine (1.2.51) .. .. 55·00 60·00

952–53. *Nos.* 441, 443 *and* 446 *optd with Type* O **5**.

193 **153** 7 c. blue (3.11.52) .. .. .. 1·40 1·40
194 **151** 20 c. grey (1.4.52) .. .. .. 1·60 10
195 **154** $1 black (2.2.53) .. .. .. 10·00 11·00
193/5 .. .. *Set of* 3 11·50 11·00

953 (1 Sept)–61. *Nos.* 450/4 *and* 462 *optd with Type* O **4** *(1 to 5 c.) or* O **5** *(50 c.).*

196 **158** 1 c. purple-brown 15 10
197 2 c. green 20 10
198 3 c. carmine 20 10
199 4 c. violet 30 10
200 5 c. ultramarine 30 10
201 **160** 50 c. deep bluish green (2.11.53) .. 3·00 1·75
a. Opt Type O **6** (24.4.61*) .. 2·25 2·25
196/201 .. .. *Set of* 6 3·00 1·90

*Earliest recorded date.

955–56. *Nos.* 463/4 *and* 466/7 *optd with Type* O **4**.

202 **161** 1 c. purple-brown (12.11.56) .. 20 20
203 2 c. green (19.1.56) 15 10
204 4 c. violet (23.7.56) 40 10
205 5 c. bright blue (11.1.55) 15 10
202/5 .. .. *Set of* 5 80 30

955–62. *Nos.* 477 *and* 488 *optd with Type* O **5**.

206 **165** 10 c. purple-brown (21.2.55) .. 40 10
a. Opt Type O **6** (28.3.62*) .. 40 90
207 **176** 20 c. green (4.12.56) .. .. .. 1·75 10
a. Opt Type O **6** (10.4.62*) .. 5·00 40

*Earliest recorded date.

1963 (15 May). *Nos.* 527/8 *and* 530/1 *optd as Type* O **4**.

O208 1 c. chocolate .. .. 40 3·75
O209 2 c. green .. .. 40 3·50
a. Type O **4** omitted (vert pair with normal) £600
O210 4 c. carmine-red .. .. 40 1·75
O211 5 c. ultramarine 40 90
O208/11 .. .. *Set of* 4 1·40 9·00

No. O209a comes from the top row of an upper pane on which the overprint was misplaced downwards by one row. Owing to the margin between the panes the top row of the bottom pane had the overprint at the top of the stamp.

OFFICIAL SPECIAL DELIVERY STAMPS

1923 (May). *Nos.* S3/4 *punctured as Type* O **1**.

OS1 S **1** 10 c. yellowish green .. .. .. — 85·00
OS2 S **2** 20 c. carmine-red .. .. .. — 70·00

1927 (29 June). *60th Anniv of Confederation. No.* S5 *punctured as Type* O **1**.

OS3 S **3** 20 c. orange .. .. — 80·00

1930 (2 Sept). *Inscr* "TWENTY CENTS" *at foot. No.* S6 *punctured as Type* O **1**.

OS4 S **4** 20 c. brown-red .. .. .. — 65·00

1932 (24 Dec). *Inscr* "CENTS" *at foot. No.* S7 *punctured as Type* O **1**.

OS5 S **4** 20 c. brown-red .. .. .. — 65·00

1935 (1 June). *No.* S8 *punctured as Type* O **1**.

OS6 S **5** 20 c. scarlet .. .. — 65·00

1938–39. *Nos.* S9/10 *punctured as Type* O **1**.

OS7 S **6** 10 c. green .. .. — 38·00
OS8 20 c. scarlet .. .. — 60·00

1939 (1 Mar). *No.* S11 *punctured as Type* O **1**.

OS9 S **6** 10 c. on 20 c. scarlet .. .. .. — 60·00

1939 (1 July). *Inscr* "CENTS" *at foot. No.* S7 *punctured as Type* O **2**.

OS10 S **4** 20 c. brown-red .. .. .. £150 80·00

1939 (1 July). *No.* S8 *punctured as Type* O **2**.

OS11 S **5** 20 c. scarlet .. .. 85·00 38·00

1939 (1 July). *No.* S9 *punctured as Type* O **2**.

OS12 S **6** 10 c. green .. .. 7·00 4·50

1939 (1 July). *No.* S11 *punctured as Type* O **2**.

OS13 S **6** 10 c. on 20 c. scarlet .. .. .. £100 50·00

1942–43. *Nos.* S12/14 *punctured as Type* O **2**. *(a) Postage*

OS14 S **8** 10 c. green .. .. 9·00 6·50

(b) Air

OS15 S **9** 16 c. ultramarine .. .. .. 17·00 13·00
OS16 17 c. ultramarine .. .. .. 10·00 8·00

1946–47. *Nos.* S15/17 *punctured as Type* O **2**. *(a) Postage*

OS17 S **10** 10 c. green .. .. 6·50 4·50

(b) Air

OS18 S **11** 17 c. ultramarine (circumflex accent) 26·00 22·00
OS19 17 c. ultramarine (grave accent) .. 55·00 55·00

1950. *No.* S15 *optd as Type* O **3**, *but larger.*

OS20 S **10** 10 c. green .. .. 17·00 21·00

1950 (2 Oct). *No.* S15 *optd as Type* O **4**, *but larger.*

OS21 S **10** 10 c. green .. .. 26·00 27·00

The use of official stamps was discontinued on 31 December 1963.

Cape of Good Hope *see* South Africa

see South Africa

Cayman Islands

The first post office was opened at Georgetown in April 1889. The stamps of Jamaica with the following cancellations were used until 19 February 1901. At some stage, probably around 1891, a supply of the Jamaica 1889 1d., No. 27, was overprinted "CAYMAN ISLANDS", but these stamps were never issued. Two surviving examples are known, one unused and the other cancelled at Richmond in Jamaica.

Types of Jamaica

2

3

4

8

11

13

PRICES OF NOS. Z1/27. These are for a single stamp showing a clear impression of the postmark. Nos. Z1, 2, 6/8, 11/13, 18, 22 and Z25 are known used on cover and these are worth considerably more.

GEORGETOWN, GRAND CAYMAN

Z 1

Z 2

Z 3

Stamps of JAMAICA *cancelled with Type* Z **1** *in purple.*

1889 *to* **1894.**

Z1 **8** ½d. yellow-green (No. 16) £400
Z2 **11** 1d. purple and mauve (No. 27) £400
Z2a **2** 2d. slate (No. 20*a*) £3250
Z3 **11** 2d. green (No. 28) £750
Z4 2½d. dull purple and blue (No. 29) .. £900
Z5 **4** 4d. red-orange (No. 22) £1800

Stamps of JAMAICA *cancelled with Type* Z **2** *in purple or black.*

1895 *to* **1898.**

Z6 **8** ½d. yellow-green (No. 16) £450
Z7 **11** 1d. purple and mauve (No. 27) £375
Z8 2½d. dull purple and blue (No. 29) £650
Z9 **3** 3d. sage-green (No. 21) £2500

Stamps of JAMAICA *cancelled with Type* Z **3**.

1898 *to* **1901.**
Z10 **8** ½d. yellow-green (No. 16) £375
a. Green (No. 16*a*) £375
Z11 **11** 1d. purple and mauve (No. 27) £375
Z12 **13** 1d. red (No. 31) (1900) £375
Z13 **11** 2½d. dull purple and blue (No. 29) £550

OFFICIAL STAMPS

Stamps of JAMAICA *cancelled with Type* Z **1** *in purple.*

1890 *to* **1894.**
Z14 **8** ½d. green (No. O1) (*opt* 17–17½ *mm long*) .. £750
Z15 ½d. green (No. O3) (*opt* 16 *mm long*) (1893) £1200
Z16 **11** 1d. rose (No. O4) £900
Z17 2d. grey (No. O5) £1800

Stamps of JAMAICA *cancelled with Type* Z **2** *in purple or black.*

1895 *to* **1898.**
Z18 **8** ½d. green (No. O3) £1300
Z19 **11** 1d. rose (No. O4) £2500
Z20 2d. grey (No. O5) £2500

STAKE BAY, CAYMAN BRAC

Z 4 Z 5

Stamps of JAMAICA *cancelled with Type* Z **4**.

1898 *to* **1900.**
Z21 **8** ½d. yellow-green (No. 16) £2250
Z22 **11** 1d. purple and mauve (No. 27) £2500
Z23 2d. green (No. 28) £3000
Z24 2½d. dull purple and blue (No. 29) £2500

Stamps of JAMAICA *cancelled with Type* Z **5**.

1900 *to* **1901.**
Z25 **8** ½d. yellow-green (No. 16) £2500
Z26 **11** 1d. purple and mauve (No. 27) £2000
Z27 **13** 1d. red (No. 31) £2000
Z28 **11** 2½d. dull purple and blue (No. 29) £1800

PRICES FOR STAMPS ON COVER TO 1945

Nos. 1/2	*from* × 25
Nos. 3/12	*from* × 5
Nos. 13/16	*from* × 4
Nos. 17/19	*from* × 10
Nos. 25/34	*from* × 5
Nos. 35/52*b*	*from* × 4
Nos. 53/67	*from* × 5
Nos. 69/83	*from* × 4
Nos. 84/95	*from* × 6
Nos. 96/9	*from* × 5
Nos. 100/11	*from* × 4
Nos. 112/14	*from* × 6
Nos. 115/26	*from* × 2

DEPENDENCY OF JAMAICA

1

2

3

(T **1/3**, **8/9** and **12/13** typo D.L.R.)

1900 (Nov). *Wmk Crown CA. P* 14.
1 **1** ½d. deep green .. .. 6·50 16·00
a. Pale green .. .. 3·50 12·00
2 1d. rose-carmine .. .. 2·50 1·75
a. Pale carmine .. .. 8·50 8·00
1/2 Optd "Specimen" .. .. *Set of* 2 90·00

Dented frame under "A" (R. 1/6 of left pane)

1902 (Jan)–**03.** *Wmk Crown CA. P* 14.
3 **2** ½d. green (15.9.02) .. .. .. 4·00 23·00
a. Dented frame .. .. .. 75·00
4 1d. carmine (6.3.03) .. .. .. 8·50 7·50
a. Dented frame £110
5 **2** 2½d. bright blue .. .. 7·00 10·00
a. Dented frame £110
6 6d. brown .. .. 25·00 55·00
a. Dented frame £225
7 **3** 1s. orange .. .. 60·00 £110
a. Dented frame £325
3/7 .. .. *Set of* 5 95·00 £180
3/7 Optd "Specimen" .. .. *Set of* 5 £160

1905 (Feb–18 Oct). *Wmk Mult Crown CA. P* 14.
8 **2** ½d. green .. .. 4·50 6·00
a. Dented frame .. .. 70·00
9 1d. carmine (18 Oct) .. .. .. 13·00 16·00
a. Dented frame £160
10 2½d. bright blue .. .. 4·50 3·00
a. Dented frame .. .. 85·00
11 6d. brown .. .. 16·00 35·00
a. Dented frame £200
12 **3** 1s. orange .. .. 32·00 48·00
a. Dented frame £275
8/12 .. .. *Set of* 5 60·00 95·00

1907 (13 Mar). *Wmk Mult Crown CA. P* 14.
13 **3** 4d. brown and blue .. .. .. 27·00 48·00
a. Dented frame £225
14 **2** 6d. olive and rose .. .. .. 27·00 55·00
a. Dented frame £225
15 **3** 1s. violet and green .. .. .. 45·00 65·00
a. Dented frame £300
16 5s. salmon and green £170 £275
a. Dented frame £950
13/16 .. .. *Set of* 4 £225 £400
13/16 Optd "Specimen" .. .. *Set of* 4 £180

One Halfpenny.
(4)

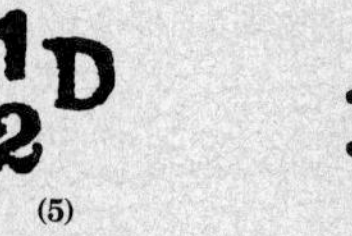

(5)

1D
(6)

1907 (30 Aug). *No.* 9 *surch at Govt Printing Office, Kingston, with T* **4**.
17 **2** ½d. on 1d. carmine .. .. .. 38·00 55·00
a. Dented frame £325

1907 (Nov). *No.* 16 *handstamped at Georgetown P.O. with T* **5** *or* **6**.
18 **3** ½d. on 5s. salmon and green (26 Nov) .. £225 £300
a. Surch inverted £22000
b. Surch double £9000 £9000
c. Surch double, one inverted .. ..
d. Surch omitted (in pair with normal) £32000
e. Dented frame £900
19 1d. on 5s. salmon and green (23 Nov) .. £225 £300
a. Surch double £14000
b. Surch inverted £35000
c. Dented frame £950

The ½d. on 5s. may be found with the figures "1" or "2" omitted, owing to defective handstamping.

8

9

2½D
(10)

1907 (27 Dec)–**09.** *Chalk-surfaced paper* (3*d. to* 10*s.*). *P* 14.

(*a*) *Wmk Mult Crown CA*
25 **8** ½d. green .. .. 1·50 3·50
26 1d. carmine .. .. 1·00 65
27 2½d. ultramarine (30.3.08) .. .. 2·75 3·50
28 **9** 3d. purple/*yellow* (30.3.08) .. .. 2·75 6·50
29 4d. black and red/*yellow* (30.3.08) .. 48·00 65·00
30 **8** 6d. dull and bright purple (2.10.08) .. 7·50 30·00
a. Dull purple and violet-purple .. 28·00 45·00
31 **9** 1s. black/*green* (5.4.09) .. .. 5·50 18·00
32 5s. green and red/*yellow* (30.3.08) .. 35·00 55·00

(*b*) *Wmk Crown CA* (30.3.08)
33 **9** 1s. black/*green* .. .. .. 48·00 70·00
34 **8** 10s. green and red/*green* £160 £225
25/34 .. .. *Set of* 10 £250 £400
25/34 (*except* 31) Optd "Specimen" .. *Set of* 9 £275

1908 (12 Feb). *No.* 13 *handstamped locally with T* **10**.
35 **3** 2½d. on 4d. brown and blue £1500 £2250
a. Surch double £30000 £18000
b. Dented frame £7500

No. 35 should only be purchased when accompanied by an expert committee's certificate or similar form of guarantee.

MANUSCRIPT PROVISIONALS. During May and June 1908 supplies of ½d. and 1d. stamps became exhausted, and the payment of postage was indicated by the Postmistress, Miss Gwendolyn Parsons, using a manuscript endorsement. Such endorsements were in use from 12 May to 1 June.

Price on cover
MP1 "(Postage Paid G.A.P.)" (12 May to 1 June) .. £2500
MP1*a* "(Postage Paid G.A.P.) ½ or 1d." (23 May) .. £3750

In October of the same year there was a further shortage of ¼d. stamps and the manuscript endorsements were again applied by either the new Postmaster, William Graham McCausland, or by Miss Parsons who remained as his assistant.

MP2 "Pd ¼d. W.G. McC." (4 to 27 October) £250
MP2*a* "¼d Pd./W.G. McC" (14 October) £1000
MP3 "Paid" (7 October) £5500
MP4 "Pd ¼d" (8 October) £4500
MP5 "(Paid ¼GAP. asst.)" (15 October) £4000

No. MP2 exists in different inks and formats.

Manuscript endorsement for the 2½d. rate is also known, but this is thought to have been done by oversight.

A 1d. surcharge on 4d. (No. 29), issued in mid-May, wa intended as a revenue stamp and was never authorised fo postal use (*price* £225 *un.*). Used examples were either cancelle by favour or passed through the post in error. Exists wi surcharge inverted (*price* £1600 *un.*), surcharge double (*pri* £2500 *un.*) or surcharge double, both inverted (*price* £2500 *un*

11

12

13

1908 (30 June)–**09.** *Wmk Mult Crown CA. Litho. P* 14.
38 **11** ¼d. brown (Optd S. £65) 90 3
a. Grey-brown (2.09) .. .. .. 1·75 7

1912 (24 Apr)–**20.** *Die I. Wmk Mult Crown CA. Chalk-surface paper* (3*d. to* 10*s.*). *P* 14.
40 **13** ¼d. brown (10.2.13) 60 3
41 **12** ½d. green .. .. 2·50 4·2
42 1d. red (25.2.13) .. .. .. 3·25 2·2
43 **13** 2d. pale grey .. .. 80 8·0
44 **12** 2½d. bright blue (26.8.14) .. .. 7·00 9·0
a. Deep bright blue (9.11.17) .. 16·00 23·0
45 **13** 3d. purple/*yellow* (26.11.14) .. .. 12·00 35·0
a. White back (19.11.13) .. .. 3·25 7·5
b. On lemon (12.3.18) (Optd S. £50) 2·25 16·0
c. On orange-buff (1920) .. .. 9·00 27·0
d. On buff (1920) .. ..
e. On pale yellow (1920) .. .. 3·50 27·0
46 4d. black and red/*yellow* (25.2.13) .. 75 8·0
47 **12** 6d. dull and bright purple (25.2.13) .. 3·50 6·5
48 **13** 1s. black/*green* (15.5.16) (Optd S. £50) 3·50 23·0
a. White back (19.11.13) .. .. 2·75 3·0
49 2s. purple and bright blue/*blue* .. 9·50 45·0
50 3s. green and violet .. .. .. 19·00 60·0
51 5s. green and red/*yellow* (26.8.14) .. 70·00 £14
52 **12** 10s. deep green and red/*green* (26.11.14)
(Optd S. £80) .. .. .. 90·00 £16
a. White back (19.11.13) .. .. 80·00 £14
b. On blue-green, olive back (5.10.18) 75·00 £16
40/52*b* .. .. *Set of* 13 £180 £40
40/4, 45*a*, 46/7, 48*a*, 49/51, 52*a* Optd "Specimen"
Set of 13 £325

WAR STAMP. 1½d
(14)

WAR STAMP. 1½d
(15)

1½d
Straight serif (Left-hand pane R. 10/2)

1917 (26 Feb). *T* **12** *surch with T* **14** *or* **15** *at Kingston Jamaica.*
53 **14** 1½d. on 2½d. deep blue .. .. .. 4·75 8·
a. No fraction bar .. .. .. 80·00 £1
b. Missing stop after "STAMP" (R.1/4) £300
54 **15** 1½d. on 2½d. deep blue .. .. .. 1·40 4·
a. No fraction bar .. .. .. 50·00 95·
b. Straight serif .. .. .. 60·00 £1

On No. 53 "WAR STAMP" and "1½d." were appli separately.

WAR STAMP 1½d
(16)

WAR STAMP 1½d
(17)

WAR STAMP 1½d.
(18)

1917 (4 Sept). *T* **12** *surch with T* **16** *or* **17** *by D.L.R.*
55 **16** 1½d. on 2½d. deep blue £650 £180
56 **17** 1½d. on 2½d. deep blue (Optd S. £100) 20 4
a. Short opt (right pane R. 10/1) ..
x. Wmk reversed .. .. .. 75·00

De La Rue replaced surcharge Type **16** by Type **17** (whic shows different figures) after only a few sheets as it did n adequately obliterate the original face value. A small quantit said to be 3½ sheets, of Type **16** was included in th consignment in error.

1919–20. *T* **12** *and* **13** (2½*d. special printing*), *optd only,* *surch in addition at Kingston* (*No.* 58) *or by D.L.R.* (*others*).
57 **16** ½d. green (4.2.19) .. .. .. 20 1·7
a. Short opt (right pane R. 10/1) .. 20·00
58 **18** 1½d. on 2d. grey (10.3.20) .. .. 1·25 6·5
59 **17** 1½d. on 2½d. orange (4.12.19) 60 8
a. Short opt (right pane R. 10/1) ..
57, 59 Optd "Specimen" .. .. *Set of* 2 80·00

The ½d. stamps on *buff* paper, and later consignments of th 2d. T **13** on *pinkish*, derived their colour from the paper in whic they were packed for despatch from England.

Nos. 56a, 57a and 59a show the overprint 2 mm high instea of 2½ mm.

A further surcharge as No. 58, but in red, was prepared i Jamaica during April 1920, but these were not issued.

19

20 King William IV and King George V

21 (4 Apr)–**26.** *P* 14. (*a*) *Wmk Mult Crown CA.*

No.	Type	Description	Unused	Used
	19	3d. purple/*orange-buff*	1·50	7·00
		aw. Wmk inverted	55·00	
		ay. Wmk inverted and reversed ..	55·00	
		b. Purple/pale yellow	45·00	60·00
		bw. Wmk inverted		
2		4d. red/*yellow* (1.4.22)	80	3·75
3		1s. black/*green*	1·25	8·50
		x. Wmk reversed		
4		5s. yellow-green/*pale yellow*	16·00	60·00
		a. Deep green/pale yellow	60·00	95·00
		b. Blue-green/pale yellow	65·00	£110
		c. Deep green/orange-buff (19.11.21) ..	90·00	£150
7		10s. carmine/*green* (19.11.21)	55·00	90·00
)/7		.. .. *Set of* 5	70·00	£150
)/7 Optd "Specimen"		.. .. *Set of* 5	£180	

(*b*) *Wmk Mult Script CA*

No.	Type	Description	Unused	Used
9	**19**	¼d. yellow-brown (1.4.22)	40	1·25
		y. Wmk inverted and reversed ..	75·00	
0		½d. pale grey-green (1.4.22)	50	30
		w. Wmk inverted		
		y. Wmk inverted and reversed ..		
1		1d. deep carmine-red (1.4.22)	1·10	85
2		1½d. orange-brown	1·75	30
3		2d. slate-grey (1.4.22)	1·75	3·50
4		2½d. bright blue (1.4.22)	50	45
		x. Wmk reversed		
5		3d. purple/*yellow* (29.6.23)	50	3·00
		y. Wmk inverted and reversed ..	55·00	
6		4½d. sage-green (29.6.23)	1·75	3·00
7		6d. claret (1.4.22)	5·50	28·00
		a. Deep claret	19·00	35·00
9		1s. black/*green* (15.5.25)	8·00	30·00
0		2s. violet/*blue* (1.4.22)	14·00	19·00
1		3s. violet (1.4.22)	23·00	16·00
2		5s. green/*yellow* (15.2.25)	24·00	42·00
3		10s. carmine/*green* (5.9.26)	55·00	75·00
9/83		.. .. *Set of* 14	£120	£200
9/53 Optd "Specimen"		.. .. *Set of* 14	£325	

A.S.R." PROVISIONAL. On the night of 9/10 November 932 the Cayman Brac Post Office at Stake Bay, and its ontents, was destroyed by a hurricane. Pending the arrival of eplacement stamp stocks and cancellation the Postmaster, Mr. . S. Rutty, initialled covers to indicate that postage had been aid. Those destined for overseas addresses additionally eceived a "Postage Paid" machine postmark in red when they assed through Kingston, Jamaica.

No.	Description	*Price on cover*
MP6	Endorsed "A.S.R." in manuscript	£4000
MP7	Endorsed "A.S.R." in manuscript and "Postage Paid" machine postmark in red	£6500

These emergency arrangements lasted until 19 December.

(Recess Waterlow)

932 (5 Dec). *Centenary of the "Assembly of Justices and Vestry". Wmk Mult Script CA. P* 12½.

No.	Type	Description	Unused	Used
4	**20**	¼d. brown	1·25	90
		a. "A" of "CA" missing from wmk ..	£1000	
5		½d. green	2·50	7·00
		a. "A" of "CA" reversed in wmk ..	£1200	
36		1d. scarlet	2·50	5·50
37		1½d. red-orange	2·00	2·00
		a. "A" of "CA" missing from wmk ..		
8		2d. grey	2·00	2·50
9		2½d. ultramarine	2·00	1·25
0		3d. olive-green	2·50	4·00
1		6d. purple	8·50	19·00
2		1s. black and brown	16·00	28·00
3		2s. black and ultramarine	42·00	70·00
4		5s. black and green	80·00	£120
5		10s. black and scarlet	£250	£350
4/95		.. .. *Set of* 12	£350	£500
4/95 Perf "Specimen"		.. .. *Set of* 12	£450	

No. 85a shows one "A" of the watermark reversed so that its ead points to right when seen from the back. It is believed that his stamp may also exist with the "A" missing. An example of he 1½d., No. 87, is known with the "A" missing from a vatermark in the right-hand sheet margin.

Examples of all values are known showing a forged George Town postmark dated "DE 31 1932".

21 Cayman Islands

24 Queen or Pink Conch Shells

(Recess Waterlow)

1935 (1 May)–**36.** *T* **21, 24** *and similar designs. Wmk Mult Script CA. P* 12½.

No.	Type	Description	Unused	Used
96	**21**	¼d. black and brown	30	80
97	–	½d. ultramarine & yellow-green (1.1.36)	1·00	1·00
98	–	1d. ultramarine and scarlet	3·00	2·25
99	**24**	1½d. black and orange	1·50	1·75
100	–	2d. ultramarine and purple	3·50	1·10
101	–	2½d. blue and black (1.1.36)	3·00	1·25
102	**21**	3d. black and olive-green	2·00	3·00
103	–	6d. bright purple and black (1.1.36) ..	8·50	4·00
104	–	1s. ultramarine and orange (1.1.36) ..	6·00	6·50
105	–	2s. ultramarine and black	45·00	32·00
106	–	5s. green and black	48·00	48·00
107	**24**	10s. black and scarlet	70·00	85·00
96/107		.. .. *Set of* 12	£170	£170
96/107 Perf "Specimen"		.. .. *Set of* 12	£250	

Designs: *Horiz*—½d., 2d., 1s. Cat boat; 1d., 2s. Red-footed Booby; 2½d., 6d. 5s. Hawksbill Turtles.

Examples of all values are known showing a forged George Town postmark dated "AU 23 1936"

1935 (6 May). *Silver Jubilee. As Nos. 91/4 of Antigua.*

No.	Description	Unused	Used
108	½d. black and green	15	60
	f. Diagonal line by turret	24·00	
	h. Dot by flagstaff	38·00	
109	2½d. brown and deep blue	1·00	1·00
110	6d. light blue and olive-green	1·00	3·00
	h. Dot by flagstaff	£120	
	i. Dash by turret	£120	
111	1s. slate and purple	6·00	6·00
	h. Dot by flagstaff	£180	
	i. Dash by turret	£190	
108/11	.. .. .. *Set of* 4	7·50	9·50
108/11 Perf "Specimen"	.. .. *Set of* 4	90·00	

For illustrations of plate varieties see Catalogue Introduction.

1937 (13 May). *Coronation Issue. As Nos. 95/7 of Antigua. P* 11×11½.

No.	Description	Unused	Used
112	½d. green	30	40
113	1d. carmine	50	20
114	2½d. blue	95	40
112/14	.. .. .. *Set of* 3	1·60	90
112/14 Perf "Specimen"	.. .. *Set of* 3	75·00	

26 Beach View

27 Dolphin (fish) (*Coryphaena hippurus*)

(Recess D.L.R. (½d., 2d., 6d., 1s., 10s.), Waterlow (others))

1938 (5 May)–**48.** *T* **26/7** *and similar designs. Wmk Mult Script CA (sideways on ¼d., 1d., 1½d., 2½d., 3d., 2s., 5s.). Various perfs.*

No.	Type	Description	Unused	Used
115	**26**	¼d. red-orange (*p* 12½)	30	55
		a. Perf 13½×12½ (16.7.43) ..	10	55
116	**27**	½d. green (*p* 13×11½)	75	55
		a. Perf 14 (16.7.43)	1·25	1·40
		ab. "A" of "CA" missing from wmk ..	£1000	
117	–	1d. scarlet (*p* 12½)	30	75
118	**26**	1½d. black (*p* 12½)	30	10
119	–	2d. violet (*p* 11½×13)	2·00	40
		a. Perf 14 (16.7.43)	60	30
120	–	2½d. bright blue (*p* 12½)	40	20
120*a*	–	2½d. orange (*p* 12½) (25.8.47) ..	1·75	50
121	–	3d. orange (*p* 12½)	40	15
121*a*	–	3d. bright blue (*p* 12½) (25.8.47) ..	1·75	30
122	–	6d. olive-green (*p* 11½×13)	8·50	4·00
		a. Perf 14 (16.7.43)	2·00	1·25
		b. Brownish ol (*p* 11½×13) (8.7.47)	3·00	1·50
123	**27**	1s. red-brown (*p* 13×11½)	4·50	1·50
		a. Perf 14 (16.7.43)	4·00	2·00
		ab. "A" of "CA" missing from wmk ..	£1100	
124	**26**	2s. yellow-green (*shades*) (*p* 12½) ..	48·00	14·00
		a. Deep green (16.7.43)	25·00	9·00
125	–	5s. carmine-lake (*p* 12½)	32·00	15·00
		a. Crimson (1948)	55·00	22·00
126	–	10s. chocolate (*p* 11½×13)	23·00	9·00
		a. Perf 14 (16.7.43)	21·00	9·00
115/26a		.. .. *Set of* 14	80·00	35·00
115/26 Perf "Specimen"		.. .. *Set of* 14	£275	

Designs: *Horiz* (*as T* **26**)—1d., 3d. Cayman Islands map; 2½d., 5s. *Rembro* (schooner). *Vert* (*as T* **27**)—2d., 6d., 10s. Hawksbill Turtles.

Stop after "1946" (R.2/1)

1946 (26 Aug). *Victory. As Nos. 110/11 of Antigua.*

No.	Description	Unused	Used
127	1½d. black	20	10
128	3d. orange-yellow	20	10
	a. Stop after "1946"	14·00	
127/8 Perf "Specimen"	.. .. *Set of* 2	65·00	

1948 (29 Nov). *Royal Silver Wedding. As Nos.* 112/13 *of Antigua.*

No.	Description	Unused	Used
129	½d. green	10	10
130	10s. violet-blue	13·00	10·00

1949 (10 Oct). *75th Anniv of Universal Postal Union. As Nos.* 114/17 *of Antigua.*

No.	Description	Unused	Used
131	2½d. orange	30	30
132	3d. deep blue	1·50	1·25
133	6d. olive	60	1·25
134	1s. red-brown	60	30
131/4	.. .. *Set of* 4	2·75	2·75

31 Cat Boat

32 Coconut Grove, Cayman Brac

(Recess B.W.)

1950 (2 Oct). *T* **31/2** *and similar horiz designs. Wmk Mult Script CA. P* 11½ × 11.

No.	Description	Unused	Used
135	¼d. bright blue and pale scarlet	15	60
136	½d. reddish violet and emerald-green ..	15	1·25
137	1d. olive-green and deep blue	60	75
138	1½d. green and brown	30	75
139	2d. reddish violet and rose-carmine ..	1·00	1·50
140	2½d. turquoise and black	50	60
141	3d. bright green and light blue	1·40	1·50
142	6d. red-brown and blue	2·00	1·25
143	9d. scarlet and grey-green	4·00	2·00
144	1s. brown and orange	3·25	2·75
145	2s. violet and reddish purple	7·50	8·50
146	5s. olive-green and violet	12·00	7·00
147	10s. black and scarlet	14·00	13·00
135/47	.. .. *Set of* 13	42·00	35·00

Designs:—1d. Green Turtle; 1½d. Thatch rope industry; 2d. Cayman seamen; 2½d. Map of Cayman Islands; 3d. Parrotfish; 6d. Bluff, Cayman Brac; 9d. Georgetown harbour; 1s. Turtle in "crawl"; 2s. *Ziroma* (schooner); 5s. Boat-building; 10s. Government Offices, Grand Cayman.

44 South Sound Lighthouse, Grand Cayman

45 Queen Elizabeth II

1953 (2 Mar)–**62**. *Designs previously used for King George VI issue but with portrait of Queen Elizabeth II as in T* **44/5**. *Wmk Mult Script CA. P* 11½×11 *or* 11×11½ (*4d., £1*).

No.	Description	Unused	Used
148	¼d. deep bright blue & rose-red (21.2.55)	85	50
	a. Bright blue and bright rose-red (5.12.56)	1·75	90
149	½d. purple and bluish green (7.7.54) ..	20	50
150	1d. brown-olive and indigo (7.7.54) ..	70	40
151	1½d. deep green and red-brown (7.7.54) ..	50	20
152	2d. reddish violet and cerise (2.6.54) ..	3·00	85
153	2½d. turquoise-blue and black (2.6.54) ..	3·50	80
154	3d. bright green and blue (21.2.55) ..	4·00	60
155	4d. black and deep blue	2·00	40
	a. Black and greenish blue (13.10.54) ..	17·00	17·00
	b. Black and deep bright blue (10.7.62)	14·00	14·00
156	6d. lake-brown and deep blue (7.7.54) ..	1·75	30
157	9d. scarlet and bluish green (2.6.54) ..	4·00	30
158	1s. brown and red-orange (21.2.55) ..	3·25	20
159	2s. slate-violet & reddish purple (21.2.55)	12·00	7·50
160	5s. olive-green and slate-violet (21.2.55)	14·00	4·50
161	10s. black and rose-red (21.2.55)	14·00	7·50
161*a*	£1 blue (6.1.59)	32·00	10·00
148/61*a*	.. .. *Set of* 15	80·00	30·00

Designs: *Horiz*—¼d. Cat boat; ½d. Coconut grove, Cayman Brac; 1d. Green Turtle; 1½d. Thatch rope industry; 2d. Cayman seamen; 2½d. Map of Cayman Islands; 3d. Parrotfish; 6d. Bluff, Cayman Brac; 9d. Georgetown harbour; 1s. Turtle in "crawl"; 2s. *Ziroma* (schooner); 5s. Boat-building; 10s. Government Offices, Grand Cayman.

1953 (2 June). *Coronation. As No.* 120 *of Antigua, but ptd by B.W.*

No.	Description	Unused	Used
162	1d. black and emerald	30	80

46 Arms of the Cayman Islands

(Photo D.L.R.)

1959 (4 July). *New Constitution. Wmk Mult Script CA. P* 12.

No.	Type	Description	Unused	Used
163	**46**	2½d. black and light blue	45	1·40
164		1s. black and orange	55	35

CROWN COLONY

47 Cuban Amazon

48 Cat Boat

(Recess B.W.)

1962 (28 Nov)–**64**. *T* **47/8** *and similar designs.* W w **12**. *P* 11×11½ (*vert*) *or* 11½×11 (*horiz*).

No.	Description	Unused	Used
165	¼d. emerald and red	30	70
	a. Emerald and rose (18.2.64)	2·00	2·25
166	1d. black and yellow-olive	60	20
167	1½d. yellow and purple	2·75	80
168	2d. blue and deep brown	60	30
169	2½d. violet and bluish green	85	80
170	3d. bright blue and carmine	30	10
171	4d. deep green and purple	80	60
172	6d. bluish green and sepia	3·25	30

173 9d. ultramarine and purple .. .. .. 1·25 40
174 1s. sepia and rose-red 80 10
175 1s. 3d. bluish green and orange-brown .. 3·50 1·75
176 1s. 9d. deep turquoise and violet .. 13·00 1·25
177 5s. plum and deep green .. .. .. 8·00 5·50
178 10s. olive and blue .. .. 14·00 8·00
179 £1 carmine and black .. .. .. 19·00 15·00
165/79 .. .. *Set of* 15 60·00 30·00

Designs: *Horiz*—1½d. *Schomburgkia thomsoniana* (orchid); 2d. Map of Cayman Islands; 2½d. Fisherman casting net; 3d. West Bay Beach; 4d. Green Turtle; 6d. *Lydia E. Wilson* (schooner); 1s. Iguana; 1s. 3d. Swimming Pool, Cayman Brac; 1s. 9d. Water sports; 5s. Fort George. *Vert*—9d. Angler with King Mackerel; 10s. Coat of Arms; £1 Queen Elizabeth II.

1963 (4 June). *Freedom from Hunger. As No.* 146 *of Antigua.*
180 1s. 9d. carmine 30 15

1963 (2 Sept). *Red Cross Centenary. As Nos.* 147/8 *of Antigua.*
181 1d. red and black 20 65
182 1s. 9d. red and blue .. .. 1·10 1·60

1964 (23 April). *400th Birth Anniv of William Shakespeare. As No.* 164 *of Antigua.*
183 6d. magenta 10 10

1965 (17 May). *I.T.U. Centenary. As Nos.* 166/7 *of Antigua.*
184 1d. blue and light purple 15 10
185 1s. 3d. bright purple and green 40 35

1965 (25 Oct). *International Co-operation Year. As Nos.* 168/9 *of Antigua.*
186 1d. reddish purple and turquoise-green .. 15 10
187 1s. deep bluish green and lavender 50 25

1966 (24 Jan). *Churchill Commemoration. As Nos.* 170/3 *of Antigua.*
188 ¼d. new blue 10 90
w. Wmk inverted .. .. .. 24·00
189 1d. deep green 20 10
190 1s. brown 50 10
w. Wmk inverted .. .. .. 4·50 5·00
191 1s. 9d. bluish violet 70 65
188/91 .. .. *Set of* 4 1·25 1·50

1966 (4 Feb). *Royal Visit. As Nos.* 174/5 *of Antigua.*
192 1d. black and ultramarine 60 20
193 1s. 9d. black and magenta .. .. .. 2·25 65

1966 (1 July). *World Cup Football Championships. As Nos.* 176/7 *of Antigua.*
194 1½d. violet, yellow-green, lake & yellow-brn 15 10
195 1s. 9d. chocolate, blue-grn, lake & yell-brn 50 25

1966 (20 Sept). *Inauguration of W.H.O. Headquarters, Geneva. As Nos.* 178/9 *of Antigua.*
196 2d. black, yellow-green and light blue .. 50 15
197 1s. 3d. black, light purple and yellow-brown 1·25 60

62 Telephone and Map

(Des V. Whiteley. Litho Harrison)

1966 (5 Dec). *International Telephone Links.* W w **12**. *P* 14½ × 14.
198 **62** 4d. red, black, greenish blue & ol-grn 20 20
199 9d. violet-blue, black, brown-red & lt grn 20 20

1966 (12 Dec*). *20th Anniv of U.N.E.S.C.O. As Nos.* 196/8 *of Antigua.*
200 1d. slate-violet, red, yellow and orange .. 15 10
201 1s. 9d. orange-yellow, violet and deep olive 45 10
202 5s. black, bright purple and orange .. 1·25 55
200/2 .. .. *Set of* 3 1·75 65

*This is the local date of issue; the Crown Agents released the stamps on 1 December.

63 B.A.C. One Eleven 200/400 Airliner over Cayman Schooner

(Des V. Whiteley. Photo Harrison)

1966 (17 Dec). *Opening of Cayman Jet Service.* W w **12**. *P* 14½.
203 **63** 1s. black, new blue and olive-green .. 50 30
204 1s. 9d. deep purple-brown, ultramarine and emerald 50 35

64 Water-skiing

(Des G. Vasarhelyi. Photo Harrison)

1967 (1 Dec). *International Tourist Year. T* **64** *and similar horiz designs. Multicoloured.* W w **12**. *P* 14½ × 14.
205 4d. Type **64** 50 10
a. Gold omitted £190
206 6d. Skin diving 50 30
207 1s. Sport fishing 50 30
208 1s. 9d. Sailing 60 75
205/8 .. .. *Set of* 4 1·90 1·25

A used copy of No. 207 is known with yellow omitted.

68 Former Slaves and Emblem

(Des and photo Harrison)

1968 (3 June). *Human Rights Year.* W w **12**. *P* 14½ × 14.
209 **68** 3d. deep bluish green, black and gold .. 10 10
w. Wmk inverted 60 80
210 9d. brown, gold and myrtle-green .. 10 10
211 5s. ultramarine, gold and myrtle-green 30 70
209/11 .. .. *Set of* 3 40 80

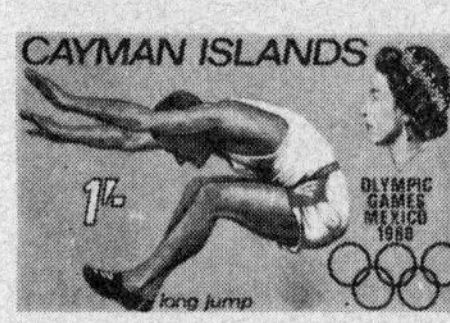

69 Long-jumping

(Des R. Granger Barrett. Litho P.B.)

1968 (1 Oct). *Olympic Games, Mexico. T* **69** *and similar multi-coloured designs.* W w **12**. *P* 13½.
212 1s. Type **69** 10 10
213 1s. 3d. High jumping 15 25
214 2s. Pole vaulting (*vert*) 15 40
212/14 .. .. *Set of* 3 30 65

72 "The Adoration of the Shepherds" (Fabritius)

(Des and photo Harrison)

1968–69. *Christmas. T* **72** *and similar horiz design. Centres multicoloured; country name and frames in gold; value and back-ground in colours given. P* 14 × 14½.

(*a*) *W* w **12**. (18.11.68)
215 **72** ¼d. brown 10 20
a. Gold omitted £190
216 – 1d. bluish violet 10 10
217 **72** 6d. bright blue 15 10
218 – 8d. cerise 15 15
219 **72** 1s. 3d. bright green 20 25
220 – 2s. grey 25 35

(*b*) *No wmk* (8.1.69)
221 **72** ¼d. bright purple 10 20
215/21 .. .. *Set of* 7 80 1·10

Design:—1d., 8d., 2s. "The Adoration of the Shepherds" (Rembrandt).

74 Grand Cayman Thrush

76 Arms of the Cayman Islands

(Des G. Vasarhelyi. Litho Format)

1969 (5 June). *Designs as T* **74** *and T* **76** *in black, ochre and re*[d] *(£1) or multicoloured (others). No wmk. P* 14.
222 ¼d. Type **74** 10 7
223 1d. Brahmin Cattle (*horiz*) 10 1
224 2d. Blowholes on the coast (*horiz*) .. 10 1
225 2½d. Map of Grand Cayman (*horiz*) .. 15 1
226 3d. Georgetown scene (*horiz*) 15 1
227 4d. Royal Poinciana (*horiz*) 30 1
228 6d. Cayman Brac and Little Cayman on Chart (*horiz*) 30 1
229 8d. Motor vessels at berth (*horiz*) .. 40 1
230 1s. Basket-making (*horiz*) 20 1
231 1s. 3d. Beach scene (*horiz*) .. .. 35 1·5
232 1s. 6d. Straw-rope making (*horiz*) .. 50 1·2
233 2s. Great Barracuda (*horiz*) .. .. 1·25 8
234 4s. Government House (*horiz*) 50 8
235 10s. Type **76** .. .. 1·00 2·2
236 £1 Queen Elizabeth II (*vert*) .. .. 1·75 2·5
222/36 .. .. *Set of* 15 6·00 9·0

1969 (11 Aug). *As No.* 222, *but wmk* w **12** (*sideways*).
237 **74** ¼d. multicoloured 30 6

(New Currency. 100 cents = 1 dollar.)

C-DAY
8th September 1969 ¼C

(89)

1969 (8 Sept). *Decimal Currency. No.* 237, *and as Nos.* 223/36, *bu*[t] *wmk* w **12** (*sideways on horiz designs*), *surch as T* **89**.
238 ¼ c. on ¼d. Type **74** 10 7
239 1 c. on 1d. Brahmin Cattle 10 1
240 2 c. on 2d. Blowholes on the coast .. 10 1
241 3 c. on 4d. Royal Poinciana 10 1
242 4 c. on 2½d. Map of Grand Cayman .. 10 1
243 5 c. on 6d. Cayman Brac and Little Cayman on Chart 10 1
244 7 c. on 8d. Motor vessels at berth .. 10 1
245 8 c. on 3d. Georgetown scene 15 1
246 10 c. on 1s. Basket-making 25 1
247 12 c. on 1s. 3d. Beach scene .. .. 35 1·2
248 15 c. on 1s. 6d. Straw-rope making .. 45 7
249 20 c. on 2s. Great Barracuda .. .. 1·25 1·5
250 40 c. on 4s. Government House 45 8
251 $1 on 10s. Type **76** .. .. .. 1·50 2·5
w. Wmk inverted .. .. ..
252 $2 on £1 Queen Elizabeth II .. .. 2·00 3·2
238/52 .. .. *Set of* 15 6·00 9·5

90 "Virgin and Child" (Vivarini)

92 "Noli me tangere" (Titian)

(Des adapted by G. Drummond. Photo Harrison)

1969 (14 Nov*). *Christmas. Multicoloured; background colou*[r] *given.* W w **12** (*sideways on* 1, 7 *and* 20 c.). *P* 14½.
253 **90** ¼ c. orange-red 10 1
w. Wmk inverted .. .. .. 3·50 5·0
254 ¼ c. magenta 10 1
w. Wmk inverted .. .. .. 3·50 5·0
255 ¼ c. emerald 10 1
a. Gold frame omitted £150
w. Wmk inverted .. .. .. 1·00 1·7
256 ¼ c. new blue 10 1
w. Wmk inverted .. .. .. 3·50 5·0
257 – 1 c. ultramarine 10 1
258 **90** 5 c. orange-red 10 1
259 – 7 c. myrtle-green 10 1
260 **90** 12 c. emerald 15 1
261 – 20 c. brown-purple 20 2
253/61 .. .. *Set of* 9 45 4

Design:—1, 7, 20 c. "The Adoration of the Kings" (Gossaert).

*This is the local release date. The Crown Agents released th[e] stamps on 4 November.

(Des L. Curtis. Litho D.L.R.)

1970 (23 Mar). *Easter. Paintings multicoloured; frame colou*[r] *given. P* 14.
262 **92** ¼ c. carmine-red 10 1
263 ¼ c. deep green 10 1
264 ¼ c. yellow-brown 10 1
265 ¼ c. pale violet 10 1
266 10 c. chalky blue 25 1
267 12 c. chestnut 30 1
268 40 c. plum 40 4
262/8 .. .. *Set of* 7 90 6

93 Barnaby (*Barnaby Rudge*) **97** Grand Cayman Thrush

(Des Jennifer Toombs. Photo Harrison)

70 (17 June). *Death Centenary of Charles Dickens. T* **93** *and similar vert designs.* W w **12** (*sideways**). P 14½×14.

9 1 c. black, olive-green and greenish yellow .. 10 10
w. Wmk Crown to right of CA .. .. — 3·00
) 12 c. black, lake-brown and red 25 10
20 c. black, ochre-brown and gold 30 10
2 40 c. black, bright ultramarine and new blue 35 25
9/72 .. .. *Set of* 4 85 35

Designs:—12 c. Sairey Gamp (*Martin Chuzzlewit*); 20 c. Mr. cawber and David (*David Copperfield*); 40 c. The archioness" (*The Old Curiosity Shop*).

*The normal sideways watermark shows Crown to left of CA, *seen from the back of the stamp.*

70 (8 Sept). *Decimal Currency. Designs as Nos. 223/37, but with values inscr in decimal currency as T* **97**. W w **12** *sideways* on cent values*).

3 ¼ c. Type **97** 10 10
4 1 c. Brahmin Cattle 10 10
5 2 c. Blowholes on the coast 10 10
6 3 c. Royal Poinciana 20 10
7 4 c. Map of Grand Cayman 20 10
3 5 c. Cayman Brac and Little Cayman on Chart 35 10
w. Wmk Crown to right of CA .. .. 11·00
9 7 c. Motor vessels at berth 30 10
0 8 c. Georgetown scene 30 10
1 10 c. Basket-making 30 10
2 12 c. Beach scene 90 45
3 15 c. Straw-rope making .. .. .. 1·25 2·50
4 20 c. Great Barracuda .. .. .. 2·50 1·25
5 40 c. Government House 85 75
6 $1 Type **76** .. .. 1·25 4·25
w. Wmk inverted .. .. .. 9·00
7 $2 Queen Elizabeth II .. .. .. 2·00 4·75
3/87 .. .. *Set of* 15 9·50 13·00

*The normal sideways watermark shows Crown to left of CA, *seen from the back of the stamp.*

98 The Three Wise Men

(Des G. Drummond. Litho Format)

70 (8 Oct). *Christmas. T* **98** *and similar horiz design.* W w **12** (*sideways**). P 14.

8 **98** ¼ c. apple-green, grey and emerald .. 10 10
w. Wmk Crown to right of CA .. 5·00 5·00
9 – 1 c. black, lemon and turquoise-green 10 10
0 **98** 5 c. grey, red-orange and crimson .. 10 10
1 – 10 c. black, lemon and orange-red .. 10 10
2 **98** 12 c. grey, pale turquoise & ultramarine 15 10
3 – 20 c. black, lemon and green 20 15
8/93 .. .. *Set of* 6 55 30

Design:—1, 10, 20 c. Nativity scene and Globe.

*The normal sideways watermark shows Crown to left of CA, *seen from the back of the stamp.*

100 Grand Cayman Terrapin

(Des V. Whiteley. Photo Harrison)

71 (28 Jan). *Turtles. T* **100** *and similar diamond-shaped designs.* W w **12** (*sideways*, reading from inscr to "ISLANDS"*). P 14½×14.

4 5 c. Type **100** 30 25
w. Wmk Crown to right of CA .. .. 16·00
5 7 c. Green Turtle 35 25
w. Wmk Crown to right of CA .. .. 55·00
6 12 c. Hawksbill Turtle 55 30
7 20 c. Turtle Farm .. .. 1·00 1·40
4/7 .. .. *Set of* 4 2·00 2·00

*The normal sideways watermark shows Crown to left of CA, *seen from the back of the stamp.*

101 *Dendrophylax fawcettii* **102** "Adoration of the Kings" (French, 15th Cent)

(Des Sylvia Goaman. Litho Questa)

1971 (7 Apr). *Orchids. T* **101** *and similar vert designs. Multicoloured.* W w **12**. P 14.

298 ¼ c. Type **101** 10 70
299 2 c. *Schomburgkia thomsoniana* 40 60
300 10 c. *Vanilla claviculata* 90 50
301 40 c. *Oncidium variegatum* .. .. .. 3·00 3·50
298/301 .. .. *Set of* 4 4·00 4·75

(Des Jennifer Toombs. Litho Questa)

1971 (15 Oct*). *Christmas. T* **102** *and similar vert designs. Multicoloured.* W w **12**. P 14.

302 ¼ c. Type **102** 10 10
w. Wmk inverted .. .. 2·00
303 1 c. "The Nativity" (Parisian, 14th Cent.) 10 10
304 5 c. "Adoration of the Magi" (Burgundian, 15th Cent.) 10 10
305 12 c. Type **102** 20 15
306 15 c. As 1 c. 20 25
307 20 c. As 5 c. 25 35
302/7 .. .. *Set of* 6 70 80
MS308 113×115 mm. Nos. 302/7 .. .. 1·25 2·25
w. Wmk inverted £225

*This is the local date of issue. The Crown Agents released the stamps on 27 September.

103 Turtle and Telephone Cable

(Des Anglo Arts Associates. Litho Walsall)

1972 (10 Jan). *Co-Axial Telephone Cable.* W w **12** (*sideways**). P 14.

309 **103** 2 c. multicoloured 10 10
310 10 c. multicoloured 15 10
w. Wmk Crown to right of CA .. 8·00
311 40 c. multicoloured 30 40
w. Wmk Crown to right of CA .. 75
309/11 .. .. *Set of* 3 45 45

*The normal sideways watermark shows Crown to left of CA, *as seen from the back of the stamp.*

104 Court House Building

(Des C. Abbott. Litho Questa)

1972 (15 Aug). *New Government Buildings. T* **104** *and similar horiz design. Multicoloured.* W w **12**. P 13½.

312 5 c. Type **104** 10 10
313 15 c. Legislative Assembly Building 10 10
314 25 c. Type **104** 15 15
315 40 c. As 15 c. 20 30
312/15 .. .. *Set of* 4 35 45
MS316 121×108 mm. Nos. 312/15 .. .. 70 2·00
w. Wmk inverted .. .. .. 30·00

105 Hawksbill Turtle and Queen or Pink Conch

(Des (from photograph by D. Groves) and photo Harrison)

1972 (20 Nov). *Royal Silver Wedding. Multicoloured; background colour given.* W w **12**. P 14 × 14½.

317 **105** 12 c. deep slate-violet 15 10
318 30 c. yellow-olive 15 20
a. Blue omitted* £425
w. Wmk inverted .. .. .. 3·00

*The omission of the blue colour results in the Duke's suit appearing sepia instead of deep blue.

106 $1 Coin and Note **107** "The Way of Sorrow"

(Des and photo D.L.R.)

1973 (15 Jan). *First Issue of Currency. T* **106** *and similar horiz designs. Multicoloured.* W w **12** (*sideways**). P 13.

319 3 c. Type **106** 20 10
320 6 c. $5 Coin and note 20 10
321 15 c. $10 Coin and note 60 20
322 25 c. $25 Coin and note 80 35
319/22 .. .. *Set of* 4 1·60 60
MS323 128×107 mm. Nos. 319/22 .. .. 3·25 3·25
w. Wmk Crown to right of CA .. .. 70·00

*The normal sideways watermark shows Crown to left of CA, *as seen from the back of the stamp.*

(Des G. Drummond. Litho Questa)

1973 (11 Apr*). *Easter. T* **107** *and similar multicoloured designs showing stained-glass windows.* W w **12** (*sideways on 10 and 12 c.*). P 14½.

324 10 c. Type **107** 15 10
325 12 c. "Christ Resurrected" 20 10
326 20 c. "The Last Supper" (*horiz*) 25 15
327 30 c. "Christ on the Cross" (*horiz*) 30 25
324/7 .. .. *Set of* 4 80 45
MS328 122 × 105 mm. Nos. 324/7. Imperf .. 1·00 1·60

*This is the local date of issue; the Crown Agents released the stamps on 15 March.

108 "The Nativity" (Sforza Book of Hours) **109** White-winged Dove

(Des J. Cooter. Litho Questa)

1973 (2 Oct). *Christmas. T* **108** *and similar vert design.* W w **12** (*sideways*). P 14.

329 **108** 3 c. multicoloured 10 10
330 – 5 c. multicoloured 10 10
331 **108** 9 c. multicoloured 15 10
332 – 12 c. multicoloured 15 10
333 **108** 15 c. multicoloured 15 15
334 – 25 c. multicoloured 20 25
329/34 .. .. *Set of* 6 65 50

Design:—5, 12, 25 c. "The Adoration of the Magi" (Breviary of Queen Isabella).

1973 (14 Nov). *Royal Wedding. As Nos. 165/6 of Anguilla. Centre multicoloured.* W w **12** (*sideways*). P 13½.

335 10 c. sage-green 10 10
336 30 c. bright mauve 15 10

(Des M. Goaman. Litho Walsall)

1974 (2 Jan). *Birds (1st series). T* **109** *and similar vert designs. Multicoloured.* W w **12** (*sideways*). P 14.

337 3 c. Type **109** .. .. 2·00 20
338 10 c. Vitelline Warbler .. .. .. 2·75 20
339 12 c. Antillean Grackle .. .. .. 2·75 25
340 20 c. West Indian Red-bellied Woodpecker .. 4·25 65
341 30 c. Stripe-headed Tanager .. .. .. 5·50 1·50
342 50 c. Yucatan Vireo .. .. 7·00 3·25
337/42 .. .. *Set of* 6 22·00 5·50

See also Nos. 383/8.

110 Old School Building

(Des PAD Studio. Litho Questa)

1974 (1 May). *25th Anniv of University of West Indies. T* **110** *and similar horiz designs. Multicoloured.* W w **12** (*sideways*). P 14.

343 12 c. Type **110** 10 10
344 20 c. New Comprehensive School 15 10
345 30 c. Creative Arts Centre, Mona 15 45
343/5 .. .. *Set of* 3 30 55

111 Hermit Crab and Staghorn Coral

(Des J.W. Litho Kynoch Press)

1974 (1 Aug). *Multicoloured designs as T* **111** (*size* 41½ × 27 *mm*). W w **12** (*sideways on* $1 *and* $2). *P* 14.

346	1 c. Type **111**	3·50	1·25
347	3 c. Treasure-chest and Lion's Paw	3·50	75
348	4 c. Treasure and Spotted Scorpionfish	50	70
349	5 c. Flintlock pistol and Brain Coral	3·00	75
350	6 c. Blackbeard and Green Turtle	35	2·25
351	9 c. Jewelled pomander and Porkfish	3·50	6·50
352	10 c. Spiny Lobster and treasure	4·50	80
353	12 c. Jewelled sword and dagger, and Sea-fan	35	1·60
354	15 c. Cabrit's Murex (*Murex cabritii*) and treasure	45	1·25
355	20 c. Queen or Pink Conch (*Strombus gigas*) and treasure	10·00	1·75
356	25 c. Hogfish and Treasure	45	70
357	40 c. Gold chalice and sea-whip	3·00	1·25
358	$1 Coat of arms (*vert*)	2·75	3·25
359	$2 Queen Elizabeth II (*vert*)	4·00	14·00
346/59	*Set of* 14	35·00	32·00

See also Nos. 364/6, 412/19 and 445/52.

112 Sea Captain and Ship (Shipbuilding)

(Des G. Vasarhelyi. Litho D.L.R.)

1974 (7 Oct). *Local Industries. T* **112** *and similar horiz designs. Multicoloured.* W w **12**. *P* 14×13½.

360	8 c. Type **112**	15	10
	w. Wmk inverted	20	20
361	12 c. Thatcher and cottages	15	10
	w. Wmk inverted	30	30
362	20 c. Farmer and plantation	25	20
	w. Wmk inverted	40	40
360/2	*Set of* 3	50	35
MS363	92×132 mm. Nos. 360/2	1·25	2·50
	w. Wmk inverted	2·25	

1974–75. *As Nos.* 346/7 *and design of* 351, *but* W w **12** (*sideways**).

364	1 c. Type **111** (29.9.75)	3·00	1·50
365	3 c. Treasure-chest and Lions-paw (12.11.74)	4·50	2·00
	w. Wmk Crown to right of CA	4·50	
366	8 c. Jewelled pomander and Porkfish (16.12.74)	2·50	8·50
364/6	*Set of* 3	9·00	11·00

*The normal sideways watermark shows Crown to left of CA, *as seen from the back of the stamp.*

Nos. 367/79 vacant.

113 Arms of Cinque Ports and Lord Warden's Flag   **114** "The Crucifixion"

(Des P. Powell. Litho D.L.R.)

1974 (30 Nov). *Birth Centenary of Sir Winston Churchill. T* **113** *and similar vert design. Multicoloured.* W w **12** (*sideways**). *P* 13½×14.

380	12 c. Type **113**	15	10
381	50 c. Churchill's coat of arms	45	70
	w. Wmk Crown to right of CA (pair)	32·00	
MS382	98×86 mm. Nos. 380/1	60	1·60

*The normal sideways watermark shows Crown to left of CA on Nos. 380/1 or Crown to right of CA on **MS**382, *as seen from the back of the stamp.*

(Des M. Goaman. Litho Questa)

1975 (1 Jan). *Birds (2nd series). Multicoloured designs as T* **109**. W w **12** (*sideways*). *P* 14.

383	3 c. Common Flicker	70	45
384	10 c. Black-billed Whistling Duck	1·25	45
385	12 c. Yellow Warbler	1·40	65
386	20 c. White-bellied Dove	2·00	2·00
387	30 c. Magnificent Frigate Bird	3·25	4·25
388	50 c. Cuban Amazon	3·75	10·00
	a. Error. Wmk Lesotho W **53** (inverted)	£600	
383/8	*Set of* 6	11·00	16·00

(Des PAD Studio. Litho D.L.R.)

1975 (24 Mar). *Easter. French Pastoral Staffs. T* **114** *and similar vert design showing "The Crucifixion" (different). Multicoloured.* W w **12** (*sideways*). *P* 13½ × 14.

389 **114**	15 c. multicoloured	10	15
390 –	35 c. multicoloured	20	30
MS391	128 × 98 mm. Nos. 389/90. W w **12** (*upright*)	65	2·50
	a. Error. Imperf		

See also Nos. 396/**MS**398.

115 Israel Hands

(Des J.W. Litho Harrison)

1975 (25 July). *Pirates. T* **115** *and similar horiz designs. Multicoloured.* W w **12** (*sideways**). *P* 14.

392	10 c. Type **115**	20	10
393	12 c. John Fenn	20	10
394	20 c. Thomas Anstis	40	35
	w. Wmk Crown to right of CA	55·00	
395	30 c. Edward Low	55	1·25
392/5	*Set of* 4	1·25	1·60

*The normal sideways watermark shows Crown to left of CA, *as seen from the back of the stamp.*

(Des PAD Studio. Litho Questa)

1975 (31 Oct). *Christmas. Vert designs as T* **114** *showing "Virgin and Child with Angels" (both different).* W w **14**. *P* 14.

396	12 c. multicoloured	10	10
397	50 c. multicoloured	30	30
MS398	113 × 85 mm. Nos. 396/7	1·00	2·50

116 Registered Cover, Government House and Sub-Post Office

(Des J. Cooter. Litho Questa)

1976 (12 Mar). *75th Anniv of First Cayman Is. Postage Stamp. T* **116** *and similar horiz designs. Multicoloured.* W w **14** (*sideways*). *P* 13½.

399	10 c. Type **116**	15	10
400	20 c. ½d. stamp and 1890–94 postmark	20	15
401	30 c. 1d. stamp and 1908 surcharge	30	25
402	50 c. ½d. and 1d. stamps	45	50
399/402	*Set of* 4	1·00	85
MS403	117 × 147 mm. Nos. 399/402	2·50	3·00

117 Seals of Georgia, Delaware and New Hampshire

(Des P. Powell. Litho J.W.)

1976 (29 May). *Bicentenary of American Revolution. T* **117** *and similar horiz designs showing seals of the States given. Multicoloured.* W w **14** (*sideways*). *P* 13½ × 14.

404	10 c. Type **117**	50	15
405	15 c. S. Carolina, New Jersey and Maryland	65	20
406	20 c. Virginia, Rhode Is. and Massachusetts	75	25
407	25 c. New York, Connecticut and N. Carolina	75	35
408	30 c. Pennsylvania seal, Liberty Bell and U.S. Great Seal	90	40
404/8	*Set of* 5	3·25	1·25
MS409	166 × 124 mm. Nos. 404/8. P 14	5·00	8·00

118 Racing Dinghies   **119** Queen Elizabeth II and Westminster Abbey

(Des C. Abbott. Litho D.L.R.)

1976 (16 Aug). *Olympic Games, Montreal. T* **118** *and similar vert design. Multicoloured.* W w **14**. *P* 14.

410	20 c. Type **118**	40	10
411	50 c. Racing dinghy	70	50

1976 (3 Sept)–**78.** *As Nos.* 347/9, 352, 355, 358/9 *and* 366, *bu* W w **14** (*upright on* $1, *inverted on* $2, *sideways on others*). *Chalk surfaced paper* (4, 5 *c. and* $1) *or ordinary paper* (*others*).

412	3 c. Treasure-chest and Lion's Paw	1·00	3·5
	a. Chalk-surfaced paper (19.10.77)	4·50	4·5
413	4 c. Treasure and Spotted Scorpionfish (19.10.77)	1·25	4·0
414	5 c. Flintlock pistol and Brain Coral (19.10.77)	4·50	4·5
415	8 c. Jewelled pomander and Porkfish	7·50	3·0
	a. Chalk-surfaced paper (19.10.77)	9·00	4·7
416	10 c. Spiny Lobster and treasure	2·00	2·7
	a. Chalk-surfaced paper (27.1.78)	2·00	3·0
417	20 c. Queen or Pink Conch (*Strombus gigas*) and treasure	3·50	3·0
	a. Chalk-surfaced paper (27.1.78)	3·50	5·0
418	$1 Coat of arms (19.10.77)	6·50	8·5
419	$2 Queen Elizabeth II	7·50	6·5
	a. Chalk-surfaced paper (19.10.77)	11·00	17·0
412/19	*Set of* 8	30·00	32·0

Nos. 420/6 vacant.

(Des BG Studio. Litho Questa)

1977 (7 Feb). *Silver Jubilee. T* **119** *and similar multicoloure designs.* W w **14** (*sideways on* 50 *c.*). *P* 13½.

427	8 c. Prince of Wales' visit, 1973	10	2
	w. Wmk inverted	8·00	
428	30 c. Type **119**	15	4
	w. Wmk inverted	27·00	
429	50 c. Preparation for the Anointing (*horiz*)	30	7
427/9	*Set of* 3	50	1·2

120 Scuba Diving

(Des Jennifer Toombs. Litho J.W.)

1977 (25 July). *Tourism. T* **120** *and similar horiz designs. Mult coloured.* W w **14** (*sideways*). *P* 13½.

430	5 c. Type **120**	10	1
431	10 c. Exploring a wreck	15	1
432	20 c. Royal Gramma ("Fairy Basslet") (fish)	45	2
433	25 c. Sergeant Major (fish)	55	3
430/3	*Set of* 4	1·10	6
MS434	146×89 mm. Nos. 430/3. P 14½	2·00	3·5

121 *Composia fidelissima* (moth)

(Des J. Cooter. Litho Enschedé)

1977 (2 Dec). *Butterflies and Moth. T* **121** *and similar hori designs. Multicoloured.* W w **14** (*sideways*). *P* 14×13.

435	5 c. Type **121**	65	1
436	8 c. *Heliconius charithonia*	70	1
437	10 c. *Danaus gilippus*	70	1
438	15 c. *Agraulis vanillae*	90	4
439	20 c. *Junonia evarete*	1·00	4
440	30 c. *Anartia jatrophae*	1·25	7
435/40	*Set of* 6	4·75	1·7

122 *Southward* (liner)   **123** "The Crucifixion" (Dürer)

(Des G. Hutchins. Litho Questa)

1978 (23 Jan). *New Harbour and Cruise Ships. T* **122** *an similar multicoloured designs.* W w **14** (*sideways* on* 3, 5 *c.* *P* 14×14½ (3, 5 *c.*) *or* 14½×14 (*others*).

441	3 c. Type **122**	20	1
	w. Wmk Crown to right of CA	16·00	
442	5 c. *Renaissance* (liner)	20	1
443	30 c. New harbour (*vert*)	80	2
444	50 c. *Daphne* (liner) (*vert*)	1·00	5
441/4	*Set of* 4	2·00	8

*The normal sideways watermark shows Crown to left of CA *as seen from the back of the stamp.*

(Litho Walsall)

78 (16 Mar)–**80**. *Designs as Nos.* 346/7, 349, 352, 355 *and* 357/9 *but smaller,* 40 × 26 *or* 26 × 40 *mm. W* w **14** (*sideways on* 1 *to* 40 *c.*). *Chalk-surfaced paper.*
5 1 c. Type **111** .. .. 1·00 1·25
6 3 c. Treasure-chest and Lion's Paw .. 80 50
7 5 c. Flintlock pistol and Brain Coral (11.12.79) .. .. 2·00 2·50
48 10 c. Spiny Lobster and treasure (25.5.78) 1·60 60
49 20 c. Queen or Pink Conch (*Strombus gigas*) and treasure (25.5.78) .. .. 3·25 1·25
50 40 c. Gold chalice and sea-whip (1979*) .. 15·00 20·00
51 $1 Coat of arms (30.7.80) .. .. 16·00 8·00
52 $2 Queen Elizabeth II (3.4.80) .. .. 6·00 24·00
45/52 .. .. *Set of* 8 42·00 50·00
*Supplies of No. 450 were sent to Cayman Islands on 7 May 979. It is not known when these stamps were first placed on le.
Nos. 453/8 vacant.

(Des Jennifer Toombs. Litho Cartor)

78 (20 Mar). *Easter and 450th Death Anniv of Dürer. T* **123** *and similar vert designs. W* w **14** (*inverted on* 20 *c.*). *P* 12.
59 10 c. magenta and black 20 10
w. Wmk inverted .. .. 16·00
60 15 c. yellow and black 30 15
w. Wmk inverted .. .. 14·00
61 20 c. turquoise-green and black 40 20
w. Wmk upright .. .. ..
62 30 c. lilac and black 55 35
w. Wmk inverted .. .. 2·00
59/62 .. .. *Set of* 4 1·25 70
MS463 120×108 mm. Nos. 459/62 .. .. 3·50 4·50
w. Wmk inverted .. .. .. 4·50
Designs:—15 c. "Christ at Emmaus"; 20 c. "The Entry into Jerusalem"; 30 c. "Christ washing Peter's Feet".

124 "Explorers" Singing Game

125 Yale of Beaufort

(Des Walsall. Litho Questa)

978 (25 Apr). *3rd International Council Meeting of Girls' Brigade. T* **124** *and similar vert designs. Multicoloured. W* w **14**. *P* 14.
64 3 c. Type **124** 20 10
65 10 c. Colour party 30 10
66 20 c. Girls and Duke of Edinburgh Award interests 60 20
67 50 c. Girls using domestic skills .. .. 1·10 80
64/7 .. .. *Set of* 4 2·00 1·10

(Des C. Abbott. Litho Questa)

978 (2 June). *25th Anniv of Coronation. T* **125** *and similar vert designs. P* 15.
68 30 c. apple-green, deep magenta and silver .. 20 25
a. Sheetlet. Nos. 468/70 × 2 .. .. 1·10
69 30 c. multicoloured 20 25
70 30 c. apple-green, deep magenta and silver .. 20 25
68/70 .. .. *Set of* 3 55 65
Designs:—No. 468, Type **125**; No. 469, Queen Elizabeth II; o. 470, Barn Owl.
Nos. 468/70 were printed together in small sheets of 6, ontaining two *se-tenant* strips of 3, with horizontal gutter argin between.

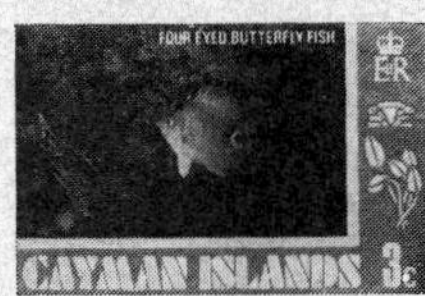

126 Four-eyed Butterflyfish

(Des G. Hutchins, Litho Walsall)

978 (29 Aug). *Fish (1st series). T* **126** *and similar horiz designs. Multicoloured. W* w **14** (*sideways*). *P* 14.
71 3 c. Type **126** 25 10
72 5 c. Grey Angelfish 30 10
73 10 c. Squirrelfish 45 10
74 15 c. Queen Parrotfish 60 30
75 20 c. Spanish Hogfish 70 35
76 30 c. Queen Angelfish 80 50
71/6 .. .. *Set of* 6 2·75 1·25
Examples of the 15 c. value inscribed "SERGEANT MAJOR ISH" and 20 c. inscribed "PARROT FISH" were prepared, but not ssued for postal purposes.
See also Nos. 483/8.

127 Lockheed L.18 Lodestar

(Des A. Theobald. Litho Format)

1979 (5 Feb). *25th Anniv of Owen Roberts Airfield. T* **127** *and similar horiz designs. Multicoloured. W* w **14** (*sideways*). *P* 14½ × 14.
477 3 c. Type **127** 25 10
478 5 c. Consolidated PBY-5A Catalina .. 25 10
479 10 c. Vickers Viking 1B 30 10
480 15 c. B.A.C. One Eleven 475 on tarmac .. 55 20
481 20 c. Piper PA-31 Cheyenne II, Bell 47G Trooper helicopter and Hawker Siddeley H.S.125 .. .. .. 65 30
482 30 c. B.A.C. One Eleven 475 over airfield 90 45
477/82 .. .. *Set of* 6 2·50 1·10

128 Trumpetfish

(Des R. Granger Barrett. Litho Questa)

1979 (20 Apr). *Fish (2nd series). T* **128** *and similar horiz designs. Multicoloured. W* w **14** (*sideways**). *P* 14.
483 1 c. Type **128** 10 10
w. Wmk Crown to right of CA .. .. 26·00
484 3 c. Nassau Grouper 25 10
485 5 c. French Angelfish 25 10
w. Wmk Crown to right of CA .. .. 3·50
486 10 c. Schoolmaster Snapper 35 10
487 20 c. Banded Butterflyfish 55 25
488 50 c. Black-barred Soldierfish .. .. 1·00 70
483/8 .. .. *Set of* 6 2·25 1·25
*The normal sideways watermark shows Crown to left of CA, *as seen from the back of the stamp.*

129 1900 1d. Stamp

(Des J.W. Litho Walsall)

1979 (15 Aug). *Death Centenary of Sir Rowland Hill. T* **129** *and similar horiz designs showing stamps and Sir Rowland Hill. W* w **14** (*sideways*). *P* 13½.
489 5 c. black, rose-carmine and grey-blue .. 10 10
490 10 c. multicoloured 15 10
491 20 c. multicoloured 20 25
489/91 .. .. *Set of* 3 30 30
MS492 138 × 90 mm. 50 c. multicoloured .. 55 65
Designs:—10 c. Great Britain 1902 3d.; 20 c. 1955 £1 definitive; 50 c. 1908 2½d.

130 Holy Family and Angels

(Des G. Vasarhelyi. Litho Secura, Singapore)

1979 (20 Nov). *Christmas. T* **130** *and similar horiz designs. Multicoloured. W* w **14** (*sideways**). *P* 13½×13.
493 10 c. Type **130** 15 10
w. Wmk Crown to right of CA 35
494 20 c. Angels appearing before shepherds .. 20 10
w. Wmk Crown to right of CA 45
495 30 c. Nativity scene 30 20
w. Wmk Crown to right of CA 65
496 40 c. Wise men following star 40 30
w. Wmk Crown to right of CA 85
493/6 .. .. *Set of* 4 95 60
*The normal sideways watermark shows Crown to left of CA, *as seen from the back of the stamp.*

131 Local Rotary Project

(Des Walsall. Litho Secura, Singapore)

1980 (14 Feb). *75th Anniv of Rotary International. T* **131** *and similar designs in black, bistre-yellow and deep ultramarine. W* w **14** (*sideways on* 20 *c.*). *P* 13½ × 13 (20 *c.*) *or* 13 × 13½ (*others*).
497 20 c. Type **131** 20 15
498 30 c. Paul P. Harris (founder) (*vert*) 25 20
499 50 c. Rotary anniversary emblem (*vert*) .. 35 30
a. Black (Royal cypher, and face value) omitted £750
497/9 .. .. *Set of* 3 70 60

132 Walking Mail Carrier (late 19th-century)

(Des J.W. Litho Walsall)

1980 (6 May). *"London 1980" International Stamp Exhibition. T* **132** *and similar horiz designs. Multicoloured. W* w **14** (*sideways*). *P* 14.
500 5 c. Type **132** 10 10
501 10 c. Delivering mail by cat boat (late 19th-century) 15 10
502 15 c. Mounted mail carrier (early 20th-century) 20 10
503 30 c. Horse-drawn waggonette (early 20th-century) 30 15
504 40 c. Postman on bicycle (mid 20th-century) .. 30 15
505 $1 Motor transport (late 20th-century) .. 65 55
500/5 .. .. *Set of* 6 1·50 1·00

133 Queen Elizabeth the Queen Mother at the Derby, 1976

134 American Thorny Oyster (*Spondylus americanus*)

(Des and litho Harrison)

1980 (4 Aug). *80th Birthday of Queen Elizabeth the Queen Mother. W* w **14** (*sideways*). *P* 14.
506 **133** 20 c. multicoloured 20 25

(Des J.W. Litho Walsall)

1980 (12 Aug). *Shells (1st series). T* **134** *and similar horiz designs. Multicoloured. W* w **14** (*sideways*). *P* 14½ × 14.
507 5 c. Type **134** 50 10
508 10 c. West Indian Murex (*Murex brevifrons*) 50 10
509 30 c. Angular Triton (*Cymatium femorale*) 85 40
510 50 c. Caribbean Vase (*Vasum muricatum*) 1·00 80
507/10 .. .. *Set of* 4 2·50 1·25
See also Nos. 565/8 and 582/5.

135 Lantana

136 Juvenile Tarpon and Fire Sponge

(Des G. Hutchins. Litho Rosenbaum Bros, Vienna)

1980 (21 Oct). *Flowers (1st series). T* **135** *and similar horiz designs. Multicoloured. W* w **14** (*sideways*). *P* 13½.
511 5 c. Type **135** 10 10
512 15 c. Bauhinia 25 10
513 30 c. Hibiscus Rosa 35 10
514 $1 Milk and Wine Lily .. .. .. 1·00 75
511/14 .. .. *Set of* 4 1·50 85
See also Nos. 541/4.

(Des G. Drummond. Litho J.W.)

1980 (9 Dec)–**82**. *Flora and Fauna of the Mangrove Swamp. Vert designs as T* **136**. *Multicoloured. W* w 14. *P* 13½×13.

A. *Without imprint date*
515A 3 c. Type **136** .. .. 50 1·50
516A 5 c. Flat Tree or Mangrove-root Oyster (*Isognomon alatus*) .. .. .. 60 1·00
517A 10 c. Mangrove Crab 40 80
518A 15 c. Lizard and *Phyciodes phaon* (butterfly) .. .. 1·00 1·50
519A 20 c. Louisiana Heron .. .. 1·50 2·00
520A 30 c. Red Mangrove flower .. .. .. 70 1·00
521A 40 c. Red Mangrove seeds .. .. .. 75 1·00
522A 50 c. Waterhouse's Leaf-nosed Bat .. 1·25 1·50
523A $1 Black-crowned Night Heron .. 4·50 4·50
524A $2 Cayman Islands coat of arms .. 1·50 3·75
525A $4 Queen Elizabeth II .. .. .. 2·25 4·75
515A/25A .. .. *Set of* 11 13·00 21·00

B. *With imprint date at foot of designs* (14.6.82)
515B 3 c. Type **136** .. .. 5·00 4·00
516B 5 c. Flat Tree or Mangrove-root Oyster (*Isognomon alatus*) .. .. .. 1·00 70
517B 10 c. Mangrove Crab .. .. 1·25 80
518B 15 c. Lizard and *Phyciodes phaon* (butterfly) .. .. 4·00 1·75
519B 20 c. Louisiana Heron .. .. 2·50 2·00
520B 30 c. Red Mangrove flower .. .. .. 1·50 1·50

521B 40 c. Red Mangrove seeds .. .. 1·50 1·50
522B 50 c. Waterhouse's Leaf-nosed Bat .. 2·00 2·00
523B $1 Black-crowned Night Heron .. 5·00 4·50
524B $2 Cayman Islands coat of arms .. 3·75 4·00
525B $4 Queen Elizabeth II .. .. 6·50 11·00
515B/25B .. .. .. *Set of* 11 30·00 30·00

Imprint dates: "1982", Nos. 515B/25B; "1984", No. 516B; "1985", Nos. 516B/24B.

For stamps in these designs, but watermark w 16, see Nos. 626 and 631/2.

137 Eucharist

138 Wood Slave

(Des Jennifer Toombs. Litho Questa)

1981 (17 Mar). *Easter. T* **137** *and similar vert designs. Multicoloured. W* w **14**. *P* 14.
526 3 c. Type **137** 10 10
527 10 c. Crown of thorns 10 10
528 20 c. Crucifix 20 10
529 $1 Lord Jesus Christ 70 80
526/9 .. .. *Set of* 4 90 90

(Des R. Granger Barrett. Litho Rosenbaum Bros, Vienna)

1981 (16 June). *Reptiles and Amphibians. T* **138** *and similar horiz designs. Multicoloured. W* w **14** (*sideways**). *P* 13½.
530 20 c. Type **138** 30 20
w. Wmk Crown to left of CA .. 70
531 30 c. Cayman Iguana 45 35
w. Wmk Crown to left of CA .. 90
532 40 c. Lion Lizard 55 45
w. Wmk Crown to left of CA .. 1·00
533 50 c. Terrapin ("Hickatee") 65 55
w. Wmk Crown to right of CA .. 1·25
530/3 .. .. .. *Set of* 4 1·75 1·40

*The normal sideways watermark shows Crown to right of CA on Nos. 530/2 and to left on No. 533, *as seen from the back of the stamp.*

139 Prince Charles

140 Disabled Scuba Divers

(Des J.W. Litho Walsall)

1981 (22 July). *Royal Wedding. T* **139** *and similar vert designs. Multicoloured. W* w **14**. *P* 14.
534 20 c. Wedding bouquet from Cayman Islands 15 10
535 30 c. Type **139** 20 10
536 $1 Prince Charles and Lady Diana Spencer 50 75
534/6 .. .. *Set of* 3 75 80

(Des J.W. Litho Walsall)

1981 (29 Sept). *International Year for Disabled Persons. T* **140** *and similar horiz designs. Multicoloured. W* w **14** (*sideways*). *P* 14.
537 5 c. Type **140** 10 10
538 15 c. Old School for the Handicapped 25 20
539 20 c. New School for the Handicapped .. 30 25
540 $1 Disabled people in wheelchairs, by the sea 1·25 85
537/40 .. .. *Set of* 4 1·60 1·25

(Des G. Hutchins. Litho Questa)

1981 (20 Oct). *Flowers* (*2nd series*). *Horiz designs as T* **135**. *Multicoloured. W* w **14** (*sideways*). *P* 13½.
541 3 c. Bougainvillea 10 10
542 10 c. Morning Glory 20 10
543 20 c. Wild Amaryllis 45 25
544 $1 Cordia .. .. 1·75 1·75
541/4 .. .. *Set of* 4 2·25 2·00

141 Dr. Robert Koch and Microscope

142 Bride and Groom walking down Aisle

(Des and litho Walsall)

1982 (24 Mar). *Centenary of Robert Koch's Discovery of Tubercle Bacillus. T* **141** *and similar multicoloured designs. W* w **14** (*sideways on* 15 *c, inverted on* 30 *c.*). *P* 14½.
545 15 c. Type **141** 25 25
546 30 c. Koch looking through microscope (*vert*) 45 45
547 40 c. Microscope (*vert*) 70 70
548 50 c. Dr. Robert Koch (*vert*) 80 80
545/8 .. .. *Set of* 4 2·00 2·00

(Des Jennifer Toombs. Litho J.W.)

1982 (1 July). *21st Birthday of Princess of Wales. T* **142** *and similar vert designs. Multicoloured. W* w **14**. *P* 13.
549 20 c. Cayman Islands coat of arms .. 30 35
550 30 c. Lady Diana Spencer in London, June 1981 .. .. 60 45
w. Wmk inverted .. .. 3·50
551 40 c. Type **142** 60 65
552 50 c. Formal portrait .. .. .. 1·75 90
w. Wmk inverted .. .. 6·00
549/52 .. .. *Set of* 4 3·00 2·10

143 Pitching Tent

144 "Madonna and Child with the Infant Baptist"

(Des L. Walker. Litho Questa)

1982 (24 Aug). *75th Anniv of Boy Scout Movement. T* **143** *and similar horiz designs. Multicoloured. W* w **14** (*sideways*). *P* 14.
553 3 c. Type **143** 15 10
554 20 c. Scouts camping 55 40
555 30 c. Cub Scouts and Leaders 70 55
556 50 c. Boating skills .. .. .. 1·10 85
553/6 .. .. *Set of* 4 2·25 1·75

(Des PAD Studio. Litho Questa)

1982 (26 Oct). *Christmas. Raphael Paintings. T* **144** *and similar vert designs. Multicoloured. W* w **14**. *P* 14½ × 14.
557 3 c. Type **144** 10 10
558 10 c. "Madonna of the Tower" 20 20
w. Wmk inverted .. ..
559 20 c. "Ansidei Madonna" 35 35
560 30 c. "Madonna and Child" 50 50
w. Wmk inverted .. ..
557/60 .. .. .. *Set of* 4 1·00 1·00

145 Mace

(Des and litho Walsall)

1982 (9 Nov). *150th Anniv of Representative Government. T* **145** *and similar horiz designs. Multicoloured. W* w **14** (*sideways*). *P* 14½ × 14.
561 3 c. Type **145** 10 20
562 10 c. Old Courthouse 20 20
563 20 c. Commonwealth Parliamentary Association coat of arms 35 45
564 30 c. Legislative Assembly building .. 50 90
561/4 .. .. *Set of* 4 1·00 1·60

(Des J.W. Litho Format)

1983 (11 Jan). *Shells* (*2nd series*). *Horiz designs as T* **134**. *Multicoloured. W* w **14** (*sideways*). *P* 13½ × 13.
565 5 c. Colourful Atlantic Moon (*Natica canrena*) 15 10
566 10 c. King Helmet (*Cassis tuberosa*) .. 25 20
567 20 c. Rooster-tail Conch (*Strombus gallus*) 45 40
568 $1 Reticulated Cowrie-helmet (*Cypraecassis testiculus*) .. .. .. 1·75 3·50
565/8 .. .. .. *Set of* 4 2·40 3·75

146 Legislative Building, Cayman Brac

(Des C. Abbott. Litho Questa)

1983 (15 Feb). *Royal Visit. T* **146** *and similar multicoloured designs. W* w **14** (*sideways on* 20 *c.,* 30 *c.*). *P* 14.
569 20 c. Type **146** 45 35
570 30 c. Legislative Building, Grand Cayman .. 60 50
571 50 c. Duke of Edinburgh (*vert*) .. .. 1·25 90
572 $1 Queen Elizabeth II (*vert*) .. .. 2·00 2·00
569/72 .. .. *Set of* 4 4·00 3·25
MS573 113 × 94 mm. Nos. 569/72 (wmk sideways) 4·00 4·25

147 Satellite View of Earth

(Des J.W. Litho Questa)

1983 (14 Mar). *Commonwealth Day. T* **147** *and similar hor designs. Multicoloured. W* w **14** (*sideways*). *P* 14.
574 3 c. Type **147** 10 1
575 15 c. Cayman Islands and Commonwealth flags 25 3
576 20 c. Fishing 30 3
577 40 c. Portrait of Queen Elizabeth II 60 6
574/7 .. .. *Set of* 4 1·10 1·2

148 MRCU Cessna 188 Ag Wagon Aircraft

149 *Song of Norway* (cruise liner)

(Des Harrison. Litho Questa)

1983 (10 Oct). *Bicentenary of Manned Flight. T* **148** *and simil horiz designs. Multicoloured. W* w **14** (*sideways*). *P* 14.
578 3 c. Type **148** 50
579 10 c. Consolidated PBY-5A Catalina .. 70
580 20 c. Boeing 727-200 .. .. .. 1·50 1·
581 40 c. Hawker Siddeley H.S. 748 .. .. 2·00 3·
578/81 .. .. *Set of* 4 4·25 4·

(Des J.W. Litho Questa)

1984 (18 Jan). *Shells* (*3rd series*). *Horiz designs as T* **134**. *Mul coloured. W* w **14** (*sideways*). *P* 14 × 14½.
582 3 c. Florida Moon (*Natica floridana*) .. 60
583 10 c. Austin's Cone (*Conus atractus austini*) 85
584 30 c. Leaning Dwarf Triton (*Colubraria obscura*) .. .. 2·25 2·
585 50 c. Filose or Threaded Turban (*Turbo cailletii*) .. .. 2·50 3·
582/5 .. .. *Set of* 4 5·50 6·

(Des G. Vasarhelyi and L. Curtis. Litho Questa)

1984 (18 June). *250th Anniv of "Lloyd's List" (newspaper). T* **1** *and similar vert designs. Multicoloured. W* w **14**. *P* 14½ × 14.
586 5 c. Type **149** 25
587 10 c. View of old harbour 35
588 25 c. Wreck of *Ridgefield* (freighter) .. 1·00 1·
589 50 c. *Goldfield* (schooner) .. .. .. 1·60 2·
586/9 .. .. *Set of* 4 2·75 3·
MS590 105×75 mm. $1 *Goldfield* (schooner) (*different*) .. .. 2·10 2·

U.P.U. CONGRESS
HAMBURG 1984

(150)

151 Snowy Egret

1984 (18 June). *Universal Postal Union Congress, Hamburg. N* 589 *optd with T* **150**.
591 50 c. Schooner *Goldfield* .. .. .. 1·00 1·

(Des Josephine Martin. Litho Questa)

1984 (15 Aug). *Birds of the Cayman Islands* (1*st series*). *T* **1** *and similar horiz designs. Multicoloured. W* w **14** (*sideway P* 14 × 14½.
592 5 c. Type **151** 90
593 10 c. Bananaquit 90
594 35 c. Belted Kingfisher .. .. .. 2·75 2
595 $1 Brown Booby .. .. 5·50 7
592/5 .. .. *Set of* 4 9·00 9

See also Nos. 627/30.

152 Couple on Beach at Sunset

153 *Schomburgkia thomsoniana* (var. *minor*)

(Des G. Wilby. Litho Questa)

.984 (17 Oct). *Christmas. Local Festivities. T* **152** *and similar vert designs. Multicoloured.* W w **14** *(sideways). P* 14.

96 5 c. Type **152** 50 75
a. Horiz strip of 4. Nos. 596/9 .. .. 1·75
97 5 c. Family and schooner 50 75
98 5 c. Carol singers 50 75
99 5 c. East End bonfire 50 75
.00 25 c. Yachts 70 85
a. Horiz strip of 4. Nos. 600/3 .. .. 2·50
01 25 c. Father Christmas in power-boat .. 70 85
02 25 c. Children on beach 70 85
03 25 c. Beach party 70 85
96/603 .. .. *Set of* 8 4·25 5·75
1S604 59×79 mm. $1 As No. 599, but larger, 27×41 mm .. .. 2·10 2·25

Nos. 596/9 and 600/3 were each printed together, *se-tenant*, in orizontal strips of 4 throughout the sheets, the four designs of ach value forming a composite picture of a beach scene at night 5 c.) or in the daytime (25 c.).

(Des Liza Horstman. Litho J.W.)

985 (13 Mar). *Orchids. T* **153** *and similar vert designs. Multicoloured.* W w **14**. *P* 14×13½.

605 5 c. Type **153** 80 20
606 10 c. *Schomburgkia thomsoniana* 90 20
607 25 c. *Encyclia plicata* .. .. .. 2·25 1·00
608 50 c. *Dendrophylax fawcettii* .. .. .. 3·00 2·75
605/8 .. .. *Set of* 4 6·25 3·75

154 Freighter Aground **155** Athletics

(Des Walsall. Litho J.W.)

1985 (22 May). *Shipwrecks. T* **154** *and similar horiz designs. Multicoloured.* W w **14** *(sideways). P* 14.

609 5 c. Type **154** 80 30
610 25 c. Submerged sailing ship .. .. 2·50 95
611 35 c. Wrecked trawler .. .. .. 2·75 2·25
612 40 c. Submerged wreck on its side .. .. 3·00 3·00
609/12 .. .. *Set of* 4 8·00 6·00

(Des Harrison. Litho Walsall)

1985 (14 Aug). *International Youth Year. T* **155** *and similar multicoloured designs.* W w **14** *(sideways on 5 c., 15 c.). P* 14×14½ *(5, 15 c.) or* 14½×14 *(others).*

613 5 c. Type **155** 20 20
614 15 c. Students in library 35 30
615 25 c. Football *(vert)* 65 55
616 50 c. Netball *(vert)* .. .. .. 1·25 2·00
613/16 .. .. *Set of* 4 2·25 2·75

156 Morse Key (1935) **157** Magnificent Frigate Bird

(Des G. Vasarhelyi. Litho Walsall)

1985 (25 Oct). *50th Anniv of Telecommunications System. T* **156** *and similar vert designs. Multicoloured.* W w **16**. *P* 14.

617 5 c. Type **156** 40 30
618 10 c. Hand cranked telephone 45 30
w. Wmk inverted £150
619 25 c. Tropospheric scatter dish (1966) .. 1·25 80
w. Wmk inverted .. .. ..
620 50 c. Earth station dish aerial (1979) .. 2·00 3·00
617/20 .. .. *Set of* 4 3·50 4·00

(Des A. Theobald. Litho Format)

1986 (21 Apr). *60th Birthday of Queen Elizabeth II. Vert designs as T* **110** *of Ascension. Multicoloured.* W w **16**. *P* 14×14½.

621 5 c. Princess Elizabeth at wedding of Lady May Cambridge, 1931 .. .. .. 10 20
622 10 c. In Norway, 1955 .. .. .. 15 20
623 25 c. Queen inspecting Royal Cayman Islands Police, 1983 .. .. .. 1·25 75
624 50 c. During Gulf tour, 1979 .. .. .. 75 1·25
625 $1 At Crown Agents Head Office, London, 1983 .. .. 1·10 2·25
621/5 .. .. *Set of* 5 3·00 4·25

(Litho J.W.)

1986 (Apr). *As No.* 516B, *but* W w **16**. "1986" *imprint date. P* 13½×13.

626 5 c. Mangrove Root Oyster .. .. .. 4·00 4·25

(Des Harrison. Litho Questa)

1986 (21 May). *Birds of the Cayman Islands (2nd series). T* **157** *and similar multicoloured designs.* W w **16** *(sideways on* 10, 40 c.). *P* 14.

627 10 c. Type **157** .. .. 1·25 50
628 25 c. Black-billed Whistling Duck *(vert)* .. 1·75 1·25
629 35 c. La Sagra's Flycatcher *(vert)* .. .. 2·00 2·25
630 40 c. Yellow-faced Grassquit .. .. 2·25 3·00
627/30 .. .. *Set of* 4 6·50 6·25

(Litho Questa)

1986 (June). *As Nos.* 516B/17B, *but different printer and* W w **16**. "1986" *imprint date. P* 14.

631 5 c. Mangrove Root Oyster .. .. .. 4·50 4·00
632 10 c. Mangrove Crab .. .. .. 4·50 4·00

(Des D. Miller. Litho Walsall)

1986 (23 July) *Royal Wedding. Square designs as T* **112** *of Ascension. Multicoloured.* W w **16**. *P* 14½×14.

633 5 c. Prince Andrew and Miss Sarah Ferguson 25 10
634 50 c. Prince Andrew aboard H.M.S. *Brazen* .. 1·25 1·40

158 Red Coral Shrimp **159** Golf

(Des D. Miller. Litho Walsall)

1986 (15 Sept). *Marine Life. T* **158** *and similar vert designs. Multicoloured.* W w **14**. *P* 13½×13.

635 5 c. Type **158** 40 50
636 10 c. Yellow Crinoid 40 50
637 15 c. *Calcinus tibicen* (hermit crab) 35 60
638 20 c. Tube dwelling Anemone 35 80
639 25 c. Christmas Tree Worm .. .. 45 1·75
640 35 c. Porcupinefish .. .. .. 70 2·00
641 50 c. Orangeball Anemone .. .. .. 80 3·50
642 60 c. *Astrophyton muricatum* (basket starfish) .. .. 3·00 5·00
643 75 c. Flamingo Tongue (*Cyphoma gibbosus*) 5·50 6·50
644 $1 *Condylactis gigantea* (sea anemone) .. 1·40 2·50
645 $2 Diamond Blenny .. .. .. 2·25 4·25
646 $4 Rough File Shell (*Lima scabra*) .. 4·00 6·50
635/46 .. .. *Set of* 12 18·00 30·00

No. 644 is incorrectly inscribed "Conolylactis gigantea".

Imprint dates: "1986", Nos. 635/46; "1987", Nos. 635/8, 644/6; "1990", Nos. 635/41, 644/5.

For the 10 c. value with watermark w **16** see No. 696.

(Des L. Curtis. Litho Walsall)

1987 (26 Jan). *Tourism. T* **159** *and similar horiz designs. Multicoloured.* W w **16** *(sideways). P* 13×13½.

647 10 c. Type **159** .. .. 1·50 75
648 15 c. Sailing .. .. 1·75 85
649 25 c. Snorkelling .. .. 1·90 1·25
650 35 c. Paragliding .. .. 2·00 1·75
651 $1 Game fishing .. .. .. 3·50 6·00
647/51 .. .. *Set of* 5 9·50 9·50

160 Ackee **161** Lion Lizard

(Des Jennifer Toombs. Litho Questa)

1987 (20 May). *Cayman Islands Fruits. T* **160** *and similar vert designs. Multicoloured.* W w **16**. *P* 14½×14.

652 5 c. Type **160** 20 30
w. Wmk inverted .. .. ..
653 25 c. Breadfruit 55 45
w. Wmk inverted .. .. .. 8·50
654 35 c. Pawpaw 75 60
655 $1 Soursop .. .. 2·00 3·25
652/5 .. .. *Set of* 4 3·25 4·25

(Des I. Loe. Litho Questa)

1987 (26 Aug). *Lizards. T* **161** *and similar horiz designs. Multicoloured.* W w **16** *(sideways). P* 13½×14.

656 10 c. Type **161** 60 20
657 50 c. Iguana .. .. 1·75 1·40
658 $1 Anole .. .. 2·50 2·50
656/8 .. .. *Set of* 3 4·25 3·75

162 Poinsettia **163** *Hemiargus ammon* and *Strymon martialis*

(Des Annette Robinson. Litho Walsall)

1987 (18 Nov). *Flowers. T* **162** *and similar square designs. Multicoloured.* W w **16**. *P* 14½×14.

659 5 c. Type **162** 40 20
660 25 c. Periwinkle .. .. 1·25 60
661 35 c. Yellow Allamanda .. .. .. 1·50 1·00
662 75 c. Blood Lily .. .. 2·50 2·50
659/62 .. .. *Set of* 4 5·00 3·75

(Des Jane Thatcher. Litho Questa)

1988 (29 Mar). *Butterflies. T* **163** *and similar horiz designs. Multicoloured.* W w **16** *(sideways). P* 14.

663 5 c. Type **163** .. .. 1·00 50
664 25 c. *Phocides pigmalion* .. .. .. 2·25 75
665 50 c. *Anaea troglodyta* .. .. .. 3·50 3·25
666 $1 *Papilio andraemon* .. .. .. 4·25 4·25
663/6 .. .. *Set of* 4 10·00 8·00

164 Green Heron **165** Cycling

(Des Jane Thatcher. Litho Walsall)

1988 (27 July). *Herons. T* **164** *and similar vert designs. Multicoloured.* W w **16**. *P* 14.

667 5 c. Type **164** .. .. 1·00 50
668 25 c. Louisiana Heron .. .. .. 2·00 65
669 50 c. Yellow-crowned Night Heron .. .. 2·75 2·75
670 $1 Little Blue Heron .. .. .. 3·25 4·00
667/70 .. .. *Set of* 4 8·00 7·00

(Des L. Curtis. Litho Walsall)

1988 (21 Sept). *Olympic Games, Seoul. T* **165** *and similar horiz designs. Multicoloured.* W w **16** *(sideways). P* 14×14½.

671 10 c. Type **165** 90 45
672 50 c. Cayman Airways Boeing 727 airliner and national team .. .. .. 1·75 1·75
673 $1 Sailing .. .. 2·00 2·50
671/3 .. .. *Set of* 3 4·25 4·25
MS674 53×60 mm. $1 Tennis. W w **14** (sideways) 3·25 2·75

166 Princess Alexandra

167 George Town Post Office and Cayman Postmark on Jamaica 1d., 1889

(Des N. Harvey. Litho B.D.T.)

1988 (1 Nov). *Visit of Princess Alexandra. T* **166** *and similar vert design. Multicoloured.* W w **14**. *P* 15×14.

675 5 c. Type **166** 75 50
676 $1 Princess Alexandra in evening dress .. 4·00 3·50

(Des L. Curtis. Litho Questa)

1989 (12 Apr). *Centenary of Cayman Islands Postal Service. T* **167** *and similar horiz designs. Multicoloured.* W w **16** *(sideways). P* 14×14½.

677 5 c. multicoloured 55 40
678 25 c. yellowish green, black and new blue 1·50 70
679 35 c. multicoloured .. .. .. 1·50 1·00
680 $1 multicoloured .. .. .. 4·25 4·50
677/80 .. .. *Set of* 4 7·00 6·00

Designs:—25 c. *Orinoco* (mail steamer) and 1900 ½d. stamp; 35 c. G.P.O., Grand Cayman and "London 1980" $1 stamp; $1 Cayman Airways B.A.C. One Eleven 200/400 and 1966 1s. Jet Service stamp.

168 Captain Bligh ashore in West Indies **169** Panton House

(Des Jane Hartley. Litho B.D.T.)

1989 (24 May). *Captain Bligh's Second Breadfruit Voyage, 1791-93. T* **168** *and similar vert designs. Multicoloured. W* w **16**. *P* 14.

681 50 c. Type **168** .. .. 2·75 3·25
a. Horiz strip of 5. Nos. 681/5 .. .. 12·00
682 50 c. H.M.S. *Providence* (sloop) at anchor .. 2·75 3·25
683 50 c. Breadfruit in tubs and H.M.S. *Assistant* (transport) .. .. .. 2·75 3·25
684 50 c. Sailors moving tubs of breadfruit .. 2·75 3·25
685 50 c. Midshipman and stores .. .. 2·75 3·25
681/5 .. .. *Set of* 5 12·00 14·00

Nos. 681/5 were printed together, *se-tenant* as a composite design, in horizontal strips of five throughout the sheet.

(Des S. Conlin. Litho Walsall)

1989 (18 Oct). *Architecture. T* **169** *and similar square designs showing George Town buildings. Multicoloured. W* w **14**. *P* 14½×14.

686 5 c. Type **169** 30 30
687 10 c. Town Hall and Clock Tower 30 30
688 25 c. Old Court House 70 50
689 35 c. Elmslie Memorial Church 80 70
690 $1 Post Office .. .. 2·00 2·75
686/90 .. .. *Set of* 5 3·75 4·00

170 Map of Grand Cayman, 1773, and Surveying Instruments

171 French Angelfish

(Des N. Shewring. Litho Walsall)

1989 (15 Nov). *Island Maps and Survey Ships. T* **170** *and similar horiz designs. Multicoloured. W* w **16** (*sideways*). *P* 14×14½.

691 5 c. Type **170** 70 70
692 25 c. Map of Cayman Islands, 1956, and surveying instruments .. .. 2·00 1·25
693 50 c. H.M.S. *Mutine*, 1914 .. .. .. 3·00 3·50
694 $1 H.M.S. *Vidal*, 1956 .. .. .. 4·50 5·00
691/4 .. .. *Set of* 4 9·00 9·50

1990 (Mar). *As No.* 636, *but W* w **16**. "1990" *imprint date. P* 13½×13.

696 10 c. Yellow Crinoid .. .. .. 1·60 2·00

(Des D. Miller. Litho Questa)

1990 (25 Apr). *Angelfishes. T* **171** *and similar horiz designs. Multicoloured. W* w **16** (*sideways*). *P* 14.

707 10 c. Type **171** .. .. 1·00 50
708 25 c. Grey Angelfish .. .. .. 2·00 90
709 50 c. Queen Angelfish .. .. .. 3·00 3·50
710 $1 Rock Beauty .. .. 4·50 5·00
707/10 .. .. *Set of* 4 9·50 9·00

(Des D. Miller. Litho Questa)

1990 (4 Aug). *90th Birthday of Queen Elizabeth the Queen Mother. Vert designs as T* **134** (50 *c.*) *or* **135** ($1) *of Ascension. W* w **16**. *P* 14×15 (50 *c.*) *or* 14½ ($1).

711 50 c. multicoloured .. .. .. 1·25 2·00
712 $1 black and blue .. .. .. 2·50 3·25

Designs:—50 c. Silver Wedding photograph, 1948; $1 King George VI and Queen Elizabeth with Winston Churchill, 1940.

172 *Danaus eresimus*

173 Goes Weather Satellite

(Des G. Drummond. Litho Questa)

1990 (24 Oct). *"EXPO 90" International Garden and Greenery Exhibition, Osaka. Butterflies. T* **172** *and similar horiz designs. Multicoloured. W* w **16** (*sideways*). *P* 14.

713 5 c. Type **172** 65 50
714 25 c. *Brephidium exilis* .. .. .. 1·50 1·10
715 35 c. *Phyciodes phaon* .. .. .. 1·75 1·25
716 $1 *Agraulis vanillae* .. .. .. 4·00 6·00
713/16 .. .. *Set of* 4 7·00 8·00

(Des A. Theobald. Litho Questa)

1991 (8 Aug). *International Decade for Natural Disaster Reduction. T* **173** *and similar horiz designs. Multicoloured. W* w **16** (*sideways*). *P* 14.

717 5 c. Type **173** 75 50
718 30 c. Meteorologist tracking hurricane .. 1·75 1·10
719 40 c. Damaged buildings .. .. .. 2·00 1·25
720 $1 U.S. Dept of Commerce weather reconnaisance Lockheed WP-3D Orion 4·50 6·50
717/20 .. .. *Set of* 4 8·00 8·50

174 Angels and *Datura candida*

175 Coconut Palm

(Des Jennifer Toombs. Litho Questa)

1991 (6 Nov). *Christmas. T* **174** *and similar horiz designs. Multicoloured. W* w **16** (*sideways*). *P* 14.

721 5 c. Type **174** 40 40
722 30 c. Mary and Joseph going to Bethlehem and *Allamanda cathartica* .. .. 1·00 60
723 40 c. Adoration of the Kings and *Euphorbia pulcherrima* .. .. 1·40 90
724 60 c. Holy Family and *Guaiacum officinale* 2·00 3·00
721/4 .. .. *Set of* 4 4·25 4·50

(Des D. Miller. Litho Enschede)

1991 (11 Dec). *Island Scenes. T* **175** *and similar multicoloured designs. W* w **14** (*sideways on horiz designs*). *P* 12½×13 (*vert*) *or* 13×12½ (*horiz*).

725 5 c. Type **175** 40 30
726 15 c. Beach scene (*horiz*) 60 30
727 20 c. Poincianas in bloom (*horiz*) 60 35
728 30 c. Blowholes (*horiz*) 70 50
a. Silver (inscr and face value) omitted
729 40 c. Police band (*horiz*) .. .. .. 2·50 1·40
730 50 c. *Song of Norway* (liner) at George Town 1·75 1·40
731 60 c. The Bluff, Cayman Brac (*horiz*) .. 1·75 1·75
732 80 c. Coat of arms .. .. 1·50 2·00
733 90 c. View of Hell (*horiz*) .. .. .. 1·60 2·00
734 $1 Game fishing (*horiz*) .. .. .. 2·00 2·00
735 $2 *Nieuw Amsterdam* (1983) and *Holiday* (liners) in harbour .. .. .. 4·25 4·50
736 $8 Queen Elizabeth II .. .. .. 13·00 15·00
725/36 .. .. *Set of* 12 27·00 28·00

Imprint dates: "1991", Nos. 725/36; "1994", No. 725.

(Des D. Miller. Litho Questa ($1), Leigh-Mardon Ltd, Melbourne (others))

1992 (6 Feb). *40th Anniv of Queen Elizabeth II's Accession. Horiz designs as T* **143** *of Ascension. W* w **16** (*sideways*) (30, 40 *c.*) *or* w **14** (*sideways*) (*others*). *P* 14.

737 5 c. Caymans' house 30 30
738 20 c. Sunset over islands 80 50
739 30 c. Beach 90 65
740 40 c. Three portraits of Queen Elizabeth .. 1·00 1·00
741 $1 Queen Elizabeth II .. .. .. 2·00 3·50
737/41 .. .. *Set of* 5 4·50 5·50

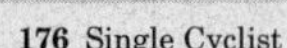

176 Single Cyclist

177 Woman and Donkey with Panniers

(Des G. Vasarhelyi. Litho Questa)

1992 (5 Aug). *Olympic Games, Barcelona. Cycling. T* **176** *and similar horiz designs. Multicoloured. W* w **14** (*sideways*). *P* 14.

742 15 c. Type **176** .. .. 1·00 55
743 40 c. Two cyclists .. .. 1·75 1·50
744 60 c. Cyclist's legs .. .. 2·25 2·75
745 $1 Two pursuit cyclists .. .. .. 3·00 3·50
742/5 .. .. *Set of* 4 7·25 7·50

(Des O. Ball. Litho Enschedé)

1992 (21 Oct). *Island Heritage. T* **177** *and similar vert designs. Multicoloured. W* w **14**. *P* 14×13½.

746 5 c. Type **177** 40 40
747 30 c. Fisherman weaving net .. .. 1·00 75
748 40 c. Maypole dancing .. .. .. 1·25 95
749 60 c. Basket making .. .. .. 2·25 3·00
750 $1 Cooking on caboose .. .. .. 2·75 3·50
746/50 .. .. *Set of* 5 7·00 7·75

178 Yellow Stingray

179 Turtle and Sailing Dinghies

(Des G. Drummond. Litho Cartor)

1993 (16 June). *Rays. T* **178** *and similar horiz designs. Multicoloured. W* w **14** (*sideways*). *P* 13½.

751 5 c. Type **178** 60 50
752 30 c. Southern Stingray .. .. .. 1·50 1·25
753 40 c. Spotted Eagle-ray .. .. .. 1·75 1·50
754 $1 Manta .. .. 3·50 4·50
751/4 .. .. *Set of* 4 6·50 7·00

(Des D. Miller. Litho B.D.T.)

1993 (30 Sept). *Tourism. T* **179** *and similar vert designs. Multicoloured. W* w **14**. *P* 13½.

755 15 c. Type **179** 60 70
a. Horiz strip of 5. Nos. 755/9 .. .. 2·75
b. Booklet pane. Nos. 755/64 .. .. 6·50
756 15 c. Tourist boat, fishing launch and scuba diver 60 70
757 15 c. Golf 60 70
758 15 c. Tennis 60 70
759 15 c. Pirates and ship 60 70
760 30 c. Liner, tourist launch and yacht .. 85 1·00
a. Horiz strip of 5. Nos. 760/4 .. .. 3·75
761 30 c. George Town street .. .. .. 85 1·00
762 30 c. Tourist submarine .. .. .. 85 1·00
763 30 c. Motor-scooter riders and cyclists .. 85 1·00
764 30 c. Cayman Airways Boeing 737 airliners 85 1·00
755/64 .. .. *Set of* 10 6·50 7·50

Nos. 755/9 and 760/4 were each printed together, *se-tenant*, in horizontal strips of 5 throughout the sheets. Booklet pane No. 755b contains both *se-tenant* strips as a block of 10 with the horizontal edges of the pane imperforate and margins at left and right.

180 Cuban Amazon with Wings spread

181 *Ionopsis utricularioides* and Manger

(Des O. Ball. Litho Leigh-Mardon Ltd, Melbourne)

1993 (29 Oct). *Endangered Species. Cuban Amazon ("Grand Cayman Parrot"). T* **180** *and similar square designs. Multicoloured. W* w **14**. *P* 14.

765 5 c. Type **180** 60 60
766 5 c. On branch with wings folded 60 60
767 30 c. Head of parrot .. .. .. 1·60 1·75
768 30 c. Pair of parrots .. .. .. 1·60 1·75
765/8 .. .. *Set of* 4 4·00 4·25

(Des Jennifer Toombs. Litho B.D.T.)

1993 (6 Dec). *Christmas. Orchids. T* **181** *and similar horiz designs. Multicoloured. W* w **16** (*sideways*). *P* 13½×14.

769 5 c. Type **181** 60 45
770 40 c. *Encyclia cochleata* and shepherd .. 1·50 85
771 60 c. *Vanilla pompona* and wise men .. 2·00 3·00
772 $1 *Oncidium caymanense* and Virgin Mary .. .. 3·25 4·25
769/72 .. .. *Set of* 4 6·50 7·75

182 Queen Angelfish

183 Flags of Great Britain and Cayman Islands

(Des D. Miller and A. Robinson. Litho Enschedé)

1994 (18 Feb). *"Hong Kong '94" International Stamp Exhibition. Reef Life. Sheet* 121×85 *mm containing T* **182** *and similar vert designs. Multicoloured. W* w **14** (*sideways*). *P* 14½×13.

MS773 60 c. Type **182**; 60 c. Diver with Porkfish and Spot-finned Hogfish; 60 c. Rock Beauty and Royal Gramma; 60 c. French Angelfish and Banded Butterflyfish .. .. 7·00 7·50

(Des D. Miller. Litho Questa)

1994 (22 Feb). *Royal Visit. T* **183** *and similar vert designs. Multicoloured. W* w **14**. *P* 14½×14.

774 5 c. Type **183** 40 35
775 15 c. Royal Yacht *Britannia* .. .. 1·00 70
776 30 c. Queen Elizabeth II .. .. .. 1·25 1·00
777 $2 Queen Elizabeth and Prince Philip disembarking .. .. 4·50 6·50
774/7 .. .. *Set of* 4 6·50 7·75

184 Black-billed Whistling Duck
185 *Electrostrymon angelia*

(Des Josephine Martin. Litho Walsall)

94 (21 Apr). *Black-billed Whistling Duck ("West Indian Whistling Duck"). T* **184** *and similar multicoloured designs.* W w **16** (*sideways on* 15 c., 20 c.). *P* 14½.

8 5 c. Type **184** .. 60 55
9 15 c. Duck landing on water (*horiz*) .. 1·00 60
0 20 c. Duck preening (*horiz*) .. 1·10 70
1 80 c. Duck flapping wings .. 2·75 3·50
2 $1 Adult and duckling .. 3·25 3·75
8/82 .. *Set of* 5 8·00 8·25
S783 71×45 mm. $1 As No. 782, but including Cayman Islands National Trust symbol .. 6·00 7·00

(Des K. McGee. Litho Enschedé)

94 (16 Aug). *Butterflies. T* **185** *and simlar vert designs. Multicoloured. W w* **14** (*sideways*). *P* 13½×14.

4 10 c. Type **185** .. 50 75
a. Vert pair. Nos. 784/5 .. 1·00 1·50
5 10 c. *Eumaeus atala* .. 50 75
6 $1 *Eurema daira* .. 3·00 3·50
a. Vert pair. Nos. 786/7 .. 6·00 7·00
7 $1 *Urbanus dorantes* .. 3·00 3·50
4/7 .. *Set of* 4 6·00 7·50

Nos. 784/5 and 786/7 were printed together, *se-tenant*, in ertical pairs throughout the sheets.

186 H.M.S. *Convert* (frigate)
187 Young Green Turtles

(Des B. Dare. Litho Enschedé)

994 (12 Oct). *Bicentenary of Wreck of Ten Sail off Grand Cayman. T* **186** *and similar square designs. Multicoloured. W w* **14** (*sideways*). *P* 13×14.

88 10 c. Type **186** .. 35 35
89 10 c. Merchant brig and full-rigged ship .. 35 35
90 15 c. Full-rigged ship near rock .. 55 45
91 20 c. Long boat leaving full-rigged ship .. 65 55
92 $2 Merchant brig .. 4·00 6·00
88/92 .. *Set of* 5 5·50 7·00

(Des Doreen McGuiness. Litho Questa)

995 (28 Feb). *Sea Turtles. T* **187** *and similer horiz designs. Multicoloured. W w* **16** (*sideways*). *P* 14.

93 10 c. Type **187** .. 45 40
94 20 c. Kemp's Ridley Turtle .. 70 45
95 25 c. Hawksbill Turtle .. 80 50
96 30 c. Leatherback Turtle .. 85 60
97 $1.30, Loggerhead Turtle .. 3·25 3·75
98 $2 Pacific Ridley Turtles .. 4·25 5·00
93/8 .. *Set of* 6 9·25 9·50
IS799 167×94 mm. Nos. 793/8 .. 9·25 10·00

188 Running
189 Queen Elizabeth the Queen Mother

(Des B. Dare. Litho Questa)

995 (15 Apr). *C.A.R.I.F.T.A. and I.A.A.F. Games, George Town. T* **188** *and similar horiz designs. Multicoloured. W w* **14** (*sideways*). *P* 14½.

0 10 c. Type **188** .. 50 40
1 20 c. High jumping .. 80 60
2 30 c. Javelin throwing .. 1·00 80
3 $1.30, Yachting .. 3·50 5·00
0/3 .. *Set of* 4 5·25 6·25
S804 100×70 $2 Athletes with medals .. 4·25 5·50

es R. Watton. Litho Cartor (Nos. 805/8) or Questa (No. **MS**809))

995 (8 May). *50th Anniv of End of Second World War. Multicoloured designs as T* **161** *of Ascension. W w* **14** (*sideways*). *P* 13½.

5 10 c. Members of Cayman Home Guard .. 65 45
6 25 c. *Comayagua* (freighter) .. 1·50 80
807 40 c. U-boat *U125* .. 1·75 1·50
808 $1 U.S. Navy *L-3* airship .. 3·25 4·75
805/8 .. *Set of* 4 6·50 6·75
MS809 75×85 mm. $1.30, Reverse of 1939–45 War Medal (*vert*). Wmk upright. P 14 .. 2·50 3·00

(Des N. Shewring. Litho Walsall)

1995 (25 Aug). *95th Birthday of Queen Elizabeth the Queen Mother. Sheet* 70×90 *mm. W w* **14** (*sideways*). *P* 14½.

MS810 **189** $4 multicoloured .. 8·00 9·00

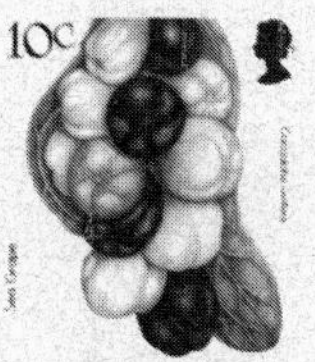

190 Ox and Christ Child
191 Sea Grape

(Des Doreen McGuiness. Litho Walsall)

1995 (1 Nov). *Christmas. Nativity Animals. T* **190** *and similar vert designs. Multicoloured. W w* **14**. *P* 14×13½.

811 10 c. Type **190** .. 45 30
812 20 c. Sheep and lamb .. 75 45
813 30 c. Donkey .. 90 60
814 $2 Camels .. 4·75 6·50
811/14 .. *Set of* 4 6·25 7·00
MS815 160×75 mm. Nos. 811/14 .. 6·25 7·00

(Des I. Loe. Litho B.D.T.)

1996 (21 Mar). *Wild Fruit. T* **191** *and similar vert designs. Multicoloured. W w* **16**. *P* 14.

816 10 c. Type **191** .. 30 30
817 25 c. Guava .. 65 50
818 40 c. West Indian Cherry .. 90 70
819 $1 Tamarind .. 2·00 3·00
816/19 .. *Set of* 4 3·50 4·00

192 Dinghy Sailing
193 Guitar and Score of National Song

(Des G. Vasarhelyi. Litho Walsall)

1996 (19 June). *Centenary of Modern Olympic Games. T* **192** *and similar vert designs. Multicoloured. W w* **16**. *P* 14×13½.

820 10 c. Type **192** .. 25 25
821 20 c. Sailboarding .. 50 55
822 30 c. Dinghy sailing (*different*) .. 70 80
823 $2 Running .. 3·75 5·00
820/3 .. *Set of* 4 4·75 6·00

(Des N. Shewring. Litho Questa)

1996 (26 Sept). *National Identity. T* **193** *and similar square designs. Multicoloured. W w* **14**. *P* 14.

824 10 c. Type **193** .. 15 30
825 20 c. Cayman Airways Boeing 737-200 .. 30 35
826 25 c. Queen Elizabeth opening Legislative Assembly .. 35 40
827 30 c. Seven Mile Beach .. 40 45
828 40 c. Scuba diver and Stingrays .. 60 65
829 60 c. Children at turtle farm .. 90 95
830 80 c. Cuban Amazon ("Cayman Parrot") (national bird) .. 1·10 1·25
831 90 c. Silver Thatch Palm (national tree) .. 1·25 1·40
832 $1 Cayman Islands flag .. 1·50 1·60
833 $2 Wild Banana Orchid (national flower) 3·00 3·25
834 $4 Cayman Islands coat of arms .. 5·75 6·00
835 $6 Cayman Islands currency .. 8·75 9·00
824/35 .. *Set of* 12 24·00 25·00

Imprint dates: "1996", Nos. 824/35; "1997", No. 824.

For miniature sheet containing No. 830 with "1997" imprint date see No. **MS**840.

OMNIBUS ISSUES

Details, together with prices for complete sets, of the various Omnibus issues from the 1935 Silver Jubilee series to date are included in a special section following Zimbabwe at the end of Volume 2.

194 "Christmas Time on North Church Street" (Joanne Sibley)
195 Children accessing Internet

(Des D. Miller. Litho Questa)

1996 (12 Nov). *Christmas. Paintings. T* **194** *and similar square designs. Multicoloured. W w* **14** (*sideways*). *P* 14.

836 10 c. Type **194** .. 25 25
837 25 c. "Gone Fishing" (Lois Brezinsky) .. 50 50
838 30 c. "Claus Encounters" (John Doak) .. 60 70
839 $2 "A Caymanian Christmas" (Debbie van der Bol) .. 3·75 5·50
836/9 .. *Set of* 4 4·50 6·25

(Des D. Miller. Litho Questa)

1997 (3 Feb). *"HONG KONG '97" International Stamp Exhibition. Sheet* 130×90 *mm, containing design as No.* 830 *with "1997" imprint date. Multicoloured. W w* **14** (*inverted*). *P* 14.

MS840 80 c. Cuban Amazon ("Cayman Parrot") 1·50 2·00

(Des N. Shewring (No. **MS**847), D. Miller (others). Litho Questa (No. **MS**847), B.D.T.(others))

1997 (10 July). *Golden Wedding of Queen Elizabeth and Prince Philip. Multicoloured designs as T* **173** *of Ascension. W w* **14**. *P* 13½.

841 10 c. Queen Elizabeth .. 35 40
a. Horiz pair. Nos. 841/2 .. 70 80
842 10 c. Prince Philip and Prince Charles at Trooping the Colour .. 35 40
843 30 c. Prince William horse riding, 1989 .. 75 90
a. Horiz pair. Nos. 843/4 .. 1·50 1·75
844 30 c. Queen Elizabeth and Prince Philip at Royal Ascot .. 75 90
845 40 c. Prince Philip at the Brighton Driving Trials .. 80 1·00
a. Horiz pair. Nos. 845/6 .. 1·60 2·00
846 40 c. Queen Elizabeth at Windsor Horse Show, 1993 .. 80 1·00
841/6 .. *Set of* 6 3·50 4·00
MS847 110×70 mm. $1 Queen Elizabeth and Prince Philip in landau (*horiz*). Wmk sideways. P 14×14½ .. 2·00 2·50

Nos. 841/2, 843/4 and 845/6 were each printed together, *se-tenant*, in horizontal pairs throughout the sheets with the backgrounds forming a composite design.

(Des O. Bell. Litho Walsall)

1997 (10 Oct). *Telecommunications. T* **195** *and similar horiz designs. Multicoloured. W w* **16** (*sideways*). *P* 14×14½.

848 10 c. Type **195** .. 30 25
849 25 c. Cable & Wireless cable ship .. 60 45
850 30 c. New area code "345" on children's T-shirts .. 70 60
851 60 c. Satellite dish .. 1·25 1·75
848/51 .. *Set of* 4 2·50 2·75

196 Santa in Hammock
197 West Indian Whistling Duck

(Des R. Watton. Litho Cartor)

1997 (3 Dec). *Christmas. T* **196** *and similar vert designs. Multicoloured. W w* **14**. *P* 13.

852 10 c. Type **196** .. 20 20
853 30 c. Santa with children on the Bluff .. 40 45
854 40 c. Santa playing golf .. 80 70
855 $1 Santa scuba diving .. 1·40 2·00
852/5 .. *Set of* 4 2·50 3·00

(Des D. Miller. Litho Questa)

1998 (31 Mar). *Diana, Princess of Wales Commemoration. Vert designs as T* **177** *of Ascension. Multicoloured. W w* **16** (*Nos.* 856/7). *P* 14½×14.

856 10 c. Wearing gold earrings, 1997 .. 25 25
857 20 c. Wearing black hat .. 45 45
MS858 145×70 mm. 10 c. As No. 856; 20 c. As No. 857; 40 c. With bouquet, 1995; $1 Wearing black and white blouse, 1983. W w **14** (sideways) (*sold at* $1.70 + 30 c. *charity premium*) .. 3·50 4·00

(Des A. Theobald. Litho B.D.T.)

1998 (1 Apr). *80th Anniv of the Royal Air Force. Horiz designs as T* **178** *of Ascension. Multicoloured. W w* **14** (*sideways*). *P* 14.

859 10 c. Hawker Horsley .. 30 30
860 20 c. Fairey Hendon .. 45 45
861 25 c. Hawker Siddeley Gnat .. 55 60
862 30 c. Hawker Siddeley Dominie .. 65 75
859/62 .. *Set of* 4 1·75 1·90
MS863 110×77 mm. 40 c. Airco D.H.9; 60 c. Spad 13 Scout; 80 c. Airspeed Oxford; $1 Martin Baltimore .. 5·00 5·50

(Des N. Shewring. Litho Cartor)

1998 (12 Oct). *Birds.* *T* **197** *and similar vert designs. Multicoloured. W* w **14**. *P* 13½.

864	10 c. Type **197**	15	20
865	20 c. Magnificent Frigate Bird	30	35
866	60 c. Red-footed Booby	90	95
867	$1 Grand Cayman Parrot	1·50	1·60
864/7	.. .. *Set of* 4	2·75	3·00

198 Santa at the Blowholes

(Des R. Watton. Litho Questa)

1998 (20 Nov). *Christmas. T* **198** *and similar horiz designs. Multicoloured. W* w **16** *(sideways). P* 14½.

868	10 c. Type **198**	15	20
869	30 c. Santa diving on wreck of *Capt. Keith Tibbetts*	40	45
870	40 c. Santa at Pedro Castle	60	65
871	60 c. Santa arriving on Little Cayman ..	1·50	1·60
868/71	.. .. *Set of* 4	2·50	2·75

STAMP BOOKLETS

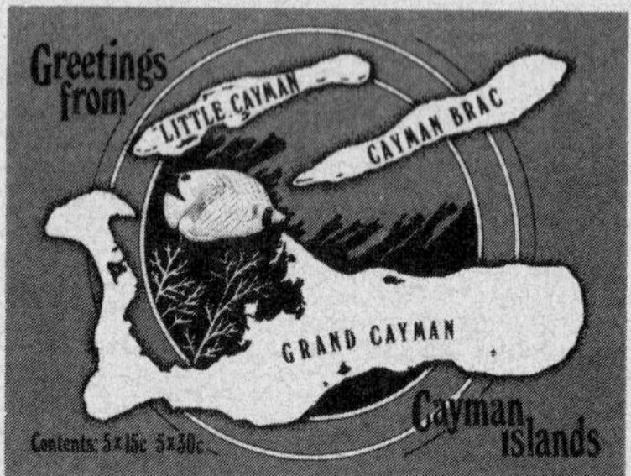

B 1

1993 (30 Sept). *Tourism. Deep ultramarine and bright greenish blue cover as Type* B **1**. *Pane attached by selvedge.*

SB1	$2.25, booklet containing pane of five 15 c. and five 30 c. (No. 755b)	6·50

B 2

1994 (12 Oct). *Bicentenary of Wreck of Ten Sail off Grand Cayman. Multicoloured covers as Type* B **2**. *Stamps attached by selvedge.*

SB2	$1 booklet containing block of ten 10 c. stamps (No. 788)	1·60
SB3	$1.50, booklet containing block of ten 15 c. stamps (No. 790)	2·40
SB4	$2 booklet containing block of ten 20 c. stamps (No. 791)	3·25

B 3

1996 (26 Sept). *National Identity. Multicoloured covers as Type* B **3** *illustrating stamp design enclosed. Stamps attached by selvedge.*

SB5	$1 booklet containing block of ten 10 c. stamps (No. 824)	1·50
SB6	$3 booklet containing block of ten 30 c. stamps (No. 827)	4·25
SB7	$4 booklet containing block of ten 40 c. stamps (No. 828)	5·75

Ceylon *see* Sri Lanka

Channel Islands

These issues are now listed under GREAT BRITAIN after the Postal Fiscal Issues.

China—British Post Offices *see after* Hong Kong

Christmas Island *see after* Australia

Cocos (Keeling) Islands *see after* Australia

Cook Islands

(Rarotonga)

This group of fifteen islands was originally also known as the Hervey Islands. A British Protectorate was declared over the group by the local Vice-Consul on 20 September 1888.

Before the introduction of the Cook Islands Post Office mail was forwarded via Auckland, New Zealand.

PRICES FOR STAMPS ON COVER TO 1945	
Nos. 1/4	*from* × 5
Nos. 5/74	*from* × 4
Nos. 75/145	*from* × 3

Watermarks of New Zealand used for Cook Islands (including Aitutaki and Penrhyn Island)

W 12*b*

W 38

W 43

W 98

Types of New Zealand Definitives overprinted or surcharged for Cook Islands (including Aitutaki and Penrhyn Island)

23

27

28

31

34

42

51

52

53

60

61

72

F 4

F 6

BRITISH PROTECTORATE

1

2 Queen Makea Takau

3 White Tern or Torea

(Des F. Moss. Typo Govt Printing Office, Wellington)

1892 (19 Apr). *No wmk. Toned paper. P* 12½.

No.	Type	Description	Unused	Used
1	**1**	1d. black	27·00	26·00
		b. White paper	26·00	26·00
		ba. Imperf between (vert pair)	£8500	
2		1½d. mauve	40·00	38·00
		a. Imperf (pair)	£9000	
		b. White paper	40·00	38·00
3		2½d. blue	40·00	38·00
		a. White paper	40·00	38·00
4		10d. carmine	£140	£130
		a. White paper	£160	£130
1/4		*Set of* 4	£200	£200

Nos. 1/4 were printed in sheets of 60 (6×10) from plates constructed from a matrix of 6 slightly different types.

(Eng A. E. Cousins. Typo Govt Printing Office, Wellington)

1893 (28 July)–**1900.** *W* **12***b of New Zealand* (N Z *and Star wide apart*) (*sideways on T* **3**). (*a*) *P* 12 × 11½.

No.	Type	Description	Unused	Used
5	**2**	1d. brown	32·00	45·00
6		1d. blue (3.4.94)	7·00	1·75
		a. Perf 12×11½ and 12½ mixed	†	£1000
7		1½d. mauve	7·00	6·00
8		2½d. rose	35·00	23·00
		a. *Rose-carmine*	60·00	55·00
		ab. Perf 12×11½ and 12½ mixed	£1700	
9		5d. olive-black	15·00	13·00
10		10d. green	65·00	48·00
5/10		*Set of* 6	£140	£110
		(*b*) *P* 11 (July 1896–1900)		
11	**3**	½d. steel blue (1st setting) (11.99)	28·00	45·00
		a. Upper right "d" omitted	£1400	
		b. Second setting	18·00	22·00
		ba. *Deep blue* (1900)	4·00	4·75
12	**2**	1d. blue	4·25	4·50
13		1d. deep brown/*cream* (4.99)	13·00	13·00
		a. Wmk sideways		
		b. *Bistre-brown* (1900)	16·00	17·00
14		1½d. deep lilac	8·50	6·50
		a. *Deep mauve* (1900)	8·50	6·50
15	**3**	2d. brown/*thin toned* (7.98)	9·50	6·50
		a. *Deep brown* (1900)	8·00	6·50
16	**2**	2½d. pale rose	45·00	38·00
		a. *Deep rose* (1900)	14·00	9·00
17		5d. olive-black	24·00	17·00
18	**3**	6d. purple/*thin toned* (7.98)	24·00	28·00
		a. *Bright purple* (1900)	19·00	20·00
19	**2**	10d. green	17·00	42·00
20	**3**	1s. red/*thin toned* (7.98)	60·00	70·00
		a. *Deep carmine* (1900)	48·00	48·00
11/20*a*		*Set of* 10	£140	£150

Examples of the 1d., 1½d., 2½d. and 5d. perforated 11 and on laid paper are perforation trials.

On the 1st setting of the ½d. the face values are misplaced in each corner. As corrected in the second setting the face values are correctly positioned in each corner.

ONE
HALF
PENNY

(4)

(5)

1899 (24 Apr). *No.* 12 *surch with T* **4** *by Govt Printer, Rarotonga.*

No.	Type	Description	Unused	Used
21	**2**	½d. on 1d. blue	32·00	40·00
		a. Surch inverted	£800	£850
		b. Surch double	£950	£750

NEW ZEALAND TERRITORY

On 8 and 9 October 1900 the chiefs of all the main islands, except Aitutaki, ceded their territory to the British Crown. On 11 June 1901 all the islands, including Aitutaki, were transferred by Great Britain to New Zealand control.

1901 (8 Oct). *No.* 13 *optd with T* **5** *by Govt Printer, Rarotonga.*

No.	Type	Description	Unused	Used
22	**2**	1d. brown	£180	£140
		a. Crown inverted	£1800	£1400
		c. Optd with crown twice	£1500	£1500

1902. *No wmk. P* 11.

No.	Type	Description	Unused	Used
		(*a*) *Medium white Cowan paper* (Feb)		
23	**3**	½d. blue-green	6·00	6·50
24	**2**	1d. dull rose	8·50	11·00
		(*b*) *Thick white Pirie paper* (May)		
25	**3**	½d. yellow-green	3·75	4·00
		a. Imperf horiz (vert pair)	£1100	
26	**2**	1d. rose-red	11·00	11·00
		a. *Rose-lake*	9·50	6·50
27		2½d. dull blue	11·00	21·00

NEW ZEALAND WATERMARKS. In W **43** the wmk units are in vertical columns widely spaced and the sheet margins are unwatermarked or wmkd "NEW ZEALAND POSTAGE" in large letters.

In W **98** the wmk units are arranged alternately in horizontal rows closely spaced and are continued into the sheet margins.

Stamps with W **98** sideways show the star to the left of NZ, *as seen from the back*. Sideways inverted varieties have the star to the right, *as seen from the back*.

1902 (Sept). *W* **43** *of New Zealand* (*single-lined* NZ *and Star, close together; sideways on T* **2**). *P* 11.

No.	Type	Description	Unused	Used
28	**3**	½d. yellow-green	2·25	3·25
		a. *Grey-green*	17·00	32·00
29	**2**	1d. rose-pink	4·00	3·00
30		1½d. deep mauve	3·25	8·00
31	**3**	2d. deep brown	4·00	10·00
		a. No figures of value	£1800	£2750
		b. Perf 11 × 14	£1100	
32	**2**	2½d. deep blue	3·75	6·50
33		5d. olive-black	35·00	48·00
34	**3**	6d. purple	32·00	28·00
35	**2**	10d. green	48·00	85·00
36	**3**	1s. carmine	48·00	65·00
		a. Perf 11 × 14	£1300	
28/36		*Set of* 9	£150	£225

Stamps in Type **3** were printed from a master plate with the value added by a series of separate duty plates. One sheet of the 2d. missed this second pass through the press and was issued without value.

1909–11. *W* **43** *of New Zealand.*

No.	Type	Description	Unused	Used
37	**3**	½d. green (*p* 14½×14) (1911)	5·50	7·00
38	**2**	1d. deep red (*p* 14)	27·00	25·00
		a. Wmk sideways (24.12.09)	11·00	9·00

1913–19. *W* **43** *of New Zealand (sideways on T* **3**). *Chalk-surfaced paper.*
39 **3** ½d. deep green (*p* 14) (1915) .. .. .. 3·75 12·00
a. Wmk upright .. .. 4·75 10·00
40 **2** 1d. red (*p* 14) (7.13) .. .. .. 3·75 3·75
41 1d. red (*p* 14 × 14½) (1914) .. .. 5·00 5·00
42 1½d. deep mauve (*p* 14) (1915) .. .. 85·00 45·00
43 1½d. deep mauve (*p* 14 × 15) (1916) .. 7·50 3·75
44 **3** 2d. deep brown (*p* 15 × 14) (1919) .. 5·00 42·00
45 **2** 10d. green (*p* 14 × 15) (1918) .. .. 13·00 75·00
46 **3** 1s. carmine (*p* 15 × 14) (1919).. .. 27·00 75·00
39/46 .. .. *Set of* 6 55·00 £180

RAROTONGA

APA PENE

(8)

1919 (Apr–July). *Stamps of New Zealand surch as T* **8**.

(*a*) *T* **53**. *W* **43**. *De La Rue chalk-surfaced paper. P* 14×15
47 1d. carmine (No. 405) (B.) (June) .. 85 1·75

(*b*) *T* **60** (*recess*). *W* **43**. *Cowan unsurfaced paper. P* 14×13½.
48 2½d. blue (No. 419) (R.) (June) .. .. 2·25 6·00
a. Perf 14×14½ .. .. 2·00 2·25
b. Vert pair. Nos. 48/a .. .. .. 20·00 45·00
49 3d. chocolate (No. 420) (B.) .. .. 2·00 7·00
a. Perf 14×14½ .. .. 2·25 1·50
b. Vert pair. Nos. 49/a .. .. .. 22·00 50·00
50 4d. bright violet (No. 422) (B.) .. .. 2·00 5·50
a. Re-entry (Pl 20 R. 1/6) .. .. 60·00
b. Re-entry (Pl 20 R. 4/10) .. .. 60·00
c. Perf 14×14½ .. .. 1·75 4·00
d. Vert pair. Nos. 50 and 50c .. .. 20·00 55·00
51 4½d. deep green (No. 423) (B.) .. .. 2·00 6·50
a. Perf 14×14½ .. .. 1·75 6·50
b. Vert pair. Nos. 51/a .. .. .. 20·00 65·00
52 6d. carmine (No. 425) (B.) (June) .. 3·00 8·00
a. Perf 14×14½ .. .. 1·75 5·00
b. Vert pair. Nos. 52/a .. .. .. 38·00 80·00
53 7½d. red-brown (No. 426a) (B.) .. .. 1·50 5·50
54 9d. sage-green (No. 429) (R.) .. .. 3·25 12·00
a. Perf 14×14½ .. .. 2·00 12·00
b. Vert pair. Nos. 54/a .. .. .. 38·00 95·00
55 1s. vermilion (No. 430) (B.) (June) .. 11·00 29·00
a. Perf 14×14½ .. .. 2·75 15·00
b. Vert pair. Nos. 55/a .. .. .. 48·00 £110

(*c*) *T* **61** (*typo*). *W* **43**. *De La Rue chalk-surfaced paper. P* 14×15
56 ½d. green (No. 435) (R.) (June) 40 80
57 1½d. orange-brown (No. 438) (R.) (June) .. 40 75
58 2d. yellow (No. 439) (R.) .. .. .. 1·25 1·25
59 3d. chocolate (No. 440) (B.) (July) .. 2·50 8·50
47/59 .. .. *Set of* 13 19·00 55·00

9 Capt. Cook landing

10 Wharf at Avarua

11 "Capt. Cook" (Dance)

12 Palm Tree

13 Huts at Arorangi

14 Avarua Harbour

R.2/8 R.3/6 R.5/2
Double derrick flaws

(Des, eng and recess Perkins, Bacon & Co)

1920 (23 Aug). *No wmk. P* 14.
70 **9** ½d. black and green .. .. .. 4·00 14·00
71 **10** 1d. black and carmine-red .. .. 4·00 12·00
a. Double derrick flaw (R.2/8, 3/6 or 5/2) 12·00
72 **11** 1½d. black and dull blue .. .. 8·00 8·50
73 **12** 3d. black and chocolate .. .. 2·25 5·50
74 **13** 6d. brown and yellow-orange .. .. 2·25 8·50
75 **14** 1s. black and violet .. .. .. 5·00 17·00
70/5 .. .. *Set of* 6 23·00 60·00

Examples of the 1d. and 1s. with centre inverted were not supplied to the Post Office.

RAROTONGA

(15)

RAROTONGA

Trimmed overprint (R. 1/6 and R. 3/7)

1921 (Oct)–**23**. *Postal Fiscal stamps as Type* F **4** *of New Zealand optd with T* **15**. *W* **43** *(sideways). Chalk-surfaced "De La Rue" paper. P* 14½×14.
76 2s. deep blue (No. F111) (R.) .. .. 27·00 55·00
a. Trimmed opt .. .. 90·00
b. Carmine opt (1923) £140 £160
ba. Trimmed opt £400
77 2s. 6d. grey-brown (No. F112) (B.) .. 18·00 50·00
a. Trimmed opt .. .. 70·00
78 5s. yellow-green (No. F115) (R.) .. .. 27·00 65·00
a. Trimmed opt .. .. 90·00
79 10s. maroon (No. F120) (B.) .. .. 48·00 85·00
a. Trimmed opt £150
80 £1 rose-carmine (No. F123) (B.) .. .. 80·00 £140
a. Trimmed opt £250
76/80 .. .. *Set of* 5 £180 £350
See also Nos. 85/9.

16 Te Po, Rarotongan Chief

17 Harbour, Rarotonga and Mt Ikurangi

(2½d. from a print; 4d. des A. H. Messenger. Plates by P.B. Recess Govt Ptg Office, Wellington)

1924–27. *W* **43** *of New Zealand. P* 14.
81 **9** ½d. black and green (13.5.26) .. .. 4·50 7·50
82 **10** 1d. black and deep carmine (10.11.24) 6·00 1·75
a. Double derrick flaw (R.2/8, 3/6 or 5/2) 16·00
83 **16** 2½d. red-brown and steel blue (15.10.27) 5·00 20·00
84 **17** 4d. green and violet (15.10.27) .. 8·00 15·00
81/4 .. .. *Set of* 4 21·00 40·00

1926 (Feb–May). *As Nos.* 76/80, *but on thick, opaque white chalk-surfaced "Cowan" paper.*
85 2s. blue (No. F131) (C.) £100 £150
a. Trimmed opt £300
86 2s. 6d. deep grey-brown (No. F132) (B.) 50·00 85·00
87 5s. yellow-green (No. F135) (R.) (May) .. 50·00 75·00
a. Trimmed opt £140
88 10s. brown-red (No. F139) (B.) (May) .. 55·00 90·00
89 £1 rose-pink (No. F142) (B.) (May) .. 80·00 £130
85/9 .. .. *Set of* 5 £300 £475

1926 (Oct)–**28**. *T* **72** *of New Zealand, overprinted with T* **15**.

(*a*) *Jones chalk-surfaced paper.*
90 2s. deep blue (No. 466) (R.) .. .. 10·00 40·00

(*b*) *Cowan thick, opaque chalk-surfaced paper*
91 2s. light blue (No. 469) (R.) (18.6.27) .. 15·00 40·00
92 3s. pale mauve (No. 470) (R.) (30.1.28) .. 16·00 42·00
90/2 .. .. *Set of* 3 38·00 £110

TWO PENCE (18) **COOK ISLANDS.** (19)

1931 (Mar). *Surch with T* **18**. *P* 14. (*a*) *No wmk.*
93 **11** 2d. on 1½d. black and blue (R.) .. 9·00 2·75

(*b*) *W* **43** *of New Zealand*
94 **11** 2d. on 1½d. black and blue (R.) .. 4·25 9·00

1931 (12 Nov)–**32**. *Postal Fiscal stamps as Type* F **6** *of New Zealand. W* **43**. *Thick, opaque, white chalk-surfaced Cowan paper. P* 14.

(*a*) *Optd with T* **15**
95 2s. 6d. deep brown (No. F147) (B.) .. 9·50 20·00
96 5s. green (No. F149) (R.) .. .. .. 16·00 48·00
97 10s. carmine-lake (No. F155) (B.) .. .. 35·00 80·00
98 £1 pink (No. F158) (B.) .. .. .. 80·00 £130

(*b*) *Optd with T* **19** (3.32)
98*a* £3 green (No. F164) (R.) £160 £325
98*b* £5 indigo-blue (No. F168) (R.) £170 £300
The £3 and £5 values were mainly used for fiscal purposes.

20 Capt. Cook landing

21 Capt. Cook

22 Double Maori Canoe

23 Natives working Cargo

24 Port of Avarua

25 R.M.S. *Monowai*

26 King George V

(Des L. C. Mitchell. Recess P.B.)

1932 (15 Mar–2 May). *No wmk. P* 13.
99 **20** ½d. black and deep green .. .. 3·50 15·0
a. Perf 14 .. .. 28·00 90·0
100 **21** 1d. black and lake .. .. .. 5·00 4·0
a. Centre inverted £2500 £250
b. Perf compound of 13 and 14 .. £180 £20
c. Perf 14 .. .. 15·00 19·0
101 **22** 2d. black and brown .. .. .. 2·75 5·0
a. Perf 14 .. .. 9·00 18·0
102 **23** 2½d. black and deep blue .. .. 6·50 48·0
a. Perf 14 .. .. 13·00 48·0
103 **24** 4d. black and bright blue .. .. 20·00 55·0
a. Perf 14 .. .. 10·00 48·0
b. Perf 14×13 .. .. .. 30·00 90·0
c. Perf compound of 14 and 13 .. 50·00 £10
104 **25** 6d. black and orange .. .. .. 24·00 48·0
a. Perf 14 .. .. 4·00 13·0
105 **26** 1s. black and violet (*p* 14) (2 May) .. 8·00 20·0
99/105 .. .. *Set of* 7 35·00 £14

Nos. 100b and 103c come from sheets reperforated 14 o arrival at Wellington. No. 100b comes from the first vertic column of a sheet and has 14 at left and No. 103c from the thi or fourth vertical column with 13 at left or right.

Other major errors exist on this issue, but these are not liste as they originated from printer's waste which appeared on th market in 1935.

(Recess from P.B. plates at Govt Printing Office, Wellington)

1933–36. *W* **43** *of New Zealand (Single* N Z *and Star). P* 14.
106 **20** ½d. black and deep green .. .. 1·00 3·5
w. Wmk inverted .. .. .. — 75·
107 **21** 1d. black and scarlet (1935) .. .. 1·00 1·7
w. Wmk inverted and reversed ..
108 **22** 2d. black and brown (1936) .. .. 1·25 4
109 **23** 2½d. black and deep blue .. .. 1·50 2·2
110 **24** 4d. black and bright blue .. .. 1·50 4
111 **25** 6d. black and orange-yellow (1936) .. 1·75 2·2
112 **26** 1s. black and violet (1936) .. .. 27·00 28·0
106/12 .. .. *Set of* 7 32·00 35·0

SILVER JUBILEE OF KING GEORGE V. 1910 - 1935.

(27)

Normal letters
B K E N
B K E N
Narrow letters

1935 (7 May). *Silver Jubilee. Optd with T* **27** *(wider vertic spacing on 6d.). Colours changed. W* **43** *of New Zealand. P* 1
113 **21** 1d. red-brown and lake .. .. 60 1·1
a. Narrow "K" in "KING" .. .. 2·75
b. Narrow "B" in "JUBILEE" .. 4·50
114 **23** 2½d. dull and deep blue (R.) .. .. 1·00 2·0
a. Narrow first "E" in "GEORGE" .. 3·50 5·0
115 **25** 6d. green and orange .. .. 3·50 5·5
a. Narrow "N" in "KING" .. .. 16·00
113/15 .. .. *Set of* 3 4·50 7·5

1936 (15 July)–**44**. *Stamps of New Zealand optd with T* 1 *W* **43**. *P* 14.

(*a*) *T* **72**. *Cowan thick, opaque chalk-surfaced paper*
116 2s. light blue (No. 469) .. .. .. 12·00 45·
117 3s. pale mauve (No. 470) .. .. .. 13·00 65·

(*b*) *Type* F **6**. *Cowan thick, opaque chalk-surfaced paper*
118 2s. 6d. deep brown (No. F147) .. .. 17·00 60·0
119 5s. green (No. F149) (R.) .. .. .. 20·00 80·0
120 10s. carmine-lake (No. F155) .. .. 40·00 £1
121 £1 pink (No. F158) .. .. .. 60·00 £1
118/21 .. .. *Set of* 4 £120 £3

(*c*) *Type* F **6**. *Thin, hard, chalk-surfaced Wiggins, Teape pape*
122 2s. 6d. dull brown (No. F170) (12.40) .. 85·00 90·0
123 5s. green (No. F172) (R.) (10.40) .. £300 £3
123*a* 10s. pale carmine-lake (No. F177) (11.44) £120 £1
123*b* £3 green (No. F183) (R.) (date?) .. £325 £5
122/3*b* .. .. *Set of* 4 £700 £10

COOK IS'DS.

(28)

IS'DS.

Small second "S" (R. 1/2)

1937 (1 June). *Coronation. Nos.* 599/601 *of New Zealand (ins "12th MAY 1937") optd with T* **28**.
124 1d. carmine 40
a. Small second "S" .. .. .. 11·00
125 2½d. Prussian blue 80
a. Small second "S" .. .. .. 20·00
126 6d. red-orange 80
a. Small second "S" .. .. .. 20·00
124/6 .. .. *Set of* 3 1·75

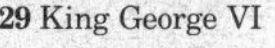

29 King George VI **30** Native Village

31 Native Canoe **32** Tropical Landscape

es J. Berry (2s., 3s., and frame of 1s.). Eng B.W. Recess Govt Ptg. Office, Wellington)

38 (2 May). *W* **43** *of New Zealand. P* 14.
7 **29** 1s. black and violet .. .. .. 7·00 9·00
8 **30** 2s. black and red-brown .. .. 18·00 10·00
w. Wmk inverted .. .. ..
9 **31** 3s. light blue and emerald-green .. 40·00 30·00
7/9 .. .. *Set of* 3 60·00 45·00

(Recess B.W.)

40 (2 Sept). *Surch as in T* **32.** *W* **98** *of New Zealand. P* 13½ × 14.
0 **32** 3d. on 1½d. black and purple 40 50
Type **32** was not issued without surcharge.

943–54. *Postal Fiscal stamps as Type* F **6** *of New Zealand optd with T* **19**. *W* **98**. *Wiggins, Teape chalk-surfaced paper. P* 14.
31 2s. 6d. dull brown (No. F170) (3.46) .. 26·00 42·00
w. Wmk inverted (2.4.51) .. .. 13·00 17·00
32 5s. green (No. F172) (R.) (11.43) .. .. 7·50 18·00
w. Wmk inverted (5.54) .. .. .. 16·00 18·00
33 10s. pale carmine-lake (No. F177) (10.48) 48·00 70·00
w. Wmk inverted (10.51) .. .. 40·00 65·00
34 £1 pink (No. F179) (11.47) .. .. 45·00 70·00
w. Wmk inverted (19.5.54) .. .. 45·00 70·00
35 £3 green (No. F183) (R.) (1946?) .. £425 £600
w. Wmk inverted (28.5.53) .. .. 55·00 £160
36 £5 indigo-blue (No. F184) (R.) (25.10.50) £225 £350
w. Wmk inverted (19.5.54) £250 £375
31/6 .. .. *Set of* 6 £350 £600
The £3 and £5 were mainly used for fiscal purposes.

(Recess Govt Ptg Office, Wellington)

944–46. *W* **98** *of New Zealand (sideways on ½d. 1d., 1s., and 2s.). P* 14.
37 **20** ½d. black and deep green (11.44) .. 1·00 3·50
w. Wmk sideways inverted .. .. 7·00
38 **21** 1d. black and scarlet (3.45) .. .. 2·00 35
w. Wmk sideways inverted .. .. 10·00
39 **22** 2d. black and brown (2.46) .. .. 1·25 4·25
40 **23** 2½d. black and deep blue (5.45) .. 65 1·75
41 **24** 4d. black and blue (4.44) .. .. 3·50 7·50
y. Wmk inverted and reversed .. 40·00 40·00
42 **25** 6d. black and orange (6.44) .. .. 1·25 1·75
43 **29** 1s. black and violet (9.44) .. .. 1·25 2·25
44 **30** 2s. black and red-brown (8.45) .. 26·00 25·00
45 **31** 3s. light blue & emerald-green (6.45) 28·00 25·00
37/45 .. .. *Set of* 9 60·00 65·00

COOK
ISLANDS
(33)

946 (4 June). *Peace. Nos.* 668, 670, 674/5 *of New Zealand optd with T* **33** *(reading up and down at sides on 2d.).*
46 1d. green (Parliament House) 30 10
47 2d. purple (Royal family) (B.) 30 40
48 6d. chocolate and vermilion (Coat of arms, foundry and farm) 30 40
49 8d. black and carmine ("St. George") (B.) 30 40
46/9 .. .. *Set of* 4 1·10 1·10

34 Ngatangiia Channel, Rarotonga **41** Map and Statue of Capt. Cook

(Des J. Berry. Recess Waterlow)

1949 (1 Aug)–**61.** *T* **34, 41** *and similar designs. W* **98** *of New Zealand (sideways on shilling values). P* 13½ × 13 *(horiz) or* 13 × 13½ *(vert).*
150 ½d. violet and brown .. .. .. 10 1·00
151 1d. chestnut and green .. .. .. 3·50 2·00
152 2d. reddish brown and scarlet .. .. 1·00 2·00
153 3d. green and ultramarine .. .. 1·25 2·00
aw. Wmk inverted £100
b. Wmk sideways (white opaque paper) (22.5.61) .. .. 3·50 2·50
154 5d. emerald-green and violet .. .. 4·00 1·50
155 6d. black and carmine .. .. .. 4·25 2·75
156 8d. olive-green and orange .. .. 55 3·75
w. Wmk inverted .. .. .. 85·00 50·00
157 1s. light blue and chocolate .. .. 4·25 3·75
158 2s. yellow-brown and carmine .. .. 3·00 11·00
w. Wmk sideways inverted .. ..
159 3s. light blue and bluish green .. .. 8·50 17·00
150/9 .. .. *Set of* 10 27·00 42·00

Designs: *Horiz*—1d. Capt. Cook and map of Hervey Islands; 2d. Rarotonga and Revd. John Williams; 3d. Aitutaki and palm trees; 5d. Rarotonga Airfield; 6d. Penrhyn village; 8d. Native hut. *Vert*—2s. Native hut and palms; 3s. *Matua* (inter-island freighter).

See note on white opaque paper below No. 736 of New Zealand.

42 Queen Elizabeth II

(Des J. Berry. Photo Harrison)

1953 (25 May). *Coronation. T* **42** *and similar vert design. W* **98**. *P* 14×14½.
160 3d. brown .. .. 1·00 75
161 6d. slate-grey .. .. 1·25 1·25
Design:—6d. Westminster Abbey.

1/6

(44)

1960 (1 Apr). *No.* 154 *surch with T* **44**.
162 1s. 6d. on 5d. emerald-green and violet .. 30 30

45 Tiare Maori **48** White Tern

52 Queen Elizabeth II **53** Island Scene

(Des J. Berry. Recess (1s. 6d.), litho (others) B.W.)

1963 (4 June). *T* **45, 48, 52/3** *and similar designs. W* **98** *of New Zealand (sideways). P* 13½×13 *(1d., 2d., 8d.),* 13×13½ *(3d., 5d., 6d., 1s.) or* 13½ *(others).*
163 1d. emerald-green and yellow 45 40
164 2d. brown-red and yellow 20 40
165 3d. yellow, yellow-green & reddish violet .. 70 40
166 5d. blue and black .. .. 8·00 75
167 6d. red, yellow and green .. .. .. 1·00 30
168 8d. black and blue .. .. 3·50 1·25
169 1s. orange-yellow and yellow-green.. .. 40 30
170 1s. 6d. bluish violet .. .. 2·75 2·00
171 2s. bistre-brown and grey-blue .. .. 1·00 75
172 3s. black and yellow-green .. .. .. 1·25 1·00
173 5s. bistre-brown and blue .. .. .. 10·00 3·25
163/73 .. .. *Set of* 11 26·00 9·50

Designs: *Vert (as T* **45**)—2d. Fishing god; 8d. Long-tailed Tuna. *Horiz (as T* **48**)—3d. Frangipani; 6d. Hibiscus; 1s. Oranges. (*As T* **53**)—3s. Administration Centre, Mangaia; 5s. Rarotonga.

56 Eclipse and Palm **57** N.Z. Ensign and Map

(Des L. C. Mitchell. Litho B.W.)

1965 (31 May). *Solar Eclipse Observation, Manuae Island. W* **98** *of New Zealand. P* 13½.
174 **56** 6d. black, yellow and light blue .. 20 10

SELF-GOVERNMENT

(Des R. M. Conly (4d.), L. C. Mitchell (10d., 1s.), J. Berry (1s. 9d.). Litho B.W.)

1965 (16 Sept). *Internal Self-Government. T* **57** *and similar horiz designs. W* **98** *of New Zealand (sideways). P* 13½.
175 4d. red and blue 20 10
176 10d. multicoloured 20 15
177 1s. multicoloured 20 15
178 1s. 9d. multicoloured .. .. .. 50 1·00
175/8 .. .. *Set of* 4 1·00 1·25

Designs:—10d. London Missionary Society Church; 1s. Proclamation of Cession, 1900; 1s. 9d. Nikao School.

In Memoriam
SIR WINSTON CHURCHILL
1874 - 1965
(61)

Airmail
(62)

1966 (24 Jan). *Churchill Commemoration. Nos.* 171/3 *and* 175/7 *optd with T* **61**, *in red.*
179 4d. red and blue 75 30
a. "l" for "1" in "1874" .. .. .. 3·00
180 10d. multicoloured .. .. .. 1·50 45
a. Opt inverted £160
b. "l" for "1" in "1874" .. .. .. 5·00
181 1s. multicoloured .. .. .. 1·50 65
a. Opt inverted £100
b. "l" for "1" in "1874" .. .. .. 5·00
182 2s. bistre-brown and grey-blue .. .. 1·50 1·25
a. "l" for "1" in "1874" .. .. .. 5·00
183 3s. black and yellow-green .. .. 1·50 1·25
a. "l" for "1" in "1874" .. .. .. 5·00
184 5s. bistre-brown and blue .. .. 2·00 1·75
a. "l" for "1" in "1874" .. .. .. 10·00
179/84 .. .. *Set of* 6 8·00 5·00

The lower case "l" for "1" in "1874" occurred on R. 6/5 for all values and additionally on R. 12/5 for the 2s., 3s. and 5s.

1966 (22 Apr). *Air. Various stamps optd with T* **62** *or surch also.*
185 6d. red, yellow and green (No. 167) .. 1·25 20
186 7d. on 8d. black and blue (No. 168) .. 1·50 25
187 10d. on 3d. yellow, yellow-green and reddish violet (No. 165) .. .. .. 1·00 15
188 1s. orange-yellow & yellow-green (No. 169) 1·00 15
189 1s. 6d. bluish violet (No. 170) .. .. 1·50 1·25
190 2s. 3d. on 3s. black & yellow-grn (No. 172) 1·00 65
191 5s. bistre-brown and blue (No. 173) .. 1·75 1·50
192 10s. on 2s. bistre-brown & grey-bl (No. 171) 1·75 10·00
193 £1 pink (No. 134) .. .. .. 12·00 17·00
a. Aeroplane omitted .. .. .. 27·00 42·00
w. Wmk inverted .. .. .. 12·00 16·00
185/93 .. .. *Set of* 9 20·00 27·00

No. 193a occurred in all stamps of the last vertical row as insufficient aeroplane symbols were available. There are also numerous other varieties on all values, notably aeroplanes of different sizes and broken first "i" with dot missing owing to damaged type.

PRINTERS. The following stamps were printed by Heraclio Fournier, Spain except *where otherwise stated.* The process used was photogravure until No. **MS**1247 and lithography thereafter.

63 "Adoration of the Magi" (Fra Angelico)

1966 (28 Nov). *Christmas. T* **63** *and similar multicoloured designs. P* 13×12 *(horiz) or* 12×13 *(vert).*
194 1d. Type **63** 50 60
a. Perf 13×14½ 10 10
195 2d. "The Nativity" (Memling) (*vert*) .. 11·00 11·00
a. Perf 14½×13 .. .. 20 10
196 4d. "Adoration of the Magi" (Velazquez) 1·00 1·00
a. Perf 13×14½ 30 15
197 10d. "Adoration of the Magi" (Bosch) .. 2·00 4·50
a. Perf 13×14½ 30 20
198 1s. 6d. "Adoration of the Shepherds" (J. de Ribera) (*vert*) .. .. 20·00 6·50
a. Perf 14½×13 .. .. 40 35
194/8 .. .. *Set of* 5 30·00 21·00
194a/8a .. .. *Set of* 5 1·10 70

68 Tennis, and Queen Elizabeth II

(Des V. Whiteley)

1967 (12 Jan). *2nd South Pacific Games, Nouméa. T* **68** *and similar horiz designs in orange-brown, black and new blue* (1d.) *or multicoloured (others). P* 13½. (*a*) *Postage.*

No.	Description	Unused	Used
199	½d. Type **68**	10	10
200	1d. Netball and Games emblem	10	10
201	4d. Boxing and Cook Islands' team badge	10	10
202	7d. Football and Queen Elizabeth II	20	15
	(*b*) *Air*		
203	10d. Running and Games emblem	20	15
204	2s. 3d. Running and Cook Islands' team badge	25	30
199/204	*Set of* 6	70	65

(New Currency, 100 cents = 1 dollar)

1c (74) **2½c** (I) **2½c** (II)

1967 (3 Apr–6 June). *Decimal Currency. Nos.* 134, 135w, 136, 163/70 *and* 172/5 *surch as T* **74** *by the Government Printer. Sterling values unobliterated except No.* 218.

No.	Description	Unused	Used
205	1 c. on 1d. emerald-green and yellow (4.5)	45	1·25
206	2 c. on 2d. brown-red and yellow	10	10
207	2½ c. on 3d. yell, yellow-grn & reddish vio (I)	20	10
	a. Horiz pair. Nos. 207/8	40	20
208	2½ c. on 3d. yellow, yellow-green & reddish violet (II)	20	10
209	3 c. on 4d. red and blue	15	10
210	4 c. on 5d. blue and black (4.5)	5·50	30
211	5 c. on 6d. red, yellow and green	15	10
212	5 c. on 6d. black, yellow and light blue	5·00	40
213	7 c. on 8d. black and blue	30	10
214	10 c. on 1s. orange-yellow and yellow-green	15	10
215	15 c. on 1s. 6d. bluish violet (R.) (4.5.67)	2·00	1·00
216	30 c. on 3s. black & yellow-green (R.) (4.5.67)	15·00	4·50
217	50 c. on 5s. bistre-brown & blue (R.) (4.5.67)	4·00	1·25
218	$1 and 10s. on 10d. mult (R.) (4.5.67)	15·00	6·50
219	$2 on £1 pink (R.) (6.6.67)	50·00	70·00
220	$6 on £3 green (R.) (6.6.67)	95·00	£110
221	$10 on £5 blue (R.) (6.6.67)	£150	£170
	w. Wmk inverted	£150	£170
205/18	*Set of* 14	42·00	13·00

The two types of the 2½ c. occur on alternate vertical rows within the sheet.

The surcharge on No. 218 is $1 and its equivalent of 10s. in the old currency. The "10d." is obliterated by three bars.

A large number of minor varieties exist in these surcharges, such as wrong fount letter "C" and figures.

75 Village Scene. Cook Islands 1d. Stamp of 1892 and Queen Victoria (from "Penny Black")

(Des V. Whiteley)

1967 (3 July). *75th Anniv of First Cook Islands Stamps. T* **75** *and similar horiz designs. Multicoloured. P* 13½.

No.	Description	Unused	Used
222	1 c. (1d.) Type **75**	10	10
223	3 c. (4d.) Post Office, Avarua, Rarotonga and Queen Elizabeth II	15	10
224	8 c. (10d.) Avarua, Rarotonga and Cook Islands 10d. stamp of 1892	30	10
225	18 c. (1s. 9d.) *Moana Roa* (inter-island ship), Douglas DC-3 aircraft, map and Captain Cook	1·40	25
222/5	*Set of* 4	1·75	40
MS226	134×109 mm. Nos. 222/5	1·75	2·75

The face values are expressed in decimal currency and in the sterling equivalent.

Each value was issued in sheets of 8 stamps and 1 label.

79 Hibiscus

80 Queen Elizabeth II

81 Queen Elizabeth and Flowers

Two types of $4

I. Value 32½ mm long. Coarse screen.
II. Value 33½ mm long. Finer screen.

(Floral designs from paintings by Kay Billings)

1967 (31 July)–**71**. *Multicoloured designs as T* **79/81**. *P* 14×13½.

No.	Description	Unused	Used
	A. *Without fluorescent security markings*		
227A	½ c. Type **79**	10	10
228A	1 c. *Hibiscus syriacus* (27×37 *mm*)	10	10
229A	2 c. Frangipani (27×37 *mm*)	10	10
230A	2½ c. *Clitoria ternatea* (27×37 *mm*)	20	10
231A	3 c. "Suva Queen" (27×37 *mm*)	55	10
232A	4 c. Water Lily ("WALTER LILY") (27×37 *mm*)	70	1·00
233A	4 c. Water Lily (27×37 *mm*)	2·00	2·50
234A	5 c. *Bauhinia bipinnata rosea* (27×37 *mm*)	35	10
235A	6 c. Hibiscus (27×37 *mm*)	40	10
236A	8 c. *Allamanda cathartica* (27×37 *mm*)	40	10
237A	9 c. Stephanotis (27×37 *mm*)	40	10
238A	10 c. *Poinciana regia flamboyant* (27×37 *mm*)	40	10
239A	15 c. Frangipani (27×37 *mm*) (11.8.67)	40	10
240A	20 c. Thunbergia (27×37 *mm*) (11.8.67)	4·50	1·25
241A	25 c. Canna Lily (27×37 *mm*) (11.8.67)	80	30
242A	30 c. *Euphorbia pulcherrima poinsettia* (27×37 *mm*) (11.8.67)	65	50
243A	50 c. *Gardinia taitensis* (27×37 *mm*) (11.8.67)	1·00	55
244A	$1 Type **80** (31.8.67)	2·25	80
245A	$2 Type **80** (31.8.67)	4·75	1·50
246A	$4 Type **81** (I) (30.4.68)	2·00	4·00
247A	$6 Type **81** (30.4.68)	2·50	5·50
247cA	$8 Type **81** (21.4.69)	7·00	14·00
248A	$10 Type **81** (12.7.68)	6·00	12·00
227A/48A	*Set of* 22	32·00	38·00
	B. *With fluorescent security markings*		
227B	½ c. Type **79** (9.2.70)	20	10
228B	1 c. *Hibiscus syriacus* (27×37 *mm*) (9.2.70)	20	10
229B	2 c. Frangipani (27×37 *mm*) (9.2.70)	20	10
230B	2½ c. *Clitoria ternatea* (27×37 *mm*) (9.2.70)	20	10
231B	3 c. "Suva Queen" (27×37 *mm*) (9.2.70)	40	10
233B	4 c. Water Lily (27×37 *mm*) (9.2.70)	2·50	10
234B	5 c. *Bauhinia bipinnata rosea* (27×37 *mm*) (9.2.70)	30	10
235B	6 c. Hibiscus (27×37 *mm*) (9.2.70)	30	10
236B	8 c. *Allamanda cathartica* (27×37 *mm*) (9.2.70)	30	10
237B	9 c. Stephanotis (27×37 *mm*) (9.2.70)	30	10
238B	10 c. *Poinciana regia flamboyant* (27×37 *mm*) (9.2.70)	30	10
239B	15 c. Frangipani (27×37 *mm*) (9.2.70)	40	10
240B	20 c. Thunbergia (27×37 *mm*) (9.2.70)	3·50	75
241B	25 c. Canna Lily (27×37 *mm*) (9.2.70)	1·00	15
242B	30 c. *Euphorbia pulcherrima poinsettia* (27×37 *mm*) (9.2.70)	2·00	40
243B	50 c. *Gardinia taitensis* (27×37 *mm*) (9.2.70)	2·00	40
244B	$1 Type **80** (12.10.70)	1·75	80
245B	$2 Type **80** (12.10.70)	3·50	1·50
246B	$4 Type **81** (I) (11.11.70)	35·00	48·00
	a. Type II (14.7.71)	7·00	8·50
247B	$6 Type **81** (12.2.71)	11·00	6·00
247cB	$8 Type **81** (3.5.71)	15·00	10·00
248B	$10 Type **81** (14.6.71)	17·00	12·00
227B/48B	*Set of* 22	60·00	35·00

The "WALTER" spelling error occurred on all stamps in one of the four post office sheets which went to make up the printing sheet and this was corrected in later supplies.

FLUORESCENT PAPER. This is on paper treated with fluorescent security markings, in the form of faint multiple coats of arms. Stamps exist with these markings inverted. In addition an invisible synthetic gum has been used which prevents curling and is suitable for use in the tropics without interleaving the sheets.

Some of the above are known with these markings omitted and can be distinguished when in unused condition from the original printings without markings by their synthetic invisible gum.

97 "Ia Orana Maria"

1967 (24 Oct). *Gauguin's Polynesian Paintings. T* **97** *and similar designs. Multicoloured. P* 13.

No.	Description	Unused	Used
249	1 c. Type **97**	10	10
250	3 c. "Riders on the Beach"	15	10
251	5 c. "Still Life with Flowers"	20	10
252	8 c. "Whispered Words"	25	10
253	15 c. "Maternity"	50	15
254	22 c. "Why are you angry?"	65	20
249/54	*Set of* 6	1·60	55
MS255	156 × 132 mm. Nos. 249/54	1·75	1·25

The 5 c. includes an inset portrait of Queen Elizabeth.

MINIMUM PRICE

The minimum price quote is 10p which represents a handling charge rather than a basis for valuing common stamps. For further notes about prices see introductory pages.

98 "The Holy Family" (Rubens)

HURRICANE RELIEF PLUS 5c

(99)

1967 (4 Dec). *Christmas. Renaissance Paintings. T* **98** *and simil[illegible] designs. Multicoloured. P* 12 × 13.

No.	Description	Unused	Used
256	1 c. Type **98**	10	[illegible]
257	3 c. "Adoration of the Magi" (Dürer)	10	[illegible]
258	4 c. "The Lucca Madonna" (J. van Eyck)	10	[illegible]
259	8 c. "The Adoration of the Shepherds" (J. da Bassano)	15	[illegible]
260	15 c. "Adoration of the Shepherds" (El Greco)	30	[illegible]
261	25 c. "Madonna and Child" (Correggio)	35	[illegible]
256/61	*Set of* 6	90	[illegible]

1968 (12 Feb). *Hurricane Relief. Nos.* 231A, 233A, 251, 238[illegible] 241A *and* 243/4A *surch as T* **99** *by Govt Printer, Rarotonga.*

No.	Description	Unused	Used
262	3 c. + 1 c. "Suva Queen"	15	[illegible]
263	4 c. + 1 c. Water Lily	15	[illegible]
264	5 c. + 2 c. "Still Life with Flowers"	20	[illegible]
	a. Black surch albino		
265	10 c. + 2 c. *Poinciana regia flamboyant*	20	[illegible]
266	25 c. + 5 c. Canna Lily	25	[illegible]
267	50 c. + 10 c. *Gardinia taitensis*	30	[illegible]
268	$1 + 10 c. Type **80**	50	[illegible]
262/8	*Set of* 7	1·60	[illegible]

The surcharge on No. 268 is as T **99**, but with seriffed letters. O[illegible] No. 264 silver blocking obliterates the design area around th[illegible] lettering.

100 "Matavai Bay, Tahiti" (J. Barralet)

101 "*Resolution* and *Discovery*" (J. Webber)

(Des J. Berry)

1968 (12 Sept). *Bicentenary of Captain Cook's First Voyage [illegible] Discovery. Multicoloured. Invisible gum. P* 13.

No.	Description	Unused	Used
	(*a*) *Postage. Vert designs as T* **100**		
269	½ c. Type **100**	10	[illegible]
270	1 c. "Island of Huaheine" (John Cleveley)	15	[illegible]
271	2 c. "Town of St. Peter and St. Paul, Kamchatka" (J. Webber)	45	[illegible]
272	4 c. "The Ice Islands" (Antarctica: W. Hodges)	60	[illegible]
	(*b*) *Air. Horiz designs as T* **101**		
273	6 c. Type **101**	1·00	[illegible]
274	10 c. "The Island of Tahiti" (W. Hodges)	1·00	[illegible]
275	15 c. "Karakakooa, Hawaii" (J. Webber)	1·25	[illegible]
276	25 c. "The Landing at Middleburg" (J. Sherwin)	1·50	[illegible]
269/76	*Set of* 8	5·50	[illegible]

Each value was issued in sheets of 10 stamps and 2 labels.

FLUORESCENT PAPER. From No. 277, *unless otherwis[illegible] stated*, all issues are printed on paper treated with fluorescen[illegible] security markings with invisible synthetic gum. These marking[illegible] may be inverted or omitted in error.

102 Sailing

103 "Madonna and Child" (Titian)

968 (21 Oct). *Olympic Games, Mexico. T* **102** *and similar horiz designs. Multicoloured. P* 13.
77 1 c. Type **102** 10 10
78 5 c. Gymnastics 10 10
79 15 c. High-jumping 20 10
30 20 c. High-diving 20 10
31 30 c. Cycling 40 20
32 50 c. Hurdling 40 25
77/82 .. .. *Set of* 6 1·10 60
Each value was issued in sheets of 10 stamps and 2 labels.

968 (2 Dec). *Christmas. Paintings. T* **103** *and similar vert designs. Multicoloured. P* 13½.
33 1 c. Type **103** 10 10
84 4 c. "The Holy Family with Lamb" (Raphael) 15 10
85 10 c. "The Virgin of the Rosary" (Murillo) .. 25 10
86 20 c. "Adoration of the Kings" (Memling) .. 40 10
87 30 c. "Adoration of the Magi" (Ghirlandaio) .. 45 10
83/7 .. .. *Set of* 5 1·25 30
IS288 114 × 177 mm. Nos. 283/7 plus label .. 1·60 1·60

104 Camp-fire Cooking

969 (6 Feb). *Diamond Jubilee of New Zealand Scout Movement and Fifth National (New Zealand) Jamboree. T* **104** *and similar square designs. Multicoloured. P* 13½.
39 ½ c. Type **104** 10 10
90 1 c. Descent by rope 10 10
91 5 c. Semaphore 10 10
92 10 c. Tree-planting 15 10
93 20 c. Constructing a shelter 25 10
94 30 c. Lord Baden-Powell and island scene .. 40 15
89/94 .. .. *Set of* 6 90 35
Each value was issued in sheets of 10 stamps and 2 labels.

105 High Jumping

1969 (7 July). *Third South Pacific Games, Port Moresby. T* **105** *and similar triangular designs. Multicoloured. Without fluorescent security markings. P* 13 × 13½.
295 ½ c. Type **105**.. .. .. 10 30
296 ½ c. Footballer 10 30
297 1 c. Basketball 50 40
298 1 c. Weightlifter 50 40
299 4 c. Tennis-player 50 50
300 4 c. Hurdler 50 50
301 10 c. Javelin-thrower.. .. .. 55 50
302 10 c. Runner 55 50
303 15 c. Golfer .. .. 1·75 1·50
304 15 c. Boxer .. .. 1·75 1·50
295/304 .. .. *Set of* 10 6·00 6·00
MS305 174 × 129 mm. Nos. 295/304 plus two labels 6·00 6·00
Each value was issued in sheets containing 5 *se-tenant* pairs of both designs and 2 labels.

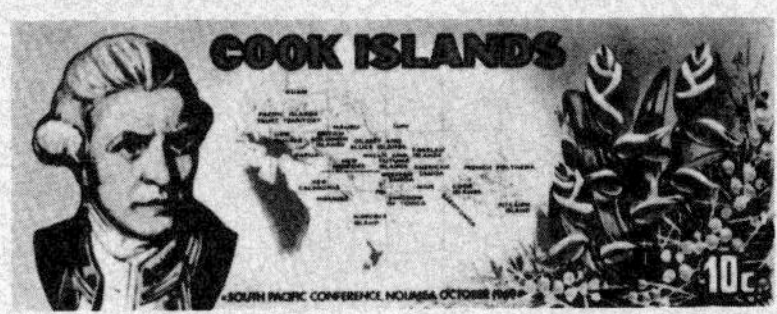

106 Flowers, Map and Captain Cook

1969 (8 Oct). *South Pacific Conference, Nouméa. T* **106** *and similar horiz designs. Multicoloured. Without fluorescent security markings. P* 13.
306 5 c. Flowers, map and Premier Albert Henry 50 20
307 10 c. Type **106** .. .. 1·00 75
308 25 c. Flowers, map and N.Z. arms .. .. 1·00 95
309 30 c. Queen Elizabeth II, map and flowers .. 1·00 1·10
306/9 .. .. *Set of* 4 3·25 2·75

PRICES OF SETS

Set prices are given for many issues, generally those containing three stamps or more. Definitive sets include one of each value or major colour change, but do not cover different perforations, die types or minor shades. Where a choice is possible the set prices are based on the cheapest versions of the stamps included in the listings.

107 "Virgin and Child with Saints Jerome and Dominic" (Lippi) 108 "The Resurrection of Christ" (Raphael)

1969 (21 Nov). *Christmas. Paintings. T* **107** *and similar designs. Multicoloured. Without fluorescent security markings. P* 13.
310 1 c. Type **107** 10 10
311 4 c. "The Holy Family" (Fra Bartolomeo) .. 10 10
312 10 c. "The Adoration of the Shepherds" (A. Mengs) 15 10
313 20 c. "Madonna and Child with Saints" (R. Campin) 25 20
314 30 c. "The Madonna of the Basket" (Correggio) 25 30
310/14 .. .. *Set of* 5 70 60
MS315 132 × 97 mm. Nos. 310/14 .. .. .. 1·50 1·50
Each value was issued in sheets of 9 stamps and 1 label.

1970 (12 Mar). *Easter. Paintings. T* **108** *and similar vert designs showing "The Resurrection of Christ" by the artists named. Multicoloured. P* 13.
316 4 c. Type **108** 10 10
317 8 c. Dirk Bouts 10 10
318 20 c. Altdorfer 15 10
319 25 c. Murillo 20 10
316/19 .. .. *Set of* 4 50 20
MS320 132 × 162 mm. Nos. 316/19 .. .. .. 1·25 1·25
Each value was issued in sheets of 8 stamps and 1 label.

KIA ORANA
APOLLO 13
ASTRONAUTS
Te Atua to
Tatou Irinakianga
(109)

1970 (17–30 Apr). *Apollo* 13. *Nos.* 233, 236, 239/40, 242 *and* 245/6 *optd with T* **109** (4 c. *to* $2) *or with first three lines only in larger type* ($4), *by Govt Printer. Without fluorescent security markings.*
321 4 c. Water Lily 10 10
a. Opt albino .. .. 25·00
322 8 c. *Allamanda cathartica* 10 10
323 15 c. Frangipani 10 10
324 20 c. Thunbergia 15 15
325 30 c. *Euphorbia pulcherrima poinsettia* .. 20 20
326 $2 Type **80** 60 90
327 $4 Type **81** (30.4) .. .. 28·00 45·00
a. With fluorescent security markings .. 1·25 2·75
321/7 .. .. *Set of* 7 2·00 3·75

110 The Royal Family

(Des V. Whiteley (5 c.), J. Berry ($1))

1970 (12 June). *Royal Visit to New Zealand. T* **110** *and similar horiz designs. Multicoloured. P* 13.
328 5 c. Type **110** 65 30
329 30 c. Captain Cook and H.M.S. *Endeavour* .. 2·75 1·75
330 $1 Royal Visit commemorative coin .. 4·00 3·00
328/30 .. .. *Set of* 3 6·75 4·50
MS331 145 × 97 mm. Nos. 328/30 .. .. .. 9·00 9·50
Each value was issued in sheets of 8 stamps and 1 label.

FIFTH ANNIVERSARY
SELF-GOVERNMENT
AUGUST 1970
(113)

FOUR
DOLLARS
$4.00
(114)

1970 (27 Aug). *5th Anniv of Self-Government Nos.* 328/30 *optd with T* **113** (30 c. *and* $1), *or in single line in silver around frame of stamp* (5 c.).
332 5 c. Type **110** 40 15
333 30 c. Captain Cook and H.M.S. *Endeavour* .. 1·25 35
334 $1 Royal Visit commemorative coin .. 2·00 90
332/4 .. .. *Set of* 3 3·25 1·25

1970 (11 Nov). *Nos.* 247c *and* 248 *surch with T* **114** *by Govt Printer, Rarotonga. Without fluorescent security markings.*
335 **81** $4 on $8 multicoloured .. .. .. 35·00 28·00
a. With fluorescent security markings 2·00 2·50
336 $4 on $10 multicoloured .. .. .. 40·00 48·00
a. With fluorescent security markings 1·50 1·50
There are variations in the setting of this surcharge and also in the rule.

115 Mary, Joseph and Christ in Manger

PLUS 20c
UNITED
KINGDOM
SPECIAL
MAIL SERVICE
(116)

(Des from De Lisle Psalter)

1970 (30 Nov). *Christmas. T* **115** *and similar square designs. Multicoloured. P* 13.
337 1 c. Type **115** 10 10
338 4 c. Shepherds and Apparition of the Angel 10 10
339 10 c. Mary showing Child to Joseph 15 10
340 20 c. The Wise Men bearing Gifts 20 10
341 30 c. Parents wrapping Child in swaddling clothes 25 15
337/41 .. .. *Set of* 5 65 35
MS342 100 × 139 mm. Nos. 337/41 plus label .. 90 1·50
Each value was issued in sheets of 5 stamps and 1 label. Stamps from the miniature sheet are smaller, since they do not have the buff parchment border as on the stamps from the sheets.

1971. *Nos.* 242B *and* 243B *surch as T* **116**.
343 30 c. + 20 c. *Euphorbia pulcherrima poinsettia* (25.2) 30 50
344 50 c. + 20 c. *Gardinia taitensis* (8.3) .. .. 1·00 1·75
The premium of 20 c. was to prepay a private delivery service fee in Great Britain during the postal strike. The mail was sent by air to a forwarding address in the Netherlands. No. 343 was intended for ordinary airmail ½ oz letters, and No. 344 included registration fee.
The postal strike ended on 8 March and both stamps were withdrawn on 12 March.

117 Wedding of Princess Elizabeth and Prince Philip

(Des from photographs. Litho Format)

1971 (11 Mar). *Royal Visit of H.R.H. The Duke of Edinburgh. T* **117** *and similar horiz designs. Multicoloured. P* 13½.
345 1 c. Type **117** 20 50
346 4 c. Queen Elizabeth, Prince Philip, Princess Anne and Prince Charles at Windsor .. 60 1·10
347 10 c. Prince Philip sailing .. .. .. 80 1·25
348 15 c. Prince Philip in polo gear .. .. 80 1·25
349 25 c. Prince Philip in naval uniform, and the Royal Yacht *Britannia* .. .. .. 1·50 2·00
345/9 .. .. *Set of* 5 3·50 5·50
MS350 168 × 122 mm. Nos 345/9 plus printed labels in positions 1, 3, 4, and 6 .. .. .. 4·25 8·00
Each value was issued in sheets of 7 stamps and 2 labels.

(118)

(119)

1971 (8 Sept). *Fourth South Pacific Games, Tahiti. Nos.* 238B, 241B *and* 242B *optd with T* **118** *in black, or surch as T* **119** *in blue.*
351 10 c. *Poinciana regia flamboyant* 10 10
352 10 c. + 1 c. *Poinciana regia flamboyant* .. 10 10
353 10 c. + 3 c. *Poinciana regia flamboyant* .. 10 10
354 25 c. Canna Lily 15 10
355 25 c. + 1 c. Canna Lily 15 10
356 25 c. + 3 c. Canna Lily 15 10

357 30 c. *Euphorbia pulcherrima poinsettia* .. 15 10
358 30 c. + 1 c. *Euphorbia pulcherrima poinsettia* 15 10
359 30 c. + 3 c. *Euphorbia pulcherrima poinsettia* 15 10
351/9 .. .. *Set of* 9 1·10 50
The stamps additionally surcharged 1 c. or 3 c. helped to finance the Cook Islands' team at the games.

10c ≡

(120)

121 "Virgin and Child" (Bellini)

1971 (20 Oct). *Nos.* 230B, 233B, 236B/7B *and* 239B *surch with T* **120**.
360 10 c. on 2½ c. *Clitoria ternatea* 15 25
361 10 c. on 4 c. Water Lily 15 25
362 10 c. on 8 c. *Allamanda cathartica* 15 25
a. Surch inverted £140
363 10 c. on 9 c. Stephanotis 15 25
364 10 c. on 15 c. Frangipani 15 25
a. Surch double .. .. 95·00
360/4 .. .. *Set of* 5 65 1·10

1971 (30 Nov). *Christmas. T* **121** *and similar vert designs showing different paintings of the "Virgin and Child", by Bellini. P* 13.
365 1 c. multicoloured 10 10
366 4 c. multicoloured 10 10
367 10 c. multicoloured 25 10
368 20 c. multicoloured 50 10
369 30 c. multicoloured 50 20
365/9 .. .. *Set of* 5 1·25 35
MS370 135 × 147 mm. Nos. 365/9 .. .. 1·75 2·25
MS371 92 × 98 mm. 50 c. + 5 c. "The Holy Family in a Garland of Flowers (Jan Brueghel and Pieter van Avont) (41 × 41 *mm*) .. .. 75 1·40
Each value was issued in sheets of 8 stamps and 1 label.

SOUTH PACIFIC COMMISSION FEB. 1947 - 1972

(122)

123 St. John

1972 (17 Feb). *25th Anniv of South Pacific Commission. No.* 244B *optd with T* **122**.
372 **80** $1 multicoloured 40 75

(Des from De Lisle Psalter)

1972 (6 Mar). *Easter. T* **123** *and similar vert designs. Multicoloured. P* 13.
373 5 c. Type **123** 10 10
374 10 c. Christ on the Cross 10 10
375 30 c. Mary, Mother of Jesus 25 25
373/5 .. .. *Set of* 3 35 35
MS376 79 × 112 mm. Nos. 373/5 forming triptych of "The Crucifixion" .. .. 80 2·25
Stamps from the miniature sheet do not have a border around the perforations, and are therefore smaller than stamps from sheets.

HURRICANE RELIEF PLUS 2c

(124)

Hurricane Relief Plus 5c

(125)

1972 (30 Mar). *Hurricane Relief. Nos.* 373/5 *surch as T* **124**, *and Nos.* 239B, 241B *and* 243B *surch as T* **125**, *by Govt Printer, Rarotonga.*
377 5 c. + 2 c. Type **123** (R.) 10 10
a. Albino surch .. .. 50·00
378 10 c. + 2 c. Christ on the Cross (R.) 15 15
379 15 c. + 5 c. Frangipani 20 20
380 25 c. + 5 c. Canna Lily 20 20
381 30 c. + 5 c. Mary, Mother of Jesus 20 20
a. Albino surch .. ..
382 50 c. + 10 c. *Gardinia taitensis* 25 25
377/82 .. .. *Set of* 6 90 90

126 Rocket heading for Moon **127**

1972 (17 Apr). *Apollo Moon Exploration Flights. T* **126/7** *and similar horiz designs. Multicoloured. P* 13.
383 5 c. Type **126** 20 10
384 5 c. Type **127** 20 10
385 10 c. Lunar module and astronaut 20 10
386 10 c. Astronaut and experiment 20 10
387 25 c. Command capsule and Earth 25 15
388 25 c. Lunar Rover 25 15
389 30 c. Sikorsky S-61B SH-3 Sea King helicopter 45 15
390 30 c. Splashdown 45 15
383/90 .. .. *Set of* 8 2·00 70
MS391 83×205 mm. Nos. 383/90 .. .. 3·50 4·75
These were issued in horizontal *se-tenant* pairs of each value, forming one composite design.

HURRICANE RELIEF Plus 2c

(128)

129 High-jumping

1972 (24 May). *Hurricane Relief. Nos.* 383/91 *surch as T* **128**.
392 5 c. + 2 c. Type **126** 10 10
393 5 c. + 2 c. Type **127** 10 10
394 10 c. + 2 c. Lunar module and astronaut .. 10 10
395 10 c. + 2 c. Astronaut and experiment .. 10 10
396 25 c. + 2 c. Command capsule and Earth 15 15
397 25 c. + 2 c. Lunar Rover 15 15
398 30 c. + 2 c. Sikorsky S-61B SH-3 Sea King helicopter 15 15
399 30 c. + 2 c. Splashdown 15 15
392/9 .. .. *Set of* 8 75 75
MS400 83×205 mm. No. **MS**391 surch 3 c. on each stamp .. .. 2·50 3·50

1972 (26 June). *Olympic Games, Munich. T* **129** *and similar vert designs. Multicoloured. P* 13½.
401 10 c. Type **129** 20 10
402 25 c. Running 40 15
403 30 c. Boxing 40 20
401/3 .. .. *Set of* 3 90 40
MS404 88 × 78 mm. 50 c. + 5 c. Pierre de Coubertin 1·00 2·00
MS405 84 × 133 mm. Nos. 401/3 plus *se-tenant* label 1·25 2·00
Each value was issued in sheets of 8 stamps and 1 label.

130 "The Rest on the Flight into Egypt" (Caravaggio)

131 Marriage Ceremony

1972 (11 Oct). *Christmas T* **130** *and similar vert designs. Multicoloured. P* 13.
406 1 c. Type **130** 10 10
407 5 c. "Madonna of the Swallow" (Guercino) 25 10
408 10 c. "Madonna of the Green Cushion" (Solario) 35 10
409 20 c. "Madonna and Child" (di Credi) .. 55 20
410 30 c. "Madonna and Child" (Bellini) 85 30
406/10 .. .. *Set of* 5 1·90 60
MS411 141 × 152 mm. Nos. 406/10 plus *se-tenant* label in position 1 .. .. 2·75 2·75
MS412 101 × 82 mm. 50 c + 5 c. "The Holy Night" (Correggio) (31 × 43 *mm*) .. .. .. 75 1·50
Each value was issued in sheets of 9 stamps and 1 label.

1972 (20 Nov). *Royal Silver Wedding. T* **131** *and similar black and silver designs. P* 13.
413 5 c. Type **131** 25 15
414 10 c. Leaving Westminster Abbey 35 40
415 15 c. Bride and Bridegroom (40 × 41 *mm*) .. 45 65
416 30 c. Family Group (67 × 40 *mm*) 55 90
413/16 .. .. *Set of* 4 1·40 1·90
The 5, 10 and 15 c. values were each issued in sheets of 8 stamps and 1 label.

132 Taro Leaf

133 "Noli me Tangere" (Titian)

1973 (15 Mar). *Silver Wedding Coinage. T* **132** *and simila designs showing coins. P* 13.
417 1 c. black, rosy carmine and gold 10 1
418 2 c. black, bright blue and gold 10 1
419 5 c. black, green and silver 10 1
420 10 c. black, royal blue and silver 20 1
421 20 c. black, deep blue-green and silver .. 30 1
422 50 c. black, carmine and silver 50 1
423 $1 black, bright blue and silver 75 3
417/23 .. .. *Set of* 7 1·75 5
Designs: *As T* **132**—2 c. Pineapple; 5 c. Hibiscus. 46×30 *m* —10 c. Oranges; 20 c. White Tern; 50 c. Striped Bonito. 32×5 *mm*—$1 Tangaroa.
Each value was issued in sheets of 20 stamps and 1 label.

1973 (9 Apr). *Easter. T* **133** *and similar vert designs. Multi coloured. P* 13.
424 5 c. Type **133** 15 1
425 10 c. "The Descent from the Cross" (Rubens) .. 20 1
426 30 c. "The Lamentation of Christ" (Dürer) .. 25 1
424/6 .. .. *Set of* 3 55 2
MS427 132 × 67 mm. Nos. 424/6 .. .. .. 55 1·2
Each value was issued in sheets of 15 stamps and 1 label.

1973 (30 Apr). *Easter. Children's Charity. Designs as Nos.* 424/ *in separate Miniature Sheets* 67 × 87 *mm, each with a face valu of* 50 *c.* + 5 *c. P* 13 × 14.
MS428 As Nos. 424/6 .. .. *Set of 3 sheets* 90 1·7

134 Queen Elizabeth II in Coronation Regalia

TENTH ANNIVERSARY CESSATION OF NUCLEAR TESTING TREATY

(135)

1973 (1 June). *20th Anniv of Queen Elizabeth's Coronation P* 14 × 13½.
429 **134** 10 c. multicoloured 50 9
MS430 64 × 89 mm. 50 c. as 10 c. P 13 × 14 .. 2·50 2·2
The perforated portion of **MS**430 is similar to No. 429, but has no borders.
No. 429 was issued in sheets of 5 stamps and 1 label.

1973 (25 July). *Tenth Anniv of Treaty Banning Nuclear Testing Nos.* 234B, 236B, 238B, *and* 240B/242B *optd with T* **135**.
431 5 c. *Bauhinia bi-pinnata rosea* 10 10
432 8 c. *Allamanda cathartica* 10 10
433 10 c. *Poinciana regia flamboyant* 10 10
434 20 c. Thunbergia 15 15
435 25 c. Canna Lily 20 15
436 30 c. *Euphorbia pulcherrima poinsettia* .. 20 15
431/6 .. .. *Set of* 6 70 65

136 Tipairua

1973 (17 Sept). *Maori Exploration of the Pacific. T* **136** *and similar horiz designs showing sailing craft. Multicoloured. P* 13.
437 ½ c. Type **136** 10 10
438 1 c. Wa'a Kaulua 10 10
439 1½ c. Tainui 15 10
440 5 c. War canoe 50 15
441 10 c. Pahi 70 15
442 15 c. Amastasi .. .. 1·25 65
443 25 c. Vaka .. .. 1·50 80
437/443 .. .. *Set of* 7 3·75 1·75

137 The Annunciation

138 Princess Anne

1973 (30 Oct). *Christmas. T* **137** *and similar vert designs showing scenes from a 15th-century Flemish "Book of Hours". Multicoloured. P* 13.
444 1 c. Type **137** 10 10
445 5 c. The Visitation 10 10
446 10 c. Annunciation to the Shepherds .. 10 10
447 20 c. Epiphany 15 10
448 30 c. The Slaughter of the Innocents .. 20 15
444/8 .. .. *Set of* 5 40 30
MS449 121 × 128 mm. Nos. 444/8 plus *se-tenant* label .. .. 55 1·40
Each value was issued in sheets of 14 stamps and 1 label.
See also No. **MS**454.

1973 (14 Nov). *Royal Wedding. T* **138** *and similar vert designs. Multicoloured. P* 14 × 13½.
450 25 c. Type **138** 20 10
451 30 c. Capt. Mark Phillips 25 10
452 50 c. Princess Anne and Capt. Phillips .. 30 15
450/2 .. .. *Set of* 3 65 30
MS453 119 × 100 mm. No. 450/2 plus *se-tenant* label. P 13 .. .. 55 35
Each value was issued in sheets of 8 stamps and 1 label.

1973 (3 Dec). *Christmas. Children's Charity. Designs as Nos. 444/8 in separate Miniature Sheets 50 × 70 mm, each with a face value of 50 c. + 5 c.*
MS454 As Nos. 444/8 .. .. *Set of 5 sheets* 75 80

139 Running

140 "Jesus carrying the Cross" (Raphael)

1974 (24 Jan). *Commonwealth Games, Christchurch. T* **139** *and similar multicoloured designs. P* 14 × 13½ (1 *and* 3 c.) *or* 13½ × 14 (*others*).
455 1 c. Diving (*vert*) 10 10
456 3 c. Boxing (*vert*) 10 10
457 5 c. Type **139** 10 10
458 10 c. Weightlifting 10 10
459 30 c. Cycling 20 25
455/9 .. .. *Set of* 5 40 40
MS460 115 × 90 mm. 50 c. Discobolus .. 40 55
Each value was issued in sheets of 15 stamps and 1 label.

1974 (25 Mar). *Easter. T* **140** *and similar vert designs. Multicoloured. P* 13½.
461 5 c. Type **140** 10 10
462 10 c. "The Holy Trinity" (El Greco) .. 15 10
463 30 c. "The Deposition of Christ" (Caravaggio) 25 20
461/3 .. .. *Set of* 3 40 30
MS464 130 × 70 mm. Nos. 461/3 .. .. 1·50 50
Each value was issued in sheets of 20 stamps and 1 label.

1974 (22 Apr). *Easter. Children's Charity. Designs as Nos. 461/3 in separate Miniature Sheets 59 × 87 mm, each with a face value of 50 c. + 5 c.*
MS465 As Nos. 461/3 .. .. *Set of 3 sheets* 70 1·40

141 Grey Bonnet (*Phalium glaucum*)

142 Queen Elizabeth II

1974 (17 May)–75. *Horiz designs as T* **141** *showing sea-shells* (½ *to* 60 *c.*), *T* **142** *or larger horiz design* ($4 *to* $10). *Multicoloured. P* 14×13½ ($4 *to* $10) *or* 13½ (*others*).
466 ½ c. Type **141** 30 10
467 1 c. Common Pacific Vase (*Vasum turbinellum*) 30 10
468 1½ c. True Heart Cockle (*Corculum cardissa*) 30 10
469 2 c. Terebellum Conch (*Terebellum terebellum*) 30 10
470 3 c. Bat Volute (*Cymbiola vespertilio*) .. 45 10
471 4 c. Gibbose Conch (*Strombus gibberulus gibbosus*) 50 10
472 5 c. Common Hairy Triton (*Cymatium pileare*) 50 10
473 6 c. Serpent's-head Cowrie (*Cypraea caputserpentis*) 50 90
474 8 c. Granulate Frog Shell (*Bursa granularis*) 60 10
475 10 c. Fly-spotted Auger (*Terebra areolata*) 60 10
476 15 c. Episcopan Mitre (*Mitra mitra*) .. 70 20
477 20 c. Butterfly Moon (*Natica alapapilionis*) 1·00 20
478 25 c. Royal Oak Scallop (*Cryptopecten pallium*) .. .. 1·00 30
479 30 c. Soldier Cone (*Conus miles*) .. 1·00 30
480 50 c. Textile or Cloth of Gold Cone (*Conus textile*) (26.8.74) .. .. 7·50 4·50
481 60 c. Red-mouth Olive (*Oliva miniacea miniacea*) (26.8.74) .. .. 7·50 4·50
482 $1 Type **142** (26.8.74) .. .. 3·00 4·50
483 $2 Type **142** (27.1.75) .. .. 2·50 2·25
484 $4 Queen Elizabeth II and seashells (17.3.75) .. .. 3·50 5·50
485 $6 As $4 (29.4.75) .. .. 14·00 7·00
486 $8 As $4 (30.5.75) .. .. 15·00 8·50
487 $10 As $4 (30.6.75) .. .. 18·00 9·00
466/87 .. .. *Set of* 22 70·00 42·00
Nos. 484/7 are larger, 60×39 mm.

143 Footballer and Australasian Map

144 Obverse and Reverse of Commemorative $2·50 Silver Coin

1974 (5 July). *World Cup Football Championships, West Germany. T* **143** *and similar horiz designs. Multicoloured. P* 13.
488 25 c. Type **143** 20 10
489 50 c. Map and Munich Stadium .. 35 25
490 $1 Footballer, stadium and World Cup .. 55 45
488/90 .. .. *Set of* 3 1·00 70
MS491 89 × 100 mm. Nos. 488/90 .. 1·00 2·75
Each value was issued in sheets of 8 stamps and 1 label.

1974 (22 July). *Bicentenary of Capt. Cook's Second Voyage of Discovery. T* **144** *and similar vert design. P* 14.
492 $2.50, silver, black and violet .. 13·00 7·00
493 $7.50, silver, black and deep turquoise-green 27·00 13·00
MS494 73 × 73 mm. Nos. 492/3 .. .. 40·00 48·00
Design:—$7.50. As T **144** but showing $7.50 coin.
Each value was issued in sheets of 5 stamps and 1 label.

145 Early Stamps of Cook Islands

146 "Madonna of the Goldfinch" (Raphael)

1974 (16 Sept). *Centenary of Universal Postal Union. T* **145** *and similar horiz designs. Multicoloured. P* 13½ × 14.
495 10 c. Type **145** 20 15
496 25 c. Old landing strip, Rarotonga, and stamp of 1898 .. .. 35 40
497 30 c. Post Office, Rarotonga, and stamp of 1920 40 40
498 50 c. U.P.U. emblem and stamps .. 45 65
495/8 .. .. *Set of* 4 1·25 1·40
MS499 118 × 79 mm. Nos. 495/8. P 13 .. 1·25 1·75
Each value was issued in sheets of 8 stamps and 1 label.

1974 (15 Oct). *Christmas. T* **146** *and similar vert designs. Multicoloured. P* 13.
500 1 c. Type **146** 10 10
501 5 c. "The Sacred Family" (Andrea del Sarto) 20 10
502 10 c. "The Virgin adoring the Child" (Correggio) 25 10
503 20 c. "The Holy Family" (Rembrandt) .. 40 20
504 30 c. "The Virgin and Child" (Rogier Van Der Weyden) 50 30
500/504 .. .. *Set of* 5 1·25 60
MS505 114 × 133 mm. Nos. 500/4 plus *se-tenant* label .. .. 1·75 2·00
Each value was issued in sheets of 15 stamps and 1 label.
See also No. **MS**512.

147 Churchill and Blenheim Palace

1974 (20 Nov). *Birth Centenary of Sir Winston Churchill. T* **147** *and similar horiz designs. Multicoloured. P* 13 × 14.
506 5 c. Type **147** 20 10
507 10 c. Churchill and Houses of Parliament .. 20 10
508 25 c. Churchill and Chartwell .. 30 20
509 30 c. Churchill and Buckingham Palace .. 30 25
510 50 c. Churchill and St. Paul's Cathedral .. 40 50
506/10 .. .. *Set of* 5 1·25 1·00
MS511 108 × 114 mm. Nos. 506/10 plus *se-tenant* label .. .. 2·25 1·25
Each value was issued in sheets of 5 stamps and 1 label.

1974 (9 Dec). *Christmas. Children's Charity. Designs as Nos. 500/504 in separate miniature sheets 53 × 69 mm, each with a face value of 50 c. + 5 c.*
MS512 As Nos. 500/4 .. .. *Set of 5 sheets* 1·25 1·25

148 Vasco Nuñez de Balboa and Discovery of Pacific Ocean (1513).

1975 (3 Feb). *Pacific Explorers. T* **148** *and similar horiz designs. Multicoloured. P* 13.
513 1 c. Type **148** 15 10
514 5 c. Fernando de Magellanes and map (1520) 65 20
515 10 c. Juan Sebastian del Cano and *Vitoria* (1520) .. .. 1·25 20
516 25 c. Friar de Urdaneta and ship (1564–67) 2·25 75
517 30 c. Miguel Lopez de Legazpi and ship (1564–67) .. .. 2·25 80
513/17 .. .. *Set of* 5 6·00 1·90

149 "Apollo" Capsule

1975 (15 July). *"Apollo-Soyuz" Space Project. T* **149** *and similar horiz designs. Multicoloured. P* 13½.
518 25 c. Type **149** 30 15
519 25 c. "Soyuz" capsule 30 15
520 30 c. "Soyuz" crew 35 15
521 30 c. "Apollo" crew 35 15
522 50 c. Cosmonaut within "Soyuz" .. 40 25
523 50 c. Astronauts within "Apollo" .. 40 25
518/23 .. .. *Set of* 6 1·90 1·00
MS524 119 × 119 mm. Nos. 518/23. P 13 × 14 .. 1·75 1·75
Each value was issued in sheets containing 9 horizontal *se-tenant* pairs of the two designs, together with 2 labels.

150 $100 Commemorative Gold Coin

1975 (8 Aug). *Bicentenary of Captain Cook's Second Voyage. P* 13.
525 **150** $2 brown, gold and bluish violet .. 3·75 1·75
No. 525 was issued in sheets of 5 stamps and 1 label.

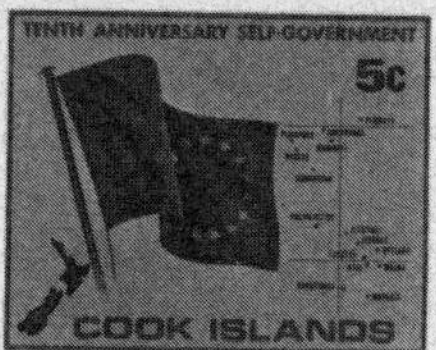

151 Cook Islands' Flag and Map

1975 (8 Aug). *Tenth Anniv of Self-Government. T* **151** *and similar multicoloured designs. P* 13.
526 5 c. Type **151** 40 10
527 10 c. Premier Sir Albert Henry and flag (*vert*) 45 10
528 25 c. Rarotonga and flag 80 30
526/8 . . . . *Set of* 3 1·50 45

152 "Madonna by the Fireside" (R. Campin) **153** "Entombment of Christ" (Raphael)

1975 (1 Dec). *Christmas. T* **152** *and similar vert designs. Multicoloured. P* $13\frac{1}{2}$.
529 6 c. Type **152** 15 10
530 10 c. "Madonna in the Meadow" (Raphael) . . 20 10
531 15 c. "Madonna of the Oak" (attrib Raphael) . . 25 10
532 20 c. "Adoration of the Shepherds" (J. B. Maino) 30 15
533 35 c. "The Annunciation" (Murillo) 45 20
529/33 . . . . *Set of* 5 1·25 45
MS534 110 × 124 mm. Nos. 529/33 . . . . 1·25 90

1975 (15 Dec). *Christmas. Children's Charity. Designs as Nos.* 529/33 *in separate miniature sheets* 53 × 71 *mm, each with a face value of* 75 *c.* + 5 *c.*
MS535 As Nos. 529/33 . . . . *Set of 5 sheets* 1·10 1·25
a. Error. Miniature sheet as No. 531 imperf £250

1976 (29 Mar). *Easter. T* **153** *and similar square designs. Multicoloured. P* 13.
536 7 c. Type **153** 30 10
537 15 c. "Pietà" (Veronese) 50 15
538 35 c. "Pietà" (El Greco) 75 25
536/8 . . . . *Set of* 3 1·40 40
MS539 144 × 57 mm. Nos. 536/8 . . . . 1·50 85
Each value was issued in sheets of 20 stamps and 1 label.

1976 (3 May). *Easter. Children's Charity. Designs as Nos.* 536/8 *in separate miniature sheets* 69 × 69 *mm. each with a face value of* 60 *c.* + 5 *c.*
MS540 As Nos. 536/8 . . . . *Set of 3 sheets* 1·10 1·40

154 Benjamin Franklin and H.M.S. *Resolution*

1976 (29 May). *Bicentenary of American Revolution. T* **154** *and similar horiz designs. Multicoloured. P* 13.
541 $1 Type **154** . . . . 7·50 1·50
542 $2 Captain Cook and H.M.S. *Resolution* . . 9·50 2·50
MS543 118×58 mm. $3 Cook, Franklin and H.M.S. *Resolution* (74×31 *mm*) . . . . . . 17·00 8·00
Each value was issued in sheets of 5 stamps and 1 label.

Royal Visit July 1976

(**155**)

1976 (9 July). *Visit of Queen Elizabeth to the U.S.A. Nos.* 541/3 *optd with T* **155**.
544 $1 Type **154** . . . . 5·00 1·50
545 $2 Captain Cook and H.M.S. *Resolution* . . 7·00 2·50
MS546 $3 Cook, Franklin and H.M.S. *Resolution* 8·00 5·50

156 Hurdling **157** "The Visitation"

1976 (22 July). *Olympic Games, Montreal. T* **156** *and similar square designs. Multicoloured. P* 13.
547 7 c. } Type **156** 20 10
548 7 c. } 20 10
549 15 c. } Hockey 40 15
550 15 c. } 40 15
551 30 c. } Fencing 40 15
552 30 c. } 40 15
553 35 c. } Football 40 20
554 35 c. } 40 20
547/54 . . . . *Set of* 8 2·40 1·10
MS555 104 × 146 mm. Nos. 547/54 . . . . 2·40 2·00
Each value was issued in sheets containing 5 horizontal *se-tenant* pairs and 2 labels. In each pair the first stamp has the face-value on the right, the second has it on the left. Illustrated is the left-hand stamp of the 7 c. design.

1976 (12 Oct). *Christmas. T* **157** *and similar vert designs showing Renaissance sculptures. Multicoloured. P* 14 × $13\frac{1}{2}$.
556 6 c. Type **157** 10 10
557 10 c. "Adoration of the Shepherds" 10 10
558 15 c. "Adoration of the Shepherds" (*different*) 15 10
559 20 c. "The Epiphany" 20 20
560 35 c. "The Holy Family" 25 25
556/60 . . . . *Set of* 5 70 60
MS561 116 × 110 mm. Nos. 556/60. P 13. . . . 85 1·75
Each value was issued in sheets of 20 stamps and 1 label.

1976 (2 Nov.) *Christmas. Children's Charity. Designs as Nos.* 556/60 *in separate miniature sheets* 66 × 80 *mm, each with a face value of* 75 *c.* + 5 *c.*
MS562 As Nos. 556/60 . . . . *Set of 5 sheets* 1·10 1·10

158 Obverse and Reverse of $5 Mangaia Kingfisher Coin

1976 (15 Nov). *National Wildlife and Conservation Day. P* 13.
563 **158** $1 multicoloured . . . . 1·75 1·25
No. 563 was issued in sheets of 5 stamps and 1 label.

159 Imperial State Crown **160** "Christ on the Cross"

1977 (7 Feb). *Silver Jubilee. T* **159** *and similar vert designs. Multicoloured. P* 13.
564 25 c. Type **159** 40 40
565 25 c. Queen with regalia 40 40
566 50 c. Westminster Abbey 50 50
567 50 c. Coronation Coach 50 50
568 $1 Queen and Prince Philip 80 80
569 $1 Royal Visit, 1974 . . . . . . 80 80
564/9 . . . . *Set of* 6 3·00 3·00
MS570 130× 136 mm. As Nos. 564/9 (borders and "COOK ISLANDS" in a different colour) . . . . 2·25 2·00
The two designs of each value are printed horizontally *se-tenant* throughout the sheet, and stamps from **MS**570 have borders and "COOK ISLANDS" in a different colour.

1977 (28 Mar). *Easter and 400th Birth Anniv of Rubens. T* **160** *and similar vert designs. Multicoloured. P* 14 × $13\frac{1}{2}$.
571 7 c. Type **160** 35 10
572 15 c. "Christ on the Cross" 55 15
573 35 c. "The Deposition of Christ" . . . . 1·10 30
571/3 . . . . *Set of* 3 1·75 50
MS574 118 × 65 mm. Nos. 571/3. P 13 . . . . 1·75 1·60
Each value was issued in sheets of 24 stamps and 1 label.

1977 (18 Apr). *Easter. Children's Charity. Designs as Nos.* 571/3 *in separate miniature sheets* 60 × 79 *mm, each with a face value of* 60 *c.* + 5 *c. P* 13 × 14.
MS575 As Nos. 571/3 . . . . *Set of 3 sheets* 1·00 1·00

161 "Virgin and Child" (Memling) **162** Obverse and Reverse of $5 Cook Islands Swiftlet Coin

1977 (3 Oct). *Christmas. T* **161** *and similar vert designs. Multicoloured. P* 14.
576 6 c. Type **161** 20 10
577 10 c. "Madonna and Child with Saints and Donors" (Memling) 20 10
578 15 c. "Adoration of the Kings" (Geertgen) . . 30 10
579 20 c. "Virgin and Child with Saints" (Crivelli) 40 15
580 35 c. "Adoration of the Magi" (16th-cent Flemish School) 50 20
576/80 . . . . *Set of* 5 1·40 50
MS581 118 × 111 mm. Nos. 576/80. P $13\frac{1}{2}$ . . 1·40 1·75
Each value was issued in sheets of 24 stamps and 1 label.

1977 (31 Oct). *Christmas. Children's Charity. Designs as Nos.* 576/80 *in separate miniature sheets* 69 × 69 *mm, each with a face value of* 75 *c.* + 5 *c.*
MS582 As Nos. 576/80 . . . . *Set of 5 sheets* 1·00 1·25

1977 (15 Nov). *National Wildlife and Conservation Day. P* 13.
583 **162** $1 multicoloured . . . . . . 2·00 1·25
No. 583 was issued in sheets containing 10 stamps and 2 labels.

163 Captain Cook and H.M.S. *Resolution* (from paintings by N Dance and H. Roberts)

1978 (20 Jan). *Bicentenary of Discovery of Hawaii. T* **163** *and similar horiz designs. Multicoloured. P* $13\frac{1}{2}$.
584 50 c. Type **163** . . . . 1·50 60
585 $1 Earl of Sandwich, and Cook landing at Owhyhee (from paintings by Thomas Gainsborough and J. Cleveley) . . . . 2·00 1·00
586 $2 Obverse and reverse of $200 coin and Cook monument, Hawaii . . . . 3·25 1·75
584/6 . . . . *Set of* 3 6·00 3·00
MS587 118 × 95 mm. Nos. 584/86 . . . . 7·00 9·00
Each value was issued in sheets of 5 stamps and 1 label.

164 "Pieta" (Van der Weyden) **165** Queen Elizabeth II

1978 (20 Mar). *Easter. Paintings from National Gallery, London. T* **164** *and similar horiz designs. Multicoloured. P* 13.
588 15 c. Type **164** 40 15
589 35 c. "The Entombment" (Michelangelo) . . 50 30
590 75 c. "The Supper at Emmaus" (Caravaggio) 75 55
588/90 . . . . *Set of* 3 1·50 90
MS591 114 × 96 mm. Nos. 588/90 . . . . 1·50 2·00
Each value was issued in sheets of 5 stamps and 1 label.

1978 (10 Apr). *Easter. Children's Charity. Designs as Nos.* 588/90 *in separate miniature sheets,* 85 × 72 *mm, each with a face value of* 60 *c.* + 5 *c. P* $13\frac{1}{2}$.
MS592 As Nos. 588/90 . . . . *Set of 3 sheets* 1·10 1·10

1978 (6 June). *25th Anniv of Coronation. T* **165** *and similar vert designs. Multicoloured. P* 13.
593 50 c. Type **165** 25 30
594 50 c. The Lion of England 25 30
595 50 c. Imperial State Crown 25 30
596 50 c. Statue of Tangaroa (god) 25 30
597 70 c. Type **165** 25 30
598 70 c. Sceptre with Cross 25 30
599 70 c. St. Edward's Crown 25 30
600 70 c. Rarotongan staff god 25 30
593/600 . . . . *Set of* 8 1·75 2·00
MS601 103 × 142 mm. Nos. 593/600*. . . . 1·00 1·50
Each value was issued in sheets containing the 4 designs and 2 labels.
* In No **MS**601 the designs of Nos. 595 and 599 are transposed.

5c ═

(**166**)

1978 (10 Nov). *Nos.* 466, 468, 473/4 *and* 478/81 *surch as T* **166**.
602 5 c. on $1\frac{1}{2}$ c. True Heart Cockle (*Corculum cardissa*) (Silver) 40 10
603 7 c. on $\frac{1}{2}$ c. Type **141** 45 15
604 10 c. on 6 c. Serpent's-head Cowrie (*Cypraea caputserpentis*) (Gold) 50 15
605 10 c. on 8 c. Granulate Frog Shell (*Bursa granularis*) (Gold) 50 15
606 15 c. on $\frac{1}{2}$ c. Type **141** 50 20
607 15 c. on 25 c. Royal Oak Scallop (*Cryptopecten pallium*) (Silver) 50 20
608 15 c. on 30 c. Soldier Cone (*Conus miles*) . . 50 20

9 15 c. on 50 c. Textile or Cloth of Gold Cone (*Conus textile*) (Silver) 50 20
0 15 c. on 60 c. Red-mouth Olive (*Oliva miniacea miniacea*) (Gold) 50 20
1 17 c. on ½ c. Type **141** 80 25
2 17 c. on 50 c. Textile or Cloth of Gold Cone (*Conus textile*) (Silver) 80 25
2/12 .. .. *Set of* 11 5·50 1·75

1728 · 250th ANNIVERSARY OF COOK'S BIRTH · 1978

(167)

978 (13 Nov). 250*th Birth Anniv of Captain Cook. Nos.* 584/7 *optd with T* **167** *on silver.*
3 50 c. Type **163** .. .. 2·00 75
4 $1 Earl of Sandwich, and Cook landing at Owhyhee (from paintings by Thomas Gainsborough and J. Cleveley) .. .. .. 2·25 1·00
5 $2 Obverse and reverse of $200 coin and Cook monument, Hawaii .. .. .. 2·50 2·00
13/15 .. .. *Set of* 3 6·00 3·25
S616 Nos. 613/15 .. .. 17·00 17·00

168 Obverse and Reverse of $5 Pitcairn Warblers Coin

978 (15 Nov). *National Wildlife and Conservation Day. P* 13.
17 **168** $1 multicoloured .. .. 1·60 1·00

169 "The Virgin and Child" (Van der Weyden)

170 Virgin with Body of Christ

1978 (8 Dec). *Christmas. Paintings. T* **169** *and similar vert designs. Multicoloured. P* 13.
618 15 c. Type **169** 35 10
619 17 c. "The Virgin and Child" (Crivelli) .. 35 15
620 35 c. "The Virgin and Child" (Murillo) .. 65 30
618/20 .. .. *Set of* 3 1·25 50
MS621 107 x 70 mm. Nos. 618/20 .. .. .. 1·50 1·50

1979 (12 Jan). *Christmas. Children's Charity. Designs as Nos.* 618/20 *in separate miniature sheets 57 x 87 mm. each with a face value of* 75 *c.* + 5 *c. P* 13½
MS622 As Nos. 618/20 .. .. *Set of 3 sheets* 1·00 1·00

1979 (5 Apr). *Easter. Details of Painting "Descent" by Gaspar de Crayar. T* **170** *and similar vert designs. Multicoloured. P* 13.
623 10 c. Type **170** 25 10
624 12 c. St. John 30 20
625 15 c. Mary Magdalene 35 25
626 20 c. Weeping angels 45 30
623/6 .. .. *Set of* 4 1·25 75
MS627 83 × 100 mm. As Nos. 623/6, but each with charity premium of 2 c. 65 75
Stamps from No. **MS**627 are slightly smaller, 32 × 40 mm, and are without borders.

171 "Captain Cook" (James Weber)

172 Post-Rider

1979 (23 July). *Death Bicentenary of Captain Cook. T* **171** *and similar vert designs. Multicoloured. P* 14 × 13.
628 20 c. Type **171** 40 20
629 30 c. H.M.S. *Resolution* 70 35
630 35 c. H.M.S. *Royal George* (ship of the line) 70 45
631 50 c. "Death of Captain Cook" (George Carter) 70 60
628/31 .. .. *Set of* 4 2·25 1·40
MS632 78×112 mm. Nos. 628/31 .. .. 1·75 1·25
Stamps from No. **MS**632 have black borders.

1979 (10 Sept). *Death Centenary of Sir Rowland Hill. History of Mail Transport. T* **172** *and similar square designs. Multicoloured. P* 14.
633 30 c. Type **172** 25 20
634 30 c. Mail coach 25 20
635 30 c. Automobile 25 20
636 30 c. Diesel train 25 20
637 35 c. *Cap-Hornier* (full-rigged ship) .. 30 20
638 35 c. River steamer 30 20
639 35 c. *Deutschland* (liner) 30 20
640 35 c. *United States* (liner) 30 20
641 50 c. Balloon *Le Neptune* 40 25
642 50 c. Junkers F13 airplane 40 25
643 50 c. Airship LZ-127 *Graf Zeppelin* .. 40 25
644 50 c. Concorde 40 25
633/44 .. .. *Set of* 12 3·50 2·40
MS645 132×104 mm. Nos. 633/44 .. .. 3·50 5·50
Nos. 633/6, 637/40 and 641/4 were each printed together, *se-tenant*, in blocks of 4 throughout the sheets.

6c 

(173)

1979 (12 Sept). *Nos.* 466, 468 *and* 481 *surch as T* **173**.
646 6 c. on ½ c. Type **141** (Gold) 20 30
647 10 c. on 1½ c. Cockle shell (Silver) .. 25 20
a. Surch inverted .. .. 90·00
648 15 c. on 60 c. Olive shell (Gold) 40 40
646/8 .. .. *Set of* 3 75 80

174 Brother and Sister

175 "Apollo 11" Emblem

1979 (10 Oct). *International Year of the Child. T* **174** *and similar horiz designs. Multicoloured. P* 13.
649 30 c. Type **174** 25 25
650 50 c. Boy with tree drum 40 40
651 65 c. Children dancing 50 50
649/51 .. .. *Set of* 3 1·00 1·00
MS652 102 × 75 mm. As Nos. 649/51, but each with charity premium of 5 c. P 13½ × 13 .. .. 1·00 1·50
Designs for stamps from No. **MS**652 are as Nos. 649/51 but have I.Y.C. emblem in red.

1979 (7 Nov). 10*th Anniv of Moon Landing. T* **175** *and similar vert designs. Multicoloured. P* 14.
653 30 c. Type **175** 40 50
654 50 c. Crew of "Apollo 11" 50 70
655 60 c. Astronaut on Moon 65 75
656 65 c. Command module after splashdown .. 70 85
653/6 .. .. *Set of* 4 2·00 2·50
MS657 119 × 105 mm. Nos. 653/6. P 13½ .. 2·50 2·50

176 Obverse and Reverse of $5 Rarotongan Fruit Dove Coin

177 Glass Christmas Tree Ornaments

1979 (15 Nov). *National Wildlife and Conservation Day. P* 13 × 14.
658 **176** $1 multicoloured .. .. 1·60 2·50

1979 (14 Dec). *Christmas. T* **177** *and similar vert designs. Multicoloured. P* 13½. (a) *Postage.*
659 6 c. Type **177** 10 10
660 10 c. Hibiscus flower and star 10 10
661 12 c. Poinsettia flower, bells and candle .. 15 10
662 15 c. Poinsettia leaves and Tiki (god) 15 15

(*b*) *Air*
663 20 c. Type **177** 20 15
664 25 c. As 10 c. 25 20
665 30 c. As 12 c. 30 25
666 35 c. As 15 c. 35 30
659/66 .. .. *Set of* 8 1·40 1·10

1980 (15 Jan). *Christmas. Children's Charity. Designs as Nos.* 659/66 *with additional premiums. (a) Postage.*
667 6 c. + 2 c. Type **177** 10 10
668 10 c. + 2 c. Hibiscus flower and star 15 15
669 12 c. + 2 c. Poinsettia flower, bells and candle 15 20
670 15 c. + 2 c. Poinsettia leaves and Tiki (god) 15 20

(*b*) *Air*
671 20 c. + 4 c. Type **177** 15 25
672 25 c. + 4 c. As 10 c. 15 25
673 30 c. + 4 c. As 12 c. 20 30
674 35 c. + 4 c. As 15 c. 25 35
667/74 .. .. *Set of* 8 1·00 1·60

178 "Flagellation"

179 Dove with Olive Twig

1980 (31 Mar). *Easter. Illustrations by Gustave Doré. T* **178** *and similar vert designs in sepia and gold. P* 13.
675 20 c. Type **178** 25 20
676 20 c. "Crown of Thorns" 25 20
677 30 c. "Jesus Insulted" 35 30
678 30 c. "Jesus Falls" 35 30
679 35 c. "The Crucifixion" 40 30
680 35 c. "The Descent from the Cross" 40 30
675/80 .. .. *Set of* 6 1·75 1·40
MS681 120 × 110 mm. As Nos. 675/80, but each with charity premium of 2 c. .. .. .. 1·10 1·50
Nos. 675/6, 677/8 and 679/80 were each printed together, *se-tenant*, in vertical pairs throughout the sheet.

1980 (23 Apr). *Easter. Children's Charity. Designs as Nos.* 675/80 *in separate miniature sheets* 60 × 71 *mm, each with a face value of* 75 *c.* + 5 *c. P* 13.
MS682 As Nos. 675/80 .. .. *Set of* 6 *sheets* 90 1·50

1980 (27 May). 75*th Anniv of Rotary International. T* **179** *and similar horiz designs. Multicoloured. P* 14.
683 30 c. Type **179** 35 35
684 35 c. Hibiscus flower 40 40
685 50 c. Ribbons 50 50
683/5 .. .. *Set of* 3 1·10 1·10
MS686 72 × 113 mm. Nos. 683/5 but each with premium of 3 c. P 13½ .. .. 1·10 1·50

ZEAPEX STAMP EXHIBITION–AUCKLAND 1980

(180)

181 Queen Elizabeth the Queen Mother

1980 (22 Aug). *"Zeapex 80" International Stamp Exhibition, Auckland. Nos.* 633/45 *optd with T* **180** *in black on silver background.*
687 30 c. Type **172** 30 25
688 30 c. Mail coach 30 25
689 30 c. Automobile 30 25
690 30 c. Diesel train 30 25
691 35 c. *Cap-Hornier* (full-rigged ship) .. 35 30
692 35 c. River steamer 35 30
693 35 c. *Deutschland* (liner) 35 30
694 35 c. *United States* (liner) 35 30
695 50 c. Balloon *Le Neptune* 50 35
696 50 c. Junkers F13 airplane 50 35
697 50 c. Airship LZ-127 *Graf Zeppelin* .. 50 35
698 50 c. Concorde 50 35
687/98 .. .. *Set of* 12 4·25 3·25
MS699 132×104 mm. Nos. 687/98 .. .. 6·00 6·00

1980 (22 Aug). *"Zeapex 80" International Stamp Exhibition, Auckland. As No.* **MS**681 *but containing stamps without charity premium of* 2 *c. optd "Zeapex '80 Auckland + 10 c" in black on gold background.*
MS700 120 × 110 mm. Nos. 675/80 (*sold at* $1.80) 80 1·75
Stamps from No. **MS**700 are unaffected by the overprint which appears on the sheet margin.

1980 (23 Sept). 80*th Birthday of Queen Elizabeth the Queen Mother. P* 13.
701 **181** 50 c. multicoloured 80 90
MS702 64× 78 mm. **181** $2 multicoloured .. 1·25 1·75

182 Satellites orbiting Moon

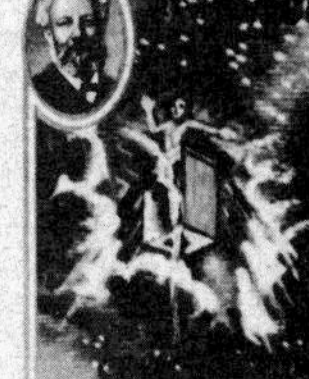

183 Scene from novel *From the Earth to the Moon*

1980 (7 Nov). *350th Death Anniv of Johannes Kepler (astronomer). T* **182** *and similar horiz designs. Multicoloured. P* 13.

703 12 c. Type **182** 50 35
704 12 c. Space-craft orbiting Moon 50 35
705 50 c. Space-craft orbiting Moon (*different*) 1·00 80
706 50 c. Astronaut and Moon vehicle 1·00 80
703/6 *Set of* 4 2·75 2·10
MS707 122 × 122 mm. Nos. 703/6 2·75 2·75

Nos. 703/4 and 705/6 were each printed together, *se-tenant*, in horizontal pairs throughout the sheet.

1980 (7 Nov). *75th Death Anniv of Jules Verne (author). T* **183** *and similar vert designs showing scenes from the novel "From the Earth to the Moon". P* 13.

708 20 c. multicoloured (green background) 45 35
709 20 c. multicoloured (brown background) 45 35
710 30 c. multicoloured (mauve background) 55 45
711 30 c. multicoloured (blue background) 55 45
708/11 *Set of* 4 1·75 1·40
MS712 121 × 122 mm. Nos. 708/11 2·00 2·00

Nos. 708/9 and 710/11 were each printed together, *se-tenant*, in horizontal pairs throughout the sheet.

184 *Siphonogorgia*

185 Annunciation

1980 (21 Nov)–**82**. *Corals* (1*st series*). *Multicoloured designs as T* 184. *P* 13 (1 *c. to* $1) *or* 14 × 13½ ($2 *to* $10).

713 1 c. Type **184** 20 20
714 1 c. *Pavona praetorta* 20 20
715 1 c. *Stylaster echinatus* 20 20
716 1 c. *Tubastraea* 20 20
717 3 c. *Millepora alcicornis* 25 20
718 3 c. *Junceella gemmacea* 25 20
719 3 c. *Fungia fungites* 25 20
720 3 c. *Heliofungia actiniformis* 25 20
721 4 c. *Distichopora violacea* 25 20
722 4 c. *Stylaster* 25 20
723 4 c. *Gonipora* 25 20
724 4 c. *Caulastraea echinulata* 25 20
725 5 c. *Ptilosarcus gurneyi* 25 20
726 5 c. *Stylophora pistillata* 25 20
727 5 c. *Melithaea squamata* 25 20
728 5 c. *Porites andrewsi* 25 20
729 6 c. *Lobophyllia bemprichii* 25 20
730 6 c. *Palauastrea ramosa* 25 20
731 6 c. *Bellonella indica* 25 20
732 6 c. *Pectinia alcicornis* 25 20
733 8 c. *Sarcophyton digitatum* 25 20
734 8 c. *Melithaea albitincta* 25 20
735 8 c. *Plerogyra sinuosa* 25 20
736 8 c. *Dendrophyllia gracilis* 25 20
737 10 c. Type **184** (19.12.80) 30 20
738 10 c. As No. 714 (19.12.80) 30 20
739 10 c. As No. 715 (19.12.80) 30 20
740 10 c. As No. 716 (19.12.80) 30 20
741 12 c. As No. 717 (19.12.80) 30 20
742 12 c. As No. 718 (19.12.80) 30 20
743 12 c. As No. 719 (19.12.80) 30 20
744 12 c. As No. 720 (19.12.80) 30 20
745 15 c. As No. 721 (19.12.80) 30 20
746 15 c. As No. 722 (19.12.80) 30 20
747 15 c. As No. 723 (19.12.80) 30 20
748 15 c. As No. 724 (19.12.80) 30 20
749 20 c. As No. 725 (19.12.80) 35 30
750 20 c. As No. 726 (19.12.80) 35 30
751 20 c. As No. 727 (19.12.80) 35 30
752 20 c. As No. 728 (19.12.80) 35 30
753 25 c. As No. 729 (19.12.80) 35 30
754 25 c. As No. 730 (19.12.80) 35 30
755 25 c. As No. 731 (19.12.80) 35 30
756 25 c. As No. 732 (19.12.80) 35 30
757 30 c. As No. 733 (19.12.80) 40 30
758 30 c. As No. 734 (19.12.80) 40 30
759 30 c. As No. 735 (19.12.80) 40 30
760 30 c. As No. 736 (19.12.80) 40 30
761 35 c. Type **184** (16.3.81) 45 35
762 35 c. As No. 714 (16.3.81) 45 35
763 35 c. As No. 715 (16.3.81) 45 35
764 35 c. As No. 716 (16.3.81) 45 35
765 50 c. As No. 717 (16.3.81) 65 75
766 50 c. As No. 718 (16.3.81) 65 75
767 50 c. As No. 719 (16.3.81) 65 75
768 50 c. As No. 720 (16.3.81) 65 75
769 60 c. As No. 721 (16.3.81) 75 75
770 60 c. As No. 722 (16.3.81) 75 75
771 60 c. As No. 723 (16.3.81) 75 75
772 60 c. As No. 724 (16.3.81) 75 75
773 70 c. As No. 725 (13.4.81) 2·50 75
774 70 c. As No. 726 (13.4.81) 2·50 75
775 70 c. As No. 727 (13.4.81) 2·50 75
776 70 c. As No. 728 (13.4.81) 2·50 75
777 80 c. As No. 729 (13.4.81) 2·50 80
778 80 c. As No. 730 (13.4.81) 2·50 80
779 80 c. As No. 731 (13.4.81) 2·50 80
780 80 c. As No. 732 (13.4.81) 2·50 80
781 $1 As No. 733 (20.5.81) 3·75 1·00
782 $1 As No. 734 (20.5.81) 3·75 1·00
783 $1 As No. 735 (20.5.81) 3·75 1·00
784 $1 As No. 736 (20.5.81) 3·75 1·00
785 $2 As No. 723 (27.11.81) 12·00 3·00
786 $3 As No. 720 (27.11.81) 12·00 3·00
787 $4 As No. 726 (11.1.82) 4·50 10·00
788 $6 As No. 715 (11.1.82) 6·00 13·00
789 $10 As No. 734 (5.3.82) 27·00 32·00
713/89 *Set of* 77 £100 80·00

Nos. 761/84 are 30 × 40 mm and Nos. 785/9, which include a portrait of Queen Elizabeth II in each design, are 55 × 35 mm in size.

The four designs of each value to the $1 were printed together, *se-tenant*, in horizontal strips of 4 (Nos. 713/60) or in blocks of 4 (Nos. 761/84) throughout the sheet.

For similar designs with redrawn frames and inscriptions see Nos. 966/94.

1980 (1 Dec). *Christmas. Illustrations from* 13*th-century French Prayer Book. T* **185** *and similar vert designs. Multicoloured. P* 14 × 13½.

801 15 c. Type **185** 25 15
802 30 c. Visitation 35 25
803 40 c. Nativity 45 30
804 50 c. Epiphany 60 40
801/4 *Set of* 4 1·50 1·00
MS805 89 × 114 mm. Nos. 801/4. P 13½ 1·50 1·50

1981 (9 Jan). *Christmas. Children's Charity. Designs as Nos.* 801/4 *in separate miniature sheets* 55 × 68 *mm, each with a face value of* 75 *c.* + 5 *c. Imperf.*

MS806 As Nos. 801/4 *Set of 4 sheets* 1·50 1·50

186 "The Crucifixion" (from book of Saint-Amand)

187 Prince Charles

1981 (10 Apr). *Easter. Illustrations from* 12*th-century French Prayer Books. T* **186** *and similar horiz designs. Multicoloured. P* 13½ × 14.

807 15 c. Type **186** 20 20
808 25 c. "Placing in Tomb" (from book of Ingeburge) 30 30
809 40 c. "Mourning at the Sepulchre" (from book of Ingeburge) 40 40
807/9 *Set of* 3 80 80
MS810 72 × 116 mm. As Nos. 807/9 but each with charity premium of 2 c. P 13½ 90 90

1981 (28 Apr). *Easter. Children's Charity. Designs as Nos.* 807/9 *in separate miniature sheets* 64 × 53 *mm, each with a face value of* 75 *c.* +5 *c. Imperf.*

MS811 As Nos. 807/9 *Set of 3 sheets* 1·10 1·10

1981 (29 July). *Royal Wedding. T* **187** *and similar vert design. Multicoloured. P* 14.

812 $1 Type **187** 50 1·10
813 $2 Prince Charles and Lady Diana Spencer 60 1·40
MS814 106 × 59 mm. Nos. 812/13. P 13½ 1·40 2·50

Nos. 812/13 were each printed in small sheets of 4.

188 Footballers

+
5
c

(**189**)

1981 (20 Oct). *World Cup Football Championship, Spain* (1982). *T* **188** *and similar horiz designs showing footballers. Multicoloured. P* 13½ × 14.

815 20 c. Type **188** 40 20
816 20 c. Figures to right of stamp 40 20
817 30 c. Figures to left 50 30
818 30 c. Figures to right 50 30
819 35 c. Figures to left 50 35
820 35 c. Figures to right 50 35
821 50 c. Figures to left 65 45
822 50 c. Figures to right 65 45
815/22 *Set of* 8 3·75 2·40
MS823 180 × 94 mm. As Nos. 815/22, but each stamp with a charity premium of 3 c. P 13½ 4·50 6·00

The two designs of each value were printed together, *se-tenant*, in horizontal pairs throughout the sheet, forming composite designs.

1981 (10 Nov). *International Year for Disabled Persons. Nos.* 812/14 *surch as T* **189**.

824 $1 + 5 c. Type **187** 1·00 2·00
825 $2 + 5 c. Prince Charles and Lady Diana Spencer 1·40 3·00
MS826 106 × 59 mm. $1 + 10 c., $2 + 10 c. As Nos. 824/5 2·00 4·00

Nos. 824/6 have commemorative inscriptions overprinted on the sheet margins.

190 "Holy Virgin with Child"

191 Princess of Wales (inscr "21st Birthday")

1981 (14 Dec). *Christmas. Details from Paintings by Ruben[s]. T* **190** *and similar vert designs. Multicoloured. P* 14 × 13½.

827 8 c. Type **190** 55 2
828 15 c. "Coronation of St. Catherine" 65 3
829 40 c. "Adoration of the Shepherds" 90 8
830 50 c. "Adoration of the Magi" 1·00 1·0
827/30 *Set of* 4 2·75 2·0
MS831 86 × 110 mm. As Nos. 827/30, but each with a charity premium of 3 c. P 13½ 3·00 3·5

1982 (18 Jan). *Christmas. Children's Charity. Designs as Nos* 827/30 *in separate miniature sheets* 62 × 78 *mm, each with a fac[e] value of* 75 *c.* + 5 *c.*

MS832 As Nos. 827/30 *Set of 4 sheets* 3·50 4·0

1982 (21 June). 21*st Birthday of Princess of Wales. T* **191** *an[d] similar horiz designs. Multicoloured. P* 14.

833 $1.25, Type **191** 1·75 1·5
a. Pair. Nos. 833/4 3·50 3·0
834 $1.25, As Type **191**, but inscr "1 July 1982" 1·75 1·5
835 $2.50, Princess (*different*) (inscr "21st Birthday") 2·50 2·2
a. Pair. Nos. 835/6 5·00 4·5
836 $2·50, As No. 835, but inscr "1 July 1982" 2·50 2·2
833/6 *Set of* 4 7·50 6·5
MS837 92 × 72 mm. $1.25, Type **191**; $2.50, As No. 835. Both inscribed "21st Birthday 1 July 1982". P 13½ 4·50 3·7

The two designs for each value were printed together, *se-tenant* in small sheets of 4.

ROYAL BIRTH · 21 JUNE 1982

(**192**)

1982 (12 July). *Birth of Prince William of Wales* (1*st issue*). *No[s]* 812/14 *optd as T* **192**.

838 $1 Type **187** (optd with T **192**) 1·50 1·2
a. Pair. Nos. 838/9 3·00 2·5
839 $1 Type **187** (optd "PRINCE WILLIAM OF WALES") 1·50 1·2
840 $2 Prince Charles and Lady Diana Spencer (optd with T **192**) 2·50 2·0
a. Pair. Nos. 840/1 5·00 4·0
841 $2 Prince Charles and Lady Diana Spencer (optd. "PRINCE WILLIAM OF WALES") 2·50 2·0
838/41 *Set of* 4 7·00 6·0
MS842 106 × 59mm. Nos. 812/13 optd "21 JUNE 1982. ROYAL BIRTH" 4·50 4·5

1982 (3 Aug). *Birth of Prince William of Wales* (2*nd issue*) *Designs as Nos.* 833/7 *but with changed inscriptions. Multi[-]coloured. P*14.

843 $1.25, As Type **191** (inscr "Royal Birth") 1·40 1·0
a. Pair. Nos. 843/4 2·75 2·0
844 $1.25, As Type **191** (inscr "21 June 1982") 1·40 1·0
845 $2.50, As No. 835 (inscr "Royal Birth") 2·00 1·5
a. Pair. Nos. 845/6 4·00 3·0
846 $2.50, As No. 835 (inscr "21 June 1982") 2·00 1·5
843/6 *Set of* 4 6·00 4·5
MS847 92 × 73 mm. $1.25, As Type **191**; $2.50, As No. 835. Both inscribed "Royal Birth 21 June 1982". P 13½ 4·00 2·75

193 "The Accordionist" (inscr "Serenade")

194 Franklin D. Roosevelt

(Litho Format)

1982 (10 Sept). *Norman Rockwell (painter) Commemoration. T* **193** *and similar vert designs. Multicoloured. P* 13½ × 14.

848 5 c. Type **193** 15 10
849 10 c. "Spring" (inscr "The Hikers") 20 15
850 20 c. "The Doctor and the Doll" 25 25
851 30 c. "Home from Camp" 25 30
848/51 *Set of* 4 75 70

982 (30 Sept). *Air. American Anniversaries. T* **194** *and similar vert designs. Multicoloured. P* 14.
52 60 c. Type **194** .. .. 1·50 80
53 80 c. Benjamin Franklin .. .. 1·75 1·00
54 $1.40, George Washington .. .. 2·00 1·50
52/4 .. .. *Set of* 3 4·75 3·00
IS855 116 × 60 mm. Nos. 852/4. P 13½ .. .. 4·75 3·00
Anniversaries:—60 c. Roosevelt birth centenary; 80 c. "Articles f Peace" negotiations bicentenary; $1.40, Washington 250th birth nniv.

195 "Virgin with Garlands" (detail) (Rubens) and Princess Diana with Prince William

196 Princess Diana and Prince William

982 (30 Nov). *Christmas. T* **195** *and similar horiz designs depicting different details from Rubens' painting "Virgin with Garlands". P* 13½ × 14.
56 35 c. multicoloured 95 60
57 48 c. multicoloured .. .. 1·50 1·00
58 60 c. multicoloured .. .. 1·75 1·75
59 $1.70, multicoloured .. .. 2·50 3·25
56/9 .. .. *Set of* 4 6·00 6·00
MS860 104 × 83 mm. 60 c × 4. Designs, each 27 × 32 mm, forming complete painting "Virgin with Garlands". P 13 × 13½ .. .. 4·50 5·00

1982 (30 Nov). *Christmas. Birth of Prince William of Wales. Children's Charity. Sheet* 73 × 59 *mm. P* 13.
MS861 **196** 75 c. + 5 c. multicoloured .. .. 2·00 2·75
No. **MS**861 comes with 4 different background designs showing details from painting "Virgin with Garlands" (Rubens).

197 Statue of Tangaroa

198 Scouts using Map and Compass

1983 (14 Mar). *Commonwealth Day. T* **197** *and similar vert designs. Multicoloured. P* 14 × 13½.
862 60 c. Type **197** 55 60
863 60 c. Rarotonga oranges 55 60
864 60 c. Rarotonga Airport 55 60
865 60 c. Prime Minister Sir Thomas Davis .. 55 60
862/5 .. .. *Set of* 4 2·00 2·10
Nos. 862/5 were issued together, *se-tenant*, in blocks of four throughout the sheet.

1983 (5 Apr). *75th Anniv of Boy Scout Movement and 125th Birth Anniv of Lord Baden-Powell. T* **198** *and similar vert designs. Multicoloured. P* 13.
866 12 c. Type **198** 60 20
867 12 c. Hiking 60 20
868 36 c. Campfire cooking 90 40
869 36 c. Erecting tent 90 40
870 48 c. Hauling on rope .. .. 1·10 55
871 48 c. Using bos'n's chair .. .. 1·10 55
872 60 c. Digging hole for sapling .. .. .. 1·25 70
873 60 c. Planting sapling .. .. 1·25 70
866/73 .. .. *Set of* 8 7·00 3·25
MS874 161 × 132 mm. As Nos. 866/73, but each with a premium of 2 c. .. .. 4·50 5·50
The two designs of each value were printed together, *se-tenant*, in horizontal pairs throughout the sheets.

XV WORLD JAMBOREE

(199)

1983 (4 July). *15th World Scout Jamboree, Alberta, Canada. Nos.* 866/74 *optd with T* **199** *(Nos.* 875, 877, 879, 881*) or with* "ALBERTA, CANADA 1983" *(others)*.
875 12 c. Type **198** 55 20
876 12 c. Hiking 55 20
877 36 c. Campfire cooking 80 40
878 36 c. Erecting tent 80 40
879 48 c. Hauling on rope 95 55
880 48 c. Using bos'n's chair 95 55
881 60 c. Digging hole for sapling .. .. .. 1·10 70
882 60 c. Planting sapling .. .. 1·10 70
875/82 .. .. *Set of* 8 6·00 3·25
MS883 161 × 132 mm. As Nos. 875/82, but each with a premium of 2 c. .. .. 2·75 3·25
The two designs of each value were printed together, *se-tenant*, in horizontal pairs throughout the sheet. In each such pair the left-hand design is overprinted with Type **199** and the right-hand with "ALBERTA, CANADA 1983".

18c (200) **$5.60** (201)

1983 (12–30 Aug). *Various stamps surch. (a) Nos.* 733/6, 745/8, 753/64 *and* 773/6 *as T* **200**.
884 18 c. on 8 c. multicoloured (No. 733) 75 50
885 18 c. on 8 c. multicoloured (No. 734) 75 50
886 18 c. on 8 c. multicoloured (No. 735) 75 50
887 18 c. on 8 c. multicoloured (No. 736) 75 50
888 36 c. on 15 c. multicoloured (No. 745) .. .. 1·25 85
889 36 c. on 15 c. multicoloured (No. 746) .. .. 1·25 85
890 36 c. on 15 c. multicoloured (No. 747) .. .. 1·25 85
891 36 c. on 15 c. multicoloured (No. 748) .. .. 1·25 85
892 36 c. on 30 c. multicoloured (No. 757) .. .. 1·25 85
893 36 c. on 30 c. multicoloured (No. 758) .. .. 1·25 85
894 36 c. on 30 c. multicoloured (No. 759) .. .. 1·25 85
895 36 c. on 30 c. multicoloured (No. 760) .. .. 1·25 85
896 36 c. on 35 c. multicoloured (No. 761) (30.8.83) .. 1·25 85
897 36 c. on 35 c. multicoloured (No. 762) (30.8.83) .. 1·25 85
898 36 c. on 35 c. multicoloured (No. 763) (30.8.83) .. 1·25 85
899 36 c. on 35 c. multicoloured (No. 764) (30.8.83) .. 1·25 85
900 48 c. on 25 c. multicoloured (No. 753) .. .. 1·50 1·25
901 48 c. on 25 c. multicoloured (No. 754) .. .. 1·50 1·25
902 48 c. on 25 c. multicoloured (No. 755) .. .. 1·50 1·25
903 48 c. on 25 c. multicoloured (No. 756) .. .. 1·50 1·25
904 72 c. on 70 c. multicoloured (No. 773) .. .. 2·50 1·75
905 72 c. on 70 c. multicoloured (No. 774) .. .. 2·50 1·75
906 72 c. on 70 c. multicoloured (No. 775) .. .. 2·50 1·75
907 72 c. on 70 c. multicoloured (No. 776) .. .. 2·50 1·75

(b) Nos. 788/9, 813, 835/6 *and* 854, *as T* **201** *in gold*
908 96 c. on $1.40, George Washington .. .. 2·00 2·00
909 96 c. on $2 Prince Charles and Lady Diana Spencer .. .. 8·50 5·50
a. Surch double £130
b. Error. Surch on No. 840 .. .. .. 16·00
ba. Pair, Nos. 909 b/c .. .. .. 32·00
c. Error. Surch on No. 841 .. .. .. 16·00
910 96 c. on $2·50 Princess Diana (inscr "21st Birthday") (30.8.83) .. .. .. 3·00 3·00
911 96 c. on $2.50. As No. 910 but inscr "1 July 1982" (30.8.83) .. .. 3·00 3·00
912 $5.60 on $6 *Stylaster echinatus* .. .. 23·00 18·00
913 $5.60 on $10 *Melithaea albitincta* (30.8.83) .. 23·00 18·00
884/913 .. .. *Set of* 30 85·00 65·00
The surcharge on No. 908 is printed in gold on a black background, over the old value.

202 Union Flag

203 Dish Aerial, Satellite Earth Station

1983 (9 Sept). *Cook Islands Flags and Ensigns. T* **202** *and similar horiz designs. Multicoloured. P* 13½ × 14. *(a) Postage. Gold frames.*
914 6 c. Type **202** 35 25
915 6 c. Group Federal flag 35 25
916 12 c. Raratonga ensign 50 30
917 12 c. Flag of New Zealand 50 30
918 15 c. Cook Islands' flag (1973–79) 50 30
919 15 c. Cook Islands' National flag 50 30

(b) Air. Silver frames and backgrounds changed
920 20 c. Type **202** 60 40
921 20 c. Group Federal flag 60 40
922 30 c. Raratonga ensign 70 45
923 30 c. Flag of New Zealand 70 45
924 35 c. Cook Islands' flag (1973–79) 75 50
925 35 c. Cook Islands' National flag 75 50
914/25 .. .. *Set of* 12 6·00 4·00
MS926 Two sheets, each 132 × 120 mm. (a) Nos. 914/19; (b) Nos. 920/5. P 13 .. .. .. 2·25 4·00
The two designs of each value were issued as *se-tenant* horizontal pairs within the sheets.

1983 (10 Oct). *World Communications Year. T* **203** *and similar vert designs showing satellites. P* 13.
927 36 c. multicoloured 50 50
928 48 c. multicoloured 65 65
929 60 c. multicoloured .. .. 85 1·00
930 96 c. multicoloured .. .. 1·40 2·00
927/30 .. .. *Set of* 4 3·00 3·75
MS931 90 × 65 mm. $2 multicoloured .. .. 2·25 3·25

204 "La Belle Jardinière"

205 Montgolfier Balloon 1783

1983 (14 Nov). *Christmas. 500th Birth Anniv of Raphael. T* **204** *and similar vert designs. Multicoloured. P* 14 × 13½.
932 12 c. Type **204** 70 40
933 18 c. "Madonna and Child with Five Saints" .. 95 60
934 36 c. "Madonna and Child with St. John" .. 1·60 1·60
935 48 c. "Madonna of the Fish" .. .. .. 2·00 2·00
936 60 c. "The Madonna of the Baldacchino" .. 2·50 3·50
932/6 .. .. *Set of* 5 7·00 7·25
MS937 139 × 113 mm. As Nos. 932/6 but each with a premium of 3 c. .. .. 2·00 2·50
Nos. 932/6 were each printed in small sheets of 5 stamps and 1 label.

1983 (9 Dec). *Christmas. 500th Birth Anniv of Raphael. Children's Charity. Designs as Nos.* 932/6 *in separate miniature sheets* 66 × 82 *mm., each with a face value of* 85 *c.* + 5 *c. P* 13.
MS938 As Nos. 932/6 .. .. *Set of* 5 *sheets* 4·25 3·75

1984 (16 Jan). *Bicentenary of Manned Flight* (1983). *T* **205** *and similar vert designs. Multicoloured. P* 13.
939 36 c. Type **205** 50 50
940 48 c. Adorne's ascent, Strasbourg, 1784 .. 60 60
941 60 c. Balloon driven by sails, 1785 .. .. 75 85
942 72 c. Ascent of man on horse, 1798 .. .. 90 1·00
943 96 c. Godard's aerial acrobatics, 1850 .. 1·00 1·25
939/43 .. .. *Set of* 5 3·25 3·75
MS944 104 × 85 mm. $2.50, Blanchard and Jeffries crossing Channel, 1785 .. .. 1·50 2·25
MS945 122 × 132 mm. As Nos. 939/43 but each with a premium of 5 c. .. .. 1·50 2·25
Nos. 939/43 were each printed in small sheets of 5 stamps and 1 label.

206 Cuvier's Beaked Whale

207 Athens, 1896

1984 (10 Feb). *Save the Whales. T* **206** *and similar horiz designs. Multicoloured. P* 13.
946 10 c. Type **206** 50 50
947 18 c. Risso's Dolphin 75 75
948 20 c. True's Beaked Whale 75 75
949 24 c. Long-finned Pilot Whale 80 80
950 30 c. Narwhal 90 90
951 36 c. White Whale (Beluga) .. .. .. 1·10 1·10
952 42 c. Common Dolphin .. .. 1·40 1·40
953 48 c. Commerson's Dolphin .. .. .. 1·60 1·60
954 60 c. Bottle-nosed Dolphin .. .. .. 1·90 1·90
955 72 c. Sowerby's Beaked Whale .. .. .. 2·00 2·00
956 96 c. Common Porpoise .. .. 2·50 2·50
957 $2 Boutu .. .. 3·25 3·25
946/57 .. .. *Set of* 12 16·00 16·00

1984 (8 Mar). *Olympic Games, Los Angeles. T* **207** *and similar vert designs showing official posters of earlier Games. Multicoloured. P* 13½.
958 18 c. Type **207** 40 40
959 24 c. Paris, 1900 .. .. 45 45
960 36 c. St. Louis, 1904 .. .. 55 55
961 48 c. London, 1948 .. .. 65 65
962 60 c. Tokyo, 1964 .. .. 75 75
963 72 c. Berlin, 1936 .. .. 90 90
964 96 c. Rome, 1960 .. .. 1·00 1·00
965 $1.20 Los Angeles, 1930 .. .. 1·25 1·25
958/65 .. .. *Set of* 8 5·50 5·50

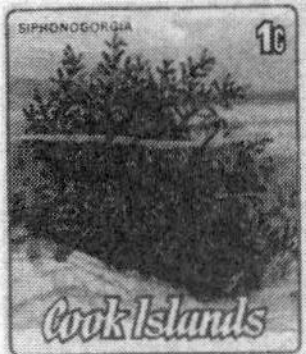

208 *Siphonogorgia*

$3.60

(209)

1984 (23 Mar–10 Aug). *Corals (2nd series). (a) Designs as No.* 713 *etc, but with redrawn frames and inscriptions as in T* **208**. *Multi-coloured. P* 13.

966 1 c. Type **208** 30 10
967 2 c. *Millepora alcicornis* 30 10
968 3 c. *Distichopora violacea* 40 10
969 5 c. *Ptilosarcus gurneyi* 45 10
970 10 c. *Lobophyllia bemprichii* 50 10
971 12 c. *Sarcophyton digitatum* 60 15
972 14 c. *Pavona praetorta* 60 15
973 18 c. *Junceella gemmacea* 70 20
974 20 c. *Stylaster* 70 20
975 24 c. *Stylophora pistillata* 70 20
976 30 c. *Palauastrea ramosa* 1·00 25
977 36 c. *Melithaea albitincta* 1·25 30
978 40 c. *Stylaster echinatus* 1·25 30
979 42 c. *Fungia fungites* 1·25 35
980 48 c. *Gonipora* 1·25 35
981 50 c. *Melithaea squamata* (15 May) 1·75 45
982 52 c. *Bellonella indica* (15 May) 1·75 60
983 55 c. *Plerogyra sinuosa* (15 May) 1·75 65
984 60 c. *Tubastraea* (15 May) 1·90 70
985 70 c. *Heliofungia actiniformis* (15 May) 2·00 85
986 85 c. *Caulastraea echinulata* (15 May) 2·25 1·00
987 96 c. *Porites andrewsi* (15 May) 2·50 1·10
988 $1.10, *Pectinia alcicornis* (15 May) 2·50 1·40
989 $1.20, *Dendrophyllia gracilis* (15 May) 2·50 1·50

(*b*) *Nos.* 785/9 *surch as T* **209** *in gold on black*

990 $3.60 on $2 *Gonipora* (28 June) 5·50 4·00
991 $4.20 on $3 *Heliofungia actiniformis* (28 June) 6·00 5·00
992 $5 on $4 *Stylophora pistillata* (28 June) 6·50 5·50
993 $7.20 on $6 *Stylaster echinatus* (20 July) 8·50 8·50
994 $9.60 on $10 *Melithaea albitincta* (10 Aug) 10·00 10·00
966/94 *Set of* 29 60·00 40·00

Equestrian
Team Dressage
Germany

(210)

1984 (24 Aug). *Olympic Gold Medal Winners. Nos.* 963/5 *optd as T* **210**.

995 72 c. Berlin, 1936 (optd T **210**) 60 65
996 96 c. Rome, 1960 (optd "Decathlon Daley Thompson Great Britain") 80 85
997 $1.20 Los Angeles, 1930 (optd "Four Gold Medals Carl Lewis U.S.A." 1·00 1·10
995/7 *Set of* 3 2·25 2·40

211 Capt. Cook's Cottage, Melbourne

1984 (20 Sept). *"Ausipex" International Stamp Exhibition, Melbourne. T* **211** *and similar horiz designs. Multicoloured. P* 13.

998 36 c. Type **211** 1·25 1·25
999 48 c. "H.M.S. *Endeavour* careened for Repairs" (Sydney Parkinson) 2·25 2·25
1000 60 c. "Cook's landing at Botany Bay" (E. Phillips Fox) 3·00 3·00
1001 $2 "Capt. James Cook" (John Webber) 3·50 3·50
998/1001 *Set of* 4 9·00 9·00
MS1002 140 × 100 mm. As Nos. 998/1001, but each stamp with a face value of 90 c. 7·50 7·50

Commemorating-
15 Sept. 1984

(212)

213 "Virgin on Throne with Child" (Giovanni Bellini)

1984 (15 Oct). *Birth of Prince Henry. Nos.* 812 *and* 833/6 *optd or surch (No.* 1007) *as T* **212**.

1003 $1.25, Type **191** (optd with T **212**) (Gold) 1·50 1·10
a. Pair. Nos. 1003/4 3·00 2·25
1004 $1.25, As Type **191**, but inscr "1 July 1982" (optd "Birth H.R.H. Prince Henry") (Gold) 1·50 1·10
1005 $2.50, Princess Diana (inscr "21st Birthday") (optd with T **212**) (Gold) 2·25 2·00
a. Pair. Nos. 1005/6 4·50 4·00
1006 $2.50, As No. 835, but inscr "1 July 1982" (optd "Birth H.R.H. Prince Henry") (Gold) 2·25 2·00
1007 $3 on $1 Type **187** (surch "Royal Birth Prince Henry 15 Sept. 1984") (Sil.) 4·50 4·00
1003/7 *Set of* 5 11·00 9·25

1984 (21 Nov). *Christmas. T* **213** *and similar vert designs. Multi-coloured. P* 14.

1008 36 c. Type **213** 1·00 40
1009 48 c. "Virgin and Child" (anonymous, 15th century) 1·10 60
1010 60 c. "Virgin and Child with Saints" (Alvise Vivarini) 1·40 80
1011 96 c. "Virgin and Child with Angels" (H. Memling) 1·75 1·60
1012 $1.20, "Adoration of Magi" (G. Tiepolo) 2·00 2·00
1008/12 *Set of* 5 6·50 4·75
MS1013 120 × 113 mm. As Nos. 1008/12, but each with a premium of 5 c. P 13½ 2·75 3·00

1984 (10 Dec). *Christmas. Designs as Nos.* 1008/12 *in separate miniature sheets,* 62 × 76 *mm, each with a face value of* 95 *c.* + 5 *c. P* 13½.

MS1014 As Nos. 1008/12 *Set of* 5 *sheets* 4·25 4·50

214 Downy Woodpecker

1985 (23 Apr). *Birth Bicentenary of John J. Audubon (ornithologist). T* **214** *and similar vert designs showing original paintings. Multicoloured. P* 13 × 13½.

1015 30 c. Type **214** 2·25 1·25
1016 55 c. Black-throated Blue Warbler 2·50 1·75
1017 65 c. Yellow-throated Warbler 2·75 2·25
1018 75 c. Chestnut-sided Warbler 3·00 2·75
1019 95 c. Dickcissel 3·25 3·00
1020 $1.15, White-crowned Sparrow 3·25 3·50
1015/20 *Set of* 6 15·00 13·00
MS1021 Three sheets, each 76 × 75 mm. (a) $1.30, Red-cockaded Woodpecker. (b) $2.80, Seaside Sparrow. (c) $5.30, Zenaida Dove *Set of* 3 *sheets* 12·00 8·50

215 "The Kingston Flyer" (New Zealand)

(Des and litho Format)

1985 (14 May). *Famous Trains. T* **215** *and similar horiz designs. Multicoloured. Ordinary paper. P* 14 × 13½.

1022 20 c. Type **215** 50 50
1023 55 c. Class 625 locomotive (Italy) 65 85
1024 65 c. Gotthard electric locomotive (Switzerland) 70 90
1025 75 c. Union Pacific diesel locomotive No. 6900 (U.S.A.) 90 1·10
1026 95 c. Canadian National "Super Continental" type diesel locomotive (Canada) 90 1·25
1027 $1.15, TGV express train (France) 95 1·00
1028 $2.20, "The Flying Scotsman" (Great Britain) 1·00 2·50
1029 $3.40, "Orient Express" 1·10 3·75
1022/9 *Set of* 8 6·00 11·00

No. 1023 is inscribed "640" in error.

Nos. 1022/9 exist imperforate from stock dispersed by the liquidator of Format International Security Printers Ltd.

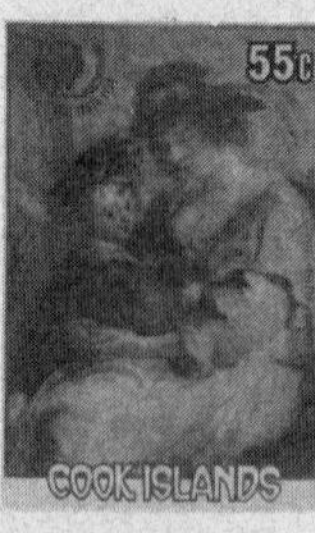

216 "Helena Fourment" (Peter Paul Rubens)

217 "Lady Elizabeth, 1908" (Mabel Hankey)

1985 (6 June). *International Youth Year. T* **216** *and similar vert designs. Multicoloured. P* 13.

1030 55 c. Type **216** 2·50 2·25
1031 65 c. "Vigee-Lebrun and Daughter" (E. Vigee-Lebrun) 2·75 2·75
1032 75 c. "On the Terrace" (P. Renoir) 3·00 3·00
1033 $1.30, "Young Mother Sewing" (M. Cassatt) 3·75 4·00
1030/3 *Set of* 4 11·00 11·00
MS1034 103 × 106 mm. As Nos. 1030/3, but each with a premium of 10 c. 5·00 5·00

1985 (28 June). *Life and Times of Queen Elizabeth the Que[en] Mother. T* **217** *and similar vert designs showing painting[s]. Multicoloured. P* 13.

1035 65 c. Type **217** 40
1036 75 c. "Duchess of York, 1923" (Savely Sorine) 45
1037 $1.15, "Duchess of York, 1925" (Philip de Laszlo) 55
1038 $2.80, "Queen Elizabeth, 1938" (Sir Gerald Kelly) 1·40 2·
1035/8 *Set of* 4 2·50 3·
MS1039 69 × 81 mm. $5.30, As $2.80 2·50 3·

Nos. 1035/8 were each printed in small sheets of 4 stamps.

For these designs in a miniature sheet, each with a face val[ue] of 55 c., see No. **MS**1079.

218 Albert Henry (Prime Minister, 1965–78)

219 Golf

1985 (29 July). *20th Anniv of Self-Government. T* **218** *an[d] similar vert designs. Multicoloured. P* 13.

1040 30 c. Type **218** 80 6
1041 50 c. Sir Thomas Davis (Prime Minister, 1978–Apr 1983 and from Nov 1983) 1·25 9
1042 65 c. Geoffrey Henry (Prime Minister, Apr–Nov 1983) 1·50 1·5
1040/2 *Set of* 3 3·25 2·7
MS1043 134 × 70 mm. As Nos. 1040/2, but each stamp with a face value of 55 c. 1·25 1·4

1985 (29 July). *South Pacific Mini Games, Rarotonga. T* **21[9]** *and similar vert designs. Multicoloured. P* 14.

1044 55 c. Type **219** 4·00 3·5
1045 65 c. Rugby 4·00 4·0
1046 75 c. Tennis 5·50 6·0
1044/6 *Set of* 3 12·00 12·0
MS1047 126 × 70 mm. Nos. 1044/6, but each with a premium of 10 c. P 13½ 10·00 11·0

220 Sea Horse, Gearwheel and Leaves

221 "Madonna of the Magnificat"

1985 (29 July). *Pacific Conferences, Rarotonga. P* 13.

1048 **220** 55 c. black, gold and rosine 85 65
1049 65 c. black, gold and violet 95 80
1050 75 c. black, gold and blue-green 1·25 1·10
1048/50 *Set of* 3 2·75 2·25
MS1051 126 × 81 mm. As Nos. 1048/50, but each stamp with a face value of 50 c. 1·25 1·40

No. 1048 shows the South Pacific Bureau for Economic Co-operation logo and is inscribed "S.P.E.C. Meeting, 30 July–1 Aug 1985, Rarotonga". No. 1049 also shows the S.P.E.C. logo, but is inscribed "South Pacific Forum, 4–6 Aug 1985, Rarotonga". No. 1050 shows the Pacific Islands Conference logo and the inscription "Pacific Islands Conference, 7–10 Aug 1985, Rarotonga".

1985 (18 Nov). *Christmas. Virgin and Child Paintings b[y] Botticelli. T* **221** *and similar vert designs. Multicoloured. P* 14.

1052 55 c. Type **221** 1·75 6
1053 65 c. "Madonna with Pomegranate" 1·90 6
1054 75 c. "Madonna and Child with Six Angels" 2·25 1·0
1055 95 c. "Madonna and Child with St. John" 2·50 1·4
1052/5 *Set of* 4 7·50 3·2
MS1056 90 × 104 mm. As Nos. 1052/5, but each stamp with a face value of 50 c. P 13½ 3·75 3·7

1985 (9 Dec). *Christmas. Virgin and Child Paintings by Botticelli. Square designs* (46 × 46 *mm*) *as Nos.* 1052/5 *in separate miniature sheets,* 50 × 51 *mm, with face values of* $1.20, $1.45, $2.20 *and* $2.75. *Imperf.*

MS1057 As Nos. 1052/5 *Set of* 4 *sheets* 9·00 11·00

222 "The Eve of the Deluge" (John Martin)

223 Queen Elizabeth II

1986 (13 Mar). *Appearance of Halley's Comet. Paintings. T* **222** *and similar vert designs. Multicoloured. P* 14.

1058 55 c. Type **222** .. .. 1·25 1·25
1059 65 c. "Lot and his Daughters" (Lucas van Leyden) .. .. 1·40 1·40
1060 75 c. "Auspicious Comet" (from treatise *c* 1587) .. .. 1·50 1·50
1061 $1.25, "Events following Charles I" (Herman Saftleven) .. .. 2·25 2·25
1062 $2 "Ossian receiving Napoleonic Officers" (Anne Louis Girodet-Trioson) .. 3·00 3·00
1058/62 .. .. *Set of* 5 8·50 8·50
MS1063 130×100 mm. As Nos. 1058/62, but each with a face value of 70 c. P 13½ .. .. 4·00 5·50
MS1064 84×63 mm. $4 "Halley's Comet of 1759 over the Thames" (Samuel Scott). P 13½ .. 5·00 6·50

1986 (21 Apr). *60th Birthday of Queen Elizabeth II. T* **223** *and similar vert designs showing formal portraits. P* 13×13½.

1065 95 c. multicoloured .. .. 1·10 1·50
1066 $1.25, multicoloured .. .. 1·40 1·75
1067 $1.50, multicoloured .. .. 1·50 2·00
1065/7 .. .. *Set of* 3 3·50 4·75
MS1068 Three sheets, each 44×75 mm. As Nos. 1065/7, but with face values of $1.10, $1.95 and $2.45 .. .. .. *Set of* 3 *sheets* 8·00 9·00

224 U.S.A. 1847 Franklin 5 c. Stamp and H.M.S. *Resolution* at Rarotonga

225 Head of Statue of Liberty

1986 (21 May). *"Ameripex '86" International Stamp Exhibition, Chicago. T* **224** *and similar horiz designs. Multicoloured. P* 14.

1069 $1 Type **224** .. .. 4·50 3·75
1070 $1.50, Chicago .. .. 3·50 4·25
1071 $2 1975 definitive $2, Benjamin Franklin and H.M.S. *Resolution* .. .. .. 5·50 5·50
1069/71 .. .. *Set of* 3 12·00 12·00

1986 (4 July). *Centenary of Statue of Liberty. T* **225** *and similar vert designs. Multicoloured. P* 14.

1072 $1 Type **225** 75 85
1073 $1.25, Hand and torch of Statue .. .. 90 1·10
1074 $2.75, Statue of Liberty .. .. .. 2·00 2·50
1072/4 .. .. *Set of* 3 3·25 4·00

226 Miss Sarah Ferguson

(227)

1986 (23 July). *Royal Wedding. T* **226** *and similar multicoloured designs. P* 14 ($1, $2) *or* 13½×13 ($3).

1075 $1 Type **226** .. .. 1·00 1·25
1076 $2 Prince Andrew .. .. 1·75 2·25
1077 $3 Prince Andrew and Miss Sarah Ferguson (57×31 *mm*) .. .. 2·50 3·00
1075/7 .. .. *Set of* 3 4·75 6·00
Nos. 1075/7 were each printed in small sheets of 4 stamps.

1986 (4 Aug). *"Stampex '86" Stamp Exhibition, Adelaide. No.* **MS**1002 *optd with T* **227** *in gold (circle) and black (inscr) only on design as No.* 1001.

MS1078 90 c.×4 multicoloured .. .. .. 5·50 6·50
The "Stampex '86" exhibition emblem is also overprinted on the sheet margin.

1986 (4 Aug). *86th Birthday of Queen Elizabeth the Queen Mother. Designs as Nos.* 1035/8 *in miniature sheet,* 91×116 *mm, each stamp with a face value of* 55 c. *Multicoloured. P* 13×13½.

MS1079 55 c.×4. As Nos. 1035/8 .. .. 4·50 5·00

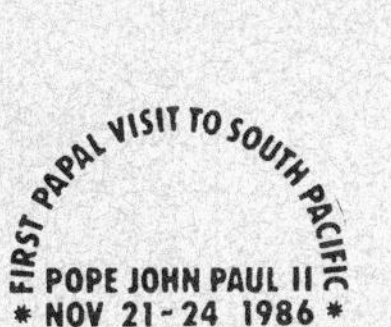

228 "The Holy Family with St. John the Baptist and St. Elizabeth"

(229)

1986 (17 Nov). *Christmas. Paintings by Rubens. T* **228** *and similar vert designs. Multicoloured. P* 13½.

1080 55 c. Type **228** .. .. 1·25 90
1081 $1.30, "Virgin with the Garland" .. 2·25 2·00
1082 $2.75, "The Adoration of the Magi" (detail) .. .. 4·25 4·00
1080/2 .. .. *Set of* 3 7·00 6·25
MS1083 140×100 mm. As Nos. 1080/2, but each size 36×46 mm with a face value of $2.40 .. 11·00 12·00
MS1084 80×70 mm. $6.40, As No. 1081 but size 32×50 mm .. .. 11·00 12·00

1986 (21 Nov). *Visit of Pope John Paul II to South Pacific. Nos.* 1080/4 *surch as T* **229** *in silver.*

1085 55 c. + 10 c. Type **228** .. .. 2·50 1·75
1086 $1.30 + 10 c. "Virgin with the Garland" 3·25 2·25
1087 $2.75 + 10 c. "The Adoration of the Magi" (detail) .. .. 5·50 3·75
1085/7 .. .. *Set of* 3 10·00 7·00
MS1088 140×100 mm. As Nos. 1085/7, but each size 36×46 mm with a face value of $2.40 + 10 c. 11·00 12·00
MS1089 80×70 mm. $6.40 + 50 c. As No. 1086 but size 32×50 mm .. .. 11·00 12·00

10c **(230)**

HURRICANE RELIEF +50c **(231)**

1987 (10–12 Feb). *Various stamps surch as T* **230** *by N.Z. Govt Printer.*

(*a*) *On Nos.* 741/56, 761/76 *and* 787/8

1090 10 c. on 15 c. *Distichopora violacea* (11.2) .. 10 10
1091 10 c. on 15 c. *Stylaster* (11.2) 10 10
1092 10 c. on 15 c. *Gonipora* (11.2) 10 10
1093 10 c. on 15 c. *Caulastraea echinulata* (11.2) 10 10
1094 10 c. on 25 c. *Lobophyllia bemprichii* (11.2) 10 10
1095 10 c. on 25 c. *Palauastrea ramosa* (11.2) .. 10 10
1096 10 c. on 25 c. *Bellonella indica* (11.2) .. 10 10
1097 10 c. on 25 c. *Pectinia alcicornis* (11.2) .. 10 10
1098 18 c. on 12 c. *Millepora alcicornis* (11.2) .. 15 15
1099 18 c. on 12 c. *Junceella gemmacea* (11.2) .. 15 15
1100 18 c. on 12 c. *Fungia fungites* (11.2) .. 15 15
1101 18 c. on 12 c. *Heliofungia actiniformis* (11.2) 15 15
1102 18 c. on 20 c. *Ptilosarcus gurneyi* (11.2) .. 15 15
1103 18 c. on 20 c. *Stylophora pistillata* (11.2) .. 15 15
1104 18 c. on 20 c. *Melithaea squamata* (11.2) .. 15 15
1105 18 c. on 20 c. *Porites andrewsi* (11.2) .. 15 15
1106 55 c. on 35 c. Type **184** (11.2) 40 45
1107 55 c. on 35 c. *Pavona praetorta* (11.2) .. 40 45
1108 55 c. on 35 c. *Stylaster echinatus* (11.2) .. 40 45
1109 55 c. on 35 c. *Tubastraea* (11.2) 40 45
1110 65 c. on 50 c. As No. 1098 (11.2) 45 50
1111 65 c. on 50 c. As No. 1099 (11.2) 45 50
1112 65 c. on 50 c. As No. 1100 (11.2) 45 50
1113 65 c. on 50 c. As No. 1101 (11.2) 45 50
1114 65 c. on 60 c. As No. 1090 (11.2) 45 50
1115 65 c. on 60 c. As No. 1091 (11.2) 45 50
1116 65 c. on 60 c. As No. 1092 (11.2) 45 50
1117 65 c. on 60 c. As No. 1093 (11.2) 45 50
1118 75 c. on 70 c. As No. 1102 (11.2) 55 60
1119 75 c. on 70 c. As No. 1103 (11.2) 55 60
1120 75 c. on 70 c. As No. 1104 (11.2) 55 60
1121 75 c. on 70 c. As No. 1105 (11.2) 55 60
1122 $6.40 on $4 *Stylophora pistillata* .. 4·50 4·75
1123 $7.20 on $6 *Stylaster echinatus* .. .. 5·00 5·25

(*b*) *On Nos.* 812/13 *in gold* (12 Feb)

1124 $9.40 on $1 Type **187** .. .. .. 15·00 16·00
1125 $9.40 on $2 Prince Charles and Lady Diana Spencer .. .. 15·00 16·00

(*c*) *On Nos.* 835/6 *in gold* (12 Feb)

1126 $9.40 on $2.50 Princess of Wales (inscr "21st Birthday") .. .. 15·00 16·00
1127 $9.40 on $2.50 As No. 1126, but inscr "1 July 1982" .. .. 15·00 16·00

(*d*) *On Nos.* 966/8, 971/2, 975, 979/80, 982 *and* 987/9

1128 5 c. on 1 c. Type **208** 10 10
1129 5 c. on 2 c. *Millepora alcicornis* 10 10
1130 5 c. on 3 c. *Distichopora violacea* 10 10
1131 5 c. on 12 c. *Sarcophyton digitatum* .. 10 10
1132 5 c. on 14 c. *Pavona praetorta* 10 10
1133 18 c. on 24 c. *Stylophora pistillata* 15 15
1134 55 c. on 52 c. *Bellonella indica* 40 45
1135 65 c. on 42 c. *Fungia fungites* 45 50
1136 75 c. on 48 c. *Gonipora* 55 60
1137 95 c. on 96 c. *Porites andrewsi* 70 75
1138 95 c. on $1.10 *Pectinia alcicornis* 70 75
1139 95 c. on $1.20 *Dendrophyllia gracilis* .. 70 75

(*e*) *On Nos.* 998/1001 *in gold (No.* 1143) *or gold (value) and black (bars) (others)* (12 Feb)

1140 $1.30 on 36 c. Type **211** .. .. .. 1·40 1·50
1141 $1.30 on 48 c. "The *Endeavour* careened for Repairs" (Sydney Parkinson) .. 1·40 1·50
1142 $1.30 on 60 c. "Cook's landing at Botany Bay" (E. Phillips Fox) .. .. .. 1·40 1·50
1143 $1.30 on $2 "Capt. James Cook" (John Webber) .. .. 1·40 1·50

(*f*) *On Nos.* 1065/7 *in gold* (12 Feb)

1144 **223** $2.80 on 95 c. multicoloured .. .. 7·00 7·50
1145 – $2.80 on $1.25 multicoloured .. .. 7·00 7·50
1146 – $2.80 on $1.50 multicoloured .. .. 7·00 7·50

(*g*) *On Nos.* 1075/7 *in gold (value) and black (bars)* (12 Feb)

1147 $2.80 on $1 Type **226** .. .. .. 6·00 6·50
a. Black opt (bars) omitted £110
1148 $2.80 on $2 Prince Andrew .. .. 6·00 6·50
1149 $2.80 on $3 Prince Andrew and Miss Sarah Ferguson (57×31 *mm*) .. .. 6·00 6·50
1090/149 .. .. *Set of* 60 £100 £120

1987 (17 June). *Various stamps surch as T* **230**.

(*a*) *On Nos.* 785/6 *and* 789

1150 $2.80 on $2 *Gonipora* .. .. .. 2·10 2·25
1151 $5 on $3 *Heliofungia actiniformis* .. .. 4·00 4·25
1152 $9.40 on $10 *Melithaea albitincta* .. .. 7·50 7·75

(*b*) *On Nos.* 838/42 *(in gold on Nos.* 1153/6)

1153 $9.40 on $1 Type **187** (No. 838) .. 7·50 7·75
a. Pair. Nos. 1153/4 .. .. .. 15·00 16·00
1154 $9.40 on $1 Type **187** (No. 839) .. .. 7·50 7·75
1155 $9.40 on $2 Prince Charles and Lady Diana Spencer (No. 840) .. .. 7·50 7·75
a. Pair. Nos. 1155/6 .. .. .. 15·00 16·00
1156 $9.40 on $2 Prince Charles and Lady Diana Spencer (No. 841) .. .. 7·50 7·75
1150/6 .. .. *Set of* 7 40·00 40·00
MS1157 106×59 mm. $9.20 on $1 Type **187**; $9.20 on $2 Prince Charles and Lady Diana Spencer .. .. 12·00 15·00

1987 (30 June–31 July). *Hurricane Relief Fund. Various stamps surch as T* **231**.

(*a*) *On Nos.* 1035/9 *in silver*

1158 65 c. + 50 c. Type **217** 80 85
1159 75 c. + 50 c. "Duchess of York, 1923" (Savely Sorine) .. .. 85 1·00
1160 $1.15 + 50 c. "Duchess of York, 1925" (Philip de Laszlo) .. .. .. 1·10 1·40
1161 $2.80 + 50 c. "Queen Elizabeth, 1938" (Sir Gerald Kelly) .. .. .. 2·25 2·75
MS1162 69×81 mm. $5.30 + 50 c. As $2.80 + 50 c. .. .. 4·50 6·00

(*b*) *On Nos.* 1058/62 *(in silver on Nos.* 1164/6)

1163 55 c. + 50 c. Type **222** 75 80
1164 65 c. + 50 c. "Lot and his Daughters" (Lucas van Leyden) 80 85
1165 75 c. + 50 c. "Auspicious Comet" (from treatise *c* 1587) 85 90
1166 $1.25 + 50 c. "Events following Charles I" (Herman Saftleven) .. .. .. 1·25 1·40
1167 $2 + 50 c. "Ossian receiving Napoleonic Officers" (Anne Louis Girodet-Trioson) .. .. 1·75 2·00

(*c*) *On Nos.* 1065/8 *(in silver on No.* 1169) (31 July)

1168 **223** 95 c. + 50 c. multicoloured .. .. 1·00 1·10
1169 – $1.25 + 50 c. multicoloured .. .. 1·25 1·40
1170 – $1.50 + 50 c. multicoloured .. .. 1·40 1·50
MS1171 Three sheets, each 44×75 mm. As Nos. 1168/70, but with face values of $1.10 + 50 c., $1.95 + 50 c., $2.45 + 50 c. *Set of* 3 *sheets* 7·00 8·50

(*d*) *On Nos.* 1069/71 *(in silver on No.* 1172)

1172 $1 + 50 c. Type **224** .. .. 2·00 2·00
1173 $1.50 + 50 c. Chicago .. .. .. 1·75 2·00
1174 $2 + 50 c. 1975 definitive $2, Benjamin Franklin and H.M.S. *Resolution* .. 2·75 2·75

(*e*) *On Nos.* 1072/4 *(in silver on Nos.* 1175 *and* 1177)

1175 $1 + 50 c. Type **225** .. .. .. 1·00 1·25
1176 $1.25 + 50 c. Hand and torch of Statue .. 1·25 1·50
1177 $2.75 + 50 c. Statue of Liberty .. .. 2·25 2·75

(*f*) *On Nos.* 1075/7 *in silver* (31 July)

1178 $1 + 50 c. Type **226** .. .. .. 1·00 1·25
1179 $2 + 50 c. Prince Andrew .. .. .. 1·75 2·00
1180 $3 + 50 c. Prince Andrew and Miss Sarah Ferguson (57×31 *mm*) .. .. .. 2·40 2·75

(*g*) *On Nos.* 1080/4 *in silver*

1181 55 c. + 50 c. Type **228** 75 80
1182 $1.30 + 50 c. "Virgin with the Garland" .. 1·25 1·40
1183 $2.75 + 50 c. "The Adoration of the Magi" (detail) .. .. 2·25 2·40
MS1184 140×100 mm. As No. 1181/3, but each size 36×46 mm with a face value of $2.40 + 50 c. 7·00 8·50
MS1185 80×70 mm. $6.40 + 50 c. As No. 1182, but size 32×50 mm. .. .. 4·75 6·00

(*h*) *On Nos.* 1122, 1134/7 *and* 1150/1

1186 55 c. + 25 c. on 52 c. *Bellonella indica* .. 70 70
1187 65 c. + 25 c. on 42 c. *Fungia fungites* .. 80 80
1188 75 c. + 25 c. on 48 c. *Gonipora* 90 90
1189 95 c. + 25 c. on 96 c. *Porites andrewsi* .. 1·10 1·10
1190 $2.80 + 50 c. on $2 *Gonipora* .. .. 2·75 2·75
1191 $5 + 50 c. on $3 *Heliofungia actiniformis* 4·50 4·50
1192 $6.40 + 50 c. on $4 *Stylophora pistillata* .. 6·00 6·00
1158/92 .. .. *Set of* 31 45·00 48·00

ROYAL WEDDING FORTIETH ANNIVERSARY

(232)

1987 (20 Nov). *Royal Ruby Wedding. Nos.* 484 *and* 787 *optd with T* **232** *in black on gold.*

1193 $4 Queen Elizabeth II and seashells .. 4·50 4·50
1194 $4 Queen Elizabeth II and *Stylophora pistillata* .. .. 4·50 4·50

233 "The Holy Family" (Rembrandt)

1987 (7 Dec). *Christmas. T* **233** *and similar horiz designs showing different paintings of the Holy Family by Rembrandt. P* 13½.
1195 $1.25, multicoloured .. .. .. 2·25 2·00
1196 $1.50, multicoloured .. .. .. 2·75 2·25
1197 $1.95, multicoloured .. .. .. 4·00 3·50
1195/7 .. .. *Set of* 3 8·00 7·00
MS1198 100×140 mm. As Nos. 1195/7, but each size 47×36 mm with a face value of $1.15 .. 6·00 7·50
MS1199 70×80 mm. $6 As No. 1196, but size 40×31 mm. P 13×13½ .. .. 8·50 9·50

234 Olympic Commemorative $50 Coin

(Des G. Vasarhelyi)

1988 (26 Apr). *Olympic Games, Seoul. T* **234** *and similar vert designs. Multicoloured. P* 13½×14.
1200 $1.50, Type **234** .. .. 2·75 2·25
a. Horiz strip of 3. Nos. 1200/2 .. .. 7·50
1201 $1.50, Olympic torch and Seoul Olympic Park .. .. 2·75 2·25
1202 $1.50, Steffi Graf playing tennis and Olympic medal .. .. 2·75 2·25
1200/2 .. .. *Set of* 3 7·50 6·00
MS1203 131×81 mm. $10 Combined design as Nos. 1200/2, but measuring 114×47 mm. P 13½ 11·00 12·00
Nos. 1200/2 were printed together, *se-tenant*, in horizontal strips of 3 throughout the sheet, each strip forming a composite design.

MILOSLAV MECIR
CZECHOSLOVAKIA
GOLD MEDAL WINNER
MEN'S TENNIS

(**235**)

1988 (12 Oct). *Olympic Tennis Medal Winners, Seoul. Nos.* 1200/3 *optd as T* **235**.
1204 $1.50, Type **234** (optd with T **235**) .. 2·25 2·25
a. Horiz strip of 3. Nos. 1204/6 .. .. 6·00
1205 $1.50, Olympic torch and Seoul Olympic Park (optd "TIM MAYOTTE UNITED STATES GABRIELA SABATINI ARGENTINA SILVER MEDAL WINNERS") .. .. 2·25 2·25
1206 $1.50, Steffi Graf playing tennis and Olympic medal (optd "GOLD MEDAL WINNER STEFFI GRAF WEST GERMANY") .. .. .. 2·25 2·25
1204/6 .. .. *Set of* 3 6·00 6·00
MS1207 131×81 mm. $10 Combined design as Nos. 1200/2, but measuring 114×47 mm. (optd "GOLD MEDAL WINNER SEOUL OLYMPIC GAMES STEFFI GRAF -WEST GERMANY") .. 10·00 11·00

236 "Virgin and Child" **237** "Apollo II" leaving Earth

1988 (11 Nov). *Christmas. T* **236** *and similar vert designs showing paintings of "The Nativity"* ($6.40) *or different versions of "Virgin and Child" by Dürer. P* 13½.
1208 70 c. multicoloured .. .. .. 2·00 2·00
1209 85 c. multicoloured .. .. .. 2·25 2·25
1210 95 c. multicoloured .. .. .. 2·50 2·50
1211 $1.25, multicoloured .. .. .. 3·25 3·25
1208/11 .. .. *Set of* 4 9·00 9·00
MS1212 80 × 100 mm. $6.40, multicoloured (45 × 60 *mm*) .. .. 6·50 8·50

(Des G. Vasarhelyi)

1989 (14 July). *20th Anniv of First Manned Landing on Moon. T* **237** *and similar horiz designs. Multicoloured. P* 13.
1213 40 c. Type **237** .. .. 1·25 1·25
a. Horiz pair. Nos. 1213/14 .. .. 2·50 2·50
1214 40 c. Lunar module over Moon .. .. 1·25 1·25
1215 55 c. Armstrong stepping onto Moon .. 1·40 1·40
a. Horiz pair. Nos. 1215/16 .. .. 2·75 2·75
1216 55 c. Astronaut on Moon .. .. .. 1·40 1·40
1217 65 c. Working on lunar surface .. .. 1·75 1·75
a. Horiz pair. Nos. 1217/18 .. .. 3·50 3·50
1218 65 c. Conducting experiment .. .. 1·75 1·75
1219 75 c. "Apollo 11" leaving Moon .. .. 1·75 1·75
a. Horiz pair. Nos. 1219/20 .. .. 3·50 3·50
1220 75 c. Splashdown in South Pacific .. 1·75 1·75
1213/20 .. .. *Set of* 8 11·00 11·00
MS1221 108×91 mm. $4.20, Astronauts on Moon .. .. 5·00 6·00
Nos. 1213/14, 1215/16, 1217/18 and 1219/20 were each printed together, horizontally *se-tenant*, in sheets of 12.

238 Rarotonga Flycatcher

(Des G. Drummond)

1989 (4 Oct). *Endangered Birds of the Cook Islands. T* **238** *and similar horiz designs. Multicoloured.* (a) *Postage. P* 13½×13
1222 15 c. Type **238** .. .. .. 1·75 1·75
1223 20 c. Pair of Rarotonga Flycatchers .. 1·75 1·75
1224 65 c. Pair of Rarotongan Fruit Doves .. 2·75 2·75
1225 70 c. Rarotongan Fruit Dove .. .. 2·75 2·75
1222/5 .. .. *Set of* 4 8·00 8·00

(b) *Air. P* 13½
MS1226 Four sheets, each 70×53 mm. As Nos. 1222/5, but with face values of $1, $1.25, $1.50, $1.75 and each size 50×32 mm. .. *Set of* 4 *sheets* 5·50 7·50

239 Villagers

1989 (24 Nov). *Christmas. T* **239** *and similar multicoloured designs showing details from "Adoration of the Magi" by Rubens. P* 13.
1227 70 c. Type **239** .. .. 1·25 1·25
1228 85 c. Virgin Mary .. .. 1·40 1·50
1229 95 c. Christ Child .. .. 1·50 1·75
1230 $1.50, Boy with gift .. .. .. 2·00 2·75
1227/30 .. .. *Set of* 4 5·50 6·50
MS1231 85×120 mm. $6.40, "Adoration of the Magi" (45×60 mm). P 13½ .. .. .. 9·00 10·00

240 Revd. John Williams and L.M.S. Church **241** "Woman writing Letter" (Terborch)

(Des Jennifer Toombs)

1990 (19 Feb). *Christianity in the Cook Islands. T* **240** *and similar square designs. Multicoloured. P* 13.
1232 70 c. Type **240** 75 80
1233 85 c. Mgr. Bernardine Castanié and Roman Catholic Church .. .. 90 1·10
1234 95 c. Elder Osborne Widstoe and Mormon Church .. .. 1·00 1·40
1235 $1.60, Dr. J. E. Caldwell and Seventh Day Adventist Church .. .. .. 1·75 2·00
1232/5 .. .. *Set of* 4 4·00 5·25
MS1236 90×90 mm. As Nos. 1232/5, but each with a face value of 90 c. P 13½ .. .. 4·75 6·00

1990 (2 May). *150th Anniv of the Penny Black. T* **241** *and similar vert designs showing paintings. Multicoloured. P* 13½.
1237 85 c. Type **241** .. .. 1·10 1·25
1238 $1.15, "George Gisze" (Holbein the Younger) .. .. 1·50 1·75
1239 $1.55, "Mrs. John Douglas" (Gainsborough) .. .. 1·90 2·25
1240 $1.85, "Portrait of a Gentleman" (Dürer) 2·25 2·50
1237/40 .. .. *Set of* 4 6·00 7·00
MS1241 82×150 mm. As Nos. 1237/40, but each with a face value of $1.05 .. .. .. 8·50 9·50

242 Sprinting **243** Queen Elizabeth the Queen Mother

(Des G. Vasarhelyi)

1990 (15 June)–**91**. *Olympic Games, Barcelona, and Winter Olympic Games, Albertville (1st issue)* (1992). *T* **242** *and similar horiz designs. Multicoloured. P* 14.
1242 $1.85, Type **242** .. .. .. 4·00 4·50
a. Horiz strip of 3. Nos. 1242/4 .. 11·00
1243 $1.85, Cook Islands $50 commemorative coin .. .. 4·00 4·50
1244 $1.85, Skiing .. .. 4·00 4·50
1242/4 .. .. *Set of* 3 11·00 12·00
MS1245 109×52 mm. $6.40, As Nos. 1242/4, but 80×26 mm. P 13½ (12.2.91) .. .. 12·00 13·00
Nos. 1242/4 were printed together, *se-tenant*, in horizontal strips of 3 throughout the sheet of 18.
See also Nos. 1304/10.

1990 (20 July). *90th Birthday of Queen Elizabeth the Queen Mother. P* 13½.
1246 **243** $1.85, multicoloured .. .. .. 3·75 4·25
MS1247 66×101 mm. **243** $6.40, multicoloured 8·50 10·00

244 "Adoration of the Magi" (Memling) (**245**)

(Litho Questa)

1990 (29 Nov). *Christmas. Religious Paintings. T* **244** *and similar multicoloured designs. Ordinary paper. P* 14.
1248 70 c. Type **244** .. .. 1·10 1·10
1249 85 c. "Holy Family" (Lotto) .. .. 1·25 1·25
1250 95 c. "Madonna and Child with Saints John and Catherine" (Titian) .. .. 1·60 1·75
1251 $1.50, "Holy Family" (Titian) .. .. 2·75 3·25
1248/51 .. .. *Set of* 4 6·00 6·50
MS1252 98×110 mm, $6.40, "Madonna and Child enthroned, surrounded by Saints" (Vivarini) (*vert*) .. .. 8·00 9·00

1990 (5 Dec). *"Birdpex '90" Stamp Exhibition, Christchurch, New Zealand. No.* **MS**1226 *optd with T* **245**.
MS1253 Four sheets, each 70×53 mm. As Nos. 1222/5, but with face values of $1, $1.25, $1.50, $1.75 and each size 50×32 mm .. *Set of* 4 *sheets* 11·00 12·00

65th BIRTHDAY

246 Columbus (engraving by Theodoro de Bry) (**247**)

1991 (14 Feb). *500th Anniv of Discovery of America by Columbus* (1992) (*1st issue*). *P* 13½×13.
1254 **246** $1 multicoloured .. .. .. 2·00 2·25
See also Nos. 1302/3.

1991 (22 Apr). *65th Birthday of Queen Elizabeth II. No.* 789 *optd with T* **247** *in gold.*
1255 $10 *Melithaea albitincta* .. .. .. 13·00 14·00

248 "Adoration of the Child" (G. delle Notti)

(Des G. Vasarhelyi. Litho Questa)

991 (12 Nov). *Christmas. Religious Paintings. T* **248** *and similar multicoloured designs. Ordinary paper. P* 14.

256 70 c. Type **248** . . . . 1·50 1·50
257 85 c. "The Birth of the Virgin" (B. Murillo) 1·75 1·75
258 $1.15, "Adoration of the Shepherds" (Rembrandt) . . . . . . 2·25 2·25
259 $1.50, "Adoration of the Shepherds" (L. le Nain) . . . . 3·25 3·75
256/9 . . . . *Set of* 4 8·00 8·50
MS1260 79×103 mm. $6.40, "Madonna and Child" (Lippi) (*vert*) . . . . 9·00 10·00

249 Red-breasted Wrasse **250** Tiger

(Litho Questa (5 c. to $2), Fournier ($3 to $15))

992 (22 Jan)–**94**. *Reef Life* (1st *series*). *T* **249** *and similar horiz designs. Multicoloured with white borders. Ordinary paper* (5 *c. to* $2) *or fluorescent security markings* ($3 *to* $15). *P* 14 (5 *c. to* $2) *or* 14×13½ ($3 *to* $15).

.261 5 c. Type **249** 40 40
.262 10 c. Blue Sea Star 40 40
.263 15 c. Bicoloured Angelfish ("Black and Gold Angelfish") 55 55
.264 20 c. Spotted Pebble Crab 70 70
.265 25 c. Black-tipped Grouper ("Black-tipped Cod") 70 70
.266 30 c. Spanish Dancer 70 70
.267 50 c. Regal Angelfish 90 90
.268 80 c. Big-scaled Soldierfish ("Squirrel Fish") . . . . 1·25 1·25
1269 85 c. Red Pencil Sea Urchin (23.3.92) . . 2·50 2·50
1270 90 c. Red-spotted Rainbowfish (23.3.92) . . 2·50 2·50
1271 $1 Cheek-lined Wrasse (23.3.92) . . 2·50 2·50
1272 $2 Long-nosed Butterflyfish (23.3.92) . . 2·50 2·50
1273 $3 Red-spotted Rainbowfish (25.10.93) . . 2·25 2·50
1274 $5 Blue Sea Star (25.10.93) . . . . 3·75 4·25
1275 $7 *Pygoplites diacanthus* (6.12.93) . . 7·00 8·00
1276 $10 Spotted Pebble Crab (31.1.94) . . 7·25 8·00
1277 $15 Red Pencil Sea Urchin (9.9.94) . . 13·00 14·00
1261/77 . . . . *Set of* 17 45·00 45·00

The 25 c., 50 c., $1 and $2 include a silhouette of the Queen's head.

Nos. 1273/7 are larger, 55×34 mm, and show a portrait of Queen Elizabeth II at left.

For some of these designs in a larger size, 40×30 mm, and with light cinnamon borders, see Nos. 1342/52.

(Litho B.D.T.)

1992 (6 June)–**93**. *Endangered Wildlife. T* **250** *and similar horiz designs. Multicoloured. Ordinary paper. P* 14.

1279 $1.15, Type **250** . . . . 1·25 1·25
1280 $1.15, Indian Elephant (7.6.92) . . . . 1·25 1·25
1281 $1.15, Brown Bear (8.6.92) . . . . 1·25 1·25
1282 $1.15, Black Rhinoceros (9.6.92) . . . . 1·25 1·25
1283 $1.15, Chimpanzee (10.6.92) . . . . 1·25 1·25
1284 $1.15, Argali (11.6.92) . . . . 1·25 1·25
1285 $1.15, Heaviside's Dolphin (13.7.92) . . 1·25 1·25
1286 $1.15, Eagle Owl (14.7.92) . . . . 1·25 1·25
1287 $1.15, Bee Hummingbird (15.7.92) . . 1·25 1·25
1288 $1.15, Puma (16.7.92) . . . . 1·25 1·25
1289 $1.15, European Otter (17.7.92) . . . . 1·25 1·25
1290 $1.15, Red Kangaroo (18.7.92) . . . . 1·25 1·25
1291 $1.15, Jackass Penguin (2.11.92) . . 1·25 1·25
1292 $1.15, Asian Lion (3.11.92) . . . . 1·25 1·25
1293 $1.15, Peregrine Falcon (4.11.92) . . 1·25 1·25
1294 $1.15, Persian Fallow Deer (5.11.92) . . 1·25 1·25
1295 $1.15, Key Deer (6.11.92) . . . . 1·25 1·25
1296 $1.15, Alpine Ibex (7.11.92) . . . . 1·25 1·25
1297 $1.15, Mandrill (1.2.93) . . . . 1·25 1·25
1298 $1.15, Gorilla (2.2.93) . . . . 1·25 1·25
1299 $1.15, *Vanessa atalanta* (butterfly) (3.2.93) 1·25 1·25
1300 $1.15, Takin (4.2.93) . . . . 1·25 1·25
1301 $1.15, Ring-tailed Lemur (5.2.93) . . 1·25 1·25
1279/1301 . . . . . . *Set of* 23 26·00 26·00

251 Columbus and Landing in New World

(Des G. Vasarhelyi. Litho B.D.T.)

1992 (22 May–21 Sept). *500th Anniv of Discovery of America by Columbus* (2nd *issue*). *Ordinary paper. P* 14×14½.

1302 **251** $6 multicoloured . . . . . . 6·50 7·50
MS1303 128×84 mm. $10 As T **251**, but detail of landing party only (40×29 *mm*). P 15×14 (21 Sept) . . . . 7·00 8·50

MINIMUM PRICE

The minimum price quote is 10p which represents a handling charge rather than a basis for valuing common stamps. For further notes about prices see introductory pages.

252 Football and $50 Commemorative Coin

(Des G. Vasarhelyi. Litho B.D.T.)

1992 (24 July). *Olympic Games, Barcelona* (2nd *issue*). *T* **252** *and similar horiz designs. Multicoloured. Ordinary paper. P* 13.

1304 $1.75, Type **252** . . . . 2·50 2·50
a. Horiz strip of 3. Nos. 1304/06 . . 6·75
1305 $1.75, Olympic Gold medal . . . . 2·50 2·50
1306 $1.75, Basketball and $10 coin . . . . 2·50 2·50
1307 $2.25, Running . . . . 3·50 3·50
a. Horiz strip of 3. Nos. 1307/09 . . 9·50
1308 $2.25, $10 and $50 coins . . . . 3·50 3·50
1309 $2.25, Cycling . . . . 3·50 3·50
1304/09 . . . . *Set of* 6 16·00 16·00
MS1310 155×91 mm. $6.40, Javelin throwing 9·00 10·00

Nos. 1304/06 and 1307/09 were each printed together, *se-tenant*, in horizontal strips of 3 throughout the sheets.

253 Festival Poster

ROYAL VISIT
(254)

(Litho B.D.T.)

1992 (16 Oct). *6th Festival of Pacific Arts, Rarotonga. T* **253** *and similar vert designs. Multicoloured. Ordinary paper. P* 15×14.

1311 80 c. Type **253** . . . . 1·00 1·10
1312 85 c. Seated Tangaroa carving . . . . 1·00 1·10
1313 $1 Seated Tangaroa carving (*different*) 1·10 1·25
1314 $1.75, Standing Tangaroa carving . . 2·00 2·50
1311/14 . . . . *Set of* 4 4·50 5·50

1992 (16 Oct). *Royal Visit by Prince Edward. Nos.* 1311/14 *optd with T* **254**.

1315 80 c. Type **253** . . . . 1·25 1·25
1316 85 c. Seated Tangaroa carving . . . . 1·25 1·25
1317 $1 Seated Tangaroa carving (*different*) 1·40 1·40
1318 $1.75, Standing Tangaroa carving . . 2·75 2·75
1315/18 . . . . *Set of* 4 6·00 6·00

255 "Worship of Shepherds" (Parmigianino)

256 Queen in Garter Robes

1992 (20 Nov). *Christmas. Religious Paintings by Parmigianino. T* **255** *and similar vert designs. Multicoloured. Ordinary paper. P* 13½.

1319 70 c. Type **255** . . . . 1·00 1·00
1320 85 c. "Virgin with Long Neck" . . . . 1·25 1·25
1321 $1.15, "Virgin with Rose" . . . . 1·50 1·75
1322 $1.90, "St. Margaret's Virgin" . . . . 2·75 3·75
1319/22 . . . . *Set of* 4 6·00 7·00
MS1323 86×102 mm. $6.40, As 85 c., but larger (36×46 *mm*) . . . . 8·00 9·00

(Litho B.D.T.)

1992 (10 Dec). *40th Anniv of Queen Elizabeth II's Accession. T* **256** *and similar vert designs. Multicoloured. Ordinary paper. P* 13½.

1324 80 c. Type **256** . . . . 1·50 1·50
1325 $1.15, Queen at Trooping the Colour . . 1·75 1·90
1326 $1.50, Queen in evening dress . . . . 2·50 2·75
1327 $1.95, Queen with bouquet . . . . 3·00 3·25
1324/7 . . . . *Set of* 4 8·00 8·50

257 Coronation Ceremony

(Des G. Vasarhelyi. Litho B.D.T.)

1993 (2 June). *40th Anniv of Coronation. T* **257** *and similar horiz designs. Multicoloured. P* 14.

1328 $1 Type **257** . . . . 1·75 1·75
1329 $2 Coronation photograph by Cecil Beaton 3·00 3·25
1330 $3 Royal family on balcony . . . . 4·25 4·50
1328/30 . . . . *Set of* 3 8·00 8·50

258 "Virgin with Child" (Filippo Lippi)

1993 (8 Nov). *Christmas. Religious Paintings. T* **258** *and similar vert designs. Multicoloured. Ordinary paper. P* 13½ ($4) *or* 14 (*others*).

1331 70 c. Type **258** 80 80
1332 85 c. "Bargellini Madonna" (Lodovico Carracci) 95 95
1333 $1.15, "Virgin of the Curtain" (Rafael Sanzio) . . . . 1·40 1·60
1334 $2.50, "Holy Family" (Agnolo Bronzino) 3·25 3·75
1335 $4 "Saint Zachary Virgin" (Parmigianino) (32×47 *mm*) . . . . 4·00 5·00
1331/5 . . . . *Set of* 5 9·50 11·00

259 Skiing, Flags and Ice Skating (*illustration further reduced. Actual size* 94×28 *mm*)

(Litho Questa)

1994 (11 Feb). *Winter Olympic Games, Lillehammer. P* 13½×14.

1336 **259** $5 multicoloured . . . . . . 6·00 7·00

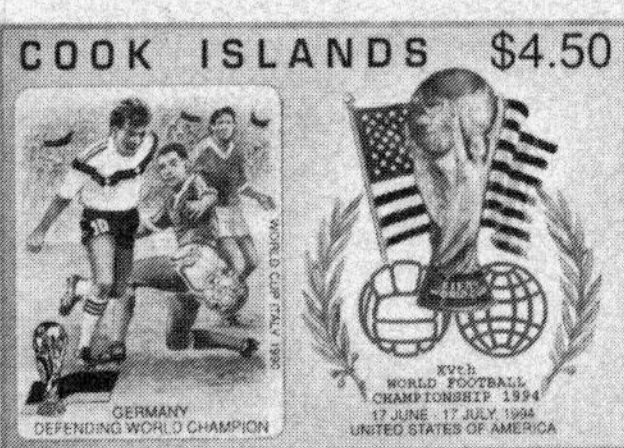

260 Cup on Logo with German and Argentinian Players

(Des G. Vasarhelyi. Litho B.D.T.)

1994 (17 June). *World Cup Football Championship, U.S.A. P* 14×14½.

1337 **260** $4.50, multicoloured . . . . . . 4·50 5·50

261 Neil Armstrong taking First Step on Moon

(Litho B.D.T.)

1994 (20 July). *25th Anniv of First Moon Landing. T* **261** *and similar horiz designs. Multicoloured. P* 14.

1338	$2.25, Type **261**	3·50	3·50
	a. Sheetlet. Nos. 1338/41×2	25·00	
1339	$2.25, Astronaut on Moon and view of Earth	3·50	3·50
1340	$2.25, Astronaut and flag	3·50	3·50
1341	$2.25, Astronaut with reflection in helmet visor	3·50	3·50
1338/41	.. .. *Set of* 4	12·50	12·50

Nos. 1338/41 were printed together, *se-tenant*, in sheetlets of 8 (2×4), containing two of each design, with Nos. 1338/9 in the top two rows and Nos. 1340/1 in the bottom two. Each row shows two different designs with a half stamp-size *se-tenant* label in the centre.

(Litho B.D.T.)

1994 (24 Oct). *Reef Life (2nd series). As Nos.* 1261 *and* 1263/71, *but each* 40×30 *mm and with light cinnamon borders. P* 15×14.

1342	5 c. Type **249**	30	30
1344	15 c. Bicoloured Angelfish	40	40
1345	20 c. Spotted Pebble Crab	45	45
1346	25 c. Black-tipped Grouper	50	50
1347	30 c. Spanish Dancer	50	50
1348	50 c. Regal Angelfish	60	60
1349	80 c. Big-scaled Soldierfish	85	85
1350	85 c. Red Pencil Sea Urchin	85	85
1351	90 c. Red-spotted Rainbowfish	90	90
1352	$1 Cheek-lined Wrasse	1·00	1·00
1342/52	.. .. *Set of* 10	5·50	5·50

Nos. 1261 and 1263/71, which were printed by Questa, are 35×27 mm and have white borders.

262 Actors in Outrigger Canoe

263 "The Virgin and Child" (Morales)

(Litho B.D.T.)

1994 (23 Nov)–**97.** *Release of* The Return of Tommy Tricker *(film shot in Cook Islands). T* **262** *and similar horiz designs showing scenes from film. Multicoloured. P* 14.

1359	85 c. Type **262**	1·10	1·25
	a. Sheetlet. Nos. 1359/64	6·00	
1360	85 c. Male and female dancers	1·10	1·25
1361	85 c. European couple on beach ..	1·10	1·25
1362	85 c. Aerial view of island	1·10	1·25
1363	85 c. Two female dancers	1·10	1·25
1364	85 c. Cook Islands couple on beach	1·10	1·25
1364*a*	90 c. Type **262** (28.8.97)	65	70
	ab. Sheetlet. Nos. 1364*a/f*	4·00	
1364*b*	90 c. As No. 1360 (28.8.97)	65	70
1364*c*	90 c. As No. 1361 (28.8.97)	65	70
1364*d*	90 c. As No. 1362 (28.8.97)	65	70
1364*e*	90 c. As No. 1363 (28.8.97)	65	70
1364*f*	90 c. As No. 1364 (28.8.97)	65	70
1359/64*f*	.. .. *Set of* 12	10·00	11·50

Nos. 1359/64 and 1364*a/f* were each printed together, *se-tenant*, in sheetlets of 6.

(Litho B.D.T.)

1994 (30 Nov). *Christmas. Religious Paintings. T* **263** *and similar vert designs. Multicoloured. P* 14.

1365	85 c. Type **263**	1·10	1·25
	a. Block of 4. Nos. 1365/8	4·00	
1366	85 c. "Adoration of the Kings" (Gerard David)	1·10	1·25
1367	85 c. "Adoration of the Kings" (Foppa) ..	1·10	1·25
1368	85 c. "The Madonna and Child with St. Joseph and Infant Baptist" (Baroccio)	1·10	1·25
1369	$1 "Madonna with Iris" (Dürer) ..	1·25	1·40
	a. Block of 4. Nos. 1369/72	4·50	
1370	$1 "Adoration of the Shepherds" (Le Nain)	1·25	1·40
1371	$1 "The Virgin and Child" (school of Leonardo)	1·25	1·40
1372	$1 "The Mystic Nativity" (Botticelli) ..	1·25	1·40
1365/72	.. .. *Set of* 8	8·50	9·50

Nos. 1365/8 and 1369/72 were printed together, *se-tenant*, in blocks of 4 throughout the sheets.

264 Pirates (*Treasure Island*)

(Des G. Vasarhelyi. Litho B.D.T.)

1994 (12 Dec). *Death Centenary of Robert Louis Stevenson (author). T* **264** *and similar horiz designs. Multicoloured. P* 14×15.

1373	$1.50, Type **264**	1·60	1·90
	a. Block of 4. Nos. 1373/6	5·75	
1374	$1.50, Duel (*David Balfour*)	1·60	1·90
1375	$1.50, Mr. Hyde (*Dr. Jekyll and Mr. Hyde*)	1·60	1·90
1376	$1.50, Rowing boat and sailing ship (*Kidnapped*)	1·60	1·90
1373/6	.. .. *Set of* 4	5·75	7·00

Nos. 1373/6 were printed together, *se-tenant*, in blocks of 4 throughout the sheet.

265 U.N. and National Flags with Peace Doves

(Des G. Vasarhelyi. Litho B.D.T.)

1995 (17 July). *50th Anniv of United Nations. P* 13.

1377	**265** $4.75, multicoloured	4·75	6·00

266 Queen Elizabeth the Queen Mother and Coat of Arms

(Des G. Vasarhelyi. Litho B.D.T.)

1995 (31 Aug). *95th Birthday of Queen Elizabeth the Queen Mother. P* 13.

1378	**266** $5 multicoloured	6·00	7·00

267 German Delegation signing Unconditional Surrender at Rheims

(Litho B.D.T.)

1995 (4 Sept). *50th Anniv of End of Second World War. T* **267** *and similar horiz design. Multicoloured. P* 13.

1379	$3.50, Type **267**	4·75	5·50
	a. Pair. Nos. 1379/80	9·50	11·00
1380	$3.50, Japanese delegation on U.S.S. *Missouri*, Tokyo Bay	4·75	5·50

Nos. 1379/80 were printed together, *se-tenant* horizontally and vertically, in sheets of 4.

(Des G. Vasarhelyi. Litho B.D.T.)

1995 (12 Oct). *50th Anniv of Food and Agriculture Organization. Horiz design as T* **265**. *Multicoloured. P* 13×13½.

1381	$4.50, F.A.O. and U.N. emblems	4·75	6·00

268 Green Turtle

269 Emblem and Throwing the Discus

(Litho B.D.T.)

1995 (20 Nov). *Year of the Sea Turtle. T* **268** *and similar horiz designs. Multicoloured. P* 13½×14.

1382	85 c. Type **268**	1·60	1·60
1383	$1 Hawksbill Turtle	1·75	1·75
1384	$1.75, Green Turtle on beach	2·75	2·75
1385	$2.25, Young Hawksbill Turtles hatching	3·25	3·25
1382/5	.. .. *Set of* 4	8·50	8·50

(Litho B.D.T.)

1996 (12 Jan). *Olympic Games, Atlanta. T* **269** *and simil horiz designs. Multicoloured. P* 14.

1386	85 c. Type **269**	1·10	1·1
1387	$1 Athlete with Olympic Torch ..	1·40	1·4
1388	$1.50, Running	1·90	1·9
1389	$1.85, Gymnastics	2·25	2·2
1390	$2.10, Ancient archery	2·50	2·5
1391	$2.50, Throwing the javelin	2·75	2·7
1386/91	.. .. *Set of* 6	10·50	10·5

270 Queen Elizabeth II

28th South Pacific Forum

(**271**)

(Des G. Vasarhelyi. Litho)

1996 (21 June). *70th Birthday of Queen Elizabeth II. T* **270** *an similar vert designs. Multicoloured. P* 14.

1392	$1.90, Type **270**	2·25	2·2
1393	$2.25, Wearing tiara	2·75	2·7
1394	$2.75, In Garter robes	3·00	3·0
1392/4	.. .. *Set of* 3	7·25	7·2
MS1395	103×152 mm. Designs as Nos. 1392/4, but each with a face value of $2.50	9·50	10·5

1997 (12 Sept). *28th South Pacific Forum. Nos.* 1364*a/f opt with T* **271** (*Nos.* 1396, 1399/400) *or* "12–22 September 1997 (*Nos.* 1397/8 *and* 1401), *all in silver.*

1396	90 c. Type **262**	90	1·0
	a. Sheetlet. Nos. 1396/1401	4·75	
1397	90 c. As No. 1360	90	1·0
1398	90 c. As No. 1361	90	1·0
1399	90 c. As No. 1362	90	1·0
1400	90 c. As No. 1363	90	1·0
1401	90 c. As No. 1364	90	1·0
1396/1401	.. .. .. *Set of* 6	4·75	5·5

272 *Lampides boeticus* (female)

(Litho B.D.T.)

1997 (22 Oct)–**98.** *Butterflies. T* **272** *and similar horiz designs Multicoloured. P* 13×13½ (5 *c. to* $1) *or* 13½ ($1.50 *to* $15).

1402	5 c. Type **272**	10	1
1403	10 c. *Vanessa atalanta*	10	1
1404	15 c. *Lampides boeticus* (male)	10	1
1405	20 c. *Papilio godeffroyi*	15	2
1406	25 c. *Danaus hamata*	15	2
1407	30 c. *Xois sesara*	20	2
1408	50 c. *Vagrans egista*	30	3
1409	70 c. *Parthenos sylvia*	45	5
1410	80 c. *Hyblaea sanguinea* (12.11.97) ..	50	55
1411	85 c. *Melanitis leda* (12.11.97)	55	60
1412	90 c. *Ascalapha odorata* (12.11.97) ..	55	60
1413	$1 *Precis villida* (12.11.97)	65	70
1414	$1.50, *Parthenos sylvia* (11.3.98) ..	95	1·00
1415	$2 *Lampides boeticus* (female) (11.3.98)	1·25	1·40
1416	$3 *Precis villida* (11.3.98)	1·90	2·00
1417	$4 *Melanitis leda* (19.6.98)	2·50	2·75
1418	$5 *Vagrans egista* (19.6.98)	3·25	3·50
1419	$7 *Hyblaea sanguinea* (18.9.98) ..	4·50	4·75
1420	$10 *Vanessa atalanta* (18.9.98)	6·25	6·50
1421	$15 *Papilio godeffroyi* (13.11.98) ..	9·00	9·50
1402/21	.. .. *Set of* 19	33·00	35·00

The $1 includes an outline portrait of Queen Elizabeth II. Nos. 1414/21 are larger, 41×25 mm, with the Queen's portrait included on the $4 to $15.

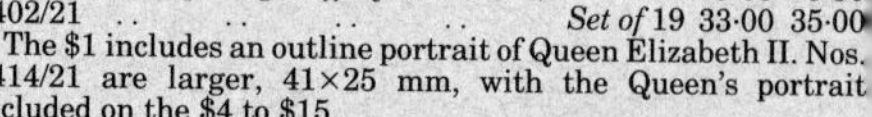

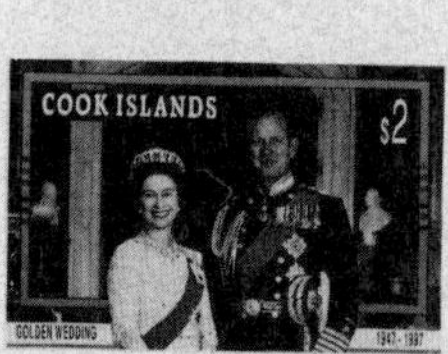

273 Queen Elizabeth and Prince Philip

274 Diana, Princess of Wales

1997 (20 Nov). *Golden Wedding of Queen Elizabeth and Prince Philip. P* 14.

1424	**273** $2 multicoloured	1·75	2·00
MS1425	76×102 mm. **273** $5 multicoloured ..	4·50	5·00

1998 (18 Mar). *Diana, Princess of Wales Commemoration. Litho. P* 14.

1426	$1.15, Type **274**	1·10	1·25
	a. Sheetlet. No. 1426×5 plus label ..	5·00	
MS1427	70×100 mm. $3.50, Princess Diana and guard of honour	3·00	3·50

No. 1426 was printed in sheetlets of 5 stamps with a label at top left.

+ $1

CHILDREN'S CHARITIES

(275)

998 (20 Nov). *Children's Charities. No.* **MS**1427 *surch with T* **275** *in silver.*

MS1428	70×100 mm. $3.50+$1 Princess Diana and guard of honour	3·50	4·00

STAMP BOOKLETS

1982 (June). *Royal Wedding. Multicoloured cover, 130×74 mm, showing Prince and Princess of Wales. Stitched.*

SB1	$6 booklet containing $1 and $2 (Nos. 812/13), each in pair	4·25

OFFICIAL STAMPS

O.H.M.S. (O 1) O.H.M.S. (O 2)

1975 (17 Mar–19 May). *Nos.* 228/31, 233, 235/7, 239/40, 243/5 *and* 246c/7 *optd with Type* O **1** (5, 10, 18, 25 *and* 30 c. *surch also), in black and silver*

O 1	1 c. *Hibiscus syriacus*		
O 2	2 c. Frangipani		
O 3	3 c. "Suva Queen"		
O 4	4 c. Water Lily		
O 5	5 c. on 2½ c. *Clitoria ternatea*		
O 6	8 c. *Allamanda cathartica*		
O 7	10 c. on 6 c. Hibiscus		
O 8	18 c. on 20 c. Thunbergia		
O 9	25 c. on 9 c. Stephanotis		
O10	30 c. on 15 c. Frangipani		
O11	50 c. *Gardinia taitensis*		
O12	$1 Type **80**		
O13	$2 Type **80**		
O14	$4 Type **81** (19 May)		
O15	$6 Type **81** (19 May)		
O1/15	*Set of* 15	†	15·00

These stamps were only sold to the public cancelled-to-order and not in unused condition.

1978 (19 Oct)–**79**. *Nos.* 466/7, 474, 478/81, 484/5, 542 *and* 568/9 *optd or surch* (2, 5, 10, 15, 18 *and* 35 c.) *as Type* O **2**.

O16	1 c. Common Pacific Vase (*Vasum turbinellum*) (Silver)	60	10
O17	2 c. on ½ c. Type **141**	60	10
O18	5 c. on ½ c. Type **141**	60	10
O19	10 c. on 8 c. Granulate Frog Shell (*Bursa granularis*) (Silver)	65	10
O20	15 c. on 50 c. Textile or Cloth of Gold Cone (*Conus textile*) (Silver)	90	10
O21	18 c. on 60 c. Red-mouth Olive (*Oliva miniacea miniacea*) (Silver)	90	15
O22	25 c. Royal Oak Scallop (*Cryptopecten pallium*)	1·00	20
O23	30 c. Soldier Cone (*Conus miles*) (Silver)	1·00	25
O24	35 c. on 60 c. Red-mouth Olive (*Oliva miniacea miniacea*) (Silver)	1·25	30
O25	50 c. Textile or Cloth of Gold Cone (*Conus textile*) (Silver)	1·75	35
O26	60 c. Red-mouth Oliva (*Oliva miniacea miniacea*) (Silver)	2·00	45
O27	$1 Queen and Prince Philip (Silver)	4·00	65
O28	$1 Royal Visit, 1974 (Silver)	4·00	65
O29	$2 Captain Cook and H.M.S. *Resolution*	7·00	2·25
O30	$4 Queen Elizabeth II and seashells (15.2.79)	12·00	2·25
O31	$6 As $4 (15.2.79)	12·00	3·50
O16/31	*Set of* 16	45·00	10·00

These stamps were originally only sold to the public cancelled-to-order and not in unused condition. They were made available to overseas collectors in mint condition during 1980.

75c

O.H.M.S. (O 3) O.H.M.S. (O 4)

O.H.M.S. (O 5)

1985 (10 July)–**90**. (*a*) *Nos.* 969/74, 976, 978, 981, 984/6 *and* 988/9 *optd or surch as Type* O **3** *by silver foil embossing.*

O32	5 c. *Ptilosarcus gurneyi*	50	50
O33	10 c. *Lobophyllia bemprichii*	50	50
	a. Opt double, one albino	50·00	
O34	12 c. *Sarcophyton digitatum* (5.5.86)	1·50	60
O35	14 c. *Pavona praetorta* (5.5.86)	1·50	60
O36	18 c. *Junceella gemmacea* (5.5.86)	1·50	60
O37	20 c. *Stylaster*	60	50
O38	30 c. *Palauastrea ramosa*	60	50
O39	40 c. *Stylaster echinatus*	60	50
O40	50 c. *Melithaea squamata* (5.5.86)	2·25	70
O41	55 c. on 85 c. *Caulastraea echinulata*	70	50
	a. "O.H.M.S." albino	†	—
O42	60 c. *Tubastraea*	70	60
O43	70 c. *Heliofungia actiniformis* (5.5.86)	2·50	85
O44	$1.10, *Pectinia alcicornis*	1·10	90
O45	$2 on $1.20, *Dendrophyllia gracilis*	2·00	1·75

(*b*) *Nos.* 862/5 *surch with Type* O **4** *by gold foil embossing*

O46	75 c. on 60 c. Type **197** (5.5.86)	2·75	1·00
O47	75 c. on 60 c. Rarotonga oranges (5.5.86)	2·75	1·00
O48	75 c. on 60 c. Rarotonga Airport (5.5.86)	2·75	1·00
O49	75 c. on 60 c. Prime Minister Sir Thomas Davis (5.5.86)	2·75	1·00

(*c*) *Nos.* 786/9 *surch as T* **209** *in silver and black further optd with Type* O **5** *by silver foil embossing.*

O50	$5 on $3 *Heliofungia actiniformis* (5.5.86)	7·00	4·75
O51	$9 on $4 *Stylophora pistillata* (30.5.89)	8·00	8·25
O52	$14 on $6 *Stylaster echinatus* (12.7.89)	12·50	13·00
O53	$18 on $10 *Melithaea albitincta* (4.6.90)	17·00	17·00
O32/53	*Set of* 22	65·00	50·00

O.H.M.S. (O 6)

1995 (24 Feb)–**98.** *Nos.* 1261/72 *optd with Type* O **3** *and Nos.* 1273/6 *with Type* O **6**, *both by silver foil embossing.*

O54	5 c. Type **249**	10	10
O55	10 c. Blue Sea Star	10	10
O56	15 c. Bicoloured Angelfish	10	15
O57	20 c. Spotted Pebble Crab	15	20
O58	25 c. Black-tipped Grouper	15	20
O59	30 c. Spanish Dancer	20	25
O60	50 c. Regal Angelfish	30	35
O61	80 c. Big-scaled Soldierfish	50	55
O62	85 c. Red Pencil Sea Urchin	55	60
O63	90 c. Red-spotted Rainbowfish	55	60
O64	$1 Cheek-lined Wrasse (15.5.95)	65	70
O65	$2 Long-nosed Butterflyfish (15.5.95)	1·25	1·40
O66	$3 Red-spotted Rainbowfish (17.7.98)	1·90	2·00
O67	$5 Blue Sea Star (17.7.98)	3·25	3·50
O68	$7 *Pygoplites diacanthus* (17.7.98)	4·50	4·75
O69	$10 Spotted Pebble Crab (12.11.98)	6·25	6·50
O54/69	*Set of* 16	20·00	21·00

AITUTAKI

Stamps of COOK ISLANDS were used in Aitutaki from 1892 until 1903.

PRICES FOR STAMPS ON COVER TO 1945

Nos. 1/7	*from* × 4
Nos. 9/14	*from* × 3
Nos. 15/29	*from* × 4
Nos. 30/2	*from* × 6

A. NEW ZEALAND DEPENDENCY

The island of Aitutaki, under British protection from 1888, was annexed by New Zealand on 11 June 1901.

Stamps of New Zealand overprinted or surcharged. For illustrations of New Zealand watermarks and definitive types see the beginning of Cook Islands.

AITUTAKI. (1) — **Ava Pene.** (2) ½d.

Tai Pene. (3) 1d. — **Rua Pene Ma Te Ava.** (4) 2½d.

Toru Pene. (5) 3d. — **Ono Pene.** (6) 6d.

Tai Tiringi. (7) 1s.

1903 (29 June)–**11**. *T* **23**, **27/8**, **31**, **34** *and* **42** *surch with T* **1** *at top and T* **2** *to* **7** *at foot. Thin, hard Cowan paper. W* **43**.

(*a*) *P* 14

1 ½d. green (No. 302) (R.) .. .. .. 4·25 6·50
2 1d. carmine (No. 303) (B.) .. .. .. 4·75 5·50
3 2½d. deep blue (No. 320*a*) (R.) (9.11) .. 8·00 18·00
a. "Ava" without stop £130 £170
1/3 .. .. *Set of* 3 15·00 27·00

(*b*) *P* 11

4 2½d. blue (No. 308) (R.) .. .. .. 11·00 12·00
5 3d. yellow-brown (No. 309) (B.) .. .. 15·00 15·00
6 6d. rose-red (No. 312*a*) (B.) .. .. 28·00 25·00
7 1s. bright red (No. 315*a*) (B.) .. .. 55·00 85·00
a. "Tiringi" without stop (R. 7/12) .. £400 £550
b. Orange-red .. .. .. 65·00 95·00
ba. "Tiringi" without stop (R. 7/12) .. £500 £650
c. Orange-brown £140 £160
ca. "Tiringi" without stop (R. 7/12) .. £1000 £1200
4/7 .. .. *Set of* 4 £100 £120

Nos. 1/2 and 4/7 were placed on sale in Auckland on 12 June 1903.

There were four states of the overprint used for No. 3. On the first the "no stop" variety (No. 3a) occurs on R. 6/8, on the second it appears on R. 1/4, 2/4 and 6/8, on the third on R. 5/8 and 6/8, and on the fourth all stops are present.

AITUTAKI.

Ono Pene.

(8)

1911–16. *T* **51** *and* **53** *surch with T* **1** *at top and T* **2** *or* **3** *at foot and T* **52** *surch as T* **8**. *P* 14×15 (½*d.*, 1*d.*) *or* 14×14½ (*others*).

9 ½d. green (No. 387) (R.) (9.11) .. .. 1·00 2·75
10 1d. carmine (No. 405) (B.) (2.13) .. .. 3·00 9·50
11 6d. carmine (No. 392) (B.) (23.5.16) .. 40·00 90·00
12 1s. vermilion (No. 394) (B.) (9.14) .. 55·00 £140
9/12 .. .. *Set of* 4 90·00 £225

1916–17. *T* **60** (*recess*) *surch as T* **8**. *W* **43**. *P* 14×13½.

13 6d. carmine (No. 425) (B.) (6.6.16) .. .. 14·00 50·00
a. Perf 14×14½ .. .. 7·50 25·00
b. Vert pair. Nos. 13/13a .. .. .. 50·00 £150
14 1s. vermilion (No. 430) (B.) (3.17) .. .. 28·00 90·00
a. Perf 14×14½ .. .. 35·00 90·00
ab. "Tai" without dot (R. 8/9, 9/12, 10/12) .. £225 £425
ac. "Tiringi" without dot on second "i" (R. 8/12, 10/7) £275 £425
ad. "Tiringi" without dot on third "i" (R. 8/11) £350 £550
b. Vert pair. Nos. 14/14a £140 £350

1917–18. *T* **60** (*recess*) *optd* "AITUTAKI" *only, as in T* **8**. *W* **43**. *P* 14×13½.

15 2½d. blue (No. 419) (R.) (12.18) .. .. 2·00 15·00
a. Perf 14×14½ .. .. 1·75 15·00
b. Vert pair. Nos. 15/15a .. .. .. 40·00 £130
16 3d. chocolate (No. 420) (B.) (1.18) .. .. 1·75 18·00
a. Perf 14×14½ .. .. 1·50 18·00
b. Vert pair. Nos. 16/16a .. .. .. 38·00 £140
17 6d. carmine (No. 425) (B.) (11.17) .. .. 7·50 21·00
a. Perf 14×14½ .. .. 4·75 20·00
b. Vert pair. Nos. 17/17a .. .. .. 50·00 £140
18 1s. vermilion (No. 430) (B.) (11.17) .. .. 17·00 38·00
a. Perf 14×14½ .. .. 12·00 27·00
b. Vert pair. Nos. 18/18a .. .. .. 75·00 £180
15/18 .. .. *Set of* 4 18·00 70·00

1917–20. *T* **53** *and* **61** (*typo*) *optd* "AITUTAKI" *only, as in T* **8**. *W* **43**. *P* 14×15.

19 ½d. green (No. 435) (R.) (2.20) .. .. 1·00 5·50
20 1d. carmine (No. 405) (B.) (5.20) .. .. 3·25 20·00
21 1½d. slate (No. 437) (R.) (11.17) .. .. 3·75 30·00
22 1½d. orange-brown (No. 438) (R.) (2.19) .. 80 7·00
23 3d. chocolate (No. 440) (B.) (6.19) .. .. 3·50 14·00
19/23 .. .. *Set of* 5 11·00 70·00

(Des and recess Perkins, Bacon & Co)

1920 (23 Aug). *T* **9/14** *of Cook Islands, but inscr* "AITUTAKI". *No wmk. P* 14.

24 ½d. black and green .. .. .. 3·50 24·00
25 1d. black and dull carmine .. .. .. 3·50 17·00
a. Double derrick flaw (R.2/8, 3/6 or 5/2) 11·00
26 1½d. black and sepia .. .. .. 6·00 12·00
27 3d. black and deep blue .. .. .. 2·00 14·00
28 6d. red-brown and slate .. .. .. 5·00 14·00
29 1s. black and purple .. .. .. 9·50 16·00
24/9 .. .. *Set of* 6 26·00 85·00

(Recess Govt Printing Office, Wellington)

1924–27. *T* **9/10** *and* **16** *of Cook Islands, but inscr* "AITUTAKI". *W* **43** *of New Zealand. P* 14.

30 ½d. black and green (5.27) .. .. .. 2·00 9·00
31 1d. black and deep carmine (10.24) .. .. 6·00 6·50
a. Double derrick flaw (R.2/8, 3/6 or 5/2) 15·00
32 2½d. black and dull blue (10.27) .. .. 7·50 50·00
30/2 .. .. *Set of* 3 14·00 60·00

Cook Islands stamps superseded those of Aitutaki on 15 March 1932. Separate issues were resumed in 1972.

B. PART OF COOK ISLANDS

On 9 August 1972, Aitutaki became a Port of Entry into the Cook Islands, and at the close of business on the previous day, Cook Islands stamps were withdrawn from sale there. Whilst remaining part of the Cook Islands, Aitutaki has a separate postal service.

(New Currency. 100 cents = 1 dollar)

PRINTERS. The following stamps, *unless otherwise stated*, were printed, in photogravure until No. **MS**613 and in lithography thereafter, by Heraclio Fournier, Spain. All such issues are, *unless otherwise stated*, on paper treated with fluorescent security markings, and with synthetic gum. The fluorescent markings can be found inverted or omitted.

(9)

Aitutaki

(10)

(Optd by Govt Printer, Wellington)

1972 (9 Aug). *Nos.* 227B *etc. of Cook Is. optd with T* **9** (*applied horizontally on* $1), *by New Zealand Govt Printer.*

33 ½ c. Type **79** 30 80
34 1 c. *Hibiscus syriacus* .. .. .. 70 1·40
35 2½ c. *Clitoria ternatea* .. .. .. 2·25 7·00
36 4 c. Water Lily (No. 233B) 70 85
37 5 c. *Bauhinia bi-pinnata rosea* .. .. 2·50 7·50
38 10 c. *Poinciana regia flamboyant* .. .. 2·50 5·50
39 20 c. Thunbergia .. .. 1·25 1·00
40 25 c. Canna Lily .. .. 70 1·00
41 50 c. *Gardinia taitensis* .. .. .. 2·75 2·75
42 $1 Type **80** .. .. 4·00 5·50
*a. Shade** .. .. 20·00
33/42 .. .. *Set of* 10 16·00 30·00

* No. 42*a* has the border flowers predominantly in a carmine colour instead of scarlet, and may be due to a missing yellow colour.

1972 (27 Oct). *Christmas. Nos.* 406/8 *of Cook. Is. optd in silver with T* **10**.

43 **130** 1 c. multicoloured 10 10
44 – 5 c. multicoloured 15 15
45 – 10 c. multicoloured 15 25
43/5 .. .. *Set of* 3 30 40

1972 (20 Nov). *Royal Silver Wedding. As Nos.* 413 *and* 415 *of Cook Is., but inscr* "COOK ISLANDS Aitutaki".

46 **131** 5 c. black and silver .. .. .. 3·50 2·75
47 – 15 c. black and silver .. .. .. 1·50 1·50

AITUTAKI

(11)

(12)

1972 (24 Nov). *No.* 245B *of Cook Is. optd with T* **11** *by Govt Printer, Rarotonga.*

48 **80** $2 multicoloured 50 75
a. Optd "AJTUTAKI" for "AITUTAKI" (R. 2/4) .. .. 25·00
b. On No. 245A (gum arabic printing) .. 50·00
ba. Optd "AJTUTAKI" for "AITUTAKI" (R. 2/4) .. ..

1972 (11 Dec). *Nos.* 227B *etc of Cook Is. optd with T* **12**, *by Heraclio Fournier.*

49 ½ c. Type **79** 15 10
50 1 c. *Hibiscus syriacus* 15 10
51 2½ c. *Clitoria ternatea* 20 10
52 4 c. Water Lily (No. 233B) 25 15
53 5 c. *Bauhinia bi-pinnata rosea* 25 15
54 10 c. *Poinciana regia flamboyant* 35 25
55 20 c. Thunbergia .. .. 1·00 50
56 25 c. Canna Lily 50 55
57 50 c. *Gardinia taitensis* 75 90
58 $1 Type **80** .. .. 1·25 1·75
49/58 .. .. *Set of* 10 4·25 4·00

13 "Christ Mocked" (Grünewald)

AITUTAKI

(14)

1973 (6 Apr). *Easter. T* **13** *and similar vert designs. Mult coloured. P* 13.

59 1 c. Type **13** 15
60 1 c. "St. Veronica" (Van der Weyden) .. 15
61 1 c. "The Crucified Christ with Virgin Mary, Saints and Angels" (Raphael) 15
62 1 c. "Resurrection" (Piero della Francesca) .. 15
63 5 c. "The Last Supper" (Master of Amiens) .. 20
64 5 c. "Condemnation" (Holbein) 20
65 5 c. "Christ on the Cross" (Rubens) 20
66 5 c. "Resurrection" (El Greco) 20
67 10 c. "Disrobing of Christ" (El Greco) 25
68 10 c. "St. Veronica" (Van Oostsanen) 25
69 10 c. "Christ on the Cross" (Rubens) 25
70 10 c. "Resurrection" (Bouts) 25
59/70 .. .. *Set of* 12 2·25 1·2

Nos. 59/62, 63/6 and 67/70 were each printed together, *se-tenan* in blocks of 4 throughout the sheet.

1973 (14 May). *Silver Wedding Coinage. Nos.* 417/23 *of Cook I. optd in silver and black as T* **14**.

71 1 c. black, rosy carmine and gold 10
72 2 c. black, bright blue and gold 10
73 5 c. black, green and silver 15
74 10 c. black, royal blue and silver 20
75 20 c. black, deep blue-green and silver .. 30 1
76 50 c. black, carmine and silver 50 3
77 $1 black, bright blue and silver 70 4
71/7 .. .. *Set of* 7 1·90 1·0

TENTH ANNIVERSARY
CESSATION
OF
NUCLEAR TESTING
TREATY

(15)

16 Red Hibiscus and Princess Anne

1973 (13 Aug). *Tenth Anniv of Treaty Banning Nuclear Testing Nos.* 236B, 238B, 240B *and* 243B *of Cook Is. optd with T* **15** *an T* **12** *together.*

78 8 c. *Allamanda cathartica* 15
79 10 c. *Poinciana regia flamboyant* 15
80 20 c. Thunbergia 30
81 50 c. *Gardinia taitensis* 70
78/81 .. .. *Set of* 4 1·10

1973 (14 Nov). *Royal Wedding. T* **16** *and similar horiz design Multicoloured. P* 13½ × 14.

82 25 c. Type **16** 25
83 30 c. Capt. Phillips and Blue Hibiscus .. 25
MS84 114 × 65 mm. Nos. 82/3. P 13 50

17 "Virgin and Child" (Montagna)

18 Rose-branch Murex (*Murex ramosus*)

1973 (10 Dec). *Christmas. T* **17** *and similar vert designs showing "The Virgin and Child" by the artists listed. Multicoloured. P* 13½.

85 1 c. Type **17** 10
86 1 c. Crivelli 10
87 1 c. Van Dyck 10
88 1 c. Perugino 10
89 5 c. Veronese (child at shoulder) 25
90 5 c. Veronese (child on lap) 25
91 5 c. Cima 25
92 5 c. Memling 25
93 10 c. Memling 25
94 10 c. Del Colle 25
95 10 c. Raphael 25
96 10 c. Lotto 25
85/96 .. .. *Set of* 12 2·00

Nos. 85/8, 89/92 and 93/6 were each printed together, *se-tenant*, in blocks of 4 throughout the sheet.

1974 (31 Jan)–**75**. *T* **18** *and similar horiz designs showing sea-shells. Multicoloured. P* 13.

97 ½ c. Type **18** 90 80
98 1 c. New Caledonia Nautilus (*Nautilus macromphallus*) 90 80

9 2 c. Common or Major Harp (*Harpa major*) 90 80
0 3 c. Striped Bonnet (*Phalium flammiferum*) 90 80
1 4 c. Mole Cowrie (*Cypraea talpa*) .. 90 80
2 5 c. Pontifical Mitre (*Mitra stictica*) .. 90 80
3 8 c. Trumpet Triton (*Charonia tritonis*) .. 90 80
4 10 c. Venus Comb Murex (*Murex pecten*) .. 90 80
5 20 c. Red-mouth Olive (*Oliva miniacea marrati*) .. .. 1·25 80
6 25 c. Ruddy Frog Shell (*Bursa rubeta*) .. 1·25 80
7 60 c. Widest Pacific Conch (*Strombus latissimus*) .. .. 3·00 1·25
8 $1 Maple-leaf Triton or Winged Frog Shell (*Biplex perca*) .. .. 2·50 1·40
9 $2 Queen Elizabeth II and Marlin-spike Auger (*Terebra maculata*) (20.1.75) .. 6·00 9·00
0 $5 Queen Elizabeth II and Tiger Cowrie (*Cypraea tigris*) (28.2.75) .. .. 27·00 10·00
/110 .. .. *Set of* 14 42·00 27·00
Nos. 109/110 are larger, 53×25 mm.

19 Bligh and H.M.S. *Bounty*

(Des G. Vasarhelyi)

974 (11 Apr). *William Bligh's Discovery of Aitutaki. T* **19** *and similar horiz designs. Multicoloured. P* 13½.
4 1 c. Type **19** 25 35
5 1 c. H.M.S. *Bounty* 25 35
6 5 c. Bligh, and H.M.S. *Bounty* at Aitutaki 55 45
7 5 c. Aitutaki chart of 1856 .. .. .. 55 45
8 8 c. Capt. Cook and H.M.S. *Resolution* .. 85 60
9 8 c. Map of Aitutaki and inset location map 85 60
4/19 .. .. *Set of* 6 3·00 2·50
Nos. 114/15, 116/17 and 118/19 were each printed together, *se-tenant*, in horizontal and vertical pairs throughout the sheet.
See also Nos. 123/8.

20 Aitutaki Stamps of 1903, and Map

21 "Virgin and Child" (Hugo van der Goes)

74 (15 July). *Centenary of Universal Postal Union. T* **20** *and similar horiz design. Multicoloured. P* 13½ × 14.
0 25 c. Type **20** 65 50
1 50 c. Stamps of 1903 and 1920, and map .. 85 75
S122 66 × 75 mm. Nos. 120/1. P 13 .. .. 1·50 2·50
Each value was issued in sheets of 5 stamps and 1 label.

974 (9 Sept). *Air. As Nos.* 114/119, *but larger* (46 × 26 *mm*), *denominations changed, and inscr* "AIR MAIL".
3 10 c. Type **19** 60 40
4 10 c. H.M.S. *Bounty* 60 40
5 25 c. Bligh, and H.M.S. *Bounty* at Aitutaki 70 50
6 25 c. Aitutaki chart of 1856 .. .. .. 70 50
7 30 c. Capt. Cook and H.M.S. *Resolution* .. 80 50
8 30 c. Map of Aitutaki and inset location map 80 50
23/8 .. .. *Set of* 6 3·75 2·50
Nos. 123/4, 125/6 and 127/8 were each printed together, *se-tenant*, in horizontal and vertical pairs throughout the sheet.

974 (11 Oct). *Christmas. T* **21** *and similar vert designs showing "Virgin and Child" by the artists listed. Multicoloured. P* 13.
29 1 c. Type **21** 10 10
30 5 c. Bellini 10 10
31 8 c. Gerard David 10 10
32 10 c. Antonello da Messina 10 10
33 25 c. Joos van Cleve 20 20
34 30 c. Master of the Life of St. Catherine .. 20 20
29/34 .. .. *Set of* 6 65 65
S135 127 × 134 mm. Nos. 129/34 .. .. 1·40 1·60
Each value was issued in sheets of 15 stamps and 1 label.

22 Churchill as Schoolboy

+1c

(23)

1974 (29 Nov). *Birth Centenary of Sir Winston Churchill. T* **22** *and similar vert designs. Multicoloured. P* 13½.
136 10 c. Type **22** 25 25
137 25 c. Churchill as young man.. .. .. 30 40
138 30 c. Churchill with troops 35 45
139 50 c. Churchill painting 45 60
140 $1 Giving "V" sign .. .. 85 1·10
136/40 .. .. *Set of* 5 2·00 2·50
MS141 115 × 108 mm. Nos. 136/40 plus *se-tenant* label. P 13 .. .. 2·25 2·00
Each value was issued in sheets of 5 stamps and 1 label.

1974 (2 Dec). *Children's Christmas Fund. Nos.* 129/34 *surch with T* **23**.
142 1 c. + 1 c. multicoloured 10 10
143 5 c. + 1 c. multicoloured 10 10
144 8 c. + 1 c. multicoloured 10 10
145 10 c. + 1 c. multicoloured 10 10
146 25 c. + 1 c. multicoloured 20 20
147 30 c. + 1 c. multicoloured 20 20
142/7 .. .. *Set of* 6 55 55

24 Soviet and U.S. Flags

25 "Madonna and Child with Saints Francis and John" (Lorenzetti)

1975 (24 July). *"Apollo-Soyuz" Space Project. T* **24** *and similar horiz design. Multicoloured. P* 13 × 14.
148 25 c. Type **24** 30 20
149 50 c. Daedalus and space capsule 40 30
MS150 123 × 61 mm. Nos. 148/9 .. .. 1·25 1·10
Each value was issued in sheets of 8 stamps and 1 label.

1975 (24 Nov). *Christmas. T* **25** *and similar vert designs. Multicoloured. P* 13½.
151 6 c. ⎫
152 6 c. ⎬ Type **25** .. .. 10 10 (each)
153 6 c. ⎭
154 7 c. ⎫
155 7 c. ⎬ "Adoration of the Kings" (Van der Weyden) .. .. 10 10 (each)
156 7 c. ⎭
157 15 c. ⎫
158 15 c. ⎬ "Madonna and Child Enthroneth with Saints Onufrius and John the Baptist" (Montagna) .. .. .. 15 15 (each)
159 15 c. ⎭
160 20 c. 20 15
161 20 c. "Adoration of the Shepherds" (Reni) .. 20 15
162 20 c. 20 15
151/62 .. .. *Set of* 12 1·50 1·40
MS163 104 × 201 mm. Nos. 151/62. P 13.. .. 2·25 2·50
Nos. 151/3, 154/6, 157/9 and 160/2 were each printed together, *se-tenant*, in horizontal strips of 3 throughout the sheet, forming composite designs. Type **25** shows the left-hand stamp of the 6 c. design.

1975 (19 Dec). *Children's Christmas Fund. Nos.* 151/62 *surch as T* **23**, *in silver.*
164 6 c. + 1 c. 10 10
165 6 c. + 1 c. Type **25** 10 10
166 6 c. + 1 c. 10 10
167 7 c. + 1 c. 10 10
168 7 c. + 1 c. "Adoration of the Kings" (Van der Weyden) 10 10
169 7 c. + 1 c. 10 10
170 15 c. + 1 c. 15 15
171 15 c. + 1 c. "Madonna and Child" (Montagna) 15 15
172 15 c. + 1 c. 15 15
173 20 c. + 1 c. 20 20
174 20 c. + 1 c. "Adoration of the Shepherds" (Reni) 20 20
175 20 c. + 1 c. 20 20
164/75 .. .. *Set of* 12 1·50 1·50

26 "The Descent" (detail, 15th-cent Flemish School)

27 "The Declaration of Independence" (detail)

1976 (5 Apr). *Easter. Various vert designs showing portions of "The Descent" as in T* **26**. *P* 13.
176 **26** 15 c. multicoloured 15 10
177 – 30 c. multicoloured 20 15
178 – 35 c. multicoloured 25 20
176/8 .. .. *Set of* 3 55 40
MS179 87 × 67 mm. Nos. 176/8 forming a complete picture of "The Descent". P 12½ × 13 .. .. 1·00 1·25
Stamps from No. **MS**179 have no borders and are therefore smaller than stamps from the sheets.
Each value was issued in sheets of 8 stamps and 1 label.

1976 (1 June). *Bicentenary of American Revolution. T* **27** *and similar vert designs showing paintings by John Trumbull. Multicoloured. P* 13.
180 30 c. 30 15
181 30 c. Type **27** 30 15
182 30 c. 30 15
183 35 c. 35 15
184 35 c. "The Surrender of Lord Cornwallis at Yorktown" 35 15
185 35 c. 35 15
186 50 c. 40 20
187 50 c. "The Resignation of General Washington" 40 20
188 50 c. 40 20
180/8 .. .. *Set of* 9 2·75 1·40
MS189 132 × 120 mm. Nos. 180/8. P 13 .. .. 2·75 1·75
Nos. 180/2, 183/5 and 186/8 were each printed together, *se-tenant*, in horizontal strips of 3 throughout the sheet, forming composite designs. Each sheet includes 3 stamp-size labels. Type **27** shows the left-hand stamp of the 30 c. design.
Stamps from No. **MS**189 have their borders in a different colour and come with a different inscription.

28 Cycling

1976 (15 July). *Olympic Games, Montreal. T* **28** *and similar horiz designs. Multicoloured. P* 13 × 14.
190 15 c. Type **28** 30 15
191 35 c. Sailing 45 20
192 60 c. Hockey 70 25
193 70 c. Sprinting 70 30
190/3 .. .. *Set of* 4 1·90 80
MS194 107 × 97 mm. Nos. 190/3 .. .. 1·90 1·25
Stamps from No. **MS**194 have borders of a different colour.
Each value was issued in sheets of 5 stamps and 1 label.

ROYAL VISIT JULY 1976

(29)

30 "The Visitation"

1976 (30 July). *Visit of Queen Elizabeth to the U.S.A. Nos.* 190/**MS**194 *optd with T* **29**.
195 15 c. Type **28** 35 15
196 35 c. Sailing 45 25
197 60 c. Hockey 70 40
198 70 c. Sprinting 70 45
195/8 .. .. *Set of* 4 2·00 1·10
MS199 107 × 97 mm. Nos. 195/8 .. .. .. 2·00 2·00

1976 (18 Oct). *Christmas. T* **30** *and similar vert designs. Figures in gold; background colours given. P* 13.
200 6 c. ⎫ deep bluish green 10 10
201 6 c. ⎭ 10 10
202 7 c. ⎫ dull brown-purple 10 10
203 7 c. ⎭ 10 10
204 15 c. ⎫ deep blue 10 10
205 15 c. ⎭ 10 10
206 20 c. ⎫ reddish violet 15 15
207 20 c. ⎭ 15 15
200/207 .. .. *Set of* 8 60 60
MS208 128 × 96 mm. As Nos. 200/207 but with borders on three sides .. .. 1·00 1·40
Designs:—No. 201, Angel; No. 202, Angel; No. 203, Shepherds; No. 204, Joseph; No. 205, Mary and the Child; No. 206, Wise Man; No. 207, Two Wise Men.
Nos. 200/1, 202/3, 204/5 and 206/7 were each printed together, *se-tenant*, in horizontal pairs throughout the sheet, forming composite designs. Type **30** shows the left-hand stamp of the 6 c. design.

+1c

(31)

32 Alexander Graham Bell and First Telephone

1976 (19 Nov). *Children's Christmas Fund. Nos.* 200/**MS**208 *surch in silver as T* **31**.
209 6 c. + 1 c. ⎫ "The Visitation" 10 10
210 6 c. + 1 c. ⎭ 10 10
211 7 c. + 1 c. ⎫ "Angel and Shepherds" 10 10
212 7 c. + 1 c. ⎭ 10 10
213 15 c. + 1 c. ⎫ "The Holy Family" 15 15
214 15 c. + 1 c. ⎭ 15 15
215 20 c. + 1 c. ⎫ "The Magi" 15 15
216 20 c. + 1 c. ⎭ 15 15
209/16 .. .. *Set of* 8 70 70
MS217 128 × 96 mm. As Nos. 209/216 but with a premium of "+ 2 c." and borders on three sides .. 80 1·40

1977 (3 Mar). *Telephone Centenary* (1976). *T* **32** *and similar horiz design. P* 13.
218 25 c. black, gold and dull scarlet 20 15
219 70 c. black, gold and lilac 40 40
MS220 116 × 59 mm. As Nos. 218/19 but with different colours .. .. 70 1·00
Design:—70 c. Earth Station and satellite.

33 "Christ on the Cross" (detail)

1977 (31 Mar). *Easter and 400th Birth Anniv of Rubens. T* **33** *and similar horiz designs. Multicoloured. P* 13½ × 14.
221 15 c. Type **33** 45 15
222 20 c. "Lamentation for Christ" 60 20
223 35 c. "Christ with Straw" 75 25
221/3 .. .. *Set of* 3 1·60 55
MS224 115 × 57 mm. Nos. 221/3. P 13 × 12½ .. 1·60 1·60
Each value was issued in sheets of 8 stamps and 1 label.

34 Capt. Bligh, George III and H.M.S. *Bounty*

1977 (21 Apr). *Silver Jubilee. T* **34** *and similar horiz designs. Multicoloured. P* 13.
225 25 c. Type **34** 35 35
226 35 c. Rev. Williams, George IV and Aitutaki Church 40 40
227 50 c. Union Jack, Queen Victoria and island map 45 45
228 $1 Balcony scene, 1953 .. .. .. 50 50
225/8 .. .. *Set of* 4 1·50 1·50
MS229 130 × 87 mm. Nos. 225/8 but with gold borders. P 13½ × 13 .. .. 1·25 1·25
Each value was issued in sheets of 5 stamps and 1 label.

35 The Shepherds

+1c

(36)

1977 (14 Oct). *Christmas. T* **35** *and similar vert designs. Multicoloured. P* 13½ × 14.
230 6 c. Type **35** 10 10
231 6 c. Angel 10 10
232 7 c. Mary, Jesus and ox 10 10
233 7 c. Joseph and donkey 10 10
234 15 c. Three Kings 10 10
235 15 c. Virgin and Child 10 10
236 20 c. Joseph 10 10
237 20 c. Mary and Jesus on donkey 10 10
230/7 .. .. *Set of* 8 55 55
MS238 130 × 95 mm. Nos. 230/7 .. .. .. 70 1·25
Each design covers two stamps; Type **35** shows the left-hand stamp of the 6 c. design.

1977 (15 Nov). *Children's Christmas Fund. Nos.* 230/7 *surch with T* **36**.
239 6 c. + 1 c. } Type **35** 10 10
240 6 c. + 1 c. } 10 10
241 7 c. + 1 c. } The Holy Family 10 10
242 7 c. + 1 c. } 10 10
243 15 c. + 1 c. } The Three Kings with Virgin 15 10
244 15 c. + 1 c. } and Child 15 10
245 20 c. + 1 c. } Flight into Egypt 15 10
246 20 c. + 1 c. } 15 10
239/46 .. .. *Set of* 8 75 55
MS247 130 × 95 mm. As Nos. 239/46 but each with premium of "+ 2 c." 70 85

37 Hawaiian Goddess

38 "Christ on the Way to Calvary" (Martini)

1978 (19 Jan). *Bicentenary of Discovery of Hawaii. T* **37** *and similar multicoloured designs. P* 13½.
248 35 c. Type **37** 35 25
249 50 c. Figurehead of H.M.S. *Resolution* (*horiz*) 60 40
250 $1 Hawaiian temple figure 70 70
248/50 .. .. *Set of* 3 1·50 1·25
MS251 168 × 75 mm. Nos. 248/50 .. .. 1·50 2·25

1978 (17 Mar). *Easter. Details of Paintings from Louvre, Paris. T* **38** *and similar horiz designs. Multicoloured. P* 13½ × 14.
252 15 c. Type **38** 15 10
253 20 c. "Piéta of Avignon" (E. Quarton) .. 20 10
254 35 c. "Pilgrims at Emmaus" (Rembrandt) .. 25 15
252/4 .. .. *Set of* 3 55 30
MS255 108 × 83 mm. Nos. 252/4 .. .. .. 75 75
Each value was printed in two panes of 9 within the sheet, both panes including one *se-tenant* stamp-size label.

1978 (17 Mar). *Easter. Children's Charity. Designs as Nos.* 252/4, *but smaller* (34 × 26 *mm*) *and without margins, in separate miniature sheets* 75 × 58 *mm, each with a face value of* 50 c. + 5 c. *P* 14.
MS256 As Nos. 252/4 .. .. *Set of* 3 *sheets* 1·40 1·00

39 Yale of Beaufort

40 "Adoration of the Infant Jesus"

1978 (15 June). *25th Anniv of Coronation. T* **39** *and similar vert designs. Multicoloured. P* 13½ × 13.
257 $1 Type **39** 30 50
258 $1 Queen Elizabeth II 30 50
259 $1 Aitutaki ancestral statue 30 50
257/9 .. .. *Set of* 3 80 1·40
MS260 98 × 127 mm. Nos. 257/9 × 2 .. .. 75 75
Stamps from No. **MS**260 have coloured borders, the upper row in lavender and the lower in apple-green.
Nos. 257/9 were printed together, *se-tenant*, in small sheets of 6, containing two horizontal strips of 3.

1978 (4 Dec). *Christmas. 450th Death Anniv of Dürer. T* **40** *and similar vert designs. Multicoloured. P* 13 × 14.
261 15 c. Type **40** 35 15
262 17 c. "The Madonna with Child" 40 15
263 30 c. "The Madonna with the Iris" 55 20
264 35 c. "The Madonna of the Siskin" 60 25
261/4 .. .. *Set of* 4 1·75 65
MS265 101 × 109 mm. As Nos. 261/4 but each with premium of "+ 2 c." .. .. 1·50 1·00
Nos. 261/4 were each printed in small sheets of 6, including 1 *se-tenant* stamp-size label.

41 "Captain Cook" (Nathaniel Dance)

42 Girl with Flowers

1979 (20 July). *Death Bicentenary of Captain Cook. Paintings. T* **41** *and similar vert designs. Multicoloured. P* 14 × 13½.
266 50 c. Type **41** .. .. 1·00 80
267 75 c. "H.M.S. *Resolution* and *Adventure* at Matavai Bay" (William Hodges) .. 1·75 95
MS268 94 × 58 mm. Nos. 266/7. P 13½ .. 2·00 2·25

1979 (1 Oct). *International Year of the Child. T* **42** *and similar vert designs. Multicoloured. P* 14 × 13½.
269 30 c. Type **42** 15 15
270 35 c. Boy playing guitar 20 20
271 65 c. Children in canoe 30 30
269/71 .. .. *Set of* 3 60 60
MS272 104 × 80 mm. As Nos. 269/71, but each with a premium of "+ 3 c." .. .. 70 1·00

43 "Man writing a Letter" (painting by G. Metsu)

44 "The Burial of Christ" (detail, Quentin Metsys)

1979 (14 Nov). *Death Centenary of Sir Rowland Hill. T* **43** *a[nd] similar horiz designs. Multicoloured. P* 13.
273 50 c. Type **43** 45
274 50 c. Sir Rowland Hill with Penny Black, 1903 ½d. and 1911 1d. stamps 45
275 50 c. "Girl in Blue reading a Letter" (painting by J. Vermeer) 45
276 65 c. "Woman writing a Letter" (painting by G. Terborch) 50
277 65 c. Sir Rowland Hill with Penny Black, 1903 3d. and 1920 ½d. stamps 50
278 65 c. "Lady reading a Letter" (painting by J. Vermeer) 50
273/8 .. .. *Set of* 6 2·50 2·
MS279 151 × 85 mm. 30 c. × 6. As Nos. 273/8 .. 1·75 2·
Nos. 273/5 and 276/8 were printed together, *se-tenant*, in ho[ri]zontal strips of 3, the sheet having two panes separated by margi[n], one containing 273/5 × 3, the other containing 276/8 × 3.

1980 (3 Apr). *Easter. T* **44** *and similar vert designs showi[ng] different details of painting "The Burial of Christ" by Quent[in] Metsys. P* 13.
280 20 c. multicoloured 40
281 30 c. multicoloured 50
282 35 c. multicoloured 65
280/2 .. .. *Set of* 3 1·40
MS283 93 × 71 mm. As Nos. 280/2, but each with premium of "+ 2 c." 75

45 Einstein as Young Man

46 Ancestor Figure, Aitutaki

1980 (21 July). *25th Death Anniv of Albert Einstein (physicis[t]). T* **45** *and similar vert designs. Multicoloured. P* 14 × 13½.
284 12 c. Type **45** 50
285 12 c. Atom and "$E=mc^2$" equation 50
286 15 c. Einstein as middle-aged man 55
287 15 c. Cross over nuclear explosion (Nuclear Test Ban Treaty, 1963) 55
288 20 c. Einstein as old man 65
289 20 c. Hand over bomb explosion (Nuclear Test Ban Treaty, 1963) 65
284/9 .. .. *Set of* 6 3·00 3·
MS290 113 × 118 mm. Nos. 284/9. P 13½ .. 3·00 3·
Nos. 284/5, 286/7 and 288/9 were each printed together, [*se-*]*tenant*, in horizontal pairs throughout the sheet.

1980 (26 Sept). *South Pacific Festival of Arts. T* **46** *and simi[lar] vert designs. Multicoloured. P* 13½.
291 6 c. Type **46** 10
292 6 c. Staff god image, Rarotonga 10
293 6 c. Trade adze, Mangaia 10
294 6 c. Carved image of Tangaroa, Rarotonga .. 10
295 12 c. Wooden image, Aitutaki 10
296 12 c. Hand club, Rarotonga 10
297 12 c. Carved mace "god", Mangaia 10
298 12 c. Fisherman's god, Rarotonga 10
299 15 c. Ti'i image, Aitutaki 15
300 15 c. Fisherman's god, Rarotonga (*different*) .. 15
301 15 c. Carved mace "god", Cook Islands .. 15
302 15 c. Carved image of Tangaroa, Rarotonga (*different*) 15
303 20 c. Chief's headdress, Aitutaki 15
304 20 c. Carved "mace" god, Cook Islands (*different*) 15
305 20 c. Staff god image, Rarotonga (*different*) .. 15
306 20 c. Carved image of Tangaroa, Rarotonga (*different*) 15
291/306 .. .. *Set of* 16 1·60 1
MS307 134 × 194 mm. Nos. 291/306 .. .. 1·60 1
The four designs of each value were printed together, *se-tena[nt]*, in blocks of 4 throughout the sheet.

47 Virgin and Child (13th-century)

48 "Mourning Virgin"

1980 (21 Nov). *Christmas. Sculptures. T* **47** *and similar v[ert] designs showing various Virgin and Child works from [the] periods given. Multicoloured. P* 13.
308 15 c. Type **47** 20
309 20 c. 14th-century 20
310 25 c. 15th-century 20
311 35 c. 15th-century (*different*) 30
308/11 .. .. *Set of* 4 80
MS312 82 × 120 mm. As Nos. 306/11 but each with premium of 2 c. 70

1981 (31 Mar). *Easter. Details of Sculpture "Burial of Christ" by Pedro Roldan. T* **48** *and similar vert designs. P* 14.
313 30 c. gold and myrtle-green 25 25
314 40 c. gold and deep reddish lilac 30 30
315 50 c. gold and Prussian blue 30 30
313/15 . . . . . . *Set of* 3 75 75
MS316 107 × 60 mm. As Nos. 313/15 but each with premium of 2 c. 75 85
Designs:—40 c. "Christ"; 50 c. "Saint John".

49 Gouldian Finch (*Poephila gouldiae*)

50 Prince Charles

1981 (6 Apr)–**82**. *Birds (1st series). Multicoloured designs as T* **49**. *P* 14 × 13½ (1 *to* 10 c.), 13½ × 14 (15 *to* 70 c.) *or* 13 ($1 *to* $4).
317 1 c. Type **49** 45 30
318 1 c. Common Starling (*Sturnus vulgaris*) . . 45 30
319 2 c. Golden Whistler (*Pachycephala pectoralis*) 50 30
320 2 c. Scarlet Robin (*Petroica multicolor*) . . 50 30
321 3 c. Rufous Fantail (*Rhipidura rufifrous*) . . 60 30
322 3 c. Peregrine Falcon (*Falco peregrinus*) . . 60 30
323 4 c. Java Sparrow (*Padda oryzivora*) . . 70 30
324 4 c. Barn Owl (*Tyto alba*) 70 30
325 5 c. Tahitian Lory (*Vini peruviana*) 70 30
326 5 c. White-breasted Wood Swallow (*Artamus leucorhynchus*) 70 30
327 6 c. Purple Swamphen (*Porphyrio porphyrio*) 70 30
328 6 c. Rock Dove (*Columba livia*) 70 30
329 10 c. Chestnut-breasted Mannikin (*Lonchura castaneothorax*) 90 30
330 10 c. Zebra Dove (*Geopelia striata*) 90 30
331 12 c. Eastern Reef Heron (*Egretta sacra*) . . 1·00 40
332 12 c. Common Mynah (*Acridotheres tristis*) . . 1·00 40
333 15 c. Whimbrel (*Numenius phaeopus*) (*horiz*) (8.5.81) . . . . . . 1·25 40
334 15 c. Black-browed Albatross (*Diomeda melanophris*) (*horiz*) (8.5.81) . . . . 1·25 40
335 20 c. American Golden Plover (*Pluvialis dominica*) (*horiz*) (8.5.81) . . . . 1·50 55
336 20 c. White Tern (*Gygis alba*) (*horiz*) (8.5.81) 1·50 55
337 25 c. Spotbill Duck (*Anas superciliosa*) (*horiz*) (8.5.81) . . . . . . 1·75 70
338 25 c. Brown Booby (*Sula leucogaster*) (*horiz*) (8.5.81) . . . . . . 1·75 70
339 30 c. Great Frigate Bird (*Fregata minor*) (*horiz*) (8.5.81) . . . . 2·00 85
340 30 c. Pintail (*Anas acuta*) (*horiz*) (8.5.81) . . 2·00 85
341 35 c. Long-billed Reed Warbler (*Conopoderas caffra caffra*) (14.1.82) . . . . 2·25 1·00
342 35 c. Pomarine Skua (*Stercorarius pomarinus*) (14.1.82) . . . . . . 2·25 1·00
343 40 c. Banded Rail (*Gallirallus philippensis goodsoni*) (14.1.82) . . . . 2·75 1·25
344 40 c. Spotted Triller (*Lalage maculosa pumila*) (14.1.82) . . . . . . 2·75 1·25
345 50 c. Royal Albatross (*Diomedea epomophora*) (14.1.82) . . . . . . 3·00 1·50
346 50 c. Stephen's Lory (*Vini stepheni*) (14.1.82) 3·00 1·50
347 70 c. Red-headed Parrot Finch (*Erythrura cyaneovirens*) (14.1.82) . . . . 5·50 3·00
348 70 c. Orange Dove (*Ptilinopus victor victor*) (14.1.82) . . . . . . 5·50 3·00
349 $1 Blue-headed Flycatcher (*Myiagra azureocapilla whitneyi*) (15.2.82) . . . . 5·50 3·75
350 $2 Red-bellied Flycatcher (*Myiagra vanikorensis rufiventris*) (15.5.82) . . . . 8·00 8·00
351 $4 Red Munia (*Amandava amandava*) (19.3.82) . . . . . . 14·00 14·00
352 $5 Flat-billed Kingfisher (*Halcyon recurvirostris*) (19.3.82) . . . . 15·00 16·00
317/52 . . . . . . *Set of* 36 80·00 60·00
The two designs of each value (1 c. to 70 c.) were printed together, *se-tenant*, in horizontal and vertical pairs throughout the sheet.
Nos. 341/8 are 35 × 27 mm and Nos. 349/52, which include a portrait of Queen Elizabeth II, 35 × 48 mm in size.
See also Nos. 475/94 for redrawn designs as Type **65**.
Nos. 353/90 are vacant.

1981 (10 June). *Royal Wedding. T* **50** *and similar multicoloured designs. P* 14 ($1.40) *or* 13 × 13½ (*others*).
391 60 c. Type **50** 30 40
392 80 c. Lady Diana Spencer 40 55
393 $1.40, Prince Charles and Lady Diana (87 × 70 *mm*) 60 80
391/3 . . . . . . *Set of* 3 1·10 1·60

(**51**) **52** Footballers

53 "The Holy Family"

1981 (23 Nov). *International Year for Disabled Persons. Nos.* 391/3 *surch with T* **51** *on gold background.*
394 60 c. + 5 c. Type **50** . . . . . . 70 1·00
395 80 c. + 5 c. Lady Diana Spencer . . . . 1·00 1·50
396 $1. 40 + 5 c.Prince Charles and Lady Diana . . . . . . 1·75 2·75
394/6 . . . . . . *Set of* 3 3·00 4·75
Nos. 394/6 have commemorative inscriptions overprinted on the sheet margins.

1981 (30 Nov). *World Cup Football Championship, Spain* (1982). *T* **52** *and similar horiz designs showing footballers. Multicoloured. P* 14.
397 12 c. Ball to left of stamp 50 35
398 12 c. Ball to right 50 35
399 15 c. Ball to right 55 40
400 15 c. Ball to left 55 40
401 20 c. Ball to left 55 50
402 20 c. Ball to right 55 50
403 25 c. Type **52** 60 55
404 25 c. "ESPANA 82" inscr on printed background 60 55
397/404 . . . . . . *Set of* 8 4·00 3·25
MS405 100 × 137 mm. 12 c. + 2 c., 15 c. + 2 c., 20 c. + 2 c., 25 c. + 2 c., each × 2. As Nos. 397/404 3·50 3·00
The two designs of each value were printed together, *se-tenant*, in horizontal pairs throughout the sheet.

1981 (10 Dec). *Christmas. Details from Etchings by Rembrandt. T* **53** *and similar designs in purple-brown and gold. P* 14.
406 15 c. Type **53** 45 45
407 30 c. "Virgin with Child" 70 70
408 40 c. "Adoration of the Shepherds" (*horiz*) . . 95 95
409 50 c. "The Holy Family" (*horiz*) . . . . 1·25 1·25
406/9 . . . . . . *Set of* 4 3·00 3·00
MS410 Designs as Nos. 406/9 in separate miniature sheets, 65 × 82 mm or 82 × 65 mm, each with a face value of 80 c. + 5 c. P 14 × 13½ . . . . *Set of* 4 *sheets* 3·25 3·00

54 Princess of Wales

21 JUNE 1982 · PRINCE WILLIAM OF WALES

(**55**)

1982 (24 June). *21st Birthday of Princess of Wales. T* **54** *and similar vert designs. Multicoloured. P* 14.
411 70 c. Type **54** . . . . . . 1·00 60
412 $1 Prince and Princess of Wales . . . . 1·25 75
413 $2 Princess Diana (*different*) . . . . 2·75 1·50
411/13 . . . . . . *Set of* 3 4·50 2·75
MS414 82 × 91 mm. Nos. 411/13 . . . . 4·25 2·75
Nos. 411/13 were each printed in small sheets of 6 including two *se-tenant* stamp-size labels. The silver markings in the margins of the individual stamps differ for each position in the sheetlet.

1982 (13 July). *Birth of Prince William of Wales (1st issue). Nos.* 391/3 *optd as T* **55**.
415 60 c. Type **50** (optd with T **55**) . . . . 1·25 1·00
a. Pair. Nos. 415/16 . . . . . . 2·50 2·00
416 60 c. Type **50** (optd "COMMEMORATING THE ROYAL BIRTH") . . . . 1·25 1·00
417 80 c. Lady Diana Spencer (optd with T **55**) . . 1·40 1·10
a. Pair. Nos. 417/18 . . . . . . 2·75 2·10
418 80 c. Lady Diana Spencer (optd "COMMEMORATING THE ROYAL BIRTH") . . 1·40 1·10
419 $1.40, Prince Charles and Lady Diana (87 × 70 *mm*) (optd as T **55**) . . . . 1·75 1·40
a. Pair. Nos. 419/20 . . . . . . 3·50 2·75
420 $1.40, Prince Charles and Lady Diana (87 × 70 *mm*) (optd "COMMEMORATING THE ROYAL BIRTH") . . . . 1·75 1·40
415/20 . . . . . . *Set of* 6 8·00 6·25
Nos. 415/16, 417/18 and 419/20 were each printed together in *se-tenant* pairs, horiz and vert, throughout the sheets.

1982 (5 Aug). *Birth of Prince William of Wales (2nd issue). As Nos.* 411/14, *but inscr* "ROYAL BIRTH 21 JUNE 1982 PRINCE WILLIAM OF WALES". *Multicoloured. P* 14.
421 70 c. Type **54** 70 60
422 $1 Prince and Princess of Wales 80 75
423 $2 Princess Diana (*different*) . . . . 1·60 1·50
421/3 . . . . . . *Set of* 3 2·75 2·50
MS424 81 × 91 mm. Nos. 421/3 . . . . 4·25 3·00

56 "Virgin and Child" (12th-century sculpture)

57 Aitutaki Bananas

1982 (10 Dec). *Christmas. Religious Sculptures. T* **56** *and similar vert designs. Multicoloured. P* 13.
425 18 c. Type **56** 60 60
426 36 c. "Virgin and Child" (12th-century) . . 75 75
427 48 c. "Virgin and Child" (13th-century) . . 90 90
428 60 c. "Virgin and Child" (15th-century) . . 1·25 1·25
425/8 . . . . . . *Set of* 4 3·25 3·25
MS429 99 × 115 mm. As Nos. 425/8 but each with 2 c. charity premium . . . . . . 2·50 2·75
Nos. 425/8 were each printed in small sheets of 6 including one *se-tenant*, stamp size, label, depicting the Prince and Princess of Wales with Prince William.

1983 (14 Mar). *Commonwealth Day. T* **57** *and similar horiz designs. Multicoloured. P* 13.
430 48 c. Type **57** . . . . . . 1·10 50
431 48 c. Ancient Ti'i image . . . . 1·10 50
432 48 c. Tourist canoeing . . . . . . 1·10 50
433 48 c. Captain William Bligh and chart . . 1·10 50
430/3 . . . . . . *Set of* 4 4·00 1·75
Nos. 430/3 were issued together, *se-tenant*, in blocks of four throughout the sheet.

58 Scouts around Campfire

15th WORLD SCOUT JAMBOREE

(**59**)

1983 (18 Apr). *75th Anniv of Boy Scout Movement, T* **58** *and similar horiz designs. Multicoloured. P* 13½ × 14.
434 36 c. Type **58** 55 55
435 48 c. Scout saluting 70 70
436 60 c. Scouts hiking 75 75
434/6 . . . . . . *Set of* 3 1·75 1·75
MS437 78 × 107 mm. As Nos. 434/6 but each with premium of 3 c. P 13 . . . . . . 2·00 2·25

1983 (11 July). *15th World Scout Jamboree, Alberta, Canada. Nos.* 434/7 *optd with T* **59**.
438 36 c. Type **58** 80 45
439 48 c. Scout saluting . . . . . . 1·00 55
440 60 c. Scouts hiking . . . . . . 1·25 75
438/40 . . . . . . *Set of* 3 2·75 1·60
MS441 78 × 107 mm. As Nos. 438/40 but each with a premium of 3 c. . . . . . . 2·00 2·50

60 Modern Sport Balloon

18c (**61**)

$1.20 (**62**)

1983 (22 July). *Bicentenary of Manned Flight. T* **60** *and similar vert designs showing different modern sport balloons. P* 14 × 13.
442 18 c. multicoloured 55 30
443 36 c. multicoloured 75 50
444 48 c. multicoloured 90 60
445 60 c. multicoloured . . . . . . 1·00 80
442/5 . . . . . . *Set of* 4 2·75 2·00
MS446 64 × 80 mm. $2.50, multicoloured (48½ × 28½ *mm*) . . . . . . 1·90 2·50
Nos. 442/5 were each issued in small sheets of 4 stamps.

1983 (22 Sept). *Various stamps surch.*

(*a*) *Nos.* 335/48 *and* 352 *as T* **61**
447 18 c. on 20 c. American Golden Plover (*Pluvialis dominica*) . . . . 2·50 75
448 18 c. on 20 c. White Tern (*Gygis alba*) . . 2·50 75
449 36 c. on 25 c. Spotbill Duck (*Anas superciliosa*) . . . . . . 3·50 1·00
450 36 c. on 25 c. Brown Booby (*Sula leucogaster*) 3·50 1·00
451 36 c. on 30 c. Great Frigate Bird (*Fregata minor*) . . . . . . 3·50 1·00
452 36 c. on 30 c. Pintail (*Anas acuta*) . . 3·50 1·00
453 36 c. on 35 c. Long-billed Reed Warbler (*Conopoderas caffra caffra*) . . 3·50 1·00
454 36 c. on 35 c. Pomarine Skua (*Stercorarius pomarinus*) . . . . . . 3·50 1·00
455 48 c. on 40 c. Banded Rail (*Gallirallus philippensis goodsoni*) . . . . 4·00 1·25
456 48 c. on 40 c. Spotted Triller (*Lalage maculosa pumila*) . . . . . . 4·00 1·25
457 48 c. on 50 c. Royal Albatross (*Diomedea epomophora*) . . . . . . 4·00 1·25
458 48 c. on 50 c. Stephen's Lory (*Vini stepheni*) 4·00 1·25
459 72 c. on 70 c. Red-headed Parrot Finch (*Erythrura cyaneovirens*) . . 7·00 2·00
460 72 c. on 70 c. Orange Dove (*Ptilinopus victor victor*) . . . . . . 7·00 2·00
461 $5.60 on $5 Flat-billed Kingfisher (*Halcyon recurvirostris*) . . . . 20·00 8·50

(*b*) *Nos.* 392/3 *and* 412/13 *as T* **62**
462 96 c. on 80 c. Lady Diana Spencer (Gold) 3·00 2·50
a. Error. Surch on No. 417 . . . . 12·00
ab. Pair. Nos. 462/a/b . . . . 25·00
b. Error. Surch on No. 418 . . . . 12·00

463 96 c. on $1 Prince and Princess of Wales .. 2·75 2·00
464 $1.20 on $1.40, Prince Charles and Lady Diana (Gold) .. .. 3·00 2·50
a. Error. Surch on No. 419 .. .. .. 12·00
ab. Pair. Nos. 464a/b .. .. .. 25·00
b. Error. Surch on No. 420 .. .. .. 12·00
465 $1.20 on $2, Princess Diana .. .. 2·75 2·00
447/65 .. .. *Set of* 19 75·00 30·00

On Nos. 462 and 464 the gold surcharge is printed on a black obliterating panel over the original face value.

63 International Mail

64 "Madonna of the Chair"

1983 (29 Sept). *World Communications Year. T* **63** *and similar vert designs. Multicoloured. P* 14 × 13½.
466 48 c. Type **63** 65 50
467 60 c. Telecommunications 95 70
468 96 c. Space satellites .. .. 1·40 1·00
466/8 .. .. *Set of* 3 2·75 2·00
MS469 126 × 53 mm. Nos. 466/8. P 13 .. .. 2·50 2·50

1983 (21 Nov). *Christmas. 500th Birth Anniv of Raphael. T* **64** *and similar horiz designs. Multicoloured. P* 13½ × 14.
470 36 c. Type **64** 65 30
471 48 c. "The Alba Madonna" 80 40
472 60 c. "Conestabile Madonna" .. .. .. 1·10 55
470/2 .. .. *Set of* 3 2·25 1·10
MS473 95 × 116 mm. As Nos. 470/2, but each with a premium of 3 c. P 13 .. .. 2·25 1·40

1983 (15 Dec). *Christmas. 500th Birth Anniv of Raphael. Children's Charity. Designs as Nos. 470/2 in separate miniature sheets 46 × 47 mm, but each with different frames and a face value of 85 c. + 5 c. Imperf.*
MS474 As Nos. 470/2 .. .. *Set of 3 sheets* 3·25 2·75

65 Gouldian Finch

66 Javelin-throwing

1984 (13 Feb–2 July). *Birds (2nd series). Designs as Nos. 317 etc. but with redrawn frames and inscriptions as in T* **65**. *Multicoloured. P* 13 × 13½ *($3 to $9.60) or* 14 *(others).*
475 2 c. Type **65** .. .. 1·25 1·00
476 3 c. Common Starling .. .. 1·25 1·00
477 5 c. Scarlet Robin .. .. 1·50 1·10
478 10 c. Golden Whistler .. .. 1·50 1·10
479 12 c. Rufous Fantail .. .. 1·50 1·10
480 18 c. Peregrine Falcon .. .. 2·00 1·50
481 24 c. Barn Owl .. .. 2·00 1·50
482 30 c. Java Sparrow .. .. 2·00 1·50
483 36 c. White-breasted Wood Swallow .. .. 2·00 1·50
484 48 c. Tahitian Lory .. .. 2·00 1·50
485 50 c. Rock Dove (26 Mar) .. .. .. 2·50 2·00
486 60 c. Purple Swamphen (26 Mar) .. .. 2·50 2·00
487 72 c. Zebra Dove (26 Mar) .. .. .. 2·50 2·00
488 96 c. Chestnut-breasted Mannikin (26 Mar) .. 2·50 2·00
489 $1.20, Common Mynah (26 Mar) .. .. 2·50 2·75
490 $2.10, Eastern Reef Heron (30 Apr) .. 3·50 3·75
491 $3 Blue-headed Flycatcher (30 × 42 *mm*) (30 Apr) .. .. 6·50 6·00
492 $4.20, Red-bellied Flycatcher (30 × 42 *mm*) (5 June) .. .. 3·75 6·00
493 $5.60, Red Munia (30 × 42 *mm*) (5 June) 4·50 7·00
494 $9.60, Flat-billed Kingfisher (30 × 42 *mm*) (2 July) .. .. 7·50 10·00
475/94 .. .. *Set of* 20 50·00 50·00

1984 (24 July). *Olympic Games, Los Angeles. T* **66** *and similar vert designs showing Memorial Coliseum and various events. Multicoloured. P* 13 × 13½.
495 36 c. Type **66** 35 35
496 48 c. Shot-putting 40 45
497 60 c. Hurdling 45 55
498 $2 Basketball .. .. 1·75 1·50
495/8 .. .. *Set of* 4 2·75 2·50
MS499 88 × 117 mm. As Nos. 495/8, but each with a charity premium of 5 c. .. .. 3·00 3·25

1984 (21 Aug). *Olympic Gold Medal Winners. Nos. 495/8 optd as T* **209** *of Cook Islands in gold on black background.*
500 36 c. Type **66** (optd "Javelin Throw Tessa Sanderson Great Britain") 35 35
501 48 c. Shot-putting (optd "Shot Put Claudia Losch Germany") 40 45
502 60 c. Hurdling (optd "Heptathlon Glynis Nunn Australia") 45 55
503 $2 Basketball (optd "Team Basketball United States") .. .. 1·75 1·50
500/3 .. .. *Set of* 4 2·75 2·50

67 Capt. William Bligh and Chart

15.9.84 Birth
Prince Henry
$3

(**68**)

1984 (14 Sept). *"Ausipex" International Stamp Exhibition, Melbourne. T* **67** *and similar horiz designs. Multicoloured. P* 14.
504 60 c. Type **67** .. .. 3·25 3·25
505 96 c. H.M.S. *Bounty* and map .. .. .. 3·50 3·50
506 $1.40, Aitutaki stamps of 1974, 1979 and 1981 with map .. .. 3·50 3·50
504/6 .. .. *Set of* 3 9·00 9·00
MS507 85 × 113 mm. As Nos. 504/6, but each with a premium of 5 c. P 13½ .. .. 6·00 4·00

1984 (10 Oct). *Birth of Prince Henry (1st issue). No. 391 surch with T* **68** *in gold.*
508 $3 on 60 c. Type **50** .. .. 2·75 3·25

On No. 508 the gold surcharge is printed on a black obliterating panel over the original face value.

69 The Annunciation

70 Princess Diana with Prince Henry

1984 (16 Nov). *Christmas. Details from Altarpiece, St. Paul's Church, Palencia, Spain. T* **69** *and similar vert designs. Multicoloured. P* 13½ × 13.
509 36 c. Type **69** 30 35
510 48 c. The Nativity 40 45
511 60 c. The Epiphany 45 50
512 96 c. The Flight into Egypt 75 80
509/12 .. .. *Set of* 4 1·75 1·90
MS513 Designs as Nos. 509/12 in separate miniature sheets, each 45 × 53 mm and with a face value of 90 c. + 7 c. Imperf. .. .. *Set of 4 sheets* 2·50 3·25

1984 (10 Dec). *Birth of Prince Henry (2nd issue). T* **70** *and similar vert designs. Multicoloured. P* 14.
514 48 c. Type **70** .. .. 1·50 1·25
515 60 c. Prince William with Prince Henry .. 1·50 1·50
516 $2.10, Prince and Princess of Wales with children .. .. 3·00 3·00
514/16 .. .. *Set of* 3 5·50 5·25
MS517 113 × 65 mm. As Nos. 514/16, but each with a face value of 96 c. + 7 c. P 13½ .. .. .. 5·00 3·25

71 Grey Kingbird

72 The Queen Mother, aged Seven

1985 (22 Mar). *Birth Bicentenary of John J. Audubon (ornithologist). T* **71** *and similar vert designs showing original paintings. Multicoloured. P* 13.
518 55 c. Type **71** .. .. 1·10 1·10
519 65 c. Bohemian Waxwing .. .. .. 1·25 1·25
520 75 c. Summer Tanager .. .. 1·40 1·40
521 95 c. Common Cardinal .. .. 1·50 1·50
522 $1.15, White-winged Crossbill .. .. 1·90 1·90
518/22 .. .. *Set of* 5 6·50 6·50

1985 (14 June). *Life and Times of Queen Elizabeth the Queen Mother. T* **72** *and similar horiz designs. Multicoloured. P* 13.
523 55 c. Type **72** 45 50
524 65 c. Engagement photograph, 1922 .. .. 50 55
525 75 c. With young Princess Elizabeth 60 65
526 $1.30, With baby Prince Charles .. .. 1·00 1·10
523/6 .. .. *Set of* 4 2·25 2·50
MS527 75 × 49 mm. $3 Queen Mother on her 63rd birthday .. .. 2·25 2·40

Nos. 523/6 were each printed in sheetlets of 4.
For these stamps in a miniature sheet see No. **MS**550.

73 "The Calmady Children" (T. Lawrence)

1985 (16 Sept). *International Youth Year. T* **73** *and similar horiz designs. Multicoloured. P* 13.
528 75 c. Type **73** .. .. 2·00 1·40
529 90 c. "Madame Charpentier's Children" (Renoir) .. .. 2·00 1·75
530 $1.40, "Young Girls at Piano" (Renoir) .. 2·50 2·75
528/30 .. .. *Set of* 3 6·00 5·50
MS531 103 × 104 mm. As Nos. 528/30, but each with a premium of 10 c. .. .. 4·25 3·25

74 "Adoration of the Magi" (Giotto) and *Giotto* Spacecraft

1985 (15 Nov). *Christmas. Appearance of Halley's Comet (1st issue). T* **74** *and similar multicoloured designs. P* 13.
532 95 c. Type **74** .. .. 1·50 1·50
533 95 c. As Type **74** but showing *Planet A* spacecraft .. .. 1·50 1·50
534 $1.15, Type **74** .. .. 1·50 1·50
535 $1.15, As No. 533 .. .. 1·50 1·50
532/5 .. .. *Set of* 4 5·50 5·50
MS536 52 × 55 mm. $6.40, As Type **74** but without spacecraft (30 × 31 *mm*). Imperf .. .. 11·00 8·50

Nos. 532/3 and 534/5 were each printed together, *se-tenant*, in horizontal pairs throughout the sheets.

75 Halley's Comet, A.D. 684 (from "Nuremberg Chronicle")

76 Queen Elizabeth II on Coronation Day (from photo by Cecil Beaton)

1986 (25 Feb). *Appearance of Halley's Comet (2nd issue). T* **75** *and similar multicoloured designs. P* 13½ × 13.
537 90 c. Type **75** 90 90
538 $1.25, Halley's Comet, 1066 (from Bayeux Tapestry) .. .. 1·10 1·10
539 $1.75, Halley's Comet, 1456 (from "Lucerne Chronicles") .. .. 1·50 1·50
537/9 .. .. *Set of* 3 3·25 3·25
MS540 107 × 82 mm. As Nos. 537/9, but each with a face value of 95 c. .. .. 2·75 2·50
MS541 65 × 80 mm. $4.20, "Melencolia I" (Albrecht Dürer woodcut) (61 × 76 *mm*). Imperf .. 4·25 3·50

1986 (21 Apr). *60th Birthday of Queen Elizabeth II. T* **76** *and similar vert design. Multicoloured. P* 14.
542 95 c. Type **76** .. .. 85 1·00
MS543 58 × 68 mm. $4.20, As T **76**, but showing more of the portrait without oval frame. P 13½ 5·50 5·50

No. 542 was printed in sheetlets of five stamps and one stamp-size label at top left.

77 Head of Statue of Liberty

78 Prince Andrew and Miss Sarah Ferguson

1986 (27 June). *Centenary of Statue of Liberty. T* **77** *and similar horiz design. Multicoloured. P* 14.
544 $1 Type **77** .. .. 1·25 1·25
545 $2.75, Statue of Liberty at sunset .. .. 2·75 2·75
MS546 91 × 79 mm. As Nos. 544/5, but each with a face value of $1.25. P 13½ .. .. .. 2·50 2·50

986 (23 July). *Royal Wedding. P* 14.
547 **78** $2 multicoloured .. .. .. 2·00 2·00
MS548 85×70 mm. **78** $5 mult. P 13½ .. .. 6·50 8·00
No. 547 was printed in sheetlets of 5 stamps and one stamp-size label at top left.

986 (4 Aug). *"Stampex '86" Stamp Exhibition, Adelaide. No.* MS507 *with "Ausipex" emblems obliterated in gold.*
MS549 As Nos. 504/6, but each with a premium of 5 c. .. .. 9·00 10·00
The "Stampex '86" exhibition emblem is overprinted on the heet margin.

986 (4 Aug). *86th Birthday of Queen Elizabeth the Queen Mother. Nos.* 523/6 *in miniature sheet,* 132×82 *mm. P* 13½×13.
MS550 Nos. 523/6 .. .. 7·50 8·50

+10c

) "St. Anne with Virgin and Child" (**80**)

986 (21 Nov). *Christmas. Paintings by Dürer. T* **79** *and similar vert designs. Multicoloured. P* 13½.
51 75 c. Type **79** .. .. 1·25 1·25
52 $1.35, "Virgin and Child" .. .. .. 1·75 1·75
53 $1.95, "The Adoration of the Magi" .. 2·25 2·25
54 $2.75, "Madonna of the Rosary" .. .. 3·00 3·00
51/4 .. .. *Set of* 4 7·50 7·50
IS555 88×125 mm. As Nos. 551/4, but each stamp with a face value of $1.65 .. .. 12·00 13·00

986 (25 Nov). *Visit of Pope John Paul II to South Pacific. Nos.* 551/5 *surch with T* **80** *in silver.*
56 75 c. + 10 c. Type **79** .. .. .. 2·50 2·50
57 $1.35 + 10 c. "Virgin and Child" .. .. 3·00 3·00
58 $1.95 + 10 c. "The Adoration of the Magi" 3·50 3·50
59 $2.75 + 10 c. "Madonna of the Rosary" .. 5·00 5·00
56/9 .. .. *Set of* 4 12·50 12·50
IS560 88 × 125 mm. As Nos. 556/9, but each stamp with a face value of $1.65 + 10 c. .. 14·00 14·00

2.50

Royal Wedding 40th Anniv

(**81**) (**82**)

87 (29 Apr). *Hurricane Relief Fund. Nos.* 544/5, 547, 551/4 *and* 556/9 *surch with T* **81** *in black (Nos.* 563, 569) *or silver (others).*
1 75 c. + 50 c. Type **79** .. .. 2·00 2·00
2 75 c. + 10 c. + 50 c. Type **79** .. .. 2·25 2·25
3 $1 + 50 c. Type **77** .. .. 2·50 2·50
4 $1.35 + 50 c. "Virgin and Child" (Dürer) .. 2·75 2·75
5 $1.35 + 10 c. + 50 c. "Virgin and Child" (Dürer) .. .. 2·75 2·75
6 $1.95 + 50 c. "The Adoration of the Magi" (Dürer) .. .. 3·25 3·25
7 $1.95 + 10 c. + 50 c. "The Adoration of the Magi" (Dürer) .. .. 3·25 3·25
8 $2 + 50 c. Type **78** .. .. 3·25 3·25
9 $2.75 + 50 c. Statue of Liberty at sunset .. 3·75 3·75
0 $2.75 + 50 c. "Madonna of the Rosary" (Dürer) .. .. 3·75 3·75
1 $2.75 + 10 c. + 50 c. "Madonna of the Rosary" (Dürer) .. .. 3·75 3·75
1/71 .. .. *Set of* 11 30·00 30·00

87 (20 Nov). *Royal Ruby Wedding. Nos.* 391/3 *surch as T* **82**.
2 $2.50 on 60 c. Type **50** .. .. .. 2·50 2·50
3 $2.50 on 80 c. Lady Diana Spencer .. .. 2·50 2·50
4 $2.50 on $1.40, Prince Charles and Lady Diana (87×70 *mm*) .. .. 2·50 2·50
2/4 .. .. *Set of* 3 6·75 6·75
On Nos. 572/4 the original values are obliterated in gold.

83 "Angels" (detail from "Virgin with Garland")

1987 (10 Dec). *Christmas. T* **83** *and similar designs showing different details of angels from "Virgin with Garland" by Rubens. P* 13×13½.
575 70 c. multicoloured .. .. 1·50 1·50
576 85 c. multicoloured .. .. 1·50 1·50
577 $1.50, multicoloured .. .. 2·50 2·50
578 $1.85, multicoloured .. .. 2·75 2·75
575/8 .. .. *Set of* 4 7·50 7·50
MS579 92×120 mm. As Nos. 575/8, but each with a face value of 95 c. .. .. 8·00 9·00
MS580 96×85 mm. $6 "Virgin with Garland" (*diamond*, 56×56 *mm*). P 13 .. .. .. 10·00 11·00

84 Chariot Racing and Athletics

(Des G. Vasarhelyi. Litho Questa)

1988 (22 Aug). *Olympic Games, Seoul. T* **84** *and similar horiz designs showing ancient and modern Olympic sports. Multicoloured. P* 14½.
581 70 c. Type **84** .. .. 1·50 1·50
582 85 c. Greek runners and football .. .. 1·60 1·60
583 95 c. Greek wrestling and handball .. .. 1·75 1·75
584 $1.40, Greek hoplites and tennis .. .. 2·50 2·50
581/4 .. .. *Set of* 4 6·50 6·50
MS585 103×101 mm. As Nos. 581 and 584, but each with face value of $2 .. .. 6·50 7·50

1988 (10 Oct). *Olympic Medal Winners, Los Angeles. Nos.* 581/4 *optd as T* **235** *of Cook Islands.*
586 70 c. Type **84** (optd "FLORENCE GRIFFTH JOYNER UNITED STATES 100 M AND 200 M") .. .. 1·10 1·25
587 85 c. Greek runners and football (optd "GELINDO BORDIN ITALY MARATHON") .. .. 1·25 1·40
588 95 c. Greek wrestling and handball (optd "HITOSHI SAITO JAPAN JUDO") .. 1·40 1·60
589 $1.40, Greek hoplites and tennis (optd "STEFFI GRAF WEST GERMANY WOMEN'S TENNIS") .. .. .. 2·00 2·25
586/9 .. .. *Set of* 4 5·25 6·00

85 "Adoration of the Shepherds" (detail)

1988 (2 Nov). *Christmas. T* **85** *and similar multicoloured designs showing paintings by Rembrandt. P* 13½.
590 55 c. Type **85** .. .. 1·25 1·25
591 70 c. "The Holy Family" .. .. 1·50 1·50
592 85 c. "Presentation in the Temple" .. .. 1·60 1·60
593 95 c. "The Holy Family" (*different*) .. .. 1·75 1·75
594 $1.15, "Presentation in the Temple" (*different*) .. .. 1·90 1·90
590/4 .. .. *Set of* 5 7·25 7·25
MS595 85 × 101 mm. $4.50, As Type **85** but 52 × 34 mm. P 14 .. .. 5·50 6·50

86 H.M.S. *Bounty* leaving Spithead and King George III

(Des Jennifer Toombs)

1989 (3 July). *Bicentenary of Discovery of Aitutaki by Capt. Bligh. T* **86** *and similar horiz designs. Multicoloured. P* 13½×13.
596 55 c. Type **86** .. .. 1·75 1·75
597 65 c. Breadfruit plants .. .. 2·00 2·00
598 75 c. Old chart showing Aitutaki and Capt. Bligh .. .. 2·25 2·25
599 95 c. Native outrigger and H.M.S. *Bounty* off Aitutaki .. .. 2·50 2·50
600 $1.65, Fletcher Christian confronting Bligh .. .. 3·00 3·00
596/600 .. .. *Set of* 5 10·50 10·50
MS601 94×72 mm. $4.20, "Mutineers casting Bligh adrift" (Robert Dodd) (60×45 *mm*). P 13½ 7·50 8·50

87 "Apollo 11" Astronaut on Moon

88 Virgin Mary

1989 (28 July). *20th Anniv of First Manned Landing on Moon. T* **87** *and similar horiz designs. Multicoloured. P* 13½×13.
602 75 c. Type **87** .. .. 1·50 1·50
603 $1.15, Conducting experiment on Moon .. 2·00 2·00
604 $1.80, Astronaut on Moon carrying equipment .. .. 3·00 3·00
602/4 .. .. *Set of* 3 6·00 6·00
MS605 105×86 mm. $6.40, Astronaut on Moon with U.S. flag (40×27 *mm*). P 13½ .. .. 7·00 8·00

1989 (20 Nov). *Christmas. T* **88** *and similar vert designs showing details from "Virgin in the Glory" by Titian. Multicoloured. P* 13½×13.
606 70 c. Type **88** .. .. 1·75 1·75
607 85 c. Christ Child .. .. 2·25 2·25
608 95 c. Angel .. .. 2·50 2·50
609 $1.25, Cherubs .. .. 3·00 3·00
606/9 .. .. *Set of* 4 8·50 8·50
MS610 80×100 mm. $6 "Virgin in the Glory" (45×60 *mm*). P 13½ .. .. 8·00 9·00

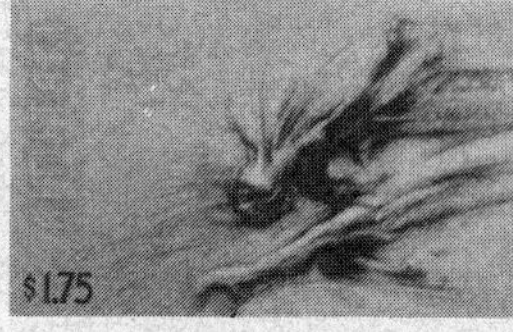

89 Human Comet striking Earth

Ninetieth Birthday

(**90**)

1990 (16 Feb). *Protection of the Environment. T* **89** *and similar horiz design. Multicoloured. P* 13½×13.
611 $1.75, Type **89** .. .. 2·25 2·25
a. Horiz pair. Nos. 611/12 .. .. .. 4·50 4·50
612 $1.75, Comet's tail .. .. 2·25 2·25
MS613 108×43 mm. $3 As Nos. 611/12 .. .. 3·50 4·50
Nos. 611/12 were printed together, *se-tenant*, in horizontal pairs throughout the sheet, each pair forming a composite design.

1990 (16 July). *90th Birthday of Queen Elizabeth the Queen Mother. No.* **MS**550 *optd with T* **90** *in black on gold on each stamp.*
MS614 132×82 mm. Nos. 523/6 .. .. .. 8·50 9·50

91 "Madonna of the Basket" (Correggio)

COMMEMORATING 65th BIRTHDAY OF H.M. QUEEN ELIZABETH II

(**92**)

(Litho Questa)

1990 (28 Nov). *Christmas. Religious Paintings. T* **91** *and similar multicoloured designs. Ordinary paper. P* 14.
615 70 c. Type **91** .. .. 1·25 1·25
616 85 c. "Virgin and Child" (Morando) .. .. 1·40 1·40
617 95 c. "Adoration of the Child" (Tiepolo) .. 1·50 1·50
618 $1.75, "Mystic Marriage of St. Catherine" (Memling) .. .. 2·25 2·25
615/18 .. .. *Set of* 4 5·75 5·75
MS619 165×93 mm. $6 "Donne Triptych" (Memling) (*horiz*) .. .. 8·00 9·00

1990 (5 Dec). *"Birdpex '90" Stamp Exhibition, Christchurch, New Zealand. Nos.* 349/50 *optd as T* **245** *of Cook Islands.*
620 $1 Blue-headed Flycatcher .. .. .. 3·00 3·00
621 $2 Red-bellied Flycatcher .. .. .. 4·00 4·00

1991 (22 Apr). 65*th Birthday of Queen Elizabeth II. No.* 352 *optd with T* **92**.
622 $5 Flat-billed Kingfisher (*Halcyon recurvirostris*) .. .. .. 7·50 8·50

93 "The Holy Family" (A. Mengs)

94 Hurdling

(Des G. Vasarhelyi. Litho Questa)

1991 (13 Nov). *Christmas. Religious Paintings. T* **93** *and similar vert designs. Multicoloured. Ordinary paper. P* 14.
623 80 c. Type **93** .. .. 1·25 1·25
624 90 c. "Virgin and the Child" (Lippi) .. 1·40 1·40
625 $1.05, "Virgin and Child" (A. Dürer) .. 1·60 1·60
626 $1.75, "Adoration of the Shepherds" (G. de la Tour) .. .. .. 2·25 2·25
623/6 .. .. *Set of* 4 6·00 6·00
MS627 79×103 mm. $6 "The Holy Family" (Michelangelo) .. .. 9·00 10·00

(Des G. Vasarhelyi. Litho B.D.T.)

1992 (29 July). *Olympic Games, Barcelona. T* **94** *and similar horiz designs. Multicoloured. Ordinary paper. P* 14.
628 95 c. Type **94** .. .. 1·50 1·50
629 $1.25, Weightlifting .. .. 1·75 1·75
630 $1.50, Judo .. .. 2·25 2·25
631 $1.95, Football .. .. 2·75 2·75
628/31 .. .. *Set of* 4 7·50 7·50

95 Vaka Motu Canoe

96 "Virgin's Nativity" (detail) (Reni)

(Litho B.D.T.)

1992 (16 Oct). 6*th Festival of Pacific Arts, Rarotonga. T* **95** *and similar horiz designs showing sailing canoes. Multicoloured. Ordinary paper. P* 14×15.
632 30 c. Type **95** 65 65
633 50 c. Hamatafua 80 80
634 95 c. Alia Kalia Ndrua .. .. .. 1·50 1·50
635 $1.75, Hokule'a Hawaiian .. .. .. 2·25 2·50
636 $1.95, Tuamotu Pahi .. .. .. 2·50 2·75
632/6 .. .. *Set of* 5 7·00 7·50

1992 (16 Oct). *Royal Visit by Prince Edward. Nos.* 632/6 *optd with T* **254** *of Cook Islands.*
637 30 c. Type **95** 75 75
638 50 c. Hamatafua .. .. 1·00 1·00
639 95 c. Alia Kalia Ndrua .. .. .. 1·75 1·75
640 $1.75, Hokule'a Hawaiian .. .. .. 2·50 2·75
641 $1.95, Tuamotu Pahi .. .. .. 2·50 2·75
637/41 .. .. *Set of* 5 7·75 8·00

1992 (19 Nov). *Christmas. Different details from "Virgin's Nativity" by Guido Reni. T* **96** *and similar vert designs. Ordinary paper. P* 13½.
642 80 c. multicoloured .. .. 1·25 1·25
643 90 c. multicoloured .. .. 1·40 1·40
644 $1.05, multicoloured .. .. 1·60 1·60
645 $1.75, multicoloured .. .. 2·25 2·25
642/5 .. .. *Set of* 4 6·00 6·00
MS646 101×86 mm. $6 multicoloured (as $1.05, but larger (36×46 *mm*)) .. .. .. 5·50 6·50

97 The Departure from Palos

(Litho B.D.T.)

1992 (11 Dec). 500*th Anniv of Discovery of America by Columbus. T* **97** *and similar horiz designs. Multicoloured. Ordinary paper. P* 14×15.
647 $1.25, Type **97** .. .. 2·25 2·50
648 $1.75, Map of voyages .. .. 2·75 3·00
649 $1.95, Columbus and crew in New World .. 3·25 3·50
647/9 .. .. *Set of* 3 7·50 8·00

98 Queen Victoria and King Edward VII

(Litho B.D.T.)

1993 (4 June). 40*th Anniv of Coronation. T* **98** *and similar horiz designs. Multicoloured. P* 14.
650 $1.75, Type **98** .. .. 2·25 2·25
a. Horiz strip of 3. Nos. 650/2 .. .. 6·00
651 $1.75, King George V and King George VI 2·25 2·25
652 $1.75, Queen Elizabeth II in 1953 and 1986 2·25 2·25
650/2 .. .. *Set of* 3 6·00 6·00
Nos. 650/2 were printed together, *se-tenant*, in horizontal strips of 3 throughout the sheet.

99 "Madonna and Child" (Nino Pisano)

100 Ice Hockey

1993 (29 Oct). *Christmas. Religious Sculptures. T* **99** *and similar vert designs. Multicoloured. Ordinary paper. P* 13½ ($3) *or* 14 (*others*).
653 80 c. Type **99** 80 80
654 90 c. "Virgin on Rosebush" (Luca della Robbia) 85 85
655 $1.15, "Virgin with Child and St. John" (Juan Francisco Rustici) .. .. 1·25 1·25
656 $1.95, "Virgin with Child" (Miguel Angel) 2·00 2·00
657 $3 "Madonna and Child" (Jacopo della Quercia) (32×47 *mm*) .. .. 3·00 3·00
653/7 .. .. *Set of* 7 7·00 7·00

(Litho B.D.T.)

1994 (11 Feb). *Winter Olympic Games, Lillehammer. T* **100** *and similar horiz designs. Multicoloured. P* 14.
658 $1.15, Type **100** .. .. 2·00 2·00
a. Horiz strip of 3. Nos. 658/60 .. .. 5·50
659 $1.15, Ski-jumping .. .. 2·00 2·00
660 $1.15, Cross-country skiing .. .. .. 2·00 2·00
658/60 .. .. *Set of* 3 5·50 5·50
Nos. 658/60 were printed together, *se-tenant*, in horizontal strips of 3 throughout the sheet.

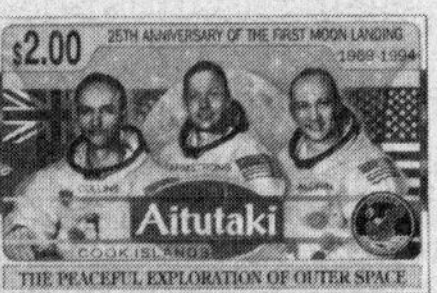

101 *Ipomoea pes-caprae*

102 Cook Islands and U.S.A. Flags with Astronauts Collins, Armstrong and Aldrin

(Des G. Drummond. Litho Questa ($3, $5, $8), B.D.T. (others))

1994 (17 Feb)–**97**. *Flowers. T* **101** *and similar vert designs. Multicoloured. P* 13½×14 ($3, $5, $8) *or* 13½ (*others*).
661 5 c. Type **101** 10 10
662 10 c. *Plumeria alba* 10 10
663 15 c. *Hibiscus rosa-sinensis* 10 15
664 20 c. *Allamanda cathartica* 15 20
665 25 c. *Delonix regia* 15 20
666 30 c. *Gardenia taitensis* 20 25
667 50 c. *Plumeria rubra* 30 35
668 80 c. *Ipomoea littoralis* 50 55
669 85 c. *Hibiscus tiliaceus* 55 60
670 90 c. *Erythrina variegata* 55 60
671 $1 *Solandra nitida* (29.4.94) 65 70
672 $2 *Cordia subcordata* (29.4.94) .. ..
673 $3 *Hibiscus rosa-sinensis* (*different*) 1·25 1·40
(34×47 *mm*) (18.11.94) .. .. 1·90 2·00
674 $5 As $3 (34×47 *mm*) (18.11.94) .. 3·25 3·50
675 $8 As $3 (34×47 *mm*) (21.11.97) .. 5·00 5·25
661/75 .. .. *Set of* 15 14·50 15·50
Nos. 671/5 include a portrait of Queen Elizabeth II at top right.

(Des G. Vasarhelyi. Litho B.D.T.)

1994 (20 July). 25*th Anniv of First Moon Landing. T* **102** *and similar horiz design. Multicoloured. P* 14.
676 $2 Type **102** .. .. 4·00 4·00
a. Pair. Nos. 676/7 .. .. .. 8·00 8·00
677 $2 "Apollo 11" re-entering atmosphere and landing in sea .. .. 4·00 4·00
Nos. 676/7 were printed together, *se-tenant*, in horizontal or vertical pairs throughout the sheet.

103 "The Madonna of the Basket" (Correggio)

104 Battle of Britain

(Litho B.D.T.)

1994 (30 Nov). *Christmas. Religious Paintings. T* **103** *an[d] similar vert designs. Multicoloured. P* 14.
678 85 c. Type **103** .. .. 1·00 1·1
a. Block of 4. Nos. 678/81 .. .. 3·50
679 85 c. "The Virgin and Child with Saints" (Memling) .. .. 1·00 1·
680 85 c. "The Virgin and Child with Flowers" (Dolci) .. .. 1·00 1·
681 85 c. "The Virgin and Child with Angels" (Bergognone) .. .. 1·00 1·
682 90 c. "Adoration of the Kings" (Dosso) .. 1·00 1·
a. Block of 4. Nos. 682/5 .. .. 3·50
683 90 c. "The Virgin and Child" (Bellini) .. 1·00 1·
684 90 c. "The Virgin and Child" (Schiavone) .. 1·00 1·
685 90 c. "Adoration of the Kings" (Dolci) .. 1·00 1·
678/85 .. .. *Set of* 8 7·00 8·
Nos. 678/81 and 682/5 were printed together, *se-tenant*, i[n] blocks of 4 throughout the sheets.
No. 678 is inscribed "Corregio" in error.

(Litho B.D.T.)

1995 (4 Sept). 50*th Anniv of End of Second World War. T* **1[04]** *and similar horiz design. Multicoloured. P* 13.
686 $4 Type **104** .. .. 5·50 6·
a. Pair. Nos. 686/7 .. .. .. 11·00 12·
687 $4 Battle of Midway .. .. .. 5·50 6·
Nos. 686/7 were printed together, *se-tenant* horizontally ar[nd] vertically, in sheets of 4.

105 Queen Elizabeth the Queen Mother

(Des G. Vasarhelyi. Litho B.D.T.)

1995 (14 Sept). 95*th Birthday of Queen Elizabeth the Qu[een] Mother. P* 13.
688 **105** $4 multicoloured .. .. .. 5·50 6

106 Globe, Doves, United Nations Emblem and Headquarters

(Des G. Vasarhelyi. Litho B.D.T.)

1995 (18 Oct). 50*th Anniv of United Nations. P* 13×13½.
689 **106** $4.25, multicoloured .. .. .. 4·50 5

107 Green Turtle

(Litho B.D.T.)

995 (1 Dec). *Year of the Sea Turtle. T* **107** *and similar horiz designs. Multicoloured. P* 13½×14.
90 95 c. Type **107** .. .. 1·50 1·50
91 $1.15, Leatherback Turtle .. .. 1·75 1·75
92 $1.50, Olive Ridley Turtle .. .. 2·00 2·00
93 $1.75, Loggerhead Turtle .. .. 2·50 2·50
90/3 .. .. *Set of* 4 7·00 7·00

108 Queen Elizabeth II

(Des G. Vasarhelyi. Litho)

996 (24 June). *70th Birthday of Queen Elizabeth II. P* 14.
94 **108** $4.50, multicoloured .. .. .. 6·00 6·50

109 Baron Pierre de Coubertin, Torch and Opening of 1896 Olympic Games

(Des G. Vasarhelyi. Litho)

996 (11 July). *Centenary of Modern Olympic Games. T* **109** *and similar horiz design. Multicoloured. P* 14.
95 $2 Type **109** .. .. 2·75 3·00
a. Pair. Nos. 695/6 .. .. .. 5·50 6·00
96 $2 Athletes and American flag, 1996 .. 2·75 3·00
Nos. 695/6 were printed together, *se-tenant*, in horizontal and ertical pairs within sheets of four.

110 Princess Elizabeth and Lieut. Philip Mountbatten with King George VI and Queen Elizabeth, 1947

111 Diana, Princess of Wales

997 (20 Nov). *Golden Wedding of Queen Elizabeth and Prince Philip. P* 14.
97 **110** $2.50, multicoloured .. .. .. 2·00 2·25
MS698 76×102 mm. **110** $6 multicoloured .. 5·25 5·75

998 (15 Apr). *Diana, Princess of Wales Commemoration. Multicoloured. Litho. P* 14.
99 $1 Type **111** 65 70
a. Sheetlet. No. 699×5 plus label .. 3·25
MS700 70×100 mm. $4 Diana, Princess of Wales 3·25 3·50
No. 699 was printed in sheetlets of 5 stamps with a label at top ight.

998 (19 Nov). *Children's Charities. No.* **MS**700 *surch as T* **275** *of Cook Islands in silver.*
MS701 70×100 mm. $4+$1 Diana, Princess of Wales .. .. 3·75 4·00

STAMP BOOKLETS

982 (June). *Royal Wedding. Cover as No.* SB1 *of Cook Islands, but inscr* "Aitutaki".
SB1 $5.60, booklet containing 60 c. and 80 c. (Nos. 391/2), each in block of 4 .. .. .. 5·50

OFFICIAL STAMPS

O.H.M.S.

(O 1)

978 (3 Nov)–**79**. *Nos.* 98/105, 107/10 *and* 227/8 *optd or surch (Nos.* O8/9 *and* O15) *as Type* O 1.
O 1 1 c. New Caledonia Nautilus (*Nautilus macromphallus*) 90 10
O 2 2 c. Common or Major Harp (*Harpa major*) 1·00 10
O 3 3 c. Striped Bonnet (*Phalium flammiferum*) .. .. 1·00 10
O 4 4 c. Mole Cowrie (*Cypraea talpa*) (Gold) 1·00 10
O 5 5 c. Pontifical Mitre (*Mitra stictica*) .. 1·00 10
O 6 8 c. Trumpet Triton (*Charonia tritonis*) .. 1·25 10
O 7 10 c. Venus Comb Murex (*Murex pecten*) 1·50 15
O 8 15 c. on 60 c. Widest Pacific Conch (*Strombus latissimus*) .. .. 2·50 20
O 9 18 c. on 60 c. Widest Pacific Conch (*Strombus latissimus*) .. .. 2·50 20
O10 20 c. Red-mouth Olive (*Oliva miniacea miniacea*) (Gold) .. .. 2·50 20
O11 50 c. Union Jack, Queen Victoria and island map .. .. 1·00 55
O12 60 c. Widest Pacific Conch (*Strombus latissimus*) .. .. 10·00 70
O13 $1 Maple-leaf Triton or Winged Frog Shell (*Biplex perca*) .. .. .. 10·00 85
O14 $2 Queen Elizabeth II and Marlin-spike Auger (*Terebra maculata*) (20.2.79) 9·00 1·00
O15 $4 on $1 Balcony scene, 1953 (Sil.) (20.2.79) .. .. 2·50 1·00
O16 $5 Queen Elizabeth II and Tiger Cowrie (*Cypraea tigris*) (20.2.79) .. .. 11·00 1·75
O1/16 .. .. *Set of* 16 50·00 6·00
These stamps were originally only sold to the public cancelled-to-order and not in unused condition.
They were made available to overseas collectors in mint condition during 1980.

75c

O.H.M.S. (O 2) O.H.M.S. (O 3)

1985 (9 Aug)–**90**. *(a) Nos.* 351/2, 475 *and* 477/94 *optd or surch as Type* O 2 *by foil embossing in blue* ($14, $18) *or emerald (others).*
O17 2 c. Type **65** 35 35
O18 5 c. Scarlet Robin 45 45
O19 10 c. Golden Whistler 50 50
O20 12 c. Rufous Fantail 55 55
O21 18 c. Peregrine Falcon .. .. .. 1·00 1·00
O22 20 c. on 24 c. Barn Owl .. .. .. 1·00 1·00
O23 30 c. Java Sparrow 75 75
O24 40 c. on 36 c. White-breasted Wood Swallow 90 90
O25 50 c. Rock Dove .. .. 1·00 1·00
O26 55 c. on 48 c. Tahitian Lory .. .. 1·00 1·00
O27 60 c. Purple Swamphen .. .. .. 1·25 1·25
O28 65 c. on 72 c. Zebra Dove .. .. .. 1·25 1·25
O29 80 c. on 96 c. Chestnut-breasted Mannikin 1·25 1·25
O30 $1.20, Common Mynah (15.6.88) .. 1·75 1·75
O31 $2.10, Eastern Reef Heron (15.6.88) .. 2·75 2·75
O32 $3 Blue-headed Flycatcher (30×42 *mm*) (1.10.86) .. .. 3·50 3·50
O33 $4.20, Red-bellied Flycatcher (30×42 *mm*) (1.10.86) .. .. .. 5·00 5·00
O34 $5.60, Red Munia (30×42 *mm*) (1.10.86) 6·00 6·00
O35 $9.60, Flat-billed Kingfisher (30×42 *mm*) (1.10.86) .. .. .. 9·00 9·00
O36 $14 on $4 Red Munia (35×48 *mm*) .. 12·00 12·00
O37 $18 on $5 Flat-billed Kingfisher (35×48 *mm*) (2.7.90) .. .. .. 14·00 14·00

(b) Nos. 430/3 *surch as Type* O 3 *by gold foil embossing*
O38 75 c. on 48 c. Type **57** 80 80
O39 75 c. on 48 c. Ancient Ti'i image 80 80
O40 75 c. on 48 c. Tourist canoeing 80 80
O41 75 c. on 48 c. Captain William Bligh and chart 80 80
O17/41 .. .. *Set of* 25 60·00 60·00

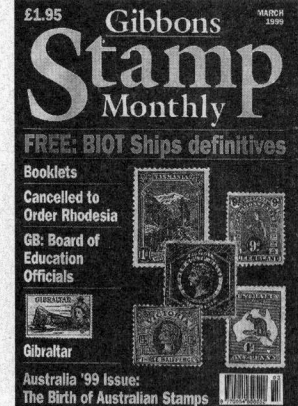

PENRHYN ISLAND

Stamps of COOK ISLANDS were used on Penrhyn Island from late 1901 until the issue of the surcharged stamps in May 1902.

PRICES FOR STAMPS ON COVER TO 1945	
No. 1	*from* × 25
No. 3	—
Nos. 4/5	*from* × 25
Nos. 6/8	—
Nos. 9/10	*from* × 50
Nos. 11/13	—
Nos. 14/18	*from* × 3
Nos. 19/23	*from* × 2
Nos. 24/37	*from* × 3
Nos. 38/40	*from* × 5

A. NEW ZEALAND DEPENDENCY

The island of Penrhyn, under British protection from 0 September 1888, was annexed by New Zealand on 11 June 901.

Stamps of New Zealand overprinted or surcharged. For illustrations of New Zealand watermarks and definitive types see the beginning of Cook Islands.

PENRHYN ISLAND.
½ PENI.
(1)

PENRHYN ISLAND.
TAI PENI.
(2) 1d.

PENRHYN ISLAND.
2½ PENI.
(3)

902 (5 May). *T* **23, 27** *and* **42** *surch with T* **1, 2** *and* **3.**

(a) Thick, soft Pirie paper. No wmk. P 11

1 2½d. blue (No. 260) (R.) .. 2·50 6·50
a. "½"and "P" spaced (all stamps in 8th vert row) .. 13·00 27·00

(b) Thin, hard Basted Mills paper. W **38** *of New Zealand.*

(i) *P* 11

3 1d. carmine (No. 286) (Br.) .. £850 £900

(ii) *P* 14

4 ½d. green (No. 287) (R.) .. 80 4·25
a. No stop after "ISLAND" .. £150 £200
5 1d. carmine (No. 288) (Br.) .. 3·25 14·00

(iii) *Perf compound of* 11 *and* 14

6 1d. carmine (No. 290) (Br.) .. £750 £800

(iv) *Mixed perfs*

7 ½d. green (No. 291) (R.) .. £1000
8 1d. carmine (No. 292) (Br.) .. £1200

(c) Thin, hard Cowan paper. W **43** *of New Zealand.* (i) *P* 14

9 ½d. green (No. 302) (R.) .. 1·40 4·25
a. No stop after "ISLAND" (R. 10/6) .. £130 £170
0 1d. carmine (No. 303) (B.) .. 1·00 3·00
a. No stop after "ISLAND" (R. 10/6) .. 48·00 80·00

(ii) *Perf compound of* 11 *and* 14

1 1d. carmine (No. 305) (B.) .. £6000

(iii) *Mixed perfs*

2 ½d. green (No. 306) (R.) .. £1100 £1200
3 1d. carmine (No. 307) (B.) .. £425 £475

PENRHYN ISLAND.
(4)

Toru Pene.
(5) 3d.

Ono Pene.
(6) 6d.

Tahi Silingi.
(7) 1s.

903 (28 Feb). *T* **28, 31** *and* **34** *surch with name at top, T* **4**, *and values at foot, T* **5/7**. *Thin, hard Cowan paper. W* **43** *(sideways) of New Zealand. P* 11.

4 3d. yellow-brown (No. 309) (B.) .. 10·00 20·00
5 6d. rose-red (No. 312*a*) (B.) .. 15·00 32·00
6 1s. brown-red (No. 315) (B.) .. 50·00 55·00
a. Bright red .. 48·00 48·00
b. Orange-red .. 55·00 55·00
4/16 .. *Set of* 3 65·00 90·00

914 (May)–**15**. *T* **51/2** *surch with T* **1** (½d.) *or optd with T* **4** *at top and surch with T* **6/7** *at foot.*

9 ½d. yellow-green (No. 387) (C.) (5.14) .. 80 6·50
a. No stop after "ISLAND" .. 30·00 70·00
b. No stop after "PENI" (R. 3/17) .. 90·00 £160
c. Vermilion opt (1.15) .. 80 6·50
ca. No stop after "ISLAND" .. 10·00 42·00
cb. No stop after "PENI" (R. 3/5, 3/17) .. 40·00 90·00
2 6d. carmine (No. 393) (B.) (8.14) .. 27·00 70·00
3 1s. vermilion (No. 394) (B.) (8.14) .. 48·00 95·00
9/23 .. *Set of* 3 65·00 £150

The "no stop after ISLAND" variety occurs on R. 1/4, 1/10, /16, 1/22, 6/4, 6/10, 6/16 and 6/22 of the carmine surcharge, No. 9, and on these positions plus R. 1/12, 1/24, 6/12 and 6/24 for he vermilion, No. 19c.

1917 (Nov)–**20.** *Optd as T* 4.

(a) T **60** *(recess). W* **43** *of New Zealand. P* 14×13½.

24 2½d. blue (No. 419) (R.) (10.20) .. 3·00 7·50
a. Perf 14×14½ .. 2·00 4·50
ab. No stop after "ISLAND" (R. 10/8) .. £150 £250
b. Vert pair. Nos. 24/4a .. 50·00 80·00
25 3d. chocolate (No. 420) (B.) (6.18) .. 12·00 60·00
a. Perf 14×14½ .. 9·50 60·00
b. Vert pair. Nos. 25/5a .. 70·00 £190
26 6d. carmine (No. 425) (B.) (1.18) .. 8·00 24·00
a. Perf 14×14½ .. 5·00 16·00
ab. No stop after "ISLAND" (R. 10/8) .. £325 £450
b. Vert pair. Nos. 26/6a .. 55·00 £120
27 1s. vermilion (No. 430) (B.) (12.17) .. 15·00 40·00
a. Perf 14×14½ .. 12·00 30·00
ab. No stop after "ISLAND" (R. 10/8) .. £350 £475
b. Vert pair. Nos. 27/7a .. £110 £200
24/7 .. *Set of* 4 25·00 £100

(b) T **61** *(typo). W* **43** *of New Zealand. P* 14×15

28 ½d. green (No. 435) (R.) (2.20) .. 1·00 2·00
a. No stop after "ISLAND" (R. 2/24) .. 85·00 £120
b. Narrow spacing .. 6·00 8·50
29 1½d. slate (No. 437) (R.) .. 6·50 14·00
a. Narrow spacing .. 18·00 35·00
30 1½d. orange-brown (No. 438) (R.) (2.19) .. 60 14·00
a. Narrow spacing .. 5·00 35·00
31 3d. chocolate (No. 440) (B.) (6.19) .. 3·50 16·00
a. Narrow spacing .. 15·00 45·00
28/31 .. *Set of* 4 10·50 42·00

The narrow spacing variety occurs on R. 1/5–8, 4/21–4, 7/5–8 and 9/21–4.

(Recess P.B.)

1920 (23 Aug). *As T* **9/14** *of Cook Islands, but inscr* "PENRHYN". *No wmk. P* 14.

32 ½d. black and emerald .. 1·00 12·00
a. Part imperf block of 4 .. £1200
33 1d. black and deep red .. 1·50 12·00
a. Double derrick flaw (R.2/8, 3/6 or 5/2) 5·50
34 1½d. black and deep violet .. 6·50 17·00
35 3d. black and red .. 2·50 8·00
36 6d. red-brown and sepia .. 3·25 20·00
37 1s. black and slate-blue .. 10·00 23·00
32/7 .. *Set of* 6 22·00 80·00

No. 32a comes from sheets on which two rows were imperforate between horizontally and the second row additionally imperforate vertically.

Examples of the ½d. and 1d. with centre inverted were not supplied to the Post Office.

(Recess Govt Printing Office, Wellington)

1927–29. *As T* **9/10** *and* **16** *of Cook Islands, but inscr* "PENRHYN". *W* **43.** *P* 14.

38 ½d. black and green (5.29) .. 5·50 18·00
39 1d. black and deep carmine (14.3.28) .. 5·50 14·00
a. Double derrick flaw (R.2/8, 3/6 or 5/2) 16·00
40 2½d. red-brown and dull blue (10.27) .. 2·75 22·00
38/40 .. *Set of* 3 12·00 48·00

Cook Islands stamps superseded those of Penrhyn Islands on 15 March 1932. Separate issues were resumed in 1973.

B. PART OF COOK ISLANDS

The following issues are for use in all the islands of the Northern Cook Islands group.

(New Currency. 100 cents = 1 dollar)

PRINTERS. The notes above No. 33 of Aitutaki concerning printers and gum also apply here. Stamps printed by Fournier from No. 472 onwards are in lithography.

PENRHYN
NORTHERN
(8)

PENRHYN
NORTHERN
(9)

1973 (24 Oct–14 Nov). *Nos.* 228/45 *of Cook Is optd with T* **8** *(without "NORTHERN" on $1, $2).*

A. Without fluorescent security markings. Gum arabic

41A 1 c. multicoloured .. 80
42A 2 c. multicoloured .. 1·25
43A 3 c. multicoloured .. 1·75
44A 4 c. multicoloured (No. 233) .. 2·00
a. Optd on Cook Is No. 232 .. 24·00
45A 5 c. multicoloured .. 2·50
46A 6 c. multicoloured .. 2·50
47A 8 c. multicoloured .. 2·75
48A 15 c. multicoloured .. 4·25
50A 50 c. multicoloured .. 10·00
51A $1 multicoloured .. 12·00
52A $2 multicoloured (14.11) .. 15·00
41A/52A .. *Set of* 11 50·00

B. With fluorescent security markings. PVA gum.

41B 1 c. multicoloured .. 10 10
42B 2 c. multicoloured .. 10 10
43B 3 c. multicoloured .. 20 10
44B 4 c. multicoloured (No. 233) .. 10 10
45B 5 c. multicoloured .. 10 10
46B 6 c. multicoloured .. 20 30
47B 8 c. multicoloured .. 30 40
48B 15 c. multicoloured .. 45 50
49B 20 c. multicoloured .. 1·50 80
50B 50 c. multicoloured .. 90 1·75
51B $1 multicoloured .. 90 2·25
52B $2 multicoloured (14.11) .. 90 2·50
41B/52B .. *Set of* 12 5·00 7·50

1973 (14 Nov). *Royal Wedding. Nos.* 450/2 *of Cook Is optd as T* **9**, *in silver.*

53 **138** 25 c. multicoloured .. 30 20
54 – 30 c. multicoloured .. 30 20
55 – 50 c. multicoloured .. 30 20
53/5 .. *Set of* 3 80 55

10 Yellow Boxfish

11 Penrhyn Stamps of 1902

1974 (15 Aug)–**75.** *Multicoloured. (a) T* **10** *and similar horiz designs showing fishes. P* 13½.

56 ½ c. Type **10** .. 50 50
57 1 c. Diamond Fingerfish .. 70 50
58 2 c. Emperor Angelfish .. 80 50
59 3 c. Copper-banded Butterflyfish .. 80 50
60 4 c. Ornate Butterflyfish .. 80 50
61 5 c. Black-backed Butterflyfish .. 80 50
62 8 c. Latticed Butterflyfish .. 80 50
63 10 c. Saddle Butterflyfish .. 85 50
64 20 c. Regal Angelfish .. 1·75 50
65 25 c. Pennant Coralfish .. 1·75 50
66 60 c. Harlequin Sweetlips .. 2·50 90
67 $1 *Balistipus undulatus* .. 2·75 1·25

(b) Larger designs, 63×25 mm. P 13×12½.

68 $2 Birds-eye view of Penrhyn (12.2.75) .. 4·50 12·00
69 $5 Satellite view of Australasia (12.3.75) 4·50 6·00
56/69 .. *Set of* 14 21·00 23·00

1974 (27 Sept). *Centenary of Universal Postal Union. T* **11** *and similar vert design. Multicoloured. P* 13.

70 25 c. Type **11** .. 20 30
71 50 c. Stamps of 1920 .. 35 40

Each value was issued in sheets of 8 stamps and 1 label.

12 "Adoration of the Kings" (Memling)

1974 (30 Oct). *Christmas. T* **12** *and similar horiz designs. Multicoloured. P* 13.

72 5 c. Type **12** .. 20 25
73 10 c. "Adoration of the Shepherds" (Hugo van der Goes) .. 25 25
74 25 c. "Adoration of the Magi" (Rubens) .. 40 35
75 30 c. "The Holy Family" (Borgianni) .. 45 50
72/5 .. *Set of* 4 1·10 1·25

13 Churchill giving "V" Sign

(14)

1974 (30 Nov.) *Birth Centenary of Sir Winston Churchill. T* **13** *and similar vert design. P* 13.

76 30 c. agate and gold .. 35 85
77 50 c. myrtle-green and gold .. 45 90

Design:—50 c. Full-face portrait.

1975 (24 July). *"Apollo-Soyuz" Space Project. No.* 69 *optd with T* **14**.

78 $5 Satellite view of Australasia .. 1·75 2·50

15 "Virgin and Child" (Bouts)

16 "Pietà"

1975 (21 Nov). *Christmas. T* **15** *and similar vert designs showing the "Virgin and Child". Multicoloured. P* 14 × 13.

79 7 c. Type **15** .. 40 10
80 15 c. Leonardo da Vinci .. 70 20
81 35 c. Raphael .. 1·10 35
79/81 .. *Set of* 3 2·00 60

1976 (19 Mar). *Easter and 500th Birth Anniv of Michelangelo. T* **16** *and similar vert designs. P* 14 × 13.
82 15 c. sepia and gold 25 15
83 20 c. blackish purple and gold.. .. .. .. 30 15
84 35 c. myrtle-green and gold 40 20
82/4 .. .. *Set of* 3 85 45
MS85 112 × 72 mm. Nos. 82/4 .. .. 85 1·25
Each value was issued in sheets of 8 stamps and 1 label.

17 "Washington crossing the Delaware" (E. Leutze) **18** Running

1976 (20 May). *Bicentenary of American Revolution. T* **17** *and similar vert designs. Multicoloured. P* 13.
86 30 c. } 30 15
87 30 c. } Type **17**.. .. .. 30 15
88 30 c. } 30 15
89 50 c. } 40 20
90 50 c. } "The Spirit of '76" (A. M. Willard) .. 40 20
91 50 c. } 40 20
86/91 .. .. *Set of* 6 1·90 95
MS92 103 × 103 mm. Nos. 86/91. P 13 .. .. 2·00 2·50
Nos. 86/8 and 89/91 were each printed together, *se-tenant*, in horizontal strips of 3 throughout the sheet, forming composite designs. Each sheet includes 3 stamp-size labels. Type **17** shows the left-hand stamp of the 30 c. design.

1976 (9 July). *Olympic Games, Montreal. T* **18** *and similar horiz designs. Multicoloured. P* 14.
93 25 c. Type **18** 25 15
94 30 c. Long Jumping 30 15
95 75 c. Throwing the Javelin 55 25
93/5 .. .. *Set of* 3 1·00 50
MS96 86 × 128 mm. Nos. 93/5. P 14 × 13 .. 1·10 2·00

19 "The Flight into Egypt" **20** The Queen in Coronation Robes

1976 (20 Oct). *Christmas. Dürer Engravings. T* **19** *and similar horiz designs. P* 13.
97 7 c. black and silver 15 10
98 15 c. steel blue and silver 25 15
99 35 c. violet and silver 35 25
97/9 .. .. *Set of* 3 65 45
Designs:—15 c. "Adoration of the Magi"; 35 c. "The Nativity".

1977 (24 Mar). *Silver Jubilee. T* **20** *and similar vert designs. Multicoloured. P* 13.
100 50 c. Type **20** 25 60
101 $1 Queen and Prince Philip.. .. .. 35 65
102 $2 Queen Elizabeth II 50 80
100/2 .. .. *Set of* 3 1·00 1·90
MS103 128 × 87 mm. Nos. 100/2. P 13 .. .. 1·00 1·50
Stamps from the miniature sheet have silver borders.

21 "The Annunciation" **22** Iiwi

1977 (23 Sept). *Christmas. T* **21** *and similar designs showing illustrations by J. S. von Carolsfeld. P* 13.
104 7 c. light stone, purple-brown and gold .. 40 15
105 15 c. pale rose, deep maroon and gold .. 60 15
106 35 c. blackish green, pale green and gold .. 1·00 30
104/6 .. .. *Set of* 3 1·75 55
Designs:—15 c. "The Announcement to the Shepherds"; 35 c. "The Nativity".

1978 (19 Jan). *Bicentenary of Discovery of Hawaii. T* **22** *and similar vert designs showing Hawaiian birds or artefacts. Multicoloured. P* 13.
107 20 c. Type **22** 80 30
108 20 c. Elgin cloak 80 30
109 30 c. Apapane 90 40
110 30 c. Feather image of a god 90 40
111 35 c. Moorhen 90 45
112 35 c. Feather cape, helmet and staff 90 45
113 75 c. Hawaii O-o .. .. 1·50 80
114 75 c. Feather image and cloak .. .. .. 1·50 80
107/14 .. .. *Set of* 8 7·50 3·50
MS115 Two sheets each 78 × 119 mm containing (a) Nos. 107, 109, 111, 113; (b) Nos. 108, 110, 112, 114.. .. .. 6·50 8·50
Nos. 107/8, 109/10, 111/12 and 113/14 were each printed together, *se-tenant*, in horizontal and vertical pairs throughout the sheet.

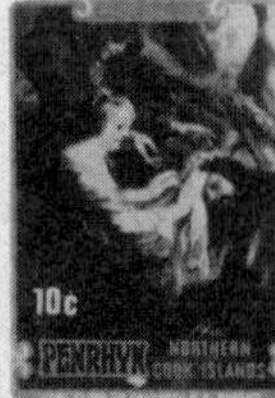

23 "The Road to Calvary" **24** Royal Coat of Arms

1978 (10 Mar). *Easter and 400th Birth Anniv of Rubens. T* **23** *and similar vert designs. Multicoloured. P* 13.
116 10 c. Type **23** 20 10
117 15 c. "Christ on the Cross" 25 15
118 35 c. "Christ with Straw" 45 25
116/18 .. .. *Set of* 3 80 45
MS119 87 × 138 mm. Nos. 116/18 .. .. .. 1·00 1·60
Stamps from No. **MS**119 are slightly larger (28 × 36 mm.)

1978 (17 Apr). *Easter. Children's Charity. Designs as Nos.* 116/18 *in separate miniature sheets.* 49 × 68 *mm, each with a face value of* 60 *c.* + 5 *c. P* 12½–13.
MS120 As Nos. 116/18 .. .. *Set of 3 sheets* 90 1·50

1978 (24 May). *25th Anniv of Coronation. T* **24** *and similar vert designs. P* 13.
121 90 c. black, gold and deep lilac 30 60
122 90 c. multicoloured 30 60
123 90 c. black, gold and deep bluish green .. 30 60
121/3 .. .. *Set of* 3 90 1·60
MS124 75 × 122 mm. Nos. 121/3 .. .. .. 1·10 2·00
Designs:—No. 122, Queen Elizabeth II; No. 123, New Zealand coat of arms.
Nos. 121/3 were printed together in small sheets of 6, containing two *se-tenant* strips of 3, with horizontal gutter margin between.

25 "Madonna of the Pear" **26** Sir Rowland Hill and G.B. Penny Black Stamp

1978 (29 Nov). *Christmas. 450th Death Anniv of Dürer. T* **25** *and similar vert design. Multicoloured. P* 14.
125 30 c. Type **25** 65 30
126 35 c. "The Virgin and Child with St. Anne" .. 65 30
MS127 101 × 60 mm. Nos. 125/6. P 13½.. .. 1·50 1·75
Nos. 125/6 were each printed in small sheets of 6.

1979 (26 Sept). *Death Centenary of Sir Rowland Hill. T* **26** *and similar vert designs. Multicoloured. P* 13½ × 14.
128 75 c. Type **26** 50 55
129 75 c. 1974 Centenary of Universal Postal Union 25 c. and 50 c. commemoratives .. 50 55
130 90 c. Sir Rowland Hill.. .. .. .. 60 70
131 90 c. 1978 25th anniv of Coronation 90 c. (Queen Elizabeth II) commemorative .. 60 70
128/31 .. .. *Set of* 4 2·00 2·25
MS132 116 × 58 mm. Nos. 128/31 .. .. 1·90 2·25
Stamps from No. **MS**132 have cream backgrounds.
Nos. 128/9 and 130/1 were each printed together, *se-tenant*, in horizontal and vertical pairs throughout small sheets of 8.

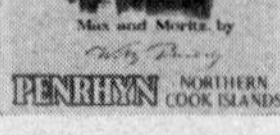

27 Max and Moritz **28** "Christ carrying Cross" (Book of Ferdinand II)

1979 (20 Nov). *International Year of the Child. Illustrations from Max and Moritz stories by Wilhelm Busch. T* **27** *and similar horiz designs. Multicoloured. P* 13.
133 12 c. Type **27** 20 10
134 12 c. Max and Moritz looking down chimney .. 20 10
135 12 c. Max and Moritz making off with food .. 20 10
136 12 c. Cook about to beat dog 20 10
137 15 c. Max sawing through bridge 25 10
138 15 c. Pursuer approaching bridge 25 1
139 15 c. Bridge collapsing under pursuer .. 25 1
140 15 c. Pursuer in river 25 1
141 20 c. Baker locking shop 30 2
142 20 c. Max and Moritz coming out of hiding .. 30 2
143 20 c. Max and Moritz falling in dough .. 30 2
144 20 c. Max and Moritz after being rolled into buns by baker 30 2
133/44 .. .. *Set of* 12 2·75 1·5
Nos. 133/6, 137/40 and 141/4 were each printed together, *se-tenant*, in sheets of 4, either with or without labels containing extracts from the books on the top and bottom selvedge.

1980 (28 Mar). *Easter. Scenes from 15th-century Prayer Books. T* **28** *and similar vert designs. Multicoloured. P* 13.
145 12 c. Type **28** 15 2
146 20 c. "The Crucifixion" (William Vrelant, Book of Duke of Burgundy) 20 2
147 35 c. "Descent from the Cross" (Book of Ferdinand II) 30 4
145/7 .. .. *Set of* 3 55 8
MS148 111×65 mm. Nos. 145/7 .. .. 55 1·0
Stamps from No. **MS**148 have cream borders.

1980 (28 Mar). *Easter. Children's Charity. Designs as Nos.* 145/7 *in separate miniature sheets* 54 × 85 *mm, each with a face value of* 70 *c.* + 5 *c.*
MS149 As Nos. 145/7 .. .. *Set of 3 sheets* 75 1·0

29 "Queen Elizabeth, 1937" (Sir Gerald Kelly) **30** Falk Hoffman, D.D.R. (platform diving) (gold)

1980 (17 Sept). *80th Birthday of Queen Elizabeth the Queen Mother. P* 13.
150 **29** $1 multicoloured .. .. .. 1·25 1·2
MS151 55 × 84 mm. **29** $2.50 multicoloured .. 1·60 1·6

1980 (14 Nov). *Olympic Games, Moscow. Medal Winners. T* **30** *and similar vert designs. Multicoloured. P* 13½.
152 10 c. Type **30** 10 1
153 10 c. Martina Jaschke, D.D.R. (platform diving) (gold) 10 1
154 20 c. Tomi Polkolainen, Finland (archery) (gold) 15 1
155 20 c. Kete Losaberidse, U.S.S.R. (archery) (gold) 15 1
156 30 c. Czechoslovakia (football) (gold) 20 2
157 30 c. D.D.R. (football) (silver) 20 2
158 50 c. Barbel Wockel, D.D.R. (200-metre dash) (gold) 30 3
159 50 c. Pietro Mennea, Italy (200-metre dash) (gold) 30 3
152/9 .. .. *Set of* 8 1·40 1·4
MS160 150 × 106 mm. Nos. 152/9. P 13 .. .. 1·40 1·7
Stamps from No. **MS**160 have gold borders.
Nos. 152/3, 154/5, 156/7 and 158/9 were each printed together, *se-tenant*, in horizontal pairs throughout the sheet.

31 "The Virgin of Counsellors" (Luis Dalmau) **32** Amatasi

1980 (5 Dec). *Christmas. Paintings. T* **31** *and similar vert designs. Multicoloured. P* 13.
161 20 c. Type **31** 15 1
162 35 c. "Virgin and Child" (Serra brothers) .. 20 2
163 50 c. "The Virgin of Albocacer" (Master of the Porciuncula) 30 3
161/3 .. .. *Set of* 3 60 6
MS164 135 × 75 mm. Nos. 161/3 .. .. .. 1·50 1·5

1980 (5 Dec). *Christmas. Children's Charity. Designs as Nos.* 161/3 *in separate miniature sheets,* 54 × 77 *mm, each with a face value of* 70 *c.* + 5 *c.*
MS165 As Nos. 161/3 .. .. *Set of 3 sheets* 1·50 1·5

1981 (16 Feb-21 Sept). *Sailing Craft and Ships (1st series). Multicoloured designs as T* **32**. *P* 14 *(Nos.* 166/85*),* 13 × 14½ *(Nos.* 186/205*) or* 13½ (Nos. 206/8*).*
166 1 c. Type **32** 20
167 1 c. Ndrua 20
168 1 c. Waka 20
169 1 c. Tongiaki 20
170 3 c. Va'a Teu'ua 40
171 3 c. *Vitoria*, 1500 40
172 3 c. *Golden Hind*, 1560 40
173 3 c. *Boudeuse*, 1760 40
174 4 c. H.M.S. *Bounty*, 1787 50
175 4 c. *L'Astrolabe*, 1811 50

4 c. *Star of India*, 1861 .. .. .. 50 15
4 c. *Great Republic*, 1853 .. .. .. 50 15
6 c. *Balcutha*, 1886 .. .. 50 20
6 c. *Coonatto*, 1863 .. .. 50 20
6 c. *Antiope*, 1866 .. .. 50 20
6 c. *Teaping*, 1863 .. .. 50 20
10 c. *Preussen*, 1902 .. .. 50 75
10 c. *Pamir*, 1921 .. .. 50 75
10 c. *Cap Hornier*, 1910 .. .. .. 50 75
10 c. *Patriarch*, 1869 .. .. 50 75
15 c. As Type **32** (16 Mar) 50 85
15 c. As No. 167 (16 Mar) 50 85
15 c. As No. 168 (16 Mar) 50 85
15 c. As No. 169 (16 Mar) 50 85
20 c. As No. 170 (16 Mar) 50 85
20 c. As No. 171 (16 Mar) 50 85
20 c. As No. 172 (16 Mar) 50 85
20 c. As No. 173 (16 Mar) 50 85
30 c. As No. 174 (16 Mar) 50 95
30 c. As No. 175 (16 Mar) 50 95
30 c. As No. 176 (16 Mar) 50 95
30 c. As No. 177 (16 Mar) 50 95
50 c. As No. 178 (16 Mar) .. .. .. 1·00 1·75
50 c. As No. 179 (16 Mar) .. .. .. 1·00 1·75
50 c. As No. 180 (16 Mar) .. .. .. 1·00 1·75
50 c. As No. 181 (16 Mar) .. .. .. 1·00 1·75
$1 As No. 182 (15 May) .. .. .. 2·00 1·50
$1 As No. 183 (15 May) .. .. .. 2·00 1·50
$1 As No. 184 (15 May) .. .. .. 2·00 1·50
$1 As No. 185 (15 May) .. .. .. 2·00 1·50
$2 *Cutty Sark*, 1869 (26 June) .. .. 4·50 3·25
$4 *Mermerus*, 1872 (26 June) .. .. 9·00 5·00
$6 H.M.S. *Resolution* and *Discovery*, 1776–80 (21 Sept) .. .. 15·00 12·00
/208 .. .. *Set of* 43 48·00 42·00
Nos. 186/205 are 41 × 25 mm and Nos. 206/8 47 × 33 mm in size.
On Nos. 166/205 the four designs of each value were printed ether, *se-tenant*, in blocks of 4 throughout the sheet.
For redrawn versions of these designs in other face values see s. 337/55.

33 "Jesus at the Grove" (Veronese)

34 Prince Charles as Young Child

31 (5 Apr). *Easter. Paintings. T* **33** *and similar vert designs. Multicoloured. P* 14.
30 c. Type **33** 40 20
40 c. "Christ with Crown of Thorns" (Titian) .. 55 25
50 c. "Pietá" (Van Dyck) 60 30
/20 .. .. *Set of* 3 1·40 65
221 110 × 68 mm. Nos. 218/20. P 13½ .. 2·75 2·00

31 (5 Apr). *Easter. Children's Charity. Designs as Nos.* 218/20 *in separate miniature sheets* 70 × 86 *mm., each with a face value of* 70 *c.* + 5 *c. P* 13½.
222 As Nos. 218/20 .. .. *Set of* 3 *sheets* 1·50 1·50

31 (10 July). *Royal Wedding. T* **34** *and similar vert designs. Multicoloured. P* 14.
40 c. Type **34** 20 35
50 c. Prince Charles as schoolboy 25 40
60 c. Prince Charles as young man 25 40
70 c. Prince Charles in ceremonial Naval uniform 25 45
80 c. Prince Charles as Colonel-in-Chief, Royal Regiment of Wales 25 45
/7 .. .. *Set of* 5 1·10 1·90
228 99 × 89 mm. Nos. 223/7 .. .. .. 1·25 2·00
Nos. 223/7 were each printed in small sheets of 6 including one *tenant* stamp-size label.

31 (30 Nov). *International Year for Disabled Persons. Nos.* 223/8 *surch as T* **51** *of Aitutaki.*
40 c.+ 5 c. Type **34** 20 50
50 c.+ 5 c. Prince Charles as schoolboy .. 25 55
60 c.+ 5 c. Prince Charles as young man .. 25 55
70 c.+ 5 c. Prince Charles in ceremonial Naval uniform 25 60
80 c.+ 5 c. Prince Charles as Colonel-in-Chief, Royal Regiment of Wales.. .. .. 25 65
/33 .. .. *Set of* 5 1·10 2·50
234 99 × 89 mm. As Nos. 229/33, but 10 c. premium on each stamp .. .. 1·10 3·00
Nos. 229/34 have commemorative inscriptions overprinted on sheet margins.

35 Footballer

36 "The Virgin on a Crescent"

1981 (7 Dec). *World Cup Football Championship, Spain* (1982). *T* **35** *and similar vert designs showing footballers. Multicoloured. P* 13.
235 15 c. Type **35** 20 15
236 15 c. Footballer wearing orange jersey with black and mauve stripes.. .. .. .. 20 15
237 15 c. Player in blue jersey 20 15
238 35 c. Player in blue jersey 30 25
239 35 c. Player in red jersey 30 25
240 35 c. Player in yellow jersey with green stripes 30 25
241 50 c. Player in orange jersey 40 35
242 50 c. Player in mauve jersey 40 35
243 50 c. Player in black jersey 40 35
235/43 .. .. *Set of* 9 2·40 2·00
MS244 113 × 151 mm. As Nos. 235/43, but each stamp with a premium of 3 c. .. .. .. 4·75 2·75
The three designs of each value were printed together, *se-tenant*, in horizontal strips of 3 throughout the sheet.

1981 (15 Dec). *Christmas. Details from Engravings by Dürer. T* **36** *and similar vert designs in violet, deep reddish purple and stone. P* 13 × 13½.
245 30 c. Type **36** .. .. 90 1·00
246 40 c. "The Virgin at the Fence" .. .. 1·25 1·40
247 50 c. "The Holy Virgin and Child" .. .. 1·50 1·75
245/7 .. .. *Set of* 3 3·25 3·75
MS248 134 × 75 mm. As Nos. 245/7, but each stamp with a premium of 2 c. .. .. .. 2·25 2·25
MS249 Designs as Nos. 245/7 in separate miniature sheets, 58 × 85 mm, each with a face value of 70 c. + 5 c. P 14 × 13½ .. .. *Set of* 3 *sheets* 1·75 1·75

37 Lady Diana Spencer as Baby

(**38**)

1982 (1 July). *21st Birthday of Princess of Wales. T* **37** *and similar vert designs. Multicoloured. P* 14.
250 30 c. Type **37** 30 30
251 50 c. As young child 40 45
252 70 c. As schoolgirl 60 60
253 80 c. As teenager 70 80
254 $1.40, As young lady.. .. .. .. 1·10 1·25
250/4 .. .. *Set of* 5 2·75 3·00
MS255 87 × 110 mm. Nos. 250/4 .. .. .. 4·50 3·50

1982 (30 July). *Birth of Prince William of Wales. Nos.* 223/8 *optd with T* **38**.
256 40 c. Type **34** 40 45
257 50 c. Prince Charles as schoolboy 50 60
258 60 c. Prince Charles as young man 55 65
259 70 c. Prince Charles in ceremonial Naval uniform 60 70
260 80 c. Prince Charles as Colonel-in-Chief, Royal Regiment of Wales 70 80
256/60 .. .. *Set of* 5 2·50 3·00
MS261 99 × 89 mm. Nos. 256/60 .. .. .. 6·00 7·00

1982 (6 Sept). *Birth of Prince William of Wales. As Nos.* 250/5 *but with changed inscriptions. Multicoloured. P* 13½ × 14.
262 30 c. As Type **37** (inscr "21 JUNE 1982. BIRTH OF PRINCE WILLIAM OF WALES") .. 30 30
263 30 c. As Type **37** (inscr "COMMEMORATING THE BIRTH OF PRINCE WILLIAM OF WALES") 30 30
264 50 c. As No. 251 (inscr. "21 JUNE 1982. BIRTH OF PRINCE WILLIAM OF WALES") .. 45 45
265 50 c. As No. 251 (inscr "COMMEMORATING THE BIRTH OF PRINCE WILLIAM OF WALES") 45 45
266 70 c. As No. 252 (inscr "21 JUNE 1982. BIRTH OF PRINCE WILLIAM OF WALES") .. 65 65
267 70 c. As No. 252 (inscr "COMMEMORATING THE BIRTH OF PRINCE WILLIAM OF WALES") 65 65
268 80 c. As No. 253 (inscr "21 JUNE 1982. BIRTH OF PRINCE WILLIAM OF WALES") .. 65 65
269 80 c. As No. 253 (inscr "COMMEMORATING THE BIRTH OF PRINCE WILLIAM OF WALES") 65 65
270 $1.40, As No. 254 (inscr "21 JUNE 1982. BIRTH OF PRINCE WILLIAM OF WALES") .. .. 1·25 1·25
271 $1.40, As No. 254 (inscr "COMMEMORATING THE BIRTH OF PRINCE WILLIAM OF WALES") .. .. .. 1·25 1·25
262/71 .. .. *Set of* 10 6·00 6·00
MS272 88 × 109 mm. As **MS**255 (stamps inscr "21 JUNE 1982. ROYAL BIRTH PRINCE WILLIAM OF WALES" .. .. 3·50 3·25
Nos. 262/3, 264/5, 266/7, 268/9 and 270/1 were printed together, *se-tenant*, in sheets of 5 stamps and 1 label, there being three examples of the "21 JUNE 1982 . . ." and two of the "COMMEMORATING . . ." in each sheet.

ALTERED CATALOGUE NUMBERS

Any Catalogue numbers altered from the last edition are shown as a list in the introductory pages.

39 "Virgin and Child" (detail, Joos Van Cleve)

40 Red Coral

1982 (10 Dec). *Christmas. Details from Renaissance Paintings of "Virgin and Child". T* **39** *and similar vert designs. Multicoloured. P* 14 × 13½.
273 35 c. Type **39** 30 40
274 48 c. "Virgin and Child" (Filippino Lippi) .. 45 55
275 60 c. "Virgin and Child" (Cima da Conegliano) 60 70
273/5 .. .. *Set of* 3 1·25 1·50
MS276 134 × 73 mm. As Nos. 273/5 but each with 2 c. charity premium. P 13 .. .. .. 1·00 2·00
Nos. 273/5 were each printed in small sheets of 6 including one *se-tenant*, stamp size, label, depicting the Prince and Princess of Wales with Prince William.

1982 (10 Dec). *Christmas. Children's Charity. Designs as Nos.* 273/5, *but without frames, in separate miniature sheets,* 60 × 85 *mm, each with a face value of* 70 *c.* + 5 *c. P* 13.
MS277 As Nos. 273/5 .. .. *Set of* 3 *sheets* 1·25 1·60

1983 (14 Mar). *Commonwealth Day. T* **40** *and similar vert designs. Multicoloured. P* 13.
278 60 c. Type **40** 50 55
279 60 c. Aerial view of Penrhyn atoll 50 55
280 60 c. Eleanor Roosevelt on Penrhyn during Second World War 50 55
281 60 c. Map of South Pacific 50 55
278/81 .. .. *Set of* 4 1·75 2·00
Nos. 278/81 were issued together, *se-tenant*, in blocks of four throughout the sheet.

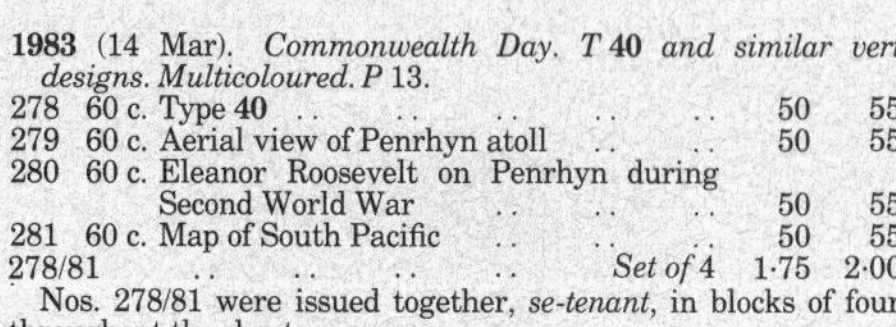

41 Scout Emblem and Blue Tropical Flower

XV
WORLD
JAMBOREE
CANADA
1983

(**42**)

1983 (5 Apr). *75th Anniv of Boy Scout Movement. T* **41** *and similar horiz designs. Multicoloured. P* 13 × 14.
282 36 c. Type **41** .. .. 1·50 65
283 48 c. Emblem and pink flower .. .. .. 1·75 75
284 60 c. Emblem and orange flower .. .. 1·75 1·00
282/4 .. .. *Set of* 3 4·50 2·25
MS285 86 × 46 mm. $2 As 48 c., but with elements of design reversed .. .. 2·40 3·00

1983 (8 July). *15th World Scout Jamboree, Alberta, Canada. Nos.* 282/5 *optd with T* **42**.
286 36 c. Type **41** .. .. 1·25 40
287 48 c. Emblem and pink flower .. .. .. 1·50 55
288 60 c. Emblem and orange flower .. .. 1·60 75
286/8 .. .. *Set of* 3 4·00 1·60
MS289 86 × 46 mm. $2 As 48 c., but with elements of design reversed .. .. 2·40 3·50

43 School of Sperm Whales

44 *Mercury* (cable ship)

1983 (29 July). *Whale Conservation. T* **43** *and similar vert designs. Multicoloured. P* 13.
290 8 c. Type **43** .. .. 1·00 70
291 15 c. Harpooner preparing to strike .. .. 1·40 95
292 35 c. Whale attacking boat .. .. .. 2·00 1·40
293 60 c. Dead whales marked with flags.. .. 3·00 2·00
294 $1 Dead whales on slipway .. .. .. 3·75 3·00
290/4 .. .. *Set of* 5 10·00 7·25

1983 (23 Sept). *World Communications Year. T* **44** *and similar horiz designs. Multicoloured. P* 13.
295 36 c. Type **44** 80 35
296 48 c. Men watching cable being laid 85 45
297 60 c. *Mercury (different)* .. .. .. 1·10 60
295/7 .. .. *Set of* 3 2·50 1·25
MS298 115 × 90 mm. As Nos. 295/7 but each with charity premium of 3 c. .. .. 1·50 1·60
On No. **MS**298 the values are printed in black and have been transposed with the World Communications Year logo.

1983 (26 Sept). *Various stamps surch as T* **200** *of Cook Islands.*

(*a*) *Nos.* 182/5, 190/7 *and* 206

299 18 c. on 10 c. *Preussen*, 1902 .. .. .. 20 20
300 18 c. on 10 c. *Pamir*, 1921 .. .. .. 20 20
301 18 c. on 10 c. *Cap Hornier*, 1910 .. .. 20 20
302 18 c. on 10 c. *Patriarch*, 1869 .. .. 20 20
303 36 c. on 20 c. Va'a Teu'ua 35 35
304 36 c. on 20 c. *Vitoria*, 1500 .. .. 35 35
305 36 c. on 20 c. *Golden Hind*, 1560 .. .. 35 35
306 36 c. on 20 c. *Boudeuse*, 1760 .. .. 35 35
307 36 c. on 30 c. H.M.S. *Bounty*, 1787 .. 35 35
308 36 c. on 30 c. *L'Astrolabe*, 1811 .. .. 35 35
309 36 c. on 30 c. *Star of India*, 1861 .. .. 35 35
310 36 c. on 30 c. *Great Republic*, 1853 .. 35 35
311 $1.20 on $2 *Cutty Sark*, 1869 .. .. 1·40 1·40

(*b*) *Nos.* 252/3

312 72 c. on 70 c. Princess Diana as schoolgirl .. 2·00 1·50
313 96 c. on 80 c. Princess Diana as teenager .. 2·25 1·75
299/313 .. .. *Set of* 15 8·50 7·00

1983 (28 Oct). *Nos.* 208, 225/6, 254 *and* 268/9 *surch as T* **200** *of Cook Islands.*

314 48 c. on 60 c. Prince Charles as young man (Gold) .. .. 3·50 1·50
a. Error. Surch on No. 258 .. .. .. 6·00 5·00
315 72 c. on 70 c. Prince Charles in ceremonial Naval uniform .. .. 4·00 1·75
a. Error. Surch on No. 259 .. .. .. 7·00 5·00
316 96 c. on 80 c. As No. 253 (inscr "21 JUNE 1982...") .. .. 2·75 1·00
a. Error. Surch on No. 260 .. .. .. 8·00 5·50
317 96 c. on 80 c. As No. 253 (inscr "COMMEMORATING...") .. .. 1·75 1·00
318 $1.20 on $1.40, Princess Diana as young lady 3·25 1·50
319 $5.60 on $6, H.M.S. *Resolution* and *Discovery*, 1776–80 .. .. 15·00 6·50
314/19 .. .. *Set of* 6 27·00 12·00

45 George Cayley's Airship Design, 1837

1983 (31 Oct). *Bicentenary of Manned Flight. T* **45** *and similar horiz designs. Multicoloured. P* 13.

A. *Inscr* "NORTHERN COOK ISLANDS"

320A 36 c. Type **45** .. .. 1·00 80
321A 48 c. Dupuy de Lome's man-powered airship, 1872 .. .. 1·25 90
322A 60 c. Santos Dumont's *Airship No. 6*, 1901 1·50 1·25
323A 96 c. Lebaudy-Juillot's practical airship No. 1 *La Jaune*, 1902 .. .. 2·25 1·75
324A $1.32, Airship LZ-127 *Graf Zeppelin*, 1929 .. .. 3·00 2·50
320A/4A .. .. *Set of* 5 8·00 6·50
MS325A 113×138 mm. Nos. 320A/4A .. 6·50 11·00

B. *Corrected spelling optd in black on silver over original inscription*

320B 36 c. Type **45** 30 35
321B 48 c. Dupuy de Lome's man-powered airship, 1872 .. .. 40 45
322B 60 c. Santos Dumont's *Airship No. 6*, 1901 45 50
323B 96 c. Lebaudy-Juillot's practical airship No. 1 *La Jaune*, 1902 .. .. 75 80
324B $1.32, Airship LZ-127 *Graf Zeppelin*, 1929 .. .. 1·00 1·10
320B/4B .. .. *Set of* 5 2·75 3·00
MS325B 113×138 mm. Nos. 320B/4B .. .. 2·25 4·25

46 "Madonna in the Meadow" **47** Waka

1983 (30 Nov). *Christmas. 500th Birth Anniv of Raphael. T* **46** *and similar vert designs. Multicoloured. P* 13.

326 36 c. Type **46** 60 40
327 42 c. "Tempi Madonna" 60 40
328 48 c. "The Smaller Cowper Madonna" .. 80 50
329 60 c. "Madonna della Tenda" 95 60
326/9 .. .. *Set of* 4 2·75 1·75
MS330 87 × 115 mm. As Nos. 326/9 but each with a charity premium of 3 c. .. .. .. 2·75 2·50

1983 (1 Dec). *Nos.* 266/7, 227 *and* 270/1 *surch as T* **200** *of Cook Islands.*

331 72 c. on 70 c. As No. 252 (inscr "21 JUNE 1982...") .. .. 1·50 80
332 72 c. on 70 c. As No. 252 (inscr "COMMEMORATING...") 80 60
333 96 c. on 80 c. Prince Charles as Colonel-in-Chief, Royal Regiment of Wales .. .. 1·50 65
334 $1.20 on $1.40, As No. 254 (inscr "21 JUNE 1982...") .. .. 1·75 70
335 $1.20 on $1.40, As No. 254 (inscr "COMMEMORATING...") .. .. 1·25 65
331/5 .. .. *Set of* 5 6·00 3·00

1983 (28 Dec). *Christmas. 500th Birth Anniv of Raphael. Children's Charity. Designs as Nos.* 326/9 *in separate miniature sheets*, 65 × 84 *mm, each with a face value of* 75 c. + 5 c. *P* 13.

MS336 As Nos. 326/9 .. .. *Set of* 4 *sheets* 2·00 3·00

1984 (8 Feb–15 June). *Sailing Craft and Ships (2nd series). Designs as Nos.* 166, *etc. but with redrawn frames, inscriptions and compass rose at top right as in T* **47**. *Multicoloured. P* 13 × 13½ ($9.60), 13 ($3, $5) *or* 11 (*others*).

337 2 c. Type **47** 20 50
338 4 c. Amatasi 30 50
339 5 c. Ndrua 30 50
340 8 c. Tongiaki 40 60
341 10 c. *Vitoria* 40 60
342 18 c. *Golden Hind* 50 70
343 20 c. *Boudeuse* 50 70
344 30 c. H.M.S. *Bounty* 60 70
345 36 c. *L'Astrolabe* 60 70
346 48 c. *Great Republic* 60 70
347 50 c. *Star of India* (21 Mar) 60 70
348 60 c. *Coonatto* (21 Mar) 60 70
349 72 c. *Antiope* (21 Mar) 60 70
350 80 c. *Balcutha* (21 Mar) 70 70
351 96 c. *Cap Hornier* (21 Mar) 85 85
352 $1.20, *Pamir* (21 Mar) .. .. .. 2·50 1·40
353 $3 *Mermerus* (41 × 31 *mm*) (4 May) .. 5·00 3·00
354 $5 *Cutty Sark* (41 × 31 *mm*) (4 May) .. 5·50 5·00
355 $9.60, H.M.S. *Resolution* and *Discovery* (41×31 *mm*) (15 June) .. .. .. 13·00 12·00
337/55 .. .. *Set of* 19 30·00 28·00

48 Olympic Flag

1984 (20 July). *Olympic Games, Los Angeles. T* **48** *and similar horiz designs. Multicoloured. P* 13½ × 13.

356 35 c. Type **48** 30 35
357 60 c. Olympic torch and flags 50 55
358 $1.80, Ancient athletes and Coliseum .. 1·50 1·60
356/8 .. .. *Set of* 3 2·10 2·25
MS359 103×86 mm. As Nos. 356/8 but each with a charity premium of 5 c. .. .. .. 2·40 2·50

49 Penrhyn Stamps of 1978, 1979 and 1981

1984 (20 Sept). *"Ausipex" International Stamp Exhibition, Melbourne. T* **49** *and similar horiz design. Multicoloured. P* 13½ × 13.

360 60 c. Type **49** 50 75
361 $1.20, Location map of Penrhyn .. .. 1·00 1·25
MS362 90 × 90 mm. As Nos. 360/1, but each with a face value of 96 c. .. .. 1·75 2·00

$2

Birth of
Prince Henry
15 Sept. 1984

(**50**)

51 "Virgin and Child" (Giovanni Bellini)

1984 (18 Oct). *Birth of Prince Henry. Nos.* 223/4 *and* 250/1 *surch as T* **50**.

363 $2 on 30 c. Type **37** .. .. .. 1·40 1·50
364 $2 on 40 c. Type **34** .. .. .. 1·60 1·75
365 $2 on 50 c. Prince Charles as schoolboy .. 1·60 1·75
366 $2 on 50 c. Lady Diana as young child (Gold) 1·40 1·50
363/6 .. .. *Set of* 4 5·50 6·00

1984 (15 Nov). *Christmas. Paintings of the Virgin and Child by different artists. T* **51** *and similar vert designs. Multicoloured. P* 13 × 13½.

367 36 c. Type **51** 60 35
368 48 c. Lorenzo di Credi 75 45
369 60 c. Palma the Older 80 50
370 96 c. Raphael .. .. 1·00 80
367/70 .. .. *Set of* 4 2·75 1·90
MS371 93 × 118 mm. As Nos. 367/70, but each with a charity premium of 5 c. .. .. .. 2·50 3·00

1984 (10 Dec). *Christmas. Children's Charity. Designs as Nos.* 367/70, *but without frames, in separate miniature sheets* 67 × 81 *mm, each with a face value of* 96 c. + 10 c. *P* 13½.

MS372 As Nos. 367/70 .. .. *Set of* 4 *sheets* 3·25 3·25

52 Harlequin Duck

1985 (9 Apr). *Birth Bicentenary of John J. Audubon (ornitho-ogist). T* **52** *and similar horiz designs showing origin- paintings. Multicoloured. P* 13.

373 20 c. Type 52 .. .. 2·00 1·7
374 55 c. Sage Grouse .. .. 2·75 2·7
375 65 c. Solitary Sandpiper .. .. .. 3·00 3·(
376 75 c. Dunlin .. .. 3·25 3·5
373/6 .. .. *Set of* 4 10·00 10·(
MS377 Four sheets, each 70×53 mm. As Nos. 373/6, but each with a face value of 95 c. .. 7·50 6·(

53 Lady Elizabeth Bowes-Lyon, 1921 **54** "The House in the Wood"

1985 (24 June). *Life and Times of Queen Elizabeth the Quee- Mother. T* **53** *and similar vert designs, each deep bluish viole- silver and yellow. P* 13.

378 75 c. Type **53** .. .. 40 (
379 95 c. With baby Princess Elizabeth, 1926 .. 50 8
380 $1.20, Coronation Day, 1937 .. .. 65 1·
381 $2.80, On her 70th birthday .. .. 1·25 2·
378/81 .. .. *Set of* 4 2·50 4·
MS382 66×90 mm. $5 The Queen Mother .. 2·40 3·2

Nos. 378/81 were each printed in small sheets of 4 stamps. For these stamps in a miniature sheet see No. **MS**403.

1985 (10 Sept). *International Youth Year and Birth Centena- of Jacob Grimm (folklorist). T* **54** *and similar vert desig- Multicoloured. P* 13×13½.

383 75 c. Type **54** .. .. 2·00 2·
384 95 c. "Snow-White and Rose-Red" .. .. 2·25 2·
385 $1.15, "The Goose Girl" .. .. .. 2·50 2·
383/5 .. .. *Set of* 3 6·00 6·

55 "The Annunciation"

1985 (25 Nov). *Christmas. Paintings by Murillo. T* **55** *a- similar horiz designs. Multicoloured. P* 14.

386 75 c. Type **55** .. .. 1·25 1
387 $1.15, "Adoration of the Shepherds" .. 1·75 1·
388 $1.80, "The Holy Family" .. .. .. 2·50 2·
386/8 .. .. *Set of* 3 5·00 5·
MS389 66×131 mm. As Nos. 386/8, but each with a face value of 95 c. P 13½ .. .. .. 2·75 3·
MS390 Three sheets, each 66×72 mm. As Nos. 386/8, but with face values of $1.20, $1.45 and $2.75. P 13½ .. .. .. *Set of* 3 *sheets* 4·50 4·

56 Halley's Comet

1986 (4 Feb). *Appearance of Halley's Comet. T* **56** *and simi- horiz design showing details of the painting "Fire and Ice" Camille Rendal. Multicoloured. P* 13½×13.

391 $1.50, Type **56** .. .. 1·75 1
392 $1.50, Stylised *Giotto* spacecraft .. .. 1·75 1
MS393 108×43 mm. $3 As Nos. 391/2 (104×39 *mm*). Imperf .. .. 2·25 2

Nos. 391/2 were printed together, *se-tenant*, in horizon- pairs throughout the sheet, forming a composite design of complete painting.

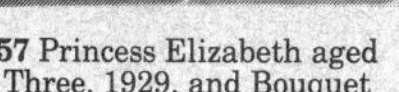

57 Princess Elizabeth aged Three, 1929, and Bouquet

58 Statue of Liberty under Construction, Paris

986 (21 Apr). *60th Birthday of Queen Elizabeth II. T* **57** *and similar horiz designs. Multicoloured. P* 13½×13 ($2.50) *or* 14 (*others*).
94 95 c. Type **57** .. .. 1·00 80
95 $1.45, Profile of Queen Elizabeth and St. Edward's Crown .. .. 1·50 1·25
96 $2.50, Queen Elizabeth aged three and in profile with Imperial State Crown (56×30 *mm*) .. .. 2·25 2·00
94/6 .. .. *Set of* 3 4·25 3·50

986 (27 June). *Centenary of Statue of Liberty (1st issue). T* **58** *and similar vert designs, each black, gold and yellow-green. P* 13×13½.
97 95 c. Type **58** 65 70
98 $1.75, Erection of Statue, New York .. 1·10 1·25
99 $3 Artist's impression of Statue, 1876 .. 2·10 2·25
97/9 .. .. *Set of* 3 3·50 3·75
See also No. **MS**412.

$2.00

59 Prince Andrew and Miss Sarah Ferguson

(**60**)

986 (23 July). *Royal Wedding. T* **59** *and similar vert design. Multicoloured. P* 13.
00 $2.50, Type **59** .. .. 3·50 3·50
01 $3.50, Profiles of Prince Andrew and Miss Sarah Ferguson .. .. 4·00 4·00
Nos. 400/1 were each printed in sheetlets of 4 stamps and 2 amp-size labels.

986 (4 Aug). *"Stampex '86" Stamp Exhibition, Adelaide. No.* **MS**362 *surch with T* **60** *in black on gold.*
IS402 $2 on 96 c.×2 .. .. 6·00 7·00
The "Stampex '86" exhibition emblem is overprinted on the eet margin.

986 (4 Aug). *86th Birthday of Queen Elizabeth the Queen Mother. Nos.* 378/81 *in miniature sheet,* 90×120 *mm. P* 13×13½.
IS403 Nos. 378/81 .. .. 8·50 9·00

SOUTH PACIFIC PAPAL VISIT 21 TO 24 NOVEMBER 1986 +10c

61 "The Adoration of the Shepherds"

(**62**)

986 (20 Nov). *Christmas. Engravings by Rembrandt. T* **61** *and similar vert designs, each red-brown, yellow-ochre and gold. P* 13.
04 65 c. Type **61** .. .. 1·75 1·75
05 $1.75 "Virgin and Child" .. .. 3·00 3·00
06 $2.50 "The Holy Family" .. .. 4·25 4·25
04/6 .. .. *Set of* 3 8·00 8·00
IS407 120×87 mm. As Nos. 404/6, but each size 31×39 mm with a face value of $1.50. P 13½×13 .. .. 8·50 9·00

986 (24 Nov). *Visit of Pope John Paul II to South Pacific. Nos.* 404/7 *surch as T* **62** *in greenish blue.*
08 65 c. + 10 c. Type **61** .. .. 2·25 2·00
09 $1.75 + 10 c. "Virgin and Child" .. .. 3·75 3·50
10 $2.50 + 10 c. "The Holy Family" .. .. 4·50 4·00
08/10 .. .. *Set of* 3 9·50 8·50
IS411 120×87 mm. As Nos. 408/10, but each size 31×39 mm with a face value of $1.50 + 10 c. .. 9·50 9·00

63 Head and Torch of Statue of Liberty

1987 (15 Apr). *Centenary of Statue of Liberty (1986) (2nd issue). Two sheets, each* 122×122 *mm, containing T* **63** *and similar multicoloured designs. Litho. P* 14×13½ (*vert*) *or* 13½×14 (*horiz*).
MS412 Two sheets (a) 65 c. Type **63**; 65 c. Torch at sunset; 65 c. Restoration workers with flag; 65 c. Statue and Manhattan skyline; 65 c. Workers and scaffolding. (b) 65 c. Workers on Statue crown (*horiz*); 65 c. Aerial view of Ellis Island (*horiz*); 65 c. Ellis Island Immigration Centre (*horiz*); 65 c. View from Statue to Ellis Island and Manhattan (*horiz*); 65 c. Restoration workers (*horiz*) .. .. .. *Set of* 2 *sheets* 9·00 11·00

Fortieth Royal Wedding
Anniversary 1947–87

(**64**)

1987 (20 Nov). *Royal Ruby Wedding. Nos.* 68/9 *optd with T* **64** *in magenta.*
413 $2 Birds-eye view of Penrhyn .. .. 2·00 2·25
414 $5 Satellite view of Australasia .. .. 3·50 4·25

65 "The Garvagh Madonna"

66 Athletics

1987 (11 Dec). *Christmas. Religious Paintings by Raphael. T* **65** *and similar vert designs. Multicoloured. P* 13½.
415 95 c. Type **65** .. .. 1·50 1·50
416 $1.60, "The Alba Madonna" .. .. 2·00 2·00
417 $2.25, "The Madonna of the Fish" .. 3·00 3·00
415/17 .. .. *Set of* 3 6·00 6·00
MS418 91×126 mm. As Nos. 415/17, but each with a face value of $1.15 .. .. 10·00 10·50
MS419 70×86 mm. $4.80, As No. 417, but size 36×39 mm .. .. 11·00 11·50

1988 (29 July). *Olympic Games, Seoul. T* **66** *and similar horiz designs. Multicoloured. P* 13½×13 (*horiz*) *or* 13×13½ (*vert*).
420 55 c. Type **66** 65 65
421 95 c. Pole vaulting (*vert*) .. .. .. 1·00 1·00
422 $1.25, Shotputting .. .. 1·40 1·40
423 $1.50, Lawn Tennis (*vert*) .. .. .. 2·25 1·75
421/3 .. .. *Set of* 4 4·75 4·25
MS424 110×70 mm. As Nos. 421 and 423, but each with a face value of $2.50 .. .. .. 4·00 5·00

1988 (14 Oct). *Olympic Gold Medal Winners, Seoul. Nos.* 420/4 *optd as T* **235** *of Cook Islands.*
425 55 c. Type **66** (optd "CARL LEWIS UNITED STATES 100 METERS") 70 60
426 95 c. Pole vaulting (optd "LOUISE RITTER UNITED STATES HIGH JUMP") .. 1·00 90
427 $1.25, Shot putting (optd "ULF TIMMERMANN EAST GERMANY SHOT-PUT") .. .. 1·50 1·25
428 $1.50, Lawn Tennis (optd "STEFFI GRAF WEST GERMANY WOMEN'S TENNIS") .. .. 2·75 1·40
425/8 .. .. *Set of* 4 5·50 3·75
MS429 110×70 mm. $2.50, As No. 421 (optd "JACKIE JOYNER-KERSEE United States Heptathlon"); $2.50, As No. 423 (optd "STEFFI GRAF West Germany Women's Tennis MILOSLAV MECIR Czechoslovakia Men's Tennis") .. .. 4·50 5·50

67 "Virgin and Child"

68 Neil Armstrong stepping onto Moon

1988 (9 Nov). *Christmas. T* **67** *and similar designs showing different "Virgin and Child" paintings by Titian. P* 13×13½.
430 70 c. multicoloured 90 90
431 85 c. multicoloured .. .. 1·00 1·00
432 95 c. multicoloured .. .. 1·25 1·25
433 $1.25, multicoloured .. .. 1·50 1·50
430/3 .. .. *Set of* 4 4·25 4·25
MS434 100 × 80 mm. $6.40, As Type **67**, but diamond-shaped (57 × 57 *mm*). P 13 .. .. 6·00 7·00

(Des G. Vasarhelyi)

1989 (24 July). *20th Anniv of First Manned Landing on Moon. T* **68** *and similar horiz designs. Multicoloured. P* 14.
435 55 c. Type **68** 70 60
436 75 c. Astronaut on Moon carrying equipment 85 75
437 95 c. Conducting experiment on Moon .. 1·10 95
438 $1.25, Crew of "Apollo 11" .. .. 1·40 1·25
439 $1.75, Crew inside "Apollo 11" .. .. 1·75 1·60
435/9 .. .. *Set of* 5 5·25 4·75

69 Virgin Mary

1989 (17 Nov). *Christmas. T* **69** *and similar multicoloured designs showing details from "The Nativity" by Dürer. P* 13.
440 55 c. Type **69** 80 80
441 70 c. Christ Child and cherubs 90 90
442 85 c. Joseph .. .. 1·25 1·25
443 $1.25, Three women .. .. 1·60 1·60
440/3 .. .. *Set of* 4 4·00 4·00
MS444 88×95 mm. $6.40, "The Nativity" (31×50 *mm*) .. .. 6·50 7·50

70 Queen Elizabeth the Queen Mother

1990 (24 July). *90th Birthday of Queen Elizabeth the Queen Mother. P* 13½.
445 **70** $2.25, multicoloured .. .. .. 2·50 2·50
MS446 85×73 mm. **70** $7.50, multicoloured .. 10·00 11·00

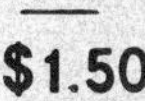

71 "Adoration of the Magi" (Veronese)

(**72**)

(Litho Questa)

1990 (26 Nov). *Christmas. Religious Paintings. T* **71** *and similar vert designs. Multicoloured. Ordinary paper. P* 14.
447 55 c. Type **71** .. .. 1·00 1·00
448 70 c. "Virgin and Child" (Quentin Metsys) .. 1·40 1·40
449 85 c. "Virgin and Child Jesus" (Hugo van der Goes) .. .. 1·60 1·60
450 $1.50, "Adoration of the Kings" (Jan Gossaert) .. .. 2·50 2·50
447/50 .. .. *Set of* 4 6·00 6·00
MS451 108×132 mm. $6.40, "Virgin and Child with Saints, Francis, John the Baptist, Zenobius and Lucy" (Domenico Veneziano) .. .. 6·00 7·00

1990 (5 Dec). *"Birdpex '90" Stamp Exhibition, Christchurch, New Zealand. Nos.* 373/6 *surch as T* **72** *in red (Nos 452, 455) or black (others).*
452 $1.50 on 20 c. Type **52** .. .. .. 1·50 1·75
453 $1.50 on 55 c. Sage Grouse .. .. .. 1·50 1·75
454 $1.50 on 65 c. Solitary Sandpiper .. .. 1·50 1·75
455 $1.50 on 75 c. Dunlin .. .. 1·50 1·75
452/5 .. .. *Set of* 4 5·50 6·25

COMMEMORATING 65th
BIRTHDAY OF H.M.
QUEEN ELIZABETH II

(73)

1991 (22 Apr). *65th Birthday of Queen Elizabeth II. No.* 208 *optd with T* **73**.
456 $6 H.M.S. *Resolution* and *Discovery*, 1776–80 .. .. 9·00 10·00

74 "The Virgin and Child with Saints" (G. David)

(Des G. Vasarhelyi. Litho Questa)

1991 (11 Nov). *Christmas. Religious Paintings. T* **74** *and similar multicoloured designs. Ordinary paper. P* 14.
457 55 c. Type **74** .. .. 1·00 1·00
458 85 c. "Nativity" (Tintoretto) .. .. .. 1·50 1·50
459 $1.15, "Mystic Nativity" (Botticelli) .. 1·75 1·75
460 $1.85, "Adoration of the Shepherds" (B. Murillo) .. .. .. 2·75 3·25
457/60 .. .. *Set of* 4 6·25 6·75
MS461 79×103 mm. $6.40, "The Madonna of the Chair" (Raphael) (*vert*) .. .. .. 8·50 9·50

(Des G. Vasarhelyi. Litho B.D.T.)

1992 (27 July). *Olympic Games, Barcelona. Horiz designs as T* **94** *of Aitutaki. Multicoloured. Ordinary paper. P* 14.
462 75 c. Running .. .. 1·25 1·25
463 95 c. Boxing .. .. 1·50 1·50
464 $1.15, Swimming .. .. .. 1·60 1·60
465 $1.50, Wrestling .. .. 1·75 1·75
462/5 .. .. *Set of* 4 5·50 5·50

75 Marquesan Canoe

(Litho B.D.T.)

1992 (16 Oct). *6th Festival of Pacific Arts, Rarotonga. T* **75** *and similar horiz designs. Multicoloured. Ordinary paper. P* 14×15.
466 $1.15, Type **75** .. .. 1·40 1·40
467 $1.75, Tangaroa statue from Rarotonga .. 1·90 1·90
468 $1.95, Manihiki canoe .. .. .. 2·00 2·00
466/8 .. .. *Set of* 3 4·75 4·75

1992 (16 Oct). *Royal Visit by Prince Edward. Nos.* 466/8 *optd with T* **254** *of Cook Islands.*
469 $1.15, Type **75** .. .. 1·75 1·75
470 $1.75, Tangaroa statue from Rarotonga .. 2·50 2·50
471 $1.95, Manihiki canoe .. .. .. 3·00 3·00
469/71 .. .. *Set of* 3 6·50 6·50

76 "Virgin with Child and Saints" (Borgognone)

77 Vincente Pinzon and *Nina*

1992 (18 Nov). *Christmas. Religious Paintings by Ambrogio Borgognone. T* **76** *and similar vert designs. Multicoloured. Ordinary paper. P* 13½.
472 55 c. Type **76** 75 75
473 85 c. "Virgin on Throne" .. .. .. 1·10 1·10
474 $1.05, "Virgin on Carpet" .. .. .. 1·40 1·40
475 $1.85, "Virgin of the Milk" .. .. .. 2·25 2·25
472/5 .. .. *Set of* 4 5·00 5·00
MS476 101×86 mm. $6.40, As 55 c., but larger (36×46 *mm*) .. .. 6·50 7·50

(Litho B.D.T.)

1992 (4 Dec). *500th Anniv of Discovery of America by Columbus. T* **77** *and similar vert designs. Multicoloured. Ordinary paper. P* 15×14.
477 $1.15, Type **77** .. .. 2·00 2·00
478 $1.35, Martin Pinzon and *Pinta* .. .. 2·25 2·25
479 $1.75, Christopher Columbus and *Santa Maria* .. .. 3·00 3·00
477/9 .. .. *Set of* 3 6·50 6·50

78 Queen Elizabeth II in 1953

79 Bull-mouth Helmet

(Des G. Vasarhelyi. Litho B.D.T.)

1993 (4 June). *40th Anniv of Coronation. P* 14.
480 **78** $6 multicoloured .. .. .. 6·50 8·00

(Des G. Drummond. Litho Questa ($3 to $10), B.D.T. (others))

1993 (18 Oct)–**98**. *Marine Life. T* **79** *and similar horiz designs. Multicoloured. P* 14×13½ ($3 *to* $10) *or* 13½×14 (*others*).
481 5 c. Type **79** 10 10
482 10 c. Daisy Coral 10 10
483 15 c. Hydroid Coral 10 15
484 20 c. Feather-star 15 20
485 25 c. Sea Star 15 20
486 30 c. Varicose Nudibranch 20 25
487 50 c. Smooth Sea Star 30 35
488 70 c. Black-lip Pearl Oyster 45 50
489 80 c. Four-coloured Nudibranch (3.12.93) .. 50 55
490 85 c. Prickly Sea Cucumber (3.12.93) .. 55 60
491 90 c. Organ Pipe Coral (3.12.93) 55 60
492 $1 Blue Sea Lizard (3.12.93) 65 70
493 $2 Textile Cone shell (3.12.93) .. .. 1·25 1·40
494 $3 Starfish (21.11.94) .. .. .. 1·90 2·00
495 $5 As $3 (21.11.94) .. .. .. 3·25 3·50
496 $8 As $3 (17.11.97) .. .. .. 5·00 5·25
497 $10 As $3 (1.10.98) .. .. .. 6·25 6·50
481/97 .. .. *Set of* 17 21·00 22·50
Nos. 494/7 are larger, 47×34 mm, and include a portrait of Queen Elizabeth II at top right.

80 "Virgin on Throne with Child" (detail) (Tura)

81 Neil Armstrong stepping onto Moon

1993 (2 Nov). *Christmas. T* **80** *and similar vert designs showing different details from "Virgin on Throne with Child" (Cosme Tura). Ordinary paper. P* 13½ ($4.50) *or* 14 (*others*).
499 55 c. multicoloured .. .. 1·00 1·00
500 85 c. multicoloured .. .. 1·50 1·50
501 $1.05, multicoloured .. .. .. 1·75 1·75
502 $1.95, multicoloured .. .. .. 2·75 3·00
503 $4.50, multicoloured (32×47 *mm*) .. 6·00 7·00
499/503 .. .. *Set of* 5 11·50 13·00

(Des G. Vasarhelyi. Litho B.D.T.)

1994 (20 July). *25th Anniv of First Moon Landing. P* 14.
504 **81** $3.25, multicoloured .. .. .. 5·50 6·00

82 "The Virgin and Child with Sts. Paul and Jerome" (Vivarini)

(Litho B.D.T.)

1994 (30 Nov). *Christmas. Religious Paintings. T* **82** *and similar vert designs. Multicoloured. P* 14.
505 90 c. Type **82** .. .. 1·10 1·25
a. Block of 4. Nos. 505/8 .. .. 4·00
506 90 c. "The Virgin and Child with St. John" (Luini) .. .. 1·10 1·25
507 90 c. "The Virgin and Child with Sts. Jerome and Dominic" (Lippi) .. .. .. 1·10 1·25
508 90 c. "Adoration of the Shepherds" (Murillo) 1·10 1·25
509 $1 "Adoration of the Kings" (detail of angels) (Reni) .. .. .. 1·10 1·25
a. Block of 4. Nos. 509/12 .. .. 4·00
510 $1 "Madonna and Child with the Infant Baptist" (Raphael) .. .. .. 1·10 1·25
511 $1 "Adoration of the Kings" (detail of manger) (Reni) .. .. .. 1·10 1·25
512 $1 "Virgin and Child" (Borgognone) .. 1·10 1·25
505/12 .. .. *Set of* 8 8·00 9·00
Nos. 505/8 and 509/12 were printed together, *se-tenant*, in blocks of 4 throughout the sheets.

83 Battleship Row burning, Pearl Harbor

(Litho B.D.T.)

1995 (4 Sept). *50th Anniv of End of Second World War. T* **83** *and similar horiz design. Multicoloured. P* 13.
513 $3.75, Type **83** .. .. 4·25 4·75
a. Pair. Nos. 686/7 .. .. .. 8·50 9·50
514 $3.75, Boeing B-25 Superfortress *Enola Gay* over Hiroshima .. .. .. 4·25 4·75
Nos. 513/14 were printed together, *se-tenant* horizontally and vertically, in sheets of 4.

84 Queen Elizabeth the Queen Mother at Remembrance Day Ceremony

(Des G. Vasarhelyi. Litho B.D.T.)

1995 (14 Sept). *95th Birthday of Queen Elizabeth the Queen Mother. P* 13.
515 **84** $4.50, multicoloured .. .. .. 6·00 7·0

85 Anniversary Emblem, United Nations Flag and Headquarters

(Des G. Vasarhelyi. Litho B.D.T.)

1995 (20 Oct). *50th Anniv of United Nations. P* 13×13½.
516 **85** $4 multicoloured .. .. .. 4·00 5·

86 Loggerhead Turtle

87 Queen Elizabeth II and Rose

(Litho B.D.T.)

1995 (7 Dec). *Year of the Sea Turtle. T* **86** *and similar ve designs. Multicoloured. P* 13½×14.
517 $1.15, Type **86** .. .. 1·75 2·
a. Horiz pair. Nos. 517/18 .. .. 3·50 4·
518 $1.15, Hawksbill Turtle .. .. .. 1·75 2·
519 $1.65, Olive Ridley Turtle .. .. .. 2·25 2·
a. Horiz pair. Nos. 519/20 .. .. 4·50 5·
520 $1.65, Green Turtle .. .. .. 2·25 2·
517/20 .. .. *Set of* 4 7·25 8·
Nos. 517/18 and 519/20 were printed together, *se-tenant*, in horizontal pairs throughout the sheets.

(Des G. Vasarhelyi. Litho)

996 (20 June). *70th Birthday of Queen Elizabeth II. P* 14.
21 **87** $4.25, multicoloured .. .. 4·75 5·50

88 Olympic Flame, National Flags and Sports

(Des G. Vasarhelyi. Litho B.D.T.)

996 (12 July). *Centenary of Modern Olympic Games. P* 14.
22 **88** $5 multicoloured .. .. 5·50 6·00

89 Royal Wedding, 1947

90 Diana, Princess of Wales with Sons

997 (20 Nov). *Golden Wedding of Queen Elizabeth and Prince Philip. P* 14.
23 **89** $3 multicoloured .. .. 2·50 2·75
S524 42×28 mm. **89** $4 multicoloured .. 3·50 4·00

998 (7 May). *Diana, Princess of Wales Commemoration. Litho. P* 14.
25 **90** $1.50, multicoloured .. .. 95 1·00
a. Sheetlet. No. 525×5 plus label .. 4·75
S526 70×100 mm. **90** $3.75, multicoloured .. 3·00 3·25
No. 525 was printed in sheetlets of 5 stamps with a label at top ft.

998 (19 Nov). *Children's Charities. No.* **MS526** *surch as T* **275** *of Cook Islands in silver.*
S527 70×100 mm. **90** $3.75+$1 multicoloured 3·00 3·25

STAMP BOOKLETS

1982 (June). *Royal Wedding. Cover as No.* SB1 *of Cook Islands, but inscr* "Penrhyn".
SB1 $4.50, booklet containing 40 c. and 50 c. (Nos. 223/4), each in block of 5 and 1 label .. 4·75

OFFICIAL STAMPS

O.H.M.S.

(O 1)

1978 (14 Nov). *Nos.* 57/66, 89/91 *and* 101/2 *optd or surch* (*Nos.* O8/9 *and* O12) *as Type* O **1**.

O 1	1 c. Diamond Fingerfish	15	10
O 2	2 c. Emperor Angelfish	15	10
O 3	3 c. Copper-banded Butterflyfish ..	25	10
O 4	4 c. Ornate Butterflyfish	25	10
O 5	5 c. Black-backed Butterflyfish	30	10
O 6	8 c. Latticed Butterflyfish	35	15
O 7	10 c. Saddle Butterflyfish	40	15
O 8	15 c. on 60 c. Harlequin Sweetlips ..	45	25
O 9	18 c. on 60 c. Harlequin Sweetlips ..	50	25
O10	20 c. Regal Angelfish	50	25
O11	25 c. Pennant Coralfish (Silver)	55	30
O12	30 c. on 60 c. Harlequin Sweetlips ..	55	35
O13	50 c. } "The Spirit of '76" (A. M. Willard) (Gold)	90	55
O14	50 c. } "The Spirit of '76" (A. M. Willard) (Gold)	90	55
O15	50 c. } "The Spirit of '76" (A. M. Willard) (Gold)	90	55
O16	$1 Queen and Prince Philip (Silver) ..	2·25	65
O17	$2 Queen Elizabeth II (Gold)	4·00	80
O1/17	.. .. *Set of* 17	12·00	4·50

These stamps were originally only sold to the public cancelled-to-order and not in unused condition. They were made available to overseas collectors in mint condition during 1980.

65c

O.H.M.S. (O 2)

O.H.M.S. (O 3)

1985 (15 Aug)–**87**. (*a*) *Nos.* 206/8, 337/47 *and* 349/55 *optd or surch as Type* O **2** *by foil embossing in red* ($2, $4, $6) *or silver* (*others*)

O18	2 c. Type **47**	30	30
O19	4 c. Amatasi	30	30
O20	5 c. Ndrua	30	30
O21	8 c. Tongiaki	30	30
O22	10 c. *Vitoria*	30	30
O23	18 c. *Golden Hind*	50	50
O24	20 c. *Boudeuse*	50	50
O25	30 c. H.M.S. *Bounty*	50	50
O26	40 c. on 36 c. *L'Astrolabe*	55	50
O27	50 c. *Star of India*	60	50
O28	55 c. on 48 c. *Great Republic*	60	50
O29	75 c. on 72 c. *Antiope* (29.4.86)	1·00	70
O30	75 c. on 96 c. *Cap Hornier* (29.4.86) ..	1·00	70
O31	80 c. *Balcutha* (29.4.86)	1·00	70
O32	$1.20, *Pamir* (29.4.86)	1·25	1·00
O33	$2 *Cutty Sark* (29.4.86)	2·00	1·60
O34	$3 *Mermerus* (29.4.86)	3·00	2·40
O35	$4 *Mermerus* (29.4.86)	4·00	3·25
O36	$5 *Cutty Sark* (2.11.87)	5·00	4·00
O37	$6 H.M.S. *Resolution* and *Discovery* (2.11.87)	6·00	5·00
O38	$9.60, H.M.S. *Resolution* and *Discovery* (2.11.87)	9·50	7·25

(*b*) *Nos.* 278/81 *surch as Type* O **3** *by silver foil embossing*

O39	65 c. on 60 c. Type **40**	70	60
O40	65 c. on 60 c. Aerial view of Penrhyn atoll ..	70	60
O41	65 c. on 60 c. Eleanor Roosevelt on Penrhyn during Second World War	70	60
O42	65 c. on 60 c. Map of South Pacific	70	60
O18/42	.. .. *Set of* 25	35·00	30·00

O.H.M.S.

(O 4)

1998 (20 July–30 Sept). *Nos.* 481/93 *optd with Type* O **4** *in silver.*

O43	5 c. Type **79**	10	10
O44	10 c. Daisy Coral	10	10
O45	15 c. Hydroid Coral	10	15
O46	20 c. Feather-star	15	20
O47	25 c. Sea Star	15	20
O48	30 c. Varicose Nudibranch	20	25
O49	50 c. Smooth Sea Star	30	35
O50	70 c. Black-lip Pearl Oyster	45	50
O51	80 c. Four-coloured Nudibranch	50	55
O52	85 c. Prickly Sea Cucumber	55	60
O53	90 c. Organ Pipe Coral	55	60
O54	$1 Blue Sea Lizard	65	70
O55	$2 Textile Cone shell (30 Sept)	1·25	1·40
O43/55	.. .. *Set of* 13	4·75	5·50

Cyprus

Cyprus was part of the Turkish Ottoman Empire from 1571.

The first records of an organised postal service date from 1871 when a post office was opened at Nicosia (Lefkosa) under the jurisdiction of the Damascus Head Post Office. Various stamps of Turkey from the 1868 issue onwards are known used from this office, cancelled "KIBRIS", in Arabic, within a double-lined oblong. Manuscript cancellations have also been reported. The records report the opening of a further office at Larnaca (Tuzla) in 1873, but no cancellation for this office has been identified.

To provide an overseas postal service the Austrian Empire opened a post office in Larnaca during 1845. Stamps of the Austrian Post Offices in the Turkish Empire were placed on sale there from 1 June 1864 and were cancelled with an unframed straight-line mark or circular date stamp. This Austrian post office closed on 6 August 1878.

BRITISH ADMINISTRATION

Following the convention with Turkey, Great Britain assumed the administration of Cyprus on 11 July 1878 and the first post office, as part of the British G.P.O. system, was opened at Larnaca on 27 July 1878. Further offices as Famagusta, Kyrenia, Limassol, Nicosia and Paphos followed in September 1878.

The stamps of Great Britain were supplied to the various offices as they opened and continued to be used until the Cyprus Administration assumed responsibility for the postal service on 1 April 1880. With the exception of "969" (Nicosia) similar numeral cancellations had previously been used at offices in Great Britain.

Numeral postmarks for Headquarters Camp, Nicosia ("D48") and Polymedia (Polemidhia) Camp, Limassol ("D47") were supplied by the G.P.O. in London during January 1881. These cancellations had three bars above and three bars below the numeral. Similar marks, but with four bars above and below, had previously been used in London on newspapers and bulk mail.

Although both three bar cancellations subsequently occur on Cyprus issues only isolated examples have been found on loose Great Britain stamps and there are no known covers or pieces which confirm such usage in Cyprus.

For illustrations of the postmark types see BRITISH POST OFFICES ABROAD notes, following GREAT BRITAIN.

FAMAGUSTA

Stamps of GREAT BRITAIN *cancelled* "982" *as Type* **9**

1878 *to* **1880–81.**
Z1 ½d. rose-red (1870–79) (Plate Nos. 11, 13) .. £700
Z2 1d. rose-red (1864–79) £475
Plate Nos. 145, 174, 181, 193, 202, 206, 215, 217
Z3 2d. blue (1858–69) (Plate Nos. 13, 14, 15) .. £950
Z4 2½d. rosy mauve (1876) (Plate Nos. 13, 16) .. £1100
Z5 6d. grey (1874–80) (Plate No. 15) .. ..
Z6 1s. green (1873–77) (Plate No. 12) £1900
Z7 1s. orange-brown (1881) (Plate No. 14) £2500

KYRENIA

Stamps of GREAT BRITAIN *cancelled* "974" *as Type* **9**

1878 *to* **1880.**
Z 8 ½d. rose-red (1870–79) (Plate No. 13) .. ..
Z 9 1d. rose-red (1864–79) .. .. .. *From* £500
Plate Nos. 168, 171, 193, 196, 206, 207, 209, 220.
Z10 2d. blue (1858–69) (Plate Nos. 13, 15) .. *From* £800
Z11 2½d. rosy mauve (1876–79) .. .. *From* £950
Plate Nos. 12, 13, 14, 15.
Z12 4d. sage-green (1877) (Plate No. 16) .. ..
Z13 6d. grey (1874–80) (Plate No. 16) .. ..

LARNACA

Stamps of GREAT BRITAIN *cancelled* "942" *as Type* **9**

1878 *to* **1880–81.**
Z14 ½d. rose-red (1870–79) .. .. .. *From* £250
Plate Nos. 11, 12, 13, 14, 15, 19, 20.
Z15 1d. rose-red (1864–79) .. .. .. *From* £170
Plate Nos. 129, 131, 146, 154, 170, 171, 174, 175, 176, 177, 178, 179, 181, 182, 183, 184, 187, 188, 190, 191, 192, 193, 194, 195, 196, 197, 198, 199, 200, 201, 202, 203, 204, 205, 206, 207, 208, 209, 210, 212, 213, 214, 215, 216, 217, 218, 220, 221, 222, 225.
Z16 1½d. lake-red (1870) (Plate No. 3) £1700
Z17 2d. blue (1858–69) (Plate Nos. 9, 13, 14, 15) .. £200
Z18 2½d. rosy mauve (1876–79) .. .. *From* 50·00
Plate Nos. 4, 5, 6, 8, 9, 10, 11, 12, 13, 14, 15, 16, 17.
Z19 2½d. blue (1880–81) (Plate Nos. 17, 18, 19, 20) .. £500
Z20 2½d. blue (1881) (Plate No. 21) £500
Z21 4d. sage-green (1877) (Plate Nos. 15, 16) .. £550
Z22 6d. grey (1874–76) (Plate Nos. 15, 16, 17) .. £500
Z23 6d. pale buff (1872–73) (Plate No. 11) £1900
Z24 8d. orange (1876) £4250
Z25 1s. green (1873–77) (Plate Nos. 12, 13) .. £900
Z26 1s. orange-brown (1881) (Plate No. 14) .. £1800
Z27 5s. rose (1874) (Plate No. 2) £4500

LIMASSOL

Stamps of GREAT BRITAIN *cancelled* "975" *as Type* **9**

1878 *to* **1880.**
Z28 ½d. rose-red (1870–79) (Plate Nos. 11, 13, 15, 19) £450
Z29 1d. rose-red (1864–79) .. .. .. *From* £275
Plate Nos. 159, 160, 171, 173, 174, 177, 179, 184, 187, 190, 193, 195, 196, 197, 198, 200, 202, 206, 207, 208, 209, 210, 213, 215, 216, 218, 220, 221, 222, 225
Z30 1½d. lake-red (1870–74) (Plate No. 3) £1800
Z31 2d. blue (1858–69) (Plate Nos. 14, 15) .. *From* £375
Z32 2½d. rosy-mauve (1876–80) .. .. .. *From* £150
Plate Nos. 11, 12, 13, 14, 15, 16.
Z33 2½d. blue (1880) (Plate Nos. 17, 19, 20) .. *From* £1200
Z34 4d. sage-green (Plate No. 16) £700

NICOSIA

Stamps of GREAT BRITAIN *cancelled* "969" *as Type* **9**

1878 *to* **1880–81.**
Z35 ½d. rose-red (1870–79) £450
Plate Nos. 12, 13, 14, 15, 20.
Z36 1d. rose-red (1864–79) .. .. .. *From* £275
Plate Nos. 170, 171, 174, 189, 190, 192, 193, 195, 196, 198, 200, 202, 203, 205, 206, 207, 210, 212, 214, 215, 218, 221, 222, 225.
Z37 2d. blue (1858–69) (Plate Nos. 14, 15) £450
Z38 2½d. rosy mauve (1876–79) .. .. *From* £170
Plate Nos. 10, 11, 12, 13, 14, 15, 16.
Z39 2½d. blue (1880) (Plate No. 20) .. .. ..
Z42 4d. sage-green (1877) (Plate No. 16) £800
Z43 6d. grey (1873) (Plate No. 16) £800

PAPHOS

Stamps of GREAT BRITAIN *cancelled* "981" *as Type* **9**

1878 *to* **1880.**
Z44 ½d. rose-red (1870–79) (Plate Nos. 13, 15) ..
Z45 1d. rose-red (1864–79) .. .. .. *From* £500
Plate Nos. 196, 201, 202, 204, 206, 213, 217.
Z46 2d. blue (1858–69) (Plate No. 15) £850
Z47 2½d. rosy mauve (1876–79) .. .. *From* £500
Plate Nos. 13, 14, 15, 16.

PRICES FOR STAMPS ON COVER TO 1945

No. 1	*from* × 10
No. 2	*from* × 50
No. 3	*from* × 100
No. 4	*from* × 8
Nos. 5/6	—
Nos. 7/10	*from* × 15
Nos. 11/15	*from* × 5
No. 16	—
Nos. 16*a*/24	*from* × 10
No. 25	*from* × 40
No. 26	—
No. 27	*from* × 10
No. 28	—
No. 29	*from* × 30
Nos. 31/5*a*	*from* × 10
Nos. 36/7	—
Nos. 40/9	*from* × 8
Nos. 50/71	*from* × 5
Nos. 74/99	*from* × 4
Nos. 100/2	—
Nos. 103/17	*from* × 4
No. 117*a*	—
Nos. 118/31	*from* × 5
No. 132	—
Nos. 133/43	*from* × 5
Nos. 144/7	*from* × 6
Nos. 148/63	*from* × 5

PERFORATION. Nos. 1/122 are perf 14.

Stamps of Great Britain overprinted

CYPRUS (1)   CYPRUS (2)

(Optd by D.L.R.)

1880 (1 Apr).
1 **1** ½d. rose £100 £100
a. Opt double (Plate 15) .. .. † £11000

Plate No.	*Un.*	*Used.*	*Plate No.*	*Un.*	*Used*
12. ..	£170	£250	19. ..	£4250	£700
15. ..	£100	£100			

2 **2** 1d. red .. .. 9·00 28·00
a. Opt double (Plate 208) .. £13000
aa. Opt double (Plate 218) .. £4250
b. Vert pair, top stamp without opt (Plate 208) £15000

174. ..	£1200	£1200	208. ..	90·00	48·00
181. ..	£325	£170	215. ..	10·00	45·00
184. ..	£10000	£2250	216. ..	13·00	28·00
193. ..	£600	†	217. ..	9·00	45·00
196. ..	£550	†	218. ..	14·00	45·00
201. ..	9·50	48·00	220. ..	£350	£375
205. ..	42·00	42·00			

3 **2** 2½d. rosy mauve .. .. .. 2·00 6·50
a. Large thin "C" (Plate 14) (BK, JK) 38·00 £150
b. Large thin "C" (Plate 15) (BK, JK) 60·00 £350
w. Wmk inverted (Plate 15) £180

14. ..	2·00	6·50	15. ..	3·00	19·00

4 **2** 4d. sage-green (Plate 16) £120 £200
5 6d. grey (Plate 16) £500 £650
6 1s. green (Plate 13) £650 £450
No. 3 has been reported from Plate 9.

HALF-PENNY (3) 18 mm   HALF-PENNY (4) 16 or 16½ mm

HALF-PENNY (5) 13 mm   30 PARAS (6)

(Optd by Govt Ptg Office, Nicosia)

1881 (Feb–June). *No. 2 surch.*
7 **3** ½d. on 1d. red (Feb) .. .. .. 70·00 85·0
a. "HALFPENN" (BG, LG) (*all plates*) .. .. .. *From* £1700 £170

Plate No.	*Un.*	*Used.*	*Plate No.*	*Un.*	*Use*
174. ..	£150	£300	215. ..	£600	£65
181. ..	£140	£160	216. ..	70·00	85·0
201. ..	85·00	£110	217. ..	£750	£65
205. ..	70·00	85·00	218. ..	£425	£55
208. ..	£160	£275	220. ..	£250	£30

8 **4** ½d. on 1d. red (Apr) £120 £16
a. Surch double (Plates 201 and 216) £2250 £225

201. ..	£120	£160	218. ..	—	–
216. ..	£350	£400			

9 **5** ½d. on 1d. red (1 June) .. .. 45·00 65·0
aa. Surch double (Plate 205) £650
ab. Surch double (Plate 215) £450 £55
b. Surch treble (Plate 205) £3000
ba. Surch treble (Plate 215) £650
bc. Surch treble (Plate 218) £2750
c. Surch quadruple (Plate 205) .. £3250
ca. Surch quadruple (Plate 215) .. £3250

205. ..	£200	—	217. ..	£120	75·(
215. ..	45·00	65·00	218. ..	65·00	90·(

The surcharge on No. 8 was handstamped; the others were applied by lithography.

(New Currency: 40 paras = 1 piastre, 180 piastres = £1)

1881 (June). *No. 2 surch with T* **6** *by lithography.*
10 **6** 30 paras on 1d. red .. .. .. £100 80·0
a. Surch double, one invtd (Plate 216) £3250
aa. Surch double, one invtd (Plate 220) £1300 £100

201. ..	£120	85·00	217. ..	£170	£16(
216. ..	£100	80·00	220. ..	£150	£16(

7   ½ (8)   ½   30 PARAS (9)

(Typo D.L.R.)

1881 (1 July). *Die I. Wmk Crown CC.*
11 **7** ½ pi. emerald-green .. .. .. £180 42·0
w. Wmk inverted £400
12 1 pi. rose .. .. £350 30·0
13 2 pi. blue .. .. £450 30·0
w. Wmk inverted .. .. .. — £40
14 4 pi. pale olive-green £900 £27
15 6 pi. olive-grey £1300 £42

Stamps of Queen Victoria initialled "J.A.B." or overprinte "POSTAL SURCHARGE" with or without the same initials we employed for accounting purposes between the Chief Post Offi and sub-offices, the initials are those of the then Postmaster, Mr. A. Bulmer.

"US" damaged at foot
(Left pane R. 5/5)

1882 (May)–**86.** *Die I*. Wmk Crown CA.*
16 **7** ½ pi. emerald-green (5.82) £4000 33
a. Dull green (4.83) .. .. 10·00 8
b. Top left triangle detached .. — 95·(
17 30 pa. pale mauve (7.6.82) .. .. 55·00 18·(
a. Top left triangle detached .. — £2
b. Damaged "US" .. .. .. — £2
18 1 pi. rose (3.83) .. .. .. 70·00 1·2
a. Top left triangle detached .. — £1
19 2 pi. blue (4.83) .. .. .. 95·00 1·2
a. Top left triangle detached .. — £1
20 4 pi. deep olive-green (10.83) .. .. £475 28·(
a. Pale olive-green .. .. .. £350 22·(
b. Top left triangle detached .. — £3
21 6 pi. olive-grey (7.82) .. .. .. 38·00 16·(
a. Top left triangle detached .. — £2
22 12 pi. orange-brown (1886) (Optd S. £650) £160 32·(
a. Top left triangle detached .. — £4
16*a*/22 .. .. *Set of* 7 £700 80·(

*For description and illustrations of Dies I and II s Introduction.

For illustration of "top left triangle detached" variety s above No. 21 of Antigua.

See also Nos. 31/7.

(Surch litho by Govt Ptg Office, Nicosia)

1882. *Surch with T* **8**/**9**. (*a*) *Wmk Crown CC.*
23 **7** ½ on ½ pi. emerald-green (6.82) .. .. £475 75·
24 30 pa. on 1 pi. rose (22.5.82) £1400 £1

(*b*) *Wmk Crown CA*
25 **7** ½ on ½ pi. emerald-green (27.5.82) .. £120 6·
a. Surch double .. .. † £27

NEW INFORMATION

The editor is always interested to correspond wi people who have new information that w improve or correct the Catalogue.

1/2	1/2
(10)	

11

Varieties of numerals:

1	1	1
Normal	Large	Small

2	2
Normal	Large

1886 (Apr). *Surch with T* **10** (*fractions approx 6 mm apart*) *in typography.*

(a) Wmk Crown CC

6	**7**	1/2 on 1/2 pi. emerald-green	£12000	

(b) Wmk Crown CA

7	**7**	1/2 on 1/2 pi. emerald-green	£225	70·00
		a. Large "2" at right	—	£750

1886 (May–June). *Surch with T* **10** (*fractions approx 8 mm apart*) *in typography.*

(a) Wmk Crown CC

8	**7**	1/2 on 1/2 pi. emerald-green	£6500	£425
		a. Large "1" at left	—	£1700
		b. Small "1" at right	£11000	£2250
		c. Large "2" at left	—	£2250

(b) Wmk Crown CA

9	**7**	1/2 on 1/2 pi. emerald-green (June)	£300	8·00
		a. Large "1" at left	£2000	£200
		b. Small "1" at right	£2750	£275
		c. Large "2" at left	£2500	£275
		d. Large "2" at right	£2500	£275

Nos. 28/9 were surcharged in a setting of 60. The large "1" at left and large "2" at right both occur in the fourth vertical row, the large "2" at left in the fifth vertical row and the small "1" at right in the top horizontal row.

A third type of this surcharge is known with the fractions spaced approximately 10 mm apart on CA paper with postmarks from August 1886. This may be due to the shifting of type.

1892–94. *Die II. Wmk Crown CA.*

1	**7**	1/2 pi. dull green	3·25	50
2		30 pa. mauve	3·50	3·50
		a. Damaged "US"	£110	
3		1 pi. carmine	8·50	1·00
4		2 pi. ultramarine	11·00	1·00
5		4 pi. olive-green	50·00	26·00
		a. Pale olive-green	16·00	22·00
6		6 pi. olive-grey (1894)	£120	£500
7		12 pi. orange-brown (1893)	£120	£325
1/7		*Set of* 7	£250	£750

1894 (14 Aug)–**96**. *Colours changed and new values. Die II. Wmk Crown CA.*

0	**7**	1/2 pi. green and carmine (1896)	4·00	70
		w. Wmk inverted		
1		30 pa. bright mauve and green (1896)	2·00	75
		a. Damaged "US"	85·00	
2		1 pi. carmine and blue (1896)	4·00	80
3		2 pi. blue and purple (1896)	5·00	80
4		4 pi. sage-green and purple (1896)	12·00	3·75
5		6 pi. sepia and green (1896)	9·00	10·00
6		9 pi. brown and carmine	15·00	12·00
7		12 pi. orange-brown and black (1896)	14·00	50·00
8		18 pi. greyish slate and brown	42·00	45·00
9		45 pi. grey-purple and blue	90·00	£120
0/9		*Set of* 10	£170	£200
0/9 Optd "Specimen"		*Set of* 10	£300	

(Typo D.L.R.)

1902–04. *Wmk Crown CA.*

0	**11**	1/2 pi. green and carmine (12.02)	3·25	60
		w. Wmk inverted	60·00	40·00
1		30 pa. violet and green (2.03)	4·50	2·00
		a. Mauve and green	13·00	5·50
2		1 pi. carmine and blue (9.03)	12·00	2·25
3		2 pi. blue and purple (2.03)	38·00	7·50
4		4 pi. olive-green and purple (9.03)	26·00	16·00
5		6 pi. sepia and green (9.03)	38·00	95·00
6		9 pi. brown and carmine (5.04)	95·00	£180
7		12 pi. chestnut and black (4.03)	12·00	42·00
8		18 pi. black and brown (5.04)	65·00	£120
9		45 pi. dull purple and ultramarine (10.03)	£200	£500
0/9		*Set of* 10	£450	£850
0/9 Optd "Specimen"		*Set of* 10	£450	

Broken top left triangle (Left pane R.7/5)

1904–10. *Wmk Mult Crown CA.*

60	**11**	5 pa. bistre and black (14.1.08)	60	30
		a. Broken top left triangle	40·00	
61		10 pa. orange and green (12.06)	2·00	30
		aw. Wmk inverted	—	65·00
		b. Yellow and green	32·00	5·50
		bw. Wmk inverted	—	75·00
		c. Broken top left triangle	50·00	
62		1/2 pi. green and carmine (1.7.04)	3·75	15
		a. Broken top left triangle	70·00	
		w. Wmk inverted	75·00	50·00
63		30 pa. purple and green (1.7.04)	10·00	1·00
		a. Violet and green (1910)	10·00	1·75
		b. Broken top left triangle	£130	
		c. Damaged "US"	£130	
64		1 pi. carmine and blue (11.04)	3·25	70
		a. Broken top left triangle	80·00	
65		2 pi. blue and purple (11.04)	4·50	1·00
		a. Broken top left triangle	£100	
66		4 pi. olive-green and purple (2.05)	9·00	6·00
		a. Broken top left triangle	£150	
67		6 pi. sepia and green (17.7.04)	9·50	11·00
		a. Broken top left triangle	£150	
68		9 pi. brown and carmine (30.5.04)	23·00	7·50
		a. Yellow-brown and carmine	18·00	18·00
		aw. Wmk inverted	90·00	60·00
		b. Broken top left triangle	£225	
69		12 pi. chestnut and black (4.06)	21·00	30·00
		a. Broken top left triangle	£225	
70		18 pi. black and brown (16.6.04)	27·00	9·50
		a. Broken top left triangle	£300	
71		45 pi. dull purple and ultram (15.6.04)	70·00	£130
60/71		*Set of* 12	£160	£180
60/1 Optd "Specimen"		*Set of* 2	£120	

12

13

Broken bottom left triangle (Right pane R.10/6)

(Typo D.L.R.)

1912 (July)–**15.** *Wmk Mult Crown CA.*

74	**12**	10 pa. orange and green (11.12)	3·00	1·60
		a. Wmk sideways	†	£2000
		b. Orange-yellow & brt green (8.15)	2·25	60
		ba. Broken bottom left triangle	55·00	
75		1/2 pi. green and carmine	1·75	20
		a. Yellow-green and carmine	5·50	1·60
		ab. Broken bottom left triangle	75·00	
		w. Wmk inverted	†	£750
76		30 pa. violet and green (3.13)	2·00	50
		a. Broken bottom left triangle	55·00	
		w. Wmk inverted		
77		1 pi. rose-red and blue (9.12)	3·75	1·25
		a. Carmine and blue (1.15?)	12·00	4·00
		ab. Broken bottom left triangle	£110	
78		2 pi. blue and purple (7.13)	6·50	1·25
		a. Broken bottom left triangle	90·00	
79		4 pi. olive-green and purple	3·75	3·75
		a. Broken bottom left triangle	70·00	
80		6 pi. sepia and green	3·00	7·50
		a. Broken bottom left triangle	70·00	
81		9 pi. brown and carmine (3.15)	21·00	22·00
		a. Yellow-brown and carmine	22·00	24·00
		b. Broken bottom left triangle	£250	
82		12 pi. chestnut and black (7.13)	9·00	24·00
		b. Broken bottom left triangle	£150	
83		18 pi. black and brown (3.15)	22·00	24·00
		a. Broken bottom left triangle	£200	
84		45 pi. dull purple and ultramarine (3.15)	65·00	£110
		a. Broken bottom left triangle	£375	
74/84		*Set of* 11	£120	£170
74/84 Optd "Specimen"		*Set of* 11	£350	

1921–23. (*a*) *Wmk Mult Script CA.*

85	**12**	10 pa. orange and green	3·00	3·50
		a. Broken bottom left triangle	65·00	
86		10 pa. grey and yellow (1923)	10·00	6·50
		a. Broken bottom left triangle	£140	
87		30 pa. violet and green	2·50	40
		a. Broken bottom left triangle	60·00	
		w. Wmk inverted		
		y. Wmk inverted and reversed	†	£550
88		30 pa. green (1923)	6·00	40
		a. Broken bottom left triangle	90·00	
89		1 pi. carmine and blue	11·00	20·00
		a. Broken bottom left triangle	£120	
90		1 pi. violet and red (1922)	3·00	3·25
		a. Broken bottom left triangle	65·00	
91		1½ pi. yellow and black (1922)	3·25	3·75
		a. Broken bottom left triangle	70·00	
92		2 pi. blue and purple	13·00	8·00
		a. Broken bottom left triangle	£150	
93		2 pi. carmine and blue (1922)	9·00	22·00
		a. Broken bottom left triangle	£130	
94		2¾ pi. blue and purple (1922)	7·00	9·00
		a. Broken bottom left triangle	£120	
95		4 pi. olive-green and purple	8·00	12·00
		a. Broken bottom left triangle	£130	
		w. Wmk inverted	†	£550
96	**12**	6 pi. sepia and green (1923)	11·00	55·00
		a. Broken bottom left triangle	£150	
97		9 pi. brown and carmine (1922)	25·00	60·00
		a. Yellow-brown and carmine	60·00	90·00
		b. Broken bottom left triangle	£275	
98		18 pi. black and brown (1923)	55·00	£130
		a. Broken bottom left triangle	£350	
99		45 pi. dull purple and ultramarine (1923)	£150	£250
		a. Broken bottom left triangle	£650	
85/99		*Set of* 15	£275	£500
85/99 Optd "Specimen"		*Set of* 15	£475	

(b) Wmk Mult Crown CA (1923)

100	**12**	10s. green and red/*pale yellow*	£350	£650
		a. Broken bottom left triangle	£1700	
101		£1 purple and black/*red*	£1000	£1400
		a. Broken bottom left triangle	£3500	
100/1 Optd "Specimen"		*Set of* 2	£500	

Examples of Nos. 96/101 are known showing a forged Limassol postmark dated "14 MR 25".

1924–28. *Chalk-surfaced paper.* (*a*) *Wmk Mult Crown CA.*

102	**13**	£1 purple and black/*red*	£300	£550

(b) Wmk Mult Script CA

102	**13**	1/4 pi. grey and chestnut	80	15
		w. Wmk inverted	†	£750
104		1/2 pi. black	2·00	5·50
105		3/4 pi. green	1·75	90
106		1 pi. purple and chestnut	1·50	50
107		1½ pi. orange and black	1·50	4·75
108		2 pi. carmine and green	1·75	8·00
109		2¾ pi. bright blue and purple	2·75	2·25
110		4 pi. sage-green and purple	2·50	2·00
111		4½ pi. black and orange/*emerald*	3·00	3·00
112		6 pi. olive-brown and green	3·00	4·50
113		9 pi. brown and purple	4·50	3·50
114		12 pi. chestnut and black	7·00	48·00
115		18 pi. black and orange	17·00	4·50
116		45 pi. purple and blue	28·00	35·00
117		90 pi. green and red/*yellow*	70·00	£150
117*a*		£5 blk/*yellow* (1928) (Optd S. £900)	£2750	£5500

Examples of No. 117*a* are known showing a forged Registered Nicosia postmark dated "6 MAY 35".

CROWN COLONY

1925. *Wmk Mult Script CA. Chalk-surfaced paper* (1/2, 3/4 *and* 2 *pi.*)

118	**13**	1/2 pi. green	1·75	85
119		3/4 pi. brownish black	1·75	10
120		1½ pi. scarlet	2·25	30
121		2 pi. yellow and black	4·25	2·00
122		2½ pi. bright blue	1·75	30
102/122		*Set of* 21 *to* £1	£400	£700
102/22 Optd "Specimen"		*Set of* 21	£600	

In the above set the fraction bar in the value is horizontal. In Nos. 91, 94, 107 and 109 it is diagonal.

14 Silver Coin of Amathus, 6th-cent B.C.

16 Map of Cyprus

(Recess B.W.)

1928 (1 Feb). *50th Anniv of British Rule. T* **14**, **16** *and similar designs. Wmk Mult Script CA. P* 12.

123	3/4 pi. deep dull purple	2·50	80
124	1 pi. black and greenish blue	2·75	1·00
125	1½ pi. scarlet	4·00	2·00
126	2½ pi. light blue	3·00	2·00
127	4 pi. deep brown	4·00	6·00
128	6 pi. blue	5·00	18·00
129	9 pi. maroon	6·00	10·00
130	18 pi. black and brown	16·00	17·00
131	45 pi. violet and blue	32·00	45·00
132	£1 blue and bistre-brown	£200	£300
123/132	*Set of* 10	£225	£350
123/32 Optd "Specimen"	*Set of* 10	£500	

Designs: *Vert*—1 pi. Zeno (philosopher); 2½ pi. Discovery of body of St Barnabas; 4 pi. Cloister, Abbey of Bella Paise; 9 pi. Tekke of Umm Haram; 18 pi. Statue of Richard I, Westminster; 45 pi. St. Nicholas Cathedral, Famagusta (now Lala Mustafa Pasha Mosque); £1 King George V. *Horiz*—6 pi. Badge of Cyprus.

24 Ruins of Vouni Palace

25 Small Marble Forum, Salamis

30 St. Sophia Cathedral, Nicosia (now Selimiye Mosque)

31 Bayraktar Mosque, Nicosia

(Recess Waterlow)

1934 (1 Dec). *T* **24/5, 30/1** *and similar designs. Wmk Mult Script CA* (*sideways on* ½ *pi.,* 1½ *pi.,* 2½ *pi.,* 4½ *pi.,* 6 *pi.,* 9 *pi. and* 18 *pi.*). *P* 12½.
133 ¼ pi. ultramarine and orange-brown .. 75 50
a. Imperf between (vert pair) .. £18000 £15000
134 ½ pi. green 80 90
a. Imperf between (vert pair) .. £10000 £11000
135 ¾ pi. black and violet 90 10
a. Imperf between (vert pair) .. £20000
136 1 pi. black and red-brown 80 80
a. Imperf between (vert pair) .. £12000 £12000
b. Imperf between (horiz pair) .. £10000
137 1½ pi. carmine 90 55
138 2½ pi. ultramarine .. .. .. 1·25 1·50
139 4½ pi. black and crimson .. .. 3·00 3·25
140 6 pi. black and blue .. .. .. 7·00 12·00
141 9 pi. sepia and violet .. .. .. 4·50 4·00
142 18 pi. black and olive-green .. .. 40·00 27·00
143 45 pi. green and black .. .. .. 60·00 45·00
133/43 .. .. *Set of* 11 £110 85·00
133/43 Perf "Specimen" .. .. *Set of* 11 £275

Designs: *Horiz*.—¾ pi. Church of St. Barnabas and St. Hilarion, Peristerona; 1 pi. Roman theatre, Soli; 1½ pi. Kyrenia Harbour; 2½ pi. Kolossi Castle; 45 pi. Forest scene, Troodos. *Vert*—9 pi. Queen's Window, St. Hilarion Castle; 18 pi. Buyuk Khan, Nicosia.

1935 (6 May). *Silver Jubilee. As Nos.* 91/4 *of Antigua, but ptd by Waterlow & Sons. P* 11 × 12.
144 ¾ pi. ultramarine and grey .. .. 1·75 40
145 1½ pi. deep blue and scarlet .. .. 3·50 2·50
l. Kite and horizontal log £160
146 2½ pi. brown and deep blue .. .. 3·75 1·50
147 9 pi. slate and purple .. .. .. 13·00 11·00
144/7 .. .. *Set of* 4 20·00 14·00
144/7 Perf "Specimen" .. .. *Set of* 4 £130

For illustration of plate variety see Catalogue Introduction.

1937 (12 May). *Coronation. As Nos.* 95/7 *of Antigua. P* 11×11½.
148 ¾ pi. grey 60 20
149 1½ pi. carmine 90 80
150 2½ pi. blue .. .. 2·00 1·25
148/50 .. .. *Set of* 3 3·25 2·00
148/50 Perf "Specimen" .. .. *Set of* 3 £100

35 Vouni Palace

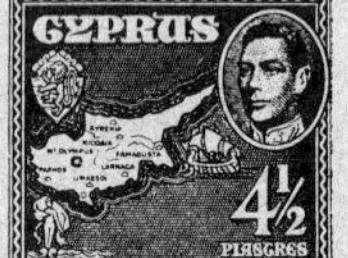
36 Map of Cyprus

37 Othello's Tower, Famagusta

38 King George VI

(Recess Waterlow)

1938 (12 May)–**1951**. *T* **35** *to* **38** *and other designs as* 1934, *but with portrait of King George VI. Wmk Mult Script CA. P* 12½.
151 **35** ¼ pi. ultramarine and orange-brown .. 20 20
152 **25** ½ pi. green 30 10
152*a* – ½ pi. violet (2.7.51) .. .. .. 1·75 20
153 – ¾ pi. black and violet .. .. .. 14·00 40
154 – 1 pi. orange 40 10
a. Perf 13½ × 12½ (1944) .. .. £375 26·00
155 – 1½ pi. carmine .. .. 5·00 1·50
155*a* – 1½ pi. violet (15.3.43) 30 30
155*ab* – 1½ pi. green (2.7.51) .. .. .. 2·25 40
155*b* – 2 pi. black and carmine (2.2.42) .. 40 10
c. Perf 12½ × 13½ (10.44) .. 1·75 5·50
156 – 2½ pi. ultramarine .. .. .. 17·00 2·50
156*a* – 3 pi. ultramarine (2.2.42) 80 15
156*b* – 4 pi. ultramarine (2.7.51) .. .. 3·00 30
157 **36** 4½ pi. grey 40 10
158 **31** 6 pi. black and blue .. .. .. 65 1·00
159 **37** 9 pi. black and purple .. .. .. 1·75 20
160 – 18 pi. black and olive-green .. .. 5·00 85
a. Black and sage-green (19.8.47) .. 7·50 1·50
161 – 45 pi. green and black .. .. .. 14·00 2·50
162 **38** 90 pi. mauve and black .. .. .. 20·00 4·50
163 £1 scarlet and indigo .. .. .. 45·00 21·00
151/63 .. .. *Set of* 19 £110 32·00
151/63 Perf "Specimen" .. .. *Set of* 16 £375

Designs: *Horiz*—¾ pi., 2 pi. Peristerona Church; 1 pi. Soli Theatre; 1½ pi. Kyrenia Harbour; 2½ pi., 3 pi., 4 pi. Kolossi Castle; 45 pi. Forest scene. *Vert*—18 pi. Buyuk Khan, Nicosia.

1946 (21 Oct). *Victory. As Nos.* 110/11 *of Antigua.*
164 1½ pi. deep violet 15 10
165 3 pi. blue 15 15
164/5 Perf "Specimen" .. .. *Set of* 2 90·00

MINIMUM PRICE

The minimum price quote is 10p which represents a handling charge rather than a basis for valuing common stamps. For further notes about prices see introductory pages.

Extra decoration (R. 3/5)

1948 (20 Dec). *Royal Silver Wedding. As Nos.* 112/13 *of Antigua.*
166 1½ pi. violet 50 20
a. Extra decoration .. .. .. 30·00
167 £1 indigo .. .. 42·00 48·00

1949 (10 Oct). *75th Anniv of Universal Postal Union. As Nos.* 114/17 *of Antigua but inscr* "CYPRUS" (*recess*).
168 1½ pi. violet 90 70
169 2 pi. carmine-red .. .. 2·00 1·50
170 3 pi. deep blue .. .. 1·25 1·00
171 9 pi. purple .. .. 1·50 1·10
168/71 .. .. *Set of* 4 5·00 3·75

1953 (2 June). *Coronation. As No.* 120 *of Antigua, but ptd by B.W.*
172 1½ pi. black and emerald 65 10

(New Currency. 1000 mils. = £1)

39 Carobs

42 Mavrovouni Copper Pyrites Mine

49 St. Hilarion Castle

52 Coins of Salamis, Paphos, Citium and Idalium

(Recess B.W.)

1955 (1 Aug)–**60**. *T* **39, 42, 49, 52** *and similar designs. Wmk Mult Script CA. P* 13½ (*Nos.* 183/5) *or* 11½ (*others*).
173 2 m. blackish brown 10 40
174 3 m. blue-violet 10 15
175 5 m. brown-orange 50 10
a. Orange-brown (17.9.58) .. .. 2·50 30
176 10 m. deep brown and deep green .. 75 10
177 15 m. olive-green and indigo .. .. 2·50 45
aa. Yellow-olive and indigo (17.9.58) .. 11·00 2·25
a. Bistre and indigo (14.6.60) .. .. 19·00 7·50
178 20 m. brown and deep bright blue .. 80 15
179 25 m. deep turquoise-blue .. .. 1·50 60
a. Greenish blue (17.9.58) .. .. 8·50 3·75
180 30 m. black and carmine-lake .. .. 1·00 10
181 35 m. orange-brown & deep turquoise-blue 55 40
182 40 m. deep green and sepia .. .. 1·00 60
183 50 m. turquoise-blue and reddish brown .. 85 30
184 100 m. mauve and bluish green .. .. 11·00 60
185 250 m. deep grey-blue and brown .. .. 9·00 6·50
186 500 m. slate and purple .. .. .. 24·00 11·00
187 £1 brown-lake and slate .. .. 24·00 28·00
173/87 .. .. *Set of* 15 70·00 45·00

Designs: *Vert* (*as T* **40**)—3 m. Grapes; 5 m. Oranges. (*as T* **52**)—£1 Arms of Byzantium, Lusignan, Ottoman Empire and Venice. *Horiz* (as *T* **42**)—15 m. Troodos Forest; 20 m. Beach of Aphrodite; 25 m. 5th-century B.C. coin of Paphos; 30 m. Kyrenia; 35 m. Harvest in Mesaoria; 40 m. Famagusta Harbour. (*as T* **50**)—100 m. Hala Sultan Tekke; 250 m. Kanakaria Church.

ΚΥΠΡΙΑΚΗ
ΔΗΜΟΚΡΑΤΙΑ
KIBRIS
CUMHURİYETİ

(**54** "Cyprus Republic") **55** Map of Cyprus

1960 (16 Aug)–**61**. *Nos.* 173/87 *optd as T* **54**, *in blue by B.W. Opt larger on Nos.* 191/7 *and in two lines on Nos.* 198/202.
188 2 m. blackish brown 20 40
189 3 m. blue-violet 20 15
190 5 m. brown-orange .. .. .. 1·00 10
a. Orange-brown (15.8.61) .. .. 1·75 10
191 10 m. deep brown and deep green .. 70 10
192 15 m. yellow-bistre and indigo 75 10
a. Olive-green and indigo .. .. £110 30·00
b. Brownish bis & dp ind (10.10.61) .. 4·25 2·50
193 20 m. brown and deep bright blue .. 40 60
a. Opt double .. .. .. † £9000
194 25 m. deep turquoise-blue .. .. 1·25 55
a. Greenish blue (7.2.61) .. .. 14·00 6·00
195 30 m. black and carmine-lake .. .. 1·75 10
a. Opt double .. .. .. † £15000
196 35 m. orange-brown & dp turquoise-blue 1·75 20
197 40 m. deep green and sepia .. .. 2·00 1·25
198 50 m. turquoise-blue and reddish brown 2·00 40
199 100 m. mauve and bluish green .. .. 9·00 40
200 250 m. deep grey-blue and brown .. .. 25·00 2·00
201 500 m. slate and purple .. .. .. 40·00 15·00
202 £1 brown-lake and slate .. .. 60·00 48·00
188/202 .. .. *Set of* 15 £130 60·00

Only two used examples of No. 195a are known.

(Recess B.W.)

1960 (16 Aug). *Constitution of Republic. W* w **12.** *P* 11½.
203 **55** 10 m. sepia and deep green 30 10
204 30 m. ultramarine and deep brown .. 65 10
205 100 m. purple and deep slate .. .. 2·00 1·75
203/5 .. .. *Set of* 3 2·75 1·75

PRINTERS. All the following stamps to No. 715 were designed by A. Tassos and lithographed by Aspioti-Elka, Athens, *unless otherwise stated.*

56 Doves

(Des T. Kurpershoek)

1962 (19 Mar). *Europa. P* 14 × 13.
206 **56** 10 m. purple and mauve 10 10
207 40 m. ultramarine and cobalt 20 15
208 100 m. emerald and pale green 20 20
206/8 .. .. *Set of* 3 40 40

57 Campaign Emblem

1962 (14 May). *Malaria Eradication. P* 14 × 13½.
209 **57** 10 m. black and olive-green 20 15
210 30 m. black and brown 40 15

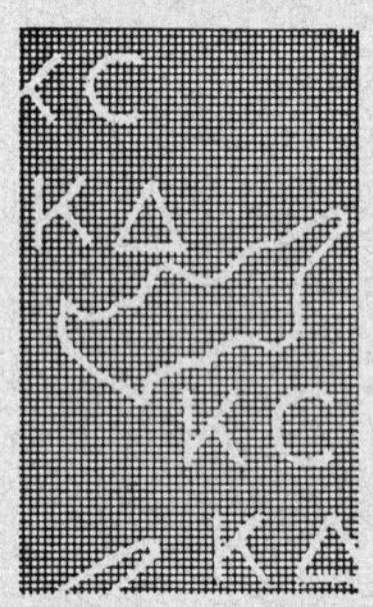

58 Mult K C K Δ and Map

WATERMARK VARIETIES. The issues printed by Aspioti-Elka with W **58** are known with the vertical stamps having the watermark normal or inverted and the horizontal stamps with the watermark reading upwards or downwards. Such varieties are not given separate listing.

62 Selimiye Mosque, Nicosia

63 St. Barnabas's Church

1962 (17 Sept). *T* **62/3** *and similar designs. W* **58** (*sideways on* 25, 30, 40, 50, 250 *m.*, £1). *P* 13½ × 14 (*vert*) *or* 14 × 13½ (*horiz*).
211 3 m. deep brown and orange-brown 10 30
212 5 m. purple and grey-green 10 10
213 10 m. black and yellow-green 15 10
214 15 m. black and reddish purple 20 15
215 25 m. deep brown and chestnut 30 20
216 30 m. deep blue and light blue 20 10
217 35 m. light green and blue 35 10
218 40 m. black and violet-blue .. .. 1·25 1·50
219 50 m. bronze-green and bistre 50 10
220 100 m. deep brown and yellow-brown .. 3·50 30
221 250 m. black and cinnamon .. .. 8·00 2·25
222 500 m. deep brown and light green .. 15·00 10·00
223 £1 bronze-green and grey .. .. 16·00 26·00
211/23 .. .. *Set of* 13 40·00 35·00

Designs: *Vert*—3 m. Iron Age jug; 5 m. Grapes; 10 m. Bronze head of Apollo; 35 m. Head of Aphrodite; 100 m. Hala Sultan Tekke; 500 m. Mouflon. *Horiz*—30 m. Temple of Apollo Hylates; 40 m. Skiing, Troodos; 50 m. Salamis Gymnasium; 250 m. Bella Paise Abbey; £1 St. Hilarion Castle.

72 Europa "Tree"

(Des L. Weyer)

1963 (28 Jan). *Europa.* W **58** (*sideways*). *P* 14 × 13½.
224 **72** 10 m. bright blue and black 75 20
225 40 m. carmine-red and black .. .. 3·00 2·00
226 150 m. emerald-green and black .. 12·00 6·00
224/6 .. .. *Set of* 3 14·00 7·50

73 Harvester **75** Wolf Cub in Camp

1963 (21 Mar). *Freedom from Hunger. T* **73** *and similar vert design.* W **58**. *P* 13½ × 14.
227 25 m. ochre, sepia and bright blue 30 25
228 75 m. grey, black and lake .. .. 1·75 1·00
Design:— 75 m. Demeter, Goddess of Corn.

1963 (21 Aug). *50th Anniv of Cyprus Scout Movement and Third Commonwealth Scout Conference, Platres. T* **75** *and similar vert designs. Multicoloured.* W **58**. *P* 13½ × 14.
229 3 m. Type **75** 10 20
230 20 m. Sea Scout 45 10
231 150 m. Scout with Mouflon .. .. .. 1·50 2·25
229/31 .. .. *Set of* 3 1·75 2·25
MS231*a* 110×90 mm. Nos. 229/31 (*sold at* 250 *m.*). Imperf £110 £200

78 Nurse tending Child **79** Children's Centre, Kyrenia

1963 (9 Sept). *Centenary of Red Cross.* W **58** (*sideways on* 100 *m.*). *P* 13½ × 14 (10 *m.*) *or* 14 × 13½ (100 *m.*).
232 **78** 10 m. red, blue, grey-bl, chestnut & blk 50 15
233 **79** 100 m. red, green, black and blue .. 2·50 3·50

80 "Co-operation" (emblem) (**81**)

(Des A. Holm)

1963 (4 Nov). *Europa.* W **58** (*sideways*). *P* 14 × 13½.
234 **80** 20 m. buff, blue and violet .. .. 1·25 40
235 30 m. grey, yellow and blue .. .. 1·75 40
236 150 m. buff, blue and orange-brown .. 8·00 9·00
234/6 .. .. *Set of* 3 10·00 9·00

1964 (5 May). *U.N. Security Council's Cyprus Resolutions. March,* 1964, *Nos.* 213, 216, 218/20, *optd with T* **81** *in blue by Govt Printing Office, Nicosia.*
237 10 m. black and yellow-green 20 10
238 30 m. deep blue and light blue 20 10
239 40 m. black and violet-blue 20 20
240 50 m. bronze-green and bistre 20 10
241 100 m. deep brown and yellow-brown .. 25 50
237/41 .. .. *Set of* 5 95 85

82 Soli Theatre

1964 (15 June). *400th Birth Anniv of Shakespeare. T* **82** *and similar horiz designs. Multicoloured.* W **58**. *P* 13½ × 13.
242 15 m. Type **82** 40 15
243 35 m. Curium Theatre 40 15
244 50 m. Salamis Theatre 40 15
245 100 m. Othello Tower and scene from *Othello* .. 1·00 2·00
242/5 .. .. *Set of* 4 2·00 2·25

86 Running **89** Europa "Flower"

1964 (6 July). *Olympic Games, Tokyo. T* **86** *and similar designs.* W **58** (*sideways,* 25 *m.* 75 *m.*). *P* 13½ × 14 (10 *m.*) *or* 14 × 13½ (*others*)
246 10 m. brown, black and yellow 15 10
247 25 m. brown, blue and blue-grey 35 10
248 75 m. brown, black and orange-red 50 65
246/8 .. .. *Set of* 3 90 75
MS248*a* 110 × 90 mm. Nos. 246/8 (*sold at* 250 *m.*). Imperf .. .. 6·00 14·00
Designs: *Horiz*—25 m. Boxing; 75 m. Charioteers.

(Des G. Bétemps)

1964 (14 Sept). *Europa.* W **58**. *P* 13½ × 14.
249 **89** 20 m. chestnut and light ochre 60 10
250 30 m. ultramarine and light blue .. 75 10
251 150 m. olive and light blue-green .. 5·25 8·00
249/51 .. .. *Set of* 3 6·00 8·00

90 Dionysus and Acme **91** Silenus (satyr)

1964 (26 Oct). *Cyprus Wines. T* **90/1** *and similar multicoloured designs.* W **58** (*sideways,* 10 *m., or* 100 *m.*). *P* 14 × 13½ (*horiz*) 13½ × 14 (*vert*).
252 10 m. Type **90** 25 10
253 40 m. Type **91** 55 85
254 50 m. Commandaria Wine (*vert*) 60 10
255 100 m. Wine factory (*horiz*) .. .. .. 2·00 1·75
252/5 .. .. *Set of* 4 3·00 2·50

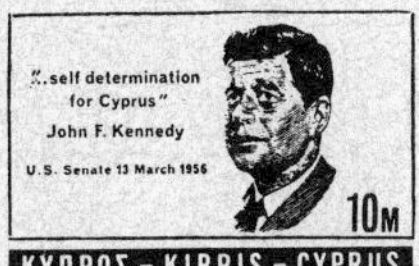

94 President Kennedy

1965 (15 Feb). *President Kennedy Commemoration.* W **58** (*sideways*). *P* 14 × 13½.
256 **94** 10 m. ultramarine 10 10
257 40 m. green 25 25
258 100 m. carmine-lake 30 25
256/8 .. .. *Set of* 3 55 50
MS258*a* 110 × 90 mm. Nos. 256/8 (*sold at* 250 *m.*). Imperf .. .. 3·00 6·50

95 "Old Age" **96** "Maternity"

1965 (12 Apr). *Introduction of Social Insurance Law. T* **95/6** *and similar design.* W **58**. *P* 13½×12 (75 *m.*) *or* 13½×14 (*others*).
259 30 m. drab and dull green 20 10
260 45 m. light grey-green, blue & dp ultramarine 30 10
261 75 m. red-brown and flesh .. .. .. 1·50 2·25
259/61 .. .. *Set of* 3 1·75 2·25
Design: *Vert as T* **95**—45 m. "Accident".

98 I.T.U. Emblem and Symbols

1965 (17 May). *I.T.U. Centenary,* W **58** (*sideways*). *P* 14 × 13½.
262 **98** 15 m. black, brown and yellow 75 20
263 60 m. black, green and light green .. 4·75 2·50
264 75 m. black, indigo and light blue .. 5·50 4·00
262/4 .. .. *Set of* 3 10·00 6·00

99 I.C.Y. Emblem

1965 (17 May). *International Co-operation Year.* W **58** (*sideways*). *P* 14 × 13½.
265 **99** 50 m. brown, dp green & lt yellow-brown 75 10
266 100 m. purple, dp green & lt purple .. 1·25 70

100 Europa "Sprig"

U. N.
Resolution
on Cyprus
18 Dec. 1965
(**101**)

(Des H. Karlsson)

1965 (27 Sept). *Europa.* W **58** (*sideways*). *P* 14×13½.
267 **100** 5 m. black, orange-brown and orange 20 10
268 45 m. black, orange-brown & lt emer 1·25 1·50
269 150 m. black, orange-brown & lt grey 3·00 3·75
267/9 .. .. *Set of* 3 4·00 4·75

1966 (31 Jan). *U.N. General Assembly's Cyprus Resolution,* 18 *December* 1965. *Nos.* 211, 213, 216 *and* 221 *optd with T* **101**, *in blue by Govt Printing Office, Nicosia.*
270 3 m. deep brown and orange-brown .. 10 25
271 10 m. black and yellow-green 10 10
272 30 m. deep blue and light blue 10 15
273 250 m. black and cinnamon .. .. .. 55 1·75
270/3 .. .. *Set of* 4 70 2·00

102 Discovery of St. Barnabas's Body **104** St. Barnabas (icon)

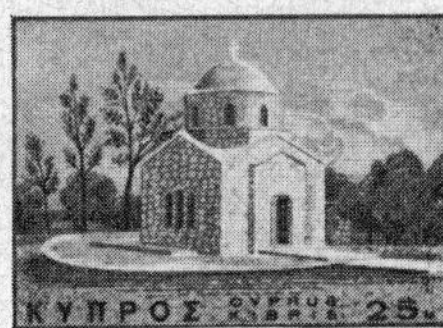

103 St. Barnabas's Chapel

105 "Privileges of Cyprus Church"
(*Actual size* 102 × 82 *mm*)

1966 (25 Apr). *1900th Death Anniv of St. Barnabas.* W **58** (*sideways on* 15 *m.,* 100 *m.,* 250 *m.*). *P* 14 × 13 (25 *m*). *or* 13 × 14 (*others*).
274 **102** 15 m. multicoloured 10 10
275 **103** 25 m. drab, black and blue 20 10
276 **104** 100 m. multicoloured .. .. .. 65 1·75
274/6 .. .. *Set of* 3 80 1·75
MS277 110 × 91 mm. **105** 250 m. mult. Imperf .. 4·25 13·00

NEW INFORMATION

The editor is always interested to correspond with people who have new information that will improve or correct the Catalogue.

5 M

Ξ

(106) 107 General K. S. Thimayya and U. N. Emblem

1966 (30 May). *No. 211 surch with T* **106** *by Govt Printing Office, Nicosia.*

278 5 m. on 3 m. deep brown & orange-brown 10 10

1966 (6 June) *General Thimayya Commemoration. W* **58** *(sideways). P* 14 × 13.

279 **107** 50 m. black and light orange-brown .. 30 10

108 Europa "Ship"

(Des G. and J. Bender)

1966 (26 Sept). *Europa. W* **58**. *P* 13½ × 14.

280	**108**	20 m. green and blue	25	10
281		30 m. bright purple and blue	25	10
282		150 m. bistre and blue	1·75	3·00
280/2		.. .. *Set of* 3	2·00	3·00

110 Church of St. James, Trikomo **119** Vase of 7th Century B.C.

120 Bronze Ingot-stand

1966 (21 Nov)–**69**. *T* **110**, **119/20** *and similar designs. W* **58** *(sideways on* 3, 15, 25, 50, 250, 500 *m.,* £1*). P* 12×13 *(*3 *m.),* 13×12 *(*5, 10 *m.),* 14×13½ *(*15, 25, 50 *m.),* 13½×14 *(*20, 30, 35, 40, 100 *m.) or* 13×14 *(others).*

283	3 m. grey-green, buff, black & light blue	40	20
284	5 m. bistre, black and steel-blue	10	10
	a. Brownish bistre, black and steel-blue (18.4.69)	45	20
285	10 m. black and bistre	15	15
286	15 m. black, chestnut & light orange-brown	15	10
287	20 m. black, slate and brown	1·25	90
288	25 m. black, drab and lake-brown ..	30	10
289	30 m. black, yellow-ochre and turquoise ..	50	20
290	35 m. yellow, black and carmine-red ..	50	30
291	40 m. black, grey and new blue	70	30
	a. Grey (background) omitted ..		
292	50 m. black, slate and brown	90	10
293	100 m. black, red, pale buff and grey ..	3·75	15
294	250 m. olive-green, black & lt yellow-ochre	1·50	40
295	500 m. multicoloured	2·25	70
296	£1 black, drab and slate	2·50	6·00
283/96	.. .. .. *Set of* 14	13·00	8·50

Designs: *Horiz (as T* **110**)—3 m. Stavrovouni Monastery. (*As T* **119**)—15 m. Minoan wine ship of 700 B.C. (painting); 25 m. Sleeping Eros (marble statue); 50 m. Silver coin of Alexander the Great. *Vert (as T* **110**)—10 m. Zeno of Cibium (marble bust). (*As T* **119**)—20 m. Silver coin of Evagoras I; 30 m. St. Nicholas Cathedral, Famagusta; 35 m. Gold sceptre from Curium; 40 m. Silver dish from 7th century. (*As T* **120**)—500 m. "The Rape of Ganymede" (mosaic); £1 Aphrodite (marble statue).

OMNIBUS ISSUES

Details, together with prices for complete sets, of the various Omnibus issues from the 1935 Silver Jubilee series to date are included in a special section following Zimbabwe at the end of Volume 2.

123 Power Station, Limassol **124** Cogwheels

1967 (10 Apr). *First Development Programme. T* **123** *and similar designs but horiz. Multicoloured. W* **58** *(sideways on* 15 *to* 100 *m.). P* 13½ × 14 *(*10 *m.) or* 14 × 13½ *(others).*

297	10 m. Type **123**	10	10
298	15 m. Arghaka-Maghounda Dam	15	10
299	35 m. Troodos Highway	20	10
300	50 m. Hilton Hotel, Nicosia	20	10
301	100 m. Famagusta Harbour	20	90
297/301	.. .. *Set of* 5	75	1·10

(Des O. Bonnevalle)

1967 (2 May). *Europa. W* **58**. *P* 13½ × 14.

302	**124**	20 m. olive-green, green & pale yell-grn	25	10
303		30 m. reddish violet, lilac and pale lilac	25	10
304		150 m. brown, light reddish brown and pale yellow-brown	1·00	2·00
302/4		.. .. *Set of* 3	1·40	2·00

125 Throwing the Javelin

126 Running (amphora) and Map of Eastern Mediterranean
(*Actual size* 97 × 77 *mm*)

1967 (4 Sept). *Athletic Games, Nicosia. T* **125** *and similar designs and T* **126**. *Multicoloured. W* **58**. *P* 13½ × 13.

305	15 m. Type **125**	20	10
306	35 m. Running	20	35
307	100 m. High-jumping	30	85
305/7	.. .. *Set of* 3	60	1·10
MS308	110×90 mm. 250 m. Type **126** (wmk sideways). Imperf	1·60	6·50

127 Ancient Monuments **128** St. Andrew Mosaic

1967 (16 Oct). *International Tourist Year. T* **127** *and similar horiz designs. Multicoloured. W* **58**. *P* 13 × 13½.

309	10 m. Type **127**	10	10
310	40 m. Famagusta Beach	15	70
311	50 m. Hawker Siddeley Comet 4 at Nicosia Airport	15	10
312	100 m. Skier and youth hostel	20	75
309/12	.. .. *Set of* 4	50	1·50

1967 (8 Nov). *Centenary of St. Andrew's Monastery. W* **58** *(sideways). P* 13 × 13½.

313 **128** 25 m. multicoloured 10 10

129 "The Crucifixion" (icon) **130** The Three Magi

(Photo French Govt Ptg Wks, Paris)

1967 (8 Nov). *Cyprus Art Exhibition, Paris. P* 12½ × 13½.

314 **129** 50 m. multicoloured 10 10

1967 (8 Nov). *20th Anniv of U.N.E.S.C.O. W* **58** *(sideways). P* 13 × 13½.

315 **130** 75 m. multicoloured 20 20

131 Human Rights Emblem over Stars **132** Human Rights and U.N. Emblems

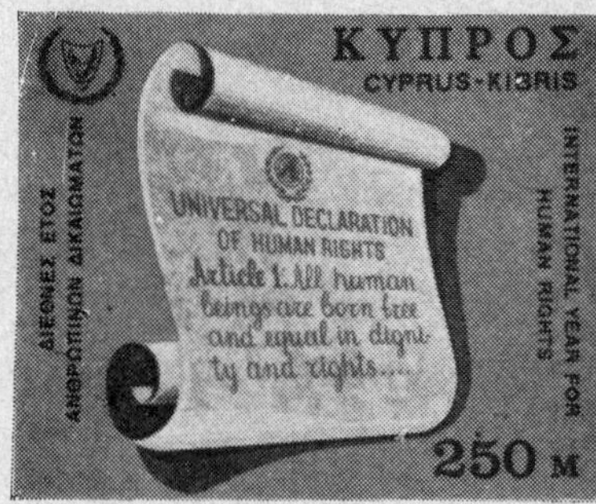

133 Scroll of Declaration
(*Actual size* 95 × 75½ *mm*)

1968 (18 Mar). *Human Rights Year. W* **58**. *P* 13 × 14.

316	**131**	50 m. multicoloured	10	10
317	**132**	90 m. multicoloured	30	70
MS318		95 × 75½ mm. **133** 250 m. multicoloured. W **58** (sideways). Imperf.	1·00	4·75

134 Europa "Key"

(Des H. Schwarzenbach)

1968 (29 Apr). *Europa. W* **58** *(sideways). P* 14 × 13.

319	**134**	20 m. multicoloured	20	10
320		30 m. multicoloured	20	10
321		150 m. multicoloured	60	2·00
319/21		.. .. *Set of* 3	90	2·00

135 U.N. Children's Fund Symbol and Boy drinking Milk **136** Aesculapius

1968 (2 Sept). *21st Anniv of U.N.I.C.E.F. W* **58** *(sideways). P* 14 × 13.

322 **135** 35 m. yellow-brown, carmine-red & blk 10 10

1968 (2 Sept). *20th Anniv of W.H.O. W* **58**. *P* 13 × 14.

323 **136** 50 m. black, green and light olive .. 10 10

137 Throwing the Discus

138 I.L.O. Emblem

68 (24 Oct). *Olympic Games, Mexico. T* **137** *and similar designs. Multicoloured.* W **58** (*sideways on* 100 *m.*). P 14 × 13 (100 *m.*) *or* 13 × 14 (*others*).
4 10 m. Type **137** 10 10
5 25 m. Sprint finish 10 10
6 100 m. Olympic Stadium (*horiz*) 20 95
4/6 .. .. *Set of* 3 30 1·00

69 (3 Mar). 50*th Anniv of International Labour Organization.* W **58**. P 12 × 13½.
7 **138** 50 m. yellow-brown, blue and light blue 15 10
8 90 m. yellow-brown, black and pale grey 15 40

139 Mercator's Map of Cyprus, 1554

140 Blaeu's Map of Cyprus, 1635

969 (7 Apr). *First International Congress of Cypriot Studies.* W **58** (*sideways*). P 14 × 14½.
29 **139** 35 m. multicoloured 20 30
30 **140** 50 m. multicoloured 20 10
a. Wmk upright .. .. — 2·75
ab. Grey (shading on boats and cartouche) omitted £225

141 Europa Emblem

142 Common Roller

(Des L. Gasbarra and G. Belli)

969 (28 Apr). *Europa.* W **58** (*sideways*). P 14 × 13½.
31 **141** 20 m. multicoloured 20 10
32 30 m. multicoloured 20 10
33 150 m. multicoloured .. .. 80 2·00
31/3 .. .. *Set of* 3 1·10 2·00

969 (7 July). *Birds of Cyprus. T* **142** *and similar designs. Multicoloured.* W **58** (*sideways on horiz designs*). P 13½ × 12 (*horiz designs*) *or* 12 × 13½ (*vert designs*).
34 5 m. Type **142** 40 15
35 15 m. Audouin's Gull 60 15
36 20 m. Cyprus Warbler 60 15
37 30 m. Jay (*vert*) 60 15
38 40 m. Hoopoe (*vert*) 65 30
39 90 m. Eleanora's Falcon (*vert*) .. .. .. 1·50 5·00
34/9 .. .. *Set of* 6 4·00 5·50
The above were printed on glazed Samuel Jones paper with very faint watermark.

143 "The Nativity" (12th-century Wall Painting)

145 "Virgin and Child between Archangels Michael and Gabriel" (6th–7th-century Mosaic) (*Actual size* 102 × 81 *mm*)

1969 (24 Nov). *Christmas. T* **143** *and similar horiz design, and T* **145**. *Multicoloured.* W **58** (*sideways*). P 13½ × 13.
340 20 m. Type **143** 15 10
341 45 m. "The Nativity" (14th-century wall painting) 15 20
MS342 110 × 90 mm. 250 m. Type **145**. Imperf .. 4·00 12·00
a. Grey and light brown omitted .. £1600

146 Mahatma Gandhi

1970 (26 Jan). *Birth Centenary of Mahatma Gandhi.* W **58** (*sideways*). P 14 × 13½.
343 **146** 25 m. ultramarine, drab and black .. 15 10
344 75 m. yellow-brown, drab and black .. 20 65

147 "Flaming Sun"

148 Gladioli

(Des L. le Brocquy)

1970 (4 May). *Europa.* W **58** (*sideways*). P 14 × 13.
345 **147** 20 m. brown, greenish yellow & orange 20 10
346 30 m. new blue, greenish yellow & orge 20 10
347 150 m. bright purple, greenish yell & orge 80 2·25
345/7 .. .. *Set of* 3 1·10 2·25

1970 (3 Aug). *European Conservation Year. T* **148** *and similar vert designs. Multicoloured.* W **58**. P 13 × 13½.
348 10 m. Type **148** 10 10
349 50 m. Poppies 15 10
350 90 m. Giant fennel .. .. 50 1·40
348/50 .. .. *Set of* 3 65 1·40

149 I.E.Y. Emblem

150 Mosaic

151 Globe, Dove and U.N. Emblem

(Des G. Simonis (75 m.))

1970 (7 Sept). *Anniversaries and Events.* W **58** (*sideways on horiz designs*). P 13×14 (5 *m.*), *or* 14×13 (*others*).
351 **149** 5 m. black, red-brown & lt yellow-brn 10 10
352 **150** 15 m. multicoloured 10 10
353 **151** 75 m. multicoloured 15 60
351/3 .. .. *Set of* 3 30 70
Events:—5 m. International Education Year; 15 m. 50th General Assembly of International Vine and Wine Office; 75 m. 25th anniv of United Nations.

152 Virgin and Child

153 Cotton Napkin

(Photo Harrison)

1970 (23 Nov). *Christmas. Wall-painting from Church of Panayia Podhythou, Galata. T* **152** *and similar multicoloured designs.* P 14 × 14½.
354 25 m. Archangel (facing right) 15 20
a. Horiz strip of 3. Nos. 354/6 40
355 25 m. Type **152** 15 20
356 25 m. Archangel (facing left) 15 20
357 75 m. Virgin and Child between Archangels 15 30
354/7 .. .. *Set of* 4 55 80
The 75 m. is horiz, size 42 × 30 mm, and the 25 m. values are vert, size as T **152**.
Nos. 354/6 were issued in *se-tenant* strips of three, throughout the sheet. The triptych thus formed is depicted in its entirety on the 75 m. value.

1971 (22 Feb). *Multicoloured designs as T* **153**. W **58** (*sideways on horiz designs*). (*a*) *Vert designs* 23 × 33 *mm.* P 12 × 13½.
358 3 m. Type **153** 30 55
359 5 m. St. George and Dragon (19th-cent bas-relief) 10 10

(*b*) *Vert* (10, 20, 25, 40, 50, 75 *m.*) *or horiz* (15, 30, 90 *m.*) *designs, each* 24 × 37 *or* 37 × 24 *mm.* P 13 × 14 (15, 30, 90 *m*) *or* 14 × 13 (*others*)
360 10 m. Woman in festival costume 15 30
361 15 m. Archaic Bichrome Kylix (cup) 20 10
a. Vert laid paper .. .. 1·00
362 20 m. A pair of donors (St. Mamas Church) 35 50
363 25 m. "The Creation" (6th-cent mosaic) .. 30 10
364 30 m. Athena and horse-drawn chariot (4th-cent B.C. terracotta) 30 10
365 40 m. Shepherd playing pipe (14th-cent fresco) .. .. 1·00 90
366 50 m. Hellenistic head (3rd cent B.C.) .. 80 10
367 75 m. "Angel" (mosaic detail), Kanakaria Church .. .. 1·75 1·00
368 90 m. Mycenaean silver bowl .. .. .. 2·00 1·50

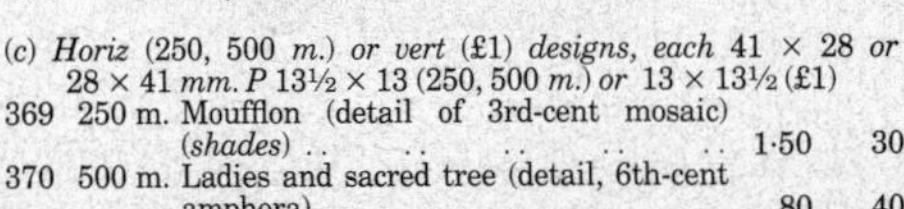

(*c*) *Horiz* (250, 500 *m.*) *or vert* (£1) *designs, each* 41 × 28 *or* 28 × 41 *mm.* P 13½ × 13 (250, 500 *m.*) *or* 13 × 13½ (£1)
369 250 m. Moufflon (detail of 3rd-cent mosaic) (*shades*) .. .. 1·50 30
370 500 m. Ladies and sacred tree (detail, 6th-cent amphora) 80 40
371 £1 Horned god from Enkomi (12th-cent bronze statue) .. .. 1·50 60
358/71 .. .. *Set of* 14 10·00 5·50

154 Europa Chain

155 Archbishop Kyprianos

(Des H. Haflidason)

1971 (3 May). *Europa.* W **58** (*sideways*). P 14 × 13
372 **154** 20 m. pale blue, ultramarine and black 20 10
373 30 m. apple green, myrtle-green & blk 20 10
374 150 m. lemon, bright green and black .. 90 2·25
372/4 .. .. *Set of* 3 1·10 2·25
The above were printed on glazed paper with very faint watermark.

1971 (9 July). 150*th Anniv. of Greek War of Independence. T* **155** *and similar multicoloured designs.* W **58** (*sideways on* 30 *m.*). P 13½ × 12½ (30 *m.*) *or* 12½ × 13½ (*others*).
375 15 m. Type **155** 10 10
376 30 m. "Taking the Oath" (*horiz*) 10 10
377 100 m. Bishop Germanos, flag and freedom-fighters 20 50
375/7 .. .. *Set of* 3 30 55

156 Kyrenia Castle

157 Madonna and Child in Stable

1971 (20 Sept). *Tourism. T* **156** *and similar multicoloured designs. W* **58** *(sideways on* 15 *and* 100 *m.). P* 13½ × 13 (15 *m.,* 100 *m.) or* 13 × 13½ *(others).*
378 15 m. Type **156** 10 10
379 25 m. Gourd on sunny beach (*vert*) .. 10 10
380 60 m. Mountain scenery (*vert*) 20 60
381 100 m. Church of St. Evlalios, Lambousa .. 20 65
378/81 .. .. *Set of* 4 45 1·25

1971 (22 Nov). *Christmas. T* **157** *and similar vert designs. Multicoloured. W* **58**. *P* 13 × 14.
382 10 m. Type **157** 10 10
a. Horiz strip of 3. Nos. 382/4 35
383 50 m. The Three Wise Men 15 35
384 100 m. The Shepherds 20 35
382/4 .. .. *Set of* 3 35 70
The 10 m. was issued in sheets of 100, and all three values were printed horizontally *se-tenant* in sheets of 36, the order being 50, 10 and 100 m.

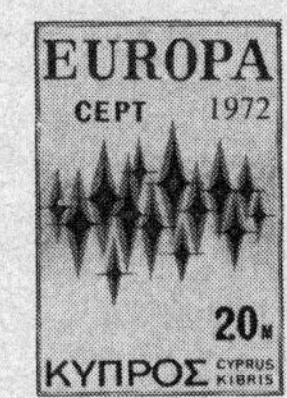

158 Heart **159** "Communications"

1972 (11 Apr). *World Heart Month. W* **58** *(sideways). P* 13½×12.
385 **158** 15 m. multicoloured 10 10
386 50 m. multicoloured 20 45

(Des P. Huovinen)

1972 (22 May). *Europa. W* **58**. *P* 12½ × 13½.
387 **159** 20 m. yellow-orge, sepia & pale grey-brn 20 15
388 30 m. yell-orge, brt dp ultram & cobalt 20 15
389 150 m. yellow-orange, myrtle-green and pale-turquoise-green .. .. 1·60 3·25
387/9 .. .. *Set of* 3 1·75 3·25

160 Archery

1972 (24 July). *Olympic Games, Munich. T* **160** *and similar horiz designs. Multicoloured. W* **58** *(sideways). P* 14×13.
390 10 m. Type **160** 10 10
391 40 m. Wrestling 15 15
392 100 m. Football .. .. 35 1·10
390/2 .. .. *Set of* 3 50 1·25

161 Stater of Marion **162** Bathing the Child Jesus

1972 (25 Sept). *Ancient Coins of Cyprus (1st series), T* **161** *and similar horiz designs. W* **58** *(sideways), P* 14 × 13.
393 20 m. pale turquoise-blue, black and silver .. 20 10
394 30 m. pale violet-blue, black and silver .. 20 10
395 40 m. brownish stone, black and silver .. 20 20
396 100 m. light salmon-pink, black and silver .. 60 1·00
393/6 .. .. *Set of* 4 1·10 1·25
Coins:—30 m. Stater of Paphos; 40 m. Stater of Lapithos, 100 m. Stater of Idalion.
See also Nos. 486/9.

1972 (20 Nov). *Christmas. T* **162** *and similar vert designs showing portions of a mural in the Church of the Holy Cross of Agiasmati. Multicoloured. W* **58** *(sideways on* **MS**400). *P* 13 × 14.
397 10 m. Type **162** 10 10
398 20 m. The Magi 10 10
399 100 m. The Nativity 15 30
397/9 .. .. *Set of* 3 30 35
MS400 100×90 mm. 250 m. Showing the mural in full. Imperf .. .. 1·10 4·50

163 Mount Olympus, Troodos

1973 (13 Mar). *29th Internation Ski Federation Congress. T* **163** *and similar horiz design. Multicoloured. W* **58** *(sideways). P* 14 × 13.
401 20 m. Type **163** 10 10
402 100 m. Congress emblem 25 35

164 Europa "Posthorn"

(Des I. Anisdahl)

1973 (7 May). *Europa. W* **58** *(sideways). P* 14 × 13.
403 **164** 20 m. multicoloured 15 10
404 30 m. multicoloured 15 10
405 150 m. multicoloured .. .. .. 1·10 2·75
403/5 .. .. *Set of* 3 1·25 2·75

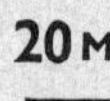

165 Archbishop's Palace, Nicosia **(166)**

1973 (23 July). *Traditional Architecture. T* **165** *and similar multicoloured designs. W* **58** *(sideways on* 20 *and* 100 *m.). P* 14 × 13 (20 *and* 100 *m.) or* 13 × 14 *(others).*
406 20 m. Type **165** 10 10
407 30 m. House of Hajigeorgajis Cornessios, Nicosia (*vert*) 10 10
408 50 m. House at Gourri, 1850 (*vert*) 15 10
409 100 n. House at Rizokarpaso, 1772 .. .. 40 75
406/9 .. .. *Set of* 4 65 90

1973 (24 Sept). *No.* 361 *surch with T* **166**.
410 20 m. on 15 m. Archaic Bichrome Kylix (cup) 15 15
a. Vert laid paper 80
b. Surch inverted .. .. ..

167 Scout Emblem **168** Archangel Gabriel

1973 (24 Sept). *Anniversaries and Events. T* **167** *and similar designs. W* **58** *(sideways on* 25 *and* 35 *m.). P* 13×14 (10, 50 *and* 100 *m.) or* 14×13 *(others).*
411 10 m. yellow-olive and deep brown 20 10
412 25 m. deep blue, and slate-lilac 20 10
413 35 m. light brown-olive, stone and sage-green 20 25
414 50 m. dull blue and indigo 20 10
415 100 m. brown and sepia.. .. .. .. 50 80
411/15 .. .. *Set of* 5 1·10 1·10
Designs and Events: *Vert*—10 m. Type **167** (60th anniv of Cyprus Boy Scouts); 50 m. Airline emblem (25th anniv of Cyprus Airways); 100 m. Interpol emblem (50th anniv of Interpol). *Horiz*—25 m. Outline of Cyprus and E.E.C. nations (Association of Cyprus with the E.E.C.); 35 m. F.A.O. emblem (Tenth anniv of F.A.O.).

1973 (26 Nov). *Christmas. Murals from Araka Church. T* **168** *and similar multicoloured designs. W* **58** *(sideways on* 100 *m.). P* 14×13 (100 *m.) or* 13×14 *(others).*
416 10 m. Type **168** 10 10
417 20 m. Madonna and Child 10 10
418 100 m. Araka Church (*horiz*) 40 75
416/18 .. .. *Set of* 3 45 75

169 Grapes **170** "The Rape of Europa" (Silver Stater of Marion)

1974 (18 Mar). *Products of Cyprus. T* **169** *and similar vert designs. Multicoloured. W* **58**. *P* 13 × 14.
419 25 m. Type **169** 10 15
420 50 m. Grapefruit 20 50
a. Horiz strip of 3, Nos. 420/2 55
421 50 m. Oranges 20 50
422 50 m. Lemons 20 50
419/22 .. .. *Set of* 4 65 1·50
Nos. 420/2 were printed together, horizontally *se-tenant* throughout the sheet.

1974 (29 Apr). *Europa. W* **58**. *P* 13½ × 14.
423 **170** 10 m. multicoloured 15 1
424 40 m. multicoloured 35 3
425 150 m. multicoloured .. .. 1·10 2·7
423/5 .. .. *Set of* 3 1·40 2·7

REFUGEE
FUND
ΤΑΜΕΙΟΝ
ΠΡΟΣΦΥΓΩΝ
GÖÇMENLER
FONU

10M

171 Title Page of A. Kyprianos' "History of Cyprus" (1788) **(172)**

1974 (22 July*). *Second International Congress of Cypri[…] Studies. T* **171** *and similar multicoloured designs. W* **58** *(side[…] ways on* 25 *m. and* **MS**429). *P* 14 × 13½ (25 *m.) or* 13½ × 1[…] *(others).*
426 10 m. Type **171** 10 1
427 25 m. Solon (philosopher) in mosaic (*horiz*) .. 15 1
428 100 m. "St. Neophytos" (wall painting).. .. 60 7
426/8 .. .. *Set of* 3 70 8
MS429 111 × 90 mm. 250 m. Ortelius' map of Cyprus and Greek Islands, 1584. Imperf .. .. 1·75 6·0
*Although this is the date appearing on first day covers th[…] stamps were not put on sale until the 24th.

1974 (1 Oct). *Obligatory Tax. Refugee Fund No.* 359 *surch wit[…] T* **172**.
430 10 m. on 5 m. St. George and Dragon.. .. 10 1

SECURITY
COUNCIL
RESOLUTION
353
20 JULY 1974

(173) **174** "Refugees"

1974 (14 Oct). *U.N. Security Council Resolution* 353. *Nos.* 36[…] 365, 366 *and* 369 *optd as T* **173**.
431 10 m. Woman in festival costume 20 1
432 40 m. Shepherd playing pipe 25 5
433 50 m. Hellenistic head.. .. .. .. 25 1
434 250 m. Moufflon (*shades*) .. .. .. 60 2·5
431/4 .. .. *Set of* 4 1·10 2·7

1974 (2 Dec). *Obligatory Tax. Refugee Fund. W* **58** *(sideways[…] P* 12 × 12½.
435 **174** 10 m. black and light grey 10 1

175 "Virgin and Child between Two Angels", Stavros Church

1974 (2 Dec). *Christmas. T* **175** *and similar multicoloure[…] designs showing wall-paintings. W* **58** *(sideways on* 10 *m. an[…]* 100 *m.). P* 13 × 14 (50 *m.) or* 14 × 13 *(others).*
436 10 m. Type **175** 10 1
437 50 m. "Adoration of the Magi", Ayios Neophytos Monastery (*vert*) 20 1
438 100 m. "Flight into Egypt", Ayios Neophytos Monastery 25 4
436/8 .. .. *Set of* 3 45 5

176 Larnaca–Nicosia Mail-coach, 1878 **177** "The Distaff" (M. Kashalos)

(Photo Harrison)

1975 (17 Feb). *Anniversaries and Events. T* **176** *and simila[…] designs. No wmk. P* 14.
439 **176** 20 m. multicoloured .. .. 25 1[…]
440 – 30 m. ultramarine, slate-blk & dull orge 25 6[…]
441 **176** 50 m. multicoloured .. .. 25 1[…]
442 – 100 m. multicoloured .. .. 40 1·4[…]
439/42 .. .. *Set of* 4 1·00 2·0[…]
Designs and Events:—20 m., 50 m. Type **176** (Centenary o[…] Universal Postal Union). *Vert*—30 m. "Disabled Persons" (Eighth European Meeting of International Society for th[…] Rehabilitation of Disabled Persons); 100 m. Council flag (25t[…] anniv of Council of Europe).

(Photo Harrison)

975 (28 Apr). *Europa. T* **177** *and similar vert designs. Multi-coloured. P* 13½ × 14½.

43 20 m. Type **177** 25 40
a. Horiz strip of 3. Nos. 443/5 80
44 30 m. "Nature Morte" (C. Savva) 25 50
45 150 m. "Virgin and Child of Liopetri" (G. P. Georghiou) 40 80
43/5 .. .. *Set of* 3 80 1·50

Nos. 443/5 were printed horizontally *se-tenant* throughout the eet.

178 Red Cross Flag over Map

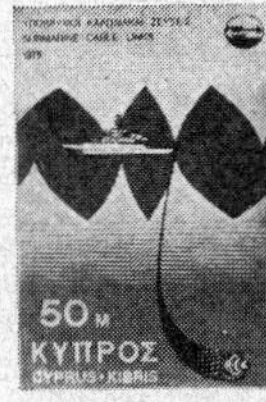

179 Submarine Cable Links

975 (4 Aug). *Anniversaries and Events. T* **178** *and similar horiz designs. P* 12½×13½ (25 *m.*) *or* 13½×12½ (*others*).

46 25 m. multicoloured 25 10
47 30 m. turquoise-green and greenish blue .. 25 10
48 75 m. red-brown, orge-brn & pale blue-grey 35 90
46/8 .. .. *Set of* 3 75 1·00

Designs and Events: *Vert*—25 m. Type **178** (25th anniversary Cyprus Red Cross). *Horiz*—30 m. Nurse and lamp nternational Nurses' Day); 75 m. Woman's Steatite Idol nternational Women's Year).

975 (13 Oct). *Telecommunications Achievements. T* **179** *and similar design. W* **58** (*sideways on* 100 *m.*). *P* 12 × 13½ (50 *m.*) *or* 13½ × 12 (100 *m.*).

49 50 m. multicoloured 40 10
50 100 m. orange-yellow, dull violet and lilac .. 50 90

Design: *Horiz*—100 m. International subscriber dialling.

10M
═

(180)

181 Human-figured Vessel, 19th-Century

976 (5 Jan). *No.* 358 *surch with T* **180**.

51 10 m. on 3 m. Cotton napkin 20 50

976 (3 May). *Europa. Ceramics. T* **181** *and similar vert designs. Multicoloured. W* **58**. *P* 13×14.

52 20 m. Type **181** 20 10
53 60 m. Composite vessel, 2100–2000 B.C. .. 50 80
54 100 m. Byzantine goblet .. .. .. 90 1·75
52/4 .. .. *Set of* 3 1·40 2·40

182 Self-help Housing

183 Terracotta Statue of Youth

976 (3 May). *Economic Reactivation. T* **182** *and similar horiz designs. Multicoloured. W* **58** (*sideways*). *P* 14 × 13.

55 10 m. Type **182** 10 10
56 25 m. Handicrafts 20 20
57 30 m. Reafforestation 20 20
58 60 m. Air Communications 35 55
55/8 .. .. *Set of* 4 75 90

976 (7 June). *Cypriot Treasures. T* **183** *and similar designs. W* **58** (*sideways on horiz designs, upright on vert designs*). *Ordinary cream paper. P* 12 × 13½ (5, 10 *m.*), 13 × 14 (20, 25, 30 *m.*), 14 × 13 (40, 50, 60 *m.*), 13½ × 12 (100 *m.*) *or* 13 × 13½ (250 *m. to* £1).

59 5 m. multicoloured 10 60
60 10 m. multicoloured 15 40
61 20 m. red, yellow and black 30 40
62 25 m. multicoloured 30 10
63 30 m. multicoloured 30 10
64 40 m. grey-green, light olive-bistre and black 45 45
65 50 m. buff, brown and black 45 10
66 60 m. multicoloured 45 20
67 100 m. multicoloured 50 40
68 250 m. deep dull blue, grey and black .. .. 80 1·50
69 500 m. black, stone and deep blue-green .. 80 2·00
70 £1 multicoloured .. .. 1·25 2·25
59/70 .. .. *Set of* 12 5·25 7·50

Sizes:—23 × 34 *mm*, 5 m., 10 m.; 34 × 23 *mm*, 100 m.; 24 × 37 *mm*, 20, 25, 30 m.; 37 × 24 *mm*, 40, 50, 60 m.; 28 × 41 *mm*, others.

Designs:—10 m. Limestone head; 20 m. Gold necklace from Lambousa; 25 m. Terracotta warrior; 30 m. Statue of a priest of Aphrodite; 40 m. Bronze tablet; 50 m. Mycenaean crater; 60 m. Limestone sarcophagus; 100 m. Gold bracelet from Lambousa; 250 m. Silver dish from Lambousa; 500 m. Bronze stand; £1 Statue of Artemis.

184 Olympic Symbol

185 "George Washington" (G. Stuart)

(Litho Harrison)

1976 (5 July). *Olympic Games, Montreal. T* **184** *and similar designs. P* 14.

471 20 m. carmine-red, black and yellow 10 10
472 60 m. multicoloured 20 30
473 100 m. multicoloured 30 55
471/3 .. .. *Set of* 3 55 80

Designs: *Horiz*—60, 100 m. Olympic symbols (*different*).

1976 (5 July). *Bicentenary of American Revolution. W* **58**. *P* 13 × 13½.

474 **185** 100 m. multicoloured 40 30

186 Children in Library

187 Archangel Michael

1976 (27 Sept). *Anniversaries and Events. T* **186** *and similar vert designs. W* **58**. *P* 13½×12½ (50 *m.*) *or* 13½ (*others*).

475 40 m. multicoloured 20 15
476 50 m. yellow-brown and black 20 10
477 80 m. multicoloured 45 60
475/7 .. .. *Set of* 3 75 75

Designs and Events:—40 m. Type **186** (Promotion of Children's Books); 50 m. Low-cost housing (HABITAT Conference, Vancouver); 80 m. Eye protected by hands (World Health Day).

(Litho Harrison)

1976 (15 Nov). *Christmas. T* **187** *and similar vert designs, showing icons from Ayios Neophytis Monastery. Multicoloured. P* 12½.

478 10 m. Type **187** 15 10
479 15 m. Archangel Gabriel 15 10
480 150 m. The Nativity 60 80
478/80 .. .. *Set of* 3 80 80

188 "Cyprus 74" (wood-engraving by A. Tassos)

189 "View of Prodhromos" (A. Diamantis)

1977 (10 Jan)–**82**. *Obligatory Tax. Refugee Fund. W* **58**. *Ordinary cream paper. P* 13 × 12½.

481 **188** 10 m. grey-black 20 10
a. Chalk-surfaced cream paper (3.5.82)* .. ..

*Earliest known date of use.

For 1 c. value, see Nos. 634/b, 729 and 747.

1977 (2 May). *Europa. Paintings. T* **189** *and similar horiz designs. Multicoloured. No wmk. P* 13½×13.

482 20 m. Type **189** 15 10
483 60 m. "Springtime at Monagroulli" (T. Kanthos) 30 60
484 120 m. "Old Port, Limassol" (V. Ioannides) .. 60 1·50
482/4 .. .. *Set of* 3 95 2·00

190 Overprinted 500 m. Stamp of 1960

191 Bronze Coin of Emperor Trajan

1977 (13 June). *Silver Jubilee. W* **58**. *P* 13 × 13½.

485 **190** 120 m. multicoloured 30 30

(Litho Harrison)

1977 (13 June). *Ancient Coins of Cyprus* (2*nd series*). *T* **191** *and similar horiz designs. P* 14.

486 10 m. brownish black, gold and ultramarine .. 15 10
487 40 m. brownish black, silver and pale blue .. 30 30
488 60 m. brownish black, silver and dull orange .. 35 35
489 100 m. brownish black, gold and blue-green .. 50 95
486/9 .. .. *Set of* 4 1·10 1·50

Designs:—40 m. Silver tetradrachm of Demetrios Poliorcetes; 60 m. Silver tetradrachm of Ptolemy VIII; 100 m. Gold Octadrachm of Arsinoe II.

192 Archbishop Makarios in Ceremonial Robes

193 Embroidery, Pottery and Weaving

1977 (10 Sept). *Death of Archbishop Makarios. T* **192** *and similar vert designs. Multicoloured. P* 13 × 13½.

490 20 m. Type **192** 15 10
491 60 m. Archbishop and doorway 20 10
492 250 m. Head and shoulders portrait .. .. 50 1·10
490/2 .. .. *Set of* 3 75 1·10

1977 (17 Oct). *Anniversaries and Events. T* **193** *and similar horiz designs. Multicoloured. W* **58** (*sideways*). *P* 13½ × 13.

493 20 m. Type **193** 10 10
494 40 m. Map of Mediterranean 15 20
495 60 m. Gold medals 20 20
496 80 m. "Sputnik" 20 85
493/6 .. .. *Set of* 4 60 1·25

Events:—20 m. Revitalisation of handicrafts; 40 m. "Man and the Biosphere" Programme in the Mediterranean region; 60 m. Gold medals won by Cypriot students in the Orleans Gymnasiade; 80 m. 60th anniv of Russian October Revolution.

194 "Nativity"

(Litho Harrison)

1977 (21 Nov). *Christmas. T* **194** *and similar horiz designs showing children's paintings. Multicoloured. P* 14 × 13½.

497 10 m. Type **194** 10 10
498 40 m. "The Three Kings" 10 10
499 150 m. "Flight into Egypt" 25 80
497/9 .. .. *Set of* 3 35 90

195 Demetrios Libertis

196 Chrysorrhogiatissa Monastery Courtyard

(Des A. Ioannides)

1978 (6 Mar). *Cypriot Poets. T* **195** *and similar horiz design. W* **58** (*sideways*). *P* 14 × 13.

500 40 m. dull brown and olive-bistre 10 10
501 150 m. grey, grey-black and light red 30 80

Design:—150 m. Vasilis Michaelides.

(Litho Harrison)

1978 (24 Apr). *Europa. Architecture. T* **196** *and similar horiz designs. Multicoloured. P* 14 × 13½.

502 25 m. Type **196** 15 10
503 75 m. Kolossi Castle 25 35
504 125 m. Municipal Library, Paphos .. .. 45 1·50
502/4 .. .. *Set of* 3 75 1·75

197 Archbishop of Cyprus, 1950–77

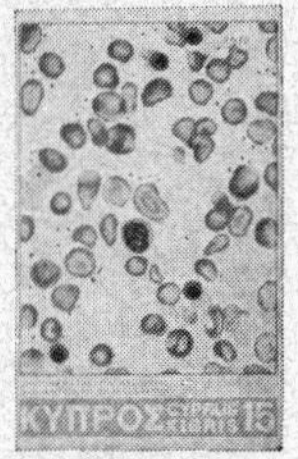

198 Affected Blood Corpuscles (Prevention of Thalassaemia)

(Des A. Ioannides (300 m.). Photo Harrison)

1978 (3 Aug). *Archbishop Makarios Commemoration. T* **197** *and similar vert designs. Multicoloured. P* 14 × 15.
505 15 m. Type **197** 15 20
a. Silver (inscr and emblem) omitted .. † —
b. Horiz strip of 5. Nos. 505/9 85
ba. Imperf (horiz strip of 5) ..
bb. Silver omitted (horiz strip of 5) ..
506 25 m. Exiled in Seychelles, 9 March 1956–28 March 1957 .. .. 15 20
507 50 m. President of the Republic, 1960–77 .. 20 25
508 75 m. "Soldier of Christ" 20 30
509 100 m. "Fighter for Freedom" 25 35
a. Silver (inscr and emblem) omitted ..
505/9 .. .. *Set of* 5 85 1·10
MS510 110 × 80 mm. 300 m. "The Great Leader". Imperf .. .. 1·40 3·00

Nos. 505/9 were printed together, *se-tenant*, in horizontal strips of 5 throughout the sheet.

Sheets of this issue are known with the silver omitted completely or only from the first or last vertical rows.

(Des A. Ioannides)

1978 (23 Oct). *Anniversaries and Events. T* **198** *and similar designs. P* 13½×14 (15, 35 *m.*) *or* 14×13½ (*others*).
511 15 m. multicoloured 10 10
512 35 m. multicoloured 15 10
513 75 m. black and grey 20 30
514 125 m. multicoloured 35 80
511/14 .. .. *Set of* 4 70 1·10

Designs and Events. *Vert*—35 m. Aristotle (sculpture) (2300th death anniversary). *Horiz*—75 m. "Heads" (Human Rights); 125 m. Wright brothers and Wright Flyer I (75th anniversary of powered flight).

199 Icon Stand

200 Aphrodite (statue from Soli)

(Litho Harrison)

1978 (4 Dec). *Christmas. T* **199** *and similar vert designs showing icon stands. P* 14 × 14½.
515 15 m. multicoloured 10 10
516 35 m. multicoloured 15 10
517 150 m. multicoloured 40 60
515/17 .. .. *Set of* 3 60 65

(Des G. Simonis. Litho Harrison)

1979 (12 Mar). *Aphrodite (Greek goddess of love and beauty) Commemoration (1st issue). T* **200** *and similar horiz design showing Aphrodite emerging from the sea at Paphos (legendary birthplace). Multicoloured. P* 14 × 13½.
518 75 m. Type **200** 25 10
519 125 m. Aphrodite on a shell (detail from "Birth of Venus" by Botticelli) .. 35 25

See also Nos. 584/5.

201 Van, Larnaca–Nicosia Mail-coach and Envelope

202 Peacock Wrasse (*thalassoma pavo*)

(Des G. Simonis)

1979 (30 Apr). *Europa. Communications. T* **201** *and similar horiz designs. Multicoloured. W* **58** (*sideways*). *P* 14 × 13.
520 25 m. Type **201** 15 10
521 75 m. Radar, satellite and early telephone .. 30 20
522 125 m. Aircraft, ship and envelopes 65 80
520/2 .. .. *Set of* 3 1·00 1·00

1979 (25 June). *Flora and Fauna. T* **202** *and similar multicoloured designs. W* **58** (*sideways on* 25 *and* 125 *m.*). *P* 13½ × 12 (25, 125 *m.*) *or* 12 × 13½ (*others*).
523 25 m. Type **202** 15 10
524 50 m. Black Partridge (*Francolinus francolinus*) (*vert*) 45 40
525 75 m. Cedar (*Cedar brevifolia*) (*vert*) .. 45 30
526 125 m. Mule (*Equus mulus*) .. .. .. 50 1·25
523/6 .. .. *Set of* 4 1·40 1·75

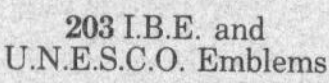

203 I.B.E. and U.N.E.S.C.O. Emblems

204 "Jesus" (from Church of the Virgin Mary of Arakas, Lagoudhera)

(Des Mrs. A. Kalathia (25 m.), A. Ioannides (others). Litho Harrison)

1979 (1 Oct). *Anniversaries and Events. T* **203** *and similar designs in black, yellow-brown and yellow-ochre* (50 *m.*) *or multicoloured* (*others*). *P* 12½.
527 15 m. Type **203** 10 10
528 25 m. Graphic design of dove and stamp album (*horiz*) 10 10
529 50 m. Lord Kitchener and map of Cyprus (*horiz*) 20 15
530 75 m. Child's face (*horiz*) 25 10
531 100 m. Graphic design of footballers (*horiz*) .. 30 20
532 125 m. Rotary International emblem and "75" 30 75
527/32 .. .. *Set of* 6 1·10 1·25

Events:—15 m. 50th anniversary of International Bureau of Education; 25 m. 20th anniversary of Cyprus Philatelic Society; 50 m. Centenary of Cyprus Survey; 75 m. International Year of the Child; 100 m. 25th anniversary of U.E.F.A. (European Football Association); 125 m. 75th anniversary of Rotary International.

1979 (5 Nov). *Christmas. Icons. T* **204** *and similar vert designs. Multicoloured. W* **58**. *P* 13 × 13½ (35 *m.*) *or* 13½ × 14 (*others*).
533 15 m. Type **204** 10 10
534 35 m. "Nativity" (from the Iconostasis of the Church of St. Nicholas, Famagusta District) (29 × 41 *mm*) 10 10
535 150 m. "Holy Mary" (from Church of the Virgin Mary of Arakas, Lagoudhera) 25 30
533/5 .. .. *Set of* 3 35 40

205 1880 ½d. Stamp with "969" (Nicosia) Postmark

206 St. Barnabas (Patron Saint of Cyprus)

1980 (17 Mar). *Cyprus Stamp Centenary. T* **205** *and similar horiz designs. Multicoloured. W* **58** (*sideways*). *P* 13½ × 13.
536 40 m. Type **205** 10 10
537 125 m. 1880 2½d. stamp with "974" (Kyrenia) postmark 15 15
538 175 m. 1880 1s. stamp with "942" (Larnaca) postmark 15 20
536/8 .. .. *Set of* 3 30 35
MS539 105 × 85 mm. 500 m. 1880 1d., ½d., 2½d., 4d., 6d. and 1s. stamps (90 × 75 *mm*). Imperf .. 70 85

(Photo Harrison)

1980 (28 Apr). *Europa. Personalities. T* **206** *and similar vert design. Multicoloured. P* 12½.
540 40 m. Type **206** 15 10
541 125 m. Zeno of Citium (founder of the Stoic philosophy) 30 20
a. Pale Venetian red omitted £100

The pale Venetian red colour on No. 541 appears as an overlay on the bust. On No. 541a the bust is pure grey.

207 Sailing

208 Gold Necklace, Arsos (7th-century BC)

(Des A. Ioannides)

1980 (23 June). *Olympic Games, Moscow. T* **207** *and similar horiz designs. Multicoloured. W* **58** (*sideways*). *P* 13½ × 13.
542 40 m. Type **207** 10 10
543 125 m. Swimming 20 20
544 200 m. Gymnastics 25 25
542/4 .. .. *Set of* 3 50 50

1980 (15 Sept). *Archaeological Treasures. Multicoloured designs as T* **208**. *W* **58** (*sideways on* 15, 40, 150 *and* 500 *m.*). *Chalk-surfaced cream paper. P* 14 × 13 (15, 40, 150 *and* 500 *m.*) *or* 13 × 14 (*others*).
545 10 m. Type **208** 30 45
546 15 m. Bronze cow, Vouni Palace (5th-century B.C.) (*horiz*) 30 45
547 25 m. Amphora, Salamis (6th-century B.C.) .. 30 10
548 40 m. Gold finger-ring, Enkomi (13th-century B.C.) (*horiz*) 40 30
549 50 m. Bronze cauldron, Salamis (8th-century B.C.) 40 10
550 75 m. Funerary stele, Marion (5th-century B.C.) 80 70
551 100 m. Jug (15–14th-century B.C.) 85 15
552 125 m. Warrior (Terracotta) (6–5th-century B.C.) 85 15
553 150 m. Lions attacking bull (bronze relief), Vouni Palace (5th-century B.C.) (*horiz*) 1·00 15
554 175 m. Faience rhyton, Kition (13th-century B.C.) .. .. 1·00 55
555 200 m. Bronze statue of Ingot God, Enkomi (12th-century B.C.) .. .. .. 1·00
556 500 m. Stone bowl, Khirokitia (6th-millennium B.C.) (*horiz*) .. .. 1·00 1·
557 £1 Ivory plaque, Salamis (7th-century B.C.) 1·25 1·
558 £2 "Leda and the Swan" (mosaic), Kouklia (3rd-century A.D.) .. .. .. 2·50 2·
545/58 .. .. *Set of* 14 10·50 6·

209 Cyprus Flag

210 Peace Dove and Head Silhouette

1980 (1 Oct). 20*th Anniv of Republic. T* **209** *and similar multi-coloured designs. P* 13½ × 13 (125 *m.*) *or* 13 × 14 (*others*).
559 40 m. Type **209** 10
560 125 m. Signing Treaty of Establishment (41 × 29 *mm*) 20
561 175 m. Archbishop Makarios 35
559/61 .. .. *Set of* 3 60

(Des A. Ioannides)

1980 (29 Nov). *International Palestinian Solidarity Day. T* **2**[illegible] *and similar horiz design showing Peace Dove and hea[d] silhouettes. W* **58** (*sideways*). *P* 13½ × 13.
562 40 m. grey and black 20 2
a. Horiz pair. Nos. 562/3 .. .. .. 55 5
563 125 m. grey and black 35 3

Nos. 562/3 were printed together, *se-tenant*, in horizontal pai[rs] throughout the sheet.

211 Pulpit, Tripiotis Church, Nicosia

212 Folk-dancing

1980 (29 Nov). *Christmas. T* **211** *and similar vert designs. Mult[i]coloured. W* **58**. *P* 13 × 14.
564 25 m. Type **211** 10
565 100 m. Holy Doors, Panayia Church, Paralimni (24 × 37 *mm*) 15
566 125 m. Pulpit, Ayios Lazaros Church, Larnaca 15
564/6 .. .. *Set of* 3 30

(Litho Harrison)

1981 (4 May). *Europa. Folklore. T* **212** *and similar vert desig[ns] showing folk-dancing from paintings by T. Photiades. P* 14.
567 40 m. multicoloured 30
568 175 m. multicoloured 60 5

213 Self-portrait

214 *Ophrys kotschyi*

1981 (15 June). 500*th Anniv of Leonardo da Vinci's Visit. T* **21**[3] *and similar multicoloured designs. W* **58** (*sideways on* 125 *m.*). *P* 12 × 14 (125 *m.*) *or* 13½ × 14 (*others*).
569 50 m. Type **213** 40 1
570 125 m. "The Last Supper" (50 × 25 *mm*) .. 70 4
571 175 m. Cyprus lace and Milan Cathedral .. 95 6
569/71 .. .. *Set of* 3 1·90 1·0

(Des A. Tassos)

1981 (6 July). *Cypriot Wild Orchids. T* **214** *and similar ve[rt] designs. Multicoloured. W* **58**. *P* 13½ × 14.
572 25 m. Type **214** 50 6
a. Block of 4. Nos. 572/5 .. .. 2·25
573 50 m. *Orchis punctulata* 60 7
574 75 m. *Ophrys argolica elegans* 70 8
575 150 m. *Epipactis veratrifolia* 75 9
572/5 .. .. *Set of* 4 2·25 2·7

Nos. 572/5 were printed together, *se-tenant*, in blocks of throughout the sheet.

215 Heinrich von Stephan

216 "The Lady of the Angels" (from Church of the Transfiguration of Christ, Palekhori)

(Des A. Tassos (200 m.), A. Ioannides (others))

81 (28 Sept). *Anniversaries and Events. T* **215** *and similar oriz designs. W* **58** *(sideways). P* 13½×13.

6 25 m. brown-olive, dp yellow-green & brt bl .. 15 10
7 40 m. multicoloured 15 10
8 125 m. black, vermilion and deep yellow-green 30 25
9 150 m. multicoloured 35 30
) 200 m. multicoloured 40 35
5/80 .. .. *Set of* 5 1·25 95

Designs and Events:—25 m. Type **215** (150th birth niversary of Henrich von Stephan (founder of U.P.U.); 40 m. ylised man holding dish of food (World Food Day); 125 m. ylised hands (International Year for Disabled Persons);) m. Stylised building and flower (European Campaign for ban Renaissance); 200 m. Prince Charles, Lady Diana encer and St. Paul's Cathedral (Royal Wedding).

81 (16 Nov). *Christmas. Murals from Nicosia District Churches. T* **216** *and similar multicoloured designs. W* **58** *(side-ways on 25 and 125 m.). P* 12½.

1 25 m. Type **216** 20 10
2 100 m. "Christ Pantokrator" (from Church of Madonna of Arakas, Lagoudera) (*vert*) 60 20
3 125 m. "Baptism of Christ" (from Church of Our Lady of Assinou, Nikitari) .. 70 30
1/3 .. .. *Set of* 3 1·25 50

217 "Louomene" (statue of Aphrodite bathing, 250 B.C.)

218 Naval Battle with Greek Fire, 985 A.D.

982 (12 Apr). *Aphrodite (Greek goddess of love and beauty) Commemoration (2nd issue). T* **217** *and similar vert design. Multicoloured. W* **58**. *P* 13½×14.

34 125 m. Type **217** 80 45
35 175 m. "Anadyomene" (Aphrodite emerging from the waters) (Titian) 95 65

(Des G. Simonis. Photo Harrison)

982 (3 May). *Europa. Historical Events. T* **218** *and similar horiz design. Multicoloured. P* 12½.

36 40 m. Type **218** 60 10
37 175 m. Conversion of Roman Proconsul Sergius Paulus to Christianity, Paphos, 45 A.D. 1·00 2·50

219 Monogram of Christ (mosaic)

100 =

(220)

982 (5 July). *World Cultural Heritage. T* **219** *and similar multi-coloured designs. W* **58** *(sideways on 50 and 225 m.). P* 13½ × 14 *(125 m.) or* 12½ *(others).*

88 50 m. Type **219** 25 10
89 125 m. Head of priest-king of Paphos (sculp-ture) (24 × 37 *mm*) 50 25
90 225 m. Theseus (Greek god) (mosaic) .. 75 95
88/90 .. .. *Set of* 3 1·40 1·10

982 (6 Sept). *No. 550 surch with T* **220** *by Govt Ptg Office, Nicosia.*

91 100 m. on 75 m. Funerary stele, Marion (5th-century B.C.) 50 50

221 Cyprus and Stylised "75"

222 Holy Communion—The Bread

1982 (8 Nov). *75th Anniv of Boy Scout Movement. T* **221** *and similar multicoloured designs. W* **58** *(sideways on 100 m. and 175 m.). P* 12½ × 13½ *(125 m.) or* 13½ × 12½ *(others).*

592 100 m. Type **221** 40 20
593 125 m. Lord Baden-Powell (*vert*) 45 30
594 175 m. Camp-site 55 55
592/4 .. .. *Set of* 3 1·25 95

1982 (6 Dec). *Christmas. T* **222** *and similar designs. W* **58** *(sideways on 25 and 250 m.). P* 12½ × 12 *(25 and 250 m.) or* 13½ × 14 *(100 m.).*

595 25 m. multicoloured 10 10
596 100 m. gold and black 30 15
597 250 m. multicoloured .. .. 70 1·00
595/7 .. .. *Set of* 3 1·00 1·10

Designs: *Vert*—100 m. Holy Chalice. *Horiz*—250 m. Holy Communion—The Wine.

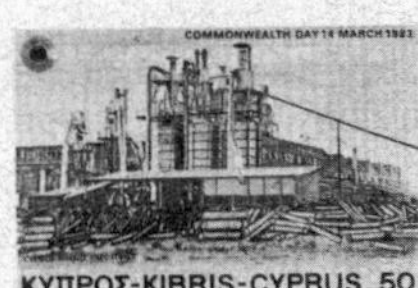

223 Cyprus Forest Industries' Sawmill

1983 (14 Mar). *Commonwealth Day. T* **223** *and similar horiz designs. Multicoloured. W* **58** *(sideways). P* 14 × 13½.

598 50 m. Type **223** 10 10
599 125 m. "Ikarios and the Discovery of Wine" (3rd-cent mosaic) 20 25
600 150 m. Folk-dancers, Commonwealth Film and Television Festival, 1980 .. .. 25 35
601 175 m. Royal Exhibition Building, Melbourne (Commonwealth Heads of Government Meeting, 1981) 25 40
598/601 .. .. *Set of* 4 70 1·00

224 Cyprosyllabic Inscription (6th-cent B.C.)

225 *Pararge aegeria*

(Des G. Simonis. Photo Harrison)

1983 (3 May). *Europa. T* **224** *and similar horiz design. Multi-coloured. P* 14½ × 14.

602 50 m. Type **224** 40 10
603 200 m. Copper ore, ingot (Enkomi 1400-1250 B.C.) and bronze jug (2nd-cent A.D.) .. 1·10 2·40

1983 (28 June). *Butterflies. T* **225** *and similar horiz designs. Multicoloured. W w* **58**. *P* 12½.

604 60 m. Type **225** 25 20
605 130 m. *Aricia agestis* 45 25
606 250 m. *Glaucopsyche melanops* .. .. 85 2·00
604/6 .. .. *Set of* 3 1·40 2·25

(New Currency: 100 cents = £1 (Cyprus))

1c =

(226)

227 View of Power Station

1983 (3 Oct). *Nos. 545/56 surch as T* **226** *by Govt Printing Office, Nicosia.*

607 1 c. on 10 m. Type **208** 35 40
608 2 c. on 15 m. Bronze cow, Vouni Palace (5th-century B.C.) 35 40
609 3 c. on 25 m. Amphora, Salamis (6th-century B.C.) 35 20
610 4 c. on 40 m. Gold finger-ring, Enkomi (13th-century B.C.) 40 20
611 5 c. on 50 m. Bronze cauldron, Salamis (8th-century B.C.) 50 50
612 6 c. on 75 m. Funerary stele, Marion (5th-century B.C.) 50 20
613 10 c. on 100 m. Jug (15–14th-century B.C.) .. 50 40
614 13 c. on 125 m. Warrior (Terracotta) (6–5th-century B.C.) 60 50
615 15 c. on 150 m. Lions attacking bull (bronze relief), Vouni Palace (5th-century B.C.) 70 55
616 20 c. on 200 m. Bronze statue of Ingot God, Enkomi (12th-century B.C.) 70 65
617 25 c. on 175 m. Faience rhyton, Kition (13th-century B.C.) .. .. 80 1·10
618 50 c. on 500 m. Stone bowl, Khirokitia (6th-millennium B.C.) .. .. 1·00 2·00
607/18 .. .. *Set of* 12 6·00 6·50

1983 (27 Oct). *Anniversaries and Events. T* **227** *and similar vert designs. Multicoloured. W* **58**. *P* 13 × 14.

619 3 c. Type **227** 10 20
620 6 c. W.C.Y. logo 20 15
621 13 c. *Sol Olympia* (liner) and *Polys* (tanker) 40 35
622 15 c. Human Rights emblem and map of Europe 40 25
623 20 c. Nicos Kazantzakis (poet) 45 75
624 25 c. Archbishop Makarios in church 50 75
619/24 .. .. *Set of* 6 1·75 2·25

Events:—3 c. 30th anniv of the Cyprus Electricity Authority; 6 c. World Communications Year; 13 c. 25th anniv of International Maritime Organization; 15 c. 35th anniv of Universal Declaration of Human Rights; 20 c. Birth centenary; 25 c. 70th birth anniv.

228 St. Lazaros Church, Larnaca

229 Waterside Cafe, Larnaca

1983 (12 Dec). *Christmas. Church Towers. T* **228** *and similar vert designs. Multicoloured. W* **58**. *P* 12×13½.

625 4 c. Type **228** 15 10
626 13 c. St. Varvara Church, Kaimakli, Nicosia 40 35
627 20 c. St. Ioannis Church, Larnaca .. .. 70 1·50
625/7 .. .. *Set of* 3 1·10 1·75

(Litho Harrison)

1984 (6 Mar). *Old Engravings. T* **229** *and similar horiz designs. Each pale stone and black. P* 14½ × 14 *(6 c.) or* 14 *(others).*

628 6 c. Type **229** 15 10
629 20 c. Bazaar at Larnaca (30 × 25 *mm*) .. 40 85
630 30 c. Famagusta Gate, Nicosia (30 × 25 *mm*) 65 1·50
628/30 .. .. *Set of* 3 1·10 2·25
MS631 110 × 85 mm. 75 c. "The Confession" (St. Lazarus Church, Larnaca) .. .. .. 1·60 2·00

230 C.E.P.T. 25th Anniversary Logo

(Des J. Larrivière. Litho Harrison)

1984 (30 Apr). *Europa. W* **58**. *P* 12½.

632 **230** 6 c. apple-green, deep bl-green & blk .. 50 10
633 15 c. light blue, dull ultram & blk .. 1·10 2·50

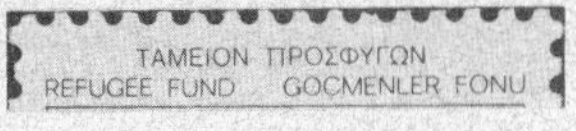

A. Waddington ptgs (Nos. 634/*a*)

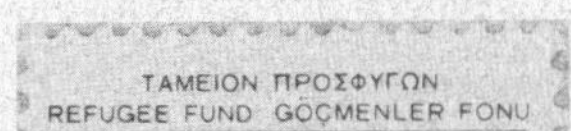

B. Aspioti-Elka ptg (No. 634*b*)

(Des A. Tassos)

1984 (18 June)–**87**. *Obligatory Tax. Refugee Fund. Design as T* **188** *but new value and* "1984" *date. P* 13×12½.

(*a*) *Litho J.W. W* **58**. *Chalk-surfaced cream paper*

634 1 c. grey-black (A) 10 10
a. Wmk sideways. Ordinary paper (21.2.87)* 70 70

(*b*) *Litho Aspioti-Elka. W* **58**. *Chalk-surfaced cream paper*

634*b* 1 c. grey-black (B) (3.11.87)* 65 65

*Earliest known date of use.

In addition to the redrawn inscriptions there are other minor differences between the work of the two printers.

For a further version of this design, showing "1974" at top right, see Nos. 729, 747 and 807.

231 Running

(Des. K. Haine. Litho Harrison)

1984 (18 June). *Olympic Games. Los Angeles. T* **231** *and similar horiz designs. Multicoloured. W* **58** *(sideways). P* 14.

635 3 c. Type **231** 20 10
636 4 c. Olympic column 20 20
637 13 c. Swimming 55 75
638 20 c. Gymnastics .. .. 80 1·50
635/8 .. .. *Set of* 4 1·60 2·25

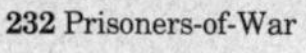

232 Prisoners-of-War

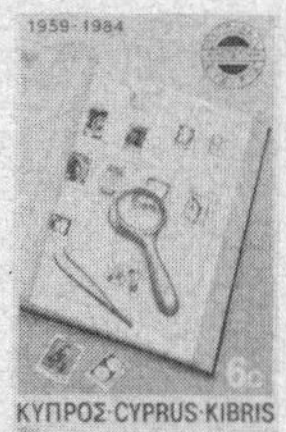

233 Open Stamp Album (25th Anniv of Cyprus Philatelic Society)

1984 (20 July). *10th Anniv of Turkish Landings in Cyprus. T* **232** *and similar horiz design. Multicoloured. P* 14 × 13½.

639 15 c. Type **232** 40 45
640 20 c. Map and burning buildings 50 55

(Des P. St. Antoniades (6 c.), A. Ioannides (10 c.), Harrison (others). Litho Harrison)

1984 (15 Oct). *Anniversaries and Events. T* **233** *and similar multicoloured designs.* **W 58** *(sideways on horiz designs). P* 12½.

641 6 c. Type **233** 30 20
642 10 c. Football in motion (*horiz*) (50th anniv of Cyprus Football Association) 45 30
643 15 c. "Dr. George Papanicolaou" (medical scientist – birth cent) 60 50
644 25 c. Antique map of Cyprus and ikon (*horiz*) (International Symposia on Cartography and Medieval Paleography) .. .. 1·00 2·00
641/4 .. .. *Set of* 4 2·10 2·75

234 St. Mark (miniature from 11th-century Gospel)

235 Autumn at Platania, Troodos Mountains

(Des and litho Harrison)

1984 (26 Nov). *Christmas. Illuminated Gospels. T* **234** *and similar vert designs. Multicoloured.* **W 58**. *P* 12½.

645 4 c. Type **234** 30 10
646 13 c. Beginning of St. Mark's Gospel 75 50
647 20 c. St. Luke (miniature from 11th-century Gospel) .. .. 1·25 2·00
645/7 .. .. *Set of* 3 2·10 2·40

(Des and litho Harrison)

1985 (18 Mar.) *Cyprus Scenes and Landscapes. T* **235** *and similar multicoloured designs. Ordinary white paper. P* 14 × 15 *(6 c., 20 c., 25 c., £1, £5) or* 15 × 14 *(others).*

648 1 c. Type **235** 20 40
649 2 c. Ayia Napa Monastery 20 40
650 3 c. Phini Village—panoramic view .. 20 30
651 4 c. Kykko Monastery 20 20
652 5 c. Beach at Makronissos, Ayia Napa .. 20 20
653 6 c. Village street, Omodhos (*vert*) .. 30 20
654 10 c. Panoramic sea view 40 35
655 13 c. Windsurfing 55 25
656 15 c. Beach at Protaras 65 25
657 20 c. Forestry for development (*vert*) .. 80 50
658 25 c. Sunrise at Protaras (*vert*) .. .. 1·00 1·00
659 30 c. Village house, Pera .. .. .. 1·25 1·25
660 50 c. Apollo Hylates Sanctuary, Curium .. 2·00 1·75
661 £1 Snow on Troodos Mountains (*vert*) .. 3·50 3·00
662 £5 Personification of Autumn, House of Dionyssos, Paphos (*vert*) .. .. 13·00 15·00
648/62 .. .. *Set of* 15 22·00 23·00

236 Clay Idols of Musicians (7/6th Century B.C.)

237 Cyprus Coat of Arms (25th Anniv of Republic)

(Des and litho Harrison)

1985 (6 May). *Europa. European Music Year. T* **236** *and similar horiz design. Multicoloured.* **W 58** *(sideways). P* 12½.

663 6 c. Type **236** 85 35
664 15 c. Violin, lute, flute and score from the "Cyprus Suite" .. .. 1·40 2·00

(Des G. Simonis (4 c., 13 c.), Harrison (others). Litho Harrison)

1985 (23 Sept). *Anniversaries and Events. T* **237** *and similar designs. P* 14½ *(4, 20 c.) or* 14 × 13½ *(others).*

665 4 c. multicoloured 30 15
666 6 c. multicoloured 35 15
667 13 c. multicoloured .. .. 75 1·25
668 15 c. black, olive-black and yellow-orange .. 1·25 1·25
669 20 c. multicoloured .. .. 80 2·00
665/9 .. .. *Set of* 5 3·00 4·25

Designs and Events: *Horiz* (43×30 *mm*)—6 c. "Barn of Liopetri" (detail) (Pol. Georghiou) (30th anniv of EOKA Campaign); 13 c. Three profiles (International Youth Year); 15 c. Solon Michaelides (composer and conductor) (European Music Year). *Vert* (*as T* **237**)—20 c. U.N. Building, New York, and flags (40th anniv of United Nations Organization).

238 "The Visit of the Madonna to Elizabeth" (Lambadistis Monastery, Kalopanayiotis)

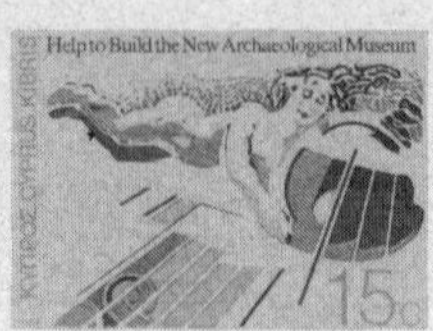

239 Figure from Hellenistic Spoon Handle

(Des and litho Harrison)

1985 (18 Nov). *Christmas. Frescoes from Cypriot Churches. T* **238** *and similar vert designs. Multicoloured. P* 12½.

670 4 c. Type **238** 30 10
671 13 c. "The Nativity" (Lambadistis Monastery, Kalopanayiotis) 80 65
672 20 c. "Candlemas-day" (Asinou Church) .. 1·25 2·00
670/2 .. .. *Set of* 3 2·10 2·50

(Des A. Ioannides. Litho Harrison)

1986 (17 Feb). *New Archaeological Museum Fund. T* **239** *and similar horiz designs. Multicoloured. P* 15 × 14.

673 15 c. Type **239** 70 45
674 20 c. Pattern from early Ionian helmet and foot from statue 80 75
675 25 c. Roman statue of Eros and Psyche .. 1·00 95
676 30 c. Head of statue .. .. 1·25 1·10
673/6 .. .. *Set of* 4 3·25 3·00
MS677 111 × 90 mm. Nos. 673/6 (*sold at* £1) .. 12·00 16·00

Two-thirds of the amount received from sales of Nos. 673/7 was devoted to the construction of a new Archaeological Museum, Nicosia.

No. 676 also commemorates the 50th anniversary of the Department of Antiquities.

240 Cyprus Moufflon and Cedars

(Des G. Simonis)

1986 (28 Apr). *Europa. Protection of Nature and the Environment. T* **240** *and similar horiz design. Multicoloured.* **W 58** *(sideways). P* 14 × 13.

678 7 c. Type **240** 50 30
679 17 c. Greater Flamingos at Larnaca Salt Lake .. .. 1·75 2·50

241 Cat's-paw Scallop (*Manupecten pesfelis*)

=
7c

(242)

(Des T. Katsoulides)

1986 (1 July). *Sea Shells. T* **241** *and similar horiz designs. Multicoloured.* **W 58** *(sideways). P* 14 × 13½.

680 5 c. Type **241** 40 15
681 7 c. Atlantic Trumpet Triton (*Charonia variegata*) 45 15
682 18 c. Purple Dye Murex (*Murex brandaris*) 1·00 70
683 25 c. Yellow Cowrie (*Cypraea spurca*) .. 1·50 2·00
680/3 .. .. *Set of* 4 3·00 2·75

1986 (13 Oct). *Nos.* 653 *and* 655 *surch as T* **242**.

684 7 c. on 6 c. Village street, Omodhos (*vert*) .. 40 30
685 18 c. on 13 c. Windsurfing .. .. .. 1·10 60

For 15 c. on 4 c. see No. 730.

243 Globe, Outline Map of Cyprus and Barn Swallows (Overseas Cypriots' Year)

(Des T. Katsoulides)

1986 (13 Oct). *Anniversaries and Events. T* **243** *and simil horiz designs. Multicoloured.* **W 58** *(sideways). P* 13½ × 13.

686 15 c. Type **243** .. .. 1·00
687 18 c. Halley's Comet over Cyprus beach (40 × 23 *mm*) .. .. 1·25 2·
a. Horiz pair. Nos. 687/8 .. .. .. 2·50 4·
688 18 c. Comet's tail over sea and Edmond Halley (40 × 23 *mm*) .. .. .. 1·25 2·
686/8 .. .. *Set of* 3 3·25 4·

Nos. 687/8 were printed together, *se-tenant*, in horizont pairs throughout the sheet, each pair forming a compos design.

244 Pedestrian Crossing

245 "The Nativity" (Church of Panayia tou Araka)

(Des A. Ioannides)

1986 (10 Nov). *Road Safety Campaign. T* **244** *and similar ho designs. Multicoloured.* **W 58** *(sideways). P* 14 × 13.

689 5 c. Type **244** .. .. 1·00
690 7 c. Motor cycle crash helmet .. .. 1·10
691 18 c. Hands fastening car seat belt .. .. 2·25 3·
689/91 .. .. *Set of* 3 4·00 3·

(Des G. Simonis)

1986 (24 Nov). *Christmas. International Peace Year. T* **245** *ar similar vert designs showing details of Nativity frescoes fro Cypriot churches. Multicoloured.* **W 58** *(inverted). P* 13½ × 1

692 5 c. Type **245** 40
693 15 c. Church of Panayia tou Moutoulla .. 1·00
694 17 c. Church of St. Nicholas tis Steyis .. 1·25 2·
692/4 .. .. *Set of* 3 2·40 2·

246 Church of Virgin Mary, Asinou

(Des and photo Harrison)

1987 (22 Apr). *Troodos Churches on the World Heritage Lis T* **246** *and similar horiz designs. Multicoloured. P* 12½.

695 15 c. Type **246** .. .. 1·00 1·
a. Sheetlet. Nos. 695/703 .. .. .. 8·00
696 15 c. Fresco of Virgin Mary, Moutoulla's Church .. .. 1·00 1·
697 15 c. Church of Virgin Mary, Podithou .. 1·00 1·
698 15 c. Fresco of Three Apostles, St. Ioannis Lampadistis Monastery .. .. 1·00 1·
699 15 c. Annunciation fresco, Church of the Holy Cross, Pelentriou .. .. .. 1·00 1·
700 15 c. Fresco of Saints, Church of the Cross, Ayiasmati .. .. 1·00 1·
701 15 c. Fresco of Archangel Michael and Donor, Pedoula's Church of St. Michael 1·00 1·
702 15 c. Church of St. Nicolaos, Steyis .. .. 1·00 1·
703 15 c. Fresco of Prophets, Church of Virgin Mary, Araka .. .. 1·00 1·
695/703 .. .. *Set of* 9 8·00 9·

Nos. 695/703 were printed together, *se-tenant*, in sheetlets nine.

247 Proposed Central Bank of Cyprus Building

(Des G. Simonis)

1987 (11 May). *Europa. Modern Architecture. T* **247** *ar similar horiz design.* **W 58** *(sideways). P* 14 × 13½.

704 7 c. multicoloured 50
705 18 c. black, brownish grey and sage-green .. 1·10 2·

Design:—18 c. Headquarters complex, Cyprus Telecommun cations Authority.

248 Remains of Ancient Ship and Kyrenia Castle

(Des Y. Pantsopoulos)

987 (3 Oct). *Voyage of "Kyrenia II" (replica of ancient ship). T* **248** *and similar horiz designs. Multicoloured. W* **58** *(sideways). P* 14×13½.

06 2 c. Type **248**.. .. .. 30 20
07 3 c. *Kyrenia II* under construction, 1982–5 30 90
08 5 c. *Kyrenia II* at Paphos, 1986 .. .. 55 20
09 17 c. *Kyrenia II* at New York, 1986 .. .. 1·40 90
06/9 .. .. *Set of* 4 2·25 2·00

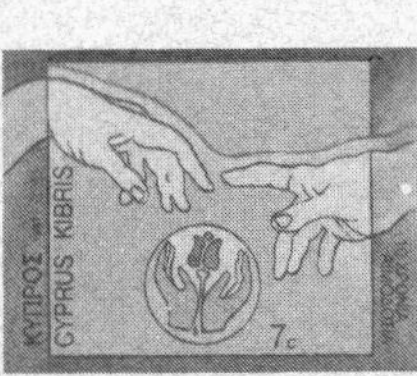

249 Hands (from Michelangelo's *Creation*) and Emblem (10th anniv of Blood Donation Co-ordinating Committee)

250 Nativity Crib

(Des A. Ioannides)

1987 (2 Nov). *Anniversaries and Events. T* **249** *and similar horiz designs. Multicoloured. W* **58** *(sideways). P* 14×13½.

710 7 c. Type **249**.. .. .. 50 25
711 15 c. Snail with flowered shell and countryside (European Countryside Campaign) 1·10 40
712 20 c. Symbols of ocean bed and Earth's crust ("Troodos '87" Ophiolites and Oceanic Lithosphere Symposium) .. .. 1·40 3·00
710/12 .. .. *Set of* 3 2·75 3·25

(Des A. Ioannides)

1987 (30 Nov). *Christmas. Traditional Customs. T* **250** *and similar square designs. Multicoloured. W* **58** *(sideways). P* 14.

713 5 c. Type **250**.. .. .. 35 15
714 15 c. Door knocker decorated with foliage .. 1·10 35
715 17 c. Bowl of fruit and nuts .. .. .. 1·25 2·00
713/15 .. .. *Set of* 3 2·40 2·25

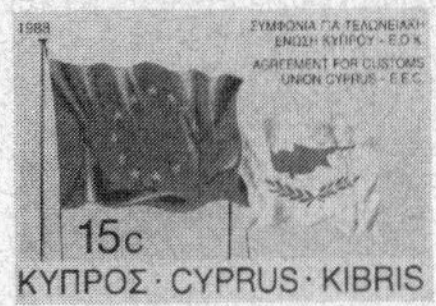

251 Flags of Cyprus and E.E.C.

(Des G. Simonis. Litho Alexandros Matsoukis, Athens)

1988 (11 Jan). *Cypriot–E.E.C. Customs Union. T* **251** *and similar horiz design. Multicoloured. W* **58**. *P* 13×13½.

716 15 c. Type **251** .. .. 80 1·50
717 18 c. Outline maps of Cyprus and E.E.C. countries 80 80

252 Intelpost Telefax Terminal

(Des A. Ioannides. Litho Alexandros Matsoukis, Athens)

1988 (9 May). *Europa. Transport and Communications. T* **252** *and similar horiz designs. Multicoloured. W* **58**. *P* 14×14½.

718 7 c. Type **252** 65 75
a. Horiz pair. Nos. 718/19 .. .. .. 1·25 1·50
719 7 c. Car driver using mobile telephone .. 65 75
720 18 c. Nose of Cyprus Airways airliner and Greater Flamingos .. .. 1·75 2·25
a. Horiz pair. Nos. 720/1 .. .. .. 3·50 4·50
721 18 c. Boeing 737 airliner in flight and Greater Flamingos .. .. 1·75 2·25
718/21 .. .. *Set of* 4 4·25 5·50

The two designs of each value were printed together, *se-tenant*, in horizontal pairs throughout the sheet of ten.

253 Sailing

254 Conference Emblem

(Des A. Ioannides. Photo Courvoisier)

1988 (27 June). *Olympic Games, Seoul. T* **253** *and similar vert designs. Multicoloured. Granite paper. P* 12.

722 5 c. Type **253** 30 20
723 7 c. Athletes at start 35 40
724 10 c. Shooting 40 70
725 20 c. Judo .. .. 90 1·50
722/5 .. .. *Set of* 4 1·75 2·50

(Des A. Ioannides. Litho M. A. Moatsos, Athens)

1988 (5 Sept). *Non-Aligned Foreign Ministers' Conference, Nicosia. T* **254** *and similar horiz designs. W* **58** *(sideways). P* 14×13½.

726 1 c. black, pale blue and emerald 10 10
727 10 c. multicoloured 45 70
728 50 c. multicoloured .. .. 2·25 2·50
726/8 .. .. *Set of* 3 2·50 3·00

Designs:— 10 c. Emblem of Republic of Cyprus; 50 c. Nehru, Tito, Nasser and Makarios.

255 "Cyprus 74" (wood-engraving by A. Tassos)

256 "Presentation of Christ at the Temple" (Church of Holy Cross tou Agiasmati)

(Des A. Tassos. Litho M. A. Moatsos, Athens)

1988 (12 Sept). *Obligatory Tax. Refugee Fund. Design as Nos. 634/b, but with upper and lower inscriptions redrawn and "1974" added as in T* **255**. *W* **58**. *Chalk-surfaced paper. P* 13×12½.

729 **255** 1 c. brownish black and brownish grey .. 20 20

For this design printed in photogravure and perforated 11½ see No. 747, in lithography perforated 13 see No. 807 and in lithography perforated 14½×13½ see No. 892.

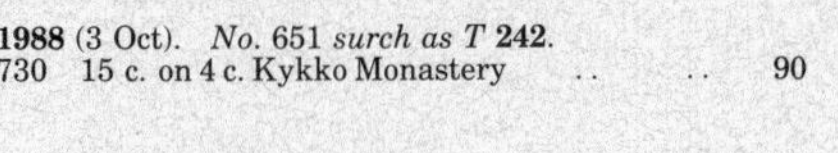

1988 (3 Oct). *No. 651 surch as T* **242**.

730 15 c. on 4 c. Kykko Monastery 90 70

(Des G. Simonis. Litho M. A. Moatsos, Athens)

1988 (28 Nov). *Christmas. T* **256** *and similar vert designs showing frescoes from Cypriot churches. Multicoloured. W* **58**. *P* 13½ × 14.

731 5 c. Type **256** 30 20
732 15 c. "Virgin and Child" (St. John Lampadistis Monastery) 70 25
733 17 c. "Adoration of the Magi" (St. John Lampadistis Monastery) .. .. 1·00 1·75
731/3 .. .. *Set of* 3 1·75 2·00

257 Human Rights Logo

258 Basketball

(Des G. Simonis. Litho M. A. Moatsos, Athens)

1988 (10 Dec). *40th Anniv of Universal Declaration of Human Rights. W* **58** *(inverted). P* 13½ × 14.

734 **257** 25 c. azure, dull violet-blue and cobalt .. 90 1·25

(Des A. Ioannides. Litho Alexandros Matsoukis, Athens)

1989 (10 Apr). *Third Small European States' Games, Nicosia. T* **258** *and similar horiz designs. Multicoloured. P* 13½.

735 1 c. Type **258** 10 15
736 5 c. Javelin 20 15
737 15 c. Wrestling 45 20
738 18 c. Athletics .. .. 60 1·00
735/8 .. .. *Set of* 4 1·25 1·40
MS739 109×80 mm. £1 Angel and laurel wreath (99×73 *mm*). Imperf .. .. 4·50 6·00

259 Lingri Stick Game

(Des S. Michael. Litho Alexandros Matsoukis, Athens)

1989 (8 May). *Europa. Children's Games. T* **259** *and similar horiz designs. Multicoloured. P* 13×13½.

740 7 c. Type **259** 65 75
a. Horiz pair. Nos. 740/1 .. .. .. 1·25 1·50
741 7 c. Ziziros 65 75
742 18 c. Sitsia .. .. 80 1·00
a. Horiz pair. Nos. 742/3 .. .. .. 1·60 2·00
743 18 c. Leapfrog .. .. 80 1·00
740/3 .. .. *Set of* 4 2·50 3·25

Nos. 740/1 and 742/3 were each printed together, *se-tenant*, in horizontal pairs throughout the sheets.

MACHINE LABELS. From 29 May 1989 gummed labels in the above design, ranging in value from 1 c. to £99.99, were available from machines at Eleftheria Square P.O., Nicosia ("001") and District P.O., Limassol ("002").

260 "Universal Man"

261 Stylized Human Figures

(Des A. Ioannides. Photo Courvoisier)

1989 (7 July). *Bicentenary of the French Revolution. Granite paper. P* 11½.

744 **260** 18 c. multicoloured 60 60

(Des A. Ioannides. Litho Alexandros Matsoukis, Athens)

1989 (4 Sept). *Centenary of Interparliamentary Union (15 c.) and 9th Non-Aligned Summit Conference, Belgrade (30 c.). T* **261** *and similar vert design. Multicoloured. P* 13½.

745 15 c. Type **261** 50 40
746 30 c. Conference logo .. .. 1·00 1·10

(Photo Courvoisier)

1989 (4 Sept). *Obligatory Tax. Refugee Fund. As T* **255**, *but inscr "1989" or "1990". Granite paper. P* 11½.

747 **255** 1 c. brownish black and brownish grey .. 45 30

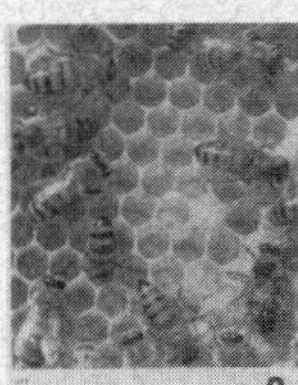

262 Worker Bees tending Larvae

263 Outstretched Hand and Profile (aid for Armenian earthquake victims)

(Litho Alexandros Matsoukis, Athens)

1989 (16 Oct). *Bee-keeping. T* **262** *and similar vert designs. Multicoloured. P* 13½.

748 3 c. Type **262** 15 20
749 10 c. Bee on Rock-rose flower 40 50
750 15 c. Bee on Lemon flower 60 50
751 18 c. Queen and worker bees 65 90
748/51 .. .. *Set of* 4 1·60 1·90

(Des A. Ioannides. Litho Alexandros Matsoukis, Athens)

1989 (13 Nov). *Anniversaries and Events. T* **263** *and similar vert designs. Multicoloured. P* 13½.

752 3 c. Type **263** 15 40
753 5 c. Airmail envelope (Cyprus Philatelic Society F.I.P. membership) 25 10
754 7 c. Crab symbol and daisy (European Cancer Year) 45 90
755 17 c. Vegetables and fish (World Food Day) 75 90
752/5 .. .. *Set of* 4 1·40 2·00

264 Winter (detail from "Four Seasons")

265 Hands and Open Book (International Literacy Year)

(Litho Alexandros Matsoukis, Athens)

1989 (29 Dec). *Roman Mosaics from Paphos. T* **264** *and similar multicoloured designs showing details. P* 13 (1, 5, 7, 15 *c.*), 13×13½ (2, 4, 18, 40 *c.*), 13½×13 (3, 10, 20, 25 *c.*) *or* 14 (50 *c.*, £1, £3).
756 1 c. Type **264** 10 10
757 2 c. Personification of Crete (32×24 *mm*) 10 10
758 3 c. Centaur and Maenad (24×32 *mm*) 10 10
759 4 c. Poseidon and Amymone (32×24 *mm*) 15 15
760 5 c. Leda 20 20
761 7 c. Apollon 25 25
762 10 c. Hermes and Dionysos (24×32 *mm*) 30 30
763 15 c. Cassiopeia 50 45
764 18 c. Orpheus (32×24 *mm*) 55 50
765 20 c. Nymphs (24×32 *mm*) 65 60
766 25 c. Amazon (24×32 *mm*) 75 70
767 40 c. Doris (32×24 *mm*) . . . . 1·40 1·25
768 50 c. Heracles and the Lion (39×27 *mm*) 1·60 1·50
769 £1 Apollon and Daphne (39×27 *mm*) . . 3·00 3·00
770 £3 Cupid (39×27 *mm*) . . . . 8·00 8·25
756/70 . . . . *Set of* 15 17·00 17·00

(Des A. Ioannides. Litho Alexandros Matsoukis, Athens)

1990 (3 Apr). *Anniversaries and Events. T* **265** *and similar horiz designs. Multicoloured. P* 13½.
771 15 c. Type **265** 55 50
772 17 c. Dove and profiles (83rd Inter-Parliamentary Conference, Nicosia) . . 65 90
773 18 c. Lions International emblem (Lions Europa Forum, Limassol) 75 90
771/3 . . . . *Set of* 3 1·75 2·10

266 District Post Office, Paphos

(Des A. Ioannides. Litho Alexandros Matsoukis, Athens)

1990 (10 May). *Europa. Post Office Buildings. T* **266** *and similar horiz design. Multicoloured. P* 13×13½.
774 7 c. Type **266** 80 25
775 18 c. City Centre Post Office, Limassol . . 1·10 1·50

267 Symbolic Lips (25th anniv of Hotel and Catering Institute)

(Des A. Ioannides. Litho Alexandros Matsoukis, Athens)

1990 (9 July). *European Tourism Year. T* **267** *and similar horiz designs. Multicoloured. P* 14.
776 5 c. Type **267** 25 20
777 7 c. Bell tower, St. Lazarus Church (1100th anniv) 30 25
778 15 c. Butterflies and woman . . . . 1·25 40
779 18 c. Birds and man . . . . . . 1·50 3·00
776/9 . . . . *Set of* 4 3·00 3·50

268 Sun (wood carving)

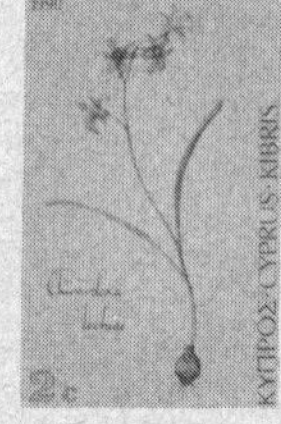

269 *Chionodoxa lochiae*

(Des A. Ioannides. Photo Courvoisier)

1990 (29 Sept). *30th Anniv of Republic. T* **268** *and similar square designs. Multicoloured. Granite paper. P* 11½.
780 15 c. Type **268** 55 45
781 17 c. Bulls (pottery design) 65 60
782 18 c. Fishes (pottery design) 75 70
783 40 c. Tree and birds (wood carving) . . 1·40 2·75
780/3 . . . . *Set of* 4 3·00 4·00
MS784 89×89 mm. £1 30th Anniversary emblem. Imperf . . . . 3·75 5·50

(Litho Alexandros Matsoukis, Athens)

1990 (5 Nov). *Endangered Wild Flowers. T* **269** *and similar vert designs taken from book illustrations by Elektra Megaw. Multicoloured. P* 13½×13.
785 2 c. Type **269** 30 60
786 3 c. *Pancratium maritimum* 30 60
787 5 c. *Paeonia mascula* 45 20
788 7 c. *Cyclamen cyprium* 50 25
789 15 c. *Tulipa cypria* 85 30
790 18 c. *Crocus cyprius* . . . . . . 1·10 2·50
785/90 . . . . *Set of* 6 3·25 4·00

270 "Nativity"

271 Archangel

(Litho Alexandros Matsoukis, Athens)

1990 (3 Dec). *Christmas. 16th-Century Icons. T* **270** *and similar vert designs. Multicoloured. P* 13½.
791 5 c. Type **270** 25 20
792 15 c. "Virgin Hodegetria" 65 30
793 17 c. "Nativity" (*different*) . . . . 90 2·25
791/3 . . . . *Set of* 3 1·60 2·50

(Des A. Ioannides. Photo Courvoisier)

1991 (28 Mar). *6th-century Mosaics from Kanakaria Church. T* **271** *and similar vert designs. Multicoloured. Granite paper. P* 12.
794 5 c. Type **271** 20 15
795 15 c. Christ Child 75 20
796 17 c. St. James . . . . 1·00 1·25
797 18 c. St. Matthew . . . . 1·00 1·75
794/7 . . . . *Set of* 4 2·75 3·00

272 *Ulysses* Spacecraft

273 Young Pied Wheatear

(Des G. Simonis. Litho Alexandros Matsoukis, Athens)

1991 (6 May). *Europa. Europe in Space. T* **272** *and similar horiz design. Multicoloured. P* 13×13½.
798 7 c. Type **272** 60 20
799 18 c. *Giotto* and Halley's Comet . . . . 1·25 2·00

(Des A. Ioannides. Litho Alexandros Matsoukis, Athens)

1991 (4 July). *Pied ("Cyprus") Wheatear. T* **273** *and similar horiz designs. Multicoloured. P* 13½.
800 5 c. Type **273** 35 30
801 7 c. Adult bird in autumn plumage . . 40 30
802 15 c. Adult male in breeding plumage . . 70 45
803 30 c. Adult female in breeding plumage . . 1·25 2·25
800/3 . . . . *Set of* 4 2·40 3·00

274 Mother and Child with Tents

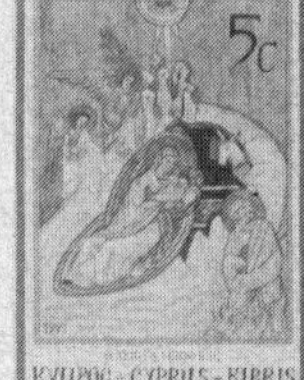

275 The Nativity

(Des A. Ioannides. Litho Alexandros Matsoukis, Athens)

1991 (7 Oct). *40th Anniv of U.N. Commission for Refugees. T* **274** *and similar horiz designs, each brown, orange-brown and silver. P* 13½.
804 5 c. Type **274** 25 15
805 15 c. Three pairs of legs 90 65
806 18 c. Three children . . . . 1·10 2·00
804/6 . . . . *Set of* 3 2·00 2·50

(Litho Alexandros Matsoukis, Athens)

1991 (7 Oct). *Obligatory Tax. Refugee Fund. As T* **255**, *but inscr* "1991", "1992", "1993" *or* "1994". *Chalk-surfaced paper. P* 13.
807 **255** 1 c. brownish black and olive-grey . . 15 15

(Des Revd. D. Demosthenous. Litho Alexandros Matsoukis, Athens)

1991 (25 Nov). *Christmas. T* **275** *and similar vert designs. Multicoloured. P* 13½.
808 5 c. Type **275** 20 15
a. Sheetlet of 9. Nos. 808/10×3 . . 3·75
809 15 c. Saint Basil 50 40
810 17 c. Baptism of Jesus . . . . . . 80 1·50
808/10 . . . . *Set of* 3 1·40 1·90
Nos. 808/10 were issued in separate sheets of 20 and in *se-tenant* sheetlets of 9.

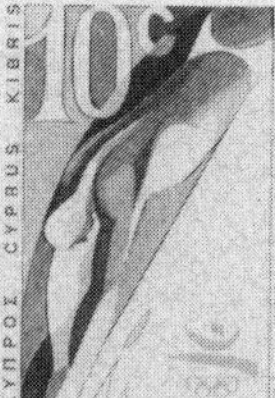

276 Swimming

277 World Map and Emblem ("EXPO '92" Worlds Fair, Seville)

(Des A. Ioannides. Photo Courvoisier)

1992 (3 Apr). *Olympic Games, Barcelona. T* **276** *and simila vert designs. Multicoloured. Granite paper. P* 12.
811 10 c. Type **276** 50 3
812 20 c. Long jump 85 7
813 30 c. Running . . . . 1·25 1·2
814 35 c. Discus . . . . 1·40 2·2
811/14 . . . . *Set of* 4 3·50 4·0

(Des S. Karamallakis. Litho Alexandros Matsoukis, Athens)

1992 (20 Apr). *Anniversaries and Events. T* **277** *and simila horiz designs. Multicoloured. P* 14.
815 20 c. Type **277** . . . . 1·00 8
816 25 c. European map and football (10th Under-16 European Football Championship) . . . . 1·40 9
817 30 c. Symbols of Learning (inauguration of University of Cyprus) . . . . 1·40 2·7
815/17 . . . . *Set of* 3 3·50 4·0

278 Compass Rose and Map of Voyage

279 *Chamaeleo chamaeleon*

(Des G. Simonis. Litho Alexandros Matsoukis, Athens)

1992 (29 May). *Europa. 500th Anniv of Discovery of Americ by Columbus. T* **278** *and similar horiz designs. Multicoloured P* 13×13½.
818 10 c. Type **278** . . . . 90 1·2
a. Horiz pair. Nos. 818/19 . . . . 1·75 2·5
819 10 c. "Departure from Palos" (R. Balaga) . . 90 1·2
820 30 c. Fleet of Columbus . . . . . . 1·40 1·7
a. Horiz pair. Nos. 820/1 . . . . 2·75 3·5
821 30 c. Christopher Columbus . . . . 1·40 1·7
818/21 . . . . *Set of* 4 4·00 5·5
Nos. 818/19 and 820/1 were printed together, *se-tenant*, i separate sheets, each horizontal pair forming a composit design.

(Litho Alexandros Matsoukis, Athens)

1992 (14 Sept). *Reptiles. T* **279** *and similar horiz designs Multicoloured. P* 13½.
822 7 c. Type **279** 55 3
823 10 c. *Lacerta laevis troodica* (lizard) . . 65 4
824 15 c. *Mauremys caspica* (turtle) . . 90 8
825 20 c. *Coluber cypriensis* (snake) . . 1·00 2·0
822/5 . . . . *Set of* 4 2·75 3·2

280 Minoan Wine Ship of 7th-century B.C.

281 "Visitation of the Virgin Mary to Elizabeth", Church of the Holy Cross, Pelendri

(Des S. Vasiliou. Litho Alexandros Matsoukis, Athens)

1992 (9 Nov). *7th International Maritime and Shippin Conference, Nicosia. P* 14.
826 **280** 50 c. multicoloured . . . . . . 2·50 2·7

(Litho Alexandros Matsoukis, Athens)

1992 (9 Nov). *Christmas. Church Fresco Paintings. T* **281** *an similar vert designs. Multicoloured. P* 13½.
827 7 c. Type **281** 40 2
828 15 c. "Virgin and Child Enthroned", Church of Panayia tou Araka 75 6
829 20 c. "Virgin and Child", Ayios Nicolaos tis Stegis Church . . . . . . 1·10 1·9
827/9 . . . . *Set of* 3 2·00 2·5

NEW INFORMATION

The editor is always interested to correspond wit people who have new information that wi improve or correct the Catalogue.

282 School Building and Laurel Wreath

283 "Motherhood" (bronze sculpture, Nicos Dymiotis)

(Des A. Ladommates. Litho Alexandros Matsoukis, Athens)

1993 (15 Feb). *Centenary of Pancyprian Gymnasium (secondary school). P* 14.
830 **282** 10 c. multicoloured 60 50

(Litho Alexandros Matsoukis, Athens)

1993 (5 Apr). *Europa. Contemporary Art. T* **283** *and similar multicoloured design. P* 13½.
831 10 c. Type **283** 50 40
832 30 c. "Motherhood" (painting, Christoforos Savva) (*horiz*) . . . . . . 1·25 2·00

284 Women Athletes (13th European Cup for Women)

285 Red Squirrelfish

Two types of 20 c.:
I. Incorrectly inscribed "MUFFLON ENCOURAGEMENT CUP"
II. Inscription corrected to "MOUFFLON ENCOURAGEMENT CUP"

(Des Maria Trillidou (10 c.), G. Simonis (25 c.), M. Christou (others). Litho Alexandros Matsoukis, Athens)

1993 (24 May–24 June). *Anniversaries and Events. T* **284** *and similar multicoloured designs. P* 14.
833 7 c. Type **234** 40 30
834 10 c. Scout symbols (80th anniv of Scouting in Cyprus) (*vert*) 55 40
835 20 c. Water-skier, dolphin and gull (Moufflon Encouragement Cup) (I) 10·00 10·00
a. Type II (24 June) 95 95
836 25 c. Archbishop Makarios III and monastery (80th birth anniv) . . 1·40 1·75
833/6 . . . . *Set of* 4 3·00 3·00

No. 835 was withdrawn on 2 June 1993, after the spelling error had been spotted. No. 835a, with the spelling corrected, was placed on sale from 24 June.

(Des A. Ioannides. Litho Alexandros Matsoukis, Athens)

1993 (6 Sept). *Fishes. T* **285** *and similar horiz designs. Multicoloured. P* 13½.
837 7 c. Type **285** 40 25
838 15 c. Red Scorpionfish 65 55
839 20 c. Painted Comber 75 85
840 30 c. Grey Triggerfish . . . . 1·40 2·00
837/40 . . . . *Set of* 4 2·75 3·25

286 Conference Emblem

(Des A. Ioannides. Litho Alexandros Matsoukis, Athens)

1993 (4 Oct). *12th Commonwealth Summit Conference. P* 13½.
841 **286** 35 c. orange-brown and pale ochre . . 1·60 1·90
842 40 c. bistre-brown and ochre . . . . 1·90 2·40

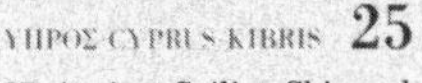

287 Ancient Sailing Ship and Modern Coaster

288 Cross from Stavrovouni Monastery

(Des G. Simonis. Litho Alexandros Matsoukis, Athens)

1993 (4 Oct). *"Maritime Cyprus '93" International Shipping Conference, Nicosia. P* 13½×14.
843 **287** 25 c. multicoloured . . . . . . 1·40 1·40

(Litho Alexandros Matsoukis, Athens)

1993 (22 Nov). *Christmas. Church Crosses. T* **288** *and similar multicoloured designs. P* 13½.
844 7 c. Type **288** 30 25
845 20 c. Cross from Lefkara 75 75
846 25 c. Cross from Pedoulas (*horiz*) . . . . 1·00 1·75
844/6 . . . . *Set of* 3 1·90 2·50

289 Copper Smelting

290 Symbols of Disability (Persons with Special Needs Campaign)

(Des G. Simonis. Litho Alexandros Matsoukis, Athens)

1994 (1 Mar). *Europa. Discoveries. Ancient Copper Industry. T* **289** *and similar horiz design. Multicoloured. P* 13×13½.
847 10 c. Type **289** 50 35
848 30 c. Ingot, ancient ship and map of Cyprus 1·25 1·75

(Des E. Hadjimichael (7 c., 25 c.), S. Karamallakis (others). Litho Alexandros Matsoukis, Athens)

1994 (9 May). *Anniversaries and Events. T* **290** *and similar vert designs. Multicoloured. P* 13½.
849 7 c. Type **290** 40 25
850 15 c. Olympic rings in flame (Centenary of International Olympic Committee) . . 65 55
851 20 c. Peace Doves (World Gymnasiade, Nicosia) 80 80
852 25 c. Adults and unborn baby in tulip (International Year of the Family) . . 1·10 1·75
849/52 . . . . *Set of* 4 2·75 3·00

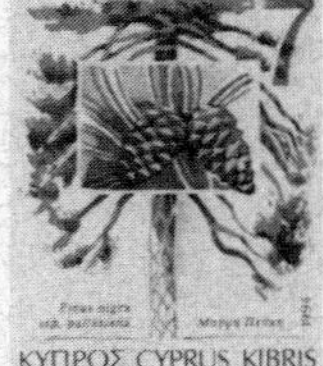

291 Houses, Soldier and Family

292 Black Pine

(Des A. Ioannides. Litho Alexandros Matsoukis, Athens)

1994 (27 June). *20th Anniv of Turkish Landings in Cyprus. T* **291** *and similar horiz design. Multicoloured. P* 14.
853 10 c. Type **291** 50 40
854 50 c. Soldier and ancient columns . . . . 2·00 3·00

(Des A. Ioannides. Litho Alexandros Matsoukis, Athens)

1994 (10 Oct). *Trees. T* **292** *and similar vert designs. Multicoloured. P* 13½×14.
855 7 c. Type **292** 30 25
856 15 c. Cyprus Cedar 55 55
857 20 c. Golden Oak 70 80
858 30 c. Strawberry Tree . . . . 1·10 1·75
855/8 . . . . *Set of* 4 2·40 3·00

293 Airliner, Route Map and Emblem

294 "Virgin Mary" (detail) (Philip Goul)

(Des G. Simonis. Litho Alexandros Matsoukis, Athens)

1994 (21 Nov). *50th Anniv of International Civil Aviation Organization. P* 14.
859 **293** 30 c. multicoloured . . . . . . 1·50 1·50

(Litho Alexandros Matsoukis, Athens)

1994 (21 Nov). *Christmas. Church Paintings. T* **294** *and similar horiz designs. Multicoloured. P* 13½.
860 7 c. Type **294** 35 25
861 20 c. "The Nativity" (detail) (Byzantine) . . 85 70
862 25 c. "Archangel Michael" (detail) (Goul) . . 1·10 1·90
860/2 . . . . *Set of* 3 2·10 2·50

295 Woman from Paphos wearing Foustani

296 "Hearth Room" Excavation, Alassa, and Frieze

(Des A. Ioannides. Litho Alexandros Matsoukis, Athens)

1994 (27 Dec). *Traditional Costumes. T* **295** *and similar vert designs. Multicoloured. Cream paper. With "1994" imprint date. P* 13½× 13.
863 1 c. Type **295** 10 10
864 2 c. Bride from Karpass 10 10
865 3 c. Woman from Paphos wearing sayia . . 10 10
866 5 c. Woman from Messaoria wearing foustani 10 10
867 7 c. Bridegroom 15 20
868 10 c. Shepherd from Messaoria 25 30
869 15 c. Woman from Nicosia in festive costume 35 40
870 20 c. Woman from Karpass wearing festive sayia 50 55
871 25 c. Woman from Pitsillia 60 65
872 30 c. Woman from Karpass wearing festive doupletti 70 75
873 35 c. Countryman 80 85
874 40 c. Man from Messaoria in festive costume 95 1·00
875 50 c. Townsman . . . . 1·25 1·40
876 £1 Townswoman wearing festive sarka 2·40 2·50
863/76 . . . . *Set of* 14 5·50 6·50

For £1 on white paper and perforated 14 see No. 958.

(Des A. Ladommatos. Litho Alexandros Matsoukis, Athens)

1995 (27 Feb). *3rd International Congress of Cypriot Studies, Nicosia. T* **296** *and similar multicoloured designs. P* 14.
877 20 c. Type **296** 75 75
878 30 c. Hypostyle hall, Kalavasos, and Mycenaean amphora . . . . . . 1·00 1·50
MS879 110×80 mm. £1 Old Archbishop's Palace, Nicosia (107×71 *mm*). Imperf . . . . . . 3·50 4·50

297 Statue of Liberty, Nicosia (left detail)

298 Nazi Heads on Peace Dove over Map of Europe

(Des G. Simonis. Litho Alexandros Matsoukis, Athens)

1995 (31 Mar). *40th Anniv of Start of E.O.K.A. Campaign. T* **297** *and similar vert designs showing different details of the statue. Multicoloured. P* 13×13½.
880 20 c. Type **297** . . . . 90 1·10
a. Horiz strip of 3. Nos. 880/2 . . . . 2·40
881 20 c. Centre detail (face value at top right) 90 1·10
882 20 c. Right detail (face value at bottom right) 90 1·10
880/2 . . . . *Set of* 3 2·40 3·00

Nos. 880/2 were printed together, *se-tenant*, in horizontal strips of 3 forming a composite design.

(Des Toulla Paphitis. Litho Alexandros Matsoukis, Athens)

1995 (8 May). *Europa. Peace and Freedom. T* **298** *and similar vert design. Multicoloured. P* 13½.
883 10 c. Type **298** 50 35
884 30 c. Concentration camp prisoner and peace dove . . . . 1·25 1·75

299 Symbolic Figure holding Healthy Food

300 European Union Flag and European Culture Month Logo

(Des Liza Petridou-Mala. Litho Alexandros Matsoukis, Athens)

1995 (26 June). *Healthy Living. T* **299** *and similar multicoloured designs. P* 13½.
885 7 c. Type **299** 25 25
886 10 c. "AIDS" and patients (*horiz*) 50 50
887 15 c. Drug addict (*horiz*) 55 55
888 20 c. Smoker and barbed wire . . . . 75 1·00
885/8 . . . . *Set of* 4 1·75 2·10

(Des G. Simonis (Nos. 889/90), N. Rangos (No. **MS**891). Litho Oriental Press, Bahrain (Nos. 889/90) or Alexandros Matsoukis, Athens (No. **MS**891))

1995 (18 Sept). *European Culture Month and "Europhilex '95" International Stamp Exhibition, Nicosia. T* **300** *and similar horiz designs. Royal blue, orange-yellow and pale stone (No.* **MS**891*) or multicoloured (others). P* 13×13½.

889 20 c. Type **300** — 55 — 60
890 25 c. Map of Europe and Cypriot church — 70 — 75
MS891 95×86 mm. 50 c. Peace dove (42×30 *mm*); 50 c. European Cultural Month symbol (42×30 *mm*). P 14 — 3·75 — 4·50

A limited quantity of No. **MS**891 was surcharged "£5" on each stamp and sold at "Europhilex '95" on 27 and 28 October 1995.

(Litho Oriental Press, Bahrain)

1995 (24 Oct). *Obligatory Tax. Refugee Fund. As T* **255**, *but inscr* "1995", "1996", "1997" *or* "1998". *Chalk-surfaced paper. P* 14½×13½.

892 **255** 1 c. brownish black and olive-grey — 10 — 10

301 Peace Dove with Flags of Cyprus and United Nations

302 Reliquary from Kykko Monastery

(Des S. Hadjimichael (10, 25 c.), S. Karamallakis (15 c.), E. Georgiades (20 c.), Litho Oriental Press, Bahrain)

1995 (24 Oct). *Anniversaries and Events. T* **301** *and similar multicoloured designs. P* 13×13½ *(horiz) or* 13½×13 *(vert).*

893 10 c. Type **301** (50th anniv of United Nations) — 30 — 35
894 15 c. Hand pushing ball over net (Centenary of volleyball) *(vert)* — 55 — 50
895 20 c. Safety pin on leaf (European Nature Conservation Year) *(vert)* — 65 — 65
896 25 c. Clay pigeon contestant (World Clay Target Shooting Championship) — 75 — 1·10
893/6 *Set of* 4 — 2·00 — 2·40

(Des S. Karamallakis. Litho Oriental Press, Bahrain)

1995 (27 Nov). *Christmas. T* **302** *and similar vert designs showing different reliquaries of Virgin and Child from Kykko Monastery. P* 13½×13.

897 7 c. multicoloured — 20 — 25
898 20 c. multicoloured — 60 — 60
899 25 c. multicoloured — 75 — 1·10
897/9 *Set of* 3 — 1·40 — 1·75

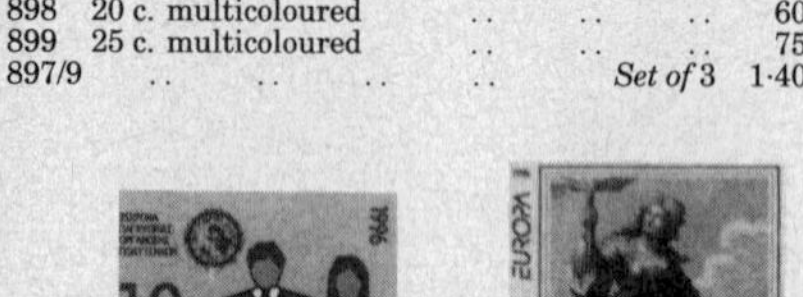

303 Family (25th anniv of Pancyprian Organisation of Large Families)

304 Maria Synglitiki

(Des Liza Petridou-Mala. Litho Oriental Press, Bahrain)

1996 (4 Jan). *Anniversaries and Events. T* **303** *and similar vert designs. Multicoloured. P* 13½×13.

900 10 c. Type **303** — 45 — 35
901 20 c. Film camera (Centenary of cinema) — 75 — 70
902 35 c. Silhouette of parent and child in globe (50th anniv of U.N.I.C.E.F.) — 1·40 — 1·40
903 40 c. "13" and Commonwealth emblem (13th Conference of Commonwealth Speakers and Presiding Officers) — 1·50 — 2·00
900/3 *Set of* 4 — 3·75 — 4·00

(Des G. Simonis. Litho Oriental Press, Bahrain)

1996 (8 Apr). *Europa. Famous Women. T* **304** *and similar vert design. Multicoloured. P* 14.

904 10 c. Type **304** — 40 — 30
905 30 c. Queen Caterina Cornaro — 1·00 — 1·25

305 High Jump

306 Watermill

(Des M. Christou. Litho Oriental Press, Bahrain)

1996 (10 June). *Centennial Olympic Games, Atlanta. T* **305** *and similar horiz designs. Multicoloured. P* 13×13½.

906 10 c. Type **305** — 40 — 30
907 20 c. Javelin — 75 — 65
908 25 c. Wrestling — 85 — 95
909 30 c. Swimming — 95 — 1·40
906/9 *Set of* 4 — 2·75 — 3·00

(Des E. Georgiades. Litho Oriental Press, Bahrain)

1996 (23 Sept). *Mills. T* **306** *and similar vert designs. Multicoloured. P* 13½×13.

910 10 c. Type **306** — 40 — 40
911 15 c. Olivemill — 55 — 50
912 20 c. Windmill — 70 — 80
913 25 c. Handmill — 80 — 1·10
910/13 *Set of* 4 — 2·25 — 2·50

307 Icon of Our Lady of Iberia, Moscow

308 "The Nativity" (detail)

(Des D. Komissarov (Nos. 914,917), G. Simonis (Nos. 915/16). Litho State Ptg Wks, Moscow)

1996 (13 Nov). *Cyprus–Russia Joint Issue. Orthodox Religion. T* **307** *and similar square designs. Multicoloured. P* 11½.

914 30 c. Type **307** — 1·10 — 1·25
a. Block of 4. Nos. 914/17 — 4·00
915 30 c. Stravrovouni Monastery, Cyprus — 1·10 — 1·25
916 30 c. Icon of St. Nicholas, Cyprus — 1·10 — 1·25
917 30 c. Iberia Gate, Moscow — 1·10 — 1·25
914/17 *Set of* 4 — 4·00 — 4·50

Nos. 914/17 were printed together, *se-tenant*, in blocks of 4 throughout the sheet.

Stamps in similar designs were also issued by Russia.

(Litho Oriental Press, Bahrain)

1996 (2 Dec). *Christmas. Religious Murals from Church of the Virgin of Asinou. T* **308** *and similar multicoloured designs. P* 13½×13 *(25 c.) or* 13×13½ *(others).*

918 7 c. Type **308** — 30 — 25
919 20 c. "Virgin Mary between the Archangels Gabriel and Michael" — 75 — 60
920 25 c. "Christ bestowing Blessing" *(vert)* — 1·10 — 1·40
918/20 *Set of* 3 — 1·90 — 2·00

309 Basketball

310 "The Last Supper"

(Des S. Karamallakis. Litho Oriental Press, Bahrain)

1997 (24 Mar). *Final of European Basketball Cup. P* 13½×13.

921 **309** 30 c. multicoloured — 1·10 — 1·10

(Des G. Koumouros. Litho Oriental Press, Bahrain)

1997 (24 Mar). *Easter. Religious Frescoes from Monastery of St. John Lambadestis. T* **310** *and similar horiz design. Multicoloured. P* 13×13½.

922 15 c. Type **310** — 50 — 50
923 25 c. "The Crucifixion" — 75 — 1·00

311 Kori Kourelleni and Prince

312 *Oedipoda miniata* (grasshopper)

(Des Liza Petridou-Mala. Litho Oriental Press, Bahrain)

1997 (5 May). *Europa. Tales and Legends. T* **311** *and similar vert design. Multicoloured. P* 13½×13.

924 15 c. Type **311** — 50 — 40
925 30 c. Digenis and Charon — 90 — 1·25

(Des A. Ladommatos. Litho Oriental Press, Bahrain)

1997 (30 June). *Insects. T* **312** *and similar horiz designs. Multicoloured. P* 13×13½.

926 10 c. Type **312** — 30 — 30
927 15 c. *Acherontia atropos* (hawk moth) — 50 — 40
928 25 c. *Daphnis nerii* (hawk moth) — 90 — 95
929 35 c. *Ascalaphus macaronius* (owl-fly) — 1·10 — 1·50
926/9 *Set of* 4 — 2·50 — 2·75

313 Archbishop Makarios III and Chapel

314 The Nativity

(Des C. Sophocleous. Litho Oriental Press, Bahrain)

1997 (1 Aug). *20th Death Anniv of Archbishop Makarios III. P* 13×13½.

930 **313** 15 c. multicoloured — 35 — 40

(Des G. Koumouros. Litho Oriental Press, Bahrain)

1997 (17 Nov). *Christmas. Byzantine Frescos from the Monastery of St. John Lambadestis. T* **314** *and similar vert designs. Multicoloured. P* 13½×13.

931 10 c. Type **314** — 20 — 25
932 25 c. Three Kings following the star — 65 — 65
933 30 c. Flight into Egypt — 85 — 1·00
931/3 *Set of* 3 — 1·50 — 1·75

315 Green Jasper

316 Players competing for Ball

(Des A. Ladommatos. Litho Oriental Press, Bahrain)

1998 (9 Mar). *Minerals. T* **315** *and similar horiz designs. Multicoloured. P* 13.

934 10 c. Type **315** — 25 — 30
935 15 c. Iron Pyrite — 35 — 45
936 25 c. Gypsum — 60 — 70
937 30 c. Chalcedony — 70 — 1·00
934/7 *Set of* 4 — 1·75 — 2·25

(Des C. Sophocleous. Litho Oriental Press, Bahrain)

1998 (4 May). *World Cup Football Championship, France. P* 14.

938 **316** 35 c. multicoloured — 80 — 85

317 Cataclysmos Festival, Larnaca

318 Mouflon Family Group

(Des S. Vassiliou (15 c.), A. Ladommatos (30 c.). Litho Oriental Press, Bahrain)

1998 (4 May). *Europa. Festivals. T* **317** *and similar horiz design. Multicoloured. P* 14.

939 15 c. Type **317** — 35 — 40
940 30 c. House of Representatives, Nicosia (Declaration of Independence) — 70 — 75

(Des S. Hadjimichael. Litho Oriental Press, Bahrain)

1998 (22 June). *Endangered Species. Cyprus Mouflon. T* **318** *and similar horiz designs. Multicoloured. P* 13×13½.

941 25 c. Type **318** — 60 — 65
a. Block of 4. Nos. 941/4 — 2·40
942 25 c. Mouflon herd — 60 — 65
943 25 c. Head of ram — 60 — 65
944 25 c. Ram on guard — 60 — 65
941/4 *Set of* 4 — 2·40 — 2·50

Nos. 941/4 were printed together, *se-tenant*, in blocks of 4 throughout the sheet.

(Litho Oriental Press, Bahrain)

1998 (22 June). *As No.* 876, *but different printer. White paper. With imprint date* ("1998"). *P* 14.

958 £1 Townswoman wearing festive sarka — 2·40 — 2·50

319 Flames and Globe Emblem

320 World "Stamp" and Magnifying Glass

(Des S. Vassiliou. Litho Oriental Press, Bahrain)

1998 (9 Oct). *50th Anniv of Universal Declaration of Human Rights. P* 14.

959	**319**	50 c. multicoloured	1·25	1·40

(Des T. Kakoullis. Litho Oriental Press, Bahrain)

1998 (9 Oct). *World Stamp Day. P* 14.

960	**320**	30 c. multicoloured	70	75
		a. Booklet pane of 8	5·50	

No. 960a has the horizontal edges of the pane imperforate and margins at left and right.

321 "The Annunciation"

(Des T. Kakoullis. Litho Oriental Press, Bahrain)

1998 (16 Nov). *Christmas. T* **321** *and similar vert designs showing religious murals. Multicoloured. P* 14.

961	10 c. Type **321**	25	30
962	25 c. "The Nativity"	60	65
963	30 c. "The Baptism of Christ"	70	75
961/3	. . . . . . *Set of* 3	1·50	1·60
MS964	102×75 mm. Nos. 961/3	1·50	1·60

STAMP BOOKLETS

Stamp-vending machines were introduced by the Cyprus Post Office in 1962. These were originally fitted to provide stamps to the value of 50 m., but in 1979 some were converted to accept 100 m. coins and, a year later, others were altered to supply 150, 200 or 300 m. worth of stamps.

The stamps contained in these booklets were a haphazard selection of low values to the required amount, attached by their sheet margins to the cardboard covers. From 1968 these covers carried commercial advertising and details of postage rates.

Following the change of currency in 1983 the machines were converted to supply 5, 10, 20 or 30 c. booklets.

B 1 World "Stamp" and Magnifying Glass

1998 (9 Oct). *World Stamp Day. Multicoloured cover as Type* B **1**. *Pane attached by selvedge.*

SB1	£2.40, booklet containing pane of 8 30 c. (No. 960a)	5·50

TURKISH CYPRIOT POSTS

After the inter-communal clashes during December 1963, a separate postal service was established on 6 January 1964 between some of the Turkish Cypriot areas, using handstamps inscribed "KIBRIS TURK POSTALARI". During 1964, however, an agreement was reached between representatives of the two communities for the restoration of postal services. This agreement, to which the United Nations representatives were a party, was ratified in November 1966 by the Republic's Council of Ministers. Under the scheme postal services were provided for the Turkish Cypriot communities in Famagusta, Larnaca, Limassol, Lefka, Nicosia and Paphos staffed by Turkish Cypriot employees of the Cypriot Department of Posts.

On 8 April 1970 5 m. and 15 m. locally-produced labels, originally designated "Social Aid Stamps", were issued by the Turkish Cypriot community and these can be found on commercial covers. These local stamps are outside the scope of this catalogue.

On 29 October 1973 Nos. 1/7 were placed on sale, but were used only on mail between the Turkish Cypriot areas.

Following the intervention by the Republic of Turkey on 20 July 1974 these stamps replaced issues of the Republic of Cyprus in that part of the island, north and east of the Attila Line, controlled by the Autonomous Turkish Cypriot Administration.

(Currency. 1000 mils = £1)

1 50th Anniversary Emblem

KIBRIS
TÜRK
FEDERE
DEVLETİ
13.2.1975

30M

(2)

(Des F. Direkoglu Miss E. Ata and G. Pir. Litho Darbhane, Istanbul)

1974 (27 July*). *50th Anniv of Republic of Turkey. T* **1** *and similar designs in vermilion and black (15 m.) or multicoloured (others). P* 12 × 11½ *(vert) or* 11½ × 12 *(horiz).*
1 3 m. Woman sentry *(vert)* .. .. .. 30·00 30·00
2 5 m. Military Parade, Nicosia 60 40
3 10 m. Man and woman with Turkish flags *(vert)* 50 20
4 15 m. Type **1** .. .. 2·50 1·50
5 20 m. Atatürk statue, Kyrenia Gate, Nicosia *(vert)* 70 20
6 50 m. "The Fallen" *(vert)* .. .. .. 2·00 1·50
7 70 m. Turkish flag and map of Cyprus .. 16·00 16·00
1/7 .. .. *Set of* 7 48·00 48·00

*This is the date on which Nos. 1/7 became valid for international mail.

On 13 February 1975 a Turkish Cypriot Federated State was proclaimed in that part of Cyprus under Turkish occupation and later 9,000 Turkish Cypriots were transferred from the South to the North of the island.

1975 (3 Mar). *Proclamation of the Turkish Federated State of Cyprus. Nos. 3 and 5 surch as T* **2** *by Halkin Sesi, Nicosia.*
8 30 m. on 20 m. Atatürk statue, Kyrenia Gate, Nicosia .. .. 75 1·00
9 100 m. on 10 m. Man and woman with Turkish flags .. .. 1·25 2·00

On No. 9 the surcharge appears at the top of the stamp and the inscription at the bottom.

3 Namik Kemal's Bust, Famagusta

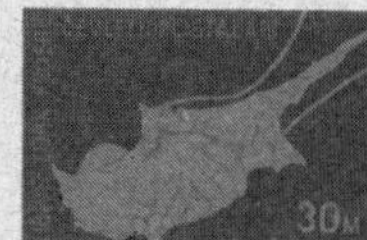

4 Map of Cyprus

(Des I. Özişik. Litho Güzel Sanatlar Matbaasi, Ankara)

1975 (21 Apr). *Multicoloured designs as T* **3**. *Imprint at foot with date* "1975". *P* 13.
10 3 m. Type **3** 15 40
11 10 m. Atatürk Statue, Nicosia 15 10
12 15 m. St. Hilarion Castle 25 20
13 20 m. Atatürk Square, Nicosia 35 20
14 25 m. Famagusta Beach 35 30
15 30 m. Kyrenia Harbour 45 10
16 50 m. Lala Mustafa Pasha Mosque, Famagusta *(vert)* 50 10
17 100 m. Interior, Kyrenia Castle 80 90
18 250 m. Castle walls, Kyrenia .. .. .. 1·25 2·75
19 500 m. Othello Tower, Famagusta *(vert)* .. 2·25 5·00
10/19 .. .. *Set of* 10 6·00 9·00

See also Nos. 37/8.

(Des B. Erkmen (30 m.), S. Tuga (50 m.), N. Cünes (150 m). Litho Ajans-Türk Matbaasi, Ankara)

1975 (20 July). *"Peace in Cyprus". T* **4** *and similar multicoloured designs. P* 13.
20 30 m. Type **4** 30 15
21 50 m. Map, laurel and broken chain 35 20
22 150 m. Map and laurel-sprig on globe *(vert)* .. 90 1·00
20/2 .. .. *Set of* 3 1·40 1·25

5 "Pomegranates" (I. V. Guney)

(Litho Güzel Sanatlar Matbaasi, Ankara)

1975 (29 Dec). *Europa. Paintings. T* **5** *and similar horiz design. Multicoloured. P* 13.
23 90 m. Type **5** 80 60
24 100 m. "Harvest Time" (F. Direkoglu) 95 60

10 M ——

(6)

7 "Expectation"

1976 (28 Apr). *Nos. 16/17 surch as T* **6** *at Govt Printing House, Nicosia in horizontal clichés of* 10.
25 10 m. on 50 m. Lala Mustafa Pasha Mosque, Famagusta 50 70
26 30 m. on 100 m. Interior, Kyrenia Castle .. 50 80

(Litho Ajans-Türk Matbaasi, Ankara)

1976 (3 May). *Europa. T* **7** *and similar vert design showing ceramic statuette. Multicoloured. P* 13.
27 60 m. Type **7** 40 80
28 120 m. "Man in Meditation" 60 90

8 Carob

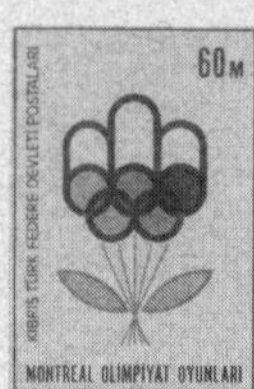

9 Olympic Symbol "Flower"

(Des S. Atlihan. Litho Güzel Sanatlar Matbaasi, Ankara)

1976 (28 June). *Export Products—Fruits. T* **8** *and similar horiz designs. Multicoloured. P* 13.
29 10 m. Type **8** 25 10
30 25 m. Mandarin 30 10
31 40 m. Strawberry 40 25
32 60 m. Orange 50 65
33 80 m. Lemon .. .. 55 1·75
29/33 .. .. *Set of* 5 1·75 2·50

(Des C. Mutver (60 m.), A. B. Kocamanoglu (100 m.). Litho Güzel Sanatlar Matbaasi, Ankara)

1976 (17 July). *Olympic Games. Montreal. T* **9** *and similar horiz design. Multicoloured. P* 13.
34 60 m. Type **9** 25 20
35 100 m. Olympic symbol and doves 35 25

10 Kyrenia Harbour

11 Liberation Monument, Karaeglanoglu (Ay. Georghios)

(Des I. Özişik. Litho Ajans-Türk Matbaasi, Ankara)

1976 (2 Aug). *New design (5 m.) or as Nos. 12/13 but redrawn with lettering altered and new imprint at foot with date* "1976". *P* 13.
36 5 m. Type **10** 40 15
37 15 m. St. Hilarion Castle 40 15
38 20 m. Atatürk Square, Nicosia 40 15
36/8 .. .. *Set of* 3 1·10 40

Nos. 39/46 vacant.

(Des D. Erimez and C. Gizer. Litho Ajans-Türk Matbaasi, Ankara)

1976 (1 Nov). *Liberation Monument. T* **11** *and similar vert design. P* 13.
47 **11** 30 m. lt turquoise-blue, lt flesh & black 15 20
48 – 150 m. light verm, light flesh & blk 35 45

No. 48 shows a different view of the Monument.

12 Hotel, Salamis Bay

(Litho Türk Tarih Kurumu Basimevi, Ankara)

1977 (2 May). *Europa. T* **12** *and similar horiz design. Multicoloured. P* 13.
49 80 m. Type **12** 65 8
50 100 m. Kyrenia Port 75 8

13 Pottery

14 Arap Ahmet Pasha Mosque, Nicosia

(Litho Güzel Sanatlar Matbaasi, Ankara)

1977 (27 June). *Handicrafts. T* **13** *and similar designs. Multicoloured. P* 13.
51 15 m. Type **13** 10 10
52 30 m. Decorated gourds *(vert)* 10 10
53 125 m. Basketware 30 50
51/3 .. .. *Set of* 3 40 65

(Litho APA Ofset Basimevi, Istanbul)

1977 (2 Dec). *Turkish Buildings in Cyprus. T* **14** *and similar horiz designs. Multicoloured. P* 13.
54 20 m. Type **14** 10 10
55 40 m. Paphos Castle 10 10
56 70 m. Bekir Pasha aqueduct 15 20
57 80 m. Sultan Mahmut library 15 25
54/7 .. .. *Set of* 4 45 60

15 Namik Kemal (bust) and House, Famagusta

16 Old Man and Woman

(Des B. Ozak. Litho Ticaret Matbaacilik TAS, Izmir)

1977 (21 Dec). *Namik Kemal (patriotic poet). T* **15** *and similar multicoloured design. P* 12½ × 13 *(30 m.) or* 13 × 12½ *(140 m.)*
58 30 m. Type **15** 15 15
59 140 m. Namik Kemal (portrait) *(vert)* 35 60

(New Currency. 100 kurus = 1 lira)

(Des G. Pir. Litho Ajans-Türk Matbaasi, Ankara)

1978 (17 Apr). *Social Security. T* **16** *and similar vert designs. P* 13×13½.
60 150 k. black, yellow and blue 10 10
61 275 k. black, red-orange and green 15 15
62 375 k. black, blue and red-orange 25 20
60/2 .. .. *Set of* 3 45 40

Designs:—275 k. Injured man with crutch; 375 k. Woman with family.

17 Oratory in Büyük Han, Nicosia

18 Motorway Junction

(Des I. Özisik. Litho APA Ofset Basimevi, Istanbul)

1978 (2 May). *Europa. T* **17** *and similar horiz design. Multicoloured. P* 13.
63 225 k. Type **17** 30 30
64 450 k. Cistern in Selimiye Mosque, Nicosia .. 60 70

(Litho APA Ofset Basimevi, Istanbul)

1978 (10 July). *Communications. T* **18** *and similar horiz designs. Multicoloured. P* 13.
65 75 k. Type **18** 15 10
66 100 k. Hydrofoil 15 10
67 650 k. Boeing 720 at Ercan Airport 50 35
65/7 .. .. *Set of* 3 70 45

19 Dove with Laurel Branch

20 Kemal Atatürk

es E. Kaya (725 k.), C. Kirkbesoglu (others). Litho APA Ofset Basimevi, Istanbul)

78 (13 Sept). *National Oath. T* **19** *and similar designs. P* 13.
150 k. orange-yellow, violet and black 10 10
225 k. black, Indian red and orange-yellow . . 10 10
725 k. black, cobalt and orange-yellow . . 20 20
/70 . . . . *Set of* 3 35 35
Designs: *Vert*—225 k. "Taking the Oath". *Horiz*—725 k. Symlic dove.

es C. Mutver. Litho Türk Tarih Kurumu Basimevi, Ankara)

78 (10 Nov). *Kemal Atatürk Commemoration. P* 13.
20 75 k. pale turquoise-grn & turq-grn . . 10 10
450 k. pale flesh and light brown . . 15 15
650 k. pale blue and light blue 20 25
/3 . . . . *Set of* 3 40 40

50 Krs.

(21)

22 Gun Barrel with Olive Branch and Map of Cyprus

79 (4 June). *Nos.* 30/3 *surch as T* **21**, *by Govt Printing Office, Lefkosa*
50 k. on 25 m. Mandarin 10 10
1 l. on 40 m. Strawberry 15 10
3 l. on 60 m. Orange 15 10
5 l. on 80 m. Lemon 35 15
/7 . . . . *Set of* 4 65 30

(Des N. Dündar. Litho Ajans-Türk Matbaasi, Ankara)

79 (20 July). *5th Anniv of Turkish Peace Operation in Cyprus. Sheet* 72×52 *mm. Imperf.*
S78 **22** 15 l. black, deep turquoise-blue and pale green . . . . 80 1·25

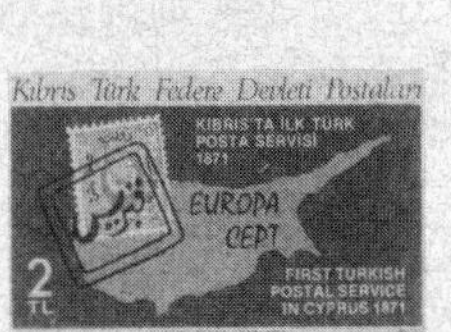

23 Postage Stamp and Map of Cyprus

24 Symbolised Microwave Antenna

(Des S. Mumcu. Litho Ajans-Türk Matbaasi, Ankara)

979 (20 Aug). *Europa. Communications. T* **23** *and similar horiz designs. Multicoloured. P* 13.
9 2 l. Type **23** 10 10
) 3 l. Postage stamps, building and map . . 10 10
8 l. Telephones, Earth and satellite 20 30
9/81 . . . . *Set of* 3 35 45

(Litho Ticaret Matbaacilik TAS, Izmir)

979 (24 Sept). *50th Anniv of International Consultative Radio Committee. P* 13 × 12½.
2 **24** 2 l. multicoloured 20 10
3 5 l. multicoloured 20 10
4 6 l. multicoloured 25 15
2/4 . . . . *Set of* 3 60 30

25 School Children

26 Lala Mustafa Pasha Mosque, Magusa

Des H. Hastürk (1½ l.), G. Akansel (4½ l.), P. Yalyali (6 l.). Litho APA Ofset Basimevi, Istanbul)

979 (29 Oct). *International Year of the Child. Children's Drawings. T* **25** *and similar multicoloured designs. P* 13.
5 1½ l. Type **25** 25 15
6 4½ l. Children and globe (*horiz*) 40 20
7 6 l. College children 60 20
5/7 . . . . *Set of* 3 1·10 50

Des S. Mumcu (20 1.), I. Özişik (others). Litho Ajans-Türk Matbaasi, Ankara)

980 (23 Mar). *Islamic Commemorations. T* **26** *and similar vert designs. Multicoloured. P* 13.
8 2½ l. Type **26** 10 10
9 10 l. Arap Ahmet Pasha Mosque, Lefkosa . . 30 15
0 20 l. Mecca and Medina 50 20
8/90 . . . . *Set of* 3 80 40
Commemorations:—2½ l. 1st Islamic Conference in Turkish Cyprus; 10 l. General Assembly of World Islam Congress; 20 l. Moslem Year 1400AH.

27 Ebu-Su'ud Efendi (philosopher)

28 Omer's Shrine, Kyrenia

(Litho Ajans-Türk Matbaasi, Ankara)

1980 (23 May). *Europa. Personalities. T* **27** *and similar vert design. Multicoloured. P* 13.
91 5 l. Type **27** 20 10
92 30 l. Sultan Selim II 70 40

(Litho Guzel Sanatlar Matbaasi, Ankara)

1980 (25 June). *Ancient Monuments, T* **28** *and similar horiz designs. P* 13.
93 2½ l. new blue and stone 10 10
94 3½ l. grey-green and pale rose-pink 10 10
95 5 l. lake and pale blue-green 15 10
96 10 l. deep mauve and pale green 30 10
97 20 l. dull ultramarine & pale greenish yellow 50 25
93/7 . . . . *Set of* 5 95 45
Designs:—3½ l. Entrance gate, Famagusta; 5 l. Funerary monuments (16th-century), Famagusta; 10 l. Bella Paise Abbey, Kyrenia; 20 l. Selimiye Mosque, Nicosia.

29 Cyprus 1880 6d.

30 Dome of the Rock

31 Extract from World Muslim Congress Statement in Turkish

(Des S. Mumcu. Litho Ajans-Türk Matbaasi, Ankara)

1980 (16 Aug). *Cyprus Stamp Centenary. T* **29** *and similar designs showing stamps. P* 14.
98 7½ l. black, drab and grey-olive 20 10
99 15 l. brown, grey-blue and blue 25 15
100 50 l. black, rose and grey 65 55
98/100 . . . . *Set of* 3 1·00 70
Designs: *Horiz*:—15 l. Cyprus 1960 Constitution of the Republic 30 m. commemorative. *Vert*—50 l. Social Aid local, 1970.

(Litho Guzel Sanatlar Matbaasi, Ankara)

1980 (16 Oct). *Palestinian Solidarity. T* **30** *and similar multicoloured design. P* 13.
101 15 l. Type **30** 25 15
102 35 l. Dome of the Rock (*horiz*) 65 30

(Des S. Mumcu. Litho Turk Tarih Kurumu Basimevi, Ankara)

1981 (24 Mar). *Solidarity with Islamic Countries Day. T* **31** *and similar vert design showing extract from World Muslim Congress statement. P* 13.
103 1 l. rosine, stone and olive-sepia 15 15
104 35 l. black, pale blue-green and myrtle-green 55 85
Design:—35 l. Extract in English

32 "Atatürk" (F. Duran)

33 Folk-dancing

(Litho Ajans-Türk Matbaasi, Ankara)

1981 (19 May). *Atatürk Stamp Exhibition, Lefkosa. P* 13.
105 **32** 20 l. multicoloured 25 35
No. 105 was printed in sheets of 100, including 50 *se-tenant* stamp-size labels.

(Litho Ticaret Matbaacilik TAS, Izmir)

1981 (29 June). *Europa, Folklore. T* **33** *and similar horiz design showing folk-dancing. P* 12½ × 13.
106 10 l. multicoloured 35 15
107 30 l. multicoloured 60 35

MINIMUM PRICE

The minimum price quote is 10p which represents a handling charge rather than a basis for valuing common stamps. For further notes about prices see introductory pages.

34 "Kemal Atatürk" (I. Calli)

35 Wild Convolvulus

(Litho Basim Ofset, Ankara)

1981 (23 July). *Birth Centenary of Kemal Atatürk. Sheet* 70 × 95 *mm. Imperf.*
MS108 **34** 150 l. multicoloured . . . . . . 1·10 1·25

(Litho Turk Tarih Kurumu Basimevi, Ankara)

1981 (28 Sept)–**82**. *Flowers, Multicoloured designs as T* **35**. *P* 13.
109 1 l. Type **35** 10 10
110 5 l. Persian Cyclamen (*horiz*) (22.1.82) . . 10 10
111 10 l. Spring Mandrake (*horiz*) 10 10
112 25 l. Corn Poppy 15 10
113 30 l. Wild Arum (22.1.82) 20 10
114 50 l. Sage-leaved Rock Rose (*horiz*) (22.1.82) 30 20
115 100 l. *Cistus salviaefolius L.* (22.1.82) . . 55 30
116 150 l. Giant Fennel (*horiz*) . . . . . . 1·00 90
109/16 . . . . *Set of* 8 2·25 1·50

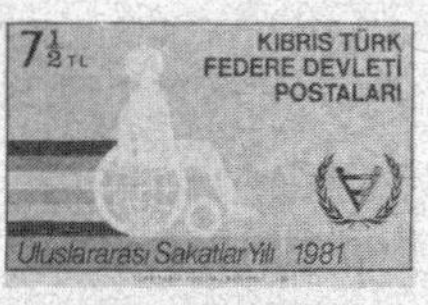

36 Stylized Disabled Person in Wheelchair

37 Turkish and Palestinian Flags

(Des H. Ulucam (7½ l.), N. Kozal (others). Litho Türk Tarih Kurumu Basimevi, Ankara)

1981 (16 Oct). *Commemorations. T* **36** *and similar multicoloured designs. P* 13.
117 7½ l. Type **36** 30 35
118 10 l. Heads of people of different races, peace dove and barbed wire (*vert*) 50 55
119 20 l. People of different races reaching out from globe, with dishes (*vert*) 75 85
117/19 . . . . *Set of* 3 1·40 1·60
Commemorations:—7½ l. International Year for Disabled Persons; 10 l. Anti-apartheid Publicity; 20 l. World Food Day.

(Des H. Ulucam. Litho Türk Tarih Kurumu Basimevi, Ankara)

1981 (29 Nov). *Palestinian Solidarity. P* 13.
120 **37** 10 l. multicoloured 30 40

38 Prince Charles and Lady Diana Spencer

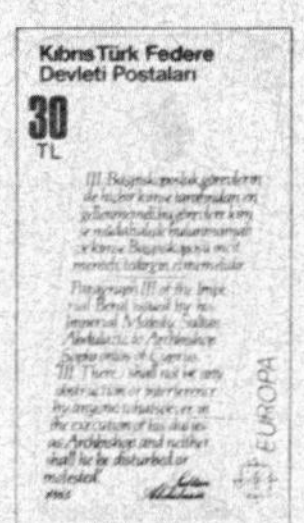

39 Charter issued by Sultan Abdul Aziz to Archbishop Sophronios

(Des H. Ulucam. Litho Türk Tarih Kurumu Basimevi, Ankara)

1981 (30 Nov). *Royal Wedding. P* 13
121 **38** 50 l. multicoloured . . . . . . 1·00 85

(Des H. Ulucam, Litho Tezel Ofset, Lefkosa)

1982 (30 July). *Europa (CEPT). Sheet* 83 × 124 *mm containing T* **39** *and similar vert design. Multicoloured. P* 12½ × 13.
MS122 30 l. × 2. Type **39**; 70 l. × 2, Turkish forces landing at Tuzla, 1571 . . . . 4·50 5·00

40 Buffavento Castle

41 "Wedding" (A. Örek)

(Des H. Ulucam (Nos. 123/5). Litho Tezel Ofset, Lefkosa)

1982 (20 Aug). *Tourism. T* **40** *and similar multicoloured designs. P* 12.

123	5 l. Type **40**	10	10
124	10 l. Windsurfing (*horiz*)	15	10
125	15 l. Kantara Castle (*horiz*)	25	15
126	30 l. Shipwreck (300 B.C.) (*horiz*)	50	40
123/6	*Set of* 4	90	65

(Litho Ajans-Türk Matbaasi, Ankara)

1982 (3 Dec). *Paintings* (1*st series*). *T* **41** *and similar multicoloured design. P* 13.

127	30 l. Type **41**	15	30
128	50 l. "Carob Pickers" (O. Naxim Selenge) (*vert*)	30	70

See also Nos. 132/3, 157/8, 176/7, 185/6, 208/9, 225/7, 248/50, 284/5, 315/16, 328/9, 369/70 and 436/7.

42 Cross of Lorraine, Koch and Bacillus (Cent of Koch's Discovery of Tubercle Bacillus)

43 "Calloused Hands" (Salih Oral)

(Des H. Ulucam. Litho Tezel Ofset, Lefkosa)

1982 (15 Dec.) *Anniversaries and Events. T* **42** *and similar multicoloured designs. P* 12.

129	10 l. Type **42**	1·00	40
130	30 l. Spectrum on football pitch (World Cup Football Championships, Spain)	1·75	1·00
131	70 l. "75" and Lord Baden-Powell (75th anniv of Boy Scout movement and 125th birth anniv) (*vert*)	2·25	3·50
129/31	*Set of* 3	4·50	4·50

(Litho Ajans-Türk Matbaasi, Ankara)

1983 (16 May). *Paintings* (2*nd series*). *T* **43** *and similar vert design. Multicoloured. P* 13.

132	30 l. Type **43**	90	1·40
133	35 l. "Malya—Limassol Bus" (Emin Cizenel)	90	1·40

44 Old Map of Cyprus by Piri Reis

45 First Turkish Cypriot 10 m. Stamp

(Litho Türk Tarih Kurumu Basimevi, Ankara)

1983 (30 June). *Europa. Sheet* 82 × 78 *mm, containing T* **44** *and similar horiz design. Multicoloured. P* 13.

MS134	100 l. Type **44**; 100 l. Cyprus as seen from "Skylab"	2·25	3·25

(Des E. Ata (15 l.), A. Hasan (20 l.), G. Pir (25 l.), H. Ulucam (others). Litho Ajans-Türk Matbaasi, Ankara)

1983 (1 Aug). *Anniversaries and Events. T* **45** *and similar multicoloured designs commemorating World Communications Year* (30, 50 *l.*) *or* 25*th Anniv. of T.M.T.* (*Turkish Cypriot Resistance Organization*). *P* 13.

135	15 l. Type **45**	50	50
136	20 l. "Turkish Achievements in Cyprus" (*horiz*))	60	60
137	25 l. "Liberation Fighters"	70	70
138	30 l. Dish aerial and telegraph pole (*horiz*)	85	90
139	50 l. Dove and envelopes (*horiz*)	1·75	2·25
135/9	*Set of* 5	4·00	4·50

46 European Bee Eater

Kuzey Kıbrıs
Türk Cumhuriyeti
15.11.1983

15 ❀

(47)

(Des E. Cizenel. Litho Ajans-Türk Matbaasi, Ankara)

1983 (10 Oct). *Birds of Cyprus. T* **46** *and similar horiz designs. Multicoloured. P* 13.

140	10 l. Type **46**	80	1·00
	a. Block of 4. Nos. 140/3	4·00	
141	15 l. Goldfinch	1·00	1·10
142	50 l. European Robin	1·25	1·40
143	65 l. Golden Oriole	1·40	1·50
140/3	*Set of* 4	4·00	4·50

Nos. 140/3 were printed together, *se-tenant*, in blocks of 4 throughout the sheet.

1983 (7 Dec). *Establishment of the Republic. Nos.* 109, 111/12 *and* 116 *surch as T* **47** (*No.* 145) *or optd only*.

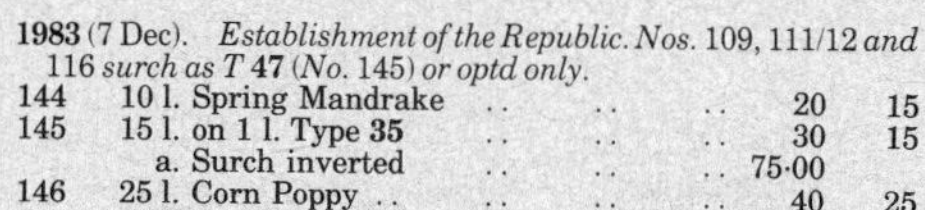

144	10 l. Spring Mandrake	20	15
145	15 l. on 1 l. Type **35**	30	15
	a. Surch inverted	75·00	
146	25 l. Corn Poppy	40	25
147	150 l. Giant Fennel	2·25	3·25
144/7	*Set of* 4	2·75	3·50

48 C.E.P.T. 25th Anniversary Logo.

49 Olympic Flame

(Des J. Larrivière. Litho Tezel Ofset, Lefkosa)

1984 (30 May). *Europa. P* 12 × 12½.

148	**48**	50 l. lemon, chestnut and black	2·25	3·00
		a. Pair. Nos. 148/9	4·50	6·00
149		100 l. pale blue, bright blue and black	2·25	3·00

Nos. 148/9 were printed together, *se-tenant*, in horizontal and vertical pairs throughout the sheet.

(Des H. Ulucam. Litho Tezel Ofset, Lefkosa)

1984 (19 June). *Olympic Games, Los Angeles. T* **49** *and similar multicoloured designs. P* 12½ × 12 (10 *l.*) *or* 12 × 12½ (*others*).

150	10 l. Type **49**	15	10
151	20 l. Olympic events within rings (*horiz*)	25	25
152	70 l. Martial arts event (*horiz*)	50	1·50
150/2	*Set of* 3	80	1·60

50 Atatürk Cultural Centre

51

(Des H. Ulucam. Litho Tezel Ofset, Lefkosa)

1984 (20 July). *Opening of Atatürk Cultural Centre, Lefkosa. W* **51**. *P* 12 × 12½.

153	**50**	120 l. stone, black and chestnut	1·25	1·75

52 Turkish Cypriot Flag and Map

(Des C. Guzeloglu (20 l.), M. Gozbebek (70 l.). Litho Tezel Ofset Lefkosa)

1984 (20 July). 10*th Anniv of Turkish Landings in Cyprus. T* **52** *and similar horiz design. W* **51**. *Multicoloured. P* 12 × 12½.

154	20 l. Type **52**	50	25
155	70 l. Turkish Cypriot flag within book	1·00	2·00

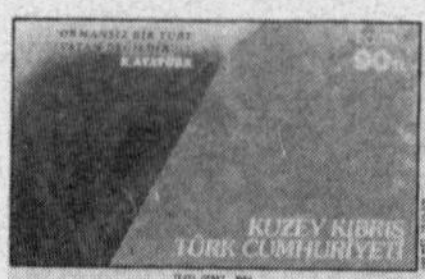

53 Burnt and Replanted Forests

(Des H. Ulucam. Litho Tezel Ofset, Lefkosa)

1984 (20 Aug). *World Forestry Resources. W* **51**. *P* 12 × 12½.

156	**53**	90 l. multicoloured	1·25	1·75

ALTERED CATALOGUE NUMBERS

Any Catalogue numbers altered from the last edition are shown as a list in the introductory pages.

54 "Old Turkish Houses, Nicosia" (Cevdet Cagdas)

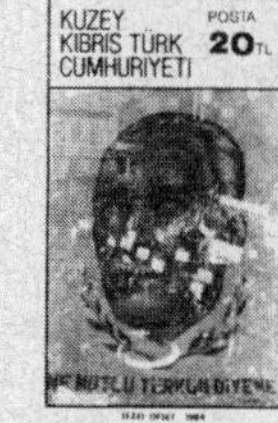

55 Kemal Atatürk Flag and Crown

(Litho Tezel Ofset, Lefkosa)

1984 (21 Sept). *Paintings* (3*rd series*). *T* **54** *and similar ho design. Multicoloured. W* **51**. *P* 13 × 12½.

157	20 l. Type **54**	50	
158	70 l. "Scenery" (Olga Rauf)	1·10	2·

See also Nos. 176/7, 185/6, 208/9, 225/7, 248/50, 284/5, 315/1 and 328/9.

(Des H. Ulucam (20 l.), F. Isiman (70 l.). Litho Tezel Ofset, Lefkosa)

1984 (15 Nov). 1*st Anniv of Turkish Republic of Northern Cypr T* **55** *and similar multicoloured design. W* **51** (*sideways on* 20 *inverted on* 70 *l.*). *P* 12½.

159	20 l. Type **55**	50	
160	70 l. Legislative Assembly voting for Republic (*horiz*)	1·10	2·

56 Taekwondo Bout

57 "Le Regard" (Saulo Mercader)

(Des H. Ulucam. Litho Tezel Ofset, Lefkosa)

1984 (10 Dec). *International Taekwondo Championship, Girn T* **56** *and similar horiz design. W* **51** (*sideways on* 10 *l.*). *P* 12½

161	10 l. black, pale cinnamon and grey-black	40	
162	70 l. multicoloured	1·60	2·

Design:—70 l. Emblem and flags of competing nations.

(Litho Tezel Ofset, Lefkosa)

1984 (10 Dec). *Exhibition by Saulo Mercader* (*artist*). *T* **57** *an similar multicoloured design. W* **51** (*sideways on* 20 *l. P* 12½ × 13 (20 *l.*) *or* 13 × 12½ (70 *l.*).

163	20 l. Type **57**	30	
164	70 l. "L'equilibre de L'esprit (*horiz*)	1·10	2·

58 Musical Instruments and Music

59 Dr. Fazil Kucuk (politician)

(Des H. Ulucam. Litho Tezel Ofset, Lefkosa)

1984 (10 Dec). *Visit of Nurnberg Chamber Orchestra. W* **51** (*side ways*). *P* 12½.

165	**58**	70 l. multicoloured	1·50	2·2

(Des Y. Calli (20 l.), E. Cizenel (70 l.). Litho Tezel Ofset, Lefkosa)

1985 (15 Jan). 1*st Death Anniv of Dr. Fazil Kucuk* (*politician T* **59** *and similar vert design. Multicoloured. W* **51** (*inverted o* 70 *l.*) *P* 12½ × 12.

166	20 l. Type **59**	30	3
167	70 l. Dr. Fazil Kucuk reading newspaper	95	2·0

60 Goat

61 George Frederick Handel

(Des E. Cizenel. Litho Tezel Ofset, Lefkosa)

85 (29 May). *Domestic Animals. T* **60** *and similar horiz designs. Multicoloured. W* **51**. *P* 12×12½.

8 100 l. Type **60** 55 30
9 200 l. Cow and calf 90 80
0 300 l. Ram .. .. 1·25 2·00
1 500 l. Donkey .. .. 2·00 3·25
8/71 .. .. *Set of* 4 4·25 5·75

(Litho Tezel Ofset, Lefkosa)

85 (26 June). *Europa. Composers. T* **61** *and similar vert designs. W* **51** *(sideways). P* 12½×12.

2 20 l. brown-purple, myrtle-green & pale grn 2·00 2·50
a. Block of 4. Nos. 172/5 .. .. .. 8·00
3 20 l. brown-purple, lake-brown & pale pink 2·00 2·50
4 100 l. brown-purple, steel blue & pale grey-bl 2·50 3·00
5 100 l. brown-purple, bistre-brown & pale cinn 2·50 3·00
2/5 .. .. *Set of* 4 8·00 10·00

Designs:—No. 172, Type **61**; 173, Guiseppe Domenico Scarti; 174, Johann Sebastian Bach; 175, Buhurizade Mustafa Itri endi.

Nos. 172/5 were printed together, *se-tenant*, in blocks of four roughout the sheet.

(Litho Tezel Ofset, Lefkosa)

85 (15 Aug). *Paintings (4th series). Vert designs as T* **54**. *Multicoloured. W* **51**. *P* 12½×13.

6 20 l. "Village Life" (Ali Atakan) 60 50
7 50 l. "Woman carrying Water" (Ismet V. Güney) .. .. 1·40 2·50

62 Heads of Three Youths **63** Parachutist (Aviation League)

(Des H. Uluçam. Litho Tezel Ofset, Lefkosa)

85 (29 Oct). *International Youth Year. T* **62** *and similar horiz design. Multicoloured. W* **51** *(sideways). P* 12×12½.

8 20 l. Type **62** 75 40
9 100 l. Dove and globe .. .. 3·50 4·00

(Des H. Uluçam. Litho Tezel Ofset, Lefkosa)

85 (29 Nov). *Anniversaries and Events. T* **63** *and similar designs. W* **51** *(inverted on Nos. 181/2, sideways on Nos. 183/4). P* 12×12½ *(Nos. 183/4) or* 12½×12 *(others).*

0 20 l. multicoloured .. .. 1·00 30
1 50 l. grey-black, light brown and dull ultramarine .. .. 1·50 1·00
2 100 l. light brown .. .. 1·75 2·50
3 100 l. multicoloured .. .. 1·75 2·50
4 100 l. multicoloured .. .. 1·75 2·50
0/4 .. .. *Set of* 5 7·00 8·00

Designs: *Vert*—No. 181, Louis Pasteur (Centenary of Discovery of Rabies vaccine); 182, İsmet İnönü (Turkish statesman) birth centenary (1984). *Horiz*—183, "40" in figures and symbolic flower (40th anniv of United Nations Organization); 184, Patient receiving blood transfusion (Prevention of Thalassemia).

(Litho Tezel Ofset, Lefkosa)

86 (20 June). *Paintings (5th series). Horiz designs as T* **54**. *Multicoloured. W* **51** *(sideways). P* 13×12½.

5 20 l. "House with Arches" (Gönen Atakol) .. 50 30
6 100 l. "Atatürk Square" (Yalkin Muhtaroğlu) .. .. 1·75 1·75

64 Griffon Vulture **65** Karagöz Show Puppets

(Des E. Çizenel (100 l.), H. Uluçam (200 l.). Litho Tezel Ofset, Lefkosa)

986 (20 June). *Europa. Protection of Nature and the Environment. Sheet* 82×76 *mm. containing T* **64** *and similar horiz design. Multicoloured. W* **51** *(sideways). P* 12×12½.

MS187 100 l. Type **64**: 200 l. Litter on Cyprus landscape .. .. 6·00 5·50

(Des Y. Yazgin. Litho Tezel Ofset, Lefkosa)

986 (25 July). *Karagöz Folk Puppets. W* **51** *(inverted). P* 12½×13.

88 **65** 100 l. multicoloured .. .. 2·25 2·00

66 Old Bronze Age Composite Pottery **67** Soldiers, Defence Force Badge and Atatürk (10th anniv of Defence Forces)

(Litho Tezel Ofset, Lefkosa)

1986 (15 Sept). *Archaeological Artifacts. Cultural Links with Anatolia. T* **66** *and similar multicoloured designs. W* **51** *(sideways on* 10, 50 *l., inverted on* 20, 100 *l.). P* 12×12½ (10, 50 *l.*) *or* 12½×12 (20, 100 *l.*).

189 10 l. Type **66** 55 20
190 20 l. Late Bronze Age bird jug (*vert*) .. 95 30
191 50 l. Neolithic earthenware pot .. .. 1·75 1·75
192 100 l. Roman statue of Artemis (*vert*) .. 2·25 3·25
189/92 .. .. *Set of* 4 5·00 5·00

(Des. H. Uluçam (No. 196). Litho Tezel Ofset, Lefkosa)

1986 (13 Oct). *Anniversaries and Events. T* **67** *and similar multicoloured designs. W* **51** *(inverted on* 20, 50 *l., sideways on others). P* 12½×12 *(vert) or* 12×12½ *(horiz).*

193 20 l. Type **67** 80 30
194 50 l. Woman and two children (40th anniv of Food and Agriculture Organization) .. 1·40 1·40
195 100 l. Football and world map (World Cup Football Championship, Mexico) (*horiz*) .. .. 2·75 3·25
196 100 l. Orbit of Halley's Comet and *Giotto* spacecraft (*horiz*) .. .. 2·75 3·25
193/6 .. .. *Set of* 4 7·00 7·50

68 Güzelyurt Dam and Power Station **69** Prince Andrew and Miss Sarah Ferguson

(Litho Tezel Ofset, Lefkosa)

1986 (17 Nov). *Modern Development (1st series). T* **68** *and similar horiz designs. Multicoloured. W* **51** *(sideways). P* 12×12½.

197 20 l. Type **68** .. .. 1·25 30
198 50 l. Low cost housing project, Lefkosa .. 1·40 1·25
199 100 l. Kyrenia Airport .. .. 3·25 3·50
197/9 .. .. *Set of* 3 5·50 4·50

See also Nos. 223/4 and 258/63.

(Litho Tezel Ofset, Lefkosa)

1986 (20 Nov). *60th Birthday of Queen Elizabeth II and Royal Wedding. T* **69** *and similar vert design. Multicoloured. W* **51** *(inverted). P* 12½×13.

200 100 l. Type **69** .. .. 1·50 2·00
a. Pair. Nos. 200/1 .. .. 3·00 4·00
201 100 l. Queen Elizabeth II .. .. 1·50 2·00

Nos. 200/1 were printed together, *se-tenant*, in horizontal and vertical pairs throughout the sheet.

70 Locomotive No. 11 and Trakhoni Station

(Des H. Uluçam (50 l.). Litho Tezel Ofset, Lefkosa)

1986 (31 Dec). *Cyprus Railway. T* **70** *and similar horiz design. Multicoloured. W* **51** *(sideways). P* 12×12½.

202 50 l. Type **70** .. .. 3·00 2·75
203 100 l. Locomotive No. 1 .. .. 3·50 3·75

Kuzey Kıbrıs Türk Cumhuriyeti

(71)

1987 (18 May). *Nos.* 94, 96/7 *and* 113 *optd as T* **71** *or surch also.*

204 10 l. deep mauve and pale green 50 70
205 15 l. on 3½ l. grey-green and pale rose-pink 50 70
206 20 l. dull ultramarine & pale greenish yellow 55 75
207 30 l. multicoloured .. .. 70 1·10
204/7 .. .. *Set of* 4 2·00 3·00

(Litho Tezel Ofset, Lefkosa)

1987 (27 May). *Paintings (6th series). Vert designs as T* **54**. *Multicoloured. W* **51** *(inverted). P* 12½×13.

208 50 l. "Shepherd" (Feridun Işiman) .. .. 1·25 1·25
209 125 l. "Pear Woman" (Mehmet Uluhan) .. 1·75 2·75

72 Modern House (architect A. Vural Behaeddin) **73** Kneeling Folk Dancer

(Des H. Uluçam (50 l.). Litho Tezel Ofset, Lefkosa)

1987 (30 June). *Europa. Modern Architecture. T* **72** *and similar horiz design. Multicoloured. W* **51** *(sideways). P* 12×12½.

210 50 l. Type **72** .. .. 1·00 30
a. Perf 12×imperf .. .. 1·75 3·00
ab. Booklet pane. Nos. 210a/11a, each × 2 7·00
211 200 l. Modern house (architect Necdet Turgay) .. .. 1·75 3·00
a. Perf 12 × imperf .. .. 1·75 3·00

Nos. 210a and 211a come from 500 l. stamp booklets containing *se-tenant* pane No. 210ab.

(Des B. Ruhi. Litho Tezel Ofset, Lefkosa)

1987 (20 Aug). *Folk Dancers. T* **73** *and similar vert designs. Multicoloured. W* **51** *(inverted). P* 12½×12.

212 20 l. Type **73** 60 20
213 50 l. Standing male dancer 90 40
214 200 l. Standing female dancer .. .. .. 2·00 1·75
215 1000 l. Woman's headdress .. .. 4·75 6·50
212/15 .. .. *Set of* 4 7·50 8·00

74 Regimental Colour (1st Anniv of Infantry Regiment) **75** Ahmet Beliğ Pasha (Egyptian judge)

(Des H. Uluçam. Litho Tezel Ofset, Lefkosa)

1987 (30 Sept–2 Nov). *Anniversaries and Events. T* **74** *and similar multicoloured designs. W* **51** *(inverted on vert designs, sideways on horiz). P* 12½×12 *(vert) or* 12×12½ *(horiz).*

216 50 l. Type **74** .. .. 1·25 75
217 50 l. Pres. Denktash and Turgut Özal (1st anniv. of Turkish Prime Minister's visit) (*horiz*) (2.11) .. .. .. 1·25 75
218 200 l. Emblem and Crescent (5th Islamic Summit Conference, Kuwait) .. .. 2·25 3·25
219 200 l. Emblem and laurel leaves (Membership of Pharmaceutical Federation) (*horiz*) .. .. 2·25 3·25
216/19 .. .. *Set of* 4 6·25 7·25

(Des H. Uluçam. Litho Tezel Ofset, Lefkosa)

1987 (22 Oct). *Turkish Cypriot Personalities. T* **75** *and similar vert designs. W* **51** *(inverted). P* 12½×12.

220 **75** 50 l. brown and greenish yellow .. 65 40
221 – 50 l. multicoloured 65 40
222 – 125 l. multicoloured .. .. 1·50 3·00
220/2 .. .. *Set of* 3 2·50 3·50

Designs:—50 l. (No. 221) Mehmet Emin Pasha (Ottoman Grand Vizier); 125 l. Mehmet Kâmil Pasha (Ottoman Grand Vizier).

76 Tourist Hotel, Girne **77** *Piyale Pasha* (tug)

(Des A. Erduran. Litho Tezel Ofset, Lefkosa)

1987 (20 Nov). *Modern Development (2nd series). T* **76** *and similar horiz design. Multicoloured. W* **51** *(sideways). P* 12×12½.

223 150 l. Type **76** .. .. 1·50 1·50
224 200 l. Dogu Akdeniz University .. .. 1·75 2·25

(Litho Tezel Ofset, Lefkosa)

1988 (2 May). *Paintings (7th series). Multicoloured designs as T* **54**. *W* **51** *(inverted on* 20, 150 *l, sideways on* 50 *l.). P* 12½×13 (20, 150 *l.) or* 13×12½ (50 *l.).*

225   20 l. "Woman making Pastry" (Ayhan Mentes) (*vert*) 50 20
226   50 l. "Chair Weaver" (Osman Güvenir) .. 75 75
227   150 l. "Woman weaving a Rug" (Zekâi Yesiladali) (*vert*) .. .. .. 1·75 3·25
225/7 .. .. *Set of* 3 2·75 3·75

(Des H. Uluçam. Litho Tezel Ofset, Lefkosa)

1988 (31 May). *Europa. Transport and Communications. T* **77** *and similar multicoloured design. W* **51** *(sideways on* 200 *l., inverted on* 500 *l.). P* 12×12½ (200 *l.) or* 12½×12 (500 *l.).*

228   200 l. Type **77** .. .. 1·75 75
229   500 l. Dish aerial and antenna tower, Selvilitepe (*vert*) .. .. .. 2·50 4·00

No. 229 also commemorates the 25th anniversary of Bayrak Radio and Television Corporation.

78 Lefkosa

79 Bülent Ecevit

(Litho Tezel Ofset, Lefkosa)

1988 (17 June). *Tourism. T* **78** *and similar horiz designs. Multicoloured. W* **51** *(sideways). P* 12×12½.

230   150 l. Type **78** 80 80
231   200 l. Gazi-Magusa .. .. 90 1·00
232   300 l. Girne .. .. 1·50 2·00
230/2 .. .. *Set of* 3 2·75 3·50

(Litho Tezel Ofset, Lefkosa)

1988 (20 July). *Turkish Prime Ministers. T* **79** *and similar vert designs. Multicoloured. W* **51**. *P* 12½×12.

233   50 l. Type **79** 60 75
234   50 l. Bülent Ulusu 60 75
235   50 l. Turgut Ozal 60 75
233/5 .. .. *Set of* 3 1·60 2·00

80 Red Crescent Members on Exercise

81 Hodori the Tiger (Games mascot) and Fireworks

(Des N. Kozal. Litho Tezel Ofset, Lefkosa)

1988 (8 Aug). *Civil Defence. W* **51** *(sideways). P* 12×12½.

236 **80** 150 l. multicoloured .. .. .. 1·25 1·50

(Des E. Cizenel (200 l.), N. Kozal (250 l.), H. Uluçam (400 l.). Litho Tezel Ofset, Lefkosa)

1988 (17 Sept). *Olympic Games, Seoul. T* **81** *and similar horiz designs. Multicoloured. W* **51** *(sideways). P* 12×12½.

237   200 l. Type **81** .. .. 80 1·00
      a. Imperf (pair) .. .. .. 70·00
238   250 l. Athletics .. .. 1·00 1·25
239   400 l. Shot and running track with letters spelling "SEOUL" .. .. .. 1·50 2·00
237/9 .. .. *Set of* 3 3·00 3·75

82 Sedat Simavi (journalist)

83 "Kemal Atatürk" (I. Calli)

(Des H. Uluçam (Nos. 241/3). Litho Tezel Ofset, Lefkosa)

1988 (17 Oct). *Anniversaries and Events. T* **82** *and similar designs. W* **51** *(inverted on Nos.* 240, 243 *and* 245, *sideways on Nos.* 241 *and* 244). *P* 12½×12 *(vert) or* 12×12½ *(horiz).*

240   50 l. olive-green 25 25
241   100 l. multicoloured 50 45
242   300 l. multicoloured .. .. 70 1·00
243   400 l. multicoloured .. .. 1·50 1·75
244   400 l. multicoloured .. .. 1·00 1·75
245   600 l. multicoloured .. .. 2·00 2·50
240/5 .. .. *Set of* 6 5·50 7·00

Designs: *Horiz*—No. 241, Stylised figures around table and flags of participating countries (International Girne Conferences); 244, Presidents Gorbachev and Reagan signing treaty (Summit Meeting). *Vert*—No. 242, Cogwheels as flowers (North Cyprus Industrial Fair); 243, Globe (125th anniv of International Red Cross); 245, "Medical Services" (40th anniv of W.H.O.).

(Litho Tezel Ofset, Lefkosa)

1988 (10 Nov). *50th Death Anniv of Kemal Atatürk. Sheet* 72 × 102 *mm containing T* **83** *and similar vert designs. Multicoloured. W* **51** *(inverted). P* 12½ × 12.

MS246 250 l. Type **83**; 250 l. "Kemal Atatürk" (N. Ismail); 250 l. In army uniform; 250 l. In profile .. .. 2·00 2·00

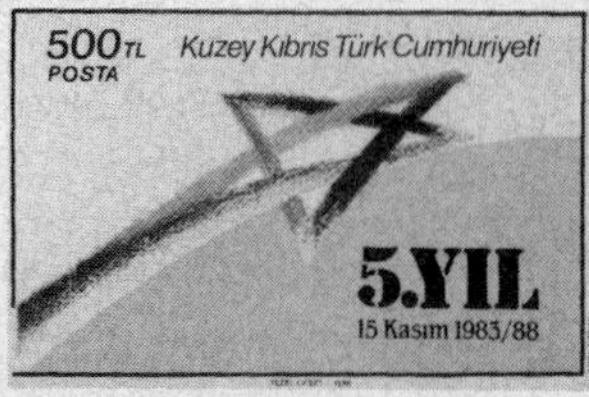

84 Abstract Design

(Des E. Cizenel. Litho Tezel Ofset, Lefkosa)

1988 (15 Nov). *5th Anniv of Turkish Republic of Northern Cyprus. Sheet* 98 × 76 *mm. W* **51** *(sideways). Imperf.*

MS247 **84** 500 l. multicoloured .. .. .. 2·25 1·75

(Litho Tezel Ofset, Lefkosa)

1989 (28 Apr). *Paintings (8th series). Multicoloured designs as T* **54**. *W* **51** *(sideways on* 150, 400 *l., inverted on* 600 *l.). P* 12½×13 (600 *l.) or* 13×12½ *(others).*

248   150 l. "Dervis Pasa Mansion, Lefkosa" (Inci Kansu) 90 60
249   400 l. "Gamblers' Inn, Lefkosa" (Osman Güvenir) .. .. 1·75 2·25
250   600 l. "Mosque, Paphos" (Hikmet Ulucam) (*vert*) .. .. 2·50 3·00
248/50 .. .. *Set of* 3 4·75 5·25

85 Girl with Doll

86 Meeting of Presidents Vassiliou and Denktash

(Des N. Kozal. Litho Tezel Ofset, Lefkosa)

1989 (31 May). *Europa. Children's Games. T* **85** *and similar vert design. Multicoloured. W* **51**. *P* 12½×12.

251   600 l. Type **85** .. .. 1·75 1·25
      a. Imperf × p 12 .. .. .. 2·00 3·25
      ab. Booklet pane. Nos. 251a/2a, each ×2 7·50
252   1000 l. Boy with kite .. .. .. 2·00 3·25
      a. Imperf × p 12 .. .. .. 2·00 3·25

Nos. 251a and 252a come from 3200 l. stamp booklets containing *se-tenant* pane No. 251ab.

(Litho Tezel Ofset, Lefkosa)

1989 (30 June). *Cyprus Peace Summit, Geneva,* 1988. *W* **51** *(sideways). P* 12×12½.

253 **86** 500 l. deep rose-red and black .. .. 1·25 1·25

87 Chukar Partridge

88 Road Construction

(Des E. Cizenel. Litho Tezel Ofset, Lefkosa)

1989 (31 July). *Wildlife. T* **87** *and similar horiz designs. Multicoloured. W* **51** *(sideways). P* 12×12½.

254   100 l. Type **87** 65 25
255   200 l. Cyprus Hare 70 35
256   700 l. Black Partridge .. .. .. 2·50 2·00
257   2000 l. Red Fox .. .. 3·00 3·50
254/7 .. .. *Set of* 4 6·00 5·50

(Litho Tezel Ofset, Lefkosa)

1989 (29 Sept). *Modern Development (3rd series). T* **88** *and similar multicoloured designs. W* **51** *(sideways on* 100, 700 *l.). P* 12×12½ (100, 700 *l.) or* 12½×12 *(others).*

258   100 l. Type **88** 15 10
259   150 l. Laying water pipeline (*vert*) .. 20 20
260   200 l. Seedling trees (*vert*) 30 30
261   450 l. Modern telephone exchange (*vert*) .. 75 1·00
262   650 l. Steam turbine power station (*vert*) 1·00 1·50
263   700 l. Irrigation reservoir .. .. 1·25 1·75
258/63 .. .. *Set of* 6 3·25 4·25

MINIMUM PRICE

The minimum price quote is 10p which represents a handling charge rather than a basis for valuing common stamps. For further notes about prices see introductory pages.

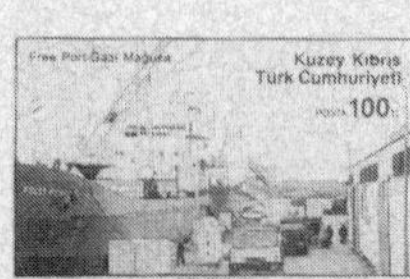

89 Unloading Freighter at Quayside (15th anniv of Gazi Magusa Free Port)

90 Erdal Inonu

(Des E. Çizenel (450, 600 l.), Ö. Özünalp (500 l.), S. Oral (1000 l.). Litho Tezel Ofset, Lefkosa)

1989 (17 Nov). *Anniversaries. T* **89** *and similar designs. W* 5 *(inverted on* 450 *l., sideways on others). P* 12½×13 (450 *l.)* 12×12½ *(others).*

264   100 l. multicoloured 35
265   450 l. black, dull ultramarine & scar- verm 80
266   500 l. black, yellow-ochre and olive-grey .. 80
267   600 l. black, vermilion and new blue .. 1·10 1·
268   1000 l. multicoloured .. .. .. 2·00 2·
264/8 .. .. *Set of* 5 4·50 5·

Designs: *Vert* (26×47 *mm*)—450 l. Airmail letter and stylize bird (25th anniv of Turkish Cypriot postal service). *Horiz* (*T* **89**)—500 l. Newspaper and printing press (centenary of *Sad* newspaper); 600 l. Statue of Aphrodite, lifebelt and seabi (30th anniv of International Maritime Organization); 1000 Soldiers (25th anniv of Turkish Cypriot resistance).

(Litho Tezel Ofset, Lefkosa)

1989 (15 Dec). *Visit of Professor Erdal Inonu (Turkis politician). W* **51** *(inverted). P* 12½×12.

269 **90** 700 l. multicoloured 50

91 Mule-drawn Plough

92 Smoking Ashtray and Drinks

(Des N. Kozal. Litho Tezel Ofset, Lefkosa)

1989 (25 Dec). *Traditional Agricultural Implements. T* **91** *an similar multicoloured designs. W* **51** *(sideways on* 150, 450 *l P* 12½×12 (550 *l.) or* 12×12½ *(others).*

270   150 l. Type **91** 15
271   450 l. Ox-drawn threshing sledge .. 50
272   550 l. Olive press (*vert*) 60
270/2 .. .. *Set of* 3 1·10 1·

(Des O. Ozünalp (200 l.), H. Ulucam (700 l). Litho Tezel Ofse Lefkosa)

1990 (19 Apr). *World Health Day. T* **92** *and similar ho design. Multicoloured. W* **51** *(sideways). P* 12×12½.

273   200 l. Type **92** 50
274   700 l. Smoking cigarette and heart .. 1·00 1·

93 Yenierenköy Post Office

94 Song Thrush

(Des H. Billur. Litho Tezel Ofset, Lefkosa)

1990 (31 May). *Europa. Post Office Buildings. T* **93** *an similar horiz design. Multicoloured. W* **51** *(sideways P* 12×12½.

275   1000 t. Type **93** 90
276   1500 t. Atatürk Meydani Post Office .. 1·60 2·
MS277 105×72 mm. Nos. 275/6, each × 2 .. 5·50 6·

(Des H. Billur. Litho Tezel Ofset, Lefkosa)

1990 (5 June). *World Environment Day. T* **94** *and similar ve designs showing birds. Multicoloured. W* **51** *(inverte P* 12½×12.

278   150 l. Type **94** .. .. 1·00
279   300 l. Blackcap .. .. 1·50
280   900 l. Black Redstart .. .. .. 2·25 2·
281   1000 l. Chiff-chaff .. .. 2·25 3·
278/81 .. .. *Set of* 4 6·25 6·

95 Two Football Teams

96 Amphitheatre, Soli

(Des H. Billur (1000 l.). Litho Tezel Ofset, Lefkosa)

1990 (8 June). *World Cup Football Championship, Italy. T* **95** *and similar horiz design. Multicoloured. W* **51** *(sideways). P* 12×12½.

282 300 l. Type **95** 75 50
283 1000 l. Championship symbol, globe and ball 2·50 3·00

(Litho Tezel Ofset, Lefkosa)

1990 (31 July). *Paintings (9th series). Multicoloured designs as T* **54**. *W* **51** *(sideways on 300 l.). P* 13×12½ *(300 l.) or* 12½×13 *(1000 l.).*

284 300 l. "Abstract" (Filiz Ankaçç) 25 25
285 1000 l. Wooden sculpture (S. Tekman) *(vert)* 85 1·50

(Litho Tezel Ofset, Lefkosa)

1990 (24 Aug). *Tourism. T* **96** *and similar vert design. Multicoloured. W* **51**. *P* 12½.

286 150 l. Type **96** 40 20
287 1000 l. Swan mosaic, Soli .. .. .. 1·75 2·50

97 Kenan Evren and Rauf Denktas

98 Road Signs and Heart wearing Seat Belt

(Litho Tezel Ofset, Lefkosa)

1990 (19 Sept). *Visit of President Kenan Evren of Turkey. W* **51** *(sideways). P* 12½.

288 **97** 500 l. multicoloured .. .. .. 1·00 1·00

(Des H. Billur. Litho Tezel Ofset, Lefkosa)

1990 (21 Sept). *Traffic Safety Campaign. T* **98** *and similar horiz designs. Multicoloured. W* **51** *(sideways). P* 12½.

289 150 l. Type **98** 50 25
290 300 l. Road signs, speeding car and spots of blood 75 50
291 1000 l. Traffic lights and road signs .. 2·25 2·75
289/91 .. .. *Set of* 3 3·25 3·25

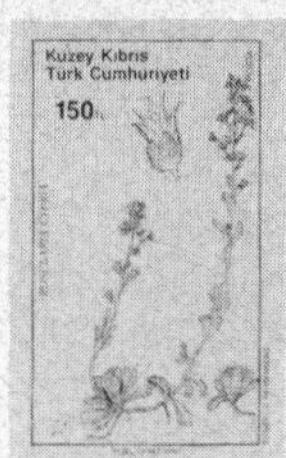

99 Yildirim Akbulut

100 *Rosularia cypria*

(Litho Tezel Ofset, Lefkosa)

1990 (1 Oct). *Visit of Turkish Prime Minister Yildrim Akbulut. W* **51** *(inverted). P* 12½.

292 **99** 1000 l. multicoloured .. .. .. 1·10 1·10

(Des D. Viney and P. Jacobs (200, 1500 l.), D. Viney and C. Hessenberg (others). Litho Tezel Ofset, Lefkosa)

1990 (31 Oct). *Plants. T* **100** *and similar vert designs. Multicoloured. W* **51**. *P* 12½.

293 150 l. Type **100** 30 20
294 200 l. *Silene fraudratrix* 40 30
295 300 l. *Scutellaria sibthorpii* 45 35
296 600 l. *Sedum lampusae* 65 70
297 1000 l. *Onosma caespitosum* .. .. 90 1·25
298 1500 l. *Arabis cypria* .. .. .. 1·25 1·75
293/8 .. .. *Set of* 6 3·50 4·00

101 Kemal Atatürk at Easel (wood carving)

250 TL

(102)

(Des M. Uzel (300 l.), H. Billur (750 l.). Litho Tezel Ofset, Lefkosa)

1990 (24 Nov). *International Literacy Year. T* **101** *and similar horiz design. Multicoloured. W* **51** *(sideways). P* 12½.

299 300 l. Type **101** 40 35
300 750 l. Globe, letters and books .. .. 1·00 1·40

1991 (3 June). *Nos. 189, 212 and 293 surch as T* **102**.

301 250 l. on 10 l. Type **66** 50 50
302 250 l. on 20 l. Type **73** 50 50
303 500 l. on 150 l. Type **100** 75 75
a. Surch inverted .. .. .. 50·00
301/3 .. .. *Set of* 3 1·60 1·60

PRINTER. Issues from Nos. 304/5 onwards were printed in lithography by the State Printing Works, Lefkosa, *unless otherwise stated.*

103 *Ophrys lapethica*

104 *Hermes* (projected shuttle)

1991 (8 July). *Orchids (1st series). T* **103** *and similar vert design. Multicoloured. W* **51** *(inverted). P* 14.

304 250 l. Type **103** .. .. 1·00 60
305 500 l. *Ophrys kotschyi* .. .. .. 1·75 2·00

See also Nos. 311/14

1991 (29 July). *Europa. Europe in Space. Sheet* 78×82 *mm containing T* **104** *and similar vert design. Multicoloured. W* **51**. *P* 12½.

MS306 2000 l. Type **104**; 2000 l. *Ulysses* (satellite) .. .. 4·00 4·00

105 Kucuk Medrese Fountain, Lefkosa

106 Symbolic Roots (Year of Love to Yunus Emre)

(Des H. Billur)

1991 (9 Sept). *Fountains. T* **105** *and similar horiz designs. Multicoloured. W* **51** *(sideways). P* 12½.

307 250 l. Type **105** 30 15
308 500 l. Cafer Pasa Fountain, Magusa .. 40 30
309 1500 l. Sarayönü Square Fountain, Lefkosa 70 80
310 5000 l. Arabahmet Mosque Fountain, Lefkosa .. .. 1·75 2·50
307/10 .. .. *Set of* 4 2·75 3·25

1991 (10 Oct). *Orchids (2nd series). Vert designs as T* **103**. *Multicoloured. W* **51**. *P* 14.

311 100 l. *Serapias levantina* 30 20
312 500 l. *Dactylorhiza romana* 70 50
313 2000 l. *Orchis simia* .. .. .. 2·00 2·50
314 3000 l. *Orchis sancta* .. .. .. 2·50 3·00
311/14 .. .. *Set of* 4 5·00 5·75

1991 (5 Nov). *Paintings (10th series). Multicoloured designs as T* **54**. *W* **51**. *P* 12½×13.

315 250 l. "Hindiler" (S. Çizel) *(vert)* .. 50 35
316 500 l. "Düsme" (A. Mene) *(vert)* .. .. 1·00 1·25

(Des K. Sarikavak (250 l.), H. Billur (500, 1500 l.))

1991 (20 Nov). *Anniversaries and Events. T* **106** *and similar designs. W* **51** *(sideways on 1500 l., inverted on others). P* 12×12½ *(1500 l.) or* 12½×12 *(others).*

317 250 l. greenish yellow, black & brt mag .. 25 25
318 500 l. multicoloured 45 50
319 500 l. multicoloured 45 50
320 1500 l. multicoloured .. .. .. 1·75 2·00
317/20 .. .. *Set of* 4 2·75 3·00

Designs: *Vert*—No. 318, Mustafa Cagatay commemoration; No. 319, University building (5th anniv of Eastern Mediterranean University). *Horiz*—No. 320, Mozart (death bicent).

107 Four Sources of Infection

108 Lighthouse, Gazimagusa

1991 (13 Dec). *AIDS Day. W* **51** *(sideways). P* 12×12½.

321 **107** 1000 l. multicoloured .. .. .. 1·10 1·10

(Des H. Billur)

1991 (16 Dec). *Lighthouses. T* **108** *and similar horiz designs. Multicoloured. W* **51** *(sideways). P* 12×12½.

322 250 l. Type **108** 65 35
323 500 l. Ancient lighthouses, Girne harbour 1·00 80
324 1500 l. Modern lighthouse, Girne harbour .. 2·25 2·75
322/4 .. .. *Set of* 3 3·50 3·50

109 Elephant and Hippopotamus Fossils, Karaoglanoglu

1991 (27 Dec). *Tourism (1st series). T* **109** *and similar horiz designs. Multicoloured. W* **51** *(sideways). P* 12.

325 250 l. Type **109** 50 30
326 500 l. Roman fish ponds, Lambusa .. 65 45
327 1500 l. Roman remains, Lambusa .. .. 1·50 2·25
325/7 .. .. *Set of* 3 2·40 2·75

See also Nos. 330/3 and 351/2.

1992 (31 Mar). *Paintings (11th series). Multicoloured designs as T* **54**, *but* 31×49 *mm. W* **51** *(sideways). P* 14.

328 500 l. "Ebru" (A. Kandulu) 40 20
329 3500 l. "Street in Lefkosa" (I. Tatar) .. 1·60 2·25

1992 (21 Apr). *Tourism (2nd series). Multicoloured designs as T* **109**. *W* **51** *(sideways). P* 14×13½ *(1500 l.) or* 13½×14 *(others).*

330 500 l. Bugday Camii, Gazimagusa .. 30 30
331 500 l. Clay pigeon shooting 30 30
332 1000 l. Salamis Bay Hotel, Gazimagusa .. 60 80
333 1500 l. Casino, Girne *(vert)* .. .. 90 1·50
330/3 .. .. *Set of* 4 1·90 2·50

110 Fleet of Columbus and Early Map

(Des H. Billur)

1992 (29 May). *Europa. 500th Anniv of Discovery of America by Columbus. Sheet,* 80×76 *mm, containing T* **110** *and similar horiz design. Multicoloured. W* **51** *(sideways). P* 13½×14.

MS334 1500 l. Type **110**; 3500 l. Christopher Columbus and signature .. .. .. 2·00 2·50

111 Green Turtle

112 Gymnastics

(Des H. Billur)

1992 (30 June). *World Environment Day. Sea Turtles. Sheet,* 105×75 *mm, containing T* **111** *and similar horiz design. W* **51** *(sideways). P* 13½×14.

MS335 1000 l. × 2, Type **111**: 1500 l. × 2, Loggerhead Turtle .. .. 3·00 3·25

(Des H. Billur)

1992 (25 July). *Olympic Games, Barcelona. T* **112** *and similar multicoloured designs. W* **51** *(inverted on 500 l., sideways on 1000, 1500 l.). P 14×13½ (500 l.) or 13½×14 (others).*

336 500 l. Type **112** 45 55
a. Horiz pair. Nos. 336/7 .. .. 90 1·10
337 500 l. Tennis 45 55
338 1000 l. High jumping (*horiz*) 70 80
339 1500 l. Cycling (*horiz*) .. .. .. 1·00 1·25
336/9 .. .. *Set of* 4 2·40 2·75

Nos. 336/7 were printed together, *se-tenant*, in horizontal pairs throughout the sheet.

113 New Generating Station, Girne

(Des H. Billur (Nos. 341/2), Therese Coustry (No. 343))

1992 (30 Sept). *Anniversaries and Events (1st series). T* **113** *and similar horiz designs. Multicoloured. W* **51** *(sideways). P* 14.

340 500 l. Type **113** 30 20
341 500 l. Symbol of Housing Association (15th anniv) 30 20
342 1500 l. Domestic animals and birds (30th anniv of Veterinary Service) .. 1·50 1·75
343 1500 l. Cat (International Federation of Cat Societies Conference) .. .. 1·50 1·75
340/3 .. .. *Set of* 4 3·25 3·50

114 Airliner over Runway

(Des H. Billur)

1992 (20 Nov). *Anniversaries and Events (2nd series). T* **114** *and similar horiz designs. Multicoloured. W* **51** *(sideways). P* 13½×14.

344 1000 l. Type **114** (17th anniv of civil aviation) 80 80
345 1000 l. Meteorological instruments and weather (18th anniv of Meteorological Service) 80 80
346 1200 l. Surveying equipment and map (14th anniv of Survey Department) .. 1·00 1·25
344/6 .. .. *Set of* 3 2·40 2·50

115 Zübiye

116 Painting by Turksal Ince

(Des A. Erduran)

1992 (14 Dec). *International Conference on Nutrition, Rome. Turkish Cypriot Cuisine. T* **115** *and similar horiz designs. W* **51** *(sideways). P* 13½×14.

347 2000 l. Type **115** 70 80
348 2500 l. Çiçek Dolmasi 80 90
349 3000 l. Tatar Böregi .. .. .. 90 1·00
350 4000 l. Şeftali Kebabi .. .. .. 1·10 1·25
347/50 .. .. *Set of* 4 3·25 3·50

1993 (1 Apr). *Tourism (3rd series). Horiz designs as T* **109**. *Multicoloured. W* **51** *(sideways). P* 13½×14.

351 500 l. Saint Barnabas Church and Monastery, Salamis 30 15
352 10000 l. Ancient pot .. .. .. 2·25 2·50

(Des T. Ince and I. Onsoy)

1993 (5 May). *Europa. Contemporary Art. Sheet* 79×69 *mm containing T* **116** *and similar vert design. Multicoloured. W* **51**. *P* 14.

MS353 2000 l. Type **116**; 3000 l. Painting by Ilkay Onsoy .. .. 1·50 1·75

ALTERED CATALOGUE NUMBERS

Any Catalogue numbers altered from the last edition are shown as a list in the introductory pages.

117 Olive Tree, Girne

118 Traditional Houses

1993 (11 June). *Ancient Trees. T* **117** *and similar vert designs. Multicoloured. W* **51** *(inverted). P* 14.

354 500 l. Type **117** 15 15
355 1000 l. River red gum, Kyrenia Gate, Lefkosa 25 25
356 3000 l. Oriental plane, Lapta 70 90
357 4000 l. Calabrian pine, Cinarli .. .. 85 1·25
354/7 .. .. *Set of* 4 1·75 2·25

(Des H. Billur)

1993 (20 Sept). *Arabahmet District Conservation Project, Lefkosa. T* **118** *and similar horiz design. Multicoloured. W* **51** *(sideways). P* 13½×14.

358 1000 l. Type **118** 50 40
359 3000 l. Arabahmet street .. .. .. 1·50 2·00

119 National Flags turning into Doves

120 Kemal Atatürk

(Des H. Ulucam (5000 l.), H. Billur (others))

1993 (15 Nov). *10th Anniv of Proclamation of Turkish Republic of Northern Cyprus. T* **119** *and similar designs. W* **51** *(sideways on Nos. 361/3). P 14×13½ (No. 360) or 13½×14 (others).*

360 500 l. carmine-red, black and new blue .. 20 15
361 500 l. rosine and new blue 20 15
362 1000 l. carmine-red, black and new blue .. 30 30
363 5000 l. multicoloured .. .. .. 1·40 2·00
360/3 .. .. *Set of* 4 1·90 2·40

Designs: *Horiz*—No. 361, National flag forming figure "10"; No. 362, Dove carrying national flag; No. 363, Map of Cyprus and figure "10" wreath.

(Des H. Billur (Nos. 365/8))

1993 (27 Dec). *Anniversaries. T* **120** *and similar multicoloured designs. W* **51** *(inverted on No. 364 or sideways on others). P 14×13½ (No. 364) or 13½×14 (others).*

364 500 l. Type **120** (55th death anniv) .. 20 20
365 500 l. Stage and emblem (30th anniv of Turkish Cypriot theatre) (*horiz*) .. 20 20
366 1500 l. Branch badges (35th anniv of T.M.T. organization) (*horiz*) 35 45
367 2000 l. World map and computer (20th anniv of Turkish Cypriot news agency) (*horiz*) 45 55
368 5000 l. Ballet dancers and Caykovski'nin (Death centenary) (*horiz*) .. 1·40 2·00
364/8 .. .. *Set of* 5 2·40 3·00

121 "Söyle Falci" (Göral Ozkan)

1994 (31 Mar). *Art (12th series). T* **121** *and similar vert design. Multicoloured. W* **51**. *P* 14.

369 1000 l. Type **121** 15 20
370 6500 l. "IV. Hareket" (sculpture) (Senol Ozdevrim) .. .. 85 1·40

See also Nos. 436/7

122 Dr. Kucuk and Memorial

1994 (1 Apr). *10th Death Anniv of Dr. Fazil Kucuk (politician). W* **51** *(sideways). P* 14.

371 **122** 1500 l. multicoloured 30 40

123 Neolithic Village, Girne

(Des H. Billur)

1994 (16 May). *Europa. Archaeological Discoveries. Sheet* 73×79 *mm containing T* **123** *and similar horiz design. Multicoloured. W* **51** *(sideways). P* 13½×14.

MS372 8500 l. Type **123**; 8500 l. Neolithic man and implements .. .. 4·00 4·00

124 Peace Doves and Letters over Pillar Box

125 World Cup Trophy

(Des H. Billur)

1994 (30 June). *30th Anniv of Turkish Cypriot Postal Service. W* **51** *(sideways). P* 13½×14.

373 **124** 50000 l. multicoloured .. .. .. 2·75 3·50

(Des H. Billur)

1994 (30 June). *World Cup Football Championship, U.S.A. T* **125** *and similar multicoloured design. W* **51** *(sideways on 10000 l.). P 14×13½ (2500 l.) or 13½×14 (10000 l.).*

374 2500 l. Type **125** 30 2
375 10000 l. Footballs on map of U.S.A. (*horiz*) 1·25 1·5

126 Peace Emblem

127 Cyprus 1934 4½ pi. Stamp and Karpas Postmark

(Des H. Billur (2500, 8500 l.))

1994 (20 July). *20th Anniv of Turkish Landings in Cyprus. T* **126** *and similar designs. W* **51** *(sideways on horiz designs). P 14×13½ (2500 l.) or 13½×14 (others).*

376 2500 l. greenish yellow, emerald and black 30 30
377 5000 l. multicoloured 50 50
378 7000 l. multicoloured 70 70
379 8500 l. multicoloured 90 90
376/9 .. .. *Set of* 4 2·25 2·25

Designs: *Horiz*—5000 l. Memorial; 7000 l. Sculpture; 8500 l. Peace doves forming map of Cyprus and flame.

1994 (15 Aug). *Postal Centenary. T* **127** *and similar horiz designs. Multicoloured. W* **51** *(sideways). P* 13½×14.

380 1500 l. Type **127** 20 20
381 2500 l. Turkish Cypriot Posts 1979 Europa 2 l. and Gazimagusa postmark .. 30 30
382 5000 l. Cyprus 1938 6 pi. and Bey Keuy postmark 50 50
383 7000 l. Cyprus 1955 100 m. and Aloa postmark 70 70
384 8500 l. Cyprus 1938 18 pi. and Pyla postmark 90 90
380/4 .. .. *Set of* 5 2·40 2·40

128 Trumpet Triton (*Charonia tritonis*)

***

1500 TL

(129)

1994 (15 Nov). *Sea Shells. T* **128** *and similar horiz designs. Multicoloured. W* **51** *(sideways). P* 13½×14.
385 2500 l. Type **128** 45 30
386 12500 l. Mole Cowrie (*Cypraea talpa*) .. 1·25 1·50
387 12500 l. Giant Tun (*Tonna galea*) .. .. 1·25 1·50
385/7 .. .. *Set of* 3 2·75 3·00

1994 (12 Dec)–**95**. *Nos.* 280, 295, 315 *and* 317 *surch as T* **129**.
388 1500 l. on 250 l. Type **106** 10 10
389 2000 l. on 900 l. Black Redstart (21.4.95) .. 50 50
390 2500 l. on 250 l. "Hindiler" (S. Çizel) .. 20 20
391 3500 l. on 300 l. *Scutellaria sibthorpii* (21.4.95) 50 50
388/91 .. .. *Set of* 4 1·10 1·10
Nos. 389/90 show the surcharge value horizontally.

130 Donkeys on Mountain

131 Peace Dove and Globe

1995 (10 Feb). *European Conservation Year. T* **130** *and similar horiz designs. W* **51** *(sideways). P* 13½×14.
392 2000 l. Type **130** 20 20
393 3500 l. Coastline 30 30
394 15000 l. Donkeys in field .. .. 1·25 1·75
392/4 .. .. *Set of* 3 1·60 2·00

(Des H. Billur)

1995 (20 Apr). *Europa. Peace and Freedom. Sheet* 72×78 *mm containing T* **131** *and similar horiz design. W* **51** *(sideways). P* 13½×14.
MS395 15000 l. Type **131**; 15000 l. Peace doves over map of Europe .. .. 1·60 1·75

132 Sini Katmeri

133 *Papilio machaon*

1995 (29 May). *Turkish Cypriot Cuisine. T* **132** *and similar horiz designs. Multicoloured. W* **51** *(sideways). P* 13½×14.
396 3500 l. Type **132** 20 20
397 10000 l. Kolokas musakka and bullez kizartma 55 55
398 14000 l. Enginar dolmasi .. .. 90 1·10
396/8 .. .. *Set of* 3 1·50 1·75

(Des H. Billur)

1995 (30 June). *Butterflies. T* **133** *and similar horiz designs. Multicoloured. W* **51** *(sideways). P* 13½×14.
399 3500 l. Type **133** 30 15
400 4500 l. *Charaxes jasius* 35 20
401 15000 l. *Cynthia cardui* .. .. 1·00 1·10
402 30000 l. *Vanessa atalanta* .. .. 1·75 2·00
399/402 .. .. *Set of* 4 3·00 3·00

134 Forest

135 Beach, Girne

1995 (7 Aug). *Obligatory Tax. Forest Regeneration Fund. P* 14×13½.
403 **134** 1000 l. emerald and black 60 20
No. 403 was for compulsory use on all mail, in addition to the normal postage, between 7 August and 6 February 1996. It was intended to provide funds for the replanting of those forests destroyed by fire in June 1995. A similar 50000 l. stamp was issued for fiscal use only.

1995 (21 Aug). *Tourism. T* **135** *and similar multicoloured designs. W* **51** *(sideways on horiz designs). P* 13½×14 *(horiz) or* 14×13½ *(vert).*
404 3500 l. Type **135** 15 15
405 7500 l. Sail boards 35 35
406 15000 l. Ruins of Salamis (*vert*) 70 80
407 20000 l. St. George's Cathedral, Gazimagusa (*vert*) .. .. 90 1·00
404/7 .. .. *Set of* 4 1·90 2·10

136 Süleyman Demirel and Rauf Denktas

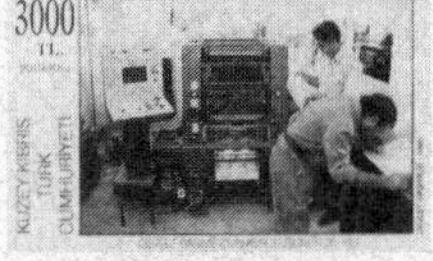
137 Stamp Printing Press

1995 (21 Aug). *Visit of President Süleyman Demirel of Turkey. W* **51** *(sideways). P* 14.
408 **136** 5000 l. multicoloured 20 20

(Des H. Billur (Nos. 410/14))

1995 (7 Nov). *Anniversaries. T* **137** *and similar designs. W* **51** *(sideways on horiz designs). P* 14×13½ *(No.* 414*) or* 13½×14 *(others).*
409 3000 l. multicoloured 40 40
410 3000 l. multicoloured 40 40
411 5000 l. multicoloured 70 70
412 22000 l. dull ultramarine, new blue & black 1·00 1·25
413 30000 l. multicoloured .. .. 1·40 1·75
414 30000 l. multicoloured .. .. 1·40 1·75
409/14 .. .. *Set of* 6 4·75 5·50
Designs: *Horiz*—No. 409, Type **137** (20th anniv od State Printing Works); No. 410, Map of Turkey (75th anniv of Turkish National Assembly); No. 411, Louis Pasteur (chemist) and microscope (Death centenary); No. 412, United Nations anniversary emblem (50th anniv); No. 413, Guglielmo Marconi (radio pioneer) and dial (Centenary of first radio transmissions). *Vert*—No. 414, Stars and reel of film (Centenary of cinema).

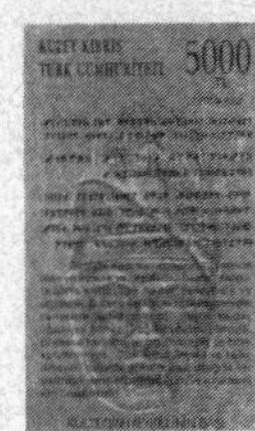
138 Kültegin Epitaph and Sculpture

139 "Bosnia" (sculpture)

(Des H. Billur)

1995 (28 Dec). *Centenary of Deciphering of Orhon Epitaphs. T* **138** *and similar vert design. W* **51**. *P* 14.
415 5000 l. Type **138** 35 35
416 10000 l. Epitaph and tombstone 65 75

(Des S. Ozdevrim)

1996 (31 Jan). *Support for Moslems in Bosnia and Herzegovina. W* **51** *(inverted). P* 14×13½.
417 **139** 10000 l. multicoloured 60 70

140 Striped Red Mullet

141 Palm Trees

(Des H. Billur)

1996 (29 Mar). *Fishes. T* **140** *and similar horiz designs. Multicoloured. W* **51** *(sideways). P* 13½×14.
418 6000 l. Type **140** 40 30
419 10000 l. Peacock Wrasse 60 45
420 28000 l. Common Two-banded Seabream .. 1·00 1·25
421 40000 l. Dusky Grouper .. .. 1·50 1·75
418/21 .. .. *Set of* 4 3·25 3·25

1996 (26 Apr). *Tourism. T* **141** *and similar multicoloured designs. W* **51** *(sideways on horiz designs). P* 14×13½ *(vert) or* 13½×14 *(horiz).*
422 100000 l. Type **141** 40 45
423 150000 l. Pomegranate 60 65
424 250000 l. Ruins of Bella Paise Abbey (*horiz*) 1·00 1·10
425 500000 l. Traditional dancers (*horiz*) .. 2·00 2·10
422/5 .. .. *Set of* 4 4·00 4·25

142 Beria Remzi Ozoran

143 Established Forest

(Des H. Billur)

1996 (31 May). *Europa. Famous Women. T* **142** *and similar horiz design. Multicoloured. W* **51** *(sideways). P* 13½×14.
426 15000 l. Type **142** 50 25
427 50000 l. Kadriye Hulusi Hacibulgur .. .. 1·40 1·75

1996 (28 June). *World Environment Day. Sheet* 72×78 *mm containing T* **143** *and similar horiz design. Multicoloured. W* **51** *(sideways). P* 13½×14.
MS428 50000 l. Type **143**; 50000 l. Conifer plantation .. .. 2·75 3·00

144 Basketball

145 Symbolic Footballs

(Des H. Billur)

1996 (31 July). *Olympic Games, Atlanta. Sheet* 105×74 *mm containing T* **144** *and similar horiz designs. Multicoloured. W* **51** *(sideways). P* 13½×14.
MS429 15000 l. Type **144**; 15000 l. Discus throwing; 50000 l. Javelin throwing; 50000 l. Volleyball .. .. 2·75 3·00

(Des H. Billur)

1996 (31 Oct). *European Football Championship, England. T* **145** *and similar horiz design. Multicoloured. W* **51** *(sideways). P* 13½×14.
430 15000 l. Type **145** 55 55
a. Pair. Nos. 430/1 .. .. 1·50 1·50
431 35000 l. Football and flags of participating nations .. .. 1·00 1·00
In addition to separate sheets Nos. 430/1 were also available in pairs, *se-tenant* horizontally and vertically.

146 Houses on Fire (Auxiliary Fire Service)

147 *Amanita phalloides*

(Des O. Oker (10000 l.), H. Billur (50000, 75000 l.))

1996 (23 Dec). *Anniversaries and Events. T* **146** *and similar multicoloured designs. W* **51** *(inverted on* 20000 *l., sideways on others). P* 14×13½ *(*20000 *l.) or* 13½×14 *(others).*
432 10000 l. Type **146** 30 30
433 20000 l. Colour party (20th anniv of Defence Forces) (*vert*) 40 40
434 50000 l. Children by lake (Nasreddin-Hoca Year) 85 85
435 75000 l. Flowers (Children's Rights) .. 1·25 1·25
432/5 .. .. *Set of* 4 2·50 2·50

1997 (31 Jan). *Arts (13th series). Multicoloured designs as T* **121**. *W* **51** *(sideways). P* 14.
436 25000 l. "City" (Lebibe Sonuc) (*horiz*) .. 50 30
437 70000 l. "Woman opening Letter" (Ruzen Atakan) (*horiz*) .. .. 1·40 1·60

(Des H. Billur)

1997 (31 Mar). *Fungi. T* **147** *and similar vert designs. Multicoloured. W* **51** *(inverted). P* 14×13½.
438 15000 l. Type **147** 30 30
439 25000 l. *Morchella esculenta* 45 45
440 25000 l. *Pleurotus eryngii* 45 45
441 70000 l. *Amanita muscaria* .. .. .. 1·25 1·25
438/41 .. .. *Set of* 4 2·25 2·25

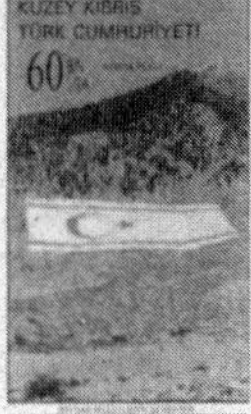
148 Flag on Hillside

149 Mother and Children playing Leapfrog

(Des H. Billur)

1997 (23 Apr). *Besparmak Mountains Flag Sculpture. W* **51** *(inverted). P* 14×13½.
442 **148** 60000 l. multicoloured .. .. .. 1·00 1·00

(Des H. Billur)

1997 (30 May). *Europa. Tales and Legends. T* **149** *and similar horiz design. Multicoloured. W* **51** *(sideways). P* 13½×14.
443 25000 l. Type **149** 45 30
444 70000 l. Apple tree and well .. .. 1·25 1·50

150 Prime Minister Necmettin Erbakan of Turkey

151 Golden Eagle

1997 (20 June). *Visit of the President and the Prime Minister of Turkey. T* **150** *and similar multicoloured design. W* **51** *(sideways on 80000 l.). P* 14×13½ *(vert) or* 13½×14 *(horiz).*
445 15000 l. Type **150** 30 20
446 80000 l. President Suleyman Demirel of Turkey *(horiz)* .. .. .. 1·25 1·50

(Des H. Billur)

1997 (31 July). *Birds of Prey. T* **151** *and similar vert designs. Multicoloured. W* **51**. *P* 14×13½.
447 40000 l. Type **151** 60 60
448 40000 l. Eleonora's Falcon 60 60
449 75000 l. Common Kestrel .. .. .. 1·00 1·10
450 100000 l. Honey Buzzard .. .. .. 1·25 1·40
447/50 .. .. *Set of* 4 3·00 3·25

152 Coin of Sultan Abdulaziz, 1861–76

153 Open Book and Emblem

1997 (28 Oct). *Rare Coins. T* **152** *and similar vert designs. Multicoloured. W* **51**. *P* 14×13½.
451 25000 l. Type **152** 15 20
452 40000 l. Coin of Sultan Mahmud II, 1808–39 .. .. 25 30
453 75000 l. Coin of Sultan Selim II, 1566–74 45 50
454 100000 l. Coin of Sultan Mehmed V, 1909–18 .. .. 60 65
451/4 .. .. *Set of* 4 1·40 1·60

(Des H. Billur.)

1997 (22 Dec). *Anniversaries. T* **153** *and similar designs. W* **51** *(sideways on horiz designs). P* 13½×14 *(horiz) or* 14×13½ *(vert).*
455 25000 l. multicoloured 15 20
456 40000 l. multicoloured 25 30
457 100000 l. black, brt scarlet & yellow ochre 60 65
458 150000 l. multicoloured .. .. 95 1·00
455/8 .. .. *Set of* 4 1·90 2·10

Designs: *Horiz*—25000 l. Type **153** (Centenary of Turkish Cypriot Scouts); 40000 l. Guides working in field (90th anniv of Turkish Cypriot Guides); 150000 l. Rudolf Diesel and first oil engine (Centenary of the diesel engine). *Vert*—100000 l. Couple and symbols (AIDS prevention campaign).

154 Ahmet and Ismet Sevki

155 *Agrion splendens* (dragonfly)

1998 (28 Jan). *Ahmet and Ismet Sevki (photographers) Commemoration. T* **154** *and similar multicoloured design. W* **51** *(sideways on 40000 l.). P* 13½×14 *(horiz) or* 14×13½ *(vert).*
459 40000 l. Type **154** 20 25
460 105000 l. Ahmet Sevki *(vert)* 40 45

(Des H. Billur)

1998 (30 Mar). *Useful Insects. T* **155** *and similar horiz designs. Multicoloured. W* **51** *(sideways). P* 13½×14.
461 40000 l. Type **155** 20 25
462 65000 l. *Ascalaphus macaronius* (owl-fly) 30 35
463 125000 l. *Podalonia hirsuta* 50 55
464 150000 l. *Rhyssa persuasoria* 60 65
461/4 .. .. *Set of* 4 1·60 1·75

156 Wooden Double Door

157 Legislative Assembly Building (Republic Establishment Festival)

(Des H. Billur)

1998 (30 Apr). *Old Doors. T* **156** *and similar vert design showing different door. W* **51**. *P* 14×13½.
465 115000 l. multicoloured 50 55
466 140000 l. multicoloured 60 65

(Des H. Billur)

1998 (30 May). *Europa. Festivals. T* **157** *and similar multicoloured design. W* **51** *(sideways on 40000 l., inverted on 150000 l.). P* 13½×14 *(horiz) or* 14×13½ *(vert).*
467 40000 l. Type **157** 20 25
468 150000 l. Globe, flags and map (Int Children's Folk Dance Festival) *(vert)* 60 65

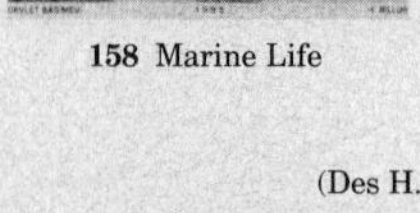

158 Marine Life

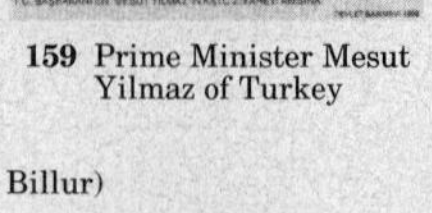

159 Prime Minister Mesut Yilmaz of Turkey

(Des H. Billur)

1998 (30 June). *International Year of the Ocean. T* **158** *and similar horiz design showing different underwater scene. W* **51** *(sideways). P* 13½×14.
469 40000 l. multicoloured 20 25
470 90000 l. multicoloured 35 40

1998 (20 July). *Prime Minister Yilmaz's Visit to Northern Cyprus. W* **51** *(sideways). P* 13½×14.
471 **159** 75000 l. multicoloured 30 35

160 Pres. Sulyman Demirel of Turkey

161 Victorious French Team

1998 (25 July). *President Demirel's "Water for Peace" Project. T* **160** *and similar multicoloured design. W* **51** *(inverted on 75000 l., sideways on 175000 l.). P* 14×13½ *(vert) or* 13½×14 *(horiz).*
472 75000 l. Type **160** 30 35
473 175000 l. Turkish and Turkish Cypriot leaders with inflatable water tank *(horiz)* 65 70

1998 (31 July). *World Cup Football Championship, France. T* **161** *and similar multicoloured design. W* **51** *(sideways on 75000 l., inverted on 175000 l.). P* 13½×14 *(horiz) or* 14×13½ *(vert).*
474 75000 l. Type **161** 30 35
475 175000 l. World Cup trophy *(vert)* 65 70

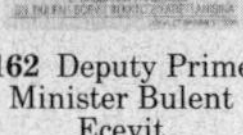

162 Deputy Prime Minister Bulent Ecevit

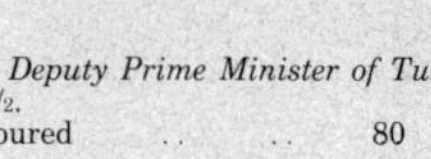

163 Itinerant Tinsmiths

1998 (5 Sept). *Visit of the Deputy Prime Minister of Turkey. W* **51** *(inverted). P* 14×13½.
476 **162** 200000 l. multicoloured 80 85

(Des H. Billur)

1998 (26 Oct). *Local Crafts. T* **163** *and similar multicoloured designs. W* **51** *(sideways on horiz designs, inverted on vert). P* 13½×14 *(horiz designs) or* 14×13½ *(others).*
477 50000 l. Type **163** 20 25
478 75000 l. Basket weaver *(vert)* 30 35
479 130000 l. Grinder sharpening knife *(vert)* .. 60 65
480 400000 l. Wood carver .. .. .. 1·90 2·00
477/80 .. .. *Set of* 4 3·00 3·25

164 Stylised Satellite Dish

(Des H. Billur and H. Ulucam)

1998 (15 Nov). *Anniversaries. T* **164** *and similar multicoloured designs (except No. 483). W* **51** *(inverted on 175000 l., sideways on others). P* 14×13½ *(175000 l.) or* 13½×14 *(others).*
481 50000 l. Type **164** 20 25
482 75000 l. Stylised birds and "15" 30 35
483 75000 l. "75" and Turkish flag (rosine, black and dull orange) 30 35
484 175000 l. Scroll, "50" and quill pen *(vert)* .. 75 80
481/4 .. .. *Set of* 4 1·50 1·75
MS485 72×78 mm. 75000 l. As No. 482; 75000 l. Map of Northern Cyprus 60 65

Anniversaries—No. 481, 35th anniv of Bayrak Radio and Television; Nos. 482, **MS**485, 15th anniv of Turkish Republic of Northern Cyprus; No. 483, 75th anniv of Turkish Republic; No. 484, 50th anniv of Universal Declaration of Human Rights.

STAMP BOOKLETS

Following the inauguration of the Turkish Cypriot postal service in 1974 several postmasters continued to use the covers previously supplied by the Cyprus Post Office in conjunction with Turkish Cypriot Posts issues.

1987 (30 June). *Europa. Modern Architecture. Black on bluish grey cover, 61×50 mm, showing Europa symbols. Pane attached by selvedge.*
SB1 500 l. booklet containing *se-tenant* pane of 4 (No. 210ab) .. .. 7·00

1989 (31 May). *Europa. Children's Games. Black on pale blue-green cover, 62×48 mm, showing Europa symbols. Pane attached by selvedge.*
SB2 3200 l. booklet containing *se-tenant* pane of 4 (No. 251ab) .. .. 7·50

Cyrenaica
see British Occupation of Italian Colonies

Dominica

CROWN COLONY

A British packet agency was operating on Dominica from bout 1778, the date of the earliest known use of a postal iarking. This was replaced by a branch office of the British i.P.O. which opened at Roseau on 8 May 1858. The stamps of ireat Britain were used from that date until 1 May 1860, after which the colonial authorities assumed responsibility for the postal service. Until the introduction of Nos. 1/3 in 1874 No. CC1 and later handstamps were utilised.

For illustrations of handstamp and postmark types see BRITISH POST OFFICES ABROAD notes, following GREAT BRITAIN.

ROSEAU

CROWNED-CIRCLE HANDSTAMPS

CC1 CC 1 DOMINICA (Black or R.) (17.5.1845)
Price on cover £500

No. CC1 is also known struck in black on various adhesive stamps as late as 1883.

Stamps of GREAT BRITAIN *cancelled* "A 07" *as Type* **2**.

1858 *to* **1860**

Z1 1d. rose-red (1857), *perf* 14 .. £200
Z2 2d. blue (1858) (Plate No. 7) .. £650
Z3 4d. rose (1857) .. £275
Z4 6d. lilac (1856) .. £275
Z5 1s. green .. £1100

PRICES FOR STAMPS ON COVER TO 1945

Nos. 1/3	*from* × 25
No. 4	*from* × 40
No. 5	*from* × 100
No. 6	*from* × 40
Nos. 7/8	*from* × 100
No. 9	*from* × 40
Nos. 10/12	*from* × 15
Nos. 13/15	*from* × 100
No. 17	*from* × 50
Nos. 18/a	—
No. 19	*from* × 40
Nos. 20/5	*from* × 30
No. 26	—
Nos. 27/90	*from* × 5
No. 91	—
Nos. 92/8	*from* × 10
Nos. 99/109	*from* × 3
Nos. R1/3	*from* × 15
No. R4	*from* × 50
No. R6	*from* × 3

ONE PENNY

1 (2) (3) (4)

½ 1/2 HALF PENNY

(Typo D.L.R.)

1874 (4 May). *Wmk Crown CC. P* 12½.

1 1 1d. lilac .. £150 42·00
2 6d. green .. £550 90·00
3 1s. dull magenta .. £325 65·00

NCE — Normal; NCE — Malformed "CE" (R.10/6)

1877–79. *Wmk Crown CC. P* 14.

4 1 ½d. olive-yellow (1879) .. 9·00 42·00
5 1d. lilac .. 4·50 1·75
a. Bisected vert or diag (½d.) (on cover or card) .. † £1600
w. Wmk inverted .. 50·00
6 2½d. red-brown (1879) .. £225 26·00
w. Wmk inverted
7 4d. blue (1879) .. £110 2·50
a. Malformed "CE" in "PENCE" .. £1500 £225
8 6d. green .. £150 20·00
9 1s. magenta .. £120 48·00

1882 (25 Nov)–**83.** *No. 5 bisected vertically and surch.*

10 2 ½ (d.), in *black*, on half 1d. .. £140 35·00
a. Surch inverted .. £950 £800
b. Surcharges *tête-bêche* (pair) .. £1600
11 3 ½ (d.), in *red*, on half 1d. (12.82) .. 28·00 13·00
a. Surch inverted .. £950 £450
c. Surch double .. £1600 £650
12 4 ½d. in *black*, on half 1d. (3.83) .. 48·00 20·00
b. Surch double .. £800

Type 4 is found reading up or down.

1883–86. *Wmk Crown CA. P* 14.

13 1 ½d. olive-yellow .. 2·00 8·50
14 1d. lilac (1886) .. 23·00 8·50
a. Bisected (½d.) (on cover) .. † £1800
15 2½d. red-brown (1884) .. £140 2·00
w. Wmk inverted .. £250

Half Penny (5) — One Penny (6)

1886 (Mar). *Nos. 8 and 9 surch locally.*

17 5 ½d. on 6d. green .. 4·00 3·50
18 6 1d. on 6d. green .. £20000 £10000
a. Thick bar (approx 1 mm) .. † £16000
19 1d. on 1s. magenta .. 14·00 14·00
a. Surch double .. £5000 £2750

It is believed that only two sheets of the 1d. on 6d. were surcharged. On one of these sheets the six stamps in the top row showed the thick bar variety, No. 18a.

1886–90. *Wmk Crown CA. P* 14.

20 1 ½d. dull green .. 1·50 4·50
22 1d. rose (1887) .. 12·00 13·00
a. Deep carmine (1889) .. 2·75 4·50
b. Bisected (½d.) (on cover) .. † £1800
w. Wmk inverted
23 2½d. ultramarine (1888) .. 3·75 4·50
24 4d. grey .. 2·00 3·75
a. Malformed "CE" in "PENCE" .. £160 £200
25 6d. orange (1888) .. 6·00 32·00
26 1s. dull magenta (1890) .. £150 £250
20/6 .. *Set of* 6 £150 £275
20/5 Optd "Specimen" .. *Set of* 5 £225

The stamps of Dominica were superseded by the general issue for Leeward Islands on 31 October 1890, but the sets following were in concurrent use with the stamps inscribed "LEEWARD ISLANDS" until 31 December 1939, when the island came under the administration of the Windward Islands.

9 "Roseau from the Sea" (Lt. Caddy)

10

(T **9** to **11** typo D.L.R.)

1903 (1 Sept)–**07.** *Wmk Crown CC (sideways* on T* **9**). *Ordinary paper. P* 14.

27 9 ½d. green and grey-green .. 3·75 2·25
a. Chalk-surfaced paper (1906) .. 11·00 15·00
28 1d. grey and red .. 7·50 75
a. Chalk-surfaced paper (1906) .. 23·00 5·50
29 2d. green and brown .. 2·50 4·50
a. Chalk-surfaced paper (1906) .. 23·00 32·00
30 2½d. grey and bright blue .. 4·50 3·75
a. Chalk-surfaced paper (3.9.07) .. 18·00 32·00
31 3d. dull purple and grey-black .. 8·00 3·00
a. Chalk-surfaced paper (1906) .. 30·00 26·00
32 6d. grey and chestnut .. 4·25 16·00
33 1s. magenta and grey-green .. 24·00 35·00
a. Chalk-surfaced paper (1906) .. 70·00 £130
34 2s. grey-black and purple .. 24·00 27·00
35 2s. 6d. grey-green and maize .. 17·00 70·00
36 10 5s. black and brown .. 90·00 £140
27/36 .. *Set of* 10 £170 £275
27/36 Optd "Specimen" .. *Set of* 10 £130

*The normal sideways watermark shows Crown to right of CC, *as seen from the back of the stamp.*

1907–08. *Wmk Mult Crown CA (sideways* on T* **9**). *Chalk-surfaced paper. P* 14.

37 9 ½d. green .. 1·50 2·50
38 1d. grey and red .. 2·00 30
39 2d. green and brown .. 5·00 15·00
40 2½d. grey and bright blue .. 4·50 19·00
41 3d. dull purple and grey-black .. 4·00 13·00
42 6d. black and chestnut .. 48·00 75·00
43 1s. magenta and grey-green (1908) .. 3·75 48·00
44 2s. grey-black and purple (1908) .. 22·00 32·00
45 2s. 6d. grey-green and maize (1908) .. 22·00 55·00
46 10 5s. black and brown (1908) .. 60·00 60·00
37/46 .. *Set of* 10 £160 £275

*The normal sideways watermark shows Crown to right of CA, *as seen from the back of the stamp.*

Examples of Nos. 27/36 and 37/46 are known showing a forged Gen. Post Office Dominica postmark dated "JU 1 11".

11

WAR TAX
ONE HALFPENNY
(12)

1908–21. *Wmk Mult Crown CA (sideways* on T* **9**), *Chalk-surfaced paper (3d., 6d., 1s.). P* 14.

47 9 ½d blue-green .. 3·00 3·50
aw. Wmk Crown to left of CA .. 2·50 2·50
b. Deep green (wmk Crown to left of CA) (1918) .. 3·50 1·75
48 1d. carmine-red .. 3·00 30
aw. Wmk Crown to left of CA .. 3·50 40
b. Scarlet (1916) .. 1·50 40
bw. Wmk Crown to left of CA .. 1·00 50
49 9 2d. grey (1909) .. 3·25 12·00
aw. Wmk Crown to left of CA .. 3·00 15·00
b. Slate (wmk Crown to left of CA) (1918) .. 3·50 12·00
50 2½d. blue .. 8·50 6·00
aw. Wmk Crown to left of CA .. — 9·00
b. Bright blue (1918) .. 5·00 9·00
bw. Wmk Crown to left of CA .. 6·00 12·00
51 3d. purple/*yellow* (1909) .. 3·00 4·25
a. Ordinary paper (wmk Crown to left of CA) (1912) .. 3·00 4·50
ab. *On pale yellow* (1920) .. 8·50 12·00
52 6d. dull and bright purple (1909) .. 10·00 15·00
a. Ordinary paper. *Dull purple* (wmk Crown to left of CA) (1915) .. 3·50 18·00
53 1s. black/*green* (1910) .. 2·75 2·75
a. Ordinary paper (wmk Crown to left of CA) (1912) (Optd S. (in red) £35) 3·00 4·00
53*b* 2s. purple and deep blue/*blue* (wmk Crown to left of CA) (1919) .. 25·00 70·00
53*c* 2s. 6d. black and red/*blue* (wmk Crown to left of CA) (1921) .. 25·00 80·00
54 11 5s. red and green/*yellow* (1914) .. 55·00 80·00
47/54 .. *Set of* 10 £110 £250
48/54 Optd "Specimen" (1s. optd in black) *Set of* 9 £180

*The normal sideways watermark shows Crown to right of CA, *as seen from the back of the stamp.*

1916 (Sept). *No. 47b surch with T* **12** *by De La Rue.*

55 9 ½d. on ½d. deep green (R.) .. 10 75
a. Small "O" in "ONE" .. 6·50 16·00

No. 55a occurs on ten stamps within each sheet of 60.

1918 (18 Mar). *No. 47b optd with T* **12** *locally, from D.L.R. plate, but with* "ONE HALF-PENNY" *blanked out.*

56 9 ½d. deep green (Blk.) .. 1·75 5·00

The blanking out of the surcharge was not completely successful so that it almost always appears as an albino to a greater or lesser extent.

WAR TAX
(14)

1918 (June)–**19.** *Nos. 47b and 51a optd with T* **14** *by De La Rue.*

57 9 ½d. deep green .. 10 30
58 3d. purple/*yellow* (R.) (1919) .. 65 3·50

WAR TAX =1½D.= (15) — 1 ½D. Short Fraction Bar (R.6/4)

1919. *As No. 50aw, but colour changed, surch with T* **15** *by De La Rue.*

59 9 1½d. on 2½d. orange (R.) .. 10 55
a. Short fraction bar .. 7·50 30·00
b. "C" and "A" missing from wmk

No. 59b shows the "C" omitted from one impression with the "A" missing from the next one to the left (as seen from the back of the stamp). The "C" is badly distorted in the second watermark.

1920 (1 June). *As No. 59, but without* "WAR TAX".

60 9 1½d. on 2½d. orange (Blk.) .. 2·00 4·00
a. Short fraction bar .. 55·00 70·00
55/60 Optd "Specimen" .. *Set of* 6 £170

1921–22. *Wmk Mult Script CA (sideways*). Chalk-surfaced paper (6d.). P* 14.

62 9 ½d. blue-green .. 1·75 12·00
63 1d. carmine-red .. 1·25 3·00
w. Wmk Crown to right of CA .. — 12·00
64 1½d. orange .. 2·75 9·50
65 2d. grey .. 2·75 3·25
66 2½d. bright blue .. 1·75 8·50
67 6d. purple .. 2·50 35·00
69 2s. purple and blue/*blue* (1922) .. 30·00 70·00
70 2s. 6d. black and red/*blue* .. 30·00 70·00
62/70 .. *Set of* 8 65·00 £190
62/70 Optd "Specimen" .. *Set of* 8 £140

*The normal sideways watermark shows Crown to left of CA, *as seen from the back of the stamp.*

The 1½d. has figures of value, in the lower corner and no ornamentation below words of value.

16

(Typo D.L.R.)

1923 (1 Mar)–**33.** *Chalk-surfaced paper. P* 14.

(*a*) *Wmk Mult Script CA (sideways*)*

71 16 ½d. black and green .. 1·50 30
72 1d. black and bright violet .. 1·75 1·25
73 1d. black and scarlet (1933) .. 9·00 90
74 1½d. black and scarlet .. 2·00 65
75 1½d. black and red-brown (1933) .. 9·00 60
76 2d. black and grey .. 1·75 40
77 2½d. black and orange-yellow .. 1·00 8·50
78 2½d. black and ultramarine (1927) .. 3·50 1·75
79 3d. black and ultramarine .. 1·00 11·00
80 3d. black and red/*yellow* (1927) .. 1·25 1·00
81 4d. black and brown .. 2·00 4·50
82 6d. black and bright magenta .. 3·50 5·50
83 1s. black/*emerald* .. 2·00 2·75
84 2s. black and blue/*blue* .. 7·50 14·00
85 2s. 6d. black and red/*blue* .. 18·00 15·00
86 3s. black and purple/*yellow* (1927) .. 3·00 9·00
87 4s. black and red/*emerald* .. 9·50 17·00
88 5s. black and green/*yellow* (1927) .. 22·00 42·00

(b) *Wmk Mult Crown CA (sideways*)*

89 16 3s. black and purple/*yellow* .. .. 4·00 55·00
90 5s. black and green/*yellow* .. .. 9·00 42·00
91 £1 black and purple/*red* £225 £325
71/91 .. .. *Set of* 21 £300 £500
71/91 Optd/Perf "Specimen" .. .. *Set of* 21 £350

*The normal sideways watermark shows Crown to left of CA, *as seen from the back of the stamp.*

Examples of most values are known showing a forged G.P.O. Dominica postmark dated "MY 19 27".

1935 (6 May). *Silver Jubilee. As Nos. 91/4 of Antigua.*

92 1d. deep blue and carmine 75 20
f. Diagonal line by turret .. .. 35·00
h. Dot by flagstaff .. .. 50·00
93 1½d. ultramarine and grey .. .. 1·25 55
f. Diagonal line by turret .. .. 45·00
h. Dot by flagstaff .. .. 65·00
94 2½d. brown and deep blue .. .. 1·40 2·25
95 1s. slate and purple .. .. 1·50 3·25
h. Dot by flagstaff £110
i. Dash by turret £110
92/5 .. .. .. *Set of* 4 4·50 5·50
92/5 Perf "Specimen" .. .. *Set of* 4 75·00

For illustrations of plate varieties see Catalogue Introduction.

1937 (12 May). *Coronation. As Nos. 95/7 of Antigua. P 11×11½.*

96 1d. carmine 40 10
97 1½d. yellow-brown 40 10
98 2½d. blue .. .. .. 60 1·25
96/8 .. .. .. *Set of* 3 1·25 1·25
96/8 Perf "Specimen" .. .. *Set of* 3 55·00

17 Fresh Water Lake

18 Layou River

(Recess Waterlow)

1938 (15 Aug)–**47.** *T* **17/18** *and similar horiz designs. Wmk Mult Script CA. P 12½.*

99 17 ½d. brown and green 10 15
100 18 1d. grey and scarlet 20 20
101 – 1½d. green and purple 30 70
102 – 2d. carmine and grey-black 50 90
103 – 2½d. purple and bright blue .. .. 4·00 1·75
a. Purple & bright ultramarine (8.42) 20 1·25
104 18 3d. olive-green and brown 30 40
104*a* – 3½d. ultramarine and purple (15.10.47) 1·50 1·25
105 17 6d. emerald-green and violet .. 1·75 90
105*a* 7d. green and yellow-brown (15.10.47) 1·50 1·25
106 – 1s. violet and olive-green .. .. 2·25 80
106*a* 18 2s. slate and purple (15.10.47) .. 4·50 8·00
107 17 2s. 6d. black and vermilion .. .. 12·00 4·75
108 18 5s. light blue and sepia .. .. 7·50 8·00
108*a* – 10s. black and brown-orange (15.10.47) 12·00 14·00
99/108*a* .. .. .. *Set of* 14 40·00 38·00

Designs:–1½d., 2½d., 3½d. Picking limes; 2d., 1s., 10s. Boiling Lake.

21 King George VI

(Photo Harrison)

1940 (15 Apr)–**42.** *Wmk Mult Script CA. Chalk-surfaced paper. P 15×14.*

109 21 ¼d. chocolate 60 15
a. Ordinary paper (1942) 10 10
99/109 Perf "Specimen" .. .. *Set of* 15 £225

1946 (14 Oct). *Victory. As Nos. 110/11 of Antigua.*

110 1d. carmine 20 10
111 3½d. blue 20 10
110/11 Perf "Specimen" .. .. *Set of* 2 48·00

1948 (1 Dec). *Royal Silver Wedding. As Nos. 112/13 of Antigua.*

112 1d. scarlet 15 10
113 10s. red-brown .. .. .. 7·50 20·00

(New Currency. 100 cents = 1 B.W.I., later East Caribbean dollar)

1949 (10 Oct). *75th Anniv of Universal Postal Union. As Nos. 114/17 of Antigua.*

114 5 c. blue 15 15
115 6 c. brown .. .. .. 75 1·50
116 12 c. purple 30 80
117 24 c. olive 30 30
114/17 .. .. .. *Set of* 4 1·40 2·50

1951 (16 Feb). *Inauguration of B.W.I. University College. As Nos. 118/19 of Antigua.*

118 3 c. yellow-green and reddish violet 50 45
119 12 c. deep green and carmine 50 30

22 King George VI

23 Drying Cocoa

(Photo Harrison (½ c.). Recess B.W. (others))

1951 (1 July). *T* **22** *and designs as T* **23**. *Wmk Mult Script CA. Chalk-surfaced paper (½ c.). P 15×14 (½ c.), 13½×13 ($2.40), 13×13½ (others).*

120 ½ c. chocolate 10 15
121 1 c. black and vermilion 10 30
b. "A" of "CA" missing from wmk .. £500
c. "JA" for "CA" in wmk £500
122 2 c. red-brown and deep green 10 20
a. "C" of "CA" missing from wmk .. † —
b. "A" of "CA" missing from wmk .. £600
123 3 c. green and reddish violet 15 70
a. "C" of "CA" missing from wmk ..
c. "JA" for "CA" in wmk £500
124 4 c. brown-orange and sepia 30 70
a. "C" of "CA" missing from wmk .. £600
b. "A" of "CA" missing from wmk .. £600
125 5 c. black and carmine 85 30
a. "C" of "CA" missing from wmk .. £800
b. "A" of "CA" missing from wmk .. £800
126 6 c. olive and chestnut 90 30
a. "C" of "CA" missing from wmk ..
b. "A" of "CA" missing from wmk .. £1000
127 8 c. blue-green and blue 60 60
b. "A" of "CA" missing from wmk ..
128 12 c. black and bright green .. .. 45 1·25
a. "C" of "CA" missing from wmk .. £1200
129 14 c. blue and violet .. .. 95 1·25
a. "C" of "CA" missing from wmk .. £1200
b. "A" of "CA" missing from wmk .. † —
c. "JA" for "CA" in wmk .. ..
130 24 c. reddish violet and rose-carmine .. 75 30
a. "C" of "CA" missing from wmk .. £1200
131 48 c. bright green and red-orange .. 2·50 6·50
a. "C" of "CA" missing from wmk .. £1200
b. "A" of "CA" missing from wmk .. £1200
c. "JA" for "CA" in wmk .. ..
132 60 c. carmine and black .. .. 2·50 5·00
133 $1.20, emerald and black .. .. 4·00 5·00
a. "C" of "CA" missing from wmk .. £1400
b. "A" of "CA" missing from wmk .. £1400
134 $2.40, orange and black .. .. 22·00 29·00
120/34 .. .. .. *Set of* 15 30·00 45·00

Designs: *Horiz*—2 c., 60 c. Making Carib baskets; 3 c., 48 c. Lime plantation; 4 c. Picking oranges; 5 c. Bananas; 6 c. Botanical Gardens; 8 c. Drying vanilla beans; 12 c., $1.20, Fresh Water Lake; 14 c. Layou River; 24 c. Boiling Lake. *Vert*—$2.40, Picking oranges.

Examples of Nos. 121b, 122b, 124b, 125b, 126b, 129b, 131b and 133b show traces of the *left leg* of the "A", *as seen from the back of the stamp.*

Nos. 121c, 123c, 129c and 131c may represent an attempt to repair the missing "C" variety.

NEW
CONSTITUTION
1951
(34)

1951 (15 Oct). *New Constitution. Nos. 123, 125, 127 and 129 optd with T* **34** *by B.W.*

135 3 c. green and reddish violet 15 70
136 5 c. black and carmine 15 70
137 8 c. blue-green and blue (R.) 15 15
a. "JA" for "CA" in wmk .. ..
138 14 c. blue and violet (R.) 15 20
b. "A" of "CA" missing from wmk .. £900
135/8 .. .. .. *Set of* 4 55 1·60

1953 (2 June). *Coronation. As No. 120 of Antigua.*

139 2 c. black and deep green 20 10

35 Queen Elizabeth II

36 Mat Making

37 Picking Oranges

38 Canoe Making

(Photo Harrison (½ c.). Recess B.W. (others))

1954 (1 Oct)–**62.** *Designs previously used for King George VI issue, but with portrait of Queen Elizabeth II as in T* **35/8**. *Wmk Mult Script CA. P 15×14 (½ c.), 13½×13 ($2.40), 13×13½ (others).*

140 35 ½ c. brown 10 30
141 – 1 c. black and vermilion 10 10
142 – 2 c. chocolate and myrtle-green .. 55 90
a. Chocolate and grey-green (13.3.62) 6·00 6·50
143 – 3 c. green and purple .. .. 1·25 30
144 36 3 c. black and carmine (15.10.57) .. 3·25 1·75
145 37 4 c. brown-orange and sepia 20 10
146 – 5 c. black and carmine-red .. .. 1·25 30
147 38 5 c. light blue & sepia-brown (15.10.57) 10·00 90
a. Blue and sepia (13.3.62) .. 17·00 5·50
148 – 6 c. bronze-green and red-brown .. 40 10
149 – 8 c. deep green and deep blue 75 10
150 – 10 c. green and brown (15.10.57) .. 5·00 1·75
a. Green and deep brown (17.7.62) .. 6·00 80
151 – 12 c. black and emerald 50 10
152 – 14 c. blue and purple 30 10
153 – 24 c. purple and carmine 40 10
154 – 48 c. green and red-orange .. .. 1·25 6·00
155 36 48 c. deep brown and violet (15.10.57) .. 1·25 80
156 – 60 c. rose-red and black .. .. 1·00 1·50
157 – $1.20, emerald and black .. .. 16·00 6·00
158 – $2.40, yellow-orange and black .. 16·00 14·00
140/58 .. .. .. *Set of* 19 55·00 29·00

Designs: *Horiz*—1 c. Drying cocoa; 2 c., 60 c. Making Carib baskets; 3 c. (No. 143), 48 c. (No. 154) Lime plantation; 5 c. (No. 146) Bananas; 6 c. Botanical Gardens; 8 c. Drying vanilla beans; 10 c. Bananas (*different*); 12 c., $1.20, Fresh Water Lake; 14 c. Layou River; 24 c. Boiling Lake. *Vert*—$2.40, Picking oranges.

1958 (22 Apr). *Inauguration of British Caribbean Federation. As Nos. 135/7 of Antigua.*

159 3 c. deep green 35 10
160 6 c. blue 50 90
161 12 c. scarlet 70 10
159/61 .. .. .. *Set of* 3 1·40 1·00

40 Seashore at Rosalie

48 Traditional Costume

Two types of 14 c.

I. Eyes of model looking straight ahead.
II. Eyes looking to her right.

(Des S. Scott. Photo Harrison)

1963 (16 May)–**65.** *T* **40, 48** *and similar designs. W w 12 (upright). P 14×14½ (vert) or 14½×14 (horiz).*

162 1 c. green, blue and sepia 10 75
163 2 c. bright blue 30 10
w. Wmk inverted .. .. .. — 10·00
164 3 c. blackish brown and blue 90 90
165 4 c. green, sepia and slate-violet .. 10 10
166 5 c. magenta 30 10
167 6 c. green, bistre and violet 10 10
168 8 c. green, sepia and black 10 10
169 10 c. sepia and pink 10 10
170 12 c. green, blue and blackish brown .. 45 10
171 14 c. multicoloured (I) 70 10
171*a* 14 c. multicoloured (II) (1.4.65) .. 2·50 2·00
172 15 c. yellow, green and brown .. 1·00 10
w. Wmk inverted .. .. .. — 18·00
173 24 c. multicoloured .. .. 8·00 20
174 48 c. green, blue and black 75 40
175 60 c. orange, green and black .. .. 1·00 60
176 $1.20, multicoloured .. .. 6·50 80
177 $2.40, blue, turquoise and brown .. 3·25 2·00
178 $4.80, green, blue and brown .. .. 9·00 20·00
162/78 .. .. .. *Set of* 17 29·00 22·00

Designs: *Vert*—2 c., 5 c. Queen Elizabeth II; 24 c. Imperial Amazon; $2.40, Trafalgar Falls; $4.80, Coconut Palm. *Horiz*—3 c. Sailing canoe; 4 c. Sulphur springs; 6 c. Road making; 8 c. Dug-out canoe; 10 c. Crapaud (toad); 12 c. Scott's Head; 15 c. Bananas; 48 c. Goodwill; 60 c. Cocoa tree; $1.20, Coat of Arms.

See also Nos. 200/4.

1963 (4 June). *Freedom from Hunger. As No. 146 of Antigua.*

179 15 c. reddish violet 15 10

1963 (2 Sept). *Red Cross Centenary. As Nos. 147/8 of Antigua.*

180 5 c. red and black 15 3
181 15 c. red and blue 30 5

1964 (23 April). *400th Birth Anniv of William Shakespeare. As No. 164 of Antigua.*

182 15 c. bright purple 10 10
w. Wmk inverted .. .. 1·50

1965 (17 May). *I.T.U. Centenary. As Nos. 166/7 of Antigua.*

183 2 c. light emerald and blue 10 10
184 48 c. turquoise-blue and grey 30 2

1965 (25 Oct). *International Co-operation Year. As Nos. 168/9 of Antigua.*

185 1 c. reddish purple and turquoise-green .. 10 2
186 15 c. deep bluish green and lavender .. 20 10

1966 (24 Jan). *Churchill Commemoration. As Nos. 170/3 of Antigua.*

187 1 c. new blue 10 3
a. Gold omitted £550
188 5 c. deep green 10 1
189 15 c. brown 20 1
190 24 c. bluish violet 30 2
187/90 .. .. .. *Set of* 4 55 5

No. 187a occured on the bottom row of a sheet.

An example of the 1 c. is known showing the gold face value printed double.

1966 (4 Feb). *Royal Visit. As Nos. 174/5 of Antigua.*

191 5 c. black and ultramarine .. .. 1·00 2
192 15 c. black and magenta .. .. 1·50 3

1966 (1 July). *World Cup Football Championships. As Nos. 176/7 of Antigua.*

193 5 c. violet, yellow-green, lake & yellow-brown 20 1
194 24 c. chocolate, blue-green, lake & yell-brown 65 1

1966 (20 Sept). *Inauguration of W.H.O. Headquarters, Geneva. As Nos. 178/9 of Antigua.*

195 5 c. black, yellow-green and light blue .. 10 1
196 24 c. black, light purple and yellow-brown .. 20 1

1966 (1 Dec). *20th Anniv of U.N.E.S.C.O. As Nos. 196/8 of Antigua.*

197 5 c. slate-violet, red, yellow and orange .. 15 1
198 15 c. orange-yellow, violet and deep olive .. 35 1
199 24 c. black, bright purple and orange .. 40 1
197/9 .. .. .. *Set of* 3 80 3

966 (30 Dec)–**67**. *As Nos.* 165, 167/9 *and* 172 *but wmk* w **12** *sideways.*
00 4 c. green, sepia and slate-violet (16.5.67) .. 1·25 90
01 6 c. green, bistre and violet 20 15
02 8 c. green, sepia and black 40 10
03 10 c. sepia and pink (16.5.67) 70 10
04 15 c. yellow, green and brown (16.5.67) .. 70 10
00/4 .. .. *Set of* 5 3·00 1·25

ASSOCIATED STATEHOOD

56 Children of Three Races

(Des and photo Harrison)

967 (2 Nov). *National Day.* *T* **56** *and similar horiz designs. Multicoloured.* *W* w **12**. *P* 14½.
05 5 c. Type **56** 10 10
06 10 c. The *Santa Maria* and motto 30 10
07 15 c. Hands holding motto ribbon 15 15
08 24 c. Belaire dancing 15 15
05/8 .. .. *Set of* 4 60 30

57 John F. Kennedy

(Des G. Vasarhelyi. Litho D.L.R.)

968 (20 Apr). *Human Rights Year.* *T* **57** *and similar horiz designs. Multicoloured.* *W* w **12** *(sideways). P* 14 × 13½.
09 1 c. Type **57** 10 10
10 10 c. Cecil A. E. Rawle 10 10
a. Imperf (pair) .. .. 90·00
11 12 c. Pope John XXIII 50 15
12 48 c. Florence Nightingale 35 20
13 60 c. Albert Schweitzer 35 20
09/13 .. .. *Set of* 5 1·25 65

ASSOCIATED STATEHOOD (58)   **NATIONAL DAY 3 NOVEMBER 1968** (59)

968 (8 July). *Associated Statehood. As Nos.* 162, 170 *and* 174, *but wmk sideways, or Nos.* 163/4, 166, 170, 171*a*, 173, 175/8 *and* 200/4 *optd with T* **58**.
14 1 c. green, blue and sepia (Sil.) 10 10
15 2 c. bright blue (Sil.) 10 10
16 3 c. blackish brown and blue (Sil.) 30 10
17 4 c. green, sepia and slate-violet (Sil.) .. 10 10
18 5 c. magenta (Sil.) 10 10
19 6 c. green, bistre and violet 10 10
20 8 c. green, sepia and black 10 10
21 10 c. sepia and pink (Sil.) 55 10
22 12 c. green, blue and blackish brown (Sil.) (wmk sideways) 10 10
a. Wmk upright 10 10
24 14 c. multicoloured (II) (Sil.) 10 10
25 15 c. yellow, green and brown (Sil.) 10 10
26 24 c. multicoloured (Sil.) .. .. .. 3·50 10
27 48 c. green, bl & blk (Sil.) (wmk sideways) .. 55 90
a. Wmk upright 40 75
28 60 c. orange, green and black 90 70
29 $1.20, multicoloured .. .. 1·00 1·75
30 $2.40, blue, turquoise and brown (Sil.) .. 1·25 2·25
31 $4.80, green, blue and brown (Sil.) .. .. 1·25 4·50
14/31 .. .. *Set of* 17 8·50 9·50
The 2, 5, 6, 8 and 10 c. values exist with PVA gum as well as gum arabic.

968 (3 Nov). *National Day. Nos.* 162/4, 171 *and* 176 *optd with T* **59**.
32 1 c. green, blue and sepia 10 10
a. Opt inverted .. .. 45·00
33 2 c. bright blue 10 10
a. Opt double .. .. 30·00
34 3 c. blackish brown and blue 10 10
a. Opt inverted .. .. 30·00
35 14 c. multicoloured (I) 10 10
a. Opt double .. .. 70·00
36 $1.20, multicoloured 55 40
a. Opt double .. .. 30·00
b. Vert pair, one opt omitted, other opt double £150
32/6 .. .. *Set of* 5 60 40
The above set was put on sale by the New York Agency on 1 November but not sold locally until the 3 November.

60 Forward shooting at Goal

(Des M. Shamir (1 c., 60 c.), K. Plowitz (5 c., 48 c.). Litho B.W.)

1968 (25 Nov). *Olympic Games, Mexico.* *T* **60** *and similar horiz designs. Multicoloured. P* 11½ × 11.
237 1 c. Type **60** 10 10
a. Horiz pair. Nos. 237/8 .. .. .. 10 10
238 1 c. Goalkeeper trying to save goal 10 10
239 5 c. Swimmers about to dive 10 10
a. Horiz pair. Nos. 239/40 .. .. .. 10 10
240 5 c. Swimmers diving 10 10
241 48 c. Javelin-throwing 15 15
a. Horiz pair. Nos. 241/2 .. .. .. 30 30
242 48 c. Hurdling 15 15
243 60 c. Basketball 65 15
a. Horiz pair. Nos. 243/4 .. .. .. 1·25 30
244 60 c. Basketball players 65 15
237/44 .. .. *Set of* 8 1·50 70
Nos. 237/44 were issued in sheets of 40 containing two panes of *se-tenant* pairs.

61 "The Small Cowper Madonna" (Raphael)   **62** "Venus and Adonis" (Rubens)

(Photo Delrieu, Paris)

1968 (23 Dec). *Christmas. P* 12½ × 12.
245 **61** 5 c. multicoloured 10 10
Three other values were issued: 12 c. "Madonna of the Chair" (Raphael); 24 c. "Madonna and Child" (Italo-Byzantine, XVI century); $1.20 "Madonna and Child" (Byzantine, XIII century). Sizes as T **61**.
These only come from miniature sheets, containing two *se-tenant* strips of each value.

(Litho D.L.R.)

1969 (30 Jan). *20th Anniv of World Health Organisation. Paintings. T* **62** *and similar vert designs. Multicoloured. W* w **12**. *P* 15.
246 5 c. Type **62** 20 10
247 15 c. "The Death of Socrates" (J.-L. David) .. 30 10
248 24 c. "Christ and the Pilgrims of Emmaus" (Velasquez) 30 10
249 50 c. "Pilate washing his Hands" (Rembrandt) 50 40
246/9 .. .. *Set of* 4 1·10 50

66 Picking Oranges

67 "Strength in Unity" Emblem and Fruit Trees

(Des K. Plowitz. Litho Harrison)

1969 (10 Mar). *Tourism. T* **66** *and similar horiz designs. Multicoloured. W* w **12**. *P* 14½.
250 10 c. Type **66** 15 10
a. Horiz pair. Nos. 250/1 .. .. .. 30 15
251 10 c. Woman, child and ocean scene 15 10
252 12 c. Fort Yeoung Hotel 30 10
a. Horiz pair. Nos. 252/3 .. .. .. 60 20
253 12 c. Red-necked Amazons 30 10
254 24 c. Calypso band 30 15
a. Horiz pair. Nos. 254/5 .. .. .. 60 30
w. Wmk inverted .. .. 28·00
255 24 c. Women dancing 30 15
w. Wmk inverted .. .. 28·00
256 48 c. Underwater life 30 25
a. Horiz pair. Nos. 256/7 .. .. .. 60 50
257 48 c. Skin-diver and turtle 30 25
250/7 .. .. *Set of* 8 1·90 1·00
Each denomination was printed *se-tenant* throughout the sheet. The 12 c. values are on cream coloured paper.

(Litho B.W.)

1969 (July). *First Anniv of CARIFTA (Caribbean Free Trade Area). T* **67** *and similar horiz designs. Multicoloured. P* 13½ × 13.
258 5 c. Type **67** 10 10
259 8 c. Hawker Siddeley H.S.748 aircraft, emblem and island 25 15
260 12 c. Chart of Caribbean Sea and emblem .. 25 20
261 24 c. Steamship unloading, tug and emblem .. 30 20
258/61 .. .. *Set of* 4 75 60

71 "Spinning"

72 Mahatma Gandhi Weaving and Clock Tower, Westminster

(Litho B.W.)

1969 (10 July). *50th Anniv of International Labour Organisation. T* **71** *and similar vert designs showing paintings of people at work by J. Millet, bordered by flags of member-nations of the I.L.O. Multicoloured. No wmk. P* 13 × 13½.
262 15 c. Type **71** 10 10
263 30 c. "Threshing" 15 15
264 38 c. "Flax-pulling" 15 15
262/4 .. .. *Set of* 3 30 30

(Des G. Vasarhelyi. Litho Format)

1969 (20 Oct). *Birth Centenary of Mahatma Gandhi. T* **72** *and similar horiz designs. Multicoloured. P* 14½.
265 6 c. Type **72** 30 10
266 38 c. Gandhi, Nehru and Mausoleum 50 15
267 $1.20, Gandhi and Taj Mahal .. .. 1·00 75
265/7 .. .. *Set of* 3 1·60 90
Nos. 265/7 are incorrectly inscribed "Ghandi".

75 "Saint Joseph"

(Des G. Vasarhelyi. Litho Govt Printer, Jerusalem)

1969 (3 Nov). *National Day. Stained Glass Windows. T* **75** *and similar vert designs. Multicoloured. P* 14.
268 6 c. Type **75** 10 10
269 8 c. "Saint John" 10 10
270 12 c. "Saint Peter" 10 10
271 60 c. "Saint Paul" 30 50
268/71 .. .. *Set of* 4 40 60
Nos. 268/71 were printed in sheets of 16 (4 × 4) containing 12 stamps and four printed labels in the top row: The labels each contain two lines of a patriotic poem by W. O. M. Pond, the first letter from each line spelling "DOMINICA".

79 Queen Elizabeth II

80 Purple-throated Carib and Flower

81 Government Headquarters

82 Coat of Arms

(Photo D.L.R.)

1969 (26 Nov)–**72**. *T* **79/82** *and similar horiz designs. Multicoloured. W* **41** *of Singapore (Half-check Pattern) (60 c. to $4.80) or no wmk (others). Chalk-surfaced paper. P* 13½×14 (½ *c.*), 14×13½ (1 *to* 50 *c.*) *or* 14 (60 *c. to* $4.80).
272 ½ c. Type **79** .. .. 10 1·50
a. Glazed paper (1972) 30 70
273 1 c. Type **80** .. .. 30 1·50
a. Glazed paper (1972) .. .. .. 1·50 80

274	2 c. Poinsettia	15	10
	a. Glazed paper (1972)	50	20
275	3 c. Red-necked Pigeon	2·00	2·00
	a. Glazed paper (1972)	1·75	80
276	4 c. Imperial Amazon	2·00	2·00
	a. Glazed paper (1972)	1·75	70
277	5 c. *Battus polydamas* (butterfly)	2·00	65
	a. Glazed paper (1972)	1·75	80
278	6 c. *Dryas julia* (butterfly)	2·00	2·25
	a. Glazed paper (1972)	1·75	2·25
279	8 c. Shipping Bananas	20	10
	a. Glazed paper (1972)	40	20
280	10 c. Portsmouth Harbour	20	10
	a. Glazed paper (1972)	35	20
281	12 c. Copra processing plant	20	10
	a. Glazed paper (1972)	35	20
282	15 c. Straw workers	20	10
	a. Glazed paper (1972)	35	25
283	25 c. Timber plant	30	10
	a. Glazed paper (1972)	40	25
284	30 c. Pumice mine	1·50	90
	a. Glazed paper (1972)	1·50	70
285	38 c. Grammar school and playing field	8·00	1·75
	a. Glazed paper (1972)	8·50	13·00
286	50 c. Roseau Cathedral	50	45
	a. Glazed paper (1972)	80	80
287	60 c. Type **81**	55	1·25
288	$1.20, Melville Hall Airport (40×27 *mm*)	1·00	1·75
289	$2.40, Type **82**	1·00	3·50
290	$4.80, Type **79** (26×39 *mm*)	1·75	6·50
272/90	*Set of* 19	21·00	23·00
272a/86a	*Set of* 15	20·00	20·00

99 "Virgin and Child with St. John" (Perugino)

101 Astronaut's First Step onto the Moon

(Des G. Vasarhelyi. Litho B.W.)

1969 (19 Dec). *Christmas. Paintings. T* **99** *and similar vert designs. Multicoloured. P* 14 × 14½.

291	6 c. "Virgin and Child with St. John" (Lippi)	10	10
292	10 c. "Holy Family with the Lamb" (Raphael)	10	10
293	15 c. Type **99**	10	10
294	$1.20, "Madonna of the Rose Hedge" (Botticelli)	35	40
291/4	*Set of* 4	35	40
MS295	89 × 76 mm. Nos. 293/4. Imperf	90	90

(Des G. Vasarhelyi. Photo Banknote Printing Office, Helsinki)

1970 (6 Feb*). *Moon Landing. T* **101** *and similar horiz designs. Multicoloured. P* 12½.

296	½ c. Type **101**	10	10
297	5 c. Scientific Experiment on the Moon, and Flag	15	10
298	8 c. Astronauts collecting Rocks	15	10
299	30 c. Module over the Moon	30	15
300	50 c. Moon Plaque	40	25
301	60 c. Astronauts	40	30
296/301	*Set of* 6	1·25	80
MS302	116 × 112 mm. Nos. 298/301. Imperf	2·00	2·00

*This is the date of release in Dominica, but the above were released by the Philatelic Agency in the U.S.A. on 2 February.

107 Giant Green Turtle

(Des G. Drummond. Litho Kyodo Printing Co, Tokyo)

1970 (7 Sept). *Flora and Fauna. T* **107** *and similar horiz designs. Multicoloured. P* 13.

303	6 c. Type **107**	50	20
304	24 c. Atlantic Flyingfish	60	40
305	38 c. Anthurium lily	70	65
306	60 c. Imperial and Red-necked Amazons	3·25	4·75
303/6	*Set of* 4	4·50	5·50
MS307	160×111 mm. Nos. 303/6	5·50	6·00

108 18th-Century National Costume

109 Scrooge and Marley's Ghost

(Des G. Drummond from local designs. Litho Questa)

1970 (30 Oct). *National Day. T* **108** *and similar horiz designs. Multicoloured. P* 14.

308	5 c. Type **108**	10	10
309	8 c. Carib Basketry	10	10
310	$1 Flag and Chart of Dominica	30	40
308/10	*Set of* 3	30	40
MS311	150 × 85 mm. Nos. 308/10 plus three labels	50	1·40

(Des R. Granger Barrett. Litho Questa)

1970 (23 Nov). *Christmas and Charles Dickens' Death Centenary. T* **109** *and similar vert designs showing scenes from "A Christmas Carol". Multicoloured. P* 14 × 14½.

312	2 c. Type **109**	10	10
313	15 c. Fezziwig's Ball	20	10
314	24 c. Scrooge and his Nephew's Party	20	10
315	$1.20, Scrooge and the Ghost of Christmas Present	65	60
312/15	*Set of* 4	1·00	70
MS316	142 × 87 mm. Nos. 312/15	1·00	3·25

110 "The Doctor" (Sir Luke Fildes)

(Des G. Vasarhelyi. Litho Questa)

1970 (28 Dec). *Centenary of British Red Cross. T* **110** *and similar horiz designs. Multicoloured. P* 14½ × 14.

317	8 c. Type **110**	10	10
318	10 c. Hands and Red Cross	10	10
319	15 c. Flag of Dominica and Red Cross Emblem	15	10
320	50 c. "The Sick Child" (E. Munch)	50	35
317/20	*Set of* 4	75	40
MS321	108 × 76 mm. Nos. 317/20	1·25	2·50

111 Marigot School

(Des G. Vasarhelyi. Litho Questa)

1971 (1 Mar). *International Education Year* (1970). *T* **111** *and similar horiz designs. Multicoloured. P* 13½.

322	5 c. Type **111**	10	10
323	8 c. Goodwill Junior High School	10	10
324	14 c. University of West Indies (Jamaica)	10	10
325	$1 Trinity College, Cambridge	25	30
322/5	*Set of* 4	30	30
MS326	85 × 85 mm. Nos. 324/5	50	1·00

112 Waterfall

(Des O. Bonnevalle. Litho Questa)

1971 (22 Mar). *Tourism. T* **112** *and similar horiz designs. Multicoloured. P* 13½.

327	5 c. Type **112**	15	10
328	10 c. Boat-building	15	10
329	30 c. Sailing	25	10
330	50 c. Yacht and motor launch	40	30
327/30	*Set of* 4	85	45
MS331	130 × 86 mm. Nos. 327/30	85	1·00

113 UNICEF Symbol in "D"

114 German Boy Scout

(Des G. Drummond. Litho Questa)

1971 (14 June). *25th Anniv of UNICEF. P* 14.

332	**113**	5 c. bluish violet, black and gold	10	10
333		10 c. yellow, black and gold	10	10
334		38 c. green, black and gold	10	10
335		$1.20 orange, black and gold	30	45
332/5		*Set of* 4	40	55
MS336		84 × 79 mm. Nos. 333 and 335	50	1·10

(Litho Format)

1971 (18 Oct). *World Scout Jamboree, Asagiri, Japan. T* **114** *and similar vert designs showing Boy Scouts from the nations listed. Multicoloured. W* w **12**. *P* 11.

337	20 c. Type **114**	15	15
338	24 c. Great Britain	20	15
339	30 c. Japan	25	20
340	$1 Dominica	50	1·75
337/40	*Set of* 4	1·00	2·00
MS341	114 × 102 mm. Nos. 339/40	1·00	2·00

The above were printed on thick paper and the watermark is very faint.

Both No. 340 and the $1 value from the miniature sheet show the national flag of the Dominican Republic in error.

"Dominica" on the scout's shirt pocket is omitted on the $1 value from the miniature sheet.

115 Groine at Portsmouth

(Des V. Whiteley. Litho Format)

1971 (15 Nov). *National Day. T* **115** *and similar multicoloured designs. P* 13½.

342	8 c. Type **115**	10	10
343	15 c. Carnival scene	10	10
344	20 c. Carifta Queen (*vert*)	10	10
345	50 c. Rock of Atkinson (*vert*)	20	25
342/5	*Set of* 4	30	30
MS346	63 × 89 mm. $1.20, As 20 c. P 15	45	7[illegible]

116 Eight Reals Piece, 1761

(Des G. Drummond. Litho Questa)

1972 (7 Feb). *Coins. T* **116** *and similar designs. P* 14.

347	10 c. black, silver and violet	10	1[illegible]
348	30 c. black, silver and yellowish green	15	1[illegible]
349	35 c. black, silver and bright blue	20	2[illegible]
350	50 c. black, silver and vermilion	40	1·4[illegible]
347/50	*Set of* 4	75	1·6[illegible]
MS351	86 × 90 mm. Nos. 349/50	1·00	1·6[illegible]

Designs: *Horiz*—30 c. Eleven and three bitt pieces, 1798. *Vert*—35 c. Two reals and two bitt pieces, 1770; 50 c. Mocos, Pieces-of-eight and eight reals-eleven bitts piece, 1798.

117 Common Opossum

(Des R. Granger Barrett. Litho Questa)

1972 (3 June). *U.N. Conference on the Human Environment, Stockholm. T* **117** *and similar horiz designs. Multicoloured. W* w **12** (*sideways*). *P* 14.

352	½ c. Type **117**	10	1[illegible]
353	35 c. Brazilian Agouti (rodent)	40	1[illegible]
354	60 c. Orchid	2·50	5[illegible]
355	$1.20, Hibiscus	2·50	1·6[illegible]
352/5	*Set of* 4	5·00	2·0[illegible]
MS356	139×94 mm. Nos. 352/5	7·00	9·0[illegible]

118 Sprinter

(Des R. Granger Barrett. Litho Format)

1972 (16 Oct*). *Olympic Games, Munich. T* **118** *and similar multicoloured designs. P* 14.

357	30 c. Type **118**	10	1[illegible]
358	35 c. Hurdler	15	1[illegible]
359	58 c. Hammer-thrower (*vert*)	20	2[illegible]
360	72 c. Long-jumper (*vert*)	40	4[illegible]
357/60	*Set of* 4	75	7[illegible]
MS361	98 × 96 mm. Nos. 359/60. P 15	75	9[illegible]

*This is the local release date; the American philatelic agency released the stamps on 9 October.

119 General Post Office

(Des G. Vasarhelyi. Litho Format)

72 (1 Nov). *National Day. T* **119** *and similar horiz designs. Multicoloured. P* 13½.
2 10 c. Type **119** 10 10
3 20 c. Morne Diablotin 10 10
4 30 c. Rodney's Rock 15 15
2/4 .. .. *Set of* 3 30 30
S365 83 × 96 mm. Nos. 363/4. P 15 .. .. 50 70

120 Bananas and Imperial Amazon

(Des (from photograph by D. Groves) and photo Harrison)

72 (20 Nov). *Royal Silver Wedding. Multicoloured; background colour given. W w* **12**. *P* 14 × 14½.
6 **120** 5 c. yellow-olive 20 10
a. Deep yellow-olive 50 25
7 $1 myrtle-green 60 40
w. Wmk inverted .. .. .. 3·50

121 "The Adoration of the Shepherds" (Caravaggio)

122 Launching of Weather Satellite

(Des G. Vasarhelyi. Litho Format)

72 (4 Dec*). *Christmas. T* **121** *and similar vert designs. Multicoloured. P* 13½.
8 8 c. Type **121** 10 10
9 14 c. "The Myosotis Virgin" (Rubens).. .. 10 10
0 30 c. "Madonna and Child with St. Francesca Romana" (Gentileschi) 15 10
1 $1 "Adoration of the Kings" (Mostaert) .. 50 90
8/71 .. .. *Set of* 4 70 1·00
S372 102 × 79 mm. Nos. 370/1. Imperf.. .. 90 80

*This is the date of release in Dominica; the stamps were put sale by the Philatelic agency in the U.S.A. on 27 November.
No. 368 is wrongly attributed to Boccaccino in the design.

(Des G. Vasarhelyi. Litho Format)

73 (16 July). *I.M.O./W.M.O. Centenary. T* **122** *and similar multicoloured designs. P* 14½.
3 ½ c. Type **122** 10 10
4 1 c. Nimbus satellite 10 10
5 2 c. Radiosonde balloon 10 10
6 30 c. Radarscope (*horiz*) 15 15
7 35 c. Diagram of pressure zones (*horiz*) .. 20 20
8 50 c. Hurricane shown by satellite (*horiz*) .. 30 35
9 $1 Computer weather-map (*horiz*) 60 65
3/9 .. .. *Set of* 7 1·25 1·40
S380 90 × 105 mm. Nos. 378/9 .. .. .. 90 1·75

123 Going to Hospital

124 Cyrique Crab

(Des G. Vasarhelyi. Litho Format)

73 (20 Aug). *25th Anniv of W.H.O. T* **123** *and similar horiz designs. Multicoloured. P* 14½.
1 ½ c. Type **123** 10 10
2 1 c. Maternity care 10 10
3 2 c. Smallpox inoculation 10 10
4 30 c. Emergency service 30 15
5 35 c. Waiting for the doctor 35 15
6 50 c. Medical examination 45 25
7 $1 Travelling doctor 65 60
1/7 .. .. *Set of* 7 1·75 1·10
S388 112 × 110 mm. Nos. 386/7. P 14 × 14½ .. 75 1·25
a. Perf 14½ .. .. 45·00 45·00

(Des G. Drummond. Litho Format)

1973 (15 Oct). *Flora and Fauna. T* **124** *and similar vert designs. Multicoloured. P* 14½.
389 ½ c. Type **124** 10 10
390 22 c. Blue Land-crab 35 10
391 25 c. Bread Fruit 35 15
392 $1.20, Sunflower .. .. 1·00 2·00
389/92 .. .. *Set of* 4 1·50 2·00
MS393 91 × 127 mm. Nos. 389/92 .. .. .. 2·50 4·00

125 Princess Anne and Captain Mark Phillips

(Des G. Drummond. Litho Format)

1973 (14 Nov). *Royal Wedding. P* 13½.
394 **125** 25 c. multicoloured 10 10
395 – $2 multicoloured 30 30
MS396 79 × 100 mm. 75 c. as 25 c. and $1.20 as $2 40 30

No. 395 is as T **125**, but the portrait has a different frame.
Nos. 394/5 were each issued in small sheets of five stamps and one stamp-size label.

126 "Adoration of the Kings" (Brueghel)

(Des M. Shamir. Litho Format)

1973 (26 Nov). *Christmas. T* **126** *and similar horiz designs. Multicoloured. P* 14½.
397 ½ c. Type **126** 10 10
398 1 c. "Adoration of the Magi" (Botticelli) .. 10 10
399 2 c. "Adoration of the Magi" (Dürer) .. 10 10
400 12 c. "Mystic Nativity" (Botticelli) 20 10
401 22 c. "Adoration of the Magi" (Rubens) .. 25 10
402 35 c. "The Nativity" (Dürer) 25 10
403 $1 "Adoration of the Shepherds" (Giorgione) 90 55
397/403 .. .. *Set of* 7 1·60 80
MS404 122 × 98 mm. Nos. 402/3 .. .. .. 1·25 1·10

127 Carib Basket-weaving

(Des G. Drummond. Litho Format)

1973 (17 Dec). *National Day. T* **127** *and similar multicoloured designs. P* 13½.
405 5 c. Type **127** 10 10
406 10 c. Staircase of the Snake 10 10
407 50 c. Miss Caribbean Queen (*vert*) 15 15
408 50 c. Miss Carifta Queen (*vert*) 15 15
409 $1 Dance group 25 30
405/9 .. .. *Set of* 5 50 60
MS410 95×127 mm. Nos. 405/6 and 409 .. 40 65

128 University Centre, Dominica

(Des G. Drummond. Litho Format)

1974 (21 Jan). *25th Anniv of West Indies University. T* **128** *and similar horiz designs. Multicoloured. P* 14½.
411 12 c. Type **128** 10 10
412 30 c. Graduation ceremony 10 10
413 $1 University coat of arms 25 35
411/13 .. .. *Set of* 3 30 35
MS414 97 × 131 mm. Nos. 411/13 .. .. .. 30 55

OMNIBUS ISSUES

Details, together with prices for complete sets, of the various Omnibus issues from the 1935 Silver Jubilee series to date are included in a special section following Zimbabwe at the end of Volume 2.

129 Dominicia 1d. Stamp of 1874 and Map

130 Footballer and Flag of Brazil

(Des G. Drummond. Litho Format)

1974 (27 May). *Stamp Centenary. T* **129** *and similar horiz designs. Multicoloured. P* 14½.
415 ½ c. Type **129** 10 10
416 1 c. 6d. stamp of 1874 and posthorn 10 10
417 2 c. 1s. stamp of 1874 and arms 10 10
418 10 c. Type **129** 20 10
419 50 c. As 1 c. 60 30
420 $1.20, As 2 c. 75 70
415/20 .. .. *Set of* 6 1·50 1·00
MS421 105 × 121 mm. Nos. 418/20 .. .. 1·50 1·50

(Des V. Whiteley. Litho Format)

1974 (12 Aug). *World Cup Football Championship, West Germany. T* **130** *and similar vert designs, showing footballers and flags of the countries given. Multicoloured. P* 14½.
422 ½ c. Type **130** 10 10
423 1 c. West Germany 10 10
424 2 c. Italy 10 10
425 30 c. Scotland 50 10
426 40 c. Sweden 50 10
427 50 c. Netherlands 55 35
428 $1 Yugoslavia 90 90
422/8 .. .. *Set of* 7 2·25 1·50
MS429 89 × 87 mm. Nos. 427/8 .. .. .. 70 80

131 Indian Hole

(Des G. Vasarhelyi. Litho Format)

1974 (1 Nov). *National Day. T* **131** *and similar horiz designs. Multicoloured. P* 13½.
430 10 c. Type **131** 10 10
431 40 c. Teachers' Training College 10 10
432 $1 Bay Oil distillery plant, Petite Savanne 50 45
430/2 .. .. *Set of* 3 60 45
MS433 96 × 143 mm. Nos. 430/2 .. .. .. 60 65

132 Churchill with "Colonist"

(Des G. Drummond. Litho Format)

1974 (25 Nov). *Birth Centenary of Sir Winston Churchill. T* **132** *and similar horiz designs. Multicoloured. P* 14½.
434 ½ c. Type **132** 10 10
435 1 c. Churchill and Eisenhower 10 10
436 2 c. Churchill and Roosevelt 10 10
437 20 c. Churchill and troops on assault-course .. 15 10
438 45 c. Painting at Marrakesh 25 10
439 $2 Giving the "V" sign .. .. .. 80 1·00
434/9 .. .. *Set of* 6 1·10 1·10
MS440 126 × 100 mm. Nos. 438/9. P 13 .. .. 1·10 1·75

133 Mailboats *Orinoco* (1851) and *Geesthaven* (1974)

134 "The Virgin and Child" (Tiso)

(Des G. Drummond. Litho Format)

1974 (4 Dec). *Centenary of Universal Postal Union. T* **133** *and similar horiz designs. Multicoloured. P* 13.
441 10 c. Type **133** 20 10
442 $2 De Havilland D.H.4 (1918) and Boeing 747-100 (1974) .. .. .. 80 1·00
MS443 107×93 mm. $1.20 as 10 c. and $2.40 as $2 .. .. 1·00 1·40

Nos. 442 and **MS**443 are inscr "De Haviland"
Nos. 441/2 were issued either in sheets of 50 or in sheets of five stamps and one inscribed label.

(Des M. Shamir. Litho Questa)

1974 (16 Dec). *Christmas. T* **134** *and similar vert designs. Multicoloured. P* 14.
444 ½ c. Type **134** 10 10
445 1 c. "Madonna and Child with Saints" (Costa) 10 10
446 2 c. "The Nativity" (School of Rimini, 14th-cent) 10 10
447 10 c. "The Rest on the Flight into Egypt" (Romanelli) 20 10
448 25 c. "Adoration of the Shepherds" (da Sermoneta) 35 10
449 45 c. "The Nativity" (Guido Reni) 45 10
450 $1 "The Adoration of the Magi" (Caselli) .. 65 40
444/50 .. .. *Set of* 7 1·60 60
MS451 114 × 78 mm. Nos. 449/50 .. .. 60 1·00

135 Queen Triggerfish

(Des G. Vasarhelyi. Litho Format)

1975 (2 June). *Fishes. T* **135** *and similar horiz designs. Multicoloured. P* 14.
452 ½ c. Type **135** 10 10
453 1 c. Porkfish 10 10
454 2 c. Sailfish 10 10
455 3 c. Swordfish 10 10
456 20 c. Great Barracuda .. .. .. 1·00 50
457 $2 Nassau Grouper .. .. .. 4·25 2·75
452/7 .. .. *Set of* 6 5·00 3·25
MS458 104×80 mm. No. 457. P 13 .. .. 3·25 6·00

136 *Myscelia antholia*

(Des J. W. Litho Format)

1975 (28 July). *Dominican Butterflies. T* **136** *and similar horiz designs. Multicoloured. P* 14½.
459 ½ c. Type **136** 10 40
460 1 c. *Lycorea ceres* 10 40
461 2 c. *Anaea marthesia* ("*Siderone nemesis*") 15 40
462 6 c. *Battus polydamas* 60 55
463 30 c. *Anartia lytrea* .. .. 1·75 70
464 40 c. *Morpho peleides* .. .. 2·00 75
465 $2 *Dryas julia* .. .. 3·75 7·50
459/65 .. .. *Set of* 7 7·50 9·50
MS466 108 × 80 mm. No. 465. P 13 .. .. 3·00 4·25

137 *Yare* (cargo liner)

(Des J. W. Litho Questa)

1975 (1 Sept). *"Ships Tied to Dominica's History". T* **137** *and similar horiz designs. Multicoloured. P* 14.
467 ½ c. Type **137** 20 35
468 1 c. *Thames II* (liner), 1890 .. .. 20 35
469 2 c. *Lady Nelson* (cargo liner) 20 35
470 20 c. *Lady Rodney* (cargo liner) .. .. 1·00 35
471 45 c. *Statesman* (freighter) .. .. 1·25 55
472 50 c. *Geestcape* (freighter) .. .. .. 1·25 80
473 $2 *Geeststar* (freighter) .. .. .. 3·25 4·50
467/73 .. .. *Set of* 7 6·50 6·50
MS474 78×103 mm. Nos. 472/3 .. .. 3·00 5·00

138 "Women in Agriculture"

139 Miss Caribbean Queen, 1975

(Litho Questa)

1975 (20 Oct). *International Women's Year. T* **138** *and similar horiz design. Multicoloured. P* 14.
475 10 c. Type **138** 10 10
476 $2 "Women in Industry and Commerce" .. 40 60

(Litho Format)

1975 (6 Nov). *National Day. T* **139** *and similar multicoloured designs. P* 14 × 13½ (*vert*) *or* 13½ × 14 (*horiz*).
477 5 c. Type **139** 10 10
478 10 c. Public Library (*horiz*) 10 10
479 30 c. Citrus Factory (*horiz*) 10 10
480 $1 National Day Trophy 25 50
477/80 .. .. *Set of* 4 35 60
MS481 130×98 mm. Nos. 478/80. Imperf .. 50 1·40

140 "Virgin and Child" (Mantegna)

141 Hibiscus

(Des M. Shamir. Litho Questa)

1975 (24 Nov). *Christmas. T* **140** *and similar vert designs showing "Virgin and Child". Multicoloured. P* 14.
482 ½ c. Type **140** 10 10
483 1 c. Fra Filippo Lippi 10 10
484 2 c. Bellini 10 10
485 10 c. Botticelli 15 10
486 25 c. Bellini 25 10
487 45 c. Correggio 30 10
488 $1 Dürer 55 50
482/88 .. .. *Set of* 7 1·10 70
MS489 139 × 85 mm. Nos. 487/88 .. .. 1·00 1·50

(Des J.W. Litho Format)

1975 (8 Dec)–**78.** *T* **141** *and similar multicoloured designs.*

(*a*) *Size as T* **141**. *P* 14½

490 ½ c. Type **141** 10 50
491 1 c. African Tulip 15 50
492 2 c. Castor Oil Tree 15 50
493 3 c. White Cedar Flower 15 50
494 4 c. Egg Plant 15 50
495 5 c. Needlefish ("Gare") 20 50
496 6 c. Ochro 20 60
497 8 c. Zenaida Dove .. .. 2·25 60
498 10 c. Screw Pine 20 15
a. Perf 13½ (1978) .. .. .. 25·00
499 20 c. Mango Longue 30 15
500 25 c. Crayfish 35 15
501 30 c. Common Opossum ("Manicou") .. 90 80

(*b*) *Size* 28 × 44 *mm* ($10) *or* 44 × 28 *mm* (*others*). *P* 13½

502 40 c. Bay Leaf Groves 90 80
503 50 c. Tomatoes 55 50
504 $1 Lime Factory 75 65
505 $2 Rum Distillery .. .. 1·75 3·50
506 $5 Bay Oil Distillery .. .. .. 2·25 5·00
507 $10 Queen Elizabeth II .. .. .. 3·00 15·00
490/507 .. .. *Set of* 18 13·00 27·00

Nos. 490/2, 494/9 and 501/7 exist imperforate from stock dispersed by the liquidator of Format International Security Printers Ltd.

142 American Infantry

143 Rowing

(Des J.W. Litho Format)

1976 (12 Apr). *Bicentenary of American Revolution. T* **142** *and similar vert designs. Multicoloured. P* 14½.
508 ½ c. Type **142** 10 10
509 1 c. British three-decker, 1782 .. .. 10 10
510 2 c. George Washington 10 10
511 45 c. British sailors 55 10
512 75 c. British ensign 80 40
513 $2 Admiral Hood .. .. 1·25 1·25
508/13 .. .. *Set of* 6 2·50 1·75
MS514 105 × 92 mm. Nos. 512/13. P 13 .. .. 2·00 3·50

(Des J.W. Litho Format)

1976 (24 May). *Olympic Games, Montreal. T* **143** *and similar vert designs. Multicoloured. P* 14½.
515 ½ c. Type **143** 10 10
516 1 c. Shot putting 10 10
517 2 c. Swimming 10 10
518 40 c. Relay 15 10
519 45 c. Gymnastics 15 10
520 60 c. Sailing 20 20
521 $2 Archery 55 80
515/21 .. .. *Set of* 7 1·10 1·10
MS522 90 × 104 mm. Nos. 520/1. P 13 .. .. 1·25 1·75

Nos. 516/21 exist imperforate from stock dispersed by the liquidator of Format International Security Printers Ltd.

144 Ringed Kingfisher

145 Viking Spacecraft System

(Des G. Drummond. Litho Format)

1976 (28 June). *Wild Birds. T* **144** *and similar multicolou designs. P* 14½.
523 ½ c. Type **144** 10
524 1 c. Mourning Dove 15
525 2 c. Green Heron 15
526 15 c. Broad-winged Hawk .. .. .. 1·25
527 30 c. Blue-headed Hummingbird .. .. 1·75
528 45 c. Bananaquit .. .. 2·50 1
529 $2 Imperial Amazon .. .. .. 9·00 14
523/9 .. .. *Set of* 7 13·50 16
MS530 133 × 101 mm. Nos. 527/9. P 13 .. .. 11·00 16

Nos. 523/5 exist imperforate from stock dispersed by t liquidator of Format International Security Printers Ltd.

1976 (26 July). *West Indian Victory in World Cricket Cup. As N 559/60 of Barbados.*
531 15 c. Map of the Caribbean 75 1
532 25 c. Prudential Cup 75 1

(Des PAD Studio. Litho Format)

1976 (20 Sept). *Viking Space Mission. T* **145** *and similar mu coloured designs. P* 14½.
533 ½ c. Type **145** 10
534 1 c. Launching pad (*horiz*) 10
535 2 c. Titan IIID and Centaur DII 10
536 3 c. Orbiter and lander capsule 10
537 45 c. Capsule, parachute unopened 30
538 75 c. Capsule, parachute opened 40
539 $1 Lander descending (*horiz*) 45
540 $2 Space vehicle on Mars (*horiz*) 60 1
533/40 .. .. *Set of* 8 1·75 2
MS541 104 × 78 mm. Nos. 539/40. P 13 .. .. 1·10 2

146 "Virgin and Child with Saints Anthony of Padua and Roch" (Giorgione)

147 Island Craft Co-operative

(Des M. Shamir. Litho Questa)

1976 (1 Nov). *Christmas. T* **146** *and similar vert designs show "Virgin and Child" by the artists named. Multicoloured. P* 14.
542 ½ c. Type **146** 10
543 1 c. Bellini 10
544 2 c. Mantegna 10
545 6 c. Mantegna (*different*) 10
546 25 c. Memling 15
547 45 c. Correggio 20
548 $3 Raphael .. .. 1·00 1
542/8 .. .. *Set of* 7 1·40 1
MS549 140 × 85 mm. 50 c. as No. 547 and $1 as No. 548 .. .. 1·00 1

(Des G. Drummond. Litho Questa)

1976 (22 Nov). *National Day. T* **147** *and similar horiz desig Multicoloured. P* 13½.
550 10 c. Type **147** 10
551 50 c. Harvesting bananas 15
552 $1 Boxing plant 30
550/2 .. .. *Set of* 3 45
MS553 96 × 122 mm. Nos. 550/2 50

148 American Giant Sundial (*Architectonica nobilis*)

149 The Queen Crowned and Enthroned

(Des J.W. Litho Questa)

'6 (20 Dec). *Shells. T* **148** *and similar vert designs. Multi-
oloured. P* 14.
½ c. Type **148** 10 10
1 c. Flame Helmet (*Cassis flammea*) .. 10 10
2 c. Mouse Cone (*Conus mus*) 10 10
20 c. Caribbean Vase (*Vasum muricatum*) 45 10
40 c. West Indian Fighting Conch (*Strombus pugilis*) 70 25
50 c. Short Coral Shell (*Coralliophila abbreviata*) 70 25
$3 Apple Murex (*Murex pomum*) .. 3·00 2·75
/60 .. .. *Set of* 7 4·50 3·00
561 101×55 mm. $2 Long-spined Star Shell
Astraea phoebia) .. .. 1·75 2·25

(Des J.W. Litho Questa)

7 (7 Feb). *Silver Jubilee. T* **149** *and similar horiz designs.
Iulticoloured. P* 14 × 13½.
½ c. Type **149** 10 10
1 c. Imperial State Crown 10 10
45 c. Queen Elizabeth and Princess Anne .. 15 10
$2 Coronation Ring 25 30
$2.50, Ampulla and Spoon 30 40
2/6 .. .. *Set of* 5 60 70
567 104 × 79 mm. $5 Queen Elizabeth and
Prince Philip .. .. 75 1·25
Nos. 562/6 also exist perf 12×11½ (*Price for set of* 5 50p *mint used*) from additional sheetlets of 5 stamps and one label. mps perforated 14×13½ are from normal sheets of 40. mps from the sheets of 5 have the arch at left in a different our.

150 Joseph Haydn

151 Hiking

(Des J.W. Litho Questa)

77 (25 Apr). *150th Death Anniv of Ludwig van Beethoven.
T* **150** *and similar vert designs. Multicoloured. P* 14.
½ c. Type **150** 10 10
1 c. Scene from "Fidelio" 10 10
2 c. Maria Casentini (dancer) 10 10
15 c. Beethoven and pastoral scene 25 10
30 c. "Wellington's Victory" 35 10
40 c. Henriette Sontag (singer) 35 10
$2 The young Beethoven .. .. .. 1·10 2·00
3/74 .. .. *Set of* 7 1·75 2·25
575 138 × 93 mm. Nos. 572/4 .. .. .. 1·50 3·25

(Des J.W. Litho Questa)

77 (8 Aug). *Caribbean Scout Jamboree, Jamaica. T* **151** *and similar horiz designs. Multicoloured. P* 14.
½ c. Type **151** 10 10
1 c. First-aid 10 10
2 c. Camping 10 10
45 c. Rock climbing 35 15
50 c. Canoeing 40 20
$3 Sailing .. .. 2·00 1·75
5/81 .. .. *Set of* 6 2·50 2·00
582 111 × 113 mm. 75 c. Map reading and $2
Campfire singsong .. .. 1·60 1·75

152 Holy Family

ROYAL VISIT
W.I. 1977

(153)

(Des G. Vasarhelyi. Litho Questa)

77 (17 Nov). *Christmas. T* **152** *and similar horiz designs showing book miniatures from Foix Book of Hours* ($3) *or De Lisle Psalter (others). Multicoloured. P* 14.
½ c. Type **152** 10 10
1 c. Angel and Shepherds 10 10
2 c. Holy Baptism 10 10
6 c. Flight into Egypt 15 10
15 c. Three Kings with gifts 15 10
45 c. Holy Family in the Temple 30 10
$3 Flight into Egypt (*different*) .. .. 1·25 1·10
3/9 .. .. *Set of* 7 1·75 1·40
590 113 × 85 mm. 50 c. Virgin and Child; $2
Flight into Egypt (*different*) 60 75

77 (28 Nov). *Royal Visit. Nos.* 562/7 *optd with T* **153** *above "JUBILEE". P* 12×11½.
½ c. Type **149** 10 10
1 c. Imperial State Crown 10 10
45 c. Queen Elizabeth and Princess Anne 15 10
a. Opt in top left-hand corner (*p* 14×13½) 15 10
$2 Coronation Ring 45 55
a. Opt in top left-hand corner (*p* 14×13½) 30 30
$2.50, Ampulla and Spoon 50 70
a. Opt in top left-hand corner (*p* 14×13½) 35 35
1/5 .. .. *Set of* 5 1·00 1·40
596 104×79 mm. $5 Queen Elizabeth and
Prince Philip (opt to left of face value) .. 1·00 1·50
a. Optd "W.I. 1977" only on stamp .. 12·00 15·00
No. **MS**596a is overprinted "W.I. 1977" beneath "ROYAL VISIT" scription to left of stamp design. Overprint as T **153**, but in one e, appears at top left of *miniature sheet*.

154 "Sousouelle Souris"

(Des L. Honychurch and J.W. Litho Questa)

1978 (9 Jan). *"History of Carnival". T* **154** *and similar horiz designs. Multicoloured. P* 14.
597 ½ c. Type **154** 10 10
598 1 c. Sensay costume 10 10
599 2 c. Street musicians 10 10
600 45 c. Douiette band 15 10
601 50 c. Pappy Show wedding 15 10
602 $2 Masquerade band 45 60
597/602 .. .. *Set of* 6 75 75
MS603 104 × 88 mm. $2.50 as No. 602 .. .. 60 85

155 Col. Charles Lindbergh and Ryan NYP Special *Spirit of St. Louis*

156 Queen receiving Homage

(Des G. Drummond. Litho Format)

1978 (13 Mar). *Aviation Anniversaries. T* **155** *and similar horiz designs. Multicoloured. P* 14½.
604 6 c. Type **155** 20 10
605 10 c. Ryan NYP Special *Spirit of St. Louis*, New York, 20 May 1927 .. .. 25 10
606 15 c. Lindbergh and map of Atlantic .. 35 10
607 20 c. Lindbergh reaches Paris, 21 May 1927 45 10
608 40 c. Airship LZ-1, Lake Constance, 1900 55 20
609 60 c. Count F. von Zeppelin and airship LZ-2, 1906 .. .. 65 30
610 $3 Airship LZ-127 *Graf Zeppelin*, 1928 1·40 1·10
604/10 .. .. *Set of* 7 3·50 1·75
MS611 139×108 mm. 50 c. Ryan NYP Special *Spirit of St. Louis* in mid-Atlantic; $2 Airship LZ-127 *Graf Zeppelin*, 1928 .. .. .. 1·00 1·10
The 6, 10, 15, 20 and 50 c. values commemorate the 50th anniversary of first solo transatlantic flight by Col. Charles Lindbergh; the other values commemorate anniversaries of various Zeppelin airships.
No. **MS**611 exists imperforate from stock dispersed by the liquidator of Format International Security Printers Ltd.

(Des J.W. Litho Questa)

1978 (2 June). *25th Anniv of Coronation. T* **156** *and similar vert designs. Multicoloured. P* 14.
612 45 c. Type**156** 15 10
613 $2 Balcony scene 30 30
614 $2.50, Queen and Prince Philip 40 40
612/14 .. .. *Set of* 3 75 65
MS615 76 × 107 mm. $5 Queen Elizabeth II .. 75 75
Nos. 612/14 also exist perf 12 (*Price for set of* 3 75p *mint or used*) from additional sheetlets of 3 stamps and 1 label. Stamps perforated 14 come from sheets of 50. The stamps from sheetlets have changed background or inscription colours.

157 Wright Flyer III

158 "Two Apostles" (Rubens)

(Des G. Vasarhelyi. Litho Format)

1978 (10 July). *75th Anniv of Powered Flight. T* **157** *and similar horiz designs. Multicoloured. P* 14½.
616 30 c. Type **157** 15 15
617 40 c. Wright Type A, 1908 .. .. .. 20 20
618 60 c. Flyer I 25 25
619 $2 Flyer I (*different*) 85 85
616/19 .. .. *Set of* 4 1·25 1·25
MS620 116×89 mm. $3 Wilbur and Orville Wright .. .. 90 1·00
Nos. 616/20 exist imperforate from stock dispersed by the liquidator of Format International Security Printers Ltd.

(Des BG Studio. Litho Questa)

1978 (16 Oct). *Christmas. Paintings. T* **158** *and similar vert designs. Multicoloured. P* 14.
621 20 c. Type **158** 10 10
622 45 c. "The Descent from the Cross" (Rubens) 15 10
623 50 c. "St Ildefonso receiving the Chasuble" (Rubens) 15 10
624 $3 "The Assumption of the Virgin" (Rubens) 35 80
621/4 .. .. *Set of* 4 60 90
MS625 113 × 83 mm. $2 "The Holy Family" (Sebastiano del Piombo*) 75 75
*This painting was incorrectly attributed to Rubens on the stamp.

INDEPENDENT

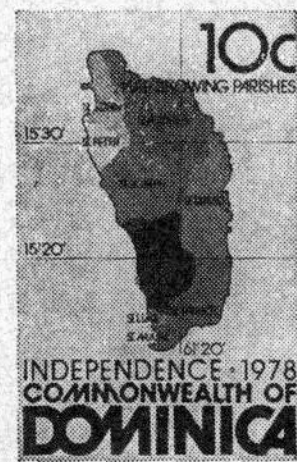

159 Map showing Parishes

INDEPENDENCE
3rd NOVEMBER
1978

(160)

(Des J.W. Litho Questa)

1978 (3 Nov). *Independence. T* **159** *and similar vert designs. Multicoloured. P* 14.
626 10 c. Type **159** 40 15
627 25 c. *Sabinea carinalis* (National flower) .. 45 15
628 45 c. New National flag 50 15
629 50 c. Coat of arms 50 30
630 $2 Patrick John (Prime Minister) .. .. 60 1·50
626/30 .. .. *Set of* 5 2·25 2·00
MS631 113 × 90 mm. $2.50, Type **159** .. .. 1·00 1·25

1978 (3 Nov)–**79**. *Independence. Nos.* 490/507 (10 c. *now perf* 13½) *optd as T* **160** *by typography*.
632 ½ c. Type **141** 40 10
633 1 c. African Tulip 45 10
634 2 c. Castor Oil Tree 45 10
635 3 c. White Cedar Flower 50 15
636 4 c. Egg Plant 50 15
637 5 c. Needlefish 50 15
638 6 c. Ochro 50 15
639 8 c. Zenaida Dove .. .. 2·25 20
640 10 c. Screw Pine 50 15
a. Perf 14½. Litho opt (7.79) .. .. 1·00 45
641 20 c. Mango Longue 60 15
642 25 c. Crayfish 70 20
643 30 c. Common Opossum 70 20
644 40 c. Bay Leaf Groves 70 25
a. Litho opt (7.79) 70 40
645 50 c. Tomatoes 80 30
646 $1 Lime Factory 80 65
647 $2 Rum Distillery .. .. 1·00 1·00
648 $5 Bay Oil Distillery .. .. .. 1·50 2·25
649 $10 Queen Elizabeth II .. .. .. 2·00 4·50
a. Litho opt (7.79) .. .. 2·75 6·50
632/49 .. .. *Set of* 18 13·00 10·00
For History of Aviation gold foil stamps see Appendix at the end of the Dominica listing.

161 Sir Rowland Hill

162 Children and Canoe

(Des BG Studio. Litho Questa)

1979 (19 Mar). *Death Centenary of Sir Rowland Hill. T* **161** *and similar vert designs. P* 14.
650 25 c. multicoloured 10 10
651 45 c. multicoloured 15 10
652 50 c. black, reddish violet and magenta .. 15 10
653 $2 black, magenta and yellow 35 65
650/3 .. .. *Set of* 4 65 80
MS654 186 × 96 mm. $5 black and vermilion .. 1·00 1·25
Designs:—45 c. Great Britain 1840 2d. blue; 50 c. 1874 1d. stamp; $2 Maltese Cross cancellations; $5 Penny Black.
Nos. 650/3 also exist perf 12 (*Price for set of* 4 80p *mint or used*) from additional sheetlets of 5 stamps and 1 label. Shades of these stamps differ from those perforated 14 which come from sheets of 40.

(Des BG Studio. Litho Questa)

1979 (23 Apr). *International Year of the Child. T* **162** *and similar horiz designs. Multicoloured. P* 14.
655 30 c. Type **162** 25 15
656 40 c. Children with bananas 25 25
657 50 c. Children playing cricket .. .. .. 1·25 80
658 $3 Child feeding rabbits .. .. .. 1·75 2·00
655/8 .. .. *Set of* 4 3·25 2·75
MS659 117 × 85 mm. $5 Child with catch of fish .. 1·00 1·50

MINIMUM PRICE

The minimum price quote is 10p which represents a handling charge rather than a basis for valuing common stamps. For further notes about prices see introductory pages.

163 Nassau Grouper

(Des G. Drummond. Litho Questa)

1979 (21 May). *Marine Wildlife. T* **163** *and similar horiz designs. Multicoloured. P* 14.
660 10 c. Type **163** 40 15
661 30 c. Striped Dolphin 70 35
662 50 c. White-tailed Tropic Bird . . . . 2·25 65
663 60 c. Brown Pelican . . . . 2·25 1·50
664 $1 Long-finned Pilot Whale . . . . 2·50 1·75
665 $2 Brown Booby . . . . 3·00 4·50
660/5 . . . . *Set of* 6 10·00 8·00
MS666 120 × 94 mm. $3 Elkhorn Coral . . . . 2·00 1·75
No. 661 is inscribed "SPOTTED DOLPHIN" in error.

164 H.M.S. *Endeavour*

(Des J.W. Litho Questa)

1979 (16 July). *Death Bicentenary of Captain Cook. T* **164** *and similar horiz designs. Multicoloured. P* 14.
667 10 c. Type **164** 65 30
668 50 c. H.M.S. *Resolution* . . . . 1·10 1·00
669 60 c. H.M.S. *Discovery* . . . . 1·25 1·50
670 $2 Detail of Cook's chart of New Zealand, 1770 . . . . 1·60 2·50
667/70 . . . . *Set of* 4 4·25 4·75
MS671 97 × 90 mm. $5 Captain Cook and signature . . . . 1·50 2·00

165 Cooking at Camp-fire **166** Colvillea

(Des M. Diamond. Litho Questa)

1979 (30 July). *50th Anniv of Girl Guide Movement in Dominica. T* **165** *and similar horiz designs. Multicoloured. P* 14.
672 10 c. Type **165** 20 10
673 20 c. Pitching emergency rain tent 25 10
674 50 c. Raising Dominican flag 35 10
675 $2.50, Singing and dancing to accordion . . 90 80
672/5 . . . . *Set of* 4 1·50 85
MS676 110 × 86 mm. $3 Guides of different age-groups . . . . 75 1·25

(Des J.W. Litho Questa)

1979 (3 Sept). *Flowering Trees. T* **166** *and similar vert designs. Multicoloured. P* 14.
677 20 c. Type **166** 15 10
678 40 c. Lignum Vitae 20 15
679 60 c. Dwarf Poinciana 30 25
680 $2 Fern Tree 70 90
677/80 . . . . *Set of* 4 1·25 1·25
MS681 114 × 89 mm. $3 Perfume Tree . . . . 75 1·10

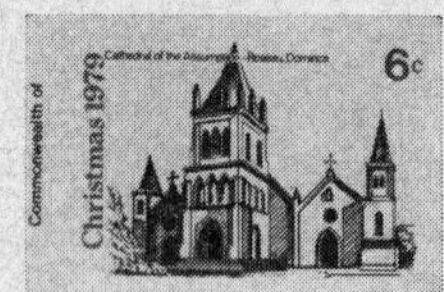

167 Cathedral of the Assumption, Roseau

(Des W. Grout. Litho Questa)

1979 (11 Oct). *Christmas. Cathedrals. T* **167** *and similar multi-coloured designs. P* 14.
682 6 c. Type **167** 10 10
683 45 c. St. Paul's, London (*vert*) 15 10
684 60 c. St. Peter's, Rome 15 10
685 $3 Notre Dame, Paris (*vert*) 55 60
682/5 . . . . *Set of* 4 75 70
MS686 113 × 85 mm. 40 c. St. Patrick's, New York; $2 Cologne Cathedral (*both vert*) 50 80

HURRICANE RELIEF

(168)

169 Mickey Mouse and Octopus playing Xylophone

1979 (29 Oct). *Hurricane Relief. Nos.* 495, 502 *and* 506/7 *optd as T* **168**.
687 5 c. Gare 10 10
688 40 c. Bay Leaf Groves 10 10
689 $5 Bay Oil Distillery . . . . 1·00 1·25
690 $10 Queen Elizabeth II . . . . 1·25 1·75
687/90 . . . . *Set of* 4 2·25 2·75

(Litho Format)

1979 (2 Nov). *International Year of the Child. Walt Disney Cartoon Characters. T* **169** *and similar vert designs showing characters playing musical instruments. Multicoloured. P* 11.
691 ½ c. Type **169** 10 10
692 1 c. Goofy playing guitar on rocking-horse . . 10 10
693 2 c. Mickey Mouse playing violin and Goofy playing bagpipes 10 10
694 3 c. Donald Duck playing drum with pneumatic drill 10 10
695 4 c. Minnie Mouse playing saxophone on roller-skates 10 10
696 5 c. Goofy as one-man-band 10 10
697 10 c. Dale being blown from French horn by Horace Horsecollar 10 10
698 $2 Huey, Dewey and Louie playing bass . . 2·00 2·00
699 $2.50, Donald Duck playing piano and Huey playing trumpet . . . . 2·00 2·25
691/9 . . . . *Set of* 9 4·00 4·25
MS700 127 × 102 mm. $3 Mickey Mouse playing piano. P 13½ . . . . 2·50 3·00

170 Hospital Ward

(Des BG Studio. Litho Questa)

1980 (31 Mar). *75th Anniv of Rotary International. T* **170** *and similar horiz designs. Multicoloured. P* 14.
701 10 c. Type **170** 10 10
702 20 c. Electric-cardiogram 15 10
703 40 c. Site for mental hospital 20 15
704 $2.50, Paul P. Harris (founder) 55 90
701/4 . . . . *Set of* 4 80 1·10
MS705 128 × 113 mm. $3 Interlocking cogs of Rotary emblem and globe 60 80

1980 (6 May). *"London 1980" International Stamp Exhibition. As Nos.* 650/3 *optd with T* **262** *of Grenada. P* 12.
706 25 c. multicoloured 25 10
707 45 c. multicoloured 30 15
708 50 c. olive-brown, blue and rose-red 30 15
709 $2 olive-brown, vermilion and yellow . . 80 60
706/9 . . . . *Set of* 4 1·50 80

171 Shot Putting

(Des J.W. Litho Questa)

1980 (27 May). *Olympic Games, Moscow. T* **171** *and similar horiz designs. Multicoloured. P* 14.
710 30 c. Type **171** 15 10
711 40 c. Basketball 60 15
712 60 c. Swimming 35 20
713 $2 Gymnastics 60 65
710/13 . . . . *Set of* 4 1·50 90
MS714 114 × 86 mm. $3 The Marathon 70 90

172 "Supper at Emmaus" (Caravaggio)

(Des J.W. Litho Questa)

1980 (22 July). *Famous Paintings. T* **172** *and similar mu coloured designs. P* 13½.
715 20 c. Type **172** 20
716 25 c. "Portrait of Charles I Hunting" (Van Dyck) (*vert*) 20
717 30 c. "The Maids of Honour" (Velasquez) (*vert*) 25
718 45 c. "The Rape of the Sabine Women" (Poussin) 25
719 $1 "Embarkation for Cythera" (Watteau) . . 50
720 $5 "Girl before a Mirror" (Picasso) (*vert*) . . 1·40 1
715/20 . . . . *Set of* 6 2·50 2
MS721 114 × 111 mm. $3 "The Holy Family" (Rembrandt) (*vert*) 60

173 Scene from "Peter Pan"

(Litho Walsall)

1980 (1 Oct). *Christmas. Scenes from Walt Disney's Cartoon F "Peter Pan". T* **173** *and similar horiz designs. P* 11.
722 ½ c. multicoloured 10
723 1 c. multicoloured 10
724 2 c. multicoloured 10
725 3 c. multicoloured 10
726 4 c. multicoloured 10
727 5 c. multicoloured 10
728 10 c. multicoloured 10
729 $2 multicoloured . . . . 2·25 1
730 $2.50, multicoloured . . . . 2·25 1
722/30 . . . . *Set of* 9 4·50 3
MS731 124 × 98 mm. $4 multicoloured (*vert*) . . 3·50 3

174 Queen Elizabeth the Queen Mother in Doorway

(Litho Questa)

1980 (20 Oct). *80th Birthday of Queen Elizabeth the Qu Mother. P* 12.
732 **174** 40 c. multicoloured 25
a. Perf 14 15
733 $2.50, multicoloured 65
a. Perf 14 45
MS734 85×66 mm. **174** $3 multicoloured . . 75 2
Stamps perforated 12 are from normal sheets of 50. Th perforated 14 come either from similar sheets or from sheet of nine with inscribed sheet margins.

175 Douglas Bay

(Des G. Drummond. Litho Questa)

1981 (12 Feb). *Dominica Safari. T* **175** *and similar multicolou designs. P* 14.
735 20 c. Type **175** 10
736 30 c. Valley of Desolation 10
737 40 c. Emerald Pool (*vert*) 10
738 $3 Indian River (*vert*) 75 1
735/8 . . . . *Set of* 4 85 1
MS739 84 × 104 mm. $4 Trafalgar Falls (*vert*) . . 1·10 1

(Litho Format)

1981 (30 Apr). *50th Anniv of Walt Disney's Cartoon Charac Pluto. Vert designs as T* **169**. *Multicoloured. P* 13½ × 14.
740 $2 Pluto and Fifi . . . . 1·25 1
MS741 128 × 102 mm. $4 Pluto in scene from film *Pluto's Blue Note* . . . . 2·00 2

176 Forest Thrush **177** Windsor Castle

(Des P. Barrett. Litho Questa)

31 (30 Apr). *Birds. T* **176** *and similar horiz designs. Multi-coloured. P* 14.

2	20 c. Type **176**	55	30
3	30 c. Wied's Crested Flycatcher	65	35
4	40 c. Blue-hooded Euphonia	75	45
5	$5 Lesser Antillean Pewee	3·50	4·75
2/5	*Set of* 4	5·00	5·25
S746	121 × 95 mm. $3 Imperial Amazon	2·50	1·75

(Des J.W. Litho Questa)

81 (23 June). *Royal Wedding. T* **177** *and similar vert designs. Multicoloured. P* 14.

7	45 c. Prince Charles and Lady Diana Spencer	10	10
	a. Perf 12	40	65
8	60 c. Type **177**	15	15
	a. Perf 12	40	65
9	$4 Prince Charles as helicopter pilot	50	75
	a. Perf 12	40	65
7/9	*Set of* 3	65	85
S750	96×82 mm. $5 Westland HU Mk 5 Wessex helicopter of Queen's Flight	85	90

Nos. 747a/9a also exist from additional sheetlets of five amps and one label with changed background colours.

178 Lady Diana Spencer **179** Ixora

(Manufactured by Walsall)

81 (23 June). *Royal Wedding. T* **178** *and similar vert designs. Multicoloured. Roul 5×imperf*. Self-adhesive.*

51	25 c. Type **178**	20	35
	a. Booklet pane. Nos. 751/2, each × 3	2·50	
52	$2 Prince Charles	70	1·00
53	$5 Prince Charles and Lady Diana Spencer	1·75	2·50
	a. Booklet pane of 1	1·75	
51/3	*Set of* 3	2·40	3·50

*The 25 c. and $2 values were separated by various mbinations of rotary knife (giving a straight edge) and ulette. The $5 value exists only with straight edges.

Nos. 751/3 were only issued in $11.75 stamp booklets.

(Litho Questa)

81 (2 Nov). *Christmas. Horiz designs as T* **169** *showing scenes from Walt Disney's cartoon film "Santa's Workshop". P* 13½.

54	½ c. multicoloured	10	10
55	1 c. multicoloured	10	10
56	2 c. multicoloured	10	10
57	3 c. multicoloured	10	10
58	4 c. multicoloured	15	10
59	5 c. multicoloured	15	10
60	10 c. multicoloured	20	10
61	45 c. multicoloured	1·50	30
62	$5 multicoloured	4·25	4·50
54/62	*Set of* 9	5·75	4·75
S763	129 × 103 mm. $4 multicoloured	4·00	3·50

(Des P. Barrett. Litho Questa)

981 (1 Dec)–85. *Plant-Life. Horiz designs as T* **179**. *Multi-coloured. A. Without imprint date. P* 14

64A	1 c. Type **179**	10	50
65A	2 c. Flamboyant	10	50
66A	4 c. Poinsettia	15	40
67A	5 c. Bois Caribe (national flower of Dominica)	15	20
68A	8 c. Annatto or Roucou	20	20
69A	10 c. Passion Fruit	30	10
70A	15 c. Breadfruit or Yampain	55	15
71A	20 c. Allamanda or Buttercup	40	15
72A	25 c. Cashew Nut	40	15
73A	35 c. Soursop or Couassol	45	30
74A	40 c. Bougainvillea	45	30
75A	45 c. Anthurium	50	35
76A	60 c. Cacao or Cocoa	1·25	70
77A	90 c. Pawpaw Tree or Papay	70	1·00
78A	$1 Coconut Palm	1·50	1·00
79A	$2 Coffee Tree or Café	1·00	2·75
80A	$5 Heliconia or Lobster Claw	3·00	9·50
81A	$10 Banana/Fig	4·00	13·00
64A/81A	*Set of* 18	13·50	27·00

3. *With imprint date at foot of design. P* 14 (15, 60 *c.*) *or* 12 (*others*)

69B	10 c. Passion Fruit (1984)	1·00	30
	a. Perf 14 (7.85)	1·00	60
770B	15 c. Breadfruit or Yampain (7.85)	3·00	1·25
776B	60 c. Cacao or Cocoa (7.85)	4·25	2·50
778B	$1 Coconut Palm (1984)	1·75	2·00
780B	$5 Heliconia or Lobster Claw (1984)	3·25	5·50
781B	$10 Banana Fig (1984)	5·00	11·00
769B/81B	*Set of* 6	16·00	20·00

Imprint dates: "1984", Nos. 769B, 778B, 780B, 781B; "1985", Nos. 769Ba, 770B, 776B, 780B.

180 Curb slope for Wheelchairs **181** "Olga Picasso in an Armchair"

(Des BG Studio. Litho Format)

1981 (22 Dec). *International Year for Disabled Persons. T* **180** *and similar vert designs. Multicoloured. P* 14½.

782	45 c. Type **180**	55	25
783	60 c. Bus with invalid step	60	35
784	75 c. Motor car controls adapted for handicapped	70	40
785	$4 Bus with wheelchair ramp	2·00	2·50
782/5	*Set of* 4	3·50	3·25
MS786	82 × 96 mm. $5 Specially designed elevator control panel	4·25	3·00

(Des J.W. Litho Format)

1981 (30 Dec). *Birth Centenary of Picasso. T* **181** *and similar vert designs. Multicoloured. P* 14½.

787	45 c. Type **181**	65	25
788	60 c. "Bathers"	75	50
789	75 c. "Woman in Spanish Costume"	80	60
790	$4 "Detail of Dog and Cock"	1·75	3·00
787/90	*Set of* 4	3·50	4·00
MS791	140 × 115 mm. $5 "Sleeping Peasants" (detail)	4·00	3·50

(Litho Questa)

1982 (29 Jan). *World Cup Football Championship, Spain. Walt Disney Cartoon Characters. Horiz designs as T* **169**. *Multi-coloured. P* 14 × 13½.

792	½ c. Goofy chasing ball with butterfly net	10	10
793	1 c. Donald Duck with ball in beak	10	10
794	2 c. Goofy as goalkeeper	10	10
795	3 c. Goofy looking for ball	10	10
796	4 c. Goofy as park attendant puncturing ball with litter spike	10	10
797	5 c. Pete and Donald Duck playing	10	10
798	10 c. Donald Duck after kicking rock instead of ball	15	10
799	60 c. Donald Duck feeling effects of a hard game and Daisy Duck dusting ball	1·50	1·25
800	$5 Goofy hiding ball under his jersey from Mickey Mouse	5·50	6·50
792/800	*Set of* 9	6·75	7·00
MS801	132 × 105 mm. $4 Dale making off with ball	3·75	3·25

182 "Gone Fishing" **183** Elma Napier (first woman elected to B.W.I. Legislative Council)

(Des M.B.I. Studios. Litho Questa)

1982 (10 Mar). *Norman Rockwell (painter) Commemoration. T* **182** *and similar vert designs. Multicoloured. P* 14 × 13½.

802	10 c. Type **182**	10	10
803	25 c. "Breakfast"	15	10
804	45 c. "The Marbles Champ"	30	30
805	$1 "Speeding Along"	55	55
802/5	*Set of* 4	95	95

No. 802 is inscribed "Golden Days" and No. 803 "The Morning News".

(Des BG Studio. Litho Questa)

1982 (15 Apr). *Decade for Women. T* **183** *and similar horiz designs. Multicoloured. P* 14.

806	10 c. Type **183**	10	10
807	45 c. Margaret Mead (anthropologist)	30	30
808	$1 Mabel ("Cissy") Caudeiron (folk song composer and historian)	55	55
809	$4 Eleanor Roosevelt	2·25	2·25
806/9	*Set of* 4	2·75	2·75
MS810	92 × 63 mm. $3 Florence Nightingale	2·00	3·00

184 George Washington and Independence Hall, Philadelphia **185** *Anaea dominicana*

(Des J.W. Litho Format)

1982 (1 May). *250th Birth Anniv of George Washington* (45, 90 *c.*) *and Birth Centenary of Franklin D. Roosevelt* (60 *c.*, $2). *T* **184** *and similar horiz designs. Multicoloured. P* 14½.

811	45 c. Type **184**	40	25
812	60 c. Franklin D. Roosevelt and Capitol, Washington D.C.	45	35
813	90 c. Washington at Yorktown (detail, "The Surrender of Cornwallis" by Trumbull)	60	55
814	$2 Construction of dam (from W. Gropper's mural commemorating Roosevelt's "New Deal")	1·00	1·60
811/14	*Set of* 4	2·25	2·50
MS815	115 × 90 mm. $5 Washington and Roosevelt with U.S.A. flags of 1777 and 1933	2·25	3·25

Nos. 813 and **MS**815 exist imperforate from stock dispersed by the liquidator of Format International Security Printers Ltd.

(Des P. Barrett. Litho Questa)

1982 (1 June). *Butterflies. T* **185** *and similar vert designs. Multi-coloured. P* 14.

816	15 c. Type **185**	1·50	35
817	45 c. *Heliconius charithonia*	2·50	65
818	60 c. *Hypolimnas misippus*	2·75	1·75
819	$3 *Biblis hyperia*	5·50	6·00
816/19	*Set of* 4	11·00	8·00
MS820	77×105 mm. $5 *Marpesia petreus*	7·00	5·00

186 Prince and Princess of Wales **187** Scouts around Campfire

(Des PAD Studio. Litho Questa)

1982 (1 July). *21st Birthday of Princess of Wales. T* **186** *and similar vert designs. Multicoloured. P* 14½ × 14.

821	45 c. Buckingham Palace	20	10
822	$2 Type **186**	50	70
823	$4 Princess of Wales	80	1·25
821/3	*Set of* 3	1·40	1·75
MS824	103 × 75 mm. $5 Princess Diana (*different*)	2·00	2·25

Nos. 821/3 also exist in sheetlets of 5 stamps and 1 label.

(Des R. Sauber. Litho Questa)

1982 (3 Aug). *75th Anniv of Boy Scout Movement. T* **187** *and similar multicoloured designs. P* 14.

825	45 c. Type **187**	1·25	50
826	60 c. Temperature study, Valley of Desolation	1·75	1·25
827	75 c. Learning about native birds	2·25	1·50
828	$3 Canoe trip along Indian River	4·25	5·50
825/8	*Set of* 4	8·50	8·00
MS829	99 × 70 mm. $5 Dominican scouts saluting the flag (*vert*)	2·25	3·25

1982 (30 Aug). *Birth of Prince William of Wales. Nos. 821/4 optd with T* **171** *of Antigua.*

830	45 c. Buckingham Palace	30	30
831	$2 Type **186**	80	1·10
832	$4 Princess of Wales	1·40	1·90
830/2	*Set of* 3	2·25	3·00
MS833	103 × 75 mm. $5 Princess Diana (*different*)	2·00	2·75

Nos. 830/2 also exist in sheetlets of 5 stamps and 1 label.

188 "Holy Family of Francis I" **189** Cuvier's Beaked Whale

(Des Design Images. Litho Questa)

1982 (3 Nov). *Christmas. Raphael Paintings. T* **188** *and similar vert designs. Multicoloured. P* 13½ × 14.
834 25 c. Type **188** 15 10
835 30 c. "Holy Family of the Pearl" 15 15
836 90 c. "Canigiani Holy Family" 45 55
837 $4 "Holy Family of the Oak Tree" . . . . 1·50 1·50
834/7 . . . . *Set of* 4 2·00 2·00
MS838 95 × 125 mm. $5 "Holy Family of the Lamb" . . . . 1·75 2·00

(Des J. Cooter. Litho Questa)

1983 (15 Feb). *Save the Whales. T* **189** *and similar horiz designs. P* 14.
839 45 c. Type **189**. . . . . 2·00 65
840 60 c. Humpback Whale . . . . . . 2·25 1·75
841 75 c. Black Right Whale . . . . . . 2·25 2·25
842 $3 Melon-headed Whale . . . . . . 4·50 6·50
839/42 . . . . *Set of* 4 10·00 10·00
MS843 99 × 72 mm. $5 Pygmy Sperm Whale . . 4·00 4·00

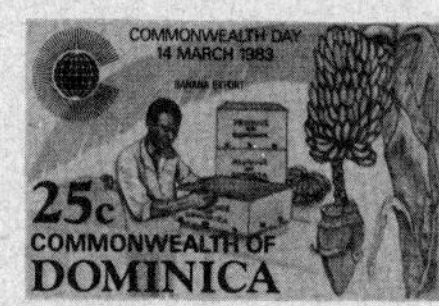

190 Banana Export

(Des R. Vigurs. Litho Questa)

1983 (14 Mar). *Commonwealth Day. T* **190** *and similar horiz designs. Multicoloured. P* 14.
844 25 c. Type **190** 15 15
845 30 c. Road building 15 20
846 90 c. Community nursing 40 45
847 $3 Tourism—handicrafts . . . . . . 1·00 1·50
844/7 . . . . *Set of* 4 1·50 2·10

191 Map and Satellite Picture of Hurricane

(Des G. Vasarhelyi. Litho Questa)

1983 (18 Apr). *World Communications Year. T* **191** *and similar horiz designs. Multicoloured. P* 14.
848 45 c. Type **191** 20 25
849 60 c. Aircraft-to-ship transmission 30 35
850 90 c. Satellite communications 40 45
851 $2 Shortwave radio . . . . 95 1·00
848/51 . . . . *Set of* 4 1·75 1·90
MS852 110 × 85 mm. $5 Communications satellite 2·50 2·75

192 Short-Mayo Composite

(Des W. Wright. Litho Format)

1983 (19 July). *Bicentenary of Manned Flight. T* **192** *and similar horiz designs. Multicoloured. P* 14½.
853 45 c. Type **192** 50 30
854 60 c. Macchi M.39 Schneider Trophy seaplane 75 85
855 90 c. Fairey Swordfish torpedo bomber . . 1·10 1·40
856 $4 Airship LZ-3 . . . . 3·25 4·75
853/6 . . . . *Set of* 4 5·00 6·50
MS857 105 × 79 mm. $5 *Double Eagle II* (balloon) 1·50 2·75
Nos. 856/7 exist imperforate from stock dispersed by the liquidator of Format International Security Printers Ltd.

193 Duesenberg "SJ", 1935

(Des R. Sauber. Litho Questa)

1983 (1 Sept). *Classic Motor Cars. T* **193** *and similar horiz designs. Multicoloured. P* 14.
858 10 c. Type **193** 30 15
859 45 c. Studebaker "Avanti", 1962 . . . . 50 25
860 60 c. Cord "812", 1936 . . . . 60 35
861 75 c. MG "TC", 1945 . . . . 65 50
862 90 c. Camaro "350 SS", 1967 . . . . . . 75 60
863 $3 Porsch "356", 1948 . . . . . . 1·50 1·60
858/63 . . . . *Set of* 6 3·75 3·00
MS864 110 × 75 mm. $5 Ferrari "312 T", 1975 . . 2·00 2·75

194 "Charity"

(Des Design Images. Litho Format)

1983 (4 Oct). *Christmas. 500th Birth Anniv of Raphael. T* **194** *and similar horiz designs. Multicoloured. P* 13½.
865 45 c. Type **194** 40 30
866 60 c. "Hope" 45 50
867 90 c. "Faith" 60 60
868 $4 "The Cardinal Virtues" . . . . . . 1·50 3·00
865/8 . . . . *Set of* 4 2·75 4·00
MS869 101 × 127 mm. $5 "Justice" . . . . 1·50 2·75
Nos. 867 and **MS**869 exist imperforate from stock dispersed by the liquidator of Format International Security Printers Ltd.

195 Plumbeous Warbler **196** Donald Duck

(Des Jennifer Toombs. Litho Questa)

1984 (24 Apr). *Birds. T* **195** *and similar horiz designs. Multicoloured. P* 14.
870 5 c. Type **195**. . . . . 1·60 90
871 45 c. Imperial Amazon . . . . . . 3·50 75
872 60 c. Blue-headed Hummingbird . . . . 3·75 3·00
873 90 c. Red-necked Amazon . . . . . . 5·00 5·50
870/3 . . . . *Set of* 4 12·50 9·00
MS874 72 × 72 mm. $5 Greater Flamingos . . 3·75 4·50

(Litho Format)

1984 (1 May). *Easter. T* **196** *and similar vert designs showing Disney cartoon characters and eggs. Multicoloured. P* 11.
875 ½ c. Type **196** 10 10
876 1 c. Mickey Mouse 10 10
877 2 c. Tortoise and Hare 10 10
878 3 c. Brer Rabbit and Brer Bear 10 10
879 4 c. Donald Duck (*different*) 10 10
880 5 c. White Rabbit 10 10
881 10 c. Thumper 10 10
882 $2 Pluto . . . . 3·25 2·75
883 $4 Pluto (*different*) . . . . . . 4·50 4·00
875/83 . . . . *Set of* 9 7·50 6·50
MS884 126 × 100 mm. $5 Chip and Dale. P 13½ × 14 . . . . 3·50 4·00

197 Gymnastics **198** *Atlantic Star*

(Des R. Sauber. Litho Questa)

1984 (14 May). *Olympic Games, Los Angeles. T* **197** *and similar vert designs. Multicoloured. P* 14.
885 30 c. Type **197** 20 25
886 45 c. Javelin-throwing 30 35
887 60 c. High diving 40 45
888 $4 Fencing . . . . 2·00 2·50
885/8 . . . . *Set of* 4 2·50 3·25
MS889 104 × 85 mm. $5 Equestrian event . . 3·25 3·25

(Des W. Wright. Litho Questa)

1984 (14 June). *Shipping. T* **198** *and similar horiz designs. Multicoloured. P* 14.
890 45 c. Type **198**. . . . . 1·75 75
891 60 c. *Atlantic* (liner) . . . . 2·00 1·75
892 90 c. Carib fishing boat . . . . . . 2·50 2·50
893 $4 *Norway* (liner) . . . . 6·00 8·00
890/3 . . . . *Set of* 4 11·00 11·50
MS894 106 × 79 mm. $5 *Santa Maria*, 1492 . . 3·75 5·50

19th UPU
CONGRESS HAMBURG

(**199**) **200** *Guzmania lingulata*

1984 (19 June). *Universal Postal Union Congress, Hambur*
Nos. 769A *and* 780A *optd with T* **199**.
895 10 c. Passion Fruit 10
896 $5 Heliconia or Lobster Claw . . . . 2·75 3·

(Des P. Barrett. Litho Questa)

1984 (13 Aug). *"Ausipex" International Stamp Exhibitio Melbourne. Bromilaids. T* **200** *and similar vert designs. Mul coloured. P* 14.
897 45 c. Type **200** 30
898 60 c. *Pitcairnia angustifolia* 40
899 75 c. *Tillandsia fasciculata* 50
900 $3 *Aechmea smithiorum* . . . . . . 2·00 3·
897/900 . . . . *Set of* 4 2·75 4·
MS901 75 × 105 mm. $5 *Tillandsia utriculata* . . 2·75 4·

201 "The Virgin and Child with Young St John" (Correggio) **202** "Before the Start" (Edgar Degas)

(Litho Format)

1984 (30 Oct). *450th Death Anniv of Correggio (painter). T* 2
and similar vert designs. Multicoloured. P 15.
902 25 c. Type **201** 45
903 60 c. "Christ bids Farewell to the Virgin Mary" 70
904 90 c. "Do not Touch Me" 90
905 $4 "The Mystical Marriage of St Catherine" 2·00 3·
902/5 . . . . *Set of* 4 3·50 4·
MS906 89 × 60 mm. $5 "The Adoration of the Magi" . . . . 1·75 3·

(Litho Format)

1984 (30 Oct). *150th Birth Anniv of Edgar Degas (painte*
T **202** *and similar multicoloured designs. P* 15.
907 30 c. Type **202** 45
908 45 c. "Race on the Racecourse" 60
909 $1 "Jockeys at the Flagpole" . . . . 1·10 1·
910 $3 "Racehorses at Longchamp" . . . . 2·50 3·
907/10 . . . . *Set of* 4 4·25 4·
MS911 89 × 60 mm. $5 "Self-portrait" (*vert*) . . 2·00 3·

203 Tabby **204** Hawker Siddeley H.S.748

(Des. I. MacLaury. Litho Format)

1984 (12 Nov). *Cats. T* **203** *and similar horiz designs. Mult coloured. P* 15.
912 10 c. Type **203** 20
913 15 c. Calico Shorthair 25
914 20 c. Siamese 35
915 25 c. Manx 40
916 45 c. Abyssinian 65
917 60 c. Tortoise-shell Longhair 80
918 $1 Cornish Rex . . . . 1·40 1·
919 $2 Persian . . . . 2·00 3·
920 $3 Himalayan . . . . 2·75 4·
921 $5 Burmese . . . . 3·75 7·
912/21 . . . . *Set of* 10 11·50 15·
MS922 105 × 75 mm. $5 Grey Burmese, Persian and American Shorthair . . . . 3·25 6·
Nos. 912, 916 and **MS**922 exist imperforate from stoc dispersed by the liquidator of Format International Securi Printers Ltd.

(Des Bonny Redecker. Litho Questa)

984 (26 Nov). *40th Anniv of International Civil Aviation Organisation. T* **204** *and similar vert designs. Multicoloured. P* 14.
23 30 c. Type **204** .. .. 1·25 35
24 60 c. De Havilland D.H.C.6 Twin Otter 100 2·00 80
25 $1 Britten Norman Islander .. .. 2·25 1·40
26 $3 De Havilland D.H.C.6 Twin Otter 100 (*different*) .. .. 4·00 4·50
23/6 .. .. *Set of* 4 8·50 6·25
1S927 102×75 mm. $5 Boeing 747-200 .. 3·25 3·50

205 Donald Duck, Mickey Mouse and Goofy with Father Christmas

206 Mrs. M. Bascom presenting Trefoil to Chief Guide Lady Baden-Powell

(Litho Questa)

1984 (30 Nov). *Christmas. Walt Disney Cartoon Characters. T* **205** *and similar vert designs. Multicoloured. P* 12 ($2) *or* 13½ × 14 (*others*).
928 45 c. Type **205** .. .. 1·25 30
929 60 c. Donald Duck as Father Christmas with toy train .. .. 1·50 70
930 90 c. Donald Duck as Father Christmas in sleigh .. .. 2·00 1·75
931 $2 Donald Duck and nephews in sledge .. 3·25 3·75
932 $4 Donald Duck in snow with Christmas tree 4·25 5·50
928/32 .. .. *Set of* 5 11·00 11·00
MS933 127 × 102 mm. $5 Donald Duck and nephews opening present .. .. .. 3·50 4·00
No. 931 was printed in sheetlets of 8 stamps.

(Des Marlise Najaka. Litho Questa)

1985 (28 Feb). *75th Anniv of Girl Guide Movement. T* **206** *and similar multicoloured designs. P* 14.
934 35 c. Type **206** 60 30
935 45 c. Lady Baden-Powell inspecting Dominican Brownies 80 35
936 60 c. Lady Baden-Powell with Mrs. M. Bascom and Mrs. A. Robinson (Guide leaders) .. 1·00 65
937 $3 Lord and Lady Baden-Powell (*vert*) .. 2·50 3·50
934/7 .. .. *Set of* 4 4·50 4·25
MS938 77 × 105 mm. $5 Flags of Dominica and Girl Guide Movement .. .. .. 3·50 4·00

(Litho Questa)

1985 (4 Apr). *Birth Bicentenary of John J. Audubon (ornithologist) (1st issue). Multicoloured designs as T* **198** *of Antigua showing original paintings. P* 14.
939 45 c. Clapper Rail .. .. 1·10 30
940 $1 Black and White Warbler (*vert*) .. 2·00 1·25
941 $2 Broad-winged Hawk (*vert*) .. .. 2·75 2·75
942 $3 Ring-necked Duck .. .. .. 3·50 3·25
939/42 .. .. *Set of* 4 8·50 6·75
MS943 101×73 mm. $5 Reddish Egret .. .. 3·50 3·75
Nos. 939/42 were each printed in sheetlets of five stamps and one stamp-size label which appears in the centre of the bottom row.
See also Nos. 1013/17.

207 Student with Computer

208 The Queen Mother visiting Sadlers Wells Opera

(Des BG Studio. Litho Questa)

1985 (30 Apr). *Duke of Edinburgh's Award Scheme. T* **207** *and similar vert designs. Multicoloured. P* 14.
944 45 c. Type **207** 35 30
945 60 c. Assisting doctor in hospital 75 40
946 90 c. Two youths hiking 90 80
947 $4 Family jogging .. .. 2·75 3·75
944/7 .. .. *Set of* 4 4·25 4·75
MS948 100×98 mm. $5 Duke of Edinburgh .. 2·75 3·00

(Des J.W. Litho Questa)

1985 (15 July). *Life and Times of Queen Elizabeth the Queen Mother. T* **208** *and similar vert designs. Multicoloured. P* 14.
949 60 c. Type **208** 75 50
950 $1 Fishing in Scotland 80 60
951 $3 On her 84th birthday .. .. .. 1·90 2·25
949/51 .. .. *Set of* 3 3·00 3·00
MS952 56×85 mm. $5 Attending Garter ceremony, Windsor Castle .. .. 3·00 3·00

209 Cricket Match ("Sports")

210 Two Players competing for Ball

(Des S. Heinmann. Litho Questa)

1985 (22 July). *International Youth Year. T* **209** *and similar horiz designs. Multicoloured. P* 14.
953 45 c. Type **209** .. .. 3·50 1·50
954 60 c. Bird-watching ("Environmental Study") 3·75 2·25
955 $1 Stamp collecting ("Education") .. 4·00 3·25
956 $3 Boating ("Leisure") .. .. .. 5·50 7·50
953/6 .. .. *Set of* 4 15·00 13·00
MS957 96×65 mm. $5 Young people linking hands .. .. 2·75 4·00

(Des Susan David. Litho Questa)

1985 (2 Sept). *300th Birth Anniv of Johann Sebastian Bach (composer). Vert designs as T* **206** *of Antigua showing antique musical instruments. P* 14.
958 45 c. multicoloured .. .. 1·50 40
959 60 c. multicoloured .. .. 1·75 60
960 $1 multicoloured .. .. 2·25 1·00
961 $3 multicoloured .. .. 4·00 3·50
958/61 .. .. *Set of* 4 8·50 5·00
MS962 109×75 mm. $5 black .. .. .. 4·00 4·50
Designs:—45 c. Cornett; 60 c. Coiled trumpet; $1 Piccolo; $3 Violoncello piccolo; $5 Johann Sebastian Bach.

(Litho Format)

1985 (25 Oct). *Royal Visit. Multicoloured designs as T* **207** *of Antigua. P* 14½.
963 60 c. Flags of Great Britain and Dominica .. 1·00 70
964 $1 Queen Elizabeth II (*vert*) .. .. 1·25 1·75
965 $4 Royal Yacht *Britannia* .. .. .. 2·75 5·50
963/5 .. .. *Set of* 3 4·50 7·00
MS966 111×83 mm. $5 Map of Dominica .. 3·50 4·00

(Litho Questa)

1985 (11 Nov). *150th Birth Anniv of Mark Twain (author). Horiz designs as T* **118** *of Anguilla showing Walt Disney cartoon characters in scenes from "Tom Sawyer". Multicoloured. P* 14×13½.
967 20 c. "The glorious whitewasher" 65 30
968 60 c. "Aunt Polly's home dentistry" .. .. 1·25 75
969 $1 "Aunt Polly's pain killer" .. .. 1·75 1·25
970 $1.50, Mickey Mouse balancing on fence .. 2·25 3·00
971 $2 "Lost in the cave with Becky" .. .. 2·75 3·50
967/71 .. .. *Set of* 5 7·75 8·00
MS972 126×101 mm. $5 Mickey Mouse as pirate .. .. 5·50 6·50

(Des Walt Disney Productions. Litho Questa)

1985 (11 Nov). *Birth Bicentenaries of Grimm Brothers (folklorists). Horiz designs as T* **119** *of Anguilla showing Walt Disney cartoon characters in scenes from "Little Red Cap". Multicoloured. P* 14×13½.
973 10 c. Little Red Cap (Daisy Duck) meeting the Wolf 30 20
974 45 c. The Wolf at the door 85 30
975 90 c. The Wolf in Grandmother's bed .. 1·75 1·75
976 $1 The Wolf lunging at Little Red Cap .. 2·00 1·75
977 $3 The Woodsman (Donald Duck) chasing the Wolf .. .. 3·75 5·00
973/7 .. .. *Set of* 5 7·75 8·00
MS978 126×101 mm. $5 The Wolf falling into cooking pot .. .. 5·00 5·50

(Litho Format)

1985 (27 Nov). *40th Anniv of United Nations Organization. Horiz designs as T* **208** *of Antigua showing United Nations (New York) stamps. Multicoloured. P* 14½.
979 45 c. Lord Baden-Powell and 1984 International Youth Year 35 c. 70 50
980 $2 Maimonides (physician) and 1966 W.H.O Building 11 c. .. .. .. 3·00 3·25
981 $3 Sir Rowland Hill (postal reformer) and 1976 25th anniv of U.N. Postal Administration 13 c. .. .. .. 3·00 3·50
979/81 .. .. *Set of* 3 6·00 6·50
MS982 110×85 mm. $5 "Apollo" spacecraft .. 2·75 3·25

(Des J. Iskowitz. Litho Questa)

1986 (26 Mar). *World Cup Football Championship, Mexico. T* **210** *and similar vert designs. Multicoloured. P* 14.
983 45 c. Type **210** .. .. 1·75 40
984 60 c. Player heading ball .. .. .. 2·00 1·50
985 $1 Two players competing for ball (*different*) .. .. 2·25 1·75
986 $3 Player with ball .. .. 4·50 6·00
983/6 .. .. *Set of* 4 9·50 8·75
MS987 114×84 mm. $5 Three players .. .. 8·00 10·00

NEW INFORMATION

The editor is always interested to correspond with people who have new information that will improve or correct the Catalogue.

211 Police in Rowing Boat pursuing River Pirates, 1890

211 Police in Rowing Boat pursuing River Pirates, 1890

(Des J. Iskowitz. Litho Questa)

1986 (27 Mar). *Centenary of Statue of Liberty. T* **211** *and similar multicoloured designs. P* 14.
988 15 c. Type **211** .. .. 1·50 65
989 25 c. Police patrol launch, 1986 .. .. 2·00 85
990 45 c. Hoboken Ferry Terminal, *c* 1890 .. 2·00 85
991 $4 Holland Tunnel entrance and staff, 1986 .. .. 4·50 6·00
988/91 .. .. *Set of* 4 9·00 7·50
MS992 104×76 mm. $5 Statue of Liberty (*vert*) .. 4·00 5·00

(Des W. Hanson. Litho Questa)

1986 (17 Apr). *Appearance of Halley's Comet (1st issue). Horiz designs as T* **123** *of Anguilla. Multicoloured. P* 14.
993 5 c. Nasir al Din al Tusi (Persian astronomer) and Jantal Mantar Observatory, Delhi 15 15
994 10 c. Bell XS-1 Rocket Plane breaking sound barrier for first time, 1947 .. .. 20 15
995 45 c. Halley's Comet of 1531 (from "Astronomicum Caesareum", 1540) 55 30
996 $4 Mark Twain and quotation, 1910 .. 2·75 3·75
993/6 .. .. *Set of* 4 3·25 4·00
MS997 104×71 mm. $5 Halley's Comet over Dominica .. .. 3·00 3·50
See also Nos. 1032/6.

(Des and litho Questa)

1986 (5 May). *60th Birthday of Queen Elizabeth II. Vert designs as T* **125** *of Anguilla. P* 14.
998 2 c. multicoloured 10 15
999 $1 multicoloured 70 80
1000 $4 multicoloured .. .. 2·00 3·00
998/1000 .. .. *Set of* 3 2·50 3·50
MS1001 120×85mm. $5 black and grey-brown .. 2·75 3·75
Designs:—2 c. Wedding photograph, 1947; $1 Queen meeting Pope John Paul II, 1982; $4 Queen on royal visit, 1971; $5 Princess Elizabeth with corgis, 1936.

212 Mickey Mouse and Pluto mounting Stamps in Album

213 William I

(Des Walt Disney Productions. Litho Format)

1986 (22 May). *"Ameripex" International Stamp Exhibition, Chicago. T* **212** *and similar horiz designs showing Walt Disney cartoon characters. Multicoloured. P* 11.
1002 25 c. Type **212** 60 40
1003 45 c. Donald Duck examining stamp under magnifying glass 80 65
1004 60 c. Chip n'Dale soaking and drying stamps .. .. 1·10 1·50
1005 $4 Donald Duck as scoutmaster awarding merit badges to Nephews .. .. 3·50 6·00
1002/5 .. .. *Set of* 4 5·50 7·75
MS1006 127×101 mm. $5 Uncle Scrooge conducting stamp auction. P 14×13½ .. .. 4·00 7·00
No. 1003 exists imperforate from stock dispersed by the liquidator of Format International Security Printers Ltd.

(Des Mary Walters. Litho Questa)

1986 (9 June). *500th Anniv of Succession of House of Tudor to English Throne (1985). T* **213** *and similar vert designs. Multicoloured. P* 14.
1007 10 c. Type **213** 40 40
1008 40 c. Richard II 80 80
1009 50 c. Henry VIII 90 90
1010 $1 Charles II .. .. 1·75 1·75
1011 $2 Queen Anne .. .. 2·75 3·00
1012 $4 Queen Victoria .. .. 3·75 4·50
1007/12 .. .. *Set of* 6 9·25 10·00
Nos. 1007/12 were each issued in sheetlets of five stamps and one stamp-size label showing the monarch's consort.

(Litho Questa)

1986 (18 June). *Birth Bicentenary of John J. Audubon (ornithologist) (1985) (2nd issue). Multicoloured designs as T* **198** *of Antigua showing original paintings. P* 12½×12 (25 c., $4) *or* 12×12½ (*others*).
1013 25 c. Black-throated Diver .. .. .. 1·50 50
1014 60 c. Great Blue Heron (*vert*) .. .. 2·00 1·50
1015 90 c. Yellow-crowned Night Heron (*vert*) 2·00 2·25
1016 $4 Common Shoveler .. .. .. 4·50 6·50
1013/16 .. .. *Set of* 4 9·00 9·75
MS1017 73×103 mm. $5 Canada Goose. P 14 .. 10·00 12·00
Nos. 1013/16 were each issued in sheetlets of five stamps and one stamp-size label, which appears in the centre of the bottom row.

(Litho Questa)

1986 (1 July). *Royal Wedding. Vert designs as T* **213** *of Antigua. Multicoloured. P* 14.
1018 45 c. Prince Andrew and Miss Sarah Ferguson 35 30
1019 60 c. Prince Andrew.. .. .. 45 45
1020 $4 Prince Andrew climbing aboard aircraft .. .. 2·00 3·00
1018/20 .. .. *Set of* 3 2·50 3·25
MS1021 88×88 mm. $5 Prince Andrew and Miss Sarah Ferguson (*different*) .. .. .. 3·50 4·50

1986 (15 Sept). *World Cup Football Championship Winners, Mexico. Nos.* 983/7 *optd with T* **216** *of Antigua in gold.*
1022 45 c. Type **210** .. .. 1·50 55
1023 60 c. Player heading ball .. .. 1·75 1·50
1024 $1 Two players competing for ball .. 2·25 2·50
1025 $3 Player with ball .. .. 5·00 7·00
1022/5 .. .. *Set of* 4 9·50 10·50
MS1026 114×84 mm. $5 Three players.. .. 8·50 11·00

214 "The Virgin at Prayer" **215** Broad-winged Hawk

(Litho Questa)

1986 (2 Dec). *Christmas. Paintings by Dürer. T* **214** *and similar vert designs. Multicoloured. P* 14.
1027 45 c. Type **214** .. .. 1·00 35
1028 60 c. "Madonna and Child".. .. .. 1·50 1·25
1029 $1 "The Madonna with the Pear" .. 2·00 2·25
1030 $3 "Madonna and Child with St. Anne" .. 5·50 8·50
1027/30 .. .. *Set of* 4 9·00 11·00
MS1031 76×102 mm. $5 "The Nativity" .. 8·00 11·00

1986 (16 Dec). *Appearance of Halley's Comet (2nd issue). Nos.* 993/7 *optd as T* **218** *of Antigua (in silver on $5).*
1032 5 c. Nasir al Din al Tusi (Persian astronomer) and Jantal Mantar Observatory, Delhi 15 15
1033 10 c. Bell XS-1 Rocket Plane breaking sound barrier for first time, 1947 .. 20 15
1034 45 c. Halley's Comet of 1531 (from "Astronomicum Caesareum", 1540) .. 55 30
1035 $4 Mark Twain and quotation, 1910 .. 2·75 3·50
1032/5 .. .. *Set of* 4 3·25 3·75
MS1036 104×71 mm. $5 Halley's Comet over Dominica .. .. 3·25 3·50

(Des S. Heinmann. Litho Format)

1987 (20 Jan). *Birds of Dominica. T* **215** *and similar vert designs. Multicoloured. Without imprint date. P* 15.
1037 1 c. Type **215** 20 40
1038 2 c. Ruddy Quail Dove 20 40
1039 5 c. Red-necked Pigeon 30 40
1040 10 c. Green Heron 30 15
1041 15 c. Moorhen 40 20
1042 20 c. Ringed Kingfisher 40 20
1043 25 c. Brown Pelican.. .. .. .. 40 20
1044 35 c. White-tailed Tropic Bird 40 30
1045 45 c. Red-legged Thrush 50 30
1046 60 c. Purple-throated Carib 65 45
1047 90 c. Magnificent Frigate Bird 70 70
1048 $1 Brown Trembler 80 80
1049 $2 Black-capped Petrel .. .. .. 1·25 4·00
1050 $5 Barn Owl .. .. 3·00 5·00
1051 $10 Imperial Amazon .. .. .. 5·00 9·50
1037/51 .. .. *Set of* 15 13·00 20·00
For similar stamps, with imprint date and perforated 14, 12 or 12½×11½ see Nos. 1241/54.

(Des J. Iskowitz. Litho Format)

1987 (16 Feb). *America's Cup Yachting Championship. Multicoloured designs as T* **222** *of Antigua. P* 15.
1052 45 c. *Reliance*, 1903.. .. .. .. 50 30
1053 60 c. *Freedom*, 1980.. .. .. .. 60 55
1054 $1 *Mischief*, 1881.. .. .. .. 80 90
1055 $3 *Australia*, 1977 .. .. .. 1·75 3·00
1052/5 .. .. *Set of* 4 3·25 4·25
MS1056 113×83 mm. $5 *Courageous*, 1977 (*horiz*) .. .. 3·00 5·50

(Litho Questa)

1987 (24 Mar). *Birth Centenary of Marc Chagall (artist). Multicoloured designs as T* **225** *of Antigua. P* 13½×14.
1057 25 c. "Artist and His Model" 40 15
1058 35 c. "Midsummer Night's Dream" .. 40 25
1059 45 c. "Joseph the Shepherd" 50 25
1060 60 c. "The Cellist" 70 50
1061 90 c. "Woman with Pigs" .. .. .. 1·00 1·00
1062 $1 "The Blue Circus" .. .. .. 1·00 1·00
1063 $3 "For Vava" .. .. 2·25 3·00
1064 $4 "The Rider" .. .. 2·50 3·00
1057/64 .. .. *Set of* 8 8·00 8·00
MS1065 Two sheets, each 110×95 mm. (a) $5 "Purim" (104×89 *mm*). (b) $5 "Firebird" (stage design) (104×89 *mm*) .. *Set of* 2 *sheets* 4·50 6·00

216 Poulsen's Triton **217** *Cantharellus cinnabarinus*

(Des L. Birmingham. Litho Format)

1987 (11 May). *Sea Shells. T* **216** *and similar designs. P* 15.
1066 35 c. multicoloured 20 20
1067 45 c. bluish violet, black and bright rose .. 25 25
1068 60 c. multicoloured 30 40
1069 $5 multicoloured .. .. 2·40 4·00
1066/9 .. .. *Set of* 4 2·75 4·25
MS1070 109×75 mm. $5 multicoloured.. .. 3·25 5·50
Designs: *Vert*—45 c. Elongate Janthina; 60 c. Banded Tulip; $5 (No. 1069) Deltoid Rock Shell. *Horiz*—$5 (No. **MS**1070) Junonia Volute.
No. 1066 is inscribed "TIRITON" in error.

(Des BG Studio. Litho Questa)

1987 (15 June). *"Capex '87" International Stamp Exhibition, Toronto. Mushrooms of Dominica. T* **217** *and similar horiz designs. Multicoloured. P* 14.
1071 45 c. Type **217** .. .. 1·50 50
1072 60 c. *Boletellus cubensis* .. .. .. 2·00 1·25
1073 $2 *Eccilia cystiophorus* .. .. .. 4·25 4·50
1074 $3 *Xerocomus guadelupae* .. .. 4·50 5·00
1071/4 .. .. *Set of* 4 11·00 10·00
MS1075 85×85 mm. $5 *Gymnopilus chrysopellus* 8·50 10·00

218 Discovery of Dominica, 1493 **219** "Virgin and Child with St. Anne" (Dürer)

(Des I. MacLaury. Litho Format)

1987 (27 July). *500th Anniv of Discovery of America (1992) (1st issue). T* **218** *and similar horiz designs. Multicoloured. P* 15.
1076 10 c. Type **218** 40 25
1077 15 c. Caribs greeting Columbus's fleet .. 50 30
1078 45 c. Claiming the New World for Spain .. 65 35
1079 60 c. Wreck of *Santa Maria* 80 60
1080 90 c. Fleet leaving Spain .. .. .. 1·00 1·00
1081 $1 Sighting the New World .. .. 1·10 1·25
1082 $3 Trading with Indians .. .. .. 2·25 3·00
1083 $5 Building settlement .. .. .. 3·25 4·00
1076/83 .. .. *Set of* 8 9·00 9·75
MS1084 Two sheets, each 109×79 mm. (a) $5 Fleet off Dominica, 1493. (b) $5 Map showing Columbus's route, 1493 .. *Set of* 2 *sheets* 5·00 7·00
See also Nos. 1221/5, 1355/63, 1406/14, 1547/53 and 1612/13.

(Des G. Welker. Litho Questa)

1987 (28 Sept). *Milestones of Transportation. Multicoloured designs as T* **226** *of Antigua. P* 14.
1085 10 c. H.M.S. *Warrior* (first ironclad warship), 1860 .. .. 50 50
1086 15 c. MAGLEV-MLU 001 (fastest train), 1979 .. .. 60 60
1087 25 c. *Flying Cloud* (fastest clipper passage New York–San Francisco) (*vert*) .. 70 70
1088 35 c. First elevated railway, New York, 1868 (*vert*) 80 80
1089 45 c. Peter Cooper's locomotive, *Tom Thumb* (first U.S. passenger locomotive), 1829 .. .. 80 80
1090 60 c. *Spray* (Slocum's solo circumnavigation), 1895–8 (*vert*) 90 90
1091 90 c. *Sea-Land Commerce* (fastest Pacific passage), 1973 (*vert*) .. .. 1·25 1·25
1092 $1 First cable cars, San Francisco, 1873 .. 1·40 1·40
1093 $3 "Orient Express", 1883 .. .. 3·00 3·00
1094 $4 *Clermont* (first commercial paddle-steamer), 1807 .. .. 3·25 3·25
1085/94 .. .. *Set of* 10 12·00 12·00

(Litho Questa)

1987 (16 Nov). *Christmas. Religious Paintings. T* **219** *and similar vert designs. Multicoloured. P* 14.
1095 20 c. Type **219** 30 15
1096 25 c. "Virgin and Child" (Murillo).. .. 30 15
1097 $2 "Madonna and Child" (Foppa) .. 1·50 2·25
1098 $4 "Madonna and Child" (Da Verona) .. 2·75 4·00
1095/8 .. .. *Set of* 4 4·25 6·00
MS1099 100×78 mm. $5 "Angel of the Annunciation" (anon, Renaissance period) .. .. 2·50 3·50

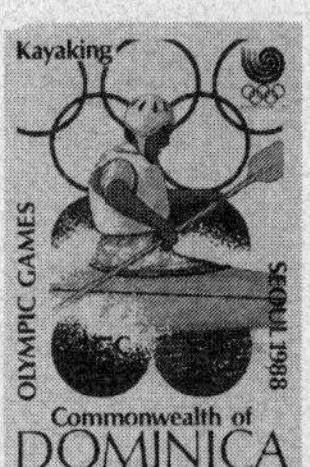

220 Three Little Pigs in People Mover, Walt Disney World **221** Kayak Canoeing

(Des Walt Disney Company. Litho Questa)

1987 (22 Dec). *60th Anniv of Mickey Mouse (Walt Disn… cartoon character). T* **220** *and similar multicoloured desig… showing cartoon characters in trains. P* 13½×14.
1100 20 c. Type **220** 45 3
1101 25 c. Goofy driving horse tram, Disneyland 45 3
1102 45 c. Donald Duck in *Roger E. Broggie*, Walt Disney World 75 6
1103 60 c. Goofy, Mickey Mouse, Donald Duck and Chip n'Dale aboard Big Thunder Mountain train, Disneyland 85 7
1104 90 c. Mickey Mouse in *Walter E. Disney*, Disneyland .. .. 1·40 1·2
1105 $1 Mickey and Minnie Mouse, Goofy, Donald and Daisy Duck in monorail, Walt Disney World .. .. .. 1·50 1·4
1106 $3 Dumbo flying over *Casey Jr* .. .. 3·25 3·7
1107 $4 Daisy Duck and Minnie Mouse in *Lilly Belle*, Walt Disney World .. .. 3·75 4·5
1100/7 .. .. *Set of* 8 11·00 11·5
MS1108 Two sheets, each 127×101 mm. (a) $5 Seven Dwarfs in Rainbow Caverns Mine train, Disneyland (*horiz*). (b) $5 Donald Duck and Chip n'Dale on toy train (from film *Out of Scale*) (*horiz*). P 14×13½ .. *Set of* 2 *sheets* 5·50 7·0

(Des and litho Questa)

1988 (15 Feb). *Royal Ruby Wedding. Vert designs as T* **234** *Antigua. P* 14.
1109 45 c. multicoloured 85 3
1110 60 c. deep brown, black and light green .. 1·00 7
1111 $1 multicoloured .. .. .. 1·25 1·0
1112 $3 multicoloured .. .. .. 2·50 3·5
1109/12 .. .. *Set of* 4 5·00 5·0
MS1113 102×76 mm. $5 multicoloured .. 3·00 3·7
Designs:— 45 c. Wedding portrait with attendants, 1947; 60 … Princess Elizabeth with Prince Charles, *c.* 1950; $1 Princes… Elizabeth and Prince Philip with Prince Charles and Princes… Anne, 1950; $3 Queen Elizabeth; $5 Princess Elizabeth i… wedding dress, 1947.

(Des D. Miller. Litho Questa)

1988 (14 Mar). *Olympic Games, Seoul. T* **221** *and similar ve… designs. Multicoloured. P* 14.
1114 45 c. Type **221** 75 3
1115 60 c. Taekwon-do .. .. 1·00 1·0
1116 $1 High diving .. .. 1·10 1·2
1117 $3 Gymnastics on bars .. .. .. 2·25 4·0
1114/17 .. .. *Set of* 4 4·50 6·0
MS1118 81×110 mm. $5 Football .. .. 2·50 3·5

222 Carib Indian **223** White-tailed Tropic Bird

(Des K. Gromell. Litho Format)

1988 (13 Apr). *"Reunion '88" Tourism Programme. T* **222** *an… similar multicoloured designs. P* 15.
1119 10 c. Type **222** 10 1
1120 25 c. Mountainous interior (*horiz*) .. 10 1
1121 35 c. Indian River.. .. .. .. 10 1
1122 60 c. Belaire dancer and tourists 15 3
1123 90 c. Boiling Lake 20 6
1124 $3 Coral reef (*horiz*) .. .. .. 60 1·6
1119/24 .. .. *Set of* 6 85 2·5
MS1125 112×82 mm. $5 Belaire dancer .. 1·75 4·0

1988 (1 June). *Stamp Exhibitions. Nos.* **MS**1084 *and* 1092/… *optd as T* **241** *of Antigua showing various emblems.*
1126 $1 First cable cars, San Francisco, 1873 (optd "FINLANDIA 88", Helsinki) .. 75 7…
1127 $3 "Orient Express", 1883 (optd "INDEPENDENCE 40", Israel) .. 1·75 2·0…
a. Opt albino .. ..
MS1128 Two sheets, each 109 × 79 mm. (a) $5 Fleet off Dominica, 1493 (optd "OLYMPHILEX '88", Seoul). (b) $5 Map showing Columbus's route, 1493 (optd "Praga '88", Prague) *Set of* 2 *sheets* 4·25 5·5…

(Des S. Barlow. Litho Questa)

988 (25 July). *Dominica Rain Forest Flora and Fauna. T* **223** *and similar vert designs. Multicoloured. P* 14½×14.

129 45 c. Type **223** 50 50
a. Sheetlet. Nos. 1129/48 .. .. 9·00
130 45 c. Blue-hooded Euphonia 50 50
131 45 c. Smooth-billed Ani 50 50
132 45 c. Scaly-breasted Thrasher 50 50
133 45 c. Purple-throated Carib 50 50
134 45 c. *Marpesia petreus* and *Strymon maesites* (butterflies) 50 50
135 45 c. Brown Trembler 50 50
136 45 c. Imperial Amazon 50 50
137 45 c. Mangrove Cuckoo 50 50
138 45 c. *Dynastes hercules* (beetle) 50 50
139 45 c. *Historis odius* (butterfly) 50 50
140 45 c. Red-necked Amazon 50 50
141 45 c. Tillandsia (plant) 50 50
142 45 c. Bananaquit and *Polystacha luteola* (plant) 50 50
143 45 c. False Chameleon 50 50
144 45 c. Iguana 50 50
145 45 c. *Hypolimnas misippus* (butterfly) .. 50 50
146 45 c. Green-throated Carib 50 50
147 45 c. Heliconia (plant) 50 50
148 45 c. Agouti 50 50
129/48 .. .. *Set of* 20 9·00 9·00

Nos. 1129/48 were printed together, *se-tenant*, in a sheetlet of 0 forming a composite design.

224 Battery Hens

225 Gary Cooper

(Des J. Martin. Litho Questa)

988 (5 Sept). *10th Anniv of International Fund for Agricultural Development. T* **224** *and similar multicoloured designs. P* 14.

149 45 c. Type **224** 50 30
150 60 c. Pig 70 65
151 90 c. Cattle .. .. 95 1·25
152 $3 Black Belly Sheep .. .. .. 2·25 4·00
149/52 .. .. *Set of* 4 4·00 5·50
MS1153 95×68 mm. $5 Tropical fruits (*vert*) .. 2·25 3·50

(Des Lynda Bruscheni. Litho Questa)

1988 (8 Sept). *Entertainers. T* **225** *and similar vert designs. Multicoloured. P* 14.

1154 10 c. Type **225** 40 20
1155 35 c. Josephine Baker 50 35
1156 45 c. Maurice Chevalier 55 35
1157 60 c. James Cagney 60 50
1158 $1 Clark Gable 80 70
1159 $2 Louis Armstrong .. .. .. 1·25 1·50
1160 $3 Liberace .. .. 1·75 2·25
1161 $4 Spencer Tracy .. .. .. 2·25 3·00
1154/61 .. .. *Set of* 8 7·25 8·00
MS1162 Two sheets, each 105×75 mm. (a) $5 Humphrey Bogart. (b) $5 Elvis Presley. *Set of* 2 *sheets* 7·00 8·00

(Des Mary Walters. Litho Questa)

1988 (29 Sept). *Flowering Trees. Horiz designs as T* **242** *of Antigua. Multicoloured. P* 14.

1163 15 c. Sapodilla 10 10
1164 20 c. Tangerine 10 10
1165 25 c. Avocado Pear 10 10
1166 45 c. Amherstia 20 25
1167 90 c. Lipstick Tree 40 55
1168 $1 Cannonball Tree 45 55
1169 $3 Saman .. .. 1·25 1·75
1170 $4 Pineapple .. .. 1·60 2·00
1163/70 .. .. *Set of* 8 3·75 4·75
MS1171 Two sheets, each 96 × 66 mm. (a) $5 Lignum Vitae. (b) $5 Sea Grape *Set of* 2 *sheets* 4·50 6·00

(Litho Questa)

1988 (10 Oct). *500th Birth Anniv of Titian (artist). Vert designs as T* **238** *of Antigua. Multicoloured. P* 13½ × 14.

1172 25 c. "Jacopo Strada" 15 15
1173 35 c. "Titian's Daughter Lavinia" 20 20
1174 45 c. "Andrea Navagero" 25 25
1175 60 c. "Judith with Head of Holoferenes" .. 30 30
1176 $1 "Emilia di Spilimbergo" 50 50
1177 $2 "Martyrdom of St. Lawrence" .. 1·00 1·25
1178 $3 "Salome" .. .. 1·60 2·00
1179 $4 "St. John the Baptist" .. .. 1·90 2·50
1172/9 .. .. *Set of* 8 5·50 6·50
MS1180 Two sheets, each 110 × 95 mm. (a) $5 "Self Portrait". (b) $5 "Sisyphus" *Set of* 2 *sheets* 4·25 6·00

PRICES OF SETS

Set prices are given for many issues, generally those containing three stamps or more. Definitive sets include one of each value or major colour change, but do not cover different perforations, die types or minor shades. Where a choice is possible the set prices are based on the cheapest versions of the stamps included in the listings.

226 Imperial Amazon

227 President and Mrs. Kennedy

(Des K. Gromell. Litho Questa)

1988 (31 Oct). *10th Anniv of Independence. T* **226** *and similar multicoloured designs. P* 14.

1181 20 c. Type **226** 90 40
1182 45 c. Dominica 1874 1d. stamp and landscape (*horiz*) 90 30
1183 $2 1978 Independence 10 c. stamp and landscape (*horiz*) .. .. .. 1·50 2·75
1184 $3 Carib Wood (national flower) .. 1·75 3·25
1181/4 .. .. *Set of* 4 4·50 6·00
MS1185 116 × 85 mm. $5 Government Band (*horiz*) .. .. 2·25 3·50

(Des J. Martin. Litho Questa)

1988 (22 Nov). *25th Death Anniv of John F. Kennedy (American statesman). T* **227** *and similar multicoloured designs. P* 14.

1186 20 c. Type **227** 10 10
1187 25 c. Kennedy sailing 10 10
1188 $2 Outside Hyannis Port house .. 80 1·50
1189 $4 Speaking in Berlin (*vert*) .. .. 1·60 2·50
1186/9 .. .. *Set of* 4 2·40 3·75
MS1190 100 × 71 mm. $5 President Kennedy (*vert*) .. .. 2·10 3·50

228 Donald Duck's Nephews decorating Christmas Tree

229 Raoul Wallenberg (diplomat) and Swedish Flag

(Des Walt Disney Co. Litho Questa)

1988 (1 Dec). *Christmas. "Mickey's Christmas Mall". T* **228** *and similar vert designs showing Walt Disney cartoon characters. Multicoloured. P* 13½ × 14.

1191 60 c. Type **228** 55 65
a. Sheetlet. Nos. 1191/8 .. .. 4·00
1192 60 c. Daisy Duck outside clothes shop .. 55 65
1193 60 c. Winnie the Pooh in shop window .. 55 65
1194 60 c. Goofy with parcels 55 65
1195 60 c. Donald Duck as Father Christmas .. 55 65
1196 60 c. Mickey Mouse contributing to collection 55 65
1197 60 c. Minnie Mouse 55 65
1198 60 c. Chip n' Dale with peanut 55 65
1191/8 .. .. *Set of* 8 4·00 4·75
MS1199 Two sheets, each 127 × 102 mm. (a) $6 Mordie Mouse with Father Christmas. (b) $6 Mickey Mouse at West Indian market *Set of* 2 *sheets* 6·50 8·00

Nos. 1191/8 were printed together, *se-tenant* as a composite design, in sheetlets of eight.

(Des J. Genzo. Litho B.D.T.)

1988 (9 Dec). *40th Anniv of Universal Declaration of Human Rights. T* **229** *and similar multicoloured design. P* 14.

1200 $3 Type **229** .. .. 2·00 2·50
MS1201 92 × 62 mm. $5 Human Rights Day logo (*vert*) .. .. 2·50 3·25

230 Greater Amberjack

(Des J. Iskowitz. Litho Questa)

1988 (22 Dec). *Game Fishes. T* **230** *and similar horiz designs. Multicoloured. P* 14.

1202 10 c. Type **230** 20 15
1203 15 c. Blue Marlin 20 15
1204 35 c. Cobia 35 30
1205 45 c. Dolphin (fish) 45 30
1206 60 c. Cero 60 55
1207 90 c. Mahogany Snapper 85 95
1208 $3 Yellow-finned Tuna .. .. 2·50 3·25
1209 $4 Rainbow Parrotfish .. .. 3·00 3·75
1202/9 .. .. *Set of* 8 7·50 8·50
MS1210 Two sheets, each 104×74 mm. (a) $5 Manta. (b) $5 Tarpon .. *Set of* 2 *sheets* 7·50 9·00

231 Leatherback Turtle

Men's c-1, 500m
O. Heukrodt DDR

(**232**)

(Des W. Wright. Litho Questa)

1988 (29 Dec). *Insects and Reptiles. T* **231** *and similar horiz designs. Multicoloured. P* 14.

1211 10 c. Type **231** 45 35
1212 25 c. *Danaus plexippus* (butterfly) .. 1·25 75
1213 60 c. Green Anole (lizard) .. .. .. 1·60 1·25
1214 $3 *Mantis religiosa* (mantid) .. .. 4·00 6·50
1211/14 .. .. *Set of* 4 6·50 8·00
MS1215 119×90 mm. $5 *Dynastes hercules* (beetle) .. .. 3·00 4·50

1989 (20 Mar). *Olympic Medal Winners, Seoul. Nos.* 1114/18 *optd as T* **232** (*horizontally on No.* **MS**1220).

1216 45 c. Type **221** (optd with T **232**) 20 25
1217 60 c. Taekwon-do (optd "Women's Fly-weight N. Y. Choo S. Korea") 25 35
1218 $1 High diving (optd "Women's Platform Y. Xu China") 40 60
1219 $3 Gymnastics on bars (optd "V. Artemov USSR") .. .. 1·25 1·75
1216/19 .. .. *Set of* 4 1·90 2·75
MS1220 81×110 mm. $5 Football (optd "USSR defeated Brazil 3-2 on penalty kicks after a 1-1 tie") .. .. 3·00 3·75

(Des D. Miller. Litho Questa)

1989 (8 May). *500th Anniv of Discovery of America by Columbus (1992) (2nd issue). Pre-Columbian Carib Society. Designs as T* **247** *of Antigua, but horiz. Multicoloured. P* 14.

1221 20 c. Carib canoe 20 20
1222 35 c. Hunting with bows and arrows .. 30 20
1223 $1 Dugout canoe making 70 90
1224 $3 Shield contest .. .. .. 1·75 2·75
1221/4 .. .. *Set of* 4 2·75 3·50
MS1225 87×71 mm. $6 Ceremonial dance .. 2·75 4·00

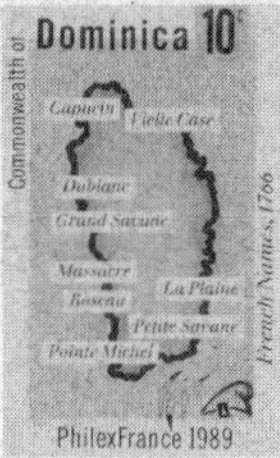

233 Map of Dominica, 1766

234 *Papilio homerus*

(Des U. Purins. Litho B.D.T.)

1989 (17 July). *"Philexfrance 89" International Stamp Exhibition, Paris. T* **233** *and similar multicoloured designs. P* 14.

1226 10 c. Type **233** 45 30
1227 35 c. French coin of 1653 (*horiz*) 65 40
1228 $1 French warship, 1720 (*horiz*) .. 1·40 1·25
1229 $4 Coffee plant (*horiz*) .. .. .. 2·00 3·00
1226/9 .. .. *Set of* 4 4·00 4·50
MS1230 98×98 mm. $5 Exhibition inscription (*horiz*) (black, grey and greenish yellow) .. 3·00 4·00

(Litho Questa)

1989 (31 Aug). *Japanese Art. Paintings by Taikan. Designs as T* **250** *of Antigua, but vert. Multicoloured. P* 13½×14.

1231 10 c. "Lao-tzu" (detail) 10 10
1232 20 c. "Red Maple Leaves" (panels 1 and 2) 10 10
1233 45 c. "King Wen Hui learns a Lesson from his Cook" (detail) 20 25
1234 60 c. "Red Maple Leaves" (panels 3 and 4) 25 35
1235 $1 "Wild Flowers" (detail) 40 50
1236 $2 "Red Maple Leaves" (panels 5 and 6) 85 1·00
1237 $3 "Red Maple Leaves" (panels 7 and 8) 1·25 1·60
1238 $4 "Indian Ceremony of Floating Lamps on the River" (detail) .. .. 1·75 2·10
1231/8 .. .. *Set of* 8 4·25 5·50
MS1239 Two sheets (a) 78×102 mm. $5 "Innocence" (detail). (b) 101×77 mm. $5 "Red Maple Leaves" (detail) .. .. *Set of* 2 *sheets* 5·50 7·00

Nos. 1231/8 were each printed in sheetlets of 10 containing two vertical strips of 5 stamps separated by printed labels commemorating Emperor Hirohito.

(Litho Questa)

1989 (31 Aug)–**91**. *As Nos.* 1038/46 *and* 1048/51 *but with* "1989" *imprint date. P* 14.

1241 2 c. Ruddy Quail Dove 40 60
a. Perf 12 (1990) 40 60
b. Perf 12½×11½ (1991) 40 60
1242 5 c. Red-necked Pigeon 50 40
a. Perf 12 (1990) 50 40
b. Perf 12½×11½ (1991) 50 40
1243 10 c. Green Heron 50 15
a. Perf 12 (1990) 50 15
b. Perf 12½×11½ (1991) 50 15
1244 15 c. Moorhen 60 30
a. Perf 12 (1990) 60 30
b. Perf 12½×11½ (1991) 60 30
1245 20 c. Ringed Kingfisher 65 40
a. Perf 12 (1990) 65 40
b. Perf 12½×11½ (1991) 65 40

1246 25 c. Brown Pelican 65 40
a. Perf 12 (1990) 65 40
b. Perf 12½×11½ (1991) 65 40
1247 35 c. White-tailed Tropic Bird 80 30
a. Perf 12 (1990) 80 30
b. Perf 12½×11½ (1991) 80 30
1248 45 c. Red-legged Thrush .. .. .. 1·00 30
a. Perf 12 (1990) .. .. 1·00 30
b. Perf 12½×11½ (1991) .. .. .. 1·00 30
1249 60 c. Purple-throated Carib .. .. 1·50 70
a. Perf 12 (1990) .. .. 1·50 70
b. Perf 12½×11½ (1991) .. .. .. 1·50 70
1251 $1 Brown Trembler .. .. 1·60 1·25
a. Perf 12 (1990) .. .. 1·60 1·25
b. Perf 12½×11½ (1991) .. .. .. 1·60 1·25
1252 $2 Black-capped Petrel .. .. .. 2·50 3·50
a. Perf 12 (1990) .. .. 2·50 3·50
b. Perf 12½×11½ (1991) .. .. .. 2·50 3·50
1253 $5 Barn Owl .. .. 5·50 7·00
a. Perf 12 (1990) .. .. 5·50 7·00
b. Perf 12½×11½ (1991) .. .. .. 5·50 7·00
1254 $10 Imperial Amazon .. .. 7·50 11·00
a. Perf 12 (1989) .. .. 7·50 11·00
b. Perf 12½×11½ (1991) .. .. .. 7·50 11·00
1241/54 .. .. *Set of* 13 21·00 23·00

Nos. 1241b/54b show a larger hole on every sixth perforation, both vertically and horizontally.

(Des W. Wright. Litho Questa)

1989 (11 Sept). *Butterflies. T* **234** *and similar horiz designs. Multicoloured. P* 14.

1255 10 c. Type **234** 40 30
1256 15 c. *Morpho peleides* 45 30
1257 25 c. *Dryas julia* 65 30
1258 35 c. *Parides gundlachianus* 70 30
1259 60 c. *Danaus plexippus* .. .. .. 1·00 75
1260 $1 *Agraulis vanillae* .. .. .. 1·25 1·25
1261 $3 *Phoebis avellaneda* .. .. .. 2·75 3·25
1262 $5 *Papilio andraemon* .. .. .. 3·75 5·00
1255/62 .. .. *Set of* 8 10·00 10·00
MS1263 Two sheets. (a) 105×74 mm. $6 *Adelpha cytherea*. (b) 105×79 mm. $6 *Adelpha iphicla* *Set of* 2 *sheets* 8·00 9·00

235 *Oncidium pusillum*

236 "Apollo 11" Command Module in Lunar Orbit

(Des W. Hanson Studio. Litho Questa)

1989 (28 Sept). *Orchids. T* **235** *and similar vert designs. Multicoloured. P* 14.

1264 10 c. Type **235** 35 30
1265 35 c. *Epidendrum cochleata* 70 30
1266 45 c. *Epidendrum ciliare* 75 40
1267 60 c. *Cyrtopodium andersonii* .. .. 1·00 80
1268 $1 *Habenaria pauciflora* .. .. 1·25 1·25
1269 $2 *Maxillaria alba* .. .. .. 2·00 2·25
1270 $3 *Selenipedium palmifolium* .. .. 2·50 2·75
1271 $4 *Brassavola cucullata* .. .. 3·25 3·75
1264/71 .. .. *Set of* 8 10·50 10·50
MS1272 Two sheets, each 108×77 mm. (a) $5 *Oncidium lanceanum*. (b) $5 *Comparettia falcata* *Set of* 2 *sheets* 8·00 9·00

(Litho Questa)

1989 (31 Oct). 20*th Anniv of First Manned Landing on Moon. T* **236** *and similar multicoloured designs. P* 14.

1273 10 c. Type **236** 30 30
1274 60 c. Neil Armstrong leaving lunar module 70 70
1275 $2 Edwin Aldrin at Sea of Tranquility .. 1·60 2·00
1276 $3 Astronauts Armstrong and Aldrin with U.S. flag .. .. 2·00 2·50
1273/6 .. .. *Set of* 4 4·25 5·00
MS1277 62×77 mm. $6 Launch of "Apollo 11" (*vert*) .. .. 4·50 6·00

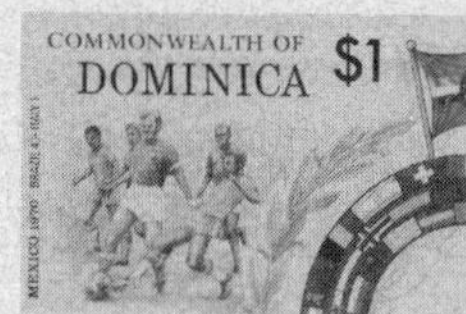

237 Brazil v Italy Final, 1970

(Des G. Vasarhelyi. Litho Questa)

1989 (8 Nov). *World Cup Football Championship, Italy* (1*st issue*). *T* **237** *and similar horiz designs. Multicoloured. P* 14.

1278 $1 Type **237** .. .. 1·50 1·75
a. Sheetlet. Nos. 1278/81 .. .. 5·50
1279 $1 England v. West Germany, 1966 .. 1·50 1·75
1280 $1 West Germany v. Holland, 1974 .. 1·50 1·75
1281 $1 Italy v. West Germany, 1982 .. 1·50 1·75
1278/81 .. .. *Set of* 4 5·50 6·50
MS1282 106×86 mm. $6 Two players competing for ball .. .. 4·00 4·75

Nos. 1278/81 were printed together, *se-tenant*, in a sheetlet of 4 stamps, forming a composite central design of a football surrounded by flags of competing nations.

See also Nos. 1383/7.

238 George Washington and Inauguration, 1789

(Des W. Hanson Studio. Litho Questa)

1989 (17 Nov). *"World Stamp Expo '89" International Stamp Exhibition, Washington* (1*st issue*). *Bicentenary of the U.S. Presidency. T* **238** *and similar horiz designs. Multicoloured. P* 14.

1283 60 c. Type **238** 50 50
a. Sheetlet. Nos. 1283/8 .. .. 2·75
1284 60 c. John Adams and Presidential Mansion, 1800 .. .. 50 50
1285 60 c. Thomas Jefferson, Graff House, Philadelphia and Declaration of Independence 50 50
1286 60 c. James Madison and U.S.S. *Constitution* defeating H.M.S. *Guerriere*, 1812 .. .. 50 50
1287 60 c. James Monroe and freed slaves landing in Liberia 50 50
1288 60 c. John Quincy Adams and barge on Erie Canal 50 50
1289 60 c. Millard Fillmore and Perry's fleet off Japan 50 50
a. Sheetlet. Nos. 1289/94 .. .. 2·75
1290 60 c. Franklin Pierce, Jefferson Davis and San Xavier Mission, Tucson .. 50 50
1291 60 c. James Buchanan, "Buffalo Bill" Cody carrying mail and Wells Fargo Pony Express stamp 50 50
1292 60 c. Abraham Lincoln and U.P.U. Monument, Berne 50 50
1293 60 c. Andrew Johnson, polar bear and Mt. McKinley, Alaska 50 50
1294 60 c. Ulysses S. Grant and Golden Spike Ceremony, 1869 .. .. .. 50 50
1295 60 c. Theodore Roosevelt and steam shovel excavating Panama Canal .. 50 50
a. Sheetlet. Nos. 1295/1300 .. 2·75
1296 60 c. William H. Taft and Admiral Peary at North Pole 50 50
1297 60 c. Woodrow Wilson and Curtiss JN-4 "Jenny" on first scheduled airmail flight, 1918 .. .. 50 50
1298 60 c. Warren G. Harding and airship U.S.S. *Shenandoah* at Lakehurst 50 50
1299 60 c. Calvin Coolidge and Lindbergh's Ryan NYP Special *Spirit of St. Louis* on trans-Atlantic flight 50 50
1300 60 c. Mt. Rushmore National Monument 50 50
1301 60 c. Lyndon B. Johnson and Earth from Moon as seen by "Apollo 8" crew .. 50 50
a. Sheetlet. Nos. 1301/6 .. .. 2·75
1302 60 c. Richard Nixon and visit to Great Wall of China 50 50
1303 60 c. Gerald Ford and *Gorch Fock* (German cadet barque) at Bicentenary of Revolution celebrations 50 50
1304 60 c. Jimmy Carter and Pres. Sadat of Egypt with Prime Minister Begin of Israel 50 50
1305 60 c. Ronald Reagan and space shuttle *Columbia* 50 50
1306 60 c. George Bush and Grumman TBF Avenger (fighter-bomber) 50 50
1283/1306 .. .. *Set of* 24 11·00 11·00

Nos. 1283/8, 1289/94, 1295/1300 and 1301/6 were printed together, *se-tenant*, in sheetlets of six stamps.

(Des Design Element. Litho Questa)

1989 (17 Nov). *"Expo '89" International Stamp Exhibition, Washington* (2*nd issue*). *Landmarks of Washington. Sheet* 77×62 *mm. containing horiz design as T* **257** *of Antigua. Multicoloured. P* 14.

MS1307 $4 The Capitol .. .. 2·50 3·25

(Des Walt Disney Co. Litho Questa)

1989 (30 Nov). *Mickey Mouse in Hollywood. Horiz designs as T* **267** *of Antigua showing Walt Disney cartoon characters. Multicoloured. P* 14×13½.

1308 20 c. Mickey Mouse reading script 40 40
1309 35 c. Mickey Mouse giving interview .. 55 55
1310 45 c. Mickey and Minnie Mouse with newspaper and magazines 65 65
1311 60 c. Mickey Mouse signing autographs 75 75
1312 $1 Trapped in dressing room .. .. 1·25 1·25
1313 $2 Mickey and Minnie Mouse with Pluto in limousine .. .. 2·00 2·50
1314 $3 Arriving at Awards ceremony .. 2·25 2·75
1315 $4 Mickey Mouse accepting award .. 2·40 2·75
1308/15 .. .. *Set of* 8 9·00 10·50
MS1316 Two sheets, each 127×102 mm. (a) $5 Mickey Mouse leaving footprints at cinema. (b) $5 Goofy interviewing .. .. *Set of* 2 *sheets* 7·50 8·50

(Litho Questa)

1989 (4 Dec). *Christmas. Paintings by Botticelli. Vert designs as T* **259** *of Antigua. Multicoloured. P* 14.

1317 20 c. "Madonna in Glory with Seraphim" 40 30
1318 25 c. "The Annunciation" 40 30
1319 35 c. "Madonna of the Pomegranate" .. 55 40
1320 45 c. "Madonna of the Rosegarden" .. 65 45
1321 60 c. "Madonna of the Book" 80 60
1322 $1 "Madonna under a Baldachin" .. 1·00 90
1323 $4 "Madonna and Child with Angels" 3·00 4·50
1324 $5 "Bardi Madonna" .. .. .. 3·50 4·75
1317/24 .. .. *Set of* 8 9·25 11·00
MS1325 Two sheets, each 71×96 mm. (a) $5 "The Mystic Nativity". (b) $5 "The Adoration of the Magi" .. .. .. *Set of* 2 *sheets* 7·00 9·00

240 Lady Olave Baden-Powell and Agatha Robinson

241 Jawaharlal Nehru

(Des A. Fagbohun. Litho Questa)

1989 (27 Dec). 60*th Anniv of Girl Guides in Dominica. T* **240** *and similar multicoloured design showing Guide leaders. P* 14.

1326 60 c. Type **240** .. .. 1·00 1·00
MS1327 70×99 mm. $5 Dorris Stockmann and Judith Pestaina (*horiz*) .. .. .. 3·50 4·00

(Des A. Fagbohun. Litho Questa)

1989 (29 Dec). *Birth Centenary of Jawaharlal Nehru (Indian statesman). T* **241** *and similar multicoloured design. P* 14.

1328 60 c. Type **241** .. .. 1·50 1·25
MS1329 101×72 mm. $5 Parliament House, New Delhi (*horiz*) .. .. 3·50 4·00

242 Cocoa Damselfish

(Des P. Chinelli. Litho Questa)

1990 (21 May). *Tropical Fishes. T* **242** *and similar horiz designs. Multicoloured. P* 14.

1330 45 c. Type **242** 45 50
a. Sheetlet. Nos. 1330/47 .. .. 7·00
1331 45 c. Stinging Jellyfish 45 50
1332 45 c. Dolphin (fish) 45 50
1333 45 c. Atlantic Spadefish and Queen Angelfish 45 50
1334 45 c. French Angelfish 45 50
1335 45 c. Blue-striped Grunt 45 50
1336 45 c. Porkfish 45 50
1337 45 c. Great Hammerhead 45 50
1338 45 c. Atlantic Spadefish 45 50
1339 45 c. Great Barracuda 45 50
1340 45 c. Southern Stingray 45 50
1341 45 c. Black Grunt 45 50
1342 45 c. Spot-finned Butterflyfish 45 50
1343 45 c. Dog Snapper 45 50
1344 45 c. Band-tailed Puffer 45 50
1345 45 c. Four-eyed Butterflyfish 45 50
1346 45 c. Lane Snapper 45 50
1347 45 c. Green Moray 45 50
1330/47 .. .. *Set of* 18 7·00 8·00

Nos. 1330/47 were printed together, *se-tenant*, in sheetlets of 18, forming a composite design.

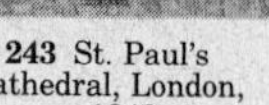

243 St. Paul's Cathedral, London, *c.* 1840

244 Blue-headed Hummingbird

(Des M. Pollard. Litho B.D.T.)

1990 (18 June). 150*th Anniv of the Penny Black and "Stamp World London 90" International Stamp Exhibition. T* **243** *and similar square designs. P* 13½.

1348 45 c. deep blue-green and black 50 25
1349 50 c. greenish blue and black 55 35
1350 60 c. greenish blue and black 65 45
1351 90 c. deep blue-green and black 85 85
1352 $3 deep ultramarine and black .. 2·25 3·00
1353 $4 deep ultramarine and black .. 2·75 3·50
1348/53 .. .. *Set of* 6 6·75 7·50
MS1354 Two sheets. (a) 103×79 mm. $5 brown-ochre and black. (b) 85×86 mm. $5 dull vermilion and blackish brown .. *Set of* 2 *sheets* 6·50 7·50

Designs:—50 c. British Post Office "accelerator" carriage, 1830; 60 c. St. Paul's and City of London; 90 c. Travelling post office, 1838; $3 "Hen and chickens" delivery cycle, 1883; $4 London skyline; $5 (a) As Type **243**; (b) Motor mail van, 1899.

(Des Mary Walters. Litho B.D.T.)

990 (19 July). *500th Anniv of Discovery of America by Columbus* (1992) (*3rd issue*). *New World Natural History–Seashells. Vert designs as T* **260** *of Antigua. Multicoloured. P* 14.

355 10 c. Reticulated Cowrie-helmet (*Cypraecassis testiculus*) .. 30 30
356 20 c. West Indian Chank (*Turbinella angulata*) .. 40 40
357 35 c. West Indian Fighting Conch (*Strombus pugilis*) .. 50 35
358 60 c. True Tulip (*Fasciolaria tulipa*) .. 75 60
359 $1 Sunrise Tellin (*Tellina radiata*) .. 1·00 1·00
360 $2 Crown Cone (*Conus regius*) .. 1·75 2·50
361 $3 Common Dove Shell (*Columbella mercatoria*) .. 2·50 3·25
362 $4 Common or Atlantic Fig Shell (*Ficus communis*) .. 2·75 3·25
355/62 .. *Set of* 8 9·00 10·50
MS1363 Two sheets, each 102×70 mm. (a) $5 King Helmet (*Cassis tuberosa*). (b) $5 Giant Tun (*Tonna galea*) .. *Set of* 2 *sheets* 6·50 7·50

(Des Mary Walters. Litho B.D.T.)

990 (26 July). *Birds. T* **244** *and similar vert designs. Multicoloured. P* 14.

364 10 c. Type **244** .. 35 35
365 20 c. Black-capped Petrel .. 45 45
366 45 c. Red-necked Amazon .. 65 40
367 60 c. Black Swift .. 80 70
368 $1 Troupial .. 1·25 1·25
369 $2 Common Noddy .. 2·00 2·50
370 $4 Lesser Antillean Pewee .. 3·25 3·50
371 $5 Little Blue Heron .. 3·75 4·25
364/71 .. *Set of* 8 11·00 12·00
MS1372 Two sheets, each 103×70 mm. (a) $6 Imperial Amazon. (b) $6 House Wren *Set of* 2 *sheets* 7·00 8·00

(Litho Questa)

990 (10 Sept). *90th Birthday of Queen Elizabeth the Queen Mother. Vert designs as T* **266** *of Antigua showing recent photographs of The Queen Mother. P* 14.

373 20 c. multicoloured .. 20 15
374 45 c. multicoloured .. 35 25
375 60 c. multicoloured .. 60 60
376 $3 multicoloured .. 2·25 3·00
373/6 .. *Set of* 4 3·00 3·50
MS1377 80×90 mm. $5 multicoloured .. 2·75 3·50

(Des B. Grout. Litho Questa)

990 (6 Nov). *Olympic Games, Barcelona* (1992) (*1st issue*). *Vert designs as T* **268** *of Antigua. Multicoloured. P* 14.

378 45 c. Tennis .. 75 40
379 60 c. Fencing .. 75 50
380 $2 Swimming .. 1·60 2·75
381 $3 Yachting .. 2·25 3·00
378/81 .. *Set of* 4 4·75 6·00
MS1382 100×70 mm. $5 Rowing .. 4·25 5·50
See also Nos. 1603/11.

245 Barnes, England

(Des Young Phillips Studio. Litho Questa)

1990 (6 Nov). *World Cup Football Championship, Italy* (*2nd issue*). *T* **245** *and similar multicoloured designs. P* 14.

1383 15 c. Type **245** .. 40 30
1384 45 c. Romario, Brazil .. 70 30
1385 60 c. Franz Beckenbauer, West Germany manager .. 85 70
1386 $4 Lindenberger, Austria .. 3·25 5·00
1383/6 .. *Set of* 4 4·75 5·75
MS1387 Two sheets, each 105×90 mm. (a) $6 McGrath, Ireland (*vert*). (b) $6 Litovchenko, Soviet Union (*vert*) .. *Set of* 2 *sheets* 7·50 8·50

246 Mickey Mouse riding Herschell-Spillman Frog

247 *Craterellus cornucopioides*

(Des Walt Disney Co. Litho Questa)

1990 (13 Dec). *Christmas. T* **246** *and similar multicoloured designs showing Walt Disney cartoon characters and American carousel animals. P* 13½×14.

1388 10 c. Type **246** .. 30 20
1389 15 c. Huey, Duey and Louie on Allan Herschell elephant .. 35 25
1390 25 c. Donald Duck on Allan Herschell polar bear .. 45 30
1391 45 c. Goofy on Dentzel goat .. 70 30
1392 $1 Donald Duck on Zalar giraffe .. 1·00 1·00
1393 $2 Daisy Duck on Herschell-Spillman stork .. 1·75 2·25
1394 $4 Goofy on Dentzel lion .. 3·00 3·75
1395 $5 Daisy Duck on Stein and Goldstein palomino stander .. 3·50 4·00
1388/95 .. *Set of* 8 10·00 11·00
MS1396 Two sheets, each 127×101mm. (a) $6 Mickey, Morty and Ferdie Mouse on Philadelphia Toboggan Company swan chariot (*horiz*). P 14×13½. (b) $6 Mickey and Minnie Mouse with Goofy on Philadelphia Toboggan Company winged griffin chariot. P 13½×14 *Set of* 2 *sheets* 8·50 11·00

(Des W. Hanson Studio. Litho Walsall)

1991 (26 Mar). *Cog Railways. Multicoloured designs as T* **275** *of Antigua. P* 14.

1397 10 c. Steam locomotive, Glion–Roches De Naye rack railway, 1890 .. 30 30
1398 35 c. Electric railcar, Mt Pilatus rack railway .. 45 30
1399 45 c. Schynige Platte rack railway train .. 50 30
1400 60 c. Steam train on Bugnli Viaduct, Furka–Oberalp rack railway (*vert*) .. 75 75
1401 $1 Jungfrau rack railway train, 1910 .. 1·00 1·25
1402 $2 Testing Pike's Peak railcar, Switzerland, 1983 .. 1·75 2·25
1403 $4 Brienz–Rothorn railway locomotive, 1991 .. 3·00 4·00
1404 $5 Steam locomotive, Arth–Rigi, 1890 3·50 4·25
1397/404 .. *Set of* 8 10·00 12·00
MS1405 Two sheets. (a) 100×70 mm. $6 Swiss Europa stamps of 1983 showing Riggenbach's locomotive of 1871 (50×37 *mm*). (b) 90×68 mm. $6 Brunig line train and Sherlock Holmes (50×37 *mm*). P 13½ .. *Set of* 2 *sheets* 8·00 9·50

(Des T. Agans. Litho Questa)

1991 (8 Apr). *500th Anniv of Discovery of America by Columbus* (1992) (*4th issue*). *History of Exploration. Horiz designs as T* **277** *of Antigua. Multicoloured. P* 14.

1406 10 c. Gil Eannes sailing south of Cape Bojador, 1433–34 .. 25 25
1407 25 c. Alfonso Baldaya sailing south to Cape Blanc, 1436 .. 35 35
1408 45 c. Bartolomeu Dias in Table Bay, 1487 45 35
1409 60 c. Vasco da Gama on voyage to India, 1497–99 .. 55 50
1410 $1 Vallarte the Dane off African coast 75 90
1411 $2 Aloisio Cadamosto in Cape Verde Islands, 1456–58 .. 1·40 1·75
1412 $4 Diogo Gomes on River Gambia, 1457 2·75 3·50
1413 $5 Diogo Cao off African coast, 1482–85 3·25 3·75
1406/13 .. *Set of* 8 8·50 10·00
MS1414 Two sheets, each 105×71 mm. (a) $6 Green-winged Macaw and bow of *Santa Maria*. (b) $6 Blue and Yellow Macaw and caravel *Set of* 2 *sheets* 7·50 8·50

(Des Walt Disney Co. Litho Questa)

1991 (22 May). *"Phila Nippon '91" International Stamp Exhibition, Tokyo. Multicoloured designs as T* **279** *of Antigua showing Walt Disney cartoon characters in Japanese costumes. P* 14×13½ (*horiz*) *or* 13½×14 (*vert*).

1415 10 c. Donald Duck as Shogun's guard (*horiz*) .. 20 20
1416 15 c. Mickey Mouse as Kabuki actor (*horiz*) 25 25
1417 25 c. Minnie and Mickey Mouse as bride and groom (*horiz*) .. 35 25
1418 45 c. Daisy Duck as geisha .. 45 25
1419 $1 Mickey Mouse in Sokutai court dress 85 85
1420 $2 Goofy as Mino farmer .. 1·60 2·00
1421 $4 Pete as Shogun .. 2·75 3·25
1422 $5 Donald Duck as Samurai (*horiz*) .. 3·25 3·75
1415/22 .. *Set of* 8 8·75 9·75
MS1423 Two sheets, each 127×112 mm. (a) $6 Mickey Mouse as Noh actor. (b) $6 Goofy as Kabubei-jishi dancer .. *Set of* 2 *sheets* 8·50 10·00

(Litho Questa)

1991 (3 June). *Fungi. T* **247** *and similar vert designs. Multicoloured. P* 14.

1424 10 c. Type **247** .. 50 40
1425 15 c. *Coprinus comatus* .. 60 40
1426 45 c. *Morchella esculenta* .. 85 40
1427 60 c. *Cantharellus cibarius* .. 1·10 70
1428 $1 *Lepista nuda* .. 1·40 1·10
1429 $2 *Suillus luteus* .. 2·00 2·50
1430 $4 *Russula emetica* .. 3·25 3·75
1431 $5 *Armillaria mellea* .. 3·25 3·75
1424/31 .. *Set of* 8 11·50 11·50
MS1432 Two sheets, each 100×70 mm. (a) $6 *Fistulina hepatica*. (b) $6 *Lactarius volemus* *Set of* 2 *sheets* 8·50 10·00

(Des D. Miller. Litho Walsall)

1991 (17 June). *65th Birthday of Queen Elizabeth II. Horiz designs as T* **280** *of Antigua. Multicoloured. P* 14.

1433 10 c. Queen and Prince William on Buckingham Palace Balcony, 1990 .. 30 20
1434 60 c. The Queen at Westminster Abbey, 1988 .. 75 50
1435 $2 Queen and Prince Philip in Italy, 1990 1·60 2·00
1436 $4 The Queen at Ascot, 1986 .. 2·50 3·00
1433/6 .. *Set of* 4 4·75 5·00
MS1437 68×90 mm. $5 Separate portraits of Queen and Prince Philip .. 3·75 4·25

(Des D. Miller. Litho Walsall)

1991 (17 June). *10th Wedding Anniv of the Prince and Princess of Wales. Horiz designs as T* **280** *of Antigua. Multicoloured. P* 14.

1438 15 c. Prince and Princess of Wales in West Germany, 1987 .. 40 25
1439 40 c. Separate photographs of Prince, Princess and sons .. 70 25
1440 $1 Separate photographs of Prince William and Prince Henry .. 95 95
1441 $5 Prince Charles at Caister and Princess Diana in Thailand .. 3·50 4·50
1438/41 .. *Set of* 4 5·00 5·50
MS1442 68×90 mm. $5 Prince Charles, and Princess Diana with sons on holiday .. 3·75 4·25

(Litho Walsall)

1991 (8 July). *Death Centenary of Vincent van Gogh* (*artist*) (1990). *Multicoloured designs as T* **278** *of Antigua. P* 13½.

1443 10 c. "Thatched Cottages" (*horiz*) .. 30 30
1444 25 c. "The House of Père Eloi" (*horiz*) .. 45 30
1445 45 c. "The Midday Siesta" (*horiz*) .. 65 30
1446 60 c. "Portrait of a Young Peasant" .. 85 70
1447 $1 "Still Life: Vase with Irises against a Yellow Background" .. 1·25 1·10
1448 $2 "Still Life: Vase with Irises" (*horiz*) 1·75 2·00
1449 $4 "Blossoming Almond Tree" (*horiz*) .. 3·00 3·75
1450 $5 "Irises" (*horiz*) .. 3·25 4·25
1443/50 .. *Set of* 8 10·50 11·50
MS1451 Two sheets, (a) 77×102 mm. $6 "Doctor Gachet's Garden in Auvers". (b) 102×77 mm. $6 "A Meadow in the Mountains: Le Mas de Saint-Paul" (*horiz*). Imperf .. *Set of* 2 *sheets* 8·00 9·00

(Des Walt Disney Co. Litho Questa)

1991 (6 Aug). *International Literacy Year* (1990). *Multicoloured designs as T* **269** *of Antigua showing scenes from Disney cartoon film* The Little Mermaid. *P* 14×13½.

1452 10 c. Ariel, Flounder and Sebastian (*horiz*) 25 25
1453 25 c. King Triton (*horiz*) .. 35 30
1454 45 c. Sebastian playing drums (*horiz*) .. 50 30
1455 60 c. Flotsam and Jetsam taunting Ariel (*horiz*) .. 75 55
1456 $1 Scuttle, Flounder and Ariel with pipe (*horiz*) .. 1·00 1·00
1457 $2 Ariel and Flounder discovering book (*horiz*) .. 1·75 2·00
1458 $4 Prince Eric and crew (*horiz*) .. 3·00 3·50
1459 $5 Ursula the Sea Witch (*horiz*) .. 3·50 4·00
1452/9 .. *Set of* 8 10·00 11·00
MS1460 Two sheets, each 127×102 mm. (a) $6 Ariel without tail (*horiz*). P 14×13½. (b) $6 Ariel and Prince Eric dancing. P 13½×14. *Set of* 2 *sheets* 8·50 9·00

248 Empire State Building, New York

249 Japanese Aircraft leaving Carrier *Akagi*

(Des W. Wright. Litho Questa)

1991 (12 Aug). *World Landmarks. T* **248** *and similar multicoloured designs. P* 14.

1461 10 c. Type **248** .. 40 30
1462 25 c. Kremlin, Moscow (*horiz*) .. 40 30
1463 45 c. Buckingham Palace, London (*horiz*) 60 30
1464 60 c. Eiffel Tower, Paris .. 75 60
1465 $1 Taj Mahal, Agra (*horiz*) .. 2·00 1·50
1466 $2 Opera House, Sydney (*horiz*) .. 3·00 3·00
1467 $4 Colosseum, Rome (*horiz*) .. 3·50 4·00
1468 $5 Pyramids, Giza (*horiz*) .. 3·75 4·50
1461/8 .. *Set of* 8 13·00 13·00
MS1469 Two sheets, each 100×68 mm. (a) $6 Galileo on Leaning Tower, Pisa (*horiz*). (b) $6 Emperor Shi Huang and Great Wall of China (*horiz*) .. *Set of* 2 *sheets* 11·00 12·00

(Des W. Wright. Litho Questa)

1991 (2 Sept). *50th Anniv of Japanese Attack on Pearl Harbor. T* **249** *and similar horiz designs. Multicoloured. P* 14.

1470 10 c. Type **249** .. 25 25
1471 15 c. U.S.S. *Ward* (destroyer) and Consolidated PBY-5 Catalina flying boat attacking midget submarine .. 30 30
1472 45 c. Second wave of Mitsubishi A6M Zero-Sen aircraft leaving carriers .. 40 30
1473 60 c. Japanese Mitsubishi A6M Zero-Sen's attacking Kaneche naval airfield .. 75 60
1474 $1 U.S.S. *Breeze*, *Medusa* and *Curtiss* (destroyers) sinking midget submarine .. 1·00 1·00
1475 $2 U.S.S. *Nevada* (battleship) under attack .. 1·75 2·00
1476 $4 U.S.S. *Arizona* (battleship) sinking 3·00 3·50
1477 $5 Mitsubishi A6M Zero-Sen aircraft 3·50 4·00
1470/7 .. *Set of* 8 9·75 11·00
MS1478 Two sheets, each 118×78 mm. (a) $6 Mitsubishi A6M Zero-Sen over anchorage. (b) $6 Mitsubishi A6M Zero-Sen attacking Hickam airfield .. *Set of* 2 *sheets* 8·50 10·00

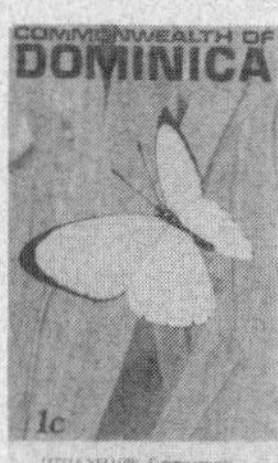

250 *Eurema venusta*

251 Symbolic Cheque

(Litho Cartor)

1991 (14 Oct)–**93.** *Butterflies. T* **250** *and similar vert designs. Multicoloured. P* 13½.
1479 1 c. Type **250** 30 60
1480 2 c. *Agraulis vanillae* 30 60
1481 5 c. *Danaus plexippus* 40 60
1482 10 c. *Biblis hyperia* 40 15
1483 15 c. *Dryas julia* 50 15
1484 20 c. *Phoebis agarithe* 50 20
1485 25 c. *Junonia genoveva* 50 20
1486 35 c. *Battus polydamas* 60 30
1487 45 c. *Leptotes cassius* 60 30
1487*a* 55 c. *Ascia monuste* (11.1.93) 75 55
1488 60 c. *Anaea dominicana* 70 35
1488*a* 65 c. *Hemiargus hanno* (11.1.93) 75 55
1489 90 c. *Hypolimnas misippus* 80 55
1490 $1 *Urbanus proteus* 80 60
1490*a* $1.20, *Historis odius* (11.1.93) .. .. 1·00 1·25
1491 $2 *Phoebis sennae* .. .. .. 1·50 2·00
1492 $5 *Cynthia cardui* ("*Vanessa cardui*") .. 2·50 3·50
1493 $10 *Marpesia petreus* .. .. .. 4·75 6·00
1494 $20 *Anartia jatrophae* .. .. .. 9·50 12·00
1479/94 .. .. *Set of* 19 24·00 27·00

(Des J. Iskowitz. Litho Questa)

1991 (1 Nov). *Birth Centenary of Charles de Gaulle (French statesman)* (1990). *Designs as T* **283** *of Antigua showing De Gaulle in uniform. P* 14.
1495 45 c. agate 75 75
MS1496 70×100 mm. $5 agate and deep ultramarine .. .. 3·50 4·00
No. 1495 is a vertical design.

(Litho Questa)

1991 (1 Nov). *40th Anniv of Credit Union Bank. T* **251** *and similar design. P* 14.
1497 10 c. grey-black and black 20 20
1498 60 c. multicoloured 80 80
Design: *Horiz*—60 c. Credit Union symbol.

252 "18th-Century Creole Dress" (detail) (Agostino Brunias)

253 Island Beach

(Litho Questa)

1991 (1 Nov). *Creole Week. T* **252** *and similar multicoloured designs. P* 14.
1499 45 c. Type **252** 50 25
1500 60 c. Jing Ping band 70 60
1501 $1 Creole dancers .. .. 1·00 1·40
1499/501 .. .. *Set of* 3 2·00 2·00
MS1502 100×70 mm. $5 "18th-century Stick-fighting Match" (detail) (Agostino Brunias) (*horiz*) .. .. 4·00 5·00

(Litho Cartor)

1991 (18 Nov). *Year of Environment and Shelter. T* **253** *and similar horiz designs. Multicoloured. P* 14.
1503 15 c. Type **253** 15 15
1504 60 c. Imperial Amazon .. .. .. 2·00 1·25
MS1505 Two sheets. (a) 100×70 mm. $5 River estuary. (b) 70×100 mm. $5 As 60 c. *Set of* 2 *sheets* 9·00 10·00

(Litho Walsall)

1991 (2 Dec). *Christmas. Religious Paintings by Jan van Eyck. Vert designs as T* **287** *of Antigua. Multicoloured. P* 12.
1506 10 c. "Virgin Enthroned with Child" (detail) 40 20
1507 20 c. "Madonna at the Fountain" .. 50 30
1508 35 c. "Virgin in a Church" 60 30
1509 45 c. "Madonna with Canon van der Paele" 70 30
1510 60 c. "Madonna with Canon van der Paele" (detail) .. .. 1·00 60
1511 $1 "Madonna in an Interior" .. .. 1·25 1·00
1512 $3 "The Annunciation" .. .. 2·50 3·50
1513 $5 "The Annunciation" (*different*) .. 3·50 5·50
1506/13 .. .. *Set of* 8 9·50 10·50
MS1514 Two sheets, each 102×127 mm. (a) $5 "Virgin and Child with Saints and Donor". (b) $5 "Madonna with Chancellor Rolin". P 14 *Set of* 2 *sheets* 9·00 11·00

(Des D. Miller. Litho Questa)

1992 (13 Mar). *40th Anniv of Queen Elizabeth II's Accession. Horiz designs as T* **288** *of Antigua. Multicoloured. P* 14.
1515 10 c. Coastline 10 10
1516 15 c. Mountains overlooking small village 10 10
1517 $1 River estuary 45 60
1518 $5 Waterfall .. .. 2·25 3·00
1515/18 .. .. *Set of* 4 2·75 3·50
MS1519 Two sheets, each 74×97 mm. (a) $6 Roseau. (b) $6 Mountain stream *Set of* 2 *sheets* 5·50 7·00

254 Cricket Match

255 Columbus and *Dynastes hercules* (beetle)

(Des Mary Walters. Litho B.D.T.)

1992 (30 Mar). *Centenary of Botanical Gardens* (1991). *T* **254** *and similar vert designs. Multicoloured. P* 14.
1520 10 c. Type **254** 20 20
1521 15 c. Scenic Entrance 20 20
1522 45 c. Traveller's Tree 30 25
1523 60 c. Bamboo House 40 30
1524 $1 The Old Pavilion 60 60
1525 $2 *Ficus benjamina* .. .. .. 1·10 1·50
1526 $4 Cricket match (*different*) .. .. 2·25 2·75
1527 $5 Thirty-five Steps .. .. .. 2·50 3·00
1520/7 .. .. *Set of* 8 6·75 8·00
MS1528 Two sheets, each 104×71 mm. (a) $6 Past and present members of national cricket team. (b) $6 The Fountain .. *Set of* 2 *sheets* 6·50 7·50

(Litho Questa)

1992 (21 Apr). *Easter. Religious Paintings. Multicoloured designs as T* **291** *of Antigua. P* 14×13½ (*horiz*) *or* 13½×14 (*vert*).
1529 10 c. "The Supper at Emmaus" (Van Honthorst) 20 20
1530 15 c. "Christ before Caiaphas" (Van Honthorst) (*vert*) 25 25
1531 45 c. "The Taking of Christ" (De Boulogne) 40 30
1532 60 c. "Pilate washing his Hands" (Preti) (*vert*) 55 45
1533 $1 "The Last Supper" (detail) (Master of the Church of S. Francisco d'Evora) .. 75 75
1534 $2 "The Three Marys at the Tomb" (detail) (Bouguereau) (*vert*) .. .. 1·50 1·75
1535 $3 "Denial of St. Peter" (Terbrugghen) 1·75 2·25
1536 $5 "Doubting Thomas" (Strozzi) .. 2·75 3·50
1529/36 .. .. *Set of* 8 7·50 8·50
MS1537 Two sheets, each 72×102 mm. (a) $6 "The Crucifixion" (detail) (Grünewald) (*vert*). (b) $6 "The Resurrection" (detail) (Caravaggio) (*vert*) .. .. .. *Set of* 2 *sheets* 7·00 8·50

(Litho B.D.T.)

1992 (4 May). *"Granada '92" International Stamp Exhibition, Spain. Art of Diego Rodriguez Velásquez. Multicoloured designs as T* **292** *of Antigua. P* 13×13½.
1538 10 c. "Pope Innocent X" (detail) 20 15
1539 15 c. "The Forge of Vulcan" (detail) .. 20 15
1540 45 c. "The Forge of Vulcan" (different detail) 40 25
1541 60 c. "Queen Mariana of Austria" (detail) 55 40
1542 $1 "Pablo de Valladolid" 70 70
1543 $2 "Sebastián de Morra" .. .. 1·50 2·00
1544 $3 "King Felipe IV" (detail) .. .. 1·75 2·25
1545 $4 "King Felipe IV" .. .. .. 2·25 2·50
1538/45 .. .. *Set of* 8 6·75 7·50
MS1546 Two sheets, each 120×95 mm. (a) $6 "The Drunkards" (110×81 *mm*). (b) $6 "Surrender of Breda" (110×81 *mm*). Imperf *Set of* 2 *sheets* 7·00 8·00

(Des R. Brown. Litho Questa)

1992 (18 May). *500th Anniv of Discovery of America by Columbus* (*5th issue*). *World Columbian Stamp "Expo '92", Chicago. T* **255** *and similar multicoloured designs. P* 14.
1547 10 c. Type **255** 15 15
1548 25 c. Columbus and *Leptodactylus fallax* (frog) 20 15
1549 75 c. Columbus and Red-necked Amazon (bird) 60 60
1550 $2 Columbus and *Ameiva fuscata* (lizard) 1·25 1·75
1551 $4 Columbus and Royal Gramma (fish) 2·25 2·75
1552 $5 Columbus and *Rosa sinensis* (flower) 2·50 3·00
1547/52 .. .. *Set of* 6 6·25 7·50
MS1553 Two sheets, each 100×67 mm. (a) $6 Ships of Columbus (*horiz*). (b) $6 *Mastophyllum scabricolle* (katydid) (*horiz*) .. *Set of* 2 *sheets* 6·50 7·50

(Des R. Brown. Litho Questa)

1992 (28 May). *"Genova '92" International Thematic Stamp Exhibition. Hummingbirds. Horiz designs as T* **295** *of Antigua. Multicoloured. P* 14.
1554 10 c. Female Purple-throated Carib .. 20 20
1555 15 c. Female Rufous-breasted Hermit .. 20 20
1556 45 c. Male Puerto Rican Emerald .. 50 30
1557 60 c. Female Antillean Mango 60 45
1558 $1 Male Green-throated Carib 95 85
1559 $2 Male Blue-headed Hummingbird .. 1·50 1·75
1560 $4 Female Eastern Streamertail .. 2·50 2·75
1561 $5 Female Antillean Crested Hummingbird .. .. 2·75 3·00
1554/61 .. .. *Set of* 8 8·25 8·50
MS1562 Two sheets, each 105×72 mm. (a) $6 Jamaican Mango ("Green Mango"). (b) $6 Vervain Hummingbird .. *Set of* 2 *sheets* 8·00 9·00

(Des D. Burkhart. Litho Questa)

1992 (23 June). *Prehistoric Animals. Multicoloured designs as T* **290** *of Antigua, but horiz. P* 14.
1563 10 c. Head of Camptosaurus 20 20
1564 15 c. Edmontosaurus 20 20
1565 25 c. Corythosaurus 30 20
1566 60 c. Stegosaurus 60 45
1567 $1 Torosaurus 95 85
1568 $3 Euoplocephalus .. .. .. 2·00 2·25
1569 $4 Tyrannosaurus .. .. .. 2·50 2·75
1570 $5 Parasaurolophus .. .. .. 2·75 3·00
1563/70 .. .. *Set of* 8 8·50 9·00
MS1571 Two sheets, each 100×70 mm. (a) $6 As 25 c. (b) $6 As $1 .. .. *Set of* 2 *sheets* 9·50 10·00

256 Trumpetfish and Blue Chromis

(Des I. MacLaury. Litho B.D.T.)

1992 (20 July). *Marine Life. T* **256** *and similar horiz designs. P* 14.
1572/1601 65 c.×30 multicoloured .. .. 12·00 13·00
MS1602 Two sheets, each 73×105 mm. (a) $6 multicoloured (Harlequin Bass). (b) $6 multicoloured (Flamefish) .. *Set of* 2 *sheets* 9·00 10·00
Nos. 1572/86 and 1587/1601 were each issued in *se-tenant* sheetlets of 15 (3×5) showing reef marine life by day or by night.

(Litho Questa)

1992 (10 Aug). *Olympic Games, Barcelona* (*2nd issue*). *Vert designs as T* **268** *of Antigua. Multicoloured. P* 14.
1603 10 c. Archery 15 15
1604 15 c. Two-man canoeing 15 15
1605 25 c. Men's 110 metres hurdles 20 15
1606 60 c. Men's high jump 40 30
1607 $1 Greco-Roman wrestling 65 65
1608 $2 Men's gymnastics – rings .. .. 1·25 1·75
1609 $4 Men's gymnastics – parallel bars .. 2·50 3·00
1610 $5 Equestrian dressage .. .. 3·00 3·25
1603/10 .. .. *Set of* 8 7·50 8·50
MS1611 Two sheets, each 100×70 mm. (a) $6 Women's platform diving. (b) $6 Men's hockey *Set of* 2 *sheets* 7·00 8·50

(Des F. Paul ($1), J. Esquino ($2). Litho Questa)

1992 (2 Sept). *500th Anniv of Discovery of America by Columbus* (*6th issue*). *Organization of East Caribbean States. Vert designs as Nos.* 1670/1 *of Antigua. Multicoloured. P* 14½.
1612 $1 Columbus meeting Amerindians .. 65 65
1613 $2 Ships approaching island .. .. 1·10 1·25

(Litho Questa)

1992 (2 Nov). *Hummel Figurines. Vert designs as T* **302** *of Antigua. Multicoloured. P* 14.
1614 20 c. Angel playing violin 15 15
1615 25 c. Angel playing recorder 15 15
1616 55 c. Angel playing lute 35 35
1617 65 c. Seated angel playing trumpet .. 45 45
1618 90 c. Angel on cloud with lantern .. 60 60
1619 $1 Angel with candle 65 65
1620 $1.20, Flying angel with Christmas tree 75 1·00
1621 $6 Angel on cloud with candle .. .. 4·25 5·00
1614/21 .. .. *Set of* 8 6·50 7·50
MS1622 Two sheets, each 97×127 mm. (a) Nos. 1614/17. (b) Nos. 1618/21 .. *Set of* 2 *sheets* 6·50 8·00

257 Brass *Reno* Locomotive, Japan (1963)

(Des W. Hanson. Litho B.D.T.)

1992 (11 Nov). *Toy Trains from Far Eastern Manufacturers. T* **257** *and similar multicoloured designs. P* 14.
1623 15 c. Type **257** 15 15
1624 25 c. Union Pacific *Golden Classic* locomotive, China (1992) 20 20
1625 55 c. L.M.S. third class brake carriage, Hong Kong (1970s) 40 40
1626 65 c. Brass Wabash locomotive, Japan (1958) 50 50
1627 75 c. Pennsylvania "Duplex" type locomotive, Korea (1991) 60 60

628 $1 Streamlined locomotive, Japan (post 1945) 70 70
629 $3 Japanese National Railways Class "C62" locomotive, Japan (1960) .. 2·00 2·50
630 $5 Tinplate friction driven trains, Japan (1960s) .. .. 2·75 3·25
623/30 .. .. *Set of* 8 6·50 7·50
MS1631 Two sheets, each 119×87 mm. (a) $6 *Rocket's* tender, Japan (1972) (multicoloured) ($51^1/_2$×40 *mm*). (b) $6 American model steam train presented to Emperor of Japan, 1854 (black, blackish olive and flesh) (40×$51^1/_2$ *mm*). P 13 .. .. *Set of 2 sheets* 7·00 8·00

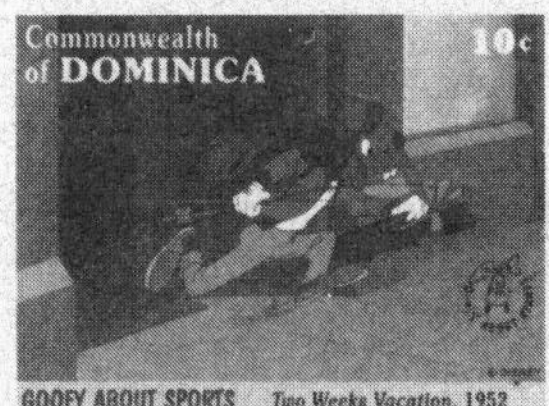

258 Goofy in *Two Weeks Vacation*, 1952

(Des Walt Disney Co. Litho Questa)

1992 (17 Nov). *60th Anniv of Goofy (Disney cartoon character). T* **258** *and similar multicoloured designs showing sports from cartoon films. P* 14×$13^1/_2$.
1632 10 c. Type **258** 35 15
1633 15 c. *Aquamania*, 1961 .. .. .. 45 15
1634 25 c. *Goofy Gymnastics*, 1949 .. .. 50 15
1635 45 c. *How to Ride a Horse*, 1941 .. .. 70 25
1636 $1 *Foul Hunting*, 1947 .. .. .. 1·00 65
1637 $2 *For Whom the Bulls Toil*, 1953 .. 1·75 2·00
1638 $4 *Tennis Racquet*, 1949 .. .. 2·25 2·75
1639 $5 *Double Dribble*, 1946 .. .. 2·50 3·00
1632/9 .. .. *Set of* 8 8·50 8·25
MS1640 Two sheets, each 128×102 mm. (a) $6 *The Goofy Sports Story*, 1956 (*vert*). (b) $6 *Aquamania*, 1961 (*different*) (*vert*). P $13^1/_2$×14 *Set of 2 sheets* 8·50 9·50

259 Airship LZ-127 *Graf Zeppelin*, 1929

260 Elvis Presley

(Des W. Wright and W. Hanson (Nos. 1641, 1655, **MS**1656a), W. Wright and L. Fried (Nos. 1645, 1654, **MS**1656b), J. Genzo (Nos. 1649, **MS**1656d), W. Wright (others). Litho Questa)

1992 (30 Dec). *Anniversaries and Events. T* **259** *and similar vert designs. Multicoloured. P* 14.
1641 25 c. Type **259** 15 15
1642 45 c. Elderly man on bike 30 25
1643 45 c. Elderly man with seedling 30 25
1644 45 c. Elderly man and young boy fishing 30 25
1645 90 c. Space Shuttle *Atlantis* 60 60
1646 90 c. Konrad Adenauer (German statesman) 60 60
1647 $1.20, Sir Thomas Lipton and *Shamrock N* (yacht) 75 75
1648 $1.20, Snowy Egret (bird) 75 75
1649 $1.20, Wolfgang Amadeus Mozart .. 75 75
1650 $2 Pulling fishing net ashore .. .. 1·25 1·25
1651 $3 Helen Keller (lecturer) .. .. 1·75 1·75
1652 $4 Eland (antelope) .. .. .. 2·50 2·50
1653 $4 Map of Allied Zones of Occupation, Germany, 1949 .. .. .. 2·50 2·50
1654 $4 Earth Resources satellite .. .. 2·50 2·50
1655 $5 Count von Zeppelin .. .. .. 2·75 3·00
1641/55 .. .. *Set of* 15 16·00 16·00
MS1656 Five sheets. (a) 100×70 mm. $6 Airship propeller. (b) 100×70 mm. $6 "Mir" Russian space station with "Soyuz". (c) 70×100 mm. $6 Cologne Cathedral. (d) 100×70 mm. $6 Rhinoceros Hornbill (bird). (e) 100×70 mm. $6 Monostatos from *The Magic Flute* .. *Set of 5 sheets* 15·00 16·00

Anniversaries and Events:—Nos. 1641, 1655, **MS**1656a, 75th death anniv of Count Ferdinand von Zeppelin; Nos. 1642/4, International Day of the Elderly; Nos. 1645, 1654, **MS**1656b, International Space Year; Nos. 1646, 1653, **MS**1656c, 25th death anniv of Konrad Adenauer; No. 1647, Americas Cup Yachting Championship; Nos. 1648, 1652, **MS**1656d, Earth Summit '92, Rio; Nos. 1649, **MS**1656e, Death bicent of Mozart; No. 1650, International Conference on Nutrition, Rome; No. 1651, 75th anniv of International Association of Lions Clubs.

No. **MS**1656b is inscribed "M.I.R." and No. **MS**1656d "Rhinocerus Hornbill", both in error.

(Litho Walsall)

1993 (24 Mar). *Bicentenary of the Louvre, Paris. Vert designs as T* **305** *of Antigua. Multicoloured. P* 12.
1657 $1 "Madonna and Child with St. Catherine and a Rabbit" (left detail) (Titian) .. 65 70
a. Sheetlet. Nos. 1657/64 .. .. 4·75
1658 $1 "Madonna and Child with St. Catherine and a Rabbit" (right detail) (Titian) .. 65 70
1659 $1 "Women at her Toilet" (Titian) .. 65 70
1660 $1 "The Supper at Emmaus" (left detail) (Titian) 65 70
1661 $1 "The Supper at Emmaus" (right detail) (Titian) 65 70
1662 $1 "The Pastoral Concert" (Titian) .. 65 70
1663 $1 "An Allegory, perhaps of Marriage" (detail) (Titian) 65 70
1664 $1 "An Allegory, perhaps of Marriage" (different detail) (Titian) 65 70
1657/64 .. .. *Set of* 8 4·75 5·00
MS1665 70×100 mm. $6 "The Ship of Fools" (Bosch) (52×85 *mm*). P $14^1/_2$ .. .. .. 3·50 4·00

Nos. 1657/64 were printed together, *se-tenant*, in sheetlets of 8 stamps and one centre label.

(Des A. Nahigian. Litho Walsall)

1993 (24 Mar). *15th Death Anniv of Elvis Presley (singer). T* **260** *and similar vert designs. Multicoloured. P* 14.
1666 $1 Type **260** 70 70
a. Strip of 3. Nos. 1666/8 .. .. 1·90
1667 $1 Elvis with guitar 70 70
1668 $1 Elvis with microphone 70 70
1666/8 .. .. *Set of* 4 1·90 1·90

Nos. 1666/8 were printed together, horizontally and vertically *se-tenant*, in sheetlets of 9 (3×3).

261 Plumbeous Warbler

262 School Crest

(Des Tracy Pedersen. Litho Questa)

1993 (30 Apr). *Birds. T* **261** *and similar vert designs. Multicoloured. P* 14.
1669 90 c. Type **261** 70 80
a. Sheetlet. Nos. 1669/80 .. .. 7·50
1670 90 c. Black Swift 70 80
1671 90 c. Blue-hooded Euphonia 70 80
1672 90 c. Rufous-throated Solitaire 70 80
1673 90 c. Ringed Kingfisher 70 80
1674 90 c. Blue-headed Hummingbird 70 80
1675 90 c. Bananaquit 70 80
1676 90 c. Brown Trembler 70 80
1677 90 c. Forest Thrush 70 80
1678 90 c. Purple-throated Carib 70 80
1679 90 c. Ruddy Quail Dove 70 80
1680 90 c. Least Bittern 70 80
1669/80 .. .. *Set of* 12 7·50 8·50
MS1681 Two sheets, each 100×70 mm. (a) $6 Imperial Amazon. (b) $6 Red-necked Amazon *Set of 2 sheets* 7·00 7·50

Nos. 1669/80 were printed together, *se-tenant*, in sheetlets of 12 forming a composite design.

(Litho Questa)

1993 (17 May). *Centenary of Dominica Grammar School. T* **262** *and similar horiz designs. Multicoloured. P* 14.
1682 25 c. Type **262** 15 10
1683 30 c. V. Archer (first West Indian headmaster) 20 20
1684 65 c. Hubert Charles (first Dominican headmaster) 35 45
1685 90 c. Present school buildings 50 65
1682/5 .. .. *Set of* 4 1·10 1·25

263 Leatherback Turtle on Beach

(Des S. Barlowe. Litho Walsall)

1993 (26 May). *Turtles. T* **263** *and similar horiz designs. Multicoloured. P* 14.
1686 25 c. Type **263** 50 15
1687 55 c. Hawksbill Turtle swimming .. 70 40
1688 65 c. Atlantic Ridley Turtle 80 50
1689 90 c. Green Turtle laying eggs .. .. 1·00 70
1690 $1 Green Turtle swimming .. .. 1·00 70
1691 $2 Hawksbill Turtle swimming (*different*) .. .. 1·50 2·00
1692 $4 Loggerhead Turtle .. .. .. 2·25 2·75
1693 $5 Leatherback Turtle swimming .. 2·25 2·75
1686/93 .. .. *Set of* 8 9·00 9·00
MS1694 Two sheets, each 99×70 mm. (a) $6 Green Turtle hatchling. (b) $6 Head of Hawksbill Turtle .. .. *Set of 2 sheets* 7·00 8·00

264 Ford "Model A", 1928

(Des W. Wright. Litho Walsall)

1993 (28 May). *Centenaries of Henry Ford's First Petrol Engine (90 c., $5, $6) and Karl Benz's First Four-wheeled Car (others). T* **264** *and similar horiz designs. Multicoloured. P* 14.
1695 90 c. Type **264** 70 50
1696 $1.20, Mercedes Benz car winning Swiss Grand Prix, 1936 .. .. .. 1·00 1·00
1697 $4 Mercedes Benz car winning German Grand Prix, 1935 .. .. .. 2·50 2·75
1698 $5 Ford "Model T", 1915 .. .. 2·50 2·75
1695/8 .. .. *Set of* 4 6·00 6·25
MS1699 Two sheets, each 99×70 mm. (a) $3 Benz "Viktoria", 1893; $3 Mercedes Benz sports coupe, 1993. (b) $6 Ford "G.T.40", Le Mans, 1966 ($57^1/_2$×48 *mm*) .. .. .. *Set of 2 sheets* 7·00 8·00

(Des Kerri Schiff. Litho Questa)

1993 (10 June). *40th Anniv of Coronation. Vert designs as T* **307** *of Antigua. P* $13^1/_2$×14.
1700 20 c. multicoloured 10 10
a. Sheetlet. Nos. 1700/3×2 .. .. 5·50
1701 25 c. reddish brown and black 10 10
1702 65 c. multicoloured 30 35
1703 $5 multicoloured .. .. .. 2·25 2·40
1700/3 .. .. *Set of* 4 2·75 3·00
MS1704 71×101 mm. $6 multicoloured. P 14 4·00 4·50

Designs:—20 c. Queen Elizabeth II at Coronation (photograph by Cecil Beaton); 25 c. Queen wearing King Edward's Crown during Coronation ceremony; 65 c. Coronation coach; $5 Queen and Queen Mother in carriage. ($28^1/_2$×$42^1/_2$ *mm*)—$6 "Queen Elizabeth II, 1969" (detail) (Norman Hutchinson).

Nos. 1700/3 were printed together in sheetlets of 8 containing two *se-tenant* blocks of 4.

265 New G.P.O. and Duke of Edinburgh

(Des Kerri Schiff (Nos. 1712, 1719, **MS**1721f). Litho Questa)

1993 (30 July). *Anniversaries and Events. T* **265** *and similar designs. Each reddish brown, deep brown and black (Nos. 1707, 1717,* **MS**1721b) *or multicoloured (others). P* 14.
1705 25 c. Type **265** 10 10
1706 25 c. "Bather with Beach Ball" (Picasso) (*vert*) 10 10
1707 65 c. Willy Brandt and Pres. Eisenhower, 1959 .. .. 30 35
1708 90 c. As Type **265**, but portrait of Queen Elizabeth II 40 45
1709 90 c. "Portrait of Leo Stein" (Picasso) (*vert*) 40 45
1710 90 c. Monika Holzner (Germany) (speed skating) (*vert*) 40 45
1711 90 c. "Self-portrait" (Marian Szczyrbula) (*vert*) 40 45
1712 90 c. Prince Naruhito and engagement photographs 40 45
1713 $1.20, 16th-century telescope (*vert*) .. 55 60
1714 $3 "Bruno Jasienski" (Tytus Czyzewski) (*vert*) .. .. 1·40 1·50
1715 $3 Modern observatory (*vert*) .. .. 1·40 1·50
1716 $4 Ray Leblanc and Tim Sweeney (U.S.A.) (ice hockey) (*vert*) .. .. 1·90 2·00
1717 $5 "Wilhelm Unde" (Picasso) (*vert*) .. 2·25 2·40
1718 $5 Willy Brandt and N.K. Winston at World's Fair, 1964 .. .. .. 2·25 2·40
1719 $5 Masako Owada and engagement photographs .. .. .. 2·25 2·40
1720 $5 Pres. Clinton and wife applauding 2·25 2·40
1705/20 .. .. *Set of* 16 16·00 18·00
MS1721 Seven sheets, each 105×75 mm (a, c and f) or 75×105 mm (others). (a) $5 Copernicus (*vert*). (b) $6 "Man with Pipe" (detail) (Picasso) (*vert*). (c) $6 Willy Brandt, 1972. (d) $6 Toni Nieminen (Finland) (120 metre ski jump) (*vert*). (e) $6 "Miser" (detail) (Tadeusz Makowski) (*vert*). (f) $6 Masako Owada (*vert*). (g) $6 Pres. W. Clinton (*vert*) .. .. .. *Set of 7 sheets* 19·00 20·00

Anniversaries and Events:—Nos. 1705, 1708, Opening of New General Post Office Building; Nos. 1706, 1709, 1717, **MS**1721b, 20th death anniv of Picasso (artist); Nos. 1707, 1718, **MS**1721c, 80th birth anniv of Willy Brandt (German politician); Nos. 1710, 1716, **MS**1721d, Winter Olympic Games '94, Lillehammer; Nos. 1711, 1714, **MS**1721e, "Polska '93" International Stamp Exhibition, Poznań; Nos. 1712, 1719, **MS**1721f, Marriage of Crown Prince Naruhito of Japan; Nos. 1713, 1715, **MS**1721a, 450th death anniv of Copernicus (astronomer); Nos. 1720, **MS**1721g, Inauguration of U.S. President William Clinton.

No. 1714 is inscribed "Tyrus" in error.

COVER PRICES

Cover factors are quoted at the beginning of each country for most issues to 1945. An explanation of the system can be found on page x. The factors quoted do not, however, apply to philatelic covers.

266 Hugo Eckener in New York Parade, 1928

267 Maradona (Argentina) and Buchwald (Germany)

(Des W. Wright. Litho Walsall)

1993 (30 July). *Aviation Anniversaries. T* **266** *and similar multicoloured designs. P* 14.

1722 25 c. Type **266** 30 15
1723 55 c. English Electric Lightning F.2 (fighter) 50 40
1724 65 c. Airship LZ-127 *Graf Zeppelin* over Egypt, 1929 .. .. 60 55
1725 $1 Boeing 314A (flying boat) on trans-Atlantic mail flight 80 75
1726 $2 Astronaut carrying mail to the Moon 1·50 1·75
1727 $4 Airship LZ-11 *Viktoria Luise* over Kiel harbour, 1912 .. .. .. 2·50 3·00
1728 $5 Supermarine Spitfire (*vert*) .. .. 2·50 3·00
1722/8 .. .. *Set of* 7 8·00 8·75
MS1729 Three sheets, each 99×70 mm. (a) $6 Hugo Eckener (42½×57 *mm*). (b) $6 Royal Air Force crest (42½×57 *mm*). (c) $6 Jean-Pierre Blanchard's hot air balloon, 1793 (*vert*) *Set of* 3 *sheets* 8·75 9·50

Anniversaries:—Nos. 1722, 1724, 1727, **MS**1729a, 125th birth anniv of Hugo Eckener (airship commander); Nos. 1723, 1728, **MS**1729b, 75th anniv of Royal Air Force; Nos. 1725/6, **MS**1729c, Bicentenary of First Airmail Flight.

(Des Rosemary DeFiglio. Litho Questa)

1993 (8 Sept). *World Cup Football Championship, U.S.A.* (1994) (1*st issue*). *T* **267** *and similar vert designs. Multicoloured. P* 14.

1730 25 c. Type **267** 30 15
1731 55 c. Ruud Gullit (Netherlands) 50 40
1732 65 c. Chavarria (Costa Rica) and Bliss (U.S.A.) 55 45
1733 90 c. Diego Maradona (Argentina) .. 70 60
1734 90 c. Leonel Alvares (Colombia) 70 60
1735 $1 Altobelli (Italy) and Yong-hwang (South Korea) 75 70
1736 $2 Stopyra (France) .. .. .. 1·25 1·50
1737 $5 Renquin (Belgium) and Yaremtchuk (Russia) .. .. 2·25 3·00
1730/7 .. .. *Set of* 8 6·25 6·75
MS1738 Two sheets. (a) 73×103 mm. $6 Nestor Fabbri (Argentina). (b) 103×73 mm. $6 Andreas Brehme (Germany) .. .. *Set of* 2 *sheets* 5·50 6·50

See also Nos. 1849/56.

268 Ornate Chedi, Wat Phra Boromathat Chaiya

(Des Kerri Schiff. Litho Questa)

1993 (4 Oct). *Asian International Stamp Exhibitons. T* **268** *and similar vert designs. Multicoloured. P* 13½×14.

(*a*) *"Indopex '93", Surabaya, Indonesia*

1739 25 c. Type **268** 40 15
1740 55 c. Temple ruins, Sukhothai 65 45
1741 90 c. Prasat Hin Phimai, Thailand 80 65
1742 $1.65, Arjuna and Prabu Gilling Wesi puppets .. .. 1·00 1·10
a. Sheetlet. Nos. 1742/7 .. .. 5·50
1743 $1.65, Loro Blonyo puppet .. .. 1·00 1·10
1744 $1.65, Yogyanese puppets .. .. 1·00 1·10
1745 $1.65, Wayang gedog puppet, Ng Setro 1·00 1·10
1746 $1.65, Wayang golek puppet .. .. 1·00 1·10
1747 $1.65, Wayang gedog puppet, Raden Damar Wulan .. .. .. 1·00 1·10
1748 $5 Main sanctuary, Prasat Phanom Rung, Thailand .. .. .. 3·25 3·50
1739/48 .. .. *Set of* 10 10·00 10·00
MS1749 105×136 mm. $6 Sculpture of Majaphit noble, Pura Sada .. .. 3·50 4·00

(*b*) *"Taipei '93", Taiwan*

1750 25 c. Aw Boon Haw Gardens, Causeway Bay 40 15
1751 65 c. Observation building, Kenting Park 65 45
1752 90 c. Tzu-en pagoda on lakeshore, Taiwan 80 65
1753 $1.65, Chang E kite .. .. .. 1·00 1·10
a. Sheetlet. Nos. 1753/8 .. .. 5·50
1754 $1.65, Red Phoenix and Rising Sun kite 1·00 1·10
1755 $1.65, Heavenly Judge kite .. .. 1·00 1·10
1756 $1.65, Monkey King kite .. .. 1·00 1·10
1757 $1.65, Goddess of Luo River kite .. 1·00 1·10
1758 $1.65, Heavenly Maiden kite .. .. 1·00 1·10
1759 $5 Villa, Lantau Island .. .. 3·25 3·50
1750/9 .. .. *Set of* 10 10·00 10·00
MS1760 105×136 mm. $6 Jade sculpture of girl, Liao Dynasty .. .. 3·50 4·00

(*c*) *"Bangkok '93", Thailand*

1761 25 c. Tugu Monument, Java 40 15
1762 55 c. Candi Cangkuang mon, West Java 65 45
1763 90 c. Merus, Pura Taman Ayun, Mengwi 80 65
1764 $1.65, Hun Lek puppets of Rama and Sita .. .. 1·00 1·10
a. Sheetlet. Nos. 1764/9 .. .. 5·50
1765 $1.65, Burmese puppet .. .. 1·00 1·10
1766 $1.65, Burmese puppets .. .. 1·00 1·10
1767 $1.65, Demon puppet at Wat Phra Kaew 1·00 1·10
1768 $1.65, Hun Lek puppet performing Khun Chang .. .. 1·00 1·10
1769 $1.65, Hun Lek puppets performing Ramakien .. .. 1·00 1·10
1770 $5 Stone mosaic, Ceto .. .. 3·25 3·50
1761/70 .. .. *Set of* 10 10·00 10·00
MS1771 105×136 mm. $6 Thai Stone carving 3·50 4·00

Nos. 1742/7, 1753/8 and 1764/9 were each printed together, *se-tenant*, in sheetlets of 6.

No. 1753 is inscribed "Chang E Rising Up th the Moon" in error.

269 Willie

(Des Rosemary DeFiglio. Litho Questa)

1993 (1 Nov). Willie the Operatic Whale. *T* **269** *and similar multicoloured designs showing scenes from Walt Disney's cartoon film. P* 14×13½.

1772 $1 Type **269** 75 80
a. Sheetlet. Nos. 1772/80 .. .. 6·00
1773 $1 Willie's pelican friend 75 80
1774 $1 Willie singing to seals 75 80
1775 $1 Willie singing *Lucia* 75 80
1776 $1 Willie in *Pagliacci* 75 80
1777 $1 Willie as Mephistopheles 75 80
1778 $1 Tetti Tatti searching for Willie .. 75 80
1779 $1 Whalers listening to Willie 75 80
1780 $1 Tetti Tatti with harpoon gun 75 80
1772/80 .. .. *Set of* 9 6·00 6·50
MS1781 Two sheets. (a) 130×102 mm. $6 Seals listening to Willie. P 14×13½. (b) 97×118 mm. $6 Willie in Heaven (*vert*). P 13½×14. *Set of* 2 *sheets* 6·50 7·00

Nos. 1772/80 were printed together, *se-tenant*, in sheetlets of 9.

270 "Adoration of the Magi" (detail) (Dürer)

(Litho Cartor)

1993 (8 Nov). *Christmas. Religious Paintings. T* **270** *and similar designs. Black, pale lemon and red* (*Nos.* 1782/5, **MS**1790a) *or multicoloured* (*others*). *P* 13.

1782 25 c. Type **270** 35 10
1783 55 c. "Adoration of the Magi" (different detail) (Dürer) 55 30
1784 65 c. "Adoration of the Magi" (different detail) (Dürer) 65 35
1785 90 c. "Adoration of the Magi" (different detail) (Dürer) 80 50
1786 90 c. "Madonna of Foligno" (detail) (Raphael) 80 50
1787 $1 "Madonna of Foligno" (different detail) (Raphael) 90 60
1788 $3 "Madonna of Foligno" (different detail) (Raphael) .. .. .. 2·00 2·75
1789 $5 "Madonna of Foligno" (different detail) (Raphael) .. .. .. 2·75 3·75
1782/9 .. .. *Set of* 8 8·00 8·00
MS1790 Two sheets, each 105×130 mm. (a) $6 "Adoration of the Magi" (different detail) (Dürer) (*horiz*). (b) $6 "Madonna of Foligno" (different detail) (Raphael) .. .. *Set of* 2 *sheets* 7·00 8·00

(Des W. Hanson. Litho Questa)

1994 (18 Feb). *"Hong Kong '94" International Stam Exhibition* (1*st issue*). *Horiz designs as T* **317** *of Antiguc Multicoloured. P* 14.

1791 65 c. Hong Kong 1988 Peak Tramway 50 c. stamp and skyscrapers 50 6
a. Horiz pair. Nos. 1791/2 .. .. 1·00 1·2
1792 65 c. Dominica 1991 Cog Railways $5 stamp and Hong Kong Peak tram .. 50 6

Nos. 1791/2 were printed together, *se-tenant*, in horizonta pairs throughout the sheet with the centre part of each pai forming the composite design.

(Des Kerri Schiff. Litho Questa)

1994 (18 Feb). *"Hong Kong '94" International Stam Exhibition* (2*nd issue*). *Tang Dynasty Jade. Multicolourec designs as T* **318** *of Antigua, but vert. P* 14.

1793 65 c. Horse .. .. 40 5(
a. Sheetlet. Nos. 1793/8 .. .. 2·25
1794 65 c. Cup with handle .. .. .. 40 5(
1795 65 c. Vase with birthday peaches .. 40 5(
1796 65 c. Vase .. .. 40 5(
1797 65 c. Fu Dog with puppy .. .. .. 40 5(
1798 65 c. Drinking cup .. .. .. 40 5(
1793/8 .. .. *Set of* 6 2·25 2·75

Nos. 1793/8 were printed together, *se-tenant*, in sheetlets of 6.

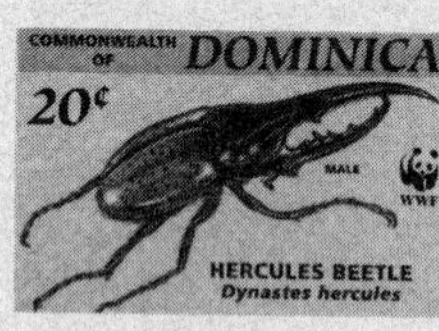

271 Male *Dynastes hercules* (beetle)

272 *Laelio-cattleya*

(Litho Questa)

1994 (15 Mar). *Endangered Species. Birds and Insects. T* **271** *and similar horiz designs. Multicoloured. P* 14.

1799 20 c. Type **271** 20 15
1800 25 c. Male *Dynastes hercules* (*different*) .. 20 15
1801 65 c. Male *Dynastes hercules* (*different*) .. 45 35
1802 90 c. Female *Dynastes hercules* 60 55
1803 $1 Imperial Amazon ("Imperial Parrot") 90 75
1804 $2 *Marpesia petreus* (butterfly) .. 1·50 2·00
1805 $3 *Hypolimnus misippus* (butterfly) .. 2·00 2·25
1806 $5 Purple-throated Carib .. .. 2·75 3·25
1799/1806 .. .. .. *Set of* 8 7·75 8·50
MS1807 Two sheets, each 98×70 mm. (a) $6 Blue-headed Hummingbird. (b) $6 *Libytheana fulvescens* (butterfly) .. .. *Set of* 2 *sheets* 7·50 8·50

Nos. 1803/7 do not carry the W.W.F Panda emblem.

Nos. 1799/1802 were also available in vertical *se-tenant* strips of 4 from sheetlets of 12.

(Des Mary Walters. Litho Questa)

1994 (4 Apr). *Orchids. T* **272** *and similar vert designs. Multicoloured. P* 14.

1808 20 c. Type **272** 35 15
1809 25 c. *Sophrolaelio cattleya* 35 15
1810 65 c. *Odontocidium* 70 45
1811 90 c. *Laelio-cattleya* (*different*) 90 75
1812 $1 *Cattleya* .. .. 1·00 75
1813 $2 *Odontocidium* (*different*) .. .. 1·50 2·00
1814 $3 *Epiphronitis* .. .. .. 2·00 2·50
1815 $4 *Oncidium* .. .. 2·00 2·50
1808/15 .. .. *Set of* 8 8·00 8·50
MS1816 Two sheets, each 100×70 mm. (a) $6 *Cattleya* (*different*). (b) $6 *Schombo cattleya* *Set of* 2 *sheets* 7·50 8·00

273 *Russula matoubenis*

274 *Appias drusilla*

(Litho Questa)

1994 (18 Apr). *Fungi. T* **273** *and similar vert designs. Multicoloured. P* 14.

1817 20 c. Type **273** 35 15
1818 25 c. *Leptonia caeruleocapitata* 35 15
1819 65 c. *Inocybe littoralis* 70 45
1820 90 c. *Russula hygrophytica* 90 75
1821 $1 *Pyrrhoglossum lilaceipes* .. .. 1·00 75
1822 $2 *Hygrocybe konradii* .. .. .. 1·40 1·90
1823 $3 *Inopilus magnificus* .. .. .. 1·75 2·25
1824 $5 *Boletellus cubensis* .. .. .. 2·50 3·00
1817/24 .. .. *Set of* 8 8·00 8·50
MS1825 Two sheets, each 110×85 mm. (a) $6 *Lentinus strigosus*. (b) $6 *Gerronema citrinum* *Set of* 2 *sheets* 7·50 8·00

(Litho Questa)

994 (3 May). *Butterflies. T* **274** *and similar horiz designs. Multicoloured. P* 14.
826 20 c. Type **274** 35 15
827 25 c. *Didonis biblis* . . 35 15
828 55 c. *Eurema daira* . . 70 45
829 65 c. *Hypolimnas misippus* . . 75 45
830 $1 *Phoebis agarithe* . . 1·00 75
831 $2 *Marpesia petreus* . . 1·50 1·90
832 $3 *Libytheana fulvescens* . . 1·75 2·50
833 $5 *Precis evarete* . . 2·50 3·00
826/33 . . *Set of* 8 8·00 8·50
MS1834 Two sheets, each 100×70 mm. (a) $6 *Chlorostrymon maesites*. (b) $6 *Vanessa cardui* *Set of 2 sheets* 7·50 8·00

275 Dachshund

ROYAL VISIT
FEBRUARY 19, 1994

(276)

(Litho Questa)

1994 (17 May). *Chinese New Year ("Year of the Dog"). T* **275** *and similar vert designs. Multicoloured. P* 14.
1835 20 c. Type **275** . . 35 15
1836 25 c. Beagle . . 35 15
1837 55 c. Greyhound . . 65 45
1838 90 c. Jack Russell Terrier . . 90 75
1839 $1 Pekingese . . 1·00 75
1840 $2 Wire Fox Terrier . . 1·50 1·75
1841 $4 English Toy Spaniel . . 2·25 2·50
1842 $5 Irish Setter . . 2·25 2·50
1835/42 . . *Set of* 8 8·25 8·00
MS1843 Two sheets, each 102×72 mm. (a) $6 Welsh Corgi. (b) $6 Labrador Retriever *Set of 2 sheets* 7·50 8·50

1994 (27 June). *Royal Visit. Nos.* 1700/4 *optd as T* **276** *(in three lines on No.* 1845 *and in silver on the sheet margin only of No.* **MS**1848).
1844 20 c. multicoloured . . 50 55
a. Sheetlet. Nos. 1844/7×2 . . 7·50
1845 25 c. reddish brown and black . . 50 55
1846 65 c. multicoloured . . 80 90
1847 $5 multicoloured . . 2·50 2·75
1844/7 . . *Set of* 4 3·75 4·25
MS1848 71×101 mm. $6 multicoloured . . 3·75 4·25

277 Des Armstrong (U.S.A.)

(Litho Questa)

1994 (5 July–28 Dec). *World Cup Football Championship, U.S.A. (2nd issue). T* **277** *and similar horiz designs. Multicoloured. P* 14.
1849 25 c. Jefferey Edmund (Dominica) (28 Dec) 10 10
1850 $1 Type **277** . . 45 50
a. Sheetlet. Nos. 1850/5 . . 2·50
1851 $1 Dennis Bergkamp (Netherlands) . . 45 50
1852 $1 Roberto Baggio (Italy) . . 45 50
1853 $1 Rai (Brazil) . . 45 50
1854 $1 Cafu (Brazil) . . 45 50
1855 $1 Marco van Basten (Netherlands) . . 45 50
1849/55 . . *Set of* 7 2·75 3·00
MS1856 Two sheets. (a) 70×100 mm. $6 Roberto Mancini (Italy). (b) 100×70 mm. $6 Player and Stanford Stadium, San Francisco *Set of 2 sheets* 7·50 8·00
Nos. 1850/5 were printed together, *se-tenant*, in sheetlets of 6.

(Litho Questa)

1994 (18 July). *10th Caribbean Scout Jamboree. T* **278** *and similar multicoloured designs. P* 14.
1857 20 c. Type **278** . . 35 15
1858 25 c. Cooking over campfire . . 35 15
1859 55 c. Erecting tent . . 60 30
1860 65 c. Serving soup . . 70 45
1861 $1 Corps of drums . . 1·00 75
1862 $2 Planting tree . . 1·50 2·00
1863 $4 Sailing dinghy . . 2·25 2·50
1864 $5 Saluting . . 2·25 2·50
1857/64 . . *Set of* 8 8·00 8·00
MS1865 Two sheets, each 100×70 mm. (a) $6 Early scout troop. (b) $6 Pres. Crispin Sorhaindo (chief scout) (*vert*) . . *Set of 2 sheets* 7·50 8·00

(Des W. Hanson. Litho B.D.T.)

1994 (26 July). *25th Anniv of First Moon Landing. Horiz designs as T* **326** *of Antigua. Multicoloured. P* 14.
1866 $1 Crew of "Apollo 14" . . 70 80
a. Sheetlet. Nos. 1866/71 . . 3·75
1867 $1 "Apollo 14" mission logo . . 70 80
1868 $1 Lunar module *Antares* on Moon . . 70 80
1869 $1 Crew of "Apollo 15" . . 70 80
1870 $1 "Apollo 15" mission logo . . 70 80
1871 $1 Lunar crater on Mt Hadley . . 70 80
1866/71 . . *Set of* 6 3·75 4·25
MS1872 99×106 mm. $6 "Apollo 11" logo and surface of Moon . . 4·00 4·50
Nos. 1866/71 were printed together, *se-tenant*, in sheetlets of 6.

(Des Kerri Schiff. Litho B.D.T.)

1994 (26 July). *Centenary of International Olympic Committee. Gold Medal Winners. Horiz designs as T* **327** *of Antigua. Multicoloured. P* 14.
1873 55 c. Urike Meyfarth (Germany) (high jump), 1984 . . 35 30
1874 $1.45, Dieter Baumann (Germany) (5000 metres), 1992 . . 90 1·25
MS1875 106×76 mm. $6 Ji Hoon Chae (South Korea) (500 metres speed skating), 1994 . . 3·25 3·75

(Des A. Melville-Brown. Litho B.D.T.)

1994 (26 July). *Centenary of First English Cricket Tour to the West Indies (1995). Multicoloured designs as T* **329** *of Antigua. P* 14.
1876 55 c. David Gower (England) (*vert*) . . 40 30
1877 90 c. Curtly Ambrose (West Indies) and Wisden Trophy . . 60 60
1878 $1 Graham Gooch (England) (*vert*) . . 70 80
1876/8 . . *Set of* 3 1·50 1·50
MS1879 76×96 mm. $3 First English touring team, 1895 . . 1·90 2·00

(Des J. Batchelor. Litho B.D.T.)

1994 (26 July). *50th Anniv of D-Day. Horiz designs as T* **331** *of Antigua. Multicoloured. P* 14.
1880 65 c. American Waco gliders . . 50 35
1881 $2 British Horsa glider . . 1·40 1·60
1882 $3 British glider and troops attacking Pegasus Bridge . . 1·75 2·00
1880/2 . . *Set of* 3 3·25 3·50
MS1883 107×77 mm. $6 British Hadrian glider 3·50 4·00

(Des Kerri Schiff. Litho Questa (Nos. 1884/93), B.D.T. (Nos. 1894/7))

1994 (26 July). *"Philakorea '94" International Stamp Exhibition, Seoul. T* **279** *and similar multicoloured designs. P* 13 *(Nos.* 1884/93) *or* 14 *(others).*
1884 55 c. Type **279** . . 40 50
a. Sheetlet. Nos. 1884/93 . . 3·50
1885 55 c. Bird with yellow, pink and red flowers 40 50
1886 55 c. Pair of birds and yellow flowers . . 40 50
1887 55 c. Chickens and flowers . . 40 50
1888 55 c. Pair of birds and pink flowers . . 40 50
1889 55 c. Ducks and flowers . . 40 50
1890 55 c. Blue bird and red flowers . . 40 50
1891 55 c. Pheasant and flowers . . 40 50
1892 55 c. Stork and flowers . . 40 50
1893 55 c. Deer and flowers . . 40 50
1894 65 c. P'alsang-jon Hall (38×24 *mm*) . . 50 55
1895 90 c. Popchu-sa Temple (38×24 *mm*) . . 65 65
1896 $2 Uhwajong Pavilion (38×24 *mm*) . . 1·25 1·50
1884/96 . . *Set of* 13 5·50 7·00
MS1897 100×70 mm. $4 Spirit Post Guardian (38×24 *mm*). P 14 . . 2·50 3·00
Nos. 1884/93 were printed together, *se-tenant*, in sheetlets of 10 and show screen paintings.

(Des Alvin White Studio. Litho Questa)

1994 (3 Oct). *65th Anniv of Mickey Mouse (1993). T* **280** *and similar multicoloured designs showing Walt Disney cartoon characters. P* 13½×14.
1898 20 c. Type **280** . . 35 15
1899 25 c. Clarabelle Cow . . 35 15
1900 55 c. Horace Horsecollar . . 60 35
1901 65 c. Mortimer Mouse . . 70 45
1902 $1 Joe Piper . . 1·00 75
1903 $3 Mr. Casey . . 2·00 2·25
1904 $4 Chief O'Hara . . 2·25 2·50
1905 $5 Mickey and The Blot . . 2·25 2·50
1898/1905 . . *Set of* 8 8·50 8·25
MS1906 Two sheets, each 127×102 mm. (a) $6 Minnie Mouse with Tanglefoot. P 13½×14. (b) $6 Minnie and Pluto (*horiz*). P 14×13½ *Set of 2 sheets* 7·50 8·00

(Des R. Rundo. Litho B.D.T.)

1994 (1 Dec). *Entertainers. T* **281** *and similar vert designs. Multicoloured. P* 14.
1907 20 c. Sonia Lloyd (folk singer) . . 20 20
1908 25 c. Ophelia Marie (singer) . . 20 20
1909 55 c. Edney Francis (accordion player) . . 50 40
1910 65 c. Norman Letang (saxophonist) . . 60 45
1911 90 c. Edie André (steel-band player) . . 70 70
1912 90 c. Type **281** . . 70 80
a. Sheetlet. Nos. 1912/20 . . 5·50
1913 90 c. Marilyn Monroe wearing necklace . . 70 80
1914 90 c. In yellow frilled dress . . 70 80
1915 90 c. In purple dress . . 70 80
1916 90 c. Looking over left shoulder . . 70 80
1917 90 c. Laughing . . 70 80
1918 90 c. In red dress . . 70 80
1919 90 c. Wearing gold cluster earrings . . 70 80
1920 90 c. In yellow dress . . 70 80
1907/20 . . *Set of* 14 7·50 8·00
MS1921 Two sheets, each 106×76 mm. (a) $6 Marilyn Monroe with top hat. (b) $6 With arms above head . . *Set of 2 sheets* 7·50 7·50
Nos. 1912/20 were printed together, *se-tenant*, in sheetlets of 9.
No. 1907 is inscribed "Llyod" in error.

(Litho Questa)

1994 (2 Dec). *Christmas. Religious Paintings. Vert designs as T* **336** *of Antigua. Multicoloured. P* 13½×14.
1922 20 c. "Madonna and Child" (Luis de Morales) . . 25 10
1923 25 c. "Madonna and Child with Yarn Winder" (De Morales) . . 25 10
1924 55 c. "Our Lady of the Rosary" (detail) (Zurbaran) . . 40 30
1925 65 c. "Dream of the Patrician" (detail) (Murillo) . . 50 35
1926 90 c. "Madonna of Charity" (El Greco) . . 70 45
1927 $1 "The Annunciation" (Zurbaran) . . 75 50
1928 $2 "Mystical Marriage of St. Catherine" (Jusepe de Ribera) . . 1·25 1·75
1929 $3 "The Holy Family with St. Bruno and Other Saints" (detail) (De Ribera) . . 1·50 2·00
1922/9 . . *Set of* 8 5·00 5·00
MS1930 Two sheets. (a) 136×97 mm. $6 "Adoration of the Shepherds" (detail) (Murillo). (b) 99×118 mm. $6 "Vision of the Virgin to St. Bernard" (detail) (Murillo) . . *Set of 2 sheets* 7·50 8·50

(Litho Questa)

1994 (16 Dec). *First Recipients of Order of the Caribbean Community. Horiz designs as Nos.* 2046/8 *of Antigua. Multicoloured. P* 14.
1931 25 c. Sir Shridath Ramphal . . 20 10
1932 65 c. William Demas . . 50 50
1933 90 c. Derek Walcott . . 70 80
1931/3 . . *Set of* 3 1·25 1·25

18th World Scout Jamboree
Mondial, Holland, May 6, 1995

(282)

283 Wood Duck

1995 (21 Mar). *18th World Scout Jamboree, Netherlands. Nos.* 1860, *and* 1863/5 *optd with T* **282** *(sideways, reading upwards on No.* **MS**1937b).
1934 65 c. Serving soup . . 30 35
1935 $4 Sailing dinghy . . 1·75 1·90
1936 $5 Saluting . . 2·10 2·25
1934/6 . . *Set of* 3 4·00 4·25
MS1937 Two sheets, each 100×70 mm. (a) $6 Early scout troop. (b) $6 Pres. Crispin Sorhaindo (chief scout) (*vert*) . . *Set of 2 sheets* 5·25 5·50

(Des R. Rundo. Litho Questa)

1995 (15 Apr). *Water Birds. T* **283** *and similar multicoloured designs. P* 14.
1938 25 c. Type **283** . . 10 10
1939 55 c. Mallard . . 25 30
1940 65 c. Blue-winged Teal . . 30 35
1941 65 c. Cattle Egret (*vert*) . . 30 35
a. Sheetlet. Nos. 1941/52 . . 3·50
1942 65 c. Snow Goose (*vert*) . . 30 35
1943 65 c. Peregrine Falcon (*vert*) . . 30 35
1944 65 c. Barn Owl (*vert*) . . 30 35
1945 65 c. Black-crowned Night Heron (*vert*) . . 30 35
1946 65 c. Common Grackle (*vert*) . . 30 35
1947 65 c. Brown Pelican (*vert*) . . 30 35

278 Scout Backpacking

279 Pink Bird and Red Flowers Screen Painting

280 Dippy Dawg

281 Marilyn Monroe

1948 65 c. Great Egret (*vert*) 30 35
1949 65 c. Ruby-throated Hummingbird (*vert*) 30 35
1950 65 c. Laughing Gull (*vert*) 30 35
1951 65 c. Greater Flamingo (*vert*) 30 35
1952 65 c. Moorhen (*vert*) 30 35
1953 $5 Red-eared Conure ("Blood Eared Parakeet") .. .. 2·10 2·25
1938/53 .. .. *Set of* 16 6·25 7·00
MS1954 Two sheets, each 105×75 mm. (a) $5 Trumpeter Swan (*vert*). (b) $6 White-eyed Vireo *Set of* 2 *sheets* 4·75 5·00

Nos. 1941/52 were printed together, *se-tenant*, in sheetlets of 12 with the background forming a composite design.

No. 1946 is inscribed "Common Gralkle" in error.

284 Pig's Head facing Right

285 Paul Harris (founder) and Emblem

(Des Y. Lee. Litho Questa)

1995 (21 Apr). *Chinese New Year ("Year of the Pig"). T* **284** *and similar multicoloured designs. P* 14½.
1955 25 c. Type **284** 10 10
a. Horiz strip of 3. Nos. 1955/7 .. 85
1956 65 c. Pig facing to the front 30 35
1957 $1 Pig facing left 45 50
1955/7 .. .. *Set of* 3 85 95
MS1958 101×50 mm. Nos. 1955/7 .. .. 85 90
MS1959 105×77 mm. $2 Two pigs (*horiz*) .. 85 90

Nos. 1955/7 were printed together, *se-tenant*, in horizontal strips of 3 throughout the sheet.

(Litho Questa)

1995 (18 May). *50th Anniv of End of Second World War in Europe. Horiz designs as T* **340** *of Antigua. Multicoloured. P* 14.
1960 $2 German Panther tank in the Ardennes 85 90
a. Sheetlet. Nos. 1960/7 .. .. .. 6·75
1961 $2 American fighter-bomber 85 90
1962 $2 American mechanized column crossing the Rhine 85 90
1963 $2 Messerschmitt Me 163B Komet and Allied bombers 85 90
1964 $2 V2 rocket on launcher 85 90
1965 $2 German U-boat surrendering .. 85 90
1966 $2 Heavy artillery in action 85 90
1967 $2 Soviet infantry in Berlin 85 90
1960/7 .. .. *Set of* 8 6·75 7·00
MS1968 106×76 mm. $6 Statue and devastated Dresden (56½×42½ *mm*) .. .. .. 2·50 2·75

Nos. 1960/7 were printed together, *se-tenant*, in sheetlets of 8 with the stamps arranged in two horizontal strips of 4 separated by a gutter showing liberation of Dachau.

(Litho Questa)

1995 (21 July). *90th Anniv of Rotary International. T* **285** *and similar horiz design. P* 14.
1969 $1 lake-brown, reddish purple and black 45 50
MS1970 70×100 mm. $6 vermilion and black .. 2·50 2·75

Design:—$6 Rotary emblems.

(Des J. Batchelor. Litho Questa)

1995 (21 July). *50th Anniv of End of Second World War in the Pacific. Horiz designs as T* **340** *of Antigua. Multicoloured. P* 14.
1971 $2 Mitsubishi A6M Zero-Sen torpedo-bomber 85 90
a. Sheetlet. Nos. 1971/6 .. .. .. 5·00
1972 $2 Aichi D3A "Val" dive bomber .. 85 90
1973 $2 Nakajima B5N "Kate" bomber .. 85 90
1974 $2 *Zuikaku* (Japanese aircraft carrier) .. 85 90
1975 $2 *Akagi* (Japanese aircraft carrier) .. 85 90
1976 $2 *Ryuho* (Japanese aircraft carrier) .. 85 90
1971/6 .. .. *Set of* 6 5·00 5·25
MS1977 108×76 mm. $6 Japanese torpedo-bomber at Pearl Harbor .. .. .. 2·50 2·75

Nos. 1971/6 were printed together, *se-tenant*, in sheetlets of 6 with the stamps arranged in two horizontal strips of 3 separated by a gutter showing U.S. dive-bombers attacking Japanese aircraft carrier *Soryu*.

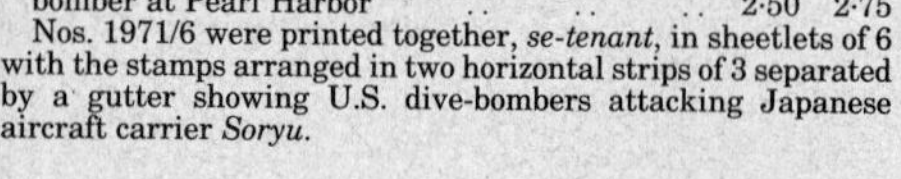

286 Boxing

287 Market Customers

(Des A. De Lorenzo. Litho Questa)

1995 (21 July). *Olympic Games, Atlanta (1st issue) (1996). T* **286** *and similar multicoloured designs. P* 14.
1978 15 c. Type **286** 10 10
1979 20 c. Wrestling 10 10
1980 25 c. Judo 10 10
1981 55 c. Fencing 25 30
1982 65 c. Swimming 30 35
1983 $1 Gymnastics (*vert*) 45 50
1984 $2 Cycling (*vert*) 85 90
1985 $5 Volleyball .. .. 2·10 2·25
1978/85 .. .. *Set of* 8 4·50 4·75
MS1986 Two sheets, each 104×74 mm. (a) $6 Show jumping. (b) $6 Football (*vert*) *Set of* 2 *sheets* 5·25 5·50

See also Nos. 2122/46 and 2213/14

(Des L. Fried. Litho Questa)

1995 (16 Aug). *50th Anniv of United Nations. Vert designs as T* **341** *of Antigua. Multicoloured. P* 14.
1987 65 c. Signatures and U.S. delegate .. 30 35
a. Horiz strip of 3. Nos. 1987/9 .. 1·60
1988 $1 U.S. delegate 45 50
1989 $2 Governor Stassen (U.S. delegate) .. 85 90
1987/9 .. .. *Set of* 3 1·60 1·75
MS1990 100×71 mm. $6 Winston Churchill .. 2·50 2·75

Nos. 1987/9 were printed together in sheets of 9 (3×3) containing three *se-tenant* horizontal strips, each forming a composite design.

(Des L. Fried. Litho Questa)

1995 (16 Aug). *50th Anniv of Food and Agriculture Organization. T* **287** *and similar multicoloured designs. P* 14.
MS1991 110×74 mm. 90 c., $1, $2 Panorama of Dominican market .. .. 1·60 1·75
MS1992 101×71 mm. $6 Women irrigating crops (*horiz*) .. .. 2·50 2·75

(Litho Questa)

1995 (16 Aug). *95th Birthday of Queen Elizabeth the Queen Mother. Vert designs as T* **344** *of Antigua. P* 13½×14.
1993 $1.65, orange-brown, pale brown and black 70 75
a. Sheetlet. Nos. 1993/6, each × 2 .. 5·50
1994 $1.65, multicoloured 70 75
1995 $1.65, multicoloured 70 75
1996 $1.65, multicoloured 70 75
1993/6 .. .. *Set of* 4 2·75 3·00
MS1997 103×126 mm. $6 multicoloured .. 2·50 2·75

Designs:—No. 1993, Queen Elizabeth the Queen Mother (pastel drawing); No. 1994, Holding bouquet of flowers; No. 1995, At desk (oil painting); No. 1996, Wearing blue dress; No. **MS**1997, Wearing ruby and diamond tiara and necklace.

Nos. 1993/6 were printed together in sheetlets of 8, containing two *se-tenant* horizontal strips of 4.

288 Monoclonius

289 Oscar Sánchez (1987 Peace)

(Des B. Regal. Litho Questa)

1995 (8 Sept). *"Singapore '95" International Stamp Exhibition. Prehistoric Animals. T* **288** *and similar multicoloured designs. P* 14.
1998 20 c. Type **288** 10 10
1999 25 c. Euoplocephalus 10 10
2000 55 c. Head of Coelophysis 25 30
2001 65 c. Head of Compsognathus 30 35
2002 90 c. Dimorphodon 40 45
a. Horiz strip of 4. Nos. 2002/5 .. 1·60
2003 90 c. Ramphorynchus 40 45
2004 90 c. Head of Giant Alligator 40 45
2005 90 c. Pentaceratops 40 45
2006 $1 Ceratosaurus (*vert*) 45 50
a. Sheetlet. Nos. 2006/17 .. .. 5·50
2007 $1 Comptosaurus (*vert*) 45 50
2008 $1 Stegosaur (*vert*) 45 50
2009 $1 Camarasaurs (*vert*) 45 50
2010 $1 Baronyx (*vert*) 45 50
2011 $1 Dilophosaurus (*vert*) 45 50
2012 $1 Dromaeosaurids (*vert*) 45 50
2013 $1 Deinonychus (*vert*) 45 50
2014 $1 Dinicthys (Terror Fish) (*vert*) .. 45 50
2015 $1 Head of Carcharodon (Giant-toothed Shark) (*vert*) 45 50
2016 $1 Nautiloid (*vert*) 45 50
2017 $1 Trilobite (*vert*) 45 50
1998/2017 .. .. .. *Set of* 20 7·75 8·50
MS2018 Two sheets. (a) 95×65 mm. $5 Sauropelta. (b) 65×95 mm. $6 Triceratops (*vert*) *Set of* 2 *sheets* 4·75 5·00

Nos. 2002/5 and 2006/17 were printed together, *se-tenant*, in horizontal strips of 4 (Nos. 2002/5) or sheetlets of 12 (Nos. 2006/17), each forming composite designs.

Nos. 2002/5 do not carry the "Singapore '95" exhibition logo.

(Des R. Rundo. Litho Questa)

1995 (27 Oct). *Centenary of Nobel Prize Trust Fund. T* **289** *an similar vert designs. Multicoloured. P* 14.
2019 $2 Type **289** 85 9
a. Sheetlet. Nos. 2019/24 .. .. 5·00
2020 $2 Ernst Chain (1945 Medicine) .. 85 9
2021 $2 Aage Bohr (1975 Physics) 85 9
2022 $2 Jaroslav Seifert (1984 Literature) .. 85 9
2023 $2 Joseph Murray (1990 Medicine) .. 85 9
2024 $2 Jaroslav Heyrovsky (1959 Chemistry) 85 9
2025 $2 Adolf von Baeyer (1905 Chemistry) .. 85 9
a. Sheetlet. Nos. 2025/30 .. .. 5·00
2026 $2 Eduard Buchner (1907 Chemistry) .. 85 9
2027 $2 Carl Bosch (1931 Chemistry) .. 85 9
2028 $2 Otto Hahn (1944 Chemistry) 85 9
2029 $2 Otto Diels (1950 Chemistry) 85 9
2030 $2 Kurt Alder (1950 Chemistry) .. 85 9
2019/30 .. .. *Set of* 12 10·00 10·5
MS2031 76×106 mm. $2 Emil von Behring (1901 Medicine) 85 9

Nos. 2019/24 and 2025/30 were printed together, *se-tenant*, i sheetlets of 6 with the backgrounds forming designs of the Nobe Medal.

(Litho Questa)

1995 (30 Nov). *Christmas. Religious Paintings. Vert design as T* **357** *of Antigua. Multicoloured. P* 13½×14.
2032 20 c. "Madonna and Child with St. John" (Pontormo) 10 1
2033 25 c. "The Immaculate Conception" (Murillo) 10 1
2034 55 c. "The Adoration of the Magi" (Filippino Lippi) 25 3
2035 65 c. "Rest on the Flight into Egypt" (Van Dyck) 30 3
2036 90 c. "The Holy Family" (Van Dyck) .. 40 4
2037 $5 "The Annunciation" (Van Eyck) .. 2·10 2·2
2032/7 .. .. *Set of* 6 3·25 3·7
MS2038 Two sheets, each 102×127 mm. (a) $5 "Madonna and Child Reading" (detail) (Van Eyck). (b) $6 "The Holy Family" (detail) (Ribera) *Set of* 2 *sheets* 5·25 5·5

(Litho Questa)

1995 (10 Dec). *Centenary of Sierra Club (environmenta protection society) (1992). Endangered Species. Multicoloure designs as T* **320** *of Antigua. P* 14.
2039 $1 Florida Panther 45 5
a. Sheetlet. Nos. 2039/47 .. .. 4·00
2040 $1 Manatee 45 5
2041 $1 Sockeye Salmon 45 5
2042 $1 Key Deer facing left 45 5
2043 $1 Key Deer doe 45 5
2044 $1 Key Deer stag 45 5
2045 $1 Wallaby with young in pouch .. 45 5
2046 $1 Wallaby feeding young 45 5
2047 $1 Wallaby and young feeding 45 5
2048 $1 Florida Panther showing teeth (*horiz*) 45 5
a. Sheetlet. Nos. 2048/56 .. .. 4·00
2049 $1 Head of Florida Panther (*horiz*) .. 45 5
2050 $1 Manatee (*horiz*) 45 5
2051 $1 Pair of Manatees (*horiz*) 45 5
2052 $1 Pair of Sockeye Salmon (*horiz*) .. 45 5
2053 $1 Sockeye Salmon spawning (*horiz*) .. 45 5
2054 $1 Pair of Southern Sea Otters (*horiz*) .. 45 5
2055 $1 Southern Sea Otter with front paws together (*horiz*) 45 5
2056 $1 Southern Sea Otter with front paws apart (*horiz*) 45 5
2039/56 .. .. *Set of* 18 8·00 9·0

Nos. 2039/47 and 2048/56 were printed together, *se-tenant*, in sheetlets of 9.

290 Street Scene

1995 (27 Dec). *"A City of Cathay" (Chinese scroll painting) T* **290** *and similar multicoloured designs. Litho. P* 14½.
2057 90 c. Type **290** 40 4
a. Horiz strip of 5. Nos. 2057/61 .. 2·00
2058 90 c. Street scene and city wall 40 4
2059 90 c. City gate and bridge 40 4
2060 90 c. Landing stage and junk 40 4
2061 90 c. River bridge 40 4
2062 90 c. Moored junks 40 4
a. Horiz strip of 5. Nos. 2062/6 .. 2·00
2063 90 c. Two rafts on river 40 4
2064 90 c. Two junks on river 40 4
2065 90 c. Roadside tea house 40 4
2066 90 c. Wedding party on the road 40 4
2057/66 .. .. *Set of* 10 4·00 4·5
MS2067 Two sheets, each 106×77 mm. (a) $2 City street and sampan; $2 Footbridge. (b) $2 Stern of sampan (*vert*); $2 Bow of sampan (*vert*) *Set of* 2 *sheets* 3·75 4·0

Nos. 2057/61 (showing inscriptions in black) and Nos. 2062/6 (showing inscriptions in chestnut) were each issued in sheets of 20 containing four *se-tenant* strips of 5, with each horizontal row separated by imperforate gutters incorporating inscribed labels.

NEW INFORMATION

The editor is always interested to correspond with people who have new information that will improve or correct the Catalogue.

291 "Bindo Altoviti" (Raphael)

292 Rat

(Litho Questa)

1995 (27 Dec). *Paintings by Raphael. T* **291** *and similar vert designs. Multicoloured. P* 13½×14.

2068 $2 Type **291** 85 90
2069 $2 "Pope Leo with Nephews" 85 90
2070 $2 "Agony in the Garden" 85 90
2068/70 . . . . . . *Set of* 3 2·50 2·50
MS2071 110×80 mm. $6 "Pope Leo X with Cardinals Giulio de Medici and Luigi dei Rossi" (detail) . . . . 2·50 2·75

(Des Y. Lee. Litho Questa)

1996 (16 Jan). *Chinese New Year ("Year of the Rat"). T* **292** *and similar vert designs showing rats and Chinese symbols. Multicoloured. P* 14½.

2072 25 c. black, violet and chestnut 10 10
a. Horiz strip of 3. Nos. 2072/4 . . 85
2073 65 c. black, orange-vermilion & deep green 30 35
2074 $1 black, magenta and blue 45 50
2072/4 . . . . . . *Set of* 3 85 95
MS2075 100×50 mm. Nos. 2072/4 . . . . 85 90
MS2076 105×77 mm. $2 black, grey-green and reddish violet (two rats) 85 90

Nos. 2072/4 were printed together, *se-tenant*, in horizontal strips of 3 throughout sheets of 12.

293 Mickey and Minnie Mouse (Year of the Rat)

(Litho Questa)

1996 (16 Jan). *Chinese Lunar Calendar. T* **293** *and similar horiz designs showing Walt Disney cartoon characters. Multicoloured. P* 14×13½.

2077 55 c. Type **293** 25 30
a. Sheetlet. Nos. 2077/88 . . . . 3·00
2078 55 c. Casey Jones (Year of the Ox) . . 25 30
2079 55 c. Tigger, Pooh and Piglet (Year of the Tiger) 25 30
2080 55 c. White Rabbit (Year of the Rabbit) . . 25 30
2081 55 c. Dragon playing flute (Year of the Dragon) 25 30
2082 55 c. Snake looking in mirror (Year of the Snake) 25 30
2083 55 c. Horace Horsecollar and Clarabelle Cow (Year of the Horse) 25 30
2084 55 c. Black Lamb and blue birds (Year of the Ram) 25 30
2085 55 c. King Louis reading book (Year of the Monkey) 25 30
2086 55 c. Cock playing lute (Year of the Cock) 25 30
2087 55 c. Mickey and Pluto (Year of the Dog) 25 30
2088 55 c. Pig building bridge (Year of the Pig) 25 30
2077/88 . . . . . . *Set of* 12 3·00 3·50
MS2089 Two sheets. (a) 127×102 mm. $3 Basil the Great Mouse Detective (Year of the Rat). (b) 102×127 mm. $6 Emblems for 1996, 1997 and 2007 . . . . *Set of* 2 *sheets* 4·00 4·25

Nos. 2077/88 were printed together, *se-tenant*, in sheetlets of 12.

294 Steam Locomotive *Dragon*, Hawaii

(Des R. Sauber. Litho B.D.T.)

1996 (29 Jan). *Trains of the World. T* **294** *and similar horiz designs. Multicoloured. P* 14.

2090 $2 Type **294** 85 90
a. Sheetlet. Nos. 2090/8 . . . . 7·50
2091 $2 Class 685 steam locomotive *Regina*, Italy 85 90
2092 $2 Class 745 steam locomotive, Calazo to Padua line, Italy 85 90
2093 $2 Mogul steam locomotive, Philippines . . 85 90
2094 $2 Class 23 and 24 steam locomotives, Germany 85 90
2095 $2 Class BB-15000 electric locomotive *Stanislaus*, France 85 90
2096 $2 Class "Black Five" steam locomotive, Scotland 85 90
2097 $2 Diesel-electric locomotive, France . . 85 90
2098 $2 L.N.E.R. Class A4 steam locomotive, *Sir Nigel Gresley*, England 85 90
2099 $2 Class 9600 steam locomotive, Japan 85 90
a. Sheetlet. Nos. 2099/107 . . . . 7·50
2100 $2 "Peloponnese Express" train, Greece . . 85 90
2101 $2 Porter type steam locomotive, Hawaii 85 90
2102 $2 Steam locomotive *Holand*, Norway . . 85 90
2103 $2 Class 220 diesel-hydraulic locomotive, Germany 85 90
2104 $2 Steam locomotive, India 85 90
2105 $2 East African Railways Class 29 steam locomotive 85 90
2106 $2 Electric trains, Russia 85 90
2107 $2 Steam locomotive, Austria 85 90
2090/107 . . . . . . *Set of* 18 15·00 16·00
MS2108 Two sheets, each 103×73 mm. (a) $5 L.M.S. steam locomotive *Duchess of Hamilton*, England. (b) $6 Diesel locomotives, China *Set of* 2 *sheets* 4·75 5·00

Nos. 2090/8 and 2099/107 were each printed together, *se-tenant*, in sheetlets of 9 with enlarged illustrated top margins.

295 Horse-drawn Gig, 1965

(Des R. Sauber. Litho B.D.T.)

1996 (29 Jan). *Traditional Island Transport. T* **295** *and similar horiz designs. Multicoloured. P* 14.

2109 65 c. Type **295** 30 35
2110 90 c. Early automobile, 1910 . . . . 40 45
2111 $2 Lorry, 1950 . . . . 85 90
2112 $3 Bus, 1955 . . . . 1·25 1·40
2109/12 . . . . . . *Set of* 4 2·75 3·00

296 Giant Panda

1996 (15 May). *"CHINA '96" 9th Asian International Stamp Exhibition, Peking. Giant Pandas. T* **296** *and similar multicoloured designs. Litho. P* 13½×14.

2113 55 c. Type **296** 25 30
a. Sheetlet. Nos. 2113/16 × 2 . . . . 2·00
2114 55 c. Panda on rock 25 30
2115 55 c. Panda eating bamboo shoots . . 25 30
2116 55 c. Panda on all fours 25 30
2113/16 . . . . . . *Set of* 4 1·00 1·10
MS2117 Two sheets. (a) 90×125 mm. $2 Huangshan Mountain, China (50×75 *mm*). P 12. (b) 160×125 mm. $3 Panda sitting (50×37 *mm*). P 14×13½ . . . . *Set of* 2 *sheets* 2·10 2·25

Nos. 2113/16 were printed together, *se-tenant*, in sheetlets of 8 containing two of each design.

(Litho Questa)

1996 (16 May). *70th Birthday of Queen Elizabeth II. Vert designs as T* **364** *of Antigua. Multicoloured. P* 13½×14.

2118 $2 As Type **364** of Antigua 85 90
a. Strip of 3. Nos. 2118/20 . . . . 2·50
2119 $2 Queen in robes of Order of St. Michael and St. George 85 90
2120 $2 Queen in blue dress with floral brooch 85 90
2118/20 . . . . . . *Set of* 3 2·50 2·75
MS2121 103×125 mm. $6 Queen at Trooping the Colour. P 13½×14 . . . . . . 2·50 2·75

Nos. 2118/20 were printed together, *se-tenant*, in horizontal and vertical strips of 3 throughout the sheet.

297 Moscow Stadium, 1980

(Litho B.D.T.)

1996 (7 June). *Olympic Games, Atlanta (2nd issue). Previous Medal Winners. T* **297** *and similar multicoloured designs. P* 14.

2122 20 c. Type **297** 10 15
2123 25 c. Hermine Joseph (running) (*vert*) . . 10 15
2124 55 c. Zimbabwe women's hockey team, 1980 . . . . 25 30
2125 90 c. Jerome Romain (long jump) (*vert*) . . 40 45
2126 90 c. Sammy Lee (diving), 1948 and 1952 (*vert*) 40 45
a. Sheetlet. Nos. 2126/34 . . . . 3·50
2127 90 c. Bruce Jenner (decathalon), 1976 (*vert*) 40 45
2128 90 c. Olga Korbut (gymnastics), 1972 (*vert*) 40 45
2129 90 c. Steffi Graff (tennis), 1988 (*vert*) . . 40 45
2130 90 c. Florence Griffith-Joyner (track and field), 1988 (*vert*) 40 45
2131 90 c. Mark Spitz (swimming), 1968 and 1972 (*vert*) 40 45
2132 90 c. Li Ning (gymnastics), 1984 (*vert*) . . 40 45
2133 90 c. Erika Salumae (cycling), 1988 (*vert*) 40 45
2134 90 c. Abebe Bikila (marathon), 1960 and 1964 (*vert*) 40 45
2135 90 c. Ulrike Meyfarth (high jump), 1972 and 1984 (*vert*) 40 45
a. Sheetlet. Nos. 2135/43 . . . . 3·50
2136 90 c. Pat McCormick (diving), 1952 and 1956 (*vert*) 40 45
2137 90 c. Takeichi Nishi (equestrian), 1932 (*vert*) 40 45
2138 90 c. Peter Farkas (Greco-Roman wrestling), 1992 (*vert*) 40 45
2139 90 c. Carl Lewis (track and field), 1984, 1988 and 1992 (*vert*) 40 45
2140 90 c. Agnes Keleti (gymnastics), 1952 and 1956 (*vert*) 40 45
2141 90 c. Yasuhiro Yamashita (judo), 1984 (*vert*) 40 45
2142 90 c. John Kelly (single sculls), 1920 (*vert*) 40 45
2143 90 c. Naim Suleymanoglu (weightlifting), 1988 and 1992 (*vert*) 40 45
2144 $1 Polo (*vert*) 45 50
2145 $2 Greg Louganis (diving), 1976, 1984 and 1988 . . . . 85 90
2122/45 . . . . . . *Set of* 24 9·00 10·00
MS2146 Two sheets, each 105×75 mm. (a) $5 Joan Benoit (marathon), 1984 (*vert*). (b) $5 Milt Campbell (discus) . . . . *Set of* 2 *sheets* 4·25 4·50

Nos. 2126/34 and 2135/43 were each printed together, *se-tenant*, in sheetlets of 9, the backgrounds forming composite designs.

(Litho Questa)

1996 (31 July). *50th Anniv of U.N.I.C.E.F. Multicoloured designs as T* **366** *of Antigua. P* 14.

2147 20 c. Child and globe (*horiz*) 10 10
2148 55 c. Child with syringe and stethoscope (*horiz*) 25 30
2149 $5 Doctor and child (*horiz*) . . . . 2·10 2·25
2147/9 . . . . . . *Set of* 3 2·40 2·50
MS2150 74×104 mm. $5 African child . . 2·10 2·25

(Des R. Sauber. Litho Questa)

1996 (31 July). *3000th Anniv of Jerusalem. Vert designs as T* **367** *of Antigua. Multicoloured. P* 14.

MS2151 114×95 mm. 90 c. Shrine of the Book, Israel Museum; $1 Church of All Nations; $2 The Great Synagogue . . . . 1·60 1·75
MS2152 104×74 mm. $5 Hebrew University, Mount Scopus . . . . 2·10 2·25

(Des J. Iskowitz. Litho Questa)

1996 (31 July). *Centenary of Radio. Entertainers. Multicoloured designs as T* **368** *of Antigua. P* 13½×14.

2153 90 c. Artie Shaw 40 45
2154 $1 Benny Goodman 45 50
2155 $2 Duke Ellington 85 90
2156 $4 Harry James . . . . 1·75 1·90
2153/6 . . . . . . *Set of* 4 3·25 3·50
MS2157 70×99 mm. $6 Tommy and Jimmy Dorsey. P 14×13½ (*horiz*) . . . . 2·50 2·75

298 Irene Peltier in National Dress

299 Humphrey Bogart as Sam Spade

(Litho Questa)

1996 (31 July). *Local Entertainers. T* **298** *and similar vert designs. Multicoloured. P* 13½×14.

2158 25 c. Type **298** 10 15
2159 55 c. Rupert Bartley (steel-band player) . . 25 30
2160 65 c. Rosemary Cools-Lartigue (pianist) . . 30 35
2161 90 c. Celestine 'Orion' Theophile (singer) 40 45
2162 $1 Cecil Bellot (band master) 45 50
2158/62 . . . . . . *Set of* 5 1·50 1·75

1996 (31 July). *Centenary of Cinema. Screen Detectives. T* **299** *and similar vert designs. Multicoloured. Litho. P* 13½×14.
2163 $1 Type **299** 45 50
a. Sheetlet. Nos. 2163/71 .. .. 4·00
2164 $1 Sean Connery as James Bond .. 45 50
2165 $1 Warren Beatty as Dick Tracy .. 45 50
2166 $1 Basil Rathbone as Sherlock Holmes .. 45 50
2167 $1 William Powell as the Thin Man .. 45 50
2168 $1 Sidney Toler as Charlie Chan .. 45 50
2169 $1 Peter Sellers as Inspector Clouseau .. 45 50
2170 $1 Robert Mitchum as Philip Marlowe .. 45 50
2171 $1 Peter Ustinov as Hercule Poirot .. 45 50
2163/71 .. .. *Set of* 9 4·00 4·50
MS2172 105×75 mm. $6 Margaret Rutherford as Miss Marple .. .. 2·50 2·75
Nos. 2163/71 were printed together, *se-tenant*, in sheetlets of 9.

300 Scribbled Filefish

301 Anthony Trollope and Postal Scenes

(Litho Questa)

1996 (1 Oct). *Fishes. T* **300** *and similar horiz designs. Multicoloured. P* 14½×13½.
2173 1 c. Type **300** 10 10
2174 2 c. Lionfish 10 10
2175 5 c. Porcupinefish 10 10
2176 10 c. Powder-blue Surgeonfish 10 10
2177 15 c. Red Hind 10 10
2178 20 c. Golden Butterflyfish 10 10
2179 25 c. Copper-banded Butterflyfish .. 10 15
2180 35 c. Pennant Coralfish 15 20
2181 45 c. Spotted Drum 20 25
2182 55 c. Blue-girdled Angelfish 25 30
2183 60 c. Scorpionfish 25 30
2184 65 c. Harlequin Sweetlips 30 35
2185 90 c. Flame Angelfish 40 45
2186 $1 Queen Triggerfish 45 50
2187 $1.20, Spotlight Parrotfish 50 55
2188 $1.45, Black Durgon 65 70
2189 $2 Glass-eyed Snapper 85 90
2190 $5 Balloonfish .. .. 2·10 2·25
2191 $10 Creole Wrasse .. .. .. 4·25 4·50
2192 $20 Sea Bass .. .. 8·75 9·00
2173/92 .. .. *Set of* 20 19·00 20·00
For these designs in a smaller format, 24×21 mm, see Nos. 2374/91.

(Litho Questa)

1996 (1 Oct). *World Post Day. T* **301** *and similar vert designs. Multicoloured. P* 14.
2193 10 c. Type **301** 10 10
2194 25 c. Anthony Trollope and Dominican Postmen 10 15
2195 55 c. *Yare* (mail steamer) 25 30
2196 65 c. Rural Post Office 30 35
2197 90 c. Postmen carrying mail 40 45
2198 $1 Grumman Goose (seaplane) and 1958 Caribbean Federation 12 c. stamp .. 45 50
2199 $2 Old and new Post Offices and 1978 Independence 10 c. stamp 85 90
2193/9 .. .. *Set of* 7 2·00 2·25
MS2200 74×104 mm. $5 18th-centenary naval officer .. .. 2·10 2·25

302 "Enthroned Madonna and Child" (S. Veneziano)

303 "Herdboy playing the Flute" (Li Keran)

(Litho Questa)

1996 (25 Nov). *Christmas. Religious Paintings. T* **302** *and similar multicoloured designs. P* 14.
2201 25 c. Type **302** 10 10
2202 55 c. "Noli Me Tangere" (Fra Angelico) .. 25 30
2203 65 c. "Madonna and Child Enthroned" (Angelico) 30 35
2204 90 c. "Madonna of Corneto Tarquinia" (F. Lippi) 40 45
2205 $2 "The Annunciation" and "Adoration of the Magi" (School of Angelico) .. 85 90
2206 $5 "Madonna and Child of the Shade" (Angelico) .. .. .. 2·10 2·25
2201/6 .. .. *Set of* 6 4·00 4·50
MS2207 Two sheets. (a) 76×106 mm. $6 "Coronation of the Virgin" (Angelico). (b) 106×76 mm. $6 "Holy Family with St. Barbara" (Veronese) (*horiz*) .. .. *Set of* 2 *sheets* 5·25 5·50

(Des Y. Lee. Litho Questa)

1997 (10 Jan). *Lunar New Year ("Year of the Ox"). Paintings by Li Keran. T* **303** *and similar vert designs. Multicoloured. P* 14.
2208 90 c. Type **303** 40 45
a. Sheetlet. Nos. 2208/11×2 .. .. 3·00
2209 90 c. "Playing Cricket in the Autumn" .. 40 45
2210 90 c. "Listening to the Summer Cicada" .. 40 45
2211 90 c. "Grazing in the Spring" 40 45
2208/11 .. .. *Set of* 4 1·60 1·75
MS2212 76×106 mm. $2 "Return in Wind and Rain" (34×51 *mm*). P 14½ 85 90
Nos. 2208/11 were printed together *se-tenant*, in sheetlets of 8 containing two of each design.

304 Lee Lai-shan (Gold medal – Wind Surfing, 1996)

(Des Y. Lee. Litho)

1997 (12 Feb). *Olympic Games, Atlanta (3rd issue). T* **304** *and similar multicoloured design. P* 15×14.
2213 $2 Type **304** 85 95
a. Sheetlet. No. 2213×3 .. .. 2·50
MS2214 97×67 mm. $5 Lee Lai-shan wearing Gold medal (37×50 *mm*). P 14 .. .. 2·10 2·25
No. 2213 was printed in sheets of 3, with an enlarged illustrated left-hand margin.

305 *Meticella metis*

1997 (1 Apr). *Butterflies. T* **305** *and similar multicoloured designs. Litho. P* 14.
2215 55 c. Type **305** 25 30
a. Sheetlet. Nos. 2215/23 .. .. 2·25
2216 55 c. *Coeliades forestan* 25 30
2217 55 c. *Papilio dardanus* 25 30
2218 55 c. *Mylothris chloris* 25 30
2219 55 c. *Poecilmitis thysbe* 25 30
2220 55 c. *Myrina silenus* 25 30
2221 55 c. *Bematistes aganice* 25 30
2222 55 c. *Euphaedra neophron* 25 30
2223 55 c. *Precis hierta* 25 30
2224 90 c. *Coeliadas forestan* (*vert*) 40 45
a. Sheetlet. Nos. 2224/31 .. .. 3·25
2225 90 c. *Spialia spio* (*vert*) 40 45
2226 90 c. *Belenois aurota* (*vert*) 40 45
2227 90 c. *Dingana bowkom* (*vert*) 40 45
2228 90 c. *Charaxes jasius* (*vert*) 40 45
2229 90 c. *Catacroptera cloanthe* (*vert*) .. 40 45
2230 90 c. *Colias electo* (*vert*) 40 45
2231 90 c. *Junonia archesia* (*vert*) 40 45
2215/31 .. .. *Set of* 17 5·50 6·00
MS2232 Two sheets, each 102×71 mm. $6 *Eurytela dryope*. (b) $6 *Acraea natalica* *Set of* 2 *sheets* 5·25 5·50
Nos. 2215/23 and 2224/31 were printed together, *se-tenant*, in sheetlets of 8 (Nos. 2224/31) or 9 (Nos. 2215/23) with the backgrounds forming composite designs.
No. 2230 is inscribed "*Collas electo*" in error.

(Des M. Freedman and Dena Rubin. Litho Questa)

1997 (7 Apr). *50th Anniv of U.N.E.S.C.O. Multicoloured designs as T* **374** *of Antigua. P* 14×13½ (*horiz*) *or* 13½×14 (*vert*).
2233 55 c. Temple roof, China 25 30
2234 65 c. The Palace of Diocletian, Split, Croatia 30 35
2235 90 c. St. Mary's Cathedral, Hildesheim, Germany 40 45
2236 $1 The Monastery of Rossanou, Mount Athos, Greece 45 50
2237 $1 Carved face, Copan, Honduras (*vert*) 45 50
a. Sheetlet. Nos. 2237/44 and centre label .. .. 3·50
2238 $1 Cuzco Cathedral, Peru (*vert*) .. 45 50
2239 $1 Church, Olinda, Brazil (*vert*) .. 45 50
2240 $1 Canaima National Park, Venezuela (*vert*) 45 50
2241 $1 Galapagos Islands National Park, Ecuador (*vert*) 45 50
2242 $1 Church ruins, La Santisima Jesuit Missions, Paraguay (*vert*) 45 50
2243 $1 San Lorenzo Fortress, Panama (*vert*) 45 50
2244 $1 Fortress, National Park, Haiti (*vert*) 45 50
2245 $2 Scandola Nature Reserve, France .. 85 90
2246 $4 Church of San Antao, Portugal .. 1·75 1·90
2233/46 .. .. *Set of* 14 7·50 7·25
MS2247 Two sheets, each 127×102 mm. (a) $6 Chengde Lakes, China. (b) $6 Pavilion, Kyoto, Japan .. .. .. *Set of* 2 *sheets* 5·25 5·50
Nos. 2237/44 were printed together, *se-tenant*, in sheetlets of 8 with a centre label.
No. 2234 is inscribed "DICELECIAN" in error.

306 Tanglefoot and Minnie

307 Afghan Hound

(Litho Questa)

1997 (15 Apr)–**98**. *Disney Sweethearts. T* **306** *and similar multicoloured designs. P* 13½×14.
2248 25 c. Type **306** 10 15
2249 35 c. Mickey and Minnie kissing on ship's wheel 15 20
2250 55 c. Pluto and kitten 25 30
2251 65 c. Clarabelle Cow kissing Horace Horsecollar 30 35
2252 90 c. Elmer Elephant and tiger 40 45
2253 $1 Minnie kissing Mickey in period costume 45 50
2254 $2 Donald Duck and nephew 85 90
2255 $4 Dog kissing Pluto .. .. .. 1·75 1·90
2248/55 .. .. *Set of* 8 4·25 4·50
MS2256 Three sheets. (a) 126×100 mm. $5 Simba and Nala in *The Lion King*. P 13½×14 (16.6.98). (b) 133×104 mm. $6 Mickey covered in lipstick and Minnie (*horiz*). P 14×13½. (c) 104×124 mm $6 Mickey and Pluto. P 13½×14 *Set of* 3 *sheets* 7·25 7·50

(Litho Questa)

1997 (24 Apr). *Cats and Dogs. T* **307** *and similar vert designs. Multicoloured. P* 14.
2257 20 c. Type **307** 10 15
2258 25 c. Cream Burmese 10 15
2259 55 c. Cocker Spaniel 25 30
2260 65 c. Smooth Fox Terrier 30 35
2261 90 c. West Highland White Terrier .. 40 45
2262 90 c. St. Bernard puppies 40 45
a. Sheetlet. Nos. 2262/7 .. .. 2·40
2263 90 c. Boy with Grand Basset 40 45
2264 90 c. Rough Collie 40 45
2265 90 c. Golden Retriever 40 45
2266 90 c. Golden Retriever, Tibetan Spaniel and Smooth Fox Terrier 40 45
2267 90 c. Smooth Fox Terrier 40 45
2268 $1 Snowshoe 45 50
2269 $2 Sorrell Abyssinian 85 90
2270 $2 British Bicolour Shorthair 85 90
a. Sheetlet. Nos. 2270/5 .. .. 5·00
2271 $2 Maine Coon and Somali kittens .. 85 90
2272 $2 Maine Coon kitten 85 90
2273 $2 Lynx Point Siamese 85 90
2274 $2 Blue Burmese kitten and White Persian 85 90
2275 $2 Persian kitten 85 90
2276 $5 Torbie Persian .. .. .. 2·10 2·25
2257/76 .. .. *Set of* 20 12·50 13·00
MS2277 Two sheets, each 106×76 mm. (a) $6 Silver Tabby. (b) $6 Shetland Sheepdog *Set of* 2 *sheets* 5·25 5·50
Nos. 2262/7 and 2270/5 were each printed together, *se-tenant*, in sheetlets of 6 with the backgrounds forming composite design.

308 *Oncidium altissimum*

309 "Mary, Mary Quite Contrary"

(Litho Questa)

1997 (10 May). *Orchids of the Caribbean. T* **308** *and similar multicoloured designs. P* 14.
2278 20 c. Type **308** 10 10
2279 25 c. *Oncidium papilio* 10 15
2280 55 c. *Epidendrum fragrans* 25 30
2281 65 c. *Oncidium lanceanum* 30 35
2282 90 c. *Campylocentrum micranthum* .. 40 45
2283 $1 *Brassavola cucculata* (*horiz*) .. 45 50
a. Sheetlet. Nos. 2283/8 .. .. 2·75
2284 $1 *Epidendrum ibaguense* (*horiz*) .. 45 50
2285 $1 *Ionopsis utricularioides* (*horiz*) .. 45 50
2286 $1 *Rodriguezia lanceolata* (*horiz*) .. 45 50
2287 $1 *Oncidium cebolleta* (*horiz*) 45 50
2288 $1 *Epidendrum ciliare* (*horiz*) 45 50
2289 $4 *Pogonia rosea* .. .. .. 1·75 1·90
2278/89 .. .. *Set of* 12 5·50 6·00
MS2290 Two sheets, each 106×76 mm. (a) $5 *Oncidium ampliatum* (*horiz*). (b) $5 *Starhopea grandiflora* (*horiz*) .. .. *Set of* 2 *sheets* 4·25 4·50
Nos. 2283/8 were printed together, *se-tenant*, in sheetlets of 6 with the backgrounds forming a composite design.

(Des R. Rundo. Litho Questa)

997 (29 May). *300th Anniv of Mother Goose Nursery Rhymes. Sheet* 72×102 *mm. P* 14.
MS2291 **309** $6 multicoloured .. .. 2·50 2·75

(Litho Questa)

997 (29 May). *10th Anniv of Chernobyl Nuclear Disaster. Vert designs as T* **376** *of Antigua. Multicoloured. P* 13½.
292 $2 As Type **376** of Antigua 85 90
293 $2 As Type **376** of Antigua; but inscribed "CHABAD'S CHILDREN OF CHERNOBYL" at foot 85 90

(Des J. Iskowitz. Litho Questa)

997 (29 May). *50th Death Anniv of Paul Harris (founder of Rotary International). Horiz designs as T* **377** *of Antigua. Multicoloured. P* 14.
294 $2 Paul Harris and irrigation project, Honduras 85 90
MS2295 78×107 mm. $6 Paul Harris with Rotary and World Community Service emblems 2·50 2·75

(Litho Questa)

997 (29 May). *Golden Wedding of Queen Elizabeth and Prince Philip. Horiz designs as T* **378** *of Antigua. Multicoloured. P* 14.
2296 $1 Queen Elizabeth II 45 50
a. Sheetlet. Nos. 2296/301 .. .. 2·75
2297 $1 Royal Coat of Arms 45 50
2298 $1 Queen Elizabeth and Prince Philip in shirt sleeves 45 50
2299 $1 Queen Elizabeth and Prince Philip in naval uniform 45 50
2300 $1 Buckingham Palace 45 50
2301 $1 Prince Philip 45 50
2296/301 .. .. *Set of* 6 2·75 3·00
MS2302 100×71 mm. $6 Queen Elizabeth and Prince Philip with flower arrangement .. 2·50 2·75
Nos. 2296/301 were printed together, *se-tenant*, in sheetlets of 6.

(Des J. Iskowitz. Litho Questa)

1997 (29 May). *"Pacific '97" International Stamp Exhibition, San Francisco. Death Centenary of Heinrich von Stephan (founder of the U.P.U.). Horiz designs as T* **379** *of Antigua. P* 14.
2303 $2 violet 85 90
a. Sheetlet. Nos. 2303/5 .. .. 2·50
2304 $2 chestnut 85 90
2305 $2 sepia 85 90
2303/5 .. .. *Set of* 3 2·50 2·75
MS2306 82×119 mm. $6 dull blue and grey-blue 2·50 2·75
Designs:—No. 2303, Kaiser Wilhelm II and Heinrich von Stephan; No. 2304, Heinrich von Stephan and Mercury; No. 2305, Early Japanese postal messenger; No. MS2306, Heinrich von Stephan and Russian postal dog team, 1859.
Nos. 2303/5 were printed together, *se-tenant*, in sheets of 3 with enlarged right-hand margin.

310 "Ichigaya Hachiman Shrine"

311 Hong Kong Skyline at Dusk

(Litho Questa)

1997 (29 May). *Birth Bicentenary of Hiroshige (Japanese painter). "One Hundred Famous Views of Edo". T* **310** *and similar vert designs. Multicoloured. P* 13½×14.
2307 $1.55, Type **310** 65 70
a. Sheetlet. Nos. 2307/12 .. .. 3·75
2308 $1.55, "Blossoms on the Tama River Embankment" 65 70
2309 $1.55, "Kumano Junisha Shrine, Tsunohazu" 65 70
2310 $1.55, "Benkei Moat from Soto-Sakurada to Kojimachi" 65 70
2311 $1.55, "Kinokuni Hill and View of Akasak Tameike" 65 70
2312 $1.55, "Naito Shinjuku, Yotsuya" .. 65 70
2307/12 .. .. *Set of* 6 3·75 4·00
MS2313 Two sheets, each 102×127 mm. (a) $6 "Sanno Festival Procession at Kojimachi l-chome". (b) $6 "Kasumigaseki" *Set of* 2 *sheets* 5·25 5·50
Nos. 2307/12 were printed together, *se-tenant*, in sheetlets of 6.

(Des R. Sauber. Litho Questa)

1997 (29 May). *175th Anniv of Brothers Grimm's Third Collection of Fairy Tales. The Goose Girl. Multicoloured designs as T* **380** *of Antigua. P* 13½×14.
2314 $2 Goose Girl with horse 85 90
a. Sheet. Nos. 2314/16 .. .. 2·50
2315 $2 Geese in front of castle 85 90
2316 $2 Goose Girl 85 90
2314/16 .. .. *Set of* 3 2·50 2·75
MS2317 124×96 mm. $6 Goose Girl (*horiz*). P 14×13½ .. .. 2·50 2·75
Nos. 2314/16 were printed together, *se-tenant*, in sheetlets of 3 with illustrated margins.

(Des Y. Lee. Litho Questa)

1997 (1 July). *Return of Hong Kong to China. T* **311** *and similar vert designs. Multicoloured. P* 14×13½.
2318 65 c. Type **311** 30 35
a. Sheetlet. Nos. 2318/20 and 2324 .. 2·40
2319 90 c. Type **311** 40 45
2320 $1 Type **311** 45 50
2321 $1 Hong Kong at night 45 50
a. Sheetlet. No. 2321×4 .. .. 1·75
2322 $1.45, Hong Kong by day 65 70
a. Sheetlet. No. 2322×4 .. .. 2·50
2323 $2 Hong Kong at night (*different*) .. 85 90
a. Sheetlet. No. 2323×4 .. .. 3·25
2324 $3 Type **311** .. .. 1·25 1·40
2318/24 .. .. *Set of* 7 4·25 4·50
Nos. 2318/20 and 2324 were printed, *se-tenant*, in sheetlets of 4 with illustrated left-hand margin. Nos. 2321/3 were also printed in sheetlets of 4, but containing stamps of one value only.

312 Yukto Kasaya (Japan) (ski jump), 1972

313 Joffre Robinson (former Credit Union President)

(Litho Questa)

1997 (15 July). *Winter Olympic Games, Nagano, Japan* (1998). *T* **312** *and similar vert designs. Multicoloured. P* 14.
2325 20 c. Type **312** 10 15
2326 25 c. Jens Weissflog (Germany) (ski jump), 1994 .. .. 10 15
2327 55 c. Anton Maier (Norway) (100m men's speed skating), 1968 .. .. 25 30
2328 55 c. Ljubov Egorova (Russia) (women's 5 km cross-country skiing), 1994 .. 25 30
2329 65 c. Swedish ice hockey team, 1994 .. 30 35
2330 90 c. Bernhard Glass (Germany) (men's single luge), 1980 .. .. .. 40 45
2331 $1 Type **312** 45 50
a. Sheetlet. Nos. 2331/4, each × 2 .. 3·50
2332 $1 As No. 2326 .. .. 45 50
2333 $1 As No. 2327 .. .. 45 50
2334 $1 Christa Rethenburger (Germany) (women's 100m speed skating), 1988 45 50
2335 $4 Frank-Peter Roetsch (Germany) (men's biathlon), 1988 .. .. 1·75 1·90
2325/35 .. .. *Set of* 11 6·50 6·75
MS2336 Two sheets, each 106×76 mm. (a) $5 Charles Jewtraw (U.S.A.) (men's 500m speed skating), 1924. (b) $5 Jacob Tullin Thams (Norway) (ski jumping), 1924 .. *Set of* 2 *sheets* 4·25 4·50
Nos. 2331/4 were printed together, *se-tenant*, in sheetlets of 8 containing two of each design.

(Litho Questa)

1997 (21 July). *World Cup Football Championship, France* (1998). *Designs as T* **383** *of Antigua. Multicoloured (except Nos. 2343/4, 2348, 2350, 2353/4). P* 13½×14.
2337 20 c. Klinsmann, Germany (*vert*) .. 10 10
2338 55 c. Bergkamp, Holland (*vert*) 25 30
2339 65 c. Ravanelli, Italy (*vert*) 30 35
2340 65 c. Wembley Stadium, England .. 30 35
a. Sheetlet. Nos. 2340/7 and central label 2·40
2341 65 c. Bernabeu Stadium, Spain 30 35
2342 65 c. Maracana Stadium, Brazil 30 35
2343 65 c. Stadio Torino, Italy (grey-black) .. 30 35
2344 65 c. Centenary Stadium, Uruguay (grey-black) 30 35
2345 65 c. Olympiastadion, Germany 30 35
2346 65 c. Rose Bowl, U.S.A. 30 35
2347 65 c. Azteca Stadium, Mexico 30 35
2348 65 c. Meazza, Italy (grey-black) 30 35
a. Sheetlet. Nos. 2348/55 and label 2·40
2349 65 c. Matthaus, Germany 30 35
2350 65 c. Walter, West Germany (grey-black) 30 35
2351 65 c. Maradona, Argentina 30 35
2352 65 c. Beckenbauer, Germany 30 35
2353 65 c. Moore, England (grey-black) .. 30 35
2354 65 c. Dunga, Brazil (grey-black) 30 35
2355 65 c. Zoff, Italy 30 35
2356 90 c. Klinkladze, Georgia (*vert*) 40 45
2357 $2 Shearer, England (*vert*) 85 90
2358 $4 Dani, Portugal (*vert*) .. .. 1·75 1·90
2337/58 .. .. *Set of* 22 8·25 9·50
MS2359 Two sheets. (a) 102×126 mm. $5 Mario Kempes, Argentina (*vert*). (b) 126×102 mm. $6 Ally McCoist, Scotland (*vert*) .. *Set of* 2 *sheets* 4·75 5·00
Nos. 2340/7 and 2348/55 were each printed together, *se-tenant*, in sheetlets of 8 stamps and 1 label

(Litho Questa)

1997 (15 Aug). *40th Anniv of Co-operative Credit Union League. T* **313** *and similar designs. P* 14×13½.
2360 25 c. deep blue and black 10 10
2361 55 c. myrtle-green and black 25 30
2362 65 c. maroon and black 30 35
2363 90 c. multicoloured 40 45
2360/3 .. .. *Set of* 4 1·00 1·25
MS2364 94×106 mm. $5 multicoloured .. 2·10 2·25
Designs: *Horiz* (*as T* **313**)—55 c. Sister Alicia (founder); 65 c. Lorrel Bruce (first Credit Union President). *Vert* (30×60 *mm*)—$5 Sister Alicia, Joffre Robinson and Lorrel Bruce.

314 Louis Pasteur

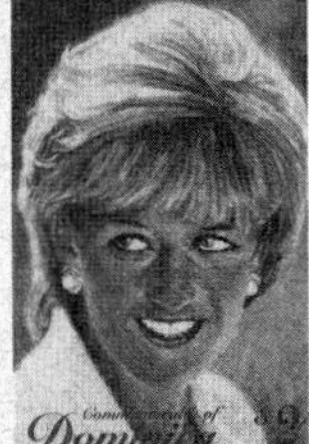
315 Diana, Princess of Wales

(Des J. Iskowitz. Litho Questa)

1997 (1 Sept). *Medical Pioneers. T* **314** *and similar vert designs. P* 14.
2365 20 c. purple-brown 10 10
2366 25 c. bright rose and orange-vermilion .. 10 15
2367 55 c. deep violet 25 30
2368 65 c. orange-red and yellow-brown .. 30 35
2369 90 c. greenish yellow and olive-yellow .. 40 45
2370 $1 bright blue and dull ultramarine .. 45 50
2371 $2 black 85 90
2372 $3 deep brown-red and yellow-brown .. 1·25 1·50
2365/72 .. .. *Set of* 8 3·50 3·75
MS2373 Two sheets, each 70×100 mm. (a) $5 multicoloured. (b) $6 multicoloured *Set of* 2 *sheets* 4·75 5·00
Designs:—25 c. Christiaan Barnard (first heart transplant); 55 c. Sir Alexander Fleming (discovery of penicillin); 65 c. Camillo Golgi (neurologist); 90 c. Jonas Salk (discovery of polio vaccine); $1 Har Gobind Khorana (genetics); $2 Elizabeth Black (first woman doctor); $3 Sir Frank MacFarlane Burnet (immunologist); $5 (No. **MS**2373a) Sir Alexander Fleming (*different*); $6 (No. **MS**2373b), Louis Pasteur (*different*).

(Litho Questa)

1997 (Oct)–**98**. *Fishes. As Nos.* 2175/92, *but smaller,* 24×21 *mm. P* 13×13½.
2374 5 c. Porcupinefish 10 10
2375 10 c. Powder-blue Surgeonfish 10 10
2376 15 c. Red Hind 10 10
2377 20 c. Golden Butterflyfish 10 10
2378 25 c. Copper-banded Butterflyfish 10 15
2379 35 c. Pennant Coralfish 15 20
2380 45 c. Spotted Drum 20 25
2381 55 c. Blue-girdled Angelfish 25 30
2382 60 c. Scorpionfish 25 30
2383 65 c. Harlequin Sweetlips 30 35
2384 90 c. Flame Angelfish 40 45
2385 $1 Queen Triggerfish 45 50
2386 $1.20, Spotlight Parrotfish 50 55
2387 $1.45, Black Durgon 65 70
2388 $2 Glass-eyed Snapper 85 90
2389 $5 Balloonfish .. .. 2·10 2·25
2390 $10 Creole Wrasse (1998) .. .. 4·25 4·50
2391 $20 Sea Bass (1998) .. .. .. 8·75 9·00
2374/91 .. .. *Set of* 18 19·00 20·00

(Des J. Iskowitz. Litho Questa)

1997 (20 Oct). *Diana, Princess of Wales Commemoration. T* **315** *and similar vert designs. Multicoloured. P* 14.
2392 $2 Type **315** 85 90
a. Sheetlet. Nos. 2392/5 .. .. 3·25
2393 $2 Wearing diamond-drop earrings .. 85 90
2394 $2 Resting head on hand 85 90
2395 $2 Wearing tiara 85 90
2392/5 .. .. *Set of* 4 3·25 3·50
MS2396 76×106 mm. $5 Diana, Princess of Wales .. .. 2·10 2·25
Nos. 2392/5 were printed together, *se-tenant*, in sheetlets of 4 with enlarged illustrated margins.

316 "Echo et Narcisse" (Toile)

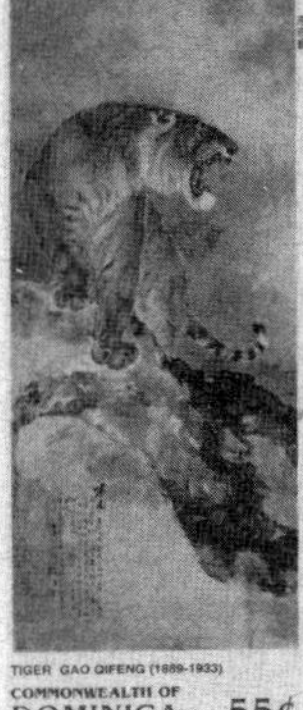

317 "Tiger" (Gao Qifeng)

(Litho Questa)

1997 (10 Nov). *Christmas. Paintings. T* **316** *and similar multicoloured designs. P* 14.
2397 20 c. Type **316** 10 10
2398 55 c. "The Archangel Raphael leaving the Family of Tobias" (Rembrandt) .. 25 30
2399 65 c. "Seated Nymphs with Flute" (Francois Boucher) 30 35
2400 90 c. "Angel" (Rembrandt) 40 45
2401 $2 "Dispute" (Raphael) 85 90
2402 $4 "Holy Trinity" (Raphael) .. .. 1·75 1·90
2397/402 .. .. *Set of* 6 3·75 4·25
MS2403 Two sheets, each 114×104 mm. (a) $6 "Study Muse" (Raphael) (*horiz*). (b) "Christ on the Mount of Olives" (El Greco) (*horiz*) *Set of* 2 *sheets* 5·25 5·50

(Des Y. Lee. Litho Questa)

1998 (5 Jan). *Chinese New Year ("Year of the Tiger"). T* **317** *and similar multicoloured designs by different painters of the Ling-Nan School. P* 14½.

2404 55 c. Type **317** 25 30
a. Sheetlet. Nos. 2404/7 .. .. 1·40
2405 65 c. "Tiger" (Zhao Shao'ang) 30 35
2406 90 c. "Tiger" (Gao Jianfu) 40 45
2407 $1.20, Tiger" (*different*) (Gao Jianfu) .. 50 55
2404/7 .. .. *Set of* 4 1·40 1·75
MS2408 95×65 mm. $3 "Spirit of Kingship" (Gao Jianfu) (48×40 *mm*) .. .. 1·25 1·50

Nos. 2404/7 were printed together, *se-tenant*, in sheetlets of 4 with illustrated margins.

318 Akira Kurosawa

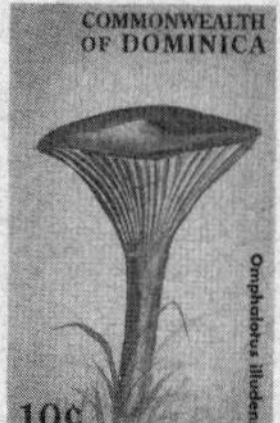

319 *Omphalotus illudens*

(Des J. Iskowitz. Litho Questa)

1998 (9 Feb). *Millennium Series. Famous People of the Twentieth Century. T* **318** *and similar designs. Multicoloured (except Nos.* 2411, 2414/15 *and* **MS**2417*). P* 14.

(*a*) *Japanese Cinema Stars*

2409 $1 Type **318** 45 50
a. Sheetlet. Nos. 2409/16 .. .. 3·50
2410 $1 *Rashomon* directed by Kurosawa (56×42 *mm*) 45 50
2411 $1 Toshiro Mifune in *Seven Samurai* (black and slate) (56×42 *mm*) .. 45 50
2412 $1 Toshiro Mifune 45 50
2413 $1 Yasujiro Ozu 45 50
2414 $1 *Late Spring* directed by Ozu (black and slate) (56×42 *mm*) 45 50
2415 $1 Sessue Hayakawa in *Bridge on the River Kwai* (orange-brown, red-brown and black) (56×42 *mm*) 45 50
2416 $1 Sessue Hayakawa 45 50
2409/16 .. .. *Set of* 8 3·50 4·00
MS2417 110×80 mm. $6 Akira Kurosawa (orange-brown, red-brown and black) .. .. 2·50 2·75

(*b*) *Sporting Record Holders. Multicoloured.*

2418 $1 Jesse Owens (winner of four Olympic gold medals, Berlin, 1936) 45 50
a. Sheetlet. Nos. 2418/25 .. .. 3·50
2419 $1 Owens competing at Berlin (56×42 *mm*) 45 50
2420 $1 Isaac Berger competing (56×42 *mm*) 45 50
2421 $1 Isaac Berger (weightlifter) 45 50
2422 $1 Boris Becker (Wimbledon champion) 45 50
2423 $1 Boris Becker on court (56×42 *mm*) .. 45 50
2424 $1 Ashe with Wimbledon trophy (56×42 *mm*) 45 50
2425 $1 Arthur Ashe (1st African-American Wimbledon singles champion, 1975) .. 45 50
2418/25 .. .. *Set of* 8 3·50 4·00
MS2426 $6 Franz Beckenbauer (captain of German football team) (*horiz*) .. .. .. 2·50 2·75

Nos. 2409/16 and 2418/25 were each printed together, *se-tenant*, in sheetlets of 8 with illustrated margins.

(Des T. Wood. Litho Questa)

1998 (2 Mar). *Fungi of the World. T* **319** *and similar vert designs. Multicoloured. P* 14.

2427 10 c. Type **319** 10 15
2428 15 c. *Inocybe fastigiata* 10 15
2429 20 c. *Marasmius plicatulus* 10 15
2430 50 c. *Mycena lilacifolia* 20 25
2431 55 c. *Armillaria straminea* and *Calastrina argiolus* (butterfly) 25 30
2432 90 c. *Tricholomopsis rutilans* and *Melitaea didyma* (butterfly) 45 50
2433 $1 *Lepiota naucina* 45 50
a. Sheetlet. Nos. 2433/41 .. .. 4·50
2434 $1 *Cortinarius violaceus* 45 50
2435 $1 *Boletus aereus* 45 50
2436 $1 *Tricholoma aurantium* 45 50
2437 $1 *Lepiota procera* 45 50
2438 $1 *Clitocybe geotropa* 45 50
2439 $1 *Lepiota acutesquamosa* 45 50
2440 $1 *Tricholoma saponaceum* 45 50
2441 $1 *Lycoperdon gemmatum* 45 50
2442 $1 *Boletus ornatipes* 45 50
a. Sheetlet. Nos. 2442/50 .. .. 4·50
2443 $1 *Russula xerampelina* 45 50
2444 $1 *Cortinarius collinitus* 45 50
2445 $1 *Agaricus meleagris* 45 50
2446 $1 *Coprinus comatus* 45 50
2447 $1 *Amanita caesarea* 45 50
2448 $1 *Amanita brunnescens* 45 50
2449 $1 *Amanita muscaria* 45 50
2450 $1 *Morchella esculenta* 45 50
2427/50 .. .. *Set of* 24 10·50 12·00
MS2451 76×106 mm. $6 *Cortinarius violaceus* 2·50 2·75

Nos. 2433/41 and 2442/50 were each printed together, *se-tenant*, in sheetlets of 9 with composite background designs.

NEW INFORMATION

The editor is always interested to correspond with people who have new information that will improve or correct the Catalogue.

320 Topsail Schooner

(Des K. Gromoll. Litho Questa)

1998 (16 Mar). *History of Sailing Ships. T* **320** *and similar horiz designs. Multicoloured. P* 14.

2452 55 c. Type **320** 25 30
a. Sheetlet. Nos. 2452/7, each × 2 .. 3·00
2453 55 c. *Golden Hind* (Drake) 25 30
2454 55 c. *Moshulu* (barque) 25 30
2455 55 c. *Bluenose* (schooner) 25 30
2456 55 c. Roman merchant ship 25 30
2457 55 c. *Gazela Primiero* (barquentine) .. 25 30
2458 65 c. Greek war galley 30 35
2459 90 c. Egyptian felucca 40 45
2460 $1 Viking longship 45 50
2461 $2 Chinese junk 85 90
2452/61 .. .. *Set of* 10 3·50 4·00
MS2462 Two sheets, each 106×76 mm. (a) $5 *Pinta* (Columbus). (b) $5 Chesapeake Bay skipjack .. .. *Set of* 2 *sheets* 4·25 4·50

Nos. 2452/7 were printed together, *se-tenant*, in sheetlets of 12 containing two of each design.

No. 2457 is inscribed "GAZELA PRIMERIRO", and both Nos. 2458/9 "EGPYTIAN FELUCCA", all in error.

321 *Steamboat Willie*, 1928

(Litho Questa)

1998 (16 June). 70*th Anniv of Mickey and Minnie Mouse. T* **321** *and similar multicoloured designs. P* 14×13½.

2463 25 c. Type **321** 10 15
a. Sheetlet. Nos. 2463/9 .. .. 4·25
2464 55 c. *The Brave Little Tailor*, 1938 .. 25 30
2465 65 c. *Nifty Nineties*, 1941 .. .. 30 35
2466 90 c. *Mickey Mouse Club*, 1955 .. .. 40 45
2467 $1 Mickey and Minnie at opening of Walt Disney World, 1971 .. .. 45 50
2468 $1.45, *Mousercise Mickey and Minnie*, 1980 .. .. 65 70
2469 $5 *Runaway Brain*, 1995 (97×110 *mm*) 2·10 2·25
2463/9 .. .. *Set of* 7 4·25 4·50
MS2470 Two sheets, each 130×104 mm. (a) $5 Walt Disney with Mickey and Minnie Mouse. (b) $5 Mickey and Minnie at 70th birthday party with Donald and Daisy Duck, Goofy and Pluto. Imperf .. .. .. *Set of* 2 *sheets* 4·25 4·50

Nos. 2463/9 were printed together, *se-tenant*, in sheetlets of 7 in which No. 2469 is imperforate at top, right and foot.

322 Big-crested Penguin ("Erect Crested Penguin")

(Des D. Burkhart. Litho Questa)

1998 (4 Aug). *Sea Birds. T* **322** *and similar horiz designs. Multicoloured. P* 14.

2471 25 c. Type **322** 10 15
2472 65 c. Humboldt Penguin 30 35
2473 90 c. Knot 40 45
2474 90 c. Crested Tern 40 45
a. Sheetlet. Nos. 2474/85 .. .. 4·75
2475 90 c. Franklin's Gull 40 45
2476 90 c. Australian Pelican 40 45
2477 90 c. Fairy Prion 40 45
2478 90 c. Andean Gull 40 45
2479 90 c. Blue-eyed Cormorant ("Imperial Shag") 40 45
2480 90 c. Grey Phalarope ("Red Phalarope") .. 40 45
2481 90 c. Hooded Grebe 40 45
2482 90 c. Least Auklet 40 45
2483 90 c. Little Grebe 40 45
2484 90 c. Pintado Petrel ("Cape Petrel") .. 40 45
2485 90 c. Slavonian Grebe ("Horned Grebe") .. 40 45
2486 $1 Audubon's Shearwater 45 50
2471/86 .. .. *Set of* 16 6·00 6·75
MS2487 Two sheets, each 100×70 mm. (a) $5 Blue-footed Booby. (b) $5 Fulmar *Set of* 2 *sheets* 4·00 4·25

Nos. 2474/85 were printed together, *se-tenant*, in sheetlets of 12, with the backgrounds forming a composite design.

323 Jetstar II

(Des S. Gardner. Litho Questa)

1998 (17 Aug). *Modern Aircraft. T* **323** *and similar hor[iz] designs. P* 14.

2488 20 c. Type **323** 10 1
2489 25 c. AN 225 .. .. 10 1
2490 55 c. L.I.A.T. Dash-8 .. .. .. 25 3
2491 65 c. Cardinal Airlines, Beech-99 .. 30 3
2492 90 c. American Airlines Eagle 40 4
2493 $1 SR 71 "Blackbird" spy plane .. 45 5
a. Sheetlet. Nos. 2493/500 .. .. 3·50
2494 $1 Stealth Bomber 45 5
2495 $1 Northrop YF23 .. .. .. 45 5
2496 $1 F-14A Tomcat 45 5
2497 $1 F-15 Eagle S 45 5
2498 $1 MiG 29 Fulcrum 45 5
2499 $1 Europa X5 .. .. 45 5
2500 $1 Camion 45 5
2501 $1 E 400 .. .. 45 5
a. Sheetlet. Nos. 2501/8 .. .. 3·50
2502 $1 CL-215 C-GKDN amphibian .. 45 5
2503 $1 Piper Jet 45 5
2504 $1 Beech Hawker 45 5
2505 $1 Lockheed YF22 .. .. .. 45 5
2506 $1 Piper Seneca V 45 5
2507 $1 CL-215 amphibian 45 5
2508 $1 Vantase 45 5
2509 $2 Itansa HFB 320 .. .. .. 85 9
2488/509 .. .. *Set of* 22 9·25 9·7
MS2510 Two sheets (a) 88×69 mm. $6 F1 Fighter. (b) 69×88 mm. $6 Sea Hopper seaplane *Set of* 2 *sheets* 5·25 5·5

Nos. 2493/500 and 2501/8 were each printed together *se-tenant*, in sheetlets of 8 with enlarged illustrated margins.

324 Stylised Americas

325 "The Painter and his Model"

(Litho Questa)

1998 (1 Sept). 50*th Anniv of Organization of American States. P* 13½×14.

2511 **324** $1 multicoloured 45 5

(Des Diane Catherines. Litho Questa)

1998 (1 Sept). 25*th Death Anniv of Pablo Picasso (painter). T* **325** *and similar multicoloured designs. P* 14½.

2512 90 c. Type **325** 40 4
2513 $1 "The Crucifixion" 45 5
2514 $2 "Nude with Raised Arms" (*vert*) .. 85 9
2512/14 .. .. *Set of* 3 1·60 1·7
MS2515 122×102 mm. $6 "Cafe at Royan" .. 2·50 2·7

326 365 GT 2+2

327 Mahatma Gandhi

(Des F. Rivera. Litho Questa)

1998 (1 Sept). *Birth Centenary of Enzo Ferrari (car manufacturer). T* **326** *and similar horiz designs. Multicoloured. P* 14.

2516 55 c. Type **326** 25 30
2517 90 c. Boano/Ellena 250 GT 40 45
2518 $1 375 MM coupe 45 50
2516/18 .. .. *Set of* 3 1·10 1·25
MS2519 104×70 mm. $5 212 (91×34 *mm*). P 14×14½ .. .. 2·10 2·25

(Des J. Iskowitz. Litho Questa)

1998 (1 Sept). 50*th Death Anniv of Mahatma Gandhi. T* **327** *and similar vert design. Multicoloured. P* 14.

2520 90 c. Type **327** 40 45
a. Sheetlet of 4 .. .. .. 1·60
MS2521 106×75 mm. $6 Gandhi spinning thread 2·50 2·75

No. 2520 was issued in sheetlets of 4 with enlarged illustrated margins at top and right.

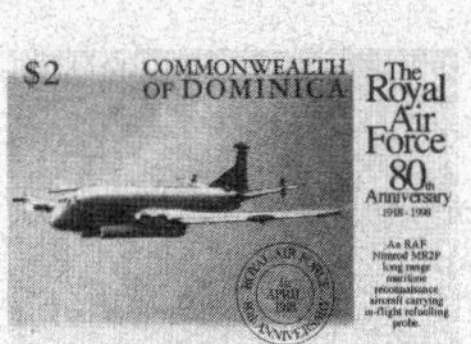

328 H.S. 801 Nimrod MR2P (reconnaissance)

329 Scout Saluting

(Des D. Miller. Litho Questa)

1998 (1 Sept). *80th Anniv of Royal Air Force. T* **328** *and similar horiz designs. Multicoloured. P* 14.

2522	$2 Type **328**	85	90
	a. Sheetlet. Nos. 2522/5	3·25	
2523	$2 Lockheed C-130 Hercules (transport)	85	90
2524	$2 Panavia Tornado GR1	85	90
2525	$2 Lockheed C-130 Hercules landing ..	85	90
2522/5	.. .. *Set of* 4	3·25	3·50

MS2526 Two sheets, each 90×68 mm. (a) $5 Bristol F2B fighter and Golden Eagle (bird) (b) $6 Hawker Hart and EF-2000 Euro-fighter *Set of* 2 *sheets* 4·75 5·00

Nos. 2522/5 were printed together, *se-tenant*, in sheetlets of 4 with enlarged illustrated margins.

No. 2525 is inscribed "Panavia Tornado GR1" in error.

(Litho Questa)

1998 (1 Sept). *19th World Scout Jamboree, Chile. T* **329** *and vert designs. Multicoloured. P* 14.

2527	65 c. Type **329**	30	35
2528	$1 Scout handshake	45	50
2529	$2 International Scout flag	85	90
2527/9	.. .. .. *Set of* 3	1·60	1·75
MS2530	76×106 mm. $5 Lord Baden-Powell ..	2·10	2·25

330 Fridman Fish

Save the Turtles

(331)

(Litho Questa)

1998 (7 Sept). *International Year of the Ocean. T* **330** *and similar horiz designs. Multicoloured. P* 14.

2531	25 c. Type **330**	10	15
2532	55 c. Hydrocoral	25	30
2533	65 c. Feather-star	30	35
2534	90 c. Royal Angelfish	40	45
2535	$1 Monk Seal	45	50
	a. Sheetlet. Nos. 2535/43	4·00	
2536	$1 Galapagos Penguin	45	50
2537	$1 Manta Ray	45	50
2538	$1 Hawksbill Turtle	45	50
2539	$1 Moorish Idols	45	50
2540	$1 Nautilus	45	50
2541	$1 Giant Clam	45	50
2542	$1 Tubeworms	45	50
2543	$1 Nudibranch	45	50
2544	$1 Spotted Dolphins	45	50
	a. Sheetlet. Nos. 2544/52	4·00	
2545	$1 Atlantic Sailfish	45	50
2546	$1 Sailfin Flying Fish	45	50
2547	$1 Fairy Basslet	45	50
2548	$1 Atlantic Spadefish	45	50
2549	$1 Leatherback Turtle	45	50
2550	$1 Blue Tang	45	50
2551	$1 Coral-banded Shrimp	45	50
2552	$1 Rock Beauty	45	50
2531/52	.. .. *Set of* 22	9·00	10·00

MS2553 Two sheets, each 110×85 mm. (a) $5 Humpback Whale and calf (56×41 *mm*). (b) $6 Leafy Sea-dragon (56×41 *mm*) .. *Set of* 2 *sheets* 4·75 5·00

Nos. 2535/43 and 2544/52 were each printed together, *se-tenant*, in sheetlets of 9, with the backgrounds forming composite designs.

1998 (14 Sept). *Save the Turtles Campaign. Nos.* 1686/7, 1689/90 *and* 1692 *optd with T* **331**.

2554	25 c. Type **263**	10	15
2555	55 c. Hawksbill Turtle swimming ..	25	30
2556	90 c. Green Turtle laying eggs	40	45
2557	$1 Green Turtle swimming	45	50
2558	$4 Loggerhead Turtle	1·75	1·90
2554/8	.. .. *Set of* 5	2·75	3·25

332 Northern Cardinal

(Litho B.D.T.)

1998 (1 Dec). *Christmas. Birds. T* **332** *and similar vert designs. Multicoloured. P* 14.

2559	25 c. Type **332**	10	15
2560	55 c. Eastern Bluebird	25	30
2561	65 c. Carolina Wren	30	35
2562	90 c. Blue Jay	40	45
2563	$1 Evening Grosbeak	45	50
2564	$2 Bohemian Waxwing	85	90
2559/64	.. .. *Set of* 6	2·25	2·50

MS2565 Two sheets, each 70×97 mm. (a) $5 Northern Parula. (b) $6 Painted Bunting *Set of* 2 *sheets* 4·75 5·00

STAMP BOOKLETS

1981 (23 June). *Royal Wedding. Multicoloured cover,* 165×92 *mm, showing Prince Charles and Lady Diana Spencer on front and St. Paul's Cathedral on back. Stitched.*

SB1 $11.75, booklet containing *se-tenant* pane of 6 (No. 751a) and pane of 1 (No. 753a) .. .. 8·00

POSTAL FISCALS

REVENUE (R 1) **Revenue** (R 2)

1879–88. *Optd with Type* R **1** *by De La Rue. P* 14. (a) *Wmk Crown CC.*

R1	1	1d. lilac	75·00	8·00
		a. Bisected vert (½d.) on cover ..	†	—
R2		6d. green	3·00	20·00
		w. Wmk inverted	£100	
R3		1s. magenta	9·00	16·00
R1/3		.. .. .. *Set of* 3	80·00	38·00
		(b) *Wmk Crown CA*		
R4	1	1d. lilac (1888)	3·25	3·25

1888. *Optd with Type* R **2** *locally. Wmk Crown CA.*

R6	1	1d. rose	£250	65·00

Appendix

The following stamps have either been issued in excess of postal needs, or have not been made available to the public in reasonable quantities at face value. Miniature sheets, imperforate stamps etc., are excluded from this section.

1978–79

History of Aviation. $16 × 30, each embossed on gold foil.

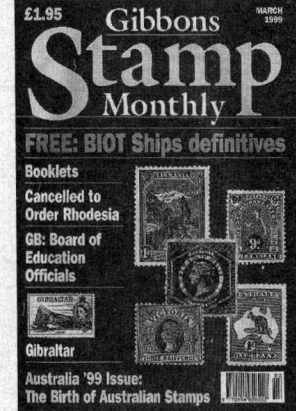

East Africa (G.E.A.)
see Tanzania

East Africa and Uganda Protectorates
see Kenya, Uganda and Tanzania

Egypt

TURKISH SUZERAINTY

In 1517 Sultan Selim I added Egypt to the Ottoman Empire, and it stayed more or less under Turkish rule until 1805, when Mohammed Ali became governor. He established a dynasty of governors owing nominal allegiance to the Sultan of Turkey until 1914.

Khedive Ismail

18 January 1863–26 June 1879

He obtained the honorific title of Khedive (viceroy) from the Sultan in 1867.

The operations of British Consular Post Offices in Egypt date from August 1839 when the first office, at Alexandria, was opened. Further offices at Suez (8 January 1847) and Cairo (1856) followed.

Great Britain stamps were issued to all three offices in August 1859 and continued to be used there until they closed, Cairo on 30 July 1873 and the others on 30 March 1878. "B 01" cancellations as Type **2** were issued to both Alexandria and Cairo. Cancellations with this number as Types **8**, **12** and **15** were only used at Alexandria.

Before 1 July 1873 combination covers showing Great Britain stamps and the first issue of Egypt exist with the latter paying the internal postage to the British Post Office at Alexandria.

Stamps issued after 1877 can be found with the Egyptian cancellation "Port Said", but these are on letters posted from British ships.

For cancellations used during the 1882 and 1885 campaigns, see BRITISH FORCES IN EGYPT at the end of the listing.

For illustrations of the handstamp and postmark types see BRITISH POST OFFICES ABROAD NOTES, following GREAT BRITAIN.

ALEXANDRIA

CROWNED-CIRCLE HANDSTAMPS

CC1 CC1b ALEXANDRIA (R.) (13.5.1843) *Price on cover* £1300

Stamps of GREAT BRITAIN *cancelled* "B 01" *as in Types* **2** *(also used at Cairo)*, **8**, **12** *or* **15**.

1859 (Aug) *to* **1878.**
Z 1 ½d. rose-red (1870–79) *From* 18·00
Plate Nos. 5, 6, 8, 10, 13, 14, 15, 19, 20.
Z 2 1d. rose-red (1857) 6·50
Z 3 1d. rose-red (1861) (Alph IV)
Z 4 1d. rose-red (1864–79) *From* 9·00
Plate Nos. 71, 72, 73, 74, 76, 78, 79, 80, 81, 82, 83, 84, 85, 86, 87, 88, 89, 90, 91, 92, 93, 94, 95, 96, 97, 98, 99, 101, 102, 103, 104, 106, 107, 108, 109, 110, 111, 112, 113, 114, 115, 117, 118, 119, 120, 121, 122, 123, 124, 125, 127, 129, 130, 131, 133, 134, 136, 137, 138, 139, 140, 142, 143, 144, 145, 146, 147, 148, 149, 150, 152, 154, 156, 157, 158, 159, 160, 162, 163, 165, 168, 169, 170, 171, 172, 174, 175, 177, 179, 180, 181, 182, 183, 185, 188, 190, 198, 200, 203, 206, 210, 220.
Z 5 2d. blue (1858–69) *From* 9·00
Plate Nos. 7, 8, 9, 13, 14, 15.
Z 6 2½d. rosy mauve (1875) (blued *paper*) *From* 60·00
Plate Nos. 1, 2.
Z 7 2½d. rosy mauve (1875–6) (Plate Nos. 1, 2, 3) 27·00
Z 8 2½d. rosy mauve (*Error of Lettering*) £1300
Z 9 2½d. rosy mauve (1876–79) *From* 21·00
Plate Nos. 3, 4, 5, 6, 7, 8, 9.
Z10 3d. carmine-rose (1862) £110
Z11 3d. rose (1865) (Plate No. 4) 55·00
Z12 3d. rose (1867–73) (Plate Nos. 4, 5, 6, 7, 8, 9) *From* 21·00
Z13 3d. rose (1873–76) *From* 21·00
Plate Nos. 11, 12, 14, 15, 16, 18, 19.
Z15 4d. rose (1857) 40·00
Z16 4d. red (1862) (Plate Nos. 3, 4) *From* 40·00
Z17 4d. vermilion (1865–73) 23·00
Plate Nos. 7, 8, 9, 10, 11, 12, 13, 14.
Z18 4d. vermilion (1876) (Plate No. 15) £140
Z19 4d. sage-green (1877) (Plate No. 15) 90·00
Z20 6d. lilac (1856) 45·00
Z21 6d. lilac (1862) (Plate Nos. 3, 4) *From* 40·00
Z22 6d. lilac (1865–67) (Plate Nos. 5, 6) *From* 32·00
Z23 6d. lilac (1867) (Plate No. 6) 42·00
Z24 6d. violet (1867–70) (Plate Nos. 6, 8, 9) *From* 30·00
a. Imperf (Plate No. 8) £1200
Z25 6d. buff (1872–73) (Plate Nos. 11, 12) *From* 55·00
Z26 6d. chestnut (1872) (Plate No. 11) 27·00
Z27 6d. grey (1873) (Plate No. 12) 70·00
Z28 6d. grey (1874–76) (Plate Nos. 13, 14, 15) *From* 21·00
Z29 9d. straw (1862) £140
Z30 9d. bistre (1862)
Z31 9d. straw (1865)
Z32 9d. straw (1867)
Z33 10d. red-brown (1867) £120
Z34 1s. green (1856) £100
Z35 1s. green (1862) 60·00
Z36 1s. green (1862) ("K" *variety*)
Z37 1s. green (1865) (Plate No. 4) 30·00
Z38 1s. green (1867–73) (Plate Nos. 4, 5, 6, 7) *From* 12·00
Z39 1s. green (1873–77) *From* 27·00
Plate Nos. 8, 9, 10, 11, 12, 13.
Z40 2s. blue (1867) 95·00
Z41 5s. rose (1867–74) (Plate Nos. 1, 2) *From* £250

CAIRO

CROWNED-CIRCLE HANDSTAMPS

CC2 CC **6** CAIRO (R. or Blk.) (23.3.1859) *Price on cover* £1800
Cancellation "B 01" as Type **2** (also issued at Alexandria) was used to cancel mail franked with Great Britain stamps between April 1859 and June 1873.

SUEZ

CROWNED-CIRCLE HANDSTAMPS

CC3 CC **1** SUEZ (B. *or* Black) (16.7.1847) *Price on cover* £2000

Stamps of GREAT BRITAIN *cancelled* "B 02" *as in Types* **2** *and* **8**, *or with circular date stamp as Type* **5**.

1859 (Aug) *to* **1878.**
Z42 ½d. rose-red (1870–79) 27·00
Plate Nos. 6, 10, 11, 12, 13, 14.
Z43 1d. rose-red (1857) 8·50
Z44 1d. rose-red (1864–79) *From* 10·00
Plate Nos. 73, 74, 78, 79, 80, 81, 83, 84, 86, 87, 90, 91, 93, 94, 96, 97, 100, 101, 106, 107, 108, 110, 113, 118, 119, 120, 121, 122, 123, 124, 125, 129, 130, 131, 134, 136, 137, 138, 140, 142, 143, 144, 145, 147, 148, 149, 150, 151, 152, 153, 154, 156, 158, 159, 160, 161, 162, 163, 164, 165, 166, 167, 168, 170, 174, 176, 177, 178, 179, 180, 181, 182, 184, 185, 186, 187, 189, 190, 205.
Z45 2d. blue (1858–69) *From* 13·00
Plate Nos. 8, 9, 13, 14, 15.
Z46 2½d. rosy mauve (1875) (blued *paper*) *From* 55·00
Plate Nos. 1, 2, 3.
Z47 2½d. rosy mauve (1875–76) (Plate Nos. 1, 2, 3) *From* 30·00
Z48 2½d. rosy mauve (*Error of Lettering*) £1300
Z49 2½d. rosy mauve (1876–79) *From* 24·00
Plate Nos. 3, 4, 5, 6, 7, 8, 9, 10.
Z50 3d. carmine-rose (1862) £120
Z51 3d. rose (1865) (Plate No. 4) 60·00
Z52 3d. rose (1867–73) (Plate Nos. 5, 6, 7, 8, 10)
Z53 3d. rose (1873–76) (Plate Nos. 12, 16) *From* 24·00
Z54 4d. rose (1857) 50·00
Z55 4d. red (1862) (Plate Nos. 3, 4) *From* 42·00
Z56 4d. vermilion (1865–73) *From* 27·00
Plate Nos. 7, 8, 9, 10, 11, 12, 13, 14.
Z57 4d. vermilion (1876) (Plate No. 15)
Z58 4d. sage-green (1877) (Plate No. 15) 95·00
Z59 6d. lilac (1856) 45·00
Z60 6d. lilac (1862) (Plate Nos. 3, 4) *From* 40·00
Z61 6d. lilac (1865–67) (Plate Nos. 5, 6) *From* 32·00
Z62 6d. lilac (1867) (Plate No. 6) 42·00
Z63 6d. violet (1867–70) (Plate Nos. 6, 8, 9) *From* 32·00
Z64 6d. buff (1872–73) (Plate Nos. 11, 12) *From* 60·00
Z65 6d. pale chestnut (Plate No. 12) (1872) £2250
Z66 6d. chestnut (1872) (Plate No. 11) 27·00
Z67 6d. grey (1873) (Plate No. 12) 75·00
Z68 6d. grey (1874–76) (Plate Nos. 13, 14, 15, 16) *From* 23·00
Z69 8d. orange (1876)
Z70 9d. straw (1862) £150
a. Thick paper
Z71 9d. bistre (1862)
Z72 9d. straw (1867)
Z73 10d. red-brown (1867) £150
Z74 1s. green (1856) £100
Z75 1s. green (1862) 65·00
Z76 1s. green (1862) ("K" *variety*)
Z77 1s. green (1865) (Plate No. 4) 40·00
Z78 1s. green (1867–73) (Plate Nos. 4, 5, 6, 7) *From* 12·00
Z79 1s. green (1873–77) *From* 27·00
Plate Nos. 8, 9, 10, 11, 12.
Z80 2s. blue (1867) £150
Z81 5s. rose (1867–74) (Plate Nos. 1, 2) *From* £275

PRICES FOR STAMPS ON COVER

Nos. 1/41	*from* × 8
Nos. 42/3	*from* × 30
Nos. 44/83	*from* × 5
Nos. 84/97	*from* × 2
Nos. D57/70	*from* × 12
Nos. D71/86	*from* × 5
Nos. D84/103	*from* × 2
Nos. O64/87	*from* × 5
Nos. O88/101	*from* × 2

(Currency: 40 paras = 1 piastre)

1

2

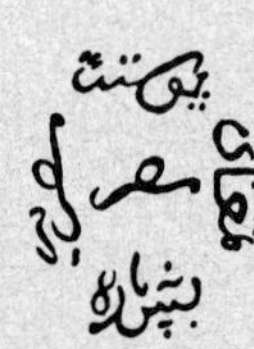
(3)

(Printed by Pellas Bros, Genoa. Litho, except for 1 pi. (typo). Black inscription (T **3**) litho, except on 1 pi. and 2 pi. (typo))

1866 (1 Jan). *Various designs as T* **1** *with black inscriptions a[s] T* **3**. *The lowest group of characters indicates the value. 1 pi. n[o] wmk, others W* **2** (*inverted*). *P* 12½.
1 5 pa. grey 32·00 24·0
a. Greenish grey 32·00 24·0
b. Imperf (pair) £180
c. Imperf between (pair) £300
d. Perf 12½×13 and compound 48·00 45·0
e. Perf 13 £250 £30
w. Wmk upright £250 £20
2 10 pa. brown 50·00 28·0
a. Imperf (pair) £160
b. Imperf between (pair) £350
c. Perf 12½×13 and compound 80·00 48·0
d. Perf 12½×15 £250 £27
e. Perf 13 £170 £19
w. Wmk upright 60·00 28·0
3 20 pa. pale blue 70·00 27·0
a. Greenish blue 70·00 27·0
b. Imperf (pair) £240
c. Imperf between (pair) £400
d. Perf 12½×13 and compound £100 80·0
e. Perf 13 £425 £25
w. Wmk upright 70·00 27·0
4 1 pi. claret 55·00 4·2
a. Imperf (pair) £100
b. Imperf between (pair) £400
c. Perf 12½×13 and compound 90·00 20·0
d. Perf 13 £300 £19
5 2 pi. yellow 90·00 40·0
a. Orange-yellow 90·00 40·0
b. Imperf (pair)
c. Imperf between (pair) £350 £35
d. Bisected diag (1 pi.) (on cover) † £225
e. Perf 12½×13 and compound £120 45·0
f. Perf 12½×15 £130
w. Wmk upright 90·00 40·0
6 5 pi. rose £250 £17
a. Imperf (pair)
b. Imperf between (pair) £1000
c. Perf 12½×13 and compound £275
d. Error. Inscr 10 pi., perf 12½×15 £900 £75
da. Imperf £500
w. Wmk upright £250 £17
7 10 pi. slate £275 £25
a. Imperf (pair)
b. Imperf between (pair) £2000
c. Perf 12½×13 and compound £425 £42
d. Perf 13 £1600
w. Wmk upright £275 £25

The 2 pi. bisected was authorised for use between 16 and 31 July 1867.

Stamps perforated 13 all round occured only in the corner of a sheet and so are very rare; of the 10 pi. only 1 example has been recorded unused. Compound perforations occur in many combinations. So many sheets were received imperforate or part-perforated that some stock was passed to V. Penasson of Alexandria who applied the 12½×15 gauge.

The two halves of each background differ in minor details of the ornamentation. All values can be found with either half at the top.

Proofs of all values exist on smooth paper, without watermark. Beware of forgeries.

All values also exist with the watermark reversed (*same price as upright*) or inverted and reversed (*same price as inverted*).

4

5

6

(Des F. Hoff. Litho V. Penasson, Alexandria)

1867 (1 Aug)–**69.** *W* **6** (*impressed on reverse*). *P* 15×12½.
11 **4** 5 pa. orange-yellow 24·00 8·00
a. Imperf (pair)
b. Imperf between (horiz pair) £170
w. Wmk inverted £250 £200
12 10 pa. dull lilac 70·00 8·50
b. Bright mauve (7.69) 48·00 9·00
ba. Bisected diag (5 pa.) (on piece) (12.71) † £750
w. Wmk inverted £300 £200
13 20 pa. deep blue-green £100 13·00
a. Pale blue-green £100 13·00
b. Yellowish green (7.69) £110 12·00
w. Wmk inverted £350 £200

No.	Type	Description	Unused	Used
	5	1 pi. dull rose-red *to* rose	10·00	90
		a. Lake	£120	32·00
		b. Imperf (pair)	£100	
		c. Imperf between (horiz pair)	£170	
		d. Bisected diag (20 pa.) (on piece)	†	£750
		e. Rouletted	55·00	
		w. Wmk inverted	50·00	30·00
		2 pi. bright blue	£110	15·00
		a. Pale blue	£110	15·00
		b. Imperf (pair)		
		c. Imperf between (pair)	£425	
		d. Bisected diag (1 pi.) (on cover)	†	—
		e. Perf 12½	£225	
		w. Wmk inverted	£400	£300
		5 pi. brown	£300	£180
		w. Wmk inverted	£500	£300

Each value was engraved four times, the resulting blocks eing used to form sheets of 200. There are therefore four types owing minor variations for each value.

No. 12ba was used on newspapers.

Stamps printed both sides, both imperf and perf, come from prinrs' waste. The 1 pi. rose without watermark is a proof.

7

8 (Side panels transposed and inverted)

8*a* (I)

8*a* (II)

ATERMARK 8*a*. There are two types of this watermark hich, as they are not always easy to distinguish, we do not list parately. Type II is slightly wider and less deep and the escent is flatter than in Type I. The width measurement for ype I is generally about 14 mm and for Type II about 15 mm, ıt there is some variation within the sheets for both types.

Nos. 26/43, 45/7*a*, 49/*a*, 50/1 and 57 come with Type I only. os. 44*a*, 48/*a*, 52, 54*b*, 73/7 and 78 exist with both types of atermark (but No. 83 and official overprints on these stamps ill require research); our prices are generally for Type II. Other atermarked issues between 1888 and 1907 have Type II atermarks only.

872 (1 Jan)–**75.** *T* **7** (*the so-called "Penasson" printing**). *Thick opaque paper. W* **8***a. P* 12½×13½.

A. LITHOGRAPHED

No.	Type	Description	Unused	Used
6	**7**	20 pa. blue (*shades*)	£120	50·00
		a. Imperf (pair)		
		b. Imperf between (pair)	—	£2000
		c. Perf 13½	£200	55·00
		w. Wmk inverted	£200	75·00
7		1 pi. red (*shades*)	£225	8·00
		a. Perf 13½	£500	17·00
		w. Wmk inverted	£600	25·00

B. TYPOGRAPHED

No.	Type	Description	Unused	Used
8	**7**	5 pa. brown (*shades*)	7·00	4·50
		a. Perf 13½	24·00	9·00
		w. Wmk inverted	£100	60·00
9		10 pa. mauve	6·00	3·00
		a. Perf 13½	6·00	3·00
		w. Wmk inverted	40·00	25·00
0		20 pa. blue (*shades*)	48·00	3·75
		a. Perf 13½	75·00	20·00
		w. Wmk inverted	45·00	30·00
1		1 pi. rose-red	48·00	1·00
		a. Bisected (20 pa.) (on piece with No. 31) (7.75)	†	£600
		b. Perf 13½	75·00	3·50
		w. Wmk inverted	35·00	25·00
2		2 pi. chrome-yellow	80·00	4·00
		a. Bisected (1 pi.) (on piece)	†	£650
		b. Perf 13½	18·00	4·00
		w. Wmk inverted		
3		2½ pi. violet	75·00	12·00
		a. Perf 13½	£700	£190
		w. Wmk inverted	90·00	30·00
4		5 pi. yellow-green	£180	32·00
		a. Tête-bêche (pair)		
		b. Perf 13½	£275	55·00
		w. Wmk inverted	£200	90·00

*The lithographed stamps are now believed to have been printed by Penasson, but the typographed by the Government Printing Works at Bûlâq, Cairo.

The lithographed and typographed stamps each show the characteristic differences between these two processes:—

The typographed stamps show the coloured lines of the design impressed into the paper and an accumulation of ink along the margins of the lines.

The lithographed stamps are essentially flat in appearance, without the heaping of the ink. Many of the 20 pa. show evidence of retouching, particularly of the outer frame lines.

The 1 p. bisected was used at Gedda or Scio and the 2 pi. vertically bisected at Gallipoli.

See also the footnote below No. 41.

1874 (Oct)–**75.** *Typo from new stereos at Bûlâq, on thinner paper. W* **8***a. P* 12½.

No.	Type	Description	Unused	Used
35	**8**	5 pa. brown (4.75)	7·00	3·75
		a. Tête-bêche (vert pair)	35·00	35·00
		b. Tête-bêche (horiz pair)	£275	£300
		c. Imperf (pair)		
		d. Imperf between (pair)	£100	£120
		ew. Wmk inverted	7·00	3·75
		f. Perf 13½×12½	9·00	3·75
		fa. Tête-bêche (vert pair)	60·00	60·00
		fb. Tête-bêche (horiz pair)	£325	£350
		fw. Wmk inverted	9·00	3·75
36	**7**	10 pa. grey-lilac (*shades*)	8·00	2·75
		a. Tête-bêche (vert pair)	£140	£160
		b. Tête-bêche (horiz pair)		
		c. Imperf (pair)		
		dw. Wmk inverted		
		e. Perf 13½×12½	14·00	3·25
		ea. Tête-bêche (vert pair)	£140	£160
		eb. Tête-bêche (horiz pair)		
		ew. Wmk inverted	15·00	3·50
37		20 pa. grey-blue (*shades*)	85·00	3·00
		b. Bisected diag (10 pa.) (on cover)	†	—
		cw. Wmk inverted		
		d. Perf 13½×12½	8·50	2·50
		da. Imperf between (pair)	£300	
38		1 pi. red (*shades*)	4·75	65
		a. Tête-bêche (vert pair)	90·00	90·00
		b. Tête-bêche (horiz pair)	£300	£300
		c. Imperf (pair)		
		d. Imperf between (pair)	—	80·00
		ew. Wmk inverted	8·00	1·50
		f. Perf 13½×12½	60·00	1·25
		fa. Tête-bêche (vert pair)	£350	£350
		fb. Tête-bêche (horiz pair)		
		fw. Wmk inverted	75·00	7·50
39		2 pi. yellow	70·00	3·00
		a. Tête-bêche (pair)	£400	£400
		bw. Wmk inverted	85·00	7·50
		c. Perf 13½×12½	5·50	5·50
		ca. Tête-bêche (pair)	£400	£400
		cb. Bisected diag (1 pi.) (on cover)	†	£2500
		cw. Wmk inverted	7·50	6·50
		d. Perf 12½×13½	60·00	11·00
		da. Tête-bêche (pair)	£850	
		dw. Wmk inverted	75·00	14·00
40		2½ pi. violet	8·50	5·00
		a. Tête-bêche (pair)	£350	
		bw. Wmk inverted	12·00	7·50
		c. Perf 12½×13½	48·00	19·00
		ca. Tête-bêche (pair)	£1000	90·00
		cw. Wmk inverted	45·00	25·00
41		5 pi. green	55·00	19·00
		a. Imperf (pair)		
		bw. Wmk inverted	£100	50·00
		c. Perf 12½×13½	£300	£275

The 2 pi. bisected was used at Jedda.

The 1872 printings have a thick line of colour in the top margin of the sheet and the other margins are all plain, an exception being the 5 pa., which on the majority of the sheets has the line at the righthand side of the sheet. The 1874–75 printings have a wide fancy border all round every sheet.

The 1872 printings are on thick opaque paper, with the impressions sharp and clear. The 1874–75 printings are on thinner paper, often semi-transparent and oily in appearance, and having the impressions very blurred and badly printed. These are only general distinctions and there are a number of exceptions.

The majority of the 1874–75 stamps have blind or defective perforations, while the 1872 stamps have clean-cut perfs.

The two printings of the 5 pa. to 1 pi. values can be identified by their perforation gauges, which are always different; the 5 pa. also differs in the side panels (Types **7** and **8**). Only the perf 12½×13½ varieties of the three higher values may need to be distinguished. As well as the general points noted above the following features are also helpful:

2 pi. In the 1872 issue the left-hand Arabic character in the top inscription is one complete shape, resembling an inverted "V" with a horizontal line on top. In the 1874 issue the character has three separate components, a line with two dots below.

2½ pi. There is a distinct thinning of the frame line in the top right-hand corner of the 1872 issue. This sometimes takes the form of a short white line within the frame.

5 pi. In the 1872 issue the top frame line is split for its entire length; in the 1874 issue the line is solid for all or most of its length. The 1872 printing always has a white dot above the "P" of "PIASTRE"; this dot appears on only a few positions of the 1874 printing.

There seem to be many different compositions of the sheets containing the *tête-bêche* varieties, settings being known with 1, 3, 9 and 10 inverted stamps in various sheets. Sheets of the 5 pa. are known with 9 of the 20 horizontal rows inverted, giving vertical *tête-bêche* pairs; four stamps were inverted within their row giving four horizontal *tête-bêche* pairs.

(9)

1879 (1 Jan). *Stamps of* 1874 *surch as T* **9** *at Bûlâq. P* 12½.

No.	Type	Description	Unused	Used
42	**7**	5 pa. on 2½ pi. violet	6·00	6·00
		a. Surch inverted	70·00	70·00
		b. Tête-bêche (pair)	£3500	
		c. Imperf (pair)		
		dw. Wmk inverted	7·50	7·50
		e. Perf 12½×13½	6·50	8·00
		ea. Surch inverted	£140	£140
		eb. Tête-bêche (pair)		
		ew. Wmk inverted	8·00	10·00
43		10 pa. on 2½ pi. violet	10·00	10·00
		a. Surch inverted	75·00	75·00
		b. Tête-bêche (pair)	£1500	
		c. Imperf (pair)		
		dw. Wmk inverted	15·00	15·00
		e. Perf 12½×13½	15·00	15·00
		ea. Surch inverted	£110	£110
		eb. Tête-bêche (pair)	£1500	
		ew. Wmk inverted	25·00	25·00

ALTERED CATALOGUE NUMBERS

Any Catalogue numbers altered from the last edition are shown as a list in the introductory pages.

10

11

12

13 14 15

(Typo De La Rue)

1879 (1 Apr). *Ordinary paper. W* **8***a* (*inverted on* 10 *pa.*). *P* 14.

No.	Type	Description	Unused	Used
44	**10**	5 pa. deep brown	1·00	30
		a. Pale brown	1·00	30
		w. Wmk inverted	£120	£100
45	**11**	10 pa. reddish lilac	50·00	3·00
46	**12**	20 pa. pale blue	60·00	1·75
		w. Wmk inverted	90·00	15·00
47	**13**	1 pi. rose	24·00	10
		a. Pale rose	24·00	10
		w. Wmk inverted	60·00	10·00
48	**14**	2 pi. orange	26·00	50
		a. Orange-yellow	22·00	80
		w. Wmk inverted	30·00	2·00
49	**15**	5 pi. green	55·00	8·50
		a. Blue-green	55·00	7·50
		w. Wmk inverted	50·00	9·00

See also Nos. 50/6

Khedive Tewfik

26 June 1879–7 January 1892

British troops were landed in Egypt in 1882 to secure the Suez Canal against a nationalist movement led by Arabi Pasha. Arabi was defeated at Tel-el-Kebir and British troops remained in Egypt until 1954. A British resident and consul-general advised the Khedive. Holders of this post were Sir Evelyn Baring (Lord Cromer), 1883–1907; Sir Eldon Gorst, 1907–11; and Lord Kitchener, 1911–14.

1881–1902. *Colours changed. Ordinary paper. W* **8***a* (*inverted on No.* 50). *P* 14.

No.	Type	Description	Unused	Used
50	**11**	10 pa. claret (1.81)	48·00	5·50
51		10 pa. bluish grey (25.1.82)	7·00	1·75
		w. Wmk inverted	40·00	3·00
52		10 pa. green (15.12.84)	70	40
		w. Wmk inverted	20·00	3·00
53	**12**	20 pa. rose-carmine (15.12.84)	10·00	55
		a. Bright rose	10·00	50
		w. Wmk inverted	35·00	7·00
54	**13**	1 pi. blue (15.12.84)	4·00	20
		a. Deep ultramarine	5·50	20
		b. Pale ultramarine	3·00	20
		cw. Wmk inverted	26·00	10·00
		d. Chalk-surfaced paper. *Ultramarine* (1902)	2·50	10
		da. Blue	2·50	10
		dw. Wmk inverted	75·00	40·00
55	**14**	2 pi. orange-brown (1.8.93)	12·00	30
		aw. Wmk inverted	80·00	40·00
		b. Chalk-surfaced paper (1902)	12·00	10
		ba. Orange	22·00	1·00
		bw. Wmk inverted		
56	**15**	5 pi. pale grey (15.12.84)	13·00	50
		a. Slate	11·00	40
		bw. Wmk inverted		
		c. Chalk-surfaced paper. *Slate-grey* (1902)	16·00	15

(17)

1884 (1 Feb). *Surch with T* **17** *at Bûlâq.*

No.	Type	Description	Unused	Used
57	**15**	20 pa. on 5 pi. green	7·00	1·25
		a. Surch inverted	65·00	60·00
		w. Wmk inverted	50·00	30·00

(New Currency: 1000 milliemes = 100 piastres = £1 Egyptian)

18

19

20

21

22

1888 (1 Jan)–**1909.** *Ordinary paper. W* **8***a. P* 14.
58 **18** 1 m. pale brown 75 10
a. *Deep brown* 1·50 10
bw. Wmk inverted 25·00 4·00
c. Chalk-surfaced paper. *Pale brown* (1902) 70 10
ca. *Deep brown* 75 10
cw. Wmk inverted 40·00 5·00
59 **19** 2 m. blue-green 60 10
a. *Green* 60 10
bw. Wmk inverted 40·00 5·00
c. Chalk-surfaced paper. *Green* (1902) 50 10
cw. Wmk inverted 40·00 5·00
60 **20** 3 m. maroon (1.1.92) 2·25 1·00
61 3 m. yellow (1.8.93) 2·50 30
a. *Orange-yellow* 2·25 15
bw. Wmk inverted 45·00 15·00
c. Chalk-surfaced paper. *Orange-yellow* (1902) 1·75 10
cw. Wmk inverted 75·00 30·00
62 **21** 4 m. verm (*chalk-surfaced paper*) (1906) 1·25 10
a. Bisected (2 m.) (on cover) (11.09) † —
63 5 m. rose-carmine 1·50 10
a. *Bright rose* 1·50 10
b. *Aniline rose* 2·75 10
cw. Wmk inverted
d. Chalk-surfaced paper. *Rose* (1902) 1·50 10
da. *Deep aniline rose* 3·25 20
64 **22** 10 p. mauve (1.1.89) 15·00 80
a. *Aniline mauve* 18·00 80
bw. Wmk inverted
c. Chalk-surfaced paper. *Mauve* (1902) 22·00 50
No. 62a was used at Giza.

Khedive Abbas Hilmi

7 January 1892–19 December 1914

A set of three values, in a common design showing Cleopatra and a Nile boat, was prepared in 1895 for the Nile Winter Fête, but not issued. Examples survive from the De La Rue archives.

29 Nile Felucca

30 Cleopatra with Head-dress of Isis

31 Ras-el-Tin Palace, Alexandria

35 Pylon of Karnak Temple, Luxor

37 Rock Temples of Abu Simbel

(Typo D.L.R.)

1914 (8 Jan). *W* **8***a. P* 13½×14 (1 *m. to* 10 *m.*) *or* 14 (20 *m. to* 200 *m.*).
73 **29** 1 m. sepia 60 40
74 **30** 2 m. green 80 20
w. Wmk inverted
75 **31** 3 m. yellow-orange 60 35
a. Double impression
w. Wmk inverted — 3·00
76 – 4 m. vermilion 1·25 65
w. Wmk inverted — 1·75
77 – 5 m. lake 1·25 10
a. Wmk sideways star to right* (booklets) 10·00 20·00
aw. Wmk sideways star to left 10·00 20·00
w. Wmk inverted 15·00 10·00
78 – 10 m. dull blue 2·50 10
w. Wmk inverted — 15·00
79 **35** 20 m. olive 6·50 30
w. Wmk inverted — 6·00
80 – 50 m. purple 11·00 40
w. Wmk inverted — 50·00
81 **37** 100 m. slate 12·00 60
82 – 200 m. maroon 26·00 3·50
73/82 *Set of* 10 55·00 6·00

Designs: *As T* **29**—4 m. Pyramids at Giza; 5 m. Sphinx; 10 m. Colossi of Thebes. *As T* **35**—50 c. Cairo Citadel; 200 m. Aswân Dam.

*The normal sideways watermark shows the star to the right of the crescent, *as seen from the back of the stamp.*

All the above exist imperforate, but imperforate stamps without watermark are proofs.

See also Nos. 84/95.

BRITISH PROTECTORATE

On 18 December 1914, after war with Turkey had begun, Egypt was declared to be a British protectorate. Abbas Hilmi was deposed, and his uncle, Hussein Kamil, was proclaimed Sultan of Egypt.

Sultan Hussein Kamil

19 December 1914–9 October 1917

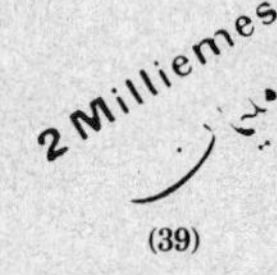

(**39**)

1915 (15 Oct). *No.* 75 *surch with T* **39**, *at Bûlâq.*
83 **31** 2 m. on 3 m. yellow-orange 55 1·00
a. Surch inverted £200 £200
b. Surch double, one albino £120
w. Wmk inverted

Sultan Ahmed Fuad

9 October 1917–15 March 1922

40

(A)

(B)

41 Statue of Rameses II **42**

(Typo Harrison)

1921–22. *As Nos.* 73/82 *and new designs* (15 *m.*). *W* **40**. *P* 14 (20, 50, 100 *m.*) *or* 13½×14 (*others*).
84 **29** 1 m. sepia (A) 80 1·25
a. Two dots omitted (B) (R. 10/10) 35·00 45·00
w. Wmk inverted 10·00 7·50
85 **30** 2 m. green 3·25 3·25
a. Imperf between (pair)
w. Wmk inverted 15·00 10·00
86 2 m. vermilion (1922) 2·00 55
w. Wmk inverted 15·00 10·00
87 **31** 3 m. yellow-orange (12.21) 2·75 1·10
w. Wmk inverted 16·00 10·00
88 – 4 m. green (1922) 3·50 4·50
w. Wmk inverted — 10·00
89 – 5 m. lake (1.21) 2·75 10
a. Imperf between (pair)
w. Wmk inverted 15·00 10·00
90 – 5 m. pink (11.21) 2·75 10
w. Wmk inverted 15·00 10·00
91 – 10 m. dull blue 2·75 20
w. Wmk inverted — 10·00
92 – 10 m. lake (9.22) 1·75 15
w. Wmk inverted — 10·00
93 **41** 15 m. indigo (3.22) 3·00 15
w. Wmk inverted — 8·00
94 **42** 15 m. indigo 18·00 2·75
w. Wmk inverted 20·00 10·00
95 **35** 20 m. olive 7·50 30
w. Wmk inverted 20·00 10·00
96 – 50 m. purple 10·00 65
w. Wmk inverted 18·00 12·00
97 **37** 100 m. slate (1922) 70·00 6·50
84/97 *Set of* 13 95·00 16·00

Type **42** was printed first; but because the inscription at right was erroneous the stamps were withheld and the corrected Type **41** printed and issued. Type **42** was released later.

STAMP BOOKLETS

1903 (1 Jan). *Black on pink cover inscr* "Egyptian Post Office" *in English and French. Stapled.*
SB1 121 m. booklet containing twenty-four 5 m. (No. 63c) in blocks of 6
Price reduced to 120 m. from 1 July 1911.

1903 (1 July). *Black on blue cover inscr* "Egyptian Post Office" *in English and French. Stapled.*
SB2 73 m. booklet containing twenty-four 3 m. (No. 61ab) in blocks of 6

1911 (1 July). *Black on pink cover inscr* "Egyptian Post Office" *in English and Arabic. Stapled.*
SB3 120 m. Contents as No. SB1

1914 (8 Jan). *Black on pink cover inscr* "Egyptian Post Office" *in English and Arabic. Stapled.*
SB4 125 m. booklet containing twenty-four 5 m. (No. 77a) in blocks of 6

1919 (1 Jan). *Black on pink cover inscr* "Egyptian Post Office" *in English and Arabic. Stapled.*
SB5 120 m. Contents as No. SB4

1921 (12 June). *Deep blue on pink cover inscr* "POST OFFICE" *in English and Arabic. Stapled.*
SB6 120 m. booklet containing twenty-four 5 m. (No. 89) in blocks of 6
a. Stitched

1921 (Nov). *Deep blue or pink cover inscr* "POST OFFICE" *in English and Arabic. Stapled.*
SB7 120 m. booklet containing twenty-four 5 m. (No. 90) in blocks of 6

POSTAGE DUE STAMPS

D 16

D 23

D 24

(Des L. Barkhausen. Litho V. Penasson, Alexandria)

1884 (1 Jan). *W* **6** (*impressed on reverse*). *P* 10½.
D57 D **16** 10 pa. red 40·00 9·
a. Imperf (pair)
b. Imperf between (pair) £110
w. Wmk inverted 75·00 15·
D58 20 pa. red £100 24·
w. Wmk inverted £190 40·
D59 1 pi. red £120 38·
w. Wmk inverted £200 £1
D60 2 pi. red £200 10·
w. Wmk inverted £300 20·
D61 5 pi. red 14·00 35·
w. Wmk inverted 30·00 40·

1886 (1 Aug). *No wmk. P* 10½.
D62 D **16** 10 pa. rose-red 50·00 8
a. Imperf between (pair) 90·00
D63 20 pa. rose-red £200 32·
a. Imperf between (pair)
D64 1 pi. rose-red 27·00 5·
a. Imperf between (pair) £120 £1
D65 2 pi. rose-red 27·00 3·
a. Imperf between (pair) £120

Specialists distinguish four types of each value in both the issues.

(Litho V. Penasson, Alexandria)

1888 (1 Jan). *No wmk. P* 11½.
D66 D **23** 2 m. green 9·50 14·
a. Imperf between (pair) £170 £1
D67 5 m. rose-carmine 26·00 13·
D68 1 p. blue £120 35·
a. Imperf between (pair) £170
D69 2 p. orange £140 12·
D70 5 p. grey £190 £1
a. With stop after left-hand "PIASTRES" £250 £2

Specialists distinguish four types of each value. No. D7 occurs on all examples of one of these types in the sheet exce that on R. 2/1.

Beware of forgeries of the 5 p.

(Typo De La Rue)

1889 (Apr)–**1907.** *Ordinary paper. W* **8***a. P* 14.
D71 D **24** 2 m. green 7·00
a. Bisected (1 m.) (on cover with unbisected 2 m.) † £2
bw. Wmk inverted 8·00
c. Chalk-surfaced paper (1903) 12·00
D72 4 m. maroon 2·25
aw. Wmk inverted 4·00 1·
b. Chalk-surfaced paper (1903) 2·50 5·
D73 1 p. ultramarine 5·50
aw. Wmk inverted 7·50
b. Chalk-surfaced paper (1903) 5·50
D74 2 p. orange 5·50
a. Bisected diagonally (1 p.) (on cover) †
bw. Wmk inverted 5·00
c. Chalk-surfaced paper (1907) 5·00

See also Nos. D84/6 for stamps with watermark sideways.

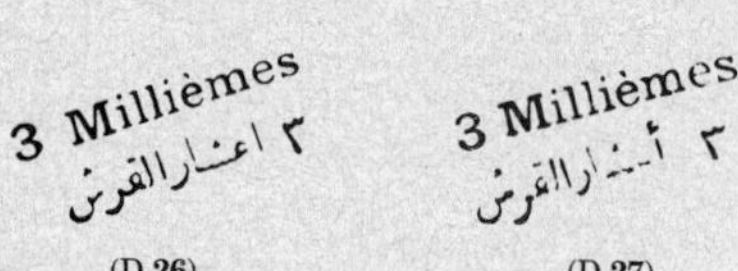

(D 26) (D 27)

Type D **26**

The Arabic figure at right is less than 2 mm from the ne character, which consists of a straight stroke only.

Type D **27**

The distance is 3 mm and the straight character has a comm like character above it. There are other minor differences.

1898 (7 May)–**1907.** *No.* D74 *surch at Bûlâq. Ordinary pape*

(*a*) *With Type* D **26**
D75 D **24** 3 m. on 2 p. orange 55 2·
a. Surch inverted 60·00 75·
b. Pair, one without surch
c. Arabic "2" for "3"
d. Arabic "3" over "2" £100

No. D75c occurred in the first printing on positions 10, 20, 3 40, 50 and 60 of the pane of 60 (the Arabic figure is th right-hand character of the second line–see illustration on pa xvii). In the second printing the correct figure was printed on t to form No. D75d. The error was corrected in subseque printings.

(*b*) *With Type* D **27** (11.04)
D76 D **24** 3 m. on 2 p. orange 3·25 10·
a. Surch inverted 50·00 60·
b. Surch double £200
c. Chalk-surfaced paper (1907)

915–17. *As Nos.* D71/3 *but wmk sideways**.
84 D 24 2 m. bright green .. .. 9·00 3·00
w. Wmk star to left of crescent (1917) .. .. 16·00 10·00
85 4 m. maroon .. .. 9·00 9·00
w. Wmk star to left of crescent (1917) .. .. 19·00
86 1 p. dull ultramarine .. .. .. 16·00 8·00
w. Wmk star to left of crescent (1917) .. .. 13·00 8·50

*The normal sideways watermark shows star to right of escent, *as seen from the back of the stamp.*

D 43

D 44

(Typo Harrison)

921 (Oct)–22. *Chalk-surfaced paper.* W **40** (*sideways**). P 14×13½.
98 D 43 2 m. green .. .. 2·75 3·25
w. Wmk stars below crescents .. 9·00 3·25
99 2 m. scarlet (1922) .. .. .. 1·00 1·50
w. Wmk stars below crescents .. 7·50 4·00
100 4 m. scarlet .. .. 5·00 12·00
101 4 m. green .. .. 2·50 1·00
w. Wmk stars below crescents .. 12·00 5·00
102 D 44 10 m. deep slate-blue (11.21) .. 4·50 15·00
103 10 m. lake (1922) .. .. .. 5·50 70
w. Wmk stars below crescents .. 10·00 4·00
98/103 .. .. *Set of* 6 19·00 29·00

*The normal sideways watermark shows the stars above the escents.

OFFICIAL STAMPS

O 25

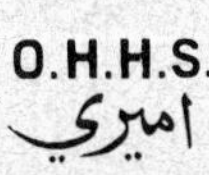
(O 28)

"O.H.H.S."
(O 29)

(Typo De La Rue)

893 (1 Jan)–09. *Ordinary paper.* W **8a**. P 14.
064 O 25 (–) chestnut .. .. 1·60 10
a. Chalk-surfaced paper (1903) ..
bw. Wmk inverted .. ..
c. Wmk sideways star to right. Chalk-surfaced paper (1.1.09) .. 10·00 7·50
cw. Wmk sideways star to left ..

From 1 January 1907 No. O64 was used on most official mail addresses within Egypt. In 1907 it was replaced by Nos. 073/8, but the new printing with watermark sideways was ssued in 1909 for use on unregistered official mail to Egyptian ddresses.

After No. O64c was withdrawn in 1914 the remaining stock vas surcharged 1 p., 2 p., 3 p. or 5 p. for fiscal use.

907 (1 Feb). *Nos.* 54da, 56c, 58c, 59c, 61c *and* 63d *optd with Type* O **28** *by De La Rue.*
073 18 1 m. pale brown .. .. .. 1·75 30
074 19 2 m. green .. .. 3·50 10
a. Opt double .. .. ..
075 20 3 m. orange-yellow .. .. .. 2·75 1·25
076 21 5 m. rose .. .. 4·50 10
077 13 1 p. blue .. .. 2·00 20
078 15 5 p. slate-grey .. .. .. 16·00 1·25
073/8 .. .. *Set of* 6 27·00 2·75

Nos. O73/8 were used on all official mail from February 1907 intil 1 January 1909 after which their use was restricted to egistered items and those sent to addresses overseas.

913 (Nov). *No.* 63d *optd at Bûlâq.*

(*a*) *With Type* O **29**
079 21 5 m. rose .. .. — £300
a. Opt inverted .. .. ..

(*b*) *As Type* O **29** *but without inverted commas*
080 21 5 m. rose .. .. 4·25 40
a. No stop after "S" (R. 11/10) .. 45·00 15·00
b. Opt inverted .. .. .. £200 75·00

O.H.H.S. اميرى
(O 38)

O.H.H.S. أميرى
(O 39)

O.H.H.S. أميرى
(O 43)

914 (Dec)–15. *Stamps of* 1902–6 *and* 1914 *optd with Type* O **38** *at Bûlâq.*
083 29 1 m. sepia (1.15) .. .. .. 1·25 3·25
a. No stop after "S" (R. 10/10) .. 12·00 25·00
084 19 2 m. green (3.15) .. .. .. 3·00 3·75
a. No stop after "S" .. .. 14·00 23·00
b. Opt inverted .. .. .. 35·00 35·00
c. Opt double £325
085 31 3 m. yellow-orange (3.15) .. .. 2·00 3·25
a. No stop after "S" (R. 10/10) .. 14·00 25·00
086 21 4 m. vermilion (12.14) .. .. .. 3·50 1·75
a. Opt inverted £190 £140
b. Pair, one without opt .. ..
087 – 5 m. lake (1.15) .. .. .. 3·50 80
a. No stop after "S" (R. 10/10) .. 15·00 22·00
083/7 .. .. *Set of* 5 12·00 11·50

No. O84a occurs on different positions in the two printings of his value.

1915 (Oct). *Nos.* 59ab, 62 *and* 77 *optd lithographically with Type* O **39** *at Bûlâq.*
O88 19 2 m. green .. .. 1·60 2·75
a. Opt inverted .. .. .. 20·00 20·00
b. Opt double .. .. .. 25·00
O89 21 4 m. vermilion .. .. 3·25 4·25
O90 – 5 m. lake .. .. 4·00 1·25
a. Pair, one without opt £275

1922. *Nos.* 84, *etc optd lithographically with Type* O **43** *at Bûlâq.*
O 98 29 1 m. sepia (A) (28.6) .. .. .. 3·50 8·50
a. Two dots omitted (B) £200
w. Wmk inverted .. ..
O 99 30 2 m. vermilion (16.6) .. .. 7·00 12·00
O100 31 3 m. yellow-orange (28.6) .. .. 65·00 £130
O101 – 5 m. pink (13.3) .. .. .. 17·00 4·00

Egypt was declared to be an independent kingdom on 15 March 1922, and Sultan Ahmed Fuad became king.

Later stamp issues will be found listed in Part 19 (*Middle East*) of this catalogue.

EGYPTIAN POST OFFICES ABROAD

From 1865 Egypt operated various post offices in foreign countries. No special stamps were issued for these offices and use in them of unoverprinted Egyptian stamps can only be identified by the cancellation. Stamps with such cancellations are worth more than the used prices quoted in the Egypt listings.

Such offices operated in the following countries. An * indicates that details will be found under that heading elsewhere in the catalogue.

ETHIOPIA

A B

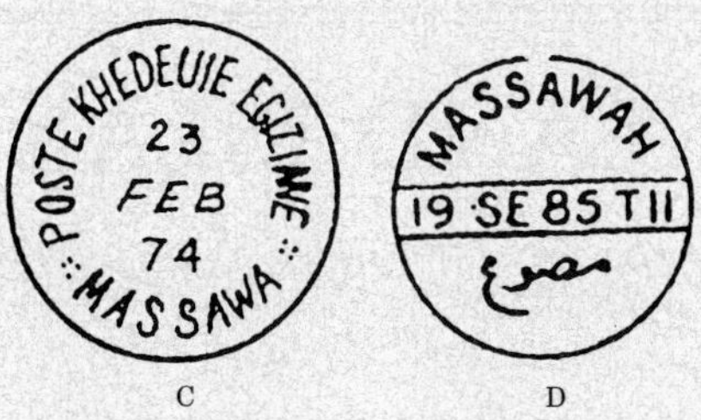

C D

MASSAWA. *Open* Nov 1867 *to* 5 Dec 1885. *Postmark types* A (*also without* REGIE), B, C, D. *An Arabic seal type is also known on stampless covers.*

SENHIT (near Keren). *Open* 1878 *to* April 1885. *Only one cover, cancelled* "Mouderie Senhit" *in* 1879, *is known, together with one showing a possible hand-drawn cancellation.*

A post office is also recorded at Harar, but no postal marking has so far been reported.

SOMALILAND*

Unoverprinted stamps of Egypt used from 1876 until 1884.

SUDAN*

Unoverprinted stamps of Egypt used from 1867 until 1897.

TURKISH EMPIRE

E F

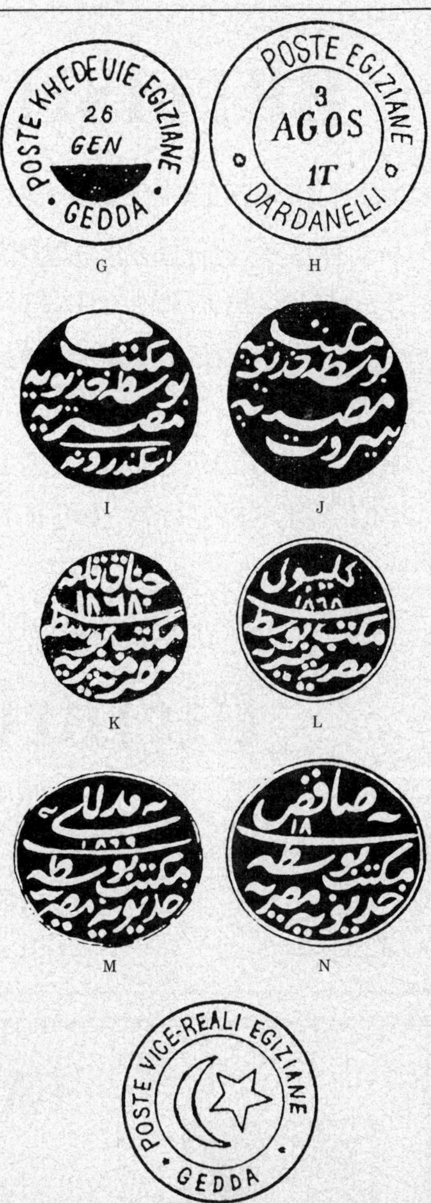

G H
I J
K L
M N
O

The offices are listed according to the spelling on the cancellation. The present-day name (if different) and country are given in brackets.

ALESSANDRETTA (Iskenderun, Turkey). *Open* 14 July 1870 *to* 15 Feb 1872. *Postmark types* E, I.
BAIROUT (Beirut, Lebanon). *Open* 14 July 1870 *to* 30 June 1881. *Postmark types* E, J.
CAVALA (Kavala, Greece). *Open* 14 July 1870 *to* 15 Feb 1872. *Postmark type* E.
COSTANTINOPOLI (Istanbul, Turkey). *Open* 13 June 1865 *to* 30 June 1881. *Postmark types* E, F, O.
DARDANELLI (Canakkle, Turkey). *Open* 10 June 1868 *to* 30 June 1881. *Postmark types* H, K.
DJEDDAH, *see* GEDDA.
GALIPOLI (Gelibolu, Turkey). *Open* 10 June 1868 *to* 30 June 1881. *Postmark types* E, L.
GEDDA, DJEDDAH (Jeddah, Saudi Arabia). *Open* 8 June 1865 *to* 30 June 1881. *Postmark types* F, G (*also with year replacing solid half-circle*), O (*all spelt* GEDDA), D (*spelt* DJEDDAH).
IAFFA (Jaffa, Israel). *Open* 14 July 1870 *to* 15 Feb 1872. *Postmark type* E.
LAGOS (Port Lago, Greece). *Open* 14 July 1870 *to* 15 Feb 1872. *Postmark type* E.
LATAKIA (Syria). *Open* 14 July 1870 *to* 15 Feb 1872. *Postmark type* E.
LEROS (Aegean Is.). *Open* May *to* December 1873 *and* July *to* September 1874. *Postmark type* E.
MERSINA (Mersin, Turkey). *Open* 14 July 1870 *to* 15 Feb 1872. *Postmark type* E.
METELINO (Lesbos, Greece). *Open* 14 July 1870 *to* 30 June 1881. *Postmark types* E, M.
RODI (Rhodes, Greece). *Open* 13 Aug 1872 *to* 30 June 1881. *Postmark type* E.
SALONNICCHI (Thessaloniki, Greece). *Open* 14 July 1870 *to* 15 Feb 1872. *Postmark type* E.
SCIO (Chios, Aegean Is.). *Open* 14 July 1870 *to* 30 June 1881. *Postmark types* E, N.
SMIRNE (Izmir, Turkey). *Open* 14 Nov 1865 *to* 30 June 1881. *Postmark types* E (*also without* "V. R."), F.
TENEDOS (Bozcaada, Turkey). *Open* 14 July 1870 *to* 15 June 1871. *Postmark type* E.
TRIPOLI (Lebanon). *Open* 14 July 1870 *to* 30 June 1881. *Postmark type* E.
VOLO (Volos, Greece). *Open* 14 July 1870 *to* 15 Feb 1872. *Postmark type* E.

BRITISH FORCES IN EGYPT

Following the rise of a nationalist movement led by Arabi asha, and serious disturbances in Alexandria, British troops anded at Ismalia in August 1882 and defeated the nationalists t Tel-el-Kebir on 13 September. During the initial stages of the ccupation a British Army Post Office, staffed by volunteers rom the Post Office Rifles, operated in Cairo. It is believed that he office closed in October 1882, but a similar facility also perated during the closing stages of the Gordon Relief xpedition in 1885.

ZA 1

Stamps of GREAT BRITAIN *cancelled with Type* ZA **1**.

882 (Aug–Oct).

ZA1	½d. rose-red (Plate No. 20)	
ZA2	½d. green (1880)	£300
ZA3	1d. Venetian red (1880)	
ZA4	1d. lilac (1881)	£175
ZA5	2½d. blue (1881) (Plate Nos. 21, 22, 23)	£100

885.

ZA6	1d. lilac (1881)	£300
ZA7	2½d. lilac (1884)	£225
ZA8	5d. green (1884)	£500

From 1 November 1932, to 29 February 1936 members of the British Forces in Egypt and their families were allowed to send etters to the British Isles at reduced rates. Special seals which vere on sale in booklets at N.A.A.F.I. Institutes and Canteens were sed instead of Egyptian stamps, and were stuck on the back of the nvelopes, letters bearing the seals being franked on the front with hand-stamp inscribed "EGYPT POSTAGE PREPAID" in a ouble circle surmounted by a crown.

PRICES FOR STAMPS ON COVER

Nos. A1/9	*from* × 5
No. A10	*from* × 2
No. A11	*from* × 5
No. A12	*from* × 100
No. A13	*from* × 20
No. A14	*from* × 200
No. A15	*from* × 20

A 1

A 2

(Des Lt.-Col. C. Fraser. Typo Hanbury, Tomsett & Co, London)

1932 (1 Nov)–**33**. *P* 11. (*a*) *Inscr* "POSTAL SEAL".

A1	A 1	1 p. deep blue and red	65·00	3·25

(*b*) *Inscr* "LETTER SEAL"

A2	A 1	1 p. deep blue and red (8.33)	23·00	85

(Des Sgt. W. F. Lait. Litho Walker & Co, Amalgamated Press, Cairo)

1932 (26 Nov)–**35**. *Christmas Seals. P* 11½.

A3	A 2	3 m. black/*azure*	48·00	70·00
A4		3 m. brown-lake (13.11.33)	7·50	45·00
A5		3 m. deep blue (17.11.34)	7·00	22·00
A6		3 m. vermilion (23.11.35)	1·25	26·00
		a. Pale vermilion (19.12.35)	7·00	15·00

A 3

(Des Miss Waugh. Photo Harrison)

1934 (1 June)–**35**. (*a*) *P* 14½ × 14.

A7	A 3	1 p. carmine	35·00	75
A8		1 p. green (5.12.34)	4·00	4·00

(*b*) *P* 13½ × 14

A9	A 3	1 p. carmine (24.4.35)	2·00	2·00

JUBILEE
COMMEMORATION
1935

(A 4)

1935 (6 May). *Silver Jubilee. As No.* A9, *but colour changed and optd with Type* A **4**, *in red.*

A10	A 3	1 p. ultramarine	£200	£180

Xmas 1935
3 Milliemes

(A 5)

1935 (16 Dec). *Provisional Christmas Seal. No.* A9 *surch with Type* A **5**.

A11	A 3	3 m. on 1 p. carmine	15·00	70·00

The seals and letter stamps were replaced by the following Army Post stamps issued by the Egyptian Postal Administration. No. A9 was accepted for postage until 15 March 1936.

A **6** King Fuad I

A **7** King Farouk

W **48** of Egypt

(Types A **6**/A **7**. Photo Survey Dept, Cairo)

1936. W **48** *of Egypt. P* 13½×14.

A12	A **6**	3 m. green (9.11.36)	1·00	90
A13		10 m. carmine (1.3.36)	2·50	10
		w. Wmk inverted		

1939 (12 Dec). W **48** *of Egypt. P* 13×13½.

A14	A **7**	3 m. green	1·50	3·25
A15		10 m. carmine	2·25	10
		w. Wmk inverted		

These stamps were withdrawn in April 1941 but the concession, without the use of special stamps, continued until October 1951 when the postal agreement was abrogated.

SUEZ CANAL COMPANY

PRICES FOR STAMPS ON COVER

Nos. 1/4	*from* × 20

100 Centimes = 1 Franc

In 1856 a concession to construct the Suez Canal was granted to Ferdinand de Lesseps and the Compagnie Universelle du Canal Maritime de Suez was formed. Work began in 1859 and the canal was opened on 17 November 1869. In November 1875 the Khedive sold his shares in the company to the British Government, which then became the largest shareholder.

The company transported mail free of charge between Port Said and Suez from 1859 to 1867, when it was decided that payment should be made for the service and postage stamps were introduced in July 1868. Letters for destinations beyond Port Said or Suez required additional franking with Egyptian or French stamps.

The imposition of charges for the service was not welcomed by the public and in August the Egyptian Government agreed to take it over.

1

(Litho Chézaud, Ainé & Tavernier, Paris)

1868 (8 July). *Imperf.*

1	1	1 c. black	£250	£1000
2		5 c. green	85·00	£500
3		20 c. blue	75·00	£500
4		40 c. pink	£130	£750

Shades of all values exist.

Stamps can be found showing parts of the papermaker's watermark "LA+-F" (La Croix Frères).

These stamps were withdrawn from sale on 16 August 1868 and demonetised on 31 August.

Many forgeries exist, unused and cancelled. The vast majority of these forgeries show vertical lines, instead of cross-hatching, between "POSTES" and the central oval. It is believed that other forgeries, which do show cross-hatching, originate from the plate of the 40 c. value which is missing from the company's archives. These are, however, on thin, brittle paper with smooth shiny gum.

Falkland Islands

PRICES FOR STAMPS ON COVER TO 1945

No. 1	*from* × 60
No. 2	*from* × 40
Nos. 3/4	*from* × 10
No. 5	—
Nos. 6/10	*from* × 30
Nos. 11/12	*from* × 15
Nos. 13/17	*from* × 10
Nos. 17*b/c*	*from* × 100
Nos. 18/21	*from* × 10
Nos. 22/*b*	*from* × 30
Nos. 23/4	*from* × 100
Nos. 25/6	*from* × 30
No. 27	*from* × 20
No. 28	*from* × 40
No. 29	*from* × 5
Nos. 30/*b*	*from* × 50
No. 30*c*	*from* × 15
No. 31	*from* × 5
Nos. 32/8	*from* × 15
Nos. 41/2	—
Nos. 43/8	*from* × 12
Nos. 49/50	—
Nos. 60/5	*from* × 10
Nos. 66/9	—
Nos. 70/1	*from* × 10
Nos. 72/*b*	—
Nos. 73/9	*from* × 4
No. 80	—
No. 115	*from* × 2
Nos. 116/19	*from* × 20
Nos. 120/2	*from* × 6
Nos. 123/6	—
Nos. 127/34	*from* × 5
Nos. 135/8	—
Nos. 139/45	*from* × 50
Nos. 146/63	*from* × 5

CROWN COLONY

FALKLAND
PAID.
ISLANDS.

1

2

1869–76. *The Franks.*

FR1	1	In black, *on cover*	£6500
FR2	2	In red, *on cover* (1876)	£12000

On *piece*, No. FR1 on white or coloured paper £85; No. FR2 on white £130. The use of these franks ceased when the first stamps were issued.

The first recorded use of No. FR1 is on a cover to London datestamped 4 January 1869.

3

½d.

(4)

In the ½d., 2d., 2½d. and 9d. the figures of value in the lower corners are replaced by small rosettes and the words of value are in colour.

NOTE. Nos. 1, 2, 3, 4, 8, 10, 11 and 12 exist with one or two sides imperf from the margin of the sheets.

(Recess B.W.)

1878–79. *No wmk. P* 14, 14½.

1	3	1d. claret (19.6.78)	£550	£325
2		4d. grey-black (Sept 1879)	£1000	£150
		a. On wmkd paper	£2500	£500
3		6d. blue-green (19.6.78)	50·00	50·00
4		1s. bistre-brown (1878)	50·00	50·00

No. 2a shows portions of the papermaker's watermark—"R. TURNER, CHAFFORD MILLS"—in ornate double-lined capitals.

NOTES. The dates shown for Nos. 5/12 and 15/38 are those on which the printer delivered the various printings to the Crown Agents. Several months could elapse before the stamps went on sale in the Colony, depending on the availability of shipping.

The plates used for these stamps did not fit the paper so that the watermark appears in all sorts of positions on the stamp. Well centred examples are scarce. Examples can also be found showing parts of the marginal watermarks, either CROWN AGENTS horizontally in letters 12 mm high or "CROWN AGENTS FOR THE COLONIES" vertically in 7 mm letters. Both are in double-lined capitals.

Many stamps between Nos. 5 and 38 can be found with the watermark reversed, inverted or both, in addition to those noted above where such variations are a constant feature.

Aron R. Halberstam Philatelists, Ltd.

For Falkland Islands and the Entire

British Commonwealth

Pre-1960 only

Call or write to request a price list detailing our comprehensive stock of singles and sets, organized by country, Scott and Gibbons catalogue numbers, and condition (Mounted, Unmounted, and Used)
Or send us your wants list

We accept payment by sterling cheque at current rate of exchange, or

P.O.B. 150168, Van Brunt Station
Brooklyn, NY 11215-0168, U.S.A.
Tel: +001 718 788 3978
Fax: +001 718 965 3099
Email: aron.halberstam@cwix.com

Thinking of selling? We are eager buyers of collections and accumulations. Contact us with details of what you have to offer.

THE ACCLAIMED RANGE OF STANLEY GIBBONS LUXURY HINGELESS ALBUMS

Internationally Recognised
You will find, like collectors all around the world, that Stanley Gibbons' range of Luxury Hingeless albums offers the very ultimate in quality, convenience and style.

Catering for a Variety of Countries
Attractively bound in deeply padded navy blue leatherette, each album is richly embossed with the country's national crest on the cover and spine, and presented in its own matching slipcase.

Contains Clearly Defined Album Leaves
Inside each album, the finest quality printed leaves have been expertly arranged with spaces for each stamp and selected illustrations and descriptions for your guidance.

Features Tailor-Made Mounts
Designed to save you time and money, clear protective mounts are already affixed in place to enable easy insertion of your stamps.

Item No. 5451	Falkland Islands Lux Vol.1 Album (1878-1995)
Item No. 5452	Falkland Islands Lux Vol.2 Album (1996-date)
Item No. 5455	Falkland Dependencies (1944-date)
Item No. 5458	British Antarctic Territoy page 8 only (1963-date)

For further information on these or other outstanding Stanley Gibbons albums, catalogues and accessories phone FREE on 0800 611 622 for your FREE Mail Order Colour Brochure

STANLEY GIBBONS PUBLICATIONS
5 Parkside, Christchurch Road,
Ringwood, Hants, England BH24 3SH
Tel: +44 (0)1425 472363 Fax: +44 (0)1425 470247
email: sales@stangib.demon.co.uk
Internet: http://www.stangib.com

882 (22 Nov). *Wmk Crown CA (upright). P* 14, 14½.
3 3 1d. dull claret £325 £120
a. Imperf vert (horiz pair) £42000
y. Wmk inverted and reversed .. £375 £200
4d. grey-black .. .. £225 65·00
w. Wmk inverted £375 £150

885 (23 Mar)–87. *Wmk Crown CA (sideways*). P* 14, 14½.
7 3 1d. pale claret .. .. 55·00 38·00
w. Wmk Crown to right of CA .. .. 75·00 50·00
x. Wmk sideways reversed .. .. £150 90·00
y. Wmk Crown to right of CA and reversed .. .. £150 90·00
8 1d. brownish claret (3.10.87) .. .. 80·00 35·00
a. Bisected (on cover) (1891) † .. .. † £2000
w. Wmk Crown to right of CA .. .. 90·00 42·00
x. Wmk sideways reversed £120 £100
y. Wmk Crown to right of CA and reversed £150 £120
9 4d. pale grey-black .. .. .. £400 42·00
w. Wmk Crown to right of CA .. .. £425 50·00
x. Wmk sideways reversed £500 £150
y. Wmk Crown to right of CA and reversed £500 £100
0 4d. grey-black (3.10.87) .. .. .. £325 35·00
w. Wmk Crown to right of CA .. .. £325 35·00
x. Wmk sideways reversed .. .. £550 90·00
y. Wmk Crown to right of CA and reversed .. .. £450 60·00

*The normal sideways watermark shows Crown to left of CA, s *seen from the back of the stamp.*
†See note below No. 14.

889 (26 Sept)–91. *Wmk Crown CA (upright). P* 14, 14½.
1 3 1d. red-brown (21.5.91) .. .. .. £130 60·00
a. Bisected (on cover)* .. .. .. † £2250
x. Wmk reversed £275 £150
2 4d. olive grey-black .. .. .. £110 45·00
w. Wmk inverted £325 £200
x. Wmk reversed £250 £100
See note below No. 14.

891 (Jan). *Nos.* 8 *and* 11 *bisected diagonally and each half handstamped with T* 4.
3 3 ½d. on half of 1d. brownish claret (No. 8) £500 £300
a. Unsevered pair £2250 £1000
b. Unsevered pair *se-tenant* with unsurcharged whole stamp .. £12000
c. Bisect *se-tenant* with unsurcharged whole stamp .. .. .. † £1100
4 ½d. on half 1d. red-brown (No. 11) .. £550 £250
a. Unsevered pair £2500 £1200
b. Bisect *se-tenant* with unsurcharged whole stamp .. .. .. † £1000

891 PROVISIONALS. In 1891 the postage to the United ingdom and Colonies was reduced from 4d. to 2½d. per half unce. As no ½d. or 2½d. stamps were available the bisection of he 1d. was authorised from 1 January 1891. This authorisation as withdrawn on 11 January 1892, although bisects were ccepted for postage until July of that year. The ½d. and 2½d. amps were placed on sale from 10 September 1891.

Cork Cancel used in 1891

The Type **4** surcharge was not used regularly; unsurcharged isects being employed far more frequently. Genuine bisects should e cancelled with the cork cancel illustrated above. The use of any her postmark, including a different cork cancel, requires date vidence linked to known mail ship sailings to prove authenticity. Posthumous strikes of the surcharge on "souvenir" bisects sually show a broken "2" and/or a large full stop. These are known n bisected examples of No. 18 and on varieties such as surcharge verted, double or sideways. Forgeries exist of all these rovisionals.

891 (10 Sept*)–1902. *Wmk Crown CA (upright). P* 14, 14½.
5 3 ½d. blue-green (Aug–Nov 1891) .. 19·00 26·00
x. Wmk reversed £200 £200
y. Wmk inverted and reversed .. £200 £200
6 ½d. green (20.5.92) .. .. .. 16·00 15·00
ax. Wmk reversed £100 £100
ay. Wmk inverted and reversed .. £200 £200
b. Deep dull green (15.4.96) .. .. 40·00 30·00
7 ½d. deep yellow-green (1894–95) .. 17·00 21·00
ay. Wmk inverted and reversed .. £100 £100
b. Yellow-green (19.6.99) .. .. 2·00 2·50
c. Dull yellowish green (13.1.1902) .. 4·50 3·25
cx. Wmk reversed £200 £200
8 1d. orange red-brown (14.10.91) .. 60·00 48·00
a. Brown .. .. 80·00 50·00
w. Wmk inverted £500 £250
x. Wmk reversed £150 £150
9 1d. reddish chestnut (20.4.92) .. .. 40·00 42·00
0 1d. orange-brn (wmk reversed) (18.1.94) 38·00 38·00
1 1d. claret (23.7.94) .. .. .. 80·00 80·00
x. Wmk reversed .. .. .. 50·00 48·00
2 1d. Venetian red (pale to deep) (1895–96) 15·00 14·00
ax. Wmk reversed .. .. .. 9·00 10·00
b. Venetian claret (1898?) .. .. 28·00 12·00
3 1d. pale red (19.6.99) .. .. .. 5·00 2·00
x. Wmk reversed £150 £150
4 1d. orange-red (13.1.1902) .. .. 8·50 3·50
5 2d. purple (pale to deep) (1895–98) .. 6·50 12·00
x. Wmk reversed £225 £250
6 2d. reddish purple (15.4.96) .. .. 5·00 11·00
7 2½d. pale chalky ultramarine (8.91) .. £110 38·00
28 3 2½d. dull blue (19.11.91) .. .. .. £100 18·00
x. Wmk reversed £225 £200
29 2½d. Prussian blue (18.1.94) £225 £140
30 2½d. ultramarine (1894–96) .. .. 20·00 8·50
ax. Wmk reversed .. .. .. 35·00 10·00
b. Pale ultramarine (10.6.98) .. .. 26·00 12·00
bx. Wmk reversed .. .. .. £100 75·00
c. Deep ultramarine (18.9.1901) .. 28·00 28·00
cx. Wmk reversed £180 £180
31 4d. brownish black (wmk reversed) (18.1.94) £550 £275
32 4d. olive-black (11.5.95) .. .. 10·00 21·00
33 6d. orange-yellow (19.11.91) £150 £120
x. Wmk reversed .. .. .. 42·00 38·00
34 6d. yellow (15.4.96) .. .. .. 27·00 35·00
35 9d. pale reddish orange (15.11.95) .. 28·00 55·00
x. Wmk reversed £180 £200
y. Wmk inverted and reversed .. £275 £275
36 9d. salmon (15.4.96) .. .. .. 32·00 48·00
x. Wmk reversed £180 £200
37 1s. grey-brown (15.11.95) .. .. 42·00 45·00
x. Wmk reversed £120 £120
38 1s. yellow-brown (15.4.96) .. .. 40·00 40·00
w. Wmk inverted £120 £120
15/38 .. .. *Set of* 8 £120 £150
15, 26, 28, 33, 35 Optd "Specimen" *Set of* 5 £600

*The ½d. and 2½d. were first placed on sale in the Falkland Islands on 10 September 1891. Such stamps came from the August 1891 printing. It is now believed that the stock of the May printings sent to the Falkland Islands was lost at sea.

The 2½d. ultramarine printing can sometimes be found in a violet shade, but the reason for this is unknown.

5

6

(Recess B.W.)

1898 (5 Oct). *Wmk Crown CC. P* 14, 14½.
41 5 2s. 6d. deep blue £200 £250
42 6 5s. red £160 £200
41/2 Optd "Specimen" .. .. *Set of* 2 £450

7

8

(Recess D.L.R.)

1904 (16 July)–12. *Wmk Mult Crown CA. P* 14.
43 7 ½d. yellow-green .. .. .. 4·25 1·50
aw. Wmk inverted £150 £110
b. Pale yell-grn (on thick paper) (6.08) 12·00 9·00
bw. Wmk inverted .. .. ..
c. Deep yellow-green (7.11) .. .. 9·00 3·00
44 1d. vermilion .. .. 9·00 1·50
aw. Wmk inverted £150 £120
ax. Wmk reversed £225 £200
b. Wmk sideways (7.06) .. .. 1·00 2·25
c. Thick paper (1908) .. .. .. 12·00 1·75
cw. Wmk inverted £250 £200
cx. Wmk reversed £300 £200
d. Dull coppery red (on thick paper) (3.08) .. .. £170 35·00
dx. Wmk reversed £450 £200
e. Orange-vermilion (7.11) .. .. 9·00 2·25
ex. Wmk reversed £250 £250
45 2d. purple (27.12.04) .. .. .. 11·00 26·00
ax. Wmk reversed £110 £110
b. Reddish purple (13.1.12) £225 £275
46 2½d. ultramarine (*shades*) .. .. 29·00 7·50
aw. Wmk inverted £130 £130
ay. Wmk inverted and reversed .. — £350
b. Deep blue (13.1.12) £225 £180
47 6d. orange (27.12.04) .. .. .. 38·00 48·00
48 1s. brown (27.12.04) .. .. .. 40·00 32·00
49 8 3s. green £140 £130
aw. Wmk inverted £950
b. Deep green (4.07) £120 £120
bx. Wmk reversed £950 £650
50 5s. red (27.12.04) £140 £150
43/50 .. .. *Set of* 8 £325 £350
43/50 Optd "Specimen" .. .. *Set of* 8 £450

Examples of Nos. 41/50 and earlier issues are known with a forged Falkland Islands postmark dated "OCT 15 10".

For details of South Georgia underprint, South Georgia provisional handstamps and Port Foster handstamp see under FALKLAND ISLANDS DEPENDENCIES.

9

10

Des B. MacKennal. Eng J. A. C. Harrison. Recess D.L.R.)

1912 (3 July)–20. *Wmk Mult Crown CA. P* 13¾×14 (*comb*) (½d. *to* 1s.) *or* 14 (*line*) (3s. *to* £1).
60 9 ½d. yellow-green .. .. .. 2·75 3·50
a. Perf 14 (line). *Dp yell-green* (1914) 18·00 35·00
b. Perf 14 (line). *Deep olive* (1918) .. 24·00 80·00
c. Deep olive (4.19) .. .. .. 3·50 22·00
ca. Printed both sides .. .. .. † £5500
d. Dull yellowish green (on thick greyish paper) (1920) .. .. 4·50 26·00
61 1d. orange-red .. .. 4·75 2·50
a. Perf 14 (line). *Orange-vermilion* (1914, 1916) .. .. .. 20·00 2·25
b. Perf 14 (line). *Vermilion* (1918) .. † £550
c. Orange-vermilion (4.19) .. .. 3·50 3·00
d. Orange-vermilion (on thick greyish paper) (1920) .. .. .. 7·00 2·00
dx. Wmk reversed £130
62 2d. maroon .. .. 20·00 23·00
a. Perf 14 (line). *Dp reddish pur* (1914) 80·00 75·00
b. Perf 14 (line). *Maroon* (4.18) .. 80·00 75·00
c. Deep reddish purple (4.19) .. .. 7·00 16·00
63 2½d. deep bright blue .. .. .. 18·00 21·00
a. Perf 14 (line). *Dp bright blue* (1914) 26·00 27·00
b. Perf 14 (line). *Deep blue* (1916, 4.18) 26·00 27·00
c. Deep blue (4.19) .. .. .. 7·00 17·00
64 6d. yellow-orange (6.7.12) .. .. 14·00 20·00
aw. Wmk inverted £275 £300
b. Brown-orange (4.19) .. .. .. 11·00 35·00
65 1s. light bistre-brown (6.7.12) .. .. 30·00 30·00
a. Pale bistre-brown (4.19) .. .. 48·00 85·00
b. Brn (on thick greyish paper) (1920) 32·00 £130
66 10 3s. slate-green .. .. 70·00 80·00
67 5s. deep rose-red .. .. .. 70·00 95·00
a. Reddish maroon (1914) £170 £190
b. Maroon (1916) .. .. .. 70·00 95·00
bx. Wmk reversed £1800 £1100
68 10s. red/*green* (11.2.14) £150 £225
69 £1 black/*red* (11.2.14) £325 £375
60/9 (*inc* 67*b*) .. .. .. *Set of* 11 £650 £850
60/9 (*inc* 67*a*) Optd "Specimen" .. *Set of* 11 £1300

The exact measurement of the comb perforation used for Type **9** is 13.7 × 13.9. The line perforation, used for the 1914, 1916 and 1918 printings and for all the high values in Type **10**, measured 14.1 × 14.1.

It was previously believed that all examples of the 1d. in vermilion with the line perforation were overprinted to form No. 71, but it has now been established that some unoverprinted sheets of No. 61b were used during 1919.

Many of the sheets showed sheets from the left-hand side in a lighter shade than those from the right. It is believed that this was due to the weight of the impression. Such differences are particularly noticeable on the 2½d. 1916 and 1918 printings where the lighter shades, approaching milky blue in appearance, are scarce.

All 1919 printings show weak impressions of the background either side of the head caused by the poor paper quality.

Examples of all values are known with forged postmarks, including one of Falkland Islands dated "5 SP 19" and another of South Shetlands dated "20 MR 27".

WAR STAMP

(11)

2½D

(12)

1918 (22 Oct*)–20. *Optd by Govt Printing Press, Stanley, with T* 11.
70 9 ½d. deep olive (line perf) (No. 60b) .. 1·00 6·50
a. Yellow-green (No. 60) (4.19) .. 13·00
ab. Albino opt £1100
b. Deep olive (comb perf) (No. 60c) (4.19) 50 6·50
c. Dull yellowish green (on thick greyish paper) (No. 60*d*) (5.20) .. .. 10·00 65·00
cx. Wmk reversed £150
71 1d. vermilion (line perf) (No. 61b) .. 2·00 16·00
a. Opt double, one albino £400
b. Orge-verm (line perf) (No. 61a) (4.19) 12·00 †
c. Orge-verm (comb perf) (No. 61*c*) (4.19) 50 3·50
ca. Opt double £1600
cx. Wmk reversed £250
d. Orange-vermilion (on thick greyish paper) (No. 61*d*) (5.20) .. .. .. 75·00 £150
72 1s. light bistre-brown (No. 65) .. .. 30·00 60·00
a. Pale bistre-brown (No. 65*a*) (4.19) .. 4·00 42·00
ab. Opt double, one albino £1200
ac. Opt omitted (in pair with normal) .. £6000
b. Brown (on thick greyish paper) (No. 65*b*) (5.20) .. .. 7·00 42·00
ba. Opt double, one albino £1200
bw. Wmk inverted £150 £200
bx. Wmk reversed £450

*Earliest known postal use. Cancellations dated 8 October were applied much later.

There were five printings of the "WAR STAMP" overprint, but all, except that in May 1920, used the same setting. Composition of the five printings was as follows:

October 1918. Nos. 70, 71 and 72
January 1919. Nos. 70, 71 and 72
April 1919. Nos. 70/*b*, 71*b*/*c* and 72*a*
October 1919. Nos. 70*b*, 71*c* and 72*a*
May 1920. Nos. 70*c*, 71*d* and 72*b*.

It is believed that the entire stock of No. 70*a* was sold to stamp dealers. Only a handful of used examples are known which may have subsequently been returned to the colony for cancellation.

No. 71ca exists in a block of 12 (6×2) from the bottom of a sheet on which the first stamp in the bottom row shows a single overprint, but the remainder have overprint double.

Examples of Nos. 70/2 are known with a forged Falkland Islands postmark dated "5 SP 19".

1921–28. *Wmk Mult Script CA. P* 14.
73 9 ½d. yellowish green .. .. .. 3·00 4·00
a. Green (1925) .. .. .. 3·00 4·00
74 1d. dull vermilion (1924) .. .. 5·00 1·25
aw. Wmk inverted .. .. .. † £1000
ay. Wmk inverted and reversed .. £190
b. Orange-vermilion (shades) (1925) .. 5·50 1·25

75 **9** 2d. deep brown-purple (8.23) .. .. 10·00 6·00
aw. Wmk inverted .. .. .. — £900
ax. Wmk reversed £950
b. Purple-brown (1927) .. .. 12·00 14·00
c. Reddish maroon (1.28) .. .. 8·00 17·00
cy. Wmk inverted and reversed ..
76 2½d. deep blue .. .. 22·00 16·00
a. Indigo (28.4.27) .. .. .. 16·00 20·00
b. Deep steel-blue (1.28) .. .. 5·50 16·00
c. Prussian blue (10.28) £300 £450
77 2½d. deep purple/*pale yellow* (8.23) .. 4·50 32·00
a. Pale purple/pale yellow (1925) .. 4·25 32·00
y. Wmk inverted and reversed .. £225
78 6d. yellow-orange (1925) .. .. 8·00 35·00
w. Wmk inverted £160
x. Wmk reversed £850
79 1s. deep ochre .. .. 16·00 48·00
80 **10** 3s. slate-green (8.23) .. .. .. 80·00 £130
73/80 .. .. *Set of* 8 £110 £225
73/80 (*incl* 76*a*) Optd "Specimen" *Set of* 9 £550

Dates quoted above are those of despatch from Great Britain.

No. 76c only occurred in part of the October 1928 printing. The remainder were in the deep steel-blue shade of the January 1928 despatch, No. 76*b*.

1928 (7 Feb). *No. 75a surch with T* **12**.
115 **9** 2½d. on 2d. purple-brown .. £650 £750
a. Surch double £30000

No. 115 was produced on South Georgia during a shortage of 2½d. stamps. The provisional was withdrawn on 22 February 1928.

13 Fin Whale and Gentoo Penguins **14**

(Recess P.B.)

1929 (2 Sept)–**36**. *P* 14 (*comb*). (*a*) *Wmk Mult Script CA*.
116 **13** ½d. green .. .. 80 3·00
a. Line perf (1936) .. .. .. 4·00 8·00
117 1d. scarlet .. .. 2·50 80
a. Line perf. *Deep red* (1936) .. 6·00 14·00
118 2d. grey .. .. 2·25 2·00
119 2½d. blue .. .. 2·50 2·25
120 **14** 4d. orange (*line perf*) (18.2.32) .. 12·00 13·00
a. Deep orange (1936) .. .. 27·00 48·00
121 **13** 6d. purple .. .. 13·00 13·00
a. Line perf. *Reddish purple* (1936) 35·00 25·00
122 1s. black/*emerald* .. .. .. 17·00 26·00
a. Line perf. *On bright emerald* (1936) 22·00 27·00
123 2s. 6d carmine/*blue* .. .. .. 35·00 40·00
124 5s. green/*yellow* .. .. .. 60·00 75·00
125 10s. carmine/*emerald* £100 £140
(*b*) *Wmk Mult Crown CA*
126 **13** £1 black/*red* £275 £375
116/26 .. .. .. *Set of* 11 £450 £600
116/26 Perf "Specimen" .. .. *Set of* 11 £1000

Two kinds of perforation exist:
A. Comb perf 13.9:—original values of 1929.
B. Line perf 13.9×14.2 or 14.2 (small holes)—4d. and 1936 printings of ½d., 1d., 6d. and 1s. On some sheets the last vertical row of perforations shows larger holes.

Examples of most values are known with forged postmarks, including one of Port Stanley dated "14 JY 31" and another of South Georgia dated "AU 30 31".

15 Romney Marsh Ram

26 King George V

(Des (except 6d.) by G. Roberts. Eng and recess B.W.)

1933 (2 Jan–Apr). *Centenary of British Administration. T* **15**, **26** *and similar designs. Wmk Mult Script CA. P* 12.
127 ½d. black and green .. .. 1·50 5·00
128 1d. black and scarlet .. .. 3·50 2·25
129 1½d. black and blue .. .. 10·00 13·00
130 2d. black and brown .. .. 9·00 21·00
131 3d. black and violet .. .. 11·00 14·00
132 4d. black and orange .. .. 11·00 15·00
133 6d. black and slate .. .. 48·00 55·00
134 1s. black and olive-green .. .. .. 38·00 55·00
135 2s. 6d. black and violet £130 £150
136 5s. black and yellow £500 £650
a. Black and yellow-orange (Apr) .. £1000 £1200
137 10s. black and chestnut £500 £700
138 £1 black and carmine £1300 £1800
127/138 .. .. .. *Set of* 12 £2250 £3000
127/38 Perf "Specimen" .. .. *Set of* 12 £2250

Designs: *Horiz*—1d. Iceberg; 1½d. Whale-catcher *Bransfield*; 2d. Port Louis; 3d. Map of Falkland Islands; 4d. South Georgia; 6d. Fin Whale; 1s. Government House, Stanley. *Vert*—2s. 6d. Battle Memorial; 5s. King Penguin; 10s. Coat of Arms.

Examples of all values are known with forged Port Stanley postmarks dated "6 JA 33". Some values have also been seen with part strikes of the forged Falkland Islands postmark mentioned below Nos. 60/9 and 70/2.

1935 (7 May). *Silver Jubilee. As Nos.* 91/4 *of Antigua, but printed by B.W. P* 11 × 12.
139 1d. deep blue and scarlet .. .. .. 2·75 40
b. Short extra flagstaff £300 £190
d. Flagstaff on right-hand turret .. £190 £150
e. Double flagstaff £225 £170
140 2½d. brown and deep blue .. .. .. 8·00 1·60
b. Short extra flagstaff £650 £325
d. Flagstaff on right-hand turret .. £225 £160
e. Double flagstaff £325 £190
l. Re-entry on value tablet (R. 8/1) .. £200 £100
141 4d. green and indigo .. .. .. 9·00 4·00
b. Short extra flagstaff £475 £300
d. Flagstaff on right-hand turret .. £300 £190
e. Double flagstaff £350 £225
142 1s. slate and purple .. .. .. 8·00 3·25
a. Extra flagstaff £2750 £2250
b. Short extra flagstaff £500 £300
c. Lightning conductor £1200 £650
d. Flagstaff on right-hand turret .. £450 £300
e. Double flagstaff £500 £325
139/42 .. .. .. *Set of* 4 25·00 8·50
139/42 Perf "Specimen" .. .. *Set of* 4 £275

For illustrations of plate varieties see Catalogue Introduction.

1937 (12 May). *Coronation. As Nos.* 95/7 *of Antigua. P* 11×11½.
143 ½d. green 30 10
144 1d. carmine 40 45
145 2½d. blue 80 55
143/5 .. .. .. *Set of* 3 1·40 1·00
143/5 Perf "Specimen" .. .. *Set of* 3 £160

27 Whales' Jaw Bones

(Des G. Roberts (Nos. 146, 148/9, 158 and 160/3), K. Lellman (No. 159). Recess B.W.)

1938 (3 Jan)–**50**. *Horiz designs as T* **27**. *Wmk Mult Script CA. P* 12.
146 ½d. black and green (*shades*) 30 75
147 1d. black and carmine .. .. .. 26·00 80
a. Black and scarlet .. .. .. 3·00 85
148 1d. black and violet (14.7.41) .. .. 2·50 1·75
a. Black and purple-violet (1.43) .. 6·00 1·75
149 2d. black and deep violet .. .. 1·00 50
150 2d. black and carmine-red (14.7.41) .. 75 2·25
a. Black and red (1.43) .. .. 2·25 1·00
151 2½d. black and bright blue 75 30
152 2½d. black and blue (15.6.49) .. .. 5·50 6·50
153 3d. black and blue (14.7.41) .. .. 6·50 2·25
a. Black and deep blue (1.43) .. .. 8·50 2·25
154 4d. black and purple .. .. .. 2·75 50
155 6d. black and brown .. .. .. 3·25 1·50
156 6d. black (15.6.49) .. .. .. 4·25 3·75
157 9d. black and grey-blue .. .. .. 13·00 80
158 1s. pale blue .. .. 65·00 18·00
a. Deep blue (1941) .. .. .. 16·00 2·50
159 1s. 3d. black and carmine-red (11.12.46) .. 2·25 1·40
160 2s. 6d. slate .. .. 55·00 10·00
161 5s. bright blue and pale brown .. £110 55·00
b. Indigo and yellow-brown (1942) .. £500 £110
c. Blue and buff-brown (9.2.50) .. £130 £160
162 10s. black and orange .. .. .. 55·00 27·00
163 £1 black and violet .. .. .. £110 48·00
146/63 .. .. .. *Set of* 18 £350 £140
146/63 (*ex* 152, 156) Perf "Specimen" *Set of* 16 £950

Designs:—Nos. 147 and 150, Black-necked Swan; Nos. 148/9, Battle Memorial; Nos. 151 and 153, Flock of sheep; Nos. 152 and 154, Magellan Goose; Nos. 155/6, *Discovery II* (polar supply vessel); No. 157, *William Scoresby* (research ship); No. 158, Mount Sugar Top; No. 159; Turkey Vultures; No. 160 Gentoo Penguins; No. 161, Southern Sealion; No. 162, Deception Island; No. 163, Arms of Falkland Islands.

1946 (7 Oct). *Victory. As Nos.* 110/11 *of Antigua*.
164 1d. dull violet 30 15
165 3d. blue 45 15
164/5 Perf "Specimen" .. .. *Set of* 2 £140

1948 (1 Nov). *Royal Silver Wedding. As Nos.* 112/13 *of Antigua*.
166 2½d. ultramarine .. .. 2·00 70
167 £1 mauve .. .. 90·00 55·00

1949 (10 Oct). *75th Anniv of Universal Postal Union. As Nos.* 114/17 *of Antigua*.
168 1d. violet .. .. 1·50 75
169 3d. deep blue .. .. 5·00 2·00
170 1s. 3d. deep blue-green .. .. .. 4·00 2·25
171 2s. blue .. .. 4·00 7·50
168/71 .. .. .. *Set of* 4 13·00 11·00

39 Sheep

43 Arms of the Colony

(Des from sketches by V. Spencer. Recess Waterlow)

1952 (2 Jan). *T* **39**, **43** *and similar designs. Wmk Mult Scri CA. P* 13×13½ (*vert*) *or* 13½×13 (*horiz*).
172 ½d. green 70
173 1d. scarlet .. .. 1·25
174 2d. violet .. .. 3·25 2·
175 2½d. black and light ultramarine 95
176 3d. deep ultramarine .. .. .. 1·00 1·
177 4d. reddish purple .. .. .. 7·50 1·
178 6d. bistre-brown .. .. .. 12·00 1·
179 9d. orange-yellow .. .. .. 9·00 2·
180 1s. black .. .. 20·00
181 1s. 3d. orange .. .. .. 12·00 5·
182 2s. 6d. olive-green .. .. .. 16·00 7·
183 5s. purple .. .. 8·50 6·
184 10s. grey .. .. 20·00 17·
185 £1 black .. .. 25·00 17·
172/185 .. .. *Set of* 14 £120 55·

Designs: *Horiz*—1d. *Fitzroy* (supply ship); 2d. Magellan Goos 2½d. Map of Falkland Islands; 4d. Auster Autocrat aircraft; 6 *John Biscoe I* (research ship); 9d. View of the Two Sisters; 1s. 3 Kelp goose and gander; 10s. Southern Sealion and Sou American Fur Seal; £1 Hulk of *Great Britain*. *Vert*—1s. Gent Penguins; 2s. 6d. Sheep-shearing; 5s. Battle Memorial.

1953 (4 June). *Coronation. As No.* 120 *of Antigua*.
186 1d. black and scarlet .. .. 80 1·

53 *John Biscoe I* (research ship)

54 Austral Thrush

(Recess Waterlow)

1955–57. *Designs previously used for King George VI issue b with portrait of Queen Elizabeth II as in T* **53**. *Wmk Mult Scr CA. P* 13 × 13½ (*vert*) *or* 13½ × 13 (*horiz*).
187 ½d. green (2.9.57) 70 1
188 1d. scarlet (2.9.57) .. .. 1·25 1
189 2d. violet (3.9.56) .. .. 2·75 4·
190 6d. deep yellow-brown (1.6.55) .. .. 6·50
191 9d. orange-yellow (2.9.57) .. .. .. 17·00 17·
192 1s. black (15.7.55) .. .. 5·00 1·
187/92 .. .. .. *Set of* 6 30·00 23·

Designs: *Horiz*—½d. Sheep; 1d. *Fitzroy* (supply ship); 2 Magellan Goose; 9d. View of Two Sisters. *Vert*—1s. Gent Penguins.

(Des from sketches by S. Scott. Recess Waterlow, then D.L. (from 9.1.62 onwards))

1960 (10 Feb)–**66**. *T* **54** *and similar horiz designs. W w (upright). P* 13½.
193 ½d. black and myrtle-green .. .. 4·00
a. Black and green (DLR) (9.1.62) .. 12·00 4·
aw. Wmk inverted £2000 £10
194 1d. black and scarlet .. .. .. 1·50
a. Black and carmine-red (DLR) (15.7.63) 10·00 3·
195 2d. black and blue .. .. .. 3·25 1·
a. Black and deep blue (DLR) (25.10.66) 17·00 14·
196 2½d. black and yellow-brown .. .. 1·50
197 3d. black and olive 80
198 4d. black and carmine .. .. .. 1·25
199 5½d. black and violet .. .. .. 1·75 1·
200 6d. black and sepia .. .. .. 2·00
201 9d. black and orange-red .. .. .. 2·00
202 1s. black and maroon 80
203 1s. 3d. black and ultramarine .. .. 10·00 12·
204 2s. black and brown-red .. .. .. 27·00 2·
a. Black and lake-brown (DLR) (25.10.66) £120 42·
205 5s. black and turquoise .. .. .. 27·00 11·
206 10s. black and purple .. .. .. 48·00 13·
207 £1 black and orange-yellow .. .. 48·00 27·
193/207 .. .. .. *Set of* 15 £150 60·

Designs:—1d. Southern Black-backed Gull; 2d. Gent Penguins; 2½d. Long-tailed Meadowlark; 3d. Magellan Geese; Falkland Islands Flightless Steamer Ducks; 5½d. Rockhop Penguin; 6d. Black-browed Albatross; 9d. Silvery Grebe; Magellanic Oystercatchers; 1s. 3d. Chilean Teal; 2s. Kelp Gee 5s. King Cormorants; 10s. Common Caracara; £1 Black-neck Swan.

Waterlow

De La Rue

Waterlow printings were from Frame Plates 1 or 2. The De Rue printings of the ½d., 1d., 2d. and 2s. are all from Fra Plate 2 and can be distinguished by the finer lines of shading the Queen's face, neck and shoulders (appearing as a white fa and also the very faint cross hatching left of the face. Apart fr this the shades differ in varying degrees. Frame Plate 1 w used by De La Rue to print initial supplies of the 6d. and th stamps have little to distinguish them from the origi printing. Frame Plate 2 was subsequently used for this va which, although it shows the usual plate characteristics, d not differ in shade from the Waterlow printing.

For the ½d. with watermark sideways see No. 227.

69 Morse Key

70 One-valve Receiver

(Des M. Goaman. Photo Enschedé)

:962 (5 Oct). *50th Anniv of Establishment of Radio Communications. T* **69/70** *and similar vert design.* W w **12**. *P* 11½ × 11.
:08 **69** 6d. carmine-lake and orange .. .. 1·00 30
:09 **70** 1s. deep bluish green and yellow-olive 1·25 35
'10 – 2s. deep violet and ultramarine .. 1·25 1·50
w. Wmk inverted .. .. .. 50·00
:08/10 .. .. *Set of* 3 3·25 1·90
Design:—2s. Rotary Spark Transmitter.

:963 (4 June). *Freedom from Hunger. As No.* 146 *of Antigua.*
11 1s. ultramarine .. .. 13·00 1·25

:963 (2 Sept). *Red Cross Centenary. As Nos.* 147/8 *of Antigua.*
12 1d. red and black .. .. 5·00 50
13 1s. red and blue .. .. 20·00 6·00

:964 (23 April). *400th Birth Anniv of William Shakespeare. As No.* 164 *of Antigua.*
:14 6d. black .. .. 1·00 40

72 H.M.S. *Glasgow*

(Recess D.L.R.)

964 (8 Dec) *50th Anniv of the Battle of the Falkland Islands. T* **72** *and similar designs.* W w **12**. *P* 13 × 14 (2*s.*) *or* 13 (*others*).
:15 2½d. black and red .. .. .. 9·00 3·25
:16 6d. black and light blue 75 25
a. Centre Type **72** £17000
:17 1s. black and carmine-red 75 75
w. Wmk inverted £1100
:18 2s. black and blue 50 75
:15/18 .. .. *Set of* 10·00 4·50
Designs: *Horiz*—6d. H.M.S. *Kent*; 1s. H.M.S. *Invincible*. *Vert*—2s. Battle Memorial.
It is believed that No. 216a came from a sheet which was first printed with the centre of the 2½d. and then accidently included among the supply of the 6d. value and thus received the wrong frame. There have been seventeen reports of stamps showing the error, although it is believed that some of these *may* refer to the same example.

:965 (26 May). *I.T.U. Centenary. As Nos.* 166/7 *of Antigua.*
:19 1d. light blue and deep blue 75 20
w. Wmk inverted £500
:20 2s. lilac and bistre-yellow .. .. .. 9·00 1·50

:965 (25 Oct). *International Co-operation Year. As Nos.* 168/9 *of Antigua.*
:21 1d. reddish purple and turquoise-green .. 2·00 20
:22 1s. deep bluish green and lavender .. .. 7·50 1·10

:966 (24 Jan). *Churchill Commemoration. As Nos.* 170/3 *of Antigua.*
:23 ½d. new blue 65 50
:24 1d. deep green .. .. 2·25 15
w. Wmk inverted .. .. .. 6·00
:25 1s. brown .. .. 6·50 2·00
w. Wmk inverted .. .. .. 55·00
:26 2s. bluish violet .. .. 5·50 2·00
:23/6 .. .. *Set of* 4 13·50 4·25

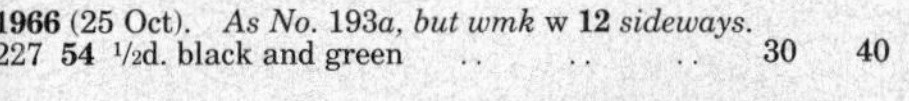

1966 (25 Oct). *As No.* 193*a*, *but wmk* w **12** *sideways.*
:27 **54** ½d. black and green 30 40

76 Globe and Human Rights Emblem

77 Dusty Miller

(Des M. Farrar Bell. Photo Harrison)

:968 (4 July). *Human Rights Year.* W w **12**. *P* 14 × 14½.
:28 **76** 2d. multicoloured 60 20
a. Yellow omitted ("1968" white) .. £900
:29 6d. multicoloured 70 20
:30 1s. multicoloured 70 20
:31 2s. multicoloured 70 30
:28/31 .. .. *Set of* 4 2·40 80

Two types of £1:
Type I. Pale brown shading does not extend to foot of design.
Type II. Pale brown shading to foot of design.

(Des Sylvia Goaman)

1968 (9 Oct)–**71**. *Flowers. Designs as T* **77**. *Chalk-surfaced paper.* W w **12** (*sideways on vert designs*). *P* 14.
232 ½d. multicoloured .. .. 15 1·60
233 1½d. multicoloured 30 15
234 2d. multicoloured 40 15
235 3d. multicoloured .. .. 4·75 65
236 3½d. multicoloured 30 15
237 4½d. multicoloured .. .. 1·25 1·75
238 5½d. olive-yellow, brown and yellow-green 1·25 1·75
239 6d. carmine, black and yellow-green .. 60 20
240 1s. multicoloured .. .. 60 1·00
w. Wmk inverted .. .. 80·00
241 1s. 6d. multicoloured .. .. 4·50 11·00
242 2s. multicoloured .. .. 5·50 6·50
243 3s. multicoloured .. .. 8·00 7·00
244 5s. multicoloured .. .. 27·00 13·00
245 £1 multicoloured (Type I) .. .. 13·00 2·00
a. Type II (15.2.71) .. .. .. 20·00 3·50
232/45 .. .. *Set of* 14 60·00 42·00
Designs: *Horiz*—1½d. Pig Vine; 3½d. Sea Cabbage; 5½d. Arrowleaf Marigold; 6d. Diddle Dee; 1s. Scurvy Grass; 5s. Felton's Flower. *Vert*—2d. Pale Maiden; 3d. Dog Orchid; 4½d. Vanilla Daisy; 1s. 6d. Prickly Burr; 2s. Fachine; 3s. Lavender; £1 Yellow Orchid.
For stamps inscribed in decimal currency see Nos. 276/88, 293/5 and 315.

91 De Havilland D.H.C.2 Beaver Seaplane

(Des V. Whiteley. Litho Format)

1969 (8 Apr). *21st Anniv of Government Air Services. T* **91** *and similar horiz designs. Multicoloured.* W w **12** (*sideways*). *P* 14.
246 2d. Type **91** 35 30
247 6d. Noorduyn Norseman V 40 35
248 1s. Auster Autocrat 50 35
249 2s. Falkland Islands Arms .. .. 1·25 1·75
246/9 .. .. *Set of* 4 2·25 2·50

92 Holy Trinity Church, 1869

(Des G. Drummond. Litho Format)

1969 (30 Oct). *Centenary of Bishop Stirling's Consecration. T* **92** *and similar horiz designs.* W w **12** (*sideways*). *P* 14.
250 2d. black, grey and apple-green 50 60
251 6d. black, grey and orange-red 50 60
252 1s. black, grey and lilac 50 60
253 2s. multicoloured 70 75
250/3 .. .. *Set of* 4 2·00 2·25
Designs:—6d. Christ Church Cathedral, 1969; 1s. Bishop Stirling; 2s. Bishop's Mitre.

96 Mounted Volunteer

97 S.S. *Great Britain* (1843)

(Des R. Granger Barrett. Litho B.W.)

1970 (30 Apr). *Golden Jubilee of Defence Force. T* **96** *and similar designs. Multicoloured.* W w **12** (*sideways on* 2*d. and* 1*s.*). *P* 13.
254 2d. Type **96** .. .. 1·90 70
255 6d. Defence Post (*horiz*) .. .. 2·00 70
256 1s. Corporal in Number One Dress Uniform 2·00 70
257 2s. Defence Force Badge (*horiz*) .. .. 3·00 75
254/7 .. .. *Set of* 4 8·00 2·50

(Des V. Whiteley. Litho J.W.)

1970 (30 Oct). *Restoration of S.S. "Great Britain". T* **97** *and views of the ship at different dates. Multicoloured.* W w **12** (*sideways**). *P* 14½×14.
258 2d. Type **97** .. .. 1·75 40
259 4d. In 1845 .. .. 2·00 1·00
w. Wmk Crown to right of CA .. .. 15·00
260 9d. In 1876 .. .. 2·00 1·00
261 1s. In 1886 .. .. 2·00 1·00
w. Wmk Crown to right of CA £700
262 2s. In 1970 .. .. 2·00 1·00
258/62 .. .. *Set of* 5 8·75 4·00
*The normal sideways watermark shows Crown to left of CA, *as seen from the back of the stamp.*

½p

(98)

99 Dusty Miller

1971 (15 Feb). *Decimal Currency. Nos.* 232/44 *surch as T* **98**. W w **12** (*sideways on vert designs*). *P* 14.
263 ½p. on ½d. multicoloured 25 20
264 1p. on 1½d. multicoloured 30 15
a. Error. Surch 5p. £375
b. Do. but surch at right £1000
c. Surch albino £100
d. Surch albino in pair with normal .. £3000
265 1½p. on 2d. multicoloured 30 15
266 2p. on 3d. multicoloured 50 20
267 2½p. on 3½d. multicoloured 30 20
268 3p. on 4½d. multicoloured 30 20
269 4p. on 5½d. olive-yellow, brown & yell-grn 30 20
270 5p. on 6d. carmine, black and yellow-green 30 20
271 6p. on 1s. multicoloured .. .. .. 6·00 4·25
272 7½p. on 1s. 6d. multicoloured .. .. 8·00 5·50
273 10p. on 2s. multicoloured .. .. .. 8·50 3·00
274 15p. on 3s. multicoloured .. .. .. 6·50 2·75
275 25p. on 5s. multicoloured .. .. .. 7·00 3·25
263/75 .. .. *Set of* 13 35·00 18·00

1972 (1 June). *As Nos.* 232/44, *but Glazed, ordinary paper and with values inscr in decimal currency as T* **99**. W w **12** (*sideways on* ½, 1½, 2, 3, 7½, 10 *and* 15*p.*). *P* 14.
276 ½p. multicoloured .. .. 35 4·00
277 1p. multicoloured (as 1½d.) 30 40
278 1½p. multicoloured (as 2d.) .. .. .. 30 3·50
279 2p. multicoloured (as 3d.) .. .. .. 13·00 1·25
280 2½p. multicoloured (as 3½d.) .. .. .. 35 3·50
281 3p. multicoloured (as 4½d.) .. .. .. 35 1·25
282 4p. olive-yellow, brown & yell-grn (as 5½d.) 40 50
283 5p. carmine, black and yellow-green (as 6d.) 40 55
284 6p. multicoloured (as 1s.) .. .. .. 20·00 9·50
285 7½p. multicoloured (as 1s. 6d.) .. .. 1·50 4·00
286 10p. multicoloured (as 2s.) .. .. .. 8·00 4·50
287 15p. multicoloured (as 3s.) .. .. .. 4·50 5·00
288 25p. multicoloured (as 5s.) .. .. .. 4·50 6·00
276/88 .. .. *Set of* 13 48·00 35·00
See also Nos. 293/5 and 315.

100 Romney Marsh Sheep and Southern Sealions

(Des (from photograph by D. Groves) and photo Harrison)

1972 (20 Nov). *Royal Silver Wedding. Multicoloured; background colour given.* W w **12**. *P* 14×14½.
289 **100** 1p. grey-green 40 40
290 10p. bright blue 85 85

1973 (14 Nov). *Royal Wedding. As Nos.* 165/6 *of Anguilla. Centre multicoloured.* W w **12** (*sideways*). *P* 13½.
291 5p. bright mauve 25 10
292 15p. brown-ochre 35 20

1974 (25 Feb–18 Oct). *As Nos.* 276, 279 *and* 284, *but wmk upright on* ½*p. and* 2*p. and sideways* on* 6*p. P* 14.
293 ½p. multicoloured (18.10.74) .. .. 12·00 28·00
w. Wmk inverted £180
294 2p. multicoloured .. .. 20·00 3·25
w. Wmk inverted £325
295 6p. multicoloured (28.3.74) .. .. 2·00 2·25
w. Wmk Crown to right of CA £400
293/5 .. .. *Set of* 3 30·00 30·00
*The normal sideways watermark shows Crown to left of CA. *as seen from the back of the stamp.*

101 South American Fur Seal

102 19th-Century Mail-coach

(Des J. Cooter. Litho Walsall)

1974 (6 Mar). *Tourism. T* **101** *and similar horiz designs. Multicoloured.* W w **12**. *P* 14.
296 2p. Type **101** .. .. 2·25 1·00
297 4p. Trout-fishing .. .. 3·00 1·25
298 5p. Rockhopper penguins .. .. .. 9·50 2·50
299 15p. Long-tailed Meadowlark .. .. 12·00 4·25
296/9 .. .. *Set of* 4 24·00 8·00

(Des PAD Studio. Litho Questa)

1974 (31 July). *Centenary of Universal Postal Union. T* **102** *and similar vert designs. Multicoloured. W* w **12** (*sideways*). *P* 14.

300	2p. Type **102** ..	25	25
301	5p. Packet ship, 1841	35	45
302	8p. First U.K. aerial post, 1911	40	55
303	16p. Ship's catapult mail, 1920's	60	75
300/3	*Set of* 4	1·40	1·75

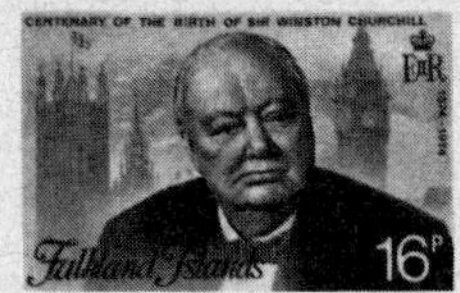

103 Churchill and Houses of Parliament

(Des G. Vasarhelyi. Litho Enschedé)

1974 (30 Nov). *Birth Centenary of Sir Winston Churchill. T* **103** *and similar horiz design. Multicoloured. W* w **12**. *P* 13½.

304	16p. Type **103**	1·40	1·60
305	20p. Churchill with H.M.S. *Inflexible* and H.M.S. *Invincible*, 1914	1·40	1·90
MS306	108×83 mm. Nos. 304/5	8·00	7·00
	w. Wmk inverted	£170	

104 H.M.S. *Exeter*

105 Seal and Flag Badge

(Des J.W. Litho Harrison)

1974 (13 Dec). *35th Anniv of the Battle of the River Plate. T* **104** *and similar horiz designs. Multicoloured. W* w **12** (*sideways**). *P* 14.

307	2p. Type **104**	3·00	1·60
	w. Wmk Crown to right of CA	10·00	6·00
308	6p. H.M.N.Z.S. *Achilles* ..	4·50	3·50
	w. Wmk Crown to right of CA	8·00	3·50
309	8p. *Admiral Graf Spee*	5·00	4·50
	w. Wmk Crown to right of CA	85·00	50·00
310	16p. H.M.S. *Ajax* ..	8·50	15·00
	w. Wmk Crown to right of CA	24·00	17·00
307/10	*Set of* 4	19·00	22·00

*The normal sideways watermark shows Crown to left of CA, *as seen from the back of the stamp.*

(Des PAD Studio. Litho Walsall)

1975 (28 Oct). *50th Anniv of Heraldic Arms. T* **105** *and similar vert designs. Multicoloured. W* w **14** (*inverted*). *P* 14.

311	2p. Type **105** ..	70	35
312	7½p. Coat of arms, 1925	1·40	1·40
313	10p. Coat of arms, 1948	1·60	1·60
314	16p. Arms of the Dependencies, 1952	2·25	3·25
311/14	*Set of* 4	5·50	6·00

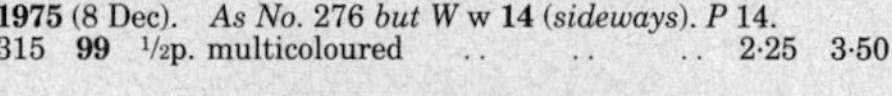

1975 (8 Dec). *As No. 276 but W* w **14** (*sideways*). *P* 14.

315 **99**	½p. multicoloured	2·25	3·50

106 ½p. Coin and Brown Trout

(Des G. Drummond. Litho Questa)

1975 (31 Dec). *New Coinage. T* **106** *and similar horiz designs each showing coin. Multicoloured. W* w **12** (*sideways**). *P* 14.

316	2p. Type **106**	85	50
	w. Wmk Crown to right of CA ..	60·00	
317	5½p. Gentoo Penguin and 1p. coin	1·25	1·40
318	8p. Magellan Goose and 2p. coin	1·60	1·60
319	10p. Black-browed Albatross and 5p. coin	1·75	1·75
320	16p. Southern Sealion and 10p. coin	1·90	2·25
316/20	*Set of* 5	6·75	6·75

*The normal sideways watermark shows Crown to left of CA, *as seen from the back of the stamp.*

107 Gathering Sheep

(Des PAD Studio. Litho J.W.)

1976 (28 Apr). *Sheep Farming Industry. T* **107** *and similar horiz designs. Multicoloured. W* w **14** (*sideways*). *P* 13½.

321	2p. Type **107** ..	55	40
322	7½p. Shearing ..	1·25	1·50
323	10p. Dipping ..	1·60	1·60
324	20p. Shipping ..	2·25	3·00
321/4	*Set of* 4	5·00	6·00

108 The Queen awaiting Anointment

(Des M. and G. Shamir; adapted J.W. Litho Questa)

1977 (7 Feb–1 Nov). *Silver Jubilee. T* **108** *and similar horiz designs. Multicoloured. P* 13½. (*a*) *W* w **14** (*sideways*).

325	6p. Visit of Prince Philip, 1957	2·00	1·25
326	11p. Queen Elizabeth, ampulla and anointing spoon	30	75
	a. Booklet pane of 4 with blank margins (1.11.77) ..	75	
327	33p. Type **108** ..	40	1·25
	a. Booklet pane of 4 with blank margins (1.11.77) ..	1·00	
	(*b*) *W* w **12** (*sideways*) (*from booklets only*) (1.11.77)		
327*b*	6p. Visit of Prince Philip,1957	2·75	4·00
	b*a*. Booklet pane of 4 with blank margins ..	10·00	
325/7*b*	*Set of* 4	5·00	6·50

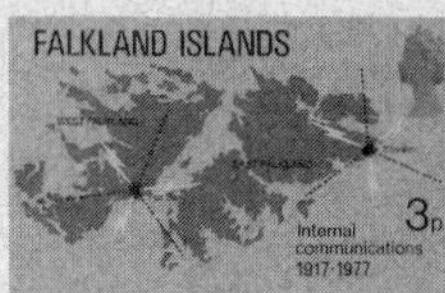

109 Map of Falkland Islands

(Des K. Penny. Litho Questa)

1977 (24 Oct). *Telecommunications. T* **109** *and similar horiz designs. Multicoloured. W* w **14** (*sideways**). *P* 14½.

328	3p. Type **109**	60	15
329	11p. Ship to shore communications	1·00	40
	w. Wmk Crown to right of CA ..		
330	40p. Telex and telephone service ..	2·75	1·75
328/30	*Set of* 3	4·00	2·10

*The normal sideways watermark shows Crown to left of CA, *as seen from the back of the stamp.*

110 *A.E.S.*, 1957–74

(Des J. Smith; adapted R. Granger Barrett. Litho Questa)

1978 (25 Jan)–**82.** *Mail Ships. Horiz designs as T* **110**. *Multicoloured. W* w **14** (*sideways**). *P* 14. A. *Without imprint date.*

331A	1p. Type **110**	20	30
332A	2p. *Darwin*, 1957–73	30	30
333A	3p. *Merak-N.*, 1951–2	25	80
	w. Wmk Crown to right of CA	£190	
334A	4p. *Fitzroy*, 1936–57	30	40
335A	5p. *Lafonia*, 1936–41	30	30
336A	6p. *Fleurus*, 1924–33	30	40
337A	7p. *Falkland*, 1914–34 ..	30	1·50
338A	8p. *Oravia*, 1900–12	35	50
339A	9p. *Memphis*, 1890–97 ..	35	50
340A	10p. *Black Hawk*, 1873–80	35	50
341A	20p. *Foam*, 1863–72	1·75	1·50
342A	25p. *Fairy*, 1857–61	2·00	3·00
343A	50p. *Amelia*, 1852–54	2·25	4·00
	w. Wmk Crown to right of CA	£250	
344A	£1 *Nautilus*, 1846–48 ..	4·00	7·00
345A	£3 *Hebe*, 1842–46	11·00	16·00
331A/45A	*Set of* 15	21·00	32·00
	B. *With imprint date* ("1982") *at foot* (1.12.82†)		
331B	1p. Type **110**	45	1·00
332B	2p. *Darwin*, 1957–73	50	1·00
333B	3p. *Merak-N.*, 1951–2	65	1·00
334B	4p. *Fitzroy*, 1936–57	65	1·25
335B	5p. *Lafonia*, 1936–41	65	1·25
336B	6p. *Fleurus*, 1924–33	65	1·25
337B	7p. *Falkland*, 1914–34 ..	70	1·25
338B	8p. *Oravia*, 1900–12	70	1·25
339B	9p. *Memphis*, 1890–97 ..	70	1·25
340B	10p. *Black Hawk*, 1873–80	70	1·25
341B	20p. *Foam*, 1863–72	1·25	1·75
342B	25p. *Fairy*, 1857–61	1·25	2·50
343B	50p. *Amelia*, 1852–54	2·25	3·00
344B	£1 *Nautilus*, 1846–48 ..	2·50	4·50
345B	£3 *Hebe*, 1842–46	5·50	9·50
331B/45B	*Set of* 15	17·00	30·00

*The normal sideways watermark shows Crown to left of CA, *as seen from the back of the stamp.*

†Nos. 331B/45B were available from the Crown Agents in London on 13 July 1982.

111 Short Hythe at Stanley

(Des L. McCombie. Litho Walsall)

1978 (28 Apr). *26th Anniv of First Direct Flight, Southampton Port Stanley. T* **111** *and similar horiz design. Multicoloure* W w **14** (*sideways*). *P* 14.

346	11p. Type **111**	2·75	2·5
347	33p. Route map and Short Hythe	3·25	3·0

112 Red Dragon of Wales

113 First Fox Bay P.O. and 1d. Stamp of 1878

(Des C. Abbott. Litho Questa)

1978 (2 June). *25th Anniv of Coronation. T* **112** *and similar ve designs. P* 15.

348	25p. bistre, bright blue and silver	60	1·0
	a. Sheetlet. Nos. 348/50 × 2	3·00	
349	25p. multicoloured	60	1·0
350	25p. bistre, bright blue and silver	60	1·0
348/50	*Set of* 3	1·60	2·7

Designs:—No. 348, Type **112**; No. 349, Queen Elizabeth II; N 350, Hornless Ram.

Nos. 348/50 were printed together in small sheets of 6, containir two *se-tenant* strips of 3, with horizontal gutter margin between.

(Des J. Cooter. Litho B.W.)

1978 (8 Aug). *Centenary of First Falkland Is Postage Stamp T* **113** *and similar vert designs. Multicoloured. W* w 1 *P* 13½ × 13.

351	3p. Type **113**	25	
352	11p. Second Stanley P.O. and 4d. stamp of 1879 ..	40	
353	15p. New Island P.O. and 6d. stamp of 1878	50	
	w. Wmk inverted	£700	
354	22p. First Stanley P.O. and 1s. stamp of 1878 ..	80	1·(
351/4	*Set of* 4	1·75	2·1

114 *Macrocystis pyrifera*

115 Britten Norman Islander over Falkland Islands

(Des I. Strange. Litho Questa)

1979 (19 Feb). *Kelp and Seaweed. T* **114** *and similar mul coloured designs. W* w **14** (*sideways on* 11 *and* 15p.). *P* 14.

355	3p. Type **114** ..	30	
356	7p. *Durvillea* sp	50	
357	11p. *Lessonia* sp (*horiz*)	65	
358	15p. *Callophyllis* sp (*horiz*)	85	
359	25p. *Iradaea* sp	1·00	1·
355/9	*Set of* 5	3·00	3·

(Des G. Hutchins. Litho Rosenbaum Bros, Vienna)

1979 (1 May). *Opening of Stanley Airport. T* **115** *and simil horiz designs showing diagrammatic drawings. Mul coloured. W* w **14** (*sideways**). *P* 13½.

360	3p. Type **115**	30	
	w. Wmk Crown to right of CA ..	30·00	
361	11p. Fokker F.27 Friendship over South Atlantic	70	
	w. Wmk Crown to left of CA	50·00	
362	15p. Fokker F.28 Fellowship over Airport	80	
	w. Wmk Crown to left of CA	35·00	
363	25p. Cessna 172 Skyhawk, Britten Norman Islander, Fokker F.27 Friendship and Fokker F.28 Fellowship over runway	1·50	
	w. Wmk Crown to left of CA	3·50	
360/3	*Set of* 4	3·00	2·

*The normal sideways watermark shows Crown to left of C on the 3p. and Crown to right of CA on the other values, *all seen from the back of the stamp.*

COVER PRICES

Cover factors are quoted at the beginning of eac country for most issues to 1945. An explanation the system can be found on page x. The facto quoted do not, however, apply to philatelic cover

116 Sir Rowland Hill and 1953 Coronation 1d. Commemorative

(Des J.W. Litho Questa)

979 (27 Aug). *Death Centenary of Sir Rowland Hill. T* **116** *and similar multicoloured designs showing stamps and portrait. W* w **14** (*sideways* on* 3 *and* 25*p.*). *P* 14.

54	3p. Type **116**	25	25
	w. Wmk Crown to left of CA	2·00	
65	11p. 1878 1d. stamp (*vert*)	40	70
66	25p. Penny Black	60	85
	w. Wmk Crown to left of CA	£200	
64/6	*Set of* 3	1·10	1·60
IS367	137×98 mm. 33p. 1916 5s. stamp (*vert*)	85	1·50

*The normal sideways watermark shows Crown to right of 'A, *as seen from the back of the stamp.*

117 Mail Drop by De Havilland D.H.C.2 Beaver Aircraft

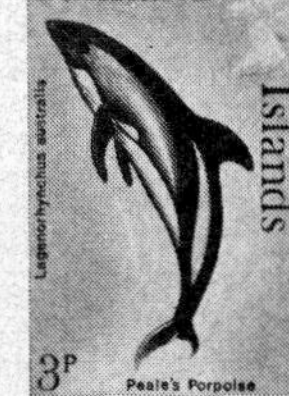

118 Peale's Dolphin

(Des A. Peake; adapted J.W. Litho Questa)

979 (26 Nov). *Centenary of U.P.U. Membership. T* **117** *and similar horiz designs. Multicoloured.* W w **14** (*sideways**). *P* 14.

68	3p. Type **117**	20	20
	w. Wmk Crown to right of CA	2·00	
69	11p. Mail by horseback	45	55
70	25p. Mail by schooner *Gwendolin*	75	1·00
68/70	*Set of* 3	1·25	1·60

*The normal sideways watermark shows Crown to left of CA, *as seen from the back of the stamp.*

(Des I. Strange. Litho Harrison)

980 (25 Feb). *Dolphins and Porpoises. T* **118** *and similar designs.* W w **14** (*sideways* on* 6, 7, 15 *and* 25*p.*). *P* 14.

71	3p. black, chestnut and blue	40	40
	w. Wmk inverted	£190	
72	6p. multicoloured	50	50
73	7p. multicoloured	50	50
74	11p. black, new blue and rose-red	70	80
75	15p. black, chestnut and greyish blue	80	1·00
	w. Wmk Crown to right of CA	55·00	
76	25p. multicoloured	1·00	1·60
71/6	*Set of* 6	3·50	4·25

Designs: *Horiz*—6p. Commerson's Dolphin; 7p. Hourglass Dolphin; 15p. Dusky Dolphin; 25p. Killer Whale. *Vert*—11p. Spectacled Porpoise.

*The normal sideways watermark shows Crown to left of CA, *as seen from the back of the stamp.*

119 1878 Falkland Islands Postmark

(Des G. Hutchins. Litho Walsall)

1980 (6 May). *"London 1980" International Stamp Exhibition. T* **119** *and similar horiz designs showing postmarks.* W w **14** (*sideways*). *P* 14.

377	11p. black, gold and light blue	30	30
	a. Block of 6. Nos. 377/82	1·50	
378	11p. black, gold and greenish yellow	30	30
379	11p. black, gold and blue-green	30	30
380	11p. black, gold and pale violet	30	30
381	11p. black, gold and claret	30	30
382	11p. black, gold and flesh	30	30
377/82	*Set of* 6	1·50	1·50

Designs:—No. 377, Type **119**; No. 378, 1915 New Island; No. 379, 1901 Falkland Islands; No. 380, 1935 Port Stanley; No. 381, 1952 Port Stanley first overseas airmail; No. 382, 1934 Fox Bay.

Nos. 377/82 were printed together, *se-tenant*, as a sheetlet, containing one of each design.

120 Queen Elizabeth the Queen Mother at Ascot, 1971

(Des Harrison. Litho Questa)

1980 (4 Aug). *80th Birthday of Queen Elizabeth the Queen Mother.* W w **14** (*sideways*). *P* 14.

383 **120**	11p. multicoloured	40	30

121 Forster's Caracara

(Des I. Strange. Litho Secura, Singapore)

1980 (11 Aug). *Birds of Prey. T* **121** *and similar horiz designs. Multicoloured.* W w **14** (*sideways**). *P* 13×13½.

384	3p. Type **121**	50	25
	w. Wmk Crown to left of CA	3·25	
385	11p. Red-backed Buzzard	80	60
	w. Wmk Crown to left of CA	£350	
386	15p. Common Caracara	95	75
	w. Wmk Crown to left of CA	£375	
387	25p. Peregrine Falcon	1·25	1·00
	w. Wmk Crown to left of CA	1·25	
384/7	*Set of* 4	3·25	2·40

*The normal sideways watermark shows Crown to right of CA, *as seen from the back of the stamp.*

122 Stanley

(Des C. Abbott. Litho Rosenbaum Bros, Vienna)

1981 (7 Jan). *Early Settlements. T* **122** *and similar horiz designs. Multicoloured.* W w **14** (*sideways**). *P* 14.

388	3p. Type **122**	15	15
389	11p. Port Egmont	30	35
390	25p. Port Louis	60	65
	w. Wmk Crown to left of CA	£300	
391	33p. Mission House, Keppel Island	70	80
	w. Wmk Crown to left of CA	£225	
388/91	*Set of* 4	1·60	1·75

*The normal sideways watermark shows Crown to right of CA, *as seen from the back of the stamp.*

123 Sheep

(Des P. Oxenham. Litho Questa)

1981 (9 Jan). *Farm Animals. T* **123** *and similar horiz designs. Multicoloured.* W w **14** (*sideways**). *P* 14.

392	3p. Type **123**	20	30
393	11p. Cattle	35	55
	w. Wmk Crown to right of CA	£140	
394	25p. Horse	70	1·25
	w. Wmk Crown to right of CA	80·00	
395	33p. Dogs	1·00	1·50
392/5	*Set of* 4	2·00	3·25

*The normal sideways watermark shows Crown to left of CA, *as seen from the back of the stamp.*

124 Bowles and Carver, 1779

125 Wedding Bouquet from Falkland Islands

(Des I. Strange. Litho Walsall)

1981 (22 May). *Early Maps. T* **124** *and similar horiz designs in black, dull rose and stone* (26*p.*) *or multicoloured* (*others*). W w **14** (*sideways**). *P* 14.

396	3p. Type **124**	25	30
397	10p. J. Hawkesworth, 1773	45	55
	w. Wmk Crown to right of CA	£170	
398	13p. Eman. Bowen, 1747	55	75
399	15p. T. Boutflower, 1768	55	85
400	25p. Philippe de Pretot, 1771	65	90
401	26p. Bellin *Petite Atlas Maritime*, Paris, 1764	65	90
396/401	*Set of* 6	2·75	3·75

*The normal sideways watermark shows Crown to left of CA, *as seen from the back of the stamp.*

(Des and litho J.W.)

1981 (22 July). *Royal Wedding. T* **125** *and similar vert designs. Multicoloured.* W w **14**. *P* 13½ × 13.

402	10p. Type **125**	30	40
	w. Wmk inverted	65·00	
403	13p. Prince Charles riding	40	50
	w. Wmk inverted	35·00	
404	52p. Prince Charles and Lady Diana Spencer	70	1·00
402/4	*Set of* 3	1·25	1·75

126 "Handicrafts"

127 "The Adoration of the Holy Child" (16th-century Dutch artist)

(Des BG Studio. Litho Questa)

1981 (28 Sept*). *25th Anniv of Duke of Edinburgh Award Scheme. T* **126** *and similar vert designs. Multicoloured.* W w **14**. *P* 14.

405	10p. Type **126**	15	20
406	13p. "Camping"	20	30
407	15p. "Canoeing"	30	40
408	26p. Duke of Edinburgh	35	60
405/8	*Set of* 4	90	1·40

*This is the local date of issue. The Crown Agents released the stamps in London on 14 September.

(Des BG Studio. Litho Walsall)

1981 (9 Nov*). *Christmas. Paintings. T* **127** *and similar vert designs. Multicoloured.* W w **14**. *P* 14.

409	3p. Type **127**	20	20
410	13p. "The Holy Family in an Italian Landscape" (17th-century Genoan artist)	35	45
411	26p. "The Holy Virgin" (Reni)	55	75
409/11	*Set of* 3	1·00	1·25

*This is the local date of issue. The Crown Agents released the stamps in London on 2 November.

128 Patagonian Sprat

(Des I. Strange. Litho Questa)

1981 (7 Dec). *Shelf Fishes. T* **128** *and similar multicoloured designs.* W w **14** (*sideways on* 5, 15 *and* 25*p.*). *P* 14 × 13½ (13, 26*p.*) *or* 13½ × 14 (*others*).

412	5p. Type **128**	20	20
413	13p. Gunther's Rockcod (*vert*)	35	35
414	15p. Argentine Hake	40	40
415	25p. Southern Blue Whiting	60	75
416	26p. Grey-tailed Skate (*vert*)	60	75
412/16	*Set of* 5	1·90	2·25

129 *Lady Elizabeth*, 1913

(Des J. Smith. Litho Questa)

1982 (15 Feb). *Shipwrecks. T* **129** *and similar horiz designs. Multicoloured.* W w **14** (*sideways*). *P* 14½.

417	5p. Type **129**	30	50
418	13p. *Capricorn*, 1882	35	70
419	15p. *Jhelum*, 1870	40	85
420	25p. *Snowsquall*, 1864	55	1·10
421	26p. *St. Mary*, 1890	55	1·10
417/21	*Set of* 5	1·90	3·75

PRICES OF SETS

Set prices are given for many issues, generally those containing three stamps or more. Definitive sets include one of each value or major colour change, but do not cover different perforations, die types or minor shades. Where a choice is possible the set prices are based on the cheapest versions of the stamps included in the listings.

ARGENTINE OCCUPATION

2 April to 15 June 1982

Following incidents, involving the illegal presence of Argentine scrap-metal workers on the dependency of South Georgia from 18 March 1982, Argentine forces attacked Port Stanley, the capital of the Falkland Islands early in the morning of 2 April. The small garrison of Royal Marines was overwhelmed and the Governor forced to agree to a cease-fire, before being deported.

South Georgia was occupied by the Argentines on the following day.

British forces, dispatched from the United Kingdom, recaptured South Georgia on 25 April, and, after landing at various points on East Falkland, forced the surrender of the Argentine troops throughout the islands on 15 June.

The last mail to be dispatched from the Falkland Islands prior to the invasion left on 31 March. The Port Stanley Post Office was closed on 2 April, when all current issues were withdrawn. From 5 April an Argentine post office operated in the town, initially accepting mail without stamps, which was then cancelled by a postmark inscribed "ISLAS MALVINAS". Any letters tendered franked with Falkland Islands issues had these cancelled by ball-point pen. A limited range of Argentine stamps was placed on sale from 8 April. The Argentine definitive overprinted "LAS MALVINAS SON ARGENTINAS" for use throughout the country, was also available.

Following the Argentine surrender a rudimentary mail service was operating by 17 June, but the Port Stanley Post Office did not re-open until 24 June.

The last mail from South Georgia before the invasion was sent out on 16 March, although items remaining in the post office there were evacuated by the Deputy Postmaster when he was deported to the United Kingdom by the Argentines. The first mail left after recapture by the British on 2 May.

BRITISH ADMINISTRATION RESTORED

130 Charles Darwin

131 Falkland Islands Coat of Arms

(Des L. Curtis. Litho Questa)

1982 (5 July*). *150th Anniv of Charles Darwin's Voyage. T* **130** *and similar horiz designs. Multicoloured. W* w **14** *(sideways). P* 14.

422	5p. Type **130**	..	20	25
423	17p. Darwin's microscope	..	50	60
424	25p. Falkland Islands Wolf ("Warrah")	..	65	80
425	34p. H.M.S. *Beagle*	..	85	1·10
	a. Pale brown (background to side panels) omitted	..	£750	
422/5		*Set of* 4	2·00	2·50

*It was initially intended that these stamps were to be issued on 19 April. First Day covers were prepared, postmarked with this date, but, because of the Argentine invasion, the stamps were not actually released until 5 July. A postmark showing the actual date of issue was struck alongside the stamps on the First Day covers.

(Des C. Abbott. Litho J.W.)

1982 (16 Aug). *21st Birthday of Princess of Wales. T* **131** *and similar vert designs. Multicoloured. W* w **14**. *P* 13.

426	5p. Type **131**	..	15	20
427	17p. Princess at Royal Opera House, Covent Garden, November 1981	..	30	40
428	37p. Bride and groom in doorway of St Paul's		50	70
429	50p. Formal portrait	..	65	90
426/9		*Set of* 4	1·40	2·00

132 Map of Falkland Islands

(Des PAD Studio. Litho Format)

1982 (13 Sept). *Rebuilding Fund. W* w **14** *(sideways*). P* 11.

430 **132**	£1 + £1 multicoloured	..	2·40	4·50
	w. Wmk Crown to right of CA	..	75·00	

*The normal sideways watermark shows Crown to left of CA, *as seen from the back of the stamp.*

1st PARTICIPATION
COMMONWEALTH GAMES 1982

(**133**)

134 Blackish Cinclodes

1982 (7 Oct). *Commonwealth Games, Brisbane. Nos.* 335B *and* 342B *optd with T* **133**.

431	5p. *Lafonia*, 1936–41	..	15	30
432	25p. *Fairy*, 1857–61	..	60	1·10

(Des I. Strange. Litho W. S. Cowells Ltd)

1982 (6 Dec). *Birds of the Passerine Family. T* **134** *and similar vert designs. Multicoloured. W* w **14** *(inverted on* 10*p.). P* 15 × 14½.

433	5p. Type **134**	..	25	30
434	10p. Black-chinned Siskin	..	35	40
	w. Wmk upright	..	40·00	
435	13p. Short-billed Marsh Wren	..	40	45
436	17p. Black-throated Finch	..	45	55
437	25p. Correndera Pipit	..	55	75
438	34p. Dark-faced Ground Tyrant	..	70	95
433/8		*Set of* 6	2·40	3·00

Imperforate examples of all values, except the 34p., exist from printer's waste which escaped destruction. Some are known on unwatermarked paper with thick red lines across the face of the stamps.

135 Raising Flag, Port Louis, 1833

136 1933 British Administration Centenary 3d. Commemorative

(Des I. Strange and J. Sheridan. Litho Questa)

1983 (3 Jan). *150th Anniv of British Administration. T* **135** *and similar multicoloured designs. W* w **14** *(sideways on* 2, 10, 15, 25 *and* 50*p.). P* 14 × 13½ (1, 5, 20, 40*p.*, £1, £2) *or* 13½ × 14 *(others).*

439	1p. Type **135**	..	20	30
440	2p. Chelsea pensioners and barracks, 1849 (*horiz*)	..	30	40
441	5p. Development of wool trade, 1874	..	30	40
442	10p. Ship-repairing trade, 1850–1890 (*horiz*)		60	70
443	15p. Government House, early 20th century (*horiz*)	..	70	80
444	20p. Battle of Falkland Islands, 1914	..	90	1·25
445	25p. Whalebone Arch, 1933 (*horiz*)	..	90	1·25
446	40p. Contribution to War effort, 1939–45	..	1·40	1·60
447	50p. Duke of Edinburgh's visit, 1957 (*horiz*)	..	1·50	2·00
448	£1 Royal Marine uniforms	..	2·00	3·00
449	£2 Queen Elizabeth II	..	2·75	4·50
439/49		*Set of* 11	10·00	14·50

(Des L. Curtis. Litho Questa)

1983 (28 Mar*). *Commonwealth Day. T* **136** *and similar multicoloured designs. W* w **14** *(sideways on* 5*p.*, 17*p.*). *P* 14.

450	5p. Type **136**	..	15	15
451	17p. 1933 British Administration Centenary ½d. commemorative	..	30	35
452	34p. 1933 British Administration Centenary 10s. commemorative (*vert*)	..	60	80
453	50p. 1983 British Administration 150th anniversary £2 commemorative (*vert*)	..	75	1·00
450/3		*Set of* 4	1·60	2·10

*This is the local date of issue: the Crown Agents released the stamps on 14 March.

137 British Army advancing across East Falkland

(Des A. Theobald. Litho Questa)

1983 (14 June). *First Anniv of Liberation. T* **137** *and similar horiz designs. Multicoloured. W* w **14** *(sideways). P* 14.

454	5p. Type **137**	..	25	30
455	13p. S.S. *Canberra* and M.V. *Norland* at San Carlos	..	40	60
456	17p. R.A.F. Hawker Siddeley Harrier fighter	..	45	70
457	50p. H.M.S. *Hermes* (aircraft carrier)	..	1·00	1·40
454/7		*Set of* 4	1·90	2·75
MS458	169×130 mm. Nos. 454/7. P 12	..	2·00	3·00

138 Diddle Dee

(Des A. Chater. Litho Questa)

1983 (10 Oct). *Native Fruits. T* **138** *and similar horiz design. Multicoloured. W* w **14** *(sideways). P* 14.

459	5p. Type **138**	..	20	
460	17p. Tea Berry	..	30	
461	25p. Mountain Berry	..	45	
462	34p. Native Strawberry	..	65	
459/62		*Set of* 4	1·40	1·9

139 Britten Norman Islander

(Des Harrison. Litho Questa)

1983 (14 Nov). *Bicentenary of Manned Flight. T* **139** *and similar horiz designs. Multicoloured. W* w **14** *(sideways). P* 14.

463	5p. Type **139**	..	15	
464	13p. De Havilland D.H.C.2 Beaver	..	35	
465	17p. Noorduyn Norseman V	..	40	
466	50p. Auster Autocrat	..	1·00	1·
463/6		*Set of* 4	1·75	2·

17 p

(**140**)

17 p

(**140***a*)

1984 (3 Jan). *Nos.* 443 *and* 445 *surch as T* **140** *by Govt Printer, Port Stanley.*

467	17p. on 15p. Government House, early 20th century (figures as Type **140**)	..	60	
	a. Surch figures as Type **140***a*	..	90	1·
468	22p. on 25p. Whalebone Arch, 1933	..	65	

The surcharge setting used for the 17p. contained 2 examples as Type **140** and 23 as Type **140***a*.

141 *Araneus cinnabarinus* (juvenile spider)

142 *Wavertree* (sail merchantman)

(Des I. Strange. Litho Questa)

1984 (3 Jan)–**86**. *Insects and Spiders. T* **141** *and similar horiz designs. Multicoloured. W* w **14** *(sideways). P* 14×14½.

A. *Without imprint date*

469A	1p. Type **141**	..	20	
470A	2p. *Alopophion occidentalis* (fly)	..	2·00	1·
471A	3p. *Pareuxoina falkandica* (moth)	..	40	
472A	4p. *Lissopterus quadrinotatus* (beetle)	..	30	
473A	5p. *Issoria cytheris* (butterfly)	..	30	
474A	6p. *Araneus cinnabarinus* (adult spider)		30	
475A	7p. *Trachysphyrus penai* (fly)	..	30	
476A	8p. *Caphornia ochricraspia* (moth)	..	30	
477A	9p. *Caneorhinus biangulatus* (weevil)	..	30	
478A	10p. *Syrphus octomaculatus* (fly)	..	30	
479A	20p. *Malvinius compressiventris* (weevil)		2·25	
480A	25p. *Metius blandus* (beetle)	..	75	
481A	50p. *Parudenus falkandicus* (cricket)	..	1·00	1·
482A	£1 *Emmenomma beauchenieus* (spider)		1·75	2·
483A	£3 *Cynthia carye* (butterfly)	..	4·00	6·
469A/83A		*Set of* 15	13·00	17·

B. *With "1986" imprint date at foot of design*

470B	2p. *Alopophion occidentalis* (fly) (19.5.86)		2·75	2

(Des A. Theobald. Litho Questa)

1984 (7 May). *250th Anniv of "Lloyd's List" (newspaper). T* **142** *and similar vert designs. Multicoloured. W* w **14**. *P* 14½ × 14.

484	6p. Type **142**	..	55	
485	17p. *Bjerk* (whale catcher) at Port Stanley		1·10	
486	22p. *Oravia* (liner) stranded	..	1·10	
487	52p. *Cunard Countess* (liner)	..	1·60	2·
484/7		*Set of* 4	3·75	3·

OMNIBUS ISSUES

Details, together with prices for complete sets of the various Omnibus issues from the 193[illegible] Silver Jubilee series to date are included in a special section following Zimbabwe at the end of Volume 2.

143 Ship, Lockheed C-130 Hercules Aircraft and U.P.U. Logo

144 Great Grebe

(Des E. Nisbet, adapted L. Curtis. Litho Questa)

1984 (25 June). *Universal Postal Union Congress, Hamburg. W* w **14** *(sideways). P* 14.
488 **143** 22p. multicoloured 55 75

(Des I. Strange. Litho Questa)

1984 (6 Aug). *Grebes. T* **144** *and similar vert designs. Multicoloured. W* w **14**. *P* 14½.
489 17p. Type **144** .. .. 1·25 1·25
490 22p. Silvery Grebe .. .. 1·40 1·40
491 52p. White-tufted Grebe .. .. .. 3·00 4·75
489/91 .. .. *Set of* 3 5·00 6·75

145 Black-browed Albatross

146 Technical Drawing of Class "Wren" Locomotive

(Des I. Strange. Litho Questa)

1984 (5 Nov). *Nature Conservation. T* **145** *and similar vert designs. Multicoloured. W* w **14**. *P* 14½ × 14.
492 6p. Type **145** .. .. 1·25 80
493 17p. Tussock grass .. .. .. 1·25 1·10
494 22p. Dusky Dolphin and Southern Sealion 1·40 1·40
495 52p. Rockcod (fish) and krill .. .. 2·00 3·00
492/5 .. .. *Set of* 4 5·50 5·50
MS496 130×90 mm. Nos. 492/5 .. .. 5·50 6·00

(Des C. Abbott. Litho Questa)

1985 (18 Feb). *70th Anniv of Camber Railway. T* **146** *and similar horiz designs, each black, deep brown and pale cinnamon. W* w **14** *(sideways). P* 14.
497 7p. Type **146** 35 30
498 22p. Sail-propelled trolley 60 90
499 27p. Class "Wren" locomotive at work .. 65 1·25
500 54p. "Falkland Islands Express" passenger train (75×25 *mm*) .. .. .. 1·10 2·00
497/500 .. .. *Set of* 4 2·40 4·00

147 Construction Workers' Camp

148 The Queen Mother on 84th Birthday

(Des N. Shewring. Litho Questa)

1985 (12 May). *Opening of Mount Pleasant Airport. T* **147** *and similar horiz designs. Multicoloured. W* w **16** *(sideways). P* 14½×14.
501 7p. Type **147** 75 40
502 22p. Building construction .. .. .. 1·40 90
503 27p. Completed airport .. .. .. 1·60 1·10
504 54p. Lockheed L-1011 TriStar 500 airliner over runway .. .. 2·00 2·50
501/4 .. .. *Set of* 4 5·25 4·50

(Des A. Theobald (£1), C. Abbott (others). Litho Questa)

1985 (7 June). *Life and Times of Queen Elizabeth the Queen Mother. T* **148** *and similar vert designs. Multicoloured. W* w **16**. *P* 14½×14.
505 7p. Attending reception at Lancaster House 25 20
506 22p. With Prince Charles, Mark Phillips and Princess Anne at Falklands Memorial Service 60 50
w. Wmk inverted .. .. 14·00
507 27p. Type **148** 70 60
508 54p. With Prince Henry at his christening (from photo by Lord Snowdon) .. .. 1·25 1·25
505/8 .. .. *Set of* 4 2·50 2·25
MS509 91×73 mm £1 With Princess Diana at Trooping the Colour. Wmk sideways .. .. 2·25 2·25

149 Captain J. McBride and H.M.S. *Jason*, 1765

150 Painted Keyhole Limpet (*Fissurella picta*)

(Des O. Bell. Litho Questa)

1985 (30 Sept). *Early Cartographers. T* **149** *and similar horiz designs. Multicoloured. W* w **14** *(sideways). P* 14×14½.
510 7p. Type **149** .. .. 1·00 40
511 22p. Commodore J. Byron and H.M.S. *Dolphin* and *Tamar*, 1765 .. .. .. 1·40 80
512 27p. Vice-Admiral R. FitzRoy and H.M.S. *Beagle*, 1831 .. .. 1·50 85
513 54p. Admiral Sir B. J. Sullivan and H.M.S. *Philomel*, 1842 .. .. .. 2·00 1·75
510/13 .. .. *Set of* 4 5·50 3·50

(Des I. Strange. Litho Questa)

1985 (4 Nov). *Early Naturalists. Vert designs as T* **35** *of British Antarctic Territory. Multicoloured. W* w **14**. *P* 14½×14.
514 7p. Philibert Commerson and Commerson's Dolphin 85 40
515 22p. René Primevère Lesson and *Lessonia* sp. (kelp) .. .. 1·50 1·10
516 27p. Joseph Paul Gaimard and Common Diving Petrel .. .. .. 1·90 1·90
517 54p. Charles Darwin and *Calceolaria darwinii* .. .. 2·25 2·75
514/17 .. .. *Set of* 4 6·00 5·50

(Des I. Strange. Litho Questa)

1986 (10 Feb). *Seashells. T* **150** *and similar horiz designs. Multicoloured. W* w **16** *(sideways). P* 14×14½.
518 7p. Type **150** 65 60
519 22p. *Provocator palliata* (*Odontocymbiola magellanica*) .. .. 1·25 1·40
520 27p. Patagonian or Falkland Scallop (*Chlamys lischkei*) .. .. .. 1·40 2·25
521 54p. Rough Thorn Drupe (*Acanthina monodon imbricata*) .. .. .. 2·25 3·50
518/21 .. .. *Set of* 4 5·00 7·00

(Des A. Theobald. Litho Format)

1986 (21 Apr). *60th Birthday of Queen Elizabeth II. Vert designs as T* **110** *of Ascension. Multicoloured. W* w **16**. *P* 14×14½.
522 10p. With Princess Margaret at St Paul's, Walden Bury, Welwyn, 1932 .. .. 20 25
523 24p. Queen making Christmas television broadcast, 1958 .. .. .. 35 50
524 29p. In robes of Order of the Thistle, St. Giles Cathedral, Edinburgh, 1962 .. .. 35 60
525 45p. Aboard Royal Yacht *Britannia*, U.S.A., 1976 .. .. 1·00 1·25
526 58p. At Crown Agents Head Office, London, 1983 .. .. 80 1·50
522/6 .. .. *Set of* 5 2·40 3·50

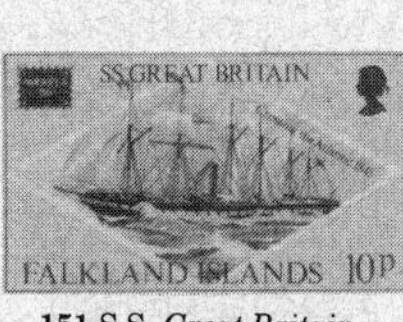

151 S.S. *Great Britain* crossing Atlantic, 1845

152 Head of Rockhopper Penguin

(Des O. Bell. Litho Format)

1986 (22 May). *"Ameripex '86" International Stamp Exhibition, Chicago. Centenary of Arrival of S.S. "Great Britain" in Falkland Islands. T* **151** *and similar horiz designs. Multicoloured. W* w **16** *(sideways*). P* 14.
527 10p. Type **151** 40 50
528 24p. Beached at Sparrow Cove, 1937 .. 50 70
529 29p. Refloated on pontoon, 1970 .. .. 55 80
530 58p. Undergoing restoration, Bristol, 1986 80 2·00
w. Wmk Crown to right of CA .. .. 60·00
527/30 .. .. *Set of* 4 2·00 3·50
MS531 109×109 mm. Nos. 527/30. Wmk upright 2·00 3·25
*The normal sideways watermark shows Crown to left of CA, *as seen from the back of the stamp.*

(Des I. Strange. Litho Questa)

1986 (25 Aug). *Rockhopper Penguins. T* **152** *and similar vert designs. Multicoloured. W* w **16**. *P* 14½×14.
532 10p. Type **152** .. .. 1·00 60
533 24p. Rockhopper Penguins at sea .. .. 1·50 1·75
534 29p. Courtship display .. .. .. 1·75 2·00
535 58p. Adult with chick .. .. .. 2·25 4·00
532/5 .. .. *Set of* 4 6·00 7·50

NEW INFORMATION

The editor is always interested to correspond with people who have new information that will improve or correct the Catalogue.

153 Prince Andrew and Miss Sarah Ferguson presenting Polo Trophy, Windsor

154 Survey Party, Sapper Hill

(Des D. Miller. Litho Questa)

1986 (10 Nov). *Royal Wedding. T* **153** *and similar vert designs. Multicoloured. W* w **16**. *P* 14½×14.
536 17p. Type **153** 75 50
537 22p. Prince Andrew and Duchess of York on wedding day 85 65
538 29p. Prince Andrew in battledress at opening of Fox Bay Mill .. .. .. 1·10 90
536/8 .. .. *Set of* 3 2·40 1·90

(Des L. Curtis. Litho Questa)

1987 (9 Feb). *Bicentenary of Royal Engineers' Royal Warrant. T* **154** *and similar horiz designs. Multicoloured. W* w **16** *(sideways). P* 14×14½.
539 10p. Type **154** .. .. 1·25 80
540 24p. Mine clearance by robot .. .. 1·75 1·50
541 29p. Boxer Bridge, Stanley .. .. .. 2·00 2·50
542 58p. Unloading mail, Mount Pleasant Airport .. .. 2·75 4·00
539/42 .. .. *Set of* 4 7·00 8·00

155 Southern Sea Lion

156 *Suillus luteus*

(Des I. Strange. Litho Questa)

1987 (27 Apr). *Seals. T* **155** *and similar horiz designs. Multicoloured. W* w **16** *(sideways). P* 14½.
543 10p. Type **155** 70 55
544 24p. Falkland Fur Seal .. .. .. 1·50 90
545 29p. Southern Elephant Seal .. .. 1·60 1·50
546 58p. Leopard Seal .. .. 2·25 2·50
543/6 .. .. *Set of* 4 5·50 5·00

(Des I. Strange. Litho Questa)

1987 (14 Sept). *Fungi. T* **156** *and similar vert designs. Multicoloured. W* w **16**. *P* 14½×14.
547 10p. Type **156** .. .. 1·40 75
548 24p. *Mycena* sp. .. .. 2·25 1·75
549 29p. *Hygrophorous adonis* ("*Camarophyllus adonis*") .. .. 2·50 3·00
550 58p. *Gerronema schusteri* .. .. .. 3·50 4·50
547/50 .. .. *Set of* 4 8·75 9·00

157 Victoria Cottage Home, *c* 1912

158 Morris Truck, Fitzroy, 1940

(Des D. Hartley. Litho Questa)

1987 (8 Dec). *Local Hospitals. T* **157** *and similar horiz designs. Multicoloured. W* w **16** *(sideways). P* 14.
551 10p. Type **157** 40 25
552 24p. King Edward VII Memorial Hospital, *c* 1914 .. .. 75 55
553 29p. Churchill Wing, King Edward VII Memorial Hospital, *c* 1953 .. .. 85 60
554 58p. Prince Andrew Wing, New Hospital, 1987 .. .. 1·40 1·25
551/4 .. .. *Set of* 4 3·00 2·40

(Des D. Hartley. Litho Questa)

1988 (11 Apr). *Early Vehicles. T* **158** *and similar horiz designs. Multicoloured. W* w **16** *(sideways). P* 14.
555 10p. Type **158** 40 25
556 24p. Citroen "Kegresse" half-track, San Carlos, 1929 .. .. 75 55
557 29p. Ford one ton truck, Port Stanley, 1933 85 60
558 58p. Ford "Model T" car, Darwin, 1935 .. 1·40 1·25
555/8 .. .. *Set of* 4 3·00 2·40

159 Kelp Goose

(Des I. Strange. Litho Walsall)

1988 (25 July). *Falkland Islands Geese. T* **159** *and similar horiz designs. Multicoloured. W* w **16** (*sideways*). *P* 13½×14.

559 10p. Type **159** .. .. 1·75 45
560 24p. Magellan ("Upland") Goose .. .. 2·25 70
561 29p. Ruddy-headed Goose .. .. .. 2·50 80
562 58p. Ashy-headed Goose .. .. .. 3·50 2·00
559/62 .. .. *Set of* 4 9·00 3·50

(Des D. Miller (10, 24p.), E. Nesbit and D. Miller (29, 58p.). Litho Format)

1988 (14 Nov). *300th Anniv of Lloyd's of London. Multicoloured designs as T* **123** *of Ascension. W* w **14** (*sideways on* 24, 29*p*.). *P* 14.

563 10p. Silver from Lloyd's Nelson Collection 40 30
564 24p. Falkland Islands hydroponic market garden (*horiz*) 75 65
565 29p. *A.E.S.* (mail ship) (*horiz*) .. .. 1·00 75
566 58p. *Charles Cooper* (full-rigged ship), 1866 1·50 1·25
w. Wmk inverted .. .. .. 28·00
563/6 .. .. *Set of* 4 3·25 2·75

160 *Padua* (barque)

(Des A. Theobald. Litho Questa)

1989 (28 Feb)–**90**. *Cape Horn Sailing Ships. T* **160** *and similar multicoloured designs. W* w **14** (*sideways on horiz designs*). *P* 14.

567 1p. Type **160** 60 60
568 2p. *Priwall* (barque) (*vert*) .. .. .. 1·25 1·25
569 3p. *Passat* (barque) .. .. 1·25 1·25
570 4p. *Archibald Russell* (barque) (*vert*) .. 80 80
571 5p. *Pamir* (barque) (*vert*) 80 80
572 6p. *Mozart* (barquentine) .. .. .. 1·25 1·25
573 7p. *Pommern* (barque) .. .. .. 1·00 1·00
574 8p. *Preussen* (full-rigged ship) .. .. 1·00 1·00
575 9p. *Fennia* (barque) .. .. 1·25 1·25
576 10p. *Cassard* (barque) .. .. .. 1·00 1·00
577 20p. *Lawhill* (barque) .. .. .. 1·75 2·00
578 25p. *Garthpool* (barque) .. .. .. 1·75 2·00
579 50p. *Grace Harwar* (full-rigged ship) .. 2·75 3·00
580 £1 *Criccieth Castle* (full-rigged ship) .. 6·50 7·50
581 £3 *Cutty Sark* (full-rigged ship) (*vert*) .. 8·50 8·50
582 £5 *Flying Cloud* (full-rigged ship) (2.1.90) 11·00 9·00
567/82 .. .. *Set of* 16 38·00 38·00

For 2, 3, 6, 9p. and £1 values watermarked w **16** and with imprint dates see Nos. 613/25.

161 Southern Right Whale

(Des I. Strange. Litho Questa)

1989 (15 May). *Baleen Whales. T* **161** *and similar horiz designs. Multicoloured. W* w **16** (*sideways*). *P* 13½×14.

583 10p. Type **161** 90 40
584 24p. Minke Whale .. .. 1·50 85
585 29p. Humpback Whale .. .. .. 1·75 1·25
586 58p. Blue Whale .. .. 2·50 2·50
583/6 .. .. *Set of* 4 6·00 4·50

162 "Gymkhana" (Sarah Gilding)

163 Vice-Admiral Sturdee and H.M.S. *Invincible* (battle cruiser)

(Adapted G. Vasarhelyi. Litho Walsall)

1989 (16 Sept). *Sports Associations' Activities. T* **162** *and similar horiz designs showing children's drawings. Multicoloured. W* w **16** (*sideways*). *P* 14.

587 5p. Type **162** 20 20
588 10p. "Steer Riding" (Karen Steen) 30 30
589 17p. "Sheep Shearing" (Colin Shepherd) .. 45 45
590 24p. "Sheepdog Trials" (Rebecca Edwards) 60 70
591 29p. "Horse Racing" (Dilys Blackley) .. 70 80
592 45p. "Sack Race" (Donna Newell) .. .. 1·00 1·10
587/92 .. .. *Set of* 6 3·00 3·25

(Des C. Collins. Litho B.D.T.)

1989 (8 Dec). *75th Anniv of Battle of the Falkland Islands and 50th Anniv of Battle of the River Plate. T* **163** *and similar vert designs. Multicoloured. W* w **16**. *P* 13½.

593 10p. Type **163** 30 30
594 24p. Vice-Admiral Graf von Spee and *Scharnhorst* (German cruiser) 70 75
595 29p. Commodore Harwood and H.M.S. *Ajax* (cruiser) 80 85
596 58p. Captain Langsdorff and *Admiral Graf Spee* (German pocket battleship) .. 1·50 2·00
593/6 .. .. *Set of* 4 3·00 3·50

164 Southern Sea Lions on Kidney Island

165 Supermarine Spitfire Mk 1 *Falkland Islands I*

(Des I. Strange. Litho Questa)

1990 (9 Apr). *Nature Reserves and Sanctuaries. T* **164** *and similar vert designs. Multicoloured. W* w **16**. *P* 14½.

597 12p. Type **164** 45 35
598 26p. Black-browed Albatrosses on Beauchene Island .. .. .. 1·00 70
599 31p. Penguin colony on Bird Island .. 1·10 80
600 62p. Tussock grass on Elephant Jason Island .. .. 1·40 1·40
597/600 .. .. *Set of* 4 3·50 3·00

(Des A. Theobald. Litho B.D.T.)

1990 (3 May). *"Stamp World London 90" International Stamp Exhibition, London. Presentation Spitfires. T* **165** *and similar horiz designs. Multicoloured. W* w **14** (*sideways*). *P* 14.

601 12p. Type **165** 50 35
602 26p. Supermarine Spitfire Mk 1 *Falkland Islands VII* 90 70
603 31p. Cockpit and wing of *Falkland Islands I* 1·00 80
604 62p. Squadron scramble, 1940 .. .. 1·40 1·40
601/4 .. .. *Set of* 4 3·50 3·00
MS605 114×100 mm. £1 Supermarine Spitfire Mk 1 in action, 1940 .. .. 3·00 2·50

For No. **MS**605 with additional inscription see No. **MS**628.

(Des D. Miller. Litho Questa)

1990 (4 Aug). *90th Birthday of Queen Elizabeth the Queen Mother. Vert designs as T* **134** (26*p*.) *or* **135** (£1) *of Ascension. W* w **16**. *P* 14×15 (26*p*.) *or* 14½ (£1).

606 26p. multicoloured 75 65
607 £1 brownish black and deep carmine-red 2·50 2·75

Designs:—26p. Queen Mother in Dover; £1 On bridge of lincr *Queen Elizabeth*, 1946.

166 Black-browed Albatrosses

167 *Gavilea australis*

(Des I. Strange. Litho Questa)

1990 (3 Oct). *Black-browed Albatross. T* **166** *and similar vert designs. Multicoloured. W* w **16**. *P* 13½×14.

608 12p. Type **166** 60 50
609 26p. Female with egg .. .. .. 1·25 1·00
610 31p. Adult and chick .. .. .. 1·50 1·25
611 62p. Black-browed Albatross in flight .. 2·50 3·00
608/11 .. .. *Set of* 4 5·25 5·25

1991 (7 Jan). *As Nos.* 568/9, 572, 575 *and* 580, *but W* w **16** (*sideways on horiz designs*) *and with* "1991" *imprint date added at foot. P* 14.

613 2p. *Priwall* (barque) (*vert*) 60 70
614 3p. *Passat* (barque) 60 70
617 6p. *Mozart* (barquentine) 70 65
620 9p. *Fennia* (barque) 80 80
625 £1 *Criccieth Castle* (full-rigged ship) .. 2·75 3·25
613/25 .. .. *Set of* 5 5·00 5·50

(Des A. Theobald. Litho B.D.T.)

1991 (18 Mar). *Second Visit of H.R.H. The Duke of Edinburg*[h.] *As No.* **MS**605, *but with Exhibition emblem replaced* [b]*y* "SECOND VISIT OF HRH THE DUKE OF EDINBURGH". W w **16** (*sideways*). *P* 14.

MS628 114×100 mm. £1 Spitfire Mk. I in action, 1940 .. .. 5·50 7·0[0]

The margin of No. **MS**628 also shows the Exhibition emble[m] omitted and has the same commemorative inscription added.

(Des I. Strange. Litho Questa)

1991 (18 Mar). *Orchids. T* **167** *and similar vert design*[s.] *Multicoloured. W* w **14**. *P* 14×13½.

629 12p. Type **167** .. .. 60 6[0]
630 26p. Dog Orchid .. .. 1·00 1·0[0]
631 31p. *Chlorea gaudichaudii* .. .. 1·25 1·5[0]
632 62p. Yellow Orchid .. .. .. 2·25 3·2[5]
629/32 .. .. *Set of* 4 4·50 5·7[5]

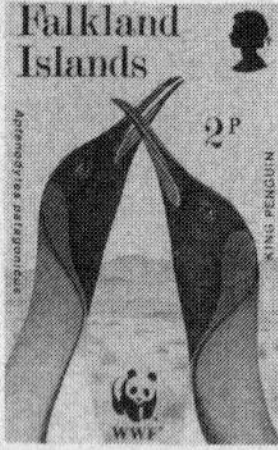

168 Heads of Two King Penguins

169 ½d and 2½d Stamps of September 1891

(Des I. Strange. Litho Questa)

1991 (26 Aug). *Endangered Species. King Penguin. T* **168** *an*[d] *similar vert designs. Multicoloured. W* w **16**. *P* 14.

633 2p. Type **168** 50
634 6p. Female incubating egg 70
635 12p. Female with two chicks .. .. 1·00
636 20p. Penguin underwater .. .. .. 1·25 1·
637 31p. Parents feeding their chick .. .. 1·50 1·
638 62p. Courtship dance .. .. .. 2·25 2·
633/8 .. .. *Set of* 6 6·50 7·

Nos. 637/8 do not include the W.W.F. panda emblem.

(Des D. Miller. Litho Questa)

1991 (10 Sept). *Centenary of Bisected Surcharges. T* **169** *an*[d] *similar horiz designs. Multicoloured. W* w **16** (*sideways*). *P* 14½.

639 12p. Type **169** 60 5
640 26p. Cover of March 1891 franked with strip of five ½d bisects .. .. .. 1·00 1·0
641 31p. Unsevered pair of ½d. surcharge .. 1·25 1·5
642 62p. *Isis* (mail ship) .. .. 2·00 3·
639/42 .. .. *Set of* 4 4·25 5·

(Des R. Watton. Litho Walsall)

1991 (12 Dec). *500th Anniv of Discovery of America* [b]*y Columbus and Re-enactment Voyages. Horiz designs as T* **14**[2] *of Ascension. Multicoloured. W* w **14** (*sideways*). *P* 13½×14.

643 14p. Map of re-enactment voyages and *Eye of the Wind* (cadet brig) 60 6
644 29p. Compass rose and *Soren Larsen* (cadet brigantine) .. .. 1·25 1·4
645 34p. *Santa Maria, Pinta* and *Nina* .. 1·50 1·7
646 68p. Columbus and *Santa Maria* .. .. 2·50 4·
643/6 .. .. *Set of* 4 5·25 7·

(Des D. Miller. Litho Questa (68p.), Walsall (others))

1992 (6 Feb). *40th Anniv of Queen Elizabeth II's Accessio*[n.] *Horiz designs as T* **143** *of Ascension. Multicoloured. W* w **1**[4] (*sideways*). *P* 14.

647 7p. "Stanley through the Narrows" (A. Asprey) 35
648 14p. "Hill Cove" (A. Asprey) 60
649 29p. "San Carlos Water" (A. Asprey) .. 95
650 34p. Three portraits of Queen Elizabeth .. 1·25 1·
651 68p. Queen Elizabeth II .. .. .. 1·75 2·
647/51 .. .. *Set of* 5 4·50 4·

170 Laying Foundation Stone, 1890

171 Captain John Davis and Backstaff

(Des N. Shewring. Litho Questa)

1992 (21 Feb). *Centenary of Christ Church Cathedral, Stanle*[y.] *T* **170** *and similar multicoloured designs. W* w **16** (*sideways* [on] 68*p*.). *P* 14½.

652 14p. Type **170** 65
653 29p. Interior of Cathedral, 1920 .. .. 1·25 1·
654 34p. Bishop's chair .. .. .. 1·50 1·
655 68p. Cathedral in 1900 (*horiz*) .. .. 1·90 1·
652/5 .. .. *Set of* 4 4·75 4·

(Des N. Shewring. Litho Questa)

92 (14 June). *10th Anniv of Liberation. Square designs as T* **146** *of Ascension. Multicoloured. W w* **14** *(sideways). P* 14.

6 14p. + 6p. San Carlos Cemetery .. .. 75 1·25
7 29p. + 11p. War Memorial, Port Stanley .. 1·40 1·75
8 34p. + 16p. South Atlantic medal .. 1·60 1·90
9 68p. + 32p. Government House, Port Stanley .. .. 2·75 3·00
6/9 .. .. *Set of* 4 6·00 7·00
S660 115×115 mm. Nos. 656/9 .. .. 6·00 7·00

The premiums on Nos. 656/60 were for the S.S.A.F.A.

(Des R. Watton. Litho Questa)

92 (14 Aug). *400th Anniv of First Sighting of the Falkland Islands. T* **171** *and similar horiz designs. Multicoloured. W w* **14** *(sideways). P* 14½.

1 22p. Type **171** .. .. 1·00 80
2 29p. Capt. John Davis .. .. 1·25 1·10
3 34p. Queen Elizabeth I and Queen Elizabeth II .. .. 1·50 1·50
4 68p. *Desire* sighting Falkland Islands .. 2·25 3·00
1/4 .. .. *Set of* 4 5·50 5·75

172 Private, Falkland Islands Volunteers, 1892

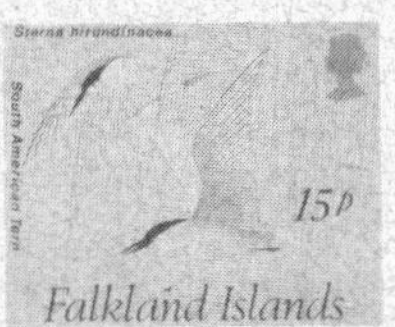

173 South American Tern

(Des C. Collins. Litho Questa)

992 (1 Oct). *Centenary of Falkland Islands Defence Force and 50th Anniv of Affiliation to West Yorkshire Regiment. T* **172** *and similar vert designs. Multicoloured. W w* **14**. *P* 14.

65 7p. Type **172** 30 30
66 14p. Officer, Falkland Islands Defence Corps, 1914 .. .. 50 50
67 22p. Officer, Falkland Islands Defence Force, 1920 .. .. 70 70
68 29p. Private, Falkland Islands Defence Force, 1939–45 .. .. 90 90
69 34p. Officer, West Yorkshire Regiment, 1942 .. .. 1·25 1·25
70 68p. Private, West Yorkshire Regiment, 1942 .. .. 2·00 2·10
65/70 .. .. *Set of* 6 5·00 5·25

(Des I. Strange. Litho Questa)

993 (2 Jan). *Gulls and Terns. T* **173** *and similar horiz designs. Multicoloured. W w* **16** *(sideways). P* 14×14½.

71 15p. Type **173** 75 65
72 31p. Brown-hooded Gull ("Pink breasted Gull") .. .. 1·25 1·25
73 36p. Magellan Gull .. .. 1·40 1·60
74 72p. Southern Black-backed Gull ("Dominican Gull") .. .. 2·50 3·50
71/4 .. .. *Set of* 4 5·50 6·25

174 *Queen Elizabeth* 2

(Des N. Shewring. Litho Questa)

993 (22 Jan). *Visit of the* Queen Elizabeth 2 *(cruise liner). Sheet* 60×42 *mm. W w* **14** *(sideways). P* 14.

MS675 **174** £2 multicoloured .. .. .. 5·25 5·50

(Des A. Theobald. Litho Questa)

993 (1 Apr). *75th Anniv of Royal Air Force. Horiz designs as T* **149** *of Ascension. Multicoloured. W w* **14** *(sideways*). P* 14.

76 15p. Avro Vulcan B.1A 65 85
77 15p. Lockheed C-130K Hercules 65 85
78 15p. Boeing-Vertol CH-47 Chinook .. 65 85
79 15p. Lockheed L-1011 TriStar 500 .. 65 85
76/9 .. .. *Set of* 4 2·40 3·00
MS680 110×77 mm. 36p. Hawker Siddeley Andover CC.2; 36p. Westland Wessex HC-2 helicopter; 36p. Panavia Tornado F Mk 3; 36p. McDonnell Douglas F-4M Phantom II .. 3·75 4·75
w. Wmk Crown to right of CA .. ..

*The normal sideways watermark shows Crown to left of CA, *as seen from the back of the stamp.*

175 Short-finned Squid

176 *Great Britain* in Drydock, Bristol

(Des O. Ball. Litho Questa)

1993 (1 July). *Fisheries. T* **175** *and similar horiz designs. Multicoloured. W w* **16** *(sideways). P* 14.

681 15p. Type **175** 60 60
682 31p. Catch of Whip-tailed Hake .. .. 1·25 1·40
683 36p. *Falklands Protector* (fisheries patrol vessel) .. .. 1·50 1·75
684 72p. Britten Norman Islander patrol aircraft and fish factory ship .. 2·25 3·50
681/4 .. .. *Set of* 4 5·00 6·50

(Des O. Ball. Litho Questa)

1993 (19 July). *150th Anniv of Launch of* Great Britain *(liner). T* **176** *and similar vert design. Multicoloured. W w* **16**. *P* 14×13½.

685 8p. Type **176** 50 50
686 £1 *Great Britain* at sea .. .. .. 2·75 4·00

177 *Explorer* (liner)

178 Pony

(Des N. Shewring. Litho Questa)

1993 (1 Oct). *Tourism. T* **177** *and similar horiz designs. Multicoloured. W w* **14** *(sideways). P* 14.

687 16p. Type **177** 75 60
688 34p. Rockhopper Penguins .. .. 1·50 1·25
689 39p. *World Discoverer* (liner) .. .. 1·75 1·75
690 78p. *Columbus Caravelle* (liner) .. .. 2·25 2·75
687/90 .. .. *Set of* 4 5·50 5·75

(Des E. Tenney. Litho Walsall)

1993 (1 Dec). *Pets. T* **178** *and similar multicoloured designs. W w* **16** *(sideways on 8p., 16p., 34p.; inverted on 39p.). P* 14×14½ *(horiz) or* 14½×14 *(vert).*

691 8p. Type **178** 50 50
692 16p. Lamb 65 65
693 34p. Puppy and cat .. .. .. 1·50 1·75
694 39p. Kitten *(vert)* .. .. .. 1·60 2·00
695 78p. Collie dog *(vert)* .. .. .. 2·50 3·50
691/5 .. .. *Set of* 5 6·00 7·50

1994 (18 Feb). *"Hong Kong '94" International Stamp Exhibition. Nos. 691/5 additionally inscribed with the exhibition logo as T* **154** *of Ascension.*

696 8p. Type **178** 50 50
697 16p. Lamb 65 65
698 34p. Puppy and cat .. .. .. 1·50 1·75
699 39p. Kitten *(vert)* .. .. .. 1·60 2·00
700 78p. Collie dog *(vert)* .. .. .. 2·50 3·50
696/700 .. .. *Set of* 5 6·00 7·50

On the vertical designs "FALKLAND ISLANDS" ranges left instead of being centred as on Nos. 694/5.

179 Goose Barnacles

180 Dockyard Blacksmith's Shop and Sir James Clark Ross (explorer)

(Des T. Chater. Litho Walsall)

1994 (4 Apr). *Inshore Marine Life. T* **179** *and similar multicoloured designs. W w* **16** *(sideways on horiz designs). P* 14.

701 1p. Type **179** 20 40
702 2p. Painted Shrimp *(horiz)* 30 40
703 8p. Patagonian Copper Limpet *(horiz)* .. 50 50
704 9p. Eleginops ("Mullet") *(horiz)* .. 50 50
705 10p. Sea Anemones *(horiz)* 50 50
706 20p. Flathead Eelpout *(horiz)* 75 75
707 25p. Spider Crab *(horiz)* 80 80
708 50p. Lobster Krill .. .. .. 1·40 1·50
709 80p. Falkland Skate *(horiz)* .. .. 2·00 2·25
710 £1 Centollón Crab *(horiz)* .. .. 2·25 2·50
711 £3 Wilton's Notothen ("Rock Cod") *(horiz)* 6·00 6·25
712 £5 Octopus .. .. 10·00 10·50
701/12 .. .. *Set of* 12 23·00 24·00

A similar 5p. value, showing a smelt and incorrectly inscribed "Austro Menidia Smithii", was withdrawn before issue.

For miniature sheet containing £1, wmk w **14** and with imprint date, see No. **MS**784.

(Des J. Peck. Litho Questa)

1994 (1 July). *150th Anniv of Founding of Stanley. T* **180** *and similar horiz designs. Multicoloured. W w* **14** *(sideways). P* 14.

713 9p. Type **180** 50 50
714 17p. 21 Fitzroy Road (home of Chaplain James Moody) 75 60
715 30p. Stanley Cottage (built by Dr. Henry Hamblin) .. .. 1·25 1·25
716 35p. Pioneer Row and Sgt-maj Henry Felton 1·50 1·75
717 40p. Government House (designed by Governor R. Moody) .. .. .. 1·60 1·90
718 65p. View of Stanley and Edward Stanley, Earl of Derby (Secretary of State for the Colonies) .. .. 2·25 3·00
713/18 .. .. *Set of* 6 7·00 8·00

181 Lockheed L-1011 TriStar over Gypsy Cove

(Des J. Peck. Litho Walsall)

1994 (24 Oct). *Falkland Beaches. T* **181** *and similar horiz designs. Multicoloured. W w* **16** *(sideways). P* 14.

719 17p. Type **181** 75 60
720 35p. Cruise ship off Sea Lion Island .. 1·40 1·25
721 40p. Britten Norman Islander aircraft at Pebble Island .. .. 1·75 1·75
722 65p. Landrover at Volunteer Beach .. 2·00 3·00
719/22 .. .. *Set of* 4 5·50 6·00

182 Mission House, Keppel Island

183 *Lupinus arboreus*

(Des G. Vasarhelyi. Litho Questa)

1994 (1 Dec). *150th Anniv of South American Missionary Society. T* **182** *and similar horiz designs. Multicoloured. W w* **16** *(sideways). P* 14.

723 5p. Type **182** 20 30
724 17p. Thomas Bridges (compiler of Yahgan dictionary) 50 50
725 40p. Fuegian Indians .. .. .. 1·10 1·50
726 65p. Capt. Allen Gardiner and *Allen Gardiner* (schooner) .. .. .. 1·50 2·25
723/6 .. .. *Set of* 4 3·00 4·00

(Des I. Strange. Litho Questa)

1995 (3 Jan). *Flowering Shrubs. T* **183** *and similar vert designs. Multicoloured. W w* **16**. *P* 14½×14.

727 9p. Type **183** 40 40
728 17p. *Hebe elliptica* 60 55
729 30p. *Fuschia magellanica* 85 85
730 35p. *Berberis ilicifolia* .. .. .. 90 1·00
731 40p. *Ulex europaeus* .. .. .. 95 1·10
732 65p. *Hebe x franciscana* .. .. .. 1·75 2·50
727/32 .. .. *Set of* 6 5·00 5·75

184 Magellanic Oystercatcher

(Des I. Strange. Litho B.D.T.)

1995 (1 Mar). *Shore Birds. T* **184** *and similar horiz designs. Multicoloured. W w* **16** *(sideways). P* 13½.

733 17p. Type **184** 85 60
734 35p. Rufous-chested Dotterel .. .. 1·40 1·25
735 40p. Blackish Oystercatcher .. .. 1·50 1·50
736 65p. Two-banded Plover .. .. .. 2·50 3·50
733/6 .. .. *Set of* 4 5·50 6·00

(Des R. Watton. Litho Questa)

1995 (8 May). *50th Anniv of End of Second World War. Multicoloured designs as T* **161** *of Ascension. W* w **14** *(sideways). P* 14.

737 17p. Falkland Islands contingent in Victory Parade 60 60
738 35p. Governor Sir Alan Cardinall on Bren gun-carrier .. .. 1·10 1·10
739 40p. H.M.A.S. *Esperance Bay* (troopship) 1·25 1·50
740 65p. H.M.S. *Exeter* (cruiser) .. .. 2·25 3·50
737/40 .. .. *Set of* 4 4·75 6·00
MS741 75×85 mm. £1 Reverse of 1939–45 War Medal (*vert*). Wmk upright .. .. .. 2·50 3·25

185 Ox and Cart

186 Kelp Geese

(Des N. Shewring. Litho B.D.T.)

1995 (1 Aug). *Transporting Peat. T* **185** *and similar horiz designs. Multicoloured. W* w **16** *(sideways). P* 14.

742 17p. Type **185** 60 50
743 35p. Horse and cart .. .. 1·10 1·10
744 40p. Caterpillar tractor pulling sleigh .. 1·25 1·25
745 65p. Lorry .. .. 2·25 3·00
742/5 .. .. *Set of* 4 4·75 5·25

(Des Sonia Felton. Litho B.D.T.)

1995 (11 Sept). *Wildlife. T* **186** *and similar vert designs. Multicoloured. W* w **16**. *P* 13½.

746 35p. Type **186** .. .. 1·10 1·10
a. Sheetlet. Nos. 746/51 .. .. 5·75
747 35p. Black-browed Albatross .. .. 1·10 1·10
748 35p. Blue-eyed Cormorants .. .. 1·10 1·10
749 35p. Magellanic Penguins .. .. 1·10 1·10
750 35p. Fur Seals .. .. 1·10 1·10
751 35p. Rockhopper Penguins .. .. 1·10 1·10
746/51 .. .. *Set of* 6 5·75 5·75

Nos. 746/51 were printed together, *se-tenant*, in sheetlets of 6, with the backgrounds forming a composite design.

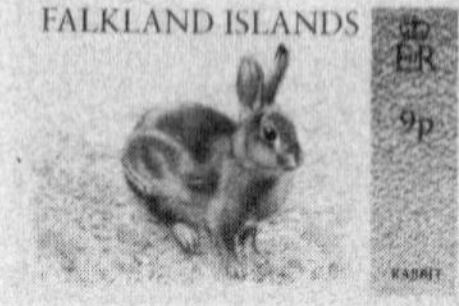

187 Cottontail Rabbit

(Des A. Robinson. Litho Walsall)

1995 (6 Nov). *Introduced Wild Animals. T* **187** *and similar horiz designs. Multicoloured. W* w **14** *(sideways). P* 14.

752 9p. Type **187** 45 45
753 17p. Brown Hare 65 55
754 35p. Guanacos .. .. 1·10 1·25
755 40p. Fox .. .. 1·25 1·40
756 65p. Otter .. .. 1·90 2·50
752/6 .. .. *Set of* 5 4·75 5·50

188 Princess Anne and Government House

(Des D. Miller. Litho Walsall)

1996 (30 Jan). *Royal Visit. T* **188** *and similar horiz designs. Multicoloured. W* w **14** *(sideways). P* 14½×14.

757 9p. Type **188** 45 45
758 19p. Falklands War Memorial, San Carlos Cemetery 75 65
759 30p. Christ Church Cathedral .. .. 1·10 1·10
760 73p. Helicopter over Goose Green .. 2·50 3·00
757/60 .. .. *Set of* 4 4·25 4·75

(Des D. Miller. Litho B.D.T.)

1996 (21 Apr). *70th Birthday of Queen Elizabeth II. Vert designs as T* **165** *of Ascension, each incorporating a different photograph of the Queen. W* w **14**. *P* 13½.

761 17p. Steeple Jason 60 50
762 40p. *Tamar* (container ship) .. .. 1·50 1·25
763 45p. New Island .. .. 1·50 1·40
764 65p. Falkland Islands Community School 1·60 1·60
761/4 .. .. *Set of* 4 4·75 4·25
MS765 64×66 mm. £1 Queen Elizabeth II .. 2·40 3·00

189 Mounted Postman, *c*. 1890

(Des A. Theobald. Litho Walsall)

1996 (8 June). *"CAPEX '96" International Stamp Exhibition, Toronto. Mail Transport. T* **189** *and similar horiz designs. Multicoloured. W* w **16** *(sideways). P* 14.

766 9p. Type **189** 50 45
767 40p. Noorduyn Norseman V seaplane .. 1·50 1·25
768 45p. *Forrest* (freighter) at San Carlos .. 1·60 1·40
769 76p. De Havilland D.H.C.2 Beaver seaplane 2·50 2·50
766/9 .. .. *Set of* 4 5·50 5·00
MS770 110×80 mm. £1 L.M.S. Class "Jubilee" steam locomotive No. 5606 *Falkland Islands* (47×31 *mm*). P 13½×14 .. .. .. 2·40 3·25

190 Southern Bottlenose Whale

(Des E. King. Litho Walsall)

1996 (2 Sept). *Beaked Whales. T* **190** *and similar horiz designs. Multicoloured. W* w **14** *(sideways). P* 13½×14.

771 9p. Type **190** 30 30
772 30p. Cuvier's Beaked Whale 80 80
773 35p. Straptoothed Beaked Whale 90 90
774 75p. Gray's Beaked Whale .. .. 1·90 1·90
771/4 .. .. *Set of* 4 3·50 3·50

191 Magellanic Penguins performing Courtship Dance

(Des I. Strange. Litho Walsall)

1997 (2 Jan). *Magellanic Penguins. T* **191** *and similar horiz designs. Multicoloured. W* w **14** *(sideways). P* 14½.

775 17p. Type **191** 55 45
776 35p. Penguin in burrow .. .. .. 1·00 85
777 40p. Adult and chick .. .. .. 1·10 90
778 65p. Group of Penguins swimming .. 1·60 1·60
775/8 .. .. *Set of* 4 3·75 3·50

192 Black Pejerry

193 Coral Fern

(Des T. Chater and D. Miller. Litho Questa)

1997 (3 Feb). *"HONG KONG '97" International Stamp Exhibition. Sheet* 130×90 *mm. W* w **14** *(sideways). P* 14.
MS779 **192** £1 multicoloured .. .. .. 2·50 2·50

(Des I. Strange. Litho Walsall)

1997 (3 Mar). *Ferns. T* **193** *and similar vert designs. Multicoloured. W* w **14**. *P* 14½.

780 17p. Type **193** 55 45
781 35p. Adder's Tongue Fern .. .. .. 1·00 1·00
782 40p. Fuegian Tall Fern .. .. .. 1·10 1·10
783 65p. Small Fern .. .. 1·60 1·75
780/3 .. .. *Set of* 4 3·75 3·75

(Des T. Chater. Litho Walsall)

1997 (20 June). *Return of Hong Kong to China. Sheet* 130×90 *mm, containing design as No.* 710. *With imprint date. W* w **14** *(sideways). P* 14.
MS784 £1 Centollón Crab .. .. .. 2·50 2·50

COVER PRICES

Cover factors are quoted at the beginning of each country for most issues to 1945. An explanation of the system can be found on page x. The factors quoted do not, however, apply to philatelic covers.

(Des N. Shewring (No. **MS**791), D. Miller (others). Litho Quest

1997 (10 July). *Golden Wedding of Queen Elizabeth and Prin Philip. Multicoloured designs as T* **173** *of Ascension. W* w **1** *P* 14½.

785 9p. Queen Elizabeth holding bouquet, 1993 40
a. Horiz pair. Nos. 785/6 80
786 9p. Prince Philip and horse, 1985 .. 40
787 17p. Queen Elizabeth in phaeton at Trooping the Colour, 1996 65
a. Horiz pair. Nos. 787/8 .. .. 1·25
788 17p. Prince Philip in R.A.F. uniform .. 65
789 40p. Queen Elizabeth wearing red coat, 1986 .. .. 1·00
a. Horiz pair. Nos. 789/90 .. .. 2·00
790 40p. Prince William and Princess Beatrice on horseback .. .. 1·00
785/90 .. .. *Set of* 6 3·50
MS791 110×71 mm. £1.50, Queen Elizabeth and Prince Philip in landau (*horiz*). W w **14** (sideways). P 14×14½ .. .. .. 3·50

Nos. 785/6, 787/8 and 789/90 were each printed togethe *se-tenant*, in horizontal pairs throughout the sheets with t backgrounds forming composite designs.

194 Bull Point Lighthouse

(Des J. Peck. Litho Walsall)

1997 (4 Aug*). *Lighthouses. T* **194** *and similar horiz design Multicoloured. W* w **14** *(sideways). P* 14.

792 9p. Type **194** 40
793 30p. Cape Pembroke Lighthouse 90
794 £1 Cape Meredith Lighthouse .. .. 2·40
792/4 .. .. *Set of* 3 3·25

*This is the local date of issue. The Crown Agents released t stamps in London on 4 July.

195 Forster's Caracara

196 Merryweather and Son Greenwich Gem Fire Engine

(Des Sonia Felton. Litho Questa)

1997 (6 Oct). *Endangered Species. T* **195** *and similar hor designs. Multicoloured. W* w **16** *(sideways). P* 14½.

795 17p. Type **195** 70
796 19p. Southern Sealion 70
797 40p. Felton's Flower .. .. .. 1·25
798 73p. Trout .. .. 2·25
795/8 .. .. *Set of* 4 4·50

(Des N. Shewring. Litho Questa)

1998 (26 Feb). *Centenary of Falkland Islands Fire Servi T* **196** *and similar vert designs. Multicoloured. W* w **1** *P* 14½×14.

799 9p. Type **196** 40
800 17p. Merryweather's Hatfield trailer pump 60
801 40p. Coventry Climax Godiva trailer pump 1·25
802 65p. Carmichael Bedford "Type B" water tender .. .. 2·00
799/802 .. .. *Set of* 4 3·75

(Des D. Miller. Litho Questa)

1998 (31 Mar). *Diana, Princess of Wales Commemoration. Ve designs as T* **177** *of Ascension. W* w **14** *(sideways). P* 14½×1
MS803 145×70 mm. 30p. Wearing black jacket, 1990; 30p. Wearing red dress, 1988; 30p. Resting head on hand, 1991; 30p. Wearing landmine protection clothing, Angola (*sold at* £1.20 + 20p. *charity premium*) .. .. 3·25

197 Tawny-throated Dotterel

198 *Penelope*, 1926

(Des A. Robinson. Litho Questa)

1998 (14 July). *Rare Visiting Birds. T* **197** *and similar hor designs. Multicoloured. W* w **14** *(sideways). P* 14.

(*a*) *Designs* 39½×23½ *mm*

804 1p. Type **197** 10
805 2p. Hudsonian Godwit 10
806 5p. Eared Dove 10
807 9p. Great Grebe 20

8	10p.	Chilian Lapwing ("Southern Lapwing")	20	25
9	16p.	Buff-necked Ibis	30	35
10	30p.	Ashy-headed Goose	60	65
11	65p.	Red-legged Cormorant ("Red-legged Shag")	1·25	1·40
12	88p.	Argentine Shoveler ("Red Shoveler")	1·75	1·90
13	£1	Red-fronted Coot	2·00	2·10
14	£3	Chilian Flamingo	6·00	6·25
15	£5	Fork-tailed Flycatcher	10·00	10·50

(*b*) *Booklet stamps. Designs* 35×22 *mm*

16	9p.	Roseate Spoonbill	20	25
	a.	Booklet pane. Nos. 816×2, 817×8 and 2 stamp-size labels	3·00	
17	17p.	Austral Conure ("Austral Parakeet")	35	40
18	35p.	American Kestrel	70	75
	a.	Booklet pane. No. 818×6	4·00	
04/18		.. .. *Set of* 15	23·00	24·00

(Litho Questa)

998 (30 Sept). *Local Vessels. T* **198** *and similar multicoloured designs.* W w **14** (*sideways*). *P* 14.

19	17p.	Type **198**	55	45
20	35p.	*Ilen*, 1926	95	95
21	40p.	*Weddell*, 1940	1·10	1·10
22	65p.	*Lively*, 1940 (31×22 *mm*)	1·60	1·75
19/22		.. .. *Set of* 4	3·75	3·75

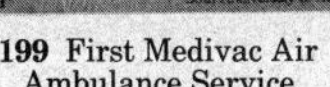

199 First Medivac Air Ambulance Service

200 Marine at Port Egmont, Saunders Island, 1766

(Des N. Shewring. Litho Questa)

998 (1 Dec). *50th Anniv of Falkland Islands Government Air Service. T* **199** *and similar horiz design. Multicoloured.* W w **14** (*sideways*). *P* 14.

23	17p.	Type **199**	35	40
24	£1	F.I.G.A.S. aircraft over map	2·00	2·10

(Des V. Ambrus. Litho Walsall)

998 (8 Dec). *Royal Marine Uniforms. T* **200** *and similar vert designs. Multicoloured.* W w **14**. *P* 14½×14.

25	17p.	Type **200**	35	40
26	30p.	Officer at Port Louis, East Falklands, 1833	60	65
27	35p.	Corporal and H.M.S. *Kent* (cruiser), 1914	70	75
28	65p.	Bugler at Government House, 1976 ..	1·25	1·40
25/8		.. .. *Set of* 4	2·75	3·00

201 Altar, St. Mary's Church

(Litho Walsall)

999 (12 Feb). *Centenary of St. Mary's Church. T* **201** *and similar horiz designs. Multicoloured.* W w **16** (*sideways*). *P* 14.

329	17p.	Type **201**	35	40
330	40p.	St. Mary's Church	80	85
331	75p.	Laying of foundation stone, 1899 ..	1·50	1·60
329/31		.. .. *Set of* 3	2·50	2·75

202 H.M.S. *Beagle* (Darwin)

(Des R. Watton. Litho Walsall)

1999 (5 Mar). *"Australia '99" World Stamp Exhibition, Melbourne. Maritime History. T* **202** *and similar horiz designs. Multicoloured.* W w **16** (*sideways*). *P* 14.

832	25p.	Type **202**	50	55
833	35p.	H.M.A.S. *Australia* (battle cruiser) ..	70	75
834	40p.	*Canberra* (liner)	80	85
835	50p.	*Great Britain* (steam/sail)	1·00	1·10
	a.	Horiz pair. Nos. 835/6	2·00	
836	50p.	All-England Cricket Team, 1861–62	1·00	1·10
832/6		.. .. *Set of* 5	4·00	4·25

Nos. 835/6 were printed together, *se-tenant*, in horizontal pairs throughout the sheet.

STAMP BOOKLETS

1977 (1 Nov). *Silver Jubilee. Multicoloured cover,* 117×79 *mm, showing Norroy and Ulster King of Arms. Stapled.*

SB1 £2 booklet containing 6p., 11p. and 33p., each in pane of 4 (Nos. 326a, 327a, 327ba) .. .. 10·00

1978 (27 Nov). *Mail Ships. Black and blue-green cover,* 99×57 *mm, showing* Hebe *on front and* Darwin *on back. Stapled.*

SB2 £1 booklet containing 1p., 3p., 5p., 6p., 10p. (Nos. 331A, 333A, 335A/6A, 340A) each in block of 4 24·00

1979 (4 June). *Mail Ships. Black and bright new blue cover,* 99×57 *mm, showing* Nautilus *on front and* A.E.S. *on back. Stapled.*

SB3 £1 booklet. Contents as No. SB2 .. .. 11·00

1980 (14 July). *Mail Ships. Black and red cover,* 100×59 *mm, showing* Amelia *on front and* Merak-N *on back. Stapled.*

SB4 £1 booklet. Contents as No. SB2 .. .. 5·50

1982 (23 Feb). *Mail Ships. Black and grey cover,* 99×58 *mm, showing* Fairy *on front and* Fitzroy *on back. Stapled.*

SB5 £1 booklet. Contents as No. SB2 .. .. 4·75

1985 (18 Feb). *Black and azure cover,* 95×64 *mm, with example of stamp No. 471A affixed. Stapled.*

SB6 £2.24, booklet containing eight 2p. and four each 7p., 20p., 25p. (Nos. 470A, 475A, 479A, 480A) in blocks of 4 .. .. 21·00

1988 (2 Feb). *Black and greenish grey cover,* 95×64 *mm, with example of stamp No. 470A affixed. Stapled.*

SB7 £2.52, booklet containing eight 4p. and four each 10p., 20p., 25p. (Nos. 472A, 478A/80A) in blocks of 4 .. .. 15·00

1988 (26 Sept). *Black and pale green cover,* 95×64 *mm, with example of stamp No. 471A affixed. Stapled.*

SB8 £2.52, booklet containing 1p., 4p., 6p., 8p., 9p., 10p., 25p. (Nos. 469A, 472A, 474A, 476A/8A, 480A), each in block of 4 .. .. .. 7·00

1990 (29 Oct). *Cape Horn Sailing Ships. Black and greenish yellow showing No.* 575 *(No.* SB9*) or pale blue showing No.* 578 *(No.* SB10*) covers, each* 104×55 *mm. Panes attached by selvedge.*

SB9 60p. booklet containing 3p., 9p. (Nos. 569, 575), each in block of 5 .. .. 6·50

SB10 £1.55, booklet containing 6p., 25p. (Nos. 572, 578), each in block of 5 .. .. .. 8·50

1998 (14 July). *Rare Visiting Birds. Multicoloured covers,* 86×52 *mm, showing Roseate Spoonbill (No.* SB11*) or American Kestrel (No.* SB12*). Panes attached by selvedge.*

SB11 £1.54, booklet containing pane of two 9p., eight 17p. and 2 stamp-size labels (No. 816a) .. 3·00

SB12 £2.10, booklet containing pane of six 35p. (No. 818a) .. .. 4·25

POSTAGE DUE STAMPS

D 1 King Penguin

(Des O. Bell. Litho Questa)

1991 (7 Jan). W w **14** (*sideways*). *P* 15×14.

D1 D 1	1p. brown-lake and cerise	10	10
D2	2p. red-orange and pale orange ..	10	10
D3	3p. brown-ochre and chrome-yellow ..	10	10
D4	4p. deep blue-green & light blue-green	10	10
D5	5p. greenish blue & light greenish blue	10	15
D6	10p. deep violet-blue and cobalt ..	20	25
D7	20p. deep reddish violet and lilac ..	40	45
D8	50p. yellowish green and apple-green ..	1·00	1·10
D1/8	.. .. *Set of* 8	1·90	2·10

FALKLAND ISLANDS DEPENDENCIES

PRICES FOR STAMPS ON COVER TO 1945
Nos. A1/D8 *from* × 20

A. GRAHAM LAND

For use at Port Lockroy (established 16 February 1944) and Hope Bay (established 12 February 1945) bases.

Falkland Islands definitive stamps with face values of 1s. 3d. and above were valid for use from Graham Land in conjunction with Nos. A1/8 and subsequently Nos. G1/16.

Stamps of FALKLAND ISLANDS *cancelled at Port Lockroy or Hope Bay with Graham Land circular datestamps between* 16 February 1944 *and* 31 January 1954.

1938–50. *King George VI* (*Nos.* 159/63).
Z1 1s. 3d. black and carmine-red .. .. 75·00
Z2 2s. 6d. slate .. .. 30·00
Z3 5s. indigo and yellow-brown £130
Z4 10s. black and orange .. .. 40·00
Z5 £1 black and violet .. .. 60·00

1952. *King George VI* (*Nos.* 181/5)
Z 6 1s. 3d. orange .. ..
Z 7 2s. 6d. olive-green .. ..
Z 8 5s. purple .. ..
Z 9 10s. grey .. ..
Z10 £1 black .. ..

GRAHAM LAND

DEPENDENCY OF

(A 1)

1944 (12 Feb)–**45.** *Falkland Islands Nos.* 146, 148, 150, 153/5, 157 *and* 158*a optd with Type* A 1, *in red, by B.W.*
A1 ½d. black and green .. .. 30 1·75
a. Blue-black and green £550 £375
A2 1d. black and violet .. .. 30 1·00
A3 2d. black and carmine-red .. .. .. 40 1·00
A4 3d. black and blue .. .. 30 1·00
A5 4d. black and purple .. .. 3·00 1·75
A6 6d. black and brown .. .. 13·00 2·25
a. Blue-black and brown (24.9.45) .. 20·00
A7 9d. black and grey-blue .. .. .. 1·00 1·25
A8 1s. deep blue .. .. 1·00 1·25
A1/8 .. .. *Set of* 8 17·00 10·00
A1/8 Perf "Specimen" .. .. *Set of* 8 £325

B. SOUTH GEORGIA

The stamps of Falkland Islands were used at the Grytviken whaling station on South Georgia from 3 December 1909.

Mr. J. Innes Wilson, the Stipendary Magistrate whose duties included those of postmaster, was issued with a stock of stamps, values ½d. to 5s., together with an example of the current "FALKLAND ISLANDS" circular datestamp. This was used to cancel the stamps, but, as it gave no indication that mail had originated at South Georgia, a straight-line handstamp inscribed "SOUTH GEORGIA", or subsequently "South Georgia", was also supplied. It was intended that this should be struck directly on to each letter or card below the stamp, but it can sometimes be found struck across the stamp instead.

The use of the "South Georgia" handstamp continued after the introduction of the "SOUTH GEORGIA" circular datestamp in June 1910 apparently for philatelic purposes, but no example has been reported used after June 1912.

SOUTH GEORGIA.

Z 1

South Georgia.

Z 2

		On piece	On cover /card
ZU1	Example of Type Z 1 used in conjunction with "FALKLAND ISLANDS" postmark (22 Dec 1909 to 30 March 1910) *Price from*	£1000	£3750
ZU2	Example of Type Z 2 used in conjunction with "FALKLAND ISLANDS" postmark (May 1910) .. .. *Price from*	£750	£3000
ZU3	Example of Type Z 2 used in conjunction with "SOUTH GEORGIA" postmark (June 1910 to June 1912) .. *Price from*	£250	£900

Stamps of FALKLAND ISLANDS *cancelled at Grytviken with South Georgia circular datestamps between* June 1910 *and* 31 January 1954.

1891–1902. *Queen Victoria* (*Nos.* 32, 36 *and* 38)
Z11 4d. olive-black £130
Z12 9d. salmon £130
Z13 1s. yellow-brown £140

1904–12. *King Edward VII* (*Nos.* 43/50).
Z14 ½d. green .. .. 11·00
Z15 1d. vermilion .. .. 11·00
d. Dull coppery red (on thick paper) .. 35·00
Z16 2d. purple .. .. 50·00
b. Reddish purple £275
Z17 2½d. ultramarine .. .. 20·00
b. Deep blue £180
Z18 6d. orange £100
Z19 1s. brown £100
Z20 3s. green £200
Z21 5s. red £250

SOUTH GEORGIA PROVISIONAL HANDSTAMPS. During October 1911 the arrival of the German South Polar Expedition at Grytviken, South Georgia, resulted in the local supply of stamps becoming exhausted. The Acting Magistrate, Mr. E. B. Binnie, who was also responsible for the postal facilities, produced a handstamp reading "Paid at (or At) SOUTH GEORGIA" which, together with a manuscript indication of the postage paid and his signature, was used on mail from 18 October 1911 to January 1912. Further examples, signed by John Innes Wilson, are known from February 1912, but these may be philatelic.
PH1 "Paid 1 at SOUTH GEORGIA EBB" *Price on cover* £4250
PH1*a* "Paid 1 At SOUTH GEORGIA EBB" (16 Dec) *Price on cover* £4500
PH2 "Paid 2½ at SOUTH GEORGIA EBB" *Price on cover* £4750
PH2*a* "Paid 2½ At SOUTH GEORGIA EBB" (16 Dec) *Price on cover* £5250

1912–23. *King George V. Wmk Mult Crown CA* (*Nos.* 60/9).
Z22 ½d. green .. .. 15·00
a. Perf 14 (line). *Deep yellow-green* .. 35·00
d. Dull yellowish green (on thick greyish paper) 30·00
Z23 1d. orange-red .. .. 10·00
a. Perf 14 (line). *Orange-vermilion* .. 10·00
d. Orange-vermilion .. .. 10·00
Z24 2d. maroon .. .. 40·00
Z25 2½d. deep bright blue .. .. 25·00
c. Deep blue .. .. 25·00
Z26 6d. yellow-orange .. .. 50·00
b. Brown-orange .. .. 40·00
ba. Bisected (diag) (3d.) (on cover) (3.23) .. £11000
Z27 1s. bistre-brown £100
b. Brown (on thick greyish paper) £150
Z28 3s. slate-green £150
Z29 5s. deep rose-red £180
a. Reddish maroon £275
b. Maroon £225
Z30 10s. red/*green* £275
Z31 £1 black/*red* £425

1918–20. "WAR STAMP" *ovpts* (*Nos.* 70/2)
Z32 ½d. deep olive .. .. 15·00
Z33 1d. vermilion .. .. 15·00
Z34 1s. light bistre-brown .. .. 80·00

1921–28. *King George V. Wmk Mult Script CA* (*Nos.* 73/80).
Z35 ½d. yellowish green .. .. 5·00
Z36 1d. dull vermilion .. .. 4·00
Z37 2d. deep brown-purple .. .. 25·00
Z38 2½d. deep blue .. .. 22·00
a. Bisected (diag) (1d.) (on cover) (3.23) .. £7000
b. Prussian blue £450
Z39 2½d. deep purple/*pale yellow* .. .. .. 45·00
Z40 6d. yellow-orange .. .. 50·00
Z41 1s. deep ochre .. .. 60·00
Z42 3s. slate-green £150

1928 PROVISIONAL. For listing of the 2½d. on 2d. surcharge issued at Grytviken on 7 February 1928 see No. 115 of Falkland Islands.

1929–36. *King George V. Whale and Penguins design* (*Nos.* 116/26).
Z43 ½d. green .. .. 5·00
Z44 1d. scarlet .. .. 4·00
Z45 2d. grey .. .. 10·00
Z46 2½d. blue .. .. 4·00
Z47 4d. orange .. .. 20·00
Z48 6d. purple .. .. 30·00
Z49 1s. black/*emerald* .. .. 35·00
Z50 2s. 6d. carmine/*blue* .. .. 75·00
Z51 5s. green/*yellow* £110
Z52 10s. carmine/*emerald* £200
Z53 £1 black/*red* £500
Examples of most values are known with forged postmarks dated "Au 30" in 1928, 1930 and 1931.

1933. *Centenary of British Administration* (*Nos.* 127/38).
Z54 ½d. black and green .. .. 7·00
Z55 1d. black and scarlet .. .. 4·00
Z56 1½d. black and blue .. .. 16·00
Z57 2d. black and brown .. .. 23·00
Z58 3d. black and violet .. .. 17·00
Z59 4d. black and orange .. .. 19·00
Z60 6d. black and slate .. .. 65·00
Z61 1s. black and olive-green .. .. .. 65·00
Z62 2s. 6d. black and violet £180
Z63 5s. black and yellow £700
a. Black and yellow-orange £1300
Z64 10s. black and chestnut £750
Z65 £1 black and carmine £2000

1935. *Silver Jubilee* (*Nos.* 139/42).
Z66 1d. deep blue and scarlet .. .. .. 3·00
Z67 2½d. brown and deep blue .. .. .. 4·00
Z68 4d. green and indigo .. .. 5·00
Z69 1s. slate and purple .. .. 5·00

1937. *Coronation* (*Nos.* 143/5).
Z70 ½d. green .. .. 2·00
Z71 1d. carmine .. .. 2·00
Z72 2½d. blue .. .. 2·00

1938–50. *King George VI* (*Nos.* 146/63).
Z73 ½d. black and green .. .. 3·00
Z74 1d. black and carmine .. .. 5·00
a. Black and scarlet .. .. 2·00
Z75 1d. black and violet .. .. 4·50
Z76 2d. black and deep violet .. .. .. 6·00
Z77 2d. black and carmine-red .. .. .. 7·00
Z78 2½d. black and bright blue (No. 151) .. 2·00
Z79 3d. black and blue .. .. 6·00
Z80 4d. black and purple .. .. 6·00
Z81 6d. black and brown .. .. 8·00
Z82 9d. black and grey-blue .. .. 10·00
Z83 1s. pale blue 30
a. Deep blue 30
Z84 1s. 3d. black and carmine-red 30
Z85 2s. 6d. slate 20
Z86 5s. bright blue and pale brown £1
a. Indigo and yellow-brown £1
b. Blue and buff-brown £1
Z87 10s. black and orange 40
Z88 £1 black and violet 60

Falkland Islands definitive stamps with values of 1s. 3d. a above continued to be valid from South Georgia after t introduction of Nos. B1/8 and subsequently Nos. G1/16.

1952. *King George VI* (*Nos.* 181/5).
Z89 1s. 3d. orange 25
Z90 2s. 6d. olive-green .. ..
Z91 5s. purple .. ..
Z92 10s. grey .. ..
Z93 £1 black .. ..

1944 (3 Apr)–**45.** *Falkland Islands Nos.* 146, 148, 150, 153 157 *and* 158*a optd* "SOUTH GEORGIA/DEPENDENCY OF *in red, as Type* A **1** *of Graham Land.*
B1 ½d. black and green .. .. .. 30 1·
a. Wmk sideways £2500
B2 1d. black and violet .. .. .. 30 1·
B3 2d. black and carmine-red .. .. 40 1·
B4 3d. black and blue .. .. .. 30 1·
B5 4d. black and purple .. .. .. 3·00 1·
B6 6d. black and brown .. .. .. 13·00 2·
a. Blue-black and brown (24.9.45) .. 20·00
B7 9d. black and grey-blue .. .. .. 1·00 1·
B8 1s. deep blue .. .. 1·00 1·
B1/8 .. .. *Set of* 8 17·00 10·
B1/8 Perf "Specimen" .. .. *Set of* 8 £325
For later issues, see after No. G44.

C. SOUTH ORKNEYS

Used from the *Fitzroy* in February 1944 and at Laurie Isla (established January 1946).

Falkland Islands definitive stamps with face values of 1s. and above were valid for use from the South Orkneys conjunction with Nos. C1/8 and subsequently Nos. G1/16.

Stamps of FALKLAND ISLANDS *cancelled on the* Fitzroy, *Laurie Island or at Signy Island with South Orkneys circu datestamps between* 21 February 1944 *and* 31 January 19

1938–50. *King George VI* (*Nos.* 160/3).
Z95 2s. 6d. slate 30
Z96 5s. indigo and yellow-brown £1
Z97 10s. black and orange .. .. 40·
Z98 £1 black and violet .. .. 60·

1952. *King George VI* (*Nos.* 181/5).
Z 99 1s. 3d. orange .. ..
Z100 2s. 6d. olive-green .. ..
Z101 5s. purple .. ..
Z102 10s. grey .. ..
Z103 £1 black .. ..

1944 (21 Feb)–**45.** *Falkland Islands Nos.* 146, 148, 150, 153/5, 1 *and* 158*a optd* "SOUTH ORKNEYS/DEPENDENCY OF", *in as Type* A **1** *of Graham Land.*
C1 ½d. black and green .. .. .. 30 1·
C2 1d. black and violet .. .. .. 30 1·
w. Wmk inverted £3750
C3 2d. black and carmine-red .. .. 40 1·
C4 3d. black and blue .. .. .. 30 1·
C5 4d. black and purple .. .. .. 3·00 1·
C6 6d. black and brown .. .. .. 13·00 2·
a. Blue-black and brown (24.9.45) .. 20·00
C7 9d. black and grey-blue .. .. .. 1·00 1·
C8 1s. deep blue .. .. 1·00 1·
C1/8 .. .. *Set of* 8 17·00 10·
C1/8 Perf "Specimen" .. .. *Set of* 8 £325

D. SOUTH SHETLANDS

Postal facilities were first provided at the Port Foster whali station on Deception Island for the 1912–13 whaling season a were available each year between November and the followi April until March 1931.

No postmark was provided for the 1912–13 season and t local postmaster was instructed to cancel stamps on cover with straight-line "PORT FOSTER" handstamp. Most letters cancelled subsequently received a "FALKLAND ISLAND circular postmark dated between 19 and 28 March 1913. It known that only low value stamps were available at Port Foste Higher values, often with other "FALKLAND ISLAND postmark dates, were, it is believed, subsequently "made order".

Stamps of FALKLAND ISLANDS *cancelled at Port Foste Deception Island with part of* "PORT FOSTER" *straight-li handstamp.*

1904–12. *King Edward VII* (*Nos.* 43/4).
Z104 ½d. deep yellow-green £12
Z105 1d. orange-vermilion £12

1912. *King George V. Wmk Mult Crown CA* (*No.* 60).
Z106 ½d. yellow-green £12

Stamps of FALKLAND ISLANDS *cancelled at Port Foster wi part of oval* "DECEPTION ISLAND SOUTH SHETLAND *postmark in black or violet between* 1914 *and* 1927.

1904–12. *King Edward VII* (*No.* 43*c*)
Z108 ½d. deep yellow-green £2

1912–20. *King George V. Wmk Mult Crown CA* (*Nos.* 60/9).
Z110 ½d. yellow-green .. .. 75·
Z111 1d. orange-red .. .. 75·
Z112 2d. maroon £1
Z113 2½d. deep bright blue £1

114 6d. yellow-orange £120
115 1s. light bistre-brown £140
116 3s. slate-green £300
117 5s. deep rose-red £350
118 10s. red/*green* £450
119 £1 black/*red* £550

918–20. "WAR STAMP" *ovpts* (*Nos.* 70/2).
120 ½d. deep olive £100
121 1d. vermilion £100
122 1s. light bistre-brown £200

921–28. *King George V. Wmk Mult Script CA* (*Nos.* 73/80).
123 ½d. yellowish green £100
126 2½d. deep blue £130
129 1s. deep ochre £150

Stamps of FALKLAND ISLANDS *cancelled at Port Foster with* "SOUTH SHETLANDS" *circular datestamp between* 1923 *and* March 1931

1912–20. *King George V. Wmk Mult Crown CA* (*Nos.* 60/9).
Z131 1d. orange-vermilion .. .. 50·00
Z132 2d. deep reddish purple .. .. .. 60·00
Z133 6d. brown-orange .. .. 80·00
Z134 3s. slate-green £160
Z135 5s. maroon £180
Z136 10s. red/*green* £300
Z137 £1 black/*red* £500

Examples of all values are known with forged postmarks dated "20 MR 27".

1918–20. "WAR STAMP" *ovpts* (*Nos.* 70/2).
Z139 1d. vermilion .. ..
Z140 1s. light bistre brown .. ..

1921–28. *King George V. Wmk Mult Script CA* (*Nos.* 73/80).
Z141 ½d. yellowish green .. .. 35·00
Z142 1d. dull vermilion .. .. 35·00
Z143 2d. deep brown-purple .. .. 50·00
Z144 2½d. deep blue .. .. 40·00
Z145 2½d. deep purple/*pale yellow* .. .. .. 75·00
Z146 6d. yellow-orange .. .. 60·00
Z147 1s. deep ochre .. .. 60·00
Z148 3s. slate-green £160

1929. *King George V. Whale and Penguins design* (*Nos.* 116/26).
Z149 ½d. green .. .. 50·00
Z150 1d. scarlet .. .. 50·00
Z151 2d. grey .. .. 70·00
Z152 2½d. blue .. .. 60·00
Z153 6d. purple .. .. 80·00
Z154 1s. black/*emerald* .. .. 80·00
Z155 2s. 6d. carmine/*blue* £110
Z156 5s. green/*yellow* £120
Z157 10s. carmine/*emerald* £250
Z158 £1 black/*red* £550

The whaling station at Port Foster was abandoned at the end of the 1930–31 season.

It was reoccupied as a Falkland Islands Dependencies Survey base on 3 February 1944.

Falkland Islands definitive stamps with face values of 1s. 3d. and above were valid for use from the South Shetlands in conjunction with Nos. D1/8 and subsequently Nos. G1/16.

Stamps of FALKLAND ISLANDS *cancelled at Port Foster or Admiralty Bay with South Shetlands circular datestamps between* 5 February 1944 *and* 31 January 1954

1938–50. *King George VI* (*Nos.* 160/3).
Z159 2s. 6d. slate .. .. 30·00
Z160 5s. indigo and yellow-brown £130
Z161 10s. black and orange .. .. 40·00
Z162 £1 black and violet .. .. 60·00

1952. *King George VI* (*Nos.* 181/5).
Z163 1s. 3d. orange .. ..
Z164 2s. 6d. olive-green .. ..
Z165 5s. purple .. ..
Z166 10s. grey .. ..
Z167 £1 black .. ..

1944 (5 Feb)–**45.** *Falkland Islands Nos.* 146, 148, 150, 153/5, 157 *and* 158*a optd* "SOUTH SHETLANDS/DEPENDENCY OF", *in red, as Type* A 1 *of Graham Land.*
D1 ½d. black and green .. .. .. 30 1·75
D2 1d. black and violet .. .. .. 30 1·00
D3 2d. black and carmine-red .. .. .. 40 1·00
D4 3d. black and blue .. .. 30 1·00
D5 4d. black and purple .. .. .. 3·00 1·75
D6 6d. black and brown .. .. .. 13·00 2·25
a. Blue-black and brown (24.9.45) .. 20·00
D7 9d. black and grey-blue .. .. .. 1·00 1·25
D8 1s. deep blue .. .. 1·00 1·25
D1/8 .. .. *Set of* 8 17·00 10·00
D1/8 Perf "Specimen" .. .. *Set of* 8 £325

From 12 July 1946 to 16 July 1963, Graham Land, South Georgia, South Orkneys and South Shetlands used FALKLAND ISLANDS DEPENDENCIES stamps.

E. FALKLAND ISLANDS DEPENDENCIES

For use at the following bases:
Adelaide Island (Graham Land) (*opened* 1961)
Admiralty Bay (South Shetlands) (*opened* January 1948, *closed* January 1961)
Anvers Island (Graham Land) (*opened* February 1955, *closed* 10 January 1958)
Argentine Islands (Graham Land) (*opened* 1947)
Danco Coast ("Base O") (Graham Land) (*opened* 30 March 1956, *closed* 1958)
Deception Island (South Shetlands)
Grytviken (South Georgia)
Halley Bay (Coats Land) (*opened* 1956)
Hope Bay (Graham Land) (*closed* 4 February 1949, *opened* February 1952)
Laurie Island (South Orkneys) (*closed* 1947)
Loubet Coast ("Base W") (Graham Land) (*opened* 1955, *closed* 1959)
Marguerite Bay (Graham Land) (*opened* March 1955, *closed* 1960)
Port Lockroy (Graham Land) (*closed* 16 January 1962)
Prospect Point ("Base J") (Graham Land) (*opened* 1956, *closed* 1958)
Shackleton (Coats Land) (*opened* 1956, *closed* 1957)
Signy Island (South Orkneys) (*opened* 1946)
Stonington Island (Graham Land) (*opened* 1946, *closed* 1950, *opened* 1958, *closed* 1959, *opened* 1960)

G 1

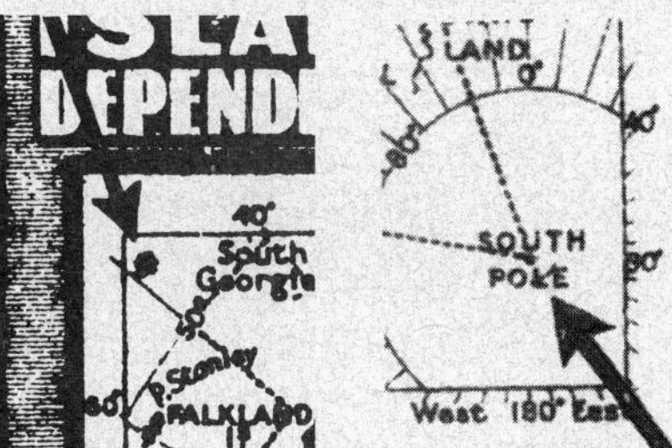

Extra island (Plate 1 R. 3/9) "SOUTH POKE" flaw (Plate 2 R. 6/8)

Missing "T" in "S. Shetland Is." (Plate 1 R. 1/2)

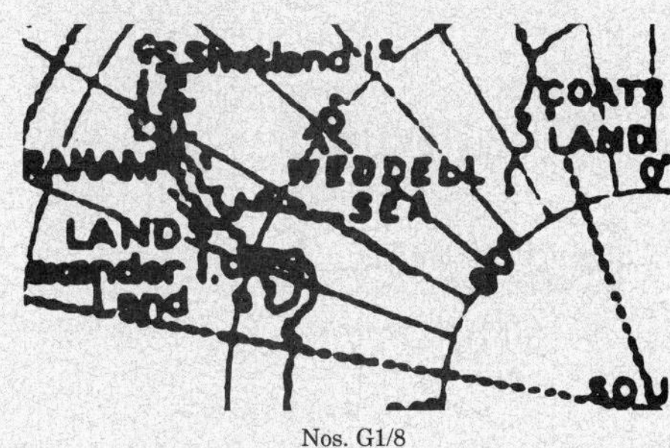

Nos. G1/8

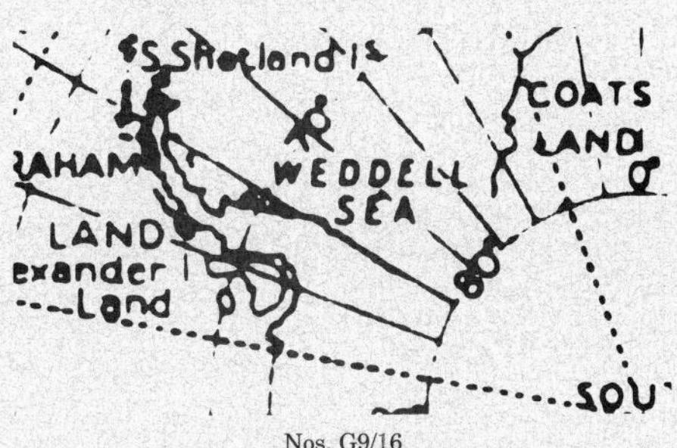

Nos. G9/16

On Nos. G9 to G16 the map is redrawn; the "0°" meridian does not pass through the "S" of "COATS", the "n" of "Alexander" is not joined to the "L" of "Land" below, and the loops of letters "s" and "t" are generally more open.

(Map litho, frame recess D.L.R.)

1946 (12 July*)–**49.** *Wmk Mult Script CA* (*sideways*). *P* 12.

(*a*) *Map thick and coarse*
G 1 G 1 ½d. black and green .. .. 1·00 2·00
a. Extra island .. .. .. 55·00
b. Missing "T" .. .. .. 55·00
c. "SOUTH POKE" .. .. 55·00
G 2 1d. black and violet .. .. 1·25 1·75
a. Extra island .. .. .. 60·00
b. Missing "T" .. .. .. 60·00
G 3 2d. black and carmine .. .. 1·25 2·50
a. Extra island .. .. .. 65·00
b. Missing "T" .. .. .. 65·00
G 4 3d. black and blue .. .. 1·25 4·00
a. Extra island .. .. .. 70·00
b. Missing "T" .. .. .. 70·00
G 5 4d. black and claret .. .. 2·25 4·75
c. "SOUTH POKE" .. .. 85·00
G 6 6d. black and orange .. .. 3·25 4·75
a. Extra island £100
b. Missing "T" £100
c. "SOUTH POKE" £100
d. Black and ochre .. .. 48·00 90·00
da. Extra island £250
db. Missing "T" £250
dc. "SOUTH POKE" £250
G 7 9d. black and brown .. .. 2·00 3·25
c. "SOUTH POKE" .. .. 90·00
G 8 1s. black and purple .. .. 2·00 4·25
c. "SOUTH POKE" .. .. 90·00
G1/8 .. .. *Set of* 8 13·00 24·00
G1/8 Perf "Specimen" .. .. *Set of* 8 £450

(*b*) *Map thin and clear* (16.2.48)
G 9 G 1 ½d. black and green .. .. 2·25 9·50
a. Recess frame printed double, one albino and inverted £850
G10 1d. black and violet .. .. 1·50 13·00
G11 2d. black and carmine .. .. 4·75 18·00
G11*a* 2½d. black and deep blue (6.3.49) .. 7·50 7·00
G12 3d. black and blue .. .. .. 2·75 4·50
G13 4d. black and claret .. .. 16·00 18·00
G14 6d. black and orange .. .. 22·00 11·00
G15 9d. black and brown .. .. 22·00 10·00
G16 1s. black and purple .. .. 23·00 10·00
G9/16 .. .. *Set of* 9 90·00 90·00

*This is the date of issue for South Georgia. Nos. G1/8 were released in London on 11 February.

In Nos. G1/8 a variety with a gap in the 80th parallel occurs six times in each sheet of all values in positions R. 1/4, 1/9, 3/4, 3/9, 5/4 and 5/9 (*Price for set of* 8 *£40 mint, in pairs with normal*).

A constant variety, dot on "T" of "SOUTH", occurs on R. 5/2, 5/4, 5/6, 5/8 and 5/10 of all values of the "thin map" set with the exception of the 2½d.

1946 (4 Oct*). *Victory. As Nos.* 110/11 *of Antigua.*
G17 1d. deep violet 50 15
G18 3d. blue 75 15
G17/18 Perf "Specimen" .. .. *Set of* 2 £120

*This is the date of issue for South Georgia. The stamps were placed on sale from the South Orkneys on 17 January 1947, from the South Shetlands on 30 January 1947 and from Graham Land on 10 February 1947.

1948 (6 Dec). *Royal Silver Wedding. As Nos.* 112/13 *of Antigua, but* 1s. *in recess.*
G19 2½d. ultramarine .. .. 1·25 1·00
G20 1s. violet-blue .. .. 2·25 1·75

1949 (10 Oct). *75th Anniv of U.P.U. As Nos.* 114/17 *of Antigua.*
G21 1d. violet .. .. 1·50 1·50
G22 2d. carmine-red .. .. 5·00 2·50
G23 3d. deep blue .. .. 4·00 1·25
G24 6d. red-orange .. .. 7·00 3·00
G21/4 .. .. *Set of* 4 16·00 7·50

1953 (4 June). *Coronation. As No.* 120 *of Antigua.*
G25 1d. black and violet .. .. 1·10 1·25

G 2 *John Biscoe I*, 1947–52 G 3 *Trepassey*, 1945–47

(Recess Waterlow, then D.L.R. (from 27.3.62))

1954 (1 Feb)–**62.** *Types* G 2/3 *and similar designs showing ships. Wmk Mult Script CA. P* 12½.
G26 ½d. black and bluish green .. .. 30 1·75
a. Black and deep green (DLR) (17.4.62) 5·50 13·00
G27 1d. black and sepia-brown .. .. 1·25 1·50
a. Black and sepia (DLR) (27.3.62) .. 14·00 18·00
G28 1½d. black and olive .. .. .. 2·00 1·25
a. Black and yellow-olive (DLR) (21.9.62) 8·50 3·00
G29 2d. black and rose-red .. .. .. 1·25 20
G30 2½d. black and yellow-ochre .. .. 1·25 15
G31 3d. black and deep bright blue .. .. 1·25 15
G32 4d. black and bright reddish purple .. 3·25 55
G33 6d. black and deep lilac .. .. .. 3·25 55
G34 9d. black .. .. 3·25 1·00
G35 1s. black and brown .. .. .. 3·25 90
G36 2s. black and carmine .. .. .. 19·00 10·00
G37 2s. 6d. black and pale turquoise .. .. 19·00 6·00
G38 5s. black and violet .. .. .. 40·00 6·50

G39 10s. black and blue .. .. 55·00 18·00
G40 £1 black .. .. 90·00 48·00
G26/40 .. .. *Set of* 15 £200 85·00

Designs: *Horiz*—1½d. *Wyatt Earp*, 1934–36; 2d. *Eagle*, 1944–45; 2½d. *Penola*, 1934–37; 3d. *Discovery II*, 1929–37; 4d. *William Scoresby*, 1926–46; 1s. *Deutschland*, 1910–12; 2s. *Pourquoi-pas?*, 1908–10; 10s. *Antarctic*, 1901–03. *Vert*—6d. *Discovery*, 1925–27; 9d. *Endurance*, 1914–16; 2s. 6d. *Français*, 1903–05; 5s. *Scotia*, 1902–04; £1 *Belgica*, 1897–99.

TRANS-ANTARCTIC EXPEDITION 1955-1958

(G 4)

1956 (30 Jan). *Trans-Antarctic Expedition. Nos.* G27, G30/1 *and* G33 *optd with Type* G **4**.

G41 1d. black and sepia-brown 10 30
G42 2½d. black and yellow-ochre 55 50
G43 3d. black and deep bright blue 55 30
G44 6d. black and deep lilac 55 30
G41/4 .. .. *Set of* 4 1·50 1·25

The stamps of Falkland Islands Dependencies were withdrawn on 16 July 1963 after Coats Land, Graham Land, South Orkneys and South Shetlands had become a separate colony, known as British Antarctic Territory.

F. SOUTH GEORGIA

From 17 July 1963 South Georgia and South Sandwich Islands used stamps inscribed "South Georgia".

1 Reindeer

2 South Sandwich Islands

(Des D.L.R. (No. 16), M. Goaman (others). Recess D.L.R.)

1963 (17 July)–**69.** *T* **1/2** *and similar designs. Ordinary or glazed paper* (*No.* 16). *W* w **12**. *P* 15.

1 ½d. brown-red 50 75
a. Perf 14 × 15 (13.2.67) .. .. 1·00 1·50
2 1d. violet-blue 70 50
3 2d. turquoise-blue .. .. .. 1·00 60
4 2½d. black .. .. 4·50 2·00
5 3d. bistre .. .. 2·50 30
6 4d. bronze-green .. .. .. 4·50 80
7 5½d. deep violet .. .. .. 2·00 30
8 6d. orange 75 30
9 9d. blue .. .. 4·00 1·50
10 1s. purple 75 30
11 2s. yellow-olive and light blue .. .. 18·00 4·50
12 2s. 6d. blue .. .. 21·00 4·00
13 5s. orange-brown .. .. .. 21·00 4·00
14 10s. magenta .. .. 42·00 10·00
15 £1 ultramarine .. .. 85·00 48·00
16 £1 grey-black (1.12.69) .. .. .. 10·00 16·00
1/16 .. .. *Set of* 16 £190 80·00

Designs: *Vert*—2d. Sperm Whale; 3d. South American Fur Seal; 6d. Light-mantled Sooty Albatross; 10s. Plankton and Krill; £1 (No. 16) King Penguins. *Horiz*—2½d. Chinstrap and King Penguins; 4d. Fin Whale; 5½d. Southern Elephant-Seal; 9d. *R2* (whale-catcher); 1s. Leopard Seal; 2s. Shackleton's Cross; 2s. 6d. Wandering Albatross; 5s. Southern Elephant-seal and South American Fur Seal; £1 (No. 15) Blue Whale.

1970 (22 Jan). *As No.* 1, *but wmk* w **12** *sideways and on glazed paper.*

17 ½d. brown-red .. .. 2·50 2·25

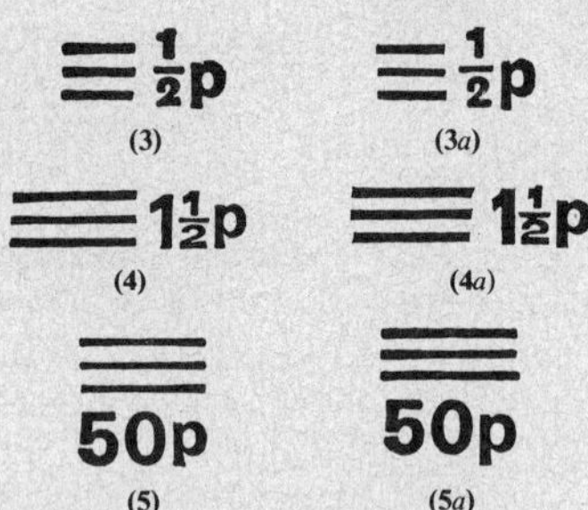

(**3**) (**3*a***)
(**4**) (**4*a***)
(**5**) (**5*a***)

1971 (15 Feb)–**76.** *Decimal Currency. Nos.* 17 *and* 2/14 *surch as T* **3/4**. *Nos.* 18/a *wmk sideways, glazed paper. Others wmk upright, ordinary paper.*

18 ½p. on ½d. brown-red (T **3**) .. .. 1·50 1·60
a. Surch with T **3*a*** (16.6.72) .. .. 1·00 90
b. Do. Wmk upright (24.8.73) .. .. 3·25 5·00
19 1p. on 1d. violet-blue .. .. .. 1·50 55
a. Glazed paper (1.12.72) .. .. 2·25 1·50
b. Do. but wmk sideways (9.3.76) .. .. 1·00 4·00
20 1½p. on 5½d. deep violet (T **4**) .. .. 3·00 2·25
b. Surch with T **4*a***. Glazed paper (24.8.73) 7·00 4·50
21 2p. on 2d. turquoise-blue 70 50
22 2½p. on 2½d. black .. .. .. 1·50 40
23 3p. on 3d. bistre .. .. 1·00 50
24 4p. on 4d. bronze-green 90 50
25 5p. on 6d. orange 90 30
26 6p. on 9d. blue .. .. 1·50 70
27 7½p. on 1s. purple .. .. 2·00 70
28 10p. on 2s. yellow-olive and light blue .. 32·00 15·00
29 15p. on 2s. 6d. blue .. .. .. 13·00 11·00
30 25p. on 5s. orange-brown .. .. .. 10·00 9·00
31 50p. on 10s. magenta (Type **5**) .. .. 35·00 16·00
a. Surch with Type **5*a***. Glazed paper (1.12.72) .. .. 10·00 21·00
b. Do. but wmk sideways (9.3.76) .. .. 15·00 32·00
18/31a .. .. *Set of* 14 70·00 50·00

The surcharge on No. 19b shows a larger "p".

See also Nos. 53/66.

6 *Endurance* beset in Weddell Sea

(Des R. Granger Barrett. Litho A. & M.)

1972 (5 Jan). *50th Death Anniv of Sir Ernest Shackleton. T* **6** *and similar horiz designs. Multicoloured. W* w **12** (*sideways**). *P* 13½.

32 1½p. Type **6** .. .. 1·00 1·25
w. Wmk Crown to right of CA .. .. 3·50
33 5p. Launching the longboat *James Caird* 1·25 1·75
w. Wmk Crown to right of CA .. .. 4·00
34 10p. Route of the *James Caird* .. .. 1·75 2·00
w. Wmk Crown to right of CA .. .. 4·25
35 20p. Sir Ernest Shackleton and the *Quest* 2·00 2·25
w. Wmk Crown to right of CA .. .. 4·50
32/5 .. .. *Set of* 4 5·50 6·50

*The normal sideways watermark shows Crown to left of CA, *as seen from the back of the stamp.*

7 Southern Elephant-Seal and King Penguins

(Des (from photograph by D. Groves) and photo Harrison)

1972 (20 Nov). *Royal Silver Wedding. Multicoloured; background colour given. W* w **12**. *P* 14 × 14½.

36 **7** 5p. slate-green 75 35
w. Wmk inverted .. .. .. 48·00
37 10p. bluish violet 75 35

1973 (1 Dec*). *Royal Wedding. As Nos.* 165/6 *of Anguilla. Centre multicoloured. W* w **12** (*sideways*). *P* 13½.

38 5p. brown-ochre 25 10
39 15p. chalky blue 35 20

*This is the local date of issue: the Crown Agents released the stamps on 14 November.

8 Churchill and Westminster Skyline

9 Captain Cook

(Des L. Curtis. Litho Questa)

1974 (14 Dec*). *Birth Centenary of Sir Winston Churchill. T* **8** *and similar horiz design. Multicoloured. W* w **12** (*sideways*). *P* 14½.

40 15p. Type **8** .. .. 1·50 1·25
41 25p. Churchill and warship .. .. 1·50 1·25
MS42 122 × 98 mm. Nos. 40/1 .. .. 6·00 6·00

*This is the local date of issue: the Crown Agents released the stamps on 30 November.

(Des J. Cooter. Litho Questa)

1975 (26 Apr). *Bicentenary of Possession by Captain Cook. T* **9** *and similar horiz designs. Multicoloured. W* w **12** (*sideways on* 8 *and* 16*p.*). *P* 13.

43 2p. Type **9** .. .. 2·25 1·25
44 8p. H.M.S. *Resolution* .. .. .. 3·50 2·00
45 16p. Possession Bay .. .. .. 3·75 2·25
43/5 .. .. *Set of* 3 8·50 5·00

NEW INFORMATION

The editor is always interested to correspond with people who have new information that will improve or correct the Catalogue.

10 *Discovery* and Biological Laboratory

11 Queen and Retinue after Coronation

(Des J. W. Litho Format)

1976 (21 Dec). *50th Anniv of "Discovery" Investigations. T* **10** *an similar vert designs. Multicoloured. W* w **14**. *P* 14.

46 2p. Type **10** .. .. 1·50 4
47 8p. *William Scoresby* and water-sampling bottles .. .. 1·75 6
48 11p. *Discovery II* and plankton net .. .. 2·00 6
49 25p. Biological Station and krill .. .. 2·50 9
46/9 .. .. *Set of* 4 7·00 2·4

(Des G. Drummond. Litho Questa)

1977 (7 Feb). *Silver Jubilee. T* **11** *and similar horiz design Multicoloured. W* w **14** (*sideways**). *P* 13½.

50 6p. Visit by Prince Philip, 1957 .. .. 50 3
51 11p. Queen Elizabeth and Westminster Abbey 70 3
w. Wmk Crown to right of CA .. .. 80·00
52 33p. Type **11** 80 5
50/2 .. .. *Set of* 3 1·75 1·0

*The normal sideways watermark shows Crown to left of CA *as seen from the back of the stamp.*

1977 (17 May)–**78.** *As Nos.* 18a *etc., but W* w **14** (*inverted o* 1*p*, 5*p*.; *upright on* 3*p. and* 50*p*.; *sideways* on others*). *Glaze paper.*

53 ½p. on ½d. brown-red .. .. .. 1·50 2·0
w. Wmk Crown to right of CA .. .. 45·00
54 1p. on 1d. violet-blue (16.8.77) .. .. 80 1·7
w. Wmk upright £275
55 1½p. on 5½d. deep violet (16.8.77) .. .. 90 1·7
w. Wmk Crown to right of CA £375
57 2½p. on 2½d. black (16.8.77) .. .. 12·00 3·5
58 3p. on 3d. bistre (16.8.77) .. .. .. 7·00 3·5
w. Wmk inverted £375
59 4p. on 4d. bronze-green (16.8.77) .. .. 20·00 14·0
w. Wmk Crown to right of CA £550
60 5p. on 6d. orange .. .. 2·50 2·7
w. Wmk upright .. .. 2·50 2·7
62 7½p. on 1s. purple (16.8.77) .. .. 9·00 20·0
w. Wmk Crown to right of CA (31.7.78) .. 1·75 8·0
63 10p. on 2s. yellow-olive & light blue (16.8.77) 6·00 11·0
w. Wmk Crown to right of CA (31.7.78) .. 1·75 8·0
64 15p. on 2s. 6d. blue (16.8.77) .. .. 9·00 20·0
w. Wmk Crown to right of CA (31.7.78) .. 2·00 8·0
65 25p. on 5s. orange-brown (16.8.77) .. 11·00 22·0
w. Wmk Crown to right of CA (31.7.78) .. 1·75 8·0
66 50p. on 10s. pale magenta (12.78) .. .. 1·75 7·5
53/66 .. .. *Set of* 12 48·00 60·0

*The normal sideways watermark shows Crown to left of CA *as seen from the back of the stamp.*

Surcharges on the above differ from those on Nos. 18a/30 b having straight outlines and being slightly more slender. Th change in paper also results in the colours appearing brighter

12 Fur Seal

13 H.M.S. *Resolution*

(Des C. Abbott. Litho Questa)

1978 (2 June). *25th Anniv of Coronation. T* **12** *and similar ver designs. P* 15.

67 25p. indigo, ultramarine and silver .. .. 35 1·1
a. Sheetlet. Nos. 67/9 × 2 .. .. .. 1·75
68 25p. multicoloured .. .. 35 1·1
69 25p. indigo, ultramarine and silver .. .. 35 1·1
67/9 .. .. *Set of* 3 90 3·0

Designs:—No. 67, Panther of Henry VI; No. 68, Queen Elizabet II; No. 69, Type **12**.

Nos. 67/9 were printed together in small sheets of 6, containin two *se-tenant* strips of 3, with horizontal gutter margin between.

(Des and litho (25p. also embossed) Walsall)

1979 (14 Feb). *Bicentenary of Captain Cook's Voyages*, 1768–79 *T* **13** *and similar vert designs. Multicoloured. P* 11.

70 3p. Type **13** .. .. 1·50 1·2
71 6p. *Resolution* and map of South Georgia and S. Sandwich Isles showing route .. .. 1·50 1·0
72 11p. King Penguin (based on drawing by George Forster) .. .. 2·50 2·2
73 25p. Flaxman/Wedgwood medallion of Captain Cook .. .. 2·75 2·7
70/3 .. .. *Set of* 4 7·50 6·5

From 5 May 1980 South Georgia and South Sandwich Island used stamps inscribed FALKLAND ISLANDS DEPENDENCIES

G. FALKLAND ISLANDS DEPENDENCIES

For use in South Georgia and South Sandwich Islands.

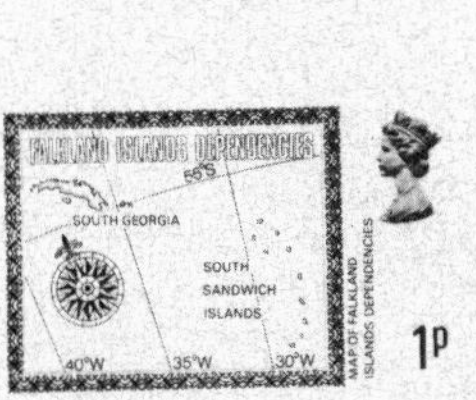
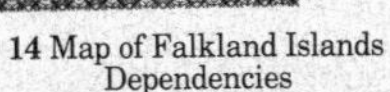

14 Map of Falkland Islands Dependencies

15 Magellanic Clubmoss

(Des and litho J.W.)

1980 (5 May)–**84**. *Horiz designs as T* **14**. *Multicoloured*. W w **14** (*sideways*). *P* 13½. A. *Without imprint date*

74A	1p. Type **14**	30	30
75A	2p. Shag Rocks	30	30
76A	3p. Bird and Willis Islands	30	30
77A	4p. Gulbrandsen Lake	30	30
78A	5p. King Edward Point	30	30
79A	6p. Sir Ernest Shackleton's Memorial Cross, Hope Point	60	30
80A	7p. Sir Ernest Shackleton's Grave, Grytviken	60	40
81A	8p. Grytviken Church	50	40
82A	9p. Coaling Hulk *Louise* at Grytviken	50	45
83A	10p. Clerke Rocks	50	45
84A	20p. Candlemas Island	2·75	1·75
85A	25p. Twitcher Rock and Cook Island, Southern Thule	2·75	1·75
86A	50p. R.R.S. *John Biscoe II* in Cumberland Bay	1·00	2·00
87A	£1 R.R.S. *Bransfield* in Cumberland Bay	1·25	2·75
88A	£3 H.M.S. *Endurance* in Cumberland Bay	3·00	6·50
74A/88A	*Set of* 15	13·00	16·00

B. *With imprint date* ("1984") *at foot* (3.5.84)

74B	1p. Type **14**	25	70
75B	2p. Shag Rocks	25	70
76B	3p. Bird and Willis Islands	25	70
77B	4p. Gulbrandsen Lake	25	70
78B	5p. King Edward Point	35	70
79B	6p. Sir Ernest Shackleton's Memorial Cross, Hope Point	30	70
80B	7p. Sir Ernest Shackleton's Grave, Grytviken	30	70
81B	8p. Grytviken Church	30	70
82B	9p. Coaling Hulk *Louise* at Grytviken	30	70
83B	10p. Clerke Rocks	50	70
84B	20p. Candlemas Island	2·00	1·50
85B	25p. Twitcher Rock and Cook Island, Southern Thule	2·00	2·25
86B	50p. R.R.S. *John Biscoe II* in Cumberland Bay	2·00	2·50
74B/86B	*Set of* 13	8·00	12·00

For some of these designs watermarked W **16** (sideways) see Nos. 148/52.

(Des L. McCombie. Litho Rosenbaum Bros, Vienna)

1981 (5 Feb). *Plants. T* **15** *and similar vert designs. Multicoloured*. W w **14** (*inverted on* 25p.). *P* 14.

89	3p. Type **15**	20	25
	w. Wmk inverted	7·00	
90	6p. Alpine Cat's-tail	20	30
91	7p. Greater Burnet	20	30
	w. Wmk inverted	£275	
92	11p. Antarctic Bedstraw	20	35
93	15p. Brown Rush	25	45
	a. Light brown (Queen's head and territory inscr) omitted	£1800	
94	25p. Antarctic Hair Grass	35	75
	w. Wmk upright	£275	
89/94	*Set of* 6	1·25	2·25

16 Wedding Bouquet from Falkland Islands Dependencies

17 Introduced Reindeer during Calving, Spring

(Des J.W. Litho Format)

1981 (22 July). *Royal Wedding. T* **16** *and similar vert designs. Multicoloured*. W w **14**. *P* 14.

95	10p. Type **16**	15	30
96	13p. Prince Charles dressed for skiing	20	35
97	52p. Prince Charles and Lady Diana Spencer	65	85
95/7	*Set of* 3	90	1·40

(Des A. Theobald. Litho Format)

1982 (29 Jan). *Reindeer. T* **17** *and similar horiz designs. Multicoloured*. W w **14** (*sideways*). *P* 14.

98	5p. Type **17**	25	65
99	13p. Bull at rut, Autumn	30	85
100	25p. Reindeer and mountains, Winter	40	1·40
101	26p. Reindeer feeding on tussock grass, late Winter	40	1·40
98/101	*Set of* 4	1·25	3·75

18 *Gamasellus racovitzai* (tick)

19 Lady Diana Spencer at Tidworth, Hampshire, July 1981

(Des I. Loe. Litho Questa)

1982 (16 Mar). *Insects. T* **18** *and similar vert designs. Multicoloured*. W w **14**. *P* 14.

102	5p. Type **18**	15	25
103	10p. *Alaskozetes antarcticus* (mite)	25	35
104	13p. *Cryptopygus antarcticus* (spring-tail)	25	40
105	15p. *Notiomaso australis* (spider)	30	45
106	25p. *Hydromedion sparsutum* (beetle)	50	70
107	26p. *Parochlus steinenii* (midge)	50	70
102/7	*Set of* 6	1·75	2·50

(Des C. Abbott. Litho Format)

1982 (7 Sept). *21st Birthday of Princess of Wales. T* **19** *and similar vert designs. Multicoloured*. W w **14**. *P* 13½ × 14.

108	5p. Falklands Islands Dependencies coat of arms	10	15
109	17p. Type **19**	40	35
	a. Perf 13½	2·75	6·50
110	37p. Bride and groom on steps of St Paul's	45	80
111	50p. Formal portrait	1·00	1·10
108/11	*Set of* 4	1·75	2·25

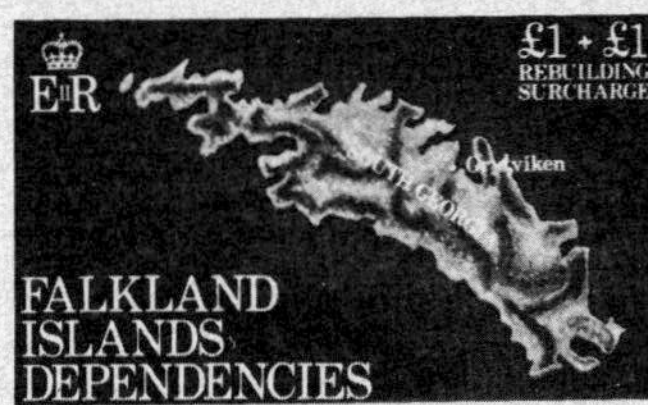

20 Map of South Georgia

(Des PAD Studio. Litho Format)

1982 (13 Sept). *Rebuilding Fund*. W w **14** (*sideways**). *P* 11.

112	**20**	£1 + £1 multicoloured	2·40	4·00
		w. Wmk Crown to right of CA	80·00	

*The normal sideways watermark shows Crown to left of CA, *as seen from the back of the stamp.*

21 Westland Whirlwind

22 *Euphausia superba*

(Des Harrison. Litho Questa)

1983 (23 Dec). *Bicentenary of Manned Flight. T* **21** *and similar horiz designs. Multicoloured*. W w **14** (*sideways*). *P* 14.

113	5p. Type **21**	30	30
114	13p. Westland AS.1 Wasp helicopter	55	65
115	17p. Vickers Supermarine Walrus II	60	70
116	50p. Auster Autocrat	1·40	1·50
113/16	*Set of* 4	2·50	2·75

(Des N. Weaver. Litho Questa)

1984 (23 Mar). *Crustacea. T* **22** *and similar vert designs. Multicoloured*. W w **14**. *P* 14½ × 14.

117	5p. Type **22**	40	20
118	17p. *Glyptonotus antarcticus*	70	50
119	25p. *Epimeria monodon*	85	60
120	34p. *Serolis pagenstecheri*	1·10	80
117/20	*Set of* 4	2·75	1·90

23 Zavodovski Island

(Des. J.W. Litho Questa)

1984 (8 Nov). *Volcanoes of South Sandwich Islands. T* **23** *and similar horiz designs. Multicoloured*. W w **14** (*sideways*). *P* 14 × 14½.

121	6p. Type **23**	80	80
122	17p. Mt Michael, Saunders Island	2·00	1·60
123	22p. Bellingshausen Island	2·00	1·75
124	52p. Bristol Island	2·50	3·25
121/4	*Set of* 4	6·50	6·75

24 Grey-headed Albatross

25 The Queen Mother

(Des I. Loe. Litho Questa)

1985 (5 May). *Albatrosses. T* **24** *and similar horiz designs. Multicoloured*. W w **14** (*sideways*). *P* 14½.

125	7p. Type **24**	1·50	75
126	22p. Black-browed Albatross	2·25	1·25
127	27p. Wandering Albatross	2·50	1·40
128	54p. Light-mantled Sooty Albatross	3·25	2·25
125/8	*Set of* 4	8·50	5·00

(Des A. Theobald (£1), C. Abbott (others). Litho Questa)

1985 (23 June). *Life and Times of Queen Elizabeth the Queen Mother. T* **25** *and similar vert designs. Multicoloured*. W w **16**. *P* 14½ × 14.

129	7p. At Windsor Castle on Princess Elizabeth's 14th birthday, 1940	30	30
130	22p. With Princess Anne, Lady Sarah Armstrong-Jones and Prince Edward at Trooping the Colour	60	70
131	27p. Type **25**	70	80
	w. Wmk inverted	10·00	
132	54p. With Prince Henry at his christening (from photo by Lord Snowdon)	1·25	1·40
129/32	*Set of* 4	2·50	2·75
MS133	91 × 73 mm. £1 Disembarking from Royal Yacht *Britannia*. Wmk sideways	2·25	2·75

(Des I. Strange. Litho Questa)

1985 (4 Nov). *Early Naturalists. Vert designs as T* **35** *of British Antarctic Territory. Multicoloured*. W w **14**. *P* 14½ × 14.

134	7p. Dumont d'Urville and *Durvillea antarctica* (kelp)	1·25	1·00
135	22p. Johann Reinhold Forster and King Penguin	2·25	2·00
136	27p. Johann Georg Adam Forster and Tussock Grass	2·25	2·25
137	54p. Sir Joseph Banks and Dove Prion	3·00	3·50
134/7	*Set of* 4	8·00	8·00

1985 (18 Nov). *As Nos.* 84/8 *but W* w **16** (*sideways*). *With imprint date* ("1985"). *P* 13½.

148	20p. Candlemas Island	2·50	4·50
149	25p. Twitcher Rock and Cook Island, Southern Thule	3·00	4·50
150	50p. R.R.S. *John Biscoe* in Cumberland Bay	3·00	4·50
151	£1 R.R.S. *Bransfield* in Cumberland Bay	3·00	4·50
152	£3 H.M.S. *Endurance* in Cumberland Bay	8·00	8·00
148/52	*Set of* 5	17·00	23·00

Under the new constitution, effective 3 October 1985, South Georgia and South Sandwich Islands ceased to be dependencies of the Falkland Islands. Issues inscribed for the separate territory are listed under SOUTH GEORGIA AND SOUTH SANDWICH ISLANDS.

Fiji

PRICES FOR STAMPS ON COVER TO 1945

Nos. 1/9	*from* × 6
Nos. 10/34	*from* × 5
Nos. 35/59	*from* × 8
Nos. 60/3	—
Nos. 64/9	*from* × 20
Nos. 70/5	*from* × 5
Nos. 76/103	*from* × 8
Nos. 104/14	*from* × 5
Nos. 115/24	*from* × 4
Nos. 125/37	*from* × 3
Nos. 138/241	*from* × 4
Nos. 242/5	*from* × 3
Nos. 246/8	*from* × 8
Nos. 249/66*b*	*from* × 2
No. 267	*from* × 8
Nos. D1/5*c*	*from* × 4
Nos. D6/10	*from* × 20
Nos. D11/18	*from* × 15

King Cakobau 1852–Oct 1874

Christian missionaries reached Fiji in 1835 and early letters are known to and from their mission stations, sent via Sydney, Hobart or Auckland.

In 1852 Cakobau, the chief of the island of Bau, declared himself King of Fiji and converted to Christianity two years later. Internal problems and difficulties with the American government led the king to offer to cede Fiji to Great Britain. The offer was refused, but resulted in the appointment of a British Consul in 1858. A Consular Post Office operated from September 1858 until 1872 and franked mail with New South Wales stamps from 1863.

The destruction of plantations in the Confederacy during the American Civil War led to an increased demand for Fijian cotton and this upsurge in commercial activity encouraged the *Fiji Times* newspaper on Levuka to establish a postal service on 1 November 1870.

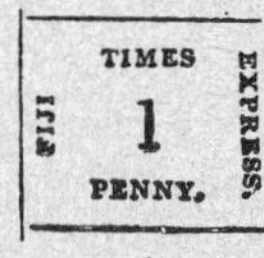

1

(Type-set and printed at the office of *The Fiji Times*, Levuka, Ovalau, Fiji)

1870 (1 Nov)–**71.** *Rouletted in the printing.* (*a*) *Quadrillé paper.*

1	**1**	1d. black/*rose*	£3250	£3500
2		3d. black/*rose*	£3000	£3000
3		6d. black/*rose*	£2000	£2000
4		1s. black/*rose*	£1500	£1800

(*b*) *Laid bâtonné paper* (1871)

5	**1**	1d. black/*rose*	£900	£1800
		a. Vert strip of 4. Nos. 5, 7/9	£35000	
6		3d. black/*rose*	£1500	£2750
7		6d. black/*rose*	£1100	£1800
8		9d. black/*rose*	£1700	£2750
		a. Comma after "EXPRESS" (R.4/4)	£2250	
9		1s. black/*rose*	£1000	£1400

Nos. 1/4 were printed *se-tenant* as a sheet of 24 (6 × 4) with the 6d. stamps in the first horizontal row, the 1s. in the second, the 1d. in the third and the 3d. in the fourth. Nos. 5/9 were produced from the same plate on which three of the 3d. impressions had been replaced with three 9d. values.

The issued stamps showed the vertical frame lines continuous from top to bottom of the sheet with the horizontal rules broken and not touching the verticals. Used examples are cancelled in manuscript or by the star cancellation used at Bua.

There are no reprints of these stamps, but the 1d., 3d., 6d. and 1s. are known in the correct type on *yellow wove* paper and are believed to be proofs.

There are also three different sets of imitations made by the proprietors of *The Fiji Times* to meet the demands of collectors:—

The first was produced in 1876 on *white wove* or *vertically laid* paper, rouletted on dotted lines and arranged in sheets of 40 (5 rows of 8) comprising 1d., 3d., 6d., 9d. and 1s.; the horizontal frame lines are continuous and the vertical ones broken.

The second was produced before 1888 on *thick rosy mauve wove* paper, rouletted on dotted lines and arranged in sheets of 30 (5 rows of 6) comprising 1s., 9d., 6d., 3d. and 1d.; the vertical frame lines are continuous and the horizontal ones broken.

The third only came to light in the 1960s and is rare, only one complete sheet being recorded, which has since been destroyed. The sheet arrangement is the same as Nos. 1/4, which suggests that this was the first imitation to be produced. It is on *off-white wove* paper, rouletted on closely dotted or solid lines, with vertical frame lines continuous and the horizontal ones broken, as in the originals. These differ from the proofs mentioned above in that the lettering is slightly larger and the figures also differ.

King Cakobau established a formal government in June 1871 and stamps for the royal post office were ordered from Sydney. These arrived in October 1871 and the postal service was placed on a firm basis by the First Postal Act in December of that year. Under its terms the *Fiji Times* service closed on 17 January 1872 and the British Consular Post Office followed six months later.

2

3

Two Cents

(4)

(Eng and electrotyped by A. L. Jackson. Typo Govt Printing Office, Sydney)

1871 (Oct). *Wove paper. Wmk* "FIJI POSTAGE" *in small sans-serif capitals across the middle row of stamps in the sheet. P* 12½.

10	**2**	1d. blue	50·00	£120
11		3d. pale yellow-green	£110	£350
12	**3**	6d. rose	£120	£275

The 3d. differs from T **2** in having a white circle containing square dots surrounding the centre.

All three values are known *imperf*, but were not issued in that condition.

See notes after No. 33b.

1872 (13 Jan). *Surch as T* **4**, *in local currency, by Govt Ptg Office, Sydney.*

13	**2**	2 c. on 1d. pale blue	50·00	65·00
		a. Deep blue	28·00	48·00
14		6 c. on 3d. yellow-green	65·00	65·00
15	**3**	12 c. on 6d. carmine-rose	85·00	75·00

CROWN COLONY

King Cakobau renewed his offer to cede Fiji to Great Britain and this took place on 12 October 1874.

V.R. (5) V.R. (6) 2d. (7)

Varieties:—

V.R. V.R.

(*Enlarged*)

Cross pattée stop Inverted "A"

Cross pattée stop after "R" (R. 3/6).
Round raised stop after "V" (R. 3/8).
Round raised stops after "V" and "R" (R. 3/9).
Inverted "A" for "V" (R. 3/10).
No stop after "R" (R. 2/3 on T **5**, R. 5/3 on T **6**).
Large stop after "R" (R. 5/10).

(Optd at *Polynesian Gazette* Office, Levuka)

1874 (10 Oct). *Nos.* 13/15 *optd.* (*a*) *With T* **5**.

16	**2**	2 c. on 1d. blue	£800	£200
		a. No stop after "R"	£2250	£1000
		b. Cross pattée stop after "R"	£2250	£1000
		c. Round raised stop after "V"	£2250	£1000
		d. Round raised stops after "V" and "R"	£2250	£1000
		e. Inverted "A" for "V"	£2250	£1000
17		6 c. on 3d. green	£1200	£550
		a. No stop after "R"	£3250	£1500
		b. Cross pattée stop after "R"	£3250	£1500
		c. Round raised stop after "V"	£3250	£1500
		d. Round raised stops after "V" and "R"	£3250	£1500
		e. Inverted "A" for "V"	£3250	£1500
18	**3**	12 c. on 6d. rose	£500	£170
		a. No stop after "R"	£2000	£1000
		b. Cross pattée stop after "R"	£2000	£1000
		c. Round raised stop after "V"	£2000	£1000
		d. Round raised stops after "V" and "R"	£2000	£1000
		e. Inverted "A" for "V"	£2000	£1000
		f. Opt inverted	—	£3750

(*b*) *With T* **6**

19	**2**	2 c. on 1d. blue	£900	£225
		a. No stop after "R"	£2250	£1000
		f. Large stop after "R"		
20		6 c. on 3d. green	£1600	£800
		a. No stop after "R"	£3250	£1500
21	**3**	12 c. on 6d. rose	£650	£180
		a. No stop after "R"	£2000	£1000
		b. Opt inverted	£4250	

Nos. 16/21 were produced in sheets of 50 (10 × 5) of which the top three rows were overprinted with Type **5** and the lower two with Type **6**.

1875. *Stamps of* 1874 *surch at* Polynesian Gazette *Office, Levuka, with T* **7**.

(*a*) *In red* (May)

22	**2**	2d. on 6 c. on 3d. green (No. 17)	£425	£150
		a. No stop after "R"	£1500	£650
		b. Cross pattée stop after "R"	£1500	£650
		c. Round raised stop after "V"	£1500	£650
		d. Round raised stops after "V" and "R"	£1500	£650
		e. Inverted "A" for "V"	£1500	£650
		f. No stop after "2d" (R. 1/2)	£1500	£650
23		2d. on 6 c. on 3d. green (No. 20)	£550	£225
		a. No stop after "R"	£1500	£650
		b. Stop between "2" and "d" (R. 5/7)	£1500	£650

(*b*) *In black* (30 Sept)

24	**2**	2d. on 6 c. on 3d. green (No. 17)	£1100	£400
		a. No stop after "R"	£2750	£1200
		b. Cross pattée stop after "R"	£2750	£1200
		c. Round raised stop after "V"	£2750	£1200
		d. Round raised stops after "V" and "R"	£2750	£1200
		e. Inverted "A" for "V"	£2750	£1200
		f. No stop after "2d" (R. 1/2)	£2750	£1200
		g. "V.R." double		
25		2d. on 6 c. on 3d. green (No. 20)	£1500	£550
		a. No stop after "R"	£2750	£1200
		b. Stop between "2" and "d" (R. 5/7)	£2750	£1200
		c. "V.R." double	—	£3250

1875 (20 Nov). *No.* 15 *surch at* Polynesian Gazette *Office, Levuka, with T* **7** *and* "V.R." *at one operation.* (*a*) "V.R." *T* **5**.

26	**3**	2d. on 12 c. on 6d. rose	£1200	£550
		aa. Round raised stop after "R"		
		a. Inverted "A" for "V" (R. 1/3, 2/8, 4/4)	£1500	£700
		b. Do. and round raised stop after "V" (R. 3/3, 3/6, 3/8, 3/10)	£1400	£650
		c. As "a" and round raised stops after "R" and "V" (R. 3/2, 3/9)	£1600	£750
		d. Surch double	—	£3000

(*b*) "V.R." *T* **6**

27	**3**	2d. on 12 c. on 6d. rose	£1200	£550
		a. Surch double	—	£3250

The setting used for Nos. 26/7 was similar to that of Nos. 16/21, but the fourth stamp in the fourth row had a Type **5** "V.R." instead of a Type **6**.

The position of No. 26aa is not known.

VR (8) Two Pence (9)

(Typo Govt Printing Office, Sydney, from plates of 1871)

1876–77. *On paper previously lithographed* "VR" *as T* **8**, *the 3d. surch with T* **9**. *P* 12½. (*a*) *Wove paper* (31.1.76).

28	**2**	1d. grey-blue	50·00	48·00
		a. Dull blue	50·00	48·00
		b. Doubly printed	£550	
		c. Void corner (R. 2/1)	£475	£275
		d. Imperf vert (horiz pair)	£850	
29		2d. on 3d. pale green	40·00	50·00
		a. Deep green	38·00	50·00
30	**3**	6d. pale rose	60·00	60·00
		a. Dull rose	48·00	50·00
		b. Carmine-rose	55·00	50·00
		c. Doubly printed	£2500	

(*b*) *Laid paper* (5.1.77)

31	**2**	1d. blue	13·00	24·00
		a. Deep blue	14·00	24·00
		b. Void corner (R. 2/1)	£250	£190
		c. Imperf vert (horiz pair)	£650	
32		2d. on 3d. yellow-green	55·00	65·00
		a. Deep yellow-green	55·00	65·00
		b. Imperf between (pair)	£850	
		c. Perf 10	£300	
		ca. Imperf vert (horiz pair)		
		d. Perf 11	£300	
33	**3**	6d. rose	48·00	27·00
		a. Carmine-rose	48·00	35·00
		b. Imperf vert (horiz pair)	£650	

The 3d. *green* is known without the surcharge T **9** on wove paper and also without the surcharge and the monogram. In this latter condition it can only be distinguished from No. 11 by its colour, which is a fuller, deeper yellow-green.

Stamps on both wove and laid paper *imperf* are from printer's trial or waste sheets and were not issued.

All values are known on laid paper without the monogram "VR" and the 3d. stamp also without the surcharge but these are also believed to be from printer's trial sheets and were never issued. Being on laid paper they are easily distinguishable from Nos. 10/12.

1877 (12 Oct). *Optd with T* **8** *and surch as T* **9**. *Laid paper. P* 12½.

34	**2**	4d. on 3d. mauve	85·00	25·00
		a. Imperf vert (horiz pair)	£850	

10

11

A Four Pence

B Four Pence

Type A: Length 12½ mm
Type B: Length 14 mm
Note also the different shape of the two "e"s.

(Typo from new plates made from original dies of 1871 with "CR" altered to "VR" at Govt Printing Office, Sydney. 2d. and 4d. made from old 3d. die.)

1878–99. *Surcharges as T* **9** *or as Types* A *or* B *for 4d. value. Wove paper with paper-maker's name* "T. H. SAUNDERS" *or* "SANDERSON" *in double-lined capitals extending over seven stamps in each full sheet.* (*a*) *P* 12½ (1878–80).

35	**10**	1d. pale ultramarine (19.2.79)	6·50	6·50
		a. Ultramarine	10·00	7·50
36		2d. on 3d. green (17.10.78)	4·50	14·00
37		2d. yellow-green (1.9.79)	12·00	8·00
		a. Blue-green	24·00	13·00
		b. Error. Ultramarine	£25000	
38	**11**	6d. rose (30.7.80)	£100	17·00

(*b*) *P* 10 (1881–90)

39	**10**	1d. dull blue (11.5.82)	42·00	3·00
		a. Ultramarine	13·00	2·75
		b. Cambridge blue (12.7.83)	42·00	3·25
40		2d. yellow-green (20.10.81)	10·00	1·00
		a. Blue-green	20·00	4·25
41		4d. on 1d. mauve (29.1.90)	30·00	20·00
42		4d. on 2d. pale mauve (A) (23.5.83)	70·00	9·00
		a. Dull purple	70·00	9·00
43		4d. on 2d. dull purple (B) (7.11.88)	—	£140
44		4d. mauve (13.9.90)	48·00	
		a. Deep purple	48·00	50·00
45	**11**	6d. pale rose (11.3.85)	70·00	15·00
		a. Bright rose	14·00	14·00

(*c*) *P* 10 × 12½ (1881–82)

46	**10**	1d. ultramarine (11.5.82)	85·00	26·00
47		2d. green (20.10.81)	£160	48·00
48	**11**	6d. rose (20.10.81)	£325	42·00

(*d*) *P* 12½ × 10 (1888–90)

49	**10**	1d. ultramarine (1890)	—	£300
49*a*		2d. green (1888)		

(*e*) *P* 10 × *nearly* 12 (3.9.86)

50	**10**	1d. ultramarine	65·00	9·00
51		2d. yellow-green	60·00	7·50

(*f*) *P nearly* 12 × 10 (1886–88)

51*a*	**10**	1d. dull blue (7.11.88)	£225	35·00
51*b*		2d. yellow-green (3.9.86)		
52	**11**	6d. rose (1887)		

(*g*) *P* 11 × 10 (1892–93)

53	**10**	1d. ultramarine (18.8.92)	10·00	7·50
54		4d. pale mauve (18.8.92)	8·50	9·00
55	**11**	6d. pale rose (14.2.93)	6·50	15·00
		a. Rose	11·00	18·00

(*h*) *P* 11 (1897–99)

56	**10**	4d. mauve (14.7.96)	10·00	7·00
57	**11**	6d. dull rose (14.7.96)	25·00	38·00
		a. Printed both sides (12.99)	£900	£750
		b. Bright rose	38·00	38·00

(*i*) *P* 11 × *nearly* 12 (1896)*

58	**10**	4d. deep purple (14.7.96)	28·00	
		a. Bright purple	7·50	6·50
59	**11**	6d. rose (23.7.96)	30·00	
		a. Bright rose	7·00	3·75

(*j*) *Imperf* (1882–90)

60 10 1d. ultramarine
61 2d. yellow-green
62 4d. on 2d. pale mauve
63 11 6d. rose

*Under this heading are included stamps from several perforating machines with a gauge varying between 11·6 and 12.

No. 37b was printed in the colour of the 1d. in error. Only four examples have been reported, one of which was subsequently destroyed.

In the absence of detailed information on dates of issue printing dates are quoted for Nos. 35/63 and 76/103.

12 13

(Typo Govt Printing Office, Sydney)

1881–99. *Paper-maker's name wmkd as previous issue.*

(*a*) *P* 10 (19.10.81)

64 12 1s. pale brown 75·00 16·00
a. Deep brown 75·00 18·00

(*b*) *P* 11 × 10 (1894)

65 12 1s. pale brown 35·00 35·00

(*c*) *P* 11 (1897)

66 12 1s. pale brown 35·00 14·00

(*d*) *P* 11 × *nearly* 12 (5.99)

67 12 1s. pale brown 32·00 9·00
a. Brown 32·00 9·00
b. Deep brown 45·00 45·00

(*e*) *P nearly* 12 × 11 (3.97)

68 12 1s. brown 45·00 40·00

Dates given of earliest known use.
Forgeries exist.

(Centre typo, frame litho Govt Printing Office, Sydney)

1882 (23 May). *Toned paper wmkd with paper-maker's name "Cowan" in old English outline type once in each sheet. P* 10.

69 13 5s. dull red and black 55·00 35·00

In July 1900, an electrotyped plate of a 5s. stamp was made and stamps were printed from it with pale orange-red centre and grey-black frame; these are known *perf* 10, *perf nearly* 12, and *imperf*. These stamps were sold as remainders with a special obliteration dated "15 Dec., 00," but were not issued for postal use. The design differs in many particulars from the issued stamp.

2½d. (14) **2½d.** (15)

T 14. Fraction bar 1 mm from "2".
T 15. Fraction bar 2 mm from "2".

(Stamps typo in Sydney and surch at Govt Printing Office, Suva)

1891 (1 Jan). *T* 10 *surch. P* 10.

70 14 2½d. on 2d. green 40·00 48·00
71 15 2½d. on 2d. green £130 £140

½d. (16) **5d** (17)

FIVE PENCE (18) 2 mm spacing
FIVE PENCE (19) 3 mm spacing

1892 (1 Mar)–**93.** *P* 10. (*a*) *Surch on T* **10**.

72 16 ½d. on 1d. dull blue 45·00 65·00
a. Ultramarine 38·00 60·00
73 17 5d. on 4d. deep purple (25.7.92) 48·00 65·00
a. Dull purple 48·00 65·00

(*b*) *Surch on T* 11

74 18 5d. on 6d. brownish rose (30.11.92) 55·00 65·00
a. Bright rose 55·00 60·00
b. Perf 10 × 12½
75 19 5d. on 6d. rose (4.1.93) 70·00 80·00
a. Deep rose 60·00 70·00
b. Brownish rose 60·00

20

21 Native Canoe

22

(Typo in Sydney)

1891–1902. *Wmk in sheet, either* "SANDERSON" *or* "NEW SOUTH WALES GOVERNMENT" *in outline capitals.*

(*a*) *P* 10 (1891–94)

76 20 ½d. slate-grey (26.4.92) 4·25 3·50
77 21 1d. black (19.9.94) 7·50 3·75
78 2d. pale green (19.9.94) 90·00 9·50
79 22 2½d. chocolate (8.6.91) 35·00 12·00
80 21 5d. ultramarine (14.2.93) 75·00 48·00

(*b*) *P* 11 × 10 (1892–93)

81 20 ½d. slate-grey (20.10.93) 4·50 13·00
82 21 1d. black (14.2.93) 4·75 2·50
83 2d. green (14.2.93) 9·00 3·50
84 22 2½d. chocolate (17.8.92) 19·00 18·00
a. Brown 7·00 6·50
b. Yellowish brown
85 21 5d. ultramarine (14.2.93) 9·50 7·50

(*c*) *P* 11 (1893–96)

86 20 ½d. slate-grey (2.6.96) 3·00 5·50
a. Greenish slate 2·50 6·00
87 21 1d. black (31.10.95) 3·00 3·00
88 1d. pale mauve (2.6.96) 3·75 1·00
a. Rosy mauve 4·25 1·00
89 2d. dull green (17.3.94) 4·75 80
a. Emerald-green 6·00 2·00
90 22 2½d. brown (31.10.95) 17·00 7·50
a. Yellowish brown 13·00 14·00
91 21 5d. ultramarine (14.2.93) £200

(*d*) *P* 10 × *nearly* 12 (1893–94)

93 21 1d. black (20.7.93) 13·00 5·50
94 2d. dull green (19.9.94) £550 £275

(*e*) *P nearly* 12 × 10 (19.9.94)

94*a* 20 ½d. pale grey

(*f*) *Perf nearly* 12 (1894–98)

95 20 ½d. greenish slate (19.9.94) 2·75 7·50
a. Grey 26·00
96 21 1d. black (19.9.94) £180 23·00
97 1d. rosy mauve (4.5.98) 4·75 7·00
98 2d. dull green (19.9.94) 85·00 35·00

(*g*) *P* 11 × *nearly* 12 (1895–97)

99 20 ½d. greenish slate (8.10.97) 1·00 2·50
100 21 1d. black (31.10.95) £325
101 1d. rosy mauve (14.7.96) 3·75 80
a. Pale rosy mauve 3·75 2·00
102 2d. dull green (26.7.97) 30·00 4·00
103 22 2½d. brown (26.7.97) 11·00 17·00
a. Yellow-brown 5·00 5·00

(*h*) *P nearly* 12 × 11 (1897–98)

103*b* 20 ½d. greenish slate (8.10.97) 4·00
103*c* 21 1d. rosy mauve (10.2.97) 10·00
103*d* 2d. dull green (4.5.98) £200

The 2½d. brown is known *doubly printed*, but only occurs in the remainders and with the special obliteration (*Price* £100 *cancelled-to-order*). It was never issued for postal use.

23

24

(Typo D.L.R.)

1903 (1 Feb). *Wmk Crown CA. P* 14.

104 23 ½d. green and pale green 2·25 1·75
105 1d. dull purple and black/*red* 12·00 55
106 24 2d. dull purple and orange 3·50 1·25
107 23 2½d. dull purple and blue/*blue* 14·00 8·00
108 3d. dull purple and purple 1·50 4·50
109 24 4d. dull purple and black 1·50 2·50
110 23 5d. dull purple and green 1·50 5·00
111 24 6d. dull purple and carmine 1·50 2·50
112 23 1s. green and carmine 10·00 45·00
113 24 5s. green and black 42·00 95·00
114 23 £1 grey-black and ultramarine £300 £375
104/14 *Set of* 11 £350 £475
104/14 Optd "Specimen" *Set of* 11 £300

1904–9. *Wmk Mult Crown CA. Chalk-surfaced paper* (1s.). *P* 14.

115 23 ½d. green and pale green 9·00 3·00
116 1d. purple and black/*red* 20·00 10
117 1s. green and carmine (1909) 26·00 40·00
115/17 *Set of* 3 50·00 40·00

1906–12. *Colours changed. Wmk Mult Crown CA. Chalk-surfaced paper* (6d. to £1). *P* 14.

118 23 ½d. green (1908) 10·00 3·25
119 1d. red (1906) 5·00 10
120 2½d. bright blue (1910) 6·00 7·50
121 24 6d. dull purple (1910) 8·50 22·00
122 23 1s. black/*green* (1911) 4·00 10·00
123 24 5s. green and red/*yellow* (1911) 48·00 55·00
124 23 £1 purple and black/*red* (1912) £300 £300
118/24 *Set of* 7 £325 £350
119/24 Optd "Specimen" *Set of* 6 £300

Nos. 112/14, 117 and 120/4 are known with a forged registered postmark of Suva dated "10 DEC 1909".

25

26

WAR STAMP (27)

(Typo D.L.R.)

1912 (Oct)–**23.** *Die I. Wmk Mult Crown CA. Chalk-surfaced paper* (5d. to £1). *P* 14.

125 26 ¼d. brown (1.4.16) 1·75 30
a. Deep brown (1917) 1·25 40
y. Wmk inverted and reversed
126 25 ½d. green 1·50 95
a. Yellow-green (1916) 8·50 8·50
b. Blue-green (1917) 1·25 50
w. Wmk inverted 75·00
y. Wmk inverted and reversed 75·00
127 25 1d. carmine 2·00 10
a. Bright scarlet (1916) 2·00 75
b. Deep rose (1916) 8·50 1·75
128 26 2d. greyish slate (5.14) 1·75 10
a. Wmk sideways
129 25 2½d. bright blue (5.14) 3·50 3·50
130 3d. purple/*yellow* (5.14) 4·00 4·25
a. Wmk sideways £350 £425
b. On lemon (1915) 2·00 8·50
c. On pale yellow (1921) 1·75 13·00
ca. "A" of "CA" missing from wmk
cw. Wmk inverted
d. Die II. *On pale yellow* (1922) 2·50 24·00
131 26 4d. black and red/*yellow* (5.14) 21·00 19·00
a. On lemon 4·00 15·00
b. On orange-buff (1920) 50·00 65·00
c. On pale yellow (1921) 8·00 14·00
cw. Wmk inverted
d. Die II. *On pale yellow* (1922) (Optd S. £35) 3·75 20·00
132 25 5d. dull purple and olive-green (5.14) 5·50 10·00
133 26 6d. dull and bright purple (5.14) 2·00 5·00
134 25 1s. black/*green* (10.13) 1·25 14·00
a. White back (4.14) 1·00 8·00
b. On blue-green, olive back (1916) 4·75 10·00
c. On emerald back (1921) (Optd S. £35) 5·50 30·00
d. Die II. *On emerald back* (1922) 3·50 21·00
135 26 2s. 6d. black and red/*blue* (19.1.16) 32·00 28·00
136 5s. green and red/*yellow* 32·00 40·00
137 25 £1 purple and black/*red* (5.14) £250 £275
a. Die II (1923) £250 £275
125/37 *Set of* 13 £275 £325
125/37 Optd "Specimen" *Set of* 13 £425

1915 (1 Dec)–**19.** *Optd with T* **27** *by Govt Printer, Suva.*

138 25 ½d. green
a. Yellow-green (1916) 60 3·50
b. Blue-green (1917) 60 2·50
c. Opt inverted £500
d. Opt double
139 1d. carmine 22·00 23·00
a. Bright scarlet 1·50 75
ab. Horiz pair, one without opt £5000
c. Opt inverted £650
d. Deep rose (1919) 1·75 1·75
138/9 H/S "Specimen" *Set of* 2 £120

No. 139ab occurred on one pane of 120 only, the overprint being so misplaced that all the stamps of the last vertical row escaped it entirely.

Nos. 140/227 are no longer used.

1922–29. *Die II. Wmk Mult Script CA. Chalk-surfaced paper* (1s. to 5s.). *P* 14.

228 26 ¼d. deep brown (1923) 2·50 22·00
229 25 ½d. green (1923) 75 2·25
w. Wmk inverted
230 1d. carmine-red 2·50 2·00
231 1d. violet (6.1.27) 1·25 10
232 26 1½d. scarlet (6.1.27) 4·00 3·25
233 2d. grey 1·25 10
a. Face value omitted £7000
234 25 3d. bright blue (1924) 2·75 1·25
235 26 4d. black and red/*lemon* (1924) 5·00 7·00
a. On pale yellow (1929) 30·00 24·00
236 25 5d. dull purple and sage-green (1927) 1·50 2·00
237 26 6d. dull and bright purple 2·00 1·25
238 25 1s. black/*emerald* (1924) 4·00 6·00
w. Wmk inverted
239 26 2s. purple and blue/*blue* (6.1.27) 28·00 60·00
240 2s. 6d. black and red/*blue* (1925) 11·00 32·00
241 5s. green and red/*pale yellow* (1926) 30·00 65·00
228/41 *Set of* 14 85·00 £180
228/41 Optd "Specimen" *Set of* 14 £300

The 2d. imperforate with watermark Type **10** of Ireland came from a trial printing and was not issued.

Only one example of No. 233a is known. It was caused by an obstruction during the printing of the duty plate.

1935 (6 May). *Silver Jubilee. As Nos.* 91/4 *of Antigua.*

242 1½d. deep blue and carmine 80 5·00
a. Deep blue and aniline red 5·50 15·00
b. Frame printed double, one albino £1000
f. Diagonal line by turret 45·00
h. Dot by flagstaff 80·00
i. Dash by turret 80·00
243 2d. ultramarine and grey 1·50 35
f. Diagonal line by turret 60·00
g. Dot to left of chapel £100
244 3d. brown and deep blue 2·50 3·00
f. Diagonal line by turret 90·00
h. Dot by flagstaff £140
i. Dash by turret £140
245 1s. slate and purple 4·50 4·50
a. Frame printed double, one albino £1500
f. Diagonal line by turret £140
h. Dot by flagstaff £180
242/5 *Set of* 4 8·50 11·50
242/5 Perf "Specimen" *Set of* 4 85·00

For illustrations of plate varieties see Catalogue Introduction.

1937 (12 May). *Coronation. As Nos.* 95/7 *of Antigua. P* 11×11½.

246 1d. purple 60 45
247 2d. grey-black 60 1·25
248 3d. Prussian blue 60 1·25
246/8 *Set of* 3 1·60 2·75
246/8 Perf "Specimen" *Set of* 3 55·00

PRICES OF SETS

Set prices are given for many issues, generally those containing three stamps or more. Definitive sets include one of each value or major colour change, but do not cover different perforations, die types or minor shades. Where a choice is possible the set prices are based on the cheapest versions of the stamps included in the listings.

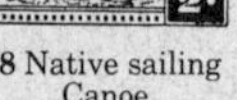

28 Native sailing Canoe

29 Native Village

30 Camakua (canoe)

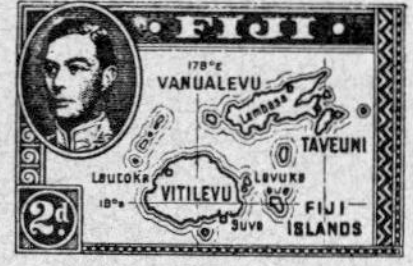

31 Map of Fiji Islands

Two Dies of Type **30**:

Die I Empty Canoe — Die II Native in Canoe

Two Dies of Type **31**:

Die I Without "180°" — Die II With "180°"

Extra palm frond (R. 5/8)

Extra line (R. 2/1)

Spur on arms medallion (Pl 2 R. 4/2) (ptg of 26 Nov 1945)

(Des V. E. Ousey (½d., 1s., 2s. 6d.), Miss C. D. Lovejoy (1d., 1½d., 5d.), Miss I. Stinson (3d., 5s.) and A. V. Guy (2d. (Nos. 253/4), 2½d., 6d., 2s.). Recess De La Rue (½d., 1½d., 2d., (Nos. 253/5a), 2½d., 6d., 8d., 1s. 5d., 1s. 6d.), Waterlow (others))

1938 (5 Apr)–**1955.** *T* **28/31** *and similar designs. Wmk Mult Script CA. Various perfs.*

No.	Type	Description	Unused	Used
249	**28**	½d. green (*p* 13½)	20	60
		a. Perf 14 (5.41)	20·00	3·50
		b. Perf 12 (8.48)	70	2·75
		ba. Extra palm frond	35·00	
250	**29**	1d. brown and blue (*p* 12½)	40	20
251	**30**	1½d. carmine (Die I) (*p* 13½)	15·00	35
252		1½d. carmine (Die II) (*p* 13½) (1.10.40)	1·40	3·00
		a. Deep carmine (10.42)	4·00	1·25
		b. Perf 14 (6.42)	18·00	18·00
		c. Perf 12 (21.7.49)	90	1·25
253	**31**	2d. brown and green (Die I) (*p* 13½)	38·00	40
		a. Extra line	£250	40·00
254		2d. brown & green (Die II) (*p* 13½) (1.10.40)	16·00	16·00
255	–	2d. grn & magenta (*p* 13½) (19.5.42)	40	60
		a. Perf 12 (27.5.46)	55	70
256	**31**	2½d. brown & grn (Die II) (*p* 14) (6.1.42)	60	85
		a. Perf 13½ (1.44)	70	80
		b. Perf 12 (19.1.48)	80	50
257	–	3d. blue (*p* 12½)	1·00	30
		a. Spur on arms medallion	£140	
258	–	5d. blue and scarlet (*p* 12½)	42·00	10·00
259	–	5d. yell-green & scar (*p* 12½) (1.10.40)	20	30
260	**31**	6d. black (Die I) (*p* 13×12)	60·00	12·00
261		6d. black (Die II) (*p* 13½) (1.10.40)	3·00	2·00
		a. Violet-black (1.44)	25·00	27·00
		b. Perf 12. *Black* (5.6.47)	1·50	1·50
261*c*	–	8d. carmine (*p* 14) (15.11.48)	1·00	1·50
		d. Perf 13 (7.6.50)	70	2·75
262	–	1s. black and yellow (*p* 12½)	75	60
263	–	1s. 5d. black & carm (*p* 14) (13.6.40)	20	10
263*a*	–	1s. 6d. ultramarine (*p* 14) (1.8.50)	3·50	2·75
		b. Perf 13 (16.2.55)	1·25	15·00
264	–	2s. violet and orange (*p* 12½)	2·50	40
265	–	2s. 6d. green and brown (*p* 12½)	2·50	1·50
266	–	5s. green and purple (*p* 12½)	2·50	1·75
266*a*	–	10s. orange & emer (*p* 12½) (13.3.50)	32·00	40·00
266*b*	–	£1 ultram & carm (*p* 12½) (13.3.50)	48·00	50·00
249/66*b*		*Set of* 22	£250	£120
249/66 excl 261*c* and 263*a* Perf "Specimen"		*Set of* 18	£450	

Designs: *Horiz* (*as T* **30**)—2d. (Nos. 255/a) Government Offices. (*As T* **29**)—3d. Canoe and arms of Fiji; 8d., 1s. 5d., 1s. 6d. Arms of Fiji; 2s. Suva Harbour; 2s. 6d. River scene; 5s. Chief's hut. *Vert* (*as T* **29**)—5d. Sugar cane; 1s. Spearing fish by torchlight; 10s. Paw-paw Tree; £1 Police bugler.

2½d.

(42)

1941 (10 Feb). *No.* 254 *surch with T* **42** *by Govt Printer, Suva.*

No.	Type	Description	Unused	Used
267	**31**	2½d. on 2d. brown and green	55	20

1946 (17 Aug). *Victory. As Nos.* 110/11 *of Antigua.*

No.	Description	Unused	Used
268	2½d. green	10	75
	a. Printed double, one albino	£250	
269	3d. blue	10	10
268/9 Perf "Specimen"	*Set of* 2	60·00	

1948 (17 Dec). *Royal Silver Wedding. As Nos.* 112/13 *of Antigua.*

No.	Description	Unused	Used
270	2½d. green	40	75
271	5s. violet-blue	14·00	6·50

1949 (10 Oct). *75th Anniv of U.P.U. As Nos.* 114/17 *of Antigua.*

No.	Description	Unused	Used
272	2d. bright reddish purple	30	30
273	3d. deep blue	2·25	2·00
274	8d. carmine-red	45	1·25
275	1s. 6d. blue	45	1·00
272/5	*Set of* 4	3·00	4·00

43 Children Bathing

44 Rugby Football

(Recess B.W.)

1951 (17 Sept). *Health Stamps. Wmk Mult Script CA. P* 13½.

No.	Type	Description	Unused	Used
276	**43**	1d. + 1d. brown	10	60
277	**44**	2d. + 1d. green	30	60

1953 (2 June). *Coronation. As No.* 120 *of Antigua.*

No.	Description	Unused	Used
278	2½d. black and green	50	30

45 Arms of Fiji

(Recess D.L.R.)

1953 (16 Dec). *Royal Visit. Wmk Mult Script CA. P* 13.

No.	Type	Description	Unused	Used
279	**45**	8d. deep carmine-red	15	15

NEW INFORMATION

The editor is always interested to correspond with people who have new information that will improve or correct the Catalogue.

46 Queen Elizabeth II (after Annigoni)

47 Government Offices

48 Loading Copra

49 Sugar Cane Train

50 Preparing Bananas for Export

51 Gold Industry

(Des V. E. Ousey (½d., 1s., 2s. 6d.), A. V. Guy (6d.). Recess D.L.R (½d., 2d., 6d., 8d.), Waterlow (1s., 2s. 6d., 10s., £1) B.W. (others))

1954 (1 Feb)–**59**. *T* **46/51** *and similar designs previously used for King George VI issue (but with portrait of Queen Elizabeth II as in T* **47**). *Wmk Mult Script CA. P* 12 (2*d.*), 13 (8*d.*), 12½ (6*d.*, 1*s.*, 2*s.* 6*d.*, 10*s.*, £1), 11½×11 (3*d.*, 1*s.* 6*d.*, 2*s.*, 5*s.*) *or* 11½ (½*d.*, 1*d.*, 1½*d.*, 2½*d.*).

No.	Type	Description	Unused	Used
280	–	½d. myrtle-green (1.7.54)	15	1·00
281	**46**	1d. turquoise-blue (1.6.56)	1·25	10
282		1½d. sepia (1.10.56)	70	30
283	**47**	2d. green and magenta	1·25	30
284	**46**	2½d. blue-violet (1.10.56)	1·25	10
285	**48**	3d. brown and reddish violet (1.10.56)	2·50	20
		a. Brown & dp reddish vio (10.11.59)	6·50	60
287	–	6d. black (1.7.54)	2·25	75
288	–	8d. deep carmine-red (1.7.54)	1·75	1·25
		a. Carmine-lake (6.3.58)	5·50	1·75
289	–	1s. black and yellow	2·25	10
290	**49**	1s. 6d. blue and myrtle-green (1.10.56)	18·00	90
291	**50**	2s. black and carmine (1.10.56)	5·50	30
292	–	2s. 6d. bluish green and brown	1·25	30
		a. Bluish green & red-brown (14.9.54)	1·25	10
293	**51**	5s. ochre and blue (1.10.56)	25·00	1·25
294	–	10s. orange and emerald (1.7.54)	12·00	20·00
295	–	£1 ultramarine and carmine (1.7.54)	42·00	18·00
280/95		*Set of* 15	£100	40·00

Designs: *Vert* (22½ × 36 *mm*)—½d. Fijians sailing canoe. (25 × 31 *mm*)—1s. Spearing fish by torchlight; 10s. Paw-paw tree; £1 Police bugler. *Horiz* (36 × 22½ *mm*)—6d. Map of Fiji. (31 × 25 *mm*)—8d. Arms of Fiji; 2s. 6d. River scene.

52 River Scene

53 Cross of Lorraine

(Recess B.W.)

1954 (1 Apr). *Health Stamps. Wmk Mult Script CA. P* 11 × 11½.

No.	Type	Description	Unused	Used
296	**52**	1½d. + ½d. bistre-brown and green	10	50
297	**53**	2½d. + ½d. orange and black	10	10

54 Queen Elizabeth II (after Annigoni)

55 Fijian beating Lali

56 Hibiscus

60 Red Shining Parrot

(Des M. Goaman: Photo Harrison (8d., 4s.). Recess. B.W. (others))

1959–63. *T* **54/6**, **60** *and similar designs. Wmk Mult Script CA. P* 11½ (*T* **46** *and* **54**), 11½ × 11 (6*d*., 10*d*., 1*s*., 2*s*. 6*d*., 10*s*., £1), 14½ × 14 (8*d*.) *or* 14 × 14½ (4*s*).

298 **46** ½d. emerald-green (14.11.61) 15 90
299 **54** 1d. deep ultramarine (3.12.62).. .. 1·75 1·00
300 1½d. sepia (3.12.62) .. .. .. 1·25 30
301 **46** 2d. rose-red (14.11.61) 50 10
302 2½d. orange-brown (3.12.62) .. .. 1·50 2·25
303 **55** 6d. carmine and black (14.11.61) .. 1·25 10
304 **56** 8d. scarlet, yellow, green & blk (1.8.61) 50 25
305 – 10d. brown and carmine (1.4.63) .. 1·75 50
306 – 1s. light blue and blue (14.11.61) .. 1·50 10
307 – 2s. 6d. black and purple (14.11.61) .. 12·00 10
308 **60** 4s. red, green, blue & slate-grn (13.7.59) 1·75 1·75
309 – 10s. emerald and deep sepia (14.11.61) .. 6·50 3·00
310 – £1 black and orange (14.11.61) .. 22·00 5·50
298/310 .. .. *Set of* 13 45·00 13·00

Designs: *Horiz* (*as T* **55**)—10d. Yaqona ceremony; 1s. Location map; 2s. 6d. Nadi Airport; 10s. Cutting sugar-cane; £1 Arms of Fiji.

Nos. 299 and 311 have turtles either side of "Fiji" instead of shells.

63 Queen Elizabeth II

64 International Dateline

65 White Orchid

66 Orange Dove

(Des M. Goaman. Photo Harrison (3d., 9d. 1s. 6d., 2s., 4s., 5s.). Recess B.W. (others))

1962 (3 Dec)–**67**. *W* w **12** (*upright*). *P* 11½ (1*d*., 2*d*.), 12½ (3*d*.), 11½×11 (6*d*., 10*d*., 1*s*., 2*s*. 6*d*., 10*s*., £1), 14½×14 (9*d*., 2*s*.) *or* 14×14½ (1*s*. 6*d*., 4*s*., 5*s*.).

311 **54** 1d. deep ultramarine (14.1.64) .. 70 2·00
312 **46** 2d. rose-red (3.8.65) 45 10
313 **63** 3d. multicoloured 25 10
w. Wmk inverted .. .. ..
314 **55** 6d. carmine and black (9.6.64) .. 2·00 10
315 **56** 9d. scarlet, yellow, grn & ultram (1.4.63) 90 65
316 – 10d. brown and carmine (14.1.64) .. 60 50
317 – 1s. light blue and blue (24.1.66*) .. 2·50 45
318 **64** 1s. 6d. red, yellow, gold, black & blue 2·75 90
a. Error. Wmk sideways £700
319 **65** 2s. yellow-green, green and copper .. 16·00 3·00
a. Apple-green, grn & copper (16.5.67) 23·00 3·75
320 – 2s. 6d. black and purple (3.8.65) .. 2·00 70
a. Black and deep purple (8.67) .. 1·75 70
321 **60** 4s. red, yellow-green, blue & grn (1.4.64) 5·50 2·75
322 4s. red, green, blue & slate-grn (1.3.66) 3·50 3·50
323 **66** 5s. red, yellow and grey .. .. 14·00 35
w. Wmk inverted £110
324 – 10s. emerald and deep sepia (14.1.64) .. 7·00 6·00
325 – £1 black and orange (9.6.64) .. .. 18·00 11·00
311/25 .. .. *Set of* 15 65·00 28·00

Designs: *Horiz* (*as T* **55**)—10d. Yaqona Ceremony; 1s. Location map; 2s. 6d. Nadi Airport; 10s. Cutting sugar-cane; £1 Arms of Fiji.

*This is the earliest known used date in Fiji and it was not released by the Crown Agents until 1 November.

The 3d. value exists with PVA gum as well as gum arabic.

For 4s. with watermark sideways see No. 359.

ROYAL VISIT

1963

(67)

ROYAL VISIT 1963

(68)

1963 (1 Feb). *Royal Visit. Nos.* 313 *and* 306 *optd with T* **67**/8.
326 **67** 3d. multicoloured 20 10
327 **68** 1s. light blue and blue 20 10

1963 (4 June). *Freedom from Hunger. As No.* 146 *of Antigua.*
328 2s. ultramarine .. .. 2·50 70

69 Running

(**73** C.S. *Retriever*.)

(Des M. Goaman. Photo Harrison)

1963 (6 Aug). *First South Pacific Games, Suva. T* **69** *and similar designs. W* w **12**. *P* 14½.
329 3d. red-brown, yellow and black 25 10
330 9d. red-brown, violet and black .. .. 35 1·40
331 1s. red-brown, green and black 35 10
332 2s. 6d. red-brown, light blue and black .. 90 1·00
329/32 .. .. *Set of* 4 1·75 2·25

Designs: *Vert*—9d. Throwing the discus; 1s. Hockey. *Horiz*—2s. 6d. High-jumping.

1963 (2 Sept). *Red Cross Centenary. As Nos.* 147/8 *of Antigua.*
333 2d. red and black 50 10
334 2s. red and blue .. .. 2·25 2·50

1963 (3 Dec). *Opening of COMPAC (Trans-Pacific Telephone Cable). No.* 317 *optd with T* **73** *by B.W.*
335 1s. light blue and blue 40 10

74 Jamborette Emblem

75 Scouts of Three Races

(Des V. Whiteley assisted by Norman L. Joe, Asst. D.C., Fiji Scouts for Jamboree emblem. Photo Harrison)

1964 (4 Aug). *50th Anniv of Fijian Scout Movement. W* w **12**. *P* 12½.
336 **74** 3d. multicoloured 15 20
337 **75** 1s. violet and yellow-brown 15 25

76 Flying-boat *Aotearoa*

78 *Aotearoa* and Map

(Des V. Whiteley. Photo Harrison)

1964 (24 Oct). *25th Anniv of First Fiji-Tonga Airmail Service. T* **76**, **78** *and similar design. W* w **12**. *P* 14½ × 14 (1*s*.) *or* 12½ (*others*).
338 3d. black and vermilion 40 10
339 6d. vermilion and bright blue 70 85
340 1s. black and turquoise-blue 70 85
338/40 .. .. *Set of* 3 1·60 1·60

Design: *Vert* (*as T* **76**)—6d. De Havilland D.H.114 Heron 2.

1965 (17 May). *I.T.U. Centenary. As Nos.* 166/7 *of Antigua.*
341 3d. blue and rose-carmine 35 10
342 2s. orange-yellow and bistre 80 25

1965 (25 Oct). *International Co-operation Year. As Nos.* 168/9 *of Antigua.*
343 2d. reddish purple and turquoise-green .. 20 10
344 2s. 6d. deep bluish green and lavender .. 60 25

1966 (24 Jan). *Churchill Commemoration. As Nos.* 170/3 *of Antigua.*
345 3d. new blue 70 10
346 9d. deep green 90 40
347 1s. brown 90 10
348 2s. 6d. bluish violet .. .. .. 1·00 50
345/8 .. .. *Set of* 4 3·25 1·00

1966 (1 July). *World Cup Football Championships. As Nos.* 176/7 *of Antigua.*
349 2d. violet, yellow-green, lake & yellow-brn .. 20 10
350 2s. chocolate, blue-green, lake & yellow-brn 50 20

79 H.M.S. *Pandora* approaching Split Island, Rotuma

(Des V. Whiteley. Photo Enschedé)

1966 (29 Aug). *175th Anniv of Discovery of Rotuma. T* **79** *and similar horiz designs. Multicoloured. W* w **12** (*sideways*). *P* 14 × 13.
351 3d. Type **79** 30 10
352 10d. Rotuma Chiefs 30 10
353 1s. 6d. Rotumans welcoming H.M.S. *Pandora* 40 30
351/3 .. .. *Set of* 3 90 40

1966 (20 Sept). *Inauguration of W.H.O. Headquarters, Geneva. As Nos.* 178/9 *of Antigua.*
354 6d. black, yellow-green and light blue .. 1·00 25
355 2s. 6d. black, light purple and yellow-brown 2·50 1·75

ALTERED CATALOGUE NUMBERS

Any Catalogue numbers altered from the last edition are shown as a list in the introductory pages.

LEGISLATIVE ASSEMBLY

82 Running

(Des V. Whiteley. Photo Harrison)

1966 (5 Dec*). *2nd South Pacific Games, Nouméa. T* **82** *and similar designs. W* w **12** (*sideways on* 9*d*.). *P* 14½ × 14 (9*d*.) *or* 14 × 14½ (*others*).
356 3d. black, chestnut and yellow-olive .. 10 10
357 9d. black, chestnut and greenish blue .. 15 15
358 1s. multicoloured 15 15
356/8 .. .. *Set of* 3 30 30

Designs: *Vert*—9d. Putting the shot. *Horiz*—1s. Diving.

*These were not released in London until 8.12.66.

1967 (16 Feb). *As No.* 321 *but wmk* w **12** *sideways.*
359 **60** 4s. red, yellow-green, blue and green .. 3·25 1·25

85 Military Forces Band

(Des G. Vasarhelyi. Photo Enschedé)

1967 (20 Oct). *International Tourist Year. T* **85** *and similar horiz designs. Multicoloured. W* w **12** (*sideways*). *P* 14 × 13.
360 3d. Type **85** 40 10
361 9d. Reef diving 20 10
362 1s. Beqa fire walkers 20 10
363 2s. *Oriana* (cruise liner) at Suva 55 15
360/3 .. .. *Set of* 4 1·25 30

89 Bligh (bust), H.M.S. *Providence* and Chart

91 Bligh's Tomb

90 "*Bounty*'s longboat being chased in Fiji waters"

(Des V. Whiteley. Photo Harrison)

1967 (11 Dec). *150th Death Anniv of Admiral Bligh. W* w **12** (*sideways on* 1*s*.). *P* 12½ × 13 (1*s*.) *or* 15 × 14 (*others*).
364 **89** 4d. multicoloured 10 10
365 **90** 1s. multicoloured 10 10
366 **91** 2s. 6d. multicoloured 15 15
364/6 .. .. *Set of* 3 30 30

92 Simmonds Spartan Seaplane

(Des V. Whiteley. Photo Harrison)

1968 (5 June). *40th Anniv of Kingsford Smith's Pacific Flight via Fiji. T* **92** *and similar horiz designs. W* w **12**. *P* 14 × 14½.
367 2d. black and green 15 10
368 6d. greenish blue, black and lake 15 10
369 1s. deep violet and turquoise-green 20 10
370 2s. orange-brown and blue 30 15
367/70 .. .. *Set of* 4 70 30

Designs—6d. Hawker Siddeley H.S.748 and airline insignias; 1s. Fokker F.VIIa/3M *Southern Cross* and crew; 2s. Lockheed 8D Altair *Lady Southern Cross* monoplane.

96 Bure Huts

97 Eastern Reef Heron (after Belcher)

98 Sea Snake

99 Queen Elizabeth and Arms of Fiji

(Des G. Hamori (½d., 1d., 9d.), W. O. Cernohorsky (2d., 4s.) H. S. Robinson (4d., 10d.), D. W. Blair (6d., 5s.), P. D. Clarke (1s.), G. Vasarhelyi (2s. 6d.), W. O. Cernohorsky and E. Jones (3s.), E. Jones and G. Hamori (10s.), E. Jones (£1). Adapted V. Whiteley. Photo D.L.R.)

1968 (15 July). *T* **96/9** *and similar designs. W w* **12** *(sideways on all vert designs). P* 14 × 13½ *(2s., 2s. 6d., 5s., £1),* 13½ × 14 *(3d., 1s., 1s. 6d., 4s., 10s.) or* 13½ × 13 *(others).*

371 ½d. multicoloured 10 10
372 1d. deep greenish blue, red and yellow .. 10 10
373 2d. new blue, brown and ochre 10 10
374 3d. blackish green, blue and ochre 35 10
375 4d. multicoloured 80 50
376 6d. multicoloured 25 10
377 9d. multicoloured 15 50
378 10d. royal blue, orange and blackish brown .. 1·25 20
379 1s. Prussian blue and brown-red 20 10
380 1s. 6d. multicoloured .. .. .. 3·25 4·00
381 2s. turquoise, black and rosine .. .. 75 2·00
382 2s. 6d. multicoloured 75 75
383 3s. multicoloured .. .. 2·75 6·00
384 4s. yellow-ochre, black and olive .. .. 6·00 2·75
385 5s. multicoloured .. .. 3·00 2·50
386 10s. lake-brown, black and ochre .. .. 1·50 3·50
387 £1 multicoloured .. .. 1·50 6·00
371/87 .. .. *Set of* 17 14·00 26·00

Designs: *Horiz* (*as T* **96**)—1d. Passion Flowers; 2d. Chambered or Pearly Nautilus; 4d. *Psilogramma jordana* (moth); 6d. Pennant Coralfish; 9d. Bamboo raft; 10d. *Asota woodfordi* (moth); 3s. Golden Cowrie shell. *Vert* (*as T* **97**)—1s. Black Marlin; 1s. 6d. Orange-breasted Honeyeaters (after Belcher); 4s. Mining industry; 10s. Ceremonial whale's tooth. *Horiz* (*as T* **98**)—2s. 6d. Outrigger canoes; 5s. Bamboo Orchids.

113 Map of Fiji, W.H.O. Emblem and Nurses

(Des V. Whiteley. Litho D.L.R.)

1968 (9 Dec). *20th Anniv of World Health Organization. T* **113** *and similar horiz designs. Multicoloured. W w* **12** *(sideways). P* 14.

388 3d. Type **113** 15 10
389 9d. Transferring patient to Medical Ship *Vuniwai* 20 10
390 3s. Recreation 25 20
388/90 .. .. *Set of* 3 55 30

(New Currency. 100 cents = 1 dollar.)

116 Passion Flowers

117 Fijian Soldiers overlooking the Solomon Islands

1969 (13 Jan)–**70.** *Decimal Currency. Designs as Nos.* 371/87, *but with values inscr in decimal currency as T* **116**. *W w* **12** *(sideways on vert designs) Chalk-surfaced paper. P* 14 × 13½ (20, 25, 50 *c.* $2) 13½ × 14 (3, 10, 15, 40 *c.*, $1) *or* 13½ × 13 (*others*).

391 **116** 1 c. deep greenish blue, red and yellow .. 10 10
392 – 2 c. new blue, brown and ochre (as 2d.) .. 10 10
393 **97** 3 c. blackish green, blue and ochre .. 30 10
394 – 4 c. multicoloured (as 4d.) .. .. 1·50 10
395 – 5 c. multicoloured (as 6d.) 20 10
396 **96** 6 c. multicoloured 10 10
397 – 8 c. multicoloured (as 9d.) 10 10
398 – 9 c. royal blue, orange and blackish brown (as 10d.) .. .. .. 1·50 1·50
399 – 10 c. Prussian blue and brown-red (as 1s.) 20 10
400 – 15 c. multicoloured (as 1s. 6d.) .. .. 9·00 4·25
401 **98** 20 c. turquoise, black and rosine .. 1·00 80
402 – 25 c. multicoloured (as 2s. 6d.) .. .. 1·00 30
403 – 30 c. multicoloured (as 3s.) .. .. 6·50 1·75
404 – 40 c. yellow-ochre, black and olive (as 4s.) 6·50 4·00
405 – 50 c. multicoloured (as 5s.) .. .. 4·50 30
a. Glazed, ordinary paper (3.9.70) .. 10·00 1·50
406 – $1 lake-brown, black and ochre (as 10s.) 1·50 60
a. Glazed, ordinary paper (3.9.70) .. 4·00 3·50
407 **99** $2 multicoloured .. .. .. 1·50 4·00
391/407 .. .. .. *Set of* 17 25·00 15·00

(Des G. Drummond. Photo Harrison)

1969 (23 June). *25th Anniv of Fijian Military Forces' Solomons Campaign. T* **117** *and similar horiz designs. W w* **12**. *P* 14.

408 3 c. yellow-brown, black and bright emerald 20 10
409 10 c. multicoloured 25 10
410 25 c. multicoloured 35 20
408/10 .. .. *Set of* 3 70 30

Designs:—10 c. Regimental Flags and Soldiers in full dress and battledress; 25 c. Cpl. Sefanaia Sukanaivalu and Victoria Cross.

120 Javelin Thrower

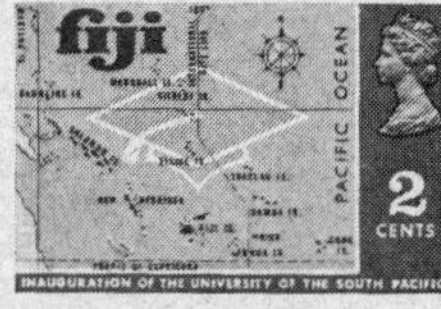

123 Map of South Pacific and "Mortar-board"

(Des L. Curtis. Photo Harrison)

1969 (18 Aug). *3rd South Pacific Games. Port Moresby. T* **120** *and similar vert designs. W w* **12** *(sideways*). P* 14½×14.

411 4 c. black, brown and vermilion 10 10
w. Wmk Crown to right of CA .. .. 3·00
412 8 c. black, grey and new blue 10 10
413 20 c. multicoloured 20 20
411/13 .. .. *Set of* 3 30 30

Designs:—8 c. Yachting; 20 c. Games medal and winners' rostrum.

*The normal sideways watermark shows Crown to left of CA, *as seen from the back of the stamp.*

(Des G. Drummond. Photo Harrison)

1969 (10 Nov). *Inauguration of University of the South Pacific. T* **123** *and similar horiz designs. Multicoloured. W w* **12**. *P* 14 × 15.

414 2 c. Type **123** 10 15
415 8 c. R.N.Z.A.F. badge and Short S.25 Sunderland flying boat over Laucala Bay (site of University) 15 10
416 25 c. Science students at work 25 15
w. Wmk inverted .. .. .. 2·00 1·50
414/16 .. .. *Set of* 3 45 30

(126)

127 Chaulmugra Tree, Makogai

1970 (4 Mar). *Royal Visit. Nos.* 392, 399 *and* 402 *optd with T* **126**.

417 2 c. new blue, brown and ochre 10 20
418 10 c. Prussian blue and brown-red 10 10
419 25 c. multicoloured 20 10
417/19 .. .. *Set of* 3 35 30

(Des G. Drummond. Photo Harrison)

1970 (25 May). *Closing of Leprosy Hospital, Makogai. T* **127** *and similar designs. W w* **12** *(sideways* on* 10 *c.). P* 14×14½.

420 2 c. multicoloured 10 10
421 10 c. pale turquoise-green and black .. 20 10
a. Pair. Nos. 421/2 .. .. .. 40 20
w. Wmk Crown to right of CA .. .. 4·50
422 10 c. turquoise-blue, black and magenta .. 20 10
w. Wmk Crown to right of CA .. .. 4·50
423 30 c. multicoloured 35 50
420/3 .. .. *Set of* 4 70 70

Designs: *Vert*—No. 421, "Cascade" (Semisi Maya); No. 422, "Sea Urchins" (Semisi Maya). *Horiz*—No. 423, Makogai Hospital.

*The normal sideways watermark shows Crown to left of CA, *as seen from the back of the stamp.*

Nos. 421/2 were printed together, *se-tenant*, throughout the sheet.

131 Abel Tasman and Log, 1643

(Des V. Whiteley. Litho D.L.R.)

1970 (18 Aug). *Explorers and Discoverers. T* **131** *and similar horiz designs. W w* **12** *(sideways*). P* 13×12½.

424 2 c. black, brown and turquoise 40 25
w. Wmk Crown to right of CA .. .. 45·00
425 3 c. multicoloured 80 25
426 8 c. multicoloured 80 15
427 25 c. multicoloured 60 15
424/7 .. .. *Set of* 4 2·40 70

Designs:—3 c. Captain Cook and H.M.S. *Endeavour*, 1774; 8 c. Captain Bligh and longboat, 1789; 25 c. Fijian and ocean-going canoe.

*The normal sideways watermark shows Crown to left of CA, *as seen from the back of the stamp.*

MINIMUM PRICE

The minimum price quote is 10p which represents a handling charge rather than a basis for valuing common stamps. For further notes about prices see introductory pages.

INDEPENDENT

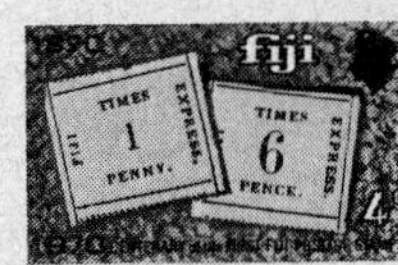

135 King Cakobau and Cession Stone

139 1d. and 6d. Stamps of 1870

(Des J.W. Litho Format)

1970 (10 Oct). *Independence. T* **135** *and similar horiz designs. Multicoloured. W w* **12** *(sideways). P* 14.

428 2 c. Type **135** 10 10
429 3 c. Children of the World 10 10
430 10 c. Prime Minister and Fijian flag 10 10
431 25 c. Dancers in costume 20 20
428/31 .. .. *Set of* 4 30 30

The design for the 10 c. value does not incorporate the Queen's head profile.

(Des V. Whiteley. Photo Harrison)

1970 (2 Nov). *Stamp Centenary. T* **139** *and similar horiz designs. Multicoloured. W w* **12** *(sideways on* 15 *c.). P* 14½ × 14.

432 4 c. Type **139** 15 10
433 15 c. Fijian stamps of all reigns (61×21 *mm*) 40 15
434 20 c. *Fiji Times* office and modern G.P.O. 40 15
w. Wmk inverted .. .. .. 45·00
432/4 .. .. *Set of* 3 85 35

140 Grey-backed White Eye

141 Masked Shining Parrot

(Des G. Drummond. Litho Questa)

1971 (6 Aug)–**72.** *Birds and Flowers. Vert designs as T* **140/1**. *Multicoloured. W w* **12** *(upright).*

(*a*) *Size as T* **140**. *P* 13½×14

435 1 c. *Cirrhopetalum umbellatum* (4.1.72) .. 15 30
436 2 c. Cardinal Honeyeater (22.11.71) .. 10 10
437 3 c. *Calanthe furcata* (23.6.72) 85 20
438 4 c. *Bulbophyllum sp nov* (23.6.72) .. 75 60
439 5 c. Type **140** 35 10
w. Wmk inverted .. .. .. — 5·00
440 6 c. *Phaius tancarvilliae* (23.6.72) .. 5·50 3·25
441 8 c. Blue-headed Flycatcher (22.11.71) .. 35 10
442 10 c. *Acanthephippium vitiense* (4.1.72) .. 40 10
443 15 c. *Dendrobium tokai* (23.6.72) .. .. 5·00 1·25
444 20 c. Slaty Flycatcher .. .. .. 1·50 30

(*b*) *Size as T* **141**. *P* 14

445 25 c. Yellow-faced Honeyeater (22.11.71) .. 2·75 20
446 30 c. *Dendrobium gordonii* (4.1.72) .. .. 10·00 90
447 40 c. Type **141** .. .. 4·50 50
448 50 c. White-throated Pigeon .. .. .. 3·50 50
449 $1 Collared Lory (22.11.71) .. .. 4·00 1·25
450 $2 *Dendrobium platygastrium* (4.1.72) .. 4·00 11·00
435/50 .. .. .. *Set of* 16 38·00 18·00

See also Nos. 459/73 and 505/20.

142 Women's Basketball

143 Community Education

(Des R. Granger Barrett. Litho Questa)

1971 (6 Sept). *Fourth South Pacific Games, Tahiti. T* **142** *and similar vert designs. W w* **12**. *P* 14.

451 8 c. multicoloured 10 10
452 10 c. cobalt, black and brown 10 10
453 25 c. pale turquoise-green, black and brown .. 30 25
451/3 .. .. *Set of* 3 45 30

Designs:—10c. Running; 25 c. Weightlifting.

(Des V. Whiteley. Litho Questa)

1972 (7 Feb). *25th Anniv of South Pacific Commission. T* **143** *and similar vert designs. Multicoloured. W w* **12**. *P* 14.

454 2 c. Type **143** 10 10
455 4 c. Public Health 10 10
456 50 c. Economic Growth 35 65
454/6 .. .. *Set of* 3 40 70

144 "Native Canoe"

145 Flowers, Conch and Ceremonial Whale's Tooth

(Des locally and adapted by A. B. New. Litho Questa)

972 (10 Apr). *South Pacific Festival of Arts, Suva. W* w **12**. *P* 14.
57 **144** 10 c. black, orange and new blue .. 10 10

972 (17 Nov)–**74**. *As Nos.* 436/41, 443/5 *and* 447/50, *but W* w **12** (*sideways**).
59 2 c. Cardinal Honey-eater (12.12.73) .. 45 8·50
60 3 c. *Calanthe furcata* (8.3.73) .. .. 1·75 45
w. Wmk Crown to left of CA (15.3.74) .. 1·75 80
61 4 c. *Bulbophyllum sp nov* (11.4.73) .. 6·00 45
62 5 c. Type **140** (8.3.73) .. .. .. 4·00 2·25
w. Wmk Crown to right of CA .. .. 7·50
63 6 c. *Phaius tancarvilliae* (11.4.73) .. 6·00 1·25
64 8 c. Blue-crested Broadbill (11.4.73) .. 3·75 75
66 15 c. *Dendrobium tokai* (11.4.73) .. .. 3·50 2·25
467 20 c. Slaty Flycatcher .. .. .. 13·00 2·00
468 25 c. Yellow-faced Honeyeater (11.4.73) .. 1·75 90
470 40 c. Type **141** (15.3.74) .. .. .. 3·00 5·00
471 50 c. White-throated Pigeon (15.3.74) .. 3·00 3·50
472 $1 Collared Lory .. .. 5·00 6·00
473 $2 *Dendrobium platygastrium* .. .. 7·00 6·00
459/73 .. .. *Set of* 13 50·00 35·00
*The normal sideways watermark shows Crown to right of CA on the 3 c. and Crown to left of CA on the remainder, *as seen from the back of the stamp.*

(Des (from photograph by D. Groves) and photo Harrison)

972 (20 Nov). *Royal Silver Wedding. Multicoloured; background colour given. W* w **12**. *P* 14 × 14½.
474 10 c. slate-green 20 15
475 25 c. bright purple 30 15
a. Blue printing omitted* £200
*The omission of the blue colour results in the Duke's suit appearing brown instead of deep blue.

HURRICANE RELIEF +10c

(146)

147 Line Out

1972 (4 Dec). *Hurricane Relief. Nos.* 400 *and* 403 *surch as T* **146**, *by the Reserve Bank of Australia.*
476 15 c. + 5 c. multicoloured 15 15
477 30 c. + 10 c. multicoloured 15 15

(Des J.W. Litho Questa)

1973 (9 Mar). *Diamond Jubilee of Fiji Rugby Union. T* **147** *and similar vert designs. Multicoloured. W* w **12** (*sideways*). *P* 14.
478 2 c. Type **147** .. .. 30 1·40
479 8 c. Body tackle 45 10
480 25 c. Conversion .. .. 1·00 40
478/80 .. .. *Set of* 3 1·60 1·60

148 Forestry Development

149 Christmas

(Des J.W. from local ideas. Litho Questa)

1973 (23 July). *Development Projects. T* **148** *and similar horiz designs. Multicoloured. W* w **12**. *P* 14.
481 5 c. Type **148** 10 10
482 8 c. Rice irrigation scheme 10 10
483 10 c. Low income housing 10 10
484 25 c. Highway construction 20 30
481/4 .. .. *Set of* 4 45 45

(Des L. Curtis. Litho Questa)

1973 (26 Oct). *Festivals of Joy. T* **149** *and similar vert designs. Multicoloured. W* w **12** (*sideways*). *P* 14.
485 3 c. Type **149** 10 10
486 10 c. Diwali 10 10
487 20 c. Id-ul-Fitar 15 15
488 25 c. Chinese New Year 15 15
485/8 .. .. *Set of* 4 35 40

150 Athletics

151 Bowler

(Des G. Drummond. Litho Questa)

1974 (7 Jan). *Commonwealth Games, Christchurch. T* **150** *and similar vert designs. Multicoloured. W* w **12** (*sideways*). *P* 14.
489 3 c. Type **150** 15 10
490 8 c. Boxing 15 10
491 50 c. Bowling 50 75
489/91 .. .. *Set of* 3 70 80

(Des Hon. P. Snow. Adapted J.W. Litho Questa)

1974 (21 Feb). *Cricket Centenary. T* **151** *and similar multi-coloured designs. W* w **12** (*sideways** *on* 3 *and* 25 *c.*). *P* 14.
492 3 c. Type **151** 50 25
w. Wmk Crown right of CA .. .. 3·50
493 25 c. Batsman and wicketkeeper .. .. 1·00 35
w. Wmk Crown to right of CA .. .. 3·00
494 40 c. Fielder (*horiz*) .. .. .. 1·50 90
492/4 .. .. *Set of* 3 2·75 1·40
*The normal sideways watermark shows Crown to left of CA, *as seen from the back of the stamp.*

152 Fijian Postman

(Des L. Curtis. Litho Format)

1974 (22 May). *Centenary of the Universal Postal Union. T* **152** *and similar horiz designs. Multicoloured. W* w **12**. *P* 14.
495 3 c. Type **152** 10 10
496 8 c. Loading mail onto *Fijian Princess* .. 10 10
497 30 c. Fijian post office and mail bus .. 20 25
498 50 c. B.A.C. One Eleven 200/400 modern aircraft .. .. 35 1·60
495/8 .. .. *Set of* 4 60 1·75

153 Cubs lighting Fire

154 Cakobau Club and Flag

(Des E. W. Roberts. Litho Questa)

1974 (20 Aug). *First National Scout Jamboree, Lautoka. T* **153** *and similar multicoloured designs. W* w **12** (*sideways** *on* 40 *c.*). *P* 14.
499 3 c. Type **153** 15 10
500 10 c. Scouts reading map 20 10
501 40 c. Scouts and Fijian flag (*vert*) .. .. 65 2·00
w. Wmk Crown to right of CA .. .. 65·00
499/501 .. .. *Set of* 3 90 2·00
*The normal sideways watermark shows Crown to left of CA, *as seen from the back of the stamp.*

(Des J.W. Litho Enschedé)

1974 (9 Oct). *Centenary of Deed of Cession and Fourth Anniv of Independence. T* **154** *and similar horiz designs. Multicoloured. W* w **12** (*sideways on* 8 *and* 50 *c.*). *P* 13½ × 13 (3 *c.*) *or* 13 × 13½ (*others*).
502 3 c. Type **154** 10 10
503 8 c. King Cakobau and Queen Victoria .. 10 10
504 50 c. Raising the Royal Standard at Nasova Ovalau 30 80
502/4 .. .. *Set of* 3 40 85

1975 (9 Apr)–**77**. *As Nos.* 435/44 *and* 446/50, *but W* w **14** (*sideways on* 1 *and* 10 *c*).
505 1 c. *Cirrhopetalum umbellatum* .. .. 75 3·25
506 2 c. Cardinal Honey-eater .. .. 75 3·25
507 3 c. *Calanthe furcata* .. .. .. 40 3·25
508 4 c. *Bulbophyllum sp nov* (3.9.76) .. 3·50 10
509 5 c. Type **140** .. .. 1·25 3·25
w. Wmk inverted .. .. .. 5·00
510 6 c. *Phaius tancarvilliae* (3.9.76) .. .. 2·75 20
511 8 c. Blue-crested Broadbill (3.9.76) .. 35 10
512 10 c. *Acanthephippium vitiense* 40 90
513 15 c. *Dendrobium tokai* (3.9.76) .. .. 2·50 60
514 20 c. Slaty Flycatcher (15.7.77) .. .. 3·00 55
516 30 c. *Dendrobium gordonii* (3.9.76) .. 6·00 95
517 40 c. Type **141** (3.9.76) .. .. .. 3·50 60
w. Wmk inverted .. .. ..
518 50 c. White-throated Pigeon (3.9.76) .. 3·50 65
519 $1 Collared Lory (3.9.76) .. .. 3·50 2·00
520 $2 *Dendrobium platygastrium* (3.9.76) .. 2·50 2·00
505/20 .. .. *Set of* 15 30·00 19·00

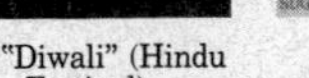

155 "Diwali" (Hindu Festival)

156 Steam Locomotive No. 21

(Des Jennifer Toombs. Litho Walsall)

1975 (31 Oct). *Festivals of Joy. T* **155** *and similar vert designs. Multicoloured. W* w **14** (*inverted*). *P* 14.
521 3 c. Type **155** 10 10
522 15 c. "Id-Ul-Fitar" (Muslim Festival) 10 10
523 25 c. Chinese New Year 15 15
524 30 c. Christmas 20 85
521/4 .. .. *Set of* 4 40 1·00
MS525 121×101 mm. Nos. 521/4. W w **14** (sideways*) .. .. 1·25 6·00
a. Imperf between (vert) £1100
w. Wmk Crown to right of CA .. .. 30·00
*The normal sideways watermark on **MS**525 shows Crown to left of CA, *as seen from the back of the stamp.*

(Des R. Granger Barrett. Litho Questa)

1976 (26 Jan). *Sugar Trains. T* **156** *and similar horiz designs. Multicoloured. W* w **14** (*sideways*). *P* 14.
526 4 c. Type **156** 25 10
527 15 c. Diesel locomotive No. 8 .. .. 75 40
528 20 c. Diesel locomotive No. 1 .. .. 85 80
529 30 c. Free passenger train .. .. .. 1·10 2·00
526/9 .. .. *Set of* 4 2·75 3·00

157 Fiji Blind Society and Rotary Symbols

(Des V. Whiteley Studio. Litho J.W.)

1976 (26 Mar). *40th Anniv of Rotary in Fiji. T* **157** *and similar horiz design. W* w **14** (*sideways*). *P* 13.
530 10 c. ultramarine, pale sage-green and black .. 15 10
531 25 c. multicoloured 40 50
Design:—25 c. Ambulance and Rotary symbol.

158 De Havilland D.H.A.3 Drover 1

(Des P. Powell. Litho Questa)

1976 (1 Sept). *25th Anniv of Air Services. T* **158** *and similar horiz designs. Multicoloured. W* w **14**. *P* 13½ × 14.
532 4 c. Type **158** 40 20
533 15 c. B.A.C. One Eleven 200/400 .. .. 1·00 1·50
534 25 c. Hawker Siddeley H.S.748 .. .. 1·25 1·75
535 30 c. Britten Norman "long nose" Trislander 1·25 3·75
532/5 .. .. *Set of* 4 3·50 6·50

159 The Queen's Visit to Fiji, 1970

160 Map of the World

(Des L. Curtis. Litho Questa)

1977 (7 Feb). *Silver Jubilee. T* **159** *and similar vert designs. Multicoloured. W* w **14**. *P* 13½.

536	10 c. Type **159**	10	10
537	25 c. King Edward's Chair	15	10
538	30 c. Queen wearing cloth-of-gold supertunica	25	15
	w. Wmk inverted	4·75	
536/8	.. .. *Set of* 3	40	30

(Des J.W. Litho Walsall)

1977 (12 Apr). *E.E.C./A.C.P.* Council of Ministers Conference, Fiji. T* **160** *and similar horiz design. Multicoloured. W* w **14** (*sideways*). *P* 14.

539	4 c. Type **160**	10	10
540	30 c. Map of Fiji group..	30	1·00

*A.C.P. = African, Caribbean, Pacific Group.

161 *Hibiscus rosa-sinensis*

(Des V. Whiteley Studio. Litho Walsall)

1977 (27 Aug). *21st Anniv of Fiji Hibiscus Festival. T* **161** *and similar horiz designs. W* w **14** (*sideways*). *P* 14.

541	**161**	4 c. multicoloured	10	10
542	–	15 c. multicoloured	15	15
543	–	30 c. multicoloured	25	25
544	–	35 c. multicoloured	40	50
541/4		.. .. *Set of* 4	80	90

Nos. 542/44 show different varieties of *H rosa-sinensis.*

162 Drua

163 White Hart of Richard II

(Des P. Powell. Litho Questa)

1977 (7 Nov). *Canoes. T* **162** *and similar horiz designs. Multicoloured. W* w **14** (*sideways*). *P* 14.

545	4 c. Type **162**	15	10
546	15 c. Tabilai	30	20
547	25 c. Takai	35	25
548	40 c. Camakua	55	80
545/8	.. .. *Set of* 4	1·25	1·25

(Des C. Abbott. Litho Questa)

1978 (21 Apr). *25th Anniv of Coronation. T* **163** *and similar vert designs. P* 15.

549	25 c. bistre, blue-green and silver	15	20
	a. Sheetlet. Nos. 549/51 × 2	80	
550	25 c. multicoloured	15	20
551	25 c. bistre, blue-green and silver	15	20
549/51	.. .. .. *Set of* 3	40	55

Designs:—No. 549, Type **163**; No. 550, Queen Elizabeth II; No. 551, Banded Iguana.

Nos. 549/51 were printed together in small sheets of 6, containing two *se-tenant* strips of 3, with horizontal gutter margin between.

164 Defence Force surrounding Fokker F.VIIa/3M *Southern Cross*, Suva

(Des A. Theobald. Litho Harrison)

1978 (26 June). *Aviation Anniversaries. T* **164** *and similar horiz designs. Multicoloured. W* w **14** (*sideways*). *P* 14.

552	4 c. Type **164**	20	10
553	15 c. *Southern Cross* prior to leaving Naselai Beach	40	30
554	25 c. Wright Flyer 1	55	60
555	30 c. Bristol F2B "Brisfit"	55	85
552/5	.. .. .. *Set of* 4	1·50	1·60

Anniversaries—25 c. 75th of powered flight; 30 c. 60th of R.A.F.; others, 50th of first trans-Pacific flight by Kingsford-Smith.

165 Shallow Wooden Oil Dish in shape of Human Figure

166 Advent Crown with Candles (Christmas)

(Des J. Cooter. Litho Questa)

1978 (14 Aug). *Fijian Artifacts. T* **165** *and similar multicoloured designs. W* w **14** (*sideways on* 15 *and* 25 *c.*). *P* 14.

556	4 c. Type **165**	10	10
557	15 c. Necklace of cachalot teeth (*horiz*) ..	10	10
558	25 c. Double water bottle (*horiz*)	15	10
559	30 c. Finely carved Ula or throwing club ..	15	15
556/9	.. .. *Set of* 4	35	35

(Des Jennifer Toombs. Litho Harrison)

1978 (30 Oct). *Festivals. T* **166** *and similar horiz designs. Multicoloured. W* w **14** (*sideways*). *P* 14.

560	4 c. Type **166**	10	10
561	15 c. Lamps (Diwali)	15	10
562	25 c. Coffee pot, cups and fruit (Id-Ul-Fitr) ..	20	10
563	40 c. Lion (Chinese New Year)	35	40
560/3	.. .. *Set of* 4	65	60

167 Banded Iguana

(Des L. Curtis and G. Drummond. Litho Questa)

1979 (19 Mar). *Endangered Wildlife. T* **167** *and similar horiz designs. Multicoloured. W* w **14** (*sideways*). *P* 14.

564	4 c. Type **167**	50	10
565	15 c. Tree Frog..	1·00	15
566	25 c. Long-legged Warbler	3·75	40
567	30 c. Pink-billed Parrot Finch..	3·75	2·00
564/7	.. .. *Set of* 4	8·00	2·40

168 Women with Dholak

(Des J.W. Litho Questa)

1979 (11 May). *Centenary of Arrival of Indians. T* **168** *and similar horiz designs. Multicoloured. W* w **14** (*sideways*). *P* 14.

568	4 c. Type **168**	10	10
569	15 c. Men sitting round tanoa..	10	10
570	30 c. Farmer and sugar cane plantation ..	15	10
571	40 c. Sailing ship *Leonidas*	40	25
568/71	.. .. *Set of* 4	60	45

169 Soccer

(Des BG Studio. Litho Questa)

1979 (2 July). *6th South Pacific Games. T* **169** *and similar horiz designs. Multicoloured. W* w **14** (*sideways*). *P* 14.

572	4 c. Type **169**	20	10
573	15 c. Rugby Union	40	20
574	30 c. Lawn tennis	80	80
575	40 c. Weightlifting	80	1·10
572/5	.. .. *Set of* 4	2·00	2·00

170 Indian Child and Map of Fiji

(Des D. Bowen. Litho Walsall)

1979 (17 Sept). *International Year of the Child. T* **170** *and simil horiz designs showing children and map of Fiji. Multicoloure W* w **14** (*sideways*). *P* 14½ × 14.

576	4 c. + 1 c. Type **170**	10	
577	15 c. + 2 c. European child	15	
578	30 c. + 3 c. Chinese child	15	
579	40 c. + 4 c. Fijian child	15	
576/9	.. .. *Set of* 4	45	

171 Old Town Hall, Suva

(Des J.W. Litho Questa (1, 2, 3, 4, 10, 15, 20, 30 c., $5) Harrison (others))

1979 (11 Nov)–**94.** *Architecture. Multicoloured designs T* **171**. *W* w **14** (*sideways* on horiz designs*). *Chalk-surface paper* (1, 2, 3, 4, 10, 15, 20, 30 *c.*, $5). *P* 13½×13 ($1), 13×13 ($2), 13×14 ($5) *or* 14 (*others*).

A. *Without imprint date at foot*

580A	1 c. Type **171**	15	6
	c. Ordinary paper (13.6.80)	70	1·2
581A	2 c. Dudley Church, Suva	45	7
	c. Ordinary paper (13.6.80)	75	1·5
582A	3 c. Fiji International Telecommunications Building, Suva	35	8
	c. Ordinary paper (13.6.80)	85	1·5
583A	5 c. Lautoka Mosque (22.12.80) ..	15	1
	w. Wmk Crown to right of CA ..	†	-
584A	6 c. General Post Office, Suva (22.12.80)	15	5
585A	10 c. Fiji Visitors' Bureau, Suva	20	1
	c. Ordinary paper (13.6.80)	85	1·5
586A	12 c. Public School, Levuka (22.12.80) ..	20	9
587A	15 c. Colonial War Memorial Hospital, Suva	40	3
	c. Ordinary paper (13.6.80)	75	1·5
588A	18 c. Labasa Sugar Mill (22.12.80) ..	20	3
	w. Wmk Crown to right of CA ..	—	15·0
589A	20 c. Rewa Bridge, Nausori	55	3
	c. Ordinary paper (13.6.80)	1·25	1·7
590A	30 c. Sacred Heart Cathedral, Suva (*vert*)	65	5
	c. Ordinary paper (13.6.80)	30	1·2
591A	35 c. Grand Pacific Hotel, Suva (22.12.80)	30	1·0
592A	45 c. Shiva Temple, Suva (22.12.80) ..	40	4
593A	50 c. Serua Island Village (22.12.80) ..	40	4
594A	$1 Solo Rock Lighthouse (30×46 *mm*) (22.12.80)	2·50	1·7
595A	$2 Baker Memorial Hall, Nausori (46×30 *mm*) (22.12.80)	1·40	1·9
595*c*A	$5 Government House, Suva (46×30 *mm*)	2·00	4·0
580A/95*c*A	.. .. .. *Set of* 17	9·00	13·0

B. *With imprint date*

580B	1 c. Type **171** (12.94)	60	1·2
581B	2 c. Dudley Church, Suva (19.11.86) ..	40	2
	c. Ordinary paper (2.84)	30	2
582B	3 c. Fiji International Telecommunications Building, Suva (11.93) ..	1·25	1·7
582*d*B	4 c. Lautoka Mosque (11.93)	1·75	2·5
	e. Ordinary paper (11.91)	1·75	2·5
583B	5 c. As 4 c. (1.84)	30	1
584B	6 c. General Post Office, Suva (15.6.83)	15	1
585B	10 c. Fiji Visitors' Bureau, Suva (*ordinary paper*) (11.91)	1·25	1·7
586B	12 c. Public School, Levuka (11.93) ..	55	1·2
587B	15 c. Colonial War Memorial Hospital, Suva (*ordinary paper*) (11.91) ..	1·25	1·2
589B	20 c. Rewa Bridge, Nausori (11.93) ..	1·50	1·5
593B	50 c. Serua Island Village (*chalk-surfaced paper*) (22.8.94)	1·75	1·7
580B/93B	.. .. .. *Set of* 11	9·50	12·0

*The normal sideways watermark show Crown to left of CA *as seen from the back of the stamp.*

Imprint dates: "1983", Nos. 581Bc, 583B, 584B; "1986", No 581B; "1991", Nos. 581Bc, 582Be, 585B, 587B; "1993", Nos 581B, 582B, 582*d*B, 586B, 589B; "1994", Nos. 580B/1B, 582*d*B 586B, 589B, 593B.

For these designs and similar 8 c. watermarked w **16** see Nos 719/35.

172 *Southern Cross*, 1873

(Des L. Dunn. Litho Secura, Singapore)

1980 (28 Apr). *"London 1980" International Stamp Exhibition Mail-carrying Ships. T* **172** *and similar horiz designs Multicoloured. W* w **14** (*sideways**). *P* 13½.

596	6 c. Type **172**	30	1(
	w. Wmk Crown to right of CA	17·00	
597	20 c. *Levuka*, 1910	40	1(

8 45 c. *Matua*, 1936 . . . . 55 40
9 50 c. *Oronsay*, 1951 . . . . . . 55 55
w. Wmk Crown to right of CA . . . . 17·00
6/9 . . . . *Set of* 4 1·60 1·00
*The normal sideways watermark shows Crown to left of CA, *seen from the back of the stamp.*

173 Sovi Bay

(Des BG Studio. Litho Questa)

980 (18 Aug). *Tourism. T* **173** *and similar horiz designs. Multicoloured. W* w **14** (*sideways*). *P* 13½ × 14.
00 6 c. Type **173** 10 10
01 20 c. Evening scene, Yanuca Island 15 15
02 45 c. Dravuni Beach 20 40
03 50 c. Wakaya Island 20 45
00/3 . . . . *Set of* 4 50 95

174 Official Opening of Parliament, 1979

(Des J. Cooter. Litho J.W.)

980 (6 Oct). 10*th Anniv of Independence. T* **174** *and similar multicoloured designs. W* w **14** (*sideways on* 6 *and* 45 *c.*). *P* 13.
04 6 c. Type **174** 10 10
05 20 c. Fiji coat of arms (*vert*) 15 10
06 45 c. Fiji flag 20 20
07 50 c. Queen Elizabeth II (*vert*). 25 35
04/7 . . . . *Set of* 4 55 60

175 "Coastal Scene" (painting, Semisi Maya)
176 Prince Charles Sailing

(Des J.W. Litho Questa)

1981 (21 Apr). *International Year for Disabled Persons. T* **175** *and similar multicoloured designs. W* w **14** (*sideways on* 6 *and* 35 *c.*). *P* 14.
608 6 c. Type **175** 10 10
609 35 c. "Underwater Scene" (painting, Semisi Maya) 35 30
610 50 c. Semisi Maya (disabled artist) at work (*vert*) 40 40
611 60 c. "Peacock" (painting, Semisi Maya) (*vert*) 45 45
608/11 . . . . *Set of* 4 1·10 1·10

(Des J.W. Litho Questa)

1981 (22 July). *Royal Wedding. T* **176** *and similar vert designs. Multicoloured. W* w **14**. *P* 14.
612 6 c. Wedding bouquet from Fiji 10 10
613 45 c. Type **176** 30 15
614 $1 Prince Charles and Lady Diana Spencer 50 60
612/14 . . . . *Set of* 3 70 75

177 Operator Assistance Centre
178 "Eat Fiji Foods"

(Des A. Theobald. Litho Format)

1981 (17 Aug). *Telecommunications. T* **177** *and similar horiz designs. Multicoloured. W* w **14** (*sideways*). *P* 14.
615 6 c. Type **177** 10 10
616 35 c. Microwave station 45 50
617 50 c. Satellite earth station 60 75
618 60 c. Cable ship *Retriever* 80 90
615/18 . . . . *Set of* 4 1·75 2·00

(Des J.W. Litho Format)

1981 (21 Sept). *World Food Day. W* w **14**. *P* 14½ × 14.
619 **178** 20 c. multicoloured 30 10

179 Ratu Sir Lala Sukuna (first Speaker, Legislative Council)

(Des A. Theobald. Litho Format)

1981 (19 Oct). *Commonwealth Parliamentary Association Conference, Suva. T* **179** *and similar horiz designs. W* w **14** (*sideways*). *P* 14.
620 6 c. black, buff and orange-brown 10 10
621 35 c. multicoloured 30 30
622 50 c. multicoloured 45 45
620/2 . . . . *Set of* 3 75 75
MS623 73 × 53 mm. 60 c. multicoloured . . . . 70 1·00
Designs:—35 c. Mace of the House of Representatives; 50 c. Suva Civic Centre; 60 c. Flags of C.P.A. countries.

180 Bell P-39 Airacobra

(Des A. Theobald. Litho Walsall)

1981 (7 Dec). *World War II Aircraft. T* **180** *and similar horiz designs. Multicoloured. W* w **14** (*sideways*). *P* 14.
624 6 c. Type **180** . . . . 1·00 10
625 18 c. Consolidated PBY-5 Catalina . . . . 1·75 40
626 35 c. Curtiss P-40E Warhawk . . . . . . 2·00 95
627 60 c. Short Singapore III . . . . . . 2·50 5·00
624/7 . . . . *Set of* 4 6·50 5·75

181 Scouts constructing Shelter

(Des B. Melton. Litho Questa)

1982 (22 Feb). 75*th Anniv of Boy Scout Movement. T* **181** *and similar multicoloured designs. W* w **14** (*sideways on* 6 *and* 45 *c.*). *P* 14½.
628 6 c. Type **181** 15 10
629 20 c. Scouts sailing (*vert*) 50 30
630 45 c. Scouts by campfire 85 50
631 60 c. Lord Baden-Powell (*vert*) . . . . 1·00 1·00
628/31 . . . . *Set of* 4 2·25 1·75

182 Fiji Soldiers at U.N. Checkpoint

(Des J.W. Litho Format)

1982 (10 May*). *Disciplined Forces. T* **182** *and similar horiz designs. Multicoloured. W* w **14** (*sideways*). *P* 14.
632 12 c. Type **182** 30 10
633 30 c. Soldiers engaged in rural development 60 45
634 40 c. Police patrol . . . . 1·50 1·25
635 70 c. *Kiro* (minesweeper) . . . . . . 1·50 3·00
632/5 . . . . *Set of* 4 3·50 4·25
*This is the local release date. The Crown Agents released the stamps in London on 3 May.

183 Footballers and Fiji Football Association Logo
184 Bride and Groom leaving St. Paul's

(Des A. Theobald. Litho Walsall)

1982 (15 June). *World Cup Football Championship, Spain. T* **183** *and similar horiz designs. W* w **14** (*sideways**). *P* 14.
636 6 c. rosine, black and lemon 10 10
637 18 c. multicoloured 25 20
w. Wmk Crown to right of CA . . . . 40·00
638 50 c. multicoloured 70 70
639 90 c. multicoloured . . . . 1·10 2·00
w. Wmk Crown to right of CA . . . . 3·50
636/9 . . . . *Set of* 4 1·90 2·75
Designs:—18 c. Footballers and World Cup emblem; 50 c. Footballer and Bernabeu Stadium; 90 c. Footballers and Naranjito (mascot).
*The normal sideways watermark shows Crown to left of CA, *as seen from the back of the stamp.*

(Des C. Abbott. Litho Harrison)

1982 (1 July). 21*st Birthday of Princess of Wales. T* **184** *and similar vert designs. Multicoloured. W* w **14**. *P* 14½ × 14.
640 20 c. Fiji coat of arms 20 15
641 35 c. Lady Diana Spencer at Broadlands, May 1981 . . . . 35 25
642 45 c. Type **184** 40 40
643 $1 Formal portrait . . . . 1·00 2·25
640/3 . . . . *Set of* 4 1·75 2·75

185 Prince Philip
186 Baby Jesus with Mary and Joseph

(Des C. Abbott. Litho Format)

1982 (1 Nov). *Royal Visit. T* **185** *and similar multicoloured designs. W* w **14**. *P* 14.
644 6 c. Type **185** 30 15
645 45 c. Queen Elizabeth II . . . . . . 80 2·25
MS646 128 × 88 mm. Nos. 644/5 and $1 Royal Yacht *Britannia* (*horiz*). Wmk sideways . . . . 2·50 3·00

(Des G. Wilby. Litho Questa)

1982 (22 Nov). *Christmas. T* **186** *and similar horiz designs. Multicoloured. W* w **14** (*sideways*). *P* 14 × 14½.
647 6 c. Type **186** 10 10
648 20 c. Three Wise Men presenting gifts . . 30 20
649 35 c. Carol-singing 45 35
647/9 . . . . *Set of* 3 75 55
MS650 94 × 42 mm. $1 "Faith" (from the "Three Virtues" by Raphael) . . . . . . 1·25 1·50

187 Red-throated Lorikeet
188 Bure in Traditional Village

(Des N. Arlott. Litho Questa)

1983 (14 Feb). *Parrots. T* **187** *and similar vert designs. Multicoloured. W* w **14**. *P* 14.
651 20 c. Type **187** . . . . 1·25 15
652 40 c. Blue-crowned Lory . . . . . . 1·60 40
653 55 c. Masked Shining Parrot . . . . 1·75 1·00
654 70 c. Red Shining Parrot . . . . . . 2·00 2·75
651/4 . . . . *Set of* 4 6·00 3·75

(Des B. Melton. Litho Questa)

1983 (14 Mar). *Commonwealth Day. T* **188** *and similar horiz designs. Multicoloured. W* w **14** (*sideways*). *P* 14.
655 8 c. Type **188** 10 10
656 25 c. Barefoot firewalkers 20 15
657 50 c. Sugar industry 30 35
658 80 c. Kava "Yagona" ceremony 55 70
655/8 . . . . *Set of* 4 1·00 1·10

Fiji 8c
Nawanawa
Cordia subcordata
189 First Manned Balloon Flight, 1783
190 Nawanawa

(Des Harrison. Litho Questa)

1983 (18 July). *Bicentenary of Manned Flight. T* **189** *and similar horiz designs. Multicoloured. W* w **14** (*sideways*). *P* 14.
659 8 c. Type **189** 25 10
660 20 c. Wright brothers' Flyer 1 . . . . 45 30
661 25 c. Douglas Super DC-3 . . . . . . 50 40
662 40 c. De Havilland D.H.106 Comet 1 . . 75 60
663 50 c. Boeing 747 . . . . 90 70
664 58 c. Space Shuttle . . . . 1·00 80
659/64 . . . . *Set of* 6 3·50 2·50

(Des Harrison. Litho Format)

1983 (3 Oct*). *Flowers (1st series). T* **190** *and similar vert designs. Multicoloured. W* w **14**. *P* 14×14½.
665 8 c. Type **190** 10 10
666 25 c. Rosawa 30 30
667 40 c. Wareraga 40 50
668 $1 Saburo .. .. 80 1·40
665/8 .. .. *Set of* 4 1·40 2·00
*This is the local release date. The Crown Agents issued the stamps in London on 26 September.
See also Nos. 680/3.

191 Fijian beating Lali and Earth Satellite Station
192 *Dacryopinax spathularia*

(Des Garden Studio. Litho Questa)

1983 (7 Nov). *World Communications Year. W* w **14**. *P* 13½.
669 **191** 50 c. multicoloured 50 80

(Des Jennifer Toombs. Litho Enschedé)

1984 (9 Jan). *Fungi. T* **192** *and similar multicoloured designs. W* w **14** (*sideways on* 50 *c. and* $1). *P* 13½ × 13 (8 *c. to* 40 *c.*) *or* 13 × 13½ (*others*).
670 8 c. Type **192** 85 15
w. Wmk inverted .. ..
671 15 c. *Podoscypha involuta* .. .. 1·25 25
672 40 c. *Lentinus squarrosulus* .. .. 2·25 1·00
673 50 c. *Scleroderma cepa* ("*Scleroderma flavidum*") (*horiz*) .. .. 2·25 1·25
674 $1 *Phillipsia domingensis* (*horiz*) .. .. 2·75 3·50
670/4 .. .. *Set of* 5 8·50 5·50

193 *Tui Lau* (freighter) on Reef

(Des L. Curtis. Litho Questa)

1984 (7 May). *250th Anniv of "Lloyd's List" (newspaper). T* **193** *and similar vert designs. Multicoloured. W* w **14**. *P* 14½ × 14.
675 8 c. Type **193** 55 10
676 40 c. *Tofua* (cargo liner) .. .. 1·25 80
677 55 c. *Canberra* (liner) .. .. 1·25 1·50
678 60 c. *NedLloyd Madras* (freighter) at Suva wharf .. .. 1·40 1·75
675/8 .. .. *Set of* 4 4·00 3·75

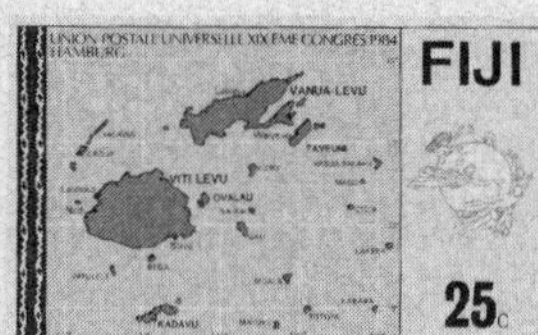

194 Map of Fijian Islands

(Des J. Cooter. Litho Questa)

1984 (14 June). *Universal Postal Union Congress, Hamburg. Sheet* 77 × 65 *mm. W* w **14** (*sideways*). *P* 14½.
MS679 **194** 25 c. multicoloured .. .. 1·50 1·00

(Des Harrison. Litho Format)

1984 (9 July). *Flowers (2nd series). Vert designs as T* **190**. *W* w **14**. *P* 14×14½.
680 15 c. Drividrivi 25 25
681 20 c. Vesida 35 40
682 50 c. Vuga 50 90
683 70 c. Qaiqi .. .. 60 1·40
680/3 .. .. *Set of* 4 1·50 2·75

195 Prize Bull, Yalavou Cattle Scheme

(Des D. Hartley-Marjoram. Litho Walsall)

1984 (17 Sept). *"Ausipex" International Stamp Exhibition, Melbourne. T* **195** *and similar multicoloured designs. W* w **14** (*sideways** *on* 8, 40 *c. and* $1). *P* 14½×14 (25 *c.*) *or* 14×14½ (*others*).
684 8 c. Type **195** 25 10
685 25 c. Wailoa Power Station (*vert*) 55 40
686 40 c. Air Pacific Boeing 737 airliner .. .. 1·40 1·10
687 $1 Container ship *Fua Kavenga* .. .. 1·40 2·75
w. Wmk Crown to right of CA .. .. 1·40
684/7 .. .. *Set of* 4 3·25 3·75
*The normal sideways watermark shows Crown to left of CA, *as seen from the back of the stamp.*

196 The Stable at Bethlehem

(Des G. Vasarhelyi. Litho Format)

1984 (5 Nov). *Christmas. Children's Paintings. T* **196** *and similar multicoloured designs. W* w **14** (*sideways on horiz designs*). *P* 14.
688 8 c. Type **196** 10 10
689 20 c. Outrigger canoe 30 20
690 25 c. Father Christmas and Christmas tree .. 30 25
691 40 c. Going to church 40 70
692 $1 Decorating Christmas tree (*vert*) .. .. 70 1·75
688/92 .. .. *Set of* 5 1·50 2·75

197 *Danaus plexippus*
198 Outrigger Canoe off Toberua Island

(Des Annette Robinson. Litho Questa)

1985 (4 Feb). *Butterflies. T* **197** *and similar multicoloured designs. W* w **14** (*sideways on* 8 *c. and* 25 *c.*). *P* 14.
693 8 c. Type **197** .. .. 1·25 15
694 25 c. *Hypolimnas bolina* .. .. 2·25 60
695 40 c. *Lampides boeticus* (*vert*) .. .. .. 3·00 2·00
696 $1 *Precis villida* (*vert*) .. .. 4·00 6·50
693/6 .. .. *Set of* 4 9·50 8·25

(Des D. Miller. Litho B.D.T.)

1985 (1 Apr). *"Expo '85" World Fair, Japan. T* **198** *and similar vert designs. Multicoloured. W* w **14**. *P* 14.
697 20 c. Type **198** 50 30
698 25 c. Wainivula Falls 85 40
699 50 c. Mana Island 95 90
700 $1 Sawa-I-Lau Caves .. .. 1·25 2·25
697/700 .. .. *Set of* 4 3·25 3·50

199 With Prince Charles at Garter Ceremony
200 Horned Squirrelfish

(Des A. Theobald ($1), C. Abbott (others). Litho Questa)

1985 (7 June). *Life and Times of Queen Elizabeth the Queen Mother. T* **199** *and similar vert designs. Multicoloured. W* w **16**. *P* 14½ × 14.
701 8 c. With Prince Andrew on her 60th Birthday 10 10
702 25 c. Type **199** 35 40
703 40 c. The Queen Mother at Epsom Races .. 50 80
704 50 c. With Prince Henry at his christening (from photo by Lord Snowdon) .. .. 65 1·25
701/4 .. .. *Set of* 4 1·40 2·25
MS705 91 × 73 mm. $1 With Prince Andrew at Royal Wedding, 1981. Wmk sideways .. .. 1·50 2·00

(Des M. Raj. Litho Questa)

1985 (23 Sept). *Shallow Water Marine Fishes. T* **200** *and similar horiz designs. Multicoloured. W* w **14** (*sideways*). *P* 14½.
706 40 c. Type **200** .. .. 1·50 55
707 50 c. Yellow-banded Goatfish .. .. .. 1·75 1·10
708 55 c. Yellow-edged Lyretail ("Fairy Cod") .. 1·75 1·75
709 $1 Peacock Hind .. .. 2·75 4·50
706/9 .. .. *Set of* 4 7·00 7·00

201 Collared Petrel
202 Children and "Peace for Fiji and the World" Slogan

(Des Doreen McGuinness. Litho Walsall)

1985 (4 Nov). *Seabirds. T* **201** *and similar vert design. Multicoloured. W* w **14**. *P* 14 × 13½.
710 15 c. Type **201** .. .. 1·75 5
711 20 c. Lesser Frigate Bird .. .. 2·00 5
712 50 c. Brown Booby .. .. 3·25 3·5
713 $1 Crested Tern .. .. 5·00 7·0
710/13 .. .. *Set of* 4 11·00 10·5

(Des A. Theobald. Litho Format)

1986 (21 Apr). *60th Birthday of Queen Elizabeth II. Ve designs as T* **110** *of Ascension. Multicoloured. W* w 1 *P* 14 × 14½.
714 20 c. With Duke of York at Royal Tournament, 1936 .. .. 20 2
715 25 c. Royal Family on Palace balcony after Princess Margaret's wedding, 1960 .. 20 2
716 40 c. Queen inspecting guard of honour, Suva, 1982 .. .. 25 4
717 50 c. In Luxembourg, 1976 .. .. 30 6
718 $1 At Crown Agents Head Office, London, 1983 .. .. 45 1·6
714/18 .. .. *Set of* 5 1·25 2·7

(Litho Harrison (4 c. (1988 ptg), 8 c.) or Questa (others))

1986 (Apr)–**91**. *As Nos.* 580/2, 582*d*, 585, 587, 589, 591, 593/ *and new value. W* w **16** (*sideways on* 1, 2, 3, 4, 8, 10, 15, 20, 3 50 *c.*). *Chalk-surfaced paper* (2 *c.*). *With imprint date P* 14×13½ ($1) *or* 14 (*others*).
719 1 c. Type **171** (11.3.91) .. .. .. 60 1·2
720 2 c. Dudley Church, Suva 30 3
a. Ordinary paper (11.3.91) 30 3
721 3 c. Fiji International Telecommunications Building, Suva (1.6.88) 30 3
722 4 c. Lautoka Mosque (1.6.88) 30 3
724 8 c. Public School, Levuka (as No. 586) (1.12.86) .. .. 1·50 1·5
725 10 c. Fiji Visitors Bureau, Suva (1.3.90) .. 20 3
726 15 c. Colonial War Memorial Hospital, Suva (11.3.91) 30 2
730 20 c. Rewa Bridge, Nausori (1.6.88) 75 7
732 35 c. Grand Pacific Hotel, Suva (11.3.91) .. 1·10 1·5
734 50 c. Serua Island Village (11.3.91) .. .. 1·60 2·0
735 $1 Solo Rock Lighthouse (30×46 *mm*) (11.3.91) .. .. 4·00 5·0
719/35 .. .. *Set of* 11 10·00 12·0
From the 11 March 1991 printing all values were produced by Questa. The 4 c. (No. 722) was the only stamp in this issue to be printed by both Harrison and Questa.
Imprint dates: "1986", Nos. 720, 724; "1988", Nos. 720/2, 730 "1990", Nos. 725, 730; "1991", Nos. 719, 720a, 721/2, 725/6, 732 734/5; "1992", Nos. 719, 721/2, 726, 730, 732, 734/5.

(Des G. Vasarhelyi. Litho Format)

1986 (23 June). *International Peace Year. T* **202** *and simila vert design. Multicoloured. W* w **16**. *P* 14½.
736 8 c. Type **202** 25 1
737 40 c. Peace dove and houses .. .. .. 65 1·0

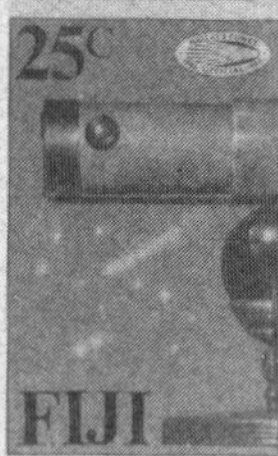

203 Halley's Comet in Centaurus Constellation and Newton's Reflector
204 Ground Frog

(Des D. Hartley. Litho B.D.T.)

1986 (7 July). *Appearance of Halley's Comet. T* **203** *and simila vert designs. Multicoloured. W* w **16**. *P* 13½.
738 25 c. Type **203** .. .. 1·25 4
739 40 c. Halley's Comet over Lomaiviti .. .. 1·50 8
740 $1 *Giotto* spacecraft photographing Comet nucleus .. .. 2·50 4·7
738/40 .. .. *Set of* 3 4·75 5·5

(Litho Format)

1986 (1 Aug). *Reptiles and Amphibians. T* **204** *and simila horiz designs. Multicoloured. W* w **16** (*sideways*). *P* 14½.
741 8 c. Type **204** 55 1
742 20 c. Burrowing Snake .. .. 1·00 3
743 25 c. Spotted Gecko .. .. 1·10 3
744 40 c. Crested Iguana .. .. 1·25 9
745 50 c. Blotched Skink .. .. 1·40 3·0
746 $1 Speckled Skink .. .. 1·75 5·0
741/6 .. .. *Set of* 6 6·25 8·5

205 Gatawaka

206 Weasel Cone (*Conus mustelinus*)

(Des M. Raj. Litho Walsall)

1986 (10 Nov). *Ancient War Clubs. T* **205** *and similar vert designs. Multicoloured. W w* **16**. *P* 14.

747	25 c. Type **205**	80	35
748	40 c. Siriti	1·00	60
749	50 c. Bulibuli	1·25	1·40
750	$1 Culacula	2·25	2·75
747/50	*Set of* 4	4·75	4·50

(Des A. Riley. Litho Format)

1987 (26 Feb). *Cone Shells of Fiji. T* **206** *and similar vert designs. Multicoloured. W w* **16**. *P* 14×14½.

751	15 c. Type **206**	80	25
752	20 c. Pertusus Cone (*Conus pertusus*)	90	35
753	25 c. Admiral Cone (*Conus ammiralis*)	1·00	40
754	40 c. Leaden Cone (*Conus scabriusculus*)	1·40	1·25
755	50 c. Imperial Cone (*Conus imperialis*)	1·50	2·50
	w. Wmk inverted		
756	$1 Geography Cone (*Conus geographus*)	2·00	4·25
	w. Wmk inverted		
751/6	*Set of* 6	7·00	8·00

207 Tagimoucia Flower

(208)

(Des M. Raj. Litho Format)

1987 (23 Apr). *Tagimoucia Flower. Sheet* 72×55 *mm. W w* **14** (*sideways*). *P* 14½.

MS757 **207**	$1 multicoloured	2·75	2·00

1987 (13 June). *"Capex '87" International Stamp Exhibition, Toronto. No.* **MS**757 *optd with T* **208**.

MS758	72×55 mm. $1 Type **207**	5·00	2·00

Stamps from Nos. **MS**757 and **MS**758 are identical as the overprint on **MS**758 appears on the margin of the sheet.

209 Traditional Fijian House

(Des National Focal Point, adapted L. Curtis. Litho Format)

1987 (20 July). *International Year of Shelter for the Homeless. T* **209** *and similar horiz design. Multicoloured. W w* **16** (*sideways*). *P* 14.

759	55 c. Type **209**	45	50
760	70 c. Modern bungalows	55	60

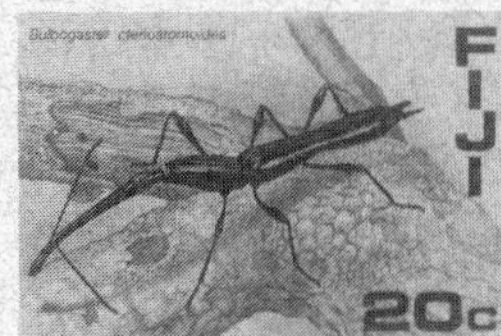

210 *Bulbogaster ctenostomoides* (stick insect)

(Des R. Lewington. Litho Walsall)

1987 (7 Sept). *Fijian Insects. T* **210** *and similar horiz designs. Multicoloured. W w* **16** (*sideways*). *P* 13½×14.

761	20 c. Type **210**	1·25	30
762	25 c. *Paracupta flaviventris* (beetle)	1·40	35
763	40 c. *Cerambyrhynchus schoenherri* (beetle)	1·75	1·25
764	50 c. *Rhinoscapha lagopyga* (weevil)	1·75	2·25
765	$1 *Xixuthrus heros* (beetle)	2·75	5·00
761/5	*Set of* 5	8·00	8·00

REPUBLIC

Following a military coup on 25 September 1987 Fiji was declared a republic on 7 October. The Governor-General resigned on 15 October 1987 and Fiji's Commonwealth membership lapsed until 1 October 1997 when the country was readmitted following further constitutional changes.

211 The Nativity

212 Windsurfer and Beach

(Des G. Vasarhelyi. Litho Walsall)

1987 (19 Nov). *Christmas. T* **211** *and similar multicoloured designs. W w* **16** (*sideways on* 40 *c.*, 50 *c.*). *P* 14×13½ (*vert*) *or* 13½×14 (*horiz*).

766	8 c. Type **211**	40	10
767	40 c. The Shepherds (*horiz*)	1·25	40
768	50 c. The Three Kings (*horiz*)	1·75	90
769	$1 The Three Kings presenting gifts	2·25	2·50
766/9	*Set of* 4	5·00	3·50

(Des Ahgrafik. Litho Questa)

1988 (27 Apr). *"Expo '88" World Fair, Brisbane. W w* **16** (*sideways*). *P* 14.

770 **212**	30 c. multicoloured	1·00	50

213 Woman using Fiji "Nouna" (stove)

214 Pottery Bowl

(Litho Questa)

1988 (14 June). *Centenary of International Council of Women. W w* **16** (*sideways*). *P* 14.

771 **213**	45 c. multicoloured	75	60

(Des N. Ahmed. Litho Questa)

1988 (29 Aug). *Ancient Fijian Pottery. T* **214** *and similar multicoloured designs. W w* **14** (*sideways*) (69 *c.*) *or w* **16** (*others, sideways on* 75 *c.*). *P* 14.

772	9 c. Type **214**	15	10
773	23 c. Cooking pot	25	25
774	58 c. Priest's drinking vessel	50	90
775	63 c. Drinking vessel	55	1·10
776	69 c. Earthenware oil lamp	60	1·25
777	75 c. Cooking pot with relief pattern (*vert*)	70	1·40
772/7	*Set of* 6	2·50	4·50

215 Fiji Tree Frog

216 *Dendrobium mohlianum*

(Des Doreen McGuinness. Litho Walsall)

1988 (3 Oct). *Fiji Tree Frog. T* **215** *and similar vert designs. Multicoloured. W w* **16**. *P* 14×13½.

778	18 c. Type **215**	1·60	50
779	23 c. Frog climbing grass stalks	1·75	1·10
780	30 c. On leaf	2·25	2·50
781	45 c. Moving from one leaf to another	3·00	4·00
778/81	*Set of* 4	7·75	7·25

(Des M. Raj. Litho Walsall)

1988 (21 Nov). *Native Flowers. T* **216** *and similar vert designs. Multicoloured. W w* **14**. *P* 14.

782	9 c. Type **216**	45	15
783	30 c. *Dendrobium cattilare*	70	45
784	45 c. *Degeneria vitiensis*	70	70
785	$1 *Degeneria roseiflora*	1·25	2·00
782/5	*Set of* 4	2·75	3·00

217 Battle of Solferino, 1859

(Des L. Curtis. Litho Questa)

1989 (6 Feb). *125th Anniv of International Red Cross. T* **217** *and similar designs. W w* **16** (*sideways on* 58, 69 *c.*). *P* 13½ × 14 (*horiz*) *or* 14 × 13½ (*vert*).

786	58 c. multicoloured	90	80
787	63 c. multicoloured	1·00	1·00
788	69 c. multicoloured	1·25	1·25
789	$1 black and bright scarlet	1·40	1·50
786/9	*Set of* 4	4·00	4·00

Designs: *Vert*—63 c. Henri Dunant (founder); $1 Anniversary logo. *Horiz*—69 c. Fijian Red Cross worker with blood donor.

218 Plan of *Bounty*'s Launch

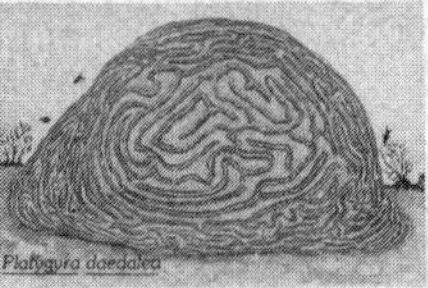

219 *Platygyra daedalea*

(Des Jennifer Toombs. Litho Questa)

1989 (28 Apr). *Bicentenary of Captain Bligh's Boat Voyage. T* **218** *and similar horiz designs. Multicoloured. W w* **16** (*sideways*). *P* 14×14½.

790	45 c. Type **218**	1·50	50
791	58 c. Cup, bowl and Bligh's journal	1·60	1·25
792	80 c. Bligh and extract from journal	2·00	2·75
793	$1 *Bounty*'s launch and map of Fiji	2·75	3·00
790/3	*Set of* 4	7·00	6·75

(Des M. Raj. Litho Harrison)

1989 (21 Aug). *Corals. T* **219** *and similar multicoloured designs. W w* **14** (*sideways on* 46, 60 *c.*). *P* 14.

794	46 c. Type **219**	1·75	75
795	60 c. *Caulastrea furcata*	2·00	1·75
796	75 c. *Acropora echinata* (*vert*)	2·25	2·25
797	90 c. *Acropora humilis* (*vert*)	2·50	2·75
794/7	*Set of* 4	7·75	6·75

220 Goalkeeper

221 Congregation in Church

(Des S. Noon. Litho Questa)

1989 (25 Sept). *World Cup Football Championship, Italy* (1990). *T* **220** *and similar horiz designs. Multicoloured. W w* **16** (*sideways*). *P* 14×14½.

798	35 c. Type **220**	1·00	40
799	63 c. Goalkeeper catching ball	1·75	2·00
800	70 c. Player with ball	1·90	2·25
801	85 c. Tackling	2·00	2·75
798/801	*Set of* 4	6·00	6·75

(Des L. Curtis. Litho Questa)

1989 (1 Nov). *Christmas. T* **221** *and similar vert designs. Multicoloured. W w* **14**. *P* 14½×14.

802	9 c. Type **221**	25	10
803	45 c. *Delonix regia* (Christmas tree)	75	35
804	$1 The Nativity	1·50	2·00
805	$1.40, Fijian children under *Delonix regia* (tree)	1·75	3·00
802/5	*Set of* 4	3·75	5·00

222 River Snapper

223 1968 3d. Eastern Reef Heron Definitive

(Des M. Raj. Litho Questa)

1990 (23 Apr). *Freshwater Fishes. T* **222** *and similar horiz designs. Multicoloured. W* w **16** (*sideways*). *P* 14½.

806 50 c. Type **222** . . . . 2·00 70
807 70 c. Kner's Grunter ("Orange-spotted Therapon") . . . . 2·50 2·75
808 85 c. Spotted Scat . . . . 2·75 3·00
809 $1 Rock Flagtail . . . . 3·25 3·75
806/9 . . . . *Set of* 4 9·50 9·25

(Des D. Miller. Litho Questa)

1990 (1 May). *"Stamp World London 90" International Stamp Exhibition, London. Sheet,* 120×70 *mm, containing T* **223** *and similar vert design. Multicoloured. W* w **16** (*sideways*). *P* 14.

MS810 $1 Type **223**; $2 1968 1s. 6d. Orange-breasted Honeyeaters definitive . . . . 6·00 7·50

224 Vertiver Grass Contours

225 *Dacrydium nidulum*

(Des Ahgrafik. Litho Questa)

1990 (23 July). *Soil Conservation. T* **224** *and similar multicoloured designs. W* w **14** (*sideways on* 50, 70, 90 *c.*). *P* 14.

811 50 c. Type **224** 85 50
812 70 c. Mulching . . . . 1·10 1·50
813 90 c. Hillside contour cultivation . . . . 1·40 1·90
814 $1 Land use rotation (*vert*) . . . . 1·50 2·25
811/14 . . . . *Set of* 4 4·25 5·50

(Des M. Raj. Litho Questa)

1990 (2 Oct). *Timber Trees. T* **225** *and similar vert designs. Multicoloured. W* w **14**. *P* 14.

815 25 c. Type **225** 65 20
816 35 c. *Decussocarpus vitiensis* 75 30
817 $1 *Agathis vitiensis* . . . . 2·25 2·75
818 $1.55, *Santalum yasi* . . . . 3·00 4·50
815/18 . . . . *Set of* 4 6·00 7·00

226 "Hark the Herald Angels sing"

227 Sigatoka Sand Dunes

(Des Jennifer Toombs. Litho Walsall)

1990 (26 Nov). *Christmas. Carols. T* **226** *and similar horiz designs. Multicoloured. W* w **14** (*sideways*). *P* 14.

819 10 c. Type **226** 25 10
820 35 c. "Still the Night, Holy the Night" . . 60 30
821 65 c. "Joy to the World!" . . . . 1·00 1·50
822 $1 "The Race that long in Darkness pined" 1·75 2·50
819/22 . . . . *Set of* 4 3·25 4·00

(Des L. Curtis. Litho Leigh-Mardon Ltd, Melbourne)

1991 (25 Feb). *Environmental Protection. T* **227** *and similar square designs. Multicoloured. P* 14.

823 35 c. Type **227** . . . . 1·00 30
824 50 c. Monu and Monuriki Islands . . . . 1·50 90
825 65 c. Ravilevu Nature Reserve, Taveuni . . 1·60 2·25
826 $1 Colo-I-Suva Forest Park . . . . 2·50 3·25
823/6 . . . . *Set of* 4 6·00 6·00

228 H.M.S. *Pandora* (frigate)

229 *Scylla serrata*

(Des D. Miller. Litho Questa)

1991 (8 Aug). *Bicentenary of Discovery of Rotuma Island. T* **228** *and similar horiz designs. Multicoloured. W* w **14** (*sideways*). *P* 14.

827 54 c. Type **228** . . . . 1·75 85
828 70 c. Map of Rotuma . . . . . . 2·00 2·25
829 75 c. Natives welcoming H.M.S. *Pandora* . . 2·00 2·25
830 $1 Mount Soloroa and Uea Island . . 2·75 3·50
827/30 . . . . *Set of* 4 7·75 8·00

(Des Katrina Hindle. Litho Questa)

1991 (26 Sept). *Mangrove Crabs. T* **229** *and similar horiz designs. Multicoloured. W* w **14** (*sideways*). *P* 14×14½.

831 38 c. Type **229** 70 35
832 54 c. *Metopograpsus messor* 95 85
833 96 c. *Parasesarma erythrodactyla* . . 1·75 2·50
834 $1.65, *Cardisoma carnifex* . . . . 2·50 3·75
831/4 . . . . *Set of* 4 5·50 6·75

230 Mary and Joseph travelling to Bethlehem

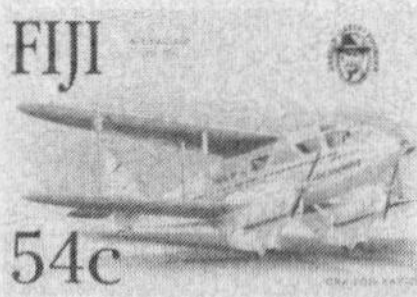

231 De Havilland D.H.89 Dragon Rapide of Fiji Airways

(Des A. Wheatcroft. Litho Leigh-Mardon Ltd, Melbourne)

1991 (31 Oct). *Christmas. T* **230** *and similar horiz designs. Multicoloured. W* w **16**. *P* 14.

835 11 c. Type **230** 30 10
a. Error. Wmk w **14** . . . . . . † —
836 75 c. Manger scene . . . . . . 1·25 1·25
837 96 c. Presentation in the Temple . . . . 1·50 2·50
838 $1 Infant Jesus with symbols . . . . 1·60 2·50
835/8 . . . . *Set of* 4 4·25 5·75

(Des D. Wood. Litho Questa)

1991 (18 Nov). *40th Anniv of Air Pacific. T* **231** *and similar horiz designs. Multicoloured. W* w **16** (*sideways*). *P* 14½.

839 54 c. Type **231** . . . . 1·50 1·00
840 75 c. Douglas DC-3 . . . . . . 2·00 2·25
841 96 c. Aerospatiale/Aeritalia ATR 42 . . 2·25 2·75
842 $1.40, Boeing 767 . . . . . . 2·75 3·50
839/42 . . . . *Set of* 4 7·75 8·50

232 Ethnic Dancers

(Des. W. Addison. Litho Leigh-Mardon Ltd, Melbourne)

1992 (23 Mar). *"Expo 92" World's Fair, Seville, Spain. T* **232** *and similar horiz designs. W* w **14** (*sideways*). *P* 14½×14.

843 27 c. Type **232** 55 40
844 75 c. Peoples of Fiji . . . . . . 1·25 1·75
845 96 c. Gold bars and sugar cane train . . 3·50 3·75
846 $1.40, *Queen Elizabeth 2* (cruise liner) at Suva . . . . 3·75 4·00
843/6 . . . . *Set of* 4 8·00 9·00

233 *Tabusoro*

234 Running

(Des O. Bell. Litho Walsall)

1992 (22 June). *Inter-Islands Shipping. T* **233** *and similar horiz designs. Multicoloured. W* w **14** (*sideways*). *P* 13½×14.

847 38 c. Type **233** . . . . 1·50 55
848 54 c. *Degei II* . . . . 2·00 1·40
849 $1.40, *Dausoko* . . . . . . 3·25 3·75
850 $1.65, *Nivanga* . . . . . . 3·25 3·75
847/50 . . . . *Set of* 4 9·00 8·50

(Des M. Chandler. Litho Enschedé)

1992 (30 July). *Olympic Games, Barcelona. T* **234** *and similar vert designs. Multicoloured. W* w **14**. *P* 13½.

851 20 c. Type **234** 65 20
852 86 c. Yachting . . . . 2·25 2·25
853 $1.34, Swimming . . . . . . 2·75 3·25
854 $1.50, Judo . . . . 2·75 3·25
851/4 . . . . *Set of* 4 7·75 8·00

235 European War Memorial, Levuka

(Des L. Curtis. Litho Leigh-Mardon Ltd, Melbourne)

1992 (21 Sept). *Historic Levuka (former capital). T* **235** *and similar multicoloured designs. W* w **14** (*sideways on horiz designs*). *P* 14½.

855 30 c. Type **235** 30 30
856 42 c. Map of Fiji 45 55
857 59 c. Beach Street . . . . 65 1·00
858 77 c. Sacred Heart Church (*vert*) . . . . 80 1·50
859 $2 Deed of Cession site (*vert*) . . . . 1·75 3·25
855/9 . . . . *Set of* 5 3·50 6·00

236 The Nativity

(Des G. Vasarhelyi. Litho Leigh-Mardon Ltd, Melbourne)

1992 (17 Nov). *Christmas. T* **236** *and similar horiz designs. Multicoloured. W* w **14** (*sideways*). *P* 15×14½.

860 12 c. Type **236** 40 10
861 77 c. Shepherds and family giving presents 1·60 1·60
862 83 c. Shepherds at manger and giving presents to pensioners . . . . 1·75 1·75
863 $2 Wise Men and collecting Fiji produce 3·25 4·50
860/3 . . . . *Set of* 4 6·25 7·00

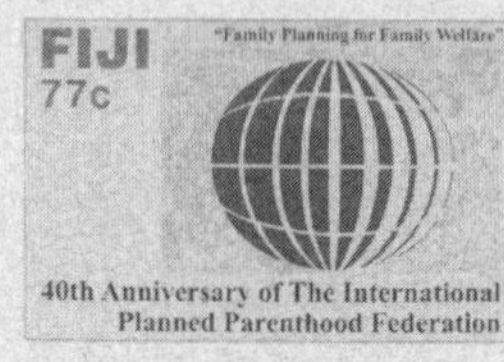

237 International Planned Parenthood Federation Logo

(Des D. Bowen. Litho Leigh-Mardon Ltd, Melbourne)

1992 (2 Dec). *40th Anniv of International Planned Parenthood Federation. T* **237** *and similar horiz design. Multicoloured. W* w **14** (*sideways*). *P* 15×14½.

864 77 c. Type **237** 85 85
865 $2 Man weeping and pregnant mother with children . . . . 2·50 3·25

238 Dove and Peace Corps Emblem

239 Fijian Players performing Cibi (traditional dance)

(Des O. Bell. Litho Leigh-Mardon Ltd, Melbourne)

1993 (22 Feb). *25th Anniv of Peace Corps in Fiji. T* **238** *and similar horiz designs. Multicoloured. W* w **14**. *P* 14½.

866 59 c. Type **238** 85 75
867 77 c. Handshake . . . . 1·10 1·40
868 $1 Educational symbols . . . . . . 1·50 1·75
869 $2 Symbols of home businesses scheme 2·25 3·25
866/9 . . . . *Set of* 4 5·00 6·50

(Des R. Larson. Litho Questa)

1993 (26 Mar). *Hong Kong Rugby Sevens Competition. T* **239** *and similar vert designs. Multicoloured. W* w **16**. *P* 14×15.

870 77 c. Type **239** . . . . 1·25 1·40
871 $1.06, Players and map of Pacific . . 1·75 2·50
872 $2 Scrum and stadium . . . . . . 2·75 3·50
870/2 . . . . *Set of* 3 5·25 6·75

(Des A. Theobald. Litho Questa)

1993 (1 Apr). *75th Anniv of Royal Air Force. Horiz designs as T* **149** *of Ascension. Multicoloured. W* w **14** (*sideways*). *P* 14.

873 59 c. Gloster Gauntlet II 90 75
874 77 c. Armstrong Whitworth Whitley Mk V 1·10 1·40
875 83 c. Bristol F2b "Brisfit" . . . . . . 1·25 1·60
876 $2 Hawker Tempest Mk V . . . . 1·90 3·00
873/6 . . . . *Set of* 4 4·75 6·00

MS877 110×77 mm. $1 Vickers Vildebeest III; $1 Handley Page Hampden; $1 Vickers FB-27 Vimy; $1 British Aerospace Hawk T.1. . . 4·50 5·50

240 *Chromodoris fidelis*

241 Mango

(Des G. Drummond. Litho Leigh-Mardon Ltd, Melbourne)

1993 (27 July). *Nudibranchs. T* **240** *and similar horiz designs. Multicoloured.* W w **14**. *P* 14.

878 12 c. Type **240** 40 10
879 42 c. *Halgerda carlsoni* 90 55
880 53 c. *Chromodoris lochi* .. .. 1·25 1·00
881 83 c. Blue Sea Lizard (*Glaucus atlanticus*) 1·75 2·00
882 $1 *Phyllidia bourguini* .. .. 1·90 2·25
883 $2 Spanish Dancer (*Hexabranchus sanguineus*) .. .. 3·00 3·75
878/83 .. .. *Set of* 6 8·25 8·75

(Des Katrina Hindle. Litho Cartor)

1993 (25 Oct). *Tropical Fruits. T* **241** *and similar vert designs. Multicoloured.* W w **14**. *P* 13½.

884 30 c. Type **241** 85 45
885 42 c. Guava .. .. 1·10 80
886 $1 Lemon .. .. 2·25 2·25
887 $2 Soursop .. .. 4·00 4·50
884/7 .. .. *Set of* 4 7·50 7·25

242 *Anaphaesis java*

243 The Last Supper

(Des I. Loe and D. Miller. Litho Enschedé (No. **MS**889))

1994 (18 Feb). *"Hong Kong '94" International Stamp Exhibition.*

(*a*) *No.* **MS**877 *optd as T* **154** *of Ascension on each stamp*

MS888 110×77 mm. $1 Vickers Vildebeest III; $1 Handley Page Hampden; $1 Vickers FB-27 Vimy; $1 British Aerospace Hawk T.1 .. 4·50 6·00

(*b*) *Sheet 122×85 mm containing T* **242** *and similar vert designs showing butterflies. Multicoloured.* W w **14** (*sideways*). *P* 14½×13.

MS889 $1 Type **242**; $1 *Euploea leucostictos*; $1 *Vagrans egista*; $1 *Acraea andromache* .. 4·50 6·00

No. **MS**888 also shows "HONG KONG '94 EXHIBITION" overprinted on the bottom margin.

(Des R. Larson. Litho Enschedé)

1994 (31 Mar). *Easter. T* **243** *and similar multicoloured designs.* W w **14** (*sideways on horiz designs*). *P* 14×15 (*horiz*) *or* 15×14 (*vert*).

890 59 c. Type **243** 80 60
891 77 c. The Crucifixion (*vert*) .. .. 1·00 1·25
892 $1 The Resurrection .. .. 1·60 2·00
893 $2 Examining Christ's wounds (*vert*) .. 2·75 4·00
890/3 .. .. *Set of* 4 5·50 7·00

244 Sagati

245 White-collared Kingfisher on Branch

(Des I. Loe. Litho Walsall)

1994 (6 June). *Edible Seaweeds. T* **244** *and similar vert designs. Multicoloured.* W w **16**. *P* 14½×14.

894 42 c. Type **244** 80 45
895 83 c. Nama .. .. 1·50 1·75
896 $1 Lumicevata .. .. 2·00 2·25
897 $2 Lumiwawa .. .. 3·25 4·50
894/7 .. .. *Set of* 4 6·75 8·00

(Des Doreen McGuinness. Litho Questa)

1994 (16 Aug). *White-collared Kingfisher. Sheet 98×84 mm, containing T* **245** *and similar vert design. Multicoloured.* W w **14**. *P* 14×13½.

MS898 $1.50, Type **245**; $1.50, Kingfisher with crab in beak .. .. 6·50 7·00

246 *Neoveitchia storckii*

247 Father Ioane Batita

(Des N. Shewring. Litho Questa)

1994 (31 Aug). *"Singpex '94" International Stamp Exhibition. Endemic Palm. Sheet 97×69 mm, containing T* **246** *and similar vert design. Multicoloured.* W w **16**. *P* 14.

MS899 $1.50, Type **246**; $1.50, Palm flowers .. 5·50 6·50

(Des S. Noon. Litho Leigh-Mardon Ltd, Melbourne)

1994 (16 Dec). *150th Anniv of Arrival of Catholic Missionaries in Fiji. T* **247** *and similar vert designs.* W w **14**. *P* 14.

900 23 c. Type **247** 25 25
901 31 c. Local catechist 30 30
902 44 c. Sacred Heart Cathedral, Suva .. 40 60
903 63 c. Lomary Church 55 85
904 81 c. Pope Gregory XVI .. .. .. 90 1·25
905 $2 Pope John Paul II .. .. .. 2·00 2·75
900/5 .. .. *Set of* 6 4·00 5·50

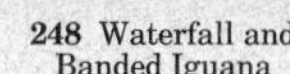

248 Waterfall and Banded Iguana

249 Fiji ("Red-headed") Parrot Finch

(Des B. Dare. Litho Questa)

1995 (27 Mar). *Eco-Tourism in Fiji. Sheet 140×80 mm containing T* **248** *and similar square designs. Multicoloured.* W w **16** (*sideways*). *P* 14.

MS906 81 c. Type **248**; 81 c. Mountain trekkers and Fiji Tree Frog; 81 c. Bilibili River trip and White-collared Kingfisher; 81 c. Historic sites and Flying Fox .. .. 4·25 5·00

(Des R. Watton. Litho Cartor (Nos. 907/10) or Questa (No. **MS**911))

1995 (8 May). *50th Anniv of End of Second World War. Multicoloured designs as T* **161** *of Ascension.* W w **14** (*sideways*). *P* 13½.

907 13 c. Fijian soldiers guarding crashed Japanese Mitsubishi A6M Zero-Sen aircraft 50 20
908 63 c. American spotter plane landing on Kameli Airstrip, Solomon Islands .. 1·40 1·25
909 87 c. Corporal Sukanaivalu and Victoria Cross .. .. 1·75 2·25
910 $1.12, H.M.S. *Fiji* (cruiser) .. .. 2·25 2·50
907/10 .. .. *Set of* 4 5·50 5·50

MS911 75×85 mm. $2 Reverse of 1939–45 War Medal (*vert*). Wmk upright. P 14 .. .. 2·25 2·75

(Des A. Robinson. Litho Enschedé)

1995 (25 July–7 Nov). *Birds. T* **249** *and similar vert designs. Multicoloured.* W w **14**. *P* 13½×13.

912 1 c. Type **249** (7 Nov) 10 10
913 2 c. Golden Whistler (7 Nov) 10 10
914 3 c. Versicoloured Flycatcher ("Ogea Flycatcher") (7 Nov) 10 10
915 4 c. Peale's Pigeon (7 Nov) 10 10
916 6 c. Blue-headed Flycatcher ("Blue-crested Broadbill") (7 Nov) 10 10
917 13 c. Island Thrush 10 10
918 23 c. Many-coloured Fruit Dove 15 20
919 31 c. Green Heron ("Mangrove Heron") .. 20 25
920 44 c. Purple Swamphen 25 30
921 63 c. Fiji Goshawk 40 45
922 81 c. Kandavu Fantail ("Kadavu Fantail") 50 55
923 87 c. Collared Lory (7 Nov) 55 60
924 $1 Scarlet Robin (7 Nov) 60 65
925 $2 Peregrine Falcon .. .. .. 1·25 1·40
926 $3 Barn Owl .. .. 1·75 1·90
927 $5 Masked Shining Parrot ("Yellow-breasted Musk Parrot") (7 Nov) .. 3·00 3·25
912/27 .. .. *Set of* 16 9·25 10·00

1995 (19 Aug). *"JAKARTA '95" Stamp Exhibition, Indonesia. No.* **MS**898 *optd "JAKARTA '95" and emblem on sheet margin.*

MS928 $1.50, Type **245**; $1.50, Kingfisher with crab in beak .. .. 5·50 6·50

250 *Arundina graminifolia*

251 Pres. Ratu Sir Kamisese Mara, Parliament Building and National Flag

(Des I. Loe. Litho Questa)

1995 (1 Sept). *Orchids. Sheet 100×80 mm, containing T* **250** *and similar vert design.* W w **16**. *P* 14.

MS929 $1 Type **250**; $1 *Phaius tankervilliae* .. 3·25 3·75

No. **MS**929 also includes "Singapore '95" and emblem on the sheet margin.

(Des S. Noon. Litho B.D.T.)

1995 (4 Oct). *25th Anniv of Independence. T* **251** *and similar horiz designs. Multicoloured.* W w **14** (*sideways*). *P* 13½.

930 81 c. Type **251** .. .. 90 1·00
931 87 c. Young citizens of Fiji .. .. .. 95 1·10
932 $1.06, Rugby players .. .. .. 1·25 1·60
933 $2 Boeing 747 *Island of Viti Levu* .. 2·25 2·75
930/3 .. .. *Set of* 4 4·75 5·75

252 "Praying Madonna with the Crown of Stars" (workshop of Correggio)

253 Trolling Lure

(Des D. Miller. Litho Cartor)

1995 (22 Nov). *Christmas. T* **252** *and similar vert designs. Multicoloured.* W w **14**. *P* 13×13½.

934 10 c. Type **252** 20 10
935 63 c. "Madonna and Child with Crowns" (on porcelain) 80 80
936 87 c. "The Holy Virgin with the Holy Child and St. John" (after Titian) .. .. 1·10 1·25
937 $2 "The Holy Family and St. John" (workshop of Rubens) .. .. .. 2·50 3·50
934/7 .. .. *Set of* 4 4·25 5·00

(Des B. Dare. Litho Walsall)

1996 (24 Jan). *50th Anniv of Resettlement of Banabans (inhabitants of Ocean Island) in Fiji. T* **253** *and similar multicoloured designs.* W w **14** (*sideways on horiz designs*). *P* 14½.

938 81 c. Type **253** .. .. 90 1·10
939 87 c. Banaban fishing canoes .. .. .. 95 1·10
940 $1.12, Banaban warrior (*vert*) .. .. 1·25 1·75
941 $2 Great Frigate Bird (*vert*) .. .. 3·25 3·75
938/41 .. .. *Set of* 4 5·75 7·00

254 L2B Portable Tape Recorder

255 Winged Monster and Ring (bronze), *c* 450 B.C.

(Des N. Shewring. Litho Walsall)

1996 (11 Mar). *Centenary of Radio. T* **254** *and similar vert designs. Multicoloured.* W w **14**. *P* 14½×14.

942 44 c. Type **254** 55 45
943 63 c. Broadcasting House, Fiji 75 70
944 81 c. Communications satellite .. .. 90 1·25
945 $3 Guglielmo Marconi .. .. .. 3·50 4·75
942/5 .. .. *Set of* 4 5·25 6·50

(Des G. Vasarhelyi. Litho B.D.T.)

1996 (25 Apr). *"CHINA '96" 9th Asian International Stamp Exhibition, Peking. T* **255** *and similar vert designs. Multicoloured.* W w **16**. *P* 13½.
946 63 c. Type **255** 75 65
947 81 c. Archer (terracotta sculpture), 210 B.C. 90 1·10
948 $1 Dragon plate, 1426–35 . . . . . . 1·25 1·50
949 $2 Central Asian horseman (sculpture), 706 . . . . 2·75 3·50
946/9 . . . . *Set of* 4 5·00 6·00
MS950 81×127 mm. 30 c. "Yan Deng Mountains" (painting) (48½×76 *mm*). Wmk sideways. P 13 . . . . 80 1·00

256 Hurdling

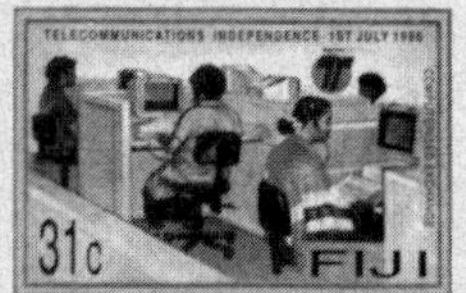
257 Computerised Telephone Exchange

(Des S. Noon. Litho Southern Colour Print, Dunedin, New Zealand)

1996 (18 June). *Centenary of Modern Olympic Games. T* **256** *and similar vert designs. Multicoloured.* W w **14**. *P* 14.
951 31 c. Type **256** 45 30
952 63 c. Judo 85 70
953 87 c. Sailboarding . . . . 1·10 1·25
954 $1.12, Swimming . . . . 1·40 1·75
951/4 . . . . *Set of* 4 3·50 3·50
MS955 59×99 mm. $2 Winning athlete, 1896. Wmk sideways . . . . 2·10 2·50

(Des G. Vasarhelyi. Litho Walsall)

1996 (1 July). *Inauguration of Independent Postal and Telecommunications Companies. T* **257** *and similar multicoloured designs.* W w **14** (*sideways on horiz designs*). *P* 14.
956 31 c. Type **257** 35 30
957 44 c. Unloading mail from aircraft . . 60 55
958 81 c. Manual telephone exchange (*vert*) . . 90 1·25
959 $1 Postman on motorbike (*vert*) . . 1·25 1·75
956/9 . . . . *Set of* 4 2·75 3·50
MS960 120×77 mm. $1.50, Fiji 1938 ½d. Sailing canoe stamp (*vert*); $1.50, Fiji 1985 20 c. "Expo '85" stamp (*vert*) . . . . *Set of 2 sheets* 3·25 4·00

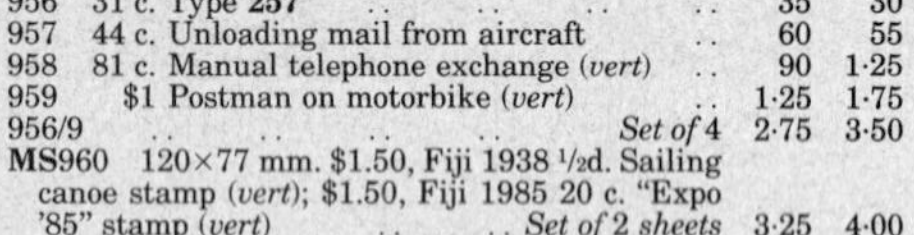

258 "Our Children Our Future"

(Adapted Jennifer Toombs. Litho Questa)

1996 (13 Aug). *50th Anniv of U.N.I.C.E.F. Children's Paintings. T* **258** *and similar horiz designs. Multicoloured.* W w **16** (*sideways*). *P* 14½.
961 81 c. Type **258** . . . . 1·00 85
962 87 c. "Village Scene" . . . . 1·10 95
963 $1 "Living in Harmony the World over" 1·25 1·50
964 $2 "Their Future" . . . . 2·25 3·25
961/4 . . . . *Set of* 4 5·00 6·00

259 First Seaplane in Fiji, 1921

(Des N. Shewring. Litho Walsall)

1996 (1 Oct). *50th Anniv of Nadi International Airport. T* **259** *and similar horiz designs. Multicoloured.* W w **16** (*sideways*). *P* 14.
965 31 c. Type **259** 40 30
966 44 c. Nadi Airport in 1946 . . . . . . 60 50
967 63 c. Arrival of first jet airliner, 1959 . . 80 80
968 87 c. Airport entrance . . . . 1·10 1·25
969 $1 Control tower . . . . 1·40 1·75
970 $2 Diagram of Global Positioning System 2·25 3·50
965/70 . . . . *Set of* 6 6·00 7·25

260 The Annunciation and Fijian beating Lali (drum)

(Des M. Raj. Litho Questa)

1996 (20 Nov). *Christmas. T* **260** *and similar horiz designs. Multicoloured.* W w **14** (*sideways*). *P* 13½×14.
971 13 c. Type **260** 20 15
972 81 c. Shepherds with sheep, and canoe . . 90 85
973 $1 Wise men on camels, and people on cross . . . . 1·25 1·40
974 $3 The Nativity, and Fijian blowing conch 3·25 4·50
971/4 . . . . *Set of* 4 5·00 6·25

261 Brahman

262 Black-throated Shrikebill

(Des G. Vasarhelyi. Litho B.D.T.)

1997 (12 Feb). *"HONG KONG '97" International Stamp Exhibition. Cattle. Sheet 130×92 mm, containing T* **261** *and similar horiz designs. Multicoloured.* W w **14** (*sideways*). *P* 14.
MS975 $1 Type **261**; $1 Friesian (Holstein); $1 Hereford; $1 Fiji draught bullock . . . . 4·00 4·50
No. **MS**975 is inscribed "FREISIAN" in error

(Des A. Robinson and Jennifer Toombs. Litho B.D.T.)

1997 (21 Feb). *"SINGPEX '97" Stamp Exhibition, Singapore. Sheet 92×78 mm.* W w **14**. *P* 14×15.
MS976 **262** $2 multicoloured . . . . . . 2·10 2·75

263 *Dendrobium biflorum*

264 Hawksbill Turtle laying Eggs

(Des M. Raj. Litho B.D.T.)

1997 (22 Apr). *Orchids. T* **263** *and similar vert designs. Multicoloured.* W w **16**. *P* 14.
977 81 c. Type **263** 90 90
978 87 c. *Dendrobium dactylodes* 95 95
979 $1.06, *Spathoglottis pacifica* . . . . 1·10 1·40
980 $2 *Dendrobium macropus* . . . . 2·25 2·75
977/80 . . . . *Set of* 4 4·75 5·50

(Des Sue Wickison. Litho B.D.T.)

1997 (26 May). *Life Cycle of Hawksbill Turtle. Sheet 140×85 mm, containing T* **264** *and similar horiz designs. Multicoloured.* W w **14** (*sideways*). *P* 14.
MS981 63 c. Type **264**; 81 c. Turtles hatching; $1.06, Young turtles swimming; $2 Adult turtle 4·50 5·50

265 Branching Hard Coral

266 Fijian Monkey-faced Bat

(Des M. Raj. Litho Walsall)

1997 (16 July). *Year of the Coral Reef. T* **265** *and similar horiz designs. Multicoloured.* W w **16** (*sideways*). *P* 14.
982 63 c. Type **265** 70 55
983 87 c. Massive Hard Coral . . . . . . 1·00 1·00
984 $1 White Soft Coral . . . . . . 1·25 1·50
985 $3 Pink Soft Coral . . . . . . 3·50 4·25
982/5 . . . . *Set of* 4 5·75 6·50

(Des Sue Wickison. Litho Enschedé)

1997 (15 Oct). *Endangered Species. Fijian Monkey-faced Bat. T* **266** *and similar vert designs showing bats. P* 13½.
986 44 c. multicoloured 50 40
987 63 c. multicoloured 70 55
988 81 c. multicoloured . . . . 95 1·00
989 $2 multicoloured . . . . 2·25 3·00
986/9 . . . . *Set of* 4 4·00 4·50
MS990 157×106 mm. Nos. 986/9, each × 2 . . 8·00 8·25

267 Waisale Serevi (Captain)

268 Shepherd and Angel

(Des G. Vasarhelyi. Litho Walsall)

1997 (31 Oct). *Fiji Rugby Club's Victory in Hong Kong Rugby Sevens Competition. T* **267** *and similar multicoloured designs.* W w **16** (*sideways*). *P* 14.
991 50 c. Type **267** 60 7
a. Sheetlet. Nos. 991/1001 . . . . 6·00
992 50 c. Taniela Qauqau 60 7
993 50 c. Jope Tuikabe 60 7
994 50 c. Leveni Duvuduvukula 60 7
995 50 c. Inoke Maraiwai 60 7
996 50 c. Aminiasi Naituyaga 60 7
997 50 c. Lemki Koroi 60 7
998 50 c. Marika Vunibaka 60 7
999 50 c. Luke Erenavula 60 7
1000 50 c. Manasa Bari 60 7
1001 $1 Fijian rugby team (56×42 *mm*) . . 80 8
991/1001 . . . . *Set of* 11 6·00 7·0
Nos. 991/1001 were printed together, *se-tenant*, in sheetlets of 11 with the 50 c. stamps arranged in two rows of 5 above an illustrated margin containing the $1.

(Des Jennifer Toombs. Litho Questa)

1997 (18 Nov). *Christmas. T* **268** *and similar horiz designs. Multicoloured.* W w **14** (*sideways*). *P* 14½.
1002 13 c. Type **268** 15 10
1003 31 c. Mary, Joseph and baby Jesus . . 35 30
1004 87 c. The Three Kings 90 90
1005 $3 Mary and baby Jesus . . . . 3·00 3·75
1002/5 . . . . *Set of* 4 4·00 4·50

269 Chief in War Dress

270 Man in Wheelchair using Computer

(Des M. Raj. Litho Questa)

1998 (20 Jan). *Traditional Chiefs' Costumes. T* **269** *and similar vert designs. Multicoloured.* W w **16**. *P* 14.
1006 81 c. Type **269** 65 65
1007 87 c. Formal dress 75 75
1008 $1.12, Presentation dress . . . . 1·00 1·25
1009 $2 War dress of Highland chief . . 1·50 2·00
1006/9 . . . . *Set of* 4 3·50 4·25

(Des G. Vasarhelyi. Litho Cartor)

1998 (13 Mar). *Asian and Pacific Decade of Disabled People. T* **270** *and similar horiz designs. Multicoloured.* W w 14 (*sideways*). *P* 13½×13.
1010 63 c. Type **270** 60 60
1011 87 c. Woman with child 80 80
1012 $1 Man at desk . . . . 90 1·00
1013 $2 Wheelchair race . . . . . . 1·60 2·00
1010/13 . . . . *Set of* 4 3·50 4·00

(Des D. Miller. Litho Questa)

1998 (31 Mar). *Diana, Princess of Wales Commemoration. Vert designs as T* **177** *of Ascension. Multicoloured.* W w **16**. *P* 14½×14.
1014 81 c. Wearing tartan jacket, 1990 . . 1·00 1·00
MS1015 145×70 mm. 81 c. As No. 1014; 81 c. Wearing blue jacket, 1991; 81 c., Wearing high-necked blouse, 1990; 81 c. Carrying bouquet. W w 14 (sideways) (*sold at $3.24 + 50 c. charity premium*) . . . . 2·75 3·25

(Des A. Theobald. Litho Enschedé)

998 (1 Apr). *80th Anniv of Royal Air Force. Horiz designs as T* **178** *of Ascension. Multicoloured.* W w **14** (*sideways*). *P* 13½×14.

016 44 c. *R34* airship 40 30
017 63 c. Handley Page Heyford 65 55
018 87 c. Supermarine Swift FR.5 .. .. 90 90
019 $2 Westland Whirlwind .. .. 1·50 1·75
016/19 .. .. *Set of* 4 3·00 3·25
IS1020 110×77 mm. $1 Sopwith Dolphin; $1 Avro 504K; $1 Vickers Warwick V; $1 Shorts Belfast .. .. 3·00 3·25

271 Pod of Sperm Whales Underwater

272 Athletics

(Des Sue Wickison. Litho Walsall)

998 (22 June). *Sperm Whales. T* **271** *and similar horiz designs. Multicoloured.* W w **14** (*sideways*). *P* 14.

021 63 c. Type **271** 65 55
022 81 c. Female and calf 80 80
023 87 c. Pod on surface 90 90
024 $2 Ceremonial whale tooth .. .. 1·60 1·75
021/4 .. .. *Set of* 4 3·50 3·50
IS1025 90×68 mm. No. 1024 .. .. .. 2·50 2·75

(Des S. Noon. Litho Questa)

998 (11 Sept). *16th Commonwealth Games, Kuala Lumpur. T* **272** *and similar vert designs. Multicoloured.* W w **16**. *P* 14.

026 44 c. Type **272** 25 30
027 63 c. Lawn bowls 40 45
028 81 c. Throwing the javelin 50 55
029 $1.12, Weightlifting 70 75
026/9 .. .. *Set of* 4 1·75 1·90
IS1030 63×77 mm. $2 Waisale Serevi (Fiji rugby captain) .. .. 1·25 1·40

273 Takia (traditional raft)

(Des J. Batchelor. Litho B.D.T.)

998 (26 Oct). *Maritime Past and Present* (*1st series*). *T* **273** *and similar horiz designs. Multicoloured.* W w **16** (*sideways*). *P* 13½.

031 13 c. Type **273** 10 10
032 44 c. Camakau (outrigger canoe) 25 30
033 87 c. Drua (outrigger canoe) 55 60
034 $3 *Pioneer* (inter-island ship) .. .. 1·75 1·90
031/4 .. .. *Set of* 4 2·50 2·75
IS1035 105×75 mm. $1.50, Camakau (outrigger canoe) .. .. 95 1·00

No. **MS**1035 also includes the "World Stamp Expo Australia '99" emblem on the margin of the sheet.

See also Nos. 1044/8.

274 "Jesus in a Manger" (Grace Lee)

(Litho Cartor)

998 (23 Nov). *Christmas. Children's Paintings. T* **274** *and similar multicoloured designs.* W w **14** (*sideways on horiz designs*). *P* 13½.

036 13 c. Type **274** 10 10
037 50 c. "A Time with Family and Friends" (Brian Guevara) 30 35
038 $1 "What Christmas Means to Me" (Naomi Tupou) (*vert*) 60 65
039 $2 "The Joy of Christmas" (Lauretta Ah Sam) (*vert*) .. .. 1·25 1·40
036/9 .. .. *Set of* 4 2·25 2·50

275 Women's Sitting Dance

(Des T. Crilley. Litho Southern Colour Print, Dunedin)

1999 (20 Jan). *Traditional Fijian Dances. T* **275** *and similar horiz designs. Multicoloured. P* 14½.

1040 13 c. Type **275** 10 10
1041 81 c. Club dance 50 55
1042 87 c. Women's fan dance 55 60
1043 $3 Kava-serving dance .. .. .. 1·75 1·90
1040/3 .. .. *Set of* 4 2·75 3·00

(Des J. Batchelor. Litho B.D.T.)

1999 (19 Mar). *Maritime Past and Present* (*2nd series*). *Horiz designs as T* **273**. *Multicoloured.* W w **16** (*sideways*). *P* 13½.

1044 63 c. *Tofua* (cargo liner) 40 45
1045 81 c. *Adi Beti* (government launch) .. 50 55
1046 $1 *Niagara* (liner) 60 65
1047 $2 *Royal Viking Sun* (liner) .. .. 1·25 1·40
1044/7 .. .. *Set of* 4 2·75 3·00
MS1048 105×75 mm. $1.50, *Maketea* (inter-island freighter) 90 95

No. **MS**1048 also includes the "Australia '99" emblem on the sheet margin.

STAMP BOOKLETS

1909. *Black and red cover. Stapled.*
SB1 2s. booklet containing eleven ½d. (No. 118) in blocks of 5 and 6, and eighteen 1d. (No. 119) in blocks of 6 .. .. £2500

1914. *Black on red cover. Stapled.*
SB2 2s. booklet containing eleven ½d. (No. 126) in blocks of 5 and 6, and eighteen 1d. (No. 127) in blocks of 6 .. .. £2000

1939 (10 Mar)–**40.** *Black on green* (*No.* SB3) *or black on pink* (*No.* SB4) *covers. No advertising pages. Stapled.*
SB3 3s. booklet containing eight ½d. and eight 1d. (Nos. 249/50) in blocks of 8 and twelve 2d. (No. 253) in blocks of 6 .. .. .. £650
a. Including four advertising pages (black on buff cover) (1940) .. ..
SB4 5s. 9d. booklet containing ten ½d. and ten 1d. (Nos. 249/50) in blocks of 10 and twenty-seven 2d. (No. 253) in blocks of 9 .. .. .. £1900
a. Including four advertising pages (1940) ..

Nos. SB3/4 were produced locally and Nos. SB3a/4a by De La Rue.

1967 (23 Jan). *Black on salmon cover. Stitched.*
SB5 2s. booklet containing eight 3d. (No. 313) in blocks of four .. .. 7·50

The first printing was not released by the Crown Agents, but a second printing was released in London on 30.6.67. The first printing had 4d. as the surface-rate for letters to the British Commonwealth on the inside back cover (*Price* £8); in the second printing this was corrected to 3d.

1969 (27 Feb). *Black on salmon cover. Stitched.*
SB6 20 c. booklet containing ten 2 c. (No. 392) in two blocks of 4 and a vert pair .. .. .. 4·50

1970 (27 Oct). *Black on salmon cover. Stitched.*
SB7 20 c. booklet containing four 1 c. and eight 2 c. (Nos. 391/2) in blocks of 4 .. .. .. 5·50

1971 (22 Nov). *Black on blue cover. Stitched.*
SB8 20 c. booklet containing 2 c. (No. 436) in block of 10 5·50

1973 (7 Sept)–**74.** *Black on blue cover. Stitched.*
SB9 20 c. booklet containing 1 c. in block of 8 and 2 c. in block of 6 (Nos. 435/6) .. .. .. 8·50
a. With 2 c. watermark sideways (No. 459) (28.3.74) .. .. 7·50

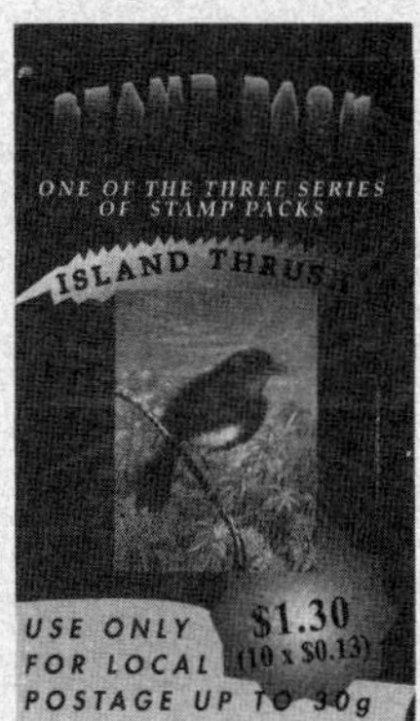

B **1** Island Thrush

1997 (13 June). *Multicoloured covers as Type* B **1**. *Stamps attached by selvedge.*
SB10 $1.30, booklet containing 13 c. (No. 917) in block of 10 80
SB11 $3.10, booklet containing 31 c. (No. 919) in block of 10 .. .. 1·75
SB12 $4.40, booklet containing 44 c. (No. 920) in block of 10 .. .. 2·75

POSTAGE DUE STAMPS

D **1**

D **2**

(Typo Govt Printer, Suva)

1917 (1 Jan). *Thick yellowish white laid paper. No gum. P* 11.
D1 D **1** ½d. black £650 £350
a. *Se-tenant* strip of 8: 1d. (×3) + ½d. + 4d. + 3d. (×3) £12000
D2 1d. black .. .. £275 70·00
D3 2d. black .. .. £225 60·00
D4 3d. black .. .. £275 75·00
D5 4d. black £650 £350

Nos. D1/2 and D4/5 were printed, *se-tenant*, in sheets of 96 (8×12) with each horizontal row containing three 1d., one ½d., one 4d. and three 3d. in that order. Only thirty-one such sheets were issued. The 2d. was printed separately in sheets of 84 (7×12). On all these sheets marginal copies were imperforate on the outer edge.

1917 (21 April)–**18.** *Narrower setting, value in ½d. as Type* D **2**.
D5*a* ½d. black £450 £225
D5*b* 1d. black £225 £110
D5*c* 2d. black (5.4.18) £800 £500

1d. and 2d. stamps must have wide margins (3½ to 4 mm) on the vertical sides to be Nos. D2 or D3. Stamps with narrow margins of approximately the same width on all four sides are Nos. D5*b* or D5*c*.

Nos. D5*a/c* were printed in separate sheets of 84 (7 × 12). The marginal copies are perforated on all sides.

D **3**

D **4**

(Typo D.L.R.)

1918 (1 June). *Wmk Mult Crown CA. P* 14.
D 6 D **3** ½d. black .. .. 3·00 14·00
D 7 1d. black .. .. 3·50 4·50
D 8 2d. black .. .. 2·75 7·50
D 9 3d. black .. .. 3·25 45·00
D10 4d. black .. .. 5·50 24·00
D6/10 .. .. *Set of* 5 16·00 85·00
D6/10 Optd "Specimen" .. .. *Set of* 5 £150

No postage due stamps were in use between 31 August 1931 and 3 July 1940.

(Typo Waterlow)

1940 (3 July). *Wmk Mult Script CA. P* 12½.
D11 D **4** 1d. emerald-green .. .. .. 6·50 55·00
D12 2d. emerald-green .. .. .. 8·50 55·00
D13 3d. emerald-green .. .. .. 11·00 60·00
D14 4d. emerald-green .. .. .. 14·00 65·00
D15 5d. emerald-green .. .. .. 15·00 65·00
D16 6d. emerald-green .. .. .. 17·00 70·00
D17 1s. carmine-lake .. .. .. 21·00 95·00
D18 1s. 6d. carmine-lake .. .. .. 22·00 £140
D11/18 .. .. *Set of* 8 £100 £550
D11/18 Perf "Specimen" .. .. *Set of* 8 £180

All values are known with forged postmarks, including one of Levuka dated "8 APR 41" and others of Suva dated "12 AUG 42", "14 AU 42" or "20 MR 45".

The use of postage due stamps was discontinued on 30 April 1946.

Gambia

PRICES FOR STAMPS ON COVER TO 1945

Nos. 1/4	*from* × 20
Nos. 5/8	*from* × 15
Nos. 10/20	*from* × 20
Nos. 21/31	*from* × 40
Nos. 32/6	*from* × 20
Nos. 37/44	*from* × 10
Nos. 45/68	*from* × 8
Nos. 69/70	*from* × 20
Nos. 72/85	*from* × 8
Nos. 86/142	*from* × 5
Nos. 143/6	*from* × 6
Nos. 147/9	*from* × 8
Nos. 150/61	*from* × 3

WEST AFRICAN SETTLEMENT

British traders were active in the River Gambia area from the beginning of the 17th century, but it was not until 1808 that it was officially recognised as a Settlement. Administration passed from the merchants to the Governor of Freetown (Sierra Leone) in 1821 and in 1843 Gambia became a separate colony with a Protectorate declared over the banks of the river for 300 miles inland in 1857. A period of colonial retrenchment in 1865 saw a return to Settlement status under Sierra Leone, but Gambia once again became a Crown Colony in 1888.

There was no government postal service before 1858.

PRICES. The prices of Nos. 1 to 8 are for fine copies, with good margins and embossing. Brilliant or poor copies can be supplied at prices consistent with their condition.

DOUBLE EMBOSSING. The majority of the stamps of T 1 with so-called "double embossing" are merely specimens in which the printing and embossing do not register accurately and have no special value. We no longer list "twice embossed" or "twice embossed, once inverted" varieties as they are considered to be outside the scope of this catalogue.

1

(Typo and embossed by D.L.R.)

1869 (18 Mar)–**72**. *No wmk. Imperf.*

1	1	4d. brown	£475	£160
2		4d. pale brown (1871)	£400	£200
3		6d. deep blue	£425	£180
3*a*		6d. blue	£500	£150
4		6d. pale blue (17.2.72)	£2250	£1000

Our prices for the 6d. pale blue, No. 4, are for stamps which are pale by comparison with specimens of the "deep blue" and "blue" colour groups listed under Nos. 3 and 3*a*. The date given is the earliest known postmark. An exceptionally pale shade is recognized by specialists and this is rare.

1874 (Aug). *Wmk Crown CC. Imperf.*

5	1	4d. brown	£350	£180
		w. Wmk inverted	£425	£225
		x. Wmk reversed	£425	£225
		y. Wmk inverted and reversed	£475	£275
6		4d. pale brown	£350	£180
7		6d. deep blue	£300	£200
		w. Wmk inverted	£375	£250
		x. Wmk reversed	£400	£250
		y. Wmk inverted and reversed	£400	£250
8		6d. blue	£300	£180
		a. Sloping label	£500	£300
		b. Wmk sideways	†	—
		w. Wmk inverted	£375	£250

SLOPING LABEL VARIETY. Traces of this flaw first occur in the 6d. imperforate on R.1/1 and R.1/5. In the perforated printings the variety on R.1/5 is much more pronounced and appears as illustrated above. Our listings are these examples from R.1/5, less noticeable varieties of this type from R.1/1, which slope from right to left, being worth less. These varieties continued to appear until the introduction of a new 6d. plate in 1893, used for No. 34.

1880–81. *Wmk Crown CC. P* 14*. A. *Wmk sideways*†

10A	1	½d. orange	£150	£120
		w. Wmk Crown to left of CC		
12A		1d. maroon	£250	£190
		w. Wmk Crown to left of CC		
		y. Wmk sideways inverted and reversed		
13A		2d. rose	80·00	45·00
		w. Wmk Crown to left of CC		
14A		3d. bright ultramarine	£300	£225
		w. Wmk Crown to left of CC		
15A		4d. brown	£300	50·00
		w Wmk Crown to left of CC	£275	45·00
16A		4d. pale brown	£275	45·00
		w. Wmk Crown to left of CC	£250	40·00
17A		6d. deep blue	£120	80·00
		c. Sloping label	£325	£225
18A		6d. blue	£120	80·00
		c. Sloping label	£325	£225
		w. Wmk Crown to left of CC		
19A		1s. green	£350	£225
20A		1s. deep green	£350	£225
		w. Wmk Crown to left of CC		
10A/20A		*Set of* 7	£1300	£800

B. *Wmk upright*

10B	1	½d. orange	6·00	11·00
11B		½d. dull orange	6·00	11·00
		w. Wmk inverted	35·00	
		x. Wmk reversed	30·00	
12B		1d. maroon	3·50	5·00
		w. Wmk inverted	75·00	75·00
13B		2d. rose	18·00	10·00
14B		3d. bright ultramarine	65·00	30·00
14cB		3d. pale dull ultramarine	48·00	25·00
		w. Wmk inverted	60·00	40·00
15B		4d. brown	£150	14·00
		w. Wmk inverted	†	—
16B		4d. pale brown	£140	15·00
17B		6d. deep blue	75·00	45·00
		c. Sloping label	£225	£150
18B		6d. blue	75·00	45·00
		c. Sloping label	£225	£150
19B		1s. green	£190	£110
		w. Wmk inverted	†	£300
20B		1s. deep green	£190	£110
10B/20B		*Set of* 7	£425	£200

*There were three different printings of these stamps. The original supply, sent in June 1880 and covering all seven values, had watermark sideways and was perforated by a line machine. In October of the same year a further printing of the lowest five values had the watermark changed to upright, but was still with line perforation. The final printing, sent May 1881 and containing all values, also had watermark upright, but was perforated on a comb machine.

†The normal sideways watermark shows Crown to right of CC, *as seen from the back of the stamp.*

1886–93. *Wmk Crown CA* (*sideways**). *P* 14.

21	1	½d. myrtle-green (1887)	2·00	2·00
		w. Wmk Crown to right of CA	20·00	
		x. Wmk sideways reversed	30·00	
22		½d. grey-green	2·50	3·00
22*b*		1d. maroon	†	£15000
23		1d. crimson (1887)	3·75	5·00
23*a*		1d. aniline crimson	6·00	9·00
23*b*		1d. pale carmine	6·00	9·00
24		2d. orange (1887)	8·50	6·00
25		2d. deep orange	1·40	7·00
26		2½d. ultramarine (1887)	2·00	2·00
27		2½d. deep bright blue	1·75	1·25
		w. Wmk Crown to right of CA	75·00	
28		3d. slate-grey (1886)	3·50	12·00
29		3d. grey	2·25	13·00
30		4d. brown (1887)	2·75	2·00
31		4d. deep brown	2·75	2·00
		a. Wmk upright	†	£900
		w. Wmk Crown to right of CA	50·00	50·00
32		6d. yellowish olive-green (1886)	65·00	30·00
		a. Sloping label	£160	75·00
		bw. Wmk Crown to right of CA	£110	
32*c*		6d. olive-green (1887)	55·00	48·00
		ca. Sloping label	£150	£130
33		6d. bronze-green (1889)	23·00	48·00
		a. Sloping label	55·00	90·00
33*b*		6d. deep bronze-green (1889)	24·00	48·00
		ba. Sloping label	55·00	90·00
34		6d. slate-green (1893)	10·00	42·00
35		1s. violet (1887)	3·25	15·00
36		1s. deep violet	3·75	16·00
36*b*		1s. aniline violet	£1100	
21/36		*Set of* 8	24·00	70·00
21/4, 32 Optd "Specimen"		*Set of* 4	£400	

*The normal sideways watermark shows Crown to left of CA, *as seen from the back of the stamp.*

The above were printed in panes of 15 on paper intended for larger panes. Hence the watermark is sometimes misplaced or omitted and letters from "CROWN AGENTS FOR THE COLONIES" from the margin may appear on the stamps.

The ½d., 2d., 3d., 4d., 6d. (No. 32) and 1s. with watermark Crown CA are known imperforate (*price from* £1100, *unused*).

Only three examples, all used, are recorded of the 1d. maroon, No. 22*b*.

The previously listed 3d. "pearl-grey" shade has been deleted as it is impossible to distinguish from other 3d. shades when it occurs on a single stamp. Sheets from this late printing can be identified by three coloured dots in the left sheet margin and one in the right, this being the reverse of the normal arrangement.

Only three used examples are known of the 4d. with upright watermark, No. 31a.

NEW INFORMATION

The editor is always interested to correspond with people who have new information that will improve or correct the Catalogue.

CROWN COLONY

2

Normal — Malformed "S" — Repaired "S"

The Malformed "S" occurs on R. 7/3 of the left pane from Key Plate 2. This was used to print the initial supply all value[s]. Printings of the ½d., 1d. and 2½d. despatched on 24 Septemb[er] 1898 had the "S" repaired as shown above. Subsequent printing[s] of the ½d., 1d. and 3d. were from Key Plate 3.

(Typo D.L.R.)

1898 (2 May)–**1902**. *Wmk Crown CA. P* 14.

37	2	½d. dull green (*shades*)	2·00	1·7
		a. Malformed "S"	£160	
		b. Repaired "S"	£180	£15
38		1d. carmine (*shades*)	1·25	7
		a. Malformed "S"	£160	
		b. Repaired "S"	£180	
39		2d. orange and mauve	4·50	3·5
		a. Malformed "S"	£180	
40		2½d. ultramarine	1·40	1·7
		a. Malformed "S"	£160	
		b. Repaired "S"	£190	
41		3d. reddish purple and blue	13·00	12·0
		a. Malformed "S"	£225	
		b. Deep purple and ultramarine (1902)	85·00	£10
42		4d. brown and blue	7·50	26·0
		a. Malformed "S"	£200	
43		6d. olive-green and carmine	9·00	21·0
		a. Malformed "S"	£225	
44		1s. violet and green	25·00	50·0
		a. Malformed "S"	£325	
37/44		*Set of* 8	55·00	£10
37/44 Optd "Specimen"		*Set of* 8	£150	

3 — 4

Dented frame (R. 1/6 of left pane)

1902 (13 Mar)–**05**. *Wmk Crown CA. P* 14.

45	3	½d. green (19.4.02)	2·00	2·
		a. Dented frame	48·00	
46		1d. carmine	1·50	
		a. Dented frame	45·00	
47		2d. orange and mauve (14.6.02)	3·25	2·
		a. Dented frame	80·00	
48		2½d. ultramarine (14.6.02)	24·00	17·
		a. Dented frame	£180	
49		3d. purple and ultramarine (19.4.02)	12·00	3·5
		a. Dented frame	£150	
50		4d. brown and ultramarine (14.6.02)	3·00	22·
		a. Dented frame	£110	
51		6d. pale sage-green & carmine (14.6.02)	3·25	10·
		a. Dented frame	£110	
52		1s. violet and green (14.6.02)	48·00	80·
		a. Dented frame	£275	
53	4	1s. 6d. green and carmine/*yellow* (6.4.05)	5·50	15·
		a. Dented frame	£160	
54		2s. deep slate and orange (14.6.02)	42·00	55·
		a. Dented frame	£250	
55		2s. 6d. purple and brown/*yellow* (6.4.05)	15·00	55·
		a. Dented frame	£190	
56		3s. carmine and green/*yellow* (6.4.05)	19·00	55·
		a. Dented frame	£190	
45/56		*Set of* 12	£160	£27
45/56 Optd "Specimen"		*Set of* 12	£180	

04 (Aug)–**06**. *Wmk Mult Crown CA. P* 14.
3 ½d. green (9.05) 3·50 25
a. Dented frame 60·00
1d. carmine 4·00 15
a. Dented frame 75·00
2d. orange and mauve (23.2.06) 11·00 2·25
a. Dented frame £150
2½d. bright blue (8.05) 4·00 4·25
a. Bright blue and ultramarine 12·00 24·00
b. Dented frame 80·00
3d. purple and ultramarine (9.05) 5·00 2·00
a. Dented frame 95·00
4d. brown and ultramarine (23.2.06) 15·00 40·00
a. Dented frame £160
4 5d. grey and black (6.4.05) 12·00 15·00
a. Dented frame £150
3 6d. olive-green and carmine (23.2.06) 12·00 40·00
a. Dented frame £150
4 7½d. green and carmine (6.4.05) 7·00 30·00
a. Dented frame £110
10d. olive and carmine (6.4.05) 16·00 24·00
a. Dented frame £160
3 1s. violet and green (9.05) 16·00 48·00
a. Dented frame £180
4 2s. deep slate and orange (7.05) 60·00 70·00
a. Dented frame £275
/68 *Set of* 12 £150 £250
, 65/6 Optd "Specimen" *Set of* 3 70·00
See also Nos. 72/85.

HALF PENNY
(5)

ONE PENNY
(6)

06 (10 Apr). *Nos.* 55 *and* 56 *surch with T* **5** *or* **6** *by Govt Printer.*
½d. on 2s. 6d. purple and brown/*yellow* 45·00 65·00
a. Dented frame £325
1d. on 3s. carmine and green/*yellow* 55·00 30·00
a. Surch double £1800 £5000
b. Dented frame £375

No. 69 was surcharged in a setting of 30 (6 × 5), the spacing tween the words and the bars being 5 mm on rows 1, 2 and 5; and nm on rows 3 and 4. Constant varieties occur on R.2/1 (broken ") and R.5/1 (dropped "Y") of the setting.

No. 70 was surcharged in a setting of 60 (6 × 10) and a similar opped "Y" variety occurs on R.6/3 and R.8/5.

Both values were withdrawn on 24 April when fresh supplies ½d. and 1d. definitives were received from London.

09 (1 Oct). *Colours changed. Wmk Mult Crown CA. P* 14.
3 ½d. blue-green 2·75 3·00
a. Dented frame 60·00
1d. red 4·00 15
a. Dented frame 75·00
2d. greyish slate 1·60 8·50
a. Dented frame 80·00
3d. purple/*yellow* 3·00 90
a. Purple/lemon-yellow 5·50 1·75
b. Dented frame 90·00
4d. black and red/*yellow* 80 65
a. Dented frame 90·00
4 5d. orange and purple 1·50 1·25
a. Dented frame 95·00
3 6d. dull and bright purple 2·00 2·25
a. Dented frame £100
4 7½d. brown and blue 2·00 2·50
a. Dented frame £100
10d. pale sage-green and carmine 2·50 6·50
a. Dented frame £110
3 1s. black/*green* 3·00 16·00
a. Dented frame £110
4 1s. 6d. violet and green 9·50 48·00
a. Dented frame £160
2s. purple and bright blue/*blue* 14·00 19·00
a. Dented frame £160
2s. 6d. black and red/*blue* 21·00 19·00
a. Dented frame £190
3s. yellow and green 22·00 48·00
a. Dented frame £200
85 *Set of* 14 80·00 £160
85 Optd "Specimen" *Set of* 13 £225

Most values between Nos. 45 and 85 are known with forged stmarks. These include circular types of Bathurst, dated "JA 2 ", and Macarthy Island, dated "FE 17 10", and an oval gistered Gambia postmark dated "22 JU 10".

7

8

TACE
Split "A" (R. 8/3 of left pane) (ptgs to 1918)

(Typo D.L.R.)

2 (1 Sept)–**22**. *Wmk Mult Crown CA. Chalk-surfaced paper 5s.). P* 14.
7 ½d. deep green 1·00 1·25
a. Green 2·00 1·25
b. Pale green (1916) 2·75 2·75
c. Split "A" 50·00
1d. red 2·50 70
a. Rose-red 1·50 30
b. Scarlet (1916) 2·50 90
c. Split "A" 60·00
88 8 1½d. olive-green and blue-green 30 30
a. Split "A" 60·00
89 7 2d. greyish slate 45 2·50
a. Split "A" 60·00
90 2½d. deep bright blue 4·00 3·00
a. Bright blue 4·50 2·50
b. Split "A" 95·00
91 3d. purple/*yellow* 30 30
a. On lemon (1917) 13·00 18·00
b. On orange-buff (1920) 10·00 8·50
c. On pale yellow 80 75
d. Split "A" 75·00
92 4d. black and red/*yellow* 75 9·00
a. On lemon (1917) 2·25 7·00
b. On orange-buff (1920) 7·00 11·00
c. On pale yellow 1·50 6·00
d. Split "A" 85·00
w. Wmk inverted 70·00
93 8 5d. orange and purple 70 1·50
a. Split "A" 90·00
94 7 6d. dull and bright purple 70 1·75
a. Split "A" 90·00
95 8 7½d. brown and blue 1·00 6·00
a. Split "A" £130
96 10d. pale sage-green and carmine 2·00 17·00
a. Deep sage-green and carmine 2·00 15·00
b. Split "A" £150
97 7 1s. black/*green* 1·50 1·00
a. On emerald back (1921) 70 15·00
b. Split "A" 95·00
98 8 1s. 6d. violet and green 8·00 10·00
a. Split "A" £250
99 2s. purple and blue/*blue* 2·50 6·00
a. Split "A" £225
100 2s. 6d. black and red/*blue* 2·75 13·00
a. Split "A" £225
101 3s. yellow and green 7·50 20·00
a. Split "A" £325
102 5s. green and red/*pale yellow* (1922) 60·00 90·00
86/102 *Set of* 17 80·00 £160
86/102 Optd "Specimen" *Set of* 17 £325

1921–22. *Wmk Mult Script CA. Chalk-surfaced paper* (4s.). *P* 14.
108 7 ½d. dull green 30 13·00
x. Wmk reversed 70·00
109 1d. carmine-red 1·00 3·75
x. Wmk reversed 65·00 65·00
110 8 1½d. olive-green and blue-green 1·25 9·50
111 7 2d. grey 1·00 1·50
x. Wmk reversed 55·00
112 2½d. bright blue 50 4·25
113 8 5d. orange and purple 1·75 14·00
x. Wmk reversed 32·00
114 7 6d. dull and bright purple 1·75 14·00
x. Wmk reversed 20·00
115 8 7½d. brown and blue 2·00 24·00
x. Wmk reversed 20·00
116 10d. pale sage-green and carmine 7·00 15·00
x. Wmk reversed 38·00
117 4s. black and red (1922) 55·00 90·00
w. Wmk inverted 50·00 £100
108/17 *Set of* 10 65·00 £170
108/17 Optd "Specimen" *Set of* 10 £200

Forged postmarks of the types mentioned below No. 85 have also been seen on various values between No. 86 and 117. Collectors should beware of partial strikes which do not show the year date.

9

10

(Recess D.L.R.)

1922 (1 Sept)–**29**. *Portrait and shield in black. P* 14*.

(*a*) *Wmk Mult Crown CA*
118 9 4d. red/*yellow* (*a*) 1·75 1·75
119 7½d. purple/*yellow* (*a*) 2·00 6·50
120 10 1s. purple/*yellow* (*a*) 5·50 18·00
w. Wmk inverted 65·00
121 5s. green/*yellow* (*c*) 30·00 85·00
w. Wmk inverted
118/21 *Set of* 4 35·00 £100
118/21 Optd/H/S "Specimen" *Set of* 4 £140

(*b*) *Wmk Mult Script CA*
122 9 ½d. green (*abd*) 55 40
123 ½d. deep green (*bd*) (1925) 2·50 85
124 1d. brown (*abd*) 70 10
125 1½d. bright rose-scarlet (*abd*) 80 10
126 2d. grey (*ab*) 1·00 2·00
127 2½d. orange-yellow (*b*) 90 9·50
w. Wmk inverted 65·00
128 3d. bright blue (*abd*) 1·00 10
129 4d. red/*yellow* (*bd*) (1.3.27) 3·75 14·00
130 5d. sage-green (*a*) 2·00 10·00
131 6d. claret (*ad*) 1·25 30
132 7½d. purple/*yellow* (*ab*) (1927) 7·00 38·00
133 10d. blue (*a*) 4·50 18·00
134 10 1s. purple/*yellow* (*aef*) (9.24) 2·25 80
a. Blackish purple/yell-buff (*c*) (1929) 32·00 42·00
135 1s. 6d. blue (*af*) 9·50 12·00
136 2s. purple/*blue* (*ac*) 3·50 3·50
137 2s. 6d. deep green (*a*) 4·00 9·50
138 3s. bright aniline violet (*a*) 11·00 40·00
139 3s. slate-purple (*c*) (1928) £180 £350
140 4s. brown (*ace*) 4·25 16·00
141 5s. green/*yellow* (*acf*) (9.26) 12·00 32·00
142 10s. sage-green (*ce*) 70·00 £100
122/42 *Set of* 19 £120 £275
122/42 Optd "Specimen" *Set of* 19 £400

Perforations. A number of different perforating machines were used for the various printings of these stamps and the following varieties are known: (*a*) the original 14 line perforation; (*b*) 14 × 13.8 comb perforation used for Type **9**; (*c*) 13.8 × 13.7 comb perforation used for Type **10**; (*d*) 13.7 line perforation used for Type **9**; (*e*) 14 × 13.8 compound line perforation used for Type **10**; (*f*) 13.8 × 14 compound line perforation used for Type **10**. The occurrence of these perforations on the individual values is indicated by the letters shown after the colour descriptions above.

No. 139 has been faked, but note that this stamp is comb perf 13.8 × 13.7 whereas No. 138 is line perf 14 exactly. There are also shades of the slate-purple.

Most values of the above issue are known with a forged oval registered Gambia postmark dated "22 JU 10", often with the year date not shown. Collectors should exercise particular caution in buying used examples of No. 139.

1935 (6 May). *Silver Jubilee. As T* **13** *of Antigua. Recess B.W. Wmk Mult Script CA. P* 11 × 12.
143 1½d. deep blue and scarlet 50 30
a. Extra flagstaff £225
b. Short extra flagstaff £120
c. Lightning conductor £225
d. Flagstaff on right-hand turret £170
e. Double flagstaff £170
144 3d. brown and deep blue 55 70
a. Extra flagstaff £150
b. Short extra flagstaff £150
c. Lightning conductor £130
145 6d. light blue and olive-green 90 1·75
a. Extra flagstaff £140
b. Short extra flagstaff £140
c. Lightning conductor £140
d. Flagstaff on right-hand turret £250
146 1s. slate and purple 2·50 4·75
a. Extra flagstaff £200
b. Short extra flagstaff £200
c. Lightning conductor £180
d. Flagstaff on right-hand turret £325
143/6 *Set of* 4 4·00 6·50
143/6 Perf "Specimen" *Set of* 4 90·00

For illustrations of plate varieties see Catalogue Introduction. Examples of Nos. 145a and 146a are known with the extra flagstaff erased from the stamp with a sharp point.

1937 (12 May). *Coronation. As Nos.* 95/7 *of Antigua. P* 11×11½
147 1d. yellow-brown 30 15
148 1½d. carmine 30 30
149 3d. blue 55 45
147/9 *Set of* 3 1·00 80
147/9 Perf "Specimen" *Set of* 3 60·00

11 Elephant (from Colony Badge)

(Recess B.W.)

1938 (1 Apr)–**46**. *Wmk Mult Script CA. P* 12.
150 11 ½d. black and emerald-green 15 50
151 1d. purple and brown 20 40
152 1½d. brown-lake and bright carmine £140 12·00
a. Brown-lake and scarlet 2·25 2·00
b. Brown-lake and vermilion 30 1·75
152*c* 1½d. blue and black (2.1.45) 30 1·25
153 2d. blue and black 2·25 2·50
153*a* 2d. lake and scarlet (1.10.43) 60 1·75
154 3d. light blue and grey-blue 30 10
154*a* 5d. sage-green & purple-brn (13.3.41) 45 45
155 6d. olive-green and claret 1·50 35
156 1s. slate-blue and violet 2·00 10
156*a* 1s. 3d. chocolate & lt blue (28.11.46) 2·00 2·00
157 2s. carmine and blue 4·50 3·25
158 2s. 6d. sepia and dull green 12·00 2·00
159 4s. vermilion and purple 21·00 2·50
160 5s. blue and vermilion 21·00 4·00
161 10s. orange and black 21·00 7·00
150/61 *Set of* 16 80·00 26·00
150/61 Perf "Specimen" *Set of* 16 £250

1946 (6 Aug). *Victory. As Nos.* 110/11 *of Antigua.*
162 1½d. black 10 10
163 3d. blue 10 10
162/3 Perf "Specimen" *Set of* 2 55·00

1948 (24 Dec). *Royal Silver Wedding. As Nos.* 112/13 *of Antigua.*
164 1½d. black 25 10
165 £1 mauve 12·00 13·00

1949 (10 Oct). *75th Anniv of Universal Postal Union. As Nos.* 114/17 *of Antigua.*
166 1½d. blue-black 40 30
167 3d. deep blue 1·50 60
168 6d. magenta 60 30
169 1s. violet 60 30
166/9 *Set of* 4 2·75 1·40

1953 (2 June). *Coronation. As No.* 120 *of Antigua, but ptd by B.W.*
170 1½d. black and deep bright blue 40 30

12 Tapping for Palm Wine

13 Cutter

(Des Mrs O. W. Meronti. Recess D.L.R.)

1953 (2 Nov)–**59**. *T* **12/13** *and similar horiz designs. Wmk Mult Script CA. P* 13½.

No.	Type	Description	Unused	Used
171	**12**	½d. carmine-red and bluish green	30	20
		a. Carmine and bluish green (7.1.59)	1·25	1·75
172	**13**	1d. deep ultramarine and deep brown	40	30
		a. Deep ultramarine & choc (22.8.56)	2·25	1·50
173	–	1½d. deep brown and grey-black	20	50
174	–	2½d. black and carmine-red	45	70
175	–	3d. deep blue and slate-lilac	35	10
176	–	4d. black and deep blue	60	1·75
177	**12**	6d. brown and reddish purple	35	15
178	–	1s. yellow-brown and yellow-green	60	40
179	**13**	1s. 3d. ultramarine and pale blue	10·00	50
		a. Ultramarine and light blue (22.2.56)	13·00	55
180	–	2s. indigo and carmine	7·00	3·50
181	**13**	2s. 6d. deep bluish green and sepia	4·00	1·50
182	–	4s. grey-blue and Indian red	10·00	2·75
183	–	5s. chocolate and bright blue	2·50	1·50
184	–	10s. deep blue and myrtle-green	19·00	7·00
185	–	£1 green and black	12·00	9·00
171/85		*Set of* 15	60·00	26·00

Designs:—1½d., 5s. Wollof woman; 2½d., 2s. Barra canoe; 3d., 10s. S.S. *Lady Wright*; 4d., 4s. James Island; 1s., 2s. 6d. Woman hoeing; £1 Elephant and palm (from Colony Badge).

20 Queen Elizabeth II and Palm

21 Queen Elizabeth II and West African Map

(Des J. R. F. Ithier (T **20**), A. W. Morley (T **21**). Recess B.W.)

1961 (2 Dec). *Royal Visit. W w* **12**. *P* 11½.

No.	Type	Description	Unused	Used
186	**20**	2d. green and purple	30	15
187	**21**	3d. turquoise-blue and sepia	65	15
188		6d. blue and cerise	65	50
189	**20**	1s. 3d. violet and myrtle-green	65	2·00
186/9		*Set of* 4	2·00	2·50

1963 (4 June). *Freedom from Hunger. As No.* 146 *of Antigua.*

No.	Description	Unused	Used
190	1s. 3d. carmine	40	15

1963 (2 Sept). *Red Cross Centenary. As Nos.* 147/8 *of Antigua.*

No.	Description	Unused	Used
191	2d. red and black	25	10
192	1s. 3d. red and blue	65	45

SELF-GOVERNMENT

22 Beautiful Sunbird

SELF GOVERNMENT
1963

(35)

(Des V. Whiteley. Photo Harrison)

1963 (4 Nov). *Birds. Horiz designs as T* **22**. *Multicoloured. W w* **12**. *P* 12½ × 13.

No.	Description	Unused	Used
193	½d. Type **22**	30	60
194	1d. Yellow-mantled Whydah	30	30
195	1½d. Cattle Egret	1·75	70
196	2d. Senegal Parrot	1·75	70
197	3d. Rose-ringed Parakeet	1·75	70
198	4d. Violet Starling	1·75	80
199	6d. Village Weaver	1·75	10
200	1s. Rufous-crowned Roller	1·25	10
201	1s. 3d. Red-eyed Dove	12·00	1·40
202	2s. 6d. Double-spurred Francolin	9·00	2·50
203	5s. Palm-nut Vulture	9·00	2·75
204	10s. Orange-cheeked Waxbill	13·00	7·00
205	£1 African Emerald Cuckoo	28·00	14·00
193/205	*Set of* 13	70·00	28·00

1963 (7 Nov). *New Constitution. Nos.* 194, 197, 200/1 *optd with T* **35**.

No.	Description	Unused	Used
206	1d. Yellow-mantled Whydah	10	30
207	3d. Rose-ringed Parakeet	25	10
208	1s. Rufous-crowned Roller	25	10
	a. Opt double		† £4000
209	1s. 3d. Red-eyed Dove	30	45
206/9	*Set of* 4	75	85

1964 (23 Apr). *400th Birth Anniv of William Shakespeare. As No.* 164 *of Antigua.*

No.	Description	Unused	Used
210	6d. bright blue	10	10
	w. Wmk inverted	35·00	35·00

INDEPENDENT

36 Gambia Flag and River

37 Arms

(Des V. Whiteley. Photo Harrison)

1965 (18 Feb). *Independence. P* 14½.

No.	Type	Description	Unused	Used
211	**36**	½d. multicoloured	10	20
212	**37**	2d. multicoloured	10	10
213	**36**	7½d. multicoloured	30	25
214	**37**	1s. 6d. multicoloured	35	25
211/14		*Set of* 4	70	65

INDEPENDENCE
1965

(38)

39 I.T.U. Emblem and Symbols

1965 (18 Feb). *Nos.* 193/205 *optd with T* **38** *or with date centred* (*1d., 2d., 3d., 4d., 1s., 5s.*).

No.	Description	Unused	Used
215	½d. Type **22**	30	60
216	1d. Yellow-mantled Whydah	30	20
217	1½d. Cattle Egret	60	60
218	2d. Senegal Parrot	70	30
219	3d. Rose-ringed Parakeet	70	15
220	4d. Violet Starling	70	70
221	6d. Village Weaver	70	10
222	1s. Rufous-crowned Roller	70	10
223	1s. 3d. Red-eyed Dove	70	10
224	2s. 6d. Double-spurred Francolin	70	50
225	5s. Palm-nut Vulture	70	65
226	10s. Orange-cheeked Waxbill	1·60	1·50
227	£1 African Emerald Cuckoo	6·00	7·00
215/27	*Set of* 13	13·00	11·00

(Des V. Whiteley. Photo Harrison)

1965 (17 May). *I.T.U. Centenary. P* 14½.

No.	Type	Description	Unused	Used
228	**39**	1d. silver and Prussian blue	20	10
229		1s. 6d. gold and bluish violet	80	30

THE GAMBIA. From this point onwards stamps are inscribed "The Gambia".

40 Sir Winston Churchill and Houses of Parliament

(Des Jennifer Toombs. Photo Harrison)

1966 (24 Jan). *Churchill Commemoration. P* 14 × 14½.

No.	Type	Description	Unused	Used
230	**40**	1d. multicoloured	10	10
231		6d. multicoloured	20	10
232		1s. 6d. multicoloured	40	65
230/2		*Set of* 3	65	75

41 Red-cheeked Cordon Bleu

42 Pin-tailed Whydah

(Des V. Whiteley. Photo Harrison)

1966 (18 Feb). *Birds. Horiz designs as T* **41**, *and T* **42**. *Multicoloured. P* 14 × 14½ (£1) *or* 12 × 13 (*others*).

No.	Description	Unused	Used
233	½d. Type **41**	75	40
234	1d. White-faced Whistling Duck	30	40
235	1½d. Red-throated Bee Eater	30	40
236	2d. Lesser Pied Kingfisher	4·25	40
237	3d. Golden Bishop	30	10
238	4d. African Fish Eagle	50	30
239	6d. Yellow-bellied Green Pigeon	40	10
240	1s. Blue-bellied Roller	40	10
241	1s. 6d. African Pygmy Kingfisher	75	30
242	2s. 6d. Spur-winged Goose	75	70
243	5s. Cardinal Woodpecker	75	75
244	10s. Violet Turaco	75	2·75
245	£1 Type **42**	1·00	6·50
233/45	*Set of* 13	10·00	12·00

The ½d., 1d. and 2d. to 1s. values exist with PVA gum as well as gum arabic.

54 Arms, Early Settlement and Modern Buildings

(Photo, arms die-stamped Harrison)

1966 (24 June). *150th Anniv of Bathurst. P* 14½ × 14.

No.	Type	Description	Unused
246	**54**	1d. silver, brown and yellow-orange	10
247		2d. silver, brown and light blue	10
248		6d. silver, brown and light emerald	10
249		1s. 6d. silver, brown and light magenta	15
246/9		*Set of* 4	30

55 I.T.Y. Emblem and Hotels

(Des and photo (emblem die-stamped) Harrison)

1967 (20 Dec). *International Tourist Year. P* 14½ × 14.

No.	Type	Description	Unused
250	**55**	2d. silver, brown and apple-green	10
251		1s. silver, brown and orange	10
252		1s. 6d. silver, brown and magenta	15
250/2		*Set of* 3	30

56 Handcuffs

(Des V. Whiteley. Photo Enschedé)

1968 (15 July). *Human Rights Year. T* **56** *and similar ho designs. Multicoloured. P* 14 × 13.

No.	Description	Unused
253	1d. Type **56**	10
254	1s. Fort Bullen	10
255	5s. Methodist Church	30
253/5	*Set of* 3	35

59 Queen Victoria, Queen Elizabeth II and 4d. Stamp of 1869

(Des G. Drummond. Photo and embossing (cameo head) Harriso

1969 (20 Jan). *Gambia Stamp Centenary. P* 14½ × 13½.

No.	Type	Description	Unused	Used
256	**59**	4d. sepia and yellow-ochre	20	
257		6d. Prussian blue and deep yellow-green	20	
258	–	2s. 6d. multicoloured	70	1
256/8		*Set of* 3	1·00	1

Design:—2s. 6d. Queen Elizabeth II with 4d. and 6d. stamps 1869.

In the 6d. value the stamp illustrated is the 6d. of 1869.

61 Catapult-Ship *Westfalen* launching Dornier Do-J II 10-t Wal

(Des L. Curtis. Litho Format)

1969 (15 Dec). *35th Anniv of Pioneer Air Services. T* **61** *a similar horiz designs showing various forms of transport, m of South Atlantic and Lufthansa emblem. Multicolour P* 13½×14.

No.	Description	Unused	Used
259	2d. Type **61**	35	
260	1s. Dornier Do-J II 10-t Wal *Boreas* flying boat	45	
261	1s. 6d. Airship LZ-127 *Graf Zeppelin*	55	1·
259/61	*Set of* 3	1·25	1

REPUBLIC

63 Athlete and Gambian Flag

(Des Jennifer Toombs. Litho Format)

970 (16 July). *Ninth British Commonwealth Games, Edinburgh.* P 14.

62	63	1d. multicoloured	10	10
63		1s. multicoloured	10	10
64		5s. multicoloured	30	30
62/4		*Set of* 3	35	30

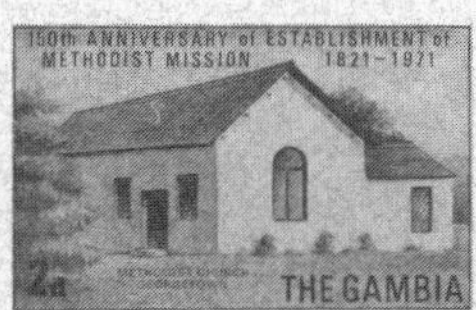

64 President Sir Dawda Kairaba Jawara and State House

(Des G. Vasarhelyi. Litho Questa)

970 (2 Nov). *Republic Day. T* **64** *and similar multicoloured designs. P* 14.

65		2d. Type **64**	10	10
66		1s. President Sir Dawda Jawara	15	10
67		1s. 6d. President and flag of Gambia	30	20
65/7		*Set of* 3	45	30

The 1s. and 1s. 6d. are both vertical designs.

65 Methodist Church, Georgetown

(Des J. Cooter. Litho Questa)

971 (16 Apr). *150th Anniv of Establishment of Methodist Mission. T* **65** *and similar multicoloured designs. P* 14.

68		2d. Type **65**	10	10
69		1s. Map of Africa and Gambian flag (*vert*)	15	10
70		1s. 6d. John Wesley and scroll (*horiz*)	15	20
68/70		*Set of* 3	30	30

(New Currency. 100 bututs = 1 dalasy)

66 Yellow-finned Tunny

(Des J.W. Litho Format)

971 (1 July). *New Currency. Fishes. Horiz designs as T* **66**. *Multicoloured. P* 14.

71	2 b. Type **66**	10	40
72	4 b. Peter's Mormyrid	10	15
73	6 b. Four-winged Flyingfish	15	40
74	8 b. African Sleeper Goby	15	40
75	10 b. Yellow-tailed Snapper	20	15
76	13 b. Rock Hind	20	40
77	25 b. West African Eel Catfish	35	40
78	38 b. Tiger Shark	55	45
79	50 b. Electric Catfish	70	55
80	63 b. Black Swampeel	80	1·50
81	1 d. 25, Small-toothed Sawfish	1·40	2·50
82	2 d. 50, Great Barracuda	2·00	4·50
83	5 d. Brown Bullhead	2·25	7·00
71/83	*Set of* 13	8·00	17·00

67 Mungo Park in Scotland

(Des J.W. from ideas by P. J. Westwood. Litho Questa)

971 (10 Sept). *Birth Bicentenary of Mungo Park (explorer). T* **67** *and similar horiz designs. Multicoloured. W w* **12** *(sideways). P* 13½ × 13.

84	4 b. Type **67**	20	10
85	25 b. Dug-out canoe	45	30
86	37 b. Death of Mungo Park, Busa Rapids	75	1·25
84/6	*Set of* 3	1·25	1·50

68 Radio Gambia

(Des G. Drummond. Litho Questa)

1972 (1 July). *Tenth Anniv of Radio Gambia. T* **68** *and similar horiz design. P* 14.

287	**68**	4 b. orange-ochre and black	10	10
288	–	25 b. light new blue, red-orange and black	10	25
289	**68**	37 b. bright green and black	20	70
287/9		*Set of* 3	30	90

Design:—25 b. Broadcast-area map.

69 High Jumping

70 Manding Woman

(Des and litho D.L.R.)

1972 (31 Aug). *Olympic Games, Munich. P* 13.

290	**69**	4 b. multicoloured	10	10
291		25 b. multicoloured	15	15
292		37 b. multicoloured	15	20
290/2		*Set of* 3	30	30

(Des C. Abbott. Litho Questa)

1972 (16 Oct). *International Conference on Manding Studies, London. T* **70** *and similar vert designs. Multicoloured. P* 14 × 14½.

293	2 b. Type **70**	10	10
294	25 b. Musician playing the Kora	15	15
295	37 b. Map of Mali Empire	25	25
293/5	*Set of* 3	40	40

71 Children carrying Fanal

72 Groundnuts

(Des L. Curtis. Litho Enschedé)

1972 (1 Dec). *Fanals (Model Boats). T* **71** *and similar horiz design. Multicoloured. P* 13 × 13½.

296	2 b. Type **71**	10	10
297	1 d. 25, Fanal with lanterns	30	45

(Des locally; adapted G. Drummond. Litho Harrison)

1973 (31 Mar). *Freedom from Hunger Campaign. P* 14½ × 14.

298	**72**	2 b. multicoloured	10	10
299		25 b. multicoloured	15	10
300		37 b. multicoloured	25	20
298/300		*Set of* 3	40	30

73 Planting and Drying Rice

74 Oil Palm

(Des PAD Studio. Litho J.W.)

1973 (30 Apr). *Agriculture (1st series). T* **73** *and similar vert designs. Multicoloured. P* 14.

301	2 b. Type **73**	10	10
302	25 b. Guinea Corn	20	15
303	37 b. Rice	25	25
301/3	*Set of* 3	45	40

(Des PAD Studio. Litho Format)

1973 (16 July). *Agriculture (2nd series). T* **74** *and similar vert designs. Multicoloured. P* 12.

304	2 b. Type **74**	10	10
305	25 b. Limes	30	30
306	37 b. Oil palm (fruits)	40	40
304/6	*Set of* 3	65	65

75 Cassava

(Des PAD Studio. Litho Questa)

1973 (15 Oct). *Agriculture (3rd series). T* **75** *and similar horiz design. Multicoloured. P* 14.

307	2 b. Type **75**	10	10
308	50 b. Cotton	40	25

76 O.A.U. Emblem

(Des and litho D.L.R.)

1973 (1 Nov). *Tenth Anniv of O.A.U. P* 13½ × 13.

309	**76**	4 b. multicoloured	10	10
310		25 b. multicoloured	15	10
311		37 b. multicoloured	15	20
309/11		*Set of* 3	30	30

77 Red Cross

78 Arms of Banjul

(Des J. Cooter. Litho Questa)

1973 (30 Nov). *25th Anniv of Gambian Red Cross. P* 14 × 14½.

312	**77**	4 b. dull orange-red, and black	10	10
313		25 b. dull orange-red, black and new blue	15	15
314		37 b. dull orange-red, black & lt yell-grn	20	20
312/14		*Set of* 3	35	35

(Des and litho D.L.R.)

1973 (17 Dec). *Change of Bathurst's Name to Banjul. P* 13½ × 13.

315	**78**	4 b. multicoloured	10	10
316		25 b. multicoloured	15	15
317		37 b. multicoloured	15	20
315/17		*Set of* 3	30	30

79 U.P.U. Emblem

(Des and litho D.L.R.)

1974 (24 Aug). *Centenary of Universal Postal Union. P* 13½.

318	**79**	4 b. multicoloured	10	10
319		37 b. multicoloured	20	30

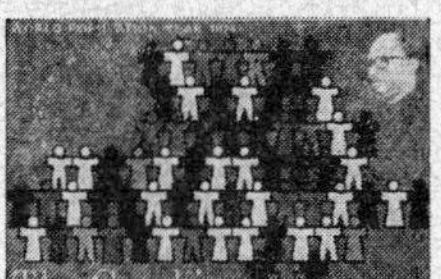

80 Churchill as Harrow Schoolboy

81 "Different Races"

(Des and litho J.W.)

1974 (30 Nov). *Birth Centenary of Sir Winston Churchill. T* **80** *and similar vert designs. Multicoloured. P* 13½.

320	4 b. Type **80**	10	10
321	37 b. Churchill as 4th Hussars officer	25	15
322	50 b. Churchill as Prime Minister	40	60
320/2	*Set of* 3	65	75

(Des G. Vasarhelyi. Litho Questa)

1974 (16 Dec). *World Population Year. T* **81** *and similar horiz designs. Multicoloured. P* 14.

323	4 b. Type **81**	10	10
324	37 b. "Multiplication and Division of Races"	15	15
325	50 b. "World Population"	20	25
323/5	*Set of* 3	35	40

82 Dr. Schweitzer and River Scene

(Des G. Vasarhelyi. Litho Walsall)

1975 (14 Jan). *Birth Centenary of Dr. Albert Schweitzer. T* **82** *and similar horiz designs. Multicoloured. P* 14.

326 10 b. Type **82** 20 10
327 50 b. Surgery scene 55 25
328 1 d. 25, River journey. . . . . 1·00 55
326/8 . . . . *Set of* 3 1·60 75

83 Dove of Peace **84** Development Graph

(Des and litho D.L.R.)

1975 (18 Feb). *10th Anniv of Independence. T* **83** *and similar horiz designs. Multicoloured. P* 13.

329 4 b. Type **83** 10 10
330 10 b. Gambian flag 10 10
331 50 b. Gambian arms 15 10
332 1 d. 25, Map of The Gambia 35 40
329/32 . . . . *Set of* 4 50 55

(Des PAD Studio. Litho Questa)

1975 (31 Mar). *Tenth Anniv of African Development Bank. T* **84** *and similar vert designs. Multicoloured. P* 14½.

333 10 b. Type **84** 10 10
334 50 b. Symbolic plant 20 15
335 1 d. 25, Bank emblem and symbols 55 60
333/5 . . . . *Set of* 3 70 75

85 Statue of "David" (Michelangelo) **86** School Building

(Des C. Abbott. Litho Walsall)

1975 (14 Nov). *500th Birth Anniv of Michelangelo. T* **85** *and similar multicoloured designs. P* 14½ × 14 (1 d. 25) *or* 14 × 14½ (*others*).

336 10 b. Type **85** 15 10
337 50 b. "Madonna of the Steps" 45 15
338 1 d. 25, "Battle of the Centaurs" (*horiz*) . . 75 1·25
336/8 . . . . *Set of* 3 1·25 1·40

(Des G. Vasarhelyi. Litho Format)

1975 (17 Nov). *Centenary of Gambia High School. T* **86** *and similar horiz designs. Multicoloured. P* 14½.

339 10 b. Type **86** 10 10
340 50 b. Pupil with scientific apparatus 15 10
341 1 d. 50, School crest 35 35
339/41 . . . . *Set of* 3 50 40

87 "Teaching"

(Des A. B. Oliver; adapted by Jennifer Toombs. Litho Questa)

1975 (15 Dec). *International Women's Year. T* **87** *and similar horiz designs. Multicoloured. P* 14½.

342 4 b. Type **87** 10 10
343 10 b. "Planting rice" 10 10
344 50 b. "Nursing" 35 15
345 1 d. 50, "Directing traffic" 85 35
342/5 . . . . *Set of* 4 1·25 55

88 Woman playing Golf

89 American Militiaman

(Des R. Granger Barrett. Litho J.W.)

1976 (18 Feb). *11th Anniv of Independence. T* **88** *and similar horiz designs. Multicoloured. P* 14½ × 14.

346 10 b. Type **88** 55 10
347 50 b. Man playing golf. . . . . 1·50 20
348 1 d. 50, President playing golf . . . . . . 2·25 70
346/8 . . . . *Set of* 3 3·75 90

(Des C. Abbott. Litho Questa)

1976 (15 May). *Bicentenary of American Revolution. T* **89** *and similar vert designs. Multicoloured. P* 14 × 13½.

349 25 b. Type **89** 20 10
350 50 b. Soldier of the Continental Army 30 20
351 1 d. 25, Independence Declaration 40 60
349/51 . . . . *Set of* 3 80 80
MS352 110 × 80 mm. Nos. 349/51 . . . . . . 1·40 4·00

90 Mother and Child **91** Serval

(Des G. Vasarhelyi. Litho Questa)

1976 (28 Oct). *Christmas. P* 14.

353 **90** 10 b. multicoloured 10 10
354 50 b. multicoloured 15 10
355 1 d. 25, multicoloured 50 45
353/5 . . . . *Set of* 3 60 50

(Des G. Drummond. Litho Questa)

1976 (29 Nov). *Abuko Nature Reserve* (1*st series*). *T* **91** *and similar horiz designs. Multicoloured. P* 13½.

356 10 b. Type **91** . . . . 2·25 20
357 25 b. Bushbuck . . . . 3·25 20
358 50 b. Sitatunga . . . . 4·50 40
359 1 d. 25, Leopard . . . . 10·00 2·00
356/9 . . . . *Set of* 4 18·00 2·50
MS360 137 × 110 mm. Nos. 356/9 . . . . . . 23·00 9·00

See also Nos. 400/3, 431/5 and 460/3.

92 Festival Emblem and Gambian Weaver

(Des E. N. Sillah; adapted C. Abbott. Litho Walsall)

1977 (12 Jan). *Second World Black and African Festival of Arts and Culture, Nigeria. P* 14.

361 **92** 25 b. multicoloured 15 10
362 50 b. multicoloured 20 15
363 1 d. 25, multicoloured 50 70
361/3 . . . . *Set of* 3 75 85
MS364 118 × 114 mm. Nos. 361/3 . . . . . . 1·75 3·75

93 The Spurs and Jewelled Sword

(Des PAD Studio. Litho Questa)

1977 (7 Feb). *Silver Jubilee. T* **93** *and similar horiz design. Multicoloured. P* 13½.

365 25 b. Queen's visit, 1961 25
366 50 b. Type **93** 20
367 1 d. 25, Oblation of the sword 30
365/7 . . . . *Set of* 3 65

94 Stone Circles, Kuntaur

(Des J.W. Litho Questa)

1977 (18 Feb). *Tourism. T* **94** *and similar horiz designs. Multicoloured. P* 14.

368 25 b. Type **94** 10
369 50 b. Ruined fort, James Island 20
370 1 d. 25, Mungo Park Monument 70
368/70 . . . . *Set of* 3 90

95 Widow of Last Year **96** Endangered Animals

(Des PAD Studio. Litho Questa)

1977 (1 July)–**79**. *Flowers and Shrubs. Multicoloured designs T* **95**. *Chalk-surfaced paper* (*No.* 376*a*) *or ordinary paper* (*othe P* 14.

371 2 b. Type **95** 10
a. Chalk-surfaced paper (23.11.79). . . . 40
372 4 b. White Water-lily 10
a. Chalk-surfaced paper (23.11.79). . . . 40
373 6 b. Fireball Lily 10
a. Chalk-surfaced paper (22.6.79) 40
374 8 b. Cocks-comb 10
a. Chalk-surfaced paper (23.11.79). . . . 30
375 10 b. Broad Leaved Ground Orchid . . . . 2·00
a. Chalk-surfaced paper (23.11.79). . . . 2·00
376 13 b. Fibre Plant (pale yellow background) . . 15
376*a* 13 b. Fibre Plant (pale olive-grey background) (*chalk-surfaced paper*) (25.7.79) . . . . 2·75 3
377 25 b. False Kapok 15
a. Chalk-surfaced paper (16.3.78) 55
378 38 b. Baobab 25
a. Chalk-surfaced paper (23.11.79). . . . 60
379 50 b. Coral Tree 35
a. Chalk-surfaced paper (16.3.78) 75
380 63 b. Gloriosa Lily 40
a. Chalk-surfaced paper (23.11.79). . . . 85
381 1 d. 25, Bell-flowered Mimosa 60 1
a. Chalk-surfaced paper (23.11.79). . . . 1·00 1·
382 2 d. 50, Kindin Dolo 65 1
383 5 d. African Tulip Tree . . . . 85 2·
371/83 . . . . *Set of* 14 7·50 9·

The 6 to 38 b., 1 d. 25 and 2 d. 50 are vertical designs.

(Des N. Fortey (10, 50 b.), D. J. Thorp (25 b.), M. Langley (1 d. 2 Litho Questa)

1977 (15 Oct). *Banjul Declaration. T* **96** *and similar vert desig P* 14.

384 10 b. black and light new blue. 25
385 25 b. multicoloured 40
386 50 b. multicoloured 65
387 1 d. 25, black and light vermilion . . . . . . 1·75
384/7 . . . . *Set of* 4 2·75 1·

Designs:—25 b. Extract from Declaration; 50 b. Declaration full; 1 d. 25, Endangered insects and flowers.

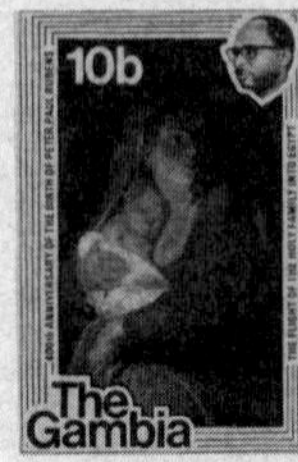

97 "Flight into Egypt" **98** Dome of the Rock, Jerusalem

(Des BG Studio and Enschedé. Litho Enschedé)

1977 (15 Dec). *400th Birth Anniv of Rubens. T* **97** *and similar v designs. Multicoloured. P* 13½ × 14.

388 10 b. Type **97** 15
389 25 b. "The Education of the Virgin" 25
390 50 b. "Clara Serena Rubens" 50
391 1 d. "Madonna with Saints" 90
388/91 . . . . *Set of* 4 1·60 1·

Nos. 388/91 were each printed in small sheets of 6 including 1 *tenant* stamp-size label.

(Des J. Cooter. Litho Questa)

)78 (3 Jan). *Palestinian Welfare. P* 14½ × 14.
)2 **98** 8 b. multicoloured 50 15
)3 25 b. multicoloured .. .. 2·00 85

99 Walking on a Greasy Pole

100 Lion

(Des J.W. Litho Harrison)

)78 (18 Feb). *13th Anniv of Independence. T* **99** *and similar vert designs showing scenes from the Independence Regatta. Multicoloured. P* 14.
)4 10 b. Type **99** 10 10
)5 50 b. Pillow fighting 20 10
)6 1 d. 25, Long rowing boat 45 45
)4/6 .. .. *Set of* 3 60 55

(Des Jennifer Toombs. Litho Questa)

78 (15 Apr). *25th Anniv of Coronation. T* **100** *and similar vert designs. P* 15.
)7 1 d. black, agate and orange-yellow 20 45
a. Sheetlet. Nos. 397/9 × 2 .. .. .. 1·00
)8 1 d. multicoloured 20 45
)9 1 d. black, agate and orange-yellow 20 45
)7/9 .. .. *Set of* 3 50 1·25
Designs:—No. 397, White Greyhound of Richmond; No. 398, ..een Elizabeth II; No. 399, Type **100**.
Nos. 397/9 were printed together in small sheets of 6, containing *..o se-tenant* strips of 3, with horizontal gutter margin between.

101 Verreaux's Eagle Owl

102 M.V. *Lady Wright* (previous vessel)

(Des M. Bryan. Litho Questa)

)78 (28 Oct). *Abuko Nature Reserve (2nd series). T* **101** *and similar vert designs. Multicoloured. P* 14 × 13½.
)0 20 b. Type **101** .. .. 5·00 50
)1 25 b. Lizard Buzzard .. .. 5·00 50
)2 50 b. African Harrier Hawk .. .. .. 8·00 2·00
)3 1 d. 25, Long-crested Eagle .. .. .. 12·00 8·00
)0/3 .. .. *Set of* 4 27·00 10·00

(Des A. Theobald. Litho Questa)

)78 (1 Dec). *New River Vessel "Lady Chilel Jawara" Commemoration. T* **102** *and similar horiz designs. Multicoloured. P* 14.
)4 8 b. Type **102** 15 10
)5 25 b. *Lady Chilel Jawara* (sectional view) .. 40 25
)6 1 d. *Lady Chilel Jawara* .. .. .. 1·25 1·10
)4/6 .. .. *Set of* 3 1·60 1·25

25b

103 Police Service

(104)

(Des G. Vasarhelyi. Litho Questa)

)79 (18 Feb). *14th Anniv of Independence. T* **103** *and similar horiz designs. Multicoloured. P* 14.
)7 10 b. Type **103** 60 10
)8 50 b. Fire service .. .. 1·10 25
)9 1 d. 25, Ambulance service .. .. .. 1·40 80
)07/9 .. .. *Set of* 3 2·75 1·00

)79 (5–26 Mar). *Nos.* 376 *and* 380/1 *surch as T* **104**.
10 25 b. on 13 b. Fibre Plant 20 35
11 25 b. on 63 b. Gloriosa Lily (26.3.79) 15 20
12 25 b. on 1 d. 25, Bell-flowered Mimosa (26.3.79) 15 20
10/12 .. .. *Set of* 3 45 65

105 "Ramsgate Sands" (detail showing Children playing on Beach)

(Des C. Abbott. Litho Questa)

1979 (25 May). *International Year of the Child. T* **105** *and similar multicoloured designs showing the painting "Ramsgate Sands" by William Powell Frith. P* 14 × 13½ (25 *b.*) *or* 13½ × 14 (*others*).
413 10 b. Type **105** 10 10
414 25 b. Detail showing child paddling (*vert*) .. 20 10
415 1 d. Complete painting (60 × 23 *mm*) .. 60 60
413/15 .. .. *Set of* 3 80 65

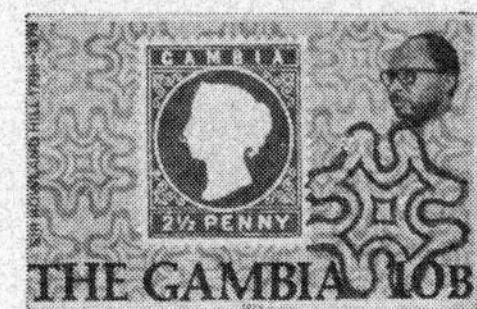

106 1883 2½d. Stamp

(Des J.W. Litho Questa)

1979 (16 Aug). *Death Centenary of Sir Rowland Hill. T* **106** *and similar horiz designs showing stamps. Multicoloured. P* 14.
416 10 b. Type **106** 10 10
417 25 b. 1869 4d. 15 10
418 50 b. 1965 7½d. Independence commemorative 20 20
419 1 d. 25, 1935 1½d. Silver Jubilee commemorative 40 50
416/19 .. .. *Set of* 4 75 80
MS420 109 × 83 mm. No. 419 .. .. .. 65 1·00

107 Satellite Earth Station under Construction

108 "Apollo 11" leaving Launch Pad

(Des A. Theobald. Litho Questa)

1979 (20 Sept). *Abuko Satellite Earth Station. T* **107** *and similar horiz designs. Multicoloured. P* 14.
421 25 b. Type **107** 20 10
422 50 b. Satellite Earth Station (completed) .. 30 20
423 1 d. "Intelsat" satellites 65 60
421/3 .. .. *Set of* 3 1·00 80

(Des and litho Walsall)

1979 (17 Oct). *10th Anniv of Moon Landing. T* **108** *and similar vert designs. Multicoloured.* (*a*) *Sheet stamps. P* 14.
424 25 b. Type **108** 20 10
425 38 b. "Apollo 11" in Moon orbit 25 20
426 50 b. Splashdown 30 40
424/6 .. .. *Set of* 3 65 60

(*b*) *Booklet stamps. Roul* 5 × *imperf.* Self-adhesive*
427 25 b. Type **108** 25 55
a. Booklet pane. Nos. 427/9, each × 2 .. 1·60
428 38 b. As No. 425 .. .. 30 55
429 50 b. As No. 426 .. .. 30 55
430 2 d. Lunar module on Moon .. .. .. 1·50 2·25
a. Booklet pane of 1 .. .. 1·50
*Nos. 427/9 are separated by various combinations of rotary-knife (giving a straight edge) and roulette. No. 430 exists only with straight edges.

109 *Acraea zetes*

(Des J. Cooter. Litho Questa)

1980 (3 Jan). *Abuko Nature Reserve* (3*rd series*). *Butterflies. T* **109** *and similar horiz designs. Multicoloured. P* 13½.
431 25 b. Type **109** .. .. 2·50 20
432 50 b. *Precis hierta* .. .. 3·00 50
433 1 d. *Graphium leonidas* .. .. .. 5·00 1·00
434 1 d. 25, *Charaxes jasius* .. .. .. 5·00 1·10
431/4 .. .. *Set of* 4 14·00 2·50
MS435 145×122 mm. Nos. 431/4 .. .. .. 22·00 4·50

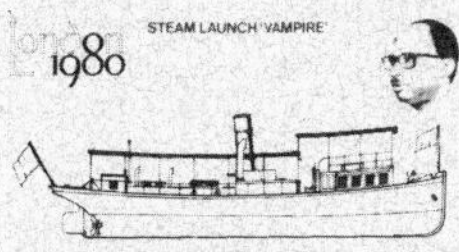

110 Steam Launch *Vampire*

(Des C. Abbott. Litho Harrison)

1980 (6 May). *"London 1980" International Stamp Exhibition. Mail Boats. T* **110** *and similar multicoloured designs. P* 14 (10, 25 *b.*) *or* 13 × 14 (*others*).
436 10 b. Type **110** 25 10
437 25 b. T.S.S. *Lady Denham* 35 10
438 50 b. T.S.C.M.Y. *Mansa Kila Ba* (49 × 26 *mm*) 40 20
439 1 d. 25, T.S.S. *Prince of Wales* (49 × 26 *mm*) .. 65 60
436/9 .. .. *Set of* 4 1·50 85

111 Queen Elizabeth the Queen Mother

(Des and litho Harrison)

1980 (4 Aug). *80th Birthday of Queen Elizabeth the Queen Mother. P* 14.
440 **111** 67 b. multicoloured 30 35

112 Phoenician Trading Vessel

113 "Madonna and Child" (Francesco de Mura)

(Des A. Theobald. Litho Walsall)

1980 (2 Oct). *Early Sailing Vessels. T* **112** *and similar horiz designs. Multicoloured. P* 14½ × 14.
441 8 b. Type **112** 10 10
442 67 b. Egyptian sea-going vessel 40 20
443 75 b. Portuguese caravel 50 30
444 1 d. Spanish galleon 70 50
441/4 .. .. *Set of* 4 1·50 1·00

(Des BG Studio. Litho Questa)

1980 (23 Dec). *Christmas. Paintings. T* **113** *and similar vert designs. Multicoloured. P* 14.
445 8 b. Type **113** 10 10
446 67 b. "Praying Madonna with Crown of Stars" (workshop of Correggio) 25 25
447 75 b. "La Zingarella" (workshop replica of Correggio painting) 25 30
445/7 .. .. *Set of* 3 50 60

114 New Atlantic Hotel

(Des BG Studio. Litho Format)

1981 (18 Feb). *World Tourism Conference, Manila. T* **114** *and similar horiz designs. Multicoloured. P* 14.
448 25 b. Type **114** 15 10
449 75 b. Ancient stone circle 30 40
450 85 b. Conference emblem 40 50
448/50 .. .. *Set of* 3 75 90

115 1979 Abuko Satellite Earth Station 50 b. Commemorative

116 Prince Charles in Naval Uniform

(Des BG Studio. Litho Questa)

1981 (17 May). *World Telecommunications Day. T* **115** *and similar horiz designs. P* 14.

No.	Description		Mint	Used
451	50 b. multicoloured	.. ..	30	20
452	50 b. multicoloured	.. ..	30	20
453	85 b. black and brown-ochre	.. ..	50	45
451/3	.. ..	*Set of* 3	1·00	75

Designs:—No. 452, 1975 Birth Centenary of Dr. Albert Schweitzer 50 b. commemorative; No. 453, I.T.U. and W.H.O. emblems.

(Des and litho J.W.)

1981 (22 July). *Royal Wedding. T* **116** *and similar vert designs. Multicoloured. P* 13½ × 13.

No.	Description		Mint	Used
454	75 b. Wedding bouquet from Gambia	.. ..	20	20
455	1 d. Type **116**	.. ..	25	30
456	1 d. 25, Prince Charles and Lady Diana Spencer	.. ..	30	35
454/6	.. ..	*Set of* 3	65	75

117 Planting-out Seedlings

(Des Jennifer Toombs. Litho Format)

1981 (4 Sept). *10th Anniv of West African Rice Development Association. T* **117** *and similar horiz designs. Multicoloured. P* 14.

No.	Description		Mint	Used
457	10 b. Type **117**	.. ..	10	10
458	50 b. Care of the crops	.. ..	25	35
459	85 b. Winnowing and drying	.. ..	40	55
457/9	.. ..	*Set of* 3	65	85

118 Bosc's Monitor

(Des J. Cooter. Litho Format)

1981 (17 Nov). *Abuko Nature Reserve (4th series). Reptiles. T* **118** *and similar horiz designs. Multicoloured. P* 14.

No.	Description		Mint	Used
460	40 b. Type **118**	.. ..	3·00	20
461	60 b. Dwarf Crocodile	.. ..	3·50	60
462	80 b. Royal Python	.. ..	4·50	1·00
463	85 b. Chameleon	.. ..	4·50	1·00
460/3	.. ..	*Set of* 4	14·00	2·50

60B

119 Examination Room (**120**)

(Des PAD Studio. Litho Walsall)

1982 (16 Mar). *30th Anniv of West African Examinations Council. T* **119** *and similar horiz designs. Multicoloured. P* 14.

No.	Description		Mint	Used
464	60 b. Type **119**	.. ..	50	30
465	85 b. First High School	.. ..	65	45
466	1 d. 10, Council's office	.. ..	85	55
464/6	.. ..	*Set of* 3	1·75	1·10

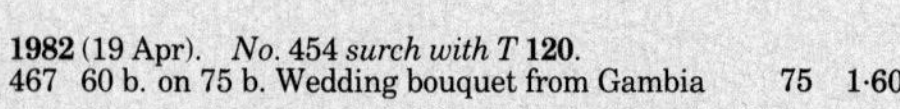

1982 (19 Apr). *No.* 454 *surch with T* **120**.

No.	Description	Mint	Used
467	60 b. on 75 b. Wedding bouquet from Gambia	75	1·60

121 Tree-planting ("Conservation")

(Des L. Curtis. Litho Harrison)

1982 (16 May). *75th Anniv of Boy Scout Movement. T* **121** *and similar horiz designs. Multicoloured. P* 14.

No.	Description		Mint	Used
468	85 b. Type **121**	.. ..	2·00	1·25
469	1 d. 25, Woodworking	.. ..	2·25	2·50
470	1 d. 27, Lord Baden-Powell	.. ..	2·50	3·25
468/70	.. ..	*Set of* 3	6·00	6·25

122 Gambia Football Team **123** Gambia Coat of Arms

(Des A. Theobald. Litho Questa)

1982 (13 June). *World Cup Football Championship, Spain. T* **122** *and similar horiz designs. Multicoloured. P* 14.

No.	Description		Mint	Used
471	10 b. Type **122**	.. ..	20	10
472	1 d. 10, Gambian team practice	.. .. ..	1·10	70
473	1 d. 25, Bernabéu Stadium, Madrid	.. ..	1·10	75
474	1 d. 55, FIFA World Cup	.. ..	1·25	80
471/4	.. ..	*Set of* 4	3·25	2·10
MS475	114 × 85 mm. Nos. 471/4	.. ..	4·00	4·50

(Des C. Abbott. Litho Walsall)

1982 (1 July). *21st Birthday of Princess of Wales. T* **123** *and similar vert designs. Multicoloured. P* 14½ × 14.

No.	Description		Mint	Used
476	10 b. Type **123**	.. ..	10	10
477	85 b. Princess at Cardiff City Hall, October 1981	.. ..	30	20
478	1 d. 10, Bride and groom returning to Buckingham Palace	.. ..	35	35
479	2 d. 50, Formal portrait	.. ..	1·25	1·00
476/9	.. ..	*Set of* 4	1·75	1·40

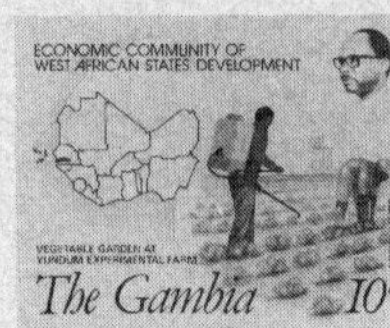

124 Vegetable Garden at Yundum Experimental Farm

(Des Harrison. Litho Questa)

1982 (5 Nov). *Economic Community of West African States Development. T* **124** *and similar horiz designs. Multicoloured. P* 14 × 14½.

No.	Description		Mint	Used
480	10 b. Type **124**	.. ..	30	15
481	60 b. Banjul/Kaolack microwave tower	..	2·00	2·25
482	90 b. Soap factory, Denton Bridge, Banjul	..	2·00	3·00
483	1 d. 25, Control tower, Yundum Airport	..	3·00	3·50
480/3	.. ..	*Set of* 4	6·50	8·00

125 *Kassina cassinoides*

(Des PAD Studio. Litho Questa)

1982 (2 Dec). *Frogs. T* **125** *and similar horiz designs. Multicoloured. P* 14.

No.	Description		Mint	Used
484	10 b. Type **125**	.. ..	80	20
485	20 b. *Hylarana galamensis*	.. ..	1·75	30
486	85 b. *Euphlyctis occipitalis*	.. ..	2·75	2·00
487	2 d. *Kassina senegalensis*	.. ..	4·25	7·50
484/7	.. ..	*Set of* 4	8·50	9·00

CENTENARY OF THE SISTERS OF ST. JOSEPH OF CLUNY 1883-1983
THE GAMBIA 10b

126 Satellite View of Gambia **127** Blessed Anne Marie Javouhey (foundress of the Order)

(Des Walsall. Litho Questa)

1983 (14 Mar). *Commonwealth Day. T* **126** *and similar horiz designs. Multicoloured. P* 14.

No.	Description		Mint	Used
488	10 b. Type **126**	.. ..	10	10
489	60 b. Batik cloth	.. ..	20	45
490	1 d. 10, Bagging groundnuts	.. .. ..	35	65
491	2 d. 10, Gambia flag	.. ..	55	1·25
488/91	.. ..	*Set of* 4	1·00	2·25

(Des G. Vasarhelyi. Litho Format)

1983 (8 Apr). *Centenary of Sisters of St. Joseph of Cluny's Work in Gambia. T* **127** *and similar multicoloured design. P* 13½.

No.	Description		Mint	Used
492	10 b. Type **127**	.. ..	10	10
493	85 b. Bathurst Hospital, nun and school-children (*horiz*)	.. ..	45	50

128 Canoes

(Des A. Theobald. Litho Walsall)

1983 (11 July). *River Craft. T* **128** *and similar horiz desig Multicoloured. P* 14.

No.	Description		Mint	Used
494	1 b. Type **128**	.. ..	15	
495	2 b. Upstream ferry	.. .. ..	20	
496	3 b. Dredger	.. ..	20	
497	4 b. *Sir Dawda* (harbour launch)	..	30	
498	5 b. Cargo liner	.. ..	30	
499	10 b. *Lady Dale* (60 ft launch)	.. ..	30	
500	20 b. *Shonga* (container ship)	.. ..	45	
501	30 b. Large sailing canoe	.. .. ..	45	
502	40 b. *Lady Wright* (river steamer)	..	65	
503	50 b. Container ship (*different*)	.. ..	65	
504	75 b. Fishing boats	.. .. ..	75	
505	1 d. Tug with groundnut barges	.. ..	90	
506	1 d. 25, Groundnut canoe	.. ..	1·00	1·
507	2 d. 50, *Banjul* (car ferry)	.. ..	1·75	2·
508	5 d. *Bintang Bolong* (freighter)	.. ..	2·50	4·
509	10 d. *Lady Chilel Jawara* (river vessel)	..	4·00	6·
494/509	.. ..	*Set of* 16	13·00	18·

Nos. 494/509 come with a pattern of blue fluorescent secur markings, resembling rosettes, printed on the reverse beneath t gum.

129 Osprey in Tree

(Des N. Arlott. Litho Questa)

1983 (12 Sept). *The Osprey. T* **129** *and similar horiz desig Multicoloured. P* 14.

No.	Description		Mint	Used
510	10 b. Type **129**	.. ..	1·50	
511	60 b. Osprey	.. ..	2·50	2
512	85 b. Osprey with catch	.. .. ..	3·00	3
513	1 d. 10, In flight	.. ..	3·50	4
510/13	.. ..	*Set of* 4	9·50	9

130 Local Ferry

(Des L. Curtis. Litho Questa)

1983 (10 Oct). *World Communications Year. T* **130** *and simi horiz designs. Multicoloured. P* 14.

No.	Description		Mint	Used
514	10 b. Type **130**	.. ..	10	
515	85 b. Telex operator	.. .. ..	45	
516	90 b. Radio Gambia	.. .. ..	45	
517	1 d. 10, Loading mail onto Douglas DC-9-80 Super Eighty aircraft	.. ..	1·00	
514/17	.. ..	*Set of* 4	1·75	1

131 "St. Paul preaching at Athens" (detail) (Raphael)

(Des C. Abbott. Litho Questa)

1983 (1 Nov). *500th Birth Anniv of Raphael. T* **131** *and simi designs. P* 14.

No.	Description		Mint	Used
518	60 b. multicoloured	.. ..	35	
519	85 b. multicoloured	.. ..	45	
520	1 d. multicoloured	.. ..	50	
518/20	.. ..	*Set of* 3	1·10	1
MS521	105 × 83 mm. 2 d. multicoloured	.. ..	1·50	1

Nos. 519/21 show different details of "St. Paul preaching Athens", the 85 b. and 1 d. being horizontal and the 2 d. vertical

MINIMUM PRICE

The minimum price quote is 10p which represe a handling charge rather than a basis for valui common stamps. For further notes about pric see introductory pages.

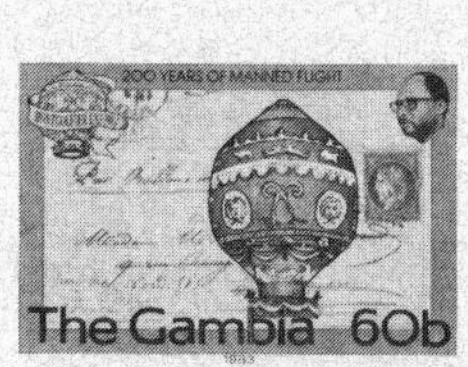

132 Montgolfier Balloon and Siege of Paris Cover — **133** Shot-putting

(Des Harrison. Litho Questa)

983 (12 Dec). *Bicentenary of Manned Flight. T* **132** *and similar horiz designs. Multicoloured. P* 14.
22 60 b. Type **132** 35 40
a. Booklet pane. Nos. 522/3, each × 2 .. 1·60
23 85 b. Douglas DC-10 aircraft and flown cover 45 50
24 90 b. Junkers W.33 seaplane *Atlantis* and Hans Bertram cover 45 50
a. Booklet pane. Nos. 524/5, each × 2 .. 2·25
25 1 d. 25, Lunar module and H. E. Sieger's space cover 65 70
26 4 d. Airship LZ-127 *Graf Zeppelin* .. 2·00 3·00
a. Booklet pane of 1 .. .. .. 2·00
22/6 .. .. *Set of* 5 3·50 4·50
Nos. 522/6 come with a pattern of blue fluorescent security arkings, resembling rosettes, printed on the reverse beneath the um.
No. 526 only exists from booklets.

On 14 December 1983 four provisional surcharges, 1 d. 50 on d. 25 (No. 439), 1 d. 50 on 1 d. 25 (No. 473), 2d. on 1 d. 25 (No. 456) nd 2 d. on 1 d. 10 (No. 478), were issued in very limited quantities, ere being, it is believed, no more than 600 complete sets (*Price for t of* 4 £110 *mint*).

(Des G. Vasarhelyi. Litho Questa)

984 (30 Mar). *Olympic Games, Los Angeles (1st issue). T* **133** *and similar multicoloured designs. P* 11.
27 60 b. Type **133** 25 30
28 85 b. High jumping (*horiz*) 35 40
29 90 b. Wrestling 35 40
30 1 d. Gymnastics 40 45
31 1 d. 25, Swimming (*horiz*) 50 55
32 2 d. Diving 80 85
27/32 .. .. *Set of* 6 2·40 2·75
MS533 100 × 80 mm. 5 d. Yachting. P 13½ × 14 2·00 2·25
See also Nos. 555/8.

134 Goofy

(Litho Format)

984 (27 Apr). *Easter. T* **134** *and similar vert designs showing Walt Disney cartoon characters painting eggs. P* 11.
34 1 b. Type **134** 10 10
35 2 b. Mickey Mouse 10 10
36 3 b. Huey, Dewey and Louie 10 10
37 4 b. Goofy (*different*) 10 10
38 5 b. Donald Duck 10 10
39 10 b. Chip 'n Dale 10 10
40 60 b. Pluto 35 40
41 90 b. Scrooge McDuck 50 60
42 5 d. Morty and Ferdie .. .. .. 2·25 2·75
34/42 .. .. *Set of* 9 3·00 3·75
MS543 125 × 100 mm. 5 d. Donald Duck (*different*). P 13½ × 14 .. .. 3·50 3·50

135 Young Crocodiles Hatching — **136** Port Banjul

(Des Doreen McGuinness. Litho Format)

984 (23 May). *Endangered Species. The Nile Crocodile. T* **135** *and similar horiz designs. Multicoloured. P* 14.
44 4 b. Type **135** 45 45
45 6 b. Adult carrying young 45 45
46 90 b. Adult .. .. 4·00 2·75
47 1 d. 50, Crocodile at riverbank .. .. 5·00 6·50
44/7 .. .. *Set of* 4 9·00 9·00
MS548 126×94 mm. As Nos. 544/7, but without W.W.F. logo .. .. 4·50 7·00
Nos. 544/8 come with a pattern of blue fluorescent security arkings, resembling rosettes, printed on the reverse beneath e gum.

(Des C. Collins. Litho Questa)

1984 (1 June). 250*th Anniv of "Lloyd's List" (newspaper). T* **136** *and similar vert designs. Multicoloured. P* 14½ × 14.
549 60 b. Type **136** 60 50
550 85 b. Bulk carrier 75 80
551 90 b. Sinking of the *Dagomba* 75 90
552 1 d. 25, 19th century frigate .. .. .. 1·25 1·60
549/52 .. .. *Set of* 4 3·00 3·50
Nos. 549/52 come with a pattern of blue fluorescent security markings, resembling rosettes, printed on the reverse beneath the gum.

19th UPU CONGRESS HAMBURG
(137)

138 Sprinting

1984 (19 June). *Universal Postal Union Congress, Hamburg. Nos.* 507/8 *optd with T* **137.**
553 2 d. 50, *Banjul* (car ferry) .. .. .. 1·00 1·50
554 5 d. *Bintang Bolong* (ferry) .. .. .. 1·75 2·50

(Des G. Vasarhelyi. Litho Walsall)

1984 (27 July). *Olympic Games, Los Angeles (2nd issue). T* **138** *and similar horiz designs. Multicoloured. P* 14.
555 60 b. Type **138** 25 30
556 85 b. Long jumping 35 40
557 90 b. Long-distance running 35 40
558 1 d. 25, Triple jumping 50 55
555/8 .. .. *Set of* 4 1·25 1·50
Nos. 555/8 come with a pattern of blue fluorescent security markings, resembling rosettes, printed on the reverse beneath the gum.

139 Airship LZ-127 *Graf Zeppelin*

(Des D. Hartley-Marjoram. Litho Questa)

1984 (1 Nov). 50*th Anniv of Gambia–South America Trans-atlantic Flights. T* **139** *and similar horiz designs. Multi-coloured. P* 14.
559 60 b. Type **139** .. .. 1·10 1·00
560 85 b. Dornier Do-J II 10-t Wal on S.S. *Westfalen* .. .. 1·60 1·75
561 90 b. Dornier DO-18 .. .. 1·75 2·50
562 1 d. 25, Dornier Do-J II 10-t Wal .. .. 1·75 2·75
559/62 .. .. *Set of* 4 5·50 7·25
Nos. 559/62 come with a pattern of blue fluorescent security markings, resembling rosettes, printed on the reverse beneath the gum.

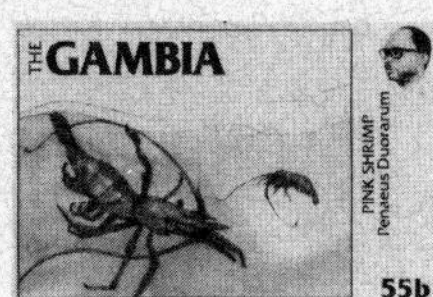

140 Pink Shrimp

(Des Pam Johnson. Litho Questa)

1984 (27 Nov). *Marine Life. T* **140** *and similar horiz designs. Multicoloured. P* 14.
563 55 b. Type **140** 35 30
564 75 b. Atlantic Loggerhead Turtle 55 40
565 1 d. 50, Portuguese Man-of-War .. .. 90 1·00
566 2 d. 35, Fiddler Crab .. .. .. 1·40 1·60
563/6 .. .. *Set of* 4 2·75 3·00
MS567 105×70 mm. 5 d. Cowrie Snail .. .. 2·75 4·00

141 *Antanartia hippomene*

(Des Pam Johnson. Litho Questa)

1984 (27 Nov). *Butterflies. T* **141** *and similar horiz designs. Multicoloured. P* 14.
568 10 b. Type **141** 30 20
569 85 b. *Pseudacraea eurytus* 80 90
570 90 b. *Charaxes lactitinctus* 80 90
571 3 d. *Graphium pylades* .. .. .. 2·00 3·75
568/71 .. .. *Set of* 4 3·50 5·25
MS572 105×75 mm. 5 d. *Eurema hapale* .. 10·00 9·50

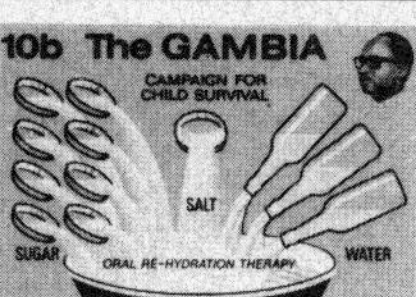

142 Oral Re-hydration Therapy

(Des L. Curtis. Litho Harrison)

1985 (27 Feb). *Campaign for Child Survival. T* **142** *and similar horiz designs. P* 14.
573 10 b. black, cobalt and deep cinnamon .. 10 10
574 85 b. multicoloured 35 45
575 1 d. 10, multicoloured 45 65
576 1 d. 50, multicoloured 60 80
573/6 .. .. *Set of* 4 1·25 1·75
Designs:—85 b. Growth monitoring; 1 d. 10, Health care worker with women and babies ("Promotion of breast feeding"); 1 d. 50, Universal immunisation.
Nos. 573/6 come with a pattern of blue fluorescent security markings, resembling rosettes, printed on the reverse beneath the gum.

143 Women at Market — **144** Turkey Vulture

(Des G. Vasarhelyi. Litho Format)

1985 (11 Mar). *Women and Development. T* **143** *and similar horiz design. Multicoloured. P* 14.
577 60 b. Type **143** 25 35
578 85 b. Type **143** 35 50
579 1 d. Woman office worker 40 60
580 1 d. 25, As 1 d. 50 90
577/80 .. .. *Set of* 4 1·40 2·10
Nos. 577/80 come with a pattern of blue fluorescent security markings, resembling rosettes, printed on the reverse beneath the gum.

(Des and litho Questa)

1985 (15 July). *Birth Bicentenary of John J. Audubon (ornithologist). T* **144** *and similar multicoloured designs showing original paintings. P* 14.
581 60 b. Type **144** .. .. 1·40 75
582 85 b. American Anhinga .. .. .. 1·60 1·50
583 1 d. 50, Green Heron .. .. .. 2·00 3·25
584 5 d. Wood Duck .. .. 3·25 5·50
581/4 .. .. *Set of* 4 7·50 10·00
MS585 100×70 mm. 10 d. Great Northern Diver (inscr "Common Loon") (*horiz*) .. .. .. 4·25 4·00

GOLD MEDALLIST
CLAUDIA LOCH
WEST GERMANY

145 The Queen Mother — **(146)**

(Des J.W. Litho Questa)

1985 (29 July). *Life and Times of Queen Elizabeth the Queen Mother. T* **145** *and similar vert designs. Multicoloured. P* 14.
586 85 b. The Queen Mother and King George VI reviewing Home Guard 25 30
587 3 d. Type **145** .. .. 80 1·00
588 5 d. The Queen Mother with posy .. .. 1·40 1·75
586/8 .. .. *Set of* 3 2·25 2·75
MS589 56×85 mm. 10 d. The Queen Mother in Garter robes .. .. 2·50 3·25

(Des Walt Disney Studios. Litho Questa)

1985 (30 Oct). 150*th Birth Anniv of Mark Twain (author). Horiz designs as T* **118** *of Anguilla showing Walt Disney cartoon characters in scenes from "Life on the Mississippi". Multicoloured. P* 14×13½.
590 1 d. 50, Mickey Mouse steering the *Calamity Jane* 90 90
591 2 d. Mickey and Minnie Mouse at antebellum mansion .. .. 1·25 1·25
592 2 d. 50, Donald Duck and Goofy heaving the lead .. .. 1·50 1·50
593 3 d. Poker game aboard the *Gold Dust* .. 1·60 1·60
590/3 .. .. *Set of* 4 4·75 4·75
MS594 126×101 mm. 10 d. Mickey Mouse and riverboat .. .. 5·50 4·25

(Des Walt Disney Productions. Litho Questa)

1985 (30 Oct). *Birth Bicentenaries of Grimm Brothers (folklorists). Designs as T* **119** *of Anguilla, but vert, showing Walt Disney cartoon characters in scenes from "Faithful John". Multicoloured. P* 13½ × 14.
595 60 b. The King (Mickey Mouse) and portrait of the Princess (Minnie Mouse) 40 40
596 85 b. The King showing the Princess his treasures 50 50
597 2 d. 35, Faithful John (Goofy) playing trumpet .. .. 1·10 1·40
598 5 d. Faithful John turned to stone .. .. 2·25 2·50
595/8 .. .. *Set of* 4 3·75 4·25
MS599 126 × 101 mm. 10 d. Faithful John after recovery .. .. 6·00 5·00

1985 (11 Nov). *Olympic Gold Medal Winners, Los Angeles. Nos.* 527/33 *optd as T* **146**.
600 60 b. Type **133** (optd with T **146**) 40 40
601 85 b. High jumping (optd "GOLD MEDALLIST ULRIKE MEYFARTH WEST GERMANY") 50 50
602 90 b. Wrestling (optd "GOLD MEDALLIST PASQUALE PASSARELLI WEST GERMANY") 50 50
603 1 d. Gymnastics (optd "GOLD MEDALLIST LI NING CHINA") 55 55
604 1 d. 25, Swimming (optd "GOLD MEDALLIST MICHAEL GROSS WEST GERMANY") 70 70
605 2 d. Diving (optd "GOLD MEDALLIST SYLVIE BERNIER CANADA") .. 1·00 1·00
600/5 .. .. *Set of* 6 3·25 3·25
MS606 100 × 80 mm. 5 d. Yachting (opt "GOLD MEDAL STAR CLASS U.S.A.") .. .. .. 1·75 1·90

147 Inspecting Maize

(Des J. Farleo. Litho Questa)

1985 (15 Nov). *United Nations Anniversaries. T* **147** *and similar horiz designs. Multicoloured. P* 14.
607 60 b. Type **147** 40 35
608 85 b. Football match, Independence Stadium, Banjul 50 40
609 1 d. 10, Rice fields 60 60
610 2 d. Central Bank of The Gambia .. .. 85 1·00
611 3 d. Cow and calf .. .. 1·50 1·75
612 4 d. Banjul harbour .. .. 2·00 2·25
613 5 d. Gambian fruits .. .. 2·25 2·50
614 6 d. Oyster Creek Bridge .. .. .. 2·50 3·00
607/14 .. .. *Set of* 8 9·50 10·50
Nos. 607, 609, 611 and 613 commemorate the 40th anniversary of the Food and Agriculture Organization and Nos. 608, 610, 612 and 614 the 40th anniversary of the United Nations Organization.

148 Fishermen in Fotoba, Guinea

149 "Virgin and Child" (Dieric Bouts)

(Des B. Bundock. Litho Questa)

1985 (24 Dec). *50th Anniv of Diocese of The Gambia and Guinea. T* **148** *and similar horiz designs. Multicoloured. P* 14.
615 60 b. Type **148** 30 30
616 85 b. St. Mary's Primary School, Banjul .. 30 40
617 1 d. 10, St. Mary's Cathedral, Banjul .. 35 65
618 1 d. 50, Mobile dispensary at Christy Kunda 50 85
615/18 .. .. *Set of* 4 1·25 2·00

(Des Mary Walters. Litho Format)

1985 (24 Dec). *Christmas. Religious Paintings. T* **149** *and similar vert designs. Multicoloured. P* 15.
619 60 b. Type **149** 20 25
620 85 b. "The Annunciation" (Robert Campin) .. 25 30
621 1 d. 50, "Adoration of the Shepherds" (Gerard David) 45 50
622 5 d. "The Nativity" (Gerard David) .. 1·60 1·75
619/22 .. .. *Set of* 4 2·25 2·50
MS623 106 × 84 mm. 10 d. "Adoration of the Magi" (Hieronymus Bosch) .. .. 3·50 4·00
No. **MS**623 exists imperforate from stock dispersed by the liquidator of Format International Security Printers Ltd.

150 Enrolment Card

(Des N. Waldman. Litho Questa)

1985 (27 Dec). *75th Anniv of Girl Guide Movement. T* **150** *and similar multicoloured designs. P* 14.
624 60 b. Type **150** 40 30
625 85 b. 2nd Bathurst Company centre .. 50 35
626 1 d. 50, Lady Baden-Powell (*vert*) .. .. 70 1·00
627 5 d. Miss Rosamond Fowlis (Gambian Guide Association leader) (*vert*) .. 2·00 3·75
624/7 .. .. *Set of* 4 3·25 4·75
MS628 97 × 67 mm. 10 d. Gambian Girl Guides (*vert*) .. .. 4·50 6·00

151 Girl and Village Scene

152 Two Players competing for Ball

(Des B. Bundock. Litho Questa)

1985 (31 Dec). *International Youth Year. T* **151** *and similar horiz designs. Multicoloured. P* 14.
629 60 b. Type **151** 25 30
630 85 b. Youth and wrestling bout 30 35
631 1 d. 10, Girl and Griot storyteller 40 85
632 1 d. 50, Youth and crocodile pool .. .. 50 1·10
629/32 .. .. *Set of* 4 1·25 2·40
MS633 106 × 76 mm. 5 d. Herdsman with cattle .. 2·00 3·00

(Des W. Hanson. Litho Questa)

1986 (18 Apr). *Appearance of Halley's Comet* (*1st issue*). *Horiz designs as T* **123** *of Anguilla. Multicoloured. P* 14.
634 10 b. Maria Mitchell (astronomer) and Kitt Peak National Observatory, Arizona .. 40 20
635 20 b. Neil Armstrong, first man on Moon, 1969 .. .. 55 25
636 75 b. "Skylab 4" and Comet Kohoutek, 1973 85 65
637 1 d. N.A.S.A.'s infra-red astronomical satellite and Halley's Comet .. .. 1·00 80
638 2 d. Comet of 1577 from Turkish painting .. 1·50 1·50
639 10 d. N.A.S.A.'s International Cometary Explorer .. .. 4·00 5·50
634/9 .. .. *Set of* 6 7·50 8·00
MS640 102 × 70 mm. 10 d. Halley's Comet .. 5·00 6·50
See also Nos. 679/84.

(Des and litho Questa)

1986 (21 Apr). *60th Birthday of Queen Elizabeth II. Vert designs as T* **125** *of Anguilla. P* 14.
641 1 d. black and yellow 25 30
642 2 d. 50, multicoloured 65 80
643 10 d. multicoloured .. .. 2·50 3·50
641/3 .. .. *Set of* 3 3·00 4·25
MS644 120 × 85 mm. 10 d. black and grey-brown 2·50 3·00
Designs:—No. 641, Duke of York and family, Royal Tournament, 1936; 642, Queen attending christening, 1983; 643, In West Germany, 1978; **MS**644, Duchess of York with her daughters, Balmoral, 1935.

(Des J. Birdsong. Litho Questa)

1986 (2 May). *World Cup Football Championship, Mexico. T* **152** *and similar vert designs. Multicoloured. P* 14.
645 75 b. Type **152** 75 60
646 1 d. Player kicking ball .. .. .. 1·00 85
647 2 d. 50, Player kicking ball (*different*) .. 2·00 2·25
648 10 d. Player heading ball .. .. .. 5·00 6·00
645/8 .. .. *Set of* 4 8·00 8·75
MS649 100 × 70 mm. 10 d. Goalkeeper saving goal .. .. 7·50 7·00

153 Mercedes "500" (1986)

(Des P. Rhymer. Litho Format)

1986 (31 May). *"Ameripex" International Stamp Exhibition, Chicago. Centenary of First Benz Motor Car* (1985). *T* **153** *and similar horiz designs. Multicoloured. P* 15.
650 25 b. Type **153** 20 15
651 75 b. Cord "810" (1935) 50 40
652 1 d. Borgward "Isabella Coupe" (1957) .. 70 60
653 1 d. 25, Lamborghini "Countach" (1985/6) 80 70
654 2 d. Ford "Thunderbird" (1955) .. .. 90 1·25
655 2 d. 25, Citroen "DS19" (1956) .. .. 90 1·6
656 5 d. Bugatti "Atlante" (1936) .. .. 1·25 3·0
657 10 d. Horch "853" (1936) .. .. .. 1·75 5·0
650/7 .. .. *Set of* 8 6·00 11·5
MS658 Two sheets, each 100 × 70 mm. (a) 12 d. Benz "8/20" (1913). (b) 12 d. Steiger "10/50" (1924) .. .. .. *Set of* 2 *sheets* 6·00 12·0
The 25 b. value is inscribed "MECEDES" and the 10 d. "LAR BENZ".
Nos. 650/2 and 657 exist imperforate from stock dispersed b the liquidator of Format International Security Printers Ltd.

(Des J. Iskowitz. Litho Questa)

1986 (10 June). *Centenary of Statue of Liberty* (*1st issue Multicoloured designs as T* **211** *of Dominica showing th Statue of Liberty and immigrants to the U.S.A. P* 14.
659 20 b. John Jacob Astor (financier) 10 1
660 1 d. Jacob Riis (journalist) 40 5
661 1 d. 25, Igor Sikorsky (aeronautics engineer) 60 6
662 5 d. Charles Boyer (actor) .. .. .. 2·50 2·5
659/62 .. .. *Set of* 4 3·25 3·2
MS663 114 × 80 mm. 10 d. Statue of Liberty (*vert*) .. .. 4·00 4·5
See also Nos. 705/14

(Litho Questa)

1986 (1 July). *Royal Wedding. Vert designs as T* **213** *Antigua. Multicoloured. P* 14.
664 1 d. Prince Andrew and Miss Sarah Ferguson 40 4
665 2 d. 50, Prince Andrew .. .. .. 1·00 1·4
666 4 d. Prince Andrew as helicopter pilot .. 1·60 2·0
664/6 .. .. *Set of* 3 2·75 3·5
MS667 88 × 88 mm. 7 d. Prince Andrew and Miss Sarah Ferguson (*different*) .. .. .. 4·25 3·5

1986 (16 Sept). *World Cup Football Championship Winner Mexico. Nos.* 645/9 *optd with T* **216** *of Antigua in gold.*
668 75 b. Type **152** 30 4
669 1 d. Player kicking ball 40 5
670 2 d. 50, Player kicking ball (*different*) .. 1·00 1·2
671 10 d. Player heading ball .. .. .. 4·25 4·7
668/71 .. .. *Set of* 4 5·25 6·
MS672 100 × 70 mm. 10 d. Goalkeeper saving goal .. .. 4·50 4·

154 Minnie Mouse (Great Britain)

(Des Walt Disney Co. Litho Format)

1986 (4 Nov). *Christmas. T* **154** *and similar vert design showing Walt Disney cartoon characters posting letters i various countries. Multicoloured. P* 11.
673 1 d. Type **154** 75 6
674 1 d. 25, Huey (U.S.A.) 80 8
675 2 d. Huey, Dewey and Louie (France) .. 1·25 1·4
676 2 d. 35, Kanga and Roo (Australia) .. .. 1·40 1·7
677 5 d. Goofy (Germany) .. .. 2·25 3·0
673/7 .. .. *Set of* 5 5·75 6·7
MS678 127 × 101 mm. 10 d. Goofy (Sweden). P 13½ × 14 .. .. 4·75 5·5
Nos. 673/8 also show the emblem of "Stockholmia '8 International Stamp Exhibition.

1986 (21 Dec). *Appearance of Halley's Comet* (*2nd issue*). *No 634/40 optd with T* **218** *of Antigua in silver.*
679 10 b. Maria Mitchell (astronomer) and Kitt Peak National Observatory, Arizona .. 30 1
680 20 b. Neil Armstrong, first man on Moon, 1969 .. .. 50 2
681 75 b. "Skylab 4" and Comet Kohoutek, 1973 75 5
682 1 d. N.A.S.A.'s infra-red astronomical satellite and Halley's Comet 85 6
683 2 d. Comet of 1577 from Turkish painting 1·40 1·7
684 10 d. N.A.S.A.'s International Cometary Explorer .. .. 3·75 6·0
679/84 .. .. *Set of* 6 6·75 8·2
MS685 102 × 70 mm. 10 d. Halley's Comet .. 3·00 4·2

155 Bugarab and Tabala

156 "Snowing"

(Des B. Bundock. Litho Format)

987 (21 Jan). *Manding Musical Instruments. T* **155** *and similar multicoloured designs. P* 15.
86 75 b. Type **155** 15 20
87 1 d. Balaphong and fiddle 15 25
88 1 d. 25, Bolongbato and konting (*vert*) .. 20 35
89 10 d. Antique and modern koras (*vert*) .. 1·60 3·00
86/9 .. .. *Set of* 4 1·90 3·50
IS690 100×70 mm. 12 d. Sabarr .. .. 1·90 2·50

(Litho Questa)

987 (6 Feb). *Birth Centenary of Marc Chagall (artist). T* **156** *and similar multicoloured designs. P* 13½×14.
91 75 b. Type **156** 40 40
92 85 b. "The Boat" 50 50
93 1 d. "Maternity" 65 65
94 1 d. 25, "The Flute Player" 75 75
95 2 d. 35, "Lovers and the Beast" .. .. 1·25 1·25
96 4 d. "Fishers at Saint Jean" .. .. .. 2·00 2·00
97 5 d. "Entering the Ring" .. .. .. 2·50 2·50
98 10 d. "Three Acrobats" .. .. 3·75 3·75
91/8 .. .. *Set of* 8 10·50 10·50
IS699 Two sheets. (a) 110×68 mm. 12 d. "The Cattle Driver" (104×61 *mm*). (b) 109×95 mm. 12 d. "The Sabbath" (104×89 *mm*). Imperf. *Set of* 2 *sheets* 7·50 8·50

157 *America*, 1851

158 Arm of Statue of Liberty

(Des S. Heinmann. Litho Questa)

987 (3 Apr). *America's Cup Yachting Championship. T* **157** *and similar horiz designs. Multicoloured. P* 14.
00 20 b. Type **157** 20 15
01 1 d. *Courageous*, 1974 .. .. 35 35
02 2 d. 50, *Volunteer*, 1887 .. .. 75 1·10
03 10 d. *Intrepid*, 1967 .. .. 2·25 3·25
00/3 .. .. *Set of* 4 3·25 4·25
IS704 114×89 mm. 12 d. *Australia II*, 1983 .. 3·25 2·50

(Des P. Kaplan. Litho Questa)

987 (9 Apr). *Centenary of Statue of Liberty* (1986) (*2nd issue*). *T* **158** *and similar multicoloured designs. P* 14.
05 1 b. Type **158** 10 10
06 2 b. Launch passing Statue (*horiz*) 10 10
07 3 b. Schooner passing Statue (*horiz*) .. 10 10
08 5 b. U.S.S. *John F. Kennedy* (aircraft carrier) and *Queen Elizabeth 2* (liner) (*horiz*) 10 10
09 50 b. Checking Statue for damage .. 40 40
10 75 b. Cleaning in progress 55 55
11 1 d. Working on Statue 70 70
12 1 d. 25, Statue and fireworks 80 80
13 10 d. Statue illuminated .. .. .. 4·25 4·25
14 12 d. Statue and fireworks (*different*) .. 4·50 4·50
05/14 .. .. *Set of* 10 10·50 10·50

159 *Lantana camara*

160 Front of Mail Bus

(Des Dot Barlowe. Litho Questa)

987 (25 May). *Flowers of Abuko Nature Reserve. T* **159** *and similar vert designs. Multicoloured. P* 14.
15 75 b. Type **159** 15 15
16 1 d. *Clerodendrum thomsoniae* 15 20
17 1 d. 50, *Haemanthus multiflorus* 25 30
18 1 d. 70, *Gloriosa simplex* 25 35
19 1 d. 75, *Combretum microphyllum* 30 40
20 2 d. 25, *Eulophia quineensis* 35 45
21 5 d. *Erythrina senegalensis* .. .. 80 1·25
22 15 d. *Dichrostachys glomerata* .. .. 2·40 3·50
15/22 .. .. *Set of* 8 4·25 6·00
IS723 Two sheets, each 100×70 mm. (a) 15 d. *Costus spectabilis*. (b) 15 d. *Strophanthus preussii* *Set of* 2 *sheets* 4·75 6·50

(Des BG Studio. Litho Questa)

987 (15 June). *"Capex '87" International Stamp Exhibition, Toronto and 10th Anniv of Gambia Public Transport Corporation. Mail Buses. T* **160** *and similar multicoloured designs. P* 14.
24 20 b. Type **160** 40 20
25 75 b. Bus in Banjul (*horiz*) 70 45
26 1 d. Passengers queuing for bus (*horiz*) .. 70 45
27 10 d. Two buses on rural road .. .. 3·00 5·00
24/7 .. .. *Set of* 4 4·25 5·50
IS728 77×70 mm. 12 d. Parked bus fleet (*horiz*) 3·00 3·75

161 Basketball

162 "A Partridge in a Pear Tree"

(Litho Questa)

1987 (3 July). *Olympic Games, Seoul* (1988) (*1st issue*). *T* **161** *and similar vert designs. Multicoloured. P* 14.
729 50 b. Type **161** 35 20
730 1 d. Volleyball 50 35
731 3 d. Hockey (*horiz*) .. .. 1·10 85
732 10 d. Handball (*horiz*) .. .. 2·50 2·25
724/32 .. .. *Set of* 4 4·00 3·25
MS733 101×85 mm. 15 d. Football (*horiz*) .. 2·75 2·75
See also Nos. 779/83.

(Des Dot Barlowe. Litho Questa)

1987 (2 Nov). *Christmas. T* **162** *and similar multicoloured designs showing a Victorian couple in scenes from carol "The Twelve Days of Christmas". P* 14.
734 20 b. Type **162** 20 25
a. Sheetlet. Nos. 734/45 .. .. .. 7·00
735 40 b. "Two turtle doves" 20 25
736 60 b. "Three French hens" 20 25
737 75 b. "Four calling birds" 30 35
738 1 d. "Five golden rings" 30 35
739 1 d. 25, "Six geese a-laying" 40 45
740 1 d. 50, "Seven swans a-swimming" .. 40 45
741 2 d. "Eight maids a-milking" 50 55
742 3 d. "Nine ladies dancing" 70 75
743 5 d. "Ten lords a-leaping" .. .. .. 1·00 1·10
744 10 d. "Eleven pipers piping" .. .. .. 1·60 1·75
745 12 d. "Twelve drummers drumming" .. 1·90 2·00
734/45 .. .. *Set of* 12 7·00 7·75
MS746 100×70 mm. 15 d. Exchanging presents (*horiz*) .. .. 2·40 3·25
Nos. 734/45 were printed together, *se-tenant*, in sheetlets of twelve.

163 Campfire Singsong

(Litho Questa)

1987 (9 Nov). *World Scout Jamboree, Australia. T* **163** *and similar horiz designs. Multicoloured. P* 14.
747 75 b. Type **163** 50 30
748 1 d. Scouts examining African Katydid .. 60 40
749 1 d. 25, Scouts watching Red-tailed Tropic Bird 75 75
750 2 d. Scouts helping bus passenger .. .. 2·75 3·75
747/50 .. .. *Set of* 4 4·25 4·75
MS751 72×98 mm. 15 d. Scouts on field trip .. 4·00 5·00

(Des Walt Disney Company. Litho Questa)

1987 (9 Dec). *60th Anniv of Mickey Mouse (Walt Disney cartoon character) (1st issue). Multicoloured designs as T* **220** *of Dominica, but horiz. P* 14×13½.
752 60 b. Morty and Ferdie examining Trevithick's locomotive, 1804 .. .. .. 25 25
753 75 b. Clarabelle Cow in "Empire State Express", 1893 .. .. 30 30
754 1 d. Donald Duck inspecting Stephenson's *Rocket*, 1829 .. .. 40 40
755 1 d. 25, Piglet and Winnie the Pooh with Santa Fe Railroad locomotive, 1920 .. 45 45
756 2 d. Donald and Daisy Duck with Pennsylvania Railroad Class GG1 electric locomotive, 1933 .. .. 70 70
757 5 d. Mickey Mouse in *Stourbridge Lion*, 1829 .. .. 1·60 1·75
758 10 d. Goofy in *Best Friend of Charleston*, 1830 .. .. 2·75 3·00
759 12 d. Brer Bear and Brer Rabbit with Union Pacific diesel locomotive No. M10001, 1934 .. .. 3·00 3·25
752/9 .. .. *Set of* 8 8·50 9·00
MS760 Two sheets, each 127×101 mm. (a) 15 d. Chip n'Dale in *The General*, 1855. (b) 15 d. Donald Duck and Mickey Mouse in modern French "TGV" train .. .. *Set of* 2 *sheets* 7·50 8·00
See also Nos. 849/58.

164 Common Duiker and Acacia

165 Wedding Portrait, 1947

(Des Mary Walters. Litho Format)

1988 (9 Feb). *Flora and Fauna. T* **164** *and similar multicoloured designs. P* 15.
761 50 b. Type **164** 20 10
762 75 b. Red-billed Hornbill and casuarina (*vert*) 30 15
763 90 b. West African Dwarf Crocodile and rice 30 20
764 1 d. Leopard and papyrus (*vert*) 30 20
765 1 d. 25, Crowned Crane and millet .. 40 30
766 2 d. Waterbuck and baobab tree (*vert*) .. 40 60
767 3 d. Oribi and Senegal palm .. .. 50 1·10
768 5 d. Hippopotamus and papaya (*vert*) .. 80 1·60
761/8 .. .. *Set of* 8 2·75 3·75
MS769 98×69 mm. (a) 12 d. Red-throated Bee Eater and acacia (*vert*). (b) 12 d. Eastern White Pelican .. .. *Set of* 2 *sheets* 3·75 4·50
No. **MS**769 exists imperforate from stock dispersed by the liquidator of Format International Security Printers Ltd.

(Des and litho Questa)

1988 (15 Mar). *Royal Ruby Wedding. T* **165** *and similar vert designs. P* 14.
770 75 b. deep brown, black and brown-orange 30 15
771 1 d. deep brown, black and bright new blue 40 20
772 3 d. multicoloured .. .. 90 1·00
773 10 d. multicoloured .. .. 2·25 3·25
770/3 .. .. *Set of* 4 3·50 4·25
MS774 100×75 mm. 15 d. multicoloured .. 2·25 3·25
Designs:— 1 d. Engagement photograph; 3 d. Wedding portrait, 1947 (*different*); 10 d. Queen Elizabeth II and Prince Philip (photo by Karsh), 1986; 15 d. Wedding portrait with page, 1947.

1988 (19 Apr). *Stamp Exhibitions. Nos.* 689, 703, 722 *and* 726 *optd as T* **241** *of Antigua with various emblems.*
775 1 d. Passengers queuing for bus (optd "Independence 40", Israel) 25 25
776 10 d. Antique and modern koras (optd "FINLANDIA 88", Helsinki) .. .. .. 2·00 2·50
777 10 d. *Intrepid* (yacht), 1967 (optd "Praga '88", Prague) .. .. 2·00 2·50
778 15 d. *Dichrostachys glomerata* (optd "OLYMPHILEX '88", Seoul) .. .. 2·75 3·00
775/8 .. .. *Set of* 4 6·25 7·50

(Des A. DiLorenzo. Litho Questa)

1988 (3 May). *Olympic Games, Seoul (2nd issue). Multicoloured designs as T* **161**. *P* 14.
779 1 d. Archery 15 20
780 1 d. 25, Boxing 20 25
781 5 d. Gymnastics .. .. 80 1·10
782 10 d. Start of 100 metre race (*horiz*) .. 1·60 2·25
779/82 .. .. *Set of* 4 2·50 3·50
MS783 74×102 mm. 15 d. Medal winners on rostrum .. .. 2·40 3·25

166 Red Cross Flag (125th anniv)

(Des W. Wright. Litho Questa)

1988 (15 May). *Anniversaries and Events. T* **166** *and similar multicoloured designs. P* 14.
784 50 b. Type **166** 55 55
785 75 b. "Friendship" 7 spacecraft (25th anniv of first American manned Earth orbit) 60 60
786 1 d. British Airways Concorde (10th anniv of Concorde London–New York service) 1·00 1·00
787 1 d. 25, Ryan NYP Special *Spirit of St. Louis* (60th anniv of first solo transatlantic flight) .. .. 1·00 1·00
788 2 d. North American X-15 (20th anniv of fastest aircraft flight) .. .. .. 1·40 1·40
789 3 d. Bell XS-1 rocket plane (40th anniv of first supersonic flight) .. .. .. 1·50 1·50
790 10 d. English and Spanish galleons (400th anniv of Spanish Armada) .. .. 3·50 3·50
791 12 d. *Titanic* (75th anniv of sinking) .. 3·75 3·75
784/91 .. .. *Set of* 8 12·00 12·00
MS792 Two sheets. (a) 113×85 mm. 15 d. Kaiser Wilhelm Memorial Church, Berlin (*vert*) (750th anniv of Berlin). (b) 121×90 mm. 15 d. Kangaroo (Bicentenary of Australian Settlement) *Set of* 2 *sheets* 4·75 7·00

(Litho Questa)

1988 (7 July). *500th Birth Anniv of Titian (artist). Vert designs as T* **238** *of Antigua. Multicoloured. P* 13½×14.
793 25 b. "Emperor Charles V" 20 20
794 50 b. "St. Margaret and the Dragon" .. 35 35
795 60 b. "Ranuccio Farnese" 40 40
796 75 b. "Tarquin and Lucretia" 55 55
797 1 d. "The Knight of Malta" 70 70
798 5 d. "Spain succouring Faith" .. .. 2·25 2·50
799 10 d. "Doge Francesco Venier" .. .. 3·50 3·50
800 12 d. "Doge Grimani before the Faith" (detail) .. .. 3·75 3·75
793/800 .. .. *Set of* 8 10·50 10·50
MS801 110×95 mm. (a) 15 d. "Jealous Husband" (detail). (b) 15 d. "Venus blindfolding Cupid" *Set of* 2 *sheets* 4·75 7·00

NEW INFORMATION

The editor is always interested to correspond with people who have new information that will improve or correct the Catalogue.

167 John Kennedy sailing

(Des G. Hinlecky. Litho Questa)

1988 (1 Sept). *25th Death Anniv of President John F. Kennedy. T* **167** *and similar multicoloured designs. P* 14.

802 75 b. Type **167** 15 15
803 1 d. Kennedy signing Peace Corps legislation, 1962 .. .. .. 15 20
804 1 d. 25, Speaking at U.N., New York (*vert*) 20 25
805 12 d. Grave and eternal flame, Arlington National Cemetery (*vert*) .. .. 1·90 2·75
802/5 .. .. *Set of* 4 2·10 3·00
MS806 99×72 mm. 15 d. John F. Kennedy (*vert*) 2·40 3·50

168 Airship LZ-127 *Graf Zeppelin* (first regular air passenger service), 1910

169 Emmett Kelley

(Des A. Fagbohun. Litho Questa)

1988 (1 Nov). *Milestones of Transportation. T* **168** *and similar multicoloured designs. P* 14.

807 25 b. Type **168** 45 35
808 50 b. Stephenson's *Locomotion* (first permanent public railway), 1825 .. 70 50
809 75 b. G.M. *Sun Racer* (first world solar challenge), 1987 .. .. .. 80 65
810 1 d. Sprague's *Premiere* (first operational electric tramway), 1888 .. .. 1·00 80
811 1 d. 25, *Gold Rush* Bicycle (holder of man-powered land speed record), 1986 .. 1·00 85
812 2 d. 50 Robert Goddard and rocket launcher (first liquid fuel rocket), 1925 1·40 1·25
813 10 d. *Orukter Amphibolos* (first steam traction engine), 1805 .. .. 3·50 3·25
814 12 d. *Sovereign of the Seas* (largest cruise liner), 1988 .. .. .. 3·50 3·50
807/14 .. .. *Set of* 8 11·00 10·00
MS815 Two sheets, each 71 × 92 mm. (a) 15 d. U.S.S. *Nautilus* (first nuclear-powered submarine), 1954 (*vert*). (b) 15 d. Fulton's *Nautilus* (first fish-shaped submarine), 1800's (*vert*) .. .. *Set of 2 sheets* 5·50 7·00

No. 807 is incorrectly inscribed "LZ-7".

(Des J. Iskowitz. Litho Questa)

1988 (9 Nov). *Entertainers. T* **169** *and similar multicoloured designs. P* 14.

816 20 b. Type **169** 10 10
817 1 d. Gambia National Ensemble 25 25
818 1 d. 25, Jackie Gleason 30 30
819 1 d. 50, Laurel and Hardy 40 40
820 2 d. 50, Yul Brynner 75 75
821 3 d. Cary Grant 95 95
822 10 d. Danny Kaye .. .. 3·00 3·00
823 20 d. Charlie Chaplin .. .. .. 5·50 5·50
816/23 .. .. *Set of* 8 10·00 10·00
MS824 Two sheets. (a) 110 × 77 mm. 15 d. Marx Brothers (*horiz*). (b) 70 × 99 mm. 15 d. Fred Astaire and Rita Hayworth (*horiz*) *Set of 2 sheets* 9·50 9·50

170 Prince Henry the Navigator and Caravel

171 Projected Space Plane and Ernst Mach (physicist)

(Des A. Fagbohun. Litho Questa)

1988 (1 Dec). *Exploration of West Africa. T* **170** *and similar multicoloured designs. P* 14.

825 50 b. Type **170** 60 60
826 75 b. Jesse Ramsden's sextant, 1785 .. 70 70
827 1 d. 15th-century hourglass 80 80
828 1 d. 25, Prince Henry the Navigator and Vasco da Gama 95 95
829 2 d. 50, Vasco da Gama and ship .. .. 1·60 1·60
830 5 d. Mungo Park and map of Gambia River (*horiz*) .. .. 2·50 2·50
831 10 d. Map of West Africa, 1563 (*horiz*) .. 3·75 3·75
832 12 d. Portuguese caravel (*horiz*) .. .. 4·00 4·00
825/32 .. .. *Set of* 8 13·50 13·50
MS833 Two sheets, each 65 × 100 mm. (a) 15 d. Ship from Columbus's fleet off Gambia. (b) 15 d. 15th-century ship moored off Gambia *Set of 2 sheets* 4·75 6·00

(Des G. Welker. Litho Questa)

1988 (12 Dec). *350th Anniv of Publication of Galileo's "Discourses". Space Achievements. T* **171** *and similar multicoloured designs. P* 14.

834 50 b. Type **171** 30 30
835 75 b. OAO III astronomical satellite and Niels Bohr (physicist) 40 40
836 1 d. Space shuttle, projected space station and Robert Goddard (physicist) (*horiz*) 45 45
837 1 d. 25, Jupiter probe, 1979, and Edward Barnard (astronomer) (*horiz*) .. 60 60
838 2 d. Hubble Space Telescope and George Hale (astronomer) 75 75
839 3 d. Earth-to-Moon laser measurement and Albert Michaelson (physicist) (*horiz*) .. 85 85
840 10 d. HEAO-2 *Einstein* orbital satellite and Albert Einstein (physicist) .. .. 2·50 2·50
841 20 d. *Voyager* (first non-stop round-the-world flight), 1987, and Wright Brothers (aviation pioneers) (*horiz*) .. 4·50 4·50
834/41 .. .. *Set of* 8 9·25 9·25
MS842 Two sheets. (a) 99 × 75 mm. 15 d. Great Red Spot on Jupiter (*horiz*). (b) 88 × 71 mm. 15 d. Neil Armstrong (first man on Moon), 1969 *Set of 2 sheets* 6·00 7·00

172 Passing Out Parade

(Des J. Genzo. Litho Questa)

1989 (10 Feb). *Army Day. T* **172** *and similar multicoloured designs. P* 14.

843 75 b. Type **172** 25 25
844 1 d. Standards of The Gambia Regiment .. 25 25
845 1 d. 25, Side drummer in ceremonial uniform (*vert*) 30 30
846 10 d. Marksman with Atlantic Shooting Cup (*vert*) .. .. 2·00 2·00
847 15 d. Soldiers on assault course (*vert*) .. 2·75 2·75
848 20 d. Gunner with 105 mm field gun .. 3·00 3·00
843/8 .. .. *Set of* 6 7·75 7·75

173 Mickey Mouse, 1928

174 "Le Coup de Lance" (detail)

(Des Walt Disney Company. Litho B.D.T.)

1989 (6 Apr). *60th Birthday of Mickey Mouse (2nd issue). T* **173** *and similar multicoloured designs. P* 13.

849 2 d. Type **173** 55 65
a. Sheetlet of 9. Nos. 849/57 .. .. 4·50
850 2 d. Mickey Mouse, 1931 .. .. .. 55 65
851 2 d. Mickey Mouse, 1936 .. .. .. 55 65
852 2 d. Mickey Mouse, 1955 .. .. .. 55 65
853 2 d. Mickey Mouse, 1947 .. .. .. 55 65
854 2 d. Mickey Mouse as magician, 1940 .. 55 65
855 2 d. Mickey Mouse with palette, 1960 .. 55 65
856 2 d. Mickey Mouse as Uncle Sam, 1976 .. 55 65
857 2 d. Mickey Mouse, 1988 .. .. .. 55 65
849/57 .. .. *Set of* 9 4·50 5·25
MS858 138×109 mm. 15 d. Mickey Mouse at 60th birthday party (132×103 *mm*). Imperf .. 3·50 3·50

Nos. 849/57 were printed together, *se-tenant* as a composite design, in sheetlets of nine.

(Litho Questa)

1989 (14 Apr). *Easter. Religious Paintings by Rubens. T* **174** *and similar vert designs showing details. Multicoloured. P* 13½×14.

859 50 b. Type **174** 25 25
860 75 b. "Flagellation of Christ" 35 35
861 1 d. "Lamentation for Christ" 35 35
862 1 d. 25, "Descent from the Cross" 40 40
863 2 d. "Holy Trinity" 60 70
864 5 d. "Doubting Thomas" .. .. .. 1·25 1·50
865 10 d. "Lamentation over Christ" .. .. 2·00 2·50
866 12 d. "Lamentation with Virgin and St. John" .. .. 2·25 2·75
859/66 .. .. *Set of* 8 6·75 8·00
MS867 Two sheets each 96×110 mm. (a) 15 d. "The Last Supper". (b) 15 d. "Raising of the Cross" .. .. .. *Set of 2 sheets* 4·50 5·50

175 African Emerald Cuckoo

176 *Druryia antimachus*

(Des W. Wright. Litho Questa)

1989 (24 Apr). *West African Birds. T* **175** *and similar hori designs. Multicoloured. P* 14.

868 20 b. Type **175** 60 3
869 60 b. Grey-headed Bush Shrike 85 5
870 75 b. South African Crowned Crane .. 90 5
871 1 d. Secretary Bird .. .. .. 1·00 6
872 2 d. Red-billed Hornbill .. .. .. 1·50 1·0
873 5 d. Superb Sunbird .. .. .. 2·00 2·7
874 10 d. Pearl-spotted Owlet ("Little Owl") .. 2·75 4·0
875 12 d. Bateleur .. .. 2·75 4·0
868/75 .. .. *Set of* 8 11·00 12·0
MS876 Two sheets, each 115×86 mm. (a) 15 d. Ostrich. (b) 15 d. Red-billed Fire Finch *Set of 2 sheets* 7·00 8·0

(Des Mary Walters. Litho Questa)

1989 (15 May). *Butterflies of Gambia. T* **176** *and similar ver designs. Multicoloured. P* 14.

877 50 b. Type **176** 30 30
878 75 b. *Euphaedra neophron* 45 45
879 1 d. *Aterica rabena* 45 45
880 1 d. 25, *Salamis parhassus* 55 55
881 5 d. *Precis rhadama* .. .. .. 1·75 2·00
882 10 d. *Papilio demodocus* .. .. .. 2·25 2·50
883 12 d. *Charaxes etesipe* .. .. .. 2·50 2·75
884 15 d. *Danaus formosa* .. .. .. 2·50 2·75
877/84 .. .. *Set of* 8 9·75 10·50
MS885 Two sheets, each 99×68 mm. (a) 15 d. *Euptera pluto*. (b) 15 d. *Euphaedra ceres* *Set of 2 sheets* 8·00 9·00

177 Class "River" Steam Locomotive No. 021, 1959, Nigeria

PHILEXFRANCE '89

(**178**)

(Des A. Fagbohun. Litho Walsall)

1989 (15 June). *African Steam Locomotives. T* **177** *and similar multicoloured designs. P* 14.

886 50 b. Type **177** 35 35
887 75 b. Class 14A steam locomotive, Rhodesia 45 45
888 1 d. British-built steam locomotive No. 120, Sudan 55 55
889 1 d. 25, Steam locomotive, 1925, U.S.A. .. 65 65
890 5 d. North British steam locomotive, 1955 1·75 1·75
891 7 d. Scottish-built steam locomotive No. 120, 1926 .. .. 2·00 2·00
892 10 d. East African Railways Class 1T steam tank locomotive .. .. .. 2·25 2·25
893 12 d. American-built steam locomotive, Ghana .. .. 2·50 2·50
886/93 .. .. *Set of* 8 9·50 9·50
MS894 Two sheets, each 82×58 mm. (a) 15 d. East African Railways Class 25 steam locomotive No. 2904 (*vert*). (b) 15 d. East African Railways Class 25 steam locomotive No. 3700A (*vert*) .. .. *Set of 2 sheets* 6·00 7·00

1989 (23 June). *"Philexfrance '89" International Stam Exhibition, Paris. Nos.* 686/90 *optd with T* **178**.

895 75 b. Type **155** 10 1
896 1 d. Balaphong and fiddle 15 2
897 1 d. 25, Bolongbato and konting (*vert*) .. 20 2
898 10 d. Antique and modern koras (*vert*) .. 1·50 2·2
895/8 .. .. *Set of* 4 1·75 2·5
MS899 100×70 mm. 12 d. Sabarr .. .. 1·40 2·0

(Litho Questa)

1989 (7 July). *Japanese Art. Multicoloured designs as T* **250** *o Antigua. P* 13½×14.

900 50 b. "Sparrow and Bamboo" (Hiroshige) (*vert*) 40 3
901 75 b. "Peonies and a Canary" (Hokusai) (*vert*) 50 4
902 1 d. "Crane and Marsh Grasses" (Hiroshige) (*vert*) 60 4
903 1 d. 25, "Crossbill and Thistle" (Hokusai) (*vert*) 70 6
904 2 d. "Cuckoo and Azalea" (Hokusai) (*vert*) 90 8
905 5 d. "Parrot on a Pine Branch" (Hiroshige) (*vert*) .. .. 1·50 1·7
906 10 d. "Mandarin Ducks in a Stream" (Hiroshige) (*vert*) .. .. .. 2·25 2·5
907 12 d. "Bullfinch and Drooping Cherry" (Hokusai) (*vert*) .. .. .. 2·25 2·5
900/7 .. .. *Set of* 8 8·25 8·5
MS908 Two sheets, each 102×77 mm. (a) 15 d. "Tit and Peony" (Hiroshige). (b) 15 d. "Peony and Butterfly" (Shigenobou). P 14×13½ *Set of 2 sheets* 5·50 6·5

Nos. 900/7 were each printed in sheets of 10 containing tw vertical strips of 5 stamps separated by printed label commemorating Emperor Hirohito.

179 Rialto Bridge, Venice

180 *Vitex doniana*

(Des L. Fried. Litho B.D.T.)

989 (25 Aug). *World Cup Football Championship, Italy* (1990) (*1st issue*). *T* **179** *and similar horiz designs, each showing landmarks and players. Multicoloured. P* 14.

09 75 b. Type **179** 45 45
10 1 d. 25, The Baptistery, Pisa 60 60
11 7 d. Casino, San Remo 2·25 2·75
12 12 d. Colosseum, Rome 3·00 3·50
09/12 *Set of* 4 5·50 6·50
IS913 Two sheets, each 104×78 mm. (a) 15 d. St. Mark's Cathedral, Venice. (b) 15 d. Piazza Colonna, Rome *Set of 2 sheets* 6·50 7·50

See also Nos. 1064/8.

(Des Jennifer Toombs. Litho Questa)

989 (18 Sept). *Medicinal Plants. T* **180** *and similar vert designs. Multicoloured. P* 14.

14 20 b. Type **180** 20 20
15 50 b. *Ricinus communis* 30 30
16 75 b. *Palisota hirsuta* 45 45
17 1 d. *Smilax kraussiana* 55 55
18 1 d. 25, *Aspilia africana* 65 65
19 5 d. *Newbouldia laevis* 1·75 2·00
20 8 d. *Monodora tenuifolia* 1·90 2·50
21 10 d. *Gossypium arboreum* 2·00 2·50
14/21 *Set of* 8 7·00 8·25
IS922 Two sheets, each 87×72 mm. (a) 15 d. *Kigelia africana*. (b) 15 d. *Spathodea campanulata* *Set of 2 sheets* 7·00 8·00

181 Lookdown

(Des Mary Walters. Litho B.D.T.)

989 (19 Oct). *Fishes. T* **181** *and similar horiz designs. Multicoloured. P* 14.

23 20 b. Type **181** 25 25
24 75 b. Boarfish 55 55
25 1 d. Grey Triggerfish 65 65
26 1 d. 25, Skipjack Tuna 75 75
27 2 d. Striped Rudderfish 95 95
28 4 d. Atlantic Manta 1·60 1·75
29 5 d. Flat-headed Grey Mullet 1·75 1·90
30 10 d. Ladyfish 2·75 3·25
23/30 *Set of* 8 8·25 9·00
IS931 Two sheets, each 104×72 mm. (a) 15 d. Porcupinefish. (b) 15 d. Shortfin Mako *Set of 2 sheets* 8·00 9·00

(Des Walt Disney Co. Litho Questa)

989 (29 Nov). *"World Stamp Expo '89" International Stamp Exhibition, Washington* (*1st issue*). *Horiz designs as T* **256** *of Antigua, each showing Walt Disney cartoon characters and American carousel horses. Multicoloured. P* 14×13½.

32 20 b. Little Hiawatha on Daniel Muller Indian Pony 40 30
33 50 b. Morty on Herschell-Spillman stander 60 50
34 75 b. Goofy on Gustav Dentzel stander 75 65
35 1 d. Mickey Mouse on Daniel Muller armoured stander 80 70
36 1 d. 25, Minnie Mouse on jumper from Smithsonian Collection 90 80
37 2 d. Webby on Illion "American Beauty" 1·25 1·10
38 8 d. Donald Duck on Zalar jumper 3·00 3·50
39 10 d. Mickey Mouse on Parker bucking horse 3·00 3·50
32/9 *Set of* 8 9·50 10·00
IS940 Two sheets, each 127×102 mm. (a) 12 d. Donald, Mickey and Goofy in carousel car. (b) 12 d. Donald's nephews on Roman chariot horses *Set of 2 sheets* 8·00 9·00

(Des Design Element. Litho Questa)

989 (29 Nov). *"World Stamp Expo '89" International Stamp Exhibition, Washington* (*2nd issue*). *Landmarks of Washington. Sheet* 78×61 *mm containing horiz design as T* **257** *of Antigua. Multicoloured. P* 14.

IS941 10 d. White House 1·40 2·00

183 Mickey and Minnie Mouse in Pierce-Arrow, 1922

(Des Walt Disney Co. Litho Questa)

1989 (29 Nov). *Christmas. T* **183** *and similar horiz designs showing Walt Disney cartoon characters with cars. Multicoloured. P* 14×13½.

942 20 b. Type **183** 50 25
943 50 b. Goofy in Spyker, 1919 70 45
944 75 b. Donald and Grandma Duck with Packard, 1929 80 55
945 1 d. Mickey Mouse driving Daimler, 1920 85 65
946 1 d. 25, Mickey Mouse in Hispano "Suiza", 1924 90 90
947 2 d. Mickey and Minnie Mouse in Opel "Laubfrosch", 1924 1·25 1·25
948 10 d. Donald Duck driving Vauxhall "30/98", 1927 3·25 4·00
949 12 d. Goofy with Peerless, 1923 3·25 4·00
942/9 *Set of* 8 10·50 11·00
MS950 Two sheets, each 127×102 mm. (a) 15 d. Mickey and Minnie Mouse picnicking by Stutz "Blackhawk Speedster", 1928. (b) 15 d. Donald Duck, Mickey and Minnie Mouse in Bentley "Supercharged", 1930 *Set of 2 sheets* 9·00 11·00

184 Charles Nicolle (typhus transmission) and Vaccination

185 *Bulbophyllum lepidum*

(Des J. Iskowitz. Litho Walsall)

1989 (12 Dec). *Great Medical Discoveries. T* **184** *and similar horiz designs. Multicoloured. P* 14.

951 20 b. Type **184** 40 20
952 50 b. Paul Ehrlich (immunization pioneer) and medical examination 50 30
953 75 b. Selman Waksman (discoverer of streptomycin) and T.B. clinic 65 40
954 1 d. Edward Jenner (smallpox vaccination), and Jenner conducting experiment, 1796 75 50
955 1 d. 25, Robert Koch (developer of tuberculin test) and Gambian using vaccination gun 90 75
956 5 d. Sir Alexander Fleming (discoverer of penicillin) and doctor giving injection 2·00 2·25
957 8 d. Max Theiler (developer of yellow fever vaccine) and child clinic 2·50 2·75
958 10 d. Louis Pasteur (bacteriologist) and health survey 2·50 2·75
951/8 *Set of* 8 9·00 9·00
MS959 Two sheets, each 121×86 mm. (a) 15 d. Hughes 369 Viking medical helicopter. (b) 15 d. B.A.C. One Eleven Nightingale C.9 medical relief plane *Set of 2 sheets* 7·50 8·50

No. **MS**959a is incorrectly inscribed "Vicking".

(Des Mary Walters. Litho Walsall)

1989 (18 Dec). *Orchids. T* **185** *and similar vert designs. Multicoloured. P* 14.

960 20 b. Type **185** 30 30
961 75 b. *Tridactyle tridactylites* 55 55
962 1 d. *Vanilla imperialis* 70 70
963 1 d. 25, *Oeceoclades maculata* 80 90
964 2 d. *Polystachya affinis* 1·10 1·25
965 4 d. *Ancistrochilus rothschildianus* 1·90 2·25
966 5 d. *Angraecum distichum* 2·00 2·25
967 10 d. *Liparis guineensis* 3·50 4·00
960/7 *Set of* 8 9·75 11·00
MS968 Two sheets, each 99×67 mm. (a) 15 d. *Plectrelminthus caudatus*. (b) 15 d. *Eulophia guineensis* *Set of 2 sheets* 8·50 8·50

186 John Newcombe

187 Lunar Module *Eagle*

(Des D. Miller. Litho Questa)

1990 (2 Jan). *Wimbledon Tennis Champions. T* **186** *and similar vert designs. Multicoloured. P* 14½.

969 20 b. Type **186** 10 10
a. Vert pair. Nos. 969/70 20 20
970 20 b. Mrs. G. W. Hillyard 10 10
971 50 b. Roy Emerson 20 20
a. Vert pair. Nos. 971/2 40 40
972 50 b. Dorothy Chambers 20 20
973 75 b. Donald Budge 30 30
a. Vert pair. Nos. 973/4 60 60
974 75 b. Suzanne Lenglen 30 30
975 1 d. Laurence Doherty 35 35
a. Vert pair. Nos. 975/6 70 70
976 1 d. Helen Wills Moody 35 35
977 1 d. 25, Bjorn Borg 40 40
a. Vert pair. Nos. 977/8 80 80
978 1 d. 25, Maureen Connolly 40 40
979 4 d. Jean Borotra 1·00 1·00
a. Vert pair. Nos. 979/80 2·00 2·00
980 4 d. Maria Bueno 1·00 1·00
981 5 d. Anthony Wilding 1·00 1·00
a. Vert pair. Nos. 981/2 2·00 2·00
982 5 d. Louise Brough 1·00 1·00
983 7 d. Fred Perry 1·40 1·40
a. Vert pair. Nos. 983/4 2·75 2·75
984 7 d. Margaret Court 1·40 1·40
985 10 d. Bill Tilden 2·00 2·00
a. Vert pair. Nos. 985/6 4·00 4·00
986 10 d. Billie Jean King 2·00 2·00
987 12 d. Rod Laver 2·25 2·25
a. Vert pair. Nos. 987/8 4·50 4·50
988 12 d. Martina Navratilova 2·25 2·25
969/88 *Set of* 20 16·00 16·00
MS989 Two sheets, each 101×76 mm. (a) 15 d. Rod Laver (*different*). (b) 15 d. Martina Navratilova (*different*) *Set of 2 sheets* 8·50 9·50

The two designs for each value were printed together, *se-tenant*, in vertical pairs throughout the sheets of 20.

(Des K. Gromell. Litho B.D.T.)

1990 (16 Feb). *20th Anniv of First Manned Landing on Moon* (1989). *T* **187** *and similar multicoloured designs. P* 14.

990 20 b. Type **187** 35 20
991 50 b. Lift-off of "Apollo 11" (*vert*) 45 30
992 75 b. Neil Armstrong stepping on to Moon 60 45
993 1 d. Buzz Aldrin and American flag 65 55
994 1 d. 25, "Apollo 11" emblem (*vert*) 75 60
995 1 d. 75, Crew of "Apollo 11" 90 90
996 8 d. Lunar Module *Eagle* on Moon 2·50 3·00
997 12 d. Recovery of "Apollo 11" after splash-down 2·75 3·25
990/7 *Set of* 8 8·00 8·25
MS998 Two sheets, each 110×89 mm. (a) 15 d. Neil Armstrong (*vert*). (b) 15 d. View of Earth from Moon (*vert*) *Set of 2 sheets* 6·50 7·50

188 Bristol Type 142 Blenheim Mk 1

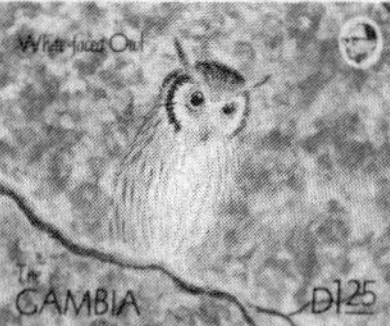

189 White-faced Scops Owl

(Des J. Batchelor. Litho B.D.T.)

1990 (8 May). *R.A.F. Aircraft of Second World War. T* **188** *and similar horiz designs. Multicoloured. P* 14.

999 10 b. Type **188** 35 30
1000 20 b. Fairey Battle 45 30
1001 50 b. Bristol Type 142 Blenheim Mk IV 55 40
1002 60 b. Vickers-Armstrong Wellington Mk 1c 60 40
1003 75 b. Armstrong Whitworth Whitley Mk V 60 40
1004 1 d. Handley Page Hampden Mk 1 70 45
1005 1 d. 25, Supermarine Spitfire Mk 1A and Hawker Hurricane Mk I 80 50
1006 2 d. Avro Manchester 1·00 80
1007 3 d. Short Stirling Mk I 1·25 1·25
1008 5 d. Handley Page Halifax Mk I 1·50 1·75
1009 10 d. Avro Type 683 Lancaster Mk III 2·25 2·75
1010 12 d. De Havilland D.H.98 Mosquito Mk IV 2·25 2·75
999/1010 *Set of* 12 11·00 11·00
MS1011 Two sheets, each 107×77 mm. (a) 15 d. Supermarine Spitfire Mk 1A. (b) 15 d. Avro Type 683 Lancaster Mk III (*different*) *Set of 2 sheets* 6·50 8·00

(Des Jennifer Toombs. Litho B.D.T.)

1990 (14 May). *African Birds. T* **189** *and similar horiz designs. Multicoloured. P* 14.

1012 1 d. 25, Type **189** 50 55
a. Sheetlet. Nos. 1012/31 9·00
1013 1 d. 25, Village Weaver 50 55
1014 1 d. 25, Red-throated Bee Eater 50 55
1015 1 d. 25, Brown Harrier Eagle 50 55
1016 1 d. 25, Red Bishop 50 55
1017 1 d. 25, Scarlet-chested Sunbird 50 55
1018 1 d. 25, Red-billed Hornbill 50 55
1019 1 d. 25, Mosque Swallow 50 55
1020 1 d. 25, White-faced Whistling Duck 50 55
1021 1 d. 25, African Fish Eagle 50 55
1022 1 d. 25, Eastern White Pelican 50 55
1023 1 d. 25, Carmine Bee Eater 50 55
1024 1 d. 25, Hadada Ibis 50 55
1025 1 d. 25, Egyptian Plover 50 55
1026 1 d. 25, Variable Sunbird 50 55
1027 1 d. 25, African Skimmer 50 55
1028 1 d. 25, Woodland Kingfisher 50 55
1029 1 d. 25, African Jacana 50 55
1030 1 d. 25, African Pygmy Goose 50 55
1031 1 d. 25, Hammerkop 50 55
1012/31 *Set of* 20 9·00 10·00

Nos. 1012/31 were printed together, *se-tenant*, in sheetlets of twenty, forming a composite design of birds at a lake.

190 Penny Black

191 Flag and National Assembly Building

(Des S. Pollard. Litho Questa)

1990 (4 June). *150th Anniv of the Penny Black. P* 14.
1032 **190** 1 d. 25, black and bright ultramarine 75 50
1033 12 d. black and scarlet .. .. 3·00 3·75
MS1034 79×73 mm. **190** 15 d. black, silver and dull orange .. .. 3·50 4·50
The design of No. **MS**1034 is without the additional stamps behind the Penny Black as shown on Type **190**.

(Des and litho Questa)

1990 (5 June). *25th Anniv of Independence. T* **191** *and similar vert designs. Multicoloured. P* 14.
1035 1 d. Type **191** 40 25
1036 3 d. Pres. Sir Dawda Jawara 50 50
1037 12 d. Map of Yundum airport and Boeing 707 airliner .. .. 3·50 4·00
1035/7 .. .. *Set of* 3 4·00 4·25
MS1038 100×69 mm. 18 d. State arms .. 3·50 4·50

192 Baobab Tree

(Des W. Hanson Studio. Litho Questa)

1990 (14 June). *Gambian Life. T* **192** *and similar multicoloured designs. P* 14.
1039 5 b. Type **192** 10 30
1040 10 b. Woodcarving, Albert Market, Banjul 10 30
1041 20 b. President Jawara planting seedling (*vert*) 10 10
1042 50 b. Sailing canoe and map 40 10
1043 75 b. Batik fabric 20 10
1044 1 d. Hibiscus and Bakau beach 30 20
1045 1 d. 25, Bougainvilla and Tendaba Camp 30 20
1046 2 d. Shrimp fishing and sorting 45 35
1047 5 d. Groundnut oil mill, Denton Bridge .. 80 1·25
1048 10 d. Handicraft pot and kora (musical instrument) .. .. 1·50 2·25
1049 15 d. *Ansellia africana* (orchid) (*vert*) .. 3·75 4·00
1050 30 d. *Euriphene gambiae* (butterfly) and ancient stone ring near Georgetown 6·50 7·50
1039/50 .. .. *Set of* 12 13·00 15·00

193 Daisy Duck at 10 Downing Street

194 Lady Elizabeth Bowes-Lyon in High Chair

(Des Walt Disney Co. Litho Questa)

1990 (19 June). *"Stamp World London 90" International Stamp Exhibition. T* **193** *and similar multicoloured designs each showing Walt Disney cartoon characters in England. P* 14.
1051 20 b. Type **193** 30 30
1052 50 b. Goofy in Trafalgar Square 35 35
1053 75 b. Mickey Mouse on White Cliffs of Dover (*horiz*) 50 50
1054 1 d. Mickey Mouse at Tower of London .. 50 50
1055 5 d. Mickey Mouse and Goofy at Hampton Court Palace (*horiz*) .. .. 1·75 2·00
1056 8 d. Mickey Mouse by Magdalen Tower, Oxford .. .. 2·00 2·50
1057 10 d. Mickey Mouse on Old London Bridge (*horiz*) .. .. 2·25 2·75
1058 12 d. Scrooge McDuck and Rosetta Stone, British Museum (*horiz*) .. .. 2·25 2·75
1051/8 .. .. *Set of* 8 9·00 10·50
MS1059 Two sheets, each 125×100 mm. (a) 18 d. Mickey Mouse and Donald Duck at Piccadilly Circus (*horiz*). (b) 18 d. Mickey Mouse steering tug on River Thames (*horiz*) .. *Set of* 2 *sheets* 9·00 11·00

(Des Young Phillips Studio. Litho Questa)

1990 (19 July). *90th Birthday of Queen Elizabeth the Queen Mother. T* **194** *and similar vert portraits*, 1900–09. *P* 14.
1060 6 d. black, dp magenta & greenish yellow 1·25 1·60
a. Strip of 3. Nos. 1060/2 .. .. 3·25
1061 6 d. black, dp magenta & greenish yellow 1·25 1·60
1062 6 d. black, dp magenta & greenish yellow 1·25 1·60
1060/2 .. .. *Set of* 3 3·25 4·25
MS1063 90×75 mm. 18 d. multicoloured .. 3·50 4·50
Designs:—Nos. 1061, **MS**1063, Lady Elizabeth Bowes-Lyon as a young girl; No. 1062, Lady Elizabeth Bowes-Lyon with wild flowers.
Nos. 1060/2 were printed together, horizontally and vertically *se-tenant*, in sheetlets of 9 (3×3).

195 Vialli, Italy

196 Summit Logo

(Des Young Phillips Studio. Litho Questa)

1990 (24 Sept). *World Cup Football Championship, Italy* (*2nd issue*). *T* **195** *and similer vert designs. Multicoloured. P* 14.
1064 1 d. Type **195** 30 30
1065 1 d. 25, Cannegia, Argentina 35 35
1066 3 d. Marchena, Costa Rica 80 90
1067 5 d. Shaiba, United Arab Emirates .. 1·10 1·40
1064/7 .. .. *Set of* 4 2·25 2·75
MS1068 Two sheets, each 75×92 mm. (a) 18 d. Hagi, Rumania. (b) 18 d. Van Basten, Netherlands .. .. .. *Set of* 2 *sheets* 8·00 8·50

(Des B. Grout. Litho Questa)

1990 (1 Nov). *Olympic Games, Barcelona* (1992) (*1st issue*). *Multicoloured designs as T* **268** *of Antigua. P* 14.
1069 20 b. Men's discus 35 15
1070 50 b. Men's 100 metres 45 20
1071 75 b. Women's 400 metres 55 30
1072 1 d. Men's 200 metres 60 40
1073 1 d. 25, Women's rhythmic gymnastics .. 65 50
1074 3 d. Football .. .. 1·25 1·50
1075 10 d. Men's marathon .. .. .. 2·50 3·25
1076 12 d. "Tornado" class yachting .. .. 2·50 3·25
1069/76 .. .. *Set of* 8 8·00 8·50
MS1077 Two sheets, each 101×71 mm. (a) 15 d. Parade of national flags (*horiz*). (b) 15 d. Opening ceremony (*horiz*) .. .. *Set of* 2 *sheets* 7·00 8·00
See also Nos. 1289/97 and 1351/63.

(Litho Questa)

1990 (24 Dec). *Christmas. Paintings by Renaissance Masters. Multicoloured designs as T* **272** *of Antigua, but vert. P* 13½×14.
1078 20 b. "The Annunciation, with St. Emidius" (detail) (Crivelli) 20 10
1079 50 b. "The Annunciation" (detail) (Campin) 30 10
1080 75 b. "The Solly Madonna" (detail) (Raphael) 40 20
1081 1 d. 25, "The Tempi Madonna" (Raphael) 40 30
1082 2 d. "Madonna of the Linen Window" (detail) (Raphael) 55 50
1083 7 d. "The Annunciation, with St. Emidius" (different detail) (Crivelli) .. .. 1·75 2·50
1084 10 d. "The Orleans Madonna" (Raphael) .. 2·00 2·50
1085 15 d. "Madonna and Child" (detail) (Crivelli) .. .. 2·50 3·25
1078/85 .. .. *Set of* 8 7·25 8·50
MS1086 72×101 mm. 15 d. "Niccolini-Cowper Madonna" (Raphael) .. .. 4·00 5·00

(Litho Questa)

1990 (24 Dec). *350th Death Anniv of Rubens. Multicoloured designs as T* **273** *of Antigua. P* 14×13½.
1087 20 b. "The Lion Hunt" (sketch) 15 15
1088 75 b. "The Lion Hunt" (detail) 25 25
1089 1 d. "The Tiger Hunt" (detail) 30 30
1090 1 d. 25, "The Tiger Hunt" (different detail) 35 35
1091 3 d. "The Tiger Hunt" (different detail) .. 75 80
1092 5 d. "The Boar Hunt" (detail) .. .. 1·10 1·25
1093 10 d. "The Lion Hunt" (different detail) .. 1·75 2·25
1094 15 d. "The Tiger Hunt" (different detail) .. 2·40 3·00
1087/94 .. .. *Set of* 8 6·25 7·50
MS1095 Four sheets. (a) 100×71 mm. 15 d. "The Boar Hunt". P 14×13½. (b) 100×71 mm. 15 d. "The Lion Hunt". P 14×13½. (c) 100×71 mm. 15 d. "The Crocodile and Hippopotamus Hunt". P 14×13½. (d) 71×100 mm. 15 d. "St. George slays the Dragon" (*vert*). P 13½×14
Set of 4 *sheets* 12·00 13·00

(Litho Questa)

1991 (2 Jan). *World Summit for Children, New York. P* 14.
1096 **196** 1 d. multicoloured 40 40

(Des Walt Disney Co. Litho Questa)

1991 (14 Feb). *International Literacy Year* (1990). *Multicoloured designs as T* **269** *of Antigua showing scenes from Disney cartoon film* The Sword in the Stone. *P* 14×13½.
1097 3 d. Sir Kay and Wart searching for lost arrow (*horiz*) .. .. .. 1·00 1·10
a. Sheetlet. Nos. 1097/105 .. 8·00
1098 3 d. Merlin the Magician (*horiz*) .. 1·00 1·10
1099 3 d. Merlin teaching Wart (*horiz*) .. 1·00 1·10
1100 3 d. Wart writing on blackboard (*horiz*) 1·00 1·10
1101 3 d. Wart transformed into bird and Madame Mim (*horiz*) .. .. 1·00 1·10
1102 3 d. Merlin and Madame Mim (*horiz*) .. 1·00 1·10
1103 3 d. Madame Mim transformed into dragon (*horiz*) .. .. .. 1·00 1·10
1104 3 d. Wart pulling sword from stone (*horiz*) 1·00 1·10
1105 3 d. King Arthur on throne (*horiz*) .. 1·00 1·10
1097/105 .. .. *Set of* 9 8·00 9·00
MS1106 Two sheets, each 131×106 mm. (a) 20 d. Sword in stone. (b) 20 d. Merlin. P 13½×14
Set of 2 *sheets* 13·00 14·00
Nos. 1097/105 were printed together, *se-tenant*, in sheetlets of 9.

197 *Bebearia senegalensis*

198 *Papilio dardanus*

(Des Mary Walters. Litho Questa)

1991 (13 May). *Wildlife. T* **197** *and similar multicoloure designs. P* 14.
1107 1 d. Type **197** 30 3
a. Sheetlet. Nos. 1107/22 .. .. 4·25
1108 1 d. *Graphium ridleyanus* (butterfly) .. 30
1109 1 d. *Precis antilope* (butterfly) 30
1110 1 d. *Charaxes ameliae* (butterfly) .. 30
1111 1 d. Addax 30
1112 1 d. Sassaby 30
1113 1 d. Civet 30
1114 1 d. Green Monkey 30
1115 1 d. Spur-winged Goose 30
1116 1 d. Red-billed Hornbill 30
1117 1 d. Osprey 30
1118 1 d. Glossy Ibis 30
1119 1 d. Egyptian Plover 30
1120 1 d. Golden-tailed Woodpecker 30
1121 1 d. Green Wood Hoopoe 30
1122 1 d. Gaboon Viper 30
1123 1 d. 50, Red-billed Fire Finch 40 4
a. Sheetlet. Nos. 1123/38 .. .. 5·50
1124 1 d. 50, Leaf-Love 40 4
1125 1 d. 50, Piapiac 40 4
1126 1 d. 50, African Emerald Cuckoo .. 40 4
1127 1 d. 50, Red Colobus Monkey 40 4
1128 1 d. 50, African Elephant 40 4
1129 1 d. 50, Duiker 40 4
1130 1 d. 50, Giant Eland 40 4
1131 1 d. 50, Oribi 40 4
1132 1 d. 50, Western African Dwarf Crocodile 40 4
1133 1 d. 50, Crowned Crane 40 4
1134 1 d. 50, Jackal 40 4
1135 1 d. 50, Yellow-throated Longclaw .. 40 4
1136 1 d. 50, Abyssinian Ground Hornbill .. 40 4
1137 1 d. 50, *Papilio hesperus* 40 4
1138 1 d. 50, *Papilio antimachus* 40 4
1139 5 d. Martial Eagle .. .. .. 1·00 1·1
a. Sheetlet. Nos. 1139/54 .. .. 14·00
1140 5 d. Red-cheeked Cordon-bleu .. .. 1·00 1·
1141 5 d. Red Bishop .. .. 1·00 1·
1142 5 d. Eastern White Pelican .. .. 1·00 1·
1143 5 d. Patas Monkey .. .. .. 1·00 1·
1144 5 d. Vervet Monkey .. .. .. 1·00 1·
1145 5 d. Roan Antelope .. .. .. 1·00 1·
1146 5 d. Western Hartebeest .. .. .. 1·00 1·
1147 5 d. Waterbuck .. .. 1·00 1·
1148 5 d. Warthog .. .. 1·00 1·
1149 5 d. Spotted Hyena .. .. .. 1·00 1·
1150 5 d. Olive Baboon .. .. .. 1·00 1·
1151 5 d. *Palla decius* .. .. 1·00 1·
1152 5 d. *Acraea pharsalus* .. .. .. 1·00 1·
1153 5 d. *Neptidopsis ophione* .. .. 1·00 1·
1154 5 d. *Acraea caecilia* .. .. .. 1·00 1·
1107/154 .. .. *Set of* 48 24·00 27·
MS1155 Three sheets, each 101×69 mm. (a) 18 d. African Spoonbill (*vert*). (b) 18 d. White-billed Buffalo Weaver (*vert*). (c) 18 d. Lion (*vert*) .. .. *Set of* 3 *sheets* 10·00 12·
Nos. 1107/22, 1123/38 and 1139/54 were printed together, *s tenant*, in sheetlets of 16, each forming a composite design.

(Des L. Nelson. Litho Questa)

1991 (1 June). *Butterflies. T* **198** *and similar vert design Multicoloured. P* 14.
1156 20 b. Type **198** 50
1157 50 b. *Bematistes poggei* 70
1158 1 d. *Vanessa cardui* 80
1159 1 d. 50, *Amphicallia tigris* 90
1160 3 d. *Hypolimnas dexithea* .. .. 1·50 1·
1161 8 d. *Acraea egina* .. .. .. 2·00 2·
1162 10 d. *Salamis temora* .. .. .. 2·00 2·
1163 15 d. *Precis octavia* .. .. .. 2·75 3·
1156/63 .. .. *Set of* 8 10·00 11·
MS1164 Four sheets, each 100×70 mm. (a) 18 d. *Danaus chrysippus*. (b) 18 d. *Charaxes jasius* (male). (c) 18 d. *Papilio demodocus*. (d) 18 d. *Papilio nireus* .. .. .. *Set of* 4 *sheets* 14·00 14·

(Des D. Miller. Litho Walsall)

1991 (12 Aug). *65th Birthday of Queen Elizabeth II. Hor designs as T* **280** *of Antigua. Multicoloured. P* 14.
1165 50 b. The Queen and Prince Charles at Windsor polo match 30 2
1166 1 d. The Queen and Princess Anne at the Derby, 1988 45
1167 1 d. 25, The Queen at the Royal London Hospital, 1970 .. .. .. 55 5
1168 12 d. The Queen and Prince Philip at Balmoral, 1976 .. .. .. 3·00 3·5
1165/8 .. .. *Set of* 4 3·75 4·2
MS1169 68×90 mm. 18 d. Separate photographs of The Queen and Prince Philip .. .. 3·50 4·2

(Des D. Miller. Litho Walsall)

1991 (12 Aug). *10th Wedding Anniv of Prince and Princess Wales. Horiz designs as T* **280** *of Antigua. Multicoloure P* 14.
1170 20 b. Prince and Princess with sons in June, 1989 .. .. 35 2
1171 75 b. Separate photographs of Prince, Princess and sons 60 5

72 1 d. 50, Prince Henry on first day of school, 1987, and Prince William at polo match 70 70
73 15 d. Separate photographs of Prince and Princess of Wales .. .. 3·50 4·00
70/3 .. .. Set of 4 4·75 5·00
S1174 68×90 mm. 18 d. The family in Italy, 1985 .. .. 4·00 4·50

(Des Walt Disney Co. Litho Questa)

91 (22 Aug). *"Phila Nippon '91" International Stamp Exhibition, Tokyo. Multicoloured designs as T* **279** *of Antigua showing Walt Disney cartoon chartacters playing Japanese sports and games. P* 14×13½ *(horiz) or* 13½ × 14 *(vert).*
75 50 b. Donald Duck and Mickey Mouse playing "go" *(horiz)* 40 30
76 75 b. Morty, Ferdie and Pete as Sumo wrestlers *(horiz)* 55 40
77 1 d. Minnie Mouse, Clarabelle Cow and Daisy Duck playing battledore and shuttlecock *(horiz)* 60 45
78 1 d. 25, Goofy and Mickey at Okinawa bullfight 70 55
79 5 d. Mickey flying hawk .. .. 1·75 1·75
80 7 d. Mickey, Minnie and Donald playing "jan-ken-pon" .. .. 2·00 2·25
81 10 d. Goofy as archer *(horiz)* .. .. .. 2·25 2·50
82 15 d. Morty and Ferdie flying kites .. .. 2·75 3·00
75/82 .. .. Set of 8 10·00 10·00
S1183 Four sheets, each 127×102 mm. (a) 20 d. Mickey climbing Mt Fuji. (b) 20 d. Mickey fishing. (c) 20 d. Scrooge McDuck and Mickey playing football. (d) 20 d. Goofy playing baseball. *Set of 4 sheets* 14·00 15·00

(Des Walt Disney Co. Litho Questa)

91 (28 Aug). *International Literacy Year* (1990). *Multi-coloured designs as T* **269** *of Antigua showing Walt Disney cartoon characters in Kipling's "Just So" stories. P* 14×13½.
84 50 b. "How the Whale got his Throat" *(horiz)* 40 30
85 75 b. "How the Camel got his Hump" *(horiz)* 55 40
86 1 d. "How the Leopard got his Spots" *(horiz)* 60 45
87 1 d. 25, "The Elephant's Child" *(horiz)* .. 70 55
88 1 d. 50, "The Singsong of Old Man Kangaroo" *(horiz)* 85 70
89 7 d. "The Crab that played with the Sea" *(horiz)* .. .. 2·00 2·25
90 10 d. "The Cat that walked by Himself" *(horiz)* .. .. 2·25 2·50
91 15 d. "The Butterfly that Stamped" *(horiz)* 2·75 3·00
84/91 .. .. Set of 8 9·00 9·00
S1192 Four sheets, each 127×102 mm. (a) 20 d. Mickey Mouse reading story to Morte and Ferdie *(horiz)*. P 14×13½. (b) 20 d. "How the Rhinoceros got his Skin" *(horiz)*. P 14×13½. (c) 20 d. "How the Alphabet was made". P 13½×14. (d) 20 d. "How the first Letter was written". P 13½×14 .. .. *Set of 4 sheets* 14·00 15·00

199 Canadian Pacific Steel Cupola Caboose

200 Tiger Shark

(Litho Cartor)

91 (12 Sept). *Railway Brake-vans. T* **199** *and similar multicoloured designs. P* 14×13½.
93 1 d. Type 19 .. .. 25 25
a. Sheetlet. Nos. 1193/1201 .. .. 2·00
94 1 d. Cumberland & Pennsylvania Railroad four-wheeled caboose, U.S.A. 25 25
95 1 d. Ferrocarril Interoceanico caboose, Mexico 25 25
96 1 d. Northern Pacific Railroad steel cupola caboose, U.S.A. 25 25
97 1 d. Morriston & Erie Railroad four-wheeled caboose, U.S.A. 25 25
98 1 d. Burlington Northern Railroad streamlined cupola caboose, U.S.A. .. 25 25
99 1 d. McCloud River Railroad caboose-coach, U.S.A. 25 25
200 1 d. Santa Fe Railroad wide-vision caboose, U.S.A. 25 25
201 1 d. Frisco Railroad wide-vision caboose, U.S.A. 25 25
202 1 d. 50, Colorado & Southern Railroad four-wheeled caboose, U.S.A. 35 40
a. Sheetlet. Nos. 1202/10 .. .. 2·75
203 1 d. 50, Santa Fe Railroad transfer caboose, U.S.A. 35 40
204 1 d. 50, Canadian National wooden cupola caboose 35 40
205 1 d. 50, Union Pacific steel transfer caboose, U.S.A. 35 40
206 1 d. 50, Virgina & Truckee Railroad caboose-coach, U.S.A. 35 40
207 1 d. 50, British Railways standard brake van 35 40
208 1 d. 50, International Railways of Central America caboose 35 40
209 1 d. 50, Northern Pacific Railroad steel cupola caboose, U.S.A. 35 40
210 1 d. 50, Burlington Northern Railroad wooden caboose, U.S.A. 35 40
211 2 d. Oahu Railway caboose, Hawaii .. 40 50
a. Sheetlet. Nos. 1211/19 .. .. 3·25
212 2 d. British Railways standard brake van 40 50
213 2 d. Union Pacific steel wide-view caboose, U.S.A. 40 50
1214 2 d. Belt Railway of Chicago four-wheeled caboose, U.S.A. 40 50
1215 2 d. McCloud River Railroad four-wheeled caboose, U.S.A. 40 50
1216 2 d. Angelina County Lumber Co caboose, U.S.A. 40 50
1217 2 d. Coahuila & Zacatecas caboose, Mexico 40 50
1218 2 d. United Railways of Yucatan caboose, Mexico 40 50
1219 2 d. Rio Grande Railroad steel cupola caboose, U.S.A. 40 50
1193/219 .. .. Set of 27 8·00 9·25
MS1220 Three sheets, each 79×56 mm. (a) 20 d. Wooden caboose on steam goods train. P 13×12. (b) 20 d. Pennsylvania Railroad steel caboose on electric goods train *(vert)*. P 12×13. (c) 20 d. Wooden caboose on passenger train and railwayman with flag *(vert)*. P 12×13 *Set of 3 sheets* 12·00 13·00

Nos. 1193/1201, 1202/10 and 1211/19 were printed together, *se-tenant*, in sheetlets of 9.

(Des R. Sauber. Litho Questa)

1991 (28 Oct). *Fishes. T* **200** *and similar horiz designs. Multicoloured. P* 14×14½.
1221 20 b. Type **200** 15 15
1222 25 b. Common Jewelfish 15 15
1223 50 b. Five-spotted Cichlid 25 25
1224 75 b. Small-toothed Sawfish 25 25
1225 1 d. Spotted Tilapia 30 30
1226 1 d. 25, Dwarf Jewelfish 35 35
1227 1 d. 50, Five-spotted Jewelfish 40 40
1228 3 d. Lion-headed Cichlid 65 65
1229 10 d. Egyptian Mouthbrooder .. .. .. 2·00 2·50
1230 15 d. Burton's Mouthbrooder .. .. .. 2·75 3·50
1221/30 .. .. Set of 10 6·50 7·50
MS1231 Two sheets, each 118×83 mm. (a) 18 d. Great Barracuda. (b) 18 d. Yellow-tailed Snapper *Set of 2 sheets* 8·50 9·50

(Litho Questa)

1991 (9 Nov). *Hummel Figurines. Vert designs as T* **302** *of Antigua. Multicoloured. P* 14.
1232 20 b. Waving children 10 10
1233 75 b. Children under umbrella 15 15
1234 1 d. Girl kissing friend 20 20
1235 1 d. 50, Children at window 30 30
1236 2 d. 50, Two girls in aprons 45 45
1237 5 d. Two boys in bow ties 85 85
1238 10 d. Two girls sitting on fence with birds 1·75 2·00
1239 15 d. Boy and girl in Swiss costume .. 2·50 3·00
1232/9 .. .. Set of 8 5·50 6·50
MS1240 Two sheets, each 98×128 mm. (a) 4 d. × 4 As Nos. 1233/5 and 1239. (b) 5 d. × 4 As Nos. 1232 and 1236/8 .. .. *Set of 2 sheets* 7·00 8·00

(Litho Questa)

1991 (5 Dec). *Death Centenary of Vincent van Gogh (artist). Multicoloured designs as T* **278** *of Antigua. P* 14×13½ *(horiz) or* 13½×14 *(vert).*
1241 20 b. "The Old Cemetery Tower at Nuenen in the Snow" *(horiz)* 15 15
1242 25 b. "Head of Peasant Woman with White Cap" 15 15
1243 50 b. "The Green Parrot" 20 20
1244 75 b. "Vase with Carnations" 20 20
1245 1 d. "Vase with Red Gladioli" 25 25
1246 1 d. 25, "Beach at Scheveningen in Calm Weather" *(horiz)* 30 30
1247 1 d. 50, "Boy cutting Grass with Sickle" *(horiz)* 35 35
1248 2 d. "Coleus Plant in a Flowerpot" (detail) 40 40
1249 3 d. "Self-portrait, 1887" 60 60
1250 4 d. "Self-portrait" *(different)* 70 70
1251 5 d. "Self-portrait" *(different)* 85 85
1252 6 d. "Self-portrait, 1887" *(different)* .. 1·25 1·25
1253 8 d. "Still Life with Bottle, Two Glasses, Cheese and Bread" (detail) .. .. 1·75 1·75
1254 10 d. "Still Life with Cabbage, Clogs and Potatoes" *(horiz)* .. .. 2·25 2·25
1255 12 d. "Montmartre: The Street Lamps" .. 2·75 2·75
1256 15 d. "Head of a Peasant Woman with Brownish Cap" .. .. 3·00 3·00
1241/56 .. .. Set of 16 13·50 13·50
MS1257 Four sheets, each 127×102 mm. (a) 20 d. "The Potato Eaters" *(horiz)*. (b) 20 d. "Montmartre: Quarry and Mills" *(horiz)*. (c) 20 d. "Autumn Landscape" *(horiz)*. (d) 20 d. "Arles: View from the Wheat Fields" (detail) *(horiz)*. Imperf .. .. *Set of 4 sheets* 15·00 16·00

(Litho Walsall)

1991 (23 Dec). *Christmas. Religious Paintings by Fra Angelico. Vert designs as T* **287** *of Antigua. Multicoloured. P* 12.
1258 20 b. "The Madonna of Humility" 10 10
1259 50 b. "Madonna and Child with Angels" .. 20 20
1260 75 b. "Virgin and Child with Angels" .. 25 25
1261 1 d. "The Annunciation" 30 30
1262 1 d. 25, "Presentation in the Temple" .. 35 35
1263 5 d. "The Annunciation" *(different)* .. 1·25 1·50
1264 10 d. "Madonna della Stella" .. .. 2·00 2·50
1265 15 d. "Naming of St. John the Baptist" .. 2·50 3·25
1258/65 .. .. Set of 8 6·25 7·50
MS1266 Two sheets, each 102×128 mm. (a) 20 d. "Coronation of the Virgin". (b) 20 d. "Annunciation and Adoration of the Magi". P 14 *Set of 2 sheets* 7·00 8·00

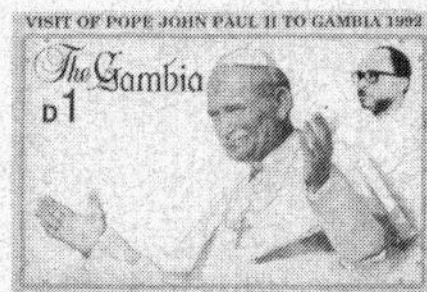

201 Son House **202** Pope John Paul II

(Des R. Sauber. Litho Questa)

1992 (12 Feb). *Famous Blues Singers. T* **201** *and similar vert designs. Multicoloured. P* 14.
1267 20 b. Type **201** 15 15
1268 25 b. W. C. Handy 15 15
1269 50 b. Muddy Waters 30 30
1270 75 b. Lightnin Hopkins 40 40
1271 1 d. Ma Rainey 45 45
1272 1 d. 25, Mance Lipscomb 50 50
1273 1 d. 50, Mahalia Jackson 60 60
1274 2 d. Ella Fitzgerald 70 70
1275 3 d. Howlin Wolf 85 85
1276 5 d. Bessie Smith .. .. 1·25 1·25
1277 7 d. Leadbelly .. .. 1·50 1·50
1278 10 d. Joe Willie Wilkins .. .. .. 2·00 2·00
1267/78 .. .. Set of 12 8·00 8·00
MS1279 Three sheets, each 110×78 mm. (a) 20 d. String Drum. (b) 20 d. Elvis Presley. (c) 20 d. Billie Holiday .. .. *Set of 3 sheets* 11·00 12·00

(Des G. Vasarhelyi. Litho Questa)

1992 (20 Feb). *Papal Visit. T* **202** *and similar horiz designs. Multicoloured. P* 14.
1280 1 d. Type **202** 40 40
1281 1 d. 25, Pope John Paul II and Pres. Sir Dawda Jawara 50 50
1282 20 d. Gambian and Papal flags .. .. 4·75 5·50
1280/2 .. .. Set of 3 5·00 5·75
MS1283 104×70 mm. 25 d. Pope giving blessing 6·00 7·00

A 50 d. value, as Type **202**, but embossed on gold foil, exists from a limited printing.

(Des D. Miller. Litho Questa)

1992 (2 Mar). *40th Anniv of Queen Elizabeth II's Accession. Horiz designs as T* **288** *of Antigua. Multicoloured. P* 14.
1284 20 b. Pottery market 10 10
1285 50 b. Ruins of early fort 20 20
1286 1 d. Fishing boat 30 30
1287 15 d. Canoes on beach .. .. 2·75 3·50
1284/7 .. .. Set of 4 3·00 3·75
MS1288 Two sheets, each 75×97 mm. (a) 20 d. *Lady Chilel Jawara* (river vessel). (b) 20 d. River ferry being loaded .. .. *Set of 2 sheets* 7·50 8·50

203 N. Comaneci (Rumania) (combined gymnastic events) and Map of Barcelona

(Litho Questa)

1992 (16 Mar). *Olympic Games, Barcelona (2nd issue). Past Medal Winners. T* **203** *and similar multicoloured designs. P* 14.
1289 20 b. Type **203** 10 10
1290 50 b. D. Moorcroft (G.B.) (5000 metres) and map 20 20
1291 75 b. M. Nemeth (Hungary) (javelin) and decorative tiles 25 25
1292 1 d. J. Pedraza (Mexico) (20k walk) and decorative plate 30 30
1293 1 d. 25, "Soling" class yachting (Brazil), state arms and flag 40 40
1294 1 d. 50, Women's hockey (G.D.R.) and Barcelona building 45 45
1295 12 d. M. Jordan (U.S.A.) (basketball) and map .. .. 2·50 3·25
1296 15 d. V. Borzov (U.S.S.R.) (100 metres) and galleon .. .. 3·00 3·50
1289/96 .. .. Set of 8 6·50 7·50
MS1297 Two sheets. (a) 82×112 mm. 20 d. Silhouette of flamenco dancer on map *(vert)*. (b) 112×82 mm. 20 d. Silhouette of bull on map *Set of 2 sheets* 7·25 7·50

204 Mickey Mouse as Christopher Columbus

205 *Hibiscus rosa-sinensis*

(Des Walt Disney Co. Litho Questa)

1992 (8 Apr). *International Stamp Exhibitions. T* **204** *and similar multicoloured designs showing Walt Disney cartoon characters. P* 13½×14.

(*a*) *"Granada '92", Spain. Voyage of Columbus*
1298 20 b. Type **204** 30 15
1299 75 b. Mickey's plans derided 45 25
1300 1 d. 50, Mickey lands in America .. 65 60
1301 15 d. Mickey presents treasure to Minnie 3·25 4·00
1298/1301 .. .. .. *Set of* 4 4·25 4·50
MS1302 127×102 mm. 18 d. Mickey embarks for America .. .. 3·50 4·00

(*b*) *World Columbian Stamp "Expo '92". Chicago Landmarks*
1303 50 b. Navy Pier 10 10
1304 1 d. Wrigley Building 20 25
1305 1 d. 25, University of Chicago 25 30
1306 12 d. Alder Planetarium .. .. .. 1·75 2·75
1303/6 .. .. *Set of* 4 2·00 3·00
MS1307 127×102 mm. 18 d. Goofy hanging over Chicago (*horiz*). P 14×13½ .. .. .. 3·50 4·00

(Litho Questa)

1992 (16 Apr). *Easter. Religious Paintings. Multicoloured designs as T* **291** *of Antigua, but vert. P* 13½×14.
1308 20 b. "Christ presented to the People" (Rembrandt) 10 10
1309 50 b. "Christ carrying the Cross" (Grünewald) 20 20
1310 75 b. "The Crucifixion" (Grünewald) .. 25 25
1311 1 d. "The Crucifixion" (Rubens) 30 30
1312 1 d. 25, "The Road to Calvary" (detail) (Tintoretto) 35 35
1313 1 d. 50, "The Road to Calvary" (Tintoretto) (*different*) 40 40
1314 15 d. "The Crucifixion" (Masaccio) .. 2·75 3·25
1315 20 d. "The Descent from the Cross" (detail) (Rembrandt) .. .. .. 3·50 4·00
1308/15 .. .. *Set of* 8 7·00 8·00
MS1316 Two sheets, each 72×101 mm. (a) 25 d. "The Crowning with Thorns" (detail) (Van Dyck). (b) 25 d. "The Crowning with Thorns" (detail) (Titian) .. .. .. *Set of* 2 *sheets* 8·50 9·50

(Des Mary Walters. Litho B.D.T.)

1992 (21 July). *Flowers. T* **205** *and similar vert designs. Multicoloured. P* 14.
1317 20 b. Type **205** 10 10
1318 50 b. *Monodora myristica* 20 20
1319 75 b. *Bombax costatum* 25 25
1320 1 d. *Oncoba spinosa* 30 30
1321 1 d. 25, *Combretum grandiflorum* .. 35 35
1322 1 d. 50, *Rothmannia longiflora* 40 40
1323 2 d. *Clerodendrum splendens* 55 55
1324 5 d. *Mussaenda erythrophylla* .. .. 1·10 1·25
1325 10 d. *Nauclea latifolia* .. .. .. 1·75 2·00
1326 12 d. *Clerodendrum capitatum* .. .. 1·90 2·25
1327 15 d. *Costus spectabilis* .. .. .. 2·50 2·75
1328 18 d. *Strophanthus preussii* .. .. 2·75 3·00
1317/28 .. .. *Set of* 12 11·00 12·00
MS1329 Four sheets, each 102×71 mm. (a) 20 d. *Bougainvillea glabra*. (b) 20 d. *Nymphaea*. (c) 20 d. *Adansonia digitata*. (d) 20 d. *Clitoria ternatea* .. .. *Set of* 4 *sheets* 12·00 13·00

206 *Joven Antonia* (River Gambia)

(Des C. Abbott. Litho Questa)

1992 (3 Aug). *River Boats of the World. T* **206** *and similar horiz designs. Multicoloured. P* 14.
1330 20 b. Type **206** 10 10
1331 50 b. *Dresden* (River Elbe) 20 20
1332 75 b. *Medway Queen* (River Medway) .. 25 25
1333 1 d. *Lady Wright* (River Gambia) .. 30 30
1334 1 d. 25, *Devin* (River Vltava) 35 35
1335 1 d. 50, *Lady Chilel Jawara* (River Gambia) 40 50
1336 5 d. *Robert Fulton* (River Hudson) .. 1·10 1·25
1337 10 d. *Coonawarra* (River Murray) .. 1·75 2·00
1338 12 d. *Nakusp* (River Columbia) .. .. 2·00 2·25
1339 15 d. *Lucy Ashton* (Firth of Clyde) .. 2·50 2·75
1330/9 .. .. *Set of* 10 8·00 9·00
MS1340 Two sheets, each 107×69 mm. (a) 20 d. *City of Cairo* (Mississippi). (b) 20 d. *Rüdesheim* (Rhine) .. .. *Set of* 2 *sheets* 8·00 9·00

(Des W. Wright. Litho Questa)

1992 (8 Aug). *50th Anniv of Japanese Attack on Pearl Harbor. Horiz designs as T* **286** *of Antigua. Multicoloured. P* 14½.
1341 2 d. U.S.S. *Pennsylvania* (battleship) .. 80 90
a. Sheetlet. Nos. 1341/50 .. .. 7·00
1342 2 d. Japanese Mitsubishi AGM Zero-Sen aircraft over Pearl Harbor 80 90
1343 2 d. U.S.S. *Ward* (destroyer) sinking midget submarine 80 90
1344 2 d. Ford Naval Station under attack .. 80 90
1345 2 d. Agency report of Japanese attack .. 80 90
1346 2 d. Newspaper headline 80 90
1347 2 d. Japanese troops on Guam 80 90
1348 2 d. U.S. forces regaining Wake Island .. 80 90
1349 2 d. North American B-25B Mitchell bomber raid on Japan 80 90
1350 2 d. American Douglas SBD Dauntless dive bomber attacking Japanese carrier, Midway 80 90
1341/50 .. .. *Set of* 10 7·00 8·00
Nos. 1341/50 were printed together, *se-tenant*, in sheetlets of 10 with the stamps arranged in two horizontal strips of 5 separated by a gutter showing dogfight over Pearl Harbor.

207 Women's Double Sculls

208 Pres. Jawara playing Golf and Map of Australia

(Litho Questa)

1992 (10 Aug). *Winter Olympic Games, Albertville, and Olympic Games, Barcelona (3rd issue). T* **207** *and similar multicoloured designs. P* 14.
1351 20 b. Type **207** 10 10
1352 50 b. Men's kayak (*vert*) 20 20
1353 75 b. Women's rapid precision pistol shooting 25 25
1354 1 d. Judo (*vert*) 30 30
1355 1 d. 25, Men's javelin (*vert*) 35 35
1356 1 d. 50, Men's vaulting horse (*vert*) .. 40 40
1357 2 d. Men's downhill skiing (*vert*) .. 55 55
1358 3 d. Windsurfing (*vert*) 70 75
1359 5 d. Men's high jump .. .. .. 1·10 1·25
1360 10 d. Four-man bobsled (*vert*) .. .. 1·90 2·25
1361 12 d. 90 metre ski-jump (*vert*) .. .. 2·00 2·50
1362 15 d. Men's slalom skiing .. .. 2·40 2·75
1351/62 .. .. *Set of* 12 9·00 10·50
MS1363 Four sheets, each 100×70 mm. (a) 18 d. Table tennis (*vert*). (b) 18 d. Men's 500 metre speed skating. (c) 18 d. Women's 200 metre backstroke. (d) 18 d. Pairs figure skating (*vert*) *Set of* 4 *sheets* 13·00 14·00

(Litho B.D.T.)

1992 (21 Sept). *"Genova '92" International Thematic Stamp Exhibition. Dinosaurs. Vert designs as T* **290** *of Antigua. Multicoloured. P* 14.
1364 20 b. Dryosaurus 15 10
1365 25 b. Saurolophus 15 10
1366 50 b. Allosaurus 20 20
1367 75 b. Fabrosaurus 25 25
1368 1 d. Deinonychus 30 30
1369 1 d. 25, Cetiosaurus 35 35
1370 1 d. 50, Camptosaurus 35 35
1371 2 d. Ornithosuchus 45 45
1372 3 d. Spinosaurus 60 60
1373 5 d. Ornithomimus .. .. .. 1·00 1·00
1374 10 d. Kentrosaurus .. .. .. 1·75 2·00
1375 12 d. Schlermochus .. .. .. 1·90 2·25
1364/75 .. .. *Set of* 12 6·50 7·00
MS1376 Three sheets, each 104×75 mm. (a) 25 d. As No. 1366. (b) 25 d. As No. 1369. (c) 25 d. As No. 1371 .. .. .. *Set of* 3 *sheets* 14·00 15·00

(Des Kerri Schiff. Litho Questa)

1992 (28 Oct). *Postage Stamp Mega Event, New York. Sheet 100×70 mm containing horiz design as T* **299** *of Antigua. Multicoloured. P* 14.
MS1377 18 d. Immigration Centre, Ellis Island 3·75 4·00

(Litho Questa)

1992 (3 Nov). *Christmas. Religious Paintings. Vert designs as T* **300** *of Antigua. Multicoloured. P* 13½×14.
1378 50 b. "The Holy Family" (Raphael) .. 20 20
1379 75 b. "The Little Holy Family" (Raphael) 25 25
1380 1 d. "The Little Holy Family" (detail) (Raphael) 30 30
1381 1 d. 25, "Escape to Egypt" (Melchior Broederlam) 35 35
1382 1 d. 50, "Flight into Egypt" (Adriaen Isenbrant) 35 35
1383 2 d. "The Holy Family" (El Greco) .. 45 45
1384 2 d. "Flight into Egypt" (detail) (Cosimo Tura) 45 45
1385 2 d. "Flight into Egypt" (detail) (Master of Hoogstraelen) 45 45
1386 4 d. "The Holy Family" (Bernard van Orley) 80 90
1387 5 d. "Holy Family with Infant Jesus Sleeping" (detail) (Charles Le Brun) 95 1·10
1388 10 d. "Rest on The Flight to Egypt" (Orazio Gentileschi) .. .. .. 1·75 2·25
1389 12 d. "Rest on The Flight to Egypt" (detail) (Orazio Gentileschi) .. .. 1·90 2·50
1378/89 .. .. *Set of* 12 7·50 8·50
MS1390 Three sheets, each 102×77 mm. (a) 25 d. "The Holy Family" (detail) (Giorgione). (b) 25 d. "Flight into Egypt" (detail) (Vittore Carpaccio). (c) 25 d. "Rest on The Flight to Egypt" (detail) (Simone Cantarino) *Set of* 3 *sheets* 11·00 12·00

(Des Walt Disney Co. Litho Questa)

1992 (16 Nov). *60th Anniv of Goofy (Disney cartoon character). Multicoloured designs as T* **258** *of Dominica. P* 14×13½.
1391 50 b. Goofy in *Orphan's Benefit*, 1934 .. 30 20
1392 75 b. Goofy and Donald Duck in *Moose Hunters*, 1937 .. .. .. 40 30
1393 1 d. Goofy in *Mickey's Amateurs*, 1937 .. 50 40
1394 1 d. 25, Goofy, Donald and Mickey Mouse in *Lonesome Ghosts*, 1937 .. .. 55 55
1395 5 d. Goofy, Donald and Mickey in *Boat Builders*, 1938 .. .. .. 1·40 1·40
1396 7 d. Goofy, Donald and Mickey in *The Whalers*, 1938 .. .. .. 1·75 2·00
1397 10 d. Goofy and Wilbur the grasshopper in *Goofy and Wilbur*, 1939 .. .. 2·00 2·25
1398 15 d. Goofy in *Saludos Amigos*, 1941 .. 2·50 2·75
1391/8 .. .. *Set of* 8 8·50 9·00
MS1399 Two sheets, each 127×102 mm. (a) 20 d. Goofy in *The Band Concert*, 1935 (*vert*). (b) 20 d. Goofy today (*vert*). P 13½×14 .. *Set of* 2 *sheets* 8·00 9·00

(Litho B.D.T.)

1992 (8 Dec). *Open Golf Championships. T* **208** *and simil[...] multicoloured designs. P* 14.
1400 20 b. Type **208** 15
1401 1 d. Pres. Jawara and Gambia Open trophy 45
1402 1 d. 50, Pres. Jawara (winner of Gambia Open, 1985) 55
1403 2 d. Pres. Jawara and map of Japan .. 70
1404 3 d. Pres. Jawara and map of U.S.A. .. 80
1405 5 d. Gambia Open trophy .. .. 1·40 1·6[...]
1406 10 d. Pres. Jawara and map of Scotland 2·50 2·[...]
1407 12 d. Pres. Jawara and map of Italy .. 2·50 2·7[...]
1400/7 .. .. *Set of* 8 8·00 9·[...]
MS1408 Two sheets. (a) 106×71 mm. 10 d. Pres. Jawara playing shot. (b) 67×99 mm. 18 d. Flag of Gambia (*horiz*) .. .. *Set of* 2 *sheets* 8·00 8·5[...]

209 Launch of European "Ariane 4"

210 Peace Corps and Gambian Flags

(Des W. Wright and L. Fried (Nos. 1409, 1419, **MS**1423[...] W. Wright and W. Hanson (Nos. 1411, 1422, **MS**1423[...] W. Wright (others). Litho B.D.T.)

1993 (7 Jan). *Anniversaries and Events. T* **209** *and simil[...] multicoloured designs. P* 14.
1409 2 d. Type **209** 50
1410 2 d. Konrad Adenauer and Berlin Airlift (*horiz*) 50
1411 2 d. Airship LZ-129 *Hindenburg*, 1928 (*horiz*) 50
1412 5 d. *Santa Maria* (*horiz*) .. .. 1·25 1·[...]
1413 6 d. Jentink's Duiker (*horiz*) .. .. 1·40 1·[...]
1414 7 d. World map and emblem (*horiz*) .. 1·40 1·[...]
1415 9 d. Wolfgang Amadeus Mozart .. 1·75 1·[...]
1416 10 d. Lions Club emblem .. .. .. 1·75 1·[...]
1417 10 d. *Enterprise* (yacht), 1930 .. .. 1·75 1·[...]
1418 10 d. Imperial Amazon ("Sisserou Parrot") 1·75 1·[...]
1419 12 d. American space shuttle .. .. 2·00 2·[...]
1420 12 d. Fleet of Columbus (*horiz*) .. .. 2·00 2·[...]
1421 15 d. Adenauer and returning prisoners of war (*horiz*) .. .. 2·40 2·[...]
1422 18 d. Airship LZ-1, 1900 (*horiz*) .. .. 3·00 3·[...]
1409/22 .. .. *Set of* 14 20·00 20·[...]
MS1423 Six sheets. (a) 104×76 mm. 18 d. Nose of projected European space station "Hermes". (b) 113×87 mm. 18 d. Konrad Adenauer. (c) 85×65 mm. 18 d. Count von Zeppelin. (d) 103×75 mm. 18 d. Green-winged Macaw and bow of ship. (e) 85×65 mm. 18 d. Globe. (f) 99×69 mm. 18 d. Dancers from *The Marriage of Figaro* *Set of* 6 *sheets* 18·00 20·[...]
Anniversaries and Events:—Nos. 1409, 1419, **MS**1423[...] International Space Year; Nos. 1410, 1421, **MS**1423b, 25[...] death anniv of Konrad Adenauer (German statesman); No[...] 1411, 1422, **MS**1423c, 75th death anniv of Count Ferdinand v[...] Zeppelin; Nos. 1412, 1420, **MS**1423d, 500th anniv of Discove[...] of America by Columbus; Nos. 1413, 1418, **MS**1423e, Ear[...] Summit '92, Rio; No. 1414, International Conference [...] Nutrition, Rome; Nos. 1415, **MS**1423f, Death bicent of Moza[...] No. 1416, 75th anniv of International Association of Lio[...] Clubs; No. 1417, Americas Cup Yachting Championship.
No. 1409 is inscribed "Arienne 4" and No. 1411 "LZ-127", bo[...] in error.

(Des A. Nahigian. Litho Walsall)

1993 (7 Jan). *15th Death Anniv of Elvis Presley (singer)* (1992[...] *Vert designs as Nos. 1666/8 of Dominica. Multicoloured. P* 1[...]
1424 3 d. Elvis Presley 70
a. Strip of 3. Nos. 1424/6 .. .. 1·90
1425 3 d. Elvis with guitar 70
1426 3 d. Elvis with microphone 70
1424/6 .. .. *Set of* 3 1·90 1·[...]
Nos. 1424/6 were printed together, horizontally and vertical[...] *se-tenant*, in sheetlets of 9 (3×3).

(Litho Walsall)

1993 (7 Jan). *Bicentenary of the Louvre, Paris. Vert designs [...] T* **305** *of Antigua showing paintings. Multicoloured. P* 12.
1427 3 d. "St. John the Baptist" (Da Vinci) .. 55
a. Sheetlet. Nos. 1427/34 .. .. 4·00
1428 3 d. "Virgin of the Rocks" (Da Vinci) .. 55
1429 3 d. "Bacchus" (Da Vinci) 55
1430 3 d. "Lady of the Court, Milan" (Da Vinci) 55
1431 3 d. "Virgin of the Rocks" (detail) (Da Vinci) 55
1432 3 d. "Mona Lisa" (Da Vinci) 55
1433 3 d. "Mona Lisa" (detail) (Da Vinci) .. 55
1434 3 d. Sketches for "Two Horsemen" (Da Vinci) 55
1435 3 d. "The Oath of Horatii" (left detail) (David) 55
a. Sheetlet. Nos. 1435/42 .. .. 4·00
1436 3 d. "The Oath of Horatii" (right detail) (David) 55
1437 3 d. "The Love of Paris and Helen" (detail) (David) 55
1438 3 d. "The Sabine Women" (detail) (David) 55
1439 3 d. "Leonidas at Thermopylae" (detail) (David) 55
1440 3 d. "The Coronation of Napoleon" (left detail) (David) 55
1441 3 d. "The Coronation of Napoleon" (centre detail) (David) 55
1442 3 d. "The Coronation of Napoleon" (right detail) (David) 55

43	3 d. "Peasant Family at Home" (detail) (L. le Nain)	55	60
	a. Sheetlet. Nos. 1443/50	4·00	
44	3 d. "Smoking Room" (left detail) (L. le Nain)	55	60
45	3 d. "Smoking Room" (right detail) (L. le Nain)	55	60
46	3 d. "The Cart" (detail) (L. le Nain)	55	60
47	3 d. "Peasants' Repast" (detail) (L. le Nain)	55	60
48	3 d. "Portrait in an Interior" (detail) (L. le Nain)	55	60
49	3 d. "Portrait in an Interior" (different detail) (L. le Nain)	55	60
50	3 d. "The Forge" (L. le Nain)	55	60
27/50	*Set of* 24	12·00	13·00

S1451 Two sheets, each 70×100 mm. (a) 20 d. 'Allegory of Victory" (M. le Nain) (52×86 *mm*). b) 20 d. "Madame Vigee-Le Brun and Daughter" Le Brun) (52×86 *mm*). P 14½ .. *Set of* 2 *sheets* 8·00 9·00

Nos. 1427/34, 1435/42 and 1443/50 were each printed ether, *se-tenant*, in sheetlets of 8 stamps and one centre label.

Nos. 1432/3 are incorrectly inscribed "Monna Lisa".

(Litho Questa)

93 (3 Mar). *25th Anniv of United States Peace Corps. P* 14.

52 **210**	2 d. multicoloured	60	60

211 Jackie Robinson and Ruby Dee (*The Jackie Robinson Story*)

(Des P. Wolff. Litho Questa)

93 (25 Mar). *Baseball Films. T* **211** *and similar multicoloured designs. P* 13.

53	3 d. Type **211**	60	70
	a. Sheetlet. Nos. 1453/60	4·25	
54	3 d. Robert DeNiro (*Bang the Drum Slowly*)	60	70
55	3 d. James Earl Jones and Billy Dee Williams (*The Bingo Long Travelling All-Stars and Motor Kings*)	60	70
56	3 d. Kevin Costner and Susan Sarandon (*Bull Durham*)	60	70
57	3 d. Cast photograph (*Eight Men Out*)	60	70
58	3 d. Ray Liotta (*Field of Dreams*)	60	70
59	3 d. Charlie Sheen (*Major League*)	60	70
60	3 d. Tom Selleck (*Mr. Baseball*)	60	70
61	3 d. Wallace Beery, 1927, and Elliott Gould, 1986 (*Casey at the Bat*)	60	70
	a. Sheetlet. Nos. 1461/8	4·25	
62	3 d. Anna Nilsson and Babe Ruth (*Babe comes Home*)	60	70
63	3 d. Joe Brown (*Elmer the Great*)	60	70
64	3 d. Bud Abbott and Lou Costello (*The Naughty Nineties*)	60	70
65	3 d. Frank Sinatra, Gene Kelly and Esther Williams (*Take Me Out to the Ball Game*)	60	70
66	3 d. Tab Hunter and Gwen Verdon (*Damn Yankees*)	60	70
67	3 d. Dan Dailey (*The Pride of St. Louis*)	60	70
68	3 d. John Candy and Richard Pryor (*Brewster's Millions*)	60	70
53/68	*Set of* 16	8·75	10·00

S1469 Four sheets, each 132×107 mm. (a) 20 d. John Goodman (*The Babe*). (b) 20 d. Ronald Reagan (*The Winning Team*). (c) 20 d. Tom Hanks and Madonna (*A League of Their Own*) (*vert*). (d) 20 d. Robert Redford (*The Natural*) (*vert*) .. *Set of* 4 *sheets* 15·00 17·00

Nos. 1453/60 and 1461/8 were each printed together, -tenant, in sheetlets of 8.

212 Giraffe

213 Long-tailed Pangolin hanging by Tail

(Des D. Burkhart. Litho Questa)

93 (5 Apr). *Animals of West Africa. T* **212** *and similar vert designs. Multicoloured. P* 14.

70	2 d. Type **212**	40	45
	a. Sheetlet. Nos. 1470/81	4·25	
71	2 d. Baboon	40	45
72	2 d. Caracal	40	45
73	2 d. Large-spotted Genet	40	45
74	2 d. Bushbuck	40	45
75	2 d. Red-fronted Gazelle	40	45
76	2 d. Red-flanked Duiker	40	45
77	2 d. Cape Buffalo	40	45
78	2 d. African Civet	40	45
79	2 d. Side-striped Jackal	40	45
1480	2 d. Ratel	40	45
1481	2 d. Striped Polecat	40	45
1482	5 d. Vervet	70	75
	a. Sheetlet. Nos. 1482/93	8·25	
1483	5 d. Blackish-green Guenon	70	75
1484	5 d. Long-tailed Pangolin	70	75
1485	5 d. Leopard	70	75
1486	5 d. Elephant	70	75
1487	5 d. Hunting Dog	70	75
1488	5 d. Spotted Hyena	70	75
1489	5 d. Lion	70	75
1490	5 d. Hippopotamus	70	75
1491	5 d. Nile Crocodile	70	75
1492	5 d. Aardvark	70	75
1493	5 d. Warthog	70	75
1470/93	*Set of* 24	12·50	13·00
MS1494	101×72 mm. 20 d. As No. 1483	3·75	4·00

Nos. 1470/81 and 1482/93 were each printed together, *se-tenant*, in sheetlets of 12, with the backgrounds forming composite designs.

(Des D. Burkhart. Litho Questa)

1993 (15 Apr). *Endangered Species. Long-tailed Pangolin. T* **213** *and similar vert designs. Multicoloured. P* 14.

1495	1 d. 25, Type **213**	45	25
1496	1 d. 50, Sitting on branch	55	40
1497	2 d. Climbing up branch	65	60
1498	5 d. Climbing down branch	1·60	2·00
1495/8	*Set of* 4	3·00	3·00
MS1499	72×100 mm. 20 d. As No. 1496	4·00	4·50

214 Osprey

215 Rose-ringed Parakeet

(Des W. Wright. Litho Questa)

1993 (15 Apr). *Birds of Prey. T* **214** *and similar multicoloured designs. P* 14.

1500	1 d. 25, Type **214**	80	50
1501	1 d. 50, Egyptian Vulture (*horiz*)	90	50
1502	2 d. Martial Eagle	1·00	55
1503	3 d. Ruppell's Griffon (*horiz*)	1·25	75
1504	5 d. Augur Buzzard	1·50	1·25
1505	8 d. Greater Kestrel	2·00	2·25
1506	10 d. Secretary Bird	2·25	2·50
1507	15 d. Bateleur (*horiz*)	2·50	3·25
1500/7	*Set of* 8	11·00	10·50

MS1508 Two sheets, each 108×80 mm. (a) 20 d. Owl ("Tawny Owl") (57×42½ *mm*). (b) 20 d. Verreaux's Eagle (57×42½ *mm*) *Set of* 2 *sheets* 8·50 9·00

(Des W. Wright. Litho Questa)

1993 (15 Apr). *African Birds. T* **215** *and similar vert designs. Multicoloured. P* 14.

1509	2 d. Type **215**	1·00	1·10
	a. Sheetlet. Nos. 1509/20	11·00	
1510	2 d. Variable Sunbird	1·00	1·10
1511	2 d. Red-billed Hornbill	1·00	1·10
1512	2 d. Red-billed Fire Finch	1·00	1·10
1513	2 d. Go-away Bird	1·00	1·10
1514	2 d. Burchell's Gonolek ("Crimson-breasted Shrike")	1·00	1·10
1515	2 d. Grey-headed Bush Shrike	1·00	1·10
1516	2 d. Western Nicator	1·00	1·10
1517	2 d. Egyptian Plover	1·00	1·10
1518	2 d. Congo Peafowl	1·00	1·10
1519	2 d. Painted Snipe	1·00	1·10
1520	2 d. South African Crowned Crane	1·00	1·10
1509/20	*Set of* 12	11·00	12·00

Nos. 1509/20 were printed together, *se-tenant*, in sheetlets of 12.

No. 1509a exists imperforate from a limited printing.

(Des Kerri Schiff. Litho Questa)

1993 (2 June). *40th Anniv of Coronation. Vert designs as T* **307** *of Antigua. P* 13½×14.

1521	2 d. multicoloured	60	75
	a. Sheetlet. Nos. 1521/4×2	8·00	
1522	5 d. multicoloured	1·00	1·25
1523	8 d. reddish brown and black	1·25	1·50
1524	10 d. multicoloured	1·50	1·60
1521/4	*Set of* 4	4·00	4·50
MS1525	70×100 mm. 20 d. multicoloured. P 14	4·00	4·50

Designs: (38×47 *mm*)—2 d. Queen Elizabeth II at Coronation (photograph by Cecil Beaton); 5 d. Orb and Sceptre; 8 d. Sir Winston Churchill; 10 d. Queen Elizabeth II at Trooping the Colour. (28½×42½ *mm*)—20 d. "Queen Elizabeth II, 1972" (detail) (Joe King).

Nos. 1521/4 were printed together in sheetlets of 8 containing two *se-tenant* blocks of 4.

216 Hugo Eckener and LZ-127 *Graf Zeppelin*

(Litho Questa)

1993 (7 June). *Aviation Anniversaries. T* **216** *and similar multicoloured designs. P* 14.

1526	2 d. Type **216**	55	50
1527	2 d. Guyot's balloon, 1785 (*vert*)	55	50
1528	5 d. Zeppelin LZ-3 *Luftschiffe 3* and crown	1·00	1·00
1529	5 d. Sopwith Snipe (fighter)	1·00	1·00
1530	8 d. Eckener and LZ-127 *Graf Zeppelin*	1·60	1·75
1531	10 d. *Comte D'Artois* (hot air balloon), 1785 (*vert*)	1·90	2·00
1532	15 d. Royal Aircraft Factory S.E.5 (fighter)	2·40	2·50
1526/32	*Set of* 7	8·00	8·25

MS1533 Three sheets. (a) 105×84 mm. 20 d. Eckener and LZ-127 *Graf Zeppelin* (airship). (b) 84×105 mm. 20 d. Blanchard's balloon, 1785 (*vert*). (c) 84×105 mm. 20 d. Avro 504k (biplane) *Set of* 3 *sheets* 13·00 14·00

Anniversaries:—Nos. 1526, 1528, 1530, **MS**1533a, 125th birth anniv of Hugo Eckener (airship pioneer); Nos. 1527, 1531, **MS**1533b, Bicentenary of first airmail flight; Nos. 1529, 1532, **MS**1533c, 75th anniv of Royal Air Force.

Nos. 1526 and **MS**1533a are incorrectly inscribed "Zeppelin Luftschiffe 3". All three stamps and the miniature sheet for Eckener's birth anniversary are inscribed with the wrong dates, 1870–1940 instead of 1868–1954.

217 Henry Ford and "Model T", 1910

218 Marilyn Monroe

(Des R. Sauber. Litho Questa)

1993 (7 June). *Centenaries of Henry Ford's First Petrol Engine (Nos. 1534/45) and Karl Benz's First Four-wheeled Car (Nos. 1546/57). T* **217** *and similar horiz designs. Multicoloured. P* 14.

1534	2 d. Type **217**	45	50
	a. Sheetlet. Nos. 1534/45	4·75	
1535	2 d. Car of 1896	45	50
1536	2 d. Henry Ford with Barney Oldfield and "999", 1902	45	50
1537	2 d. Henry Ford, 1893, and car of 1896	45	50
1538	2 d. "Model A", 1903	45	50
1539	2 d. "Model T" with roof lowered, 1908	45	50
1540	2 d. "Model T" with roof raised, 1908	45	50
1541	2 d. "Model K", 1906	45	50
1542	2 d. "Model A", 1931	45	50
1543	2 d. "Model A", 1906	45	50
1544	2 d. "Model N", 1906	45	50
1545	2 d. "Model F", 1905	45	50
1546	2 d. Benz "Velo", 1894	45	50
	a. Sheetlet. Nos. 1546/57	4·75	
1547	2 d. Car of 1894	45	50
1548	2 d. Three-wheeled car of 1885 from side	45	50
1549	2 d. "Mannheim", 1905	45	50
1550	2 d. Car of 1892	45	50
1551	2 d. Car of 1900 from front	45	50
1552	2 d. Racing car of 1911 from side	45	50
1553	2 d. "Velo", 1893	45	50
1554	2 d. Black car of 1900 from side	45	50
1555	2 d. Red car of 1900 from side	45	50
1556	2 d. Racing car of 1911 from front	45	50
1557	2 d. Three-wheeled car of 1885 from back	45	50
1534/57	*Set of* 24	9·50	11·00

MS1558 Two sheets, each 132×115 mm. (a) 20 d. Ford car of 1896. (b) 20 d. Benz car of 1900 *Set of* 2 *sheets* 7·50 8·00

Nos. 1534/45 and 1546/57 were each printed together, *se-tenant*, in sheetlets of 12 with the backgrounds forming composite designs.

(Des Susan Rini. Litho B.D.T.)

1993 (26 July). *Musical Entertainers. T* **218** *and similar vert designs. P* 14.

1559/93 3 d.×35 multicoloured .. .. .. 27·00 28·00

Nos. 1559/93 were issued as four sheetlets, three of nine different designs (Nos. 1559/85) and one of eight (Nos. 1586/93), depicting Marilyn Monroe (Nos. 1559/67), Elvis Presley (Nos. 1568/76), Madonna (Nos. 1577/85) and Buddy Holly, Otis Redding, Bill Haley, Dinah Washington, musical instruments, Ritchie Valens, Clyde McPhatter, Elvis Presley (Nos. 1586/93).

219 Siamese

220 "Woman with a Comb" (Picasso)

(Des R. Sauber. Litho Questa)

1993 (13 Sept). *Oriental Cats. T* **219** *and similar multicoloured designs. P* 14.

1594	2 d. Type **219**	75	75
	a. Sheetlet. Nos. 1594/1605	8·00	
1595	2 d. Colourpoint Longhair sitting	75	75

1596 2 d. Burmese 75 75
1597 2 d. Birman 75 75
1598 2 d. Snowshoe 75 75
1599 2 d. Tonkinese 75 75
1600 2 d. Foreign Shorthair stretching 75 75
1601 2 d. Balinese 75 75
1602 2 d. Oriental Shorthair 75 75
1603 2 d. Foreign Shorthair lying 75 75
1604 2 d. Colourpoint Longhair with black face standing 75 75
1605 2 d. Colourpoint Longhair with white face standing 75 75
1594/1605 .. .. *Set of* 12 8·00 8·00
MS1606 Two sheets, each 121×90 mm. (a) 20 d. Colourpoint shorthair (*vert*). (b) 20 d. Burmese (*vert*) .. .. *Set of* 2 *sheets* 7·75 8·00

Nos. 1594/1605 were printed together, *se-tenant*, in sheetlets of 12 with the background forming a composite design.

No. **MS**1606 exists imperforate from a limited printing.

(Des R. Sauber. Litho Questa)

1993 (13 Sept). *Royal Dogs. Horiz designs as T* **219**. *Multicoloured. P* 14.

1607 2 d. Shih Tzu (Emperor of China) .. 70 75
a. Sheetlet. Nos. 1607/18 .. .. 7·50
1608 2 d. Skye Terrier (Queen Victoria) .. 70 75
1609 2 d. Berner Laufhund (King Louis XVI, France) 70 75
1610 2 d. Boxer (King Francis I, France) .. 70 75
1611 2 d. Welsh Corgi (Queen Elizabeth II) .. 70 75
1612 2 d. Dumfrieshire (Princess Anne) .. 70 75
1613 2 d. Lurcher (King George VI) 70 75
1614 2 d. Welsh Corgi (Princess Anne) .. 70 75
1615 2 d. Pekinese (Empress Ts'Eu-Hi, China) 70 75
1616 2 d. Papillon (King Louis XIII, France) .. 70 75
1617 2 d. Otterhound (King John) 70 75
1618 2 d. Pug (Napoleon I, France) 70 75
1607/18 .. .. *Set of* 12 7·50 8·00
MS1619 Two sheets, each 120×90 mm. (a) 20 d. Cairn Terrior (Mary, Queen of Scots). (b) 20 d. Long-haired Dachshund (Queen Victoria) *Set of* 2 *sheets* 7·75 8·00

Nos. 1607/18 were printed together, *se-tenant*, in sheetlets of 12 with the background forming a composite design.

No. **MS**1619 exists imperforate from a limited printing.

(Des Kerri Schiff. Litho Questa)

1993 (27 Sept). *Asian International Stamp Exhibitions. Multicoloured designs as T* **268** *of Dominica. P* 13½×14.

(*a*) "*Indopex '93*", *Surabaya, Indonesia*

1620 20 b. National Monument and statue, Jakarta 20 20
1621 20 b. Pura Taman Ayun Temple, Bali .. 20 20
1622 2 d. Guardian statue, Singosari Palace, Java 60 60
1623 2 d. Candi Jawi, Java 60 60
1624 5 d. Telek Luh mask .. .. .. 1·40 1·40
a. Sheetlet. Nos. 1624/9 .. .. 7·50
1625 5 d. Jero Gde mask .. .. .. 1·40 1·40
1626 5 d. Barong Macan mask .. .. 1·40 1·40
1627 5 d. Monkey mask .. .. .. 1·40 1·40
1628 5 d. Mata Gde mask .. .. .. 1·40 1·40
1629 5 d. Jauk Kras mask .. .. .. 1·40 1·40
1630 5 d. "Tree Mask" (Soedibio) .. .. 1·40 1·40
a. Sheetlet. Nos. 1630/5 .. .. 7·50
1631 5 d. "Dry Lizard" (Hendra Gunawan) .. 1·40 1·40
1632 5 d. "The Corn Eater" (Sudjana Kerton) 1·40 1·40
1633 5 d. "Night Watchman" (Djoko Pekik) .. 1·40 1·40
1634 5 d. "Hunger" (Kerton) .. .. .. 1·40 1·40
1635 5 d. "Arje Player" (Soedjojono) .. .. 1·40 1·40
1636 5 d. Central Temple, Lara Djonggrang .. 1·40 1·40
1637 5 d. Irian Jaya Monument, Jakarta .. 1·40 1·40
1638 15 d. Brahma and Siva Temples, Java .. 2·75 3·25
1639 15 d. Date of the Year Temple, Java .. 2·75 3·25
1620/39 .. .. *Set of* 20 20·00 21·00
MS1640 Two sheets, each 135×105 mm. (a) 18 d. Tomb effigies, Torajaland (*horiz*). (b) 18 d. Relief from Borobudur, Java (*horiz*). P 14×13½. *Set of* 2 *sheets* 7·50 8·00

(*b*) "*Taipei '93*", *Taiwan*

1641 20 b. Fawang Si Pagoda, Henan 20 20
1642 20 b. Wanshoubao Pagoda, Shashi .. 20 20
1643 2 d. Red Pavilion, Shibaozhai 60 60
1644 2 d. Songyue Si Pagoda, Henan 60 60
1645 5 d. Pottery camel (walking) .. .. 1·40 1·40
a. Sheetlet. Nos. 1645/50 .. .. 7·50
1646 5 d. Pottery horse and rider .. .. 1·40 1·40
1647 5 d. Pottery camel (standing with mouth closed) .. .. 1·40 1·40
1648 5 d. Yellow-glazed pottery horse .. 1·40 1·40
1649 5 d. Pottery camel (standing with mouth open) .. .. 1·40 1·40
1650 5 d. Pottery saddled horse .. .. 1·40 1·40
1651 5 d. Qianlong vase .. .. .. 1·40 1·40
a. Sheetlet. Nos. 1651/6 .. .. 7·50
1652 5 d. Small wine cup .. .. .. 1·40 1·40
1653 5 d. Mei-ping vase .. .. .. 1·40 1·40
1654 5 d. Urn vase .. .. 1·40 1·40
1655 5 d. Tureen .. .. 1·40 1·40
1656 5 d. Lidded potiche .. .. .. 1·40 1·40
1657 5 d. Tianning Si Pagoda, Beijing .. 1·40 1·40
1658 5 d. Bond Centre, Hong Kong .. .. 1·40 1·40
1659 15 d. Forbidden City pavilion, Beijing .. 2·75 3·25
1660 15 d. Xuanzhuang Pagoda, Shenxi .. 2·75 3·25
1641/60 .. .. *Set of* 20 20·00 21·00
MS1661 Two sheets, each 135×105 mm. (a) 18 d. Seated Buddha, Shanhua Temple, Shanxi. P 13½×14. (b) 18 d. Statues, Upper Huayan Si Temple, Datong (*horiz*). P 14×13½. *Set of* 2 *sheets* 7·50 8·00

(*c*) "*Bangkok '93*", *Thailand*

1662 20 b. Sanctuary of Prasat Phanom Wan .. 20 20
1663 20 b. Lai Kham Vihan, Chiang Mai .. 20 20
1664 2 d. Upmarket spirit shrine, Bangkok .. 60 60
1665 2 d. Walking Buddha statue, Wat Phra Si Ratana Mahathat 60 60
1666 5 d. "Early Fruit Stand" .. .. .. 1·40 1·40
a. Sheetlet. Nos. 1666/71 .. .. 7·50
1667 5 d. "Scene Rendered in Chinese Style" .. 1·40 1·40
1668 5 d. "Buddha descends from Tauatimsa" 1·40 1·40
1669 5 d. "Sang Thong Tales" (detail) .. 1·40 1·40
1670 5 d. "The Damned in Hell" .. .. 1·40 1·40
1671 5 d. "King Sanjaya travels on Elephant" 1·40 1·40
1672 5 d. U Thong C Buddha (bronze) .. 1·40 1·40
a. Sheetlet. Nos. 1672/7 .. .. 7·50
1673 5 d. Seated Buddha (bronze) .. .. 1·40 1·40
1674 5 d. Phra Chai Buddha (ivory and gold) 1·40 1·40
1675 5 d. Buddha (bronze) .. .. .. 1·40 1·40
1676 5 d. U Thong A Buddha (bronze) .. 1·40 1·40
1677 5 d. Crowned Buddha (bronze) .. .. 1·40 1·40
1678 5 d. Statue of Buddha, Wat Mahathat .. 1·40 1·40
1679 5 d. The Gopura of Prasat Phanom Rung 1·40 1·40
1680 15 d. Slender Chedis, Mongkon .. .. 2·75 3·25
1681 15 d. The Prang of Prasat Hin Phimai .. 2·75 3·25
1662/81 .. .. *Set of* 20 20·00 21·00
MS1682 Two sheets, each 135×105 mm. (a) 18 d. Khon (Thai dance drama). P 13½×14. (b) 18 d. Ceramics (*horiz*). P 14×13½ .. *Set of* 2 *sheets* 7·50 8·00

Nos. 1624/9, 1630/5, 1645/50, 1651/6, 1666/71 and 1672/7 were each printed, *se-tenant*, in sheetlets of 6.

(Litho Cartor (Nos. 1686, 1690, **MS**1691c) or Questa (others))

1993 (7 Oct). *Anniversaries and Events. T* **220** *and similar multicoloured designs. P* 14 (*Nos.* 1683/5, 1687/9) *or* 13½×14 (*Nos.* 1686, 1690).

1683 2 d. Type **220** 65 65
1684 2 d. Niedzica Castle (*horiz*) 65 65
1685 5 d. "The Mirror" (Picasso) .. .. 1·25 1·25
1686 5 d. Early astronomical instrument .. 1·25 1·25
1687 7 d. "Woman on a Pillow" (Picasso) .. 1·50 1·50
1688 10 d. "Honegger's Liturgical Symphony" (Marian Bogusz) (*horiz*) .. .. 2·00 2·25
1689 10 d. "Pont-Neut in Paris" (Hanna Rudzka-Cybisowa) (*horiz*) .. .. .. 2·00 2·25
1690 10 d. Modern Telescope .. .. .. 2·00 2·25
1683/90 .. .. *Set of* 8 10·00 11·00
MS1691 Three sheets. (a) 75×105 mm. 18 d. "The Three Dancers" (detail) (Picasso). P 14. (b) 105×75 mm. 18 d. "When You enter here, Whisper my Name soundlessly" (detail) (Henryk Waniek) (*horiz*). P 14. (c) 102×74 mm. 18 d. Copernicus. P 12×13 .. *Set of* 3 *sheets* 11·00 12·00

Anniversaries and Events:—Nos. 1683, 1685, 1687, **MS**1691a, 20th death anniv of Picasso (artist); Nos. 1684, 1688/9, **MS**1691b, "Polska '93" International Stamp Exhibition, Poznań; Nos. 1686, 1690, **MS**1691c, 450th death anniv of Copernicus (astronomer).

The captions printed on Nos. 1684 and 1689 are transposed in error.

No. **MS**1691b is inscribed "WHISPERT" in error.

221 Mudville Player at the Plate

(Des Rosemary DeFiglio. Litho Questa)

1993 (25 Oct). Casey at the Bat. *T* **221** *and similar multicoloured designs showing scenes from Walt Disney's cartoon film. P* 14×13½.

1692 2 d. Type **221** 75 80
a. Sheetlet. Nos. 1692/1700 .. .. 6·00
1693 2 d. Mudville player out 75 80
1694 2 d. Umpire and player arguing 75 80
1695 2 d. Fans applauding 75 80
1696 2 d. Casey reading newspaper at plate .. 75 80
1697 2 d. Casey letting second pitch go by .. 75 80
1698 2 d. Over-confident Casey 75 80
1699 2 d. Casey's striking out 75 80
1700 2 d. Casey striking out at night 75 80
1692/1700 .. .. .. *Set of* 9 6·00 6·50
MS1701 Two sheets, each 129×103 mm. (a) 20 d. Mudville manager. P 14×13½. (b) 20 d. Pitcher (*vert*). P 13½×14 .. .. *Set of* 2 *sheets* 8·50 9·00

Nos. 1692/1700 were printed together, *se-tenant*, in sheetlets of 9.

(Des Rosemary DeFiglio, Litho Cartor)

1993 (22 Nov). *World Cup Football Championship* 1994, *U.S.A. (1st issue). Multicoloured designs as T* **310** *of Antigua. P* 13½×14.

1702 1 d. 25, Hannich (Hungary) and Stopyra (France) 65 40
1703 1 d. 50, Labd (Morocco) and Gary Lineker (England) 75 50
1704 2 d. Segota (Canada) and Morozov (Russia) 90 65
1705 3 d. Roger Milla (Cameroun) .. .. 1·10 1·10
1706 5 d. Rodax (Austria) and Weiss (Czechoslovakia) .. .. 1·40 1·50
1707 10 d. Claesen (Belgium), Bossis and Amoros (France) .. .. 2·00 2·25
1708 12 d. Candida (Brazil) and Ramirez (Costa Rica) .. .. 2·25 2·50
1709 15 d. Silva (Brazil) and Michel Platini (France) .. .. 2·50 2·75
1702/9 .. .. *Set of* 8 10·50 10·50
MS1710 Two sheets, each 100×70 mm. (a) 25 d. Muller (Brazil) and McDonald (Ireland) (*horiz*). (b) 25 d. Diego Maradona (Argentina) and Matthaeus (Germany) (*horiz*). P 13 *Set of* 2 *sheets* 9·75 10·00

See also Nos. 1882/90.

(Litho Questa)

1993 (1 Dec). *Christmas. Religious Paintings. Designs a[s] T* **270** *of Dominica. Black, pale lemon and red* (*Nos.* 1712/1[3], 1715/17 *and* **MS**1719b) *or multicoloured* (*others*). *P* 13½×14

1711 25 b. "The Adoration of the Magi" (detail) (Rubens) 20 2
1712 1 d. "The Holy Family with Joachim and Anna" (Dürer) 45 2
1713 1 d. 50, "The Annunciation" (Dürer) .. 60 3
1714 2 d. "The Adoration of the Magi" (different detail) (Rubens) 75 5
1715 2 d. "The Virgin Mary worshipped by Albrecht Bonstetten" (Dürer) .. 75 5
1716 7 d. "The Holy Family with Two Angels in a Portico" (detail) (Dürer) .. .. 2·00 2·5
1717 10 d. "Virgin on a Throne, crowned by an Angel" (Dürer) .. .. .. 2·25 2·5
1718 15 d. "The Adoration of the Magi" (different detail) (Rubens) .. .. .. 2·50 3·2
1711/18 .. .. *Set of* 8 8·50 9·0
MS1719 Two sheets, each 102×127 mm. (a) 20 d. "The Adoration of the Magi" (different detail) (Rubens). P 13½×14. (b) 20 d. "The Holy Family with Two Angels in a Portico" (different detail) (Dürer) (*horiz*). P 14×13½ .. *Set of* 2 *sheets* 7·75 8·5

(Des Kerri Schiff. Litho Questa)

1993 (15 Dec). *Famous Paintings by Rembrandt and Matisse Multicoloured designs as T* **316** *of Antigua. P* 13½×14.

1720 50 b. "A Man in a Cap" (Rembrandt) .. 40 2
1721 1 d. 50, "Pierre Matisse" (Matisse) .. 70 3
1722 2 d. "Man with a Gold Helmet" (Rembrandt) 75 5
1723 2 d. "Auguste Pellerin" (Matisse) .. 75 5
1724 5 d. "Andre Derain" (Matisse) .. .. 1·50 1·5
1725 7 d. "A Franciscan Monk" (Rembrandt) 2·00 2·5
1726 12 d. "The Young Sailor (II)" (Matisse) .. 2·50 3·2
1727 15 d. "The Apostle Paul" (Rembrandt) .. 2·50 3·2
1720/7 .. .. *Set of* 8 10·00 11·0
MS1728 Two sheets, each 127×102 mm. (a) 20 d. "Dr. Tulp demonstrating the Anatomy of the Arm" (detail) (Rembrandt) (*horiz*). (b) 20 d. "Pianist and Draughts Players" (detail) (Matisse) (*horiz*). P 14×13½ .. .. *Set of* 2 *sheets* 8·00 9·0

222 Mickey Mouse performing Ski Ballet

(Des Alvin White Studios. Litho Questa)

1993 (20 Dec). *Winter Sports. T* **222** *and similar vert designs showing Walt Disney cartoon characters. Multicoloured P* 13½×14.

1729 50 b. Type **222** 30 15
1730 75 b. Clarabelle and Horace ice dancing .. 40 15
1731 1 d. Donald Duck and Dale speed skating 45 20
1732 1 d. 25, Donald in biathlon 50 20
1733 4 d. Donald and nephews in bob-sled .. 1·40 1·40
1734 5 d. Goofy on luge .. .. .. 1·50 1·50
1735 7 d. Minnie Mouse figure skating .. 2·00 2·50
1736 10 d. Goofy downhill skiing .. .. 2·25 2·50
1737 15 d. Goofy playing ice hockey .. .. 2·50 3·00
1729/37 .. .. *Set of* 9 10·00 10·50
MS1738 Two sheets, each 128×102 mm. (a) 20 d. Minnie mogul skiing. (b) 20 d. Goofy cross-country skiing .. .. .. *Set of* 2 *sheets* 7·50 8·50

(Des W. Hanson. Litho Questa)

1994 (18 Feb). "*Hong Kong '94*" *International Stam[p] Exhibition (1st issue). Horiz design as T* **317** *of Antigua Multicoloured. P* 14.

1739 1 d. 50, Hong Kong 1979 $2 Butterflies stamp and "Spring Garden" (M. Bruce) (left detail) 40 5
a. Horiz pair. Nos. 1739/40 .. .. 80 1·00
1740 1 d. 50, Gambia 1990 50 d. Gambian Life stamp and "Spring Garden" (M. Bruce) (right detail) 40 50
MS1741 82×117 mm. 20 d. Hong Kong 1970 Chinese New Year 10 c. stamp .. .. 3·25 3·50

Nos. 1739/40 were printed together, *se-tenant*, in horizonta[l] pairs throughout the sheet with the centre part of each pai[r] forming the complete painting.

(Des Kerri Schiff. Litho Questa)

1994 (18 Feb). "*Hong Kong '94*" *International Stam[p] Exhibition (2nd issue). Qin Dynasty Terracotta Figures Multicoloured designs as T* **318** *of Antigua, but vert. P* 14.

1742 1 d. 50, Warriors and horses 40 50
a. Sheetlet. Nos. 1742/7 .. .. 2·25
1743 1 d. 50, Head of warrior 40 50
1744 1 d. 50, Kneeling warrior 40 50
1745 1 d. 50, Chariot driver 40 50
1746 1 d. 50, Dog 40 50
1747 1 d. 50, Warriors as excavated 40 50
1742/7 .. .. *Set of* 6 2·25 2·75

Nos. 1742/7 were printed together, *se-tenant*, in sheetlets of 6

223 Pluto the Racer, 1934–35

224 Ludwig von Drake and Easter Bunny

(Des Alvin White Studios. Litho Questa)

4 (11 Apr). *Chinese New Year ("Year of the Dog"). T* **223** *ɪd similar multicoloured designs showing Walt Disney ɪrtoon dogs. P* 13½×14.

8 25 b. Type **223** 20 15
9 50 b. Fifi, 1933 .. .. 30 20
0 75 b. Pluto Jnr, 1942 .. .. .. 40 30
1 1 d. 25, Goofy and Bowser 50 30
2 1 d. 50, Butch, 1940 .. .. .. 60 35
3 2 d. Toliver, 1936 .. .. .. 70 50
4 3 d. Ronnie, 1946 .. .. .. 90 90
5 5 d. Primo, 1950 .. .. 1·25 1·25
6 8 d. Pluto's kid brother, 1946 .. .. 1·75 2·00
7 10 d. The army mascot, 1942 .. .. 1·90 2·25
8 12 d. Pluto and Fifi's puppies, 1937 .. 2·00 2·50
9 18 d. Bent Tail Jnr, 1949 .. .. .. 2·75 3·25
8/59 .. .. *Set of* 12 12·00 12·50
1760 Three sheets, each 127×102 mm. (a) 0 d. Pluto and Fifi's puppies, 1937 (*different*). 13½×14. (b) 20 d. Pluto and Dinah, 1950. 13½×14. (c) 20 d. Pflip (*horiz*). P 14×13½ *Set of* 3 *sheets* 11·00 12·00

Io. 1748/59 were issued in small sheets of 10 (5×2). No. 1748 exists as a sheetlet of 6 (3×2).
Ios. 1758 and **MS**1760a are inscribed "DINAH'S PUPPIES" error.

(Des Alvin White Studios. Litho Questa)

4 (11 Apr). *Easter. T* **224** *and similar vert designs showing Valt Disney cartoon characters. Multicoloured. P* 13½×14.

1 25 b. Type **224** 20 10
2 50 b. Minnie Mouse and Daisy Duck carrying banner 30 10
3 3 d. Mickey Mouse wearing top hat .. 90 75
4 4 d. Von Drake holding hatching egg .. 1·00 1·00
5 5 d. Donald Duck pushing trolley full of eggs .. .. 1·25 1·25
6 8 d. Bunny taking photograph of Von Drake .. .. 1·50 1·75
7 10 d. Goofy dressed as Easter Bunny .. 1·75 2·25
8 12 d. Von Drake holding dinosaur egg .. 2·00 2·50
1/8 .. .. *Set of* 8 8·00 8·50
1769 Two sheets. (a) 102×123 mm. 20 d. Mickey and Minnie. (b) 123×102 mm. 20 d. udwig von Drake .. .. *Set of* 2 *sheets* 7·50 8·50

(Litho Questa)

94 (25 Apr). *Centenary of Sierra Club (environmental protection society) (1992). Endangered Environments. Multicoloured designs as T* **320** *of Antigua. P* 14. 70 80

70 5 d. Briksdal Fjord .. .. .. 3·75
a. Sheetlet. Nos. 1770/5 .. .. 70 80
71 5 d. Glacier, Briksdal Fjord 70 80
72 5 d. Waterfall, Briksdal Fjord 70 80
73 5 d. Frozen lake, Yosemite 70 80
74 5 d. Cliffs and river, Yosemite 70 80
75 5 d. Forest, Yosemite 70 80
76 5 d. Mother and child, Tibetan Plateau .. 5·00
a. Sheetlet. Nos. 1776/83 .. .. 70 80
77 5 d. Yellowstone in winter 70 80
78 5 d. Ross Island 70 80
79 5 d. Mount Erebus 70 80
80 5 d. Tibetan Plateau 70 80
81 5 d. Waterfall, Yellowstone 70 80
82 5 d. Sunset on the Serengeti 70 80
83 5 d. Dead trees, Ansel Adams Wilderness
84 5 d. Ansel Adams Wilderness in winter (*horiz*) 70 80
a. Sheetlet. Nos. 1784/91 .. .. 5·00
85 5 d. Ansel Adams Wilderness in summer (*horiz*) 70 80
86 5 d. Ridge on Mount Erebus (*horiz*) .. 70 80
87 5 d. Mount Erebus from a distance (*horiz*) 70 80
88 5 d. Prince William Sound (*horiz*) .. 70 80
89 5 d. Geysers, Yellowstone (*horiz*) .. 70 80
90 5 d. Local dwelling, Tibetan Plateau (*horiz*) 70 80
91 5 d. Sierra Club Centennial emblem (*horiz*) 70 80
92 5 d. Frozen lake, Prince William Sound (*horiz*) 70 80
a. Sheetlet. Nos. 1792/7 .. .. 3·75
93 5 d. Forest, Prince William Sound (*horiz*) 70 80
94 5 d. Baobab Tree, Serengeti (*horiz*) .. 70 80
95 5 d. Plains, Serengeti (*horiz*) 70 80
96 5 d. Volcano, Ross Island (*horiz*) .. 70 80
97 5 d. Mountains, Ross Island (*horiz*) .. 70 80
70/97 .. .. *Set of* 28 17·00 20·00

Nos. 1770/5, 1776/83, 1784/91 and 1792/7 were each printed gether, *se-tenant*, in two sheetlets of 6 (Nos. 1770/5 and 92/7) or two sheetlets of 8 (Nos. 1776/91).

ALTERED CATALOGUE NUMBERS

ny Catalogue numbers altered from the last dition are shown as a list in the introductory pages.

225 *Oeceoclades maculata*

226 "Girl with a Kitten" (Perronneau)

(Des Wendy Smith-Griswold. Litho Questa)

1994 (1 May). *Orchids. T* **225** *and similar multicoloured designs. P* 14.

1798 1 d. Type **225** 35 20
1799 1 d. 25, *Angraecum distichum* (*horiz*) .. 45 30
1800 2 d. *Plectrelminthus caudatus* 60 35
1801 5 d. *Tridactyle tridactylites* (*horiz*) .. 1·25 1·25
1802 8 d. *Bulbophyllum lepidum* (*horiz*) .. 1·40 1·50
1803 10 d. *Angraecum eburneum* .. .. 1·60 1·90
1804 12 d. *Eulophia guineensis* .. .. 1·75 2·00
1805 15 d. *Angraecum eichleranum* (*horiz*) .. 2·00 2·50
1798/1805 .. .. .. *Set of* 8 8·50 9·00
MS1806 Two sheets, each 100×70 mm. (a) 25 d. *Vanilla imperialis*. (b) 25 d. *Ancistrochilus rothschildianus* (*horiz*) .. .. *Set of* 2 *sheets* 8·00 9·00

(Des Kerri Schiff. Litho Questa)

1994 (11 July). *Cats. T* **226** *and similar multicoloured designs showing paintings of cats. P* 14.

1807 5 d. Type **226** 90 90
a. Sheetlet. Nos. 1807/18 .. .. 9·50
1808 5 d. "Still Life with Cat and Fish" (Chardin) 90 90
1809 5 d. "Tinkle a Cat" 90 90
1810 5 d. "Naughty Puss!" (advertisement) .. 90 90
1811 5 d. "Cats" (T.-A. Steinlen) 90 90
1812 5 d. "Girl in Red with Cat and Dog" (Phillips) 90 90
1813 5 d. "Cat, Butterfly and Begonia" (Harunobu) 90 90
1814 5 d. "Cat and Kitten" (Pamela Higgins) 90 90
1815 5 d. "Woman with a Cat" (Renoir) .. 90 90
1816 5 d. "Minnie from Outskirts of the Village" (Thrall) 90 90
1817 5 d. "The Fisher" (Raphael Tuck postcard) 90 90
1818 5 d. "Artist and His Family" (detail) (Vaenius) 90 90
1819 5 d. "The Arena" (Harold Weston) (*horiz*) 90 90
a. Sheetlet. Nos. 1819/30 .. .. 9·50
1820 5 d. "Cat killing a Bird" (Picasso) (*horiz*) 90 90
1821 5 d. "Cat and Butterfly" (Hokusai) (*horiz*) 90 90
1822 5 d. "Winter: Cat on a Cushion" (Steinlen) (*horiz*) 90 90
1823 5 d. "Rattown Tigers" (Prang) (*horiz*) .. 90 90
1824 5 d. "Cat on the Floor" (Steinlen) (*horiz*) 90 90
1825 5 d. "Cat and Kittens" (*horiz*) 90 90
1826 5 d. "Cats looking over Fence" (Prang) (*horiz*) 90 90
1827 5 d. "Little White Kittens into Mischief" (Ives) (*horiz*) 90 90
1828 5 d. "Cat Bathing" (Hiroshige) (*horiz*) .. 90 90
1829 5 d. "Playtime" (Tuck postcard) (*horiz*) .. 90 90
1830 5 d. "Summer: Cat on a Balustrade" (Steinlen) (*horiz*) 90 90
1807/30 .. .. *Set of* 24 19·00 19·00
MS1831 Two sheets, each 100×70 mm. (a) 20 d. "The Graham Children" (detail) (William Hogarth). (b) 20 d. "The Morning Rising" (detail) (Michel Lepicie) (*horiz*) .. .. *Set of* 2 *sheets* 7·50 8·50

Nos. 1807/18 and 1819/30 were printed together, *se-tenant*, in sheetlets of 12.

227 Patas Monkey

228 *Mylothris rhodope*

(Des D. Burkhart. Litho Questa)

1994 (1 Aug). *Monkeys. T* **227** *and similar vert designs. Multicoloured. P* 14.

1832 1 d. Type **227** 35 20
1833 1 d. 50, Collared Mangabey 55 30
1834 2 d. Black and White Colobus 60 35
1835 5 d. Mona Monkey .. .. .. 1·10 1·10
1836 8 d. Kirk's Colobus .. .. .. 1·50 1·75
1837 10 d. Vervet .. .. 1·75 2·00
1838 12 d. Red Colobus .. .. .. 2·00 2·25
1839 15 d. Guinea Baboon .. .. .. 2·25 2·50
1832/9 .. .. *Set of* 8 9·00 9·50
MS1840 Two sheets, each 106×77 mm. (a) 25 d. Head of Guinea Baboon. (b) 25 d. Head of Collared Mangabey .. .. *Set of* 2 *sheets* 9·00 9·50

(Des W. Hanson. Litho B.D.T.)

1994 (16 Aug). *25th Anniv of First Moon Landing. Horiz designs as T* **326** *of Antigua. Multicoloured. P* 14.

1841 2 d. Yuri Gagarin (first cosmonaut) .. 50 55
a. Sheetlet. Nos. 1841/9 .. .. 4·00
1842 2 d. Valentina Tereshkova (first woman in Space) 50 55
1843 2 d. Ham (first chimpanzee in Space) .. 50 55
1844 2 d. Alexei Leonov (first man to walk in Space) 50 55
1845 2 d. Neil Armstrong (first man on Moon) 50 55
1846 2 d. Svetlana Savitskaya (first woman to walk in Space) 50 55
1847 2 d. Marc Garneau (first Canadian in Space) 50 55
1848 2 d. Vladimir Komarov (first Soviet Space casualty) 50 55
1849 2 d. Ulf Merbold (first German in Space) 50 55
1841/9 .. .. *Set of* 9 4·00 4·50
MS1850 81×81 mm. 30 d. "Apollo 11" crew at news conference .. .. 6·00 6·50

Nos. 1841/9 were printed together, *se-tenant*, in sheetlets of 9.

(Des Kerri Schiff. Litho Questa)

1994 (16 Aug). *Centenary of International Olympic Committee. Gold Medal Winners. Multicoloured designs as T* **327** *of Antigua, but vert. P* 14.

1851 1 d. 50, Daley Thompson (Great Britain) (decathlon), 1980 and 1984 .. .. 40 30
1852 5 d. Heide Marie Rosendohl (Germany) (long jump), 1972 .. .. .. 1·10 1·25
MS1853 106×76 mm. 20 d. Sweden (ice hockey), 1994 .. .. 4·00 4·50

(Des J. Batchelor. Litho Questa)

1994 (16 Aug). *50th Anniv of D-Day. Horiz designs as T* **331** *of Antigua. Multicoloured. P* 14.

1854 50 b. *Soema* (Dutch sloop) 40 40
1855 75 b. H.M.S. *Belfast* (cruiser) 50 50
1856 1 d. U.S.S. *Texas* (battleship) 60 60
1857 2 d. *Georges Leygues* (French cruiser) .. 1·00 1·00
1854/7 .. .. *Set of* 4 2·25 2·25
MS1858 105×76 m. 20 d. H.M.S. *Ramillies* (battleship) firing broadside .. .. .. 4·00 4·50

(Des Kerri Schiff. Litho Questa (Nos. 1859, 1870/2) or B.D.T. (Nos. 1860/9))

1994 (16 Aug). *"Philakorea '94" International Stamp Exhibition, Seoul. Multicoloured designs as T* **281** *of Dominica. P* 14 *(50 b., 2 d., 3 d.) or* 13½×14 *(others).*

1859 50 b. Kungnakchon Hall (38×25 *mm*) .. 20 20
1860 1 d. Soldiers on horses 30 30
a. Sheetlet. Nos. 1860/9 .. .. 2·75
1861 1 d. Soldiers defending fort 30 30
1862 1 d. Archers 30 30
1863 1 d. General on horse 30 30
1864 1 d. Three soldiers in battle 30 30
1865 1 d. Army in retreat 30 30
1866 1 d. Archers using fire arrows 30 30
1867 1 d. Horsemen attacking fort 30 30
1868 1 d. Women in summer house 30 30
1869 1 d. Old man, child and house 30 30
1870 2 d. Kettle of Popchusa (38×25 *mm*) .. 50 50
1871 3 d. Pomun tourist resort (38×25 *mm*) .. 55 55
1859/71 .. .. *Set of* 13 3·75 3·75
MS1872 98×68 mm. 20 d. Tomb guardian, Taenung (38×25 *mm*). P 14 .. .. 4·00 4·50

Nos. 1860/9 were printed together, *se-tenant*, in sheetlets of 10 showing screen paintings of the "Sanguozhi".

(Des B. Hargreaves. Litho Questa)

1994 (18 Aug). *Butterflies. T* **228** *and similar horiz designs. Multicoloured. P* 14.

1873 1 d. Type **228** 40 25
1874 1 d. 25, *Iolaphilus menas* 55 35
1875 2 d. *Neptis nemetes* 65 40
1876 5 d. *Antanartia delius* .. .. .. 1·10 1·10
1877 8 d. *Acraea caecilia* .. .. .. 1·40 1·60
1878 10 d. *Papilio nireus* .. .. .. 1·50 1·75
1879 12 d. *Papilio menestheus* .. .. 1·75 2·25
1880 15 d. *Iolaphilus julus* .. .. .. 2·00 2·50
1873/80 .. .. *Set of* 8 8·50 9·25
MS1881 Two sheets, each 97×68 mm. (a) 25 d. *Bematistes epaea*. (b) 25 d. *Colotis evippe* *Set of* 2 *sheets* 8·50 9·50

229 Bobby Charlton (England)

230 *Suillus luteus*

(Litho Questa)

1994 (1 Sept). *World Cup Football Championships, U.S.A. (2nd issue). T* **229** *and similar vert designs. Multicoloured. P* 14.

1882 50 b. Type **229** 30 20
1883 75 b. Ferenc Puskas (Hungary) 35 25
1884 1 d. Paolo Rossi (Italy) 40 25
1885 2 d. Biri Biri (Spain) 60 40
1886 3 d. Diego Maradona (Argentina) .. 75 60
1887 8 d. Johann Cruyff (Netherlands) .. 1·40 1·60
1888 10 d. Franz Beckenbauer (Germany) .. 1·50 1·75

1889 15 d. Thomas Dooley (U.S.A.) 2·00 2·50
1882/9 *Set of* 8 6·50 6·75
MS1890 Two sheets, each 70×100 mm. (a) 25 d. Pelé (Brazil). (b) 25 d. Gordon Banks (England) *Set of 2 sheets* 9·00 9·50

(Des Mary Walters. Litho Questa)

1994 (30 Sept). *Fungi. T* **230** *and similar vert designs. Multicoloured. P* 14.
1891 5 d. Type **230** 90 90
a. Sheetlet. Nos. 1891/9 7·00
1892 5 d. *Bolbitius vitellinus* 90 90
1893 5 d. *Clitocybe nebularis* 90 90
1894 5 d. *Omphalotus olearius* 90 90
1895 5 d. *Auricularia auricula* 90 90
1896 5 d. *Macrolepiota rhacodes* 90 90
1897 5 d. *Volvariella volvacea* 90 90
1898 5 d. *Psilocybe coprophila* 90 90
1899 5 d. *Suillus granulatus* 90 90
1900 5 d. *Agaricus campestris* 90 90
a. Sheetlet. Nos. 1900/8 7·00
1901 5 d. *Lepista nuda* 90 90
1902 5 d. *Podaxis pistillaris* 90 90
1903 5 d. *Oudemansiella radicata* 90 90
1904 5 d. *Schizophyllum commune* 90 90
1905 5 d. *Chlorophyllum molybdites* 90 90
1906 5 d. *Hypholoma fasciculare* 90 90
1907 5 d. *Mycena pura* 90 90
1908 5 d. *Ganoderma lucidum* 90 90
1891/1908 *Set of* 18 14·00 14·00
MS1909 Two sheets, each 100×70 mm. (a) 20 d. *Leucoagaricus naucinus.* (b) 20 d. *Cyathus striatus* *Set of 2 sheets* 8·00 9·00
Nos. 1891/9 and 1900/8 were printed together, *se-tenant*, in sheetlets of 9.

(Litho Questa)

1994 (5 Dec). *Christmas. Religious Paintings. Vert designs as T* **336** *of Antigua. Multicoloured. P* 13½×14.
1910 50 b. "Expectant Madonna with St. Joseph" (French 15th-century) 20 10
1911 75 b. "Rest of the Holy Family" (Louis le Nain) 30 20
1912 1 d. "Rest on the Flight into Egypt" (Antoine Watteau) 35 20
1913 2 d. "Rest on the Flight into Egypt" (Jean-Honore Fragonard) 50 40
1914 2 d. "Rest on the Flight into Egypt" (Francois Boucher) 50 40
1915 2 d. "Noon" (Claude Lorrain) 50 40
1916 10 d. "The Holy Family" (Nicolas Poussin) 2·00 2·50
1917 12 d. "Mystical Marriage of St. Catherine" (Pierre-Francois Mignard) 2·00 2·50
1910/17 *Set of* 8 5·50 6·00
MS1918 Two sheets, each 122×87 mm. (a) 25 d. "Adoration of the Shepherds" (detail) (Mathieu le Nain). (b) 25 d. "The Nativity by Torchlight" (detail) (Louis le Nain) *Set of 2 sheets* 9·00 10·00

231 Marilyn Monroe **232** Elvis as a Child

(Des R. Rundo. Litho Questa)

1995 (8 Jan). *Marilyn Monroe (American entertainer) Commemoration. T* **231** *and similar vert designs. Multicoloured. P* 14.
1919 4 d. Type **231** 70 80
a. Sheetlet. Nos. 1919/27 5·50
1920 4 d. Wearing pendant necklace 70 80
1921 4 d. In blue jacket 70 80
1922 4 d. With sun-glasses on head 70 80
1923 4 d. Looking over right arm 70 80
1924 4 d. Wearing gold beret and jacket 70 80
1925 4 d. Wearing hooped earrings 70 80
1926 4 d. Smiling 70 80
1927 4 d. Laughing 70 80
1919/27 *Set of* 9 5·50 6·50
MS1928 Two sheets, each 70×100 mm. (a) 25 d. Marilyn Monroe in red dress. (b) 25 d. With pendant earrings *Set of 2 sheets* 7·50 8·00
Nos. 1919/27 were printed together, *se-tenant*, in sheetlets of 9.

(Des Isabelle Tanner. Litho Questa)

1995 (8 Jan). *60th Birth Anniv of Elvis Presley (singer). T* **232** *and similar vert designs. Multicoloured. P* 14.
1929 4 d. Type **232** 70 80
a. Sheetlet. Nos. 1929/37 5·50
1930 4 d. Wearing white shirt 70 80
1931 4 d. With his mother Gladys 70 80
1932 4 d. With his wife Priscilla 70 80
1933 4 d. With large gold medallion 70 80
1934 4 d. In army uniform 70 80
1935 4 d. In purple shirt 70 80
1936 4 d. Wearing stetson 70 80
1937 4 d. With his daughter Lisa-Marie 70 80
1929/37 *Set of* 9 5·50 6·50
Nos. 1929/37 were printed together, *se-tenant*, in sheetlets of 9.

233 Pteranodon **234** Pig (Chinese characters in bright green)

(Des R. Sauber. Litho Questa)

1995 (6 Feb). *Prehistoric Animals. T* **233** *and similar multicoloured designs. P* 14.
1938 2 d. Type **233** 40 40
a. Sheetlet. Nos. 1938/49 4·25
1939 2 d. Archaeopteryx 40 40
1940 2 d. Rhamphorhynchus 40 40
1941 2 d. Ornithomimus 40 40
1942 2 d. Stegosaurus 40 40
1943 2 d. Heterodontosaurus 40 40
1944 2 d. Lystrosaurus 40 40
1945 2 d. Euoplocephalus 40 40
1946 2 d. Coelophysis 40 40
1947 2 d. Staurikosaurus 40 40
1948 2 d. Giantoperis 40 40
1949 2 d. Diarthrognathus 40 40
1950 3 d. Archaeopteryx 50 50
a. Sheetlet. Nos. 1950/61 5·50
1951 3 d. Vangehuanosaurus 50 50
1952 3 d. Celophysis 50 50
1953 3 d. Plateosaurus 50 50
1954 3 d. Baryonyx 50 50
1955 3 d. Ornitholestes 50 50
1956 3 d. Dryosaurus 50 50
1957 3 d. Estemmenosuchus 50 50
1958 3 d. Macroplata 50 50
1959 3 d. Shonisaurus 50 50
1960 3 d. Muraeonosaurus 50 50
1961 3 d. Archelon 50 50
1938/61 *Set of* 24 9·50 9·50
MS1962 Four sheets, each 100×70 mm. (a) 20 d. Bactrosaurus. (b) 22 d. Tyrannosaurus rex (*vert*). (c) 25 d. Triceratops (*vert*). (d) 25 d. Spinosaurus *Set of 4 sheets* 13·00 15·00
Nos. 1938/49 and 1950/61 were each printed together, *se-tenant*, in sheetlets of 12 stamps forming composite designs.

(Des Y. Lee. Litho Questa)

1995 (4 May). *Chinese New Year ("Year of the Pig"). T* **234** *and similar horiz designs showing symbolic pigs. P* 14½.
1963 **234** 3 d. scarlet-vermilion, black & brt grn 35 40
a. Sheetlet. Nos. 1963/6 1·40
1964 – 3 d. multicoloured (characters in deep ultramarine) 35 40
1965 – 3 d. reddish orange, orange-vermilion and black (characters in white) 35 40
1966 – 3 d. dull rose, scarlet-vermilion and black (characters in black) 35 40
1963/6 *Set of* 4 1·40 1·60
MS1967 76×106 mm. 10 d. deep magenta and orange-vermilion (three pigs) 1·10 1·25
Nos. 1963/6 were printed together, *se-tenant*, in sheetlets of 4.

235 Great White Egret **236** Rural Road

(Litho B.D.T.)

1995 (8 May). *Water Birds. T* **235** *and similar horiz designs. Multicoloured. P* 14.
1968 2 d. Type **235** 20 25
1969 3 d. Pintails 35 40
a. Sheetlet. Nos. 1969/80 4·25
1970 3 d. Fulvous Whistling Duck 35 40
1971 3 d. Garganey 35 40
1972 3 d. White-faced Whistling Duck 35 40
1973 3 d. White-backed Duck 35 40
1974 3 d. Egyptian Goose 35 40
1975 3 d. African Pygmy Geese 35 40
1976 3 d. Little Bitterns 35 40
1977 3 d. Redshanks 35 40
1978 3 d. Ringed Plovers 35 40
1979 3 d. Black-winged Stilt 35 40
1980 3 d. Squacco Herons 35 40
1981 8 d. Hammerkop 90 95
1982 10 d. Common Shovelers 1·10 1·25
1983 12 d. Crowned Crane 1·40 1·50
1968/83 *Set of* 16 7·75 8·75
MS1984 Two sheets, each 106×76 mm. (a) 25 d. Ferruginous Ducks. (b) 25 d. Moorhen *Set of 2 sheets* 6·00 6·25
Nos. 1969/80 were printed together, *se-tenant*, in sheetlets of 12, forming a composite design.

(Litho Questa)

1995 (30 May). *20th Anniv of Economic Community of West African States (E.C.O.W.A.S.). T* **236** *and similar vert design. Multicoloured. P* 14.
1985 2 d. Type **236** 20 25
1986 5 d. Pres. Yayah Jammeh 60 65

237 Leather Back Turtle **238** First Stage of Lariat Knot

(Des J. Barbarus and G. Lott. Litho B.D.T.)

1995 (20 June). *Marine Life. T* **237** *and similar multicolour designs. P* 14.
1987 3 d. Type **237** 35
a. Sheetlet. Nos. 1987/98 4·25
1988 3 d. Tiger Shark 35
1989 3 d. Powder-blue Surgeonfish 35
1990 3 d. Emperor Angelfish 35
1991 3 d. Blue Parrotfish 35
1992 3 d. Clown Triggerfish 35
1993 3 d. Seahorse 35
1994 3 d. Lionfish 35
1995 3 d. Moray Eel 35
1996 3 d. Melon Butterflyfish 35
1997 3 d. Octopus 35
1998 3 d. Common Stingray 35
1999 8 d. Stoplight Parrotfish ("Multicolored Parrot Fish") (*vert*) 90
a. Horiz strip of 4. Nos. 1999/2002 3·50
2000 8 d. Stoplight Parrotfish ("Sparisoma viride") (*vert*) 90
2001 8 d. Queen Parrotfish (*vert*) 90
2002 8 d. Bicoloured Parrotfish (*vert*) 90
1987/2002 *Set of* 16 7·75 8·
MS2003 Two sheets, each 98×68 mm. (a) 25 d. Queen Angelfish (*Angelicthys isabelita*). (b) 25 d. Rock Beauty (*Holacanthus ciliaris*) *Set of 2 sheets* 6·00 6·
Nos. 1987/98 and 1999/2002 were printed together, *se-tena* in sheetlets of 12 (Nos. 1987/98) or horizontal strips of 4 (N 1999/2002) with the backgrounds forming composite designs.
No. 1991 is inscribed "BLUE PARRO FISH" in error.

(Des P. Chinelli. Litho Questa)

1995 (14 July). *18th World Scout Jamboree, Netherlan T* **238** *and similar vert designs. Multicoloured. P* 14.
MS2004 Two sheets, each 101×65 mm. (a) 2 d. Type **238**; 2 d. Second stage of knot with ropes end at right; 2 d. Completed Lariat knot. (b) 5 d. Completed Bowline knot; 10 d. Second stage of knot; 12 d. First stage of knot *Set of 2 sheets* 3·75 4
MS2005 Two sheets, each 72×102 mm. (a) 25 d. Scout in rope using Hitch knot. (b) 25 d. Injured scout supported by Bowline knot *Set of 2 sheets* 5·75 6

(Des L. Fried. Litho B.D.T.)

1995 (1 Aug). *50th Anniv of End of Second World War Europe. Film Stars. Black and scarlet (Nos. 2008 and 2010) multicoloured designs (others) as T* **340** *of Antigua. P* 14.
2006 3 d. Peter Lawford 60
a. Sheetlet. Nos. 2006/13 4·25
2007 3 d. Gene Tierney and Dana Andrews 60
2008 3 d. Groucho and Harpo Marx 60
2009 3 d. James Stewart 60
2010 3 d. Chico and Zeppo Marx 60
2011 3 d. Tyrone Power 60
2012 3 d. Cary Grant and Ingrid Bergman 60
2013 3 d. Veronica Lake 60
2006/13 *Set of* 8 4·25 4·
MS2014 105×75 mm. 25 d. "A Lady Fights Back" film poster (*vert*) 4·50 5·
Nos. 2006/13 were printed together, *se-tenant*, in sheetlets 8 with the stamps arranged in two horizontal strips of separated by a gutter showing Laurel and Hardy, Anna Neag and Orson Wells.
No. 2012 is inscribed "BERMAN" in error.

(Des Bryna Waldman. Litho)

1995 (1 Aug). *50th Anniv of United Nations. Vert designs T* **341** *of Antigua. Multicoloured. P* 14.
2015 3 d. Children in class 35
a. Horiz strip of 3. Nos. 2015/17 1·00
2016 3 d. Teacher helping child 35
2017 3 d. Child writing on blackboard 35
2015/17 *Set of* 3 1·00 1·
MS2018 104×74 mm. 25 d. Nurse weighing baby 3·00 3·
Nos. 2015/17 were printed together in sheets of 9 containi three *se-tenant* horizontal strips, each forming a composi design.

(Des Bryna Waldman. Litho)

1995 (1 Aug). *50th Anniv of Food and Agricultu Organization. Vert designs as T* **342** *of Antigu Multicoloured. P* 14.
2019 3 d. Woman carrying sack on head 35
a. Horiz strip of 3. Nos. 2019/21 1·00
2020 3 d. Two men carrying sacks 35
2021 3 d. Man carrying sack 35
2019/21 *Set of* 3 1·00 1·
MS2022 104×74 mm. 25 d. Fisherman with net 3·00 3·
Nos. 2019/21 were printed together in sheets of 9 containi three *se-tenant* horizontal strips, each forming a composi design.

239 Paul Harris (founder) and Rotary Emblem

240 Kenichi Fukui (1981 Chemistry)

95 (1 Aug). *90th Anniv of Rotary International. T* **239** *and similar horiz design. Multicoloured. Litho. P* 14.
23 15 d. Type **239** .. .. 1·75 1·90
S2024 75×105 mm. 20 d. National flag and Rotary emblem .. .. 2·25 2·40

(Litho Questa)

95 (1 Aug). *95th Birthday of Queen Elizabeth the Queen Mother. Vert designs as T* **344** *of Antigua. P* 13½×14.
25 5 d. orange-brown, pale brown and black 60 65
a. Sheetlet. Nos. 2025/8×2 .. .. 4·75
26 5 d. multicoloured 60 65
27 5 d. multicoloured 60 65
28 5 d. multicoloured 60 65
25/8 .. .. *Set of* 4 2·40 2·50
S2029 102×126 mm. 25 d. multicoloured .. 3·00 3·25
Designs:—No. 2025, Queen Elizabeth the Queen Mother astel drawing); No. 2026, Wearing blue hat and dress; No. 27, At desk (oil painting); No. 2028, Wearing green hat and ess; No. **MS**2029, Wearing lavender hat and dress.
Nos. 2025/8 were printed together in sheetlets of 8 containing o *se-tenant* horizontal strips of 4.

(Des J. Batchelor. Litho Questa)

95 (1 Aug). *50th Anniv of End of Second World War in the Pacific. Horiz designs as T* **340** *of Antigua. Multicoloured. P* 14.
30 5 d. Fairey Firefly 60 65
a. Sheetlet. Nos. 2030/5 .. .. 3·50
31 5 d. Fairey Barracuda Mk III 60 65
32 5 d. Supermarine Seafire II 60 65
33 5 d. H.M.S. *Repulse* (battle cruiser) .. 60 65
34 5 d. H.M.S. *Illustrious* (aircraft carrier) 60 65
35 5 d. H.M.S. *Exeter* (cruiser) 60 65
30/5 .. .. *Set of* 6 3·50 4·00
S2036 108×76 mm. 25 d. Kamikaze aircraft heading for British cruiser .. .. .. 3·00 3·25
Nos. 2030/5 were printed together, *se-tenant*, in sheetlets of 6 th the stamps arranged in two horizontal strips of 3 separated a gutter showing Lord Louis Mountbatten and the sinking of .M.S. *Kelly*.

(Des Shayna Magid. Litho Questa)

95 (1 Aug). *Centenary of Nobel Prize Trust Fund. Past Prize Winners. T* **240** *and similar vert designs. Multicoloured. P* 14.
37 2 d. Type **240** 20 25
38 3 d. Gustav Stresemann (1929 Peace) .. 35 40
39 5 d. Thomas Mann (1929 Literature) .. 60 65
40 5 d. Marie Curie (1911 Chemistry) .. 60 65
a. Sheetlet. Nos. 2040/8 .. .. 5·25
41 5 d. Adolf Butenandt (1939 Chemistry) .. 60 65
42 5 d. Susumu Tonegawa (1987 Medicine) .. 60 65
43 5 d. Nelly Sachs (1966 Literature) .. 60 65
44 5 d. Yasunari Kawabata (1968 Literature) 60 65
45 5 d. Hideki Yukawa (1949 Physics) .. 60 65
46 5 d. Paul Ehrlich (1908 Medicine) .. 60 65
47 5 d. Bisaku Sato (1974 Peace) 60 65
48 5 d. Carl von Ossietsky (1935 Peace) .. 60 65
49 8 d. Albert Schweitzer (1952 Peace) .. 90 95
50 12 d. Leo Esaki (1973 Physics) .. .. 1·40 1·50
51 15 d. Lech Walesa (1983 Peace) .. .. 1·75 1·90
37/51 .. .. *Set of* 15 10·50 11·50
S2052 75×105 mm. 25 d. Willy Brandt (1971 Peace) .. .. 3·00 3·25
Nos. 2040/8 were printed together, *se-tenant*, in sheetlets of 9, rming a composite design.
No. 2048 is dated "1974" and No. 2051 inscribed "Lech alsea", both in error.

241 Bruce Jenner (U.S.A.) (decathlon)

(Des A. Di Lorenzo. Litho Questa)

995 (17 Aug). *Olympic Games, Atlanta* (1996) (*1st issue*). *T* **241** *and similar multicoloured designs. P* 14.
053 1 d. Type **241** 10 15
054 1 d. 25, Greg Louganis (U.S.A.) (diving) 15 20
055 1 d. 50, Michael Gross (Germany) (50 metre butterfly) 20 25
056 2 d. Vasily Alexeev (Russia) (weight-lifting) 20 25
057 3 d. Ewing (U.S.A.) and Corbalan (Spain) (basketball) 35 40
058 3 d. Stefano Cerioni (Italy) (fencing) (*vert*) 35 40
a. Sheetlet. Nos. 2058/65 .. .. 2·75

2059 3 d. Alberto Cova (Italy) (10000 metres) (*vert*) 35 40
2060 3 d. Mary Lou Retton (U.S.A.) (gymnastics) (*vert*) 35 40
2061 3 d. Vladimir Artemov (Russia) (gymnastics) (*vert*) 35 40
2062 3 d. Florence Griffith-Joyner (U.S.A.) (400 metre relay) (*vert*) 35 40
2063 3 d. Brazil (football) (*vert*) 35 40
2064 3 d. Nelson Vails (U.S.A.) (sprint cycling) (*vert*) 35 40
2065 3 d. Cheryl Miller (U.S.A.) (basketball) (*vert*) 35 40
2066 5 d. U.S.A. v Brazil (men's volleyball) .. 60 65
2067 10 d. Svenden (West Germany) and Fernandez (U.S.A.) (water polo) .. 1·10 1·25
2068 15 d. Pertii Karppinen (Finland) (single sculls) .. .. 1·75 1·90
2053/68 .. .. *Set of* 16 7·25 8·25
MS2069 Two sheets, each 71×101 mm. (a) 25 d. Karen Stives (U.S.A.) (equestrian) (*vert*). (b) 25 d. Edwin Moses (U.S.A.) (400 metre hurdles) (*vert*) .. .. *Set of* 2 *sheets* 6·00 6·25
Nos. 2058/65 were printed together, *se-tenant*, in sheetlets of 8.
No. 2059 is inscribed "Alberto Covo" and No. 2064 "Nelson Valis", both in error.
See also Nos. 2281/303.

242 Rotary Emblem and Rotarians supporting School for the Deaf

243 *Zantedeschia rehmannii*

(Litho Questa)

1995 (5 Sept). *Local Rotary and Boy Scout Projects. T* **242** *and similar multicoloured designs. P* 14.
2070 2 d. Type **242** 20 25
2071 5 d. Scout wood badge course, 1980 .. 60 65
2072 5 d. Scout Commissioner M. J. E. Sambou (*vert*) 60 65
2070/2 .. .. *Set of* 3 1·40 1·50

(Des Mary Walters. Litho Questa)

1995 (2 Oct). *African Flowers. T* **243** *and similar vert designs. Multicoloured. P* 14.
2073 2 d. Type **243** 20 25
2074 3 d. *Kigelia africana* 35 40
a. Sheetlet. Nos. 2074/82 .. .. 3·25
2075 3 d. *Hibiscus schizopelatus* 35 40
2076 3 d. *Dombeya mastersii* 35 40
2077 3 d. *Agapanthus orientalis* 35 40
2078 3 d. *Strelitzia reginae* 35 40
2079 3 d. *Spathodea companulata* 35 40
2080 3 d. *Rhodolaena bakeriana* 35 40
2081 3 d. *Gazania rigens* 35 40
2082 3 d. *Ixianthes retzioides* 35 40
2083 3 d. *Canarina abyssinica* 35 40
a. Sheetlet. Nos. 2083/91 .. .. 3·25
2084 3 d. *Nerine bowdenii* 35 40
2085 3 d. *Zantedeschia aethiopica* 35 40
2086 3 d. *Aframomum sceptrum* 35 40
2087 3 d. *Schotia brachypetala* 35 40
2088 3 d. *Catharanthus roseus* 35 40
2089 3 d. *Protea grandiceps* 35 40
2090 3 d. *Plumbago capensis* 35 40
2091 3 d. *Uncarina grandidieri* 35 40
2092 5 d. *Euadenia eminens* 60 65
2093 10 d. *Passiflora vitifolia* .. .. .. 1·10 1·25
2094 15 d. *Dietes grandiflora* .. .. .. 1·75 1·90
2073/94 .. .. *Set of* 22 10·00 11·00
MS2095 Two sheets, each 106×75 mm. (a) 25 d. *Eulophia quartiniana*. (b) 25 d. *Gloriosa simplex* *Set of* 2 *sheets* 6·00 6·25
Nos. 2074/82 and 2083/91 were printed together, *se-tenant*, in sheetlets of 9 forming composite background designs.

244 Children outside Huts

1995 (9 Oct). *Kinderdorf International S.O.S. Children's Villages. T* **244** *and similar multicoloured designs. Litho. P* 14.
2096 2 d. Type **244** 20 25
2097 2 d. Charity worker with children (*vert*) 20 25
2098 5 d. Children at party 60 65
2096/8 .. .. *Set of* 3 1·00 1·10

245 Roy Orbison

1995 (1 Dec). *History of Rock n' Roll Music. T* **245** *and similar vert designs. Multicoloured. Litho. P* 13½×14.
2099 3 d. Type **245** 35 40
a. Sheetlet. Nos. 2099/107 .. .. 3·25
2100 3 d. Mick Jagger 35 40
2101 3 d. Bruce Springsteen 35 40
2102 3 d. Jimi Hendrix 35 40
2103 3 d. Bill Hailey 35 40
2104 3 d. Gene Vincent 35 40
2105 3 d. Buddy Holly 35 40
2106 3 d. Jerry Lee Lewis 35 40
2107 3 d. Chuck Berry 35 40
2099/107 .. .. *Set of* 9 3·25 3·50
MS2108 116×86 mm. 25 d. Elvis Presley .. 3·00 3·25
Nos. 2099/2107 were printed together, *se-tenant*, in sheetlets of 9 forming a composite design.

1995 (1 Dec). *Centenary of Cinema. Vert designs as T* **245** *depicting James Dean. Multicoloured. Litho. P* 13½×14.
2109 3 d. As a boy 35 40
a. Sheetlet. Nos. 2109/17 .. .. 3·25
2110 3 d. On motorbike 35 40
2111 3 d. With sports car and trophy 35 40
2112 3 d. Close-up portrait 35 40
2113 3 d. Facing left 35 40
2114 3 d. Holding girl 35 40
2115 3 d. *Rebel without a Cause* (film) .. 35 40
2116 3 d. *Giant* (film) 35 40
2117 3 d. *East of Eden* (film) 35 40
2109/17 .. .. *Set of* 9 3·25 3·50
MS2118 116×86 mm. 25 d. James Dean in *Rebel without a Cause* .. .. 3·00 3·25
Nos. 2109/17 were printed together, *se-tenant*, in sheetlets of 9 forming a composite design.

(Litho Questa)

1995 (18 Dec). *Christmas. Religious Paintings. Vert designs as T* **357** *of Antigua. Multicoloured. P* 13½×14.
2119 75 b. "Madonna and Child" (Maria della Vallicella) 10 10
2120 1 d. "Madonna" (Giotto) 10 10
2121 2 d. "The Flight into Egypt" (Luca Giordano) 20 25
2122 5 d. "The Epiphany" (Bondone) 60 65
2123 8 d. "Virgin and Child" (Burgkmair) .. 90 95
2124 12 d. "Madonna" (Bellini) .. .. .. 1·40 1·50
2119/24 .. .. *Set of* 6 3·25 3·50
MS2125 Two sheets, each 101×127 mm. (a) 25 d. "Christ" (Carpaccio). (b) 25 d. "Madonna and Child" (Rubens) .. .. .. *Set of* 2 *sheets* 5·75 6·00

246 Terminal Building

247 U.P.U. Emblem

(Litho Questa)

1995 (21 Dec). *Opening of New Terminal Building, Banjul International Airport. P* 14.
2126 **246** 1 d. multicoloured 10 10
2127 2 d. multicoloured 20 25
2128 3 d. multicoloured 35 40
2129 5 d. multicoloured 60 65
2126/9 .. .. *Set of* 4 1·25 1·40

(Litho Questa)

1995 (21 Dec). *121st Anniv of Universal Postal Union. P* 14.
2130 **247** 1 d. black and deep bluish violet .. 10 10
2131 2 d. black and bright greenish blue .. 20 25
2132 3 d. black and bright scarlet 35 40
2133 7 d. black and bright emerald .. 80 85
2130/3 .. .. *Set of* 4 1·40 1·60

COVER PRICES

Cover factors are quoted at the beginning of each country for most issues to 1945. An explanation of the system can be found on page x. The factors quoted do not, however, apply to philatelic covers.

248 Commerson's Dolphin

(Litho Questa)

1995 (22 Dec). *Whales and Dolphins. T* **248** *and similar multicoloured designs. P* 14.

2134 2 d. Type **248** 20 25
2135 3 d. Bryde's Whale 35 40
a. Sheetlet. Nos. 2135/43 .. .. 3·00
2136 3 d. Sperm Whale 35 40
2137 3 d. Humpback Whale 35 40
2138 3 d. Sei Whale 35 40
2139 3 d. Blue Whale 35 40
2140 3 d. Grey Whale 35 40
2141 3 d. Fin Whale 35 40
2142 3 d. Killer Whale 35 40
2143 3 d. Right Whale 35 40
2144 3 d. Northern Right Whale Dolphin .. 35 40
a. Sheetlet. Nos. 2144/52 .. .. 3·00
2145 3 d. Spotted Dolphin 35 40
2146 3 d. Common Dolphin 35 40
2147 3 d. Pacific White-sided Dolphin .. 35 40
2148 3 d. Atlantic Humpbacked Dolphin .. 35 40
2149 3 d. Atlantic White-sided Dolphin .. 35 40
2150 3 d. White-beaked Dolphin 35 40
2151 3 d. Striped Dolphin 35 40
2152 3 d. Risso's Dolphin 35 40
2153 5 d. Narwhal 60 65
2154 8 d. True's Beaked Whale 90 95
2155 10 d. Rough-toothed Dolphin .. .. 1·10 1·25
2134/55 .. .. *Set of* 22 9·00 10·00
MS2156 Two sheets, each 110×80 mm. (a) 25 d. Beluga and Clymene Dolphin. (b) 25 d. Bowhead Whale and Blue Shark (*vert*) .. *Set of* 2 *sheets* 5·75 6·00

Nos. 2135/43 and 2144/52 were printed together, *se-tenant*, in sheetlets of 9 forming composite designs.

249 Big Pete as Seminole with Alligator

(Des Alvin White Studios. Litho Questa)

1995 (22 Dec). *Disney Cowboys and Indians. T* **249** *and similar multicoloured designs showing Walt Disney cartoon characters. P* 14×13½.

2157 15 b. Type **249** 10 10
2158 20 b. Donald Duck as Chinook fisherman 10 10
2159 25 b. Huey, Dewey and Louie as Blackfoot braves 10 10
2160 30 b. Minnie Mouse shooting bottles .. 10 10
2161 40 b. Donald riding bull 10 10
2162 50 b. Mickey Mouse branding steer .. 10 10
2163 2 d. Donald in Tlingit mask 20 25
2164 3 d. Mickey bronco-busting 35 40
2165 12 d. Grandma Duck with lasso .. .. 1·40 1·50
2166 15 d. Mickey in Pomo canoe .. .. 1·75 1·90
2167 15 d. Goofy as ranch hand .. .. 1·75 1·90
2168 20 d. Goofy and Minnie with Navaho weaving .. .. 2·25 2·50
2157/68 .. .. *Set of* 12 8·00 9·00
MS2169 Four sheets, each 127×102 mm. (a) 25 d. Minnie as Massachusetts squaw. P 14×13½. (b) 25 d. Minnie as Shoshoni squaw (*vert*). P 13½×14. (c) 25 d. Pluto singing to the Moon (*vert*). P 13½×14. (d) 25 d. Donald and steer (*vert*). P 13½×14 .. .. *Set of* 4 *sheets* 11·50 12·00

250 Rat

251 "Don Tiburcio Pérez y Cuervo (detail) (Goya)

(Des Y. Lee. Litho Questa)

1996 (2 Jan). *Chinese New Year* ("*Year of the Rat*"). *T* **250** *and similar horiz designs showing different stylised rats. P* 14½.

2170 63 b. multicoloured 10 10
a. Horiz strip of 4. Nos. 2170/3 .. 85
2171 75 b. multicoloured 10 10
2172 1 d. 50, multicoloured 20 25
2173 4 d. multicoloured 45 50
2170/3 .. .. *Set of* 4 85 1·00
MS2174 84×68 mm. 3 d. × 4 As Nos. 2170/3 .. 1·40 1·50
MS2175 76×106 mm. 10 d. orange-vermilion, deep violet and yellow-brown .. .. 1·10 1·25

Nos. 2170/3 were printed together, *se-tenant*, as horizontal strips of 4 in sheets of 12.

(Litho Questa)

1996 (29 Jan). *125th Anniv of Metropolitan Museum of Art, New York. T* **251** *and similar multicoloured designs. P* 14.

2176/83 4 d. × 8 (Type **251**; "Jean Antoine Moltedo" (Ingres); "The Letter" (Corot); "General Etienne Gerard" (David); "Portrait of the Artist" (Van Gogh); "Joseph Henri Altés" (Degas); "Princess de Broglie" (Ingres); "Lady at the Table" (Cassatt))
a. Sheetlet. Nos. 2176/83 .. .. 3·50
2184/91 4 d. × 8 ("Broken Eggs" (Greuze); "Johann Joachim Wincklemann" (Mengs); "Col. George Coussmaker" (Reynolds); "Self Portrait with Pupils" (Labille-Guiard); "Courtesan holding a Fan" (Utamaro); "The Woodgatherers" (Gainsborough); "Mrs Grace Elliott" (Gainsborough); "The Drummond Children" (Raeburn))
a. Sheetlet. Nos. 2184/91 .. .. 3·50
2192/9 4 d. × 8 ("Sunflowers" (Monet); "Still Life with Pansies" (Fantin-Latour); "Parisians enjoying the Parc" (Monet); "La Mére Larchevêque" (Pissarro); "Rue de L'Epicerie, Rouen" (Pissarro); "The Abduction of Rebecca" (Delacroix); "Daughter, Abraham-Ben-Chimol" (Delacroix); "Christ on Lake of Gennesaret" (Delacroix))
a. Sheetlet. Nos. 2192/9 .. .. 3·50
2200/7 4 d. × 8 ("Henry Prince of Wales" (Peake); "Saints Peter, Martha, Mary and Leonard" (Correggio); "Marriage Feast at Cana" (Juan de Flandes); "Portrait of One of Wedigh Family" (Holbein); "Guillaume Budé" (Clouet); "Portrait of a Cardinal" (El Greco); "St. Jerome as a Cardinal" (El Greco); "Portrait of a Man" (Titian))
a. Sheetlet. Nos. 2200/7 .. .. 3·50
2176/207 .. .. *Set of* 32 14·00 14·50
MS2208 Four sheets, each 95×70 mm containing horiz designs, 81×53 mm. (a) 25 d. "Israelites gathering Manna in the Desert" (Rubens). (b) 25 d. "Henry IV at the Battle of Ivry" (Rubens). (c) 25 d. "The Creation of the World and the Expulsion from Paradise" (Giovanni di Paolo). (d) 25 d. "The Harvesters" (Bruegel). P 14 *Set of* 4 *sheets* 12·00 12·50

Nos. 2176/83, 2184/91, 2192/9 and 2200/7 were each printed together, *se-tenant*, in sheetlets of 8 stamps and one centre label.

252 Fire-eater

253 Bruce Lee

(Litho Questa)

1996 (29 Jan). *Fire-eating in the Gambia. T* **252** *and similar designs. P* 14.

2209 1 d. multicoloured 10 10
2210 2 d. multicoloured (*horiz*) 20 25
2211 3 d. multicoloured 35 40
2212 7 d. multicoloured (*horiz*) 80 85
2209/12 .. .. *Set of* 4 1·40 1·60

(Des Y. Lee. Litho)

1996 (1 Apr). *Bruce Lee (film star) Commemoration. T* **253** *and similar vert designs showing different portraits. Multicoloured. P* 14.

2213 3 d. Wearing cap and mask 45 50
a. Sheetlet. Nos. 2213/21 .. .. 3·25
2214 3 d. Type **253** 35 40
2215 3 d. Facing left 35 40
2216 3 d. Wearing blue jumper and with hand to face 35 40
2217 3 d. Wearing buff jacket 35 40
2218 3 d. Wearing brown jacket (Chinese characters in chestnut) 35 40
2219 3 d. Wearing black shirt (Chinese characters in lilac) 35 40
2220 3 d. Wearing white shirt 35 40
2221 3 d. Bare-chested 35 40
2213/21 .. .. *Set of* 9 3·25 3·50
MS2222 Two sheets. (a) 140×85 mm. 5 d. Deng Xiao Ping (Chinese leader) (78×51 *mm*). P 13. (b) 70×100 mm. 25 d. Bruce Lee. P 14 *Set of* 2 *sheets* 6·25 6·50

Nos. 2213/21 were printed together, *se-tenant*, in numbered sheetlets of 9, which also included "CHINA '96 9th Asian International Philatelic Exhibition" emblem on the sheet margin.

254 Donald Duck and Big Pete giving Blood

(Litho Questa)

1996 (12 Apr). *Voluntary Activities. T* **254** *and similar h*[…] *designs showing Walt Disney cartoon characters. Mu*[…] *coloured. P* 14×13½.

2223 1 d. Type **254** 10
2224 4 d. Daisy Duck and Minnie Mouse adopting pets 45
2225 5 d. Goofy as one-man band raising money for the needy 60
2226 10 d. Goofy teaching outdoor skills .. 1·10 1
2227 15 d. Minnie teaching reading .. .. 1·75 1
2228 20 d. Donald, Mickey and Goofy as volunteer fire fighters .. .. 2·25 2
2223/9 .. .. *Set of* 6 6·25 6
MS2229 Two sheets, each 127×102 mm. (a) 25 d. Minnie counting whales. (b) 25 d. Mickey planting roadside sapling .. *Set of* 2 *sheets* 5·75 6

255 Roan Antelope

(Litho Questa)

1996 (15 Apr). *Wildlife. T* **255** *and similar multicolou*[…] *designs. P* 14.

2230 3 d. Type **255** 35
a. Sheetlet. Nos. 2230/5 each × 2 .. 4·25
2231 3 d. Lesser Bushbaby 35
2232 3 d. Black Leopard 35
2233 3 d. Guinea Forest Red Colobus .. 35
2234 3 d. Kobs 35
2235 3 d. Common Eland 35
2236 4 d. African Buffalo 45
a. Sheetlet. Nos. 2236/44 .. .. 4·00
2237 4 d. Herd of Topi 45
2238 4 d. Vervet 45
2239 4 d. Hippopotamuses 45
2240 4 d. Waterbuck 45
2241 4 d. Senegal Chameleon 45
2242 4 d. Western Green Mamba 45
2243 4 d. Slender-snouted Crocodile .. 45
2244 4 d. Adanson's Mud Turtle 45
2245 15 d. African Civet .. .. .. 1·75 1
2230/45 .. .. *Set of* 16 7·75 8
MS2246 Two sheets, each 98×68 mm. (a) 25 d. Lion (*vert*). (b) 25 d. Chimpanzee (*vert*) *Set of* 2 *sheets* 5·75 6

Nos. 2230/5 and 2236/44 were printed together, *se-tenant*, […] sheetlets of 12 (Nos. 2230/5 × 2) or 9 (Nos. 2236/44), the lat[…] forming a composite design.

(Litho Questa)

1996 (9 May). *70th Birthday of Queen Elizabeth II. Mul*[…] *coloured designs as T* **364** *of Antigua showing differe*[…] *photographs. P* 13½×14.

2247 8 d. As Type **364** of Antigua 90
a. Strip of 3. Nos. 2247/9 .. .. 2·75
2248 8 d. Wearing tiara facing right 90
2249 8 d. Wearing tiara facing left 90
2247/9 .. .. *Set of* 3 2·75 3
MS2250 125×104 mm. 25 d. Buckingham Palace (*horiz*). P 14×13½ .. .. 3·00 3

Nos. 2247/9 were printed together, *se-tenant*, in horizon[…] and vertical strips of 3 throughout sheets of 9.

256 Pumper Hose Cart, U.S.A. (1850)

1996 (27 May). *Classic Road Transport. T* **256** *and simi*[…] *horiz designs showing fire engines (Nos. 2251/6) or cars (N*[…] *2257/62). Multicoloured. Litho. P* 14.

2251 4 d. Type **256** 45
a. Sheetlet. Nos. 2251/6 .. .. 2·75
2252 4 d. Steam fire engine, U.S.A. (1891) .. 45
2253 4 d. Lausitzer engine, Germany (1864) .. 45
2254 4 d. Chemical engine, Great Britain (1902) 45

55 4 d. Motor fire engine, Great Britain (1904) 45 50
56 4 d. Colonia No. 5 engine, Germany (1860) 45 50
57 4 d. Fiat Tipo 510, Italy (1912) 45 50
a. Sheetlet. Nos. 2257/62 .. .. 2·75
58 4 d. Toyota Model 4B Phaeton, Japan (1936) 45 50
59 4 d. Nag C4B, Germany (1924) 45 50
60 4 d. Cadillac, U.S.A. (1903) 45 50
61 4 d. Bentley, Great Britain (1925) .. 45 50
62 4 d. Renault Model AX, France (1909) .. 45 50
51/62 .. .. *Set of* 12 5·50 6·00
S2263 (a) 76×58 mm. 25 d. Amoskeag Steamer fire engine), U.S.A. (1865). (b) 81×59 mm. 25 d. Mitsubishi Model A, Japan (1917) *Set of* 2 *sheets* 5·75 6·00
Nos. 2251/6 and 2257/62 were each printed together, *tenant*, in sheetlets of 6.

257 Bulgarian Team

258 Ray Ewry (U.S.A.) (standing high jump), 1912

96 (8 June). *European Football Championship, England. T* **257** *and similar multicoloured designs. Litho. P* 14×13½.
64 2 d. Type **257** 20 25
65 2 d. Croatian team 20 25
66 2 d. Czech Republic team 20 25
67 2 d. Danish team 20 25
68 2 d. English team 20 25
69 2 d. French team 20 25
70 2 d. German team 20 25
71 2 d. Dutch team 20 25
72 2 d. Italian team 20 25
73 2 d. Portuguese team 20 25
74 2 d. Rumanian team 20 25
75 2 d. Russian team 20 25
76 2 d. Scottish team 20 25
77 2 d. Spanish team 20 25
78 2 d. Swiss team 20 25
79 2 d. Turkish team 20 25
64/79 .. .. *Set of* 16 3·25 4·00
S2280 Sixteen sheets. (a) 115×85 mm. 25 d. Danish team celebrating (43×28 *mm*). (b) 85×115 mm. 25 d. Ruud Gullit (Netherlands) (28×43 *mm*). (c) 85×115 mm. 25 d. Gary McAllister (Scotland) (28×43 *mm*). (d) 115×85 mm. 25 d. Oleg Salenko (Russia) (28×43 *mm*). (e) 85 ×115 mm. 25 d. Hami Mandirali (Turkey) (28×43 *mm*). (f) 85×115 mm. 25 d. Hristo Stoitchkov (Bulgaria) (28×43 *mm*). (g) 115×85 mm. 25 d. European Championship Trophy (28×43 *mm*). (h) 85×115 mm. 25 d. Davor Suker (Croatia) (28×43 *mm*). (i) 115×85 mm. 25 d. Jurgen Klinsmann (Germany) (43×28 *mm*). (j) 85×115 mm. 25 d. Juan Goikoetxea (Spain) (28×43 *mm*). (k) 85×115 mm. 25 d. Eusebio (Portugal) (28×43 *mm*). (l) 115×85 mm. 25 d. Bryan Robson (England) (28×43 *mm*). (m) 85×115 mm. 25 d. Roberto Baggio (Italy) (28×43 *mm*) (n) 85×115 mm. 25 d. Christophe Ohrel (Switzerland) (28×43 *mm*). (o) 85×115 mm. 25 d. Pavel Hapal (Czech Republic) (43×28 *mm*). (p) 85×115 mm. 25 d. Gheorge Hagi (Rumania) (28×43 *mm*). P 14 .. .. *Set of* 16 *sheets* 48·00 50·00
Nos. 2264/79 were each printed in sheetlets of 8 stamps with central label.

(Des Y. Lee. Litho Questa)

996 (18 July). *Olympic Games, Atlanta (2nd issue). Previous Gold Medal Winners. T* **258** *and similar multicoloured designs. P* 14.
281 1 d. Type **258** 10 10
282 2 d. Fanny Durack (Australia) (100m freestyle swimming), 1912 .. .. 20 25
283 3 d. Fu Mingxia (China) (platform diving), 1992 .. .. 30 35
a. Sheetlet. Nos. 2283/91 .. .. 2·50
284 3 d. H. Henkel (Germany) (high jump) 1992 .. .. 30 35
285 3 d. Spanish team (soccer), 1992 .. 30 35
286 3 d. Jackie Joyner-Kersee (U.S.A.) (heptathlon), 1988 and 1992 .. 30 35
287 3 d. T. Gutsu (Russia) (gymnastics), 1992 30 35
288 3 d. M. Johnson (U.S.A.) (400m running), 1992 .. .. 30 35
289 3 d. Lin Li (China) (200m medley swimming), 1992 .. .. .. 30 35
290 3 d. G. Devers (U.S.A.) (100m running), 1992 .. .. 30 35
291 3 d. Michael Powell (U.S.A.) (long jump), 1992 .. .. 30 35
292 3 d. Japanese volleyball team, 1964 .. 30 35
a. Sheetlet. Nos. 2292/2300 .. .. 2·50
293 3 d. Li Neng (China) (floor exercises), 1984 30 35
294 3 d. S. Bubka (U.S.S.R.) (pole vault), 1988 30 35
295 3 d. Nadia Comaneci (Romania) (gymnastics), 1976 .. .. .. 30 35
296 3 d. Edwin Moses (U.S.A.) (400m hurdles), 1984 .. .. 30 35
297 3 d. Victor Scherbo (Russia) (gymnastics), 1992 .. .. 30 35
298 3 d. Evelyn Ashford (U.S.A.) (100m running), 1984 .. .. .. 30 35
299 3 d. Mohammed Ali (U.S.A.) (light heavyweight boxing), 1960 .. .. 30 35

2300 3 d. Carl Lewis and C. Smith (U.S.A.) (400m relay), 1984 .. .. .. 30 35
2301 5 d. Stockholm Olympic arena, 1912 .. 60 65
2302 10 d. Jim Thorpe (U.S.A.) (decathalon and pentathlon), 1912 .. .. .. 1·10 1·25
2281/2302 .. .. .. *Set of* 22 7·00 8·50
MS2303 Two sheets each 100×70 mm. 25 d. Michael Gross (Germany) (butterfly swimming), 1984 and 1988 (*horiz*). 25 d. Ulrike Meyfarth (Germany) (high jump), 1972 and 1984 *Set of* 2 *sheets* 5·75 6·00
Nos. 2283/91 and 2292/2300 were printed together, *se-tenant*, in sheetlets of 9.

(Litho Questa)

1996 (25 July). *50th Anniv of U.N.I.C.E.F. Multicoloured designs as T* **366** *of Antigua. P* 14.
2304 63 b. Boy holding shoes 10 10
2305 3 d. Girl being inoculated 35 40
2306 8 d. Boy holding ladle 90 95
2307 10 d. Child with blanket .. .. .. 1·10 1·25
2304/7 .. .. *Set of* 4 2·40 2·75
MS2308 105×75 mm. 25 d. Boy being inoculated (*horiz*) .. .. 3·00 3·25

259 Roman Officer and Pillar of Absalom

260 Jacqueline Kennedy Onassis in Wedding Dress

(Des J. Genzo. Litho Questa)

1996 (25 July). *3000th Anniv of Jerusalem. T* **259** *and similar multicoloured designs. P* 14.
2309 1 d. 50, Type **259** 20 25
2310 2 d. Turk and Gate of Mercy 20 25
2311 3 d. Ancient Greek and Church of the Holy Sepulchre 35 40
2312 10 d. Modern Hasidic Jew at Wailing Wall 1·10 1·25
2309/12 .. .. *Set of* 4 1·75 2·25
MS2313 100×70 mm. 25 d. City coat of arms (*vert*) .. .. 3·00 3·25

(Des J. Genzo. Litho Questa)

1996 (25 July). *Centenary of Radio. Entertainers. Vert designs as T* **368** *of Antigua. Multicoloured. P* 13½×14.
2314 1 d. Glenn Miller 10 10
2315 4 d. Louis Armstrong 45 50
2316 5 d. Nat "King" Cole 60 65
2317 10 d. The Andrew Sisters .. .. .. 1·10 1·25
2314/17 .. .. *Set of* 4 2·25 2·50
MS2318 105×74 mm. 25 d. President Truman 3·00 3·25
No. 2314 is inscribed "Glen Miller" in error.

(Des Zina Sanders (Nos. 2319/27 and **MS**2336), R. Sauber (Nos. 2328/35). Litho Questa)

1996 (22 Aug). *Famous People of the 20th Century. T* **260** *and similar vert designs. Multicoloured. P* 14.
2319 5 d. Type **260** 60 65
a. Sheetlet. Nos. 2319/27 .. .. 5·50
2320 5 d. Jaqueline Kennedy and White House 60 65
2321 5 d. Jaqueline Kennedy wearing pink hat 60 65
2322 5 d. Jaqueline Kennedy and motor yacht 60 65
2323 5 d. Jacqueline Kennedy wearing red jumper 60 65
2324 5 d. Jacqueline Kennedy and horse .. 60 65
2325 5 d. Jacqueline Kennedy on book .. 60 65
2326 5 d. Jacqueline Kennedy in blue dress and three rows of pearls 60 65
2327 5 d. Jacqueline Kennedy and corner of fountain 60 65
2328 5 d. President John Kennedy 60 65
a. Sheetlet. Nos. 2328/35 .. .. 4·75
2329 5 d. Jacqueline Kennedy (inscr in capitals) 60 65
2330 5 d. Willy Brandt 60 65
2331 5 d. Marilyn Monroe 60 65
2332 5 d. Mao Tse-tung 60 65
2333 5 d. Sung Ching Ling 60 65
2334 5 d. Charles De Gaulle 60 65
2335 5 d. Marlene Dietrich 60 65
2319/35 .. .. .. *Set of* 17 10·00 11·00
MS2336 105×74 mm. 25 d. Jacqueline Kennedy (*different*) .. .. 3·00 3·25
Nos. 2319/27 and 2328/35 were each printed together, *se-tenant*, in sheetlets of 9 or 8.
No. 2330 is inscr "WILLIE BRANDT", No. 2331 "MARYLYN MONROE" and No. 2332 "MAO TSE TONG", all in error.

PRICES OF SETS

Set prices are given for many issues, generally those containing three stamps or more. Definitive sets include one of each value or major colour change, but do not cover different perforations, die types or minor shades. Where a choice is possible the set prices are based on the cheapest versions of the stamps included in the listings.

261 Richard Petty's 1969 Ford

262 Elvis Presley with Microphone

(Des W. Wright. Litho Questa)

1996 (26 Aug). *Richard Petty (stock car driver) Commemoration. T* **261** *and similar horiz designs. Multicoloured. P* 14.
2337 5 d. Type **261** 60 65
a. Sheetlet. Nos. 2337/42 .. .. 3·50
2338 5 d. Richard Petty 60 65
2339 5 d. Dodge Magnum, 1978 .. .. 60 65
2340 5 d. Pontiac, 1987 .. .. .. 60 65
2341 5 d. Pontiac, 1989 .. .. .. 60 65
2342 5 d. Dodge Daytona, 1975 .. .. 60 65
2337/42 .. .. *Set of* 6 3·50 4·00
MS2343 104×74 mm. 25 d. Plymouth, 1972 (84×27 *mm*) .. .. 3·00 3·25
Nos. 2337/42 were printed together, *se-tenant*, in sheetlets of 6.

1996 (26 Aug). *Results of European Football Championship, England. As Nos.* 2265/6, 2268, 2270, 2272, 2275 *and* **MS**2280 *(d, h, i, l, m, o), but each additionally inscribed with date and match result. Multicoloured. Litho. P* 14×13½.
2344 2 d. Croatian team ("23/6/96 Germany 2, Croatia 1") 20 25
2345 2 d. Czech Republic team ("9/6/96 Germany 2, Czech Rep. 0") 20 25
2346 2 d. English team ("26/6/96 Germany 6, England 5") 20 25
2347 2 d. German team ("30/6/96 Germany 2, Czech Rep. 1") 20 25
2348 2 d. Italian team ("19/6/96 Germany 0, Italy 0") 20 25
2349 2 d. Russian team ("16/6/96 Germany 3, Russia 0") 20 25
2344/9 .. .. *Set of* 6 1·25 1·50
MS2350 Six sheets. (a) 114×84 mm. 25 d. Oleg Salenko (Russia) (28×43 *mm*) ("16/6/96 Germany 3, Russia 0"). (b) 84×114 mm. 25 d. Davor Suker (Croatia) (28×43 *mm*) ("23/6/96 Germany 2, Croatia 1"). (c) 114×84 mm. 25 d. Jurgen Klinsmann (Germany) (43×28 *mm*) ("Final 30/6/96 Germany 2, Czech Republic 1"). (d) 114×84 mm. 25 d. Bryan Robson (England) (28×43 *mm*) ("26/6/96 Germany 6 England 5"). (e) 84×114 mm. 25 d. Roberto Baggio (Italy) (28×43 *mm*) ("19/6/96 Germany 0 Italy 0"). (f) 84×114 mm. 25 d. Pavel Hapal (Czech Rep) (43×28 *mm*) ("9/6/96 Germany 2 Czech Republic 0") .. .. .. *Set of* 6 *sheets* 18·00 19·00
On No. **MS**2350 the dates and match results are shown on the sheet margins.

(Des Y. Lee. Litho Questa)

1996 (8 Sept). *Elvis Presley Commemoration. T* **262** *and similar vert designs showing different portraits. Multicoloured. P* 14.
2351 5 d. Type **262** 60 65
a. Sheetlet. Nos. 2351/6 .. .. 3·50
2352 5 d. In dinner jacket 60 65
2353 5 d. In Mexican outfit 60 65
2354 5 d. Wearing blue jumper 60 65
2355 5 d. In leather jacket 60 65
2356 5 d. Wearing lei 60 65
2351/6 .. .. *Set of* 6 3·50 4·00
Nos. 2351/6 were printed together, *se-tenant*, in numbered sheetlets of 6 with an illustrated margin.

263 Bob Dylan

264 Supermarine Spitfire Prototype K5054

(Des J. Iskowitz. Litho Questa)

1996 (8 Sept). *Rock and Roll Legends. Bob Dylan. P* 14.
2357 **263** 5 d. multicoloured 60 65
No. 2357 was issued in sheet of 16 with an enlarged illustrated right-hand margin.

(Des W. Wright. Litho Questa)

1996 (13 Sept). *65th Anniv of Britain's Victory in Schneider Trophy Air Race. T* **264** *and similar horiz designs. Multicoloured. P* 13½×14.
2358 4 d. Type **264** 45 50
a. Sheetlet. Nos. 2358/66 .. .. 4·00
2359 4 d. First production Spitfire K9787 .. 45 50

No.	Description	Unused	Used
2360	4 d. Spitfire Mk 1A in Battle of Britain	45	50
2361	4 d. Spitfire Lfmk IXE with D-Day markings	45	50
2362	4 d. Spitfire Mk XII (first with "Griffon" engine)	45	50
2363	4 d. Spitfire Mk XIVC with jungle markings	45	50
2364	4 d. Spitfire XIX of Royal Swedish Air Force	45	50
2365	4 d. Spitfire Mk XIX	45	50
2366	4 d. Spitfire FMk 22/24 (final variant) ..	45	50
2367	4 d. Spitfire Mk XIX of Royal Swedish Air Force (from below)	45	50
	a. Sheetlet. Nos. 2367/75	4·00	
2368	4 d. Spitfire Mk VB of United States Army Air Corps	45	50
2369	4 d. Spitfire Mk VC of French Air Force	45	50
2370	4 d. Spitfire Mk VB of Soviet Air Force	45	50
2371	4 d. Spitfire Mk IXE of Netherlands East Indies Air Force	45	50
2372	4 d. Spitfire Mk IXE of Israeli Air Force	45	50
2373	4 d. Spitfire Mk VIII of Royal Australian Air Force	45	50
2374	4 d. Spitfire Mk VB of Turkish Air Force	45	50
2375	4 d. Spitfire Mk XI of Royal Danish Air Force	45	50
2358/75	.. .. *Set of* 18	8·00	9·00

MS2376 Two sheets, each 97×67 mm. (a) 25 d. Supermarine S 6B S1595 seaplane taking off (42×29 *mm*). (b) 25 d. Supermarine S 6B S1595 in flight (42×29 *mm*). P 14 .. *Set of 2 sheets* 5·75 6·00

Nos. 2358/66 and 2367/75 were each printed together, *se-tenant*, in sheetlets of 9.

265 Egyptian Plover

266 Sylvester Stallone as Rocky Balboa

(Des D. Burkhart. Litho Questa)

1996 (22 Oct)–**97.** *Birds. T* **265** *and similar square designs. Multicoloured. P* 14.

No.	Description	Unused	Used
2377	50 b. Type **265**	10	10
2378	63 b. Painted Snipe	10	10
2379	75 b. Golden-breasted Bunting	10	10
2380	1 d. Bateleur	10	10
2381	1 d. 50, Didric Cuckoo	20	25
2382	2 d. Turtle Dove	20	25
2383	3 d. Village Weaver	35	40
2384	4 d. Common Roller	45	50
2385	5 d. Cut-Throat	60	65
2386	10 d. Hoopoe	1·10	1·25
2387	15 d. White-faced Scops Owl	1·75	1·90
2388	20 d. Narina Trogon	2·25	2·40
2389	25 d. Lesser Pied Kingfisher	3·00	3·25
2390	30 d. Common Kestrel	3·50	3·75
2391	40 d. Temminck's Courser (25.3.97) ..	4·75	5·00
2392	50 d. European Bee-eater (25.3.97) ..	5·75	6·00
2377/92	.. .. .. *Set of* 16	23·00	24·00

No. 2388 is inscribed "TROGAN" in error

(Litho Questa)

1996 (18 Nov). *Christmas. Religious Paintings. Designs as T* **369** *of Antigua, showing different details of "Assumption of the Madonna" (Tiziano Vecellio) (Nos. 2393/8). P* 13½×14.

No.	Description	Unused	Used
2393	1 d. multicoloured	10	10
2394	1 d. 50, multicoloured	20	25
2395	2 d. multicoloured	20	25
2396	3 d. multicoloured	35	40
2397	10 d. multicoloured	1·10	1·25
2398	15 d. multicoloured	1·75	1·90
2393/8	.. .. .. *Set of* 6	3·50	4·00

MS2399 Two sheets, each 76×106 mm. (a) 25 d. blackish brown, black and yellow-brown ("Adoration of the Magi" (F. Lippi)) (*horiz*). P 14×13½. (b) 25 d. carmine-red, black and pale brown-rose ("Virgin and Child with Infant St. John" (Raphael)). P 13½×14 .. *Set of 2 sheets* 5·75 6·00

(Des Shannon. Litho Questa)

1996 (21 Nov). *20th Anniv of* Rocky (*film*). *Sheet* 143×182 *mm. P* 14×13½.

MS2400 **266** 10 d.×3 multicoloured .. .. 3·50 3·75

267 Ox

268 "Arch 22" Monument

(Des Y. Lee. Litho Questa)

1997 (16 Jan). *Chinese New Year ("Year of the Ox"). T* **267** *and similar horiz designs showing symbolic oxen. P* 14½.

No.	Description	Unused	Used
2401	63 b. multicoloured	10	10
	a. Horiz strip of 4. Nos. 2401/4 ..	1·00	
2402	75 b. multicoloured	10	10
2403	1 d. 50, multicoloured	20	25
2404	4 d. multicoloured	45	50
2401/4	.. .. .. *Set of* 4	85	95

MS2405 84×68 mm. 3 d. × 4. As Nos. 2401/4 1·40 1·50

MS2406 76×106 mm. 10 d. multicoloured (ox and sleeping peasant) (39½×24½ *mm*). P 14 1·10 1·25

Nos. 2401/4 were printed together, *se-tenant*, as horizontal strips of 4 in sheets of 12.

(Litho Questa)

1997 (28 Jan). *Economic Development. T* **268** *and similar multicoloured designs. P* 14.

No.	Description	Unused	Used
2407	63 b. Type **268**	10	10
2408	1 d. Tractor (*horiz*)	10	10
2409	1 d. 50, Man planting rice	20	25
2410	2 d. As Type **268**, but with white panel at top	20	25
2411	3 d. Model of Banjul International Airport terminal building (*horiz*)	35	40
2412	5 d. Chamoi Bridge (*horiz*)	60	65
2407/12	.. .. .. *Set of* 6	1·25	1·75

MS2413 Two sheets. (a) 106×76 mm. 20 d. Workers in rice field (*horiz*). (b) 76×106 mm. 25 d. As Type **268** .. .. *Set of 2 sheets* 5·25 5·50

269 Monkey King extinguishing Fire on Flame Mountain

270 Jackie Chan

1997 (28 Jan). *Mickey Mouse's Journey to the West. T* **269** *and similar multicoloured designs showing Disney cartoon characters. Litho. P* 14×13½.

No.	Description	Unused	Used
2414	2 d. Type **269**	20	25
	a. Sheetlet. Nos. 2414/19	1·25	
2415	2 d. Demon Ox and Monkey King fighting	20	25
2416	2 d. Mickey, Donald, Monkey King and Master San Tsang	20	25
2417	2 d. Fighting the Spider Demon ..	20	25
2418	2 d. Fighting the White Skeleton Demon	20	25
2419	2 d. The real and the fake Monkey King	20	25
2420	3 d. Monkey King trapped in furnace ..	35	40
	a. Sheetlet. Nos. 2420/5	2·10	
2421	3 d. Monkey King with magic weapon ..	35	40
2422	3 d. Type **269**	35	40
2423	3 d. At the Gate of South Heaven ..	35	40
2424	3 d. Tasting the celestial peaches ..	35	40
2425	3 d. Monkey King rescued from Five-Finger Mountain	35	40
2414/25	.. .. .. *Set of* 12	3·25	4·00

MS2426 Four sheets, each 134×109 mm. (a) 5 d. Mickey and Donald with Master San Tsang (*vert*). P 13½×14. (b) 10 d. Monkey King, Mickey and monkeys. P 14×13½. (c) 10 d. Monkey King, Mickey and tortoise (*vert*). P 13½×14. (d) 15 d. Mickey and Minnie with Buddhist scriptures. P 14×13½ .. .. *Set of 4 sheets* 4·75 5·00

Nos. 2414/19 and 2420/5 were each printed together, *se-tenant*, in sheetlets of 6.

Nos. 2414/25 were re-issued on the 15 September 1998 with the margins of the sheetlets overprinted "70TH ANNIVERSARY OF MICKEY & MINNIE" and the "HAPPY BIRTHDAY" logo. The logo was also added to the margins of No. **MS**2426.

(Des Y. Lee. Litho Questa)

1997 (12 Feb). *"HONG KONG '97" International Stamp Exhibition. Jackie Chan (film star). T* **270** *and similar multicoloured designs. P* 14.

No.	Description	Unused	Used
2427	4 d. Type **270**	45	50
	a. Sheetlet. Nos. 2427/34	3·50	
2428	4 d. Wearing red jacket	45	50
2429	4 d. In open-necked shirt	45	50
2430	4 d. Bare-chested	45	50
2431	4 d. Wearing black jacket	45	50
2432	4 d. Wearing black and white spotted shirt	45	50
2433	4 d. Wearing white T-shirt and red anorak	45	50
2434	4 d. Wearing white sleeveless T-shirt ..	45	50
2427/34	.. .. .. *Set of* 8	3·50	4·00

MS2435 76×106 mm. 25 d. Jackie Chan in action (*horiz*) .. .. 3·00 3·25

Nos. 2427/34 were printed together, *se-tenant*, in sheetlets of 8.

271 Clouded Leopard

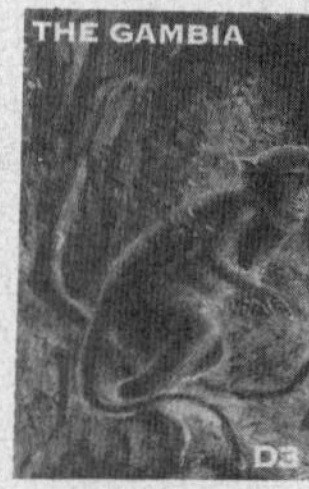

272 Monkey

1997 (24 Feb). *Endangered Species. T* **271** *and similar h[oriz] designs. Multicoloured. Litho. P* 14.

No.	Description	Unused	Used
2436	1 d. 50, Type **271**	20	
	a. Sheetlet. Nos. 2436/55	4·00	
2437	1 d. 50, Audouin's Gull	20	
2438	1 d. 50, Leatherback Turtle	20	
2439	1 d. 50, White Eared-Pheasant	20	
2440	1 d. 50, Kakapo	20	
2441	1 d. 50, Right Whale	20	
2442	1 d. 50, Black-footed Ferret	20	
2443	1 d. 50, Dwarf Lemur	20	
2444	1 d. 50, Peacock Pheasant	20	
2445	1 d. 50, Brown Hyena	20	
2446	1 d. 50, Cougar	20	
2447	1 d. 50, Gharial	20	
2448	1 d. 50, Monk Seal	20	
2449	1 d. 50, Mountain Gorilla	20	
2450	1 d. 50, Blyth's Tragopan	20	
2451	1 d. 50, Malayan Tapir	20	
2452	1 d. 50, Black Rhinoceros	20	
2453	1 d. 50, Polar Bear	20	
2454	1 d. 50, Red Colobus	20	
2455	1 d. 50, Tiger	20	
2456	1 d. 50, Arabian Oryx	20	
	a. Sheetlet. Nos. 2456/75	4·00	
2457	1 d. 50, Baiji	20	
2458	1 d. 50, Ruffed Lemur	20	
2459	1 d. 50, California Condor	20	
2460	1 d. 50, Blue-headed Quail Dove ..	20	
2461	1 d. 50, Numbat	20	
2462	1 d. 50, Congo Peacock	20	
2463	1 d. 50, White Uakari	20	
2464	1 d. 50, Eskimo Curlew	20	
2465	1 d. 50, Gouldian Finch	20	
2466	1 d. 50, Coelacanth	20	
2467	1 d. 50, Toucan Barbet	20	
2468	1 d. 50, Snow Leopard	20	
2469	1 d. 50, Queen Alexandra's Birdwing ..	20	
2470	1 d. 50, Dalmatian Pelican	20	
2471	1 d. 50, Chaco Tortoise	20	
2472	1 d. 50, Giant Catfish	20	
2473	1 d. 50, Helmeted Hornbill	20	
2474	1 d. 50, White-eyed River Martin ..	20	
2475	1 d. 50, Fluminense Swallowtail ..	20	
2436/75	.. .. *Set of* 40	8·00	10[...]

MS2476 Three sheets, each 103×72 mm. (a) 25 d. Giant Panda; (b) 25 d. Humpback Whale; (c) 25 d. Japanese Crane .. *Set of 3 sheets* 8·75 9[...]

Nos. 2436/55 and 2456/75 were each printed, *se-tenant*, [in] sheetlets of 20, with enlarged top margins incorporating [...] "HONG KONG '97" International Stamp Exhibition.

1997 (24 Feb). The Jungle Book *by Rudyard Kipling. T* [...] *and similar vert designs. Multicoloured. Litho. P* 14.

No.	Description	Unused	Used
2477	3 d. Type **272**	35	
	a. Sheetlet. Nos. 2477/88	4·25	
2478	3 d. Baloo (bear)	35	
2479	3 d. Elephant	35	
2480	3 d. Monkey and temple	35	
2481	3 d. Bagheera (panther)	35	
2482	3 d. Buffalo	35	
2483	3 d. Mandrill	35	
2484	3 d. Shere Khan (tiger)	35	
2485	3 d. Rama (wolf)	35	
2486	3 d. Kaa (cobra)	35	
2487	3 d. Mongoose	35	
2488	3 d. Mowgli	35	
2477/88	.. .. *Set of* 12	4·25	4[...]

Nos. 2477/88 were printed together, *se-tenant*, in sheetlets [of] 12 with the background forming a composite design.

273 *Polyporus squamosus*

(Litho Questa)

1997 (10 Mar). *Fungi. T* **273** *and similar multicolour[ed] designs. P* 14.

No.	Description	Unused	Used
2489	1 d. Type **273**	10	
2490	3 d. *Armillaria tabescens*	35	
2491	4 d. *Amanita caesarea* (*vert*)	45	
	a. Sheetlet. Nos. 2491/9	4·00	
2492	4 d. *Lepiota procera* (*vert*)	45	
2493	4 d. *Hygrophorus psittacinus* (*vert*) ..	45	
2494	4 d. *Russula xerampelina* (*vert*)	45	
2495	4 d. *Laccaria amethystina* (*vert*)	45	
2496	4 d. *Coprinus micaceus* (*vert*)	45	
2497	4 d. *Boletus edulis* (*vert*)	45	
2498	4 d. *Morchella esculenta* (*vert*)	45	
2499	4 d. *Otidea auricula* (*vert*)	45	
2500	5 d. *Collybia velutipes*	60	
2501	10 d. *Sarcoscypha coccinea*	1·10	1·[...]
2489/501	.. .. *Set of* 13	6·25	7·[...]

MS2502 76×106 mm. 25 d. *Volvariella bombycina* .. .. 3·00 3·[...]

Nos. 2491/9 were printed together, *se-tenant*, in sheetlets of [...]

(Des M. Freedman and Dena Rubin, Litho Questa)

1997 (24 Mar). *50th Anniv of U.N.E.S.C.O. Multicolour[ed] designs as T* **374** *of Antigua. P* 14×13½ (*horiz*) *or* 13½× [...] (*vert*).

No.	Description	Unused	Used
2503	1 d. Cloister, Horyu-ji, Japan	10	
2504	2 d. Great Wall, China	20	
2505	3 d. Statues, Ayutthaya, Thailand ..	35	
2506	4 d. Ascension Convent, Santa Maria, Philippines	45	
2507	4 d. Mount Nimba Nature Reserve, Guinea (*vert*)	45	
	a. Sheetlet. Nos. 2507/14 and 1 central label	3·50	

08 4 d. Banc d'Argun National Park, Mauritania (*vert*) 45 50
09 4 d. Doorway, Marrakesh, Morocco (*vert*) 45 50
10 4 d. Ichkeul National Park, Tunisia (*vert*) 45 50
11 4 d. Village pottery, Mali (*vert*) 45 50
12 4 d. Hippopotamus, Salonga National Park, Zaire (*vert*) 45 50
13 4 d. Timgad Roman Ruins, Algeria (*vert*) 45 50
14 4 d. Wooden statue, Benin (*vert*) .. 45 50
15 4 d. Temple, Magao Caves, China (*vert*) 45 50
a. Sheetlet. Nos. 2515/22 and 1 central label .. .. 3·50
16 4 d. Statue, Magao Caves (*vert*) 45 50
17 4 d. Domes, Magao Caves (*vert*) 45 50
518 4 d. Great Wall from the air, China (*vert*) 45 50
519 4 d. Statue, Great Wall (*vert*) 45 50
520 4 d. Bronze Bird, Imperial Palace, China (*vert*) 45 50
521 4 d. Temples, Imperial Palace, China (*vert*) 45 50
522 4 d. Dragon statue, Imperial Palace (*vert*) 45 50
523 4 d. Kyoto Gardens, Japan (*vert*) .. 45 50
a. Sheetlet. Nos. 2523/30 and 1 central label .. .. 3·50
24 4 d. Himeji Castle, Japan (*vert*) 45 50
25 4 d. Horyu-ji Temple, Japan (*vert*) .. 45 50
26 4 d. Buddha, Horyu-ji, Japan (*vert*) .. 45 50
27 4 d. Yakushima Forest, Japan (*vert*) .. 45 50
28 4 d. Ancient tree, Yakushima Forest, Japan (*vert*) 45 50
529 4 d. Temple, Kyoto, Japan (*vert*) .. 45 50
530 4 d. Pavilion, Kyoto, Japan (*vert*) .. 45 50
531 5 d. Riverside houses, Inselstadt, Germany 60 65
a. Sheetlet. Nos. 2531/5 and 1 corner label .. .. 3·00
532 5 d. Rosaleda Gardens, Bamberg, Germany 60 65
533 5 d. Bamberg Cathedral, Germany .. 60 65
534 5 d. Timbered house, Maulbronn, Germany 60 65
535 5 d. Maulbronn Monastery, Germany .. 60 65
536 5 d. Ruins at Delphi, Greece 60 65
a. Sheetlet. Nos. 2536/40 and 1 corner label .. .. 3·00
537 5 d. Rhodes waterfront, Greece 60 65
538 5 d. Knights' Hospital, Rhodes, Greece .. 60 65
539 5 d. Temple, Delphi, Greece 60 65
540 5 d. Delphi from air, Greece 60 65
541 5 d. Foliage, Shirakami-Sanchi, Japan .. 60 65
a. Sheetlet. Nos. 2541/5 and 1 corner label .. .. 3·00
542 5 d. Notice board, Shirakami-Sanchi, Japan 60 65
543 5 d. Tower, Himeji Castle, Japan .. 60 65
544 5 d. Roof tops, Himeji Castle, Japan .. 60 65
545 5 d. Gateway, Himeji Castle, Japan .. 60 65
546 10 d. Komodo Dragons, Indonesia .. 1·10 1·40
547 15 d. Ancient hut, Timbuktu, Mali .. 1·75 1·90
503/47 .. .. *Set of* 44 23·00 26·00
IS2548 Four sheets, each 127×102 mm. (a) 25 d. Plitvice Lakes National Park, Croatia; (b) 25 d. Ruins of Kilwa Kisiwani, Tanzania; (c) 25 d. Santa Maria de Alcobaca cloisters, Portugal; (d) 25 d. Watergarden, Kyoto, Japan *Set of 4 sheets* 11·50 12·00

Nos. 2507/14, 2515/22 and 2523/30 were each printed ogether, *se-tenant*, in sheetlets of 8 stamps with a centre label nd Nos. 2531/5, 2536/40 and 2541/5 in sheetlets of 5 stamps ith a top left-hand corner label.

274 Minnie Mouse, 1928

997 (1 May). *Minnie Mouse Through the Years. T* **274** *and similar vert designs showing Disney cartoon character in years stated. Multicoloured. Litho. P* 13½×14.

549 4 d. Type **274** 45 50
a. Sheetlet. Nos. 2549/57 .. .. 4·00
550 4 d. In 1933 .. .. 45 50
551 4 d. In 1934 .. .. 45 50
552 4 d. In 1937 .. .. 45 50
553 4 d. In 1938 .. .. 45 50
554 4 d. In 1941 .. .. 45 50
555 4 d. In 1950 .. .. 45 50
556 4 d. In 1990 .. .. 45 50
557 4 d. In 1997 .. .. 45 50
549/57 .. .. .. *Set of* 9 4·00 4·50
IS2558 133×108 mm. 25 d. In 1987 .. .. 3·00 3·25

Nos. 2549/57 were printed together, *se-tenant*, in sheetlets of .

OMNIBUS ISSUES

Details, together with prices for complete sets, of the various Omnibus issues from the 1935 Silver Jubilee series to date are included in a special section following Zimbabwe at the end of Volume 2.

275 Dipstick

(Des Alvin White Studios. Litho Questa)

1997 (1 May). 101 Dalmatians. *T* **275** *and similar multi-coloured designs showing Disney cartoon characters. P* 13½×14 (*vert*) *or* 14×13½ (*horiz*).

2559 50 b. Type **275** 10 10
a. Sheetlet. Nos. 2559/64 35
2560 50 b. Fidget 10 10
2561 50 b. Jewel 10 10
2562 50 b. Lucky 10 10
2563 50 b. Two-Tone 10 10
2564 50 b. Wizzer 10 10
2565 2 d. Two puppies playing (*horiz*) .. 20 25
a. Sheetlet. Nos. 2565/73 .. .. 1·75
2566 2 d. Puppy and pig (*horiz*) 20 25
2567 2 d. Two puppies with butterfly (*horiz*) .. 20 25
2568 2 d. Puppy lying on back (*horiz*) .. 20 25
2569 2 d. Puppy with ball (*horiz*) 20 25
2570 2 d. Puppy with bone (*horiz*) 20 25
2571 2 d. One puppy pulling another puppy's tail (*horiz*) 20 25
2572 2 d. Two puppies pulling third puppy's ears (*horiz*) 20 25
2573 2 d. Puppy with teddy bear (*horiz*) .. 20 25
2574 3 d. Puppy asleep on biscuit box (*horiz*) 35 40
a. Sheetlet. Nos. 2574/82 .. .. 3·25
2575 3 d. Puppy with hose (*horiz*) 35 40
2576 3 d. Puppy and bottle (*horiz*) 35 40
2577 3 d. Puppy and biscuit bowl (*horiz*) .. 35 40
2578 3 d. Puppy wearing hat (*horiz*) 35 40
2579 3 d. Three puppies with lipstick (*horiz*) .. 35 40
2580 3 d. Puppy tying another up with string (*horiz*) 35 40
2581 3 d. Two puppies and lunch box (*horiz*) .. 35 40
2582 3 d. Three puppies and computer (*horiz*) 35 40
2559/82 .. .. *Set of* 24 5·25 6·00
MS2583 Six sheets, each 127×103 mm. (a) 25 d. Sheep and puppies (*horiz*). (b) 25 d. Cruella de Vil (*horiz*). (c) 25 d. Puppy looking at photograph (*horiz*). (d) 25 d. Puppies in mail sack. (e) 25 d. Two puppies covered in paint (*horiz*). (f) 25 d. Two puppies playing computer game (*horiz*). *Set of 6 sheets* 17·00 18·00

Nos. 2559/64, 2565/73 and 2574/82 were each printed together, *se-tenant*, in sheetlets of 6 (Nos. 2559/64) or 9 (others).

276 Juventus Team, 1897

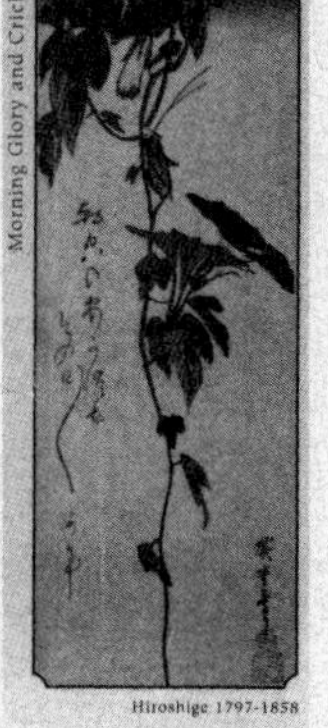

277 "Morning Glory and Cricket"

1997 (9 May). *Centenary of Juventus Football Team. T* **276** *and similar horiz designs. Multicoloured. Litho. P* 14×13½.

2584 5 d. Type **276** 60 65
a. Sheetlet. Nos. 2584/9 .. .. 3·50
2585 5 d. Centenary emblem and player .. 60 65
2586 5 d. Giampiero Boniperti 60 65
2587 5 d. Roberto Bettega 60 65
2588 5 d. Juventus team, 1996 .. .. 60 65
2589 5 d. Juventus '97 logo 60 65
2584/89 .. .. *Set of* 6 3·50 4·00

Nos. 2584/9 were printed together, *se-tenant*, in sheetlets of 6.

(Des R. Rundo. Litho Questa)

1997 (20 May). 300*th Anniv of Mother Goose Nursery Rhymes. Horiz design as T* **309** *of Dominica. Sheet* 72×102 *mm. Multicoloured. P* 14.

MS2590 25 d. Young girl ("I'll Tell You a Story") 3·00 3·25

(Litho Questa)

1997 (20 May). 10*th Anniv of Chernobyl Nuclear Disaster. Vert designs as T* **376** *of Antigua . Multicoloured. P* 13½.

2591 15 d. As Type **376** of Antigua .. .. 1·75 1·90
2592 15 d. As No. 2591 but inscribed "CHABAD'S CHILDREN OF CHERNOBYL" .. .. 1·75 1·90

(Des J. Iskowitz. Litho Questa)

1997 (20 May). 50*th Death Anniv of Paul Harris (founder of Rotary International). Horiz designs as T* **377** *of Antigua. Multicoloured. P* 14.

2593 10 d. Rotary President Sydney Pascall planting tree of friendship .. .. 1·10 1·25
MS2594 78×108 mm. 25 d. Paul Harris and Preserve Planet Earth emblem .. .. 3·00 3·25

(Litho Questa)

1997 (20 May). *Golden Wedding of Queen Elizabeth and Prince Philip. Horiz designs as T* **378** *of Antigua. Multicoloured. P* 14.

2595 4 d. Queen Elizabeth II 45 50
a. Sheetlet. Nos. 2595/600 .. .. 2·75
2596 4 d. Royal coat of arms 45 50
2597 4 d. Queen Elizabeth and Prince Philip applauding 45 50
2598 4 d. Queen Elizabeth and Prince Philip taking the salute 45 50
2599 4 d. Royal Yacht *Britannia* 45 50
2600 4 d. Prince Philip 45 50
2595/600 .. .. .. *Set of* 6 2·75 3·00
MS2601 100×70 mm. 20 d. Princess Elizabeth, 1948 .. .. 2·25 2·40

Nos. 2595/600 were printed together, *se-tenant*, in sheetlets of 6.

(Des J. Iskowitz. Litho Questa)

1997 (20 May). *"Pacific '97" International Stamp Exhibition, San Francisco. Death Centenary of Henrich von Stephan (founder of U.P.U.). Horiz designs as T* **379** *of Antigua. P* 14.

2602 5 d. deep magenta 60 65
a. Sheetlet. Nos. 2602/4 .. .. 1·75
2603 5 d. chestnut 60 65
2604 5 d. turquoise-green and black 60 65
2602/4 .. .. .. *Set of* 3 1·75 1·90
MS2605 82×118 mm. 25 d. turquoise-green and black .. .. 3·00 3·25

Designs:—No. 2602, Von Stephan and Otto von Bismarck; No. 2603, Von Stephan and Mercury; No. 2604, Mail wagon, Boston, 1900; No. **MS**2605, Von Stephan and Hamburg–Lubeck postilion.

Nos. 2602/4 were printed together, *se-tenant*, in sheetlets of 3 with enlarged illustrated right-hand margin.

1997 (20 May). *Birth Bicentenary of Hiroshige (Japanese painter). T* **277** *and similar vert designs. Multicoloured. Litho. P* 13½×14.

2606/11 4 d. × 6 (Type **277**; "Dragonfly and Begonia"; "Two Ducks swimming among Reeds"; "A Black-naped Oriole perched on a Stem of Rose Mallow"; "A Pheasant on a Snow-covered Pine"; "A Cuckoo flying through the Rain")
a. Sheetlet. Nos. 2606/11 .. .. 2·75
2612/17 4 d. × 6 ("An Egret among Rushes"; "Peacock and Peonies"; "Three Wild Geese flying across the Moon"; "A Cock in the Snow"; "A Pheasant and Bracken"; "Peonies")
a. Sheetlet. Nos. 2612/17 .. .. 2·75
2618/23 4 d. × 6 ("Sparrow and Bamboo"; "Mandarin Ducks on an Icy Pond with Brown Leaves falling"; "Blossoming Plum Tree"; "Java Sparrow and Magnolia"; "Chinese Bellflowers and Miscanthus"; "A Small Black Bird clinging to a Tendril of Ivy")
a. Sheetlet. Nos. 2618/23 .. .. 2·75
2624/9 5 d. × 6 ("Sparrows and Camellia in Snow"; "Parrot on a Branch of Pine"; "A Long-tailed Blue Bird on a Branch of Flowering Plum"; "Sparrow and Bamboo"; "Bird in a Tree"; "A Wild Duck swimming beneath Snow-laden reeds")
a. Sheetlet. Nos. 2624/9 .. .. 3·50
2630/5 5 d. × 6 ("Kingfisher above a Yellow-flowered Water Plant"; "Wagtail and Roses"; "A Mandarin Duck on a Snowy Bank"; "A Japanese White-eye on a Persimmon Branch"; "Sparrows and Camellia in Snow"; "Kingfisher and Moon above a Yellow-flowered Water Plant")
a. Sheetlet. Nos. 2630/5 .. .. 3·50
2636/41 5 d. × 6 ("Sparrow and Bamboo by Night"; "Birds Flying over Waves"; "Blossoming Plum Tree with Full Moon"; "Kingfisher and Iris"; "A Blue-and-White Flycatcher on a Hibiscus Flower"; "Mandarin Ducks in Snowfall")
a. Sheetlet. Nos. 2636/41 .. .. 3·50
2606/41 .. .. .. *Set of* 35 15·00 16·00
MS2642 Six sheets each 95×120 mm. (a) 25 d. Hawk on perch. (b) 25 d. Two green birds on branch. (c) 25 d. Kingfisher hovering. (d) 25 d. "Three Wild Geese flying across moon". (e) 25 d. Red parrot on branch. (f) 25 d. White bird on flowering bush .. .. *Set of 6 sheets* 17·00 18·00

Nos. 2606/11, 2612/17, 2618/23, 2624/9, 2630/5 and 2636/41 were each printed together, *se-tenant*, in sheetlets of 6.

(Des R. Rundo. Litho Questa)

1997 (20 May). 175*th Anniv of Brothers Grimm's Third Collection of Fairy Tales. Little Red Riding Hood. Multicoloured designs as T* **380** *of Antigua. P* 13½×14.

2643 10 d. Grandma's cottage .. .. .. 1·10 1·25
a. Sheetlet. Nos. 2643/5 .. .. 3·25
2644 10 d. Little Red Riding Hood .. .. 1·10 1·25
2645 10 d. The Wolf .. .. 1·10 1·25
2643/5 .. .. .. *Set of* 3 3·25 3·50
MS2646 124×96 mm. 10 d. Little Red Riding Hood (*horiz*). P 14×13½ .. .. .. 1·10 1·25

Nos. 2643/5 were printed together, *se-tenant*, in sheetlets of 3 with an illustrated margin.

278 Coelophysis chasing Ornitholestes

(Des W. Wright. Litho Questa)

1997 (23 June). *Dinosaurs. T* **278** *and similar horiz designs. Multicoloured. P* 14.

2647 50 b. Type **278** 10 10
2648 63 b. Spinosaurus 10 10
2649 75 b. Kentrosaurus 10 10
2650 1 d. Ceratosaurus 10 10
2651 1 d. 50, Stygimoloch 20 25
2652 2 d. Troodon 20 25
2653 3 d. Velociraptor 35 40
2654 4 d. Triceratops 45 50
2655 4 d. Anurognathus 45 50
a. Sheetlet. Nos. 2655/63 .. .. 4·00
2656 4 d. Pteranodon 45 50
2657 4 d. Pterosaurus 45 50
2658 4 d. Saltasaurus 45 50
2659 4 d. Agathaumus 45 50
2660 4 d. Stegosaurus 45 50
2661 4 d. Albertosaurus libratus 45 50
2662 4 d. Three Lesothosauruses running .. 45 50
2663 4 d. Five Lesothosauruses running .. 45 50
2664 4 d. Tarbosaurus bataar 45 50
a. Sheetlet. Nos. 2664/72 .. .. 4·00
2665 4 d. Brachiosaurus 45 50
2666 4 d. Styracosasaurus 45 50
2667 4 d. Baryonyx 45 50
2668 4 d. Coelophysis 45 50
2669 4 d. Carnotaurus 45 50
2670 4 d. Compsognathus longipes 45 50
2671 4 d. Compsognathus "Elegant Jaw" .. 45 50
2672 4 d. Stenonychosaurus 45 50
2673 5 d. Protoceratops 60 65
2674 10 d. Ornithomimus .. .. .. 1·10 1·25
2675 15 d. Stegosaurus .. .. 1·75 1·90
2676 20 d. Ankylosaurus saichania .. .. 2·25 2·40
2647/76 .. .. *Set of* 30 15·00 17·00

MS2677 Two sheets, each 106×81 mm. (a) 25 d. Head of Deinonychus (50×37 *mm*). (b) 25 d. Seismosaurus (88×27 *mm*) .. *Set of* 2 *sheets* 5·75 6·00

Nos. 2655/63 and 2664/72 were each printed together, *se-tenant*, in sheetlets of 9 with the backgrounds forming composite designs.

279 Margaret Thatcher and Deng Xiaoping toasting Joint Declaration, 1984

1997 (1 July). *Return of Hong Kong to China. T* **279** *and similar horiz designs. Multicoloured. Litho. P* 14.

2678 3 d. Type **279** 35 40
a. Sheetlet. Nos. 2678/81 .. .. 1·40
2679 3 d. Signing Joint Declaration on Hong Kong, 1984 .. .. .. 35 40
2680 3 d. Signing Joint Declaration on Macao, 1987 .. .. 35 40
2681 3 d. Deng Xiaoping toasting Prime Minister Anibal Silva of Portugal .. 35 40
2682 4 d. Hong Kong in 1843 and Governor Sir Henry Pottinger 45 50
a. Sheetlet. Nos. 2682/4 .. .. 1·40
2683 4 d. Kowloon in 1860 and Governor Sir Hercules Robinson 45 50
2684 4 d. Reception in New Territories, 1898, and Governor Sir Henry Blake .. 45 50
2685 5 d. Governor Sir Henry Pottinger and British warship 60 65
a. Sheetlet. Nos. 2685/7 .. .. 1·75
2686 5 d. Governor Christopher Patten and Lantau Bridge 60 65
2687 5 d. Chief Executive C.H. Tung and Hong Kong by night 60 65
2688 6 d. Signing the Treaty of Nanking, 1842 70 75
a. Sheetlet. Nos. 2688/90 .. .. 2·10
2689 6 d. Signing the Japanese Surrender of Hong Kong, 1945 .. .. .. 70 75
2690 6 d. Signing of the Sino-British Joint Declaration, 1984 .. .. .. 70 75
2678/90 .. .. *Set of* 13 6·50 7·25

Nos. 2678/81, 2682/4, 2685/7 and 2688/90 were each printed together, *se-tenant*, in sheetlets of 4 (Nos. 2678/81) or 3 (others).

280 Great Mosque, Samarra, Iran

281 Downhill Skiing

(Des W. Wright. Litho Questa)

1997 (15 July). *Natural and Man-made Wonders of the World. T* **280** *and similar multicoloured designs. P* 14 (*Nos.* 2691/6) *or* 13½×14 (*others*).

2691 63 b. Type **280** 10 10
2692 75 b. Moai statues, Easter Island (*horiz*) .. 10 10
2693 1 d. Golden Gate Bridge, San Francisco (*horiz*) 10 10
2694 1 d. 50, The Statue of Liberty, New York 20 25
2695 2 d. The Parthenon, Athens (*horiz*) .. 20 25
2696 3 d. Pyramid of the Sun, Mexico (*horiz*) 35 40
2697 5 d. The Rock of Gibraltar (*horiz*) .. 60 65
a. Sheetlet. Nos. 2697/702 .. .. 3·50
2698 5 d. St. Peter's Basilica, Rome (*horiz*) .. 60 65
2699 5 d. Santa Sophia, Istanbul (*horiz*) .. 60 65
2700 5 d. "Gateway to the West" monument, St. Louis (*horiz*) 60 65
2701 5 d. Great Wall of China (*horiz*) .. 60 65
2702 5 d. City of Carcassonne, France (*horiz*) 60 65
2703 5 d. Stonehenge, England (*horiz*) .. 60 65
a. Sheetlet. Nos. 2703/8 .. .. 3·50
2704 5 d. Hughes HK-1 *Spruce Goose* flying boat (World's largest aircraft) (*horiz*) 60 65
2705 5 d. Hoverspeed "Seacat" catamaran (fastest Atlantic crossing by a commercial catamaran) (*horiz*) .. 60 65
2706 5 d. "Thrust 2" car (official land speed record) (*horiz*) 60 65
2707 5 d. Stepped Pyramid, Egypt (*horiz*) .. 60 65
2708 5 d. L.N.E.R. Class A4 *Mallard* (fastest steam locomotive),1938 (*horiz*) .. 60 65
2691/708 .. .. *Set of* 18 8·00 9·00

MS2709 Three sheets, each 98×68 mm. (a) 25 d. Mount Everest (42×28 *mm*). P 14. (b) 25 d. The Grand Canyon, Colorado (42×28 *mm*). P 14. (c) 25 d. Washington Monument (33×51 *mm*). P 15 *Set of* 3 *sheets* 9·00 9·25

Nos. 2697/702 and 2703/8 were each printed together, *se-tenant*, in sheetlets of 6.

No. 2702 is inscribed "CARCASSONNNE" in error.

(Litho B.D.T.)

1997 (21 July). *Winter Olympic Games, Nagano* (1998). *T* **281** *and similar multicoloured designs. P* 14.

2710 5 d. Type **281** 60 65
2711 5 d. Two-man bob-sleigh (*vert*) 60 65
a. Sheetlet. Nos. 2711/19 .. .. 5·50
2712 5 d. Freestyle skiing (*vert*) 60 65
2713 5 d. Speed skating (*vert*) 60 65
2714 5 d. Downhill skiing (No. 8 on bib) (*vert*) 60 65
2715 5 d. Womens figure skating (*vert*) .. 60 65
2716 5 d. Downhill skiing (No. 4 on bib) (*vert*) 60 65
2717 5 d. Pairs figure skating (*vert*) 60 65
2718 5 d. Cross-country (*vert*) 60 65
2719 5 d. Ski jumping (*vert*) 60 65
2720 5 d. One-man luge 60 65
a. Sheetlet. Nos. 2720/8 .. .. 5·50
2721 5 d. Ice hockey 60 65
2722 5 d. Four-man bob-sleigh 60 65
2723 5 d. Ski-jumping 60 65
2724 5 d. Curling 60 65
2725 5 d. Figure skating 60 65
2726 5 d. Speed skating 60 65
2727 5 d. Biathlon 60 65
2728 5 d. Downhill skiing (*different*) 60 65
2729 10 d. One-man luge .. .. .. 1·10 1·25
2730 15 d. Speed skating .. .. .. 1·75 1·90
2731 20 d. Ice hockey .. .. 2·25 2·40
2710/31 .. .. *Set of* 22 17·00 18·00

MS2732 Two sheets. (a) 97×67 mm. 25 d. Bob-sleigh. (b) 67×97 mm. 25 d. Pairs figure skating (*vert*) .. .. *Set of* 2 *sheets* 5·75 6·00

Nos. 2711/19 and 2720/8 were each printed togther, *se-tenant*, in sheetlets of 9.

282 Brown Pelican

(Des J. Ruff. Litho Questa)

1997 (4 Aug). *Sea Birds. T* **282** *and similar multicoloured designs. P* 14.

2733 3 d. Type **282** 35 40
a. Sheetlet. Nos. 2733/44 .. .. 4·25
2734 3 d. Galapagos Penguin 35 40
2735 3 d. Red-billed Tropic Bird 35 40
2736 3 d. Little Tern 35 40
2737 3 d. Dunlin 35 40
2738 3 d. Kittiwake 35 40
2739 3 d. Atlantic Puffin 35 40
2740 3 d. Wandering Albatross 35 40
2741 3 d. Masked Booby 35 40
2742 3 d. Glaucous Winged Gull 35 40
2743 3 d. Arctic Tern 35 40
2744 3 d. Piping Plover 35 40
2745 5 d. Roseate Tern 60 65
2746 10 d. Red-legged Cormorant .. .. 1·10 1·25
2747 15 d. Blue-footed Booby .. .. .. 1·75 1·90
2748 20 d. Sanderling .. .. 2·25 2·40
2733/48 .. .. *Set of* 16 10·00 11·00

MS2749 Two sheets, each 106×76 mm. (a) 23 d. Long-tailed Skua (*vert*). (b) 23 d. Osprey (*vert*) *Set of* 2 *sheets* 2·50 2·75

Nos. 2733/44 were printed together, *se-tenant*, in sheetlets of 12.

The captions on Nos. 2745/6 are transposed in error.

283 Scottish Fold Cat

284 Diana, Princess of Wales

(Des D. Burkhart. Litho Questa)

1997 (12 Aug). *Cats and Dogs. T* **283** *and similar ho designs. Multicoloured. P* 14.

2750 63 b. Type **283** 10
2751 75 b. Dalmatian 10
2752 1 d. Rottweiler 10
2753 1 d. 50, American Curl cat 20
2754 2 d. British Bi-colour cat 20
2755 3 d. Newfoundland 35
2756 3 d. Devon Rex cat 35
2757 4 d. Great Dane 45
2758 5 d. Burmilla cat 60
a. Sheetlet. Nos. 2758/63 .. .. 3·50
2759 5 d. Blue Burmese cat 60
2760 5 d. Korat cat 60
2761 5 d. British Tabby cat 60
2762 5 d. Foreign White cat 60
2763 5 d. Somali cat 60
2764 5 d. Akita 60
a. Sheetlet. Nos. 2764/9 .. .. 3·50
2765 5 d. Welsh Corgi 60
2766 5 d. German Shepherd 60
2767 5 d. Saint Bernard 60
2768 5 d. Bullmastiff 60
2769 5 d. Malamute 60
2770 6 d. Silver Tabby cat 70
2771 10 d. Old English Sheepdog .. .. 1·10 1·
2772 15 d. Queensland Heeler cat .. .. 1·75 1·
2773 20 d. Abyssinian cat .. .. .. 2·25 2·
2750/73 .. .. *Set of* 24 14·50 16·

MS2774 Four sheets, each 107×78 mm. (a) 25 d. Cornish Rex cat. (b) 25 d. Siamese cat. (c) 25 d. Boxer. (d) 25 d. Doberman Pinscher *Set of* 4 *sheets* 12·00 12·

Nos. 2758/63 and 2764/9 were each printed togeth *se-tenant*, in sheetlets of 6.

(Litho Questa)

1997 (4 Sept). *World Cup Football Championship, Fra* (1998). *Designs as T* **383** *of Antigua. P* 14×13½ (*horiz*) 13½×14 (*vert*).

2775 1 d. black 10
2776 1 d. 50, black 20
2777 2 d. black 20
2778 3 d. black 35
2779/86 4 d. × 8 mult or agate (Nos. 2782/3)
a. Sheetlet. Nos. 2779/86 and central label .. .. 3·50
2787/94 4 d. × 8 multicoloured or blk (No. 2788)
a. Sheetlet. Nos. 2787/94 and central label .. .. 3·50
2795/802 4 d. × 8 blackish brown (Nos. 2795/6, 2800 and 2802) or multicoloured
a. Sheetlet. Nos. 2795/802 and central label .. .. .. 3·50
2803/10 4 d. × 8 multicoloured
a. Sheetlet. Nos. 2803/10 and central label .. .. 3·50
2811 5 d. black 60
2812 10 d. black .. .. 1·10 1·
2775/812 .. .. *Set of* 38 16·50 18·

MS2813 Four sheets, each 102×127 mm. (a) 25 d. multicoloured. (b) 25 d. multicoloured. (c) 25 d. black. (d) 25 d. blackish brown *Set of* 4 *sheets* 12·00 12·

Designs: *Horiz*—No. 2775, Uruguay team, 1950; No. 277 West German team, 1954; No 2777, Brazilian team, 1970; N 2778, Brazilian team, 1962; No. 2779, Brazilian team, 1994; N 2780, Argentine team, 1986; No. 2781, Brazilian team, 197 No. 2782, Italian team, 1934; No. 2783, Uruguay team, 195 No. 2784, English team, 1966; No. 2785, Brazilian team, 196 No. 2786, West German team, 1990; No. 2787, Mario Kemp Argentina (1978); No. 2788, Joseph Gaetjens, U.S.A. (195 (inscr "ADEMIR BRAZIL" in error); No. 2789, Muller, We Germany (1970); No. 2790, Lineker, England (1986); No. 279 Eusebio, Portugal (1966); No. 2792, Schillaci, Italy (1990); N 2793, Lato, Poland (1974); No. 2794, Rossi, Italy (1982); N 2811, Italian team, 1938; No. 2812, Uruguay team, 1930; N **MS**2813a, Philippe Albert, Belgium; No. **MS**2813b, Junin Brazil; No. **MS**2813c, Eusebio, Portugal; No. **MS**2813d, Pe Brazil. *Vert*—No. 2795, Moore, England (1996); No. 279 Fritzwalter, West Germany (1954); No. 2797, Beckenbau West Germany (1974); No. 2798, Zoff, Italy (1982); No. 279 Maradona, Argentina (1986); No. 2800, Passarella, Argenti (1978); No. 2801, Mattahus, West Germany (1990); No. 280 Dunga, Brazil (1994); No. 2803, Kinkladze, Georgia; No. 280 Shearer, England; No. 2805, Dani, Portugal; No. 2806, Wea Portugal; No. 2807, Ravanelli, Italy; No. 2808, Raducioi Rumania; No. 2809, Schmeichel, Denmark; No. 281 Bergkamp, Holland;

Nos. 2779/86, 2787/94, 2795/802 and 2803/10 were ea printed together, *se-tenant*, in sheetlets of 8 stamps and central label.

NEW INFORMATION

The editor is always interested to correspond wi people who have new information that w improve or correct the Catalogue.

(Des J. Iskowitz. Litho Questa)

1997 (26 Nov). *Diana, Princess of Wales Commemoration. T* **284** *and similar vert designs each red-brown and black* (*Nos.* 2814/17). *P* 14.
2814 10 d. Type **284** . . . . 1·10 1·25
a. Sheetlet. Nos. 2814/17 . . . . 4·50
2815 10 d. Wearing open-necked shirt . . . . 1·10 1·25
2816 10 d. Wearing polo-neck jumper . . . . 1·10 1·25
2817 10 d. Wearing diamond-drop earrings . . 1·10 1·25
2814/17 . . . . *Set of* 4 4·50 5·00
MS2818 76×106 mm. 25 d. Diana, Princess of Wales (multicoloured) . . . . . . 3·00 3·25
Nos. 2814/17 were printed together, *se-tenant*, in sheetlets of 4 with enlarged illustrated margins.

(Litho B.D.T.)

1997 (8 Dec). *Christmas. Paintings. Vert designs as T* **386** *of Antigua. Multicoloured. P* 14.
2819 1 d. "Angel" (Rembrandt) 10 15
2820 1 d. 50, "Initiation into the Rites of Dionysus", Villa dei Misteri . . 20 25
2821 2 d. "Pair of Erotes with Purple Cloaks" 20 25
2822 3 d. "The Ecstasy of Saint Theresa" (Gianlorenzo Bernini) 35 40
2823 5 d. "Virgin and Child with Angels" (Matthias Grunewald) 60 65
2824 10 d. "Angel playing the Organ" (Stefan Lochner) . . . . . . 1·10 1·25
2819/24 . . . . *Set of* 6 2·50 3·00
MS2825 Two sheets, each 105×95 mm. (a) 25 d. "The Rest on the Flight into Egypt" (Caravaggio). (b) 25 d. "The Education of Cupid" (Titian) . . . . . . *Set of 2 sheets* 5·75 6·00
No. **MS**2825b is inscribed "TITAN" in error.

285 Tiger

286 Class 91 Electric Train, Great Britain

(Des Y. Lee. Litho Questa)

1998 (5 Jan). *Chinese New Year* ("*Year of the Tiger*"). *T* **285** *and similar horiz designs. Multicoloured. P* 14½.
2826 3 d. Type **285** ("GAMBIA" in emerald) . . 35 40
a. Sheetlet. Nos. 2826/9 . . . . 1·40
2827 3 d. Tiger ("GAMBIA" in magenta) . . 35 40
2828 3 d. Tiger "(GAMBIA" in lilac) 35 40
2829 3 d. Tiger ("GAMBIA" in deep violet-blue) 35 40
2826/9 . . . . *Set of* 4 1·40 1·60
MS2830 73×103 mm. 10 d. Tiger (42×28 *mm*) 1·10 1·25
Nos. 2826/9 were printed together, *se-tenant*, in sheetlets of 4.

(Des R. Sauber. Litho Questa)

1998 (19 May). *Trains of the World. T* **286** *and similar horiz designs. Multicoloured. P* 14.
2831 5 d. Type **286** 60 65
a. Sheetlet. Nos. 2831/6 . . . . 3·75
2832 5 d. Class 26 steam locomotive No. 3450 *Red Devil*, South Africa 60 65
2833 5 d. TGV express train, France 60 65
2834 5 d. People Mover railcar, Great Britain . . 60 65
2835 5 d. ICE high speed train, Germany . . 60 65
2836 5 d. Montmartre funicular car, France . . 60 65
2837 5 d. Burlington Northern SD70 diesel locomotive No. 9716, U.S.A. 60 65
a. Sheetlet. Nos. 2837/42 . . . . 3·75
2838 5 d. L.N.E.R. Class A4 steam locomotive *Mallard*, 1938 . . . . . . 60 65
2839 5 d. Baldwin steam locomotive, Peru . . 60 65
2840 5 d. Amtrak Class ARM-7 electric locomotive, U.S.A. 60 65
2841 5 d. Rack steam locomotive No. B2503, Amberawa, Java 60 65
2842 5 d. Beyer-Peacock steam locomotive No. 3108, Pakistan 60 65
2831/42 . . . . *Set of* 12 7·50 7·75
MS2843 Two sheets, each 84×110 mm. (a) 25 d. Futuristic monorail train, Great Britain. (b) 25 d. Southern Pacific GS4 stream-lined steam locomotive, U.S.A. . . . . *Set of 2 sheets* 5·75 6·00
Nos. 2831/6 and 2837/42 were each printed together, *se-tenant*, in sheetlets of 6.
No. 2832 is inscribed "BEACONSFIELD CHINA", No. 2836 "MOUNTMAETRE FUNICULAR" and No. 2840 "SWEDEN RAIL 125 MPH", all in error.

287 Yellow Orchid

288 Wright *Flyer I*, 1903

(Des R. Martin. Litho Questa)

1998 (2 June). *African Flowers. T* **287** *and similar multicoloured designs. P* 14.
2844 75 b. Type **287** 10 10
2845 1 d. 50, Transvaal Daisy 20 25
2846 3 d. Torch Lily 35 40
2847 4 d. *Ancistrochilus rothschildianus* . . 45 50
2848 5 d. *Adenium multiflorum* (*horiz*) . . 60 65
a. Sheetlet. Nos. 2848/53 . . . . 3·75
2849 5 d. *Huernia namaquensis* (*horiz*) . . 60 65
2850 5 d. *Gloriosa superba* (*horiz*) 60 65
2851 5 d. *Strelitzia reginae* (*horiz*) 60 65
2852 5 d. *Passiflora mollissima* (*horiz*) . . 60 65
2853 5 d. *Bauhinia variegata* (*horiz*) 60 65
2854 10 d. *Polystachya vulcanica* . . . . 1·10 1·25
2855 15 d. Gladiolus . . . . 1·75 1·90
2844/55 . . . . *Set of* 12 7·50 8·25
MS2856 Two sheets, each 106×76 mm. (a) 25 d. *Aerangis rhodosticta*. (b) 25 d. *Ansella gigantea* *Set of 2 sheets* 5·75 6·00
Nos. 2848/53 were printed together, *se-tenant*, in sheetlets of 6, forming a composite background design.

1998 (16 June). *History of Aviation. T* **288** *and similar horiz designs. Multicoloured. Litho. P* 14.
2857 5 d. Type **288** 60 65
a. Sheetlet. Nos. 2857/62 . . . . 3·50
2858 5 d. Curtiss A-1 seaplane, 1910 . . . . 60 65
2859 5 d. Farman biplane, 1907 . . . . 60 65
2860 5 d. Bristol monoplane, 1911 . . . . 60 65
2861 5 d. Antoinette IV, 1908 . . . . . . 60 65
2862 5 d. Sopwith "Bat Boat" amphibian, 1912 60 65
2863 5 d. Short Type 38, 1913 . . . . . . 60 65
a. Sheetlet. Nos. 2863/8 . . . . 3·50
2864 5 d. Fokker F.VIIb/3m, 1925 . . . . 60 65
2865 5 d. Junkers J.13, 1919 . . . . . . 60 65
2866 5 d. Pitcairn "Mailwing", 1927 . . . . 60 65
2867 5 d. Douglas, 1920 . . . . 60 65
2868 5 d. Curtiss T-32 Condor II airliner, 1934 60 65
2857/68 . . . . *Set of* 12 7·00 7·75
MS2869 Two sheets, each 106×76 mm. (a) 25 d. Albatross, 1913 (84×28 *mm*). (b) 25 d. Boeing 247 airliner, 1932 (84×28 *mm*) . . *Set of 2 sheets* 6·00 6·25
Nos. 2857/62 and 2863/8 were each printed together, *se-tenant*, in sheetlets of 6, forming composite background designs.
No. 2857 is dated "1902" in error.

289 Mulan

290 Chinese Junk

(Des Walt Disney Co. Litho)

1998 (1 July). Mulan (*film*). *T* **289** *and similar vert designs showing Disney cartoon characters. Multicoloured. P* 13½×14.
2870 4 d. Type **289** 45 50
a. Sheetlet. Nos. 2870/7 . . . . 3·50
2871 4 d. Mushu 45 50
2872 4 d. Little Brother 45 50
2873 4 d. Cri-kee 45 50
2874 4 d. Grandmother Fa 45 50
2875 4 d. Fa Li 45 50
2876 4 d. Fa Zhou 45 50
2877 4 d. Mulan and Khan 45 50
2878 5 d. Mulan riding Khan 60 65
a. Sheetlet. Nos. 2878/85 . . . . 4·75
2879 5 d. Shang 60 65
2880 5 d. Chi-fu 60 65
2881 5 d. Chien-po 60 65
2882 5 d. Yao 60 65
2883 5 d. Ling 60 65
2884 5 d. Shan-yu 60 65
2885 5 d. Mulan, Shang and Mushu 60 65
2870/85 . . . . *Set of* 16 8·25 9·00
MS2886 Four sheets. (a) 102×127 mm. 25 d. Mulan and Khan. (b) 127×102 mm. 25 d. Mulan and firework. (c) 127×102 mm. 25 d. Mulan in front of house. (d) 127×102 mm. 25 d. Mulan performing karate kick . . . . *Set of 4 sheets* 12·00 12·50
Nos. 2870/7 and 2878/85 were each printed together, *se-tenant*, in sheetlets of 8.

(Des D. Keren, R. Sauber and Zina Saunders. Litho Questa)

1998 (12 Oct). *Millennium Series. Famous People of the Twentieth Century. Multicoloured designs as T* **318** *of Dominica. P* 14.

(*a*) *Famous Jazz Musicians*
2887 4 d. Sidney Bechet 45 50
a. Sheetlet. Nos. 2887/94 . . . . 3·50
2888 4 d. Sidney Bechet playing saxophone (53×38 *mm*) 45 50
2889 4 d. Duke Ellington conducting (53×38 *mm*) 45 50
2890 4 d. Duke Ellington 45 50
2891 4 d. Louis Armstrong 45 50
2892 4 d. Louis Armstrong playing trumpet (53×38 *mm*) 45 50
2893 4 d. Charlie "Bird" Parker playing saxophone (53×38 *mm*) 45 50
2894 4 d. Charlie "Bird" Parker 45 50

(*b*) *Famous Theatrical Composers*
2895 4 d. Cole Porter 45 50
a. Sheetlet. Nos. 2895/902 . . . . 3·50
2896 4 d. *Born to Dance* (Cole Porter) (53×38 *mm*) 45 50
2897 4 d. *Porgy and Bess* (George Gershwin) (53×38 *mm*) 45 50
2898 4 d. George Gershwin 45 50
2899 4 d. Rogers and Hammerstein 45 50
2900 4 d. *The King and I* (Rogers and Hammerstein) (53×38 *mm*) . . 45 50
2901 4 d. *West Side Story* (Leonard Bernstein) (53×38 *mm*) 45 50
2902 4 d. Leonard Bernstein 45 50
2887/902 . . . . *Set of* 16 7·00 8·00
MS2903 Two sheets, each 76×106 mm. (a) 25 d. Ella Fitzgerald. (b) 25 d. "Oh How I Hate to Get Up in the Morning" (Irving Berlin) *Set of 2 sheets* 6·00 6·25
Nos. 2887/94 and 2895/902 were each printed together, *se-tenant*, in sheetlets of 8 with enlarged illustrated margins.

(Litho Questa)

1998 (15 Oct). *Ships. T* **290** *and similar multicoloured designs. P* 14.
2904 2 d. Type **290** 20 25
2905 3 d. H.M.S. *Victory* (ship of the line, 1765) 35 40
2906 5 d. *Santa Maria* (Columbus) 60 65
a. Sheetlet. Nos. 2906/11 . . . . 3·50
2907 5 d. *Mary Rose* (galleon) 60 65
2908 5 d. *Mayflower* (Pilgrim Fathers) . . 60 65
2909 5 d. *Ark Royal* (galleon, 1587) 60 65
2910 5 d. H.M.S. *Beagle* (Darwin) 60 65
2911 5 d. H.M.S. *Bounty* (Bligh) 60 65
2912 5 d. H.M.S. *Dreadnought* (battleship) . . 60 65
a. Sheetlet. Nos. 2912/17 . . . . 3·50
2913 5 d. American Truxton Class cruiser . . 60 65
2914 5 d. *Queen Mary* (liner) 60 65
2915 5 d. *Canberra* (liner) 60 65
2916 5 d. *Queen Elizabeth* (liner) 60 65
2917 5 d. *Queen Elizabeth II* (liner) 60 65
2918 10 d. British County Class destroyer . . 1·10 1·25
2919 15 d. Viking longship . . . . . . 1·75 1·90
2904/19 . . . . *Set of* 16 11·50 12·50
MS2920 Two sheets. (a) 70×100 mm. 25 d. *Cutty Sark* (clipper) (41×56 *mm*). (b) 100×70 mm. 25 d. *Sovereign of the Seas* (liner) (56×41 *mm*) *Set of 2 sheets* 6·00 6·25
Nos. 2906/11 and 2912/17 were each printed together, *se-tenant*, in sheetlets of 6.

291 Captain Edward Smith

292 Mahatma Gandhi

1998 (15 Oct). Titanic *Commemoration. T* **291** *and similar designs. Litho. P* 14.
2921 5 d. yellow-brown, black and dull violet-blue 60 65
a. Sheetlet. Nos. 2921/6 . . . . 3·50
2922 5 d. yellow-brown, black & deep violet-blue 60 65
2923 5 d. yellow-brown and black 60 65
2924 5 d. dull violet-blue and black 60 65
2925 5 d. dull mauve and black 60 65
2926 5 d. dull mauve and black 60 65
2921/6 . . . . *Set of* 6 3·50 3·75
MS2927 Three sheets, each 110×85 mm. (a) 25 d. multicoloured. (b) 25 d. sepia and black. (c) 25 d. multicoloured . . . . *Set of 3 sheets* 9·00 9·25
Designs: *Vert*—No. 2921, Type **291**; No. 2922, Mrs. J. J. "Molly" Brown (passenger); No. 2923, Newspaper boy with placard; No. 2924, Benjamin Guggenheim (passenger); No. 2925, Isidor Strauss (passenger); No. 2926, Ida Strauss (passenger). *Horiz*—No. **MS**2927a, *Titanic* on postcard; No. **MS**2927b, *Titanic* sinking; No. **MS**2927c, Wreckage of *Titanic* on seabed.
Nos. 2921/6 were printed together, *se-tenant*, in sheetlets of 6 with enlarged illustrated margins.

(Des M. Leboeuf. Litho Questa)

1998 (29 Oct). 50*th Death Anniv of Mahatma Gandhi. T* **292** *and similar multicoloured designs. P* 14.
2928 10 d. Type **292** . . . . 1·10 1·25
a. Sheetlet. Nos. 2928/31 . . . . 4·25
2929 10 d. Gandhi on Salt March with Mrs. Sarojini Naidu (53×38 *mm*) . . 1·10 1·25
2930 10 d. Gandhi spinning yarn (53×38 *mm*) 1·10 1·25
2931 10 d. Gandhi in 1916 . . . . . . 1·10 1·25
2928/31 . . . . *Set of* 4 4·25 5·00
MS2932 53×71 mm. 25 d. Gandhi writing . . 3·00 3·25
Nos. 2928/31 were printed together, *se-tenant*, in sheetlets of 4 with enlarged illustrated margins.

(Des Diana Catherines. Litho Questa)

1998 (29 Oct). 25*th Death Anniv of Pablo Picasso* (*painter*). *Multicoloured designs as T* **325** *of Dominica. P* 14½.
2933 3 d. "Death of Casagemas" 35 40
2934 5 d. "Seated Woman" (*vert*) 60 65
2935 10 d. "Mother and Child" (*vert*) . . . . 1·10 1·25
2933/5 . . . . *Set of* 3 2·00 2·25
MS2936 102×126 mm. 25 d. "Child playing with toy truck" (*vert*) . . . . 3·00 3·25

(Des D. Miller. Litho Questa)

1998 (29 Oct). *80th Anniv of Royal Air Force. Horiz designs as T* **328** *of Dominica. Multicoloured. P* 14.

2937 5 d. Sepecat Jaguar GR1A (from above) .. 60 65
a. Sheetlet. Nos. 2937/40 .. .. 2·40
2938 5 d. Panavia Tornado GR1A 60 65
2939 5 d. Sepecat Jaguar GR1A (side view) .. 60 65
2940 5 d. BAe Hawk 200 .. .. .. 60 65
2941 5 d. Sepecat Jaguar GR1A firing Sparrow missile 60 65
a. Sheetlet. Nos. 2941/4 .. .. 2·40
2942 5 d. BAe Harrier GR7 firing SNEB rockets 60 65
2943 5 d. Panavia Tornado GR1 firing AIM-9L missile 60 65
2944 5 d. Panavia Tornado GR1 in low level flight 60 65
2945 7 d. Panavia Tornado GR1 (facing left) .. 80 85
a. Sheetlet. Nos. 2945/8 .. .. 3·00
2946 7 d. BAe Hawk T1A 80 85
2947 7 d. Sepecat Jaguar GR1A 80 85
2948 7 d. Panavia Tornado GR1 (facing right) 80 85
2937/48 .. .. *Set of* 12 7·75 8·50
MS2949 Six sheets, each 90×68 mm. (a) 20 d. EF-2000 Eurofighter. (b) 25 d. Bristol F2B Fighter and bird of prey in flight. (c) 25 d. Falcon's head and Bristol F2B Fighter. (d) 25 d. Bristol F2B Fighter and Golden Eagle (bird). (e) 25 d. Lancaster and EF-2000 Eurofighter. (f) 25 d. Lightning and EF-2000 Eurofighter *Set of* 6 *sheets* 17·00 18·00

Nos. 2937/40, 2941/4 and 2945/8 were each printed together, *se-tenant*, in sheetlets of 4.

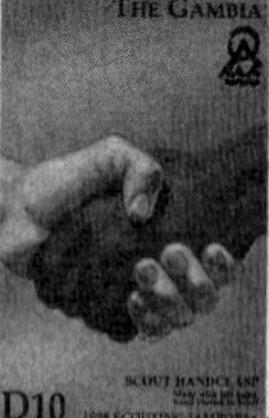

293 Scout Handshake

294 "Mule-drivers from Tetuan"

(Litho Questa)

1998 (29 Oct). *19th World Scout Jamboree, Chile. T* **293** *and similar vert designs. Multicoloured (except No.* **MS**2953). *P* 14.

2950 10 d. Type **293** .. .. .. 1·10 1·25
a. Sheetlet. Nos. 2950/2 .. .. 3·25
2951 10 d. Dinghy sailing .. .. .. 1·10 1·25
2952 10 d. Scout salute .. .. .. 1·10 1·25
2950/2 .. .. *Set of* 3 3·25 3·75
MS2953 47×61 mm. 25 d. Lord Baden-Powell (olive-bistre and black) .. .. .. 3·00 3·25

Nos. 2950/2 were printed together, *se-tenant*, in sheetlets of 3 with illustrated margins.

1998 (29 Oct). *Birth Bicentenary of Eugène Delacroix (painter). T* **294** *and similar multicoloured designs. Litho. P* 14.

2954 4 d. Type **294** 45 50
a. Sheetlet. Nos. 2954/61 .. .. 3·50
2955 4 d. "Encampment of Arab Mule-drivers" 45 50
2956 4 d. "An Orange Seller" 45 50
2957 4 d. "The Banks of the River" 45 50
2958 4 d. "View of Tangier from the Seashore" 45 50
2959 4 d. "Arab Horses fighting in a Stable" .. 45 50
2960 4 d. "Horses at the Trough" 45 50
2961 4 d. "The Combat of Giaour and Hassan" 45 50
2962 4 d. "Turk on a Sofa, Smoking" 45 50
a. Sheetlet. Nos. 2962/9 .. .. 3·50
2963 4 d. "View of Tangier" 45 50
2964 4 d. "The Spanish Coast at Salobrena" .. 45 50
2965 4 d. "The Aissaouas" 45 50
2966 4 d. "The Sea from the Cliffs of Dieppe" .. 45 50
2967 4 d. "The Fanatics of Tangier" 45 50
2968 4 d. "Arab Musicians" 45 50
2969 4 d. "An Arab Camp at Night" 45 50
2954/69 .. .. *Set of* 16 7·00 8·00
MS2970 Two sheets. (a) 100×85 mm. 25 d. "Massacre at Chios". (b) 85×100 mm. 25 d. "Self-portrait" (*vert*) .. .. *Set of* 2 *sheets* 6·00 6·25

Nos. 2954/61 and 2962/8 were printed together in sheetlets of 8, each containing two *se-tenant* horizontal strips of 4 separated by a gutter showing the paintings depicted on Nos. 2956, 2961 or 2965 and 2968.

The captions on the sheet margins for Nos. 2966 and 2967 are transposed in error.

295 Puppy in Stocking

296 Rabbit

(Litho B.D.T.)

1998 (1 Dec). *Christmas. T* **295** *and similar vert designs. Multicoloured. P* 14.

2971 1 d. Type **295** 10 15
2972 2 d. Giraffe in Christmas wreath .. 20 25
2973 3 d. Rainbow Bee Eater (bird) with bauble 35 40
2974 4 d. Deer 45 50
2975 5 d. Fawn 60 65
2976 10 d. Puppy in gift box .. .. .. 1·10 1·25
2971/6 .. .. *Set of* 6 2·75 3·00
MS2977 Two sheets, each 105×76 mm. (a) 25 d. Brown Classic Tabby. (b) 25 d. Basset Hound and Rough Collie .. .. *Set of* 2 *sheets* 6·00 6·25

(Des Y. Lee. Litho Questa)

1999 (4 Jan). *Chinese New Year ("Year of the Rabbit"). T* **296** *similar horiz designs. Multicoloured. P* 14½.

2978 3 d. Type **296** 35 40
a. Sheetlet. Nos. 2978/81 .. .. 1·40
2979 3 d. Rabbit looking over shoulder .. 35 40
2980 3 d. Rabbit facing left 35 40
2981 3 d. Rabbit running 35 40
2978/81 .. .. *Set of* 4 1·40 1·60
MS2982 73×103 mm. 10 d. Rabbit (42×28 *mm*). P 14 .. .. 1·10 1·25

Nos. 2978/81 were printed together, *se-tenant*, in sheetlets of 4.

STAMP BOOKLETS

1979 (17 Oct). *Tenth Anniv of Moon Landing. Multicoloured cover, 165×93 mm, showing "Apollo 11" on the front and Abuko Satellite Earth Station on the back. Pane attached by selvedge.*

SB1 4 d. 26, booklet containing *se-tenant* pane of 6 (No. 427a) and pane of 1 (No. 430a) .. .. 2·75

The cover of No. SB1 is folded five times "concertina fashion" and when opened out measures 165×465 mm.

1983 (12 Dec). *Bicentenary of Manned Flight. Bistre-brown and bright scarlet cover, 121×81 mm, showing Bicentenary of Manned Flight logo on front and advertisement on reverse. Stitched.*

SB2 11 d. 20, booklet containing *se-tenant* panes of 4 (Nos. 522a, 524a) and pane of 1 (No. 526a) 5·75

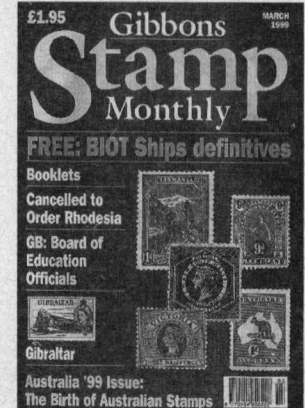

Ghana
(*formerly* Gold Coast)

GOLD COAST

Gold Coast originally consisted of coastal forts, owned by the Royal African Company, trading with the interior. In 1821, due to raids by the Ashanti king, the British Government took over the forts, together with some of the hinterland, and the Gold Coast was placed under the Governor of Sierra Leone.

The administration was handed back to a merchantile company in 1828, but the forts returned to British Government rule in 1843. The colony was reconstituted by Royal Charter on 24 July, 1874, and at that time also included the settlement at Lagos which became a separate colony in January, 1886.

Following the end of the final Ashanti War the whole of the territory was annexed in September 1901.

A postal service was established at Cape Coast Castle in 1853. There is no record of British stamps being officially issued in the Colony before 1875, apart from those used on board the ships of the West African Squadron, but examples do, however, exist cancelled by Gold Coast postmarks.

CROWN COLONY

PRICES FOR STAMPS ON COVER TO 1945	
Nos. 1/3	*from* × 15
Nos. 4/8	*from* × 20
Nos. 9/10	*from* × 10
Nos. 11/20	*from* × 25
Nos. 22/5	—
Nos. 26/34	*from* × 10
Nos. 35/6	*from* × 20
Nos. 38/69	*from* × 6
Nos. 70/98	*from* × 3
Nos. 100/2	—
Nos. 103/12	*from* × 5
Nos. 113/16	*from* × 3
Nos. 117/19	*from* × 4
Nos. 120/32	*from* × 3
Nos. D1/4	*from* × 8

1

ONE
PENNY.

(2)

(Typo D.L.R.)

1875 (1 July). *Wmk Crown CC. P* 12½.
1 1 1d. blue .. £425 80·00
2 4d. magenta .. £400 £110
3 6d. orange .. £600 65·00

1876–84. *Wmk Crown CA. P* 14.
4 1 ½d. olive-yellow (1879) .. 48·00 22·00
5 1d. blue .. 14·00 6·50
a. Bisected (½d.) (on cover) (1884) .. † £3000
w. Wmk inverted .. £150 75·00
6 2d. green (1879) .. 60·00 9·00
a. Bisected (1d.) (on cover) (1884) .. † £2500
b. Quartered (½d.) (on cover) (1884) .. † £4000
7 4d. magenta .. £150 6·00
a. Bisected (2d.) (on cover) (1884) .. † £4500
b. Quartered (1d.) (on cover) (1884) .. † £6000
w. Wmk inverted .. £300
8 6d. orange .. 90·00 18·00
a. Bisected (3d.) (on cover) (1884) .. † £5500
b. Sixth (1d.) (on cover) (1884) .. † £7000

During 1884 some values were in short supply and the use of bisects and other divided stamps is known as follows:
No. 5a. Used as part of 2½d. rate from Accra and Quittah
No. 6a. Used as 1d. rate from Addah, Cape Coast Castle, Quittah, Salt Pond, Secondee and Winnebah
No. 6b. Used as part of 2½d. rate from Cape Coast Castle
No. 7a. Used as 2d. or as part of 2½d. rate from Quittah
No. 7b. Used as 1d. rate from Appam, Axim, Cape Coast Castle and Winnebah
No. 8a. Used as 3d. rate from Secondee
No. 8b. Used as 1d. rate from Cape Coast Castle and Winnebah.

Examples of bisects used on piece are worth about 10% of the price quoted for those on cover.

1883 (May)? *No. 7 surch locally.*
8c 1 "1d." on 4d. magenta

1883. *Wmk Crown CA. P* 14.
9 1 ½d. olive-yellow (January) .. £150 60·00
10 1d. blue (May) .. £850 60·00

PENNY

Short "P" and distorted "E" (Pl 1 R. 5/6) ("P" repaired for Pl 2)

1884 (Aug)–**91.** *Wmk Crown CA. P* 14.
11 1 ½d. green .. 1·75 65
a. Dull green .. 1·50 60
w. Wmk inverted .. 75·00
12 1d. rose-carmine .. 2·25 50
a. Carmine .. 2·25 50
b. Bisected (½d.) (on cover) .. † £3500
c. Short "P" and distorted "E" .. 55·00
13 1 2d. grey .. 7·50 3·50
aw. Wmk inverted .. £120 £120
b. Slate .. 1·50 50
c. Bisected (1d.) (on cover) .. † £4000
d. Quartered (½d.) (on cover)
14 2½d. ultramarine and orange (13.3.91) .. 2·75 50
15 3d. olive-yellow (9.89) .. 6·00 4·50
a. Olive .. 5·50 4·25
16 4d. deep mauve (3.85) .. 5·00 1·25
a. Rosy mauve .. 7·50 3·00
17 6d. orange (1.89) .. 4·75 4·50
a. Orange-brown .. 4·75 4·50
b. Bisected (3d.) (on cover)
18 1s. violet (1888) .. 29·00 12·00
a. Bright mauve .. 3·50 1·25
19 2s. yellow-brown (1888) .. 80·00 35·00
a. Deep brown .. 32·00 15·00
11/19*a* .. *Set of* 9 50·00 25·00
14/15, 18/19 Optd "Specimen" .. *Set of* 4 £150

During 1884 to 1886 and in 1889 some values were in short supply and the use of bisects and other divided stamps is known as follows:
No. 12b. Used as part of 2½d. rate from Cape Coast Castle
No. 13c. Used as 1d. or as part of 2d. rate from Cape Coast Castle, Chamah, Dixcove and Elmina
No. 13d. Used as part of 2½d. rate from Cape Coast Castle
No. 17b. Used as 3d. from Appam

1889 (Mar). *No. 17 surch with T* **2**.
20 1 1d. on 6d. orange .. £100 48·00
a. Surch double .. † £2750

In some sheets examples may be found with the bar and "PENNY" spaced 8 mm, the normal spacing being 7 mm.

USED HIGH VALUES. Until the introduction of airmail in 1929 there was no postal use for values over 10s. Post Offices did, however, apply postal cancellations to high value stamps required for telegram fees.

3

4

1889 (Sept)–**94.** *Wmk Crown CA. P* 14.
22 3 5s. dull mauve and blue .. 60·00 12·00
23 10s. dull mauve and red .. 75·00 15·00
a. Dull mauve and carmine .. £450 £160
24 20s. green and red .. £3250
25 20s. dull mauve and black/*red* (4.94) .. £150 35·00
w. Wmk inverted .. £200 75·00
22/5 Optd "Specimen" .. *Set of* 4 £450

No. 24 was withdrawn from sale in April 1893 when a large part of the stock was stolen. No 20s. stamps were available until the arrival of the replacement printing a year later.

1898 (May)–**1902.** *Wmk Crown CA. P* 14.
26 3 ½d. dull mauve and green .. 1·75 75
27 1d. dull mauve and rose .. 1·75 40
aw. Wmk inverted .. — 75·00
27*b* 4 2d. dull mauve and orange-red (1902) 35·00 90·00
28 3 2½d. dull mauve and ultramarine .. 4·25 4·00
29 4 3d. dull mauve and orange .. 4·50 1·25
30 6d. dull mauve and violet .. 5·50 1·25
31 3 1s. green and black (1899) .. 8·50 9·50
32 2s. green and carmine .. 9·00 17·00
33 5s. green and mauve (1900) .. 48·00 26·00
34 10s. green and brown (1900) .. £130 50·00
26/34 .. *Set of* 10 £225 £180
26/34 Optd "Specimen" .. *Set of* 10 £180

1901 (6 Oct). *Nos. 28 and 30 surch with T* **2**.
35 1d. on 2½d. dull mauve and ultramarine .. 1·75 3·00
a. "ONE" omitted .. £1000
36 1d. on 6d. dull mauve and violet .. 1·75 3·00
a. "ONE" omitted .. £250 £550

6

7

8

1902. *Wmk Crown CA. P* 14.
38 6 ½d. dull purple and green (Aug) .. 75 40
39 1d. dull purple and carmine (May) .. 1·00 15
w. Wmk inverted .. — 42·00
40 7 2d. dull purple and orange-red (Apr) .. 14·00 7·00
w. Wmk inverted
41 6 2½d. dull purple and ultramarine (Aug) 4·50 9·00
42 7 3d. dull purple and orange (Aug) .. 2·75 1·50
43 6d. dull purple and violet (Aug) .. 2·75 1·50
w. Wmk inverted .. — 55·00
44 6 1s. green and black (Aug) .. 9·00 3·00
45 2s. green and carmine (Aug) .. 12·00 16·00
46 5s. green and mauve (Aug) .. 32·00 75·00
47 10s. green and brown (Aug) .. 48·00 £120
48 20s. purple and black/*red* (Aug) .. £130 £170
38/48 .. *Set of* 11 £225 £350
38/48 Optd "Specimen" .. *Set of* 11 £200

Examples of Nos. 45/8 are known showing a forged Accra postmark dated "25 MAR 1902".

1904–06. *Wmk Mult Crown CA. Ordinary paper* (½d. *to* 6d.) *or chalk-surfaced paper* (2s. 6d.).
49 6 ½d. dull purple and green (3.06) .. 2·50 5·50
50 1d. dull purple and carmine (10.04) .. 4·50 20
a. Chalk-surfaced paper (5.06) .. 6·00 1·75
w. Wmk inverted
51 7 2d. dull purple and orange-red (11.04) 4·00 50
a. Chalk-surfaced paper (8.06) .. 18·00 1·50
52 6 2½d. dull purple and ultramarine (6.06) 45·00 35·00
53 7 3d. dull purple and orange (8.05) .. 48·00 4·50
a. Chalk-surfaced paper (4.06) .. 11·00 60
54 6d. dull purple and violet (3.06) .. 42·00 1·75
a. Chalk-surfaced paper (9.06) .. 38·00 1·25
57 2s. 6d. green & yell (3.06) (Optd S. £45) 27·00 95·00
49/57 .. *Set of* 7 £120 £120

1907–13. *Wmk Mult Crown CA. Ordinary paper* (½d. *to* 2½d. *and* 2s.) *or chalk-surfaced paper* (3d. *to* 1s., 2s. 6d., 5s.). *P* 14.
59 6 ½d. dull green (5.07) .. 2·00 30
a. Blue-green (1909) .. 4·75 1·25
60 1d. red (2.07) .. 4·25 30
61 7 2d. greyish slate (4.09) .. 2·00 40
62 6 2½d. blue (4.07) .. 3·50 1·75
w. Wmk inverted
63 7 3d. purple/*yellow* (16.4.09) .. 6·00 55
64 6d. dull and deep purple (12.08) .. 13·00 55
a. Dull and bright purple (1911) .. 3·50 3·50
65 6 1s. black/*green* (10.09) .. 6·50 50
66 2s. purple and blue/*blue* (1910) .. 5·00 16·00
a. Chalk-surfaced paper (1912) .. 14·00 16·00
67 7 2s. 6d. blue and red/*blue* (1911) .. 25·00 65·00
68 6 5s. green and red/*yellow* (1913) .. 55·00 £130
59/68 .. *Set of* 10 £100 £190
59/68 Optd "Specimen" .. *Set of* 10 £225

A 10s. green and red on green, and a 20s. purple and black on red, both Type **6**, were prepared for use but not issued. Both exist overprinted "Specimen" (*Price for* 10s. *in this condition* £300).

(Typo D.L.R.)

1908 (Nov). *Wmk Mult Crown CA. P* 14.
69 8 1d. red (Optd S. £45) .. 2·25 10

9

10

11

(Typo D.L.R.)

1913–21. *Die I. Wmk Mult Crown CA. Chalk-surfaced paper* (3d. *to* 20s.). *P* 14.
70 9 ½d. green .. 1·25 1·00
a. Yellow-green (1916) .. 1·90 1·25
72 10 1d. red .. 60 10
a. Scarlet (1917) .. 75 50
74 11 2d. grey .. 1·50 2·50
a. Slate-grey (1920) .. 7·50 6·50
w. Wmk inverted .. † £110
76 9 2½d. bright blue .. 3·75 90
x. Wmk reversed .. † £110
77 11 3d. purple/*yellow* (8.15) (Optd S. £32) 1·25 50
aw. Wmk inverted .. — 55·00
b. White back (9.13) .. 30 40
c. On orange-buff (1919) .. 3·25 6·50
cw. Wmk inverted
d. On buff (1920)
e. Die II. *On pale yellow* (1921) .. 26·00 5·00
78 6d. dull and bright purple .. 2·00 2·25
79 9 1s. black/*green* .. 1·25 1·25
a. Wmk sideways
bw. Wmk inverted
c. On blue-green, olive back (1916) (Optd S. £32) .. 3·50 75
cw. Wmk inverted
d. On emerald back (1920) (Optd S. £32) .. 2·00 2·00
e. Die II. *On emerald back* (1921) (Optd S. £38) .. 1·50 50
ew. Wmk inverted
80 2s. purple and blue/*blue* .. 7·00 2·00
aw. Wmk inverted .. — £120
b. Die II (1921) .. £140 65·00
81 11 2s. 6d. black and red/*blue* .. 5·00 13·00
a. Die II (1921) .. 22·00 35·00
82 9 5s. green & red/*yell* (1916) (Optd S. £42) 6·50 45·00
a. White back (10.13) .. 8·50 48·00
b. On orange-buff (1919) .. 65·00 70·00
c. On buff (1920)
d. On pale yellow (1921) .. 95·00 £120
e. Die II. *On pale yellow* (1921) .. 29·00 £120
ew. Wmk inverted .. £130
83 10s. green and red/*green* .. 45·00 80·00
a. On blue-green, olive back (1916) .. 18·00 65·00
b. On emerald back (1921) .. 30·00 95·00
84 20s. purple and black/*red* .. £120 80·00
70/84 .. *Set of* 12 £150 £190
70/6, 77*b*, 78/81, 82*a*/4 Optd "Specimen" *Set of* 12 £250

The 10s. and 20s. were withdrawn locally from September 1920 and, in common with other Gold Coast stamps, were not available to stamp dealers from the Crown Agents in London.

WAR TAX

ONE PENNY

(12)

13 King George V and Christiansborg Castle

1918 (17 June). *Surch with T* **12**.
85 10 1d. on 1d. red (Optd S. £50) .. 30 40

1921–24. *Die I* (15s., £2) *or Die II* (*others*). *Wmk Mult Script CA. Chalk-surfaced paper* (6d. *to* £2). *P* 14.
86 9 ½d. green .. 30 30
87 10 1d. chocolate-brown (1922) .. 30 10
88 11 1½d. red (1922) .. 90 10
89 2d. grey .. 90 30

90 **9** 2½d. yellow-orange (1922) .. .. .. 50 8·00
91 **11** 3d. bright blue (1922) 90 60
94 6d. dull and bright purple .. .. .. 90 3·00
95 **9** 1s. black/*emerald* (1924) .. .. 2·00 3·00
96 2s. purple and blue/*blue* (1923) .. .. 2·50 3·25
97 **11** 2s. 6d. black and red/*blue* (1924) .. 5·50 15·00
98 **9** 5s. green and red/*pale yellow* (1924) .. 9·00 40·00
100 **11** 15s. dull purple and green (Die I) .. £110 £275
a. Die II (1924) (Optd S. £100) .. £100 £250
102 £2 green and orange (Die I) £350 £800
86/100a .. .. *Set of* 12 £110 £275
86/102 Optd "Specimen" .. .. *Set of* 13 £350

The Duty plate for the 1½d., 15s. and £2 has the words "GOLD COAST" in distinctly larger letters.

Examples of Nos. 100/a and 102 are known showing parts of forged Accra postmarks. These are dated "3 MAY 44" and "8 MAY 44", but are invariably positioned so that the year date is not shown.

(Des W. Palmer. Photo Harrison)

1928 (1 Aug). *Wmk Mult Script CA. P* 13½×15.
103 **13** ½d. blue-green 50 40
104 1d. red-brown 50 10
105 1½d. scarlet .. .. 50 1·50
106 2d. slate 50 20
107 2½d. orange-yellow .. .. .. 1·25 3·50
108 3d. bright blue 55 40
109 6d. black and purple 75 40
110 1s. black and red-orange .. .. 1·75 75
111 2s. black and bright violet .. .. 14·00 4·00
112 5s. carmine and sage-green .. .. 45·00 38·00
103/12 .. .. *Set of* 10 60·00 45·00
103/12 Optd "Specimen" .. .. *Set of* 10 £180

1935 (6 May). *Silver Jubilee. As Nos.* 91/4 *of Antigua, but printed by B.W. P* 11 × 12.
113 1d. ultramarine and grey-black 60 50
a. Extra flagstaff £120
b. Short extra flagstaff £120
c. Lightning conductor .. .. .. 85·00
d. Flagstaff on right-hand turret .. £130
114 3d. brown and deep blue .. .. .. 3·00 6·00
a. Extra flagstaff £120
c. Lightning conductor £100
115 6d. green and indigo .. .. .. 4·25 9·50
a. Extra flagstaff £120
b. Short extra flagstaff £190
c. Lightning conductor £100
d. Flagstaff on right-hand turret .. £225
116 1s. slate and purple .. .. .. 3·25 9·50
a. Extra flagstaff £130
b. Short extra flagstaff £150
c. Lightning conductor £120
113/16 .. .. *Set of* 4 10·00 23·00
113/16 Perf "Specimen" .. .. *Set of* 4 85·00

For illustrations of plate varieties see Catalogue Introduction.

1937 (12 May). *Coronation. As Nos.* 95/7 *of Antigua. P* 11×11½.
117 1d. buff .. .. 1·00 1·25
118 2d. slate .. .. 1·10 2·75
119 3d. blue .. .. 1·25 1·25
117/19 .. .. *Set of* 3 3·00 4·75
117/19 Perf "Specimen" .. .. *Set of* 3 50·00

14

15 King George VI and Christiansborg Castle, Accra

(Recess B.W.)

1938 (1 Apr)–**44**. *Wmk Mult Script CA. P* 11½×12 (1s. 3d., 10s.) *or* 12 (*others*).
120 **14** ½d. green .. .. 1·75 90
a. Perf 12×11½ (1940) 40 50
121 1d. red-brown .. .. 1·75 30
a. Perf 12×11½ (1939) 40 10
122 1½d. scarlet .. .. 1·75 1·00
a. Perf 12×11½ (1940) 40 50
123 2d. slate .. .. 1·75 70
a. Perf 12×11½ (1940) 40 10
124 3d. blue .. .. 1·75 45
a. Perf 12×11½ (1940) 40 35
125 4d. magenta .. .. 2·25 2·00
a. Perf 12×11½ (1942) .. .. 70 1·25
126 6d. purple .. .. 2·50 45
a. Perf 12×11½ (1939) 70 20
127 9d. orange .. .. 2·50 90
a. Perf 12×11½ (1944) 90 55
128 **15** 1s. black and olive-green .. .. 4·50 1·75
a. Perf 11½×12 (1940) .. .. 1·00 50
129 1s. 3d. brown & turquoise-bl (12.4.41) 2·00 40
130 2s. blue and violet .. .. .. 14·00 8·50
a. Perf 11½×12 (1940) .. .. 4·50 8·00
131 5s. olive-green & carmine .. .. 25·00 11·00
a. Perf 11½×12 (1940) .. .. 8·00 11·00
132 10s. black and violet (7.40) .. .. 7·00 16·00
120/32 .. .. *Set of* 13 24·00 35·00
120/32 Perf "Specimen" .. .. *Set of* 13 £170

All values except 1s. 3d. and 10s. exist in two perforations: (*a*) Line-perforated 12, from early printings; (*b*) Comb-perforated 12×11.8 (vertical design) or 11.8×12 (horiz design) from later printings. The 1s. 3d. and 10s. only exist comb-perforated 11.8×12.

The ½d. and 1d. values exist in coils constructed from normal sheets.

1946 (14 Oct). *Victory. As Nos.* 110/11 *of Antigua. P* 13½×14.
133 2d. slate-violet .. .. 11·00 2·25
a. Perf 13½ 10 10
134 4d. claret .. .. 1·50 2·75
a. Perf 13½ .. .. 75 2·75
133/4 Perf "Specimen" .. .. *Set of* 2 50·00

16 Northern Territories Mounted Constabulary

17 Christiansborg Castle

(Des B. A. Johnston (1½d.), M. Ziorkley and B. A. Abban (2d.), P.O. draughtsman (2½d.), C. Gomez (1s.), M. Ziorkley (10s.); others from photographs. Recess B.W.)

1948 (1 July). *T* **16/17** *and similar designs. Wmk Mult Script CA. P* 12 × 11½ (*vert*) *or* 11½ × 12 (*horiz*).
135 ½d. emerald-green 20 30
136 1d. blue 15 15
137 1½d. scarlet .. .. 1·25 70
138 2d. purple-brown 55 10
139 2½d. yellow-brown and scarlet .. .. 2·00 2·50
140 3d. light blue .. .. 4·00 45
141 4d. magenta .. .. 3·50 1·25
142 6d. black and orange 30 30
143 1s. black and vermilion 60 30
144 2s. sage-green and magenta .. .. 3·00 2·00
145 5s. purple and black .. .. .. 20·00 4·50
146 10s. black and sage-green .. .. 8·00 4·50
135/46 .. .. *Set of* 12 40·00 15·00
135/46 Perf "Specimen" .. .. *Set of* 12 £225

Designs: *Horiz*—1½d. Emblem of Joint Provincial Council; 2½d. Map showing position of Gold Coast; 3d. Nsuta manganese mine; 4d. Lake Bosumtwi; 1s. Breaking cocoa pods; 2s. Gold Coast Regt Trooping the Colour; 5s. Surfboats. *Vert*—2d. Talking drums; 6d. Cocoa farmer; 10s. Forest.

Nos. 135/6 exist in coils constructed from normal sheets.

1948 (20 Dec). *Royal Silver Wedding. As Nos.* 112/13 *of Antigua.*
147 1½d. scarlet 30 30
148 10s. grey-olive .. .. 12·00 17·00

1949 (10 Oct). *75th Anniv of U.P.U. As Nos.* 114/17 *of Antigua.*
149 2d. red-brown 30 30
150 2½d. orange .. .. 2·00 1·75
151 3d. deep blue 50 70
152 1s. blue-green 50 50
149/52 .. .. *Set of* 4 3·00 3·00

28 Northern Territories Mounted Constabulary

(Recess B.W.)

1952 (19 Dec)–**54**. *Designs previously used for King George VI issue, but with portrait of Queen Elizabeth II, as in T* **28**. *Portrait faces left on* ½*d.,* 4*d.,* 6*d.,* 1*s. and* 5*s. Wmk Mult Script CA. P* 12 × 11½ (*vert*) *or* 11½ × 12 (*horiz*).
153 ½d. yellow-brown and scarlet (1.4.53) .. 10 10
a. Bistre-brown and scarlet (7.4.54) .. 10 20
154 1d. deep blue (1.3.54) 30 10
155 1½d. emerald-green (1.4.53) .. .. 30 1·25
156 2d. chocolate (1.3.54) 30 10
157 2½d. scarlet 35 35
158 3d. magenta (1.4.53) 50 10
159 4d. blue (1.4.53) 30 30
160 6d. black and orange (1.3.54) 30 15
161 1s. black and orange-red (1.3.54) .. 30 15
162 2s. brown-olive and carmine (1.3.54) .. 11·00 85
163 5s. purple and black (1.3.54) .. .. 17·00 5·00
164 10s. black and olive-green (1.3.54) .. 14·00 12·00
153/64 .. .. *Set of* 12 40·00 18·00

Designs: *Horiz*—½d. Map showing position of Gold Coast; 1d. Christiansborg Castle; 1½d. Emblem of Joint Provincial Council; 3d. Nsuta manganese mine; 4d. Lake Bosumtwi; 1s. Breaking cocoa pods; 2s. Gold Coast Regt Trooping the Colour; 5s. Surfboats. *Vert*—2d. Talking drums; 6d, Cocoa farmer; 10s. Forest.

Nos. 153*a*/4 exist in coils constructed from normal sheets.

1953 (2 June). *Coronation. As No.* 120 *of Antigua, but ptd by B.W.*
165 2d. black and sepia 60 10

Gold Coast became the Dominion of Ghana on 6 March 1957.

GHANA

DOMINION

***CANCELLED REMAINDERS.** In 1961 remainders of some issues of 1957 to 1960 were put on the market cancelled-to-order in such a way as to be indistinguishable from genuine postally used copies for all practical purposes. Our used quotations which are indicated by an asterisk are the same for cancelled-to-order or postally used copies.

29 Dr. Kwame Nkrumah, Palm-nut Vulture and Map of Africa

GHANA
INDEPENDENCE
6TH MARCH,
1957.
(30)

(Photo Harrison)

1957 (6 Mar). *Independence. Wmk Mult Script CA. P* 14 × 14½.
166 **29** 2d. scarlet 10 10
167 2½d. green 10 15
168 4d. brown 10 15
169 1s. 3d. deep blue 15 15
166/9 .. .. *Set of* 4 40 45

1957 (6 Mar)–**58**. *Nos.* 153*a*/64 *of Gold Coast optd as T* **30**.
170 ½d. bistre-brown and scarlet 10 10
a. Olive-brown and scarlet 10 10
171 1d. deep blue (R.) 10 10
172 1½d. emerald-green 10 10
173 2d. chocolate (26.5.58) 30 30
174 2½d. scarlet (26.5.58) .. .. .. 1·00 1·25
175 3d. magenta 30 10
176 4d. blue (26.5.58) .. .. .. 3·75 6·00
177 6d. black and orange (R.) 10 10
a. Opt double .. .. † £275
178 1s. black and orange-red 10 10
179 2s. brown-olive and carmine 60 10
180 5s. purple and black 75 10
181 10s. black and olive-green 75 60
170/81 .. .. *Set of* 12 7·00 7·50

Nos. 173/4 and 176 were officially issued on 26 May 195 although, in error, small quantities were sold at certain post office when the rest of the set appeared.

Nos. 170 and 171 exist in coils constructed from normal sheets.

31 Viking Ship

(Des W. Wind. Recess E. A. Wright Bank Note Co., Philadelphia

1957 (27 Dec). *Inauguration of Black Star Shipping Line. T* 3 *and similar horiz designs. No wmk. P* 12.
182 2½d. emerald-green 70 2
a. Imperf between (vert pair) £350
b. Imperf between (horiz pair) £350
183 1s. 3d. deep blue .. .. 1·00 1·2
a. Imperf horiz (vert pair) £400
184 5s. bright purple .. .. 1·50 3·0
a. Imperf vert (horiz pair) £475
182/4 .. .. *Set of* 3 2·75 4·0

Designs:—1s. 3d. Galleon; 5s. M.V. *Volta River*.

PRINTERS. Nos. 185/**MS**568 were printed in photogravure b Harrison & Sons *except where otherwise stated.*

34 Ambassador Hotel, Accra

35 Ghana Coat of Arms

1958 (6 Mar). *First Anniv of Independence. T* **34/5** *and simila designs. Wmk Mult Script CA. P* 14½ × 14 (2*s.*) *or* 14 × 14½ (*others*).
185 ½d. black, red, yellow, green and carmine .. 10 1
186 2½d. black, red, green and yellow 10 1
187 1s. 3d. black, red, yellow, green and blue .. 30 1
188 2s. red, yellow, blue, green, brown and black 45 3
185/8 .. .. *Set of* 4 75 4

Designs: *Horiz as T* **34**—2½d. State Opening of Parliament 1s. 3d. National Monument.

38 Map showing the Independent African States

39 Map of Africa and Flaming Torch

(Des R. Milton)

1958 (15 Apr). *First Conference of Independent African States Accra. Wmk Mult Script CA. P* 13½ × 14½ (2½*d.,* 3*d*) *o* 14½ × 13½ (*others*).
189 **38** 2½d. black, bistre and bright carmine-red 10 10
190 3d. black, bistre, brown and bright green 10 10
191 **39** 1s. black, yellow, red and dull blue .. 20 10
192 2s. 6d. black, yellow, red and dull violet 40 35
189/92 .. .. *Set of* 4 60 40

40 Palm-nut Vulture over Globe
41 Bristol 175 Britannia 309 Airliner

(Des M. Goaman (2½d., 2s. 6d.), R. Milton (1s. 3d.), W. Wind (2s.))

1958 (15 July). *Inauguration of Ghana Airways. T* **40/1** *and similar designs. Wmk Mult Script CA. P* 15 × 14 (2s. 6d.) *or* 14 × 15 (*others*).

193	2½d. black, yellow-bistre & rose-carmine	45	10
194	1s. 3d. multicoloured	90	20
195	2s. multicoloured	1·00	55
196	2s. 6d. black and bistre	1·00	95
193/6	*Set of* 4	3·00	1·60

Designs: *Horiz* (*as T* **41**)—2s. Boeing 377 Stratocruiser and Yellow-nosed Albatross. (*As T* **40**)—2s. 6d. Palm-nut Vulture and Vickers VC-10 aircraft.

PRIME MINISTER'S VISIT, U.S.A. AND CANADA

(44)

45

1958 (18 July). *Prime Minister's Visit to the United States and Canada. Nos.* 166/9 *optd with T* **44**.

197	**29**	2d. scarlet	10	10
198		2½d. green	10	10
199		4d. brown	10	15
200		1s. 3d. deep blue	15	25
197/200		*Set of* 4	30	45

(Des W. Wind)

1958 (24 Oct). *United Nations Day. Wmk Mult Script CA. P* 14 × 14½.

201	**45**	2½d. purple-brown, green and black	10	10
202		1s. 3d. purple-brown, blue and black	20	10
203		2s. 6d. purple-brown, violet and black	25	35
201/3		*Set of* 3	40	40

46 Dr. Nkrumah and Lincoln Statue, Washington
47

(Des M. Goaman)

1959 (12 Feb). *150th Birth Anniv of Abraham Lincoln. W* **47**. *P* 14 × 14½.

204	**46**	2½d. pink and deep purple	10	10
205		1s. 3d. light blue and blue	15	10
206		2s. 6d. orange-yellow & dp olive-green	20	20
204/6		*Set of* 3	30	30
MS206*a*		102 × 77 mm. Nos. 204/6. Imperf	55	1·75

48 Kente Cloth and Traditional Symbols

(Des Mrs. T. Sutherland (½d.), M. Karoly (2½d.), K. Antubam (1s. 3d.), A. M. Medina (2s.))

1959 (6 Mar). *Second Anniv of Independence. T* **48** *and similar multicoloured designs. W* **47**. *P* 14½ × 14 (2s.) *or* 14 × 14½ (*others*).

207	½d. Type **48**	10	10
208	2½d. Talking drums and elephant-horn blower	10	10
209	1s. 3d. "Symbol of Greeting" (*vert*)	15	10
210	2s. Map of Africa, Ghana flag and palms	30	1·00
207/10	*Set of* 4	50	1·10

52 Globe and Flags

(Des Mrs. H. Potter)

1959 (15 Apr). *Africa Freedom Day. W* **47** (*sideways*). *P* 14½ × 14.

211	**52**	2½d. multicoloured	15	10
212		8½d. multicoloured	15	20

53 "God's Omnipotence"
54 Nkrumah Statue, Accra

55 Ghana Timber
56 Volta River

65*a* Red-fronted Gazelle

Two Types of ½d. and 3d:

I. Inscr "GOD'S OMNIPOTENCE"
II. Inscr "GYE NYAME"

(Des Mrs. T. Sutherland (½d., 3d.), Ghana Information Bureau (source of 1d. and 2d.), O. Haulkland (1½d.), A. Medina (2½d., 4d.), M. Goaman (6d., 1s. 3d., 2s. 6d.), W. Wind (11d., 1s., 2s., 5s.), W. H. Brown (10s.), M. Shamir (£1)).

1959 (5 Oct)–**61**. *T* **53/6**, **65***a*, *and similar multicoloured designs. W* **47** (*sideways on horiz designs*). *P* 11½ × 12 (½d.), 12 × 11½ (1d.), 14 × 14½ (1½d., 11d., 1s., 2s. *and* 5s.), 14 × 15 (10s.) *or* 14½ × 14 (*others*). (*a*) *Postage.*

213	½d. Type **53** (I)	10	10
	a. Type II (29.4.61)	30	10
214	1d. Type **54**	10	10
215	1½d. Type **55**	10	10
216	2d. Type **56**	10	10
217	2½d. Cocoa bean	10	10
218	3d. "God's Omnipotence" (I)	10	10
	a. Type II (29.4.61)	30	10
219	4d. Diamond and Mine	4·50	65
220	6d. Red-crowned Bishop	50	10
	a. Green (flag) omitted	65·00	
221	11d. Golden Spider Lily	25	10
222	1s. Shell Ginger	25	10
223	2s. 6d. Great Blue Turaco	2·25	15
224	5s. Tiger Orchid	5·50	50
225	10s. Jewel Cichlid	1·50	70
225*a*	£1 Type **65***a* (29.4.61)	12·00	4·75
	(*b*) *Air*		
226	1s. 3d. Pennant-winged Nightjar	2·50	10
227	2s. Crowned Cranes	1·75	10
213/27	*Set of* 16	28·00	6·00

Nos. 217/224 and 226/7 are as Types **55/6**, the 11d., 1s., 5s. and 2s. (air) being vertical and the remainder horizontal. No. 225 is as Type **65***a*.

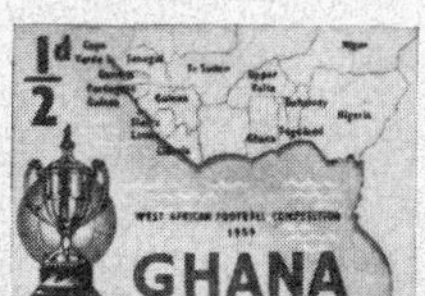

68 Gold Cup and West African Map

(Des K. Lehmann (½d., 3d.), M. & G. Shamir (1d.), W. Wind (8d.), and K. Antubam (2s. 6d.))

1959 (15 Oct). *West African Football Competition*, 1959. *T* **68** *and similar multicoloured designs. W* **47** (*sideways on horiz designs*). *P* 14 × 14½ (1d., 2s. 6d) *or* 14½ × 14 (*others*).

228	½d. Type **68**	10	10*
229	1d. Footballers (*vert*)	10	10*
230	3d. Goalkeeper saving ball	15	10*
231	8d. Forward attacking goal	70	15*
232	2s. 6d. "Kwame Nkrumah" Gold Cup (*vert*)	1·00	15*
228/32	*Set of* 5	1·75	40*

73 The Duke of Edinburgh and Arms of Ghana

(Des A. S. B. New)

1959 (24 Nov). *Visit of the Duke of Edinburgh to Ghana. W* **47** (*sideways*). *P* 15 × 14.

233	**73**	3d. black and magenta	30	10*

74 Ghana Flag and Talking Drums
75 Ghana Flag and U.N. Emblem

(Des K. Antubam (2s. 6d.), A. Medina (others))

1959 (10 Dec). *United Nations Trusteeship Council. T* **74/5** *and similar multicoloured designs. W* **47** (*sideways on* 3d.). *P* 14½ × 14 (3d.) *or* 14 × 14½ (*others*).

234	3d. Type **74**	10	10*
235	6d. Type **75**	10	10*
236	1s. 3d. Ghana flag and U.N. emblem (*vert*)	30	15*
237	2s. 6d. "Totem Pole" (*vert*)	40	15*
234/7	*Set of* 4	75	45*

78 Eagles in Flight
79 Fireworks

(Des A. Medina (½d.), M. Goaman (3d.), W. Wind (1s. 3d., 2s.))

1960 (6 Mar). *Third Anniv of Independence. T* **78/9** *and similar vert designs. Multicoloured. W* **47**. *P* 14 × 14½.

238	½d. Type **78**	10	10*
239	3d. Type **79**	10	10*
240	1s. 3d. "Third Anniversary"	30	10*
241	2s. "Ship of State"	30	15*
238/41	*Set of* 4	70	30*

82 "A" of National Flags

(Des W. Wind)

1960 (15 Apr). *Africa Freedom Day. T* **82** *and similar horiz designs. Multicoloured. W* **47** (*sideways*). *P* 14½ × 14.

242	3d. Type **82**	10	10*
243	6d. Letter "f"	20	10*
244	1s. Letter "d"	20	10*
242/4	*Set of* 3	40	20*

REPUBLIC

85 President Nkrumah

(Des A. Medina (3d., 10s.), W. Wind (1s. 3d., 2s.))

1960 (1 July). *Republic Day. T* **85** *and similar multicoloured designs. W* **47**. *P* 14½ × 14 (10s.) *or* 14 × 14½ (*others*).

245	3d. Type **85**	10	10
246	1s. 3d. Ghana flag	30	10
247	2s. Torch of Freedom	40	20
248	10s. Arms of Ghana (*horiz*)	90	1·25
245/8	*Set of* 4	1·50	1·50
MS248*a*	102 × 77 mm. Nos. 245/8. Imperf	40	1·25

89 Olympic Torch **90** Athlete

(Des A. Medina (T **89**), W. Wind (T **90**))

1960 (15 Aug). *Olympic Games. W* **47** *(sideways on T* **90**). *P* 14 × 14½ *(T* **89**) *or* 14½ × 14 *(T* **90**).

249 **89** 3d. multicoloured 10 10
250 6d. multicoloured 15 10
251 **90** 1s. 3d. multicoloured 25 10
252 2s. 6d. multicoloured 35 45
249/52 .. .. *Set of* 4 70 55

91 President Nkrumah **94** U.N. Emblem and Ghana Flag

(Des M. Goaman (3d., 6d.), W. Wind (1s. 3d.))

1960 (21 Sept). *Founder's Day. T* **91** *and similar multicoloured designs. W* **47** *(sideways on 3d.). P* 14½ × 14 *(3d.) or* 14 × 14½ *(others).*

253 3d. Type **91** 10 10
254 6d. President Nkrumah *(vert)* 10 10
255 1s. 3d. Flag-draped column over map of African *(vert)* 20 20
253/5 .. .. *Set of* 3 30 30

(Des M. Goaman (3d., 1s. 3d.), W. Wind (6d.))

1960 (10 Dec). *Human Rights Day. T* **94** *and similar vert designs. W* **47**. *P* 14 × 14½.

256 3d. multicoloured 10 10
257 6d. yellow, black and blue 20 10
258 1s. 3d. multicoloured 40 30
256/8 .. .. *Set of* 3 60 40

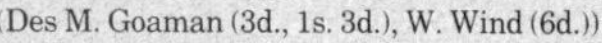

Designs:—6d. U.N. emblem and Torch; 1s. 3d. U.N. emblem.

97 Talking Drums **100** Eagle on Column

(Des M. Goaman (3d.), A. S. B. New (6d.), W. Wind (2s.))

1961 (15 Apr). *Africa Freedom Day. T* **97** *and similar designs. W* **47** *(sideways on 2s.). P* 14½ × 14 *(2s.) or* 14 × 14½ *(others).*

259 3d. multicoloured 10 10
260 6d. red, black and green 20 10
261 2s. multicoloured 50 45
259/61 .. .. *Set of* 3 70 50

Designs: *Vert.*—6d. Map of Africa. *Horiz*—2s. Flags and map.

(Des A. S. B. New (3d.), M. Shamir (1s. 3d.), W. Wind (2s.))

1961 (1 July). *First Anniv of Republic. T* **100** *and similar vert designs. Multicoloured. W* **47**. *P* 14 × 14½.

262 3d. Type **100** 10 10
263 1s. 3d. "Flower" 10 10
264 2s. Ghana flags 20 70
262/4 .. .. *Set of* 3 30 80

103 Dove with Olive Branch **106** Pres. Nkrumah and Globe

(Des V. Whiteley)

1961 (1 Sept). *Belgrade Conference. T* **103** *and similar designs. W* **47** *(sideways on 1s. 3d., 5s.). P* 14 × 14½ *(3d.) or* 14½ × 14 *(others).*

265 3d. yellow-green 10 10
266 1s. 3d. deep blue 15 10
267 5s. bright reddish purple 60 50
265/7 .. .. *Set of* 3 70 55

Designs: *Horiz.*—1s. 3d. World map, chain and olive branch; 5s. Rostrum, conference room.

(Des A. Medina (3d.), M. Goaman (1s. 3d.), Miriam Karoly (5s.))

1961 (21 Sept). *Founder's Day. T* **106** *and similar multicoloured designs. W* **47** *(sideways on 3d.). P* 14½ × 14 *(3d.) or* 14 × 14½ *(others).*

268 3d. Type **106** 10 10
269 1s. 3d. President and Kente Cloth *(vert)* .. 35 10
270 5s. President in national costume *(vert)* .. 1·25 2·50
268/70 .. .. *Set of* 3 1·50 2·50

MS270*a* Three sheets 106 × 86 mm (3d.) or 86 × 106 mm (others) each with Nos. 268/70 in block of four. Imperf .. .. *Three sheets* 5·50 14·00

The 1s. 3d. Miniature Sheet is known with the brown colour omitted.

109 Queen Elizabeth II and African Map

(Des M. Goaman)

1961 (9 Nov). *Royal Visit. W* **47**. *P* 14½ × 14.

271 **109** 3d. multicoloured 15 10
272 1s. 3d. multicoloured 75 20
273 5s. multicoloured .. .. .. 2·50 3·50
271/3 .. .. *Set of* 3 3·00 3·50

MS273*a* 106 × 84 mm. No. 273 in block of four. Imperf .. .. 4·50 8·50

110 Ships in Tema Harbour

(Des C. Bottiau. Litho Enschedé & Sons)

1962 (10 Feb). *Opening of Tema Harbour. T* **110** *and similar horiz designs. Multicoloured. No wmk. P* 14 × 13. *(a) Postage.*

274 3d. Type **110** 15 10

(b) Air

275 1s. 3d. Douglas DC-8 aircraft and ships at Tema 80 15
276 2s. 6d. As 1s. 3d. .. .. 1·00 1·50
274/6 .. .. *Set of* 3 1·75 1·50

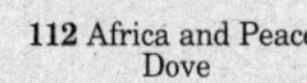

112 Africa and Peace Dove **113** Compass over Africa

(Des R. Hegeman. Litho Enschedé)

1962 (6 Mar). *First Anniv of Casablanca Conference. No wmk. P* 13 × 14. *(a) Postage.*

277 **112** 3d. multicoloured 10 10

(b) Air

278 **112** 1s. 3d. multicoloured 30 15
279 2s. 6d. multicoloured .. .. .. 40 1·10
277/9 .. .. *Set of* 3 70 1·25

(Des R. Hegeman)

1962 (24 Apr). *Africa Freedom Day. W* **47**. *P* 14 × 14½.

280 **113** 3d. sepia, blue-green and reddish purple 10 10
281 6d. sepia, blue-green and orange-brown 10 15
282 1s. 3d. sepia, blue-green and red .. 15 15
280/2 .. .. *Set of* 3 30 30

COVER PRICES

Cover factors are quoted at the beginning of each country for most issues to 1945. An explanation of the system can be found on page x. The factors quoted do not, however, apply to philatelic covers.

114 Ghana Star and "Five Continents" **115** Atomic Bomb-burst "Skull"

(Des M. Goaman (3d.), M. Shamir (6d.), W. Wind (1s. 3d.))

1962 (21 June). *Accra Assembly, T* **114/15** *and similar ve*
design. W **47**. *P* 14 × 14½.

283 3d. black and lake-red 10 1
284 6d. black and scarlet 25 3
285 1s. 3d. turquoise 30 4
283/5 .. .. *Set of* 3 55 7

Design:—1s. 3d. Dove of Peace.

117 Patrice Lumumba **118** Star over Two Columns

(Des A. S. B. New)

1962 (30 June). *1st Death Anniv of Lumumba. W* **47**. *P* 14½ × 1

286 **117** 3d. black and orange-yellow 10 1
287 6d. black, green and lake 10 3
288 1s. 3d. black, pink and black-green .. 15 3
286/8 .. .. *Set of* 3 30 6

(Des A. S. B. New (3d.), A. Medina (6d.), M. Goaman (1s. 3d.) Lith
Enschedé)

1962 (1 July). *2nd Anniv of Republic. T* **118** *and similar multi*
coloured designs. P 14 × 13½ *(1s. 3d.) or* 13½ × 14 *(others).*

289 3d. Type **118** 10 1
290 6d. Flaming torch 20 3
291 1s. 3d. Eagle trailing flag *(horiz)* 40 5
289/91 .. .. *Set of* 3 60 8

121 President Nkrumah **125** Campaign Emblem

(Litho Enschedé)

1962 (21 Sept). *Founder's Day. T* **121** *and similar vert designs*
P 13 × 14½.

292 1d. multicoloured 10 1
293 3d. multicoloured 10 1
294 1s. 3d. black and bright blue 30 1
295 2s. multicoloured 30 4
292/5 .. .. *Set of* 4 70 6

Designs:—3d. Nkrumah medallion; 1s. 3d. President Nkrumah
and Ghana Star; 2s. Laying "Ghana" Brick.

1962 (3 Dec). *Malaria Eradication. W* **47**. *P* 14 × 14½.

296 **125** 1d. cerise 15 1
297 4d. yellow-green .. .. 50 1·0
298 6d. bistre 50 3
299 1s. 3d. bluish violet 60 9
296/9 .. .. *Set of* 4 1·60 2·0
MS299*a* 90 × 115 mm. Nos. 296/9. Imperf .. 75 1·5

126 Campaign Emblem **129** Map of Africa

1963 (21 Mar). *Freedom from Hunger. T* **126** *and similar designs.* W **47** *(sideways on 4d., 1s. 3d.). P 14 × 14½ (1d.) or 14½ × 14 (others).*
300 1d. multicoloured 15 10
301 4d. sepia, yellow and orange.. .. .. .. 75 45
302 1s. 3d. ochre, black and green .. .. .. 1·60 80
300/2 .. .. *Set of 3* 2·25 1·25
Designs: *Horiz*—4d. Emblem in hands; 1s. 3d. World map and emblem.

1963 (15 Apr). *Africa Freedom Day. T* **129** *and similar designs.* W **47** *(sideways on 4d.). P 14½ × 14 (4d.) or 14 × 14½ (others).*
303 1d. gold and red 10 10
304 4d. red, black and yellow 10 10
305 1s. 3d. multicoloured 35 10
306 2s. 6d. multicoloured .. .. 50 1·25
303/6 .. .. *Set of 4* 85 1·40
Designs: *Horiz*—4d. Carved stool. *Vert*—1s. 3d. Map and bowl of fire; 2s. 6d. Topi (antelope) and flag.

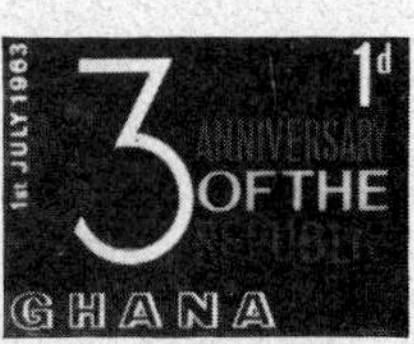

133 Red Cross **137** "3rd Anniversary"

(Des R. Hegeman (4d.), M. Shamir (others))

1963 (28 May). *Red Cross Centenary. T* **133** *and similar multicoloured designs.* W **47** *(sideways on 1½d., 4d.). P 14½ × 14 (1d., 1s. 3d.) or 14 × 14½ (others).*
307 1d. Type **133** 60 15
308 1½d. Centenary emblem *(horiz)* .. .. 90 1·25
309 4d. Nurses and child *(horiz)* .. .. 2·25 20
310 1s. 3d. Emblem, globe and laurel .. .. 3·50 2·00
307/10 .. .. *Set of 4* 6·50 3·25
MS310*a* 102 × 127 mm. Nos. 307/10. Imperf .. 2·75 11·00

(Des M. Goaman (1d., 4d.), R. Hegeman (others))

1963 (1 July). *3rd Anniv of Republic. T* **137** *and similar multicoloured designs.* W **47** *(sideways on 1d., 4d.). P 14½ × 14 (horiz) or 14 × 14½ (vert).*
311 1d. Type **137** 10 10
312 4d. Three Ghanaian flags 10 10
a. Black (stars on flag) omitted .. .. † £300
313 1s. 3d. Map, flag and star *(vert)* 35 15
314 2s. 6d. Flag and torch *(vert)* .. .. .. 55 1·50
311/14 .. .. *Set of 4* 1·00 1·50

141 President Nkrumah and Ghana Flag **145** Rameses II, Abu Simbel

(Des R. Hegeman (1d., 4d.), M. Shamir (1s. 3d.), G. Rose (5s.))

1963 (21 Sept). *Founder's Day. T* **141** *and similar designs.* W **47** *(sideways on 1s. 3d., 5s.). P 14 × 14½ (vert) or 14½ × 14 (horiz).*
315 1d. multicoloured 10 10
316 4d. multicoloured 15 10
317 1s. 3d. multicoloured 30 10
a. Green omitted .. .. 60·00
318 5s. yellow and bright reddish purple .. 65 75
315/18 .. .. *Set of 4* 1·00 80
Designs: *Vert*—4d. Nkrumah and flag. *Horiz*—1s. 3d. Nkrumah and fireworks; 5s. Symbol of Wisdom.

(Des M. Farrar Bell and R. Hegeman. Litho (1½d., 2d.) or photo (others) Enschedé)

1963 (1 Nov). *Nubian Monuments Preservation. T* **145** *and similar multicoloured designs. No wmk. P 11½ × 11 (vert) or 11 × 11½ (horiz).*
319 1d. Type **145** 15 10
320 1½d. Rock paintings *(horiz)* 20 65
321 2d. Queen Nefertari *(horiz)* 20 10
322 4d. Sphinx, Sebua 35 15
323 1s. 3d. Rock Temple, Abu Simbel *(horiz)* .. 80 90
319/23 .. .. *Set of 5* 1·60 1·75

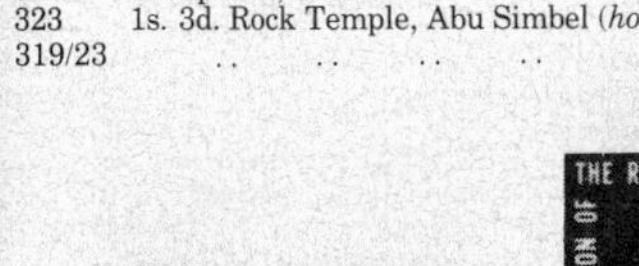

150 Class 248 Steam Locomotive and Diesel-electric Locomotive No. 1401 **151** Eleanor Roosevelt and "Flame of Freedom"

(Des H. L. W. Stevens)

1963 (1 Dec). *60th Anniv of Ghana Railway.* W **47** *(sideways). P 14½ × 14.*
324 **150** 1d. multicoloured 10 10
325 6d. multicoloured 60 10
326 1s. 3d. multicoloured .. .. .. 1·25 60
327 2s. 6d. multicoloured .. .. .. 2·25 2·25
324/7 .. .. *Set of 4* 3·75 2·75

(Des R. Hegeman and F. H. Savage. Photo Enschedé)

1963 (10 Dec). *15th Anniv of Declaration of Human Rights. T* **151** *and similar multicoloured designs. No wmk. P 11 × 11½ (1s. 3d.) or 11½ × 11 (others).*
328 1d. Type **151** 10 10
329 4d. Type **151** 10 10
330 6d. Eleanor Roosevelt 10 10
331 1s. 3d. Eleanor Roosevelt and emblems *(horiz)* 15 15
328/31 .. .. *Set of 4* 30 30
No. 329 differs from No. 328 in the arrangement of the trailing "flame" and of the background within the circular emblem.

154 Sun and Globe Emblem **155** Harvesting Corn on State Farm

1964 (15 June). *International Quiet Sun Years.* W **47** *(sideways). Each blue, yellow, red and green; background colours given. P 14½.*
332 **154** 3d. pale brown 15 10
333 6d. pale grey 25 10
334 1s. 3d. mauve 25 15
332/4 .. .. *Set of 3* 60 30
MS334*a* 90 × 90 mm. No. 334 in block of four. Imperf .. .. 70 2·50
Nos. 332/4 each exist in a miniature sheet of 12 in different colours (i.e. 3d. in colours of 6d.; 6d. in colours of 1s. 3d.; 1s. 3d. in colours of 3d.) but these were not generally available to the public.

(Des M. Shamir. Photo Govt Printer, Israel)

1964 (1 July). *4th Anniv of Republic. T* **155** *and similar horiz designs. P 13 × 14.*
335 3d. olive, brown and yellow-olive 10 10
336 6d. bluish green, brown and turquoise-green 10 10
337 1s. 3d. brown-red, brown and salmon-red .. 10 10
338 5s. multicoloured 40 70
335/8 .. .. *Set of 4* 55 75
MS338*a* 126 × 100 mm. Nos. 335/8. Imperf .. 55 2·00
ab. Olive (central design and face value of 3d.) omitted .. .. ..
Designs:—6d. Oil refinery, Tema; 1s. 3d. "Communal Labour"; 5s. Procession headed by flag.

159 Globe and Dove **163** Pres. Nkrumah and Hibiscus Flowers

(Des M. Shamir. Litho Lewin-Epstein Ltd, Bat Yam, Israel)

1964 (15 July). *1st Anniv of African Unity Charter. T* **159** *and similar designs. P 14.*
339 3d. multicoloured 10 10
340 6d. deep bronze-green and red 10 10
341 1s. 3d. multicoloured 15 10
342 5s. multicoloured 45 70
339/42 .. .. *Set of 4* 65 75
Designs: *Vert*—6d. Map of Africa and quill pen; 5s. Planting flower. *Horiz*—1s. 3d. Hitched rope on map of Africa.

1964 (21 Sept). *Founder's Day.* W **47** *(sideways). P 14 × 14½.*
343 **163** 3d. sepia, red, deep green and light blue 10 10
344 6d. sepia, red, deep green and yellow .. 15 10
345 1s. 3d. sepia, red, deep green and grey .. 25 10
346 2s. 6d. sepia, red, dp grn & light emerald 40 60
343/6 .. .. *Set of 4* 75 70
MS346*a* 90 × 122 mm. No. 346 in block of four. Imperf .. .. 70 2·50

IMPERFORATE STAMPS. Many issues, including miniature sheets, from here onwards exist imperforate, but these were not sold at post offices.

164 Hurdling

(Des A. S. B. New (No. 352))

1964 (25 Oct). *Olympic Games, Tokyo. T* **164** *and similar multicoloured designs.* W **47** *(sideways on 1d., 2½d., 6d., 5s.). P 14½ × 14 (horiz) or 14 × 14½ (vert).*
347 1d. Type **164** 10 10
348 2½d. Running .. .. 10 1·25
349 3d. Boxing *(vert)* 10 10
350 4d. Long-jumping *(vert)* 10 10
351 6d. Football *(vert)* 15 10
352 1s. 3d. Athlete holding Olympic Torch *(vert)* 20 10
353 5s. Olympic Rings and flags.. .. .. 85 3·25
347/53 .. .. *Set of 7* 1·40 4·25
MS353*a* 128 × 102 mm. Nos. 351/3. Imperf .. 75 2·50

171 G. Washington Carver (botanist) and Plant **173** African Elephant

(Des M. Shamir)

1964 (7 Dec). *U.N.E.S.C.O. Week.* W **47**. *P 14½.*
354 **171** 6d. deep blue and green 15 10
355 – 1s. 3d. reddish purple & greenish blue 75 10
w. Wmk inverted .. .. .. 11·00
356 **171** 5s. sepia and orange-red .. .. 2·10 4·00
354/6 .. .. *Set of 3* 2·75 4·00
MS356*a* 127×77 mm. Nos. 354/6. Imperf .. 75 2·00
Design:—1s. 3d. Albert Einstein (scientist) and atomic symbol.

(Des A. S. B. New (No. 360). Photo Enschedé)

1964 (14 Dec). *Multicoloured designs as T* **173**. *P 11½ × 11 (vert) or 11 × 11½ (horiz).*
357 1d. Type **173** 50 50
358 1½d. Secretary Bird *(horiz)* .. .. 1·00 2·25
359 2½d. Purple Wreath (flower) .. .. 60 2·25
360 3d. Grey Parrot .. .. .. 1·50 50
361 4d. Blue-naped Mousebird *(horiz)* .. 1·50 70
362 6d. African Tulip Tree *(horiz)* 60 30
363 1s. 3d. Violet Starling *(horiz)* .. .. 1·75 1·25
364 2s. 6d. Hippopotamus *(horiz)* .. .. 1·75 5·50
357/64 .. .. *Set of 8* 8·25 12·00
MS364*a* (a) 150×86 mm. Nos. 357/9. (b) 150×110 mm. Nos. 360/4. Imperf *Set of 2 sheets* 5·50 14·00

181 I.C.Y. Emblem **182** I.T.U. Emblem and Symbols

(Litho Enschedé)

1965 (22 Feb). *International Co-operation Year. P 14 × 12½.*
365 **181** 1d. multicoloured 35 60
366 4d. multicoloured .. .. .. 1·25 95
367 6d. multicoloured .. .. .. 1·50 60
368 1s. 3d. multicoloured .. .. .. 1·75 2·75
365/8 .. .. *Set of 4* 4·25 4·50
MS368*a* 100 × 100 mm. No. 368 in block of four. Imperf .. .. 2·50 5·00

(Litho Enschedé)

1965 (12 Apr). *I.T.U. Centenary. P 13½.*
369 **182** 1d. multicoloured 15 15
370 6d. multicoloured 55 15
371 1s. 3d. multicoloured .. .. .. 1·00 25
372 5s. multicoloured .. .. .. 2·25 2·75
369/72 .. .. *Set of 4* 3·50 3·00
MS372*a* 132 × 115 mm. Nos. 369/72. Imperf .. 4·50 8·00

183 Lincoln's Home

(Des M. Farrar Bell (6d.), A. S. B. New (1s. 3d., 5s.), R. Hegeman (2s.))

1965 (17 May). *Death Centenary of Abraham Lincoln. T* **183** *and similar square-shaped designs.* W **47** *(sideways). P 12½.*
373 6d. multicoloured 15 10
374 1s. 3d. black, red and blue 25 15
375 2s. black, orange-brown and greenish yellow 30 30
376 5s. black and red .. .. 70 1·50
373/6 .. .. *Set of 4* 1·25 1·75
MS376*a* 115 × 115 mm. Nos. 373/6. Imperf .. 1·25 3·50
ab. Green (part of flag on 6d.) omitted ..
Designs:—1s. 3d. Lincoln's Inaugural Address; 2s. Abraham Lincoln; 5s. Adaptation of U.S. 90 c. Lincoln Stamp of 1869.

(New Currency. 100 pesewas = 1 cedi)

187 Obverse (Pres. Nkrumah) and Reverse of 5 p. Coin

(Photo Enschedé)

1965 (19 July). *Introduction of Decimal Currency. T* **187** *and similar horiz designs. Multicoloured. P* 11 × 13 (5 *p.*, 10 *p.*), 13 × 12½ (25 *p.*) *or* 13½ × 14 (50 *p.*).

377 5 p. Type **187** 25 10
378 10 p. As Type **187** 30 10
379 25 p. Size 63 × 39 mm.. .. .. .. 1·00 1·00
380 50 p. Size 71 × 43½ mm .. .. .. 2·00 2·25
377/80 .. .. *Set of* 4 3·25 3·00

The coins in Nos. 378/80 are all circular and express the same denominations as on the stamps.

₵2·40
Ghana New Currency
19th July. 1965.

(188)

1965 (19 July). *Nos.* 214, 216 *and* 218*a*/27 *surch as T* **188** *diagonally upwards*, (D) *or horizontally*, (H), *by Govt Printer, Accra.*

(*a*) *Postage*

381 1 p. on 1d. multicoloured (R.) (D) .. 10 10
a. Surch inverted .. .. 15·00
b. Surch double .. .. 45·00
382 2 p. on 2d. multicoloured (Ultram.) (H) .. 10 10
a. Surch inverted .. .. ..
b. Surch double .. .. 10·00
c. Surch on back only .. .. ..
d. Surch on front and back .. ..
e. Red surch .. .. 26·00
f. Orange surch .. .. 26·00
g. Indigo surch .. ..
ga. Surch sideways .. .. ..
383 3 p. on 3d. multicoloured (II) (Br.) (H) .. 95 4·50
a. Surch inverted .. .. 18·00
b. Indigo surch .. .. ..
384 4 p. on 4d. multicoloured (B.) (H) .. 3·75 45
a. Surch inverted .. .. 35·00
b. Surch double .. .. ..
c. Red surch .. .. ..
385 6 p. on 6d. multicoloured (Blk.) (H) .. 50 10
a. Surch inverted .. .. 8·50
b. Surch double .. .. 15·00
c. Horiz pair, one without surch .. .. 50·00
d. Green (flag) omitted .. .. .. 60·00
386 11 p. on 11d. multicoloured (W.) (D) .. 25 10
a. Surch inverted .. .. 11·00
387 12 p. on 1s. multicoloured (B.) (D) .. 25 10
a. Surch double .. .. ..
b. Surch double, one albino inverted
c. Black surch .. .. 9·00
ca. Surch inverted .. .. 9·00
388 30 p. on 2s. 6d. multicoloured (B.) (H).. .. 3·00 2·25
389 60 p. on 5s. multicoloured (B.) (D) .. 4·50 70
a. Surch double (G. + B.) .. .. 25·00
390 1 c. 20 on 10s. multicoloured (B.) (D) .. 75 2·25
a. Surch double (G. + B.) .. .. 85·00
391 2 c. 40 on £1 multicoloured (B.) (D) .. 1·00 6·00

(*b*) *Air*

392 15 p. on 1s. 3d. multicoloured (W.) (H) .. 2·00 50
a. Surch inverted .. .. ..
393 24 p. on 2s. multicoloured (G.) (D) .. 2·50 30
a. Surch on front and back .. .. 25·00
381/93 .. .. *Set of* 13 16·00 15·00

On the diagonal surcharges the values are horizontal.

The 30 p. was not released in Ghana until 30 July and the 3 p. sometime later.

Numerous minor varieties exist.

189 "OAU" and Flag

190 "OAU", Heads and Flag

191 "OAU" Emblem and Flag

192 African Map and Flag

1965 (21 Oct). *O.A.U. Summit Conference, Accra. T* **189/92** *and similar horiz designs. Multicoloured. W* **47** (*sideways* except on* 6*p.*). *P* 14 (*T* **189/91**) *or* 14½×14 (*others*).

394 1 p. Type **189** 10 10
a. Red (part of flag) omitted .. .. 70·00
395 2 p. Type **190** 10 10
396 5 p. Type **191** 10 10
397 6 p. Type **192** 10 10
398 15 p. "Sunburst", map and flag 20 30
399 24 p. "O.A.U." on map, and flag 35 60
w. Wmk top of G to left .. ..
394/9 .. .. *Set of* 6 75 1·10

*The 1 p. also exists with the watermark facing left or right, but positional blocks are required to show the two types. The normal sideways watermark has top of G to right, *as seen from the back of the stamp.*

195 Goalkeeper saving Ball

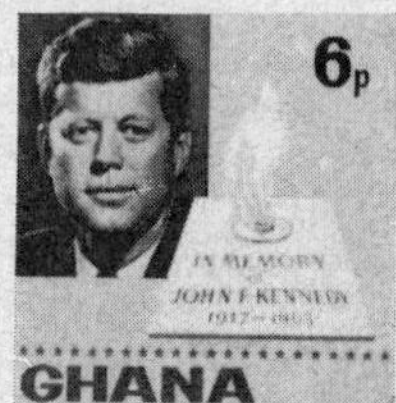

198 Pres. Kennedy and Grave Memorial

(Photo Enschedé)

1965 (15 Nov). *African Soccer Cup Competition. T* **195** *and similar multicoloured designs. P* 13 × 14 (15 *p.*) *or* 14 × 13 (*others*).

400 6 p. Type **195** 20 10
401 15 p. Player with ball (*vert*) 35 25
402 24 p. Players, ball and soccer cup 45 50
400/2 .. .. *Set of* 3 90 75

(Des A. S. B. New (No. 405))

1965 (15 Dec)–**66**. *2nd Anniv of President Kennedy's Death. T* **198** *and similar square-shaped designs. W* **47** (*sideways*). *P* 12½.

403 6 p. multicoloured 15 10
404 15 p. violet, red and green 25 35
405 24 p. black and reddish violet 30 60
406 30 p. dull purple and black 40 75
403/6 .. .. *Set of* 4 1·00 1·60
MS407 114½ × 114 mm. Nos. 403/6. Imperf (21.3.66) .. .. 3·75 6·50

Designs:—15 p. Pres. Kennedy and Eternal Flame; 24 p. Pres. Kennedy and memorial inscription; 30 p. President Kennedy.

202 Section of Dam and Generators

Black Stars Retain Africa Cup
21st Nov. 1965

(206)

(Des A. S. B. New (No. 411). Photo Enschedé)

1966 (22 Jan). *Volta River Project. T* **202** *and similar horiz designs. P* 11 × 11½.

408 6 p. multicoloured 15 10
409 15 p. multicoloured 20 15
410 24 p. multicoloured 25 20
411 30 p. black and new blue 35 50
408/11 .. .. *Set of* 4 85 85

Designs:—15 p. Dam and Lake Volta; 24 p. Word "GHANA" as dam; 30 p. "Fertility".

1966 (7 Feb). *"Black Stars" Victory in African Soccer Cup Competition. Nos.* 400/2 *optd with T* **206**, *in black.*

412 6 p. Type **195** 20 10
a. Green opt .. .. 20·00
b. Green opt double, one inverted ..
c. Stop after "Nov" omitted (R. 5/1) ..
413 15 p. Player with ball 35 20
414 24 p. Players, ball and cup 45 35
a. Opt inverted* .. .. 26·00
ab. Vert pair, one without opt, the other with opt inverted .. .. ..
b. Error. Opt for 15 p. on 24 p. inverted*
c. Stop after "Nov" omitted (R. 5/1) ..
412/14 .. .. *Set of* 3 90 60

*In No. 414a the overprint reads downwards (top right to bottom left), but in No. 414b it reads upwards (bottom right to top left).

DATES OF ISSUE of miniature sheets are approximate as they are generally released some time after the related ordinary stamps, but it is known that the G.P.O. sometimes applied first-day cancellations months after the dates shown on the cancellations.

207 W.H.O. Building and Ghana Flag

1966 (1 July). *Inauguration of W.H.O. Headquarters, Geneva. T* **207** *and similar horiz design. Multicoloured. W* **47** *P* 14½ × 14.

415 6 p. Type **207** 50 1
416 15 p. Type **207** .. .. 1·25 6
417 24 p. W.H.O. Building and emblem .. .. 1·40 1·2
418 30 p. As 24 p. .. .. 1·60 2·2
415/18 .. .. *Set of* 4 4·25 3·7
MS419 120 × 101 mm. Nos. 415/18. Imperf (11.66) 17·00 18·0

209 Atlantic Herring

214 African "Links" and Ghana Flag

(Des O. Hamann. Photo Enschedé)

1966 (10 Aug). *Freedom from Hunger. T* **209** *and similar horiz designs. Multicoloured. P* 14 × 13.

420 6 p. Type **209** 15 10
421 15 p. Turbot 35 15
422 24 p. Spadefish 65 35
423 30 p. Red Snapper 80 90
424 60 p. Blue-finned Tuna .. .. .. 2·00 3·50
420/4 .. .. *Set of* 5 3·50 4·50
MS425 126×109 mm. No. 423 in block of four. Imperf (Nov) .. .. 8·00 12·00

(Photo Enschedé)

1966 (11 Oct). *Third Anniv of African Charter. T* **214** *and similar multicoloured designs. P* 13½.

426 6 p. Type **214** 15 10
427 15 p. Flags as "Quill", and diamond (*horiz*) .. 35 45
428 24 p. Ship's wheel, map and cocoa bean (*horiz*) 40 60
426/8 .. .. *Set of* 3 80 1·00

217 Player heading Ball, and Jules Rimet Cup

1966 (14 Nov). *World Cup Football Championships, England. T* **217** *and similar horiz designs. Multicoloured. W* **47**. *P* 14½ × 14.

429 5 p. Type **217** 30 10
430 15 p. Goalkeeper clearing ball 70 20
w. Wmk inverted .. .. 1·60
431 24 p. Player and Jules Rimet Cup (replica) 85 35
432 30 p. Players and Jules Rimet Cup (replica) 1·10 1·25
433 60 p. Players with ball .. .. .. 1·75 4·75
w. Wmk inverted .. .. ..
429/33 .. .. *Set of* 5 4·25 6·00
MS434 120×102 mm. 60 p. (block of four). Imperf 19·00 19·00

ALTERED CATALOGUE NUMBERS

Any Catalogue numbers altered from the last edition are shown as a list in the introductory pages.

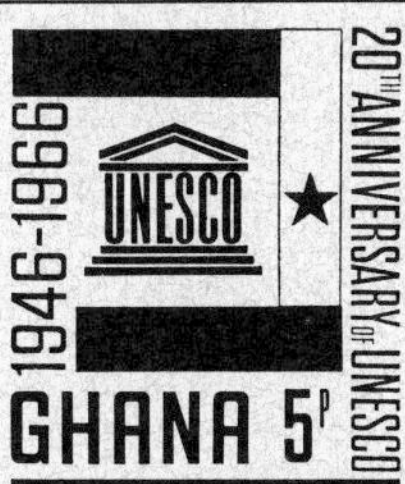

222 U.N.E.S.C.O. Emblem

1966 (23 Dec). *20th Anniv of U.N.E.S.C.O. W* **47** (*sideways*). *P* 14½.
435 **222** 5 p. multicoloured 25 15
436 15 p. multicoloured 60 40
437 24 p. multicoloured 90 85
438 30 p. multicoloured .. .. .. 1·25 2·25
439 60 p. multicoloured .. .. .. 2·25 4·75
435/9 .. .. *Set of* 5 4·75 7·50
MS440 140 × 115 mm. Nos. 435/9. Imperf .. 18·00 20·00

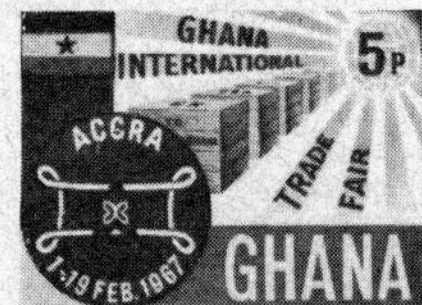

223 Fair Emblem and Crates

1967 (1 Feb). *Ghana Trade Fair, Accra. T* **223** *and similar multi-coloured designs. W* **47** (*sideways on* 24 *p.*). *P* 14 × 14½ (24 *p.*) *or* 14½ × 14 (*others*).
441 5 p. Type **223** 10 10
442 15 p. Fair emblem and world map 15 20
443 24 p. Shipping and flags (*vert*) 25 30
444 36 p. Fair emblem and hand-held hoist .. 40 1·90
441/4 .. .. *Set of* 4 70 2·25

(New Currency. 100 new pesewas = 1 new cedi (1·2 old cedi))

1½Np (227) NȻ2.00 (228)

229 Ghana Eagle and Flag

1967 (23 Feb). *Nos.* 216, 219/23, 225/6 *and* 393 *surch as T* **227/8.**

(*a*) *Postage*
445 1½ n.p. on 2d. multicoloured (Blk.) .. 3·50 4·00
446 3½ n.p. on 4d. multicoloured (R.) .. 4·00 85
a. Surch double, one sideways ..
447 5 n.p. on 6d. multicoloured (R.) .. 1·25 50
448 9 n.p. on 11d. multicoloured (W.) .. 30 20
449 10 n.p. on 1s. multicoloured (W.) .. 30 30
450 25 n.p. on 2s. 6d. multicoloured (R.) .. 3·50 4·50
451 1 n.c. on 10s. multicoloured (R.) .. 3·00 14·00
452 2 n.c. on £1 multicoloured (R.) .. .. 6·00 24·00

(*b*) *Air*
453 12½ n.p. on 1s. 3d. multicoloured (W.) .. 4·00 2·00
454 20 n.p. on 24 p. on 2s. multicoloured (R.) 4·00 3·00
445/54 .. .. *Set of* 10 27·00 48·00

Inverted surcharges in a different type face on the 3½, 5 and 25 n.p. are fakes.

(Des M. Shamir)

1967 (24 Feb). *First Anniv of February 24 Revolution. W* **47** (*sideways*). *P* 14 × 14½.
455 **229** 1 n.p. multicoloured 10 15
456 4 n.p. multicoloured 10 10
457 12½ n.p. multicoloured 40 60
458 25 n.p. multicoloured .. .. .. 85 2·50
455/8 .. .. *Set of* 4 1·25 3·00
MS459 89 × 108 mm. Nos. 455/8. Perf or imperf .. 6·50 12·00

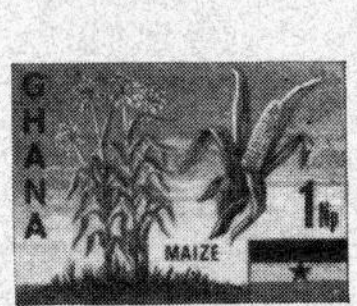

230 Maize

231 Forest Kingfisher

235 Rufous-crowned Roller

236 Akosombo Dam

1967 (1 June–4 Sept). *T* **230/1, 235/6** *and similar designs. W* **47** (1½, 2, 4, 50 *n.p. and* 1 *n.c.*) *or sideways* (*others*). *P* 11½ × 12 (1, 8 *n.p.*), 12 × 11½ (4 *n.p.*), 14 × 14½ (1½, 2, 2½, 20 *n.p.*, 2 *n.c.* 50) *or* 14½ × 14 (*others*).
460 1 n.p. multicoloured 10 10
a. Salmon omitted** .. ..
461 1½ n.p. multicoloured .. .. .. 90 1·75
a. Blue omitted* .. .. .. 75·00
b. Green printed double, once inverted†
c. Green omitted† .. .. ..
462 2 n.p. multicoloured (4.9) 10 10
a. Green (part of flag omitted ..
b. Gold (frame) omitted .. ..
w. Wmk inverted .. .. .. 10·00
463 2½ n.p. multicoloured (4.9) 35 10
a. Wmk upright .. .. .. 10·00
ab. Face value omitted £180
464 3 n.p. multicoloured 20 40
a. Green (part of flag) omitted ..
465 4 n.p. multicoloured .. .. .. 1·50 10
a. Green (part of flag) omitted .. 38·00
b. Red (part of flag) omitted ..
c. Black (star, bird markings and shadow) omitted .. .. .. 65·00
466 6 n.p. multicoloured 15 50
467 8 n.p. multicoloured 15 10
468 9 n.p. multicoloured (4.9) 75 10
469 10 n.p. multicoloured 15 10
470 20 n.p. deep blue and new blue (4.9) .. 20 10
471 50 n.p. multicoloured .. .. .. 4·50 1·50
472 1 n.c. multicoloured (4.9.) .. .. 2·25 75
473 2 n.c. multicoloured (4.9.) .. .. 2·00 3·50
474 2 n.c. 50, multicoloured .. .. .. 3·50 7·50
460/74 .. .. *Set of* 15 15·00 14·50

Designs: *Vert* (*as T* **231**)—2 n.p. The Ghana Mace; 2½ n.p. Commelina; 20 n.p. Bush Hare; 2 n.c. Frangipani; 2 n.c. 50, Seat of State. *Horiz* (*as T* **236**)—3 n.p. West African Lungfish; 9 n.p. Chameleon; 10 n.p. Tema Harbour; 50 n.p. Black-winged Stilt; 1 n.c. Wooden Stool. (*As T* **230**)—8 n.p. Adomi Bridge.

*In this stamp the blue not only affects the bird but is printed over the yellow background to give the value in green, so that its omission results in the value also being omitted.

**This affects the maize flowers, corn and foreground.

†This affects the feather-tips and the flag.

The 2 n.p. and 20 n.p. were officially issued on 4 September but small quanties of both were released in error on 1 June. The 2½ n.p. is also known to have been released in error in June.

245 Kumasi Fort

249 "Luna 10"

(Des O. Hamann)

1967 (1 July). *Castles and Forts. T* **245** *and similar designs. Multicoloured. W* **47** (*diagonal*). *P* 14½.
475 4 n.p. Type **245** 25 10
476 12½ n.p. Christiansborg Castle and British galleon .. .. 1·00 1·00
477 20 n.p. Elmina Castle and Portuguese galleon .. .. 1·40 2·75
478 25 n.p. Cape Coast Castle and Spanish galleon .. .. 1·75 3·50
475/8 .. .. *Set of* 4 4·00 6·50

(Des M. Shamir. Photo Enschedé)

1967 (16 Aug). *"Peaceful Use of Outer Space". T* **249** *and similar square designs. Multicoloured. P* 13½ × 14.
479 4 n.p. Type **249** 10 10
480 10 n.p. "Orbiter 1" 10 35
481 12½ n.p. Man in Space 20 70
479/81 .. .. *Set of* 3 35 1·00
MS482 140 × 90 mm. Nos. 479/81. Imperf .. 1·25 2·75

252 Scouts and Camp-fire

(Photo Enschedé)

1967 (18 Sept). *50th Anniv of Ghanaian Scout Movement. T* **252** *and similar horiz designs. Multicoloured. P* 14½ × 13.
483 4 n.p. Type **252** 20 10
484 10 n.p. Scout on march 50 50
485 12½ n.p. Lord Baden-Powell .. .. .. 70 1·75
483/5 .. .. *Set of* 3 1·25 2·00
MS486 167 × 95 mm. Nos. 483/5. Imperf .. .. 6·00 9·50

255 U.N. Headquarters Building

256 General View of U.N. H.Q., Manhattan

(Litho D.L.R.)

1967 (20 Nov). *United Nations Day* (24 *October*). *P* 13½.
487 **255** 4 n.p. multicoloured 10 10
488 10 n.p. multicoloured 10 15
489 **256** 50 n.p. multicoloured 30 70
490 2 n.c. 50, multicoloured .. .. 1·00 4·00
487/90 .. .. *Set of* 4 1·25 4·50
MS491 76 × 75 mm. No. 490. Imperf (4.12.67) .. 2·75 9·50

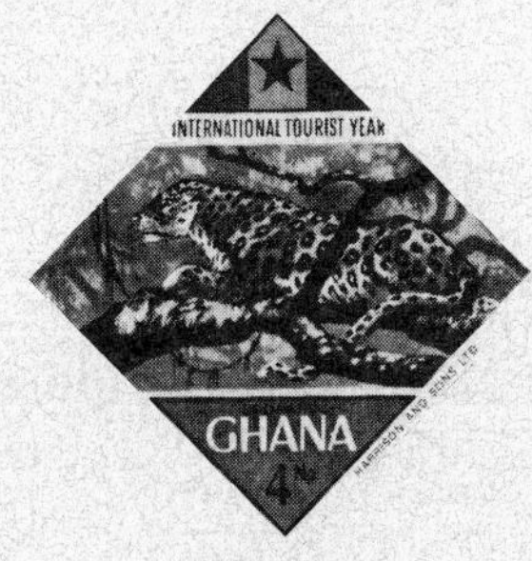

257 Leopard

1967 (28 Dec). *International Tourist Year. T* **257** *and similar diamond-shaped designs. Multicoloured. W* **47** (*diagonal*). *P* 12½.
492 4 n.p. Type **257** .. .. 1·00 20
493 12½ n.p. *Papilio demodocus* (butterfly) .. 2·50 1·50
494 20 n.p. Carmine Bee Eater .. .. 3·00 3·50
495 50 n.p. Waterbuck .. .. 3·00 7·00
492/5 .. .. *Set of* 4 8·50 11·00
MS496 126 × 126 mm. Nos. 493/5. Imperf .. 15·00 16·00

261 Revolutionaries entering Accra

(Litho D.L.R.)

1968 (24 Feb). *2nd Anniv of February Revolution. T* **261** *and similar horiz designs. Multicoloured. P* 14.
497 4 n.p. Type **261** 10 10
498 12½ n.p. Marching troops 20 20
499 20 n.p. Cheering people 30 40
500 40 n.p. Victory celebrations .. .. 50 1·25
497/500 .. .. *Set of* 4 1·00 1·75

265 Microscope and Cocoa Beans

1968 (18 Mar). *Cocoa Research. T* **265** *and similar horiz design. Multicoloured. W* **47** (*sideways*). *P* 14½ × 14.
501 2½ n.p. Type **265** 10 40
502 4 n.p. Microscope and cocoa tree, beans and pods 10 10
503 10 n.p. Type **265** 15 20
504 25 n.p. As 4 n.p. .. .. 60 1·10
501/4 .. .. *Set of* 4 80 1·50
MS505 102 × 102 mm. Nos. 501/4. Imperf . .. 2·25 3·50

267 Kotoka and Flowers

271 Tobacco

(Des A. S. B. New (No. 508) and F. Mate (others) Litho D.L.R.)

1968 (17 Apr). *1st Death Anniv of Lt.-Gen. E. K. Kotoka. T* **267** *and similar multicoloured designs. P* 14.

506 4 n.p. Type **267** 10 10
507 12½ n.p. Kotoka and wreath 20 30
508 20 n.p. Kotoka in civilian clothes 35 75
509 40 n.p. Lt.-Gen. Kotoka (*vert*) 50 1·60
506/9 *Set of* 4 1·00 2·50

(Des A. S. B. New (5 n.p.))

1968 (19 Aug). *Flora and Fauna. T* **271** *and similar vert designs. Multicoloured. W* **47** (*sideways*). *P* 14×14½.

510 4 n.p. Type **271** 15 10
511 5 n.p. North African Crested Porcupine 15 60
512 12½ n.p. Rubber 50 75
513 20 n.p. *Cymothoe sangaris* (butterfly) 2·25 2·75
514 40 n.p. *Charaxes ameliae* (butterfly) 2·50 4·75
510/14 *Set of* 5 5·00 8·00
MS515 88×114 mm. Nos. 510, 512/14. Imperf 3·50 8·00

276 Surgeons, Flag and W.H.O. Emblem

277 Hurdling

(Photo Enschedé)

1968 (11 Nov). *20th Anniv of World Health Organization. P* 14 × 13.

516 **276** 4 n.p. multicoloured 25 10
517 12½ n.p. multicoloured 60 40
518 20 n.p. multicoloured 95 1·10
519 40 n.p. multicoloured 1·50 3·00
516/19 *Set of* 4 3·00 4·00
MS520 132 × 110 mm. Nos. 516/19. Imperf 3·75 6·50

1969 (10 Jan). *Olympic Games, Mexico* (1968). *T* **277** *and similar vert designs. Multicoloured. W* **47** (*sideways*). *P* 14 × 14½.

521 4 n.p. Type **277** 10 10
522 12½ n.p. Boxing 20 30
523 20 n.p. Torch, Olympic Rings and flags 40 75
524 40 n.p. Football 70 2·50
521/4 *Set of* 4 1·25 3·25
MS525 89 × 114 mm. Nos. 521/4. Imperf (17.1.69) 3·50 6·00

281 U.N. Building

285 Dr. J. B. Danquah

(Litho D.L.R.)

1969 (1 Feb). *United Nations Day* (1968). *T* **281** *and similar square-shaped designs. Multicoloured. P* 13½.

526 4 n.p. Type **281** 10 10
527 12½ n.p. Native stool, staff and U.N. emblem 15 25
528 20 n.p. U.N. building and emblem over Ghanaian flag 20 35
529 40 n.p. U.N. emblem encircled by flags 40 1·25
526/9 *Set of* 4 75 1·75
MS530 127 × 117 mm. No. 526/9. Imperf 75 3·25

1969 (7 Mar). *Human Rights Year. T* **285** *and similar horiz design. Multicoloured. W* **47** (*sideways on* **MS**535). *P* 14½ × 14.

531 4 n.p. Type **285** 10 10
532 12½ n.p. Dr. Martin Luther King 20 35
533 20 n.p. As 12½ n.p. 35 75
534 40 n.p. Type **285** 50 1·60
531/4 *Set of* 4 1·00 2·50
MS535 116 × 50 mm. Nos. 531/4. Imperf (17.4.69) 80 3·00

287 Constituent Assembly Building

1969 (10 Sept). *Third Anniv of the Revolution. T* **287** *and similar horiz design. W* **47** (*sideways on* **MS**540). *P* 14½ × 14.

536 4 n.p. Type **287** 10 10
537 12½ n.p. Arms of Ghana 10 10
538 20 n.p. Type **287** 15 15
539 40 n.p. As 12½ n.p. 20 35
536/9 *Set of* 4 40 60
MS540 114 × 89 mm. Nos. 536/9. Imperf 70 2·25

NEW CONSTITUTION
1969

(289)

290 Map of Africa and Flags

1969 (1 Oct). *New Constitution. Nos.* 460/74 *optd with T* **289** *in various positions by Government Press, Accra.*

541 1 n.p. multicoloured (Horiz) 10 1·00
542 1½ n.p. multicoloured (Vert down) 85 2·00
a. Opt vert up 6·00
b. Horiz opt 25·00
ba. Opt omitted (in vert pair with normal) £180
543 2 n.p. multicoloured (Vert up) 10 1·50
a. Opt vert down 5·00
b. Opt double 12·00
544 2½ n.p. multicoloured (Vert up) 10 1·25
a. Opt vert down 18·00
545 3 n.p. multicoloured (Horiz) 60 1·50
a. Opt inverted 15·00
546 4 n.p. multicoloured (Y.) (Vert down) 2·25 30
a. Black opt (vert down) 7·00 1·25
b. Black opt (vert up) 10·00
c. Red opt (vert down) 18·00
d. Opt double (White vert down + yellow vert up) 27·00
547 6 n.p. multicoloured (Horiz) 15 1·50
548 8 n.p. multicoloured (Horiz) 15 1·00
549 9 n.p. multicoloured (Horiz) 15 1·50
550 10 n.p. multicoloured (Horiz) 20 85
551 20 n.p. deep blue and new blue (Vert up) 35 90
a. Opt vert down 20·00
552 50 n.p. multicoloured (Horiz) 5·00 5·50
a. Opt double
553 1 n.c. multicoloured (Horiz) 1·75 7·00
554 2 n.c. multicoloured (R.) (Vert up) 2·75 8·00
a. Opt double (vert up and down)
555 2 n.c. 50, multicoloured (Vert down) 2·75 9·50
541/55 *Set of* 15 14·00 38·00

The 1 n.p. is known with the overprint inverted, "NEW CONSTITUTION" appearing between the stamps across the perforations.

(Litho D.L.R.)

1969 (4 Dec). *Inauguration of Second Republic. T* **290** *and similar vert designs. Multicoloured. P* 14.

556 4 n.p. Type **290** 10 10
557 12½ n.p. Figure "2", branch and Ghanaian colours 20 10
558 20 n.p. Hands receiving egg 35 30
559 40 n.p. Type **290** 60 70
556/9 *Set of* 4 1·10 1·00

293 I.L.O. Emblem and Cog-wheels

1970 (5 Jan). *50th Anniv of International Labour Organisation. W* **47** (*sideways*). *P* 14½ × 14.

560 **293** 4 n.p. multicoloured 10 10
561 12½ n.p. multicoloured 20 25
562 20 n.p. multicoloured 30 45
560/2 *Set of* 3 55 70
MS563 117 × 89 mm. Nos. 560/2. Imperf 70 2·50

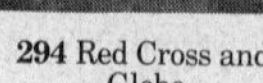

294 Red Cross and Globe

298 General Kotoka, Vickers VC-10 and Airport

1970 (2 Feb). *50th Anniv of League of Red Cross Societies. T* **294** *and similar multicoloured designs. W* **47** (*sideways on* 4 *n.p.*). *P* 14 × 14½ (4 *n.p.*) *or* 14½ × 14 (*others*).

564 4 n.p. Type **294** 30 10
565 12½ n.p. Henri Dunant and Red Cross emblem (*horiz*) 40 20
w. Wmk inverted
566 20 n.p. Patient receiving medicine (*horiz*) 50 55
567 40 n.p. Patient having arm bandaged (*horiz*) 75 1·40
564/7 *Set of* 4 1·75 2·00
MS568 114×89 mm. Nos. 564/7. Imperf 2·00 6·00

NEW INFORMATION

The editor is always interested to correspond with people who have new information that will improve or correct the Catalogue.

(Des G. Vasarhelyi. Litho D.L.R.)

1970 (17 Apr). *Inauguration of Kotoka Airport. T* **298** *and simila horiz designs. Multicoloured. P* 13 × 13½.

569 4 n.p. Type **298** 15 1
570 12½ n.p. Control tower and tail of Vickers VC-10 25 1
571 20 n.p. Aerial view of airport 40 3
572 40 n.p. Airport and flags 75 8
569/72 *Set of* 4 1·40 1·2

302 Lunar Module landing on Moon

306 Adult Education

(Des A. Medina (4 n.p., 12½ n.p.), G. Vasarhelyi (others). Lith D.L.R.)

1970 (15 June). *Moon Landing. T* **302** *and similar multicolour designs. P* 12½.

573 4 n.p. Type **302** 30 1
574 12½ n.p. Astronaut's first step onto the Moon 85 6
575 20 n.p. Astronaut with equipment on Moon (*horiz*) 1·25 1·4
576 40 n.p. Astronauts (*horiz*) 2·25 3·0
573/6 *Set of* 4 4·25 4·5
MS577 142 × 142 mm. Nos. 573/6. Imperf (with or without simulated perfs) 4·50 12·0

On 18 September 1970 Nos. 573/6 were issued overprinte "PHILYMPIA LONDON 1970" but it is understood that only 90 sets were made available for sale in Ghana and we do not conside that this is sufficient to constitute normal postal use. The miniatur sheet was also overprinted but not issued in Ghana.

(Litho D.L.R.)

1970 (10 Aug). *International Education Year. T* **306** *and simila horiz designs. Multicoloured. P* 13.

578 4 n.p. Type **306** 10 1
579 12½ n.p. International education 20 2
580 20 n.p. "Ntesie" and I.E.Y. symbols 35 3
581 40 n.p. Nursery schools 60 8
578/81 *Set of* 4 1·10 1·2

310 Saluting March-Past

314 *Crinum ornatum*

(Litho D.L.R.)

1970 (1 Oct). *First Anniv of the Second Republic. T* **310** *an similar horiz designs. Multicoloured. P* 13 × 13½.

582 4 n.p. Type **310** 10 1
583 12½ n.p. Busia declaration 15 1
584 20 n.p. Doves symbol 25 3
585 40 n.p. Opening of Parliament 50 6
582/5 *Set of* 4 90 1·0

(Des G. Vasarhelyi. Photo Harrison)

1970 (2 Nov). *Flora and Fauna. T* **314** *and similar horiz designs. Multicoloured. W* **47** (*sideways*). *P* 14½ × 14.

586 4 n.p. Type **314** 1·50 10
w. Wmk inverted 7·00
587 12½ n.p. Lioness 1·50 85
588 20 n.p. *Anselia africana* (flower) 1·60 1·25
589 40 n.p. African Elephant 4·75 5·50
586/9 *Set of* 4 8·50 7·00

315 Kuduo Brass Casket

(Des G. Vasarhelyi. Photo Harrison)

1970 (7 Dec). *Monuments and Archaeological Sites in Ghana T* **315** *and similar horiz designs. Multicoloured. W* **47** *P* 14½ × 14.

590 4 n.p. Type **315** 15 1C
w. Wmk inverted
591 12½ n.p. Akan traditional house 40 2C
592 20 n.p. Larabanga Mosque 55 5C
593 40 n.p. Funerary clay head 70 1·1C
590/3 *Set of* 4 1·60 1·75
MS594 89×71 mm. Nos. 590, 592 and 12½ n.p. Basilica of Pompeii, 40 n.p. Pistrinum of Pompeii (wmk sideways). Imperf (2.71) 5·00 7·5C

316 Trade Fair Building

(Des G. Drummond (4 n.p., 50 n.p.), A. Larkins (others). Photo Harrison)

1971 (5 Feb). *International Trade Fair, Accra. T* **316** *and similar multicoloured designs. W* **47** *(sideways, except 50 n.p.). P* 14 × 14½ *(50 n.p.) or* 14½ × 14 *(others).*

595	4 n.p. Type **316**	10	10
596	12½ n.p. Cosmetics and Pharmaceutical Goods	60	20
597	20 n.p. Vehicles	65	25
598	40 n.p. Construction Equipment	95	95
599	50 n.p. Transport and Packing Case (*vert*)	1·10	1·10
595/9	*Set of* 5	3·00	2·25

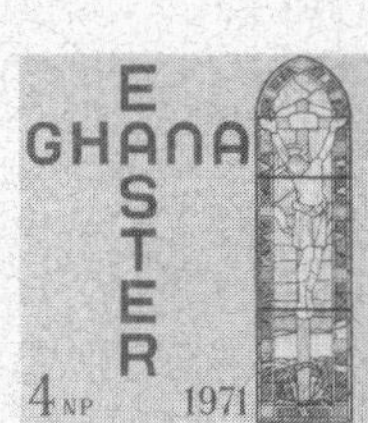

317 Christ on the Cross

318 Corn Cob

(Des from stained-glass windows. Litho D.L.R.)

1971 (19 May). *Easter. T* **317** *and similar square designs. Multicoloured. P* 13.

600	4 n.p. Type **317**	20	10
601	12½ n.p. Christ and Disciples	45	45
602	20 n.p. Christ blessing Disciples	65	1·10
600/2	*Set of* 3	1·10	1·50

(Photo Harrison)

1971 (15 June). *Freedom from Hunger Campaign. W* **47.** *P* 14 × 14½.

603 **318**	4 n.p. multicoloured	10	10
604	12½ n.p. multicoloured	35	60
605	20 n.p. multicoloured	65	1·10
603/5	*Set of* 3	1·00	1·60

Remainder stocks of the above were overprinted on the occasion of the death of Lord Boyd Orr and the 4 n.p. surcharged 60 n.p.

It is understood that 8,070 sets from the New York Agency were overprinted locally and returned to the Agency. Limited remainders of these stamps (only 330 of the 60 n.p.) were sold at the G.P.O. We do not list these as they were not freely on sale in Ghana.

319 Guides Emblem and Ghana Flag

320 Child-care Centre

(Des and litho Questa)

1971 (22 July). *Ghana Girl Guides Golden Jubilee. T* **319** *and similar horiz designs each with Guides Emblem. Multicoloured. P* 14.

606	4 n.p. Type **319**	20	10
607	12½ n.p. Mrs. E. Ofuatey-Kodjoe (founder) and guides with flags	60	50
608	20 n.p. Guides laying stones	90	90
609	40 n.p. Camp-fire and tent	1·50	1·75
610	50 n.p. Signallers	1·75	2·00
606/10	*Set of* 5	4·50	4·75
MS611	133 × 105 mm. Nos. 606/10. Imperf	11·00	13·00

(Des and litho D.L.R.)

1971 (7 Aug). *Y.W.C.A. World Council Meeting, Accra. T* **320** *and similar horiz designs. Multicoloured. P* 13.

612	4 n.p. Type **320**	10	10
613	12½ n.p. Council meeting	10	15
614	20 n.p. School typing-class	15	30
615	40 n.p. Building Fund Day	30	60
612/15	*Set of* 4	55	1·00
MS616	84 × 83 mm. Nos. 612/15. Imperf	70	2·00

321 Firework Display

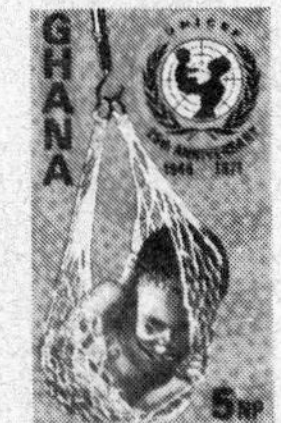

322 Weighing Baby

(Photo Harrison)

1971 (22 Nov). *Christmas. T* **321** *and similar horiz designs. Multicoloured. W* **47** *(sideways on 3 and 6 n.p.). P* 14 × 14½ *(1 n.p.) or* 14½ × 14 *(others).*

617	1 n.p. Type **321**	10	60
618	3 n.p. African Nativity	15	70
619	6 n.p. The flight into Egypt	15	70
617/19	*Set of* 3	30	1·75

(Litho D.L.R.)

1971 (20 Dec). *25th Anniv of U.N.I.C.E.F. T* **322** *and similar multicoloured designs, each showing the U.N.I.C.E.F. symbol. No wmk* (**MS**624) *or W* **47** *(sideways on 5 and 30 n.p.). P* 13.

620	5 n.p. Type **322**	10	10
621	15 n.p. Mother and child (*horiz*)	20	30
622	30 n.p. Nurse	30	70
623	50 n.p. Young boy (*horiz*)	50	2·25
620/3	*Set of* 4	1·00	3·00
MS624	111 × 120 mm. Nos. 620/3. Imperf	3·00	6·50

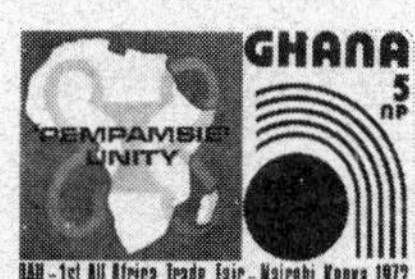

323 Unity Symbol and Trade Fair Emblem

(Litho Questa)

1972 (23 Feb). *All-Africa Trade Fair. T* **323** *and similar horiz designs. Multicoloured. W* **47.** *P* 14.

625	5 n.p. Type **323**	10	10
626	15 n.p. Horn of Plenty	15	30
627	30 n.p. Fireworks on map of Africa	25	70
628	60 n.p. "Participating Nations"	35	2·00
629	1 n.c. As No. 628	50	2·50
625/9	*Set of* 5	1·10	5·00

All designs include the Trade Fair Emblem as in T **323**.

On 24 June 1972, on the occasion of the Belgian International Philatelic Exhibition, Nos. 625/9 were issued overprinted "BELGICA 72" in red. Only very limited supplies were sent to Ghana (we understand not more than 900 sets), and for this reason we do not list them.

(New Currency. 100 pesewas = 1 cedi = 0.8 (1967) new cedi)

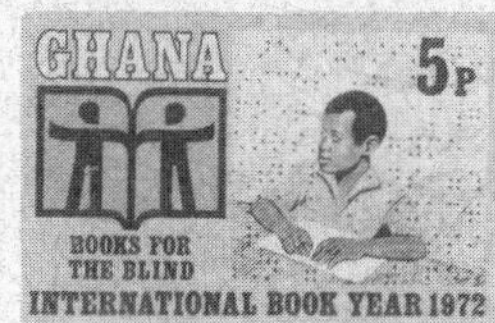

324 Books for the Blind

(Des and litho D.L.R.)

1972 (21 Apr). *International Book Year. T* **324** *and similar multicoloured designs. P* 13.

630	5 p. Type **324**	20	10
631	15 p. Children's books	55	50
632	30 p. Books for recreation	1·00	1·25
633	50 p. Books for students	1·75	2·75
634	1 c. Book and flame of knowledge (*vert*)	2·50	3·75
630/4	*Set of* 5	5·50	7·50
MS635	99 × 106 mm. Nos. 630/4. Imperf	8·00	11·00

325 *Hypoxis urceolata*

(Litho D.L.R.)

1972 (3 July). *Flora and Fauna. T* **325** *and similar horiz designs. Multicoloured. P* 13½.

636	5 p. Type **325**	30	10
637	15 p. Mona Monkey	65	65
638	30 p. *Crinum ornatum*	5·50	4·00
639	1 c. De Winton's Tree Squirrel	6·00	8·00
636/9	*Set of* 4	11·00	11·50

326 Football

(Litho D.L.R.)

1972 (5 Sept). *Olympic Games, Munich. T* **326** *and similar horiz designs. Multicoloured. P* 13.

640	5 p. Type **326**	15	10
641	15 p. Running	25	20
642	30 p. Boxing	50	65
643	50 p. Long-jumping	80	2·00
644	1 c. High-jumping	1·25	3·25
640/4	*Set of* 5	2·75	5·50
MS645	86 × 43 mm. 40 p. as No. 642 *se-tenant* with 60 p. as No. 640	2·25	6·50

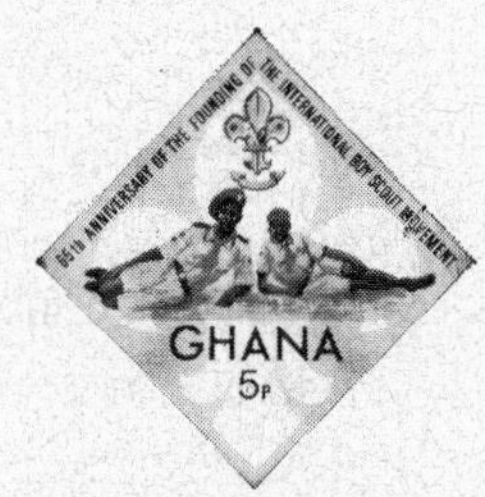

327 Senior Scout and Cub

(Litho Questa)

1972 (2 Oct). *65th Anniv of Boy Scouts. T* **327** *and similar diamond-shaped designs. Multicoloured. P* 13½.

646	5 p. Type **327**	30	10
647	15 p. Scout and tent	65	45
648	30 p. Sea scouts	1·25	1·25
649	50 p. Leader with cubs	1·60	2·00
650	1 c. Training school	3·00	3·50
646/50	*Set of* 5	6·00	6·50
MS651	110 × 110 mm. 40 p. as 30 p.; 60 p. as 1 c.	3·25	5·50

328 "The Holy Night" (Correggio)

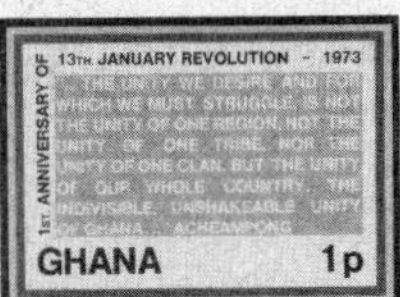

329 Extract from Speech

(Des G. Vasarhelyi and L. Apelt. Litho Questa)

1972 (1 Dec). *Christmas. T* **328** *and similar vert designs. Multicoloured. P* 13½.

652	1p. Type **328**	10	10
653	3p. "Adoration of the Kings" (Holbein the Elder)	10	10
654	15p. "Madonna of the Passion" (School of Ricco)	40	30
655	30p. "King Melchior"	70	70
656	60p. "King Gaspar, Mary and Jesus"	1·00	2·00
657	1 c. "King Balthasar"	1·50	3·00
652/7	*Set of* 6	3·25	5·50
MS658	139×90 mm. Nos. 655/7. Imperf	8·00	9·00

Nos. 655/7 are from a 16th-cent. Norman stained-glass window.

(Des and litho D.L.R.)

1973 (10 Apr). *First Anniv of January 13 Revolution. T* **329** *and similar multicoloured designs. P* 13 × 14 *(5, 15 p.) or* 14 × 13 *(others).*

659	1 p. Type **329**	10	10
660	3 p. Market scene	10	10
661	5 p. Selling bananas (*vert*)	10	10
662	15 p. Farmer with hoe and produce (*vert*)	20	25
663	30 p. Market traders	30	40
664	1 c. Farmer cutting palm-nuts	70	1·40
659/64	*Set of* 6	1·25	1·90
MS665	90 × 55 mm. 40 p. as 1 c. and 60 p. Miners	70	2·25

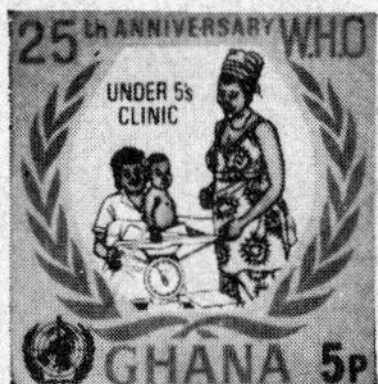

330 Under 5's Clinic

(Litho D.L.R.)

1973 (24 July). *25th Anniv of W.H.O. T* **330** *and similar square designs. Multicoloured. P* 13½.

666	5 p. Type **330**	10	10
667	15 p. Radiography	25	30
668	30 p. Immunisation	35	50
669	50 p. Starving child	50	1·25
670	1 c. W.H.O. H.Q., Geneva	75	2·25
666/70	*Set of* 5	1·75	4·00

1st WORLD SCOUTING CONFERENCE IN AFRICA

(331)

1973 (14 Aug). *First World Scouting Conference, Nairobi/Addis Ababa. Nos.* 646/51 *optd with T* **331**.
671 5 p. Type **327** 10 15
672 15 p. Scout and tent 35 60
673 30 p. Sea scouts .. .. 60 1·40
674 50 p. Leader with cubs.. .. .. .. 80 2·00
675 1 c. Training school .. .. 1·50 3·00
671/5 .. .. *Set of* 5 3·00 6·50
MS676 110 × 110 mm. 40 p. as 30 p.; 60 p. as 1 c. 2·00 6·50

332 Poultry Farming

(Litho Questa)

1973 (11 Sept). *Tenth Anniv of World Food Programme. T* **332** *and similar horiz designs. Multicoloured. P* 14.
677 5 p. Type **332** 10 10
678 15 p. Mechanisation 15 15
679 50 p. Cocoa harvest 40 90
680 1 c. F.A.O. H.Q., Rome .. .. .. 60 1·90
677/80 .. .. *Set of* 4 1·00 2·75
MS681 92 × 104 mm. 40 p. as 15 p.; 60 p. as 1 c. 60 2·25

333 "Green Alert"

(Litho D.L.R.)

1973 (1 Oct). *50th Anniv of Interpol. T* **333** *and similar horiz designs. Multicoloured. P* 13.
682 5 p. Type **333** 15 10
683 30 p. "Red Alert" 75 80
684 50 p. "Blue Alert" .. .. 1·50 1·75
685 1 c. "Black Alert" .. .. 3·00 4·00
682/5 .. .. *Set of* 4 4·75 6·00

334 Handshake

(Litho Format)

1973 (22 Oct). *Tenth Anniv of O.A.U. T* **334** *and similar horiz designs. Multicoloured. P* 14 × 14½.
686 5 p. Type **334** 10 10
687 30 p. Africa Hall, Addis Ababa 15 30
688 50 p. O.A.U. emblem .. .. 20 1·00
689 1 c. "X" in colours of Ghana flag .. .. 35 1·50
686/9 .. .. *Set of* 4 70 2·50

335 Weather Balloon

336 Epiphany Scene

(Des G. Vasarhelyi. Litho Format)

1973 (16 Nov). *I.M.O./W.M.O. Centenary. T* **335** *and similar horiz designs. Multicoloured. P* 14 × 14½.
690 5 p. Type **335** 10 10
691 15 p. Satellite "Tiros" 15 20
692 30 p. Computer weather map 30 65
693 1 c. Radar .. .. 60 2·25
690/3 .. .. *Set of* 4 1·00 2·75
MS694 120 × 95 mm. 40 p. as 15 p.; 60 p. as 30 p. 1·25 3·25

(Litho D.L.R.)

1973 (10 Dec). *Christmas. T* **336** *and similar vert designs. Multicoloured. P* 14.
695 1 p. Type **336** 10 10
696 3 p. Madonna and Child 10 10
697 30 p. "Madonna and Child" (Murillo) 30 75
698 50 p. "Adoration of the Magi" (Tiepolo) .. 45 1·00
695/8 .. .. *Set of* 4 1·25 2·75
MS699 77 × 103 mm. Nos. 695/8. Imperf.. .. 1·25 3·00

337 "Christ carrying the Cross" (Thomas de Kolozsvar)

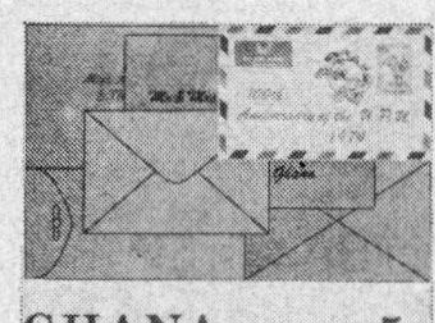

338 Letters

(Des M. Shamir and A. Larkins. Litho D.L.R.)

1974 (17 Apr). *Easter. T* **337** *and similar vert designs. P* 14.
700 5 p. multicoloured 10 10
701 30 p. bright blue, silver and sepia 20 35
702 50 p. light orange-vermilion, silver and sepia 30 60
703 1 c. dull yellow-green, silver and sepia .. 50 1·25
700/3 .. .. *Set of* 4 90 2·00
MS704 111 × 106 mm. 15 p. as No. 700, 20 p. as No. 701, 25 p. as No. 702. Imperf .. .. 80 1·75
Designs (from 15th-century English carved alabaster):—30 p. "The Betrayal"; 50 p. "The Deposition"; 1 c. "The Risen Christ and Mary Magdalene".

(Des A. Larkins. Litho Questa)

1974 (21 May). *Centenary of Universal Postal Union. T* **338** *and similar horiz designs. Multicoloured. P* 14½.
705 5 p. Type **338** 10 10
706 9 p. U.P.U. Monument and H.Q. 10 15
707 50 p. Airmail letter .. .. 35 1·00
708 1 c. U.P.U. Monument and Ghana stamp .. 60 1·75
705/8 .. .. *Set of* 4 1·00 2·75
MS709 108 × 90 mm. 20 p. as No. 705, 30 p. as No. 706, 40 p. as No. 707, 60 p. as No. 708 .. .. 75 1·60
Nos. 705/8 were issued both in sheets of 30 and in sheets of 5 stamps and 1 label.

1974 (7 June). *"Internaba 1974" Stamp Exhibition, Basle. Nos.* 705/9 *additionally inscribed* "INTERNABA 1974".
710 5 p. Type **338** 10 10
711 9 p. U.P.U. Monument and H.Q. 10 15
712 50 p. Airmail letter .. .. 30 1·00
713 1 c. U.P.U. Monument and Ghana stamp .. 45 1·75
710/13 .. .. *Set of* 4 80 2·75
MS714 108 × 90 mm. 20 p. as No. 710; 30 p. as No. 711; 40 p. as No. 712; 60 p. as No. 713 .. .. 1·50 4·00

339 Footballers

(Des G. Vasarhelyi. Litho Format)

1974 (17 June). *World Cup Football Championships, West Germany. T* **339** *and similar horiz designs showing footballers. P* 14½.
715 **339** 5 p. multicoloured 10 10
716 – 30 p. multicoloured 25 60
717 – 50 p. multicoloured 35 85
718 – 1 c. multicoloured .. .. 50 1·50
715/18 .. .. *Set of* 4 1·00 2·75
MS719 148 × 94 mm. 25, 40, 55 and 60 p. as Nos. 715/18 .. .. 1·00 3·25
Nos. 715/18 also exist perf 13 (*price for set of* 4 £1 *mint*, £3.25 *used*) from additional sheetlets of 5 stamps and 1 label. Stamps perforated 14½ are from normal sheets of 25.
The sheetlets, together with No. **MS**719, exist imperforate from stock dispersed by the liquidator of Format International Security Printers Ltd.

340 Roundabout

WEST GERMANY WINNERS

(341)

(Des and litho B.W.)

1974 (16 July). *Change to Driving on the Right. T* **340** *and similar designs. P* 13½ (5 *and* 15 p.) *or* 14½ × 14 (*others*).
720 5 p. bright yellow-grn, rose-vermilion & blk 10 10
721 15 p. lavender, dull red and black 25 35
722 30 p. multicoloured 45 60
723 50 p. multicoloured .. .. 70 1·10
724 1 c. multicoloured .. .. 1·40 2·00
720/4 .. .. *Set of* 5 2·75 3·75
Designs: *Horiz*—15 p. Warning triangle sign. *Vert* (29 × 42 *mm*)—30 p. Highway arrow and slogan; 50 p. Warning hands; 1 c. Car on symbolic hands.

1974 (30 Aug). *West Germany's Victory in World Cup. Nos.* 715/19 *optd with T* **341**. *P* 14½.
725 **339** 5 p. multicoloured 10 10
726 – 30 p. multicoloured 35 40
727 – 50 p. multicoloured 50 55
728 – 1 c. multicoloured .. .. 90 1·25
725/8 .. .. *Set of* 4 1·75 2·10
MS729 148 × 94 mm. 25, 40, 55, 60 p. as Nos. 725/8 .. .. 1·25 2·50
This overprint also exists on the stamps perforated 13 mentioned below No. **MS**719 (*Price for set of* 4 £2 *mint or used*).

342 "Planned Family"

(Des and litho D.L.R.)

1974 (12 Sept). *World Population Year. T* **342** *and similar horiz designs. Multicoloured. P* 12½.
730 5 p. Type **342** 10 10
731 30 p. Family planning clinic 25 35
732 50 p. Immunization 35 60
733 1 c. Population census enumeration.. .. 60 1·40
730/3 .. .. *Set of* 4 1·10 2·25

343 Angel

APOLLO
SOYUZ
JULY 15, 1975

(344)

(Des A. Medina (5 and 7 p.), A. Larkins (others). Litho D.L.R.)

1974 (19 Dec). *Christmas. T* **343** *and similar multicoloured designs. P* 13½.
734 5 p. Type **343** 10 10
735 7 p. The Magi (*diamond* 47 × 47 *mm*) .. 10 10
736 9 p. The Nativity 10 10
737 1 c. The Annunciation .. .. .. 60 1·40
734/7 .. .. *Set of* 4 80 1·50
MS738 128 × 128 mm. 15 p. Type **343**; 30 p. as 7 p.; 45 p. as 9 p.; 60 p. as 1 c. Imperf .. .. .. 80 2·50

1975 (15 Aug). *"Apollo–Soyuz" Space Link. Nos.* 715/19 *optd with T* **344**. *P* 14½.
739 5 p. multicoloured 10 10
740 30 p. multicoloured 25 25
741 50 p. multicoloured 45 55
742 1 c. multicoloured 70 80
739/42 .. .. *Set of* 4 1·25 1·50
MS743 148 × 94 mm. 25, 40, 55, 60 p. as Nos. 739/42 .. .. 1·25 2·00
This overprint also exists on the stamps perforated 13 mentioned below No. **MS**719 (*Price for set of* 4 £6 *mint*, £7 *used*).

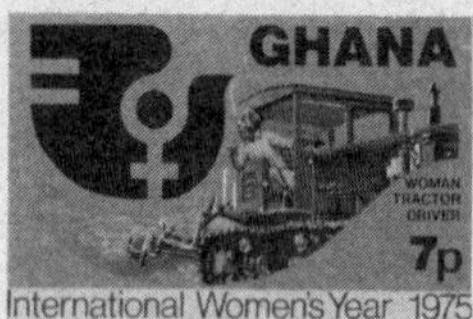

345 Tractor Driver

(Des and litho D.L.R.)

1975 (3 Sept). *International Women's Year. T* **345** *and similar horiz designs each showing I.W.Y. emblem. Multicoloured. P* 14 × 13½.
744 7 p. Type **345** 25 10
745 30 p. Motor mechanic 75 35
746 60 p. Factory workers 90 80
747 1 c. Cocoa research .. .. 1·10 1·40
744/7 .. .. *Set of* 4 2·75 2·40
MS748 136 × 110 mm. 15, 40, 65 and 80 p. as Nos. 744/7. Imperf .. .. 2·00 6·00

346 Angel

(Litho D.L.R.)

1975 (31 Dec). *Christmas. T* **346** *and similar horiz designs. P* 14 × 13½.

749	2 p. multicoloured	10	10
750	5 p. greenish yellow and light green	10	10
751	7 p. greenish yellow and light green	10	10
752	30 p. greenish yellow and light green	20	20
753	1 c. greenish yellow and light green	50	1·00
749/53	*Set of* 5	80	1·25
MS754	98 × 87 mm. 15, 40, 65 and 80 p. as Nos. 750/3. Imperf	90	3·00

Designs:—5 p. Angel with harp; 7 p. Angel with lute; 30 p. Angel with viol; 1 c. Angel with trumpet.

347 Map Reading

(Litho Format)

1976 (5 Jan). *14th World Scout Jamboree, Norway. T* **347** *and similar horiz designs. Multicoloured. P* 13½ × 14.

755	7 p. Type **347**	20	10
756	30 p. Sailing	60	90
757	60 p. Hiking	90	2·25
758	1 c. Life-saving	1·10	2·50
755/8	*Set of* 4	2·50	5·25
MS759	133 × 99 mm. 15, 40, 65 and 80 p. as Nos. 755/8	2·25	6·50

Nos. 755/9 exist imperforate from stock dispersed by the liquidator of Format International Security Printers Ltd.

348 Bottles (litre)

(Litho D.L.R.)

1976 (5 Jan). *Metrication Publicity. T* **348** *and similar horiz designs. Multicoloured. P* 14.

760	7 p. Type **348**	15	10
761	30 p. Scales (kilogramme)	40	40
762	60 p. Tape measure and bale of cloth (metre)	80	1·00
763	1 c. Ice, thermometer and kettle (temperature)	1·25	1·75
760/3	*Set of* 4	2·40	2·75

349 Fair Site

(Litho Format)

1976 (6 Apr). *International Trade Fair, Accra. T* **349** *and similar horiz designs. P* 13½.

764 **349**	7 p. multicoloured	10	10
765 –	30 p. multicoloured	20	20
766 –	60 p. multicoloured	35	60
767 –	1 c. multicoloured	55	1·00
764/7	*Set of* 4	1·10	1·60

Nos. 765/7 are as T **349** but show different views of the Fair.

Nos. 764/7 exist imperforate from stock dispersed by the liquidator of Format International Security Printers Ltd.

'INTERPHIL' 76
BICENTENNIAL
EXHIBITION

(350)

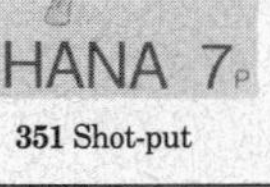

351 Shot-put

1976 (28 May). *Interphil Stamp Exhibition, Philadelphia. Nos. 755/9 optd with T* **350** *in blue.*

768	7 p. Type **347**	15	15
769	30 p. Sailing	35	50
770	60 p. Hiking	55	75
771	1 c. Life-saving	80	1·25
768/71	*Set of* 4	1·75	2·40
MS772	133 × 99 mm. 15, 40, 65 and 80 p. as Nos. 768/71	1·50	2·50

Nos. 768/71 exist imperforate from stock dispersed by the liquidator of Format International Security Printers Ltd.

(Des PAD Studio. Litho Format)

1976 (9 Aug). *Olympic Games, Montreal. T* **351** *and similar vert designs. Multicoloured. P* 13½.

773	7 p. Type **351**	15	10
774	30 p. Football	30	25
775	60 p. Women's 1500 metres	45	50
776	1 c. Boxing	60	80
773/6	*Set of* 4	1·40	1·50
MS777	103 × 135 mm. 15, 40, 65 and 80 p. as Nos. 773/6	1·50	1·50

Nos. 773/6 also exist perf 15 (*Price for set of* 4 £2·25 *mint or used*) from additional sheetlets of 5 stamps and 1 label. Stamps perforated 13½ are from normal sheets of 30. The sheetlets also exist imperforate from stock dispersed by the liquidator of Format International Security Printers Ltd.

352 Supreme Court

(Litho D.L.R.)

1976 (7 Sept). *Centenary of Supreme Court. T* **352** *and similar horiz designs. P* 14.

778 **352**	8 p. multicoloured	10	10
779 –	30 p. multicoloured	20	25
780 –	60 p. multicoloured	35	50
781 –	1 c. multicoloured	60	1·00
778/81	*Set of* 4	1·10	1·75

Nos. 779/81 show different views of the Court Building.

353 Examination for River Blindness

(Des and litho D.L.R.)

1976 (28 Oct). *Prevention of Blindness. T* **353** *and similar horiz designs. Multicoloured. P* 14 × 13½.

782	7 p. Type **353**	65	10
783	30 p. Entomologist	1·75	1·40
784	60 p. Normal vision	2·75	2·75
785	1 c. Blackfly eradication	4·25	4·50
782/5	*Set of* 4	8·50	8·00

354 Fireworks Party, Christmas Eve

(Des A. Adom & A. Larkins. Litho D.L.R.)

1976 (15 Dec). *Christmas. T* **354** *and similar horiz designs. Multicoloured. P* 13.

786	6 p. Type **354**	15	10
787	8 p. Children and gifts	15	10
788	30 p. Christmas feast	50	30
789	1 c. As 8 p.	1·10	1·75
786/9	*Set of* 4	1·75	2·00
MS790	122 × 98 mm. 15, 40, 65 and 80 p. as Nos. 786/9. Imperf	2·00	4·00

355 "Gallows Frame" Telephone and Alexander Graham Bell

EAST GERMANY
WINNERS

(356)

(Des A. Larkins. Litho Format)

1976 (17 Dec). *Telephone Centenary. T* **355** *and similar horiz designs showing telephones and Alexander Graham Bell. Multicoloured. P* 13.

791	8 p. Type **355**	20	10
792	30 p. 1895 telephone	30	30
793	60 p. 1929 telephone	50	70
794	1 c. 1976 telephone	75	1·25
791/4	*Set of* 4	1·60	2·00
MS795	125 × 92 mm. 15, 40, 65 and 80 p. as Nos. 791/4	1·50	1·75

1977 (22 Feb). *Olympic Winners. Nos. 773/7 optd with the name of the country given, as T* **356.** *P* 13½.

796	7 p. East Germany	15	15
797	30 p. East Germany	35	40
798	60 p. U.S.S.R.	45	85
799	1 c. U.S.A.	65	1·50
796/9	*Set of* 4	1·40	2·50
MS800	103 × 135 mm. 15, 40, 65 and 80 p. as Nos. 796/9	2·25	2·50

357 Dipo Dancers and Drum Ensemble

(Des A. Larkins. Litho Format)

1977 (24 Mar). *Second World Black and African Festival of Arts and Culture, Nigeria. T* **357** *and similar horiz designs. Multicoloured. P* 13½.

801	8 p. Type **357**	15	15
802	30 p. Arts and Crafts	30	60
803	60 p. Acon music and dancing priests	50	1·25
804	1 c. African huts	60	2·00
801/4	*Set of* 4	1·40	3·50
MS805	164 × 120 mm. 15, 40, 65 and 80 p. as Nos. 801/4	1·40	1·50

PRINCE CHARLES
VISITS GHANA
17th TO 25th
MARCH, 1977

(358)

1977 (2 June). *Prince Charles's Visit to Ghana. Nos. 791/5 optd with T* **358**.

806	8 p. Type **355**	50	55
807	30 p. 1895 telephone	1·25	1·00
808	60 p. 1929 telephone	1·75	2·00
809	1 c. 1976 telephone	2·25	2·50
806/9	*Set of* 4	5·25	5·50
MS810	125 × 92 mm. 15, 40, 65 and 80 p. as Nos. 806/9	8·00	8·50

359 Olive Colobus

360 "Le Chapeau de Paille" (Rubens—400th Birth Anniv)

(Des PAD Studio. Litho Format)

1977 (22 June). *Wildlife. T* **359** *and similar horiz designs. Multicoloured. P* 13½.

811	8 p. Type **359**	45	15
812	20 p. Temminck's Giant Squirrel	1·25	80
813	30 p. Hunting Dog	1·75	1·25
814	60 p. African Manatee	3·00	2·75
811/14	*Set of* 4	5·75	4·50
MS815	140 × 101 mm. 15, 40, 65 and 80 p. as Nos. 811/14	5·50	5·50

No. **MS**815 exists imperforate from stock dispersed by the liquidator of Format International Security Printers Ltd.

(Des PAD Studio. Litho Format)

1977 (Sept). *Painters' Anniversaries. T* **360** *and similar vert designs. Multicoloured. P* 14 × 13½.

816	8 p. Type **360**	25	10
817	30 p. "Isabella of Portugal" (Titian—500th Birth Anniv)	50	40
818	60 p. "Duke and Duchess of Cumberland" (Gainsborough—250th Birth Anniv)	65	65
819	1 c. "Rubens and Isabella Brandt"	85	1·25
816/19	*Set of* 4	2·00	2·25
MS820	99 × 149 mm. 15, 40, 65 and 80 p. as Nos. 816/19	2·25	2·25

No. **MS**820 exists imperforate from stock dispersed by the liquidator of Format International Security Printers Ltd.

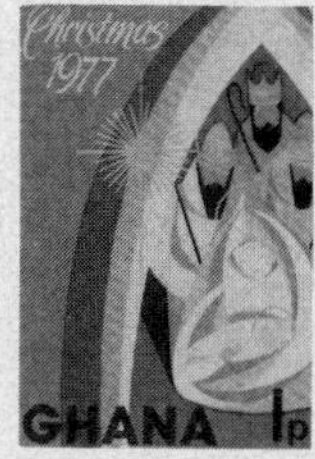

361 The Magi, Madonna and Child

REFERENDUM 1978
VOTE EARLY
(362)

(Litho De La Rue, Colombia)

1977 (30 Dec). *Christmas. T* **361** *and similar multicoloured designs. P* 14 (1 *p.*, 8 *p.*) *or* 14 × 13½ (*others*).
821 1 p. Type **361** 10 10
822 2 p. Choir from Abossey Okai (45 × 27 *mm*) 10 10
823 6 p. Methodist Church, Wesley, Accra (45 × 27 *mm*) . . 10 10
824 8 p. Madonna and Child . . 10 10
825 30 p. Holy Spirit Cathedral, Accra (45 × 27 *mm*) . . 40 50
826 1 c. Ebeneezer Presbyterian Church, Accra (45 × 27 *mm*) . . 1·25 1·60
821/6 . . *Set of* 6 1·75 2·25
MS827 122 × 97 mm. 15, 40, 65 and 80 p. as Nos. 822/3 and 825/6. Imperf . . 1·75 3·75
Nos. 822/3 and 825/6 all have as a background the score to the carol "Hark the Herald Angels Sing".

1978 (Mar). *1978 Referendum. Nos.* 821/7 *optd with T* **362** *by De La Rue, Colombia.*
828 1 p. Type **361** . . 10 10
829 2 p. Choir from Abossey Okai . . 10 10
830 6 p. Methodist Church, Wesley, Accra . . 10 10
831 8 p. Madonna and Child . . 10 10
832 30 p. Holy Spirit Cathedral, Accra . . 40 50
833 1 c. Ebeneezer Presbyterian Church, Accra 1·25 1·50
828/33 . . *Set of* 6 1·75 2·10
MS834 122 × 97 mm. 15, 40, 65, 80 p. as Nos. 829/30 and 832/3 . . 27·00 17·00

363 Cutting Bananas

(Litho De La Rue, Colombia)

1978 (15 May). *Operation "Feed Yourself". T* **363** *and similar horiz designs. Multicoloured. P* 14.
835 2 p. Type **363** . . 10 10
836 8 p. Home produce . . 10 10
837 30 p. Market . . 25 35
838 60 p. Fishing . . 60 60
839 1 c. Mechanisation . . 80 1·25
835/9 . . *Set of* 5 1·60 2·10

364 Wright Flyer III

"CAPEX 78
JUNE 9-18 1978"
(365)

(Des J.W. Litho Format)

1978 (6 June). *75th Anniv of Powered Flight. T* **364** *and similar vert designs. P* 14 × 13½.
840 8 p. black, deep brown and brown-ochre . . 20 10
841 30 p. black, deep brown and blue-green . . 40 30
842 60 p. black, deep brown and rosine . . 60 60
843 1 c. black, deep brown and ultramarine . . 1·75 1·10
840/3 . . *Set of* 4 2·75 1·90
MS844 167 × 100 mm. 15, 40, 65, 80 p. as Nos. 840/3 . . 2·50 1·75
Designs:—30 p. Handley Page H.P.42; 60 p. De Havilland D.H.106 Comet 1; 1 c. Concorde.
No. 841 exists imperforate from stock dispersed by the liquidator of Format International Security Printers Ltd.

1978 (9 June). *"CAPEX 1978" International Stamp Exhibition, Toronto. Nos.* 840/4 *optd with T* **365**.
845 8 p. black, deep brown and brown-ochre . . 15 15
846 30 p. black, deep brown and blue-green . . 25 25
847 60 p. black, deep brown and rosine . . 50 50
848 1 c. black, deep brown and ultramarine . . 1·10 80
845/8 . . *Set of* 4 1·75 1·50
MS849 167 × 100 mm. 15, 40, 65, 80 p. as Nos. 845/8 . . 1·75 2·00

366 Players and African Cup Emblem

(Litho Format)

1978 (1 July). *Football Championships. T* **366** *and similar horiz designs. Multicoloured. P* 13½ × 14.
850 8 p. Type **366** . . 20 15
851 30 p. Players and African Cup emblem (*different*) . . 25 30
852 60 p. Players and World Cup emblem . . 40 60
853 1 c. Goalkeeper and World Cup emblem . . 55 1·00
850/3 . . *Set of* 4 1·25 1·90
MS854 111 × 105 mm. 15, 40, 65, 80 p. as Nos. 850/3 . . 1·10 1·25
The 8 and 30 p. values commemorate the African Nations Cup; the other values the World Cup Football Championship, Argentina.
Nos. 850/3 exist imperforate from stock dispersed by the liquidator of Format International Security Printers Ltd.

367 "The Betrayal"

"GHANA WINNERS"
(368)

(Litho Format)

1978 (15 July). *Easter. Details from drawings by Dürer. T* **367** *and similar vert designs. P* 14 × 13½.
855 11 p. black and bright reddish violet . . 10 10
856 39 p. black and flesh . . 25 30
857 60 p. black and orange-yellow . . 40 45
858 1 c. black and pale yellow-green . . 60 65
855/8 . . *Set of* 4 1·25 1·40
Designs:—39 p. "The Crucifixion"; 60 p. "The Deposition"; 1 c. "The Resurrection".

1978 (21 Aug). *Ghana—Winners of African Nations Football Cup and Argentina—Winners of World Cup Football Championship. Nos.* 850/1 *and* **MS**854 *optd with T* **368** *and Nos.* 852/3 *optd* "ARGENTINA WINS".
859 8 p. Type **366** . . 15 15
860 30 p. Players and African Cup emblem (*different*) . . 25 30
861 60 p. Players and World Cup emblem . . 35 45
862 1 c. Goalkeeper and World Cup emblem . . 55 75
859/62 . . *Set of* 4 1·10 1·50
MS863 111 × 105 mm. 15, 40, 65, 80 p. as Nos. 859/62 but all opt with T **368** . . 1·00 1·10
Nos. 859/60 exist imperforate from stock dispersed by the liquidator of Format International Security Printers Ltd.

369 *Bauhinia purpurea*

(Litho Format)

1978 (20 Nov). *Flowers. T* **369** *and similar vert designs. Multicoloured. P* 14 × 13½.
864 11 p. Type **369** . . 15 10
865 39 p. *Cassia fistula* . . 30 55
866 60 p. *Plumeria acutifolia* . . 40 70
867 1 c. *Jacaranda mimosifolia* . . 45 1·00
864/7 . . *Set of* 4 1·10 2·10
No. 864 exists imperforate from stock dispersed by the liquidator of Format International Security Printers Ltd.

ALTERED CATALOGUE NUMBERS

Any Catalogue numbers altered from the last edition are shown as a list in the introductory pages.

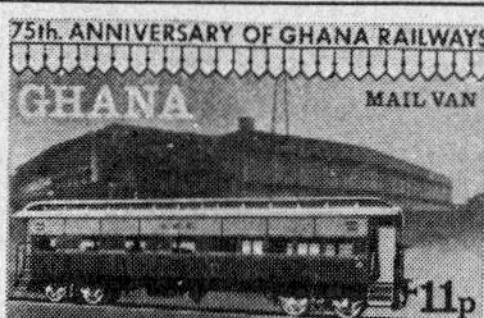

370 Mail Van

(Litho Format)

1978 (4 Dec). *75th Anniv of Ghana Railways. T* **370** *and simila horiz designs. Multicoloured. P* 13½ × 14.
868 11 p. Type **370** . . 25 1(
869 39 p. Pay and bank car . . 35 65
870 60 p. Steam locomotive No. 1 *Amanful*, 1922 40 1·0(
871 1 c. Diesel-electric locomotive No. 1651, 1960 . . 40 1·4(
868/71 . . *Set of* 4 1·25 2·75
Nos. 868/71 exist imperforate from stock dispersed by the liquidator of Format International Security Printers Ltd.

371 "Orbiter" Spacecraft

(Litho Format)

1979 (5 July). *"Pioneer" Venus Space Project. T* **371** *and simila horiz designs. Multicoloured. P* 14 × 13½.
872 11 p. Type **371** . . 15 1
873 39 p. "Multiprobe" spacecraft . . 25 3
874 60 p. "Orbiter" and "Multiprobe" spacecraft in Venus orbit . . 40 4
875 3 c. Radar chart of Venus . . 60 1·6
872/5 . . *Set of* 4 1·25 2·2
MS876 135 × 94 mm. 15, 40, 65 p., 2 c. as Nos. 872/5. Imperf . . 1·10 1·2

372 "O Come All Ye Faithful"

373 Dr. J. B. Danquah (lawyer and nationalist)

(Litho D.L.R.)

1979 (20 Dec). *Christmas. Opening Lines and Scenes from wel known Carols. T* **372** *and similar horiz designs. Multicoloured P* 14 × 14½.
877 8 p. Type **372** . . 10 1(
878 10 p. "O Little Town of Bethlehem" . . 10 1(
879 15 p. "We Three Kings of Orient Are" . . 10 1(
880 20 p. "I Saw Three Ships come Sailing By" . . 10 1
881 2 c. "Away in a Manger" . . 40 8(
882 4 c. "Ding Dong Merrily on High" . . 65 1·4(
877/82 . . *Set of* 6 1·25 2·4(
MS883 110 × 95 mm. 25, 65 p., 1, 2 c. as Nos. 877, 879 and 881/2 . . 75 1·0(

(Litho D.L.R.)

1980 (21 Jan). *Great Ghanaians. T* **373** *and similar vert designs Multicoloured. P* 14 × 13½.
884 20 p. Type **373** . . 15 1
885 65 p. John Mensah Sarbah (nationalist) . . 20 2
886 80 p. Dr. J. E. K. Aggrey (educationalist) . . 25 3
887 2 c. Dr. Kwame Nkrumah (nationalist) . . 40 4
888 4 c. G. E. (Paa) Grant (lawyer) . . 70 1·1
884/8 . . *Set of* 5 1·50 1·7

374 Tribesman ringing Clack Bells

375 Children in Classroom

(Des G. Vasarhelyi. Litho Format)

1980 (12 Mar). *Death Centenary of Sir Rowland Hill* (1979). *T* **374** *and similar horiz designs. Multicoloured.* (*a*) *P* 14½.
889 20 p. Type **374** . . 15 1
890 65 p. Chieftain with Golden Elephant staff . . 30 3
891 2 c. Tribesman banging drums . . 50 1·0
892 4 c. Chieftain with ivory and gold staff . . 75 2·0(
889/92 . . *Set of* 4 1·50 3·0(

(b) P 13½
93 25 p. Type 374 .. 15 20
94 50 p. As 65 p. .. 30 40
95 1 c. As 2 c. .. 50 85
96 5 c. As 4 c. .. 1·25 3·00
93/6 .. *Set of* 4 2·00 4·00
S897 115 × 86 mm. Nos. 893/6. P 14½ .. 1·00 1·50
Nos. 893/6 were each printed in small sheets of 6 including one *e-tenant* stamp-size label.

(Des J.W. Litho Questa)

980 (2 Apr). *International Year of the Child* (1979). *T* 375 *and similar vert designs. Multicoloured. P* 14½.
98 20 p. Type 375 .. 15 15
99 65 p. Children playing football .. 30 45
00 2 c. Children playing in boat .. 50 1·00
01 4 c. Mother and child .. 75 1·75
98/901 .. *Set of* 4 1·50 3·00
S902 156 × 94 mm. 25, 50 p., 1, 3 c. as Nos. 898/901 .. 1·25 1·75

"LONDON 1980"
6th - 14th May 1980
(376)

"PAPAL VISIT"
8th - 9th May
1980
(377)

980 (6 May). *"London 1980" International Stamp Exhibition. Nos.* 889/97 *optd with T* 376. (a) *P* 14½.
03 20 p. Type 374 .. 15 15
04 65 p. Chieftain with Golden Elephant staff .. 25 50
05 2 c. Tribesman banging drums .. 50 1·25
06 4 c. Chieftain with ivory and gold staff .. 75 2·25
03/6 .. *Set of* 4 1·50 3·75
(b) *P* 13½
07 25 p. Type 374 .. 60 1·00
08 50 p. As 65 p. .. 90 1·50
09 1 c. As 2 c. .. 1·50 2·25
10 5 c. As 4 c. .. 3·50 4·50
07/10 .. *Set of* 4 6·00 8·25
MS911 115 × 86 mm. Nos. 907/10. P 14½ .. 1·00 2·00

980 (8 May). *Papal Visit. Nos.* 898/902 *optd with T* 377.
12 20 p. Type 375 .. 45 25
13 65 p. Children playing football .. 90 60
14 2 c. Children playing in boat .. 1·50 1·40
15 4 c. Mother and child .. 2·25 2·50
12/15 .. *Set of* 4 4·50 4·25
MS916 156 × 94 mm. 25, 50 p., 1, 3 c. as Nos. 912/15 .. 9·00 7·50

378 Parliament House
379 Boeing 737 Airliner and Map of West Africa

(Litho Questa)

980 (4 Aug). *Third Republic Commemoration. T* 378 *and similar horiz designs. Multicoloured. P* 14.
17 20 p. Type 378 .. 10 10
18 65 p. Supreme Court .. 20 25
19 2 c. The Castle .. 40 70
17/19 .. *Set of* 3 60 95
MS920 72 × 113 mm. 25 p., 1, 3 c. As Nos. 917/19 60 1·10

(Litho Questa)

980 (5 Nov). *Fifth Anniv of E.C.O.W.A.S. (Economic Community of West African States). T* 379 *and similar horiz designs showing symbols named and map of West Africa. Multicoloured. P* 14.
21 20 p. Type 379 .. 10 10
22 65 p. Radio antenna .. 15 20
23 80 p. Cog-wheels .. 20 25
24 2 c. Corn ear .. 35 50
21/4 .. *Set of* 4 70 90

380 "O.A.U."
381 "The Adoration of the Magi"

(Litho Questa)

1980 (26 Nov). *Organisation of African Unity First Economic Summit, Nigeria. T* 380 *and similar vert designs. Multicoloured. P* 14½ × 14.
925 20 p. Type 380 .. 10 10
926 65 p. Banner with maps of Africa and Ghana .. 15 20
927 80 p. Map of Africa .. 15 25
928 2 c. Ghana flag, banner and map of Africa .. 20 65
925/8 .. *Set of* 4 55 1·00

(Litho Format)

1980 (10 Dec). *Christmas. Paintings by Fra Angelico. T* 381 *and similar vert designs. Multicoloured. P* 14.
929 15 p. Type 381 .. 10 10
930 20 p. "The Virgin and Child enthroned with four Angels" .. 10 10
931 2 c. "The Virgin and Child enthroned with eight Angels" .. 35 80
932 4 c. "The Annunciation" .. 60 1·60
929/32 .. *Set of* 4 1·00 2·25
MS933 77 × 112 mm. 25, 50 p., 1, 3 c. As Nos. 929/32 .. 75 1·25

382 "Health"
383 Narina Trogon

(Litho Format)

1980 (18 Dec). *75th Anniv of Rotary International. T* 382 *and similar horiz designs. Multicoloured. P* 14.
934 20 p. Type 382 .. 10 10
935 65 p. Rotary emblem and motto with maps of World and Ghana .. 15 30
936 2 c. Rotary emblem, globe and outstretched hands .. 35 85
937 4 c. "Eradication of Hunger" .. 60 1·50
934/7 .. *Set of* 4 1·10 2·50
MS938 121 × 93 mm. 25, 50 p., 1, 3 c. As Nos. 934/7 .. 1·10 2·00

(Des G. Drummond. Litho Harrison)

1981 (12 Jan). *Birds. T* 383 *and similar vert designs. Multicoloured. P* 14.
939 20 p. Type 383 .. 1·25 15
940 65 p. White-crowned Robin Chat .. 2·25 50
941 2 c. Swallow-tailed Bee Eater .. 2·75 1·75
942 4 c. Rose-ringed Parakeet .. 4·25 3·25
939/42 .. *Set of* 4 9·50 5·00
MS943 89×121 mm. 25, 50 p., 1, 3 c. As Nos. 939/42. P 14½ .. 5·00 4·00

384 Pope John Paul II and Archbishop of Canterbury with President Limann during Papal Visit
385 Royal Yacht *Britannia*

(Litho Format)

1981 (3 Mar). *First Anniv of Papal Visit. P* 14 × 13½.
944 **384** 20 p. multicoloured .. 25 15
945 65 p. multicoloured .. 45 55
946 80 p. multicoloured .. 60 70
947 2 c. multicoloured .. 1·10 2·00
944/7 .. *Set of* 4 2·25 3·00

(Des J.W. Litho Questa)

1981 (8 July–16 Sept). *Royal Wedding. T* 385 *and similar vert designs. Multicoloured.* (i) *Sheet stamps* (8 July). (a) *P* 14.
948 20 p. Prince Charles and Lady Diana Spencer 10 10
949 80 p. Prince Charles on visit to Ghana .. 15 20
950 4 c. Type 385 .. 50 80
948/50 .. *Set of* 3 60 1·00
MS951 95 × 85 mm. 7 c. St. Paul's Cathedral .. 70 1·25
(b) *P* 12
952 65 p. As 20 p. .. 15 25
953 1 c. As 80 p. .. 25 35
954 3 c. Type 385 .. 70 1·10
952/4 .. *Set of* 3 1·00 1·50
(ii) *Booklet stamps. P* 14 (16 Sept)
955 2 c. Type 385 .. 1·00 1·50
a. Booklet pane. Nos. 955/6 each × 2 .. 4·00
956 5 c. As 20 p. .. 1·00 2·75
The 65 p., 1 and 3 c. values were each printed in small sheets of 6 including one *se-tenant* stamp-size label.
The above exist imperforate from a restricted printing (*price for Nos.* 948/50 *set of* 3 £5, **MS**951 £6, *Nos.* 952/4 *set of* 3 £7.50 *and booklet pane No.* 955a £12, *all mint*).

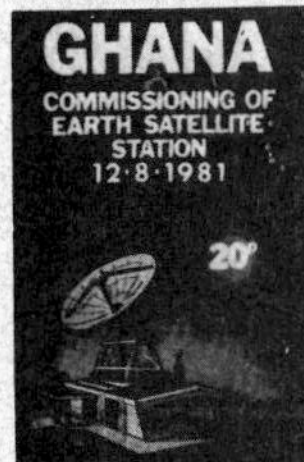

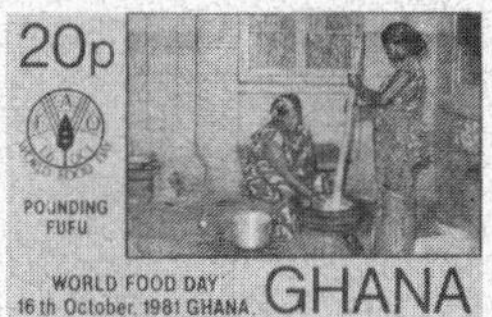

386 Earth Satellite Station
387 Pounding Fufu

(Litho Questa)

1981 (28 Sept). *Commissioning of Earth Satellite Station. T* 386 *and similar vert designs. Multicoloured. P* 14.
957 20 p. Type 386 .. 10 10
958 65 p. Satellites beaming signals to Earth .. 15 15
959 80 p. Satellite .. 15 20
960 4 c. Satellite orbiting Earth .. 1·00 1·50
957/60 .. *Set of* 4 1·25 1·75
MS961 112 × 100 mm. 25 p., 50 p., 1 c., 3 c. As Nos. 957/60 .. 70 1·40

(Des BG Studio. Litho Format)

1981 (16 Oct). *World Food Day. T* 387 *and similar horiz designs. Multicoloured. P* 13½ × 14.
962 20 p. Type 387 .. 10 10
963 65 p. Plucking Cocoa .. 25 35
964 80 p. Preparing Banku .. 35 45
965 2 c. Garri processing .. 75 2·25
962/5 .. *Set of* 4 1·25 2·75
MS966 131 × 99 mm. 25 p., 50 p., 1 c., 3 c. As Nos. 962/5 .. 1·00 1·50

388 "The Betrothal of St. Catherine of Alexandria" (Lucas Cranach)
389 Blind Person

(Des Clover Mill. Litho Format)

1981 (26 Nov). *Christmas. Details from Paintings. T* 388 *and similar vert designs. Multicoloured. P* 15.
967 15 p. Type 388 .. 15 10
968 20 p. "Angelic Musicians play for Mary and Child" (Aachener Altares) .. 15 10
969 65 p. "Child Jesus embracing his Mother" (Gabriel Metsu) .. 20 15
970 80 p. "Madonna and Child" (Fra Filippo Lippi) 20 20
971 2 c. "The Madonna with Infant Jesus" (Barnaba da Modena) .. 40 70
972 4 c. "The Immaculate Conception" (Murillo) 45 1·10
967/72 .. *Set of* 6 1·40 2·00
MS973 82 × 102 mm. 6 c. "Madonna and Child with Angels" (Hans Memling) .. 1·00 2·25

(Des G. Vasarhelyi. Litho Questa)

1982 (8 Feb). *International Year for Disabled Persons. T* 389 *and similar horiz designs. Multicoloured. P* 14.
974 20 p. Type 389 .. 10 10
975 65 p. Disabled person with crutches .. 30 35
976 80 p. Blind child reading braille .. 40 45
977 4 c. Disabled people helping one another .. 1·75 2·25
974/7 .. *Set of* 4 2·25 2·75
MS978 109 × 85 mm. 6 c. Group of disabled people 2·75 3·00

390 African Clawless Otter
391 *Precis westermanni*

(Des G. Drummond. Litho Harrison)

1982 (22 Feb). *Flora and Fauna. T* 390 *and similar vert designs. Multicoloured. P* 14.
979 20 p. Type 390 .. 25 15
980 65 p. Bushbuck .. 60 40
981 80 p. Aardvark .. 70 50
982 1 c. Scarlet Bell Tree .. 85 60
983 2 c. Glory-Lilies .. 1·60 1·25
984 4 c. Blue-Pea .. 2·75 2·25
979/84 .. *Set of* 6 6·00 4·75
MS985 76 × 100 mm. 5 c. Chimpanzee .. 2·00 5·00

(Litho Harrison)

1982 (3 May). *Butterflies. T* **391** *and similar vert designs. Multicoloured. P* 14.
986 20 p. Type **391** 70 15
987 65 p. *Papilio menestheus* .. .. 1·50 1·00
988 2 c. *Antanartia delius* .. .. 2·50 3·50
989 4 c. *Charaxes castor* .. .. 4·00 4·75
986/9 .. .. *Set of* 4 8·00 8·50
MS990 98×123 mm. 25 p., 50 p., 1 c., 3 c. As Nos. 986/9. P 14½ .. .. 9·00 12·00

392 Scouts planting Tree

(Des M. Diamond. Litho Format)

1982 (1 June). *75th Anniv of Boy Scout Movement. T* **392** *and similar multicoloured designs. P* 14½ × 15.
991 20 p. Type **392** 35 15
992 65 p. Scouts cooking on camp-fire 90 65
993 80 p. Sea Scouts sailing .. .. 1·25 85
994 3 c. Scouts observing elephant .. .. 2·50 3·25
991/4 .. .. *Set of* 4 4·50 4·50
MS995 101 × 71 mm. 5 c. Lord Baden-Powell (*vert*). P 15 × 14½ .. .. 2·75 6·50

393 Initial Stages of Construction

(Des C. Tetteh. Litho Questa)

1982 (28 June). *Kpong Hydro-Electric Project. T* **393** *and similar horiz designs. Multicoloured. P* 14.
996 20 p. Type **393** 65 10
997 65 p. Truck removing rubble .. .. .. 1·40 45
998 80 p. Hydro-electric turbines .. .. .. 1·60 65
999 2 c. Aerial view of completed plant .. .. 3·00 1·60
996/9 .. .. *Set of* 4 6·00 2·50

394 Footballers

(Des M. and S. Gerber Studio. Litho Format)

1982 (19 July). *World Cup Football Championship, Spain. T* **394** *and similar horiz designs showing footballers.* (a) *P* 14½.
1000 **394** 20 p. multicoloured 10 10
1001 – 65 p. multicoloured 30 35
1002 – 80 p. multicoloured 40 45
1003 – 4 c. multicoloured .. .. 1·50 2·00
1000/3 .. .. *Set of* 4 2·00 2·50
MS1004 110 × 90 mm. 6 c. multicoloured .. .. 3·75 2·75

(*b*) *P* 14 × 14½
1005 **394** 30 p. multicoloured 20 20
1006 – 80 p. multicoloured (as No. 1001) 35 45
1007 – 1 c. multicoloured (as No. 1002) 40 55
1008 – 3 c. multicoloured (as No. 1003) .. .. 1·00 1·60
1005/8 .. .. *Set of* 4 1·75 2·50

Nos. 1005/8 were each printed in small sheets including one *se-tenant*, stamp-size, label.

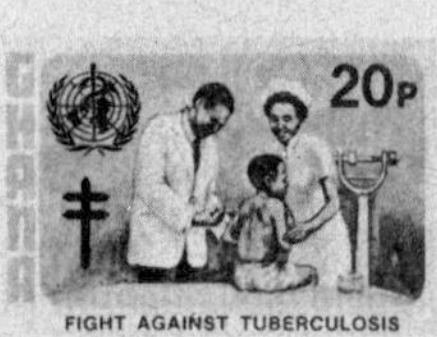

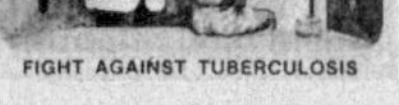

395 The Fight against Tuberculosis

396 The Shepherds worship Jesus

(Des M. Diamond. Litho Harrison)

1982 (9 Aug). *Centenary of Robert Koch's Discovery of Tubercle Bacillus. T* **395** *and similar horiz designs. Multicoloured. P* 14.
1009 20 p. Type **395** 70 20
1010 65 p. Robert Koch .. .. 1·60 1·25
1011 80 p. Robert Koch in Africa .. .. .. 2·00 1·75
1012 1 c. Centenary of discovery of Tuberculosis .. 2·25 2·75
1013 2 c. Robert Koch and Nobel Prize, 1905 .. 3·25 4·00
1009/13 .. .. *Set of* 5 9·00 9·00

(Des E. Mensah. Litho Format)

1982 (22 Dec). *Christmas. T* **396** *and similar vert designs. Multicoloured. P* 14½.
1014 15 p. Type **396** 10 10
1015 20 p. Mary, Joseph and baby Jesus 10 10
1016 65 p. The Three Kings sight star 25 30
1017 4 c. Winged Angel .. .. 1·00 1·75
1014/17 .. .. *Set of* 4 1·25 2·00
MS1018 90 × 110 mm. 6 c. The Three Kings with Jesus .. .. 90 1·75

Nos. 1017/18 exist imperforate from stock dispersed by the liquidator of Format International Security Printers Ltd.

397 Ghana and Commonwealth Flags with Coat of Arms

WINNER ITALY
3–1
(398)

(Des J.W. Litho Format)

1983 (14 Mar). *Commonwealth Day. T* **397** *and similar vert designs. Multicoloured. P* 14½.
1019 20 p. Type **397** 25 15
1020 55 p. Satellite view of Ghana 45 65
1021 80 p. Minerals of Ghana .. .. 1·00 1·25
1022 3 c. African Fish Eagle .. .. 2·75 4·25
1019/22 .. .. *Set of* 4 4·00 5·75

Nos. 1021/2 exist imperforate from stock dispersed by the liquidator of Format International Security Printers Ltd.

1983 (30 May). *Italy's Victory in World Cup Football Championship* (1982). *Nos.* 1000/8 *optd with T* **398**, *in gold.* (*a*) *P* 14½.
1023 **394** 20 p. multicoloured 10 10
1024 – 65 p. multicoloured 15 15
1025 – 80 p. multicoloured 15 20
1026 – 4 c. multicoloured .. .. 1·25 1·75
1023/6 .. .. *Set of* 4 1·40 2·00
MS1027 110 × 90 mm. 6 c. multicoloured .. .. 1·50 1·50

(*b*) *P* 14 × 14½
1028 **394** 30 p. multicoloured 15 30
1029 – 80 p. multicoloured 50 80
1030 – 1 c. multicoloured 60 95
1031 – 3 c. multicoloured .. .. 1·50 2·00
1028/31 .. .. *Set of* 4 2·50 3·50

No. **MS**1027 has an additional overprint, "FINAL: ITALY V. W. GERMANY", on the sheet margin.

INFLATION HANDSTAMPS. During 1983 the value of the Ghanaian currency fell drastically and as a result, there was a considerable rise in postal rates.

To cope with this situation supplies of past commemorative issues were made available from the post offices, many being hand-stamped "NOT FOR PHILATELIC USE" in one line within a frame. These handstamps were usually applied in blue, haphazardly across the sheet with examples so far reported on Nos. 656/7, 664, 670, 680, 689, 703, 708, 718, 746/7, 753, 757, 762/3, 766, 775, 780/1, 791, 793, 799, 814, 817, 846/7, 850/1, 853, 856/7, 860, 865, 867, 869, 875 and 882.

(398*a*)

399 Short-finned Pilot Whale

1983 (Oct). *No.* 470 *surch with T* **398***a*.
1031*a* 1 c. on 20 n.p. deep blue and new blue 40 40
ab. Surch triple .. .. ..
ac. Surch double .. .. ..
ad. Surch double, one inverted .. ..

(Des J. Iskowitz. Litho Format)

1983 (15 Nov). *Coastal Marine Mammals. T* **399** *and similar horiz designs. Multicoloured. P* 14½.
1032 1 c. Type **399** .. .. 1·00 1·00
1033 1 c. 40, Risso's Dolphin .. .. .. 1·10 1·10
1034 2 c. 30, False Killer Whale .. .. .. 1·25 1·25
1035 3 c. Spinner Dolphin .. .. 1·60 1·60
1036 5 c. Atlantic Hump-backed Dolphin .. 2·00 2·00
1032/6 .. .. *Set of* 5 6·25 6·25
MS1037 117 × 76 mm. 6 c. As 5 c. .. .. 1·25 1·00

No. **MS**1037 exists imperforate from stock dispersed by the liquidator of Format International Security Printers Ltd.

400 Banded Jewelfish

401 Communication Devices

(Des and litho D.L.R.)

1983 (12 Dec). *T* **400** *and similar designs. P* 14.
1038 5 p. multicoloured 30 2
1039 10 p. multicoloured 30 2
1040 20 p. multicoloured 40 2
1041 50 p. deep grey-green, yellow-orange and black 40 3
1042 1 c. yellow-orange, violet-blue and black .. 50 2
1043 2 c. multicoloured 50 3
1044 3 c. multicoloured 80 3
1045 4 c. multicoloured 40 4
1046 5 c. multicoloured 50 4
1047 10 c. multicoloured .. .. 65 1·0
1038/47 .. .. *Set of* 10 4·25 3·2

Designs: *Horiz*—10 p. Banded Jewelfish (*different*); 2 c. Je airliner. *Vert*—20 p. *Haemanthus rupestris*; 50 p. Mounte warrior; 1 c. Scorpion; 3 c. White-collared Mangabey; 4 c Demidoff's Galago; 5 c. *Kaemferia nigerica*; 10 c. Grey-backe Camaroptera.

(Des PAD Studio. Litho Questa)

1983 (13 Dec). *World Communications Year. T* **401** *and simila vert designs. Multicoloured. P* 14.
1048 1 c. Type **401** 15 2
1049 1 c. 40, Satellite dish aerial 20 3
1050 2 c. 30, Cable and cable-laying ship 35 5
1051 3 c. Switchboard operators 40 6
1052 5 c. Aircraft cockpit and air traffic controllers 55 8
1048/52 .. .. *Set of* 5 1·50 2·4
MS1053 95 × 70 mm. 6 c. Space satellite 30 5

402 Children receiving Presents

403 Soldiers with Rifles

(Des Designs Images. Litho Questa)

1983 (28 Dec). *Christmas. T* **402** *and similar multicoloure designs. P* 14 × 13½ (*70 p. and 3 c.*) *or* 14½ × 14 (*others*).
1054 70 p. Type **402** 20
1055 1 c. Nativity and Star of Bethlehem (28 × 36 *mm*) 20
1056 1 c. 40, Children celebrating (28 × 36 *mm*) .. 35
1057 2 c. 30, Family praying (28 × 36 *mm*) .. 45 1·
1058 3 c. Dancing to bongo drum .. .. .. 55 1·
1054/8 .. .. *Set of* 5 1·60 2·
MS1059 70 × 90 mm. 6 c. As 2 c. 30 .. .. 30 1·

(Des and litho B.D.T.)

1984 (26 Jan). *Namibia Day. T* **403** *and similar vert designs. P* 1
1060 50 p. blue-green and black 10
1061 1 c. multicoloured 10
1062 1 c. 40, new blue, bright blue and black .. 15 1
1063 2 c. 30, multicoloured 20 2
1064 3 c. multicoloured 25 3
1060/4 .. .. *Set of* 5 65 7

Designs:—1 c. Soldiers supported by tank; 1 c. 40, Mache cutting chains; 2 c. 30, Peasant woman; 3 c. Soldiers and artille support.

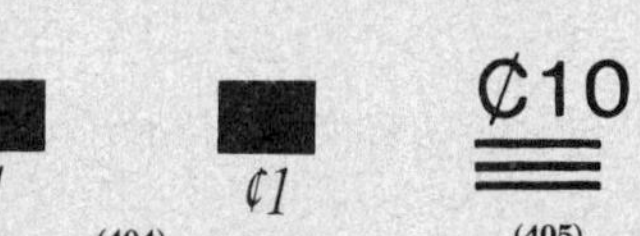

(404) **(405)**

1984 (8 Feb)–**85**. (*a*) *Nos.* 948/52 *and* 954 *surch as T* **404**
1065 1 c. on 20 p. Prince Charles and Lady Diana Spencer .. .. 2·50 3·0
1066 9 c. on 65 p. Prince Charles and Lady Diana Spencer (1985) .. .. .. 3·00 4·0
1067 9 c. on 80 p. Prince Charles on visit to Ghana .. .. 3·00 4·0
a. Imperf (pair) with surch inverted .. £275
1068 20 c. on 3 c. Type **385** (1985) .. .. 3·50 6·0
1069 20 c. on 4 c. Type **385** .. .. .. 3·50 6·0
MS1070 95 × 85 mm. 60 c. on 7 c. St. Paul's Cathedral .. .. 1·40 3·0

The above exist imperforate from a restricted printing (*Pri for Nos.* 1065, 1067, 1069 *set of* 3 £8, *Nos.* 1066 *and* 1068 *set of* £10 *and No.* **MS**1070 £20, *all mint*).

(*b*) *Nos.* 991/2 *and* 994/5 *surch as T* **405**
1071 10 c. on 20 p. Type **392** 40
1072 19 c. on 65 p. Scouts cooking on camp-fire .. 80
1073 30 c. on 3 c. Scouts observing elephant .. 1·50 1·
MS1074 101 × 71 mm. 60 c. on 5 c. Lord Baden-Powell .. .. 1·50 3·

(*c*) *Nos.* 1000/6 *and* 1008 *surch as T* **405**
1075 **394** 1 c. on 20 p. multicoloured 30
1076 – 9 c. on 65 p. multicoloured 70
1077 – 9 c. on 3 c. multicoloured 70
1078 **394** 10 c. on 30 p. multicoloured 70
1079 – 10 c. on 80 p. mult (No. 1002) .. 70
1080 – 20 c. on 4 c. mult (No. 1006) .. 1·50 1·
1081 – 20 c. on 4 c. multicoloured .. .. 1·50 1·
MS1082 110 × 90 mm. 60 c. on 6 c. multicoloured 1·50 2·

(*d*) *Nos.* 1019/22 *surch as T* **405**
1083 1 c. on 20 p. Type **397** 10
1084 9 c. on 55 p. Satellite view of Ghana .. 40
1085 30 c. on 80 p. Minerals of Ghana .. .. 1·50 1·
1086 50 c. on 3 c. African Fish Eagle .. .. 2·50 3·

(e) *Nos.* 1023/9 *and* 1031 *surch as T* **405**

087 **394** 1 c. on 20 p. multicoloured 10 10
088 – 9 c. on 65 p. multicoloured 40 45
089 – 9 c. on 3 c. multicoloured 40 45
090 **394** 10 c. on 30 p. multicoloured 40 45
091 – 10 c. on 80 p. mult (No. 1025) .. 40 45
092 – 20 c. on 80 p. mult (No. 1029) .. 80 85
093 – 20 c. on 4 c. multicoloured 80 85
IS1094 110×90 mm. 60 c. on 6 c. multicoloured 1·00 2·00
065/9, 1071/3, 1075/81, 1083/93 .. *Set of* 26 30·00 35·00

c10

19TH U.P.U CONGRESS - HAMBURG

(406)

984 (19 June). *Universal Postal Union Congress, Hamburg. Nos.* 1035/7 *surch as T* **406**.
095 10 c. on 3 c. Spinner Dolphin 40 45
096 50 c. on 5 c. Atlantic Hump-backed Dolphin .. .. 2·10 2·25
IS1097 117×76 mm. 60 c. on 6 c. As No. 1096 .. 2·50 3·50

407 Cross and Crown of Thorns

408 Women's 400 Metre Race

(Litho Format)

984 (26 June). *Easter. T* **407** *and similar vert designs. Multicoloured. P* 15.
098 1 c. Type **407** 10 10
099 1 c. 40, Christ praying 10 10
100 2 c. 30, The Resurrection 10 10
101 3 c. Palm Sunday 10 15
102 50 c. Christ on the road to Emmaus .. 1·10 2·25
098/102 .. .. *Set of* 5 1·25 2·40
IS1103 102×86 mm. 60 c. Type **407** .. .. 1·00 2·50
No. 1098 exists imperforate from stock dispersed by the iquidator of Format International Security Printers Ltd.

(Des P. Cox and J. Iskowitz. Litho Format)

984 (13 Aug). *Olympic Games, Los Angeles. T* **408** *and similar vert designs. Multicoloured. P* 15.
104 1 c. Type **408** 10 10
105 1 c. 40, Boxing 15 10
106 2 c. 30, Hockey 20 15
107 3 c. Men's 400 metre hurdles race .. 20 15
108 50 c. Rhythmic gymnastics .. .. .. 2·40 3·50
104/8 .. .. *Set of* 5 2·75 3·50
MS1109 103×78 mm. 70 c. Football .. .. 2·50 3·50
No. 1108 is inscribed "RYTHMIC" in error.
Nos. 1104/8 exist imperforate from stock dispersed by the iquidator of Format International Security Printers Ltd.

409 *Amorphophallus johnsonii*

410 Young Bongo

(Litho Harrison)

984 (24 Aug). *Flowers. T* **409** *and similar vert designs. Multicoloured. P* 14.
110 1 c. Type **409** 10 10
111 1 c. 40, *Pancratium trianthum* 10 10
112 2 c. 30, *Eulophia cucullata* 15 15
113 3 c. *Amorphophallus abyssinicus* 15 15
114 50 c. *Chlorophytum togoense* .. .. 3·00 5·00
110/14 .. .. *Set of* 5 3·00 5·00
IS1115 70×96 mm. 60 c. Type **409** .. .. 2·00 3·50

(Des Susan David. Litho B.D.T.)

984 (7 Sept). *Endangered Antelopes. T* **410** *and similar horiz designs. Multicoloured. P* 14.
116 1 c. Type **410** 30 20
117 2 c. 30, Bongo bucks fighting 55 55
118 3 c. Bongo family 70 70
119 20 c. Bongo herd in high grass .. .. 2·50 3·50
116/19 .. .. *Set of* 4 3·50 4·50
IS1120 Two sheets, each 100×71 mm. (a) 70 c. Head of Kob; (b) 70 c. Head of Bush buck *Set of 2 sheets* 9·00 12·00

411 Dipo Girl

412 The Three Wise Men Bringing Gifts

(Des and litho B.D.T.)

1984 (3 Oct). *Ghanaian Culture. T* **411** *and similar vert designs. Multicoloured. P* 14.
1121 1 c. Type **411** 10 10
1122 1 c. 40, Adowa dancer 10 10
1123 2 c. 30, Agbadza dancer 10 15
1124 3 c. Damba dancer 10 15
1125 50 c. Dipo dancer .. .. 1·75 3·00
1121/5 .. .. *Set of* 5 1·90 3·25
MS1126 70×84 mm. 70 c. Mandolin player. P 14×15 .. .. 2·00 3·00

(Litho D.L.R.)

1984 (19 Nov). *Christmas. T* **412** *and similar vert designs. Multicoloured. P* 12×12½.
1127 70 p. Type **412** 10 10
1128 1 c. Choir of angels 10 10
1129 1 c. 40, Mary and shepherds at manger .. 10 10
1130 2 c. 30, The flight into Egypt 10 15
1131 3 c. Simeon blessing Jesus 10 15
1132 50 c. Holy Family and angels .. .. 1·75 3·00
1127/32 .. .. *Set of* 6 1·90 3·25
MS1133 70×90 mm. 70 c. Type **412** .. .. 2·00 2·75

VALERIE
BRISCO-HOOKS
U.S.A.

(413)

414 The Queen Mother attending Church Service

1984 (3 Dec). *Olympic Medal Winners, Los Angeles. Nos.* 1104/9 *optd as T* **413** *in gold.*
1134 1 c. Type **408** (optd with T **413**) 10 10
1135 1 c. 40, Boxing (optd "U.S. WINNERS") .. 10 10
1136 2 c. 30, Field hockey (optd "PAKISTAN (FIELD HOCKEY)") 10 10
1137 3 c. Men's 400 metre hurdles race (optd "EDWIN MOSES U.S.A.") 10 10
1138 50 c. Rhythmic gymnastics (optd "LAURI FUNG CANADA") .. .. .. 1·50 1·60
1134/8 .. .. *Set of* 5 1·60 1·75
MS1139 103×78 mm. 70 c. Football (optd "FRANCE") .. .. 1·75 2·50
Nos. 1135 and **MS**1139 have the overprint in one line and Nos. 1136/8 in two.

(Des J.W. Litho Questa)

1985 (24 July). *Life and Times of Queen Elizabeth the Queen Mother. T* **414** *and similar vert designs. Multicoloured. P* 14.
1140 5 c. Type **414** 10 15
1141 12 c. At Ascot Races 25 30
1142 100 c. At Clarence House on her 84th birthday .. .. 1·75 2·50
1140/2 .. .. *Set of* 3 1·75 2·75
MS1143 56×84 mm. 110 c. With Prince Charles at Garter ceremony .. .. 1·75 3·00
Stamps as Nos. 1140/2, but with face values of 8 c., 20 c. and 70 c., exist from additional sheetlets of 5 plus a label issued December 1985. These also have changed background colours and are perforated 12×12½ (*Price for set of 3 stamps* £2.25 *mint*).
Nos. 1140/3 and the stamps from the additional sheetlets also exist surcharged "90th Birthday 4th August 1990", but are reported not to have been available in Ghana.

415 Moslems going to Mosque

416 Youths clearing Refuse ("Make Ghana Clean")

(Des E. Mensah. Litho B.D.T.)

1985 (1 Aug.) *Islamic Festival of Id-el-Fitr. T* **415** *and similar vert designs. Multicoloured. P* 14.
1144 5 c. Type **415** 25 20
1145 8 c. Moslems at prayer 35 30
1146 12 c. Pilgrims visiting the Dome of the Rock 55 45
1147 18 c. Preaching the Koran 70 60
1148 50 c. Banda Nkwanta Mosque, Accra, and map of Ghana .. .. 1·75 1·60
1144/8 .. .. *Set of* 5 3·25 2·75

(Des E. Mensah. Litho Questa)

1985 (9 Aug). *International Youth Year. T* **416** *and similar vert designs. Multicoloured. P* 14×13½.
1149 5 c. Type **416** 10 10
1150 8 c. Planting sapling ("Make Ghana Green") 15 15
1151 12 c. Youth carrying bananas ("Feed Ghana") 20 25
1152 100 c. Open-air class ("Educate Ghana") .. 1·60 2·25
1149/52 .. .. *Set of* 4 1·75 2·50
MS1153 103×78 mm. 110 c. As 8 c. .. .. 1·75 3·00

417 Honda "Interceptor", 1984

418 Fork-tailed Flycatcher

(Litho Questa)

1985 (9 Sept). *Centenary of the Motorcycle. T* **417** *and similar multicoloured designs. P* 14.
1154 5 c. Type **417** 55 55
1155 8 c. DKW, 1938 .. .. 65 75
1156 12 c. BMW "R 32", 1923 .. .. .. 1·00 1·00
1157 100 c. NSU, 1900 .. .. 5·50 7·00
1154/7 .. .. *Set of* 4 7·00 8·50
MS1158 78×108 mm. 110 c. Zündapp, 1973 (*vert*) .. .. 4·50 4·75

(Litho Questa)

1985 (16 Oct). *Birth Bicentenary of John J. Audubon (ornithologist). T* **418** *and similar vert designs showing original paintings. Multicoloured. P* 14.
1159 5 c. Type **418** .. .. 1·25 50
1160 8 c. Barred Owl .. .. 2·25 2·00
1161 12 c. Black-throated Mango .. .. 2·25 2·00
1162 100 c. White-crowned Pigeon .. .. 6·00 9·50
1159/62 .. .. *Set of* 4 10·50 12·50
MS1163 85×115 mm. 110 c. Downy Woodpecker 6·00 3·50
No. 1159 is inscribed "York-tailed Fly Catcher" in error.
Nos. 1159/63 also exist imperforate from a limited printing.

419 United Nations Building, New York

(Des Mary Walters. Litho D.L.R.)

1985 (24 Oct). *40th Anniv of United Nations Organization. T* **419** *and similar horiz designs. Multicoloured. P* 14½ (18 c.) *or* 14½×14 (*others*).
1164 5 c. Type **419** 10 10
1165 8 c. Flags of member nations and U.N. Building 15 15
1166 12 c. Dove with olive branch 15 25
1167 18 c. General Assembly 25 35
1168 100 c. Flags of Ghana and United Nations .. .. 1·25 1·75
1164/8 .. .. *Set of* 5 1·60 2·40
MS1169 90×70 mm. 110 c. United Nations (New York) 1955 4 cent 10th anniv stamp .. .. 1·25 1·75
Nos. 1164/9 also exist imperforate from a limited printing.

420 Coffee

(Des J. Iskowitz. Litho B.D.T.)

1985 (4 Nov). *20th Anniv of United Nations Conference on Trade and Development. T* **420** *and similar horiz designs showing export products. Multicoloured. P* 14.
1170 5 c. Type **420** 10 10
1171 8 c. Cocoa 15 15
1172 12 c. Timber 25 25
1173 18 c. Bauxite .. .. 1·25 90
1174 100 c. Gold .. .. 6·50 8·50
1170/4 .. .. *Set of* 5 7·50 9·00
MS1175 104×74 mm. 110 c. Agricultural produce and plate of food. P 15×14 .. .. 2·00 2·50

421 Growth Monitoring

(Des E. Mensah. Litho B.D.T.)

1985 (16 Dec). *U.N.I.C.E.F. Child Survival Campaign. T* **421** *and similar horiz designs. Multicoloured. P* 14.

1176	5 c.	Type **421**	30	10
1177	8 c.	Oral rehydration therapy	50	30
1178	12 c.	Breast feeding	70	40
1179	100 c.	Immunization	3·00	4·50
1176/9		.. .. *Set of* 4	4·00	4·75
MS1180		99×69 mm. 110 c. Campaign logo. P 15×14	1·75	2·25

422 Airline Stewardess and Boys with Stamp Album

(Litho Questa)

1986 (27 Oct). *"Ameripex" International Stamp Exhibition, Chicago. T* **422** *and similar multicoloured designs. P* 14.

1181	5 c.	Type **422**	15	15
1182	25 c.	Globe and Douglas DC-10 aircraft	60	45
1183	100 c.	Ghana Airways stewardess (*vert*) ..	2·25	3·00
1181/3		.. .. *Set of* 3	2·75	3·25
MS1184		90×70 mm. 150 c. Stamp collecting class	2·25	2·50

Nos. 1181/4 also exist imperforate from a limited printing.

423 Kejetia Roundabout, Kumasi   **424** Tackling

(Litho B.D.T.)

1986 (10 Nov). *"Inter-Tourism '86" Conference. T* **423** *and similar horiz designs. Multicoloured. P* 14.

1185	5 c.	Type **423**	10	10
1186	15 c.	Fort St. Jago, Elmina	30	30
1187	25 c.	Tribal warriors	45	45
1188	100 c.	Chief holding audience	1·75	3·25
1185/8		.. .. *Set of* 4	2·40	3·75
MS1189		110×70 mm. 150 c. African Elephants. P 15 × 14	3·75	5·50

(Litho D.L.R.)

1987 (16 Jan). *World Cup Football Championship, Mexico* (1986). *T* **424** *and similar vert designs. Multicoloured. P* 14×14½.

1190	5 c.	Type **424**	15	10
1191	15 c.	Player taking control of ball ..	25	15
1192	25 c.	Player kicking ball	40	25
1193	100 c.	Player with ball	1·40	1·25
1190/3		.. .. *Set of* 4	2·00	1·50
MS1194		90×70 mm. 150 c. Player kicking ball (*different*)	1·50	2·00

Nos. 1190/4 also exist imperforate from a limited printing.

425 Fertility Doll   **426** Children of Different Races, Peace Doves and Sun

(Litho D.L.R.)

1987 (22 Jan). *Ghanaian Fertility Dolls. T* **425** *and similar vert designs showing different dolls. P* 14×14½.

1195	**425**	5 c.	multicoloured	10	10
1196	–	15 c.	multicoloured	20	15
1197	–	25 c.	multicoloured	35	25
1198	–	100 c.	multicoloured	1·25	1·50
1195/8			.. .. *Set of* 4	1·60	1·75
MS1199			90×70 mm. **425** 150 c. multicoloured ..	1·50	2·00

(Litho D.L.R.)

1987 (2 Mar). *International Peace Year* (1986). *T* **426** *and similar multicoloured designs. P* 14×14½ (100 *c*.) *or* 14½×14 (*others*).

1200	5 c.	Type **426**	15	10
1201	25 c.	Plough, peace dove and rising sun ..	75	25
1202	100 c.	Peace dove, olive branch and globe (*vert*)	2·50	3·00
1200/2		.. .. *Set of* 3	3·00	3·00
MS1203		90×70 mm. 150 c. Dove perched on plough (*vert*). P 14×14½..	1·75	2·25

427 Lumber and House under Construction   **428** Demonstrator and Arms breaking Shackles

(Des and litho B.D.T.)

1987 (10 Mar). *"Gifex '87" International Forestry Exposition, Accra. T* **427** *and similar horiz designs. Multicoloured. P* 14.

1204	5 c.	Type **427**	10	10
1205	15 c.	Planks and furniture	15	15
1206	25 c.	Felled trees	30	25
1207	200 c.	Logs and wood carvings	1·90	2·25
1204/7		.. .. *Set of* 4	2·25	2·50

(Des W. Hanson. Litho D.L.R.)

1987 (8 Apr). *Appearance of Halley's Comet* (1986). *Horiz designs as T* **123** *of Anguilla. Multicoloured. P* 14½×14.

1208	5 c.	Mikhail Lomonosov (scientist) and Chamber of Curiosities, St. Petersburg	20	10
1209	25 c.	Lunar probe "Surveyor 3", 1966 ..	70	30
1210	200 c.	Wedgwood plaques for Isaac Newton, 1790, and "Apollo 11" Moon landing, 1968	3·25	2·25
1208/10		.. .. *Set of* 3	3·75	2·40
MS1211		100×70 mm. 250 c. Halley's Comet ..	3·50	2·75

Nos. 1208/11 also exist imperforate from a limited printing.

(Litho D.L.R.)

1987 (18 May). *Solidarity with the People of Southern Africa. T* **428** *and similar vert designs. Multicoloured. P* 14×14½.

1212	5 c.	Type **428**	10	10
1213	15 c.	Miner and gold bars	40	15
1214	25 c.	Xhosa warriors	30	25
1215	100 c.	Nelson Mandela and shackles ..	1·25	2·00
1212/15		.. .. *Set of* 4	1·75	2·25
MS1216		70×90 mm. 150 c. Nelson Mandela ..	1·50	2·00

429 Aerophones

(Litho D.L.R.)

1987 (13 July). *Musical Instruments. T* **429** *and similar horiz designs. Multicoloured. P* 14½×14.

1217	5 c.	Type **429**	10	10
1218	15 c.	Xylophone	15	15
1219	25 c.	Chordophones	30	25
1220	100 c.	Membranophones	1·00	1·25
1217/20		.. .. *Set of* 4	1·40	1·50
MS1221		90×70 mm. 200 c. Idiophones	1·90	2·25

430 Woman filling Water Pot at Pump   **431** Ga Women preparing Kpokpoi for Homowo Festival

(Litho B.D.T.)

1987 (21 Sept). *International Year of Shelter for the Homeless. T* **430** *and similar horiz designs. Multicoloured. P* 14.

1222	5 c.	Type **430**	10	10
1223	15 c.	Building house from breeze-blocks	15	15
1224	25 c.	Modern village with stream ..	25	25
1225	100 c.	Modern houses with verandahs ..	1·25	1·25
1222/5		.. .. *Set of* 4	1·50	1·50

(Litho Format)

1988 (6 Jan). *Ghana Festivals. T* **431** *and similar vert designs. Multicoloured. P* 15.

1226	5 c.	Type **431**	10	1
1227	15 c.	Efute hunters with deer, Aboakyir festival	15	1
1228	25 c.	Fanti chief dancing at Odwira festival	25	2
1229	100 c.	Chief in palanquin, Yam festival ..	1·25	1·2
1226/9		.. .. *Set of* 4	1·50	1·5

432 Port Installation   **433** Nurse giving Injection

(Litho National Ptg Wks, Havana)

1988 (26 Jan). *5th Anniversary of 31 December Revolution* (1987). *T* **432** *and similar horiz designs. Multicoloured. P* 13

1230	5 c.	Type **432**	1·00	4
1231	15 c.	Repairing railway line	7·00	2·2
1232	25 c.	Planting cocoa	1·25	5
1233	100 c.	Miners with ore truck	7·50	7·5
1230/3		.. .. *Set of* 4	15·00	9·5

(Litho Format)

1988 (1 Feb). *U.N.I.C.E.F. Global Immunization Campaign. T* **433** *and similar vert designs. Multicoloured. P* 15.

1234	5 c.	Type **433**	20	1
1235	15 c.	Girl receiving injection	25	2
1236	25 c.	Schoolgirl crippled by polio	35	5
1237	100 c.	Nurse giving oral vaccine to baby ..	60	2·2
1234/7		.. .. *Set of* 4	1·25	2·75

434 Fishing   **435** Akwadjan Men

(Des E. Mensah. Litho National Ptg Wks, Havana)

1988 (14 Apr). *10th Anniv of International Fund for Agricultural Development. T* **434** *and similar horiz designs. Multicoloured. P* 13.

1238	5 c.	Type **434**	45	2
1239	15 c.	Women harvesting crops	70	3
1240	25 c.	Cattle	85	4
1241	100 c.	Village granaries	2·50	4·2
1238/41		.. .. *Set of* 4	4·00	4·7

(Litho Questa)

1988 (9 May). *Tribal Costumes. T* **435** *and similar vert designs. Multicoloured. P* 14.

1242	5 c.	Type **435**	15	1
1243	25 c.	Banaa man	35	2
1244	250 c.	Agwasen woman	1·50	2·0
1242/4		.. .. *Set of* 3	1·75	2·0

₵20.00

(436)

₵20.00

(436*a*)

₵50.00

(437)

₵50

(437*a*)

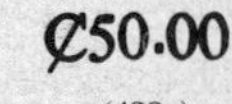

₵50.00

(438)

₵50.00

(438*a*)

88 (19 July)–**90**. *Nos.* 460, 464/6, 469/70, 1031*a*, 1038/42, 1044 *and* 1046 *surch as T* **436/8***a*.

45 – 20 c. on 50 p. dp grey-green, yell-orge & blk (No. 1041) (surch as T **436**) 30 15
a. Horiz pair, one without surch
b. Surch inverted .. .. † —
46 – 20 c. on 1 c. yell-orge, vio-blue & black (No. 1042) (surch T **436**) (9.88) 30 15
a. Surch double .. .. ..
b. Surch double, one albino ..
c. Surch double, one albino and one inverted .. .. ..
d. Surch double, one inverted (T **436** + **436***a*) .. ..
e. Pair, one without surch ..
f. Surch sideways .. ..
g. Surch triple .. .. ..
h. "2" omitted (R. 4/3) .. ..
46*m* – 20 c. on 1 c. yellow-orange, violet-bl & blk (No. 1042) (surch T **436***a*)
ma. Surch double .. .. ..
mb. Surch double, one inverted ..
mc. Surch double, one sideways ..
md. Surch inverted .. ..
me. Pair, one without surch ..
mf. Albino surch .. .. ..
mg. Small "0"'s in surch (R. 2/6) ..
mh. Space between "C 20." and "00" (R. 1/5) .. .. ..
47 – 50 c. on 10 n.p. multicoloured (No. 469) (surch T **437**) 30 25
a. Vert pair, one without surch ..
b. Surch inverted .. ..
48 – 50 c. on 20 n.p. deep blue & new blue (No. 470) (surch T **437***a*) (1990) 2·50 45
49 – 50 c. on 20 n.p. deep blue and new blue (No. 470) (surch as T **437**, reading down) (1990) .. .. 2·50 45
a. Surch double .. .. ..
50 – 50 c. on 10 p. multicoloured (No. 1039) (surch T **438**) (9.88) .. 30 15
a. Pair, one without surch ..
50*d* – 50 c. on 10 p. multicoloured (No. 1039) (surch T **438***a*) .. ..
da. Pair, one without surch ..
db. Surch inverted .. ..
dc. Surch on front and back ..
dd. Surch on front and surch inverted on back .. ..
de. Surch on front and double surch, one inverted, one sideways, on back .. ..
51 – 50 c. on 1 c. on 20 n.p. deep blue and new blue (No. 1031*a*) (surch T **437***a*) (1990) .. .. 2·50 45
a. Surch inverted .. ..
b. Pair, one without surch ..
c. Surch omitted, inverted on back
d. Albino surch (T **437***a*) .. ..
52 – 50 c. on 1 c. on 20 n.p. deep blue and new blue (No. 1031*a*) (surch as T **437** reading down) (1990) .. 2·50 45
a. Surch double .. .. ..
b. "5C0.00" (R. 1/2) .. ..
c. Surch omitted, inverted on back
d. Albino surch .. .. ..
e. Surch as T **437** reading up ..
ea. Surch double, both reading up
eb. Surch double, reading up and down .. ..
ec. Surch triple, two reading up (one albino) and one reading down
ed. "5C0.00" (R. 6/4) .. ..
ee. Pair, one without surch ..
53 – 50 c. on 1 c. on 20 n.p. deep blue and new blue (No. 1031*a*) (horiz surch as T **437**) (1991) .. 2·50 45
54 – 50 c. on 1 c. yellow-orge, violet-blue and black (No. 1042) (surch as T **436**) (1990) .. .. .. 2·50 45
a. Decimal point omitted from surcharge (R. 4/6) .. ..
55 **230** 60 c. on 1 n.p. multicoloured (surch as T **437**) (1990) .. .. .. 2·00 45
a. Surch inverted .. ..
b. Surch double .. .. ..
c. Surch double, one inverted ..
d. Surch double, one sideways ..
e. Surch double, one albino ..
f. Surch triple .. .. ..
g. Surch triple, one albino ..
h. Surch on front, inverted surch on back .. .. ..
i. Pair, one without surch ..
256 **235** 60 c. on 4 n.p. mult (surch as T **437**) 2·50 30
a. Surch double .. .. ..
b. Surch double, one inverted ..
c. Surch double, one albino ..
d. Surch inverted .. ..
257 – 60 c. on 3 c. multicoloured (No. 1044) (surch as T **438**) (1989) .. 50 30
a. Decimal point omitted from surch (R. 4/5) .. .. ..
b. Vert pair, one without surch ..
258 **400** 80 c. on 5 p. mult (surch as T **437**)
a. Pair, one without surch ..
b. Surch double .. .. ..
259 – 80 c. on 5 c. multicoloured (No. 1046) (surch as T **438**) (1990) .. 3·25 3·50
260 – 100 c. on 3 n.p. multicoloured (No. 464) (surch as T **437**) (1990) .. 5·50 5·50
a. Surch inverted .. ..
261 – 100 c. on 20 n.p. deep blue and new blue (No. 470) (surch as T **437**) 50 55
a. Horiz pair, one without surch
262 – 100 c. on 20 p. multicoloured (No. 1040) (surch as T **436**) (9.88) .. 50 55
a. Surch double, one sideways ..
b. Horiz pair, one without surch
c. Surch inverted .. ..

1263 – 100 c. on 3 c. multicoloured (No. 1044) (surch as T **438***a*) (1990) .. 50 55
1264 **236** 200 c. on 6 n.p. mult (surch as T **437**) 50 65
a. Surch double .. .. ..

Other handstamped and manuscript surcharges can be found used during 1988–89, but it is understood that only those listed above were issued by the postal authorities.

440 Boxing **441** Nutrition Lecture

(Litho Questa)

1988 (10 Oct). *Olympic Games, Seoul. T* **440** *and similar horiz designs. Multicoloured. P* 14.

1265 20 c. Type **440** 20 15
1266 60 c. Athletics 55 55
1267 80 c. Discus-throwing 60 80
1268 100 c. Javelin-throwing .. .. .. 70 1·10
1269 350 c. Weightlifting .. .. .. 1·75 3·00
1265/9 .. .. *Set of* 5 3·50 5·00
MS1270 75×105 mm. 500 c. As 80 c. .. .. 4·00 3·00

Nos. 1265/70 also exist imperforate from a limited printing.

(Litho B.D.T.)

1988 (14 Dec). 125*th Anniv of International Red Cross. T* **441** *and similar vert designs. Multicoloured. P* 14.

1271 20 c. Type **441** 40 15
1272 50 c. Red Cross volunteer with blind woman 90 90
1273 60 c. Distributing flood relief supplies .. 1·00 1·00
1274 200 c. Giving first aid .. .. .. 2·50 3·25
1271/4 .. .. *Set of* 4 4·25 4·75

442 Tropical Forest **443** "African Solidarity"

(Litho B.D.T.)

1988 (19 Dec). *Christmas. T* **442** *and similar multicoloured designs. P* 14.

1275 20 c. Type **442** 15 10
1276 60 c. Christ Child (*vert*) 35 35
1277 80 c. Virgin and Child with Star (*vert*) .. 50 60
1278 100 c. Three Wise Men following Star .. 60 70
1279 350 c. Symbolic Crucifixion (*vert*) .. 2·00 2·50
1275/9 .. .. *Set of* 5 3·25 3·75
MS1280 100×70 mm. 500 c. Virgin and Child (*vert*) .. .. 2·50 2·75

Nos. 1275/80 also exist imperforate from a limited printing.

(Litho B.D.T.)

1989 (3 Jan). 25*th Anniv of Organization of African Unity* (1988). *T* **443** *and similar multicoloured designs. P* 14.

1281 20 c. Type **443** 10 10
1282 50 c. O.A.U. Headquarters, Addis Ababa 15 20
1283 60 c. Emperor Haile Selassie and Ethiopian flag (*horiz*) 20 25
1284 200 c. Kwame Nkrumah (former Ghanaian President) and flag (*horiz*) 60 85
1281/4 .. .. *Set of* 4 90 1·25

444 "Amor"

A. ZUELOW
DDR
60 KG
(**445**)

(Litho B.D.T.)

1989 (16 Jan). 500*th Birth Anniversary of Titian* (*artist*). *T* **444** *and similar vert designs. Multicoloured. P* 14.

1285 20 c. Type **444** 40 15
1286 60 c. "The Appeal" 90 65
1287 80 c. "Bacchus and Ariadne" (detail) .. 1·00 85
1288 100 c. "Portrait of Musician" .. .. 1·10 1·60
1289 350 c. "Philip II seated" .. .. .. 2·75 4·50
1285/9 .. .. *Set of* 5 5·50 7·00
MS1290 77×115 mm. 500 c. "Portrait of a Gentleman" .. .. 2·50 2·75

1989 (23 Jan). *Olympic Medal Winners, Seoul. Nos.* 1265/70 *optd as T* **445**.

1291 20 c. Type **440** (optd with T **445**) .. 10 10
1292 60 c. Athletics (optd "G. BORDIN ITALY MARATHON") 20 25
1293 80 c. Discus-throwing (optd "J. SCHULT DDR") 25 30
1294 100 c. Javelin-throwing (optd "T. KORJUS FINLAND") 30 35
1295 350 c. Weightlifting (optd "B. GUIDIKOV BULGARIA 75 KG") .. .. 1·00 1·10
1291/5 .. .. *Set of* 5 1·60 1·90
MS1296 75×105 mm. 500 c. As 80 c. (optd "GOLD J. SCHULT DDR SILVER R. OUBARTAS USSR BRONZE R. DANNEBERG W. GERMANY" on sheet margin) .. .. 2·10 2·10

¢100 ¢100 C60
(**446**) (**447**)

1989 (3 July–20 Nov). *Various stamps surch as T* **446/7**.

(*a*) *On Nos.* 949/50 *and* 952/4 (20 Nov)

1297 80 c. on 65 p. Prince Charles and Lady Diana Spencer 35 40
1298 100 c. on 80 p. Prince Charles on visit to Ghana 45 50
1299 100 c. on 1 c. Prince Charles on visit to Ghana 45 50
1300 300 c. on 3 c. Type **385** .. .. .. 1·25 1·60
1301 500 c. on 4 c. Type **385** .. .. .. 2·25 2·75
1297/1301 .. .. .. *Set of* 5 4·25 5·25

(*b*) *On Nos.* 1048/51 *and* **MS**1053 (18 Sept)

1302 60 c. on 1 c. Type **401** 50 50
1303 80 c. on 1 c. 40, Satellite dish aerial .. 65 65
1304 200 c. on 2 c. 30, Cable and cable-laying ship .. .. 1·75 2·00
1305 300 c. on 3 c. Switchboard operators .. 2·00 2·25
1302/5 .. .. *Set of* 4 4·50 4·75
MS1306 95×70 mm. 500 c. on 6 c. Space satellite .. .. 4·50 5·50

(*c*) *On Nos.* 1104/7 *and* **MS**1109

1307 60 c. on 1 c. Type **408** 30 30
1308 80 c. on 1 c. 40, Boxing 40 40
1309 200 c. on 2 c. 30, Hockey .. .. .. 1·25 1·60
1310 300 c. on 3 c. Men's 400 metre hurdles race 1·40 1·75
1307/10 .. .. *Set of* 4 3·00 3·50
MS1311 103×78 mm. 600 c. on 70 c. Football 3·00 4·00

(*d*) *On Nos.* 1134/7 *and* **MS**1139

1312 60 c. on 1 c. Type **408** (optd with T **413**) 85 90
1313 80 c. on 1 c. 40, Boxing (optd "U.S. WINNERS") .. .. 1·10 1·25
1314 200 c. on 2 c. 30, Field hockey (optd "PAKISTAN (FIELD HOCKEY)") 3·25 3·50
1315 300 c. on 3 c. Men's 400 metre hurdles race (optd "EDWIN MOSES U.S.A.") .. 3·50 3·75
1312/15 .. .. *Set of* 4 8·00 8·50
MS1316 103×78 mm. 600 c. on 70 c. Football (optd "FRANCE") .. .. 5·00 5·50

(*e*) *On Nos.* 1140/3 (20 Nov)

1317 80 c. on 5 c. Type **414** 35 40
1318 250 c. on 12 c. At Ascot Races .. .. 1·10 1·75
1319 300 c. on 100 c. At Clarence House on her 84th birthday .. .. .. 1·25 1·75
1317/19 .. .. *Set of* 3 2·50 3·50
MS1320 56×84 mm. 500 c. on 110 c. With Prince Charles at Garter Ceremony .. .. 3·25 4·00

(*f*) *On Nos.* 1159/61 *and* **MS**1163 (20 Nov)

1321 80 c. on 5 c. Type **418** .. .. .. 1·00 1·00
1322 100 c. on 8 c. Barred Owl .. .. .. 2·25 2·25
1323 300 c. on 12 c. Black-throated Mango .. 2·50 3·00
1321/3 .. .. *Set of* 3 5·00 5·50
MS1324 500 c. on 110 c. Downy Woodpecker .. 6·00 6·50

(*g*) *On Nos.* 1190/2 *and* **MS**1194

1325 60 c. on 5 c. Type **424** 45 45
1326 200 c. on 15 c. Player taking control of ball 1·50 2·00
1327 300 c. on 25 c. Player kicking ball .. 2·00 2·50
1325/7 .. .. *Set of* 3 3·50 4·50
MS1328 90×70 mm. 600 c. on 150 c. Player kicking ball (*different*) .. .. 5·00 5·50

(*h*) *As Nos.* 1190/2 *and* **MS**1194, *but with unissued* "WINNERS" *opt as T* **216** *of Antigua* (18 Sept)

1329 60 c. on 5 c. Type **424** 30 30
1330 200 c. on 15 c. Player taking control of ball 1·00 1·50
1331 300 c. on 25 c. Player kicking ball .. 1·40 2·00
1329/31 .. .. *Set of* 3 2·40 3·50
MS1332 90×70 mm. 600 c. on 150 c. Player kicking ball (*different*) .. .. 3·75 4·50

(*i*) *On Nos.* 1208/11

1333 60 c. on 5 c. Mikhail Lomonosov (scientist) and Chamber of Curiosities, St. Petersburg 65 55
1334 80 c. on 25 c. Lunar probe "Surveyor 3", 1966 .. .. 85 70
1335 500 c. on 200 c. Wedgwood plaques for Isaac Newton, 1790, and "Apollo 11" Moon landing, 1968 .. .. .. 3·25 4·50
1333/5 .. .. *Set of* 3 4·25 5·25
MS1336 100×70 mm. 750 c. on 250 c. Halley's Comet .. .. 4·00 5·00
a. Surch double, one inverted .. .. ..

(*j*) *As Nos.* 1208/11, *but with unissued logo opt as T* **218** *of Antigua* (18 Sept)

1337 60 c. on 5 c. Mikhail Lomonosov (scientist) and Chamber of Curiosities, St. Petersburg 35 40
1338 80 c. on 25 c. Lunar probe "Surveyor 3", 1966 .. .. 45 50
1339 500 c. on 200 c. Wedgwood plaques for Isaac Newton, 1790, and "Apollo 11" Moon landing, 1968 .. .. .. 2·50 4·00
1337/9 .. .. *Set of* 3 3·00 4·50
MS1340 100×70 mm. 750 c. on 250 c. Halley's Comet .. .. 5·50 6·50

The stamps, as Nos. 1140/3, from additional sheetlets also exist surcharged as 80 c. on 20 c., 200 c. on 8 c. and 250 c. on 70 c.

On No. **MS**1336a the inverted surcharge occurs towards the bottom left of the miniature sheet.

448 French Royal Standard and Field Gun

449 Storming the Bastille

(Litho B.D.T.)

1989 (7 July). *"Philexfrance 89" International Stamp Exhibition, Paris. T* **448** *and similar multicoloured designs. P* 14.

1341 20 c. Type **448** 50 25
1342 60 c. Regimental standard, 1789, and French infantryman .. .. 1·00 90
1343 80 c. Revolutionary standard, 1789, and pistol .. .. 1·25 1·00
1344 350 c. Tricolour, 1794, and musket .. 3·25 5·00
1341/4 .. .. *Set of* 4 5·50 6·50
MS1345 77×106 mm. 600 c. Street plan of Paris, 1789 (*horiz*) .. .. 3·00 3·50

(Litho Questa)

1989 (21 Aug). *Japanese Art. Portraits. Multicoloured designs as T* **250** *of Antigua. P* 13½×14.

1346 20 c. "Minamoto-no-Yoritomo" (Fujiwara-no-Takanobu) (*vert*) 20 20
1347 50 c. "Takami Senseki" (Watanabe Kazan) (*vert*) 30 30
1348 60 c. "Ikkyu Sojun" (study) (Bokusai) (*vert*) 35 35
1349 75 c. "Nakamura Kuranosuka" (Ogata Korin) (*vert*) 40 40
1350 125 c. "Portrait of a Lady" (Kyoto branch, Kano School) (*vert*) 65 70
1351 150 c. "Portrait of Zemmui" (anon, 12th-century) (*vert*) 70 75
1352 200 c. "Ono no Komachi the Poetess" (Hokusai) (*vert*) .. .. .. 90 1·00
1353 500 c. "Kobo Daisi as a Child" (anon) (*vert*) 2·25 3·00
1346/53 .. .. *Set of* 8 5·00 6·00
MS1354 Two sheets, each 102×77 mm. (a) 500 c. "Kodai-no-Kimi" (attr Fujiwara-no-Nobuzane) (*vert*). P 13½×14. (b) 500 c. "Emperor Hanazono" (Fujiwara-no-Goshin). P 14×13½ *Set of* 2 *sheets* 8·00 8·00

Nos. 1346/53 were each printed in sheetlets of 10 containing two vertical strips of 5 stamps separated by printed labels commemorating Emperor Hirohito.

(Litho B.D.T.)

1989 (22 Sept). *Bicentenary of the French Revolution. T* **449** *and similar multicoloured designs. P* 14×13½ (*vert*) *or* 13½×14 (*horiz*).

1355 20 c. Type **449** 35 20
1356 60 c. Declaration of Human Rights .. 60 50
1357 80 c. Storming the Bastille (*horiz*) .. 80 75
1358 200 c. Revolution monument (*horiz*) .. 1·75 2·00
1359 350 c. Tree of Liberty (*horiz*) .. .. 2·50 3·25
1355/9 .. .. *Set of* 5 5·50 6·00

450 *Collybia fusipes*

451 "The Course of True Love . . "

(Des L. Nelson. Litho B.D.T.)

1989 (2 Oct). *Fungi* (1*st series*). *T* **450** *and similar vert designs. Multicoloured. P* 14.

1360 20 c. Type **450** 25 25
1361 50 c. *Coprinus comatus* 40 40
1362 60 c. *Xerocomus subtomentosus* 40 45
1363 80 c. *Lepista nuda* 55 55
1364 150 c. *Suillus placidus* 95 95
1365 200 c. *Lepista nuda* (*different*) .. 1·25 1·25
1366 300 c. *Marasmius oreades* .. .. 1·75 1·75
1367 500 c. *Agaricus campestris* .. .. 3·00 3·00
1360/7 .. .. *Set of* 8 7·75 7·75
MS1368 Two sheets, each 110×80 mm. (a) 600 c. *Boletus rhodoxanthus*. (b) 600 c. *Amanita rubescens* .. .. .. *Set of* 2 *sheets* 7·50 8·00

Nos. 1360/8 also exist imperforate from a limited printing.

See also Nos. 1489/97.

(Des N. Waldman. Litho Walsall)

1989 (9 Oct). *425th Birth Anniv of Shakespeare. T* **451** *and similar vert designs showing lines and scenes from* A Midsummer Night's Dream. *Multicoloured. P* 13½×13.

1369 40 c. Type **451** 60 60
a. Sheetlet. Nos. 1369/89 .. .. 11·00
1370 40 c. "Love looks not with the eye, but with the mind" 60 60
1371 40 c. "Nature here shows art" 60 60
1372 40 c. "Things growing are not ripe till their season" 60 60
1373 40 c. "He is defiled that draws a sword on thee" 60 60
1374 40 c. "It is not enough to speak, but to speak true" 60 60
1375 40 c. "Thou art as wise as thou art beautiful" 60 60
1376 40 c. Wildcat in wood (face value at left) .. 60 60
1377 40 c. Man 60 60
1378 40 c. Woman with flower 60 60
1379 40 c. King and queen 60 60
1380 40 c. Bottom 60 60
1381 40 c. Wildcat in wood (face value at right) 60 60
1382 40 c. Woman 60 60
1383 40 c. Leopard 60 60
1384 40 c. Tree trunk and man 60 60
1385 40 c. Meadow flowers 60 60
1386 40 c. Mauve flowers 60 60
1387 40 c. Plants 60 60
1388 40 c. Lion 60 60
1389 40 c. Fern and flowers 60 60
1369/89 .. .. *Set of* 21 11·00 11·00

Nos. 1369/89 were printed together, *se-tenant*, as a sheetlet of 21, forming a composite design.

(Des Mary Walters. Litho B.D.T.)

1989 (16 Oct)–**90**. *Birds. Multicoloured designs as T* **244** *of Dominica. P* 14.

1390 20 c. Bronze Mannikin (*horiz*) 30 10
1391 50 c. African Pied Wagtail (*horiz*) .. 45 30
1392 60 c. African Pygmy Kingfisher (inscr "*Halcyon malimbicus*") (*horiz*) .. 1·25 1·75
1392*a* 60 c. African Pygmy Kingfisher (inscr "*Ispidina picta*") (6.90) (*horiz*) .. 1·25 1·50
1393 80 c. Blue-breasted Kingfisher (inscr "*Ispidina picta*") (*horiz*) .. .. 1·75 2·25
1393*a* 80 c. Blue-breasted Kingfisher (inscr "*Halcyon malimbicus*") (*horiz*) (6.90) .. .. 1·50 2·00
1394 150 c. Striped Kingfisher .. .. .. 1·10 1·25
1395 200 c. Shikra .. .. 1·25 1·40
1396 300 c. Grey Parrot .. .. .. 1·50 1·75
1397 500 c. Black Kite .. .. .. 2·50 3·25
1390/7 .. .. *Set of* 10 11·50 14·00
MS1398 Two sheets. (a) 128×83 mm. 600 c. Cinnamon-breasted Rock Bunting and Barn Swallow (*horiz*). (b) 83×128 mm. 600 c. Senegal Puff-back Flycatcher .. .. *Set of* 2 *sheets* 12·00 13·00

The original printings of Nos. 1392/3 had the Latin names of the birds transposed. Corrected versions of the two designs were supplied during 1990.

Nos. 1390/8 also exist imperforate from a limited printing.

452 Command Module *Columbia* orbiting Moon

(Des K. Gromell. Litho B.D.T.)

1989 (6 Nov). *20th Anniv of First Manned Landing on Moon. T* **452** *and similar horiz designs. Multicoloured. P* 14.

1399 20 c. Type **452** 30 15
1400 80 c. Neil Armstrong's footprint on Moon 50 60
1401 200 c. Edwin Aldrin on Moon .. .. 1·25 1·75
1402 300 c. "Apollo 11" capsule on parachutes 1·60 2·00
1399/1402 .. .. .. *Set of* 4 3·25 4·00
MS1403 Two sheets, each 100×72 mm. (a) 500 c. Launch of "Apollo 11". (b) 500 c. Earth seen from Moon .. .. *Set of* 2 *sheets* 5·50 7·00

453 Desertification of Pasture

(Litho B.D.T.)

1989 (15 Nov). *World Environment Day. T* **453** *and similar horiz designs. Multicoloured. P* 14.

1404 20 c. Type **453** 50 15
1405 60 c. Wildlife fleeing bush fire 90 80
1406 400 c. Industrial pollution .. .. 2·75 3·50
1407 500 c. Erosion .. .. 3·00 3·75
1404/7 .. .. *Set of* 4 6·50 7·50

454 *Bebearia arcadius*

455 Great Ribbed Cockle (*Cardium costatum*)

(Des Mary Walters. Litho B.D.T.)

1990 (20 Feb). *Butterflies. T* **454** *and similar horiz desig Multicoloured. P* 14.

1408 20 c. Type **454** 35
1409 60 c. *Charaxes laodice* 50
1410 80 c. *Euryphura porphyrion* 60
1411 100 c. *Neptis nicomedes* 70
1412 150 c. *Citrinophila erastus* 90
1413 200 c. *Aethiopana honorius* .. .. 1·25 1
1414 300 c. *Precis westermanni* .. .. 1·50 1
1415 500 c. *Cymothoe hypatha* .. .. 2·00 2
1408/15 .. .. *Set of* 8 7·00 7
MS1416 Two sheets, each 104×72 mm. (a) 600 c. *Telipna acraea*. (b) 600 c. *Pentila abraxas* *Set of* 2 *sheets* 8·50 9

Nos. 1408/16 also exist imperforate from a limited printing

(Des E. Mensah. Litho D.L.R.)

1990 (23 Feb). *Seashells. T* **455** *and similar vert desig Multicoloured. P* 14×14½.

1417 20 c. Type **455** 60
1418 60 c. Elephant's Snout (*Cymbium glans*) 75
1419 80 c. Garter Cone (*Conus genuanus*) .. 85
1420 200 c. Tankerville's Ancilla (*Amalda tankervillii*) .. .. .. 2·00 2·
1421 350 c. Coronate Prickly-winkle (*Tectarius coronatus*) .. .. 2·75 3·
1417/21 .. .. *Set of* 5 6·25 6·

Nos. 1417/18 show the shell descriptions transposed in err

456 Nehru welcoming President Nkrumah of Ghana

(Des E. Mensah. Litho D.L.R.)

1990 (27 Mar). *Birth Centenary of Jawaharlal Nehru (Indi statesman). T* **456** *and similar multicoloured desigr P* 14½×14 (*horiz*) *or* 14×14½ (*others*).

1422 20 c. Type **456** 60
1423 60 c. Nehru addressing Bandung Conference, 1955 75
1424 80 c. Nehru with garland and flowers (*vert*) 80
1425 200 c. Nehru releasing pigeon (*vert*) .. 1·25 1·
1426 350 c. Nehru (*vert*) .. .. .. 1·75 2·
1422/6 .. .. *Set of* 5 4·75 4·

457 Wyon Medal, 1838

458 Anniversary Emblem

(Des S. Pollard. Litho B.D.T.)

1990 (23 May). *150th Anniv of Penny Black. T* **457** *and simil horiz designs. P* 13½.

1427 20 c. black and reddish violet 30
1428 60 c. black and deep grey-green 45
1429 80 c. black and reddish violet 60
1430 200 c. black and deep grey-green .. .. 1·25 1
1431 350 c. black and deep grey-green .. .. 1·75 2
1432 400 c. black and rosine .. .. .. 1·75 2
1427/32 .. .. *Set of* 6 5·50 5
MS1433 Two sheets, each 112×83 mm. (a) 600 c. red-brown and black; (b) 600 c. deep brown, buff and black .. .. .. *Set of* 2 *sheets* 6·00 7

Designs:—60, 600 c. (No. **MS**1433b) Bath mail coach, 18 80 c. Leeds mail coach, 1840; 200 c. Proof of Queen's he engraved by Heath, 1840; 350 c. Master die, 1840; 400 c. Lond mail coach, 1840; 600 c. (No. **MS**1433a) Printing the Pen Black.

Nos. 1427/33 also exist imperforate from a limited printing

(Litho D.L.R.)

1990 (5 June). *Tenth Anniv* (1989) *of 4 June Revolution. T 4 and similar vert designs. Multicoloured. P* 14½×14.

1434 20 c. Type **458** 15
1435 60 c. Foodstuffs 20
1436 80 c. Cocoa 25
1437 200 c. Mining .. .. 1·50 1
1438 350 c. Scales of Justice and sword .. 1·75 2
1434/8 .. .. *Set of* 5 3·50 4

459 Map of Africa and Satellite Network

(Litho D.L.R.)

990 (12 July). *25th Anniv of Intelsat Satellite System.* T **459** *and similar horiz designs. Multicoloured.* P 14×14½.
439 20 c. Type **459** .. 20 20
440 60 c. Map of Americas .. 30 30
441 80 c. Map of Asia and Pacific .. 35 35
442 200 c. Map of South America and Africa .. 90 1·00
443 350 c. Map of Indian Ocean and Pacific .. 1·50 2·00
439/43 .. *Set of* 5 3·00 3·50

460 Housewife using Telephone

461 Blue Flycatcher

(Litho D.L.R.)

990 (16 July). *Second Anniversary of Introduction of International Direct Dialling Service.* T **460** *and similar horiz designs. Multicoloured.* P 14×14½.
444 20 c. Type **460** .. 25 20
445 60 c. Businessman using telephone .. 35 35
446 80 c. Man using phonecard telephone .. 40 40
447 200 c. Public telephones for internal and IDD services .. 90 1·00
448 350 c. Satellite station .. 1·50 2·00
444/8 .. *Set of* 5 3·00 3·50

(Des W. Wright. Litho Questa)

1990 (25 Oct). *African Tropical Rain Forest.* T **461** *and similar multicoloured designs.* P 14×14½.
1449 40 c. Type **461** .. 55 60
a. Sheetlet. Nos. 1449/68 .. 10·00
1450 40 c. Boomslang (snake) .. 55 60
1451 40 c. Superb Sunbird .. 55 60
1452 40 c. Bateleur .. 55 60
1453 40 c. Yellow-casqued Hornbill .. 55 60
1454 40 c. *Salamis temora* (butterfly) .. 55 60
1455 40 c. Potto .. 55 60
1456 40 c. Leopard .. 55 60
1457 40 c. Bongo .. 55 60
1458 40 c. Grey Parrot .. 55 60
1459 40 c. Okapi .. 55 60
1460 40 c. Gorilla .. 55 60
1461 40 c. Flap-necked Chameleon .. 55 60
1462 40 c. West African Dwarf Crocodile .. 55 60
1463 40 c. Python .. 55 60
1464 40 c. Giant Ground Pangolin .. 55 60
1465 40 c. *Pseudacraea boisduvali* (butterfly) .. 55 60
1466 40 c. North African Crested Porcupine .. 55 60
1467 40 c. Rosy-columned Aerangis (orchid) .. 55 60
1468 40 c. *Cymothoe sangaris* (butterfly) .. 55 60
1449/68 .. *Set of* 20 10·00 11·00
MS1469 100×75 mm. 600 c. Head of Leopard (*vert*). P 14½×14 .. 4·50 5·00

Nos. 1449/68 were printed together, *se-tenant*, as a sheetlet of 20, forming a composite design.

462 Jupiter

463 *Eulophia guineensis*

(Des K. Gromell. Litho Questa)

1990 (13 Dec). *Space Flight of* "Voyager 2". T **462** *and similar multicoloured designs.* P 14.
1470 100 c. Type **462** .. 70 70
a. Sheetlet. Nos. 1470/8 .. 5·75
1471 100 c. Neptune and Triton .. 70 70
1472 100 c. Ariel, moon of Uranus .. 70 70
1473 100 c. Saturn from Mimas .. 70 70
1474 100 c. Saturn .. 70 70
1475 100 c. Rings of Saturn .. 70 70
1476 100 c. Neptune .. 70 70
1477 100 c. Uranus from Miranda .. 70 70
1478 100 c. Volcano on Io .. 70 70
1470/8 .. *Set of* 9 5·75 5·75
MS1479 Two sheets. (a) 111×81 mm. 600 c. "Voyager 2" spacecraft (*vert*). (b) 80×111 mm. 600 c. Lift off of "Voyager 2" (*vert*) *Set of* 2 *sheets* 4·50 5·00

Nos. 1470/8 were printed together, *se-tenant*, as a sheetlet of 9.

(Litho B.D.T.)

1990 (17 Dec). *Orchids.* T **463** *and similar vert designs. Multicoloured.* P 14.
1480 20 c. Type **463** .. 45 45
1481 40 c. *Eurychone rothschildiana* .. 60 60
1482 60 c. *Bulbophyllum barbigerum* .. 80 80
1483 80 c. *Polystachya galeata* .. 1·10 1·10
1484 200 c. *Diaphananthe kamerunensis* .. 1·75 1·75
1485 300 c. *Podangis dactyloceras* .. 2·00 2·00
1486 400 c. *Ancistrochilus rothschildianus* .. 2·00 2·00
1487 500 c. *Rangaeris muscicola* .. 2·00 2·00
1480/7 .. *Set of* 8 9·50 9·50
MS1488 Two sheets, each 101×70 mm. (a) 600 c. *Bolusiella imbricata.* (b) 600 c. *Diaphananthe rutila* .. *Set of* 2 *sheets* 8·50 9·00

464 *Coprinus atramentarius*

(Litho B.D.T.)

1990 (18 Dec). *Fungi* (2nd series). T **464** *and similar horiz designs. Multicoloured.* P 14.
1489 20 c. Type **464** .. 60 45
1490 50 c. *Marasmius oreades* .. 80 65
1491 60 c. *Oudemansiella radicata* .. 90 70
1492 80 c. *Boletus edulis* ("Cep") .. 1·10 90
1493 150 c. *Hebeloma crustuliniforme* .. 1·50 1·50
1494 200 c. *Coprinus micaceus* .. 1·75 1·75
1495 300 c. *Macrolepiota procera* ("*Lepiota procera*") .. 2·00 2·00
1496 500 c. *Amanita phalloides* .. 2·50 2·50
1489/96 .. *Set of* 8 10·00 9·50
MS1497 Two sheets, each 104×82 mm. (a) Nos. 1489, 1491/2 and 1496. (b) Nos. 1490 and 1493/5 *Set of* 2 *sheets* 7·00 8·00

465 Italian and Swedish Players chasing Ball

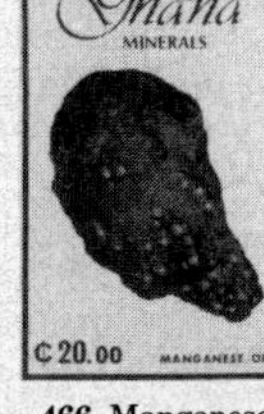

466 Manganese Ore

(Des Young Phillips Studio. Litho Questa)

1990 (18 Dec). *World Cup Football Championship, Italy.* T **465** *and similar multicoloured designs.* P 14.
1498 20 c. Type **465** .. 35 20
1499 50 c. Egyptian player penetrating Irish defence .. 45 30
1500 60 c. Cameroon players celebrating .. 50 30
1501 80 c. Rumanian player beating challenge .. 60 40
1502 100 c. Russian goalkeeper Dassayev .. 75 65
1503 150 c. Roger Milla of Cameroon (*vert*) .. 1·10 1·10
1504 400 c. South Korean player challenging opponent .. 2·00 2·25
1505 600 c. Klinsman of West Germany celebrating .. 2·50 3·00
1498/505 .. *Set of* 8 7·50 7·50
MS1506 Two sheets, each 88×98 mm. (a) 800 c. United Arab Emirates player watching ball. (b) 800 c. Colombian player .. *Set of* 2 *sheets* 5·50 6·50

(Litho Questa)

1990 (24 Dec). *350th Death Anniv of Rubens. Multicoloured designs as* T **273** *of Antigua, but vert.* P 13½×14.
1507 20 c. "Duke of Mantua" .. 20 20
1508 50 c. "Jan Brant" .. 30 30
1509 60 c. "Portrait of a Young Man" .. 30 30
1510 80 c. "Michel Ophovius" .. 40 40
1511 100 c. "Caspar Gevaerts" .. 55 55
1512 200 c. "Head of Warrior" (detail) .. 85 1·00
1513 300 c. "Study of a Bearded Man" .. 1·25 1·50
1514 400 c. "Paracelsus" .. 1·75 2·00
1507/14 .. *Set of* 8 5·00 5·50
MS1515 Two sheets, each 71×100 mm. (a) 600 c. "Warrior with two Pages" (detail). (b) 600 c. "Archduke Ferdinand" (detail) .. *Set of* 2 *sheets* 7·00 8·00

(Des E. Mensah. Litho D.L.R.)

1991 (2 May). *Minerals.* T **466** *and similar vert designs. Multicoloured.* P 14½×14.
1516 20 c. Type **466** .. 55 30
1517 60 c. Iron ore .. 70 60
1518 80 c. Bauxite ore .. 90 75
1519 200 c. Gold ore .. 2·00 2·00
1520 350 c. Diamond .. 3·00 4·00
1516/20 .. *Set of* 5 6·50 7·00
MS1521 70×90 mm. 600 c. Uncut and cut diamonds .. 5·50 6·50

PRICES OF SETS

Set prices are given for many issues, generally those containing three stamps or more. Definitive sets include one of each value or major colour change, but do not cover different perforations, die types or minor shades. Where a choice is possible the set prices are based on the cheapest versions of the stamps included in the listings.

467 Dance Drums

468 *Amorphophallus dracontioides*

(Des E. Mensah. Litho D.L.R.)

1991 (9 May). *Tribal Drums.* T **467** *and similar vert designs. Multicoloured.* P 14½×14.
1522 20 c. Type **467** .. 20 20
1523 60 c. Message drums .. 50 40
1524 80 c. War drums .. 60 50
1525 200 c. Dance drums (different) .. 1·25 1·50
1526 350 c. Ceremonial drums .. 1·75 2·50
1522/6 .. *Set of* 5 3·75 4·50
MS1527 70×90 mm. 600 c. Drum with carrying strap .. 3·75 5·50

(Des E. Mensah. Litho D.L.R.)

1991 (15 May). *Flowers* (1st series). T **468** *and similar vert designs. Multicoloured.* P 14½×14.
1528 20 c. Type **468** .. 55 25
1529 60 c. *Anchomanes difformis* .. 75 50
1530 80 c. *Kaemferia nigerica* .. 85 70
1531 200 c. *Aframomum sceptrum* .. 2·00 2·25
1532 350 c. *Amorphophallus flavovirens* .. 2·25 3·25
1528/32 .. *Set of* 5 5·75 6·25
MS1533 70×90 mm. 600 c. *Amorphophallus flavovirens* (different) .. 3·75 5·00

(Des E. Mensah. Litho D.L.R.)

1991 (17 May). *Flowers* (2nd series). *Vert designs as* T **468**, *but inscr* "GHANA" *in block capitals. Multicoloured.* P 14½×14.
1534 20 c. *Urginea indica* .. 55 25
1535 60 c. *Hymenocallis littoralis* .. 75 50
1536 80 c. *Crinum jagus* .. 1·25 70
1537 200 c. *Dipcadi tacazzeanum* .. 2·00 2·25
1538 350 c. *Haemanthus rupestris* .. 2·25 3·25
1534/8 .. *Set of* 5 6·00 6·25
MS1539 70×90 mm. 600 c. *Urginea indica* (different) .. 3·75 5·00

469 Transport and Telecommunication Symbols

470 Drawing of Scout from First Handbook

(Des E. Mensah. Litho Francoise-Charles Oberthur)

1991 (21 June). *40th Anniv of United Nations Development Programme.* T **469** *and similar vert designs. Multicoloured.* P 13½×14.
1540 20 c. Type **469** .. 30 20
1541 60 c. Agricultural research .. 50 40
1542 80 c. Literacy .. 60 55
1543 200 c. Advances in agricultural crop growth 1·25 1·50
1544 350 c. Industrial symbols .. 1·75 2·50
1540/4 .. *Set of* 5 4·00 4·75

(Des W. Hanson Studio. Litho B.D.T.)

1991 (18 July). *50th Death Anniv of Lord Baden-Powell.* T **470** *and similar designs.* P 14.
1545 20 c. black and pale buff .. 50 20
1546 50 c. grey, pale blue and black .. 70 40
1547 60 c. multicoloured .. 70 45
1548 80 c. black and pale buff .. 80 55
1549 100 c. multicoloured .. 95 75
1550 200 c. multicoloured .. 1·75 1·75
1551 500 c. multicoloured .. 2·50 3·00
1552 600 c. multicoloured .. 2·75 3·50
1545/52 .. *Set of* 8 9·50 9·50
MS1553 Two sheets. (a) 104×75 mm. 800 c. multicoloured; (b) 74×105 mm. 800 c. mult *Set of* 2 *sheets* 6·00 7·50

Designs: *Vert*—50 c. Lord Baden-Powell; 80 c. Handbook illustration by Norman Rockwell; 500 c. Scout at prayer. *Horiz*—60 c. Hands holding Boy Scout emblem; 100 c. Mafeking Siege 1d. Goodyear stamp and African runner; 200 c. Scouts with blitz victim, London, 1944; 600 c. Mafeking Siege 1d. Goodyear stamp; 800 c. (**MS**1553a) Scout camp; 800 c. (**MS**1553b) Envelope from Mafeking Siege.

471 Women sorting Fish

(Litho D.L.R.)

1991 (22 July). *Chorkor Smoker (fish smoking process). T* **471** *and similar horiz designs. Multicoloured. P* 14×14½.

1554 20 c. Type **471** 30 20
1555 60 c. Cleaning the ovens 55 40
1556 80 c. Washing fish 65 55
1557 200 c. Laying fish on pallets .. .. 1·25 1·50
1558 350 c. Stacking pallets over ovens .. 1·75 2·50
1554/8 .. .. *Set of* 5 4·00 4·75

472 African Hind

(Des E. Mensah. Litho B.D.T.)

1991 (29 July). *Fishes. T* **472** *and similar horiz designs. Multicoloured. P* 14.

1559 20 c. Type **472** 25 25
1560 50 c. Shrew Squeaker 40 40
1561 80 c. West African Triggerfish 55 55
1562 100 c. Stonehead 70 70
1563 200 c. Lesser Pipefish .. .. 1·50 1·50
1564 300 c. Aba .. .. 1·60 1·60
1565 400 c. Jewel Cichlid .. .. 1·75 1·75
1566 500 c. Smooth Hammerhead .. .. .. 1·90 1·90
1559/66 .. .. *Set of* 8 7·75 7·75
MS1567 Two sheets, each 108×81 mm. (a) 800 c. Bayad. (b) 800 c. Eastern Flying Gurnard *Set of* 2 *sheets* 6·00 7·00

(Litho B.D.T.)

1991 (12 Aug). *Death Centenary of Vincent van Gogh (artist) (1990). Multicoloured designs as T* **278** *of Antigua. P* 13.

1568 20 c. "Reaper with Sickle" 35 25
1569 50 c. "The Thresher" 55 40
1570 60 c. "The Sheaf-Binder" 60 50
1571 80 c. "The Sheep-Shearers" 70 65
1572 100 c. "Peasant Woman cutting Straw" .. 85 80
1573 200 c. "The Sower" .. .. 1·60 1·75
1574 500 c. "The Plough and the Harrow" (*horiz*) 2·25 2·50
1575 600 c. "The Woodcutter" .. .. .. 2·25 2·50
1568/75 .. .. *Set of* 8 8·25 8·50
MS1576 Two sheets, each 117×80 mm. (a) 800 c. "Evening: The Watch" (*horiz*). (b) 800 c. "Evening: The End of the Day" (*horiz*). Imperf *Set of* 2 *sheets* 7·00 8·00

473 Gamal Nasser (Egypt) and Conference Hall

474 Green-winged Pytilia

(Litho Cartor)

1991 (2 Sept). *10th Non-Aligned Ministers' Conference, Accra. T* **473** *and similar horiz designs showing statesmen. Multicoloured. P* 13½.

1577 20 c. Type **473** 50 30
1578 60 c. Josip Tito (Yugoslavia) 55 45
1579 80 c. Pandit Nehru (India) .. .. .. 1·75 1·25
1580 200 c. Kwame Nkrumah (Ghana) .. .. 1·75 2·25
1581 350 c. Achmad Sukarno (Indonesia) .. 1·90 3·00
1577/81 .. .. *Set of* 5 5·75 6·50

(Des S. Barlowe. Litho Questa)

1991 (14 Oct). *Birds. T* **474** *and similar vert designs. Multicoloured. P* 14½×14.

1582/1629 80 c. × 16, 100 c. × 32 *Set of* 48 22·00 25·00
MS1630 Three sheets, each 107×86 mm. (a) 800 c. Marabou Stork. (b) 800 c. African Fish Eagle. (c) 800 c. Saddle-bill Stork *Set of* 3 *sheets* 8·50 9·50

Nos. 1582/1629 were issued together, *se-tenant*, as three sheetlets of 16 forming composite designs. The 80 c. values show Green-winged Pytilia, Orange-cheeked Waxbill, African Paradise Flycatcher, Great Blue Turaco ("Blue Plantain-eater"), Red Bishop, Splendid Glossy Starling, Red-faced Lovebird, African Palm Swift, Narina Trogon, Tawny Eagle, Bateleur, Hoopoe, Secretary Bird, African White-backed Vulture, White-necked Bald Crow ("Bare-headed Rockfowl"), Abyssinian Ground Hornbill, and the 100 c. African Open-bill Stork, African Spoonbill, Pink-backed Pelican, Little Bittern, Purple Swamphen ("King Reed-hen"), Saddle-bill Stork, Glossy Ibis, White-faced Whistling Duck, Black-headed Heron, Hammerkop, African Darter, Woolly-necked Stork, Yellow-billed Stork, Black-winged Stilt, Goliath Heron, African Jacana ("Lily Trotter"), Shikra, Abyssinian Roller, Carmine Bee Eater, Pin-tailed Whydah, Purple Glossy Starling, Yellow-mantled Whydah, Pel's Fishing Owl, Crested Touraco, Red-cheeked Cordon-bleu, Olive-bellied Sunbird, Red-billed Hornbill, Red-billed Quelea, South African Crowned Crane, Blue Quail, Egyptian Vulture and Helmet Guineafowl.

475 *Nularda* (beetle)

476 Boti Falls

(Litho Cartor)

1991 (25 Oct). *Insects. T* **475** *and similar horiz designs. Multicoloured. P* 14×13½.

1631 20 c. Type **475** 50 20
1632 50 c. *Zonocrus* (grasshopper) 65 30
1633 60 c. *Gryllotalpa africana* (mole cricket) 70 30
1634 80 c. Weevil 80 60
1635 100 c. *Coenagrion* (dragonfly) 90 70
1636 150 c. *Sahlbergella* (fly) .. .. .. 1·25 1·60
1637 200 c. *Anthia* (ant) .. .. 1·40 1·75
1638 350 c. *Megacephala* (beetle) .. .. 2·00 2·75
1631/8 .. .. *Set of* 8 7·50 7·50
MS1639 106×79 mm. 600 c. *Lacetus* (lacewing). P 13×12 .. .. 5·00 6·00

(Litho R. Alhelou Marfo Co Ltd, Accra)

1991 (21 Nov)–**96**. *T* **476** *and similar multicoloured designs. P* 13½.

1639*a* 20 c. Oil palm fruit (4.93) 10 10
ab. Imperf (horiz pair) .. .. .. † —
1640 50 c. Type **476** 15 10
a. Imperf (pair) .. ..
1641 60 c. Larabanga Mosque (*horiz*) (12.12.91) 10 10
a. Black (inscriptions) omitted ..
1642 80 c. Fort Sebastian, Shama (*horiz*) (12.12.91) 10 10
1643 100 c. Cape Coast Castle (*horiz*) (12.12.91) 20 20
a. Black (inscriptions) omitted .. † —
b. Perf 14 (1996) .. .. ..
1644 200 c. White-toothed Cowrie (*Cyraea leucodon*) (*horiz*) (12.12.91) .. 40 30
a. Black (inscriptions) omitted ..
b. Perf 14 (1996) .. .. ..
1645 400 c. True Achatina (*Achatina achatina*) (*horiz*) (12.12.91) 70 55
a. Perf 14 (1996) .. .. ..
1639*a*/45 .. .. *Set of* 7 1·50 1·40

Examples of No. 1643a have been seen used on commercial cover.

Nos. 1643b and 1645a show "GHANA" and the face value in black redrawn.

(Litho Walsall)

1991 (23 Dec). *Christmas. Religious Paintings. Vert designs as T* **287** *of Antigua. Multicoloured. P* 12.

1646 20 c. "Adoration of the Magi" (Bosch) .. 35 20
1647 50 c. "The Annunciation" (Campin) .. 50 30
1648 60 c. "Virgin and Child" (detail) (Bouts) 55 30
1649 80 c. "Presentation in the Temple" (Memling) 65 50
1650 100 c. "Virgin and Child enthroned with Angel and Donor" (Memling) .. 85 65
1651 200 c. "Virgin and Child with Saints and Donor" (Van Eyck) .. .. 1·50 1·75
1652 400 c. "St. Luke painting the Virgin" (Van der Weyden) .. .. .. 2·50 3·00
1653 700 c. "Virgin and Child" (Bouts) .. 3·50 4·50
1646/53 .. .. *Set of* 8 9·50 10·00
MS1654 Two sheets, each 103×128 mm. (a) 800 c. "Virgin and Child standing in a Niche" (Van der Weyden). (b) 800 c. "The Annunciation" (Memling). P 14 .. .. *Set of* 2 *sheets* 6·50 8·00

477 Women collecting Water from Bore Hole

478 Mount Fuji and Flying Fish

(Litho R. Alhelou Marfo Co Ltd, Accra)

1992 (2 Feb). *Decade of Revolutionary Progress. T* **477** *and similar horiz designs. Multicoloured. P* 14×13½.

1655 20 c. Type **477** 15 10
1656 50 c. Miners 20 15
1657 60 c. Wood carver 20 15
1658 80 c. Forestry 25 20
1659 200 c. Cacao tree 50 75
1660 350 c. Village electrification .. .. 75 1·00
1655/60 .. .. *Set of* 6 1·90 2·00

(Litho B.D.T.)

1992 (16 Feb). *"Phila Nippon '91" International Stamp Exhibition, Tokyo. T* **478** *and similar horiz designs. Multicoloured. P* 14.

1661 20 c. Type **478** 35 30
1662 60 c. Itsukushima Jingu Shrine 45 40
1663 80 c. Geisha 60 50
1664 100 c. Samurai house 80 70
1665 200 c. Bonsai tree .. .. 1·50 1·50
1666 400 c. Olympic Sports Hall .. .. .. 2·00 2·25
1667 500 c. Great Buddha (statue) .. .. 2·25 2·50
1668 600 c. Nagoya Castle .. .. 2·40 2·75
1661/8 .. .. *Set of* 8 9·25 9·75
MS1669 Two sheets, each 109×80 mm. (a) 800 c. Takamatsu Castle. (b) 800 c. Heian Shrine *Set of* 2 *sheets* 7·50 8·50

479 East and West Germans celebrating

480 Steam Side-tank Locomotive, 1903

(Litho Questa)

1992 (17 Feb). *Reunification of Germany. T* **479** *and similar multicoloured designs. P* 14.

1670 20 c. Type **479** 30 20
1671 60 c. Signing Reunification Treaty .. 40 40
1672 80 c. Chariot on Brandenburg Gate and fireworks 45 45
1673 1000 c. Germans with unified currency .. 5·50 7·00
1670/3 .. .. *Set of* 4 6·00 7·25
MS1674 Three sheets. (a) 109×78 mm. 400 c. Doves and Brandenburg Gate; 400 c. Chancellor Kohl and Prime Minister De Maizière. (b) 125×87 mm. 800 c. Chancellor Kohl and members of last German Democratic Republic administration. (c) 130×92 mm. 300 c. President Gorbachev (*vert*); 300 c. Chancellor Kohl (*vert*); 300 c. Map of Western Germany (face value in black) (*vert*); 300 c. Map of Eastern Germany (face value in white) (*vert*) .. *Set of* 3 *sheets* 7·50 8·50

(Des W. Hanson. Litho B.D.T.)

1992 (2 Mar). *Ghanaian Railways. T* **480** *and similar horiz designs. Multicoloured. P* 14.

1675 20 c. Type **480** 40 30
1676 50 c. A1A-A1A diesel locomotive .. 60 40
1677 60 c. First class coach, 1931 .. .. 60 45
1678 80 c. Railway inspection coach No. 2212 70 70
1679 100 c. Steam locomotive No. 401 on Kumasi turntable 90 90
1680 200 c. Cocoa wagon, 1921 .. .. .. 1·40 1·50
1681 500 c. Steam locomotive No. 223 *Prince of Wales* .. .. 2·25 2·50
1682 600 c. Cattle wagon .. .. 2·25 2·50
1675/82 .. .. *Set of* 8 8·00 8·25
MS1683 Two sheets. (a) 106×76 mm. 800 c. Beyer-Garratt steam locomotive No. 301, 1943. (b) 76×106 mm. 800 c. German-built steam locomotive .. .. .. *Set of* 2 *sheets* 7·50 8·50

(Litho Questa)

1992 (3 Mar). *Olympic Games, Albertville and Barcelona. Past Medal Winners. Multicoloured designs as T* **204** *of Gambia. P* 14.

1684 20 c. E. Blay (Ghana) (boxing) and windmill 30 20
1685 60 c. M. Ahey (Ghana) (athletics) and Catalan coat of arms 50 35
1686 80 c. T. Wilson (U.S.A.) (70 metres ski jump) and grapes 60 50
1687 100 c. Four-man Bob-sleighing (East Germany) and passport 75 75
1688 200 c. G. Louganis (U.S.A.) (platform diving) and decorative vase .. 1·25 1·25
1689 300 c. L. Visser (Netherlands) (5000 metres speed skating) and wine bottle cork 1·50 1·60
1690 350 c. J. Passler (Italy) (biathlon) and lily 1·60 1·75
1691 400 c. M. Retton (U.S.A.) (gymnastics) and silhouette of castle .. .. .. 1·75 2·00
1692 500 c. J. Hingsen (West Germany) (decathlon) and gold and silver coins 1·75 2·00
1693 600 c. R. Neubert (West Germany) (heptathlon) and leather work .. 1·75 2·00
1684/93 .. .. *Set of* 10 10·50 11·00
MS1694 Two sheets. (a) 112×82 mm. 800 c. Silhouette of windmill. (b) 82×112 mm. 800 c. Silhouette of folk dancer (*vert*) .. *Set of* 2 *sheets* 8·50 9·50

481 *Angides lugubris*

482 *Danaus chrysippus*

(Litho B.D.T.)

1992 (30 Mar). *Reptiles. T* **481** *and similar horiz designs Multicoloured. P* 14.

1695 20 c. Type **481** 20 20
1696 50 c. *Kinixys erosa* (tortoise) 30 30
1697 60 c. *Agama agama* (lizard) 30 30
1698 80 c. *Chameleo gracilis* (chameleon) .. 40 40
1699 100 c. *Naja melanleuca* (snake) 50 50
1700 200 c. *Crocodylus niloticus* (crocodile) .. 90 1·1
1701 400 c. *Chelonia mydas* (turtle) .. .. 1·75 2·0
1702 500 c. *Varanus exanthematicus* (lizard) .. 1·90 2·25
1695/1702 .. .. .. *Set of* 8 5·50 6·25
MS1703 94×66 mm. 600 c. Tortoise and snake 2·75 3·50

(Litho Questa)

·92 (13 Apr). *Easter. Religious Paintings. Multicoloured designs as T* **291** *of Antigua.* P 13½×14.
04 20 c. "The Four Apostles" (detail) (Dürer) (*vert*) 25 20
'05 50 c. "The Last Judgement" (detail) (Rubens) (*vert*) 35 30
06 60 c. "The Four Apostles" (different detail) (Dürer) (*vert*) 35 30
'07 80 c. "The Last Judgement" (different detail) (Rubens) (*vert*) 50 40
'08 100 c. "Crucifixion" (Rubens) (*vert*) .. 60 50
'09 200 c. "The Last Judgement" (different detail) (Rubens) (*vert*) .. .. 1·10 1·25
'10 500 c. "Christum Videre" (Rubens) (*vert*) 2·00 2·50
'11 600 c. "The Last Judgement" (different detail) (Rubens) (*vert*) .. .. 2·25 2·75
'04/11 .. .. *Set of* 8 6·50 7·50
S1712 Two sheets. (a) 69×100 mm. 800 c. "Last Communion of St. Francis of Assisi" (detail) (Rubens) (*vert*). P 13½×14. (b) 100×69 mm. 800 c. "Scourging the Money Changers from the Temple" (detail) (El Greco). P 14×13½ *Set of* 2 *sheets* 7·50 8·50

(Litho B.D.T.)

·92 (4 May). *"Granada '92" International Stamp Exhibition, Spain. Spanish Paintings. Multicoloured designs as T* **292** *of Antigua.* P 13½×13 (*horiz*) or 13×13½ (*vert*).
713 20 c. "Two Men at Table" (Velázquez) (*horiz*) 20 20
714 60 c. "Christ in the House of Mary and Martha" (detail) (Velázquez) (*horiz*) 30 30
715 80 c. "The Supper at Emmaus" (Velázquez) (*horiz*) 40 40
716 100 c. "Three Musicians" (Velázquez) (*horiz*) 50 50
717 200 c. "Old Woman Cooking Eggs" (Velázquez) 90 90
718 400 c. "Old Woman Cooking Eggs" (detail) (Velázquez) .. .. .. 1·60 1·60
719 500 c. "The Surrender of Breda" (detail) (Velázquez) .. .. .. 1·75 1·75
720 700 c. "The Surrender of Breda" (different detail) (Velázquez) .. .. 2·00 2·00
713/20 .. .. *Set of* 8 7·00 7·00
MS1721 Two sheets. (a) 95×120 mm. 900 c. "The Waterseller of Seville" (Velázquez) (86×111 *mm*). (b) 120×95 mm. 900 c. "They still Say that Fish is Expensive" (Joaquín Sorolla y Bastida) (111×86 *mm*). Imperf .. .. *Set of* 2 *sheets* 7·50 8·50

(Des L. Nelson. Litho Walsall)

·992 (25 May). *"Genova '92" International Thematic Stamp Exhibition. Butterflies. T* **482** *and similar vert designs. Multicoloured.* P 14.
722 20 c. Type **482** 50 30
723 60 c. *Papilio dardanus* 80 45
724 80 c. *Cynthia cardui* 90 60
725 100 c. *Meneris tulbaghia* .. .. .. 1·00 75
726 200 c. *Salamis temora* .. .. .. 1·50 1·60
727 400 c. *Charaxes jasius* .. .. .. 2·00 2·50
728 500 c. *Precis oenone* .. .. .. 2·25 2·50
729 700 c. *Precis sophia* .. .. .. 2·50 2·75
722/9 .. .. *Set of* 8 10·00 10·00
MS1730 Two sheets, each 100×70 mm. (a) 900 c. *Papilio demodocus.* (b) 900 c. *Precis octavia* *Set of* 2 *sheets* 7·50 8·50

Examples of Nos. 1722/30 overprinted "40th Anniversary of the Accession of HM Queen Elizabeth II 1952–1992" in silver are reported as not having been issued in Ghana.

(Litho Walsall)

·992 (1 June). *Prehistoric Animals. Vert designs as T* **290** *of Antigua. Multicoloured.* P 14.
731 20 c. Iguanodon 35 25
732 50 c. Anchisaurus 50 35
733 60 c. Heterodontosaurus 55 35
734 80 c. Ouranosaurus 60 45
735 100 c. Anatosaurus 75 55
736 200 c. Elaphrosaurus .. .. .. 1·25 1·50
737 500 c. Coelophysis .. .. .. 2·25 2·75
738 600 c. Rhamphorynchus .. .. .. 2·50 3·00
731/8 .. .. *Set of* 8 8·00 8·25
MS1739 Two sheets, each 100×70 mm. (a) 1500 c. As 200 c. (b) 1500 c. As 500 c. *Set of* 2 *sheets* 9·00 10·00

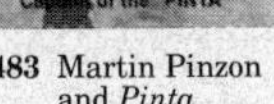

483 Martin Pinzon and *Pinta*

484 Olive-grey Ancilla (*Agaronia hiatula*)

(Des J.-L. Puvilland. Litho Questa)

·992 (20 July). *World Columbian Stamp "Expo '92", Chicago. 500th Anniv of Discovery of America by Columbus. T* **483** *and similar vert designs. Multicoloured.* P 14.
·740 200 c. Type **483** 90 90
a. Sheetlet. Nos. 1740/7 .. .. 6·50
·741 200 c. Vincente Pinzon and *Nina* .. 90 90
·742 200 c. Columbus and Father Marchena at La Rabida 90 90
1743 200 c. Columbus in his cabin 90 90
1744 200 c. Fleet sights land 90 90
1745 200 c. Columbus on Samana Cay .. 90 90
1746 200 c. Wreck of *Santa Maria* 90 90
1747 200 c. Amerindians at Spanish Court .. 90 90
1740/7 .. .. *Set of* 8 6·50 6·50
MS1748 122×86 mm. 500 c. Columbus and *Santa Maria* .. .. 2·75 3·50

Nos. 1740/7 were printed together, *se-tenant*, in sheetlets of 8.

(Litho Questa)

1992 (30 Sept–5 Oct). *Shells. T* **484** *and similar vert designs. Multicoloured.* P 14.
1749 20 c. Type **484** 20 20
1750 20 c. Radula Cerith (*Tympanotonus fuscatus radula*) (5 Oct) 20 20
1751 60 c. Rugose Donax (*Donax rugosus*) .. 30 30
1752 60 c. Horned Murex (*Murex cornutus*) (5 Oct) 30 30
1753 80 c. Concave Ear Moon (*Sinum concavum*) 40 40
1754 80 c. Triple Tivella (*Tivella tripla*) (5 Oct) 40 40
1755 200 c. *Pila africana* 90 90
1756 200 c. Rat Cowrie (*Cypraea stercoraria*) (5 Oct) 90 90
1757 350 c. *Thais hiatula* .. .. .. 1·60 1·60
1758 350 c. West African Helmet (*Cassis tessellata*) (5 Oct) .. .. .. 1·60 1·60
1749/58 .. .. *Set of* 10 6·00 6·00
MS1759 Two sheets, each 87×117 mm. (a) 600 c. Fanel Moon (*Natica fanel*). (b) 600 c. Giant Hairy Melongena (*Pugilina moria*) .. *Set of* 2 *sheets* 6·00 7·00

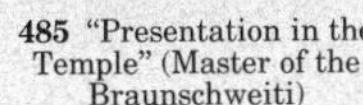

485 "Presentation in the Temple" (Master of the Braunschweiti)

486 *Calappa rubroguttata*

(Litho Questa)

1992 (16 Dec). *Christmas. Religious Paintings. T* **485** *and similar vert designs. Multicoloured.* P 13½×14.
1760 20 c. Type **485** 20 20
1761 50 c. "Presentation in the Temple" (detail) (Master of St. Severin) 30 30
1762 60 c. "The Visitation" (Sebastiano del Piombo) 30 30
1763 80 c. "The Visitation" (detail) (Giotto) .. 40 40
1764 100 c. "The Circumcision" (detail) (Studio of Bellini) 50 50
1765 200 c. "The Circumcision" (Studio of Garofalo) 90 90
1766 500 c. "The Visitation" (Studio of Van der Weyden) .. .. 1·60 1·60
1767 800 c. "The Visitation" (detail) (Studio of Van der Weyden) .. .. .. 1·90 1·90
1760/7 .. .. *Set of* 8 5·50 5·50
MS1768 Two sheets, each 77×102 mm. (a) 900 c. "Presentation in the Temple" (Bartolo di Fredi). (b) 900 c. "The Visitation" (larger detail) (Giotto) *Set of* 2 *sheets* 6·50 7·50

(Litho Francoise-Charles, Oberthur)

1993 (15 Feb). *Crabs. T* **486** *and similar horiz designs. Multicoloured.* P 13½×14.
1769 20 c. Type **486** 40 20
1770 60 c. *Cardisoma amatum* 60 25
1771 80 c. *Maia squinado* 70 25
1772 400 c. *Ocypoda cursor* .. .. .. 1·40 1·60
1773 800 c. *Grapus grapus* .. .. .. 2·00 2·50
1769/73 .. .. *Set of* 5 4·50 4·25
MS1774 127×97 mm. Nos. 1769/72 .. .. 3·50 4·00

487 *Clerodendrum thomsoniae*

488 Zeppelin LZ-3 entering Floating Hangar, Lake Constance

(Litho Questa)

1993 (1 Mar). *Flowers. T* **487** *and similar vert designs. Multicoloured.* P 14.
1775 20 c. Type **487** 20 15
1776 20 c. *Lagerstroemia flos-reginae* 20 15
1777 60 c. *Cassia fistula* 35 25
1778 60 c. *Spathodea campanulata* 35 25
1779 80 c. *Hildegardia barteri* 40 25
1780 80 c. *Mellitea ferrugenea* 40 25
1781 200 c. *Petrea volubilis* 60 75
1782 200 c. *Ipomoea asarifolia* 60 75
1783 350 c. *Bryphyllum pinnatum* .. .. 90 1·00
1784 350 c. *Ritchiea reflexa* .. .. .. 90 1·00
1775/84 .. .. *Set of* 10 4·50 4·25
MS1785 Two sheets, each 86×125 mm. (a) 50 c. As No. 1777; 100 c. As No. 1783; 150 c. As No. 1782; 300 c. As No. 1779. (b) 50 c. As No. 1778; 100 c. As No. 1776; 150 c. As No. 1780; 300 c. As No. 1784 .. .. .. *Set of* 2 *sheets* 4·50 5·00

(Des W. Wright and W. Hanson (Nos. 1786, 1792, **MS**1793a). W. Wright and L. Fried (Nos. 1787, 1791, **MS**1793b). J. Genzo (Nos. 1790, **MS**1793d). W. Wright (others). Litho B.D.T.)

1993 (8 Mar). *Anniversaries and Events. T* **488** *and similar multicoloured designs.* P 14.
1786 20 c. Type **488** 55 30
1787 100 c. Launch of European "Ariane 4" rocket (*vert*) 90 75
1788 200 c. Leopard .. .. 1·60 1·75
1789 300 c. Colosseum and fruit .. .. 1·75 2·00
1790 400 c. Mozart (*vert*) .. .. .. 2·00 2·25
1791 600 c. Launch of Japanese "H-1" rocket (*vert*) .. .. 2·50 2·75
1792 800 c Zeppelin LZ-10 *Schwaben* .. .. 2·75 3·00
1786/92 .. .. *Set of* 7 11·00 11·50
MS1793 Four sheets. (a) 106×76 mm. 900 c. Count Ferdinand von Zeppelin (*vert*). (b) 76×106 mm. 900 c. Launch of American space shuttle (*vert*). (c) 106×76 mm. 900 c. Bongo. (d) 99×69 mm. 900 c. Cherubino from *The Marriage of Figaro* (*vert*) .. .. .. *Set of* 4 *sheets* 12·00 13·00

Anniversaries and Events:—Nos. 1786, 1792, **MS**1793a, 75th death anniv of Count Ferdinand von Zeppelin; Nos. 1787, 1791, **MS**1793b, International Space Year; Nos. 1788, **MS**1793c, Earth Summit '92, Rio; No. 1789, International Conference on Nutrition, Rome; Nos. 1790, **MS**1793d, Death bicent of Mozart.

(Litho Walsall)

1993 (8 Mar). *Bicentenary of the Louvre, Paris. Multicoloured designs as T* **305** *of Antigua.* P 12.
1794 200 c. "Carnival Minuet" (left detail) (Giovanni Domenico Tiepolo) .. 85 1·00
a. Sheetlet. Nos. 1794/1801 .. .. 6·25
1795 200 c. "Carnival Minuet" (centre detail) (Giovanni Domenico Tiepolo) .. 85 1·00
1796 200 c. "Carnival Minuet" (right detail) (Giovanni Domenico Tiepolo) .. 85 1·00
1797 200 c. "The Tooth Puller" (left detail) (Giovanni Domenico Tiepolo) .. 85 1·00
1798 200 c. "The Tooth Puller" (right detail) (Giovanni Domenico Tiepolo) .. 85 1·00
1799 200 c. "Rebecca at the Well" (Giovanni Battista Tiepolo) .. .. 85 1·00
1800 200 c. "Presenting Christ to the People" (left detail) (Giovanni Battista Tiepolo) .. .. 85 1·00
1801 200 c. "Presenting Christ to the People" (right detail) (Giovanni Battista Tiepolo) .. .. 85 1·00
1794/1801 .. .. *Set of* 8 6·25 7·25
MS1802 100×70 mm. 700 c. "Chancellor Seguier" (Charles le Brun) (85×52 *mm*). P 14½ 2·10 2·40

Nos. 1794/1801 were printed together, *se-tenant*, in sheetlets of 8 stamps and one centre label.

489 Energy Foods

(Litho Questa)

1993 (22 Mar). *International Conference on Nutrition, Rome. T* **489** *and similar horiz designs. Multicoloured.* P 14.
1803 20 c. Type **489** 20 15
1804 60 c. Body-building foods 30 20
1805 80 c. Protective foods 35 25
1806 200 c. Disease prevention equipment .. 80 90
1807 400 c. Quality control and preservation of fish products .. .. .. 1·50 1·75
1803/7 .. .. *Set of* 5 2·75 3·00

490 Kwame Nkrumah Mausoleum

491 Resurrection Egg

(Litho Questa)

1993 (8 Apr). *Proclamation of Fourth Republic. T* **490** *and similar multicoloured designs. P* 14.

1808 50 c. Type **490** 20 15
1809 100 c. Kwame Nkrumah Conference Centre 35 25
1810 200 c. Book of Constitution (*vert*) .. 80 80
1811 350 c. Independence Square (*vert*) .. 1·60 1·75
1812 400 c. Christiansborg Castle (*vert*) .. 1·75 2·00
1808/12 .. .. .. *Set of* 5 4·25 4·50

(Des Kerri Schiff. Litho Questa)

1993 (26 Apr). *Easter. Faberge Eggs. T* **491** *and similar multicoloured designs. P* 14.

1813 50 c. Type **491** 40 15
1814 80 c. Imperial Red Cross egg with Resurrection triptych 65 25
1815 100 c. Imperial Uspensky Cathedral egg 75 25
1816 150 c. Imperial Red Cross egg with portraits .. .. 1·10 65
1817 200 c. Orange Tree egg .. .. .. 1·25 1·25
1818 250 c. Rabbit egg .. .. 1·25 1·50
1819 400 c. Imperial Coronation egg .. .. 2·00 2·50
1820 900 c. Silver-gilt enamel Easter egg .. 3·25 4·00
1813/20 .. .. *Set of* 8 9·50 9·50
MS1821 Two sheets, each (a) 73×100 mm. 1000 c. Renaissance egg. (b) 100×73 mm. 1000 c. Egg charms (*horiz*) .. .. *Set of 2 sheets* 7·75 8·25

(Des W. Wright. Litho Questa)

1993 (3 May). *Centenary of Henry Ford's First Petrol Engine (Nos. 1823/4,* **MS**1826b) *and Karl Benz's First Four-wheeled Car (others). Horiz designs as T* **264** *of Dominica. Multicoloured. P* 14.

1822 150 c. Mercedes Benz "300 SLR", Mille Miglia, 1955 .. .. .. 75 50
1823 400 c. Ford "Depot Wagon", 1920 .. 1·75 1·75
1824 600 c. Ford "Mach 1 Mustang", 1970 .. 2·25 2·50
1825 800 c. Mercedes Benz racing car, Monaco Grand Prix, 1937 .. .. .. 3·50 4·00
1822/5 .. .. *Set of* 4 7·50 8·00
MS1826 Two sheets, each 110×80 mm. (a) 1000 c. Mercedes Benz "Type 196" racing car, 1955 ($85^1/_2\times28^1/_2$ *mm*). (b) 1000 c. Ford "Super T", 1910 ($85^1/_2\times28^1/_2$ *mm*) .. *Set of 2 sheets* 7·75 8·25

(Des W. Wright. Litho Questa)

1993 (3 May). *Aviation Anniversaries. Multicoloured designs as T* **266** *of Dominica. P* 14.

1827 50 c. LZ-127 *Graf Zeppelin* over Alps (*vert*) 50 30
1828 150 c. Zeppelin LZ-7 *Deutschland* .. 85 55
1829 400 c. Avro Vulcan jet bomber .. .. 1·75 1·75
1830 400 c. U.S. Mail Ford 4-AT Trimotor .. 1·75 1·75
1831 600 c. Nieuport 27 (*vert*) .. .. .. 2·25 2·25
1832 600 c. Loading mail on LZ-127 *Graf Zeppelin* (*vert*) .. .. .. 2·25 2·25
1833 800 c. Zeppelin LZ-10 *Schwaben* .. .. 3·50 4·00
1827/33 .. .. *Set of* 7 11·50 11·50
MS1834 Three sheets, each 111×80 mm. (a) 1000 c. LZ-127 *Graf Zeppelin*. (b) 1000 c. S.E.5A, 1918. (c) 1000 c. Early airmail flight by Walter Edwards between Portland and Vancouver ($57\times42^1/_2$ *mm*) .. .. *Set of 3 sheets* 11·50 12·00
Anniversaries:—Nos. 1827/8, 1833, **MS**1834a, 125th birth anniv of Hugo Eckener (airship commander); Nos. 1829, 1831, **MS**1834b, 75th anniv of Royal Air Force; Nos. 1830, 1832, **MS**1834c, Bicentenary of First Airmail Flight.

492 African Buffalo

40TH ANNIVERSARY
OF CORONATION
H.M. ELIZABETH II

(**493**)

(Des T. Muse. Litho Questa)

1993 (24 May). *Wild Animals. T* **492** *and similar horiz designs. Multicoloured. P* 14.

1835 20 c. Type **492** 25 15
1836 50 c. Giant Forest Hog 30 20
1837 60 c. Potto 40 25
1838 80 c. Bay Duiker 50 30
1839 100 c. Royal Antelope 60 35
1840 200 c. Serval 90 90
1841 500 c. Golden Cat .. .. 1·75 2·00
1842 800 c. *Megaloglossus woermanni* (bat) .. 3·00 3·50
1835/42 .. .. *Set of* 8 7·00 7·00
MS1843 Two sheets, each 68×98 mm. (a) 900 c. Dormouse. (b) 900 c. White-collared Mangabey *Set of 2 sheets* 7·00 7·50

1993 (18 June). *40th Anniv of Coronation. Nos.* 1549/53 *optd with T* **493**.

1844 100 c. multicoloured 50 25
1845 200 c. multicoloured 90 70
1846 500 c. multicoloured .. .. .. 2·50 2·75
1847 600 c. multicoloured .. .. .. 2·75 3·00
1844/7 .. .. *Set of* 4 6·00 6·00
MS1848 Two sheets. (a) 104×75 mm. 800 c. mult. (b) 74×105 mm. 800 c. mult *Set of 2 sheets* 6·75 7·50
The sheets of No. **MS**1848 also carry a commemorative overprint on the margin.

35 YEARS OF
ROTARY INTERNATIONAL
GHANA 1958

(**494**)

GHANA
RED CROSS SOCIETY
FOUNDED 1932

(**495**)

1993 (18 June). *35th Anniv of Rotary International and 60th Anniv of Ghana Red Cross Society (1992). Nos.* 1562 *and* 1564/7 *optd with T* **494** *(Nos.* 1849, 1852, **MS**1853a) *or T* **495** *(others).*

1849 100 c. Stonehead 50 25
1850 300 c. Aba (R.) .. .. 1·50 1·50
1851 400 c. Jewel Cichlid (R.) .. .. .. 1·75 1·75
1852 500 c. Smooth Hammerhead .. .. 2·00 2·25
1849/52 .. .. *Set of* 4 5·25 5·25
MS1853 Two sheets, each 108×81 mm. (a) 800 c Bayad. (b) 800 c. Eastern Flying Gurnard (R.) *Set of 2 sheets* 7·00 7·50
The sheets of No. **MS**1853 also carry a commemorative overprint on the margin.

496 *Cantharellus cibarius*

497 "The Actor" (Picasso)

(Des L. Nelson (Nos. 1861/2, 1866/8), E. Mensah (others). Litho Questa)

1993 (30 July). *Mushrooms. T* **496** *and similar vert designs. Multicoloured. P* 14.

1854 20 c. Type **496** 40 25
1855 50 c. *Russula cyanoxantha* 50 30
1856 60 c. *Clitocybe rivulosa* 55 30
1857 80 c. *Cortinarius elatior* 60 35
1858 80 c. *Mycena galericulata* 60 35
1859 200 c. *Tricholoma gambosum* .. .. 1·00 1·00
1860 200 c. *Boletus edulis* .. .. .. 1·00 1·00
1861 200 c. *Lepista saeva* .. .. .. 1·00 1·00
1862 250 c. *Gyroporus castaneus* .. .. 1·10 1·10
1863 300 c. *Boletus chrysenteron* .. .. 1·25 1·25
1864 350 c. *Nolanea sericea* .. .. .. 1·40 1·40
1865 350 c. *Hygrophorus puniceus* ("*Hygrophorus puiceus*") .. .. .. 1·40 1·40
1866 500 c. *Gomphidius glutinosus* .. .. 1·60 1·75
1867 600 c. *Russula olivacea* .. .. .. 1·75 2·00
1868 1000 c. *Russula aurata* .. .. .. 2·25 2·75
1854/68 .. .. *Set of* 15 14·50 14·50
MS1869 Two sheets, each 85×130 mm. (a) 50 c. As No. 1856; 100 c. As No. 1858; 150 c. As No. 1860; 1000 c. As No. 1864. (b) 100 c. As Type **496**; 150 c. As No. 1857; 300 c. As No. 1859; 600 c. As No. 1865 .. .. *Set of 2 sheets* 9·50 11·00

(Litho Cartor (Nos. 1871, 1873, **MS**1877c/d), Questa (others))

1993 (19 Oct). *Anniversaries and Events. T* **497** *and similar multicoloured designs. P* $13^1/_2\times14$ *(Nos.* 1871, 1873) *or* 14 *(others).*

1870 20 c. Type **497** 30 20
1871 20 c. Early astronomical equipment .. 30 20
1872 80 c. "Portrait of Allan Stein" (Picasso) .. 40 25
1873 200 c. Modern telescope 80 80
1874 200 c. "Tattoo" (Lesek Sobocki) 80 80
1875 600 c. "Prison" (Sasza Blonder) .. .. 2·00 2·50
1876 800 c. "Seated Male Nude" (Picasso) .. 2·75 3·25
1870/6 .. .. *Set of* 7 6·50 7·25
MS1877 Four sheets. (a) 75×105 mm. 900 c. "Guernica" (Picasso). P 14. (b) 75×105 mm. 1000 c. "Bajika o Czlowieku Szczesliwym" (detail) (Antoni Mickalak) (*horiz*). P 14. (c) 105×75 mm. 1000 c. Copernicus (face value at top left). P 12×13. (d) 105×75 mm. 1000 c. Copernicus (face value at centre top). P 12×13 *Set of 4 sheets* 14·00 15·00
Anniversaries and Events:—Nos. 1870, 1872, 1876, **MS**1877a, 20th death anniv of Picasso (artist); Nos. 1871, 1873, **MS**1877c/d, 450th death anniv of Copernicus (astronomer); Nos. 1874/5, **MS**1877b, "Polska '93" International Stamp Exhibition, Poznań.

498 Abedi Pele (Ghana)

499 Common Turkey

(Litho Questa)

1993 (1 Dec). *World Cup Football Championship, U.S.A. (1st issue). T* **498** *and similar vert designs. Multicoloured. P* 13×14.

1878 50 c. Type **498** 50 25
1879 80 c. Pedro Troglio (Argentina) 60 30
1880 100 c. Fernando Alvez (Uruguay) 70 40
1881 200 c. Franco Baresi (Italy) .. .. 1·25 1·00
1882 250 c. Gomez (Colombia) and Katanec (Yugoslavia) .. .. .. 1·25 1·
1883 600 c. Diego Maradona (Argentina) .. 2·50 2·
1884 800 c. Hasek (Czechoslovakia) and Wynalda (U.S.A.) .. .. .. 3·00 3·
1885 1000 c. Lothar Matthaeus (Germany) .. 3·50 4·
1878/85 .. .. *Set of* 8 12·00 12·
MS1886 Two sheets, each 70×100 mm. (a) 1200 c. Rabie Yassein (Egypt) and Ruud Gullit (Netherlands). (b) 1200 c. Giuseppe Giannini (Italy). P 13 .. .. .. *Set of 2 sheets* 11·00 12·
See also Nos. 2037/43.

(Litho Questa)

1993 (8 Dec). *Domestic Animals. T* **499** *and similar ho[rizontal] designs. Multicoloured. P* 14.

1887 50 c. Type **499** 50
1888 100 c. Goats 70
1889 150 c. Muscovy Ducks .. .. .. 1·00
1890 200 c. Donkeys .. .. 1·25 1·
1891 250 c. Red Junglefowl cock .. .. 1·25 1·
1892 300 c. Pigs .. .. 1·40 1·
1893 400 c. Helmet Guineafowl .. .. 1·75 1·
1894 600 c. Dog .. .. 2·50 2·
1895 800 c. Red Junglefowl hen .. .. 3·00 3·
1896 1000 c. Sheep .. .. 3·50 4·
1887/96 .. .. *Set of* 10 15·00 15·
MS1897 Two sheets, each 133×106 mm. (a) 100 c. As No. 1888; 250 c. No. 1894; 350 c. No. 1892; 500 c. No. 1896. (b) 100 c. No. 1893; 250 c. As No. 1891; 350 c. No. 1895; 500 c. Type **499** *Set of 2 sheets* 9·50 10·

(Litho Questa)

1993 (20 Dec). *Christmas. Religious Paintings. Designs* [as] *T* **270** *of Dominica. Black, pale lemon and red* (Nos. 189[8/9], 1900/1, 1905 *and* **MS**1906a) *or multicoloured (other[s]). P* $13^1/_2\times14$.

1898 50 c. "Adoration of the Magi" (Dürer) .. 50
1899 100 c. "The Virgin and Child with St. John and an Angel" (Botticelli) .. 70
1900 150 c. "Mary as Queen of Heaven" (Dürer) 90
1901 200 c. "Saint Anne" (Dürer) .. .. 1·00
1902 250 c. "The Madonna of the Magnificat" (Botticelli) .. .. .. 1·10
1903 400 c. "The Madonna of the Goldfinch" (Botticelli) .. .. .. 1·75 1·
1904 600 c. "The Virgin and Child with the young St. John the Baptist" (Botticelli) .. .. .. 2·25 2·
1905 1000 c. "Adoration of the Shepherds" (Dürer) .. .. 3·00 4·
1898/1905 .. .. .. *Set of* 8 10·00 9·
MS1906 Two sheets, each 102×128 mm. (a) 1000 c. "Madonna in a Circle" (detail) (Dürer). P $13^1/_2\times14$. (b) 1000 c. "Mystic Nativity" (detail) (Botticelli) (*horiz*). P $14\times13^1/_2$ .. *Set of 2 sheets* 8·00 9·

500 Doll

501 Mickey Mouse in *Steamboat Willie*, 1928

(Des E. Mensah. Litho Questa)

1994 (24 Jan). *Traditional Crafts. T* **500** *and similar ve[rt] designs. Multicoloured. P* 14.

1907 50 c. Type **500** 25
1908 50 c. Pot with "head" lid 25
1909 200 c. Bead necklace 60
1910 200 c. Snake charmers (statuette) .. 60
1911 250 c. Hoe 60
1912 250 c. Scabbard 60
1913 600 c. Pipe .. .. 1·50 1·7
1914 600 c. Deer (carving) .. .. .. 1·50 1·7
1915 1000 c. Mask .. .. 2·25 2·5
1916 1000 c. Doll (*different*) .. .. .. 2·25 2·5
1907/16 .. .. *Set of* 10 9·25 10·0
MS1917 Two sheets, each 95×128 mm. (a) 100 c. As Type **500**; 250 c. As No. 1909; 350 c. As No. 1911; 500 c. As No. 1913. (b) 100 c. As No. 1908; 250 c. As No. 1910; 350 c. As No. 1912; 500 c. As No. 1914 .. .. .. *Set of 2 sheets* 4·50 5·5

(Des W. Hanson. Litho Questa)

1994 (18 Feb). *"Hong Kong '94" International Stam[p] Exhibition (1st issue). Horiz designs as T* **317** *of Antigu[a]. Multicoloured. P* 14.

1918 200 c. Hong Kong 1986 50 c. "Expo '86" stamp and tram 70
a. Horiz pair. Nos. 1918/19 .. .. 1·40 1·
1919 200 c. Ghana 1992 20 c. Railways stamp and tram 70
Nos. 1918/19 were printed together, *se-tenant*, in horizont[al] pairs throughout the sheet with the centre part of each pa[ir] forming the complete design.

(Des Kerri Schiff. Litho Questa)

994 (18 Feb). *"Hong Kong '94" International Stamp Exhibition (2nd issue). Imperial Palace Clocks. Designs as T* **318** *of Antigua, but vert. Multicoloured.* P 14.
920 100 c. Windmill clock 60 65
a. Sheetlet. Nos. 1920/5 .. .. 3·25
921 100 c. Horse clock 60 65
922 100 c. Balloon clock 60 65
923 100 c. Zodiac clock 60 65
924 100 c. Shar-pei Dog clock 60 65
925 100 c. Cat clock 60 65
920/5 .. .. .. *Set of* 6 3·25 3·50
Nos. 1920/5 were printed together, *se-tenant*, in sheetlets of 6.

(Litho Questa)

994 (1 Mar). *65th Anniv of Mickey Mouse (Walt Disney cartoon character)* (1993). *T* **501** *and similar vert designs showing scenes from various cartoon films.* P 13½×14.
926 50 c. Type **501** 30 15
927 100 c. *The Band Concert*, 1935 .. .. 40 20
928 150 c. *Moose Hunters*, 1937 .. .. 45 35
929 200 c. *Brave Little Tailor*, 1938 .. .. 55 50
930 250 c. *Fantasia*, 1940 .. .. .. 60 60
931 400 c. *The Nifty Nineties*, 1941 .. .. 1·25 1·50
932 600 c. *Canine Caddy*, 1941 .. .. 1·50 1·75
933 1000 c. *Mickey's Christmas Carol*, 1983 .. 2·25 2·50
926/33 .. .. .. *Set of* 8 6·50 6·75
IS1934 Two sheets, each 127×102 mm. (a) 1200 c. *Mickey's Elephant*, 1936. (b) 1200 c. *Mickey's Amateurs*, 1937 .. *Set of* 2 *sheets* 5·50 6·00
No. 1929 is inscribed "TAYLOR" in error. The dates on Nos. 927 and 1932 are incorrectly shown as "1937" and "1944".

(Litho Questa)

994 (6 Apr). *Easter. Hummel Figurines. Vert designs as T* **302** *of Antigua. Multicoloured.* P 14.
935 50 c. Boy hiker 30 15
936 100 c. Girl with basket behind back .. 40 20
937 150 c. Boy with rabbits 45 35
938 200 c. Boy holding basket 55 50
939 250 c. Girl with chicks 60 60
940 400 c. Girl with lamb .. .. .. 1·25 1·50
941 600 c. Girl waving red handkerchief with lamb .. .. 1·50 1·75
942 1000 c. Girl with basket and posy .. 2·25 2·50
935/42 .. .. .. *Set of* 8 6·50 6·75
IS1943 Two sheets, each 93×126 mm. (a) 50 c. As No. 1935; 150 c. As No. 1942; 500 c. As No. 1936; 1200 c. As No. 1938. (b) 200 c. As No. 1940; 300 c. As No. 1939; 500 c. As No. 1941; 1000 c. As No. 1937 .. .. .. *Set of* 2 *sheets* 7·50 8·00

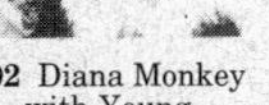

502 Diana Monkey with Young

503 Norwegian Forest Cat

(Des S. Barlowe. Litho Questa)

994 (16 May). *Wildlife. T* **502** *and similar multicoloured designs.* P 14.
944 50 c. Type **502** 30 15
a. Horiz strip of 4. Nos. 1944 and 1947/9 .. .. 3·00
945 100 c. Bushbuck (*horiz*) 40 20
946 150 c. Spotted Hyena (*horiz*) 45 35
947 200 c. Diana Monkey on branch facing left 50 40
948 500 c. Diana Monkey on branch facing right .. .. 1·00 1·25
949 800 c. Head of Diana Monkey .. .. 1·50 1·75
950 1000 c. Aardvark (*horiz*) .. .. 1·75 2·00
944/50 .. .. .. *Set of* 7 5·50 5·50
IS1951 Two sheets, each 106×76 mm. (a) 2000 c. Leopard. (b) 2000 c. Waterbuck *Set of* 2 *sheets* 8·00 9·00
In addition to normal sheets of each value Nos. 1944 and 947/9 were also available in sheets of 12 with the stamps vailable both vertically and horizontally *se-tenant.*
Designs of Nos. 1944 and 1947/9 include the W.W.F. Panda mblem.

(Des Jennifer Toombs. Litho Questa)

994 (6 June). *Cats. T* **503** *and similar horiz designs. Multicoloured.* P 14.
952 200 c. Type **503** 40 40
a. Sheetlet. Nos. 1952/63 .. .. 4·25
953 200 c. Blue Longhair 40 40
954 200 c. Red Self Longhair 40 40
955 200 c. Black Longhair 40 40
956 200 c. Chinchilla 40 40
957 200 c. Dilute Calico Longhair 40 40
958 200 c. Blue Tabby and White Longhair .. 40 40
959 200 c. Ruby Somali 40 40
960 200 c. Blue Smoke Longhair 40 40
961 200 c. Calico Longhair 40 40
1962 200 c. Brown Tabby Longhair 40 40
1963 200 c. Balinese 40 40
1964 200 c. Sorrel Abyssinian 40 40
a. Sheetlet. Nos. 1964/75 .. .. 4·25
1965 200 c. Silver Classic Tabby 40 40
1966 200 c. Chocolate-point Siamese 40 40
1967 200 c. Brown Tortie Burmese 40 40
1968 200 c. Exotic Shorthair 40 40
1969 200 c. Havana Brown 40 40
1970 200 c. Devon Rex 40 40
1971 200 c. Black Manx 40 40
1972 200 c. British Blue Shorthair 40 40
1973 200 c. Calico American Wirehair 40 40
1974 200 c. Spotted Oriental Siamese 40 40
1975 200 c. Red Classic Tabby 40 40
1952/75 .. .. .. *Set of* 24 8·50 8·50
MS1976 Two sheets, each 102×89 mm. (a) 2000 c. Brown Mackerel Tabby Scottish Fold. (b) 2000 c. Seal-point Colourpoint .. *Set of* 2 *sheets* 8·50 9·00
Nos. 1952/63 and 1964/75 were printed together, *se-tenant*, in sheetlets of 12.
No. 1957 is inscribed "Dilut" in error.

504 Red-bellied Paradise Flycatcher

(Des Mary Walters. Litho Questa)

1994 (13 June). *Birds. T* **504** *and similar horiz designs. Multicoloured.* P 14.
1977 200 c. Type **504** 50 50
a. Sheetlet. Nos. 1977/88 .. .. 5·50
1978 200 c. Many-coloured Bush Shrike .. 50 50
1979 200 c. Broad-tailed Paradise Whydah .. 50 50
1980 200 c. White-crowned Robin Chat .. 50 50
1981 200 c. Violet Turaco ("Violet Plantain-eater") 50 50
1982 200 c. Village Weaver 50 50
1983 200 c. Red-crowned Bishop 50 50
1984 200 c. Common Shoveler 50 50
1985 200 c. Spur-winged Goose 50 50
1986 200 c. African Crake 50 50
1987 200 c. Purple Swamphen ("King Reed-hen") 50 50
1988 200 c. African Tiger Bittern 50 50
1989 200 c. Oriole Warbler ("Moho") 50 50
a. Sheetlet. Nos. 1989/2000 .. .. 5·50
1990 200 c. Superb Sunbird 50 50
1991 200 c. Blue-breasted Kingfisher 50 50
1992 200 c. African Blue Cuckoo Shrike .. 50 50
1993 200 c. Great Blue Turaco ("Blue Plantain-eater") 50 50
1994 200 c. Greater Flamingo 50 50
1995 200 c. African Jacana ("Lily-trotter") .. 50 50
1996 200 c. Black-crowned Night Heron .. 50 50
1997 200 c. Black-winged Stilt 50 50
1998 200 c. White-spotted Crake 50 50
1999 200 c. African Pygmy Goose 50 50
2000 200 c. African Pitta 50 50
1977/2000 .. .. .. *Set of* 24 11·00 11·00
MS2001 Two sheets, each 113×83 mm. (a) 2000 c. African Spoonbill. (b) 2000 c. Goliath Heron .. .. .. *Set of* 2 *sheets* 8·50 9·50
Nos. 1977/88 and 1989/2000 were printed together, *se-tenant*, in sheetlets of 12.

505 Women at Stand-pipe

(Litho Questa)

1994 (11 July). *First Anniversary of Fourth Republic. T* **505** *and similar horiz designs. Multicoloured.* P 14.
2002 50 c. Type **505** 25 15
2003 100 c. Presenting certificate to farmers 35 20
2004 200 c. Village electricity supply 50 35
2005 600 c. Bridge .. .. .. 1·25 1·50
2006 800 c. National Theatre .. .. 1·50 1·75
2007 1000 c. Lighting Perpetual Flame .. 1·75 2·00
2002/7 .. .. .. *Set of* 6 5·00 5·50

(Des W. Hanson. Litho B.D.T.)

1994 (20 July). *25th Anniv of First Moon Landing. Horiz designs as T* **326** *of Antigua showing scientists. Multicoloured.* P 14.
2008 300 c. Sigmund Jahn 80 90
a. Sheetlet. Nos. 2008/16 .. .. 6·50
2009 300 c. Ulf Merbold 80 90
2010 300 c. Hans Wilhelm Schegal 80 90
2011 300 c. Ulrich Walter 80 90
2012 300 c. Reinhard Furrer 80 90
2013 300 c. Ernst Messerschmid 80 90
2014 300 c. Mamoru Mohri 80 90
2015 300 c. Klaus-Dietrich Flade 80 90
2016 300 c. Chaiki Naito-Mukai 80 90
2008/16 .. .. .. *Set of* 9 6·50 7·00
MS2017 130×118 mm. 2000 c. Poster for *Frau im Mond* (film) by Fritz Lang .. .. 5·00 5·50
Nos. 2008/16 were printed together, *se-tenant*, in sheetlets of 9.

(Des Kerri Schiff. Litho B.D.T.)

1994 (20 July). *Centenary of International Olympic Committee. Gold Medal Winners. Designs as T* **327** *of Antigua, but vert. Multicoloured.* P 14.
2018 300 c. Dieter Modenburg (Germany) (high jump), 1984 .. .. 60 65
2019 400 c. Ruth Fuchs (Germany) (javelin), 1972 and 1976 .. .. .. 80 85
MS2020 77×106 mm. 1500 c. Jans Weissflog (Germany) (ski jump), 1994 .. .. 3·25 3·50

(Des J. Batchelor. Litho B.D.T.)

1994 (20 July). *50th Anniv of D-Day. Horiz designs as T* **331** *of Antigua. Multicoloured.* P 14.
2021 60 c. H.M.S. *Roberts* (monitor) 50 50
2022 100 c. H.M.S. *Warspite* (battleship) .. 70 70
2023 200 c. U.S.S. *Augusta* (cruiser) .. .. 1·00 1·00
2021/3 .. .. .. *Set of* 3 2·00 2·00
MS2024 107×76 mm. 1500 c. U.S.S. *Nevada* (battleship) firing salvo .. .. .. 4·00 4·25

(Des Kerri Schiff. Litho Questa (Nos. 2027/34), B.D.T. (others))

1994 (20 July). *"Philakorea '94" International Stamp Exhibition, Seoul. Multicoloured designs as T* **279** *of Dominica.* P 14 (*Nos.* 2025/6, 2035) *or* 13 (*others*).
2025 20 c. Ch'unghak-dong village elder in traditional costume (24½×38 *mm*) 15 15
2026 150 c. Stone Pagoda, Punhwangsa (24½×38 *mm*) 40 40
2027 250 c. Character with eggs 45 50
a. Sheetlet. Nos. 2027/34 .. .. 3·25
2028 250 c. Character with pair of birds on house 45 50
2029 250 c. Character with cock 45 50
2030 250 c. Character with dragon and pagoda 45 50
2031 250 c. Character with orange flowers .. 45 50
2032 250 c. Character with parrot and pagoda 45 50
2033 250 c. Character with plant 45 50
2034 250 c. Character with fish 45 50
2035 300 c. Traditional country house, Andong (24½×34 *mm*) 50 55
2025/35 .. .. .. *Set of* 11 4·25 4·50
MS2036 100×70 mm. 1500 c. Temple judges deliberating (42½×28½ *mm*). P 14 .. 3·25 3·50
Nos. 2027/34 were printed together, *se-tenant*, in sheetlets of 8 and show illuminated Korean characters.

506 Dennis Bergkamp (Netherlands)

(Litho Questa)

1994 (22 July). *World Cup Football Championship, U.S.A.* (*2nd issue*). *T* **506** *and similar multicoloured designs.* P 14.
2037 200 c. Type **506** 45 50
a. Sheetlet. Nos. 2037/42 .. .. 2·40
2038 200 c. Lothar Matthaus (Germany) .. 45 50
2039 200 c. Giuseppe Signori (Italy) 45 50
2040 200 c. Carlos Valderama (Colombia) .. 45 50
2041 200 c. Jorge Campos (Mexico) 45 50
2042 200 c. Tony Meola (U.S.A.) 45 50
2037/42 .. .. .. *Set of* 6 2·40 2·75
MS2043 Two sheets, each 100×70 mm. (a) 1200 c. Giants' Stadium, New Jersey (*vert*). (b) 1200 c. Citrus Bowl, Orlando (*vert*) *Set of* 2 *sheets* 5·00 5·50
Nos. 2037/42 were printed together, *se-tenant*, in sheetlets of 6.

507 Common ("Crowned") Duiker

508 Northern Region Dancer

(Des E. Mensah. Litho Questa)

1994 (1 Sept). *Duikers (Antelopes). T* **507** *and similar horiz designs. Multicoloured.* P 14.
2044 50 c. Type **507** 30 15
2045 100 c. Red-flanked Duiker 40 25
2046 200 c. Yellow-backed Duiker 60 40
2047 400 c. Ogilby's Duiker .. .. .. 1·00 1·25
2048 600 c. Bay Duiker .. .. .. 1·25 1·50
2049 800 c. Jentink's Duiker .. .. .. 1·50 1·75
2044/9 .. .. .. *Set of* 6 4·50 4·75
MS2050 Two sheets, each 106×76 mm. (a) 2000 c. Red Forest Duiker. (b) 2000 c. Black Duiker .. .. .. *Set of* 2 *sheets* 8·00 8·50

(Litho Questa)

1994 (5 Dec). *Christmas. Religious Paintings. Vert designs as T* **336** *of Antigua. Multicoloured. P* 13½×14.

2051 100 c. "Madonna of the Annunciation" (Simone Martini) 30 15
2052 200 c. "Madonna and Child" (Niccolo di Pietro Gerini) 45 20
2053 250 c. "Virgin and Child on the Throne with Angels and Saints" (Raffaello Botticini) 55 45
2054 300 c. "Madonna and Child with Saints" (Antonio Fiorentino) 75 75
2055 400 c. "Adoration of the Magi" (Bartolo di Fredi) 90 90
2056 500 c. "The Annunciation" (Cima da Congeliano) .. .. 1·00 1·00
2057 600 c. "Virgin and Child with the Young St. John the Baptist" (workshop of Botticelli) .. .. 1·25 1·50
2058 1000 c. "The Holy Family" (Giorgione) .. 1·75 2·25
2051/8 .. .. *Set of* 8 6·25 6·50
MS2059 Two sheets, each 135×95 mm. (a) 2000 c. "Adoration of the Kings" (detail showing Holy Family) (Giorgione). (b) 2000 c. "Adoration of the Kings" (detail showing King and attendants) (Giorgione) .. .. *Set of 2 sheets* 8·00 8·50

(Litho B.D.T.)

1994 (9 Dec). *Panafest '94 (2nd Pan-African Historical Theatre Festival). T* **508** *and similar vert designs. Multicoloured. P* 13½×13.

2060 50 c. Type **508** 20 15
2061 100 c. Traditional artefacts 35 25
2062 200 c. Chief with courtiers 65 60
2063 400 c. Woman in ceremonial costume .. 1·25 1·25
2064 600 c. Cape Coast Castle .. .. .. 1·75 2·00
2065 800 c. Clay figurines .. .. .. 2·25 2·75
2060/5 .. .. *Set of* 6 6·00 6·25

509 Red Cross Stretcher-bearers

510 Fertility Doll

(Des E. Mensah. Litho Questa)

1994 (20 Dec). *75th Anniv of Red Cross. T* **509** *and similar horiz designs. Multicoloured. P* 14.

2066 50 c. Type **509** 30 15
2067 200 c. Worker with children 50 35
2068 600 c. Workers erecting tents .. .. 1·25 1·50
2066/8 .. .. *Set of* 3 1·75 1·75
MS2069 147×99 mm. Nos. 2066/7 and 1000 c. As 600 c. .. .. 2·40 2·50

(Des E. Mensah. Litho Questa)

1994 (20 Dec). *Fertility Dolls. T* **510** *and similar vert designs showing different dolls. P* 14.

2070 50 c. multicoloured 15 10
2071 100 c. multicoloured 20 15
2072 150 c. multicoloured 30 25
2073 200 c. multicoloured 35 30
2074 400 c. multicoloured 60 60
2075 600 c. multicoloured 75 80
2076 800 c. multicoloured .. .. .. 90 1·00
2077 1000 c. multicoloured .. .. .. 1·00 1·25
2070/7 .. .. *Set of* 8 3·75 4·00
MS2078 147×99 mm. Nos. 2071, 2074/5 and 250 c. As 1000 c. .. .. 3·50 4·00

511 Ghanaian Family

512 Control Tower and Emblem

(Des E. Mensah. Litho Questa)

1994 (20 Dec). *International Year of the Family. T* **511** *and similar vert designs. Multicoloured. P* 14.

2079 50 c. Type **511** 15 15
2080 100 c. Teaching carpentry 25 15
2081 200 c. Child care 40 25
2082 400 c. Care for the elderly 60 60
2083 600 c. Learning pottery 85 95
2084 1000 c. Adult education students .. 1·25 1·50
2079/84 .. .. *Set of* 6 3·25 3·25

(Des E. Mensah. Litho Questa)

1994 (24 Dec)–**95.** *50th Anniv of International Civil Aviation Organization. T* **512** *and similar horiz designs. Multicoloured. P* 14. (*a*) *Inscr* "50th Anniversary Of Ghana Civil Aviation Authority"

2085 100 c. Type **512** 30
2086 400 c. Communications equipment .. 80
2087 1000 c. Airliner taking off .. .. 1·60
2085/7 .. .. *Set of* 3 2·40

(*b*) *Inscr* "50th Anniversary Of The International Civil Aviation Organisation (I.C.A.O.)" (4.95)

2088 100 c. Type **512** 30 20
2089 400 c. Communications equipment .. 80 80
2090 1000 c. Airliner taking off .. .. 1·60 1·75
2088/90 .. .. *Set of* 3 2·40 2·50

Nos. 2085/7 were withdrawn from post offices in Ghana soon after issue when it was realised that the wrong organisation had been commemorated. Supplies were, however, distributed by the New York philatelic agent.

513 Pluto, Donald Duck and Chip n'Dale around Table

(Des Alvin White Studio. Litho Questa)

1995 (2 Feb). *60th Anniv of Donald Duck. T* **513** *and similar multicoloured designs showing Walt Disney cartoon characters at birthday party. P* 14×13½.

2091 40 c. Type **513** 25 15
2092 50 c. Mickey Mouse and pup with banner 25 15
2093 60 c. Daisy Duck with balloons .. 25 20
2094 100 c. Goofy making cake 30 20
2095 150 c. Goofy on roller blades delivering cake 40 30
2096 250 c. Donald pinning donkey tail on Goofy 50 50
2097 400 c. Ludwig von Drake singing to Pluto 70 70
2098 500 c. Grandma Duck giving cake to puppies 80 80
2099 1000 c. Mickey and Minnie Mouse at piano 1·40 1·75
2100 1500 c. Pluto with bone and ball .. 2·25 2·75
2091/100 .. .. *Set of* 10 6·25 6·75
MS2101 Two sheets. (a) 117×95 mm. 2000 c. Donald blowing out birthday candles (*vert*). (b) 95×117 mm. 2000 c. Donald wearing party hat (*vert*). P 13½×14 .. .. *Set of 2 sheets* 6·50 7·00

514 Fort Appolonia, Beyin

(Des E. Mensah. Litho B.D.T.)

1995 (3 Apr). *Forts and Castles of Ghana. T* **514** *and similar multicoloured designs. P* 14.

2102 50 c. Type **514** 10 10
2103 200 c. Fort Patience, Apam 10 15
2104 250 c. Fort Amsterdam, Kormantin .. 15 20
2105 300 c. Fort St. Jago, Elmina 15 20
2106 400 c. Fort William, Anomabo 20 25
2107 600 c. Kumasi Fort 30 35
2102/7 .. .. *Set of* 6 1·00 1·25
MS2108 Two sheets, each 102×72 mm. (a) 800 c. Elmina Castle (*vert*). (b) 1000 c. Fort St. Antonio, Axim .. .. *Set of 2 sheets* 90 95

515 Cochem Castle, Germany

(Des R. Sauber. Litho B.D.T.)

1995 (3 Apr). *Castles of the World. T* **515** *and similar horiz designs. Multicoloured. P* 14.

2109 150 c. Type **515** 10 10
2110 500 c. Windsor Castle, England 25 30
a. Sheetlet. Nos. 2110/18 .. .. 2·25
2111 500 c. Osaka Castle, Japan 25 30
2112 500 c. Vaj Dahunyad Castle, Hungary .. 25 30
2113 500 c. Karlstejn Castle, Czech Republic .. 25 30
2114 500 c. Kronborg Castle, Denmark .. 25 30
2115 500 c. Alcázar of Segovia, Spain 25 30
2116 500 c. Chambourd Castle, France .. 25 30
2117 500 c. Linderhof Castle, Germany .. 25 30
2118 500 c. Red Fort, Delhi, India 25 30
2119 600 c. Hohenzollern Castle, Germany .. 30 35
2120 800 c. Uwajima Castle, Japan 40
2121 1000 c. Hohenschwangau Castle, Germany 50
2109/21 .. .. *Set of* 13 3·25 3·
MS2122 Two sheets, each 102×72 mm. (a) 2500 c. Neuschwanstein Castle, Germany (b) 2500 c. Himeji Castle, Japan .. *Set of 2 sheets* 2·50 3·

Nos. 2110/18 were printed together, *se-tenant*, in sheetlets 9.

516 European Pochard ("Eurasian Pochard")

517 Cycling

(Litho B.D.T.)

1995 (28 Apr). *Ducks. T* **516** *and similar horiz design Multicoloured. P* 14.

2123 200 c. Type **516** 10
2124 400 c. African Pygmy Goose 20
a. Sheetlet. Nos. 2124/35 .. .. 2·40
2125 400 c. Southern Pochard 20
2126 400 c. Cape Teal 20
2127 400 c. Ruddy Shelduck 20
2128 400 c. Fulvous Whistling Duck 20
2129 400 c. White-faced Whistling Duck .. 20
2130 400 c. Ferruginous Duck ("Ferruginous White-eye") 20
2131 400 c. Hottentot Teal 20
2132 400 c. African Black Duck 20
2133 400 c. African Yellow-bill 20
2134 400 c. Bahama Pintail ("White-checked Pintail Duck") 20
2135 400 c. Hartlaub's Duck 20
2136 500 c. Maccoa Duck 25
2137 800 c. Cape Shoveler 40
2138 1000 c. Red-crested Pochard 50
2123/38 .. .. *Set of* 16 3·50 4·2
MS2139 Two sheets, each 104×74 mm. (a) 2500 c. Roseate Tern. (b) 2500 c. Common Shoveler ("Northern Shoveler") .. *Set of 2 sheets* 2·50 3·

Nos. 2124/35 were printed together, *se-tenant*, in sheetlets 12 with the backgrounds forming a composite design.

Nos. 2128 is inscribed "Wistling" in error.

(Des J. Iskowitz. Litho Questa)

1995 (2 May). *Olympic Games, Atlanta* (1996) (*1st issu T* **517** *and similar vert designs. Multicoloured. P* 14.

2140 300 c. Type **517** 15
a. Sheetlet. Nos. 2140/51 .. .. 1·75
2141 300 c. Archery 15
2142 300 c. Diving 15
2143 300 c. Swimming 15
2144 300 c. Women's Gymnastics 15
2145 300 c. Fencing 15
2146 300 c. Boxing 15
2147 300 c. Men's Gymnastics 15
2148 300 c. Javelin 15
2149 300 c. Tennis 15
2150 300 c. Football 15
2151 300 c. Equestrian 15
2152 500 c. Carl Lewis (U.S.A.) 25
2153 800 c. Eric Liddell (Great Britain) .. 40
2154 900 c. Jesse Owens (U.S.A.) 45
2155 1000 c. Jim Thorpe (U.S.A.) 50
2140/55 .. .. *Set of* 16 3·25 4·
MS2156 Two sheets, each 70×100 mm. (a) 1200 c. Pierre de Coubertin (founder of International Olympic Committee). (b) 1200 c. John Akii Bua (Uganda) .. *Set of 2 sheets* 1·25 1·

Nos. 2140/51 were printed together, *se-tenant*, in sheetlets 12 with the backgrounds forming a composite design.

See Nos. 2334/55.

518 *Cymothoe beckeri* (butterfly)
519 Ghanaian Scouts

(Des E. Mensah. Litho Ikam Security Ptg Ltd, Accra)

1995 (19 June)–**97.** *T* **518** *and similar multicoloured design P* 13½×14 (*vert*) *or* 14×13½ (*horiz*).

2157 400 c. Type **518** 20
2158 500 c. *Graphium policenes* (butterfly) .. 25
2158*a* 550 c. Atumpan drums (*vert*) (30.5.97) .. 25
2158*b* 800 c. *Cyrestis camillus* (butterfly) (*vert*) (4.6.97) 40
2159 1000 c. African Long-tailed Hawk (*vert*) .. 50
2159*a* 1100 c. Kente cloth (7.6.97) 55
2160 2000 c. Swordfish .. .. .. 1·00 1·
2161 3000 c. Guinean Fingerfish .. .. 1·50 1·
2162 5000 c. Purple Heron (*vert*) .. .. 2·50 2·
2157/62 .. .. *Set of* 9 7·00 7·

(Des R. Rundo. Litho Questa)

1995 (6 July). *18th World Scout Jamboree, Netherlands. T* **519** *and similar vert designs showing Ghanaian scouts. P* 14.
2163 400 c. multicoloured 20 25
a. Horiz strip of 3. Nos. 2163/5 . . 1·10
2164 800 c. multicoloured 40 45
2165 1000 c. multicoloured 50 55
2163/5 . . . . . . *Set of* 3 1·10 1·25
MS2166 70×100 mm. 1200 c. multicoloured . . 60 65
Nos. 2163/5 were printed together in sheets of 9 containing three *se-tenant* horizontal strips of 3.

(Des W. Wright. Litho B.D.T.)

1995 (6 July). *50th Anniv of End of Second World War in Europe. Multicoloured designs as T* **340** *of Antigua. P* 14.
2167 400 c. Winston Churchill 20 25
a. Sheetlet. Nos. 2167/74 . . . . 1·60
2168 400 c. Gen. Dwight D. Eisenhower . . 20 25
2169 400 c. Air Marshal Sir Arthur Tedder . . 20 25
2170 400 c. Field-Marshal Sir Bernard Montgomery 20 25
2171 400 c. Gen. Omar Bradley 20 25
2172 400 c. Gen. Charles de Gaulle 20 25
2173 400 c. French resistance fighters 20 25
2174 400 c. Gen. George S. Patton 20 25
2167/74 . . . . . . *Set of* 8 1·60 2·00
MS2175 104×74 mm. 1200 c. "GIVE ME FIVE YEARS & YOU WILL NOT RECOGNISE GERMANY AGAIN" quote by Adolf Hitler in English and German (42×57 *mm*) 60 65
Nos. 2167/74 were printed together, *se-tenant*, in sheetlets of 8 with the stamps arranged in two horizontal strips of 4 separated by a gutter showing celebrations around the Arc de Triomphe.

520 Trygve Lie (1946–52) and United Nations Building

521 Preserving Fish

(Litho Questa)

1995 (6 July). *50th Anniv of United Nations. Secretary-Generals. T* **520** *and similar multicoloured designs. P* 14.
2176 200 c. Type **520** 10 15
a. Sheetlet. Nos. 2176/81 . . . . 1·40
2177 300 c. Dag Hammarskjold (1953–61) . . 15 20
2178 400 c. U. Thant (1961–71) 20 25
2179 500 c. Kurt Waldheim (1972–81) . . 25 30
2180 600 c. Javier Perez de Cuellar (1982–91) . . 30 35
2181 800 c. Boutrous Boutrous-Ghali (1992) . . 40 45
2176/81 . . . . . . *Set of* 6 1·40 1·75
MS2182 104×74 mm. 1200 c. U.N. flag (*horiz*) 60 65
Nos. 2176/81 were printed together, *se-tenant*, in sheetlets of 6.

(Litho Questa)

1995 (6 July). *50th Anniv of Food and Agriculture Organization. T* **521** *and similar horiz designs. Multicoloured. P* 14.
2183 200 c. Type **521** 10 15
2184 300 c. Fishermen with fish traps 15 20
2185 400 c. Ox-drawn plough 20 25
2186 600 c. Harvesting bananas 30 35
2187 800 c. Planting saplings 40 45
2183/7 . . . . . . *Set of* 5 1·10 1·40
MS2188 100×70 mm. 2000 c. Canoe and cattle 1·00 1·10

522 National Flag and Rotary Emblem

523 Seismosaurus

(Litho Questa)

1995 (6 July). *90th Anniv of Rotary International. T* **522** *and similar multicoloured design. P* 14.
2189 600 c. Type **522** 30 35
MS2190 94×65 mm. 1200 c. Ghanaian Rotary banner (*vert*) 60 65

(Litho Questa)

1995 (6 July). *95th Birthday of Queen Elizabeth the Queen Mother. Vert designs as T* **344** *of Antigua. Multicoloured. P* 13½×14.
2191 600 c. orange-brown, pale brown and black 30 35
a. Sheetlet. Nos. 2191/4×2 . . . . 2·10
2192 600 c. multicoloured 30 35
2193 600 c. multicoloured 30 35
2194 600 c. multicoloured 30 35
2191/4 . . . . . . *Set of* 4 1·10 1·40
MS2195 102×127 mm. 2500 c. multicoloured . . 1·25 1·40
Designs:—No. 2191, Queen Elizabeth the Queen Mother (pastel drawing); No. 2192, Wearing light blue hat and floral dress; No. 2193, At desk (oil painting); No. 2194, Wearing red hat and dress; No. **MS**2195, Wearing pale blue hat and jacket.
Nos. 2191/4 were printed together in sheetlets of 8, containing two *se-tenant* strips of 4.

(Des J. Batchelor. Litho Questa)

1995 (6 July). *50th Anniv of End of Second World War in the Pacific. Medals. Horiz designs as T* **340** *of Antigua. Multicoloured. P* 14.
2196 500 c. Navy Cross and Purple Heart, U.S.A. 25 30
a. Sheetlet. Nos. 2196/2201 . . . . 1·50
2197 500 c. Air Force Cross and Distinguished Flying Cross, Great Britain . . 25 30
2198 500 c. Navy and Marine Corps Medal and Distinguished Service Cross, U.S.A. 25 30
2199 500 c. Distinguished Service Medal and Distinguished Conduct Medal, Great Britain 25 30
2200 500 c. Military Medal and Military Cross, Great Britain 25 30
2201 500 c. Distinguished Service Cross and Distinguished Service Order, Great Britain 25 30
2196/2201 . . . . . . *Set of* 6 1·50 1·75
MS2202 108×76 mm. 1200 c. Congressional Medal of Honor, U.S.A. 60 65
Nos. 2196/2201 were printed together, *se-tenant*, in sheetlets of 6 with the stamps arranged in two horizontal strips of 3 separated by a gutter showing American troops in Japan.

(Litho Questa)

1995 (8 Aug). *"Singapore '95" International Stamp Exhibition. Prehistoric Animals. T* **523** *and similar multicoloured designs. P* 14.
2203 400 c. Type **523** 20 25
a. Sheetlet. Nos. 2203/11 . . . . 1·75
2204 400 c. Supersaurus 20 25
2205 400 c. Ultrasaurus 20 25
2206 400 c. Saurolophus 20 25
2207 400 c. Lambeosaurus 20 25
2208 400 c. Parasaurolophus 20 25
2209 400 c. Triceratops 20 25
2210 400 c. Styracosaurus 20 25
2211 400 c. Pachyrhinosaurus 20 25
2212 400 c. Peteinosaurus 20 25
a. Sheetlet. Nos. 2212/20 . . . . 1·75
2213 400 c. Quetzalcoatlus 20 25
2214 400 c. Eudimorphodon 20 25
2215 400 c. Allosaurus 20 25
2216 400 c. Daspletosaurus 20 25
2217 400 c. Tarbosaurus bataar 20 25
2218 400 c. Velociraptor mongoliensis . . 20 25
2219 400 c. Herrerasaurus 20 25
2220 400 c. Coelophysis 20 25
2203/20 . . . . . . *Set of* 18 3·50 4·50
MS2221 Two sheets, each 106×76 mm. (a) 2500 c. Tyrannosaurus rex (*horiz*). (b) 2500 c. Albertosaur (*horiz*) . . . . *Set of* 2 *sheets* 2·50 2·75
Nos. 2203/11 and 2212/20 were printed together, *se-tenant*, in sheetlets of 9, each forming a composite design.

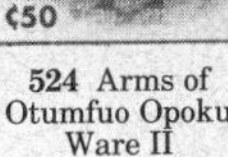

524 Arms of Otumfuo Opoku Ware II

525 Nelson Mandela (1993 Peace)

(Litho Ikam Security Ptg Ltd, Accra)

1995 (9 Aug). *Silver Jubilee of Otumfuo Opoku Ware II (King of Ashanti). T* **524** *and similar vert designs. Multicoloured. P* 13½×13.
2222 50 c. Type **524** 10 10
2223 100 c. Silver casket 10 10
2224 200 c. Golden stool 10 15
2225 400 c. Busummuru sword bearer . . 20 25
2226 600 c. Otumfuo Opoku Ware II . . 30 35
2227 800 c. Otumfro Opoku Ware II under umbrella 40 45
2228 1000 c. Mponponsuo sword bearer . . 50 55
2222/8 . . . . . . *Set of* 7 1·60 1·75

(Des R. Sauber. Litho Questa)

1995 (2 Oct). *Centenary of Nobel Prize Trust Fund. Past Prize Winners. T* **525** *and similar vert designs. Multicoloured. P* 14.
2229 400 c. Type **525** 20 25
a. Sheetlet. Nos. 2229/37 . . . . 1·75
2230 400 c. Albert Schweitzer (1952 Peace) . . 20 25
2231 400 c. Wole Soyinka (1986 Literature) . . 20 25
2232 400 c. Emil Fischer (1902 Chemistry) . . 20 25
2233 400 c. Rudolf Mossbauer (1961 Physics) . . 20 25
2234 400 c. Archbishop Desmond Tutu (1984 Peace) 20 25
2235 400 c. Max Born (1954 Physics) . . 20 25
2236 400 c. Max Planck (1918 Physics) . . 20 25
2237 400 c. Herman Hesse (1946 Literature) . . 20 25
2229/37 . . . . . . *Set of* 9 1·75 2·25
MS2238 104×75 mm. 1200 c. Paul Ehrlich (1908 Medicine) and map 60 65
Nos. 2229/37 were printed together, *se-tenant*, in sheetlets of 9.

(Litho Questa)

1995 (1 Dec). *Christmas. Religious Paintings. Vert designs as T* **357** *of Antigua. Multicoloured. P* 13½×14.
2239 50 c. "The Child Jesus and the Young St. John" (Murillo) 10 10
2240 80 c. "Rest on the Flight into Egypt" (Memling) 10 10
2241 300 c. "Holy Family" (Van Dyck) . . 15 20
2242 600 c. "Enthroned Madonna and Child" (Uccello) 30 35
2243 800 c. "Madonna and Child" (Van Eyck) 40 45
2244 1000 c. "Head of Christ" (Rembrandt) . . 50 55
2239/44 . . . . . . *Set of* 6 1·40 1·60
MS2245 Two sheets, each 101×127 mm. (a) 2500 c. "The Holy Family" (Pulzone). (b) 2500 c. "Madonna and Child with Two Saints" (Montagna) . . . . *Set of* 2 *sheets* 2·50 2·75

526 Ernemann Camera (1903)

527 John Lennon

(Des H. Friedman. Litho Questa)

1995 (8 Dec). *Centenary of Cinema. T* **526** *and similar vert designs. Multicoloured. P* 13½×14.
2246 400 c. Type **526** 20 25
a. Sheetlet. Nos. 2246/54 . . . . 1·75
2247 400 c. Charlie Chaplin 20 25
2248 400 c. Rudolph Valentino 20 25
2249 400 c. Will Rogers 20 25
2250 400 c. Greta Garbo 20 25
2251 400 c. Jackie Cooper 20 25
2252 400 c. Bette Davis 20 25
2253 400 c. John Barrymore 20 25
2254 400 c. Shirley Temple 20 25
2246/54 . . . . . . *Set of* 9 1·75 2·25
MS2255 106×76 mm. 2500 c. Laurel and Hardy 1·25 1·40
Nos. 2246/54 were printed together, *se-tenant*, in sheetlets of 9.
No. 2246 is inscribed "ERNMANN" in error.

(Litho Questa)

1995 (8 Dec). *John Lennon (musician) Commemoration. T* **527** *and similar vert designs. Multicoloured. P* 14 *(No. 2265) or* 13½×14 *(others).*
2256 400 c. Type **527** . . . . . . 1·10 1·10
a. Sheetlet. Nos. 2256/64 . . . . 10·00
2257 400 c. Full face portrait (green background) 1·10 1·10
2258 400 c. With guitar . . . . . . 1·10 1·10
2259 400 c. Wearing glasses and caftan . . 1·10 1·10
2260 400 c. Full face portrait (verm background) 1·10 1·10
2261 400 c. Wearing headphones . . . . 1·10 1·10
2262 400 c. Wearing purple T-shirt . . . . 1·10 1·10
2263 400 c. Full face portrait (blue background) 1·10 1·10
2264 400 c. Facing right . . . . . . 1·10 1·10
2265 400 c. As No. 2263, but smaller (24×39 *mm*) . . . . . . 1·10 1·10
2256/65 . . . . . . *Set of* 10 10·00 10·00
MS2266 102×73 mm. 2000 c. John Lennon playing guitar . . . . . . 6·00 6·50
Nos. 2256/64 were printed together, *se-tenant*, in sheetlets of 9.
No. 2265 was printed in sheetlets of 16 with a large illustrated margin at right.

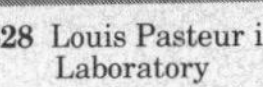

528 Louis Pasteur in Laboratory

529 Rat Musicians

(Des E. Mensah. Litho Questa)

1995 (13 Dec). *Death Centenary of Louis Pasteur (scientist). T* **528** *and similar vert designs. Multicoloured. P* 14.
2267 600 c. Type **528** 30 35
a. Sheetlet. Nos. 2267/71 . . . . 1·50
2268 600 c. Pasteur injecting rabid dog . . 30 35
2269 600 c. Pasteur and microscope slide . . 30 35
2270 600 c. Laboratory equipment and birds . . 30 35
2271 600 c. Yeast vats 30 35
2267/71 . . . . . . *Set of* 5 1·50 1·75
Nos. 2267/71 were printed together, *se-tenant*, in sheetlets of 5.

(Des Y. Lee. Litho Questa)

1996 (28 Jan). *Chinese New Year ("Year of the Rat"). T* **529** *and similar designs. P* 14.
2272 250 c. orange-brown, violet and rosine .. 15 20
a. Horiz strip of 4. Nos. 2272/5 .. 60
2273 250 c. orange-brown, violet and rosine .. 15 20
2274 250 c. orange-brown, violet and rosine .. 15 20
2275 250 c. orange-brown, violet and rosine .. 15 20
2272/5 .. .. *Set of* 4 60 80
MS2276 142×60 mm. As Nos. 2272/5, but face values and "GHANA" in rosine instead of white 60 80
MS2277 106×75 mm. 1000 c. scarlet-vermilion and yellow-orange 50 55
Designs: *Vert*—No. 2272, Type **529**; No. 2273, Rats carrying banners; No. 2274, Rats carrying palanquin; No. 2275, Rats with offerings. *Horiz*—No. **MS**2277, Four rats carrying palanquin.
Nos. 2272/5 were printed together, *se-tenant*, in horizontal strips of 4 throughout the sheets.

(Litho Questa)

1996 (12 Feb). *125th Anniv of Metropolitan Museum of Art, New York. Multicoloured designs as T* **251** *of Gambia. P* 13½×14.
2278 400 c. "Portrait of a Man" (Van der Goes) 20 25
a. Sheetlet. Nos. 2278/85 plus centre label .. .. 1·60
2279 400 c. "Paradise" (detail) (Di Paolo) .. 20 25
2280 400 c. "Portrait of a Young Man" (Messina) 20 25
2281 400 c. "Tommaso Portinari" (detail) (Memling) 20 25
2282 400 c. "Maria Portinari" (detail) (Memling) 20 25
2283 400 c. "Portrait of a Lady" (detail) (Ghirlandaio) 20 25
2284 400 c. "St. Christopher and the Infant Christ" (Ghirlandaio) 20 25
2285 400 c. "Francesco D'Este" (detail) (Weyden) 20 25
2286 400 c. "The Interrupted Sleep" (Boucher) 20 25
a. Sheetlet. Nos. 2286/93 plus centre label .. .. 1·60
2287 400 c. "Diana and Cupid" (detail) (Batoni) 20 25
2288 400 c. "Boy blowing Bubbles" (Chardin) .. 20 25
2289 400 c. "Ancient Rome" (detail) (Pannini) .. 20 25
2290 400 c. "Modern Rome" (detail) (Pannini) .. 20 25
2291 400 c. "The Calmady Children" (Lawrence) 20 25
2292 400 c. "The Triumph of Marius" (detail) (Tiepolo) 20 25
2293 400 c. "Garden at Vaucression" (detail) (Vuillard) 20 25
2278/93 .. .. *Set of* 16 3·25 4·00
MS2294 Two sheets, each 95×70 mm. (a) 2500 c. "The Epiphany" (detail) (Giotto) (80×56 *mm*). (b) 2500 c. "The Calling of Matthew" (detail) (Hemessen) (80×56 *mm*). P 14 .. *Set of* 2 *sheets* 2·50 2·75
Nos. 2278/85 and 2286/93 were each printed together, *se-tenant*, in sheetlets of 8 stamps and one centre label.

530 Toco Toucan

531 Pagoda of Kaiyuan Si Temple, Fujian

(Des Y. Lee. Litho)

1996 (15 Apr). *Wildlife of the Rainforest. T* **530** *and similar vert designs. Multicoloured. P* 14.
2295 400 c. Type **530** 20 25
a. Sheetlet. Nos. 2295/2306 .. .. 2·40
2296 400 c. Two-toed Sloth 20 25
2297 400 c. Orang-utan 20 25
2298 400 c. Crested Hawk Eagle 20 25
2299 400 c. Tiger 20 25
2300 400 c. Yellow-billed Stork 20 25
2301 400 c. Green-winged Macaw 20 25
2302 400 c. Common Squirrel-monkey .. 20 25
2303 400 c. Crab-eating Macaque 20 25
2304 400 c. *Cithaerias menander* and *Ithomiidae* (butterflies) 20 25
2305 400 c. *Coryptophanes cristatus* and *Gekkonidae* (lizards) 20 25
2306 400 c. Boa Constrictor 20 25
2307 400 c. Hoatzin 20 25
a. Sheetlet. Nos. 2307/18 .. .. 2·40
2308 400 c. Western Tarsier 20 25
2309 400 c. Golden Lion Tamarin 20 25
2310 400 c. *Pteropus gouldii* (bat) 20 25
2311 400 c. Guianan Cock of the Rock .. 20 25
2312 400 c. Resplendent Quetzal 20 25
2313 400 c. Tree Frog and Poison-arrow Frog .. 20 25
2314 400 c. Ring-tailed Lemur 20 25
2315 400 c. Iguana 20 25
2316 400 c. *Heliconius burneyi* (butterfly) .. 20 25
2317 400 c. Vervain Hummingbird 20 25
2318 400 c. Verreauv's Sifaka 20 25
2295/2318 .. .. .. *Set of* 24 4·75 6·00
MS2319 Two sheets, each 74×104 mm. (a) 3000 c. King of Saxony Bird of Paradise. (b) 3000 c. King Vulture .. .. *Set of* 2 *sheets* 3·00 3·25
Nos. 2295/2306 and 2307/18 were each printed together, *se-tenant*, in sheetlets of 12.

1996 (13 May). *"CHINA '96" 9th Asian International Stamp Exhibition. Pagodas. T* **531** *and similar vert designs. Multicoloured. Litho. P* 14.
2320 400 c. Type **531** 20 25
a. Sheetlet. Nos. 2320/3×2 .. .. 1·60
2321 400 c. Kaiyuan Si Temple, Hebei .. 20 25
2322 400 c. Fogong Si Temple, Shanxi 20 25
2323 400 c. Xiangshan, Beijing 20 25
2320/3 .. .. *Set of* 4 80 1·00
MS2324 Two sheets. (a) 100×70 mm. 1000 c. Baima Si Temple, Henan. (b) 143×98 mm. 1000 c. Gold statue (38×50 *mm*) *Set of* 2 *sheets* 1·00 1·10
Nos. 2320/3 were printed together, *se-tenant*, in sheetlets of 8 containing two of each design.

(Litho Questa)

1996 (10 June). *70th Birthday of Queen Elizabeth II. Multicoloured designs as T* **364** *of Antigua showing different photographs. P* 13½×14.
2325 1000 c. As Type **364** of Antigua 50 55
a. Strip of 3. Nos. 2325/7 .. .. 1·50
2326 1000 c. In blue hat and coat 50 55
2327 1000 c. Wearing straw hat and carrying bouquet 50 55
2325/7 .. .. *Set of* 3 1·50 1·60
MS2328 125×103 mm. 2500 c. In open carriage at Trooping the Colour (*horiz*). P 14×13½ .. 1·25 1·40
Nos. 2325/7 were printed together, *se-tenant*, in horizontal and vertical strips of 3 throughout the sheet.

532 Serafim Todorow (Bulgaria)

533 Ancient Greek Wrestlers

(Litho B.D.T.)

1996 (27 June). *50th Anniv of International Amateur Boxing Association. T* **532** *and similar vert designs. Multicoloured. P* 14.
2329 300 c. Type **532** 15 20
2330 400 c. Oscar de la Hoya (U.S.A.) .. 20 25
2331 800 c. Ariel Hernandez (Cuba) 40 45
2332 1500 c. Arnoldo Mesa (Cuba) 80 85
2329/32 .. .. *Set of* 4 1·50 1·75
MS2333 80×110 mm. 3000 c. Tadahiro Sasaki (Japan) .. .. 1·50 1·60

(Litho B.D.T.)

1996 (27 June). *Olympic Games, Atlanta (2nd issue). Previous Medal Winners. T* **533** *and similar multicoloured designs. P* 14.
2334 300 c. Type **533** 15 20
2335 400 c. Aileen Riggin, 1920 (U.S.A.) .. 20 25
a. Sheetlet. Nos. 2335/43 .. .. 1·75
2336 400 c. Pat McCormick, 1952 (U.S.A.) .. 20 25
2337 400 c. Dawn Fraser, 1956 (Australia) .. 20 25
2338 400 c. Chris von Saltza, 1960 (U.S.A.) .. 20 25
2339 400 c. Anita Lonsbrough, 1960 (Great Britain) 20 25
2340 400 c. Debbie Meyer, 1968 (U.S.A.) .. 20 25
2341 400 c. Shane Gould, 1972 (Australia) .. 20 25
2342 400 c. Petra Thuemer, 1976 (Germany) .. 20 25
2343 400 c. Marjorie Gestring, 1936 (U.S.A.) .. 20 25
2344 400 c. Abedi Pele (Ghana) (*vert*) 20 25
a. Sheetlet. Nos. 2344/52 .. .. 1·75
2345 400 c. Quico Navarez (Spain) (*vert*) .. 20 25
2346 400 c. Heino Hanson (Denmark) (*vert*) .. 20 25
2347 400 c. Mostafa Ismail (Egypt) (*vert*) .. 20 25
2348 400 c. Anthony Yeboah (Ghana) (*vert*) .. 20 25
2349 400 c. Jurgen Klinsmann (Germany) (*vert*) 20 25
2350 400 c. Cobi Jones (U.S.A.) (*vert*) 20 25
2351 400 c. Franco Baresi (Italy) (*vert*) .. 20 25
2352 400 c. Igor Dobrovolski (Russia) (*vert*) .. 20 25
2353 500 c. Wilma Rudolph (U.S.A.) (track and field, 1960) 25 30
2354 600 c. Olympic Stadium, 1960, and Roman landmarks 30 35
2355 800 c. Ladies Kayak pairs, 1960 (Soviet Union) 40 45
2334/55 .. .. *Set of* 22 4·50 5·75
MS2356 Two sheets, each 110×80 mm. (a) 2000 c. Tracy Caulkins (U.S.A.) (200m freestyle, 1984). (b) 2000 c. Kornelia Ender (Germany) (200m freestyle, 1976) .. .. *Set of* 2 *sheets* 2·00 2·10
Nos. 2335/43 (swimming and diving) and 2344/52 (football) were each printed together, *se-tenant*, in sheetlets of 9, with the backgrounds forming composite designs.

PRICES OF SETS

Set prices are given for many issues, generally those containing three stamps or more. Definitive sets include one of each value or major colour change, but do not cover different perforations, die types or minor shades. Where a choice is possible the set prices are based on the cheapest versions of the stamps included in the listings.

534 E. W. Agyare (35 years service with Ghana Broadcasting)

535 Fiddles

(Litho Questa)

1996 (31 July). *Local Broadcasting. P* 14.
2357 **534** 100 c. multicoloured 10

(Litho Questa)

1996 (31 July). *50th Anniv of U.N.I.C.E.F. Multicolour designs as T* **366** *of Antigua. P* 14.
2358 400 c. Ghanaian child 20
2359 500 c. Mother and child 25
2360 600 c. Mother and child drinking .. 30
2358/60 .. .. *Set of* 3 75
MS2361 74×104 mm. 1000 c. Young child .. 50

(Des Jennifer Toombs. Litho Questa)

1996 (31 July). *3000th Anniv of Jerusalem. Multicolour designs as T* **367** *of Antigua. P* 14½.
2362 400 c. St. Stephen's Gate and *Jasminum mesnyi* 20
2363 600 c. The Citadel, Tower of David and *Nerium oleander* 30
2364 800 c. Chapel of the Ascension and *Romulea bulbocodium* 40
2362/4 .. .. *Set of* 3 90 1·
MS2365 65×80 mm. 2000 c. Russian Orthodox Church of St. Mary Magdalene (48×30 *mm*). P 14 .. .. 1·00 1·

(Des R. Sauber. Litho Questa)

1996 (31 July). *Centenary of Radio. Entertainers. Mul coloured designs as T* **368** *of Antigua. P* 13½×14.
2366 500 c. Frank Sinatra 25
2367 600 c. Judy Garland 30
2368 600 c. Bing Crosby 30
2369 800 c. Martin and Lewis 40
2366/9 .. .. *Set of* 4 1·25 1·
MS2370 81×110 mm. 2000 c. Edgar Bergen and Charlie McCarthy .. .. 1·00 1·

(Des M. Freedman and Dena Rubin. Litho Questa)

1996 (31 July). *50th Anniv of U.N.E.S.C.O. Multicolour designs as T* **374** *of Antigua. P* 14×13½ *(1000 c.) or* 13½×1 *(others)*.
2371 400 c. The Citadel, Haiti (*vert*) 20
2372 800 c. Ait-Ben-Hadou (fortified village), Morocco (*vert*) 40
2373 1000 c. Spissky Hrad, Slovakia 50
2371/3 .. .. *Set of* 3 1·10 1·2
MS2374 106×76 mm. 2000 c. Cape Coast Castle, Ghana. P 14×13½ .. .. 1·00 1·

1996 (5 Aug). *Musical Instruments. T* **535** *and similar ve designs. Multicoloured. Litho. P* 14.
2375 500 c. Type **535** 45
a. Sheetlet. Nos. 2375/9 .. .. 2·25
2376 500 c. Proverbial drum 45
2377 500 c. Double clapless bell and castanet .. 45
2378 500 c. Gourd rattle 45
2379 500 c. Horns 45
2375/9 .. .. *Set of* 5 2·25 2·
Nos. 2375/9 were printed together, *se-tenant*, in sheetlets of

536 Ariel, Flounder and Sebastian

(Des Alvin White Studios. Litho Questa)

1996 (25 Aug). *Disney Friends. T* **536** *and simila multicoloured designs showing Disney cartoon character. P* 14×13½.
2380 60 c. Type **536** 10 1
2381 60 c. Pinocchio and Jiminy Cricket .. 10 1
2382 60 c. Cogsworth and Lumiere 10 1
2383 60 c. Copper and Tod 10 1
2384 60 c. Pocahontas, Meeko and Flit .. 10 1
2385 60 c. Bambi, Flower and Thumper .. 10
2386 150 c. As No. 2381 10
a. Sheetlet. Nos. 2386/94 .. .. 1·75
2387 200 c. Type **536** 10 1
2388 200 c. As No. 2383 .. .. .. 10 1
2389 300 c. As No. 2385 .. .. .. 15 2
2390 350 c. As No. 2382 .. .. .. 20 2
2391 450 c. As No. 2384 .. .. .. 25 3
2392 600 c. Aladdin and Abu 30 3
2393 700 c. Penny and Rufus 35 4

394 800 c. Mowgli and Baloo 40 45
380/94 .. .. *Set of* 15 1·90 2·25
MS2395 Two sheets. (a) 98×124 mm. 3000 c. Winnie the Pooh (*vert*). P 13½×14. (b) 133×108 mm. 3000 c. Simba and Timon .. *Set of* 2 *sheets* 3·00 3·25
Nos. 2386/94 were printed together, *se-tenant*, in sheetlets of

(Des Shannon. Litho Questa)

996 (21 Nov). 20*th Anniv of* Rocky (*film*). *Sheet* 143×182 *mm, containing vert design as T* **266** *of Gambia. Multi-coloured. P* 14×13½.
MS2396 2000 c.×3 Sylvester Stallone in *Rocky II* 3·00 3·25
No. **MS**2396 was printed with an enlarged illustrated left and margin.

537 Herd Boy and Ox

538 The Tomb of Dr. Hideyo Noguchi

(Des Y. Lee. Litho Questa)

1997 (22 Jan). *Chinese New Year* (*"Year of the Ox"*). *"The Herd Boy and Weaver". T* **537** *and similar vert designs. Each lake-brown, silver and black. P* 13½×14.
2397 500 c. Type **537** 25 30
a. Sheetlet. Nos. 2397/405 .. .. 2·25
2398 500 c. Ox and weaver in lake 25 30
2399 500 c. Weaver at work 25 30
2400 500 c. Herd boy with dying Ox 25 30
2401 500 c. Weaver flying out of window .. 25 30
2402 500 c. Herd boy carrying children .. 25 30
2403 500 c. Family separated by "river" .. 25 30
2404 500 c. Petitioning the emperor 25 30
2405 500 c. Family reunited 25 30
2397/405 .. .. *Set of* 9 2·25 2·40
Nos. 2397/405 were printed together, *se-tenant*, in sheetlets of 9 with an enlarged illustrated right-hand margin.

1997 (3 Mar). 120*th Birth Anniv of Dr. Hideyo Noguchi* (*bacteriologist*). *T* **538** *and similar vert designs. Multicoloured. Litho. P* 14.
2406 1000 c. Type **538** 50 55
a. Sheetlet. Nos. 2406/10 .. .. 2·50
2407 1000 c. Dr. Hideyo Noguchi 50 55
2408 1000 c. Birthplace of Dr. Noguchi at Sanjogarta 50 55
2409 1000 c. Noguchi Institute, Legon 50 55
2410 1000 c. Noguchi Gardens, Accra 50 55
2406/10 .. .. *Set of* 5 2·50 2·75
MS2411 Two sheets, each 67×97 mm. (a) 3000 c. Dr. Noguchi in his laboratory. (b) 3000 c. Statue of Dr. Noguchi .. .. .. *Set of* 2 *sheets* 3·00 3·25
Nos. 2406/10 were printed together, *se-tenant*, in sheetlets of 5.

539 Dipo Hairstyle

540 Independence Anniversary Emblem

1997 (3 Mar). *Ghanaian Women's Hairstyles. T* **539** *and similar vert designs. Multicoloured. Litho. P* 14.
2412 1000 c. Type **539** 50 55
a. Sheetlet. Nos. 2412/16 .. .. 2·50
2413 1000 c. Oduku with flowers 50 55
2414 1000 c. Dansinkran 50 55
2415 1000 c. Mbobom 50 55
2416 1000 c. Oduku with hair pins 50 55
2417 1000 c. African Corn Row 50 55
a. Sheetlet. Nos. 2417/21 .. .. 2·50
2418 1000 c. Chinese Raster 50 55
2419 1000 c. Chinese Raster with top knot .. 50 55
2420 1000 c. Corn Row 50 55
2421 1000 c. Mbakaa 50 55
2412/21 .. .. *Set of* 10 5·00 5·50
Nos. 2412/16 and 2417/21 were each printed together, *se-tenant*, in sheetlets of 5.

(Des J. Iskowitz (No. **MS**2427b), Dena Rubin (others). Litho B.D.T.)

1997 (6 Mar). 40*th Anniv of Independence. T* **540** *and similar multicoloured designs. P* 14.
2422 200 c. Type **540** 10 10
2423 200 c. President J. J. Rawlings (*vert*) .. 1·50 1·50
2424 550 c. Dr. Kwame Nkrumah (first President) (*vert*) 30 35
2425 800 c. Children in class 40 45
2426 1100 c. Akosombo Dam 55 60
2422/6 .. .. *Set of* 5 2·50 2·75
MS2427 Two sheets. (a) 70×100 mm. 2000 c. Dr. Nkrumah proclaiming independence (*vert*). (b) 101×141 mm. 3000 c. United Nations Secretary-General Kofi Annan (37×50 *mm*) *Set of* 2 *sheets* 2·50 2·75
No. 2423 was withdrawn on 22 March at the request of the Office of the President.
No. 2425 is inscribed "Acheivement" in error

(Litho Questa)

1997 (8 Apr). 10*th Anniv of Chernobyl Nuclear Disaster. Vert designs as T* **376** *of Antigua. Multicoloured. P* 13½.
2428 800 c. As Type **376** of Antigua 40 45
2429 1000 c. As No. 2428, but inscribed "CHABAD'S CHILDREN OF CHERNOBYL" at foot 50 55

541 Deng Xiaoping

542 Jackie Gleason

(Des Y. Lee. Litho Questa)

1997 (25 Apr). *Deng Xiaoping* (*Chinese statesman*) *Commemoration. T* **541** *and similar vert designs showing different portraits. Multicoloured. P* 14×13½.
2430 300 c. Type **541** 15 20
a. Sheetlet. Nos. 2430, 2432, 2434 and 2436 .. .. 1·25
2431 500 c. Looking thoughtful 25 30
a. Sheetlet. Nos. 2431, 2433, 2435 and 2437 .. .. 1·40
2432 600 c. Wearing glasses 30 35
2433 600 c. Delivering speech 30 35
2434 800 c. As No. 2432 .. .. .. 40 45
2435 800 c. As No. 2433 .. .. .. 40 45
2436 1000 c. Type **541** 50 55
2437 1000 c. As No. 2431 .. .. .. 50 55
2430/7 .. .. *Set of* 8 2·75 3·25
MS2438 Two sheets, each 101×70 mm. (a) 3000 c. Deng Xiaoping making speech (47×34 *mm*). (b) 4000 c. Deng Xiaoping with hand raised (47×34 *mm*) .. .. .. *Set of* 2 *sheets* 3·75 4·00
Nos. 2430, 2432, 2434 and 2436, and 2431, 2433, 2435 and 2437 were each printed together, *se-tenant*, in sheetlets of 4 with an enlarged illustrated margin at left or right.

(Des J. Iskowitz. Litho Questa)

1997 (29 May). 50*th Death Anniv of Paul Harris* (*founder of Rotary International*). *Horiz designs as T* **377** *of Antigua. Multicoloured. P* 14.
2439 2000 c. Paul Harris and Egyptian patient receiving polio vaccination .. .. 1·00 1·10
MS2440 78×107 mm. 3000 c. Paul Harris with Rotary and PolioPlus emblems .. .. 1·50 1·60

(Litho Questa)

1997 (29 May). *Golden Wedding of Queen Elizabeth and Prince Philip. Horiz designs as T* **378** *of Antigua. Multicoloured. P* 14.
2441 800 c. Queen Elizabeth II 40 45
a. Sheetlet. Nos. 2441/6 .. .. 2·40
2442 800 c. Royal coat of arms 40 45
2443 800 c. Queen Elizabeth and Prince Philip waving 40 45
2444 800 c. Queen Elizabeth and Prince Philip on offical visit 40 45
2445 800 c. Queen in Irish State Coach .. 40 45
2446 800 c. Prince Philip in 1947 .. .. 40 45
2441/6 .. .. *Set of* 6 2·40 2·75
MS2447 100×71 mm. 3000 c. Princess Elizabeth in 1947 .. .. 1·50 1·60
Nos. 2441/6 were printed together, *se-tenant*, in sheetlets of 6.

(Des J. Iskowitz. Litho Questa)

1997 (29 May). *"Pacific '97" International Stamp Exhibition, San Francisco. Death Centenary of Heinrich von Stephan* (*founder of the U.P.U.*). *Horiz designs as T* **379** *of Antigua. P* 14.
2448 1000 c. deep blue 50 55
a. Sheetlet. Nos. 2448/50 .. .. 1·50
2449 1000 c. orange-brown 50 55
2450 1000 c. pale Indian red 50 55
2448/50 .. .. *Set of* 3 1·50 1·60
MS2451 82×119 mm. 3000 c. turquoise-green 1·50 1·60
Designs:—No. 2448, Early motor car; No. 2449, Von Stephan and Mercury; No. 2450, Blanchard's balloon flight, 1784; No. **MS**2451, African messenger.
Nos. 2448/50 were printed together, *se-tenant*, in sheetlets of 3 with enlarged illustrated right-hand margin.

(Litho Questa)

1997 (29 May). *Birth Bicentenary of Hiroshige* (*Japanese painter*). *"One Hundred Famous Views of Edo". Vert designs as T* **310** *of Dominica. Multicoloured. P* 13½×14.
2452 600 c. "Nihonbashi Bridge and Edobashi Bridge" 30 35
a. Sheetlet. Nos. 2452/7 .. .. 1·75
2453 600 c. "View of Nihonbashi Tori 1-chome" 30 35
2454 600 c. "Open Garden at Fukagawa Hachiman Shrine" 30 35
2455 600 c. "Inari Bridge and Minato Shrine, Teppozu" 30 35
2456 600 c. "Bamboo Yards, Kyobashi Bridge" 30 35
2457 600 c. "Hall of Thirty-Three Bays, Fukagawa" 30 35
2452/7 .. .. *Set of* 6 1·75 1·90
MS2458 Two sheets, each 102×127 mm. (a) 3000 c. "Sumiyoshi Festival, Tsukudajima". (b) 3000 c. "Teppozu and Tsukjji Honganji Temple" *Set of* 2 *sheets* 3·00 3·25
Nos. 2452/7 were printed together, *se-tenant*, in sheetlets of 6.

(Des E. Mensah (No. **MS**2468b), Zina Saunders (others). Litho Questa)

1997 (1 July). *Famous Comedians. T* **542** *and similar vert designs. Multicoloured. P* 13½×14.
2459 600 c. Type **542** 30 35
a. Sheetlet. Nos. 2459/67 .. .. 2·75
2460 600 c. Danny Kaye 30 35
2461 600 c. John Cleese 30 35
2462 600 c. Lucille Ball 30 35
2463 600 c. Jerry Lewis 30 35
2464 600 c. Sidney James 30 35
2465 600 c. Louis Defuenes 30 35
2466 600 c. Mae West 30 35
2467 600 c. Bob Hope 30 35
2459/67 .. .. *Set of* 9 2·75 3·25
MS2468 Two sheets. (a) 83×113 mm. 3000 c. Groucho Marx. P 13½×14. (b) 76×106 mm. 2000 c. Professor Ajax Bukana in front of curtain; 2000 c. Professor Ajax Bukana (*different*) (*both* 28×42 *mm*). P 14 *Set of* 2 *sheets* 2·50 2·75
Nos. 2459/67 were printed together, *se-tenant*, in sheetlets of 9.

543 *Galerina calyptrata*

544 African Pygmy Angelfish

(Litho Questa)

1997 (9 July). *Fungi of the World. T* **543** *and similar vert designs. Multicoloured. P* 14.
2469 200 c. Type **543** 10 15
2470 300 c. *Lepiota ignivolvata* 15 20
2471 400 c. *Omphalotus olearius* 20 25
2472 550 c. *Amanita phalloides* 30 35
2473 600 c. *Entoloma conferendum* 30 35
2474 800 c. *Entoloma nitidum* 40 45
2475 800 c. *Coprinus picaceus* 40 45
a. Sheetlet. Nos. 2475/80 .. .. 2·40
2476 800 c. *Stropharia aurantiaca* 40 45
2477 800 c. *Cortinarius splendens* 40 45
2478 800 c. *Gomphidius roseus* 40 45
2479 800 c. *Russula sardonia* 40 45
2480 800 c. *Geastrum schmidelia* 40 45
2469/80 .. .. *Set of* 12 3·75 4·50
MS2481 Two sheets, each 73×103 mm. (a) 3000 c. *Craterellus cornucopioides*. (b) 3000 c. *Mycena crocata* .. .. .. *Set of* 2 *sheets* 3·00 3·25
Nos. 2475/80 were printed together, *se-tenant*, in sheetlets of 6.

(Litho Questa)

1997 (12 July). *World Football Championship, France* (1998). *Horiz designs as T* **383** *of Antigua. Multicoloured. P* 14×13½.
2482 200 c. Azteca Stadium, Mexico 10 10
2483 300 c. The Rose Bowl, U.S.A. 15 20
2484 400 c. Stadio Giuseppe Meazza, Italy .. 20 25
2485 500 c. Olympiastadion, Germany .. 25 30
2486 600 c. Patrick Kluivert, Netherlands .. 30 35
a. Sheetlet. Nos. 2486/93 and central label .. .. 2·40
2487 600 c. Roy Keane, Republic of Ireland .. 30 35
2488 600 c. Abedi Ayew Pele, Ghana 30 35
2489 600 c. Peter Schmeichel, Denmark .. 30 35
2490 600 c. Roberto di Matteo, Italy 30 35
2491 600 c. Bebeto, Brazil 30 35
2492 600 c. Steve McManaman, England .. 30 35
2493 600 c. George Oppon Weah, Liberia .. 30 35
2494 1000 c. Maracana Stadium, Brazil .. 50 55
2495 2000 c. Bernabeu Stadium, Spain .. 1·00 1·10
2482/95 .. .. *Set of* 14 4·50 5·50
MS2496 Two sheets. (a) 127×102 mm. 3000 c. David Seaman, England. (b) 102×127 mm. 3000 c. Juninho, Brazil .. .. *Set of* 2 *sheets* 3·00 3·25
Nos. 2486/93 were printed together, *se-tenant*, in sheetlets of 8 stamps and 1 central label.

(Des R. Martin. Litho Questa)

1997 (15 July). *Marine Life. T* **544** *and similar horiz designs. Multicoloured. P* 14.
2497 400 c. Type **544** 20 25
2498 500 c. Violet-crested Turaco 25 30
a. Sheetlet. Nos. 2498/509 .. .. 3·00
2499 500 c. Pied Avocet 25 30
2500 500 c. Bottle-nosed Dolphin 25 30
2501 500 c. Bottle-nosed Dolphin and Long-toed Lapwing 25 30
2502 500 c. Longfinned Spadefish 25 30
2503 500 c. Imperial Angelfish and Manta .. 25 30
2504 500 c. Raccoon Butterflyfish and African Pompano 25 30

2505 500 c. Silvertip Shark 25 30
2506 500 c. Longfin Banner Fish 25 30
2507 500 c. Longfin Banner Fish and Manta .. 25 30
2508 500 c. Rust Parrotfish 25 30
2509 500 c. Coral Trout 25 30
2510 600 c. Angelfish 30 35
2511 800 c. Broomtail Wrasse 40 45
2512 1000 c. Indian Butterflyfish 50 55
2497/512 .. .. *Set of* 16 4·50 5·25
MS2513 Two sheets, each 106×76 mm. (a) 3000 c. King Angelfish. (b) 3000 c. Crown Butterflyfish .. .. .. *Set of* 2 *sheets* 3·00 2·25
Nos. 2498/509 were printed together, *se-tenant*, in sheetlets of 12 with the backgrounds forming a composite design.

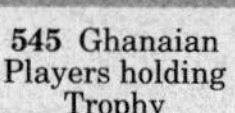

545 Ghanaian Players holding Trophy

546 *Eurychone rothschildiana*

1997 (25 July). *J.V.C. Under-17 World Soccer Champions* (1995). *T* **545** *and similar multicoloured designs. Litho. P* 13½×13 (*vert*) *or* 13×13½ (*horiz*).
2514 200 c. + 50 c. Type **545** 15 20
2515 550 c. + 50 c. Ghana football team (*horiz*) 30 35
2516 800 c. + 50 c. Abu Iddrisu 45 50
2517 1100 c. + 50 c. Emmanuel Bentil (captain) 60 65
2518 1500 c. + 50 c. Basiru Gambo 80 85
2514/18 .. .. *Set of* 5 2·25 2·50

(Des Jennifer Toombs. Litho Questa)

1997 (1 Aug). *Flowers of the World. T* **546** *and similar multicoloured designs. P* 14×14½ (*horiz*) *or* 14½×14 (*vert*).
2519 200 c. Type **546** 10 10
2520 550 c. *Bulbophyllum lepidum* 30 35
2521 800 c. *Ansellia africana* 40 45
2522 800 c. *Strophanthus preusii* (*vert*) .. 40 45
a. Sheetlet. Nos. 2522/30 .. .. 3·50
2523 800 c. *Ancistrochilus rothschildlanus* (*vert*) 40 45
2524 800 c. *Mussaendra arcuata* (*vert*) .. 40 45
2525 800 c. *Microcoelia guyoniane* (*vert*) .. 40 45
2526 800 c. *Gloriosa simplex* (*vert*) 40 45
2527 800 c. *Brachycorythis kalbreyeri* (*vert*) .. 40 45
2528 800 c. *Aframomum sceptrum* (*vert*) .. 40 45
2529 800 c. *Thunbergia alata* (*vert*) 40 45
2530 800 c. *Clerodendrum thomsoniae* (*vert*) .. 40 45
2531 1100 c. *Combbretum grandiflorum* .. 60 65
2519/31 .. .. *Set of* 13 5·00 5·75
MS2532 Two sheets each 82×77 mm. (a) 3000 c. *Kigelia africana* (*vert*). (b) 3000 c. *Spathodea campanulata* (*vert*) .. .. *Set of* 2 *sheets* 3·00 3·75
Nos. 2522/30 were printed together, *se-tenant*, in sheetlets of 9 with the backgrounds forming a composite design.

547 Goldfinch

548 Havana Cat

(Des D. Burkhart. Litho B.D.T.)

1997 (20 Oct). *Birds of Africa. T* **547** *and similar vert designs. Multicoloured. P* 14.
2533 200 c. Type **547** 10 10
2534 300 c. Cape Puff-back Flycatcher ("Batis") 15 20
2535 400 c. Red-headed Barbet 20 25
2536 500 c. African White-necked Raven .. 25 30
2537 600 c. Purple Grenadier 30 35
2538 800 c. Black Bustard 40 45
a. Sheetlet. Nos. 2538/46 .. .. 3·50
2539 800 c. Lapwing 40 45
2540 800 c. Lichtenstein's Sandgrouse .. 40 45
2541 800 c. Red-crested Turaco 40 45
2542 800 c. White-browed Coucal 40 45
2543 800 c. Lilac-breasted Roller 40 45
2544 800 c. Golden Pipet 40 45
2545 800 c. Burchell's Gonolek 40 45
2546 800 c. Blackcap 40 45
2547 1000 c. Zebra Waxbill 50 55
2533/47 .. .. *Set of* 5 5·00 5·25
MS2548 Two sheets, each 106×75 mm. (a) 3000 c. Shaft-tailed Whydah. (b) 3000 c. Yellow-tufted Malachite Sunbird *Set of* 2 *sheets* 3·00 3·25
Nos. 2538/46 were printed together, se-tenant, in sheetlets of 9.

(Des D. Burkhart. Litho Questa)

1997 (20 Oct). *Cats and Dogs. T* **548** *and similar horiz designs. Multicoloured. P* 14.
2549 20 c. Type **548** 10 10
2550 50 c. Singapura cat 10 10
2551 80 c. Papillon 10 10
2552 100 c. Sphinx cat 10 10
2553 150 c. British White cat 10 10
2554 200 c. Bulldog 10 15
2555 300 c. Snowshoe cat 15 20
2556 400 c. Shetland Sheepdog 20 25
2557 500 c. Schnauzer 25 30
2558 600 c. Persian cat 30 35
2559 800 c. Shih Tzu 40 45
2560 1000 c. Russian Wolfhound 50 55
a. Sheetlet. Nos. 2560/5 .. .. 3·00
2561 1000 c. Birman cat 50 55
2562 1000 c. Basset Hound 50 55
2563 1000 c. Silver Tabby cat 50 55
2564 1000 c. Afghan 50 55
2565 1000 c. Burmilla cat 50 55
2566 1000 c. Abyssinian cat 50 55
a. Sheetlet. Nos. 2566/71 .. .. 3·00
2567 1000 c. Border Terrier 50 55
2568 1000 c. Scottish Fold cat 50 55
2569 1000 c. Boston Terrier 50 55
2570 1000 c. Oriental cat 50 55
2571 1000 c. Keeshond 50 55
2572 2000 c. Chow Chow .. .. .. 1·00 1·10
2549/72 .. .. *Set of* 24 8·50 9·50
MS2573 Two sheets, each 73×100 mm. (a) 3000 c. Alaskan Malamute. (b) 3000 c. Ragdoll cat .. .. .. *Set of* 2 *sheets* 3·00 3·25
Nos. 2560/5 and 2566/71 were each printed together, *se-tenant*, in sheetlets of 6.

549 "Landscape" (Huang Binhong)

550 Diana, Princess of Wales

(Des Y. Lee. Litho Questa)

1997 (10 Nov). *Return of Hong Kong to China. T* **549** *and similar designs showing landscape paintings by Huang Binhong* (*Nos.* 2574/81 *and* **MS**2582) *or historical scenes* (*No.* **MS**2583). *P* 14.
2574 200 c. multicoloured 10 15
a. Sheetlet. Nos. 2574/81 .. .. 3·00
2575 300 c. multicoloured 15 20
2576 400 c. multicoloured 20 25
2577 500 c. multicoloured 25 30
2578 600 c. multicoloured 30 35
2579 800 c. multicoloured 40 45
2580 1000 c. multicoloured 50 55
2581 2000 c. multicoloured .. .. .. 1·00 1·10
2574/81 .. .. *Set of* 8 3·00 3·25
MS2582 138×105 mm. (a) 2000 c. multicoloured (farm). (b) 2000 c. multicoloured (mountains) (*each* 50×37 *mm*). P 14×13½ .. .. 2·00 2·10
MS2583 150×125 mm. (a) 1000 c. × 2 multicoloured (Lin Tse-Hue). (b) 1000 c. × 2 multicoloured (Gwen Tian-Pei) (*each* 63×31 *mm*) .. 2·00 2·10
Nos. 2574/81 were printed together, *se-tenant*, in sheetlets of 8.

(Litho B.D.T.)

1997 (8 Dec). *Christmas. Paintings. Vert designs as T* **386** *of Antigua. Multicoloured. P* 14.
2584 200 c. "Cupid" (Botticelli) 10 15
2585 550 c. "Zephyr and Chloris" (Botticelli) .. 30 35
2586 800 c. "Triumphant Cupid" (Caravaggio) 40 45
2587 1100 c. "The Seven Works of Mercy" (Caravaggio) 55 60
2588 1500 c. "The Toilet of Venus" (Diego Velazquez) 80 85
2589 2000 c. "Freeing of St. Peter" (Raphael) .. 1·00 1·10
2584/9 .. .. *Set of* 6 3·25 3·50
MS2590 Two sheets. (a) 95×105 mm. 5000 c. "The Cavalcanti Annunciation" (Donatello). (b) 105 x 95 mm. 5000 c. Ancient Egyptian painting of Isis and Nephthys .. .. *Set of* 2 *sheets* 5·00 5·25

(Litho Questa)

1997 (22 Dec). *Diana, Princess of Wales Commemorati*[c] *T* **550** *and similar vert designs. Multicoloured* (*except N*[os]. 2591, 2596, 2602 *and* **MS**2603b). *P* 14.
2591 1200 c. Type **550** (brown-red) 60
a. Sheetlet. Nos. 2591/6 .. .. 3·50
2592 1200 c. Wearing blue suit and holding flowers 60
2593 1200 c. Looking right 60
2594 1200 c. Sitting crossed-legged 60
2595 1200 c. With Prince William 60
2596 1200 c. Wearing spotted scarf (blue & blk) 60
2597 1200 c. Wearing pink shirt 60
a. Sheetlet. Nos. 2597/602 .. .. 3·50
2598 1200 c. Wearing red dress 60
2599 1200 c. Carrying bouquet 60
2600 1200 c. Wearing sunglasses 60
2601 1200 c. With children 60
2602 1200 c. Wearing hat (light brown & black) 60
2591/602 .. .. *Set of* 12 7·00 7·
MS2603 Two sheets. (a) 100×70 mm. 3000 c. Diana, Princess of Wales. (b) 70×100 mm. 3000 c. Diana, Princess of Wales (dull vio & blk) *Set of* 2 *sheets* 3·00 3·
Nos. 2591/6 and 2597/602 were each printed togethe[r] *se-tenant*, in sheetlets of 6.

551 Horse

552 Mortie and Ferdie (January)

(Litho Questa)

1998 (15 Jan). *Animals of the Chinese Lunar Calendar. T* 5[51] *and similar vert designs. Multicoloured. P* 13½.
2604 400 c. Type **551** 20
a. Sheetlet. Nos. 2604/15 .. .. 2·40
2605 400 c. Monkey 20
2606 400 c. Ram 20
2607 400 c. Cock 20
2608 400 c. Dog 20
2609 400 c. Ox 20
2610 400 c. Rabbit 20
2611 400 c. Pig 20
2612 400 c. Snake 20
2613 400 c. Dragon 20
2614 400 c. Tiger 20
2615 400 c. Rat 20
2604/15 .. .. *Set of* 12 2·40 2·
Nos. 2604/15 were printed together, *se-tenant*, in sheetlets [of] 12.

(Des Walt Disney Co. Litho Questa)

1998 (29 Jan). *A Year in the Life of Mickey Mouse and Frien*[ds]. *T* **552** *and similar multicoloured designs showing Walt Disn*[ey] *cartoon characters. P* 13½×14.
2616 1000 c. Type **552** 50 5
a. Sheetlet. Nos. 2616/21 .. .. 3·00
2617 1000 c. Minnie on Valentine's Day (February) 50 5
2618 1000 c. Goofy with kite (March) 50 5
2619 1000 c. Mickey, Minnie and Pluto in rain (April) 50 5
2620 1000 c. Minnie with flowers (May) .. 50 5
2621 1000 c. Daisy watering garden (June) .. 50 5
2622 1000 c. Donald at Independance Day celebrations (July) 50 5
a. Sheetlet. Nos. 2622/7 .. .. 3·00
2623 1000 c. Donald and Daisy on the beach (August) 50 5
2624 1000 c. Morty and Ferdie returning to school (September) 50 5
2625 1000 c. Hewey, Dewey and Louie at Hallowe'en (October) 50 5
2626 1000 c. Mickey on Thanksgiving Day (November) 50 5
2627 1000 c. Mickey and Minnie at Christmas (December) 50 5
2616/27 .. .. *Set of* 12 6·00 6·5
MS2628 Four sheets, each 132×107 mm. (a) 5000 c. Mickey bottle feeding calf (Spring) (*horiz*). (b) 5000 c. Minnie camping (Summer). (c) 5000 c. Goofy sweeping leaves (Autumn). (d) 5000 c. Daisy and Nephews on ice (Winter) (*horiz*). P 13½×14 (*vert*) or 14×13½ (*horiz*) *Set of* 4 *sheets* 10·00 10·5
Nos. 2616/21 and 2622/7 were each printed together, *se*-*tenant*, in sheetlets of 6.

553 Union Pacific SD60M Diesel Locomotive No. 6331, U.S.A.

554 Maya Angelou

(Des G. Bibby. Litho Questa)

1998 (26 Feb). *Trains of the World. T* **553** *and similar horiz designs. Multicoloured. P* 14.

2629 300 c. Type **553** 15 20
2630 500 c. ETR 450 high-speed train, Italy .. 25 30
2631 800 c. X200 high-speed train, Sweden .. 40 45
2632 800 c. SPS steam locomotive, Pakistan .. 40 45
a. Sheetlet. Nos. 2632/40 .. .. 3·75
2633 800 c. Class WP steam locomotive, India 40 45
2634 800 c. Class QJ steam locomotive, China 40 45
2635 800 c. Type 12 steam locomotive, Belgium 40 45
2636 800 c. Class P8 steam locomotive, Germany 40 45
2637 800 c. Class "Castle" steam locomotive, Great Britain 40 45
2638 800 c. Tank locomotive, Austria .. 40 45
2639 800 c. Class P36 steam locomotive, Russia 40 45
2640 800 c. Steam locomotive *William Mason*, U.S.A. 40 45
2641 800 c. AVE high-speed train, Spain .. 40 45
a. Sheetlet. Nos. 2641/9 .. .. 3·75
2642 800 c. Diesel locomotive, No. 1602, Luxembourg 40 45
2643 800 c. "Hikari" express train, Japan .. 40 45
2644 800 c. Santa Fe Railroad GM F7 "Warbonnet" diesel locomotive, U.S.A. 40 45
2645 800 c. Class E1500 diesel locomotive, Morocco 40 45
2646 800 c. Class "Deltic" diesel locomotive, Great Britain 40 45
2647 800 c. XPT high-speed train, Australia .. 40 45
2648 800 c. Channel Tunnel shuttle train, France and Great Britain .. 40 45
2649 800 c. Class 201 diesel locomotive, Ireland 40 45
2650 1000 c. TGV Duplex high-speed train, France 50 55
2651 2000 c. Class EL diesel locomotive, Australia .. .. 1·00 1·10
2652 3000 c. Eurostar high-speed train, Great Britain .. .. .. 1·50 1·60
2626/52 .. .. *Set of* 24 11·00 12·00
MS2653 Two sheets, each 106×76 mm. (a) 5500 c. Class "Duchess" steam locomotive heading the "Irish Mail", Great Britain (56×42 *mm*). (b) 5500 c. TGV express train, France (56×42 *mm*) .. .. .. *Set of* 2 *sheets* 5·00 5·50

Nos. 2632/40 and 2641/9 were each printed together, *se-tenant*, in sheetlets of 9.

1998 (25 Mar). *Great Writers of the 20th Century. T* **554** *and similar vert designs. Multicoloured. P* 14.

2654 350 c. Type **554** 20 25
a. Sheetlet. Nos. 2654/9 .. .. 1·25
2655 350 c. Alex Haley 20 25
2656 350 c. Charles Johnson 20 25
2657 350 c. Richard Wright 20 25
2658 350 c. Toni Cade Bambara 20 25
2659 350 c. Henri Louis Gates Jr 20 25
2654/9 .. .. *Set of* 6 1·25 1·50

Nos. 2654/9 were printed together, *se-tenant*, in sheetlets of 6.

555 Breguet Br 14 B2, France

1998 (5 May). *History of Aviation. T* **555** *and similar horiz designs. Multicoloured. Litho. P* 14.

2660 800 c. Type **555** 40 45
a. Sheetlet. Nos. 2660/8 .. .. 3·50
2661 800 c. Curtiss BF2C-1 Goshawk, U.S.A. 40 45
2662 800 c. Supermarine Spitfire Mk IX, Great Britain 40 45
2663 800 c. Fiat G.50, Italy 40 45
2664 800 c. Douglas B-18A, U.S.A. 40 45
2665 800 c. Boeing FB-5, U.S.A. 40 45
2666 800 c. Bristol F2B "Brisfit", Great Britain 40 45
2667 800 c. Hawker Fury 1, Great Britain .. 40 45
2668 800 c. Fiat CR-42, Italy 40 45
2669 800 c. Messerschmitt Bf 109 E-7, Germany 40 45
a. Sheetlet. Nos. 2669/77 .. .. 3·50
2670 800 c. Lockheed PV-2 Harpoon, U.S.A .. 40 45
2671 800 c. Airspeed Oxford Mk 1, Great Britain 40 45
2672 800 c. Junkers Ju 87D-1, Germany .. 40 45
2673 800 c. Yakovlev Yak-9D, U.S.S.R. .. 40 45
2674 800 c. North American P-51D Mustang, U.S.A. 40 45
2675 800 c. Douglas A-206 Havoc, U.S.A. .. 40 45
2676 800 c. Supermarine Attacker F1, Great Britain 40 45
2677 800 c. Mikoyan Gurevich MiG-15, U.S.S.R. 40 45
2660/77 .. .. *Set of* 18 7·00 8·00
MS2678 Two sheets, each 106×76 mm. (a) 3000 c. Supermarine Spitfires Mk 1 and Mk XIV, Great Britain (58×43 *mm*). (b) 3000 c. Mitsubishi AGM8 Reisen, Japan (58×43 *mm*) *Set of* 2 *sheets* 2·00 2·10

Nos. 2660/8 and 2669/77 were printed together, *se-tenant*, in sheetlets of 9.

NEW INFORMATION

The editor is always interested to correspond with people who have new information that will improve or correct the Catalogue.

556 *Empress of Ireland* (liner) (**557**)

(Des S. Thurston. Litho B.D.T.)

1998 (5 May). *Famous Ships. T* **556** *and similar multicoloured designs. P* 14.

2679 800 c. Type **556** 40 45
a. Sheetlet. Nos. 2679/87 .. .. 3·50
2680 800 c. *Transylvania* (liner) 40 45
2681 800 c. *Mauretania I* (liner) 40 45
2682 800 c. *Reliance* (liner) 40 45
2683 800 c. *Aquitania* (liner) 40 45
2684 800 c. *Lapland* (liner) 40 45
2685 800 c. *Cap Polonio* (liner) 40 45
2686 800 c. *France I*, 1910 (liner) 40 45
2687 800 c. *Imperator* (liner) 40 45
2688 800 c. H.M.S. *Rodney* (battleship) .. 40 45
a. Sheetlet. Nos. 2688/96 .. .. 3·50
2689 800 c. U.S.S. *Alabama* (battleship) .. 40 45
2690 800 c. H.M.S. *Nelson* (battleship) .. 40 45
2691 800 c. *Ormonde* (camouflaged liner) .. 40 45
2692 800 c. U.S.S. *Radford* (destroyer) .. 40 45
2693 800 c. *Empress of Russia* (camouflaged liner) 40 45
2694 800 c. Type XIV U-boat 40 45
2695 800 c. Japanese Type A midget submarine 40 45
2696 800 c. *Brin* (Italian submarine) 40 45
2679/96 .. .. *Set of* 18 7·00 8·00
MS2697 Two sheets, each 100×75 mm. (a) 5500 c. *Titanic* (liner) (43×57 *mm*). (b) 5500 c. *Amistad* (slave schooner) (43×57 *mm*) *Set of* 2 *sheets* 5·00 5·25

Nos. 2679/87 and 2688/96 were each printed together, *se-tenant*, in sheetlets of 9.

Nos. 2681 is inscribed "MAURITANIA" in error.

1998 (13 May). *"Israel 98" International Stamp Exhibition, Tel-Aviv. Nos.* 2362/5 *optd with T* **557**.

2698 400 c. St. Stephen's Gate and *Jasminum mesnyi* 20 25
2699 600 c. The Citadel, Tower of David and *Nerium oleander* 30 35
2700 800 c. Chapel of the Ascension and *Romulea bulbocodium* 40 45
a. Opt inverted .. .. ..
2698/700 .. .. *Set of* 3 90 1·00
MS2701 65×80 mm. 2000 c. Russian Orthodox Church of St. Mary Magdalene (48×30 *mm*) .. 1·00 1·10

No. **MS**2701 is additionally overprinted "ISRAEL 98 – WORLD STAMP EXHIBITION TEL-AVIV 13–21 MAY 1998" on the sheet margin.

558 *Renanthera imschootiana* **559** Elvis Presley

1998 (2 June). *Orchids of the World. T* **558** *and similar vert designs. Multicoloured. Litho. P* 14.

2702 800 c. Type **558** 40 45
a. Sheetlet. Nos. 2702/7 .. .. 2·40
2703 800 c. *Arachnis flos-aeris* 40 45
2704 800 c. *Restrepia lansbergi* 40 45
2705 800 c. *Paphiopedilum tonsum* 40 45
2706 800 c. *Phalaenopsis ebauche* 40 45
2707 800 c. *Pleione limprichti* 40 45
2708 800 c. *Phragmipedium schroderae* .. 40 45
a. Sheetlet. Nos. 2708/13 .. .. 2·40
2709 800 c. *Zygopetalum clayii* 40 45
2710 800 c. *Vanda coerulea* 40 45
2711 800 c. *Odontonia boussole* 40 45
2712 800 c. *Disa uniflora* 40 45
2713 800 c. *Dendrobium bigibbum* 40 45
2702/13 .. .. *Set of* 12 4·75 5·25
MS2714 Two sheets, each 98×68 mm. (a) 5500 c. *Cypripedium calceolus*. (b) 5500 c. *Sobralia candida* .. .. .. *Set of* 2 *sheets* 5·00 5·25

Nos. 2702/7 and 2708/13 were each printed together, *se-tenant*, in sheetlets of 6.

(Des Zina Saunders. Litho)

1998 (16 June). *30th Anniv of Elvis Presley's "68 Special" Television Programme. T* **559** *and similar vert designs. Multicoloured. P* 13½.

2715 800 c. Type **559** 40 45
a. Sheetlet. Nos. 2715/20 .. .. 2·40
2716 800 c. Elvis in white suit 40 45
2717 800 c. In leather jacket, holding microphone 40 45
2718 800 c. Wearing light blue jacket 40 45
2719 800 c. Elvis with silhouetted figures in background 40 45
2720 800 c. Elvis with guitar and microphone .. 40 45
2715/20 .. .. *Set of* 6 2·40 2·50

Nos. 2715/20 were printed together, *se-tenant*, in sheetlets of 6 with enlarged illustrated margins.

560 Crest of Accra Metropolitan Assembly and Surf Boats **561** Tetteh Quarshie (cocoa industry pioneer)

(Litho Cartor)

1998 (8 July). *Centenary of Accra Metropolitan Assembly. T* **560** *and similar horiz designs. Multicoloured. P* 13×13½.

2721 200 c. Type **560** 10 15
2722 550 c. King Tackie Tawiah I 30 35
2723 800 c. Achimota School 40 45
2724 1100 c. Korle Bu Hospital 60 65
2725 1500 c. Christianborg Castle 80 85
2721/5 .. .. *Set of* 5 2·10 2·40

(Litho Cartor)

1998 (8 July). *50th Anniv of Ghana Cocoa Board. T* **561** *and similar horiz designs. Multicoloured. P* 13×13½.

2726 200 c. Type **561** 10 15
2727 550 c. Ripe hybrid cocoa pods 30 35
2728 800 c. Opening cocoa pods 40 45
2729 1100 c. Fermenting cocoa beans 60 65
2730 1500 c. Loading freighter with cocoa .. 80 85
2726/30 .. .. *Set of* 5 2·10 2·40

562 Bamboo **563** Two Dolphins

(Des Kang Cheng Weng. Litho Questa)

1998 (14 July). *Oriental Flowers. T* **562** *and similar multicoloured designs. P* 14.

2731 2000 c. Type **562** .. .. 1·00 1·10
a. Sheetlet. Nos. 2731/4 .. .. 4·00
2732 2000 c. Cherry blossom .. .. .. 1·00 1·10
2733 2000 c. Yellow chrysanthemum .. .. 1·00 1·10
2734 2000 c. Orchid .. .. 1·00 1·10
2735 2000 c. Green peony .. .. .. 1·00 1·10
a. Sheetlet. Nos. 2735/8 .. .. 4·00
2736 2000 c. Red peony .. .. .. 1·00 1·10
2737 2000 c. Pink peony .. .. .. 1·00 1·10
2738 2000 c. White peony .. .. .. 1·00 1·10
2731/8 .. .. *Set of* 8 8·00 8·25
MS2739 Two sheets, each 109×85 mm. (a) 5500 c. Cherry blossom (*horiz*). (b) 5500 c. Peonies (*horiz*) .. .. *Set of* 2 *sheets* 5·00 5·25

Nos. 2731/4 and 2735/8 were each printed together, *se-tenant*, in sheetlets of 4.

(Des S. Stines. Litho Questa)

1998 (18 Aug). *International Year of the Ocean. T* **563** *and similar horiz designs. Multicoloured. P* 14.

2740 500 c. Type **563** 25 30
a. Sheetlet. Nos. 2740/55 .. .. 4·00
2741 500 c. Dolphin 25 30
2742 500 c. Seagull 25 30
2743 500 c. Least Tern 25 30
2744 500 c. Emperor Angelfish 25 30
2745 500 c. White Ear (juvenile) 25 30
2746 500 c. Blue Shark and diver 25 30
2747 500 c. Parrotfish 25 30
2748 500 c. Dottyback 25 30
2749 500 c. Blue-spotted Stingray 25 30
2750 500 c. Masked Butterflyfish 25 30
2751 500 c. Jackknife-Fish 25 30
2752 500 c. Octopus 25 30
2753 500 c. Lionfish 25 30
2754 500 c. Seadragon 25 30
2755 500 c. Rock Cod 25 30
2740/55 .. .. *Set of* 16 4·00 4·75
MS2756 Two sheets. (a) 63×98 mm. 3000 c. Great White Shark. (b) 98×63 mm. 3000 c. Devil Ray .. .. .. *Set of* 2 *sheets* 3·00 3·25

Nos. 2740/55 were printed together, *se-tenant*, in sheetlets of 16 with the backgrounds forming a composite design.

No. 2745 is inscribed "Whit Ear" in error.

STAMP BOOKLETS

1916 (Dec).
SB1 2s. booklet containing twelve ½d. and eighteen 1d. (Nos. 70*a*, 72) in blocks of 6

1961. *Red* (*No.* SB2), *yellow* (*No.* SB3) *or green* (*No.* SB4) *covers. Stitched.*
SB2 3s. booklet containing twelve 3d. (No. 218a) in blocks of 4 .. 6·00
SB3 6s. booklet containing eight 3d. and eight 6d. (Nos. 218a, 220) in blocks of 4 .. 7·50
SB4 10s. booklet containing four 3d., eight 6d. and four 1s. 3d. (Nos. 218a, 220, 226) in blocks of 4 .. 9·50

1963 (Jan). *Yellow cover. Stitched.*
SB5 6s. booklet containing twelve 4d. and four 6d. (Nos. 219/20) in blocks of four

1981 (16 Sept). *Royal Wedding. Multicoloured cover,* 120×82 *mm, showing Prince Charles and Lady Diana Spencer on front and map of Ghana on back. Stapled.*
SB6 14 c. booklet containing *se-tenant* pane of 4 (No. 955a) .. 4·50

POSTAGE DUE STAMPS

D 1

(Typo D.L.R.)

1923 (6 Mar). *Yellowish toned paper. Wmk Mult Script CA. P* 14.
D1 D 1 ½d. black .. 14·00 £100
D2 1d. black .. 75 1·25
D3 2d. black .. 13·00 9·00
D4 3d. black .. 22·00 6·00
D1/4 .. *Set of* 4 45·00 £110
D1/4 Optd "Specimen" .. *Set of* 4 70·00

A bottom marginal strip of six of No. D2 is known showing the "A" of "CA" omitted from the watermark in the margin below the third vertical column.

3d — Normal

3d — Lower serif at left of "3" missing (R. 9/1)

1/- — Row 4 (No. D8)

1/- — Row 5 (No. D8c)

The degree of inclination of the stroke on the 1s. value varies for each vertical row of the sheet: Rows 1, 2 and 6 104°, Row 3 108°, Row 4 107° and Row 5 (No. D8c) 100°.

1951–52. *Chalk-surfaced paper. Wmk Mult Script CA. P* 14.
D5 D 1 2d. black (13.12.51) .. 3·00 17·00
a. Error. Crown missing, W **9***a* .. £500
b. Error. St. Edward's Crown, W **9***b* .. £275
c. Large "d" (R. 9/6, 10/6) .. 18·00
D6 3d. black (13.12.51) .. 1·50 15·00
a. Error. Crown missing, W **9***a* .. £500
b. Error. St. Edward's Crown. W **9***b* .. £275
c. Missing serif .. 18·00
D7 6d. black (1.10.52) .. 1·75 8·00
a. Error. Crown missing, W **9***a* .. £650
b. Error. St. Edward's Crown, W **9***b* .. £450
D8 1s. black (1.10.52) .. 1·75 55·00
b. Error. St. Edward's Crown, W **9***b* .. £600
c. Upright stroke .. 12·00
D5/8 .. *Set of* 4 7·25 85·00

For illustration of No. D5c see Nos. D4/6 of Botswana.

GHANA

(D 2)

D 3

1958 (25 June). *Nos.* D5/8 *and similar* 1d. *value optd with Type* D 2 *in red.*
D 9 D 1 1d. black .. 10 20
D10 2d. black .. 10 25
c. Large "d" .. 2·25
D11 3d. black .. 10 30
a. Missing serif .. 4·00
D12 6d. black .. 15 65
D13 1s. black .. 20 1·25
c. Upright stroke .. 1·50
D9/13 .. *Set of* 5 50 2·40

(Typo De La Rue)

1958 (1 Dec). *Chalk-surfaced paper. Wmk Mult Script CA. P* 14.
D14 D 3 1d. carmine .. 10 30
D15 2d. green .. 10 30
c. Large "d" .. 2·25
D16 3d. orange .. 10 30
a. Missing serif .. 4·00
D17 6d. bright ultramarine .. 10 50
D18 1s. reddish violet .. 15 2·00
c. Upright stroke .. 1·50
D14/18 .. *Set of* 5 45 3·00

3p. Ghana New Currency 19th July, 1965.

(D 4)

1½Np

(D 5)

1965 (19 July). *Nos.* D14/18 *surch as Type* D 4 *diagonally upwards* (D) *or horiz* (H), *by Govt Printer, Accra.*
D19 D 3 1 p. on 1d. (D) .. 10 60
a. Surch inverted .. 7·50
b. Surch double
D20 2 p. on 2d. (B.) (H) .. 10 60
a. Surch inverted .. 6·00
c. Large "d" .. 2·25
D21 3 p. on 3d. (indigo) (H) .. 10 60
a. Surch inverted
b. Surch omitted (in horiz pair with normal)
c. Ultramarine surch
ca. Surch inverted .. 9·00
cb. Surch on front and back
d. Black surch
e. Missing serif .. 1·50
D22 6 p. on 6d. (R.) (H) .. 10 1·50
a. Surch inverted
b. Purple-brown surch
ba. Surch double .. 19·00
c. Green surch .. 13·00
D23 12 p. on 1s. (B.) (D) .. 15 2·00
c. Upright stroke .. 1·50
D19/23 .. *Set of* 5 45 4·75

On the diagonal surcharges the figures of value are horizontal.

No. D21b occurs in the first or second vertical row of one sheet which shows the surcharges shifted progressively to the right.

1968 (Feb)–**70.** *Nos.* D20/2 *additionally surch as Type* D 5, *in red* (1½ *n.p.*, 5 *n.p.*) *or black* (2½ *n.p.*).
D24 D 3 1½ n.p. on 2 p. on 2d. .. 5·50 4·25
a. Type D 5 double, one albino
b. Albino surch (Type D 4)
c. Large "d" .. 20·00
D25 2½ n.p. on 3 p. on 3d. (4.70?) .. 1·00 4·50
a. Type D 5 double, one albino .. 5·50
b. Missing serif .. 3·75
D26 5 n.p. on 6 p. on 6d. (1970) .. 1·00
D24/6 .. *Set of* 3 6·00

The above were three in a series of surcharges, the others being 1 n.p. on 1 p. and 10 n.p. on 12 p., which were prepared, but owing to confusion due to the two surcharges in similar currency it was decided by the authorities not to issue the stamps, however, Nos. D24/6 were issued in error.

(Litho D.L.R.)

1970. *Inscr in new currency. P* 14¼ × 14.
D27 D 3 1 n.p. carmine-red .. 80 3·25
D28 1½ n.p. green .. 80 3·75
D29 2½ n.p. yellow-orange .. 1·10 4·25
D30 5 n.p. ultramarine .. 1·75 4·50
D31 10 n.p. reddish violet .. 2·50 5·50
D27/31 .. *Set of* 5 6·50 19·00

(Litho D.L.R.)

1980–81. *Currency described as "p". P* 14½ × 14.
D32 D 3 2 p. reddish orange .. 90 2·75
D33 3 p. brown .. 90 2·75

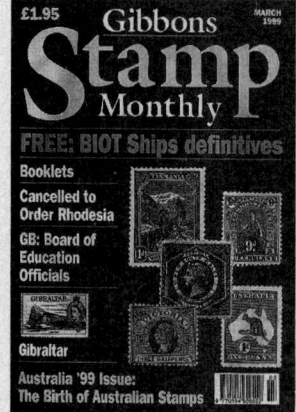

Gibraltar

CROWN COLONY

Early details of postal arrangements in Gibraltar are hard to stablish, although it is known that postal facilities were rovided by the Civil Secretary's Office from the early 1750s. ibraltar became a packet port in 1806, although the Civil ecretary's Office continued to be responsible for other mail. The wo services were amalgamated on 1 January 1857 as a Branch)ffice of the British G.P.O., the control of the postal services not everting to Gibraltar until 1 January 1886.

Spanish stamps could be used at Gibraltar from their ntroduction in 1850 and, indeed, such franking was required on etters weighing over ½ oz. sent to Spain after 1 July 1854. rom 1 July 1856 until 1 July 1875 all mail to Spain required ostage to be prepaid by Spanish stamps and these issues were upplied by the Gibraltar postal authorities, acting as a Spanish ostal Agent. The mail, forwarded under this system was ancelled at San Roque with a horizontal barred oval, later eplaced by a cartwheel type mark showing numeral 63. From 857 combination covers showing the ship mail fee paid in ritish stamps and the inland postage by Spanish issues exist.

Stamps of Great Britain were issued for use in Gibraltar from September 1857 (earliest recorded cover is dated 7 September 857) to the end of 1885.

The initial supply contained 1d., 4d. and 6d. values. No upplies of the 2d. or 1s. were sent until the consignment of)ctober 1857. No other values were supplied until early 1862.

For illustrations of the postmark types see BRITISH POST FFICES ABROAD notes, following GREAT BRITAIN.

Stamps of GREAT BRITAIN *cancelled "G" as Type* **1** (3 Sept 1857 *to* 19 Feb 1859)

Z 1 1d. red-brown (1854) Die I, *wmk* Small Crown, *Perf* 16 .. £325
Z 2 1d. red-brown (1855), Die II, *wmk* Small Crown, *perf* 16 .. £600
Z 3 1d. red-brown (1855), Die II, *wmk* Small Crown, *perf* 14 .. £275
Z 4 1d. red-brown (1855), Die II, *wmk* Large Crown, *perf* 14 .. 70·00
Z 5 1d. rose-red (1857), Die II, *wmk* Large Crown, *perf* 14 .. 20·00
Z 6 2d. blue (1855), *wmk* Small Crown, *perf* 14 .. £350
Z 7 2d. blue (1855–58), *wmk* Large Crown, *perf* 16 .. £300
Z 8 2d. blue (1855), *wmk* Large Crown, *perf* 14 *From* 55·00
Plate Nos. 5, 6.
Z 9 2d. blue (1858) (Plate No. 7) .. £225
Z10 4d. rose (1857) .. 45·00
a. Thick glazed paper
Z11 6d. lilac (1856) .. 40·00
Z12 6d. lilac (1856) (blued *paper*) .. £750
Z13 1s. green (1856) .. £100
a. Thick paper
Z14 1s. green (1856) (blued *paper*) .. £1300

Stamps of GREAT BRITAIN *cancelled "A 26" as in Types* **2, 5, 11** *or* **14** (20 Feb 1859 *to* 31 Dec 1885).

Z15 ½d. rose-red (1870–79) .. *From* 23·00
Plate Nos. 4, 5, 6, 8, 10, 11, 12, 13, 14, 15, 19, 20.
Z16 1d. red-brown (1841), *imperf* .. £1100
Z17 1d. red-brown (1855), *wmk* Large Crown, *perf* 14 .. £160
Z18 1d. rose-red (1857), *wmk* Large Crown, *perf* 14 .. 12·00
Z19 1d. rose-red (1864–79) .. *From* 19·00
Plate Nos. 71, 72, 73, 74, 76, 78, 79, 80, 81, 82, 83, 84, 85, 86, 87, 88, 89, 90, 91, 92, 93, 94, 95, 96, 97, 98, 99, 100, 101, 102, 103, 104, 105, 106, 107, 108, 109, 110, 111, 112, 113, 114, 115, 116, 117, 118, 119, 120, 121, 122, 123, 124, 125, 127, 129, 130, 131, 132, 133, 134, 135, 136, 137, 138, 139, 140, 141, 142, 143, 144, 145, 146, 147, 148, 149, 150, 151, 152, 153, 154, 155, 156, 157, 158, 159, 160, 161, 162, 163, 164, 165, 166, 167, 168, 169, 170, 171, 172, 173, 174, 175, 176, 177, 178, 179, 180, 181, 182, 183, 184, 185, 186, 187, 188, 189, 190, 191, 192, 193, 194, 195, 196, 197, 198, 199, 200, 201, 202, 203, 204, 205, 206, 207, 208, 209, 210, 211, 212, 213, 214, 215, 216, 217, 218, 219, 220, 221, 222, 223, 224, 225.
Z20 1½d. lake-red (1870) (Plate No. 3) .. £350
Z21 2d. blue (1855), *wmk* Large Crown, *perf* 14 .. £110
Plate No. 6.
Z22 2d. blue (1858–69) .. *From* 18·00
Plate Nos. 7, 8, 9, 12, 13, 14, 15.
Z23 2½d. rosy mauve (1875) (blued *paper*) .. *From* £100
Plate Nos. 1, 2, 3.
Z24 2½d. rosy mauve (1875–76) (Plate Nos. 1, 2, 3) *From* 27·00
Z25 2½d. rosy mauve (*Error of Lettering*) .. £1800
Z26 2½d. rosy mauve (1876–79) .. *From* 20·00
Plate Nos. 3, 4, 5, 6, 7, 8, 9, 10, 11, 12, 13, 14, 15, 16, 17.
Z27 2½d. blue (1880–81) (Plate Nos. 17, 18, 19, 20) *From* 12·00
Z28 2½d. blue (1881) (Plate Nos. 21, 22, 23) .. *From* 10·00
Z29 3d. carmine-rose (1862) .. £160
Z30 3d. rose (1865) (Plate No. 4) .. 48·00
Z31 3d. rose (1867–73) .. *From* 25·00
Plate Nos. 4, 5, 6, 7, 8, 9, 10.
Z32 3d. rose (1873–76) .. *From* 30·00
Plate Nos. 11, 12, 14, 15, 16, 17, 18, 19, 20.
Z33 3d. rose (1881) (Plate Nos. 20, 21)
Z34 3d. lilac (1883) (3d. *on* 3d) .. £100
Z35 4d. rose (1857) .. 45·00
Z36 4d. red (1862) (Plate Nos. 3, 4) .. *From* 45·00
Z37 4d. vermilion (1865–73) .. *From* 30·00
Plate Nos. 7, 8, 9, 10, 11, 12, 13, 14.
Z38 4d. vermilion (1876) (Plate No. 15) .. £225
Z39 4d. sage-green (1877) (Plate Nos. 15, 16) .. £100
Z40 4d. grey-brown (1880) *wmk* Large Garter .. £190
Plate No. 17.
Z41 4d. grey-brown (1880) *wmk* Crown .. *From* 38·00
Plate Nos. 17, 18.
Z42 6d. lilac (1856) .. 42·00
Z43 6d. lilac (1862) (Plate Nos. 3, 4) .. *From* 38·00
Z44 6d. lilac (1865–67) (Plate Nos. 5, 6) .. *From* 32·00
Z45 6d. lilac (1867) (Plate No. 6) .. 42·00
Z46 6d. violet (1867–70) (Plate Nos. 6, 8, 9) .. *From* 32·00
Z47 6d. buff (1872–73) (Plate Nos. 11, 12) .. *From* £180
Z48 6d. chestnut (1872) (Plate No. 11) .. 30·00
Z49 6d. grey (1873) (Plate No. 12) .. 90·00
Z50 6d. grey (1874–80) .. *From* 28·00
Plate Nos. 13, 14, 15, 16, 17.
Z51 6d. grey (1881) (Plate Nos. 17, 18) .. £180
Z52 6d. lilac (1883) (6d. *on* 6d.) .. 85·00
Z53 8d. orange (1876) .. £275
Z54 9d. bistre (1862) .. £170
Z55 9d. straw (1862) .. £600
Z56 9d. straw (1865) .. £550
Z57 9d. straw (1867) .. £160
Z58 10d. red-brown (1867) .. £150
Z59 1s. green (1856) .. £100
Z60 1s. green (1862) .. 70·00
Z61 1s. green (1862) ("K" *variety*) .. £2000
Z62 1s. green (1865) (Plate No. 4) .. 60·00
Z63 1s. green (1867–73) (Plate Nos. 4, 5, 6, 7) .. *From* 18·00
Z64 1s. green (1873–77) .. *From* 45·00
Plate Nos. 8, 9, 10, 11, 12, 13.
Z65 1s. orange-brown (1880) (Plate No. 13) .. £250
Z66 1s. orange-brown (1881) (Plate Nos. 13, 14) *From* 65·00
Z67 2s. blue (1867) .. £150
Z68 5s. rose (1867) (Plate No. 1) .. £650

1880.
Z69 ½d. deep green .. 20·00
Z70 ½d. pale green .. 20·00
Z71 1d. Venetian red .. 22·00
Z72 1½d. Venetian red .. £180
Z73 2d. pale rose .. 65·00
Z74 2d. deep rose .. 65·00
Z75 5d. indigo .. £110

1881.
Z76 1d. lilac (14 *dots*) .. 22·00
Z77 1d. lilac (16 *dots*) .. 9·00

1884.
Z78 ½d. slate-blue .. 20·00
Z79 2d. lilac .. 80·00
Z80 2½d. lilac .. 15·00
Z81 3d. lilac
Z82 4d. dull green .. £130
Z83 6d. dull green

POSTAL FISCAL
Z83*a* 1d. purple (Die 4) (1878) *wmk* Small Anchor £600
Z84 1d. purple (1881), *wmk* Orb .. £1100

PRICES FOR STAMPS ON COVER TO 1945

Nos. 1/2	*from* × 25
No. 3	*from* × 10
No. 4	*from* × 25
Nos. 5/6	*from* × 8
Nos. 7/33	*from* × 6
Nos. 39/45	*from* × 5
Nos. 46/109	*from* × 3
Nos. 110/13	*from* × 4
Nos. 114/17	*from* × 3
Nos. 118/20	*from* × 5
Nos. 121/31	*from* × 3

GIBRALTAR
(1)

1886 (1 Jan). *Contemporary types of Bermuda optd with T* **1** *by D.L.R. Wmk Crown CA. P* 14.
1 **9** ½d. dull green .. 9·00 6·00
2 **1** 1d. rose-red .. 50·00 4·00
3 **2** 2d. purple-brown .. 95·00 75·00
w. Wmk inverted
4 **11** 2½d. ultramarine .. £120 3·00
a. Optd in blue-black .. £500 £150
w. Wmk inverted
5 **10** 4d. orange-brown .. £120 85·00
6 **4** 6d. deep lilac .. £200 £180
7 **5** 1s. yellow-brown .. £400 £350
1/7 .. *Set of* 7 £850 £650
1/3, 4a/7 Optd "Specimen" .. *Set of* 7 £2500

PRINTER. All Gibraltar stamps to No. 109 were typographed by De La Rue & Co, Ltd.

2

3

4

5

1886 (Nov)–**87**. *Wmk Crown CA. P* 14.
8 **2** ½d. dull green (1.87) .. 7·00 3·50
9 **3** 1d. rose (12.86) .. 42·00 3·75
10 **4** 2d. brown-purple (12.86) .. 30·00 17·00
w. Wmk inverted .. £250
11 **5** 2½d. blue .. 70·00 2·25
w. Wmk inverted .. £150 60·00
12 **4** 4d. orange-brown (16.4.87) .. 70·00 70·00
13 6d. lilac (16.4.87) .. 95·00 95·00
14 1s. bistre (2.87) .. £180 £180
w. Wmk inverted
8/14 .. *Set of* 7 £425 £325
8/14 Optd "Specimen" .. *Set of* 7 £500
See also Nos. 39 to 45.

5 CENTIMOS
(6)

7

1889 (1 Aug). *Surch as T* **6**.
15 **2** 5 c. on ½d. green .. 6·00 14·00
16 **3** 10 c. on 1d. rose .. 10·00 6·50
17 **4** 25 c. on 2d. brown-purple .. 4·25 5·00
a. Small "I" (R.6/2) .. £100 £140
b. Broken "N" (R.10/5) .. £100 £140
18 **5** 25 c. on 2½d. bright blue .. 25·00 2·00
a. Small "I" (R.6/2) .. £300 £100
b. Broken "N" (R.10/5) .. £300 £100
19 **4** 40 c. on 4d. orange-brown .. 60·00 80·00
20 50 c. on 6d. bright lilac .. 60·00 80·00
21 75 c. on 1s. bistre .. 65·00 75·00
15/21 .. *Set of* 7 £200 £225
15/21 Optd "Specimen" .. *Set of* 7 £350

10 c., 40 c. and 50 c. values from this issue and that of 1889–96 are known bisected and used for half their value from various post offices in Morocco (*price on cover from* £500). These bisects were never authorised by the Gibraltar Post Office.

Two varieties of the figure "5" of the 5 c., 25 c., 50 c. and 75 c. may be found.

Broken "M" (Pl 2 R. 4/5)

Flat top to "C" (Pl 2 R. 4/4)

1889 (8 Oct)*–**96**. *Issue in Spanish currency. Wmk Crown CA. P* 14.
22 **7** 5 c. green .. 3·50 70
a. Broken "M" .. 90·00 50·00
w. Wmk inverted .. £180 £150
23 10 c. carmine .. 3·50 45
b. Value omitted .. £5000
24 20 c. olive-green and brown (2.1.96) .. 35·00 17·00
25 20 c. olive-green (8.7.96) .. 9·00 48·00
a. Flat top to "C" .. £140
w. Wmk inverted
26 25 c. ultramarine .. 12·00 70
a. *Deep ultramarine* .. 25·00 80
27 40 c. orange-brown .. 2·75 2·25
28 50 c. bright lilac (1890) .. 2·25 1·50
29 75 c. olive-green (1890) .. 32·00 32·00
30 1 p. bistre (11.89) .. 75·00 20·00
31 1 p. bistre and ultramarine (6.95) .. 4·00 3·50
32 2 p. black and carmine (2.1.96) .. 8·50 24·00
33 5 p. slate-grey (12.89) .. 42·00 95·00
22/33 .. *Set of* 12 £200 £225
22/4, 26/33 Optd "Specimen" .. *Set of* 11 £375
*Earliest recorded postmark date.

1898 (1 Oct). *Reissue in Sterling currency. Wmk Crown CA. P* 14.
39 **2** ½d. grey-green .. 3·50 1·25
w. Wmk inverted
40 **3** 1d. carmine .. 5·00 35
w. Wmk inverted .. † £1000
41 **4** 2d. brown-purple and ultramarine .. 17·00 1·50
42 **5** 2½d. bright ultramarine .. 22·00 40
w. Wmk inverted .. £150 60·00
43 **4** 4d. orange-brown and green .. 16·00 6·50
44 6d. violet and red .. 38·00 20·00
45 1s. bistre and carmine .. 32·00 16·00
w. Wmk inverted
39/45 .. *Set of* 7 £120 42·00
39/45 Optd "Specimen" .. *Set of* 7 £250

No. 39 is greyer than No. 8, No. 40 brighter and deeper than No. 9 and No. 42 much brighter than No. 11.

8

9

½ ½
Normal Large "2"
2½d.

This occurs on R.10/1 in each pane of 60. The diagonal stroke is also longer.

1903 (1 May). *Wmk Crown CA. P* 14.
46 **8** ½d. grey-green and green .. 9·00 8·50
47 1d. dull purple/*red* .. 27·00 60
48 2d. grey-green and carmine .. 15·00 24·00
49 2½d. dull purple and black/*blue* .. 3·50 60
a. Large "2" in "½" .. £160 90·00
50 6d. dull purple and violet .. 13·00 18·00

51 **8** 1s. black and carmine .. .. .. 27·00 30·00
52 **9** 2s. green and blue £110 £140
53 4s. dull purple and green .. .. .. 75·00 £140
54 8s. dull purple and black/*blue* £110 £140
55 £1 dull purple and black/*red* £450 £500
46/55 .. .. *Set of* 10 £750 £900
46/55 Optd "Specimen" .. .. *Set of* 10 £500

1904–8. *Wmk Mult Crown CA. Ordinary paper* (½d. *to* 2d. *and* 6d. *to* 2s.) *or chalk-surfaced paper* (*others*). *P* 14.
56 **8** ½d. dull and bright green (16.4.04*) .. 7·00 2·25
a. Chalk-surfaced paper (10.05) .. 9·50 6·00
57 1d. dull purple/*red* (6.9.04*) .. .. 5·00 40
a. Bisected (½d.) (on card) .. .. † £1200
bw. Wmk inverted .. .. ..
c. Chalk-surfaced paper (16.9.05) .. 2·25 70
58 2d. grey-green and carmine (9.1.05) .. 8·00 3·25
a. Chalk-surfaced paper (2.07) .. 7·00 3·50
59 2½d. purple and black/*blue* (4.5.07) .. 32·00 85·00
a. Large "2" in "½" £425 £700
60 6d. dull purple and violet (19.4.06) .. 22·00 16·00
a. Chalk-surfaced paper (4.08) .. 18·00 8·00
61 1s. black and carmine (13.10.05) .. 38·00 10·00
a. Chalk-surfaced paper (4.06) .. 45·00 10·00
62 **9** 2s. green and blue (2.2.05) .. .. 65·00 85·00
a. Chalk-surfaced paper (10.07) .. 75·00 80·00
63 4s. deep purple and green (6.08) .. £180 £225
64 £1 deep purple and black/*red* (15.3.08) £450 £500
56/64 .. .. *Set of* 9 £700 £800
*Earliest known date of use.

1906 (Oct)–**12.** *Colours changed. Wmk Mult Crown CA. Chalk-surfaced paper* (6d. *to* 8s.). *P* 14.
66 **8** ½d. blue-green .. .. 2·25 90
67 1d. carmine .. .. 4·25 45
a. Wmk sideways .. .. .. — £3250
w. Wmk inverted .. .. .. † £500
68 2d. greyish slate (5.10) .. .. .. 6·50 9·00
69 2½d. ultramarine (6.07) .. .. .. 4·25 1·25
a. Large "2" in "½" .. .. .. £180 95·00
70 6d. dull and bright purple (3.12) .. £120 £375
71 1s. black/*green* (1910) .. .. .. 21·00 19·00
72 **9** 2s. purple and bright blue/*blue* (4.10) 48·00 45·00
73 4s. black and carmine (4.10) .. .. 90·00 £130
x. Wmk reversed £1100
74 8s. purple and green (1911) £180 £180
66/74 .. .. *Set of* 9 £425 £650
67/74 Optd "Specimen" .. *Set of* 8 £500
Examples of many values between Nos. 46 and 74 are known showing a forged oval registered postmark dated "6 OC 10".

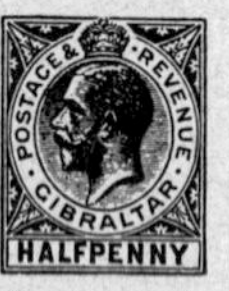

10

11

WAR TAX
(12)

1912 (17 July)–**24.** *Wmk Mult Crown CA. Ordinary paper* (½d. *to* 2½d) *or chalk-surfaced paper* (*others*). *P* 14.
76 **10** ½d. blue-green .. .. 2·50 70
a. Yellow-green (4.17) .. .. 3·00 1·50
w. Wmk inverted .. .. ..
x. Wmk reversed .. .. .. † £1000
77 1d. carmine-red .. .. .. 2·50 75
a. Scarlet (6.16) .. .. .. 2·75 1·00
78 2d. greyish slate .. .. .. 5·50 1·50
79 2½d. deep bright blue .. .. .. 3·25 1·75
a. Large "2" in "½" .. .. .. £120 90·00
b. Pale ultramarine (1917) .. .. 6·00 2·00
ba. Large "2" in "½" £250 £120
80 6d. dull purple and mauve .. .. 7·00 11·00
81 1s. black/*green* .. .. .. 7·00 3·25
a. Ordinary paper (8.18) £500
b. On blue-green, olive back (1919) .. 12·00 25·00
c. On emerald surface (12.23) .. 20·00 50·00
d. On emerald back (3.24) (Optd S. £70) 16·00 70·00
82 **11** 2s. dull purple and blue/*blue* .. .. 25·00 3·25
83 4s. black and carmine .. .. .. 29·00 55·00
84 8s. dull purple and green .. .. 70·00 85·00
85 £1 dull purple and black/*red* £140 £190
76/85 .. .. .. *Set of* 10 £250 £300
76/85 Optd "Specimen" .. .. *Set of* 10 £450

1918 (15 Apr). *Optd with T* **12** *by Beanland, Malin & Co, Gibraltar.*
86 **10** ½d. green .. .. 55 1·40
a. Opt double £650
w. Wmk inverted £350
y. Wmk inverted and reversed £350
Two printings of this overprint exist, the second being in slightly heavier type on a deeper shade of green.

3 PENCE
(I)

THREE PENCE
(II)

1921–27. *Wmk Mult Script CA. Chalk-surfaced paper* (6d. *to* 8s.). *P* 14.
89 **10** ½d. green (25.4.27) 70 90
90 1d. carmine-red (2.21) .. .. 1·50 70
91 1½d. chestnut (1.12.22) .. .. 1·25 40
a. Pale chestnut (7.24) .. .. 1·25 30
w. Wmk inverted .. .. .. † £500
93 2d. grey (17.2.21) .. .. .. 1·25 85
94 2½d. bright blue (2.21) .. .. .. 17·00 25·00
a. Large "2" in "½" £300 £350
95 3d. bright blue (I) (1.1.22) .. .. 2·50 4·25
a. Ultramarine .. .. .. 1·40 1·50
97 **10** 6d. dull purple and mauve (1.23) .. 5·50 3·75
a. Bright purple & magenta (22.7.26) 1·60 3·50
98 1s. black/*emerald* (20.6.24) .. .. 7·50 13·00
99 **11** 2s. grey-purple and blue/*blue* (20.6.24) 18·00 65·00
a. Reddish purple and blue/blue (1925) 5·50 35·00
100 4s. black and carmine (20.6.24) .. 60·00 £100
101 8s. dull purple and green (20.6.24) .. £180 £325
89/101 .. .. .. *Set of* 11 £225 £425
89/101 Optd "Specimen" .. .. *Set of* 11 £500
The ½d. exists in coils constructed from normal sheets.

1925 (15 Oct)–**32.** *New values and colours changed. Wmk Mult Script CA. Chalk-surfaced paper. P* 14.
102 **10** 1s. sage-green and black (8.1.29) .. 14·00 21·00
a. Olive and black (1932) .. .. 14·00 12·00
103 **11** 2s. red-brown and black (8.1.29) .. 9·00 29·00
104 2s. 6d. green and black .. .. 9·00 17·00
105 5s. carmine and black .. .. 13·00 48·00
106 10s. deep ultramarine and black .. 32·00 65·00
107 £1 red-orange and black (16.11.27) .. £140 £180
108 £5 violet and black (Optd S. £700) .. £1400 £3500
102/7 .. .. *Set of* 6 £190 £300
102/7 Optd/Perf "Specimen" .. *Set of* 6 £400
Examples of Nos. 83/5, 99/101 and 102/8 are known showing forged oval registered postmarks dated "24 JA 25" or "6 MY 35".

1930 (12 Apr). *T* **10** *inscribed* "THREE PENCE". *Wmk Mult Script CA. P* 14.
109 3d. ultramarine (II) (Perf S. £70) .. .. 7·50 2·00

13 The Rock of Gibraltar

(Des Capt. H. St. C. Garrood. Recess D.L.R.)

1931–33. *Wmk Mult Script CA. P* 14.
110 **13** 1d. scarlet (1.7.31) .. .. .. 1·75 2·25
a. Perf 13½×14 .. .. .. 13·00 4·75
111 1½d. red-brown (1.7.31) .. .. 1·75 2·25
a. Perf 13½×14 .. .. .. 10·00 3·75
112 2d. pale grey (1.11.32) .. .. 4·50 1·00
a. Perf 13½×14 .. .. .. 11·00 2·25
113 3d. blue (1.6.33) .. .. .. 4·50 2·75
a. Perf 13½×14 .. .. .. 19·00 26·00
110/13 .. .. *Set of* 4 11·50 7·50
110a/13a .. .. *Set of* 4 48·00 32·00
110/13 Perf "Specimen" .. .. *Set of* 4 £160
Figures of value take the place of both corner ornaments at the base of the 2d. and 3d.

1935 (6 May). *Silver Jubilee. As Nos.* 91/4 *of Antigua but ptd by B.W. P* 11 × 12.
114 2d. ultramarine and grey-black .. .. 1·60 2·50
a. Extra flagstaff .. .. .. 60·00 70·00
b. Short extra flagstaff .. .. 90·00 £100
c. Lightning conductor .. .. 60·00 70·00
d. Flagstaff on right-hand turret .. £130 £140
e. Double flagstaff £130 £140
115 3d. brown and deep blue .. .. 3·25 3·50
a. Extra flagstaff £300 £300
b. Short extra flagstaff £250 £250
c. Lightning conductor £275 £275
116 6d. green and indigo .. .. .. 8·50 12·00
a. Extra flagstaff £225 £250
b. Short extra flagstaff £300 £325
c. Lightning conductor £225 £250
117 1s. slate and purple .. .. .. 8·50 8·50
a. Extra flagstaff £200 £200
b. Short extra flagstaff £275 £275
c. Lightning conductor £200 £200
114/17 .. .. *Set of* 4 20·00 24·00
114/17 Perf "Specimen" .. .. *Set of* 4 £160
For illustrations of plate varieties see Catalogue Introduction.

1937 (12 May). *Coronation. As Nos.* 95/7 *of Antigua. P* 11×11½.
118 ½d. green 25 10
119 2d. grey-black .. .. 80 2·00
120 3d. blue .. .. 2·00 2·00
118/20 .. .. *Set of* 3 2·75 3·50
118/20 Perf "Specimen" .. .. *Set of* 3 75·00

14 King George VI

15 Rock of Gibraltar

16 The Rock (North Side)

Broken second "R" in "GIBRALTAR"
(Frame Pl.2 R.9/4)

(Des Captain H. St. C. Garrood. Recess D.L.R.)

1938 (25 Feb)–**51.** *Designs as T* **14/16**. *Wmk Mult Script CA.*
121 ½d. deep green (*p* 13½×14) 10 4
122 1d. yellow-brown (*p* 14) .. .. 23·00 2·2
a. Perf 13½ .. .. 26·00 2·2
ab. Perf 13½. Wmk sideways (1940) .. 6·00 7·0
b. Perf 13. Wmk sideways. *Red-brown* (1942) 50 5
c. Perf 13. Wmk sideways. *Deep brown* (1944) .. .. 30 3·2
d. Perf 13. *Red-brown* (1949) .. .. 1·50 1·5
123 1½d. carmine (*p* 14) .. .. .. 35·00 7
a. Perf 13½ .. .. £250 35·0
123*b* 1½d. slate-violet (*p* 13) (1.1.43) .. .. 30 1·0
124 2d. grey (*p* 14) .. .. .. 25·00 4
a. Perf 13½ 55 3
ab. Perf 13½. Wmk sideways (1939) .. £600 42·0
b. Perf 13. Wmk sideways (1943) .. 30 1·0
ba. "A" of "CA" missing from wmk .. £1200
124*c* 2d. carm (*p* 13) (*wmk sideways*) (15.7.44) 40 6
125 3d. light blue (*p* 13½) .. .. .. 15·00 1·0
a. Perf 14 .. .. £120 5·0
b. Perf 13 (1942) 30 3
ba. Greenish blue (2.51) .. .. 3·50 2·5
125*c* 5d. red-orange (*p* 13) (1.10.47) .. .. 70 1·2
126 6d. carm & grey-violet (*p* 13½) (16.3.38) 48·00 3·0
a. Perf 14 .. .. £120 1·2
b. Perf 13 (1942) .. .. .. 2·00 1·6
c. Perf 13. *Scarlet and grey-violet* (1945) 4·25 3·2
127 1s. black and green (*p* 14) (16.3.38) .. 38·00 22·0
a. Perf 13½ .. .. 60·00 7·0
b. Perf 13 (1942) .. .. .. 3·00 4·0
ba. Broken "R" £130
128 2s. black and brown (*p* 14) (16.3.38) .. 65·00 25·0
a. Perf 13½ .. .. £120 32·0
b. Perf 13 (1942) .. .. .. 3·25 6·0
ba. Broken "R" £140
129 5s. black and carmine (*p* 14) (16.3.38) 95·00 £15
a. Perf 13½ .. .. 38·00 17·0
b. Perf 13 (1944) .. .. .. 12·00 17·0
ba. Broken "R" £200
130 10s. black and blue (*p* 14) (16.3.38) .. 65·00 £12
a. Perf 13 (1943) .. .. .. 35·00 25·0
ab. Broken "R" £300
131 £1 orange (*p* 13½×14) (16.3.38) .. 38·00 45·0
121/31 .. .. *Set of* 14 £120 85·0
121/31 Perf "Specimen" .. .. *Set of* 14 £500
Designs:—½d., £1, Type **14.** *Horiz as T* **15/16**—1d., 1½d. (*both*) Type **15**; 2d. (*both*), Type **16**; 3d., 5d. Europa Point; 6d. Moorish Castle; 1s. Southport Gate; 2s. Eliott Memorial; 5s. Government House; 10s. Catalan Bay.
The ½d., 1d. and both colours of the 2d. exist in coils constructed from normal sheets. These were originally joined vertically, but because of technical problems, the 1d. and 2d. grey were subsequently issued in horizontal coils. The 2d. carmine only exists in the horizontal version.

1946 (12 Oct). *Victory. As Nos.* 110/11 *of Antigua.*
132 ½d. green 10 1
133 3d. ultramarine 30 2
132/3 Perf "Specimen" .. .. *Set of* 2 60·00

1948 (1 Dec). *Royal Silver Wedding. As Nos.* 112/13 *of Antigua.*
134 ½d. green 70 8
135 £1 brown-orange .. .. 50·00 60·0

1949 (10 Oct). *75th Anniv of Universal Postal Union. As Nos.* 114/17 *of Antigua.*
136 2d. carmine .. .. 1·00 1·1
137 3d. deep blue .. .. 2·50 1·1
138 6d. purple .. .. 2·00 1·1
139 1s. blue-green .. .. 1·60 2·5
136/9 .. .. *Set of* 4 6·50 5·2

NEW
CONSTITUTION
1950
(23)

1950 (1 Aug). *Inauguration of Legislative Council. Nos.* 124*c*, 125b, 126b *and* 127b *optd as T* **23**.
140 **16** 2d. carmine .. .. 30 1·0
141 – 3d. light blue .. .. 40 1·0
142 – 6d. carmine and grey-violet .. .. 50 1·4
a. Opt double £600 £70
143 – 1s. black and green (R.) .. .. 50 1·4
a. Broken "R" .. .. 48·00
140/3 .. .. *Set of* 4 1·50 4·2
On stamps from the lower part of the sheet of No. 142a the two impressions are almost coincident.

1953 (2 June). *Coronation. As No.* 120 *of Antigua.*
144 ½d. black and bronze-green 30 75

24 Cargo and Passenger Wharves

25 Tower of Homage, Moorish Castle

26 Arms of Gibraltar

Major re-entry causing doubling of "ALTA" in "GIBRALTAR" (R. 4/6)

(Des N. Cummings. Recess (except £1, centre litho) De La Rue)

953 (19 Oct)–**59**. *T* **24/26** *and similar designs. Wmk Mult Script CA. P* 13.

45 ½d. indigo and grey-green 15 30
46 1d. bluish green .. .. 1·50 30
a. Deep bluish green (31.12.57) .. .. 2·25 50
47 1½d. black 90 90
48 2d. deep olive-brown .. .. .. 1·25 40
a. Sepia (18.6.58) .. .. .. 2·25 90
49 2½d. carmine .. .. 3·75 85
a. Deep carmine (11.9.56) .. .. 2·75 70
aw. Wmk inverted £300
50 3d. light blue .. .. 3·25 10
a. Deep greenish blue (8.6.55) .. .. 5·50 10
b. Greenish blue (18.6.58) .. .. 7·50 20
51 4d. ultramarine .. .. 2·25 1·50
a. Blue (17.6.59) .. .. .. 8·50 5·00
52 5d. maroon 60 70
a. Major re-entry .. .. .. 19·00
b. Deep maroon (31.12.57) .. .. 1·50 1·50
ba. Major re-entry .. .. .. 24·00
153 6d. black and pale blue 40 50
a. Black and blue (24.4.57) .. .. 3·25 1·25
b. Black and grey-blue (17.6.59) .. 4·00 2·75
154 1s. pale blue and red-brown 30 60
a. Pale blue and deep red-brown (27.3.56) 30 60
155 2s. orange and reddish violet .. .. 27·00 5·50
a. Orange and violet (17.6.59) .. .. 19·00 3·50
156 5s. deep brown .. .. 24·00 12·00
157 10s. reddish brown and ultramarine .. 50·00 35·00
158 £1 scarlet and orange-yellow .. .. 50·00 38·00
145/58 .. .. *Set of* 14 £140 80·00

Designs: *Horiz as T* **24**—1d. South View from Straits; 1½d. Tuna Fishing Industry; 2d. Southport Gate; 2½d. Sailing in the Bay; 3d. *Saturnia* (liner); 4d. Coaling wharf; 5d. Airport; 6d. Europa Point; 1s. Straits from Buena Vista; 2s. Rosia Bay and Straits; 5s. Main Entrance, Government House.

Nos. 145/6, 148 and 150 exist in coils, constructed from normal sheets.

1954 (10 May). *Royal Visit. As No.* 150 *but inscr* "ROYAL VISIT 1954" *at top.*

159 3d. greenish blue 15 20

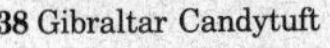

38 Gibraltar Candytuft

40 Rock and Badge of Gibraltar Regiment

39 Moorish Castle

(Des J. Celecia (½d., 2d., 2½d., 2s., 10s.), N. A. Langdon (1d., 3d., 6d., 7d., 9d., 1s.), M. Bonilla (4d.), L. V. Gomez (5s.), Sgt. T. A. Griffiths (£1). Recess (£1) or photo (others) D.L.R.)

1960 (29 Oct)–**62**. *Designs as T* **38/9**, *and T* **40**. *W* w **12** (*upright*). *P* 14 (£1) *or* 13 (*others*).

160 ½d. bright purple and emerald-green .. 15 30
161 1d. black and yellow-green 10 10
162 2d. indigo and orange-brown 15 15
163 2½d. black and blue 55 55
a. Black and grey-blue (16.10.62) .. 20 15
164 3d. deep blue and red-orange 30 10
165 4d. deep red-brown and turquoise .. 2·75 55
166 6d. sepia and emerald 70 50
167 7d. indigo and carmine-red 70 75
168 9d. grey-blue and greenish blue 50 50
169 1s. sepia and bluish green 90 40
170 2s. chocolate and ultramarine .. .. 13·00 2·25
171 5s. turquoise-blue and olive-brown .. 8·00 5·50
172 10s. yellow and blue .. .. .. 14·00 10·00
173 £1 black and brown-orange .. .. 17·00 11·00
160/73 .. .. *Set of* 14 48·00 28·00

Designs: *Horiz*—2d. St. George's Hall; 3d. The Rock by moonlight; 4d. Catalan Bay; 1s. Barbary Ape; 2s. Barbary Partridge; 5s. Blue Rock Thrush. *Vert*—2½d. The Keys; 6d. Map of Gibraltar; 7d. Air terminal; 9d. American War Memorial; 10s. Rock Lily (*Narcissus niveus*).

Vignette cylinders 2A and 2B, used for printings of the 9d. from 13 March 1962 onwards, had a finer screen (250 dots per inch instead of the 200 of the original printing).

Nos. 160/2, 164 and 166 exist in coils, constructed from normal sheets.

See also No. 199.

1963 (4 June). *Freedom from Hunger. As No.* 146 *of Antigua.*

174 9d. sepia .. .. 9·00 1·50

1963 (2 Sept). *Red Cross Centenary. As Nos.* 147/8 *of Antigua.*

175 1d. red and black .. .. 1·50 1·50
176 9d. red and blue .. .. 14·00 3·00

1964 (23 Apr). 400*th Birth Anniv of William Shakespeare. As No.* 164 *of Antigua.*

177 7d. bistre-brown 40 20

NEW CONSTITUTION 1964.

(52)

53 Red Seabream

1964 (16 Oct). *New Constitution. Nos.* 164 *and* 166 *optd with T* **52**.

178 3d. deep blue and red-orange 15 10
179 6d. sepia and emerald 15 20
a. No stop after "1964" (R.2/5) .. .. 15·00 24·00

1965 (17 May). *I.T.U. Centenary. As Nos.* 166/7 *of Antigua.*

180 4d. light emerald and yellow .. .. 4·00 50
w. Wmk inverted .. .. .. 25·00
181 2s. apple-green and deep blue .. .. 11·00 3·00

1965 (25 Oct). *International Co-operation Year. As Nos.* 168/9 *of Antigua.*

182 ½d. deep bluish green and lavender .. .. 20 1·25
183 4d. reddish purple and turquoise-green .. 1·00 80

The value of the ½d. stamp is shown as "1/2".

1966 (24 Jan). *Churchill Commemoration. As Nos.* 170/3 *of Antigua.*

184 ½d. new blue .. .. 20 1·25
w. Wmk inverted .. .. .. 28·00
185 1d. deep green 30 10
186 4d. brown .. .. 1·25 10
187 9d. bluish violet .. .. 1·25 2·00
184/7 .. .. *Set of* 4 2·75 3·00

1966 (1 July). *World Cup Football Championships. As Nos.* 176/7 *of Antigua.*

188 2½d. violet, yellow-green, lake & yellow-brn 75 30
189 6d. chocolate, blue-green, lake & yellow-brn 1·00 50

PRINTERS. All stamps from here to No. 239 were printed in photogravure by Harrison and Sons Ltd, London.

(Des A. Ryman)

1966 (27 Aug). *European Sea Angling Championships, Gibraltar. T* **53** *and similar designs. W* w **12** (*sideways on* 1s.). *P* 13½ × 14 (1s.) *or* 14 × 13½ (*others*).

190 4d. rosine, bright blue and black 20 10
191 7d. rosine, deep olive-green and black .. 30 30
a. Black (value and inscr) omitted £900
w. Wmk inverted .. .. .. 2·50
192 1s. lake-brown, emerald and black 30 30
190/2 .. .. *Set of* 3 70 60

Designs: *Horiz*—7d. Red Scorpionfish. *Vert*—1s. Stone Bass.

1966 (20 Sept). *Inauguration of W.H.O. Headquarters, Geneva. As Nos.* 178/9 *of Antigua.*

193 6d. black, yellow-green and light blue .. 2·50 1·50
194 9d. black, light purple and yellow-brown .. 3·00 1·50

56 "Our Lady of Europa"

57 H.M.S. *Victory*

(Des A. Ryman)

1966 (15 Nov). *Centenary of Re-enthronement of "Our Lady of Europa". W* w **12**. *P* 14 × 14½.

195 **56** 2s. bright blue and black 30 70

1966 (1 Dec). 20*th Anniv of U.N.E.S.C.O. As Nos.* 196/8 *of Antigua.*

196 2d. slate-violet, red, yellow and orange .. 25 10
197 7d. orange-yellow, violet and deep olive .. 60 10
198 5s. black, bright purple and orange.. .. 2·50 2·50
196/8 .. .. *Set of* 3 3·00 2·50

1966 (23 Dec). *As No.* 165 *but wmk* w **12** *sideways.*

199 4d. deep red-brown and turquoise 30 60

(Des A. Ryman)

1967 (3 Apr)–**69**. *Horiz designs as T* **57**. *Multicoloured. W* w **12**. *P* 14 × 14½.

200 ½d. Type **57** 10 15
a. Grey (sails, etc) omitted £400
201 1d. *Arab* (early steamer) 10 10
w. Wmk inverted .. .. .. 2·75 2·50
202 2d. H.M.S. *Carmania* (merchant cruiser) 15 10
a. Grey-blue (hull) omitted £2250
203 2½d. *Mons Calpe* (ferry) 30 30
204 3d. *Canberra* (liner) 20 10
w. Wmk inverted .. .. .. 21·00 6·50
205 4d. H.M.S. *Hood* (battle cruiser) 30 10
205*a* 5d. *Mirror* (cable ship) (7.7.69) .. .. 3·25 55
aw. Wmk inverted .. .. ..
206 6d. Xebec (sailing vessel) 30 50
207 7d. *Amerigo Vespucci* (Italian cadet ship) 30 45
w. Wmk inverted .. .. .. 14·00
208 9d. *Raffaello* (liner) 30 60
209 1s. *Royal Katherine* (galleon) 30 35
210 2s. H.M.S. *Ark Royal* (aircraft carrier), 1937 .. .. 3·50 2·50
211 5s. H.M.S. *Dreadnought* (nuclear submarine) .. .. 3·50 6·50
212 10s. *Neuralia* (liner) .. .. .. 14·00 22·00
213 £1 *Mary Celeste* (sailing vessel) .. .. 14·00 22·00
200/13 .. .. *Set of* 15 35·00 50·00

No. 202a results from the misaligning of the grey-blue cylinder. The bottom horizontal row of the sheet involved has this colour completely omitted except for the example above the cylinder numbers which shows the grey-blue "1A" towards the top of the stamp.

The ½d., 1d., 2d., 3d., 6d., 2s., 5s. and £1 exist with PVA gum as well as gum arabic, but the 5d. exists with PVA gum only.

Nos. 201/2, 204/5 and 206 exist in coils constructed from normal sheets.

58 Aerial Ropeway

(Des A. Ryman)

1967 (15 June). *International Tourist Year. T* **58** *and similar designs but horiz. Multicoloured. W* w **12** (*sideways on* 7*d.*). *P* 14½ × 14 (7*d.*) *or* 14 × 14½ (*others*).

214 7d. Type **58** 10 10
215 9d. Shark fishing 10 10
216 1s. Skin-diving 15 15
214/16 .. .. *Set of* 3 30 30

59 Mary, Joseph and Child Jesus

60 Church Window

1967 (1 Nov). *Christmas. W* w **12** (*sideways* on* 6*d.*). *P* 14.

217 **59** 2d. multicoloured 15 10
w. Wmk inverted .. .. .. 1·25
218 **60** 6d. multicoloured 15 10
w. Wmk Crown to right of CA £120

*The normal sideways watermark shows Crown to left of CA, *as seen from the back of the stamp.*

61 Gen. Eliott and Route Map

62 Eliott directing Rescue Operations

(Des A. Ryman)

1967 (11 Dec). 250*th Birth Anniv of General Eliott. Multicoloured designs as T* **61** (4*d. to* 1*s.*) *or T* **62**. *W* w **12** (*sideways on horiz designs*). *P* 14 × 15 (1*s.*) *or* 15 × 14 (*others*).

219 4d. Type **61** 10 10
220 9d. Heathfield Tower and Monument, Sussex (38 × 22 *mm*) 15 10
221 1s. General Eliott (22 × 38 *mm*) 15 10
222 2s. Type **62** 40 30
219/22 .. .. *Set of* 4 65 50

65 Lord Baden-Powell

(Des A. Ryman)

1968 (27 Mar). *60th Anniv of Gibraltar Scout Association. T* **65** *and similar horiz designs. W* w **12.** *P* 14 × 14½.
223 4d. buff and bluish violet 15 10
224 7d. ochre and blue-green 15 10
225 9d. bright blue, yellow-orange and black .. 20 30
226 1s. greenish yellow and emerald 20 30
223/6 .. .. *Set of* 4 65 65
Designs:—7d. Scout Flag over the Rock; 9d. Tent, scouts and salute; 1s. Scout badges.

66 Nurse and W.H.O. Emblem

68 King John signing Magna Carta

(Des A. Ryman)

1968 (1 July). *20th Anniv of World Health Organization. T* **66** *and similar horiz design. W* w **12.** *P* 14 × 14½.
227 2d. ultramarine, black and yellow 10 15
228 4d. slate, black and pink 10 15
Design:—4d. Doctor and W.H.O. emblem.

(Des A. Ryman)

1968 (26 Aug). *Human Rights Year. T* **68** *and similar vert design. W* w **12** *(sideways). P* 13½ × 14.
229 1s. yellow-orange, brown and gold 15 10
230 2s. myrtle and gold 15 20
Design:—2s. "Freedom" and Rock of Gibraltar.

70 Shepherd, Lamb and Star

72 Parliament Houses

(Des A. Ryman)

1968 (1 Nov). *Christmas. T* **70** *and similar vert design. Multi-coloured. W* w **12.** *P* 14½ × 13½.
231 4d. Type **70** 10 10
a. Gold (star) omitted £225
232 9d. Mary holding Holy Child 10 10

(Des A. Ryman)

1969 (26 May). *Commonwealth Parliamentary Association Conference. T* **72** *and similar designs. W* w **12** *(sideways on 2s.). P* 14 × 14½ *(2s.) or* 14½ × 14 *(others).*
233 4d. green and gold 10 10
234 9d. bluish violet and gold 10 10
235 2s. multicoloured 15 20
233/5 .. .. *Set of* 3 30 30
Designs: *Horiz*—9d. Parliamentary emblem and outline of "The Rock". *Vert*—2s. Clock Tower, Westminster (Big Ben) and arms of Gibraltar.

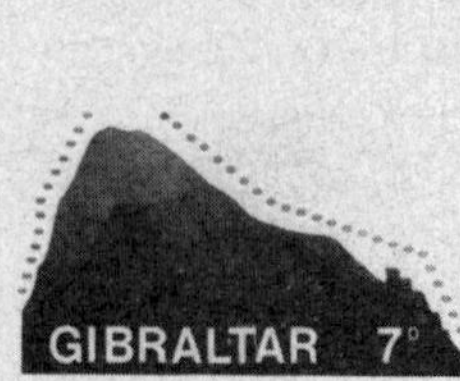

75 Silhouette of Rock, and Queen Elizabeth II

77 Soldier and Cap Badge, Royal Anglian Regiment, 1969

(Des A. Ryman)

1969 (30 July). *New Constitution. W* w **12.** *P* 14 × 13½ *(in addition, the outline of the Rock is perforated).*
236 **75** ½d. gold and orange 10 10
237 5d. silver and bright green 20 10
a. Portrait and inscr in gold and silver*
238 7d. silver and bright purple 20 10
239 5s. gold and ultramarine 70 70
236/9 .. .. *Set of* 4 1·00 85
*No. 237a was first printed with the head and inscription in gold and then in silver but displaced slightly to lower left.

(Des A. Ryman. Photo D.L.R.)

1969 (6 Nov). *Military Uniforms (1st series). T* **77** *and similar vert designs. Multicoloured. W* w **12.** *P* 14.
240 1d. Royal Artillery officer, 1758 and modern cap badge.. .. .. 20 10
241 6d. Type **77** 45 20
242 9d. Royal Engineers' Artificer, 1786 and modern cap badge 55 30
243 2s. Private, Fox's Marines, 1704 and modern Royal Marines cap badge .. .. 2·00 1·25
240/3 .. .. *Set of* 4 2·75 1·60
Nos. 240/3 have a short history of the Regiment printed on the reverse side over the gum, therefore, once the gum is moistened the history disappears.
See also Nos. 248/51, 290/3, 300/3, 313/16, 331/4, 340/3 and 363/6.

80 "Madonna of the Chair" (detail, Raphael)

83 Europa Point

(Des A. Ryman. Photo Enschedé)

1969 (1 Dec). *Christmas. T* **80** *and similar vert designs. Multi-coloured. W* w **12** *(sideways). P* 14 × *Roulette* 9.
244 5d. Type **80** 10 10
a. Strip of 3. Nos. 244/6 45
245 7d. "Virgin and Child" (detail, Morales) .. 20 20
246 1s. "The Virgin of the Rocks" (detail, Leonardo da Vinci) 20 20
244/6 .. .. *Set of* 3 45 45
Nos. 244/6 were issued together in *se-tenant* strips of three throughout the sheet.

(Des A. Ryman. Photo Enschedé)

1970 (8 June). *Europa Point. W* w **12.** *P* 13½.
247 **83** 2s. multicoloured 40 30
w. Wmk inverted .. .. .. 1·90 1·90

(Des A. Ryman. Photo D.L.R.)

1970 (28 Aug). *Military Uniforms (2nd series). Vert designs as T* **77.** *Multicoloured. W* w **12.** *P* 14.
248 2d. Royal Scots officer, 1839 and cap badge .. 35 10
249 5d. South Wales Borderers private, 1763 and cap badge.. .. .. 70 10
250 7d. Queen's Royal Regiment private, 1742 and cap badge 70 15
251 2s. Royal Irish Rangers piper, 1969 and cap badge .. .. 2·75 1·25
248/51 .. .. *Set of* 4 4·00 1·40
Nos. 248/51 have a short history of the Regiment printed on the reverse side under the gum.

88 No. 191a and Rock of Gibraltar

(Des A. Ryman. Litho D.L.R.)

1970 (18 Sept). *"Philympia 1970" Stamp Exhibition, London. T* **88** *and similar horiz design. W* w **12** *(sideways). P* 13.
252 1s. vermilion and bronze-green 15 10
253 2s. bright blue and magenta 25 55
Design:—2s. Victorian stamp (No. 23b) and Moorish Castle.
The stamps shown in the designs are well-known varieties with values omitted.

90 "The Virgin Mary" (stained-glass window by Gabriel Loire)

(Photo Enschedé)

1970 (1 Dec). *Christmas. W* w **12.** *P* 13 × 14.
254 **90** 2s. multicoloured 30 30

(New Currency: 100 pence = £1)

91 Saluting Battery, Rosia

92 Saluting Battery, Rosia, Modern View

(Des A. Ryman. Litho Questa)

1971 (15 Feb). *Decimal Currency. Designs as T* **91/2.** *W* w **1** *(sideways* on horiz designs). P* 14.
255 ½p. multicoloured 15 2
a. Pair. Nos. 255/6 .. .. .. 30 4
256 ½p. multicoloured 15 2
257 1p. multicoloured 80 3
a. Pair. Nos. 257/8 .. .. .. 1·60 6
258 1p. multicoloured 80 3
259 1½p. multicoloured 20 4
a. Pair. Nos. 259/60 .. .. .. 40 8
260 1½p. multicoloured 20 4
261 2p. multicoloured .. .. .. 1·50 1·5
a. Pair. Nos. 261/2 .. .. .. 3·00 3·0
262 2p. multicoloured .. .. .. 1·50 1·5
263 2½p. multicoloured 20 4
a. Pair. Nos. 263/4 .. .. .. 40 8
264 2½p. multicoloured 20 4
265 3p. multicoloured 20 2
a. Pair. Nos. 265/6 .. .. .. 40 4
266 3p. multicoloured 20 2
267 4p. multicoloured .. .. .. 2·00 2·0
a. Pair. Nos. 267/8 .. .. .. 4·00 4·0
268 4p. multicoloured .. .. .. 2·00 2·0
269 5p. multicoloured 30 3
a. Pair. Nos. 269/70 .. .. .. 60 6
270 5p. multicoloured 30 3
271 7p. multicoloured 65 6
aw. Wmk Crown to right of CA .. .. 45·00
b. Pair. Nos. 271/2 .. .. .. 1·25 1·2
bw. Pair. Nos. 271aw/2aw .. .. 85·00
272 7p. multicoloured 65 6
aw. Wmk Crown to right of CA .. .. 45·00
273 8p. multicoloured 70 8
a. Pair. Nos. 273/4 .. .. .. 1·40 1·6
274 8p. multicoloured 70 8
275 9p. multicoloured 70 7
a. Pair. Nos. 275/6 .. .. .. 1·40 1·4
276 9p. multicoloured 70 7
277 10p. multicoloured 80 8
aw. Wmk Crown to right of CA .. .. 75·00
b. Pair. Nos. 277/8 .. .. .. 1·60 1·6
bw. Pair. Nos. 277aw/8aw £150
278 10p. multicoloured 80 8
aw. Wmk Crown to right of CA .. .. 75·00
279 12½p. multicoloured .. .. .. 1·00 1·6
a. Pair. Nos. 279/80 .. .. .. 2·00 3·0
280 12½p. multicoloured .. .. .. 1·00 1·6
281 25p. multicoloured .. .. .. 1·10 1·6
a. Pair. Nos. 281/2 .. .. .. 2·10 3·0
282 25p. multicoloured .. .. .. 1·10 1·6
283 50p. multicoloured .. .. .. 1·25 2·5
a. Pair. Nos. 283/4 .. .. .. 2·50 5·0
284 50p. multicoloured .. .. .. 1·25 2·5
285 £1 multicoloured .. .. .. 2·00 4·0
a. Pair. Nos. 285/6 .. .. .. 4·00 8·0
286 £1 multicoloured .. .. .. 2·00 4·0
255/86 .. .. *Set of* 32 24·00 32·0
Designs (the two versions of each value show the same Gibraltar view taken from an early 19th-century print (first design) or modern photograph (second design): *Horiz*—1p. Prince George of Cambridge Quarters and Trinity Church; 1½p. The Wellington Bust, Alameda Gardens; 2p. Gibraltar from the North Bastion; 2½p. Catalan Bay; 3p. Convent Garden; 4p. The Exchange and Spanish Chapel; 5p. Commercial Square and Library; 7p. South Barracks and Rosia Magazine; 8p. Moorish Mosque and Castle; 9p. Europa Pass Road; 10p. South Barracks from Rosia Bay; 12½p. Southport Gates; 25p. Trooping the Colour, The Alameda. *Vert*—50p. Europa Pass Gorge; £1 Prince Edward's Gate.
The two designs of each value were printed together, *se-tenant*, in horizontal and vertical pairs throughout.
*The normal sideways watermark shows Crown to left of CA, *as seen from the back of the stamp.*
See also Nos. 317/20 and 344/5.

93

94 Regimental Arms

(Des A. Ryman. Photo Harrison)

1971 (15 Feb). *Coil Stamps. W* w **12.** *P* 14½ × 14.
287 **93** ½p. red-orange 15 30
a. Coil strip (287 × 2, 288 × 2 and 289 *se-tenant*) .. .. 1·00
288 1p. blue 15 30
289 2p. bright green .. .. .. 50 1·10
287/9 .. .. *Set of* 3 70 1·50

(Des A. Ryman. Litho Questa)

1971 (6 Sept). *Military Uniforms (3rd series). Multicoloured designs as T* **77,** *showing uniform and cap-badge. W* w **12.** *P* 14.
290 1p. The Black Watch (1845) 35 30
291 2p. Royal Regt of Fusiliers (1971) .. 65 30
w. Wmk inverted .. .. ..
292 4p. King's Own Royal Border Regt (1704) 1·25 50
293 10p. Devonshire and Dorset Regt (1801) .. 3·75 2·50
w. Wmk inverted .. .. .. 5·50 6·00
290/3 .. .. *Set of* 4 5·50 3·25
Nos. 290/3 have a short history of the regiment printed on the reverse side under the gum.

(Des A. Ryman. Litho Harrison)

71 (25 Sept). *Presentation of Colours to the Gibraltar Regiment. W w* **12** *(sideways). P 12½ × 12.*
4 **94** 3p. black, gold and red 30 30

95 Nativity Scene **96** Soldier Artificer, 1773

(Des A. Ryman. Photo Enschedé)

971 (1 Dec). *Christmas. T* **95** *and similar horiz design. Multicoloured. W w* **12.** *P 13 × 13½.*
95 3p. Type **95** 45 45
96 5p. Mary and Joseph going to Bethlehem .. 55 55

(Des A. Ryman. Litho Questa)

972 (6 Mar). *Bicentenary of Royal Engineers in Gibraltar. T* **96** *and similar multicoloured designs. W w* **12** *(sideways on 1 and 3p.). P 13½ × 14 (5p.) or 14 × 13½ (others).*
97 1p. Type **96** 50 30
98 3p. Modern tunneller 70 60
99 5p. Old and new uniforms and badge (*horiz*) 90 80
97/9 .. .. *Set of* 3 1·90 1·50

(Des A. Ryman. Litho Questa)

972 (19 July). *Military Uniforms (4th series). Multicoloured designs as T* **77.** *W w* **12** *(sideways). P 14.*
00 1p. Duke of Cornwall's Light Infantry, 1704 60 20
01 3p. King's Royal Rifle Corps, 1830 .. .. 1·75 40
02 7p. Officer, 37th North Hampshire, 1825 .. 2·75 70
03 10p. Royal Navy, 1972 .. .. .. 3·25 1·50
00/3 .. .. *Set of* 4 7·50 2·50
Nos. 300/303 have a short history of the Regiment printed on the reverse side under the gum.

97 "Our Lady of Europa" **98** Keys of Gibraltar and *Narcissus niveus*

(Des A. Ryman. Litho Harrison)

1972 (4 Oct). *Christmas. W w* **12** *(sideways*). P 14½×14.*
304 **97** 3p. multicoloured 10 10
w. Wmk Crown to right of CA .. 8·00
305 5p. multicoloured 10 30
w. Wmk Crown to right of CA .. 1·00
*The normal sideways watermark shows Crown to left of CA, *as seen from the back of the stamp.*
These stamps have an inscription printed on the reverse side.

(Des (from photograph by D. Groves) and photo Harrison)

1972 (20 Nov). *Royal Silver Wedding. Multicoloured; background colour given. W w* **12.** *P 14 × 14½.*
306 **98** 5p. carmine-red 20 20
w. Wmk inverted .. .. .. 38·00
307 7p. deep grey-green 20 20
w. Wmk inverted .. .. ..

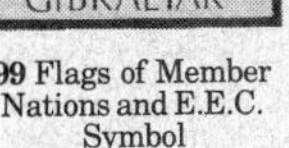

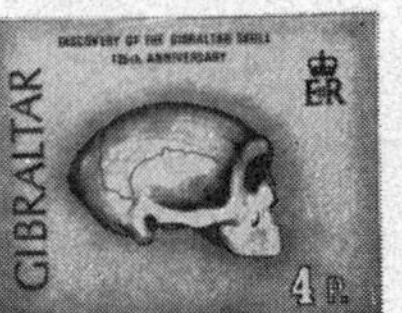

99 Flags of Member Nations and E.E.C. Symbol **100** Skull

(Des A. Ryman. Litho Questa)

1973 (22 Feb). *Britain's Entry into E.E.C. W w* **12** *(sideways). P 14½ × 14.*
308 **99** 5p. multicoloured 55 40
309 10p. multicoloured 70 60

(Des A. Ryman. Litho B.W.)

1973 (22 May). *125th Anniv of Gibraltar Skull Discovery. T* **100** *and similar horiz designs. Multicoloured. W w* **12.** *P 13 (10p.) or 13½ (others).*
310 4p. Type **100** .. .. 1·25 50
a. Gold ("GIBRALTAR") omitted .. £1700
311 6p. Prehistoric man .. .. .. 1·25 70
312 10p. Prehistoric family (40×26 *mm*) .. 1·75 1·25
310/12 .. .. *Set of* 3 3·75 2·25
Four mint examples of No. 310a have been found in presentation packs.

(Des A. Ryman. Litho Questa)

1973 (22 Aug). *Military Uniforms (5th series). Multicoloured designs as T* **77.** *W w* **12** *(sideways). P 14.*
313 1p. King's Own Scottish Borderers, 1770 .. 50 40
314 4p. Royal Welch Fusiliers, 1800 .. .. 1·50 1·00
315 6p. Royal Northumberland Fusiliers, 1736 .. 2·25 2·00
316 10p. Grenadier Guards, 1898 .. .. 3·00 4·25
313/16 .. .. *Set of* 4 6·50 7·00
Nos. 313/16 have a short history of the Regiment printed on the reverse side under the gum.

1973 (12 Sept). *As Nos. 261/2 and 267/8 but W w* **12** *upright.*
317 2p. multicoloured .. .. 1·10 1·75
a. Pair. Nos. 317/18 .. .. .. 2·10 3·50
318 2p. multicoloured .. .. 1·10 1·75
319 4p. multicoloured .. .. 1·25 1·75
a. Pair. Nos. 319/20 .. .. .. 2·50 3·50
320 4p. multicoloured .. .. 1·25 1·75
317/20 .. .. *Set of* 4 4·25 6·25

101 "Nativity" (Danckerts) **102** Victorian Pillar-box

(Des and litho Enschedé)

1973 (17 Oct). *Christmas. W w* **12.** *P 12½ × 12.*
321 **101** 4p. violet and Venetian red 35 15
322 6p. magenta and turquoise-blue .. 50 95

1973 (14 Nov). *Royal Wedding. As Nos. 165/6 of Anguilla. Centre multicoloured. W w* **12** *(sideways). P 13½.*
323 6p. turquoise 10 10
324 14p. yellow-green 20 20

(Des A. Ryman. Litho Walsall)

1974 (2 May). *Centenary of Universal Postal Union. T* **102** *and similar vert designs. Multicoloured. (a) W w* **12** *(sideways). P 14½.*
325 2p. Type **102** 15 20
326 6p. Pillar-box of George VI 25 30
327 14p. Pillar-box of Elizabeth II 40 65
325/7 .. .. *Set of* 3 70 1·00
(b) No wmk. Imperf × roul 5. Self-adhesive (from booklets)*
328 2p. Type **102** 25 90
a. Booklet pane Nos. 328/30 *se-tenant* .. 6·50
b. Booklet pane Nos. 328 × 3 and 329 × 3 .. 1·40
329 6p. As No. 326 .. .. 25 1·00
330 14p. As No. 327 .. .. 6·50 8·00
328/30 .. .. *Set of* 3 6·50 9·00
*Nos. 328/30 were separated by various combinations of rotary-knife (giving a straight edge) and roulette.

(Des A. Ryman. Litho Questa)

1974 (21 Aug). *Military Uniforms (6th series). Multicoloured designs as T* **77.** *W w* **12** *(sideways*). P 14.*
331 4p. East Lancashire Regt, 1742 .. .. 50 50
332 6p. Somerset Light Infantry, 1833 .. 70 70
333 10p. Royal Sussex Regt, 1790 .. .. 1·00 1·40
334 16p. R.A.F. officer, 1974 .. .. .. 2·25 4·00
w. Wmk Crown to right of CA £110
331/4 .. .. *Set of* 4 4·00 6·00
*The normal sideways watermark shows Crown to left of CA, *as seen from the back of the stamp.*
Nos. 331/4 have a short history of the regiment printed on the reverse side under the gum.

103 "Madonna with the Green Cushion" (Solario) **104** Churchill and Houses of Parliament

(Des A. Ryman and M. Infante. Litho Questa)

1974 (5 Nov). *Christmas. T* **103** *and similar vert design. Multicoloured. W w* **14.** *P 14.*
335 4p. Type **103** 40 30
336 6p. "Madonna of the Meadow" (Bellini) .. 60 95

(Des L. Curtis. Litho Harrison)

1974 (30 Nov). *Birth Centenary of Sir Winston Churchill. T* **104** *and similar horiz design. W w* **12.** *P 14 × 14½.*
337 6p. black, reddish purple and light lavender 25 15
338 20p. brownish black, lake-brown and light orange-red 50 75
MS339 114×93 mm. Nos. 337/8. W w **12** (sideways*). P 14 .. .. 4·50 6·00
w. Wmk Crown to right of CA £300
Design:—20p. Churchill and *King George V* (battleship).
*The normal sideways watermark shows Crown to left of CA, *as seen from the back of the stamp.*

(Des A. Ryman. Litho Questa)

1975 (14 Mar). *Military Uniforms (7th series). Multicoloured designs as T* **77.** *W w* **14.** *P 14.*
340 4p. East Surrey Regt, 1846 .. .. .. 40 30
341 6p. Highland Light Infantry, 1777 .. .. 60 50
342 10p. Coldstream Guards, 1704 .. .. 80 90
343 20p. Gibraltar Regt, 1974 .. .. .. 1·50 2·50
340/3 .. .. *Set of* 4 3·00 3·75
Nos. 340/3 have a short history of each regiment printed on the reverse side under the gum.

1975 (9 July). *As Nos. 257/8 but W w* **14** *(sideways).*
344 1p. multicoloured .. .. 1·25 1·75
a. Pair. Nos. 344/5 .. .. 2·50 3·50
345 1p. multicoloured .. .. 1·25 1·75

105 Girl Guides' Badge **106** Child at Prayer

(Des A. Ryman. Litho Harrison)

1975 (10 Oct). *50th Anniv of Gibraltar Girl Guides. W w* **12.** *P 13 × 13½.*
346 **105** 5p. gold, light blue and dull violet .. 30 45
a. *Tête-bêche* (pair) .. .. .. 75 1·00
w. Wmk inverted 45 60
347 7p. gold, sepia and light lake-brown 40 50
a. *Tête-bêche* (pair) .. .. .. 1·00 1·10
w. Wmk inverted 60 70
348 – 15p. silver, brownish black & yellow-brn 65 1·00
a. *Tête-bêche* (pair) .. .. .. 1·50 2·00
b. Silver omitted .. .. ..
w. Wmk inverted .. .. .. 85 1·25
346/8 .. .. *Set of* 3 1·25 1·75
No. 348 is as T **105** but shows a different badge.
Nos. 346/8 were each issued in sheets of 25 (5×5) with each horizontal row containing three upright stamps and two inverted.

(Des A. Ryman. Litho Walsall)

1975 (26 Nov). *Christmas. T* **106** *and similar vert designs. Multicoloured. W w* **14** *(sideways*). P 14.*
349 6p. Type **106** 40 60
aw. Wmk Crown to right of CA .. .. 6·00
b. Sheetlet. Nos. 349/54 .. .. 2·10
bw. Sheetlet. Nos. 349aw/54aw .. .. 32·00
350 6p. Angel with lute 40 60
aw. Wmk Crown to right of CA .. .. 6·00
351 6p. Child singing carols 40 60
aw. Wmk Crown to right of CA .. .. 6·00
352 6p. Three children 40 60
aw. Wmk Crown to right of CA .. .. 6·00
353 6p. Girl at prayer 40 60
aw. Wmk Crown to right of CA .. .. 6·00
354 6p. Boy and lamb 40 60
aw. Wmk Crown to right of CA .. .. 6·00
349/54 .. .. *Set of* 6 2·10 3·25
*The normal sideways watermark shows Crown to left of CA, *as seen from the back of the stamp.*
Nos. 349/54 were issued together *se-tenant* in sheetlets of 6 (3×2).

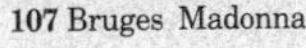

107 Bruges Madonna **108** Bicentennial Emblem and Arms of Gibraltar

(Des Jennifer Toombs. Litho Walsall)

1975 (17 Dec). *500th Birth Anniv of Michelangelo. T* **107** *and similar vert designs. Multicoloured*

(a) W w **14** *(sideways**). *P* 14

355 6p. Type **107** 20 25
356 9p. Taddei Madonna 25 40
357 15p. Pietà 35 90
w. Wmk Crown to right of CA .. .. 95·00
355/7 .. .. *Set of* 3 70 1·40

(b) No wmk. Imperf×roul 5†. Self-adhesive (from booklets)

358 6p. Type **107** 35 45
a. Booklet pane. Nos. 358/60 *se-tenant* .. 1·50
b. Booklet pane. Nos. 358×2, 359×2 and 360×2 .. .. 3·00
359 9p. As No. 356 .. .. 55 75
360 15p. As No. 357 .. .. 80 1·25
358/60 .. .. *Set of* 3 1·50 2·25

*The normal sideways watermark shows Crown to left of CA, *as seen from the back of the stamp.*

†Nos. 358/60 were separated by various combinations of rotary knife (giving a straight edge) and roulette.

(Des A. Ryman. Litho Walsall)

1976 (28 May). *Bicentenary of American Revolution. W* w **14** *(inverted). P* 14.

361 **108** 25p. multicoloured 50 50
MS362 85 × 133 mm. No. 361 × 4 .. .. .. 4·50 7·00

The edges of **MS**362 are rouletted.

(Des A. Ryman. Litho Walsall)

1976 (21 July). *Military Uniforms (8th series). Multicoloured designs as T* **77**. *W* w **14** *(inverted). P* 14.

363 1p. Suffolk Regt, 1795 .. .. .. 25 15
364 6p. Northamptonshire Regt, 1779 .. .. 50 30
365 12p. Lancashire Fusiliers, 1793 .. .. 75 55
366 25p. Ordnance Corps, 1896 .. .. .. 1·25 1·10
363/6 .. .. *Set of* 4 2·50 1·90

Nos. 363/6 have a short history of each regiment printed on the reverse side under the gum.

109 The Holy Family

110 Queen Elizabeth II, Royal Arms and Gibraltar Arms

(Des A. Ryman. Litho Questa)

1976 (3 Nov). *Christmas. T* **109** *and similar vert designs showing stained-glass windows in St. Joseph's Church, Gibraltar. Multicoloured. W* w **14**. *P* 14.

367 6p. Type **109** 25 15
368 9p. Madonna and Child 30 25
369 12p. St. Bernard 45 60
370 20p. Archangel Michael .. .. .. 70 1·25
367/70 .. .. *Set of* 4 1·50 2·00

(Des A. Ryman. Litho J.W.)

1977 (7 Feb). *Silver Jubilee. W* w **14**. *P* $13\frac{1}{2}$.

371 **110** 6p. multicoloured 25 20
372 £1 multicoloured .. .. .. 1·40 2·25
MS373 124 × 115 mm. Nos. 371/2. P 13 .. .. 1·60 2·25

The outer edges of the miniature sheet are either guillotined or rouletted.

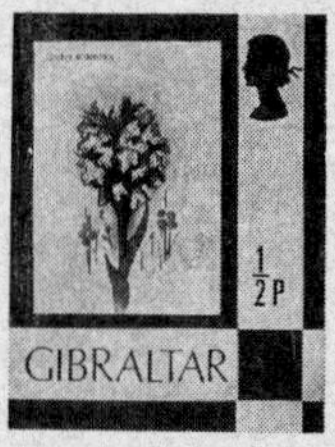

111 Toothed Orchid (*Orchis tridentata*)

(Des A. Ryman. Litho Questa)

1977 (1 Apr)–**82**. *Multicoloured designs as T* **111**. *W* w **14** *(sideways* on horiz designs; inverted on £5). Chalk-surfaced paper (15p., £5). Imprint date at foot. P* 14.

374 ½p. Type **111** .. .. 60 1·75
a. Chalk-surfaced paper (22.2.82) .. 3·25 3·25
375 1p. Red Mullet (*Mullus surmuletus*) (*horiz*) 15 10
w. Wmk Crown to right of CA .. 6·00 6·50
376 2p. *Maculinea arion* (butterfly) (*horiz*) .. 30 50
377 2½p. Sardinian Warbler (*Sylvia melanocephala*) .. .. 40 1·50
378 3p. Giant Squill (*Scilla peruviana*) .. 20 10
379 4p. Grey Wrasse (*Crenilabrus cinereus*) (*horiz*) 30 10
b. Chalk-surfaced paper (21.4.81) .. 55 55
380 5p. *Vanessa atalanta* (butterfly) (*horiz*) 50 70
381 6p. Black Kite (*Milvus migrans*) .. 1·25 30
w. Wmk inverted .. .. .. 80·00
382 9p. Shrubby Scorpion-vetch (*Coronilla valentina*) 70 70
383 10p. John Dory (fish) (*Zeus faber*) (*horiz*) 40 20
a. Chalk-surfaced paper (21.4.81) .. 70 1·00
384 12p. *Colias crocea* (butterfly) (*horiz*) .. 1·00 35
a. Chalk-surfaced paper (21.4.81) .. 4·00 4·25
384*b* 15p. Winged Asparagus Pea (*Tetragonolobus purpureus*) (12.11.80) .. 3·25 55
bw. Wmk inverted .. .. .. 80·00
385 20p. Audouin's Gull (*Larus audouinii*) .. 1·25 2·00
386 25p. Barbary Nut (iris) (*Iris sisyrinchium*) 1·25 2·00
a. Chalk-surfaced paper (21.4.81) .. 4·25 4·75
387 50p. Swordfish (*Xiphias gladius*) (*horiz*) 2·00 95
a. Chalk-surfaced paper (21.4.81) .. 5·50 6·50
388 £1 *Papilio machaon* (butterfly) (*horiz*) 4·25 4·50
389 £2 Hoopoe (*Upupa epops*) .. .. 7·50 10·00
389*a* £5 Arms of Gibraltar (16.5.79) .. 10·00 10·00
374/89*a* .. .. *Set of* 18 30·00 32·00

The ½p. to £2 values have a descriptive text printed on the reverse, beneath the gum.

*The normal sideways watermark shows Crown to left of CA, *as seen from the back of the stamp.*

Imprint dates: "1977", Nos. 374/84, 385/9; "1978", No. 382; "1979", No. 389*a*; "1980", No. 384*b*; "1981", Nos. 379b, 383a, 384a, 386a, 387a; "1982", No. 374a.

112 "Our Lady of Europa" Stamp

(Des J. Cooter. Litho Questa)

1977 (27 May). *"Amphilex 77" Stamp Exhibition. Amsterdam. T* **112** *and similar vert designs. Multicoloured. W* w **14** *(sideways on 6p.; inverted on 12p.). P* $13\frac{1}{2}$.

390 6p. Type **112** 10 20
391 12p. "Europa Point" stamp 15 30
w. Wmk upright .. .. .. 20·00
392 25p. "E.E.C. Entry" stamp 20 50
w. Wmk inverted .. .. .. 2·25
390/2 .. .. *Set of* 3 40 90

113 "The Annunciation" (Rubens)

114 Aerial View of Gibraltar

(Des A. Ryman. Litho Enschedé)

1977 (2 Nov). *Christmas and Rubens' 400th Birth Anniv. T* **113** *and similar multicoloured designs. W* w **14** *(sideways on 12p.). P* $13\frac{1}{2}$.

393 3p. Type **113** 10 10
394 9p. "The Adoration of the Magi" 25 20
395 12p. "The Adoration of the Magi" (*horiz*) .. 30 30
396 15p. "The Holy Family under the Apple Tree" 30 40
393/6 .. .. *Set of* 4 85 85
MS397 110 × 200 mm. Nos. 393/6 (wmk upright) .. 2·75 4·00

(Des A. Ryman. Litho Enschedé)

1978 (3 May). *Gibraltar from Space. P* $13\frac{1}{2}$.

398 **114** 12p. multicoloured 25 40
a. Horiz pair imperf 3 sides .. £3000
MS399 148×108 mm. 25p. multicoloured .. 80 80

Design:—25p. Aerial view of Straits of Gibraltar.

No. 398a occurs on the bottom pair from two sheets of 10 (2×5) and shows the stamps perforated at top only.

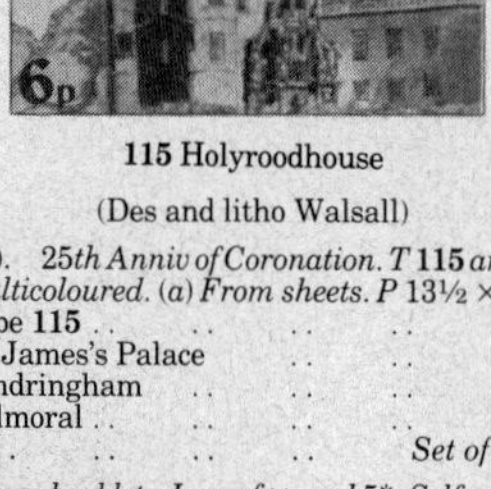

115 Holyroodhouse

(Des and litho Walsall)

1978 (12 June). *25th Anniv of Coronation. T* **115** *and similar horiz designs. Multicoloured. (a) From sheets. P* $13\frac{1}{2}$ × 14.

400 6p. Type **115** 20 15
401 9p. St. James's Palace 25 15
402 12p. Sandringham 30 30
403 18p. Balmoral 40 55
400/3 .. .. *Set of* 4 1·00 1·00

(b) From booklets. Imperf × roul 5. Self-adhesive*

404 12p. As No. 402 .. .. 35 75
a. Booklet pane. Nos. 404/5, each × 3 .. 2·00
405 18p. As No. 403 .. .. 40 90
406 25p. Windsor Castle .. .. .. 90 1·75
a. Booklet pane of 1 90
404/6 .. .. *Set of* 3 1·50 3·00

*Nos. 404/5 were separated by various combinations of rotary-knife (giving a straight edge) and roulette. No. 406 exists only with straight edges.

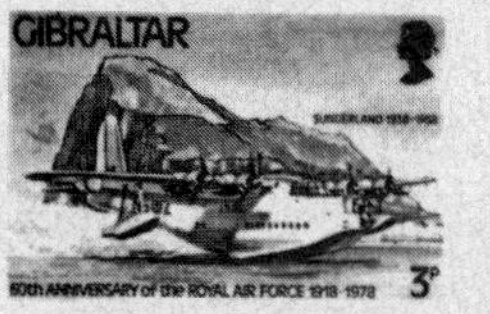

116 Short S.25 Sunderland, 1938–58

117 "Madonna with Animals"

(Des A. Theobald. Litho Harrison)

1978 (6 Sept). *60th Anniv of Royal Air Force. T* **116** *and simi horiz designs. Multicoloured. W* w **14** *(sideways). P* 14.

407 3p. Type **116** 15
408 9p. Caudron G-3, 1918 35
409 12p. Avro Shackleton M.R.2, 1953–66 .. 40
410 16p. Hawker Hunter F.6, 1954–77 .. 45
411 18p. Hawker Siddeley H.S.801 Nimrod M.R.1, 1969–78 50
407/11 .. .. *Set of* 5 1·75 2·

(Des A. Ryman. Litho Questa)

1978 (1 Nov). *Christmas. Paintings by Dürer. T* **117** *and simil vert designs. Multicoloured. W* w **14**. *P* 14.

412 5p. Type **117** 15
413 9p. "The Nativity" 20
414 12p. "Madonna of the Goldfinch" 25
415 15p. "Adoration of the Magi" 35
412/15 .. .. *Set of* 4 85 1·

118 Sir Rowland Hill and 1d. Stamp of 1886

(Des A. Ryman. Litho Format)

1979 (7 Feb). *Death Centenary of Sir Rowland Hill. T* **118** *an similar horiz designs. W* w **14** *(sideways*). P* $13\frac{1}{2}$×14.

416 3p. multicoloured 10
417 9p. multicoloured 20
418 12p. multicoloured 25
w. Wmk Crown to right of CA .. .. 70·00
419 25p. black, dull claret and yellow 35
416/19 .. .. *Set of* 4 80

Designs:—9p. Sir Rowland Hill and 1p. coil stamp of 197 12p. Sir Rowland Hill and Post Office Regulations documer 1840; 25p. Sir Rowland Hill and "G" cancellation.

*The normal sideways watermark shows Crown to left of C/ *as seen from the back of the stamp.*

119 Posthorn, Dish Antenna and Early Telephone

120 African Child

(Des A. Ryman. Litho Format)

1979 (16 May). *Europa. Communications. W* w **14** *(sideways P* $13\frac{1}{2}$.

420 **119** 3p. green and pale green 15
421 9p. lake-brown and ochre 30
422 12p. ultramarine and dull violet-blue .. 35 1·2
420/2 .. .. *Set of* 3 70 2·0

(Des G. Hutchins. Litho Walsall)

1979 (14 Nov). *Christmas. International Year of the Child. T* 12 *and similar vert designs. Multicoloured. W* w **14** *(sideways). P* 1

423 12p. Type **120** 25
a. Block of 6. Nos. 423/8 .. .. .. 1·40
424 12p. Asian child 25
425 12p. Polynesian child 25
426 12p. American Indian child 25
427 12p. Children of different races and Nativity scene 25
428 12p. European child 25
423/8 .. .. *Set of* 6 1·40 1·6

Nos. 423/8 were printed together, *se-tenant*, in blocks of 6, wit margin separating the two blocks in each sheet.

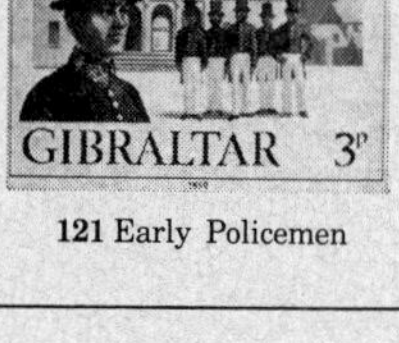

121 Early Policemen

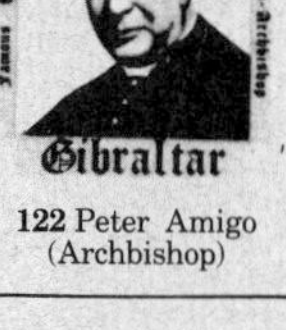

122 Peter Amigo (Archbishop)

(Des C. Abbott. Litho Questa)

980 (5 Feb). 150*th Anniv of Gibraltar Police Force. T* **121** *and similar horiz designs. Multicoloured.* W w **14** (*sideways*). *P* 14.

29 3p. Type **121** 20 10
30 6p. Policemen of 1895, early 1900s and 1980 20 15
31 12p. Policeman and police ambulance .. 25 20
32 37p. Policewoman and police motor-cyclist .. 55 90
29/32 .. .. *Set of* 4 1·10 1·25

(Des A. Ryman. Litho Questa)

980 (6 May). *Europa. Personalities. T* **122** *and similar vert designs. Multicoloured.* W w **14** (*inverted on No.* 434). *P* 14½ × 14.

33 12p. Type **122** 20 25
34 12p. Gustavo Bacarisas (artist) 20 25
35 12p. John Mackintosh (philanthropist) .. 20 25
33/5 .. .. *Set of* 3 55 70

123 Queen Elizabeth the Queen Mother

124 "Horatio Nelson" (J. F. Rigaud)

(Des Harrison. Litho Questa)

1980 (4 Aug). 80*th Birthday of Queen Elizabeth the Queen Mother.* W w **14** (*sideways*). *P* 14.

436 **123** 15p. multicoloured 30 30

(Des BG Studio. Litho Questa)

1980 (20 Aug). 175*th Death Anniv of Nelson. Paintings. T* **124** *and similar multicoloured designs.* W w **14** (*sideways on* 9 *and* 40*p.*). *P* 14.

437 3p. Type **124** 15 10
438 9p. "H.M.S. *Victory*" (*horiz*) 25 25
439 15p. "Horatio Nelson" (Sir William Beechey) 35 35
440 40p. "H.M.S. *Victory* being towed into Gibraltar" (Clarkson Stanfield) (*horiz*) .. 80 1·00
437/40 .. .. *Set of* 4 1·40 1·50
MS441 159 × 99 mm. No. 439 .. .. .. 75 1·75

Examples of the 3p. value showing Nelson facing left in error were prepared, but not issued by the Gibraltar Post Office.

125 Three Kings

126 Hercules creating Mediterranean Sea

(Des A. Ryman. Litho Questa)

1980 (12 Nov). *Christmas. T* **125** *and similar horiz design, each in deep brown and orange-yellow.* W w **14** (*sideways*). *P* 14½.

442 15p. Type **125** 25 35
a. Horiz pair. Nos. 442/3 .. .. .. 50 70
443 15p. Nativity scene 25 35

Nos. 442/3 were printed together, *se-tenant*, in horizontal pairs throughout the sheet.

(Des G. Vasarhelyi. Litho Enschedé)

1981 (24 Feb). *Europa. Folklore. T* **126** *and similar vert design. Multicoloured.* W w **14**. *P* 13½ × 13.

444 9p. Type **126** 20 15
445 15p. Hercules and Pillars of Hercules (Straits of Gibraltar) 25 35

127 Dining-room

128 Prince Charles and Lady Diana Spencer

(Des A. Ryman. Litho Harrison)

1981 (22 May). 450*th Anniv of The Convent* (*Governor's Residence*). *T* **127** *and similar square designs. Multicoloured.* W w **14** (*sideways*). *P* 14½ × 14.

446 4p. Type **127** 10 10
447 14p. King's Chapel 15 15
448 15p. The Convent 15 15
449 55p. Cloister 60 80
446/9 .. .. *Set of* 4 85 1·00

(Des A. Ryman. Litho Questa)

1981 (27 July). *Royal Wedding.* W w **14** (*sideways*). *P* 14½.

450 **128** £1 multicoloured .. .. .. 1·50 1·50

129

130 Paper Aeroplane

(Des A. Ryman. Litho Questa)

1981 (2 Sept). W w **14**. *P* 13½×14.

451 **129** 1p. black 30 30
a. Booklet pane. Nos. 451/2 and 453×3 plus printed label .. 1·40
b. Booklet pane. Nos. 451/2×2 and 453×6 plus two printed labels .. 2·00
452 4p. Prussian blue 30 30
453 15p. light green 30 30
451/3 .. .. *Set of* 3 80 80

Nos. 451/3 were only issued in 50p. and £1 stamp booklets.

(Des A. Ryman. Litho Walsall)

1981 (29 Sept*). 50*th Anniv of Gibraltar Airmail Service. T* **130** *and similar horiz designs. Multicoloured.* W w **14** (*sideways*). *P* 14½ × 14.

454 14p. Type **130** 15 15
455 15p. Airmail letters, post box and aircraft tail fin 15 15
456 55p. Jet airliner circling globe 60 70
454/6 .. .. *Set of* 3 80 90

*This is the local release date. The Crown Agents released the stamps on 21 September.

131 Carol Singers

132 I.Y.D.P. Emblem and Stylised Faces

(Des Clive Torres (15p.); Peter Parody (55p.); adapted G. Vasarhelyi. Litho Questa)

1981 (19 Nov). *Christmas. Children's Drawings. T* **131** *and similar multicoloured design.* W w **14** (*sideways on* 15*p.*). *P* 14.

457 15p. Type **131** 30 15
458 55p. Postbox (*vert*) .. .. 1·00 85

(Des A. Ryman. Litho Questa)

1981 (19 Nov). *International Year For Disabled Persons.* W w **14** (*sideways*). *P* 14 × 14½.

459 **132** 14p. multicoloured 30 30

133 Douglas DC-3

134 Crest, H.M.S. *Opossum*

(Des A. Theobald. Litho J.W.)

1982 (10 Feb). *Aircraft. Horiz designs as T* **133**. *Multicoloured.* W w **14**. *Imprint date at foot. P* 14.

460 1p. Type **133** .. .. 25 1·00
461 2p. Vickers Viking 1B .. .. 30 1·00
462 3p. Airspeed A.S.57 Ambassador 30 90
463 4p. Vickers Viscount 800 .. .. .. 40 20
464 5p. Boeing 727-100 .. .. 90 60
465 10p. Vickers 953 Vanguard .. .. .. 1·50 50
466 14p. Short S.45A Solent 2 .. .. .. 1·00 2·25
467 15p. Fokker F.27 Friendship .. .. .. 2·25 1·75
468 17p. Boeing 737 .. .. 1·00 55
469 20p. B.A.C. One Eleven .. .. 1·00 50
470 25p. Lockheed Constellation .. .. .. 3·50 3·00
471 50p. Hawker Siddeley Comet 4B .. .. 4·00 2·25
472 £1 Saro A.21 Windhover .. .. .. 5·50 2·25
473 £2 Hawker Siddeley Trident 2E .. .. 6·50 5·00
474 £5 De Havilland D.H.89A Dragon Rapide 9·00 14·00
460/74 .. .. *Set of* 15 32·00 32·00

Imprint dates: "1982", Nos. 460/74; "1985", No. 469.

For 2p. and 5p. values watermarked w **16** see Nos. 549 and 552.

(Des A. Ryman. Litho Questa)

1982 (14 Apr). *Naval Crests* (1*st series*). *T* **134** *and similar vert designs. Multicoloured.* W w **14**. *P* 14.

475 ½p. Type **134** 10 10
476 15½p. H.M.S. *Norfolk* 55 65
477 17p. H.M.S. *Fearless* 60 70
478 60p. H.M.S. *Rooke* .. .. 1·40 2·75
w. Wmk inverted .. .. 35·00
475/8 .. .. *Set of* 4 2·25 3·75

See also Nos. 493/6, 510/13, 522/5, 541/4, 565/8, 592/5, 616/19, 638/41 and 651/4.

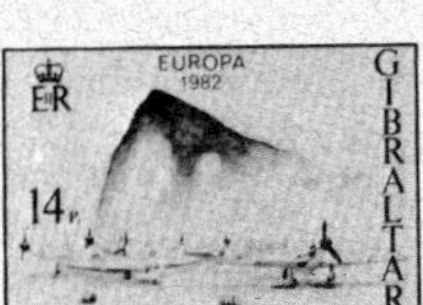

135 Hawker Hurricane Mk 1 and Supermarine Spitfires at Gibraltar

136 Gibraltar Chamber of Commerce Centenary

(Des A. Ryman. Litho Questa)

1982 (11 June). *Europa. Operation Torch. T* **135** *and similar horiz design. Multicoloured.* W w **14** (*sideways*). *P* 14.

479 14p. Type **135** 25 70
480 17p. General Giraud, General Eisenhower and Gibraltar 35 80

(Des A. Ryman. Litho Questa)

1982 (22 Sept). *Anniversaries. T* **136** *and similar vert designs. Multicoloured.* W w **14** (*sideways*). *P* 14½.

481 ½p. Type **136** 10 10
482 15½p. British Forces Postal Service centenary 30 25
483 60p. 75th anniv of Gibraltar Scout Association .. .. 1·10 1·25
481/3 .. .. *Set of* 3 1·25 1·40

137 Printed Circuit forming Map of World

(Des A. Ryman. Litho Harrison)

1982 (1 Oct). *International Direct Dialling.* W w **14** (*sideways*). *P* 14½.

484 **137** 17p. black, pale blue and bright orange 35 35

138 Gibraltar illuminated at Night and Holly

(Des A. Ryman. Litho Questa)

1982 (18 Nov). *Christmas. T* **138** *and similar horiz design. Multicoloured.* W w **14** (*sideways*). *P* 14 × 14½.

485 14p. Type **138** 45 30
486 17p. Gibraltar illuminated at night and Mistletoe 50 35

139 Yacht Marina

(Des Olympia Reyes. Litho Questa)

1983 (14 Mar). *Commonwealth Day. T* **139** *and similar multicoloured designs.* W w **14** (*sideways on* 4, 14*p.*). *P* 14.

487 4p. Type **139** 10 10
488 14p. Scouts and Guides Commonwealth Day Parade 20 15
489 17p. Flag of Gibraltar (*vert*) 25 20
490 60p. Queen Elizabeth II (from photo by Tim Graham) (*vert*) .. .. 70 1·00
487/90 .. .. *Set of* 4 1·00 1·25

140 St George's Hall Gallery

(Des A. Ryman. Litho Harrison)

1983 (21 May). *Europa. T* **140** *and similar horiz design.* W w **14** (*sideways*). *P* 13½ × 13.

491 16p. black and brown-ochre 30 35
492 19p. black and pale blue 40 40

Design:—19p. Water catchment slope.

(Des A. Ryman. Litho Questa)

1983 (1 July). *Naval Crests (2nd series). Vert designs as T* **134**. *Multicoloured. W* w **14**. *P* 14.
493 4p. H.M.S. *Faulknor* 30 10
494 14p. H.M.S. *Renown* 70 35
495 17p. H.M.S. *Ark Royal* 75 40
496 60p. H.M.S. *Sheffield* .. .. 1·75 1·50
w. Wmk inverted .. .. 28·00
493/6 .. .. *Set of* 4 3·25 2·10

141 Landport Gate, 1729

(Des Olympia Reyes. Litho Enschedé)

1983 (13 Sept). *Fortress Gibraltar in the 18th Century. T* **141** *and similar horiz designs. Multicoloured. W* w **14** *(sideways). P* 13 × 13½.
497 4p. Type **141** 20 10
498 17p. Koehler Gun, 1782 .. .. 50 45
499 77p. King's Bastion, 1779 .. .. 1·50 1·75
497/9 .. .. *Set of* 3 2·00 2·00
MS500 97 × 145 mm. Nos. 497/9 .. .. .. 2·00 2·00

142 "Adoration of the Magi" (Raphael)

143 1932 2d. Stamp and Globe

(Des A. Ryman. Litho Questa)

1983 (17 Nov). *Christmas. 500th Birth Anniv of Raphael. T* **142** *and similar multicoloured designs. W* w **14** *(sideways on 4p.). P* 14.
501 4p. Type **142** 25 10
502 17p. "Madonna of Foligno" (*vert*) 70 35
503 60p. "Sistine Madonna" (*vert*) .. .. .. 1·75 1·40
501/3 .. .. *Set of* 3 2·40 1·60

(Des E. Field. Litho Walsall)

1984 (6 Mar). *Europa. Posts and Telecommunications. T* **143** *and similar vert design. Multicoloured. W* w **14**. *P* 14½ × 14.
504 17p. Type **143** 35 50
505 23p. Circuit board and globe .. .. .. 45 1·00
w. Wmk inverted .. .. .. 95·00

144 Hockey

145 Mississippi River Boat Float

(Des A. Ryman. Litho Walsall)

1984 (25 May). *Sports. T* **144** *and similar horiz designs. Multicoloured. W* w **14** *(sideways). P* 14 × 14½.
506 20p. Type **144** 55 65
507 21p. Basketball 55 65
508 26p. Rowing .. .. 65 1·00
509 29p. Football .. .. 70 1·10
506/9 .. .. *Set of* 4 2·25 3·00

(Des A. Ryman. Litho Walsall)

1984 (21 Sept). *Naval Crests (3rd series). Vert designs as T* **134**. *Multicoloured. W* w **14**. *P* 13½ × 13.
510 20p. H.M.S. *Active* .. .. 1·60 1·75
511 21p. H.M.S. *Foxhound* .. .. 1·60 2·00
512 26p. H.M.S. *Valiant* .. .. 1·75 2·00
513 29p. H.M.S. *Hood* .. .. 1·90 2·25
w. Wmk inverted .. .. 12·00
510/13 .. .. *Set of* 4 6·25 7·25

(Des A. Ryman. Litho Questa)

1984 (7 Nov). *Christmas. Epiphany Floats. T* **145** *and similar horiz design. Multicoloured. W* w **14** *(sideways). P* 14 × 14½.
514 20p. Type **145** 40 50
515 80p. Roman Temple float .. .. 1·60 2·00

MINIMUM PRICE

The minimum price quote is 10p which represents a handling charge rather than a basis for valuing common stamps. For further notes about prices see introductory pages.

146 Musical Symbols, and Score from Beethoven's 9th (Choral) Symphony

147 Globe and Stop Polio Campaign Logo

(Des Olympia Reyes. Photo Courvoisier)

1985 (26 Feb). *Europa. European Music Year. T* **146** *and similar horiz design. Multicoloured. Granite paper. P* 12½.
516 **146** 20p. multicoloured 60 50
517 – 29p. multicoloured .. .. .. 90 2·00
The 29p. is as T **146** but shows different symbols.

(Des E. Field. Litho J.W.)

1985 (3 May). *Stop Polio Campaign. Vert designs as T* **147**. *Multicoloured. W* w **14** *(inverted). P* 13 × 13½.
518 26p. multicoloured (Type **147**) .. .. 90 1·25
a. Horiz strip of 4. Nos. 518/21 .. .. 3·25
519 26p. multicoloured ("ST" visible) .. .. 90 1·25
520 26p. multicoloured ("STO" visible) .. .. 90 1·25
521 26p. multicoloured ("STOP" visible) .. 90 1·25
518/21 .. .. *Set of* 4 3·25 4·50

Nos 518/21 were printed in horizontal *se-tenant* strips of four within the sheet. Each design differs in the position of the logo across the centre of the globe. On the left hand stamp in the strip only the letter "S" is visible, on the next "ST", on the next "STO" and on the last "STOP".

Other features of the design also differ, so that the word "Year" moves towards the top of the stamp and on No. 521 the upper logo is omitted.

(Des A. Ryman. Litho Questa)

1985 (3 July). *Naval Crests (4th series). Vert designs as T* **134**. *Multicoloured. W* w **16**. *P* 14.
522 4p. H.M.S. *Duncan* 60 10
523 9p. H.M.S. *Fury* 90 50
524 21p. H.M.S. *Firedrake* .. .. 2·00 2·00
525 80p. H.M.S. *Malaya* .. .. 4·00 6·00
522/5 .. .. *Set of* 4 6·75 7·75

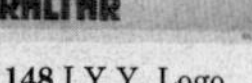
148 I.Y.Y. Logo

149 St. Joseph

(Des Olympia Reyes. Litho Walsall)

1985 (6 Sept). *International Youth Year. T* **148** *and similar horiz designs. Multicoloured. W* w **14** *(sideways). P* 14 × 14½.
526 4p. Type **148** 25 10
527 20p. Hands passing diamond .. .. .. 95 1·10
528 80p. 75th anniv logo of Girl Guide Movement 2·50 3·25
526/8 .. .. *Set of* 3 3·25 4·00

(Des A. Ryman (4p.), Olympia Reyes (80p.). Litho Cartor)

1985 (25 Oct). *Christmas. Centenary of St. Joseph's Parish Church. T* **149** *and similar vert designs. Multicoloured. W* w **16**. *P* 13½*.
529 4p. Type **149** 50 70
a. Vert pair. Nos. 529/30 .. .. .. 1·00 1·40
530 4p. St. Joseph's Parish Church 50 70
531 80p. Nativity crib .. .. 3·00 3·50
529/31 .. .. *Set of* 3 3·50 4·50

*Nos. 529/30 were printed together in panes of 25; No. 529 on rows 1, 3 and 5, and No. 530 on rows 2 and 4. *Se-tenant* vertical pairs from rows 1/2 and 3/4, forming composite designs, have the stamps separated by a line of roulettes instead of perforations. Examples of No. 529 from row 5 have perforations on all four sides.

150 *Papilio machaon* (butterfly) and The Convent.

151 1887 Queen Victoria 6d. Stamp

(Des E. Field. Litho Walsall)

1986 (10 Feb). *Europa. Nature and the Environment. T* **150** *an[d] similar horiz design. Multicoloured. W* w **16** *(sideways[)]. P* 13 × 13½.
532 22p. Type **150** .. .. 1·25 5
533 29p. Herring Gull and Europa Point .. 1·75 4·2

(Des A. Ryman. Litho Walsall)

1986 (26 Mar). *Centenary of First Gibraltar Postage Stamp[.] T* **151** *and similar vert designs showing stamps. Mult[i]coloured. W* w **16**. *P* 14 × 13½ (*44p.*) *or* 13½ × 13 (*others*).
534 4p. Type **151** 30
535 22p. 1903 Edward VII 2½d. .. .. .. 1·00 1·0
536 32p. 1912 George V 1d. .. .. .. 1·50 2·0
537 36p. 1938 George VI £1 .. .. .. 1·60 2·5
538 44p. 1953 Coronation ½d. (29 × 46 *mm*) .. 2·00 3·0
534/8 .. .. *Set of* 5 5·75 7·7
MS539 102×73 mm. 29p. 1886 "GIBRALTAR" overprint on Bermuda 1d. .. .. .. 2·25 2·5
w. Wmk inverted .. .. ..

152 Queen Elizabeth II in Robes of Order of the Bath

153 Prince Andrew and Miss Sarah Ferguson

(Des A. Ryman. Litho Walsall)

1986 (22 May). *60th Birthday of Queen Elizabeth II. W* w **16**[.] *P* 14 × 13½.
540 **152** £1 multicoloured .. .. 1·60 3·0

(Des A. Ryman. Litho Questa)

1986 (28 Aug). *Naval Crests (5th series). Vert designs as T* **134**[.] *Multicoloured. W* w **16**. *P* 14.
541 22p. H.M.S. *Lightning* .. .. .. 1·75 1·0
542 29p. H.M.S. *Hermione* .. .. .. 2·00 1·7
543 32p. H.M.S. *Laforey* .. .. 2·25 3·2
544 44p. H.M.S. *Nelson* .. .. 2·75 4·0
541/4 .. .. *Set of* 4 8·00 9·0

(Des A. Ryman. Litho Questa)

1986 (28 Aug). *Royal Wedding. Sheet* 115 × 85 *mm. W* w **16**[.] *P* 14½.
MS545 **153** 44p. multicoloured .. .. .. 1·10 2·0

154 Three Kings and Cathedral of St. Mary the Crowned

155 Neptune House

(Des M. Infante. Litho Walsall)

1986 (14 Oct). *Christmas. International Peace Year. T* **154** *and similar vert design. Multicoloured. W* w **16**. *P* 14.
546 18p. Type **154** .. .. 1·00 50
547 32p. St. Andrew's Church .. .. .. 1·50 2·75

(Litho Questa)

1986 (12 Dec)–**87**. *As Nos.* 461 *and* 464, *but W* w **16** *(sideways). With "1986" imprint date. P* 14.
549 2p. Vickers Viking 1B .. .. .. 1·50 2·50
552 5p. Boeing 727-100 (2.1.87) .. .. .. 2·00 2·50

(Des M. Infante. Litho Questa)

1987 (17 Feb). *Europa. Architecture. T* **155** *and similar horiz design. Multicoloured. W* w **16**. *P* 14½.
563 22p. Type **155** .. .. 1·50 50
564 29p. Ocean Heights .. .. 2·50 4·00

(Des A. Ryman. Litho Walsall)

1987 (15 Apr). *Naval Crests (6th series). Vert designs as T* **134**. *Multicoloured. W* w **16**. *P* 13½ × 13.
565 18p. H.M.S. *Wishart* (destroyer) .. .. 1·25 75
566 22p. H.M.S. *Charybdis* (cruiser) .. .. 1·40 1·10
567 32p. H.M.S. *Antelope* (destroyer) .. .. 1·90 3·00
568 44p. H.M.S. *Eagle* (aircraft carrier) .. .. 2·50 4·00
565/8 .. .. *Set of* 4 6·50 8·00

156 13-inch Mortar, 1783 **157** Victoria Stadium

(Des A. Ryman. Litho Format)

1987 (1 June). *Guns. T* **156** *and similar horiz designs. Multicoloured. W* w **14**. *P* 12½.

569 1p. Type **156** 20 50
570 2p. 6-inch coastal gun, 1909 .. .. 30 50
571 3p. 8-inch howitzer, 1783 .. .. .. 30 50
572 4p. Bofors "L40/70" AA gun, 1951 .. .. 40 10
573 5p. 100 ton rifled muzzle-loader, 1882 .. 40 50
574 10p. 5.25-inch heavy AA gun, 1953 .. .. 40 55
575 18p. 25-pounder gun-how, 1943 .. .. 65 80
576 19p. 64-pounder rifled muzzle-loader, 1873 .. 70 90
577 22p. 12-pounder gun, 1758 .. .. .. 70 50
578 50p. 10-inch rifled muzzle-loader, 1870 .. 1·40 3·00
579 £1 Russian 24-pounder gun, 1854 .. .. 2·50 3·50
580 £3 9.2-inch "Mk.10" coastal gun, 1935 .. 6·50 14·00
581 £5 24-pounder gun, 1779 .. .. .. 10·00 16·00
569/81 .. .. *Set of* 13 22·00 38·00

(Des A. Ryman. Litho Walsall)

1987 (16 Sept). *Bicentenary of Royal Engineers' Royal Warrant. T* **157** *and similar vert designs. Multicoloured. W* w **14**. *P* 14½.

582 18p. Type **157** .. .. 1·25 65
583 32p. Freedom of Gibraltar scroll and casket 1·75 3·00
584 44p. Royal Engineers' badge .. .. .. 2·50 4·00
582/4 .. .. *Set of* 3 5·00 7·00

158 The Three Kings

(Des Olympia Reyes. Litho Walsall)

1987 (12 Nov). *Christmas. T* **158** *and similar horiz designs. Multicoloured. W* w **16** *(sideways). P* 14½.

585 4p. Type **158** 15 10
586 22p. The Holy Family .. .. .. 90 1·00
587 44p. The Shepherds .. .. 1·75 3·25
585/7 .. .. *Set of* 3 2·50 3·75

159 *Canberra* (liner) passing Gibraltar **160** European Bee Eater

(Des Olympia Reyes. Litho Format)

1988 (16 Feb). *Europa. Transport and Communications. T* **159** *and similar horiz designs. Multicoloured. W* w **14**. *P* 14½ × 14 × *roul between se-tenant pairs.*

588 22p. Type **159** .. .. 1·50 2·25
a. Horiz pair. Nos. 588/9 .. .. 3·00 4·50
589 22p. *Gibline I* (ferry), dish aerial and Boeing 737 .. .. 1·50 2·25
590 32p. Horse-drawn carriage and modern coach .. .. 2·00 2·75
a. Horiz pair. Nos. 590/1 .. .. 4·00 5·50
591 32p. Car, telephone and Rock of Gibraltar 2·00 2·75
588/91 .. .. *Set of* 4 6·25 9·00

The two designs for each value were printed in sheets of ten, each containing five horizontal *se-tenant* pairs in which the stamps were rouletted between vertically.

(Des A. Ryman. Litho Walsall)

1988 (7 Apr). *Naval Crests (7th series). Vert designs as T* **134**. *W* w **16**. *P* 13½ × 13.

592 18p. multicoloured .. .. 1·50 65
593 22p. black, brownish black and gold .. 2·00 1·25
594 32p. multicoloured .. .. 2·25 3·25
595 44p. multicoloured .. .. 3·00 4·50
592/5 .. .. *Set of* 4 8·00 8·75

Designs:—18p. H.M.S. *Clyde*; 22p. H.M.S. *Foresight*; 32p. H.M.S. *Severn*; 44p. H.M.S. *Rodney*.

(Des Olympia Reyes. Litho B.D.T.)

1988 (15 June). *Birds. T* **160** *and similar horiz designs. Multicoloured. W* w **14** *(sideways). P* 13½.

596 4p. Type **160** 65 20
597 22p. Atlantic Puffin .. .. .. 1·50 90
598 32p. Honey Buzzard .. .. .. 2·00 3·00
599 44p. Blue Rock Thrush .. .. .. 2·50 4·25
596/9 .. .. *Set of* 4 6·00 7·50

161 *Zebu* (brigantine) **162** "Snowman" (Rebecca Falero)

(Des A. Ryman. Litho B.D.T.)

1988 (14 Sept). *Operation Raleigh. T* **161** *and similar horiz designs. Multicoloured. W* w **14**. *P* 13.

600 19p. Type **161** 65 60
601 22p. Miniature of Sir Walter Raleigh and logo 75 70
602 32p. *Sir Walter Raleigh* (expedition ship) and world map .. .. .. 1·10 1·50
600/2 .. .. *Set of* 3 2·25 2·50
MS603 135×86 mm. 22p. As No. 601; 44p. *Sir Walter Raleigh* (expedition ship) passing Gibraltar .. .. 3·75 4·25

(Des A. Ryman. Litho Questa)

1988 (2 Nov). *Christmas. Children's Paintings. T* **162** *and similar multicoloured designs. W* w **16** *(sideways). P* 14½ *(44p.) or* 14 *(others).*

604 4p. Type **162** 15 10
605 22p. "The Nativity" (Dennis Penalver) .. 55 60
606 44p. "Father Christmas" (Gavin Key) (23×31 *mm*) .. .. 1·00 1·50
604/6 .. .. *Set of* 3 1·50 2·00

163 Soft Toys and Toy Train **164** Port Sergeant with Keys

(Des Olympia Reyes. Litho Walsall)

1989 (15 Feb). *Europa. Children's Toys. T* **163** *and similar horiz design. Multicoloured. W* w **16** *(sideways). P* 13 × 13½.

607 25p. Type **163** .. .. 1·25 75
608 32p. Soft toys, toy boat and doll's house .. 1·75 2·75

(Des A. Ryman. Litho Walsall)

1989 (28 Apr). *50th Anniv of Gibraltar Regiment. T* **164** *and similar vert designs. Multicoloured. W* w **14**. *P* 13½×13.

609 4p. Type **164** 40 10
610 22p. Regimental badge and colours .. 1·25 95
611 32p. Drum major .. .. 1·75 2·25
609/11 .. .. *Set of* 3 3·00 3·00
MS612 124×83 mm. 22p. As No. 610; 44p. Former Gibraltar Defence Force badge .. 3·00 3·50

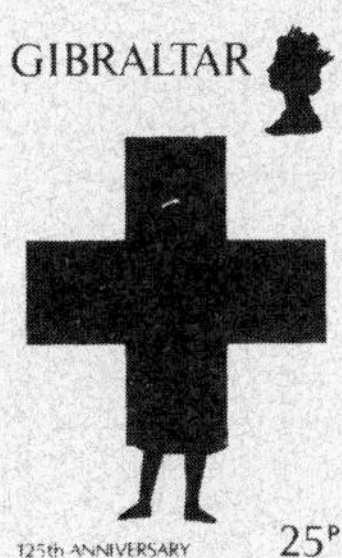

165 Nurse and Baby **166** One Penny Coin

(Des E. Field. Litho Questa)

1989 (7 July). *125th Anniv of International Red Cross. T* **165** *and similar vert designs. W* w **16**. *P* 15×14½.

613 25p. black, bright scarlet and grey-brown .. 75 60
614 32p. black, bright scarlet and grey-brown .. 95 1·60
615 44p. black, bright scarlet and grey-brown .. 1·25 2·75
613/15 .. .. *Set of* 3 2·75 4·50

Designs:—32p. Famine victims; 44p. Accident victims.

(Des A. Ryman. Litho B.D.T.)

1989 (7 Sept). *Naval Crests (8th series). Vert designs as T* **134**. *W* w **16**. *P* 14×13½.

616 22p. multicoloured .. .. .. 1·50 75
617 25p. black and gold .. .. .. 1·50 1·50
618 32p. gold, black and bright scarlet .. .. 2·00 2·25
619 44p. multicoloured .. .. .. 3·00 3·50
616/19 .. .. *Set of* 4 7·25 7·25

Designs:—22p. H.M.S. *Blankney*; 25p. H.M.S. *Deptford*; 32p. H.M.S. *Exmoor*; 44p. H.M.S. *Stork*.

(Des A. Ryman. Litho Questa)

1989 (11 Oct). *New Coinage. T* **166** *and similar vert designs in two miniature sheets. W* w **16** *(sideways). P* 14½.

MS620 72×94 mm. 4p. bronze, black & dull verm (Type **166**); 4p. bronze, blk & dp brn (two pence); 4p. silver, blk & greenish yellow (ten pence); 4p. silver, black and emerald (five pence) .. .. 1·00 1·50
MS621 100×95 mm. 22p. silver, black & reddish orge (fifty pence); 22p. gold, black & ultram (five pounds); 22p. gold, blk & orge-brn (two pounds); 22p. gold, blk & brt emer (one pound); 22p. gold, blk & brt reddish vio (obverse of coin series); 22p. silver, black and pale violet-blue (twenty pence) 4·25 5·50

167 Father Christmas in Sleigh **168** General Post Office Entrance

(Des M. Infante. Litho Questa)

1989 (11 Oct). *Christmas. T* **167** *and similar horiz designs. Multicoloured. W* w **16** *(sideways). P* 14½.

622 4p. Type **167** 15 10
623 22p. Shepherds and sheep 70 70
624 32p. The Nativity .. .. 1·10 1·75
625 44p. The Three Wise Men .. .. .. 1·75 3·00
622/5 .. .. *Set of* 4 3·25 5·00

(Des Olympia Reyes. Litho Questa)

1990 (6 Mar). *Europa. Post Office Buildings. T* **168** *and similar vert designs. Multicoloured. P* 14½×*roul between se-tenant pairs.*

626 22p. Type **168** .. .. 1·00 1·50
a. Horiz pair. Nos. 626/7 .. .. 2·00 3·00
627 22p. Interior of General Post Office .. 1·00 1·50
628 32p. Interior of South District Post Office 1·50 2·25
a. Horiz pair. Nos. 628/9 .. .. 3·00 4·50
629 32p. South District Post Office .. .. 1·50 2·25
626/9 .. .. *Set of* 4 4·50 6·50

Nos. 626/7 and 628/9 were printed in *se-tenant* horizontal pairs within separate sheets of eight, the stamps in each pair being divided by a line of roulettes.

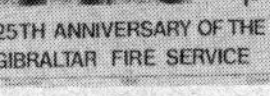

169 19th-century Firemen **170** Henry Corbould (artist) and Penny Black

(Des D. Gonzalez. Litho Questa)

1990 (2 Apr). *125th Anniv of Gibraltar Fire Service. T* **169** *and similar multicoloured designs. P* 14½×14 *(vert) or* 14×14½ *(horiz).*

630 4p. Type **169** 60 15
631 20p. Early fire engine *(horiz)* .. .. 1·50 1·00
632 42p. Modern fire engine *(horiz)* .. .. 1·75 2·75
633 44p. Fireman in breathing apparatus .. 2·00 2·75
630/3 .. .. *Set of* 4 5·25 6·00

(Des A. Ryman. Litho Questa)

1990 (3 May). *150th Anniv of the Penny Black. T* **170** *and similar vert designs. Multicoloured. P* 13½×14.

634 19p. Type **170** 85 70
635 22p. Bath Royal Mail coach 95 80
636 32p. Sir Rowland Hill and Penny Black .. 2·00 3·25
634/6 .. .. *Set of* 3 3·50 4·25
MS637 145×95 mm. 44p. Penny Black with Maltese Cross cancellation. P 14½×14 .. 3·50 3·75

(Des A. Ryman. Litho Questa)

1990 (10 July). *Naval Crests (9th series). Vert designs as T* **134**. *Multicoloured. P* 14.

638 22p. H.M.S. *Calpe* .. .. 1·50 70
639 25p. H.M.S. *Gallant* .. .. .. 1·60 1·75
640 32p. H.M.S. *Wrestler* .. .. .. 2·00 2·75
641 44p. H.M.S. *Greyhound* .. .. .. 2·50 3·75
638/41 .. .. *Set of* 4 7·00 8·00

ALTERED CATALOGUE NUMBERS

Any Catalogue numbers altered from the last edition are shown as a list in the introductory pages.

171 Model of Europort Development

172 Candle and Holly

(Des A. Ryman. Litho Questa)

1990 (10 Oct). *Development Projects. T* **171** *and similar horiz designs. Multicoloured. P* 14½.

642	22p. Type **171**	75	80
643	23p. Construction of building material factory	75	1·40
644	25p. Land reclamation	95	1·40
642/4	*Set of* 3	2·25	3·25

(Des D. Gonzalez. Litho B.D.T.)

1990 (10 Oct). *Christmas. T* **172** *and similar vert designs. Multicoloured. P* 13½.

645	4p. Type **172**	15	10
646	22p. Father Christmas	75	65
647	42p. Christmas Tree	1·50	2·25
648	44p. Nativity crib	1·50	2·25
645/8	*Set of* 4	3·50	4·75

173 Space Laboratory and Spaceplane (Colombus Development Programme)

174 Shag

(Des D. Gonzalez. Litho B.D.T.)

1991 (26 Feb). *Europa. Europe in Space. T* **173** *and similar horiz design. Multicoloured. P* 13½×13.

649	25p. Type **173**	75	75
650	32p. "ERS-1" earth resources remote sensing satellite	1·00	2·00

(Des A. Ryman. Litho Walsall)

1991 (9 Apr). *Naval Crests (10th series). Vert designs as T* **134**. *P* 13½×13.

651	4p. black, new blue and gold	35	10
652	21p. multicoloured	1·25	1·25
653	22p. multicoloured	1·25	1·25
654	62p. multicoloured	3·25	5·50
651/4	*Set of* 4	5·50	7·25

Designs:—4p. H.M.S. *Hesperus*; 21p. H.M.S. *Forester*; 22p. H.M.S. *Furious*; 62p. H.M.S. *Scylla*.

(Des Olympia Reyes. Litho B.D.T.)

1991 (30 May). *Endangered Species. Birds. T* **174** *and similar horiz designs. Multicoloured. P* 13½.

655	13p. Type **174**	85	1·10
	a. Block of 4. Nos. 655/8	3·00	
656	13p. Barbary Partridge	85	1·10
657	13p. Egyptian Vulture	85	1·10
658	13p. Black Stork	85	1·10
655/8	*Set of* 4	3·00	4·00

Nos. 655/8 were printed together, *se-tenant*, in differently arranged blocks of 4 throughout the sheet of 16.

≡ £1.05

(175)

176 "North View of Gibraltar" (Gustavo Bacarisas)

1991 (30 May). *No. 580 surch with T* **175**.

659	£1.05 on £3 9.2-inch "Mk.10" coastal gun, 1935	3·50	1·60

(Des A. Ryman. Litho B.D.T.)

1991 (10 Sept). *Local Paintings. T* **176** *and similar multicoloured designs. P* 14×15 (42*p.*) *or* 15×14 (*others*).

660	22p. Type **176**	85	50
661	26p. "Parson's Lodge" (Elena Mifsud)	1·00	1·00
662	32p. "Governor's Parade" (Jacobo Azagury)	1·50	2·25
663	42p. "Waterport Wharf" (Rudesindo Mannia) (*vert*)	2·25	3·50
660/3	*Set of* 4	5·00	6·50

NEW INFORMATION

The editor is always interested to correspond with people who have new information that will improve or correct the Catalogue.

177 "Once in Royal David's City"

178 *Danaus chrysippus*

(Des D. Gonzalez. Litho Questa)

1991 (15 Oct). *Christmas. Carols. T* **177** *and similar horiz designs. Multicoloured. P* 14×14½.

664	4p. Type **177**	20	10
665	24p. "Silent Night"	1·00	70
666	25p. "Angels We have Heard on High"	1·00	1·25
667	49p. "O Come All Ye Faithful"	1·75	3·00
664/7	*Set of* 4	3·50	4·50

(Des A. Ryman. Litho Questa)

1991 (15 Nov). *"Phila Nippon '91" International Stamp Exhibition, Tokyo. Sheet* 116×91 *mm. P* 14½.

MS668	**178** £1.05, multicoloured	3·50	4·25

179 Columbus and *Santa Maria*

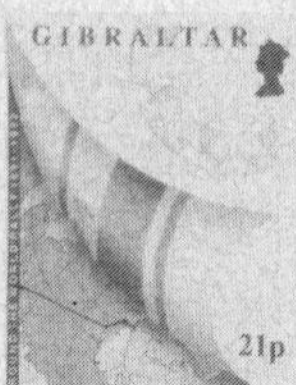

180 Compass Rose, Sail and Atlantic Map

(Des Olympia Reyes. Litho Walsall)

1992 (6 Feb). *Europa. 500th Anniv of Discovery of America by Columbus. T* **179** *and similar horiz designs. Multicoloured. P* 14½.

669	24p. Type **179**	1·00	1·50
	a. Horiz pair. Nos. 669/70	2·00	3·00
670	24p. Map of Old World and *Nina*	1·00	1·50
671	34p. Map of New World and *Pinta*	1·25	1·75
	a. Horiz pair. Nos. 671/2	2·50	3·50
672	34p. Map of Old World and look-out	1·25	1·75
669/72	*Set of* 4	4·00	6·00

The two designs of each value were printed together, *se-tenant*, in sheets of eight, the background to each horizontal pair forming a composite design.

(Des D. Miller. Litho Questa (54p), B.D.T. (others))

1992 (6 Feb). *40th Anniv of Queen Elizabeth II's Accession. Horiz designs as T* **143** *of Ascension. Multicoloured. W w* **14** (*sideways*). *P* 14.

673	4p. Gibraltar from North	15	10
674	20p. H.M.S. *Arrow* (frigate) and Gibraltar from South	60	60
675	24p. Southport Gates	75	80
676	44p. Three portraits of Queen Elizabeth	1·25	1·60
677	54p. Queen Elizabeth II	1·60	1·90
673/7	*Set of* 5	4·00	4·50

(Des E. Field. Litho B.D.T.)

1992 (15 Apr). *Round the World Yacht Rally. T* **180** *and similar multicoloured designs, each incorporating compass rose and sail. P* 13½.

678	21p. Type **180**	75	80
679	24p. Map of Indonesian Archipelago (*horiz*)	95	1·40
680	25p. Map of Indian Ocean (*horiz*)	95	1·75
678/80	*Set of* 3	2·40	3·50
MS681	108×72 mm. 21p. Type **180**; 49p. Map of Mediterranean and Red Sea	2·25	3·25

181 Holy Trinity Cathedral

182 Sacred Heart of Jesus Church

(Des M. Infante. Litho Questa)

1992 (21 Aug). *150th Anniv of Anglican Diocese of Gibraltar-in-Europe. T* **181** *and similar multicoloured designs. P* 14.

682	4p. Type **181**	20	10
683	24p. Diocesan crest and map (*horiz*)	1·00	65
684	44p. Construction of Cathedral and Sir George Don (*horiz*)	1·75	2·75
685	54p. Bishop Tomlinson	2·00	3·00
682/5	*Set of* 4	4·50	6·00

(Des W. Stagnetto. Litho B.D.T.)

1992 (10 Nov). *Christmas. Churches. T* **182** *and similar vert designs. Multicoloured. P* 14×13½.

686	4p. Type **182**	20	10
687	24p. Cathedral of St. Mary the Crowned	1·00	55
688	34p. St. Andrew's Church of Scotland	1·60	2·25
689	49p. St. Joseph's Church	2·25	3·75
686/9	*Set of* 4	4·50	6·00

183 "Drama and Music"

184 H.M.S. *Hood* (battle cruiser)

(Des E. Field. Litho Questa)

1993 (2 Mar). *Europa. Contemporary Art. T* **183** *and similar vert designs. Multicoloured. P* 14½×14.

690	24p. Type **183**	1·25	1·50
	a. Horiz pair. Nos. 690/1	2·50	3·00
691	24p. "Sculpture, Art and Pottery"	1·25	1·50
692	34p. "Architecture"	1·75	2·25
	a. Horiz pair. Nos. 692/3	3·50	4·50
693	34p. "Printing and Photography"	1·75	2·25
690/3	*Set of* 4	5·50	6·50

Nos. 690/1 and 692/3 were printed together, *se-tenant*, as horizontal pairs in sheetlets of 8 with decorative margins.

(Des D. Miller. Litho B.D.T.)

1993 (27 Apr). *Second World War Warships (1st series). Sheet* 120×79 *mm containing T* **184** *and similar horiz designs. Multicoloured. P* 14.

MS694	24p. Type **184**; 24p. H.M.S. *Ark Royal* (aircraft carrier, 1937); 24p. H.M.A.S. *Waterhen* (destroyer); 24p. U.S.S. *Gleaves* (destroyer)	6·50	6·5

See also Nos. **MS**724, **MS**748, **MS**779 and **MS**809.

185 Landport Gate

186 £sd and Decimal British Coins (25th anniv of Decimal Currency)

(Des Olympia Reyes. Litho and thermography Cartor (£5), litho Cartor (6, 7, 8, 9, 20, 30, 40p. and £2) or B.D.T. (others))

1993 (28 June)–**95**. *Architectural Heritage. T* **185** *and similar multicoloured designs. P* 13.

695	1p. Type **185**	10	10
696	2p. St. Mary the Crowned Church (*horiz*)	10	10
697	3p. Parsons Lodge Battery (*horiz*)	10	10
698	4p. Moorish Castle (*horiz*)	10	10
699	5p. General Post Office	10	10
699*a*	6p. House of Assembly (1.9.95)	10	10
699*b*	7p. Bleak House (*horiz*) (1.9.95)	15	20
699*c*	8p. General Eliott Memorial (1.9.95)	15	20
699*d*	9p. Supreme Court Building (*horiz*) (1.9.95)	20	25
700	10p. South Barracks (*horiz*)	20	25
700*a*	20p. The Convent (*horiz*) (1.9.95)	40	45
701	21p. American War Memorial	40	45
702	24p. Garrison Library (*horiz*)	50	55
703	25p. Southport Gates	50	55
704	26p. Casemates Gate (*horiz*)	50	55
704*a*	30p. St. Bernard's Hospital (1.9.95)	60	65
704*b*	40p. City Hall (*horiz*) (1.9.95)	80	85
705	50p. Central Police Station (*horiz*)	1·00	1·10
706	£1 Prince Edward's Gate	2·00	2·25
706*a*	£2 Church of the Sacred Heart of Jesus (1.9.95)	4·00	4·25
707	£3 Lighthouse, Europa Point	6·00	6·25
708	£5 Coat of arms and Fortress keys (6.6.94)	10·00	10·50
695/708	*Set of* 22	27·00	29·00

(Des W. Stagnetto. Litho Cartor)

1993 (21 Sept). *Anniversaries. T* **186** *and similar horiz designs. Multicoloured. P* 13.

709	21p. Type **186**	75	65
710	24p. R.A.F. crest with Handley Page 0/400 biplane and Panavia Tornado F Mk 3 fighter (75th anniv)	1·00	75
711	34p. Garrison Library badge and building (Bicent)	1·40	2·00
712	49p. Sir Winston Churchill and air raid (50th anniv of visit)	2·00	3·00
709/12	*Set of* 4	4·75	5·75

187 Mice decorating Christmas Tree

(Des Josie Evans. Litho Cartor)

93 (16 Nov). *Christmas. T* **187** *and similar horiz designs. Multicoloured. P* 13½.
3 5p. Type **187** 20 10
4 24p. Mice pulling cracker 90 70
5 44p. Mice singing carols .. .. .. 1·75 2·25
6 49p. Mice building snowman .. .. 1·90 2·50
3/16 .. .. *Set of* 4 4·25 5·00

188 Exploding Atom (Lord Penney)

(Des M. Braunewell. Litho Cartor)

994 (1 Mar). *Europa. Scientific Discoveries. T* **188** *and similar horiz designs. Multicoloured. P* 13½.
17 24p. Type **188** .. .. 1·00 1·25
a. Horiz pair. Nos. 717/18 .. .. 2·00 2·50
18 24p. Polonium and radium experiment (Marie Curie) .. .. .. 1·00 1·25
19 34p. First oil engine (Rudolph Diesel) .. 1·25 1·75
a. Horiz pair. Nos. 719/20 .. .. 2·50 3·50
20 34p. Early telescope (Galileo) .. .. 1·25 1·75
17/20 .. .. *Set of* 4 4·00 5·50
Nos. 717/18 and 719/20 were each printed together, *se-tenant*, n horizontal pairs in sheetlets of 8 with decorative margins.

189 World Cup and Map of U.S.A

(Des M. Braunewell. Litho Cartor)

994 (19 Apr). *World Cup Football Championship, U.S.A. T* **189** *and similar multicoloured designs. P* 13½.
21 26p. Type **189** 80 55
22 39p. Players and pitch in shape of U.S.A. 1·25 1·75
23 49p. Player's legs (*vert*) .. .. .. 1·60 2·50
21/3 .. .. *Set of* 3 3·25 4·25

(Des D. Miller. Litho Cartor)

994 (6 June). *Second World War Warships (2nd series). Sheet* 112×72 *mm containing horiz designs as T* **184**. *Multicoloured. P* 13.
1S724 5p. H.M.S. *Penelope* (cruiser); 25p. H.M.S. *Warspite* (battleship); 44p. U.S.S. *McLanahan* (destroyer); 49p. *Isaac Sweers* (Dutch destroyer) .. .. 4·50 6·00

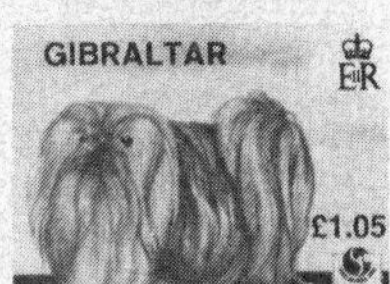

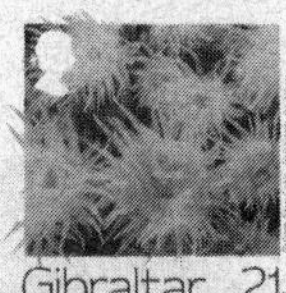

190 Pekingese **191** Golden Star Coral

(Des M. Braunewell. Litho B.D.T.)

1994 (16 Aug). *"Philakorea '94" International Stamp Exhibiton, Seoul. Sheet* 102×76 *mm. P* 13.
MS725 **190** £1.05, multicoloured .. .. 3·00 4·00

(Des M. Whyte. Litho Walsall)

1994 (27 Sept). *Marine Life. T* **191** *and similar square designs. Multicoloured. P* 14½×14.
726 21p. Type **191** 75 45
727 24p. Star Fish 90 55
728 34p. Gorgonian Sea-fan .. .. .. 1·50 2·25
729 49p. Peacock Wrasse ("Turkish Wrasse") 2·00 3·25
726/9 .. .. *Set of* 4 4·75 6·00

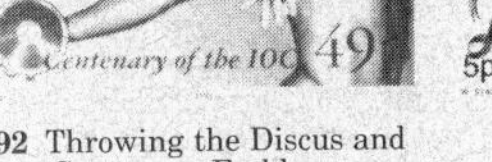

192 Throwing the Discus and Centenary Emblem **193** Great Tit

(Des S. Perera. Litho Walsall)

1994 (22 Nov). *Centenary of International Olympic Committee. T* **192** *and similar horiz design. Multicoloured. P* 14.
730 49p. Type **192** .. .. 1·50 2·00
731 54p. Javelin throwing and emblem .. 1·75 2·50

(Des W. Stagnetto. Litho B.D.T.)

1994 (22 Nov). *Christmas. Songbirds. T* **193** *and similar multicoloured designs. P* 14×13½ (*vert*) *or* 13½×14 (*horiz*).
732 5p. Type **193** 25 10
733 24p. European Robin (*horiz*) 90 70
734 34p. Blue Tit (*horiz*) .. .. .. 1·25 1·50
735 54p. Goldfinch .. .. 1·75 2·75
732/5 .. .. *Set of* 4 3·75 4·50

194 Austrian Flag, Hand and Star

(Des R. Ollington. Litho Questa)

1995 (3 Jan). *Expansion of European Union. T* **194** *and similar horiz designs. Multicoloured. P* 14.
736 24p. Type **194** 60 55
737 26p. Finnish flag, hand and star 60 60
738 34p. Swedish flag, hand and star .. .. 90 1·50
739 49p. Flags of new members and European Union emblem .. .. .. 1·60 2·50
736/9 .. .. *Set of* 4 3·25 4·50

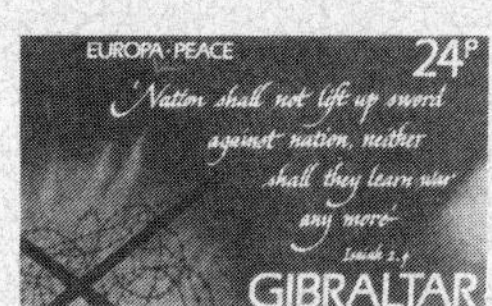

195 Barbed Wire and Quote from Isaiah Ch 2.4

(Des Jennifer Toombs. Litho B.D.T.)

1995 (28 Feb). *Europa. Peace and Freedom. T* **195** *and similar horiz designs. Multicoloured. P* 13½.
740 24p. Type **195** .. .. 70 1·00
a. Horiz pair. Nos. 740/1 .. .. 1·40 2·00
741 24p. Rainbow and hands releasing peace dove .. .. 70 1·00
742 34p. Shackles on wall and quote from Isaiah ch 61.1 .. .. 1·00 1·40
a. Horiz pair. Nos. 742/3 .. .. 2·00 2·75
743 34p. Hands and sea-birds .. .. .. 1·00 1·40
740/3 .. .. *Set of* 4 3·00 4·25
Nos. 740/1 and 742/3 were each printed together, *se-tenant*, as horizontal pairs in sheetlets of 8 with decorative margins.

196 Fairey Swordfish, I Class Destroyer and Rock of Gibraltar

(Des A. Theobald. Litho B.D.T.)

1995 (8 May). *50th Anniv of End of Second World War. Sheet* 101×66 *mm. P* 13½.
MS744 **196** £1.05, multicoloured .. .. 2·75 3·50

197 Yachting **198** Bee Orchid

(Des S. Perera. Litho B.D.T.)

1995 (8 May). *Island Games '95. T* **197** *and similar vert designs. Multicoloured. P* 14×13½.
745 24p. Type **197** 50 60
a. Booklet pane. No. 745×3, with margins all round .. .. 1·40
b. Booklet pane. Nos. 745/7, with margins all round .. .. 3·25
746 44p. Athlete on starting blocks .. .. 1·50 2·25
a. Booklet pane. No. 746×3, with margins all round .. .. 4·25
747 49p. Swimmer at start of race .. .. 1·50 2·25
a. Booklet pane. No. 747×3, with margins all round .. .. 4·25
745/7 .. .. *Set of* 3 3·25 4·50

(Des D. Miller. Litho Questa)

1995 (6 June). *Second World War Warships (3rd series). Sheet* 133×85 *mm containing horiz designs as T* **184**. *Multicoloured. P* 13½×14.
MS748 5p. H.M.S. *Calpe* (destroyer); 24p. H.M.S. *Victorious* (aircraft carrier); 44p. U.S.S. *Weehawken* (attack transport); 49p. *Savorgan de Brazza* (French sloop) .. .. 5·00 5·50

(Des R. Gorringe. Litho B.D.T.)

1995 (1 Sept). *"Singapore '95" International Stamp Exhibition. Orchids. T* **198** *and similar vert designs. Multicoloured. P* 14×14½.
749 22p. Type **198** 65 85
a. Horiz strip of 5. Nos. 749/53 .. .. 3·00
750 23p. Brown Bee Orchid 65 85
751 24p. Pyramidal Orchid 65 85
752 25p. Mirror Orchid 65 85
753 26p. Sawfly Orchid 65 85
749/53 .. .. *Set of* 5 3·00 3·75
Nos. 749/53 were printed together, *se-tenant*, in horizontal strips of 5.

199 Handshake and United Nations Emblem

(Des S. Perera. Litho B.D.T.)

1995 (24 Oct). *50th Anniv of United Nations. T* **199** *and similar horiz design. Multicoloured. P* 13½.
754 34p. Type **199** .. .. 1·10 1·10
755 49p. Peace dove and U.N. emblem .. 1·40 2·00

200 Marilyn Monroe **201** Father Christmas

(Des M. Whyte. Litho Questa)

1995 (13 Nov). *Centenary of Cinema. T* **200** *and similar horiz designs showing film stars. Multicoloured. P* 14½×14.
MS756 Two sheets, each 116×80 mm. (a) 5p. Type **200**; 25p. Romy Schneider; 28p. Yves Montand; 38p. Audrey Hepburn. (b) 24p. Ingrid Bergman; 24p. Vittorio de Sica; 24p. Marlene Dietrich; 24p. Laurence Olivier *Set of* 2 *sheets* 4·50 5·50

(Des M. Whyte. Litho B.D.T.)

1995 (27 Nov). *Christmas. T* **201** *and similar square designs. Multicoloured. P* 14.
757 5p. Type **201** 15 10
758 24p. Toys in sack 65 55
759 34p. Reindeer .. .. 90 1·25
760 54p. Sleigh over houses .. .. .. 1·25 1·75
757/60 .. .. *Set of* 4 2·75 3·25

202 Shih Tzu

(Des Doreen McGuinness. Litho B.D.T.)

1996 (24 Jan). *Puppies. T* **202** *and similar horiz designs. Multicoloured. P* 14.
761 5p. Type **202** 30 40
a. Sheetlet. Nos. 761/6 .. .. .. 3·50
762 21p. Dalmatians 60 70
763 24p. Cocker Spaniels 70 80
764 25p. West Highland White Terriers .. 70 80
765 34p. Labrador 80 85
766 35p. Boxer 80 85
761/6 .. .. *Set of* 6 3·50 4·00
Nos. 761/6 were printed together, *se-tenant*, in sheetlets of 6.
No. 762 is inscr "Dalmation" in error.

203 Princess Anne

204 West German Player, 1980

(Des R. Ollington. Litho B.D.T.)

1996 (9 Feb). *Europa. Famous Women. T* **203** *and similar horiz designs. P* 13½.

767 **203** 24p. black and yellow 75 75
768 – 24p. black and deep turquoise-green .. 75 75
769 – 34p. black and vermilion .. .. .. 1·00 1·50
770 – 34p. black and purple .. .. .. 1·00 1·50
767/70 .. .. *Set of* 4 3·25 4·00

Details:—No. 768, Princess Diana; No. 769, Queen Elizabeth II; No. 770, Queen Elizabeth the Queen Mother.

Nos. 767/70 were each printed in sheets of 10 with inscribed margins all round.

(Des S. Noon. Litho Walsall)

1996 (2 Apr). *European Football Championship, England. T* **204** *and similar vert designs showing players from previous winning teams. Multicoloured. P* 13.

771 21p. Type **204** 55 45
772 24p. French player, 1984 .. .. 65 55
773 34p. Dutch player, 1988 .. .. 95 1·10
774 £1.20, Danish player, 1992 .. .. .. 3·00 4·25
771/4 .. .. *Set of* 4 4·75 5·75
MS775 135×91 mm. As Nos. 771/4. P 13×13½ 6·00 6·50

205 Ancient Greek Athletes

206 Asian Children

(Des K. Bassford. Litho Walsall)

1996 (2 May). *Centenary of Modern Olympic Games. T* **205** *and similar horiz designs. P* 13½.

776 34p. black, deep reddish purple & brt orange 95 90
777 49p. black and grey-brown .. .. .. 1·40 1·75
778 £1.05, multicoloured .. .. 2·75 3·50
776/8 .. .. *Set of* 3 4·50 5·50

Designs:—49p. Start of early race; £1.05, Start of modern race.

(Des D. Miller. Litho Walsall)

1996 (8 June). *Second World War Warships* (4*th series*). *Sheet,* 118×84 *mm, containing horiz designs as T* **184**. *Multicoloured. P* 14.

MS779 5p. H.M.S. *Starling* (sloop); 25p. H.M.S. *Royalist* (cruiser); 49p. U.S.S. *Philadelphia* (cruiser); 54p. H.M.C.S. *Prescott* (corvette) .. 4·00 4·50

(Des S. Noon. Litho Walsall)

1996 (8 June). *50th Anniv of U.N.I.C.E.F. T* **206** *and similar horiz designs showing children from different continents. P* 13½×13.

780 21p. multicoloured 60 80
a. Horiz strip of 4. Nos. 780/3 .. .. 3·50
781 24p. multicoloured 70 90
782 49p. multicoloured .. .. 1·25 1·40
783 54p. multicoloured .. .. 1·40 1·60
780/3 .. .. *Set of* 4 3·50 4·25

Nos. 780/3 were printed together, *se-tenant*, in horizontal strips of 4 throughout the sheet.

207 Red Kites in Flight

(Des R. Gorringe. Litho Walsall)

1996 (30 Sept). *Endangered Species. Red Kite. T* **207** *and similar horiz designs. Multicoloured. P* 14½.

784 34p. Type **207** .. .. 90 1·10
a. Block of 4. Nos. 784/7 .. .. .. 3·25
785 34p. Red Kite on ground .. .. .. 90 1·10
786 34p. On rock .. .. 90 1·10
787 34p. Pair at nest .. .. 90 1·10
784/7 .. .. *Set of* 4 3·25 4·00

Nos. 784/7 were printed together, *se-tenant*, in blocks of four throughout the sheet.

208 Christmas Pudding

209 *Mary Celeste* passing Gibraltar

(Des K. Bassford. Litho Questa)

1996 (27 Nov). *Christmas. T* **208** *and similar horiz designs created from "Lego" blocks. Multicoloured. P* 14×14½.

788 5p. Type **208** 15 15
789 21p. Snowman face 60 45
790 24p. Present 70 55
791 34p. Father Christmas face .. .. .. 90 1·25
792 54p. Candle .. .. 1·25 1·90
788/92 .. .. *Set of* 5 3·25 3·75

(Des S. Tarabay. Litho Questa)

1997 (12 Feb). *Europa. Tales and Legends. The* Mary Celeste. *T* **209** *and similar square designs. Multicoloured. P* 14.

793 28p. Type **209** 70 80
794 28p. Boarding the *Mary Celeste* 70 80
795 30p. Crew leaving *Mary Celeste* 80 95
796 30p. *Mary Celeste* found by *Dei Gratia* .. 80 95
793/6 .. .. *Set of* 4 2·75 3·25

210 American Shorthair Silver Tabby

211 *Anthocharis belia euphenoides*

(Des Colleen Corlett. Litho B.D.T.)

1997 (12 Feb). *Kittens. T* **210** *and similar horiz designs. Multicoloured. P* 13½×14.

797 5p. Type **210** 30 40
a. Booklet pane. Nos. 797, 799 and 801 with margins all round .. .. .. 1·50
b. Booklet pane. Nos. 797/8 and 801/2 with margins all round .. .. .. 2·25
798 24p. Rumpy Manx Red Tabby 65 75
a. Booklet pane. Nos. 798/800 with margins all round .. .. .. 1·75
799 26p. Blue Point Birmans 65 75
a. Booklet pane. Nos. 799/802 with margins all round .. .. .. 2·50
800 28p. Red Self Longhair 70 85
801 30p. British Shorthair Tortoiseshell and White 70 85
802 35p. British Bicolour Shorthairs 80 90
797/802 .. .. *Set of* 6 3·50 4·00
MS803 132×80 mm. Nos. 797/802 with "HONG KONG '97" International Stamp Exhibition logo at bottom left .. .. 4·00 4·50
a. Booklet pane. As No. **MS**803, but without "HONG KONG '97" logo and with additional line of roulettes at left .. .. 3·50

Nos. 797/802 were only issued in £5 stamp booklets or miniature sheet No. **MS**803

(Des R. Gorringe. Litho Enschedé)

1997 (7 Apr). *Butterflies. T* **211** *and similar vert designs. Multicoloured. P* 14×13½.

804 23p. Type **211** 60 50
805 26p. *Charaxes jasius* 75 60
806 30p. *Vanessa cardui* 80 90
807 £1.20, *Iphiclides podalirius* .. .. 3·00 3·75
804/7 .. .. *Set of* 4 4·75 5·25
MS808 135×90 mm. Nos. 804/7 .. .. 4·75 5·50

(Des D. Miller. Litho Cartor)

1997 (9 June). *Second World War Warships* (5*th series*). *Sheet,* 117×82 *mm, containing horiz designs as T* **184**. *Multicoloured. P* 13½.

MS809 24p. H.M.S. *Enterprise* (cruiser); 26p. H.M.S. *Cleopatra* (cruiser); 38p. U.S.S. *Iowa* (battleship); 50p. *Orkan* (Polish destroyer) .. 3·25 3·50

212 Queen Elizabeth and Prince Philip at Carriage-driving Trials

(Des C. Abbott. Litho Questa)

1997 (10 July). *Golden Wedding of Queen Elizabeth and Prince Philip. T* **212** *and similar horiz design. Multicoloured. P* 13½.

810 £1.20, Type **212** .. .. 3·00 3·50
a. Horiz pair. Nos. 810/11 .. .. 6·00 7·00
811 £1.40 Queen Elizabeth in Trooping the Colour uniform .. .. 3·00 3·50

Nos. 810/11 were printed together, *se-tenant*, in horizontal pairs throughout the sheet.

213 Christian Dior Evening Dress

214 "Our Lady and St. Bernard" (St. Joseph's Parish Church)

(Des M. Whyte. Litho B.D.T.)

1997 (24 Oct). *Christian Dior Spring/Summer '97 Collection designed by John Galliano. T* **213** *and similar vert designs. Multicoloured. P* 13½.

812 30p. Type **213** 80 90
a. Horiz pair. Nos. 812 and 814 .. .. 2·00 2·25
813 35p. Tunic top and skirt .. .. .. 1·10 1·25
a. Horiz pair. Nos. 813 and 815 .. .. 2·50 3·00
814 50p. Ballgown .. .. 1·25 1·40
815 62p. Two-piece suit .. .. .. 1·60 1·90
812/15 .. .. *Set of* 4 4·25 5·00
MS816 110×90 mm. £1.20, Ballgown (*different*) 2·75 3·25

Nos. 812 with 814 and 813 with 815 were each printed together, *se-tenant*, in sheets of 8 with enlarged illustrated right-hand margin.

(Des S. Perera. Litho Cartor)

1997 (18 Nov). *Christmas. Stained Glass Windows. T* **214** *and similar vert designs. Multicoloured. P* 13½.

817 5p. Type **214** 15 10
818 26p. "The Epiphany" (Our Lady of Sorrows Church) 65 60
819 38p. "St. Joseph" (Our Lady of Sorrows Church) 85 90
820 50p. "The Holy Family" (St. Joseph's Parish Church) .. .. 1·25 1·40
821 62p. "The Miraculous Medal" (St. Joseph's Parish Church) .. .. .. 1·50 2·00
817/21 .. .. *Set of* 5 4·00 4·50

215 Sir Joshua Hassan

216 Wales v Brazil (1958)

(Des S. Perera. Litho Cartor)

1997 (15 Dec). *Sir Joshua Hassan (former Chief Minister) Commemoration. P* 13.

822 **215** 26p. black 55 60

(Des L. Montgomery. Litho Cartor)

1998 (23 Jan). *World Football Championship, France* (1998). *T* **216** *and similar vert designs. Multicoloured. P* 13.

823 5p. Type **216** 15 10
824 26p. Northern Ireland v France (1958) .. 65 60
825 38p. Scotland v Holland (1978) 85 90
826 $1.20, England v West Germany (1966) 2·50 3·25
823/6 .. .. *Set of* 4 3·75 4·25
MS827 153×96 mm. Nos. 823/6 .. .. 3·75 4·25

(Des D. Miller. Litho Questa)

1998 (31 Mar). *Diana, Princess of Wales Commemoration. Sheet,* 145×70 *mm, containing vert designs as T* **177** *of Ascension. Multicoloured. P* 14½×14.

MS828 26p. Wearing jacket with white fur collar, 1988; 26p. Wearing pink checked suit and hat; 38p. Wearing black jacket, 1995; 38p. Wearing blue jacket with gold embroidery, 1987 (*sold at* £1.28 + 20p. *charity premium*) .. .. 3·25 3·50

(Des A. Theobald. Litho B.D.T.)

998 (1 Apr). *80th Anniv of Royal Air Force. Horiz designs as T* **178** *of Ascension. Multicoloured. P* 14.

29 24p. Saro London (flying boat) 70 55
30 26p. Fairey Fox 75 60
31 38p. Handley Page Halifax GR.VI .. 95 95
32 50p. Hawker Siddeley Buccaneer S.2B .. 1·25 1·40
29/32 .. .. *Set of* 4 3·25 3·25
1S833 110×77 mm. 24p. Sopwith 1½ Strutter; 26p. Bristol M.IB; 38p. Supermarine Spitfire XII; 50p. Avro York .. .. 3·25 3·50

217 Miss Gibraltar saluting

218 Striped Dolphin

(Des S. Perera. Litho Cartor)

998 (22 May). *Europa. Festivals. National Day. T* **217** *and similar vert designs showing Miss Gibraltar in various costumes. Multicoloured. P* 13½×13.

334 26p. Type **217** 70 70
335 26p. In black bodice and long red skirt .. 70 70
336 38p. In black bodice and short red skirt, with Gibraltar flag .. .. .. 95 1·10
337 38p. In Genoese-style costume .. .. 95 1·10
334/7 .. .. *Set of* 4 3·00 3·25

Nos. 834/7 were each printed in sheets of 10 with enlarged illustrated right-hand margins.

(Des L. Montgomery. Litho Questa)

1998 (22 May). *International Year of the Ocean. Sheet,* 155×64 *mm, containing T* **218** *and similar multicoloured designs. P* 14.

MS838 5p. Type **218**; 5p. Common Dolphin (*vert*); 26p. Killer Whale (*vert*); £1.20, Blue Whale .. 3·75 4·00

219 Nileus (dog) with Hat and Telescope

220 "Love comforts like Sunshine after Rain" (William Shakespeare)

(Des M. Hargreaves. Litho Cartor)

1998 (1 Aug). *Bicent of Battle of the Nile. T* **219** *and similar multicoloured designs. P* 13½.

839 12p. Type **219** 35 30
a. Booklet pane. Nos. 839/41 with margins all round .. .. .. 1·75
b. Booklet pane. Nos. 839/43 with margins all round .. .. .. 3·75
840 26p. Rear-Admiral Sir Horatio Nelson .. 65 55
a. Booklet pane. No. 840 with margins all round 65
b. Booklet pane. Nos. 840×2 and 842/3 with margins all round .. .. 3·50
c. Booklet pane. Nos. 840 and 842/3 with margins all round .. .. .. 2·75
841 28p. Frances Nisbet, Lady Nelson .. 75 75
842 35p. H.M.S. *Vanguard* (ship of the line) .. 95 95
843 50p. Battle of the Nile (47×29 *mm*) .. 1·25 1·50
839/43 .. .. *Set of* 5 3·50 3·50

(Des M. Whyte. Litho Questa)

1998 (6 Oct). *Famous Quotations. T* **220** *and similar horiz designs. Multicoloured. P* 14½.

844 26p. Type **220** 55 60
845 26p. "The price of greatness is responsibility" (Sir Winston Churchill) .. 55 60
846 38p. "Hate the sin, love the sinner" (Mahatma Gandhi) 75 80
847 38p. "Imagination is more important than knowledge" (Albert Einstein) .. 75 80
844/7 .. .. *Set of* 4 2·50 2·75

Nos. 844/7 were each issued in sheets of 6 stamps and 6 half stamp-size labels showing the quotations in different languages.

221 The Nativity

(Des Petula Stone. Litho Walsall)

1998 (10 Nov). *Christmas. T* **221** *and similar vert designs. Multicoloured. P* 13½.

848 5p. Type **221** 10 10
849 26p. Star and stable 55 60
850 30p. King with gold 60 65
851 35p. King with myrrh 70 75
852 50p. King with frankincense .. .. 1·00 1·10
848/52 .. .. *Set of* 5 2·75 3·00

STAMP BOOKLETS

1909. *Black on red cover. Stapled.*
SB1 2s. ½d. booklet containing twenty-four ½d. and twelve 1d. (Nos. 66/7) in blocks of 6 .. ..

1912 (15 May). *Black on red cover with Edwardian cypher. Stapled.*
SB2 2s. ½d. booklet containing twenty-four ½d. and twelve 1d. (Nos. 76/7) in blocks of 6 .. ..

1921. *Black on red cover. Stapled.*
SB2*a* 2s. booklet containing twenty-four ½d. and twelve 1d. (Nos. 89/90) in blocks of 6 ..

B 1
(*Illustration reduced. Actual size* 152×79 *mm*)

1974 (2 May). *Centenary of Universal Postal Union. Multicoloured cover as Type* B **1**. *Stitched.*
SB3 46p. booklet containing *se-tenant* panes of 3 (No. 328a) and 6 (No. 328b) .. .. .. 7·50

1975 (17 Dec). 500*th Birth Anniv of Michelangelo. Multicoloured cover as Type* B **1**, *but* 165×91 *mm showing Michelangelo. Stitched.*
SB4 90p. booklet containing *se-tenant* panes of 3 (No. 358a) and 6 (No. 358b) .. .. .. 4·50

1978 (12 June). 25*th Anniv of Coronation. Multicoloured cover as Type* B **1**, *but* 165×92 *mm showing Buckingham Palace. Stitched.*
SB5 £1.15, booklet containing *se-tenant* pane of 6 (No. 404a) and pane of 1 (No. 406a) .. .. 2·75

B 2

1981 (2 Sept). *Black and vermilion (No.* SB6) *and black and ultramarine (No.* SB7) *covers as Type* B **2**. *Stamps attached by selvedge.*
SB6 50p. booklet containing *se-tenant* pane of 5 and 1 label (No. 451a) .. .. 1·40
SB7 £1 booklet containing *se-tenant* pane of 10 and 2 labels (No. 451b) .. .. 2·00

B 3 Moorish Castle

1993 (21 Sept). *Multicoloured covers as Type* B **3**. *Stamps affixed by selvedge.*
SB8 20p. booklet containing 5p. (No. 699) in strip of 4 40
SB9 £1.20 booklet containing 24p. (No. 702) in strip of 5 .. .. 2·40

B 4 Rock of Gibraltar and Games Events
(*Illustration reduced. Actual size* 175×97 *mm*)

1995 (8 May). *Island Games* '95. *Multicoloured cover as Type* B **4**. *Stitched.*
SB10 £4.68, booklet containing four panes of 3 (Nos. 745a/b, 746a and 747a) .. .. .. 12·00

B 5
(*Illustration reduced. Actual size* 150×80 *mm*)

1997 (12 Feb). *Kittens. Multicoloured cover as Type* B **5**. *Stitched.*
SB11 £5 booklet containing five *se-tenant* panes (Nos. 797a/b, 798a, 799a and **MS**803a) .. .. 12·00

B **6** Battle of the Nile
(*Illustration reduced. Actual size* 145×102 *mm*)

1998 (1 Aug). *Bicent of Battle of the Nile. Multicoloured cover as Type* B **6**. *Stitched.*
SB12 £5 booklet containing five panes (Nos. 839a/b and 840a/c) .. .. 12·00

POSTAGE DUE STAMPS

D 1

D 2

D 3 Gibraltar Coat of Arms

(Typo D.L.R.)

1956 (1 Dec). *Chalk-surfaced paper. Wmk Mult Script CA. P* 14.

D1	D **1**	1d. green	2·00	3·50
D2		2d. sepia	2·50	3·75
		a. Large "d" (R. 9/6, 10/6)	22·00	
D3		4d. blue	3·00	6·25
D1/3		.. .. *Set of* 3	6·75	12·00

For illustrations of No. D2a. see above No. D4 of Botswana.

1971 (15 Feb). *As Nos.* D1/3 *but inscr in decimal currency.* W w **12**. *P* 17½ × 18.

D4	D **1**	½p. green	30	80
D5		1p. sepia	30	70
D6		2p. blue	30	80
D4/6		.. .. *Set of* 3	80	2·10

(Des A. Ryman. Litho Questa)

1976 (13 Oct). W w **14**. *P* 14 × 13½.

D 7	D **2**	1p. light red-orange	15	50
D 8		3p. bright blue	15	65
D 9		5p. orange-vermilion	20	75
D10		7p. reddish violet	25	75
D11		10p. greenish slate	35	75
D12		20p. green	70	1·00
D7/12		.. .. *Set of* 6	1·60	4·00

(Des A. Ryman. Litho B.D.T.)

1984 (2 July). W w **14** (*sideways*). *P* 15×14.

D13	D **3**	1p. black	25	40
D14		3p. vermilion	35	40
D15		5p. ultramarine	40	40
D16		10p. new blue	50	40
D17		25p. deep mauve	90	1·00
D18		50p. reddish orange	1·40	1·50
D19		£1 blue-green	2·25	2·50
D13/19		.. .. *Set of* 7	5·50	6·00

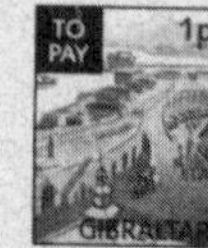

D 4 Water Port Gates

(Des Olympia Reyes. Litho B.D.T.)

1996 (30 Sept). *Gibraltar Landmarks. Type* D **4** *and similar vert designs. P* 14½×14.

D20	1p. black, emerald & bright yellow-green	10	1
D21	10p. black and bluish grey	20	25
D22	25p. black, red-brown and chestnut ..	50	55
D23	50p. black and reddish lilac	1·00	1·10
D24	£1 black, olive-brown and chestnut ..	2·00	2·10
D25	£2 black and light blue	4·00	4·25
D20/5	.. .. *Set of* 6	7·50	8·25

Designs:—10p. Naval Dockyard; 25p. Military Hospital; 50p Governor's Cottage; £1 Swans on the Laguna; £2 Catalan Bay

Gilbert and Ellice Islands

No organised postal service existed in the Gilbert and Ellice [Is]lands before the introduction of stamp issues in January 1911.

New Zealand Postal Agency was, however, provided on [Fa]nning Island, one of the Line Islands, primarily for the use of [th]e staff of the Cable & Wireless Ltd cable station which was [es]tablished in 1902. The agency opened on 29 November 1902 [an]d continued to operate until replaced by a Protectorate post [of]fice on 14 February 1939. The cable station closed in 1964. [Fa]nning Island is now known as Tabuaeran.

Z 1

[T]he following NEW ZEALAND *stamps are know postmarked on* [F]anning Island *with Type* Z 1 (*in use from November* 1902 *until* [N]ovember 1936. *The earliest known cover is postmarked* 20 [D]ecember 1902.

1882–1900 Q.V. (*p* 11) ½d., 1d., 2d. (*Nos.* 236/8)
1898 Pictorials (*no wmk*) 1d., 2d. (*Nos.* 247/8)
1900 Pictorials (*W* **38**) ½d., 2d. (*Nos.* 273, 276)
1901 1d. "Universal" (*W* **38**) (*No.* 278)
1902 1d. "Universal" (*no wmk*) (*No.* 295)
1902–09 Pictorials (*W* **43**) 2½d., 6d., 9d., 1s., 2s. (*Nos.* 312, 315, 320, 326, 328)
1907–08 Pictorials (*W* **43**) 4d. (*No.* 379)
1908 1d. "Universal" (*De La Rue paper*) 1d. (*No.* 386)
1909–12 King Edward VII (*typo*) ½d. (*No.* 387)
1909–16 King Edward VII (*recess*) 2d., 3d., 4d., 5d., 6d., 8d., 1s. (*Nos.* 388/91, 393/6, 398)
1909–26 1d. "Universal" (*W* **43**) 1d. (*Nos.* 405, 410)
1915–30 King George V (*recess*) 1½d., 2d. bright violet, 2½d., 3d., 4d. bright violet, 6d., 7½d., 9d., 1s. (*Nos.* 416/17, 419/20, 422, 425/6, 429/30)
1915–34 King George V (*typo*) ½d., 1½d. (all 3), 2d., 3d. (*Nos.* 435/40, 446, 448, 449)
1915 "WAR STAMP" opt ½d. (*No.* 452)
1920 Victory 1d., 1½d. (*Nos.* 454/5)
1922 2d. on ½d. (*No.* 459)
1923–25 Penny Postage 1d. (*No.* 460)
1926–34 Admiral design 1d. (*No.* 468)
1935–36 Pictorials ½d., 2d., 4d., 8d., 1s. (*Nos.* 556, 559, 562, 565, 567)
1935 Silver Jubilee ½d., 1d., 6d. (*Nos.* 573/5)
1936 Anzac 1d.+1d. (*No.* 592)

Z 2

[T]he following NEW ZEALAND *stamps are known postmarked* [o]n Fanning Island *with Type* Z **2** (*in use from* 7 *December* 1936 [t]o 13 *February* 1939):

1935–36 Pictorials (*W* **43**) 1d (*No.* 557)
1936–39 Pictorials (*W* **98**) ½d., 1d., 1½d. (*Nos.* 577/9)
1936 Chambers of Commerce Congress ½d. (*No.* 593)
1936 Health 1d. + 1d. (*No.* 598)
1937 Coronation 1d., 2½d., 6d. (*Nos.* 599/601)
1938–39 King George VI ½d., 1d., 1½d. (*Nos.* 603, 605, 607)

The schooner which carried the mail from Fanning Island also [c]alled at Washington Island, another of the Line group. [P]roblems arose, however, as the authorities insisted that mail [f]rom Washington must first pass through the Fanning Island [P]ostal Agency before being forwarded which resulted in [c]onsiderable delays. Matters were resolved by the opening of a [N]ew Zealand Postal Agency on Washington Island which [o]perated from 1 February 1921 until the copra plantations were [c]losed in early 1923. The postal agency was re-established on 15 [M]ay 1924, but finally closed on 30 March 1934. Covers from this [s]econd period occur with incorrectly dated postmarks. [M]anuscript markings on New Zealand Nos. 578, 599/600 and [5]92 are unofficial and were applied during the resettlement of [t]he island between 1937 and 1948. Washington Island is now [k]nown as Teraina.

NEW INFORMATION

[T]he editor is always interested to correspond with [p]eople who have new information that will improve or correct the Catalogue.

Z 3

The following NEW ZEALAND *stamps are known postmarked on Washington Island with Type* Z **3**:

1909–16 King Edward VII 5d., 8d. (*Nos.* 402, 404*b*)
1915–30 King George V (*recess*) 6d., 7½d, 8d., 9d., 1s. (*Nos.* 425/7, 429/30)
1915–34 King George V (*typo*) ½d., 1½d., 2d., 3d. (*Nos.* 435, 438/9, 449)
1915 "WAR STAMP" opt ½d (*No.* 452)
1920 Victory 1d., 1½d., 6d. (*Nos.* 454/5, 457)
1922 2d. on ½d. (*No.* 459)
1926–34 Admiral design 1d. (*No.* 468)

The above information is based on a special survey undertaken by members of the Kiribati & Tuvalu Philatelic Society and the Pacific Islands Study Circle, co-ordinated by Mr. Michael Shaw.

PRICES FOR STAMPS ON COVER TO 1945

Nos. 1/7	*from* × 5
Nos. 8/11	*from* × 10
Nos. 12/23	*from* × 6
No. 24	—
No. 26	*from* × 15
Nos. 27/30	*from* × 6
No. 35	—
Nos. 36/9	*from* × 4
Nos. 40/2	*from* × 12
Nos. 43/54	*from* × 4
Nos. D1/8	*from* × 5

BRITISH PROTECTORATE

GILBERT & ELLICE

PROTECTORATE

(1)

2 Pandanus Pine

1911 (1 Jan). *Stamps of Fiji optd with T* 1. *Wmk Mult Crown CA. Chalk-surfaced paper (5d. to 1s.).*

No.	Type	Description		
1	**23**	½d. green	4·50	38·00
2		1d. red	45·00	27·00
3	**24**	2d. grey	8·00	13·00
4	**23**	2½d. ultramarine	12·00	25·00
5		5d. purple and olive-green	38·00	65·00
6	**24**	6d. dull and bright purple	20·00	40·00
7	**23**	1s. black/*green* (R.)	20·00	45·00
1/7		*Set of* 7	£130	£225
1/7 Optd "Specimen"		*Set of* 7	£275	

The 2d. to 6d. are on special printings which were not issued without overprint.

Examples of Nos. 1/7 are known showing a forged Ocean Island postmark dated "JY 15 11".

(Recess D.L.R.)

1911 (Mar). *Wmk Mult Crown CA. P* 14.

No.	Type	Description		
8	**2**	½d. green	4·25	11·00
9		1d. carmine	2·00	6·00
10		2d. grey	1·50	6·00
11		2½d. blue	3·50	9·00
8/11		*Set of* 4	10·00	29·00
8/11 Optd "Specimen"		*Set of* 4	£140	

3

WAR TAX

(5)

(Typo D.L.R.)

1912 (May)–**24**. *Die I (½d. to 5s.) or Die II (£1). Wmk Mult Crown CA. Chalk-surfaced paper (3d. to £1). P* 14.

No.	Type	Description		
12	**3**	½d. green (7.12)	30	4·00
		a. Yellow-green (1914)	4·25	8·50
13		1d. carmine (12.12)	1·75	4·00
		a. Scarlet (1915)	3·75	9·50
14		2d. greyish slate (1.16)	13·00	20·00
15		2½d. bright blue (1.16)	1·75	11·00
16		3d. purple/*yellow* (1918)	2·50	8·50
17		4d. black and red/*yellow* (10.12)	60	5·50
18		5d. dull purple and sage-green	1·50	7·00
19		6d. dull and bright purple	1·25	7·50
20		1s. black/*green*	1·25	5·50
21		2s. purple and blue/*blue* (10.12)	14·00	28·00
22		2s. 6d. black and red/*blue* (10.12)	14·00	24·00
23		5s. green and red/*yellow* (10.12)	32·00	55·00
24		£1 purple and black/*red* (Die II) (3.24)	£600	£1400
12/24		*Set of* 13	£600	£1400
12/24 Optd "Specimen"		*Set of* 13	£550	

CROWN COLONY

1918 (June). *Optd with T* 5.

No.	Type	Description		
26	**3**	1d. red (Optd S. £60)	30	6·00

1922–27. *Die II. Wmk Mult Crown CA. Chalk-surfaced paper (10s.). P* 14.

No.	Type	Description		
27	**3**	½d. green (1923)	2·25	2·00
28		1d. violet (1927)	3·50	3·75
29		1½d. scarlet (1924)	3·50	1·50
30		2d. slate-grey	5·50	20·00
35		10s. green and red/*emerald* (3.24)	£180	£350
27/35 Optd "Specimen"		*Set of* 5	£250	

Examples of most values between Nos. 12 and 35 are known showing part strikes of the forged postmark mentioned below Nos. 1/7. Collectors should exercise particular caution when buying used examples of Nos. 24 and 35.

1935 (6 May). *Silver Jubilee. As Nos.* 91/4 *of Antigua, but ptd by B.W. P* 11 × 12.

36	1d. ultramarine and grey-black	2·25	8·00
	d. Flagstaff on right-hand turret	£150	
	e. Double flagstaff	£200	
37	1½d. deep blue and scarlet	1·75	3·50
	d. Flagstaff on right-hand turret	£150	
	e. Double flagstaff	£200	
38	3d. brown and deep blue	5·50	11·00
	d. Flagstaff on right-hand turret	£225	
	e. Double flagstaff	£250	
39	1s. slate and purple	35·00	24·00
	d. Flagstaff on right-hand turret	£350	
	e. Double flagstaff	£375	
36/9	*Set of* 4	40·00	42·00
36/9 Perf "Specimen"	*Set of* 4	£110	

For illustrations of plate varieties see Catalogue Introduction.

1937 (12 May). *Coronation. As Nos.* 95/7 *of Antigua, but ptd by D.L.R. P* 14.

40	1d. violet	35	55
41	1½d. scarlet	35	55
42	3d. bright blue	40	60
40/2	*Set of* 3	1·00	1·50
40/2 Perf "Specimen"	*Set of* 3	65·00	

6 Great Frigate Bird

7 Pandanus Pine

8 Canoe crossing Reef

(Recess B.W. (½d., 2d., 2s. 6d.), Waterlow (1d., 5d., 6d., 2s., 5s.), D.L.R. (1½d., 2½d., 3d., 1s.))

1939 (14 Jan)–**55**. *T* **6/8** *and similar horiz designs. Wmk Mult Script CA (sideways on ½d., 2d. and 2s. 6d.). P* 11½×11 (*½d., 2d., 2s. 6d.*), 12½ (*1d., 5d., 6d., 2s., 5s.*) *or* 13½ (*1½d., 2½d., 3d., 1s.*).

43	½d. indigo and deep bluish green	30	75
	a. "A" of "CA" missing from wmk		
44	1d. emerald and plum	30	1·50
45	1½d. brownish black and bright carmine	30	90
46	2d. red-brown and grey-black	50	1·00
47	2½d. brownish black and deep olive	40	70
	a. Brownish black & olive-green (12.5.43)	3·00	3·25
48	3d. brownish black and ultramarine	45	1·00
	a. Perf 12. *Black and bright blue* (24.8.55)	50	2·25
49	5d. deep ultramarine and sepia	4·25	1·25
	a. Ultramarine and sepia (12.5.43)	4·75	5·00
	b. Ultramarine & blackish brn (20.10.44)	4·25	4·25
50	6d. olive-green and deep violet	40	50
51	1s. brownish black and turquoise-green	7·50	1·75
	a. Brownish black & turquoise-bl (12.5.43)	4·50	2·00
	ab. Perf 12 (8.5.51)	3·75	13·00
52	2s. deep ultramarine and orange-red	16·00	11·00
53	2s. 6d. deep blue and emerald	17·00	14·00
54	5s. deep rose-red and royal blue	18·00	16·00
43/54	*Set of* 12	55·00	42·00
43/54 Perf "Specimen"	*Set of* 12	£250	

Designs: *As T* **6**—2d. Canoe and boat-house; 2s. 6d. Gilbert Islands canoe. *As T* **7**—5d. Ellice Islands canoe; 6d. Coconut palms; 2s. H.M.C.S. *Nimanoa*; 5s. Coat of arms. *As T* **8**—2½d. Native house; 3d. Seascape; 1s. Cantilever jetty, Ocean Island.

1946 (16 Dec). *Victory. As Nos.* 110/11 *of Antigua.*

55	1d. purple	15	30
56	3d. blue	15	30
55/6 Perf "Specimen"	*Set of* 2	55·00	

1949 (29 Aug). *Royal Silver Wedding. As Nos.* 112/13 *of Antigua.*

57	1d. violet	40	50
58	£1 scarlet	15·00	18·00

1949 (10 Oct). *75th Anniv of U.P.U. As Nos.* 114/17 *of Antigua.*

59	1d. purple	55	90
60	2d. grey-black	2·25	2·25
61	3d. deep blue	1·00	2·00
62	1s. blue	1·25	2·00
59/62	*Set of* 4	4·50	6·50

1953 (2 June). *Coronation. As No.* 120 *of Antigua.*

63	2d. black and grey-black	55	2·00

18 Great Frigate Bird

19 Loading Phosphate from Cantilever

(Recess B.W. (½d., 2d., 2s. 6d.), Waterlow (1d., 5d., 6d., 2s., 5s.), D.L.R. (2½d., 3d., 1s., 10s. and after 1962, 1d., 5d.))

1956 (1 Aug)–**62**. *Designs previously used for King George VI issue; but with portrait of Queen Elizabeth II as in T* **18**. *Wmk Mult Script CA. P* 11½×11 (½d., 2d., 2s. 6d.), 12½ (1d., 5d., 6d., 2s., 5s.) *or* 12 (2½d., 3d., 1s., 10s.).

64 ½d. black and deep bright blue .. .. 35 1·00
65 1d. brown-olive and deep violet 60 60
66 2d. bluish green and deep purple .. .. 90 2·00
a. *Bluish green and purple* (30.7.62) .. 17·00 17·00
67 2½d. black and myrtle-green 50 60
68 3d. black and carmine-red 50 60
69 5d. ultramarine and red-orange .. .. 8·50 2·50
a. *Ultramarine & brn-orge* (DLR) (30.7.62) 15·00 22·00
70 6d. chestnut and black-brown .. .. 55 1·75
71 1s. black and bronze-green .. .. 1·50 60
72 2s. deep bright blue and sepia .. .. 8·50 5·50
73 2s. 6d. scarlet and deep blue .. .. 10·00 5·50
74 5s. greenish blue and bluish green .. 12·00 8·50
75 10s. black and turquoise .. .. .. 28·00 15·00
64/75 .. .. *Set of* 12 65·00 40·00

Designs: *Horiz* (30 × 22½ *mm*)—1d. Pandanus pine; 5d. Ellice Islands canoe; 6d. Coconut palms; 2s. H.M.C.S. *Nimanoa*; 5s. Coat of arms. (35½ × 22½ *mm*)—2d. Canoe and boat-house; 2½d. Native house; 3d. Seascape; 1s. Cantilever jetty, Ocean Island; 2s. 6d. Gilbert Islands canoe; 10s. Canoe crossing reef.

See also Nos. 85/6.

(Des R. Turrell (2d.), M. Thoma (2½d), M. A. W. Hook and A. Larkins (1s.). Photo D.L.R.)

1960 (1 May). *Diamond Jubilee of Phosphate Discovery at Ocean Island. T* **19** *and similar horiz designs. W* w **12**. *P* 12.

76 2d. green and carmine-rose 70 85
77 2½d. black and olive-green 70 85
78 1s. black and deep turquoise 70 85
76/8 .. .. *Set of* 3 1·90 2·40

Designs:—2½d. Phosphate rock; 1s. Phosphate mining.

1963 (1 Aug). *Freedom from Hunger. As No.* 146 *of Antigua.*

79 10d. ultramarine .. .. 1·25 30

1963 (5 Oct). *Red Cross Centenary. As Nos.* 147/8 *of Antigua.*

80 2d. red and black .. .. 1·00 50
81 10d. red and blue .. .. 2·00 2·50

22 De Havilland D.H.114 Heron 2 and Route Map

24 De Havilland D.H.114 Heron 2 over Tarawa Lagoon

23 Eastern Reef Heron in Flight

(Des Margaret Barwick. Litho Enschedé)

1964 (20 July). *First Air Service. W* w **12** (*sideways* on 3d., 3s. 7d.*). *P* 11×11½ (1s.) *or* 11½×11 (*others*).

82 **22** 3d. blue, black and light blue 70 30
w. Wmk Crown to right of CA .. 70 30
83 **23** 1s. light blue, black and deep blue .. 90 30
84 **24** 3s. 7d. deep green, black & light emerald 1·40 1·25
82/4 .. .. *Set of* 3 2·75 1·60

*The normal sideways watermark shows Crown to left of CA, *as seen from the back of the stamp.*

(Recess B.W. (2d.), D.L.R. (6d.))

1964 (30 Oct)–**65**. *As Nos.* 66*a and* 70 *but wmk* w **12**.

85 2d. bluish green and purple .. .. 75 2·00
86 6d. chestnut and black-brown (26.4.65)* .. 1·00 2·25

*Earliest known postmark date.

1965 (4 June). *I.T.U. Centenary. As Nos.* 166/7 *of Antigua.*

87 3d. red-orange and deep bluish green .. 20 10
88 2s. 6d. turquoise-blue and light purple .. 80 20

25 Maneaba and Gilbertese Man blowing Bu Shell

26 Gilbertese Women's Dance

(Des V. Whiteley from drawings by Margaret Barwick. Litho B.W.)

1965 (16 Aug). *Vert designs as T* **25** (*½d. to 2s.*) *or horiz designs as T* **26** (*3s. 7d. to £1*). *Centres multicoloured. W* w **12**. *P* 12 × 11 (*½d. to 2s.*) *or* 11 × 12 (*3s. 7d. to £1*).

89 ½d. turquoise-green 10 10
90 1d. deep violet-blue 10 10
91 2d. bistre 10 10
92 3d. rose-red 10 10
93 4d. purple 15 10
94 5d. cerise 20 10
95 6d. turquoise-blue 20 10
96 7d. bistre-brown 25 10
97 1s. bluish violet 50 10
98 1s. 6d. lemon .. .. 1·00 65
99 2s. yellow-olive .. .. 1·00 1·25
100 3s. 7d. new blue .. .. 2·25 65
101 5s. light yellow-olive .. .. .. 2·25 80
102 10s. dull green .. .. 4·00 1·25
103 £1 light turquoise-blue .. .. .. 4·50 2·50
89/103 .. .. *Set of* 15 15·00 6·50

Designs:—1d. Ellice Islanders reef fishing by flare; 2d. Gilbertese girl weaving head garland; 3d. Gilbertese woman performing Ruoia; 4d. Gilbertese man performing Kamei; 5d. Gilbertese girl drawing water; 6d. Ellice islander performing a Fatele; 7d. Ellice youths performing spear dance; 1s. Gilbertese girl tending Ikaroa Babai plant; 1s. 6d. Ellice islanders dancing a Fatele; 2s. Ellice islanders pounding Pulaka; 5s. Gilbertese boys playing stick game; 10s. Ellice youths beating the box for the Fatele; £1 Coat of arms.

1965 (25 Oct). *International Co-operation Year. As Nos.* 168/9 *of Antigua.*

104 ½d. reddish purple and turquoise-green .. 10 10
105 3s. 7d. deep bluish green and lavender .. 60 20

1966 (24 Jan). *Churchill Commemoration. As Nos.* 170/3 *of Antigua.*

106 ½d. new blue 10 10
107 3d. deep green 20 10
108 3s. brown 35 35
109 3s. 7d. bluish violet 40 35
106/9 .. .. *Set of* 4 90 75

(New Currency, 100 cents = 1 Australian dollar)

≡2c

(40)

41 H.M.S. *Royalist*

1966 (14 Feb). *Decimal currency. Nos.* 89/103 *surch as T* **40**.

110 1 c. on 1d. deep violet-blue 10 10
111 2 c. on 2d. bistre 10 10
112 3 c. on 3d. rose-red 10 10
113 4 c. on ½d. turquoise-green 10 10
114 5 c. on 6d. turquoise-blue 15 10
115 6 c. on 4d. purple 15 10
116 8 c. on 5d. cerise 15 10
117 10 c. on 1s. bluish violet 15 10
118 15 c. on 7d. bistre-brown 80 30
119 20 c. on 1s. 6d. lemon 45 25
120 25 c. on 2s. yellow-olive 45 20
121 35 c. on 3s. 7d. new blue .. .. .. 1·25 20
122 50 c. on 5s. light yellow-olive 75 35
123 $1 on 10s. dull green 75 40
124 $2 on £1 light turquoise-blue .. .. 1·50 2·25
110/24 .. .. *Set of* 15 6·00 4·00

1966 (1 July). *World Cup Football Championships. As Nos.* 176/7 *of Antigua.*

125 3 c. violet, yellow-green, lake & yellow-brn .. 15 10
126 35 c. chocolate, blue-green, lake & yell-brn .. 45 20

1966 (20 Sept). *Inauguration of W.H.O. Headquarters, Geneva. As Nos.* 178/9 *of Antigua.*

127 3 c. black, yellow-green and light blue .. 20 10
128 12 c. black, light purple and yellow-brown .. 45 40

1966 (1 Dec). *20th Anniv of U.N.E.S.C.O. As Nos.* 196/8 *of Antigua.*

129 5 c. slate-violet, red, yellow and orange .. 25 10
130 10 c. orange-yellow, violet and deep olive .. 35 10
131 20 c. black, bright purple and orange 60 45
129/31 .. .. *Set of* 3 1·10 55

(Des V. Whiteley. Photo Harrison)

1967 (1 Sept). *75th Anniv of the Protectorate. T* **41** *and simil[ar] horiz designs. W* w **12**. *P* 14½.

132 3 c. red, blue and myrtle-green 30 5
133 10 c. multicoloured 15 1
134 35 c. sepia, orange-yellow & dp bluish green .. 30 5
132/4 .. .. *Set of* 3 65 1·0

Designs:—10 c. Trading Post; 35 c. Island family.

44 Gilbertese Women's Dance

1968 (1 Jan). *Decimal Currency. Designs as Nos.* 89/103 *but wit[h] values inscr in decimal currency as T* **44**. *W* w **12** (*sideways o[n] horiz designs*). *P* 12 × 11 (*vert*) *or* 11 × 12 (*horiz*).

135 1 c. deep violet-blue (as 1d.) 10 1
136 2 c. bistre (as 2d.) 15 1
137 3 c. rose-red (as 3d.) 15 1
138 4 c. turquoise-green (as ½d.) 15 1
139 5 c. turquoise-blue (as 6d.) 15 1
140 6 c. purple (as 4d.) 20 1
141 8 c. cerise (as 5d.) 20 1
142 10 c. bluish violet (as 1s.) 20 1
143 15 c. bistre-brown (as 7d.) 50 2
144 20 c. lemon (as 1s. 6d.) 65 1
w. Wmk inverted .. .. .. 14·00 14·0
145 25 c. yellow-olive (as 2s.) .. .. .. 1·25 2
146 35 c. new blue .. .. 1·50 2
147 50 c. light yellow-olive (as 5s.) .. .. 1·50 2·2
148 $1 dull green (as 10s.) .. .. .. 1·50 3·2
149 $2 light turquoise-blue (as £1) .. .. 4·00 3·5
135/49 .. .. *Set of* 15 11·00 9·0

45 Map of Tarawa Atoll

(Des V. Whiteley. Photo D.L.R.)

1968 (21 Nov). *25th Anniv of the Battle of Tarawa. T* **45** *an[d] similar designs. Multicoloured. W* w **12** (*sideways*). *P* 14.

150 3 c. Type **45** 20 2
151 10 c. Marines landing 20 1
152 15 c. Beach-head assault 30 3
153 35 c. Raising U.S. and British flags 40 4
150/3 .. .. *Set of* 4 1·00 1·0

46 Young Pupil against outline of Abemama Island

47 "Virgin and Child" in Pacific Setting

(Des J.W. (from original designs by Mrs V. J. Anderson and Miss A. Loveridge). Litho D.L.R.)

1969 (2 June). *End of Inaugural Year of South Pacific University. T* **46** *and similar horiz designs. W* w **12** (*sideways*). *P* 12½.

154 3 c. multicoloured 10 15
155 10 c. multicoloured 10 10
156 35 c. black, brown and grey-green 15 30
154/6 .. .. *Set of* 3 30 45

Designs:—10 c. Boy and girl students and Tarawa atoll; 35 c University graduate and South Pacific islands.

(Des Jennifer Toombs. Litho B.W.)

1969 (20 Oct). *Christmas. W* w **12** (*sideways*). *P* 11½.

157 – 2 c. olive-grn & multicoloured (*shades*) 15 2
158 **47** 10 c. olive-grn & multicoloured (*shades*) 15 1

Design:—2 c. As T **47** but foreground has grass instead of sand.

48 "The Kiss of Life"

(Des Manate Tenang Manate. Litho J.W.)

70 (9 Mar*). *Centenary of British Red Cross. W* w **12** (*sideways*). *P* 14.

9	**48**	10 c. multicoloured	20	10
0	–	15 c. multicoloured	30	35
1	–	35 c. multicoloured	60	70
9/61		*Set of* 3	1·00	1·00

Nos. 160/1 are as T **48**, but arranged differently.
*The above were released by the Crown Agents on 2 March, but t sold locally until the 9 March.

49 Foetus and Patients

(Des Jennifer Toombs. Litho Enschedé)

70 (26 June). *25th Anniv of United Nations. T* **49** *and similar horiz designs. W* w **12** (*sideways*). *P* 12½ × 13.

2	5 c. multicoloured	15	20
3	10 c. black, grey and red	15	15
4	15 c. multicoloured	20	25
5	35 c. new blue, black and turquoise-green	30	35
2/5	*Set of* 4	70	85

Designs:—10 c. Nurse and surgical instruments; 15 c. X-ray ate and technician; 35 c. U.N. emblem and map.

53 Map of Gilbert Islands

57 "Child with Halo" (T. Collis)

(Des G. Vasarhelyi. Litho Harrison)

70 (1 Sept). *Centenary of Landing in Gilbert Islands by London Missionary Society. T* **53** *and similar designs. W* w **12** (*sideways on vert designs*). *P* 14½ × 14 (2 c., 35 c.) *or* 14 × 14½ (*others*).

6	2 c. multicoloured	15	70
7	10 c. black and pale green	25	15
8	25 c. chestnut and cobalt	20	20
9	35 c. turquoise-blue, black and red	50	70
66/9	*Set of* 4	1·00	1·60

Designs: *Vert*—10 c. Sailing-ship *John Williams III*; 25 c. Rev. S. Whitmee. *Horiz*—35 c. M.V. *John Williams VII*.

(Des L. Curtis. Litho Format)

970 (3 Oct). *Christmas. Sketches. T* **57** *and similar vert designs. Multicoloured. W* w **12**. *P* 14½.

70	2 c. Type **57**	10	15
71	10 c. "Sanctuary, Tarawa Cathedral" (Mrs. A. Burroughs)	10	10
72	35 c. "Three ships inside star" (Mrs. C. Barnett)	20	20
70/2	*Set of* 3	35	35

60 Casting Nets

(Des G. Drummond. Litho Walsall)

1971 (31 May). *Multicoloured designs as T* **60**. *W* w **12** (*sideways* on* 2, 3, 4, 5, 20, 25 *and* 35 c.). *P* 14.

173	1 c. Cutting toddy (*vert*)	10	10
174	2 c. Lagoon fishing	15	30
	w. Wmk Crown to right of CA	10·00	
175	3 c. Cleaning pandanus leaves	15	15
	w. Wmk Crown to right of CA		
176	4 c. Type **60**	20	25
	w. Wmk Crown to right of CA		
177	5 c. Gilbertese canoe	35	15
	w. Wmk Crown to right of CA		
178	6 c. De-husking coconuts (*vert*)	30	45
179	8 c. Weaving pandanus fronds (*vert*)	35	15
180	10 c. Weaving a basket (*vert*)	40	15
	w. Wmk inverted	1·50	1·50
181	15 c. Tiger Shark and fishermen (*vert*)	2·50	1·50
182	20 c. Beating a rolled pandanus leaf	1·50	90
	w. Wmk Crown to right of CA	3·75	
183	25 c. Loading copra	2·00	1·00
184	35 c. Fishing at night	2·25	50
	w. Wmk Crown to left of CA	3·50	
185	50 c. Local handicrafts (*vert*)	1·50	1·50
186	$1 Weaving coconut screens (*vert*)	2·00	2·25
187	$2 Coat of Arms (*vert*)	6·50	11·00
173/87	*Set of* 15	18·00	18·00

*The normal sideways watermark shows Crown to right of CA on 35 c., and Crown to left of CA on the others, *as seen from the back of the stamp*.
See also Nos. 203/7.

61 House of Representatives

62 Pacific Nativity Scene

(Des V. Whiteley. Litho J.W.)

1971 (1 Aug). *New Constitution. T* **61** *and similar horiz design. Multicoloured. W* w **12** (*sideways*). *P* 14.

188	3 c. Type **61**	10	20
189	10 c. Maneaba Betio (Assembly hut)	20	10

(Des L. Curtis and T. Collis. Litho Questa)

1971 (1 Oct). *Christmas. T* **62** *and similar vert designs. W* w **12**. *P* 14 × 14½.

190	3 c. black, yellow and ultramarine	10	15
191	10 c. black, gold and turquoise-blue	10	10
192	35 c. black, gold and magenta	25	35
190/2	*Set of* 3	40	55

Designs:—10 c. Star and palm leaves; 35 c. Outrigger canoe and star.

63 Emblem and Young Boys

(Des G. Vasarhelyi. Litho Questa)

1971 (11 Dec). *25th Anniv of UNICEF. T* **63** *and similar horiz designs, showing UNICEF emblem and young boys. W* w **12** (*sideways*). *P* 14.

193	3 c. multicoloured	10	60
194	10 c. multicoloured	15	15
195	35 c. multicoloured	45	60
193/5	*Set of* 3	60	1·25

64 Flag and Map of South Pacific

(Des A. New. Litho Questa)

1972 (21 Feb). *25th Anniv of South Pacific Commission. T* **64** *and similar horiz designs. Multicoloured. W* w **12**. *P* 13½.

196	3 c. Type **64**	10	65
197	10 c. Flag and native boats	15	20
198	35 c. Flags of member nations	15	95
196/8	*Set of* 3	30	1·60

65 *Alveopora*

66 Star of Peace

(Des Sylvia Goaman after original designs by H. Wickison. Litho Questa)

1972 (26 May). *Coral. T* **65** *and similar horiz designs. Multicoloured. W* w **12** (*sideways**). *P* 14.

199	3 c. Type **65**	25	35
200	10 c. *Euphyllia*	30	15
201	15 c. *Melithea*	40	25
	w. Wmk Crown to left of CA	1·75	
202	35 c. *Spongodes*	80	50
199/202	*Set of* 4	1·60	1·10

*The normal sideways watermark shows Crown to right of CA, *as seen from the back of the stamp*.

1972 (7 Sept)–**73**. *As Nos.* 174, 177/8 *and* 181/2 *but W* w **12** *upright on* 2, 5 *and* 20 c.; *sideways on* 6 *and* 15 c.

203	2 c. Lagoon fishing (13.6.73)	11·00	14·00
204	5 c. Gilbertese canoe	4·00	4·50
205	6 c. De-husking coconuts (13.6.73)	11·00	15·00
206	15 c. Tiger Shark and fishermen	6·00	6·00
207	20 c. Beating a rolled pandanus leaf	6·00	6·00
203/7	*Set of* 5	35·00	40·00

(Des T. Matarena (35 c.), Father Bermond (others); adapted by Jennifer Toombs. Litho Questa)

1972 (15 Sept). *Christmas. T* **66** *and similar multicoloured designs. W* w **12** (*sideways on* 3 *and* 10 c.). *P* 13½.

208	3 c. Type **66**	10	10
209	10 c. "The Nativity"	10	10
210	35 c. Baby in "manger" (*horiz*)	20	20
208/10	*Set of* 3	30	30

67 Floral Head-dresses

(Des (from photograph by D. Groves) and photo Harrison)

1972 (20 Nov). *Royal Silver Wedding. Multicoloured; background colour given. W* w **12**. *P* 14 × 14½.

211	**67**	3 c. brown-olive	10	15
		w. Wmk inverted	6·00	
212		35 c. lake-brown	25	15
		w. Wmk inverted	38·00	

68 Funafuti ("The Land of Bananas")

69 Dancer

(Des H. Wickison; adapted J. Cooter. Litho Walsall)

1973 (5 Mar). *Legends of Island Names* (1*st series*). *T* **68** *and similar horiz designs. Multicoloured. W* w **12**. *P* 14½ × 14.

213	3 c. Type **68**	10	40
214	10 c. Butaritari ("The Smell of the Sea")	20	20
215	25 c. Tarawa ("The Centre of the World")	30	45
216	35 c. Abemama ("The Land of the Moon")	35	50
	w. Wmk inverted		
213/16	*Set of* 4	80	1·40

See also Nos. 252/5.

(Des Sister Juliette (3 c.), R. P. Turner (10 and 35 c.), C. Potts (50 c.); adapted Jennifer Toombs. Litho Questa)

1973 (24 Sept). *Christmas. T* **69** *and similar vert designs. Multicoloured. W* w **12** (*sideways**). *P* 14.

217	3 c. Type **69**	10	15
218	10 c. Canoe and lagoon	10	10
	w. Wmk Crown to right of CA	8·00	
219	35 c. Lagoon at evening	20	15
220	50 c. Map of Christmas Island	30	1·25
	w. Wmk Crown to right of CA	6·00	
217/20	*Set of* 4	60	1·50

*The normal sideways watermark shows Crown to left of CA, *as seen from the back of the stamp*.

1973 (14 Nov). *Royal Wedding. As Nos.* 165/6 *of Anguilla. Centre multicoloured. W* w **12** (*sideways*). *P* 13½.

221	3 c. pale green	10	15
222	35 c. Prussian blue	20	15

70 Meteorological Observation

(Des E. S. Cheek; adapted PAD Studio. Litho Questa)

1973 (26 Nov). *I.M.O./W.M.O. Centenary. T* **70** *and similar horiz designs. Multicoloured. W* w **12**. *P* 14.

223	3 c. Type **70**	50	30
224	10 c. Island observing-station	50	20
225	35 c. Wind-finding radar	70	25
226	50 c. World weather watch stations	1·10	1·25
223/6	*Set of* 4	2·50	1·75

71 Te Mataaua Crest

(Des J. Cooter. Litho Questa)

1974 (4 Mar). *Canoe Crests. T* **71** *and similar horiz designs showing sailing craft and the canoe crests given. Multicoloured. W* w **12**. *P* 13½.

227	3 c. Type **71**	10	10
228	10 c. Te Nimta-wawa	15	10
229	35 c. Tara-tara-venei-na	25	10
230	50 c. Te Bou-uoua	35	50
227/30	*Set of* 4	75	65
MS231	154 × 130 mm. Nos. 227/30	2·00	5·00

72 £1 Stamp of 1924 and Te Koroba (canoe)

(Des E. S. Cheek; adapted J. Cooter. Litho Questa)

1974 (10 June). *Centenary of Universal Postal Union. T* **72** *and similar horiz designs. W* w **12**. *P* 14.

232	4 c. multicoloured	.. .. ..	20	15
233	10 c. multicoloured	.. .. ..	20	10
234	25 c. multicoloured	.. .. ..	25	25
	w. Wmk inverted	.. .. ..	50·00	
235	35 c. light vermilion and black	.. ..	30	25
232/5	.. ..	*Set of* 4	85	65

Designs:—10 c. 5s. stamp of 1939 and sailing vessel *Kiakia*; 25 c. $2 stamp of 1971 and B.A.C. One Eleven airplane; 35 c. U.P.U. emblem.

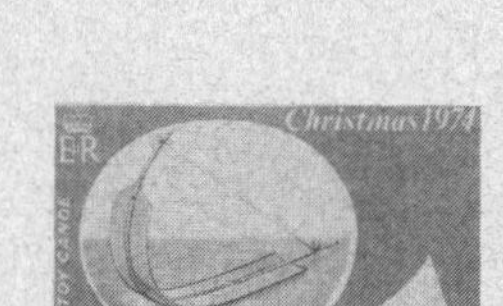

73 Toy Canoe

74 North Front Entrance, Blenheim Palace

(Des H. Wickison and G. J. Hayward; adapted J. Cooter. Litho Questa)

1974 (5 Sept). *Christmas. T* **73** *and similar horiz designs. Multicoloured. W* w **12** (*sideways**). *P* 14.

236	4 c. Type **73**	.. ..	10	15
237	10 c. Toy windmill ..	.. .. ..	15	10
	w. Wmk Crown to right of CA	.. ..	1·25	
238	25 c. Coconut "ball"	.. .. ..	20	30
239	35 c. Canoes and constellation Pleiades	..	25	35
236/9	.. ..	*Set of* 4	65	80

*The normal sideways watermark shows Crown to left of CA, *as seen from the back of the stamp.*

(Des J. Cooter. Litho Questa)

1974 (30 Nov). *Birth Centenary of Sir Winston Churchill. T* **74** *and similar vert designs. Multicoloured. W* w **14**. *P* 14.

240	4 c. Type **74**	.. ..	10	25
241	10 c. Churchill painting	.. .. ..	10	10
242	35 c. Churchill's statue, London	.. ..	25	35
240/2	.. ..	*Set of* 3	40	65

75 Barometer Crab

(Des J. Cooter. Litho Questa)

1975 (27 Jan). *Crabs. T* **75** *and similar horiz designs. Multicoloured. W* w **12** (*sideways**). *P* 14.

243	4 c. Type **75**	.. ..	40	60
	w. Wmk Crown to right of CA	.. ..	6·00	
244	10 c. *Ranina ranina*	.. .. ..	50	20
245	25 c. Pelagic Swimming Crab	.. ..	90	60
246	35 c. Ghost Crab ..	.. .. ..	1·00	1·00
243/6	.. ..	*Set of* 4	2·50	2·25

*The normal sideways watermark shows Crown to left of CA, *as seen from the back of the stamp.*

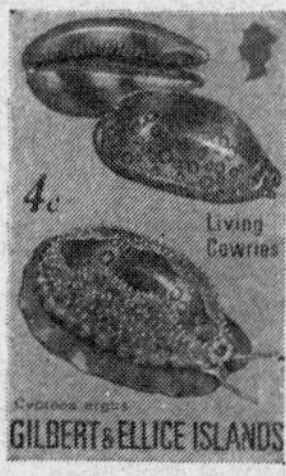

76 Eyed Cowrie (*Cypraea argus*)

77 "Christ is Born"

(Des E. S. Cheek; adapted J. Cooter. Litho Questa)

1975 (26 May). *Cowrie Shells. T* **76** *and similar vert designs. Multicoloured. W* w **14**. *P* 14.

247	4 c. Type **76**	.. ..	55	50
248	10 c. Sieve Cowrie (*Cypraea cribraria*)	..	80	15
249	25 c. Mole Cowrie (*Cypraea talpa*)	..	1·75	90
250	35 c. All-red Map Cowrie (*Cypraea mappa panerythra*)	.. ..	2·00	1·75
247/50	.. ..	*Set of* 4	4·50	3·00
MS251	146×137 mm. Nos. 247/50	.. ..	12·00	15·00

(Des J. Cooter. Litho Questa)

1975 (1 Aug). *Legends of Island Names (2nd series). Horiz designs as T* **68**. *Multicoloured. W* w **12** (*sideways**). *P* 14.

252	4 c. Beru ("The Bud")	.. .. ..	10	20
253	10 c. Onotoa ("Six Giants")	.. ..	10	10
254	25 c. Abaiang ("Land to the North")	..	20	25
	w. Wmk Crown to right of CA	.. ..	8·50	
255	35 c. Marakei ("Fish-trap floating on eaves")		30	40
252/4	.. ..	*Set of* 4	60	85

*The normal sideways watermark shows Crown to left of CA, *as seen from the back of the stamp.*

(Des C. J. Barnett (4 and 25 c.), Philatelic Advisory Committee (10 c.), P. T. Burangke (35 c.); adapted J. Cooter. Litho Questa)

1975 (22 Sept). *Christmas. T* **77** *and similar vert designs. Multicoloured. W* w **14**. *P* 14.

256	4 c. Type **77**	.. ..	20	50
257	10 c. Protestant Chapel, Tarawa	.. ..	20	30
258	25 c. Catholic Church, Ocean Island ..	..	35	90
259	35 c. Fishermen and star	.. ..	40	1·50
256/9	.. ..	*Set of* 4	1·00	2·75

POSTAGE DUE STAMPS

D 1

(Typo B.W.)

1940 (Aug). *Wmk Mult Script CA. P* 12.

D1 D 1	1d. emerald-green	.. .. ..	8·00	20·00
D2	2d. scarlet	.. .. ..	9·00	20·00
D3	3d. brown	.. .. ..	13·00	21·00
D4	4d. blue ..	.. .. ..	15·00	27·00
D5	5d. grey-green ..	.. .. ..	20·00	27·00
D6	6d. purple	.. .. ..	20·00	27·00
D7	1s. violet	.. .. ..	22·00	38·00
D8	1s. 6d. turquoise-green..	.. ..	42·00	75·00
D1/8	.. ..	*Set of* 8	£130	£225
D1/8 Perf "Specimen"	.. ..	*Set of* 8	£160	

Examples of all values are known showing a forged Post Office Ocean Island postmark dated "16 DE 46".

Stamps for the Gilbert and Ellice Islands were withdrawn on 31 December 1975 when the separate colonies of KIRIBATI (GILBERT ISLANDS) and TUVALU were created.

Gilbert Islands
***see* Kiribati**

Gold Coast
***see* Ghana**

Grenada

The earliest recorded postmark of the British administration of Grenada dates from 1784, and, although details of the early period are somewhat sparse, it would appear that the island's postal service was operated at a branch of the British G.P.O. In addition to a Packet Agency at St. George's, the capital, there was a further agency at Carriacou, in the Grenadines, which operated for a few years from 15 September 1847.

Stamps of Great Britain were supplied to the St. George's office from April 1858 until the colony assumed responsibility for the postal service on 1 May 1860. Following the take-over the crowned-circle handstamp, No. CC2, was again used until the Grenada adhesives were issued in 1861.

There was no internal postal service before 1861.

For illustrations of the handstamp and postmark types see BRITISH POST OFFICE ABROAD notes, following GREAT BRITAIN.

CARRIACOU

CROWNED-CIRCLE HANDSTAMPS

CC1 CC 1 CARRIACOU (13.11.1846) .. .. .. †

Although recorded in the G.P.O. proof book no example of No. CC1 has been reported used from Grenada.

ST. GEORGE'S

CROWNED-CIRCLE HANDSTAMPS

CC2 CC 1 GRENADA (R.) (24.10.1850) *Price on cover* £1100

Stamps of GREAT BRITAIN *cancelled* "A 15" *as Type* **2**

1858 *to* **1860**.

Z1	1d. rose-red (1857), *perf* 14 ..	.. .. ..	£350
Z2	2d. blue (1858) (Plate No. 7) .	.. .. ..	£650
Z3	4d. rose (1857)	.. .. ..	£225
Z4	6d. lilac (1856)	.. .. ..	£120
Z5	1s. green (1856)	.. .. ..	£650

PRICES FOR STAMPS ON COVER TO 1945

Nos. 1/19	*from* × 15
Nos. 20/3	*from* × 20
Nos. 24/6	*from* × 10
No. 27	*from* × 15
No. 28	—
No. 29	*from* × 10
Nos. 30/6	*from* × 20
Nos. 37/9	*from* × 10
No. 40	*from* × 30
Nos. 41/7	*from* × 10
Nos. 48/101	*from* × 4
Nos. 109/11	*from* × 8
Nos. 112/48	*from* × 4
Nos. 149/51	*from* × 10
Nos. 152/63	*from* × 4
Nos. D1/3	*from* × 25
Nos. D4/7	*from* × 12
Nos. D8/14	*from* × 20

CROWN COLONY

PRINTERS. Types **1** and **5** recess-printed by Perkins, Bacon an Co.

1

2 Small Star

(Eng C. Jeens)

1861 (3 June)–**62**. *No wmk. Wove paper.*

(*a*) *Rough perf* 14 *to* 16

1 **1**	1d. bluish green ..	.. .. ..	£4500 £30
2	1d. green (5.62) ..	.. .. ..	50·00 40·0
	a. Imperf between (horiz pair) ..	..	
3	6d. rose (*shades*)	.. .. ..	£800 90·0

(*b*) *Perf* 11 *to* 12½

3*a* **1**	6d. lake-red (6.62)	.. .. ..	£750

No. 3*a* is only known unused, and may be the result o perforating machine trials undertaken by Perkins, Bacon. It ha also been seen on horizontally laid paper (*Price* £1100).

SIDEWAYS WATERMARK. W **2/3** when sideways show tw points of star downwards.

1863–71. *W* **2** (*Small Star*). *Rough perf* 14 *to* 16.

4 **1**	1d. green (3.64)	.. ..	60·00 12·0
	a. Wmk sideways ..	.. .. ..	— 20·0
5	1d. yellowish green ..	.. .. ..	95·00 26·0
6	6d. rose (*shades*) (5.63)	.. .. ..	£600 12·0
	a. Wmk sideways ..	.. .. ..	— 60·0
7	6d. orange-red (*shades*) (5.66)	.. ..	£650 12·0
8	6d. dull rose-red (*wmk sideways*)	.. ..	£3000 £22
9	6d. vermilion (5.71)	.. .. ..	£750 12·0
	a. Double impression	.. .. ..	— £180

1873 (Jan). *W* **2** (*Small Star, sideways*). *Clean-cut perf* 15.

10 **1**	1d. deep green	.. ..	70·00 28·0
	a. Bisected diag (on cover)	.. ..	† £600
	b. Imperf between (pair)	.. ..	— £375

No. 10a, and later bisected 1d. values, were authorised unti 1881 to pay the island newspaper rate (½d.) or the newspape rate to Great Britain (1½d.). Examples also exist on covers t France.

3 Large Star

4 Broad-pointed Star

1873 (Sept)–**74**. *W* **3** (*Large Star*). *Intermediate perf* 15.

11 **1**	1d. blue-green (*wmk sideways*) (2.74)	..	60·00 18·00
	a. Double impression	.. ..	
	b. Bisected diag (on cover)	.. ..	† —
12	6d. orange-vermilion	.. .. ..	£600 26·00

POSTAGE

ONE SHILLING

5 (6)

NOTE. The early ½d., 2½d., 4d. and 1s. postage stamps wer made by surcharging the undenominated Type **5** design.

The surcharges were from two founts of type—one about 1½ mm high, the other 2 mm high—so there are short and tall letters on the same stamp; also the spacing varies considerably, so that the length of the words varies.

Examples of Type **5** with surcharges, but without the "POSTAGE" inscription, are revenue stamps.

875 (July). *Surch with T* **6**. *W* **3**. *P* 14.
3 5 1s. deep mauve (B.) £650 9·00
a. "SHLLIING" † £700
b. "NE SHILLING" † £2500
c. Inverted "S" in "POSTAGE" £3500 £500
d. "OSTAGE" † £2000

875 (Dec). *W* **3** (*Large Star, upright*).
4 1 1d. green *to* yellow-green (*p* 14) 55·00 6·00
a. Bisected diag (on cover) † £6500
5 1d. green (*p* 15) £7000 £2000

No. 14 was perforated at Somerset House. 40 sheets of No. 15 ere perforated by Perkins, Bacon to replace spoilages and to mplete the order.

878 (Aug). *W* **2** (*Small Star, sideways*). *Intermediate perf* 15.
6 1 1d. green £225 27·00
b. Bisected diag (on cover) † —
7 6d. deep vermilion £750 27·00
a. Double impression — £1500

879 (Dec). *W* **2** (*Small Star, upright*). *Rough perf* 15.
8 1 1d. pale green (*thin paper*) £300 20·00
a. Double impression
b. Bisected diag (on cover) † —

881 (Apr). *W* **2** (*Small Star, sideways*). *Rough perf* 14½.
9 1 1d. green £110 6·50
a. Bisected diag (on cover) † £6500

POSTAGE POSTAGE POSTAGE

TWO PENCE HALF-PENNY

HALF-PENNY FOUR PENCE

(7) (8) (9)

1881 (Apr). *Surch with T* **7/9**. *P* 14½. (*a*) *W* **3** (*Large Star, sideways on* ½*d.*)
20 5 ½d. pale mauve 30·00 10·00
21 ½d. deep mauve 11·00 5·50
a. Imperf (pair) £300
ab. Ditto. "OSTAGE" (R.9/4) £3250
b. Surch double £275
c. "OSTAGE" (R.9/4) £180 £130
d. No hyphen £180 £130
e. "ALF-PENNY" £3000
f. Wmk upright £300 £140
g. Ditto. "OSTAGE" (R.9/4) £1700 £750
22 2½d. rose-lake 50·00 5·50
a. Imperf (pair) £400
b. Imperf between (horiz pair) £3250
c. No stop £250 75·00
d. "PENCF" (R.8/12) £450 £180
23 4d. blue 90·00 8·00
a. Wmk sideways
b. Inverted "S" in "POSTAGE"

(*b*) *W* **4** (*Broad-pointed Star*)
24 5 2½d. rose-lake £130 48·00
a. No stop £550 £200
b. "PENCF" (R.8/12) £750 £275
25 2½d. claret £400 £120
a. No stop £1000 £475
b. "PENCF" (R.8/12) £1500 £600
25c 2½d. deep claret £600 £225
d. No stop £2250 £900
e. "PENCF" (R.8/12) £2750 £1100
26 4d. blue £225 £180

Examples of the "F" for "E" error on the 2½d. value should not be onfused with a somewhat similar broken "E" variety. The latter is lways without the stop and shows other damage to the "E". The uthentic error always occurs with the full stop shown.

The "no stop" variety occurs on R.3/4, R.6/2, R.8/3 and R.9/7.

ONE PENNY POSTAGE. POSTAGE POSTAGE

(10) (11) (12)

883 (Jan). *Revenue stamps* (*T* **5** *with green surcharge as in T* **10**) *optd for postage. W* **2** (*Small Star*). *P* 14½.

(*a*) *Optd horizontally with T* **11**.
7 5 1d. orange £250 48·00
a. "POSTAGE" inverted £1700 £1200
b. "POSTAGE" double £1200 £1100
c. Inverted "S" in "POSTAGE" £800 £600
d. Bisected diag (on cover) † £3000

(*b*) *Optd diagonally with T* **11** *twice on each stamp, the stamp being cut and each half used as* ½*d.*
8 5 Half of 1d. orange £650 £225
a. Unsevered pair £3750 £1200
b. "POSTAGE" inverted — £1100

(*c*) *Optd with T* **12**, *the stamps divided diagonally and each half used as* ½*d.*
9 5 Half of 1d. orange £200 £110
a. Unsevered pair £1200 £450

Nos. 27/9 exist with wmk either upright or sideways.

1d. Revenue stamps with "POSTAGE" added in black manuscript were used at Gouyave during February and March 883 (*Price* £2250, *used*). Similar manuscript overprints, in lack or red, were also used at Sauteurs in September 1886 *Price* £3250, *used*).

GRENADA POSTAGE / ONE PENNY — 13
d. 1 POSTAGE. — (14)
GRENADA POSTAGE & REVENUE / ONE PENNY — 15

(Typo D.L.R.)

1883. *Wmk Crown CA. P* 14.
30 **13** ½d. dull green (February) 1·00 85
a. *Tête-bêche* (vert pair) 4·00 14·00
31 1d. carmine (February) 65·00 3·25
a. *Tête-bêche* (vert pair) £225 £225
32 2½d. ultramarine (May) 6·50 85
a. *Tête-bêche* (vert pair) 24·00 50·00
33 4d. greyish slate (May) 4·50 1·75
a. *Tête-bêche* (vert pair) 17·00 55·00
34 6d. mauve (May) 3·00 3·75
a. *Tête-bêche* (vert pair) 18·00 55·00
35 8d. grey-brown (February) 8·50 12·00
a. *Tête-bêche* (vert pair) 32·00 75·00
36 1s. pale violet (April) £110 55·00
a. *Tête-bêche* (vert pair) £900
30/36 *Set of* 7 £180 65·00

Types **13** and **15** were printed in rows *tête-bêche* in the sheets, so that 50% of the stamps have inverted watermarks.

1886. *Revenue stamps* (*T* **5** *with green surch as T* **10**), *surch with T* **14**. *P* 14. (*a*) *Wmk Large Star, T* **3**.
37 **5** 1d. on 1½d. orange (October) 35·00 29·00
a. Surch inverted £300 £300
b. Surch double £475 £300
c. "THRFE" £250 £225
d. "PFNCE" £250 £225
e. "HALH" £250 £225
f. Bisected diag (on cover) † £1900
38 1d. on 1s. orange (December) 32·00 30·00
a. "POSTAGE" (no stop) £350
b. "SHILLNG" £425 £375
c. Wide space (3½ mm) between "ONE" and "SHILLING" £300 £250
d. Bisected diag (on cover) † £1900

(*b*) *Wmk Small Star, T* **2**
39 **5** 1d. on 4d. orange (November) £140 90·00

1887 (Jan). *Wmk Crown CA. P* 14.
40 **15** 1d. carmine (Optd S. £50) 60 50
a. *Tête-bêche* (vert pair) 1·75 17·00

4d. POSTAGE — (16)
HALF PENNY POSTAGE — (17)

1888 (31 Mar)–**91**. *Revenue stamps* (*T* **5** *with green surch as T* **10**) *further surcharged. W* **2**. *P* 14½, *and No.* 35.

I. *Surch with T* **16**.
(*a*) 4 *mm between value and* "POSTAGE"
41 **5** 4d. on 2s. orange 35·00 17·00
a. Upright "d" (R. 5/6) £750 £400
b. Wide space (2¼ mm) between "TWO" and "SHILLINGS" £250 £150
c. First "S" in "SHILLINGS" inverted £450 £325
d. Imperf between (horiz pair)

(*b*) 5 *mm between value and* "POSTAGE"
42 **5** 4d. on 2s. orange 60·00 28·00
a. Wide space £300 £225
b. "S" inverted £650 £550

II. *Surch as T* **17** (December 1889)
43 **5** ½d. on 2s. orange 12·00 17·00
a. Surch double £300 £325
b. Wide space £110 £130
c. "S" inverted £275 £300

POSTAGE d. AND 1 REVENUE — (18)
POSTAGE AND REVENUE 1d. — (19)
2½d. — (20)

III. *Surch with T* **18** (December 1890)
44 **5** 1d. on 2s. orange 70·00 70·00
a. Surch inverted £550
b. Wide space £325 £325
c. "S" inverted £650 £650

IV. *Surch with T* **19** (January 1891)
45 **5** 1d. on 2s. orange 50·00 50·00
a. No stop after "1d" (R.3/8) £325
b. Wide space £250 £250
c. "S" inverted £500 £500
46 **13** 1d. on 8d. grey-brown 9·00 11·00
a. *Tête-bêche* (vert pair) 40·00 60·00
b. Surch inverted £300 £275
c. No stop after "1d" (R.6/5) £250 £250

V. *Surch with T* **20** (December 1891)
47 **13** 2½d. on 8d. grey-brown (Optd S. £65) 8·00 11·00
a. *Tête-bêche* (vert pair) 40·00 60·00
b. Inverted surcharge
c. Double surcharge £750 £800
d. Double surcharge, one inverted £550 £500
e. Treble surcharge — £900
f. Treble surcharge, two inverted — £850

The wide space between "TWO" and "SHILLINGS" occurs on R. 1/4 and 10/3 of the original 2s. Revenue stamp which was printed in sheets of 120 (12×10).

The surcharges, Types **16/19**, were applied to half sheets as a setting of 60 (12×5).

There are two varieties of fraction in Type **20**, which each occur 30 times in the setting; in the one the "1" has horizontal serif and the "2" commences in a ball; in the other the "1" has sloping serif and the "2" is without ball.

See also D4/7.

21 **22** **23** Flagship of Columbus. (Columbus named Grenada "La Concepcion")

(Typo D.L.R.)

1895 (6 Sept)–**99**. *Wmk Crown CA. P* 14.
48 **22** ½d. mauve and green (9.99) 2·50 1·25
49 **21** 1d. mauve and green (5.96) 4·25 60
50 2d. mauve and brown (9.99) 40·00 32·00
x. Wmk reversed
51 2½d. mauve and ultramarine 5·00 1·25
52 **22** 3d. mauve and orange 6·50 16·00
53 **21** 6d. mauve and green 9·50 19·00
54 **22** 8d. mauve and black 12·00 35·00
55 1s. green and orange 17·00 30·00
48/55 *Set of* 8 85·00 £120
48/55 Optd "Specimen" *Set of* 8 £140

(Recess D.L.R.)

1898 (15 Aug). *400th Anniv of Discovery of Grenada by Columbus. Wmk Crown CC. P* 14
56 **23** 2½d. ultramarine (Optd S. £85) 13·00 5·50
a. Bluish paper 32·00 40·00

24 **25**

(Typo D.L.R.)

1902. *Wmk Crown CA. P* 14.
57 **24** ½d. dull purple and green 3·00 50
58 **25** 1d. dull purple and carmine 3·50 20
59 2d. dull purple and brown 3·00 8·00
60 2½d. dull purple and ultramarine 3·50 2·00
61 **24** 3d. dull purple and orange 3·50 7·00
62 **25** 6d. dull purple and green 2·50 16·00
63 **24** 1s. green and orange 3·25 22·00
64 2s. green and ultramarine 18·00 55·00
65 **25** 5s. green and carmine 38·00 55·00
66 **24** 10s. green and purple £100 £190
57/66 *Set of* 10 £160 £300
57/66 Optd "Specimen" *Set of* 10 £200

1904–6. *Wmk Mult Crown CA. Ordinary paper. P* 14.
67 **24** ½d. purple and green (1905) 17·00 22·00
68 **25** 1d. purple and carmine 9·00 2·50
69 2d. purple and brown (1905) 48·00 90·00
70 2½d. purple and ultramarine (1905) 48·00 65·00
71 **24** 3d. purple and orange (1905) 2·50 6·50
a. Chalk-surfaced paper 2·50 8·00
72 **25** 6d. purple and green (1906) 4·50 8·50
a. Chalk-surfaced paper 7·00 15·00
73 **24** 1s. green and orange (1905) 6·00 23·00
74 2s. green and ultramarine (1906) 35·00 70·00
a. Chalk-surfaced paper 25·00 75·00
75 **25** 5s. green and carmine (1906) 55·00 90·00
76 **24** 10s. green and purple (1906) £140 £225
67/76 *Set of* 10 £300 £500

Examples of most values between Nos. 57 and 76 are known showing a forged G.P.O. Grenada B.W.I. postmark dated "OC 6 09".

26 Badge of the Colony **27**

(Recess D.L.R.)

1906. *Wmk Mult Crown CA. P* 14.
77 **26** ½d. green 2·50 30
78 1d. carmine 3·50 10
y. Wmk inverted and reversed
79 2d. orange 2·00 3·00
80 2½d. blue 3·75 1·50
a. Ultramarine 7·50 3·50

(Typo D.L.R.)

1908. *Wmk Crown CA. Chalk-surfaced paper. P* 14.
82 **27** 1s. black/*green* 20·00 40·00
83 10s. green and red/*green* 80·00 £150

1908–11. *Wmk Mult Crown CA. Chalk-surfaced paper. P* 14.
84 **27** 3d. dull purple/*yellow* .. .. .. 3·25 1·75
85 6d. dull purple and purple .. .. 18·00 23·00
86 1s. black/*green* (1911) .. .. .. 5·00 4·00
87 2s. blue and purple/*blue* .. .. 18·00 12·00
88 5s. green and red/*yellow* .. .. 50·00 65·00
77/88 .. .. *Set of* 11 £180 £250
77/80, 82/5, 87/8 Optd "Specimen" *Set of* 10 £200
Examples of Nos. 82/8 are known showing a forged G.P.O. Grenada B.W.I. postmark dated "OC 6 09".

28 WAR TAX (29) WAR TAX (30)

(Typo D.L.R.)

1913 (3 Jan)–**22.** *Wmk Mult Crown CA. Chalk-surfaced paper* (3*d. to* 10*s.*). *P* 14.
89 **28** ½d. yellow-green .. .. .. 90 1·40
90 ½d. green 90 80
91 1d. red .. .. 2·25 30
92 1d. scarlet (1916) .. .. .. 2·75 60
w. Wmk inverted .. .. ..
93 2d. orange .. .. 1·50 30
94 2½d. bright blue .. .. .. 1·40 2·75
95 2½d. dull blue (1920) .. .. .. 4·25 4·25
96 3d. purple/*yellow* 65 85
a. White back (3.14) (Optd S. £30) .. 65 1·50
b. On lemon (1917) .. .. .. 3·75 8·50
c. On pale yellow (1921) .. .. 6·00 25·00
97 6d. dull and bright purple .. .. 1·25 8·00
98 1s. black/*green* .. .. .. 1·00 8·00
a. White back (3.14) (Optd S. £30) .. 1·00 5·00
b. On blue-green, olive back (1917) 48·00 80·00
c. On emerald surface .. .. 1·50 9·00
d. On emerald back (6.22) (Optd S. £30) .. .. 1·00 9·00
dw. Wmk inverted .. .. .. 75·00
99 2s. purple and blue/*blue* .. .. 4·75 11·00
100 5s. green and red/*yellow* .. .. 16·00 55·00
a. On pale yellow (1921) (Optd S. £45) 24·00 75·00
101 10s. green and red/*green* .. .. 48·00 80·00
a. On emerald back (6.22) (Optd S. £55) .. .. 50·00 £130
89/101 .. .. *Set of* 10 70·00 £140
89/101 Optd "Specimen" .. .. *Set of* 10 £150
98 Optd in black instead of red .. .. .. 30·00

1916 (1 June). *Optd by Govt Press, St. George's. With T* **29**.
109 **28** 1d. red (*shades*) (H/S S. £50) .. .. 2·25 1·75
a. Opt inverted £275
b. "T△X" .. .. 55·00 70·00
A small "A" in "WAR", 2 mm high is found on Nos. 29, 38 and 48 of the setting of 60 and a very small "A" in "TAX", 1½ mm high, on No. 11. Value about twice normal. The normal "A" is 2¼ mm high.
No. 109b is on No. 56 of the setting.

1916 (1 Sept)–**18.** *Optd with T* **30** *in London.*
111 **28** 1d. scarlet 30 20
a. Carmine-red/bluish (5.18) .. .. 3·25 1·50
w. Wmk inverted .. .. ..
111 Optd "Specimen" .. .. 40·00

1921–32. *Wmk Mult Script CA. Chalk-surfaced paper* (3*d.* (*No.* 122) *to* 10*s.*) *P* 14.
112 **28** ½d. green .. .. 1·25 15
113 1d. carmine-red 80 50
114 1d. brown (1923) .. .. .. 1·50 20
115 1½d. rose-red (6.22) .. .. .. 1·50 1·50
116 2d. orange .. .. 1·25 15
117 2d. grey (1926) .. .. .. 2·50 2·00
117*a* 2½d. dull blue .. .. 3·50 2·50
118 2½d. grey (6.22) .. .. .. 75 8·00
119 2½d. bright blue (1926) .. .. 3·50 3·25
120 2½d. ultramarine (1931) .. .. 4·25 8·00
120*a* 2½d. chalky blue and blue (1932) .. 50·00 48·00
121 3d. bright blue (6.22) .. .. 1·25 8·50
122 3d. purple/*yellow* (1926) .. .. 3·00 4·75
123 4d. black and red/*yellow* (1926) .. 1·00 3·50
124 5d. dull purple & sage-green (27.12.22) 1·50 3·75
125 6d. dull and bright purple .. .. 1·25 16·00
126 6d. black and carmine (1926) .. 2·25 2·50
127 9d. dull purple and black (27.12.22) 2·25 8·00
128 1s. black/*emerald* (1923) .. .. 2·50 32·00
129 1s. chestnut (1926) .. .. .. 3·00 10·00
130 2s. purple and blue/*black* (1922) .. 6·00 16·00
131 2s. 6d. black and carmine/*blue* (1929) 6·00 16·00
132 3s. green and violet (27.12.22) .. 6·00 27·00
133 5s. green and red/*pale yellow* (1923) 12·00 32·00
134 10s. green and red/*emerald* (1923) .. 50·00 £130
112/19, 121/34 .. .. .. *Set of* 22 £100 £275
112/34 Optd/Perf "Specimen" .. *Set of* 23 £300

31 Grand Anse Beach

32 Badge of the Colony

33 Grand Etang

34 St. George's

(Recess Waterlow)

1934 (23 Oct)–**36.** *Wmk Mult Script CA* (*sideways on T* **32**). *P* 12½.
135 **31** ½d. green 15 80
a. Perf 12½ × 13½ (1936) .. .. 3·75 35·00
136 **32** 1d. black and sepia .. .. .. 80 2·25
a. Perf 13½ × 12½ (1936) 65 35
137 **33** 1½d. black and scarlet .. .. 4·75 2·50
a. Perf 12½ × 13½ (1936) 90 55
138 **32** 2d. black and orange 90 40
139 **34** 2½d. blue 40 30
140 **32** 3d. black and olive-green .. .. 55 2·00
141 6d. black and purple .. .. .. 1·40 1·25
142 1s. black and brown .. .. .. 90 2·75
143 2s. 6d. black and ultramarine .. .. 7·00 25·00
144 5s. black and violet .. .. .. 32·00 48·00
135/144 .. .. *Set of* 10 40·00 70·00
135/44 Perf "Specimen" .. .. *Set of* 10 £160

1935 (6 May). *Silver Jubilee. As Nos.* 91/4 *of Antigua but ptd by Waterlow. P* 11×12.
145 ½d. black and green 50 75
k. Kite and vertical log .. .. 35·00
l. Kite and horizontal log .. .. 42·00
146 1d. ultramarine and grey .. .. 50 1·25
l. Kite and horizontal log .. .. 40·00
147 1½d. deep blue and scarlet .. .. 50 1·25
l. Kite and horizontal log .. .. 55·00
148 1s. slate and purple .. .. .. 5·50 15·00
l. Kite and horizontal log £140
145/8 .. .. *Set of* 4 6·25 16·00
145/8 Perf "Specimen" .. .. *Set of* 4 70·00
For illustrations of plate varieties see Catalogue Introduction.

1937 (12 May). *Coronation. As Nos.* 95/7 *of Antigua. P* 11x11½.
149 1d. violet 40 20
150 1½d. carmine 40 20
151 2½d. blue 80 30
149/51 .. .. *Set of* 3 1·40 65
149/51 Perf "Specimen" .. .. *Set of* 3 50·00

35 King George VI

(Photo Harrison)

1937 (12 July)–**50.** *Wmk Mult Script CA. Chalk-surfaced paper. P* 15×14.
152 **35** ¼d. brown .. .. 1·40 10
a. Ordinary paper (11.42) 30 60
b. Ordinary paper. *Chocolate* (1.45) 20 60
c. Chalk-surfaced paper. *Chocolate* (8.50) .. .. 50 2·50
The ordinary paper is thick, smooth and opaque.

36 Grand Anse Beach

40 Badge of the Colony

Colon flaw (R. 5/8. Corrected on ptg of Nov 1950)

(Recess D.L.R. (10s.), Waterlow (others))

1938 (16 Mar)–**50.** *As T* 31/4 (*but portrait of King George VI as in T* **36**) *and T* **40**. *Wmk Mult Script CA* (*sideways on T* **32**). *P* 12½ *or* 12 × 13 (10*s.*).
153 **36** ½d. yellow-green .. .. .. 4·50 1·00
a. Perf 12½×13½ (1938) .. .. 6·00 80
b. Perf 12½. *Blue-green* .. .. 60 1·25
ba. Perf 12½×13½. *Blue-green* .. 6·00 5·00
154 **32** 1d. black and sepia .. .. .. 1·00 20
a. Perf 13½×12½ (1938) 50 50
155 **33** 1½d. black and scarlet 50 60
a. Perf 12½×13½ (1938) .. .. 2·25 30
156 **32** 2d. black and orange 30 50
a. Perf 13½×12½ (1938) .. .. 2·50 60
157 **34** 2½d. bright blue 30
a. Perf 12½×13½ (?March 1950) .. £4000 £2
158 **32** 3d. black and olive-green .. .. 9·00 1·
a. Perf 13½×12½ (16.3.38) .. .. 6·00
ab. Perf 13½×12½. *Black and brown-olive* (1942) 30
b. Perf 12½. *Black and brown-olive* (16.8.50) .. .. 30 1·
ba. Colon flaw .. .. 48·00
159 6d. black and purple .. .. .. 1·25
a. Perf 13½×12½ (1942) .. .. 2·25
160 1s. black and brown .. .. .. 2·25
a. Perf 13½×12½ (1941) .. .. 3·50 1·
161 2s. black and ultramarine .. .. 16·00 1·
a. Perf 13½×12½ (1941) .. .. 20·00 1·
162 5s. black and violet .. .. .. 3·50 1·
a. Perf 13½×12½ (1947) .. .. 2·75 5·
163 **40** 10s. steel blue and carmine (*narrow*) (*p* 12×13) .. .. 55·00 9·
a. Perf 14. *Steel blue and bright carmine* (*narrow*) .. .. .. £180 45·
b. Perf 14. *Slate-blue and bright carmine* (*narrow*) (1943) £190 £11
c. Perf 12. *Slate-blue and bright carmine* (*narrow*) (1943) £450 £75
d. Perf 14. *Slate-blue and carmine-lake* (*wide*) (1944) .. .. .. 85·00 8·
e. Perf 14. *Blue-black and carmine* (*narrow*) (1943) .. .. .. 27·00 8·
f. Perf 14. *Blue-black and bright carmine* (*wide*) (1947) .. .. .. 25·00 25·
152/63e .. .. *Set of* 12 45·00 13·
152/63 Perf "Specimen" .. .. *Set of* 12 £225
In the earlier printings of the 10s. the paper was dampene before printing and the subsequent shrinkage produced narro frames 23½ to 23¾ mm wide. Later printings were made on dr paper producing wide frames 24¼ mm wide.
No. 163a is one of the earlier printings line perf 13.8×14. Later printings of the 10s. are line perf 14.1.
Nos. 163b/c show a blurred centre caused by the use of a wor plate.
Nos. 163a and 163b may be found with gum more or les yellow due to local climatic conditions.
Examples of No. 163c are known showing forged St. George postmarks dated "21 AU 42", "21 AU 43" or "2 OC 43".

1946 (25 Sept). *Victory. As Nos.* 110/11 *of Antigua.*
164 1½d. carmine 10
165 3½d. blue 10
164/5 Perf "Specimen" .. .. *Set of* 2 50·00

1948 (27 Oct). *Royal Silver Wedding. As Nos.* 112/13 *Antigua.*
166 1½d. scarlet 15 1
167 10s. slate-green .. .. 8·00 16·0

(New Currency. 100 cents = 1 West Indian, later Eastern Caribbean, dollar)

1949 (10 Oct). *75th Anniv of Universal Postal Union. As Nos* 114/17 *of Antigua.*
168 5 c. ultramarine 20 1
169 6 c. olive 90 9
170 12 c. magenta 35 3
171 24 c. red-brown 35 3
168/71 .. .. *Set of* 4 1·60 1·4

41 King George VI

42 Badge of the Colony

43 Badge of the Colony

(Recess B.W. (T **41**), D.L.R. (others))

1951 (8 Jan). *Wmk Mult Script CA. P* 11½ (*T* **41**), 11½ × 12½ (*T* **42**), *and* 11½ × 13 (*T* **43**).
172 **41** ½ c. black and red-brown .. .. 15 1·0
173 1 c. black and emerald-green 15 25
174 2 c. black and brown 15 30
175 3 c. black and rose-carmine 15 10
176 4 c. black and orange 35 40
177 5 c. black and violet 20 10
178 6 c. black and olive 30 60
179 7 c. black and light blue .. .. 1·75 10
180 12 c. black and purple .. .. .. 2·25 30
181 **42** 25 c. black and sepia .. .. .. 2·25 50
182 50 c. black and blue .. .. .. 6·00 40
183 $1.50, black and yellow-orange .. 7·50 5·50
184 **43** $2.50, slate-blue and carmine .. .. 5·50 5·50
172/184 .. .. *Set of* 13 24·00 13·00

1951 (16 Feb). *Inauguration of B.W.I. University College. As Nos.* 118/19 *of Antigua.*
185 3 c. black and carmine 45 20
186 6 c. black and olive 45 20

NEW CONSTITUTION

1951

(44)

1951 (21 Sept). *New Constitution. Nos.* 175/7 *and* 180 *optd with T* **44** *by B.W.*

187 **41** 3 c. black and rose-carmine 10 10
188 4 c. black and orange 10 10
189 5 c. black and violet (R.) 10 10
190 12 c. black and purple 10 15
187/90 .. .. .. *Set of* 4 30 40

1953 (3 June). *Coronation. As No.* 120 *of Antigua.*

191 3 c. black and carmine-red 20 10

45 Queen Elizabeth II — 46 Badge of the Colony — 47 Badge of the Colony

(Recess B.W. (T **45**), D.L.R. (T **46/7**))

1953 (15 June)–**59**. *Wmk Mult Script CA. P* 11½ (*T* **45**), 11½ × 12½ (*T* **46**), *or* 11½ × 13 (*T* **47**).

192 **45** ½ c. black and brown (28.12.53) .. 10 10
193 1 c. black and deep emerald 10 10
194 2 c. black and sepia (15.9.53) 30 10
195 3 c. black and carmine-red (22.2.54) .. 10 10
196 4 c. black and brown-orange (22.2.54) .. 10 10
197 5 c. black and deep violet (22.2.54) .. 10 10
198 6 c. black and olive-green (28.12.53) .. 45 85
199 7 c. black and blue (6.6.55) .. .. 1·25 10
200 12 c. black and reddish purple 30 10
201 **46** 25 c. black and sepia (10.1.55) .. .. 1·25 20
202 50 c. black and deep blue (2.12.55) .. 5·50 40
203 $1.50, black & brown-orange (2.12.55) 11·00 12·00
204 **47** $2.50, slate-blue & carmine (16.11.59) 18·00 10·00
192/204 .. .. .. *Set of* 13 35·00 21·00

On 23 December 1965, No. 203 was issued surcharged "2" but this was intended for fiscal and revenue purposes and it was not authorised to be used postally, although some are known to have passed through the mail.

For stamps in Types **45/6** watermarked w **12** see Nos. 214/20.

1958 (22 Apr). *Inauguration of British Caribbean Federation. As Nos.* 135/7 *of Antigua.*

205 3 c. deep green 35 10
206 6 c. blue 45 60
207 12 c. scarlet 55 10
205/7 .. .. *Set of* 3 1·25 70

48 Queen Victoria, Queen Elizabeth II, Mail Van and Post Office, St. George's

(Photo Harrison)

1961 (1 June). *Grenada Stamp Centenary. T* **48** *and similar horiz designs. W* w **12**. *P* 14½ × 14.

208 3 c. crimson and black 25 10
209 8 c. bright blue and orange 55 25
210 25 c. lake and blue 55 25
208/10 .. .. .. *Set of* 3 1·25 55

Designs:—8 c. Queen Victoria, Queen Elizabeth II and flagship of Columbus; 25 c. Queen Victoria, Queen Elizabeth II, *Solent I* (paddle-steamer) and Douglas DC-3 aircraft.

1963 (4 June). *Freedom from Hunger. As No.* 146 *of Antigua.*

211 8 c. bluish green 30 15

1963 (2 Sept). *Red Cross Centenary. As Nos.* 147/8 *of Antigua.*

212 3 c. red and black 15 15
213 25 c. red and blue 30 15

1964 (12 May)–**66**. *As Nos.* 194/8, 201/1, *but wmk* w **12**.

214 **45** 2 c. black and sepia 10 10
215 3 c. black and carmine-red 15 10
216 4 c. black and brown-orange 15 50
217 5 c. black and deep violet 15 10
218 6 c. black and olive-green (4.1.66) .. £190 65·00
219 12 c. black and reddish purple 20 10
220 **46** 25 c. black and sepia .. .. .. 2·25 50
214/20 .. .. .. *Set of* 7 £190 65·00

1965 (17 May). *I.T.U. Centenary. As Nos.* 166/7 *of Antigua.*

221 2 c. red-orange and yellow-olive 10 10
222 50 c. lemon and light red 25 20

1965 (25 Oct). *International Co-operation Year. As Nos.* 168/9 *of Antigua*

223 1 c. reddish purple and turquoise-green .. 10 15
224 25 c. deep bluish green and lavender 20 15

1966 (24 Jan). *Churchill Commemoration. As Nos.* 170/3 *of Antigua.*

225 1 c. new blue 10 15
226 3 c. deep green 10 15
227 25 c. brown 15 10
228 35 c. bluish violet 25 15
225/8 .. .. *Set of* 4 45 40

1966 (4 Feb). *Royal Visit. As Nos.* 174/5 *of Antigua.*

229 3 c. black and ultramarine 25 15
230 35 c. black and magenta 65 15

52 Hillsborough, Carriacou — 53 Badge of the Colony

54 Queen Elizabeth II — 55 Map of Grenada

(Des V. Whiteley. Photo Harrison)

1966 (1 Apr). *Horiz designs as T* **52**, *and T* **53/5**. *Multicoloured. W* w **12**. *P* 14½ ($1, $2, $3) *or* 14½×13½ (*others*).

231 1 c. Type **52** 20 40
232 2 c. Bougainvillea 20 10
233 3 c. Flamboyant plant 20 30
234 5 c. Levera beach 50 10
235 6 c. Carenage, St. George's 50 10
236 8 c. Annandale Falls 50 10
w. Wmk inverted .. .. ..
237 10 c. Cocoa pods 30 10
238 12 c. Inner Harbour 30 50
239 15 c. Nutmeg 30 50
240 25 c. St. George's 30 10
241 35 c. Grand Anse beach 30 10
242 50 c. Bananas .. .. 1·00 1·25
243 $1 Type **53** .. .. 7·00 2·75
244 $2 Type **54** .. .. 4·50 5·00
245 $3 Type **55** .. .. 4·50 11·00
231/45 .. .. .. *Set of* 15 18·00 20·00

1966 (1 July). *World Cup Football Championships. As Nos.* 176/7 *of Antigua.*

246 5 c. violet, yellow-green, lake & yellow-brn 10 10
247 50 c. chocolate, blue-green, lake & yelllow-brn 40 50

1966 (20 Sept). *Inauguration of W.H.O. Headquarters, Geneva. As Nos.* 178/9 *of Antigua.*

248 8 c. black, yellow-green and light blue .. 10 10
249 25 c. black, light purple and yellow-brown .. 25 20

1966 (1 Dec). *20th Anniv of U.N.E.S.C.O. As Nos.* 196/8 *of Antigua.*

250 2 c. slate-violet, red, yellow and orange .. 10 10
251 15 c. orange-yellow, violet and deep olive .. 15 10
252 50 c. black, bright purple and orange 30 60
250/2 .. .. *Set of* 3 45 65

ASSOCIATED STATEHOOD

(67) — (68)

1967 (3 Mar). *Statehood. Nos.* 232/3, 236 *and* 240 *optd with T* **67**, *in silver*

253 2 c. Bougainvillea 10 15
254 3 c. Flamboyant plant 10 10
255 8 c. Annandale Falls 15 10
256 25 c. St. George's 15 15
253/6 .. .. .. *Set of* 4 30 30

1967 (June). *World Fair, Montreal. Nos.* 232, 237, 239 *and* 243/4 *surch as T* **68** *or optd with "Expo" emblem only.*

257 1 c. on 15 c. Nutmeg 10 20
a. Surch and opt albino .. .. .. 14·00
258 2 c. Bougainvillea 10 20
259 3 c. on 10 c. Cocoa pods 10 20
w. Wmk inverted .. .. .. 7·00
260 $1 Type **53** 30 25
261 $2 Type **54** 45 30
257/61 .. .. .. *Set of* 5 70 1·00

COVER PRICES

Cover factors are quoted at the beginning of each country for most issues to 1945. An explanation of the system can be found on page x. The factors quoted do not, however, apply to philatelic covers.

ASSOCIATED STATEHOOD

(69) — 70 Kennedy and Local Flower

1967 (Oct). *Statehood. Nos.* 231/45 *optd with T* **69**.

262 1 c. Type **52** 10 10
263 2 c. Bougainvillea 10 10
264 3 c. Flamboyant plant 10 10
265 5 c. Levera beach 10 10
266 6 c. Carenage, St. George's 10 10
267 8 c. Annandale Falls 10 10
268 10 c. Cocoa pods 10 10
269 12 c. Inner Harbour 10 10
270 15 c. Nutmeg 15 10
271 25 c. St. George's 20 10
272 35 c. Grand Anse beach 55 10
273 50 c. Bananas 70 20
274 $1 Type **53** 70 60
275 $2 Type **54** .. .. 1·25 3·25
276 $3 Type **55** .. .. 2·25 3·25
262/76 .. .. .. *Set of* 15 5·50 7·50

See also No. 295

(Des M. Shamir. Photo Harrison)

1968 (13 Jan). *50th Birth Anniv of President Kennedy. T* **70** *and similar horiz designs. Multicoloured. P* 14½ × 14.

277 1 c. Type **70** 10 15
278 15 c. Type **70** 10 10
279 25 c. Kennedy and strelitzia 10 10
280 35 c. Kennedy and roses 10 10
281 50 c. As 25 c. 15 20
282 $1 As 35 c. 25 50
277/82 .. .. .. *Set of* 6 55 80

73 Scout Bugler — 76 "Near Antibes"

(Des K. Plowitz. Photo Govt Printer, Israel)

1968 (17 Feb). *World Scout Jamboree, Idaho. T* **73** *and similar vert designs. Multicoloured. P* 13 × 13½.

283 1 c. Type **73** 10 10
284 2 c. Scouts camping 10 10
285 3 c. Lord Baden-Powell 10 10
286 35 c. Type **73** 20 10
287 50 c. As 2 c. 25 20
288 $1 As 3 c. 40 40
283/8 .. .. .. *Set of* 6 85 65

(Des G. Vasarhelyi. Photo Harrison)

1968 (23 Mar). *Paintings by Sir Winston Churchill. T* **76** *and similar horiz designs. Multicoloured. P* 14 × 14½.

289 10 c. Type **76** 10 10
290 12 c. "The Mediterranean" 15 10
291 15 c. "St. Jean Cap Ferratt" 15 10
292 25 c. Type **76** 20 10
293 35 c. As 15 c. 25 10
294 50 c. Sir Winston painting 35 25
289/94 .. .. .. *Set of* 6 1·10 45

CHILDREN NEED MILK

$5

CHILDREN NEED MILK

2cts. + 3cts.

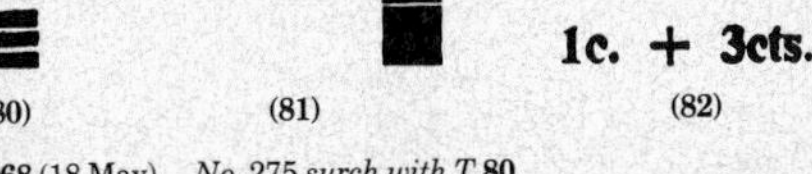

(80) — (81) — (82)

1968 (18 May). *No.* 275 *surch with T* **80**

295 **54** $5 on $2 multicoloured .. .. 1·50 2·25

1968 (22 July–19 Aug). *"Children Need Milk".*

(*a*) *Nos.* 244/5 *surch locally as T* **81** (22 July)

296 **54** 2 c. + 3 c. on $2 multicoloured 10 10
297 **55** 3 c. + 3 c. on $3 multicoloured 10 10
a. Surch inverted .. .. .. 50·00 15·00
b. Surch double .. .. .. 22·00
c. Surch double, one albino .. ..

(*b*) *Nos.* 243/4 *surch locally as T* **82** (19 Aug)

298 **53** 1 c. + 3 c. on $1 multicoloured 10 40
a. Surch on No. 274 .. .. .. 70·00 70·00
b. Surch double .. .. .. 35·00
299 **54** 2 c. + 3 c. on $2 multicoloured .. .. 13·00 45·00
a. Surch on No. 275 .. .. .. 80·00
296/9 .. .. .. *Set of* 4 13·00 45·00

83 Edith McGuire (U.S.A.) 86 Hibiscus

(Des M. Shamir. Photo Harrison)

1968 (24 Sept). *Olympic Games, Mexico. T* **83** *and similar square designs. P* 12½.

300 1 c. brown, black and blue 10 10
301 2 c. orange, brown, blue and lilac .. 10 10
a. Orange (badge, etc.) omitted ..
302 3 c. scarlet, brown and dull green .. 10 10
a. Scarlet (rings, "MEXICO" etc.) omitted £650
303 10 c. brown, black, blue and vermilion .. 15 10
304 50 c. orange, brown, blue and turquoise .. 55 65
305 60 c. scarlet, brown and red-orange .. 60 80
300/5 .. .. *Set of* 6 1·25 1·50

Designs:—2, 50 c. Arthur Wint (Jamaica); 3, 60 c. Ferreira da Silva (Brazil); 10 c. Type **83**.

Nos. 300/2 and 303/5 were issued in separate composite sheets containing three strips of three, with three *se-tenant* labels showing Greek athlete (Nos. 300/2) or Discobolos (Nos. 303/5). (*Price for two sheets £6 mint, £8 used.*)

(Des G. Vasarhelyi (No. 314*a*), V. Whiteley (75 c.), M. Shamir (others). Litho Format (Nos. 314*a* and 317*a*). Photo Harrison (others))

1968 (Oct)–**71**. *Multicoloured designs as T* **86**. *P* 13½ (*Nos.* 314*a and* 317*a*), 13½ × 14½ (*vert except No.* 314*a*) *or* 14½ × 13½ (*horiz except No.* 317*a*).

306 1 c. Type **86** 10 10
307 2 c. Strelitzia 10 10
308 3 c. Bougainvillea (1.7.69) 10 10
309 5 c. Rock Hind (*horiz*) (4.2.69) 10 10
310 6 c. Sailfish 10 10
311 8 c. Red Snapper (*horiz*) (1.7.69) 10 30
312 10 c. Marine Toad (*horiz*) (4.2.69) 10 10
313 12 c. Turtle 15 10
314 15 c. Tree Boa (*horiz*) 90 60
314*a* 15 c. Thunbergia (1970) .. .. .. 5·50 2·50
315 25 c. Greater Trinidadian Murine Opossum (4.2.69) 30 10
316 35 c. Nine-banded Armadillo (*horiz*) (1.7.69) 35 10
317 50 c. Mona Monkey 45 25
317*a* 75 c. Yacht in St. George's Harbour (*horiz*) (9.10.71) .. .. 12·00 8·50
318 $1 Bananaquit .. .. 3·00 1·50
319 $2 Brown Pelican (4.2.69) .. .. 5·00 9·00
320 $3 Magnificent Frigate Bird .. .. 4·50 5·00
321 $5 Bare-eyed Thrush (1.7.69) .. .. 7·00 16·00
306/21 .. .. *Set of* 18 35·00 40·00

Nos. 314*a*, 317*a* and the dollar values are larger—29×45½, 44×28½ and 25½×48 mm respectively.

No. 317*a* exists imperforate from stock dispersed by the liquidator of Format International Security Printers Ltd.

102 Kidney Transplant 106 "The Adoration of the Kings" (Veronese)

(Des M. Shamir. Litho B.W.)

1968 (25 Nov). *20th Anniv of World Health Organization. T* **102** *and similar vert designs. Multicoloured. P* 13 × 13½.

322 5 c. Type **102** 20 10
323 25 c. Heart transplant 30 10
324 35 c. Lung transplant 30 10
325 50 c. Eye transplant 35 50
322/5 .. .. *Set of* 4 1·10 60

(Photo Harrison)

1968 (3 Dec). *Christmas. T* **106** *and similar square designs. P* 12½.

326 5 c. multicoloured 10 10
327 15 c. multicoloured 10 10
328 35 c. multicoloured 10 10
329 $1 multicoloured 30 40
326/9 .. .. *Set of* 4 40 45

Designs:—15 c. "Madonna and Child with Sts. John and Catherine" (Titian); 35 c. "Adoration of the Kings" (Botticelli); $1 "A Warrior Adoring" (Catena).

VISIT CARIFTA EXPO '69
April 5-30
5c

(110)

1969 (Feb). *Caribbean Free Trade Area Exhibition. Nos.* 300/5 *surch in red as T* **110**.

330 5 c. on 1 c. brown, black and blue 10 10
a. Surch double .. ..
331 8 c. on 2 c. orange, brown, blue and lilac .. 10 10
a. Surch double .. ..
332 25 c. on 3 c. scarlet, brown and dull green .. 10 10
a. Surch double .. ..
333 35 c. on 10 c. brown, black, blue and vermilion 10 10
334 $1 on 50 c. orange, brown, blue & turquoise 20 30
335 $2 on 60 c. scarlet, brown and red-orange .. 35 60
a. Scarlet (rings, "MEXICO" etc) omitted † —
330/5 .. .. *Set of* 6 65 95

The centre of the composite sheets is also overprinted with a commemorative inscription publicising CARIFTA EXPO 1969 (*Price for two sheets £11 mint or used*).

111 Dame Hylda Bynoe (Governor) and Island Scene

(Des and litho D.L.R.)

1969 (1 May). *Carifta Expo* 1969. *T* **111** *and similar horiz designs. Multicoloured. P* 13 × 13½.

336 5 c. Type **111** 10 10
337 15 c. Premier E. M. Gairy and Island scene .. 10 10
338 50 c. Type **111** 10 25
339 60 c. Emblems of 1958 and 1967 World's Fairs 10 30
336/9 .. .. *Set of* 4 30 60

114 Dame Hylda Bynoe 115 "Balshazzar's Feast" (Rembrandt)

(Photo Enschedé)

1969 (8 June). *Human Rights Year. T* **114/15** *and similar multi-coloured design. P* 12½ × 13 ($1) *or* 13 × 12½ (*others*).

340 5 c. Type **114** 10 10
341 25 c. Dr. Martin Luther King (*vert*) 15 10
342 35 c. Type **114** 15 10
343 $1 Type **115** 30 45
340/3 .. .. *Set of* 4 55 55

117 Batsman and Wicket-keeper

(Des M. Shamir and L. W. Denyer. Photo Harrison)

1969 (1 Aug). *Cricket. T* **117** *and similar horiz designs. P* 14 × 14½.

344 3 c. yellow, brown and ultramarine .. 25 70
a. Yellow (caps and wicket) omitted .. £400
345 10 c. multicoloured 30 40
346 25 c. brown, ochre and myrtle-green .. 60 85
347 35 c. multicoloured 80 90
344/7 .. .. *Set of* 4 1·75 2·50

Designs:—10 c. Batsman playing defensive stroke; 25 c. Batsman sweeping ball; 35 c. Batsman playing on-drive.

Nos. 344/7 were each issued in small sheets of 9 (3 × 3) with decorative borders.

129 Astronaut handling Moon Rock

(Des G. Vasarhelyi. Photo)

1969 (24 Sept). *First Man on the Moon. T* **129** *and similar multi-coloured designs. P* 13½ (½ c.) *or* 12½ (*others*).

348 ½ c. As Type **129** but larger (56 × 35 *mm*) .. 10 10
349 1 c. Moon rocket and moon 10 10
350 2 c. Module landing 10 10
351 3 c. Declaration left on moon 10 10
352 8 c. Module leaving rocket 10 10
353 25 c. Rocket lifting-off (*vert*) 20 10
354 35 c. Spacecraft in orbit (*vert*) 20 10
355 50 c. Capsule with parachutes (*vert*) .. 30 30
356 $1 Type **129** 45 70
348/56 .. .. *Set of* 9 1·25 1·40
MS357 115 × 90 mm. Nos. 351 and 356. Imperf 1·00 2·50

130 Gandhi

(Des A. Robledo. Litho B.W.)

1969 (8 Oct). *Birth Centenary of Mahatma Gandhi. T* **130** *and similar designs. P* 11½.

358 **130** 6 c. multicoloured 15 10
359 – 15 c. multicoloured 20 10
360 – 25 c. multicoloured 30 10
361 – $1 multicoloured 75 60
358/61 .. .. *Set of* 4 1·25 75
MS362 155 × 122 mm. Nos. 358/61. Imperf .. 2·25 3·50

Designs: *Vert*—15 c. Gandhi standing; 25 c. Gandhi walking. *Horiz*—$1 Head of Gandhi.

1969

(134) 135 "Blackbeard" (Edward Teach)

1969 (23 Dec). *Christmas. Nos.* 326/9 *surch with T* **134** *in black* (2 c.) *or optd with new date only in silver* (*others*).

363 2 c. on 15 c. multicoloured 10 10
a. Surch inverted .. .. .. 40·00
364 5 c. multicoloured 10 10
a. Opt double .. .. .. 40·00
365 35 c. multicoloured 20 10
a. Opt inverted .. .. .. 40·00
b. Horiz pair, one with opt omitted .. £200
c. Opt double, one vertical .. .. 45·00
366 $1 multicoloured .. .. .. 80 1·50
a. Opt inverted .. .. .. 40·00
363/6 .. .. *Set of* 4 1·00 1·60

(Des K. Plowitz. Recess B.W.)

1970 (2 Feb). *Pirates. T* **135** *and similar vert designs. P* 13½.

367 15 c. black 35 10
368 25 c. dull green 50 10
369 50 c. lilac 90 20
370 $1 carmine .. .. 1·50 75
367/70 .. .. *Set of* 4 3·00 1·00

Designs:—25 c. Anne Bonney; 50 c. Jean Lafitte; $1 Mary Read.

5c 5c

(139) (140)

1970 (18 Mar). *No.* 348 *surch with T* **139**.

371 5 c. on ½ c. multicoloured 10 10
a. Surch double .. .. .. 25·00
b. Surch with T **140** 70 70
ba. Surch double, one inverted .. .. 40·00

141 "The Last Supper" (detail, 142 Del Sarto)

(Des and litho B.W.)

1970 (13 Apr). *Easter. Paintings. T* **141/2** *and similar vert designs. Multicoloured. P* 11½.

372 5 c. } Type **141/2** 10 15
373 5 c. } 10 15
374 15 c. } "Christ crowned with Thorns" (detail, .. 20 25
375 15 c. } Van Dyck) 20 25
376 25 c. } "The Passion of Christ" (detail, .. 25 30
377 25 c. } Memling) 25 30
378 60 c. } "Christ in the Tomb" (detail, Rubens) .. 40 55
379 60 c. } 40 55
372/9 .. .. *Set of* 8 1·60 2·25
MS380 120 × 140 mm. Nos. 376/9 .. .. 1·00 1·25

Nos. 372/9 were issued with each design spread over two *se-tenant* stamps of the same denomination.

149 Girl with Kittens in Pram

(Des A. Robledo. Litho Questa)

1970 (27 May). *Birth Bicentenary of William Wordsworth (poet). "Children and Pets". T* **149** *and similar horiz designs. Multicoloured. P* 11.
381 5 c. Type **149** 15 15
382 15 c. Girl with puppy and kitten . . 20 15
383 30 c. Boy with fishing rod and cat . . 25 20
384 60 c. Boys and girls with cats and dogs . . 40 1·10
381/4 . . *Set of* 4 90 1·40
MS385 Two sheets each 114 × 126 mm. Nos. 381, 383 and Nos. 382, 384. Imperf . . 1·25 2·00

153 Parliament of India

(Des G. Vasarhelyi. Litho Questa)

1970 (15 June). *Seventh Regional Conference of Commonwealth Parliamentary Association. T* **153** *and similar horiz designs. Multicoloured. P* 14
386 5 c. Type **153** 10 10
387 25 c. Parliament of Great Britain, Westminster . . 10 10
388 50 c. Parliament of Canada . . 15 15
389 60 c. Parliament of Grenada . . 15 15
386/9 . . *Set of* 4 40 35
MS390 126 × 90 mm. Nos. 386/9 . . 50 90

157 Tower of the Sun

(Litho Kyodo Printing Co, Tokyo)

1970 (8 Aug). *World Fair, Osaka. T* **157** *and similar multicoloured designs. P* 13.
391 1 c. Type **157** 10 10
392 2 c. Livelihood and Industry Pavilion (*horiz*) 10 10
393 3 c. Flower painting, 1634 . . 10 10
394 10 c. "Adam and Eve" (Tintoretto) (*horiz*) . . 15 10
395 25 c. O.E.C.D. (Organisation for Economic Co-operation and Development) Pavilion (*horiz*) . . 20 10
396 50 c. San Francisco Pavilion . . 45 1·25
391/6 . . *Set of* 6 90 1·50
MS397 121 × 91 mm. $1 Japanese Pavilion (56 × 34 *mm*) . . 55 1·50

164 Roosevelt and "Raising U.S. Flag on Iwo Jima"

(Litho Questa)

1970 (3 Sept). *25th Anniv of Ending of World War II. T* **164** *and similar horiz designs. Multicoloured. P* 11.
398 ½ c. Type **164** 10 10
399 5 c. Zhukov and "Fall of Berlin" . . 70 15
400 15 c. Churchill and "Evacuation at Dunkirk" 1·50 45
401 25 c. De Gaulle and "Liberation of Paris" . . 1·50 45
402 50 c. Eisenhower and "D-Day Landing" . . 2·00 1·50
403 60 c. Montgomery and "Battle of Alamein" . . 2·00 2·75
398/403 . . *Set of* 6 7·00 4·75
MS404 163 × 113 mm. Nos. 398, 400, 402/3 . . 3·25 7·00
a. Brown (panel) on 60 c. value omitted . . £700

PHILYMPIA
LONDON 1970

(169)

170 U.P.U. Emblem, Building and Transport

1970 (18 Sept). *"Philympia 1970" Stamp Exhibition, London. Nos. 353/6 optd with T* **169**
405 25 c. Rocket lifting-off 10 10
a. Albino opt . . 4·50
b. Opt inverted . . 15·00
406 35 c. Spacecraft in orbit . . 10 10
a. Opt inverted . . 40·00
407 50 c. Capsule with parachutes . . 15 15
a. Albino opt . . 3·50
408 $1 Type **129** (Sil.) (optd vert upwards) . . 20 30
a. Albino opt . . 6·50
405/8 . . *Set of* 4 40 50

The miniature sheet was also overprinted but we understand that only 300 of these were put on sale in Grenada.

(Litho Questa)

1970 (17 Oct). *New U.P.U. Headquarters Building. T* **170** *and similar multicoloured designs. P* 14.
409 15 c. Type **170** 35 10
410 25 c. As Type **170**, but modern transport . . 35 10
411 50 c. Sir Rowland Hill and U.P.U. Building . . 35 30
412 $1 Abraham Lincoln and U.P.U. Building . . 40 1·25
409/12 . . *Set of* 4 1·25 1·50
MS413 79 × 85 mm. Nos. 411/12 . . 90 3·00

The 50 c. and $1 are both vertical designs.

171 "The Madonna of the Goldfinch" (Tiepolo)

172 19th-Century Nursing

(Des G. Vasarhelyi. Litho Questa)

1970 (5 Dec). *Christmas. T* **171** *and similar vert designs. Multicoloured. P* 13½.
414 ½ c. Type **171** 10 10
415 ½ c. "The Virgin and Child with St. Peter and St. Paul" (Bouts) . . 10 10
416 ½ c. "The Virgin and Child" (Bellini) . . 10 10
417 2 c. "The Madonna of the Basket" (Correggio) 10 10
418 3 c. Type **171** 10 10
419 35 c. As No. 415 . . 20 10
420 50 c. As 2 c. . . 30 35
421 $1 As No. 416 . . 50 1·25
414/21 . . *Set of* 8 1·10 1·75
MS422 102 × 87 mm. Nos. 420/1 . . 1·25 3·00

(Des G. Vasarhelyi. Litho Questa)

1970 (12 Dec). *Centenary of British Red Cross. T* **172** *and similar horiz designs. Multicoloured. P* 14½ × 14.
423 5 c. Type **172** 20 10
424 15 c. Military Ambulance, 1918 . . 25 10
425 25 c. First-Aid Post, 1941 . . 35 10
426 60 c. Red Cross Transport, 1970 . . 90 80
423/6 . . *Set of* 4 1·50 95
MS427 113 × 82 mm. Nos. 423/6 . . 2·00 1·60
a. Error. Imperf . . 25·00

173 John Dewey and Art Lesson

(Des G. Vasarhelyi. Litho Questa)

1971 (1 May). *International Education Year* (1970). *T* **173** *and similar horiz designs. Multicoloured. P* 13½.
428 5 c. Type **173** 10 10
429 10 c. Jean-Jacques Rousseau and "Alphabetisation" . . 15 10
430 50 c. Maimonides and laboratory . . 50 15
431 $1 Bertrand Russell and mathematics class 95 40
428/31 . . *Set of* 4 1·50 55
MS432 90 × 98 mm. Nos. 430/1 . . 1·40 2·00

NEW INFORMATION

The editor is always interested to correspond with people who have new information that will improve or correct the Catalogue.

174 Jennifer Hosten and outline of Grenada

176 "Napolean reviewing the Guard" (E. Detaille)

175 French and Canadian Scouts

(Des local artist; adapted G. Drummond. Litho Format)

1971 (1 June). *Winner of "Miss World" Competition* (1970). *P* 13½.
433 **174** 5 c. multicoloured . . 10 10
434 10 c. multicoloured . . 10 10
435 15 c. multicoloured . . 15 10
436 25 c. multicoloured . . 15 10
437 35 c. multicoloured . . 15 10
438 50 c. multicoloured . . 35 55
433/8 . . *Set of* 6 80 75
MS439 92 × 89 mm. **174** 50 c. multicoloured. Printed on silk. Imperf . . 75 1·75

(Litho Format)

1971 (11 Sept). *13th World Scout Jamboree, Asagiri, Japan. T* **175** *and similar horiz designs. Multicoloured. P* 11.
440 5 c. Type **175** 10 10
441 35 c. German and American scouts . . 30 25
442 50 c. Australian and Japanese scouts . . 40 50
443 75 c. Grenada and British scouts . . 50 75
440/3 . . *Set of* 4 1·10 1·40
MS444 101 × 114 mm. Nos. 442/3 . . 1·25 2·50

(Des G. Vasarhelyi. Litho Questa)

1971 (9 Oct). *150th Death Anniversary of Napolean Bonaparte. T* **176** *and similar vert designs showing paintings. Multicoloured. P* 13½.
445 5 c. Type **176** 15 15
446 15 c. "Napoleon before Madrid" (Vernet) . . 25 15
447 35 c. "Napoleon crossing Mt St. Bernard" (David) . . 30 15
448 $2 "Napoleon in his Study" (David) . . 75 1·50
445/8 . . *Set of* 4 1·25 1·75
MS449 101 × 76 mm. No. 447. Imperf . . 1·25 1·60

177 1d. Stamp of 1861 and Badge of Grenada

(Des R. Granger Barrett. Litho Questa)

1971 (6 Nov). *110th Anniv of the Postal Service. T* **177** *and similar horiz designs. Multicoloured. W w* **12** *(sideways*). P* 11.
450 5 c. Type **177** 20 20
451 15 c. 6d. stamp of 1861 and Queen Elizabeth II 25 15
452 35 c. 1d. and 6d. stamps of 1861 and badge of Grenada . . 50 20
453 50 c. Scroll and 1d. stamp of 1861 . . 65 1·75
450/3 . . *Set of* 4 1·40 2·10
MS454 96 × 114 mm. Nos. 452/3 . . 90 1·00

* This issue is printed on thick paper and consequently the watermark is very faint.

178 Apollo Splashdown

(Des R. Granger Barrett. Litho Questa)

1971 (13 Nov). *Apollo Moon Exploration Series. T* **178** *and similar multicoloured designs. P* 11.

455 1 c. Type **178** 10 10
456 2 c. Recovery of Apollo 13 .. .. 10 10
457 3 c. Separation of Lunar Module from Apollo 14 .. .. 10 10
458 10 c. Shepard and Mitchell taking samples of moon rock 25 10
459 25 c. Moon Buggy 75 20
460 $1 Apollo 15 blast-off (*vert*) .. .. .. 2·00 3·25
455/60 .. .. *Set of* 6 2·75 3·25
MS461 77 × 108 mm. 50 c. as $1 .. .. .. 1·40 1·50

179 67th Regiment of Foot, 1787

180 "The Adoration of the Kings" (Memling)

(Des G. Vasarhelyi. Litho Format)

1971 (11 Dec). *Military Uniforms. T* **179** *and similar vert designs. Multicoloured. P* 13½.

462 ½ c. Type **179** 10 10
463 1 c. 45th Regiment of Foot, 1792 .. .. 10 10
464 2 c. 29th Regiment of Foot, 1794 .. .. 10 10
465 10 c. 9th Regiment of Foot, 1801 .. .. 45 10
466 25 c. 2nd Regiment of Foot, 1815 .. .. 85 20
467 $1 70th Regiment of Foot, 1764 .. .. 2·50 2·00
462/7 .. .. *Set of* 6 3·50 2·25
MS468 108 × 99 mm. Nos. 466/7. P 15 .. .. 2·75 3·25

(Des G. Vasarhelyi. Litho Questa)

1972 (15 Jan). *Christmas* (1971). *T* **180** *and similar vert designs. Multicoloured. P* 14 × 13½.

469 15 c. Type **180** 15 10
470 25 c. "Madonna and Child" (Michelangelo) .. 20 10
471 35 c. "Madonna and Child" (Murillo) .. 25 10
472 50 c. "The Virgin with the Apple" (Memling) 30 1·00
469/72 .. .. *Set of* 4 80 1·10
MS473 105 × 80 mm. $1 "The Adoration of the Kings" (Mostaert) .. .. 75 1·25

35c

WINTER OLYMPICS
FEB. 3-13, 1972
SAPPORO, JAPAN
(181)

VOTE
FEB. 28 1972
(182)

1972 (3 Feb). *Winter Olympic Games, Sapporo, Japan. Nos.* 462/4 *and* **MS**468 *surch or optd only* (**MS**475).

(*a*) *Postage. As T* **181**

474 $2 on 2 c. multicoloured 50 90
MS475 108 × 99 mm. Nos. 466/7 (R.) .. .. 1·00 1·25

(*b*) *Air. As T* **181**, *but additionally surch* "AIR MAIL"

476 35 c. on ½ c. multicoloured 15 25
477 50 c. on 1 c. multicoloured 15 35

1972 (25 Feb). *General Election. Nos.* 307/8, 310 *and* 315 *optd with T* **182**.

478 2 c. multicoloured 10 10
b. Stop after "1972" (R.1/2, 1/10) .. 6·00
479 3 c. multicoloured 10 10
a. Opt inverted .. .. 95·00
b. Stop after "1972" (R.1/2, 1/10) .. 6·00
480 6 c. multicoloured 10 15
b. Stop after "1972" (R.1/2, 1/10) .. 6·00
481 25 c. multicoloured 15 30
b. Stop after "1972" (R.1/2, 1/10) .. 7·50
478/81 .. .. *Set of* 4 40 60

183 King Arthur

(Litho Questa)

1972 (4 Mar). *U.N.I.C.E.F. T* **183** *and similar multicoloured designs. P* 14.

482 ½ c. Type **183** 10 10
483 1 c. Robin Hood 10 10
484 2 c. Robinson Crusoe (*vert*) 10 10
485 25 c. Type **183** 10 10
486 50 c. As No. 483 .. .. 25 40
487 75 c. As No. 484 .. .. 30 80
488 $1 Mary and her little lamb (*vert*) .. .. 45 1·10
482/8 .. .. *Set of* 7 1·10 2·25
MS489 65 × 98 mm. No. 488 .. .. .. 55 80

INTERPEX
1972
(184)

12¢
(185)

AIR MAIL
(186)

1972 (17 Mar). *"Interpex" Stamp Exhibition, New York. Nos.* 433/9 *optd with T* **184**.

490 **174** 5 c. multicoloured 10 10
491 10 c. multicoloured 10 10
492 15 c. multicoloured 10 10
493 25 c. multicoloured 10 10
494 35 c. multicoloured 15 15
a. Opt double .. .. ..
495 50 c. multicoloured 25 30
a. Vert pair, top stamp with opt omitted £100
490/5 .. .. *Set of* 6 60 65
MS496 92×89 mm. **174** 50 c. multicoloured. Printed on silk. Imperf .. .. 7·00 12·00

1972 (20 Apr). *Nos.* 306/8 *surch with T* **185**, *and No.* 433 *surch similarly, but with obliterating bars under* "12c".

497 12 c. on 1 c. Type **88** 40 55
498 12 c. on 2 c. Strelitzia 40 55
499 12 c. on 3 c. Bougainvillea 40 55
a. Horiz pair, left stamp with surch omitted .. ..
500 12 c. on 5 c. Type **174** 40 55
497/500 .. .. *Set of* 4 1·40 2·00

1972. *Air.* (*a*) *Nos.* 306/12, 314*a*/17 *and* 318/21 *optd as T* **186** *or surch in addition* (2 May)

501 5 c. Rock Hind 10 10
a. Opt double .. .. 28·00
502 8 c. Snapper 15 10
a. Opt double .. .. 60·00
503 10 c. Marine Toad 15 10
a. Opt double .. .. 40·00
504 15 c. Thunbergia 30 10
505 25 c. Greater Trinidadian Murine Opossum 35 20
a. Horiz pair, one without opt £130
506 30 c. on 1 c. Type **86** 40 25
507 35 c. Nine-banded Armadillo 40 25
508 40 c. on 2 c. Strelitzia 50 25
509 45 c. on 3 c. Bougainvillea 55 35
510 50 c. Mona Monkey 55 35
a. Horiz pair, one without opt .. .. 90·00
b. Opt double £180
511 60 c. on 5 c. Rock Hind 60 40
512 70 c. on 6 c. Sailfish 70 50
513 $1 Bananaquit .. .. 4·50 60
514 $1·35 on 8 c. Snapper .. .. .. 3·25 1·50
515 $2 Brown Pelican .. .. 6·50 4·50
516 $3 Magnificent Frigate Bird .. .. 7·00 4·50
517 $5 Bare-eyed Thrush .. .. .. 8·50 10·00

(*b*) *Nos.* 440/3 *optd as T* **186** (5 June)

518 **175** 5 c. multicoloured 75 10
519 – 35 c. multicoloured .. .. .. 2·00 30
520 – 50 c. multicoloured .. .. .. 2·25 45
521 – 75 c. multicoloured .. .. .. 3·00 1·00
501/21 .. .. *Set of* 21 38·00 23·00

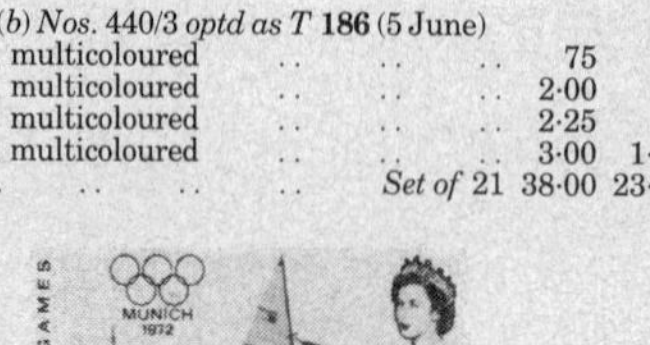

187 Yachting

(Litho Format)

1972 (8 Sept) *Olympic Games, Munich. T* **187** *and similar multicoloured designs. P* 14. (*a*) *Postage.*

522 ½ c. Type **187** 10 10
523 1 c. Show-jumping 10 10
524 2 c. Running (*vert*) 10 10
525 35 c. As 2 c. 30 10
526 50 c. As 1 c. 40 40

(*b*) *Air*

527 25 c. Boxing 25 10
528 $1 As 25 c. 65 85
522/8 .. .. *Set of* 7 1·50 1·40
MS529 82 × 85 mm. 60 c. as 25 c. and 70 c. as 1 c. 1·00 1·40

188 Badge of Grenada and Nutmegs

(Des (from photographs by D. Groves) and photo Harrison)

1972 (20 Nov). *Royal Silver Wedding. Multicoloured; background colour given. W w* **12**. *P* 14 × 14½.

530 **188** 8 c. olive-brown 10 10
531 $1 ultramarine 45 55

189 Boy Scout Saluting

190 Madonna and Child

(Des R. Granger Barrett. Litho Questa)

1972 (2 Dec). *65th Anniv of Boy Scouts. T* **189** *and similar hori[z] designs. Multicoloured. P* 14. (*a*) *Postage.*

532 ½ c. Type **189** 10 1
533 1 c. Scouts knotting ropes 10 1
534 2 c. Scouts shaking hands 10 1
535 3 c. Lord Baden-Powell 10 1
536 75 c. As 2 c. .. .. 1·10 2·7
537 $1 As 3 c. .. .. 1·25 2·7

(*b*) *Air*

538 25 c. Type **189** 50 2
539 35 c. As 1 c. 70 2
532/9 .. .. *Set of* 8 3·25 5·5
MS540 87 × 88 mm. 60 c. as 3 c., and 70 c. as 2 c. 1·50 1·5

(Des V. Whiteley. Litho Format)

1972 (9 Dec). *Christmas. T* **190** *and similar vert designs. Multi-coloured. P* 13½.

541 1 c. Type **190** 10 1
542 3 c. The Three Kings 10 1
543 5 c. The Nativity 10 1
544 25 c. Type **190** 15 1
545 35 c. As 3 c. 20 1
546 $1 As 5 c. 60 7
541/6 .. .. *Set of* 6 1·00 1·0
MS547 102 × 76 mm. 60 c. Type **190** and 70 c. as 3 c. P 15 .. .. 60 8

191 Greater Flamingoes

(Des M. and G. Shamir. Litho Questa)

1973 (26 Jan). *National Zoo. T* **191** *and similar horiz designs. Multicoloured. P* 14½.

548 25 c. Type **191** 80 3
549 35 c. Brazilian Tapir 80 3
550 60 c. Blue and Yellow Macaw, and Scarlet Macaw .. .. 1·50 1·2
551 70 c. Ocelot .. .. 1·50 1·5
548/51 .. .. *Set of* 4 4·25 3·0

192 Class II Racing Yacht

(Des V. Whiteley. Litho Format)

1973 (26 Feb). *Yachting. T* **192** *and similar horiz designs. Multi-coloured. P* 13½.

552 25 c. Type **192** 25 10
553 35 c. Harbour, St George's 30 10
554 60 c. Yacht *Bloodhound* 45 65
555 70 c. St. George's 50 75
552/5 .. .. *Set of* 4 1·40 1·40

193 Helios (Greek god) and Earth orbiting the Sun

(Des G. Vasarhelyi. Litho Format)

1973 (6 July). *I.M.O./W.M.O. Centenary. T* **193** *and similar horiz designs showing Greek Gods. Multicoloured. P* 13½.

556 ½ c. Type **193** 10 10
557 1 c. Poseidon and "Normad" storm detector 10 10
558 2 c. Zeus and radarscope 10 10
559 3 c. Iris and weather balloon 10 10
560 35 c. Hermes and "ATS-3" satellite 35 10
561 50 c. Zephyrus and diagram of pressure zones 50 30
562 75 c. Demeter and space photo 60 60
563 $1 Selene and rainfall diagram .. .. 65 1·00
556/63 .. .. *Set of* 8 2·00 2·00
MS564 123 × 92 mm. $2 Computer weather map (42 × 31 *mm*). P 13½. .. .. 90 1·25

194 Racing Class Yachts

195 Ignatius Semmelweis (obstetrician)

(Des G. Drummond. Litho Format)

973 (3 Aug). *Carriacou Regatta. T* **194** *and similar horiz designs. Multicoloured. P* 13½.

55 ½ c. Type **194** 10 10
56 1 c. Cruising Class Yacht 10 10
57 2 c. Open-decked sloops 10 10
58 35 c. *Mermaid* (sloop) 30 10
59 50 c. St. George's Harbour 35 25
70 75 c. Map of Carriacou 40 55
71 $1 Boat-building 55 70
55/71 .. .. *Set of* 7 1·40 1·40
IS572 109 × 88 mm. $2 End of Race .. .. 90 1·75

(Des G. Vasarhelyi. Litho Format)

973 (17 Sept). *25th Anniv of W.H.O. T* **195** *and similar vert designs. Multicoloured. P* 14½.

73 ½ c. Type **195** 10 10
74 1 c. Louis Pasteur 10 10
75 2 c. Edward Jenner 10 10
76 3 c. Sigmund Freud 10 10
77 25 c. Emil Von Behring (bacteriologist) .. 65 10
78 35 c. Carl Jung 75 20
79 50 c. Charles Calmette (bacteriologist) .. 1·10 80
80 $1 William Harvey .. .. 1·40 2·00
73/80 .. .. *Set of* 8 3·50 2·75
IS581 105 × 80 mm. $2 Marie Curie .. .. 1·60 1·60

196 Princess Anne and Capt. Mark Phillips

197 "Virgin and Child" (Maratti)

(Des G. Drummond. Litho Format)

973 (14 Nov). *Royal Wedding. P* 13½.

82 **196** 25 c. multicoloured 10 10
83 $2 multicoloured 30 45
IS584 79 × 100 mm. 75 c. and $1 as Nos. 582/3 .. 40 30

Nos. 582/3 were each issued in small sheets of five stamps and ne stamp-size label.

(Litho Format)

973 (10 Dec). *Christmas. T* **197** *and similar vert designs. Multicoloured. P* 14½.

85 ½ c. Type **197** 10 10
86 1 c. "Madonna and Child" (Crivelli) 10 10
87 2 c. "Virgin and Child with Two Angels" (Verrocchio) 10 10
88 3 c. "Adoration of the Shepherds" (Roberti) .. 10 10
89 25 c. "The Holy Family with the Infant Baptist" (Baroccio) 15 10
90 35 c. "The Holy Family" (Bronzino) 20 10
91 75 c. "Mystic Nativity" (Botticelli) 30 20
92 $1 "Adoration of the Kings" (Geertgen) .. 40 30
85/92 .. .. *Set of* 8 1·00 60
IS593 89 × 89 mm. $2 "Adoration of the Kings" (Mostaert) (30 × 45 *mm*). P 13½ .. .. .. 85 1·10

INDEPENDENT

INDEPENDENCE 7TH FEB. 1974

(198)

199 Creative Arts Theatre, Jamaica Campus

974 (7 Feb). *Independence. Nos.* 306/9, 311/13, 315/16 *and* 317*a*/21 *optd as T* **198**

94 1 c. Hibiscus 10 10
95 2 c. Strelitzia 10 10
96 3 c. Bougainvillea 10 10
97 5 c. Rock Hind 10 10
98 8 c. Snapper 15 10
99 10 c. Marine Toad 20 15
00 12 c. Turtle 20 15
01 25 c. Greater Trinidadian Murine Opossum 45 35
02 35 c. Nine-banded Armadillo 75 50
03 75 c. Yacht in St. George's Harbour .. 2·00 1·25
04 $1 Bananaquit .. .. 3·75 1·50
05 $2 Brown Pelican .. .. 6·00 5·00
06 $3 Magnificent Frigate Bird .. .. 8·00 6·50
07 $5 Bare-eyed Thrush .. .. .. 12·00 14·00
94/607 .. .. *Set of* 14 30·00 26·00

(Des G. Drummond. Litho Format)

1974 (10 Apr). *25th Anniv of University of West Indies. T* **199** *and similar multicoloured designs. P* 13½ × 14.

608 10 c. Type **199** 10 10
609 25 c. Marryshow House 10 10
610 50 c. Chapel, Jamaica Campus (*vert*) 20 10
611 $1 University arms (*vert*) 30 30
608/11 .. .. *Set of* 4 55 50
MS612 69 × 86 mm. $2 as No. 611 .. .. 50 90

200 Nutmeg Pods and Scarlet Mace

201 Footballers (West Germany v Chile)

(Des G. Drummond. Litho Format)

1974 (19 Aug). *Independence.* T **200** *and similar vert designs. Multicoloured. P* 13½.

613 3 c. Type **200** 10 10
614 8 c. Map of Grenada 10 10
615 25 c. Prime Minister Eric Gairy 15 10
616 35 c. Grand Anse Beach and flag 15 10
617 $1 Coat of arms 35 40
613/17 .. .. *Set of* 5 70 60
MS618 91 × 125 mm. $2 as $1 .. .. .. 55 90

(Des G. Vasarhelyi. Litho Format)

1974 (3 Sept). *World Cup Football Championships, West Germany. T* **201** *and similar multicoloured designs showing footballers of the countries given. P* 14½.

619 ½ c. Type **201** 10 10
620 1 c. East Germany v Australia 10 10
621 2 c. Yugoslavia v Brazil 10 10
622 10 c. Scotland v Zaire 10 10
623 25 c. Netherlands v Uruguay 15 10
624 50 c. Sweden v Bulgaria 20 10
625 75 c. Italy v Haiti 35 15
626 $1 Poland v Argentina 50 25
619/26 .. .. *Set of* 8 1·25 60
MS627 114 × 76 mm. $2 Country flags. P 13 .. 90 1·75

202 Early U.S. Mail-trains and Concorde

(Des G. Vasarhelyi. Litho Format)

1974 (8 Oct). *Centenary of Universal Postal Union. T* **202** *and similar horiz designs. Multicoloured. P* 14½.

628 ½ c. Type **202** 10 10
629 1 c. *Caesar* (snow) (1839) and Westland Wessex HU Mk 5 helicopter 10 10
630 2 c. Airmail transport 10 10
631 8 c. Pigeon post (1480) and telephone dial 15 10
632 15 c. 18th-century bellman and tracking antenna 30 10
633 25 c. Messenger (1450) and satellite .. 35 10
634 35 c. French pillar-box (1850) and mail-boat 50 10
635 $1 18th-century German postman and British Advanced Passenger Train .. 1·50 1·25
628/35 .. .. *Set of* 8 2·50 1·50
MS636 105×66 mm. $2 St. Gotthard mail-coach (1735). P 13 .. .. 1·00 1·75

203 Sir Winston Churchill

204 "Madonna and Child of the Eucharist" (Botticelli)

(Des G. Vasarhelyi. Litho Format)

1974 (28 Oct). *Birth Centenary of Sir Winston Churchill. T* **203** *and similar portrait design. P* 13½.

637 **203** 35 c. multicoloured 15 10
638 – $2 multicoloured 45 50
MS639 129 × 96 mm. 75 c. as 35 c. and $1 as $2 75 75

(Des. M. Shamir. Litho Format)

1974 (18 Nov). *Christmas. T* **204** *and similar vert designs, showing "The Madonna and Child" by the artists given. Multicoloured. P* 14½.

640 ½ c. Type **204** 10 10
641 1 c. Niccolo di Pietro 10 10
642 2 c. Van der Weyden 10 10
643 3 c. Bastiani 10 10
644 10 c. Giovanni 10 10
645 25 c. Van der Weyden 20 10
646 50 c. Botticelli 25 20
647 $1 Mantegna 35 50
640/7 .. .. *Set of* 8 85 80
MS648 117 × 96 mm. $2 as 1 c. P 13 .. .. 75 90

205 Yachts, Point Saline

(Des G. Drummond. Litho Format)

1975 (13 Jan)–**78.** *Multicoloured designs as T* **205**. *P* 14½ (½ *to* 50 *c.*) *or* 13½ (75 *c. to* $10).

649 ½ c. Type **205** (inscr "POINT SALINE") .. 10 40
a. Inscr "POINT SALINES" .. .. 50·00
650 1 c. Yacht club race 10 10
a. Perf 13 (1978) 10 50
651 2 c. Carenage taxi 10 10
a. Perf 13 (1978) 10 50
652 3 c. Large working boats 10 10
a. Perf 13 (1978) 10 30
653 5 c. Deep-water dock 20 10
a. Perf 13 (1978) 10 15
654 6 c. Cocoa beans in drying trays 10 10
a. Perf 13 (1978) 10 30
655 8 c. Nutmegs 55 10
656 10 c. Rum distillery, River Antoine Estate, *c* 1785 .. .. 10 10
a. Perf 13 (1978) 15 40
657 12 c. Cocoa tree 30 10
658 15 c. Fisherman at Fontenoy 10 10
a. Perf 13 (1978) 15 45
659 20 c. Parliament Building, St. George's .. 15 15
a. Perf 13 (1978) 20 55
660 25 c. Fort George cannons 20 15
a. Perf 13 (1978) 25 55
661 35 c. Pearls Airport 20 15
a. Perf 13 (1978) .. ..
662 50 c. General Post Office 25 30
a. Perf 13 (1978) 45 90
663 75 c. Carib's Leap, Sauteurs Bay (45×28 *mm*) (22.1.75) 45 50
664 $1 Carenage, St. George's (45×28 *mm*) (22.1.75) 50 70
665 $2 St. George's Harbour by night (45×28 *mm*) (22.1.75) .. .. 65 1·50
666 $3 Grand Anse Beach (45×28 *mm*) (22.1.75) .. .. 75 2·00
667 $5 Canoe Bay and Black Bay from Point Saline Lighthouse (45×28 *mm*) (22.1.75) .. .. 1·10 3·00
668 $10 Sugar-loaf Island from Levera Beach (45×28 *mm*) (26.3.75) .. .. .. 2·50 6·50
649/68 .. .. *Set of* 20 7·00 13·00

No. 649a occurs on R. 6/1 and 7/1 from plate 1A and R. 10/5 from plate 1C. It is believed that the plate was originally produced showing the incorrect inscription ("POINT SALINES") on every stamp. Each position was then individually corrected, but those noted were missed.

Nos. 649/59, 661/4 and 666/8 exist imperforate from stock dispersed by the liquidator of Format International Security Printers Ltd.

206 Sailfish

(Des V. Whiteley. Litho Format)

1975 (3 Feb). *Big Game Fishing. T* **206** *and similar horiz designs. Multicoloured. P* 14½.

669 ½ c. Type **206** 10 10
670 1 c. Blue Marlin 10 10
671 2 c. White Marlin 10 10
672 10 c. Yellow-finned Tuna 10 10
673 25 c. Wahoo 25 10
674 50 c. Dolphin (fish) 40 15
675 70 c. Giant Grouper 60 20
676 $1 Great Barracuda 80 35
669/76 .. .. *Set of* 8 2·00 70
MS677 107×80 mm. $2 Short-finned Mako. P 13 1·25 1·25

207 Granadilla Barbadine

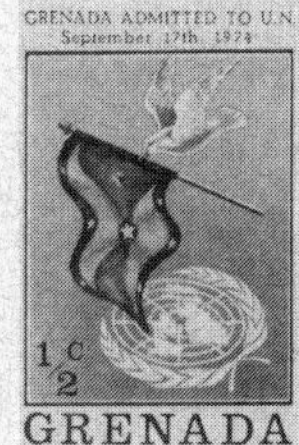

208 Dove, Grenada Flag and U.N. Emblem

(Des G. Vasarhelyi. Litho Format)

1975 (26 Feb). *Flowers. T* **207** *and similar horiz designs. Multicoloured. P* 14½.

678 ½ c. Type **207** .. 10 10
679 1 c. Bleeding Heart (Easter Lily) .. 10 10
680 2 c. Poinsettia .. 10 10
681 3 c. Cocoa flower .. 10 10
682 10 c. Gladioli .. 10 10
683 25 c. Redhead/Yellowhead .. 25 10
684 50 c. Plumbago .. 45 15
685 $1 Orange flower .. 70 25
678/85 .. *Set of* 8 1·40 55
MS686 102 × 82 mm. $2 Barbados Gooseberry. P 13 .. 1·10 1·25

(Des G. Drummond. Litho Format)

1975 (19 Mar). *Grenada's Admission to the U.N.* (1974). *T* **208** *and similar vert designs. Multicoloured. P* 14½.

687 ½ c. Type **208** .. 10 10
688 1 c. Grenada and U.N. flags .. 10 10
689 2 c. Grenada coat of arms .. 10 10
690 35 c. U.N. emblem over map of Grenada .. 15 10
691 50 c. U.N. buildings and flags .. 20 15
692 $2 U.N. emblem and scroll .. 45 45
687/92 .. *Set of* 6 80 70
MS693 122 × 91 mm. 75 c. Type **208** and $1 as 2 c. P 13 .. 65 90

CANCELLED REMAINDERS*. Some of the following issues have been remaindered, cancelled-to-order, at a fraction of their face-value. For all practical purposes these are indistinguishable from genuine postally used copies. Our used quotations which are indicated by an asterisk are the same for cancelled-to-order or postally used copies.

209 Paul Revere's Midnight Ride

210 "Blood of the Redeemer" (G. Bellini)

(Des J. Cornel (½ to 10 c.), PAD Studio (40 c. to $1), J.W. (**MS**704). Litho Format)

1975 (6 May). *Bicentenary of American Revolution (1st issue). T* **209** *and similar multicoloured designs. P* 14½.

(a) Postage. Horiz designs

694 ½ c. Type **209** .. 10 10*
695 1 c. Crispus Attucks .. 10 10*
696 2 c. Patrick Henry .. 10 10*
697 3 c. Franklin visits Washington .. 10 10*
698 5 c. Rebel troops .. 10 10*
699 10 c. John Paul Jones .. 10 10*

(b) Air. Vert designs

700 40 c. "John Hancock" (Copley) .. 35 10*
701 50 c. "Benjamin Franklin" (Roslin) .. 50 15*
702 75 c. "John Adams" (Copley) .. 70 15*
703 $1 "Lafayette" (Casanova) .. 80 20*
694/703 .. *Set of* 10 2·25 60*
MS704 Two sheets 131 × 102 mm: $2 Grenada arms and U.S. seal; $2 Grenada and U.S. flags. P 13½ .. 1·25 60*

Stamps from **MS**704 are horiz and larger: 47½ × 35mm.

Nos. 694/703 also exist perf 13 (*Price for set of* 10 £2·25 *mint or used*) from additional sheetlets of 5 stamps and 1 label. Stamps perforated 14½ are from normal sheets of 40.

See also Nos. 785/92.

(Des M. Shamir. Litho Format)

1975 (21 May). *Easter. T* **210** *and similar vert designs. Multicoloured. P* 14½.

705 ½ c. Type **210** .. 10 10*
706 1 c. "Pietà" (Bellini) .. 10 10*
707 2 c. "The Entombment" (Van der Weyden) .. 10 10*
708 3 c. "Pietà" (Bellini) .. 10 10*
709 35 c. "Pietà" (Bellini) .. 25 10*
710 75 c. "The Dead Christ" (Bellini) .. 35 10*
711 $1 "The Dead Christ supported by Angels" (Procaccini) .. 50 10*
705/11 .. *Set of* 7 1·00 30*
MS712 117 × 100 mm. $2 "Pietà" (Botticelli). P 13 75 30*

211 Wildlife Study

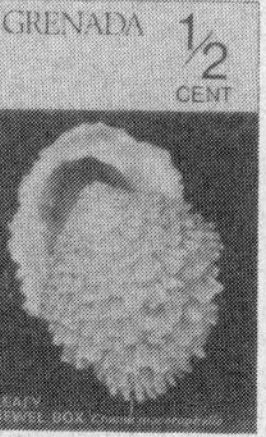

212 Leafy Jewel Box (*Chama macerophylla*)

(Des J.W. Litho Format)

1975 (2 July). *14th World Scout Jamboree, Norway. T* **211** *and similar horiz designs. Multicoloured. P* 14.

713 ½ c. Type **211** .. 10 10*
714 1 c. Sailing .. 10 10*
715 2 c. Map-reading .. 10 10*
716 35 c. First-aid .. 40 10*
717 40 c. Physical training .. 45 10*
718 75 c. Mountaineering .. 60 10*
719 $2 Sing-song .. 1·25 20*
713/19 .. *Set of* 7 2·50 40*
MS720 106 × 80 mm. $1 Boat-building .. 90 30*

(Des J.W. Litho Questa)

1975 (1 Aug). *Seashells. T* **212** *and similar vert designs. Multicoloured. P* 14.

721 ½ c. Type **212** .. 10 10*
722 1 c. Emerald Nerite (*Smaragdia viridis viridemaris*) .. 10 10*
723 2 c. Yellow American Cockle (*Trachycardium muricatum*) .. 10 10*
724 25 c. Common Purple Janthina (*Janthina janthina*) .. 85 10*
725 50 c. Atlantic Turkey Wing (*Arca zebra*) .. 1·75 10*
726 75 c. West Indian Fighting Conch (*Strombus pugilis*) .. 2·25 15*
727 $1 Noble Wentletrap (*Sthenorytis pernobilis*) .. 2·25 15*
721/7 .. *Set of* 7 6·50 60*
MS728 102×76 mm. $2 Music Volute (*Voluta musica*) .. 2·00 80*

213 *Lycorea ceres*

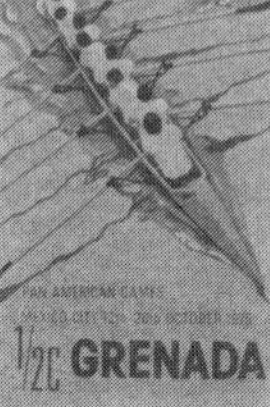

214 Rowing

(Des J.W. Litho Format)

1975 (22 Sept). *Butterflies. T* **213** *and similar vert designs. Multicoloured. P* 14.

729 ½ c. Type **213** .. 10 10*
730 1 c. *Adelpha cytherea* .. 10 10*
731 2 c. *Atlides polybe* .. 10 10*
732 35 c. *Anteos maerula* .. 80 10*
733 45 c. *Parides neophilus* .. 85 10*
734 75 c. *Nymula orestes* .. 1·25 15*
735 $2 *Euptychia cephus* .. 1·75 20*
729/35 .. *Set of* 7 4·25 50*
MS736 108×83 mm. $1 *Papilio astyalus* (sub-species *lycophron*) .. 1·25 40*

(Des J.W. Litho Questa)

1975 (13 Oct). *Pan-American Games, Mexico City. T* **214** *and similar vert designs. Multicoloured. P* 14.

737 ½ c. Type **214** .. 10 10*
738 1 c. Swimming .. 10 10*
739 2 c. Show-jumping .. 10 10*
740 35 c. Gymnastics .. 15 10*
741 45 c. Football .. 15 10*
742 75 c. Boxing .. 25 15*
743 $2 Cycling .. 65 20*
737/43 .. *Set of* 7 1·10 40*
MS744 106 × 81 mm. $1 Yachting .. 1·00 40*

215 "The Boy David" (Michelangelo)

216 "Madonna and Child" (Filippino Lippi)

(Des M. and G. Shamir. Litho J.W.)

1975 (3 Nov). *500th Birth Anniv of Michelangelo. T* **215** *and similar vert designs. Multicoloured. P* 14.

745 ½ c. Type **215** .. 10 10*
746 1 c. "Young Man" (detail) .. 10 10*
747 2 c. "Moses" .. 10 10*
748 40 c. "Prophet Zachariah" .. 40 10*
749 50 c. "St John the Baptist" .. 40 15*
750 75 c. "Judith and Holofernes" .. 70 20*
751 $2 "Doni Madonna" (detail from "Holy Family") .. 1·25 25*
745/51 .. *Set of* 7 2·50 65*
MS752 104 × 89 mm. $1 "Madonna" (head from Pietà) .. 1·00 30*

The sculpture on No. 749 though ascribed to Michelangelo, shows a work by Francesco Sangallo.

(Des M. Shamir. Litho Questa)

1975 (8 Dec). *Christmas. T* **216** *and similar vert designs showin "Virgin and Child". Multicoloured. P* 14.

753 ½ c. Type **216** .. 10 10
754 1 c. Mantegna .. 10 10
755 2 c. Luis de Morales .. 10 10
756 35 c. G. M. Morandi .. 20 10
757 50 c. Antonello da Messina .. 25 10
758 75 c. Dürer .. 30 10
759 $1 Velasquez .. 40 10
753/9 .. *Set of* 7 1·10 35
MS760 125 × 98 mm. $2 Bellini .. 90 30

217 Bananaquit

218 Carnival Time

(Des G. Drummond. Litho Questa)

1976 (20 Jan). *Flora and Fauna. T* **217** *and similar multicoloured designs. P* 14.

761 ½ c. Type **217** .. 10 10*
762 1 c. Brazilian Agouti .. 10 10*
763 2 c. Hawksbill Turtle (*horiz*) .. 10 10*
764 5 c. Dwarf Poinciana .. 10 10*
765 35 c. Black-finned Tuna ("Albacore") (*horiz*) 90 10*
766 40 c. Cardinal's Guard .. 95 10*
767 $2 Nine-banded Armadillo (*horiz*) .. 2·50 30*
761/7 .. *Set of* 7 4·00 60*
MS768 82×89 mm. $1 Belted Kingfisher .. 7·50 90*

(Des G. Drummond. Litho Questa)

1976 (25 Feb). *Tourism. T* **218** *and similar horiz designs. Multicoloured. P* 14.

769 ½ c. Type **218** .. 10 10
770 1 c. Scuba diving .. 10 10
771 2 c. Liner *Southward* at St. George's .. 10 10
772 35 c. Game fishing .. 65 10
773 50 c. St George's Golf Course .. 2·25 20
774 75 c. Tennis .. 2·50 25*
775 $1 Ancient rock carvings at Mount Rich 2·75 25*
769/75 .. *Set of* 7 7·50 80*
MS776 100×73 mm. $2 Small boat sailing .. 1·75 60*

219 "Pietà" (Master of Okolicsno)

220 Sharpshooters

(Des M. and G. Shamir. Litho Questa)

1976 (29 Mar). *Easter. T* **219** *and similar vert designs by the artists listed. Multicoloured. P* 14.

777 ½ c. Type **219** .. 10 10*
778 1 c. Correggio .. 10 10*
779 2 c. Van der Weyden .. 10 10*
780 3 c. Dürer .. 10 10*
781 35 c. Master of the Holy Spirit .. 20 10*
782 75 c. Raphael .. 45 15*
783 $1 Raphael .. 50 20*
777/83 .. *Set of* 7 1·25 50*
MS784 108 × 86 mm. $2 Crespi .. 85 60*

(Des J.W. Litho Questa)

1976 (15 Apr). *Bicentenary of American Revolution (2nd issue). T* **220** *and similar vert designs. Multicoloured. P* 14.

785 ½ c. Type **220** .. 10 10*
786 1 c. Defending the Liberty Pole .. 10 10*
787 2 c. Loading muskets .. 10 10*
788 35 c. The fight for Liberty .. 35 10*
789 50 c. Peace Treaty, 1783 .. 40 10*
790 $1 Drummers .. 65 20*
791 $3 Gunboat .. 1·25 30*
785/91 .. *Set of* 7 2·50 60*
MS792 93 × 79 mm. 75 c. as 35 c. and $2 as 50 c. 75 60*

PRICES OF SETS

Set prices are given for many issues, generally those containing three stamps or more. Definitive sets include one of each value or major colour change, but do not cover different perforations, die types or minor shades. Where a choice is possible the set prices are based on the cheapest versions of the stamps included in the listings.

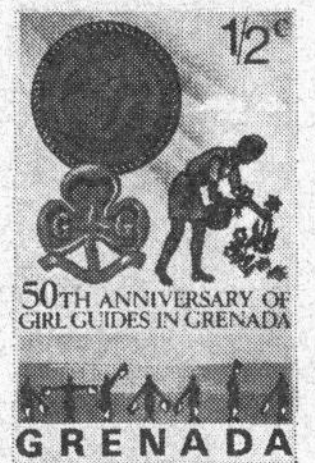

221 Nature Study

222 Volleyball

(Des G. Vasarhelyi. Litho Questa)

76 (1 June). *50th Anniv of Girl Guides in Grenada. T* **221** *and similar vert designs. Multicoloured. P* 14.

3 ½ c. Type **221** 10 10*
4 1 c. Campfire cooking 10 10*
5 2 c. First Aid 10 10*
6 50 c. Camping 65 10*
7 75 c. Home economics 90 15*
8 $2 First Aid .. .. 1·25 25*
3/8 .. .. *Set of* 6 2·50 55*
S799 111 × 85 mm. $1 Painting 85 70*

(Des J.W. Litho Questa)

76 (21 June). *Olympic Games, Montreal. T* **222** *and similar vert designs. Multicoloured. P* 14.

0 ½ c. Type **222** 10 10*
1 1 c. Cycling 10 10*
2 2 c. Rowing 10 10*
3 35 c. Judo 30 10*
4 45 c. Hockey 60 10*
5 75 c. Gymnastics 60 20*
6 $1 High jump 60 20*
0/6 .. .. *Set of* 7 2·00 60*
S807 106 × 81 mm. $3 Equestrian event .. 1·25 80*

223 "Cha-U-Kao at the Moulin Rouge"

224 Piper PA-23 Apache 235

(Des M. Shamir. Litho Questa)

976 (20 July). *75th Death Anniv of Toulouse Lautrec. T* **223** *and similar vert designs. Multicoloured. P* 14.

08 ½ c. Type **223** 10 10*
09 1 c. "Quadrille at the Moulin Rouge" 10 10*
10 2 c. "Profile of a Woman" 10 10*
11 3 c. "Salon in the Rue des Moulins" 10 10*
12 40 c. "The Laundryman" 55 10*
13 50 c. "Marcelle Lender dancing the Bolero" .. 65 10*
14 $2 "Signor Boileau at the Cafe" .. .. 1·75 25*
08/14 .. .. *Set of* 7 2·75 55*
MS815 152 × 125 mm. $1 "Woman with Boa" .. 2·00 70*

976 (26 July). *West Indian Victory in World Cricket Cup. As Nos.* 559/60 *of Barbados.*

16 35 c. Map of the Caribbean .. .. .. 1·25 35
17 $1 The Prudential Cup .. .. .. 2·75 5·00

(Des J.W. Litho Questa)

976 (18 Aug). *Airplanes. T* **224** *and similar horiz designs. Multicoloured. P* 14.

18 ½ c. Type **224** 10 10*
19 1 c. Beech 50 Twin Bonanza 10 10*
20 2 c. De Havilland D.H.C.6 Twin Otter 100 .. 10 10*
21 40 c. Britten Norman Islander 70 10*
22 50 c. De Havilland D.H.114 Heron 2 .. 75 10*
23 $2 Hawker Siddeley H.S.748 .. .. 2·50 50*
18/23 .. .. *Set of* 6 3·50 70*
MS824 75×83 mm. $3 B.A.C. One Eleven 500 .. 2·00 80*

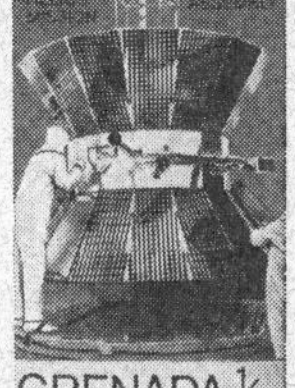

225 Satellite Assembly

226 S.S. *Geestland*

(Des PAD Studio. Litho Questa)

976 (1 Sept). *Viking and Helios Space Missions. T* **225** *and similar multicoloured designs. P* 14.

25 ½ c. Type **225** 10 10*
26 1 c. Helios satellite 10 10*
27 2 c. Helios encapsulation 10 10*
28 15 c. Systems test 10 10*
29 45 c. Viking lander (*horiz*) 20 10*
30 75 c. Lander on Mars 35 15*
31 $2 Viking encapsulation 90 25*
25/31 .. .. *Set of* 7 1·40 55*
MS832 110 × 85 mm. $3 Orbiter and lander .. 1·00 75*

(Des J.W. Litho Format)

1976 (3 Nov). *Ships. T* **226** *and similar horiz designs. Multicoloured. P* 14½.

833 ½ c. Type **226** 10 10*
834 1 c. M. V. *Federal Palm* 10 10*
835 2 c. H.M.S. *Blake* 10 10*
836 25 c. M. V. *Vistafjord* 45 10*
837 75 c. S.S. *Canberra* 90 15*
838 $1 S.S. *Regina* .. .. 1·10 20*
839 $5 S.S. *Arandora Star* .. .. .. 2·75 40*
833/39 .. .. *Set of* 7 4·75 85*
MS840 91 × 78 mm. $2 *Santa Maria* .. .. 1·60 4·00

227 "Altarpiece of San Barnaba" (Botticelli)

(Des PAD Studio. Litho Questa)

1976 (8 Dec). *Christmas. T* **227** *and similar horiz designs. Multicoloured. P* 14.

841 ½ c. Type **227** 10 10*
842 1 c. "Annunciation" (Botticelli) 10 10*
843 2 c. "Madonna of Chancellor Rolin" (Jan van Eyck) 10 10*
844 35 c. "Annunciation" (Fra Filippo Lippi) .. 15 10*
845 50 c. "Madonna of the Magnificat" (Botticelli) 20 10*
846 75 c. "Madonna of the Pomegranate" (Botticelli) 35 15*
847 $3 "Madonna with St. Cosmas and Other Saints" (Botticelli) .. .. 1·00 25*
841/7 .. .. *Set of* 7 1·50 50*
MS848 71 × 57 mm. $2 "Gypsy Madonna" (Titian) 1·00 60*

228 Alexander Graham Bell and Telephones

229 Coronation Scene

(Des G. Vasarhelyi. Litho Questa)

1976 (17 Dec). *Telephone Centenary. T* **228** *and similar horiz designs. Multicoloured. P* 14.

849 ½ c. Type **228** 10 10*
850 1 c. Telephone-users within globe 10 10*
851 2 c. Telephone satellite 10 10*
852 18 c. Telephone viewer and console 20 10*
853 40 c. Satellite and tracking stations 35 10*
854 $1 Satellite transmitting to ships 50 15*
855 $2 Dish aerial and modern telephone .. 75 25*
849/55 .. .. *Set of* 7 1·60 55*
MS856 107 × 80 mm. $5 Globe encircled by flags 1·50 75*

(Des J.W. Litho Questa (Nos. 857/62), Walsall (863/6))

1977 (8 Feb). *Silver Jubilee. T* **229** *and similar vert designs. Multicoloured. (a) Sheet stamps. P* 13½ × 14.

857 ½ c. Type **229** 10 10*
858 1 c. Sceptre and orb 10 10*
859 35 c. Queen on horseback 10 10*
860 $2 Spoon and ampulla 25 15*
861 $2.50 Queen and Prince Philip 25 15*
857/61 .. .. *Set of* 5 60 45*
MS862 103 × 79 mm. $5 Royal Visit to Grenada .. 75 60*

Nos. 857/61 also exist perf 11½×12 (*price for set of* 5 60p. *mint or used*) from additional sheetlets of 5 stamps and 1 label. They also have different frame colours to those perforated 13½×14 which come from normal sheets of 40.

(b) Booklet stamps. Roul 5 × *imperf**. *Self-adhesive*

863 35 c. As No. 861 .. .. 15 25
a. Booklet pane of 6 70
864 50 c. As No. 860 .. .. 25 1·00
a. Booklet pane. Nos. 864/6 .. .. .. 1·90
865 $1 As No. 858 .. .. 50 1·40
866 $3 As No. 859 .. .. 1·25 2·75
863/6 .. .. *Set of* 4 2·00 4·75

*No. 863/6 are separated by various combinations of rotary knife (giving a straight edge) and roulette.

230 Water Skiing

(Des G. Drummond. Litho Questa)

1977 (Apr). *Easter Water Parade. T* **230** *and similar horiz designs. Multicoloured. P* 14.

867 ½ c. Type **230** 10 10*
868 1 c. Speedboat race 10 10*
869 2 c. Row boat race 10 10*
870 22 c. Swimming 15 10*
871 35 c. Work boat race 25 10*
872 75 c. Water polo 40 15*
873 $2 Game fishing 90 25*
867/73 .. .. *Set of* 7 1·60 55*
MS874 115 × 85 mm. $3 Yacht race .. .. 1·25 75*

231 Meeting Place, Grand Anse Beach

(Litho Questa)

1977 (14 June). *Seventh Meeting of Organization of American States. P* 14.

875 **231** 35 c. multicoloured 10 10
876 $1 multicoloured 25 60
877 $2 multicoloured .. .. .. 40 1·75
875/7 .. .. *Set of* 3 65 2·25

232 Rafting

(Des G. Drummond. Litho Questa)

1977 (6 Sept). *Caribbean Scout Jamboree, Jamaica. T* **232** *and similar horiz designs. Multicoloured. P* 14.

878 ½ c. Type **232** 10 10*
879 1 c. Tug-of-war 10 10*
880 2 c. Sea Scouts regatta 10 10*
881 18 c. Camp fire 25 10*
882 40 c. Field kitchen 50 10*
883 $1 Scouts and sea scouts .. .. .. 1·00 15*
884 $2 Hiking and map reading .. .. .. 1·40 25*
878/84 .. .. *Set of* 7 2·75 60*
MS885 107 × 85 mm. $3 Semaphore .. .. 2·00 80*

233 Angel and Shepherd

Royal Visit W. I. 1977

(234)

(Des G. Vasarhelyi. Litho Questa)

1977 (3 Nov). *Christmas. T* **233** *and similar horiz designs showing ceiling panels from the church of St. Martin in Zillis. Multicoloured. P* 14.

886 ½ c. Type **233** 10 10*
887 1 c. St. Joseph 10 10*
888 2 c. Virgin and Child Fleeing to Egypt .. 10 10*
889 22 c. Angel 10 10*
890 35 c. A Magus on horseback 15 10*
891 75 c. Three horses 20 15*
892 $2 Virgin and Child 50 25*
886/92 .. .. *Set of* 7 85 50*
MS893 85 × 112 mm. $3 Magus offering gifts .. 1·00 70*

1977 (10 Nov). *Royal Visit. Nos.* 857/62 *optd with T* **234**. *P* 13½×14 (35 *c*., $2, $2.50) *or* 11½×12 (*others*).

894 ½ c. Type **229** 10 10
895 1 c. Sceptre and orb 10 10
896 35 c. Queen on horseback 10 10
897 $2 Spoon and ampulla 30 40
898 $2.50, Queen and Prince Philip 35 45
894/8 .. .. *Set of* 5 75 85
MS899 103 × 79 mm. $5 Royal Visit to Grenada 75 1·25

Nos. 894/5 only exist perforated 11½×12, but the remaining three values come perforated 13½×14 or 11½×12 (Nos. 896/8 *perf* 11½×12. *Price for set of* 3 75p *mint or used*).

235 Christjaan Eijkman (Medicine)

236 Count von Zeppelin and First Zeppelin Airship LZ-1

(Des J.W. Litho Questa)

1978 (25 Jan). *Nobel Prize Winners. T* **235** *and similar vert designs. Multicoloured. P* 14.

900 ½ c. Type **235** 10 10*
901 1 c. Sir Winston Churchill (Literature) .. 30 10*
902 2 c. Woodrow Wilson (Peace) 10 10*
903 35 c. Frederic Passy (Peace) 15 10*
904 $1 Albert Einstein (Physics) .. .. 1·00 15*
905 $3 Carl Bosch (Chemistry) .. .. .. 1·75 25*
900/5 .. .. *Set of* 6 3·00 55*
MS906 114 × 99 mm. $2 Alfred Nobel 70 60*

(Des G. Vasarhelyi. Litho Questa)

1978 (13 Feb). *75th Anniv of First Zeppelin Flight and 50th Anniv of Lindbergh's Transatlantic Flight. T* **236** *and similar horiz designs. Multicoloured. P* 14.

907 ½ c. Type **236** 10 10*
908 1 c. Lindbergh with Ryan NYP Special *Spirit of St. Louis* 10 10*
909 2 c. Airship LZ-7 *Deutschland* 10 10*
910 22 c. Lindbergh's arrival in France .. 25 10*
911 75 c. Lindbergh and Ryan NYP Special *Spirit of St. Louis* in flight 50 10*
912 $1 LZ-127 *Graf Zeppelin* over Alps .. 55 15*
913 $3 LZ-127 *Graf Zeppelin* over White House .. .. 1·25 25*
907/13 .. .. *Set of* 7 2·50 55*
MS914 103×85 mm. Lindbergh in cockpit; $2 Count von Zeppelin and airship LZ-5 .. .. 1·40 60*

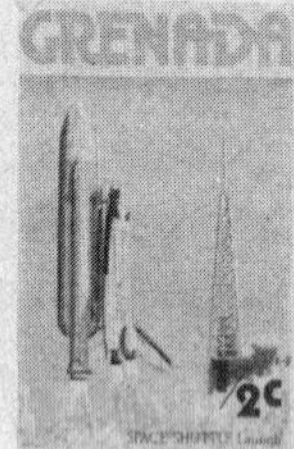
237 Rocket Launching

238 Black-headed Gull

(Des J.W. Litho Questa)

1978 (28 Feb). *Space Shuttle. T* **237** *and similar vert designs. Multicoloured. P* 14.

915 ½ c. Type **237** 10 10*
916 1 c. Booster jettison 10 10*
917 2 c. External tank jettison 10 10*
918 18 c. Space shuttle in orbit 25 10*
919 75 c. Satellite placement 55 10*
920 $2 Landing approach .. .. .. 1·25 20*
915/20 .. .. *Set of* 6 1·90 50*
MS921 103 × 85 mm. $3 Shuttle after landing .. 1·40 60*

(Des G. Drummond. Litho Questa)

1978 (9 Mar). *Wild Birds of Grenada. T* **238** *and similar vert designs. Multicoloured. P* 14.

922 ½ c. Type **238** 10 10*
923 1 c. Wilson's Petrel 10 10*
924 2 c. Killdeer 10 10*
925 50 c. White-necked Jacobin .. .. .. 1·50 10*
926 75 c. Blue-faced Booby .. .. .. 2·00 15*
927 $1 Broad-winged Hawk .. .. .. 3·00 20*
928 $2 Red-necked Pigeon .. .. .. 4·00 30*
922/8 .. .. *Set of* 7 9·50 80*
MS929 103×94 mm. $3 Scarlet Ibis .. .. 6·00 1·00*

239 "The Landing of Marie de Medici at Marseilles"

240 Ludwig van Beethoven

(Des PAD Studio. Litho Questa)

1978 (30 Mar). *400th Birth Anniv of Rubens. T* **239** *and similar vert designs showing paintings. Multicoloured. P* 13½ × 14.

930 5 c. Type **239** 10 10*
931 15 c. "Rubens and Isabella Brandt" 10 10*
932 18 c. "Marchesa Brigida Spindola-Doria" .. 10 10*
933 25 c. "Ludovicus Nonninus" 10 10*
934 45 c. "Helene Fourment and her Children" .. 15 10*
935 75 c. "Clara Serena Rubens" 25 10*
936 $3 "Le Chapeau de Paille" 60 20*
930/6 .. .. *Set of* 7 1·10 50*
MS937 65 × 100 mm. $5 "Self Portrait" .. .. 1·50 60*

(Des PAD Studio. Litho Questa)

1978 (24 Apr). *150th Death Anniv of Beethoven. T* **240** *and similar multicoloured designs. P* 14.

938 5 c. Type **240** 10 10*
939 15 c. Woman violinist (*horiz*) 15 10*
940 18 c. Musical instruments (*horiz*) 20 10*
941 22 c. Piano (*horiz*) 20 10*
942 50 c. Violins 40 10*
943 75 c. Piano and sonata score 60 15*
944 $3 Beethoven's portrait and home (*horiz*) 2·25 25*
938/44 .. .. *Set of* 7 3·50 60*
MS945 83 × 62 mm. $2 Beethoven and score .. 1·10 60*

241 King Edward's Chair

242 Queen Elizabeth II taking Salute at Trooping the Colour

(Des J.W. Litho Questa. (Nos. 946/9). Manufactured by Walsall. (Nos. 950/2))

1978 (2 May–14 June). *25th Anniv of Coronation. Multicoloured.*

(a) *Sheet stamps. Vert designs as T* **241**. *P* 14 (14 June)

946 35 c. Type **241** 10 10
947 $2 Queen with regalia 30 35
948 $2.50, St. Edward's Crown 30 40
946/8 .. .. *Set of* 3 60 75
MS949 102 × 76 mm. $5 Queen and Prince Philip 80 80

(b) *Booklet stamps. Vert designs as T* **242**. *Roul* 5 × *imperf*. Self-adhesive* (2 May)

950 25 c. Type **242** 15 15
a. Booklet pane. Nos. 950/1, each × 3 .. 80
951 35 c. Queen taking part in Maundy Thursday ceremony 15 25
952 $5 Queen and Prince Philip at Opening of Parliament .. .. 1·50 2·50
a. Booklet pane of 1 .. .. .. 1·50
950/2 .. .. *Set of* 3 1·60 2·50

Nos. 946/8 also exist perf 12 (*Price for set of* 3 75p. *mint or used*) from additional sheetlets of 3 stamps and 1 label, issued 2 June. These have different frame colours from the stamps perforated 14, which come from normal sheets of 50.

*Nos. 950/1 are separated by various combinations of rotary-knife (giving a straight edge) and roulette. No. 952 exists only with straight edges.

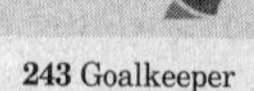
243 Goalkeeper reaching for Ball

244 Aerial Phenomena, Germany, 1561 and U.S.A., 1952

(Des M. Rubin. Litho Format)

1978 (1 Aug). *World Cup Football Championship, Argentina. T* **243** *and similar vert designs showing goalkeeper reaching for ball. P* 14½.

953 40 c. multicoloured 10 10
954 60 c. multicoloured 15 20
955 90 c. multicoloured 25 30
956 $2 multicoloured 60 60
953/6 .. .. *Set of* 4 1·00 1·00
MS957 130 × 97 mm. $2.50, multicoloured .. 1·10 1·10

(Des G. Vasarhelyi. Litho Format)

1978 (17 Aug). *U.F.O. Research. T* **244** *and similar horiz designs. Multicoloured. P* 14½.

958 5 c. Type **244** 15 10
959 35 c. Various aerial phenomena, 1950 .. 35 25
960 $3 U.F.O.'s, 1965 .. .. 2·00 1·75
958/60 .. .. *Set of* 3 2·25 1·90
MS961 112 × 89 mm. $2 Sir Eric Gairy and U.F.O. research laboratory .. .. 1·25 1·25

245 Wright Flyer III

(Des G. Vasarhelyi. Litho Questa)

1978 (28 Aug). *75th Anniv of Powered Flight. T* **245** *and similar horiz designs. Multicoloured. P* 14.

962 5 c. Type **245** 10 10
963 15 c. Flyer I, 1903 .. .. 10 10
964 18 c. Wright Type A 10 10
965 22 c. Flyer I from above 15 10
966 50 c. Orville Wright and Wright Type A .. 20 20
967 75 c. Wright Type A in Pau, France, 1908 25 25
968 $3 Wilbur Wright and Wright glider No. IV 80 70
962/8 .. .. *Set of* 7 1·40 1·25
MS969 114×85 mm. $2 Wright glider No. III 1·00 75

246 Cook and Hawaiian Feast

247 "Paumgartner Altarpiece" (detail)

(Des G. Vasarhelyi. Litho Questa)

1978 (5 Dec). *Bicentenary of Discovery of Hawaii and 250th Birt Anniv of Captain Cook. T* **246** *and similar horiz designs. Mult coloured. P* 14.

970 18 c. Type **246** 60 2
971 35 c. Cook and Hawaiian warriors 80 2
972 75 c. Cook and Honolulu Harbour .. .. 1·50 1·5
973 $3 Cook (statue) and H.M.S. *Resolution* .. 3·00 6·0
970/3 .. .. *Set of* 4 5·50 7·0
MS974 116 × 88 mm. $4 Cook and death scene .. 3·75 2·5

(Des M. Rubin. Litho Questa)

1978 (20 Dec). *Christmas. Paintings by Dürer. T* **247** *and simila vert designs. Multicoloured. P* 14.

975 40 c. Type **247** 20 1
976 60 c. "The Adoration of the Magi" 25 2
977 90 c. "The Virgin and Child" 30 2
978 $2 "Virgin and Child with St. Anne" (detail) 55 5
975/8 .. .. *Set of* 4 1·10 1·1
MS979 113 × 83 mm. $4 "Madonna and Child" .. 1·10 1·5

248 National Convention and Cultural Centre (interior)

249 *Acalypha hispida*

(Des BG Studio. Litho Questa)

1979 (8 Feb). *5th Anniv of Independence. T* **248** *and similar vert designs. Multicoloured. P* 14.

980 5 c. Type **248** 10 10
981 18 c. National Convention and Cultural Centre (exterior) 10 10
982 22 c. Easter Water Parade, 1978 .. .. 10 10
983 35 c. Sir Eric M. Gairy (Prime Minister) .. 15 10
984 $3 The Cross, Fort Frederick 60 80
980/4 .. .. *Set of* 5 80 90

(Des J.W. Litho Questa)

1979 (26 Feb). *Flowers. T* **249** *and similar vert designs. Multicoloured. P* 14.

985 18 c. Type **249** 10 10
986 50 c. *Hibiscus rosa sinensis* 25 15
987 $1 *Thunbergia grandiflora* 40 25
988 $3 *Nerium oleander* .. .. 1·10 1·10
985/8 .. .. *Set of* 4 1·60 1·40
MS989 115 × 90 mm. $2 *Lagerstroemia speciosa* 1·00 1·40

250 Birds in Flight

251 Children playing Cricket

(Des M. Rubin. Litho Questa)

1979 (15 Mar). *30th Anniv of Declaration of Human Rights. T* **250** *and similar vert design. Multicoloured. P* 14.

990 15 c. Type **250** 10 10
991 $2 Bird in flight 55 65

(Des J.W. Litho Questa)

1979 (23 Apr). *International Year of the Child* (1st issue). *T* **251** *and similar vert designs. Multicoloured. P* 14.

992 18 c. Type **251** 40 30
993 22 c. Children playing baseball 40 30
994 $5 Children playing in tree .. .. .. 3·75 6·00
992/4 .. .. *Set of* 3 4·00 6·00
MS995 114×92 mm. $4 Children with model spaceship .. .. 1·75 2·25

See also Nos. 1006/7 and 1025/34.

252 "Around the World in 80 Days"

(Des G. Vasarhelyi. Litho Questa)

979 (4 May). 150*th Birth Anniv of Jules Verne* (*author*). *T* **252** *and similar horiz designs showing scenes from his books and modern technological developments. Multicoloured. P* 14.

96 18 c. Type **252** 25 10
97 35 c. "20,000 Leagues under the Sea" 35 15
98 75 c. "From the Earth to the Moon" 50 50
99 $3 "Master of the World" .. .. .. 1·40 1·60
96/9 .. .. *Set of* 4 2·25 2·00
\1S1000 110×85 mm. $4 "Clipper of the Clouds" 1·25 1·25

253 Mail Runner, Africa (early 19th-century)

254 "The Pistol of Peace" (vaccination gun), Map of Grenada and Children

(Des J.W. Litho Questa)

1979 (23 July). *Death Centenary of Sir Rowland Hill. T* **253** *and similar horiz designs. Multicoloured. P* 14.

1001 20 c. Type **253** 10 10
1002 40 c. Pony Express, America (mid 19th-century) 10 10
1003 $1 Pigeon post 20 25
1004 $3 Mail coach, Europe (18th-19th-century) 50 80
1001/4 .. .. *Set of* 4 80 1·10
MS1005 127 × 100 mm. $5 Sir Rowland Hill and 1891 1d. on 8d. *tête-bêche* block of 4 .. .. 75 1·10

Nos. 1001/4 also exist perf 12 (*Price for set of* 4 80*p. mint or used*) from additional sheetlets of 5 stamps and 1 label, issued 8 August. These have different background colours from the stamps perforated 14, which come from normal sheets of 40.

(Des G. Vasarhelyi. Litho Questa)

1979 (20 Aug). *International Year of the Child* (2*nd Issue*). *"Grenada—First Nation 100% Immunized". P* 14.

1006 **254** 5 c. multicoloured 30 30
1007 $1 multicoloured .. .. 1·00 2·00

255 Reef Shark

(Des G. Drummond. Litho Questa)

1979 (22 Aug). *Marine Wildlife. T* **225** *and similar horiz designs. Mutlicoloured. P* 14.

1008 40 c. Type **255** 40 30
1009 45 c. Spotted Eagle Ray 40 30
1010 50 c. Many-toothed Conger 45 40
1011 60 c. Golden Olive (shell) 70 75
1012 70 c. West Indian Murex (shell) 85 90
1013 75 c. Giant Tun (shell) .. .. 90 1·00
1014 90 c. Brown Booby .. .. 2·25 2·00
1015 $1 Magnificent Frigate Bird .. .. 2·25 2·00
1008/15 .. .. *Set of* 8 7·50 7·00
MS1016 109×78 mm. $2.50, Sooty Tern .. 2·50 2·00

256 The Flight into Egypt

(Des W. Grout. Litho Questa)

1979 (19 Oct). *Christmas. Religious Tapestries. T* **256** *and similar multicoloured designs. P* 14.

1017 6 c. Type **256** 10 10
1018 25 c. The Flight into Egypt (detail) 10 10
1019 30 c. Angel (*vert*) 15 10
1020 40 c. Doge Marino Grimani (detail) (*vert*) .. 15 10
1021 90 c. The Annunciation to the Shepherds (*vert*) 30 20
1022 $1 The Flight into Egypt (Rome) (*vert*) .. 30 25
1023 $2 The Virgin in Glory (*vert*) 40 50
1017/23 .. .. *Set of* 7 1·25 1·10
MS1024 111 × 148 mm. $4 Doge Marino Grimani (*vert*) .. .. 70 1·00

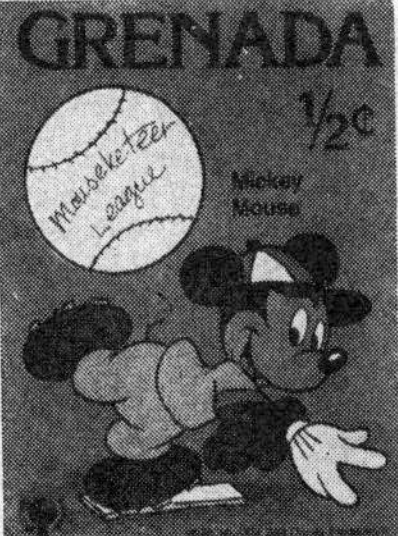

257 Mickey Mouse playing Baseball

258 Paul Harris (founder)

(Litho Format)

1979 (2 Nov). *International Year of the Child* (3*rd issue*). *Walt Disney Cartoon Characters. T* **257** *and similar vert designs showing characters playing sport. Multicoloured. P* 11.

1025 ½ c. Type **257** 10 10
1026 1 c. Donald Duck high-jumping 10 10
1027 2 c. Goofy playing basketball 10 10
1028 3 c. Goofy hurdling 10 10
1029 4 c. Donald Duck playing golf 10 10
1030 5 c. Mickey Mouse playing cricket 10 10
1031 10 c. Mickey Mouse playing football 10 10
1032 $2 Mickey Mouse playing tennis .. .. 2·75 3·00
1033 $2.50, Minnie Mouse riding horse .. .. 2·75 3·00
1025/33 .. .. *Set of* 9 5·50 6·00
MS1034 125 × 100 mm. $3 Goofy in riding gear. P 13½. .. .. 1·50 1·50

(Des J.W. Litho Questa)

1980 (25 Feb). *75th Anniv of Rotary International. T* **258** *and similar vert designs. Multicoloured. P* 14.

1035 6 c. Type **258** 10 10
1036 30 c. "Health" 20 15
1037 90 c. "Hunger" 40 30
1038 $2 "Humanity" 80 80
1035/8 .. .. *Set of* 4 1·40 1·10
MS1039 104 × 89 mm. $4 Rotary International emblem .. .. 1·00 1·60

PEOPLE'S REVOLUTION
13 MARCH 1979

(259)

1980 (28 Feb–8 Apr). *1st Anniv of Revolution* (*1st issue*). *Nos.* 651A/2A, 654A/7A, 659A, 660B *and* 662A/8A *optd with T* **259**.

1040 2 c. Carenage taxi 10 10
a. Optd on No. 651B .. .. .. 8·50
1041 3 c. Large working boats 10 10
a. Optd on No. 652B .. .. .. 8·50
1042 6 c. Cocoa beans in drying trays 10 10
1043 8 c. Nutmegs 10 10
1044 10 c. River Antoine Estate Rum Distillery, *c.* 1785 .. .. 10 10
1045 12 c. Cocoa Tree 10 10
1046 20 c. Parliament Building, St. George's .. 10 15
1047 25 c. Fort George cannons (8.4.80) 30 30
1048 50 c. General Post Office 30 30
1049 75 c. Caribs Leap, Sauteurs Bay 50 40
1050 $1 Carenage, St. George's 60 60
1051 $2 St. George's Harbour by night .. .. 1·25 2·00
1052 $3 Grand Anse Beach .. .. 1·50 3·25
1053 $5 Canoe Bay and Black Bay from Point Saline Lighthouse .. .. 2·50 5·00
1054 $10 Sugar Loaf Island from Levera Beach .. 3·75 7·50
1040/54 .. .. *Set of* 15 10·00 18·00

See also Nos. 1069/73.

260 Boxing

261 Tropical Kingbird

(Des Design Images Inc. Litho Questa)

1980 (24 Mar). *Olympic Games, Moscow. T* **260** *and similar horiz designs. Multicoloured. P* 14.

1055 25 c. Type **260** 10 10
1056 40 c. Cycling 15 15
1057 90 c. Show-jumping 20 30
1058 $2 Running .. .. 40 1·00
1055/8 .. .. *Set of* 4 75 1·40
MS1059 128 × 95 mm. $4 Sailing .. .. .. 80 1·40

(Des G. Drummond. Litho Questa)

1980 (8 Apr). *Wild Birds. T* **261** *and similar vert designs. Multicoloured. P* 14.

1060 20 c. Type **261** 85 15
1061 40 c. Rufous-breasted Hermit .. .. .. 1·25 25
1062 $1 Troupial .. .. 1·75 1·75
1063 $2 Ruddy Quail Dove .. .. 2·25 3·50
1060/3 .. .. *Set of* 4 5·50 5·00
MS1064 85×114 mm. $3 Prairie Warbler .. .. 3·75 1·75

LONDON 1980

(262)

263 Free Hot Lunch at Schools

1980 (6 May). *"London 1980" International Stamp Exhibition. Nos.* 1001/4 *optd with T* **262**. *P* 12.

1065 20 c. Type **253** 20 20
1066 40 c. Pony Express, America (mid 19th-century) 30 30
1067 $1 Pigeon Post 60 60
1068 $3 Mail coach, Europe (18th-19th-century) 1·75 1·75
1065/8 .. .. *Set of* 4 2·50 2·50

(Des M. Diamond. Litho Questa)

1980 (19 May). *1st Anniv of Revolution* (2*nd issue*). *T* **263** *and similar horiz designs. Multicoloured. P* 14.

1069 10 c. Type **263** 10 10
1070 40 c. "From tree to can" (agro-industry) .. 15 20
1071 $1 National Health care 40 45
1072 $2 New housing projects 75 90
1069/72 .. .. *Set of* 4 1·25 1·40
MS1073 110 × 85 mm. $5 Prime Minister Maurice Bishop (*vert*) .. .. 1·00 1·25

264 Jamb Statues, West Portal, Chartres Cathedral

(Des J.W. Litho Questa)

1980 (15 July). *Famous Works of Art. T* **264** *and similar horiz designs. Multicoloured. P* 13½.

1074 8 c. Type **264** 10 10
1075 10 c. "Les Demoiselles D'Avignon" (painting by Picasso) 10 10
1076 40 c. Winged Victory of Samothrace (statue) 20 20
1077 50 c. "The Night Watch" (painting by Rembrandt) 20 20
1078 $1 "Portrait of Edward VI as a Child" (painting by Holbein the Younger) .. 35 35
1079 $3 Portrait head of Queen Nefertiti (carving) 80 80
1074/9 .. .. *Set of* 6 1·50 1·50
MS1080 101 × 101 mm. $4 "Weier Haws" (detail of painting by Dürer) (*vert*) .. .. .. 1·00 1·00

265 Carib Canoes

(Des G. Drummond. Litho Questa)

1980 (9 Sept)–**84**. *Shipping. Horiz designs as T* **265**. *Multicoloured. A. Without imprint date. P* 14.

1081A ½ c. Type **265** 10 10
1082A 1 c. Boat building 10 10
1083A 2 c. Small working boat 15 10
1084A 4 c. Columbus' *Santa Maria* 40 10
1085A 5 c. West Indiaman barque, *circa* 1840 .. 40 10
1086A 6 c. *Orinoco* (paddle-steamer), *circa* 1851 .. 40 10
1087A 10 c. Working schooner 50 10
1088A 12 c. Trimaran at Grand Anse anchorage .. 50 10
1089A 15 c. Spice Island cruising yacht *Petite Amie* 50 10
1090A 20 c. Fishing pirogue .. .. 1·00 10
1091A 25 c. Harbour police launch .. .. .. 1·75 20
1092A 30 c. Grand Anse speed-boat .. .. .. 1·50 20
1093A 40 c. *Seimstrand* (freighter) .. .. .. 1·50 25
1094A 50 c. *Ariadne* (cadet schooner) .. .. 1·50 35
1095A 90 c. *Geestide* (freighter) .. .. .. 1·75 50
1096A $1 *Cunard Countess* (liner) .. .. .. 2·00 70
1097A $3 Rum-runner .. .. 3·00 4·00
1098A $5 *Statendam* (liner) off St. George's .. 4·50 7·00
1099A $10 Coastguard patrol boat .. .. .. 8·00 13·00
1081A/99A .. .. *Set of* 19 26·00 24·00

B. *With imprint date at foot of design. P* 14 ($1) *or* 12 (*others*)

1081B ½ c. Type **265** (1982) .. .. 75 1·50
1085B 5 c. West Indiaman barque, *circa* 1840 (1982) .. .. 2·00 1·25
1087B 10 c. Working schooner (1982) .. .. 2·00 60
a. Perf 14 .. .. † —
1090B 20 c. Fishing pirogue (1982) .. .. .. 2·50 95
1091B 25 c. Harbour police launch (1982) .. .. 2·25 90
a. Perf 14 .. .. 3·25 3·00
1092B 30 c. Grand Anse speed-boat (1982) .. .. 2·00 1·25
a. Perf 14 .. .. 3·75 3·00
1093B 40 c. *Seimstrand* (freighter) (1982) .. .. 3·50 1·60
1094B 50 c. *Ariadne* (cadet schooner) (1.84) .. 50 50
a. Perf 14 (1984) 55 50
1096B $1 *Cunard Countess* (liner) (1982) .. 28·00 14·00
1097B $3 Rum-runner (1982) .. .. .. 4·00 6·50

1098B $5 *Statendam* (liner) off St. George's (1982) .. .. .. 5·00 9·00
1099B $10 Coastguard patrol boat (1.84) .. 7·00 8·50
1081B/99B .. .. .. *Set of* 12 55·00 42·00

Imprint dates: "1982", Nos. 1081B, 1085B, 1087B/aB, 1090B, 1091B/aB, 1092B/aB, 1093B, 1096B/8B; "1984", Nos. 1094B/aB, 1099B.

(Litho Walsall)

1980 (25 Sept). *Christmas. Walt Disney Cartoon Scenes from "Snow White and the Seven Dwarfs". Horiz designs as T* **257**. *Multicoloured. P* 11.

1100 ½ c. Snow White at well 10 10
1101 1 c. The Wicked Queen 10 10
1102 2 c. Snow White singing to animals .. 10 10
1103 3 c. Snow White doing housework for Dwarfs 10 10
1104 4 c. The Seven Dwarfs 10 10
1105 5 c. Snow White with Dwarfs 10 10
1106 10 c. Witch offering Snow White apple .. 10 10
1107 $2.50, Snow White with Prince, and Dwarfs 3·00 1·75
1108 $3 Snow White and Prince.. .. .. 3·50 2·00
1100/8 .. .. *Set of* 9 6·50 3·75
MS1109 127 × 102 mm. $4 Snow White sleeping (*vert*) .. .. 4·25 2·00

(Litho Format)

1981 (19 Jan). *50th Anniv of Walt Disney's Cartoon Character, Pluto. Vert designs as T* **257**. *Multicoloured. P* 13½.

1110 $2 Pluto with birthday cake .. .. 1·25 1·50
MS1111 127 × 102 mm. $4 Pluto in scene from film *Pueblo Pluto* .. .. 2·25 1·75

No. 1110 was printed in small sheets of 8 stamps.

266 Revolution and Grenada Flags

1981 (13 Mar). *Festival of the Revolution. T* **266** *and similar triangular designs. Multicoloured. Litho. P* 12½.

1112 5 c. Type **266** 10 10
1113 10 c. Teacher, pupil, book and pencil ("education") 10 10
1114 15 c. Food processing plant ("industry") .. 10 10
1115 25 c. Selection of fruits and farm scene ("agriculture") 15 15
1116 40 c. Crawfish and boat ("fishing") 20 20
1117 90 c. *Cunard Countess* arriving at St. George's Harbour ("shipping") .. 50 50
1118 $1 Straw-work ("native handicrafts") .. 60 60
1119 $3 Map of Caribbean with expanded view of Grenada .. .. 1·75 1·75
1112/19 .. .. .. *Set of* 8 3·00 3·00

(Litho Format)

1981 (7 Apr). *Easter. Walt Disney Cartoon Characters. Vert designs as T* **257**. *Multicoloured. P* 11.

1120 35 c. Mickey Mouse and Goofy 40 25
1121 40 c. Donald Duck, Chip and Daisy Duck .. 40 25
1122 $2 Minnie Mouse .. .. .. 1·40 1·50
1123 $2.50, Pluto and Mickey Mouse .. 1·60 1·75
1120/3 .. .. *Set of* 4 3·50 3·25
MS1124 127×101 mm. $4 Goofy. P 13½ .. 3·00 3·50

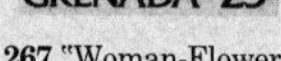

267 "Woman-Flower"

268 Prince Charles playing Polo

(Des J.W. Litho Questa)

1981 (28 Apr). *Birth Centenary of Picasso. T* **267** *and similar vert designs. Multicoloured. P* 13½ × 14.

1125 25 c. Type **267** 15 15
1126 30 c. "Portrait of Madame" 20 15
1127 90 c. "Cavalier with Pipe" 40 45
1128 $4 "Large Heads" .. .. .. 1·50 1·75
1125/8 .. .. .. *Set of* 4 2·00 2·25
MS1129 128 × 103 mm. $5 "Woman on the Banks of the Seine" (after Courbet). Imperf .. .. 4·00 1·75

(Des J.W. Litho Format)

1981 (16 June). *Royal Wedding* (1*st issue*). *T* **268** *and similar vert designs. Multicoloured.* (a) *P* 15.

1130 50 c. Prince Charles and Lady Diana Spencer 10 10
1131 $2 Holyrood House 35 50
1132 $4 Type **268** 50 75
a. Imperf (pair) £400
1130/2 .. .. .. *Set of* 3 85 1·25
MS1133 98 × 84 mm. $5 Glass Coach 75 75

(*b*) *P* 15 × 14½

1134 30 c. As 50 c. 20 20
1135 40 c. As $2 .. .. 30 30

The 30 and 40 c. values were each printed in small sheets of 6 including one *se-tenant* stamp-size label.

The $4 value, with changed background colour, also exists perforated 15×14½ (*price* 90*p. mint or used*) from similar sheetlets in addition to the original version issued in sheets of 40.

269 Lady Diana Spencer

270 "The Bath" (Mary Cassatt)

(Manufactured by Walsall)

1981 (16 June). *Royal Wedding* (2*nd issue*). *T* **269** *and similar vert designs. Multicoloured. Roul* 5 × *imperf**. *Self-adhesive.*

1136 $1 Type **269** 30 65
a. Booklet pane. Nos. 1136/7 each × 3 .. 1·60
1137 $2 Prince Charles 30 65
1138 $5 Prince Charles and Lady Diana Spencer 1·00 1·75
a. Booklet pane of 1.. .. .. .. 1·00
1136/8 .. .. *Set of* 3 1·40 2·75

*The $1 and $2 values were each separated by various combinations of rotary knife (giving a straight edge) and roulette. The $5 value exists only with straight edges.

Nos. 1136/8 were only issued in $14 stamp booklets.

(Des BG Studio. Litho Questa)

1981 (Oct). *"Decade for Women". Paintings. T* **270** *and similar multicoloured designs. P* 14.

1139 15 c. Type **270** 15 10
1140 40 c. "Mademoiselle Charlotte du Val d'Ognes" (Constance Marie Charpentier) 45 20
1141 60 c. "Self-portrait" (Mary Beale) 65 30
1142 $3 "Woman in White Stockings" (Suzanne Valadon) .. .. 2·00 1·25
1139/42 .. .. *Set of* 4 3·00 1·75
MS1143 101×77 mm. $5 "The Artist hesitating between the Arts of Music and Painting" (Angelica Kauffman) (*horiz*) .. .. .. 1·75 2·00

(Litho Questa)

1981 (Nov). *Christmas. Horiz designs as T* **257** *showing scenes from Walt Disney's cartoon film "Cinderella". P* 13½.

1144 ½ c. multicoloured 10 10
1145 1 c. multicoloured 10 10
1146 2 c. multicoloured 10 10
1147 3 c. multicoloured 10 10
1148 4 c. multicoloured 10 10
1149 5 c. multicoloured 10 10
1150 10 c. multicoloured 15 10
1151 $2.50, multicoloured .. .. .. 3·50 2·25
1152 $3 multicoloured .. .. 3·50 2·50
1144/52 .. .. *Set of* 9 7·00 4·75
MS1153 127 × 103 mm. $5 multicoloured .. 5·50 3·25

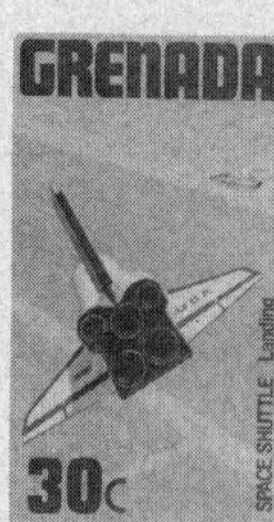

271 Landing

272 West German Footballer and Flag

(Des M. Brodie. Litho Format)

1981 (12 Nov). *Space Shuttle Project. T* **271** *and similar vert designs. Multicoloured. P* 14½.

1154 30 c. Type **271** 20 15
1155 60 c. Working in space 40 30
1156 70 c. Lift off 45 35
1157 $3 Separation .. .. 1·40 1·25
1154/7 .. .. *Set of* 4 2·25 1·75
MS1158 117 × 89 mm. $5 In orbit .. .. 1·75 1·50

(Des Clover Mill. Litho Format)

1981 (30 Nov.) *World Cup Football Championship, Spain* (1982). *T* **272** *and similar multicoloured designs. P* 14.

1159 25 c. + 10 c. Type **272** 55 30
1160 40 c. + 20 c. Argentinian footballer and flag .. 70 40
1161 50 c. + 25 c. Brazilian footballer and flag .. 80 50
1162 $1 + 50 c. English footballer and flag .. 1·25 95
1159/62 .. .. *Set of* 4 3·00 1·90
MS1163 141 × 128 mm. $5 + 50 c. Spanish orange mascot and Jules Rimet Trophy (*vert*) .. 3·50 2·00

Nos. 1159/62 were each printed in sheetlets of 12 on an overall background design showing a football.

273 General Post Office, St. George's

274 Artist without Hands

(Des J.W. Litho Format)

1981 (10 Dec). *Centenary of U.P.U. Membership. T* **273** *and similar horiz designs. Multicoloured. P* 15.

1164 25 c. Type **273** 20 15
1165 30 c. 1861 1d. stamp 25 20
1166 90 c. 1970 New U.P.U. Headquarters Building 25 c. commemorative 65 50
1167 $4 1961 Stamp Centenary 25 c. commemorative .. .. 1·75 2·00
1164/7 .. .. *Set of* 4 2·50 2·50
MS1168 113×87 mm. $5 1974 Centenary of U.P.U. ½ c. commemorative .. .. .. 3·50 3·25

(Litho Questa)

1982 (4 Feb). *International Year for the Disabled* (1981). *T* **274** *and similar vert designs. Multicoloured. P* 14.

1169 30 c. Type **274** 45 15
1170 40 c. Computer operator without hands .. 50 15
1171 70 c. Blind schoolteacher teaching braille .. 75 25
1172 $3 Midget playing drums .. .. .. 1·75 1·10
1169/72 .. .. *Set of* 4 3·00 1·50
MS1173 101 × 72 mm. $4 Auto mechanic confined to wheelchair .. .. 3·00 2·25

275 Tending Vegetable Patch

276 *Dryas julia*

(Des Design Images. Litho Format)

1982 (19 Feb). *75th Anniv of Boy Scout Movement and 125th Birth Anniv of Lord Baden-Powell. T* **275** *and similar horiz designs. Multicoloured. P* 14½.

1174 70 c. Type **275** 50 45
1175 90 c. Map-reading 55 55
1176 $1 Bee-keeping 65 65
1177 $4 Hospital reading .. .. .. 2·25 2·75
1174/7 .. .. *Set of* 4 3·50 4·00
MS1178 100 × 71 mm. $5 Presentation of trophies 2·00 2·00

(Des G. Drummond. Litho Questa)

1982 (24 Mar). *Butterflies. T* **276** *and similar vert designs. Multicoloured. P* 14.

1179 10 c. Type **276** 75 30
1180 60 c. *Phoebis agarithe* .. .. .. 2·50 1·50
1181 $1 *Anartia amathea* .. .. .. 3·00 2·00
1182 $3 *Battus polydamas* .. .. .. 4·25 7·00
1179/82 .. .. *Set of* 4 9·50 9·75
MS1183 111×85 mm. $5 *Junonia evarete* .. 7·50 3·50

277 "Saying Grace"

278 Kensington Palace

(Des M.B.I. Studio. Litho Questa)

1982 (14 Apr). *Norman Rockwell (painter) Commemoration. T* **277** *and similar vert designs. Multicoloured. P* 14 × 13½.

1184 15 c. Type **277** 35 10
1185 30 c. "Nothing Up His Sleeve" (inscr "Card Tricks") 60 15
1186 60 c. "Pharmacist" 75 25
1187 70 c. "Hobo" (inscr "Pals") 80 35
1184/7 .. .. *Set of* 4 2·25 75

(Des PAD Studio. Litho Questa)

1982 (1 July). *21st Birthday of Princess of Wales. T* **278** *and similar vert designs. Multicoloured. P* 14½ × 14.

1188 50 c. Type **278** 40 45
1189 60 c. Type **278** 80 45
1190 $1 Prince and Princess of Wales .. .. 90 1·00
1191 $2 As $1 .. .. 1·75 1·25
1192 $3 Princess of Wales .. .. .. 2·00 2·25

193 $4 As $3 . . . . 2·25 2·25
188/93 . . . . *Set of* 6 7·25 7·00
IS1194 103 × 75 mm. $5 Princess Diana (*different*) . . . . 2·50 2·00
Nos. 1188, 1190 and 1192 come from sheetlets of 5 stamps and 1 label.

279 Mary McLeod Bethune appointed Director of Negro Affairs, 1942

(Des Design Images. Litho Questa)

982 (27 July). *Birth Centenary of Franklin D. Roosevelt. T* **279** *and similar horiz designs. Multicoloured. P* 14.
195 10 c. Type **279** 10 10
196 60 c. Huddie Ledbetter ("Leadbelly") in concert (Works Progress administration) 35 20
197 $1.10, Signing bill No. 8802, 1941 (Fair Employment committee) 65 40
198 $3 Farm Security administration . . . . 1·00 80
195/8 . . . . . . *Set of* 4 1·75 1·25
IS1199 100×70 mm. $5 William Hastie, first Negro judicial appointee . . . . . . 1·50 1·50

982 (30 Aug). *Birth of Prince William of Wales. Nos.* 1188/94 *optd with T* **171** *of Antigua.*
200 50 c. Type **278** 30 60
201 60 c. Type **278** 35 35
202 $1 Prince and Princess of Wales 55 85
203 $2 As $1 . . . . 1·00 1·00
204 $3 Princess of Wales . . . . . . 1·75 1·90
205 $4 As $3 . . . . 1·90 1·90
200/5 . . . . . . *Set of* 6 5·50 6·00
MS1206 103 × 75 mm. $5 Princess Diana (*different*) . . . . 2·00 1·50
Nos. 1200, 1202 and 1204 come from sheetlets of 5 stamps and 1 label.

280 Apostle and Tormentor

(Des Clover Mill. Litho Format)

1982 (2 Sept). *Easter. Details from Painting "The Way to Calvary" by Raphael. T* **280** *and similar multicoloured designs. P* 14 × 14½ (40 c.) *or* 14½ × 14 (*others*).
1207 40 c. Type **280** 30 15
1208 70 c. Captain of the guards (*vert*) 40 25
1209 $1.10, Christ and apostle (*vert*) 60 35
1210 $4 Mourners (*vert*) . . . . . . 1·50 1·50
1207/10 . . . . . . *Set of* 4 2·50 2·00
MS1211 102 × 126 mm. $5 Christ falls beneath the cross (*vert*) . . . . 2·50 2·50

281 "Orient Express"

(Des Artists International. Litho Format)

1982 (4 Oct). *Famous Trains of the World. T* **281** *and similar horiz designs. Multicoloured. P* 15 × 14½.
1212 30 c. Type **281** 50 35
1213 60 c. "Trans-Siberian Express" 60 70
1214 70 c. "Fleche d'Or" 70 80
1215 90 c. "Flying Scotsman" . . . . . . 85 1·00
1216 $1 German Federal Railways steam locomotive . . . . 1·00 1·25
1217 $3 German National Railways Class 05 steam locomotive . . . . . . 2·25 4·00
1212/17 . . . . . . *Set of* 6 5·50 7·25
MS1218 109×81 mm. $5 "20th Century Limited" 2·50 3·00
No. 1217 exists imperforate from stock dispersed by the liquidator of Format International Security Printers Ltd.

282 Footballers

283 Killer Whale

(Des D. Miller. Litho Questa)

1982 (2 Dec). *World Cup Football Championship Winners. T* **282** *and similar horiz designs. P* 14 × 13½.
1219 60 c. multicoloured 35 35
1220 $4 multicoloured . . . . 2·00 2·00
MS1221 93×119 mm. $5 multicoloured . . 2·50 2·75

(Litho Questa)

1982 (14 Dec). *Christmas. Horiz designs as T* **257** *depicting scenes from Walt Disney's cartoon film "Robin Hood". P* 13½.
1222 ½ c. multicoloured 10 10
1223 1 c. multicoloured 10 10
1224 2 c. multicoloured 10 10
1225 3 c. multicoloured 10 10
1226 4 c. multicoloured 10 10
1227 5 c. multicoloured 10 10
1228 10 c. multicoloured 10 10
1229 $2.50, multicoloured . . . . . . 2·00 2·75
1230 $3 multicoloured . . . . 2·25 2·75
1222/30 . . . . . . *Set of* 9 4·25 5·25
MS1231 121 × 96 mm. $5 multicoloured . . . . 6·50 4·00

(Des Artists International. Litho Questa)

1983 (10 Jan). *Save the Whales. T* **283** *and similar vert designs. Multicoloured. P* 14.
1232 15 c. Type **283** . . . . 1·00 30
1233 40 c. Sperm Whale . . . . 2·25 90
1234 70 c. Blue Whale . . . . 2·75 2·75
1235 $3 Common Dolphin . . . . . . 3·50 6·50
1232/5 . . . . . . *Set of* 4 8·50 9·50
MS1236 84 × 74 mm. $5 Humpback Whale . . 6·00 4·00

284 "Construction of Ark"

(Des Design Images. Litho Format)

1983 (15 Feb). *500th Birth Anniv of Raphael. T* **284** *and similar horiz designs showing painting details. Multicoloured. P* 13½.
1237 25 c. Type **284** 20 15
1238 30 c. "Jacob's Vision" 20 20
1239 90 c. "Joseph interprets the Dreams to his Brothers" 40 45
1240 $4 "Joseph interprets Pharaoh's Dreams" 1·60 1·75
1237/40 . . . . . . *Set of* 4 2·25 2·25
MS1241 128 × 100 mm. $5 "Creation of the Animals" . . . . 1·25 1·75
Nos. 1237/41 exist imperforate from stock dispersed by the liquidator of Format International Security Printers Ltd.

285 Dentistry at Health Centre

(Des J.W. Litho Questa)

1983 (14 Mar). *Commonwealth Day. T* **285** *and similar horiz designs. Multicoloured. P* 14.
1242 10 c. Type **285** 10 10
1243 70 c. Airport runway construction 35 35
1244 $1.10, Tourism 40 55
1245 $3 Boat-building . . . . 80 1·40
1242/5 . . . . . . *Set of* 4 1·50 2·10

286 Maritime Communications via Satellite

(Des G. Vasarhelyi. Litho Questa)

1983 (29 Mar). *World Communications Year. T* **286** *and similar horiz designs. Multicoloured. P* 14.
1246 30 c. Type **286** 15 15
1247 40 c. Rural telephone installation 20 20
1248 $2.50, Satellite weather map . . . . 1·25 1·25
1249 $3 Airport control room . . . . . . 1·40 1·40
1246/9 . . . . . . *Set of* 4 2·75 2·75
MS1250 111 × 85 mm. $5 Communications satellite . . . . 2·00 2·00

NEW INFORMATION
The editor is always interested to correspond with people who have new information that will improve or correct the Catalogue.

287 Franklin Sport Sedan, 1928

(Des J. Mendola. Litho Format)

1983 (4 May). *75th Anniv of Model "T" Ford Car. T* **287** *and similar horiz designs showing cars of the 20th century. Multicoloured. P* 14½.
1251 6 c. Type **287** 15 10
1252 10 c. Delage "D8", 1933 . . . . . . 20 10
1253 40 c. Alvis, 1938 . . . . 35 25
1254 60 c. Invicta "S-type" tourer, 1931 . . . . 45 45
1255 70 c. Alfa-Romeo "1750 Gran Sport", 1930 . . 55 55
1256 90 c. Isotta Fraschini, 1930 . . . . . . 60 65
1257 $1 Bugatti "Royale Type 41" 70 65
1258 $2 BMW "328", 1938 . . . . . . 1·40 1·50
1259 $3 Marmon "V16", 1931 . . . . . . 1·60 2·25
1260 $4 Lincoln "K8" saloon, 1932 . . . . 1·90 2·75
1251/60 . . . . . . *Set of* 10 7·00 8·50
MS1261 114 × 90 mm. $5 Cougar "XR 7", 1972 . . 2·00 2·50
Nos. 1251/60 were each issued in sheets of eight stamps with a stamp-size label in the centre position.

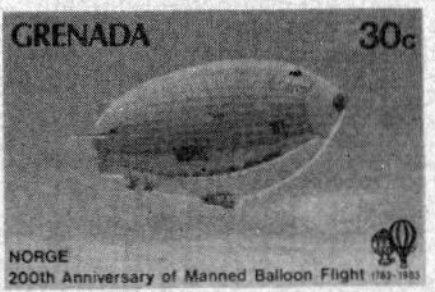

288 N.1 *Norge* (airship)

(Des W. Wright. Litho Questa)

1983 (18 July). *Bicentenary of Manned Flight. T* **288** *and similar multicoloured designs. P* 14.
1262 30 c. Type **288** 60 30
1263 60 c. Gloster VI seaplane . . . . . . 1·00 1·00
1264 $1.10, Curtiss NC-4 flying boat . . . . 3·50 4·50
1265 $4 Dornier Do-18 flying boat *Aeolus* . . 3·50 4·50
1262/5 . . . . . . *Set of* 4 6·00 6·75
MS1266 114×85 mm. $5 Modern hot-air balloon (*vert*) . . . . 2·25 2·50

289 Morty

(Litho Format)

1983 (7 Nov). *Christmas. T* **289** *and similar vert designs showing Disney cartoon characters in scenes from "It's beginning to look a lot like Christmas" (song). Multicoloured. P* 11.
1267 ½ c. Type **289** 10 10
1268 1 c. Ludwig von Drake 10 10
1269 2 c. Gyro Gearloose 10 10
1270 3 c. Pluto and Figaro 10 10
1271 4 c. Morty and Ferdie 10 10
1272 5 c. Mickey Mouse and Goofy 10 10
1273 10 c. Chip'n Dale 10 10
1274 $2.50, Mickey and Minnie Mouse . . . . 2·75 3·50
1275 $3 Donald and Grandma Duck . . . . 3·00 3·50
1267/75 . . . . . . *Set of* 9 5·75 7·00
MS1276 127 × 102 mm. $5 Goofy with Christmas tree. P 13½ . . . . 4·50 4·50

290 Daisy Duck on Pommel Horse

291 William I

(Litho Questa)

1984 (17 Jan–May). *Olympic Games, Los Angeles. T* **290** *and similar horiz designs showing Disney cartoon characters in Olympic events. Multicoloured.*

A. *Inscr* "1984 LOS ANGELES". *P* 14×13½
1277A ½ c. Type **290** 10 10
1278A 1 c. Mickey Mouse boxing 10 10
1279A 2 c. Daisy Duck in archery event . . 10 10

1280A 3 c. Clarabelle Cow on uneven bars .. 10 10
1281A 4 c. Mickey and Minnie Mouse in hurdles race 10 10
1282A 5 c. Donald Duck with Chip and Dale weightlifting 10 10
1283A $1 Little Hiawatha in single kayak .. 1·75 2·00
1284A $2 The Tortoise and the Hare in marathon .. .. 2·25 3·00
1285A $3 Mickey Mouse pole-vaulting .. 2·75 3·25
1277A/85A .. .. *Set of* 9 6·75 8·00
MS1286A 127×101 mm. $5 Donald Duck in medley relay (*vert*). P 13½×14 .. .. 5·00 3·50

B. *Inscr* "1984 OLYMPICS LOS ANGELES *and Olympic emblem. P* 12 (May)

1277B ½ c. Type **290** 10 10
1278B 1 c. Mickey Mouse boxing 10 10
1279B 2 c. Daisy Duck in archery event .. 10 10
1280B 3 c. Clarabelle Cow on uneven bars .. 10 10
1281B 4 c. Mickey and Minnie Mouse in hurdles race 10 10
1282B 5 c. Donald Duck with Chip and Dale weightlifting 10 10
1283B $1 Little Hiawatha in single kayak .. 1·75 2·00
1284B $2 The Tortoise and the Hare in marathon .. .. 2·25 3·00
1285B $3 Mickey Mouse pole-vaulting .. 2·75 3·25
1277B/85B .. .. .. *Set of* 9 6·75 8·00
MS1286B 127×101 mm. $5 Donald Duck in medley relay (*vert*). P 13½×14 .. .. 6·00 5·50

1984 (25 Jan). *British Monarchs. T* **291** *and similar vert designs. Multicoloured. Litho. P* 14.
1287 $4 Type **291** .. .. 3·00 3·25
a. Sheetlet. Nos. 1287/93 .. .. 19·00
1288 $4 William II .. .. 3·00 3·25
1289 $4 Henry I .. .. 3·00 3·25
1290 $4 Stephen .. .. 3·00 3·25
1291 $4 Henry II .. .. 3·00 3·25
1292 $4 Richard I .. .. 3·00 3·25
1293 $4 John .. .. 3·00 3·25
1294 $4 "Henry III" .. .. 3·00 3·25
a. Sheetlet. Nos. 1294/1300 .. .. 19·00
1295 $4 Edward I .. .. 3·00 3·25
1296 $4 Edward II .. .. 3·00 3·25
1297 $4 Edward III .. .. 3·00 3·25
1298 $4 Richard II .. .. 3·00 3·25
1299 $4 Henry IV .. .. 3·00 3·25
1300 $4 Henry V .. .. 3·00 3·25
1301 $4 Henry VI .. .. 3·00 3·25
a. Sheetlet. Nos. 1301/7 .. .. .. 19·00
1302 $4 Edward IV .. .. 3·00 3·25
1303 $4 Edward V .. .. 3·00 3·25
1304 $4 Richard III .. .. 3·00 3·25
1305 $4 Henry VII .. .. 3·00 3·25
1306 $4 Henry VIII .. .. 3·00 3·25
1307 $4 Edward VI .. .. 3·00 3·25
1308 $4 Lady Jane Grey .. .. .. 3·00 3·25
a. Sheetlet. Nos. 1308/14 .. .. 19·00
1309 $4 Mary I .. .. 3·00 3·25
1310 $4 Elizabeth I .. .. 3·00 3·25
1311 $4 James I .. .. 3·00 3·25
1312 $4 Charles I .. .. 3·00 3·25
1313 $4 Charles II .. .. 3·00 3·25
1314 $4 James II .. .. 3·00 3·25
1315 $4 William III .. .. 3·00 3·25
a. Sheetlet. Nos. 1315/21 .. .. 19·00
1316 $4 Mary II .. .. 3·00 3·25
1317 $4 Anne .. .. 3·00 3·25
1318 $4 George I .. .. 3·00 3·25
1319 $4 George II .. .. 3·00 3·25
1320 $4 George III .. .. 3·00 3·25
1321 $4 George IV .. .. 3·00 3·25
1322 $4 William IV .. .. 3·00 3·25
a. Sheetlet. Nos. 1322/8 .. .. .. 19·00
1323 $4 Victoria .. .. 3·00 3·25
1324 $4 Edward VII .. .. 3·00 3·25
1325 $4 George V .. .. 3·00 3·25
1326 $4 Edward VIII .. .. 3·00 3·25
1327 $4 George VI .. .. 3·00 3·25
1328 $4 Elizabeth II .. .. 3·00 3·25
1287/1328 .. .. *Set of* 42 £110 £120

Nos. 1287/93, 1294/1300, 1301/7, 1308/14, 1315/21 and 1322/8 were printed together, in small sheets of 8 including one *se-tenant* stamp-size label.

Although inscribed "Henry III" the portrait on No. 1294 is actually of Edward II.

Although announced as all being issued on 25 January 1984 the different sheetlets were distributed at monthly intervals.

292 Lantana

(Des P.U.B. Graphics. Litho Format)

1984 (9 Apr). *Flowers. T* **292** *and similar horiz designs. Multicoloured. P* 15.
1329 25 c. Type **292** 20 15
1330 30 c. Plumbago 25 20
1331 90 c. Spider Lily 70 60
1332 $4 Giant Alocasia .. .. 2·50 3·00
1329/32 .. .. *Set of* 4 3·25 3·50
MS1333 108 × 90 mm. $5 Orange Trumpet Vine 1·25 2·00

Nos. 1329/32 exist imperforate from stock dispersed by the liquidator of Format International Security Printers Ltd.

COVER PRICES

Cover factors are quoted at the beginning of each country for most issues to 1945. An explanation of the system can be found on page x. The factors quoted do not, however, apply to philatelic covers.

293 Blue Parrotfish

19TH U.P.U CONGRESS – HAMBURG
(294)

(Litho Questa)

1984 (21 May). *Coral Reef Fishes. T* **293** *and similar horiz designs. Multicoloured. P* 14.
1334 10 c. Type **293** .. .. 1·40 45
1335 30 c. Flame-backed Angelfish .. .. 2·75 1·10
1336 70 c. Painted Wrasse .. .. .. 4·00 3·25
1337 90 c. Rosy Razorfish .. .. .. 4·75 3·50
1334/7 .. .. *Set of* 4 11·50 7·50
MS1338 81×85 mm. $5 Spanish Hogfish .. 6·00 4·75

1984 (19 June). *Universal Postal Union Congress, Hamburg. Nos.* 1331/3 *optd with T* **294**.
1339 90 c. Spider Lily 60 65
1340 $4 Giant Alocasia .. .. 2·00 2·50
MS1341 108 × 90 mm. $5 Orange Trumpet Vine 1·50 2·50

295 Freighter

296 "The Night" (detail) (Correggio)

(Des Artists International. Litho Format)

1984 (16 July). *Ships. T* **295** *and similar horiz designs. Multicoloured. P* 15.
1342 40 c. Type **295** .. .. 1·25 55
1343 70 c. *Queen Elizabeth 2* .. .. .. 1·50 1·50
1344 90 c. Sailing boats .. .. 1·90 2·00
1345 $4 *Amerikanis* .. .. 6·00 8·00
1342/5 .. .. *Set of* 4 9·50 11·00
MS1346 107×80 mm. $5 Spanish galleon .. 7·00 7·00

Nos. 1342/6 exist imperforate from stock dispersed by the liquidator of Format International Security Printers Ltd.

(Litho Questa)

1984 (22 Aug). *450th Death Anniv of Correggio (painter). T* **296** *and similar vert designs showing paintings. Multicoloured. P* 14.
1347 10 c. Type **296** 45 15
1348 30 c. "The Virgin adoring the Child" .. 80 50
1349 90 c. "The Mystical Marriage of St. Catherine with St. Sebastian" .. .. 2·00 1·75
1350 $4 "The Madonna and the Fruit Basket" .. 4·50 5·50
1347/50 .. .. *Set of* 4 7·00 7·00
MS1351 54 × 73 mm. $5 "The Madonna at the Spring" .. .. 4·25 3·75

297 "L'Absinthe" (Degas)

298 Train on Puffing Billy Line, Victoria

(Litho Questa)

1984 (22 Aug). *150th Birth Anniv of Edgar Degas (painter). T* **297** *and similar multicoloured designs showing paintings. P* 14.
1352 25 c. Type **297** 80 30
1353 70 c. "Pouting" (*horiz*) .. .. .. 1·50 1·25
1354 $1.10, "The Millinery Shop" .. .. 2·00 2·00
1355 $3 "The Bellelli Family" (*horiz*) .. 3·75 4·25
1352/5 .. .. *Set of* 4 7·25 7·00
MS1356 84 × 54 mm. $5 "The Cotton Market" .. 4·25 3·75

(Des Bonny Redecker. Litho Questa)

1984 (21 Sept). *"Ausipex" International Stamp Exhibition, Melbourne. T* **298** *and similar vert designs. Multicoloured. P* 14.
1357 $1.10, Type **298** .. .. 2·25 1·75
1358 $4 Yacht *Australia II* (winner of America's Cup) .. .. 4·75 5·25
MS1359 107 × 76 mm. $5 Melbourne tram .. 3·75 4·50

299 George Stephenson's *Locomotion* (1825)

OPENING OF POINT SALINE INT'L AIRPORT
(300)

(Des J.W. Litho Format)

1984 (3 Oct). *Railway Locomotives. T* **299** *and similar horiz designs. Multicoloured. P* 15.
1360 30 c. Type **299** 80 35
1361 40 c. Braithwaite and Ericsson's *Novelty* (1829) 95 40
1362 60 c. William Norris's *Washington Farmer* (1836) .. .. 1·10 75
1363 70 c. French Crampton type (1859) .. 1·25 1·00
1364 90 c. Dutch State Railways (1873) .. 1·50 1·50
1365 $1.10, *Champion*, U.S.A. (1882) .. 1·75 2·00
1366 $2 Webb Compound type (1893) .. 2·25 3·25
1367 $4 Berlin "No. 74" (1900) .. .. 3·75 5·50
1360/7 .. .. *Set of* 8 12·00 13·00
MS1368 Two sheets, each 100×70 mm. (a) $5 Crampton *Phoenix* (1863); (b) $5 Mikado type, Japan (1897) .. .. .. *Set of* 2 *sheets* 6·00 6·50

1984 (28 Oct). *Opening of Point Saline International Airport (1st issue). Nos.* 1247 *and* 1249/50 *optd as T* **300**.
1369 40 c. Rural telephone installation 30 30
1370 $3 Airport control room .. .. 2·00 2·00
MS1371 111×85 mm. $5 Communications satellite .. .. 3·50 3·25

On No. **MS**1371 the overprint, 54 × 8 mm., appears in two lines on the sheet margin only.

See also Nos. 1393/6.

301 Donald Duck as Father Christmas looking into Mirror

(Litho Questa)

1984 (26 Nov). *Christmas. Walt Disney Cartoon Characters. T* **301** *and similar vert designs. Multicoloured. P* 12 ($2) *or* 13½ × 14 *(others)*.
1372 45 c. Type **301** .. .. 1·25 40
1373 60 c. Donald Duck filling stocking with presents .. .. 1·50 55
1374 90 c. As Father Christmas pulling a sleigh .. 2·00 1·10
1375 $2 As Father Christmas decorating Christmas tree .. .. 3·50 3·50
1376 $4 Donald Duck and nephews singing carols 5·00 5·50
1372/6 .. .. *Set of* 5 12·00 10·00
MS1377 127 × 102 mm. $5 As Father Christmas in sleigh .. .. 7·00 8·00

No. 1375 was printed in sheetlets of 8 stamps.

(Litho Questa)

1985 (11 Feb). *Birth Bicentenary of John J. Audubon (ornithologist) (1st issue). Multicoloured designs as T* **198** *of Antigua showing original paintings. P* 14.
1378 50 c. Clapper Rail (*vert*) .. .. .. 2·00 75
1379 70 c. Hooded Warbler (*vert*) .. .. 2·25 1·50
1380 90 c. Common Flicker (*vert*) .. .. 2·75 1·75
1381 $4 Bohemian Waxwing (*vert*) .. .. 5·50 8·00
1378/81 .. .. *Set of* 4 11·00 11·00
MS1382 82×112 mm. $5 Merlin ("Pigeon Hawk") .. .. 9·00 4·50

See also Nos. 1480/4.

302 Honda "XL500R"

(Des R. Sentnor. Litho Questa)

1985 (11 Mar). *Centenary of the Motor Cycle. T* **302** *and similar horiz designs. Multicoloured. P* 14.
1383 25 c. Type **302** 90 50
1384 50 c. Suzuki "GS1100ES" .. .. .. 1·40 1·00
1385 90 c. Kawasaki "KZ700" .. .. .. 2·00 2·00
1386 $4 BMW "K100" .. .. 5·50 6·50
1383/6 .. .. *Set of* 4 8·75 9·00
MS1387 109 × 81 mm. $5 Yamaha "500CC V Four" 6·50 5·00

303 "Explorer"

(Des Susan David. Litho Questa)

85 (15 Apr). *75th Anniv of Girl Guide Movement. T* **303** *and similar horiz designs, showing work for Guide badges. Multi-coloured. P* 14.
88 25 c. Type **303** .. 55 30
89 60 c. "Cook" .. 90 65
90 90 c. "Musician" .. 1·50 1·10
91 $3 "Home nurse" .. 3·00 3·50
88/91 .. *Set of* 4 5·50 5·00
S1392 97×70 mm. $5 Flags of Girl Guides and Grenada .. 2·50 2·50

304 Hawker Siddeley H.S.748 on Inaugural Flight from Barbados

(Des Susan David. Litho Questa)

85 (30 Apr). *Opening of Point Saline International Airport* (1984) (*2nd issue*). *T* **304** *and similar horiz designs. Multi-coloured. P* 14.
93 70 c. Type **304** .. 2·50 1·00
94 $1 Lockheed L-1011 TriStar 500 on inaugural flight from New York .. 3·25 1·50
95 $4 Lockheed L-1011 TriStar 500 on inaugural flight to Miami .. 6·50 8·00
93/5 .. *Set of* 3 11·00 9·50
S1396 101×72 mm. $5 Point Saline Airport terminal and Hawker Siddeley H.S.748 on tarmac .. 5·00 3·75

305 Douglas DC-8-61

(Des BG Studio. Litho Questa)

85 (15 May). *40th Anniv of International Civil Aviation Organization. T* **305** *and similar horiz designs. Multicoloured. P* 14.
97 10 c. Type **305** .. 40 20
98 50 c. Lockheed L.1649A Starliner .. 1·00 75
99 60 c. Vickers 952 Cargoliner .. 1·25 85
400 $4 De Havilland D.H.C.6 Twin Otter 200/300 .. 4·50 6·00
97/400 .. *Set of* 4 6·50 7·00
S1401 102×64 mm. $5 Hawker Siddeley H.S.748 turboprop .. 3·00 3·00

306 Model Boat Racing **307** Bird of Paradise (flower)

(Litho Format)

985 (15 June). *Water Sports. T* **306** *and similar horiz designs. Multicoloured. P* 15.
402 10 c. Type **306** .. 20 10
403 50 c. Scuba diving, Carriacou .. 45 35
404 $1.10, Windsurfers on Grand Anse Beach 75 1·10
405 $4 Windsurfing .. 2·00 4·00
402/5 .. *Set of* 4 3·00 5·00
IS1406 107×77 mm. $5 Beach scene .. 2·25 2·75
Nos. 1402/5 exist imperforate from stock dispersed by the liquidator of Format International Security Printers Ltd.

(Des Mary Walters. Litho Questa)

985 (1 July)–**88**. *Native Flowers. T* **307** *and similar vert designs. Multicoloured. Chalk-surfaced paper.*

A. *Without imprint date. P* 14
407 ½ c. Type **307** .. 40 40
 a. Perf 12 (3.86) .. 30 40
408 1 c. Passion Flower .. 50 40
 a. Perf 12 (3.86) .. 40 40
409 2 c. Oleander .. 50 40
 a. Perf 12 (3.86) .. 40 40
410 4 c. Bromeliad .. 85 40
 a. Perf 12 (3.86) .. 45 40
411 5 c. Anthurium .. 85 40
 a. Perf 12 (3.86) .. 45 40
412 6 c. Bougainvillea .. 85 50
 a. Perf 12 (3.86) .. 45 50
413 10 c. Hibiscus .. 1·00 40
 a. Perf 12 (7.86) .. 45 30
414 15 c. Ginger .. 1·75 40
 a. Perf 12 (3.86) .. 65 30
415 25 c. Poinsettia .. 1·75 40
 a. Perf 12 (3.86) .. 65 30
1416 30 c. Mexican Creeper .. 1·75 70
 a. Perf 12 (3.86) .. 65 30
1417 40 c. Angel's Trumpet .. 2·00 70
 a. Perf 12 (3.86) .. 75 50
1418 50 c. Amaryllis .. 2·00 1·00
 a. Perf 12 (3.86) .. 75 75
1419 60 c. Prickly Pear .. 2·00 1·75
 a. Perf 12 (3.86) .. 75 90
1420 70 c. Chenille Plant .. 2·00 1·75
 a. Perf 12 (7.86) .. 75 1·00
1420*b* 75 c. Cordia (1.12.88) .. 1·25 1·75
1421 $1 Periwinkle .. 3·25 2·00
 a. Perf 12 (3.86) .. 1·75 1·75
1422 $1.10, Ixora .. 3·50 2·75
 a. Perf 12 (3.86) .. 1·75 2·25
1423 $3 Shrimp Plant .. 4·75 6·00
 a. Perf 12 (3.86) .. 2·50 5·00
1424 $5 Plumbago .. 4·75 7·00
 a. Perf 12 (7.86) .. 2·50 6·00
1425 $10 *Lantana camara* (11.11.85) .. 4·75 8·50
 a. Perf 12 (12.86) .. 4·00 9·00
1425*b* $20 Peregrina (1.8.86) .. 8·50 16·00
 ba. Ordinary paper (5.8.87) .. 9·00 16·00
1407/25*b* .. *Set of* 21 42·00 45·00

B. *With imprint date. P* 14
1425*c* 10 c. Hibiscus (7.88) .. 3·00 3·25
1425*d* 30 c. Mexican Creeper (1987) .. 20 60
1425*e* 50 c. Amaryllis (1987) .. 30 75
1425*f* 60 c. Prickly Pear (1987) .. 30 1·00
1425*g* $1 Periwinkle (1987) .. 35 1·25
1425*c/g* .. *Set of* 5 3·75 6·00
Imprint dates: "1987", Nos. 1425*d/g*; "1988", No. 1425*c*.

308 The Queen Mother at Royal Opera House, London **309** Youth Gardening (Horticulture)

(Des J.W. Litho Questa)

1985 (3 July). *Life and Times of Queen Elizabeth the Queen Mother. T* **308** *and similar multicoloured designs. P* 14.
1426 $1 Type **308** .. 40 60
1427 $1.50, The Queen Mother playing snooker at London Press Club (*horiz*) .. 55 85
1428 $2.50, At Epsom Races, 1960 .. 95 1·50
1426/8 .. *Set of* 3 1·75 2·75
MS1429 56×85 mm. $5 With Prince of Wales on 80th Birthday .. 1·75 3·00
Stamps as Nos. 1426/8, but with face values of 90 c., $1 and $3, exist from additional sheetlets of 5 plus a label issued December 1985. These also have changed background colours and are perforated 12½×12 ($1) or 12×12½ (others) (*Price for set of 3 stamps £1.50 mint*).

(Des Liane Fried. Litho Format)

1985 (21 Aug). *International Youth Year. T* **309** *and similar vert designs. Multicoloured. P* 15.
1430 25 c. Type **309** .. 25 20
1431 50 c. Young people on beach (Leisure) .. 45 40
1432 $1.10, Girls in classroom (Education) .. 90 1·10
1433 $3 Nurse and young patient (Health Care) .. 2·25 2·50
1430/3 .. *Set of* 4 3·50 3·75
MS1434 111×80 mm. $5 Children of different races .. 2·00 3·00

(Des Susan David. Litho Questa)

1985 (3 Sept). *300th Birth Anniv of Johann Sebastian Bach (composer). Vert designs as T* **206** *of Antigua. P* 14.
1435 25 c. multicoloured .. 80 20
1436 70 c. multicoloured .. 1·50 85
1437 $1 multicoloured .. 2·00 1·25
1438 $3 multicoloured .. 3·00 4·00
1435/8 .. *Set of* 4 6·50 5·75
MS1439 104×74 mm. $5 black, lavender-grey and cinnamon .. 3·50 3·75
Designs:—25 c. Crumhorn; 70 c. Oboe d'amore; $1 Violin; $3 Harpsichord; $5 Johann Sebastian Bach.

310 Cub Scouts Camping

(Des A. DiLorenzo. Litho Questa)

1985 (5 Sept). *4th Caribbean Cuboree. T* **310** *and similar multicoloured designs. P* 14.
1440 10 c. Type **310** .. 30 15
1441 50 c. Cub scouts swimming ("Physical Fitness") .. 65 40
1442 $1 Stamp collecting .. 1·50 80
1443 $4 Birdwatching .. 3·50 3·00
1440/3 .. *Set of* 4 5·50 4·00
MS1444 103×75 mm. $5 Cub scouts saluting leader (*vert*) .. 3·25 3·50

(Des Mary Walters. Litho Format)

1985 (4 Nov). *Royal Visit. Multicoloured designs as T* **207** *of Antigua. P* 14½.
1445 50 c. Flags of Great Britain and Grenada .. 75 40
1446 $1 Queen Elizabeth II (*vert*) .. 1·00 1·25
1447 $4 Royal Yacht *Britannia* .. 2·50 5·00
1445/7 .. *Set of* 3 3·75 6·00
MS1448 111×83 mm. $5 Map of Grenada .. 1·75 3·25

(Des Walt Disney Productions. Litho Questa)

1985 (4 Nov). *150th Birth Anniv of Mark Twain (author). Horiz designs as T* **118** *of Anguilla showing Walt Disney cartoon characters in scenes from "The Prince and the Pauper". Multicoloured. P* 14×13½.
1449 25 c. Mortie as Tom meeting the Prince (Ferdie) .. 50 20
1450 50 c. Tom and the Prince exchanging clothes .. 70 50
1451 $1.10, The Prince with John Cantry .. 1·60 1·60
1452 $1.50, The Prince knights Mike Hendon (Goofy) .. 2·00 2·50
1453 $2 Tom and the Whipping Boy .. 2·25 2·75
1449/53 .. *Set of* 5 6·25 6·75
MS1454 124×100 mm. $5 The Prince, Tom and Mike Hendon .. 5·50 5·50

(Des Walt Disney Productions. Litho Questa)

1985 (4 Nov). *Birth Bicentenaries of Grimm Brothers (folklorists). Horiz designs as T* **119** *of Anguilla, showing Walt Disney cartoon characters in scenes from "The Fisherman and his Wife". Multicoloured. P* 14×13½.
1455 30 c. The Fisherman (Goofy) catching enchanted fish .. 55 30
1456 60 c. The Fisherman scolded by his Wife (Clarabelle) .. 80 80
1457 70 c. The Fisherman's Wife with dream cottage .. 95 95
1458 $1 The Fisherman's Wife as King .. 1·50 1·50
1459 $3 The Fisherman and Wife in their original shack .. 3·00 3·75
1455/9 .. *Set of* 5 6·00 6·50
MS1460 126×100 mm. $5 The Fisherman in boat .. 5·50 5·50

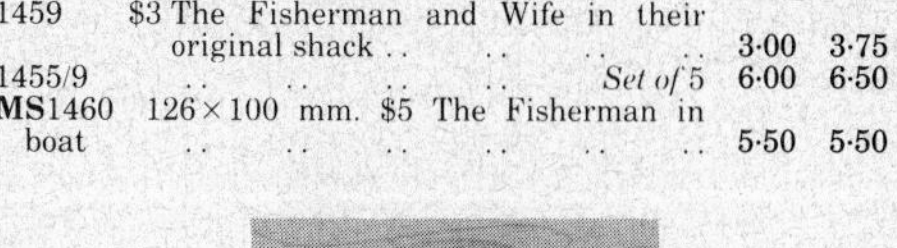

311 Red-spotted Hawkfish

(Des R. Sauber. Litho Questa)

1985 (15 Nov). *Marine Life. T* **311** *and similar horiz designs. Multicoloured. P* 14.
1461 25 c. Type **311** .. 1·25 55
1462 50 c. Spot-finned Butterflyfish .. 2·00 1·10
1463 $1.10, Fire Coral and Orange Sponges 3·25 3·25
1464 $3 Pillar Coral .. 6·00 7·50
1461/4 .. *Set of* 4 11·00 11·00
MS1465 127×100 mm. $5 Bigeye .. 3·75 4·50

(Litho Format)

1985 (22 Nov). *40th Anniv of United Nations Organization. Multicoloured designs as T* **208** *of Antigua showing United Nations (New York) stamps. P* 14½.
1466 50 c. Mary McLeod Bethune (educationist) and 1975 International Women's Year 10 c. .. 50 50
1467 $2 Maimonides (physician) and 1966 W.H.O. 5 c. .. 3·00 3·50
1468 $2.50, Alexander Graham Bell (telephone inventor) and 1956 I.T.U. 3 c. .. 3·00 3·75
1466/8 .. *Set of* 3 6·00 7·00
MS1469 110×85 mm. $5 Dag Hammarskjold (Secretary-General) (*vert*) .. 1·50 2·00

VISIT OF

PRES REAGAN

20 FEB. 1986

312 "The Adoration of the Shepherds" (Mantegna) (**313**)

(Des Mary Walters. Litho Format)

1985 (23 Dec). *Christmas. Religious Paintings. T* **312** *and similar horiz designs. Multicoloured. P* 15.
1470 25 c. Type **312** .. 20 15
1471 60 c. "Journey of the Magi" (Sassetta) .. 40 40
1472 90 c. "Madonna and Child enthroned with Saints" (Raphael) .. 50 70
1473 $4 "Nativity" (Monaco) .. 1·50 3·50
1470/3 .. *Set of* 4 2·40 4·25
MS1474 107×81 mm. $5 "Madonna and Child enthroned with Saints" (Gaddi) .. 1·75 2·50

(Des J. Iskowitz. Litho Questa)

1986 (6 Jan). *Centenary of Statue of Liberty (1st issue). Multicoloured designs as T* **211** *of Dominica. P* 15.
1475 5 c. Columbus Monument, 1893 (*vert*) .. 15 20
1476 25 c. Columbus Monument, 1986 (*vert*) .. 40 20
1477 40 c. Mounted police, Central Park, 1895 .. 1·75 1·10
1478 $4 Mounted police, 1986 .. 6·50 8·00
1475/8 .. *Set of* 4 8·00 8·50
MS1479 104×76 mm. $5 Statue of Liberty (*vert*) 2·25 2·50
See also Nos. 1644/52.

(Litho Questa)

1986 (20 Jan). *Birth Bicentenary of John J. Audubon (ornithologist) (2nd issue). Multicoloured designs as T* **198** *of Antigua. P* 12×12½.
1480 50 c. Snowy Egret .. .. 2·00 80
1481 90 c. Greater Flamingo .. .. 2·75 2·00
1482 $1.10, Canada Goose .. .. 2·75 2·50
1483 $3 Smew .. .. 4·50 6·00
1480/3 .. .. *Set of* 4 11·00 10·00
MS1484 103×72 mm. $5 Brent Goose (*horiz*). P 14 .. .. 12·00 13·00
Nos. 1480/3 were each issued in sheetlets of five stamps and one stamp-size label, which appears in the centre of the bottom row.

1986 (20 Feb). *Visit of President Reagan. Nos.* 1418A *and* 1424A *optd with T* **313**.
1485 50 c. Amaryllis 50 50
1486 $5 Plumbago .. .. 3·00 5·00

314 Methodist Church, St. Georges **315** Player with Ball

(Litho Format)

1986 (24 Feb). *Bicentenary of Methodist Church in Grenada. T* **314** *and similar horiz design. Multicoloured. P* 15.
1487 60 c. Type **314** .. .. 70 1·00
MS1488 102×73 mm. $5 St. Georges .. .. 1·40 3·00

(Des N. Waldman. Litho Questa)

1986 (6 Mar). *World Cup Football Championship, Mexico. T* **315** *and similar vert designs. Multicoloured. P* 14.
1489 50 c. Type **315** 80 55
1490 70 c. Player heading ball .. .. 1·00 1·00
1491 90 c. Player controlling ball .. .. .. 1·50 1·50
1492 $4 Player controlling ball with right foot 5·50 7·00
1489/92 .. .. *Set of* 4 8·00 9·00
MS1493 101×71 mm. $5 Player tackling .. 4·25 5·00

(Des W. Hanson. Litho Questa)

1986 (20 Mar). *Appearance of Halley's Comet (1st issue). Horiz designs as T* **123** *of Anguilla. Multicoloured. P* 14.
1494 5 c. Clyde Tombaugh (astronomer) and Dudley Observatory, New York .. 40 40
1495 20 c. N.A.S.A. – U.S.A.F. "X-24B" Space Shuttle prototype, 1973 .. .. 50 30
1496 40 c. German comet medal, 1618 .. .. 70 45
1497 $4 Destruction of Sodom and Gomorrah, 1949 B.C. .. .. 3·50 4·50
1494/7 .. .. *Set of* 4 4·50 5·00
MS1498 102×70 mm. $5 Halley's Comet over Grenada .. .. 6·50 7·00
See also Nos. 1533/7 and 1980/4.

(Litho Questa)

1986 (21 Apr). *60th Birthday of Queen Elizabeth II. Vert designs as T* **125** *of Anguilla. P* 14.
1499 2 c. black and yellow 10 15
1500 $1.50, multicoloured 60 80
1501 $4 multicoloured .. .. 1·50 2·50
1499/1501 .. .. *Set of* 3 2·00 3·00
MS1502 120×85 mm. $5 black and grey-brown .. 1·75 3·25
Designs:—2 c. Princess Elizabeth in 1951; $1.50, Queen presenting trophy at polo match, Windsor, 1965; $4 At Epsom, Derby Day, 1977; $5 King George VI and family, 1939.

(Des Walt Disney Productions. Litho Format)

1986 (22 May). *"Ameripex" International Stamp Exhibition, Chicago. Horiz designs as T* **212** *of Dominica, showing Walt Disney cartoon characters playing baseball. Multicoloured. P* 11.
1503 1 c. Goofy as pitcher 10 10
1504 2 c. Goofy as catcher 10 10
1505 3 c. Mickey Mouse striking ball and Donald Duck as catcher 10 10
1506 4 c. Huey forcing out Dewey 10 10
1507 5 c. Chip n'Dale chasing flyball 10 10
1508 6 c. Mickey Mouse, Donald Duck and Clarabelle in argument 10 10
1509 $2 Minnie Mouse and Donald Duck reading baseball rules .. .. 1·75 2·50
1510 $3 Ludwig von Drake as umpire with Goofy and Pete colliding .. .. .. 2·25 3·00
1503/10 .. .. *Set of* 8 4·00 5·50
MS1511 Two sheets, each 126×101 mm. (a) $5 Donald Duck striking ball. (b) $5 Minnie and Mickey Mouse running between bases. P 14×13½ .. .. *Set of* 2 *sheets* 11·00 13·00

(Litho Questa)

1986 (1 July). *Royal Wedding. Vert designs as T* **213** *of Antigua. Multicoloured. P* 14.
1512 2 c. Prince Andrew and Miss Sarah Ferguson 10 15
1513 $1.10, Prince Andrew 70 80
1514 $4 Prince Andrew with H.M.S. *Brazen's* Westland WG-13 Lynx helicopter .. 2·50 3·25
1512/14 .. .. *Set of* 3 3·00 3·75
MS1515 88×88 mm. $5 Prince Andrew and Miss Sarah Ferguson (*different*) .. .. .. 4·00 5·00

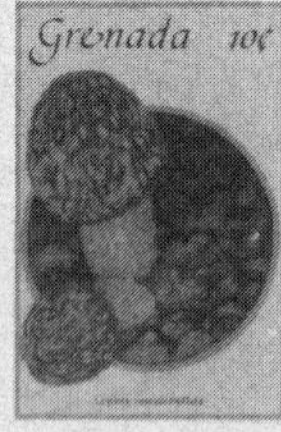

316 Brown-lined Latirus **317** *Lepiota roseolamellata*

(Des L. Birmingham. Litho Format)

1986 (15 July). *Sea Shells. T* **316** *and similar horiz designs. Multicoloured. P* 15.
1516 25 c. Type 316 .. .. 45 25
1517 60 c. Lamellose Wentletrap 75 90
1518 70 c. Atlantic Turkey Wing .. .. .. 85 1·00
1519 $4 Rooster-tail Conch .. .. .. 2·75 5·00
1516/19 .. .. *Set of* 4 4·25 6·50
MS1520 110×75 mm. $5 Angular Triton .. 3·50 5·50

(Des R. Sauber. Litho Format)

1986 (1 Aug). *Mushrooms. T* **317** *and similar vert designs. Multicoloured. P* 15.
1521 10 c. Type **317** 60 40
1522 60 c. *Lentinus bertieri* .. .. 1·75 1·75
1523 $1 *Lentinus retinervis* .. .. 2·50 2·50
1524 $4 *Eccilia cystiophorus* .. .. 5·75 7·50
1521/4 .. .. *Set of* 4 9·50 11·00
MS1525 127×100 mm. $5 *Cystolepiota eriophora* 10·00 13·00
No. MS1525 exists imperforate from stock dispersed by the liquidator of Format International Security Printers Ltd.

1986 (15 Sept). *World Cup Football Championship Winners, Mexico. Nos.* 1489/93 *optd with T* **216** *of Antigua in gold*.
1526 50 c. Type **315** 85 85
1527 70 c. Player heading ball .. .. 1·00 1·00
1528 90 c. Player controlling ball .. .. .. 1·40 1·60
1529 $4 Player controlling ball with right foot 4·50 5·00
1526/9 .. .. *Set of* 4 7·00 7·75
MS1530 101×71 mm. $5 Player tackling .. 3·50 4·50

318 Dove on Rifles and Mahatma Gandhi (Disarmament Week) **319** Cockerel and Hen

(Des Mary Walters. Litho Format)

1986 (15 Sept). *International Events. T* **318** *and similar multicoloured design. P* 15.
1531 60 c. Type **318** 50 50
1532 $4 Hands passing olive branch and Martin Luther King (International Peace Year) (*horiz*) .. .. 1·50 3·00
Nos. 1531/2 exist imperforate from stock dispersed by the liquidator of Format International Security Printers Ltd.

1986 (15 Oct). *Appearance of Halley's Comet (2nd issue). Nos.* 1494/8 *optd with T* **218** *of Antigua (in silver on $5)*.
1533 5 c. Clyde Tombaugh (astronomer) and Dudley Observatory, New York .. 60 60
1534 20 c. N.A.S.A.—U.S.A.F. "X-24B" Space Shuttle prototype, 1973 .. .. 85 60
1535 40 c. German comet medal, 1618 .. .. 1·25 70
1536 $4 Destruction of Sodom and Gomorrah, 1949 B.C. .. .. 5·00 7·00
1533/6 .. .. *Set of* 4 7·00 8·00
MS1537 102×70 mm. $5 Halley's Comet over Grenada .. .. 3·50 4·25

(Des Walt Disney Co. Litho Format)

1986 (3 Nov). *Christmas. Multicoloured designs as T* **220** *of Antigua showing Walt Disney cartoon characters. P* 11.
1538 30 c. Mickey Mouse asleep in armchair (*vert*) 35 25
1539 45 c. Young Mickey Mouse with Father Christmas (*vert*) 45 30
1540 60 c. Donald Duck with toy telephone .. 60 50
1541 70 c. Pluto with pushcart 70 70
1542 $1.10, Daisy Duck with doll .. .. 1·00 1·25
1543 $2 Goofy as Father Christmas (*vert*) .. 1·75 2·00
1544 $2.50, Goofy singing carols at piano (*vert*) 2·00 2·50
1545 $3 Mickey Mouse, Donald Duck and nephew riding toy train .. .. .. 2·25 3·00
1538/45 .. .. *Set of* 8 8·00 9·50
MS1546 Two sheets, each 127×101 mm. (a) $5 Donald Duck, Goofy and Mickey Mouse delivering presents (*vert*). P 13½×14. (b) $5 Father Christmas playing toy piano. P 14×13½ *Set of* 2 *sheets* 6·50 9·00

(Litho Questa)

1986 (17 Nov). *Fauna and Flora. T* **319** *and similar horiz designs. Multicoloured. P* 14.
1547 10 c. Type **319** 20 10
1548 30 c. Fish-eating Bat 35 20
1549 60 c. Goat 55 45
1550 70 c. Cow 60 5
1551 $1 Anthurium .. .. 1·50 1·2
1552 $1.10, Royal Poinciana .. .. .. 1·50 1·2
1553 $2 Frangipani .. .. 2·50 3·2
1554 $4 Orchid .. .. 8·50 9·5
1547/54 .. .. *Set of* 8 14·00 15·0
MS1555 Two sheets, each 104×73 mm. (a) $5 Grenada landscape. (b) $5 Horse *Set of* 2 *sheets* 12·00 13·0

320 Maserati "Biturbo" (1984) **321** Pole Vaulting

(Des J. Martin. Litho Format)

1986 (20 Nov). *Centenary of Motoring. T* **320** *and similar hori[z] designs. Multicoloured. P* 15.
1556 10 c. Type **320** 25 2
1557 30 c. AC "Cobra" (1960) 40 4
1558 60 c. Corvette (1963) 60 6
1559 70 c. Dusenberg "SJ7" (1932) 70 7
1560 90 c. Porsche (1957) .. .. 85 1·0
1561 $1.10, Stoewer (1930) .. .. .. 1·00 1·2
1562 $2 Volkswagen "Beetle" (1957) .. .. 1·60 2·0
1563 $3 Mercedes "600 Limo" (1963) .. .. 1·90 2·5
1556/63 .. .. *Set of* 8 6·50 8·0
MS1564 Two sheets, each 106 × 77 mm. (a) $5 Stutz (1914). (b) $5 Packard (1941) *Set of* 2 *sheets* 5·50 7·0

(Des BG Studio. Litho Format)

1986 (1 Dec). *Olympic Games, Seoul, South Korea* (1988). *T* **321** *and similar vert designs. Multicoloured. P* 15.
1565 10 c.+5 c. Type **321** 10 3
1566 50 c.+20 c. Gymnastics 35 6
1567 70 c.+30 c. Putting the shot 50 8
1568 $2+$1 High jumping .. .. .. 1·00 2·2
1565/8 .. .. *Set of* 4 1·75 3·5
MS1569 80 × 100 mm. $3 + $1 Swimming .. 2·00 3·2
The premiums on Nos. 1565/9 were to support the participation of the Grenada team.
Nos. 1565/8 exist imperforate from stock dispersed by the liquidator of Format International Security Printers Ltd.

(Litho Questa)

1986 (19 Dec). *Birth Centenary of Marc Chagall (artist). Designs as T* **225** *of Antigua, showing various paintings. P* 13½×14 (*vert*) *or* 14×13½ (*horiz*).
1570/1609 $1×40 multicoloured .. *Set of* 40 24·00 26·0
MS1610 Ten sheets, each 110×95 mm. $5×10 multicoloured (*each* 104×89 *mm*). Imperf *Set of* 10 *sheets* 24·00 26·0
Although announced as all being released on 19 December 1986 the issue was distributed in ten parts, each of four stamps and one miniature sheet, at monthly intervals.

(Des J. Iskowitz. Litho Format)

1987 (5 Feb). *America's Cup Yachting Championship. Vert designs as T* **222** *of Antigua. Multicoloured. P* 15.
1611 10 c. *Columbia*, 1958 .. .. 25 20
1612 60 c. *Resolute*, 1920 .. .. 55 60
1613 $1.10, *Endeavor*, 1934 .. .. .. 1·00 1·25
1614 $4 *Rainbow*, 1934 .. .. 2·25 3·50
1611/14 .. .. *Set of* 4 3·50 5·00
MS1615 113×84 mm. $5 *Weatherly*, 1962 .. 2·25 4·0

322 Virgin Mary and Outline Map of Grenada **323** Black Grouper

(Des G. Hamilton (10, 30, 50 c.), Mary Walters (others). Litho Format)

1987 (27 Apr). *500th Anniv of Discovery of America by Columbus (1992) (1st issue). T* **322** *and similar multicoloured designs. P* 15.
1616 10 c. Type **322** 20 20
1617 30 c. *Santa Maria, Pinta* and *Nina* (*horiz*) .. 60 35
1618 50 c. Columbus and outline map of Grenada 70 45
1619 60 c. Christopher Columbus 70 55
1620 90 c. King Ferdinand and Queen Isabella of Spain (*horiz*) 70 80
1621 $1.10, Map of Antilles by Columbus .. 1·10 1·00
1622 $2 Caribs with sailing raft (*horiz*) .. 1·40 2·25
1623 $3 Columbus in the New World, 1493 (contemporary drawing) .. .. 1·75 2·25
1616/23 .. .. *Set of* 8 6·50 7·00
MS1624 Two sheets, each 104×72 mm. (a) $5 Route map and Columbus' signature. (b) $5 Columbus carrying Christ Child *Set of* 2 *sheets* 6·00 7·50
Nos. 1616/23 exist imperforate from stock dispersed by the liquidator of Format International Security Printers Ltd.
See also Nos. 2051/5, 2091/9, 2222/30, 2389/95 and 2423/4.

(Des W. Wright. Litho Questa)

987 (18 May). *Milestones of Transportation. Horiz designs as T* **226** *of Antigua. Multicoloured. P* 14.

525 10 c. Cornu's first helicopter, 1907 .. 55 55
526 16 c. *Monitor* and *Merrimack* (first battle between ironclad warships), 1862 .. 60 60
527 30 c. LZ1 (first Zeppelin), 1900 .. 80 80
528 50 c. *Sirius* (first transatlantic paddle-steamer crossing), 1838 .. 85 85
529 60 c. Steam locomotive on Trans-Siberian Railway (longest line) .. 1·00 1·00
530 70 c. U.S.S. *Enterprise* (largest aircraft carrier), 1960 .. 1·25 1·25
531 90 c. Blanchard and Jeffries' balloon (first balloon across English Channel), 1785 1·40 1·40
532 $1.50, U.S.S. *Holland I* (first steam-powered submarine), 1900 .. 2·00 2·00
533 $2 *Oceanic I* (first luxury liner), 1871 2·50 2·50
534 $3 Lamborghini "Countach" (fastest commercial car), 1984 .. 2·75 2·75
525/34 .. *Set of* 10 12·00 12·00

(Des J. Martin. Litho Format)

987 (15 June). *"Capex '87" International Stamp Exhibition, Toronto. Game Fishes. T* **323** *and similar multicoloured designs. P* 15.

635 10 c. Type **323** .. 30 15
636 30 c. Blue Marlin (*horiz*) .. 40 15
637 60 c. White Marlin .. 60 55
638 70 c. Bigeye Threshershark (*horiz*) .. 70 70
639 $1 Bonefish (*horiz*) .. 90 1·00
640 $1.10, Wahoo (*horiz*) .. 1·00 1·25
641 $2 Sailfish (*horiz*) .. 1·75 2·25
642 $4 Albacore (*horiz*) .. 2·75 3·50
635/42 .. *Set of* 8 7·50 8·50
MS1643 Two sheets, each 100×70 mm. (a) $5 Yellow-finned Tuna. (b) $5 Great Barracuda (*horiz*) .. *Set of* 2 *sheets* 6·00 8·00

(Litho Questa)

987 (5 Aug). *Centenary of Statue of Liberty* (1986) (*2nd issue*). *Multicoloured designs as T* **227** *of Antigua. P* 14.

644 10 c. Computer projections of Statue and base (*horiz*) .. 15 15
645 25 c. Statue and fireworks (*horiz*) .. 20 15
646 50 c. Statue and fireworks (*different*) (*horiz*) 35 35
647 60 c. Statue and boats .. 45 45
648 70 c. Computer projections of top of Statue (*horiz*) .. 50 50
649 $1 Rear view of Statue and fireworks .. 80 80
650 $1.10, Aerial view of Statue .. 95 1·25
651 $2 Statue and flotilla .. 2·00 2·25
652 $4 *Queen Elizabeth 2* in New York Harbour .. 3·50 4·00
644/52 .. *Set of* 9 8·00 9·00

324 Alice and the Rabbit Hole

(Des Walt Disney Co. Litho Questa)

987 (9 Sept). *50th Anniv of First Full-Length Disney Cartoon Film. T* **324** *and similar designs. P* 14 × 13½.

653/1706 30 c. × 54 multicoloured *Set of* 54 15·00 16·00
MS1707 Six sheets, each 127 × 102 mm. $5 × 6 multicoloured. P 13½ × 14 (*vert*) or 14 × 13½ (*horiz*) .. *Set of* 6 *sheets* 30·00 30·00

Nos. 1653/1706 (issued as six sheetlets each of nine different designs) and No. **MS**1707 depict scenes from *Alice in Wonderland, Cinderella, Peter Pan, Pinocchio, Sleeping Beauty* and *Snow White and the Seven Dwarfs*.

325 Isaac Newton holding Apple (Law of Gravity)

(Litho Questa)

1987 (9 Sept). *Great Scientific Discoveries. T* **325** *and similar horiz designs. Multicoloured. P* 14.

1708 50 c. Type **325** .. 85 85
1709 $1.10, John Jacob Berzelius and symbols of chemical elements .. 1·75 1·75
1710 $2 Robert Boyle (law of Pressure and Volume) .. 2·50 3·00
1711 $3 James Watt and drawing of steam engine .. 3·75 4·25
1708/11 .. *Set of* 4 8·00 9·00
MS1712 105×75 mm. $5 *Voyager* (experimental aircraft) and Wright glider No. IV .. 3·00 4·00

No. 1711 is inscribed "RUDOLF DIESEL" and No. **MS**1712 "Flyer I", both in error.

326 Wade Boggs (Boston Red Sox)

International Social Security Association

(**327**)

(Des W. Storozuk. Litho Questa)

1987 (2 Nov). *All-Star Baseball Game, Oakland, California. Sheet* 114 × 82 *mm, containing T* **326** *and similar horiz design. Multicoloured. P* 14 × 13½.

MS1713 $1 Type **326**; $1 Eric Davis (Cincinnati Reds) .. 75 1·50

1987 (2 Nov). *60th Anniv of International Social Security Association. Nos.* 1413A, 1418A *and* 1423A *optd with T* **327**.

1714 10 c. Hibiscus .. 10 15
1715 50 c. Amaryllis .. 25 35
1716 $3 Shrimp Plant .. 1·40 2·25
1714/16 .. *Set of* 3 1·50 2·50

(Litho Questa)

1987 (2 Nov). *Bicentenary of U.S. Constitution. Multicoloured designs as T* **232** *of Antigua. P* 14.

1717 15 c. Independence Hall, Philadelphia (*vert*) 10 10
1718 50 c. Benjamin Franklin (Pennsylvania delegate) (*vert*) .. 25 35
1719 60 c. State Seal, Massachusetts .. 25 35
1720 $4 Robert Morris (Pennsylvania delegate) (*vert*) .. 1·75 2·75
1717/20 .. *Set of* 4 2·10 3·25
MS1721 105 × 75 mm. $5 James Madison (Virginia delegate) (*vert*) .. 2·00 3·50

Nos. 1717/20 were each issued in sheetlets of five stamps and one stamp-size label, which appears in the centre of the bottom row.

328 Goofy in "The Shadow"

329 "The Annunciation" (Fra Angelico)

(Des Walt Disney Co. Litho Questa)

1987 (16 Nov). *"Hafnia '87" International Stamp Exhibition, Copenhagen. T* **328** *and similar vert designs showing Walt Disney cartoon characters in scenes from Hans Christian Andersen's fairy tales. Multicoloured. P* 13½ × 14.

1722 25 c. Type **328** .. 50 30
1723 30 c. Mother Stork and brood in "The Storks" .. 50 30
1724 50 c. King Richard, Robin Hood and Little John (from *Robin Hood*) in "The Emperor's New Clothes" .. 75 55
1725 60 c. Goofy and Pluto in "The Tinderbox" .. 75 55
1726 70 c. Daisy and Donald Duck in "The Shepherdess and the Chimney Sweep" .. 80 70
1727 $1.50, Mickey and Minnie Mouse in "The Little Mermaid" .. 1·60 1·75
1728 $3 Clarabelle and Goofy in "The Princess and the Pea" .. 2·50 3·50
1729 $4 Minnie Mouse and Pegleg Pete in "The Marsh King's Daughter" .. 2·50 3·50
1722/9 .. *Set of* 8 9·00 10·00
MS1730 Two sheets, each 127 × 102 mm. (a) $5 Goofy in "The Flying Trunk". (b) $5 Goofy as "The Sandman" .. *Set of* 2 *sheets* 11·00 13·00

(Litho Questa)

1987 (15 Dec). *Christmas. T* **329** *and similar vert designs showing religious paintings. Multicoloured. P* 14.

1731 15 c. Type **329** .. 55 10
1732 30 c. "The Annunciation" (attr. Hubert van Eyck) .. 90 30
1733 60 c. "The Adoration of the Magi" (Januarius Zick) .. 1·75 1·40
1734 $4 "The Flight into Egypt" (Gerard David) 5·50 7·00
1731/4 .. *Set of* 4 8·00 8·00
MS1735 99 × 75 mm. $5 "The Circumcision" (Giovanni Bellini studio) .. 7·00 8·00

330 T. Albert Marryshow

(Litho Questa)

1988 (22 Jan). *Birth Centenary of T. Albert Marryshow (nationalist). P* 14.

1736 **330** 25 c. reddish brown, chestnut & brt crim 30 30

(Des and litho Questa)

1988 (15 Feb). *Royal Ruby Wedding. Vert designs as T* **234** *of Antigua. Multicoloured. P* 14.

1737 15 c. deep brown, black and bright new blue 35 10
1738 50 c. multicoloured .. 70 50
1739 $1 deep brown and black .. 1·25 2·00
1740 $4 multicoloured .. 3·00 4·00
1737/40 .. *Set of* 4 4·75 6·00
MS1741 76 × 100 mm. $5 multicoloured .. 2·25 3·25

Designs:—15 c. Wedding photograph, 1947; 50 c. Queen Elizabeth II with Prince Charles and Princess Anne, *c.* 1955; $1 Queen with Princess Anne, *c.* 1957; $4 Queen Elizabeth (from photo by Tim Graham), 1980; $5 Princess Elizabeth in wedding dress, 1947.

331 Goofy and Daisy Duck lighting Olympic Torch, Olympia

332 Scout fishing from Boat

(Des Walt Disney Company. Litho Questa)

1988 (13 Apr). *Olympic Games, Seoul. T* **331** *and similar vert designs showing Walt Disney cartoon characters. Multicoloured. P* 13½×14.

1742 1 c. Type **331** .. 10 10
1743 2 c. Donald and Daisy Duck carrying Olympic torch .. 10 10
1744 3 c. Donald Duck, Goofy and Mickey Mouse carrying flags of U.S., Korea and Spain .. 10 10
1745 4 c. Donald Duck releasing doves .. 10 10
1746 5 c. Mickey Mouse flying with rocket belt 10 10
1747 10 c. Morty and Ferdie carrying banner with Olympic motto .. 10 10
1748 $6 Donald Duck, Minnie Mouse and Hodori the Tiger (mascot of Seoul Games) .. 4·75 5·00
1749 $7 Pluto, Hodori and old post office, Seoul 4·75 5·00
1742/9 .. *Set of* 8 9·00 9·50
MS1750 Two sheets, each 127×101 mm. (a) $5 Mickey Mouse taking athlete's oath. (b) $5 Donald and Daisy Duck as athletes at Closing Ceremony .. *Set of* 2 *sheets* 8·50 9·50

1988 (19 Apr). *Stamp Exhibitions. Nos.* 1631/4 *optd as T* **241** *of Antigua with various emblems.*

1751 90 c. Blanchard and Jefferies' balloon, 1785 (optd "OLYMPHILEX '88", Seoul) .. 75 85
1752 $1.50, U.S.S. *Holland I*, 1900 (optd "INDEPENDENCE 40", Israel) .. 1·00 1·25
1753 $2 *Oceanic I*, 1871 (optd "FINLANDIA 88", Helsinki) .. 1·40 1·75
1754 $3 Lamborghini "Countach", 1984 (optd "Praga 99", Prague) .. 1·90 2·25
1751/4 .. *Set of* 4 4·50 5·50

(Des J. Martin. Litho Questa)

1988 (3 May). *World Scout Jamboree, Australia. T* **332** *and similar multicoloured designs. P* 14.

1755 20 c. Type **332** .. 40 15
1756 70 c. Scouts hiking through forest (*horiz*) .. 1·00 1·00
1757 90 c. Practicing first aid (*horiz*) .. 1·40 1·40
1758 $3 Shooting rapids in inflatable canoe .. 3·00 3·75
1755/8 .. *Set of* 4 5·25 5·75
MS1759 114×80 mm. $5 Scout with Koala .. 2·10 3·00

333 *Santa Maria de Guia* (Columbus), 1498, and Map of Rotary District

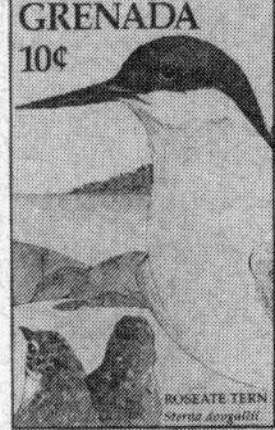

334 Roseate Tern

(Des W. Hanson. Litho Questa)

1988 (5 May). *Rotary District* 405 *Conference, St. George's. T* **333** *and similar multicoloured design. P* 13½×14.
1760 $2 Type **333** .. .. 1·00 1·25
MS1761 133×90 mm. $10 Rotary emblem (*horiz*). P 14×13½ .. .. 4·25 5·50

(Des Mary Walters. Litho Questa)

1988 (31 May). *Birds. T* **334** *and similar vert designs. Multicoloured. P* 14.
1762 10 c. Type **334** 50 20
1763 25 c. Laughing Gull 65 25
1764 50 c. Osprey .. .. 1·00 60
1765 60 c. Rose-breasted Grosbeak .. .. 1·00 60
1766 90 c. Purple Gallinule .. .. .. 1·00 90
1767 $1.10, White-tailed Tropic Bird .. .. 1·00 1·00
1768 $3 Blue-faced Booby .. .. .. 1·75 2·50
1769 $4 Common Shoveler .. .. .. 1·90 2·75
1762/9 .. .. *Set of* 8 8·00 8·00
MS1770 Two sheets, each 100×71 mm. (a) $5 Belted Kingfisher. (b) $5 Grenada Flycatcher ("Rusty-tailed Flycatcher") .. *Set of* 2 *sheets* 7·00 8·50

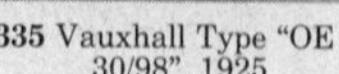
335 Vauxhall Type "OE 30/98", 1925

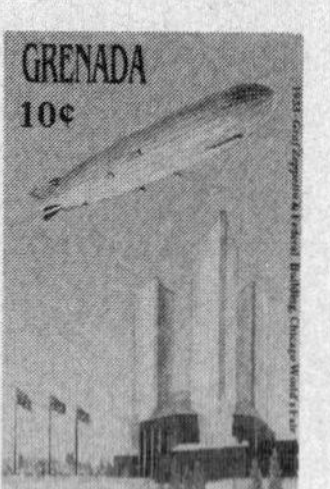

336 LZ-127 *Graf Zeppelin* over Chicago World's Fair, 1933

(Des W. Wright. Litho B.D.T.)

1988 (1 June). *Cars. T* **335** *and similar vert designs. Multicoloured. P* 13.
1771 $2 Type **335** .. .. 1·00 1·25
a. Sheetlet. Nos. 1771/80 .. .. 9·00
1772 $2 Wills "Sainte Claire", 1926 .. .. 1·00 1·25
1773 $2 Bucciali, 1928 .. .. .. 1·00 1·25
1774 $2 Irving Napier "Golden Arrow", 1929 1·00 1·25
1775 $2 Studebaker "President", 1930 .. 1·00 1·25
1776 $2 Thomas "Flyer", 1907 .. .. 1·00 1·25
1777 $2 Isotta-Fraschini "Tipo J", 1908 .. 1·00 1·25
1778 $2 Fiat 10/14HP, 1910 .. .. .. 1·00 1·25
1779 $2 Mercer "Type 35 Raceabout", 1911 .. 1·00 1·25
1780 $2 Marmon "Model 34 Cloverleaf", 1917 1·00 1·25
1781 $2 Tatra "Type 77", 1934 .. .. 1·00 1·25
a. Sheetlet. Nos. 1781/90 .. .. 9·00
1782 $2 Rolls-Royce "Phantom III", 1938 .. 1·00 1·25
1783 $2 Studebaker "Champion Starlight", 1947 .. .. 1·00 1·25
1784 $2 Porsche "Gmund", 1948 .. .. 1·00 1·25
1785 $2 Tucker, 1948 .. .. .. 1·00 1·25
1786 $2 Peerless "V-16", 1931 .. .. 1·00 1·25
1787 $2 Minerva "AL", 1931 .. .. .. 1·00 1·25
1788 $2 Reo "Royale", 1933 .. .. .. 1·00 1·25
1789 $2 Pierce Arrow "Silver Arrow", 1933 .. 1·00 1·25
1790 $2 Hupmobile "Aerodynamic", 1934 .. 1·00 1·25
1791 $2 Peugeot "404", 1965 .. .. .. 1·00 1·25
a. Sheetlet. Nos. 1791/1800 .. .. 9·00
1792 $2 Ford "Capri", 1969 .. .. .. 1·00 1·25
1793 $2 Ferrari "312T", 1975 .. .. 1·00 1·25
1794 $2 Lotus "T-79", 1978 .. .. .. 1·00 1·25
1795 $2 Williams-Cosworth "FW07", 1979 .. 1·00 1·25
1796 $2 H.R.G. "1500 Sports", 1948 .. .. 1·00 1·25
1797 $2 Crosley "Hotshot", 1949 .. .. 1·00 1·25
1798 $2 Volvo "PV444", 1955 .. .. 1·00 1·25
1799 $2 Maserati "Tipo 61", 1960 .. .. 1·00 1·25
1800 $2 Saab "96", 1963 .. .. .. 1·00 1·25
1771/1800 .. .. .. *Set of* 30 27·00 30·00
Nos. 1771/80, 1781/90 and 1791/1800 were each printed together, *se-tenant*, in sheetlets of 10.

(Litho Questa)

1988 (15 June). 500*th Birth Anniv of Titian (artist). Multicoloured designs as T* **238** *of Antigua. P* 13½×14.
1801 10 c. "Lavinia Vecellio" 10 10
1802 20 c. "Portrait of a Man" 10 10
1803 25 c. "Andrea de Franceschi" 10 15
1804 90 c. "Head of a Soldier" 40 45
1805 $1 "Man with a Flute" 45 50
1806 $2 "Lucrezia and Tarquinius" .. .. 80 1·00
1807 $3 "Duke of Mantua with Dog" .. .. 1·25 1·60
1808 $4 "La Bella di Tiziano" .. .. .. 1·60 2·00
1801/8 .. .. *Set of* 8 4·25 5·25
MS1809 Two sheets, each 110×95 mm. (a) $5 "Allegory of Alfonso D'Avalos (detail). P 13½×14. (b) $5 "Fall of Man" (detail) (*horiz*). P 14×13½ .. .. .. *Set of* 2 *sheets* 4·25 5·50

(Des W. Hanson. Litho Questa)

1988 (1 July). *Airships. T* **336** *and similar multicoloured designs. P* 14.
1810 10 c. Type **336** 20 20
1811 15 c. LZ-1 over Lake Constance, 1901 (*horiz*) 25 25
1812 25 c. *Washington* (balloon) and *George Washington Curtis* (balloon barge), 1862 .. .. 30 30
1813 45 c. LZ-129 *Hindenburg* and Maybach "Zeppelin" car (*horiz*) 40 40
1814 50 c. Goodyear Aerospace airship in Statue of Liberty Centenary Race, 1986 .. 40 40
1815 60 c. LZ-129 *Hindenburg* over Statue of Liberty, 1937 (*horiz*) 50 50
1816 90 c. Heinkel biplane docking experiment with LZ-129 *Hindenburg*, 1936 (*horiz*) 80 80
1817 $2 LZ-129 *Hindenburg* over Olympic Stadium, Berlin, 1936 .. .. .. 1·60 1·60
1818 $3 LZ-129 *Hindenburg* over Christ of the Andes Monument, 1937 .. .. .. 2·00 2·00
1819 $4 LZ-129 *Hindenburg* and *Bremen* (liner), 1936 (*horiz*) .. .. .. 2·25 2·25
1810/19 .. .. *Set of* 10 8·00 8·00
MS1820 (a) 75×95 mm. $5 LZ-127 *Graf Zeppelin*, 1930 (*horiz*). (b) 95×75 mm. $5 LZ-129 *Hindenburg*, 1935 (*horiz*) .. *Set of* 2 *sheets* 4·75 5·50

337 Tasmanian Wolf, Mickey Mouse and Pluto

338 Pineapple

(Des Walt Disney Co. Litho Questa)

1988 (1 Aug). *"Sydpex '88" National Stamp Exhibition, Sydney and* 60*th Birthday of Mickey Mouse. T* **337** *and similar horiz designs. Multicoloured. P* 14×13½.
1821 1 c. Type **337** 10 10
1822 2 c. Mickey Mouse feeding wallabies .. 10 10
1823 3 c. Mickey Mouse and Goofy with kangaroo 10 10
1824 4 c. Mickey and Minnie Mouse riding emus 10 10
1825 5 c. Mickey and Minnie Mouse with wombat 10 10
1826 10 c. Mickey Mouse and Donald Duck watching platypus 10 10
1827 $5 Mickey Mouse and Goofy photographing Blue-winged Kookaburra 4·50 5·00
1828 $6 Mickey Mouse and Koala on map of Australia .. .. 4·50 5·00
1821/8 .. .. *Set of* 8 8·50 9·50
MS1829 Two sheets, each 127×102 mm. (a) $5 Mickey Mouse with birthday cake. (b) $5 Mickey and Minnie Mouse with Rainbow Lories *Set of* 2 *sheets* 8·50 11·00

(Des J. Martin. Litho Questa)

1988 (11 Aug). 10*th Anniv of International Fund for Agricultural Development. T* **338** *and similar multicoloured designs. P* 14.
1830 25 c. Type **338** 25 15
1831 75 c. Bananas 60 60
1832 $3 Mace and nutmeg (*horiz*) .. .. 2·00 2·75
1830/2 .. .. *Set of* 3 2·50 3·25

339 Lignum Vitae

(Des W. Wright. Litho Questa)

1988 (30 Sept). *Flowering Trees and Shrubs. T* **339** *and similar horiz designs. Multicoloured. P* 14.
1833 15 c. Type **339** 15 15
1834 25 c. Saman 20 15
1835 35 c. Red Frangipani 25 20
1836 45 c. Flowering Maple 30 25
1837 60 c. Yellow Poui 40 40
1838 $1 Wild Chestnut 60 70
1839 $3 Mountain Immortelle .. .. .. 1·50 2·25
1840 $4 Queen of Flowers .. .. .. 1·75 2·50
1833/40 .. .. *Set of* 8 4·50 6·00
MS1841 Two sheets, each 117 × 88 mm. (a) $5 Flamboyant. (b) $5 Orchid Tree .. *Set of* 2 *sheets* 4·25 5·50

340 Mickey Mantle (New York Yankees)

(Des Rosemary De Figlio. Litho Questa)

1988 (28 Nov). *Major League Baseball Players (1st series). T* **340** *and similar horiz designs showing portraits or league emblems. P* 14 × 13½.
1842/1922 30 c. × 81 multicoloured .. *Set of* 81 8·75 9·50
Nos. 1842/1922 were issued as nine sheetlets, each of nine different designs.
One sheetlet was subsequently reissued with the Pete Rose stamp replaced by a label inscribed "U.S. BASEBALL SERIES I".

(Des Walt Disney Co. Litho Questa)

1988 (1 Dec). *Christmas. "Mickey's Christmas Eve". Vert designs as T* **246** *of Antigua showing Walt Disney cartoon characters. Multicoloured. P* 13½ × 14.
1923 $1 Donald Duck's nephew on mantelpiece 65 65
a. Sheetlet. Nos. 1923/30 .. .. 4·75
1924 $1 Goofy with string of popcorn .. 65 65
1925 $1 Chip n' Dale decorating Christmas tree 65 65
1926 $1 Father Christmas in sleigh 65 65
1927 $1 Donald's nephew with stocking .. 65 65
1928 $1 Donald's nephew unpacking Xmas decorations 65 65
1929 $1 Donald Duck with present 65 65
1930 $1 Mickey Mouse with present 65 65
1923/90 .. .. *Set of* 8 4·75 4·75
MS1931 Two sheets, each 127×102 mm. (a) $5 Ferdie leaving drink for Father Christmas. (b) $5 Mordie and Ferdie asleep .. *Set of* 2 *sheets* 7·00 8·50
Nos. 1923/30 were printed together, *se-tenant*, in a sheetlet of eight forming a composite design.

341 Tina Turner

342 Atlantic Railway No. 2, 1889, Canada

(Litho Questa)

1988 (5 Dec). *Entertainers. T* **341** *and similar vert designs. Multicoloured. P* 14.
1932 10 c. Type **341** 25 20
1933 25 c. Lionel Ritchie 25 20
1934 45 c. Whitney Houston 35 30
1935 60 c. Joan Armatrading 50 45
1936 75 c. Madonna 70 60
1937 $1 Elton John .. .. 1·00 80
1938 $3 Bruce Springsteen .. .. .. 2·00 2·75
1939 $4 Bob Marley .. .. 3·00 3·50
1932/9 .. .. *Set of* 8 7·25 8·00
MS1940 115×155 mm. 55 c.×2 Yoko Minamino; $1×2 Yoko Minamino (*different*) .. .. 1·90 2·75
No. 1935 is incorrectly inscribed "JOAN AMMERTRADING".

(Des T. Hadley and W. Wright. Litho B.D.T.)

1989 (23 Jan). *North American Railway Locomotives. T* **342** *and similar vert designs. Multicoloured. P* 13.
1941 $2 Type **342** .. .. 1·25 1·25
a. Sheetlet. Nos. 1941/50 .. .. 11·00
1942 $2 Virginia & Truckee Railroad "J. W. Bowker" type, 1875, U.S.A. .. .. 1·25 1·25
1943 $2 Philadelphia & Reading Railway *Ariel*, 1872, U.S.A. .. .. .. 1·25 1·25
1944 $2 Chicago & Rock Island Railroad "America" type, 1867, U.S.A. .. 1·25 1·25
1945 $2 Lehigh Valley Railroad Consolidation No. 63, 1866, U.S.A. .. .. 1·25 1·25
1946 $2 Great Western Railway *Scotia*, 1860, Canada .. .. 1·25 1·25
1947 $2 Grand Trunk Railway Class "Birkenhead", 1854, Canada .. .. 1·25 1·25
1948 $2 Camden & Amboy Railroad *Monster*, 1837, U.S.A. .. .. .. 1·25 1·25
1949 $2 Baltimore & Ohio Railroad Class "Grasshopper", 1834, U.S.A. .. 1·25 1·25
1950 $2 Peter Cooper's *Tom Thumb*, 1829, Baltimore & Ohio Railroad, U.S.A. .. 1·25 1·25
1951 $2 United Railways of Yucatan *Yucatan*, 1925, Mexico .. .. .. 1·25 1·25
a. Sheetlet. Nos. 1951/60 .. .. 11·00
1952 $2 Canadian National Railways Class T2, 1924 .. .. 1·25 1·25
1953 $2 St. Louis–San Francisco Railroad Class "Light Mikado", 1919, U.S.A. .. 1·25 1·25
1954 $2 Atlantic Coast Line Railroad Class "Light Pacific", 1919, U.S.A. .. 1·25 1·25
1955 $2 Edaville Railroad No. 7, 1913, U.S.A. 1·25 1·25
1956 $2 Denver & Rio Grande Western Railroad Class K 27, 1903, U.S.A. .. .. 1·25 1·25
1957 $2 Pennsylvania Railroad Class E-2 No. 7002, 1902, U.S.A. .. .. .. 1·25 1·25
1958 $2 Pennsylvania Railroad Class H6, 1899, U.S.A. .. .. 1·25 1·25
1959 $2 John Jarvis's *De Witt Clinton*, 1831, Mohawk & Hudson Railroad, U.S.A. 1·25 1·25
1960 $2 St. Clair Tunnel Company locomotive No. 598, 1891, Canada .. .. 1·25 1·25
1961 $2 Chesapeake & Ohio Railroad Class M-1 steam turbine electric locomotive No. 500, 1947, U.S.A. .. .. .. 1·25 1·25
a. Sheetlet. Nos. 1961/70 .. .. 11·00
1962 $2 Rutland Railroad steam locomotive No. 93, 1946, U.S.A. .. .. .. 1·25 1·25

63 $2 Pennsylvania Railroad Class T 1, 1942, U.S.A. . . 1·25 1·25
64 $2 Chesapeake & Ohio Railroad Class H-8, 1942, U.S.A. . . 1·25 1·25
65 $2 Atchison, Topeka & Santa Fe Railway Model FT diesel, 1941, U.S.A. . . 1·25 1·25
66 $2 Gulf, Mobile & Ohio Railroad Models S-1 and S-2 diesels, 1940, U.S.A. . . 1·25 1·25
67 $2 New York, New Haven & Hartford Railroad Class 15, 1937, U.S.A. . . 1·25 1·25
68 $2 Seaboard Air Line Railroad Class R, 1936, U.S.A. . . 1·25 1·25
69 $2 Newfoundland Railway Class R-2, 1930 1·25 1·25
70 $2 Canadian National Railway diesel No. 9000, 1928 . . 1·25 1·25
41/70 . . *Set of* 30 32·00 32·00

Nos. 1941/50, 1951/60 and 1961/70 were each printed gether, *se-tenant*, in sheetlets of 10.

343 Women's Long Jump (Jackie Joyner-Kersee, U.S.A.)

344 Nebulae

(Des L. Fried. Litho B.D.T.)

989 (6 Apr). *Olympic Gold Medal Winners, Seoul* (1988). *T* **343** *and similar vert designs. Multicoloured. P* 14.

971 10 c. Type **343** . . 20 20
972 25 c. Women's Singles Tennis (Steffi Graf, West Germany) . . 50 35
973 45 c. Men's 1500 metres (Peter Rono, Kenya) . . 60 40
974 75 c. Men's 1000 metres single kayak (Greg Barton, U.S.A.) . . 70 60
975 $1 Women's team foil (Italy) . . 85 75
976 $2 Women's 100 metres freestyle swimming (Kristin Otto, East Germany) . . 1·75 2·00
977 $3 Men's still rings gymnastics (Holger Behrendt, East Germany) . . 2·10 2·25
978 $4 Synchronized swimming pair (Japan) 2·40 2·50
971/8 . . *Set of* 8 8·25 8·25
IS1979 Two sheets, each 76×100 mm. (a) $6 Olympic flame. (b) $6 Runner with Olympic torch . . *Set of* 2 *sheets* 8·50 9·50

(Litho Questa)

989 (25 Apr). *Appearance of Halley's Comet* (1986) (3*rd issue*). *T* **344** *and similar horiz designs. P* 14.

980 25 c. + 5 c. multicoloured . . 40 50
981 75 c. + 5 c. black and turquoise-green . . 75 95
982 90 c. + 5 c. multicoloured . . 85 1·10
983 $2 + 5 c. multicoloured . . 1·25 1·75
980/3 . . *Set of* 4 2·75 3·75
MS1984 111×78 mm. $5 + 5 c. multicoloured. Imperf . . 3·00 4·00

Designs: (*As T* **344**)—75 c. + 5 c. Marine astronomical xperiments; 90 c. + 5 c. Moon's surface; $2 + 5 c. Edmond alley, Sir Isaac Newton and his book *Principia*. (102×69 nm)—$5 + 5 c. 17th-century warships and astrological signs.

(Litho Questa)

989 (15 May). *Japanese Art. Paintings by Hiroshige. Horiz designs as T* **250** *of Antigua. Multicoloured. P* 14×13½.

985 10 c. "Shinagawa on Edo Bay" . . 20 20
986 25 c. "Pine Trees on the Road to Totsuka" 30 30
987 60 c. "Kanagawa on Edo Bay" . . 50 50
988 75 c. "Crossing Banyu River to Hiratsuka" 55 55
989 $1 "Windy Shore at Odawara" . . 70 70
990 $2 "Snow-Covered Post Station of Mishima" . . 1·25 1·50
991 $3 "Full Moon at Fuchu" . . 1·60 1·75
992 $4 "Crossing the Stream at Okitsu" . . 2·25 2·50
985/92 . . *Set of* 8 6·50 7·25
MS1993 Two sheets, each 102×76 mm. (a) $5 "Mountain Pass at Nissaka". (b) $5 "Mt Uzu at Okabe" . . *Set of* 2 *sheets* 4·25 5·50

Nos. 1985/92 were each printed in sheetlets of 10 containing wo horizontal strips of 5 stamps separated by printed labels ommemorating Emperor Hirohito.

345 Great Blue Heron

(Des D. Bruckner. Litho Questa)

1989 (6 June)–**94**. *Birds. T* **345** *and similar multicoloured designs. P* 14.

1994 5 c. Type **345** . . 30 30
 a. Perf 11½×12½ (1993) . . 30 30
1995 10 c. Green Heron . . 30 30
 a. Perf 11½×12½ (1993) . . 30 30
1996 15 c. Turnstone . . 40 30
 a. Perf 11½×12½ (1993) . . 30 30
1997 25 c. Blue-winged Teal . . 40 20
 a. Perf 11½×12½ (1993) . . 30 20
1998 35 c. Little Ringed Plover (*vert*) . . 50 20
 a. Perf 12½×11½ (1993) . . 35 20
1999 45 c. Green-throated Carib ("Emerald-throated Hummingbird") (*vert*) . . 55 30
 a. Perf 12½×11½ (1993) . . 40 30
2000 50 c. Rufous-breasted Hermit (*vert*) . . 60 45
 a. Perf 12½×11½ (1993) . . 45 35
2001 60 c. Lesser Antillean Bull-finch (*vert*) . . 70 50
 a. Perf 12½×11½ (1993) . . 55 50
2002 75 c. Brown Pelican (*vert*) . . 80 65
 a. Perf 12½×11½ (1993) . . 60 60
2003 $1 Black-crowned Night Heron (*vert*) . . 1·00 90
 a. Perf 12½×11½ (1993) . . 80 80
2004 $3 American Kestrel ("Sparrow Hawk") (*vert*) . . 2·25 2·75
 a. Perf 12½×11½ (1993) . . 1·75 2·25
2005 $5 Barn Swallow (*vert*) . . 3·00 3·50
 a. Perf 12½×11½ (1993) . . 2·50 3·00
2006 $10 Red-billed Tropic Bird (*vert*) (13.11.89) 6·00 7·00
 a. Perf 12½×11½ (1993) . . 7·00 8·00
2007 $20 Barn Owl (*vert*) (22.1.90) . . 12·00 13·00
 a. Perf 12½×11½ (1994) . . 14·00 15·00
1994/2007 . . *Set of* 14 26·00 27·00
1994a/2007a . . *Set of* 14 26·00 28·00

Nos. 1994a/2007a show a larger perforation hole on every sixth perforation, both vertically and horizontally.

(Des D. Bruckner. Litho B.D.T.)

1989 (12 June). *World Cup Football Championship, Italy* (1990) (1*st issue*). *Vert designs as T* **252** *of Antigua. Multicoloured. P* 14.

2008 10 c. Scotland player . . 30 20
2009 25 c. England and Brazil players . . 40 30
2010 60 c. Paolo Rossi (Italy) . . 65 55
2011 75 c. Jairzinho (Brazil) . . 80 70
2012 $1 Sweden striker . . 1·00 90
2013 $2 Péle (Brazil) . . 2·00 2·00
2014 $3 Mario Kempes (Argentina) . . 2·75 2·75
2015 $4 Pat Jennings (Northern Ireland) . . 3·00 3·00
2008/15 . . *Set of* 8 10·00 9·50
MS2016 Two sheets. (a) 70×93 mm. $6 Players jumping for ball. (b) 82×71 mm. $6 Goalkeeper *Set of* 2 *sheets* 8·50 10·00

See also Nos. 2174/8 and **MS**2179.

346 Xebec and Sugar Cane

(Des T. Agans. Litho B.D.T.)

1989 (7 July). *"Philexfrance 89" International Stamp Exhibition, Paris. T* **346** *and similar horiz designs showing French sailing vessels and plantation crops. Multicoloured. P* 14.

2017 25 c. Type **346** . . 70 30
2018 75 c. Lugger and cotton . . 1·25 85
2019 $1 Full-rigged ship and cocoa . . 1·40 1·00
2020 $4 Ketch and coffee . . 3·50 5·00
2017/20 . . *Set of* 4 6·00 6·50
MS2021 114×70 mm. $6 "View of Fort and Town of St. George, 1779" (105×63 *mm*). Imperf . . 4·00 5·00

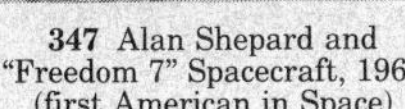

347 Alan Shepard and "Freedom 7" Spacecraft, 1961 (first American in Space)

348 *Hygrocybe occidentalis*

(Des L. Birmingham. Litho Questa)

1989 (20 July). *20th Anniv of First Manned Landing on Moon. T* **347** *and similar horiz designs. Multicoloured. P* 14.

2022 15 c. Type **347** . . 50 40
2023 35 c. "Friendship 7" spacecraft, 1962 (first manned earth orbit) . . 65 55
2024 45 c. "Apollo 8" orbiting Moon, 1968 (first manned lunar orbit) . . 75 65
2025 70 c. "Apollo 15" lunar rover, 1972 . . 1·00 85
2026 $1 "Apollo 11" emblem and lunar module *Eagle* on Moon, 1969 . . 1·25 1·10
2027 $2 "Gemini 8" and "Agena" rocket, 1966 (first space docking) . . 2·25 2·00
2028 $3 Edward White in space, 1965 (first U.S. space walk) . . 3·00 2·75
2029 $4 "Apollo 7" emblem . . 3·50 3·25
2022/9 . . *Set of* 8 11·50 10·50
MS2030 Two sheets, each 101×71 mm. (a) $5 Moon and track of "Apollo 11", 1969. (b) $5 Armstrong and Aldrin raising U.S. flag on Moon, 1969 . . *Set of* 2 *sheets* 8·00 8·00

(Des J. Cooter. Litho B.D.T.)

1989 (17 Aug). *Fungi. T* **348** *and similar vert designs. Multicoloured. P* 14.

2031 15 c. Type **348** . . 50 40
2032 40 c. *Marasmius haematocephalus* . . 65 55
2033 50 c. *Hygrocybe hypohaemacta* . . 75 65
2034 70 c. *Lepiota pseudoignicolor* . . 1·00 90
2035 90 c. *Cookeina tricholoma* . . 1·25 1·25
2036 $1.10, *Leucopaxillus gracillimus* . . 1·50 1·50
2037 $2.25, *Hygrocybe nigrescens* . . 2·75 3·00
2038 $4 *Clathrus crispus* . . 3·75 4·00
2031/8 . . *Set of* 8 11·00 11·00
MS2039 Two sheets, each 57×70 mm. (a) $6 *Mycena holoporphyra*. (b) $6 *Xeromphalina tenuipes* . . *Set of* 2 *sheets* 12·00 13·00

349 Y.W.C.A. Logo and Grenada Scenery

350 *Historis odius*

(Litho Questa)

1989 (11 Sept). *Centenary of Young Women's Christian Association. T* **349** *and similar multicoloured design. P* 14.

2040 50 c. Type **349** . . 45 45
2041 75 c. Y.W.C.A. logo and town (*horiz*) . . 80 80

(Des Deborah Dudley Max. Litho B.D.T.)

1989 (2 Oct). *Butterflies. T* **350** *and similar horiz designs. Multicoloured. P* 14.

2042 6 c. Type **350** . . 30 30
2043 30 c. *Marpesia petreus* . . 55 55
2044 40 c. *Danaus gilippus* . . 60 60
2045 60 c. *Dione juno* . . 80 80
2046 $1.10, *Agraulis vanillae* . . 1·25 1·25
2047 $1.25, *Danaus plexippus* . . 1·50 1·50
2048 $4 *Papilio androgeus* (inscr "*Battus polydamas*") . . 3·25 3·25
2049 $5 *Dryas julia* . . 3·25 3·25
2042/9 . . *Set of* 8 10·50 10·50
MS2050 Two sheets, each 87×115 mm. (a) $6 *Anartia jatrophae*. (b) $6 *Strymon simaethis* *Set of* 2 *sheets* 9·50 11·00

351 Amerindian Hieroglyph

352 Amos leaving Home

(Litho Questa)

1989 (16 Oct). 500*th Anniv of Discovery of America by Columbus* (1992) (2*nd issue*). *T* **351** *and similar vert designs showing different hieroglyphs. P* 14.

2051 45 c. brownish black, black and new blue 70 50
2052 60 c. brownish black, black & bright green 80 60
2053 $1 brownish black, black & dp reddish vio 1·25 1·00
2054 $4 brownish black, black & orange-brn 3·75 4·50
2051/4 . . *Set of* 4 6·00 6·00
MS2055 74×86 mm. $6 brownish black, black and vermilion . . 4·00 5·50

(Des Walt Disney Co. Litho Questa)

1989 (20 Nov). *"World Stamp Expo '89" International Stamp Exhibition, Washington. T* **352** *and similar multicoloured designs showing Walt Disney cartoon characters in scenes from* Ben and Me. *P* 14×13½.

2056 1 c. Type **352** . . 10 10
2057 2 c. Meeting of Benjamin Franklin and Amos . . 10 10
2058 3 c. The Franklin stove . . 10 10
2059 4 c. Ben and Amos with bi-focals . . 10 10
2060 5 c. Amos on page of *Pennsylvania Gazette* 10 10
2061 6 c. Ben working printing press . . 10 10
2062 10 c. Conducting experiment with electricity . . 10 10
2063 $5 Ben disembarking in England . . 5·00 5·50
2064 $6 Ben with Document of Agreement . . 5·50 6·00
2056/64 . . *Set of* 9 10·00 11·00
MS2065 Two sheets, each 127×101 mm. (a) $6 Benjamin Franklin teaching (*vert*). P 13½×14. (b) $6 Signatories of Declaration of Independence. P 14×13½ . . *Set of* 2 *sheets* 8·00 10·00

(Litho Questa)

1990 (4 Jan). *Christmas. Paintings by Rubens. Vert designs as T* **259** *of Antigua. Multicoloured. P* 14.
2066 20 c. "Christ in the House of Mary and Martha" 30 25
2067 35 c. "The Circumcision" 45 40
2068 60 c. "Trinity adored by Duke of Mantua and Family" 75 65
2069 $2 "Holy Family with St. Francis" .. 2·25 2·50
2070 $3 "The Ildefonso Altarpiece" .. 2·75 3·00
2071 $4 "Madonna and Child with Garland and Putti" .. .. .. 3·25 3·50
2066/71 .. .. *Set of* 6 8·75 9·25
MS2072 Two sheets, each 70×95 mm. (a) $5 "Adoration of the Magi". (b) $5 "Virgin and Child adored by Angels" .. .. *Set of* 2 *sheets* 7·50 9·00

353 Alexander Graham Bell and Early Telephone System (150th anniv of invention)

354 *Odontoglossum triumphans*

(Des J. Genzo. Litho B.D.T.)

1990 (12 Feb). *Anniversaries. T* **353** *and similar horiz designs. Multicoloured. P* 14.
2073 10 c. Type **353** 30 20
2074 25 c. George Washington and Capitol (bicent of presidential inauguration) 30 20
2075 35 c. Shakespeare and birthplace, Stratford (425th birth anniv) 50 30
2076 75 c. Nehru and Gandhi (birth cent of Nehru) .. .. 1·25 1·25
2077 $1 Dr. Hugo Eckener, Ferdinand von Zeppelin and LZ-127 *Graf Zeppelin* (80th anniv of first passenger Zeppelin) .. .. .. 1·25 1·25
2078 $2 Charlie Chaplin (birth cent) .. 2·25 2·25
2079 $3 Container ship in Hamburg Harbour (800th anniv) .. .. .. 2·50 3·00
2080 $4 Friedrich Ebert (first President) and Heidelberg gate (70th anniv of German Republic) .. .. 2·50 3·00
2073/80 .. .. *Set of* 8 9·75 10·50
MS2081 Two sheets, each 100×72 mm. (a) $6 13th-century ships in Hamburg Harbour (*vert*) (800th anniv). (b) $6 Concorde (20th anniv of first test flight) .. .. *Set of* 2 *sheets* 8·50 10·00
No. 2080 is inscribed "40th Anniversary of German Republic" in error.

(Des L. Nelson. Litho Questa)

1990 (6 Mar). *"EXPO 90" International Garden and Greenery Exhibition, Osaka. Caribbean Orchids. T* **354** *and similar vert designs. Multicoloured. P* 14.
2082 1 c. Type **354** 10 10
2083 25 c. *Oncidium splendidum* 30 20
2084 60 c. *Laelia anceps* 60 60
2085 75 c. *Cattleya trianaei* 75 75
2086 $1 *Odontoglossum rossii* .. .. 1·00 1·00
2087 $2 *Brassia gireoudiana* .. .. 1·75 1·75
2088 $3 *Cattleya dowiana* .. .. 2·25 2·25
2089 $4 *Sobralia macrantha* .. .. 2·50 2·50
2082/9 .. .. *Set of* 8 8·25 8·25
MS2090 Two sheets, each 97×68 mm. (a) $6 *Oncidium lanceanum*. (b) $6 *Laelia rubescens* *Set of* 2 *sheets* 8·50 9·50

(Des Mary Walters. Litho Questa)

1990 (16 Mar). *500th Anniv of Discovery of America by Columbus* (1992) (3*rd issue*). *New World Natural History – Butterflies. Vert designs as T* **260** *of Antigua. Multicoloured. P* 14.
2091 15 c. *Marpesia petreus* 30 20
2092 25 c. *Junonia evarete* 40 25
2093 75 c. *Siproeta stelenes* 80 70
2094 90 c. *Historis odius* 95 85
2095 $1 *Mestra cana* .. .. 1·00 90
2096 $2 *Biblis hyperia* .. .. .. 2·00 2·00
2097 $3 *Dryas julia* .. .. .. 2·50 2·75
2098 $4 *Anartia amathea* .. .. .. 2·50 2·75
2091/8 .. .. *Set of* 8 9·50 9·50
MS2099 Two sheets, each 101×69 mm. (a) $6 *Pseudolycaena marsyas*. (b) $6 *Phoebis philea* *Set of* 2 *sheets* 8·50 9·50

(Des J. Barbaris. Litho B.D.T.)

1990 (3 Apr). *Local Fauna. Multicoloured designs as T* **254** *of Antigua. P* 14.
2100 10 c. Caribbean Monk Seal 20 20
2101 15 c. Little Brown Bat 25 25
2102 45 c. Brown Rat 50 50
2103 60 c. Common Rabbit 60 60
2104 $1 Water Opossum 95 95
2105 $2 White-nosed Ichneumon .. .. 1·75 1·75
2106 $3 Little Big-eared Bat (*vert*) .. 2·25 2·25
2107 $4 Mouse Opossum .. .. .. 2·25 2·25
2100/7 .. .. *Set of* 8 8·00 8·00
MS2108 Two sheets, each 107×80 mm. (a) $6 Common Rabbit (*different*). (b) $6 Water Opossum (*different*) .. .. *Set of* 2 *sheets* 8·50 9·50

(Des W. Wright. Litho Questa)

1990 (30 Apr). *50th Anniv of Second World War. Horiz designs as T* **274** *of Antigua. Multicoloured. P* 14.
2109 25 c. British tanks during Operation Battleaxe, 1941 .. .. .. 30 30
2110 35 c. Allied tank in southern France, 1944 40 40
2111 45 c. U.S. forces landing on Guadalcanal, 1942 .. .. 45 45
2112 50 c. U.S. attack in New Guinea, 1943 .. 50 50
2113 60 c. Hoisting U.S. flag on Leyte, Phillippines, 1944 .. .. .. 60 60
2114 75 c. U.S. tanks entering Cologne, 1945 .. 75 75
2115 $1 Anzio offensive, 1944 .. .. 95 95
2116 $2 Battle of the Bismarck Sea, 1943 .. 1·75 1·75
2117 $3 U.S. battle fleet, 1944 .. .. 2·25 2·25
2118 $4 Focke Wulf Fw190A German fighter attacking Salerno landing, 1943 .. 2·50 2·50
2109/18 .. .. *Set of* 10 9·50 9·50
MS2119 111×83 mm. $6 German *U-30* submarine, 1939 .. .. 3·50 4·00

(Des Walt Disney Co. Litho Questa)

1990 (21 June). *"Stamp World London 90" International Stamp Exhibition* (1*st issue*). *Multicoloured designs as T* **193** *of Gambia showing Walt Disney cartoon characters and British trains. P* 14×13½.
2120 5 c. Mickey Mouse driving S.R. "King Arthur" Class locomotive, 1925 (*horiz*) 20 10
2121 10 c. Mickey and Minnie Mouse with *Puffing Billy*, 1813 (*horiz*) 25 10
2122 20 c. Mickey Mouse with Pluto pulling Durham colliery waggon, 1765 (*horiz*) 35 15
2123 45 c. Mickey Mouse timing L.N.E.R. locomotive No. 2509, *Silver Link*, 1935 (*horiz*) 65 25
2124 $1 Mickey Mouse and Donald Duck with locomotive No. 60149, *Amadis*, 1948 (*horiz*) .. .. 1·50 1·00
2125 $2 Goofy and Mickey Mouse with Liverpool & Manchester Railway locomotive, 1830 (*horiz*) .. .. 2·25 2·50
2126 $4 Goofy and Donald Duck with Great Northern locomotive No. 1, 1870 (*horiz*) .. .. 3·25 3·75
2127 $5 Mickey Mouse and Gyro the Mechanic with Advanced Passenger Train, 1972 (*horiz*) .. .. 3·25 3·75
2120/7 .. .. *Set of* 8 10·50 10·50
MS2128 Two sheets, each 127×101 mm. (a) $6 Minnie Mouse, Donald and Daisy Duck in Trevithick's *Catch-Me-Who-Can*, 1808 (*horiz*). P 14×13½. (b) $6 Donald Duck and *Locomotion*, 1825. P 13½×14 .. .. *Set of* 2 *sheets* 10·00 11·00
No. 2126 is inscribed "Flying Scotsman" in error.
See also No. **MS**2146.

355 U.S. Paratroop Drop over Grenada

(Litho B.D.T.)

1990 (3 July). *50th Anniv of United States' Airborne Forces. T* **355** *and similar horiz designs. Multicoloured. P* 14.
2129 75 c. Type **355** 90 90
MS2130 Two sheets, each 115×87 mm. (a) $2.50, Paratrooper landing. (b) $6 Paratroop uniforms of 1940 and 1990 .. .. *Set of* 2 *sheets* 5·50 6·50

(Des Young Phillips Studio. Litho Questa)

1990 (5 July). *90th Birthday of Queen Elizabeth the Queen Mother. Vert designs as T* **194** *of Gambia showing photographs*, 1960–69. *Multicoloured. P* 14.
2131 $2 Queen Mother in coat and hat .. 1·50 1·75
a. Strip of 3. Nos. 2131/3 .. .. 4·00
2132 $2 Queen Mother in evening dress .. 1·50 1·75
2133 $2 Queen Mother in Garter robes .. 1·50 1·75
2131/3 .. .. *Set of* 3 4·00 4·75
MS2134 90×75 mm. $6 Queen Mother (as No. 2131) .. .. 3·50 4·00
Nos. 2131/3 were printed together, horizontally and vertically *se-tenant*, in sheetlets of 9 (3×3).

(Des B. Grout. Litho Questa)

1990 (9 July). *Olympic Games, Barcelona* (1992) (1*st issue*). *Vert designs as T* **268** *of Antigua. Multicoloured. P* 14.
2135 10 c. Men's steeplechase 20 20
2136 15 c. Dressage 30 30
2137 45 c. Men's 200 m butterfly swimming .. 45 45
2138 50 c. Men's hockey 60 60
2139 65 c. Women's beam gymnastics 60 60
2140 75 c. "Flying Dutchman" class yachting .. 80 80
2141 $2 Freestyle wrestling .. .. .. 1·75 1·75
2142 $3 Men's springboard diving .. .. 2·25 2·25
2143 $4 Women's 1000 m sprint cycling .. 2·50 2·50
2144 $5 Men's basketball .. .. .. 3·25 3·25
2135/44 .. .. *Set of* 10 11·50 11·50
MS2145 Two sheets, each 101×70 mm. (a) $8 Equestrian three-day event. (b) $8 Men's 10000 metres .. .. *Set of* 2 *sheets* 9·50 11·00
See also Nos. 2414/22

COVER PRICES

Cover factors are quoted at the beginning of each country for most issues to 1945. An explanation of the system can be found on page x. The factors quoted do not, however, apply to philatelic covers.

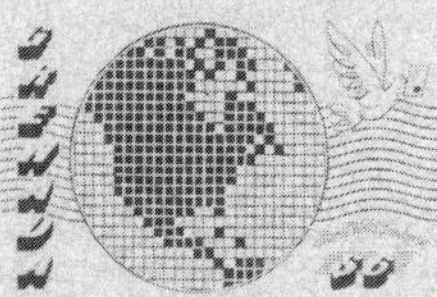

356 Map of North America and Logo

(Des M. Pollard. Litho Questa)

1990 (12 July). *"Stamp World London 90" International Stamp Exhibition* (2*nd issue*). *Sheet* 97×75 *mm. P* 14.
MS2146 **356** $6 deep mauve .. .. .. 4·00 5·0

357 Yellow Goatfish

(Des Mary Walters. Litho B.D.T.)

1990 (8 Aug). *Coral Reef Fishes. T* **357** *and similar horiz designs. Multicoloured. P* 14.
2147 10 c. Type **357** 20 20
2148 25 c. Black Margate 35 35
2149 65 c. Blue-headed Wrasse 75 75
2150 75 c. Puddingwife 85 85
2151 $1 Four-eyed Butterflyfish 95 95
2152 $2 Honey Damselfish .. .. .. 1·75 1·75
2153 $3 Queen Angelfish .. .. .. 2·25 2·25
2154 $5 Cherub Angelfish .. .. .. 3·00 3·00
2147/54 .. .. *Set of* 8 9·00 9·00
MS2155 Two sheets, each 103×72 mm. (a) $6 Smooth Trunkfish. (b) $6 Sergeant Major *Set of* 2 *sheets* 8·00 9·00

358 Tropical Mockingbird

(Des J. Anderton. Litho B.D.T.)

1990 (10 Sept). *Birds. T* **358** *and similar horiz designs. Multicoloured. P* 14.
2156 15 c. Type **358** 30 30
2157 25 c. Grey Kingbird 35 35
2158 65 c. Bare-eyed Thrush 75 75
2159 75 c. Antillean Crested Hummingbird .. 85 85
2160 $1 House Wren .. .. 1·00 1·00
2161 $2 Purple Martin .. .. .. 1·75 1·75
2162 $4 Hooded Tanager .. .. .. 2·50 2·50
2163 $5 Scaly-breasted Ground Dove .. 3·00 3·00
2156/63 .. .. *Set of* 8 3·00 3·00
MS2164 Two sheets, each 101×72 mm. (a) $6 Fork-tailed Flycatcher. (b) $6 Smooth-billed Ani 9·50 9·50
Set of 2 *sheets* 11·00 12·00

359 Coral Crab

360 Cameroun Player

(Des Deborah Dudley Max. Litho Questa)

1990 (17 Sept). *Crustaceans. T* **359** *and similar horiz designs. Multicoloured. P* 14.
2165 5 c. Type **359** 10 10
2166 10 c. Smoothtail Spiny Lobster 15 15
2167 15 c. Flamestreaked Box Crab 15 15
2168 25 c. Spotted Swimming Crab 25 25
2169 75 c. Sally Lightfoot Rock Crab 60 60
2170 $1 Spotted Spiny Lobster 80 80
2171 $3 Longarm Spiny Lobster .. .. 2·00 2·50
2172 $20 Caribbean Spiny Lobster .. .. 13·00 18·00
2165/72 .. .. *Set of* 8 15·00 20·00
MS2173 Two sheets, 106×75 mm. (a) $6 Copper Lobster. (b) $6 Spanish Lobster .. *Set of* 2 *sheets* 8·00 9·00

(Des Young Phillips Studio. Litho Questa)

1990 (24 Sept). *World Cup Football Championship, Italy* (2*nd issue*). *T* **360** *and similar vert designs. Multicoloured. P* 14.
2174 10 c. Type **360** 20 15
2175 25 c. Michel (Spain) 25 15
2176 $1 Brehme (West Germany) 85 85
2177 $5 Nevin (Scotland) .. .. .. 3·00 4·00
2174/7 .. .. *Set of* 4 3·75 4·50
MS2178 Two sheets, each 95×90 mm. (a) $6 Giannini (Italy). (b) $6 Perdomo (Uruguay) *Set of* 2 *sheets* 8·50 10·00

1990 W GERMANY 1 ARGENTINA 0

(361)

90 (30 Nov). *World Cup Football Championship, Italy* (1990) (3rd *issue*). *No.* **MS**2016a *optd with T* **361**.

S2179 70×93 mm. $6 Players jumping for ball 5·50 6·00

No. **MS**2179 shows the overprint, Type **361**, added to the list match results in the sheet margin.

(Litho Questa)

90 (31 Dec). *Christmas. Paintings by Raphael. Multicoloured designs as T* **272** *of Antigua, but vert. P* 13½×14.

80 10 c. "The Ansidei Madonna" 20 10
81 15 c. "The Sistine Madonna" 20 10
82 $1 "The Madonna of the Baldacchino" .. 1·25 70
83 $2 "The Large Holy Family" (detail) .. 2·00 2·25
84 $5 "Madonna in the Meadow" .. .. 3·50 5·00
80/4 .. .. *Set of* 5 6·50 7·25
S2185 Two sheets, each 71×101 mm. (a) $6 "Madonna of the Diadem" (detail). (b) $6 "The Madonna of the Veil" (detail) .. *Set of* 2 *sheets* 10·00 12·00

A 50 c. value in a similar design, showing "The Canigiani Holy amily" by Raphael, was prepared, but not issued.

(Litho Questa)

991 (31 Jan). 350*th Death Anniv of Rubens. Horiz designs as T* **273** *of Antigua. Multicoloured. P* 14×13½.

86 5 c. "The Brazen Serpent" (detail) .. 15 10
87 10 c. "The Garden of Love" 15 10
88 25 c. "Head of Cyrus" (detail) 30 20
89 75 c. "Tournament in Front of a Castle" .. 70 60
90 $1 "The Brazen Serpent" (different detail) 85 75
191 $2 "Judgement of Paris" (detail) .. 1·75 2·00
192 $4 "The Brazen Serpent" .. .. 2·50 3·00
193 $5 "The Karmesse" (detail) .. .. 3·00 3·25
186/93 .. .. *Set of* 8 8·50 9·00
S2194 Two sheets, each 101×70 mm. (a) $6 "Anger of Neptune" (detail). (b) $6 "The Prodigal Son" (detail) .. .. .. *Set of* 2 *sheets* 8·50 10·00

362 "The Sorcerer's Apprentice"

(Des Walt Disney Co. Litho Questa)

991 (4 Feb). 50*th Anniv of* Fantasia (*cartoon film*). *T* **362** *and similar horiz designs. Multicoloured. P* 14×13½.

195 5 c. Type **362** 20 15
196 10 c. Dancing mushrooms ("The Nutcracker Suite") 25 15
197 20 c. Pterodactyls ("The Rite of Spring") .. 45 15
198 45 c. Centaurs ("The Pastoral Symphony") 85 40
199 $1 Bacchus and Jacchus ("The Pastoral Symphony") .. .. .. 1·50 1·00
200 $2 Dancing ostrich ("Dance of the Hours") .. .. 2·50 2·75
201 $4 Elephant ballet ("Dance of the Hours") 3·25 3·75
202 $5 Diana ("The Pastoral Symphony") .. 3·25 3·75
195/202 .. .. *Set of* 8 11·00 11·00
S2203 Two sheets, each 122×102 mm. (a) $6 Mickey Mouse as the Sorcerer's Apprentice; (b) $6 Mickey Mouse with Leopold Stokowski (conductor) .. .. .. *Set of* 2 *sheets* 9·50 11·00
S2204 176×213 mm. $12 Mickey Mouse as the Sorcerer's Apprentice (*vert*). P 13½×14 .. 9·50 11·00

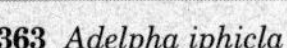

363 *Adelpha iphicla* **364** *Psilocybe cubensis*

(Des W. Wright. Litho Questa)

991 (8 Apr). *Butterflies. T* **363** *and similar horiz designs. Multicoloured. P* 14.

205 5 c. Type **363** 30 15
206 10 c. *Nymphalidae claudina* 30 20
207 15 c. *Brassolidae polyxena* 35 20
208 20 c. Zebra Longwing 40 20
209 25 c. *Marpesia corinna* 40 25
210 30 c. *Morpho hecuba* 40 30
211 45 c. *Morpho rhetenor* 55 45
212 50 c. *Dismorphia spio* 65 55
213 60 c. *Prepona omphale* 75 65
214 70 c. *Morpho anaxibia* 85 75
215 75 c. *Marpesia iole* 90 80
216 $1 *Amarynthis meneria* .. .. 1·00 90
2217 $2 *Morpho cisseis* .. .. .. 1·75 2·25
2218 $3 *Danaidae plexippus* .. .. .. 2·25 2·75
2219 $4 *Morpho achilleana* .. .. .. 2·75 3·50
2220 $5 *Calliona argenissa* .. .. .. 3·25 4·00
2205/20 .. .. *Set of* 16 15·00 16·00
MS2221 Four sheets, each 118×80 mm. (a) $6 *Anteos clorinde*. (b) $6 *Haetera piera*. (c) $6 *Papilio cresphontes*. (d) $6 *Prepona pheridames*. *Set of* 4 *sheets* 17·00 19·00

(Des T. Agans. Litho Questa)

1991 (29 Apr). 500*th Anniv of Discovery of America by Columbus* (1992) (4*th issue*). *History of Exploration. Multicoloured designs as T* **277** *of Antigua. P* 14.

2222 5 c. Vitus Bering in Bering Sea, 1728–29 20 20
2223 10 c. De Bougainville off Pacific island, 1766–69 .. .. 25 25
2224 25 c. Polynesian canoe 30 25
2225 50 c. De Mendana off Solomon Islands, 1567–69 .. .. 55 40
2226 $1 Darwin's H.M.S. *Beagle*, 1831–35 .. 1·00 1·00
2227 $2 Cook's H.M.S. *Endeavour*, 1768–71 2·50 2·50
2228 $4 Willem Schouten in LeMaire Strait, 1615–17 .. .. 3·00 3·00
2229 $5 Tasman off New Zealand, 1642–44 3·00 3·00
2222/9 .. .. *Set of* 8 9·75 9·75
MS2230 Two sheets, each 116×77 mm. (a) $6 *Santa Maria* sinking. (b) $6 Bow of *Santa Maria* (*vert*) .. .. *Set of* 2 *sheets* 7·50 8·50

(Des Walt Disney Co. Litho Questa)

1991 (6 May). *"Phila Nippon '91" International Stamp Exhibition, Tokyo. Multicoloured designs as T* **279** *of Antigua showing Walt Disney cartoon characters at Japanese festivals. P* 14×13½.

2231 5 c. Minnie Mouse and Daisy Duck at Dolls festival (*horiz*) 15 10
2232 10 c. Morty and Ferdie with Boys' Day display (*horiz*) 20 15
2233 20 c. Mickey and Minnie Mouse at Star festival (*horiz*) 35 20
2234 45 c. Minnie and Daisy folk-dancing (*horiz*) 60 35
2235 $1 Huey, Dewey and Louie wearing Eboshi headdresses (*horiz*) .. .. 1·10 85
2236 $2 Mickey and Goofy pulling decorated cart at Gion festival (*horiz*) .. .. 2·50 2·75
2237 $4 Minnie and Daisy preparing rice broth, Seven Plants festival (*horiz*) 3·25 3·50
2238 $5 Huey and Dewey with straw boat at Lanterns festival (*horiz*) .. .. 3·25 3·50
2231/8 .. .. *Set of* 8 10·50 10·50
MS2239 Three sheets, each 127×101 mm. (a) $6 Minnie Mouse in kimono. P 13½×14. (b) $6 Mickey taking photo (*horiz*). P 14×13½. (c) $6 Goofy behind fair stall (*horiz*). P 14×13½ *Set of* 3 *sheets* 13·00 14·00

(Litho Walsall)

1991 (13 May). *Death Centenary of Vincent van Gogh* (*artist*) (1990). *Multicoloured designs as T* **278** *of Antigua. P* 13½.

2240 20 c. "Blossoming Almond Branch in Glass" 15 15
2241 25 c. "La Mousmé sitting" 15 15
2242 30 c. "Still Life with Red Cabbages and Onions" (*horiz*) 20 20
2243 40 c. "Japonaiserie: Flowering Plum Tree" 30 30
2244 45 c. "Japonaiserie: Bridge in Rain" .. 30 30
2245 60 c. "Still Life with Basket of Apples" (*horiz*) 50 50
2246 75 c. "Italian Woman" 60 60
2247 $1 "The Painter on his Way to Work" .. 80 80
2248 $2 "Portrait of Pére Tanguy" .. .. 1·50 1·50
2249 $3 "Still Life with Plaster Statuette, a Rose and Two Novels" .. .. 2·25 2·25
2250 $4 "Still Life: Bottle, Lemons and Oranges" (*horiz*) .. .. .. 2·50 2·50
2251 $5 "Orchard with Blossoming Apricot Trees" (*horiz*) .. .. .. 2·75 2·75
2240/51 .. .. *Set of* 12 11·00 11·00
MS2252 Five sheets. (a) 76×102 mm. $6 "Roubine du Roi Canal with Washerwoman" (73×99 *mm*). (b) 102×76 mm. $6 "Farmhouse in a Wheatfield" (99×73 *mm*). (c) 102×76 mm. $6 "The Gleize Bridge over the Vigueirat Canal" (99×73 *mm*). (d) 102×76 mm. $6 "Rocks with Oak Tree" (99×73 *mm*). (e) 76×102 mm. $6 "Japonaiserie: Oiran" (73×99 mm). Imperf. *Set of* 5 *sheets* 18·00 21·00

(Des Mary Walters. Litho Questa)

1991 (1 June). *Fungi. T* **364** *and similar vert designs. Multicoloured. P* 14.

2253 15 c. Type **364** 40 30
2254 25 c. *Leptonia caeruleocapitata* 50 30
2255 65 c. *Cystolepiota eriophora* 90 75
2256 75 c. *Chlorophyllum molybdites* .. .. 1·00 85
2257 $1 *Xerocomus hypoxanthus* .. .. 1·25 1·10
2258 $2 *Volvariella cubensis* .. .. 2·00 2·25
2259 $4 *Xerocomus coccolobae* .. .. 3·00 3·25
2260 $5 *Pluteus chrysophlebius* .. .. 3·00 3·25
2253/60 .. .. *Set of* 8 11·00 11·00
MS2261 Two sheets, each 100×70 mm. (a) $6 *Psathyrella tuberculata*. (b) $6 *Hygrocybe miniata* .. .. *Set of* 2 *sheets* 12·00 13·00

365 Johannes Kepler (astronomer)

(Des G. Vasarhelyi. Litho Questa)

1991 (21 June). *Exploration of Mars. T* **365** *and similar horiz designs showing astronomers, spacecraft and Martian landscapes. Multicoloured. P* 14×13½.

2262/97 75 c. × 9, $1.25 × 9, $2 × 9, $7 × 9 *Set of* 36 48·00 48·00
MS2298 Three sheets, each 112×92 mm. (a) $6 Projected spacecraft. (b) $6 Mars and part of spacecraft. (c) $6 Phobos satellite over Mars. P 13×12 .. .. .. *Set of* 3 *sheets* 11·00 12·00

Nos. 2262/97 were issued as four sheetlets, each containing nine different designs of the same face values.

(Des D. Miller. Litho Walsall)

1991 (5 July). 65*th Birthday of Queen Elizabeth II. Horiz designs as T* **280** *of Antigua. Multicoloured. P* 14.

2299 15 c. Royal Family on balcony after Trooping the Colour, 1985 .. .. 15 15
2300 40 c. Queen and Prince Philip at Peterborough, 1988 .. .. .. 35 35
2301 $2 Queen and Queen Mother at Windsor, 1986 .. .. 1·50 1·75
2302 $4 Queen and Prince Philip on visit to United Arab Emirates .. .. 2·50 2·75
2299/302 .. .. *Set of* 4 4·00 4·50
MS2303 68×90 mm. $5 Separate photographs of the Queen and Prince Philip .. .. .. 3·50 4·25

(Des D. Miller. Litho Walsall)

1991 (5 July). 10*th Wedding Anniv of the Prince and Princess of Wales. Horiz designs as T* **280** *of Antigua. Multicoloured. P* 14.

2304 10 c. Prince and Princess in July 1985 .. 20 10
2305 50 c. Separate photographs of Prince, Princess and sons 55 45
2306 $1 Prince Henry at Trooping the Colour and Prince William in Majorca .. 1·00 1·00
2307 $5 Separate photographs of Prince Charles and Princess Diana .. .. 3·50 4·00
2304/7 .. .. *Set of* 4 4·75 5·00
MS2308 68×90 mm. $5 Prince, Princess and sons on holiday in Majorca .. .. .. 4·00 4·50

366 Anglican High School Pupils

(Litho Questa)

1991 (29 July). 75*th Anniv of Anglican High School* (10, 25 *c.*) *and* 40*th Anniv of University of the West Indies* (45, 50 *c.*). *T* **366** *and similar horiz designs. Multicoloured. P* 14.

2309 10 c. Type **366** 20 20
2310 25 c. Artist's impression of new Anglican High School 30 20
2311 45 c. Marryshow House, Grenada .. 55 55
2312 50 c. University Administrative Building, Barbados 65 75
2309/12 .. .. *Set of* 4 1·50 1·50

367 George Stephenson's First Locomotive, 1814 (Great Britain)

(Des G. Vasarhelyi. Litho Walsall)

1991 (2 Dec). *Great Railways of the World. T* **367** *and similar horiz designs. Multicoloured. P* 14.

2313 75 c. Type **367** 60 60
a. Sheetlet. Nos. 2313/21 .. .. 4·75
2314 75 c. George Stephenson 60 60
2315 75 c. Killingworth locomotive, 1816 (Great Britain) 60 60
2316 75 c. George Stephenson's *Locomotion*, 1825 (Great Britain) 60 60
2317 75 c. *Locomotion* in Darlington, 1825 (Great Britain) 60 60
2318 75 c. Opening of Stockton & Darlington Railway, 1825 .. .. .. 60 60
2319 75 c. Timothy Hackworth's *Royal George*, 1827 (Great Britain) 60 60
2320 75 c. *Northumbrian*, 1831 (Great Britain) 60 60
2321 75 c. *Planet*, 1830 (Great Britain) .. 60 60
2322 $1 *Old Ironsides*, 1832 (U.S.A.) .. 80 80
a. Sheetlet. Nos. 2322/30 .. .. 6·50
2323 $1 *Wilberforce*, 1832 (Great Britain) .. 80 80
2324 $1 *Der Adler*, 1835 (Germany) 80 80
2325 $1 *North Star*, 1837 (Great Britain) .. 80 80
2326 $1 London & Birmingham Railway No. 1, 1838 (Great Britain) 80 80
2327 $1 Stephenson's *Austria*, 1838 (Austria) 80 80
2328 $1 Baltimore & Ohio Railroad No. 378 *Muddigger*, 1840 (U.S.A.) 80 80
2329 $1 Baltimore & Ohio Railroad Norris, 1840 (U.S.A.) 80 80
2330 $1 *Centaur*, 1840 (Great Britain) .. 80 80
2331 $2 *Lion*, 1841 (Great Britain) .. .. 1·50 1·50
a. Sheetlet. Nos. 2331/9 .. .. 12·50
2332 $2 *Beuth*, 1843 (Germany) .. .. 1·50 1·50
2333 $2 *Derwent*, 1845 (Great Britain) .. 1·50 1·50
2334 $2 *Bets*, 1846 (Hungary) .. .. 1·50 1·50

2335 $2 Opening of Budapest to Vac railway, 1846 (Hungary) .. .. .. 1·50 1·50
2336 $2 Carriages, Stockton & Darlington Railway, 1846 (Great Britain) .. 1·50 1·50
2337 $2 "Long Boiler" type, 1847 (France) .. 1·50 1·50
2338 $2 Baldwin locomotive, 1850 (U.S.A.) .. 1·50 1·50
2339 $2 Steam locomotive, 1850 (Germany) 1·50 1·50
2313/39 .. .. *Set of* 27 23·00 23·00
MS2340 Two sheets, each 116×86 mm. (a) $6 Part of Stephenson's *Locomotion*, 1825 (Great Britain). (b) $6 Train on Liverpool & Manchester Railway, 1833 (Great Britain) .. *Set of* 2 *sheets* 9·50 11·00

Nos. 2313/21, 2322/30 and 2331/9 were printed together, *se-tenant*, in sheetlets of 9.

368 Barbu

(Des I. MacLaury. Litho Questa)

1991 (5 Dec). *Marine Life of the Sandflats. T* **368** *and similar horiz designs. Multicoloured. P* 14.

2341 50 c. Type **368** 55 55
a. Sheetlet. Nos. 2341/55 .. .. 7·50
2342 50 c. Beau Gregory 55 55
2343 50 c. Porcupinefish 55 55
2344 50 c. Queen or Pink Conch and Conchfish 55 55
2345 50 c. Hermit Crab 55 55
2346 50 c. Bluestripe Lizardfish 55 55
2347 50 c. Spot-finned Mojarra 55 55
2348 50 c. Southern Stingray 55 55
2349 50 c. Long-spined Sea Urchin and Slippery Dick 55 55
2350 50 c. Peacock Flounder 55 55
2351 50 c. West Indian Sea Star 55 55
2352 50 c. Spotted Goatfish 55 55
2353 50 c. Netted Olive and West Indian Sea Egg 55 55
2354 50 c. Pearly Razorfish 55 55
2355 50 c. Spotted Jawfish and Yellow-headed Jawfish 55 55
2341/55 .. .. *Set of* 15 7·50 7·50
MS2356 105×76 mm. $6 Short-nosed Batfish .. 7·50 8·50

Nos. 2341/55 were printed together, *se-tenant*, in sheetlets of fifteen, forming a composite design.

(Litho Walsall)

1991 (9 Dec). *Christmas. Religious Paintings by Albrecht Dürer. Vert designs as T* **287** *of Antigua. Multicoloured. P* 12.

2357 10 c. "Adoration of the Magi" (detail) .. 25 10
2358 35 c. "Madonna with the Siskin" (detail) .. 50 25
2359 50 c. "Feast of the Rose Garlands" (detail) 70 45
2360 75 c. "Virgin with the Pear" (detail) .. 1·00 70
2361 $1 "Virgin in Half-length" (detail) .. 1·25 90
2362 $2 "Madonna and Child" (detail) .. 2·25 2·50
2363 $4 "Virgin and Child with St. Anne" (detail) .. .. 3·00 3·50
2364 $5 "Virgin and Child" (detail) .. .. 3·00 3·50
2357/64 .. .. *Set of* 8 10·50 10·50
MS2365 Two sheets, each 102×127 mm. (a) $6 "Virgin with a Multitude of Animals" (detail). (b) $6 "The Nativity" (detail). P 14½×14 *Set of* 2 *sheets* 8·50 9·50

369 Goofy windsurfing

(Des Walt Disney Co. Litho Questa)

1992 (11 Feb). *Thrill Sports. T* **369** *and similar multicoloured designs showing Walt Disney cartoon characters. P* 14×13½.

2366 5 c. Type **369** 15 10
2367 10 c. Mickey Mouse skateboarding .. 20 10
2368 20 c. Daisy Duck gliding 40 10
2369 45 c. Mickey's nephews stunt kite flying 70 25
2370 $1 Donald Duck mountain biking .. 1·25 85
2371 $2 Donald and Chipmunk parachuting 2·00 2·25
2372 $4 Mickey go-karting .. .. .. 3·25 3·75
2373 $5 Minnie water skiing .. .. .. 3·25 3·75
2366/73 .. .. *Set of* 8 10·00 10·00
MS2374 Four sheets, each 128×102 mm. (a) $6 Mickey bungee jumping (*vert*). P 13½×14. (b) $6 Mickey and Minnie river rafting. P 14×13½. (c) $6 Donald's nephews playing roller hockey. P 14×13½. (d) $6 Mickey hang-gliding. P 14×13½ .. .. .. *Set of* 4 *sheets* 16·00 17·00

(Des D. Miller. Litho Questa)

1992 (2 Mar). *40th Anniv of Queen Elizabeth II's Accession. Horiz designs as T* **288** *of Antigua. Multicoloured. P* 14.

2375 10 c. Waterfall 25 15
2376 50 c. Street in St. George's 50 40
2377 $1 Colonial-style houses, St. George's .. 80 80
2378 $5 St. George's from the sea .. .. 3·25 3·50
2375/8 .. .. *Set of* 4 4·00 4·25
MS2379 Two sheets, each 75×96 mm. (a) $6 Village on hillside. (b) $6 Yacht at anchor off village .. .. *Set of* 2 *sheets* 8·00 10·00

(Litho B.D.T.)

1992 (30 Apr). *"Granada '92" International Stamp Exhibition, Spain. Spanish Paintings. Multicoloured designs as T* **292** *of Antigua. P* 13×13½ (*vert*) *or* 13½×13 (*horiz*).

2380 10 c. "The Corpus Christi Procession in Seville" (Manuel Cabral y Aguado) (*horiz*) 15 15
2381 35 c. "The Mancorbo Channel" (Carlos de Haes) 25 20
2382 50 c. "Amalia de Llano y Dotres, Countess of Vilches" (Federico de Madrazo y Kuntz) 40 40
2383 75 c. "Conchita Serrano y Domínguez, Countess of Santovenia" (Eduardo Rosales Gallina) 55 55
2384 $1 "Queen María Isabel de Braganza" (Bernardo López Piquer) 70 70
2385 $2 "The Presentation of Don John of Austria to Charles V" (detail) (Gallina) .. .. 1·40 1·75
2386 $4 "The Presentation of Don John of Austria to Charles V" (different detail) (Gallina) .. .. 2·75 3·25
2387 $5 "The Testament of Isabella the Catholic" (Gallina) (*horiz*) .. .. 3·00 3·25
2380/7 .. .. *Set of* 8 8·25 9·25
MS2388 Two sheets, each 120×95 mm. (a) $6 "The Horse Corral in the Old Madrid Bullring" (Manuel Castellano) (111×85 *mm*). (b) $6 "Meeting of Poets in Antonio Mariá Esquivel's Studio" (Antonia Mariá Esquivel y Suárez de Urbina) (111×85 *mm*). Imperf .. *Set of* 2 *sheets* 8·00 9·00

370 Green-winged Macaw

371 Gracie Fields

(Des L. Fried. Litho Questa)

1992 (7 May). *500th Anniv of Discovery of America by Columbus (5th issue). World Columbian Stamp "Expo '92", Chicago. T* **370** *and similar vert designs. Multicoloured. P* 14.

2389 10 c. Type **370** 25 15
2390 25 c. *Santa Maria* 35 20
2391 35 c. Christopher Columbus 40 30
2392 50 c. 15th-century sandglass 55 55
2393 75 c. Queen Isabella 70 80
2394 $4 Cantino map of 1502 (detail) .. 3·50 4·75
2389/94 .. .. *Set of* 6 5·25 6·00
MS2395 Two sheets, each 80×108 mm. (a) $6 Map of Genoa (detail). (b) $6 Detail of 15th-century map by Thomas Bly .. *Set of* 2 *sheets* 9·00 10·00

(Des R. Brickman. Litho Questa)

1992 (28 May). *"Genova '92" International Thematic Stamp Exhibition. Hummingbirds. Multicoloured designs as T* **295** *of Antigua, but vertical. P* 14.

2396 10 c. Ruby-throated Hummingbird .. 20 15
2397 25 c. Vervain Hummingbird 30 20
2398 35 c. Blue-headed Hummingbird 35 25
2399 50 c. Cuban Emerald 55 55
2400 75 c. Antillean Mango 75 75
2401 $2 Purple-throated Carib .. .. 1·50 1·75
2402 $4 Puerto Rican Emerald .. .. 2·75 3·25
2403 $5 Green-throated Carib .. .. 2·75 3·25
2396/403 .. .. *Set of* 8 8·25 9·25
MS2404 Two sheets, each 109×80 mm. (a) $6 Young Antillean Crested Hummingbird. (b) $6 Rufous-breasted Hermit .. *Set of* 2 *sheets* 11·00 12·00

(Des R. Jung. Litho B.D.T.)

1992 (1 June). *50th Anniv of United Service Organization (forces' entertainment programme). T* **371** *and similar vert designs. Multicoloured. P* 14.

2405 15 c. Type **371** 15 15
2406 25 c. Jack Benny 20 20
2407 35 c. Jinx Falkenburg 25 25
2408 50 c. Francis Langford 40 40
2409 75 c. Joe E. Brown 70 70
2410 $1 Phil Silvers 80 80
2411 $2 Danny Kaye .. .. .. 1·50 1·75
2412 $5 Frank Sinatra .. .. .. 3·00 3·50
2405/12 .. .. *Set of* 8 6·25 7·00
MS2413 Two sheets, each 107×80 mm. (a) $6 Bob Hope. (b) $6 Anna May Wong *Set of* 2 *sheets* 8·00 9·00

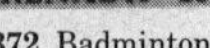

372 Badminton

373 *Matador* (yacht), Newport News Regatta

(Litho Questa)

1992 (17 June). *Olympic Games, Barcelona (2nd issue). T* **372** *and similar multicoloured designs. P* 14.

2414 10 c. Type **372** 15 15
2415 25 c. Women's long jump 20 20
2416 35 c. Women's 100 metres 30 30
2417 50 c. 1000 metres cycling sprint 50 50
2418 75 c. Decathlon (*horiz*) 70 70
2419 $2 Judo (*horiz*) .. .. 1·60 1·75
2420 $4 Women's gymnastics – asymmetrical bars .. .. 2·75 3·25
2421 $5 Men's javelin .. .. .. 2·75 3·25
2414/21 .. .. *Set of* 8 8·00 9·00
MS2422 Two sheets, each 100×70 mm. (a) $6 Men's gymnastics – vault. (b) $6 Men's gymnastics – floor exercise .. *Set of* 2 *sheets* 8·00 9·0

(Des F. Paul ($1), J. Esquino ($2). Litho Questa)

1992 (24 Aug). *500th Anniv of Discovery of America by Columbus (6th issue). Organization of East Caribbean States. As Nos.* 1670/1 *of Antigua. Multicoloured. P* 14½.

2423 $1 Columbus meeting Amerindians .. 70 7
2424 $2 Ships approaching island .. .. 1·40 1·6

(Des W. Hanson. Litho B.D.T.)

1992 (22 Oct). *Toy Trains from American Manufacturers. Multicoloured designs as T* **257** *of Dominica. P* 14.

2425 10 c. *The Blue Comet* locomotive, Boucher (1933) 15 1
2426 35 c. No. 2220 switching locomotive, Voltamp (1906) 25 2
2427 40 c. No. 221 tunnel locomotive, Knapp (1905) 30 3
2428 75 c. "Grand Canyon" locomotive, American Flyer (1931) 55 5
2429 $2 "Streamliner" tin locomotive, Hafner (1930s) 70 7
2430 $2 No. 237 switching locomotive, Elektoy (1911) .. .. 1·40 1·7
2431 $4 Parlour car, Ives (1928) .. .. 2·75 3·2
2432 $5 "Improved President's Special" locomotive, American Flyer (1927) .. 2·75 3·2
2425/32 .. .. *Set of* 8 8·00 9·0
MS2433 Two sheets, each 133×103 mm. (a) $6 No. 1122 locomotive, Ives (1921) (38½×50 *mm*). (b) $6 No. 3239 locomotive, Ives (1912) (50×38½ *mm*). P 13 .. .. .. *Set of* 2 *sheets* 8·00 9·0

(Des Kerri Schiff. Litho Questa)

1992 (28 Oct). *Postage Stamp Mega Event, New York. Sheet 100×70mm containing multicoloured design as T* **299** *of Antigua. P* 14.

MS2434 $6 Guggenheim Museum .. .. 3·50 4·2

(Litho Questa)

1992 (12 Nov). *World Regattas. T* **373** *and similar multicoloured designs. P* 14.

2435 15 c. Type **373** 20 2
2436 25 c. *Awesome*, Antigua 25 2
2437 35 c. *Mistress Quickly*, Bermuda 30 3
2438 50 c. *Emeraude*, St. Tropez 50 5
2439 $1 *Diva G*, German Admirals Cup .. 80 8
2440 $2 *Lady Be*, French Admirals Cup .. 1·50 1·7
2441 $4 *Midnight Sun*, Admirals Cup .. 2·75 3·2
2442 $5 *Carat*, Sardinia Cup .. .. 2·75 3·2
2435/42 .. .. *Set of* 8 8·00 9·0
MS2443 Two sheets, each 113×85 mm. (a) $6 Yachts, Grenada Regatta (*horiz*). (b) $6 Fastnet Race, 1979 (*horiz*) .. .. *Set of* 2 *sheets* 8·00 9·0

(Litho Questa)

1992 (16 Nov). *Christmas. Religious Paintings. Vert designs as T* **300** *of Antigua. Multicoloured. P* 13½×14.

2444 10 c. "Adoration of the Magi" (detail) (Fra Filippo Lippi) 25
2445 15 c. "Madonna adoring Child in a Wood" (Lippi) 30
2446 25 c. "Adoration of the Magi" (detail) (Botticelli) 40
2447 35 c. "The Epiphany - Adoration of the Magi" (detail) (Hieronymus Bosch) .. 45
2448 50 c. "Adoration of the Magi" (detail) (Giovanni de Paolo) 70
2449 75 c. "Adoration of the Magi" (Gentile da Fabriano) 90
2450 90 c. "Adoration of the Magi" (detail) (Juan Batista Maino) .. .. .. 1·10

451 $1 "Adoration of the Child" (Master of Liesborn) . . . . 1·25 80
452 $2 "Adoration of the Kings" (Master of Liesborn) . . . . 2·00 2·25
453 $3 "Adoration of the Three Wise Men" (Pedro Berruguete) . . . . . . 2·25 3·00
454 $4 "Adoration of the Child" (Lippi) . . 3·00 3·50
455 $5 "Adoration of the Child" (Correggio) 3·00 3·50
444/55 . . . . *Set of* 12 14·00 14·00
IS2456 Three sheets, each 72×97 mm. (a) $6 "Adoration of the Magi" (detail) (Andrea Mantegna). (b) $6 "Adoration of the Magi" (detail) (Hans Memling). (c) $6 "Adoration of the Shepherds" (La Tour) . . . . *Set of* 3 *sheets* 13·00 15·00
No. 2447 is inscribed "Hieronymous" in error.

374 Cher

375 Grenada Dove

(Des J. Genzo. Litho Questa)

992 (19 Nov). *Gold Record Award Winners.* *T* **374** *and similar vert designs. Multicoloured. P* 14.
457 90 c. Type **374** . . . . 1·25 1·25
a. Sheetlet. Nos. 2457/64 . . . . 8·50
458 90 c. Michael Jackson . . . . . . 1·25 1·25
459 90 c. Elvis Presley . . . . . . 1·25 1·25
460 90 c. Dolly Parton . . . . . . 1·25 1·25
461 90 c. Johnny Mathis . . . . . . 1·25 1·25
462 90 c. Madonna . . . . 1·25 1·25
463 90 c. Nat King Cole . . . . . . 1·25 1·25
464 90 c. Janice Joplin . . . . . . 1·25 1·25
457/64 . . . . *Set of* 8 8·50 8·50
IS2465 Two sheets, each 100×70 mm. (a) $3 Chuck Berry; $3 James Brown. (b) $3 Frank Sinatra; $3 Perry Como . . *Set of* 2 *sheets* 11·00 12·00
Nos. 2457/64 were printed together, *se-tenant,* in sheetlets of with a composite background design.

Des W. Wright and W. Hanson (Nos. 2467, 2476, **MS**2478a), W. Wright and L. Fried (Nos. 2468, 2474, **MS**2478b), J. Genzo (Nos. 2473, **MS**2478e), W. Wright (others). Litho B.D.T)

992 (15 Dec). *Anniversaries and Events.* *T* **375** *and similar multicoloured designs. P* 14.
466 10 c. Type **375** 50 40
467 25 c. Airship LZ-1 on maiden flight, 1900 (*horiz*) 70 30
468 50 c. ENDOSAT (robot plane) project (*horiz*) 75 55
469 75 c. Konrad Adenauer (German statesman) and industrial skyline (*horiz*) 80 70
470 $1.50, Golden Lion Tamarin (*horiz*) . . 2·00 2·00
471 $2 Mountain Gorilla (*horiz*) . . . . 2·50 2·50
472 $2 Outline of man and heart (*horiz*) . . 2·50 2·50
473 $3 Wolfgang Amadeus Mozart . . 3·25 3·25
474 $4 "Voyager 2" and Neptune (*horiz*) . . 3·50 3·50
475 $4 Adenauer with flag and map of West Germany (*horiz*) . . . . . . 3·50 3·50
476 $5 Count von Zeppelin and LZ-127 *Graf Zeppelin* (*horiz*) . . . . . . 3·50 3·50
477 $6 Admiral Richard Byrd (polar explorer) (*horiz*) . . . . 3·50 3·50
466/77 . . . . *Set of* 12 24·00 24·00
IS2478 Five sheets. (a) 110×80 mm. $6 Count von Zeppelin (*horiz*). (b) 110×80 mm. $6 Space shuttle recovering "Intelsat 6" satellite. (c) 110×80 mm. $6 Konrad Adenauer (*horiz*). (d) 95×70 mm. $6 Spotted Little Owl (*horiz*). (e) 100×70 mm. $6 Papageno costume from *The Magic Flute* . . . . . . *Set of* 5 *sheets* 18·00 20·00
Anniversaries and Events:—No. 2466, National bird; Nos. 467, 2476, **MS**2478a, 75th death anniv of Count Ferdinand von eppelin; Nos. 2468, 2475, **MS**2478b, International Space Year; os. 2469, 2475, **MS**2478c, 25th death anniv of Konrad denauer; Nos. 2470/1, **MS**2478d, Earth Summit '92, Rio; No. 472, United Nations World Health Organization Projects; No. 473, **MS**2478e, Death bicent of Mozart; No. 2477, 75th anniv of nternational Association of Lions Clubs.

376 Care Bear on Beach

(Des T.C.F.C. Inc. Litho Questa)

992 (15 Dec). *Ecology.* *T* **376** *and similar multicoloured design showing Care Bear cartoon characters. P* 14.
479 75 c. Type **376** 45 45
IS2480 71×101 mm. $2 Care Bear and butterfly (*vert*) . . . . 1·75 1·90

377 Samoyed and St. Basil's Cathedral, Moscow

378 Baha'i Shrine, Haifa

(Des Joan Popeio. Litho Questa)

1993 (20 Jan). *Dogs of the World.* *T* **377** *and similar horiz designs. Multicoloured. P* 14.
2481 10 c. Type **377** 40 30
2482 15 c. Chow and Ling Yin Monastery, China 50 30
2483 25 c. Boxer and Tower of London . . 55 30
2484 90 c. Basenji and Yamma Mosque, Niger 1·00 75
2485 $1 Golden Labrador and Parliament Building, Ottawa . . . . . . 1·00 80
2486 $3 St. Bernard and Parsenn, Switzerland 2·25 2·75
2487 $4 Rhodesian Ridgeback and Melrose House, South Africa . . . . 2·50 3·00
2488 $5 Afghan Hound and Mazar-i-Sharif, Afghanistan . . . . . . 2·50 3·00
2481/8 . . . . *Set of* 8 9·50 10·00
MS2489 Two sheets, each 100×70 mm. (a) $6 Australian Cattle Dog. (b) $6 Alaskan Malamute *Set of* 2 *sheets* 8·00 8·50
No. **MS**2489(a) is inscribed "Austrailian" in error.

(Litho Walsall)

1993 (8 Mar). *Bicentenary of the Louvre, Paris. Paintings by Jean-Antoine Watteau. Multicoloured designs as T* **305** *of Antigua. P* 12.
2490 $1 "The Faux-pas" 65 70
a. Sheetlet. Nos. 2490/7 . . . . 4·50
2491 $1 "Portrait of a Gentleman" 65 70
2492 $1 "Young Lady with Archlute" 65 70
2493 $1 "Young Man Dancing" 65 70
2494 $1 "Autumn, Pamona and a Cherub" . . 65 70
2495 $1 "Judgement of Paris" 65 70
2496 $1 "Pierrot" (detail) 65 70
2497 $1 "Pierrot" (different detail) 65 70
2490/7 . . . . *Set of* 8 4·50 5·00
MS2498 100×70 mm. $6 "The Embarkation for Cythère" (85×52 *mm*). P 14½ . . . . 3·75 4·50
Nos. 2490/7 were printed together, *se-tenant,* in sheetlets of 8 stamps and one centre label.

(Litho Cartor)

1993 (7 Apr). *Centenary of Baha'i Faith. P* 13½×14.
2499 **378** 75 c. multicoloured 60 60

379 *Citheronia magnifica*

380 Heliconia

(Litho Questa)

1993 (13 Apr). *Moths.* *T* **379** *and similar multicoloured designs. P* 14.
2500 10 c. Type **379** 25 25
2501 35 c. *Automeris metali* 40 25
2502 45 c. *Thysania zenobia* 50 30
2503 75 c. *Agrius cingulatus* 70 55
2504 $1 *Composia fidelissima* 80 65
2505 $2 *Synchlora xysteraria* . . . . 1·50 1·75
2506 $4 *Eumorpha labruscae* . . . . 2·50 2·75
2507 $5 *Ascalapha odorata* . . . . 2·50 2·75
2500/7 . . . . *Set of* 8 8·25 8·25
MS2508 Two sheets, each 100×70 mm. (a) $6 *Epimecis detexta* (*vert*). (b) $6 *Xylophanes titana* (*vert*) . . . . . . *Set of* 2 *sheets* 7·00 8·00

(Des D. Delouise. Litho Questa)

1993 (17 May). *Flowers.* *T* **380** *and similar multicoloured designs. P* 14.
2509 10 c. Type **380** 25 25
2510 35 c. Pansy 40 25
2511 45 c. Water Lily 50 30
2512 75 c. Bougainvillea 70 55
2513 $1 Calla Lily 80 65
2514 $2 California Poppy . . . . . . 1·50 1·75
2515 $4 Red Ginger . . . . 2·50 2·75
2516 $5 Anthurium . . . . 2·50 2·75
2509/16 . . . . *Set of* 8 8·25 8·25
MS2517 Two sheets, each 70×100 mm. (a) $6 Christmas Rose (*horiz*). (b) $6 Moth Orchid (*horiz*) . . . . . . *Set of* 2 *sheets* 7·00 8·00

(Des Kerri Schiff. Litho Questa)

1993 (2 June). *40th Anniv of Coronation. Vert designs as T* **307** *of Antigua. P* 13½×14.
2518 35 c. multicoloured 55 65
a. Sheetlet. Nos. 2518/21×2 . . . . 7·50
2519 70 c. multicoloured 70 80
2520 $1 reddish brown and black 75 85
2521 $5 multicoloured . . . . . . 2·25 2·50
2518/21 . . . . *Set of* 4 3·75 4·25
MS2522 70×100 mm. $6 multicoloured. P 14 3·75 4·50
Designs: (38×47 *mm*)—35 c. Queen Elizabeth II at Coronation (photograph by Cecil Beaton); 70 c. Sceptres; $1 Queen Elizabeth receiving sceptre from Archbishop of Canterbury; $5 Queen and Prince Philip with their children, 1960s. (28½×42½ *mm*)—$6 "Queen Elizabeth II, 1965" (detail) (Peter Greenham).
Nos. 2518/21 were printed together in sheetlets of 8 containing two *se-tenant* blocks of 4.

381 "Woman with Loaves" (Picasso)

382 Red-eyed Vireo

(Litho Questa)

1993 (1 July). *Anniversaries and Events.* *T* **381** *and similar designs. Each reddish brown, deep brown and black (Nos.* 2527, 2535, **MS**2536d) *or multicoloured (others). P* 14.
2523 25 c. Type **381** 30 20
2524 35 c. 16th-century telescope 35 20
2525 35 c. Public Library building 35 20
2526 35 c. Gaetan Boucher (speed skating, 1984) 35 20
2527 50 c. Willy Brandt with Senator Edward Kennedy (*horiz*) 40 30
2528 75 c. Carnival float (*horiz*) 50 40
2529 90 c. "Weeping Woman" (Picasso) . . 65 45
2530 $1 "Marii Prohaska" (Tyrus Czyzewski) 70 50
2531 $3 "Marysia et Burek a Geylan" (S. Wirkiewicz) . . . . . . 2·25 2·25
2532 $4 "Woman seated in Airchair" (Picasso) 2·75 2·75
2533 $4 Astronaut on Moon . . . . . . 2·75 2·75
2534 $5 Norbert Schramm (figure skating, 1984) . . . . 2·75 2·75
2535 $5 Willy Brandt and Kurt Waldheim (*horiz*) . . . . 2·75 2·75
2523/35 . . . . *Set of* 13 15·00 14·00
MS2536 Five sheets. (a) 76×107 mm. $5 Copernicus. (b) 75×105 mm. $6 "Three Women at the Spring" (detail) (Picasso). (c) 76×105 mm. $6 Women's Super G skiing medal winners, 1988 (*horiz*). (d) 105×75 mm. $6 Newspaper headline, 1974. (e) 105×76 mm. $6 "Parting" (detail) (Witold Wojtkiewicz) . . *Set of* 5 *sheets* 17·00 18·00
Anniversaries and Events:—Nos. 2523, 2529, 2532, **MS**2536b, 20th death anniv of Picasso (artist); Nos. 2524, 2533, **MS**2536a, 450th death anniv of Copernicus (astronomer); No. 2525, Centenary of Grenada Public Library (1992); Nos. 2526, 2534, **MS**2536c, Winter Olympic Games '94, Lillehammer; Nos. 2527, 2535, **MS**2536d, 80th birth anniv of Willy Brandt (German politician) (1992); No. 2528, Grenada Carnival; Nos. 2530/1, **MS**2536e, "Polska '93" International Stamp Exhibition, Poznań.

(Des R. Sauber. Litho B.D.T.)

1993 (13 July). *Songbirds.* *T* **382** *and similar horiz designs. Multicoloured. P* 14.
2537 15 c. Type **382** 35 35
a. Sheetlet. Nos. 2537/48 . . . . 7·00
2538 25 c. Fork-tailed Flycatcher ("Scissor-tailed Flycatcher") 40 40
2539 35 c. Palm Chat 45 45
2540 35 c. Chaffinch 45 45
2541 45 c. Yellow Wagtail 50 50
2542 45 c. Painted Bunting 50 50
2543 50 c. Short-tailed Pygmy Tyrant ("Short-tailed Pygmy Flycatcher") 50 50
2544 65 c. Orange-breasted Bunting ("Rainbow Bunting") 60 60
2545 75 c. Red Crossbill 60 60
2546 75 c. Akialoa 60 60
2547 $1 Yellow-throated Longclaw ("Yellow-throated Wagtail") 75 75
2548 $4 Barn Swallow . . . . . . 2·25 2·25
2537/48 . . . . *Set of* 12 7·00 7·00
MS2549 Two sheets, each 105×86 mm. (a) $6 Song Thrush. (b) $6 White-crested Laughing Thrush . . . . . . *Set of* 2 *sheets* 7·00 8·00
Nos. 2537/48 were printed together, *se-tenant,* in sheetlets of 12 with the backgrounds forming a composite design.

PRICES OF SETS

Set prices are given for many issues, generally those containing three stamps or more. Definitive sets include one of each value or major colour change, but do not cover different perforations, die types or minor shades. Where a choice is possible the set prices are based on the cheapest versions of the stamps included in the listings.

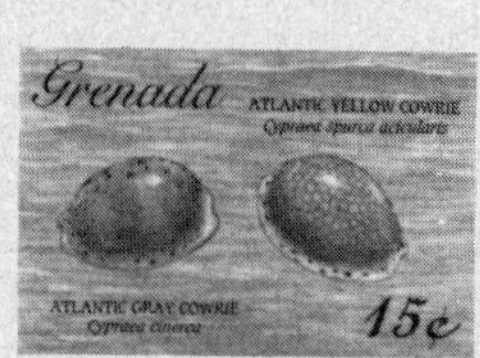

383 Atlantic Grey Cowrie (*Cypraea cinerea*) and Atlantic Yellow Cowrie (*Cypraea spurca acicularis*)

384 James K. Spensley

(Des I. MacLaury. Litho B.D.T.)

1993 (19 July). *Sea Shells. T* **383** *and similar horiz designs. Multicoloured. P* 14.

2550 15 c. Type **383** 35 35
a. Sheetlet. Nos. 2550/61 .. .. 7·00
2551 15 c. Candy-stick Tellin (*Tellina similis*) and Sunrise Tellin (*Tellina radiata*) 35 35
2552 25 c. Caribbean Vase (*Vasum muricatum*) 40 40
2553 35 c. Lightning Venus (*Pitar fulminatus*) and Royal Comb Venus (*Pitar dione*) 45 45
2554 35 c. Crown Cone (*Conus regius*) .. 45 45
2555 45 c. Reticulated Cowrie-helmet (*Cypraecassis testiculus*) 50 50
2556 50 c. Barbados Mitre (*Mitra barbadensis*) and Variegated Turret Shell (*Turritella variegata*) 50 50
2557 50 c. Common Egg Cockle (*Laevicardium laevigatum*) and Atlantic Strawberry Cockle (*Americardia media*) .. 50 50
2558 75 c. Measled Cowrie (*Cypraea zebra*) .. 60 60
2559 75 c. Rooster-tail Conch (*Strombus gallus*) 60 60
2560 $1 Lion's-paw Scallop (*Lyropecten nodosa*) and Antillean Scallop (*Lyropecten antillarum*) 75 75
2561 $4 Dog-head Triton (*Cymatium moritinctum caribbaeum*) .. .. 2·25 2·25
2550/61 .. .. *Set of* 12 7·00 7·00
MS2562 Two sheets, each 76×106 mm. (a) $6 Dyson's Keyhole Limpet (*Diodora dysoni*). (b) $6 Virgin Nerite (*Neritina virginea*) and Emerald Nerite (*Smaragdia viridis viridemaris*) *Set of* 2 *sheets* 8·50 9·00

Nos. 2550/61 were printed together, *se-tenant*, in sheetlets of 12 with the backgrounds forming a composite design.

(Litho Questa)

1993 (13 Aug). *Asian International Stamp Exhibitions. Multicoloured designs as T* **268** *of Dominica. P* 13½×14.

(*a*) *"Indopex '93", Surabaya, Indonesia*

2563 35 c. Megalithic Carving, Sumba Island .. 35 25
2564 45 c. Entrance to Gao Gajah, Bali .. 45 30
2565 $1.50, Statue of kris holder .. .. 1·00 1·00
a. Sheetlet. Nos. 2565/70 .. .. 5·50
2566 $1.50, Hanuman protecting Sita .. 1·00 1·00
2567 $1.50, Sendi of Visu mounted on Garuda 1·00 1·00
2568 $1.50, Wahana (votif figure) .. .. 1·00 1·00
2569 $1.50, Hanuman (*different*) .. .. 1·00 1·00
2570 $1.50, Singa (symbolic lion) .. 1·00 1·00
2571 $2 Loving-mother Bridge, Taroko Gorge National Park .. .. .. 1·40 1·50
2572 $4 Head of Kala over temple gateway, Northern Bali .. .. 2·50 2·75
2563/72 .. .. *Set of* 10 9·50 9·25
MS2573 104×134 mm. $6 Slow Loris .. 3·75 4·25

(*b*) *"Taipei '93", Taiwan*

2574 35 c. Fire-breathing Dragon, New Year's Fair, Chongqing 35 25
2575 45 c. Stone elephant, Ming Tomb, Nanjing 45 30
2576 $1.50, "Ornamental Cock" (Han Meilin) 1·00 1·00
a. Sheetlet. Nos. 2576/81 .. .. 5·50
2577 $1.50, "He's even afraid of Cows" (Meilin) 1·00 1·00
2578 $1.50, "On a Moonlit Night" (Meilin) .. 1·00 1·00
2579 $1.50, "Eyes that see in the Dark" (Meilin) .. .. 1·00 1·00
2580 $1.50, "He's well behaved" (Meilin) .. 1·00 1·00
2581 $1.50, "He doesn't Bite" (Meilin) .. 1·00 1·00
2582 $2 Marble peifang, Ming 13 Tombs, Beijing .. .. 1·40 1·50
2583 $4 Stone pillar, Nanjing .. .. 2·50 2·75
2574/83 .. .. *Set of* 10 9·50 9·75
MS2584 104×134 mm. $6 Orang-utan, Mt Leuser National Park .. .. .. 3·75 4·25

(*c*) *"Bangkok 1993", Thailand*

2585 35 c. Nora Nair, Prasad Phra Thepidon, Wat Phra Kaew 35 25
2586 45 c. Stucco deities at Library of Wat Phra Singh 45 30
2587 $1.50, Wooden carved horses .. .. 1·00 1·00
a. Sheetlet. Nos. 2587/92 .. .. 5·50
2588 $1.50, Wheel of the law .. .. 1·00 1·00
2589 $1.50, Lanna bronze elephant .. .. 1·00 1·00
2590 $1.50, Kendi in the form of elephant .. 1·00 1·00
2591 $1.50, Bronze duck .. .. .. 1·00 1·00
2592 $1.50, Horseman .. .. .. 1·00 1·00
2593 $2 Naga snake, Chiang Mai's Temple .. 1·40 1·50
2594 $4 Stucco figures, Wat Chang Lom .. 2·50 2·75
2585/94 .. .. *Set of* 10 9·50 9·75
MS2595 134×104 mm. $6 Elephant calf (*horiz*). P 14×13½. .. .. 3·75 4·25

Nos. 2565/70, 2576/81 and 2571/92 were each printed together, *se-tenant*, in sheetlets of 6.

No. 2590 is incorrectly inscribed "Kendi in the form of an Elphant".

(Des Rosemary DeFiglio. Litho Questa)

1993 (7 Sept). *World Cup Football Championship, U.S.A. (1994) (1st issue). Vert designs as T* **310** *of Antigua. Multicoloured. P* 14.

2596 10 c. Nikolai Larionov (Russia) 20 20
2597 25 c. Andrea Carnevale (Italy) 40 25
2598 35 c. Enzo Schifo (Belgium) and Soon-Ho Choi (South Korea) 45 25
2599 45 c. Gary Lineker (England) 50 30
2600 $1 Diego Maradona (Argentina) .. 1·00 80
2601 $2 Lothar Mattaeus (Germany) .. 1·60 1·90
2602 $4 Jan Karas (Poland) and Julio César Silva (Brazil) .. .. .. 2·25 2·75
2603 $5 Claudio Caniggia (Argentina) .. 2·50 3·00
2596/603 .. .. *Set of* 8 8·00 8·50
MS2604 Two sheets, each 75×104 mm. (a) $6 Wlodzimierz (Poland). (b) $6 José Basualdo (Argentina) .. .. .. *Set of* 2 *sheets* 7·00 8·00

See also Nos. 2721/7.

(Litho Questa)

1993 (7 Sept). *Centenary of Italian Football. T* **384** *and similar designs showing past and present Genoa players. Each blue-black, bright vermilion and black* (*Nos.* 2605/16) *or multicoloured* (*No.* **MS**2617). *P* 14.

2605 $3 Type **384** .. .. 2·00 2·00
a. Sheetlet. Nos. 2605/10 .. .. 11·00
2606 $3 Renzo de Vecchi .. .. .. 2·00 2·00
2607 $3 Giovanni de Pra' .. .. .. 2·00 2·00
2608 $3 Luigi Burlando .. .. .. 2·00 2·00
2609 $3 Felice Levratto .. .. .. 2·00 2·00
2610 $3 Guglielmo Stabile .. .. .. 2·00 2·00
2611 $3 Vittorio Sardelli .. .. .. 2·00 2·00
a. Sheetlet. Nos. 2611/16 .. .. 11·00
2612 $3 Juan Carlos Verdeal .. .. .. 2·00 2·00
2613 $3 Fosco Becattini .. .. .. 2·00 2·00
2614 $3 Julio Cesar Abadie .. .. .. 2·00 2·00
2615 $3 Luigi Meroni .. .. 2·00 2·00
2616 $3 Roberto Pruzzo .. .. .. 2·00 2·00
2605/16 .. .. *Set of* 12 22·00 22·00
MS2617 Two sheets. (a) 100×75 mm. $15 Genoa Football Club badge (29×45 *mm*). P 14. (b) 129×106 mm. $15 Genoa team of 1991–92 (48×35 *mm*). P 14×13½ .. *Set of* 2 *sheets* 21·00 22·00

Nos. 2605/10 and 2611/16 were printed together, *se-tenant*, in sheetlets of 6.

385 *The Band Concert*, 1935

(Des Rosemary DeFiglio. Litho Questa)

1993 (11 Nov). *65th Anniv of Mickey Mouse. T* **385** *and similar multicoloured designs showing Mickey Mouse in scenes from Walt Disney cartoon films. P* 14×13½.

2618 25 c. Type **385** 45 20
2619 35 c. *Mickey's Circus*, 1936 .. .. 50 20
2620 50 c. *Magician Mickey*, 1937 .. .. 60 35
2621 75 c. *Moose Hunters*, 1937 .. .. 80 60
2622 $1 *Mickey's Amateurs*, 1937 .. .. 90 80
2623 $2 *Tugboat Mickey*, 1940 .. .. 1·50 1·50
2624 $4 *Orphan's Benefit*, 1941 .. .. 2·50 2·75
2625 $5 *Mickey's Christmas Carol*, 1983 .. 2·50 2·75
2618/25 .. .. *Set of* 8 8·75 8·25
MS2626 Two sheets, each 127×102 mm. (a) $6 *Mickey's Birthday Party*, 1942. P 14×13½. (b) $6 *Mickey's Trailer*, 1938 (*vert*). P 13½×14 *Set of* 2 *sheets* 8·50 9·00

No. 2624 is inscribed "Oprhan's Benefit" in error.

(Litho Questa)

1993 (22 Nov). *Christmas. Religious Paintings. Vert designs as T* **270** *of Dominica. Black, pale lemon and red* (*Nos.* 2627/8, 2632, 2634, **MS**2635a) *or multicoloured* (*others*). *P* 13½×14.

2627 10 c. "The Nativity" (Dürer) 25 15
2628 25 c. "The Annunciation" (Dürer) .. 35 15
2629 35 c. "The Litta Madonna" (Da Vinci) .. 40 20
2630 60 c. "The Virgin and Child with St. John the Baptist and St. Anne" (Da Vinci) 50 40
2631 90 c. "The Madonna with the Carnation" (Da Vinci) 65 65
2632 $1 "Adoration of the Magi" (Dürer) .. 75 75
2633 $4 "The Benois Madonna" (Da Vinci) .. 2·50 3·00
2634 $5 "The Virgin Mary in the Sun" (Dürer) 2·50 3·00
2627/34 .. .. *Set of* 8 7·25 7·50
MS2635 Two sheets, each 102×128 mm. (a) $6 "The Holy Family with Three Hares" (detail) (Dürer). (b) $6 "Adoration of the Magi" (detail) (Da Vinci) .. .. .. *Set of* 2 *sheets* 7·00 8·00

Nos. 2629/31, 2633 and **MS**2635b are inscribed "LEONARDO DI VINCI".

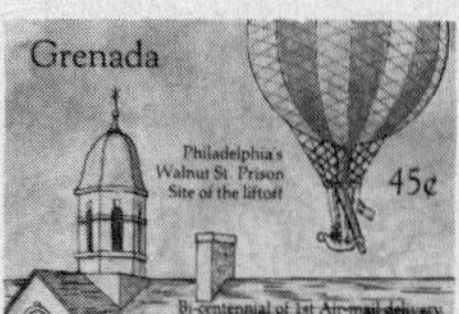

386 Blanchard's Balloon over Walnut St. Prison

(Litho Questa)

1993 (21 Dec). *Aviation Anniversaries. T* **386** *and similar multicoloured designs. P* 14.

2636 35 c. Airship LZ-127 *Graf Zeppelin* over Vienna at night 35 20
2637 45 c. Type **386** 20 25
2638 50 c. Lysander 50 35
2639 75 c. *Graf Zeppelin* over Pyramids .. 75 55
2640 $2 Blanchard waving hat from balloon (*vert*) 90 95
2641 $3 Hawker Typhoon .. .. .. 2·00 2·50
2642 $5 *Graf Zeppelin* over Rio de Janeiro .. 3·25 3·75
2636/42 .. .. *Set of* 7 7·25 7·75
MS2643 Three sheets, each 106×77 mm. (a) $6 *Graf Zeppelin*. (b) $6 Blanchard's balloon (*vert*). (c) $6 Hawker Hurricane .. *Set of* 3 *sheets* 10·50 11·00

Anniversaries:—Nos. 2636, 2639, 2642, **MS**2643a, 125th birth anniv of Hugo Eckener (airship commander); Nos. 2637, 2640, **MS**2643b, Bicentenary of First Airmail Flight; Nos. 2638, 2641, **MS**2643c, 75th anniv of Royal Air Force

387 Mercedes Benz "370 S" Cabriolet, 1932

388 Fishermen with Blue Marlin

(Des K. Gromell. Litho Questa)

1993 (21 Dec). *Centenaries of Henry Ford's First Petrol Engine* (*Nos.* 2645/6, **MS**2648b) *and Karl Benz's First Four-wheeled Car* (*others*). *T* **387** *and similar horiz designs. Multicoloured. P* 14.

2644 35 c. Type **387** 15 20
2645 45 c. Ford "Mustang", 1966 .. .. 40 30
2646 $3 Ford "Model A" Phaeton, 1930 .. 1·40 1·50
2647 $4 Mercedes Benz "300 Sl" Gullwing .. 3·50 3·75
2644/7 .. .. *Set of* 4 5·00 5·25
MS2648 Two sheets, each 76×106 mm. (a) $6 Mercedes Benz "290", 1934. (b) $6 Ford "Model A", 1903 .. .. .. *Set of* 2 *sheets* 7·00 8·00

(Des Kerri Schiff. Litho Questa)

1993 (31 Dec). *Famous Paintings by Rembrandt and Matisse. Multicoloured designs as T* **316** *of Antigua. P* 13½×14.

2649 15 c. "Self-portrait", 1900 (Matisse) .. 30 20
2650 35 c. "Self-portrait", 1629 (Rembrandt) .. 35 20
2651 45 c. "Self-portrait", 1918 (Matisse) .. 40 25
2652 50 c. "Self-portrait", 1640 (Rembrandt) .. 50 35
2653 75 c. "Self-portrait", 1652 (Rembrandt) .. 65 55
2654 $2 "Self-portrait", 1906 (Matisse) .. 1·40 1·75
2655 $4 "Self-portrait", 1900 (*different*) (Matisse) .. .. 2·50 3·25
2656 $5 "Self-portrait", 1625–31 (Rembrandt) 2·75 3·25
2649/56 .. .. *Set of* 8 8·00 8·75
MS2657 Two sheets. (a) 100×125 mm. $6 "The Painter in his Studio" (detail) (Matisse). P 13½×14. (b) 125×100 mm. $6 "The Sampling Officials of the Drapers' Guild" (detail) (Rembrandt) (*horiz*). P 14×13½ *Set of* 2 *sheets* 7·00 8·00

(Litho Questa)

1994 (21 Jan). *25th Anniv of Spice Island Billfish Tournament. T* **388** *and similar vert designs. Multicoloured. P* 14.

2658 15 c. Type **388** 30 20
2659 25 c. Sailfish and angler 35 20
2660 35 c. Yellow-finned Tuna with angler .. 50 25
2661 50 c. White Marlin with angler 60 50
2662 75 c. Catching a Sailfish 75 80
2658/62 .. .. *Set of* 5 2·25 1·75

389 National Flag and Ketch in Bay

390 *Hygrocybe acutoconica*

(Litho Questa)

1994 (8 Feb). *25th Anniv of Independence. T* **389** *and similar vert design. Multicoloured. P* 14.

2663 35 c. Type **389** 30 30
MS2664 76×106 mm. $6 Map of Grenada .. 3·50 4·00

(Des W. Hanson. Litho Questa)

1994 (18 Feb). *"Hong Kong '94" International Stamp Exhibition* (*1st issue*). *Horiz designs as T* **317** *of Antigua. Multicoloured. P* 14.

2665 40 c. Hong Kong 1971 Scouting 50 c. stamp and "Hong Kong Post Office, 1846" (left detail) (M. Bruce) 30 40
a. Horiz pair. Nos. 2665/6 .. .. 60 80

2666 40 c. Grenada 1988 Rotary $2 and "Hong Kong Post Office, 1846" (right detail) (M. Bruce) 30 40

Nos. 2665/6 were printed together, *se-tenant*, in horizontal pairs throughout the sheet with the centre part of each pair forming the complete painting.

(Des Kerri Schiff. Litho Questa)

1994 (18 Feb). *"Hong Kong '94" International Stamp Exhibition (2nd issue). Qing Dynasty Porcelain. Multicoloured designs as T* **318** *of Antigua, but vert. P* 14.

2667 45 c. Vase with dragon decoration 30 35
a. Sheetlet. Nos. 2667/72 .. .. 1·60
2668 45 c. Hat stand with brown base 30 35
2669 45 c. Gourd-shaped vase 30 35
2670 45 c. Rotating vase with openwork 30 35
2671 45 c. Candlestick with dogs 30 35
2672 45 c. Hat stand with orange base 30 35
2667/72 .. .. *Set of* 6 1·60 1·90

Nos. 2667/72 were printed together, *se-tenant*, in sheetlets of 6.

(Des Susan Carlson. Litho Questa)

1994 (6 Apr). *Fungi. T* **390** *and similar vert designs. Multicoloured. P* 14.

2673 35 c. Type **390** 35 20
2674 45 c. *Leucopaxillus gracillimus* 40 25
2675 50 c. *Leptonia caeruleocapitata* 40 30
2676 75 c. *Leucocoprinus birnbaumii* 60 50
2677 $1 *Marasmius atrorubens* 75 75
2678 $2 *Boletellus cubensis* .. .. .. 1·25 1·50
2679 $4 *Chlorophyllum molybdites* .. .. 2·25 2·40
2680 $5 *Psilocybe cubensis* .. .. .. 2·25 2·40
2673/80 .. .. *Set of* 8 7·50 7·50
MS2681 Two sheets, each 100×70 mm. (a) $6 *Mycena pura*. (b) $6 *Pyrrhoglossum lilaceipes* *Set of* 2 *sheets* 7·50 8·00

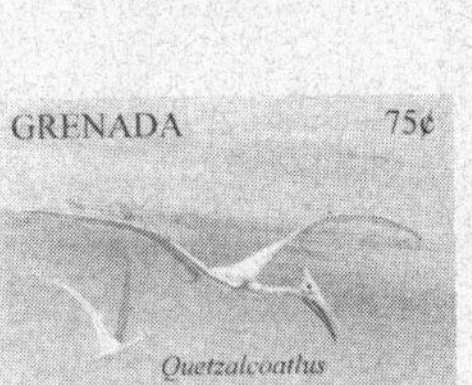

391 Quetzalcoatlus

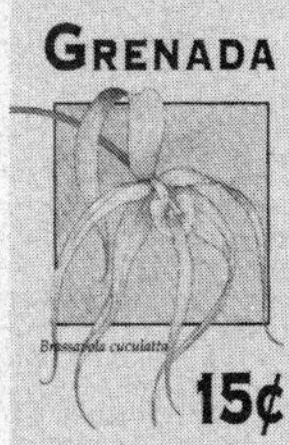

392 *Brassavola cuculatta*

(Des V. DiFate. Litho Questa)

1994 (13 Apr). *Prehistoric Animals. T* **391** *and similar multicoloured designs. P* 14.

2682 75 c. Type **391** 45 50
a. Sheetlet. Nos. 2682/93 .. .. 4·75
2683 75 c. Pteranodon ingens 45 50
2684 75 c. Tropeognathus 45 50
2685 75 c. Phobetor 45 50
2686 75 c. Alamosaurus 45 50
2687 75 c. Triceratops 45 50
2688 75 c. Tyrannosaurus rex 45 50
2689 75 c. Head of Tyrannosaurus rex .. 45 50
2690 75 c. Lambeosaurus 45 50
2691 75 c. Spinosaurus 45 50
2692 75 c. Parasaurolophus 45 50
2693 75 c. Hadrosaurus 45 50
2694 75 c. Germanodactylus 45 50
a. Sheetlet. Nos. 2694/705 .. .. 4·75
2695 75 c. Dimorphodon 45 50
2696 75 c. Ramphorynchus 45 50
2697 75 c. Apatosaurus 45 50
2698 75 c. Pterodactylus 45 50
2699 75 c. Stegosaurus 45 50
2700 75 c. Brachiosaurus 45 50
2701 75 c. Allosaurus 45 50
2702 75 c. Plesiosaurus 45 50
2703 75 c. Ceratosaurus 45 50
2704 75 c. Compsognathus 45 50
2705 75 c. Elaphosaurus 45 50
2682/705 .. .. *Set of* 24 9·50 11·00
MS2706 Two sheets. (a) 100×70 mm. $6 Pteranodon ingens (*different*). (b) 70×100 mm. $6 Head of Plateosaurus (*vert*) .. *Set of* 2 *sheets* 7·50 8·00

Nos. 2682/93 and 2694/705 were printed together, *se-tenant*, in sheetlets of 12 forming composite designs.

(Des W. Hanson. Litho B.D.T.)

1994 (4 Aug). *25th Anniv of First Moon Landing. Space Shuttle* Challenger. *Horiz designs as T* **326** *of Antigua. Multicoloured. P* 14.

2707 $2 Space Shuttle *Challenger* .. .. 1·10 1·40
a. Sheetlet. Nos. 2707/12 .. .. 6·00
2708 $2 Judith Resnick (astronaut) .. .. 1·10 1·40
2709 $2 Aircraft in memorial fly past .. .. 1·10 1·40
2710 $2 Dick Scobee (astronaut) .. .. 1·10 1·40
2711 $2 Mission logo .. .. .. 1·10 1·40
2712 $2 Michael Smith (astronaut) .. .. 1·10 1·40
2707/12 .. .. *Set of* 6 6·00 7·50
MS2713 107×76 mm. $6 *Challenger* crew .. 3·50 4·00

Nos. 2707/12 were printed together, *se-tenant*, in sheetlets of 6.

(Litho Questa)

1994 (4 Aug). *Centenary of International Olympic Committee. Gold Medal Winners. Multicoloured designs as T* **327** *of Antigua, but vert. P* 14.

2714 50 c. Heike Dreschler (Germany) (long jump), 1992 .. .. 40 30
2715 $1.50, Nadia Comaneci (Rumania) (gymnastics), 1976 and 1980 .. .. 1·10 1·25
MS2716 107×76 mm. $6 Dan Jansen (U.S.A.) (1000 metre speed skating), 1994 .. .. 3·50 4·00

(Litho Questa)

1994 (4 Aug). *International Year of the Family. Horiz design as T* **328** *of Antigua. Multicoloured. P* 14.

2717 $1 Grenadian family 55 60

(Des J. Batchelor. Litho Questa)

1994 (4 Aug). *50th Anniv of D-Day. Horiz designs as T* **331** *of Antigua. Multicoloured. P* 14.

2718 40 c. Sherman amphibious tank leaving landing craft 40 30
2719 $2 Tank on Churchill "Ark" bridging vehicle .. .. 1·40 1·50
2720 $3 Churchill "Bobbin" tank laying roadway .. .. 1·75 2·00
2718/20 .. .. *Set of* 3 3·25 3·50
MS2721 107×76 mm. $6 Churchill AVRE with fascine .. .. 3·50 4·00

(Des Kerri Schiff. Litho Questa (Nos. 2724/31, MS2733), B.D.T. (others))

1994 (4 Aug). *"Philakorea '94" International Stamp Exhibition, Seoul. Multicoloured designs as T* **279** *of Dominica. P* 13½×14 *(Nos. 2724/31) or* 14 *(others).*

2722 40 c. Wonson Park (*horiz*) 20 25
2723 $1 Pusan (*horiz*) 45 50
2724 $1 "Lady in a Hooded Cloak" (left detail) (Sin Yunbok) 45 50
a. Sheetlet. Nos. 2724/31 .. .. 3·50
2725 $1 "Lady in a Hooded Cloak" (right detail) 45 50
2726 $1 "Kiaseng House" (left detail) (Sin Yunbok) 45 50
2727 $1 "Kiaseng House" (right detail) .. 45 50
2728 $1 "Amorous Youth on a Picnic" (left detail) (Sin Yunbok) 45 50
2729 $1 "Amorous Youth on a Picnic" (right detail) 45 50
2730 $1 "Chasing a Cat" (left detail) (Sin Yunbok) 45 50
2731 $1 "Chasing a Cat" (right detail) .. 45 50
2732 $4 Korean orchestra, National Theatre, Seoul (*horiz*) .. .. .. 1·90 2·00
2722/32 .. .. *Set of* 11 6·00 6·75
MS2733 70×102 mm. $6 "Roof Tiling" (detail) (Kim Hongdo). P 14 .. .. 3·25 3·50

Nos. 2724/31, each 26×49 mm, were printed together, *se-tenant*, in sheetlets of 8. Paintings are shown across horizontal pairs without white vertical margins in the centre.

(Des Claudia Sergeant. Litho Questa)

1994 (7 Aug). *Orchids. T* **392** *and similar vert designs. Multicoloured. P* 14.

2734 15 c. Type **392** 30 20
2735 25 c. *Comparettia falcata* 40 20
2736 45 c. *Epidendrum ciliare* 50 30
2737 75 c. *Epidendrum cochleatum* 70 50
2738 $1 *Ionopsis utricularioides* 80 70
2739 $2 *Onicidium ceboletta* .. .. 1·25 1·40
2740 $4 *Onicidium luridium* .. .. 2·25 2·50
2741 $5 *Rodriquezia secunda* .. .. 2·25 2·50
2734/41 .. .. *Set of* 8 7·50 7·50
MS2742 Two sheets, each 100×70 mm. (a) $6 *Ionopsis utricularioides* (*different*). (b) $6 *Onicidium luridium* (*different*) .. *Set of* 2 *sheets* 7·50 8·00

No. MS2742(b) is inscribed "Onicium luridum" in error.

393 Tony Meola (U.S.A.)

394 Yellow-tailed Snapper

(Litho Questa)

1994 (11 Aug). *World Cup Football Championship, U.S.A. (2nd issue). T* **393** *and similar vert designs. Multicoloured. P* 14.

2743 75 c. Type **393** 45 50
a. Sheetlet. Nos. 2743/8 .. .. 2·40
2744 75 c. Steve Mark (Grenada) 45 50
2745 75 c. Gianluigi Lentini (Italy) 45 50
2746 75 c. Belloumi (Algeria) 45 50
2747 75 c. Nunoz (Spain) 45 50
2748 75 c. Lothar Matthaus (Germany) .. 45 50
2743/8 .. .. *Set of* 6 2·40 2·75
MS2749 Two sheets. (a) 99×70 mm. $6 World Cup Championship poster, 1930. (b) 70×114 mm. $6 Steve Mark (Grenada) (*different*) *Set of* 2 *sheets* 7·50 8·00

Nos. 2743/8 were printed together, *se-tenant*, in sheetlets of 6.

(Litho Questa)

1994 (1 Sept). *First Recipients of Order of the Caribbean Community. Horiz designs as Nos. 2046/8 of Antigua. Multicoloured. P* 14.

2750 15 c. Sir Shridath Ramphal 10 10
2751 65 c. William Demas 40 40
2752 $2 Derek Walcott .. .. .. 1·40 1·60
2750/2 .. .. *Set of* 3 1·60 1·75

(Des P. Gonzalez. Litho Questa)

1994 (1 Sept). *Fishes. T* **394** *and similar multicoloured designs. P* 14.

2753 15 c. Type **394** 30 20
2754 20 c. Blue Tang 30 20
2755 25 c. Porkfish (*vert*) 30 20
2756 75 c. Four-eyed Butterflyfish 65 50
2757 $1 Reid's Seahorse (*vert*) 75 70
2758 $2 Spotted Moray (*vert*) .. .. 1·25 1·50
2759 $4 Royal Gramma ("Fairy Basslet") .. 2·25 2·50
2760 $5 Queen Triggerfish (*vert*) .. .. 2·25 2·50
2753/60 .. .. *Set of* 8 7·25 7·50
MS2761 Two sheets, each 106×76 mm. (a) $6 Queen Angelfish. (b) $6 Long-spined Squirrelfish *Set of* 2 *sheets* 7·50 8·00

395 Mickey Mouse bathing Pluto

396 *Anartia amathea*

(Des Alvin White Studios. Litho Questa)

1994 (22 Sept). *Chinese New Year ("Year of the Dog"). T* **395** *and similar horiz designs showing Walt Disney cartoon characters. Multicoloured. P* 14×13½.

2762 2 c. Type **395** 10 10
2763 3 c. Dog taking mouthwash 10 10
2764 4 c. Dog with curlers in tail 10 10
2765 5 c. Brushing dog's eyelashes 10 10
2766 10 c. Giving dog manicure 15 10
2767 15 c. Mickey spraying Pluto with flea powder 20 15
2768 20 c. Dogs on display 25 20
2769 $4 Judge checking Pluto's teeth .. 2·50 3·00
2770 $5 Pluto wearing "1st Prize" rosette .. 2·50 3·00
2762/70 .. .. *Set of* 9 5·50 6·00
MS2771 Three sheets, each 127×102 mm. (a) $6 King Charles Spaniel rubbing against judge's leg. (b) $6 Pluto holding rosette. (c) $6 Pluto with No. 13 on coat .. .. *Set of* 3 *sheets* 11·00 12·00

(Des I. MacLaury. Litho Questa)

1994 (28 Sept)–**96**. *Butterflies. T* **396** *and similar vert designs. Multicoloured. A. Without imprint date. P* 14

2772A 10 c. Type **396** 10 10
2773A 15 c. *Marpesia petreus* 10 10
2774A 25 c. *Hylephila phylaeus* 10 10
2775A 35 c. *Junonia evarete* 15 20
2776A 45 c. *Pseudolycaena marsyas* 20 25
2777A 50 c. *Heliconius charitonius* 20 25
2778A 75 c. *Hypolimnas misippus* 35 40
2779A $1 *Cepheuptychia cephus* 45 50
2780A $2 *Historis odius* 85 90
2781A $3 *Phoebis philea* .. .. .. 1·25 1·40
2782A $4 *Urbanus proteus* .. .. .. 1·75 1·90
2783A $5 *Battus polydamas* .. .. .. 2·10 2·25
2784A $10 *Philaethria dido* .. .. .. 4·25 4·50
2785A $20 *Hamadryas arethusa* .. .. 8·75 9·00
2772A/85A .. .. *Set of* 14 20·00 22·00

B. *With imprint date* ("1996"). *P* 12 (7.11.96)

2774B 25 c. *Hylephila phylaeus* 10 10
2775B 35 c. *Junonia evarete* 15 20
2778cB 90 c. *Pyrgus oileus* 40 45
2779cB $1.50, *Allosmaitia piplea* 70 75
2774B/9cB .. .. *Set of* 4 1·25 1·40

(Litho Questa)

1994 (5 Dec). *Christmas. Religious Paintings by Francisco de Zurbaran. Multicoloured designs as T* **336** *of Antigua. P* 13½×14.

2786 10 c. "The Virgin and Child with St. John" (1658) 20 15
2787 15 c. "The Circumcision" 30 20
2788 25 c. "Adoration of St. Joseph" 30 20
2789 35 c. "Adoration of the Magi" 30 20
2790 75 c. "The Portiuncula" 60 45
2791 $1 "The Virgin and Child with St. John" (1662) 75 60
2792 $2 "The Virgin and Child with St. John" (1658/64) .. .. 1·25 1·25
2793 $4 "The Flight into Egypt" .. .. 2·25 2·50
2786/93 .. .. *Set of* 8 5·00 4·75
MS2794 Two sheets. (a) 74×86 mm. $6 "Our Lady of Ransom and Two Mercedarians" (detail). P 13½×14. (b) 114×100 mm. $6 "Adoration of the Shepherds" (detail) (*horiz*). P 14×13½ *Set of* 2 *sheets* 7·50 8·00

397 Grenada Dove on Nest

(Litho Questa)

1995 (10 Jan). *Birds. T* **397** *and similar multicoloured designs. P* 14.
2795 25 c. Type **397** 40 20
2796 35 c. Pair of Grenada Doves at nest .. 45 20
2797 45 c. Cuban Tody (*vert*) 50 25
2798 75 c. Grenada Dove on branch (*vert*) .. 60 60
2799 75 c. Painted Bunting 60 60
2800 $1 Grenada Dove in flight (*vert*) .. 75 75
2801 $1 Red-legged Honeycreeper 75 75
2802 $5 Green Jay .. .. 2·50 2·75
2795/802 .. .. *Set of* 8 6·00 5·50
MS2803 Two sheets, each 101×71 mm. (a) $6 Chaffinch. (b) $6 Chestnut-sided Shrike Vireo *Set of* 2 *sheets* 7·50 8·00

Nos. 2795/6, 2798 and 2800 also show the W.W.F. Panda emblem.

(Des A. Melville-Brown. Litho Questa)

1995 (12 Jan). *Centenary of First English Cricket Tour to the West Indies. Multicoloured designs as T* **329** *of Antigua. P* 14.
2804 25 c. Junior Murray (West Indies) (*vert*) .. 30 20
2805 35 c. Richie Richardson (West Indies) (*vert*) 35 25
2806 $2 Alex Stewart (England) and Wisden Trophy .. .. 1·40 1·60
2804/6 .. .. *Set of* 3 1·90 1·90
MS2807 75×95 mm. $3 West Indian team, 1994 1·75 2·00

398 Hooded Merganser

(Litho Questa)

1995 (27 Mar). *Water Birds of the World. T* **398** *and similar horiz designs. Multicoloured. P* 14.
2808 25 c. Type **398** 10 10
2809 35 c. Green-winged Teal 15 20
2810 75 c. King Eider 35 40
a. Sheetlet. Nos. 2810/21 .. .. 4·25
2811 75 c. Common Shoveler 35 40
2812 75 c. Long-tailed Duck 35 40
2813 75 c. Chiloe Wigeon 35 40
2814 75 c. Red-breasted Merganser 35 40
2815 75 c. Falcated Teal 35 40
2816 75 c. Versicolor Teal 35 40
2817 75 c. Smew 35 40
2818 75 c. Red-crested Pochard 35 40
2819 75 c. Pintail 35 40
2820 75 c. Barrow's Goldeneye 35 40
2821 75 c. Stellar's Eider 35 40
2822 $1 Harlequin Duck 45 50
2823 $3 European Wigeon .. .. .. 1·25 1·40
2808/23 .. .. *Set of* 16 6·00 6·75
MS2824 Two sheets, each 74×104 mm. (a) $5 Common Shelduck ("European Wigeon"). (b) $6 Egyptian Goose .. .. .. *Set of* 2 *sheets* 4·75 5·00

Nos. 2810/21 were printed together, *se-tenant*, in sheetlets of 12 with the background forming a composite design.

No. 2811 is inscribed "Shobeler" in error.

399 Pig Priest, China

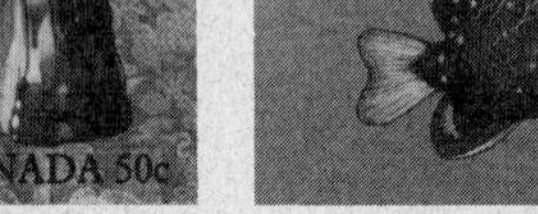

400 Yellow-tailed Damselfish

(Des R. Sauber. Litho Questa)

1995 (21 Apr). *Chinese New Year ("Year of the Pig"). T* **399** *and similar vert designs showing ornaments. Multicoloured. P* 14.
2825 50 c. Type **399** 20 25
a. Horiz strip of 3. Nos. 2825/7 .. 95
2826 75 c. Porcelain pig, Scotland 35 40
2827 $1 Seated porcelain pig, Italy 45 50
2825/7 .. .. *Set of* 3 95 1·10
MS2828 107×77 mm. $2 Jade pig, China .. 85 90

Nos. 2825/7 were printed together, *se-tenant*, in horizontal strips of 3 throughout the sheet.

(Des D. Burkhart. Litho Questa)

1995 (24 Apr). *Marine Life. T* **400** *and similar horiz designs. Multicoloured. P* 14.
2829 $1 Type **400** 45 40
a. Sheetlet. Nos. 2829/34 .. .. 2·75
2830 $1 Blue-headed Wrasse 45 50
2831 $1 Balloonfish 45 50
2832 $1 Shy Hamlet 45 50
2833 $1 Orange Tube Coral 45 50
2834 $1 Rock Beauty 45 50
2835 $1 Creole Wrasse 45 50
a. Sheetlet. Nos. 2835/43 .. .. 4·00
2836 $1 Queen Angelfish 45 50
2837 $1 Trumpetfish 45 50
2838 $1 Barred Hamlet 45 50
2839 $1 Tube Sponge 45 50
2840 $1 Porcupine Fish 45 50
2841 $1 Firecoral 45 50
2842 $1 Royal Gramma ("Fairy Basslet") .. 45 50
2843 $1 Sea Anemone 45 50
2829/43 .. .. *Set of* 15 6·75 7·50
MS2844 Two sheets, each 106×76 mm. (a) $5 Seahorse. (b) $6 Elkhorn Coral .. *Set of* 2 *sheets* 4·75 5·00

Nos. 2829/34 and 2835/43 were printed together, *se-tenant*, in sheetlets of 6 (with narrow horizontal gutter) (Nos. 2829/34) or 9 (Nos. 2835/43) forming composite designs.

401 National Flags

402 Cocker Spaniel

(Litho Questa)

1995 (27 Apr). *Grenada–Taiwan (Republic of China) Friendship. T* **401** *and similar horiz design. Multicoloured. P* 14.
2845 75 c. Type **401** 35 40
2846 $1 Prime Minister Brathwaite and President Lee Teng-hui 45 50
MS2847 76×106 mm. Nos. 2845/6 .. .. 80 90

(Des D. Burkhart. Litho Questa)

1995 (3 May). *Domestic Animals. T* **402** *and similar vert designs. Multicoloured. P* 14.
2848 10 c. Type **402** 10 10
2849 15 c. Pinto (horse) 10 10
2850 25 c. Rottweiler 10 10
2851 35 c. German Shepherd 15 20
2852 45 c. Persian (cat) 20 25
2853 50 c. Snowshoe (cat) 20 25
2854 75 c. Percheron (horse) 35 40
2855 $1 Scottish Fold (cat) 45 50
2856 $2 Arabian (horse) 85 90
2857 $3 Andalusian (horse) .. .. .. 1·25 1·40
2858 $4 C.P. Shorthair (cat) .. .. .. 1·75 1·90
2859 $5 Chihuahua .. .. 2·10 2·25
2848/59 .. .. *Set of* 12 7·50 8·25
MS2860 Three sheets, each 100×71 mm. (a) $5 Manx (cat). (b) $5 Donkey. (c) $6 Shar Pei *Set of* 3 *sheets* 6·50 6·75

(Litho Questa)

1995 (5 May). *Centenary of Sierra Club (environmental protection society) (1992). Endangered Species. Multicoloured designs as T* **320** *of Antigua. P* 14.
2861 $1 Head of Margay at night 45 50
a. Sheetlet. Nos. 2861/9 .. .. .. 4·00
2862 $1 Margay sitting 45 50
2863 $1 Head of Margay in daylight 45 50
2864 $1 Head of Andean Condor 45 50
2865 $1 Andean Condor facing right 45 50
2866 $1 Andean Condor facing left 45 50
2867 $1 White-faced Saki on branch 45 50
2868 $1 White-faced Saki showing mane .. 45 50
2869 $1 Patagonia landscape 45 50
2870 $1 Lesser Rheas feeding (*horiz*) 45 50
a. Sheetlet. Nos. 2870/8 .. .. .. 4·00
2871 $1 Pair of Lesser Rheas (*horiz*) 45 50
2872 $1 Lesser Rhea (*horiz*) 45 50
2873 $1 Sunset over snow-covered mountains, Patagonia (*horiz*) 45 50
2874 $1 Volcanic eruption, Patagonia (*horiz*) .. 45 50
2875 $1 White-faced Saki (*horiz*) 45 50
2876 $1 Common Caracara on branch (*horiz*) 45 50
2877 $1 Pair of Common Caracaras at nest (*horiz*) 45 50
2878 $1 Common Caracara facing left (*horiz*) 45 50
2861/78 .. .. *Set of* 18 8·00 9·00

Nos. 2861/9 and 2870/8 were printed together, *se-tenant*, in sheetlets of 9.

403 Grenadian Scout

404 "Swords into Ploughshares"

(Litho Questa)

1995 (8 May). *18th World Scout Jamboree, Netherlands. T* **403** *and similar horiz designs. Multicoloured. P* 14.
2879 75 c. Type **403** 35 40
a. Horiz strip of 3. Nos. 2879/81 .. 1·75
2880 $1 Scout abseiling 45 50
2881 $2 Scout saluting and national flag .. 85 90
2879/81 .. .. *Set of* 3 1·60 1·75
MS2882 107×77 mm. $6 Scouts in canoe .. 2·50 2·75

Nos. 2879/81 were printed together in sheets of 9 containing three *se-tenant* horizontal strips of 3.

(Des W. Wright. Litho Questa)

1995 (8 May). *50th Anniv of End of Second World War in Europe. Fighter Aircraft. Horiz designs as T* **340** *of Antigua. Multicoloured. P* 14.
2883 $2 Lavochkin La-7 (fighter) 85 90
a. Sheetlet. Nos. 2883/90 .. .. 6·75
2884 $2 Hawker Hurricane 85 90
2885 $2 North American P-51D Mustang .. 85 90
2886 $2 Messerschmitt Bf 109 .. .. 85 90
2887 $2 Bristol Type 152 Beaufighter .. 85 90
2888 $2 Messerschmitt Me 262 .. .. 85 90
2889 $2 Republic P-47 Thunderbolt 85 90
2890 $2 Hawker Tempest 85 90
2883/90 .. .. *Set of* 8 6·75 7·00
MS2891 106×76 mm. $6 Nose of Republic P-47 Thunderbolt .. .. 2·50 2·75

Nos. 2883/90 were printed together, *se-tenant*, in sheetlets of 8 with the stamps arranged in two horizontal strips of 4 separated by a gutter showing a dogfight.

(Des J. Iskowitz. Litho Questa)

1995 (8 May). *50th Anniv of United Nations. T* **404** *and similar multicoloured designs. P* 14.
2892 75 c. Type **404** 35 40
a. Horiz strip of 3. Nos. 2892/4 .. 1·60
2893 $1 Globe and dove 45 50
2894 $2 U.N. Building, New York 85 90
2892/4 .. .. *Set of* 3 1·50 1·60
MS2895 101×71 mm. $6 Anniversary logo (*horiz*) .. .. 2·50 2·75

Nos. 2892/4 were printed together in sheets of 9 containing three *se-tenant* horizontal strips of 3.

405 Woman with Baskets

406 National Flag and Rotary Logo

(Des J. Iskowitz. Litho Questa)

1995 (8 May). *50th Anniv of Food and Agriculture Organization. T* **405** *and similar vert designs. Multicoloured. P* 14.
2896 75 c. Type **405** 35 40
a. Horiz strip of 3. Nos. 2896/8 .. 1·60
2897 $1 Boy with basket on head 45 50
2898 $2 Men harvesting bananas 85 90
2896/8 .. .. *Set of* 3 1·50 1·60
MS2899 72×102 mm. $6 F.A.O. logo .. .. 2·50 2·75

Nos. 2896/8 were printed together in sheets of 9 containing three *se-tenant* horizontal strips of 3.

(Litho Questa)

1995 (8 May). *90th Anniv of Rotary International. T* **406** *and similar vert design. Multicoloured. P* 14.
2900 $5 Type **406** .. .. 2·10 2·25
MS2901 76×106 mm. $6 Paul Harris (founder) and logo .. .. 2·50 2·75

(Litho Questa)

1995 (8 May). *95th Birthday of Queen Elizabeth the Queen Mother. Vert designs as T* **344** *of Antigua. P* 13½×14.
2902 $1.50, orange-brown, pale brown and black 65 70
a. Sheetlet. Nos. 2902/5×2 .. .. 5·00
2903 $1.50, multicoloured 65 70
2904 $1.50, multicoloured 65 70
2905 $1.50, multicoloured 65 70
2902/5 .. .. *Set of* 4 2·50 2·75
MS2906 127×102 mm. $6 multicoloured .. 2·50 2·75

Designs:—No. 2902, Queen Elizabeth the Queen Mother (pastel drawing); No. 2903, Holding rose; No. 2904, At desk (oil painting); No. 2905, In blue hat and white coat; No. **MS**2906, Wearing floral hat.

Nos. 2902/5 were printed together in sheetlets of 8, containing two *se-tenant* horizontal strips of 4.

(Des J. Batchelor. Litho Questa)

1995 (8 May). *50th Anniv of End of Second World War in the Pacific. Horiz designs as T* **340** *of Antigua. Multicoloured. P* 14.
2907 $2 Dogfight over the Marianas 85 90
a. Sheetlet. Nos. 2907/12 .. .. 5·00
2908 $2 U.S. dive-bomber and burning aircraft carrier, Battle of Midway 85 90
2909 $2 U.S. aircraft attacking Japanese transport, Battle of the Bismarck Sea 85 90
2910 $2 *Mushashi* (Japanese battleship) on fire in Leyte Gulf 85 90
2911 $2 U.S. aircraft taking off from Henderson Field 85 90
2912 $2 Battleships at Guadalcanal 85 90
2907/12 .. .. *Set of* 6 5·00 5·25
MS2913 108×77 mm. $6 U.S. bomber .. 2·50 2·75

No. 2907/12 were printed together, *se-tenant*, in sheetlets of 6 with the stamp arranged in two horizontal strips of 3 separated by a gutter showing Doolittle's B-25 *Ruptured Duck* leaving U.S.S. *Hornet*.

407 Tian Bingyi (China) (badminton) **408** Junior Murray (West Indies)

(Litho B.D.T.)

95 (23 June). *Olympic Games, Atlanta* (1996) (1*st issue*). *T* **407** *and similar vert designs. Multicoloured. P* 14.

14 75 c. Type **407** 35 40
a. Horiz strip of 4. Nos. 2914/17 .. 1·40
15 75 c. Waldemar Leigien (Poland) and Frank Wieneke (West Germany) (judo) 35 40
16 75 c. Nelli Kim (U.S.S.R) (gymnastics) .. 35 40
17 75 c. Alessandro Andri (Italy) (shot put) .. 35 40
18 $2 Jackie Joyner (U.S.A.) (heptathlon) 85 90
a. Horiz strip of 4. Nos. 2918/21 .. 3·25
19 $2 Mitsuo Tsukahara (Japan) (gymnastics) 85 90
20 $2 Flo Hyman (U.S.A.) and Zhang Rung Fang (China) (volleyball) 85 90
21 $2 Steffi Graf (West Germany) (tennis) 85 90
14/21 .. .. *Set of* 8 4·50 5·00
S2922 Two sheets, each 72×102 mm. (a) $6 Wilma Rudolph (U.S.A.) (athletics). (b) $6 Soling class yacht .. .. .. *Set of* 2 *sheets* 5·25 5·50

Nos. 2914/17 and 2918/21 were printed together in sheets of 2 containing three *se-tenant* strips of 4.

No. **MS**2922(b) is inscribed "Sailing" in error.

See also Nos. 3102/24.

(Litho Questa)

995 (18 Aug). *Anniversaries and Events. T* **408** *and similar vert designs. Multicoloured. P* 14.

923 25 c. Type **408** (Centenary of first English cricket tour to the West Indies) .. 10 10
924 75 c. Nutmeg (Opening of Grenada Spice Factory) 35 40
925 $1 Sendall Tunnel (Centenary (1994) .. 45 50
926 $1 Caribbean Development Bank building (25th anniv) 45 50
923/6 .. .. *Set of* 4 1·25 1·50

409 Ajamu **410** Elvis Presley and Signature

(Litho Questa)

995 (5 Sept). *Local Entertainers. T* **409** *and similar vert designs. Multicoloured. P* 14.

927 35 c. Type **409** 15 20
928 35 c. Mighty Sparrow 15 20
929 50 c. Mighty Sparrow in evening dress .. 20 25
930 75 c. Ajamu (*different*) 35 40
927/30 .. .. *Set of* 4 95 1·00

(Des Y. Lee. Litho Questa)

995 (5 Sept). *Entertainment Legends. T* **410** *and similar vert design. Multicoloured. P* 14.

931 75 c. Type **410** 35 40
932 75 c. Marilyn Monroe 35 40

Nos. 2931/2 were each issued in numbered sheets of 16 ncluding an enlarged illustrated right-hand margin.

411 Elvis Presley

(Des Isabelle Tanner. Litho Questa)

1995 (5 Sept). *60th Birth Anniv of Elvis Presley* (*singer*). *T* **411** *and similar vert designs. Multicoloured. P* 14.

2933 $1 Type **411** 45 50
a. Sheetlet. Nos. 2933/41 .. .. 4·00
2934 $1 With beard 45 50
2935 $1 With long hair and microphone .. 45 50
2936 $1 Wearing white shirt 45 50
2937 $1 Wearing pink shirt and purple jacket 45 50
2938 $1 With short hair and microphone .. 45 50
2939 $1 Wearing magenta shirt 45 50
2940 $1 Wearing orange shirt 45 50
2941 $1 Wearing purple shirt 45 50
2933/41 .. .. *Set of* 9 4·00 4·50

Nos. 2933/41 were printed together, *se-tenant*, in sheetlets of 9.

412 Film Reel and Oscar Statuette

(Des J. Rosata. Litho Questa)

1995 (5 Sept). *Centenary of Cinema. T* **412** *and similar multicoloured designs. P* 13½×14.

2942 $1 Type **412** 45 50
a. Sheetlet. Nos. 2942/50 .. .. 4·00
2943 $1 "HOLLYWOOD" sign 45 50
2944 $1 Charlie Chaplin 45 50
2945 $1 Shirley Temple 45 50
2946 $1 Spencer Tracy and Katherine Hepburn 45 50
2947 $1 Marilyn Monroe 45 50
2948 $1 John Wayne 45 50
2949 $1 Marlon Brando 45 50
2950 $1 Tom Cruise 45 50
2942/50 .. .. *Set of* 9 4·00 4·50
MS2951 107×77 mm. $5 Orson Welles (*horiz*). P 14×13½ .. .. 2·10 2·25

Nos. 2942/50 were printed together, *se-tenant*, in sheetlets of 9 forming a composite design.

413 "B1 Level Vista Dome" Electric Locomotive, Japan **414** Teresa Teng

(Des D. Miller. Litho Questa)

1995 (5 Sept). *Trains of the World* (1*st series*). *T* **413** *and similar horiz designs. Multicoloured. P* 14.

2952 $1 Type **413** 45 50
a. Sheetlet. Nos. 2952/60 .. .. 4·00
2953 $1 Rolios Rail Class 25NC steam locomotive, South Africa 45 50
2954 $1 Class 460 electric locomotive, Switzerland 45 50
2955 $1 Central Railway diesel locomotive No. 605, Peru 45 50
2956 $1 X2000 tilt body train, Sweden .. 45 50
2957 $1 Via Rail Toronto to Vancouver observation car, Canada 45 50
2958 $1 Intercity 125 diesel locomotive, Great Britain 45 50
2959 $1 *The Flying Scotsman* steam locomotive, Great Britain 45 50
2960 $1 "Indian Pacific" diesel locomotive, Australia 45 50
2961 $1 ETR 450 electric train, Italy 45 50
a. Sheetlet. Nos. 2961/9 .. .. .. 4·00
2962 $1 Isparta to Bozanonu Line steam locomotive, Turkey 45 50
2963 $1 TGV train, France 45 50
2964 $1 ICE train, Germany 45 50
2965 $1 Nishi Line electric locomotive, Japan 45 50
2966 $1 "Hikari" train, Japan 45 50
2967 $1 Central Pacific Jupiter steam locomotive, U.S.A. 45 50
2968 $1 Amtrak Type 9000 electric locomotive, U.S.A. 45 50
2969 $1 *Sir Nigel Gresley* steam locomotive, Great Britain 45 50
2952/69 .. .. *Set of* 18 8·00 9·00
MS2970 Two sheets, each 106×76 mm. (a) $5 Diesel hydraulic train, Korea. (b) $6 Peking–Ulan Bator express, Mongolia .. *Set of* 2 *sheets* 4·75 5·00

Nos. 2952/60 and 2961/9 (which include the "Singapore '95" International Stamp Exhibition logo) were printed together, *se-tenant*, in sheetlets of 9.

See also Nos. 3167/83.

(Litho Questa)

1995 (29 Sept). *Teresa Teng* (*Chinese actress*) *Commemoration. T* **414** *and similar vert designs showing different portraits. Multicoloured unless otherwise indicated. P* 14 (*Nos.* 2971/86) *or* 13½×14 (*others*).

2971 35 c. Type **414** 30 30
a. Sheetlet. Nos. 2971/86 .. .. 4·25
2972 35 c. As a child (agate, ochre & orge-yellow) 30 30
2973 35 c. Wearing feather boa (black, pale grey and orange-yellow) 30 30
2974 35 c. With motor scooter 30 30
2975 35 c. Holding microphone 30 30
2976 35 c. In white sweater 30 30
2977 35 c. Playing flute 30 30
2978 35 c. With hand to hair (black, pale grey and orange-yellow) 30 30
2979 35 c. Wearing gold decorated dress .. 30 30
2980 35 c. With fan 30 30
2981 35 c. As South-sea islander 30 30
2982 35 c. With hands clasped 30 30
2983 35 c. In kimono 30 30
2984 35 c. Holding bow tie 30 30
2985 35 c. Wearing black blouse 30 30
2986 35 c. Resting on chair arm 30 30
2987 75 c. In army uniform 45 45
a. Sheetlet. Nos. 2987/95 .. .. 3·50
2988 75 c. In navy uniform 45 45
2989 75 c. In air force uniform 45 45
2990 75 c. Singing with hand outstretched (black, pale grey and orange-yellow) 45 45
2991 75 c. Singing with flower in hair 45 45
2992 75 c. Singing in blue floral dress 45 45
2993 75 c. With pink scarf 45 45
2994 75 c. In fringed dress 45 45
2995 75 c. In pale green sweater 45 45
2996 75 c. With hands to face 45 45
2971/96 .. .. *Set of* 26 8·00 8·00

Nos. 2987/96 are larger, 34×46 mm.

Nos. 2971/86 and 2987/95 were each printed together, *se-tenant*, in sheetlets of 16 with a large illustrated margin at right (Nos. 2971/86), or 9 (Nos. 2987/95).

415 Mickey Mouse fighting Big Pete **416** Albert Michelson (1907 Physics)

(Des Walt Disney Company and Rosemary DeFiglio. Litho Questa)

1995 (2 Oct). *Mickey's Pirate Adventure. T* **415** *and similar vert designs showing Walt Disney cartoon characters. Multicoloured. P* 13½×14.

2997 15 c. Type **415** 10 10
2998 25 c. Mickey with treasure chest 10 10
2999 35 c. Minnie Mouse trying on plunder .. 15 20
3000 75 c. Goofy with telescope and Mickey swimming with barrel 35 40
3001 $3 Big Pete .. .. 1·40 1·50
3002 $5 Mickey and monkey, seagull and handkerchief .. .. .. 2·25 2·40
2997/3002 .. .. *Set of* 6 4·25 4·50
MS3003 Two sheets, each 108×130 mm. (a) $6 Sea rat pirate. (b) $6 Minnie being thrown overboard by pirates .. .. *Set of* 2 *sheets* 5·50 5·75

(Des B. DuRand. Litho Questa)

1995 (18 Oct). *Centenary of Nobel Trust Fund. T* **416** *and similar vert designs. Multicoloured. P* 14.

3004 $1 Type **416** 45 50
a. Sheetlet. Nos. 3004/12 .. .. 4·00
3005 $1 Ralph Bunche (1950 Peace) 45 50
3006 $1 Edwin Neher (1991 Medicine) .. 45 50
3007 $1 Klaus Vonklitzing (1985 Physics) .. 45 50
3008 $1 Johann Deisenhofer (1988 Chemistry) 45 50
3009 $1 Max Delbruck (1969 Medicine) .. 45 50
3010 $1 J. Georg Bednorz (1987 Physics) .. 45 50
3011 $1 Feodor Lynen (1964 Medicine) .. 45 50
3012 $1 Walther Bothe (1954 Physics) .. 45 50
3013 $1 James Franck (1925 Physics) .. 45 50
a. Sheetlet. Nos. 3013/21 .. .. 4·00
3014 $1 Gustav Hertz (1925 Physics) 45 50
3015 $1 Friedrich Bergius (1931 Chemistry) .. 45 50
3016 $1 Otto Loewi (1936 Medicine) 45 50
3017 $1 Fritz Lipmann (1953 Medicine) .. 45 50
3018 $1 Otto Meyerhof (1922 Medicine) .. 45 50
3019 $1 Paul Heyse (1910 Literature) .. 45 50
3020 $1 Jane Addams (1931 Peace) 45 50
3021 $1 Carl Braun (1909 Physics) 45 50
3022 $1 Hans Dehmelt (1989 Physics) .. 45 50
a. Sheetlet. Nos. 3022/30 .. .. 4·00
3023 $1 Heinrich Böll (1972 Literature) .. 45 50
3024 $1 Georges Köhler (1984 Medicine) .. 45 50
3025 $1 Wolfgang Pauli (1945 Physics) .. 45 50
3026 $1 Sir Bernard Katz (1970 Medicine) .. 45 50
3027 $1 Ernest Ruska (1986 Physics) 45 50
3028 $1 William Golding (1983 Literature) .. 45 50
3029 $1 Hartmut Michel (1988 Chemistry) .. 45 50
3030 $1 Hans Bethe (1967 Physics) 45 50
3004/30 .. .. *Set of* 27 12·00 13·50
MS3031 Three sheets, each 105×76 mm. (a) $6 Theodore Roosevelt (1906 Peace). (b) $6 Woodrow Wilson (1919 Peace). (c) $6 Sir Winston Churchill (1953 Literature) .. *Set of* 3 *sheets* 7·50 7·75

Nos. 3004/12, 3013/21 and 3022/30 were each printed together, *se-tenant*, in sheetlets of 9 forming composite designs.

No. 3015 is inscribed "Freidrich" in error.

(Litho Questa)

1995 (28 Nov). *Christmas. Religious Paintings. Vert designs as T* **357** *of Antigua. Multicoloured. P* 13½×14.

3032 15 c. "The Madonna" (Bartolommeo Montagna) 10 10
3033 25 c. "Sacred Conversation Piece" (Bonifacio dei Pitati) 10 10
3034 35 c. "Nativity" (Van Loo) 15 20
3035 75 c. "Madonna of the Fountain" (Van Eyck) 35 40
3036 $2 "The Apparition of the Virgin to St. Philip Neri" (Giovanni Tiepolo) .. 85 90
3037 $5 "The Holy Family" (Ribera) .. 2·10 2·25
3032/7 .. .. *Set of* 6 3·25 3·75
MS3038 Two sheets. (a) 127×101 mm. $6 "Madonna and Child" (detail) (Van Dyck). (b) 101×127 mm. $6 "The Vision of St. Anthony" (detail) (Van Dyck) .. .. *Set of* 2 *sheets* 5·25 5·50

417 Pres. Ronald Reagan at Fort George

418 Pres. Ronald Reagan

(Des J. Iskowitz. Litho Questa)

1995 (8 Dec). *12th Anniv of Liberation of Grenada* (1*st issue*). *T* **417** *and similar horiz designs. Multicoloured. P* 14.

3039 75 c. Type **417** 35 40
a. Horiz strip of 3. Nos. 3039/41 .. 1·10
3040 75 c. Pres. Reagan with U.S. and Grenadian flags 35 40
3041 75 c. St. George's 35 40
3039/41 .. .. *Set of* 3 1·10 1·25
MS3042 Two sheets, each 70×100 m. (a) $5 Pres. Reagan and beach. (b) $6 Pres Reagan and waterfall .. .. .. *Set of* 2 *sheets* 4·75 5·00

Nos. 3039/41 were printed in sheets of 9 containing three *se-tenant* horizontal strips, each strip forming a composite design.

(Litho Questa)

1995 (8 Dec). *12th Anniv of Liberation of Grenada* (2*nd issue*). *T* **418** *and similar vert designs each showing Ronald Reagan. Multicoloured. P* 13½×14.

3043 $1 With wife 45 50
a. Sheetlet. Nos. 3043/51 .. .. 4·00
3044 $1 Type **418** 45 50
3045 $1 With microphones 45 50
3046 $1 Wearing stetson 45 50
3047 $1 In front of U.S. flag 45 50
3048 $1 In front of Brandenburg Gate, Berlin 45 50
3049 $1 Saluting by helicopter 45 50
3050 $1 On horseback 45 50
3051 $1 Addressing troops 45 50
3043/51 .. .. *Set of* 9 4·00 4·50

Nos. 3043/51 were printed together, *se-tenant*, in sheetlets of 9 with an enlarged illustrated right margin.

419 Pope John Paul II and Statue of Liberty

420 Rat asleep

(Des R. Rundo. Litho Questa)

1995 (13 Dec). *Papal Visit to New York. T* **419** *and similar vert designs. Multicoloured. P* 14.

3052 $1 Type **419** 45 50
3053 $1 Pope John Paul II and cathedral .. 45 50
MS3054 105×76mm. $6 Pope John Paul II .. 2·50 2·75

Nos. 3052/3 were printed separately in sheets of 9 with enlarged illustrated margin at right.

A $30 value embossed on gold foil exists from a limited printing.

(Des Y. Lee. Litho Questa)

1996 (2 Jan). *Chinese New Year* ("*Year of the Rat*"). *T* **420** *and similar designs. P* 14.

3055 **420** 75 c. buff, brown-olive and deep brown 35 40
a. Horiz strip of 3. Nos. 3055/7 .. 1·10
3056 – 75 c. salmon, deep rose-red & dp violet 35 40
3057 – 75 c. buff, dull verm & blackish green 35 40
3055/7 .. .. *Set of* 3 1·10 1·25
MS3058 95×58 mm. Nos. 3055/7 .. .. 1·10 1·25
MS3059 76×106 mm. $1 multicoloured .. 45 50

Designs: *Vert*—No. 3056, Rat eating; No. 3057, Rat asleep (T **420** reversed). *Horiz*—No. **MS**3059, Two rats.

Nos. 3055/7 were printed together, *se-tenant*, in horizontal strips of 3 throughout the sheet.

421 "Young Woman" (Dürer)

(Litho Questa)

1996 (29 Jan). *Famous Drawings and Paintings by Dürer and Rubens. T* **421** *and similar vert designs. P* 13½×14.

3060 15 c. Type **421** 10 10
3061 25 c. "Four Horsemen of the Apocalypse" (Dürer) 10 15
3062 35 c. "Assumption and Coronation of the Virgin" (Dürer) 15 20
3063 75 c. "Mulay Ahmed" (Rubens) 35 40
3064 $1 "Anthony van Dyck aged 15" (Rubens) 45 50
3065 $2 "Head of a Young Monk" (Rubens) .. 85 90
3066 $3 "A Scholar inspired by Nature" (Rubens) .. .. 1·25 1·40
3067 $5 "Hanns Dürer" (Dürer) .. .. 2·10 2·25
3060/7 .. .. *Set of* 8 5·25 5·75
MS3068 Two sheets, each 102×127 mm. (a) $5 "Martyrdom of St. Ursula" (detail) (Rubens). (b) $6 "The Death of the Virgin" (detail) (Dürer) *Set of* 2 *sheets* 4·75 5·00

422 Goofy tap-dancing

(Litho Questa)

1996 (26 Feb). *Famous Dances. T* **422** *and similar multicoloured designs showing Walt Disney cartoon characters dancing. P* 13½×14 (*vert*) *or* 14×13½ (*horiz*).

3069 35 c. Type **422** 15 20
3070 45 c. Donald Duck doing Mexican hat dance (*horiz*) 20 25
3071 75 c. Daisy Duck as hula dancer 35 40
3072 90 c. Mickey and Minnie Mouse doing the tango (*horiz*) 40 45
3073 $1 Donald and Daisy doing the jitterbug 45 50
3074 $2 Mickey and Minnie performing Ukrainian folk dance (*horiz*) .. 90 95
3075 $3 Goofy and Pluto as ballet dancers (*horiz*) .. .. 1·40 1·50
3076 $4 Mickey and Minnie line-dancing .. 1·90 2·00
3069/76 .. .. *Set of* 8 5·75 6·25
MS3077 Two sheets, each 133×109 mm. (a) $5 Minnie doing the can-can (*horiz*). (b) $6 Scrooge McDuck doing Scottish sword dance *Set of* 2 *sheets* 5·00 5·25

(Litho Questa)

1996 (8 May). *70th Birthday of Queen Elizabeth II. Vert designs as T* **364** *of Antigua showing different photographs. Multicoloured. P* 13½×14.

3078 35 c. As Type **364** of Antigua 15 20
a. Strip of 3. Nos. 3078/80 .. .. 2·25
3079 75 c. Wearing white hat 35 40
3080 $4 With bouquet .. .. .. 1·75 1·90
3078/80 .. .. *Set of* 3 2·25 2·40
MS3081 103×125 mm. $6 Queen and Prince Philip .. .. 2·50 2·75

Nos. 3078/80 were printed together, *se-tenant*, in horizontal and vertical strips of 3 throughout the sheet.

423 Ferrari "125 F1"

424 Lions' Gate, Jerusalem

(Des W. Wright. Litho)

1996 (8 May). *Ferrari Racing Cars. T* **423** *and similar hor[iz] designs. Multicoloured. P* 14.

3082 $1.50, Type **423** 65 7
a. Sheetlet. Nos. 3082/7 .. .. .. 3·75
3083 $1.50, "Tipo 625" 65 7
3084 $1.50, "P4" 65 7
3085 $1.50, "312P" 65 7
3086 $1.50, "312" Formula 1 .. .. .. 65 7
3087 $1.50, "312B" 65 7
3082/7 .. .. *Set of* 6 3·75 4·2
MS3088 100×71 mm. $6 "F333 SP" (84×28 *mm*) 2·50 2·7

Nos. 3082/7 were printed together, *se-tenant* in sheetlets of which include the "CHINA '96" International Stamp Exhibitio[n] logo on the margin.

(Litho Questa)

1996 (26 June). *50th Anniv of U.N.I.C.E.F. Multicoloure[d] designs as T* **366** *of Antigua. P* 14.

3089 35 c. Child writing in book (*horiz*) .. 15 2
3090 $2 Child planting seedling (*horiz*) .. 85 9
3091 $3 Children and U.N.I.C.E.F. emblem (*horiz*) .. .. 1·25 1·4
3089/91 .. .. *Set of* 3 2·25 2·4
MS3092 75×106 mm. $5 Young boy .. .. 2·10 2·2

(Des Rachel Deitch. Litho Questa)

1996 (26 June). *3,000th Anniv of Jerusalem. T* **424** *and simil[ar] multicoloured designs. P* 14.

3093 75 c. Type **424** 35 4
3094 $2 New Gate 85 9
3095 $3 Dung Gate .. .. 1·25 1·4
3093/5 .. .. *Set of* 3 2·40 2·5
MS3096 114×74 mm. $5 The Old City (*horiz*) 2·10 2·2

(Des J. Iskowitz. Litho Questa)

1996 (26 June). *Centenary of Radio. Entertainers. Mult[i]coloured designs as T* **368** *of Antigua. P* 13½.

3097 35 c. Jack Benny 15 2
3098 75 c. Gertrude Berg 35 4
3099 $1 Eddie Cantor 45 5
3100 $2 Groucho Marx 85 9
3097/100 .. .. *Set of* 4 1·60 1·9
MS3101 70×100 mm. $6 George Burns and Gracie Allen (*horiz*) .. .. 2·50 2·7

425 Olympic Stadium, Athens, 1896

(Litho B.D.T.)

1996 (8 July). *Olympic Games, Atlanta* (2*nd issue*). *Previou[s] Medal Winners. T* **425** *and similar multicoloured design[s]. P* 14.

3102 35 c. Gold medal of 1896 (*vert*) 15 2
3103 75 c. Type **425** 35 4
3104 $1 Boughera el Quafi (France) (Gold, 1928) 45 5
a. Sheetlet. Nos. 3104/12 .. .. 4·00
3105 $1 Gustav Jansson (Sweden) (Bronze, 1952) 45 5
3106 $1 Spiridon Louis (Greece) (Gold, 1896) 45 5
3107 $1 Basil Heatley (Great Britain) (Silver, 1964) 45 5
3108 $1 Emil Zatopek (Czechoslovakia) (Gold, 1952) 45 5
3109 $1 Frank Shorter (U.S.A.) (Gold, 1972) 45 5
3110 $1 Alain Minoun O'Kacha (France) (Gold, 1956) 45 5
3111 $1 Kokichi Tsu Uraya (Japan) (Bronze, 1964) 45 5
3112 $1 Delfo Cabrera (Argentina) (Gold, 1948) 45 5
3113 $1 Harald Sakata (U.S.A.) (Silver – light heavyweight, 1948) 45 5
a. Sheetlet. Nos. 3113/21 .. .. 4·00
3114 $1 Tom Kono (U.S.A.) (Gold – middleweight, 1952 and 1956) 45 5
3115 $1 Naim Suleymanoglu (Turkey) (Gold – featherweight, 1988) 45 5
3116 $1 Lee Hyung Kun (South Korea) (Gold – light heavyweight, 1988) 45 5
3117 $1 Vassily Alexeyev (U.S.S.R.) (Gold – super heavyweight, 1972 and 1976) 45 5
3118 $1 Chen Weiqiang (China) (Gold – featherweight, 1984) 45 5
3119 $1 Ye Huanming (China) (Gold – featherweight, 1988) 45 5
3120 $1 Manfred Nerlinger (Germany) (Silver – super heavyweight, 1988) .. 45 5
3121 $1 Joseph Depietro (U.S.A.) (Gold – bantamweight, 1948) 45 5
3122 $2 Ancient Greek runners 85 9
3123 $3 Spiridon Louis (Greece) (Gold – marathon, 1896) .. .. .. 1·25 1·4
3102/23 .. .. *Set of* 22 10·00 11·5
MS3124 Two sheets, each 75×105 mm. (a) $5 Manfred Nerlinger (Germany) (Silver – super heavyweight weightlifting, 1988) (*vert*). (b) $6 Thomas Hicks (U.S.A.) (Gold – marathon, 1904) (*vert*) .. .. *Set of* 2 *sheets* 4·75 5·0

Nos. 3104/12 (marathon runners) and 3113/21 (weightlifters) were each printed together, *se-tenant*, in sheetlets of 9, with th[e] backgrounds forming composite designs.

426 Mercedes-Benz, 1929

96 (25 July). *Classic Cars. T* **426** *and similar horiz designs. Multicoloured. Litho. P* 14.

25	35 c. Type **426**	15	20
	a. Sheetlet. Nos. 3125/8 and 3135/6	3·50	
26	50 c. Bugatti Type 35, 1927	25	30
27	75 c. J. Dusenberg, 1935	35	40
28	$1 Mercer, 1914	45	50
29	$1 Type 57C Atalante, 1939	45	50
	a. Sheetlet. Nos. 3129/34	2·50	
30	$1 Cannstatt-Daimler, 1900	45	50
31	$1 Delage, 1925	45	50
32	$1 Coventry Daimler, 1899	45	50
33	$1 Vauxhall, 1900	45	50
34	$1 T-15 Hispano-Suza, 1912	45	50
35	$2 Alfa Romeo, 1929	85	90
36	$3 Rolls Royce, 1910	1·25	1·40
25/36	*Set of* 12	6·00	6·75
S3137	Two sheets, each 66×96 mm. (a) $6 L-Head Mercer, 1915 (56×42 *mm*). (b) $6 Mercedes, 1937 (56×42 *mm*) *Set of* 2 *sheets*	5·25	5·50

Nos. 3125/8 with 3135/6 and 3129/34 were each printed gether, *se-tenant*, in sheetlets of 6.

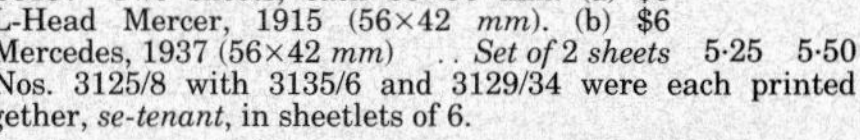

427 *Gorch Fock* (cadet barque), Germany, 1916

428 Jacqueline Kennedy

(Des R. Sauber. Litho Questa)

96 (14 Aug). *Ships. T* **427** *and similar horiz designs. Multicoloured. P* 14.

38	$1 Type **427**	45	50
	a. Sheetlet. Nos. 3138/46	4·00	
39	$1 *Henry B. Hyde*, U.S.A., 1886	45	50
40	$1 *Resolution* (galleon), Great Britain, 1652	45	50
41	$1 U.S.S. *Constitution* (frigate), U.S.A., 1797	45	50
42	$1 *Nippon Maru* (cadet ship), Japan, 1930	45	50
43	$1 *Preussen* (full-rigged sailing ship), Germany, 1902	45	50
44	$1 *Taeping* (tea clipper), Great Britain, 1852	45	50
45	$1 *Chariot of Fame, U.S.A.*, 1853	45	50
46	$1 *Star of India* (clipper), U.S.A., 1861	45	50
.47	$1 H.M.S. *Bounty*	45	50
	a. Sheetlet. Nos. 3147/55	4·00	
.48	$1 *Bismarck* (German battleship)	45	50
.49	$1 *Chuii Apoo* and two junks	45	50
.50	$1 *Lubeck* (German frigate)	45	50
.51	$1 Dutch galleon	45	50
.52	$1 *Augsburg* (German frigate)	45	50
53	$1 *Henri Grace a Dieu* (British galleon)	45	50
54	$1 H.M.S. *Prince of Wales* (battleship)	45	50
55	$1 *Santa Anna* (Spanish carrack)	45	50
38/55	*Set of* 18	8·00	9·00
S3156	Two sheets, each 104×74 mm. (a) $5 H.M.S. *Victory* (ship of the line), Great Britain, 1805. (b) $6 *Cutty Sark* (clipper), Great Britain, 1869 *Set of* 2 *sheets*	4·75	5·00

Nos. 3138/46 and 3147/55 were each printed together, -*tenant*, in sheetlets of 9.

No. 3151 is inscribed "BARBARY CORSAIR" and No. 3153 is ated to be French, both in error.

96 (26 Aug). *Jacqueline Kennedy Onassis Commemoration. T* **428** *and similar vert designs. Multicoloured. Litho. P* 14.

.57	$1 Type **428**	45	50
	a. Sheetlet. Nos. 3157/65	4·00	
158	$1 Wearing mauve blouse	45	50
159	$1 In evening dress (inscr at right)	45	50
160	$1 In evening dress (inscr at left)	45	50
161	$1 Wearing pink dress	45	50
162	$1 Wearing blue dress with collar embroidered	45	50
163	$1 Wearing white jacket and brooch	45	50
164	$1 In yellow jacket and green shirt	45	50
165	$1 Wearing black jacket	45	50
157/65	*Set of* 9	4·00	4·50
S3166	76×106 mm. $6 Jacqueline Kennedy Onassis (*different*)	2·50	2·75

Nos. 3157/65 were printed together, *se-tenant*, in sheetlets of with an enlarged illustrated left-hand margin

MINIMUM PRICE

he minimum price quote is 10p which represents handling charge rather than a basis for valuing ommon stamps. For further notes about prices see introductory pages.

429 Class C51 Locomotive of Imperial Train, Japan

(Litho Questa)

1996 (28 Aug). *Trains of the World (2nd series). T* **429** *and similar horiz designs. Multicoloured. P* 14.

3167	35 c. Type **429**	15	10
3168	75 c. "Rheingold" express, Germany	35	40
3169	$1 Atlantic Coast Line locomotive No. 153, 1894, U.S.A.	45	50
	a. Sheetlet. Nos. 3169/74	2·50	
3170	$1 Smith Compound No. 1619, Great Britain	45	50
3171	$1 Trans-Siberian Soviet Railways	45	50
3172	$1 Palatinate Railway Krauss locomotive, 1898, Germany	45	50
3173	$1 Paris, Lyons and Mediterranean line, France	45	50
3174	$1 Diesel-electric 0341 locomotive, Italy	45	50
3175	$1 Class C62 locomotive, Japan	45	50
	a. Sheetlet. Nos. 3175/80	2·50	
3176	$1 Shantung Railways locomotive, China	45	50
3177	$1 Class C57 locomotive, Japan	45	50
3178	$1 Diesel express train, Japan	45	50
3179	$1 Shanghai–Nanking Railway locomotive, China	45	50
3180	$1 Class D51 locomotive, Japan	45	50
3181	$2 *Pioneer*, 1851, U.S.A.	85	90
3182	$3 *France*, France	1·25	1·40
3167/82	*Set of* 16	7·50	8·75
MS3183	Two sheets, each 105×73 mm. (a) $5 Baden State Railways locomotive, Germany, (b) $6 Class C11 locomotive, Japan *Set of* 2 *sheets*	5·00	5·25

Nos. 3169/74 and 3175/80 were each printed together, *se-tenant*, in sheetlets of 6.

No. 3180 is inscribed "051" in error.

430 Winter Jasmine

(Des H. Friedman. Litho Questa)

1996 (9 Sept). *Flowers. T* **430** *and similar multicoloured designs. P* 14.

3184	$1 Type **430**	45	50
	a. Sheetlet. Nos. 3184/92	4·00	
3185	$1 Chrysanthemum	45	50
3186	$1 Lilac	45	50
3187	$1 Japanese Iris	45	50
3188	$1 Hibiscus	45	50
3189	$1 Sacred Lotus	45	50
3190	$1 Apple blossom	45	50
3191	$1 Gladiolus	45	50
3192	$1 Japanese Quince	45	50
3193	$1 Canterbury Bell (*vert*)	45	50
	a. Sheetlet. Nos. 3193/201	4·00	
3194	$1 Rose (*vert*)	45	50
3195	$1 Nasturtium (*vert*)	45	50
3196	$1 Daffodil (*vert*)	45	50
3197	$1 Tulip (*vert*)	45	50
3198	$1 Snapdragon (*vert*)	45	50
3199	$1 Zinnia (*vert*)	45	50
3200	$1 Sweetpea (*vert*)	45	50
3201	$1 Pansy (*vert*)	45	50
3184/201	*Set of* 18	8·00	9·00
MS3202	Two sheets. (a) 104×74 mm. $5 Aster. (b) 74×104 mm. $6 Peony (*vert*) *Set of* 2 *sheets*	4·75	6·00

Nos. 3184/92 and 3193/201 were each printed together, *se-tenant*, in sheetlets of 9 with the backgrounds forming composite designs.

431 Zeppelin L-31 (Germany)

(Des R. Rundo. Litho Questa)

1996 (9 Sept). *Airships. T* **431** *and similar horiz designs. Multicoloured. P* 14.

3203	30 c. Type **431**	15	20
	a. Sheetlet. Nos. 3203/6 and 3213/14	3·50	
3204	30 c. Zeppelin L-35 (Germany)	15	20
3205	50 c. Zeppelin L-30 (Germany)	25	30
3206	75 c. Zeppelin L-2 10 (Germany)	35	40
3207	$1.50, Zeppelin L-21 (Germany)	65	70
	a. Sheetlet. Nos. 3207/12	3·75	
3208	$1.50, Zodiac Type 13 Spiess (France)	65	70
3209	$1.50, N1 *Norge* (Roald Amundsen)	65	70
3210	$1.50, LZ-127 *Graf Zeppelin* (Germany)	65	70
3211	$1.50, LZ-129 *Hindenburg* (Germany)	65	70
3212	$1.50, Zeppelin NT (Germany)	65	70
3213	$3 Zeppelin L-3 (Germany)	1·25	1·40
3214	$3 Beardmore No. 24 (Great Britain)	1·25	1·40
3203/14	*Set of* 12	7·00	8·00
MS3215	Two sheets, each 104×74 mm. (a) $6 Zeppelin ZT (Germany). (b) $6 Zeppelin L-13 (Germany) *Set of* 2 *sheets*	5·25	5·50

Nos. 3203/6 with 3213/14 and 3207/12 were each printed together, *se-tenant*, in sheetlets of 9.

432 Horned Guan

1996 (18 Sept). *West Indian Birds. T* **432** *and similar horiz designs. Multicoloured. Litho. P* 14.

3216	$1.50, Type **432**	65	70
	a. Sheetlet. Nos. 3216/21	3·75	
3217	$1.50, St. Lucia Parrot	65	70
3218	$1.50, Black Penelopina	65	70
3219	$1.50, Grenada Dove	65	70
3220	$1.50, St. Vincent Parrot	65	70
3221	$1.50, White-breasted Trembler	65	70
3216/21	*Set of* 6	3·75	4·00
MS3222	Two sheets, each 100×70 mm. (a) $5 Semper's Warbler. (b) $6 Barbados Yellow Warbler *Set of* 2 *sheets*	4·75	5·00

Nos. 3216/21 were printed together, *se-tenant*, in sheetlets of 6 with the backgrounds forming a composite design.

The inscriptions on Nos. **MS**3222a and **MS**3222b are transposed in error.

433 Blue Whale

434 Killer Whale

1996 (18 Sept). *Whales and Turtles. T* **433** *and similar horiz designs. Multicoloured. Litho. P* 14.

3223	$1.50, Type **433**	65	70
	a. Sheetlet. Nos. 3223/8	3·75	
3224	$1.50, Humpback Whale	65	70
3225	$1.50, Right Whale	65	70
3226	$1.50, Hawksbill Turtle	65	70
3227	$1.50, Leatherback Turtle	65	70
3228	$1.50, Green Turtle	65	70
3223/8	*Set of* 6	3·75	4·00

Nos. 3223/8 were printed together, *se-tenant*, in sheetlets of 6.

(Des T. Wood. Litho Questa)

1996 (7 Nov). *Marine Life. T* **434** *and similar multicoloured designs. P* 14.

3229	$1 Type **434**	45	50
	a. Sheetlet. Nos. 3229/37	4·00	
3230	$1 Dolphin	45	50
3231	$1 Two dolphins	45	50
3232	$1 Sea Lion and Regal Angelfish	45	50
3233	$1 Dolphins and Hawksbill Turtle	45	50
3234	$1 Three Hawksbill Turtles	45	50
3235	$1 Regal Angelfish and Pennant Coralfish	45	50
3236	$1 Pennant Coralfish	45	50
3237	$1 Sea Lion and Squirrelfish	45	50
3238	$1 Brown Pelican	45	50
	a. Sheetlet. Nos. 3238/46	4·00	
3239	$1 Killer Whale (*different*)	45	50
3240	$1 Whale	45	50
3241	$1 Dolphins and Sea Lion	45	50
3242	$1 Shortfin Pilot Whale, Blue-ringed Octopus and Sea Lion	45	50
3243	$1 Hammerhead Sharks and Sea Lion	45	50
3244	$1 Blue-striped Grunts	45	50
3245	$1 Stingray and Van Gogh Fusilier	45	50
3246	$1 Van Gogh Fusilier, Ribbon Moray and percoid fish	45	50
3229/46	*Set of* 18	8·00	9·00
MS3247	Two sheets, each 106×76 mm. (a) $6 Pair of Sea Lions (*horiz*). (b) $6 Pair of Dolphins (*horiz*) *Set of* 2 *sheets*	5·25	5·50

Nos. 3229/37 and 3238/46 were each printed together, *se-tenant*, in sheetlets of 9 with the backgrounds forming composite designs.

(Litho Questa)

1996 (18 Nov). *Christmas. Religious Paintings. Vert designs as T* **369** *of Antigua. Multicoloured. P* 13½×14.

3248	25 c. "The Visitation" (Tintoretto)	10	15
3249	35 c. "Virgin with the Child" (Palma Vecchio)	15	20
3250	50 c. "The Adoration of the Magi" (Botticelli)	25	30
3251	75 c. "The Annunciation" (Titian)	35	40
3252	$1 "The Flight into Egypt" (Tintoretto)	45	50
3253	$3 "The Holy Family with the Infant Saint John" (Andrea del Sarto)	1·25	1·40
3248/53	*Set of* 6	2·25	2·75

MS3254 Two sheets, each 106×76 mm. (a) $6 "Adoration of the Magi" (Paolo Schiavo). (b) $6 "Madonna and Child with Saints" (Vincenzo Poppa) . . . . . . *Set of* 2 *sheets* 5·25 5·50
No. 3250 in inscr "Botticelli" in error.

(Des Shannon. Litho Questa)

1996 (21 Nov). 20*th Anniv of* Rocky *(film). Sheet* 143×182 *mm, containing vert design as T* **266** *of Gambia. Multicoloured. P* 14×13½.
MS3255 $2×3, Sylvester Stallone in *Rocky V* . . 2·50 2·75

435 Ox

(Des Y. Lee. Litho Walsall)

1997 (2 Jan). *Chinese New Year ("Year of the Ox"). Sheet,* 150×75 *mm, containing T* **435** *and similar triangular designs. Multicoloured. Self-adhesive on silver foil. P* 9½.
MS3256 $2 Type **435** ("GRENADA" in black); $2 Ox ("GRENADA" in pink); $2 Ox ("GRENADA" in blue) . . . . . . 2·50 2·75
No. **MS**3256 also exists on gold foil from a limited printing.

436 Mickey at Tram Stop **437** Devon Rex

(Des Speedy Studio. Litho Questa)

1997 (12 Feb). *"HONG KONG '97" International Stamp Exhibition. Mickey in Hong Kong. T* **436** *and similar multicoloured designs showing Disney cartoon characters. P* 14×13½.
3257 35 c. Type **436** . . 15 20
a. Sheetlet. Nos. 3257/60 and 3267/8 . . 3·25
3258 50 c. Mickey and Donald fishing at Victoria Harbour . . 25 30
3259 75 c. Donald and Mickey parachuting . . 35 40
3260 90 c. Mickey and Minnie visiting Bank of China . . 40 45
3261 $1 Mickey with pet parrot . . 45 50
a. Sheetlet. Nos. 3261/6 . . 2·50
3262 $1 Mickey drinking Kung-fu Tea . . 45 50
3263 $1 Mickey, Minnie and Goofy shopping at Chinese Wet Market . . 45 50
3264 $1 Mickey, Minnie and Goofy with grass-hoppers . . 45 50
3265 $1 Mickey and Goofy with lanterns . . 45 50
3266 $1 Mickey and Minnie practising Tai-chi 45 50
3267 $2 Goofy delivering bottled gas . . 90 95
3268 $3 Mickey, Minnie and Donald at *Jumbo* floating restaurant . . 1·40 1·50
3257/68 . . *Set of* 12 6·00 6·50
MS3269 Four sheets, each 132×108 mm. (a) $3 Mickey and skyscrapers *(vert)*. (b) $4 Mickey and Minnie dancing *(vert)*. (c) $5 Mickey pulling rickshaw *(vert)*. (d) $6 Mickey with noodles *(vert)*. P 13½×14 . . *Set of* 4 *sheets* 8·25 8·50
Nos. 3257/60 with 3267/8 and 3261/6 were each printed together, *se-tenant*, in sheetlets of 6.
Nos. **MS**3269a and **MS**3269c show the "HONG KONG '97" International Stamp Exhibition logo on the margins.

(Des M. Freedman and Dena Rubin. Litho Questa)

1997 (3 Apr). 50*th Anniv of U.N.E.S.C.O. Multicoloured designs as T* **374** *of Antigua. P* 14×13½ *(horiz) or* 13½×14 *(vert)*.
3270 35 c. Temple, Kyoto, Japan . . 15 20
3271 75 c. Timbered houses, Quedlinburg, Germany . . 35 40
3272 90 c. View from walls, Dubrovnik, Croatia 40 45
3273 $1 Ruins at Delphi, Greece . . 45 50
3274 $1 Bryggen Wharf, Bergen, Norway *(vert)* . . 45 50
a. Sheetlet. Nos. 3274/81 and central label . . 3·50
3275 $1 Old city, Berne, Switzerland *(vert)* . . 45 50
3276 $1 Warsaw, Poland *(vert)* . . 45 50
3277 $1 Fortress walls, Luxembourg *(vert)* . . 45 50
3278 $1 Interior of Drottningholm Palace, Sweden *(vert)* . . 45 50
3279 $1 Petajavesi Church, Finland *(vert)* . . 45 50
3280 $1 Vilnius, Lithuania *(vert)* . . 45 50
3281 $1 Jelling Church, Denmark *(vert)* . . 45 50
3282 $1 Entrance to caves, Desert of Taklamakan, China *(vert)* . . 45 50
a. Sheetlet. Nos. 3282/9 and central label 3·50
3283 $1 House, Desert of Taklamakan, China *(vert)* . . 45 50
3284 $1 Monument, Desert of Taklamakan, China *(vert)* . . 45 50
3285 $1 Palace of Cielos Purpuras, Wudang, China *(vert)* . . 45 50
3286 $1 House, Wudang, China *(vert)* . . 45 50
3287 $1 Stone Guardian, The Great Wall, China *(vert)* . . 45 50
3288 $1 Ming Dynasty statue, Wudang, China *(vert)* . . 45 50
3289 $1 The Great Wall, China *(vert)* . . 45 50
3290 $1.50, Segovia Cathedral, Spain . . 65 70
a. Sheetlet. Nos. 3290/4 and label . . 3·25
3291 $1.50, Wurtzburg, Germany . . 65 70
3292 $1.50, Plitvice Lakes, Croatia . . 65 70
3293 $1.50, Batalha Monastery, Portugal . . 65 70
3294 $1.50, River Seine, Paris, France . . 65 70
3295 $2 Tomar, Portugal . . 85 90
3296 $3 Palace of Chaillot, Paris, France . . 1·25 1·40
3270/96 . . *Set of* 27 13·00 14·50
MS3297 Three sheets, each 127×102 mm. (a) $6 Popocatepetl Monastery, Mexico. (b) $6 Woodland path, Shirakami-Sanchi, Japan. (c) $6 Interior of the Hieronymites' Monastery, Portugal . . *Set of* 3 *sheets* 7·50 7·75
Nos. 3274/81 and 3282/9 were each printed together, *se-tenant*, in sheetlets of 8 stamps with a centre label and Nos. 3290/4 in a sheetlet of 5 with a top left-hand corner label.

(Des D. Miller. Litho Questa)

1997 (10 Apr). *Cats and Dogs. T* **437** *and similar vert designs. Multicoloured. P* 14.
3298 35 c. Type **437** . . 15 20
3299 75 c. King Charles Spaniel . . 35 40
3300 90 c. Japanese Bobtail . . 40 45
3301 $1 Afghan Hound . . 45 50
3302 $1 Turkish Van . . 45 50
a. Sheetlet. Nos. 3302/10 . . 4·00
3303 $1 Ragdoll . . 45 50
3304 $1 Siberian . . 45 50
3305 $1 Egyptian Mau . . 45 50
3306 $1 American Shorthair . . 45 50
3307 $1 Bengal . . 45 50
3308 $1 Asian Longhair . . 45 50
3309 $1 Somali . . 45 50
3310 $1 Turkish Angora . . 45 50
3311 $1 Lhasa Apso . . 45 50
a. Sheetlet. Nos. 3311/19 . . 4·00
3312 $1 Rough Collie . . 45 50
3313 $1 Norwich Terrier . . 45 50
3314 $1 American Cocker Spaniel . . 45 50
3315 $1 Chinese Crested Dog . . 45 50
3316 $1 Old English Sheepdog . . 45 50
3317 $1 Standard Poodle . . 45 50
3318 $1 German Shepherd . . 45 50
3319 $1 German Shorthair Pointer . . 45 50
3320 $2 Cornish Rex . . 85 90
3321 $3 Pekingese . . 1·25 1·40
3298/321 . . *Set of* 24 11·00 12·00
MS3322 Two sheets, each 106×76 mm. (a) $6 Singapura. (b) $6 Bernese Mountain Dog *Set of* 2 *sheets* 5·25 5·50
Nos. 3302/10 (cats) and 3311/19 (dogs) were each printed together, *se-tenant*, in sheetlets of 9.

438 Dunkleosteus

(Litho Questa)

1997 (15 Apr). *Dinosaurs. T* **438** *and similar multicoloured designs. P* 14.
3323 35 c. Type **438** . . 15 20
3324 75 c. Tyrannosaurus rex . . 35 40
3325 $1.50, Sordes . . 65 70
a. Sheetlet. Nos. 3325/30 . . 3·75
3326 $1.50, Dimorphodon . . 65 70
3327 $1.50, Diplodocus . . 65 70
3328 $1.50, Allosaurus . . 65 70
3329 $1.50, Pentaceratops . . 65 70
3330 $1.50, Protoceratops . . 65 70
3331 $2 Askeptosaurus *(vert)* . . 85 90
3332 $3 Triceratops *(vert)* . . 1·25 1·40
3323/32 . . *Set of* 10 6·00 6·50
MS3333 Two sheets, each 103×74 mm. (a) $6 Tristychius *(vert)*. (b) $6 Maiasaura *(vert)* *Set of* 2 *sheets* 5·25 5·50
Nos. 3325/30 were printed together, *se-tenant*, in sheetlets of 6 with the backgrounds forming a composite design.

439 Porcelain Crab

(Des R. Rundo. Litho Questa)

1997 (2 May). *Marine Life. T* **439** *and similar multicoloured designs. P* 14.
3334 45 c. Type **439** . . 20 25
3335 75 c. Humpback Whale . . 35 40
3336 90 c. Hermit Crab . . 40 45
3337 $1 Great White Shark . . 45 50
3338 $1.50, Octopus *(vert)* . . 65
a. Sheetlet. Nos. 3338/43 . . 3·75
3339 $1.50, Lei Triggerfish *(vert)* . . 65
3340 $1.50, Lionfish *(vert)* . . 65
3341 $1.50, Harlequin Wrasse *(vert)* . . 65
3342 $1.50, Clown Fish *(vert)* . . 65
3343 $1.50, Moray Eel *(vert)* . . 65
3344 $3 Green Sea Turtle . . 1·25 1·
3345 $4 Whale Shark . . 1·75 1·
3334/45 . . *Set of* 12 8·00 8·
MS3346 Two sheets, each 106×76 mm. (a) $6 Pacific Barracudas. (b) $6 Scalloped Hammer-head Shark . . *Set of* 2 *sheets* 5·25 5·
Nos. 3338/43 were printed together, *se-tenant*, in sheetlets of 6 with the backgrounds forming a composite design.

(Des R. Rundo. Litho Questa)

1997 (28 May). 300*th Anniv of Mother Goose Nursery Rhym... Sheet* 72×102 *mm containing multicoloured design as T* 3... *of Dominica. P* 14.
MS3347 $5 Boy holding umbrella ("Rain") *(vert)* 2·10 2·

(Litho Questa)

1997 (28 May). 10*th Anniv of Chernobyl Nuclear Disast... Vert designs as T* **376** *of Antigua. P* 13½×14.
3348 $2 As Type **376** of Antigua . . 85
3349 $2 As No. 3348, but inscribed "CHABAD'S CHILDREN OF CHERNOBYL" at foot 85

(Des J. Iskowitz. Litho Questa)

1997 (28 May). 50*th Death Anniv of Paul Harris (founder Rotary International). Horiz designs as T* **377** *of Antigu... Multicoloured. P* 14.
3350 $3 Paul Harris and vocational training programme, Philippines . . 1·25 1·
MS3351 78×107 mm. $6 Hands holding globe and doves . . 2·00 2·

(Litho Questa)

1997 (28 May). *Golden Wedding of Queen Elizabeth a... Prince Philip. Horiz designs as T* **378** *of Antigua. Mu... coloured. P* 14.
3352 $1 Queen Elizabeth and Prince Philip waving . . 45
a. Sheetlet. Nos. 3352/7 . . 2·75
3353 $1 Royal coat of arms . . 45
3354 $1 Queen Elizabeth with Prince Philip in naval uniform . . 45
3355 $1 Queen Elizabeth and Prince Philip at Buckingham Palace . . 45
3356 $1 Windsor Castle . . 45
3357 $1 Prince Philip . . 45
3352/7 . . *Set of* 6 2·50 2·
MS3358 100×70 mm. $6 Queen Elizabeth with Prince Philip in naval uniform *(different)* . . 2·75 3·
Nos. 3352/7 were printed together, *se-tenant*, in sheetlets of

(Des J. Iskowitz. Litho Questa)

1997 (28 May). *"Pacific '97" International Stamp Exhibiti... San Francisco (1st issue). Death Centenary of Heinrich ... Stephan (founder of the U.P.U.). Horiz designs as T* **379** *... Antigua. P* 14.
3359 $2 turquoise-green and black . . 85
a. Sheetlet. Nos. 3359/61 . . 2·50
3360 $2 chestnut . . 85
3361 $2 dull blue . . 85
3359/61 . . *Set of* 3 2·50 2·
MS3362 82×119 mm. $6 violet and black . . 2·50 2·
Designs:—No. 3359, Postman on motorcycle; No. 3360, V... Stephan and Mercury; No. 3361, Postman on skis, Ro... Mountains, 1900s; No. **MS**3362, Von Stephan and Chin... letter carrier.
Nos. 3359/61 were printed together, *se-tenant*, in sheets o... with enlarged right-hand margin.
See also Nos. 3392/409.

(Litho Questa)

1997 (28 May). *Birth Bicentenary of Hiroshige (Japan... painter). "One Hundred Famous Views of Edo". Vert desi... as T* **310** *of Dominica. Multicoloured. P* 13½×14.
3363 $1.50, "Nihon Embankment, Yoshiwara" 65
a. Sheetlet. Nos. 3363/8 . . 3·75
3364 $1.50, "Asakusa Ricefields and Torino-machi Festival" . . 65
3365 $1.50, "Senju Great Bridge" . . 65
3366 $1.50, "Dawn inside the Yoshiwara" . . 65
3367 $1.50, "Tile Kilns and Hasiba Ferry, Sumida River" . . 65
3368 $1.50, "View from Massaki of Suijin Shrine, Uchigawa Inlet and Sekiya" . . 65
3363/8 . . *Set of* 6 3·75 4
MS3369 Two sheets, each 102×127 mm. (a) $6 "Kinryuzan Temple, Asakusa"; (b) "Night view of Saruwaka-machi" . . *Set of* 2 *sheets* 5·25 5
Nos. 3363/8 were printed together, *se-tenant*, in sheetlets o...

(Des R. Sauber. Litho Questa)

1997 (28 May). 175*th Anniv of Brothers Grimm's Th... Collection of Fairy Tales. Snow White. Vert designs as T ... of Antigua. Multicoloured. P* 14.
3370 $2 Queen looking in mirror . . 85
a. Sheetlet. Nos. 3370/2 . . 2·50
3371 $2 Snow White and the Seven Dwarfs . . 85
3372 $2 Snow White and Prince . . 85
3370/2 . . *Set of* 3 2·50 2
MS3373 124×96 mm. $6 Witch with apple . . 2·50 2
Nos. 3370/2 were printed together, *se-tenant*, in sheetlets ... with illustrated margins.

440 One-man Luge

441 Bank of China

(Litho B.D.T.)

997 (26 June). *Winter Olympic Games, Nagano, Japan. T* **440** *and similar multicoloured designs. P* 14.

374 45 c. Type **440** 20 25
375 75 c. Men's speed-skating 35 40
376 $1 One-man luge (*different*) 45 50
a. Sheetlet. Nos. 3376/84 .. .. .. 4·00
377 $1 Ski-jumping (blue ski suit) 45 50
378 $1 Downhill skiing 45 50
379 $1 Speed-skating 45 50
380 $1 Two-man bobsleigh 45 50
381 $1 Women's figure-skating 45 50
382 $1 Alpine combined 45 50
383 $1 Ice hockey 45 50
384 $1 Ski-jumping (yellow ski suit) 45 50
385 $2 Men's figure-skating 90 95
386 $3 Slalom .. .. 1·40 1·50
374/86 .. .. *Set of* 13 6·75 7·50
S3387 Two sheets, each 96×69 mm. (a) $6 Four-man bobsleigh; (b) $6 Downhill skiing (*vert*) *Set of* 2 *sheets* 5·50 5·75

Nos. 3376/84 were printed together, *se-tenant*, in sheetlets of

(Des Y. Lee. Litho Questa)

997 (1 July). *Return of Hong Kong to China. T* **441** *and similar multicoloured designs. P* 14×13½ (90 *c.*, $1) *or* 14 (*others*).

388 90 c. Type **441** 40 45
a. Sheetlet of 4 .. .. 1·60
389 $1 Skyscrapers 45 50
a. Sheetlet of 4 .. .. 1·75
390 $1.75, "Hong Kong '97" on modern buildings (63×32 *mm*) 70 75
a. Sheetlet of 3 .. .. 2·10
391 $2 Deng Xiaoping and Hong Kong (63×32 *mm*) 85 90
a. Sheetlet of 3 .. .. 2·50
388/91 .. .. *Set of* 4 2·40 2·50

Nos. 3388/91 were printed in sheetlets of 3 or 4, each with nlarged illustrated margins.

442 Minnie Mouse dancing the Hula

(Des Alvin White Studios. Litho Questa)

97 (7 Aug). *"Pacific '97" International Stamp Exhibition, San Francisco (2nd issue). Centenary of the Cinema. Minnie Mouse in* Hawaiian Holiday. *T* **442** *and similar horiz designs showing a series of cartoon frames. Multicoloured. P* 14×13½.

392 50 c. Type **442** (Frame 1) 25 30
a. Sheetlet. Nos. 3392/9 and 1 label .. 2·00
393 50 c. Frame 2 .. .. 25 30
394 50 c. Frame 3 .. .. 25 30
395 50 c. Frame 4 .. .. 25 30
396 50 c. Frame 5 .. .. 25 30
397 50 c. Frame 6 .. .. 25 30
398 50 c. Frame 7 .. .. 25 30
399 50 c. Frame 8 .. .. 25 30
400 50 c. Frame 9 .. .. 25 30
a. Sheetlet. Nos. 3400/8 .. .. .. 2·25
401 50 c. Frame 10 .. .. 25 30
402 50 c. Frame 11 .. .. 25 30
403 50 c. Frame 12 .. .. 25 30
404 50 c. Frame 13 .. .. 25 30
405 50 c. Frame 14 .. .. 25 30
406 50 c. Frame 15 .. .. 25 30
407 50 c. Frame 16 .. .. 25 30
408 50 c. Frame 17 .. .. 25 30
392/408 .. .. *Set of* 17 4·25 5·00
S3409 110×130 mm. $6 Frame 18 .. .. 2·75 3·00

Nos. 3392/9 and 3400/8 were printed together, *se-tenant*, in eetlets of 8 or 9. It is intended that the stamps should be parated and used as a flip book to produce a moving image.

OMNIBUS ISSUES

etails, together with prices for complete sets, f the various Omnibus issues from the 1935 ilver Jubilee series to date are included in a pecial section following Zimbabwe at the end of Volume 2.

443 Hercules lifting Rock

(Des Alvin White Studios. Litho Questa)

1997 (7 Aug). *Hercules* (*cartoon film*) (1*st series*). *T* **443** *and similar vert designs showing Disney cartoon characters. Multicoloured. P* 13½×14.

3410 $1 Type **443** 45 50
a. Sheetlet. Nos. 3410/17 .. .. .. 3·50
3411 $1 Pegasus 45 50
3412 $1 Megara 45 50
3413 $1 Philoktetes 45 50
3414 $1 Nessus 45 50
3415 $1 Hydra 45 50
3416 $1 Pain and Panic 45 50
3417 $1 Hades 45 50
3410/17 .. .. *Set of* 8 3·50 4·00
MS3418 Two sheets (a) 131×104 mm. $6 Hercules as a boy. (b) 104×131 mm. $6 The Muses .. .. *Set of* 2 *sheets* 5·50 5·75

Nos. 3410/17 were printed together, *se-tenant*, in sheetlets of 8.

See also Nos. 3561/85.

(Litho Questa)

1997 (11 Aug). *World Cup Football Championship, France* (1998). *Designs as T* **383** *of Antigua. Multicoloured* (*except Nos.* 3422/3 *and* 3428). *P* 13½×14 (*vert*) *or* 14×13½ (*horiz*).

3419 15 c. West German and Italian players, 1982 (*vert*) 10 10
3420 75 c. Italian player holding World Cup, 1982 (*vert*) 35 40
3421 90 c. West German and Italian players wearing "20" shirts, 1982 (*vert*) .. 40 45
3422 $1 Uruguay team, 1950 (agate) 45 50
a. Sheetlet. Nos. 3422/9 and central label 3·50
3423 $1 Brazilian team, 1958 (agate) 45 50
3424 $1 West German team, 1974 .. .. 45 50
3425 $1 Argentine team, 1986 .. .. .. 45 50
3426 $1 Italian team, 1982 .. .. .. 45 50
3427 $1 West German team, 1990 .. .. 45 50
3428 $1 Italian team, 1934 (agate) 45 50
3429 $1 Brazilian team, 1970 .. .. .. 45 50
3430 $1 Seaman, England 45 50
a. Sheetlet. Nos. 3430/7 and central label 3·50
3431 $1 Klinsmann, Germany 45 50
3432 $1 Berger, Czech Republic 45 50
3433 $1 McCoist, Scotland 45 50
3434 $1 Gascoigne, England 45 50
3435 $1 Djorkaeff, France 45 50
3436 $1 Sammer, Germany 45 50
3437 $1 Futre, Portugal 45 50
3438 $2 Italian player beating goal keeper, 1982 (*vert*) 85 90
3439 $3 Goal-mouth melee, 1982 (*vert*) .. .. 1·25 1·40
3440 $4 Two West German players tackling Italian player (*vert*) .. .. .. 1·75 1·90
3419/40 .. .. *Set of* 22 10·00 11·00
MS3441 Two sheets. (a) 102×127 mm. $6 Beckenbaur holding World Cup, Germany (*vert*). (b) 127×102 mm. $6 Moore, England *Set of* 2 *sheets* 5·25 5·50

Nos. 3422/9 and 3430/7 were each printed together, *se-tenant*, in sheetlets of 8 with central label.

444 Peacock

(Des Joni Popes. Litho Questa)

1997 (12 Aug). *Butterflies and Moths. T* **444** *and similar horiz designs. Multicoloured. P* 14.

3442 45 c. Type **444** 20 25
3443 75 c. Orange Flambeau 35 40
3444 90 c. Eastern Tailed Blue 45 50
3445 $1 Brimstone 45 50
a. Sheetlet. Nos. 3445/52 .. .. .. 3·50
3446 $1 Mocker Swallowtail 45 50
3447 $1 American Painted Lady 45 50
3448 $1 Tiger Swallowtail 45 50
3449 $1 Long Wing 45 50
3450 $1 Sunset Moth 45 50
3451 $1 Australian Blue Mountain Swallowtail 45 50
3452 $1 Bird Wing 45 50
3453 $2 Black and Red 85 90
3454 $3 Large White .. .. 1·25 1·40
3455 $4 Oriental Swallowtail .. .. .. 1·75 1·90
3442/55 .. .. *Set of* 14 8·25 9·00
MS3456 Two sheets, each 76×106 mm. (a) $5 Monarch. (b) $5 Blue Morpho .. *Set of* 2 *sheets* 4·25 4·50

Nos. 3445/52 were printed together, *se-tenant*, in sheetlets of 8.

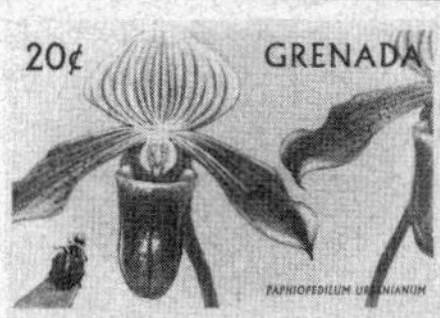

445 *Paphiopedilum urbanianum*

(Des R. Rundo. Litho B.D.T.)

1997 (4 Sept). *Orchids of the World. T* **445** *and similar multicoloured designs. P* 14.

3457 20 c. Type **445** 10 10
3458 35 c. *Trichoceros parviflorus* 15 20
3459 45 c. *Euanthe sanderiana* (*vert*) 20 25
3460 75 c. *Oncidium macranthum* (*vert*) 35 40
3461 90 c. *Psychopsis kramerianum* (*vert*) .. 40 45
3462 $1 *Oncidium hastatum* (*vert*) 45 50
3463 $2 *Broughtonia sanguinea* (*vert*) 90 95
a. Sheetlet. Nos. 3463/8 .. .. .. 5·50
3464 $2 *Anguloa virginalis* (*vert*) 90 95
3465 $2 *Dendrobium bigibbum* (*vert*) 90 95
3466 $2 *Lucasiana* (*vert*) 90 95
3467 $2 *Cymbidium* (*vert*) 90 95
3468 $2 *Cymbidium* and vase (*vert*) 90 95
3469 $2 *Odontoglossum crispum* (*vert*) 90 95
a. Sheetlet. Nos. 3469/74 .. .. .. 5·50
3470 $2 *Cattleya brabantiae* (*vert*) 90 95
3471 $2 *Cattleya bicolor* (*vert*) 90 95
3472 $2 *Trichopilia suavia* (*vert*) 90 95
3473 $2 *Encyclia mariae* (*vert*) 90 95
3474 $2 *Angraecum leonis* (*vert*) 90 95
3475 $3 *Masdevallia saltatix* (*vert*) .. .. 1·40 1·50
3476 $4 *Cattleya luteola* .. .. 1·90 2·00
3457/76 .. .. *Set of* 20 16·00 17·00
MS3477 Two sheets. (a) 76×106 mm. $6 *Laelia milleri*. (b) 106×76 mm. $6 *Oncidium onustum* *Set of* 2 *sheets* 5·50 5·75

Nos. 3463/8 and 3469/74 were each printed together, *se-tenant*, in sheetlets of 6 with the backgrounds forming composite designs.

446 *Boletus erythropus*

(Litho B.D.T.)

1997 (4 Sept). *Fungi of the World. T* **446** *and similar horiz designs. Multicoloured. P* 14.

3478 35 c. Type **446** 15 20
3479 75 c. *Armillariella mellea* 35 40
3480 90 c. *Amanita flavorubens* 40 45
3481 $1 Indigo Milky 45 50
3482 $1.50, *Agaricus solidipes* 65 70
a. Sheetlet. Nos. 3482/7 .. .. .. 3·75
3483 $1.50, Salmon Waxy Cap 65 70
3484 $1.50, Fused Maramius 65 70
3485 $1.50, Shellfish-scented Russula 65 70
3486 $1.50, Red-capped Scaber Stalk 65 70
3487 $1.50, *Calocybe gambosum* 65 70
3488 $1.50, *Boletus parasiticus* 65 70
a. Sheetlet. Nos. 3488/93 .. .. .. 3·75
3489 $1.50, *Frostis bolete* 65 70
3490 $1.50, *Amanita myscara flavilolvata* .. 65 70
3491 $1.50, *Volvariella volvacea* 65 70
3492 $1.50, Stuntz's Blue Legs 65 70
3493 $1.50, Orange-latex Milky 65 70
3494 $2 *Tylopilus balloui* 85 90
3495 $4 *Boletus parasiticus* .. .. .. 1·75 1·90
3478/95 .. .. *Set of* 18 11·00 12·00
MS3496 Two sheets, each 97×67 mm. (a) $6 *Agaricus argenteus*. (b) $6 *Omphalotus illudens* *Set of* 2 *sheets* 5·25 5·50

Nos. 3482/7 and 3488/93 were each printed together, *se-tenant*, in sheetlets of 6.

447 Princess Diana with Landmine Victims

448 "Angel" (Matthias Grünewald)

(Des R. Sauber. Litho Questa)

1997 (15 Oct). *Diana, Princess of Wales Commemoration. T* **447** *and similar horiz designs. Multicoloured. P* 14½.

3497 $1.50, Type **447** 60 65
a. Sheetlet. Nos. 3497/502 .. .. .. 3·75
3498 $1.50, With sick child 60 65
3499 $1.50, With young boy on crutches 60 65
3500 $1.50, With leper 60 65
3501 $1.50, Holding baby 60 65
3502 $1.50, Walking through minefield 60 65
3497/502 .. .. *Set of* 6 3·75 4·25
MS3503 76×106 mm. $5 With Mother Theresa 2·10 2·25

Nos. 3497/502 were printed together, *se-tenant*, in sheetlets of 6 with enlarged illustrated right-hand margin.

Two different $20 values embossed on gold foil and a $6 on silver foil showing a hologram exist from limited printings.

(Litho Questa)

1997 (5 Dec). *Christmas. Religious Paintings. T* **448** *and similar multicoloured designs. P* 14.
3504 35 c. Type **448** 15 20
3505 50 c. "St. Demetrius" (icon) 20 25
3506 75 c. Three-panelled reliquary 35 40
3507 $1 "Angel of the Annunciation" (Jan van Eyck) 45 50
3508 $3 "The Annunciation" (Simone Martini) 1·25 1·40
3509 $4 "St. Michael" (icon) .. .. .. 1·75 1·90
3504/9 .. .. *Set of* 6 4·00 4·50
MS3510 Two sheets. (a) 104×114 mm. $6 "The Coronation of the Virgin" (Fra Angelico). (b) 114×104 mm. $6 "The Annunciation" (Titian) (*horiz*) .. .. *Set of 2 sheets* 5·25 5·50

(Des Y. Lee. Litho Walsall)

1998 (5 Jan). *Chinese New Year ("Year of the Tiger"). Sheet 150×75 mm containing triangular designs as T* **435** *showing tigers. Multicoloured. Self-adhesive on silver foil. P* $9^{1}/_{2}$.
MS3511 $1.50, "GRENADA" in pink; $1.50, "GRENADA" in gold; $1.50, "GRENADA" in bronze .. .. 2·00 2·10
No. **MS**3511 also exists on gold foil

449 Black-tailed Damselfish

(Litho B.D.T.)

1988 (10 Feb). *Fishes. T* **449** *and similar horiz designs. Multicoloured. P* 14.
3512 65 c. Type **449** 30 35
3513 90 c. Yellow Sweetlips 40 45
3514 $1 Common Squirrelfish 45 50
3515 $1.50, Blue Tang 65 70
a. Sheetlet. Nos. 3515/20 .. .. 3·75
3516 $1.50, Porkfish 65 70
3517 $1.50, Banded Butterflyfish 65 70
3518 $1.50, Thread-finned Butterflyfish .. 65 70
3519 $1.50, Hooded Butterflyfish ("Red-headed") 65 70
3520 $1.50, Emperor Angelfish 65 70
3521 $1.50, Duboulay's Angelfish ("Scribbled Anglefish") 65 70
a. Sheetlet. Nos. 3521/6 .. .. 3·75
3522 $1.50, Lemon-peel Angelfish 65 70
3523 $1.50, Bandit Angelfish 65 70
3524 $1.50, Bicoloured Angelfish ("Biclor Cherub") 65 70
3525 $1.50, Palette Surgeonfish ("Regal Tang") 65 70
3526 $1.50, Yellow Tang 65 70
3527 $2 Powder-blue Surgeonfish 85 90
3512/27 .. .. *Set of* 16 9·50 10·50
MS3528 Two sheets, each 110×80 mm. (a) $6 Two-banded Anemonefish. (b) $6 Forceps Butterflyfish ("Long-nosed Butterflyfish") *Set of 2 sheets* 5·25 5·50
Nos. 3515/20 and 3521/6 were each printed together, *se-tenant*, in sheetlets of 6 with the backgrounds forming composite designs.

450 *Sophronitis grandiflora*

1998 (21 Apr). *Flowers of the World. T* **450** *and similar horiz designs. Multicoloured. Litho. P* 14.
3529 $1.50, Type **450** 65 70
a. Sheetlet. Nos. 3529/34 .. .. 3·75
3530 $1.50, *Phalaenopsis amboinensis* .. 65 70
3531 $1.50, *Zygopetalum intermedium* .. 65 70
3532 $1.50, *Paphiopedilum purpuratum* .. 65 70
3533 $1.50, *Miltonia regnellii* 65 70
3534 $1.50, *Dendrobium parishii* 65 70
3535 $1.50, *Arachnis clarkei* 65 70
a. Sheetlet. Nos. 3535/40 .. .. 3·75
3536 $1.50, *Cymbidium eburneum* 65 70
3537 $1.50, *Dendrobium chrysotoxum* .. 65 70
3538 $1.50, *Paphiopedilum insigne* 65 70
3539 $1.50, *Paphiopedilum venustum* .. 65 70
3540 $1.50, *Renanthera imschootiana* .. 65 70
3529/40 .. .. *Set of* 12 7·50 8·25
MS3541 Two sheets, each 104×72 mm. (a) $6 *Pleione maculata*. (b) $6 *Lycaste aromatica* *Set of 2 sheets* 5·25 5·50
Nos. 3529/34 and 3535/40 were each printed together, *se-tenant*, in sheetlets of 6.

COVER PRICES

Cover factors are quoted at the beginning of each country for most issues to 1945. An explanation of the system can be found on page x. The factors quoted do not, however, apply to philatelic covers.

451 Dhow

452 Arctic Skua

(Des S. Thurston. Litho Questa)

1998 (26 Apr). *Famous Ships. T* **451** *and similar horiz designs. Multicoloured. P* 14.
3542 $1 Type **451** 45 50
a. Sheetlet. Nos. 3542/50 .. .. 4·00
3543 $1 Galleon 45 50
3544 $1 Felucca 45 50
3545 $1 Schooner 45 50
3546 $1 Aircraft carrier 45 50
3547 $1 Knau 45 50
3548 $1 Destroyer 45 50
3549 $1 Viking longship 45 50
3550 $1 *Queen Elizabeth 2* (liner) 45 50
3551 $1 Brig 45 50
a. Sheetlet. Nos. 3551/9 .. .. 4·00
3552 $1 Clipper 45 50
3553 $1 Caique 45 50
3554 $1 Mississippi riverboat 45 50
3555 $1 Luxury liner 45 50
3556 $1 *Mayflower* (Pilgrim Fathers) 45 50
3557 $1 Frigate 45 50
3558 $1 Janggolan 45 50
3559 $1 Junk 45 50
3542/59 .. .. *Set of* 18 8·00 9·00
MS3560 Two sheets, each 100×75 mm. (a) $6 Nuclear submarine (58×43 *mm*). (b) $6 *Lusitania* (liner) (86×29 *mm*) .. *Set of 2 sheets* 5·25 5·50
Nos. 3542/50 and 3551/9 were each printed together, *se-tenant*, in sheetlets of 9, forming composite background designs.

1998 (16 June). Hercules (*cartoon film*) (*2nd series*). *Multicoloured designs as T* **443** *showing Disney cartoon characters. Litho. P* $13^{1}/_{2}$×14.
3561/8 10 c. × 8 Hercules and giant statue; Hercules, Pegasus and Philoktetes; Hercules and Philoktetes with shield and arrows; Hercules swinging from blades; Nessus carrying off Megara; Hercules fighting Nessus; Hercules fighting giant lion; Hercules and Pegasus leaving prints on pavement
a. Sheetlet. Nos. 3561/8 80
3569/76 $1 × 8 Baby Hercules with Zeus and Alcmene; Baby Hercules with Hades; Hades in the Underworld; Baby Hercules and young Pegasus; Baby Hercules with Pain and Panic; Baby Hercules with mortal parents; Hercules towing hay waggon; Hercules receiving gold medallion
a. Sheetlet. Nos. 3569/76 .. .. 3·50
3577/84 $1 × 8 Hercules and Megara; Megara and Hades; Hercules training with Philoktetes; Hercules confronting Hades; Giant destroying city; Zeus; Hercules saving Megara by lifting pillar; Hercules diving into sea
a. Sheetlet. Nos. 3577/84 .. .. 3·50
3561/84 .. .. *Set of* 24 7·75 8·25
MS3585 Six sheets, each 127×102 mm. (a) $6 Hades. (b) $6 Baby Pegasus. (c) $6 Hercules with sword. (d) $6 Hades on fire. (e) $6 Zeus and Hercules (*horiz*). (f) $6 Hercules and Megara riding Pegasus (*horiz*). P $13^{1}/_{2}$×14 (*vert*) or 14×$13^{1}/_{2}$ (*horiz*) .. .. .. *Set of 6 sheets* 15·00 16·00
Nos. 3561/8, 3569/76 and 3577/84 were each printed together, *se-tenant*, in sheetlets of 8.

(Des D. Brown. Litho Questa)

1998 (30 June). *Seabirds. T* **452** *and similar multicoloured designs. P* 14.
3586 90 c. Type **452** 40 45
3587 $1 Northern Fulmar (*horiz*) 45 50
a. Sheetlet. Nos. 3587/95 .. .. 4·00
3588 $1 Black-legged Kittiwake (*horiz*) .. 45 50
3589 $1 Cape Petrel (*horiz*) 45 50
3590 $1 Mediterranean Gull (*horiz*) 45 50
3591 $1 Brandt's Cormorant (*horiz*) 45 50
3592 $1 Greater Shearwater (*horiz*) 45 50
3593 $1 Black-footed Albatross (*horiz*) .. 45 50
3594 $1 Red-necked Phalarope (*horiz*) .. 45 50
3595 $1 Black Skimmer (*horiz*) 45 50
3596 $1.10, Humboldt Penguin 50 55
3597 $2 Herring Gull 85 90
3598 $3 Red Knot .. .. 1·25 1·40
3586/98 .. .. *Set of* 13 7·00 7·75
MS3599 Two sheets, each 100×70 mm. (a) $5 Black-browed Albatross. (b) $5 King Penguin *Set of 2 sheets* 4·25 4·50
Nos. 3587/95 were printed together, *se-tenant*, in sheetlets of 9, with the backgrounds forming a composite design.

453 Supermarine Spitfire Mk I

(Des M. Servino. Litho Questa)

1998 (20 July). *History of the Supermarine Spitfire* (*aircraft*) *T* **453** *and similar horiz designs showing different versions. Multicoloured. P* 14.
3600 $1.50, Type **453** 65 7
a. Sheetlet. Nos. 3600/5 .. .. .. 3·75
3601 $1.50, Mark VIII 65 7
3602 $1.50, Mark III 65 7
3603 $1.50, Mark XVI 65 7
3604 $1.50, Mark V 65 7
3605 $1.50, Mark XIX 65 7
3606 $1.50, Mark IX 65 7
a. Sheetlet. Nos. 3606/11 .. .. 3·75
3607 $1.50, Mark XIV 65 7
3608 $1.50, Mark XII 65 7
3609 $1.50, Mark XI 65 7
3610 $1.50, H.F. Mark VIII 65 7
3611 $1.50, Mark VB 65 7
3600/11 .. .. *Set of* 12 7·50 8·2
MS3612 Two sheets, each 80×106 mm. (a) $6 Mark IA. (b) $6 Mark IX (*different*) (*both* 56×41 *mm*) .. .. *Set of 2 sheets* 5·25 5·5
Nos. 3600/5 and 3606/11 were each printed together *se-tenant*, in sheetlets of 6 with enlarged illustrated top margins

454 Walrus

455 Scout saluting

1998 (19 Aug). *International Year of the Ocean. T* **454** *and similar horiz designs. Multicoloured. Litho. P* 14.
3613 75 c. Type **454** 35 4
a. Sheetlet. Nos. 3613/28 .. .. 5·50
3614 75 c. African Black-footed Penguins .. 35 4
3615 75 c. African Black-footed Penguin .. 35 4
3616 75 c. California Sealion 35 4
3617 75 c. Green Turtle 35 4
3618 75 c. Redfin Anthias 35 4
3619 75 c. Sperm Whale 35 4
3620 75 c. French Angelfish and Australian Sealion 35 4
3621 75 c. Jellyfish 35 4
3622 75 c. Sawfish 35 4
3623 75 c. Cuckoo Wrasse 35 4
3624 75 c. Garibaldi 35 4
3625 75 c. Spinecheek Anemonefish 35 4
3626 75 c. Leafy Seadragon 35 4
3627 75 c. Blue-spotted Goatfish 35 4
3628 75 c. Two-spot Gobies 35 4
3613/28 .. .. *Set of* 16 5·50 6·2
MS3629 Two sheets, each 98×68 mm. (a) $5 Atlantic Spotted Dolphins. (b) $6 Octopus *Set of 2 sheets* 4·75 5·0
Nos. 3613/28 were printed together, *se-tenant*, in sheetlets of 16 with the backgrounds forming a composite design.

(Litho Questa)

1998 (15 Sept). *50th Anniv of Organization of American States. Vert design as T* **324** *of Dominica. P* $13^{1}/_{2}$×14.
3630 $1 multicoloured 45 5

(Des Diana Catherines. Litho Questa)

1998 (15 Sept). *25th Death Anniv of Pablo Picasso* (*painter*). *Multicoloured designs as T* **325** *of Dominica. P* $14^{1}/_{2}$.
3631 45 c. "The Bathers" (*vert*) 20 2
3632 $2 "Luncheon on the Grass" 85 9
3633 $3 "The Swimmer" .. .. .. 1·25 1·4
3631/3 .. .. *Set of* 3 2·25 2·5
MS3634 102×127 mm. $5 "Tomato Plant" (*vert*) 2·10 2·2

(Des F. Rivera. Litho Questa)

1998 (15 Sept). *Birth Centenary of Enzo Ferrari* (*car manufacturer*). *Multicoloured designs as T* **326** *of Dominica. P* 14.
3635 $2 250 GT Berlinetta Lusso 85 9
a. Sheetlet. Nos. 3635/7 .. .. .. 2·50
3636 $2 250 GTO 85 9
3637 $2 250 GT Boano/Ellena cabriolet .. 85 9
3635/7 .. .. *Set of* 3 2·50 2·7
MS3638 104×70 mm. $5 246 GTS Dino (91×34 *mm*). P 14×$14^{1}/_{2}$ .. .. 2·10 2·2
Nos. 3635/7 were printed together, *se-tenant*, in sheetlets of 3

(Des G. Bibby. Litho Questa)

1998 (15 Sept). *19th World Scout Jamboree, Chile. T* **455** *and similar multicoloured designs. P* 14.
3639 $2 Type **455** 85 9
3640 $3 International Scout flag .. .. 1·25 1·4
3641 $4 Applying First Aid .. .. .. 1·75 1·9
3639/41 .. .. *Set of* 3 3·75 4·0
MS3642 106×76 mm. $6 International Scout flag (*horiz*) .. .. 2·50 2·7

(Des J. Iskowitz. Litho Questa)

1998 (15 Sept). *50th Death Anniv of Mahatma Gandhi. Vert designs as T* **327** *of Dominica. P* 14.
3643 $1 black, grey and dull mauve 45 5
a. Sheetlet of 4 .. .. 1·75
MS3644 70×100 mm. $6 multicoloured .. 2·50 2·7
Designs:—$1 Mahatma Gandhi; $6 Gandhi and spinning wheel.
No. 3643 was issued in sheetlets of 4 with enlarged illustrated margins at top and right.

(Des D. Miller. Litho Questa)

998 (15 Sept). *80th Anniv of Royal Air Force. Horiz designs as T* **328** *of Dominica. Multicoloured. P* 14.
645 $2 Supermarine Spitfire Mk IIa 85 90
a. Sheetlet. Nos. 3645/8 .. .. .. 3·25
646 $2 Supermarine Spitfire Mk IXb from above 85 90
647 $2 Supermarine Spitfire Mk IXb from side 85 90
648 $2 Hawker Hurricane Mk IIC of Battle of Britain Memorial Flight 85 90
649 $2 EF-2000 Eurofighter above clouds .. 85 90
a. Sheetlet. Nos. 3649/52 .. .. 3·25
650 $2 Nimrod MR2P (maritime reconnaissance) 85 90
651 $2 EF-2000 Eurofighter at low level .. 85 90
652 $2 C-47 Dakota (transport) 85 90
645/52 .. .. *Set of* 8 6·50 7·00
MS3653 Four sheets, each 93×70 mm. (a) $6 Bristol F2B fighter and head of Golden Eagle. (b) $6 Bristol F2B fighter and Falcon (bird). (c) $6 Jet Provost (trainer) and EF-2000 Eurofighter. (d) $6 VC10 (transport) and EF-2000 Eurofighter .. .. *Set of* 4 *sheets* 10·00 10·50
Nos. 3645/8 and 3649/52 were each printed together, *se-tenant*, in sheetlets of 4 with enlarged illustrated margins.

456 "Knights in Combat"

(Litho Questa)

1998 (15 Sept). *Birth Bicentenary of Eugène Delacroix (painter). T* **456** *and similar horiz designs. Multicoloured. P* 14.
3654 $1 Type **456** 45 50
a. Sheetlet. Nos. 3654/61 .. .. 3·50
3655 $1 "Murder of Bishop of Liége" 45 50
3656 $1 "Still Life" 45 50
3657 $1 "Battle of Nancy" 45 50
3658 $1 "Shipwreck of Don Juan" 45 50
3659 $1 "The Death of Ophelia" 45 50
3660 $1 "Attila the Hun" 45 50
3661 $1 "Arab Entertainers" 45 50
3654/61 .. .. *Set of* 8 3·50 4·00
MS3662 100×92 mm. $5 "The Capture of Constantinople" .. .. 2·10 2·25
Nos. 3654/61 were printed together in sheetlets of 8, containing two *se-tenant* horizontal strips of 4 separated by a gutter showing the paintings depicted on Nos. 3657 and 3660.

457 Flags of Grenada and CARICOM

(Des R. Sauber. Litho Questa)

1998 (15 Sept). *25th Anniv of Caribbean Community. P* 13½.
3663 **457** $1 multicoloured 45 50

459 Dove of Peace with Stars and Streamers

460 "The Angel's parting from Tobias" (Jean Bilevelt)

(Litho Walsall)

1998 (30 Nov). *Grenada's Participation in U.N. Peacekeeping Operations, Beirut,* 1982–4. *P* 14.
3672 **459** $1 multicoloured 45 50

1998 (1 Dec). *Christmas. Religious Paintings. T* **460** *and similar vert designs. Multicoloured. Litho. P* 14.
3673 35 c. Type **460** 15 20
3674 45 c. "Allegory of Faith" (Moretto Da Brescia) 20 25
3675 90 c. "Crucifixion" (Ugolino Di Tedice) .. 40 45
3676 $1 "The Triumphal Entry into Jerusalem" (Master of the Thuison Altarpiece) 45 50
3673/6 .. .. *Set of* 4 1·10 1·40

461 Blue-hooded Euphonia

(Litho B.D.T.)

1998 (1 Dec). *Christmas. Birds. T* **461** *and similar multicoloured designs. P* 13½×14.
3677 45 c. Type **461** 20 25
3678 75 c. Red-billed Whistling Duck ("Black-bellied Whistling Duck") 35 40
3679 90 c. Purple Martin 40 45
3680 $1 Imperial Amazon ("Imperial Parrot") 45 50
3681 $2 Adelaide's Warbler 85 90
3682 $3 Greater Flamingo ("Roseate Flamingo") .. .. 1·25 1·40
3677/82 .. .. *Set of* 6 3·50 3·75
MS3683 Two sheets, each 97×84 mm. (a) $5 Green-throated Carib. (b) $6 Purple-throated Carib and Canada 1898 Imperial Penny Postage 2 c. stamp (37×60 *mm*) .. .. *Set of* 2 *sheets* 4·75 5·00

1999 (4 Jan). *Chinese New Year ("Year of the Rabbit"). Sheet* 150×75 *mm containing triangular designs as T* **435** *showing rabbits. Multicoloured. Self-adhesive on silver foil. P* 9½.
MS3684 $1 "GRENADA" in green; $1 "GRENADA" in orange; $1 "GRENADA" in pink 1·25 1·40

STAMP BOOKLETS

1977 (8 Feb). *Silver Jubilee. Multicoloured cover,* 165×92 *mm, showing Queen in Coronation Coach. Stitched.*
SB1 $6.60, booklet containing 35 c. in pane of 6 (No. 863a) and *se-tenant* pane of 3 (No. 864a) .. 2·50

1978 (2 May). *25th Anniv of Coronation. Multicoloured cover,* 165×92 *mm, showing photograph of Queen Elizabeth II. Stitched.*
SB2 $6.80, booklet containing *se-tenant* pane of 6 (No. 950a) and pane of 1 (No. 952a) .. .. 2·00

1981 (16 June). *Royal Wedding. Multicoloured cover,* 95×166 *mm, showing commemorative inscription on front and Queen, Prince Charles, Lady Diana Spencer and group of Privy Councillors on back. Stitched.*
SB3 $14 booklet containing *se-tenant* pane of 6 (No. 1136a) and pane of 1 (No. 1138a) .. .. 2·50

POSTAGE DUE STAMPS

D 1

1d.

SURCHARGE
POSTAGE

(D 2)

(Typo D.L.R.)

1892 (18 Apr–Oct). (a) *Type* D 1. *Wmk Crown CA. P* 14.
D1 D 1 1d. blue-black .. .. 23·00 1·50
D2 2d. blue-black .. .. £140 1·50
D3 3d. blue-black .. .. £140 2·50
D1/3 .. .. *Set of* 3 £275 5·00

(b) *Nos.* 34 *and* 35 *surch locoally as Type* D 2
D4 13 1d. on 6d. mauve (10.92) .. .. 75·00 1·25
a. *Tête-bêche* (vert pair) £1000 £750
b. Surch double .. .. .. — £150
D5 1d. on 8d. grey-brown (8.92) .. £600 3·25
a. *Tête-bêche* (vert pair) £3000 £1300
D6 2d. on 6d. mauve (10.92) .. £140 2·50
a. *Tête-bêche* (vert pair) £1500 £1000
D7 2d. on 8d. grey-brown (8.92) .. £1100 9·50
a. *Tête-bêche* (vert pair) £4500 £2750
Nos. D4/7 were in use from August to November 1892. As supplies of Nos. D1/3 were available from April or May of that year it would not appear that they were intended for postage due purposes. There was a shortage of 1d. postage stamps in July and August, but this was alleviated by Nos. 44/5 which were still available. The provisionals *may* have been intended for postal purposes, but the vast majority appear to have been used philatelically.

1906 (July)–**11**. *Wmk Mult Crown CA. P* 14.
D 8 D 1 1d. blue-black (1911) .. .. .. 2·50 6·50
D 9 2d. blue-black .. .. 9·00 1·75
D10 3d. blue-black (9.06) .. .. .. 11·00 6·00
D8/10 .. .. *Set of* 3 20·00 13·00

1921 (Dec)–**22**. *As Type* D 1, *but inscr* "POSTAGE DUE". *Wmk Mult Script CA. P* 14.
D11 1d. black .. .. 90 1·00
D12 1½d. black (15.12.22) .. .. .. 8·50 16·00
D13 2d. black .. .. 2·00 1·75
D14 3d. black .. .. 2·00 4·25
D11/14 .. .. *Set of* 4 12·00 21·00
D11/14 Optd "Specimen" .. .. *Set of* 4 80·00

1952 (1 Mar). *As Type* D 1, *but inscr* "POSTAGE DUE". *Value in cents. Chalk-surfaced paper. Wmk Mult Script CA. P* 14.
D15 2 c. black .. .. 30 5·00
a. Error. Crown missing. W **9a** .. .. 85·00
b. Error. St. Edward Crown. W **9b** .. .. 42·00
D16 4 c. black .. .. 30 11·00
a. Error. Crown missing. W **9a** .. .. 85·00
b. Error. St. Edward Crown. W **9b** .. .. 42·00
D17 6 c. black .. .. 45 11·00
a. Error. Crown missing. W **9a** £120
b. Error. St. Edward Crown. W **9b** .. .. 80·00
D18 8 c. black .. .. 75 11·00
a. Error. Crown missing. W **9a** £200
b. Error. St. Edward Crown. W **9b** £130
D15/18 .. .. *Set of* 4 1·60 35·00

OFFICIAL STAMPS

P.R.G.

(O 1)

(= People's Revolutionary Government)

1982 (June). *Various stamps optd with Type* O 1.

(a) *Nos.* 1085A/97A *and* 1099A
O 1 5 c. West Indiaman barque, *circa* 1840 15 20
O 2 6 c. R.M.S.P. *Orinoco, circa* 1851 .. .. 15 20
O 3 10 c. Working Schooner 15 20
O 4 12 c. Trimaran at Grand Anse anchorage .. 15 20
O 5 15 c. Spice Island cruising yacht *Petite Amie* 20 20
O 6 20 c. Fishing pirogue 25 20
O 7 25 c. Harbour police launch 30 30
O 8 30 c. Grand Anse speedboat 30 30
O 9 40 c. M.V. *Seimstrand* 35 30
O10 50 c. Three-masted schooner *Ariadne* .. 40 40
O11 90 c. M.V. *Geestide* 70 80
O12 $1 M.V. *Cunard Countess* 70 80
O13 $3 Rum-runner .. .. 2·00 3·75
O14 $10 Coast-guard patrol boat.. .. .. 6·00 12·00

(b) *Nos.* 1130/2 *and* 1134/5
O15 30 c. Prince Charles and Lady Diana Spencer 1·75 2·25
O16 40 c. Holyrood House .. .. 2·25 2·75
O17 50 c. Prince Charles and Lady Diana Spencer 1·25 2·00
O18 $2 Holyrood House.. .. .. .. 2·75 3·50
O19 $4 Type **268** .. .. 6·50 8·00
O1/19.. .. .. .. *Set of* 19 23·00 35·00
The $4 from sheetlets, perforated 14½×14 and with changed background colour, also exists with the overprint (*Price £4 mint, £7 used*).

GRENADINES OF GRENADA

Part of a group of islands north of Grenada, the most important of which is Carriacou. The Grenadine islands further north are administered by St. Vincent, and their stamps are listed after that country.

GRENADINES

(1) (2)

1973 (29 Dec). *Royal Wedding. Nos. 582/4 of Grenada optd with T* **1**.

1 **196**	25 c. multicoloured	20	10
2	$2 multicoloured	70	50
	a. Albino opt		
MS3	79 × 100 mm. 75 c. and $1 as Nos. 1/2	1·00	50

1974 (29 May). *Nos. 306 etc of Grenada optd with T* **2**.

4	1 c. multicoloured	10	10
5	2 c. multicoloured	10	10
6	3 c. multicoloured	10	10
7	5 c. multicoloured	15	10
8	8 c. multicoloured	15	10
9	10 c. multicoloured	15	10
10	12 c. multicoloured	20	10
11	25 c. multicoloured	45	10
12	$1 multicoloured	2·50	45
13	$2 multicoloured	3·00	1·00
14	$3 multicoloured	3·00	1·50
15	$5 multicoloured	3·75	1·75
4/15	*Set of* 12	12·00	4·50

1974 (17 Sept). *World Cup Football Championships. As Nos. 619/27 of Grenada but additionally inscr* "GRENADINES".

16	½ c. Type **201**	10	10
17	1 c. East Germany v Australia	10	10
18	2 c. Yugoslavia v Brazil	10	10
19	10 c. Scotland v Zaire	15	10
20	25 c. Netherlands v Uruguay	20	10
21	50 c. Sweden v Bulgaria	25	15
22	75 c. Italy v Haiti	25	20
23	$1 Poland v Argentina	30	25
16/23	*Set of* 8	1·00	70
MS24	114 × 76 mm. $2 Country flags	75	80

1974 (8 Oct). *Centenary of Universal Postal Union. Designs as Nos. 628 etc of Grenada, but additionally inscr* "GRENADINES".

25	8 c. Mailboat *Caesar* (1839) and helicopter	10	10
26	25 c. Messenger (1450) and satellite	15	10
27	35 c. Airmail transport	15	10
28	$1 Type **202**	70	40
25/8	*Set of* 4	1·00	60
MS29	172×109 mm. $1 Bellman and antenna; $2 18th-century postman and British Advanced Passenger Train. P 13	1·00	1·00

1974 (11 Nov). *Birth Centenary of Sir Winston Churchill. As Nos. 637/9 of Grenada but additionally inscr* "GRENADINES".

30 **203**	35 c. multicoloured	15	10
31 –	$2 multicoloured	40	45
MS32	129 × 96 mm. 75 c. as 35 c. and $1 as $2	35	80

1974 (27 Nov). *Christmas. As Nos. 640/8 of Grenada but additionally inscr* "GRENADINES".

33	½ c. Type **204**	10	10
34	1 c. Niccolo di Pietro	10	10
35	2 c. Van der Weyden	10	10
36	3 c. Bastiani	10	10
37	10 c. Giovanni	10	10
38	25 c. Van der Weyden	10	10
39	50 c. Botticelli	15	15
40	$1 Mantegna	30	25
33/40	*Set of* 8	65	60
MS41	117 × 96 mm. $2 as 1 c.	45	60

CANCELLED REMAINDERS*. Some of the following issues have been remaindered, cancelled-to-order, at a fraction of their face value. For all practical purposes these are indistinguishable from genuine postally used copies. Our used quotations, which are indicated by an asterisk, are the same for cancelled-to-order or postally used copies.

1975 (17 Feb). *Big Game Fishing. As Nos. 669 etc of Grenada, but additionally inscr* "GRENADINES" *and background colours changed.*

42	½ c. Type **206**	10	10
43	1 c. Blue Marlin	10	10
44	2 c. White Marlin	10	10
45	10 c. Yellow-finned Tuna	10	10
46	25 c. Wahoo	15	10
47	50 c. Dolphin (fish)	20	15
48	70 c. Giant Grouper	25	20
49	$1 Great Barracuda	35	35
42/9	*Set of* 8	90	85
MS50	107×80 mm. $2 Short-finned Mako	60	90

1975 (11 Mar). *Flowers. As Nos. 678 etc of Grenada, but additionally inscr.* "GRENADINES".

51	½ c. Type **207**	10	10
52	1 c. Bleeding Heart (Easter Lily)	10	10
53	2 c. Poinsettia	10	10
54	3 c. Cocoa flower	10	10
55	10 c. Gladioli	10	10
56	25 c. Redhead/Yellowhead	10	10
57	50 c. Plumbago	20	15
58	$1 Orange flower	30	20
51/8	*Set of* 8	65	50
MS59	102 × 82 mm. $2 Barbados Gooseberry	60	70

3 "Christ Crowned with Thorns" (Titian)

4 "Dawn" (detail from Medici Tomb)

(Des M. Shamir. Litho Format)

1975 (24 June). *Easter. T* **3** *and similar vert designs showing Crucifixion and Deposition scenes by the artists listed. Multicoloured. P* 14½.

60	½ c. Type **3**	10	10*
61	1 c. Giotto	10	10*
62	2 c. Tintoretto	10	10*
63	3 c. Cranach	10	10*
64	35 c. Caravaggio	15	10*
65	75 c. Tiepolo	20	10*
66	$2 Velasquez	40	15*
60/6	*Set of* 7	70	30*
MS67	105 × 90 mm. $1 Titian. P 13	60	30

(Des M. Shamir. Litho Format)

1975 (16 July). *500th Birth Anniv of Michelangelo. T* **4** *and similar vert designs. Multicoloured. P* 14½.

68	½ c. Type **4**	10	10*
69	1 c. "Delphic Sibyl"	10	10*
70	2 c. "Giuliano de Medici"	10	10*
71	40 c. "The Creation" (detail)	15	10*
72	50 c. "Lorenzo de Medici"	15	10*
73	75 c. "Persian Sibyl"	20	10*
74	$2 "Head of Christ"	30	15*
68/74	*Set of* 7	75	35*
MS75	118 × 96 mm. $1 "The Prophet Jeremiah". P 13	75	50

1975 (12 Aug). *Butterflies. Designs as Nos. 729 etc of Grenada, but additionally inscr* "GRENADINES". *P* 14½.

76	½ c. *Morpho peleides*	10	10*
77	1 c. *Danaus eresimus* ("*Danaus gilippus*")	10	10*
78	2 c. *Dismorphia amphione*	10	10*
79	35 c. *Hamadryas feronia*	35	10*
80	45 c. *Philaethria dido*	45	10*
81	75 c. *Phoebis argante*	70	15*
82	$2 *Prepona laertes*	1·40	30*
76/82	*Set of* 7	2·75	60*
MS83	104×77 mm. $1 *Siproeta stelenes*. P 13	2·75	2·25

5 Progress "Standard" Badge

(Des J.W. Litho Format)

1975 (22 Aug). *14th World Scout Jamboree, Norway. T* **5** *and similar horiz designs. Multicoloured. P* 14½.

84	½ c. Type **5**	10	10*
85	1 c. Boatman's badge	10	10*
86	2 c. Coxswain's badge	10	10*
87	35 c. Interpreter's badge	15	10*
88	45 c. Ambulance badge	20	10*
89	75 c. Chief Scout's award	25	10*
90	$2 Queen's Scout award	35	15*
84/90	*Set of* 7	85	35*
MS91	106 × 80 mm. $1 Venture award. P 13	55	30*

6 The Surrender of Lord Cornwallis

(Des J.W. Litho Questa)

1975 (30 Sept)–**76**. *Bicentenary of American Revolution* (1st *issue*). *Multicoloured.* (a) *Horiz designs as T* **6**. *P* 14.

92	½ c. Type **6**	10	10*
93	1 c. Minute-men	10	10*
94	2 c. Paul Revere's ride	10	10*
95	3 c. Battle of Bunker Hill	10	10*
96	5 c. Fifer and drummers	10	10*
97	45 c. Backwoodsman	25	10*
98	75 c. Boston Tea Party	35	10*
99	$2 Naval engagement	80	10*
	(*b*) *Larger designs. P* 11 (16.1.76)		
100	$2 George Washington (35 × 60 *mm*)	80	35
101	$2 White House and flags (60 × 35 *mm*)	80	35
92/101	*Set of* 10	2·75	85
MS102	Two sheets 113 × 128 mm containing No. 100, and 128 × 113 mm containing No. 101. Imperf	1·40	1·40

See also Nos. 176/**MS**183

7 Fencing

8 "Madonna and Child" (Dürer)

(Des J.W. Ltd. Litho Format)

1975 (27 Oct). *Pan-American Games. Mexico City. T* **7** *and similar horiz designs. Multicoloured. P* 14½.

103	½ c. Type **7**	10	10*
104	1 c. Hurdling	10	10*
105	2 c. Pole-vaulting	10	10*
106	35 c. Weightlifting	15	10*
107	45 c. Throwing the javelin	15	10*
108	75 c. Throwing the discus	15	10*
109	$2 Diving	35	15*
103/109	*Set of* 7	75	35*
MS110	78 × 104 mm. $1 Sprinter. P 13	40	20*

1975 (5 Nov)–**76**. *As Nos.* 649A/68A *of Grenada but additionally inscribed* "GRENADINES". *Multicoloured.*

111	½ c. Yachts, Port Saline	10	30
112	1 c. Yacht Club race, St. George's	10	15
113	2 c. Carenage taxi	10	15
114	3 c. Large working boats	10	15
115	5 c. Deep-water dock, St. George's	10	15
116	6 c. Cocoa beans in drying trays	10	15
117	8 c. Nutmegs	10	15
118	10 c. Rum distillery, River Antoine Estate, *circa* 1785	10	15
119	12 c. Cocoa tree	10	15
120	15 c. Fishermen landing catch at Fontenoy	10	15
121	20 c. Parliament Building, St. George's	10	30
122	25 c. Fort George cannons	10	15
123	35 c. Pearls Airport	50	15
124	50 c. General Post Office	20	60
125	75 c. Caribs Leap, Sauteurs Bay	40	60
126	$1 Carenage, St. George's	60	85
127	$2 St. George's Harbour by night	90	2·00
128	$3 Grand Anse beach	1·10	2·50
129	$5 Canoe Bay and Black Bay from Point Saline Lighthouse	1·75	5·50
130	$10 Sugar-loaf Island from Levera Beach (1.76)	3·00	5·50
111/30	*Set of* 20	8·00	17·00

(Des M. Shamir. Litho Questa)

1975 (17 Dec). *Christmas. T* **8** *and similar vert designs showing "Virgin and Child". Multicoloured. P* 14.

131	½ c. Type **8**	10	10*
132	1 c. Dürer	10	10*
133	2 c. Correggio	10	10*
134	40 c. Botticelli	15	10*
135	50 c. Niccolo da Cremona	15	10*
136	75 c. Correggio	15	10*
137	$2 Correggio	30	15*
131/7	*Set of* 7	70	35*
MS138	114 × 102 mm. $1 Bellini	60	50*

9 Bleeding Tooth (*Nerita peloronta*)

(Des J.W. Litho Questa)

1976 (13 Jan). *Shells. T* **9** *and similar horiz designs. Multicoloured. P* 14.

139	½ c. Type **9**	10	10*
140	1 c. Toothed Donax (*Donax denticulatus*)	10	10*
141	2 c. Hawk-wing Conch (*Strombus raninus*)	10	10*
142	3 c. Atlantic Distorsio (*Distorsio clathrata*)	10	10*
143	25 c. Scotch Bonnet (*Phalium ganulatum*)	30	10*
144	50 c. King Helmet (*Cassis tuberosa*)	60	10*
145	75 c. Queen or Pink Conch (*Strombus gigas*)	85	15*
139/45	*Set of* 7	1·75	30*
MS146	79×105 mm. $2 Atlantic Trumpet Triton (*Charonia variegata*)	1·00	70*

10 Cocoa Thrush

(Des J.W. Litho Questa)

1976 (4 Feb). *Flora and Fauna. T* **10** *and similar horiz designs. Multicoloured. P* 14.

147	½ c. *Lignum vitae*	10	10*
148	1 c. Type **10**	10	10*
149	2 c. *Eurypelma* sp (spider)	10	10*
150	35 c. Hooded Tanager	1·25	10*
151	50 c. *Nyctaginaceae*	1·00	15*
152	75 c. Grenada Dove	2·50	25*
153	$1 Marine Toad	2·50	25*
147/53	*Set of* 7	6·50	70*
MS154	108 × 84 mm. $2 Blue-hooded Euphonia	3·75	1·00*

11 Hooked Sailfish

(Des G. Drummond. Litho Questa)

976 (17 Feb). *Tourism. T* **11** *and similar horiz designs. Multicoloured. P* 14.

55 ½ c. Type **11** 10 10*
56 1 c. Careened schooner, Carriacou 10 10*
57 2 c. Carriacou Annual Regatta 10 10*
58 18 c. Boat building on Carriacou 20 10*
59 22 c. Workboat race, Carriacou Regatta .. 20 10*
60 75 c. Cruising off Petit Martinique 30 20*
61 $1 Water skiing 40 20*
55/61 .. .. *Set of* 7 1·00 60*
1S162 105 × 87 mm. $2 Yacht racing at Carriacou 70 75*

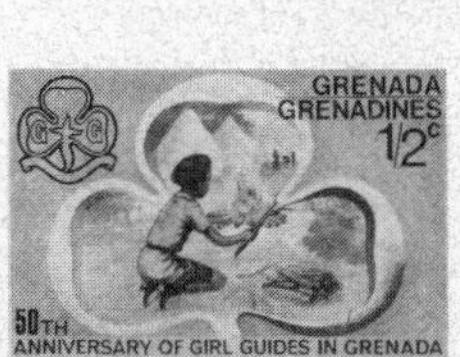

12 Making a Camp Fire 13 "Christ Mocked" (Bosch)

(Des G. Vasarhelyi. Litho Questa)

976 (17 Mar). *50th Anniv of Girl Guides in Grenada. T* **12** *and similar horiz designs. Multicoloured. P* 14.

63 ½ c. Type **12** 10 10*
64 1 c. First aid 10 10*
65 2 c. Nature study 10 10*
66 50 c. Cookery 65 15*
67 $1 Sketching .. .. 1·00 25*
63/7 .. .. *Set of* 5 1·60 50*
IS168 85 × 110 mm. $2 Guide playing guitar .. 1·00 75*

(Des PAD Studio. Litho Questa)

976 (28 Apr). *Easter. T* **13** *and similar vert designs. Multicoloured. P* 14.

69 ½ c. Type **13** 10 10*
70 1 c. "Christ Crucified" (Antonello da Messina) 10 10*
71 2 c. "Adoration of the Trinity" (Dürer) .. 10 10*
72 3 c. "Lamentation of Christ" (Dürer) .. 10 10*
73 35 c. "The Entombment" (Van der Weyden) .. 20 10*
74 $3 "The Entombment" (Raphael) 75 30*
69/74 .. .. *Set of* 6 95 50*
MS175 57 × 72 mm. $2 "Blood of the Redeemer" (G. Bellini) 65 70*

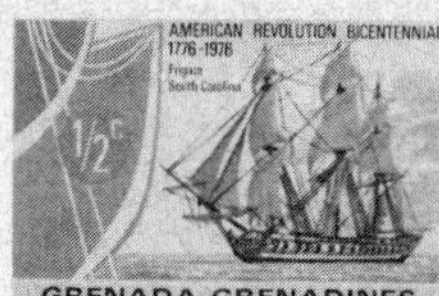

14 *South Carolina* (frigate)

(Des J.W. Litho Questa)

1976 (18 May). *Bicentenary of American Revolution* (2nd issue). *T* 14 *and similar horiz designs. Multicoloured. P* 14.

176 ½ c. Type **14** 10 10*
177 1 c. *Lee* (schooner) 10 10*
178 2 c. H.M.S. *Roebuck* (frigate) 10 10*
179 35 c. *Andrew Doria* (brig) 50 10*
180 50 c. *Providence* (sloop) 60 15*
181 $1 *Alfred* (frigate) .. .. 1·00 20*
182 $2 *Confederacy* (frigate) .. .. .. 1·50 30*
176/82 .. .. *Set of* 7 3·25 75*
MS183 72×85 mm. $3 *Revenge* (cutter) .. 1·25 1·00*

15 Piper PA-23 Apache

(Des J.W. Litho Format)

1976 (10 June). *Aircraft. T* **15** *and similar horiz designs. Multicoloured. P* 14.

184 ½ c. Type **15** 10 10*
185 1 c. Beech 50 Twin Bonanza 10 10*
186 2 c. De Havilland D.H.C.6 Twin Otter 100 10 10*
187 40 c. Britten Norman Islander 30 10*
188 50 c. De Havilland D.H.114 Heron 2 .. 40 10*
189 $2 Hawker Siddeley H.S.748 .. .. 1·25 25*
184/9 .. .. *Set of* 6 1·75 55*
MS190 71×85 mm. $3 B.A.C. One Eleven 500 1·00 1·00*

16 Cycling **17** "Virgin and Child" (Cima)

(Des J.W. Litho Format)

1976 (1 July). *Olympic Games, Montreal. T* **16** *and similar horiz designs. Multicoloured. P* 14.

191 ½ c. Type **16** 10 10*
192 1 c. Pommel horse 10 10*
193 2 c. Hurdling 10 10*
194 35 c. Shot putting 10 10*
195 45 c. Diving 15 10*
196 75 c. Sprinting 15 10*
197 $2 Rowing 35 25*
191/7 .. .. *Set of* 7 70 60*
MS198 101 × 76 mm. $3 Sailing 80 75*

(Litho Format)

1976 (19 Oct). *Christmas. T* **17** *and similar multicoloured designs. P* 13½.

199 ½ c. Type **17** 10 10*
200 1 c. "The Nativity" (Romanino) 10 10*
201 2 c. "The Nativity" (Romanino) (*different*) .. 10 10*
202 35 c. "Adoration of the Kings" (Bruegel) .. 15 10*
203 50 c. "Madonna and Child" (Girolamo) .. 20 10*
204 75 c. "Adoration of the Magi" (Giorgione) (*horiz*) 20 15*
205 $2 "Adoration of the Kings" (School of Fra Angelico) (*horiz*) 40 25*
199/205 .. .. *Set of* 7 1·00 60*
MS206 120 × 100 mm. $3 "The Holy Family" (Garofalo) .. .. 60 2·25

18 Alexander Graham Bell and First Telephone

(Des G. Vasarhelyi. Litho Questa)

1977 (28 Jan). *Telephone Centenary* (1976). *T* **18** *and similar horiz designs showing Alexander Graham Bell and telephone. Multicoloured. P* 14.

207 ½ c. Type **18** 10 10*
208 1 c. Telephone, 1895 .. .. 10 10*
209 2 c. Telephone, 1900 .. .. 10 10*
210 35 c. Telephone, 1915 .. .. 15 10*
211 75 c. Telephone, 1920 .. .. 20 10*
212 $1 Telephone, 1929 .. .. 25 15*
213 $2 Telephone, 1963 .. .. 35 25*
207/13 .. .. *Set of* 7 85 60*
MS214 107 × 78 mm. $3 Telephone, 1976 .. 1·10 75*

19 Coronation Coach 20 Royal Visit

(Des Jennifer Toombs. Litho and embossed Walsall. (Nos. 215/18). Des and litho Walsall (Nos. 219/22))

1977 (7 Feb). *Silver Jubilee. Multicoloured.*

(*a*) *Sheet stamps. Horiz designs as T* **19**. *P* 13½

215 35 c. Type **19** 10 10*
216 $2 Queen entering Abbey 20 10*
217 $4 Queen crowned 35 25*
215/17 .. .. *Set of* 3 55 35*
MS218 100 × 70 mm. $5 The Mall on Coronation Night .. .. 60 1·25

Nos. 215/17 also exist perf 11 (*Price for set of* 3 60*p. mint or used*) from additional sheetlets of 3 stamps and 1 label. These have different background colours from the stamps perforated 13½, which come from normal sheets of 25.

(*b*) *Booklet stamps. Vert designs as T* **20**. *Roul* 5 × *imperf.** *Self-adhesive*

219 35 c. Type **20** 15 20
a. Booklet pane of 6 70
220 50 c. Crown of St. Edward 40 80
a. Booklet pane. Nos. 220/2 .. .. .. 1·75

221 $2 The Queen and Prince Charles .. .. 75 1·60
222 $5 Royal Standard .. .. 90 1·75
219/22 .. .. *Set of* 4 2·00 4·00

*Nos. 219/22 are separated by various combinations of rotary knife (giving a straight edge) and roulette.

21 "Disrobing of Christ" (Fra Angelico) 22 "The Virgin adoring the Child" (Correggio)

(Des J.W. Litho Questa)

1977 (5 July). *Easter. Vert designs as T* **21** *showing paintings by the artists given. Multicoloured. P* 14.

223 ½ c. Type **21** 10 10*
224 1 c. Fra Angelico 10 10*
225 2 c. El Greco 10 10*
226 18 c. El Greco 10 10*
227 35 c. Fra Angelico 15 10*
228 50 c. Giottino 20 10*
229 $2 Antonello da Messina 50 25*
223/9 .. .. *Set of* 7 85 50*
MS230 121 × 94 mm. $3 Fra Angelico 85 75*

(Des J.W. Litho Questa)

1977 (17 Nov). *Christmas. T* **22** *and similar vert designs. Multicoloured. P* 14.

231 ½ c. Type **22** 10 10*
232 1 c. "Virgin and Child" (Giorgione) 10 10*
233 2 c. "Virgin and Child" (Morales) 10 10*
234 18 c. "Madonna della Tenda" (Raphael) .. 10 10*
235 35 c. "Rest on the Flight into Egypt" (Van Dyck) 15 10*
236 50 c. "Madonna and Child" (Lippi) 20 10*
237 $2 "Virgin and Child" (Lippi) (*different*) .. 60 25*
231/7 .. .. *Set of* 7 95 50*
MS238 114 × 99 mm. $3 "Virgin and Child with Angels and Saints" (Ghirlandaio) 85 75*

ROYAL VISIT W.I. 1977

(23)

1977 (23 Nov). *Royal Visit. Nos.* 215/18 *optd with T* **23**. *P* 13½.

239 35 c. Type **19** 10 10
240 $2 Queen entering Abbey 25 20
241 $4 Queen crowned 40 30
239/41 .. .. *Set of* 3 60 50
MS242 100 × 70 mm. $5 The Mall on Coronation Night 70 90

This overprint also exists on the stamps perforated 11, mentioned below No. MS218 (*price for set of* 3 90*p. mint or used*).

24 Life-saving

(Des G. Drummond. Litho Questa)

1977 (7 Dec). *Caribbean Scout Jamboree, Jamaica. T* **24** *and similar horiz designs. Multicoloured. P* 14.

243 ½ c. Type **24** 10 10*
244 1 c. Overnight hike 10 10*
245 2 c. Cubs tying knots 10 10*
246 22 c. Erecting a tent 15 10*
247 35 c. Gang show limbo dance 25 10*
248 75 c. Campfire cooking 40 15*
249 $3 Sea Scouts' yacht race 80 30*
243/9 .. .. *Set of* 7 1·40 65*
MS250 109 × 85 mm. $2 Pioneering project—Spring bridge .. .. 1·10 90*

25 Blast-off

(Des J.W. Litho Questa)

1978 (3 Feb). *Space Shuttle. T* **25** *and similar horiz designs. Multicoloured. P* 14.

251 ½ c. Type **25** 10 10*
252 1 c. Booster jettison 10 10*
253 2 c. External tank jettison 10 10*
254 22 c. Working in orbit 15 10*
255 50 c. Shuttle re-entry 25 10*
256 $3 Shuttle landing 85 30*
251/6 .. .. *Set of* 6 1·10 50*
MS257 85 × 103 mm. $2 Shuttle being towed .. 60 70*

26 Alfred Nobel and Physiology/Medicine Medal

(Des J.W. Litho Questa)

1978 (22 Feb). *Nobel Prize Awards. T* **26** *and similar horiz designs. Multicoloured. P* 14.

258 ½ c. Type **26** 10 10*
259 1 c. Physics and Chemistry medal 10 10*
260 2 c. Peace medal 10 10*
261 22 c. Nobel Institute, Oslo 25 10*
262 75 c. Peace Prize committee 50 15*
263 $3 Literature medal.. .. .. 1·50 30*
258/63 .. .. *Set of* 6 2·00 60*
MS264 127 × 103 mm. $2 Peace medal and Nobel's will.. .. .. 50 60*

27 German Zeppelin Stamp of 1930

(Des J.W. Litho Questa)

1978 (15 Mar). *75th Anniv of First Zeppelin Flight and 50th Anniv of Lindbergh's Trans-atlantic Flight. T* **27** *and similar horiz designs. Multicoloured. P* 14 × 13½.

265 5 c. Type **27** 20 10*
266 15 c. French Concorde stamp, 1970 .. .. 60 10*
267 25 c. Liechtenstein Zeppelin stamp, 1931 .. 20 10*
268 35 c. Panama Lindbergh stamp, 1928 .. .. 20 10*
269 50 c. Russian airship stamp, 1931 .. .. 25 10*
270 $3 Spanish Lindbergh stamp, 1930 .. .. 75 30*
265/70 .. .. *Set of* 6 2·00 50*
MS271 140×79 mm. 75 c. U.S.A. Lindbergh stamp, 1927; $2 German LZ-129 *Hindenburg* stamp, 1936 .. .. 1·10 90*

28 Coronation Ring **29** Drummer, Royal Regiment of Fusiliers.

(Des J.W. Litho Questa (Nos. 272/5). Manufactured by Walsall (Nos. 276/8))

1978 (12 Apr). *25th Anniv of Coronation. Multicoloured.*

(*a*) *Sheet stamps. Horiz designs as T* **28.** *P* 14

272 50 c. Type **28** 10 10
273 $2 Queen's Orb 25 30
274 $2.50, Imperial State Crown 30 35
272/4 .. .. *Set of* 3 60 65
MS275 97 × 67 mm. $5 Queen Elizabeth II .. 60 60

Nos. 272/4 also exist perf 12 (*Price for set of* 3 90*p. mint or used*) from additional sheetlets of 3 stamps and 1 label, issued 2 June. These have different background colours from the stamps perforated 14, which come from normal sheets of 50.

(*b*) *Booklet stamps. Vert designs as T* **29.** *Roul* 5 × *imperf.** *Self-adhesive*

276 18 c. Type **29** 15 35
a. Booklet pane. Nos. 276/7 × 3 70
277 50 c. Drummer, Royal Anglian Regiment .. 15 45
278 $5 Drum Major, Queen's Regiment.. .. 1·00 3·00
a. Booklet pane of 1.. .. .. .. 1·00
276/8 .. .. *Set of* 3 1·10 3·50

*Nos. 276/7 are separated by various combinations of rotary-knife (giving a straight edge) and roulette. No. 278 exists only with straight edges.

30 "Le Chapeau de Paille" **31** Wright Flyer I

(Litho Questa)

1978 (18 May). *400th Birth Anniv of Rubens. T* **30** *and similar vert designs. Multicoloured. P* 14.

279 5 c. Type **30** 10 10
280 15 c. "Achilles slaying Hector" 15 10
281 18 c. "Helene Fourment and her Children" .. 15 10
282 22 c. "Rubens and Isabella Brandt" 20 10
283 35 c. "The Ildefonso Altarpiece" 20 10
284 $3 "Heads of Negroes" (detail) .. .. 1·10 1·00
279/84 .. .. *Set of* 6 1·60 1·25
MS285 85 × 127 mm. $2 "Self-portrait" .. .. 70 1·00

(Des BG Studio. Litho Questa)

1978 (10 Aug). *75th Anniv of Powered Flight. T* **31** *and similar designs. P* 14.

286 5 c. black, chestnut and pale blue 10 10
287 15 c. black, vermilion and yellow-ochre .. 10 10
288 18 c. black, vermilion and yellow-ochre .. 10 10
289 25 c. multicoloured 10 10
290 35 c. black, purple and magenta 15 10
291 75 c. multicoloured 25 25
292 $3 black, magenta and new blue 75 75
286/92 .. .. *Set of* 7 1·10 1·10
MS293 126 × 83 mm. $2 black, blue and bright blue-green .. .. 75 1·00

Designs: *Vert*—15 c. Orville Wright; 18 c. Wilbur Wright. *Horiz*—25 c. Wright Flyer III; 35 c. Wright glider No. 1; 75 c. Wright Flyer I; $2 Various Wright aircraft; $3 Wright Type A.

32 Audubon's Shearwater **33** Players with Ball

(Des Jennifer Toombs. Litho Questa)

1978 (28 Sept). *Birds. T* **32** *and similar multicoloured designs. P* 14.

294 5 c. Type **32** 50 10
295 10 c. Semipalmated Plover 70 10
296 18 c. Purple-throated Carib (*horiz*) .. .. 1·00 15
297 22 c. Red-billed Whistling Duck (*horiz*) .. 1·00 20
298 40 c. Caribbean Martin (*horiz*) .. .. 1·50 35
299 $1 White-tailed Tropic Bird.. .. .. 2·25 75
300 $2 Long-billed Curlew .. .. 3·25 1·25
294/300 .. .. *Set of* 7 9·00 2·50
MS301 78 × 78 mm. $5 Snowy Egret .. .. 5·00 2·75

(Des G. Vasarhelyi. Litho Questa)

1978 (2 Nov). *World Cup Football Championship, Argentina. T* **33** *and similar vert designs showing football scenes. P* 14.

302 15 c. multicoloured 10 10
303 35 c. multicoloured 20 10
304 50 c. multicoloured 25 20
305 $3 multicoloured 80 80
302/5 .. .. *Set of* 4 1·10 90
MS306 114 × 85 mm. $2 multicoloured .. .. 80 1·25

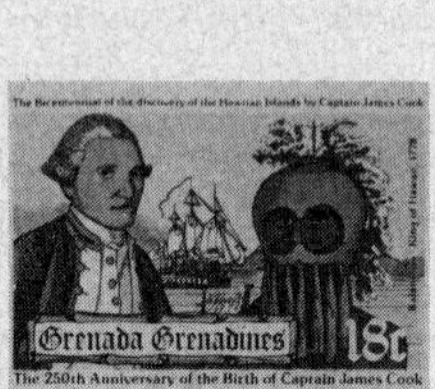

34 Captain Cook and Kalaniopu (king of Hawaii), 1778 **35** "Virgin at Prayer"

(Des BG Studio. Litho Questa)

1978 (13 Dec). *250th Birth Anniv of Captain Cook and Bicentenary of Discovery of Hawaii. T* **34** *and similar horiz designs. Multicoloured. P* 14.

307 18 c. Type **34** 45 10
308 22 c. Captain Cook and native of Hawaii .. 60 15
309 50 c. Captain Cook and death scene, 14 February 1779 .. .. 1·00 30
310 $3 Captain Cook and offering ceremony .. 2·25 1·75
307/10 .. .. *Set of* 4 3·75 2·00
MS311 171 × 113 mm. $4 H.M.S. *Resolution* (*vert*) 2·00 1·50

(Des M. Rubin. Litho Questa)

1978 (20 Dec). *Christmas. Paintings by Dürer. T* **35** *and similar vert designs. Multicoloured. P* 14.

312 40 c. Type **35** 20 10
313 60 c. "The Dresden Altarpiece" 25 15
314 90 c. "Madonna and Child with St. Anne" .. 30 15
315 $2 "Madonna and Child with Pear" 60 50
312/15 .. .. *Set of* 4 1·25 80
MS316 114 × 84 mm. $4 "Salvator Mundi" .. 1·00 1·40

36 *Strelitzia reginae* **37** Children with Pig

(Des J.W. Litho Questa)

1979 (15 Feb). *Flowers. T* **36** *and similar vert designs. Multicoloured. P* 14.

317 22 c. Type **36** 15 10
318 40 c. *Euphorbia pulcherrima* 25 15
319 $1 *Heliconia humilis* 55 30
320 $3 *Thunbergia alata* .. .. 1·25 80
317/20 .. .. *Set of* 4 2·00 1·10
MS321 114 × 90 mm. $2 *Bougainvillea glabra* .. 75 1·00

(Des G. Drummond. Litho Questa)

1979 (22 Mar). *International Year of the Child. T* **37** *and similar horiz designs. Multicoloured. P* 14.

322 18 c. Type **37** 10 10
323 50 c. Children with donkey 20 25
324 $1 Children with goats 25 30
325 $3 Children fishing 65 80
322/5 .. .. *Set of* 4 1·00 1·25
MS326 104 × 86 mm. $4 Child with coconuts .. 1·00 1·90

38 20,000 *Leagues Under the Sea*

(Des G. Vasarhelyi. Litho Questa)

1979 (20 Apr). *150th Birth Anniv of Jules Verne (author). T* **38** *and similar horiz designs showing scenes from his books and modern technological developments. Multicoloured. P* 14.

327 18 c. Type **38** 30 10
328 38 c. *From the Earth to the Moon* 35 20
329 75 c. *From the Earth to the Moon* (*different*) .. 45 35
330 $3 *Five Weeks in a Balloon* .. .. .. 85 1·00
327/30 .. .. *Set of* 4 1·75 1·50
MS331 111 × 86 mm. $4 *Around the World in* 80 *days* .. .. 1·00 1·60

39 Sir Rowland Hill and Mail Van

(Des BG Studio. Litho Questa)

1979 (30 July). *Death Centenary of Sir Rowland Hill. T* **39** *and similar horiz designs showing Sir Rowland Hill and mail transport. Multicoloured. P* 14.

332 15 c. Type **39** 10 10
333 $1 *Britanis* (cargo liner) 20 20
334 $2 Diesel mail train 30 30
335 $3 Concorde 90 70
332/5 .. .. *Set of* 4 1·25 1·10
MS336 85×67 mm. $4 Sir Rowland Hill .. .. 75 1·00

Nos. 332/5 also exist perf 12 (*Price for set of* 4 £1.25 *mint or used*) from additional sheetlets of 5 stamps and 1 label issued 6 September. These have different background colours to the stamps perforated 14, which come from normal sheets of 40.

40 "Virgin and Child Enthroned" (11th-century Byzantine) **41** Great Hammerhead

(Des G. Vasarhelyi. Litho Questa)

1979 (23 Oct). *Christmas. Sculptures. T* **40** *and similar vert designs. Multicoloured. P* 14.

337 6 c. Type **40** 10 10
338 25 c. "Presentation in the Temple" (Andre Beauneveu) 10 10
339 30 c. "Flight to Egypt", Utrecht, *circa* 1510 .. 10 10
340 40 c. "Madonna and Child" (Jacopo della Quercia) 10 10
341 90 c. "Madonna della Mela" (Luca della Robbia) 15 15
342 $1 "Madonna and Child" (Antonio Rossellino) 20 20
343 $2 "Madonna", Antwerp, 1700 .. .. .. 35 35
337/43 .. .. *Set of* 7 80 80
MS344 125 × 95 mm. $4 "Virgin", Krumau .. 65 1·10

(Des J.W. Litho Questa)

1979 (9 Nov). *Marine Life. T* **41** *and similar horiz designs. Multicoloured. P* 14 × 13½.

345 40 c. Type **41** 40 30
346 45 c. Spot-finned Butterflyfish 45 30
347 50 c. Permit (fish) 45 40
348 60 c. Threaded Turban (shell) 65 55
349 70 c. Milk Conch (shell) 75 75
350 75 c. Great Blue Heron 85 90
351 90 c. Colourful Atlantic Moon (shell) .. .. 95 1·00

2 $1 Red-footed Booby .. .. 1·50 1·75
5/52 .. .. *Set of* 8 5·50 5·50
S353 99 × 86 mm. $2.50 Collared Plover .. 2·00 1·10

42 Goofy as Doctor **43** Classroom

(Litho Format)

79 (12 Dec). *International Year of the Child. Walt Disney Cartoon Characters. T* **42** *and similar multicoloured designs showing characters at various occupations. P* 11.
4 ½ c. Type **42** 10 10
5 1 c. Mickey Mouse as admiral 10 10
6 2 c. Goofy as fireman 10 10
7 3 c. Minnie Mouse as nurse 10 10
8 4 c. Mickey Mouse as drum major 10 10
9 5 c. Donald Duck as policeman 10 10
0 10 c. Donald Duck as pilot 10 10
1 $2 Goofy as postman (*horiz*) .. .. 2·25 2·25
2 $2.50, Donald Duck as train driver (*horiz*) .. 2·25 2·25
4/62 .. .. *Set of* 9 4·50 4·50
S363 128 × 102 mm. $3 Mickey Mouse as fireman. P 13½ .. .. 1·75 2·00

80 (10 Mar). *1st Anniv of Revolution. Nos.* 116 *and* 119/30 *optd with T* **259** *of Grenada.*
4 6 c. Cocoa beans in drying trays 10 10
5 12 c. Cocoa Tree 10 10
6 15 c. Fishermen landing catch at Fontenoy .. 10 10
7 20 c. Parliament Building, St. George's .. 10 10
8 25 c. Fort George cannons 15 10
9 35 c. Pearls Airport 20 10
0 50 c. General Post Office 35 15
1 75 c. Caribs Leap, Sauteurs Bay 40 20
2 $1 Carenage, St. George's 55 30
3 $2 St. George's Harbour by night 85 70
4 $3 Grand Anse Beach .. .. .. 1·60 1·60
5 $5 Canoe Bay and Black Bay from Point Saline Lighthouse .. .. .. 2·25 2·50
6 $10 Sugar Loaf Island from Levera Beach .. 3·75 4·25
4/76 .. .. *Set of* 13 9·50 9·00

(Des BG Studio. Litho Questa)

80 (12 Mar). *75th Anniv of Rotary International. T* **43** *and similar horiz designs. Multicoloured. P* 14.
7 6 c. Type **43** 10 10
8 30 c. Rotary International emblem encircled by people of different races 20 10
9 60 c. Rotary International executive presenting doctor with cheque 35 20
0 $3 Nurses with young patients .. .. 1·60 75
7/80 .. .. *Set of* 4 2·00 1·00
S381 85 × 72 mm. $4 Paul P. Harris (founder) 1·00 1·60

44 Yellow-bellied Seedeater **45** Running

(Des G. Drummond. Litho Questa)

80 (14 Apr). *Wild Birds. T* **44** *and similar vert designs. Multicoloured. P* 14.
2 25 c. Type **44** 50 15
3 40 c. Blue-hooded Euphonia 55 20
4 90 c. Yellow Warbler .. .. 1·25 65
5 $2 Tropical Mockingbird .. .. .. 1·75 1·25
2/5 .. .. *Set of* 4 3·50 2·00
S386 83 × 110 mm. $3 Barn Owl .. .. 3·75 2·00

(Des G. Vasarhelyi. Litho Questa)

80 (21 Apr). *Olympic Games, Moscow. T* **45** *and similar horiz designs. Multicoloured. P* 14.
7 30 c. Type **45** 20 15
8 40 c. Football 15 20
9 90 c. Boxing 35 35
0 $2 Wrestling 70 75
7/90 .. .. *Set of* 4 1·25 1·25
S391 104 × 75 mm. $4 Athletes in silhouette .. 75 1·10

LONDON 1980

(46)

47 Long-jawed Squirrelfish

1980 (6 May). *"London 1980" International Stamp Exhibition. Nos.* 332/5 *optd with T* **46**. *P* 12.
392 15 c. Type **39** 15 15
393 $1 *Britanis* (cargo liner) 75 35
394 $2 Diesel mail train .. .. .. 1·50 1·00
395 $3 Concorde .. .. 2·25 2·00
392/5 .. .. *Set of* 4 4·25 3·25

(Des G. Drummond. Litho Questa)

1980 (6 Aug)–**87**. *Fishes. Horiz designs as T* **47**. *Multicoloured. P* 14. A. *Without imprint date.*
396A ½ c. Type **47** 10 10
397A 1 c. Blue Chromis 10 10
398A 2 c. Four-eyed Butterflyfish 10 10
399A 4 c. Sergeant Major 10 10
400A 5 c. Yellow-tailed Snapper 10 10
401A 6 c. Mutton Snapper 10 10
402A 10 c. Cocoa Damselfish 10 10
403A 12 c. Royal Gramma 10 10
404A 15 c. Cherub Angelfish 15 10
405A 20 c. Black-barred Soldierfish 15 10
406A 25 c. Mottled Grouper 15 15
407A 30 c. Caribbean Long-nosed Butterflyfish 15 20
408A 40 c. Puddingwife 20 25
409A 50 c. Midnight Parrotfish 25 35
410A 90 c. Red-spotted Hawkfish 40 55
411A $1 Hogfish 45 60
412A $3 Beau Gregory .. .. .. 1·25 1·50
413A $5 Rock Beauty .. .. .. 2·00 2·50
414A $10 Barred Hamlet .. .. .. 3·50 5·00
396A/414A .. .. .. *Set of* 19 8·00 10·00

B. *With imprint date at foot of design.*
396B ½ c. Type **47** (*p* 12) (1982) .. .. 7·00 8·00
402B 10 c. Cocoa Damselfish (1984) 30 30
405B 20 c. Black-barred Soldierfish (1987) .. 1·00 1·00
346B/405B .. .. *Set of* 3 7·50 8·50
Imprint dates: "1982", No. 396B; "1984", No. 402B; "1987", No. 405B.

(Litho Walsall)

1980 (7 Oct). *Christmas. Walt Disney Cartoon Scenes from "Bambi". Horiz designs as T* **42**. *Multicoloured. P* 11.
415 ½ c. Bambi with Mother 10 10
416 1 c. Bambi with quails 10 10
417 2 c. Bambi meets Thumper the rabbit .. 10 10
418 3 c. Bambi meets Flower the skunk 10 10
419 4 c. Bambi and Faline 10 10
420 5 c. Bambi with his father 10 10
421 10 c. Bambi on ice 10 10
422 $2.50, Faline with foals .. .. .. 1·75 1·25
423 $3 Bambi and Faline .. .. .. 1·75 1·25
415/23 .. .. *Set of* 9 3·50 2·50
MS424 127 × 102 mm. $4 Bambi as Prince of the Forest (*vert*) .. .. 2·00 2·00

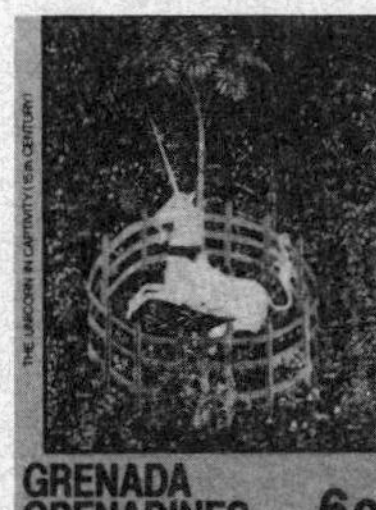

48 "The Unicorn in Captivity" (15th-century unknown artist) **49** "Bust of a Woman"

(Litho Format)

1981 (25 Jan). *Paintings. T* **48** *and similar multicoloured designs. P* 13½.
425 6 c. Type **48** 10 10
426 10 c. "The Fighting *Temeraire*" (Turner) (*horiz*) 10 10
427 25 c. "Sunday Afternoon on the Ile de la Grande-Jatte" (Georges-Pierre Seurat) (*horiz*) 15 15
428 90 c. "Max Schmitt in a Single Scull" (Thomas Eakins) (*horiz*) 45 45
429 $2 "The Burial of the Count of Orgaz" (El Greco) 85 85
430 $3 "George Washington" (Gilbert Stuart) .. 1·10 1·10
425/30 .. .. *Set of* 6 2·40 2·40
MS431 66 × 101 mm. $5 "Kaiser Karl de Grosse" (detail, Dürer) .. .. 1·75 2·00
No. MS431 exists imperforate from stock dispersed by the liquidator of Format International Security Printers Ltd.

(Litho Format)

1981 (26 Jan). *50th Anniv of Walt Disney's Cartoon Character, Pluto. Vert designs as T* **42**. *Multicoloured. P* 13½.
432 $2 Mickey Mouse serving birthday cake to Pluto 90 80
MS433 127 × 101 mm. $4 Pluto in scene from film *Pluto's Dream House* .. .. 1·75 1·75
No. 432 was printed in small sheets of 8 stamps.

(Litho Format)

1981 (14 Apr). *Easter. Walt Disney Cartoon Characters. Vert designs as T* **42**. *Multicoloured. P* 11.
434 35 c. Chip 20 20
435 40 c. Dewey 20 20
436 $2 Huey 60 60
437 $2.50, Mickey Mouse 75 75
434/7 .. .. *Set of* 4 1·60 1·60
MS438 126 × 102 mm. $4 Jiminy Cricket. P 13½ 2·00 2·00

(Des J.W. Litho Questa)

1981 (5 May). *Birth Centenary of Picasso. T* **49** *and similar vert designs. Multicoloured. P* 14.
439 6 c. Type **49** 10 10
440 40 c. Woman (study for "Les Demoiselles d'Avignon") 25 15
441 90 c. "Nude with raised Arms (The Dancer of Avignon)" 40 30
442 $4 "The Dryad" .. .. 1·25 1·25
439/42 .. .. *Set of* 4 1·75 1·50
MS443 103 × 128 mm. $5 "Les Demoiselles d'Avignon". Imperf .. .. 1·75 1·50

50 Balmoral Castle **51** Lady Diana Spencer

(Des J.W. Litho Format)

1981 (16 June). *Royal Wedding (1st issue). T* **50** *and similar vert designs. Multicoloured. (a) P* 15.
444 40 c. Prince Charles and Lady Diana Spencer 15 15
445 $2 Type **50** 35 35
446 $4 Prince Charles as parachutist 50 50
MS447 97 × 84 mm. $5 Royal Coach 90 90

(*b*) *P* 15×14½
448 30 c. As No. 444 .. .. 20 20
449 40 c. Type **50** 20 20
444/9 .. .. *Set of* 5 1·25 1·25
The 30 and 40 c. values were each printed in small sheets of 6 including one *se-tenant* stamp-size label.
The $4 value, with changed background colour, also exists perforated 15×14½ (*price* £1.10 *mint or used*) from similar sheetlets in addition to the original version from sheets of 40.

(Manufactured by Walsall)

1981 (16 June). *Royal Wedding (2nd issue). T* **51** *and similar multicoloured designs. Roul 5 × imperf*. Self-adhesive.*
450 $1 Type **51** 20 35
a. Booklet pane. Nos. 450/1 each × 3 .. 1·25
451 $2 Prince Charles 25 50
452 $5 Prince Charles and Lady Diana Spencer (*horiz*) .. .. 1·25 2·00
a. Booklet pane of 1 .. .. 1·25
450/2 .. .. *Set of* 3 1·50 2·50
*The $1 and $2 values were each separated by various combinations of rotary knife (giving a straight edge) and roulette. The $5 value exists only with straight edges.
Nos. 450/2 were only issued in $14 stamp booklets.

52 Amy Johnson (1st solo flight, Britain to Australia by Woman, May 1930) **53** Boeing 747 SCA

(Des BG Studio. Litho Questa)

1981 (13 Oct). *"Decade for Women". Famous Female Aviators. T* **52** *and similar vert designs. Multicoloured. P* 14.
453 30 c. Type **52** 45 15
454 70 c. Mme la Baronne de Laroche (1st qualified woman pilot, March 1910) 70 30
455 $1.10, Ruth Nichols (solo Atlantic flight attempt, June 1931) 80 40
456 $3 Amelia Earhart (1st North Atlantic solo flight by woman, May 1932) .. .. 1·75 1·10
453/6 .. .. *Set of* 4 3·25 1·75
MS457 90 × 85 mm. $5 Valentina Nikolayeva-Tereshkova (1st woman in space, June 1963) .. 1·25 1·40

(Litho Questa)

1981 (2 Nov). *Christmas. Horiz designs as T* **42** *showing scenes from Walt Disney's cartoon film "Lady and the Tramp". P* 13½.
458 ½ c. multicoloured 10 10
459 1 c. multicoloured 10 10
460 2 c. multicoloured 10 10
461 3 c. multicoloured 10 10
462 4 c. multicoloured 10 10
463 5 c. multicoloured 10 10
464 10 c. multicoloured 10 10
465 $2.50, multicoloured .. .. .. 2·50 1·25
466 $3 multicoloured .. .. 3·00 1·25
458/66 .. .. *Set of* 9 5·25 2·50
MS467 128 × 103 mm. $5 multicoloured .. .. 4·25 3·00

(Des M. Brodie. Litho Format)

1981 (2 Nov). *Space Shuttle Project. T* **53** *and similar horiz designs. Multicoloured. P* 14½.
468 10 c. Type **53** 30 10
469 40 c. Re-entry 65 15
470 $1.10, External tank separation .. .. 1·25 45
471 $3 Touchdown .. .. 1·75 1·00
468/71 .. .. *Set of* 4 3·50 1·50
MS472 117 × 89 mm. $5 Launch .. .. .. 2·75 2·00

54 Footballer **55** Mail Van and Stage-Coach

(Des Clover Mill. Litho Questa)

1981 (30 Nov). *World Cup Football Championship, Spain* (1982). *T* **54** *and similar vert designs showing footballers. P* 14.
473 20 c. multicoloured 15 10
474 40 c. multicoloured 20 15
475 $1 multicoloured 35 30
476 $2 multicoloured 65 55
473/6 .. .. *Set of* 4 1·25 1·00
MS477 106 × 128 mm. $4 multicoloured .. .. 1·40 1·60
Nos. 473/6 were each printed in small sheets of 6 including one *se-tenant* stamp-size label.

(Des G. Vasarhelyi. Litho Format)

1982 (13 Jan). *Centenary of U.P.U. Membership. T* **55** *and similar horiz designs. Multicoloured. P* 14½.
478 30 c. Type **55** 30 15
479 40 c. U.P.U. emblem 30 15
480 $2.50, *Queen Elizabeth 2* (liner) and sailing ship .. .. 1·50 70
481 $4 Concorde and De Havilland D.H.9 biplane .. .. 2·25 1·25
478/81 .. .. *Set of* 4 4·00 2·00
MS482 117×78 mm. $5 British Advanced Passenger Train and steam mail trains .. 3·50 2·25

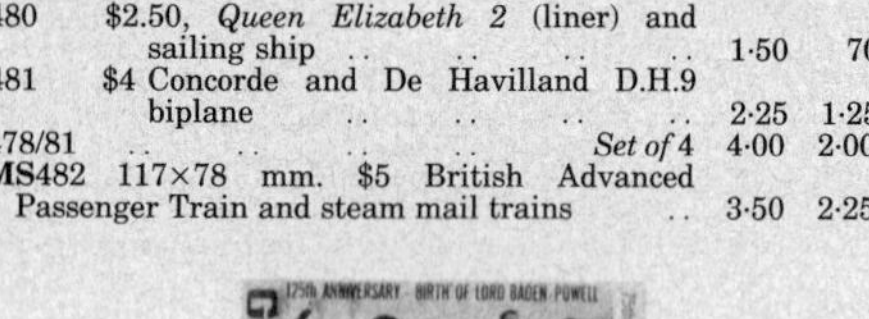

56 National Sports Meeting

(Des M. Diamond. Litho Format)

1982 (19 Feb). *75th Anniv of Boy Scout Movement and 125th Birth Anniv of Lord Baden-Powell. T* **56** *and similar horiz designs. Multicoloured. P* 14½.
483 6 c. Type **56** 15 10
484 90 c. Sea scouts sailing 50 30
485 $1.10, Handicraft 65 60
486 $3 Animal tending .. .. 1·40 1·40
483/6 .. .. *Set of* 4 2·40 2·10
MS487 100 × 71 mm. $5 Music around campfire .. 1·40 1·75

57 *Anartia jatrophae* **58** Prince and Princess of Wales

(Des J.W. Litho Questa)

1982 (24 Mar). *Butterflies. T* **57** *and similar horiz designs. Multicoloured. P* 14.
488 30 c. Type **57** 75 30
489 40 c. *Chioides vintra* 80 35
490 $1.10, *Cynthia cardui* .. .. 1·75 75
491 $3 *Historis odius* .. .. 2·75 1·60
488/91 .. .. *Set of* 4 5·50 2·75
MS492 103×77 mm. $5 *Dione juno* .. .. 3·25 2·50

(Des PAD Studio. Litho Questa)

1982 (1 July). *21st Birthday of Princess of Wales. T* **58** *and similar vert designs. Multicoloured. P* 14½ × 14.
493 50 c. Blenheim Palace 50 75
494 60 c. As 50 c. 60 75
495 $1 Type **58** .. .. 70 1·40
496 $2 Type **58** .. .. 1·50 1·50
497 $3 Princess of Wales .. .. 2·25 2·25
498 $4 As $3 .. .. 2·50 2·25
493/8 .. .. *Set of* 6 7·25 8·00
MS499 103 × 75 mm. $5 Princess Diana (*different*) 2·75 2·50
Nos. 493, 495 and 497 come from sheetlets of 5 stamps and 1 label.

PRICES OF SETS

Set prices are given for many issues, generally those containing three stamps or more. Definitive sets include one of each value or major colour change, but do not cover different perforations, die types or minor shades. Where a choice is possible the set prices are based on the cheapest versions of the stamps included in the listings.

59 "New Deal"—Soil Conservation **60** "Presentation of Christ in the Temple"

(Des M. Diamond. Litho Questa)

1982 (27 July). *Birth Centenary of Franklin D. Roosevelt. T* **59** *and similar horiz designs. Multicoloured. P* 14.
500 30 c. Type **59** 25 15
501 40 c. Roosevelt and George Washington Carver (scientist) 25 15
502 70 c. Civilian conservation corps and reafforestation 45 30
503 $3 Roosevelt with Pres. Barclay of Liberia, Casablanca Conference, 1943 .. .. 1·25 90
500/3 .. .. *Set of* 4 2·00 1·40
MS504 100 × 72 mm. $5 Roosevelt delivering address at Howard University .. .. .. 1·75 1·75

1982 (30 Aug). *Birth of Prince William of Wales. Nos. 493/9 optd with T* **171** *of Antigua*.
505 50 c. Blenheim Palace 50 50
506 60 c. As 50 c. 55 60
507 $1 Type **58** 70 75
508 $2 Type **58** .. .. 1·00 1·25
509 $3 Princess of Wales .. .. 1·25 1·75
510 $4 As $3 .. .. 1·50 1·75
505/10 .. .. *Set of* 6 5·00 6·00
MS511 103 × 75 mm. $5 Princess Diana (*different*) 2·10 2·25
Nos. 505, 507 and 509 come from sheetlets of 5 stamps and 1 label.

(Des Clover Mill. Litho Format)

1982 (2 Sept). *Easter. T* **60** *and similar vert designs depicting Easter paintings by Rembrandt. Multicoloured. P* 14½.
512 30 c. Type **60** 40 15
513 60 c. "Descent from the Cross" 55 20
514 $2 "Raising of the Cross" .. .. .. 1·25 75
515 $4 "Resurrection of Christ" .. .. .. 1·75 1·50
512/15 .. .. *Set of* 4 3·50 2·40
MS516 101 × 126 mm. $5 "The Risen Christ" .. 3·00 2·40

61 "Santa Fe", U.S.A.

(Des Artists International. Litho Format)

1982 (4 Oct). *Famous Trains of the World. T* **61** *and similar vert designs. Multicoloured. P* 15.
517 10 c. Type **61** 50 15
518 40 c. "Mistral", France 70 20
519 70 c. "Rheingold", Germany 80 45
520 $1 "ET 403", France .. .. 1·00 50
521 $1.10, Steam locomotive *Mallard*, Great Britain .. .. 1·25 60
522 $2 Tokaido Shinkansen "Hikari", Japan 1·40 90
517/22 .. .. *Set of* 6 5·00 2·50
MS523 121×95 mm. $5 "Settebello", Italy .. 2·25 2·50

62 Footballers

(Des D. Miller. Litho Questa)

1982 (2 Dec). *World Cup Football Championship Winners. T* **62** *and similar horiz designs. P* 14 × 13½.
524 60 c. multicoloured 50 35
525 $4 multicoloured .. .. 2·00 1·25
MS526 92 × 134 mm. $5 multicoloured .. .. 1·50 1·50

(Litho Questa)

1982 (14 Dec). *Christmas. Horiz designs as T* **42** *showing scenes from Walt Disney's cartoon film "The Rescuers". P* 13½.
527 ½ c. multicoloured 10 10
528 1 c. multicoloured 10 10
529 2 c. multicoloured 10 10
530 3 c. multicoloured 10 10
531 4 c. multicoloured 10 10
532 5 c. multicoloured 10 10
533 10 c. multicoloured 10 10
534 $2.50, multicoloured .. .. 2·75 1·75
535 $3 multicoloured .. .. 2·75 1·75
527/35 .. .. *Set of* 9 5·50 3·50
MS536 120 × 96 mm. $5 multicoloured .. .. 4·50 2·75

63 Short-finned Pilot Whale

(Des Artists International. Litho Questa)

1983 (10 Jan). *Save the Whales. T* **63** *and similar horiz designs. Multicoloured. P* 14.
537 10 c. Type **63** 85 55
538 60 c. Dall's Porpoise .. .. 2·00 1·75
539 $1.10, Humpback Whale .. .. .. 3·50 2·75
540 $3 Bowhead Whale .. .. 6·00 7·00
537/40 .. .. *Set of* 4 11·00 11·00
MS541 113 × 84 mm. $5 Spotted Dolphin .. 4·50 4·00

64 "David and Goliath"

(Des Design Images. Litho Format)

1983 (15 Feb). *500th Birth Anniv of Raphael. T* **64** *and similar horiz designs showing painting details. Multicoloured. P* 13½.
542 25 c. Type **64** 15 15
543 30 c. "David sees Bathsheba" 15 15
544 90 c. "Triumph of David" 30 35
545 $4 "Anointing of Solomon" 70 90
542/5 .. .. *Set of* 4 1·10 1·40
MS546 126 × 101 mm. $5 "Anointing of David" .. 80 1·10
Nos. 542/5 exist imperforate from stock dispersed by the liquidator of Format International Security Printers Ltd.

65 Voice and Visual Communication

(Des Artists International. Litho Questa)

1983 (7 Apr). *World Communications Year. T* **65** *and similar horiz designs. Multicoloured. P* 14.
547 30 c. Type **65** 10 10
548 60 c. Ambulance 25 20
549 $1.10, Westland Whirlwind helicopters .. 45 45
550 $3 Satellite .. .. 1·00 1·00
547/50 .. .. *Set of* 4 1·60 1·60
MS551 127×85 mm. $5 Diver and Bottle-nosed Dolphin .. .. 1·75 2·00

66 Chrysler "Imperial Roadster", 1931

(Des R. Sauber. Litho Format)

1983 (4 May). *75th Anniv of Model "T" Ford Car. T* **66** *and similar horiz designs showing cars of the 20th century. Multicoloured P* 14½.
552 10 c. Type **66** 15 15
553 30 c. Doble steam car, 1925 .. .. .. 25 25
554 40 c. Ford "Mustang", 1965 .. .. .. 25 30
555 60 c. Packard tourer, 1930 .. .. .. 35 40
556 70 c. Mercer "Raceabout" 1913 .. .. .. 35 40
557 90 c. Corvette "Stingray", 1963 .. .. .. 35 40
558 $1.10, Auburn "851 Supercharger Speedster", 1935 .. .. 40 45
559 $2.50, Pierce-Arrow "Silver Arrow", 1933 .. 65 95
560 $3 Duesenberg dual cowl phaeton, 1929 .. 75 1·25
561 $4 Mercedes-Benz "SSK", 1928 .. .. 75 1·50
552/61 .. .. *Set of* 10 3·75 5·50
MS562 119 × 90 mm. $5 McFarlan "Knickerbocker" cabriolet, 1923 .. .. 2·00 2·50
Nos. 552/61 were each issued in sheets of eight stamps with a stamp-size label in the centre position.

67 Short S.45A Solent 2 Flying Boat

(Des W. Wright. Litho Questa)

83 (18 July). *Bicentenary of Manned Flight. T* **67** *and similar horiz designs. Multicoloured. P* 14.
3 40 c. Type **67** 75 20
4 70 c. Curtiss R3C-2 seaplane 90 35
5 90 c. Hawker Nimrod biplane .. .. 1·10 40
6 $4 Montgolfier balloon .. .. .. 3·25 2·75
3/6 .. .. *Set of* 4 5·50 3·25
S567 112×85 mm. $5 LZ-11 *Viktoria Luise* airship) .. .. 1·75 2·00

68 Goofy **69** Weightlifting

(Litho Walsall)

83 (7 Nov). *Christmas. T* **68** *and similar vert designs showing Disney cartoon characters in scenes from "Jingle Bells" Christmas carol). Multicoloured. P* 11.
8 ½ c. Type **68** 10 10
9 1 c. Clarabelle Cow 10 10
0 2 c. Donald Duck 10 10
1 3 c. Pluto 10 10
2 4 c. Morty and Ferdie 10 10
3 5 c. Huey, Dewey and Louie 10 10
4 10 c. Daisy and Chip 'n Dale 10 10
5 $2.50, Big Bad Wolf .. .. 4·75 5·00
6 $3 Mickey Mouse .. .. 5·00 5·50
8/76 .. .. *Set of* 9 9·00 10·00
S577 102 × 124 mm. $5 Donald Duck in sleigh. P 13½ .. .. 8·00 8·00

(Des N. Waldman. Litho Questa)

84 (9 Jan). *Olympic Games, Los Angeles. T* **69** *and similar vert designs. Multicoloured. P* 14.
8 30 c. Type **69** 20 15
9 60 c. Gymnastics 45 35
0 70 c. Archery 50 40
1 $4 Sailing .. .. 1·90 1·90
8/81 .. .. *Set of* 4 2·75 2·50
S582 70 × 102 mm. $5 Basketball .. .. 2·00 2·25

70 Frangipani **71** Goofy

(Des J. Cooter. Litho Format)

84 (9 Apr). *Flowers. T* **70** *and similar vert designs. Multicoloured. P* 15.
3 15 c. Type **70** 15 10
4 40 c. Dwarf Poinciana 30 25
5 70 c. Walking Iris 55 45
6 $4 Lady's Slipper .. .. 2·25 2·50
3/6 .. .. *Set of* 4 3·00 3·00
S587 66 × 57 mm. $5 Brazilian Glory Vine .. 1·75 2·50
Nos. 583/6 exist imperforate from stock dispersed by the liquidator of Format International Security Printers Ltd.

(Litho Format)

84 (1 May). *Easter. T* **71** *and similar vert designs showing Disney cartoon characters with Easter hats. Multicoloured. P* 11.
8 ½ c. Type **71** 10 10
9 1 c. Chip and Dale 10 10
0 2 c. Daisy Duck and Huey 10 10
1 3 c. Daisy Duck 10 10
2 4 c. Donald Duck 10 10
3 5 c. Merlin and Madam Mim 10 10
4 10 c. Flower 10 10
5 $2 Minnie and Mickey Mouse .. .. .. 1·50 2·00
6 $4 Minnie Mouse .. .. 2·25 2·75
8/96 .. .. *Set of* 9 3·75 4·75
S597 126 × 100 mm. $5 Minnie Mouse (*different*). P 13½ × 14 .. .. .. 3·00 3·75

72 Bobolink

19TH U.P.U CONGRESS HAMBURG
(**73**)

(Litho Questa)

1984 (21 May). *Songbirds. T* **72** *and similar horiz designs. Multicoloured. P* 14.
598 40 c. Type **72** .. .. 1·75 1·50
599 50 c. Eastern Kingbird .. .. 2·00 1·60
600 60 c. Barn Swallow .. .. 2·25 2·00
601 70 c. Yellow Warbler .. .. 2·25 2·00
602 $1 Rose-breasted Grosbeak .. .. .. 2·50 2·50
603 $1.10, Yellowthroat .. .. 2·75 2·75
604 $2 Catbird .. .. 3·50 4·50
598/604 .. .. *Set of* 7 15·00 15·00
MS605 71 × 65 mm. $5 Fork-tailed Flycatcher .. 6·50 5·00

1984 (19 June). *Universal Postal Union Congress, Hamburg. Nos.* 585/7 *optd with T* **73**.
606 70 c. Walking Iris .. .. 1·00 1·00
607 $4 Lady's Slipper .. .. 4·50 5·00
MS608 66 × 57 mm. $5 Brazilian Glory Vine .. 2·25 3·00

74 *Geeststar* (freighter) **75** Col. Steven's Model (1825)

(Litho Format)

1984 (16 July). *Ships. T* **74** *and similar horiz designs. Multicoloured. P* 15.
609 30 c. Type **74** 75 75
610 60 c. *Daphne* (liner) .. .. 1·00 1·25
611 $1.10 *Southwind* (schooner) .. .. .. 1·25 2·00
612 $4 *Oceanic* (liner) .. .. 2·00 5·50
609/12 .. .. *Set of* 4 4·50 8·50
MS613 108×80 mm. $5 Pirate ship .. .. 3·00 4·00
No. **MS**613 exists imperforate from stock dispersed by the liquidator of Format International Security Printers Ltd.

(Litho Questa)

1984 (22 Aug). *450th Death Anniv of Correggio (painter). Multicoloured designs as T* **296** *of Grenada showing paintings. P* 14.
614 10 c. "The Hunt—Blowing the Horn" 10 10
615 30 c. "St. John the Evangelist" (*horiz*) .. 15 15
616 90 c. "The Hunt—The Deer's Head" 50 50
617 $4 "The Virgin crowned by Christ" (*horiz*) .. 2·00 2·00
614/17 .. .. *Set of* 4 2·50 2·50
MS618 73 × 63 mm. $5 "Martyrdom of the Four Saints" .. .. 2·40 3·00

(Litho Questa)

1984 (22 Aug). *150th Birth Anniv of Edgar Degas (painter). Vert designs as T* **297** *of Grenada showing paintings. Multicoloured. P* 14.
619 25 c. "The Song of the Dog" 40 15
620 70 c. "Cafe-concert" 70 50
621 $1.10, "The Orchestra of the Opera" .. 1·50 1·25
622 $3 "The Dance Lesson" .. .. .. 2·75 2·75
619/22 .. .. *Set of* 4 4·75 4·25
MS623 53 × 73 mm. $5 "Madame Camus at the Piano" .. .. 2·40 3·00

(Des Bonny Redecker. Litho Questa)

1984 (21 Sept). *"Ausipex" International Stamp Exhibition, Melbourne. Horiz designs as T* **298** *of Grenada. Multicoloured. P* 14.
624 $1.10, Queen Victoria Gardens, Melbourne 50 50
625 $4 Ayers Rock .. .. 2·00 2·00
MS626 107 × 76 mm. $5 River Yarra, Melbourne 2·00 3·00

(Des Bonny Redecker. Litho Format)

1984 (3 Oct). *Railway Locomotives. T* **75** *and similar horiz designs. Multicoloured. P* 15.
627 20 c. Type **75** 55 25
628 50 c. *Royal George* (1827) 70 50
629 60 c. *Stourbridge Lion* (1829) 75 65
630 70 c. *Liverpool* (1830) 80 85
631 90 c. *South Carolina* (1832) .. .. .. 90 1·25
632 $1.10, *Monster* (1836) .. .. 90 1·50
633 $2 *Lafayette* (1837) .. .. 1·10 2·25
634 $4 *Lion* (1838) .. .. 1·40 3·75
627/34 .. .. *Set of* 8 6·25 10·00
MS635 Two sheets, each 100×70 mm. (a) $5 Sequin's locomotive (1829); (b) $5 *Adler* (1835) *Set of* 2 *sheets* 6·00 8·00

1984 (28 Oct). *Opening of Point Saline International Airport. Nos.* 547, 549 *and* **MS**551 *optd as T* **300** *of Grenada.*
636 30 c. Type **65** 30 25
637 $1.10, Westland Whirlwind helicopters .. 95 75
MS638 127×85 mm. Diver and Bottle-nosed Dolphin .. .. 3·75 3·50
The overprint on No. **MS**638 appears on the sheet margin as for No. **MS**1371 of Grenada.

(Litho Questa)

1984 (26 Nov). *Christmas. Walt Disney Cartoon Characters. Vert designs as T* **301** *of Grenada. Multicoloured. P* 12 ($2) *or* 13½ × 14 (*others*).
639 45 c. Donald Duck, and nephews knitting Christmas stockings 70 40
640 60 c. Donald Duck and nephews sitting on sofa 80 65
641 90 c. Donald Duck getting out of bed .. 1·25 1·00
642 $2 Donald Duck putting presents in wardrobe .. .. 2·00 2·50
643 $4 Nephews singing carols outside Donald Duck's window .. .. 3·25 4·25
639/43 .. .. *Set of* 5 7·25 8·00
MS644 126×102 mm. $5 Donald Duck filming nephews .. .. 4·25 4·00
No. 642 was printed in sheetlets of 8 stamps.

(Litho Questa)

1985 (11 Feb). *Birth Bicentenary of John J. Audubon (ornithologist) (1st issue). Multicoloured designs as T* **198** *of Antigua showing original paintings. P* 14.
645 50 c. Blue-winged Teal .. .. 2·00 60
646 90 c. White Ibis .. .. 2·50 1·25
647 $1.10, Swallow-tailed Kite .. .. .. 3·50 2·00
648 $3 Moorhen ("Common Gallinule") .. .. 4·50 4·75
645/8 .. .. *Set of* 4 11·00 7·75
MS649 82×111 mm. $5 Mangrove Cuckoo (*vert*) 3·25 3·75
See also Nos. 736/40.

76 Kawasaki "750" (1972) **77** Nursing Cadets folding Bandages (Health)

(Des BG Studio. Litho Questa)

1985 (11 Mar). *Centenary of the Motor Cycle. T* **76** *and similar multicoloured designs. P* 14.
650 30 c. Type **76** 65 45
651 60 c. Honda "Goldwing GL1000" (1974) (*horiz*) .. .. 90 1·00
652 70 c. Kawasaki "Z650" (1976) (*horiz*) .. 1·00 1·10
653 $4 Honda "CBX" (1977) .. .. .. 4·00 6·50
650/3 .. .. *Set of* 4 6·00 8·00
MS654 113×76 mm. $5 BMW "R100RS" (1978) .. 3·50 4·25

(Des Susan David. Litho Questa)

1985 (15 Apr). *International Youth Year. T* **77** *and similar horiz designs. Multicoloured. P* 14.
655 50 c. Type **77** 70 45
656 70 c. Scuba diver and turtle (Environment) .. 1·00 80
657 $1.10, Yachting (Leisure) .. .. .. 1·60 1·50
658 $3 Boys playing chess (Education) .. .. 5·50 6·50
655/8 .. .. *Set of* 4 8·00 8·25
MS659 98×70 mm. $5 Hands touching globe .. 2·75 3·00

(Des BG Studio. Litho Questa)

1985 (30 Apr). *40th Anniv of International Civil Aviation Organization. Horiz designs as T* **305** *of Grenada. Multicoloured. P* 14.
660 5 c. Lockheed L.18 Lodestar 40 20
661 70 c. Hawker Siddeley H.S.748 .. .. .. 1·75 55
662 $1.10, Boeing 727-200 .. .. 2·25 90
663 $3 Boeing 707 .. .. 3·50 2·50
660/3 .. .. *Set of* 4 7·00 3·75
MS664 87×68 mm. $4 Pilatus Britten Norman Islander .. .. 3·50 3·00

78 Lady Baden-Powell (founder) and Grenadian Guide Leaders

(Des D. Francis. Litho Questa)

1985 (30 May). *75th Anniv of Girl Guide Movement. T* **78** *and similar multicoloured designs. P* 14.
665 30 c. Type **78** 40 20
666 50 c. Guide leader and guides on botany field trip 70 30
667 70 c. Guide leader and guides camping (*vert*) 95 45
668 $4 Guides sailing (*vert*) .. .. .. 3·25 2·25
665/8 .. .. *Set of* 4 4·75 3·00
MS669 100×73 mm. $5 Lord and Lady Baden-Powell (*vert*) .. .. 3·75 4·25

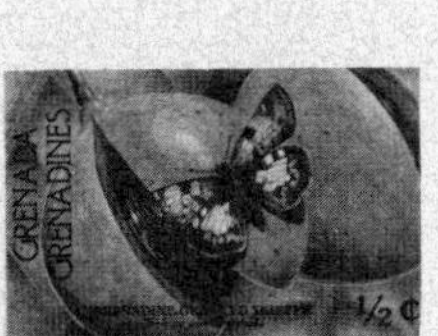

79 *Chiomara asychis* **80** The Queen Mother before Prince William's Christening

(Des I. MacLaury. Litho Questa)

1985 (17 June)–**89.** *Butterflies. T* **79** *and similar horiz designs. Multicoloured. P* 14.

670 ½ c. Type **79** 10 10
a. Perf 12 (1986) 10 10
671 1 c. *Anartia amathea* 10 10
a. Perf 12 (1986) 10 10
672 2 c. *Pseudolycaena marsyas* 10 10
a. Perf 12 (1986) 10 10
673 4 c. *Urbanus proteus* 10 10
a. Perf 12 (1986) 10 10
674 5 c. *Polygonus manueli* 15 10
a. Perf 12 (1986) 15 10
675 6 c. *Battus polydamas* 20 15
a. Perf 12 (1986) 20 15
676 10 c. *Eurema daira* 30 15
a. Perf 12 (1986) 30 15
677 12 c. *Phoebis agarithe* 45 20
a. Perf 12 (1986) 45 20
678 15 c. *Aphrissa statira* 45 20
a. Perf 12 (1986) 45 20
679 20 c. *Strymon simaethis* 60 20
a. Perf 12 (1986) 60 20
680 25 c. *Mestra cana* 60 25
a. Perf 12 (1986) 60 25
681 30 c. *Agraulis vanillae* 60 30
a. Perf 12 (1986) 60 30
682 40 c. *Junonia evarete* 75 45
a. Perf 12 (1986) 75 45
683 60 c. *Dryas julia* .. .. 1·00 65
a. Perf 12 (1986) .. .. 1·00 65
684 70 c. *Philaethria dido* .. .. 1·10 75
a. Perf 12 (1986) .. .. 1·10 75
685 $1.10, *Hamadryas feronia* .. .. .. 1·75 1·25
a. Perf 12 (1986) .. .. 1·75 1·25
686 $2.50, *Strymon rufofusca* .. .. .. 3·25 3·00
a. Perf 12 (9.86) .. .. 3·25 3·75
687 $5 *Appias drusilla* .. .. 5·00 4·75
a. Perf 12 (1986) .. .. 5·00 5·50
688 $10 *Polites dictynna* (11.11.85) .. .. 8·00 9·00
a. Perf 12 (9.86) .. .. 8·00 11·00
688*b* $20 *Euptychia cephus* (1.8.86) .. .. 12·00 14·00
ba. Perf 12 (5.89) .. .. 12·00 15·00
670/88*b* .. .. *Set of* 20 32·00 32·00
670a/88ba .. .. .. *Set of* 20 32·00 35·00

(Des J.W. Litho Questa)

1985 (3 July). *Life and Times of Queen Elizabeth the Queen Mother. T* **80** *and similar multicoloured designs. P* 14.

689 $1 Type **80** 45 60
690 $1.50, In winner's enclosure at Ascot (*horiz*) 60 75
691 $2.50, With Prince Charles at Garter ceremony, Windsor Castle .. .. 85 1·10
689/91 .. .. *Set of* 3 1·75 2·10
MS692 56 × 85 mm. $5 At opening of Royal York Hospice, London .. .. 1·75 3·00

Stamps as Nos. 689/91, but with face values of 70 c., $1.10 and $3, exist from additional sheetlets of 5 plus a label issued 28 January 1986. These also have changed background colours and are perforated 12½×12 ($1.10) or 12×12½ (others) (*Price for set of 3 stamps £1.75 mint*).

81 Scuba Diving

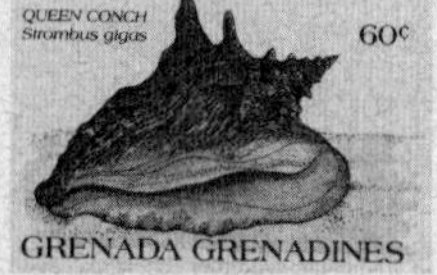

82 Queen or Pink Conch

(Des Marlise Nakaja. Litho Format)

1985 (15 July). *Water Sports. T* **81** *and similar vert designs. Multicoloured. P* 15.

693 15 c. Type **81** 30 10
694 70 c. Boys playing in waterfall 70 45
695 90 c. Water skiing 85 55
696 $4 Swimming .. .. 2·50 2·25
693/6 .. .. *Set of* 4 4·00 3·00
MS697 103 × 78 mm. $5 Scuba diver .. .. 3·25 3·25

(Des Mary Walters. Litho Questa)

1985 (1 Aug). *Marine Life. T* **82** *and similar horiz designs. Multicoloured. P* 14.

698 60 c. Type **82** 65 40
699 90 c. Porcupinefish and Fire Coral 85 55
700 $1.10, Ghost Crab .. .. 1·00 70
701 $4 West Indies Spiny Lobster .. .. 2·50 2·25
698/701 .. .. *Set of* 4 4·50 3·50
MS702 299×70 mm. $5 Long-spined Urchin .. 4·50 4·00

(Des Susan David. Litho Questa)

1985 (3 Sept). *300th Birth Anniv of Johann Sebastian Bach (composer). Vert designs as T* **206** *of Antigua. Multicoloured. P* 14.

703 15 c. Natural trumpet 50 10
704 60 c. Bass viol 85 40
705 $1.10, Flute .. .. 1·50 70
706 $3 Double flageolet .. .. 2·25 1·75
703/6 .. .. *Set of* 4 4·50 2·75
MS707 110 × 75 mm. $5 Johann Sebastian Bach 3·25 3·50

(Litho Format)

1985 (4 Nov). *Royal Visit. Multicoloured designs as T* **207** *of Antigua. P* 14½.

708 10 c. Arms of Great Britain and Grenada .. 20 20
709 $1 Queen Elizabeth II (*vert*) .. .. 1·25 1·75
710 $4 Royal Yacht *Britannia* .. .. .. 3·75 4·75
708/10 .. .. *Set of* 3 4·75 6·00
MS711 111 × 83 mm. $5 Map of Grenada Grenadines .. .. 3·75 3·75

(Litho Format)

1985 (22 Nov). *40th Anniv of United Nations Organization. Multicoloured designs as T* **208** *of Antigua showing United Nations (New York) stamps. P* 14½.

712 $1 Neil Armstrong (first man on Moon) and 1982 Peaceful Uses of Outer Space 20 c. .. 1·10 1·10
713 $2 Gandhi and 1971 Racial Equality Year 13 c. .. .. 3·25 3·75
714 $2.50, Maimonides (physician) and 1956 World Health Organization 3 c. .. .. 4·50 5·50
712/14 .. .. *Set of* 3 8·00 9·25
MS715 110 × 85 mm. $5 U.N. Under-Secretary Ralph Bunche (*vert*) .. .. 2·75 3·00

(Des Walt Disney Productions. Litho Questa)

1985 (27 Nov). *150th Birth Anniv of Mark Twain (author). Horiz designs as T* **118** *of Anguilla showing Walt Disney cartoon characters illustrating scenes from "Letters from Hawaii". Multicoloured. P* 14 × 13½.

716 25 c. Minnie Mouse dancing the hula .. 60 30
717 50 c. Donald Duck surfing 90 65
718 $1.50, Donald Duck roasting marshmallow in volcano .. .. 2·25 2·25
719 $3 Mickey Mouse and Chip'n'Dale canoeing .. .. 3·75 4·00
716/19 .. .. *Set of* 4 6·75 6·50
MS720 127 × 102 mm. $5 Mickey Mouse with cat 4·75 3·75

(Des Walt Disney Productions. Litho Questa)

1985 (27 Nov). *Birth Bicentenaries of Grimm Brothers (folklorists). Designs as T* **119** *of Anguilla, but vert, showing Walt Disney cartoon characters in scenes from "The Elves and the Shoemaker". Multicoloured. P* 13½ × 14.

721 30 c. Mickey Mouse as the unsuccessful Shoemaker 70 40
722 60 c. Two elves making shoes .. .. 1·10 85
723 70 c. The Shoemaker discovering the new shoes .. .. 1·40 1·00
724 $4 The Shoemaker's wife (Minnie Mouse) making clothes for the elves .. .. 4·25 5·00
721/4 .. .. *Set of* 4 6·75 6·50
MS725 126 × 101 mm. $5 The Shoemaker and his wife waving .. .. 5·50 5·00

83 "Madonna and Child" (Titian)

VISIT OF PRES. REAGAN
20 FEBRUARY 1986
(**84**)

(Des Mary Walters. Litho Format)

1985 (23 Dec). *Christmas. Religious Paintings. T* **83** *and similar vert designs. Multicoloured. P* 15.

726 50 c. Type **83** 45 35
727 70 c. "Madonna and Child with St. Mary and John the Baptist" (Bugiardini) .. 55 50
728 $1.10, "Adoration of the Magi" (Di Fredi) .. 90 1·40
729 $3 "Madonna and Child with Young St. John the Baptist" (Bartolomeo) .. 1·75 3·75
726/9 .. .. *Set of* 4 3·25 5·50
MS730 112×81 mm. $5 "The Annunciation" (Botticelli) .. .. 3·25 6·00

Nos. 726 and **MS**730 exist imperforate from stock dispersed by the liquidator of Format International Security Printers Ltd.

(Des J. Iskowitz. Litho Questa)

1986 (6 Jan). *Centenary of the Statue of Liberty* (1*st issue*). *Multicoloured designs as T* **211** *of Dominica. P* 15.

731 5 c. Croton Reservoir, New York (1875) .. 10 10
732 10 c. New York Public Library (1986) .. 10 10
733 70 c. Old Boathouse, Central Park (1894) .. 25 40
734 $4 Boating in Central Park (1986) .. 1·40 2·25
731/4 .. .. *Set of* 4 1·50 2·50
MS735 103 × 76 mm. $5 Statue of Liberty (*vert*) .. 2·50 3·50

See also Nos. 892/903.

(Litho Questa)

1986 (28 Jan). *Birth Bicentenary of John J. Audubon (ornithologist)* (2*nd issue*). *Horiz designs as T* **198** *of Antigua. Multicoloured. P* 12½ × 12.

736 50 c. Louisiana Heron .. .. 2·00 1·00
737 70 c. Black-crowned Night Heron .. .. 2·50 1·50
738 90 c. American Bittern .. .. 2·75 2·00
739 $4 Glossy Ibis .. .. 5·00 6·50
736/9 .. .. *Set of* 4 11·00 10·00
MS740 103 × 74 mm. $5 King Eider. P 14 .. 6·50 8·50

Nos. 736/9 were each issued in sheetlets of five stamps and one stamp-size label, which appears in the centre of the bottom row.

1986 (20 Feb). *Visit of President Reagan of U.S.A. Nos.* 684A *and* 687A *optd with T* **84**.

741 70 c. *Philaethria dido* .. .. 1·50 1·25
742 $5 *Appias drusilla* .. .. 6·50 8·00

85 Two Footballers

86 *Hygrocybe firma*

(Des BG Studio. Litho Questa)

1986 (18 Mar). *World Cup Football Championship, Mexic Vert designs as T* **85** *showing footballers. P* 14.

743 10 c. multicoloured 50 4
744 70 c. multicoloured .. .. 1·60 1·2
745 $1 multicoloured .. .. 1·90 1·7
746 $4 multicoloured .. .. 5·00 6·5
743/6 .. .. *Set of* 4 8·00 9·(
MS747 86 × 104 mm. $5 multicoloured .. .. 4·00 4·7

(Des W. Hanson. Litho Questa)

1986 (26 Mar). *Appearance of Halley's Comet* (1*st issue*). *Hor designs as T* **123** *of Anguilla. Multicoloured. P* 14.

748 5 c. Nicholas Copernicus (astronomer) and Earl of Rosse's six foot reflector telescope 40 4
749 20 c. "Sputnik I" (first satellite) orbiting Earth, 1957 .. .. 60 4
750 40 c. Tycho Brahe's notes and sketch of 1577 Comet .. .. 80 (
751 $4 Edmond Halley and 1682 Comet .. 3·75 4·5
748/51 .. .. *Set of* 4 5·00 5·5
MS752 101 × 70 mm. $5 Halley's Comet .. 3·00 3·5

The captions of Nos. 750/1 are transposed.
See also Nos. 790/4.

(Litho Questa)

1986 (21 Apr). *60th Birthday of Queen Elizabeth II. Ve designs as T* **125** *of Anguilla. P* 14.

753 2 c. black and yellow 10 1
754 $1.50, multicoloured .. .. 80 1·
755 $4 multicoloured .. .. 2·00 2·7
753/5 .. .. *Set of* 3 2·50 3·5
MS756 120 × 85 mm. $5 black and grey-brown .. 2·00 3·5

Designs:—2 c. Princesses Elizabeth and Margaret, Windsc Park, 1933; $1.50, Queen Elizabeth; $4 In Sydney, Australi 1970; $5 The Royal Family, Coronation Day, 1937.

(Des Walt Disney Productions. Litho Format)

1986 (22 May). *"Ameripex '86" International Stamp Exhibitio Chicago. Horiz designs as T* **212** *of Dominica showing Wa Disney cartoon characters. Multicoloured. P* 11.

757 30 c. Donald Duck riding mule in Grand Canyon 45 4
758 60 c. Daisy Duck, Timothy Mouse and Dumbo on Golden Gate Bridge, San Francisco .. .. 70 1·0
759 $1 Mickey Mouse and Goofy in fire engine and Chicago Watertower .. .. 1·25 1·7
760 $3 Mickey Mouse as airmail pilot and White House .. .. 3·00 4·(
757/60 .. .. *Set of* 4 5·00 6·5
MS761 126 × 101 mm. $5 Donald Duck and Mickey Mouse watching Halley's Comet over Statue of Liberty. P 14 × 13½ .. .. .. 5·00 7·5

No. 757 exists imperforate from stock dispersed by th liquidator of Format International Security Printers Ltd.

(Litho Questa)

1986 (1 July). *Royal Wedding. Vert designs as T* **213** *Antigua. Multicoloured. P* 14.

762 60 c. Prince Andrew and Miss Sarah Ferguson 55 4
763 70 c. Prince Andrew in car 65 5
764 $4 Prince Andrew with Westland WG-13 Lynx naval helicopter .. .. .. 2·75 3·
762/4 .. .. *Set of* 3 3·50 4·(
MS765 88×88 mm. $5 Prince Andrew and Miss Sarah Ferguson (*different*) .. .. .. 4·00 5·

(Des BG Studio. Litho Format)

1986 (15 July). *Mushrooms of the Lesser Antilles. T* **86** *an similar vert designs. Multicoloured. P* 15.

766 15 c. Type **86** 80 4
767 50 c. *Xerocomus coccolobae* .. .. .. 1·75 1·2
768 $2 *Volvariella cubensis* .. .. .. 3·50 4·0
769 $3 *Lactarius putidus* .. .. 4·50 5·0
766/9 .. .. *Set of* 4 9·50 9·5
MS770 76 × 80 mm. $5 *Leptonia caeruleocapitata* 9·00 11·0

No. **MS**770 exists imperforate from stock dispersed by th liquidator of Format International Security Printers Ltd.

87 Giant Atlantic or Doldorate Pyram (*Pyramidella dolabrata*)

88 Common Opossum

(Des L. Birmingham. Litho Format)

.986 (1 Aug). *Sea Shells. T* **87** *and similar multicoloured designs. P* 15.
'71 15 c. Type **87** 90 50
'72 50 c. Beau's Murex (*Murex beauii*) .. 2·00 1·25
'73 $1.10, West Indian Fighting Conch (*Strombus pugilis*) .. .. .. 2·50 2·75
'74 $4 Alphabet Cone (*Conus spurius*) .. 4·75 7·00
'71/4 .. .. *Set of* 4 9·00 10·50
AS775 109×75 mm. $5 Brown-lined Paper Bubble (*Hydatina vesicaria*) .. .. .. 6·00 8·00

986 (15 Sept). *World Cup Football Championship Winners, Mexico. Nos. 743/7 optd with T* **216** *of Antigua in gold.*
76 **85** 10 c. multicoloured 40 30
77 – 70 c. multicoloured .. .. 1·10 1·00
78 – $1 multicoloured .. .. 1·40 1·40
79 – $4 multicoloured .. .. 3·75 5·00
76/9 .. .. *Set of* 4 6·00 7·00
IS780 86×104 mm. $5 multicoloured .. .. 8·00 9·00

(Des Dot and S. Barlowe. Litho Format)

986 (15 Sept). *Wildlife. T* **88** *and similar multicoloured designs. P* 15.
'81 10 c. Type **88** 20 20
'82 30 c. Giant Toad 40 40
'83 60 c. Land Tortoise (*Testudo denticulata*) .. 80 80
'84 70 c. Murine Opossum (*vert*) 85 85
'85 90 c. Burmese Mongoose (*vert*) .. .. 90 1·00
'86 $1.10, Nine-banded Armadillo .. .. 1·00 1·25
'87 $2 Agouti .. .. 1·75 2·25
'88 $3 Humpback Whale .. .. .. 3·50 4·25
'81/8 .. .. *Set of* 8 8·50 10·00
AS789 Two sheets, each 103×72 mm. (a) $5 Mona Monkey (*vert*) (b) $5 Iguana
Set of 2 *sheets* 11·00 14·00

Nos. 781/8 exist imperforate from stock dispersed by the iquidator of Format International Security Printers Ltd.

.986 (15 Oct). *Appearance of Halley's Comet (2nd issue). Nos. 748/52 optd with T* **218** *of Antigua (in silver on 20 c., $4 and $5).*
'90 5 c. Nicholas Copernicus (astronomer) and Earl of Rosse's six foot reflector telescope 60 60
'91 20 c. "Sputnik I" (first satellite) orbiting Earth, 1957 .. .. 80 50
'92 40 c. Tycho Brahe's notes and sketch of 1577 Comet .. .. 1·00 60
'93 $4 Edmond Halley and 1682 Comet .. 5·00 6·00
'90/3 .. .. *Set of* 4 6·50 7·00
AS794 102×70 mm. $5 Halley's Comet .. 4·00 5·50

(Des Walt Disney Co. Litho Format)

986 (3 Nov). *Christmas. Multicoloured designs as T* **220** *of Antigua showing Walt Disney cartoon characters. P* 11.
'95 25 c. Chip n'Dale with hummingbird .. 25 15
'96 30 c. Robin delivering card to Mickey Mouse (*vert*) 25 20
'97 50 c. Piglet, Pooh and Jose Carioca on beach 40 30
'98 60 c. Grandma Duck feeding birds (*vert*) .. 50 40
'99 70 c. Cinderella and birds with mistletoe (*vert*) 55 50
'00 $1.50, Huey, Dewey and Louie windsurfing 1·25 1·75
01 $3 Mickey Mouse and Morty on beach with turtle .. .. 1·50 2·50
02 $4 Kittens playing on piano (*vert*) .. 2·00 3·25
95/802 .. .. *Set of* 8 6·00 8·00
AS803 Two sheets, each 127×102 mm. (a) $5 Mickey Mouse and Willie the Whale. P 14×13½. (b) $5 Bambi, Thumper and Blossom in snow (*vert*). P 13½×14 *Set of* 2 *sheets* 8·00 11·50

89 Cycling

90 Aston-Martin "Volanté" (1984)

(Des BG Studio. Litho Format)

986 (18 Nov). *Olympic Games, Seoul, South Korea (1988). T* **89** *and similar vert designs. Multicoloured. P* 15.
04 10 c.+5 c. Type **89** 30 40
05 50 c.+20 c. Sailing 60 90
06 70 c.+30 c. Gymnastics .. .. .. 75 1·10
07 $2+$1 Horse trials .. .. .. 2·25 3·00
04/7 .. .. *Set of* 4 3·50 4·75
AS808 80×100 mm. $3+$1 Marathon .. .. 3·00 4·50

The premiums on Nos. 804/8 were to support the participation f the Grenada team.

Nos. 804/8 exist imperforate from stock dispersed by the quidator of Format International Security Printers Ltd.

(Des W. Wright. Litho Format)

986 (20 Nov). *Centenary of Motoring. T* **90** *and similar horiz designs. Multicoloured. P* 15.
09 10 c. Type **90** 25 25
10 30 c. Jaguar "Mk V" (1948) 45 45
11 60 c. Nash "Ambassador" (1956) 65 65
12 70 c. Toyota "Supra" (1984) 70 70
13 90 c. Ferrari "Testarossa" (1985) 80 90
14 $1 BMW "501B" (1955) 85 95
15 $2 Mercedes-Benz "280 SL" (1968) .. 1·40 2·00
16 $3 Austro-Daimler "ADR8" (1932) .. 1·90 2·50
09/16 .. .. *Set of* 8 6·25 7·50
AS817 Two sheets, each 116 × 85 mm. (a) $5 Morgan "+8" (1977). (b) $5 Checker taxi
Set of 2 *sheets* 7·00 11·00

(Litho Questa)

1986 (19 Dec). *Birth Centenary of Marc Chagall (artist). Designs as T* **225** *of Antigua, showing various paintings. P* 13½×14 (*vert*) *or* 14×13½ (*horiz*).
818/57 $1.10×40 multicoloured .. *Set of* 40 28·00 28·00
MS858 Ten sheets, each 110×95 mm. $5×10 multicoloured (*each* 104×89 *mm*). Imperf
Set of 10 *sheets* 28·00 28·00

Although announced as all being released on 19 December 1986 the issue was distributed in ten parts, each of four stamps and one miniature sheet, at monthly intervals.

(Des J. Iskowitz. Litho Format)

1987 (5 Feb). *America's Cup Yachting Championship. Multicoloured designs as T* **222** *of Antigua. P* 15.
859 25 c. *Defender*, 1895 .. .. .. 60 40
860 45 c. *Galatea*, 1886 .. .. .. 80 60
861 70 c. *Azzurra*, 1981 .. .. .. 1·00 1·00
862 $4 *Australia II*, 1983 .. .. .. 2·00 3·50
859/62 .. .. *Set of* 4 4·00 5·00
MS863 113×83 mm. $5 *Columbia* defeating *Shamrock*, 1899 (*horiz*) .. .. .. 5·00 7·00

(Des Mary Walters. Litho Format)

1987 (27 Apr). *500th Anniv of Discovery of America by Columbus (1992) (1st issue). Vert designs as T* **322** *of Grenada. Multicoloured. P* 15.
864 15 c. Christopher Columbus 25 25
865 30 c. Queen Isabella of Castile 30 30
866 50 c. *Santa Maria* 45 50
867 60 c. Claiming the New World for Spain .. 50 60
868 90 c. Early Spanish map of Lesser Antilles .. 65 75
869 $1 King Ferdinand of Aragon 70 80
870 $2 Fort La Navidad (drawing by Columbus) 1·40 2·00
871 $3 Galley and Caribs, Hispaniola (drawing by Columbus) .. .. 1·90 2·50
864/71 .. .. *Set of* 8 5·50 7·00
MS872 Two sheets, 104×72 mm. (a) $5 Caribs pearl fishing. (b) $5 *Santa Maria* at anchor
Set of 2 *sheets* 8·50 11·00

See also Nos. 1191/5, 1224/32, 1366/74, 1494/1500 and 1519/20.

(Des W. Wright. Litho Questa)

1987 (18 May). *Milestones of Transportation. Horiz designs as T* **226** *of Antigua. Multicoloured. P* 14.
873 10 c. Saunders Roe "SR-N1" (first hovercraft), 1959 .. .. 30 30
874 15 c. Bugatti "Royale" (largest car), 1931 .. 35 35
875 30 c. Aleksei Leonov and "Voskhod II" (first spacewalk), 1965 .. .. .. 55 55
876 50 c. C.S.S. *Hunley* (first submarine to sink enemy ship), 1864 .. .. .. 75 75
877 60 c. Rolls Royce "Flying Bedstead" (first VTOL aircraft), 1954 .. .. .. 85 85
878 70 c. *Jenny Lind* (first mass produced locomotive class), 1847 .. .. .. 90 1·00
879 90 c. Duryea "Buggvaut" (first U.S. petrol-driven car), 1893 .. .. .. 1·00 1·25
880 $1.50, Steam locomotive, Metropolitan Railway, London (first underground line), 1863 .. .. 1·75 2·00
881 $2 S.S. *Great Britain* (first transatlantic crossing by screw-steamship), 1843 .. 2·25 2·50
882 $3 "Budweiser Rocket" (fastest car), 1979 2·75 3·00
873/82 .. .. *Set of* 10 10·00 11·50

(Des Susan Barrasi. Litho Format)

1987 (15 June). *"Capex '87" International Stamp Exhibition, Toronto. Game Fishes. Multicoloured designs as T* **323** *of Grenada, but horiz. P* 15.
883 6 c. Yellow Chub 15 15
884 30 c. King Mackerel 40 30
885 50 c. Short-finned Mako 55 55
886 60 c. Dolphin (fish) 60 60
887 90 c. Skipjack Tuna ("Bonito") 75 75
888 $1.10, Cobia .. .. 1·00 1·25
889 $3 Tarpon .. .. 2·25 2·75
890 $4 Swordfish .. .. 2·50 3·25
883/90 .. .. *Set of* 8 7·50 8·75
MS891 Two sheets, each 100×70 mm. (a) $5 Spotted Jewfish. (b) $5 Amberjack *Set of* 2 *sheets* 8·00 10·00

(Litho Questa)

1987 (5 Aug). *Centenary of Statue of Liberty (1986) (2nd issue). Multicoloured designs as T* **227** *of Antigua. P* 14.
892 10 c. Cleaning face of Statue 20 20
893 15 c. Commemorative lapel badges 30 30
894 25 c. Band playing and Statue 40 40
895 30 c. Band on parade and Statue 45 45
896 45 c. Face of Statue 50 50
897 50 c. Cleaning head of Statue (*horiz*) .. 55 55
898 60 c. Models of Statue (*horiz*) 65 65
899 70 c. Small boat flotilla (*horiz*) 75 85
900 $1 Unveiling ceremony 85 90
901 $1.10, Statue and Manhattan skyline .. 90 1·00
902 $2 Parade of warships .. .. .. 1·75 2·00
903 $3 Making commemorative flags .. .. 1·90 2·25
892/903 .. .. *Set of* 12 8·25 9·00

(Litho Questa)

1987 (9 Sept). *Great Scientific Discoveries. Horiz designs as T* **325** *of Grenada. Multicoloured. P* 14.
904 60 c. Newton medal 85 80
905 $1 Louis Daguerre (inventor of daguerreotype) .. .. 1·25 1·00
906 $2 Antoine Lavoisier and apparatus .. 2·25 2·75
907 $3 Rudolf Diesel and first oil engine .. 4·00 4·75
904/7 .. .. *Set of* 4 7·50 8·50
MS908 105×75 mm. $5 Halley's Comet .. 6·00 7·50

No. 907 is inscribed "JAMES WATT" in error.

(Litho Questa)

1987 (1 Nov). *Bicentenary of U.S. Constitution. Multicoloured designs as T* **232** *of Antigua. P* 14.
909 10 c. Washington addressing delegates, Constitutional Convention 25 20
910 50 c. Flag and State Seal, Georgia 85 75
911 60 c. Capitol, Washington (*vert*) 85 80
912 $4 Thomas Jefferson (statesman) (*vert*) .. 3·75 5·50
909/12 .. .. *Set of* 4 5·25 6·50
MS913 105×75 mm. $5 Alexander Hamilton (New York delegate) (*vert*) .. .. .. 3·00 4·00

Nos. 909/12 were each issued in sheetlets of five stamps and one stamp-size label, which appears in the centre of the bottom row.

(Des Walt Disney Co. Litho Questa)

1987 (16 Nov). *"Hafnia '87" International Stamp Exhibition, Copenhagen. Designs as T* **328** *of Grenada, but horiz, illustrating Hans Christian Andersen's fairy tales. Multicoloured. P* 14×13½.
914 25 c. Donald and Daisy Duck in "The Swineherd" 50 30
915 30 c. Mickey Mouse, Donald and Daisy Duck in "What the Good Man Does is Always Right" 55 35
916 50 c. Mickey and Minnie Mouse in "Little Tuk" 75 75
917 60 c. Minnie Mouse and Ferdie in "The World's Fairest Rose" 75 75
918 70 c. Mickey Mouse in "The Garden of Paradise" 80 80
919 $1.50, Goofy and Mickey Mouse in "The Naughty Boy" .. .. 2·00 2·25
920 $3 Goofy in "What the Moon Saw" .. 2·75 3·00
921 $4 Alice as "Thumbelina" .. .. .. 3·25 3·50
914/21 .. .. *Set of* 8 10·00 10·50
MS922 Two sheets, each 127×101 mm. (a) $5 Daisy Duck in "Hans Clodhopper". (b) $5 Aunt Matilda and Mickey Mouse in "Elder-Tree Mother" .. .. .. *Set of* 2 *sheets* 11·00 12·00

91 "The Virgin and Child with Saints Martin and Agnes"

92 Scout signalling with Semaphore Flags

(Litho Questa)

1987 (15 Dec). *Christmas. Religious Paintings by El Greco. T* **91** *and similar vert designs. Multicoloured. P* 14.
923 10 c. Type **91** 40 15
924 50 c. "St. Agnes" (detail from "The Virgin and Child with Saints Martin and Agnes") .. .. 1·25 75
925 60 c. "The Annunciation" .. .. .. 1·25 75
926 $4 "The Holy Family with St. Anne" .. 4·75 7·25
923/6 .. .. *Set of* 4 7·00 8·00
MS927 75×101 mm. $5 "The Adoration of the Shepherds" .. .. 7·50 8·50

(Des and litho Questa)

1988 (15 Feb). *Royal Ruby Wedding. Vert designs as T* **234** *of Antigua. Multicoloured. P* 14.
928 20 c. deep brown, black and light green .. 35 15
929 30 c. deep brown and black 40 20
930 $2 multicoloured .. .. 2·00 2·50
931 $3 multicoloured .. .. 2·50 3·25
928/31 .. .. *Set of* 4 4·75 5·50
MS932 76×100 mm. $5 multicoloured .. .. 3·50 5·00

Designs:—20 c. Queen Elizabeth II with Princess Anne, *c.* 1957; 30 c. Wedding photograph, 1947; $2 Queen with Prince Charles and Princess Anne, *c.* 1955; $3 Queen Elizabeth (from photo by Tim Graham), 1980; $5 Princess Elizabeth in wedding dress, 1947.

(Des Walt Disney Company. Litho Questa)

1988 (13 Apr). *Olympic Games, Seoul. Multicoloured designs as T* **331** *of Grenada, showing Walt Disney cartoon characters as Olympic competitors. P* 14×13½.
933 1 c. Minnie Mouse as rhythmic gymnast (*horiz*) 10 10
934 2 c. Pete and Goofy as pankration wrestlers (*horiz*) 10 10
935 3 c. Huey and Dewey as synchronized swimmers (*horiz*) 10 10
936 4 c. Huey, Dewey and Louey in hoplite race (*horiz*) 10 10
937 5 c. Clarabelle and Daisy Duck playing baseball (*horiz*) 10 10
938 10 c. Goofy and Donald Duck in horse race (*horiz*) 10 10
939 $6 Donald Duck and Uncle Scrooge McDuck windsurfing (*horiz*) .. .. 4·50 5·50
940 $7 Mickey Mouse in chariot race (*horiz*) .. 4·75 5·50
933/40 .. .. *Set of* 8 9·00 10·00
MS941 Two sheets, each 127×101 mm. (a) $5 Mickey Mouse throwing discus in pentathlon. (b) $5 Donald Duck playing tennis. P 13½×14
Set of 2 *sheets* 7·00 8·50

(Des J. Martin. Litho Questa)

1988 (3 May). *World Scout Jamboree, Australia. T* **92** *and similar multicoloured designs. P* 14.

942 50 c. Type **92** 50 35
943 70 c. Canoeing 60 50
944 $1 Cooking over campfire (*horiz*) .. 70 65
945 $3 Scouts around campfire (*horiz*) .. 2·00 3·00
942/5 .. .. *Set of* 4 3·50 4·00
MS946 110×77 mm. $5 Erecting tent (*horiz*) .. 3·50 4·50

(Des Mary Walters. Litho Questa)

1988 (31 May). *Birds. Designs as T* **334** *of Grenada, but horiz. Multicoloured. P* 14.

947 20 c. Yellow-crowned Night Heron .. 30 25
948 25 c. Brown Pelican 30 25
949 45 c. Audubon's Shearwater 40 35
950 60 c. Red-footed Booby 50 45
951 70 c. Bridled Tern 55 50
952 90 c. Red-billed Tropic Bird 70 70
953 $3 Blue-winged Teal .. .. .. 1·75 2·25
954 $4 Sora .. .. 2·00 2·75
947/54 .. .. *Set of* 8 6·00 6·75
MS955 Two sheets, each 105×75 mm. (a) $5 Purple-throated Carib. (b) $5 Little Blue Heron *Set of* 2 *sheets* 4·75 6·50

(Litho Questa)

1988 (15 June). *500th Birth Anniv of Titian (artist). Vert designs as T* **238** *of Antigua. Multicoloured. P* 13½×14.

956 15 c. "Man with Blue Eyes" 15 15
957 30 c. "The Three Ages of Man" (detail) .. 20 20
958 60 c. "Don Diego Mendoza" 35 35
959 75 c. "Emperor Charles V seated" .. 50 50
960 $1 "A Young Man in a Fur" 60 60
961 $2 "Tobias and the Angel" .. .. 1·10 1·40
962 $3 "Pietro Bembo" .. .. .. 1·60 1·90
963 $4 "Pier Luigi Farnese" .. .. 1·75 2·25
956/63 .. .. *Set of* 8 5·50 6·50
MS964 110×95 mm. (a) $5 "Sacred and Profane Love" (detail). (b) $5 "Venus and Adonis" (detail) *Set of* 2 *sheets* 7·00 8·00

(Des W. Hanson. Litho Questa)

1988 (1 July). *Airships. Multicoloured designs as T* **336** *of Grenada. P* 14.

965 10 c. LZ-129 *Hindenburg* over Sugarloaf Mountain, Rio de Janeiro, 1937 (*horiz*) 20 20
966 20 c. LZ-129 *Hindenburg* over New York, 1937 (*horiz*) 30 30
967 30 c. U.S. Navy "K" Class airships on Atlantic escort duty, 1944 (*horiz*) .. 35 35
968 40 c. LZ-129 *Hindenburg* approaching Lakehurst, 1937 .. .. .. 45 45
969 60 c. LZ-127 *Graf Zeppelin* and LZ-129 *Hindenburg* over Germany, 1936 .. 60 60
970 70 c. LZ-129 *Hindenburg* and ZR-3 *Los Angeles* moored at Lakehurst, 1936 (*horiz*) 65 70
971 $1 LZ-130 *Graf Zeppelin II* over Dover, 1939 .. .. 80 85
972 $2 LZ-8 *Ersatz Deutschland* on scheduled passenger flight, 1912 (*horiz*) .. 1·40 1·60
973 $3 LZ-127 *Graf Zeppelin* over Dome of the Rock, Jerusalem, 1931 (*horiz*) .. 1·90 2·25
974 $4 LZ-129 *Hindenburg* over Olympic stadium, Berlin, 1936 (*horiz*) .. 2·00 2·25
965/74 .. .. *Set of* 10 7·75 8·50
MS975 Two sheets (a) 76×95 mm. $5 LZ-127 *Graf Zeppelin*, 1933. (b) 95×76 mm. $5 LZ-127 *Graf Zeppelin*, 1931 (*horiz*) .. *Set of* 2 *sheets* 8·00 10·00

93 Bambi and his Mother

(Des Walt Disney Co. Litho Questa)

1988 (25 July). *Disney Animal Cartoon Films. T* **93** *and similar designs. P* 14×13½.

976/1029 30 c.×54 multicoloured .. *Set of* 54 14·00 15·00
MS1030 Six sheets, each 127×102 mm. $5×6 multicoloured. P 14×13½ (*horiz*) or 13½×14 (*vert*) .. .. *Set of* 6 *sheets* 28·00 30·00

Nos. 976/1029 (issued as six sheetlets each of nine different designs) and No. **MS**1030 depict scenes from *Bambi, Dumbo* ($5 vert), *Lady and The Tramp* ($5 vert), *The Aristocats, The Fox and the Hound* and *101 Dalmatians*.

(Des Walt Disney Co. Litho Questa)

1988 (1 Aug). *"Sydpex '88" National Stamp Exhibition, Sydney and 60th Birthday of Mickey Mouse. Horiz designs as T* **337** *of Grenada. Multicoloured. P* 14×13½.

1031 1 c. Mickey Mouse conducting at Sydney Opera House 10 10
1032 2 c. Mickey Mouse and Donald Duck at Ayers Rock 10 10
1033 3 c. Goofy and Mickey Mouse on sheep station 10 10
1034 4 c. Goofy and Mickey Mouse at Lone Pine Koala Sanctuary 10 10
1035 5 c. Mickey Mouse, Donald Duck and Goofy playing Australian football .. 10 10
1036 10 c. Mickey Mouse and Goofy camel racing 10 10
1037 $5 Donald Duck and his nephews bowling .. .. 4·50 5·00
1038 $6 Mickey Mouse with America's Cup trophy and *Australia II* (yacht) .. 5·50 6·00
1031/8 .. .. *Set of* 8 9·50 10·50
MS1039 Two sheets, each 127×102 mm. (a) $5 Goofy diving on Great Barrier Reef. (b) $5 Donald Duck, Mickey and Minnie Mouse at beach barbecue .. .. .. *Set of* 2 *sheets* 7·50 9·50

(Des W. Wright. Litho Questa)

1988 (30 Sept). *Flowering Trees and Shrubs. Multicoloured designs as T* **339** *of Grenada. P* 14.

1040 10 c. Potato Tree (*vert*) 15 15
1041 20 c. Wild Cotton 15 15
1042 30 c. Shower of Gold (*vert*) 20 20
1043 60 c. Napoleon's Button (*vert*) 35 30
1044 90 c. Geiger Tree 60 70
1045 $1 Fern Tree 70 80
1046 $2 French Cashew .. .. .. 1·25 2·00
1047 $4 Amherstia (*vert*) .. .. .. 2·00 3·00
1040/7 .. .. *Set of* 8 5·00 6·50
MS1048 Two sheets, each 117×88 mm. (a) $5 African Tulip Tree (*vert*). (b) $5 Swamp Immortelle .. .. .. *Set of* 2 *sheets* 4·25 5·50

(Des W. Wright. Litho B.D.T.)

1988 (7 Oct). *Cars. Vert designs as T* **335** *of Grenada. Multicoloured. P* 13.

1049 $2 Doble "Series E", 1925 .. .. 1·25 1·25
a. Sheetlet. Nos. 1049/58 .. .. 11·00
1050 $2 Alvis "12/50", 1926 .. .. 1·25 1·25
1051 $2 Sunbeam 3-litre, 1927 .. .. 1·25 1·25
1052 $2 Franklin "Airman", 1928 .. .. 1·25 1·25
1053 $2 Delage "D8S", 1929 .. .. 1·25 1·25
1054 $2 Mors, 1897 .. .. .. 1·25 1·25
1055 $2 Peerless "Green Dragon", 1904 .. 1·25 1·25
1056 $2 Pope-Hartford, 1909 .. .. 1·25 1·25
1057 $2 Daniels "Submarine Speedster", 1920 1·25 1·25
1058 $2 McFarlan 9.3 litre, 1922 .. .. 1·25 1·25
1059 $2 Frazer Nash "Lemans" replica, 1949 1·25 1·25
a. Sheetlet. Nos. 1059/68 .. .. 11·00
1060 $2 Pegaso "Z102", 1953 .. .. 1·25 1·25
1061 $2 Siata "Spyder V-8", 1953 .. .. 1·25 1·25
1062 $2 Kurtis-Offenhauser, 1953 .. .. 1·25 1·25
1063 $2 Kaiser-Darrin, 1954 .. .. 1·25 1·25
1064 $2 Tracta, 1930 .. .. .. 1·25 1·25
1065 $2 Maybach "Zeppelin", 1932 .. .. 1·25 1·25
1066 $2 Railton "Light Sports", 1934 .. 1·25 1·25
1067 $2 Hotchkiss, 1936 .. .. .. 1·25 1·25
1068 $2 Mercedes-Benz "W163", 1939 .. 1·25 1·25
1069 $2 Aston Martin "Vantage V8", 1982 .. 1·25 1·25
a. Sheetlet. Nos. 1069/78 .. .. 11·00
1070 $2 Porsche "956", 1982 .. .. 1·25 1·25
1071 $2 Lotus "Esprit Turbo", 1983 .. .. 1·25 1·25
1072 $2 McLaren "MP4/2", 1984 .. .. 1·25 1·25
1073 $2 Mercedes-Benz "190E 2.3-16", 1985 .. 1·25 1·25
1074 $2 Ferrari "250 GT Lusso", 1963 .. 1·25 1·25
1075 $2 Porsche "904", 1964 .. .. 1·25 1·25
1076 $2 Volvo "P1800", 1967 .. .. 1·25 1·25
1077 $2 McLaren-Chevrolet "M8D", 1970 .. 1·25 1·25
1078 $2 Jaguar "XJ6", 1981 .. .. 1·25 1·25
1049/78 .. .. .. *Set of* 30 32·00 32·00

Nos. 1049/58, 1059/68 and 1069/78 were each printed together, *se-tenant*, in sheetlets of 10.

(Des Walt Disney Co. Litho Questa)

1988 (1 Dec). *"Mickey's Christmas Parade". Multicoloured designs as T* **246** *of Antigua showing Walt Disney cartoon characters. P* 13½×14.

1079 $1 Dumbo 55 65
a. Sheetlet. Nos. 1079/86 .. .. 4·00
1080 $1 Goofy as Father Christmas 55 65
1081 $1 Minnie Mouse waving from window .. 55 65
1082 $1 Clarabelle, Mordie and Ferdie watching parade 55 65
1083 $1 Donald Duck's nephews 55 65
1084 $1 Donald Duck as drummer 55 65
1085 $1 Toy soldiers 55 65
1086 $1 Mickey Mouse on wooden horse .. 55 65
1079/86 .. .. *Set of* 8 4·00 4·75
MS1087 Two sheets, each 127 × 102 mm. (a) $7 Peter Pan and Captain Hook on float (*horiz*). (b) $7 Mickey Mouse as Father Christmas and Donald Duck in carnival train (*horiz*). P 14 × 13½ .. .. .. *Set of* 2 *sheets* 10·00 11·00

94 Middleweight Boxing (Gold, Henry Maske, East Germany)

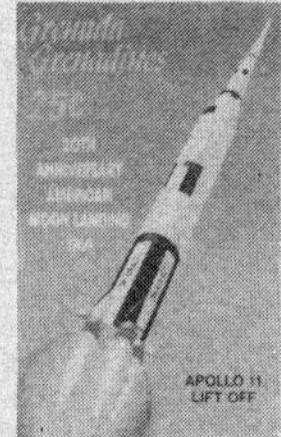

95 Launch of "Apollo 11"

(Des L. Fried. Litho B.D.T.)

1989 (13 Apr). *Olympic Medal Winners, Seoul* (1988). *T* **94** *and similar horiz designs. Multicoloured. P* 14.

1088 15 c. Type **94** 20 20
1089 50 c. Freestyle wrestling (130 kg) (Bronze, Andreas Schroeder, East Germany) .. 40 40
1090 60 c. Women's team gymnastics (Bronze, East Germany) 50 50
1091 75 c. Platform diving (Gold, Greg Louganis, U.S.A.) 55 55
1092 $1 Freestyle wrestling (52 kg) (Gold, Mitsuru Sato, Japan) 70 70
1093 $2 Men's freestyle 4×200 metres relay swimming (Bronze, West Germany) .. 1·25 1·50
1094 $3 Men's 5000 metres (Silver, Dieter Baumann, West Germany) .. .. 1·60 1·75
1095 $4 Women's heptathlon (Gold, Jackie Joyner-Kersee, U.S.A.) .. .. 2·00 2·5
1088/95 .. .. *Set of* 8 6·50 7·2
MS1096 Two sheets, each 70×100 mm. (a) $6 Weightlifting (67.5 kg) (Gold, Joachim Kunz, East Germany). (b) $6 Team Three-Day Event (Gold, West Germany) .. .. *Set of* 2 *sheets* 6·00 7·5

(Litho Questa)

1989 (15 May). *Japanese Art. Paintings by Hiroshige. Hori designs as T* **250** *of Antigua. Multicoloured. P* 14×13½.

1097 15 c. "Crossing the Oi at Shimada by Ferry" 25 2
1098 20 c. "Daimyo and Entourage at Arai" .. 30 3
1099 45 c. "Cargo Portage through Goyu" .. 50 5
1100 75 c. "Snowfall at Fujigawa" 75 7
1101 $1 "Horses for the Emperor at Chirifu" .. 85 8
1102 $2 "Rainfall at Tsuchiyama" .. .. 1·60 1·6
1103 $3 "An Inn at Ishibe" .. .. .. 2·25 2·2
1104 $4 "On the Shore of Lake Biwa at Otsu" 2·75 2·7
1097/104 .. .. .. *Set of* 8 8·25 8·2
MS1105 Two sheets, each 102×78 mm. (a) $5 "Fishing Village of Yokkaichi on the Mie". (b) $5 "Pilgrimage to Atsuta Shrine at Miya" *Set of* 2 *sheets* 4·75 6·5

Nos. 1097/104 were each printed in sheetlets of 10 containin two horizontal strips of 5 stamps separated by printed label commemorating Emperor Hirohito.

(Des D. Bruckner. Litho B.D.T.)

1989 (12 June). *World Cup Football Championship, Ital (1990) (1st issue). Multicoloured designs as T* **252** *of Antigua P* 14.

1106 15 c. World Cup trophy 40 2
1107 20 c. Flags of Argentina (winners 1986) and International Federation of Football Associations (F.I.F.A.) (*horiz*) .. 40 2
1108 45 c. Franz Beckenbauer (West Germany) with World Cup, 1974 .. .. 60 3
1109 75 c. Flags of Italy (winners 1982) and F.I.F.A. (*horiz*) 75 5
1110 $1 Péle (Brazil) with Jules Rimet trophy 90 7
1111 $2 Flags of West Germany (winners 1974) and F.I.F.A. (*horiz*) .. .. 1·40 1·7
1112 $3 Flags of Brazil (winners 1970) and F.I.F.A. (*horiz*) .. .. .. 1·75 2·5
1113 $4 Jules Rimet trophy and Brazil players 1·90 2·5
1106/13 .. .. *Set of* 8 7·25 8·0
MS1114 (a) 100×81 mm. $6 Goalkeeper (*horiz*). (b) 66×95 mm. $6 Péle with Jules Rimet trophy *Set of* 2 *sheets* 7·50 8·5

See also Nos. 1285/9.

(Des W. Wright. Litho B.D.T.)

1989 (28 June). *North American Railway Locomotives. Ver designs as T* **342** *of Grenada. Multicoloured. P* 13.

1115 $2 Morris & Essex Railroad *Dover*, 1841, U.S.A. .. .. 1·50 1·5
a. Sheetlet. Nos. 1115/24 .. .. 13·00
1116 $2 Baltimore & Ohio Railroad No. 57 *Memnon*, 1848, U.S.A. .. .. 1·50 1·5
1117 $2 Camden & Amboy Railroad *John Stevens*, 1849, U.S.A. .. .. 1·50 1·5
1118 $2 Lawrence Machine Shop *Lawrence*, 1853, U.S.A. .. .. .. 1·50 1·5
1119 $2 South Carolina Railroad *James S. Corry*, 1859, U.S.A. .. .. 1·50 1·5
1120 $2 Mine Hill & Schuylkill Haven Railroad flexible beam No. 3, 1860, U.S.A. .. 1·50 1·5
1121 $2 Delaware, Lackawanna & Western Railroad *Montrose*, 1861, U.S.A. .. 1·50 1·5
1122 $2 Central Pacific Railroad No. 68 *Pequop*, 1868, U.S.A. .. .. .. 1·50 1·5
1123 $2 Boston & Providence Railroad *Daniel Nason*, 1863, U.S.A. .. .. 1·50 1·5
1124 $2 Morris & Essex Railroad *Joe Scranton*, 1870, U.S.A. .. .. .. 1·50 1·5
1125 $2 Central Railroad of New Jersey No. 124, 1871, U.S.A. .. .. 1·50 1·5
a. Sheetlet. Nos. 1125/34 .. .. 13·00
1126 $2 Baldwin tramway steam locomotive, 1876, U.S.A. .. .. .. 1·50 1·5
1127 $2 Lackawanna & Bloomsburg Railroad *Luzerne*, 1878, U.S.A. .. .. 1·50 1·5
1128 $2 Central Mexican Railroad No. 150, 1892 1·50 1·5
1129 $2 Denver, South Park & Pacific Railroad No. 15 *Breckenridge*, 1879, U.S.A. .. 1·50 1·5
1130 $2 Miles Planting & Manufacturing Company plantation locomotive *Daisy*, 1894, U.S.A. .. .. .. 1·50 1·5
1131 $2 Central of Georgia Railroad Baldwin 854 No. 1136, 1895, U.S.A. .. .. 1·50 1·5
1132 $2 Savannah, Florida & Western Railroad No. 111, 1900, U.S.A. .. .. 1·50 1·5
1133 $2 Douglas, Gilmore & Company contractors locomotive No. 3, 1902, U.S.A. .. 1·50 1·5
1134 $2 Lehigh Valley Coal Company compressed-air locomotive No. 900, 1903, U.S.A. .. .. .. 1·50 1·5
1135 $2 Louisiana & Texas Railroad McKeen motor locomotive, 1908, U.S.A. .. 1·50 1·5
a. Sheetlet. Nos. 1135/44 .. .. 13·00
1136 $2 Clear Lake Lumber Company Type B Climax locomotive No. 6, 1910, U.S.A. 1·50 1·5
1137 $2 Blue Jay Lumber Company Heisler locomotive No. 10, 1912, U.S.A. .. 1·50 1·5
1138 $2 Stewartstown Railroad petrol locomotive No. 6, 1920s, U.S.A. .. .. 1·50 1·5
1139 $2 Bangor & Aroostock Railroad Class G No. 186, 1921, U.S.A. .. .. 1·50 1·5
1140 $2 Hammond Lumber Company Mallet locomotive No. 6, 1923, U.S.A. .. 1·50 1·5
1141 $2 Central Railway of New Jersey diesel locomotive No. 1000, 1925, U.S.A. .. 1·50 1·5
1142 $2 Atchison Topeka & Santa Fe Railroad "Super Chief" diesel express, 1935, U.S.A. .. .. 1·50 1·5
1143 $2 Norfolk & Western Railroad Class Y-6, 1948, U.S.A. .. .. .. 1·50 1·5

.44 $2 Boston & Maine Railroad Budd diesel railcar, 1949, U.S.A. .. .. .. 1·50 1·50
.15/44 .. .. *Set of* 30 38·00 38·00
Nos. 1115/24, 1125/34 and 1135/44 were each printed gether, *se-tenant*, in sheetlets of 10.

(Des Walt Disney Co. Litho Questa)

989 (7 July). *"Philexfrance 89" International Stamp Exhibition, Paris. Multicoloured designs as T* **251** *of Antigua showing Walt Disney cartoon characters in Paris. P* 14×13½ *(horiz) or* 13½×14 *(vert).*

145 1 c. Mickey Mouse and Donald Duck at Ecole Militaire inflating balloon .. 10 10
146 2 c. Mickey and Minnie Mouse on river boat passing Conciergerie 10 10
147 3 c. Mickey Mouse at Hotel de Ville *(vert)* 10 10
148 4 c. Mickey Mouse at Genie of the Bastille monument *(vert)* 10 10
149 5 c. Mickey and Minnie Mouse arriving at Opera House 10 10
150 10 c. Mickey and Minnie Mouse on tandem in Luxembourg Gardens 10 10
151 $5 Mickey Mouse in aeroplane over L'Arch de la Defense *(vert)* .. .. 5·50 6·50
152 $6 Mickey Mouse at Place Vendome *(vert)* .. .. 5·50 6·50
145/52 .. .. *Set of* 8 10·00 12·00
IS1153 Two sheets, each 127×102 mm. (a) $6 Mickey and Minnie Mouse on scooter in Place de la Concorde. (b) $6 Donald Duck, Mickey and Minnie Mouse in balloon over Versailles. P 14×13½ .. .. .. *Set of* 2 *sheets* 11·00 13·00

(Des L. Birmingham. Litho Questa)

989 (20 July). *20th Anniv of First Manned Landing on Moon. T* **95** *and similar multicoloured designs. P* 14.

154 25 c. Type **95** 30 30
155 50 c. Splashdown *(horiz)* 50 50
156 60 c. Modules in space 60 60
157 75 c. Aldrin setting up experiment *(horiz)* 70 70
158 $1 "Apollo 11" leaving Earth orbit *(horiz)* 80 80
159 $2 Moving "Apollo 11" to launch site .. 1·60 1·90
160 $3 Lunar module *Eagle* leaving Moon *(horiz)* .. .. 2·00 2·50
161 $4 *Eagle* landing on Moon .. .. 2·25 2·75
154/61 .. .. *Set of* 8 8·00 9·00
IS1162 (a) 71×100 mm. $5 Armstrong stepping onto Moon. (b) 101×72 mm. $5 Armstrong's footprint on Moon .. .. *Set of* 2 *sheets* 6·50 8·00

(Des J. Cooter. Litho B.D.T.)

989 (17 Aug). *Fungi. Vert designs as T* **348** *of Grenada. Multicoloured. P* 14.

163 6 c. *Agaricus purpurellus* (incorrectly inscr *Collybia aurea)* 35 25
164 10 c. *Podaxis pistillaris* 35 25
165 20 c. *Hygrocybe firma* 55 45
166 30 c. *Agaricus rufoaurantiacus* 65 55
167 75 c. *Leptonia howellii* .. .. .. 1·40 1·40
168 $2 *Marasmiellus purpureus* .. .. 2·50 2·75
169 $3 *Marasmius trinitatis* .. .. 3·00 3·25
170 $4 *Collybia aurea* (incorrectly inscr *Hygrocybe martinicensis)* .. .. 3·25 3·50
163/70 .. .. *Set of* 8 11·00 11·00
IS1171 Two sheets, each 56×71 mm. (a) $6 *Lentinus crinitus* (incorrectly inscr *Agaricus purpurellus*). (b) $6 *Hygrocybe martinicensis* (incorrectly inscr *Lentinus crinitus)* *Set of* 2 *sheets* 12·00 13·00

(Des Deborah Dudley Max. Litho B.D.T.)

989 (2 Oct). *Butterflies. Horiz designs as T* **350** *of Grenada. Multicoloured. P* 14.

172 25 c. *Battus polydamas* (inscr *"Papilio androgeus")* 40 40
173 35 c. *Phoebis sennae* 45 45
174 45 c. *Hamadryas feronia* 55 55
175 50 c. *Cynthia cardui* 55 55
176 75 c. *Ascia monuste* 80 80
177 90 c. *Eurema lisa* 90 90
178 $2 *Aphrissa statira* .. .. .. 2·00 2·00
179 $3 *Hypolimnas misippus* .. .. 2·50 2·50
172/9 .. .. *Set of* 8 7·50 7·50
MS1180 Two sheets, each 87×115 mm. (a) $6 *Anartia amathea*. (b) $6 *Pseudolycaena marsyas* *Set of* 2 *sheets* 9·00 11·00

96 Ethel Barrymore

97 Buddy Holly

(Des J. Genzo. Litho B.D.T.)

1989 (9 Oct). *425th Birth Anniv of Shakespeare. Shakespearean Actors. T* **96** *and similar horiz designs. Multicoloured. P* 14.

1181 15 c. Type **96** 25 25
1182 $1.10, Richard Burton .. .. .. 1·25 1·25
1183 $2 John Barrymore .. .. .. 2·00 2·00
1184 $3 Paul Robeson .. .. .. 2·25 2·25
1181/4 .. .. *Set of* 4 5·25 5·25
MS1185 103×77 mm. $6 Bando Tamasaburo and Nakamura Kanzaburo .. .. .. 4·50 5·50

(Des J. Genzo. Litho B.D.T.)

1989 (9 Oct). *Musicians. T* **97** *and similar vert designs. Multicoloured. P* 14.

1186 10 c. Type **97** 35 25
1187 25 c. Jimmy Hendrix 55 40
1188 75 c. Mighty Sparrow 70 70
1189 $4 Katsutoji Kineya .. .. .. 3·00 4·00
1186/9 .. .. *Set of* 4 4·25 4·75
MS1190 103×77 mm. $6 Kurt Weill .. .. 4·25 4·75

(Des D. Miller. Litho Questa)

1989 (16 Oct). *500th Anniv of Discovery of America by Columbus* (1992) *(2nd issue). Pre-Columbian Arawak Society. Vert designs as T* **247** *of Antigua. Multicoloured. P* 14.

1191 15 c. Arawaks canoeing 25 25
1192 75 c. Family and campfire 75 75
1193 90 c. Using stone tools 95 95
1194 $3 Eating and drinking .. .. 2·50 3·00
1191/4 .. .. *Set of* 4 4·00 4·50
MS1195 84×87 mm. $6 Making fire .. .. 3·50 4·25

(Des Walt Disney Co. Litho Questa)

1989 (17 Nov). *"World Stamp Expo '89" International Stamp Exhibition, Washington. Multicoloured designs as T* **352** *of Grenada showing Walt Disney cartoon characters illustrating proverbs from* Poor Richard's Almanack. *P* 14×13½.

1196 1 c. Scrooge McDuck with gold coins in sinking boat 10 10
1197 2 c. Robin Hood shooting apple off Friar Tuck 10 10
1198 3 c. Winnie the Pooh with honey .. 10 10
1199 4 c. Goofy, Minnie Mouse and Donald Duck exercising 10 10
1200 5 c. Pinnochio holding Jimminy Cricket 10 10
1201 6 c. Huey and Dewey putting up wallpaper 10 10
1202 8 c. Mickey Mouse asleep in storm .. 15 10
1203 10 c. Mickey Mouse as Benjamin Franklin selling *Pennsylvania Gazette* .. 15 10
1204 $5 Mickey Mouse with chicken, recipe book and egg .. .. .. 4·00 5·00
1205 $6 Mickey Mouse missing carriage .. 4·50 5·00
1196/1205 .. .. .. *Set of* 10 8·50 9·50
MS1206 Two sheets, each 127×102 mm. (a) $6 Mickey Mouse bowing. P 14×13½. (b) $6 Mickey Mouse delivering basket of food *(vert)*. P 13½×14 .. .. .. *Set of* 2 *sheets* 10·50 11·00

(Litho Questa)

1990 (4 Jan). *Christmas. Paintings by Rubens. Vert designs as T* **259** *of Antigua. Multicoloured. P* 14.

1207 10 c. "The Annunciation" 35 15
1208 15 c. "The Flight of the Holy Family into Egypt" 40 15
1209 25 c. "The Presentation in the Temple" 55 15
1210 45 c. "The Holy Family under the Apple Tree" 70 25
1211 $2 "Madonna and Child with Saints" 2·00 2·50
1212 $4 "The Virgin and Child enthroned with Saints" .. .. 3·00 4·00
1213 $5 "The Holy Family" .. .. .. 3·00 4·00
1207/13 .. .. *Set of* 7 9·00 10·00
MS1214 Two sheets, each 70×95 mm. (a) $5 "The Adoration of the Magi" (sketch). (b) $5 "The Adoration of the Magi" .. *Set of* 2 *sheets* 11·00 12·00

(Des L. Nelson. Litho Questa)

1990 (6 Mar). *"EXPO 90" International Garden and Greenery Exhibition, Osaka. Caribbean Orchids. Vert designs as T* **354** *of Grenada. Multicoloured. P* 14.

1215 15 c. *Brassocattleya* Thalie 30 30
1216 20 c. *Odontocidium* Tigersun 35 35
1217 50 c. *Odontioda* Hambuhren 55 55
1218 75 c. *Paphiopedilum* Delrosi 75 75
1219 $1 *Vuylstekeara* Yokara 95 95
1220 $2 *Paphiopedilum* Geelong .. .. 1·75 2·00
1221 $3 *Wilsonara* Tigerwood .. .. 2·00 2·25
1222 $4 *Cymbidium* Ormoulu .. .. 2·50 2·75
1215/22 .. .. *Set of* 8 8·25 9·00
MS1223 Two sheets, each 98×68 mm. (a) $6 *Odontonia* Sappho. (b) $6 *Cymbidium* Vieux Rose .. .. *Set of* 2 *sheets* 9·50 10·00

(Des Mary Walters. Litho Questa)

1990 (16 Mar). *500th Anniv of Discovery of America by Columbus* (1992) *(3rd issue). New World Natural History – Insects. Designs as T* **260** *of Antigua, but horiz. Multicoloured. P* 14.

1224 35 c. *Dynastes hercules* (beetle) 35 35
1225 40 c. *Chalcolepidius porcatus* (beetle) .. 35 35
1226 50 c. *Acrocinus longimanus* (beetle) .. 40 40
1227 60 c. *Battus polydamas* (butterfly) .. 75 75
1228 $1 *Orthemis ferruginea* (skimmer) .. 95 95
1229 $2 *Psiloptera variolosa* (beetle) .. .. 1·60 1·75
1230 $3 *Hypolimnas misippus* (butterfly) .. 2·50 2·75
1231 $4 Scarab Beetle .. .. .. 2·50 2·75
1224/31 .. .. *Set of* 8 8·50 9·00
MS1232 Two sheets, each 102×70 mm. (a) $6 *Calpodes ethlius* (butterfly). (b) $6 *Danaus plexippus* (butterfly) .. .. *Set of* 2 *sheets* 8·50 9·50

(Des J. Barbaris. Litho B.D.T.)

1990 (3 Apr). *Wildlife. Horiz designs as T* **254** *of Antigua. Multicoloured. P* 14.

1233 5 c. West Indies Giant Rice Rat .. 20 20
1234 25 c. Agouti 35 35
1235 30 c. Humpback Whale 70 65
1236 40 c. Pilot Whale 70 65
1237 $1 Spotted Dolphin 95 95
1238 $2 Egyptian Mongoose .. .. 1·75 2·00
1239 $3 Brazilian Tree Porcupine .. .. 2·25 2·75
1240 $4 American Manatee .. .. .. 2·50 3·00
1233/40 .. .. *Set of* 8 8·50 9·50
MS1241 Two sheets, each 107×80 mm. (a) $6 Caribbean Monk Seal. (b) $6 Egyptian Mongoose *(different)* .. .. .. *Set of* 2 *sheets* 8·00 9·00

(Des W. Wright. Litho Questa)

1990 (30 Apr). *50th Anniv of Second World War. Horiz designs as T* **274** *of Antigua. Multicoloured. P* 14.

1242 6 c. British Tanks in France, 1939 .. 30 30
1243 10 c. Operation "Crusader", North Africa, 1941 .. .. 30 30
1244 20 c. Retreat of the Afrika Corps, 1942 .. 40 40
1245 45 c. American landing on Aleutian Islands, 1943 .. .. .. 50 50
1246 50 c. U.S. marines landing on Tarawa, 1943 55 55
1247 60 c. U.S. army entering Rome, 1944 .. 60 60
1248 75 c. U.S. tanks crossing River Seine, 1944 70 70
1249 $1 Battle of the Bulge, 1944 .. .. 95 95
1250 $5 American infantry in Italy, 1945 .. 3·00 3·50
1251 $6 Boeing B-29 Superfortress *Enola Gay* dropping atomic bomb on Hiroshima, 1945 .. .. 3·50 3·50
1242/51 .. .. *Set of* 10 9·75 10·00
MS1252 112×84 mm. $6 St. Paul's Cathedral in London Blitz, 1940 .. .. 3·75 4·25

(Des Walt Disney Company. Litho Questa)

1990 (3 May). *"Stamp World London 90" International Stamp Exhibition (1st issue). Multicoloured designs as T* **193** *of Gambia showing Walt Disney cartoon characters at Shakespeare's sites. P* 14×13½ *(15, 60 c., $1, $5) or* 13½×14 *(others).*

1253 15 c. Daisy Duck at Ann Hathaway's Cottage *(horiz)* 40 20
1254 30 c. Minnie and Bill Mouse at Shakespeare's birthplace, Stratford 55 35
1255 50 c. Minnie Mouse in front of Mary Arden's house, Wilmcote 75 70
1256 60 c. Mickey Mouse leaning on hedge in New Place gardens, Stratford *(horiz)* 90 90
1257 $1 Mickey Mouse walking in New Place gardens, Stratford *(horiz)* .. 1·25 1·25
1258 $2 Mickey Mouse carrying books in Scholars Lane, Stratford .. .. 2·25 2·50
1259 $4 Mickey Mouse and Royal Shakespeare Theatre, Stratford .. .. .. 3·25 4·00
1260 $5 Ludwig von Drake teaching Mickey Mouse at the Stratford Grammar School *(horiz)* .. .. .. 3·25 4·00
1253/60 .. .. *Set of* 8 11·50 12·50
MS1261 Two sheets, each 126×101 mm. (a) $6 Mickey Mouse as Shakespeare. P 13½×14. (b) $6 Mickey and Minnie Mouse in rowing boat on River Avon, Stratford *(horiz)*. P 14×13½ *Set of* 2 *sheets* 11·00 12·00

(Des Young Phillips Studio. Litho Questa)

1990 (5 July). *90th Birthday of Queen Elizabeth the Queen Mother. Vert designs as T* **194** *of Gambia, showing photographs, 1970–79. Multicoloured. P* 14.

1262 $2 Queen Mother in pink hat and coat .. 1·10 1·40
a. Strip of 3. Nos. 1262/4 .. .. 3·00
1263 $2 Prince Charles and Queen Mother at Garter ceremony .. .. .. 1·10 1·40
1264 $2 Queen Mother in blue floral outfit .. 1·10 1·40
1262/4 .. .. *Set of* 3 3·00 3·75
MS1265 90×75 mm. $6 Queen Mother in Garter robes .. .. 4·00 5·00
Nos. 1262/4 were printed together, horizontally and vertically *se-tenant*, in sheetlets of 9 (3×3).

(Des M. Pollard. Litho Questa)

1990 (12 July). *"Stamp World London 90" International Stamp Exhibition (2nd issue). Sheet 97×75 mm containing horiz design as T* **356** *of Grenada. P* 14.

MS1266 $6 blue-green .. .. 5·50 6·50
Design:—$6 Map of South America and logo.

(Des J. Anderton. Litho B.D.T.)

1990 (10 Sept). *Birds. Multicoloured designs as T* **358** *of Grenada, but vert. P* 14.

1267 25 c. Yellow-bellied Seedeater 30 30
1268 45 c. Carib Grackle 50 50
1269 50 c. Black-whiskered Vireo 55 55
1270 75 c. Bananaquit 70 70
1271 $1 White-collared Swift 95 95
1272 $2 Yellow-billed Elaenia .. .. 1·50 1·50
1273 $3 Blue-hooded Euphonia .. .. 2·00 2·00
1274 $5 Eared Dove .. .. 3·25 3·25
1267/74 .. .. *Set of* 8 8·75 8·75
MS1275 Two sheets, each 101×72 mm. (a) $6 Mangrove Cuckoo. (b) $6 Scaly-breasted Thrasher .. .. .. *Set of* 2 *sheets* 8·50 10·00

(Des Deborah Dudley Max. Litho Questa)

1990 (17 Sept). *Crustaceans. Horiz designs as T* **359** *of Grenada. Multicoloured. P* 14.

1276 10 c. Slipper Lobster 20 20
1277 25 c. Green Reef Crab 30 30
1278 65 c. Caribbean Lobsterette 60 60
1279 75 c. Blind Deep Sea Lobster 70 70
1280 $1 Flattened Crab 95 95
1281 $2 Ridged Slipper Lobster .. .. 1·75 1·75
1282 $3 Land Crab .. .. 2·25 2·25
1283 $4 Mountain Crab .. .. .. 2·50 2·50
1276/83 .. .. *Set of* 8 8·25 8·25
MS1284 Two sheets, each 108×76 mm. (a) $6 Caribbean King Crab. (b) $6 Purse Crab *Set of* 2 *sheets* 8·00 9·00

98 Lineker, England

99 Angel with Star and Lantern

(Des Young Phillips Studio. Litho Questa)

1990 (24 Sept). *World Cup Football Championship, Italy* (2nd *issue*). *T* **98** *and similar vert designs. Multicoloured. P* 14.
1285 15 c. Type **98** 25 25
1286 45 c. Burruchaga, Argentina 45 45
1287 $2 Hysen, Sweden .. .. 1·75 2·25
1288 $4 Sang Ho, South Korea .. .. .. 2·75 3·75
1285/8 .. .. *Set of* 4 4·75 6·00
MS1289 Two sheets, each 76×90 mm. (a) $6 Ramos, U.S.A. (b) $6 Stojkovic, Yugoslavia *Set of* 2 *sheets* 8·50 9·50

(Des B. Grout. Litho Questa)

1990 (1 Nov). *Olympic Games, Barcelona* (1992). *Vert designs as T* **268** *of Antigua. Multicoloured. P* 14.
1290 10 c. Boxing 10 10
1291 25 c. Olympic flame 20 20
1292 50 c. Football 40 40
1293 75 c. Discus throwing 60 60
1294 $1 Pole vaulting 85 85
1295 $2 Show jumping .. .. 1·75 1·75
1296 $4 Women's basketball .. .. .. 3·00 3·25
1297 $5 Men's gymnastics .. .. .. 3·00 3·25
1290/7 .. .. *Set of* 8 9·00 9·50
MS1298 Two sheets. (a) 101×70 mm. $6 Sailboards. (b) 70×101 mm. $6 Decathlon *Set of* 2 *sheets* 8·50 9·50

(Litho Questa)

1991 (31 Jan). 350*th Death Anniv of Rubens. Multicoloured designs as T* **273** *of Antigua. P* 13½×14 (*vert*) *or* 14×13½ (*horiz*).
1299 5 c. "Adam and Eve" (Eve detail) (*vert*) .. 20 20
1300 15 c. "Esther before Ahasuerus" (detail) .. 30 20
1301 25 c. "Adam and Eve" (Adam detail) (*vert*) 40 25
1302 50 c. "Expulsion from Eden" 70 60
1303 $1 "Cain slaying Abel" (detail) (*vert*) .. 1·10 1·10
1304 $2 "Lot's Flight" .. .. 1·75 2·25
1305 $4 "Samson and Delilah" (detail) .. 2·75 3·50
1306 $5 "Abraham and Melchizedek" .. 3·25 3·50
1299/306 .. .. *Set of* 8 9·50 10·50
MS1307 Two sheets, each 101×71 mm. (a) $6 "The Meeting of David and Abigail" (detail). (b) $6 "Daniel in the Lions' Den" (detail) *Set of* 2 *sheets* 7·00 8·50

(Des Mary Walters. Litho B.D.T.)

1991 (5 Feb). *Coral Reef Fishes. Horiz designs as T* **357** *of Grenada. Multicoloured. P* 14.
1308 15 c. Barred Hamlet 40 25
1309 35 c. Long-spined Squirrelfish 70 50
1310 45 c. Red-spotted Hawkfish 75 60
1311 75 c. Bigeye .. .. 1·00 1·00
1312 $1 Balloonfish ("Spiny Puffer") .. .. 1·25 1·25
1313 $2 Small-mouthed Grunt .. .. .. 2·00 2·25
1314 $3 Harlequin Bass .. .. 2·50 2·75
1315 $4 Creole Fish .. .. 3·00 3·25
1308/15 .. .. *Set of* 8 10·50 10·50
MS1316 Two sheets, each 103×72 mm. (a) $6 Copper Sweeper. (b) $6 Royal Gramma ("Fairy Basslet") .. .. *Set of* 2 *sheets* 8·50 10·00

(Litho Questa)

1991 (1 Mar). *Christmas* (1990). *Hummel Figurines. T* **99** *and similar vert designs. Multicoloured. P* 14.
1317 10 c. Type **99** 10 10
1318 15 c. Christ Child and Angel playing mandolin 15 15
1319 25 c. Shepherd 25 25
1320 50 c. Angel with trumpet and lantern .. 50 50
1321 $1 Nativity scene 95 95
1322 $2 Christ Child and Angel holding candle 1·75 2·25
1323 $4 Angel with baskets .. .. .. 2·75 3·50
1324 $5 Angels singing .. .. 3·25 3·50
1317/24 .. .. *Set of* 8 8·75 10·00
MS1325 Two sheets, each 99×122 mm. (a) 5 c. As No. 1318; 40 c. As No. 1320; 60 c. As No. 1321; $3 As No. 1324. (b) 20 c. As Type **99**; 30 c. As No. 1319; 75 c. As No. 1322; $6 As No. 1323 *Set of* 2 *sheets* 10·00 11·00

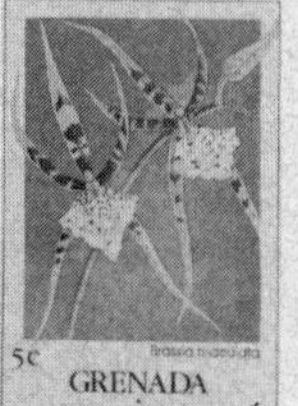

100 *Brassia maculata*

101 Donald and Daisy Duck with Solar-powered Car

(Des S. Barlowe. Litho Walsall)

1991 (1 Apr)–**92**. *Orchids. T* **100** *and similar vert designs. Multicoloured. P* 14.
1326 5 c. Type **100** 30 30
1327 10 c. *Oncidium lanceanum* 30 30
1328 15 c. *Broughtonia sanguinea* 35 20
1329 25 c. *Diacrium bicornutum* 40 20
1330 35 c. *Cattleya labiata* 40 20
1331 45 c. *Epidendrum fragrans* 50 25
1332 50 c. *Oncidium papilio* 55 30
1333 75 c. *Neocogniauxia monophylla* 70 50
1334 $1 *Epidendrum polybulbon* 80 70
1335 $2 *Spiranthes speciosa* .. .. .. 1·40 1·40
1336 $4 *Epidendrum ciliare* .. .. .. 2·25 2·75
1337 $5 *Phais tankervilliae* .. .. .. 2·50 3·00
1338 $10 *Brassia caudata* (27.11.91) .. .. 4·50 5·50
1339 $20 *Brassavola cordata* (29.6.92) .. .. 9·25 11·00
1326/39 .. .. *Set of* 14 22·00 24·00

(Des W. Wright. Litho Questa)

1991 (8 Apr). *Butterflies. Horiz designs as T* **363** *of Grenada. Multicoloured. P* 14.
1340 5 c. Crimson-patched Longwing 40 30
1341 10 c. *Morpho helena* 40 30
1342 15 c. *Morpho sulkowskyi* 55 35
1343 20 c. *Dynastor napoleon* 60 40
1344 25 c. *Pieridae callinira* 60 45
1345 30 c. *Anartia amathea* 65 50
1346 35 c. *Heliconiidae dido* 65 50
1347 45 c. *Papilionidae columbus* 75 65
1348 50 c. *Nymphalidae praeneste* 85 70
1349 60 c. *Panacea prola* .. .. 1·00 80
1350 75 c. *Dryas julia* .. .. 1·00 90
1351 $1 *Papilionidae orthosilaus* .. .. 1·25 1·10
1352 $2 *Pyrrhopyge cometes* .. .. .. 1·75 2·00
1353 $3 *Papilionidae paeon* .. .. .. 2·00 2·50
1354 $4 *Morpho cypris* .. .. 2·50 3·00
1355 $5 Choringa .. .. 3·00 3·25
1340/55 .. .. *Set of* 16 16·00 16·00
MS1356 Four sheets, each 118×80 mm. (a) $6 *Danaus plexippus*. (b) $6 *Caligo idomenides*. (c) $6 *Nymphalidae amydon*. (d) $6 *Papilio childrenae* .. .. .. *Set of* 4 *sheets* 15·00 15·00

(Des Walt Disney Co. Litho Questa)

1991 (22 Apr). *Ecology Conservation. T* **101** *and similar multicoloured designs showing Walt Disney cartoon characters. P* 14×13½.
1357 10 c. Type **101** 30 20
1358 15 c. Goofy saving water 40 20
1359 25 c. Donald and Daisy on nature hike .. 55 35
1360 45 c. Donald Duck returning chick to nest 75 55
1361 $1 Donald Duck and balloons .. .. 1·40 1·25
1362 $2 Minnie Mouse and Daisy Duck on hot day .. .. 2·25 2·50
1363 $4 Mickey's nephews cleaning beach .. 3·25 3·75
1364 $5 Donald Duck on pedal generator .. 3·25 3·75
1357/64 .. .. *Set of* 8 11·00 11·50
MS1365 Three sheets, each 127×102 mm. (a) $6 Hiawatha and felled forest. P 14×13½. (b) $6 Donald Duck recycling (*vert*). P 13½×14. (c) $6 Mickey Mouse with Arbor Day notice. P 14×13½ .. .. .. *Set of* 3 *sheets* 13·00 14·00
d. Error. Imperf (sheet) (a)) .. ..

(Des T. Agans. Litho Questa)

1991 (29 Apr). 500*th Anniv of Discovery of America by Columbus* (1992) (4*th issue*). *History of Exploration. Multicoloured designs as T* **277** *of Antigua. P* 14.
1366 15 c. Magellan's *Vitoria* rounding Cape Horn, 1519–21 .. .. .. 40 30
1367 20 c. Drake's *Golden Hind*, 1577–80 .. 40 35
1368 50 c. Cook's H.M.S. *Resolution*, 1768–71 70 60
1369 60 c. Douglas World Cruiser seaplane, 1924 70 60
1370 $1 *Sputnik I* satellite, 1957 .. .. 85 90
1371 $2 Gagarin's space flight, 1961 .. 1·50 1·75
1372 $4 Glenn's space flight, 1962 .. .. 2·50 2·75
1373 $5 Space shuttle, 1981 .. .. .. 3·00 3·25
1366/73 .. .. *Set of* 8 9·00 9·50
MS1374 Two sheets. (a) 105×78 mm. $6 Bow of *Pinta* (*vert*). (b) 78×105 mm. $6 Fleet of Columbus .. .. .. *Set of* 2 *sheets* 8·00 9·00

(Des Walt Disney Co. Litho Questa)

1991 (6 May). *"Phila Nippon '91" International Stamp Exhibition, Tokyo. Multicoloured designs as T* **279** *of Antigua showing Walt Disney cartoon characters in Japanese scenes. P* 14×13½.
1375 15 c. Minnie Mouse with silkworms (*horiz*) 30 20
1376 30 c. Mickey, Minnie, Morty and Ferdie at Torii Gate (*horiz*) 45 35
1377 50 c. Donald Duck and Mickey Mouse trying origami (*horiz*) 70 60
1378 60 c. Mickey and Minnie diving for pearls (*horiz*) 80 70
1379 $1 Minnie Mouse in kimono (*horiz*) .. 1·25 1·10
1380 $2 Mickey making masks (*horiz*) .. 2·25 2·50
1381 $4 Donald and Mickey making paper (*horiz*) .. .. 3·00 3·25
1382 $5 Minnie and Pluto making pottery (*horiz*) .. .. 3·25 3·50
1375/82 .. .. *Set of* 8 11·00 11·00
MS1383 Four sheets, each 122×102 mm. (a) $6 Mickey flower-arranging. (b) $6 Mickey carving a netsuke. (c) $6 Mickey at tea ceremony. (d) $6 Mickey making printing plate. P 13½×14 *Set of* 4 *sheets* 16·00 16·00

(Des Mary Walters. Litho Questa)

1991 (1 June). *Fungi. Vert designs as T* **364** *of Grenada. Multicoloured. P* 14.
1384 5 c. *Pyrrhoglossum pyrrhum* 25 25
1385 45 c. *Agaricus purpurellus* 75 50
1386 50 c. *Amanita craseoderma* 75 55
1387 90 c. *Hygrocybe acutoconica* .. .. 1·25 1·25
.1388 $1 *Limacella guttata* .. .. .. 1·25 1·25
1389 $2 *Lactarius hygrophoroides* .. .. 1·75 1·7
1390 $4 *Boletellus cubensis* .. .. .. 3·00 3·0
1391 $5 *Psilocybe caerulescens* .. .. 3·00 3·0
1384/91 .. .. *Set of* 8 11·00 10·5
MS1392 Two sheets, each 100×70 mm. (a) $6 *Marasmius haematocephalus*. (b) $6 *Lepiota spiculata* .. .. .. *Set of* 2 *sheets* 11·00 12·0

(Des D. Miller. Litho Walsall)

1991 (5 July). 65*th Birthday of Queen Elizabeth II. Hori designs as T* **280** *of Antigua. Multicoloured. P* 14.
1393 20 c. Queen, Prince Philip, Prince Charles and Prince William at Trooping the Colour, 1990 .. .. .. 30 2
1394 25 c. Queen and Prince Charles at polo match, 1985 .. .. .. 30 2
1395 $2 Queen and Prince Philip at Maundy service, 1989 .. .. .. 2·00 2·5
1396 $4 Queen with Queen Mother on her 87th birthday, 1987 .. .. 3·25 3·7
1393/6 .. .. *Set of* 4 5·25 6·0
MS1397 68×90 mm. $5 The Queen at Caen Hill, 1990, and Prince Philip at R.A.F. Benson, 1989 3·75 4·5

(Des D. Miller. Litho Walsall)

1991 (5 July). 10*th Wedding Anniv of Prince and Princess o Wales. Horiz designs as T* **280** *of Antigua. Multicoloured P* 14.
1398 5 c. Prince and Princess of Wales kissing, 1987 .. .. 15 1
1399 60 c. Portraits of Prince, Princess and sons 70 7
1400 $1 Prince Henry in 1988 and Prince William in 1987 .. .. .. 1·10 1·1
1401 $5 Princess Diana in 1990 and Prince Charles in 1988 .. .. .. 3·75 4·7
1398/1401 .. .. .. *Set of* 4 5·25 6·0
MS1402 68×90 mm. $5 Princess with Prince Henry in Majorca, and Prince and Princess with Prince Henry at polo match .. .. .. 4·00 4·5

(Litho Questa)

1991 (18 Nov). *Death Centenary of Vincent van Gogh* (*artist*) (1990). *Multicoloured designs as T* **278** *of Antigua. P* 13½×1 (*vert*) *or* 14×13½ (*horiz*).
1403 5 c. "Two Thistles" 20 2
1404 10 c. "Baby Marcelle Roulin" 25 2
1405 15 c. "Still Life: Basket with Six Oranges" (*horiz*) 30 1
1406 25 c. "Orchard in Blossom" 35 2
1407 45 c. "Armand Roulin" 50 3
1408 50 c. "Wood Gatherers in Snow" (detail) (*horiz*) 60 4
1409 60 c. "Almond Tree in Blossom" 70 5
1410 $1 "An Old Man" .. .. .. 1·00 1·0
1411 $2 "The Seine Bridge at Asnières" (*horiz*) 1·75 2·0
1412 $3 "Vase with Lilacs, Daises and Anemones" .. .. 2·25 2·5
1413 $4 "Self Portrait" .. .. .. 2·40 2·7
1414 $5 "Patience Escalier" .. .. .. 2·50 2·7
1403/14 .. .. *Set of* 12 11·50 11·5
MS1415 Three sheets. (a) 127×102 mm. $6 "Quay with Men unloading Sand Barges" (*horiz*). (b) 127×102 mm. $6 "Sunset: Wheat Fields near Arles" (*horiz*). (c) 102×127 mm. "Les Alyscamps". Imperf .. .. .. *Set of* 3 *sheets* 12·00 13·0

102 Sargassum Triggerfish

(Litho Questa)

1991 (5 Dec). *Reef Fishes. T* **102** *and similar horiz designs. Multicoloured. P* 14.
1416 50 c. Type **102** 70 70
a. Sheetlet. Nos. 1416/30 .. .. 9·00
1417 50 c. Tobaccofish 70 70
1418 50 c. Caribbean Long-nosed Butterflyfish 70 70
1419 50 c. Cherub Angelfish 70 70
1420 50 c. Black Jack 70 70
1421 50 c. Masked Goby and Black Jack .. 70 70
1422 50 c. Spot-finned Hogfish 70 70
1423 50 c. Royal Gramma ("Fairy Basslet") .. 70 70
1424 50 c. Orange-backed Bass 70 70
1425 50 c. Candy Basslet 70 70
1426 50 c. Black-capped Basslet 70 70
1427 50 c. Long-jawed Squirrelfish 70 70
1428 50 c. Jackknife-fish 70 70
1429 50 c. Bigeye 70 70
1430 50 c. Short Bigeye 70 70
1416/30 .. .. *Set of* 15 9·00 9·00
MS1431 106×66 mm. $6 Caribbean Flashlight Fish .. .. 7·00 8·00
Nos. 1416/30 were printed together, *se-tenant*, as a sheetlet of 15, forming a composite design.

(Litho Walsall)

1991 (9 Dec). *Christmas. Religious Paintings by Martin Schongauer. Vert designs as T* **287** *of Antigua. P* 12.
1432 10 c. black and cinnamon 30 15
1433 35 c. multicoloured 55 30
1434 50 c. multicoloured 75 50
1435 75 c. multicoloured .. .. 1·00 80
1436 $1 multicoloured .. .. 1·40 1·25
1437 $2 multicoloured .. .. 2·25 2·50
1438 $4 black and cinnamon .. .. .. 3·25 3·75

1724 $5 "Presentation at the Temple" (different detail) (Raphael) 2·50 3·00
1717/24 *Set of* 8 7·75 7·50
MS1725 Two sheets. (a) 102×128 mm. $6 "Adoration of the Shepherds" (different detail) (Dürer) (*horiz*). P 14×13½. (b) 128×102 mm. $6 "Annunciation" (detail) (Raphael). P 13½×14 *Set of* 2 *sheets* 7·00 8·00

(Litho Questa)

1993 (21 Dec). *Aviation Anniversaries. Multicoloured designs as T* **386** *of Grenada. P* 14.
1726 15 c. Avro Lancaster 30 20
1727 35 c. Blanchard's balloon crossing the River Delaware 15 20
1728 50 c. Airship LZ-127 *Graf Zeppelin* over Rio de Janeiro 50 35
1729 75 c. Hugo Eckener 65 50
1730 $3 Pres. Washington handing passport to Blanchard 1·40 1·50
1731 $5 Short Sunderland flying boat 2·50 2·75
1732 $5 Eckener in *Graf Zeppelin* 2·50 2·75
1726/32 *Set of* 7 7·25 7·50
MS1733 Three sheets. (a) 76×107 mm. $6 Supermarine Spitfire. (b) 107×76 mm. $6 Blanchard's balloon (*vert*). (c) 107×76 mm. $6 Eckener with Pres. Hoover *Set of* 3 *sheets* 10·50 11·50
Anniversaries:—Nos. 1726, 1731, **MS**1733a, 75th anniv of Royal Air Force; Nos. 1727, 1730, **MS**1733b, Bicentenary of First Airmail Flight; Nos. 1728/9, 1732, **MS**1733c, 125th birth anniv of Hugo Eckener (airship commander).

(Des K. Gromell. Litho Questa)

1993 (21 Dec). *Centenaries of Henry Ford's First Petrol Engine (Nos.* 1735/6, **MS**1738b) *and Karl Benz's First Four-wheeled Car (others). Horiz designs as T* **387** *of Grenada. Multicoloured. P* 14.
1734 25 c. Mercedes Benz "300 SLR", 1955 30 20
1735 45 c. Ford "Thunderbird", 1957 20 25
1736 $4 Ford "150-A" station wagon, 1929 1·90 2·00
1737 $5 Mercedes Benz "540 K" 2·75 3·00
1734/7 *Set of* 4 4·75 5·00
MS1738 Two sheets, 76×107 mm. (a) $6 Mercedes Benz "SSK", 1929. (b) $6 Ford "Model T", 1924 *Set of* 2 *sheets* 7·00 8·00

(Des Kerri Schiff. Litho Questa)

1993 (31 Dec). *Famous Paintings by Rembrandt and Matisse. Multicoloured designs as T* **316** *of Antigua. P* 13½×14.
1739 15 c. "Hendrickje Stoffels as Flora" (Rembrandt) 40 25
1740 35 c. "Lady and Gentleman in Black" (Rembrandt) 50 25
1741 50 c. "Aristotle with the Bust of Homer" (Rembrandt) 60 40
1742 75 c. "Interior: Flowers and Parakeets" (Matisse) 85 60
1743 $1 "Goldfish" (Matisse) 1·00 85
1744 $2 "The Girl with Green Eyes" (Matisse) 1·75 2·00
1745 $3 "Still Life with a Plaster Figure" (Matisse) 2·00 2·50
1746 $5 "Christ and the Woman of Samaria" (Rembrandt) 2·50 2·75
1739/46 *Set of* 8 8·75 8·75
MS1747 Two sheets. (a) 100×125 mm. $6 "Anna accused of stealing the Kid" (detail) (Rembrandt). P 13½×14. (b) 125×100 mm. $6 "Tea in the Garden" (detail) (Matisse) (*horiz*). P 14×13½ *Set of* 2 *sheets* 7·00 8·00

(Des W. Hanson. Litho Questa)

1994 (18 Feb). *"Hong Kong '94" International Stamp Exhibition (1st issue). Horiz designs as T* **317** *of Antigua. Multicoloured. P* 14.
1748 40 c. Hong Kong 1984 $5 aviation stamp and airliner at Kai Tak Airport 40 50
a. Horiz pair. Nos. 1748/9 80 1·00
1749 40 c. Grenada Grenadines 1988 20 c. airships stamp and junk in Kowloon Bay 40 50
Nos. 1748/9 were printed together, *se-tenant*, in horizontal pairs throughout the sheet with the centre part of each pair forming a composite design.

(Des Kerri Schiff. Litho Questa)

1994 (18 Feb). *"Hong Kong '94" International Stamp Exhibition (2nd issue). Jade Sculptures. Horiz designs as T* **318** *of Antigua. Multicoloured. P* 14.
1750 45 c. White jade brush washer 35 40
a. Sheetlet. Nos. 1750/5 1·90
1751 45 c. Archaic jade brush washer 35 40
1752 45 c. Dark green jade brush washer 35 40
1753 45 c. Green jade almsbowl 35 40
1754 45 c. Archaic jade dog 35 40
1755 45 c. Yellow jade brush washer 35 40
1750/5 *Set of* 6 1·90 2·25
Nos. 1750/5 were printed together, *se-tenant*, in sheetlets of 6.

(Des Susan Carlson. Litho Questa)

1994 (6 Apr). *Fungi. Vert designs as T* **390** *of Grenada, but with white backgrounds. Multicoloured. P* 14.
1756 35 c. *Hygrocybe hypohaemacta* 45 30
1757 45 c. *Cantharellus cinnabarinus* 55 35
1758 50 c. *Marasmius haematocephalus* 60 40
1759 75 c. *Mycena pura* 80 60
1760 $1 *Gymnopilus russipes* 90 80
1761 $2 *Calocybe cyanocephala* 1·40 1·50
1762 $4 *Pluteus chrysophlebius* 2·50 2·75
1763 $5 *Chlorophyllum molybdites* 2·50 2·75
1756/63 *Set of* 8 8·75 8·50
MS1764 Two sheets, each 100×70 mm. (a) $6 *Xeromphalina tenuipes*. (b) $6 *Collybia fibrosipes* *Set of* 2 *sheets* 7·50 8·00
No. 1757 is inscribed "Cantherellus cinnabarinus" and No. 1762 "Pleuteus chrysophlebius", both in error.

(Des V. DiFate. Litho Questa)

1994 (13 Apr). *Prehistoric Animals. Multicoloured designs as T* **391** *of Grenada. P* 14.
1765 15 c. Spinosaurus 30 25
1766 35 c. Apatosaurus (Brontosaurus) 45 30
1767 45 c. Tyrannosaurus rex 50 35
1768 55 c. Triceratops 50 40
1769 $1 Pachycephalosaurus 85 75
1770 $2 Pteranodon 1·40 1·50
1771 $4 Parasaurolophus 2·50 2·75
1772 $5 Brachiosaurus 2·50 2·75
1765/72 *Set of* 8 8·00 8·25
MS1773 Two sheets, each 100×70 mm. (a) $6 Head of Brachiosaurus (*vert*). (b) $6 Spinosaurus and Tyrannosaurus rex fighting (*vert*) *Set of* 2 *sheets* 7·50 8·00

(Des W. Hanson. Litho B.D.T.)

1994 (4 Aug). *25th Anniv of First Moon Landing. Space Shuttle* Challenger. *Multicoloured designs as T* **326** *of Antigua. P* 14.
1774 $1.10, *Challenger* crew in training 1·00 1·10
a. Sheetlet. Nos. 1774/9 5·50
1775 $1.10, Christa McAuliffe (astronaut) 1·00 1·10
1776 $1.10, *Challenger* on launch pad 1·00 1·10
1777 $1.10, Gregory Jarvis (astronaut) 1·00 1·10
1778 $1.10, Ellison Onizuka (astronaut) 1·00 1·10
1779 $1.10, Ronald McNair (astronaut) 1·00 1·10
1774/9 *Set of* 6 5·50 6·00
MS1780 107×76 mm. $6 Judith Resnick (astronaut) (*vert*) 3·75 4·25
Nos. 1774/9 were printed together, *se-tenant*, in sheetlets of 6.

(Litho Questa)

1994 (4 Aug). *Centenary of International Olympic Committee. Gold Medal Winners. Horiz designs as T* **327** *of Antigua. Multicoloured. P* 14.
1781 50 c. Silke Renk (Germany) (javelin), 1992 35 30
1782 $1.50, Mark Spitz (U.S.A.) (swimming), 1972 90 1·10
MS1783 106×77 mm. $6 Japanese team (Nordic skiing), 1994 3·25 3·75

(Litho Questa)

1994 (4 Aug). *International Year of the Family. Horiz design as T* **328** *of Antigua. P* 14.
1784 $1 Grenadines family 60 60

(Des J. Batchelor. Litho Questa)

1994 (4 Aug). *50th Anniv of D-Day. Horiz designs as T* **331** *of Antigua. Multicoloured. P* 14.
1785 40 c. Churchill bridge-laying tank 35 30
1786 $2 Sherman "Firefly" tank leaving landing craft 1·00 1·25
1787 $3 Churchill "Crocodile" flame-thrower 1·60 1·75
1785/7 *Set of* 3 2·75 3·00
MS1788 107×76 mm. $6 Sherman "Crab" flail tank 3·25 3·75

(Des Kerri Schiff. Litho Questa (Nos. 1791/8, **MS**1800), B.D.T. (others))

1994 (4 Aug). *"Philakorea '94" International Stamp Exhibition, Seoul (1st issue). Multicoloured designs as T* **281** *of Dominica. P* 13½×14 *(Nos.* 1791/8) *or* 14 *(others).*
1789 40 c. Onung Tomb (*horiz*) 30 30
1790 $1 Stone pagoda, Mt Namsam (*horiz*) 55 55
1791 $1 "Admiring Spring in the Country" (left detail) (Sin Yunbok) 55 55
a. Sheetlet. Nos. 1791/8 4·50
1792 $1 "Admiring Spring in the Country" (right detail) 55 55
1793 $1 "Woman on Dano Day" (left detail) (Sin Yunbok) 55 55
1794 $1 "Woman on Dano Day" (right detail) 55 55
1795 $1 "Enjoying Lotuses while Listening to Music" (left detail) (Sin Yunbok) 55 55
1796 $1 "Enjoying Lotuses while Listening to Music) (right detail) 55 55
1797 $1 "Women by a Crystal Stream" (left detail) (Sin Yunbok) 55 55
1798 $1 "Women by a Crystal Stream" (right detail) 55 55
1799 $4 Pusan (*horiz*) 2·25 2·25
1789/99 *Set of* 11 6·75 6·75
MS1800 70×102 mm. $6 "Blacksmith's Shop" (detail) (Kim Duksin). P 14 3·25 3·75
Nos. 1791/8, each 26×49 mm, were printed together, *se-tenant*, in sheetlets of 8. Paintings are shown across horizontal pairs without white vertical margins in the centre.

(Des Claudia Sergeant. Litho Questa)

1994 (7 Aug). *Orchids. Multicoloured designs as T* **392** *of Grenada. P* 14.
1801 15 c. *Cattleya aurantiaca* 35 25
1802 25 c. *Blettia patula* 40 25
1803 45 c. *Sobralia macrantha* 50 30
1804 75 c. *Encyclia belizensis* 70 55
1805 $1 *Sophrolaeliocattleya* 85 75
1806 $2 *Encyclia fragrans* 1·40 1·50
1807 $4 *Schombocattleya* 2·50 2·75
1808 $5 *Brassolaeliocattleya* 2·50 2·75
1801/8 *Set of* 8 8·25 8·25
MS1809 Two sheets, each 100×70 mm. (a) $6 *Ornithidium coccineum* (*horiz*). (b) $6 *Brassavola nodosa* (*horiz*) *Set of* 2 *sheets* 7·50 8·00

(Litho Questa)

1994 (11 Aug). *World Cup Football Championship, U.S.A. (2nd issue). Vert designs as T* **393** *of Grenada. Multicoloured. P* 14.
1810 75 c. Steve Mark (Grenada) 50 50
a. Sheetlet. Nos. 1810/15 2·75
1811 75 c. Jurgen Kohler (Germany) 50 50
1812 75 c. Almir (Brazil) 50 50
1813 75 c. Michael Windischmann (U.S.A.) 50 50
1814 75 c. Guiseppe Giannini (Italy) 50 50
1815 75 c. Rashidi Yekini (Nigeria) 50 50
1810/15 *Set of* 6 2·75 2·75
MS1816 Two sheets, each 99×70 mm. (a) $6 Kemari (ancient Japanese game). (b) $6 Hand holding trophy *Set of* 2 *sheets* 7·50 8·00
Nos. 1810/15 were printed together, *se-tenant*, in sheetlets of 6.

106 Mickey Mouse and Unjin Mirŭk Window from Kwanch Ok Temple

(Litho Questa)

1994 (16 Aug). *"Philakorea '94" International Stamp Exhibition, Seoul (2nd issue). T* **106** *and similar multicoloured designs showing Walt Disney cartoon characters. P* 14×13½.
1817 3 c. Type **106** 15 15
1818 4 c. Goofy imitating statue of Admiral Yi, Chŏnju 15 15
1819 5 c. Cousin Gus and Donald Duck eating dinner 15 15
1820 10 c. Mickey playing flute 20 15
1821 15 c. Goofy with Tolharubang (statue) 30 20
1822 15 c. Type **106** 30 20
1823 20 c. Mickey and Minnie at Hyang-Wonjŏng 30 20
1824 35 c. As 4 c. 40 25
1825 50 c. As 5 c. 50 35
1826 75 c. As 10 c. 70 55
1827 $1 As 15 c. 85 75
1828 $2 As 20 c. 1·40 1·50
1829 $4 Mickey as Somori-Kut shaman 2·50 2·75
1830 $5 Minnie holding ceremonial fan 2·50 2·75
1817/30 *Set of* 14 9·50 9·00
MS1831 Two sheets, each 130×103 mm. (a) $6 Minnie beating Buk drum (*vert*). (b) $6 Mickey in swimming pool at Pugok Hawaii (*vert*). P 13½×14 *Set of* 2 *sheets* 7·50 8·00

(Litho Questa)

1994 (1 Sept). *First Recipients of Order of the Caribbean Community. Horiz designs as Nos.* 2046/8 *of Antigua. Multicoloured. P* 14.
1832 25 c. Sir Shridath Ramphal 10 10
1833 50 c. William Demas 25 30
1834 $2 Derek Walcott 1·40 1·60
1832/34 *Set of* 3 1·60 1·75

(Des P. Gonzalez. Litho Questa)

1994 (1 Sept). *Fishes. Horiz designs as T* **394** *of Grenada. Multicoloured. P* 14.
1835 75 c. Porkfish 55 55
a. Sheetlet. Nos. 1835/46 6·00
1836 75 c. Blue Chromis 55 55
1837 75 c. Caribbean Reef Shark (facing left) 55 55
1838 75 c. Long-spined Squirrelfish 55 55
1839 75 c. Four-eyed Butterflyfish 55 55
1840 75 c. Blue Head 55 55
1841 75 c. Royal Gramma 55 55
1842 75 c. Sharp-nosed Puffer 55 55
1843 75 c. Reid's Seahorse 55 55
1844 75 c. Black-barred Soldierfish 55 55
1845 75 c. Red-lipped Blenny 55 55
1846 75 c. Painted Wrasse 55 55
1847 75 c. Yellow-tailed Snapper 55 55
a. Sheetlet. Nos. 1847/58 6·00
1848 75 c. Caribbean Reef Shark (facing right) 55 55
1849 75 c. Great Barracuda 55 55
1850 75 c. Red-tailed Parrotfish 55 55
1851 75 c. Blue Tang 55 55
1852 75 c. Queen Angelfish 55 55
1853 75 c. Red Hind 55 55
1854 75 c. Rock Beauty 55 55
1855 75 c. Queen Parrotfish 55 55
1856 75 c. Spanish Hogfish 55 55
1857 75 c. Spotted Moray 55 55
1858 75 c. Queen Triggerfish 55 55
1835/58 *Set of* 24 12·00 12·00
MS1859 Two sheets, each 102×72 mm. (a) $6 Head of Queen Angelfish. (b) $6 Head of Painted Wrasse *Set of* 2 *sheets* 7·50 8·00
Nos. 1835/46 and 1847/58 were printed together, *se-tenant*, in sheetlets of 12 each forming composite designs.

(Litho Questa)

1994 (5 Dec). *Christmas. Religious Paintings by Bartolome Murillo. Vert designs as T* **336** *of Antigua. Multicoloured. P* 13½×14.
1860 15 c. "The Annunciation" 20 20
1861 35 c. "The Adoration of the Shepherds" 30 20
1862 50 c. "Virgin and Child with St. Rose" 40 30
1863 50 c. "Flight into Egypt" 40 30
1864 75 c. "Virgin and Child" 60 45
1865 $1 "Virgin of the Rosary" 75 60
1866 $4 "The Holy Family" 2·25 2·75
1860/6 *Set of* 7 4·50 4·25
MS1867 Two sheets. (a) 85×95 mm. $6 "Adoration of the Shepherds" (*different*) (detail). (b) 95×125 mm. $6 "The Holy Family with a Little Bird" (detail) *Set of* 2 *sheets* 7·50 8·00

(Litho Questa)

1995 (10 Jan). *Birds. Multicoloured designs as T* **397** *of Grenada. Multicoloured. P* 14.
1868 25 c. Scaly-breasted Ground Dove (*vert*) 35 25
1869 50 c. White-winged Dove 60 45
1870 $2 Inca Dove (*vert*) 1·40 1·50
1871 $4 Mourning Dove 2·25 2·75
1868/71 *Set of* 4 4·25 4·50

(Des A. Melville-Brown. Litho Questa)

1995 (12 Jan). *Centenary of First English Cricket Tour to the West Indies. Multicoloured designs as T* **329** *of Antigua. P* 14.
1872 50 c. Mike Atherton (England) and Wisden Trophy 45 35
1873 75 c. Curtly Ambrose (West Indies) (*vert*) 65 65
1874 $1 Brian Lara (West Indies) (*vert*) 85 1·00
1872/4 *Set of* 3 1·75 1·75
MS1875 75×95 mm. $3 West Indian team, 1994 2·00 2·25

107 Aspects of London, National Flag and Map

108 Pig

(Des S. and Dot Barlowe. Litho Questa)

1995 (10 Mar). *Capitals of the World. T* **107** *and similar vert designs showing aspects of various cities, national flags and maps. Multicoloured. P* 14.
1876 $1 Type **107** 45 50
a. Sheetlet. Nos. 1876/85 4·50
1877 $1 Cairo 45 50
1878 $1 Vienna 45 50
1879 $1 Paris 45 50
1880 $1 Rome 45 50
1881 $1 Budapest 45 50
1882 $1 Moscow 45 50
1883 $1 Peking ("Beijing") 45 50
1884 $1 Tokyo 45 50
1885 $1 Washington 45 50
1876/85 *Set of* 10 4·50 5·00
Nos. 1876/85 were printed together, *se-tenant*, in sheetlets of 10.

(Des Y. Lee. Litho Questa)

1995 (21 Apr). *Chinese New Year ("Year of the Pig"). T* **108** *and similar multicoloured designs showing* "GRENADA GRENADINES" *in colours indicated. P* 14½.
1886 75 c. Type **108** (deep reddish violet) 35 40
a. Block of 4. Nos. 1886/9 1·40
1887 75 c. Pig (deep carmine) 35 40
1888 75 c. Pig (lake-brown) 35 40
1889 75 c. Pig (scarlet-vermilion) 35 40
1886/9 *Set of* 4 1·40 1·60
MS1890 Two sheets. (a) 106×77 mm. $2 Two pigs (*horiz*). (b) 67×83 mm. Nos. 1886/9 *Set of* 2 *sheets* 2·25 2·40
Nos. 1886/9 were printed together, *se-tenant*, as blocks of 4 in sheetlets of 16.

109 Bull Shark and Diver

(Des Y. Lee. Litho Questa)

1995 (3 May). *Marine Life of the Caribbean. T* **109** *and similar horiz designs. Multicoloured. P* 14.
1891 $1 Type **109** 45 50
a. Sheetlet. Nos. 1891/9 4·00
1892 $1 Great White Shark 45 50
1893 $1 Octopus and shoal of fish 45 50
1894 $1 Great Barracuda 45 50
1895 $1 Green Moray 45 50
1896 $1 Spotted Eagle Ray 45 50
1897 $1 Sea Snake 45 50
1898 $1 Stingray 45 50
1899 $1 Grouper 45 50
1900 $1 Dolphins 45 50
a. Sheetlet. Nos. 1900/8 4·00
1901 $1 Lionfish 45 50
1902 $1 Sea Turtle and Rock Beauty (fish) 45 50
1903 $1 Blue-cheeked Butterflyfish and Nurse Shark 45 50
1904 $1 Queen Angelfish 45 50
1905 $1 Grouper and Coney 45 50
1906 $1 Rainbow Eel and Spotted Moray 45 50
1907 $1 Sun Flower-star and Coral Crab 45 50
1908 $1 Octopus on sea bed 45 50
1891/1908 *Set of* 18 8·00 9·00
MS1909 Two sheets, each 107×77 mm. (a) $5 French Angelfish. (b) $6 Smooth Hammerhead *Set of* 2 *sheets* 4·75 5·00
Nos. 1891/9 and 1900/8 were printed together, *se-tenant*, in sheetlets of 9.

110 Suffolk Punch

(Des Jennifer Toombs. Litho Questa)

1995 (3 May). *Domestic Animals. T* **110** *and similar horiz designs. Multicoloured. P* 14.
1910 15 c. Type **110** 10 10
1911 25 c. Shetland pony 10 10
1912 75 c. Blue Persian (cat) 35 40
a. Sheetlet. Nos. 1912/23 4·25
1913 75 c. Sorrel Abyssinian (cat) 35 40
1914 75 c. White Angora (cat) 35 40
1915 75 c. Brown Burmese (cat) 35 40
1916 75 c. Red Tabby Exotic Shorthair (cat) 35 40
1917 75 c. Seal-point Birman (cat) 35 40
1918 75 c. Korat (cat) 35 40
1919 75 c. Norwegian Forest Cat 35 40
1920 75 c. Lilac-point Balinese (cat) 35 40
1921 75 c. British Shorthair (cat) 35 40
1922 75 c. Red Self Longhair (cat) 35 40
1923 75 c. Calico Manx (cat) 35 40
1924 75 c. Shetland Sheepdog 35 40
a. Sheetlet. Nos. 1924/35 4·25
1925 75 c. Bull Terrier 35 40
1926 75 c. Afghan Hound 35 40
1927 75 c. Scottish Terrier 35 40
1928 75 c. Labrador Retriever 35 40
1929 75 c. English Springer Spaniel 35 40
1930 75 c. Samoyed (dog) 35 40
1931 75 c. Irish Setter 35 40
1932 75 c. Border Collie 35 40
1933 75 c. Pekingese 35 40
1934 75 c. Dachshund 35 40
1935 75 c. Weimaraner (dog) 35 40
1936 $1 Arab 45 50
1937 $3 Shire horse 1·25 1·40
1910/37 *Set of* 28 10·00 11·00
MS1938 Two sheets, each 105×75 mm. (a) $6 Seal-point Colourpoint (cat). (b) $6 English Setter *Set of* 2 *sheets* 5·25 5·50
Nos. 1912/23 and 1924/35 were printed together, *se-tenant*, in sheetlets of 12.

(Litho Questa)

1995 (5 May). *Centenary of Sierra Club (environmental protection society)* (1992). *Endangered Species. Multicoloured designs as T* **320** *of Antigua. P* 14.
1939 $1 Spotted Owl 45 50
a. Sheetlet. Nos. 1939/47 4·00
1940 $1 Brown Pelican on perch 45 50
1941 $1 Head of Brown Pelican 45 50
1942 $1 Head of Jaguarundi 45 50
1943 $1 Jaguarundi looking over shoulder 45 50
1944 $1 Maned Wolf in undergrowth 45 50
1945 $1 American Wood Stork standing on two legs 45 50
1946 $1 American Wood Stork standing on one leg 45 50
1947 $1 Close-up of Maned Wolf 45 50
1948 $1 Brown Pelican (*horiz*) 45 50
a. Sheetlet. Nos. 1948/56 4·00
1949 $1 Close-up of Spotted Owl (*horiz*) 45 50
1950 $1 Spotted Owl chick (*horiz*) 45 50
1951 $1 Jaguarundi (*horiz*) 45 50
1952 $1 Central American Spider Monkey sitting with young (*horiz*) 45 50
1953 $1 Central American Spider Monkey carrying young (*horiz*) 45 50
1954 $1 Central American Spider Monkey swinging from branch (*horiz*) 45 50
1955 $1 American Wood Stork (*horiz*) 45 50
1956 $1 Pair of Maned Wolves (*horiz*) 45 50
1939/56 *Set of* 18 8·00 9·00
Nos. 1939/47 and 1948/56 were printed together, *se-tenant*, in sheetlets of 9.

(Litho Questa)

1995 (8 May). *18th World Scout Jamboree, Netherlands. Horiz designs as T* **403** *of Grenada. Multicoloured. P* 14.
1957 75 c. Grenadian scout on beach 35 40
a. Horiz strip of 3. Nos. 1957/9 1·60
1958 $1 Scout with staff on hill 45 50
1959 $2 Scout saluting and national flag 85 90
1957/9 *Set of* 3 1·60 1·75
MS1960 107×77 mm. $6 Scout snorkelling 2·50 2·75
Nos. 1957/9 were printed together in sheets of 9 containing three *se-tenant* horizontal strips of 3.

(Des W. Wright. Litho Questa)

1995 (8 May). *50th Anniv of End of Second World War in Europe. Bombers. Horiz designs as T* **340** *of Antigua. Multicoloured. P* 14.
1961 $2 Avro Type 683 Lancaster 85 90
a. Sheetlet. Nos. 1961/8 6·75
1962 $2 Junkers Ju 88 85 90
1963 $2 North American B-25 Mitchell 85 90
1964 $2 Boeing B-17 Flying Fortress 85 90
1965 $2 Petlyakov Pe-2 85 90
1966 $2 Martin B-26 Marauder 85 90
1967 $2 Heinkel He 111H 85 90
1968 $2 Consolidated B-24 Liberator 85 90
1961/8 *Set of* 8 6·75 7·00
MS1969 105×75 mm. $6 Pres. Truman and newspaper headline (57×43 *mm*) 2·50 2·75
Nos. 1961/8 were printed together, *se-tenant*, in sheetlets of 8 with the stamps arranged in two horizontal strips of 4 separated by a gutter showing a De Havilland D.H.98 Mosquito.

(Des R. Martin. Litho Questa)

1995 (8 May). *50th Anniv of United Nations. Vert designs as T* **404** *of Grenada. Multicoloured. P* 14.
1970 75 c. U. N. Headquarters, New York, and flag 35 40
a. Horiz strip of 3. Nos. 1970/2 1·60
1971 $1 Trygve Lie (first Secretary-General) 45 50
1972 $2 U.N. soldier 85 90
1970/2 *Set of* 3 1·60 1·75
MS1973 101×76 mm. $6 Peace dove over emblem 2·50 2·75
Nos. 1970/2 were printed together in sheets of 9 containing three *se-tenant* horizontal strips of 3, each forming a composite design.

(Des R. Martin. Litho Questa)

1995 (8 May). *50th Anniv of Food and Agriculture Organization. Vert designs as T* **405** *of Grenada. Multicoloured. P* 14.
1974 75 c. Man hoeing 35 40
a. Horiz strip of 3. Nos. 1974/6 1·60
1975 $1 Woman hoeing 45 50
1976 $1 Man and woman hoeing 90 95
1974/6 *Set of* 3 1·60 1·75
MS1977 106×76 mm. $6 Child eating with chopsticks 2·50 2·75
Nos. 1974/6 were printed together in sheets of 9 containing three *se-tenant* horizontal strips of 3, each forming a composite design.

(Litho Questa)

1995 (8 May). *90th Anniv of Rotary International. Multicoloured designs as T* **406** *of Grenada. P* 14.
1978 $5 Paul Harris (founder) and logo (*horiz*) 2·10 2·25
MS1979 106×76 mm. $6 Rotary Club and International logos (*horiz*) 2·50 2·75

(Litho Questa)

1995 (8 May). *95th Birthday of Queen Elizabeth the Queen Mother. Vert designs as T* **344** *of Antigua. P* 13½×14.
1980 $1.50, orange-brown, pale brown and black 65 70
a. Sheetlet. Nos. 1980/3×2 5·00
1981 $1.50, multicoloured 65 70
1982 $1.50, multicoloured 65 70
1983 $1.50, multicoloured 65 70
1980/3 *Set of* 4 2·50 2·75
MS1984 102×127 mm. $6 multicoloured 2·50 2·75
Designs:—No. 1980, Queen Elizabeth the Queen Mother (pastel drawing); No. 1981, At Remembrance Day service; No. 1982, At desk (oil painting); No. 1983, Wearing green hat; No. **MS**1984, Unveiling memorial to Blitz victims.
Nos. 1980/3 were printed together in sheetlets of 8, containing two *se-tenant* horizontal strips of 4.

(Des J. Batchelor. Litho Questa)

1995 (8 May). *50th Anniv of End of Second World War in the Pacific. Horiz designs as T* **340** *of Antigua. Multicoloured. P* 14.
1985 $2 Mitsubishi G4M1 "Betty" (bomber) 85 90
a. Sheetlet. Nos. 1985/90 5·00
1986 $2 Japanese submarine "I 14" with sea-plane on catapult 85 90
1987 $2 Mitsubishi GM31 "Nell" (bomber) 85 90
1988 $2 *Akizuki* (Japanese destroyer) 85 90
1989 $2 *Kirishima* (Japanese battleship) 85 90
1990 $2 *Asigari* (Japanese cruiser) 85 90
1985/90 *Set of* 6 5·00 5·25
MS1991 108×76 mm. $6 Japanese Aichi D3A1 "Val" dive bomber 2·50 2·75
Nos. 1985/90 were printed together, *se-tenant*, in sheetlets of 6 with the stamps arranged in two horizontal strips of 3 separated by a gutter showing Yokosuka MXY-7 "Okha" (Kamikaze airplane) attacking ships.

(Litho B.D.T.)

1995 (23 June). *Olympic Games, Atlanta* (1996). *Designs as T* **407** *of Grenada. Multicoloured. P* 14.
1992 15 c. Rosemary Ackerman (East Germany) (high jump) (*horiz*) 10 10
a. Horiz strip of 3. Nos. 1992/4 15
1993 15 c. Li Ning (China) (gymnastics) (*horiz*) 10 10
1994 15 c. Denise Parker (U.S.A.) (archery) (*horiz*) 10 10
1995 $3 Terry Carlisle (U.S.A.) (skeet shooting) (*horiz*) 1·25 1·40
a. Horiz strip of 3. Nos. 1995/7 3·75
1996 $3 Kathleen Nord (East Germany) (swimming) (*horiz*) 1·25 1·40
1997 $3 Brigit Schmidt (East Germany) (canoeing) (*horiz*) 1·25 1·40
1992/7 *Set of* 6 4·00 4·25
MS1998 Two sheets, each 102×72 mm. (a) $6 Dan Gable (U.S.A.) and Kikuo Wada (Japan) (wrestling). (b) $6 George Foreman (U.S.A.) (boxing) *Set of* 2 *sheets* 5·25 5·50
Nos. 1992/4 and 1995/7 were printed in sheets of 12 containing four *se-tenant* horizontal strips of 3.

111 Brown Pelican

(Des T. Wood. Litho Questa)

1995 (5 Sept). *Birds of the Caribbean. T* **111** *and similar horiz designs. Multicoloured. P* 14.

1999 10 c. Type **111** 10 10
2000 15 c. Black-necked Stilt 10 10
2001 25 c. Cuban Trogon 10 10
2002 35 c. Greater Flamingo 15 20
2003 75 c. Imperial Amazon 35 40
2004 $1 Pintail 45 50
2005 $1 Great Blue Heron 45 50
a. Sheetlet. Nos. 2005/12 .. .. 3·50
2006 $1 Jamaican Tody 45 50
2007 $1 Laughing Gull 45 50
2008 $1 Purple-throated Carib 45 50
2009 $1 Red-legged Thrush 45 50
2010 $1 Ruddy Duck 45 50
2011 $1 Common Shoveler 45 50
2012 $1 West Indian Red-bellied Woodpecker 45 50
2013 $2 Ringed Kingfisher 85 90
2014 $3 Stripe-headed Tanager .. .. 1·25 1·40
1999/2014 .. .. .. *Set of* 16 6·75 7·50
MS2015 Two sheets, each 104×73 mm. (a) $5 Village Weaver. (b) $5 Blue-hooded Euphonia *Set of* 2 *sheets* 4·25 4·50

Nos. 2005/12 were printed together, *se-tenant*, in sheetlets of 8, and, together with No. **MS**2015, carry the "Singapore '95" exhibition logo.

No. 2001 is inscr "Cuban Trogan", No. 2008 "Purple-throated Carb" and No. 2013 "Ringed King Fisher", all in error.

(Des Walt Disney Company and Rosemary DeFiglio. Litho Questa)

1995 (2 Oct). *Mickey's Pirate Adventure. Multicoloured designs as T* **415** *of Grenada showing Walt Disney cartoon characters. P* 14×13½.

2016 10 c. Goofy and Donald Duck with treasure chests (*horiz*) 10 10
2017 35 c. Mickey and Minnie Mouse at ship's wheel (*horiz*) 15 20
2018 75 c. Mickey, Donald and Goofy opening chest (*horiz*) 35 40
2019 $1 Big Pete and rats confronting Mickey (*horiz*) 45 50
2020 $2 Mickey, Goofy and Donald in boat (*horiz*) 90 95
2021 $5 Goofy fighting rat pirate with mop (*horiz*) .. .. 2·25 2·40
2016/21 .. .. *Set of* 6 4·00 4·50
MS2022 Two sheets, each 108×130 mm. (a) $6 Goofy and cannon-balls. (b) $6 Monkey pinching Mickey's nose. P 13½×14 .. *Set of* 2 *sheets* 5·50 5·75

(Des R. Martin. Litho Questa)

1995 (18 Oct). *Centenary of Nobel Trust Fund. Vert designs as T* **416** *of Grenada. Multicoloured. P* 14.

2023/51 75 c. × 2, $1×27 .. .. *Set of* 29 13·50 14·00
MS2052 Three sheets, each 105×76 mm. (a) $6 Sir Winston Churchill (1953 Literature). (b) $6 Willy Brandt (1971 Peace). (c) $6 Albert Schweitzer (1952 Peace) .. *Set of* 3 *sheets* 7·50 7·75

Designs:—75 c. W. Arthur Lewis (1979 Economics); Derek Walcott (1992 Literature); $1 Jules Border (1919 Medicine); René Cassin (1968 Peace); Verner von Heidenstam (1916 Literature); José Echegaray (1904 Literature); Otto Wallach (1910 Chemistry); Corneille Heymans (1938 Medicine); Ivar Giaever (1973 Physics); Sir William Cremer (1903 Peace); John Strutt (1904 Physics); James Franck (1925 Physics); Tobias Asser (1911 Peace); Carl Spitteler (1919 Literature); Christiaan Eijkman (1929 Medicine); Ragnar Granit (1967 Medicine); Frederic Passy (1901 Peace); Louis Neel (1970 Physics); Sir William Ramsay (1904 Chemistry); Philip Noel-Baker (1959 Peace); Heike Onnes (1913 Physics); Fridtjof Nansen (1922 Peace); Sir Ronald Ross (1902 Medicine); Paul Müller (1948 Medicine); Allvar Gullstrand (1911 Medicine); Gerhart Hauptmann (1912 Literature); Hans Spemann (1935 Medicine); Cecil Powell (1950 Physics); Walther Bothe (1954 Physics).

Nos. 2025/33, 2034/42 and 2043/51 were each printed together, *se-tenant*, in sheetlets of 9 forming composite designs.

No. 2027 (Von Heidenstam) is inscribed "1906" and No. 2044 is inscribed "Fridtjof Nanser", both in error.

112 Nita Naldi and Rudolph Valentino

(Des J. Iskowitz. Litho Questa)

1995 (3 Nov). *Centenary of Cinema. T* **112** *and similar multicoloured designs. P* 13½.

2053 $1 Type **112** 45 50
a. Sheetlet. Nos. 2053/61 .. .. 4·00
2054 $1 Ramon Novaro and Alice Terry .. 45 50
2055 $1 Frederic March and Joan Crawford .. 45 50
2056 $1 Clark Gable and Vivien Leigh .. 45 50
2057 $1 Barbara Stanwyck and Burt Lancaster 45 50
2058 $1 Warren Beatty and Natalie Wood .. 45 50
2059 $1 Spencer Tracy and Katharine Hepburn 45 50
2060 $1 Humphrey Bogart and Lauren Bacall 45 50
2061 $1 Omar Sharif and Julie Christie .. 45 50
2062 $1 Marion Davis 45 50
a. Sheetlet. Nos. 2062/70 .. .. 4·00
2063 $1 Marlene Dietrich 45 50
2064 $1 Lillian Gish 45 50
2065 $1 Bette Davis 45 50
2066 $1 Elizabeth Taylor 45 50
2067 $1 Veronica Lake 45 50
2068 $1 Ava Gardner 45 50
2069 $1 Grace Kelly 45 50
2070 $1 Kim Novak 45 50
2053/70 .. .. *Set of* 18 8·00 9·00
MS2071 Two sheets. (a) 72×102 mm. $6 Sophia Loren. (b) 102×72 mm. $6 Greta Garbo and John Gilbert (*horiz*) .. .. *Set of* 2 *sheets* 5·25 5·50

Nos. 2053/61 and 2062/70 were each printed together, *se-tenant*, in sheetlets of 9 forming composite designs.

(Litho Questa)

1995 (7 Nov). *Racing Cars. Multicoloured designs as T* **423** *of Grenada. P* 14.

2072 10 c. Williams-Renault Formula 1, 1990s 10 10
2073 25 c. Porsche "956", Le Mans, 1980s .. 10 15
2074 35 c. Lotus "John Player Special", 1970s 15 20
2075 75 c. Ford "GT-40", 1960s 35 40
2076 $2 Mercedes-Benz "W196", 1950s .. 85 90
2077 $3 Mercedes "SSK", 1920s .. .. 1·25 1·40
2072/7 .. .. *Set of* 6 2·75 3·00
MS2078 103×73 mm. $6 Jackie Stewart in Tyrrell-Ford, 1971 (*vert*) .. .. .. 2·50 2·75

113 Man on Donkey

114 Symbolic Rat and Candle

(Litho Questa)

1995 (7 Nov). *Local Transport. T* **113** *and similar horiz design. Multicoloured. P* 14.

2079 35 c. Type **113** 15 20
2080 75 c. Local bus 35 40

(Des W. Wright. Litho Questa)

1995 (7 Nov). *Evolution of Sailing Ships. Horiz designs as T* **427** *of Grenada. Multicoloured. P* 14.

2081 $1 *Preussen* (full-rigged ship) 45 50
a. Sheetlet. Nos. 2081/6 .. .. 2·50
2082 $1 Japanese junk 45 50
2083 $1 Caribbean pirate ship 45 50
2084 $1 *Mayflower* (Pilgrim Fathers) .. 45 50
2085 $1 Chinese junk 45 50
2086 $1 *Santa Maria* (Columbus) 45 50
2081/6 .. .. *Set of* 6 2·50 3·00
MS2087 103×73 mm. $5 Spanish galleon (56×41 *mm*) .. .. 2·10 2·25

Nos. 2081/6 were printed together, *se-tenant*, in sheetlets of 6.

(Litho Questa)

1995 (28 Nov). *Christmas. Religious Paintings. Vert designs as T* **357** *of Antigua. Multicoloured. P* 13½×14.

2088 10 c. "Immaculate Conception" (Piero di Cosimo) 10 10
2089 15 c. "St. Michael dedicating Arms to the Madonna" (Le Nain) 10 10
2090 35 c. "Annunciation" (Lorenzo di Credi) .. 15 20
2091 50 c. "The Holy Family" (Jacob Jordaens) 25 30
2092 $3 "Madonna and Child" (Lippi) .. 1·25 1·40
2093 $5 "Madonna and Child with Ten Saints" (Fiorentino) .. .. 2·10 2·25
2088/93 .. .. *Set of* 6 3·75 4·25
MS2094 102×127 mm. (a) $6 "Adoration of the Shepherds" (detail) (Van Oost). (b) $6 "Holy Family" (detail) (Del Start) .. *Set of* 2 *sheets* 5·25 5·50

(Des Y. Lee. Litho Questa)

1996 (2 Jan). *Chinese New Year ("Year of the Rat"). T* **114** *and similar multicoloured designs. P* 14½.

2095 75 c. Type **114** (dull blue background) .. 35 40
a. Block of 4. Nos. 2095/8 .. .. 1·40
2096 75 c. Type **114** (lilac background) .. 35 40
2097 75 c. Type **114** (orange-brown background) 35 40
2098 75 c. Type **114** (yellow-green background) 35 40
2095/8 .. .. *Set of* 4 1·40 1·60
MS2099 69×84 mm. Nos. 2095/8 .. .. 1·40 1·60
MS2100 76×106 mm. $2 Two rats (*horiz*) .. 85 90

Nos. 2095/8 were printed together, *se-tenant*, as blocks of 4 in sheets of 16, with the four designs showing different Chinese characters.

(Litho Questa)

1996 (29 Jan). *Works of Art by Dürer and Rubens. Vert designs as T* **421** *of Grenada. Multicoloured. P* 13½×14.

2101 15 c. "The Centaur Family" (Dürer) .. 10 10
2102 35 c. "Oriental Ruler Seated" (Dürer) .. 15 20
2103 50 c. "The Entombment" (Dürer) .. 25 30
2104 75 c. "Man in Armour" (Rubens) 35 40
2105 $1 "Peace embracing Plenty" (Rubens) 45 50
2106 $2 "Departure of Lot" (Rubens) .. 85 90
2107 $3 "The Four Evangelists" (Rubens) .. 1·25 1·40
2108 $5 "Knight, Death and Devil" (Dürer) .. 2·10 2·25
2101/8 .. .. *Set of* 8 5·50 6·00
MS2109 Two sheets, each 101×127 mm. (a) $5 "The Fathers of the Church" (detail) (Rubens). (b) $6 "St. Jerome" (detail) (Dürer) *Set of* 2 *sheets* 4·75 5·00

115 Mickey and Minnie at New Year's Day "Hopping John" Tradition

(Des Alvin White Studios. Litho Questa)

1996 (17 Apr). *Traditional Holidays. T* **115** *and similar multicoloured designs showing Walt Disney cartoon characters. P* 14×13½.

2110 25 c. Type **115** 10 15
2111 50 c. Disney characters dancing around maypole 25 30
2112 75 c. Mickey, Minnie and Pluto watching Independence Day fireworks .. 35 40
2113 90 c. Gyro Gearloose and Donald's nephews in Halloween costumes 40 45
2114 $3 Donald Duck as Puritan and nephews as Indians on Thanksgiving Day .. 1·40 1·50
2115 $4 Huey and Dewey with Hanukkah dreidle .. .. 1·90 2·00
2110/15 .. .. *Set of* 6 4·25 4·75
MS2116 Two sheets, each 124×98 mm. (a) $6 Mickey, Minnie and Donald taking part in Caribbean carnival. P 14×13½. (b) $6 Traditional pot of gold in St. Patrick's Day parade (*vert*). P 13½×14 .. *Set of* 2 *sheets* 5·50 5·75

116 Gateway in Imperial Palace, Peking

1996 (8 May). *"CHINA '96" 9th Asian International Stamp Exhibition, Peking. T* **116** *and similar multicoloured designs. Litho. P* 13.

2117 $1 Type **116** 45 50
a. Sheetlet. Nos. 2117/20 .. .. 1·75
2118 $1 Eastern end of Great Wall at Shanhaiguan 45 50
2119 $1 Great Wall fortress, Shanhaiguan .. 45 50
2120 $1 Gate of Heavenly Peace, Peking .. 45 50
2121 $1 Sun Yat-sen's Mausoleum, Nanjing .. 45 50
a. Sheetlet. Nos. 2121/4 .. .. 1·75
2122 $1 Summer Palace, Peking 45 50
2123 $1 Temple of Heaven, Peking 45 50
2124 $1 Hall of Supreme Harmony, Forbidden City, Peking 45 50
2117/24 .. .. *Set of* 8 3·50 4·00
MS2125 Three sheets. (a) 150×100 mm. $2 Traditional Chinese painting (39×50 *mm*). (b) 90×68 mm. $6 Great Wall of China from the air (39×50 *mm*). (c) 90×68 mm. $6 Marble Boat, Summer Palace, Peking (50×39 *mm*) *Set of* 3 *sheets* 6·00 6·25

Nos. 2117/20 and 2121/4 were each printed together, *se-tenant*, in sheetlets of 4.

(Litho Questa)

1996 (8 May). *70th Birthday of Queen Elizabeth II. Vert designs as T* **364** *of Antigua. Multicoloured. P* 13½×14.

2126 35 c. As Type **364** of Antigua 15 20
a. Strip of 3. Nos. 2126/8 .. .. 2·75
2127 $2 Queen wearing tiara and green dress 85 90
2128 $4 Windsor Castle .. .. .. 1·75 1·90
2126/8 .. .. *Set of* 3 2·75 3·00
MS2129 103×125 mm. $6 Queen Elizabeth at Windsor .. .. 2·50 2·75

Nos. 2126/8 were printed together, *se-tenant*, in horizontal and vertical strips of 3 throughout the sheet.

(Litho B.D.T.)

1996 (12 June). *Flowers. Multicoloured designs as T* **430** *of Grenada, but vert. P* 14.

2130 35 c. *Camellia* "Apple Blossom" 15 20
2131 75 c. *Odontoglossum* 35 40
a. Sheetlet. Nos. 2131/4×3 .. .. 4·25
2132 75 c. *Cattleya* 35 40
2133 75 c. *Paphiopedilum* "Venus's Slipper" .. 35 40
2134 75 c. *Laeliocattleya* "Marysville" 35 40
2135 75 c. Fuchsia "Citation" 35 40
a. Sheetlet. Nos. 2135/46 .. .. 4·25
2136 75 c. Fuchsia "Amy Lye" 35 40
2137 75 c. *Clysonimus* (butterfly) and temple .. 35 40
2138 75 c. *Digitalis purpurea* (foxglove) .. 35 40
2139 75 c. *Lilium martagon* "Martagon Lily" .. 35 40
2140 75 c. *Tulipa* "Coleur Cardinal" 35 40
2141 75 c. *Galanthus nivalis* (snowdrop) .. 35 40

2142 75 c. *Rosa* "Superstar" 35 40
2143 75 c. Crocus "Dutch Yellow Mammoth" .. 35 40
2144 75 c. *Lilium speciosum* (Japanese lily) .. 35 40
2145 75 c. *Lilium* "Joan Evans" 35 40
2146 75 c. *Rosa* "Rosemary Harkness" 35 40
2147 90 c. *Camellia japonica* "Extravaganza" .. 40 45
2148 $1 Chrysanthemum "Primrose Dorothy Else" 45 50
2149 $2 Dahlia "Brandaris" 85 90
2130/49 .. .. *Set of* 20 10·00 11·00
MS2150 Two sheets, each 68×98 mm. (a) $5 Narcissus "Rembrandt". (b) $6 Gladiolus "Flowersong" .. .. .. *Set of 2 sheets* 4·75 5·00

Nos. 2131/4 and 2135/46 were each printed together, *se-tenant*, in sheetlets of 12 containing three of each design (Nos. 2131/4) or with the backgrounds forming a composite design (Nos. 2135/46).

No. 2135 is inscribed "Fuschcia", No. 2143 "Mammouth" and No. **MS**2150b "Gladiollus", all in error.

(Litho Questa)

1996 (26 June). *50th Anniv of U.N.I.C.E.F. Horiz designs as T* **366** *of Antigua. Multicoloured. P* 14.

2151 75 c. Child's face 35 40
2152 $2 Child with spoon 85 90
2153 $3 Girl sewing .. .. 1·25 1·40
2151/3 .. .. *Set of* 3 2·40 2·50
MS2154 105×75 mm. $6 Mother carrying child 2·75 3·00

(Des Jennifer Toombs. Litho Questa)

1996 (26 June). *3000th Anniv of Jerusalem. Multicoloured designs as T* **367** *of Antigua, but horiz. P* 14.

MS2155 137×47 mm. $1 Pool of Bethesda and *Papaver rhoeas*; $2 Damascus Gate and *Chrysanthemum coronarium*; $3 Church of All Nations and *Myrtus communis* .. .. .. 2·75 3·00
MS2156 82×62 mm. $6 Church of the Holy Sepulchre .. .. 2·50 2·75

(Des J. Iskowitz. Litho Questa)

1996 (26 June). *Centenary of Radio. Entertainers. Multicoloured designs as T* **368** *of Antigua. P* $13^1/_2$×14.

2157 35 c. Ed Wynn 15 20
2158 75 c. Red Skelton 35 40
2159 $1 Joe Penner 45 50
2160 $3 Jerry Colonna .. .. 1·25 1·40
2157/60 .. .. *Set of* 4 2·10 2·50
MS2161 70×99 mm. $6 Bob Elliot and Ray Goulding (*horiz*). P 14×$13^1/_2$ .. .. .. 2·75 3·00

(Litho Questa)

1996 (15 July). *Olympic Games, Atlanta. Previous Medal Winners. Multicoloured designs as T* **425** *of Grenada. P* 14.

2162 35 c. Los Angeles Memorial Coliseum .. 15 20
2163 75 c. Connie Carpenter-Phinney (U.S.A.) (Cycling) 35 40
2164 $1 Josef Neckermann (Germany) (*vert*) 45 50
a. Sheetlet. Nos. 2164/72 .. .. 4·00
2165 $1 Harry Boldt (Germany) (*vert*) .. 45 50
2166 $1 Elena Petouchkova (Russia) (*vert*) .. 45 50
2167 $1 Alwin Schockemoehle (Germany) (*vert*) 45 50
2168 $1 Hans Winkler (Germany) (*vert*) .. 45 50
2169 $1 Joe Fargis (U.S.A.) (*vert*) 45 50
2170 $1 David Broome (Great Britain) (*vert*) 45 50
2171 $1 Reiner Klimke (Germany) (*vert*) .. 45 50
2172 $1 Richard Meade (Great Britain) (*vert*) 45 50
2173 $1 Julianne McNamara (U.S.A.) (*vert*) 45 50
a. Sheetlet. Nos. 2173/81 .. .. 4·00
2174 $1 Takuti Hayata (Japan) (*vert*) .. 45 50
2175 $1 Nikolai Adriana (Russia) (*vert*) .. 45 50
2176 $1 Mitch Gaylord (U.S.A.) (*vert*) .. 45 50
2177 $1 Ludmilla Tourischeva (Russia) (*vert*) 45 50
2178 $1 Karin Janz (Germany) (*vert*) .. 45 50
2179 $1 Peter Kormann (U.S.A.) (*vert*) .. 45 50
2180 $1 Sawoo Kato (Japan) (*vert*) 45 50
2181 $1 Nadia Comaneci (Rumania) (*vert*) .. 45 50
2182 $2 Mohamed Bouchighe (Algeria) (Boxing) (*vert*) 85 90
2183 $3 Jackie Joyner Kersee (U.S.A.) (Javelin) .. .. 1·25 1·40
2162/83 .. .. *Set of* 22 10·00 11·00
MS2184 Two sheets, each 103×74 mm. (a) $5 Child waving flag (*vert*). (b) $6 William Steinkraus (U.S.A.) (Show jumping) *Set of 2 sheets* 4·75 5·00

Nos. 2164/72 (equestrians) and 2173/81 (gymnasts) were each printed together, *se-tenant*, in sheetlets of 9 with the backgrounds forming composite designs.

(Des J. Puvilland. Litho B.D.T.)

1996 (25 July). *Classic Cars. Multicoloured designs as T* **426** *of Grenada. P* 14.

2185 35 c. Chevrolet Belair convertible 15 20
a. Sheetlet. Nos. 2185/8 and 2195/6 .. 3·50
2186 50 c. V.I.P. car 25 30
2187 75 c. Rolls-Royce Torpedo 35 40
2188 $1 Nissan "Cepric" type 45 50
2189 $1 Delaunay-Belleville HB6 .. .. 45 50
a. Sheetlet. Nos. 2189/94 .. .. 2·75
2190 $1 Bugatti Type-15 .. .. .. 45 50
2191 $1 Mazda Type 800 .. .. .. 45 50
2192 $1 Mercedes 24/100/140 Sport 45 50
2193 $1 MG K3 Rover 45 50
2194 $1 Plymouth Fury 45 50
2195 $2 Mercedes-Benz 500K 85 90
2196 $3 Bugatti Type-13 .. .. .. 1·25 1·40
2185/96 .. .. *Set of* 12 6·00 6·50
MS2197 Two sheets, each 106×76 mm. (a) $5 Bugatti "Roadster" Type-55. (b) $6 Lincoln Type-L .. .. *Set of 2 sheets* 4·75 5·00

Nos. 2185/8 with 2195/6 and 2189/94 were each printed together, *se-tenant*, in sheetlets of 6.

(Litho Questa)

1996 (14 Aug). *Ships. Multicoloured designs as T* **427** *of Grenada. P* 14.

2198 35 c. Grenada schooner 15 20
2199 75 c. Grenada schooner (*different*) .. 35 40
2200 $1 Athenian triremes, 1000 B.C. .. 45 50
a. Sheetlet. Nos. 2200/5 .. .. 2·75
2201 $1 Egyptian Nile galley, 30 B.C. .. 45 50
2202 $1 Bangladesh dinghi, 310 B.C. .. 45 50
2203 $1 Warship of Queen Hatshepsut, 476 B.C. 45 50
2204 $1 Chinese junk, 200 B.C. 45 50
2205 $1 Polynesian ocean-going canoe, 600 B.C. 45 50
2206 $1 *Europa* (liner), 1957 .. .. 45 50
a. Sheetlet. Nos. 2206/11 .. .. 2·75
2207 $1 *Lusitania* (liner), 1906 .. .. 45 50
2208 $1 *Queen Mary* (liner), 1936 .. .. 45 50
2209 $1 *Bianca C* (liner) 45 50
2210 $1 *France* (liner), 1952 .. .. .. 45 50
2211 $1 *Orion* (liner), 1915 .. .. .. 45 50
2198/211 .. .. *Set of* 14 6·00 6·50
MS2212 Two sheets, each 104×74 mm. (a) $5 *Queen Elizabeth 2* (liner), 1969 (56×42 *mm*). (b) $6 Viking longship, 610 (42×56 *mm*) *Set of 2 sheets* 4·75 5·00

Nos. 2200/5 and 2206/11 were each printed together, *se-tenant*, in sheetlets of 6.

117 Felix Mendelssohn

118 Man Ho Temple, 1841

1996 (26 Aug). *Composers. T* **117** *and similar vert designs. Multicoloured. Litho. P* 14.

2213 $1 Type **117** 45 50
a. Sheetlet. Nos. 2213/21 .. .. 4·00
2214 $1 Franz Schubert 45 50
2215 $1 Franz Joseph Haydn 45 50
2216 $1 Robert Schumann 45 50
2217 $1 Ludwig van Beethoven 45 50
2218 $1 Gioacchino Rossini 45 50
2219 $1 George Frederick Handel 45 50
2220 $1 Pyotr Tchaikovsky 45 50
2221 $1 Frédéric Chopin 45 50
2222 $1 Bela Bartok 45 50
a. Sheetlet. Nos. 2222/30 .. .. 4·00
2223 $1 Giacomo Puccini 45 50
2224 $1 George Gershwin 45 50
2225 $1 Leonard Bernstein 45 50
2226 $1 Kurt Weill 45 50
2227 $1 John Cage 45 50
2228 $1 Aaron Copland 45 50
2229 $1 Sergei Prokofiev 45 50
2230 $1 Igor Stravinsky 45 50
2213/30 .. .. *Set of* 18 8·00 9·00
MS2231 Two sheets, each 74×104 mm. (a) $5 Richard Strauss. (b) $6 Wolfgang Amadeus Mozart .. .. *Set of 2 sheets* 4·75 5·00

Nos. 2213/21 and 2222/30 were each printed together, *se-tenant*, in sheetlets of 9 with the backgrounds forming a composite designs.

1996 (28 Aug). *Railway Steam Locomotives. Horiz designs as T* **429** *of Grenada. Multicoloured. Litho. P* 14.

2232 $1.50, Class 38 No. 382, Germany .. 65 70
a. Sheetlet. Nos. 2232/7 .. .. 3·75
2233 $1.50, *Duchess of Hamilton*, Great Britain 65 70
2234 $1.50, Class WP, India 65 70
2235 $1.50, Class 141R *Americaine*, France .. 65 70
2236 $1.50, Class A4 *Mallard*, Great Britain .. 65 70
2237 $1.50, Class 18 No. 201, Germany .. 65 70
2238 $1.50, Class A2 *Blue Peter*, Great Britain 65 70
a. Sheetlet. Nos. 2238/43 .. .. 3·75
2239 $1.50, Class P36, Russia 65 70
2240 $1.50, Class QJ, China 65 70
2241 $1.50, Class 12, Belgium 65 70
2242 $1.50, Class "Challenger", U.S.A. .. 65 70
2243 $1.50, Class 25, South Africa 65 70
2232/43 .. .. *Set of* 12 7·75 8·25
MS2244 Two sheets, each 100×70 mm. (a) $5 Class "King", Great Britain. (b) $6 Class "Royal Scot", Great Britain .. .. *Set of 2 sheets* 4·75 5·00

Nos. 2232/7 and 2238/43 were each printed together, *se-tenant*, in sheetlets of 6.

(Litho Questa)

1996 (18 Nov). *Christmas. Religious Paintings. Vert designs as T* **369** *of Antigua showing different details from "Suffer Little Children to Come Unto Me" by Van Dyck. P* $13^1/_2$×14.

2245 15 c. multicoloured 10 10
2246 25 c. multicoloured 10 15
2247 $1 multicoloured 45 50
2248 $1.50, multicoloured 65 70
2249 $2 multicoloured 85 90
2250 $4 multicoloured .. .. 1·75 1·90
2245/50 .. .. *Set of* 6 3·75 4·00
MS2251 Two sheets, each 106×76 mm. (a) $6 "Suffer Little Children to Come Unto Me" (detail) (Van Dyck) (*horiz*). (b) $6 "Adoration of the Magi" (Rembrandt) (*horiz*). P 14×$13^1/_2$ *Set of 2 sheets* 5·25 5·50

(Des Dena Rubin. Litho B.D.T.)

1997 (12 Feb). *"HONG KONG '97" International Stan[...] Exhibition. Hong Kong Past and Present. T* **118** *and simil[...] horiz designs. Multicoloured. P* 14.

MS2252 Five sheets, each 120×96 mm. (a) $3 Type **118**; $3 Man Ho Temple, 1983. (b) $3 St. John's Cathedral, Victoria 1886; $3 St. John's Cathedral, Victoria 1983. (c) $3 Victoria Harbour, 1858; $3 Victoria Harbour, 1983. (d) $3 Water front skyscraper; $3 Aerial view of central Victoria. (e) $3 Signing of Treaty of Nanking, 1852. $3 Margaret Thatcher signing The Joint Declaration, 1984 .. .. *Set of 5 sheets* 12·50 13·

(Des M. Freedman and Dena Rubin. Litho Questa)

1997 (3 Apr). *50th Anniv of U.N.E.S.C.O. Multicoloure[...] designs as T* **374** *of Antigua. Multicoloured. P* 14×$13^1/_2$ *(hori[...] or* $13^1/_2$×14 (*vert*).

2253 15 c. Temple, Kyoto, Japan 10 1
2254 25 c. Roman ruins, Trier, Germany .. 10 1
2255 $1 Gateway, Mount Taishan, China .. 45 5
2256 $1 Temple guardian, Kyoto, Japan (*vert*) 45 5
a. Sheetlet. Nos. 2256/63 and central label .. .. 3·50
2257 $1 Temple deity, Kyoto, Japan (*vert*) .. 45 5
2258 $1 Temple lamp, Kyoto, Japan (*vert*) .. 45 5
2259 $1 Ayutthaya, Thailand (*vert*) 45 5
2260 $1 Statue, Borobudur Temple, Indonesia (*vert*) 45 5
2261 $1 Monuments at Pattadakal, India (*vert*) 45 5
2262 $1 Sleeping buddha, Polonnaruwa, Sri Lanka (*vert*) 45 5
2263 $1 Sagarmatha National Park, Nepal (*vert*) 45 5
2264 $1 Congonhas Sanctuary, Brazil (*vert*) 45 5
a. Sheetlet. No. 2264/71 and central label .. .. 3·50
2265 $1 Cartagena, Colombia (*vert*) 45 5
2266 $1 Pueblo, Guatemala (*vert*) 45 5
2267 $1 Maya statue, Honduras (*vert*) .. 45 5
2268 $1 Popocatepetl Monastery, Mexico (*vert*) 45 5
2269 $1 Galapagos Islands, Ecuador (*vert*) .. 45 5
2270 $1 Waterfall, Costa Rica (*vert*) 45 5
2271 $1 Glaciares National Park, Argentina (*vert*) 45 5
2272 $1.50, Notre Dame Cathedral, Paris, France 65 7
a. Sheetlet. Nos. 2272/6 .. .. 2·50
2273 $1.50, Timbered house, Maulbronn, Germany 65 7
2274 $1.50, Gateway, Himeji-jo, Japan .. 65 7
2275 $1.50, Lion statues, Delphi, Greece .. 65 7
2276 $1.50, Palace of Fontainebleau, France 65 7
2277 $1.50, Scandola Nature Reserve, France 65 7
2278 $2 Citadel, Dubrovnik, Croatia .. 85 9
2279 $4 Angra do Heroismo, Portugal .. 1·75 1·9
2253/79 .. .. *Set of* 7 14·00 15·0
MS2280 Three sheets, each 127×102 mm. (a) $6 Mont St. Michel, France; (b) $6 Ruins of Teotihuacau, Mexico; (c) $6 Temple, Chengde, China .. .. *Set of 3 sheets* 7·50 7·7

Nos. 2256/63 and 2264/71 were each printed togethe[r] *se-tenant*, in sheetlets of 8 stamps with a centre label and No[s.] 2272/6 in sheetlet of 5 stamps with a top left-hand corner labe[l].

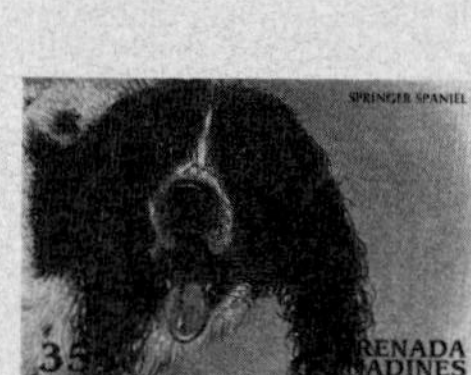

119 Springer Spaniel

120 Hong Kong

(Des R. Rundo. Litho Questa)

1997 (10 Apr). *Cats and Dogs. T* **119** *and similar multi[...] coloured designs. P* 14.

2281 35 c. Type **119** 15 2
2282 45 c. Abyssinian Blue 20 2
2283 50 c. Burmese Cream (*vert*) 25 3
2284 75 c. Doberman Pinscher 35 4
2285 90 c. Persian Tortoiseshell and White .. 40 4
2286 $1 Italian Spinone (*vert*) 45 5
2287 $1.50, Siamese Chocolate Point .. 70 7
a. Sheetlet. Nos. 2287/92 .. .. 65 7
2288 $1.50, Oriental Shorthair White .. 3·75
2289 $1.50, Burmese Sable 65 7
2290 $1.50, Abyssinian Tabby 65 7
2291 $1.50, Persian Shaded Silver 65 7
2292 $1.50, Tonkinese Natural Mink .. 65 7
2293 $1.50, Leonberger 65 7
a. Sheetlet. Nos. 2293/8 .. .. 3·75
2294 $1.50, Newfoundland 65 7
2295 $1.50, Boxer 65 7
2296 $1.50, St. Bernard 65 7
2297 $1.50, Silky Terrier 65 7
2298 $1.50, Miniature Schnauzer 65 7
2299 $2 Cocker Spaniel (*vert*) 85 9
2300 $3 Oriental Shorthair Agouti (*vert*) .. 1·25 1·4
2281/300 .. .. *Set of* 20 10·00 10·5
MS2301 Two sheets. (a) 75×105 mm. $6 Sphynx (*vert*). (b) 105×75 mm. $6 Golden Retriever puppy .. .. *Set of 2 sheets* 5·25 5·5

Nos. 2287/92 (cats) and 2293/8 (dogs) were each printe[d] together, *se-tenant*, in sheetlets of 6 with the background[s] forming composite designs.

(Litho Questa)

1997 (15 Apr). *Dinosaurs. Multicoloured designs as T* **438** *of Grenada. P* 14.
2302 45 c. Stegosaurus 20 25
2303 90 c. Diplodocus 40 45
2304 $1 Pteranodon (*vert*) 45 50
2305 $1.50, Rhamphorhynchus and head of Brachiosaurus 65 70
a. Sheetlet. Nos. 2305/10 . . . . 3·75
2306 $1.50, Archaeopteryx 65 70
2307 $1.50, Anurognathus and body of Brachiosaurus 65 70
2308 $1.50, Head of Albertosaurus 65 70
2309 $1.50, Herrerasaurus and legs of Brachiosaurus 65 70
2310 $1.50, Platyhystrix and body of Albertosaurus 65 70
2311 $2 Deinonychus and Ankylasaurus (*vert*) 85 90
2302/11 . . . . *Set of* 10 5·50 5·75
MS2312 Two sheets, each 103×74 mm. (a) $6 Allosaurus (*vert*). (b) $6 Hydacrosaurus *Set of* 2 *sheets* 5·25 5·50
Nos. 2305/10 were printed together, *se-tenant*, in sheetlets of 6 with the backgrounds forming a composite design.

(Des R. Rundo. Litho Questa)

1997 (28 May). *300th Anniv of Mother Goose Nursery Rhymes. Sheet 72×102 mm containing vert design as T* **309** *of Dominica. Multicoloured. P* 14.
MS2313 $6 Girl and sheep ("Baa, Baa, Black Sheep") . . . . 2·50 2·75

(Des J. Iskowitz. Litho Questa)

1997 (28 May). *50th Death Anniv of Paul Harris (founder of Rotary International). Horiz design as T* **377** *of Antigua. Multicoloured. P* 14.
2314 $3 Paul Harris and village women with water pump, Burkina Faso . . . . 1·25 1·40
MS2315 78×108 mm. $6 Early Rotary parade float . . . . 2·50 2·75

(Litho Questa)

1997 (28 May). *Golden Wedding of Queen Elizabeth and Prince Philip. Horiz designs as T* **378** *of Antigua. Multicoloured (except Nos. 2318/19). P* 14.
2316 $1 Engagement photograph, 1947 . . 45 50
a. Sheetlet. Nos. 2316/21 . . . . 2·75
2317 $1 Royal coat of arms 45 50
2318 $1 Queen Elizabeth and Duke of Edinburgh, 1953 (blackish brown) . . 45 50
2319 $1 Formal portrait of Queen Elizabeth with Prince Philip in uniform (blackish brown) 45 50
2320 $1 Sandringham House 45 50
2321 $1 Queen Elizabeth and Prince Philip in carriage 45 50
2316/21 . . . . *Set of* 6 2·75 3·00
MS2322 100×70 mm. $6 Wedding photograph, 1947 . . . . 2·50 2·75
Nos. 2316/21 were printed together, *se-tenant*, in sheetlets of 6.
A $20 value embossed on gold foil exists from a limited printing.

(Des J. Iskowitz. Litho Questa)

1997 (28 May). *"Pacific '97" International Stamp Exhibition, San Francisco. Death Centenary of Heinrich von Stephan (founder of the U.P.U.). Horiz design as T* **379** *of Antigua. P* 14.
2323 $1.50, olive-green 65 70
a. Sheetlet. Nos. 2323/5 . . . . 1·90
2324 $1.50, chestnut 65 70
2325 $1.50, violet 65 70
2323/5 . . . . *Set of* 3 1·90 2·10
MS2326 82×118 mm. $6 deep blue and black 2·50 2·75
Designs:—No. 2323, Pony Express, 1860; No. 2324, Von Stephan and Mercury; No. 2325, American steam locomotive; No. **MS**2326 Von Stephan and camel courier, Baghdad.
Nos. 2323/5 were printed together, *se-tenant*, in sheets of 3 with enlarged right-hand margin.

(Litho Questa)

1997 (28 May). *Birth Bicentenary of Hiroshige (Japanese painter). "One Hundred Famous Views of Edo". Horiz designs as T* **310** *of Dominica. Multicoloured. P* $13^1/_2$×14.
2327 $1.50, "Koume Embankment" 65 70
a. Sheetlet. Nos. 2327/32 . . . . 3·75
2328 $1.50, "Azuma Shrine and the Entwined Camphor" 65 70
2329 $1.50, "Yanagishima" 65 70
2330 $1.50, "Inside Akiba Shrine, Ukeji" . . 65 70
2331 $1.50, "Distant View of Kinryuzan Temple and Azuma Bridge" 65 70
2332 $1.50, "Night View of Matsuchiyama and the San'ya Canal" 65 70
2327/32 . . . . *Set of* 6 3·75 4·00
MS2333 Two sheets, each 102×127 mm. (a) $6 "Five Pines, Onagi Canal". (b) $6 "Spiral Hall, Five Hundred Rakan Temple" . . *Set of* 2 *sheets* 5·25 5·50
Nos. 2327/32 were printed together, *se-tenant*, in sheetlets of 6.

(Des R. Rundo. Litho Questa)

1997 (28 May). *175th Anniv of Brothers Grimm's Third Collection of Fairy Tales. The Fox and the Geese. Multicoloured designs as T* **380** *of Antigua. P* $13^1/_2$×14.
2334 $2 Fox and geese 85 90
a. Sheetlet. Nos. 2334/6 . . . . 2·50
2335 $2 Fox with knife and fork and geese . . 85 90
2336 $2 Fox asleep and singing geese . . 85 90
2334/6 . . . . *Set of* 3 2·50 2·75
MS2337 124×96 mm. $6 Fox (*horiz*). P 14×$13^1/_2$ 2·50 2·75
Nos. 2334/6 were printed together, *se-tenant*, in sheetlets of 3 with an illustrated margin.

(Litho B.D.T.)

1997 (26 June). *Winter Olympic Games, Nagano, Japan. Multicoloured designs as T* **440** *of Grenada. P* 14.
2338 90 c. Slalom 40 45
2339 $1 Downhill skiing 45 50
a. Sheetlet. Nos. 2339/47 . . . . 4·00
2340 $1 Freestyle ski-jumping (blue and green ski suit) 45 50
2341 $1 Curling 45 50
2342 $1 Ski-jumping (pink ski suit) 45 50
2343 $1 Four-man bobsleigh 45 50
2344 $1 Nordic combined 45 50
2345 $1 Speed skating 45 50
2346 $1 Ice hockey 45 50
2347 $1 Cross-country skiing 45 50
2348 $2 One-man luge 85 90
2349 $3 Men's figure-skating . . . . . . 1·25 1·40
2350 $5 Speed skating (*different*) . . . . 2·10 2·25
2338/50 . . . . *Set of* 13 9·00 10·00
MS2351 Two sheets, each 97×67 mm. (a) $6 Figure skating. (b) $6 One-man luge (*vert*) *Set of* 2 *sheets* 5·25 5·50
Nos. 2339/47 were printed together, *se-tenant*, in sheetlets of 9.

(Des Y. Lee. Litho Questa)

1997 (1 July). *Return of Hong Kong to China. T* **120** *and similar multicoloured designs showing modern Hong Kong through inscription. P* 14×$13^1/_2$ *(Nos. 2352/3) or* 14 *(others).*
2352 $1 multicoloured 45 50
a. Sheetlet of 4 . . . . 1·75
2353 $1.25, multicoloured 50 55
a. Sheetlet of 4 . . . . 2·00
2354 $1.50, multicoloured (63×32 *mm*) . . 65 70
a. Sheetlet of 3 . . . . 1·90
2355 $2 multicoloured (63×32 *mm*) 85 90
a. Sheetlet of 3 . . . . 2·50
2352/5 . . . . *Set of* 4 2·40 2·50
Nos. 2352/5 were printed in sheetlets of 3 or 4, each with enlarged illustrated margins.

(Litho Questa)

1997 (22 July). *Marine Life. Horiz designs as T* **439** *of Grenada. Multicoloured. P* 14.
2356 10 c. Wimplefish 10 10
2357 15 c. Clown Triggerfish 10 10
2358 25 c. Ringed Emperor Angelfish 10 15
2359 35 c. Hooded Butterflyfish 15 20
2360 45 c. Semicircle Angelfish 20 25
2361 75 c. Scribbled Angelfish 35 40
2362 90 c. Threadfin Butterflyfish 40 45
2363 $1.10, Clown Surgeonfish 50 55
2364 $2 Bottle-nosed Dolphin 85 90
2365 $5 Triggerfish . . . . 2·10 2·25
2366 $10 Lionfish . . . . 4·25 4·50
2367 $20 Jackknife Fish . . . . 8·75 9·00
2356/67 . . . . *Set of* 12 16·00 17·00

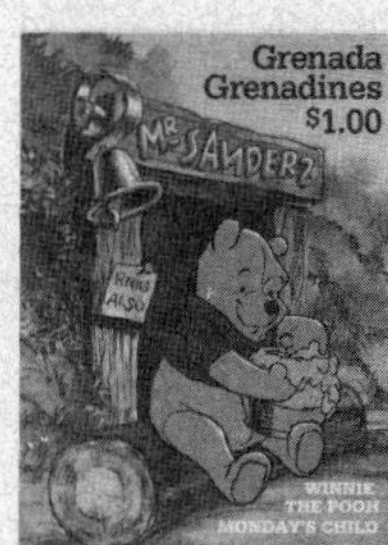

121 Winnie the Pooh as Monday's Child

(Des Alvin White Studios. Litho Questa)

1997 (7 Aug). *"Monday's Child" (poem). T* **121** *and similar vert designs showing Disney cartoon characters from Winnie the Pooh illustrating the various verses. Multicoloured. P* $13^1/_2$×14.
2368 $1 Type **121** 45 50
a. Sheetlet. Nos. 2368/73 . . . . 2·75
2369 $1 Kanga as Tuesday's child 45 50
2370 $1 Eeyore as Wednesday's child 45 50
2371 $1 Tigger as Thursday's child 45 50
2372 $1 Piglet as Friday's child 45 50
2373 $1 Rabbit as Saturday's child 45 50
2368/73 . . . . *Set of* 6 2·75 3·00
MS2374 128×107 mm. $6 Christopher Robin as Sunday's child . . . . 2·75 3·00
Nos. 2368/73 were printed together, *se-tenant*, in sheetlets of 6.

122 Snow White kissing Grumpy

(Des Alvin White Studios. Litho Questa)

1997 (7 Aug). *Disney Sweethearts. T* **122** *and similar multicoloured designs showing Disney cartoon characters kissing. P* 14×$13^1/_2$.
2375 $1 Type **122** 45 50
a. Sheetlet. Nos. 2375/83 . . . . 4·00
2376 $1 Figaro the Cat and Cleo the Fish . . 45 50
2377 $1 Peter Pan and Wendy 45 50
2378 $1 Cinderella and the Prince 45 50
2379 $1 Ariel and Eric 45 50
2380 $1 Beauty and the Prince 45 50
2381 $1 Aladdin and Jasmine 45 50
2382 $1 Pocahontas and Captain John Smith 45 50
2383 $1 Phoebus and Esmeralda 45 50
2375/83 . . . . *Set of* 9 4·00 4·50
MS2384 127×102 mm. $5 Georges Hautecourt kissing cat's tail (*vert*). P $13^1/_2$×14 . . . . 2·25 2·40
Nos. 2375/83 were printed together, *se-tenant*, in sheetlets of 9.

(Litho Questa)

1997 (11 Aug). *World Football Championship, France* (1998). *Designs as T* **383** *of Antigua. P* 14×$13^1/_2$ *(horiz) or* $13^1/_2$×14 *(vert).*
2385 10 c. steel-blue 10 10
2386 20 c. multicoloured 10 10
2387 45 c. sepia 20 25
2388 $1 black 45 50
2389 $1 sepia 45 50
a. Sheetlet. Nos. 2389/96 and central label . . . . 3·50
2390 $1 black 45 50
2391 $1 sepia 45 50
2392 $1 multicoloured 45 50
2393 $1 multicoloured 45 50
2394 $1 black 45 50
2395 $1 sepia 45 50
2396 $1 multicoloured 45 50
2397 $1 black 45 50
a. Sheetlet. Nos. 2397/404 and central label . . . . 3·50
2398 $1 black 45 50
2399 $1 black 45 50
2400 $1 black 45 50
2401 $1 black 45 50
2402 $1 black 45 50
2403 $1 black 45 50
2404 $1 black 45 50
2405 $1.50, multicoloured 65 70
2406 $5 black . . . . 2·10 2·25
2385/406 . . . . *Set of* 22 10·00 11·00
MS2407 Two sheets. (a) 127×102 mm. $6 black. (b) 102×127 mm. $6 black . . *Set of* 2 *sheets* 5·25 5·50
Designs: *Horiz*—No. 2385, Italian team, 1934; No. 2386, Angolan team; No. 2387, Brazilian team, 1958; No. 2388, Uruguay team, 1950; No. 2389, Winning England team, 1966; No. 2390, West German team, 1954; No. 2391, Uruguyan officials with Jules Rimet trophy, 1930; No. 2392, West German players celebrating, 1990; No. 2393, Maradonna (Argentine player), 1986; No. 2394, Brazilian players, 1994; No. 2395, Argentine players, 1978; No. 2396, West German player holding World Cup, 1974; No. 2405, West German team, 1974; No. 2406, Italian team, 1938; No. **MS**2407b, Paulao, Angola. *Vert*—No. 2397, Ademir, Brazil; No. 2398, Kocsis, Hungary; No. 2399, Leonidas, Brazil; No. 2400, Nejedly, Czechoslovakia; No. 2401, Schiavio, Italy; No. 2402, Stabile, Uruguay; No. 2403, Pele, Brazil; No. 2404, Fritzwalter, West Germany, No. **MS**2407a, Shearer, England.
Nos. 2389/96 and 2397/404 were each printed together, *se-tenant*, in sheetlets of 8 stamps and a central label.

1997 (12 Aug). *Butterflies. Multicoloured designs as T* **444** *of Grenada. Litho. P* 14.
2408 75 c. *Polyura dehaani* 35 40
2409 90 c. *Polyura dolon* 40 45
2410 $1 *Charaxes candiope* 45 50
2411 $1.50, *Pantaporia punctata* 65 70
2412 $1.50, *Euthalia confucius* 65 70
a. Sheetlet. Nos. 2412/17 . . . . 3·75
2413 $1.50, *Euthalia kardama* 65 70
2414 $1.50, *Limenitis albomaculata* 65 70
2415 $1.50, *Hestina assimilis* 65 70
2416 $1.50, *Kallima inachus* 65 70
2417 $1.50, *Euthalia teutoides* 65 70
2418 $1.50, *Euphaedra francina* 65 70
a. Sheetlet. Nos. 2418/23 . . . . 3·75
2419 $1.50, *Euphaedra eleus* 65 70
2420 $1.50, *Euphaedra harpalyce* 65 70
2421 $1.50, *Euphaedra cyparissa* 65 70
2422 $1.50, *Euphaedra gausape* 65 70
2423 $1.50, *Euphaedra imperialis* 65 70
2424 $2 *Charaxes etesippe* 85 90
2425 $3 *Charaxes castor* . . . . . . 1·25 1·40
2408/25 . . . . *Set of* 18 11·00 11·50
MS2426 Two sheets, each 106×76 mm. (a) $5 *Charaxes nobilis* (*vert*). (b) $6 *Charaxes numenes* (*vert*) . . . . *Set of* 2 *sheets* 4·75 5·00
Nos. 2412/17 and 2418/23 were each printed together, *se-tenant*, in sheetlets of 6 with the backgrounds forming composite designs.

123 James Dean

124 *Symphyglossum sanguineum*

(Des Shannon. Litho Questa)

1997 (22 Aug). *James Dean (actor) Commemoration. T* **123** *and similar vert designs showing different portraits. Multicoloured. P* 13½×14.

2427 $1 Type **123** .. 45 50
 a. Sheetlet. Nos. 2427/35 .. 4·00
2428 $1 Wearing purple jumper .. 45 50
2429 $1 Wearing stetson and smoking .. 45 50
2430 $1 Wearing dinner jacket and tie .. 45 50
2431 $1 Full-face portrait .. 45 50
2432 $1 Grimacing .. 45 50
2433 $1 Wearing stetson .. 45 50
2434 $1 Leaning on arms .. 45 50
2435 $1 Smoking .. 45 50
2427/35 .. *Set of* 9 4·00 4·50

Nos. 2427/35 were printed together, *se-tenant*, in sheetlets of 9 with enlarged illustrated right-hand margin.

(Des T. Wood. Litho B.D.T.)

1997 (4 Sept). *Orchids of the World. T* **124** *and similar vert designs. Multicoloured. P* 14.

2436 35 c. Type **124** .. 15 20
2437 45 c. *Doritaenopsis* "Mythic Beauty" .. 20 25
2438 75 c. *Odontoglossum cervantesii* .. 35 40
2439 90 c. *Cattleya* "Pumpernickel" .. 40 45
2440 $1 *Vanda* "Patricia Low" .. 45 50
2441/9 $1 × 9 (*Lycaste* "Aquila"; *Brassolaeliocattleya* "Dorothy Bertsch"; *Phalaenopsis* "Zuma Urchin"; *Promenaea xanthina*; *Amesiella philippinensis*; *Brassocattleya* "Angel Lace"; *Brassoepidendrum* "Peggy Ann"; *Miltonia seine*; *Sophralaeliocattleya* "Precious Stones")
 a. Sheetlet. Nos. 2441/9 .. 4·25
2450/8 $1 × 9 (*Cymbidium* "Showgirl"; *Disa blackii*; *Phalaenopsis aphrodite*; *Iwanagaara* "Apple Blossom"; *Masdevallia* "Copper Angel"; *Paphiopedilum micranthum*; *Paphiopedilum* "Clare de Lune"; *Cattleya forbesii*; *Dendrobium* "Dawn Maree")
 a. Sheetlet. Nos 2450/8 .. 4·25
2459 $1.50, *Odontonia* "Debutante" .. 65 70
2460/5 $1.50 × 6 (*Miltoniopsis* "Jean Sabourin"; *Cymbididium* "Red Beauty"; *Brassocattleya* "Green Dragon"; *Phalaenopsis* hybrid; *Laeliocattleya* "Mary Ellen Carter"; *Disa* hybrid)
 a. Sheetlet. Nos 2460/5 .. 3·75
2466/71 $1.50 × 6 (*Lycaste macrobulbon*; *Cochleanthes discolor*; *Cymbidium* "Nang Carpenter"; *Paphiopedilum* "Clare de Lune"; *Masdevallia caudata*; *Cymbidium* "Showgirl")
 a. Sheetlet. Nos 2466/71 .. 3·75
2472 $2 *Laeliocattleya* "Mini Purple" .. 85 90
2473 $3 *Phragmipedium dominiarum* .. 1·25 1·40
2436/73 .. *Set of* 38 20·00 21·00
MS2474 Two sheets, each 76×106mm. (a) $5 *Phalenopsis* "Medford Star"; (b) $6 *Brassolaeliocattleya* "Dorothy Bertsch" .. *Set of 2 sheets* 4·75 5·00

Nos. 2441/9, 2450/8, 2460/5 and 2466/71 were each printed together, *se-tenant*, in sheetlets of 9 (Nos. 2441/9, 2450/8) or 6 some with the backgrounds forming a composite design (Nos. 2460/5, 2466/71).

125 *Clitocybe metachroa*

126 Ludwig van Beethoven

(Litho Questa)

1997 (4 Sept). *Fungi. T* **125** *and similar horiz designs. Multicoloured. P* 14.

2475 75 c. Type **125** .. 35 40
2476 90 c. *Clavulinopsis helvola* .. 40 45
2477 $1 *Lycoperdon pyriforme* .. 45 50
2478 $1.50, *Auricularia auricula-judae* .. 65 70
2479 $1.50, *Entoloma incanum* .. 65 70
 a. Sheetlet. Nos. 2479/84 .. 3·75
2480 $1.50, *Coprinus atramentarius* .. 65 70
2481 $1.50, *Mycena polygramma* .. 65 70
2482 $1.50, *Lepista nuda* .. 65 70
2483 $1.50, *Pleurotis cornucopiae* .. 65 70
2484 $1.50, *Laccaria amethystina* .. 65 70
2485 $2 *Clathrus archeri* .. 85 90
2486 $3 *Lactarius trivialis* .. 1·25 1·40
2475/86 .. *Set of* 12 7·50 8·00
MS2487 Two sheets, each 106×76mm. (a) $6 *Morchella esculenta*. (b) $6 *Amanita muscaria* *Set of 2 sheets* 5·25 5·50

Nos. 2479/84 were printed together, *se-tenant*, in sheetlets of 6.

(Des Christina de Musée. Litho Questa)

1997 (10 Oct). *Classical Composers. T* **126** *and similar vert designs. Multicoloured. P* 14½.

2488 $1 Type **126** .. 45 50
 a. Sheetlet. Nos. 2488/95 and label .. 3·50
2489 $1 Pyotr Tchaikovsky .. 45 50
2490 $1 Johann Christian Bach .. 45 50
2491 $1 Frédéric Chopin .. 45 50
2492 $1 Igor Stravinsky .. 45 50
2493 $1 Franz Joseph Haydn .. 45 50
2494 $1 Gustav Mahler .. 45 50
2495 $1 Gioacchino Antonio Rossini .. 45 50
2488/95 .. *Set of* 8 3·50 4·00
MS2496 Two sheets, each 106×76mm. (a) $6 Wolfgang Amadeus Mozart. (b) $6 Franz Schubert .. *Set of 2 sheets* 5·25 5·50

Nos. 2488/95 were printed together, *se-tenant*, in sheetlets of 8 stamps and one central label.

127 Diana, Princess of Wales and Buckingham Palace

128 Tiger (hologram)

(Des Y. Lee. Litho Questa)

1997 (10 Nov). *Diana, Princess of Wales Commemoration. T* **127** *and similar horiz designs. Multicoloured. P* 14.

2497 $1.50, Type **127** .. 65 70
 a. Sheetlet. Nos. 2497/502 .. 3·75
2498 $1.50, Princess Diana and lake at Althorp 65 70
2499 $1.50, Princess Diana and Westminster Abbey .. 65 70
2500 $1.50, Princess Diana and gates to Althorp 65 70
2501 $1.50, Princess Diana in pink hat and gates to Kensington Palace .. 65 70
2502 $1.50, Princess Diana and Althorp House 65 70
2497/502 .. *Set of* 6 3·75 4·00
MS2503 115×80mm, $6 Holding bouquet (60×40 *mm*). P 14×14½ .. 2·50 2·75

Nos. 2497/502 were printed together, *se-tenant*, in sheetlets of 6 with enlarged illustrated right-hand margin.

Two different $20 values embossed on gold foil and an $8 on silver foil showing a hologram exist from limited printings.

(Litho Questa)

1997 (5 Dec). *Christmas. Religious Paintings. Multicoloured designs as T* **448** *of Grenada. P* 14.

2504 20 c. "Choir of Angels" (Simon Marmion) 10 15
2505 75 c. "The Annunciation" (Giotto) .. 35 40
2506 90 c. "Festival of the Rose Garlands" (Albrecht Dürer) .. 40 45
2507 $1.50, "Madonna with Two Angels" (Hans Memling) .. 65 70
2508 $2 "The Ognissanti Madonna" (Giotto) 85 90
2509 $3 "Angel with Candlestick" (Michelangelo) .. 1·25 1·40
2504/9 .. *Set of* 6 3·50 4·00
MS2510 Two sheets, each 114×104 mm. (a) $6 "The Rising of the Sun" (detail) (*horiz*) (Francois Boucher). (b) $6 "Cupid" (detail) (*horiz*) (Jean-Baptiste Huet) .. *Set of 2 sheets* 4·75 5·00

No. 2506 is inscribed "DUER" in error.

1997 (12 Dec). *Fishes. Multicoloured designs as T* **449** *of Grenada. Litho. P* 14.

2511 $1 Queen Angelfish .. 45 50
 a. Sheetlet. Nos. 2511/19 .. 4·00
2512 $1 Clown Triggerfish .. 45 50
2513 $1 Four-spot Butterflyfish .. 45 50
2514 $1 Yellow-tailed Damselfish .. 45 50
2515 $1 Yellow-headed Wrasse .. 45 50
2516 $1 Royal Gramma .. 45 50
2517 $1 Candy Basslet .. 45 50
2518 $1 Smooth Trunkfish .. 45 50
2519 $1 Coral Hind .. 45 50
2511/19 .. *Set of* 9 4·00 4·50
MS2520 Two sheets. (a) 102×72 mm. $6 Black-finned Reef Shark. (b) 72×102 mm. $6 Yellow-headed Jawfish (*vert*) .. *Set of 2 sheets* 5·25 5·50

Nos. 2511/19 were printed together, *se-tenant*, in sheetlets of 9 with the backgrounds forming a composite design.

1998 (10 Feb). *Chinese New Year ("Year of the Tiger"). Litho. Die-cut perf* 11.

2521 **128** $1.50, black on silver foil .. 65 70
 a. Sheetlet of 4 .. 2·75
MS2522 64×76 mm. **128** $3 black on silver foil (52×65 *mm*) .. 1·25 1·40

No. 2521 was printed in sheetlets of 4 with an overall pattern of Chinese characters which varies from stamp to stamp.

129 *Alabama* (Confederate warship)

(Des R. Sauber. Litho Questa)

1998 (7 May). *Famous Ships. T* **129** *and similar multicoloured designs. P* 14.

(*a*) *Ships of the* 1860s

2523 75 c. Type **129** .. 35 40
 a. Sheetlet. Nos. 2523/34 .. 4·00
2524 75 c. *Persia* (paddle-steamer) .. 35 40
2525 75 c. *Ariel* (clipper) .. 35 40
2526 75 c. *Florida* (Confederate cruiser) .. 35 40
2527 75 c. *Great Eastern* (paddle-steamer) .. 35 40
2528 75 c. *Jacob Bell* on fire .. 35 4
2529 75 c. *Star of India* (clipper) .. 35 4
2530 75 c. *Robert E. Lee* (Mississippi paddle-steamer) .. 35 4
2531 75 c. U.S.S. *Passaic* (monitor) .. 35 4
2532 75 c. *Madagascar* (clipper) .. 35 4
2533 75 c. H.M.S. *Devastation* (battleship) .. 35 4
2534 75 c. *General Grant* (clipper) .. 35 4

(*b*) *Ships of the American Civil War*

2535 $1 Clark Gable as Rhett Butler in *Gone with the Wind* (*vert*) .. 45 5
 a. Sheetlet. Nos. 2535/42 .. 3·50
2536 $1 Crew abandoning blockade runner wrecked on Sullivan's Island (*vert*) .. 45 5
2537 $1 Margaret Mitchell (author of *Gone with the Wind*) (*vert*) .. 45 5
2538 $1 George Alfred Trenholm (ship owner) (*vert*) .. 45 5
2539 $1 Dock Street Theatre, Charleston (*vert*) 45 5
2540 $1 *Howlett* (paddle-steamer) sinking (*vert*) .. 45 5
2541 $1 U.S.S. *Tecumseh* on fire (*vert*) .. 45 5
2542 $1 City Jail, Charleston (*vert*) .. 45 5
2523/42 .. *Set of* 20 7·50 8·7
MS2543 Two sheets, each 106×76 mm. (a) $6 *Nashville* sinking Union clipper *Harvey Birch* (57×42 *mm*). (b) $6 *Hatteras* (paddle-steamer) on fire (42×57 *mm*) .. *Set of 2 sheets* 5·00 5·2

Nos. 2523/34 were printed together, *se-tenant*, in sheetlets o 12, and Nos. 2535/42 were printed together, *se-tenant*, i sheetlets of 8 showing the stamps arranged in two horizonta strips of 4 separated by stamp-size labels.

130 Concept Strike Fighter

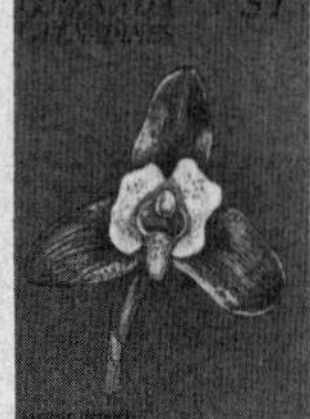

131 *Lycaste deppei*

(Litho Questa)

1998 (13 May). *Aircraft Designs of the Future. T* **130** *an similar horiz designs. Multicoloured. P* 14.

2544 70 c. Type **130** .. 30 3
2545 90 c. Concept space shuttle .. 40 4
2546 $1 Velocity 173 RG Elite .. 45 5
 a. Sheetlet. Nos. 2546/53 .. 3·50
2547 $1 Davis DA-9 .. 45 5
2548 $1 Concorde .. 45 5
2549 $1 Voyager .. 45 5
2550 $1 Factimobile .. 45 5
2551 $1 RAF 2000 .. 45 5
2552 $1 Boomerang .. 45 5
2553 $1 N1M Flying Wing .. 45 5
2554 $2 Concept air and space jet .. 85 9
2555 $3 V Jet II .. 1·25 1·4
2544/55 .. *Set of* 12 6·25 7·5
MS2556 Two sheets, each 100×70 mm. (a) $6 Concept aeropod. (b) $6 Delmar .. *Set of 2 sheets* 5·25 5·5

Nos. 2546/53 were printed together, *se-tenant*, in sheetlets o 8.

(Litho Questa)

1998 (19 May). *Orchids of the World. T* **131** *and similar ver designs. Multicoloured. P* 14.

2557 $1 Type **131** .. 45 50
 a. Sheetlet. Nos. 2557/65 .. 4·00
2558 $1 *Dendrobium victoriae* .. 45 50
2559 $1 *Dendrobium nobile* .. 45 50
2560 $1 *Cymbidium dayanum* .. 45 50
2561 $1 *Cymbidium* Starbright .. 45 50
2562 $1 *Cymbidium giganteum* .. 45 50
2563 $1 *Chysis aurea* .. 45 50
2564 $1 *Broughtonia sanguinea* .. 45 50
2565 $1 *Cattleya guttata* .. 45 50
2566 $1 *Calanthe vestita* .. 45 50
 a. Sheetlet. Nos. 2566/74 .. 4·00
2567 $1 *Cattleya bicolor* .. 45 50
2568 $1 *Laelia anceps* .. 45 50
2569 $1 *Epidendrum prismatocarpum* .. 45 50
2570 $1 *Coelogyne ochracea* .. 45 50
2571 $1 *Doritaenopsis eclantant* .. 45 50
2572 $1 *Laelia gouldiana* .. 45 50
2573 $1 *Encyclia vitellina* .. 45 50
2574 $1 *Maxillaria praestans* .. 45 50
2575 $1 *Laelia tenebrosa* .. 45 50
2576 $1.50, *Phragmipedium besseae* .. 65 70
2577 $2 *Pschopsis papilio* .. 85 90
2578 $3 *Masdevallia coccinea* .. 1·25 1·40
2557/78 .. *Set of* 22 10·50 12·00
MS2579 Two sheets, each 29×43 mm. (a) $6 *Masdevallia ignea*. (b) $6 *Encyclia brassavolae* *Set of 2 sheets* 5·25 5·50

Nos. 2557/65 and 2566/74 were each printed together, *se-tenant*, in sheetlets of 9.

1998 (30 June). *Seabirds. Multicoloured designs as T* **452** *of Grenada. Litho. P* 14.

2580 75 c. Bonaparte's Gull (*horiz*) .. 35 40
2581 90 c. Western Sandpiper (*horiz*) .. 40 45
2582 $1.50, Common Tern (*horiz*) .. 65 70
 a. Sheetlet. Nos. 2582/7 .. 3·75
2583 $1.50, Brown Pelican (*horiz*) .. 65 70
2584 $1.50, Black-legged Kittiwake and White Tern (*horiz*) .. 65 70
2585 $1.50, Herring Gull (*horiz*) .. 65 70
2586 $1.50, Lesser Noddy (*horiz*) .. 65 70

587 $1.50, Black-legged Kittiwake (*horiz*) .. 65 70
588 $1.50, Whimbrel (*horiz*) 65 70
a. Sheetlet. Nos. 2588/93 .. .. 3·75
589 $1.50, Golden White-tailed Tropic Bird (*horiz*) 65 70
590 $1.50, Arctic Tern (*horiz*) 65 70
591 $1.50, Ruddy Turnstone (*horiz*) .. 65 70
592 $1.50, Imperial Shag (*horiz*) 65 70
593 $1.50, Magellan Gull (*horiz*) 65 70
594 $2 Great Black-backed Gull (*horiz*) .. 85 90
595 $3 Dotterell (*horiz*) .. .. .. 1·25 1·40
580/95 .. .. *Set of* 16 10·00 11·50
MS2596 Two sheets, each 100×70 mm. (a) $5 Broad-billed Prion (*horiz*). (b) $5 Yellow-nosed Albatross .. .. .. *Set of* 2 *sheets* 4·25 4·50

Nos. 2582/7 and 2588/93 were each printed together, *se-tenant*, in sheetlets of 6, with the backgrounds forming composite designs.

998 (19 Aug). *International Year of the Ocean. Horiz designs as T* **454** *of Grenada. Multicoloured. Litho. P* 14.

597 75 c. Great Black-backed Gull 35 40
a. Sheetlet. Nos. 2597/608 .. .. 4·00
598 75 c. Common Dolphin 35 40
599 75 c. Seal 35 40
2600 75 c. Amazonian Catfish 35 40
2601 75 c. Shark 35 40
2602 75 c. Goldfish 35 40
2603 75 c. Cyathopharynx 35 40
2604 75 c. Killer Whale 35 40
2605 75 c. Telmatochromis 35 40
2606 75 c. Crab 35 40
2607 75 c. Octopus 35 40
2608 75 c. Turtle 35 40
2609 90 c. Two Dolphins 40 45
a. Sheetlet. Nos. 2609/20 .. .. 4·75
2610 90 c. Seal 40 45
2611 90 c. Turtle on rock 40 45
2612 90 c. Leopard Shark 40 45
2613 90 c. Flame Angelfish 40 45
2614 90 c. Syndontis 40 45
2615 90 c. Lamprologus 40 45
2616 90 c. *Krptopterus bicirrhus* 40 45
2617 90 c. *Pterophyllum scalare* 40 45
2618 90 c. Swimming Pancake 40 45
2619 90 c. Cowfish 40 45
2620 90 c. Seahorse 40 45
2597/620 .. .. *Set of* 24 8·75 10·00
MS2615 Two sheets, each 98×68 mm. (a) $6 *Tetraodon mbu*. (b) $6 Goldfish .. *Set of* 2 *sheets* 5·25 5·50

Nos. 2597/608 and 2609/20 were each printed together, *se-tenant*, in sheetlets of 12 with the backgrounds forming composite designs.

STAMP BOOKLETS

1977 (7 Feb). *Silver Jubilee. Multicoloured cover,* 165×92 *mm, showing the Queen enthroned. Stitched.*

SB1 $9.60, booklet containing 35 c. in pane of 6 (No. 219a) and *se-tenant* pane of 3 (No. 220a) .. 2·25

1978 (12 Apr). 25th *Anniv of Coronation. Multicoloured cover,* 165×92 *mm, showing the Queen's Division on parade. Stitched.*

SB2 $7.04, booklet containing *se-tenant* pane of 6 (No. 276a) and pane of 1 (No. 278a) .. .. 1·60

1981 (16 June). *Royal Wedding. Multicoloured cover,* 90×165 *mm, showing Prince Charles on front and back. Panes attached by selvedge.*

SB3 $14 booklet containing *se-tenant* pane of 6 (No. 450a) and pane of 1 (No. 452a) .. .. 2·50

The cover of No. SB3 is folded five times "concertina fashion" and when opened up measures 550×165 mm.

OFFICIAL STAMPS

1982 (June). *Various stamps optd with Type* O **1** *of Grenada.*

(*a*) *Nos.* 400/12 *and* 414

O 1 5 c. Yellow-tailed Snapper 10 15
O 2 6 c. Mutton Snapper 10 15
O 3 10 c. Cocoa Damselfish 10 15
O 4 12 c. Royal Gramma 10 15
O 5 15 c. Cherub Angelfish 10 15
O 6 20 c. Black-barred Soldierfish 10 20
O 7 25 c. Mottled Grouper 10 20
O 8 30 c. Long-snouted Butterflyfish 15 20
O 9 40 c. Puddingwife 15 25
O10 50 c. Midnight Parrotfish 20 30
O11 90 c. Red-spotted Hawkfish 40 55
O12 $1 Hogfish 40 60
O13 $3 Beau Gregory .. .. .. 1·25 2·25
O14 $10 Barred Hamlet .. .. .. 4·25 6·00

(*b*) *Nos.* 444/6 *and* 448/9

O15 30 c. Prince Charles and Lady Diana Spencer 2·00 2·00
O16 40 c. Prince Charles and Lady Diana Spencer 1·60 1·60
O17 40 c. Type **50** .. .. 2·00 2·75
O18 $2 Type **50** .. .. 2·50 3·50
O19 $4 Prince Charles as parachutist .. 6·50 8·50

The Royal Wedding $4 from sheetlets, perforated $14\frac{1}{2}$×14 and with changed background colour, also exists with this overprint (*Price £6 mint, £8 used*).

(*c*) *Nos.* 473/6

O20 **54** 20 c. multicoloured 10 20
O21 – 40 c. multicoloured 15 25
O22 – $1 multicoloured 35 70
O23 – $2 multicoloured .. .. .. 70 1·40
O1/23 .. .. *Set of* 23 20·00 29·00

Griqualand West see South Africa

Guyana
(*formerly* British Guiana)

BRITISH GUIANA

The postal service from what was to become British Guiana dates from the last years of the 18th-century, being placed on a more regular basis after the final British occupation.

An inland postal system was organised in 1850, using the adhesive stamps of British Guiana, but, until 1 May 1860, overseas mails continued to be the province of the British G.P.O. The stamps of Great Britain were supplied for use on such letters from 11 May 1858 and examples of their use in combination with British Guiana issues have been recorded.

For illustration of the handstamp and postmark type see BRITISH POST OFFICES ABROAD notes, following GREAT BRITAIN.

CROWNED-CIRCLED HANDSTAMPS

The provision of a handstamp, probably as Type CC **1**, inscribed "DEMERARA", is recorded in the G.P.O. proof book under 1 March 1856. No examples have been reported. A further handstamp, as Type CC **6**, recorded in the proof book on 17 February 1866, is known used as a cancellation in at least two instances, *circa* 1868.

GEORGETOWN (DEMERARA)

Stamps of GREAT BRITAIN *cancelled* "A 03" *as Type* **2**.

1858 to **1860**.

Z1	1d. rose-red (1857), *perf* 14	£200
Z2	4d. rose (1857)	£130
Z3	6d. lilac (1856)	£100
	a. Azure paper	
Z4	1s. green (1856)	£1100

NEW AMSTERDAM (BERBICE)

Stamps of GREAT BRITAIN *cancelled* "A 04" *as Type* **2**.

1858 to **1860**.

Z5	1d. rose-red (1857), *perf* 14	£600
Z6	2d. blue (1858) (Plate Nos. 7, 8)	£600
Z7	4d. rose (1857)	£300
Z8	6d. lilac (1856)	£200
Z9	1s. green (1856)	£1200

PRICES FOR STAMPS ON COVER TO 1945

Nos. 1/21	*from* × 3
No. 23	†
Nos. 24/7	*from* × 3
Nos. 29/115	*from* × 4
Nos. 116/24	*from* × 6
Nos. 126/36	*from* × 5
Nos. 137/59	*from* × 6
Nos. 162/5	*from* × 8
Nos. 170/4	*from* × 5
Nos. 175/89	*from* × 6
No. 192	*from* × 20
Nos. 193/210	*from* × 4
Nos. 213/15	*from* × 5
Nos. 216/21	*from* × 3
Nos. 222/4	*from* × 8
Nos. 233/50	*from* × 3
No. 251	—
Nos. 252/7	*from* × 3
Nos. 259/82	*from* × 4
Nos. 283/7	*from* × 5
Nos. 288/300	*from* × 4
Nos. 301/4	*from* × 5
Nos. 305/7	*from* × 6
Nos. 308/19	*from* × 5
Nos. D1/4	*from* × 12
Nos. O1/12	*from* × 12

CROWN COLONY

(Currency. 100 cents = 1 dollar)

1

2

(Set up and printed at the office of the *Royal Gazette*, Georgetown, British Guiana)

1850 (1 July)–**51**. *Type-set. Black impression.* (*a*) *Medium wove paper. Prices are for—I. Cut square. II. Cut round.*

No.	Type	Description	I *Used*	II *Used*
1	1	2 c. *rose* (1.3.51)	—	£70000
2		4 c. *orange*	£25000	£4000
3		4 c. *lemon-yellow* (1851)	£36000	£4500
4		8 c. *green*	£15000	£3250
5		12 c. *blue*	£5500	£2000
6		12 c. *indigo*	£9500	£2750
7		12 c. *pale blue* (1851)	£8500	£3000
		a. "2" of "12" with straight foot	—	£5000
		b. "1" of "12" omitted	†	£35000
		(*b*) *Pelure paper* (1851)		
8	1	4 c. *pale yellow*	£45000	£5000

These stamps were initialled by the postmaster, or the Post Office clerks, before they were issued. The initials are—E. T. E. D(alton), E. D. W(ight), J. B. S(mith), H. A. K(illikelley), and W. H. L(ortimer). There are several types of each value and it has been suggested that the setting contained one horizontal row of four slightly different impressions.

Ten examples of No. 1 have been recorded, including three pairs on separate covers.

(Litho Waterlow)

1852 (1 Jan). *Surface-coloured paper. Imperf.*

No.	Type	Description	*Un*	*Used*
9	2	1 c. black/*magenta*	£8500	£4250
10		4 c. black/*deep blue*	£11000	£5500

There are two types of each value.

Reprints on thicker paper and perf $12^1/_2$, were made in 1865 (*Price* £16 *either value*).

Such reprints with the perforations removed are sometimes offered as genuine originals.

CONDITION. Prices for Nos. 9 to 21 are for fine copies. Poor to medium specimens can be supplied when in stock at much lower rates.

3

4

5

(Dies eng and stamps litho Waterlow)

1853–59. *Imperf.* (*a*) *Original printing.*

No.	Type	Description	*Un*	*Used*
11	3	1 c. vermilion	£3000	£1000

This 1 c. in *reddish brown* is probably a proof (*Price* £650).

ONE CENT — A

ONE CENT — B

ONE CENT — C

ONE CENT — D

A. "O" large and 1 mm from left corner.
B. "O" small and ¾ mm from left corner.
C. "O" small and ¾ mm from left corner. "NT" widely spaced.
D. "ONE" close together, "O" 1¼ mm from left corner.

No.	Type	Description	*Un*	*Used*
		(*b*) *Fresh lithographic transfers from the* 4 c. *with varying labels of value. White line above value* (1857–59).		
12	3	1 c. dull red (A)	£2500	£900
13		1 c. brownish red (A)	£5500	£1200
14		1 c. dull red (B)	£3000	£950
15		1 c. brownish red (B)	£5500	£1300
16		1 c. dull red (C)	£3750	£1200
16*a*		1 c. brownish red (C)	—	£1500
17		1 c. dull red (D)	£9000	£4000

1853–55. *Imperf.*

No.	Type	Description	*Un*	*Used*
18	4	4 c. deep blue	£1700	£600
		a. Retouched	£2500	£850
19		4 c. blue (1854)	£1100	£425
		a. Retouched	£1700	£600
20		4 c. pale blue (1855)	£850	£325
		a. Retouched	£1500	£550

The 4 c. value was produced from transfers from the original 1 c., with the bottom inscription removed, teamed with a new face value. The join often shows as a white line or traces of it above the label of value and lower corner figures. In some stamps on the sheet this line is missing, owing to having been retouched, and in these cases a line of colour usually appears in its place.

The 1 c. and 4 c. stamps were printed in 1865 from fresh transfers of five varieties. These are on thin paper and perf $12^1/_2$ (*Price* £14 *each unused*).

1860 (May). *Figures in corners framed. Imperf.*

No.	Type	Description	*Un*	*Used*
21	5	4 c. blue	£2500	£450

6

(Type-set and printed at the *Official Gazette* by Baum and Dallas, Georgetown).

1856. (*a*) *Surface-coloured paper.*

No.	Type	Description	*Un*	*Used*
23	6	1 c. black/*magenta*	†	—
24		4 c. black/*magenta* (Feb)	†	£6000
25		4 c. black/*rose-carmine* (Sept)	£20000	£8500
26		4 c. black/*blue* (Oct)	†	£38000
		(*b*) *Paper coloured through*		
27	6	4 c. black/*deep blue* (Aug)	†	£50000

Since only one example of No. 23 is known, no market price can be given. This celebrated stamp frequently termed "the world's rarest", was last on the market in 1980.

These stamps, like those of the first issue, were initialled before being issued; the initials are—E.T.E.D (alton), E.D.W (ight), C.A. W(atson), and W.H.L (ortimer). The unique 1 c. is initialled by E.D. Wight.

The 4 c. is known in four types, differing in the position of the inscriptions.

PAPERMAKERS' WATERMARKS. Seven different papermakers' watermarks were used in the period 1860 to 1875 and stamps bearing portions of these are worth a premium.

7

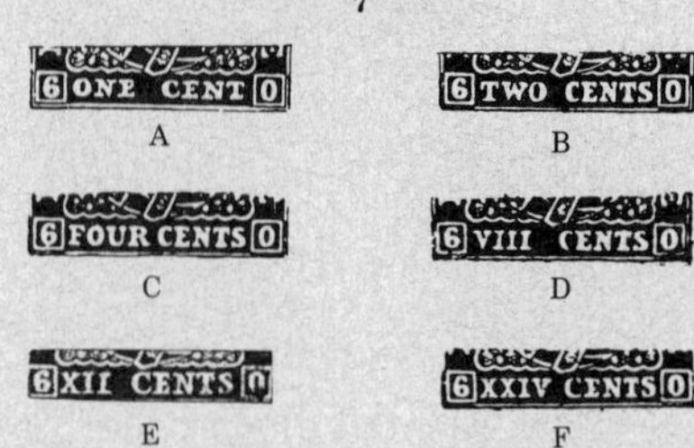

A B C D

6 XII CENTS 0 — E

6 XXIV CENTS 0 — F

(Dies eng and litho Waterlow)

1860 (July)–**63**. *Tablets of value as illustrated. Thick paper. P* 12.

No.	Type	Description	*Un*	*Used*
29	7	1 c. pale rose	£1100	£200
30		2 c. deep orange (8.60)	£160	40·00
31		2 c. pale orange	£160	40·00
32		4 c. deep blue (8.60)	£375	65·00
33		4 c. blue	£250	50·00
34		8 c. brownish rose	£400	80·00
35		8 c. pink	£325	65·00
36		12 c. lilac (12.60)	£425	35·00
37		12 c. grey-lilac	£350	32·00
38		24 c. deep green (6.63)	£950	90·00
39		24 c. green	£800	65·00

The 1 c. was reprinted in 1865 on *thin* paper, P $12^1/_2$–13, and in a different shade. *Price* £13.

The 12 c. in both shades is frequently found surcharged with a large "5d" in *red*; this is to denote the proportion of postage repayable by the colony to Great Britain for overseas letters.

1861 (3 Aug*). *Colour changed. Thick paper. P* 12.

No.	Type	Description	*Un*	*Used*
40	7	1 c. reddish brown	£300	90·00

*Earliest known postmark date.

1862–65. (*a*) *Thin paper. P* 12.

No.	Type	Description	*Un*	*Used*
41	7	1 c. brown	£375	£170
42		1 c. black (1863)	90·00	48·00
43		2 c. orange	85·00	35·00
44		4 c. blue	£100	35·00
45		4 c. pale blue	85·00	24·00
46		8 c. pink (1863)	£110	50·00
47		12 c. dull purple (1863)	£120	22·00
48		12 c. purple	£140	25·00
49		12 c. lilac	£150	35·00
50		24 c. green	£700	85·00
		(*b*) *Thin paper. P* $12^1/_2$–13 (1863)		
51	7	1 c. black	50·00	17·00
52		2 c. orange	70·00	17·00
53		4 c. blue	75·00	17·00
54		8 c. pink	£200	75·00
55		12 c. brownish lilac	£450	£100
56		24 c. green	£550	65·00

Copies are found on *pelure* paper.

No.	Type	Description	*Un*	*Used*
		(*c*) *Medium paper. P* $12^1/_2$–13		
57	7	1 c. black (1864)	45·00	28·00
58		2 c. deep orange (1864)	60·00	18·00
59		2 c. orange	65·00	16·00
60		4 c. greyish blue (1864)	75·00	14·00
61		4 c. blue	90·00	21·00
62		8 c. pink (1864)	£130	50·00
63		12 c. brownish lilac (1865)	£400	90·00
64		24 c. green (1864)	£160	50·00
65		24 c. deep green	£300	70·00
		(*d*) *Medium paper. P* 10 (Nov 1865)		
65*a*	7	12 c. grey-lilac	£375	65·00

8

9

6 ONE CENT 0 — G

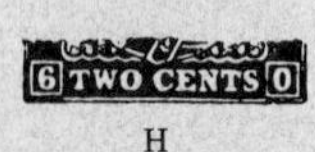

H

I

K

New transfers for the 1 c., 2 c., 8 c., and 12 c. with the spaces between values and the word "CENTS" about 1 mm.

1863–76. *Medium paper (a) P* 12½–13 (1863–68).
66 **8** 1 c. black (1866) .. .. 32·00 20·00
67 2 c. orange-red (1865) .. .. .. 40·00 4·50
68 2 c. orange .. .. 35·00 4·50
69 **9** 6 c. blue (1865) .. .. 95·00 42·00
70 6 c. greenish blue .. .. .. £100 48·00
71 6 c. deep blue .. .. £140 55·00
72 6 c. milky blue .. .. 95·00 45·00
73 **8** 8 c. pink (1868) .. .. £160 16·00
74 8 c. carmine .. .. £180 18·00
75 12 c. grey-lilac (1867) .. .. .. £400 24·00
76 12 c. brownish purple .. .. .. £475 30·00
77 **9** 24 c. green (*perf* 12) .. .. .. £200 19·00
78 24 c. yellow-green (*perf* 12) .. .. .. £120 9·50
79 24 c. yellow-green (*perf* 12½–13) .. .. £120 8·00
80 24 c. green (*perf* 12½–13) (1864) .. .. £130 9·50
81 24 c. blue-green (*perf* 12½–13) .. .. £160 19·00
82 48 c. pale red .. .. £190 45·00
83 48 c. deep red .. .. £225 48·00
84 48 c. carmine-rose .. .. £250 48·00

The 4 c. corresponding to this issue can only be distinguished from that of the previous issue by minor plating flaws.

There is a variety of the 6 c. with stop before "VICISSIM".

Varieties of most of the values of issues of 1863–64 and 1866 are to be found on both very thin and thick papers.

(*b*) *P* 10 (1866–71)
85 **8** 1 c. black (1869) .. .. 8·50 3·50
86 1 c. grey-black .. .. 9·50 6·50
87 2 c. orange (1868) .. .. 20·00 2·75
88 2 c. reddish orange .. .. 29·00 3·75
89 4 c. slate-blue .. .. 65·00 12·00
90 4 c. blue .. .. 75·00 7·50
a. Bisected (on cover) .. .. .. † £4250
b. Ditto Imperf (on cover) .. .. .. † —
91 4 c. pale blue .. .. 70·00 9·50
92 **9** 6 c. milky blue (1867) .. .. .. £100 27·00
93 6 c. ultramarine .. .. £110 42·00
94 6 c. dull blue .. .. £100 32·00
95 **8** 8 c. pink (5.71) .. .. £100 19·00
96 8 c. brownish pink .. .. £120 20·00
96*a* 8 c. carmine .. .. £170 25·00
97 12 c. pale lilac (1867) .. .. .. £190 13·00
98 12 c. grey-lilac .. .. £150 13·00
99 12 c. brownish grey .. .. £140 16·00
100 12 c. lilac .. .. £140 16·00
101 **9** 24 c. deep green .. .. £190 9·00
102 24 c. bluish green .. .. £180 8·00
103 24 c. yellow-green .. .. £140 7·50
104 48 c. crimson (1867) .. .. £275 28·00
105 48 c. red .. .. £275 24·00
104 Handstamped "Specimen" £200
104 Perf "Specimen" £160

(*c*) *P* 15 (1875–76)
106 **8** 1 c. black .. .. 38·00 7·50
107 2 c. orange-red .. .. £120 8·50
108 2 c. orange .. .. £120 8·50
109 4 c. bright blue .. .. £200 85·00
111 **9** 6 c. ultramarine .. .. £425 70·00
112 **8** 8 c. deep rose (1876) .. .. .. £190 75·00
113 12 c. lilac .. .. £500 48·00
114 **9** 24 c. yellow-green .. .. £500 35·00
115 24 c. deep green .. .. £650 50·00

There is a variety of the 48 c. with stop after "P" in "PETIMUSQUE".

Imperforate stamps of this and of the previous issue are considered to be proofs, although examples of the 24 c. imperforate from the 1869–73 period are known commercially used.

PRICES for stamps of the 1862 issue are for good average copies. Copies with roulettes on all sides very seldom occur and do not exist in marginal positions.

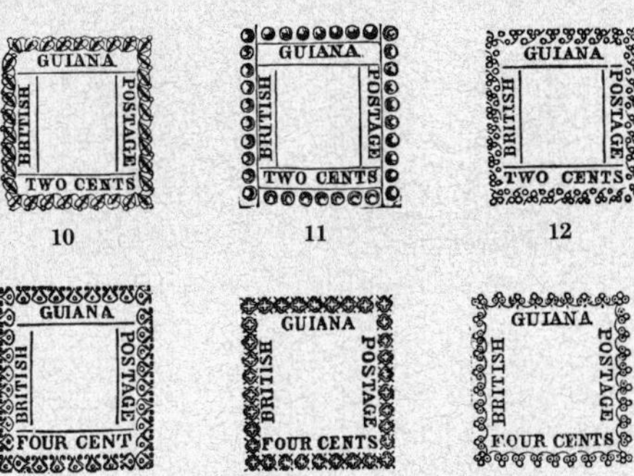

10 11 12

13 14 15

(Type-set and printed at the Office of the *Royal Gazette*, Georgetown)

1862 (Sept). *Black on coloured paper. Roul* 6.
116 **10** 1 c. *rose* £2000 £425
a. Unsigned £200
b. Wrong ornament (as T **13**) at left (R. 1/1) .. .. .. — £700
c. "1" for "I" in "BRITISH" (R. 1/5) .. — £700
117 **11** 1 c. *rose* £2750 £550
a. Unsigned £250
b. Narrow "T" in "CENTS" (R. 3/1) .. — £700
c. Wrong ornament (as T **15**) at top (R. 3/3) .. .. .. — £700
d. "1" for "I" in "BRITISH" and italic "S" in "POSTAGE" (R. 3/5) .. — £700
118 **12** 1 c. *rose* £4250 £750
a. Unsigned £450
b. "1" for "I" in "GUIANA" (R. 4/4) .. — £750
c. Wrong ornament (as T **15**) at left (R. 4/5) .. .. .. — £750
d. "C" for "O" in "POSTAGE" (R. 4/6) — £750
119 **10** 2 c. *yellow* £2000 £275
a. Unsigned £700
b. Wrong ornament (as T **13**) at left (R. 1/1) .. .. .. — £475
c. "1" for "I" in "BRITISH" (R. 1/5) .. — £475
120 **11** 2 c. *yellow* £2750 £350
a. Unsigned £750
b. "C" for "O" in "TWO" and narrow "T" in "CENTS" (R. 3/1) .. .. — £475
c. Wrong ornament (as T **15**) at top (R. 3/3) .. .. .. — £475
d. "1" for "I" in "BRITISH" and italic "S" in "POSTAGE" (R. 3/5) .. — £475
e. Italic "T" in "TWO" (R. 3/6) .. — £475
121 **12** 2 c. *yellow* £4250 £550
a. Unsigned £900
b. "1" for "I" in "GUIANA" (R. 4/4) .. — £550
c. Wrong ornament (as T **15**) at left (R. 4/5) .. .. .. — £550
d. "C" for "O" in "POSTAGE" (R. 4/6) — £550
122 **13** 4 c. *blue* £2250 £450
a. Unsigned £450
b. Wrong ornament (as T **15**) at left (R. 1/6) .. .. .. — £750
c. Wrong ornament (as T **15**) at top and italic "S" in "CENTS" (R. 2/2) .. — £750
d. Ornament omitted at right (R. 2/4) — £750
123 **14** 4 c. *blue* £3000 £600
a. Unsigned £475
b. With inner frame lines (as in T **10**/**13**) (R. 2/5–6) £4250 £1300
ba. "1" for "I" in "BRITISH" (R. 2/5) .. £4250 £1300
c. "1" for "I" in "BRITISH" and "GUIANA" (R. 4/1) .. .. .. — £750
124 **15** 4 c. *blue* £3000 £600
a. Unsigned £500
b. Wrong ornament (as T **12**) at foot (R. 3/1) .. .. .. — £750
c. Italic "S" in "CENTS" (R. 3/2) .. — £750
d. Italic "S" in "BRITISH" (R. 3/3) .. — £750

Stamps were initialled across the centre before use by the Acting Receiver-General, Robert Mather. Black was used on the 1 c., red for the 2 c. and an ink which appears white for the 4 c.

The three values of this provisional were each printed in sheets of 24 (6 × 4). The 1 c. and 2 c. were produced from the same setting of the border ornaments which contained 12 examples as Type **10** (Rows 1 and 2), 8 as Type **11** (R. 3/1 to R. 4/2) and 4 as Type **12** (R. 4/3–6).

The setting of the 4 c. contained 10 examples as Type **13** (R. 1/1 to R. 2/4), 8 as Type **14** (R. 2/5–6 and Row 4) and 6 as Type **15** (Row 3).

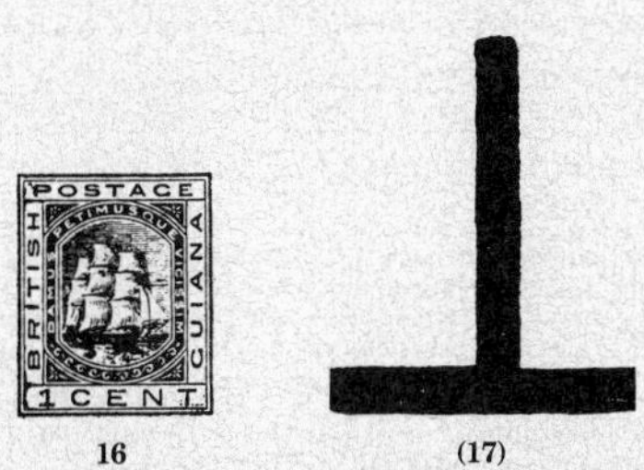

16 (17)

(Typo D.L.R.)

1876 (1 July)–**79.** *Wmk Crown CC. (a) P* 14.
126 **16** 1 c. slate .. .. 2·75 1·40
127 2 c. orange .. .. 40·00 1·50
w. Wmk inverted .. ..
128 4 c. blue .. .. £120 8·50
129 6 c. brown .. .. 75·00 6·50
130 8 c. rose £100 75
w. Wmk inverted .. ..
131 12 c. pale violet .. .. 50·00 1·25
w. Wmk inverted .. ..
132 24 c. emerald-green .. .. 60·00 3·00
w. Wmk inverted .. ..
133 48 c. red-brown .. .. £110 26·00
134 96 c. olive-bistre £475 £250
126/34 .. .. *Set of* 9 £900 £250
126/32, 134 Handstamped/Perf "Specimen" *Set of* 8 £600

(*b*) *P* 12½ (1877)
135 **16** 4 c. blue £1200 £200

(*c*) *Perf compound of* 14×12½ (1879)
136 **16** 1 c. slate .. .. — £200

1878. *Provisionals. Various stamps with old values ruled through with thick bars, in black ink, the bars varying in depth of colour.*

(*a*) *With two horiz bars* (17 Apr)
137 **16** (1 c.) on 6 c. brown .. .. .. 38·00 £100

(*b*) *Official stamps with horiz bars across* "OFFICIAL" (end Aug)
138 **8** 1 c. black .. .. £160 70·00
139 **16** 1 c. slate .. .. £120 55·00
140 2 c. orange .. .. £250 65·00

(*c*) *With horiz and vert bars as T* **17** (6 Nov)
141 **9** (1 c.) on 6 c. ultramarine (93) .. .. £130 75·00
142 **16** (1 c.) on 6 c. brown .. .. .. £250 95·00

(*d*) *Official stamps with bars across* "OFFICIAL" (23 Nov)

(i) *With two horiz bars and one vert*
144 **16** (1 c.) on 4 c. blue .. .. .. £190 90·00
145 (1 c.) on 6 c. brown .. .. .. £250 90·00
146 **8** (2 c.) on 8 c. rose £1000 £250

(ii) *With one horiz bar and one vert*
147 **16** (1 c.) on 4 c. blue .. .. .. † £1900
148 (2 c.) on 8 c. rose .. .. .. £250 95·00

1 2 2
(18) (19) (20)

1881 (21 Dec). *No. 134 with old value ruled through with bar in black ink and surch.*
149 **18** 1 on 96 c. olive-bistre .. .. .. 3·50 5·50
a. Bar in red .. ..
b. Bar omitted .. ..
150 **19** 2 on 96 c. olive-bistre .. .. .. 4·00 11·00
a. Bar in red .. ..
b. Bar omitted .. ..
151 **20** 2 on 96 c. olive-bistre .. .. .. 45·00 80·00
a. Bar in red .. ..

In the setting of 60 Type **19** occurs on the first five vertical rows and Type **20** on the sixth.

1 2 2
(21) (23) (24)

1881 (28 Dec). *Various stamps with old value ruled with bar and surch. (a) On No.* 105.
152 **21** 1 on 48 c. red .. .. 38·00 5·00
a. Bar omitted .. .. — £500

(*b*) *On Official stamps (including unissued 48 c. optd with Type* O **2**)
153 **21** 1 on 12 c. brownish purple (O4) .. .. £110 70·00
154 1 on 48 c. red-brown .. .. .. £120 90·00
155 **23** 2 on 12 c. pale violet (O11) .. .. 60·00 24·00
a. Pair. Nos. 155/6 .. .. .. £700 £750
b. Surch double £800 £400
c. Surch double (T **23** + **24**) £2000
d. Extra bar through "OFFICIAL" ..
156 **24** 2 on 12 c. pale violet (O11) £375 £275
157 **23** 2 on 24 c. emerald-green (O12) .. .. 70·00 38·00
a. Pair. Nos. 157/8 .. .. .. £850 £950
b. Surch double £900
158 **24** 2 on 24 c. emerald-green (O12) £500 £500
159 **19** 2 on 24 c. green (O5) £200 £110

On Nos. 149/59 the bar is found in various thicknesses ranging from 1 to 4 mm.

It is believed that the same composite surcharge setting of 60 (6×10) was used for Nos. 155/6 and 157/8. Type **24** occurs on R. 7/2, 4–6 and R. 8/1.

26 27

(Type-set, Baldwin & Co. Georgetown)

1882 (9 Jan). *Black impression. P* 12. *Perforated with the word* "SPECIMEN" *diagonally.*
162 **26** 1 c. *magenta* .. .. 35·00 28·00
a. Imperf between (horiz pair) .. .. † —
b. Without "SPECIMEN" £425 £300
c. "1" with foot .. .. .. 75·00 60·00
163 2 c. *yellow* .. .. 60·00 48·00
a. Without "SPECIMEN" £375 £350
b. Small "2" .. .. 60·00 48·00
164 **27** 1 c. *magenta* .. .. 35·00 28·00
a. Without "SPECIMEN" £425 £300
b. "1" with foot .. .. .. 75·00 60·00
c. Imperf between (horiz pair) .. .. † £4000
165 2 c. *yellow* .. .. 55·00 42·00
a. Bisected diagonally (1 c.) (on cover)
b. Without "SPECIMEN" £375 £350
c. Small "2" .. .. 90·00 80·00

These stamps were perforated "SPECIMEN" as a precaution against fraud. Stamps are known with "SPECIMEN" double.

The 1 c. and 2 c. stamps were printed in separate sheets; but utilising the same clichés, these being altered according to the face value required. Two settings were used, common to both values:—

1st setting. Four rows of three, T **26** being Nos. 5, 6, 7, 8, 11 and 12, and T **27** the remainder.

From this setting there were two printings of the 2 c., but only one of the 1 c.

2nd setting. Six rows of two, T **26** being Nos. 3, 7, 8, 9, 11 and 12, and T **27** the remainder.

There were two printings of each value from this setting.

Se-tenant pairs are worth about 20% more.

The "1" with foot occurs on T **27** on No. 9 in the first setting and on T **26** on No. 7 in the first printing only of the second setting.

The small "2" appears on T **26** in the first setting on Nos. 6, 7, 8 and 12 in the first printing and on Nos. 7, 8 and 12 only in the second printing: in the second setting it comes on Nos. 3, 9 and 12 in the first printing and on Nos. 9, 11 and 12 in the second printing. On T **27** the variety occurs in the first setting on No. 9 of the second printing only and in the second setting on No. 10 in both printings.

(Typo D.L.R.)

1882. *Wmk Crown C.A. P* 14.
170 **16** 1 c. slate (27 Jan) .. .. .. 8·00 20
171 2 c. orange (27 Jan) .. .. .. 20·00 15
a. Value doubly printed .. .. .. † —
x. Wmk reversed .. ..
172 4 c. blue .. .. 80·00 5·00
173 6 c. brown .. .. 5·00 6·50
w. Wmk inverted .. ..
174 8 c. rose .. .. 85·00 40
x. Wmk reversed .. ..
170/4 .. .. *Set of* 5 £180 11·00
170/4 Perf "Specimen" .. .. *Set of* 5 £250

INLAND 4 CENTS 4 CENTS
(*a*) (*b*)
Two types of "4"

2 CENTS
REVENUE
(28)

6 6
(*c*) (*d*)
Two types of "6"

1888–89. *T* **16** (*without value in lower label*) *optd*. "INLAND REVENUE", *and surch with value as T* **28**, *by D.L.R. Wmk Crown CA. P* 14.

175 1 c. dull purple (8.89) .. .. .. 1·25 20
176 2 c. dull purple (25.5.89) .. .. .. 1·25 30
177 3 c. dull purple 75 20
178 4 c. dull purple (*a*) .. .. .. 4·50 30
a. Larger figure "4" (*b*) .. .. .. 20·00 6·00
179 6 c. dull purple (*c*) .. .. .. 4·50 3·25
a. Figure 6 with straight top (*d*) .. .. 19·00 4·00
180 8 c. dull purple (8.89) .. .. .. 1·50 25
181 10 c. dull purple .. .. 6·00 2·50
182 20 c. dull purple .. .. 19·00 10·00
183 40 c. dull purple .. .. 20·00 17·00
184 72 c. dull purple (1.10.88) .. .. .. 35·00 42·00
185 $1 green (1.10.88) £400 £400
186 $2 green (1.10.88) £180 £180
187 $3 green (1.10.88) £120 £120
188 $4 green (*a*) (1.10.88) £375 £400
a. Larger figure "4" (*b*) £1000 £1100
189 $5 green (1.10.88) £225 £200
175/189 .. .. *Set of* 15 £1200 £1200

Nos. 175/89 were surcharged in settings of 60 (6×10). No. 178a occurs on all stamps in the third vertical row, No. 179a in the fourth and sixth vertical rows and No. 188a in the second vertical row.

2

(29)

30

INLAND
One
Cent
~~1 DOLLAR~~
REVENUE

(31)

1889 (6 June). *No.* 176 *surch with T* **29** *in red by* Official Gazette.

192 "2" on 2 c. dull purple .. .. .. 1·25 15

The varieties with figure "2" *inverted* or *double* were made privately by a postal employee in Demerara.

1889 (Sept). *Wmk Crown CA. P* 14.

193 **30** 1 c. dull purple and slate-grey .. 2·50 1·50
194 2 c. dull purple and orange .. .. 1·50 10
w. Wmk inverted .. ..
195 4 c. dull purple and ultramarine .. 4·50 1·50
196 4 c. dull purple and cobalt .. 19·00 2·25
197 6 c. dull purple and brown .. 35·00 11·00
198 6 c. dull purple and maroon .. 7·00 10·00
199 8 c. dull purple and rose .. 12·00 60
w. Wmk inverted .. .. — 50·00
200 12 c. dull purple and bright purple .. 18·00 1·75
200*a* 12 c. dull purple and mauve .. 8·50 2·00
201 24 c. dull purple and green .. 6·00 2·50
202 48 c. dull purple and orange-red .. 15·00 9·00
x. Wmk reversed .. ..
203 72 c. dull purple and red-brown .. 28·00 38·00
204 72 c. dull purple and yellow-brown .. 65·00 75·00
205 96 c. dull purple and carmine .. .. 65·00 70·00
x. Wmk reversed .. ..
206 96 c. dull purple and rosine .. .. 75·00 80·00
193/205 .. .. *Set of* 10 £130 £120
193/205 Optd "Specimen" .. *Set of* 10 £140

1890 (15 July). *Stamps of* 1888–89 *surch locally* "One Cent", *in red, as in T* **31**.

207 1 c. on $1 (No. 185) .. .. .. 1·00 35
a. Surch double .. .. .. — 80·00
208 1 c. on $2 (No. 186) .. .. .. 1·00 60
a. Surch double .. .. .. 75·00
209 1 c. on $3 (No. 187) .. .. .. 1·40 1·25
a. Surch double .. .. .. 85·00
210 1 c. on $4 (No. 188) .. .. .. 2·00 6·00
a. Surch double .. .. .. 75·00
b. Larger figure "4" (*b*) .. .. 10·00 25·00
207/10 .. .. *Set of* 4 4·75 7·50

1890–91. *Colours changed. Wmk Crown CA. P* 14

213 **30** 1 c. sea-green (12.90) 40 10
214 5 c. ultramarine (1.91) .. .. .. 2·75 10
215 8 c. dull purple and greenish black (10.90) .. .. 2·75 1·10
213/15 .. .. *Set of* 3 5·50 1·10
213/215 Optd "Specimen" .. *Set of* 3 60·00

32 Mount Roraima

33 Kaieteur Falls

(Recess D.L.R.)

1898 (18 July). *Queen Victoria's Jubilee. Wmk Crown CC* (*sideways* on T* **32**). *P* 14.

216 **32** 1 c. blue-black and carmine-red .. 3·50 65
w. Wmk Crown to left of CC ..
x. Wmk sideways reversed .. ..
y. Wmk sideways inverted and reversed .. ..
217 **33** 2 c. brown and indigo .. .. 11·00 1·50
a. Imperf between (horiz pair) .. £4250
218 2 c. brown and blue .. .. .. 16·00 2·00
219 **32** 5 c. deep green and sepia .. .. 35·00 3·00
a. Imperf between (horiz pair) ..
w. Wmk Crown to left of CC ..
220 **33** 10 c. blue-black and brown-red .. 16·00 20·00
221 **32** 15 c. red-brown and blue .. .. 26·00 16·00
216/21 .. .. *Set of* 5 80·00 35·00
216/21 Optd "Specimen" .. .. *Set of* 5 £100

*The normal sideways watermark on Type **32** shows Crown to right of CC, *as seen from the back of the stamp*.

A second plate was later used for the 1 c. on which the lines of shading on the mountains in the background are strengthened, and those along the ridge show distinct from each other, whereas, in the original, they are more or less blurred. In the second plate the shading of the sky is less pronounced.

TWO CENTS.

(34)

CE

Shaved "E"

35

(Surch at Printing Office of the *Daily Chronicle*, Georgetown)

1899 (24 Feb–15 June). *Surch with T* **34**.

222 **32** 2 c. on 5 c. (No. 219) (15 June) .. 2·25 1·75
a. No stop after "CENTS" .. .. 75·00 60·00
b. Comma after "CENTS" (R. 7/2) ..
c. "CINTS" (R. 4/1) .. .. .. 85·00
d. Shaved "E" (R. 6/2) .. .. 21·00
w. Wmk Crown to left of CC .. ..
223 **33** 2 c. on 10c. (No. 220) .. .. 1·75 1·75
a. No stop after "CENTS" (R. 5/5 or 2/9) 20·00 50·00
b. "GENTS" for "CENTS" (R. 5/7) .. 50·00 70·00
c. Surch inverted £350 £400
d. Shaved "E" (R. 4/2 or 3/8) .. 15·00
224 **32** 2 c. on 15 c. (No. 221) .. .. 1·25 1·25
a. No stop after "CENTS" (R. 9/2) .. 60·00 65·00
b. Surch double £500 £650
c. Surch double, one without stop ..
d. Surch inverted £375 £450
e. Surch inverted and stop omitted ..
f. Shaved "E" (R. 6/2) .. .. 16·00
222/4 .. .. *Set of* 3 4·75 4·25

No. 222c was caused by damage to the first "E" of "CENTS" which developed during surcharging. The listing is for an example with only the upright stroke of the letter visible.

There were two settings of No. 223 with the no stop and shaved "E" varieties occurring on R.5/5 and R.4/2 of the first and on R.2/9 and R.3/8 of the second.

No. 224b occurred on the first five vertical columns of one sheet, the surcharges on the right hand vertical column being normal.

Only two examples of No. 224c are known.

There is only one known example of No. 224e.

1900–7. *T* **30**. *Wmk Crown CA. P* 14

233 1 c. grey-green (1907) .. .. .. 2·25 3·25
234 2 c. dull purple and carmine .. .. 3·25 25
235 2 c. dull purple and black/*red* (1901) .. 1·00 10
236 6 c. grey-black and ultramarine (1902) .. 6·50 11·00
237 48 c. grey and purple-brown (1901) .. 50·00 35·00
a. Brownish grey and brown (1907) .. 29·00 28·00
238 60 c. green and rosine (1903) .. .. 60·00 £170
233/8 .. .. *Set of* 6 90·00 £190
233/8 Optd "Specimen" .. .. *Set of* 6 90·00

No. 233 is a reissue of No. 213 in non-fugitive ink.

1905–7. *Wmk Multiple Crown CA. Ordinary paper* (1 c. *to* 60 c.) *or chalk-surfaced paper* (72, 96 c.).

240 **30** 1 c. grey-green .. .. .. 3·50 30
aw. Wmk inverted .. ..
b. Chalk-surfaced paper .. .. 4·00 30
241 2 c. purple and black/*red* .. .. 9·00 10
a. Chalk-surfaced paper .. .. 3·50 10
242 4 c. dull purple and ultramarine .. 8·00 11·00
a. Chalk-surfaced paper .. .. 6·00 11·00
243 5 c. dull pur & bl/*bl* (1.5.05) (Optd S. £20) 11·00 6·50
a. Chalk-surfaced paper .. .. 3·50 6·50
244 6 c. grey-black and ultramarine .. 16·00 40·00
a. Chalk-surfaced paper .. .. 15·00 40·00
aw. Wmk inverted .. ..
245 12 c. dull and bright purple .. .. 22·00 32·00
a. Chalk-surfaced paper .. .. 22·00 40·00
246 24 c. dull purple and green (1906) .. 10·00 10·00
a. Chalk-surfaced paper .. .. 3·75 4·50
247 48 c. grey and purple-brown .. .. 24·00 28·00
a. Chalk-surfaced paper .. .. 14·00 20·00
248 60 c. green and rosine .. .. 25·00 85·00
a. Chalk-surfaced paper .. .. 14·00 85·00
249 72 c. purple and orange-brown (1907) .. 32·00 65·00
250 96 c. black & vermilion/*yellow* (20.11.05) (Optd S. £30) .. .. .. 35·00 45·00
240/50 .. .. *Set of* 11 £130 £275

1905. *Optd* "POSTAGE AND REVENUE". *Wmk Multiple Crown CA. Chalk-surfaced paper. P* 14.

251 **35** $2.40 green and violet (S. £75) £160 £275

1907–10. *Colours changed. Wmk Mult Crown CA. P* 14

252 **30** 1 c. blue-green .. .. .. 14·00 2·75
253 2 c. rose-red .. .. .. 14·00 10
a. Redrawn (1910) .. .. .. 8·50 10
254 4 c. brown and purple .. .. 2·25 60
255 5 c. ultramarine .. .. .. 8·50 90
256 6 c. grey and black .. .. .. 13·00 7·00
257 12 c. orange and mauve .. .. 4·00 4·00
252/7 .. .. *Set of* 6 45·00 13·50
253/7 Optd "Specimen" .. .. *Set of* 5 75·00

In No. 253a the flag at the main truck is close to the mast, whereas in the original type it appears to be flying loose from halyards. There are two background lines above the value "2 CENTS" instead of three and the "S" is further away from the end of the tablet.

37

War
Tax

(38)

(Typo D.L.R.)

1913–21. *Wmk Mult Crown CA. Chalk-surfaced paper* (4 c *and* 48 *c. to* 96 *c.*). *P* 14.

259 **37** 1 c. yellow-green .. .. .. 1·50 7
a. Blue-green (1917) .. .. .. 1·50 2
260 2 c. carmine 70 1
a. Scarlet (1916) .. .. .. 2·25 1
b. Wmk sideways .. .. .. † £150
261 4 c. brown and bright purple (1914) .. 3·75 2
aw. Wmk inverted .. .. ..
b. Deep brown and purple .. .. 3·50 2
262 5 c. bright blue .. .. .. 1·75 8
263 6 c. grey and black .. .. .. 1·75 8
264 12 c. orange and violet .. .. .. 1·00 9
265 24 c. dull purple and green (1915) .. 3·25 4·0
266 48 c. grey and purple-brown (1914) .. 16·00 16·0
267 60 c. green and rosine (1915) .. .. 15·00 48·0
268 72 c. purple and orange-brown (1915) .. 40·00 70·0
269 96 c. black and vermilion/*yellow* (1915) 30·00 60·0
a. White back (1913) .. .. .. 16·00 40·0
b. On lemon (1916) (Optd S. £30) .. 18·00 40·0
c. On pale yellow (1921) (Optd S. £30) 19·00 60·0
259/69*a* .. .. *Set of* 11 90·00 £160
259/69*a* Optd "Specimen" .. *Set of* 11 £130

1918 (4 Jan). *No.* 260*a optd with T* **38**, *by D.L.R.*

271 **37** 2 c. scarlet 50 15

The relative position of the words "WAR" and "TAX" vary considerably in the sheet.

1921–27. *Wmk Mult Script CA. Chalk-surfaced paper* (24 *c. to* 96 *c.*). *P* 14.

272 **37** 1 c. green (1922) .. .. .. 4·50 2
273 2 c. rose-carmine .. .. .. 3·00 2
w. Wmk inverted .. .. .. † £10
274 2 c. bright violet (1923) .. .. 2·50 1
275 4 c. brown and bright purple (1922) .. 4·75 1
276 6 c. bright blue (1922) .. .. 2·75 2
277 12 c. orange and violet (1922) .. .. 2·75 1·5
278 24 c. dull purple and green .. .. 2·00 4·5
279 48 c. black and purple (1926) .. .. 9·50 3·5
280 60 c. green and rosine (1926) .. .. 9·50 48·00
281 72 c. dull purple & orange-brown (1923) 17·00 48·00
282 96 c. black and red/*yellow* (1927) .. 18·00 45·00
272/82 .. .. *Set of* 11 65·00 £130
272/82 Optd "Specimen" .. .. *Set of* 11 £150

39 Ploughing a Rice Field

40 Indian shooting Fish

(Recess Waterlow)

1931 (21 July). *Centenary of County Union T* **39/40** *and similar designs. Wmk Mult Script CA. P* 12½.

283 1 c. emerald-green .. .. 2·25 7
284 2 c. brown .. .. 1·75 1
285 4 c. carmine .. .. 1·75 4
286 6 c. blue .. .. 2·00 2·5
287 $1 violet .. .. 20·00 40·0
283/7 .. .. *Set of* 5 25·00 40·0
283/7 Perf "Specimen" .. .. *Set of* 5 75·00

Designs: *Vert*—4 c., $1 Kaieteur Falls. *Horiz*—6 c. Public buildings, Georgetown.

43 Ploughing a Rice Field

44 Gold Mining

(Recess Waterlow)

1934 (1 Oct)–**51**. *T* **40** (*without dates at top of frame*), **43/4** *and similar designs. Wmk Mult Script CA* (*sideways on horiz designs*). *P* 12½.

288 **43** 1 c. green 60 5
289 **40** 2 c. red-brown .. .. 1·50 4
290 **44** 3 c. scarlet 30 1
aa. Wmk error. Crown missing .. ..
a. Perf 12½ × 13½ (30.12.43) 40 6
b. Perf 13 × 14 (28.4.49) 40 1
291 – 4 c. slate-violet .. .. .. 2·00 8
a. Imperf between (vert pair) .. .. † £1200
b. Imperf horiz (vert pair) £6500 £700
292 – 6 c. deep ultramarine .. .. .. 2·50 2·7
293 – 12 c. red-orange 10 2
a. Perf 14 × 13 (16.4.51) 20 8
294 – 24 c. purple .. .. 2·75 4·0
295 – 48 c. black .. .. 7·00 8·5
296 – 50 c. green .. .. 10·00 16·0
297 – 60 c. red-brown .. .. 26·00 27·0
298 – 72 c. purple .. .. 1·25 2·0
299 – 96 c. black .. .. 20·00 30·0
300 – $1 bright violet .. .. .. 32·00 28·0
288/300 .. .. *Set of* 13 95·00 £11
288/300 Perf "Specimen" .. .. *Set of* 13 £140

Designs: *Vert*—4 c., 50 c. Kaieteur Falls (as No. 285, but with dates omitted); 96 c. Sir Walter Raleigh and his son. *Horiz*—6 c Shooting logs over falls; 12 c. Stabroek Market 24 c. Sugar cane in punts; 48 c. Forest road; 60 c. Victoria Regia Lilies; 72 c. Mount Roraima; $1 Botanical Gardens.

1935 (6 May). *Silver Jubilee. As Nos.* 91/4 *of Antigua*.

301 2 c. ultramarine and grey 20 10
f. Diagonal line by turret .. .. 23·00
h. Dot by flagstaff .. .. .. 45·00

302 6 c. brown and deep blue .. .. 1·00 85
f. Diagonal line by turret .. .. 50·00
g. Dot to left of chapel .. .. .. 80·00
h. Dot by flagstaff .. .. .. 80·00
303 12 c. green and indigo .. .. .. 2·50 7·00
f. Diagonal line by turret .. .. 70·00
h. Dot by flagstaff £110
i. Dash by turret £110
304 24 c. slate and purple .. .. .. 4·75 7·00
h. Dot by flagstaff £150
i. Dash by turret £150
301/4 .. .. *Set of* 4 7·50 13·50
301/4 Perf "Specimen" .. .. *Set of* 4 70·00
For illustrations of plate varieties see Catalogue Introduction.

1937 (12 May). *Coronation. As Nos.* 95/7 *of Antigua, but ptd by D.L.R. P* 14.
305 2 c. yellow-brown 15 10
306 4 c. grey-black 50 30
307 6 c. bright blue .. .. 60 1·00
305/7 .. .. *Set of* 3 1·10 1·25
305/7 Perf "Specimen" .. .. *Set of* 3 50·00

53 South America

54 Victoria Regia Lilies

(Recess Waterlow)

1938 (1 Feb)–**1952**. *As earlier types but with portrait of King George VI as in T* **53/4**. *Wmk Mult Script CA. P* 12½
308 **43** 1 c. yellow-green .. .. 12·00 55
aa. Green (1944) 30 10
a. Perf 14 × 13 (1949) 30 80
309 – 2 c. slate-violet 60 10
a. Perf 13 × 14 (28.4.49) 30 10
310 **53** 4 c. scarlet and black 70 30
a. Imperf horiz (vert pair) £11000 £8500
b. Perf 13 × 14 (1952) 45 15
311 **40** 6 c. deep ultramarine 40 10
a. Perf 13 × 14 (24.10.49) 30 30
312 – 24 c. blue-green .. .. 26·00 10·00
a. Wmk sideways .. .. 1·25 10
313 – 36 c. bright violet (7.3.38) .. .. .. 2·00 20
a. Perf 13 × 14 (13.12.51) .. .. .. 2·75 30
314 – 48 c. orange 60 40
a. Perf 14×13 (8.5.51*) .. .. .. 1·50 1·25
315 – 60 c. red-brown .. .. 11·00 3·75
316 – 96 c. purple .. .. 2·50 2·75
a. Perf 12½ × 13½ (1944) .. .. 5·50 7·00
b. Perf 13 × 14 (8.2.51) .. .. .. 2·75 5·50
317 – $1 bright violet .. .. 11·00 35
a. Perf 14 × 13(1951) £300 £400
318 – $2 purple (11.6.45) .. .. .. 4·50 14·00
a. Perf 14 × 13 (9.8.50) .. .. .. 10·00 15·00
319 **54** $3 red-brown (2.7.45) .. .. .. 27·00 25·00
a. Bright red-brown (12.46) .. .. 28·00 28·00
b. Perf 14 × 13. *Red-brown* (29.10.52) .. 25·00 45·00
308a/19 .. .. *Set of* 12 55·00 40·00
308/19 Perf "Specimen" .. .. *Set of* 12 £200
Designs: *Vert*—2 c., 36 c. Kaieteur Falls; 96 c. Sir Walter Raleigh and his son. *Horiz*—24 c. Sugar cane in punts; 48 c. Forest road; 60 c. Shooting logs over falls; $1 Botanical Gardens; $2 Mount Roraima.
* Earliest known postmark date.

1946 (1 Oct). *Victory. As Nos.* 110/11 *of Antigua.*
320 3 c. carmine 10 10
321 6 c. blue 30 40
320/1 Perf "Specimen" .. .. *Set of* 2 48·00

1948 (20 Dec). *Royal Silver Wedding. As Nos.* 112/13 *of Antigua, but $3 in recess.*
322 3 c. scarlet 10 40
323 $3 red-brown .. .. 12·00 23·00

1949 (10 Oct). *75th Anniv of Universal Postal Union. As Nos.* 114/17 *of Antigua.*
324 4 c. carmine 30 20
325 6 c. deep blue 90 65
326 12 c. orange 30 45
327 24 c. blue-green 30 60
324/7 .. .. *Set of* 4 1·60 1·75

1951 (16 Feb). *University College of B.W.I. As Nos.* 118/19 *of Antigua.*
328 3 c. black and carmine 30 30
329 6 c. black and blue 30 60

1953 (2 June). *Coronation. As No.* 120 *of Antigua.*
330 4 c. black and scarlet 20 10

55 G.P.O., Georgetown

62 Felling Greenheart.

(Centre litho, frame recess ($1); recess (others). Waterlow (until 1961), then D.L.R.)

1954 (1 Dec)–**63**. *T* **55**, **62** *and similar designs. Wmk Mult Script CA. P* 12½×13* *(horiz) or* 13 *(vert).*
331 1 c. black 10 10
332 2 c. myrtle-green 10 10
333 3 c. brown-olive and red-brown .. .. 3·00 10
w. Wmk inverted .. .. ..
334 4 c. violet 20 10
a. D.L.R. ptg (5.12.61) .. .. .. 7·00 2·50
ab. Deep violet (3.1.63) .. .. .. 9·00 1·50
335 5 c. scarlet and black 30 10
w. Wmk inverted .. .. ..
336 6 c. yellow-green 10 10
a. D.L.R. ptg. *Green* (22.5.62) .. .. 40 1·50
337 8 c. ultramarine 10 10
a. D.L.R. ptg. *Blue* (19.9.61) .. .. 8·00 65
338 12 c. black and reddish brown 60 40
a. Black and light brown (13.6.56) .. 15 10
b. D.L.R. ptg. *Black and brown* (11.7.61) 16·00 3·00
339 24 c. black and brownish orange .. .. 4·50 10
a. Black and orange (13.6.56) .. .. 5·50 10
340 36 c. rose-carmine and black .. .. 2·75 90
w. Wmk inverted .. .. ..
341 48 c. ultramarine and brown-lake 60 50
a. Brt ultram & pale brown-lake (13.6.56) 40 40
ab. D.L.R. ptg (19.9.61) .. .. .. 26·00 20·00
342 72 c. carmine and emerald .. .. 12·00 2·75
a. D.L.R. ptg (17.7.62) .. .. .. 12·00 20·00
343 $1 pink, yellow, green and black .. .. 16·00 2·50
344 $2 deep mauve .. .. 16·00 5·50
a. D.L.R. ptg. *Reddish mauve* (11.7.61) 38·00 7·00
345 $5 ultramarine and black .. .. .. 12·00 20·00
a. D.L.R. ptg (19.9.61) .. .. .. 45·00 32·00
331/45 .. .. *Set of* 15 60·00 29·00
Designs: *Horiz*—2 c. Botanical Gardens; 3 c. *Victoria regia* water-lilies; 5 c. Map of Caribbean; 6 c. Rice combine-harvester; 8 c. Sugar cane entering factory; 24 c. Mining for bauxite; 36 c. Mount Roraima; $1 Channel-billed Toucan; $2 Dredging gold. *Vert*—4 c. Amerindian shooting fish; 48 c. Kaieteur Falls; 72 c. Arapaima (fish); $5 Arms of British Guiana.
The separately listed De La Rue printings are identifiable as singles by the single wide-tooth perfs at each side at the bottom of the stamps. In the Waterlow these wide teeth are at the top.
*All the Waterlow printing and early De La Rue printings of the horizontal designs measure 12.3×12.8, but De La Rue printings of 22 May 1962 and all later printings (including those on the Block CA watermark) measure 12.3×12.6.
The 1 c. and 2 c., printed by Waterlow, exist in coils constructed from normal sheets.
See also Nos. 354/65.

SELF-GOVERNMENT

70

(Photo Harrison)

1961 (23 Oct). *History and Culture Week. W w* **12** *P* 14½ × 14.
346 **70** 5 c. sepia and orange-red 20 10
347 6 c. sepia and blue-green 20 15
348 30 c. sepia and yellow-orange 45 45
346/8 .. .. *Set of* 3 75 60

1963 (14 July). *Freedom from Hunger. As No.* 146 *of Antigua.*
349 20 c. reddish violet 30 10

1963 (2 Sept). *Red Cross Centenary. As Nos.* 147/8 *of Antigua.*
350 5 c. red and black 20 20
351 20 c. red and blue 55 35

1963–65. *As Nos.* 333/44, *but wmk w* **12**.
354 3 c. brown-olive and red-brown (12.65) .. 5·50 5·50
356 5 c. scarlet and black (28.5.64) 30 10
w. Wmk inverted .. .. ..
359 12 c. black and yellowish brown (6.10.64) 20 10
360 24 c. black and bright orange (10.12.63) .. 3·25 10
361 36 c. rose-carmine and black (10.12.63) .. 60 60
362 48 c. brt ultram & Venetian red (25.11.63) 1·25 2·25
w. Wmk inverted .. .. ..
363 72 c. carmine and emerald (25.11.63) .. 4·00 20·00
364 $1 pink, yellow, green & black (10.12.63) 7·00 90
365 $2 reddish mauve (10.12.63) .. .. 9·00 14·00
354/65 .. .. *Set of* 9 28·00 38·00
There was no London release of No. 354.
The 5 c. exists in coils constructed from normal sheets.
For 1 c. value, see No. 429a.

71 Weightlifting

(Photo D.L.R.)

1964 (1 Oct). *Olympic Games, Tokyo. W w* **12**. *P* 13 × 13½.
367 **71** 5 c. orange 15 10
368 8 c. blue 15 25
369 25 c. magenta 25 40
367/9 .. .. *Set of* 3 50 65

1965 (17 May). *I.T.U. Centenary. As Nos.* 166/7 *of Antigua.*
370 5 c. emerald and yellow-olive 10 15
371 25 c. light blue and magenta 20 15

1965 (25 Oct). *International Co-operation Year. As Nos.* 168/9 *of Antigua.*
372 5 c. reddish purple and turquoise-green .. 10 10
373 25 c. deep bluish green and lavender .. 25 20

72 St. George's Cathedral, Georgetown

(Des Jennifer Toombs, Photo Harrison)

1966 (24 Jan). *Churchill Commemoration. W w* **12**. *P* 14 × 14½.
374 **72** 5 c. black, crimson and gold 50 10
375 25 c. black, blue and gold .. .. 1·40 50

1966 (3 Feb). *Royal Visit. As Nos.* 174/5 *of Antigua.*
376 3 c. black and ultramarine 50 15
377 25 c. black and magenta .. .. .. 1·50 60

GUYANA

British Guiana became independent as Guyana on 25 May 1966.

GUYANA
INDEPENDENCE
1966

(73)

1966 (26 May)–**67**. *Various stamps as Nos.* 331/45 *optd with T* **73** *by De La Rue. (a) Wmk Mult Script CA.*
378 2 c. myrtle-green 20 30
379 3 c. brown-olive and red-brown .. .. 2·50 5·00
380 4 c. violet 60 10
381 6 c. yellow-green 30 10
382 8 c. ultramarine 70 50
383 12 c. black and reddish brown 80 50
384 $5 ultramarine and black .. .. 24·00 38·00
378/84 .. .. .. *Set of* 7 25·00 40·00

(b) Wmk w **12** *(upright)*
385 1 c. black (28.2.67) 10 20
386 3 c. brown-olive and red-brown 80 10
387 4 c. violet (28.2.67) 10 50
388 5 c. scarlet and black 20 10
389 6 c. green (28.2.67) 10 20
390 8 c. ultramarine (14.3.67) .. .. 40 1·25
391 12 c. black and yellowish brown 10 10
392 24 c. black and bright orange .. .. 3·25 20
393 36 c. rose-carmine and black 30 30
394 48 c. bright ultramarine and Venetian red 3·50 8·00
395 72 c. carmine and emerald 40 50
396 $1 pink, yellow, green and black .. 1·50 35
397 $2 reddish mauve .. .. .. 1·50 75
398 $5 ultramarine and black .. .. 1·00 1·75
385/98 .. .. .. *Set of* 14 11·50 12·00

(c) Wmk w **12** *(sideways)*
399 1 c. black 10 10
400 4 c. violet 10 10
401 8 c. ultramarine 10 10
402 12 c. black and yellowish brown (28.2.67) 10 10
403 24 c. black and bright orange .. .. 2·00 40
404 36 c. rose-carmine and black (28.2.67) .. 30 90
405 48 c. bright ultramarine and Venetian red 30 30
406 72 c. carmine and emerald (28.2.67) .. 1·25 3·00
407 $1 pink, yellow, green and black (14.3.67) 2·50 3·00
407*a* $2 reddish mauve (28.2.67) .. .. 2·00 3·00
407*b* $5 ultramarine and black (28.2.67) .. 1·50 3·00
399/407*b* .. .. .. *Set of* 11 9·00 12·50
See also Nos. 420/40.

74 Flag and Map

75 Arms of Guyana

(Des V. Whiteley. Photo Harrison)

1966 (26 May). *Independence. P* 14½.
408 **74** 5 c. multicoloured 10 10
409 15 c. multicoloured 15 10
410 **75** 25 c. multicoloured 20 10
411 $1 multicoloured .. .. .. 65 1·00
408/11 .. .. *Set of* 4 90 1·00

76 Bank Building

(Des R. Granger Barrett. Photo Enschedé)

1966 (11 Oct). *Opening of Bank of Guyana. P* 13½ × 14.
412 **76** 5 c. multicoloured 10 10
413 25 c. multicoloured 10 10

CANCELLED REMAINDERS.* In 1969 remainders of some issues were put on the market cancelled-to-order in such a way as to be indistinguishable from genuine postally used copies for all practical purposes. Our used quotations which are indicated by an asterisk are the same for cancelled-to-order or postally used copies.

77 British Guiana One Cent Stamp of 1856

(Des V. Whiteley. Litho D.L.R.)

1967 (23 Feb). *World's Rarest Stamp Commemoration. P* 12½.
414 **77** 5 c. black, magenta, silver & light ochre .. 10 10*
415 25 c. black, magenta, gold and light green .. 10 10*

78 Château Margot

GUYANA
INDEPENDENCE
1966

(**82**)

(Des R. Granger Barrett. Photo Harrison)

1967 (26 May). *First Anniv of Independence. T* **78** *and similar multicoloured designs. P* 14 (6 *c.*), 14½ × 14 (15 *c.*) *or* 14 × 14½ (*others*).
416 6 c. Type **78** 10 10*
417 15 c. Independence Arch 10 10*
418 25 c. Fort Island (*horiz*) 10 10*
419 $1 National Assembly (*horiz*) 20 15
416/19 .. .. *Set of* 4 20 15

1967–68. *Stamps as Nos.* 331/45 *optd with T* **82** *locally.*

(i) *Wmk Mult Script CA*
420 1 c. black (3.10.67) 10 10
a. Opt inverted .. .. 35·00
b. Date misplaced 5 mm .. .. .. 9·00
c. Date misplaced 2 mm .. .. .. 9·00
421 2 c. myrtle-green (3.10.67) 10 10
a. "1966" for "GUYANA" .. .. .. 18·00
b. Date misplaced 5 mm .. .. .. 9·00
c. Date misplaced 2 mm .. .. .. 9·00
422 3 c. brown-olive and red-brown (3.10.67) .. 30 10
a. "1966" for "GUYANA" .. .. .. 15·00
b. Vert pair, one without opt £375
c. Date misplaced 2 mm .. .. .. 9·00
423 4 c. violet (10.67) 10 10
a. Deep violet 65 65
b. Opt inverted .. .. 45·00
424 6 c. yellow-green (11.67) 10 10
a. "1966" for "GUYANA" .. .. .. 23·00
b. Opt inverted .. .. 40·00
c. Opt double .. .. 55·00
425 8 c. ultramarine (12.67) 10 10
426 12 c. black and brown (12.67) 10 10
426*a* 24 c. black and orange (date?) .. .. £275 90·00
427 $2 reddish mauve (12.67) .. .. .. 1·00 1·75
428 $5 ultramarine and black (12.67) .. .. 1·50 2·25

(ii) *Wmk w* **12** (*upright*)
429 1 c. black (2.68) 10 30
a. Opt omitted £130
430 2 c. myrtle-green (2.68) 30 85
431 3 c. brown-olive and red-brown (3.10.67) .. 30 10
a. "1966" for "GUYANA" .. .. .. 75·00
b. Opt inverted .. .. 28·00
432 4 c. violet (2.68) 10 60
433 5 c. scarlet and black (3.10.67) .. .. 2·00 1·25
a. Deep scarlet and black .. .. .. 70 1·25
aw. Wmk inverted .. .. ..
c. Date misplaced 2 mm .. .. .. 9·00
434 6 c. yellow-green (2.68) 10 50
a. Opt double, one diagonal .. .. 70·00
435 24 c. black and bright orange (11.12.67) .. 2·25 10
a. Opt double, one diagonal (horiz pair) £180
436 36 c. rose-carmine and black (12.67) 70 10
437 48 c. bright ultram & Venetian red (12.67) 70 40
a. Opt inverted .. .. 60·00
438 72 c. carmine and emerald (12.67) .. .. 1·25 40
439 $1 pink, yellow, green and black (12.67) 3·00 50
440 $2 reddish mauve (12.67) .. .. .. 3·00 4·00
420/40 (*excl.* 426*a*) .. .. *Set of* 21 14·00 12·00

The "1966" errors occurred on R. 7/10 and were later corrected. Nos. 425/8 and 436/40 were issued in mid-December, but some were cancelled-to-order with a November date in error.

On Nos. 420b and 421b the "1" of "1966" is below the second "D" of "INDEPENDENCE" (R. 6/3). On Nos. 420c, 421c, 422c and 433c it is below the second "E" (R. 6/1).

No. 433*a* is from a printing made specially for this overprint.

NEW INFORMATION

The editor is always interested to correspond with people who have new information that will improve or correct the Catalogue.

83 "Millie" (Blue and Yellow Macaw)

84 Wicket-keeping

(Des V. Whiteley. Photo Harrison)

1967–68. *Christmas. P* 14½ × 14. (*a*) *First issue* (6 Nov 1967).
441 **83** 5 c. yellow, new blue, blk & bronze-grn 10 10*
442 25 c. yellow, new blue, black and violet .. 15 10*

(*b*) *Second issue. Colours changed* (22 Jan 1968)
443 **83** 5 c. yellow, new blue, black and red .. 10 10*
444 25 c. yellow, new blue, blk & apple-grn .. 15 10*

(Des V. Whiteley. Photo Harrison)

1968 (8 Jan). *M.C.C.'s West Indies Tour. T* **84** *and similar vert designs. P* 14.
445 5 c. Type **84** 10 10*
a. Strip of 3. Nos. 445/7 70
446 6 c. Batting 10 10*
447 25 c. Bowling 30 10*
445/7 .. .. *Set of* 3 70 15*

Nos. 445/7 were issued in small sheets of 9 containing three *se-tenant* strips.

87 Pike Cichlid

102 "Christ of St John of the Cross" (Salvador Dali)

(Des R. Granger Barrett. Photo Harrison)

1968 (4 Mar). *Multicoloured designs as T* **87**, *showing fish* (1 *to* 6 *c.*), *birds* (10 *to* 40 *c.*) *or animals* (*others*). *No wmk. P* 14 × 14½.
448 1 c. Type **87** 10 10
449 2 c. Red Piranha ("Pirai") 10 10
450 3 c. Peacock Cichlid ("Lukunani") 10 10
451 5 c. Armoured Catfish ("Hassar") 10 10
452 6 c. Black Acara ("Patua") 55 10
453 10 c. Spix's Guan (*vert*) 55 10
454 15 c. Harpy Eagle (*vert*) .. .. .. 1·60 10
455 20 c. Hoatzin (*vert*) 60 10
456 25 c. Guianan Cock of the Rock (*vert*) .. 60 10
457 40 c. Great Kiskadee (*vert*) 75 40
458 50 c. Brazilian Agouti ("Accouri") 80 50
459 60 c. White-lipped Peccary 80 10
460 $1 Paca ("Labba") 80 10
461 $2 Nine-banded Armadillo .. .. .. 1·25 2·00
462 $5 Ocelot .. .. 1·50 3·00
448/62 .. .. *Set of* 15 8·50 5·50

For Nos. 448/62 with W **106** see Nos. 485/99

(Des and photo Harrison)

1968 (25 Mar). *Easter. P* 14.
463 **102** 5 c. multicoloured 10 10*
464 25 c. multicoloured 20 10*

103 "Efficiency Year"

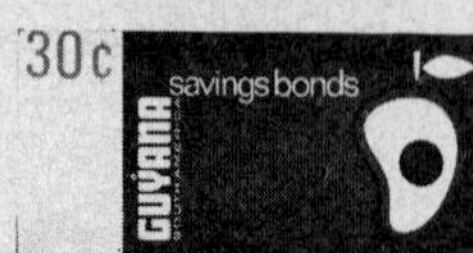

104 "Savings Bonds"

(Des W. Starzmann. Litho B.W.)

1968 (22 July). *"Savings Bonds and Efficiency". P* 14.
465 **103** 6 c. multicoloured 10 10*
466 25 c. multicoloured 10 10*
467 **104** 30 c. multicoloured 10 10*
468 40 c. multicoloured 10 10*
465/8 .. .. *Set of* 4 30 15*

105 Open Book, Star and Crescent

(Des R. Gates. Photo D.L.R.)

1968 (9 Oct). *1400th Anniv of the Holy Quran. P* 14.
469 **105** 6 c. black, gold and flesh 10 10*
470 25 c. black, gold and lilac 10 10*
471 30 c. black, gold and light apple-green .. 10 10*
472 40 c. black, gold and cobalt 10 10*
469/72 .. .. *Set of* 4 30 15*

106 Lotus Blossoms

107 Broadcasting Greetings

(Des L. Pritchard; adapted G. Vasarhelyi. Litho D.L.R.)

1968 (11 Nov). *Christmas. T* **107** *and similar vert design. W* **106**. *P* 14.
473 6 c. brown, blue and green 10 10*
474 25 c. brown, reddish violet and green .. 10 10*
475 30 c. blue-green and turquoise-green .. 10 10*
476 40 c. red and turquoise-green 10 10*
473/6 .. .. *Set of* 4 30 15*

Designs:—25 c. Type **107**; 30, 40 c. Map showing radio link, Guyana–Trinidad.

109 Festival Ceremony

(Des J. Cooter. Litho P.B.)

1969 (26 Feb). *Hindu Festival of Phagwah. T* **109** *and similar horiz design. Multicoloured. W* **106** (*sideways*). *P* 13½.
477 6 c. Type **109** 10 10
478 25 c. Ladies spraying scent 10 10
479 30 c. Type **109** 10 10
480 40 c. As 25 c. 10 10
477/80 .. .. *Set of* 4 30 20

111 "Sacrament of the Last Supper" (Dali)

112 Map showing "CARIFTA" Countries

(Photo D.L.R.)

1969 (10 Mar). *Easter. W* **106** (*sideways*). *P* 13½ × 13.
481 **111** 6 c. multicoloured 10 10
482 25 c. multicoloured 10 10
483 30 c. multicoloured 10 10
484 40 c. multicoloured 10 10
481/4 .. .. *Set of* 4 30 15

1969–71. *As Nos.* 448/62, *but Wmk* **106** (*sideways* on* 1 *to* 6 *c. and* 50 *c. to* $5). *Chalk-surfaced paper.*
485 1 c. Type **87** 10 10
486 2 c. Red Piranha ("Pirai") 10 20
487 3 c. Peacock Cichlid ("Lukunani") 10 30
488 5 c. Armoured Catfish ("Hassar") 10 10
489 6 c. Black Acara ("Patua") 10 50
490 10 c. Spix's Guan 30 40
a. Glazed paper (*wmk inverted*) (21.12.71) 1·00 3·00
491 15 c. Harpy Eagle 30 10
aw. Wmk inverted .. ..
b. Glazed paper (*wmk inverted*) (21.12.71) 1·25 3·50
492 20 c. Hoatzin 30 50
493 25 c. Guianan Cock of the Rock 30 10
a. Glazed paper (*wmk inverted*) (21.12.71) 1·50 4·25
494 40 c. Great Kiskadee 60 60
495 50 c. Brazilian Agouti ("Accouri") 35 15
496 60 c. White-lipped Peccary .. .. .. 35 1·00
497 $1 Paca ("Labba") .. .. 70 1·10
a. Glazed paper (*wmk top of blossom to right*) (21.12.71) .. .. .. 2·50 11·00

98 $2 Nine-banded Armadillo .. .. 1·00 3·25
99 $5 Ocelot .. .. 1·50 5·50
85/99 .. .. *Set of* 15 5·00 11·50

*The normal sideways watermark shows the top of the lossom to the left, *as seen from the back of the stamp.*

These were put on sale by the Crown Agents on 25 March 969 but although supplies were sent to Guyana in time they ere not released there until needed as ample supplies remained the stamps without watermark. It is understood that the 3 c. nd 5 c. were put on sale in early May 1969 followed by the 25 c. ut there are no records of when the remainder were released.

(Des J. Cooter. Litho P.B.)

969 (30 Apr). *First Anniv of CARIFTA (Caribbean Free Trade Area). T* **112** *and similar design. W* **106** *(sideways on 25 c.). P* 13½.
00 6 c. rose-red, ultramarine and turquoise-blue 10 10
01 25 c. lemon, brown and rose-red 10 10
Design: *Horiz*—25 c. "Strength in Unity".

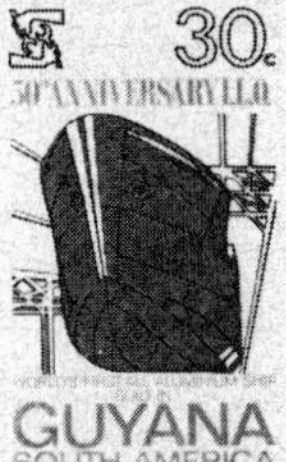

114 Building *Independence* (first aluminium ship)   **116** Scouts raising Flag

(Des R. Gates. Litho B.W.)

969 (30 Apr). *50th Anniv of International Labour Organization. T* **114** *and similar design. W* **106** *(sideways on 40 c.). P* 12 × 11 (30 c.) *or* 11 × 12 (40 c.).
02 30 c. turquoise-blue, black and silver.. .. 40 20
03 40 c. multicoloured 50 20
Design: *Horiz*—40 c. Bauxite processing plant.

(Des Jennifer Toombs. Litho B.W.)

969 (13 Aug). *Third Caribbean Scout Jamboree and Diamond Jubilee of Scouting in Guyana. T* **116** *and similar horiz design. Multicoloured. W* **106** *(sideways). P* 13.
04 6 c. Type **116** 10 10
05 8 c. Camp-fire cooking 10 10
06 25 c. Type **116** 10 10
07 30 c. As 8 c. 10 10
08 50 c. Type **116** 15 15
04/8 .. .. *Set of* 5 30 30

118 Gandhi and Spinning-wheel   **119** "Mother Sally Dance Troupe"

(Des G. Drummond. Litho Format)

969 (1 Oct). *Birth Centenary of Mahatma Gandhi. W* **106** *(sideways). P* 14½.
09 **118** 6 c. black, brown and yellowish olive .. 20 50
10 15 c. black, brown and lilac 25 50

(Des V. Whiteley (5, 25 c.), J.W. (others). Litho B.W. (5, 25 c.), D.L.R. (others))

1969 (17 Nov). *Christmas. T* **119** *and similar vert designs. Multicoloured. No wmk* (5, 25 *c.) or W* **106** *(others). P* 13½ (5, 25 *c.) or* 13×13½ *(others).*
511 5 c. Type **119** 10 10
a. Opt omitted .. .. 28·00
b. Opt double .. .. 25·00
512 6 c. City Hall, Georgetown 10 10
a. Opt omitted .. .. 28·00
b. Opt inverted .. .. 30·00
513 25 c. Type **119** 10 10
a. Opt omitted .. .. 28·00
514 60 c. As 6 c. 20 25
511/14 .. .. *Set of* 4 30 30

Nos. 511/14 are previously unissued stamps optd as in T **119** by Guyana Lithographic Co, Ltd.

REPUBLIC

121 Forbes Burnham and Map   **125** "The Descent from the Cross"

(Des L. Curtis. Litho D.L.R.)

1970 (23 Feb). *Republic Day. T* **121** *and similar designs. W* **106** *(sideways on 15 and 25 c.). P* 14.
515 5 c. sepia, ochre and pale blue 10 10
516 6 c. multicoloured 10 10
517 15 c. multicoloured 15 10
518 25 c. multicoloured 20 15
515/18 .. .. *Set of* 4 40 30
Designs: *Vert*—6 c. "Rural Self-help". *Horiz*—15 c. University of Guyana; 25 c. Guyana House.

(Des J. Cooter. Litho Questa)

1970 (24 Mar). *Easter. Paintings by Rubens. T* **125** *and similar vert design. Multicoloured. W* **106** *(inverted). P* 14 × 14½.
519 5 c. Type **125** 10 10
520 6 c. "Christ on the Cross" 10 10
521 15 c. Type **125** 20 10
522 25 c. As 6 c. 20 15
519/22 .. .. *Set of* 4 45 30

127 "Peace" and U.N. Emblem   **128** "Mother and Child" (Philip Moore)

(Des and litho Harrison)

1970 (26 Oct). *25th Anniv of United Nations. T* **127** *and similar horiz design. Multicoloured. W* **106** *(inverted). P* 14.
523 5 c. Type **127** 10 10
524 6 c. U.N. Emblem, Gold-panning and Drilling 10 10
525 15 c. Type **127** 10 10
526 25 c. As 6 c. 15 15
523/6 .. .. *Set of* 4 30 30

(Des Harrison. Litho J.W.)

1970 (8 Dec). *Christmas. W* **106.** *P* 13½.
527 **128** 5 c. multicoloured 10 10
528 6 c. multicoloured 10 10
529 15 c. multicoloured 15 15
530 25 c. multicoloured 15 15
527/30 .. .. *Set of* 4 30 30

129 National Co-operative Bank   **130** Racial Equality Symbol

(Des E. Samuels. Litho J.W.)

1971 (23 Feb). *Republic Day. W* **106** *(sideways). P* 14.
531 **129** 6 c. multicoloured 10 10
532 15 c. multicoloured 15 15
533 25 c. multicoloured 15 15
531/3 .. .. *Set of* 3 30 30

(Des E. Samuels. Litho Harrison)

1971 (22 Mar). *Racial Equality Year. W* **106** *(sideways). P* 14.
534 **130** 5 c. multicoloured 10 10
535 6 c. multicoloured 10 10
536 15 c. multicoloured 15 15
537 25 c. multicoloured 15 15
534/7 .. .. *Set of* 4 30 30

131 Young Volunteer felling Tree (from painting by J. Criswick).   **132** Yellow Allamanda

(Des and litho Harrison)

1971 (19 July). *First Anniv of Self-help Road Project. W* **106.** *P* 14.
538 **131** 5 c. multicoloured 10 10
539 20 c. multicoloured 25 10
540 25 c. multicoloured 30 10
541 50 c. multicoloured .. .. .. 45 1·75
538/41 .. .. *Set of* 4 1·00 1·75

Two types of 25 c.:

I Flowers facing up. Value in centre.

II Flowers facing down. Value to right. Colours changed.

(Des V. Whiteley (1 to 40 c.), PAD Studio (others). Litho D.L.R. (1 to 6 c.), J.W. (10 c. to 40 c.), Format (50 c. to $5))

1971 (17 Sept)–**76.** *Flowering Plants. Vert designs as T* **132.** *Multicoloured. W* **106** *(sideways on 1 c. to 40 c.). P* 13 × 13½ *(1 to 6 c.) or* 13½ *(10 c. to $5).*
542 1 c. Pitcher Plant of Mt Roraima (15.1.72) 10 10
543 2 c. Type **132** 10 10
544 3 c. Hanging Heliconia 10 10
545 5 c. Annatto tree 10 10
546 6 c. Cannon-ball tree 10 10
547 10 c. Cattleya (18.9.72) .. .. .. 3·25 10
a. Perf 13 (28.1.76) .. .. .. 3·50 10
548 15 c. Christmas Orchid (18.9.72) 80 10
a. Perf 13 (3.9.76) 65 10
549 20 c. *Paphinia cristata* (18.9.72) .. .. 3·00 20
a. Perf 13 (28.1.76) .. .. .. 4·00 20
550 25 c. Marabunta (I) (18.9.72) .. .. 4·50 6·00
550*a* 25 c. Marabunta (II) (*wmk inverted*) (20.8.73) 30 85
ab. Perf 13 (*wmk sideways*) (3.9.76) .. 45 10
551 40 c. Tiger Beard (18.9.72) .. .. 3·50 10
552 50 c. *Guzmania lingulata* (3.9.73) .. 40 85
553 60 c. Soldier's Cap (3.9.73) 30 65
554 $1 *Chelonanthus uliginoides* (3.9.73) .. 30 55
555 $2 *Norantea guianensis* (3.9.73) .. 35 55
556 $5 *Odontadenia grandiflora* (3.9.73) .. 55 55
542/56 .. .. *Set of* 16 15·00 9·00

The watermark is often indistinct, particularly on the early printings.

133 Child praying at Bedside   **134** Obverse and Reverse of Guyana $1 Coin

(Des V. Bassoo (T **133**), M. Austin (25, 50 c.). Litho J.W.)

1971 (29 Nov). *Christmas. T* **133** *and similar vert design. Multicoloured. W* **106** *(sideways on 5 c. and 20 c.). P* 13½.
557 5 c. Type **133** 10 10
558 20 c. Type **133** 10 10
559 25 c. Carnival Masquerader 10 10
560 50 c. As 25 c. 20 60
557/60 .. .. *Set of* 4 35 75

(Des G. Drummond. Litho Questa)

1972 (23 Feb). *Republic Day. T* **134** *and similar vert design. W* **106** *(sideways). P* 14½ × 14.
561 **134** 5 c. silver, black and orange-red .. 10 10
562 – 20 c. silver, black and magenta 15 10
563 **134** 25 c. silver, black and ultramarine .. 15 15
564 – 50 c. silver, black and yellow-green .. 25 45
561/4 .. .. *Set of* 4 55 70
Design:—20, 50 c. Reverse and obverse of Guyana $1 coin.

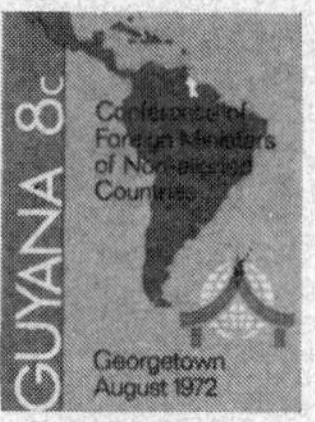

135 Hands and Irrigation Canal   **136** Map and Emblem

(Des J. Criswick. Litho J.W.)

1972 (3 Apr). *Youman Nabi (Mohammed's Birthday). W* **106.** *P* 14.
565 **135** 5 c. multicoloured 10 10
566 25 c. multicoloured 10 10
567 30 c. multicoloured 10 10
568 60 c. multicoloured 20 20
565/8 .. .. *Set of* 4 35 35

(Des J. Criswick. Litho J.W.)

1972 (20 July). *Conference of Foreign Ministers of Non-aligned Countries. W* **106.** *P* 13½.
569 **136** 8 c. multicoloured 10 10
570 25 c. multicoloured 10 10
571 40 c. multicoloured 15 15
572 50 c. multicoloured 20 20
569/72 .. .. *Set of* 4 40 40

OMNIBUS ISSUES

Details, together with prices for complete sets, of the various Omnibus issues from the 1935 Silver Jubilee series to date are included in a special section following Zimbabwe at the end of Volume 2.

137 Hand reaching for Sun

138 Joseph, Mary, and the Infant Jesus

(Des G. Bowen. Litho J.W.)

1972 (25 Aug). *First Caribbean Festival of Arts. W* **106** *(inverted on* 40, 50 *c.). P* 13½.

No.	Type	Description	Unused	Used
573	**137**	8 c. multicoloured	10	10
574		25 c. multicoloured	10	10
575		40 c. multicoloured	15	20
576		50 c. multicoloured	20	25
573/6		*Set of* 4	45	55

(Des Megan Anderson. Litho B.W.)

1972 (18 Oct). *Christmas. W* **106**. *P* 13 × 13½.

No.	Type	Description	Unused	Used
577	**138**	8 c. multicoloured	10	10
578		25 c. multicoloured	10	10
579		40 c. multicoloured	15	25
580		50 c. multicoloured	15	25
577/80		*Set of* 4	40	60

139 Umana Yana (Meeting-house)

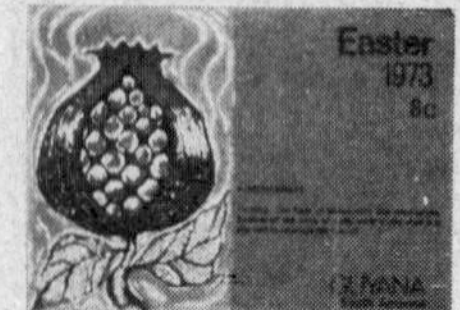

140 Pomegranate

(Des J. Cooter. Litho Questa)

1973 (23 Feb). *Republic Day. T* **139** *and similar vert design. Multicoloured. W* **106** *(inverted on* 8 *c.). P* 14.

No.	Type	Description	Unused	Used
581		8 c. Type **139**	10	10
582		25 c. Bethel Chapel	10	10
583		40 c. As 25 c.	20	20
584		50 c. Type **139**	25	20
581/4		*Set of* 4	55	50

(Des E. Samuels. Litho Format)

1973 (19 Apr). *Easter. T* **140** *and similar multicoloured design. W* **106** *(sideways on* 25 *and* 40 *c.). P* 14½ (8, 50 *c.) or* 13½ *(others).*

No.	Type	Description	Unused	Used
585		8 c. Type **140**	10	10
586		25 c. Cross and map (34 × 47 *mm*)	10	10
587		40 c. As 25 c.	10	10
588		50 c. Type **140**	15	15
585/8		*Set of* 4	35	35

141 Stylized Blood Cell

142 Steel-Band Players

(Des S. Greaves. Litho Harrison)

1973 (1 Oct). *25th Anniv of Guyana Red Cross. W* **106**. *P* 14.

No.	Type	Description	Unused	Used
589	**141**	8 c. vermilion and black	10	10
590		25 c. vermilion and bright purple	25	15
591		40 c. vermilion and ultramarine	35	50
592		50 c. vermilion and blackish olive	50	1·00
589/92		*Set of* 4	1·00	1·50

(Des E. Samuels; adapted J. Cooter. Litho Questa)

1973 (20 Nov). *Christmas. T* **142** *and similar vert design. Multicoloured. W* **106**. *P* 14 (8, 25 *c.) or* 13½ *(others).*

No.	Type	Description	Unused	Used
593		8 c. Type **142**	10	10
594		25 c. Type **142**	20	10
595		40 c. "Virgin and Child" (stained-glass window) (34 × 47 *mm*)	50	75
596		50 c. As 40 c.	55	75
593/6		*Set of* 4	1·25	1·50

143 Symbol of Progress

8c
=

(144)

(Des PAD Studio. Litho Questa)

1974 (23 Feb). *Republic Day. T* **143** *and similar vert design. Multicoloured. W* **106**. *P* 13½.

No.	Type	Description	Unused	Used
597		8 c. Type **143**	10	10
598		25 c. Wai-Wai Indian	10	10
599		40 c. Type **143**	15	30
600		50 c. As 25 c.	15	40
597/600		*Set of* 4	40	75

1974 (18 Mar). *No.* 546 *surch with T* **144**.

No.	Type	Description	Unused	Used
601		8 c. on 6 c. Cannon-ball tree	10	10

See also No. 620.

145 Kite with Crucifixion Motif

146 British Guiana 24 c. Stamp of 1874

(Des R. Savory; adapted J. Cooter. Litho Questa)

1974 (8 Apr). *Easter. T* **145** *and similar vert design. W* **106**. *P* 13½.

No.	Type	Description	Unused	Used
602	**145**	8 c. multicoloured	10	10
603	–	25 c. black and dull green	10	10
604	–	40 c. black and magenta	10	15
605	**145**	50 c. multicoloured	15	25
602/5		*Set of* 4	35	50

Design:—Nos. 603/4, "Crucifixion" in pre-Columbian style.

(Des R. Savory. Litho Harrison)

1974 (18 June). *Centenary of Universal Postal Union. T* **146** *and similar horiz design. W* **106** *(sideways on* 8 *and* 40 *c.). P* 13½ × 14 (8, 40 *c.) or* 14 *(others).*

No.	Type	Description	Unused	Used
606	**146**	8 c. multicoloured	25	10
607	–	25 c. bright yellow-green, deep slate-violet and black	35	10
608	**146**	40 c. multicoloured	35	20
609	–	50 c. bright yellow-green, reddish chestnut and black	45	45
606/9		*Set of* 4	1·25	75

Design (42 × 25 *mm*):—25 c., 50 c. U.P.U. emblem and Guyana postman.

147 Guides with Banner

148 Buck Toyeau

(Des M. Broodhagen; adapted J. Cooter. Litho Questa)

1974 (1 Aug). *Girl Guides' Golden Jubilee. T* **147** *and similar horiz design. Multicoloured. W* **106** *(sideways). P* 14½.

No.	Type	Description	Unused	Used
610		8 c. Type **147**	20	10
611		25 c. Guides in camp	30	15
612		40 c. As 25 c.	45	40
613		50 c. Type **147**	45	45
610/13		*Set of* 4	1·25	1·00
MS614		170 × 137 mm. Nos. 610/13	1·25	2·75

(Des S. Greaves and R. Granger Barrett. Litho Enschedé)

1974 (18 Nov). *Christmas. T* **148** *and similar vert designs. Multicoloured. W* **106**. *P* 13½ × 13.

No.	Type	Description	Unused	Used
615		8 c. Type **148**	10	10
616		35 c. Five-fingers and awaras	10	10
617		50 c. Pawpaw and tangerine	15	10
618		$1 Pineapple and sapodilla	30	60
615/18		*Set of* 4	55	70
MS619		127 × 94 mm. Nos. 615/18	90	2·50

1975 (20 Jan). *No.* 544 *surch as T* **144**.

No.	Type	Description	Unused	Used
620		8 c. on 3 c. Hanging Heliconia	10	10

149 Golden Arrow of Courage

150 Old Sluice Gate

(Des L. Curtis. Litho D.L.R.)

1975 (23 Feb). *Republic Day. Guyana Orders and Decorations. T* **149** *and similar vert designs. W* **106**. *P* 13½.

No.	Type	Description	Unused	Used
621		10 c. Type **149**	10	10
622		35 c. Cacique's Crown of Honour	10	15
623		50 c. Cacique's Crown of Valour	15	20
624		$1 Order of Excellence	35	60
621/4		*Set of* 4	60	90

(Des E. Samuels; adapted PAD Studio. Litho Questa)

1975 (2 May). *Silver Jubilee of International Commission on Irrigation and Drainage. T* **150** *and similar horiz design. Multicoloured. W* **106** *(sideways on* 35 *c. and* $1*). P* 14.

No.	Type	Description	Unused	Used
625		10 c. Type **150**	10	10
626		35 c. Modern sluice gate	10	15
627		50 c. Type **150**	15	30
628		$1 As 35 c.	35	60
625/8		*Set of* 4	60	1·00
MS629		162 × 121 mm. Nos. 625/8. Wmk sideways	75	2·50

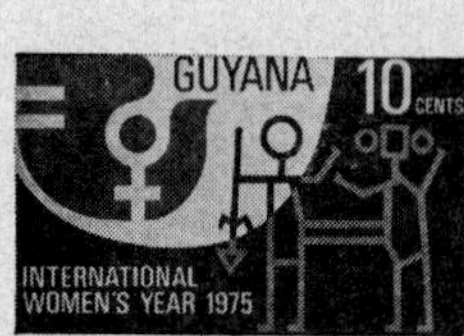

151 I.W.Y. Emblem and Rock Drawing

152 Freedom Monument

(Des C. Henriques; adapted PAD Studio. Litho Questa)

1975 (1 July). *International Women's Year. T* **151** *and similar horiz designs showing different rock drawings. W* **106** *(sideways). P* 14.

No.	Type	Description	Unused	Used
630	**151**	10 c. grey-green and yellow	10	10
631	–	35 c. reddish violet and greenish blue	15	10
632	–	50 c. royal blue and orange	20	15
633	–	$1 brown and bright blue	30	45
630/3		*Set of* 4	65	65
MS634		178 × 89 mm. Nos. 630/3	1·00	3·00

(Des PAD Studio. Litho Questa)

1975 (26 Aug). *Namibia Day. T* **152** *and similar vert design. Multicoloured. W* **106**. *P* 14.

No.	Type	Description	Unused	Used
635		10 c. Type **152**	10	10
636		35 c. Unveiling of Monument	15	10
637		50 c. Type **152**	25	15
638		$1 As 35 c.	35	35
635/8		*Set of* 4	70	60

153 G.N.S. Emblem

154 Court Building, 1875 and Forester's Badge

(Des C. Henriques; adapted PAD Studio. Litho Questa)

1975 (1 Oct*). *First Anniv of National Service. W* **106**. *P* 14.

No.	Type	Description	Unused	Used
639	**153**	10 c. greenish yellow, light green and light reddish violet	10	10
640	–	35 c. orange, lt green & reddish violet	10	10
641	–	50 c. light violet-blue, light green and light yellow-brown	15	15
642	–	$1 light mauve, dull green & lt emerald	40	40
639/42		*Set of* 4	60	60
MS643		196 × 133 mm. Nos. 639/42. W **106** (inverted)	1·10	2·00

*This is the local date of issue; the Crown Agents released the stamps a day later.

Nos. 640/2 are as T **153** but have different symbols within the circle.

(Des R. Savory; adapted PAD Studio. Litho Questa)

75 (14 Nov). *Centenary of Guyanese Ancient Order of Foresters. T* **154** *and similar horiz designs. Multicoloured.* W **106** (*sideways*). *P* 14.
4 10 c. Type **154** 10 10
5 35 c. Rock drawing of hunter and quarry . . 10 10
6 50 c. Crossed axes and bugle-horn 15 10
7 $1 Bow and arrow 40 40
4/7 . . . . *Set of* 4 60 50
3648 129 × 97 mm. Nos. 644/7 . . . . . . 75 2·25

35c

(155)

156 Shoulder Flash

76 (10 Feb). *No. 553 surch with T* **155**.
9 35 c. on 60 c. Soldier's Cap 20 15

(Des C. Henriques; adapted J.W. Litho Questa)

76 (29 Mar). *50th Anniv of the St. John Ambulance in Guyana. T* **156** *and similar vert designs.* W **106**. *P* 14.
0 **156** 8 c. silver, black and magenta 10 10
1 – 15 c. silver, black and orange 10 10
2 – 35 c. silver, black and green 20 20
3 – 40 c. silver, black and new blue 25 25
0/3 . . . . *Set of* 4 55 50
Nos. 651/3 are as T **156** but show different shoulder flashes.

157 Triumphal Arch

158 Flame in Archway

(Des C. Henriques. Litho J.W.)

76 (25 May). *Tenth Anniv of Independence. T* **157** *and similar vert designs. Multicoloured.* W **106**. *P* 13½.
4 8 c. Type **157** 10 10
5 15 c. Stylised Victoria Regia lily 10 10
6 35 c. "Onward to Socialism" 15 15
7 40 c. Worker pointing the way 15 15
4/7 . . . . *Set of* 4 35 35
S658 120×100 mm. Nos. 654/7. Wmk inverted.
P 14½ . . . . 50 1·50

76 (3 Aug). *West Indian Victory in World Cricket Cup. As Nos. 559/60 of Barbados.*
9 15 c. Map of the Caribbean . . . . . . 1·50 1·75
0 15 c. Prudential Cup . . . . 1·50 1·75

(Des G. Vasarhelyi. Litho J.W.)

76 (21 Oct). *Deepavali Festival. T* **158** *and similar vert designs. Multicoloured.* W **106**. *P* 14.
1 8 c. Type **158** 10 10
2 15 c. Flame in hand 10 10
3 35 c. Flame in bowl 15 20
4 40 c. Goddess Latchmi 15 25
1/4 . . . . *Set of* 4 35 50
S665 94 × 109 mm. Nos. 661/4 . . . . . . 50 1·50

59 Festival Emblem and "Musical Instrument"

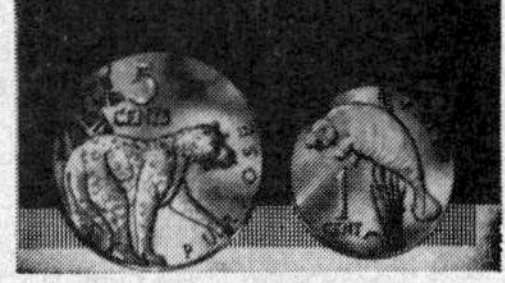

160 1 c. and 5 c. Coins

(Des C. Henriques. Litho Questa)

77 (1 Feb). *Second World Black and African Festival of Arts and Culture, Nigeria.* W **106**. *P* 14.
6 **159** 10 c. dull red, black and gold 10 10
7 35 c. deep violet, black and gold 15 10
8 50 c. ultramarine, black and gold 20 25
9 $1 blue-green, black and gold 35 75
6/9 . . . . *Set of* 4 65 1·00
S670 90 × 157 mm. Nos. 666/9 . . . . . . 75 3·00
The above were scheduled for release in 1975, and when finally issued had the original inscription obliterated and a new one applied by overprinting. Examples of Nos. 666/70 are known without overprint.

(Des J.W. Litho Questa)

1977 (26 May). *New Coinage. T* **160** *and similar horiz designs.* W **106**. *P* 14.
671 8 c. multicoloured 20 10
672 15 c. yellow-brown, grey and black 25 10
673 35 c. bright yellow-green, grey and black . . 45 30
674 40 c. carmine-red, grey and black 50 35
675 $1 multicoloured . . . . 1·25 1·25
676 $2 multicoloured . . . . 1·75 2·75
671/6 . . . . *Set of* 6 4·00 4·25
Designs:—15 c. 10 and 25 c. coins; 35 c. 50 c. and $1 coins; 40 c. $5 and $10 coins; $1 $50 and $100 coins; $2 Reverse of $1 coin.

161 Hand Pump, *circa* 1850

162 Cuffy Monument

(Des J. Porteous Wood. Litho Harrison)

1977 (15 Nov). *National Fire Prevention Week. T* **161** *and similar horiz designs. Multicoloured.* W **106**. *P* 14 × 14½.
677 8 c. Type **161** 40 10
678 15 c. Steam engine, *circa* 1860 . . . . 70 10
679 35 c. Fire engine, *circa* 1930 . . . . 1·00 60
680 40 c. Fire engine, 1977 . . . . . . 1·10 85
677/80 . . . . *Set of* 4 2·75 1·50

(Des BG Studio. Litho Questa)

1977 (7 Dec). *Cuffy Monument (commemorating 1763 Slave Revolt).* W **106**. *P* 14.
681 **162** 8 c. multicoloured 10 10
682 – 15 c. multicoloured 10 10
683 **162** 35 c. multicoloured 15 20
684 – 40 c. multicoloured 15 30
681/4 . . . . *Set of* 4 35 55
Nos. 682 and 684 show a different view of the monument.

163 American Manatee

(Des BG Studio. Litho Questa)

1978 (15 Feb). *Wildlife Conservation. T* **163** *and similar multicoloured designs.* W **106** (*sideways on* 8 *and* 15 *c.*). *P* 14.
685 8 c. Type **163** 65 10
686 15 c. Giant sea turtle 85 20
687 35 c. Harpy Eagle (*vert*) . . . . . . 3·25 1·50
688 40 c. Iguana (*vert*) . . . . 3·25 1·50
685/8 . . . . *Set of* 4 7·25 3·00

164 L. F. S. Burnham (Prime Minister) and Parliament Buildings, Georgetown

165 Dr. George Giglioli (scientist and physician)

(Des Walsall. Litho Questa)

1978 (27 Apr). *25th Anniv of Prime Minister's Entry into Parliament. T* **164** *and similar horiz designs.* W **106** (*sideways*). *P* 13½ × 14.
689 8 c. black, violet and bluish grey 10 10
690 15 c. black, light violet-blue and bluish grey . . 10 10
691 35 c. black, red and bluish grey 15 20
692 40 c. black, red-orange and bluish grey . . 15 20
689/92 . . . . *Set of* 4 40 45
MS693 176 × 118 mm. Nos. 689/92 . . . . 55 1·50
Designs:—15 c. Burnham, graduate and children ("Free Education"); 35 c. Burnham and industrial works (Nationalization of Bauxite industry); 40 c. Burnham and village scene ("The Co-operative Village").

(Des J.W. Litho Harrison)

1978 (4 Sept). *National Science Research Council. T* **165** *and similar multicoloured designs.* W **106** (*sideways on* 10 *and* 50 *c.*). *P* 13½ × 14 (10, 50 *c.*) *or* 14 × 13½ (*others*).
694 10 c. Type **165** 15 10
695 30 c. Institute of Applied Science and Technology (*horiz*) 20 15
696 50 c. Emblem of National Science Research Council 25 25
697 60 c. Emblem of Commonwealth Science Council (commemorating the 10th Meeting) (*horiz*) 25 25
694/7 . . . . *Set of* 4 75 60

166 *Prepona pheridamas*

167 *Agrias claudina*

(Des J. Cooter. Litho J.W.)

1978 (1 Oct)–**80**. *Butterflies. Horiz designs as T* **166** (5 *to* 60 *c.*) *or vert as T* **167** (*$1 to $10*). *Multicoloured.* W **106**. *P* 14 × 13½ (5 *to* 60 *c.*) *or* 13 (*$1 to $10*).
698 5 c. Type **166** . . . . 1·25 10
699 10 c. *Archonias bellona* . . . . . . 1·25 10
700 15 c. *Eryphanis polyxena* . . . . . . 1·25 10
701 20 c. *Helicopis cupido* . . . . 1·25 10
702 25 c. *Nessaea batesii* . . . . 1·50 10
702*a* 30 c. *Nymphidium mantus* (25.1.80) . . 1·25 1·75
703 35 c. *Anaea galanthis* . . . . 1·50 10
704 40 c. *Morpho rhetenor* (male) . . . . 1·50 10
705 50 c. *Hamadryas amphinome* . . . . 1·50 20
705*a* 60 c. *Papilio androgeus* (25.1.80) . . . . 1·25 1·00
706 $1 Type **167** . . . . 3·25 20
707 $2 *Morpho rhetenor* (female) . . . . 5·00 35
708 $5 *Morpho deidamia* . . . . 6·50 90
708*a* $10 *Elbella patrobas* (25.1.80) . . . . 7·50 4·25
698/708*a* . . . . *Set of* 14 32·00 8·00

168 Amerindian Stone-chip Grater in Preparation

169 Dish Aerial by Night

(Des L. Curtis. Litho Questa)

1978 (18 Dec). *National/International Heritage Year. T* **168** *and similar vert designs. Multicoloured.* W **106**. *P* 14.
709 10 c. Type **168** 10 10
710 30 c. Cassiri and decorated Amerindian jars . . 15 10
711 50 c. Fort Kyk-over-al 20 15
712 60 c. Fort Island 20 20
709/12 . . . . *Set of* 4 55 45

(Des L. Curtis. Litho Questa)

1979 (7 Feb). *Satellite Earth Station. T* **169** *and similar horiz designs. Multicoloured.* W **106** (*sideways*). *P* 14 × 14½.
713 10 c. Type **169** 10 10
714 30 c. Dish aerial by day 20 15
715 50 c. Satellite with solar veins 30 15
716 $3 Cylinder satellite . . . . 1·50 90
713/16 . . . . *Set of* 4 1·90 1·10

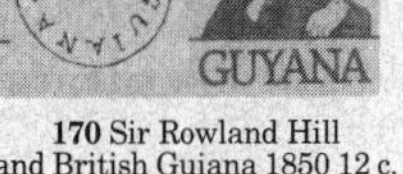

170 Sir Rowland Hill and British Guiana 1850 12 c. "Cottonreel" Stamp

171 "Me and my Sister"

(Des and litho J.W.)

1979 (11 June). *Death Centenary of Sir Rowland Hill. T* **170** *and similar multicoloured designs.* W **106** (*sideways on* 10 *and* 50 *c.*). *P* 14.
717 10 c. Type **170** 15 10
718 30 c. British Guiana 1856 1 c. black on magenta stamp (*vert*) 25 15
719 50 c. British Guiana 1898 1 c. stamp 35 25
720 $3 Printing press used for early British Guiana stamps (*vert*) . . . . . . 70 1·10
717/20 . . . . *Set of* 4 1·25 1·40

(Des J.W. Litho Questa)

1979 (20 Aug). *International Year of the Child. Paintings by local children. T* **171** *and similar multicoloured designs.* W **106** (*sideways on* 30, 50 *c. and* $3). *P* 13½.
721 10 c. Type **171** 10 10
722 30 c. "Fun with the Fowls" (*horiz*) 15 15
723 50 c. "Two Boys catching Ducks" (*horiz*) . . 20 20
724 $3 "Mango Season" (*horiz*) . . . . . . 65 1·25
721/4 . . . . *Set of* 4 90 1·50

172 "An 8 Hour Day"

173 Guyana Flag

(Des C. Rodriguez. Litho Walsall)

1979 (27 Sept). *60th Anniv of Guyana Labour Union. T* **172** *and similar multicoloured designs. W* **106** *(sideways on* 30 c.). *P* 14 × 14½ (30 c.) *or* 14½ × 14 *(others).*

725 10 c. Type **172** 10 10
726 30 c. "Abolition of Night Baking" *(horiz)* .. 10 10
727 50 c. "Introduction of the Workmen's Compensation Ordinance" 15 15
728 $3 H. N. Critchlow (founder) 55 90
725/8 .. .. *Set of* 4 75 1·10

(Des BG Studio. Litho Questa)

1980 (23 Feb). *10th Anniv of Republic. T* **173** *and similar horiz designs. W* **106** *(sideways). P* 14.

729 10 c. multicoloured 10 10
730 35 c. black and red-orange 30 10
731 60 c. multicoloured 50 20
732 $3 multicoloured 80 90
729/32 .. .. .. *Set of* 4 1·50 1·10

Designs:—35 c. View of Demerara River Bridge; 60 c. Kaieteur Falls; $3 "Makanaima the Great Ancestral Spirit of the Amerindians".

174 Common Snook

175 Children's Convalescent Home (Community Service)

(Des J.W. Litho Questa)

1980 (6 May). *"London 1980" International Stamp Exhibition. Fishes. T* **174** *and similar horiz designs. Multicoloured. W* **106** *(sideways). P* 14½.

733 35 c. Type **174** 35 25
a. Block of 12. Nos. 733/44 .. .. 3·75
734 35 c. Trahira ("Haimara") 35 25
735 35 c. Electric Eel 35 25
736 35 c. Golden Rivulus 35 25
737 35 c. Golden Pencilfish 35 25
738 35 c. Four-eyed Fish 35 25
739 35 c. Red Piranha ("Pirai") 35 25
740 35 c. Smoking Hassar 35 25
741 35 c. Manta 35 25
742 35 c. Festive Cichlid ("Flying Patwa") .. 35 25
743 35 c. Arapaima 35 25
744 35 c. Peacock Cichlid ("Lukanani") .. 35 25
733/44 .. .. .. *Set of* 12 3·75 2·75

Nos. 733/44 were printed together, *se-tenant*, in a block of 12 within the sheetlet containing one of each design.

(Des local artist; adapted J.W. Litho Walsall)

1980 (23 June). *75th Anniv of Rotary International. T* **175** *and similar multicoloured designs. P* 14.

745 10 c. Type **175** 10 10
746 30 c. Rotary Club of Georgetown and Rotary emblems 10 10
747 50 c. District 404 emblem *(vert)* 20 20
748 $3 Rotary anniversary emblem *(vert)* .. 80 80
745/8 .. .. *Set of* 4 1·00 1·10

176 "C" encircling Globe, Caduceus Emblem and Sea

177 *Virola surinamensis*

(Des L. Curtis. Litho Enschedé)

1980 (23 Sept). *25th Anniv of Commonwealth Caribbean Medical Research Council. T* **176** *and similar horiz designs. Multicoloured. W* **106** *(sideways). P* 13.

749 10 c. Type **176** 10 10
750 60 c. Researcher with microscope, Caduceus emblem, stethoscope and beach scene .. 40 20
751 $3 Caduceus emblem, "C" encircling researcher and island silhouettes .. 1·10 1·00
749/51 .. .. *Set of* 3 1·40 1·10

(Des L. Curtis. Litho Format)

1980 (1 Dec). *Christmas. Trees and Foliage. T* **177** *and similar horiz designs. Multicoloured. W* **106** *(sideways). P* 13½.

752 10 c. Type **177** 10 10
753 30 c. *Hymenaea courbaril* 20 10
754 50 c. *Mora excelsa* 30 15
755 $3 *Peltogyne venosa* .. .. .. 1·25 1·10
752/5 .. .. *Set of* 4 1·75 1·25

GUYANA 30c
TREE PORCUPINE Coendou prehensilis

178 Brazilian Tree Porcupine

1981 CONFERENCE $1·05 X

(179)

(Des G. Drummond. Litho Questa)

1981 (2 Mar–1 Sept). *Wildlife. T* **178** *and similar horiz designs. Multicoloured. W* **106** *(sideways). P* 14.

756 30 c. Type **178** 60 50
a. Sheetlet of 12. Nos. 756/67 .. .. 6·50
757 30 c. Red Howler 60 50
758 30 c. Common Squirrel-Monkey 60 50
759 30 c. Two-toed Sloth 60 50
760 30 c. Brazilian Tapir 60 50
761 30 c. Collared Peccary 60 50
762 30 c. Six-banded Armadillo 60 50
a. Perf 12 (1 Sept) 60 15
763 30 c. Tamandua ("Ant Eater") 60 50
764 30 c. Giant Anteater 60 50
765 30 c. Murine Opossum 60 50
766 30 c. Brown Four-eyed Opossum 60 50
767 30 c. Brazilian Agouti 60 50
756/67 .. .. .. *Set of* 12 6·50 5·50

Nos. 756/67 were printed together, *se-tenant*, within the sheet of 12.

No. 762a was printed in sheets of 50.

1981 (4 May). *Liberation of Southern Africa Conference. No.* 635 *surch with T* **179** *by Govt Printer.*

768 $1.05 on 10 c. Type **152** 40 30

ROYAL WEDDING 1981 $3·60 X X

(180)

GUYANA REVENUE ESSEQUIBO IS OURS 10c

181 Map of Guyana

7.20

(182)

1981 (6 May). *Royal Wedding (1st issue). Nos.* 554 *and* 556 *surch as T* **180** *by Govt Printer in blue.*

769 $3.60 on $5 *Odontadenia grandiflora* .. 1·00 1·00
a. Surch inverted £100
b. Surch double .. .. .. 18·00
c. Black surch 60 65
770 $7.20 on $1 *Chelonanthus uliginoides* .. 80 80
b. Surch double .. .. .. 20·00
c. Surch triple .. .. ..
d. Black surch .. .. .. 1·00 1·00
da. Surch on No. 556 .. .. .. 25·00

See also Nos. 841/3 and 930/6

(Surch by Govt Printer)

1981 (11 May). *W* **106** *(sideways). P* 13.

771 **181** 10 c. on 3 c. black, ind & Venetian red .. 40 10
772 30 c. on 2 c. black, ind & greenish grey .. 45 15
773 50 c. on 2 c. black, ind & greenish grey .. 55 15
774 60 c. on 2 c. black, ind & greenish grey .. 65 15
775 75 c. on 3 c. black, ind & Venetian red .. 65 20
a. Surch double .. .. .. 40·00
b. Surch triple .. .. .. 60·00
771/5 .. .. .. *Set of* 5 2·40 60

Nos. 771/5 are fiscal stamps surcharged for postal use.

See also Nos. 940/76, 988/9 and 1029.

1981 (11 May). *No.* 544 *surch with T* **182** *by Govt Printer.*

775c 720 c. on 3 c. Hanging Heliconia .. .. 70·00 15·00
ca. Surch quadruple .. .. .. 75·00

1981

(183)

1981 (8 June). *Optd with T* **183** *by Bovell's Printery.*

776 **105** 25 c. black, gold and lilac (R.) 10 10
777 30 c. black, gold & lt apple-green (R.) .. 15 10
778 – 35 c. multicoloured (No. 645) (R.) .. 15 10
779 – $1 multicoloured (No. 554) 70 40
776/9 .. .. *Set of* 4 1·00 55

210

7 X ESSEQUIBO IS OURS 15 ESSEQUIBO IS OURS 15

(184) (185) (186) (186*a*)

1981 (8 June–1 July) *Nos.* 545 *and* 556 *surch with T* **184** *(No.* 780) *or as T* **185**, *all by Bovell's Printery.*

780 75 c. on 5 c. Annatto tree 50 50
781 210 c. on $5 *Odontadenia grandiflora* .. 80 1·00
a. Surch inverted .. .. .. 60·00
781*b* 220 c. on 5 c. Annatto tree (1 July) .. 80·00 8·50

1981 (8 June). *Nos.* D8/11 *surch in black* (15 c.) *or red (others) by Bovell's Printery. A. As T* **186**.

782A **D 2** 10 c. on 2 c. black 25 1
c. Surch omitted (in vert pair with normal) .. .. ..
w. Wmk inverted .. .. ..
783A 15 c. on 12 c. bright scarlet 25 1
784A 20 c. on 1 c. olive 20 2
w. Wmk inverted .. .. ..
785A 45 c. on 2 c. black 60 2
786A 55 c. on 4 c. dull ultramarine 30 2
c. Surch inverted .. .. ..
d. Surch double, one inverted (T **186** + T **186**) .. .. ..
da. Ditto, but T **186** + T **186*a*** .. ..
e. Surch double (55 c. + 60 c.) ..
f. Vert pair, one surch inverted, one surch albino .. .. ..
w. Wmk inverted .. .. ..
788A 65 c. on 2 c. black 40 2
789A 70 c. on 4 c. dull ultramarine 80 5
w. Wmk inverted .. .. ..
790A 80 c. on 4c. dull ultramarine 35 2
c. Surch inverted .. .. ..
d. Surch omitted (in vert pair with inverted) .. .. ..
782/90A .. .. *Set of* 8 2·75 1·6

B. *As T* **186*a***

782B **D 2** 10 c. on 2 c. black 50 1
w. Wmk inverted .. .. ..
783B 15 c. on 12 c. bright scarlet 50 2
784B 20 c. on 1 c. olive 30 2
a. "ESSEOUIBO" .. .. .. 25·00
c. Surch omitted (in vert pair with normal) .. .. ..
w. Wmk inverted .. .. ..
785B 45 c. on 2 c. black 60 3
786B 55 c. on 4 c. dull ultramarine .. .. 6·50 3·5
c. Surch inverted .. .. ..
db. Surch double, one inverted (T **186*a*** + T **186**) ..
w. Wmk inverted .. .. ..
787B 60 c. on 4 c. dull ultramarine 50 1
a. "ESSEOUIBO" .. .. .. 10·00
c. Surch omitted (in vert pair with normal) .. .. ..
788B 65 c. on 2 c. black 50 2
789B 70 c. on 4 c. dull ultramarine 60 4
w. Wmk inverted .. .. ..
790B 80 c. on 4 c. dull ultramarine 50 3
782B/90B .. .. .. *Set of* 9 9·00 5·0

With the exception of No. 787 these stamps were surcharge with a setting of eighteen (three horizontal rows) as Type 18 and twelve as Type 186*a*. The two types of surcharge can therefore, be found as vertical *se-tenant* pairs.

No. 787 was produced from a setting of 12 containing Type 186*a* only. The same setting was also used for the bottom tw rows of the 20 c. on 1 c. value. The "ESSEOUIBO" error occurs o the first stamp in the second horizontal row of this setting.

Examples of 15, 45 and 60 c. surcharges are also known o stamps with watermark w **12**.

1981 1981 198

(187) (188) (189)

1981 (8 June–1 July). *Nos.* 491, 494 *and* 555 *optd with T* **187**, **18** *or* **189**, *all by Bovell's Printery.*

791 15 c. Harpy Eagle (R.) .. .. .. 8·00 10
a. Opt omitted (in vert pair with normal) † —
b. Opt double .. .. ..
c. Opt inverted .. .. .. 40·00
d. Opt in black .. .. .. 42·00 5·00
da Opt double, one inverted .. .. 40·00
792 40 c. Great Kiskadee (1.7.81) .. .. 8·50 40
a. Opt double .. .. .. 30·00
793 $2 *Norantea guianensis* (1.7.81) .. 3·00 55
791/3 .. .. .. *Set of* 3 18·00 90

x 120 50c ■ ■

(190) (191)

150

(192)

(Surch by Bovell's Printery)

1981 (1 July). *(a) Postage. (i) No.* 545 *surch with T* **190**.

794 50 c. on 5 c. Annatto tree 30 2
a. Surch inverted .. .. .. 6·00 2·0

(ii) *No.* 554 *surch as T* **191**

795 120 c. on $1 *Chelonanthus uliginoides* .. 75 4
796 140 c. on $1 *Chelonanthus uliginoides* .. 70 4

(iii) *Nos.* F7 *and* F9 *surch as T* **192**

797 150 c. on $2 *Norantea guianensis* 75 4
798 360 c. on $2 *Norantea guianensis* .. .. 3·00 6
799 720 c. on 60 c. Soldier's Cap .. .. 3·00 1·0

(iv) *Nos.* 556 *and* 716 *surch as T* **185**

0 220 c. on $3 Cylinder satellite (surch vert – reading downwards) .. .. 1·75 45
a. Surch reading upwards .. .. 30·00
1 250 c. on $5 *Odontadenia grandiflora* .. 1·25 45
2 280 c. on $5 *Odontadenia grandiflora* .. 1·50 50
3 375 c. on $5 *Odontadenia grandiflora* .. 1·75 55
a. Surch inverted .. .. ..
b. "7" of "375" omitted .. .. ..

b) *Air. No.* 843 *with commemorative opt cancelled by three bars*
4 $1.10 on $2 *Norantea guianensis* .. .. 2·00 1·75

No. 803b was subsequently corrected by the insertion of a ry uneven "7".

100

15 AIR

(193) (194)

(Surch by Bovell's Printery)

81 (1 July). *No.* 485 *surch.* (a) *Postage. With T* **193**.
5 15 c. on 1 c. Type **87** 70 20
a. Horiz strip of 3. Nos. 805/7 .. .. 2·00
b. Surch inverted .. .. .. 48·00
c. Surch double .. .. .. 40·00

(*b*) *Air. As T* **194**
6 100 c. on 1 c. Type **87** 70 40
7 110 c. on 1 c. Type **87** 70 40

Nos. 805/7 were printed together, *se-tenant*, within the same eet providing 36 examples of No. 805 and 32 each of the others. . 805 appears in the six vertical columns of Rows 3 to 8 with rizontal pairs of Nos. 806/7 in vertical columns 1, 2, 9, 10 and rtical pairs in the central six vertical columns of Rows 1, 2, 9, .

SSEQUIBO S OURS — ESSEQUIBO IS OURS — 1981

(195) (195*a*) (196)

81 (1 July). *No.* 700 *optd with T* **195** *by Bovell's Printery.*
8 15 c. *Eryphanis polyxena* .. .. .. 1·50 10
a. Opt T **195***a* .. .. .. 1·50 15
ab. "I" of "IS" omitted .. .. ..

No. 808ab is believed to occur on either R. 5/1 or R. 5/5.

81 (7 July–15 Sept). *Various stamps optd with T* **196** *by Bovell's Printery.*
9 – 15 c. multicoloured (No. 548) .. 6·00 10
a. Opt inverted .. .. ..
0 – 15 c. multicoloured (No. 659) (opt vert —reading downwards) .. .. 6·00 20
a. Opt reading upwards .. .. 26·00
b. Opt albino .. .. .. 26·00
1 – 15 c. multicoloured (No. 660) .. 4·50 20
a. Opt inverted .. .. ..
b. Vert pair, one with opt omitted
1c – 40 c. multicoloured (No. F5) .. .. — £200
2 – 50 c. multicoloured (No. 623) .. 60 20
a. Opt inverted .. .. 28·00
b. Opt double, one albino inverted 50·00
3 **150** 50 c. multicoloured .. .. 1·00 20
4 – 50 c. royal blue and orange (No. 632) 23·00 2·00
a. Opt inverted .. .. 30·00
5 – 50 c. multicoloured (No. 646) .. 2·75 20
a. Opt inverted .. .. 30·00
6 **159** 50 c. ultramarine, black and gold .. 13·00 2·00
7 – 50 c. multicoloured (No. F6) .. .. 4·00 20
8 – 60 c. multicoloured (No. 731) (15.9.81) 60 20
9 – 60 c. multicoloured (No. 750) (15.9.81) 60 20
0 – $1 multicoloured (No. 624) .. 6·00 55
a. Opt inverted .. .. 20·00
1 **159** $1 blue-green, black and gold .. 6·00 30
a. Opt inverted .. .. 30·00
2 – $2 multicoloured (No. 555) .. 9·00 75
3 – $3 multicoloured (No. 732) .. 2·50 65
a. Opt inverted .. .. 16·00
4 – $5 multicoloured (No. 556) .. 3·25 1·25

Overprints on Nos. 814/15 and 823 are vertical, reading wards.

55 55

(197) (198)

110

(199)

440 440

(200) (201)

550 550

(202) (203)

240

(204)

(Surch by Bovell's Printery)

1981 (7 July–15 Sept). (*a*) *Various stamps surch as T* **197/203**.
825 **116** 55 c. on 6 c. multicoloured (surch T **197**) (15.9.81) .. .. 4·00 80
a. Surch with T **198** .. .. .. 10·00 3·50
b. Vert pair. Nos. 825/a .. .. 14·00 4·50
826 **111** 70 c. on 6 c. multicoloured (15.9.81) .. 1·00 20
827 100 c. on 6 c. multicoloured .. .. 1·25 20
a. Surch inverted .. .. .. 3·50 75
b. Surch albino inverted .. .. 9·00
828 – 100 c. on 8 c. multicoloured (No. 505) 4·50 20
829 **152** 100 c. on $1.05 on 10 c. mult (No. 768) (surch vert—reading upwards) .. 29·00 4·00
a. Surch reading downwards .. 35·00
830 **116** 110 c. on 6 c. multicoloured .. .. 3·00 30
831 **149** 110 c. on 10 c. multicoloured (surch vert—reading downwards) .. .. 2·50 30
832 **151** 110 c. on 10 c. grey-green and yellow .. 6·00 45
833 **154** 110 c. on 10 c. multicoloured .. .. 5·00 45
834 – 125 c. on $2 multicoloured (No. 555) .. 12·00 80
835 **116** 180 c. on 6 c. multicoloured (15.9.81) .. 3·50 45
836 400 c. on 6 c. multicoloured .. .. 3·50 80
837 440 c. on 6 c. multicoloured (surch T **200**) 10·00 3·50
a. Surch with T **201** .. .. .. 2·00 55
b. Vert pair. Nos. 837/a .. .. 12·00 6·00
838 – 550 c. on $10 multicoloured (No. O21) (surch T **202**) (15.9.81) .. .. 5·50 1·00
a. Surch with T **203** .. .. .. 13·00 5·50
b. Vert pair. Nos. 838/a .. .. 17·00 8·00
839 – 625 c. on 40 c. multicoloured (No. F5) .. 14·00 1·75

(*b*) *No.* 728 *surch with T* **204**
840 – 240 c. on $3 multicoloured (15.9.81) .. 9·50 75

Nos. 825/a, 837/a and 838/a were each printed together, *se-tenant*, in vertical pairs throughout sheets containing five of these pairs plus an additional fifteen examples of Nos. 825, 837a and 838.

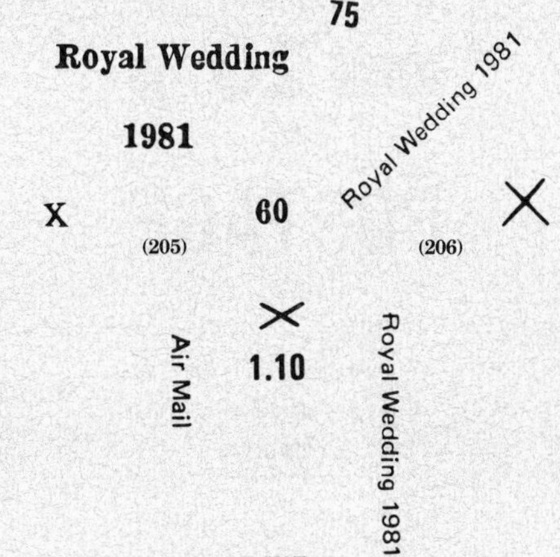

(205) (206) (207)

(Surch by Bovell's Printery)

1981 (22 July). *Royal Wedding (2nd issue).* (*a*) *Postage. Nos.* 544 *and* 556 *surch with T* **205/6**.
841 60 c. on 3 c. Hanging Heliconia 30 35
a. Surch inverted .. .. .. 55·00
b. "Royal Wedding" diagonal (as T **206**) .. 55·00
c. Surch double (T **205** + T **206**) .. .. 25·00
d. Surch T **205** double .. .. 70·00
842 75 c. on $5 *Odontadenia grandiflora* .. 30 40

(*b*) *Air. No.* 555 *surch with T* **207**
843 $1.10 on $2 *Norantea guianensis* 30 45
a. Surch double .. .. .. 38·00
b. Surch inverted .. .. .. 80·00
841/3 .. .. *Set of* 3 80 1·10

It is believed No. 841b comes from trial sheets which were accidentally included in supplies of the normal No. 841.

1831-1981 — Von Stephan — 330

Espana 82

(208) (209)

1981 (22 July). *World Cup Football Championship, Spain (1982) (1st issue). No.* 781*b optd with T* **208** *by Bovell's Printery.*
844 220 c. on 5 c. Annatto tree .. .. 1·25 40
a. Opt double .. .. .. 30·00
b. Opt double, one albino .. .. 30·00

See also Nos. 937/9 and 1218.

1981 (22 July). *150th Birth Anniv of Heinrich von Stephan (founder of U.P.U.). No.* 720 *surch with T* **209**.
845 330 c. on $3 Printing press used for early British Guiana stamps .. .. 1·50 55
a. Surch inverted .. .. .. 30·00

12

(211)

1981 (24 Aug). *No.* 452 *surch as T* **211** *by Bovell's Printery.*
847 12 c. on 12 c. on 6 c. Black Acara ("Patua") 20 25
a. Large surch omitted .. .. 15·00
b. Strip of 3. Nos. 847/9 50
c. Strip of 3. Nos. 847, 850/1 50
848 15 c. on 10 c. on 6 c. Black Acara ("Patua") 15 10
849 15 c. on 30 c. on 6 c. Black Acara ("Patua") 15 10
a. Small surch omitted .. .. 25·00
850 15 c. on 50 c. on 6 c. Black Acara ("Patua") 15 10
851 15 c. on 60 c. on 6 c. Black Acara ("Patua") 15 10

Nos. 847/51 are further surcharges on previously unissued stamps.

No. 847 exists with the smaller of the two 12 c. surcharges printed by either lithography or typography.

Nos. 847/9 and 847, 850/1 were each printed together, *se-tenant*, within the sheets providing 36 examples of No. 847 and 30 each of Nos. 848/9 or 850/1. Each sheet also contained four stamps cancelled with a black diagonal cross. In each instance No. 847 appeared in the six central vertical columns of Rows 3 to 8 with horizontal pairs of Nos. 848/9 or 850/1 in vertical columns 1, 2, 9, 10 and vertical pairs in R. 1/4–8, R. 2/4–8, R. 9/3–7 and R. 10/3–7.

214 Coromantyn Free Negro Armed Ranger, *circa* 1772 and Cuffy Monument

215 Louis Braille

(Des G. Drummond. Litho Rosenbaum Bros, Vienna)

1981 (1 Oct). *16th Anniv of Guyana Defence Force. T* **214** *and similar vert designs. Multicoloured. W* **106** *(inverted on $1). P* $13\frac{1}{2}$.
853 15 c. on 10 c. Type **214** 40 10
854 50 c. Private, 27th Foot Regiment, *circa* 1825 60 30
855 $1 on 30 c. Private, Col. Fourgeoud's Marines, *circa* 1775 .. .. .. 70 45
856 $1.10 on $3 W.O. and N.C.O., Guyana Defence Force, 1966 .. .. .. 80 70
853/6 .. .. *Set of* 4 2·25 1·40

The 15 c., $1 and $1.10 values are surcharged on previously unissued stamps.

(Des G. Vasarhelyi. Litho Questa)

1981 (2 Nov). *International Year for Disabled Persons. Famous Disabled People. T* **215** *and similar horiz designs. Multicoloured. W* **106** *(sideways). P* $13\frac{1}{2} \times 14$.
857 15 c. on 10 c. Type **215** 25 10
858 50 c. Helen Keller and Rajkumari Singh .. 50 40
859 $1 on 60 c. Beethoven and Sonny Thomas 55 50
a. Surch double .. .. .. 55·00
860 $1.10 on $3 Renoir 55 55
a. Surch double .. .. .. 30·00
857/60 .. .. *Set of* 4 1·60 1·40

The 15 c., $1 and $1.10 values are surcharged, by Bovell's Printery, on previously unissued stamps. Examples of Nos. 857, 859 and 860 are known without surcharge.

12 X 50 AIR

(216) (217)

(Surch by Bovell's Printery)

1981 (10 Nov). *Nos.* 452 *and* 489 *surch.* (*a*) *Postage. With T* **216**.
861 12 c. on 6 c. Black Acara ("Patua") (No. 452) 15 10
a. Strip of 3. Nos. 861/3 .. .. 1·25
861*b* 12 c. on 6 c. Black Acara ("Patua") (No. 489) 15 10
ba. Strip of 3. Nos. 861*b*/3*b* .. .. 1·10

(*b*) *Air. As T* **217**
862 50 c. on 6 c. Black Acara ("Patua") (No. 452) 25 15
862*b* 50 c. on 6 c. Black Acara ("Patua") (No. 489) 20 15
863 $1 on 6 c. Black Acara ("Patua") (No. 452) 50 30
863*b* $1 on 6 c. Black Acara ("Patua") (No. 489) 50 30

Nos. 861/3 were printed together, *se-tenant*, throughout the sheet. All sheets of Nos. 861*b*/3*b* and about half of Nos. 861/3 contained 36 examples of the 12 c., 35 of the 50 c. and 29 of the $1. On the remainder of the unwatermarked sheets there were the same number of the 12 c., but 34 of the 50 c. and 30 of the $1. No. 861 appeared in the six central vertical columns of Rows 3 to 8 with horizontal pairs of Nos. 862/3 in vertical columns 1, 2, 9 10 and vertical pairs in the six central vertical columns of Rows 1, 2, 9, 10. The additional $1 value on the second stage of the setting occurred on R. 9/1

1981
(218)

1981 (14 Nov). *Nos.* 548 *and* 554/5 *optd with T* **218** *in red by Bovell's Printery.*
864 15 c. Christmas Orchid .. .. .. 4·00 10
a. Optd on No. 548a .. .. .. 5·00
b. Opt inverted .. ..
865 $1 *Chelonanthus uliginoides* 40 20
866 $2 *Norantea guianensis* 90 35

110 (219) **110** (220) Nov 81 50c (221)

1981 (14 Nov). (*a*) *Nos.* 601, 620, 644, *and* O13 *surch with T* **219/20** *in blue by Bovell's Printery.*
867 110 c. on 10 c. Type **154** (surch T **219**) .. 3·00 30
868 110 c. on 110 c. on 8 c. on 3 c. Hanging Heliconia (surch T **219** + **220**) .. 3·00 40
a. Type **220** albino .. .. .. 25·00
869 110 c. on 110 c. on 8 c. on 6 c. Cannon-ball tree (surch T **219** + **220**) .. .. 3·00 40
a. Type **219** albino .. .. .. 26·00
869*b* 110 c. on 10 c. on 25 c. Marabunta (surch T **219** vert) .. .. .. 2·25 40
(*b*) *Nos.* 717, 720, 728, 749, 751 *and* 755 *surch with T* **220** *by Bovell's Printery*
870 110 c. on 10 c. Type **170** (R.) .. .. 2·00 30
a. Surch albino .. .. .. 15·00
871 110 c. on 10 c. Type **176** (B.) .. .. 8·00 50
872 110 c. on $3 Printing press used for early British Guiana stamps (R.) (surch vert) .. .. .. 1·75 30
a. Surch albino .. .. .. 15·00
873 110 c. on $3 H.N. Critchlow (B.) (surch vert) 6·50 45
874 110 c. on $3 Caduceus emblem, "C" encircling researcher, and island silhouettes (B.) .. .. .. 2·00 30
a. Surch inverted .. .. .. 15·00
b. Surch in red .. .. .. 3·25 70
ba. Surch inverted .. .. .. 15·00
bb. Surch double .. .. .. 30·00
875 110 c. on $3 *Peltogyne venosa* (B.) .. .. 4·00 50
a. Surch inverted .. .. .. 20·00
b. Surch double .. .. .. 65·00
c. Surch in red .. .. .. 48·00 6·50
(*c*) *No.* 698 *surch with T* **221** *by Herald Printing-Kitty*
876 50 c. on 5 c. Type **166** .. .. .. 5·00 20

222 Yellow Allamanda (*Allamanda cathartica*)

X X
Human Rights
Day
1981
110 AIR
(223)

1981 (14 Nov)–**82.** *Flowers. Coil stamps. Vert designs as T* **222.** *W* **106.** *P* 15 × 14.
877 15 c. on 2 c. grey-lilac, blue & turquoise-green 15 15
a. Vert pair. Nos. 877/8 .. .. 50 45
b. New blue surch (12.82) 20 10
ba. Vert pair. Nos. 877b/8b 65 50
878 15 c. on 8 c. grey-lilac, blue and mauve .. 15 15
b. New blue surch (12.82) 20 10
Design:—15 c. on 8 c. Mazaruni Pride (*Sipanea prolensis*).
Nos. 877/8 are surcharges on previously unissued stamps and were printed together, *se-tenant*, in vertical pairs throughout the coil.

1981 (14 Nov). *Air. Human Rights Day. No.* 748 *surch with T* **223** *in blue by Bovell's Printery.*
879 110 c. on $3 Rotary anniversary emblem .. 1·75 60

U.N.I.C.E.F.
1946 - 1981
125 XX
(224)

1981 (14 Nov). 35*th Anniv of U.N.I.C.E.F. No.* 724 *surch with T* **224** *by Bovell's Printery.*
880 125 c. on $3 "Mango Season" .. .. 1·00 40
a. Surch inverted .. .. .. 30·00
b. Surch double, one inverted .. .. 30·00

Cancun 81
50c
(224*a*)

1981 (14 Nov). *"Cancun 81" International Conference. No.* 698 *surch with T* **224*a*** *by Herald Printing-Kitty.*
880*a* 50 c. on 5 c. Type **166** .. .. .. 4·00 55

225 Tape Measure and Guyana Metrication Board Van

1982
(226)

(Des local artist; adapted A. Theobald. Litho Questa)

1982 (18 Jan). *Metrication. T* **225** *and similar vert designs. Multicoloured. W* **106.** *P* 14½ × 14.
881 15 c. Type **225** 25 25
a. Sheetlet of 6. Nos. 881/6 .. .. 1·40
882 15 c. "Metric man" 25 25
883 15 c. "Postal service goes metric" 25 25
884 15 c. Weighing child on metric scales.. .. 25 25
885 15 c. Canje Bridge 25 25
886 15 c. Tap filling litre bucket 25 25
881/6 .. .. *Set of* 6 1·40 1·40
Nos. 881/6 were printed together, *se-tenant*, in a sheetlet of 6.

1982 (8 Feb). *Various stamps optd with T* **226** *in blue by Autoprint.*
887 – 20 c. multicoloured (No. 549) .. .. 2·00 20
a. Optd on No. 549a .. .. .. 4·50 1·75
888 **105** 25 c. black, gold and lilac 60 15
889 – 25 c. multicoloured (No. 550*a*) .. .. 2·50 20
a. Optd on No. 550 .. .. .. 5·00 3·00
b. Optd on No. 550ab .. .. .. 4·75 2·50
See also Nos. 914/17, 919/21, 923/4, 977, 992/8, 1001, 1004, 1006/8, 1015, 1017, 1059, 1117 and OP3/4.

20c
(227)

20
(228)

POSTAGE
(229)

1982 (8 Feb). *Nos.* 506, 546 *and* 601 *surch or optd as T* **227/9** *by Bovell's Printery* (*No.* 890) *or Autoprint* (*others*).
890 20 c. on 6 c. Cannon-ball tree (surch T **227**) (G.) 35 10
891 20 c. on 6 c. Cannon-ball tree (surch T **228**) (B.) 35 10
892 25 c. Type **116** (optd T **229**) (B.) .. .. 1·00 10
893 125 c. on 8 c. on 6 c. Cannon-ball tree (surch T **228**) (B.) 35 20

230 Guyana Soldier and Flag

1982 (8 Feb). *Savings Campaign. W* **106** (*sideways*). *P* 14×14½.
894 **230** $1 multicoloured 30 30
a. Opt inverted .. .. .. 42·00
No. 894 is a fiscal stamp overprinted, by Bovell's Printery, for postal use.

110 X
BADEN POWELL
1857 - 1982
(231)

1982 (15–22 Feb). 125*th Birth Anniv of Lord Baden-Powell and* 75*th Anniv of Boy Scout Movement. Nos.* 543, 545 *and* 601 *surch as T* **231** *by Bovell's Printery.*
895 15 c. on 2 c. Type **132** (surch T **231**) (22 Feb) 10 30
a. Sheetlet of 25. Nos. 895/6, each × 8, Nos. 897/8, each × 4 and No. 899 .. 8·00
ab. Surch inverted (sheetlet of 25) ..
896 15 c. on 2 c. Type **132** (surch "Scout Movement 1907–1982") (22 Feb) 10 3
897 15 c. on 2 c. Type **132** (surch "1907–1982") (22 Feb).. .. .. .. 15 4
898 15 c. on 2 c. Type **132** (surch "1857–1982") (22 Feb).. .. .. .. 15 1
899 15 c. on 2 c. Type **132** (surch "1982") (22 Feb) 10 1
900 110 c. on 5 c. Annatto tree (surch T **231**) .. 1·00 2
a. Sheetlet of 25. Nos. 900/1, each × 8, Nos. 902/3, each × 4, and No. 904 (22 Feb) 18·00
901 110 c. on 5 c. Annatto tree (surch "Scout Movement 1907–1982") 60 2
902 110 c. on 5 c. Annatto tree (surch "1907–1982") (22 Feb).. .. .. .. 1·50 1·0
903 110 c. on 5 c. Annatto tree (surch "1857–1982") (22 Feb).. .. .. .. 1·50 1·0
904 110 c. on 5 c. Annatto tree (surch "1982") (22 Feb).. .. .. .. 60 2
a. "110" larger .. .. .. 95·00
905 125 c. on 8 c. on 6 c. Cannon-ball tree (surch T **231**) (G.) .. .. .. 1·00 2
a. Sheetlet of 25. Nos. 905/6, each × 8, Nos. 907/8, each × 4, and No. 909 (22 Feb) 20·00
906 125 c. on 8 c. on 6 c. Cannon-ball tree (surch "Scout Movement 1907–1982") (G.) .. 1·00 2
907 125 c. on 8 c. on 6 c. Cannon-ball tree (surch "1907–1982") (G.) (22 Feb) .. 1·50 1·0
908 125 c. on 8 c. on 6 c. Cannon-ball tree (surch "1857–1982") (G.) (22 Feb) .. 1·50 1·0
909 125 c. on 8 c. on 6 c. Cannon-ball tree (surch "1982") (G.) (22 Feb) 75 2
895/909 .. .. .. *Set of* 15 10·00 5·5
In addition to the sheetlets of 25, Nos. 895a, 900a and 905a, Nos 899/901, 904/6 and 909 also come from sheets containing one typ of surcharge only.
No. 904a occurs in the printing of sheets containing thi surcharge only. The "110" is in the same size as the surcharge o Type **241**.

Geo Washington 1732...1982 100
(232)

GEORGE WASHINGTON 1732 — 1982
(233)

1982 (15 Feb). 250*th Birth Anniv of George Washington. Nos.* 70 718 *and* 720 *surch as T* **232** *by Herald Printing-Kitty or op only with T* **233** *by Autoprint.*
910 100 c. on $3 Printing press used for early British Guiana stamps.. .. 45 3
911 400 c. on 30 c. British Guiana 1856 1 c. black on magenta stamp .. .. 1·60 1·2
a. Surch inverted .. .. .. 20·00
912 $5 *Morpho deidamia* (B.) .. .. 7·50 5·5
910/12 .. .. .. *Set of* 3 8·50 6·2

1982 (3 Mar). *Savings Campaign. Horiz design as T* **230.** *Mult coloured. W* **106.** *P* 14 × 14½.
913 110 c. on $5 Guyana male and female soldiers with flag 50 2
No. 913 is a fiscal stamp surcharged, by Bovell's Printery, f postal use.
See also No. 990.

45 (234) 20 (235) 210 (236)

1982 (15 Mar). *Easter. Nos.* 481/4 *optd with T* **226**, *in blue, surch as T* **234**, *all by Autoprint.*
914 **111** 25 c. multicoloured 20 1
915 30 c. multicoloured 20 1
916 45 c. on 6 c. multicoloured (B.) 20 2
917 75 c. on 40 c. multicoloured (R.) 35 2
914/17 .. .. .. *Set of* 4 85 7
No. 917 exists with the surcharge either at the right or in th centre of the design.

1982 (15 Mar). *No.* 703 *surch with T* **235** *by Herald Printin Kitty.*
918 20 c. on 35 c. *Anaea galanthis* .. .. 3·50 1

1982 (8 Apr). *No.* F5 *optd with T* **226** *and surch as T* **228** *blue, both by Autoprint.*
919 180 c. on 40 c. Tiger Beard .. .. .. 3·50 4

1982 (23 Apr). *Nos.* 555/6 *optd with T* **226** *in blue by Autoprin*
920 $2 *Norantea guianensis* 80 3
921 $5 *Odontadenia grandiflora* .. .. 1·40 7

1982 (23 Apr). *No.* 542 *surch as T* **228** *in blue by Autoprint.*
922 220 c. on 1 c. Pitcher Plant of Mt Roraima .. 1·25 4

1982 (27 Apr). *Nos.* 472 *and* 684 *optd with T* **226** *in blue Autoprint.*
923 **105** 40 c. black, gold and cobalt 35 1
924 – 40 c. multicoloured 50 2

1982 (27 Apr). *Nos.* 469, 751, 842 *and* 843 *surch as T* **228**, *vert cally* (*Nos.* 925/7), *or as T* **236** (*others*), *all in blue by Autoprin*
925 **105** 80 c. on 6 c. black, gold and flesh .. 30 2
926 85 c. on 6 c. black, gold and flesh .. 50 2
927 – 160 c. on $1.10 on $2 multicoloured (No 843) 60 3

28 – 210 c. on $3 multicoloured (No. 751) (surch reading up) .. .. 2·50 40
a. Surch reading down .. .. 12·00
29 – 235 c. on 75 c. on $5 multicoloured (No. 842) .. .. 2·50 60

The surcharge on No. 929 is as Type **236**, but horizontal.

● 85 ● 130

(237) (238)

170

(239)

(Surch by Herald Printing-Kitty)

982 (27 Apr–May). *Royal Wedding (3rd issue). Coil stamps. Nos. 841/3 surch as T* **237** *(No. 930),* **238** *(Nos. 931/2, 934/5) or* **239** *(others).*

30 85 c. on 60 c. on 3 c. Hanging Heliconia .. 2·50 50
31 130 c. on 60 c. on 3 c. Hanging Heliconia .. 1·75 45
a. Surch (as T **238**) inverted £100
32 160 c. on $1.10 on $2 *Norantea guianensis* (vert surch) .. .. 2·25 1·00
a. Surch (as T **238**) double .. .. 32·00
33 170 c. on $1.10 on $2 *Norantea guianensis* 6·00 4·50
a. Surch inverted .. .. .. 45·00
34 210 c. on 75 c. on $5 *Odontadenia grandiflora* (B.) .. .. .. 1·25 40
a. Surch (as T **238**) inverted .. .. 28·00
35 235 c. on 75 c. on $5 *Odontadenia grandiflora* .. .. 2·00 1·40
a. Surch (T **206**) omitted .. .. 75·00
b. Surch (as T **238**) double .. ..
36 330 c. on $1.10 on $2 *Norantea guianensis* 1·75 40
30/6 .. .. *Set of* 7 16·00

220 AIR

ESPANA 1982

(240)

Princess of Wales 1961 - 1982

(241)

982 (15 May). *World Cup Football Championship, Spain (2nd issue). Nos. 544, 546 and 554 optd with T* **240** *or surch also as T* **228**, *both by Autoprint.*

37 $1 *Chelonanthus uliginoides* 75 40
a. Opt inverted .. .. .. 15·00
38 110 c. on 3 c. Hanging Heliconia (B.) .. 75 25
39 250 c. on 6 c. Cannon-ball tree (B.) .. 1·00 60
37/9 .. .. *Set of* 3 2·25 1·10

See also No. 1218

(Optd Govt Printer and surch by Autoprint)

982 (17 May). *W* **106** *(sideways). P* 13.

40 **181** 15 c. on 2 c. black, ind & greenish grey 50 15
a. Opt ("ESSEQUIBO etc") omitted 18·00
41 20 c. on 2 c. black, ind & greenish grey 3·50 30
42 25 c. on 2 c. black, ind & greenish grey 5·00 20
43 30 c. on 2 c. black, ind & greenish grey 50 15
44 40 c. on 2 c. black, ind & greenish grey 8·00 30
a. Surch inverted .. .. .. 12·00
45 45 c. on 2 c. black, ind & greenish grey 1·75 45
46 50 c. on 2 c. black, ind & greenish grey 7·50 30
a. Opt ("ESSEQUIBO etc") omitted 18·00
47 60 c. on 2 c. black, ind & greenish grey 7·00 20
48 75 c. on 2 c. black, ind & greenish grey 6·00 25
49 80 c. on 2 c. black, ind & greenish grey 5·00 20
50 85 c. on 2 c. black, ind & greenish grey 75 25
51 100 c. on 3 c. black, ind and Venetian red 1·00 35
52 110 c. on 3 c. black, ind and Venetian red 80 30
53 120 c. on 3 c. black, ind and Venetian red 8·00 35
54 125 c. on 3 c. black, ind and Venetian red 2·25 35
55 130 c. on 3 c. black, ind and Venetian red 1·00 35
a. Surch inverted .. .. .. 17·00
b. Error. Nos. 952 and 955 *se-tenant*
c. Error. Nos. 955 and 956 *se-tenant*
56 150 c. on 3 c. black, ind and Venetian red 8·50 40
57 160 c. on 3 c. black, ind and Venetian red 2·00 40
58 170 c. on 3 c. black, ind and Venetian red 1·40 45
59 175 c. on 3 c. black, ind and Venetian red 6·00 45
60 180 c. on 3 c. black, ind and Venetian red 2·00 60
61 200 c. on 3 c. black, ind and Venetian red 2·25 45
62 210 c. on 3 c. black, ind and Venetian red 7·00 50
63 220 c. on 3 c. black, ind and Venetian red 8·50 50
64 235 c. on 3 c. black, ind and Venetian red 8·00 50
65 240 c. on 3 c. black, ind and Venetian red 9·00 50
66 250 c. on 3 c. black, ind and Venetian red 2·25 50
67 300 c. on 3 c. black, ind and Venetian red 12·00 55
68 330 c. on 3 c. black, ind and Venetian red 2·75 65
69 375 c. on 3 c. black, ind and Venetian red 7·00 75
70 400 c. on 3 c. black, ind and Venetian red 10·00 75
71 440 c. on 3 c. black, ind and Venetian red 4·00 75
72 500 c. on 3 c. black, ind and Venetian red 3·50 1·10
73 550 c. on 3 c. black, ind and Venetian red 4·00 1·25
974 **181** 625 c. on 3 c. black, ind and Venetian red 2·75 1·75
975 1500 c. on 2 c. black, ind & greenish grey 11·00 3·00
976 2000 c. on 2 c. black, ind & greenish grey 11·00 3·75
940/76 .. .. *Set of* 37 £160 21·00

Nos. 940/76 are fiscal stamps, surcharged for postal use, as Type **181**, but with the overprinted inscription and face value redrawn. On the 15 to 85 c., the surcharged face value is in blue, on the 100 to 625 c. in black, and on the 1500 and 2000 c. in red.

Nos. 955b/c come from the first printing of the 130 c. which had one cliché of the 110 c. surcharge (R. 4/1) and three of the 150 c. (R. 2/8–10) included in error.

For 25 c. and 40 c. surcharges in black see Nos. 988/9 and for the 25 c. in red, No. 1029.

1982 (7 June). *No. 548 optd with T* **226** *in blue by Autoprint.*

977 15 c. Christmas Orchid .. .. .. 7·00 10
a. Optd on No. 548a .. .. .. 48·00 12·00

1982 (15 June). *No. O26 optd with T* **229** *in blue by Autoprint.*

978 110 c. on 6 c. Type **116** .. .. .. 4·50 35

1982 (25 June). *Air. 21st Birthday of Princess of Wales. Nos. 542, 545 and 555 surch as T* **241** *by Bovell's Printery.*

979 110 c. on 5 c. Annatto tree (R.) 50 30
a. Surch in black .. .. .. 38·00
980 220 c. on 1 c. Pitcher Plant of Mt Roraima .. 80 60
a. Surch double .. .. 65·00
981 330 c. on $2 *Norantea guianensis* (B.) .. 90 90
a. Surch in greenish blue .. ..
ab. Surch double .. .. 48·00
979/81 .. .. *Set of* 3 2·00 1·60

GUYANA
H.R.H.
Prince William
21st June 1982
000
000000000 $1.10

(242)

H.R.H.
Prince William
21st June 1982

$2.20

(243)

1982 (12 July). *Birth of Prince William of Wales. Surch as T* **242** *(50 c. and $1.10) or with T* **243** *(others), all in blue by Autoprint.*

(a) On stamps of British Guiana

982 50 c. on 2 c. myrtle-green (No. 332) .. 40 30
a. Surch as T **243** (lines at foot) .. 50·00
983 $1.10 on 3 c. brown-olive and red-brown (No. 354) 80 50
a. Surch inverted .. .. .. 23·00
b. Surch double .. .. ..
c. Surch on No. 333 .. .. .. 80 50
ca. Surch inverted .. .. .. 55·00
cb. Surch double .. .. .. 75·00
cc. Surch as T **243** (lines at foot) .. 45·00

(b) On stamps of Guyana previously optd "GUYANA INDEPENDENCE 1966"

984 50 c. on 2 c. myrtle-green (No. 430) .. 10·00 3·25
985 $1.10 on 3 c. brn-olive & red-brn (No. 431) 17·00 3·25
a. Surch on No. 422 .. .. .. 27·00 10·00
986 $1.25 on 6 c. yellow-green (No. 389) .. 60 60
a. Surch inverted .. .. .. 28·00
b. Surch double .. .. .. 75·00
c. Surch on No. 434 .. .. .. 4·00 2·00
987 $2.20 on 24 c. black and brownish orange (No. 403) .. .. 1·50 1·50
a. Surch inverted .. .. .. 75·00
b. Surch on No. 392 .. .. .. 11·00 9·00
c. Surch on No. 435 .. .. .. 25·00 22·00
982/7 .. .. *Set of* 6 27·00 8·50

Nos. 982, 983c and 985a have Mult Script CA watermark and the remainder watermark w **12** (sideways on No. 987).

1982 (13 July). *As Nos. 942 and 944 but with surcharged face values in black by Autoprint.*

988 **181** 25 c. on 2 c. black, ind & greenish grey .. 2·25 20
989 40 c. on 2 c. black, ind & greenish grey .. 1·00 15

1982 (13 July). *Savings Campaign. Coil stamp. As No. 913 but showing inverted comma before "OURS" in overprint.*

990 110 c. on $5 Guyana male and female soldiers with flag .. .. 5·50 75

ITALY

$2.35

(244)

50

C.A. & CARIB GAMES 1982

(245)

1982 (15 July). *Italy's Victory in World Cup Football Championship. No. F7 optd as T* **240** *and surch with T* **244**, *both in blue by Autoprint.*

991 $2.35 on 180 c. on 60 c. Soldier's Cap .. 3·50 55

1982 (16 Aug). *Wildlife Protection. Nos. 687 and 733/8 optd with T* **226** *(vert on Nos. 993/8) in blue by Autoprint.*

992 35 c. Harpy Eagle .. .. 2·00 40
a. Opt inverted .. .. 32·00
993 35 c. Type **174** .. .. 2·00 40
a. Block of 6. Nos. 993/8 .. .. 12·50
994 35 c. Trahira ("Haimara") .. .. .. 2·00 40
995 35 c. Electric Eel .. .. 2·00 40
996 35 c. Golden Rivulus .. .. .. 2·00 40
997 35 c. Golden Pencilfish .. .. .. 2·00 40
998 35 c. Four-eyed Fish .. .. .. 2·00 40
992/8 .. .. *Set of* 7 12·50 2·50

1982 (16 Aug). *Central American and Caribbean Games, Havana. Nos. 542/3 surch as T* **245** *by Autoprint.*

999 50 c. on 2 c. Type **132** .. .. .. 1·00 25
a. Surch inverted .. .. † —
1000 60 c. on 1 c. Pitcher Plant of Mt Roraima .. 1·25 15

1982 (15 Sept). *No. 730 optd with T* **226** *vertically in blue by Autoprint.*

1001 35 c. black and red-orange 30 20

1982 (15 Sept). *Nos. 841 and 979 further surch as T* **228** *(No. 1003 has solid bar) in blue by Autoprint.*

1002 130 c. on 60 c. on 3 c. Hanging Heliconia .. 40 30
a. Surch as T **228** inverted £150
1003 170 c. on 110 c. on 5 c. Annatto tree 70 45
a. With six lines as in T **228** .. .. 90·00

1982 (15 Sept). *No. 841 optd with T* **226** *and surch as T* **228**, *both in blue by Autoprint.*

1004 440 c. on 60 c. on 3 c. Hanging Heliconia .. 75 45
a. T **226** and T **228** both inverted .. 32·00
b. Surch and optd on No. 841b .. .. 2·50 2·25
c. Without opt T **226** .. .. 3·00 55

No. 1004c also differs from No. 1004 by showing a "c" after the surcharge "60" on Type **205**.

Commonwealth GAMES AUSTRALIA 1982 1.25

(246)

INT. FOOD DAY 1982

(247)

1982 (27 Sept). *Commonwealth Games, Brisbane, Australia. No. 546 surch with T* **246** *in blue by Autoprint.*

1005 $1.25 on 6 c. Cannon-ball tree .. .. 1·50 30

1982 (1 Oct). *Nos. 552, 641 and 719 optd with T* **226** *(vertically reading upwards on Nos. 1007/8) in blue by Autoprint.*

1006 50 c. multicoloured (No. 552) .. .. 2·00 25
1007 50 c. lt vio-bl, lt grn & lt yell-brn (No. 641) 1·50 25
1008 50 c. multicoloured (No. 719) 60 25
a. Opt reading downwards .. ..

1982 (1 Oct). *Various Official stamps additionally optd for postal purposes as T* **229**, *but smaller (29 mm in length), all in blue by Autoprint.*

1009 15 c. Christmas Orchid (No. O23) (vert opt) .. .. 8·00 30
1010 50 c. *Guzmania lingulata* (No. O14) (vert opt) 90 15
1011 100 c. on $3 Cylinder satellite (No. O19) 1·25 35
a. Opt double .. .. .. 20·00

1982 (15 Oct). *International Food Day. No. 617 optd with T* **247** *in blue by Autoprint.*

1012 50 c. Pawpaw and tangerine .. .. .. 11·00 65

INT. YEAR OF THE ELDERLY

(248)

Dr. R. KOCH CENTENARY TBC BACILLUS DISCOVERY

(249)

F. D. ROOSEVELT 1882-1982

(250)

1982 (15 Oct). *International Year of the Elderly. No. 747 optd with T* **248** *in blue by Autoprint.*

1013 50 c. District 404 emblem .. .. .. 6·50 50

1982 (15 Oct). *Centenary of Robert Koch's Discovery of Tubercle Bacillus. No. 750 optd with T* **249** *in blue by Autoprint.*

1014 60 c. Researcher with microscope, Caduceus emblem, stethoscope and beach scene .. 2·50 30

1982 (15 Oct). *International Decade for Women. No. 633 optd with T* **226** *in blue by Autoprint.*

1015 $1 brown and bright blue .. .. .. 2·50 60
a. Opt inverted .. .. 18·00

1982 (15 Oct). *Birth Centenary of F. D. Roosevelt (American statesman). No. 706 optd with T* **250** *in blue by Autoprint.*
1016 $1 Type **167** .. .. 3·25 50

GAC Inaug. Flight Georgetown— Boa Vista, Brasil 200

(251)

50 CARICOM Heads of Gov't Conference July 1982

(252)

1982 (15 Oct). *1st Anniv of G.A.C. Inaugural Flight Georgetown to Boa Vista, Brazil. No. 842 optd with T* **226** *and surch with T* **251**, *both in blue by Autoprint.*
1017 200 c. on 75 c. on $5 *Odontadenia grandiflora* 8·00 1·40

1982 (18 Nov). *CARICOM Heads of Government Conference, Kingston, Jamaica. Nos. 881/6 surch with T* **252** *by Herald Printing-Kitty.*
1018 50 c. on 15 c. Type **225**.. .. .. .. 1·25 30
a. Sheetlet of 6. Nos. 1018/23 .. 6·75
1019 50 c. on 15 c. "Metric man" .. .. .. 1·25 30
1020 50 c. on 15 c. "Postal service goes metric" .. 1·25 30
1021 50 c. on 15 c. Weighing child on metric scales 1·25 30
1022 50 c. on 15 c. Canje Bridge .. .. .. 1·25 30
1023 50 c. on 15 c. Tap filling litre bucket .. .. 1·25 30
1018/23 .. .. *Set of* 6 6·75 1·75

CHRISTMAS 1982

(253)

15

(254)

50

(255)

1982 (1 Dec). *Christmas. Nos. 895/9 optd with T* **253** *in red by Autoprint.*
1024 15 c. on 2 c. Type **132** (surch T **231**) .. 25 15
a. Sheetlet of 25. Nos. 1024/5, each × 8, Nos. 1026/7, each × 4 and No. 1028 .. .. 14·00
1025 15 c. on 2 c. Type **132** (surch "Scout Movement 1907–1982") .. 25 15
1026 15 c. on 2 c. Type **132** (surch "1907–1982") .. 65 50
1027 15 c. on 2 c. Type **132** (surch "1857–1982") .. 65 60
1028 15 c. on 2 c. Type **132** (surch "1982") .. .. 6·50 7·00
1024/8 .. .. *Set of* 5 7·50 7·50
Nos. 1024/8 were only issued in the *se-tenant* sheetlets of 25.

1982 (15 Dec). *As No. 942 but with surcharged face value in red by Autoprint.*
1029 **181** 25 c. on 2 c. black, indigo and greenish grey 50 10

1982 (15 Dec). *Nos. 543 and 546 surch as T* **254** *by Autoprint.*
1030 15 c. on 2 c. Type **132** (B.) 15 10
1031 20 c. on 6 c. Cannon-ball tree (Blk.) 25 10
For similar surcharges in different colours see Nos. 1034/5 and 1063; and for surcharges incorporating "c" Nos. 1085/7 and 1098/9.

1982 (15 Dec). *No. 489 surch as T* **255** *by Autoprint.*
1032 50 c. on 6 c. Black Acara ("Patua") .. 20 15
1033 100 c. on 6 c. Black Acara ("Patua") .. 40 30

1983 (5 Jan). *As Nos. 1030/1, but with colours of surcharge changed.*
1034 15 c. on 2 c. Type **132** (Blk.) 10 10
1035 20 c. on 6 c. Cannon-ball tree (G.) 10 10

1983

(256)

POSTAGE

(257)

60th BIRTHDAY ANNIVERSARY OF OUR PRESIDENT 25c ALL GUYANA OUR HERITAGE

258 Guyana Flag (inscr "60th BIRTHDAY ANNIVERSARY")

1983 (1 Feb). *Optd with T* **256** *by Autoprint.*
1036 – 15 c. multicoloured (No. 655) (opt vert) 4·50 1·00
1037 – 15 c. yellow-brown, grey and black (No. 672) 60 10
1038 – 15 c. multicoloured (No. 682) (opt vert) .. 40 10
1039 **214** 15 c. on 10 c. multicoloured (opt vert) .. 35 10
1040 **215** 15 c. on 10 c. multicoloured .. 15 10
1041 – 50 c. multicoloured (No. 646) .. 4·00 25
1042 – 50 c. multicoloured (No. 696) (opt vert) .. 4·00 25
1043 – 50 c. multicoloured (No. 719) .. .. 1·50 25
1036/43 .. .. *Set of* 8 14·00 1·75
See also Nos. 1060/1, 1069/70, 1072/9*c*, 1096, 1101 and 1110/16.

1983 (1 Feb). *No. O17 optd for postal purposes with T* **257** *in red by Autoprint.*
1044 15 c. Harpy Eagle .. .. 12·00 10

1983 (8 Feb). *National Heritage. Nos. 710/12 and No. 778 surch as T* **234** *in black (No. 1045) or blue (others) by Autoprint.*
1045 90 c. on 30 c. Cassiri and decorated Amerindian jars .. .. 1·50 50
1046 90 c. on 35 c. Rock drawing of hunter and quarry 35 20
1047 90 c. on 50 c. Fork Kyk-over-al .. .. 1·50 50
1048 90 c. on 60 c. Fort Island .. .. 2·25 20
1045/8 .. .. *Set of* 4 5·00 1·25

(Des K. Everett (25 c.). Litho Format)

1983 (19 Feb). *President Burnham's 60th Birthday and 30 Years in Parliament. T* **258** *and similar multicoloured designs. W* **106** *(sideways) (25 c., $1.30). P* 13½ *($1.30) or* 14 *(others).*
1049 25 c. Type **258** 15 20
a. Horiz pair. Nos. 1049/50.. .. 25 40
1050 25 c. As T **258**, but position of flag reversed and inscr "30th ANNIVERSARY IN PARLIAMENT" 15 20
1051 $1.30, Youth display (41 × 25 *mm*).. .. 40 65
1052 $6 Presidential standard (43½ × 25 *mm*) .. 1·00 2·75
1049/52 .. .. *Set of* 4 1·50 3·50
Nos. 1049/50 were printed together, *se-tenant*, in horizontal pairs throughout the sheet.
No. 1052 exists imperforate from stock dispersed by the liquidator of Format International Security Printers Ltd.
For stamps as Nos. 1049/50, but without commemorative inscriptions, see Nos. 1108/9.

PRINTERS. Nos. 1053/1126 were surcharged or overprinted by Autoprint, Georgetown.

FIFTY CENTS

(259)

20 X

(260)

1983 (7 Mar). *Surch as T* **259**.
1053 **170** 50 c. on 10 c. mult (No. 717) (R.) .. 2·00 30
1054 – 50 c. on 400 c. on 30 c. multicoloured (No. 911) (surch vert) .. .. .. 2·50 30
1055 **152** $1 on 10 c. multicoloured (No. 635) (surch vert) .. .. 7·50 45
1056 $1 on $1.05 on 10 c. multicoloured (No. 768) (surch vert) .. .. .. 6·50 45
1056*a* – $1 on $1.10 on $2 multicoloured (No. 843).. .. .. 1·40 2·50
1057 – $1 on 220 c. on 5 c. mult (No. 844) (B.) 7·50 75
1058 – $1 on 330 c. on $2 mult (No. 981) (B.) 60 45
1059 – $1 on $12 on $1.10 on $2 mult (similar to No. P3) (B.) .. .. 3·50 2·00
1053/9.. .. .. .. *Set of* 8 28·00 6·50
Nos. 1057/9 have thin bars cancelling previous surcharges, and, in addition, No. 1059 is optd with T **226** in blue.
See also Nos. 1062 and 1080/4.

1983 (7 Mar). *No. 859 optd with T* **256**.
1060 $1 on 60 c. Beethoven and Sonny Thomas .. 6·00 45

1983 (11 Mar). *Conference of Foreign Ministers of Non-aligned Countries, New Delhi. No. 569 surch with T* **259** *and No. 570 optd with T* **256**.
1061 **136** 25 c. multicoloured (opt vert) .. .. 1·00 25
1062 50 c. on 8 c. mult (surch vert) (R.) .. 2·00 25

1983 (14 Mar). *As No. 1030, but colour of surcharge changed.*
1063 15 c. on 2 c. Type **132** (R.) .. .. .. 1·50 10

1983 (14 Mar). *No. 771 further surch with T* **260** *in blue.*
1064 **181** 20 c. on 10 c. on 3 c. black, indigo and Venetian red 55 10

Commonwealth Day 14 March 1983

$1.30

(261)

I.M.C.O. 1983 $4.80

262

1983 (14 Mar). *Commonwealth Day. Nos. 389 and 403 surch as T* **261** *in black (25 c., $1.30) or blue (others).*
1065 25 c.on 6 c. yellow-green .. .. .. 1·00 20
1066 $1.20 on 6 c. yellow-green 50 50
1067 $1.30 on 24 c. black and bright orange .. 1·50 55
1068 $2.40 on 24 c. black and bright orange .. 2·00 1·25
1065/8 .. .. *Set of* 4 4·50 2·25

1983 (17 Mar). *Easter. Nos. 482/3 optd with T* **256**.
1069 **111** 25 c. multicoloured 15 10
1070 30 c. multicoloured 30 15

1983 (17 Mar). *25th Anniv of International Maritime Organization. British Guiana fiscal stamp optd in red as T* **262**. *Wmk Mult Crown CA. P* 14.
1071 $4.80, bright blue and deep dull green .. 2·00 4·00

1983 (1 Apr). *Optd with T* **256**.
1072 **152** 50 c. mult (No. 637) (opt vert) .. 1·50 25
1073 **159** 50 c. ultramarine, black and gold (No. 668) (opt vert) .. .. 2·75 25
1073*a* – 50 c. multicoloured (No. 723) .. 25·00 2·00
1074 – 50 c. mult (No. 854) (opt vert) .. 60 25
1075 – 50 c. multicoloured (No. 858) .. 1·00 25
1076 – $1 multicoloured (No. 628) .. 5·50 45
1077 – $1 mult (No. 638) (opt vert) .. 4·75 45
1078 – $1 multicoloured (No. 675) .. 4·00 45
1079 – $1 on 30 c. mult (No. 855) (opt vert) 1·25 45
1079*a* – $3 multicoloured (No. 720) .. 17·00 90
1079*b* – $3 multicoloured (No. 724) .. 20·00 1·50
1079*c* – $3 multicoloured (No. 748) .. 65·00 7·00

1983 (1 Apr). *Surch with T* **259**, *vertically, in black (No. 1082) or blue (others).*
1080 **148** 50 c. on 8 c. multicoloured (No. 615) .. 1·75 25
1081 **162** 50 c. on 8 c. multicoloured (No. 681) .. 6·00 25
1082 **171** 50 c. on 10 c. multicoloured (No. 721) .. 3·00 25
1083 – 50 c. on 10 c. on 25 c. mult (No. O13) .. 5·00 25
1084 – 50 c. on 330 c. on $3 mult (No. 845) .. 4·00 25

1983 (2 May). *Surch as T* **254**, *but with "c" after new face value.*
1085 **105** 15 c. on 6 c. black, gold and flesh (No. 469) (B.) .. 30 10
1086 – 20 c. on 6 c. multicoloured (No. 546) .. 30 10
1087 **111** 50 c. on 6 c. multicoloured (No. 481) .. 40 30
For No. 1085 with black overprint, see No. 1098.

$1

(263)

110

(264)

ITU 1983 25

(265)

1983 (2 May). *No. 489 surch with T* **263**.
1088 $1 on 6 c. Black Acara ("Patua") .. .. 1·25 30

1983 (2 May). *No. 639 surch with T* **264** *in blue.*
1089 **153** 110 c. on 10 c. greenish yellow, light green and light reddish violet.. 1·75 50
a. Error. Surch on 35 c (No. 640) £100

1983 (2 May). *Nos. 551 and 556 surch as T* **228** *in blue.*
1090 250 c. on 40 c. Tiger Beard .. .. .. 7·50 55
1091 400 c. on $5 *Odontadenia grandiflora* .. 5·50 70

1983 (17 May). *World Telecommunications and Health Day. Nos 842 and 980 further surch as T* **265**.
1092 25 c. on 220 c. on 1 c. Pitcher Plant of Mt Roraima (surch T **265**) (R.) 30 30
a. Sheetlet of 25. Nos. 1092/3 each × 8 and No. 1094 × 9 .. .. 6·50
b. Six bars only at top .. .. ..
1093 25 c. on 220 c. on 1 c. Pitcher Plant of Mt Roraima (surch "WHO 1983 25") (R.) .. 30 30
b. Six bars only at top .. .. ..
1094 25 c. on 220 c. on 1 c. Pitcher Plant of Mt Roraima (surch "17 MAY '83 ITU/WHO 25") (R.) 30 30
b. Six bars only at top .. .. ..
1095 $4.50 on 75 c. on $5 *Odontadenia grandiflora* (surch "ITU/WHO 17 MAY 1983") (B.) .. .. 13·00 1·50
a. Surch on 235 c. on 75 c. on $5 (No. 929).. 1·75 1·25
1092/5 .. .. *Set of* 4 13·00 2·25

1983 (18 May). *30th Anniv of President's Entry into Parliament. Nos. 690 and 692 surch as T* **259**, *the former additionally optd with T* **256**.
1096 $1 on 15 c. black, light violet-blue and bluish grey .. .. 6·00 50
1097 $1 on 40 c. black, red-orange and bluish grey 9·00 50
No. **MS**693 was also reissued with examples of Nos. 1096/7 affixed over the 8 c. and 35 c. values, and an example of No. 1050 added to the righthand sheet margin. These miniature sheets, revalued to $6, numbered on the reverse and cancelled with First Day of Issue postmarks, were for presentation purposes and were not available for postage.

1983 (23 May). *Surch as T* **254**, *but with "c" after new face value.*
1098 **105** 15 c. on 6 c. black, gold and flesh (No. 469) (Blk.) 10 10
1099 – 50 c. on 6 c. multicoloured (No. 489) (Blk.) 30 30

1983 (23 May). *No. 546 surch as T* **228**, *but with "c" after new face value.*
1100 20 c. on 6 c. Cannon-ball tree 15 10

1983 (23 May). *No. 611 optd with T* **256**.
1101 25 c. Guides in camp .. .. 48·00 4·00

$1.30 120

$1

(266)

CANADA 1983

(267)

XXX

(268)

1983 (23 May). *No. 489 surch with T* **266** *in red.*
1102 $1 on 6 c. Black Acara ("Patua") .. .. 1·25 35

1983 (15 June). *15th World Scout Jamboree, Alberta. Nos. 835/6 and O25 additionally surch or optd as T* **267**.
1103 – $1.30 on 100 c. on 8 c. multicoloured .. 3·00 1·75
1104 **116** 180 c. on 6 c. multicoloured .. .. 3·00 3·00
1105 $3.90 on 400 c. on 6 c. multicoloured .. 3·50 4·50
1103/5 .. .. *Set of* 3 8·50 8·25

1983 (22 June). *Nos. 659/60 surch as T* **254**.
1106 60 c. on 15 c. Map of the Caribbean .. .. 9·00 40
1107 $1.50 on 15 c. Prudential Cup .. .. 10·00 1·25

1983 (1 July). *As Nos. 1049/50, but without commemorative inscr above flag. W* **106** *(sideways). P* 14.
1108 25 c. As Type **258** 15 15
a. Horiz pair. Nos. 1108/9 .. .. .. 30 30
1109 25 c. As No. 1050 .. .. 15 15
Nos. 1108/9 were printed together, *se-tenant* in horizontal pairs throughout the sheet.

1983 (1 July). *Optd with T* **256**.
1110 **105** 30 c. black, gold and light apple-green (No. 471) 75 20
1111 – 30 c. multicoloured (No. 695) .. .. 9·50 30
1112 – 30 c. multicoloured (No. 718) (opt vert) .. 4·50 20
1113 – 30 c. multicoloured (No. 722) .. .. 8·00 20
1114 – 30 c. multicoloured (No. 746) .. .. 14·00 20
1115 – 60 c. multicoloured (No. 697) .. .. 4·50 20
1116 – 60 c. multicoloured (No. 731) .. .. 5·50 20
1110/16 .. .. *Set of* 7 42·00 1·25

1983 (1 July). *No. 553 optd with T* **226** *in blue.*
1117 60 c. Soldier's Cap .. .. 4·00 35

1983 (1 July). *Surch as T* **264** *in blue.*
1118 **157** 120 c. on 8 c. multicoloured (No. 654) 3·25 40
1119 **159** 120 c. on 10 c. dull red, black and gold (No. 666) .. 3·50 40
1120 – 120 c. on 35 c. multicoloured (No. 622) 3·50 40
a. Surch reading upwards ..
1121 – 120 c. on 35 c. orange, light green and reddish violet (No. 640) .. 3·50 40

1983 (1 July). *Nos. 716 and 729 surch as T* **268**.
1122 120 c. on 10 c. Type **173** (R.) .. .. 3·25 40
1123 120 c. on 375 c. on $3 Cylinder satellite .. 3·00 40
No. 1123 also carries an otherwise unissued surcharge in red, reading "INTERNATIONAL SCIENCE YEAR 1982 375". As issued much of this is obliterated by two heavy bars.

CARICOM DAY 1983

120
GUYANA
(269)

60
(270)

XXX

1983 (1 July). *British Guiana No. D1a and Guyana No. D8 surch with T* **269** *in blue.*
1124 D 1 120 c. on 1 c. deep green .. .. .. 2·75 45
1125 D 2 120 c. on 1 c. olive .. .. .. 2·75 45

1983 (1 July). *CARICOM Day. No. 823 additionally surch with T* **270** *in red.*
1126 60 c. on $3 "Makanaima the Great Ancestral Spirit of the Amerindians" .. .. 1·75 35

271 *Kurupukari*

(Litho Format)

1983 (11 July*). *Riverboats. T* **271** *and similar horiz designs. W* **106**. *P* 14.
1127 30 c. black and vermilion 20 20
a. *Tête-bêche* (vert pair) 75
w. Wmk inverted 55 35
1128 60 c. black and bright reddish violet .. 35 35
a. *Tête-bêche* (vert pair) .. .. 1·00
w. Wmk inverted 65 60
1129 120 c. black and bright lemon 40 60
a. *Tête-bêche* (vert pair) .. .. 1·40
w. Wmk inverted 90 95
1130 130 c. black 40 65
a. *Tête-bêche* (vert pair) .. .. 1·40
w. Wmk inverted 90 95
1131 150 c. black and bright emerald 40 80
a. *Tête-bêche* (vert pair) .. .. 1·40
w. Wmk inverted .. .. 95 1·00
1127/31 .. .. .. *Set of* 5 1·60 2·40
Designs:—60 c. *Makouria*; 120 c. *Powis*; 130 c. *Pomeroon*; 150 c. *Lukanani*.
*Although not finally issued until 11 July First Day Covers of Nos. 1127/31 are postmarked with the intended release date of 1 July.
Nos. 1127/31 were each issued in sheets of 80 (10 × 8) with the bottom three rows inverted forming *tête-bêche* vertical pairs from Rows 5 and 6.

2.30
(272)

1983 (22 July). *Unissued Royal Wedding surcharge, similar to No. 843, surch as T* **272** *in blue by Autoprint.*
1132 $2.30 on $1.10 on $2 *Norantea guianensis* .. 60 40
1133 $3.20 on $1.10 on $2 *Norantea guianensis* .. 60 40

BW
(273)

Mont Golfier
1783-1983
(274)

1983 (5 Sept). *Bicentenary of Manned Flight and 20th Anniv of Guyana Airways. Nos. 701/2a optd as T* **273/4**, *in red (Nos. 1134/47) or blue (Nos. 1148/68) by Autoprint.*
1134 20 c. multicoloured (optd T **273**) 35 35
a. Sheetlet of 25. Nos. 1134/8 each × 4 and 1139 × 5 .. .. 7·50
1135 20 c. multicoloured (optd "LM") 35 35
1136 20 c. multicoloured (optd "GY 1963 1983") .. 35 35
1137 20 c. multicoloured (optd "JW") 35 35
1138 20 c. multicoloured (optd "CU") 35 35
1139 20 c. multicoloured (optd T **274**) 35 35
1140 25 c. multicoloured (optd "BGI") 50 25
a. Sheetlet of 25. Nos. 1140 × 2, 1141 × 8, 1142/44 each × 2, 1145 × 5 and 1146/7 each × 2 .. .. 9·00
1141 25 c. multicoloured (optd "GEO") 15 10
1142 25 c. multicoloured (optd "MIA") 50 25
1143 25 c. multicoloured (optd "BVB") 50 25
1144 25 c. multicoloured (optd "PBM") 50 25
1145 25 c. multicoloured (optd T **274**) 20 15
1146 25 c. multicoloured (optd "POS") 50 25
1147 25 c. multicoloured (optd "JFK") 50 25
1148 30 c. multicoloured (optd "AHL") 40 30
a. Sheetlet of 25. Nos. 1148/54, 1155 × 5 and 1156/68 .. .. 9·00
1149 30 c. multicoloured (optd "BCG") 40 30
1150 30 c. multicoloured (optd "BMJ") 40 30
1151 30 c. multicoloured (optd "EKE") 40 30
1152 30 c. multicoloured (optd "GEO") 40 30
1153 30 c. multicoloured (optd "GFO") 40 30
1154 30 c. multicoloured (optd "IBM") 40 30
1155 30 c. multicoloured (optd T **274**) 25 15
1156 30 c. multicoloured (optd "KAI") 40 30
1157 30 c. multicoloured (optd "KAR") 40 30
1158 30 c. multicoloured (optd "KPG") 40 30
1159 30 c. multicoloured (optd "KRG") 40 30
1160 30 c. multicoloured (optd "KTO") 40 30
1161 30 c. multicoloured (optd "LTM") 40 30
1162 30 c. multicoloured (optd "MHA") 40 30
1163 30 c. multicoloured (optd "MWJ") 40 30
1164 30 c. multicoloured (optd "MYM") 40 30
1165 30 c. multicoloured (optd "NAI") 40 30
1166 30 c. multicoloured (optd "ORJ") 40 30
1167 30 c. multicoloured (optd "USI") 40 30
1168 30 c. multicoloured (optd "VEG") 40 30
1134/68 .. .. *Set of* 35 12·50 8·00
The overprints on the 20 c. value represent airlines, on the 25 c. international airports and on the 30 c. internal airports. Those on Nos. 1150 and 1154 were incorrect and examples of the former exist with the manuscript correction "PMT".

240
(275)

240
(275*a*)

1983 (14 Sept). *No. 649 surch with T* **275** *in blue by Autoprint.*
1169 240 c. on 35 c. on 60 c. Soldier's Cap .. .. 1·25 1·00
a. Surch with T **275*a*** .. .. 1·25 1·00
b. Pair. Nos. 1169/a .. .. 2·50
Types **275** and **275*a*** occur *se-tenant* within the sheet.

FAO 1983

30
(276)

277 G.B. 1857 1d. with Georgetown "AO3" Postmark

1983 (15 Sept). *F.A.O. Fisheries Project. Nos. 485 and 487 surch as T* **276** *in red by Autoprint.*
1170 30 c. on 1 c. Type **87** 15 15
1171 $2.60 on 3 c. Peacock Cichlid ("Lukunani") .. .. .. 1·50 2·25

(Des K. Everett. Litho Format)

1983 (1 Oct). *125th Anniv of Use of Great Britain Stamps in Guyana. T* **277** *and similar square designs. P* 14½.

(*a*) *Inscriptions in black. W* **106**
1172 **277** 25 c. lake-brown and black 15 10
a. *Tête-bêche* (pair) 75
w. Wmk inverted 60
1173 – 30 c. rose-red and black 15 15
a. *Tête-bêche* (pair) 75
w. Wmk inverted 60
1174 – 60 c. bright violet and black 35 30
a. *Tête-bêche* (pair) .. .. 1·75
w. Wmk inverted .. .. 1·40
1175 – 120 c. dull green and black 75 55
a. *Tête-bêche* (pair) .. .. 3·50
w. Wmk inverted .. .. 2·75

(*b*) *Inscriptions in bright blue. W* **106** *(inverted).*
1176 **277** 25 c. lake-brown and black 15 10
a. Block of 4. Nos. 1176/9 55
1177 – 25 c. rose-red and black 15 10
1178 – 25 c. bright violet and black 15 10
1179 – 25 c. dull green and black 15 10
1180 **277** 30 c. lake-brown and black 15 15
a. Block of 4. Nos. 1180/3 55
1181 – 30 c. rose-red and black 15 15
1182 – 30 c. bright violet and black 15 15
1183 – 30 c. dull green and black 15 15
1184 **277** 45 c. lake-brown and black 30 25
a. Block of 4. Nos. 1184/7 .. .. 1·10
1185 – 45 c. rose-red and black 30 25
1186 – 45 c. bright violet and black 30 25
1187 – 45 c. dull green and black 30 25
1188 **277** 120 c. lake-brown and black 40 55
a. Block of 4. Nos. 1188/91 .. .. 1·40
1189 – 130 c. rose-red and black 40 60
1190 – 150 c. bright violet and black 40 70
1191 – 200 c. dull green and black 40 95
1172/91 .. .. *Set of* 20 4·50 5·00
Designs:—Nos. 1173, 1177, 1181, 1185, 1189, G.B. 1857 4d. rose; Nos. 1174, 1178, 1182, 1186, 1190, G.B. 1856 6d. lilac; Nos. 1175, 1179, 1183, 1187, 1191, G.B. 1856 1s. green.
Each design incorporates the "A03" postmark except Nos. 1189/91 which show mythical postmarks of the Crowned-circle type inscribed "DEMERARA", "BERBICE" or "ESSEQUIBO".
Nos. 1172/5 were each printed in sheets with the bottom row inverted, forming vertical *tête-bêche* pairs. Nos. 1176/87 were issued in sheets of 60, one for each value, with the four designs *se-tenant*. Nos. 1188/91 were issued in sheets of 20, containing five *se-tenant* blocks.

75

(278)

(279)

1983 (15 Oct). *International Communications Year. No. 716 surch with T* **278** *by Autoprint.*
1192 50 c. on 375 c. on $3 Cylinder satellite .. 4·50 30
No. 1192 also carries an otherwise unissued "375" surcharge. As issued much of this surcharge is obliterated by two groups of six thin horizontal lines.

1983 (15 Oct). *St. John Ambulance Commemoration. Nos. 650 and 653 surch as T* **279**, *vertically on No. 1194 by Autoprint.*
1193 **156** 75 c. on 8 c. silver, black and magenta .. 4·50 50
1194 – $1.20 on 40 c. silver, black and new blue 6·50 75

$1.20

Int. Food Day
1983

(280)

1918-1983

I.L.O.
(281)

1983 (15 Oct). *International Food Day. No. 616 surch with T* **280** *by Autoprint.*
1195 $1.20 on 35 c. Five-fingers and awaras .. 1·00 50

1983 (15 Oct). *65th Anniv of I.L.O. and 25th Death Anniv. of H. N. Critchlow (founder of Guyana Labour Union). No. 840 further optd with T* **281** *by Autoprint.*
1196 240 c. on $3 H. N. Critchlow .. .. .. 1·50 1·50

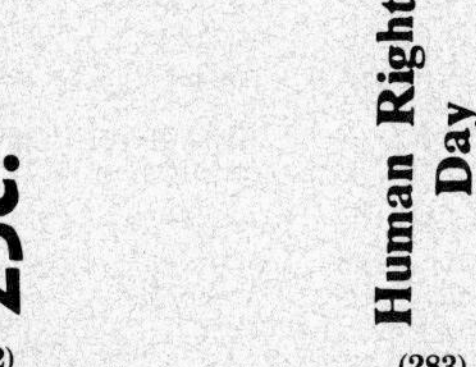

(282)

(283)

1983 (1 Nov). *Deepavali Festival. Nos. 661 and 663/4 surch as T* **282** *by Autoprint.*
1197 25 c. on 8 c. Type **158** 20 10
1198 $1.50 on 35 c. Flame in bowl .. .. 1·25 60
1199 $1.50 on 40 c. Goddess Latchmi 80 60
1197/9 .. .. *Set of* 3 2·00 1·25
On Nos. 1198/9 the original face values are obliterated by "XX" and the surcharges are horizontal.

1983 (3 Nov). *No. 732 optd with T* **226** *and No. 798 further optd with T* **256**, *both vertically reading upwards by Autoprint.*
1200 $3 "Makanaima the Great Ancestral Spirit of the Amerindians" (B.) .. .. 1·50 70
a. Opt reading downwards .. .. 15·00
1201 360 c. on $2 *Norantea guianensis* .. .. 1·75 80

1983 (15 Nov). *Wildlife Protection. Nos. 686 and 688 surch as T* **234**, *and No. 852 optd with T* **256** *by Autoprint.*
1202 30 c. Six-banded Armadillo 50 15
1203 60 c. on 15 c. Giant sea turtle 75 30
1204 $1.20 on 40 c. Iguana .. .. .. 1·25 50
1202/4 .. .. *Set of* 3 2·25 85

1983 (1 Dec). *Human Rights Day. No. 1079c optd with T* **283** *by Autoprint.*
1205 $3 Rotary anniversary emblem .. .. 2·00 1·25

LOS ANGELES
1984

125 

(284)

●●● 55

(284a)

1983 (6 Dec). *Olympic Games, Los Angeles* (1984) (1*st issue*). *Nos.* 733/44 *surch with T* **284** *by Herald Printing-Kitty or further surch with T* **284a** *by Autoprint.*
1206 55 c. on 125 c. on 35 c. Type **174** .. 25 25
a. Block of 12. Nos. 1206/17 .. 3·50
1207 55 c. on 125 c. on 35 c. Trahira ("Haimara") .. 25 25
1208 55 c. on 125 c. on 35 c. Electric Eel .. 25 25
1209 55 c. on 125 c. on 35 c. Golden Rivulus 25 25
1210 55 c. on 125 c. on 35 c. Golden Pencilfish 25 25
1211 55 c. on 125 c. on 35 c. Four-eyed Fish 25 25
1212 55 c. on 125 c. on 35 c. Red Piranha ("Pirai") .. 25 25
1213 55 c. on 125 c. on 35 c. Smoking Hassar 25 25
1214 55 c. on 125 c. on 35 c. Manta .. 25 25
1215 55 c. on 125 c. on 35 c. Festive Cichlid ("Flying Patwa") .. 25 25
1216 55 c. on 125 c. on 35 c. Arapaima .. 25 25
1217 55 c. on 125 c. on 35 c. Peacock Cichlid ("Lukanani") .. 25 25
1217*a* 125 c. on 35 c. Type **174** .. 5·50
ab. Block of 12. Nos. 1217*a/l* .. 60·00
1217*b* 125 c. on 35 c. Trahira ("Haimara") .. 5·50
1217*c* 125 c. on 35 c. Electric Eel .. 5·50
1217*d* 125 c. on 35 c. Golden Rivulus .. 5·50
1217*e* 125 c. on 35 c. Golden Pencilfish .. 5·50
1217*f* 125 c. on 35 c. Four-eyed Fish .. 5·50
1217*g* 125 c. on 35 c. Red Piranha ("Pirai") .. 5·50
1217*h* 125 c. on 35 c. Smoking Hassar .. 5·50
1217*i* 125 c. on 35 c. Manta .. 5·50
1217*j* 125 c. on 35 c. Festive Cichlid ("Flying Patwa") .. 5·50
1217*k* 125 c. on 35 c. Arapaima .. 5·50
1217*l* 125 c. on 35 c. Peacock Cichlid ("Lukanani") .. 5·50
See also Nos. 1308/17 and 1420.

1983 (14 Dec). *No.* F7 *with unissued* "ESPANA 1982" *surch, as Nos.* 938/9 *in blue, further optd with T* **256** *vertically by Autoprint.*
1218 180 c. on 60 c. Soldier's Cap .. 2·50 65
a. Opt (T **256**) omitted .. 15·00

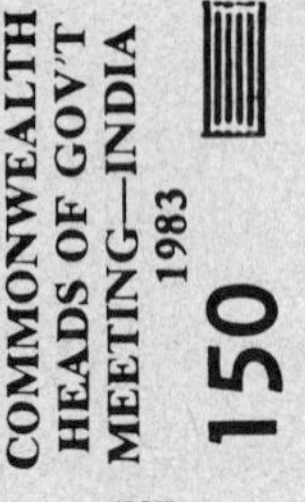

(285) (286)

1983 (14 Dec). *Commonwealth Heads of Government Meeting, New Delhi. No.* 542 *surch with T* **285** *by Autoprint.*
1219 150 c. on 1 c. Pitcher Plant of Mt Roraima .. 2·50 60

1983 (14 Dec). *Christmas. No.* 861 *further surch with T* **286** *by Autoprint.*
1220 20 c. on 12 c. on 6 c. Black Acara ("Patua") 1·50 10
a. On No. 861*b* (Wmk **106**) .. 1·50 10

1984 (8 Jan). *Nos.* 838 *and* F9 *optd as T* **229**, *but smaller* 24×6 *mm, vertically in blue by Autoprint.*
1221 $2 *Norantea guianensis* .. 3·00 70
a. Opt inverted .. 6·00
1221*b* 550 c. on $10 *Elbella patrobas* .. 11·00 7·50

17¢

(287)

1984 (Jan). *Flowers. Unissued coil stamps as T* **222** *handstamped with T* **287** *in blue.*
1222 17 c. on 2 c. grey-lilac, blue & turquoise-green 1·25 1·00
a. Vert pair. Nos. 1222/3 .. 2·50 2·00
1223 17 c. on 8 c. grey-lilac, blue and mauve .. 1·25 1·00
Nos. 1222/3 were intended for use on 8 c. postal stationery envelopes to uprate them to the new price of 25 c.

ALL
OUR HERITAGE
1984

● 25 (288)

● 25 (289)

1984

● 25 (290)

● 25 (291)

1984 (24 Feb). *Republic Day. No.* 703 *surch as T* **288/91** *in black and No.* 705*a optd as T* **288/9** *in blue by Autoprint.*
1224 25 c. on 35 c. multicoloured (surch T **288**) .. 35 20
a. Sheetlet of 25. No. 1224 × 6, Nos. 1225/7 each × 4, Nos. 1228/30 each × 2 and No. 1231 .. 21·00
1225 25 c. on 35 c. multicoloured (surch T **289**) .. 40 20
1226 25 c. on 35 c. multi (surch "REPUBLIC DAY") 40 20
1227 25 c. on 35 c. multicoloured (surch T **290**) .. 40 20
1228 25 c. on 35 c. multi (surch "BERBICE") .. 1·75 1·50
1229 25 c. on 35 c. multi (surch "DEMERARA") .. 1·75 1·50
1230 25 c. on 35 c. multi (surch "ESSEQUIBO") .. 1·75 1·50
1231 25 c. on 35 c. multicoloured (surch T **291**) .. 6·50 7·00
1232 60 c. multicoloured (opt T **288**) .. 50 30
a. Sheetlet of 25. Nos. 1232/3 each × 8 and No. 1234 × 9 .. 11·00
1233 60 c. multicoloured (opt "REPUBLIC DAY") 50 30
1234 60 c. multicoloured (opt T **289**) .. 50 30
1224/34 .. *Set of* 11 13·00 12·00

25¢ POSTAGE (+ 2.25 SURTAX)
OLYMPIC GAMES 84

(292)

1984 (1 Mar). *Guyana Olympic Committee Appeal. Nos.* 841/3 *handstamped with T* **292** *in blue.*
1235 25 c. + $2.25 on 60 c. on 3 c. Hanging Heliconia .. 2·00 4·50
1236 25 c. + $2.25 on 75 c. on $5 *Odontadenia grandiflora* .. 2·00 4·50
1237 25 c. + $2.25 on £1.10 on $2 *Norantea guianensis* .. 2·00 4·50
1235/7 .. *Set of* 3 5·50 12·00
Nos. 1235/7 come from stamp booklets, the $2.25 charity premium on each stamp being donated to the local Olympic Committee Appeal Fund. All examples of these handstamps are inverted.

PRINTERS. Nos. 1238/97 and 1302/27 were overprinted or surcharged by Autoprint, Georgetown.

Protecting
Our Heritage

(293)

XXXX
90

(294)

1984 (5 Mar). *Nature Protection. Various stamps optd with T* **293** *in black (except for No.* 1239 *in blue) with some additionally surch as T* **272** *(Nos.* 1238/40, 1250/1 *and* 1254/5*) or as T* **294** *(Nos.* 1242, 1247 *and* 1252/3*) all in blue.*
1238 20 c. on 15 c. multicoloured (No. 491) (opt + surch vert) .. 8·50 10
a. Opt T **293** in blue .. 15·00 50
1239 20 c. on 15 c. multicoloured (No. 791) (opt + surch vert) .. 8·50 10
a. Surch on No. 791a (pair) ..
1240 20 c. on 15 c. multicoloured (No. 1044) (opt + surch vert) .. 38·00 1·75
a. Opt T **293** in blue .. 15·00 1·25
1241 25 c. multicoloured (No. 550*a*) .. 11·00 10
a. On No. 550ab .. 45·00 3·50
1242 30 c. on 15 c. multicoloured (No. 548) .. 20·00 30
1243 40 c. multicoloured (No. 494) (opt vert) .. 12·00 20
1244 50 c. multicoloured (No. 552) .. 1·50 25
1245 50 c. multicoloured (No. F6) .. 1·50 25
a. Opt Type F 1 double .. 25·00
1246 60 c. multicoloured (No. 459) .. 9·50 30
a. On No. 496 .. 55·00 4·00
1247 90 c. on 40 c. multicoloured (No. 551) .. 16·00 50
a. On No. F5 .. £110 7·50
1248 180 c. on 40 c. multicoloured (No. 919) .. 16·00 90
1249 $2 multicoloured (No. 461) .. 50·00 1·50
1250 225 c. on 10 c. multicoloured (No. 490a) (opt + surch vert) .. 23·00 1·00
1251 260 c. on $1 multicoloured (No. 497a) .. 11·00 1·00
1252 320 c. on 40 c. multicoloured (No. 551) .. 12·00 2·25
1253 350 c. on 40 c. multicoloured (No. 551) .. 20·00 2·50
1254 390 c. on 50 c. multicoloured (No. 495) .. 5·00 2·50
a. On No. 458 .. 80·00 20·00
1255 450 c. on $5 multicoloured (No. 499) .. 7·00 2·50
1238/55 .. *Set of* 18 £225 15·00

1984

(295) (296)

1984 (17 Mar). *Easter. Nos.* 483 *and* 916/17 *optd with T* **295**, *and No.* 481 *surch as T* **272**, *but without decimal point, all in blue.*
1256 **111** 30 c. multicoloured .. 20 20
1257 45 c. on 6 c. multicoloured .. 25 25
1258 75 c. on 40 c. multicoloured .. 35 35
1259 130 c. on 6 c. multicoloured .. 65 60
1256/9 .. *Set of* 4 1·40 1·25
No. 1258 exists with the previous surcharge either at the right or in the centre of the design.

1984 (2 Apr). *Nos.* 937/9 *and* 991 *surch as T* **294**.
1260 75 c. on $1 *Chelonanthus uliginoides* .. 9·50 35
1261 75 c. on 110 c. on 3 c. Hanging Heliconia .. 9·50 35
1262 225 c. on 250 c. on 6 c. Cannon-ball tree .. 3·00 1·25
1263 230 c. on $2.35 on 180 c. on 60 c. Soldier's Cap 3·00 1·00

1984 (2 May). *Nos.* 899/901, 904/6 *and* 909 *surch as T* **294**.
1264 20 c. on 15 c. on 2 c. Type **132** (No. 899) .. 1·50 30
1265 75 c. on 110 c. on 5 c. Annatto tree (No. 904) 9·00 70
1266 90 c. on 110 c. on 5 c. Annatto tree (No. 900) (B.) .. 5·50 85
1267 90 c. on 110 c. on 5 c. Annatto tree (No. 901) (B.) .. 7·00 85
1268 120 c. on 125 c. on 8 c. on 6 c. Cannon-ball tree (No. 905) .. 7·00 1·00
1269 120 c. on 125 c. on 8 c. on 6 c. Cannon-ball tree (No. 906) .. 7·00 1·00
1270 120 c. on 125 c. on 8 c. on 6 c. Cannon-ball tree (No. 909) .. 2·75 1·00
1264/70 .. *Set of* 7 35·00 5·25
Nos. 1264/70 were surcharged on the sheets which contained one type of the previous surcharge only.

1984 (17 May). *World Telecommunications and Health Day. Nos.* 802 *and* 980 *surch as T* **296** *in blue.*
1271 25 c. on 220 c. on 1 c. Pitcher Plant of Mt Roraima (surch T **296**) .. 20 20
a. Sheetlet of 25. Nos. 1271/2 each × 8 and No. 1273 × 9 .. 4·50
1272 25 c. on 220 c. on 1 c. Pitcher Plant of Mt Roraima (surch "WHO DAY 1984") .. 20 20
1273 25 c. on 220 c. on 1 c. Pitcher Plant of Mt Roraima (surch "ITU/WHO DAY 1984") 20 20
1274 $4.50 on 280 c. on $5 *Odontadenia grandiflora* (surch "ITU/WHO DAY 1984") .. 1·75 1·25
1271/4 .. *Set of* 4 2·10 1·75
The surcharge is horizontal on No. 1274 and vertical on the others.

1984 (11 June). *No.* 1005 *surch vertically as T* **272**, *but without decimal point.*
1275 120 c. on $1.25 on 6 c. Cannon-ball tree .. 7·00 55

1984 (15 June). *World Forestry Conference. Nos.* 752/5 *surch as T* **272**, *but without decimal point, or optd with T* **295** *($3), and No.* 875 *surch as T* **294**.
1276 55 c. on 30 c. *Hymenaea courbaril* .. 2·75 30
1277 75 c. on 110 c. on $3 *Peltogyne venosa* (B.) .. 40 35
1278 160 c. on 50 c. *Mora excelsa* (B.) .. 75 70
1279 260 c. on 10 c. Type **177** (B.) .. 1·25 1·25
1280 $3 *Peltogyne venosa* (B.) .. 1·40 1·40
1276/80 .. *Set of* 5 6·00 3·50

1984 (18 June). *No.* 625 *surch vertically as T* **294**.
1281 55 c. on 110 c. on 10 c. Type **150** .. 75 30
1282 90 c. on 110 c. on 10 c. Type **150** (B.) .. 1·00 45
Nos. 1281/2 also carry an otherwise unissued 110 c. surcharge in blue as Type **264**.

UPU
Congress 1984
Hamburg

(297)

60

(298)

1984 (19 June). *U.P.U. Congress, Hamburg. Nos.* 1188/91 *optd with T* **297**.
1283 120 c. lake-brown and black .. 50 60
a. Block of 4. Nos. 1283/6 .. 2·25
1284 130 c. rose-red and black .. 55 70
1285 150 c. bright violet and black .. 60 75
1286 200 c. dull green and black .. 80 90
1283/6 .. *Set of* 4 2·25 2·75

1984 (21 June). *Nos.* 982/3 *and* 986/7 *surch with T* **298** *(60 c.) or as T* **272**, *but without the decimal point (others).*
1287 45 c. on 50 c. on 2 c. myrtle-green .. 60 25
1288 60 c. on $1.10 on 3 c. brown-olive and red-brown (B.) .. 2·25 40
a. Surch on No. 983c .. 2·50 40
1289 120 c. on $1.25 on 6 c. yellow-green .. 75 55
1290 200 c. on $2.20 on 24 c. black and brownish orange (B.) .. 5·50 1·10

1984 (30 June). *Nos.* 979/80 *and* 1003 *surch as T* **294**, *and No.* 981 *optd vertically with T* **295**.
1291 75 c. on 110 c. on 5 c. Annatto tree .. 60 35
1292 120 c. on 170 c. on 110 c. on 5 c. Annatto tree 80 55
1293 200 c. on 220 c. on 1 c. Pitcher Plant of Mt Roraima (B.) .. 12·00 85
1294 330 c. on $2 *Norantea guianensis* (B.) .. 1·75 1·75

CARICOM DAY 1984

60 **XX**

(299)

984 (30 June). *CARICOM Day. No.* 1200 *additionally surch with T* **299**.
295 60 c. on $3 "Makanaima the Great Ancestral Spirit of the Amerindians" 40 30

984 (30 June). *No.* 544 *surch as T* **275** *in blue.*
296 150 c. on 3 c. Hanging Heliconia .. .. 1·25 65

60
CARICOM
HEADS OF GOV'T
CONFERENCE
JULY 1984

X

(300)

301 Children and Thatched School

984 (2 July). *CARICOM Heads of Government Conference. No.* 544 *surch with T* **300** *in blue.*
297 60 c. on 3 c. Hanging Heliconia 40 30

(Litho Format)

984 (16 July). *Centenary of Guyana Teachers' Association. T* **301** *and similar horiz designs. Multicoloured. W* **106** *(sideways). P* 14.

298	25 c. Type **301**	10	15
	a. Block of 4. Nos. 1298/301	35	
299	25 c. Torch and graduates	10	15
300	25 c. Torch and target emblem	10	15
301	25 c. Teachers of 1884 and 1984 in front of school	10	15
298/301	.. .. *Set of* 4	35	55

Nos. 1298/301 were printed together, *se-tenant*, in blocks of 4 hroughout the sheet.

INT.
CHESS
FED.
1924-1984
25XX

(302)

25
TRACK
AND
FIELD

(303)

984 (20 July). *60th Anniv of International Chess Federation. No.* 1048 *optd or surch as T* **302** *or optd with T* **295**, *all in blue.*

302	25 c. on 90 c. on 60 c. Fort Island (surch T **302**)	1·00	25
	a. Sheetlet of 25. No. 1302 × 16 and No. 1303 × 9..	27·00	
303	25 c. on 90 c. on 60 c. Fort Island (opt T **295**) ..	1·75	45
304	75 c. on 90 c. on 60 c. Fort Island (surch T **302**)	1·10	40
	a. Sheetlet of 25. No. 1304 × 16 and No. 1305 × 9..	32·00	
305	75 c. on 90 c. on 60 c. Fort Island (opt T **295**) ..	2·00	70
306	90 c. on 60 c. Fort Island (opt T **302**).. ..	1·25	50
	a. Sheetlet of 25. No. 1306 × 16 and No. 1307 × 9..	35·00	
307	90 c. on 60 c. Fort Island (opt T **295**).. ..	2·25	90
302/7	.. .. *Set of* 6	8·50	2·75

Overprints as Type **295** occur in the central horizontal and ertical rows of each sheet.

984 (28 July). *Olympic Games, Los Angeles (2nd issue). No.* 1051 *surch as T* **303** *in blue.*

308	25 c. on $1.30, multicoloured (surch T **303**) ..	20	25
	a. Booklet pane of 10. No. 1308 × 4 and Nos. 1309/10, each × 3	2·50	
	b. Coil strip of 5. Nos. 1308 × 2, 1311 × 2 and 1312	4·25	
309	25 c. on $1.30, mult (surch "BOXING") ..	20	30
310	25 c. on $1.30, mult (surch "OLYMPIC GAMES 1984 LOS ANGELES") ..	20	30
311	25 c. on $1.30, mult (surch "CYCLING") ..	1·00	50
312	25 c. on $1.30, mult (surch "OLYMPIC GAMES 1984")	3·00	1·25
313	$1.20 on $1.30, multicoloured (surch T **303**)	1·00	1·10
	a. Booklet pane of 10. No. 1313 × 4 and Nos. 1314/15 each × 3	10·00	
	b. Coil strip of 5. Nos. 1313 × 2, 1316 × 2 and 1317	7·00	
314	$1.20 on $1.30, mult (surch "BOXING") ..	1·00	1·10
315	$1.20 on $1.30, mult (surch "OLYMPIC GAMES 1984 LOS ANGELES") ..	1·00	1·25
316	$1.20 on $1.30, mult (surch "CYCLING") ..	1·75	1·50
317	$1.20 on $1.30, multicoloured (surch "OLYMPIC GAMES 1984")	3·50	3·00
308/17	.. .. *Set of* 10	11·50	9·50

Nos. 1308 and 1313 come from booklets and coils, Nos. 1309/10 nd 1314/15 from booklets only, and Nos. 1311/12 and 1316/17 from oils only.

The coils were constructed from normal sheets with coil joins on very fifth stamp.

25
GIRL GUIDES 1924-1984

(304)

1984 (15 Aug). *60th Anniv of Girl Guide Movement in Guyana. Nos.* 900/9 *surch with T* **304** *in blue.*

1318	25 c. on 110 c. on 5 c. Annatto tree (No. 900)	15	15
	a. Sheetlet of 25. Nos. 1318/19, each × 8, Nos. 1320/1, each × 4 and No. 1322 ..	9·00	
1319	25 c. on 110 c. on 5 c. Annatto tree (No. 901) ..	15	15
1320	25 c. on 110 c. on 5 c. Annatto tree (No. 902) ..	50	35
1321	25 c. on 110 c. on 5 c. Annatto tree (No. 903) ..	50	35
1322	25 c. on 110 c. on 5 c. Annatto tree (No. 904) ..	4·00	4·50
1323	25 c. on 125 c. on 8 c. on 6 c. Cannon-ball tree (No. 905)..	15	15
	a. Sheetlet of 25. Nos. 1323/4, each × 8, Nos. 1325/6, each × 4 and No. 1327 ..	9·00	
1324	25 c. on 125 c. on 8 c. on 6 c. Cannon-ball tree (No. 906)..	15	15
1325	25 c. on 125 c. on 8 c. on 6 c. Cannon-ball tree (No. 907)..	50	35
1326	25 c. on 125 c. on 8 c. on 6 c. Cannon-ball tree (No. 908)..	50	35
1327	25 c. on 125 c. on 8 c. on 6 c. Cannon-ball tree (No. 909)..	4·00	4·50
1318/27	.. .. *Set of* 10	9·50	10·00

(305) —

(306) 25 130

(307) 1984

(308) 1984

(309) 1984

1984 (Sept–Nov). *Various stamps surch or optd.*

(a) As T **294** *or as T* **298** *(60 c.)*

1328	20 c. on 15 c. on 2 c. Type **132** (No. 1030) ..	30	10
1329	20 c. on 15 c. on 2 c. Type **132** (No. 1034) ..	65	10
1330	20 c. on 15 c. on 2 c. Type **132** (No. 1063) ..	1·40	10
1331	60 c. on 110 c. on 8 c. on 3 c. Hanging Heliconia (as No. 868, but without T **219**) (two vert obliterating panels) ..	29·00	
	a. One vert obliterating panel* ..	90·00	
1332	120 c. on 125 c. on 8 c. on 6 c. Cannon-ball tree (No. 893)	5·00	50
1333	120 c. on 125 c. on $2 *Norantea guianensis* (No. 834)	38·00	
1334	120 c. on 125 c. on $2 *Norantea guianensis* (No. O20)	2·00	50
1335	120 c. on 140 c. on $1 *Chelonanthus uliginoides* (No. 796)	5·50	50
1336	200 c. on 220 c. on 1 c. Pitcher Plant of Mt Roraima (No. 922) (B.)..	8·00	75
1337	320 c. on $1.10 on $2 *Norantea guianensis* (No. 804) (B.)	1·75	75
1338	350 c. on 375 c. on $5 *Odontadenia grandiflora* (No. 803) (B.)	3·25	80
1339	390 c. on 400 c. on $5 *Odontadenia grandiflora* (No. 1091) (B.)	4·00	90
1340	450 c. on $5 *Odontadenia grandiflora* (No. O16) (B.)	5·50	2·50

*The small original printing of the 60 c. surcharge has the "8 c" and "110" values obliterated by a single vertical block of six lines. On the vast majority of the supply these features were covered by two vertical blocks of six lines each.

(b) As T **305** *(figures surch, bar in ballpoint pen)*

1341	25 c. on 10 c. Cattleya (No. 547)	30·00	2·00
	a. Surch on No. 547a	50·00	3·25
1342	25 c. on 15 c. Christmas Orchid (No. 864a)..	14·00	15
1342*a*	25 c. on 35 c. on 60 c. Soldier's Cap (No. 649)	90·00	4·50

(c) As T **306** *(on Nos.* 1343/8 *the original face value is obliterated by a fleur-de-lys*

1343	25 c. on 15 c. Christmas Orchid (No. 548) ..	£120	5·00
1344	25 c. on 15 c. Christmas Orchid (No. 809) ..	60·00	3·00
1345	25 c. on 15 c. Christmas Orchid (No. 864) ..	25·00	2·25
1346	25 c. on 15 c. Christmas Orchid (No. 977) ..	13·00	10
	a. Surch on No. 977a	£120	6·00
1347	25 c. on 15 c. Christmas Orchid (No. 1009) ..	13·00	10
1348	25 c. on 15 c. Christmas Orchid (No. O23) ..	13·00	10
1349	130 c. on 110 c. on $2 *Norantea guianensis* (No. 804)	70·00	4·00
1350	130 c. on 110 c. on $2 *Norantea guianensis* (No. O22)	2·25	1·25
1351	600 c. on $7.20 on $1 *Chelonanthus uliginoides* (No. 770A)..	2·25	75
	a. With two fleur-de-lys over original opt	75	75
	b. Surch on No. 770B	2·25	1·50
	ba. With two fleur-de-lys over original opt	75	75

(d) With T **307** *(Nov)*

1352	20 c. *Paphinia cristata* (No. 549)	18·00	10
	a. Optd on No. 549a	£120	5·00
1353	$3.60 on $5 *Odontadenia grandiflora* (No. 769A)	1·50	1·50
	a. Optd on No. 769B	2·75	1·25

(e) With T **308** *vertically in blue* (Nov)

1354	50 c. on 8 c. Type **136** (No. 1062)	10·00	25
1355	60 c. on 1 c. Pitcher Plant of Mt Roraima (No. 1000)	65	25
1356	$2 *Norantea guianensis* (No. O33) ..	1·50	60

(f) With T **309**

1357	20 c. *Paphinia cristata* (No. 549)	55·00	3·25
	a. Optd on No. 549a	£120	6·00
1357*b*	20 c. *Paphina cristata* (No. 887a) ("1984" omitted)	55·00	3·25
1358	25 c. Marabunta (No. 550)	85·00	4·50
1358*a*	25 c. Marabunta (No. 889) ("1984" omitted)	85·00	4·50
1358*b*	25 c. Marabunta (No. 889b) ("1984" omitted)	35·00	2·50
1359	25 c. Marabunta (No. F4)	4·25	50
	a. Optd on No. F4a	2·00	30
1360	$3.60 on $5 *Odontadenia grandiflora* (No. 769A)	85	1·10
	a. Optd on No. 769B	85	1·40

ICAO

(310)

ICAO

(311)

1984 (6 Sept). *40th Anniv of International Civil Aviation Organization. Nos.* 981 *(with previously unissued surcharge),* 1017 *and* 1148/68 *optd as T* **310** *(30 c.) or T* **311** *(200 c.), all in blue by Autoprint.*

1361	30 c. multicoloured (No. 1148)	60	60
	a. Sheetlet of 25. Nos. 1361/71, 1372 × 2 and 1373/84	13·00	
1362	30 c. multicoloured (No. 1149)	60	60
1363	30 c. multicoloured (No. 1150)	60	60
1364	30 c. multicoloured (No. 1151)	60	60
1365	30 c. multicoloured (No. 1152)	60	60
1366	30 c. multicoloured (No. 1153)	60	60
1367	30 c. mult (No. 1154) (optd "IMB/ICAO")	60	60
1368	30 c. mult (No. 1155) (optd "KCV/ICAO")	60	60
1369	30 c. mult (No. 1156) (optd "KAI/ICAO")	60	60
1370	30 c. multicoloured (No. 1157)	60	60
1371	30 c. multicoloured (No. 1158)	60	60
1372	30 c. mult (No. 1155) (optd "1984") ..	60	60
1373	30 c. mult (No. 1155) (optd "KPM/ICAO")	60	60
1374	30 c. multicoloured (No. 1159)	60	60
1375	30 c. multicoloured (No. 1160)	60	60
1376	30 c. multicoloured (No. 1161)	60	60
1377	30 c. mult (No. 1155) (optd "PMT/ICAO")	60	60
1378	30 c. multicoloured (No. 1162)	60	60
1379	30 c. multicoloured (No. 1163)	60	60
1380	30 c. multicoloured (No. 1164)	60	60
1381	30 c. multicoloured (No. 1165)	60	60
1382	30 c. multicoloured (No. 1166)	60	60
1383	30 c. multicoloured (No. 1167)	60	60
1384	30 c. multicoloured (No. 1168)	60	60
1385	200 c. on 330 c. on $2 mult (No. 981) ..	65	70
	a. Opt T **311** omitted	35·00	
1386	200 c. on 75 c. on $5 mult (No. 1017) ..	2·25	1·75
1361/86	.. .. *Set of* 26	16·00	16·00

No. 1385 also carries an otherwise unissued surcharge "G.A.C. Inaug. Flight Georgetown—Toronto 200" in black.

1984

(312)

$1.50
X

(313)

(314)

1984 (15 Sept). *Wildlife Protection. Nos.* 756/67 *optd with T* **312** *by Autoprint.*

1387	30 c. Type **178**	30	25
	a. Sheetlet of 12. Nos. 1387/98	3·25	
1388	30 c. Red Howler	30	25
1389	30 c. Common Squirrel-Monkey	30	25
1390	30 c. Two-toed Sloth..	30	25
1391	30 c. Brazilian Tapir	30	25
1392	30 c. Collared Peccary	30	25
1393	30 c. Six-banded Armadillo..	30	25
1394	30 c. Tamandua ("Ant Eater")	30	25
1395	30 c. Giant Anteater	30	25
1396	30 c. Murine Opossum	30	25
1397	30 c. Brown Four-eyed Opossum	30	25
1398	30 c. Brazilian Agouti	30	25
1387/98	.. .. *Set of* 12	3·25	2·75

1984 (1 Oct). *Nos.* D6/7 *and* D10/11 *surch with T* **269** *in blue by Autoprint.*

1399	D **2**	120 c. on 4 c. dp ultramarine (No. D6)	3·25	45
1400		120 c. on 4 c. dull ultram (No. D10)	20·00	1·50
1401		120 c. on 12 c. reddish scarlet (No. D7)	3·25	45
1402		120 c. on 12 c. bright scarlet (No. D11)	3·25	45
1399/402		.. .. .. *Set of* 4	27·00	2·40

1984 (15 Oct). *175th Birth Anniv of Louis Braille (inventor of alphabet for the blind). No.* 1040 *surch with T* **313** *in blue by Autoprint.*

1403	$1.50 on 15 c. on 10 c. Type **215**	6·50	55

1984 (15 Oct). *International Food Day. No.* 1012 *surch with T* **314** *by Tip Torres.*
1404 150 c. on 50 c. Pawpaw and tangerine .. 1·75 55
Type **314** places a "1" alongside the original face value and obliterates the "1982" date on the previous overprint.

1984 (15 Oct). *Birth Centenary of H. N. Critchlow (founder of Guyana Labour Union). No.* 873, *surch horizontally as T* **236**, *and No.* 1196, *both optd with T* **312** *by Autoprint.*
1405 240 c. on 110 c. on $3 H. N. Critchlow (No. 873) .. .. 1·00 65
1406 240 c. on $3 H. N. Critchlow (No. 1196) .. 6·50 70

1984 (22 Oct). *Nos.* 910/12 *surch as T* **272**, *but vertically and without the decimal point, and Nos.* 1184/7 *surch as T* **234** *by Autoprint.*
1407 **277** 25 c. on 45 c. lake-brown and black .. 15 15
a. Block of 4. Nos. 1407/10 .. 55
1408 – 25 c. on 45 c. rose-red and black (No. 1185) 15 15
1409 – 25 c. on 45 c. bright violet and black (No. 1186) 15 15
1410 – 25 c. on 45 c. dull green and black (No. 1187) 15 15
1411 – 120 c. on 100 c. on $3 multicoloured (No. 910) .. .. .. 8·50 45
1412 – 120 c. on 400 c. on 30 c. multicoloured (No. 911) 90 45
1413 – 320 c. on $5 mult (No. 912) (B.) .. 16·00 1·75
1407/13 .. .. *Set of* 7 23·00 3·00

25 X

MAHA SABHA
1934-1984
(315)

Philatelic Exhibition
New York 1984
(316)

1984 (1 Nov). *Deepavali Festival. Nos.* 544/5 *surch as T* **315** *in blue by Autoprint.*
1414 25 c. on 5 c. Annatto tree 20 10
1415 $1.50 on 3 c. Hanging Heliconia.. .. 1·40 55

1984 (15 Nov). *A.S.D.A. Philatelic Exhibition, New York. Nos.* 1188/91 *optd with T* **316** *in red by Autoprint.*
1416 **277** 120 c. lake-brown and black.. .. 40 45
a. Block of 4. Nos. 1416/19 .. 1·90
1417 – 130 c. rose-red and black 45 50
1418 – 150 c. bright violet and black .. 50 55
1419 – 200 c. dull green and black 70 75
1416/19 .. .. *Set of* 4 1·90 2·00

(Litho Format)

1984 (16 Nov). *Olympic Games, Los Angeles (3rd issue). Design as No.* 1051, *but with Olympic rings and inscr* "OLYMPIC GAMES 1984 LOS ANGELES". *P* 13½.
1420 $1.20, Youth display (41 × 25 *mm*).. .. 1·50 45
No. 1420 also exists from coils of 500 or 1,000 with numbers on the reverse of each stamp.

(317)

318 Pair of Swallow-tailed Kites on Tree

1984 (24 Nov). *Nos.* 847, 861*b*, 1099 *and* 1102 *surch as T* **317**.
1421 20 c. on 12 c. on 12 c. on 6 c. mult (No. 847) 60 10
1422 20 c. on 12 c. on 6 c. mult (No. 861*b*) 65·00
1423 25 c. on 50 c. on 6 c. mult (No. 1099) .. 30 10
1424 60 c. on $1 on 6 c. multicoloured (No. 1102) 45 25
No. 1423 shows the previous surcharge obliterated by horizontal parallel lines.

(Litho Questa)

1984 (3 Dec). *Christmas. Swallow-tailed Kites. T* **318** *and similar horiz designs. Multicoloured. W* **106** *(sideways). P* 14 × 14½.
1425 60 c. Type **318** .. .. 3·00 1·75
a. Horiz strip of 5. Nos. 1425/9 .. .. 13·50
1426 60 c. Swallow-tailed Kite on branch .. 3·00 1·75
1427 60 c. Kite in flight with wings raised .. 3·00 1·75
1428 60 c. Kite in flight with wings lowered .. 3·00 1·75
1429 60 c. Kite gliding .. .. .. 3·00 1·75
1425/9 .. .. *Set of* 5 13·50 8·00
Nos. 1425/9 were printed together, *se-tenant*, in horizontal strips of 5 throughout the sheet with the backgrounds forming a composite design. Each stamp is inscribed "CHRISTMAS 1982".

319 St. George's Cathedral, Georgetown

(Litho Format)

1985 (8 Feb–Oct). *Georgetown Buildings. T* **319** *and similar horiz designs, each black and stone. W* **106** *(sideways). P* 14.
1430 25 c. Type **319** 10 10
1431 60 c. Demerara Mutual Life Assurance Building 15 25
1432 120 c. As No. 1431 .. .. 20 45
a. Horiz strip of 3. Nos. 1432/4 .. 55
b. No wmk (10.85) 40 45
ba. Horiz strip of 3. Nos. 1432b/4b .. 1·10
1433 120 c. Town Hall 20 45
b. No wmk (10.85) 40 45
1434 120 c. Victoria Law Courts.. .. .. 20 45
b. No wmk (10.85) 40 45
1435 200 c. As No. 1433 .. .. 20 75
1436 300 c. As No. 1434 .. .. 20 1·10
1430/6 .. .. *Set of* 7 1·10 3·25
Nos. 1432/4 were printed together, *se-tenant*, in horizontal strips of 3 within the sheet, forming a composite design.

International
Youth Year 1985
(320)

Republic
Day
1970-1985
(321)

1985 (15 Feb). *International Youth Year. As No.* 1420, *but W* **106** *(sideways), optd with T* **320** *by Tip Torres.*
1437 $1.20, Youth display .. .. .. 2·00 45
Examples used for this overprint all show the second line of the original inscription as "LOS ANGELLES".

1985 (22 Feb). *Republic Day. Nos* 1049/50 *and* 1052 *optd or surch as T* **321** *in red by Autoprint.*
1438 25 c. Type **238** 20 20
a. Horiz pair. Nos. 1438/9 .. .. 40 40
1439 25 c. Flag (inscr "30th ANNIVERSARY IN PARLIAMENT") 20 20
1440 120 c. on $6 Presidential standard.. .. 65 65
1441 130 c. on $6 Presidential standard.. .. 70 70
1438/41 .. .. *Set of* 4 1·60 1·60
Examples of Nos. 1438/9 overprinted "1980–1985" in error come from stock dispersed by the liquidator of Format International Security Printers Ltd.

322 Young Ocelot on Branch

International
Youth Year
1985
(323)

(Des K. Everett. Litho Format)

1985 (11 Mar)–**87**. *Wildlife Protection. T* **322** *and similar multicoloured designs. W* **106** *(inverted). A. P* 14½ (320 c., 330 c.) *or* 12½ *(others). Without imprint*
1442A 25 c. Type **322** (grey-olive background) 1·50 10
1443A 60 c. Young Ocelot (*different*) (yellow-brown background) 30 25
1444A 120 c. As No. 1443A 50 55
c. Vert strip of 3. Nos. 1444A/6A .. 1·50
1445A 120 c. Type **322** 50 55
1446A 120 c. Young Ocelot (*different*) (red-brown background) 50 55
1447A 130 c. As No. 1446A 45 60
1448A 320 c. Scarlet Macaw (28 × 46 *mm*) .. 3·00 1·50
1449A 330 c. Young Ocelot reaching for branch (28 × 46 *mm*) .. .. .. 90 1·50
1442A/9A .. .. *Set of* 8 7·00 5·00
B. *P* 14. *With imprint date at foot* (18.2.87)
1444B 120 c. As No. 1443A 15 20
c. Vert strip of 3. Nos. 1444B/6B .. 40
1445B 120 c. Type **322** 15 20
1446B 120 c. Young Ocelot (*different*) (red-brown background) 15 20
Nos. 1444/6 were printed together, *se-tenant*, in vertical strips of 3 throughout the sheet.
Examples of the 25 c. with imprint date and perforated 14 come from stock dispersed by the liquidator of Format International Security Printers Ltd.

1985 (11 Mar–11 Apr). *No.* 940 *and Revenue stamp, as T* **181**, *surch as T* **305** *with fleur-de-lys over existing value, by Tip Torres, and Nos.* 912, 1016 *and* O 24 *surch as T* **272**, *but without the decimal point, by Autoprint.*
1450 30 c. on 50 c. multicoloured (No. O24) (B.) 50 10
1451 55 c. on 2 c. black, indigo & greenish grey 65 20
a. Opt "ESSEQUIBO etc" omitted .. 10·00
1452 55 c. on 15 c. on 2 c. black, indigo and greenish grey (No. 940) 65 20
1453 90 c. on $1 multicoloured (No. 1016) (B.) .. 4·50
1454 225 c. on $5 multicoloured (No. 912) (11.4) 7·50
1455 230 c. on $5 multicoloured (No. 912) (B.) .. 7·50
1456 260 c. on $5 multicoloured (No. 912) (B.) .. 7·50 1·
1450/6 .. .. *Set of* 7 26·00 3·
On Nos. 1454/6 the surcharges are sideways.

1985 (15 Apr). *International Youth Year Save the Childre[n] Fund Campaign. Nos.* 880, 1073*a*, 1079*b and* 1082 *optd surch as T* **323** *in blue by Autoprint.*
1457 50 c. "Two Boys catching Ducks" (No. 1073*a*).. .. .. 2·00
1458 50 c. on 10 c. Type **171** (No. 1082) .. 6·00
1459 120 c. on 125 c. on $3 "Mango Season" (No. 880) .. .. 2·00
1460 $3 "Mango Season" (No. 1079*b*) .. 2·00 1·
a. Opt Type **256** ("1983") omitted .. 12·00
1457/60 .. .. *Set of* 4 11·00 1·
On Nos. 1457 and 1459/60 the overprints and surcharge [of] Type **323** are sideways.

Airy Hall
25
(324)

1985
(325)

1985 (2 May). *125th Anniv of British Guiana Post Office* (1st *issue). No.* 699 *surch as T* **324** *in blue by Autoprint.*
1461 25 c. on 10 c. multicoloured (surch T **324**) .. 50
a. Sheetlet of 25. Nos. 1461/85 .. .. 11·00
1462 25 c. on 10 c. multicoloured (surch "Belfield Arab. Coast") 50
1463 25 c. on 10 c. multicoloured (surch "Belfield E. C. Dem.") 50
1464 25 c. on 10 c. mult (surch "Belladrum") .. 50
1465 25 c. on 10 c. multicoloured (surch "Beterver-wagting") 50
1466 25 c. on 10 c. multicoloured (surch "Blair-mont Ferry") 50
1467 25 c. on 10 c. mult (surch "Boeraserie") .. 50
1468 25 c. on 10 c. mult (surch "Brahm") .. 50
1469 25 c. on 10 c. mult (surch "Bushlot") .. 50
1470 25 c. on 10 c. mult (surch "De Kinderen") .. 50
1471 25 c. on 10 c. multicoloured (surch "Fort Wellington") 50
1472 25 c. on 10 c. mult (surch "Georgetown") .. 50
1473 25 c. on 10 c. mult (surch "Hague").. .. 50
1474 25 c. on 10 c. mult (surch "Leguan") .. 50
1475 25 c. on 10 c. mult (surch "Mahaica") .. 50
1476 25 c. on 10 c. mult (surch "Mahaicony") .. 50
1477 25 c. on 10 c. multicoloured (surch "New Amsterdam") 50
1478 25 c. on 10 c. mult (surch "Plaisance") .. 50
1479 25 c. on 10 c. multicoloured (surch "No. 6 Police Station") 50
1480 25 c. on 10 c. mult (surch "Queenstown") .. 50
1481 25 c. on 10 c. mult (surch "Vergenoegen") .. 50
1482 25 c. on 10 c. mult (surch "Vigilance") .. 50
1483 25 c. on 10 c. mult (surch "Vreed-en-Hoop") 50
1484 25 c. on 10 c. mult (surch "Wakenaam") .. 50
1485 25 c. on 10 c. mult (surch "Windsor Castle") 50
1461/85 .. .. *Set of* 25 11·00 11·
The surcharged names are those of the post offices and post[al] agencies open in 1860.
See also Nos. 1694/1717, 2140/64 and 2278/301.

1985 (17 May). *I.T.U./W.H.O. Day. Nos.* 1148/68 *optd wi[th] T* **325**, *or with single capital letter, in red by Autoprint.*
1486 30 c. multicoloured (No. 1148) 50
a. Sheetlet of 25. Nos. 1486/510.. .. 11·00
1487 30 c. multicoloured (No. 1149) 50
1488 30 c. multicoloured (No. 1150) 50
1489 30 c. multicoloured (No. 1151) 50
1490 30 c. multicoloured (No. 1152) 50
1491 30 c. multicoloured (No. 1153) 50
1492 30 c. multicoloured (No. 1154) (optd "I") .. 50
1493 30 c. multicoloured (No. 1155) (optd "T") .. 50
1494 30 c. multicoloured (No. 1156) (optd "U") .. 50
1495 30 c. multicoloured (No. 1157) 50
1496 30 c. multicoloured (No. 1158) 50
1497 30 c. multicoloured (No. 1155) (optd "W") .. 50
1498 30 c. multicoloured (No. 1155) (optd "H") .. 50
1499 30 c. multicoloured (No. 1155) (optd "O") .. 50
1500 30 c. multicoloured (No. 1159) 50
1501 30 c. multicoloured (No. 1160) 50
1502 30 c. multicoloured (No. 1161) (optd "D") .. 50
1503 30 c. multicoloured (No. 1155) (optd "A") .. 50
1504 30 c. multicoloured (No. 1162) (optd "Y") .. 50
1505 30 c. multicoloured (No. 1163) 50
1506 30 c. multicoloured (No. 1164) 50
1507 30 c. multicoloured (No. 1165) 50
1508 30 c. multicoloured (No. 1166) 50
1509 30 c. multicoloured (No. 1167) 50
1510 30 c. multicoloured (No. 1168) 50
1486/1510 .. .. *Set of* 25 11·00 11·

20
(326)

CARDI
1975-1985

(327)

1985 (21 May). *No.* 861*b surch with T* **326** *by Autoprint.*
1511 20 c. on 12 c. on 6 c. Black Acara ("Patua") 2·50 1·
a. Surch on No. 861 (no wmk) .. 6·00 1·5
For a similar surcharge, but with new face value at right se[e] Nos. 1655/6.

1985 (29 May). *10th Anniv of Caribbean Agricultural Research Development Institute. No.* 544 *surch with T* **327** *in blue by Autoprint.*
1512 60 c. on 3 c. Hanging Heliconia .. .. 1·25 25

1985 (3 June). *No.* 839 *surch as Type O* **10** *by Autoprint, but with two blocks of obliterating bars over the previous surch.*
1513 600 c. on 625 c. on 40 c. Tiger Beard .. 18·00 2·50

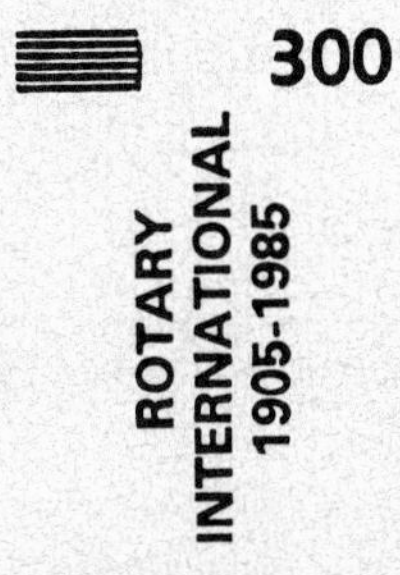

(328)

1985 (21 June). *80th Anniv of Rotary International. Nos.* 707 *and* 879 *surch as T* **328** *in red by Autoprint.*
1514 120 c. on 110 c. on $3 Rotary anniversary emblem .. .. 9·50 45
1515 300 c. on $2 *Morpho rhetenor* .. .. 6·50 2·25

No. 1205 exists with a similar 120 c. horizontal surcharge. A limited quantity was available mint, but examples are mainly found on First Day Covers (*Price £8 on First Day Cover*).

CARICOM DAY 1985

60 

(329)

1985 (28 June). *CARICOM Day. No.* 1200 *surch with T* **329** *in red.*
1516 60 c. on $3 "Makanaima the Great Ancestral Spirit of the Amerindians" .. 60 30

135th Anniversary
Cotton Reel
1850-1985

120

(330)

1985 (28 June). *135th Anniv of First British Guiana Stamps. No.* 870 *surch with T* **330** *in red.*
1517 120 c. on 110 c. on 10 c. Type **170** 65 55

"REICHENBACHIA" ISSUES. Due to the proliferation of these designs the catalogue uses the book plate numbers as description for each design. The following index gives the species on each plate and the stamp numbers on which they occur.

Series 1

Plate No. 1 – *Odontoglossum crispum* – 1578, 2112
Plate No. 2 – *Cattleya percivaliana* – 1519, 2026, 2394, 3293, 4321
Plate No. 3 – *Cypripedium sanderianum* – 1525, 2084
Plate No. 4 – *Odontoglossum rossi* – 1533, **MS**1539, 2095, **MS**2105
Plate No. 5 – *Cattleya dowiana aurea* – 1667, 1779, 1942/3, 2030, 2464
Plate No. 6 – *Coelogyne cristata maxima* – 1526, **MS**1685, 1759, 2085, 2093, 2119, **MS**2234, 2519, 2751
Plate No. 7 – *Odontoglossum insleayi splendens* – 1520, 1967
Plate No. 8 – *Laelia euspatha* – 1571, 1933, 1950
Plate No. 9 – *Dendrobium wardianum* – 1552, 1763, 1979/80, 1981*a*, 1996, 2002, 2005, 2017, 2022, 2138/9, 2387, 2748
Plate No. 10 – *Laelia autumnalis xanthotropis* – 1521, 1968, 2027, 3290, 4319
Plate No. 11 – *Phalaenopsis grandiflora aurea* – 1579, 2113
Plate No. 12 – *Cattleya lawrenceana* – 1518, 1935
Plate No. 13 – *Masdevallia shuttleworthii* and *M. xanthocorys* – 1527, 1684, 1760, 2092, 2107, 2110, 2120, 2233, 2448, 2520, 3839
Plate No. 14 – *Aeranthus sesquipedalis* – 1584, 2096, 2472
Plate No. 15 – *Cattleya mendelii* Duke of Marlborough – 1752, 1804, 2009, 2050, 2259, 2532
Plate No. 16 – *Zygopetalum intermedium* – 1559, 2090
Plate No. 17 – *Phaius humblotii* – 1732, 1792, 1885, 1965, 1977*a*, 2062, 2393
Plate No. 18 – *Chysis bractescens* – 1528, 1536, 2087, 2133
Plate No. 19 – *Masdevallia backhousiana* – 1522, 1969, 2028, 3292, 4320
Plate No. 20 – *Cattleya citrina* – 1529, **MS**1570, 1761, 2086, 2094, **MS**2106, 2121, 2449, 2521
Plate No. 21 – *Oncidium jonesianum* and *Oncidium jonesianum phaeanthum* – 1585, 2097, 2129
Plate No. 22 – *Saccolabium giganteum* – 1553, **MS**1619, 1764, 1940/1, 1989, 1997, 2006, 2018, 2023, **MS**2232, 2388, **MS**2531
Plate No. 23 – *Cypripedium io* – 1572, 1936
Plate No. 24 – *Odontoglossum blandum* – 1635, 1774, 1864/5, 1931, 1961, 2019, 2047, 2344, 2527, 2529
Plate No. 25 – *Maxillaria sanderiana* – 1530, 1762, 2108, 2111, 2122, 2522, 2752/3
Plate No. 26 – *Odontoglossum* Edward II – 1633, 2137, 2258, 2450
Plate No. 27 – *Vanda teres* – 1524, 2438
Plate No. 28 – *Odontoglossum hallii xanthoglossum* – 1580, 2114
Plate No. 29 – *Odontoglossum crispum hrubyanum* – 1531, 1537, 2088, 2134
Plate No. 30 – *Oncidium concolor* – 1532, 1538, 2089, 2135
Plate No. 31 – *Trichopilia suavis alba* – 1523, 1970, 2029, 3291, 4322
Plate No. 32 – *Cattleya superba splendens* – 1561, 2512
Plate No. 33 – *Odontoglossum luteo-purpureum* – 1634, 2098, 2342, 2479, 3827
Plate No. 34 – *Cypripedium niveum* – 1562
Plate No. 35 – *Stanhopea shuttleworthii* – 1563
Plate No. 36 – *Laelia anceps percivaliana* – 1558, 2439
Plate No. 37 – *Odontoglossum hebraicum* – 1627, 2115, 2440
Plate No. 38 – *Cypripedium oenanthum superbum* – 1560, 2445
Plate No. 39 – *Dendrobium superbiens* – 1737, 1797, 1985, 2063, 2104, 2414, 2515
Plate No. 40 – *Laelia harpophylla* – 1581, 1767, 2123, 2126, 2523, 3350
Plate No. 41 – *Lycaste skinneri* and *alba* – 1564
Plate No. 42 – *Phalaenopsis stuartiana* – 1582, 1657, 1768, 1993, 2125, 2127, 2524, 3349
Plate No. 43 – *Cattleya trianaei ernesti* – 1586, 1658, 1770, 2099, 2130/1, 2525, 3351/2
Plate No. 44 – *Sobralia xantholeuca* – 1556, 1971
Plate No. 45 – *Odontoglossum crispum kinlesideanum* – 1583, 1769, 2124, 2128, 2526, 3348
Plate No. 46 – *Cattleya trianaei schroederiana* – 1628, 2116, 2476
Plate No. 47 – *Epidendrum vitellinum* – 1557, 1972
Plate No. 48 – *Laelia anceps stella* and *barkeriana* – 1565
Plate No. 49 – *Odontoglossum harryanum* – 1554, 1765, 1912, 1964, 1966, 1994, 2003, 2007, 2015, 2024, 2749
Plate No. 50 – *Dendrobium leechianum* – 1672, 1784, 2031, 2403, 2496, 2558
Plate No. 51 – *Phalaenopsis speciosa* – 1573, 1934
Plate No. 52 – *Laelia elegans schilleriana* – 1551, 1949
Plate No. 53 – *Zygopetalum wendlandi* – 1621, 1771, 1930, 1954, 1962, 1983, 1986, 2020, 2048, 2361, 2364, E4
Plate No. 54 – *Cypripedium selligerum majus* – 1664, 1776, 2032, 2381, 2404
Plate No. 55 – *Angraecum articulatum* – 1597, 1625, 1772, 1927, 1990, 2046, 2265, 2463, 2465
Plate No. 56 – *Laelia anceps sanderiana* – 1629, 2117, 2441, 3841
Plate No. 57 – *Vanda coerulea* – 1622, 1973, 2395/6, 3828
Plate No. 58 – *Dendrobium nobile sanderianum* – 1630, 2118, 2442, 3840
Plate No. 59 – *Laelia gouldiana* – 1620, 2243, 2359
Plate No. 60 – *Odontoglossum grande* – 1682, 1789, 1944, 2038, 2514, 2528
Plate No. 61 – *Cypripedium rothschildianum* – 1574, 2356
Plate No. 62 – *Vanda sanderiana* – 1566, 2513
Plate No. 63 – *Dendrobium aureum* – 1575, 2357
Plate No. 64 – *Oncidium macranthum* – 1555, 1766, 1913, 1981/2, 1995, 2004, 2008, 2016, 2025, 2750
Plate No. 65 – *Cypripedium tautzianum* – 1598, 1626, 1773, 1963, 2021, 2049, 2221, 2434, 2437, 2530, E1
Plate No. 66 – *Cymbidium mastersi* – 1632, 2091, 2136, 2257, 2446
Plate No. 67 – *Angraecum caudatum* – 1631, 2132, 2256, 2443
Plate No. 68 – *Laelia albida* – 1734, 1794, 1884, 1937, 2056, 2378/9, 2435
Plate No. 69 – *Odontoglossum roezlii* – 1680, 1787, 2033, 2405, 2444
Plate No. 70 – *Oncidium ampliatum majus* – 1576, 2358
Plate No. 71 – *Renanthera lowii* – 1679, 1786, 1952, 1976, 2034, 2360
Plate No. 72 – *Cattleya warscewiczii* – 1577, 1951, 2429
Plate No. 73 – *Oncidium lanceanum* – 1623, 1974, 2397, 3826
Plate No. 74 – *Vanda hookeriana* – 1736, 1796, 1984, 2064, 2103, 2415, 2454
Plate No. 75 – *Cattleya labiata gaskelliana* – 1624, 1975, 2398/9, 3829
Plate No. 76 – *Epidendrum prismatocarpum* – 1751, 1803, 2058, 2453
Plate No. 77 – *Cattleya guttata leopoldi* – 1663, 1775, 1955, 1958, 2042, 2372/3
Plate No. 78 – *Oncidium splendidum* – 1669, 1781, 1959, 2043, 2451
Plate No. 79 – *Odontoglossum hebraicum aspersum* – 1670, 1782, 2035, 2100, 2343, 2406, 2473
Plate No. 80 – *Cattleya dowiana* var *chrysotoxa* – 1754, 1806, 2059, 2517
Plate No. 81 – *Cattleya trianae alba* – 1748, 1800, 1957, 2010, 2051, 2382
Plate No. 82 – *Odontoglossum humeanum* – 1753, 1805, 2011, 2052, 2260, 2516
Plate No. 83 – *Cypripedium argus* – 1671, 1783, 2039, 2466, 2480
Plate No. 84 – *Odontoglossum luteo-purpureum prionopetalum* – 1668, 1780, 2044, 2421
Plate No. 85 – *Cattleya rochellensis* – 1673, 1785, 1960, 2045, 2497, 2518
Plate No. 86 – *Odontoglossum triumphans* – 1731, 1791, 1847, 1868, 1953, 1956, 1956a, 2055, 2055a, 2264, 2362, 2377, E2, E2a, E11, (Nos. 1847, 1956a, 2055a, 2264, E2 and E11 are inscr "ONTOGLOSSUM" in error)
Plate No. 87 – *Phalaenopsis casta* – 1681, 1788, 1977, 2036, 2452, 2474, 2478
Plate No. 88 – *Oncidium tigrinum* – 1750, 1802, 2060, 2436
Plate No. 89 – *Cypripedium lemoinierianum* – 1749, 1801, 1978, 2012, 2053, 2422
Plate No. 90 – *Catasetum bungerothii* – 1738, 1798, 1938, 1947/8, 1988, 2014, 2057, 2380, 2433
Plate No. 91 – *Cattleya ballantiniana* – 1735, 1795, 1987, 2013, 2054, 2109, 2375/6, 2447
Plate No. 92 – *Dendrobium brymerianum* – 1665, 1777, 1945, 1988*a*, 2040, 2384
Plate No. 93 – *Cattleya eldorado crocata* – 1733, 1793, 1991/2, 2065, 2401, 2416
Plate No. 94 – *Odontoglossum sanderianum* – 1683, 1790, 2037, 2345, 2407, 2484
Plate No. 95 – *Cattleya labiata warneri* – 1666, 1778, 1990*a*, 2041, 2400, 2467
Plate No. 96 – *Odontoglossum schroderianum* – 1747, 1799, 2061, 2374

Series 2

Plate No. 1 – *Cypripedium morganiae burfordiense* – 2178, 2556
Plate No. 2 – *Cattleya bowringiana* – 1886, 1929, 2102, 2426
Plate No. 3 – *Dendrobium formosum* – 1919, 1998, 2389
Plate No. 4 – *Phaius tuberculosus* – 1813, 2428, 2500
Plate No. 5 – *Odontoglossum crispum mundyanum* – 1815, 2475
Plate No. 6 – *Laelia praestans* – 1881, 1999, 2390, 2624/6
Plate No. 7 – *Dendrobium phalaenopsis* var *statterianum* – 1917, 2365
Plate No. 8 – *Cypripedium boxalli atratum* – 1811, 2408
Plate No. 9 – *Odontoglossum wattianum* – 1816, 2101, 2409/10
Plate No. 10 – *Cypripedium lathamianum inversum* – 1869, 1880, 2423, 2482
Plate No. 11 – *Paphinia rugosa* and *Zygopetalum xanthinum* – 2503, E6
Plate No. 12 – *Dendrobium melanodiscus* – 1817, 2411/12, **MS**2590
Plate No. 13 – *Laelia anceps schroderiana* – 1877, 1907, 2385, 2424
Plate No. 14 – *Phaius hybridus cooksonii* – 1920, 2366/7
Plate No. 15 – *Disa grandiflora* – 1918, 1926, 2386, 2419
Plate No. 16 – *Selenipedium hybridum grande* – 2314, 2331
Plate No. 17 – *Cattleya schroederae alba* – 1872, 2413, 2610/11
Plate No. 18 – *Lycaste skinnerii armeniaca* – 1923, 1928, 1946, 2420, 2557
Plate No. 19 – *Odontoglossum excellens* – 2175
Plate No. 20 – *Laelio-cattleya elegans* var *blenheimensis* – 1916, 2000, 2391
Plate No. 21 – *Odontoglossum coradinei* – 1810, 2383, 4711
Plate No. 22 – *Odontoglossum wilckeanum* var *rothschildianum* – 1922, 2368
Plate No. 23 – *Cypripedium lawrenceanum hyeanum* – 2504, 2601, O65
Plate No. 24 – *Cattleya intermedia punctatissima* – 1887, 1914, 2418
Plate No. 25 – *Laelia purpurata* – 2067, 2576
Plate No. 26 – *Masdevallia harryana splendens* – 2505, 2596, O59
Plate No. 27 – *Selenipedium hybridum nitidissimum* – 1874, 1915, 2402, 2425
Plate No. 28 – *Cattleya mendelii* var *measuresiana* – 1924, 2369/70
Plate No. 29 – *Odontoglossum vexillarium (miltonia vexillaria)* – 1818, 2485
Plate No. 30 – *Saccolabium coeleste* – 1809, 2363, 2430
Plate No. 31 – *Cypripedium hybridum youngianum* – 2324, 2594, O57
Plate No. 32 – *Miltonia (hybrida) bleuana* – 1921, 2001, 2392
Plate No. 33 – *Laelia grandis* – 1873, 2616/19, 4712
Plate No. 34 – *Cattleya labiata* var *lueddemanniana* – 1819, 2341, 2481
Plate No. 35 – *Odontoglossum coronarium* – 2511, E9
Plate No. 36 – *Cattleya granulosa* var *schofieldiana* – 2316, 2592, O55
Plate No. 37 – *Odontoglossum (hybridum) leroyanum* – 2174
Plate No. 38 – *Cypripedium (hybridum) laucheanum* and *eyermanianum* – 1814, 2477, 2580
Plate No. 39 – *Cychnoches chlorochilon* – 2172
Plate No. 40 – *Cattleya O'Brieniana* – 2276
Plate No. 41 – *Odontoglossum ramosissimum* – 2066, 2581
Plate No. 42 – *Dendrobium phalaenopsis* var – 1812, 2427, 2499
Plate No. 43 – *Cypripedium (hybridum) pollettianum* and *maynardii* – 2216, 2593, O56
Plate No. 44 – *Odontoglossum naevium* – 1878, 2498, 2656
Plate No. 45 – *Cypripedium (hybridum) castleanum* – 1876, 1925, 2371, 2417
Plate No. 46 – *Odontoglossum cervantesii decorum* – **MS**2275, **MS**2332
Plate No. 47 – *Cattleya amethystoglossa* – 2171
Plate No. 48 – *Cattleya (hybrida) arnoldiana* – 2217, O53
Plate No. 49 – *Cattleya labiata* – 2239, 2605, 2614/15, 2646/7
Plate No. 50 – *Dendrobium (hybridum) venus* and *cassiope* – 1879, 2501, 2620/1
Plate No. 51 – *Selenipedium (hybridum) weidlichianum* – 2177, 2502
Plate No. 52 – *Cattleya mossiae* var. *reineckiana* – 2072, 2577
Plate No. 53 – *Cymbidium lowianum* – 2236, 2585, 2606
Plate No. 54 – *Oncidium loxense* – 2176, 2579
Plate No. 55 – *Cattleya (hybrida) hardyana* – **MS**2275, **MS**2332
Plate No. 56 – *Coelogyne sanderae* – 1875, 2612/13, 2627
Plate No. 57 – *Cypripedium leeanum* var *giganteum* – **MS**2275, **MS**2332
Plate No. 58 – *Coelogyne pandurata* – 2173, 2582
Plate No. 59 – *Schomburgkia sanderiana* – 2323, 2595, O61
Plate No. 60 – *Oncidium superbiens* – 2227, 2607
Plate No. 61 – *Dendrobium johnsoniae* – 2235, O58
Plate No. 62 – *Laelia hybrida behrensiana* – 2322, 2509, 2622/3
Plate No. 63 – Hybrid *Calanthes Victoria Regina, Bella* and *Burfordiense* – 2510, E8
Plate No. 64 – *Cattleya mendelii* Quorndon House var – 2238, 2608
Plate No. 65 – *Arachnanthe clarkei* – 2073, 2578
Plate No. 66 – *Zygopetalum burtii* – 2240, 2583
Plate No. 67 – *Cattleya (hybrida) parthenia* – 2318, 2584
Plate No. 68 – *Phalaenopsis sanderiana* and *intermedia portei* – 2225, 2597, O60
Plate No. 69 – *Phaius blumei* var *assamicus* – 2317, 2598, O62

Plate No. 70 – *Angraecum humblotii* – 2470, 2602, O67
Plate No. 71 – *Odontoglossum pescatorei* – 2471, 2603, O68
Plate No. 72 – *Cattleya rex* – 2193
Plate No. 73 – *Zygopetalum crinitum* – 2315, 2329,
Plate No. 74 – *Cattleya lueddemanniana alba* – 2219/20, 2222/3, 2328
Plate No. 75 – *Cymbidium (hybridum) winnianum* – 2506, O64
Plate No. 76 – Hybrid *Masdevallias courtauldiana, geleniana* and *measuresiana* – 2242
Plate No. 77 – *Cypripedium (hybridum) calypso* – 2191
Plate No. 78 – *Masdevallia chimaera* var *mooreana* – 2325
Plate No. 79 – *Miltonia phalaenopsis* – 2241, 2508
Plate No. 80 – *Lissochilus giganteus* – 2190
Plate No. 81 – *Aerides savageanum* – **MS**2275, **MS**2332
Plate No. 82 – *Thunia brymeriana* – 2069, 2483
Plate No. 83 – *Miltonia moreliana* – 2182
Plate No. 84 – *Oncidium kramerianum* – 2469, 2604, O69
Plate No. 85 – *Cattleya Victoria Regina* – 2068
Plate No. 86 – *Zygopetalum klabochorum* – 2180
Plate No. 87 – *Laelia autumnalis alba* – 2070, 2432
Plate No. 88 – *Spathoglottis kimballiana* – 2071
Plate No. 89 – *Laelio-cattleya* ("The Hon. Mrs. Astor") – 2181
Plate No. 90 – *Phaius hybridus amabilis* and *marthiae* – 2468, 2599, O63
Plate No. 91 – *Zygopetalum rostratum* – 2277
Plate No. 92 – *Coelogyne swaniana* – 2218, 2591, O54
Plate No. 93 – *Laelio-cattleya (hybrida) phoebe* – 2507, E7
Plate No. 94 – *Epidendrum atro-purpureum* var *randianum* – 2192
Plate No. 95 – *Dendrobium imperatrix* – 2226, 2600, O66
Plate No. 96 – *Vanda parishii* var *marriottiana* – 2237, 2330

CATTLEYA LAWRENCEANA
Plate No. 12 (Series 1)
25
Guyana

GUYANA

c 25 c

331 *Cattleya lawrenceana* (Plate No. 12 (Series 1))

332 Arms of Guyana

(Litho Format)

1985 (9 July). *Centenary of Publication of Sanders'* Reichenbachia (*1st issue*). *T* **331** *and similar vert designs showing orchids. Multicoloured. No wmk. P* 13½×14.

1518	25 c. Type **331**	40	30
1519	60 c. Plate No. 2 (Series 1)	50	35
1520	60 c. Plate No. 7 (Series 1)	50	35
1521	60 c. Plate No. 10 (Series 1)	50	35
1522	60 c. Plate No. 19 (Series 1)	50	35
1523	60 c. Plate No. 31 (Series 1)	50	35
1524	120 c. Plate No. 27 (Series 1)	75	55
1525	130 c. Plate No. 3 (Series 1)	75	55
1526	130 c. Plate No. 6 (Series 1)	1·10	55
1527	130 c. Plate No. 13 (Series 1)	75	55
1528	130 c. Plate No. 18 (Series 1)	2·00	55
1529	130 c. Plate No. 20 (Series 1)	1·00	55
1530	130 c. Plate No. 25 (Series 1)	75	55
1531	130 c. Plate No. 29 (Series 1)	1·50	55
1532	130 c. Plate No. 30 (Series 1)	1·50	55
1533	200 c. Plate No. 4 (Series 1)	1·50	85
1518/33	.. .. *Set of* 16	13·00	7·00

Nos. 1518/33 were printed in four sheets each of 16 orchid stamps, arranged as blocks of four of each design, and 9 examples of Type **332** which appear on the vertical and horizontal gutters between the blocks.

For 130 c. stamps as Nos. 1526/7 and 1529/30, but with watermark **106** see Nos. 1759/62.

(Litho Format)

1985 (9 July–16 Sept). *No wmk.*

1534	**332**	25 c. multicoloured (*imperf* × *p* 14)	20	25
1534*a*		25 c. multicoloured (*imperf* × *p* 13½) (16 Sept)	20	25
1534*b*		25 c. multicoloured (*p* 13½×14) ..	20	25
1535		25 c. multicoloured (*p* 13½×*imperf*)	20	25
1535*a*		25 c. mult (*p* 14×*imperf*) (16 Sept) ..	20	25
1535*b*		25 c. mult (*p* 14×13½) (16 Sept) ..	15	20
1534/5*b*		.. .. *Set of* 6	1·00	1·25

See note below No. 1533. Examples of Nos. 1534/5*b*, which were issued in booklets or coils, were cut from the gutters of the orchid sheets and the white area surrounding the design varies considerably in size. Nos. 1534, 1534*b* and 1535 occur from sheets with vertical orchid designs and Nos. 1534*a* and 1535*a*/*b* from those with horizontal designs.

See also Nos. 1807/8*b* (watermarked **106**), 1820/1*a* (additionally inscribed "1996–1986" and 2183/4*c* (within frame).

(333) (334)

1985 (9 July). *85th Birthday of Queen Elizabeth the Queen Mother* (*1st issue*). *Nos.* 1528 *and* 1531/3 *optd with T* **333** (*in two lines on No.* 1538) *or with similar opts* (*No.* **MS**1539), *all in blue by Format.*

1536	130 c. Plate No. 18 (Series 1)	60	70
1537	130 c. Plate No. 29 (Series 1)	60	70
1538	130 c. Plate No. 30 (Series 1)	60	70
1536/8	.. .. *Set of* 3	1·60	1·90
MS1539	100×126 mm. 200 c.×4 Plate No. 4 (Series 1)	3·75	5·00

The four stamps in No. **MS**1539 are overprinted "LADY BOWES-LYON 1900–1923", "DUCHESS OF YORK 1923–1937", "QUEEN ELIZABETH 1937–1952" or "QUEEN MOTHER 1952–1985", all reading upwards.

See also No. **MS**1570.

1985 (18 July). *International Youth Year. Nos.* 900/4 *surch with T* **334** *in red by Autoprint.*

1540	25 c. on 110 c. on 5 c. mult (No. 900) ..	10	10
	a. Sheetlet of 25. Nos. 1540/1, each × 8, Nos. 1542/3, each × 4 and No. 1544 ..	5·25	
1541	25 c. on 110 c. on 5 c. mult (No. 901) ..	15	15
1542	25 c. on 110 c. on 5 c. mult (No. 902) ..	35	25
1543	25 c. on 110 c. on 5 c. mult (No. 903) ..	35	25
1544	25 c. on 110 c. on 5 c. mult (No. 904) ..	2·50	2·25
1540/4	.. .. *Set of* 5	3·00	2·75

In addition to the sheetlet containing the five different original surcharges, Type **334** can also be found on the sheets of No. 900.

225

1910 - 1985

(335)

J. J. Audubon
1785-1985

240

(336)

1985 (26 July). *75th Anniv of Girl Guide Movement. No.* 612 *surch with T* **335** *by Tip Torres.*

1545	225 c. on 350 c. on 225 c. on 40 c. Guides in camp	27·00	1·75
	a. Inverted "L"'s for 1's in surcharged dates		

No. 1545a occurs on all stamps in the bottom row.

In addition to Type **335** No. 1545 also carries two otherwise unissued surcharges at top right.

Nos. 610 and 613 also exist surcharged with Type **335**. A limited quantity was available mint, but examples were mainly found on First Day Covers (*Price £25 per pair on First Day Cover*).

1985 (26 July). *Birth Bicentenary of John J. Audubon* (*ornithologist*). *No.* 992 *surch with T* **336** *by Tip Torres.*

1546	240 c. on 35 c. Harpy Eagle	19·00	2·00

1763 Revolution
GUYANA 25c

337 Leaders of the 1763 Rebellion

(338)

(Des K. Everett (150 c.). Litho Format)

1985 (29 July). *150th Anniv of Abolition of Slavery* (1984) (*1st issue*). *T* **337** *and similar horiz designs. P* 14.

1547	25 c. black and bluish grey	25	10
1548	60 c. black and mauve	20	25
1549	130 c. black and light greenish blue ..	25	50
1550	150 c. black and rose-lilac	60	55
1547/50	.. .. *Set of* 4	1·10	1·25

Designs:—60 c. Damon and Parliament Buildings, Georgetown; 130 c. Quamina and Demerara, 1823; 150 c. *Den Arendt* (slave ship), 1627.

Nos. 1549/50 exist imperforate from stock dispersed by the liquidator of Format International Security Printers Ltd.

For these designs in changed colours see Nos. 2552/5.

(Litho Format)

1985 (1 Aug). *Centenary of Publication of Sanders'* Reichenbachia (*2nd issue*). *Vert designs as T* **331** *showing orchids. Multicoloured. No wmk. P* 13½×14.

1551	25 c. Plate No. 52 (Series 1)	60	25
1552	55 c. Plate No. 9 (Series 1)	70	35
1553	55 c. Plate No. 22 (Series 1)	70	35
1554	55 c. Plate No. 49 (Series 1)	70	25
1555	55 c. Plate No. 64 (Series 1)	70	35
1556	60 c. Plate No. 44 (Series 1)	70	35
1557	60 c. Plate No. 47 (Series 1)	70	35
1558	120 c. Plate No. 36 (Series 1)	1·00	55
1559	130 c. Plate No. 16 (Series 1)	1·00	55
1560	130 c. Plate No. 38 (Series 1)	1·00	55
1561	150 c. Plate No. 32 (Series 1)	1·00	55
1562	150 c. Plate No. 34 (Series 1)	1·00	55
1563	150 c. Plate No. 35 (Series 1)	1·00	55
1564	150 c. Plate No. 41 (Series 1)	1·00	55
1565	150 c. Plate No. 48 (Series 1)	1·00	55
1566	150 c. Plate No. 62 (Series 1)	1·00	55
1551/66	.. .. *Set of* 16	12·50	6·50

Nos. 1551/66 were printed in a similar sheet format to Nos. 1518/33.

For 55 c. stamps as Nos. 1552/5, but with watermark **106** see Nos. 1763/6.

For 50 c. stamps in designs of Nos. 1554/5 see Nos. 1912/13.

1985 (16 Aug). *Signing of Guyana—Libya Friendship Treaty. No.* 621 *surch with T* **338** *by Autoprint.*

1567	150 c. on 10 c. Type **149**	9·00	2·75

ALTERED CATALOGUE NUMBERS

Any Catalogue numbers altered from the last edition are shown as a list in the introductory pages.

200

Mexico
1986
150 X 275

(339) (340) (341)

1985 (16 Aug). *Namibia Day. No. 636 surch with T* **339** *in deep carmine by Tip Torres.*
1568 150 c. on 35 c. Unveiling of Monument .. 2·75 55

1985 (16 Aug). *World Cup Football Championship. Mexico (1986) (1st issue). No. F2 surch with T* **340** *by Autoprint.*
1569 275 c. on 3 c. Hanging Heliconia .. .. 5·50 1·10
See also No. 1727.

1985 (12 Sept). *85th Birthday of Queen Elizabeth the Queen Mother (2nd issue). Sheet 120×129 mm containing No. 1529×4 optd as No.* **MS**1539, *each stamp surch with T* **341** *by Tip Torres.*
MS1570 200 c. on 130 c. × 4 Plate No. 20 (Series 1) 12·00 6·00

(Litho Format)

1985 (16 Sept). *Centenary of Publication of Sanders'* Reichenbachia *(3rd issue). Multicoloured designs as T* **331** *showing orchids. No wmk. P* 13½×14 *(Nos.* 1571/7 *and* 1584) *or* 14×13½ *(others).*
1571 25 c. Plate No. 8 (Series 1) 70 20
1572 25 c. Plate No. 23 (Series 1) 70 20
1573 25 c. Plate No. 51 (Series 1) 70 20
1574 25 c. Plate No. 61 (Series 1) 70 20
1575 25 c. Plate No. 63 (Series 1) 70 20
1576 25 c. Plate No. 70 (Series 1) 70 20
1577 25 c. Plate No. 72 (Series 1) 70 20
1578 120 c. Plate No. 1 (Series 1) *(horiz)* .. 1·00 55
1579 120 c. Plate No. 11 (Series 1) *(horiz)* .. 1·00 55
1580 120 c. Plate No. 28 (Series 1) *(horiz)* .. 1·00 55
1581 150 c. Plate No. 40 (Series 1) *(horiz)* .. 1·00 65
1582 150 c. Plate No. 42 (Series 1) *(horiz)* .. 1·00 65
1583 150 c. Plate No. 45 (Series 1) *(horiz)* .. 1·00 65
1584 200 c. Plate No. 14 (Series 1) .. .. 1·50 80
1585 200 c. Plate No. 21 (Series 1) *(horiz)* .. 1·50 80
1586 200 c. Plate No. 43 (Series 1) *(horiz)* .. 1·50 80
1571/86 .. .. *Set of* 16 14·00 6·75
Nos. 1571/86 were printed in a similar sheet format to Nos. 1518/33.
For 150 c. and 200 c. stamps as Nos. 1581/3 and 1586, but with watermark **106** see Nos. 1767/70.

120
1955-1985

1965-1985
25

(342) (343)

1985 (23 Sept). *30th Anniv of Commonwealth Caribbean Medical Research Council. Nos.* 819, 871, 874/a, 928a *and* 1014 *surch or optd (vertically reading upwards on Nos.* 1587/8) *as T* **342** *by Autoprint.*
1587 – 60 c. multicoloured (No. 819) 20 25
1588 – 60 c. multicoloured (No. 1014) .. 20 25
1589 **176** 120 c. on 110 c. on 10 c. multicoloured (No. 871) 40 45
1590 – 120 c. on 110 c. on $3 mult (No. 874) .. 40 45
1591 – 120 c. on 110 c. on $3 mult (No. 874a) .. 40 45
1592 – 120 c. on 210 c. on $3 mult (No. 928a) .. 40 45
1587/92 .. .. *Set of* 6 1·75 2·10

1985 (30 Sept). *20th Anniv of Guyana Defence Force. No.* 856 *surch as T* **343** *by Autoprint.*
1593 25 c. on $1.10 on $3 W.O. and N.C.O., Guyana Defence Force, 1966 .. 1·00 10
1594 225 c. on $1.10 on $3 W.O. and N.C.O., Guyana Defence Force, 1966 .. 2·50 1·25

1985 (5 Oct). *Fire Prevention. Nos.* 678 *and* 680 *optd with T* **325** *and surch as T* **255** *by Autoprint.*
1595 25 c. on 40 c. Fire engine, 1977 .. .. 8·00 20
1596 320 c. on 15 c. Steam engine, *circa* 1860 14·00 3·75
a. Surch double, one albino .. 55·00

(Litho Format)

1985 (7 Oct). *Centenary of Publication of Sanders'* Reichenbachia *(4th issue). Vert design as T* **331**. *Multicoloured. No wmk. P* 13½×14.
1597 60 c. Plate No. 55 (Series 1) 75 30

CRISTOBAL COLON
1492-1992
350

SIR WINSTON CHURCHILL
1965-1985

(344) (345)

1985 (12 Oct). *Columbus Day. Unissued value as T* **331** *surch with T* **344** *in red. Multicoloured. P* 13½×14.
1598 350 c. on 120 c. Plate No. 65 (Series 1) .. 4·50 2·50

1985 (15 Oct). *20th Death Anniv of Sir Winston Churchill. No.* 707 *optd with T* **345** *by Autoprint.*
1599 $2 *Morpho rhetenor* (female) .. .. 7·00 1·60

XX
1950-1985
200

United
Nations
1945-1985

POSTAGE

(346) (347) (348)

1985 (15 Oct). *35th Anniv of International Commission on Irrigation and Drainage. No.* 625 *with unissued surcharge as T* **264** *in blue further surch as T* **346** *by Autoprint.*
1600 **150** 25 c. on 110 c. on 10 c. multicoloured .. 15 10
1601 200 c. on 110 c. on 10 c. multicoloured .. 85 85

1985 (24 Oct). *40th Anniv of United Nations Organization. Nos.* 714/16, 800 *and* O19 *optd with T* **347** *by Autoprint.*
1602 30 c. multicoloured (No. 714) .. .. 1·50 10
1603 50 c. multicoloured (No. 715) .. .. 1·50 20
1604 100 c. on $3 multicoloured (No. O19) .. 1·50 40
1605 225 c. on 220 c. on $3 multicoloured (No. 800) 7·00 75
1606 $3 multicoloured (No. 716) .. .. 3·00 1·40
1602/6 .. .. *Set of* 5 13·00 2·50

1985 (29 Oct). *Nos.* 551/3, O14/15, O18, O21, OP1/2 *and* F7 *optd as T* **348** *(horizontally* 22×4 *on Nos.* 1607 *and* 1615/16) *by Autoprint.*
1607 30 c. on $2 *Norantea guianensis* (No. O18) .. 40 10
1608 40 c. Tiger Beard (No. 551) .. .. 32·00 40
1609 50 c. *Guzmania lingulata* (No. 552) .. 40 20
1610 50 c. *Guzmania lingulata* (No. O14) .. 40 20
1611 60 c. Soldier's Cap (No. 553) .. .. 3·00 25
1612 60 c. Soldier's Cap (No. O15) .. .. 2·75 25
1613 60 c. Soldier's Cap (No. F7) .. .. 1·50 25
1614 $10 *Elbella patrobas* (No. O21) .. 16·00 5·50
1615 $15 on $1 *Chelonanthus uliginoides* (No. OP1) .. .. 8·00 9·00
1616 $20 on $1 *Chelonanthus uliginoides* (No. OP2) .. .. 9·00 11·00
1607/16 .. .. *Set of* 10 65·00 24·00

150 X
Deepavali
1985

Christmas 1985

(349) (350)

1985 (1 Nov). *Deepavali Festival. Nos.* 542/3 *surch as T* **349** *by Autoprint.*
1617 25 c. on 2 c. Type **132** 20 10
1618 150 c. on 1 c. Pitcher Plant of Mt Roraima .. 1·40 55

1985 (3 Nov). *Christmas. Sheet* 120×129 *mm containing No.* 1553×4 *optd as T* **350** *in red by Format.*
MS1619 55 c. × 4 Plate No. 22 (Series 1), each with a different overprint (Type **350**, "Happy New Year", "Merry Christmas" or "Happy Holidays") .. .. 6·50 4·00

(Litho Format)

1985 (4 Nov). *Centenary of Publication of Sanders'* Reichenbachia *(5th issue). Multicoloured designs as T* **331** *showing orchids. No wmk. P* 14×13½ (60, 200 *c.) or* 13½×14 *(others).*
1620 25 c. Plate No. 59 (Series 1) 65 20
1621 30 c. Plate No. 53 (Series 1) 70 20
1622 60 c. Plate No. 57 (Series 1) *(horiz)* .. 80 35
1623 60 c. Plate No. 73 (Series 1) *(horiz)* .. 80 35
1624 60 c. Plate No. 75 (Series 1) *(horiz)* .. 80 35
1625 75 c. Plate No. 55 (Series 1) .. .. 1·00 40
1626 100 c. Plate No. 65 (Series 1) .. .. 1·25 50
1627 120 c. Plate No. 37 (Series 1) .. .. 1·25 55
1628 120 c. Plate No. 46 (Series 1) .. .. 1·25 55
1629 120 c. Plate No. 56 (Series 1) .. .. 1·25 55
1630 120 c. Plate No. 58 (Series 1) .. .. 1·25 55
1631 120 c. Plate No. 67 (Series 1) .. .. 1·25 55
1632 130 c. Plate No. 66 (Series 1) .. .. 1·40 65
1633 150 c. Plate No. 26 (Series 1) .. .. 1·50 75
1634 200 c. Plate No. 33 (Series 1) *(horiz)* .. 1·75 85
1635 225 c. Plate No. 24 (Series 1) .. .. 2·00 95
1620/35 .. .. *Set of* 16 17·00 7·50
Nos. 1620/35 were printed in a similar sheet format to Nos. 1518/33.
The 30, 75, 100 and 225 c. values show face values and "Guyana" in blue. Examples of these four stamps with face values and "Guyana" in black were prepared, but not issued.
For stamps as Nos. 1621, 1625/6 and 1635, but with watermark **106** see Nos. 1771/4.
For 50 c. in design of No. 1625 see No. 1927.

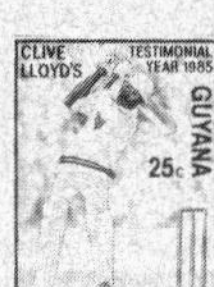

REICHENBACHIA 1886-1986

351 Clive Lloyd (cricketer) (**352**)

(Litho Format)

1985 (7 Nov). *Clive Lloyd's Testimonial Year. T* **351** *and similar vert designs. Multicoloured. W* **106** *(sideways on* $3.50). *P* 14½×14 (25 *c.),* 12½ ($3.50) *or* 14 *(others).*
1636 25 c. Type **351** 50 60
a. Horiz strip of 3. Nos. 1636/8 .. .. 1·40
1637 25 c. Clive Lloyd, bat and wicket 50 60
1638 25 c. Cricket equipment 50 60
1639 60 c. As No. 1638 (25×33 *mm*) 60 40
1640 $1.30, As No. 1637 (25×33 *mm*) .. 70 85
1641 $2.25, Type **351** (25×33 *mm*) .. .. 80 1·25
1642 $3.50, Clive Lloyd with the Prudential Cup (36×56 *mm*) .. .. .. 90 1·75
1636/42 .. .. *Set of* 7 4·00 5·50
Nos. 1636/8 were printed together, *se-tenant*, in horizontal strips of 3 throughout the sheet.

1985 (15 Nov). *Wildlife Protection. Nos.* 756/67 *optd with T* **325** *vertically in red by Autoprint.*
1643 30 c. Type **178** 75 75
a. Sheetlet of 12. Nos. 1643/54 .. .. 8·00
1644 30 c. Red Howler 75 75
1645 30 c. Common Squirrel Monkey 75 75
1646 30 c. Two-toed Sloth 75 75
1647 30 c. Brazilian Tapir 75 75
1648 30 c. Collared Peccary 75 75
1649 30 c. Six-banded Armadillo 75 75
1650 30 c. Tamandua ("Ant Eater") 75 75
1651 30 c. Giant Anteater 75 75
1652 30 c. Murine Opossum 75 75
1653 30 c. Brown Four-eyed Opossum 75 75
1654 30 c. Brazilian Agouti 75 75
1643/54 .. .. *Set of* 12 8·00 8·00

1985 (23 Dec). *Nos.* 847 *and* 861*b surch as T* **326**, *but with face value of surch at right.*
1655 20 c. on 12 c. on 12 c. on 6 c. Black Acara ("Patua") (No. 847) .. .. .. 1·50 15
1656 20 c. on 12 c. on 6 c. Black Acara ("Patua") (No. 861*b*) .. .. 1·50 15

1986 (13 Jan). *Centenary of the Appearance of* Reichenbachia *Volume I. Nos.* 1582 *and* 1586 *optd with T* **352** *in reddish violet.*
1657 150 c. Plate No. 42 (Series 1) .. .. 2·25 60
1658 200 c. Plate No. 43 (Series 1) .. .. 2·25 75

Republic Day

1986 1986

(353) (354)

1986 (22 Feb). *Republic Day. Nos.* 1108/9 *and* 1052 *optd or surch as T* **353** *by Autoprint.*
1659 25 c. As Type **258** 10 10
a. Horiz pair. Nos. 1659/60 .. .. 15 20
1660 25 c. As No. 1050 .. .. 10 10
1661 120 c. on $6 Presidential standard (surch vert) 40 45
1662 225 c. on $6 Presidential standard (surch vert) 70 75
1659/62 .. .. *Set of* 4 1·10 1·25

(Litho Format)

1986 (26 Feb). *Centenary of Publication of Sanders'* Reichenbachia *(6th issue). Vert designs as T* **331**. *Multicoloured. No wmk. P* 13½×14.
1663 40 c. Plate No. 77 (Series 1) 55 20
1664 45 c. Plate No. 54 (Series 1) 55 25
1665 50 c. Plate No. 92 (Series 1) 55 25
1666 60 c. Plate No. 95 (Series 1) 60 30
1667 75 c. Plate No. 5 (Series 1) 65 35
1668 90 c. Plate No. 84 (Series 1) 75 40
1669 150 c. Plate No. 78 (Series 1) 95 60
1670 200 c. Plate No. 79 (Series 1) .. .. 1·25 80
1671 300 c. Plate No. 83 (Series 1) .. .. 1·75 1·25
1672 320 c. Plate No. 50 (Series 1) .. .. 1·75 1·40
1673 360 c. Plate No. 85 (Series 1) .. .. 1·90 1·50
1663/73 .. .. *Set of* 11 10·00 6·50
Nos. 1663/73 were printed in a similar sheet format to Nos. 1518/33.
For stamps as Nos. 1663/73, but with watermark **106** see Nos. 1775/85.

1986 (24 Mar). *Easter. No.* 481 *optd with T* **354** *and surch as T* **317**, *but without the* "X", *both by Autoprint.*

1674 **111** 25 c. on 6 c. multicoloured 25 10
1675 50 c. on 6 c. multicoloured 40 20
1676 100 c. on 6 c. multicoloured 65 40
1677 200 c. on 6 c. multicoloured .. .. 1·25 70
1674/7 .. .. *Set of* 4 2·25 1·25

1926 1986 1926

X 150 QUEEN ELIZABETH 1986

(355) (356)

1986 (27 Mar). *60th Anniv of St. John's Ambulance in Guyana. No.* 652 *surch with T* **355** *by Autoprint.*

1678 150 c. on 35 c. silver, black and green .. 3·00 55

(Litho Format)

1986 (4 Apr). *Centenary of Publication of Sanders'* Reichenbachia (*7th issue*). *Multicoloured designs as T* **331**. *No wmk. P* 13½ × 14 (225 c.) *or* 14 × 13½ (*others*).

1679 25 c. Plate No. 71 (Series 1) (*horiz*) .. 60 20
1680 120 c. Plate No. 69 (Series 1) (*horiz*) .. 1·50 55
1681 150 c. Plate No. 87 (Series 1) (*horiz*) .. 1·75 65
1682 225 c. Plate No. 60 (Series 1) .. .. 1·75 90
1683 350 c. Plate No. 94 (Series 1) (*horiz*) .. 2·25 1·50
1679/83 .. .. *Set of* 5 7·00 3·50

Nos. 1679/83 were printed in a similar sheet format to Nos. 1518/33.

For stamps as Nos. 1679/83, but with watermark **106** see Nos. 1786/90.

1986 (21 Apr). *60th Birthday of Queen Elizabeth II. Nos.* 1526/7 *optd or surch as T* **356** *by Tip Torres.*

1684 130 c. Plate No. 13 (Series 1) .. .. 1·25 50
MS1685 100 × 126 mm. 130 c. on 130 c., 200 c. on 130 c., 260 c. on 130 c., 330 c. on 130 c., Plate No. 6 (Series 1) .. .. 4·25 4·50

The original face values on No. **MS** 1685 are obliterated by a floral pattern.

Protect the

60 GUYANA INDEPENDENCE 1966-1986 25

(357) (358)

1986 (3 May). *Wildlife Protection. Nos.* 685, 739/44 *and* 993/8 *surch as T* **357** *by Tip Torres.*

1686 60 c. on 35 c. Type **174** 35 35
a. Block of 6. Nos. 1686/91 .. 1·90
1687 60 c. on 35 c. Trahira ("Haimara") .. 35 35
1688 60 c. on 35 c. Electric Eel 35 35
1689 60 c. on 35 c. Golden Rivulus 35 35
1690 60 c. on 35 c. Golden Pencilfish 35 35
1691 60 c. on 35 c. Four-eyed Fish 35 35
1691*a* 60 c. on 35 c. Red Piranha ("Pirai") .. 4·75 2·00
ab. Block of 6. Nos. 1691*a/f* .. 25·00
1691*b* 60 c. on 35 c. Smoking Hassar .. .. 4·75 2·00
1691*c* 60 c. on 35 c. Manta .. .. 4·75 2·00
1691*d* 60 c. on 35 c. Festive Cichlid ("Flying Patwa") .. .. 4·75 2·00
1691*e* 60 c. on 35 c. Arapaima .. .. 4·75 2·00
1691*f* 60 c. on 35 c. Peacock Cichlid ("Lukanani") 4·75 2·00
1692 $6 on 8 c. Type **163** .. .. 3·00 2·50
1686/92 .. .. *Set of* 13 29·00 15·00

Nos. 1686/91 were previously overprinted with Type **226**.

On No. 1692 the previous value is covered by a fleur-de-lys.

1986 (5 May). *No.* 799 *surch as T* **326** *by Autoprint*

1693 600 c. on 720 c. on 60 c. Soldier's Cap .. 9·00 75

1986 (15 May). *125th Anniv of British Guiana Post Office* (*2nd issue*). *No.* 702*a surch as T* **324** *by Autoprint.*

1694 25 c. on 30 c. multicoloured (surch "Abary") 50 50
a. Sheetlet of 25. Nos. 1694/1704, 1705 × 2, 1706/17 .. .. .. 11·00
1695 25 c. on 30 c. mult (surch "Anna Regina") 50 50
1696 25 c. on 30 c. mult (surch "Aurora") .. 50 50
1697 25 c. on 30 c. mult (surch "Bartica Grove") 50 50
1698 25 c. on 30 c. mult (surch "Bel Air") .. 50 50
1699 25 c. on 30 c. mult (surch "Belle Plaine") .. 50 50
1700 25 c. on 30 c. multicoloured (surch "Clonbrook") 50 50
1701 25 c. on 30 c. multicoloured (surch "T.P.O. Dem. Railway") 50 50
1702 25 c. on 30 c. mult (surch "Enmore") .. 50 50
1703 25 c. on 30 c. multicoloured (surch "Fredericksburg") 50 50
1704 25 c. on 30 c. mult (surch "Good Success") 50 50
1705 25 c. on 30 c. multicoloured (surch "1986") 50 50
1706 25 c. on 30 c. mult (surch "Mariabba") .. 50 50
1707 25 c. on 30 c. multicoloured (surch "Massaruni") 50 50
1708 25 c. on 30 c. multicoloured (surch "Nigg") 50 50
1709 25 c. on 30 c. multicoloured (surch "No. 50") 50 50
1710 25 c. on 30 c. mult (surch "No. 63 Benab") 50 50
1711 25 c. on 30 c. multicoloured (surch "Philadelphia") 50 50
1712 25 c. on 30 c. mult (surch "Sisters") .. 50 50
1713 25 c. on 30 c. mult (surch "Skeldon") .. 50 50
1714 25 c. on 30 c. mult (surch "Suddie") .. 50 50
1715 25 c. on 30 c. multicoloured (surch "Taymouth Manor") 50 50
1716 25 c. on 30 c. multicoloured (surch "Wales") 50 50
1717 25 c. on 30 c. multicoloured (surch "Whim") 50 50
1694/717 .. .. *Set of* 24 11·00 11·00

The surcharged names are those of postal agencies opened between 1860 and 1880.

1986 (26 May). *20th Anniv of Independence.* (*a*) *No.* 332 *surch as T* **358** *by Autoprint, Nos.* 389, 403 *surch with* "1986", *bars and new value by Autoprint and No.* 656 *surch as T* **339** *by Tip Torres.*

1718 25 c. on 2 c. myrtle-green (No. 332) .. 15 10
1719 25 c. on 35 c. multicoloured (No. 656) .. 15 10
1720 60 c. on 2 c. myrtle-green (No. 332) .. 25 10
1721 120 c. on 6 c. yellow-green (No. 389) .. 40 20
1722 130 c. on 24 c. black & brt orange (No. 403) 4·25 30

(*b*) *Nos.* 1188/91 *surch as T* **358**, *but without* "GUYANA", *by Autoprint.*

1723 **277** 25 c. on 120 c. lake-brown, black and bright blue (No. 1188) 25 20
a. Block of 4. Nos. 1723/6 .. 1·25
1724 – 25 c. on 130 c. rose-red, black and bright blue (No. 1189) 25 20
1725 – 25 c. on 150 c. bright violet, black and bright blue (No. 1190) 25 20
1726 – 225 c. on 200 c. dull green, black and bright blue (No. 1191) 65 60
1718/26 .. .. *Set of* 9 6·00 1·75

On Nos. 1721/2 "1986" has been added below the existing overprint.

Nos. 1718 and 1720 have Mult Script CA watermark, No. 1721 watermark w **12** upright and No. 1722 watermark w **12** sideways.

225 CARICOM DAY 1986

(359) (360)

1986 (31 May). *World Cup Football Championship, Mexico* (*2nd issue*). *No.* 544 *surch with T* **359** *in blue by Autoprint.*

1727 225 c. on 3 c. Hanging Heliconia .. .. 7·50 70

1986 (28 June). *CARICOM Day. No.* 705*a optd with T* **360** *in blue by Autoprint.*

1728 60 c. *Papilio androgeus* .. .. .. 5·50 30

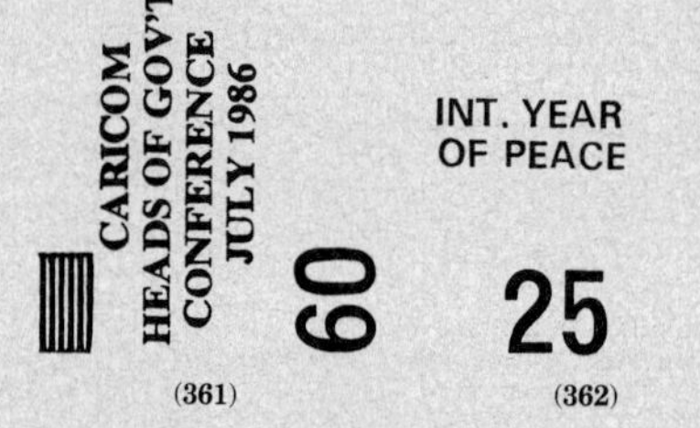

(361) (362)

1986 (1 July). *CARICOM Heads of Government Conference, Georgetown. Nos.* 544 *and* 601 *surch as T* **361** *in blue by Autoprint.*

1729 25 c. on 8 c. on 6 c. Cannon-ball Tree .. 1·00 10
1730 60 c. on 3 c. Hanging Heliconia .. .. 1·50 25

(Litho Format)

1986 (10 July). *Centenary of Publication of Sanders'* Reichenbachia (*8th issue*). *Vert designs as T* **331**. *Multicoloured. No wmk. P* 13½ × 14.

1731 30 c. Plate No. 86 (Series 1) 50 15
1732 55 c. Plate No. 17 (Series 1) 50 20
1733 60 c. Plate No. 93 (Series 1) 50 20
1734 100 c. Plate No. 68 (Series 1) 85 20
1735 130 c. Plate No. 91 (Series 1) 90 30
1736 250 c. Plate No. 74 (Series 1) .. .. 1·00 60
1737 260 c. Plate No. 39 (Series 1) .. .. 1·00 60
1738 375 c. Plate No. 90 (Series 1) .. .. 1·50 85
1731/8 .. .. *Set of* 8 6·00 2·75

Nos. 1731/8 were printed in a similar sheet format to Nos. 1518/33.

For stamps as Nos. 1731/8, but with watermark **106** see Nos. 1791/8.

For these designs with different face values see Nos. 1822, 1868 and 1884/5.

1986 (14 July). *International Peace Year. Nos.* 542 *and* 546 *surch as T* **362** *in blue* (*No.* 1739) *or black* (*others*).

1739 25 c. on 1 c. Pitcher Plant of Mt Roraima .. 20 20
a. Sheetlet of 25. No. 1739 × 24 and one label .. .. 4·00
1740 60 c. on 6 c. Cannon-ball Tree 40 40
a. Sheetlet of 25. Nos. 1740/3, each × 4, and nine labels .. .. .. 5·50
1741 120 c. on 6 c. Cannon-ball Tree 40 40
1742 130 c. on 6 c. Cannon-ball Tree 40 40
1743 150 c. on 6 c. Cannon-ball Tree 40 40
1739/43 .. .. *Set of* 5 1·60 1·60

As surcharged the sheet of No. 1739 contained a stamp without face value, overprinted "1986", in the centre position.

Nos. 1740/3 were each surcharged in blocks of four from the corner positions of the same sheet. Stamps in the central horizontal and vertical rows were without value and were overprinted with one letter of "PEACE".

363 Halley's Comet and British Guiana 1907 2 c. Stamp

(Litho Format)

1986 (19 July). *Appearance of Halley's Comet. T* **363** *and similar vert design. P* 13½ × 14.

1744 **363** 320 c. rosine, black & deep reddish lilac 30 50
a. Horiz pair. Nos. 1744/5 .. .. 60 1·00
ab. Imperf between (horiz pair) ..
1745 – 320 c. multicoloured 30 50
MS1746 76 × 50 mm. Nos. 1744/5. Imperf .. 1·50 1·25

Design:—No. 1745, Guyana 1985 320 c. Scarlet Macaw stamp.

(Litho Format)

1986 (24 July). *Centenary of Publication of Sanders'* Reichenbachia (*9th issue*). *Vert designs as T* **331**. *Multicoloured. No wmk. P* 13½ × 14.

1747 40 c. Plate No. 96 (Series 1) 60 15
1748 45 c. Plate No. 81 (Series 1) 60 15
1749 90 c. Plate No. 89 (Series 1) 80 20
1750 100 c. Plate No. 88 (Series 1) 80 20
1751 150 c. Plate No. 76 (Series 1) 90 35
1752 180 c. Plate No. 15 (Series 1) 90 40
1753 320 c. Plate No. 82 (Series 1) .. .. 1·10 70
1754 330 c. Plate No. 80 (Series 1) .. .. 1·25 90
1747/54 .. .. *Set of* 8 6·25 2·75

Nos. 1747/54 were printed in a similar sheet format to Nos. 1518/33.

For stamps as Nos. 1747/54, but with watermark **106** see Nos. 1799/1806.

1986 (28 July). *No.* 489 *surch as T* **317**, *but without the* "X".

1755 20 c. on 6 c. Patua .. .. 3·00 15

GUSIA 1936-1986

REGIONAL PHARMACY CONFERENCE 1986 130

(364) (365)

1986 (15 Aug). *50th Anniv of Guyana United Sadr Islamic Association. Nos.* 469/70 *optd or surch as T* **364** *by Autoprint.*

1756 **105** 25 c. black, gold and lilac .. .. 1·25 10
1757 $1.50 on 6 c. black, gold and flesh .. 2·50 80

1986 (19 Aug). *Regional Pharmacy Conference. No.* 545 *surch with T* **365** *in blue.*

1758 130 c. on 5 c. Annatto Tree .. .. .. 4·00 30

1986 (21 Aug)–**87**. *As previous* Reichenbachia *issues, but W* **106** (*sideways on horiz designs*). *P* 13½×14 (*vert*) *or* 14×13½ (*horiz*).

(*a*) *As Nos.* 1526/7 *and* 1529/30

1759 130 c. Plate No. 6 (Series 1) 55 20
1760 130 c. Plate No. 13 (Series 1) 55 20
1761 130 c. Plate No. 20 (Series 1) 55 20
1762 130 c. Plate No. 25 (Series 1) 55 20
1759/62 .. .. *Set of* 4 2·00 70

(*b*) *As Nos.* 1552/5

1763 55 c. Plate No. 9 (Series 1) 55 10
1764 55 c. Plate No. 22 (Series 1) 55 10
1765 55 c. Plate No. 49 (Series 1) 55 10
1766 55 c. Plate No. 64 (Series 1) 55 10
1763/6 .. .. *Set of* 4 2·00 30

(*c*) *As Nos.* 1581/3 *and* 1586

1767 150 c. Plate No. 40 (Series 1) (*horiz*) .. 45 20
1768 150 c. Plate No. 42 (Series 1) (*horiz*) .. 45 20
1769 150 c. Plate No. 45 (Series 1) (*horiz*) .. 45 20
1770 200 c. Plate No. 43 (Series 1) (*horiz*) .. 55 30
1767/70 .. .. *Set of* 4 1·75 80

(*d*) *As Nos.* 1621, 1625/6 *and* 1635

1771 30 c. Plate No. 53 (Series 1) (10.86) .. 30 10
1772 75 c. Plate No. 55 (Series 1) (1.87) .. 35 15
1773 100 c. Plate No. 65 (Series 1) (1.87) .. 35 15
1774 225 c. Plate No. 24 (Series 1) (10.86) .. 45 35
1771/4 .. .. *Set of* 4 1·25 60

(*e*) *As Nos.* 1663/73 (1987)

1775 40 c. Plate No. 77 (Series 1) .. .. 1·50 1·50
1776 45 c. Plate No. 54 (Series 1) .. .. 1·50 1·50
1777 50 c. Plate No. 92 (Series 1) .. .. 1·50 1·50
1778 60 c. Plate No. 95 (Series 1) .. .. 2·00 2·00
1779 75 c. Plate No. 5 (Series 1) .. .. 2·50 2·50

'80 90 c. Plate No. 84 (Series 1) .. .. 3·00 3·00
'81 150 c. Plate No. 78 (Series 1) .. .. 5·00 5·00
'82 200 c. Plate No. 79 (Series 1) .. .. 6·50 6·50
'83 300 c. Plate No. 83 (Series 1) .. .. 10·00 10·00
'84 320 c. Plate No. 50 (Series 1) .. .. 11·00 11·00
'85 360 c. Plate No. 85 (Series 1) .. .. 12·50 12·50
'75/85 .. .. *Set of* 11 50·00 50·00

(*f*) *As Nos.* 1679/83 (1987)

'86 25 c. Plate No. 71 (Series 1) .. .. 1·50 1·50
'87 120 c. Plate No. 69 (Series 1) .. .. 6·00 6·00
'88 150 c. Plate No. 87 (Series 1) .. .. 7·00 7·00
'89 225 c. Plate No. 60 (Series 1) .. .. 8·50 8·50
'90 350 c. Plate No. 94 (Series 1) .. .. 15·00 15·00
'86/90 .. .. *Set of* 5 32·00 32·00

(*g*) *As Nos.* 1731/8 (1987)

'91 30 c. Plate No. 86 (Series 1) .. .. 1·00 1·00
'92 55 c. Plate No. 17 (Series 1) .. .. 1·50 1·50
'93 60 c. Plate No. 93 (Series 1) .. .. 1·50 1·50
'94 100 c. Plate No. 68 (Series 1) .. .. 2·00 2·00
'95 130 c. Plate No. 91 (Series 1) .. .. 2·50 2·50
'96 250 c. Plate No. 74 (Series 1) .. .. 5·00 5·00
'97 260 c. Plate No. 39 (Series 1) .. .. 5·00 5·00
'98 375 c. Plate No. 90 (Series 1) .. .. 7·00 7·00
'91/8 .. .. *Set of* 8 20·00 20·00

(*h*) *As Nos.* 1747/54 (1987)

'99 40 c. Plate No. 96 (Series 1) .. .. 1·00 1·00
300 45 c. Plate No. 81 (Series 1) .. .. 1·00 1·00
301 90 c. Plate No. 89 (Series 1) .. .. 2·00 2·00
302 100 c. Plate No. 88 (Series 1) .. .. 2·00 2·00
303 150 c. Plate No. 76 (Series 1) .. .. 3·00 3·00
304 180 c. Plate No. 15 (Series 1) .. .. 4·00 4·00
305 320 c. Plate No. 82 (Series 1) .. .. 5·50 5·50
306 330 c. Plate No. 80 (Series 1) .. .. 6·50 6·50
799/1806 .. .. *Set of* 8 22·00 22·00

Nos. 1759/1806 were printed in a similar sheet format to Nos. 518/33.

These stamps, together with other unwatermarked values om the 1st to the 9th issues, also exist made up into two small ooks which reproduce the order of the plates in the original olumes.

Some designs in these booklets show changed face values, as etailed below, but there is no evidence that such printings were vailable for postal purposes without surcharge:

Plate No. 5 = 60 c.	Plate No. 76 = 65 c.
Plate No. 6 = 100 c.	Plate No. 77 = 45 c.
Plate No. 9 = 50 c.	Plate No. 78 = 45 c.
Plate No. 13 = 100 c.	Plate No. 79 = 60 c.
Plate No. 15 = 55 c.	Plate No. 80 = 65 c.
Plate No. 22 = 50 c.	Plate No. 81 = 55 c.
Plate No. 24 = 50 c.	Plate No. 82 = 55 c.
Plate No. 25 = 100 c.	Plate No. 83 = 75 c.
Plate No. 39 = 80 c.	Plate No. 84 = 45 c.
Plate No. 40 = 100 c.	Plate No. 85 = 45 c.
Plate No. 43 = 100 c.	Plate No. 87 = 60 c.
Plate No. 45 = 100 c.	Plate No. 88 = 65 c.
Plate No. 50 = 60 c.	Plate No. 89 = 55 c.
Plate No. 53 = 50 c.	Plate No. 90 = 40 c.
Plate No. 54 = 60 c.	Plate No. 92 = 75 c.
Plate No. 60 = 75 c.	Plate No. 93 = 80 c.
Plate No. 65 = 50 c.	Plate No. 94 = 60 c.
Plate No. 69 = 60 c.	Plate No. 95 = 75 c.
Plate No. 71 = 60 c.	Plate No. 96 = 65 c.
Plate No. 74 = 80 c.	

See also after No. 2471.

986 (21 Aug). *Booklet and Coil Stamps. As Nos.* 1534/5*b*, *but* W **106** (*sideways on Nos.* 1807*a*, 1808*a*/*b*).
807 **332** 25 c. multicoloured (*imperf* × *p* 14) 20 25
807*a* 25 c. multicoloured (*imperf* × *p* 13½) 20 25
807*b* 25 c. multicoloured (*p* 13½×14) .. 20 25
808 25 c. multicoloured (*p* 13½×*imperf*) 20 25
808*a* 25 c. multicoloured (*p* 14×*imperf*) .. 20 25
808*b* 25 c. multicoloured (*p* 14×13½) .. 20 25
807/8*b* .. .. .. *Set of* 6 1·10 1·40

The note below Nos. 1534/5*b* also applies to Nos. 1807/8*b*.

(Litho Format)

986 (23 Sept). *Centenary of Publication of Sanders'* Reichenbachia (10*th issue*). *Multicoloured designs as T* **331**. *No wmk. P* 14 × 13½ (*Nos.* 1810, 1812, 1815, 1818) *or* 13½ × 14 (*others*).
1809 30 c. Plate No. 30 (Series 2) 35 15
1810 45 c. Plate No. 21 (Series 2) (*horiz*) .. 40 15
1811 75 c. Plate No. 8 (Series 2) 65 15
1812 80 c. Plate No. 42 (Series 2) (*horiz*) .. 65 15
1813 90 c. Plate No. 4 (Series 2) 75 25
1814 130 c. Plate No. 38 (Series 2) 80 35
1815 160 c. Plate No. 5 (Series 2) (*horiz*) .. 95 40
1816 200 c. Plate No. 9 (Series 2) .. .. 1·25 50
1817 320 c. Plate No. 12 (Series 2) .. .. 2·00 70
1818 350 c. Plate No. 29 (Series 2) (*horiz*) .. 2·25 70
1819 360 c. Plate No. 34 (Series 2) .. .. 2·25 70
1809/19 .. .. *Set of* 11 11·00 3·75

Nos. 1809/19, together with Nos. 1820/1*a*, were printed in a similar sheet format to Nos. 1518/33.

(Litho Format)

1986 (23 Sept). *20th Anniv of Independence* (2*nd issue*). *T* **332** *additionally inscr "1966–1986" at foot. No wmk.*
1820 25 c. multicoloured (*imperf*×*p* 14) .. 20 25
1821 25 c. multicoloured (*p* 13½×*imperf*) .. 20 25
1821*a* 25 c. multicoloured (*p* 13½×14) .. 20 25
1820/1*a* .. .. .. *Set of* 3 55 65

Nos. 1820/1*a* together with Nos. 1809/19, were printed in the sheet format described beneath No. 1533. They were only issued in booklets or coils.

(Litho Format)

986 (26 Sept). *Centenary of Publication of Sanders'* Reichenbachia (11*th issue*). *Design as No.* 1735, *but with different face value. Multicoloured. No wmk. P* 13½ × 14.
822 40 c. Plate No. 91 (Series 1) 75 15

120 (366)

650 — 12th World Orchid Conference TOKYO JAPAN MARCH 1987 (367)

1986 (3 Oct). *Nos.* 1361/84 *surch with T* **366** *by Autoprint.*
1823 120 c. on 30 c. multicoloured (No. 1361) .. 70 70
a. Sheetlet of 25. Nos. 1823/33, 1834 × 2 and 1835/46 .. .. 15·00
1824 120 c. on 30 c. multicoloured (No. 1362) .. 70 70
1825 120 c. on 30 c. multicoloured (No. 1363) .. 70 70
1826 120 c. on 30 c. multicoloured (No. 1364) .. 70 70
1827 120 c. on 30 c. multicoloured (No. 1365) .. 70 70
1828 120 c. on 30 c. multicoloured (No. 1366) .. 70 70
1829 120 c. on 30 c. multicoloured (No. 1367) .. 70 70
1830 120 c. on 30 c. multicoloured (No. 1368) .. 70 70
1831 120 c. on 30 c. multicoloured (No. 1369) .. 70 70
1832 120 c. on 30 c. multicoloured (No. 1370) .. 70 70
1833 120 c. on 30 c. multicoloured (No. 1371) .. 70 70
1834 120 c. on 30 c. multicoloured (No. 1372) .. 70 70
1835 120 c. on 30 c. multicoloured (No. 1373) .. 70 70
1836 120 c. on 30 c. multicoloured (No. 1374) .. 70 70
1837 120 c. on 30 c. multicoloured (No. 1375) .. 70 70
1838 120 c. on 30 c. multicoloured (No. 1376) .. 70 70
1839 120 c. on 30 c. multicoloured (No. 1377) .. 70 70
1840 120 c. on 30 c. multicoloured (No. 1378) .. 70 70
1841 120 c. on 30 c. multicoloured (No. 1379) .. 70 70
1842 120 c. on 30 c. multicoloured (No. 1380) .. 70 70
1843 120 c. on 30 c. multicoloured (No. 1381) .. 70 70
1844 120 c. on 30 c. multicoloured (No. 1382) .. 70 70
1845 120 c. on 30 c. multicoloured (No. 1383) .. 70 70
1846 120 c. on 30 c. multicoloured (No. 1384) .. 70 70
1823/46 .. .. *Set of* 24 15·00 15·00

1986 (6 Oct). 12*th World Orchid Conference, Tokyo* (1*st issue*). *Unissued design as No.* 1731, *but with different face value, surch with T* **367** *by Tip Torres.*
1847 650 c. on 40 c. Plate No. 86 (Series 1) .. 7·50 3·50

No. 1847 is inscribed "ONTOGLOSSUM TRIUMPHANS" in error.

See also Nos. 2138/9.

1492-1992 CHRISTOPHER COLUMBUS 320 (368)

1986 (10–30 Oct). *Columbus Day. Unissued design as No.* 1635, *but with different face value, surch with T* **368** *by Tip Torres.*
1864 320 c. on 150 c. Plate No. 24 (Series 1) (surch in black (figures and obliterating device) and red) .. .. .. 2·50 80
1865 320 c. on 150 c. Plate No. 24 (Series 1) (entire surch in red) (30 Oct) .. 2·50 80

1986 50 (369)

AIR UNICEF 1946-1986 120 (370)

1986 (15 Oct). *International Food Day. Nos.* 1170/1 *further surch as T* **369** *by Autoprint.*
1866 50 c. on 30 c. on 1 c. Type **87** .. .. 1·25 15
1867 225 c. on $2.60 on 3 c. Peacock Cichlid ("Lukunani") .. .. .. 4·00 60

(Litho Format)

1986 (23 Oct). *Centenary of Publication of Sanders'* Reichenbachia (12*th issue*). *Vert designs as T* **331**, *one as No.* 1731 *with different face value. Multicoloured. No wmk. P* 13½ × 14.
1868 40 c. Plate No. 86 (Series 1) 50 15
1869 90 c. Plate No. 10 (Series 2) 75 30

1986 (24 Oct). *Air.* 40*th Annivs of U.N.I.C.E.F. and U.N.E.S.C.O. No.* 706 *surch as T* **370** *by Autoprint.*
1870 120 c. on $1 Type **167** (surch T **370**) .. 3·00 3·00
a. Pair. Nos. 1870/1 .. .. .. 6·00 6·00
1871 120 c. on $1 Type **167** (surch "UNESCO 1946–1986") .. .. 3·00 3·00

Nos. 1870/1 were surcharged together, *se-tenant*, in horizontal and vertical pairs throughout the sheet.

(Litho Format)

1986 (30 Oct). *Centenary of Publication of Sanders'* Reichenbachia (13*th issue*). *Vert designs as T* **331**. *Multicoloured. No wmk. P* 13½ × 14.
1872 45 c. Plate No. 17 (Series 2) 30 15
1873 50 c. Plate No. 33 (Series 2) 30 15
1874 60 c. Plate No. 27 (Series 2) 45 15
1875 75 c. Plate No. 56 (Series 2) 55 20
1876 85 c. Plate No. 45 (Series 2) 55 20
1877 90 c. Plate No. 13 (Series 2) 70 20
1878 200 c. Plate No. 44 (Series 2) .. .. 1·00 45
1879 300 c. Plate No. 50 (Series 2) .. .. 1·60 60
1880 320 c. Plate No. 10 (Series 2) .. .. 1·75 70
1881 390 c. Plate No. 6 (Series 2) .. .. 2·00 95
1872/81 .. .. *Set of* 10 8·25 3·25

Nos. 1872/81 were printed in a similar sheet format to Nos. 1518/33.

For these designs with different face values see Nos. 1907, 1915 and 1925.

25 X Deepavali 1986 (371)

CHRISTMAS 1986 20 (372)

1986 (3 Nov). *Deepavali Festival. Nos.* 543 *and* 601 *surch as T* **371** *by Autoprint.*
1882 25 c. on 2 c. Type **132** 50 10
1883 200 c. on 8 c. on 6 c. Cannon-ball Tree .. 1·50 40

(Litho Format)

1986 (25 Nov). *Centenary of Publication of Sanders'* Reichenbachia (14*th issue*). *Vert designs as T* **331**, *two as Nos.* 1732 *and* 1734 *with different face values. Multicoloured. No wmk. P* 13½ × 14.
1884 40 c. Plate No. 68 (Series 1) 90 15
1885 80 c. Plate No. 17 (Series 1) .. .. 1·50 25
1886 200 c. Plate No. 2 (Series 2) .. .. 1·75 60
1887 225 c. Plate No. 24 (Series 2) .. .. 2·00 70
1884/7 .. .. *Set of* 4 5·50 1·50

Nos. 1884/7 were printed in a similar sheet format to Nos. 1518/33.

For these designs with different face values see Nos. 1914 and 1929.

1986 (26 Nov). *Christmas. No.* 452 *surch with T* **372** *and previously unissued miniature sheet containing Nos.* 1425/9, *each surch as T* **342**, *but without dates, all in red by Autoprint.*
1888 20 c. on 6 c. Black Acara ("Patua") .. 75 10
MS1889 215×75 mm. 120 c. on 60 c. × 5 Nos. 1425/9 .. .. 6·00 6·00

1986 (373)

$15 (374)

1986 (26 Nov). *Wildlife Protection. Nos.* 756/67 *optd with T* **373** *in blue by Autoprint.*
1894 30 c. Type **178** 80 80
a. Sheetlet of 12. Nos. 1894/905.. .. 8·50
1895 30 c. Red Howler 80 80
1896 30 c. Common Squirrel-Monkey 80 80
1897 30 c. Two-toed Sloth.. .. .. .. 80 80
1898 30 c. Brazilian Tapir 80 80
1899 30 c. Collared Peccary 80 80
1900 30 c. Six-banded Armadillo.. .. .. 80 80
1901 30 c. Tamandua ("Ant Eater") 80 80
1902 30 c. Giant Anteater 80 80
1903 30 c. Murine Opossum 80 80
1904 30 c. Brown Four-eyed Opossum 80 80
1905 30 c. Brazilian Agouti 80 80
1894/905 .. .. *Set of* 12 8·50 8·50

1986 (1 Dec). *No.* 1642 *surch with T* **374** *in red by Autoprint.*
1906 $15 on $3.50, Clive Lloyd with the Prudential Cup .. .. 18·00 12·00

(Litho Format)

1986 (3 Dec). *Centenary of Publication of Sanders'* Reichenbachia *(15th issue). Design as No. 1877, but with different face value. Multicoloured. No wmk. P* 13½×14.
1907 50 c. Plate No. 13 (Series 2) 65 15

GPOC

$10 1977 1987

375 Memorial (376)

(Litho Format)

1986 (13 Dec). *President Burnham Commemoration. T* **375** *and similar multicoloured designs. P* 12½.
1908 25 c. Type **375** 10 10
1909 120 c. Map of Guyana and flags 20 20
1910 130 c. Parliament Buildings and mace .. 20 20
1911 $6 L. F. Burnham and Georgetown mayoral chain *(vert)* .. .. 60 1·25
1908/11 .. .. *Set of* 4 90 1·60

(Litho Format)

1986 (15–22 Dec). *Centenary of Publication of Sanders'* Reichenbachia *(16th issue). Multicoloured designs as Nos.* 1554/5, 1874 *and* 1887 *with different face values. W* **106** *(Nos.* 1912/13) *or no wmk (others). P* 13½×14.
1912 50 c. Plate No. 49 (Series 1) (22.12) .. 1·00 20
1913 50 c. Plate No. 64 (Series 1) .. .. 1·00 20
1914 85 c. Plate No. 24 (Series 2) .. .. 1·50 35
1915 90 c. Plate No. 27 (Series 2) .. .. 1·50 35
1912/15 .. .. *Set of* 4 4·50 1·00

(Litho Format)

1986 (27 Dec). *Centenary of Publication of Sanders'* Reichenbachia *(17th issue). Vert designs as T* **331**. *Multicoloured. No wmk. P* 13½×14.
1916 25 c. Plate No. 20 (Series 2) 35 15
1917 40 c. Plate No. 7 (Series 2) 35 15
1918 85 c. Plate No. 15 (Series 2) 50 20
1919 90 c. Plate No. 3 (Series 2) 50 20
1920 120 c. Plate No. 14 (Series 2) 65 30
1921 130 c. Plate No. 32 (Series 2) 65 30
1922 150 c. Plate No. 22 (Series 2) 80 35
1923 320 c. Plate No. 18 (Series 2) .. .. 1·25 55
1924 330 c. Plate No. 28 (Series 2) .. .. 1·25 70
1916/24 .. .. *Set of* 9 5·50 2·75
Nos. 1916/24 were printed in a similar sheet format to Nos. 1518/33.
For these designs with different face values see Nos. 1926 and 1928.

(Litho Format)

1987 (5–16 Jan). *Centenary of Publication of Sanders'* Reichenbachia *(18th issue). Multicoloured designs as Nos.* 1625, 1876, 1886, 1918 *and* 1923 *with different face values. W* **106** *(No.* 1927) *or no wmk (others). P* 13½×14.
1925 35 c. Plate No. 45 (Series 2) 40 15
1926 50 c. Plate No. 15 (Series 2) 40 15
1927 50 c. Plate No. 55 (Series 1) (16.1) .. 40 15
1928 85 c. Plate No. 18 (Series 2) 65 25
1929 90 c. Plate No. 2 (Series 2) 65 25
1925/9 .. .. *Set of* 5 2·25 85
Nos. 1925/9 were printed in a similar sheet format to Nos. 1518/33.

1987 (19 Jan). *10th Anniv of Guyana Post Office Corporation (1st issue). Unissued designs as Nos.* 1621 *and* 1635, *but with different face values, surch or optd as T* **376** *by Tip Torres.*
1930 $2.25, Plate No. 53 (Series 1) .. .. 1·25 35
1931 $10 on 150 c. Plate No. 24 (Series 1) .. 3·50 4·00
See also Nos. 2074/80.

200

200

(377) (378)

200

TWO DOLLARS

(379) (380)

1987

15.oo

(381)

(382)

120

(383)

120

(384)

1987 (9 Feb–Sept). *Various* Reichenbachia *issues surch as T* **377/84**.

(a) As T **377** *in red by Tip Torres (9 Feb)*
1932 200 c. on 40 c. Plate No. 90 (Series 1) .. 60 50

(b) As T **378** *by Tip Torres* (6 Mar)
1933 200 c. on 25 c. Plate No. 8 (Series 1) (No. 1571) 60 50
1934 200 c. on 25 c. Plate No. 51 (Series 1) (No. 1573) 60 50

(c) As T **379** *by Tip Torres (No.* 1935 *without ornament)* (6 Mar)
1935 $2 on 25 c. Plate No. 12 (Series 1) (No. 1518) 60 50
1936 $2 on 25 c. Plate No. 23 (Series 1) (No. 1572) 60 50

(d) As T **380** *by Tip Torres* (17 Mar)
1937 200 c. on 40 c. Plate No. 68 (Series 1) (No. 1884) (ornament inverted) .. 60 50
a. Ornament upright 60 50
1938 200 c. on 40 c. Plate No. 90 (Series 1) .. 60 50
1939 200 c. on 50 c. Plate No. 92 (Series 1) (No. 1665) 60 50
1940 200 c. on 50 c. Plate No. 22 (Series 1) *(wmkd)* 60 50
1941 200 c. on 55 c. Plate No. 22 (Series 1) (No. 1764) *(wmkd)* 60 50
1942 200 c. on 60 c. Plate No. 5 (Series 1) (ornament inverted) 60 50
1943 200 c. on 75 c. Plate No. 5 (Series 1) (No. 1667) (ornament inverted) .. 60 50
1944 200 c. on 75 c. Plate No. 60 (Series 1) .. 60 50
1945 200 c. on 75 c. Plate No. 92 (Series 1) .. 60 50
1946 200 c. on 85 c. Plate No. 18 (Series 2) (No. 1928) 60 50
1947 200 c. on 375 c. Plate No. 90 (Series 1) (No. 1738) 60 50
1948 200 c. on 375 c. Plate No. 90 (Series 1) (No. 1798) *(wmkd)* 60 50
1937/48 .. .. *Set of* 12 6·50 5·50

(e) As T **377** *by Tip Torres* (March)
1949 200 c. on 25 c. Plate No. 52 (Series 1) (No. 1551) 60 50
1950 200 c. on 25 c. Plate No 8 (Series 1) (No. 1571) 60 50
1951 200 c. on 25 c. Plate No. 72 (Series 1) (No. 1577) 60 50
1952 200 c. on 25 c. Plate No. 71 (Series 1) (No. 1679) (surch vert–reading downwards) 60 50
1953 200 c. on 30 c. Plate No. 86 (Series 1) (No. 1731) 60 50
1954 200 c. on 30 c. Plate No. 53 (Series 1) (No. 1771) *(wmkd)* 60 50
1955 200 c. on 40 c. Plate No. 77 (Series 1) (No. 1663) 60 50
1956 200 c. on 40 c. Plate No. 86 (Series 1) (No. 1868) 60 50
a. Inscr "ONTOGLOSSUM TRIUMPHANS" in error .. .. ..
1957 220 c. on 45 c. Plate No. 81 (Series 1) (No. 1748) 60 50
1958 200 c. on 45 c. Plate No. 77 (Series 1) .. 60 50
1959 200 c. on 45 c. Plate No. 78 (Series 1) .. 60 50
1960 200 c. on 45 c. Plate No. 85 (Series 1) .. 60 50
1961 200 c. on 50 c. Plate No. 24 (Series 1) *(wmkd)* 60 50
1962 200 c. on 50 c. Plate No. 53 (Series 1) *(wmkd)* 60 50
1963 200 c. on 50 c. Plate No. 65 (Series 1) *(wmkd)* 60 50
1964 200 c. on 55 c. Plate No. 49 (Series 1) (No. 1554) 60 50
1965 200 c. on 55 c. Plate No. 17 (Series 1) (No. 1732) 60 50
1966 200 c. on 55 c. Plate No. 49 (Series 1) (No. 1765) *(wmkd)* 60 50
1967 200 c. on 60 c. Plate No. 7 (Series 1) (No. 1520) 60 50
1968 200 c. on 60 c. Plate No. 10 (Series 1) (No. 1521) 60 50
1969 200 c. on 60 c. Plate No. 19 (Series 1) (No. 1522) 60 50
1970 200 c. on 60 c. Plate No. 31 (Series 1) (No. 1523) 60 50
1971 200 c. on 60 c. Plate No. 44 (Series 1) (No. 1556) 60 50
1972 200 c. on 60 c. Plate No. 47 (Series 1) (No. 1557) 60 50
1973 200 c. on 60 c. Plate No. 57 (Series 1) (No. 1622) (surch vert – reading down) 60 50
1974 200 c. on 60 c. Plate No. 73 (Series 1) (No. 1623) (surch vert – reading up) .. 60 50
1975 200 c. on 60 c. Plate No. 75 (Series 1) (No. 1624) (surch vert – reading down) 60 50
1976 200 c. on 60 c. Plate No. 71 (Series 1) (surch vert – reading down) 60 50
1977 200 c. on 60 c. Plate No. 87 (Series 1) (surch vert–reading down) 60 50
1977*a* 200 c. on 80 c. Plate No. 17 (Series 1) (No. 1885) .. .. 1·50 1·25
1978 225 c. on 90 c. Plate No. 89 (Series 1) (No. 1749) 65 55
1949/78 .. .. *Set of* 31 17·00 14·00

(f) As T **381** *by Gardy Ptg* (March)
1979 120 c. on 50 c. Plate No. 9 (Series 1) *(wmkd)* 50 30
1980 120 c. on 55 c. Plate No. 9 (Series 1) (No. 1552) 50 30
1981 120 c. on 55 c. Plate No. 64 (Series 1) (No. 1555) 50 30
1981*a* 120 c. on 55 c. Plate No. 9 (Series 1) (No. 1763) *(wmkd)* .. .. .. 1·50 1·00
1982 120 c. on 55 c. Plate No. 64 (Series 1) (No. 1766) *(wmkd)* 50 30
1983 $10 on 25 c. Plate No. 53 (Series 1) 2·00 2·25
1984 $12 on 80 c. Plate No. 74 (Series 1) .. 2·25 2·50
1985 $15 on 80 c. Plate No. 39 (Series 1) .. 2·75 3·00
1986 $25 on 25 c. Plate No. 53 (Series 1) .. 4·50 5·00
1979/86 .. .. *Set of* 9 13·50 13·50
Nos. 1979/82 do not show a date as part of the surcharge. On No. 1986 the surcharge is achieved by a dollar sign in front of the original face value.

(g) With T **382** *by Gardy Ptg* (June)
1987 225 c. on 40 c. Plate No. 91 (Series 1) (No. 1822) 70 60
1988 225 c. on 40 c. Plate No. 90 (Series 1) .. 70 60
1988*a* 225 c. on 50 c. Plate No. 92 (Series 1) No. 1665) .. .. 10·00 3·00
1989 225 c. on 50 c. Plate No. 22 (Series 1) *(wmkd)* 70 60
1990 225 c. on 60 c. Plate No. 55 (Series 1) (No. 1597) 70 60
1990*a* 225 c. on 60 c. Plate No. 95 (Series 1) (No. 1666) .. .. 10·00 3·00
1991 225 c. on 60 c. Plate No. 93 (Series 1) (No. 1733) 70 60
1992 225 c. on 80 c. Plate No. 93 (Series 1) .. 70 60
1993 225 c. on 150 c. Plate No. 42 (Series 1) (No. 1657) (surch vert–reading down) .. 70 60
1987/93 .. .. *Set of* 9 22·00 9·00

(h) As T **383** (July)
1994 120 c. on 50 c. Plate No. 49 (Series 1) (No. 1912) *(wmkd)* 50 40
1995 120 c. on 50 c. Plate No. 64 (Series 1) (No. 1913) *(wmkd)* 50 40
1996 120 c. on 50 c. Plate No. 9 (Series 1) *(wmkd)* 50 40
1997 120 c. on 50 c. Plate No. 22 (Series 1) *(wmkd)* 50 40
1998 120 c. on 50 c. Plate No. 3 (Series 2) .. 50 40
1999 120 c. on 50 c. Plate No. 6 (Series 2) .. 50 40
2000 120 c. on 50 c. Plate No. 20 (Series 2) .. 50 40
2001 120 c. on 50 c. Plate No. 32 (Series 2) .. 50 40
2002 120 c. on 55 c. Plate No. 9 (Series 1) (No. 1552) 50 40
2003 120 c. on 55 c. Plate No. 49 (Series 1) (No. 1554) 50 40
2004 120 c. on 55 c. Plate No. 64 (Series 1) (No. 1555) 50 40
2005 120 c. on 55 c. Plate No. 9 (Series 1) (No. 1763) *(wmkd)* 50 40
2006 120 c. on 55 c. Plate No. 22 (Series 1) (No. 1764) *(wmkd)* 50 40
2007 120 c. on 55 c. Plate No. 49 (Series 1) (No. 1765) *(wmkd)* 50 40
2008 120 c. on 55 c. Plate No. 64 (Series 1) (No. 1766) *(wmkd)* 50 40
2009 120 c. on 55 c. Plate No. 15 (Series 1) .. 50 40
2010 120 c. on 55 c. Plate No. 81 (Series 1) .. 50 40
2011 120 c. on 55 c. Plate No. 82 (Series 1) .. 50 40
2012 120 c. on 55 c. Plate No. 89 (Series 1) .. 50 40
1994/2012 .. .. *Set of* 19 8·50 7·00

(i) As T **384** *by Gardy Ptg* (Sept)

2013 120 c. on 40 c. Plate No. 91 (Series 1) (No. 1822) 50 40
2014 120 c. on 40 c. Plate No. 90 (Series 1) .. 50 40
2015 120 c. on 50 c. Plate No. 49 (Series 1) (No. 1912) (*wmkd*) 50 40
2016 120 c. on 50 c. Plate No. 64 (Series 1) (No. 1913) (*wmkd*) 50 40
2017 120 c. on 50 c. Plate No. 9 (Series 1) (*wmkd*) 50 40
2018 120 c. on 50 c. Plate No. 22 (Series 1) (*wmkd*) 50 40
2019 120 c. on 50 c. Plate No. 24 (Series 1) (*wmkd*) 50 40
2020 120 c. on 50 c. Plate No. 53 (Series 1) (*wmkd*) 50 40
2021 120 c. on 50 c. Plate No. 65 (Series 1) (*wmkd*) 50 40
2022 120 c. on 55 c. Plate No. 9 (Series 1) (No. 1763) (*wmkd*) 50 40
2023 120 c. on 55 c. Plate No. 22 (Series 1) (No. 1764) (*wmkd*) 50 40
2024 120 c. on 55 c. Plate No. 49 (Series 1) (No. 1765) (*wmkd*) 50 40
2025 120 c. on 55 c. Plate No. 64 (Series 1) (No. 1766) (*wmkd*) 50 40
2026 120 c. on 60 c. Plate No. 2 (Series 1) (No. 1519) 50 40
2027 120 c. on 60 c. Plate No. 10 (Series 1) (No. 1521) 50 40
2028 120 c. on 60 c. Plate No. 19 (Series 1) (No. 1522) 50 40
2029 120 c. on 60 c. Plate No. 31 (Series 1) (No. 1523) 50 40
2030 120 c. on 60 c. Plate No. 5 (Series 1) .. 50 40
2031 120 c. on 60 c. Plate No. 50 (Series 1) .. 50 40
2032 120 c. on 60 c. Plate No. 54 (Series 1) .. 50 40
2033 120 c. on 60 c. Plate No. 69 (Series 1) (surch vert – reading down) 50 40
2034 120 c. on 60 c. Plate No. 71 (Series 1) (surch vert – reading up) 50 40
a. Surch reading down 50 40
2035 120 c. on 60 c. Plate No. 79 (Series 1) .. 50 40
2036 120 c. on 60 c. Plate No. 87 (Series 1) (surch vert – reading up) 50 40
a. Surch reading down 50 40
2037 120 c. on 60 c. Plate No. 94 (Series 1) (surch vert – reading down) 50 40
2038 120 c. on 75 c. Plate No. 60 (Series 1) .. 50 40
2039 120 c. on 75 c. Plate No. 83 (Series 1) .. 50 40
2040 120 c. on 75 c. Plate No. 92 (Series 1) .. 50 40
2041 120 c. on 75 c. Plate No. 95 (Series 1) .. 50 40
2042 200 c. on 45 c. Plate No. 77 (Series 1) .. 50 40
2043 200 c. on 45 c. Plate No. 78 (Series 1) .. 50 40
2044 200 c. on 45 c. Plate No. 84 (Series 1) .. 50 40
2045 200 c. on 45 c. Plate No. 85 (Series 1) .. 50 40
2046 200 c. on 50 c. Plate No. 55 (Series 1) (No. 1927) (*wmkd*) 90 50
2047 200 c. on 50 c. Plate No. 24 (Series 1) (*wmkd*) 90 50
2048 200 c. on 50 c. Plate No. 53 (Series 1) (*wmkd*) 90 50
2049 200 c. on 50 c. Plate No. 65 (Series 1) (*wmkd*) 90 50
2050 200 c. on 55 c. Plate No. 15 (Series 1) .. 2·00 50
2051 200 c. on 55 c. Plate No. 81 (Series 1) .. 2·00 50
2052 200 c. on 55 c. Plate No. 82 (Series 1) .. 5·00 50
2053 200 c. on 55 c. Plate No. 89 (Series 1) .. 2·00 50
2054 225 c. on 40 c. Plate No. 91 (Series 1) (No. 1822) .. .. 1·25 60
2055 225 c. on 40 c. Plate No. 86 (Series 1) (No. 1868) .. .. 1·25 60
a. Inscr "ONTOGLOSSUM TRIUMPHANS" in error .. .. .. 1·00 60
2056 225 c. on 40 c. Plate No. 68 (Series 1) (No. 1884) 90 60
2057 225 c. on 40 c. Plate No. 90 (Series 1) .. 90 60
2058 225 c. on 65 c. Plate No. 76 (Series 1) .. 90 60
2059 225 c. on 65 c. Plate No. 80 (Series 1) .. 90 60
2060 225 c. on 65 c. Plate No. 88 (Series 1) .. 90 60
2061 225 c. on 65 c. Plate No. 96 (Series 1) .. 90 60
2062 600 c. on 80 c. Plate No. 17 (Series 1) (No. 1885) .. .. 1·50 1·50
2063 600 c. on 80 c. Plate No. 39 (Series 1) .. 1·50 1·50
2064 600 c. on 80 c. Plate No. 74 (Series 1) .. 1·50 1·50
2065 600 c. on 80 c. Plate No. 93 (Series 1) .. 1·50 1·50
2013/65 .. .. *Set of* 53 40·00 24·00

Initially some values were surcharged in sheets of sixteen orchid stamps together with nine examples of No. 2081. Subsequently, however, the surcharges appeared in the individual blocks of 4 with the arms design issued separately as Nos. 2082/3.

For 600 c. on 900 c. with surcharge as T **384** see No. 2219.

(Litho Format)

1987 (16 Feb). *Centenary of Publication of Sanders' Reichenbachia (19th issue). Vert designs as T* **331**. *Multicoloured. No wmk. P* 13½×14.

2066 180 c. Plate 41 (Series 2) .. .. .. 1·25 40
2067 230 c. Plate 25 (Series 2) .. .. .. 1·40 50
2068 300 c. Plate 85 (Series 2) .. .. .. 2·00 65
2069 330 c. Plate 82 (Series 2) .. .. .. 2·25 70
2070 425 c. Plate 87 (Series 2) .. .. .. 2·50 85
2071 440 c. Plate 88 (Series 2) .. .. .. 2·50 85
2072 590 c. Plate 52 (Series 2) .. .. .. 2·50 1·25
2073 650 c. Plate 65 (Series 2) .. .. .. 3·25 1·50
2066/73 .. .. .. *Set of* 8 16·00 6·00

Nos. 2066/73 were printed in a similar sheet format to Nos. 1518/33.

PRICES OF SETS

Set prices are given for many issues, generally those containing three stamps or more. Definitive sets include one of each value or major colour change, but do not cover different perforations, die types or minor shades. Where a choice is possible the set prices are based on the cheapest versions of the stamps included in the listings.

Post Office Corp. 1977-1987 25c (385)

1987 200 (386)

1987 (17 Feb). *10th Anniv of Guyana Post Office Corporation (2nd issue). Nos.* 543, 545, 548a *and* 601 *surch as T* **385** *in blue by Autoprint.*

2074 25 c. on 2 c. Type **132** 15 10
2075 25 c. on 5 c. Annatto tree 15 10
2076 25 c. on 8 c. on 6 c. Cannon-ball tree .. 15 10
2077 25 c. on 15 c. Christmas Orchid .. .. 1·25 10
2078 60 c. on 15 c. Christmas Orchid .. .. 2·50 15
2079 $1.20 on 2 c. Type **132** 75 65
2080 $1.30 on 15 c. Christmas Orchid .. 3·00 85
2074/80 .. .. *Set of* 7 7·00 1·75

1987 (6 Mar). *Nos.* 1534/5 *surch with T* **386** *by Tip Torres.*

2081 **332** 200 c. on 25 c. mult (*p* 13½×14) .. 85 85
2082 200 c. on 25 c. mult (*imperf* × *p* 14) 85 85
2083 200 c. on 25 c. mult (*p* 13½ × *imperf*) 85 85
2081/3 .. .. *Set of* 3 2·25 2·25

See note below No. 2065.

1987 (387) 1987 (388) 1987 (389) 1987 (390)

1987 (6 Mar–Dec). *Various* Reichenbachia *issues optd as T* **387/90**.

(a) With T **387** *by Tip Torres* (March)

2084 130 c. Plate No. 3 (Series 1) (No. 1525) .. 50 40
2085 130 c. Plate No. 6 (Series 1) (No. 1526) .. 50 40
2086 130 c. Plate No. 20 (Series 1) (No. 1529) .. 50 40
2087 130 c. Plate No. 18 (Series 1) (No. 1536) .. 50 40
2088 130 c. Plate No. 29 (Series 1) (No. 1537) .. 50 40
2089 130 c. Plate No. 30 (Series 1) (No. 1538) .. 50 40
2090 130 c. Plate No. 16 (Series 1) (No. 1559) .. 50 40
2091 130 c. Plate No. 66 (Series 1) (No. 1632) .. 50 40
2092 130 c. Plate No. 13 (Series 1) (No. 1684) .. 50 40
2093 130 c. Plate No. 6 (Series 1) (No. 1759) (*wmkd*) 50 40
2094 130 c. Plate No. 20 (Series 1) (No. 1761) (*wmkd*) 50 40
2095 200 c. Plate No. 4 (Series 1) (No. 1533) .. 60 50
2096 200 c. Plate No. 14 (Series 1) (No. 1584) 60 50
2097 200 c. Plate No. 21 (Series 1) (No. 1585) (opt vert – reading down) 60 50
2098 200 c. Plate No. 33 (Series 1) (No. 1634) (opt vert – reading down) 60 50
2099 200 c. Plate No. 43 (Series 1) (No. 1658) (opt vert – reading down) 60 50
2100 200 c. Plate No. 79 (Series 1) (No. 1670) .. 60 50
2101 200 c. Plate No. 9 (Series 2) (No. 1816) .. 60 50
2102 200 c. Plate No. 2 (Series 2) (No. 1886) .. 60 50
2103 250 c. Plate No. 74 (Series 1) (No. 1736) .. 70 60
2104 260 c. Plate No. 39 (Series 1) (No. 1737) .. 70 60
2084/2104 .. .. .. *Set of* 21 10·50 8·50
MS2105 100×129 mm. 200 c.×4 Plate 4 (Series 1) (No. **MS**1539) .. .. .. 2·00 1·75
MS2106 100×129 mm. 200 c. on 130 c.×4 Plate 20 (Series 1) (No. **MS**1570) .. .. 2·00 1·75

(b) With T **388** *by Gardy Ptg* (March)

2107 130 c. Plate No. 13 (Series 1) (No. 1527) .. 50 40
2108 130 c. Plate No. 25 (Series 1) (No. 1530) .. 50 40
2109 130 c. Plate No. 91 (Series 1) (No. 1735) .. 50 40
2110 130 c. Plate No. 13 (Series 1) (No. 1760) (*wmkd*) 50 40
2111 130 c. Plate No. 25 (Series 1) (No. 1762) (*wmkd*) 50 40
2107/11 .. .. *Set of* 5 2·25 1·75

(c) With T **389** *by Gardy Ptg* (July)

2112 120 c. Plate No. 1 (Series 1) (No. 1578) (opt vert – reading down) .. .. 2·00 60
2113 120 c. Plate No. 11 (Series 1) (No. 1579) (opt vert – reading down) .. .. 1·50 60
2114 120 c. Plate No. 28 (Series 1) (No. 1580) (opt vert – reading down) .. .. 2·00 60
2115 120 c. Plate No. 37 (Series 1) (No. 1627) .. 1·00 60
2116 120 c. Plate No. 46 (Series 1) (No. 1628) .. 4·50 60
2117 120 c. Plate No. 56 (Series 1) (No. 1629) 1·50 60
2118 120 c. Plate No. 58 (Series 1) (No. 1630) 1·50 60
2119 130 c. Plate No. 6 (Series 1) (No. 1759) (*wmkd*) .. .. 1·50 60
2120 130 c. Plate No. 13 (Series 1) (No. 1760) (*wmkd*) .. .. 1·50 60
2121 130 c. Plate No. 20 (Series 1) (No. 1761) (*wmkd*) .. .. 1·00 60
2122 130 c. Plate No. 25 (Series 1) (No. 1762) (*wmkd*) .. .. 1·25 60
2123 150 c. Plate No. 40 (Series 1) (No. 1581) (opt vert–reading down) .. .. 1·25 70
2124 150 c. Plate No. 45 (Series 1) (No. 1583) (opt vert–reading down) .. .. 1·00 70
2125 150 c. Plate No. 42 (Series 1) (No. 1657) (opt vert–reading down) .. .. 3·00 70
2126 150 c. Plate No. 40 (Series 1) (No. 1767) (*wmkd*) (opt vert–reading up) .. 1·00 70
2127 150 c. Plate No. 42 (Series 1) (No. 1768) (*wmkd*) (opt vert–reading up) .. 1·50 70
2128 150 c. Plate No. 45 (Series 1) (No. 1769) (*wmkd*) (opt vert–reading up) .. 1·25 70
2129 200 c. Plate No. 21 (Series 1) (No. 1585) (opt vert–reading down) .. .. 1·00 75
2130 200 c. Plate No. 43 (Series 1) (No. 1658) (opt vert–reading down) .. .. 3·00 75
2131 200 c. Plate No. 43 (Series 1) (No. 1770) (*wmkd*) (opt vert–reading up) .. 3·00 75
2112/31 .. .. *Set of* 20 32·00 11·50

(d) With T **390** *by Gardy Ptg* (Dec)

2132 120 c. Plate No. 67 (Series 1) (No. 1631) .. 50 40
2133 130 c. Plate No. 18 (Series 1) (No. 1536) .. 50 40
2134 130 c. Plate No. 29 (Series 1) (No. 1537) .. 50 40
2135 130 c. Plate No. 30 (Series 1) (No. 1538) .. 50 40
2136 130 c. Plate No. 66 (Series 1) (No. 1632) .. 50 40
2137 150 c. Plate No. 26 (Series 1) (No. 1633) .. 50 50
2132/7 .. .. *Set of* 6 2·75 2·25

650 12th World Orchid Conference TOKYO JAPAN (391)

28 MARCH 1927 PAA GEO-POS (392)

1987 (12 Mar). *12th World Orchid Conference, Tokyo (2nd issue). Nos.* 1552 *and* 1763 *surch with T* **391** *by Tip Torres.*

2138 650 c. on 55 c. Plate No. 9 (Series 1) (No. 1552) .. .. 3·50 2·50
2139 650 c. on 55 c. Plate No. 9 (Series 1) (No. 1763) .. .. 3·50 2·50

1987 (17 Mar). *125th Anniv of British Guiana Post Office (3rd issue). No.* 699 *surch as T* **324** *by Autoprint.*

2140 25 c. on 10 c. mult (surch "AGRICOLA") .. 50 30
a. Sheetlet of 25. Nos. 2140/64 .. 11·00
2141 25 c. on 10 c. mult (surch "BAGOTVILLE") 50 30
2142 25 c. on 10 c. mult (surch "BOURDA") .. 50 30
2143 25 c. on 10 c. mult (surch "BUXTON") .. 50 30
2144 25 c. on 10 c. mult (surch "CABACABURI") 50 30
2145 25 c. on 10 c. multicoloured (surch "CARMICHAEL STREET") .. 50 30
2146 25 c. on 10 c. multicoloured (surch "COTTON TREE") 50 30
2147 25 c. on 10 c. mult (surch "DUNOON") .. 50 30
2148 25 c. on 10 c. mult (surch "FELLOWSHIP") 50 30
2149 25 c. on 10 c. mult (surch "GROVE") .. 50 30
2150 25 c. on 10 c. mult (surch "HACKNEY") .. 50 30
2151 25 c. on 10 c. mult (surch "LEONORA") .. 50 30
2152 25 c. on 10 c. multicoloured (surch "1987") 50 30
2153 25 c. on 10 c. mult (surch "MALLALI") .. 50 30
2154 25 c. on 10 c. mult (surch "PROVIDENCE") 50 30
2155 25 c. on 10 c. mult (surch "RELIANCE") .. 50 30
2156 25 c. on 10 c. mult (surch "SPARTA") .. 50 30
2157 25 c. on 10 c. multicoloured (surch "STEWARTVILLE") 50 30
2158 25 c. on 10 c. mult (surch "TARLOGY") .. 50 30
2159 25 c. on 10 c. multicoloured (surch "T.P.O. BERBICE RIV.") 50 30
2160 25 c. on 10 c. multicoloured (surch "T.P.O. DEM. RIV.") 50 30
2161 25 c. on 10 c. multicoloured (surch "T.P.O. ESSEO. RIV.") 50 30
2162 25 c. on 10 c. multicoloured (surch "T.P.O. MASSARUNI RIV.") 50 30
2163 25 c. on 10 c. multicoloured (surch "TUSCHEN (De VRIENDEN)") .. 50 30
2164 25 c. on 10 c. multicoloured (surch "ZORG") 50 30
2140/64 .. .. *Set of* 25 11·00 6·50

The surcharged names are those of postal agencies opened by 1885.

1987 (28 Mar). *50th Anniv of First Georgetown to Port-of-Spain Flight by P.A.A. No.* 708a *optd with T* **392** *by Autoprint.*

2165 $10 *Elbella patrobas* .. .. .. 8·50 4·50

1987 (6 Apr). *No.* 704 *surch with figures only as T* **324** *by Autoprint.*

2166 25 c. on 40 c. *Morpho rhetenor* (male) .. 4·00 10

1987 120 (393) 1987 (394) CAPEX '87 (395)

1987 (21 Apr). *Easter. Nos.* 481/2 *and* 484 *optd or surch as T* **393** *by Autoprint.*

2167 **111** 25 c. multicoloured 30 10
2168 120 c. on 6 c. multicoloured 40 20
2169 320 c. on 6 c. multicoloured 75 55
2170 500 c. on 40 c. multicoloured .. .. 1·25 90
2167/70 .. .. *Set of* 4 2·40 1·50

(Litho Format)

1987 (24 Apr). *Centenary of Publication of Sanders' Reichenbachia (20th issue). Multicoloured designs as T* **331**. *No wmk. P* 13½×14 (240, 260, 500, 560 *c.*) *or* 13½×14 (*others*).

2171 240 c. Plate No. 47 (Series 2) 80 45
2172 260 c. Plate No. 39 (Series 2) 90 55

2173 275 c. Plate No. 58 (Series 2) *(horiz)* .. 90 55
2174 390 c. Plate No. 37 (Series 2) *(horiz)* .. 1·10 70
2175 450 c. Plate No. 19 (Series 2) *(horiz)* .. 1·50 90
2176 460 c. Plate No. 54 (Series 2) *(horiz)* .. 1·50 90
2177 500 c. Plate No. 51 (Series 2) .. .. 1·75 1·10
2178 560 c. Plate No. 1 (Series 2) .. .. 2·00 1·50
2171/8 .. .. *Set of* 8 9·50 6·00

Nos. 2171/8 were printed in a similar sheet format to Nos. 1518/33.

1987 (Apr). *No.* 706 *optd with T* **394** *by Autoprint.*
2179 **167** $1 multicoloured .. .. .. 3·00 15

(Litho Format)

1987 (2 June). *Centenary of Publication of Sanders Reichenbachia* (21*st issue*). *Vert designs as T* **331**. *Multicoloured. No wmk. P* 13½×14.
2180 500 c. Plate No. 86 (Series 2) .. .. 1·75 1·10
2181 520 c. Plate No. 89 (Series 2) .. .. 1·90 1·25
2182 $20 Plate No. 83 (Series 2) .. .. 6·00 7·00
2180/2 .. .. *Set of* 3 8·75 8·50

Nos. 2180/2 were printed in a similar sheet format to Nos. 1518/33, but included Nos. 2183/4 instead of Nos. 1534/5.

Two types of bird in coat of arms:

A. Bird with short tail B. Bird with long tail

(Litho Format)

1987 (2 June–29 Sept). *As T* **332**, *but within frame. No wmk.*
2183 25 c. mult (Type A) *(imperf × p 14)* .. 30 30
a. Perf 13½×14 .. .. 30 30
b. Perf 13½×imperf 30 30
2184 25 c. multicoloured (Type B) *(imperf × p 14)* (29 Sept) 30 30
a. Perf 13½×14 .. .. .. 30 30
b. Perf 13½×imperf 30 30
c. Perf 14×13½ 30 30

Nos. 2183/4 were cut from the gutters of the orchid stamps as detailed in the note below No. 1533. They were only issued in booklets or coils.

1987 (10 June). *"Capex '87" International Stamp Exhibition, Toronto. Nos.* 1744/5 *optd with T* **395**.
2185 **363** 320 c. rosine, black and dp reddish lilac 75 1·00
a. Horiz pair. Nos. 2185/6 .. 1·50 2·00
ab. Imperf between (horiz pair) ..
2186 – 320 c. multicoloured .. .. .. 75 1·00

1987 (15 July). *Commonwealth Heads of Government Meeting, Vancouver. Nos.* 1066/8 *further optd with T* **394**.
2187 $1.20 on 6 c. yellow-green 45 20
2188 $1.30 on 24 c. black and bright orange .. 3·00 30
2189 $2.40 on 24 c. black and bright orange .. 3·75 90
2187/9 .. .. *Set of* 3 6·50 1·25

(Litho Format)

1987 (22 July). *Centenary of Publication of Sanders' Reichenbachia* (22*nd issue*). *Vert designs as T* **331**. *Multicoloured. No wmk. P* 13½×14.
2190 400 c. Plate No. 80 (Series 2) .. .. 1·25 80
2191 480 c. Plate No. 77 (Series 2) .. .. 1·50 1·00
2192 600 c. Plate No. 94 (Series 2) .. .. 2·00 1·50
2193 $25 Plate No. 72 (Series 2) .. .. 6·50 8·00
2190/3 .. .. *Set of* 4 10·00 10·00

Nos. 2190/3 were printed in a similar sheet format to Nos. 1518/33.

396 Steam Locomotive No. 4 *Alexandra*

FAIREY NICHOLL
8 AUG 1927
GEO-MAZ

(397)

(Litho Format)

1987 (3 Aug–4 Dec). *Guyana Railways. T* **396** *and similar horiz designs. No wmk. P* 12½ ($10, $12) *or* 15 *(others).*
2194 **396** $1.20, bronze-green 25 30
a. Block of 4. Nos. 2194/7 90
2195 – $1.20, bronze-green 25 30
2196 – $1.20, bronze-green 25 30
2197 – $1.20, bronze-green 25 30
2198 **396** $1.20, maroon (4 Dec) 25 30
a. Block of 4. Nos. 2198/201 .. 90
2199 – $1.20, maroon (4 Dec) 25 30
2200 – $1.20, maroon (4 Dec) 25 30
2201 – $1.20, maroon (4 Dec) 25 30
2202 **396** $3.20, deep dull blue 80 90
a. Block of 5. Nos. 2202/6 .. 3·50
2203 – $3.20, deep dull blue 80 90
2204 – $3.20, deep dull blue 80 90
2205 – $3.20, deep dull blue 80 90
2206 – $3.20, deep dull blue 80 90
2207 – $3.30, brownish black (4 Dec) .. 80 90
a. Block of 5. Nos. 2207/11 .. .. 3·50
2208 **396** $3.30, brownish black (4 Dec) .. 80 90
2209 – $3.30, brownish black (4 Dec) .. 80 90
2210 – $3.30, brownish black (4 Dec) .. 80 90
2211 – $3.30, brownish black (4 Dec) .. 80 90
2212 – $10 multicoloured (4 Dec) .. .. 1·00 1·50
2213 – $12 multicoloured .. .. 1·25 1·75
2194/213 .. .. *Set of* 20 10·00 13·00

Designs: (*As T* **396**)—Nos. 2195, 2199, 2203, 2207, Front view of diesel locomotive; Nos. 2196, 2200, 2204, 2210, Steam locomotive with searchlight; Nos. 2197, 2201, 2205, 2209, Side view of diesel locomotive No. 21. (82×55 *mm*)—No. 2206, Molasses warehouses and early locomotive; No. 2211, Diesel locomotive and passenger train. (88×39 *mm*)—No. 2212, Cattle train and Parika–Rosignol Railway route map; No. 2213, Molasses train and Parika–Rosignol Railway route map.

Nos. 2194/7 and 2198/201 were each printed together, *se-tenant*, in blocks of 4, within the sheets of 40.

Nos. 2202/6 and 2207/11 were each printed together, *se-tenant*, in blocks of 5 within the sheets of 25. The order of the stamps as Type **396** differs in the $3.30 block.

1987 (7 Aug). *50th Anniv of First Flights from Georgetown to Massaruni and Mabaruma. No.* 706 *optd as T* **397** *by Autoprint.*
2214 **167** $1 multicoloured (optd T **397**) .. 4·00 4·00
a. Pair. Nos. 2214/15 .. .. 8·00 8·00
2215 $1 mult (optd "FAIREY NICHOLL 15 AUG 1927 GEO- MAB") .. 4·00 4·00

Nos. 2214/15 were overprinted together, *se-tenant*, in vertical or horizontal pairs within the sheet.

(Litho Format)

1987 (29 Sept). *Centenary of Publication of Sanders' Reichenbachia* (23*rd issue*). *Vert designs as T* **331**. *Multicoloured. No wmk. P* 13½×14.
2216 200 c. Plate No. 43 (Series 2) .. .. 2·00 65
2217 200 c. Plate No. 48 (Series 2) .. .. 2·00 65
2218 200 c. Plate No. 92 (Series 2) .. .. 2·00 65
2216/18 .. .. *Set of* 3 5·50 1·75

Nos. 2216/18 were printed in a similar sheet format to Nos. 1518/33.

(Litho Format)

1987 (9 Oct). *Centenary of Publication of Sanders' Reichenbachia* (24*th issue*). *Vert design as T* **331**, *optd as T* **384** *by Gardy Ptg* (600 *c.*). *Multicoloured. No wmk. P* 13½ × 14.
2219 600 c. on 900 c. Plate No. 74 (Series 2) .. 2·25 2·50
a. Pair. Nos. 2219/20 .. .. 7·00 7·00
2220 900 c. Plate No. 74 (Series 2) .. .. 2·25 2·50

Nos. 2219/20 were printed in a similar sheet format to Nos. 1518/33 with the surcharge on the first and last stamp of each block of four.

950

CRISTOVÃO COLOMBO
1492 — 1992

(398)

THE PASSING OF HALLEY'S COMET:
PROPHESY OF THE ARRIVAL OF
HERNAN CORTES 1519.
V CENTENARY OF THE LANDING OF
CHRISTOPHER COLUMBUS
$ 20.oo IN THE AMERICAS

(399)

1987 (9 Oct). *Columbus Day. No.* 1598 *further surch with T* **382**, *No.* 2220 *surch as T* **398** *and No.* **MS**1746 *surch with T* **399**.
2221 225 c. on 350 c. on 120 c. Plate No. 65 (Series 1) 75 40
2222 950 c. on 900 c. Plate No. 74 (Series 2) (surch with T **398**) .. .. .. 1·75 2·25
a. Horiz pair. Nos. 2222/3 .. .. 3·50 4·50
2223 950 c. on 900 c. Plate No. 74 (Series 2) (surch "950 CHRISTOPHE COLOMB 1492 — 1992") .. .. 1·75 2·25
2221/3 .. .. *Set of* 3 3·75 4·50
MS2224 76 × 50 mm. $20 on 320 c. × 2 Nos. 1744/5 .. .. 6·00 7·00

Nos. 2222/3 were surcharged together, *se-tenant*, in horizontal pairs in the sheetlet of 4.

(Litho Format)

1987 (26 Oct). *Centenary of Publication of Sanders' Reichenbachia* (25*th issue*). *Multicoloured designs as T* **331**. *No wmk. P* 13½ × 14 (575 *c.*) *or* 14 × 13½ *(others).*
2225 325 c. Plate No. 68 (Series 2) *(horiz)* .. 2·25 90
2226 420 c. Plate No. 95 (Series 2) *(horiz)* .. 2·50 1·25
2227 575 c. Plate No. 60 (Series 2) .. .. 3·00 2·25
2225/7 .. .. *Set of* 3 7·00 4·00

Nos. 2225/7, together with No. E7, were printed in a similar sheet format to Nos. 1518/33.

DEEPAVALI
1987
25

(400)

1987 (2 Nov). *Deepavali Festival. Nos.* 544/5 *surch as T* **400**.
2228 25 c. on 3 c. Hanging Heliconia 30 10
2229 $3 on 5 c. Annatto tree .. .. 1·25 60

120

CHRISTMAS
1987
20 1987

(401) (402)

1987 (9 Nov). *Christmas. No.* 452 *surch with T* **401** *in red, previously unissued miniature sheet containing Nos.* 1425/9 *each surch with T* **402** *in blue and No.* **MS**1619 *with each stamp surch with T* **382**.
2230 20 c. on 6 c. Black Acara ("Patua") .. 60 10
MS2231 215×75 mm. 120 c. on 60 c. × 5 Nos. 1425/9 .. .. 6·50 3·25
MS2232 120×129 mm. 225 c. on 55 c. × 4 Plate No. 22 (Series 1), each with a different overprint (Type **350**, "Happy New Year", "Merry Christmas" or "Happy Holidays") .. .. 1·10 1·25

1987 (20 Nov). *Royal Ruby Wedding. Nos.* 1684/5 *optd with T* **390** (130 *c.*) *or surch as T* **384** *by Gardy Ptg.*
2233 130 c. Plate No. 13 (Series 1) .. .. 1·25 30
MS2234 600 c. on 130 c. on 130 c., 600 c. on 200 c. on 130 c., 600 c. on 260 c. on 130 c., 600 c. on 330 c. on 130 c., Plate No. 6 (Series 1) .. .. 8·00 9·00

(Litho Format)

1987 (23 Nov). *Centenary of Publication of Sanders' Reichenbachia* (26*th issue*). *Vert designs as T* **331**. *Multicoloured. No wmk. P* 13½ × 14.
2235 255 c. Plate No. 61 (Series 2) .. .. 2·00 1·25
2236 290 c. Plate No. 53 (Series 2) .. .. 2·25 1·50
2237 375 c. Plate No. 96 (Series 2) .. .. 2·75 1·60
2238 680 c. Plate No. 64 (Series 2) .. .. 4·00 2·50
2239 720 c. Plate No. 49 (Series 2) .. .. 4·50 4·00
2240 750 c. Plate No. 66 (Series 2) .. .. 4·50 4·00
2241 800 c. Plate No. 79 (Series 2) .. .. 5·00 4·50
a. Face value omitted .. ..
2242 850 c. Plate No. 76 (Series 2) .. .. 5·00 4·50
a. Face value omitted .. ..
2235/42 .. .. *Set of* 8 27·00 21·00

Nos. 2235/42 were printed in a similar sheet format to Nos. 1518/33.

Nos. 2241a and 2242a occurred in the same sheet as Nos. 2276a and 2277a.

AIR

75

(403)

1987 (Nov). *Air. No.* 1620 *surch with T* **403** *by Gardy Ptg.*
2243 75 c. on 25 c. Plate No. 59 (Series 1) .. 3·00 40

ALTERED CATALOGUE NUMBERS

Any Catalogue numbers altered from the last edition are shown as a list in the introductory pages.

Protect our Heritage '87

320

PROTECT OUR
HERITAGE '87

(404) (405)

1987 (9 Dec). *Wildlife Protection. Nos.* 756/67 *optd vertically with T* **394**, *Nos.* 1432b/4b *surch with T* **404** *in red and Nos.* 1631/3, 1752/3 *and* 1847 *optd with T* **405**.

2244 30 c. Type **178** 20 15
a. Sheetlet of 12. Nos. 2244/55 .. 2·25
2245 30 c. Red Howler 20 15
2246 30 c. Common Squirrel-Monkey 20 15
2247 30 c. Two-toed Sloth 20 15
2248 30 c. Brazilian Tapir 20 15
2249 30 c. Collared Peccary 20 15
2250 30 c. Six-banded Armadillo 20 15
2251 30 c. Tamandua ("Ant Eater") 20 15
2252 30 c. Giant Anteater 20 15
2253 30 c. Murine Opossum 20 15
2254 30 c. Brown Four-eyed Opossum .. 20 15
2255 30 c. Brazilian Agouti 20 15
2256 120 c. Plate No. 67 (Series 1) 50 30
2257 130 c. Plate No. 66 (Series 1) 50 30
2258 150 c. Plate No. 26 (Series 1) 55 35
2259 180 c. Plate No. 15 (Series 1) 60 40
2260 320 c. Plate No. 82 (Series 1) 80 60
2261 320 c. on 120 c. Demerara Mutual Life Assurance Building 80 80
a. Horiz strip of 3. Nos. 2261/3 .. 2·25
b. Surch on No. 1432 .. ..
ba. Horiz strip of 3. Nos. 2261b/3b ..
2262 320 c. on 120 c. Town Hall 80 80
b. Surch on No. 1433 .. ..
2263 320 c. on 120 c. Victoria Law Courts .. 80 80
b. Surch on No. 1434 .. ..
2264 650 c. on 40 c. Plate No. 86 (Series 1) .. 2·00 2·00
2244/64 .. .. *Set of* 21 8·75 7·00

AIR

(406)

1987 (Dec). *Air. No.* 1597 *optd with T* **406**.

2265 60 c. Plate No. 55 (Series 1) .. .. 3·50 4·00

No. 2265 was only issued in $15 stamp booklets.

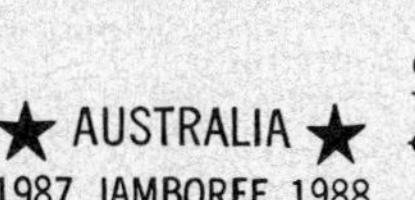
★ AUSTRALIA ★
1987 JAMBOREE 1988

(407)

* AUSTRALIA *
$10
1987 Jamboree 1988

(408)

1988 (7 Jan). *World Scout Jamboree, Australia. Nos.* 830, 837/a *and* 1104 *handstamped with T* **407** *(No. 2266) or surch with T* **408** *by Tip Torres (others), all in red.*

2266 **116** 440 c. on 6 c. multicoloured (No. 837a) (surch T **201**) .. .. .. 3·75 30
a. On No. 837 (surch T **200**) .. 8·50
2267 $10 on 110 c. on 6 c. mult (No. 830) 75 70
2268 $10 on 180 c. on 6 c. mult (No. 1104) 75 70
2269 $10 on 440 c. on 6 c. mult (No. 837) 2·50 2·00
a. On No. 837a 75 70
2266/9a .. .. *Set of* 4 5·50 2·25

IFAD
For a World
Without Hunger
25

Republic
Day
1988
25

(409) (410)

1988 (26 Jan). *10th Anniv of International Fund for Agricultural Development. Nos.* 485 *and* 487 *surch as T* **409** *by Autoprint.*

2270 25 c. on 1 c. Type **87** 30 10
2271 $5 on 3 c. Lukunani .. .. .. 1·25 70

1988 (23 Feb). *Republic Day. Nos.* 545, 548a *and* 555 *surch as T* **410** *in blue.*

2272 25 c. on 5 c. Annatto tree 10 10
2273 120 c. on 15 c. Christmas Orchid .. .. 1·75 50
2274 $10 on $2 *Noranthea guianensis* .. 2·00 1·75
2272/4 .. .. *Set of* 3 3·50 2·00

(Litho Format)

1988 (26 Feb). *Centenary of Publication of Sanders' Reichenbachia (27th issue). Four sheets, each* 102×127 *mm, containing vert designs as T* **331**. *Multicoloured. No wmk. P* 13½×14.

MS2275 (a) 320 c. Plate No. 46 (Series 2); 330 c. Plate No. 55 (Series 2); 350 c. Plate No. 57 (Series 2); 500 c. Plate No. 81 (Series 2). (b) 320 c. Plate No. 55 (Series 2); 330 c. Plate No. 46 (Series 2); 350 c. Plate No. 81 (Series 2); 500 c. Plate No. 57 (Series 2). (c) 320 c. Plate No. 57 (Series 2); 330 c. Plate No. 81 (Series 2); 350 c. Plate No. 46 (Series 2); 500 c. Plate No. 55 (Series 2). (d) 320 c. Plate No. 81 (Series 2); 330 c. Plate No. 57 (Series 2); 350 c. Plate No. 55 (Series 2); 500 c. Plate No. 46 (Series 2) *Set of* 4 *sheets* 15·00 12·00

(Litho Format)

1988 (24 Mar). *Centenary of Publication of Sanders' Reichenbachia (28th issue). Vert designs as T* **331**. *Multicoloured. No wmk. P* 13½×14.

2276 $10 Plate No. 40 (Series 2) .. .. 1·75 2·00
a. Face value omitted .. ..
2277 $12 Plate No. 91 (Series 2) .. .. 1·75 2·00
a. Face value omitted .. ..

Nos. 2276/7 were printed in a similar sheet format to Nos. 1518/33.

Nos. 2276a/7a occurred in the same sheet as Nos. 2241a and 2242a.

1988 (5 Apr). *125th Anniv of British Guiana Post Office (4th issue). No.* 702a *surch as T* **324** *by Autoprint.*

2278 25 c. on 30 c. mult (surch "Albouystown") .. 50 40
a. Sheetlet of 25. Nos. 2278/88, 2289×2, 2290/301 .. .. .. 11·00
2279 25 c. on 30 c. mult (surch "Anns Grove") .. 50 40
2280 25 c. on 30 c. mult (surch "Amacura") .. 50 40
2281 25 c. on 30 c. mult (surch "Arakaka") .. 50 40
2282 25 c. on 30 c. mult (surch "Baramanni") .. 50 40
2283 25 c. on 30 c. mult (surch "Cuyuni") .. 50 40
2284 25 c. on 30 c. mult (surch "Hope Placer") .. 50 40
2285 25 c. on 30 c. mult (surch "H M P S") .. 50 40
2286 25 c. on 30 c. multicoloured (surch "Kitty") 50 40
2287 25 c. on 30 c. mult (surch "M'M'Zorg") .. 50 40
2288 25 c. on 30 c. mult (surch "Maccaseema") 50 40
2289 25 c. on 30 c. multicoloured (surch "1988") 50 40
2290 25 c. on 30 c. mult (surch "Morawhanna") 50 40
2291 25 c. on 30 c. mult (surch "Naamryck") .. 50 40
2292 25 c. on 30 c. multicoloured (surch "Purini") 50 40
2293 25 c. on 30 c. mult (surch "Potaro Landing") 50 40
2294 25 c. on 30 c. mult (surch "Rockstone") .. 50 40
2295 25 c. on 30 c. mult (surch "Rosignol") .. 50 40
2296 25 c. on 30 c. mult (surch "Stanleytown") .. 50 40
2297 25 c. on 30 c. mult (surch "Santa Rosa") .. 50 40
2298 25 c. on 30 c. mult (surch "Tumatumari") .. 50 40
2299 25 c. on 30 c. mult (surch "Weldaad") .. 50 40
2300 25 c. on 30 c. mult (surch "Wismar") .. 50 40
2301 25 c. on 30 c. multicoloured (surch "TPO Berbice Railway") 50 40
2278/301 .. .. .. *Set of* 24 11·00 8·50

The surcharged names are those of postal agencies opened between 1886 and 1900.

120
Olympic
Games
1988

Caricom Day
1988
25

(411) (412)

1988 (3 May). *Olympic Games, Seoul (1st issue). Nos.* 1206/17 *further surch with T* **411**.

2302 120 c. on 55 c. on 125 c. on 35 c. Type **174** 70 70
a. Block of 12. Nos. 2302/13 .. .. 7·50
2303 120 c. on 55 c. on 125 c. on 35 c. Trahira ("Haimara") 70 70
2304 120 c. on 55 c. on 125 c. on 35 c. Electric Eel 70 70
2305 120 c. on 55 c. on 125 c. on 35 c. Golden Rivulus 70 70
2306 120 c. on 55 c. on 125 c. on 35 c. Golden Pencilfish 70 70
2307 120 c. on 55 c. on 125 c. on 35 c. Four-eyed Fish 70 70
2308 120 c. on 55 c. on 125 c. on 35 c. Red Piranha ("Pirai") 70 70
2309 120 c. on 55 c. on 125 c. on 35 c. Smoking Hassar 70 70
2310 120 c. on 55 c. on 125 c. on 35 c. Manta .. 70 70
2311 120 c. on 55 c. on 125 c. on 35 c. Festive Cichlid ("Flying Patwa") 70 70
2312 120 c. on 55 c. on 125 c. on 35 c. Arapaima 70 70
2313 120 c. on 55 c. on 125 c. on 35 c. Peacock Cichlid ("Lukanani") 70 70
2302/13 .. .. .. *Set of* 12 7·50 7·50

See also Nos. 2476/95

(Litho Format)

1988 (1 June). *Centenary of Publication of Sanders' Reichenbachia (29th issue). Vert designs as T* **331**. *Multicoloured. No wmk. P* 13½×14.

2314 320 c. Plate No. 16 (Series 2) 80 40
2315 475 c. Plate No. 73 (Series 2) .. .. 1·00 70
2316 525 c. Plate No. 36 (Series 2) .. .. 1·50 90
2317 530 c. Plate No. 69 (Series 2) .. .. 1·50 90
2318 $15 Plate No. 67 (Series 2) .. .. 3·00 4·00
2314/18 .. .. *Set of* 5 7·00 6·25

Nos. 2314/18 were printed in a similar sheet format to Nos. 1518/33.

1988 (15 June). *CARICOM Day. Nos.* 545/6 *and* 555 *surch as T* **412**.

2319 25 c. on 5 c. Annatto tree 15 10
2320 $1.20 on 6 c. Cannon-ball tree 30 10
2321 $10 on $2 *Norantea guianensis* .. .. 2·00 2·00
2319/21 .. .. *Set of* 3 2·25 2·00

(Litho Format)

1988 (15 June). *Centenary of Publication of Sanders' Reichenbachia (30th issue). Vert designs as T* **331**. *Multicoloured. No wmk. P* 13½×14.

2322 700 c. Plate No. 62 (Series 2) .. .. 1·50 1·25
2323 775 c. Plate No. 59 (Series 2) .. .. 1·75 1·40
2324 875 c. Plate No. 31 (Series 2) .. .. 2·00 1·50
2325 950 c. Plate No. 78 (Series 2) .. .. 2·25 1·75
2322/5 .. .. *Set of* 4 6·75 5·50

Nos. 2322/5 were printed in a similar sheet format to Nos. 1518/33.

WHO
1948-1988

1988

(413) (414)

1988 (17 June). *40th Anniv of World Health Day. No.* 705a *optd with T* **413** *or T* **414** *by Autoprint.*

2326 60 c. *Papilio androgeus* (T **413**) .. .. 7·50 8·50
a. Sheetlet of 25. Nos. 2326 and 2327×24 .. .. 9·00
2327 60 c. *Papilio androgeus* (T **414**) 15 10

Nos. 2326 and 2327 were overprinted together, *se-tenant*, in a sheetlet of 25 showing a single example of No. 2326 in the central position.

(Litho Format)

1988 (22 June). *Centenary of Publication of Sanders' Reichenbachia (31st issue). Vert design as T* **331**. *No wmk. P* 13½×14.

2328 350 c. Plate No. 74 (Series 2) 90 40

No. 2328 was printed in a similar sheet format to Nos. 1518/33.

(Litho Format)

1988 (9 July). *Centenary of Publication of Sanders Reichenbachia (32nd issue). Vert designs as T* **331**, *with Nos.* 2329/31 *additional inscr* "1985 – 1988". *No wmk. P* 13½×14.

2329 130 c. Plate No. 73 (Series 2) 85 25
2330 200 c. Plate No. 96 (Series 2) .. .. 1·00 30
2331 260 c. Plate No. 16 (Series 2) .. .. 1·50 45
2329/31 .. .. *Set of* 3 3·00 90

MS2332 Four sheets, each 102×127 mm. (a) 120 c. Plate No. 81 (Series 2); 120 c. Plate No. 57 (Series 2); 120 c. Plate No. 55 (Series 2); 120 c. Plate No. 46 (Series 2). (b) 150 c. Plate No. 57 (Series 2); 150 c. Plate No. 81 (Series 2); 150 c. Plate No. 46 (Series 2); 150 c. Plate No. 55 (Series 2). (c) 225 c. Plate No. 46 (Series 2); 225 c. Plate No. 55 (Series 2); 225 c. Plate No. 57 (Series 2); 225 c. Plate No. 81 (Series 2). (d) 305 c. Plate No. 55 (Series 2); 305 c. Plate No. 46 (Series 2); 305 c. Plate No. 81 (Series 2); 305 c. Plate No. 57 (Series 2) .. .. *Set of* 4 *sheets* 7·50 5·00

CONSERVE
TREES

CONSERVE
WATER

(415) (416)

1988 (15 July). *Conservation of Resources.*

(a) Nos. 1444B/6B *optd as T* **415** *by Gardy Ptg*

2333 120 c. Young Ocelot (No. 1444B) (opt T **415**) 50 40
a. Block of 9. Nos. 2333/41 .. 4·00
2334 120 c. Young Ocelot (No. 1444B) (opt "CONSERVE ELECTRICITY") .. 50 40
2335 120 c. Young Ocelot (No. 1444B) (opt "CONSERVE WATER") 50 40
2336 120 c. Type **322** (opt "CONSERVE ELECTRICITY") 50 40
2337 120 c. Type **322** (opt "CONSERVE WATER") 50 40
2338 120 c. Type **322** (opt T **415**) 50 40
2339 120 c. Young Ocelot (No. 1446B) (opt "CONSERVE WATER") 50 40
2340 120 c. Young Ocelot (No. 1446B) (opt T **415**) 50 40
2341 120 c. Young Ocelot (No. 1446B) (optd "CONSERVE ELECTRICITY") .. 50 40

(b) Nos. 1634, 1670, 1683 *and* 1774 *optd with T* **416** *(opt vert–reading upwards on Nos.* 2342, 2345) *by Tip Torres.*

2342 200 c. Plate No. 33 (Series 1) 50 40
2343 200 c. Plate No. 79 (Series 1) 50 40
2344 225 c. Plate No. 24 (Series 1) 50 40
2345 350 c. Plate No. 94 (Series 1) 60 60
2333/45 .. .. *Set of* 13 6·00 4·75

The three different overprints as T **415** were applied, *se-tenant*, in strips of three, both horizontally and vertically, on blocks of nine.

BEWARE
OF ANIMALS

120

(417) (418)

1988 (15 July). *Road Safety Campaign. Nos.* 2194/2201 *optd as T* **417** *by Gardy Ptg.*

2346 **396** $1.20, bronze-green (opt T **417**) .. 1·00 1·00
a. Block of four. Nos. 2346/9 .. 3·50
2347 – $1.20, bronze-green (No. 2195) (opt "BEWARE OF CHILDREN") .. 1·00 1·00
2348 – $1.20, bronze-green (No. 2196) (opt "DRIVE SAFELY") .. .. 1·00 1·00
2349 – $1.20, bronze-green (No. 2197) (opt "DO NOT DRINK AND DRIVE") 1·00 1·00

2350 **396** $1.20, maroon (opt T **417**) .. .. 1·00 1·00
a. Block of four. Nos. 2350/3 .. 3·50
2351 – $1.20, maroon (No. 2199) (opt "BEWARE OF CHILDREN") .. 1·00 1·00
2352 – $1.20, maroon (No. 2200) (opt "DRIVE SAFELY") .. .. 1·00 1·00
2353 – $1.20, maroon (No. 2201) (opt "DO NOT DRINK AND DRIVE") .. 1·00 1·00
2346/53 .. .. *Set of* 8 7·00 7·00

1988 (July). *No. 706 optd with T 414 or surch with T* **418**, *both by Autoprint.*
2354 $1 Type **167** .. .. 2·50 50
2355 120 c. on $1 Type **167** .. .. .. 2·50 50

120

(**419**)

120 **240**

(**420**) (**421**)

1988 (July–Oct). *Various* Reichenbachia *issues surch by Gardy Ptg.*

(*a*) *As T* **419**

2356 120 c. on 25 c. Plate No. 61 (Series 1) (No. 1574) 60 40
2357 120 c. on 25 c. Plate No. 63 (Series 1) (No. 1575) 60 40
2358 120 c. on 25 c. Plate No. 70 (Series 1) (No. 1576) 60 40
2359 120 c. on 25 c. Plate No. 59 (Series 1) (No. 1620) 60 40
2360 120 c. on 25 c. Plate No. 71 (Series 1) (No. 1679) (surch vert - reading down) 60 40
2361 120 c. on 30 c. Plate No. 53 (Series 1) (No. 1621) 60 40
2362 120 c. on 30 c. Plate No. 86 (Series 1) (No. 1731) 60 40
2363 120 c. on 30 c. Plate No. 30 (Series 2) (No. 1809) 60 40
a. Horiz pair, one without surch .. 2·50
2364 120 c. on 30 c. Plate No. 53 (Series 1) (No. 1771) (*wmkd*) 60 40
2365 120 c. on 30 c. Plate No. 7 (Series 2) .. 60 40
2366 120 c. on 30 c. Plate No. 14 (Series 2) ("120" at foot) 60 40
2367 120 c. on 30 c. Plate No. 14 (Series 2) ("120" at top below bars) 60 40
2368 120 c. on 30 c. Plate No. 22 (Series 2) .. 60 40
2369 120 c. on 30 c. Plate No. 28 (Series 2) ("120" at bottom right) 60 40
2370 120 c. on 30 c. Plate No. 28 (Series 2) ("120" at top left) 60 40
2371 120 c. on 35 c. Plate No. 45 (Series 2) (No. 1925) 60 40
a. Horiz pair, one without surch .. 2·50
2372 120 c. on 40 c. Plate No. 77 (Series 1) (No. 1663) ("120" at bottom right) .. 60 40
2373 120 c. on 40 c. Plate No. 77 (Series 1) (No. 1663) ("120" at top left) 60 40
2374 120 c. on 40 c. Plate No. 96 (Series 1) (No. 1747) 60 40
2375 120 c. on 40 c. Plate No. 91 (Series 1) (No. 1822) ("120" at bottom right) .. 60 40
2376 120 c. on 40 c. Plate No. 91 (Series 1) (No. 1822) ("120" at top left) 60 40
2377 120 c. on 40 c. Plate No. 86 (Series 1) (No. 1868) 60 40
2378 120 c. on 40 c. Plate No. 68 (Series 1) (No. 1884) ("120" at top left) 60 40
2379 120 c. on 40 c. Plate No. 68 (Series 1) (No. 1884) ("120" at bottom left) .. 60 40
2380 120 c. on 40 c. Plate No. 90 (Series 1) .. 60 40
2381 120 c. on 45 c. Plate No. 54 (Series 1) (No. 1664) 60 40
2382 120 c. on 45 c. Plate No. 81 (Series 1) (No. 1748) 60 40
2383 120 c. on 45 c. Plate No. 21 (Series 2) (No. 1810) 60 40
a. Vert pair, one without surch .. 2·50
2384 120 c. on 50 c. Plate No. 92 (Series 1) (No. 1665) 60 40
2385 120 c. on 50 c. Plate No. 13 (Series 2) (No. 1907) 60 40
a. Horiz pair, one without surch .. 2·50
2386 120 c. on 50 c. Plate No. 15 (Series 2) (No. 1926) 60 40
a. Horiz pair, one without surch .. 2·50
2387 120 c. on 50 c. Plate No. 9 (Series 1) (*wmkd*) 60 40
2388 120 c. on 50 c. Plate No. 22 (Series 1) (*wmkd*) 60 40
2389 120 c. on 50 c. Plate No. 3 (Series 2) .. 60 40
2390 120 c. on 50 c. Plate No. 6 (Series 2) .. 60 40
2391 120 c. on 50 c. Plate No. 20 (Series 2) .. 60 40
2392 120 c. on 50 c. Plate No. 32 (Series 2) .. 60 40
2393 120 c. on 55 c. Plate No. 17 (Series 1) (No. 1732) 60 40
2394 120 c. on 60 c. Plate No. 2 (Series 1) (No. 1519) 60 40
2395 120 c. on 60 c. Plate No. 57 (Series 1) (No. 1622) (surch vert at top - reading down) 60 40
2396 120 c. on 60 c. Plate No. 57 (Series 1) (No. 1622) (surch vert at foot - reading down) 60 40
2397 120 c. on 60 c. Plate No. 73 (Series 1) (No. 1623) (surch vert - reading up) .. 60 40
2398 120 c. on 60 c. Plate No. 75 (Series 1) (No. 1624) (surch vert at top - reading down) 60 40
2399 120 c. on 60 c. Plate No. 75 (Series 1) (No. 1624) (surch vert at foot - reading down) 60 40
2400 120 c. on 60 c. Plate No. 95 (Series 1) (No. 1666) 60 40
2401 120 c. on 60 c. Plate No. 93 (Series 1) (No. 1733) 60 40
2402 120 c. on 60 c. Plate No. 27 (Series 2) (No. 1874) 60 40
a. Horiz pair, one without surch .. 2·50
2403 120 c. on 60 c. Plate No. 50 (Series 1) .. 60 40
2404 120 c. on 60 c. Plate No. 54 (Series 1) .. 60 40
2405 120 c. on 60 c. Plate No. 69 (Series 1) (surch vert–reading up) 60 40
2406 120 c. on 60 c. Plate No. 79 (Series 1) .. 60 40
2407 120 c. on 60 c. Plate No. 94 (Series 1) (surch vert - reading down) 60 40
2408 120 c. on 70 c. Plate No. 8 (Series 2) .. 60 40
2409 120 c. on 70 c. Plate No. 9 (Series 2) ("120" at foot above bars) 60 40
2410 120 c. on 70 c. Plate No. 9 (Series 2) ("120" at top right) 60 40
2411 120 c. on 70 c. Plate No. 12 (Series 2) ("120" at foot above bars) 60 40
2412 120 c. on 70 c. Plate No. 12 (Series 2) "120" at top left) 60 40
2413 120 c. on 70 c. Plate No. 17 (Series 2) .. 60 40
2414 120 c. on 80 c. Plate No. 39 (Series 1) .. 60 40
2415 120 c. on 80 c. Plate No. 74 (Series 1) .. 60 40
2416 120 c. on 80 c. Plate No. 93 (Series 1) .. 60 40
2417 120 c. on 85 c. Plate No. 45 (Series 2) (No. 1876) 60 40
2418 120 c. on 85 c. Plate No. 24 (Series 2) (No. 1914) 60 40
a. Horiz pair, one without surch .. 2·50
2419 120 c. on 85 c. Plate No. 15 (Series 2) (No. 1918) 60 40
2420 120 c. on 85 c. Plate No. 18 (Series 2) (No. 1928) 60 40
a. Horiz pair, one without surch .. 2·50
2421 120 c. on 90 c. Plate No. 84 (Series 1) (No. 1668 .. .. 60 40
2422 120 c. on 90 c. Plate No. 89 (Series 1) (No. 1749) 60 40
2423 120 c. on 90 c. Plate No. 10 (Series 2) (No. 1869) 60 40
a. Horiz pair, one without surch .. 2·50
2424 120 c. on 90 c. Plate No. 13 (Series 2) (No. 1877) 60 40
2425 120 c. on 90 c. Plate No. 27 (Series 2) (No. 1915) 60 40
2426 120 c. on 90 c. Plate No. 2 (Series 2) (No. 1929) 60 40
a. Horiz pair, one without surch .. 2·50
2427 200 c. on 80 c. Plate No. 42 (Series 2) (No. 1812) (surch vert–reading down) .. 60 40
2428 200 c. on 90 c. Plate No. 4 (Series 2) (No. 1813) 60 40

(*b*) *As T* **420** (Sept)

2429 120 c. on 25 c. Plate No. 72 (Series 1) (No. 1577) 60 40

(*c*) *As T* **421** (Oct)

2430 240 c. on 140 c. Plate No. 30 (Series 2) .. 60 40
2431 240 c. on 140 c. Plate No. 34 (Series 2) .. 60 40
2432 240 c. on 425 c. Plate No. 87 (Series 2) (No. 2070) 60 40
2433 260 c. on 375 c. Plate No. 90 (Series 1) (No. 1738) 60 40
2356/433 .. .. *Set of* 78 40·00 27·00

Nos. 2363, 2371, 2383, 2385/6, 2402, 2418, 2420, 2423 and 2426 come from sheetlets of four on which the surcharge was applied to two of the stamps only.

On No. 2433 there are no bars and the surcharge is placed over the original face value.

CONSERVE
OUR RESOURCES + AIR

(**422**) (**423**) (**424**)

1988 (July). *Conservation of Resources. Various* Reichenbachia *issues optd with T* **422** *by Gardy Ptg.*
2434 100 c. Plate No. 65 (Series 1) (No. 1626) 60 40
2435 100 c. Plate No. 68 (Series 1) (No. 1734) 60 40
2436 100 c. Plate No. 88 (Series 1) (No. 1750) 60 40
2437 100 c. Plate No. 65 (Series 1) (No. 1773) (*wmkd*) 60 40
2438 120 c. Plate No. 27 (Series 1) (No. 1524) .. 60 40
2439 120 c. Plate No. 36 (Series 1) (No. 1558) .. 60 40
2440 120 c. Plate No. 37 (Series 1) (No. 1627) .. 60 40
2441 120 c. Plate No. 56 (Series 1) (No. 1629) .. 60 40
2442 120 c. Plate No. 58 (Series 1) (No. 1630) .. 60 40
2443 120 c. Plate No. 67 (Series 1) (No. 1631) .. 60 40
2444 120 c. Plate No. 69 (Series 1) (No. 1680) (opt vert - reading down) 60 40
2445 130 c. Plate No. 38 (Series 1) (No. 1560) .. 60 40
2446 130 c. Plate No. 66 (Series 1) (No. 1632) .. 60 40
2447 130 c. Plate No. 91 (Series 1) (No. 1735) .. 60 40
2448 130 c. Plate No. 13 (Series 1) (No. 1760) (*wmkd*) 60 40
a. Opt inverted 60 40
2449 130 c. Plate No. 20 (Series 1) (No. 1761) (*wmkd*) 60 40
2450 150 c. Plate No. 26 (Series 1) (No. 1633) .. 60 40
2451 150 c. Plate No. 78 (Series 1) (No. 1669) .. 60 40
2452 150 c. Plate No. 87 (Series 1) (No. 1681) (opt vert - reading down) 60 40
2453 150 c. Plate No. 76 (Series 1) (No. 1751) .. 60 40
2454 250 c. Plate No. 74 (Series 1) (No. 1736) .. 70 60
2434/54 .. .. *Set of* 21 11·50 7·50

The 130 c., No. 2448, exists in equal quantities with the overprint either upright or inverted.

1988 (3 Aug). *125th Anniv of International Red Cross. Nos.* 2202/5 *and* 2207/10 *optd with T* **423** *in red by Gardy Ptg.*
2455 **396** $3.20, deep dull blue 80 80
a. Vert pair. Nos. 2455 and 2457 .. 1·60 1·60
2456 – $3.20, deep dull blue (No. 2203) .. 80 80
a. Vert pair. Nos. 2456 and 2458 .. 1·60 1·60
2457 – $3.20, deep dull blue (No. 2204) .. 80 80
2458 – $3.20, deep dull blue (No. 2205) .. 80 80
2459 – $3.30, brownish black (No. 2207) .. 80 80
a. Vert pair. Nos. 2459 and 2461 .. 1·60 1·60
2460 **396** $3.30, brownish black 80 80
a. Vert pair. Nos. 2460 and 2462 .. 1·60 1·60
2461 – $3.30, brownish black (No. 2209) .. 80 80
2462 – $3.30, brownish black (No. 2210) .. 80 80
2455/62 .. .. *Set of* 8 5·50 5·50

Nos. 2455/62 were issued in vertical strips of ten, each strip containing two designs *se-tenant*.

1988 (Aug). *Air. Various* Reichenbachia *issues optd with T* **424** *by Gardy Ptg.*
2463 75 c. Plate No. 55 (Series 1) (No. 1625) .. 90 55
2464 75 c. Plate No. 5 (Series 1) (No. 1667) .. 90 55
2465 75 c. Plate No. 55 (Series 1) (No. 1772) (*wmkd*) 90 55
2466 75 c. Plate No. 83 (Series 1) 90 55
2467 75 c. Plate No. 95 (Series 1) 90 55
2463/7 .. .. *Set of* 5 4·00 2·50

(Litho Format)

1988 (15 Aug). *Centenary of Publication of Sanders'* Reichenbachia *(33rd issue). Multicoloured designs as T* **331**. *P* 13½×14 *(270 c., 360 c.) or* 14×13½ *(others).*
2468 270 c. Plate No. 90 (Series 2) 85 60
2469 360 c. Plate No. 84 (Series 2) .. .. 1·25 75
2470 550 c. Plate No. 70 (Series 2) (*horiz*) .. 2·00 1·40
2471 670 c. Plate No. 71 (Series 2) (*horiz*) .. 2·50 1·75
2468/71 .. .. *Set of* 4 6·00 4·00

Nos. 2468/71 were printed in a similar sheet format to Nos. 1518/33.

A further small bock similar to those described under Nos. 1767/1806, containing stamps showing plate numbers 1 to 48 of the second series, was issued on 23 August 1988.

Some designs in this booklet show changed face values, as detailed below, but there is no evidence that such printings were available for postal purposes without surcharge.

Plate No. 1 = 175 c.		Plate No. 25 = 140 c.
Plate No. 3 = 50 c.		Plate No. 28 = 30 c.
Plate No. 5 = 130 c.		Plate No. 29 = 130 c.
Plate No. 6 = 50 c.		Plate No. 32 = 50 c.
Plate No. 7 = 30 c.		Plate No. 33 = 100 c.
Plate No. 8 = 70 c.		Plate No. 34 = 140 c.
Plate No. 9 = 70 c.		Plate No. 37 = 175 c.
Plate No. 12 = 70 c.		Plate No. 38 = 140 c.
Plate No. 14 = 30 c.		Plate No. 39 = 175 c.
Plate No. 17 = 70 c.		Plate No. 40 = 250 c.
Plate No. 19 = 175 c.		Plate No. 41 = 140 c.
Plate No. 20 = 50 c.		Plate No. 46 = 150 c.
Plate No. 22 = 30 c.		Plate No. 47 = 175 c.

1928 — 1988
CRICKET
JUBILEE

(**425**)

1988 (5 Sept). *60th Anniv of Cricket in Guyana. Nos.* 1584, 1670, 1681 *and* 1815 *optd as T* **425** *or surch also by Gardy Ptg.*
2472 200 c. Plate No. 14 (Series 1) .. .. 9·00 11·00
2473 200 c. Plate No. 79 (Series 1) .. .. 1·00 40
2474 800 c. on 150 c. Plate No. 87 (Series 1) .. 6·00 8·00
2475 800 c. on 160 c. Plate No. 5 (Series 2) .. 3·25 3·25
2472/5 .. .. *Set of* 4 17·00 20·00

Nos. 2472 and 2474 were only issued in $20 stamp booklets.

OLYMPIC GAMES
1988

(**426**)

KOREA 1988

150

(**427**)

1988 (16 Sept). *Olympic Games, Seoul (2nd issue). (a) Nos.* 1628, 1634, 1671, 1681, 1683, 1814, 1818/19, 1880 *and* 2069 *optd as T* **426** *or surch also by Gardy Ptg.*

2476 120 c. Plate No. 46 (Series 1) 20 20
2477 130 c. Plate No. 38 (Series 2) 20 20
2478 150 c. Plate No. 87 (Series 1) 20 20
2479 200 c. Plate No. 33 (Series 1) 20 20
2480 300 c. Plate No. 83 (Series 1) 30 30
2481 300 c. on 360 c. Plate No. 34 (Series 2) .. 30 30
2482 320 c. Plate No. 10 (Series 2) 30 30
2483 330 c. Plate No. 82 (Series 2) 30 30
2484 350 c. Plate No. 94 (Series 1) (opt vert - reading up) 30 30
2485 350 c. Plate No. 29 (Series 2) 30 30

(b) Design as No. 1420, *but incorrectly inscr* "LOS ANGELLES", *optd or surch as T* **427**, *inscr* "OLYMPICS 1988" (A) *or* "KOREA 1988" (B), *by Gardy Ptg.*

2486 $1.20, multicoloured (A) 20 20
a. Horiz strip of 5. Nos. 2486, 2488, 2490, 2492 and 2494 .. .. 1·10
b. Booklet pane of 10. Nos. 2486/95 .. 14·00
2487 $1.20, multicoloured (B) 20 20
2488 130 c. on $1.20, multicoloured (A) .. 20 20
2489 130 c. on $1.20, multicoloured (B) .. 20 20
2490 150 c. on $1.20, multicoloured (A) .. 20 20
2491 150 c. on $1.20, multicoloured (B) .. 20 20
2492 200 c. on $1.20, multicoloured (A) .. 25 25
2493 200 c. on $1.20, multicoloured (B) .. 25 25
2494 350 c. on $1.20, multicoloured (A) .. 35 35
2495 350 c. on $1.20, multicoloured (B) .. 35 35
2476/95 .. .. *Set of* 20 4·50 4·50

Nos. 2486/95 were issued in $20 stamp booklets which included pane No. 2486b. Nos. 2486, 2488, 2490, 2492 and 2494 were also available from sheets containing horizontal *se-tenant* strips of 5. All values later appeared in coils of 500 or 1,000.

V CENTENARY OF
THE LANDING OF
CHRISTOPHER COLUMBUS
IN THE AMERICAS

(428)

1988 (12 Oct). *Columbus Day. Nos.* 1672/3 *optd or surch as T* **428** *by Gardy Ptg.*

2496 320 c. Plate No. 50 (Series 1) .. .. 1·00 30
2497 $15 on 360 c. Plate No. 85 (Series 1) .. 2·50 3·00

(Litho Format)

1988 (3 Nov). *Centenary of Publication of Sanders' Reichenbachia (34th issue). Multicoloured designs as T* **331**. *P* 14×13½ (130 c.) *or* 13¼×14 (*others*).

2498 100 c. Plate No. 44 (Series 2) .. .. 1·00 55
2499 130 c. Plate No. 42 (Series 2) (*horiz*) .. 1·00 55
2500 140 c. Plate No. 4 (Series 2) .. .. 1·25 65
2501 160 c. Plate No. 50 (Series 2) .. .. 1·25 65
2502 175 c. Plate No. 51 (Series 2) .. .. 1·50 75
2503 200 c. Plate No. 11 (Series 2) .. .. 1·50 75
2504 200 c. Plate No. 23 (Series 2) .. .. 1·50 75
2505 200 c. Plate No. 26 (Series 2) .. .. 1·50 75
2506 200 c. Plate No. 75 (Series 2) .. .. 1·50 75
2507 200 c. Plate No. 93 (Series 2) .. .. 1·50 75
2508 250 c. Plate No. 79 (Series 2) .. .. 1·75 90
2509 280 c. Plate No. 62 (Series 2) .. .. 1·75 1·00
2510 285 c. Plate No. 63 (Series 2) .. .. 2·00 1·00
2511 380 c. Plate No. 35 (Series 2) .. .. 2·25 1·25
2498/511 .. .. *Set of* 14 19·00 12·50

Nos. 2498/511 were printed in a similar sheet format to Nos. 2518/33.

SEASON'S
GREETINGS

120

SEASON'S
GREETINGS

(429) (430)

SEASON'S
GREETINGS

SEASON'S
GREETINGS
1988

240

(431) (432)

1988 (10 Nov). *Christmas (1st issue). Various* Reichenbachia *issues optd or surch by Gardy Ptg*

(a) With T **429**

2512 150 c. Plate No. 32 (Series 1) (No. 1561) 50 50
2513 150 c. Plate No. 62 (Series 1) (No. 1566) 50 50
2514 225 c. Plate No. 60 (Series 1) (No. 1682) 50 50
2515 260 c. Plate No. 39 (Series 1) (No. 1737) 50 50
2516 320 c. Plate No. 82 (Series 1) (No. 1753) 50 50
2517 330 c. Plate No. 80 (Series 1) (No. 1754) 50 50
2518 360 c. Plate No. 85 (Series 1) (No. 1673) 50 50

(b) As T **430** *in blue*

2519 120 c. on 100 c. Plate No. 6 (Series 1) (*wmkd*) 50 50
2520 120 c. on 100 c. Plate No. 13 (Series 1) (*wmkd*) 50 50
2521 120 c. on 100 c. Plate No. 20 (Series 1) (*wmkd*) 50 50
2522 120 c. on 100 c. Plate No. 25 (Series 1) (*wmkd*) 50 50
2523 120 c. on 100 c. Plate No. 40 (Series 1) (*horiz*) (*wmkd*) 50 50
2524 120 c. on 100 c. Plate No. 42 (Series 1) (*horiz*) (*wmkd*) 50 50
2525 120 c. on 100 c. Plate No. 43 (Series 1) (*horiz*) (*wmkd*) 50 50
2526 120 c. on 100 c. Plate No. 45 (Series 1) (*horiz*) (*wmkd*) 50 50

(c) With T **431** *in blue*

2527 225 c. Plate No. 24 (Series 1) (No. 1635) 75 75
2528 225 c. Plate No. 60 (Series 1) (No. 1682) 75 75
2529 225 c. Plate No. 24 (Series 1) (No. 1774) (*wmkd*) 75 75
2530 225 c. on 350 c. on 120 c. Plate No. 65 (Series 1) (No. 2221) 75 75
MS2531 120×129 mm. 225 c. on 55 c.×4 Plate No. 22 (Series 1) each with a different overprint (Type **350**, "Happy New Year", "Merry Christmas" or "Happy Holidays") (No. **MS**2232) 2·00 2·00

(d) With T **432**

2532 240 c. on 180 c. Plate No. 15 (Series 1) (No. 1752) 60 60
2512/30 *and* 2532 .. .. *Set of* 20 10·00 10·00

CHRISTMAS
1988
20

Protect yourself
from AIDS.
Better safe
than sorry.

(433) (434)

1988 (16 Nov). *Christmas (2nd issue). Nos.* 489, 1188/91 *and* 1449 *surch or optd as T* **433** *by Autoprint.*

2533 – 20 c. on 6 c. mult (No. 489) (R.) .. 10 10
2534 **277** 120 c. lake-brown, black & bright blue 20 25
a. Block of 4. Nos. 2534/7 .. 75
2535 – 120 c. on 130 c. rose-red, black and bright blue (No. 1189) .. 20 25
2536 – 120 c. on 150 c. bright violet, black and bright blue (No. 1190) .. 20 25
2537 – 120 c. on 200 c. dull green, black and bright blue (No. 1191) .. 20 25
2538 – 500 c. on 330 c. mult (No. 1449) (R.) 1·00 1·10
2533/8 .. .. *Set of* 6 1·60 2·00

No. 2538 shows "CHRISTMAS 1988" vertical, reading up.

1988 (1 Dec). *AIDS Information Campaign. Nos.* 707/8*a optd as T* **434** *or surch also.*

2539 120 c. on $5 *Morpho deidamia* (A) .. 1·75 1·75
a. Strip of 5. Nos. 2539/43 .. .. 8·00
2540 120 c. on $5 *Morpho deidamia* (B) .. 1·75 1·75
2541 120 c. on $5 *Morpho deidamia* (C) .. 1·75 1·75
2542 120 c. on $5 *Morpho deidamia* (D) .. 1·75 1·75
2543 120 c. on $5 *Morpho deidamia* (Type **434**) 1·75 1·75
2544 120 c. on $10 *Elbella patrobas* (A) .. 1·75 1·75
a. Strip of 5. Nos. 2544/8 .. .. 8·00
2545 120 c. on $10 *Elbella patrobas* (B) .. 1·75 1·75
2546 120 c. on $10 *Elbella patrobas* (C) .. 1·75 1·75
2547 120 c. on $10 *Elbella patrobas* (D) .. 1·75 1·75
2548 120 c. on $10 *Elbella patrobas* (Type **434**) 1·75 1·75
2549 $2 *Morpho rhetenor* (female) (Type **434**) 4·50 1·75
2550 $5 *Morpho deidamia* (Type **434**) .. 7·00 4·25
2551 $10 *Elbella patrobas* (Type **434**) .. 8·50 6·00
2539/51 .. .. *Set of* 13 35·00 26·00

Nos. 2539/43 and 2544/8 were surcharged horizontally and vertically *se-tenant* with Type **434** and four other slogans: (A) "Be compassionate towards AIDS victims."; (B) "Get information on AIDS. it may save your life."; (C) "Get the facts. Education helps to prevent AIDS."; (D) "Say no to Drugs and limit the spread of AIDS.".

(Des K. Everett (150 c.). Litho Format)

1988 (16 Dec). *150th Anniv of Abolition of Slavery* (1984) *(2nd issue). Designs as Nos.* 1547/50, *but colours changed. P* 14.

2552 **337** 25 c. black and bistre-brown .. 15 10
2553 – 60 c. black and brown-lilac 20 15
2554 – 130 c. black and blue-green 25 40
2555 – 150 c. black and dull blue 30 45
2552/5 .. .. *Set of* 4 80 1·00

Nos. 2552/5 exist imperforate from stock dispersed by the liquidator of Format International Security Printers Ltd.

1050

SALUTING WINNERS
OLYMPIC GAMES
1988

(435)

1989 (3 Jan). *Olympic Medal Winners, Seoul. Nos.* 1672, 1923 *and* 2178 *surch as T* **435** *by Gardy Ptg.*

2556 550 c. on 560 c. Plate No. 1 (Series 2) .. 1·00 1·00
2557 900 c. on 320 c. Plate No. 18 (Series 2) 1·50 1·75
2558 1050 c. on 320 c. Plate No. 50 (Series 1) 2·00 2·25
2556/8 .. .. *Set of* 3 4·00 4·50

A further small book, similar to these described under Nos. 1767/1806, containing stamps showing plate numbers 49 to 96 of the second series, was issued on 3 January 1989.

REPUBLIC DAY 1989 $5.00

(436) (437)

1989 (22 Feb). *Republic Day. Nos.* 2194/201 *and* 2212 *optd with T* **436** *in red by Gardy Ptg.*

2559 **396** $1.20, bronze-green 20 30
a. Block of 4. Nos. 2559/62 .. 70
2560 – $1.20, bronze-green (No. 2195) .. 20 30
2561 – $1.20, bronze-green (No. 2196) .. 20 30
2562 – $1.20, bronze-green (No. 2197) .. 20 30
2563 **396** $1.20, maroon 20 30
a. Block of 4. Nos. 2563/6 70
2564 – $1.20, maroon (No. 2199) 20 30
2565 – $1.20, maroon (No. 2200) 20 30
2566 – $1.20, maroon (No. 2201) 20 30
2567 – $10 multicoloured .. .. .. 1·75 2·00
2559/67 .. .. *Set of* 9 3·00 4·00

1989 (22 Feb). *Nos.* 2202/5 *and* 2207/10 *surch with T* **437** *in red.*

2568 **396** $5 on $3.20, deep dull blue .. 1·00 1·25
a. Vert pair. Nos. 2568 and 2570 .. 2·00 2·50
2569 – $5 on $3.20, deep dull blue (No. 2203) 1·00 1·25
a. Vert pair. Nos. 2569 and 2571 .. 2·00 2·50
2570 – $5 on $3.20, deep dull blue (No. 2204) 1·00 1·25
2571 – $5 on $3.20, deep dull blue (No. 2205) 1·00 1·25
2572 – $5 on $3.30, brownish blk (No. 2207) 1·00 1·25
a. Vert pair. Nos. 2572 and 2574 .. 2·00 2·50
2573 **396** $5 on $3.30, brownish black .. 1·00 1·25
a. Vert pair. Nos. 2573 and 2575 .. 2·00 2·50
2574 – $5 on $3.30, brownish blk (No. 2209) 1·00 1·25
2575 – $5 on $3.30, brownish blk (No. 2210) 1·00 1·25
2568/75 .. .. *Set of* 8 7·00 9·00

Nos. 2568/75 were issued in vertical strips of ten, each strip containing two designs *se-tenant*.

1989 (22 Feb–Mar). *Various* Reichenbachia *issues surch by Gardy Ptg.*

(a) As T **420** *in red*

2576 120 c. on 140 c. Plate No. 25 (Series 2) .. 80 80
2577 120 c. on 140 c. Plate No. 52 (Series 2) .. 80 80
2578 120 c. on 140 c. Plate No. 65 (Series 2) .. 80 80
2579 120 c. on 175 c. Plate No. 54 (Series 2) (surch vert–reading down) .. 80 80

(b) As T **421**, *but with two bars only*

2580 120 c. on 140 c. Plate No. 38 (Series 2) .. 80 80
2581 120 c. on 140 c. Plate No. 41 (Series 2) .. 80 80
2582 170 c. on 175 c. Plate No. 58 (Series 2) (Mar) 90 90
2583 250 c. on 280 c. Plate No. 66 (Series 2) (Mar) .. .. 1·25 1·25
2584 250 c. on 280 c. Plate No. 67 (Series 2) (Mar) .. .. 1·25 1·25
2585 300 c. on 290 c. Plate No. 53 (Series 2) (No. 2236) (Mar) .. .. 1·40 1·40
2576/85 .. .. *Set of* 10 8·50 8·50

TEN DOLLARS

$10.00 TEN DOLLARS

(438) (439)

1989 (22 Feb). *Nos.* 1744/5 *and* 2185/6 *surch with T* **438** (*Nos.* 2586, 2588) *or T* **439** (*Nos.* 2587, 2589), *both in red.*

2586 **363** $10 on 320 c. rosine, black and deep reddish violet (No. 1744) .. 1·50 2·00

a. Horiz pair. Nos. 2586/7 .. 3·00 4·00

2587 – $10 on 320 c. multicoloured (No. 1745) 1·50 2·00

2588 **363** $10 on 320 c. rosine, black and deep reddish violet (No. 2185) .. 1·50 2·00

a. Horiz pair. Nos. 2588/9 .. 3·00 4·00

2589 – $10 on 320 c. multicoloured (No. 2186) 1·50 2·00

2586/9 .. .. *Set of* 4 5·50 7·00

EASTER

125 POSTAGE

(440) (441)

1989 (22 Mar). *Easter. No.* 1817 *in block of four surch as T* **440**.

MS2590 97×124 mm. 125 c. on 320 c., 250 c. on 320 c., 300 c. on 320 c., 350 c. on 320 c., Plate No. 12 (Series 2) .. .. 1·75 2·00

1989 (Mar). *Nos.* O54/7, O59/63 *and* O65/9 *optd with T* **441** *or surch additionally as T* **421** *with two bars only by Gardy Ptg.*

2591 125 c. on 130 c. Plate No. 92 (Series 2) .. 60 60

2592 125 c. on 140 c. Plate No. 36 (Series 2) .. 60 60

2593 150 c. Plate No. 43 (Series 2) 60 60

2594 150 c. on 175 c. Plate No. 31 (Series 2) .. 60 60

2595 250 c. Plate No. 59 (Series 2) 75 75

2596 250 c. on 225 c. Plate No. 26 (Series 2) (surch at top) 75 75

a. Surch at foot 75 75

2597 250 c. on 230 c. Plate No. 68 (Series 2) .. 75 75

2598 250 c. on 260 c. Plate No. 69 (Series 2) (surch at top) 75 75

a. Surch in centre 75 75

2599 300 c. on 275 c. Plate No. 90 (Series 2) .. 75 75

2600 350 c. Plate No. 95 (Series 2) (opt vert – reading up) 75 75

a. Opt vert – reading down 75 75

2601 350 c. on 330 c. Plate No. 23 (Series 2) .. 75 75

2602 600 c. Plate No. 70 (Series 2) (opt vert – reading up) .. .. 1·00 1·00

2603 $12 Plate No. 71 (Series 2) (opt vert – reading up) .. .. 1·75 2·00

2604 $15 Plate No. 84 (Series 2) .. .. 2·00 2·25

2591/604 .. .. *Set of* 14 11·00 11·50

1989 (Mar). *Centenary of Publication of Sanders' Reichenbachia* (35*th issue*). *Vert designs as T* **331**. *Multicoloured. P* $13\frac{1}{2}\times14$.

2605 200 c. Plate No. 49 (Series 2) 50 50

2606 200 c. Plate No. 53 (Series 2) 50 50

2607 200 c. Plate No. 60 (Series 2) 50 50

2608 200 c. Plate No. 64 (Series 2) 50 50

2605/8 .. .. *Set of* 4 1·75 1·75

Nos. 2605/8 were printed in a similar sheet format to Nos. 1518/33.

250

(442)

1989 (Mar). *As No.* 1442, *but with imprint date, surch with T* **442**. *P* 14.

2609 **322** 250 c. on 25 c. multicoloured .. .. 1·00 15

375

RED CROSS

1948

1988

(443)

1989 (Apr). *40th Anniv of Guyana Red Cross. No.* 1872 *surch as T* **443**.

2610 375 c. on 45 c. Plate No. 17 (Series 2) .. 1·25 65

2611 425 c. on 45 c. Plate No. 17 (Series 2) .. 1·25 65

HEALTH FOR ALL

250

(444)

1989 (3 Apr). *World Health Day. Nos.* 1875 *and* 2239 *surch as T* **444**.

2612 250 c. on 75 c. Plate No. 56 (Series 2) (surch T 444) 65 65

a. Pair. Nos. 2612/13 .. .. .. 1·25 1·25

2613 250 c. on 75 c. Plate No. 56 (Series 2) (surch "ALL FOR HEALTH") 65 65

2614 675 c. on 720 c. Plate No. 49 (Series 2) (surch "ALL FOR HEALTH") .. 1·25 1·25

a. Pair. Nos. 2614/15 .. .. .. 2·50 2·50

2615 675 c. on 720 c. Plate No. 49 (Series 2) (surch as T 444) .. .. .. 1·25 1·25

2612/15 .. .. *Set of* 4 3·25 3·25

Nos. 2612/13 and 2614/15 were each issued, *se-tenant*, in horizontal and vertical pairs, within the sheets of four.

PHOTOGRAPHY 1839 - 1989

BOY SCOUTS 1909 1989

550

(445) (446)

1989 (11 Apr). *Scouting Anniversaries. Nos.* 1873, 1879, 2322, 2509 *and unissued value as No.* 1873 *optd or surch as T* **445**.

2616 250 c. on 50 c. Plate No. 33 (Series 2) (surch T 445) 60 60

a. Pair. Nos. 2616/17 .. .. .. 1·10 1·10

2617 250 c. on 50 c. Plate No. 33 (Series 2) (surch "GIRL GUIDES 1924 1989") .. 60 60

2618 250 c. on 100 c. Plate No. 33 (Series 2) (surch as T 445) 60 60

a. Pair. Nos. 2618/19 .. .. .. 1·10 1·10

2619 250 c. on 100 c. Plate No. 33 (Series 2) (surch "GIRL GUIDES 1924 1989") 60 60

2620 300 c. Plate No. 50 (Series 2) (optd as T 445) 75 75

a. Pair. Nos. 2620/1 .. .. .. 1·50 1·50

2621 300 c. Plate No. 50 (Series 2) (optd "GIRL GUIDES 1924 1989") 75 75

2622 $25 on 280 c. Plate No. 62 (Series 2) (surch "LADY BADEN POWELL 1889 – 1989") .. .. .. 3·50 4·00

2623 $25 on 700 c. Plate No. 62 (Series 2) (surch "LADY BADEN POWELL 1889 – 1989") .. .. .. 3·50 4·00

2616/23 .. .. *Set of* 8 9·50 10·50

The events commemorated are the 80th anniversary of Boy Scout Movement in Guyana, 65th anniversary of Girl Guide Movement in Guyana and birth centenary of Lady Baden-Powell.

On Nos. 2616/17 the surcharge is a "2" applied in front of the original face value to form "250".

Nos. 2616/17, 2618/19 and 2620/1 were each issued, *se-tenant*, in horizontal and vertical pairs within the sheets of four.

1989 (15 Apr). 150 *Years of Photography. No.* 1881 *surch as T* **446**.

2624 550 c. on 390 c. Plate No. 6 (Series 2) .. 70 70

a. Pair. Nos. 2624/5 .. .. .. 1·40 1·40

2625 650 c. on 390 c. Plate No. 6 (Series 2) (original value cancelled by two bars) 70 70

2626 650 c. on 390 c. Plate No. 6 (Series 2) (original value cancelled by six bars) 70 70

2624/6 .. .. *Set of* 3 1·90 1·90

No. 2624 exists either as complete sheets of four or horizontally and vertically *se-tenant* with No. 2625. No. 2626 only comes as sheets of four all showing the same surcharge.

PRICES OF SETS

Set prices are given for many issues, generally those containing three stamps or more. Definitive sets include one of each value or major colour change, but do not cover different perforations, die types or minor shades. Where a choice is possible the set prices are based on the cheapest versions of the stamps included in the listings.

I.L.O. 1919-1989

300

(447)

1989 (2 May). 70*th Anniv of International Labou*[r] *Organization. No.* 1875 *surch with T* **447**.

2627 300 c. on 75 c. Plate No. 56 (Series 2) .. 3·00 4

80c

$6.40

(448) (449)

$5

$2·55 X $6.40

(450) (451) (452)

1989 (8 May)–**92?**. *Various stamps surch*

(*a*) *As T* **448** *with short obliterating bars over original value*

2628 80 c. on 6 c. Patua (No. 452) 40 2

2629 $1 on 2 c. Type **132** (15.6.89) 40 2

2630 $2.05 on 3 c. Hanging Heliconia (No. 544) (15.6.89) 40 25

2631 $2.55 on 5 c. Annatto tree (No. 545) (15.6.89) 40 30

2632 $3.25 on 6 c. Cannon-ball tree (No. 546) (15.6.89) 40 30

2633 $5 on 6 c. Type **111** (16.8.89) 40 30

2634 $6.40 on 10 c. *Archonias bellona* (No. 699) (18.5.89) .. .. .. 2·75 75

2635 $8.90 on 60 c. *Papilio androgeus* (No. 705*a*) (26.5.89) .. .. .. 3·75 85

(*b*) *As T* **449** (*larger figures on* 80 *c.*) *without any obliterating bars*

2636 80 c. on 6 c. Patua (No. 452) 40 20

2637 $6.40 on 10 c. *Archonias bellona* (No. 699) (18.5.89) .. .. .. 2·75 75

2637*a* $7.65 on 35 c. *Anaea galanthus* (No. 703) (1992?) .. .. .. 3·25 80

2638 $7.65 on 40 c. *Morpho rhetenor* (male) (No. 704) (18.5.89) .. .. 3·25 80

2639 $8.90 on 60 c. *Papilio androgeus* (No. 705*a*) (26.5.89) .. .. .. 3·75 85

(*c*) *As T* **450** (*larger figures on* $1) *with* "X" *over original value*

2640 $1 on 2 c. Type **132** (15.6.89) 40 20

2641 $2.55 on 5 c. Annatto tree (No. 545) (15.6.89) 40 25

2642 $3.25 on 6 c. Cannon-ball tree (No. 546) 40 25

2643 $50 on $2 *Morpho rhetenor* (female) (No. 707) (B.) (5.6.89) .. .. 10·00 3·50

2644 $100 on $2 *Morpho rhetenor* (female) (No. 707) (5.6.89) .. .. .. 15·00 8·50

(*d*) *As T* **451**

2645 $5 on 6 c. Type **111** (with T **451**) (16.8.89) 40 20

2645*a* $5 on 6 c. Type **111** (as T **451**, but with "X" instead of bars at foot) (1992) .. 40 20

(*e*) *As T* **421**, *but two obliterating bars only*

2646 640 c. on 675 on 720 c. Plate No. 49 (Series 2) (surch "ALL FOR HEALTH") (No. 2614) .. .. 1·25 1·25

a. Pair. Nos. 2646/7 .. .. .. 2·50 2·50

2647 640 c. on 675 c. on 720 c. Plate No. 49 (Series 2) (surch "HEALTH FOR ALL") (No. 2615) .. .. .. 1·25 1·25

(*f*) *As T* **452**

2648 – $6.40 on $3.30, brownish black (No. 2207) .. .. 2·50 1·50

a. Vert pair. Nos. 2648 and 2650 .. 5·00 3·00

2649 **396** $6.40 on $3.30, brownish black .. 2·50 1·50

a. Vert pair. Nos. 2649 and 2651 .. 5·00 3·00

2650 – $6.40 on $3.30, brownish black (No. 2209) .. .. 2·50 1·50

2651 – $6.40 on $3.30, brownish black (No. 2210) .. .. 2·50 1·50

2652 **396** $7.65 on $3.20, deep dull blue .. 2·50 1·50

a. Vert pair. Nos. 2652 and 2654 .. 5·00 3·00

2653 – $7.65 on $3.20, dp dull blue (No. 2203) 2·50 1·50

a. Vert pair. Nos. 2653 and 2655 .. 5·00 3·00

2654 – $7.65 on $3.20, dp dull blue (No. 2204) 2·50 1·50

2655 – $7.65 on $3.20, dp dull blue (No. 2205) 2·50 1·50

2628/55 .. .. *Set of* 30 60·00 30·00

CARICOM
DAY

125

(453) 454 *Stalachtis calliope*

'89 (26 June). *CARICOM Day. No.* 1878 *surch with T* **453.**
'56 125 c. on 200 c. Plate No. 44 (Series 2) .. 1·50 30
a. Original face value cancelled by 6 thin lines .. .. 1·75 50

(Des Mary Walters. Litho Questa)

'89 (7 Sept). *Butterflies (1st series). T* **454** *and similar vert designs. Multicoloured. P* 14.
'57 80 c. Type **454** 40 10
'58 $2.25, *Morpho rhetenor* 50 10
'59 $5 *Agrias claudia* 55 10
'60 $6.40, *Marpesia marcella* 60 15
'61 $7.65, *Papilio zagreus* 65 20
'62 $8.90, *Chorinea faunus* 80 25
'63 $25 *Euptychia cephus* .. .. .. 2·25 2·25
'64 $100 *Nessaea regina* .. .. .. 6·00 7·00
'57/64 .. .. *Set of* 8 10·50 9·00
For miniature sheets accompanying this issue see Nos. MS18/19.
See also Nos. 2789/861.

AHMADIYYA
CENTENARY
1889-1989
$8·90

455 Kathryn Sullivan (first U.S woman to walk in space) (456)

(Des M. Dorfman. Litho Questa)

989 (8 Nov). 25 *Years of Women in Space. T* **455** *and similar vert designs. Multicoloured. P* 14.
665 $6.40, Type **455** 40 15
666 $12.80, Svetlana Savitskaya (first Soviet woman to walk in space) 65 35
667 $15.30, Judy Resnik and Christa McAuliffe with *Challenger* logo .. 65 35
668 $100 Sally Ride (first U.S. woman astronaut) .. .. 4·00 5·00
665/8 .. .. *Set of* 4 5·25 5·50
For miniature sheet accompanying this issue see No. **EMS**20.

989 (22 Nov). *Centenary of Ahmadiyya (Moslem organization). Nos.* 543/5 *surch as T* **456.**
669 80 c. on 2 c. Type **132** .. .. .. 1·25 40
670 $6.40 on 3 c. Hanging Heliconia .. 5·00 2·75
671 $8.90 on 5 c. Annatto tree .. .. 6·00 3·50
669/71 .. .. *Set of* 3 11·00 6·00

457 Head of Harpy Eagle 458 Channel-billed Toucan

(Des J. Barbaris. Litho Questa)

990 (23 Jan). *Endangered Species. Harpy Eagle. T* **457** *and similar vert designs. Multicoloured. P* 14.
672 $2.25, Type **457** 50 25
673 $5 Harpy Eagle with monkey prey .. 75 30
674 $8.90, Eagle on branch (facing right) .. 1·10 50
675 $30 Eagle on branch (facing left) .. 3·00 3·50
672/5 .. .. *Set of* 4 4·75 4·00

(Des J. Barbaris. Litho Questa)

990 (23 Jan). *Birds of Guyana. T* **458** *and similar multicoloured designs. P* 14.
676 $15 Type **458** 90 40
677 $25 Blue and Yellow Macaw .. .. 1·40 70
678 $50 Wattled Jacana (*horiz*) .. .. 2·75 2·25
679 $60 Hoatzin (*horiz*) .. .. .. 3·00 2·50
676/9 .. .. *Set of* 4 7·25 5·25
MS2680 Two sheets, each 110×80 mm. (a) $100 Great Kiskadee. (b) $100 Amazon Kingfisher *Set of* 2 *sheets* 9·00 9·00

(459) **460** Indian Post Runner, 1837

1990 (15 Mar). 85*th Anniv of Rotary International. Optd as T* **459** *in silver. (a) On Nos.* 2657/64
2681 80 c. Type **454** 60 20
2682 $2.25, *Morpho rhetenor* 90 30
2683 $5 *Agrias claudia* .. .. .. 1·25 30
2684 $6.40, *Marpesia marcella* .. .. 1·40 35
2685 $7.65, *Papilio zagreus* .. .. .. 1·50 50
2686 $8.90, *Chorinea faunus* .. .. .. 1·60 55
2687 $25 *Euptychia cephus* .. .. .. 2·75 3·25
2688 $100 *Nessaea regina* .. .. .. 8·00 9·00
2681/8 .. .. *Set of* 8 16·00 13·00

(*b*) *On Nos.* 2665/8
2689 $6.40, Type **455** 85 40
2690 $12.80, Svetlana Savitskaya (first Soviet woman to walk in space) .. .. 1·50 80
2691 $15.30, Judy Resnik and Christa McAuliffe with *Challenger* logo .. 1·60 90
2692 $100 Sally Ride (first U.S. woman astronaut) .. .. 6·00 7·00
2689/92 .. .. *Set of* 4 9·00 8·25

(Des G. Vasarhelyi. Litho Questa)

1990 (3 May). 150*th Anniv of Penny Black and* 500*th Anniv of Thurn and Taxis Postal Service. T* **460** *and similar horiz designs. Multicoloured. P* 14.
2693/2746 $15.30×27, $17.80×9, $20×18 *Set of* 54 23·00 26·00
MS2747 Three sheets, each 116×86 mm. (a) $150 Post boy; (b) $150 Thurn and Taxis (Northern District) 3 sgr. of 1852; (c) $150 Thurn and Taxis (Southern District) 6 k. of 1852 *Set of* 3 *sheets* 9·50 11·00
Nos. 2693/746 (issued as six sheetlets each of nine different designs) depict various forms of mail transport.

80

ROTARY
DISTRICT 405
9th CONFERENCE
MAY 1990
GEORGETOWN

90th Birthday
H.M. The Queen Mother

(461) (462)

1990 (8 May). 9*th Conference of Rotary District* 405, *Georgetown. Nos.* 1526, 1530, 1552 *and* 1554/5 *surch as T* **461.**
2748 80 c. on 55 c. Plate No. 9 (Series 1) ..
2749 80 c. on 55 c. Plate No. 49 (Series 1) ..
2750 80 c. on 55 c. Plate No. 64 (Series 1) ..
2751 $6.40, on 130 c. Plate No. 6 (Series 1) ..
2752 $6.40, on 130 c. Plate No. 25 (Series 1)
2753 $7.65, on 130 c. Plate No. 25 (Series 1)

1990 (8 June). 90*th Birthday of Queen Elizabeth the Queen Mother. Nos.* 2657/64 *surch with T* **462.**
2754 80 c. Type **454** 40 20
2755 $2.25, *Morpho rhetenor* 65 30
2756 $5 *Agrias claudia* 80 30
2757 $6.40, *Marpesia marcella* 90 35
2758 $7.65, *Papilio zagreus* .. .. .. 1·00 40
2759 $8.90, *Chorinea faunus* .. .. .. 1·25 45
2760 $25 *Euptychia cephus* .. .. .. 2·50 2·75
2761 $100 *Nessaea regina* .. .. .. 7·50 8·50
2754/61 .. .. *Set of* 8 13·50 12·00
For miniature sheets accompanying this issue see Nos. EMS31/3.

GUYANA

$2·55

463 Collared Trogon **464** *Melinaea idae*

(Litho Format)

1990 (12 Sept). *Birds. T* **463** *and similar multicoloured designs. P* 13½×14 (80 *c.*) *or* 14×13½ (*others*).
2762 80 c. Guiana Partridge (*horiz*) 10 10
2763 $2.55, Type **463** 10 10
2764 $3.25, Derby Aracari 10 10
2765 $5 Black-necked Aracari 20 20
2766 $5.10, Green Aracari 20 20
2767 $5.80, Ivory-billed Aracari 20 20
2768 $6.40, Guiana Toucanet 20 20
2769 $6.50, Sulphur-breasted Toucan .. 20 20
2770 $7.55, Red-billed Toucan 25 25
2771 $7.65, Toco Toucan 25 25
2772 $8.25, Natterers Toucanet 25 25
2773 $8.90, Welcome Trogon 25 25
2774 $9.75, Doubtful Trogon 25 25
2775 $11.40, Banded Aracari 30 30
2776 $12.65, Golden-headed Train Bearer .. 30 30
2777 $12.80, Rufous-breasted Hermit .. 30 30
2778 $13.90, Band Tail Barbthroat 30 30
2779 $15.30, White-tipped Sickle Bill .. 35 35
2780 $17.80, Black Jacobin 40 40
2781 $19.20, Fiery Topaz 40 40
2782 $22.95, Tufted Coquette 45 45
2783 $26.70, Ecuadorian Pied-tail 45 45
2784 $30 Quetzal 50 50
2785 $50 Green-crowned Brilliant 80 80
2786 $100 Emerald-chinned Hummingbird .. 1·50 1·50
2787 $190 Lazuline Sabre-wing .. .. 2·50 2·50
2788 $225 Beryline Hummingbird .. .. 2·75 2·75
2762/88 .. .. *Set of* 27 12·00 12·00

(Litho Questa)

1990 (26 Sept). *Butterflies (2nd series). T* **464** *and similar multicoloured designs. P* 14.
2789/2860 80 c., $2.55, $5, $6.40, $7.65, $8.90, $10×64, $50 and $100 .. .. *Set of* 72 9·50 10·00
MS2861 Four sheets, each 102×71 mm. (a) $150 *Heliconius aoede.* (b) $150 *Phyciodes clio* (*horiz*). (c) $190 *Thecla hemon.* (d) $190 *Nymphidium caricae* .. .. *Set of* 4 *sheets* 15·00 16·00
Designs: *Vert*—$2.55, *Rhetus dysonii*; $5 *Actinote anteas*; $6.40, *Heliconius tales*; $7.65, *Thecla telemus*; $8.90, *Theope eudocia*; $10 (No. 2795), *Heleconius vetustus*; No. 2796, *Mesosemia eumene*; No. 2797, *Parides phosphorus*; No. 2798, *Polystichtis emylius*; No. 2799, *Xanthocleis aedesia*; No. 2800, *Doxocopa agathina*; No. 2801, *Adelpha plesaure*; No. 2802, *Heliconius wallacei*; No. 2803, *Notheme eumeus*; No. 2804, *Melinaea mediatrix*; No. 2805, *Theritas coronata*; No. 2806, *Dismorphia orise*; No. 2807, *Phyciodes ianthe*; No. 2808, *Morpho aega*; No. 2809, *Zaretis isidora*; No. 2810, *Pierella lena*; No. 2811, *Heliconius silvana*; No. 2812, *Eunica alcmena*; No. 2813, *Mechanitis polymnia*; No. 2814, *Mesosemia ephyne*; No. 2815, *Thecla erema*; No. 2816, *Callizona acesta*; No. 2817, *Stalachtis phaedusa*; No. 2818, *Battus belus*; No. 2819, *Nymula phliasus*; No. 2820, *Parides childrenae*; No. 2821, *Stalachtis euterpe*; No. 2822, *Dysmathia portia*; No. 2823, *Tithorea hermias*; No. 2824, *Prepona pheridamas*; No. 2825, *Dismorphia fortunata*; No. 2826, *Hamadryas amphinome*; $50 *Heliconius vicini*; $100 *Amarynthis meneria. Horiz*—$10 (No. 2827), *Thecla falerina*; No. 2828, *Pheles heliconides*; No. 2829, *Echenias leucocyana*; No. 2830, *Heliconius xanthocles*; No. 2831, *Mesopthalma idotea*; No. 2832, *Parides aeneas*; No. 2833, *Heliconius numata*; No. 2834, *Thecla critola*; No. 2835, *Themone pais*; No. 2836, *Nymula agle*; No. 2837, *Adelpha cocala*; No. 2838, *Anaea eribotes*; No. 2839, *Prepona demophon*; No. 2840, *Selenophanes cassiope*; No. 2841, *Consul hippona*; No. 2842, *Antirrhaea avernus*; No. 2843, *Thecla telemus*; No. 2844, *Thyridia confusa*; No. 2845, *Heliconius burneyi*; No. 2846, *Parides lysander*; No. 2847, *Eunica orphise*; No. 2848, *Adelpha melona*; No. 2849, *Morpho menelaus*; No. 2850, *Nymula phylleus*; No. 2851, *Stalachtis phlegia*; No. 2852, *Theope barea*; No. 2853, *Morpho perseus*; No. 2854, *Lycorea ceres*; No. 2855, *Archonias bellona*; No. 2856; *Caeronis chorinaeus*; No. 2857, *Vila azeca*; No. 2858, *Nessaea batesii.*
Nos. 2795/2810, 2811/26, 2827/42 and 2843/58 were printed together, *se-tenant*, in sheetlets of 16 with the backgrounds forming composite designs.

465 *Vanilla inodora* **466** Ivory-billed Woodpecker

(Litho B.D.T.)

1990 (16 Oct). *Flowers. T* **465** *and similar multicoloured designs. P* 14.
2862/2965 $7.65, $8.90, $10×32, $12.80×65, $15.30, $17.80, $20, $25 and $100 *Set of* 104 12·00 13·00
MS2966 Five sheets. (a) 65×95 mm. $150 *Delonix regia* (*horiz*). (b) 86×65 mm. $150 *Hexisea bidentata* (*horiz*). (c) 70×105 mm. $150 *Galeandra devoniana* (*horiz*). (d) 68×110 mm. $150 *Lecythis ollaria.* (e) 74×104 mm. $190 *Ionopsis utricularioides* .. .. *Set of* 5 *sheets* 11·00 12·00
Designs: *Vert*—$8.90, *Epidendrum ibaguense*; $10 (No. 2864), *Dichea muricata*; No. 2865, *Octomeria erosilabia*; No. 2866, *Spiranthes orchioides*; No. 2867, *Brassavola nodosa*; No. 2868, *Epidendrum rigidum*; No. 2869, *Brassia caudata*; No. 2870, *Pleurothallis diffusa*; No. 2871, *Aspasia variegata*; No. 2872, *Stenia pallida*; No. 2873, *Cyrtopodium punctatum*; No. 2874, *Cattleya deckeri*; No. 2875, *Cryptarrhena lunata*; No. 2876, *Cattleya violacea*; No. 2877, *Caularthron bicornutum*; No. 2878, *Oncidium carthagenense*; No. 2879, *Galeandra devoniana*; No. 2880, *Bifrenaria aurantiaca*; No. 2881, *Epidendrum ciliare*; No. 2882, *Dichaea picta*; No. 2883, *Scaphyglottis violacea*; No. 2884, *Cattleya percivaliana*; No. 2885, Map and national flag; No. 2886, *Epidendrum difforme*; No. 2887, *Eulophia maculata*; No. 2888, *Spiranthes tenuis*; No. 2889, *Peristoria guttata*; No. 2890, *Pleurothallis pruinosa*; No. 2891, *Cleistes rosea*; No. 2892, *Maxillaria variabilis*; No. 2893, *Brassavola cucullata*; No. 2894, *Epidendrum moyobambae*; No. 2895, *Oncidium orthostate*; $12.80, *Maxillaria parkeri*; $12.80 (No. 2897), *Brassavola martiana*; No. 2898, *Paphinia cristata*; No. 2899, *Aganisia pulchella*; No. 2900, *Oncidium lanceanum*; No. 2901, *Lockhartia*

imbricata; No. 2902, *Caularthron bilamellatum*; No. 2903, *Oncidium nanum*; No. 2904, *Pleurothallis ovalifolia*; No. 2905, *Galeandra dives*; No. 2906, *Cycnoches loddigesii*; No. 2907, *Ada aurantiaca*; No. 2908, *Catasetum barbatum*; No. 2909, *Palmorchis pubescens*; No. 2910, *Epidendrum anceps*; No. 2911, *Huntleya meleagris*; No. 2912, *Sobralia sessilis*; $15.30, *Epidendrum nocturnum*; $17.80, *Catasetum discolor*; $20 *Scuticaria hadwenii*; $25 *Epidendrum fragrans*; $100 *Epistephium parviflorum*. *Horiz*—$12.80 (No. 2913), *Cochlospermum vitifolium*; No. 2914, *Eugenia malaccensis*; No. 2915, *Plumiera rubra*; No. 2916, *Erythrina glauca*; No. 2917, *Spathodea campanulata*; No. 2918, *Jacaranda filicifolia*; No. 2919, *Samanea saman*; No. 2920, *Cassia fistula*; No. 2921, *Abutilon integerrimum*; No. 2922, *Lagerstroemia speciosa*; No. 2923, *Tabebuia serratifolia*; No. 2924, *Guaiacum officinale*; No. 2925, *Solanum macranthum*; No. 2926, *Peltophorum roxburghii*; No. 2927, *Bauhinia variegata*; No. 2928, *Plumiera alba*; No. 2929, *Maxillaria camaridii*; No. 2930, *Vanilla pompona*; No. 2931, *Stanhopea grandiflora*; No. 2932, *Oncidium pusillum*; No. 2933, *Polycycnis vittata*; No. 2934, *Cattleya lawrenceana*; No. 2935, *Menadenium labiosum*; No. 2936, *Rodriguezia secunda*; No. 2937, *Mormodes buccinator*; No. 2938, *Otostylis brachystalix*; No. 2939, *Maxillaria discolor*; No. 2940, *Liparis elata*; No. 2941, *Gongora maculata*; No. 2942, *Koellensteinia graminea*; No. 2943, *Rudolfiella aurantiaca*; No. 2944, *Scuticaria steelei*; No. 2945, *Gloriosa rothschildiana*; No. 2946, *Pseudocalymma alliaceum*; No. 2947, *Callichlamys latifolia*; No. 2948, *Distictis riversii*; No. 2949, *Maurandya barclaiana*; No. 2950, *Beaumontia fragrans*; No. 2951, *Phaseolus caracalla*; No. 2952, *Mandevilla splendens*; No. 2953, *Solandra longiflora*; No. 2954, *Passiflora coccinea*; No. 2955, *Allamanda cathartica*; No. 2956, *Bauhinia galpini*; No. 2957, *Verbena maritima*; No. 2958, *Mandevilla sauveolens*; No. 2959, *Phryganocydia corymbosa*; No. 2960, *Jasminum sambac*.

Nos. 2864/79, 2880/95, 2897/2912, 2913/28, 2929/44 and 2945/60 were each printed together, *se-tenant*, in sheetlets of 16 with the backgrounds forming composite designs.

Nos. **MS**2966b/c and **MS**2966e show the "EXPO '90" logo on the sheet margin.

1990 (16 Nov). *Fauna. T* **466** *and similar multicoloured designs. Litho. P* 14×13½ (*vert*) *or* 13½×14 (*horiz*).
2967/86 $12.80×20 (*vert* designs showing endangered birds)
2987/3006 $12.80×20 (*vert* designs showing tropical birds)
3007/26 $12.80×20 (*vert* designs showing prehistoric animals)
3027/46 $12.80×20 (*horiz* designs showing endangered wildlife)
2967/3046 .. .. .. *Set of* 80 30·00 30·00

Designs: *Vert*—No. 2968, Cauca Guan; No. 2969, Sun Conure; No. 2970, Quetzal; No. 2971, Long-wattled Umbrellabird; No. 2972, Banded Cotinga; No. 2973, Blue-chested Parakeet; No. 2974, Rufous-bellied Chachalaca; No. 2975, Yellow-faced Amazon; No. 2976, Toucan Barbet; No. 2977, Red Siskin; No. 2978, Cock-of-the-Rock; No. 2979; Hyacinth Macaw; No. 2980, Yellow Cardinal; No. 2981, Bare-necked Umbrellabird; No. 2982, Saffron Toucanet; No. 2983, Red-billed Curassow; No. 2984, Spectacled Parrotlet; No. 2985, Lovely Cotinga; No. 2986, Black-breasted Gnateater; No. 2987, Swallow-tailed Kite; No. 2988, Hoatzin; No. 2989, Ruby-Topaz Hummingbird; No. 2990, American Black Vulture; No. 2991, Rufous-tailed Jacamar; No. 2992, Scarlet Macaw; No. 2993, Rose-breasted Thrush Tanager; No. 2994, Toco Toucan; No. 2995, Bearded Bellbird; No. 2996, Blue-crowned Motmot; No. 2997, Green Oropendola; No. 2998, Pompadour Cotinga; No. 2999; Vermilion Flycatcher; No. 3000, Blue and Yellow Macaw; No. 3001, White-barred Piculet; No. 3002, Great Razor-billed Curassow; No. 3003, Ruddy Quail Dove; No. 3004, Paradise Tanager; No. 3005, American Darter ("Anhinga"); No. 3006, Greater Flamingo; No. 3007, Palaelodus; No. 3008, Archaeotrogon; No. 3009, Vulture; No. 3010, Bradypus tridactylus; No. 3011, Natalus stramineus bat; No. 3012, Cebidae; No. 3013, Cuvieronius; No. 3014, Phororhacos; 3015, Smilodectes; No. 3016, Megatherium; No. 3017, Titanotylopus; No. 3018, Teleoceras; No. 3019, Macrauchenia; No. 3020, Mylodon; No. 3021, Smilodon; No. 3022, Glyptodon; No. 3023, Protohydrocherus; No. 3024, Archaeohyrax; No. 3025, Pyrotherium; No. 3026, Platypittamys. *Horiz*—$12.80 (No. 3027), Harpy Eagle and Hyacinth Macaw; No. 3028, Andean Condor; No. 3029, Amazonian Umbrellabird; No. 3030, Spider Monkeys; No. 3031, Hyacinth Macaws; No. 3032, Red Siskin; No. 3033, Toucan Barbet; No. 3034, Three-toed Sloth; No. 3035, Guanacos; No. 3036, Spectacled Bear; No. 3037, White-lipped Peccary; No. 3038, Maned Wolf; No. 3039, Jaguar; No. 3040, Spectacled Cayman; No. 3041, Giant Armadillo; No. 3042, Giant Anteater; No. 3043, South American River Otter; No. 3044, Yapok; No. 3045, Central American River Turtle; No. 3046, Cauca Guan.

Nos. 2967/86, 2987/3006, 3007/26 and 3027/46 were printed together, *se-tenant*, in sheetlets of 20 forming composite designs.

No. 2982 is inscribed "Toucanette" and No. 2995 inscribed "Belllbird" both in error.

For miniature sheets accompanying this issue see Nos. **EMS**34/5.

467 National Flag

1991 (26 May). 25*th Anniv of Independence. Sheet* 100×70 *mm. Litho. Imperf.*
MS3047 **467** $225 multicoloured .. .. 5·50 6·00

NEW INFORMATION

The editor is always interested to correspond with people who have new information that will improve or correct the Catalogue.

$100

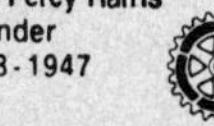

468 Ramon Folist (Cuba) (fencing, 1900) (**469**)

(Litho Cartor)

1991 (12 Aug). *Winter Olympic Games, Albertville (1st issue) and Olympic Games, Barcelona, Previous Gold Medal Winners. T* **468** *and similar multicoloured designs. P* 14×13½.
3048/3119 $15.30×9, $17.80×9, $20×18, $25 ×18 and $30×18 .. .. .. *Set of* 72 30·00 32·00
MS3120 Three sheets, each 98×70 mm. (a) $150 Johannes Kolehmainen (Finland) (10,000 metres, 1912) (*vert*). (b) $150 Paavo Nurmi (Finland) (5000 metres, 1924) (*vert*). (c) $190 Nedo Nadi (Italy) (fencing, 1920) (*vert*). P 13×13½ .. .. .. *Set of* 3 *sheets* 10·50 11·00

Designs:—$15.30 (No. 3049), Lucien Gaudin (France) (fencing, 1924); No. 3050, Ole Lilloe-Olsen (Norway) (shooting, 1924); No. 3051, Morris Fisher (U.S.A.) (rifle shooting, 1924); No. 3052, Ray Ewry (U.S.A.) (long jump, 1900); No. 3053, Hubert van Innes (Belgium) (archery, 1900); No. 3054, Alvin Kraenzlein (U.S.A.) (hurdles, 1900); No. 3055, Johnny Weissmuller (U.S.A.) (swimming, 1924); No. 3056, Hans Winkler (West Germany) (show jumping, 1956); $17.80 (No. 3057), Viktor Chukarin (Russia) (gymnastics, 1952); No. 3058, Agnes Keleti (Hungary) (gymnastics, 1952); No. 3059, Barbel Wochel (East Germany) (200 metres, 1980); No. 3060, Eric Heiden (U.S.A.) (speed skating, 1980); No. 3061, Alvodár Gerevich (Hungary) (fencing, 1932); No. 3062, Giuseppe Delfino (Italy) (fencing, 1952); No. 3063, Alexander Tikhonov (Russia) (skiing, 1980); No. 3064, Pahud de Mortanges (Netherlands) (equestrian, 1932); No. 3065 Patricia McCormick (U.S.A.) (diving, 1952); $20 (No. 3066), Olga Korbut (Russia) (gymnastics, 1972); No. 3067, Lyudmila Turischeva (Russia) (gymnastics, 1972); No. 3068, Lasse Viren (Finland) (10,000 metres, 1972); No. 3069, George Miez (Switzerland) (gymnastics, 1936); No. 3070, Roland Matthes (East Germany) (swimming, 1972); No. 3071 Pal Kovaks (Hungary) (fencing, 1936); No. 3072, Jesse Owens (U.S.A.) (200 metres, 1936); No. 3073, Mark Spitz (U.S.A.) (swimming, 1972); No. 3074, Eduardo Mangiarotti (Italy) (fencing, 1936); No. 3075, Nelli Kim (Russia) (gymnastics, 1976); No. 3076, Viktor Krovopuskov (Russia) (fencing, 1976); No. 3077, Viktor Sidiak (Russia) (fencing, 1976); No. 3078, Nikolai Andrianov (Russia) (gymnastics, 1976); No. 3079, Nadia Comaneci (Rumania) (gymnastics, 1976); No. 3080, Mitsuo Tsukahara (Japan) (gymnastics, 1976); No. 3081, Yelena Novikova-Belova (Russia) (fencing, 1976); No. 3082, John Naber (U.S.A.) (swimming, 1976); No. 3083, Kornella Ender (Rumania) (swimming, 1976); $25 (No. 3084), Lydia Skoblikova (Russia) (speed skating, 1964); No. 3085, Ivar Ballangrud (Norway) (speed skating, 1936); No. 3086, Clas Thunberg (Finland) (speed skating, 1928); No. 3087, Anton Heida (U.S.A.) (gymnastics, 1904); No. 3088, Akinori Nakayama (Japan) (gymnastics, 1968); No. 3089, Sixten Jernberg (Sweden) (skiing, 1964); No. 3090, Yevgeniy Grischin (Russia) (speed skating, 1956); No. 3091, Paul Radmilovic (East Germany) (waterpolo, 1920); No. 3092, Charles Daniels (U.S.A.) (swimming, 1904); No. 3093, Sawao Kato (Japan) (gymnastics, 1968); No. 3094, Rudolf Karpáti (Hungary) (fencing, 1948); No. 3095, Jenö Fuchs (Hungary) (fencing, 1908); No. 3096, Emil Zátopek (Czechoslovakia) (10,000 metres, 1948); No. 3097, Fanny Blankers-Koen (Netherlands) (hurdles, 1948); No. 3098, Melvin Sheppard (U.S.A.) (4 x 400 metres relay, 1908); No. 3099, Gert Fredriksson (Sweden) (kayak, 1948); No. 3100, Paul Elvstrom (Denmark) (yachting, 1948); No. 3101, Harrison Dillard (U.S.A.) (100 metres, 1948); $30 (No. 3102), Al Oerter (U.S.A.) (discus, 1956); No. 3103, Polina Atsakhova (Russia) (gymnastics, 1956); No. 3104, Takashi Ono (Japan) (gymnastics, 1956); No. 3105, Valentin Muratov (Russia) (gymnastics, 1956); No. 3106, Henri St. Cyr (Sweden) (equestrian, 1956); No. 3107, Iain Murray Rose (Australia) (swimming, 1956); No. 3108, Larisa Latynina (Russia) (gymnastics, 1956); No. 3109, Carlo Pavesi (Italy) (fencing, 1956); No. 3110, Dawn Fraser (Australia) (swimming, 1956); No. 3111, Betty Cuthbert (Australia) (400 metres, 1964); No. 3112, Vera Cáslavská (Czechoslovakia) (gymnastics, 1964); No. 3113, Galin Kulakova (Russia) (skiing, 1972); No. 3114, Yukio Endo (Japan) (gymnastics, 1972); No. 3115, Vladimir Morozov (Russia) (kayak, 1972); No. 3116, Boris Shaklin (Russia) (gymnastics, 1964); No. 3117, Don Schollander (U.S.A.) (swimming, 1964); No. 3118, Gyözö Kulscár (Hungary) (fencing, 1964); No. 3119, Christian D'Oriloa (France) (fencing, 1956).

Nos. 3048/56, 3057/65, 3066/74, 3075/83, 3084/92, 3093/3101, 3102/10 and 3111/19 were printed together, *se-tenant*, in sheetlets of 9 forming composite designs.

Sheetlets containing Nos. 3057/65, 3084/92 and 3111/19 were subsequently re-issued with Nos. 3063, 3086 and 3113 overprinted "ALBERTVILLE '92". No. **MS**3120 also exists with the 1992 venues printed on the sheet margins.

See also Nos. 3186/94 and 3246/54

1991 (29 Oct). 85*th Anniv of Rotary International* (1990).

(*a*) *Nos.* 2789/94 *and* 2859/60 *optd or surch as T* **469** (A) *or with Rotary emblem and* "1905–1990" (B)
3121 80 c. Type **464** (B) 10 10
3122 $2.55, *Rhetus dysonii* (B) 10 10
3123 $5 *Actinote anteas* (A) 10 10
3124 $6.40, *Heliconius tales* (A) 10 10
3125 $7.65, *Thecla telemus* (A) 10 10
3126 $100 on $8.90, *Theope eudocia* (A) .. 1·25 1·40
3127 $190 on $50 *Heliconius vicini* (B) .. 2·25 2·50
3128 $225 on $100 *Amarynthis meneria* (B) .. 2·50 2·75

(*b*) *Nos.* 2795/2810 *and* **MS**2861a/b *optd or surch as Nos.* 3121/8 *but some with emblems and inscriptions of other international organizations.*
3129 $10 *Heliconius vetustus* (B) 15 1
a. Sheetlet. Nos. 3129/44 .. .. 6·00
3130 $10 *Mesosemia eumene* (optd Boy Scout emblem and "1907–1992") 15 1
3131 $10 *Parides phosphorus* (optd Lions Club emblem and "1917–1992") 15 1
3132 $10 *Polystichtis emylius* (A) 15 1
3133 $10 *Xanthocleis aedesia* (optd "125 Years Red Cross" and cross) 15 1
3134 $10 *Doxocopa agathina* (optd with part Rotary emblem) 15 1
3135 $10 *Adelpha plesaure* (optd with part Rotary emblem) 15 1
3136 $10 *Heliconius wallacei* (optd "125 Years Red Cross" and cross) 15 1
3137 $10 *Notheme eumeus* (optd Lions Club emblem and "1917–1992") 15 1
3138 $10 *Melinaea mediatrix* (optd with part Rotary emblem) 15 1
3139 $10 *Theritas coronata* (optd with part Rotary emblem) 15 1
3140 $10 *Dismorphia orise* (optd Boy Scout emblem and "1907–1992") 15 1
3141 $50 on $10 *Phyciodes ianthe* (A) 65 6
3142 $75 on $10 *Morpho aega* (surch Boy Scout emblem and "1907–1992") .. .. 1·00 1·1
3143 $100 on $10 *Zaretis isidora* (surch Lions Club emblem and "1917–1992") .. 1·25 1·4
3144 $190 on $10 *Pierella lena* (B) .. .. 2·25 2·5
3121/44 .. .. *Set of* 24 12·00 13·0
MS3145 Two sheets, each 102×71 mm. (a) $400 on $150 *Heliconius aoede*. (b) $500 on $150 *Phyciodes clio* .. .. .. *Set of* 2 *sheets* 9·00 9·2

Nos. 3134/5 and 3138/9 show the Rotary Internationa emblem overprinted at the centre of the block of four.

Nos. **MS**3145a/b only show the new face values on the stamp and have international organization emblems overprinted o the sheet margins.

(Des D. Miller. Litho B.D.T.)

1991 (25 Nov). 65*th Birthday of Queen Elizabeth II and* 70*th Birthday of Prince Philip. Horiz designs as T* **280** *of Antigua Multicoloured. P* 14.
3146 $12.80, Queen and Prince Philip in evening dress 15 2
3147 $15.30, Queen Elizabeth II 15 2
3148 $100 Queen and Prince Philip .. .. 1·00 1·1
3149 $130 Prince Philip .. .. .. 1·25 1·4
3150 $150 Prince Philip in R.A.F. uniform .. 1·50 1·6
3151 $200 The Queen with Queen Elizabeth the Queen Mother .. .. .. 2·25 2·4
3146/51 .. .. *Set of* 6 5·75 6·2
MS3152 68×90 mm. $225 Queen Elizabeth II 3·00 3·2

(Des D. Miller. Litho B.D.T.)

1991 (25 Nov). 10*th Wedding Anniv of Prince and Princess o Wales. Horiz designs as T* **280** *of Antigua. Multicoloured P* 14.
3153 $8.90, Prince and Princess of Wales .. 20 2
3154 $50 Separate portraits of Princess and sons 80 8
3155 $75 Prince Charles with Prince William 1·25 1·2
3156 $190 Princess Diana with Prince Henry .. 2·75 3·0
3153/6 .. .. *Set of* 4 4·50 4·7
MS3157 68×90 mm. $225 Separate portraits of Prince Charles, Prince William and Princess Diana with Prince Henry .. .. .. 3·25 3·5

$100

Melvin Jones
Founder 1880-1961

(**470**)

1991 (26 Nov). 75*th Anniv of Lions International* (1992). (*a Nos.* 2789/94 *and* 2859/60 *optd or surch as T* **470** (A) *or wit Lions Club emblem and* "Lions International 1917–1992" (B
3158 80 c. Type **464** (B) 15 1
3159 $2.55, *Rhetus dysonii* (B) 20 1
3160 $5 *Actinote anteas* (A) 30 2
3161 $6.40, *Heliconius tales* (A) 30 2
3162 $7.65, *Thecla telemus* (A) 35 2
3163 $100 on $8.90, *Theope eudocia* (A) .. 1·50 1·5
3164 $190 on $50 *Heliconius vicini* (B) .. 2·50 2·7
3165 $225 on $100 *Amarynthis meneria* (B) .. 2·50 2·7

(*b*) *Nos.* 2843/58 *and* **MS**2861c/d *optd or surch in black or red as Nos.* 3158/65, *but some with emblems and inscriptions of other international organizations.*
3166 $10 *Thecla telemus* (optd Lions Club emblem and "1917–1992") 15 15
a. Sheetlet. Nos. 3166/81 .. .. 6·00
3167 $10 *Thyridia confusa* (optd Rotary emblem and "1905–1990") 15 15
3168 $10 *Heliconius burneyi* (optd Boy Scout emblem and "1907–1992") 15 15
3169 $10 *Parides lysander* (A) 15 15
3170 $10 *Eunica orphise* (optd "125 Years Red Cross" and cross) 15 15
3171 $10 *Adelpha melona* (optd with part Lions Club emblem) 15 15
3172 $10 *Morpho menelaus* (optd with part Lions Club emblem) 15 15
3173 $10 *Nymula phylleus* (optd "125 Years Red Cross" and cross) 15 15
3174 $10 *Stalachtis phlegia* (optd Rotary emblem and "1905–1990") 15 15
3175 $10 *Theope barea* (optd with part Lions Club emblem) 15 15

76 $10 *Morpho perseus* (optd with part Lions Club emblem) 15 15
77 $10 *Lycorea ceres* (optd Boy Scout emblem and "1907–1992") 15 15
78 $50 on $10 *Archonias bellona* (A) .. 65 65
79 $75 on $10 *Caerois chorinaeus* (surch Boy Scout emblem and "1907–1992") .. 1·00 1·10
80 $100 on $10 *Vila azeca* (surch Rotary emblem and "1905–1990") .. .. 1·25 1·40
81 $190 on $10 *Nessaea batesii* (surch Lions Club emblem and "1917–1992") .. 2·25 2·50
58/81 .. .. *Set of* 24 12·00 13·00
S3182 Two sheets, each 102×71 mm. (a) $400 on $190 *Nymphidium caricae*. (b) $500 on $190 *Thecla hemon* .. .. .. *Set of* 2 *sheets* 9·00 9·25
Nos. 3171/2 and 3175/6 show the Lions Club International emblem overprinted at the centre of the block of four.
Nos. **MS**3182a/b only show new face values on the stamps and five international organization emblems overprinted on the sheet margins.

$50
(471)

91 (29 Nov). *"Phila Nippon '91" International Stamp Exhibition, Tokyo. Sheetlets containing Nos.* 2880/95 *and* 2897/2912, *now sold as miniature sheets, and* **MS**2966d *with some stamps surch as T* 471 *and inscriptions and exhibition logo on the sheet margins, all in red.*
S3183 135×203 mm. $10×12; $25 on $10; $50 on $10; $75 on $10; $130 on $10 .. .. 5·00 5·50
S3184 135×203 mm. $12.80×12; $25 on $12.80; $50 on $12.80; $75 on $12.80; $100 on $12.80 .. .. 5·00 5·50
S3185 68×110 mm. $250 on $150 *Lecythis ollaria* .. .. 3·75 4·00

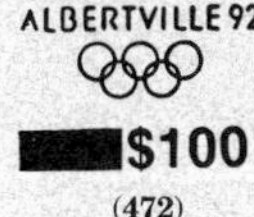

(472)

(473)

91 (3 Dec). *Winter Olympic Games, Albertville* (1992) (2*nd issue*). *Nos.* 2738/46 *optd or surch with T* 472 *or* "XVIth Olympic Winter Games in Albertville" (*No.* 3190), *in black or red.*
86/94 $20×6, $70 on $20, £100 on $20, $190 on $20 .. .. *Set of* 9 7·50 8·00

91 (19 Dec). *John F. Kennedy and Sir Winston Churchill Commemorations. Nos.* **MS**2966c *and* **MS**2966e *surch with T* 473 *in black or red.*
S3195 70×105 mm. $600 on $150 *Galeandra devoniana* (*horiz*) .. ..
S3196 74×104 mm. $600 on $190 *Ionopsis utricularioides* .. ..
No. **MS**3195 is additionally overprinted with "IN MEMORIAM John F. Kennedy 1917–1963", "First Man on Moon July 20, 1969" and "Apollo 11" emblem, and No. **MS**3196 "IN MEMORIAM Sir Winston S. Churchill 1874–1965" and 50th Anniversary World War II" on sheet margins.

GUYANA $50

474 *Akagi* (Japanese aircraft carrier)

(Des J. Batchelor. Litho Questa)

91 (23 Dec). *50th Anniv of Japanese Attack on Pearl Harbor. T* 474 *and similar horiz designs, each deep ultramarine, bright scarlet and black. P* 14½.
97 $50 Type 474 .. .. 85 85
a. Sheetlet. Nos. 3197/206 .. .. 7·50
98 $50 Beached Japanese midget submarine 85 85
99 $50 Mitsubishi A6M Zero-Sen fighter .. 85 85
200 $50 U.S.S. *Arizona* (battleship) under attack 85 85
201 $50 Aichi D3A1 "Val" dive bomber .. 85 85
202 $50 U.S.S. *California* (battleship) sinking 85 85
203 $50 Curtiss P-40 fighters taking off .. 85 85
204 $50 U.S.S. *Cassin* and U.S.S. *Downes* damaged in dry dock 85 85
205 $50 Boeing B-17 Flying Fortress crash landing at Bellows Field 85 85
206 $50 U.S.S. *Nevada* (battleship) on fire .. 85 85
197/206 .. .. *Set of* 10 7·50 7·50
Nos. 3197/206 were printed together, *se-tenant*, in sheetlets of 10 with the stamps arranged in two horizontal rows of 5 separated by an illustrated gutter showing American battleships after the attack.

475 Brandenburg Gate and Location Plan

(Des L. Fried (Nos. 3207/8, 3220, **MS**3225c), W. Hanson (Nos. 3209/11, 3221, **MS**3225d), J. Iskowitz (Nos. 3212/14, 3217/18, 3222/3, **MS**3225a/b, **MS**3225e), W. Wright (Nos. 3215/16, 3219, 3224, **MS**3225f). Litho Questa)

1991 (23 Dec). *Anniversaries and Events. T* **475** *and similar multicoloured designs. P* 14.
3207 $10 Type **475** 20 20
3208 $25 President Bush, President Lech Walesa of Poland and Brandenburg Gate 50 50
3209 $25 Scout handshake 50 50
3210 $30 Scouts hiking at Philmont Scout Ranch 60 60
3211 $40 Jamboree and Scout Movement emblems 70 70
3212 $60 General de Gaulle at Venice, 1944 90 90
3213 $75 De Gaulle with Khrushchev, 1960 1·25 1·25
3214 $75 Mozart and Castle of Laxenburg .. 1·25 1·25
3215 $75 Caroline Herschel (astronomer) and Old Town Hall, Hanover .. .. 1·25 1·25
3216 $75 Map of Switzerland and woman in Valais costume .. .. .. 1·25 1·25
3217 $80 De Gaulle at Algiers, 1958 .. .. 1·40 1·40
3218 $80 Mozart and death of Leopold II .. 1·40 1·40
3219 $80 Otto Lilienthal and *Flugzeug Nr. 3* 1·40 1·40
3220 $100 Chancellor Kohl, Foreign Minister Genscher and Brandenburg Gate .. 1·50 1·50
3221 $100 Lord Baden-Powell (*vert*) .. .. 1·50 1·50
3222 $100 De Gaulle with Pope Paul VI, 1967 1·50 1·50
3223 $100 Mozart and birthplace, Salzburg .. 1·50 1·50
3224 $100 Class P 36 steam locomotive .. 1·50 1·50
3207/24 .. .. *Set of* 18 18·00 18·00
MS3225 Six sheets. (a) 67×99 mm. $150 General De Gaulle (*vert*). (b) 75×104 mm. $190 General De Gaulle (*different*) (*vert*). (c) 101×71 mm. $190 Ceremonial helmet and statues from Brandenburg Gate. (d) 114×83 mm. $190 Rocket-flown commemorative cover, 1960. (e) 73×104 mm. $190 Mozart cameo (*vert*). (f) 103×74 mm. $190 Arms of Berne and Solothurn .. *Set of* 6 *sheets* 15·00 16·00
Anniversaries and Events:—Nos. 3207/8, 3220, **MS**3225c, Bicentenary of Brandenburg Gate, Berlin; Nos. 3209/11, 3221, **MS**3225d, 17th World Scout Jamboree, Korea; Nos. 3212/13, 3217, 3222, **MS**3225a/b, Birth centenary of Charles de Gaulle (French statesman) (1990); Nos. 3214, 3218, 3223, **MS**3225e, Death bicentenary of Mozart; No. 3215, 750th anniv of Hanover; No. 3216, **MS**3225f, 700th anniv of Swiss Confederation; No. 3219, Centenary of Otto Lilienthal's first gliding experiments; No. 3224, Centenary of Trans-Siberian Railway.
No. 3222 is inscribed "Pope John VI" in error.

476 Disney Characters Carol Singing, 1989

(Des Walt Disney Co. Litho Questa)

1991 (30 Dec). *Christmas. Walt Disney Christmas Cards. T* **476** *and similar multicoloured designs. P* 14×13½ (*horiz*) *or* 13½×14 (*vert*).
3226 80 c. Type **476** 10 10
3227 $2.55, Disney characters and carol singers in tram, 1962 .. .. 10 10
3228 $5 Donald Duck and Pluto with parcel, 1971 .. .. 10 10
3229 $6.40, "SEASON'S GREETINGS" and Mickey Mouse with candle, 1948 .. 10 10
3230 $7.65, Mickey Mouse as Father Christmas, 1947 .. .. .. 10 10
3231 $8.90, Shadow of Pinocchio with candle, 1939 .. .. 10 10
3232 $50 Three Little Pigs dancing on wolf rug, 1933 .. .. 65 65
3233 $50 Conductor and Donald Duck, 1940 (*vert*) 65 65
a. Horiz strip of 5. Nos. 3233/7 .. 3·00
3234 $50 Elephant and ostrich carol singing, 1940 (*vert*) 65 65
3235 $50 Hippo, centaurs, Pinocchio and Goofy, 1940 (*vert*) 65 65
3236 $50 Snow White, Dopey, Mickey and Minnie, 1940 (*vert*) 65 65
3237 $50 Dino, Pluto and Walt Disney, 1940 (*vert*) 65 65
3238 $50 Mickey Mouse in sleigh, 1974 (*vert*) 65 65
a. Horizontal strip of 6. Nos. 3238/43 .. 3·50
3239 $50 Three Little Pigs, Winnie the Pooh, Bambi and Thumper, 1974 (*vert*) .. 65 65
3240 $50 Baloo, King Louis, Lady and the Tramp, 1974 (*vert*) 65 65
3241 $50 Alice, Robin Hood, the Cheshire Cat and Goofy, 1974 (*vert*) 65 65
3242 $50 Dumbo, Pinocchio, Peter Pan, Tinkerbelle, Seven Dwarfs and Donald Duck, 1974 (*vert*) 65 65
3243 $50 Pluto pulling sleigh, 1974 (*vert*) .. 65 65
3244 $200 Mickey and mice carol singing, 1949 2·75 2·75
3226/44 .. .. *Set of* 19 9·00 9·00
MS3245 Eight sheets. (a) 127×101 mm. $260 Mickey, Minnie, Clarabelle and Pluto in mail coach, 1932 (*vert*). (b) 127×101 mm. $260 Mickey's House, 1935 (*vert*). (c) 101×127 mm. $260 Jose Carioca, Rooster and Donald Duck on flying carpet, 1944 (*vert*). (d) 101×127 mm. $260 Casey at the Bat and dancers, 1945. (e) 127×101 mm. $260 Mickey, Donald and Goofy on musical score, 1946. (f) 127×101 mm. $260 Picture of Winnie the Pooh, 1969. (g) 127×101 mm. $260 Father Christmas in chimney, 1969 (*vert*). (h) 101×127 mm. $260 Letters of film titles forming Mickey Mouse, 1978 (*vert*) .. *Set of* 8 *sheets* 22·00 24·00
Nos. 3233/7 and 3238/43 were each printed together, *se-tenant*, in horizontal strips of 5 or 6 throughout the sheets, each strip showing the design of the complete card.

477 Gus Gander playing Ice Hockey

(Des Walt Disney Co. Litho B.D.T.)

1991 (30 Dec). *Winter Olympic Games, Albertville* (1992) (3*rd issue*). *T* **477** *and similar horiz designs showing Walt Disney cartoon characters. Multicoloured. P* 13.
3246 $6.40, Type **477** 20 10
3247 $7.65, Mickey and Minnie Mouse in bobsleigh 20 10
3248 $8.90, Donald's Nephews on luge and skis 25 10
3249 $12.80, Goofy freestyle skiing 40 20
3250 $50 Goofy ski jumping .. .. .. 1·00 1·00
3251 $100 Donald and Daisy Duck speed skating 1·50 1·50
3252 $130 Pluto cross-country skiing .. .. 1·75 2·00
3253 $190 Mickey and Minnie Mouse ice dancing 2·50 3·00
3246/53 .. .. *Set of* 8 7·00 7·00
MS3254 Two sheets, each 125×100 mm. (a) $225 Donald's nephew curling; (b) $225 Donald Duck slalom skiing .. .. .. *Set of* 2 *sheets* 7·00 7·50

478 Columbus landing on Trinidad

479 Tom Mix in *The Great K&A Train Robbery*, 1926

(Des J. Genzo. Litho Questa)

1992 (2 Jan). *500th Anniv of Discovery of America by Columbus. T* **478** *and similar multicoloured designs. P* 14.
3255 $6.40, Type **478** 40 40
3256 $7.65, Columbus the map-maker .. 45 45
3257 $8.90, Fleet blown off course 45 45
3258 $12.80, Map of Third Voyage and Columbus in chains 55 55
3259 $15.30, Sighting land 55 55
3260 $50 *Nina* and *Pinta* 90 90
3261 $75 *Santa Maria* .. .. .. 1·25 1·25
3262 $100 Columbus trading with Amerindians 1·75 1·75
3263 $125 Crew and sea monster .. .. 2·00 2·00
3264 $130 Columbus landing on San Salvador and map of First Voyage .. .. 2·00 2·00
3265 $140 Priest and Amerindians .. .. 2·00 2·00
3266 $150 Columbus before King Ferdinand and Queen Isabella of Spain .. .. 2·00 2·00
3255/66 .. .. *Set of* 12 13·00 13·00
MS3267 Three sheets, each 126×91 mm. (a) $280 *Nina* (*vert*). (b) $280 Columbus (*vert*). (c) $280 Early map of Caribbean .. *Set of* 3 *sheets* 13·00 14·00

(Litho B.D.T.)

1992 (11 Mar). *Classic Movie Posters. T* **479** *and similar multicoloured designs. P* 14.
3268 $8.90, Type **479** 30 30
3269 $12.80, Richard Dix and Irene Dunne in *Cimarron*, 1931 .. .. .. 40 40
3270 $15.30, Fatty Arbuckle in *Buzzin' Around*, 1934 .. .. 40 40
3271 $25 Tom Tyler in *The Adventures of Captain Marvel*, 1941 .. .. 55 55
3272 $30 Boris Karloff in *The Mummy*, 1932 70 70
3273 $50 Rudolph Valentino in *A Sainted Devil*, 1924 .. .. 90 90
3274 $75 Seven posters for *A Tale of Two Cities*, 1935 .. .. 1·25 1·25
3275 $100 Chester Conklin in *A Tugboat Romeo*, 1916 .. .. 1·75 1·75
3276 $130 Douglas Fairbanks in *The Thief of Bagdad*, 1924 .. .. .. 2·00 2·00
3277 $150 Laurel and Hardy in *Bacon Grabbers*, 1929 .. .. 2·50 2·50
3278 $190 Marx Brothers in *A Night at the Opera*, 1935 .. .. 3·00 3·00
3279 $200 Orson Welles in *Citizen Kane*, 1941 3·00 3·00
3268/79 .. .. *Set of* 12 15·00 15·00
MS3280 Four sheets (a) 70×99 mm. $225 Babe Ruth in *Babe Comes Home*, 1927. (b) 70×99 mm. $225 Mae West in *She Done Him Wrong*, 1933. (c) 70×99 mm. $225 Charlie Chaplin in *The Circus*, 1928. (d) 99×70 mm. $225 Poster for never-made film *Zeppelin*, 1933. Imperf
Set of 4 *sheets* 15·00 16·00

(Litho Questa)

1992 (11 May). *Easter. Paintings by Dürer. Multicoloured designs as T* **291** *of Antigua, but vert. P* 13½×14.

3281 $6.40, "The Martyrdom of Ten Thousand" (detail) 25 10
3282 $7.65, "Adoration of the Trinity" (detail of Virgin Mary) 25 10
3283 $12.80, "The Martyrdom of Ten Thousand" (execution detail) 40 20
3284 $15.30, "Adoration of the Trinity" (different detail) 45 25
3285 $50 "The Martyrdom of Ten Thousand" (detail of bishop) .. .. .. 1·00 75
3286 $100 "Adoration of the Trinity" (different detail) .. .. 1·50 1·50
3287 $130 "The Martyrdom of Ten Thousand" (different detail) .. .. .. 1·75 2·00
3288 $190 "Adoration of the Trinity" (different detail) .. .. 3·25 3·50
3281/8 .. .. *Set of* 8 8·00 7·50
MS3289 Two sheets, each 71×101 mm. (a) $225 "The Martyrdom of Ten Thousand". (b) $225 "Adoration of the Trinity" (detail of Christ on cross) .. .. *Set of 2 sheets* 8·00 8·50

$6.40

BAHA'I HOLY
YEAR
1992

(**480**)

1992 (29 May). *Baha'i Holy Year. Nos.* 1519 *and* 1521/3 *surch as T* **480**.

3290 $6.40 on 60 c. Plate No. 10 (Series 1) (No. 1521) .. ..
3291 $7.65 on 60 c. Plate No. 31 (Series 1) (No. 1523) .. ..
3292 $8.90 on 60 c. Plate No. 19 (Series 1) (No. 1522) .. ..
3293 $50 on 60 c. Plate No. 2 (Series 1) (No. 1519) .. ..

481 Queen Elizabeth II and Duke of Edinburgh

(Litho Questa)

1992 (1 June). *40th Anniv of Queen Elizabeth II's Accession. T* **481** *and similar horiz designs. Multicoloured. P* 14.

3294 $8.90, Type **481** 25 25
3295 $12.80, Queen at Trooping the Colour .. 30 30
3296 $100 Queen at Coronation .. .. .. 2·00 2·25
3297 $130 Queen in Garter robes .. .. .. 2·25 2·50
3294/7 .. .. *Set of* 4 4·25 4·75
MS3298 Two sheets, each 119×79 mm. (a) $225 Queen in Coronation robes. (b) $225 Queen in blue dress .. .. .. *Set of 2 sheets* 8·00 8·50

482 Holy Cross Church, Annai Rupununi

483 Burmese

(Litho B.D.T.)

1992 (10 Aug). *150th Anniv of Diocese of Guyana. T* **482** *and similar multicoloured designs. P* 14.

3299 $6.40, Type **482** 15 10
3300 $50 St. Peter's Church 80 65
3301 $100 Interior of St. George's Cathedral (*vert*) .. .. 1·50 1·60
3302 $190 Map of Guyana (*vert*) .. .. .. 2·75 3·25
3299/302 .. .. *Set of* 4 4·75 5·00
MS3303 104×70 mm. $225 Religious symbols 3·75 4·25

(Des S. Barlowe. Litho Questa)

1992 (10 Aug). *Cats. T* **483** *and similar multicoloured designs. P* 14 (*Nos.* 3309/16) *or* 14½×13½ (*others*).

3304 $5 Type **483** 10 10
3305 $6.40, Turkish Van 10 10
3306 $12.80, American Shorthair 15 20
3307 $15.30, Sphynx 15 20
3308 $50 Egyptian Mau 50 55
3309 $50 Russian Blue 50 55
a. Sheetlet. Nos. 3309/16 .. .. .. 4·00
3310 $50 Havana Brown 50 55
3311 $50 Himalayan 50 55
3312 $50 Manx 50 55
3313 $50 Cornish Rex 50 55
3314 $50 Black Persian 50 55
3315 $50 Scottish Fold 50 55
3316 $50 Siamese 50 55
3317 $100 Japanese Bobtail .. .. .. 1·00 1·10
3318 $130 Abyssinian .. .. 1·25 1·40
3319 $225 Oriental Shorthair .. .. .. 2·25 2·40
3304/19 .. .. *Set of* 16 9·25 10·25
MS3320 Four sheets, each 99×69 mm. (a) $250 Chartreuse (*vert*). (b) $250 Turkish Angora (*vert*). (c) $250 Maine Coon (*vert*). (d) $250 Chinchilla (*vert*). P 13½×14½ .. *Set of 4 sheets* 10·00 10·50

Nos. 3309/16 were printed together, *se-tenant*, in sheetlets of 8.

484 Red Howler

(Des L. Nelson. Litho Questa)

1992 (10 Aug). *Animals of Guyana. T* **484** *and similar multicoloured designs. P* 14.

3321 $8.90, Type **484** 20 10
3322 $12.80, Ring-tailed Coati 25 20
3323 $15.30, Jaguar 30 20
3324 $25 Two-toed Sloth 50 30
3325 $50 Giant Armadillo .. .. 1·00 80
3326 $75 Giant Anteater .. .. 1·50 1·75
3327 $100 Capybara .. .. 1·75 1·90
3328 $130 Ocelot .. .. 2·00 2·25
3321/8 .. .. *Set of* 8 6·75 6·75
MS3329 Two sheets, each 70×100 mm. (a) $225 Woolly Opossum (*vert*). (b) $225 Night Monkey (*vert*) .. .. *Set of 2 sheets* 8·00 8·50

No. **MS**3329a is inscribed "WOLLY OPOSSUM" in error.

485 Oligocene Mammoth

486 Palomino

(Des J.-L. Puvilland. Litho Questa)

1992 (10 Aug). *Elephants. T* **485** *and similar horiz designs. Multicoloured. P* 14.

3330 $50 Type **485** .. .. 1·25 1·25
a. Sheetlet. Nos. 3330/7 .. .. .. 9·00
3331 $50 Mid-Miocene Stegodon .. .. .. 1·25 1·25
3332 $50 Pliocene Mammoth .. .. .. 1·25 1·25
3333 $50 Carthaginian elephant crossing Alps, 219 B.C. .. .. 1·25 1·25
3334 $50 Ceremonial elephant of Maharaja of Mysore, India .. .. .. 1·25 1·25
3335 $50 Elephant pulling teak trunks, Burma 1·25 1·25
3336 $50 Tiger-hunting by elephant, India .. 1·25 1·25
3337 $50 Elephant towing raft on River Kwai, Thailand .. .. 1·25 1·25
3330/7 .. .. *Set of* 8 9·00 9·00
MS3338 110×80 mm. $225 African Elephants 4·50 4·50

Nos. 3330/7 were printed together, *se-tenant*, in sheetlets of 8.

(Des S. Barlowe. Litho Questa)

1992 (10 Aug). *Horses. T* **486** *and similar horiz designs. Multicoloured. P* 14.

3339 $190 Type **486** .. .. 3·00 3·00
a. Sheetlet. Nos. 3339/46 .. .. .. 22·00
3340 $190 Appaloosa .. .. 3·00 3·00
3341 $190 Clydesdale .. .. 3·00 3·00
3342 $190 Arab .. .. 3·00 3·00
3343 $190 Morgan .. .. 3·00 3·00
3344 $190 Friesian .. .. 3·00 3·00
3345 $190 Pinto .. .. 3·00 3·00
3346 $190 Thoroughbred .. .. 3·00 3·00
3339/40 .. .. *Set of* 8 22·00 22·00
MS3347 109×80 mm. $190 Lipizzaner (47×29 *mm*) .. .. 4·00 4·25

Nos. 3339/46 were printed together, *se-tenant*, in sheetlets of 8.

No. 3340 is inscribed "APALOOSA" in error.

INT.
CONFERENCE
ON NUTRITION
1992
$6.40

(**487**)

1992 (2 Nov). *International Conference on Nutrition, Rome. Nos.* 1658 *and* 1767/9 *surch as T* **487**.

3348 $6.40 on 150 c. Plate No. 45 (Series 1) (No. 1769) .. ..
3349 $7.65 on 150 c. Plate No. 42 (Series 1) (No. 1768) .. ..
3350 $8.90 on 150 c. Plate No. 40 (Series 1) (No. 1767) .. ..
3351 $10 on 200 c. Plate No. 43 (Series 1) (No. 1658) .. ..
3352 $50 on 200 c. Plate No. 43 (Series 1) (No. 1658) .. ..

488 Marklin Swiss "Crocodile" Locomotive, 1933

(Des W. Hanson. Litho B.D.T.)

1992 (25 Nov). *"Genova '92" International Thematic Stamp Exhibition. Toy Trains from German Manufacturers. T* **488** *and similar horiz designs. Multicoloured. P* 14.

3353/61 $45 × 9 (Made by Marklin: Type **488**; French tramcar, 1902; British "Flatiron" tank engine, 1913; German switching engine, 1970; Third class carriage, 1909; American style locomotive, 1904; Zurich tramcar, 1928; Central London Railway locomotive in Paris–Orleans livery, 1904; British GWR *Great Bear* locomotive, 1909)
a. Sheetlet. Nos. 3353/61 .. .. 5·00
3362/70 $45 × 9 (Made by Marklin: LMS "Precursor" tank engine, 1923; American "Congressional Limited" passenger carriage, 1908; Swiss Type "Ae 3/6" locomotive, 1934; German Class 80, 1975; British Southern Railways third class carriage, 1926; LNWR Bowen-Cooke tank engine, 1913; London Underground "Two Penny Tube", 1901; French Paris–Orsay steeplecab, 1920; Passenger locomotive, 1895)
a. Sheetlet. Nos. 3362/70 .. .. 5·00
3371/9 $45 × 9 (Made by Marklin: American style locomotive, 1907; German passenger carriage, 1908; British Great Eastern Railway locomotive, 1908; London Underground steeplecab, 1904; Santa Fe Railroad diesel locomotive, 1962; British GNR locomotive, 1903; Caledonian Railway *Cardean*, 1906; British LNWR passenger carriage, 1903; Swiss St. Gottard Railway locomotive, 1920)
a. Sheetlet. Nos. 3371/9 .. .. 5·00
3380/8 $45 × 9 (Made by Marklin; British LB & SCR tank engine No. 22, 1920; Central London Railway steeplecab locomotive, 1904; German "Borsig" streamlined, 1935; French Paris–Lyon–Mediterranean first class carriage, 1929; American style locomotive No. 1021, 1904; French Paris–Orsay long-nose steeplecab, 1920; British LNER *Cock o' the North*, 1936; Prussian State Railways Class P8, 1975; German diesel railcar set, 1937)
a. Sheetlet. Nos. 3380/8 .. .. 5·00
3389/97 $45 × 9 (Marklin North British Railway "Atlantic", 1913; Bing British LNWR "Precursor", 1916, Marklin British GWR *King George V*, 1937; Marklin "Kaiser Train" passenger carriage, 1901; Bing side tank locomotive No. 88, 1904; Marklin steeplecab, 1912 Marklin *Adler*, 1935; Bing British GWR *County of Northampton*, 1909; Bing British Midland Railway *Black Prince*, 1908)
a. Sheetlet. Nos. 3389/97 .. .. 5·00
3398/406 $45 × 9 (Made by Bing: Midland Railway "Deeley Type" No. 483, 1909; British Midland Railway No. 2631, 1903; German Pacific, 1927; British GWR third class carriage 1926; British LSWR "M7" No. 109, 1909; Side tank engine *Pilot*, 1901; British LNWR Webb *Cauliflower*, 1912; Side tank locomotive, No. 112, 1910; British GNR "Stirling Single", 1904)
a. Sheetlet. Nos. 3398/406 .. .. 5·00
3407/15 $45 × 9 (Carette tin "Penny Bazaar" train, 1904; Winteringham locomotive, 1917; Carette British Northeastern Railway Smith Compound, 1905; Carette S.E. & C.R. steam railcar, 1908; Carette British Great Northern Railway Stirling Single No. 776, 1903; Carette British Midland Railways locomotive No. 1132M, 1911; Carette London Metropolitan Railway Co. Westinghouse locomotive No. 5,

1908; Carette Clestory carriage, 1907; Carette steam railcar No. 1, 1906)
a. Sheetlet. Nos. 3407/15 . . . . 5·00
416/24 $45 × 9 (Made by Bing: Engine and tender, 1895; British Midland Railway Single No. 650, 1913; No. 524/510 reversible locomotive, 1916; "Kaiser Train" passenger carriage, 1902; British rural station, 1915; British LSWR M7 tank locomotive, 1909; "Windcutter", 1912; British Great Central Railway *Sir Sam Fay*, 1914; Scottish Caledonian Railway *Dunalastair* locomotive, 1910)
a. Sheetlet. Nos. 3416/24 . . . . 5·00
353/424 . . . . *Set of* 72 35·00 40·00
IS3425 Eight sheets, each 116×83 mm. (a) $350 Bing contractor's locomotive No. 18, 1904 (51×39 *mm*); (b) $350 Marklin rack railway steeplecab locomotive, 1908 (51×39 *mm*); (c) $350 Bing British GWR *County of Northampton* locomotive, 1909 (51×39 *mm*); (d) $350 Marklin French Paris–Lyon–Mediterranean Pacific locomotive, 1912 (51×39 *mm*); (e) $350 Bing Pabst Blue Ribbon beer refrigerator wagon, 1925 (51×39 *mm*); (f) $350 Marklin French "Mountain Etat" locomotive, 1933 (51×39 *mm*); (g) $350 Marklin German National Railroad Class 0-1 Pacific locomotive, 1937 (51×39 *mm*); (g) $350 Marklin American *Commodore Vanderbilt* locomotive, 1937 (51×39 *mm*). P 13
Set of 8 *sheets* 30·00 32·00

Nos. 3353/61, 3362/70, 3371/9, 3380/8, 3389/97, 3398/406, 407/15 and 3416/24 were each printed together, *se-tenant*, in heetlets of nine.

(Des Kerri Schiff. Litho Questa)

992 (29 Dec). *Postage Stamp Mega Event, New York. Sheet 100×70 mm containing multicoloured design as T* **299** *of Antigua, but vert. P* 14.
IS3426 $325 Statue of Liberty . . . . 5·00 6·00

489 Aquarius

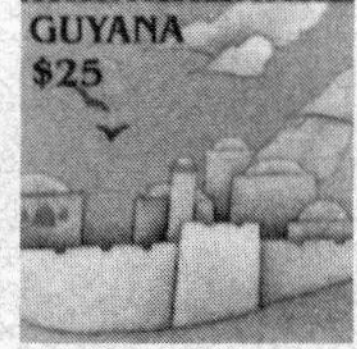

490 City Walls and Two Birds

992 (29 Dec). *Signs of the Zodiac. T* **489** *and similar horiz designs. Multicoloured. Litho. P* 14×13½.
427 $30 Type **489** 60 60
a. Sheetlet. Nos. 3427/38 . . . . 6·50
428 $30 Pisces 60 60
429 $30 Aries 60 60
430 $30 Taurus 60 60
431 $30 Gemini 60 60
432 $30 Cancer 60 60
433 $30 Leo 60 60
434 $30 Virgo 60 60
435 $30 Libra 60 60
436 $30 Scorpio 60 60
437 $30 Sagittarius 60 60
438 $30 Capricorn 60 60
427/38 . . . . *Set of* 12 6·50 6·50
Nos. 3427/38 were printed together, *se-tenant*, in sheetlets of 2.

(Des N. Waldman. Litho B.D.T.)

992 (29 Dec). *Bible Stories (1st series). David and Goliath. T* **490** *and similar square designs. Multicoloured. P* 14.
439 $25 Type **490** 50 50
a. Sheetlet. Nos. 3439/63 . . . . 11·00
440 $25 City walls and one bird at right . . 50 50
441 $25 Sun over city gateway . . 50 50
442 $25 City walls and one bird at left . . 50 50
443 $25 City walls and no birds . . 50 50
444 $25 Philistine army and edge of shield . . 50 50
445 $25 Goliath's head and torso . . 50 50
446 $25 Goliath's arm and spear . . 50 50
447 $25 Philistine army and spearhead . . 50 50
448 $25 Philistine infantry . . 50 50
449 $25 Philistine cavalry and infantry . . 50 50
450 $25 Goliath's shield . . 50 50
451 $25 Goliath's waist and thigh . . 50 50
452 $25 David with sling . . 50 50
453 $25 Israelite soldier with spear . . 50 50
454 $25 Two Israelite soldiers with spears and shields . . 50 50
455 $25 Goliath's right leg . . 50 50
456 $25 Goliath's left leg (face value at foot) 50 50
457 $25 David's legs and Israelite standard 50 50
458 $25 Three Israelite soldiers . . 50 50
459 $25 Israelite soldier and parts of two shields . . 50 50
460 $25 Israelite soldier with sword . . 50 50
461 $25 Back of Israelite soldier . . 50 50
462 $25 Israelite soldier leaning on rock . . 50 50
463 $25 Israelite soldier looking left . . 50 50
439/63 . . . . *Set of* 25 11·00 11·00
Nos. 3439/63 were printed together, *se-tenant*, forming a omposite design.
See also Nos. 4020/4116.

COVER PRICES

over factors are quoted at the beginning of each ountry for most issues to 1945. An explanation of e system can be found on page x. The factors uoted do not, however, apply to philatelic covers.

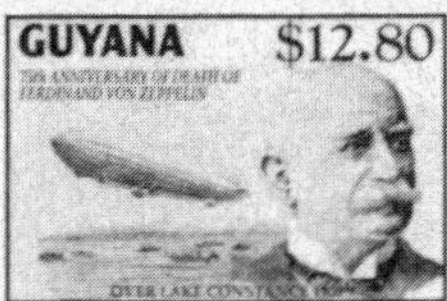

491 Count Ferdinand von Zeppelin and Airship over Lake Constance, 1909

(Des W. Hanson and W. Wright (Nos. 3464, 3474, **MS**3475a), W. Wright and L. Fried (Nos. 3465, 3472, **MS**3475b), W. Wright (others). Litho B.D.T.)

1992 (29 Dec). *Anniversaries and Events. T* **491** *and similar multicoloured designs. P* 14.
3464 $12.80, Type **491** 50 35
3465 $50 *Voyager I* and Jupiter . . . . 1·50 1·00
3466 $50 Chancellor Adenauer with President Kennedy, 1961 . . . . 1·00 1·00
3467 $100 Aeromedical airlift . . . . 2·00 2·00
3468 $100 Boutu ("Amazon Dolphin") . . . . 2·00 2·00
3469 $130 Baby gorilla . . . . 2·50 2·50
3470 $130 Mobile eye screening unit and doctor with child . . . . 2·50 2·50
3471 $130 *Stars and Stripes* (winning yacht, 1987) . . . . 2·50 2·50
3472 $130 Lift-off of *Voyager I*, 1977 . . . . 2·50 2·50
3473 $190 Adenauer with President De Gaulle of France, 1962 . . . . 3·25 3·25
3474 $225 Von Zeppelin and airship preparing for take-off, 1905 . . . . 3·50 3·50
3464/74 . . . . *Set of* 11 21·00 21·00
MS3475 Four sheets. (a) 76×105 mm. $225 Ferdinand von Zeppelin (*vert*). (b) 116×80 mm. $225 Earth from Space (*vert*). (c) 84×111 mm. $225 Konrad Adenauer (*vert*). (d) 87×111 mm. $225 *Hyperohus marmoratus* (tree frog) (*vert*)
Set of 4 *sheets* 15·00 16·00

Anniversaries and Events:—Nos. 3464, 3474, **MS**3475a, 75th death anniv of Count Ferdinand von Zeppelin; Nos. 3465, 3472, **MS**3475b, International Space Year; Nos. 3466, 3473, **MS**3475c, 75th death anniv of Konrad Adenauer (German statesman); No. 3467, United Nations World Health Organization projects; Nos. 3468/9, **MS**3475d, Earth Summit '92, Rio; No. 3470, 75th anniv of International Association of Lions Clubs; No. 3471, Americas Cup Yachting Championship.

492 Hyacinth Macaw

493 Crimson Topaz

(Des R. Duburke. Litho B.D.T.)

1993 (10 Mar). *South American Parrots. T* **492** *and similar multicoloured designs. P* 14.
3476 80 c. Type **492** 30 15
3477 $6.40, Scarlet Macaw (preening) . . 50 25
3478 $7.65, Buffon's Macaw ("Green Macaw") (*vert*) 50 25
3479 $15.30, Orange-chinned Parakeet ("Tovi Parakeet") 70 50
3480 $50 Blue and Yellow Macaw . . 1·00 80
3481 $100 Military Macaw (*vert*) . . 1·50 1·25
3482 $130 Green-winged Macaw ("Red and Green Macaw") (*vert*) . . 1·75 1·75
3483 $190 Chestnut-fronted Macaw ("Severa Macaw") . . . . 2·50 3·00
3476/83 . . . . *Set of* 8 8·00 7·00
MS3484 Two sheets, each 108×74 mm. (a) $225 Scarlet Macaw. (b) $225 Green Conure ("Green Parakeet") (*vert*) . . *Set of* 2 *sheets* 7·00 7·50

(Des P. Chenelli. Litho Questa)

1993 (10 Mar). *Birds of Guyana. T* **493** *and similar multicoloured designs. P* 14.
3485 $50 Type **493** 75 75
a. Sheetlet. Nos. 3485/96 . . . . 8·00
3486 $50 Bearded Bellbird 75 75
3487 $50 Amazonian Umbrellabird 75 75
3488 $50 Paradise Jacamar 75 75
3489 $50 Paradise Tanager 75 75
3490 $50 White-tailed Trogon 75 75
3491 $50 Scarlet Macaw 75 75
3492 $50 Hawk-headed Parrot ("Red-fan Parrot") 75 75
3493 $50 Cuvier's Toucan ("Red-billed Toucan") 75 75
3494 $50 White-faced Antcatcher ("White-plumed Antbird") 75 75
3495 $50 Crimson-hooded Manakin 75 75
3496 $50 Guianan Cock of the Rock 75 75
3485/96 . . . . *Set of* 12 8·00 8·00
MS3497 70×100 mm. $325 Tufted Coquette (*horiz*) . . . . 5·00 5·00
Nos. 3485/96 were printed together, *se-tenant*, in sheetlets of 12, with the backgrounds forming a composite design.

494 Manatee surfacing

495 Tamandua

(Des P. Chenelli. Litho Questa)

1993 (10 Mar). *Endangered Species. American Manatee* (*"Caribbean Manatee"*). *T* **494** *and similar horiz designs. Multicoloured. P* 14½.
3498 $6.40, Type **494** 40 20
3499 $7.65, Cow and calf feeding 40 20
3500 $8.90, Manatee underwater 40 20
3501 $50 Two Manatees . . . . 2·00 1·50
3498/501 . . . . *Set of* 4 2·75 1·90

(Des P. Chenelli. Litho Questa)

1993 (10 Mar). *Animals of Guyana. T* **495** *and similar vert designs. Multicoloured. P* 14.
3502 $50 Type **495** 75 75
a. Sheetlet. Nos. 3502/13 . . . . 8·00
3503 $50 Pale-throated Sloth ("Three-toed Sloth") 75 75
3504 $50 Red Howler 75 75
3505 $50 Four-eyed Opossum 75 75
3506 $50 Black Spider Monkey 75 75
3507 $50 Giant Otter 75 75
3508 $50 Red Brocket 75 75
3509 $50 Brazilian Tree Porcupine 75 75
3510 $50 Tayra 75 75
3511 $50 Brazilian Tapir 75 75
3512 $50 Ocelot 75 75
3513 $50 Giant Armadillo 75 75
3502/13 . . . . *Set of* 12 8·00 8·00
MS3514 100×70 mm. $325 Paca . . . . 4·50 5·00
Nos. 3502/13 were printed together, *se-tenant*, in sheetlets of 12, the backgrounds forming a composite design.

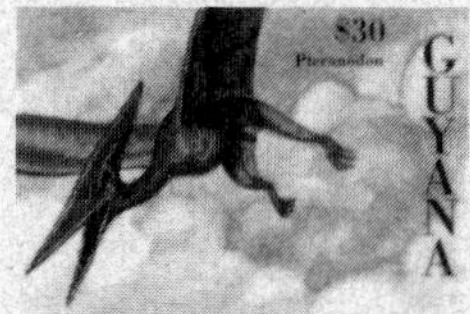

496 Pteranodon

(Des R. Sauber. Litho B.D.T.)

1993 (10 Mar). *Prehistoric Animals. T* **496** *and similar horiz designs. Multicoloured. P* 14.
3515/26 $30 × 12 (Type **496**; Cearadactylus; Eudimorphodon; Pterodactylus; Staurikosaurus; Euoplocephalus; Tuojiangosaurus; Oviraptor; Protoceratops; Panaoplosaurus; Psittacosaurus; Corythosaurus)
a. Sheetlet. Nos. 3515/26 . . . . 5·00
3527/38 $30 × 12 (Sordes; Quetzalcoatlus; Archaeopteryx in flight; Rhamphorynchus; Spinosaurus; Anchisaurus; Stegosaurus; Leaellynosaurs; Minmi; Heterdontosaurus; Lesothosaurus; Deninonychus)
a. Sheetlet. Nos. 3527/38 . . . . 5·00
3539/50 $30 × 12 (Archaeopteryx on branch; Pteranodon (*different*); Quetzalcoatlus (three); Protoavis; Dicraeosaurus; Moschops; Lystrosaurus; Dimetrondon; Staurikosaurus; Cacops; Diarthrognathus; Estemmenosuchus)
a. Sheetlet. Nos. 3539/50 . . . . 5·00
3515/50 . . . . *Set of* 36 13·50 15·00
Nos. 3515/26, 3527/38 and 3539/50 were each printed together, *se-tenant*, in sheetlets of 12, with the backgrounds forming composite designs.

(Des Kerri Schiff. Litho Questa)

1993 (2 June). *40th Anniv of Coronation. Vert designs as T* **307** *of Antigua. Multicoloured. P* 13½×14.
3551 $25 Queen Elizabeth II in Coronation robes (photograph by Cecil Beaton) . . 75 75
a. Sheetlet. Nos. 3551/4×2 . . . . 7·00
3552 $50 Royal gems . . . . 1·00 1·00
3553 $75 Queen Elizabeth and Prince Philip . . 1·25 1·40
3554 $130 Queen opening Parliament . . . . 1·50 1·75
3551/4 . . . . *Set of* 4 4·00 4·50
MS3555 69×100 mm. $325 "Queen in Coronation Robes" (Sir James Gunn) (28½×42½ *mm*). P 14 . . . . 4·25 4·50
Nos. 3551/4 were printed together, *se-tenant*, in sheetlets of 8, containing two *se-tenant* blocks of 4.

497 Gabriel Marquez (author) **498** "Bather, Paris" (Picasso)

(Des J. Genzo. Litho Questa)

1993 (26 July). *Famous People of the Twentieth Century.* *T* **497** *and similar horiz designs. Multicoloured. P* 14.

(a) Arts and Literature

3556 $50 Type **497** 50 55
a. Sheetlet. Nos. 3556/64 .. .. 4·50
3557 $50 Pablo Picasso (artist) 50 55
3558 $50 Cecil De Mille (film director) .. 50 55
3559 $50 Martha Graham (dancer) 50 55
3560 $50 Peace dove (inscr "20th Century Arts and Literature") 50 55
3561 $50 Charlie Chaplin (actor) 50 55
3562 $50 Paul Robeson (actor) 50 55
3563 $50 Rudolph Dunbar (musician) .. 50 55
3564 $50 Louis Armstrong (musician) .. 50 55
3556/64 .. .. *Set of* 9 4·00 4·75
MS3565 100×70 mm. $250 Elvis Presley (singer) (*vert*) .. .. 3·50 3·50

(b) Science and Medicine

3566 $50 Louis Leakey (archaeologist and anthropologist) 50 55
a. Sheetlet. Nos. 3566/74 .. .. 4·50
3567 $50 Jonas Salk (discoverer of polio vaccine) 50 55
3568 $50 Hideyo Noguchi (bacteriologist) .. 50 55
3569 $50 Karl Landsteiner (pathologist) .. 50 55
3570 $50 As No. 3550, but inscr "20th Century Science and Medicine" 50 55
3571 $50 Sigmund Freud (founder of psychoanalysis) 50 55
3572 $50 Louis Pasteur (chemist) 50 55
3573 $50 Madame Curie (physicist) 50 55
3574 $50 Jean Baptiste Perrin (physicist) .. 50 55
3566/74 .. .. *Set of* 9 4·50 4·75
MS3575 100×70 mm. $250 Einstein's Theory of Relativity equation (*vert*) .. .. .. 3·50 3·50

(c) Sports Personalities

3576 $50 O. J. Simpson (American football) .. 50 55
a. Sheetlet. Nos. 3576/84 .. .. 4·50
3577 $50 Rohan Kanhai (cricket) 50 55
3578 $50 Gabriela Sabatini (tennis) 50 55
3579 $50 Severiano Ballesteros (golf) .. 50 55
3580 $50 As No. 3550, but inscr "20th Century Sports" 50 55
3581 $50 Franz Beckenbauer (football) .. 50 55
3582 $50 Pele (football) 50 55
3583 $50 Wilt Chamberlain (basketball) .. 50 55
3584 $50 Nadia Comaneci (gymnastics) .. 50 55
3576/84 .. .. *Set of* 9 4·50 4·75
MS3585 100×70 mm. $250 Jackie Robinson (baseball) (*vert*) .. .. .. 3·50 3·50

(d) Peace and Humanity

3586 $100 Mahatma Gandhi (India) .. .. 1·00 1·10
a. Sheetlet. Nos. 3586/94 .. .. 9·00
3587 $100 Dalai Lama (Tibet) .. .. .. 1·00 1·10
3588 $100 Michael Manley (Jamaica) .. .. 1·00 1·10
3589 $100 Pérez de Cuéllar (U.N. Secretary-General) .. .. 1·00 1·10
3590 $100 Peace dove and globe .. .. 1·00 1·10
3591 $100 Mother Teresa (India) .. .. 1·00 1·10
3592 $100 Martin Luther King (U.S.A.) .. 1·00 1·10
3593 $100 Pres. Nelson Mandela (South Africa) 1·00 1·10
3594 $100 Raoul Wallenberg (Sweden) .. 1·00 1·10
3586/94 .. .. *Set of* 9 9·00 9·75
MS3595 100×70 mm. $250 Nobel Peace Prize scroll (*vert*) .. .. 3·50 3·50

(e) Politics

3596 $100 Nehru (India) .. .. .. 1·00 1·10
a. Sheetlet. Nos. 3596/604 .. .. 9·00
3597 $100 Dr. Eric Williams (Trinidad and Tobago) .. .. 1·00 1·10
3598 $100 Pres. John F. Kennedy (U.S.A.) .. 1·00 1·10
3599 $100 Pres. Hugh Desmond Hoyte (Guyana) 1·00 1·10
3600 $100 Peace dove and map of the Americas 1·00 1·10
3601 $100 Friedrich Ebert (Germany) .. .. 1·00 1·10
3602 $100 Pres. F. D. Roosevelt (U.S.A.) .. 1·00 1·10
3603 $100 Mikhail Gorbachev (Russia) .. 1·00 1·10
3604 $100 Sir Winston Churchill (Great Britain) 1·00 1·10
3596/604 .. .. *Set of* 9 9·00 9·75
MS3605 100×70 mm. $250 Flags of United Nations and member countries (*vert*) .. 3·50 3·50

(f) Transportation and Technology

3606 $100 Douglas DC-3 cargo plane .. .. 1·00 1·10
a. Sheetlet. Nos. 3606/14 .. .. 9·00
3607 $100 Space Shuttle .. .. .. 1·00 1·10
3608 $100 Concord .. .. 1·00 1·10
3609 $100 Count Ferdinand von Zeppelin and *Graf Zeppelin* .. .. 1·00 1·10
3610 $100 Peace dove and rocket trails .. 1·00 1·10
3611 $100 Marconi and aerial tower .. .. 1·00 1·10
3612 $100 Adrian Thompson (mountaineer) and Mt Roraima .. .. 1·00 1·10
3613 $100 "Hikari" express train, Japan .. 1·00 1·10
3614 $100 Johann von Neumann and computer 1·00 1·10
3606/14 .. .. *Set of* 6 9·00 9·75
MS3615 100×70 mm. $250 Lunar module *Eagle* on Moon .. .. 3·50 3·50

Nos. 3556/64, 3566/74, 3576/84, 3586/94, 3596/604 and 3606/14 were each printed together, *se-tenant*, in sheetlets of 9 with composite background designs on Nos. 3586/94, 3596/604 and 3606/14.

No. 3562 is inscribed "Paul Roebeson" in error.

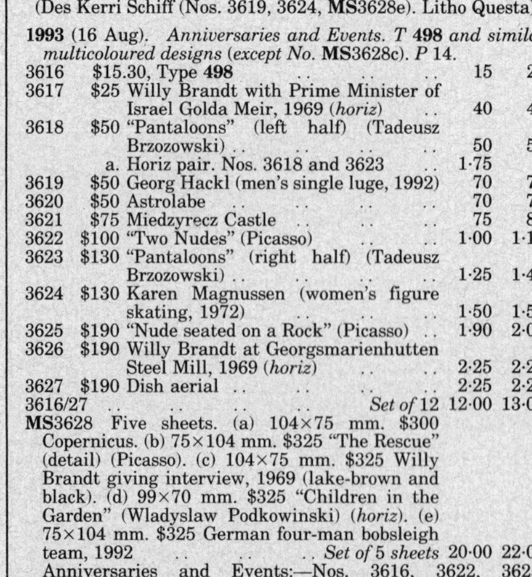

(Des Kerri Schiff (Nos. 3619, 3624, **MS**3628e). Litho Questa)

1993 (16 Aug). *Anniversaries and Events. T* **498** *and similar multicoloured designs (except No.* **MS**3628c). *P* 14.

3616 $15.30, Type **498** 15 20
3617 $25 Willy Brandt with Prime Minister of Israel Golda Meir, 1969 (*horiz*) .. 40 40
3618 $50 "Pantaloons" (left half) (Tadeusz Brzozowski) 50 55
a. Horiz pair. Nos. 3618 and 3623 .. 1·75
3619 $50 Georg Hackl (men's single luge, 1992) 70 70
3620 $50 Astrolabe 70 70
3621 $75 Miedzyrecz Castle 75 80
3622 $100 "Two Nudes" (Picasso) .. .. 1·00 1·10
3623 $130 "Pantaloons" (right half) (Tadeusz Brzozowski) .. .. 1·25 1·40
3624 $130 Karen Magnussen (women's figure skating, 1972) .. .. .. 1·50 1·50
3625 $190 "Nude seated on a Rock" (Picasso) .. 1·90 2·00
3626 $190 Willy Brandt at Georgsmarienhutten Steel Mill, 1969 (*horiz*) .. .. 2·25 2·25
3627 $190 Dish aerial .. .. 2·25 2·25
3616/27 .. .. *Set of* 12 12·00 13·00
MS3628 Five sheets. (a) 104×75 mm. $300 Copernicus. (b) 75×104 mm. $325 "The Rescue" (detail) (Picasso). (c) 104×75 mm. $325 Willy Brandt giving interview, 1969 (lake-brown and black). (d) 99×70 mm. $325 "Children in the Garden" (Wladyslaw Podkowinski) (*horiz*). (e) 75×104 mm. $325 German four-man bobsleigh team, 1992 .. .. .. *Set of* 5 *sheets* 20·00 22·00

Anniversaries and Events:—Nos. 3616, 3622, 3625, **MS**3628b, 20th death anniv of Picasso (artist); Nos. 3617, 3626, **MS**3628c, 80th birth anniv of Willy Brandt (German politician) (1992); Nos. 3618, 3621, 3623, **MS**3628d, "Polska '93" International Stamp Exhibition, Poznań; Nos. 3619, 3624, **MS**3628e, Winter Olympic Games '94, Lillehammer; Nos. 3620, 3627, **MS**3628a, 450th death anniv of Copernicus (astronomer).

Nos. 3618 and 3623 were printed together, *se-tenant*, in horizontal pairs throughout the sheet, each pair forming a composite design showing the complete painting.

499 Audie Murphy (most decorated U.S. serviceman)

(Des K. Gromoll. Litho Questa)

1993 (27 Sept). *50th Anniv of Second World War (1st issue). T* **499** *and similar horiz designs. Multicoloured. P* 14.

3629 $6.40, Type **499** 30 20
3630 $7.65, Allied troops in Normandy (8 June 1944) 30 25
3631 $8.90, American howitzer crew, Battle of Monte Cassino (18 May 1944) .. 35 30
3632 $12.80, American aircraft attacking *Yamato* (Japanese battleship), Battle of East China Sea (7 April 1945) .. 50 40
3633 $15.30, St. Basil's Cathedral, Moscow (Foreign Ministers' Conference, 19 October 1943) 50 40
3634 $50 American troops crossing Rhine at Remagen (7 March 1945) 80 65
3635 $100 Boeing B-29 Superfortresses raiding Japan from China (15 June 1944) .. 1·50 1·50
3636 $130 General Patton and map of Sicily (17 August 1943) .. .. .. 1·60 1·60
3637 $190 Destruction of *Tirpitz* (German battleship) (12 November 1944) .. 2·40 2·50
3638 $200 American forces in Brittany (1 August 1944) .. .. 2·50 2·75
3639 $225 American half-track (ceasefire in Italy, 2 May 1945) .. .. .. 2·75 3·00
3629/39 .. .. *Set of* 11 12·00 12·00
MS3640 100×69 mm. $325 Meeting of American and Russian troops on the Elbe (25 April 1945) 5·00 5·50

No. 3631 is inscribed "Monte Casino" in error.

See also Nos. 3641/60 and 3942/61.

500 R.A.A.F. Bristol Type 156 Beaufighter, Battle of the Bismarck Sea (2–4 March 1943)

501 Stuart Pearce (England)

1993 (27 Sept). *50th Anniv of Second World War (2nd issue). T* **500** *and similar horiz designs. Multicoloured. P* $14^{1}/_{2}$.

3641 $50 Type **500** 80 80
a. Sheetlet. Nos. 3641/50 .. .. 7·00
3642 $50 Lockheed P-38 Lightning attacking Admiral Yamamoto's plane, Bougainville (7 April 1943) 80 80
3643 $50 Consolidated B-24 Liberator bombers, Tarawa (17–19 September 1943) .. 80 80
3644 $50 North American B-25 Mitchell bomber, Rabaul (12 October 1943) .. 80 80
3645 $50 U.S. Navy aircraft attacking Makin (19 November 1943) 80 80
3646 $50 U.S.A.A.F. bombers on first daylight raid over Germany (27 January 1943) 80 80
3647 $50 R.A.F. De Havilland D.H.98 Mosquito bombers on first daylight raid over Berlin (30 January 1943) 80 80
3648 $50 Allied aircraft over Hamburg (24–30 July 1943) 80 80
3649 $50 Consolidated B-24 Liberators bombing Ploesti oil refineries, Rumania (1 August 1943) 80 80
3650 $50 German nightfighter attacking Allied bombers over Berlin (18 November 1943) 80 80
3651 $50 Japanese aircraft carriers during Operation 1 (7 April 1943) 80 80
a. Sheetlet. Nos. 3651/60 .. .. 7·00
3652 $50 Lt. John F. Kennedy's motor torpedo boat U.S.S. *PT109* in Blackett Strait (1 August 1943) 80 80
3653 $50 U.S.S. *Enterprise* (aircraft carrier) .. 80 80
3654 $50 American battleships bombarding Rabaul (12 October 1943) 80 80
3655 $50 American landing craft at Cape Gloucester (26 December 1943) .. 80 80
3656 $50 Commissioning of U.S.S. *Bogue* (first anti-submarine escort carrier) (February 1943) 80 80
3657 $50 Grumman FM-2 Wildcat fighters from U.S.S. *Bogue* sinking *U-118* .. 80 80
3658 $50 U-boat launching torpedo during peak of Battle of the Atlantic (March 1943) 80 80
3659 $50 Surrender of Italian fleet at Malta (10 September 1943) 80 80
3660 $50 H.M.S. *Duke of York* (battleship) sinking *Scharnhorst* (26 December 1943) 80 80
3641/60 .. .. *Set of* 20 14·00 14·00

Nos. 3641/50 and 3651/60 were each printed together, *se-tenant*, in sheetlets of 10 with the stamps arranged in two horizontal strips of 5 separated by gutters showing the Dambusters Raid (Nos. 3641/50) or the sinking of *Chuyo* (Japanese aircraft carrier) by U.S.S. *Sailfish* (Nos. 3651/60).

(Des Rosemary DeFiglio. Litho Questa)

1993 (27 Sept). *World Cup Football Championship, U.S.A. (1994) (1st issue). T* **501** *and similar multicoloured designs. P* 14.

3661 $5 Type **501** 15 1
3662 $6.40, Ronald Koeman (Netherlands) .. 15 1
3663 $7.65, Gianluca Vialli (Italy) 20 1
3664 $12.80, McStay (Scotland) and Alemao (Brazil) 30 2
3665 $15.30, Ceulemans (Belgium) and Butcher (England) 30 2
3666 $50 Dragan Stojkovic (Yugoslavia) .. 75 6
3667 $100 Ruud Gullit (Netherlands) .. .. 1·25 1·2
3668 $130 Miloslav Kadlec (Czechoslovakia) .. 1·40 1·5
3669 $150 Ramos (Uruguay) and Berthold (Germany) .. .. 1·75 2·0
3670 $190 Baggio (Italy) and Wright (England) 2·25 2·5
3671 $200 Yarentchuck (Russia) and Renquin (Belgium) .. .. 2·40 2·7
3672 $225 Timofte (Rumania) and Aleinikov (Russia) .. .. 2·50 3·0
3661/72 .. .. *Set of* 12 12·00 12·5
MS3673 Two sheets. (a) 101×73 mm. $325 Salvatore Schillaci (Italy) and José Pintos (Uruguay) (*horiz*). (b) 73×101 mm. $325 Rene Higuita (Colombia) .. .. *Set of* 2 *sheets* 8·00 8·5

See also Nos. 4142/58.

502 Sir Shridath Ramphal

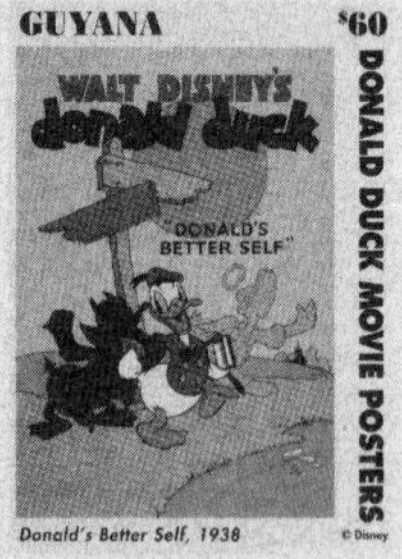

503 *Donald's Better Self,* 1938

(Litho Questa)

1993 (29 Nov). *First Recipients of Order of the Caribbean Community. T* **502** *and similar vert designs. Multicoloured. P* 14.

3674 $7.65, Type **502** 50 3
3675 $7.65, William Demas 50 3
3676 $7.65, Derek Walcott 50 3
3674/6 .. .. *Set of* 3 1·40 8

(Adapted Pauline Cianciolo. Litho Questa)

1993 (1 Dec). *Christmas. Paintings by Rubens and Dürer. Vert designs as T* **270** *of Dominica. Black, pale lemon and red (Nos. 3678, 3680/1, 3684,* **MS**3685b) *or multicoloured (others). P* $13^{1}/_{2}$×14.

3677 $6.40, "The Holy Family under the Apple Tree" (detail) (Rubens) 10 1
3678 $7.65, "The Virgin in Glory" (detail) (Dürer) 10 1
3679 $12.80, "The Holy Family under the Apple Tree" (different detail) (Rubens) .. 10 1
3680 $15.30, "The Virgin in Glory" (different detail) (Dürer) 15 2
3681 $50 "The Virgin in Glory" (different detail) (Dürer) 50 5
3682 $130 "The Holy Family under the Apple Tree" (different detail) (Rubens) .. 1·25 1·4

383 $190 "The Holy Family under the Apple Tree" (different detail) (Rubens) .. 1·90 2·00
384 $250 "The Virgin in Glory" (different detail) (Dürer) .. .. 2·50 2·75
377/84 .. .. Set of 8 6·50 7·25
S3685. Two sheets. (a) 126×101 mm. $325 "The Holy Family under the Apple Tree" (Rubens). (b) 101×126 mm. $325 "The Virgin in Glory" (woodcut by Dürer from *The Life of the Virgin*) Set of 2 sheets 6·50 7·75

(Litho Questa)

93 (6 Dec). *Bicentenary of the Louvre, Paris. Vert designs as T* **305** *of Antigua. Multicoloured. P* 13½×14.
86 $50 "Mona Lisa" (Leonardo da Vinci) 50 55
a. Sheetlet. No. 3686×8 .. .. 4·00
87/94 $50 × 8 "Self-portrait with Spectacles" (Chardin); "Infanta Maria Theresa" (Velázquez); "Spring" (Arcimboldo); "The Virgin of Sorrows" (Bouts); "The Student" (Fragonard); "François I" (Clouet); "Le Condottière" (Antonello da Messina); "La Bohémienne" (Hals)
a. Sheetlet. Nos. 3687/94 .. .. 4·00
95/702 $50 × 8 "The Village Bride" (left detail) (Greuze); "The Village Bride" (centre detail); "The Village Bride" (right detail); "Self-portrait" (Melendez); "The Knight, the Girl and the Mountain" (Baldung-Grien); "The Young Beggar" (Murillo); "The Pilgrims of Emmaus" (left detail) (Le Nain); "The Pilgrims of Emmaus" (right detail)
a. Sheetlet. Nos. 3695/3702 .. .. 4·00
703/10 $50 × 8 "Woman with a Flea" (detail) (Crespi); "The Woman with Dropsy" (detail) (Dou); "Portrait of a Couple" (Ittenbach); "Cleopatra" (Moreau); "Riches" (Vouet); "Old Man and Young Boy" (Ghirlandaio); "Louis XIV" (Rigaud); "The Drinker" (Pieter de Hooch)
a. Sheetlet. Nos. 3703/10 .. .. 4·00
711/18 $50 × 8 "Woman with a Flea" (Crespi); "Self-portrait at Easel" (Rembrandt); "Algerian Women" (detail) (Delacroix); "Head of a Young Man" (Raphael); "Venus and The Graces" (detail) (Botticelli); "Still Life with Chessboard" (detail) (Lubin Baugin); "Lady Macbeth" (Füssli); "The Smoke-filled Room" (detail) (Chardin)
a. Sheetlet. Nos. 3711/18 .. .. 4·00
719/26 $50 × 8 "The Virgin with the Rabbit" (Titian); "The Virgin with the Rabbit" (detail of head) (Titian); "The Beautiful Gardener" (detail) (Raphael); "The Lace-maker" (Vermeer); "Jeanne d'Aragon" (detail) (Raphael); "The Astronomer" (Vermeer); "The Rialto Bridge" (detail) (Canaletto); "Sigismond Malatesta" (Piero della Francesca)
a. Sheetlet. Nos. 3719/26 .. .. 4·00
386/726 .. .. Set of 41 18·00 19·00
S3727 Six sheets, each 95×70 mm. (a) $325 "Mona Lisa" and details (Leonardi da Vinci) (84×56 *mm*); (b) $325 "The Coronation of Napoleon I" (David) (84×56 *mm*); (c) $325 "Farmyard" (Jan Brueghel the Younger) (84×56 *mm*); (d) $325 "The Marriage Feast at Cana" (Veronese) (84×56 *mm*); (e) $325 "The Fortune-teller" (Caravaggio) (84×56 *mm*); (f) $325 "The Rialto Bridge" (Canaletto) (84×56 *mm*). P 12 Set of 6 sheets 3·25 3·50

Nos. 3686×8, 3687/94, 3695/702, 3703/10, 3711/18 and 719/26 were each printed together, *se-tenant*, in sheetlets of 8 amps and one centre label.

(Litho Questa)

993 (6 Dec). *Donald Duck Film Posters. T* **503** *and similar multicoloured designs. P* 13½×14 (*vert*) *or* 14×13½ (*horiz*).
728/35 $60 × 8 Type **503**; *Donald's Golf Game*, 1938; *Sea Scouts*, 1939; *Donald's Penguin*, 1939; *A Good Time for a Dime*, 1941; *Truant Officer Donald*; *Orphan's Benefit*, 1941; *Chef Donald*, 1941
a. Sheetlet. Nos. 3728/35 .. .. 4·75
736/43 $60 × 8 *The Village Smithy*; *Donald's Snow Fight*; *Donald's Garden*; *Donald's Gold Mine*; *The Vanishing Private*; *Sky Trooper*; *Bellboy Donald*; *The New Spirit*, all 1942
a. Sheetlet. Nos. 3736/43 .. .. 4·75
744/51 $60 × 8 *Saludos Amigos*, 1943; *The Eyes Have It*, 1945; *Donald's Crime*, 1945; *Straight Shooters*, 1947; *Donald's Dilemma*, 1947; *Bootle Beetle*, 1947; *Daddy Duck*, 1948; *Soup's On*, 1948
a. Sheetlet. Nos. 3744/51 .. .. 4·75
752/9 $80 × 8 *Donald's Happy Birthday*, 1949; *Sea Salts*, 1949; *Honey Harvester*, 1949; *All in a Nutshell*, 1949; *The Greener Yard*, 1949; *Slide, Donald, Slide*, 1949; *Lion Around*, 1950; *Trailer Horn*, 1950
a. Sheetlet. Nos. 3752/9 .. .. 6·50
760/7 $80 × 8 *Bee at the Beach*, 1950; *Out on a Limb*, 1950; *Corn Chips*, 1951; *Test Pilot Donald*, 1951; *Lucky Number*, 1951; *Out of Scale*, 1951; *Bee on Guard*, 1951; *Let's Stick Together*, 1952
a. Sheetlet. Nos. 3760/7 .. .. 6·50
3768/75 $80 × 8 *Trick or Treat*, 1952; *Don's Fountain of Youth*, 1953; *Rugged Bear*, 1953; *Canvas Back Duck*, 1953; *Dragon Around*, 1954; *Grin and Bear It*, 1954; *The Flying Squirrel*, 1954; *Up a Tree*, 1955
a. Sheetlet. Nos. 3768/75 .. .. 6·50
3776/81 $80 × 6 Scenes from *Pirate Gold*: In the crow's nest; Aracuan Bird carrying treasure chest; Donald with treasure map; Donald at souvenir stall; Aracuan Bird with Donald; Donald on jetty (*all horiz*)
a. Sheetlet. Nos. 3776/81 .. .. 4·75
3728/81 .. .. Set of 56 38·00 40·00
MS3782 Five sheets, each 129×103 mm. (a) $500 Book cover of *The Wise Little Hen*, 1934 (*horiz*). P 14×13½; (b) $500 Sketch for *Timber*, 1941. P 13½×14; (c) $500 Fan-card for *The Three Caballeros*, 1945 (*horiz*). P 14×13½; (c) $500 Fan-card for *Melody Time*, 1948. Imperf; (d) $500 Donald Duck. P 14×13½ .. Set of 5 sheets 25·00 26·00

Nos. 3728/35, 3736/43, 3744/51, 3752/9, 3760/7, 3768/75 and 3776/81 were each printed together, *se-tenant*, in sheetlets of 8 or 6 (Nos. 3776/81).

504 Aladdin

505 President Dr. Cheddi Jagan

(Des Walt Disney Co. Litho Questa)

1993 (6 Dec). Aladdin (*film*). *T* **504** *and similar multicoloured designs showing Disney cartoon characters. P* 13½×14 (*vert*) *or* 14×13½ (*horiz*).
3783/90 $7.65 × 8 Type **504**; Abu the monkey; Jasmine; Rajah the tiger; Jafar; Iago the parrot; The Sultan; The Genie
a. Sheetlet. Nos. 3783/90 60
3791/9 $50 × 9 Jafar and magic scarab; Tiger Head entrance, Cave of Wonders; Jafar; Aladdin and Abu at breakfast; Aladdin rescuing Jasmine; Aladdin, Jasmine and Abu; Rajah comforts Jasmine; Jafar disguised as an old man; Aladdin and Abu in treasure chamber (*all horiz*)
a. Sheetlet. Nos. 3791/9 .. .. 4·50
3800/8 $65 × 9 Aladdin with lamp and magic carpet; The Genie measuring Aladdin; Abu turned into an elephant; Aladdin in disguise at palace; Aladdin and Jasmine on magic carpet; Aladdin in disguise, Jasmine and Sultan; Aladdin fighting Jafar; Aladdin and Jasmine; The Genie with suitcase and golf clubs (*all horiz*)
a. Sheetlet. Nos. 3800/8 .. .. 5·50
3783/808 .. .. Set of 26 10·50 11·00
MS3809 Four sheets, each 127×102 mm. (a) $325 Aladdin, The Genie, Abu and magic carpet in Cave of Wonders (*horiz*); (b) $325 Aladdin in disguise on elephant; (c) $325 Aladdin and Jasmine on magic carpet (*horiz*); (d) $325 The Genie, The Sultan, Jasmine, Aladdin and Abu (*horiz*) .. .. Set of 4 sheets 13·00 13·50

Nos. 3783/90, 3791/9 and 3800/8 were printed together, *se-tenant*, in sheetlets of 8 (Nos. 3783/90) or 9 (others).

1993 (17 Dec). *1st Anniv of Election of President Jagan. T* **505** *and similar multicoloured design. Litho. P* 13½×14.
3810 $6.40, Type **505** 30 30
MS3811 97×69 mm. $325 "REBIRTH OF DEMOCRACY" emblem. P 13 .. .. 3·50 4·00

(Des W. Hanson. Litho Questa)

1994 (18 Feb). *"Hong Kong '94" International Stamp Exhibition (1st issue). Horiz designs as T* **317** *of Antigua. Multicoloured. P* 14.
3812 $50 Hong Kong 1984 Royal Hong Kong Jockey Club $1.30 stamp and Happy Valley Racecourse 70 80
a. Horiz pair. Nos. 3812/13 .. .. 1·40 1·60
3813 $50 Guyana 1992 Movie Posters $190 stamp and Happy Valley Racecourse 70 80

Nos. 3812/13 were printed together, *se-tenant*, in horizontal pairs throughout the sheet with the centre part of each pair forming a composite design.

(Des Kerri Schiff. Litho Questa)

1994 (18 Feb). *"Hong Kong '94" International Stamp Exhibition (2nd issue). Ch'ing Dynasty Snuff Boxes (Nos. 3814/19) or Porcelain (Nos. 3820/5). Multicoloured designs as T* **318** *of Antigua, but vert. P* 14.
3814 $20 Painted enamel in shape of bamboo 30 30
a. Sheetlet. Nos. 3814/19 .. .. 1·60
3815 $20 Painted enamel showing woman .. 30 30
3816 $20 Amber with lions playing ball .. 30 30
3817 $20 Agate in shape of two gourds .. 30 30
3818 $20 Glass overlay with dog design .. 30 30
3819 $20 Glass with foliage design 30 30
3820 $20 Covered jar with dragon design .. 30 30
a. Sheetlet. Nos. 3820/5 .. .. 1·60
3821 $20 Rotating brush-holder 30 30
3822 $20 Covered jar with horses design .. 30 30
3823 $20 Amphora vase with bats and peaches 30 30
3824 $20 Tea caddy with Fo dogs 30 30
3825 $20 Vase with camellias and peaches design 30 30
3814/25 .. .. Set of 12 3·25 3·25

Nos. 3814/19 and 3820/5 were each printed together, *se-tenant*, in sheetlets of 6.

$20.00 **XX**

CENTENARY
Sign For The
MAHDI
1894-1994

(**506**)

1994 (21 Mar). *Centenary of the Sign for the Mahdi. Nos.* 1622/4 *and* 1634 *surch as T* **506** *in blue.*
3826 $6 on 60 c. Plate No. 73 (Series 1) (*horiz*)
3827 $20 on 200 c. Plate No. 33 (Series 1) (*horiz*)
3828 $30 on 60 c. Plate No. 57 (Series 1) (*horiz*)
3829 $35 on 60 c. Plate No. 75 (Series 1) (*horiz*)

The surcharges on Nos. 3826 and 3828 show the third line as "MADHI".

(Litho Questa)

1994 (5 May). *Hummel Figurines. Vert designs as T* **302** *of Antigua. Multicoloured. P* 14.
3830 $20 Girl holding inscribed heart .. 20 25
3831 $25 Boy with heart under arm 25 30
3832 $35 Baker 35 40
3833 $50 Girl with pot of flowers 50 55
3834 $60 Girl with trumpet, pot plant and bird 60 65
3835 $130 Four girls .. .. 1·25 1·40
3836 $190 Boy and two girls with dog .. .. 1·90 2·00
3837 $250 Boy with cake and dog .. .. 2·50 2·75
3830/7 .. .. Set of 8 7·50 8·50
MS3838 Two sheets, each 92×124 mm. (a) $6 As No. 3835; $25 No. 3831; $30 As No. 3830; $190 No. 3836. (b) $20 As No. 3832; $35 As No. 3837; $60 No. 3834; $130 As No. 3833 Set of 2 sheets 5·00 5·25

ILO
75th Anniversary
1919-1994

$6.00

XX

(**507**)

1994 (16 May). *75th Anniv of International Labour Organization. Nos.* 1527 *and* 1629/30 *surch as T* **507**.
3839 $6 on 130 c. Plate No. 13 (Series 1) ..
3840 $30 on 120 c. Plate No. 58 (Series 1) ..
3841 $35 on 120 c. Plate No. 56 (Series 1) ..

1994 (20 May). *Centenary of Sierra Club (environmental protection society)* (1992). *Endangered Species. Multicoloured designs as T* **320** *of Antigua. P* 14.
3842 $70 Red Kangaroo with young 90 90
a. Sheetlet. Nos. 3842/9 .. .. 6·50
3843 $70 Head of American Alligator .. 90 90
3844 $70 Head of Bald Eagle 90 90
3845 $70 Giant Panda eating bamboo .. 90 90
3846 $70 Head of Red Kangaroo 90 90
3847 $70 Alaskan Brown Bear sitting .. 90 90
3848 $70 Bald Eagle 90 90
3849 $70 Head of Giant Panda 90 90
3850 $70 Red Kangaroo (*horiz*) 90 90
a. Sheetlet. Nos. 3850/7 .. .. 6·50
3851 $70 Whooping Crane facing left (*horiz*) .. 90 90
3852 $70 Male Whooping Crane in courtship display (*horiz*) 90 90
3853 $70 Whooping Crane looking right (*horiz*) 90 90
3854 $70 Alaskan Brown Bear and cub (*horiz*) 90 90
3855 $70 Alaskan Brown Bear fishing (*horiz*) 90 90
3856 $70 Bald Eagle on branch (*horiz*) .. 90 90
3857 $70 Giant Panda (*horiz*) 90 90
3858 $70 American Alligator (logo at left) (*horiz*) 90 90
a. Sheetlet. Nos. 3858/63 .. .. 4·75
3859 $70 American Alligator (logo at right) (*horiz*) 90 90
3860 $70 Italian Alps at sunrise (*horiz*) .. 90 90
3861 $70 Italian Alps and meadow (*horiz*) .. 90 90
3862 $70 Mono Lake at sunset (*horiz*) .. 90 90
3863 $70 Rock pinnacles, Mono Lake (*horiz*) .. 90 90
3864 $70 Sea Lion 90 90
a. Sheetlet. Nos. 3864/72 .. .. 7·00
3865 $70 Head of Sea Lion 90 90
3866 $70 Sea Lions on rocks 90 90
3867 $70 Rock pinnacles, Mono Lake .. 90 90
3868 $70 Sierra Club Centennial emblem (black, buff and deep blue-green) .. 90 90

3869 $70 Lake, Italian Alps 90 90
3870 $70 Summit of Matterhorn 90 90
3871 $70 Matterhorn and village 90 90
3872 $70 Clouds over Matterhorn 90 90
3842/72 .. .. *Set of* 31 24·00 24·00

Nos. 3842/9, 3850/7, 3858/63 and 3864/72 were printed together *se-tenant* in sheetlets of 8 (Nos. 3842/9 and 3850/7), 6 (Nos. 3858/63) or 9 (Nos. 3864/72).

ROYAL VISIT FEB 19-22, 1994

(508)

1994 (26 May). *Royal Visit. Nos. 3551/5 optd as T* **508** *(in three lines on $75 or two lines on* $130).
3873 $25 Queen Elizabeth II in Coronation robes (photograph by Cecil Beaton) 40 50
a. Sheetlet. Nos. 3873/6×2 .. .. 6·00
3874 $50 Royal gems 75 85
3875 $75 Queen Elizabeth and Prince Philip .. 90 1·00
3876 $130 Queen opening Parliament .. .. 1·25 1·40
3873/6 .. .. *Set of* 4 3·00 3·25
MS3877 69×100 mm. $325 "Queen in Coronation Robes" (Sir James Gunn) (28½×42½ *mm*) .. 3·50 4·00

No. **MS**3877 shows the overprint in three lines on the sheet margin.

509 *Cestrum parqui*

1994 (20 June). *Flowers. T* **509** *and similar horiz designs. Multicoloured. Litho. P* 14×13½.
3878 $6.40, Type **509** 10 10
3879 $7.65, *Brunfelsia calycina* 10 10
3880 $12.80, *Datura rosei* 10 15
3881 $15.30, *Ruellia macrantha* 15 20
3882 $50 *Portlandia albiflora* 50 55
3883 $50 *Clusia grandiflora* 50 55
a. Sheetlet. Nos. 3883/94 .. .. 6·00
3884 $50 *Begonia haageana* 50 55
3885 $50 *Fuchsia simplicicaulis* 50 55
3886 $50 *Guaiacum officinale* 50 55
3887 $50 *Pithecoctenium cynanchoides* .. 50 55
3888 $50 *Sphaeralcea umbellata* 50 55
3889 $50 *Erythrina poeppigiana* 50 55
3890 $50 *Steriphoma paradoxa* 50 55
3891 $50 *Allemanda violacea* 50 55
3892 $50 *Centropogon cornutus* 50 55
3893 $50 *Passiflora quadrangularis* 50 55
3894 $50 *Victoria amazonica* 50 55
3895 $50 *Cobaea scandens* 50 55
a. Sheetlet. Nos. 3895/906 .. .. 6·00
3896 $50 *Pyrostegia venusta* 50 55
3897 $50 *Petrea kohautiana* 50 55
3898 $50 *Hippobroma longiflora* 50 55
3899 $50 *Cleome hassleriana* 50 55
3900 $50 *Verbena peruviana* 50 55
3901 $50 *Tropaeolum peregrinum* 50 55
3902 $50 *Plumeria rubra* 50 55
3903 $50 *Selenicereus grandiflorus* 50 55
3904 $50 *Mandevilla splendens* 50 55
3905 $50 *Pereskia aculeata* 50 55
3906 $50 *Ipomoea learii* 50 55
3907 $130 *Pachystachys coccinea* .. .. 1·25 1·40
3908 $190 *Beloperone guttata* .. .. 1·90 2·00
3909 $250 *Ferdinandusa speciosa* .. .. 2·50 2·75
3878/909 .. .. *Set of* 32 19·00 20·00
MS3910 Two sheets, each 99×70 mm. (a) $325 *Lophospermum erubescens.* (b) $325 *Columnea fendleri.* P 13 .. .. *Set of* 2 *sheets* 6·50 6·75

Nos. 3883/94 and 3895/906 were printed together, *se-tenant*, in sheetlets of 12, forming composite background designs.

(Des W. Hanson. Litho)

1994 (20 June). *25th Anniv of First Moon Landing (1st issue). Horiz designs as T* **326** *of Antigua. Multicoloured. P* 14.
3911 $60 Walter Dornberger and launch of first A-4 rocket 90 90
a. Sheetlet. Nos. 3911/16 .. .. 4·75
3912 $60 Rudolph Nebel and "Surveyor 1" .. 90 90
3913 $60 Robert H. Goddard and "Apollo 7" .. 90 90
3914 $60 Kurt Debus and view of Earth from Moon ("Apollo 8") 90 90
3915 $60 James T. Webb and "Apollo 9" .. 90 90
3916 $60 George E. Mueller and "Apollo 10" lunar module 90 90
3917 $60 Wernher von Braun and launch of "Apollo 11" 90 90
a. Sheetlet. Nos. 3917/22 .. .. 4·75
3918 $60 Rocco A. Petrone and "Apollo 11" astronaut on Moon 90 90
3919 $60 Eberhard Rees and "Apollo 12" astronaut on Moon 90 90
3920 $60 Charles A. Berry and damaged "Apollo 13" 90 90
3921 $60 Thomas O. Paine and "Apollo 14" before splashdown 90 90
3922 $60 A. F. Staats and "Apollo 15" on Moon 90 90
3923 $60 Robert R. Gilruth and "Apollo 16" astronaut on Moon 90 90
a. Sheetlet. Nos. 3923/8 .. .. 4·75
3924 $60 Ernst Stuhlinger and "Apollo 17" crew on Moon 90 90
3925 $60 Christopher C. Kraft and X-30 National Aero-Space Plane 90 90
3926 $60 Rudolf Opitz and Messerschmitt Me 163B Komet (rocket engine), 1943 .. 90 90
3927 $60 Clyde W. Tombaugh and "face" on Mars 90 90
3928 $60 Hermann Oberth and scene from *The Girl in the Moon* 90 90
3911/28 .. .. *Set of* 18 13·00 13·00
MS3929 125×112 mm. $325 Frank J. Everest Jr and "Apollo 11" anniversary logo .. .. 4·50 5·00

Nos. 3911/16, 3917/22 and 3923/8 were each printed together, *se-tenant*, in sheetlets of 6.

See also Nos. 4169/87

(Des Kerri Schiff. Litho B.D.T.)

1994 (20 June). *Centenary of International Olympic Committee. Medal Winners. Multicoloured designs as T* **327** *of Antigua, but vert. P* 14.
3930 $20 Nancy Kerrigan (U.S.A.) (1994 figure skating silver) 30 30
3931 $35 Sawao Kato (Japan) (1976 gymnastics gold) 50 50
3932 $130 Florence Griffith Joyner (U.S.A.) (1988 100 and 200 metres gold) .. 1·75 2·00
3930/2 .. .. *Set of* 3 2·25 2·50
MS3933 110×80 mm. $325 Mark Wasmeier (Germany) (1994 super giant slalom and giant slalom gold) .. .. 4·00 4·50

(Des A. Melville-Brown. Litho B.D.T.)

1994 (20 June). *Centenary of First English Cricket Tour to the West Indies* (1995). *Multicoloured designs as T* **329** *of Antigua. P* 14.
3934 $20 Clive Lloyd (Guyana and West Indies) (*vert*) 40 30
3935 $35 Carl Hooper (Guyana and West Indies) and Wisden Trophy 55 50
3936 $60 Graham Hick (England) and Wisden Trophy .. .. .. 90 1·00
3934/6 .. .. *Set of* 3 1·60 1·60
MS3937 79×100 mm. $200 English team of 1895 (black and grey-brown) .. .. .. 2·50 2·75

(Des J. Batchelor. Litho B.D.T.)

1994 (20 June). *50th Anniv of D-Day. Aircraft. Horiz designs as T* **331** *of Antigua. Multicoloured. P* 14.
3938 $6 Supermarine Spitfire Mk XI fighter on photo reconnaissance 20 15
3939 $35 North American B-25 Mitchell bomber 60 50
3940 $190 Republic P-47 Thunderbolt fighters 2·50 3·00
3938/40 .. .. *Set of* 3 3·00 3·25
MS3941 109×79 mm. $325 Avro Type 683 Lancaster bomber of 419 Squadron .. .. 4·25 4·50

(Des J. Batchelor (Nos. 3942/51), W. Wright (Nos. 3952/60). Litho B.D.T.)

1994 (20 June). *50th Anniv of Second World War (3rd issue). Horiz designs as T* **500**. *Multicoloured. P* 13.
3942 $60 Paratroops drop, D-Day 80 80
a. Sheetlet. Nos. 3942/51 .. .. 7·00
3943 $60 Glider assault, D-Day 80 80
3944 $60 U.S.S. *Arkansas* (battleship) bombarding Omaha Beach, D-Day .. 80 80
3945 $60 U.S. fighters attacking train .. 80 80
3946 $60 Allied landing craft approaching beaches 80 80
3947 $60 Troops in beach obstacles 80 80
3948 $60 Commandos leaving landing craft .. 80 80
3949 $60 U.S. flail tank destroying mines .. 80 80
3950 $60 U.S. tank breaking through sea wall 80 80
3951 $60 Tanks and infantry advancing .. 80 80
3952 $60 Landings at Anzio (22 January 1944) 80 80
a. Sheetlet. Nos. 3952/61 .. .. 7·00
3953 $60 R.A.F. attacking Amiens Prison (18 February 1944) 80 80
3954 $60 Soviet Army tank in Sevastopol (9 May 1944) 80 80
3955 $60 British bren-gun carriers at the Gustav Line (19 May 1944) .. 80 80
3956 $60 D-Day landings (6 June 1944) .. 80 80
3957 $60 "V-1" over London (13 June 1944) .. 80 80
3958 $60 Allies entering Paris (19 August 1944) 80 80
3959 $60 German "V-2" rocket ready for launch (8 September 1944) 80 80
3960 $60 Sinking of *Tirpitz* (German battleship) (12 November 1944) .. 80 80
3961 $60 U.S. tanks at Bastogne (29 December 1944) 80 80
3942/61 .. .. *Set of* 20 14·00 14·00

Nos. 3942/51 and 3952/61 were each printed together, *se-tenant*, in sheetlets of 10 with the stamps arranged in two horizontal strips of 5 separated by gutters showing a D-Day Mulberry Harbour (Nos. 3942/51) or map of Europe and North Africa (Nos. 3952/61).

(Des Kerri Schiff. Litho Questa (Nos. 3964/83) or B.D.T. (others))

1994 (20 June). *"Philakorea '94" International Stamp Exhibition, Seoul (1st issue). Multicoloured designs as T* **330** *of Antigua. P* 13 *(Nos. 3964/83) or* 14 *(others).*
3962 $6 Socialist ideals statue, Pyongyang (*vert*) 10 10
3963 $25 Statue of Admiral Yi Sun-sin (*vert*) 25 30
3964 $60 Fruits and mountain peaks .. 60 65
a. Sheetlet. Nos. 3964/73 .. .. 6·00
3965 $60 Manchurian crane, bamboo and peaks 60 65
3966 $60 Rising sun and two cranes on pine .. 60 65
3967 $60 Five cranes on pine and peak .. 60 65
3968 $60 Three cranes in flight 60 65
3969 $60 Sea, rocky shore and fungi 60 65
3970 $60 Sea, rocky shore and fruit 60 65
3971 $60 Hind at seashore and fruit 60 65
3972 $60 Stag in pine forest 60 65
3973 $60 Deer and fungi by waterfall .. 60 65
3974 $60 Tops of pines and mountain peaks .. 60 65
a. Sheetlet. Nos. 3974/83 .. .. 6·00
3975 $60 Manchurian crane in flight 60 65
3976 $60 Three cranes on pine tree 60 65
3977 $60 Crane on pine tree 60 65
3978 $60 Top of fruit tree 60 65
3979 $60 Stag and two hinds on mountainside 60 6
3980 $60 Deer and fungi 60 6
3981 $60 Stag by waterfall and hind drinking 60 6
3982 $60 Pine tree, fruit and fungi 60 6
3983 $60 Fungi on mountainside 60 6
3984 $120 Sŏkkat'ap Pagoda, Pulguksa .. 1·25 1·4
3985 $130 Village Guardian (statue), Chejudo Island .. .. 1·25 1·4
3962/85 .. .. *Set of* 24 15·00 16·0
MS3986 Two sheets. (a) 104×73 mm. $325 Europeans at the Korean Court (early lithograph). (b) 73×104 mm. $325 Pagoda by Ch'urae-am Rock. P 14 .. .. *Set of* 2 *sheets* 6·50 6·7

Nos. 3964/73 and 3974/83, all 23×49 mm, were printe together, *se-tenant*, in sheetlets of 10, each sheetlet forming composite design showing panels from a screen painting longevity symbols from the late Chosun dynasty.

See also Nos. 4117/41

510 Miki Maya

1994 (20 June). *80th Anniv of Takarazuka Revue of Japa T* **510** *and similar multicoloured designs. Litho. P* 14½×15.
3987 $20 Type **510** 40 4
a. Sheetlet. Nos. 3987/94 .. .. 4·00
3988 $20 Fubuki Takane 40 4
3989 $20 Seika Kuze 40 4
3990 $20 Saki Asaji 40 4
3991 $60 Mira Anju (34×47 *mm*) 70 7
3992 $60 Yuki Amami (34×47 *mm*) 70 7
3993 $60 Maki Ichiro (34×47 *mm*) 70 7
3994 $60 Yu Shion (34×47 *mm*) 70 7
3987/94 .. .. *Set of* 8 4·00 4·2

Nos. 3987/94 were printed together, *se-tenant*, in sheetlets 8 stamps and 4 34×21½ mm labels.

511 *Heliconius melpomene*

512 Jacob

(Litho Questa)

1994 (5 July). *Butterflies. T* **511** *and similar horiz design Multicoloured. P* 14½ *(Nos. 4000/15) or* 14 *(others).*
3995 $6 Type **511** 10 1
3996 $20 *Helicopis cupido* 20 2
3997 $25 *Agrias claudina* 25 3
3998 $30 *Parides coelus* 30 3
3999 $50 *Heliconius hecale* 50 5
4000 $50 *Anaea marthesia* 50 5
a. Sheetlet. Nos. 4000/15 .. .. 8·00
4001 $50 *Brassolis astyra* 50 5
4002 $50 *Heliconius melpomene* 50 5
4003 $50 *Haetera piera* 50 5
4004 $50 *Morpho diana* 50 5
4005 $50 *Parides coelus* 50 5
4006 $50 *Catagramma pitheas* 50 5
4007 $50 *Nessaea obrinus* 50 5
4008 $50 *Automeris janus* 50 5
4009 $50 *Papilio torquatus* 50 5
4010 $50 *Eunica sophonisba* 50 5
4011 $50 *Ceratinia nise* 50 5
4012 $50 *Panacea procilla* 50 5
4013 $50 *Pyrrhogyra neaerea* 50 5
4014 $50 *Morpho deidamia* 50 5
4015 $50 *Dismorphia orise* 50 5
4016 $60 *Morpho diana* 60 6
4017 $190 *Dismorphia orise* .. .. .. 1·90 2·0
4018 $250 *Morpho deidamia* .. .. .. 2·50 2·7
3995/4018 .. .. .. *Set of* 24 14·50 15·5
MS4019 Four sheets. (a) 104×76 mm. $325 *Anaea eribotes*. P 14. (b) 104×76 mm. $325 *Eunica sophonisba*. P 14. (c) 110×80 mm. $325 *Hamadryas velutina* (39×30 *mm*). P 14½. (d) 110×80 mm. $325 *Agrias claudina* (39×30 *mm*). P 14½ .. .. *Set of* 4 *sheets* 13·00 13·5

Nos. 4000/15, which measure 39×30 mm, were printe together, *se-tenant*, in sheetlets of 16.

(Des Bryna Waldman (Nos. 4020/43), K. Tanner (Nos. 4044/91 Marilyn Abramowitz (Nos. 4092/116). Litho Questa)

1994 (4 Aug). *Bible Stories (2nd series). T* **512** *and simila square designs. Multicoloured. P* 14.

(*a*) *Joseph*

4020/43 $20 × 24 arranged as blocks of 4 depicting Jacob giving Joseph a coat of many colours (Type **512** at top left): Joseph thrown into a pit; Joseph sold as a slave; Joseph accused by Potiphar's wife; Joseph interprets Pharoah's dreams; Joseph reunited with his brothers
a. Sheetlet. Nos. 4020/43 .. .. 6·00

(b) The Parting of the Red Sea

044/67 $20 × 24 Palm trees on shore; Pyramids; Palm trees on shore and black cloud; Three palm trees; Blue and white dove; Red and white bird; Egyptian army engulfed by sea; Yellow and white dove; Red and green fishes; Egyptian chariot with wall of water at left; Chariots between walls of water; Dolphins; Two doves; Israelites and water to left; Israelites and water to right; Turquoise and purple fishes; Israelites with tree at left; Iraelites with goats; Moses; Israelites with tree at right; Israelites with woman on horse; Israelites with old man and woman carrying pack; Israelites with woman carrying young child; Israelites with cart
a. Sheetlet. Nos. 4044/67 .. .. 6·00

(c) Ruth

068/91 $20 × 24 arranged as blocks of 6 depicting Ruth and Naomi; Ruth gleaning in cornfield; Boaz establishing kinsman's rights; Naomi with Ruth, Boaz and Obed
a. Sheetlet. Nos. 4068/91 .. .. 6·00

(d) Daniel in the Lions' Den

092/116 $20 × 25 Palm fronds and hibiscus flower; Frigate bird and palm fronds; Frigate birds and tops of stone pillars; Frigate bird, pillars and sail at bottom right; Hibiscus, sails of ship and top of pillar; Yellow arum lilies and palm trees; Heads of adult and immature frigate birds and palm trees; Palm trees, butterfly and stone pillars; Two butterflies and stone pillars; Stone pillar and sailing ship; Standing heron; Purple irises and palm trees; Daniel; Angel; Donkey foal; Orchids; Lioness and two cubs; Daniel's legs and lions; Lion; Three crowns; Goat and kid; Kid; Cub and head of lion; Lioness; Heron in flight
a. Sheetlet. Nos. 4092/116 .. .. 6·00

4020/116 .. .. *Set of* 97 22·00 24·00

Nos. 4020/43, 4044/67, 4068/91 and 4092/116 were each rinted together, *se-tenant*, in sheetlets of 25 (Nos. 4092/116) or 4 (others), forming composite designs.

513 Peregrine Falcon

514 Paulo Futre (Portugal)

(Des G. Bibby. Litho Questa)

994 (16 Aug). *"Philakorea '94" International Stamp Exhibition, Seoul (2nd issue). Birds of the World. T* **513** *and similar vert designs. Multicoloured. P* 14.

117	$35 Type **513**	45	50
	a. Sheetlet. Nos. 4117/28	4·75	
118	$35 Great Spotted Woodpecker	45	50
119	$35 White-throated Kingfisher	45	50
120	$35 Peruvian Cock of the Rock	45	50
121	$35 Yellow-headed Amazon	45	50
122	$35 Victoria Crowned Pigeon	45	50
123	$35 Little Owl	45	50
124	$35 Ring-necked Pheasant	45	50
125	$35 Goldfinch	45	50
126	$35 Jay	45	50
127	$35 Sulphur-breasted Toucan	45	50
128	$35 Japanese Blue Flycatcher	45	50
129	$35 Northern Goshawk	45	50
	a. Sheetlet. Nos. 4129/40	4·75	
130	$35 Lapwing	45	50
131	$35 Ornate Umbrellabird	45	50
132	$35 Slaty-headed Parakeet	45	50
133	$35 Regent Bowerbird	45	50
134	$35 Egyptian Goose	45	50
135	$35 White-winged Crossbill	45	50
136	$35 Waxwing	45	50
137	$35 Ruff	45	50
138	$35 Hoopoe	45	50
139	$35 Superb Starling	45	50
140	$35 Great Jacamar	45	50
117/40	.. .. .. *Set of* 24	9·50	11·00

MS4141 Two sheets, each 70×100 mm. (a) $325 American Bald Eagle; (b) $325 Gould's Violetear .. .. .. *Set of* 2 *sheets* 7·50 8·00

Nos. 4117/28 and 4129/40 were each printed together, *se-tenant*, in sheetlets of 12.

(Litho B.D.T.)

1994 (1 Sept). *World Cup Football Championship, U.S.A. (2nd issue). T* **514** *and similar vert designs. Multicoloured. P* 14.

4142	$6 Type **514**	10	10
4143	$35 Lyndon Hooper (Canada)	35	40
4144	$60 Enzo Francescoli (Uruguay)	60	65
4145	$60 Paolo Maldini (Italy)	60	65
	a. Sheetlet. Nos. 4145/50	3·50	
4146	$60 Guyana player	60	65
4147	$60 Bwalya Kalusha (Zambia)	60	65
4148	$60 Diego Maradona (Argentina) ..	60	65
4149	$60 Andreas Brehme (Germany) ..	60	65
4150	$60 Eric Wynalda (U.S.A.) (pursuing ball)	60	65
4151	$60 John Doyle (U.S.A.)	60	65
	a. Sheetlet. Nos. 4151/6	3·50	
4152	$60 Eric Wynalda (U.S.A.) (kicking ball)	60	65
4153	$60 Thomas Dooley (U.S.A.)	60	65
4154	$60 Ernie Stewart (U.S.A.)	60	65
4155	$60 Marcelo Balboa (U.S.A.)	60	65
4156	$60 Bora Milutinovic (U.S.A. coach) ..	60	65
4157	$190 Freddy Rincón (Colombia)	1·90	2·00
4142/57	.. .. *Set of* 16	10·00	11·00

MS4158 Two sheets. (a) 105×75 mm. $325 "94" symbol and player. (b) 75×105 mm. $325 Oiler Watson (U.S.A.) .. .. *Set of* 2 *sheets* 6·50 6·75

Nos. 4145/50 and 4151/6 were each printed together, *se-tenant*, in sheetlets of 6, forming composite background designs.

515 Anja Fichtel (individual foil, 1988)

(Des Kerri Schiff. Litho Questa)

1994 (28 Sept). *Olympic Games, Atlanta* (1996) (*1st issue*). *Previous German Gold Medal Winners. T* **515** *and similar multicoloured designs. P* 14.

4159	$6 Type **515**	10	10
4160	$25 Annegret Richter (100 metres, 1976) (*vert*)	25	30
4161	$30 Heike Henkel (high jump, 1992) (*vert*)	30	35
4162	$35 Armin Hary (100 metres, 1960) (*vert*)	35	40
4163	$50 Heide Rosendahl (long jump, 1972) (*vert*)	50	55
4164	$60 Josef Neckermann (dressage, 1968) (*vert*)	60	65
4165	$130 Heike Drechsler (long jump, 1988) (*vert*)	1·25	1·40
4166	$190 Ulrike Mayfarth (high jump, 1984) (*vert*)	1·90	2·00
4167	$250 Michael Gross (200 metres freestyle and 100 metres butterfly, 1984) ..	2·50	2·75
4159/67	.. .. *Set of* 9	7·75	8·50

MS4168 Three sheets. (a) 105×75 mm. $135 Markus Wasmeier (skiing, 1994) (*vert*); $190 Katja Seizinger (skiing, 1994) (*vert*). (b) 105×75 mm. $325 Franziska van Almsick (swimming, 1992) (*vert*). (c) 75×105 mm. $325 Steffi Graf (tennis, 1988, 1992) (*vert*) .. *Set of* 3 *sheets* 6·50 7·00

See also Nos. 4492/4508 and 4739/88.

516 Dog Laika and Rocket, 1957

(Des J.-L. Puviland. Litho Questa)

1994 (10 Nov). *25th Anniv of First Moon Landing* (*2nd issue*). *T* **516** *and similar vert designs. Multicoloured. P* 13½×14.

4169	$60 Type **516**	80	80
	a. Sheetlet. Nos. 4169/77	6·50	
4170	$60 Yuri Gagarin (first man in space), 1961	80	80
4171	$60 John Glenn (first American to orbit Earth), 1962	80	80
4172	$60 Edward White walking in space, 1965	80	80
4173	$60 Neil Armstrong, walking on Moon and "Apollo 11" logo	80	80
4174	$60 "Luna 16" leaving Moon, 1970 ..	80	80
4175	$60 Lunar Module 1 on Moon, 1970 ..	80	80
4176	$60 Skylab 1, 1973	80	80
4177	$60 Astronauts and Apollo–Soyuz link-up, 1975	80	80
4178	$60 "Mars 3"	80	80
	a. Sheetlet. Nos. 4178/86	6·50	
4179	$60 "Mariner 10"	80	80
4180	$60 "Voyager"	80	80
4181	$60 "Pioneer"	80	80
4182	$60 "Giotto"	80	80
4183	$60 "Magellan"	80	80
4184	$60 "Galileo"	80	80
4185	$60 "Ulysses"	80	80
4186	$60 "Cassini"	80	80
4169/86	.. .. *Set of* 18	13·00	13·00

MS4187 Two sheets, each 142×104 mm. (a) $325 "Apollo 11" astronauts. (b) $325 "Galileo" *Set of* 2 *sheets* 8·50 9·00

Nos. 4169/77 and 4178/86 were each printed together, *se-tenant*, in sheetlets of 9, with the backgrounds of Nos. 4178/86 forming a composite design of Space.

517 South Carolina Railroad *Best Friend of Charleston*, 1830, U.S.A.

(Des R. Sauber. Litho Questa)

1994 (15 Nov). *History of Trains. Steam Locomotives. T* **517** *and similar horiz designs. Multicoloured. P* 14.

4188	$25 Type **517**	40	40
4189	$25 South Eastern Railway No. 285, 1882	40	40
4190	$30 Camden & Amboy Railroad No. 1 *John Bull*, 1831, U.S.A.	45	45
	a. Sheetlet. Nos. 4190/7	3·25	
4191	$30 Stephenson "Patentee" type locomotive, 1837	45	45
4192	$30 *Atlantic*, 1832	45	45
4193	$30 *Stourbridge Lion*, 1829, U.S.A. ..	45	45
4194	$30 Polonceau locomotive, 1854 ..	45	45
4195	$30 *Thomas Rogers*, 1855, U.S.A. ..	45	45
4196	$30 *Vulcan*, 1858	45	45
4197	$30 *Namur*, 1846	45	45
4198	$30 John Jarvis's *De Witt Clinton*, 1831, U.S.A.	45	45
	a. Sheetlet. Nos. 4198/205	3·25	
4199	$30 Seguin locomotive, 1829	45	45
4200	$30 Stephenson's *Planet*, 1830 ..	45	45
4201	$30 Norris locomotive, 1840	45	45
4202	$30 *Sampson*, 1867, U.S.A.	45	45
4203	$30 *Andrew Jackson*, 1832	45	45
4204	$30 *Herald*, 1831	45	45
4205	$30 *Cumberland*, 1845, U.S.A. ..	45	45
4206	$30 Pennsylvania Railroad Class K, 1880	45	45
	a. Sheetlet. Nos. 4206/13	3·25	
4207	$30 Cooke locomotive No. 11, 1885 ..	45	45
4208	$30 *John B. Turner*, 1867, U.S.A. ..	45	45
4209	$30 Baldwin locomotive, 1871	45	45
4210	$30 Richard Trevithick's locomotive, 1803	45	45
4211	$30 John Stephens' locomotive, 1825 ..	45	45
4212	$30 John Blenkinsop's locomotive, 1814	45	45
4213	$30 *Pennsylvania*, 1803	45	45
4214	$300 Mount Washington Cog Railway locomotive No. 6, 1886	3·00	3·00
4215	$300 Stroudley locomotive *Brighton*, 1872	3·00	3·00
4188/215	.. .. *Set of* 28	15·00	15·00

MS4216 Two sheets, 100×70 mm. (a) $250 Est Railway locomotive, 1878; (b) $300 *Claud Hamilton*, 1900 .. .. .. *Set of* 2 *sheets* 7·50 8·00

Nos. 4190/7, 4198/205 and 4206/13 were each printed together, *se-tenant*, in sheetlets of 8, with the stamps arranged in two horizontal strips of 4 separated by a large illustrated gutter.

No. 4198 is inscribed "West Point Foundry 1832 Locomotive" and No. 4202 "Union Iron Works os San Francisco", both in error.

(Litho Questa)

1994 (1 Dec). *Christmas. Religious Paintings. Vert designs as T* **336** *of Antigua. Multicoloured. P* 13½×14.

4217	$6 "Joseph with the Christ Child" (Guido Reni)	15	10
4218	$20 "Adoration of the Christ Child" (Girolamo Romanino)	25	25
4219	$25 "Adoration of the Christ Child with St. Barbara and St. Martin" (Raffaello Botticini)	30	30
4220	$30 "Holy Family" (Pompeo Batoni) ..	35	35
4221	$35 "Flight into Egypt" (Bartolommeo Carducci)	40	40
4222	$60 "Holy Family and the Baptist" (Andrea del Sarto)	70	70
4223	$120 "Sacred Conversation" (Cesare de Sesto)	1·50	1·75
4224	$190 "Madonna and Child with Saints Joseph and John the Baptist" (Pontormo)	2·40	2·75
4217/24	.. .. *Set of* 8	5·50	6·00

MS4225 (a) 112×93 mm. $325 "Presentation of Christ in the Temple" (Fra Bartolommeo). (b) 85×95 mm. $325 "Holy Family and St. Elizabeth and St. John the Baptist" (Francisco Primaticcio) *Set of* 2 *sheets* 7·50 8·00

518 Riker and Dr. Crusher

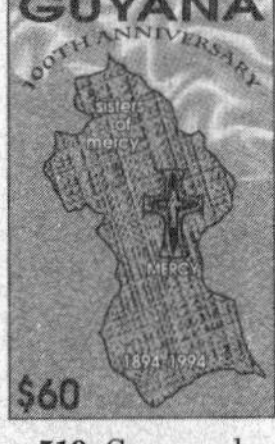

519 Cross and Map of Guyana

(Des J. Gordon. Litho Questa)

1994 (7 Dec). Star Trek Generations (*film*). *T* **518** *and similar multicoloured designs showing* Enterprise *crew in 19th-century naval uniforms* (*Nos.* 4226/34) *or in 23rd-century* (*Nos.* 4235/43). *P* 13½×14.

4226	$100 Type **518**	1·25	1·25
	a. Sheetlet. Nos. 4226/34	10·00	
4227	$100 Geordi, Dr. Crusher with Lt. Worf in chains	1·25	1·25
4228	$100 Captain Picard	1·25	1·25
4229	$100 Data and Geordi	1·25	1·25

4230 $100 "U.S.S. *Enterprise*" (sailing ship) .. 1·25 1·25
4231 $100 Captain Picard and Riker on quarterdeck .. .. 1·25 1·25
4232 $100 Data .. .. 1·25 1·25
4233 $100 Lt. Worf .. .. 1·25 1·25
4234 $100 Dr. Crusher .. .. 1·25 1·25
4235 $100 Captain Picard .. .. .. 1·25 1·25
a. Sheetlet. Nos. 4235/43 .. .. 10·00
4236 $100 Riker .. .. 1·25 1·25
4237 $100 Captain Kirk .. .. .. 1·25 1·25
4238 $100 Soron with phaser .. .. .. 1·25 1·25
4239 $100 Captains Kirk and Picard on horseback .. .. 1·25 1·25
4240 $100 Klingon women .. .. .. 1·25 1·25
4241 $100 Captains Kirk and Picard .. .. 1·25 1·25
4242 $100 Troi .. .. 1·25 1·25
4243 $100 Captain Picard and Data .. .. 1·25 1·25
4244 $100 "BOLDLY GO" film poster .. .. 1·25 1·25
4226/44 .. .. *Set of* 18 20·00 20·00
MS4245 86×103 mm. $500 U.S.S. *Enterprise* from film poster (*horiz*). P 14×13½ .. .. 5·50 6·00

Nos. 4226/34 and 4235/43 were each printed together, *se-tenant*, in sheetlets of 9. No. 4244 was printed in sheets of 9 of the one design.

Two $1000 values with designs as Nos. 4235 with 4237 and 4239 embossed on gold foil also exist from limited printings.

(Litho Questa)

1994 (12 Dec). *Centenary of Sisters of Mercy in Guyana. P* 14.
4246 **519** $60 multicoloured 80 80

(Litho Questa)

1994 (12 Dec). *First Recipients of Order of the Caribbean Community. Horiz designs as Nos.* 2046/8 *of Antigua. Multicoloured. P* 14.
4247 $60 Sir Shridath Ramphal 60 65
4248 $60 William Demas 60 65
4249 $60 Derek Walcott 60 65
4247/9 .. .. *Set of* 3 1·75 2·00

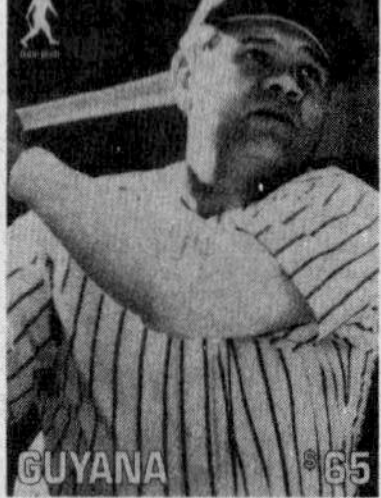

520 Garfield Sobers congratulating Brian Lara

521 Babe Ruth

(Litho Questa)

1995 (3 Feb). *Brian Lara's Achievements in Cricket. T* **520** *and similar multicoloured designs. P* 14.
4250 $20 Type **520** 20 25
4251 $30 Brian Lara setting world record for highest Test Match score (*vert*) .. 30 35
4252 $375 Lara and Chanderpaul .. .. 3·75 4·00
MS4253 70×100 mm. $300 Brian Lara (*vert*) .. 3·00 3·25

(Des J. Gordon. Litho Questa)

1995 (6 Feb). *Birth Centenary of Babe Ruth (baseball player). T* **521** *and similar designs, all reddish brown and black. P* 13½×14.
4254 $65 Type **521** 65 70
a. Sheetlet. Nos. 4254/65 .. .. 7·75
4255 $65 Preparing to bat (full-length photo) 65 70
4256 $65 Head and shoulders portrait (cap with limp brim) 65 70
4257 $65 In retirement (bare-headed) .. 65 70
4258 $65 Running (in plain shirt) 65 70
4259 $65 Head and shoulders portrait (cap with emblem and stiff brim) 65 70
4260 $65 Wearing "NEW YORK" shirt .. 65 70
4261 $65 Preparing to hit (in "NEW YORK" shirt) 65 70
4262 $65 Wearing "YANKEES" shirt .. 65 70
4263 $65 At base with bat on shoulder (in striped shirt) 65 70
4264 $65 Watching the ball (in striped shirt) 65 70
4265 $65 In cap and coat at Old Timer's Day, Yankee Stadium, 1948 .. .. 65 70
4254/65 .. .. *Set of* 12 7·75 8·50
MS4266 89×118 mm. $500 Babe Ruth (*horiz*). P 14×13½ .. .. 5·00 5·25

Nos. 4254/65 were printed together, *se-tenant*, in sheetlets of 12.

A $1000 value, showing a similar portrait, embossed on gold foil exists from a limited printing.

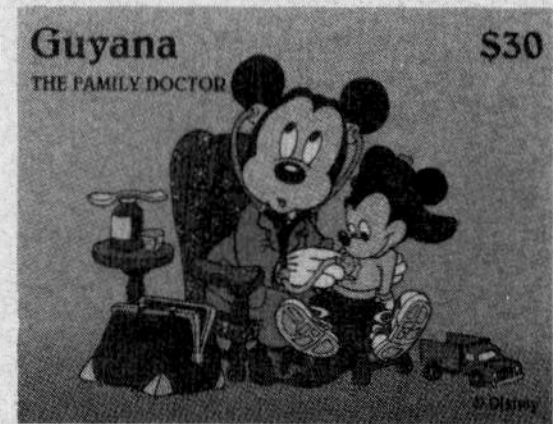

522 Mickey Mouse as Family Doctor

(Des Alvin White Studio. Litho Questa)

1995 (24 Feb). *Disney Characters at Work. T* **522** *and similar multicoloured designs. P* 14×13½ (*horiz*) *or* 13½×14 (*vert*).
4267/75 $30 × 9 Type **522**; Goofy and optometrist; Daisy Duck as nurse; Scrooge McDuck as psychiatrist; Daisy Duck as physiotherapist; Horace Horsecollar and dentist; Goofy and radiologist; Goofy as pharmacist; Big Pete as chiropractor
a. Sheetlet. Nos. 4267/75 .. .. 3·25
4276/84 $30 × 9 Mickey Mouse as vet; Donald Duck training seals; Ludwig von Duck as animal psychiatrist; Goofy as ornithologist; Daisy Duck grooming Old English Sheepdog; Minnie Mouse as herpetologist; Mickey Mouse as pet shop keeper with Pluto; J. Audubon Woodlore as park ranger; Donald Duck as aquarist
a. Sheetlet. Nos. 4276/84 .. .. 3·25
4285/93 $30 × 9 Mickey Mouse as animator with Pluto; Goofy the tailor with Mickey Mouse; Pete the glassblower with Morty; Minnie Mouse painting Clarabelle; Daisy Duck sculpting Donald; Donald Duck as potter; Chip and Dale the watchmakers; Donald Duck the locksmith; Grandma Duck making quilt;
a. Sheetlet. Nos. 4285/93 .. .. 3·25
4294/301 $35 × 8 Mickey Mouse as policeman; Donald Duck as fireman; Uncle Scrooge as ambulance driver; Grandma Duck as crossing patrol; Daisy Duck as museum attendant and Donald as visitor; Goofy as census taker and family of rabbits; Horace Horsecollar and Big Pete as street maintenance workers; Donald Duck as sanitation worker at recyling bin (*all vert*)
a. Sheetlet. Nos. 4294/301 .. .. 3·25
4302/9 $35 × 8 Mickey Mouse with Pluto driving lorry; Mickey Mouse as carpenter sawing; Goofy riding road drill; Minnie Mouse with electric drill; Donald Duck driving forklift; Minnie Mouse and Goofy as construction contractors; Mickey Mouse with Pluto as carpenter making table; Pluto driving bulldozer (*all vert*)
a. Sheetlet. Nos. 4302/9 .. .. 3·25
4310/17 $35 × 8 Mickey Mouse as plumber; Mickey Mouse the paperboy; Huey, Dewey and Louie moving furniture; Big Pete as handyman; Donald Duck and nephews house painting; Goofy as washing machine repairman; Minnie Mouse as babysitter; Daisy Duck as carer (*all vert*)
a. Sheetlet. Nos. 4310/17 .. .. 3·25
4267/317 .. .. *Set of* 51 18·00 20·00
MS4318 Six sheets. (a) 132×107 mm. $200 Goofy as surgeon. (b) 107×129 mm. $200 Goofy the zookeeper. (c) 132×107 mm. $200 Ferdie riding Pluto for photographer (*vert*). (d) 107×129 mm. $200 Horace Horsecollar campaigning for mayor. (e) 132×107 mm. $200 Minnie Mouse as carpenter and puppies. (f) 107×129 mm. $200 Minnie Mouse as maid .. .. *Set of* 6 *sheets* 14·00 15·00

Nos. 4267/75, 4276/84, 4285/93, 4294/301, 4302/9 and 4310/17 were printed together, *se-tenant*, in sheetlets of 9 (Nos. 4267/75, 4276/84 and 4285/93) or 8 (others).

No. 4271 is inscribed "PHYSICAL THEREPIST" in error.

X $20.00
SALVATION ARMY 1895 — 1995

(**523**)

524 Pig

1995 (24 Apr). *Centenary of Salvation Army. Nos.* 1519 *and* 1521/3 *surch as T* **523** *in red.*
4319 $6 on 60 c. Plate No. 10 (Series 1) ..
4320 $20 on 60 c. Plate No. 19 (Series 1) ..
4321 $30 on 60 c. Plate No. 2 (Series 1) ..
4322 $35 on 60 c. Plate No. 31 (Series 1) ..

1995 (4 May). *Chinese New Year ("Year of the Pig"). T* **524** *and similar vert designs showing symbolic pigs. Multicoloured. P* 14½.
4323 $20 Type **524** 20 25
a. Block of 4. Nos. 4323/6 .. .. 2·00
4324 $30 Pig facing left 30 35
4325 $50 Pig facing front (face value bottom right) 50 55
4326 $100 Pig facing front (face value bottom left) .. .. 1·00 1·10
4323/6 .. .. *Set of* 4 2·00 2·25
MS4327 67×89 mm. $50×4 As Nos. 4323/6 .. 2·00 2·10
MS4328 104×76 mm. $150 Pig's head .. 1·50 1·60

Nos. 4323/6 were printed together, *se-tenant*, in blocks of 4 throughout the sheet.

525 Goshawk

526 Norwegian Forest Cat

(Litho Questa)

1995 (8 May). *Birds. T* **525** *and similar vert desigr Multicoloured. P* 14½×14.
4329 $5 Type **525** 10
4330 $6 Lapwing 10
4331 $8 Ornate Umbrellabird 10
4332 $15 Slaty-headed Parakeet 10
4333 $19 Regent Bowerbird 20
4334 $20 Egyptian Goose 20
4335 $25 White-winged Crossbill 25
4336 $30 Waxwing 30
4337 $35 Ruff 35
4338 $60 Hoopoe 60
4339 $100 Superb Starling .. .. 1·00 1·
4340 $500 Great Jacamar .. .. .. 5·00 5·
4329/40 .. .. *Set of* 12 8·25 9·

(Des T. Wood. Litho Questa)

1995 (11 June). *"Singapore '95" International Star Exhibition. T* **526** *and similar vert designs. Multicoloure P* 14.
4341/52 $35 × 12 Cats (Type **526**; Scottish Fold; Red Burmese; British Blue-hair; Abyssinian; Siamese; Exotic Shorthair; Turkish Van Cat; Black Persian; Black-tipped Burmilla; Singapura; Calico Shorthair)
a. Sheetlet. Nos. 4341/52 .. .. 4·25
4353/64 $35 × 12 Dogs (Gordon Setter; Long-haired Chihuahua; Dalmatian; Afghan Hound; Old English Bulldog; Miniature Schnauzer; Clumber Spaniel; Pekingese; St. Bernard; English Cocker Spaniel; Alaskan Malamute; Rottweiler)
a. Sheetlet. Nos. 4353/64 .. .. 4·25
4365/76 $35 × 12 Horses (chestnut Thoroughbred colt; liver chestnut Quarter horse; black Friesian; chestnut Belgian; Appaloosa; Lippizaner; chestnut hunter; British Shire; Palomino; Pinto ("Seal Brown Point"); Arab; Afghanistan Kabardin)
a. Sheetlet. Nos. 4365/76 .. .. 4·25
4341/76 .. .. *Set of* 36 13·00 15·
MS4377 Three sheets, each 87×71 mm. (a) $300 Maine Coon. (b) $300 Golden Retriever. (c) $300 American Anglo-Arab .. .. *Set of* 3 *sheets* 9·00 9·

Nos. 4341/52, 4353/64 and 4365/76 were printed togeth *se-tenant*, in sheetlets of 12.

No. 4355 is inscribed "Dalmation", No. 4367 "Freisian" a No. 4370 "Lipizzanas", all in error.

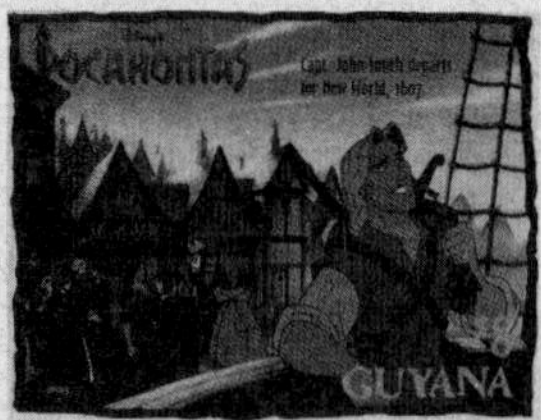

527 Captain John Smith leaving for New World, 1607

(Des Walt Disney Co. Litho Questa)

1995 (28 June–9 Oct). Pocahontas. *T* **527** *and simil multicoloured designs showing characters and scenes fr Disney cartoon film.*

(*a*) *Vert designs showing characters. P* 13½×14
4378/85 $50 × 8 Pocahontas and Meeko; John Smith; Chief Powhatan; Kocoum; Ratcliffe; Wiggins; Nakoma; Thomas
a. Sheetlet. Nos. 4378/85 .. .. 8·00

(*b*) *Horiz designs showing film scenes. P* 14×13½ (9 Oct)
4386/94 $8 × 9 Type **527**; Ratcliffe; Chief Powhatan greeted by his people; Pocahontas standing on cliff; Pocahontas, Nakoma and Meeko in canoe; Powhatan asking Pocahontas to marry Kocoum; Pocahontas receiving her mother's necklace; Pocahontas seeking guidance from Grandmother Willow; Pocahontas watching arrival of *Susan Constant*
a. Sheetlet. Nos. 4386/94 .. .. 2·50

95/403 $30 × 9 Ratcliffe claiming land for English Crown; Kekata having vision; Meeting of John Smith and Pocahontas; Namantack watching settlers; Powhatan and wounded Namantack; Pocahontas showing John Smith the colours of the wind; Nakoma finds Pocahontas with John Smith; Pocahontas offering John "Indian gold" (corn); Pocahontas, John Smith and Grandmother Willow

a. Sheetlet. Nos. 4395/403 .. .. 5·00

04/12 $35 × 9 Kocoum telling Pocahontas about the war council; Nakoma telling Kocoum to find Pocahontas; John Smith and Kocoum wrestling over knife; Powhatan sentencing John to death; Pocahontas and Grandmother Willow; Pocahontas saving John Smith; Ratcliffe under arrest; Powhatan draping his cloak over wounded John Smith; Pocahontas and John Smith saying goodbye

a. Sheetlet. Nos. 4404/12 .. .. 7·00

78/412 .. .. *Set of* 35 20·00 21·00

S4413 Four sheets. (a) 98×120 mm. $300 Meeko (9 Oct). P 14×13½. (b) 132×107 mm. $325 Pocahontas hiding. P 14×13½. (c) 132×107 mm. $325 Powhatan and Pocahontas. P 14×13½. (d) 132×107 mm. $325 Pocahontas kneeling (*vert*). P 13½×14 .. *Set of* 4 *sheets* 15·00 16·00

Nos. 4378/85, 4386/94, 4395/403 and 4404/12 were printed gether, *se-tenant*, in sheetlets of 8 (Nos. 4378/85) or 9 (others).

(Litho Questa)

95 (6 July). 95*th Birthday of Queen Elizabeth the Queen Mother. Vert designs as T* **344** *of Antigua. P* 13½×14.

14 $100 orange-brown, pale brown and black 1·00 1·10
a. Sheetlet. Nos. 4414/17×2 .. .. 8·00
15 $100 multicoloured .. .. .. 1·00 1·10
16 $100 multicoloured .. .. .. 1·00 1·10
17 $100 multicoloured .. .. .. 1·00 1·10
14/17 .. .. .. *Set of* 4 4·00 4·50
S4418 121×126 mm. $325 multicoloured .. 3·25 3·50

Designs:—No. 4414, Queen Elizabeth the Queen Mother astel drawing); No. 4415, Wearing purple hat; No. 4416, earing turquoise hat; No. 4417, At desk (oil painting); No. S4418, Wearing blue dress and mink stole

Nos. 4414/17 were printed together in sheetlets of 8, ntaining two *se-tenant* horizontal strips of 4.

528 Paul Harris (founder) and Rotary Emblem

529 Girl carrying Sack on Head

(Litho Questa)

95 (6 July). 90*th Anniv of Rotary International. T* **528** *and similar horiz design. Multicoloured. P* 14.

19 $200 Type **528** .. .. 2·00 2·10
S4420 104×74 mm. $300 Rotary emblems .. 3·00 3·25

(Des R. Martin. Litho)

95 (6 July). 50*th Anniv of Food and Agriculture Organization. T* **529** *and similar vert designs. Multicoloured. P* 14.

21 $35 Type **529** 35 40
a. Horiz strip of 3. Nos. 4421/3 .. 3·00
22 $60 Man and woman carrying sacks of food aid 60 65
23 $200 Woman holding sack .. .. .. 2·00 2·10
21/3 .. .. *Set of* 3 3·00 3·25
S4424 104×74 mm. $300 Bowl of food and F.A.O. emblem .. .. 3·00 3·25

Nos. 4421/3 were printed together in sheets of 9 (3×3) ntaining three *se-tenant* horizontal strips, each forming a mposite design.

530 Scouts around Campfire

(Litho Questa)

95 (6 July). 18*th World Scout Jamboree, Netherlands. T* **530** *and similar horiz designs. Multicoloured. P* 14.

25 $20 Type **530** 20 25
26 $25 Scout on beach 25 30
27 $30 Scouts hiking 30 35
28 $35 Scout snorkelling 35 40
29 $60 Scout saluting and flag of Guyana .. 60 65
30 $200 Scout fishing from boat .. .. 2·00 2·10
25/30 .. .. *Set of* 6 3·75 4·00
S4431 Two sheets, each 100×70 mm. (a) $300 Scouts putting up tent. (b) $300 Scouts canoeing *Set of* 2 *sheets* 6·00 6·25

(Des W. Wright. Litho Questa)

1995 (6 July). 50*th Anniv of End of World War II in Europe. Horiz designs as T* **340** *of Antigua. Multicoloured. P* 14.

4432 $60 American tank during Battle of the Bulge 60 65
a. Sheetlet. Nos. 4432/9 .. .. 4·75
4433 $60 Allied tanks crossing Siegfried Line 60 65
4434 $60 Liberated concentration camp prisoners 60 65
4435 $60 Allied plane dropping food to Dutch 60 65
4436 $60 U.S. infantry patrol, North Italy .. 60 65
4437 $60 *Daily Mail* headline announcing Hitler's death 60 65
4438 $60 Soviet tanks entering Berlin .. 60 65
4439 $60 Surrender of *U858* in U.S. waters .. 60 65
4432/9 .. .. *Set of* 8 4·75 5·25
MS4440 105×74 mm. $300 Soviet troops raising flag on Brandenburg Gate (56×42 *mm*) .. 3·00 3·25

Nos. 4432/9 were printed together, *se-tenant*, in sheetlets of 8 with the stamps arranged in two horizontal strips of 4 separated by a gutter showing sounding of ceasefire on the Western Front.

No. 4433 was incorrectly inscribed "SIGFRIED LINE".

(Des J. Batchelor. Litho Questa)

1995 (6 July). 50*th Anniv of End of Second World War in the Pacific. U.S. Ships and Aircraft. Horiz designs as T* **340** *of Antigua. Multicoloured. P* 14.

4441 $60 P61 Black Widow 60 65
a. Sheetlet. Nos. 4441/6 .. .. 3·50
4442 $60 PT boat 60 65
4443 $60 Martin B-26 Marauder bomber .. 60 65
4444 $60 U.S.S. *San Juan* (cruiser) 60 65
4445 $60 Gato class submarine 60 65
4446 $60 Destroyer 60 65
4441/6 .. .. *Set of* 6 3·50 4·00
MS4447 107×77 mm. $300 Cruiser and aircraft carrier .. .. 3·00 3·25

Nos. 4441/6 were printed together, *se-tenant*, in sheetlets of 6 with the stamps arranged in two horizontal strips of 3 separated by a gutter showing Curtiss P-40B Tomahawk II Flying Tiger aircraft.

531 Thanksgiving (U.S.A.)

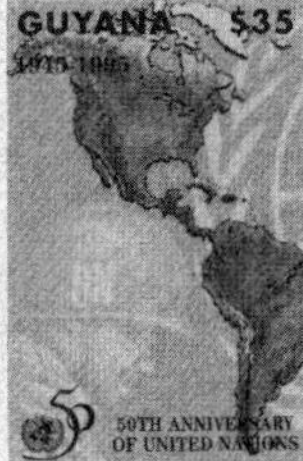

532 Map of the Americas and U.N. Soldier

(Des R. Sauber. Litho Questa)

1995 (8 Aug). *Holidays of the World. T* **531** *and similar horiz designs. Multicoloured. P* 14.

4448 $60 Type **531** 60 65
a. Sheetlet. Nos. 4448/55 .. .. 4·75
4449 $60 Christmas (Germany) 60 65
4450 $60 Hanukkah (Israel) 60 65
4451 $60 Easter (Spain) 60 65
4452 $60 Carnivale (Brazil) 60 65
4453 $60 Bastille Day (France) 60 65
4454 $60 Independence Day (India) 60 65
4455 $60 St. Patrick's Day (Ireland) 60 65
4448/55 .. .. *Set of* 8 4·75 5·25
MS4456 105×76 mm. $300 Chinese New Year (China) .. .. 3·00 3·25

Nos. 4448/55 were printed together, *se-tenant*, in sheetlets of 8, with the designs extending onto the sheetlet margin.

(Des R. Martin. Litho)

1995 (1 Sept). 50*th Anniv of United Nations. T* **532** *and similar vert designs. Multicoloured. P* 14.

4457 $35 Type **532** 35 40
a. Horiz strip of 3. Nos. 4457/9 .. 3·00
4458 $60 Map of Africa and Western Asia .. 60 65
4459 $200 Map of Eastern Asia and Australasia with refugees .. .. .. 2·00 2·10
4457/9 .. .. *Set of* 3 3·00 3·25
MS4460 74×104 mm. $300 Secretary-General Boutros Boutros Ghali .. .. .. 3·00 3·25

Nos. 4457/9 were printed together in sheets of 9 (3×3) containing three *se-tenant* horizontal strips, each forming a composite design.

533 Four-eyed Butterflyfish

534 Pole Vaulting

(Des D. Burkhart. Litho Questa)

1995 (5 Sept). *Marine Life. T* **533** *and similar multicoloured designs. P* 14.

4461 $30 Type **533** 30 35
a. Sheetlet. Nos. 4461, 4463, 4465 and 4489 .. .. 3·25
4462 $30 Lemon Shark 30 35
a. Sheetlet. Nos. 4462, 4464, 4466 and 4490 .. .. 3·25
4463 $35 Blue-headed Wrasse 35 40
4464 $35 Green Turtle 35 40
4465 $60 Three-spotted Damselfish 60 65
4466 $60 Sawfish 60 65
4467 $60 Sei Whales 60 65
a. Sheetlet. Nos. 4467/75 .. .. 5·50
4468 $60 Great Barracuda 60 65
4469 $60 Mutton Snapper 60 65
4470 $60 Hawksbill Turtle 60 65
4471 $60 Spanish Hogfish 60 65
4472 $60 Queen Angelfish 60 65
4473 $60 Porkfish 60 65
4474 $60 Trumpetfish 60 65
4475 $60 Lesser Electric Ray 60 65
4476 $60 Tiger Shark 60 65
a. Sheetlet. Nos. 4476/84 .. .. 5·50
4477 $60 Needlefish 60 65
4478 $60 Horse-eyed Jack 60 65
4479 $60 Princess Parrotfish 60 65
4480 $60 Yellow-tailed Snapper 60 65
4481 $60 Spotted Snake Eel 60 65
4482 $60 Buffalo Trunkfish 60 65
4483 $60 Cherubfish Angelfish 60 65
4484 $60 French Angelfish 60 65
4485 $80 Cocoa Damselfish (*vert*) 80 85
a. Horiz strip of 4. Nos. 4485/8 .. 3·25
4486 $80 Sergeant Major (*vert*) 80 85
4487 $80 Beaugregory (*vert*) 80 85
4488 $80 Yellow-tailed Damselfish (*vert*) .. 80 85
4489 $200 Fin-spot Wrasse .. .. .. 2·00 2·10
4490 $200 Stingray .. .. 2·00 2·10
4461/90 .. .. *Set of* 30 21·00 22·00
MS4491 Two sheets, each 100×70 mm. (a) $300 Great White Shark. (b) $300 Leatherback Turtle *Set of* 2 *sheets* 6·00 6·25

Nos. 4461, 4463, 4465 and 4489, Nos. 4462, 4464, 4466 and 4490, Nos. 4467/75 and Nos. 4476/84 were each printed together, *se-tenant*, in sheetlets of 4 or 9, the backgrounds forming composite designs.

Nos. 4485/8 were printed together, *se-tenant*, in horizontal strips of 4, each strip forming a composite background design.

(Litho B.D.T.)

1995 (9 Oct). *Olympic Games, Atlanta* (1996) (2*nd issue*). *T* **534** *and similar vert designs. Multicoloured. P* 14.

4492 $60 Type **534** 60 65
a. Sheetlet. Nos. 4492/9 .. .. 4·75
4493 $60 Long jumping 60 65
4494 $60 Woman with relay baton 60 65
4495 $60 Wrestling 60 65
4496 $60 Discus (side view) 60 65
4497 $60 Basketball 60 65
4498 $60 Boxing 60 65
4499 $60 Weightlifting 60 65
4500 $60 Shot put 60 65
a. Sheetlet. Nos. 4500/7 .. .. 4·75
4501 $60 Man in relay race 60 65
4502 $60 Female gymnast on beam 60 65
4503 $60 Cycling 60 65
4504 $60 Synchronized swimming 60 65
4505 $60 Hurdling 60 65
4506 $60 Male gymnast on pommel horse .. 60 65
4507 $60 Discus (front view) 60 65
4492/507 .. .. *Set of* 18 9·50 10·50
MS4508 Two sheets (a) 105×75 mm. $300 Athletes at start of race. (b) 75×105 mm. $300 Long jumping .. .. *Set of* 2 *sheets* 6·00 6·25

Nos. 4492/9 and 4500/7 were each printed together, *se-tenant*, in sheetlets of 8, the backgrounds forming composite designs.

535 Sand Martin

536 Queenstown Jama Masjid

(Des Mary Walters. Litho Questa)

1995 (18 Oct). *Wildlife. T* **535** *and similar vert designs. Multicoloured. P* 14.

4509 $20 Type **535** 20 25
a. Block of 4. Nos. 4509/11 and 4521 .. 3·25
4510 $35 House Martin 35 40
4511 $60 Hobby 60 65
4512 $60 Olive Colobus 60 65
a. Sheetlet. Nos. 4512/20 .. .. 5·50
4513 $60 Violet-backed Starling 60 65
4514 $60 Diana Monkey 60 65
4515 $60 African Palm Civet 60 65
4516 $60 Giraffe and zebras 60 65
4517 $60 African Linsang 60 65
4518 $60 Royal Antelope 60 65
4519 $60 Duikers 60 65
4520 $60 Palm Squirrel 60 65
4521 $200 Long-tailed Skua .. .. .. 2·00 2·10
4509/21 .. .. *Set of* 13 8·75 9·25
MS4522 Two sheets, each 110×80 mm. (a) $300 Brush Pig and Giant Forest Hog. (b) $300 Chimpanzee .. .. .. *Set of* 2 *sheets* 6·00 6·25

Nos. 4509/11 and 4521 were printed together, *se-tenant*, in blocks of 4, each block forming a composite background design.

Nos. 4512/20 were printed together, *se-tenant*, in sheetlets of 9, forming a composite background design.

(Des R. Sauber. Litho Questa)

1995 (1 Dec). *Centenary of Queenstown Jama Masjid (mosque), Georgetown. P* 14.
4523 **536** $60 multicoloured 60 65

537 Woman Soldier with Sub-machine Gun — **538** Bank Logo and Headquarters

(Des Rina Lamphe. Litho Questa)

1995 (1 Dec). *30th Anniv of Guyana Defence Force. T* **537** *and similar vert design. Multicoloured. P* 14.
4524 $6 Type **537** 10 10
4525 $60 Soldier with rifle 60 65

(Des M. Friedman. Litho Questa)

1995 (1 Dec). *25th Anniv of Caribbean Development Bank. P* 14.
4526 **538** $60 multicoloured 60 65

(Litho Questa)

1995 (4 Dec). *Christmas. Religious Paintings. Vert designs as T* **357** *of Antigua. Multicoloured. P* 13½×14.
4527 $25 "Angel of the Annunciation" (Carracci) 25 30
4528 $30 "Virgin of the Annunciation" (Carracci) 30 35
4529 $35 "Assumption of the Madonna" (Carracci) 35 40
4530 $60 "Baptism of Christ" (Carracci) .. 60 65
4531 $100 "Madonna and Child with Saints" (detail) (Carracci) .. .. .. 1·00 1·10
4532 $300 "Birth of the Virgin" (Carracci) .. 3·00 3·25
4527/32 .. .. *Set of* 6 5·50 6·00
MS4533 Two sheets, each 101×127 mm. (a) $325 "Madonna and Child enthroned with Ten Saints" (Rosso Fiorentino). (b) $325 "Mystic Marriage of St. Catherine" (Carracci) .. *Set of* 2 *sheets* 6·50 6·75

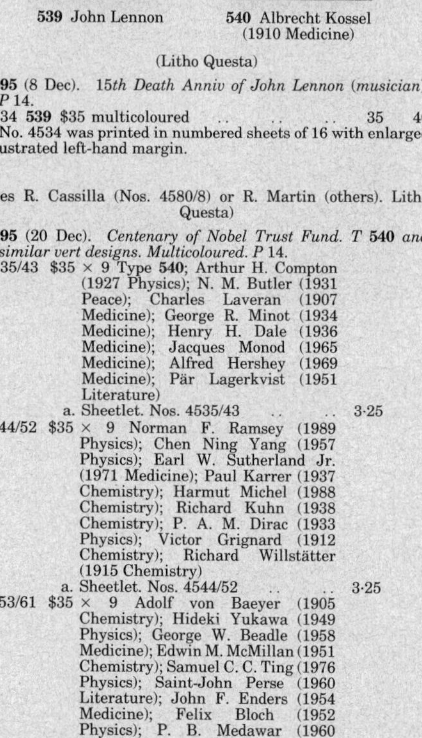

539 John Lennon — **540** Albrecht Kossel (1910 Medicine)

(Litho Questa)

1995 (8 Dec). *15th Death Anniv of John Lennon (musician). P* 14.
4534 **539** $35 multicoloured 35 40
No. 4534 was printed in numbered sheets of 16 with enlarged illustrated left-hand margin.

(Des R. Cassilla (Nos. 4580/8) or R. Martin (others). Litho Questa)

1995 (20 Dec). *Centenary of Nobel Trust Fund. T* **540** *and similar vert designs. Multicoloured. P* 14.
4535/43 $35 × 9 Type **540**; Arthur H. Compton (1927 Physics); N. M. Butler (1931 Peace); Charles Laveran (1907 Medicine); George R. Minot (1934 Medicine); Henry H. Dale (1936 Medicine); Jacques Monod (1965 Medicine); Alfred Hershey (1969 Medicine); Pär Lagerkvist (1951 Literature)
a. Sheetlet. Nos. 4535/43 .. .. 3·25
4544/52 $35 × 9 Norman F. Ramsey (1989 Physics); Chen Ning Yang (1957 Physics); Earl W. Sutherland Jr. (1971 Medicine); Paul Karrer (1937 Chemistry); Harmut Michel (1988 Chemistry); Richard Kuhn (1938 Chemistry); P. A. M. Dirac (1933 Physics); Victor Grignard (1912 Chemistry); Richard Willstätter (1915 Chemistry)
a. Sheetlet. Nos. 4544/52 .. .. 3·25
4553/61 $35 × 9 Adolf von Baeyer (1905 Chemistry); Hideki Yukawa (1949 Physics); George W. Beadle (1958 Medicine); Edwin M. McMillan (1951 Chemistry); Samuel C. C. Ting (1976 Physics); Saint-John Perse (1960 Literature); John F. Enders (1954 Medicine); Felix Bloch (1952 Physics); P. B. Medawar (1960 Medicine)
a. Sheetlet. Nos. 4553/61 .. .. 3·25
4562/70 $35 × 9 Nikolai Basov (1964 Physics); Klas Arnoldson (1908 Peace); René Sully-Prudhomme (1901 Literature); Robert W. Wilson (1978 Physics); Hugo Theorell (1955 Medicine); Nelly Sachs (1966 Literature); Hans von Euler-Chelpin (1929 Chemistry); Mairead Corrigan (1976 Peace); Willis E. Lamb Jr (1955 Physics)
a. Sheetlet. Nos. 4562/70 .. .. 3·25
4571/9 $35 × 9 Francis Crick (1962 Medicine); Manne Siegbahn 1924 Physics); Eisaku Sato (1974 Peace); Robert Koch (1905 Medicine); Edgar D. Adrian (1932 Medicine); Erwin Neher (1991 Medicine); Henry Taube (1983 Chemistry); Norman Angell (1933 Peace); Robert Robinson (1947 Chemistry)
a. Sheetlet. Nos. 4571/9 .. .. 3·25
4580/8 $35 × 9 Henri Becquerel (1903 Physics); Igor Tamm (1958 Physics); Georges Köhler (1984 Medicine); Gerhard Domagk (1939 Medicine); Yasunari Kawabata (1968 Literature); Maurice Allais (1988 Economic Sciences); Aristide Briand (1926 Peace); Pavel Cherenkov (1958 Physics); Feodor Lynen (1964 Medicine)
a. Sheetlet. Nos. 4580/8 .. .. 3·25
4535/88 .. .. *Set of* 54 20·00 21·00
MS4589 Six sheets, each 106×76 mm. (a) $300 Lech Walesa (1983 Peace). (b) $300 Heinrich Böll (1972 Literature). (c) $300 Henry A. Kissinger (1973 Peace). (d) $300 Kenichi Fukui (1981 Chemistry). (e) $300 Yasunari Kawabata (1968 Literature). (f) $300 Le Duc Tho (1973 Peace) .. .. *Set of* 6 *sheets* 18·00 19·00
Nos. 4535/43, 4544/52, 4553/61, 4562/70, 4571/9 and 4580/8 were each printed together, *se-tenant*, in sheetlets of 9, with the backgrounds forming composite designs.

541 David Copperfield

(Des R. Sauber. Litho Questa)

1995 (29 Dec). *David Copperfield (magician). T* **541** *and similar vert designs. Multicoloured. P* 13½×14.
4590 $60 Type **541** 60 65
a. Sheetlet. Nos. 4590/8 .. .. 5·50
4591 $60 David Copperfield in cloak and top hat 60 65
4592 $60 With flaming torch 60 65
4593 $60 David Copperfield in close up .. 60 65
4594 $60 Head of Statue of Liberty 60 65
4595 $60 David Copperfield climbing rope .. 60 65
4596 $60 With handcuffs 60 65
4597 $60 With woman dancer 60 65
4598 $60 David Copperfield wearing white shirt 60 65
4590/8 .. .. *Set of* 9 5·50 5·75
MS4599 76×106 mm. $300 David Copperfield with rose .. .. 3·00 3·25
Nos. 4590/8 were printed together, *se-tenant*, in sheetlets of 9, with the backgrounds forming a composite design.

542 Marilyn Monroe — **543** Rat

(Des M. Staples. Litho Questa)

1995 (29 Dec). *70th Birth Anniv of Marilyn Monroe (entertainer). T* **542** *and similar multicoloured designs. P* 13½×14.
4600 $60 Type **542** 60 65
a. Sheetlet. Nos. 4600/8 .. .. 5·50
4601 $60 Marilyn Monroe with circular earrings 60 65
4602 $60 Marilyn Monroe (deep red top right corner) 60 65
4603 $60 Marilyn Monroe (signature at bottom right) 60 65
4604 $60 With hair over left eye 60 65
4605 $60 With pink satin at left 60 65
4606 $60 With arm raised 60 65
4607 $60 With pink satin at bottom right .. 60
4608 $60 With square earring 60
4600/8 .. .. *Set of* 9 5·50 5
MS4609 76×105 mm. $300 Marilyn Monroe in pink satin dress (*horiz*). P 14×13½ .. .. 3·00 3·
Nos. 4600/8 were printed together, *se-tenant*, in sheetlets of with the background forming a composite design.

(Des Y. Lee. Litho Questa)

1995 (29 Dec). *Chinese New Year ("Year of the Rat"). T* 5 *and similar vert designs showing symbolic rats. P* 14½.
4610 $20 multicoloured 20
a. Block of 4. Nos. 4610/13 .. .. 2·00
4611 $30 multicoloured (face value bottom left) 30
4612 $50 multicoloured (face value top right) 50
4613 $100 multicoloured (face value top left) .. 1·00 1·
4610/13 .. .. *Set of* 4 2·00 2·
MS4614 68×92 mm. $50×4 As Nos. 4610/13 .. 2·00 2·
MS4615 106 x 76 mm. $150 multicoloured .. 1·50 1
Nos. 4610/13 were printed together, *se-tenant*, in blocks o throughout sheets of 16.

544 City Children

(Des M. Friedman. Litho Questa)

1996 (2 Jan). *50th Anniv of U.N.I.C.E.F. Sheet,* 110×87 *m containing T* **544** *and similar horiz designs. Multicolour P* 14.
MS4616 $1100 Type **544**; $1100 Youth worker and children (face value at top right); $1100 City children (face value at bottom right; $1100 Youth worker and children (face value at bottom right) .. .. 40·00

(Litho Questa)

1996 (29 Jan). *Paintings by Rubens. Multicoloured designs T* **421** *of Grenada. P* 13½×14.
4617 $6 "The Garden of Love" (detail) .. 10
4618 $10 "Two Sleeping Children" .. 10
4619 $20 "All Saints Day" 20
4620 $25 "Sacrifice of Abraham" 25
4621 $30 "The Last Supper" 30
4622 $35 "The Birth of Henry of Navarre" .. 35
4623 $40 Study of standing female saint .. 40
4624 $50 "The Garden of Love" (different detail) 50
4625 $60 "The Garden of Love" (different detail) 60
4626 $200 "The Martyrdom of St. Livinus" .. 2·00 2
4627 $200 "St. Francis of Paola" .. .. 2·00 2
4628 $300 "The Union of Maria de Medici and Henry IV" .. .. 3·00 3
4617/28 .. .. *Set of* 12 9·75 10
MS4629 Three sheets. (a) 70×100 mm. $325 "The Three Crosses" (56×84 *mm*). (b) 100×70 mm. $325 "Decius Mus addressing the Legions" (84×56 *mm*). (c) 100×70 mm. $325 "Triumph of Henry IV" (84×56 *mm*). P 14 .. *Set of* 3 *sheets* 9·75 10

545 Apatosaurus — **546** Giant Panda

1996 (29 Jan). *Prehistoric Animals. T* **545** *and simi multicoloured designs. Litho. P* 14.
4630/41 $35 × 12 Type **545**; Archaeopteryx; Dimorphodon; Deinonychus; Coelophysis; Tyrannosaurus; Triceratops; Anatosaurus; Saltasaurus; Allosaurus; Oviraptor; Stegosaurus
a. Sheetlet. Nos. 4630/41 .. .. 4·00
4642/53 $35 × 12 Ornithomimus; Pteranodon; Rhamphorynchus; Ornitholestes; Brachiosaurus; Parasaurolophus; Ceratosaurus; Camarasaurus; Euoplocephalus; Scutellosaurus; Compsognathus; Stegoceras
a. Sheetlet. Nos. 4642/53 .. .. 4·00
4654/65 $35 × 12 Eudimorphodon; Criorhynchus; Elasmosaurus; Rhomaleosaurus; Ceresiosaurus; Mesosaurus; Grendelius; Nothosaurus; Mixosaurus; Placodus; Coelacanth; Mosasaurus
a. Sheetlet. Nos. 4654/65 .. .. 4·00
4666/77 $35 × 12 Tarbosaurus; Hadrosaurus; Polacanthus; Psittacosaurus; Ornitholestes; Yangchuanosaurus; Scelidosaurus; Kentrosaurus; Coelophysis; Lesothosaurus; Plateosaurus; Staurikosaurus (*all vert*)
a. Sheetlet. Nos. 4666/77 .. .. 4·00
4630/77 .. .. *Set of* 48 16·00 17
MS4678 Two sheets, each 101×58 mm. (a) $60 Saurolophus; $60 Muttaburrasaurus; $60 Dicraeosaurus. (b) $60 Heterodontosaurus; $60 Compsognathus; $60 Ornithomimosaure (*all vert*) .. .. *Set of* 2 *sheets* 3·50 3

S4679 Five sheets. (a) 106×76 mm. $300 Struthiomimus. (b) 76×106 mm. $300 Tyrannosaurus rex (*vert*). (c) 76×106 mm. $300 Apatosaurus and Allosaurus. (d) 106×76 mm. $300 Quetzalcoatlus. (e) 106×76 mm. $300 Lagosuchus .. .. .. *Set of* 5 *sheets* 15·00 16·00

Nos. 4630/41, 4642/53, 4654/65 and 4666/77 were each printed gether, *se-tenant*, in sheetlets of 12, with the backgrouds rming composite designs.

96 (1 Apr). *"CHINA 96" International Stamp Exhibition, Beijing. T* **546** *and similar vert designs. Multicoloured. Litho. P* 13 (*No.* **MS**4680) *or* 14 (*Nos.* **MS**4681).

S4680 130×95 mm. $60 Summer Palace, Beijing (39×51 *mm*) 60 65

S4681 Two sheets, each 146×116 mm. (a) $60 Type **546**; $60 Panda holding bamboo stem; $60 Eating bamboo stalk; $60 On all fours. (b) $60 Panda lying on tree branch (logo at left); $60 Lying on branch (logo at right); $60 Exploring hollow in tree (logo at left); $60 Sitting on trunk (logo at right) .. .. .. *Set of* 2 *sheets* 4·75 5·00

The stamps in No. **MS**4681 form composite designs showing cks and stream (a) or dead tree (b).

COMMONWEALTH PHARMACY WEEK JUNE 16th 22nd 1996

$60.000

547 *Morchella esculenta* and *Doryphorella princeps* (leaf beetle)

(**548**)

(Des Rinah Lyamphe. Litho Questa)

96 (15 May). *Fungi of Guyana. T* **547** *and similar multi-coloured designs. P* 14.

682	$20 Type **547**	20	25
683	$25 Green-spored Mushroom	25	30
684	$30 Common Mushroom and leaf beetle ..	30	35
685	$35 Pine Cone Mushroom and *Danaus plexippus* caterpillar	35	40
686	$60 *Armillaria mellea*	60	65
	a. Sheetlet. Nos. 4686/93	4·75	
687	$60 *Gomphus floccosus*	60	65
688	$60 *Pholiota astragalina*	60	65
689	$60 *Helvellaa crispa*	60	65
690	$60 *Hygrophorus miniatus*	60	65
691	$60 *Omphalotus olearius*	60	65
692	$60 *Hygrocybe acutoconica*	60	65
693	$60 *Mycena viscosa*	60	65
694	$60 Cockle-shell Lentinus	60	65
	a. Sheetlet. Nos. 4694/7, each × 2 ..	4·75	
695	$60 *Volvariella surrecta*	60	65
696	$60 *Lepiota josserandii*	60	65
697	$60 *Boletellus betula*	60	65
698	$60 *Amanita muscaria*	60	65
	a. Sheetlet. Nos. 4698/701, each × 2 ..	4·75	
699	$60 *Russula claroflava* and *Semiotus angulatus* (click beetle)	60	65
700	$60 *Dictyophora duplicata* and *Musca domestica* (house fly)	60	65
701	$60 *Stropharia* and *Editha magnifica* (butterfly hunter)	60	65
702	$60 *Leotia viscosa*	60	65
	a. Sheetlet. Nos. 4702/5, each × 2 ..	4·75	
703	$60 *Calostoma cinnabarina*	60	65
704	$60 Stalkless Paxillus	60	65
705	$60 *Amanita spissa*	60	65
682/705	.. .. .. *Set of* 36	20·00	21·00

S4706 Two sheets, each 114×84 mm. (a) $300 *Mycena leaiana* and Yellow Crosbeak (bird). (b) $300 *Tubifera ferryginosa, Clavulina amethystina* and *Ramaria formosa* (*horiz*) *Set of* 2 *sheets* 6·00 6·25

Nos. 4686/93, 4694/7, 4698/701 and 4702/5 were each printed gether, *se-tenant*, in sheetlets of 8, containing 8 different signs (Nos. 4686/93) or two of each design (others).

Nos. 4686 and 4692 are inscribed "Armillauella mellea" and lygzocybe acutoconica", both in error.

(Litho Questa)

96 (1 June). *70th Birthday of Queen Elizabeth II. Vert designs as T* **364** *of Antigua. Multicoloured. P* 13½×14.

707	$100 As Type **364** of Antigua	1·00	1·10
	a. Strip of 3. Nos. 4707/9	3·00	
708	$100 Queen wearing green and blue jacket and hat	1·00	1·10
09	$100 Queen at State Opening of Parliament	1·00	1·10
07/9	.. .. .. *Set of* 3	3·00	3·25

S4710 103×125 mm. $325 Queen in Garter robes .. .. 3·25 3·50

Nos. 4707/9 were printed together, *se-tenant*, in horizontal d vertical strips of 3 throughout the sheet.

96 (17 June). *Commonwealth Pharmacy Week. Unissued values in designs of Nos.* 1810 *and* 1873 *surch as T* **548**.

711	$6 on 130 c. Plate No. 21 (Series 2) ..		
712	$60 on 100 c. Plate No. 33 (Series 2) ..		

(Litho Questa)

1996 (8 July). *Centenary of Radio. Entertainers. Vert designs as T* **368** *of Antigua. Multicoloured. P* 13½×14.

4713	$20 Frank Sinatra	20	25
4714	$35 Gene Autry	50	55
4715	$60 Groucho Marx	60	65
4716	$200 Red Skelton	2·00	2·10
4713/16	.. .. .. *Set of* 4	3·25	3·50
MS4717	104×74 mm. $300 Burl Ives	3·00	3·25

549 Hulda Gates

550 Long-billed Starthroat

(Des R. Sauber. Litho Questa)

1996 (8 July). *3000th Anniv of Jerusalem. T* **549** *and similar vert designs. Multicoloured. P* 14.

4718	$30 Type **549**	30	35
	a. Sheetlet. Nos. 4718/20	2·50	
4719	$35 Church of St. Mary Magdalene ..	35	40
4720	$200 Absalom's Tomb, Kidron Valley ..	2·00	2·10
4718/20	.. .. .. *Set of* 3	2·50	2·75

MS4721 105×76 mm. $300 Children's Holocaust Memorial, Yad Vashem .. .. .. 3·00 3·25

Nos. 4718/20 were printed together, *se-tenant*, in sheetlets of 3 with enlarged illustrated margin at foot.

1996 (10 July). *Birds of the World. T* **550** *and similar multicoloured designs. Litho. P* 14.

4722	$60 Type **550**	60	65
	a. Sheetlet. Nos. 4722/9	4·75	
4723	$60 Velvet-purple Coronet	60	65
4724	$60 Racquet-tailed Coquette	60	65
4725	$60 Violet-tailed Sylph	60	65
4726	$60 Broad-tailed Hummingbird	60	65
4727	$60 Blue-tufted Starthroat	60	65
4728	$60 White-necked Jacobin	60	65
4729	$60 Ruby-throated Hummingbird ..	60	65
4730	$60 Blue and Yellow Macaw	60	65
	a. Sheetlet. Nos. 4730/7	4·75	
4731	$60 Andean Condor	60	65
4732	$60 Guiana Crested Eagle	60	65
4733	$60 White-tailed Trogon	60	65
4734	$60 Toco Toucan	60	65
4735	$60 Great Horned Owl	60	65
4736	$60 Andean Cock-of-the-Rock	60	65
4737	$60 Great Curassow	60	65
4722/37	.. .. .. *Set of* 16	9·50	10·00

MS4738 Two sheets, each 101×70 mm. (a) $300 Gould's Sparkling Violet-ear. (b) $300 Ornate Hawk Eagle (*horiz*) .. *Set of* 2 *sheets* 6·00 6·25

Nos. 4722/9 and 4730/7 were each printed together, *se-tenant*, in sheetlets of 8, the backgrounds forming composite designs.

551 Pancratium (ancient Olympic event)

(Litho Questa)

1996 (19 July). *Olympic Games, Atlanta* (3rd issue). *T* **551** *and similar multicoloured designs. P* 14.

4739	$20 Type **551**	20	25
4740	$30 Olympic Stadium, Melbourne, 1956	30	35
4741/9	$50 × 9 Volleyball; Basketball; Tennis; Table tennis; Baseball; Handball; Hockey; Water polo; Football		
	a. Sheetlet. Nos. 4741/9	4·50	
4750/8	$50 × 9 Cycling; Hurdling; High jumping; Diving; Weightlifting; Canoeing; Wrestling; Gymnastics; Running (*all vert*)		
	a. Sheetlet. Nos. 4750/8	4·50	
4759/67	$50 × 9 Florence Griffith-Joyner (track and field) (U.S.A.); Ines Geissler (swimming) (Germany); Nadia Comaneci (gymnastics) (Rumania); Tatiana Gutsu (gymnastics) (Unified team); Ogla Korbut (gymnastics) (Russia); Barbara Krause (swimming) (Germany); Olga Bryzgina (track and field) (Russia); Fanny Blankers-Koen (track and field) (Holland); Irena Szewinska (track and field) (Poland) (*all vert*)		
	a. Sheetlet. Nos. 4759/67	4·50	
4768/76	$50 × 9 Gerd Wessig (Germany); Jim Thorpe (U.S.A.); Norman Read (New Zealand); Lasse Viren (Finland); Milt Campbell (U.S.A.); Abebe Bikila (Ethiopia); Jesse Owens (U.S.A.); Viktor Saneev (Russia); Waldemer Cierpinski (Germany) (all track and field) (*all vert*)		
	a. Sheetlet. Nos. 4768/76	4·50	
4777/85	$50 × 9 Ditmar Schmidt (handball) (Germany); Pam Shriver (tennis doubles) (U.S.A.); Zina Garrison (tennis doubles) (U.S.A); Hyun Jung-Hua (table tennis doubles) (Korea); Steffi Graf (tennis) (Germany); Michael Jordan (basketball) (U.S.A.); Karch Kiraly (volleyball) (U.S.A.); "Magic" Johnson (basketball) (U.S.A.); Ingolf Weigert (handball) (Germany) (*all vert*)		
	a. Sheetlet. Nos. 4777/85	4·50	
4786	$60 Leonid Spirin winning 20 kilometre walk, 1956 (*vert*)	60	65
4787	$200 Lars Hall, Gold medal winner, Modern Pentathalon, 1952 and 1956 (Sweden) (*vert*)	2·00	2·10
4739/87	.. .. .. *Set of* 49	26·00	27·00

MS4788 Two sheets. (a) 104×74 mm. $300 Carl Lewis, Gold medal winner, track and field, 1984, 1988 and 1992 (U.S.A.). (b) 74×104 mm. $300 U.S.A. defeating Korea at baseball, 1988 *Set of* 2 *sheets* 6·00 6·25

Nos. 4741/9, 4750/8, 4759/67, 4768/76 and 4777/85 (the last three showing Gold medal winners) were each printed together, *se-tenant*, in sheetlets of 9, forming composite background designs.

No. **MS**4788 (a) is inscribed "1985" in error.

552 Mickey's Bait Shop

(Des Walt Disney Co. Litho Questa)

1996 (26 July). *Mickey Mouse and Friends Outdoors. T* **552** *and similar multicoloured designs. P* 14×13½ (*horiz*) *or* 13½×14 (*vert*).

4789	$60 Type **552**	60	65
	a. Horiz strip of 3. Nos. 4789/91 ..	1·75	
4790	$60 Mickey and Pluto as lumberjacks ..	60	65
4791	$60 Mickey fishing	60	65
4792	$80 Donald Duck in BMX Bike Championships (*vert*)	80	85
	a. Horiz strip of 3. Nos. 4792/4 ..	2·25	
4793	$80 Goofy as ice hockey superstar (*vert*)	80	85
4794	$80 Donald Duck at Malibu Surf City (*vert*)	80	85
4795	$100 Mickey as naval captain (*vert*) ..	1·00	1·10
	a. Horiz strip of 3. Nos. 4795/7 ..	3·00	
4796	$100 Captain Mickey's Seamanship School (*vert*)	1·00	1·10
4797	$100 Mickey as sailor with ship's wheel and full-rigged sailing ship (*vert*) ..	1·00	1·10
4789/97	.. .. .. *Set of* 9	7·00	7·50

MS4798 Five sheets. (a) 124×101 mm. $250 Mickey as Pinkerton detective (*vert*). (b) 104×126 mm. $250 Mickey as U.S. Marshal (*vert*). (c) 125×104 mm. $250 Mickey as train conductor and Transcontinental Railroad locomotive. (d) 101×124 mm. $300 Donald Duck as mountaineer. (e) 104×124 mm. $325 Mickey as trapper (*vert*) .. .. *Set of* 5 *sheets* 13·00 13·50

Nos. 4789/91, 4792/4 and 4795/7 were each printed together, *se-tenant*, in horizontal strips of 3 throughout sheets of 9.

553 Two Gun Mickey

554 Elvis Presley

1996 (26 July). *Disney Antique Toys. T* **553** *and similar vert designs. Multicoloured. Litho. P* 13½×14.

4799	$6 Type **553**	10	10
	a. Sheetlet. Nos. 4799/806	50	
4800	$6 Wood-jointed Mickey figure	10	10
4801	$6 Donald jack-in-the-box	10	10
4802	$6 Rocking Minnie	10	10
4803	$6 Fireman Donald Duck	10	10
4804	$6 Long-billed Donald Duck	10	10
4805	$6 Painted-wood Mickey figure	10	10
4806	$6 Wind-up Jimny Cricket	10	10
4799/806	.. .. .. *Set of* 8	50	55

MS4807 Two sheets, each 131×105 mm. (a) $300 Mickey doll. (b) $300 Carousel .. *Set of* 2 *sheets* 6·00 6·50

Nos. 4799/806 were printed together, *se-tenant*, in sheetlets of 8.

1996 (8 Sept). *60th Birth Anniv of Elvis Presley* (1995). *T* **554** *and similar vert portraits. Multicoloured: background colours given. Litho. P* 13½×14.

4808 $100 carmine-red (Type **554**) . . . . 1·00 1·10
a. Sheetlet. Nos. 4808/13 . . . . 6·00
4809 $100 cerise . . . . 1·00 1·10
4810 $100 lake-brown . . . . 1·00 1·10
4811 $100 dull ultramarine . . . . . . 1·00 1·10
4812 $100 purple . . . . 1·00 1·10
4813 $100 turquoise-blue . . . . . . 1·00 1·10
4808/13 . . . . *Set of* 6 6·00 6·50

Nos. 4808/13 were printed together, *se-tenant*, in sheetlets of 6 with enlarged illustrated margins.

555 Piece of Meteorite showing Fossil

556 Birman

(Des L. Birmingham. Litho Questa)

1996 (7 Oct). *Mars Meteorite. Sheet* 104×76 *mm. P* 14½×14.

MS4814 **555** $50 multicoloured 50 60

1996 (7 Oct). *Cats of the World. T* **556** *and similar multicoloured designs. Litho. P* 14.

4815 $60 Type **556** 60 65
a. Sheetlet. Nos. 4815/23 . . . . 5·25
4816 $60 American Curl 60 65
4817 $60 Turkish Angora 60 65
4818 $60 European Shorthair (Italy) 60 65
4819 $60 Persian (Great Britain) 60 65
4820 $60 Scottish Fold 60 65
4821 $60 Sphynx (Canada) 60 65
4822 $60 Malayan (Thailand) 60 65
4823 $60 Cornish Rex (Great Britain) 60 65
4824 $60 Norwegian Forest (*vert*) 60 65
a. Sheetlet. Nos. 4824/32 . . . . 5·25
4825 $60 Russian Shorthair (*vert*) 60 65
4826 $60 European Shorthair (Italy) (*vert*) . . 60 65
4827 $60 Birman (*vert*) 60 65
4828 $60 Ragdoll (U.S.A.) (*vert*) 60 65
4829 $60 Egyptian Mau (*vert*) 60 65
4830 $60 Persian (Great Britain) (*vert*) . . 60 65
4831 $60 Turkish Angora (*vert*) 60 65
4832 $60 Siamese (*vert*) 60 65
4815/32 . . . . *Set of* 18 10·50 11·50
MS4833 Two sheets, each 107×72 mm. (a) $300 Himalayan (U.S.A.). (b) $300 Maine Coon (U.S.A.) (*vert*) . . . . *Set of* 2 *sheets* 6·00 6·25

Nos. 4815/23 and 4824/32 were each printed together, *se-tenant*, in sheetlets of 9 with the backgrounds forming composite designs.

557 Hyed Snapper

558 Snow White and Reindeer

(Des I. MacLaury (Nos. 4838/52), Rina Lyamphe (others). Litho Questa)

1996 (2 Dec). *Marine Life. T* **557** *and similar horiz designs. Multicoloured. P* 14.

4834 $6 Type **557** 10 10
4835 $6 Angelfish 10 10
4836 $20 Boxfish 20 25
4837 $25 Golden Damselfish 25 30
4838 $30 Goblin Shark and Coelacanth . . 30 35
a. Sheetlet. Nos. 4838/52 . . . . 4·50
4839 $30 "Jason" remote-controlled submersible 30 35
4840 $30 Deep-water invertebrates 30 35
4841 $30 Submarine NR-1 . . . . . . 30 35
4842 $30 Giant Squid 30 35
4843 $30 Sperm Whale 30 35
4844 $30 Volcanic vents and "Alvin" submersible 30 35
4845 $30 Air-recycling pressure suits and shipwreck 30 35
4846 $30 "Shinkai" 6500 submersible . . 30 35
4847 $30 Giant Tube Worms 30 35
4848 $30 Anglerfish 30 35
4849 $30 Six-gill Shark 30 35
4850 $30 Autonomous Underwater Vehicle ABE 30 35
4851 $30 Octopus and Viperfish 30 35
4852 $30 Swallower and Hatchetfish 30 35
4853 $35 Clown Triggerfish 35 40
4854 $60 Red Gorgonians 60 65
a. Sheetlet. Nos. 4854/62 . . . . 5·25
4855 $60 Soft Coral and Butterflyfish . . 60 65
4856 $60 Soft Coral and Slender Snapper . . 60 65
4857 $60 Common Clownfish, Anemone and Mushroom Coral 60 65
4858 $60 Anemone and Horse-eyed Jack . . 60 65
4859 $60 Splendid Coral Trout 60 65
4860 $60 Anemones 60 65
4861 $60 Brain Coral 60 65
4862 $60 Cup Coral 60 65
4863 $200 Harlequin Tuskfish . . . . . . 2·00 2·10
4834/63 . . . . *Set of* 30 12·00 14·00
MS4864 Two sheets, each 98×68 mm. (a) $300 Caribbean Flower Coral. (b) $300 Sea Anemone *Set of* 2 *sheets* 6·00 6·25

Nos. 4838/52 and 4854/62 were each printed together, *se-tenant*, in sheetlets of 15 or 9, with the backgrounds forming composite designs.

No. 4853 is inscribed "CLOWN TUGGERFISH" in error.

(Des Walt Disney Co. Litho Questa)

1996 (2 Dec). *Christmas. Disney's* Snow White and the Seven Dwarfs. *T* **558** *and similar vert designs. Multicoloured. P* 13½×14.

4865 $6 Type **558** 10 10
4866 $20 Doc with presents 20 25
4867 $25 Dopey and Sneezy 25 30
4868 $30 Sleepy, Happy and Bashful 30 35
4869 $35 Dopey and Santa Claus 35 40
4870 $60 Dopey with socks at fireplace . . 60 65
4871 $100 Dopey and Grumpy . . . . . . 1·00 1·10
4872 $200 Dopey dressed as Santa Claus . . 2·00 2·10
4865/72 . . . . *Set of* 8 4·75 5·25
MS4873 Two sheets, each 122×102 mm. (a) $300 Snow White, Doc and squirrel. (b) $300 Dopey and Christmas tree . . . . *Set of* 2 *sheets* 6·00 6·25

559 Hotel Tower

(Litho B.D.T.)

1996 (30 Dec). *50th Anniv of Hotel Tower, Georgetown. P* 14×14½.

4874 **559** $30 multicoloured 30 35

STAMP BOOKLETS

09 (14 June). *Black on pink cover without face value. Stapled.*
1 49 c. booklet containing twelve 1 c. and eighteen 2 c. (Nos. 252/3) in blocks of 6 .. ..

23. *Black on pink cover without face value. Stapled.*
2 30 c. booklet containing six 1 c. and twelve 2 c. (Nos. 272, 274) in blocks of 6 .. ..

23. *Black on pink without face value. Stapled.*
3 48 c. booklet containing twelve 1 c. and eighteen 2 c. (Nos. 272, 274) in blocks of 6 .. .. £950
a. With face value on front cover .. ..

23. *Black on red cover without face value. Stapled.*
4 72 c. booklet containing twelve 1 c., six 2 c. and twelve 4 c. (Nos. 272, 274/5) in blocks of 6 £1300

34. *Black on orange cover. Stitched.*
5 24 c. booklet containing eight 1 c. and eight 2 c. (Nos. 288/9) in blocks of 4 .. .. ..

34. *Black on orange cover. Stitched.*
36 36 c. booklet containing four 1 c., eight 2 c. and four 4 c. (Nos. 288/9, 291) in blocks of 4 ..

38. *Black on orange cover. Stitched.*
37 36 c. booklet containing four 1 c., eight 2 c. and four 4 c. (Nos. 308/10) in blocks of 4 .. £180

44. *Black on orange cover. Stitched.*
38 24 c. booklet containing eight 1 c. and eight 2 c. (Nos. 308/9) in blocks of 4 .. .. .. £140

45–49. *Black on red cover. Stitched.*
39 24 c. booklet containing 1 c., 2 c. and 3 c. (Nos. 290, 308, 309), each in block of 4 .. .. 65·00
a. Containing Nos. 290, 308aa, 309 .. .. 65·00
b. Containing Nos. 290, 308aa, 309a .. ..
c. Containing Nos. 290a, 308aa, 309 .. .. 65·00
d. Containing Nos. 290b, 308aa, 309 .. .. 65·00
e. Containing Nos. 290b, 308aa, 309a .. 65·00
f. Containing Nos. 290b, 308a, 309a .. .. 65·00

B 1

981 (1 July). *Blue cover as Type* B **1**, *printed in black. Stapled.*
B10 $6 booklet containing two 15 c. (No. 808A or B), three 50 c. on 5 c. (No. 794), two 100 c. on 1 c. (No. 806) and two 110 c. on 1 c. (No. 807) .. 4·25

B 2

981 (22 July). *Royal Wedding. Red, yellow and blue cover as Type* B **2**. *Stitched.*
B11 $5 booklet containing two 60 c. on 3 c., two 75 c. on $5 and two $1.10 on $2 (Nos. 841/3) in pairs and pane of four air mail labels .. .. 3·25

981 (1 Aug). *Green cover as Type* B **1**, *printed in black. Stapled.*
B12 $3 booklet containing ten 15 c. on 10 c. on 6 c. and ten 15 c. on 30 c. on 6 c. (Nos. 848/9) .. 4·50
B13 $3 booklet containing ten 15 c. on 50 c. on 6 c. and ten 15 c. on 60 c. on 6 c. (Nos. 850/1) .. 5·00

981 (10 Nov). *Cover as Nos.* SB12/13 *surcharged* "$5". *Stapled.*
B14 $5 on $3 booklet containing six 50 c. on 6 c. (No. 862 or 862*b*) and two $1 on 6 c. (No. 863 or 863*b*) .. .. 4·00

1981 (10 Nov). *Blue cover as Type* B **1**, *printed in black, Stapled.*
SB15 $6 booklet containing four 50 c. on 6 c. (No. 862 or 862*b*) and four $1 on 6 c. (No. 863 or 863*b*) 4·25

1982 (Apr). *Cover as Nos.* SB12/13 *surcharged* "$5". *Stapled.*
SB16 $5 on $3 booklet containing ten 20 c. on 35 c. (No. 918), two 50 c. on 6 c. (No. 862 or 862*b*) and two $1 on 6 c. (No. 863 or 863*b*) .. .. 11·00

1982 (15 June). *75th Anniv of Boy Scout Movement. Cover as No.* SB16 *further overprinted* "SCOUT MOVEMENT 1907–1982". *Stapled.*
SB17 $5 on $3 booklet containing two 125 c. on 8 c. on 6 c. and two 125 c. on 8 c. on 6 c. (Nos. 905/6) 5·00

1982 (15 June). *75th Anniv of Boy Scout Movement. Cover as No.* SB15 *overprinted* "SCOUT MOVEMENT 1907–1982" *in red. Stapled.*
SB18 $6 booklet containing two 25 c. and five 110 c. on 6 c. (Nos. 892, 978) .. .. 20·00

1982 (15 July). *75th Anniv of Boy Scout Movement. Cover as No.* SB16 *further overprinted* "SCOUT MOVEMENT 1907–1982". *Stapled.*
SB19 $5 on $3 booklet containing two 15 c. on 2 c., two 15 c. on 2 c. and four 110 c. on 6 c. (Nos. 895/6, 978) .. .. 14·00
SB20 $5 on $3 booklet containing 15 c. on 2 c., 15 c. on 2 c., 110 c. on 5 c., 110 c. on 5 c., 125 c. on 8 c. on 6 c. and 125 c. on 8 c. on 6 c. (Nos. 895/6, 900/1, 905/6) .. .. 4·00

1982 (15 July). *75th Anniv of Boy Scout Movement. Covers as No.* SB15 *overprinted* "SCOUT MOVEMENT 1907–1982" *in red. Stapled.*
SB21 $6 booklet containing four 15 c. on 2 c., four 15 c. on 2 c., four 15 c. on 2 c., three 25 c., 110 c. on 5 c., 110 c. on 5 c. and 125 c. on 8 c. on 6 c. (Nos. 895/7, 892, 900/1, 905) .. .. .. 9·00
SB22 $6 booklet containing four 15 c. on 2 c., four 15 c. on 2 c., four 15 c. on 2 c., three 25 c., 110 c. on 5 c., 110 c. on 5 c. and 125 c. on 8 c. on 6 c. (No. 895/6, 898, 892, 900/1, 906) .. .. .. 9·00

1983 (July). *Covers as Type* B **1**, *printed in black on green* ($3), *surcharged as No.* SB16 ($5) *or on blue* ($6). *Stapled.*
SB23 $3 booklet containing ten 30 c. (No. 1127) .. 3·00
SB24 $5 on $3 booklet containing twenty 25 c. (No. 1108a) .. .. 4·00
SB25 $6 booklet containing ten 60 c. (No. 1128) .. 6·00
SB26 $6 booklet containing five 120 c. (No. 1129) .. 6·00
SB27 $6 booklet containing four 150 c. (No. 1131) .. 6·00

1983 (Oct). *Covers as Type* B **1**, *printed in black on green* ($3), *surcharged as No.* SB16 ($5) *or on blue* ($6). *Stamps attached by selvedge.*
SB28 $3 booklet containing ten 30 c. (No. 1173) .. 2·25
SB29 $5 on $3 booklet containing twenty 25 c. (No. 1172) .. .. 3·25
SB30 $6 booklet containing ten 30 c. and five 60 c. (Nos. 1173/4) .. .. 2·75
SB31 $6 booklet containing ten 60 c. (No. 1174) .. 2·75
SB32 $6 booklet containing five 120 c. (No. 1175) .. 2·75

1984 (1 Mar). *Guyana Olympic Committee Appeal. Booklet No.* SB11 *with cover surcharged* "HELP SEND OUR ATHLETES TO THE 1984 OLYMPICS BOOKLET $15.00" *in blue.*
SB33 $15 on $5 booklet containing two 25 c.+2.25 c. on 60 c. on 3 c., two 25 c.+2.25 c. on 75 c. on $5 and two 25 c.+2.25 c. on $1.10 on $2 (Nos. 1235/7) and pane of four air mail labels .. 10·00

1984 (28 July). *Olympic Games, Los Angeles. Covers as Nos.* SB10 *and* SB12 *surcharged* "OLYMPIC GAMES 1984" *and* "$5.00" *on* $3 *black on green or* "$12.00" *on* $6 *black on blue.*
SB34 $5 on $3 booklet containing two panes of 10 (No. 1308a) .. .. 5·00
SB35 $12 on $6 booklet containing two panes of 10 (No. 1313a) .. .. 18·00

1985 (9 July). *Green cover as Type* B **1**, *printed in black. Stapled.*
SB36 $3 booklet containing twelve 25 c. (No. 1534) in pairs .. .. 2·25

1986 (26 May). *20th Anniv of Independence* (1*st issue*). *Green cover as Type* B **1**, *printed in black. Stamps attached by selvedge.*
SB37 $3 booklet containing 25 c. on 120 c., 25 c. on 130 c., 25 c. on 150 c. and 225 c. on 200 c. (No. 1723a) .. .. 3·25

1986 (14 July). *International Peace Year. Blue cover as Type* B **1**, *printed in black. Stamps attached by selvedge.*
SB38 $6 booklet containing twenty-four 25 c. on 1 c. (No. 1739) and label as block of 25 .. .. 3·25

1986 (21 Aug). *Green cover as Type* B **1**, *printed in black. Stapled.*
SB39 $3 booklet containing twelve 25 c. (No. 1807) in pairs .. .. 3·75

1986 (23 Sept). *20th Anniv of Independence* (2*nd issue*). *Green cover as Type* B **1**, *printed in black. Stapled.*
SB40 $3 booklet containing twelve 25 c. (No. 1820) in pairs .. .. 3·75

$5
GUYANA
Post Office
Corp.
1977 - 1987

B 3

1987 (17 Feb). *10th Anniv of Guyana Post Office Corporation. Covers as Type* B **3**, *printed in black with face value handstamped in blue. Stapled.*
SB41 $5 booklet containing twenty 25 c. (Nos. 2074/7) in strips of 5 .. .. 7·00
SB42 $20 booklet containing five 60 c., five $1.20 and five $1.30 (Nos. 2078/80), each in strips of 5, and two $2.25 (No. 1930) in pair .. .. 17·00

1987 (2 June). *Green cover as Type* B **1**, *printed in black. Stamps attached by selvedge.*
SB43 $3 booklet containing twelve 25 c. (No. 2183) in pairs .. .. 2·50

1987 (29 Sept). *Green cover as Type* B **1**, *printed in black. Stamps attached by selvedge.*
SB44 $3 booklet containing twelve 25 c. (No. 2184) in pairs .. .. 2·50

1987 (Dec). *Covers as Nos.* SB10 *and* SB12 *handstamped with new face value in blue. Stamps attached by selvedge.*
SB45 $15 on $3 booklet containing twelve $1.20 (No. 2194a) in blocks of 4 and one 60 c. (No. 2265) 8·00
SB46 $15 on $3 booklet containing twelve $1.20 (No. 2198a) in blocks of 4 and one 60 c. (No. 2265) 8·00
SB47 $24 on $6 booklet containing twenty $1.20 (No. 2194a) in blocks of 4 or 8 .. .. .. 9·00
SB48 $24 on $6 booklet containing twenty $1.20 (No. 2198a) in blocks of 4 or 8 .. .. .. 9·00

Blocks of Nos. 2194a and 2198a in booklet Nos. SB45/8 have the perforations at top and bottom removed by guillotine.

1988 (3 Sept). *60th Anniv of Cricket in Guyana. Cream covers with black inscr. Stamps attached by selvedge.*
SB49 $20 booklet containing two 200 c. and two 800 c. on 150 c. (Nos. 2472, 2474), each in pair .. 28·00
SB50 $20 booklet containing two 200 c. and two 800 c. on 150 c. (Nos. 2473/4), each in pair .. 14·00

1988 (16 Sept). *Olympic Games, Seoul. Greenish yellow covers with black inscr. Stamps attached by selvedge.*
SB51 $20 booklet containing four 25 c. (No. 1534) in pairs and *se-tenant* pane of 10 (No. 2486b) 15·00
SB52 $20 booklet containing four 25 c. (No. 1535*a*) in pairs and *se-tenant* pane of 10 (No. 2486b) 15·00

EXPRESS LETTER STAMPS

$12.oo

EXPRESS

(E 1)

1986 (10 Nov). *Various stamps surch as Type* E 1 *by Tip Torres.*
E1 $12 on 350 c. on 120 c. mult (No. 1598) .. 6·00 6·00
E2 $15 on 40 c. multicoloured (as No. 1868, but inscr "ONTOGLOSSUM") .. .. 8·00 8·00
a. Surch on No. 1868 (inscr "ODONTOGLOSSUM") .. .. 8·00 8·00
E3 $20 on $6.40, multicoloured (No. **MS**1746) 6·00 6·00
E4 $25 on 25 c. multicoloured (as No. 1621, but value changed) .. .. .. 11·00 11·00
E1/4 .. .. *Set of* 4 28·00 28·00

The surcharges on Nos. E2/3 include a pattern of leaves over the original value. On No. E4 a dollar sign has been added in front of the original value and a small maltese cross overprinted above "EXPRESS" at bottom right.

1987 (3 Mar). *No.* E3 *additionally optd with small Maltese cross above surch.*
E5 $20 on $6.40, multicoloured .. .. 6·50 6·50
a. With additional "2" optd at bottom left .. 6·50 6·50

(Litho Format)

1987 (1 Sept)–**88**. *Centenary of Publication of Sanders' Reichenbachia. Vert designs as T* **331** *additionally inscr* "EXPRESS". *Multicoloured. No wmk. P* $13^1/_2 \times 14$.
E6 $15 Plate No. 11 (Series 2) (29.9.87) .. 4·00 4·00
E7 $20 Plate No. 93 (Series 2) (17.5.88) .. 3·50 4·00
E8 $25 Plate No. 63 (Series 2) (26.10.87) .. 3·75 4·25
E9 $45 Plate No. 35 (Series 2) .. .. 7·00 8·00
E6/9 .. .. *Set of* 4 16·00 18·00

Nos. E6/9, in conjunction with postage issues, were printed in a similar sheet format to Nos. 1518/33.

EXPRESS

FORTY DOLLARS

(E 2) (*Illustration reduced. Actual size of surcharge* 64 × 36 *mm*)

1987 (Nov). *No.* 1744ab *surch with Type* E 2 *by Gardy Ptg.*
E10 $40 on $6.40, multicoloured .. .. 11·00 11·00

1987 (Dec). *No.* E 2 *additionally optd with T* **390** *by Gardy Ptg.*
E11 $15 on 40 c. multicoloured (inscr "ONTOGLOSSUM" .. .. 9·00 5·00

SPECIAL DELIVERY

$40-00

(E 3)
(*Illustration reduced. Actual size of surcharge* 80×45 *mm*)

1988 (10 Aug). *Nos.* 2206 *and* 2211 *surch as Type* E 3 *in red by Gardy Ptg.*
E12 $40 on $3.20, deep dull blue .. .. 8·50 9·00
E13 $45 on $3.30, brownish black .. .. 9·00 10·00

Nos. E12/13 were only issued in vertical strips of five, being the remainders of the sheets utilised to produce Nos. 2455/62.

EXPRESS

FORTY DOLLARS

(E 4)

1989 (Mar). *Nos.* 1744ab *and* 2185ab *surch with Type* E 4 *in red.*
E14 $40 on $6.40, multicoloured (No. 1744ab) 4·50 5·00
E15 $40 on $6.40, multicoloured (No. 2185ab) 4·50 5·00

1989 (May). *Nos.* 2206 *and* 2211 *surch as Type* E 3.
E16 $190 on $3.30, brownish black .. .. 13·00 15·00
E17 $225 on $3.20, deep dull blue .. .. 14·00 16·00

Nos. E16/17 were surcharged on the remains of the sheets utilized for Nos. 2648/55.

EXPRESS

(E 5) (E 6)

(Des Mary Walters. Litho Questa)

1989 (7 Sept). *Butterflies. Two sheets, each* 97×67 *mm, containing vert designs as T* **454** *optd with Type* E 5. *Multicoloured. P* 14.
EMS18 $130 *Phareas coeleste* .. .. .. 4·00 4·00
EMS19 $190 *Papilio torquatus* .. .. .. 5·50 5·50

(Des M. Dorfman. Litho Questa)

1989 (8 Nov). *Women in Space. Sheet,* 92×67 *mm, containing vert design as T* **455** *optd with Type* E 5. *Multicoloured. P* 14.
EMS20 $190 Valentina Tereshkova (first woman cosmonaut) .. .. .. 3·75 4·00

1989 (17 Nov). *"World Stamp Expo '89" International Stamp Exhibition, Washington. Nos.* **EMS**18/19 *optd with Type* E 6.
EMS21 $130 *Phareas coeleste* .. .. .. 3·25 3·25
EMS22 $190 *Papilio torquatus* .. .. .. 4·25 4·25

Nos. **EMS**21/22 show additional overprints on sheet margins.

1990 (15 Mar). *85th Anniv of Rotary International. Nos.* **EMS**18/20 *optd* "ROTARY INTERNATIONAL 1905–1990" *and emblem on sheet margins only.*
EMS23 $130 *Phareas coeleste* .. .. .. 3·25 3·25
EMS24 $190 *Papilio torquatus* .. .. .. 4·50 4·50
EMS25 $190 Valentina Tereshkova (first woman cosmonaut) .. .. .. 3·75 4·50
EMS23/5 .. .. *Set of* 3 10·50 11·00

1990 (3 May). *"Stamp World London '90" International Stamp Exhibition. Nos.* **EMS**18/20 *optd* "Stamp World London '90" *and emblem on sheet margins only.*
EMS26 $130 *Phareas coeleste* (R.) .. .. 3·50 3·50
a. Opt in black .. .. ..
EMS27 $190 *Papilio torquatus* .. .. .. 4·50 4·50
EMS28 $190 Valentina Tereshkova (first woman cosmonaut) .. .. .. 3·75 4·50
EMS26/8 .. .. *Set of* 3 10·50 11·00

1990 (2 June). *"Belgica '90" International Stamp Exhibition, Brussels. Nos.* **EMS**18 *and* **EMS**20 *additionally optd* "BELGICA PHILATELIC EXPOSITION 1990" *and emblem on sheet margins only.*
EMS29 $130 *Phareas coeleste* .. .. .. 3·00 3·00
EMS30 $190 Valentina Tereshkova (first woman cosmonaut) .. .. .. 3·25 3·50

1990 (8 June). *90th Birthday of Queen Elizabeth the Queen Mother. Nos.* **EMS**18/20 *optd* "90TH BIRTHDAY H.M. THE QUEEN MOTHER" *on sheet margins only.*
EMS31 $130 *Phareas coeleste* .. .. .. 2·50 2·50
EMS32 $190 *Papilio torquatus* .. .. .. 3·25 3·25
EMS33 $190 Valentina Tereshkova (first woman cosmonaut) .. .. .. 3·25 3·25
EMS31/3 .. .. *Set of* 3 8·00 8·00

(Des W. Wright. Litho)

1990 (16 Nov). *Fauna. Two sheets, each* 110×80 *mm, containing vert designs as T* **466**, *but larger* (40×55 *mm*) *inscr* "EXPRESS". *Multicoloured. P* 14.
EMS34 $130 Harpy Eagle .. .. .. 2·75 2·75
EMS35 $150 Ocelot .. .. .. 2·75 2·75

PARCEL POST STAMPS

PARCEL POST

X X PARCEL POST
$15.00 $15.00 $12.00

(P 1) (P 2)

1981 (8 June). *No.* 554 *surch as Type* P 1 *by Bovell's Printer*
P1 $15 on $1 *Chelonanthus uliginoides* .. .. 10·00 3·(
P2 $20 on $1 *Chelonanthus uliginoides* .. .. 10·00 6·(

1983 (15 Jan). *No.* 843 *surch with Type* P 2 *in blue b Autoprint.*
P3 $12 on $1.10 on $2 *Norantea guianensis* .. 3·75 2·(

Parcel Post
$12.00

(P 3)

1983 (14 Sept). *Unissued Royal Wedding surch, similar No.* 843, *further surch with Type* P 3 *in blue by Autoprint.*
P4 $12 on $1.10 on $2 *Norantea guianensis* .. 1·00 1·7

TWENTY FIVE DOLLARS
PARCEL POST 25.oo

(P 4)

1985 (25 Apr). *No.* 673 *surch with Type* P 4 *in red by Ti Torres.*
P5 $25 on 35 c. bright yellow-green, grey & black 21·00 18·(

POSTAGE DUE STAMPS

D 1

D 2

(Typo D.L.R.)

1940 (Mar)–**55**. *Wmk Mult Script CA. Chalk-surfaced pap (4 c.). P* 14.
D1 D **1** 1 c. green .. .. 3·50 6·5
a. Chalk-surfaced paper. *Deep green*, (30.4.52) .. .. 1·50 8·(
ab. W**9***a* (Crown missing) £180
ac. W**9***b* (St. Edward's Crown) .. 80·00
D2 2 c. black .. .. 13·00 2·5
a. Chalk-surfaced paper (30.4.52) .. 1·50 3·5
ab. W**9***a* (Crown missing) £150
ac. W**9***b* (St. Edward's Crown) .. 70·00
D3 4 c. bright blue (1.5.52) .. .. 30 8·(
a. W**9***a* (Crown missing) £130
b. W**9***b* (St. Edward's Crown) .. 70·00
D4 12 c. scarlet .. .. 25·00 5·(
a. Chalk-surfaced paper (19.7.55) .. 11·00 20·(
D1a/4a .. .. *Set of* 4 13·00 35·(
D1, D2 and D4 Perf "Specimen" .. *Set of* 3 50·00

(Typo D.L.R.)

1967–8. *Chalk-surfaced paper. W* w **12**. *P* 14.
D5 D **2** 2 c. black (11.12.68) .. .. .. 70 15·(
D6 4 c. deep ultramarine .. .. .. 30 4·2
D7 12 c. reddish scarlet .. .. .. 30 4·7
D5/7 .. .. *Set of* 3 1·10 22·(

1973 (24 May). *Glazed, ordinary paper. W* **106.** *P* 14.
D 8 D **2** 1 c. olive .. .. 20 3·(
D 9 2 c. black .. .. 20 3·(
D10 4 c. dull ultramarine .. .. .. 20 3·(
D11 12 c. bright scarlet .. .. .. 30 3·(
D8/11.. .. .. *Set of* 4 80 11·(

OFFICIAL STAMPS

OFFICIAL OFFICIAL OFFICIA

(O 1) (O 1*a*) (O 2)

1875. *Optd with Type* O **1** (*1 c.*) *or* O **1***a* (*others*) *by litho. P* 1(
O1 **8** 1 c. black (R.) .. .. 40·00 14·(
a. Imperf between (horiz pair) .. — £45(
O2 2 c. orange .. .. £150 14·(
O3 8 c. rose £300 £12
O4 **7** 12 c. brownish purple £1500 £47
O5 **9** 24 c. green £850 £22

Two types of the word "OFFICIAL" are found on each value. O the 1 c., the word is either 16 or 17 mm long. On the other valu the chief difference is in the shape and position of the letter "o" i "OFFICIAL". In one case the "o" is upright, in the other it slants the left.

1877. *Optd with Type* O **2** *by typo. Wmk Crown CC. P* 14.
O 6 **16** 1 c. slate . . . . £200 55·00
a. Imperf between (vert pair) . . . . — £6500
O 7 2 c. orange . . . . 90·00 15·00
O 8 4 c. blue . . . . 80·00 20·00
O 9 6 c. brown £2500 £600
O10 8 c. rose £1700 £450

Prepared for use, but not issued

O11 **16** 12 c. pale violet £900
O12 24 c. green £1000

The "OFFICIAL" overprints have been extensively forged.

The use of Official stamps was discontinued in June 1878, but was resumed in June 1981.

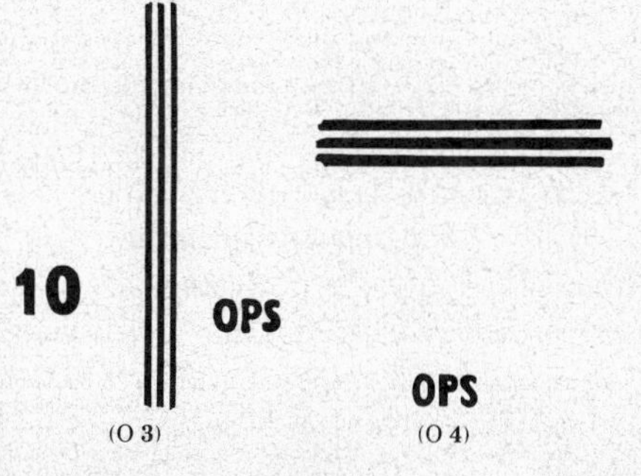
(O 3) (O 4)

OPS
(O 5)

1981 (8 June). *Nos.* 556, F4a *and* F6/7 *surch or optd with Types* O **3/5** *by Bovell's Printery.*
O13 10 c. on 25 c. Marabunta (Blk. + R.) . . 1·50 2·00
O14 50 c. *Guzmania lingulata* (R.) . . . . 1·60 30
O15 60 c. Soldier's Cap (R.) . . . . 1·25 20
O16 $5 *Odontadenia grandiflora* (opt Type O **5**) (R.) . . . . 3·00 1·75
O13/16 . . . . *Set of* 4 6·50 3·75

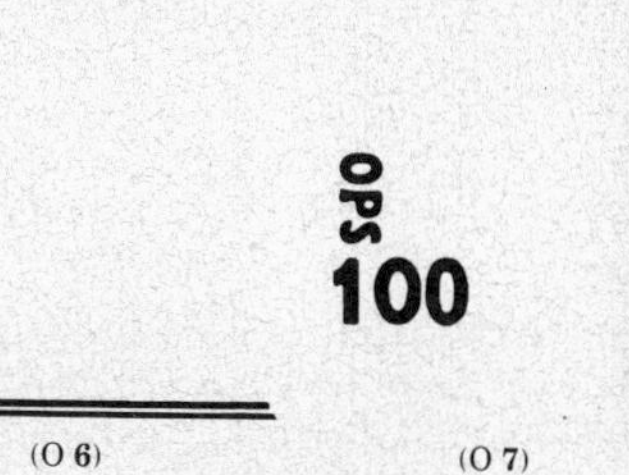
(O 6) (O 7)

1981 (1 July). (*a*) *Postage. Nos.* 491, 708*a*, 716, 834 *and* F9 *optd or surch as Types* O **5/7** *or additionally surch as T* **227**.
O17 15 c. Harpy Eagle (opt Type O **6**) . . 8·50 65
O18 30 c. on $2 *Norantea guianensis* (No. F9) (opt Type O **5**) (Blk. + R.) . . 45 30
O19 100 c. on $3 Cylinder satellite (surch Type O **7**) (Blk. + R.) . . . . 3·00 40
O20 125 c. on $2 *Norantea guianensis* (opt Type O **5**) (R.) . . . . . . 1·75 60
O21 $10 *Elbella patrobas* (opt Type O **5**) . . 7·00 8·00
(*b*) *Air. No.* 804 *optd with Type* O **5** *in red*
O22 $1.10 on $2 *Norantea guianensis* . . 1·00 2·50
a. Opt Type O **5** double £110
O17/22 . . . . *Set of* 6 20·00 11·00

1981 (7 July). *Nos.* 548, 719, 828 *and* 830 *optd with Type* O **5**.
O23 15 c. Christmas Orchid . . . . 8·00 1·50
O24 50 c. British Guiana 1898 1 c. stamp . . 1·25 35
O25 100 c. on 8 c. Camp-fire cooking . . 2·00 50
O26 110 c. on 6 c. Type **116** . . . . 3·50 1·25

OPS

OPS 250
(O 8) (O 9)

(Surch or optd by Autoprint)

1982 (17 May). (*a*) *Postage.* (i) *Various stamps optd with Type* O **8** *in blue*
O27 – 20 c. multicoloured (No. 701) . . . . 3·25 60
O28 **136** 40 c. multicoloured 75 15
O29 – 40 c. carmine-red, grey & blk (No. 674) 1·00 15
O30 – $2 multicoloured (No. 676) . . 7·00 75
O27/30 . . . . *Set of* 4 11·00 1·50
(ii) *No.* 911 *additionally surch with Type* O **9** *in blue*
O31 – 250 c. on 400 c. on 30 c. multicoloured . . 80 60
(*b*) *Air. No.* 980 *additionally optd with Type* O **8** *in blue*
O32 – 220 c. on 1 c. multicoloured . . . . 1·50 60

1982 (12 July). *No.* F9 *optd with Type* O **5** *in red by Bovell's Printery.*
O33 $2 *Norantea guianensis* . . . . . . 10·00 2·00

1982 (15 Sept). *Air. No.* 979 *optd with Type* O **8** *by Autoprint.*
O34 110 c. on 5 c. Annatto tree . . . . . . 1·75 60

1984 (2 Apr). *No.* 912 *surch as Type* O **9** *vertically, in blue (except for No.* O37 *which has "OPS" in blue and "225" in black) by Autoprint.*
O35 150 c. on $5 multicoloured . . . . . . 5·00 2·75
O36 200 c. on $5 multicoloured . . . . . . 5·50 3·00
O37 225 c. on $5 multicoloured . . . . . . 5·50 3·25
O38 230 c. on $5 multicoloured . . . . . . 5·50 3·25
O39 260 c. on $5 multicoloured . . . . . . 5·50 3·50
O40 320 c. on $5 multicoloured . . . . . . 6·50 4·00
O41 350 c. on $5 multicoloured . . . . . . 7·00 4·50
O42 600 c. on $5 multicoloured . . . . . . 8·50 5·50
O35/42 . . . . *Set of* 8 45·00 27·00

25
(O 10)

(Surch or optd by Autoprint)

1984 (25 June). *Nos.* O32 and O34 *surch as Type* O **10** (25 *c.*, 60 *c.*) *or as T* **294** (*others*), *and No.* 981 *optd vertically with Type* O **8**.
O43 25 c. on 110 c. on 5 c. Annatto tree 70 30
O44 30 c. on 110 c. on 5 c. Annatto tree (B.) . . 80 35
O45 45 c. on 220 c. on 1 c. Pitcher Plant of Mt Roraima 90 40
O46 55 c. on 110 c. on 5 c. Annatto tree . . . . 1·10 50
O47 60 c. on 220 c. on 1 c. Pitcher Plant of Mt Roraima . . . . 1·10 50
O48 75 c. on 220 c. on 1 c. Pitcher Plant of Mt Roraima . . . . 1·25 60
O49 90 c. on 220 c. on 1 c. Pitcher Plant of Mt Roraima (B.) . . . . . . 1·25 70
O50 120 c. on 220 c. on 1 c. Pitcher Plant of Mt Roraima . . . . 1·40 85
O51 130 c. on 220 c. on 1 c. Pitcher Plant of Mt Roraima (B.) . . . . . . 1·50 90
O52 330 c. on $2 *Norantea guianensis* (B.) . . 3·00 2·25
O43/52 . . . . *Set of* 10 11·50 6·50

(Litho Format)

1987 (5 Oct)–**88**. *Centenary of Publication of Sanders' Reichenbachia. Multicoloured designs as T* **331** *additionally inscr* "OFFICIAL". *No wmk. P* 14×13½ (230, 350, 600 *c.*, $12) *or* 13½×14 (*others*).
O53 120 c. Plate No. 48 (Series 2) 60 25
O54 130 c. Plate No. 92 (Series 2) 60 25
O55 140 c. Plate No. 36 (Series 2) (5.10.88) . . 60 25
O56 150 c. Plate No. 43 (Series 2) 60 25
O57 175 c. Plate No. 31 (Series 2) (5.10.88) . . 70 30
O58 200 c. Plate No. 61 (Series 2) 75 35
O59 225 c. Plate No. 26 (Series 2) 75 35
O60 230 c. Plate No. 68 (Series 2) (*horiz*) . . 75 35
O61 250 c. Plate No. 59 (Series 2) (5.10.88) . . 75 40
O62 260 c. Plate No. 69 (Series 2) (5.10.88) . . 75 40
O63 275 c. Plate No. 90 (Series 2) 75 40
O64 320 c. Plate No. 75 (Series 2) 75 50
O65 330 c. Plate No. 23 (Series 2) 85 60
O66 350 c. Plate No. 95 (Series 2) (*horiz*) . . 85 60
O67 600 c. Plate No. 70 (Series 2) (*horiz*) . . 1·25 1·25
O68 $12 Plate No. 71 (Series 2) (*horiz*) . . 2·00 2·00
O69 $15 Plate No. 84 (Series 2) . . . . 2·25 2·25
O53/69 . . . . . . *Set of* 17 14·00 9·50

Nos. O53/69 were printed in a similar sheet format to Nos. 1518/33.

OFFICIAL PARCEL POST STAMPS

1981 (8 June). *Nos.* P1/2 *optd with Type* O **5** *in red by Bovell's Printery.*
OP1 $15 on $1 *Chelonanthus uliginoides* . . . . 7·50 2·25
a. Opt in black . . . . 65·00 8·00
OP2 $20 on $1 *Chelonanthus uliginoides* . . . . 10·00 2·75

OPS
Parcel Post
$12.00
(OP 1)

1983 (15 Jan). *No.* 843 *surch with Type* OP **1**, *and optd with T* **226**, *both in blue by Autoprint.*
OP3 $12 on $1.10 on $2 *Norantea guianensis* 65·00 17·00
a. Surch Type OP **1** omitted . . . . 90·00

1983 (22 Aug). *As No.* OP3, *but additionally optd with Type* O **8** *by Autoprint.*
OP4 $12 on $1.10 on $2 *Norantea guianensis* . . 29·00 5·00

1983 (3 Nov). *No.* P4 *additionally optd with Type* O **8** *in blue by Autoprint.*
OP5 $12 on $1.10 on $2 *Norantea guianensis* . . 7·50 5·00

POSTAL FISCAL STAMPS

REVENUE
ONLY
*
(F 1)

1975 (1 Nov). *Nos.* 543/5 *and* 550*a*/56 *optd with Type* F **1**.
F 1 2 c. Type **132** 40 40
F 2 3 c. Hanging Heliconia 40 40
F 3 5 c. Annatto tree 65 30
F 4 25 c. Marabunta (Type II) . . . . . . 2·50 30
a. Optd on No. 550 (Type I) . . . . 15·00 13·00
F 5 40 c. Tiger Beard . . . . . . 5·00 30
F 6 50 c. *Guzmania lingulata* 60 40
F 7 60 c. Soldier's Cap 75 50
F 8 $1 *Chelonanthus uliginoides* . . . . 75 1·25
F 9 $2 *Norantea guianensis* . . . . . . 1·00 2·75
F10 $5 *Odontadenia grandiflora* . . . . 1·75 9·00
F1/F10 . . . . *Set of* 10 12·00 14·00

Although intended for fiscal use Nos. F1/10 were allowed, by the postal authorities, as "an act of grace" to do duty as postage stamps until 30 June 1976.

Heligoland

Stamps of HAMBURG (see Part 7 (*Germany*) of this catalogue) were used in Heligoland until 16 April 1867. The Free City of Hamburg ran the Heligoland postal service between 1796 and 1 June 1866. Its stamps continued in use on the island until replaced by Heligoland issues.

PRICES FOR STAMPS ON COVER

Nos. 1/19 *from* × 3

PRINTERS. All the stamps of Heligoland were typographed at the Imperial Printing Works, Berlin.

REPRINTS. Many of the stamps of Heligoland were subsequently reprinted at Berlin (between 1875 and 1885), Leipzig (1888) and Hamburg (1892 and 1895). Of these only the Berlin productions are difficult to distinguish from the originals so separate notes are provided for the individual values. Leipzig reprints can be identified by their highly surfaced paper and those from Hamburg by their 14 perforation. All of these reprints are worth much less than the original stamps priced below.

There was, in addition, a small reprinting of Nos. 13/19, made by the German government in 1890 for exchange purposes, but examples of this printing are far scarcer than the original stamps.

Forgeries, printed by lithography instead of typography, also exist for Nos. 1/4, 6 and 8 perforated 12½ or 13. Forged cancellations can also be found on originals and, on occasion, genuine postmarks on reprints.

1

(Currency. 16 schillings = 1 mark)

Three Dies of Embossed Head for Types **1** and **2**:

Die I Die II

Die III

Die I. Blob instead of curl beneath the chignon. Outline of two jewels at top of diadem.
Die II. Curl under chignon. One jewel at top of diadem.
Die III. Shorter curl under chignon. Two jewels at top of diadem.

(Des Wedding. Die eng E. Schilling)

1867 (Mar)–**68**. *Head Die I embossed in colourless relief. Roul.*

1	1	½ sch. blue-green and rose	£300	£800
		a. Head Die II (7.68)	£700	£1100
2		1 sch. rose and blue-green (21.3.67)	£160	£180
3		2 sch. rose and grass-green (21.3.67)	10·00	55·00
4		6 sch. green and rose	12·00	£250

For Nos. 1/4 the second colour given is that of the spandrels on the ½ and 1 sch., and of the spandrels and central background for the 2 and 6 sch.

All four values exist from the Berlin, Leipzig and Hamburg reprintings. The following points are helpful in identifying originals from Berlin reprints; for Leipzig and Hamburg reprints see general note above:

½ sch. – Reprints are all in yellowish green and show Head Die II
1 sch. – All reprints are Head Die III
2 sch. – Berlin reprints are in dull rose with a deeper blue-green
6 sch. – Originals show white specks in green. Berlin reprints have a more solid bluish green

1869 (Apr)–**73**. *Head embossed in colourless relief. P* 13½×14½.

5	1	¼ sch. rose and green (background) (I) (*quadrillé paper*) (8.73)	26·00	£1500
		a. Error. Green and rose (background) (9.73)	£110	£3000
		b. Deep rose and pale green (background) (11.73)	85·00	£1500
6		½ sch. blue-green and rose (II)	£190	£200
		a. Yellow-green and rose (7.71)	£140	£190
		b. Quadrillé paper (6.73)	95·00	£150
7		¾ sch. green and rose (I) (*quadrillé paper*) (12.73)	29·00	£1100
8		1 sch. rose and yellow-green (III) (7.71)	£140	£180
		a. Quadrillé paper. *Rose and pale blue-green* (6.73)	£120	£180
9		1½ sch. grn & rose (I) (*quadrillé paper*) (9.73)	65·00	£250

For Nos. 5/9 the second colour given is that of the spandrels on the ½ and 1 sch., of the central background on the ¼ and 1½ sch., and of the central background, side labels and side marginal lines of the ¾ sch.

No. 5a was a printing of the ¼ sch. made in the colour combination of the 1½ sch. by mistake.

A further printing of the ¼ sch. (head die I) in deep rose-red and yellowish green (background), on non-*quadrillé* paper, was made in December 1874, but not issued (*Price* £15, *unused*).

All five values exist from the Berlin, Leipzig and Hamburg reprintings. The following points are helpful in identifying originals from Berlin reprints; for Leipzig and Hamburg reprints see general note above:

¼ sch. – All Berlin and some Hamburg reprints are Head Die II
½ sch. – Berlin reprints on thinner paper with solid colour in the spandrels.
¾ sch. – Berlin reprints on thinner, non-quadrillé paper
1 sch. – Berlin reprints are on thinner paper or show many breaks in the rose line beneath "SCHILLING" at the top of the design or in the line above it at the foot.
1½ sch. – All Berlin and some Hamburg reprints are Head Die II

Berlin, Leipzig and Hamburg reprints also exist of the 2 and 6 sch., but these values do not come as perforated originals.

(New Currency. 100 pfennig = 1 mark)

2

3

4

5

(Des H. Gätke. Die eng E. Schilling (T **2**), A. Schiffner (others))

1875 (Feb)–**90**. *Head Die II on T* **2** *embossed in colourless relief. P* 13½×14½.

10	2	1 pf. (¼d.) deep green and rose	10·00	£500
11		2 pf. (½d.) deep rose and deep green	10·00	£600
12	3	3 pf. (⅝d.) pale green, red and yellow (6.76)	£225	£1100
		a. Green, red and orange (6.77)	£160	£850
13	2	5 pf. (¾d.) deep yellow-green and rose	10·00	18·00
		a. Deep green and rose (6.90)	12·00	40·00
14		10 pf. (1½d.) deep rose and deep green	30·00	20·00
		a. Scarlet and pale blue-green (5.87)	10·00	20·00
15	3	20 pf. (2½d.) rose, green and yellow (6.76)	£200	£120
		a. Rose-carmine, dp green & orge (4.80)	£150	50·00
		b. Dull red, pale green and lemon (7.88)	12·00	28·00
		c. Aniline verm, brt grn & lemon (6.90)	12·00	50·00
16	2	25 pf. (3d.) deep green and rose	12·00	26·00
17		50 pf. (6d.) rose and green	18·00	32·00
18	4	1 m. (1s.) deep green, scarlet & black (8.79)	£140	£200
		a. Perf 11½	£1000	
		b. Deep green, aniline rose & black (5.89)	£140	£200
19	5	5 m. (5s.) deep green, aniline rose, black and yellow (8.79)	£150	£950
		a. Perf 11½	£1000	
		ab. Imperf between (horiz pair)	£3500	

For stamps as Type **2** the first colour is that of the central background and the second that of the frame. On the 3 pf. the first colour is of the frame and the top band of the shield, the second is the centre band and the third the shield border. The 20 pf. is similar, but has the centre band in the same colour as the frame and the upper band on the shield in the second colour.

The 1, 2 and 3 pf. exist from the Berlin, Leipzig and Hamburg reprintings. There were no such reprints for the other values. The following points are helpful in identifying originals from Berlin reprints; for Leipzig and Hamburg reprints see general note above:

1 pf. – Berlin printings show a peculiar shade of pink
2 pf. – All reprints are much lighter in shade than the deep rose and deep green of the originals
3 pf. – Berlin reprints either show the band around the shield in brownish orange, or have this feature in deep yellow with the other two colours lighter.

Heligoland was ceded to Germany on 9 August 1890.

MINIMUM PRICE

The minimum price quote is 10p which represents a handling charge rather than a basis for valuing common stamps. For further notes about prices see introductory pages.

Hong Kong

CROWN COLONY

Hong Kong island was formally ceded to Great Britain on 26 January 1841. The Hong Kong Post Office was established in October 1841, when much of the business previously transacted through the Macao postal agency was transferred to the island. The first cancellation is known from April 1842, but local control of the posts was shortlived as the Hong Kong Office became a branch of the British G.P.O. on 15 April 1843.

The colonial authorities resumed control of the postal service on 1 May 1860 although the previously established postal agencies in the Chinese Treaty Ports remained part of the British G.P.O. system until 1 May 1868.

For illustrations of the handstamp types see BRITISH POST OFFICES ABROAD notes, following GREAT BRITAIN.

CROWNED-CIRCLE HANDSTAMPS

CC1 **CC1b** HONG KONG (R.) (17.10.1843) *Price on cover* £47
CC2 **CC1** HONG KONG (R.) (21.8.1844) *Price on cover* £70
CC3 **CC3** HONG KONG (R.) (16.6.1852) *Price on cover* £30

We no longer list the Great Britain stamps with obliteration "B 62" within oval. The Government notification dated 29 November 1862 stated that only the Hong Kong stamps to be issued on 8 December would be available for postage and the stamps formerly listed were all issued in Great Britain later than the date of the notice.

(Currency. 100 cents = 1 Hong Kong dollar)

PRICES FOR STAMPS ON COVER TO 1945

Nos. 1/27	*from* × 6
Nos. 28/36	*from* × 4
Nos. 37/9	*from* × 5
Nos. 40/4	*from* × 4
Nos. 45/8	*from* × 10
Nos. 49/50	*from* × 4
No. 51	*from* × 15
Nos. 52/61	*from* × 5
Nos. 62/99	*from* × 4
Nos. 100/32	*from* × 3
Nos. 133/6	*from* × 2
Nos. 137/9	*from* × 4
Nos. 140/68	*from* × 2
Nos. D1/12	*from* × 8
Nos. F1/11	*from* × 4
No. F12	*from* × 3
Nos. P1/3	*from* × 2

PRINTERS. All definitive issues up to 1962 were typographed by De La Rue and Co., *except for some printings between 194 and* 1945.

1

2

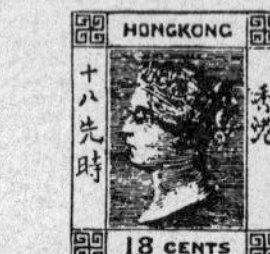

3

1862 (8 Dec)–**63**. *No wmk. P* 14.

1	1	2 c. brown	£375	85·0
		a. Deep brown (1863)	£500	£10
2		8 c. yellow-buff	£600	60·0
3		12 c. pale greenish blue	£475	48·0
4	3	18 c. lilac	£500	45·0
5		24 c. green	£900	90·0
6		48 c. rose	£2500	£325
7		96 c. brownish grey	£3500	£375

1863 (Aug)–**71**. *Wmk Crown CC. P* 14.

8	1	2 c. deep brown (11.64)	£250	27·0
		a. Brown	£110	7·0
		b. Pale yellowish brown	£130	11·0
		w. Wmk inverted	£350	40·0
		x. Wmk reversed	—	60·0
9	4	4 c. grey	£120	13·0
		a. Slate	95·00	5·5
		aw. Wmk inverted	£275	40·0
		b. Deep slate	£140	10·0
		c. Greenish grey	£275	45·0
		cw. Wmk inverted	†	£20
		d. Bluish slate	£450	21·0
		dw. Wmk inverted	£750	£10
		e. Perf 12½. *Slate* (12.70)	£8000	£27
		ew. Wmk inverted	—	£45
10		6 c. lilac	£300	9·5
		a. Mauve	£400	10·0
		w. Wmk inverted	£650	35·0
		x. Wmk reversed	—	45·0
11	1	8 c. pale dull orange (10.64)	£450	9·5
		a. Brownish orange	£400	11·0
		b. Bright orange	£350	11·0
		w. Wmk inverted	£650	45·0
		x. Wmk reversed	£650	45·0
12		12 c. pale greenish blue (4.65)	£900	29·0
		a. Pale blue	25·00	5·5
		b. Deep blue	£180	12·0
		w. Wmk inverted	—	45·0
		x. Wmk reversed	—	40·0

3	18 c. lilac (1866)	£5000	£300
	w. Wmk inverted	†	£600
	x. Wmk reversed	†	£700
	24 c. green (10.64)	£450	8·50
	a. Pale green	£550	15·00
	b. Deep green	£750	28·00
	w. Wmk inverted	—	50·00
	x. Wmk reversed	£1000	50·00
2	30 c. vermilion	£750	14·00
	a. Orange-vermilion	£650	15·00
	w. Wmk inverted	£1800	50·00
	x. Wmk reversed	—	50·00
	30 c. mauve (14.8.71)	£180	5·50
	w. Wmk inverted	£500	45·00
	x. Wmk reversed	—	50·00
	48 c. pale rose (1.65)	£950	40·00
	a. Rose-carmine	£800	23·00
	w. Wmk inverted	—	65·00
	x. Wmk reversed	—	85·00
	96 c. olive-bistre (1.65)	£25000	£550
	w. Wmk inverted	†	£1100
	96 c. brownish grey (1865)	£1000	42·00
	a. Brownish black	£1100	35·00
	w. Wmk inverted	£1400	85·00

There is a wide range of shades in this issue, of which we can only ;icate the main groups.

No. 12 is the same shade as No. 3 without wmk, the impression ving a waxy appearance.

A single used example of the 48 c. in a bright claret shade is own. No other stamps in this shade, either mint or used, have en discovered.

See also Nos. 22 and 28/31.

16 ents. (4) 28 cents. (5) 5 cents. (6) 10 cents. (7)

No. 20b

76 (Aug)–**77.** *Nos.* 13 *and* 16 *surch with T* **4** *or* **5** *by Noronha and Sons, Hong Kong.*

3	16 c. on 18 c. lilac (1.4.77)	£1900	£150
	a. Space between "n" and "t" ..	£6000	£800
	b. Space between "s" and stop	£6000	£800
	w. Wmk inverted	£4000	£500
2	28 c. on 30 c. mauve	£1000	48·00

77 (Aug). *New value. Wmk Crown CC. P* 14.

3	16 c. yellow	£1200	65·00
	w. Wmk inverted	£2250	£200

1880 (1 Mar–Sept). *Surch with T* **6** *or* **7** *by Noronha and Sons.*

23	1	5 c. on 8 c. brt orange (No. 11*b*) (Sept)	£600	85·00
		a. Surch inverted	†	£10000
		b. Surch double	†	£15000
24	3	5 c. on 18 c. lilac (No. 13)	£600	55·00
		x. Wmk reversed	£900	
25	1	10 c. on 12 c. pale blue (No. 12*a*) ..	£700	55·00
		a. Blue	£900	70·00
26	3	10 c. on 16 c. yellow (No. 22) (May) ..	£3500	£140
		a. Surch inverted	†	£40000
		b. Surch double	†	£50000
		w. Wmk inverted	†	£750
27		10 c. on 24 c. green (No. 14) (June) ..	£1200	80·00
		w. Wmk inverted	†	£180

Two examples of No. 26b are known, both used in Shanghai.

1880 (Mar–Dec). *Colours changed and new values. Wmk Crown CC. P* 14.

28	1	2 c. dull rose	£110	18·00
		a. Rose	£120	19·00
29	2	5 c. blue (Dec)	£275	30·00
		w. Wmk inverted	—	75·00
30		10 c. mauve (Nov)	£425	13·00
		w. Wmk inverted	—	50·00
31	3	48 c. brown	£950	85·00

1882 (May)–**96.** *Wmk Crown CA. P* 14.

32	1	2 c. rose-lake (7.82)	£120	24·00
		a. Rose-pink	£170	32·00
		ab. Perf 12	£70000	£70000
		w. Wmk inverted	—	75·00
33		2 c. carmine (1884)	25·00	85
		a. Aniline carmine	27·00	85
		w. Wmk inverted	—	50·00
34	2	4 c. slate-grey (1.4.96)	9·00	85
		w. Wmk inverted	—	50·00
35		5 c. pale blue	20·00	85
		a. Blue	21·00	85
		aw. Wmk inverted	£150	50·00
		x. Wmk reversed	—	£100
36		10 c. dull mauve (8.82)	£500	8·50
		w. Wmk inverted	—	75·00
37		10 c. deep blue-green (1884)	£1600	35·00
		a. Green (2.84)	£110	1·00
38		10 c. purple/*red* (1.1.91)	18·00	85
		w. Wmk inverted	£225	50·00
		x. Wmk reversed	£250	60·00
		y. Wmk inverted and reversed ..		
39		30 c. yellowish green (1.1.91)	£120	38·00
		a. Grey-green	60·00	16·00
38, 39*a* Optd "Specimen" .. *Set of* 2			£375	

Examples of No. 39 should not be confused with washed or faded stamps from the grey-green shade which tend to turn to a very yellow-green when dampened.

For other stamps with this watermark, but in colours changed to the U.P.U. scheme see Nos. 56/61.

20 CENTS (8) 50 CENTS (9) 1 DOLLAR (10)

1885 (Sept). *As Nos.* 15, 19 *and* 31, *but wmkd Crown CA, surch with T* **8** *to* **10** *by De La Rue.*

40	2	20 c. on 30 c. orange-red	85·00	5·00
		a. Surch double		
		w. Wmk inverted	£500	£100
41	3	50 c. on 48 c. yellowish brown	£300	26·00
		w. Wmk inverted	—	85·00
42		$1 on 96 c. grey-olive	£550	48·00
40/2 Optd "Specimen" .. .. *Set of* 3			£800	

7 cents. (11) 14 cents. (12)

弍 (13) (20 c.) 五十 (14) (50 c.) 壹員 (15) ($1)

1891 (1 Jan–Mar). (*a*) *Nos.* 16 *and* 37 *surch with T* **11** *or* **12** *by Noronha and Sons, Hong Kong*

43	2	7 c. on 10 c. green	60·00	7·50
		a. Antique "t" in "cents" (R.1/1) ..	£550	£150
		b. Surch double	£6000	£1300
44		14 c. on 30 c. mauve (Feb)	£120	50·00
		a. Antique "t" in "cents" (R.1/1) ..	£2250	£900

(*b*) *As Nos.* 40/2 (*surch with T* **8** *to* **10** *by De La Rue*), *but colours changed*

45	2	20 c. on 30 c. yellowish green (No. 39) ..	£160	£150
		a. Grey-green (No. 39*a*)	95·00	£130
46	3	50 c. on 48 c. dull purple	£225	£250
47		$1 on 96 c. purple/*red*	£600	£325
45*a*/7 Optd "Specimen" .. .. *Set of* 3			£650	

(*c*) *Nos.* 45/7 *with further surch, T* **13/15**, *in Chinese characters, handstamped locally* (Mar)

48	2	20 c. on 30 c. yellowish green	55·00	6·50
		a. Grey-green	25·00	4·50
49	3	50 c. on 48 c. dull purple	65·00	5·50
50		$1 on 96 c. purple/*red*	£375	22·00
		w. Wmk inverted		

The true antique "t" variety (Nos. 43a and 44a) should not be confused with a small "t" showing a short foot. In the antique "t" the crossbar is accurately bisected by the vertical stroke, which is thicker at the top. The lower curve bends towards the right and does not turn upwards to the same extent as on the normal.

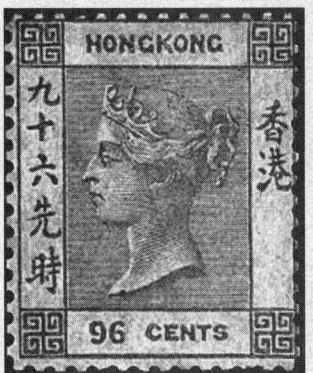

The handstamped surcharges on Nos. 48/50 were applied over the original Chinese face values. The single character for "2"

was intended to convert "30 c." to "20 c.". There were six slightly different versions of the "2" handstamp and three for the "50 c.".

A used example of No. 48 in the Royal Philatelic Collection shows surcharge Type 8 double.

The errors of the Chinese surcharges previously listed on the above issue and also on Nos. 52 and 55 are now omitted as being outside the scope of the catalogue. While some without doubt possess philatelic merit, it is impossible to distinguish between the genuine errors and the clandestine copies made to order with the original chops. No. 55c is retained as this represents a distinctly different chop which was used for the last part of the printing.

1841 Hong Kong JUBILEE 1891 (16)

10 CENTS (17)

拾 (18)

拾 (19)

1891 (22 Jan). *50th Anniversary of Colony. Optd with T* **16** *by Noronha and Sons, Hong Kong.*

51	**1**	2 c. carmine (No. 33)	£375	95·00
		b. Short "J" in "JUBILEE" (R. 1/6)	£550	£140
		b. Short "U" or "JUBILEE" (R. 1/1)	£550	£140
		c. Broken "1" in "1891" (R. 2/1)	£700	£200
		d. Tall narrow "K" in "Kong" (R. 1/3)	£1100	£425
		e. Opt double	£16000	£12000
		f. Space between "O" and "N" of "Hong" (R. 1/5)	£1500	£650

Most of the supply of No. 51, which was only on sale for three days, was overprinted from a setting of 12 (6×2) applied five times to complete each sheet. There were six printings from this setting, but a second setting, possibly of 30 or 60, was used for the seventh. Positions quoted are from the setting of twelve. Most varieties only occur in some printings and many less marked overprint flaws also exist.

The prices quoted for No. 51e are for examples on which the two impressions are distinctly separated. Examples on which the two impressions are almost coincidental are worth considerably less.

1898 (1 Apr). *Wmk Crown CA. P* 14. (a) *Surch with T* **10** *by D.L.R. and handstamped Chinese characters as T* **15**

52	**3**	$1 on 96 c. black	£130	27·00
		a. Grey-black	£130	26·00
		(b) *Surch with T* **10** *only*		
53	**3**	$1 on 96 c. black	£3000	£3750
		a. Grey-black (Optd S. £600)	£2750	£3500

1898 (1 Apr). (a) *Surch with T* **17** *by Noronha and Sons, Hong Kong*

54	**2**	10 c. on 30 c. grey-green (No. 39*a*)	£450	£750
		a. Figures "10" widely spaced ($1^1/_2$ mm)	£3500	
		b. Surch double		

Type **17** was applied in a horizontal setting of 12, No. 54a appearing on position 12 for the first printing only.

(b) *As No. 54, but with Chinese character, T* **18**, *in addition*

55	**2**	10 c. on 30 c. grey-green (No. 39*a*) (H/S S. £120)	38·00	70·00
		a. Yellowish green (Optd S. £150)	80·00	£110
		b. Figures "10" widely spaced ($1^1/_2$ mm)	£700	£800
		c. Chinese character large (Type **19**)	£850	£950
		ca. Ditto. Figures "10" widely spaced	£6500	
		d. Surch Type **17** double		

1900 (Aug)–**01**. *Wmk Crown CA. P* 14.

56	**1**	2 c. dull green	25·00	85
		w. Wmk inverted	£100	50·00
57	**2**	4 c. carmine (1901)	14·00	85
58		5 c. yellow	17·00	6·50
		w. Wmk inverted		
59		10 c. ultramarine	45·00	1·75
		w. Wmk inverted	—	65·00
60	**1**	12 c. blue (1901)	30·00	40·00
61	**2**	30 c. brown (1901)	30·00	20·00
56/61		*Set of* 6	£140	60·00
56/9, 61 Optd "Specimen"		*Set of* 5	£450	

20

21

22

23

1903 (Jan–July). *Wmk Crown CA. P* 14.

62	**20**	1 c. dull purple and brown	2·00	50
63		2 c. dull green (July)	5·50	1·50
		w. Wmk inverted		
64	**21**	4 c. purple/*red* (July)	8·00	40
65		5 c. dull green and brown-orange (July)	9·00	9·00
66		8 c. slate and violet (12 Feb)	7·00	1·25
67	**20**	10 c. purple and blue/*blue* (July)	28·00	1·25
68	**23**	12 c. green and purple/*yellow* (18 Feb)	7·00	4·25
69		20 c. slate and chestnut (June)	30·00	2·50
70	**22**	30 c. dull green and black (21 May)	32·00	16·00
71	**23**	50 c. dull green and magenta (June)	26·00	26·00
72	**20**	$1 purple and sage-green (June)	65·00	19·00
73	**23**	$2 slate and scarlet (July)	£170	£200
74	**22**	$3 slate and dull blue (July)	£180	£300
75	**23**	$5 purple and blue-green (June)	£325	£400
76	**22**	$10 slate and orange/*blue* (July)	£800	£375
62/76		*Set of* 15	£1500	£1100
62/76 Optd "Specimen"		*Set of* 15	£1100	

1904 (4 Oct)–**06**. *Wmk Mult Crown CA. Chalk-surfaced paper (8, 12 c., $3, $5) or ordinary paper (others). P* 14.

77	**20**	2 c. dull green	4·00	1·25
		a. Chalk-surfaced paper (1906)	6·00	2·50
78	**21**	4 c. purple/*red*	8·50	40
		a. Chalk-surfaced paper (1906)	4·75	40
79		5 c. dull green and brown-orange	16·00	6·00
		a. Chalk-surfaced paper (1906)	9·00	5·00
		aw. Wmk inverted		
80		8 c. slate and violet (1906)	7·50	2·00
81	**20**	10 c. purple and blue/*blue* (3.05)	12·00	75
82	**23**	12 c. green and purple/*yellow* (1906)	9·00	5·50
83		20 c. slate and chestnut	24·00	2·25
		a. Chalk-surfaced paper (1906)	20·00	2·25
		w. Wmk inverted	†	£250
84	**22**	30 c. dull green and black	24·00	12·00
		a. Chalk-surfaced paper (1906)	30·00	15·00
85	**23**	50 c. green and magenta	45·00	6·50
		a. Chalk-surfaced paper (1906)	45·00	9·50
86	**20**	$1 purple and sage-green	90·00	17·00
		a. Chalk-surfaced paper (1906)	85·00	17·00
87	**23**	$2 slate and scarlet	£150	85·00
		a. Chalk-surfaced paper (1905)	£140	75·00
88	**22**	$3 slate and dull blue (1905)	£150	£180
89	**23**	$5 purple and blue-green (1905)	£325	£300
90	**22**	$10 slate and orange/*blue* (5.05)	£1300	£900
		a. Chalk-surfaced paper (1906)	£1200	£700
77/90		*Set of* 14	£1800	£1100

1907–11. *Colours changed and new value. Wmk Mult Crown CA. Chalk-surfaced paper (6 c. and 20 c. to $2). P* 14.

91	**20**	1 c. brown (9.10)	3·00	90
92		2 c. deep green	17·00	1·75
		a. Green	17·00	1·50
93	**21**	4 c. carmine-red	4·25	40
94	**22**	6 c. orange-vermilion and purple (10.07)	15·00	3·00
95	**20**	10 c. bright ultramarine	15·00	40
96	**23**	20 c. purple and sage-green (3.11)	32·00	35·00
97	**22**	30 c. purple and orange-yellow (3.11)	45·00	18·00
98	**23**	50 c. black/*green* (3.11)	35·00	13·00
99		$2 carmine-red and black (1910)	£250	£225
91/9		*Set of* 9	£375	£275
91, 93/9 Optd "Specimen"		*Set of* 8	£650	

24

25

26

27

28

(A)

(B)

In Type A of the 25 c. the upper Chinese character in the left-hand label has a short vertical stroke crossing it at the foot. In Type B this stroke is absent.

1912 (9 Nov)–**21**. *Wmk Mult Crown CA. Chalk-surfaced paper (12 c. to $10). P* 14.

100	**24**	1 c. brown	2·00	55
		a. Black-brown	3·50	2·00
		b. Crown broken at right (R. 9/2)	£190	£140
101		2 c. deep green	5·00	30
		a. Green	5·00	30
102	**25**	4 c. carmine-red	3·75	30
		a. Scarlet (1914)	15·00	1·75
103	**26**	6 c. yellow-orange	3·75	85
		a. Brown-orange	3·75	1·25
		w. Wmk inverted		
104	**25**	8 c. grey	22·00	4·50
		a. Slate (1914)	30·00	4·50
105	**24**	10 c. ultramarine	28·00	30
		a. Deep bright ultramarine	23·00	30
106	**27**	12 c. purple/*yellow*	3·50	5·50
		a. White back (Optd S. £85) (1914)	6·50	11·00
107		20 c. purple and sage-green	4·75	90
108		25 c. purple & magenta (Type A) (1.14)	14·00	17·00
109		25 c. purple & magenta (Type B) (8.19)	£120	50·00
110	**26**	30 c. purple and orange-yellow	25·00	5·00
		a. Purple and orange	12·00	4·50
		w. Wmk inverted		
111	**27**	50 c. black/*blue-green*	11·00	1·50
		a. White back (Optd S. £130) (5.14)	10·00	4·25
		b. On blue-green, olive back (1917)	£900	26·00
		c. On emerald surface (9.19)	19·00	8·00
		d. On emerald back (Optd S. £130) (7.12.21)	20·00	6·50
112	**24**	$1 purple and blue/*blue*	32·00	2·25
		w. Wmk inverted	95·00	75·00
113	**27**	$2 carmine-red and grey-black	£100	35·00
114	**26**	$3 green and purple	£160	60·00
115	**27**	$5 green and red/*green*	£475	£300
		a. White back (Optd S. £250) (5.14)	£475	£250
		b. On blue-green, olive back (Optd S. £275) (1917)	£850	£225
		bw. Wmk inverted		
116	**26**	$10 purple and black/*red*	£475	75·00
100/16		*Set of* 17	£1300	£375
100/16 Optd "Specimen"		*Set of* 17	£1400	

No. 100b occurs on R. 9/2 of the lower right pane.

Broken flower at top right (Upper left pane R. 1/3)

1921 (Jan)–**37**. *Wmk Mult Script CA. Chalk-surfaced pap*
(12 *c. to* $5). *P* 14.

117	**24**	1 c. brown	1·00
		b. Crown broken to right (R. 9/2)	
118		2 c. blue-green	2·25
		a. Yellow-green (1932)	6·50
		bw. Wmk inverted	55·00
118*c*		2 c. grey (14.4.37)	13·00
119	**25**	3 c. grey (8.10.31)	4·00
120		4 c. carmine-rose	3·25
		a. Carmine-red (1932)	2·25
		b. Top of lower Chinese characters at right broken off (R. 9/4)	75·00
121		5 c. violet (16.10.31)	4·50
122		8 c. grey	8·00
123		8 c. orange (7.12.21)	3·00
124	**24**	10 c. bright ultramarine	2·25
		aw. Wmk inverted	85·00
124*b*	**27**	12 c. purple/*yellow* (3.4.33)	11·00
125		20 c. purple and sage-green (7.12.21)	3·50
126	**28**	25 c. purple and magenta (B) (7.12.21)	2·50
		a. Broken flower	30·00
		w. Wmk inverted	†
127	**26**	30 c. purple & chrome-yellow (7.12.21)	10·00
		a. Purple and orange-yellow	22·00
		w. Wmk inverted	£100
128	**27**	50 c. black/*emerald* (1924)	8·50
129	**24**	$1 purple and blue/*blue* (7.12.21)	22·00
130	**27**	$2 carmine-red & grey-black (7.12.21)	80·00
131	**26**	$3 green and dull purple (1926)	£140
132	**27**	$5 green and red/*emerald* (1925)	£375
117/32		*Set of* 18	£600
117/32 Optd/Perf "Specimen"		*Set of* 18	£1200

No. 120b occurs on R. 9/4 of the lower left pane.

1935 (6 May). *Silver Jubilee. As Nos.* 91/4 *of Antigua, but p*
by B.W. P 11×12.

133	3 c. ultramarine and grey-black	4·00
	c. Lightning conductor	£275
134	5 c. green and indigo	8·00
	a. Extra flagstaff	£275
	b. Short extra flagstaff	£300
	c. Lightning conductor	£250
	d. Flagstaff on right-hand turret	£300
135	10 c. brown and deep blue	20·00
136	20 c. slate and purple	38·00
	b. Short extra flagstaff	£550
	d. Flagstaff on right-hand turret	£500
	e. Double flagstaff	£500
133/6	*Set of* 4	60·00
133/6 Perf "Specimen"	*Set of* 4	£300

For illustrations of plate varieties see Catalogue Introductio

1937 (12 May). *Coronation. As Nos.* 95/7 *of Antigu*
P 11×11½.

137	4 c. green	6·00
138	15 c. carmine	12·00
139	25 c. blue	15·00
137/9	*Set of* 3	30·00
137/9 Perf "Specimen"	*Set of* 3	£180

29 King George VI

Short right leg to "R" (Right pane R. 7/3, left pane R. 3/1)

1938–52. *Wmk Mult Script CA. Chalk-surfaced paper* (80 c
$1 (*No.* 155), $2 (*No.* 157), $5 (*No.* 159), $10 (*No.* 161)). *P* 1

140	**29**	1 c. brown (24.5.38)	1·75
		a. Pale brown (4.2.52)	2·00
141		2 c. grey (5.4.38)	2·00
		a. Perf 14½×14 (28.9.45)	1·75
142		4 c. orange (5.4.38)	2·75
		a. Perf 14½×14 (28.9.45)	4·50
143		5 c. green (24.5.38)	1·25
		a. Perf 14½×14 (28.9.45)	2·50
144		8 c. red-brown (1.11.41)	1·75
		a. Imperf (pair)	£22000
145		10 c. bright violet (13.4.38)	48·00
		a. Perf 14½×14. *Dull violet* (28.9.45)	7·50
		b. Dull reddish violet (9.4.46)	5·50
		c. Reddish lilac (9.4.47)	15·00
146		15 c. scarlet (13.4.38)	1·50
147		20 c. black (1.2.46)	1·25
148		20 c. scarlet-vermilion (1.4.48)	7·00
		a. Rose-red (25.4.51)	15·00
149		25 c. bright blue (5.4.38)	24·00
150		25 c. pale yellow-olive (9.4.46)	4·75
151		30 c. yellow-olive (13.4.48)	£150
		a. Perf 14½×14. *Yellowish olive* (28.9.45)	20·00
152		30 c. blue (9.4.46)	7·00
153		50 c. reddish purple (13.4.38)	42·00
		a. Perf 14½×14. *Deep magenta* (28.9.45)	29·00
		b. Chalk-surfaced paper. *Brt purple* (9.4.47)	9·00
154		80 c. carmine (2.2.48)	5·00

.55 **29** $1 dull lilac and blue (*chalk-surfaced paper*) (27.4.38) 8·00 2·50
a. Short right leg to "R" £100
b. Ordinary paper. *Pale reddish lilac and blue* (28.9.45) 10·00 5·50
.56 $1 red-orange and green (9.4.46) 16·00 30
a. Short right leg to "R" £150
b. Chalk-surfaced paper (21.6.48) 45·00 3·50
ba. Short right leg to "R" £250
c. Chalk-surfaced paper. *Yellow-orange and green* (6.11.52) 65·00 14·00
57 $2 red-orange and green (24.5.38) 70·00 14·00
58 $2 reddish violet and scarlet (9.4.46) 26·00 1·50
a. Chalk-surfaced paper (9.4.47) 32·00 85
59 $5 dull lilac and scarlet (2.6.38) 55·00 48·00
60 $5 green and violet (9.4.46) 80·00 5·00
a. Yellowish green and violet (9.4.46) £150 16·00
ab. Chalk-surfaced paper (9.4.47) 95·00 2·75
61 $10 green and violet (2.6.38) £375 80·00
62 $10 bright lilac and blue (9.4.46) £140 23·00
a. Chalk-surfaced paper. *Reddish violet and blue* (9.4.47) £170 18·00
40/62 *Set of* 23 £750 £150
40/62 Perf "Specimen" *Set of* 23 £2000

Following bomb damage to the De La Rue works on the night of 29 December 1940 various emergency arrangements were made to complete current requisitions for Hong Kong stamps:

Nos. 141a, 143a, 145a, 151a and 153a (all printings perforated 14½×14 except the 4 c.) were printed and perforated by Bradbury, Wilkinson & Co. Ltd. using De La Rue plates. These stamps are on rough-surfaced paper.

Nos. 142a and 144 were printed by Harrison & Sons in sheets of 120 (12×10) instead of the normal 120 two panes (6×10).

Printings of the $1 and $2 values were made by Williams, Lea & Co. using De La Rue plates.

With the exception of the 8 c. it is believed that none of these printings were issued in Hong Kong before its occupation by the Japanese on 25 December 1941, although examples could be obtained in London from late 1941. The issue dates quoted are those on which the stamps were eventually released in Hong Kong following liberation in 1945.

Nos. 160/*a* were separate printings released in Hong Kong on the same day.

No. 144a. One imperforate sheet was found and most of the stamps were sold singly to the public at a branch P.O. and used for postage.

30 Street Scene **31** *Empress of Japan* (liner) and Junk

(Des W. E. Jones. Recess B.W.)

1941 (26 Feb). *Centenary of British Occupation. T* **30/1** *and similar designs. Wmk Mult Script CA (sideways on horiz designs). P* 13½ × 13 (*2 c. and 25 c.*) *or* 13 × 13½ (*others*).
63 2 c. orange and chocolate 4·00 1·75
64 4 c. bright purple and carmine 4·50 1·75
65 5 c. black and green 2·50 50
66 15 c. black and scarlet 5·50 1·00
67 25 c. chocolate and blue 12·00 3·25
68 $1 blue and orange 45·00 7·00
63/168 *Set of* 6 65·00 14·00
63/8 Perf "Specimen" *Set of* 6 £325

Designs: *Horiz*—5 c. The University; 15 c. The Harbour; $1 Falcon (clipper) and Short S.23 Empire "C" Class flying boat. *Vert*—25 c. The Hong Kong Bank.

Hong Kong was under Japanese occupation from 25 December 1941 until 30 August 1945. The Japanese post offices in the colony were closed from 31 August and mail was carried free, marked with cachets reading "HONG KONG/1945/POSTAGE PAID". Military administration lasted until 1 May 1946. Hong Kong stamps were re-introduced on 28 September 1945.

36 King George VI and Phoenix **37** Queen Elizabeth II

Extra stroke (R. 1/2)

(Des W. E. Jones. Recess D.L.R.)

1946 (29 Aug). *Victory. Wmk Mult Script CA. P* 13.
169 **36** 30 c. blue and red (*shades*) 1·75 1·25
a. Extra stroke 42·00
170 $1 brown and red 3·50 75
a. Extra stroke 75·00
169/70 Perf "Specimen" *Set of* 2 £160

HONG KONG

Spur on "N" of "KONG" (R. 2/9)

1948 (22 Dec). *Royal Silver Wedding. As Nos.* 112/13 *of Antigua.*
171 10 c. violet 2·50 80
a. Spur on "N" 50·00
172 $10 carmine £250 70·00

1949 (10 Oct). *75th Anniv of Universal Postal Union. As Nos.* 114/17 *of Antigua.*
173 10 c. violet 3·75 50
174 20 c. carmine-red 15·00 3·00
175 30 c. deep blue 12·00 1·75
176 80 c. bright reddish purple 35·00 9·50
173/6 *Set of* 4 60·00 13·00

1953 (2 June) *Coronation. As No.* 120 *of Antigua.*
177 10 c. black and slate-lilac 5·00 30

1954 (5 Jan)–**62.** *Chalk-surfaced paper* (20 c. *to* $10). *Wmk Mult Script CA. P* 14.
178 **37** 5 c. orange 1·50 20
a. Imperf (pair) £1100
179 10 c. lilac 2·50 10
aw. Wmk inverted £130
b. Reddish violet (18.7.61) 7·00 10
180 15 c. green 4·25 45
a. Pale green (6.12.55) 4·00 45
181 20 c. brown 5·00 30
182 25 c. scarlet 3·50 1·00
a. Rose-red (26.5.58) 3·00 70
183 30 c. grey 4·50 20
a. Pale grey (26.2.58) 6·50 20
184 40 c. bright blue 4·00 40
a. Dull blue (10.1.61) 9·50 70
185 50 c. reddish purple 4·75 20
186 65 c. grey (20.6.60) 19·00 7·50
187 $1 orange and green 7·50 20
188 $1.30, blue and red (20.6.60) 23·00 1·00
a. Bright blue and red (23.1.62) 42·00 2·75
189 $2 reddish violet and scarlet 12·00 40
a. Lt reddish violet & scarlet (26.2.58) 13·00 60
190 $5 green and purple 75·00 1·50
a. Yellowish green and purple (7.3.61) 90·00 2·25
191 $10 reddish violet and bright blue 60·00 8·50
a. Lt reddish violet & brt blue (26.2.58) 65·00 8·50
178/91 *Set of* 14 £200 19·00

No. 178a exists from two sheets, each of which had 90 stamps imperforate and 10 perforated on three sides only.

The 10 c. exists in coils constructed from normal sheets.

38 University Arms **39** Statue of Queen Victoria

(Des and photo Harrison)

1961 (11 Sept). *Golden Jubilee of Hong Kong University. W* w **12.** *P* 11½ × 12.
192 **38** $1 multicoloured 7·00 2·00
a. Gold ptg omitted £1300

(Des Cheung Yat-man. Photo Harrison)

1962 (4 May). *Stamp Centenary. W* w **12.** *P* 14½.
193 **39** 10 c. black and magenta 60 10
194 20 c. black and light blue 1·75 1·75
195 50 c. black and bistre 4·00 40
193/5 *Set of* 3 5·75 2·00

40 Queen Elizabeth II (after Annigoni) **41**

(Photo Harrison)

1962 (4 Oct)–**73.** *W* w **12** (*upright*). *Chalk-surfaced paper. P* 15 × 14 (*5 c. to $1*) *or* 14 × 14½ (*others*).
196 **40** 5 c. red-orange 50 50
197 10 c. bright reddish violet 1·25 10
a. Reddish violet (19.11.71) 4·00 10
ab. Glazed paper (14.4.72) 8·50 1·75
198 15 c. emerald 2·50 75
199 20 c. red-brown 1·75 75
a. Brown (13.12.71) 7·00 2·00
ab. Glazed paper (27.9.72) 13·00 8·50
200 **40** 25 c. cerise 2·50 1·50
201 30 c. deep grey-blue 2·50 10
a. Chalky blue (19.11.71) 6·50 1·75
ab. Glazed paper (27.9.72) 14·00 4·00
202 40 c. deep bluish green 2·00 30
203 50 c. scarlet 1·75 20
a. Vermilion (13.12.71) 11·00 1·75
ab. Glazed paper (27.9.72) 10·00 2·00
204 65 c. ultramarine 17·00 2·00
205 $1 sepia 17·00 30
206 **41** $1.30, multicoloured 5·00 20
a. Pale yellow omitted 35·00
b. Pale yellow inverted (horiz pair) £2750
c. Ochre (sash) omitted 25·00
d. Glazed paper (3.2.71) 12·00 2·25
da. Ochre (sash) omitted 30·00
dw. Wmk inverted 15·00
207 $2 multicoloured 7·00 40
a. Pale yellow omitted† 35·00
b. Ochre (sash) omitted 32·00
c. Pale yellow† and ochre (sash) omitted £150
dw. Wmk inverted 10·00
e. Glazed paper (1973)* £140 6·00
208 $5 multicoloured 17·00 1·25
a. Ochre (sash) omitted 35·00
bw. Wmk inverted 25·00
c. Glazed paper (3.2.71) 25·00 9·50
cw. Wmk inverted 40·00
209 $10 multicoloured 30·00 2·25
a. Ochre (sash) omitted £100
b. Pale yellow† and ochre (sash) omitted £160
cw. Wmk inverted 65·00
d. Glazed paper (1973)* £1800 £110
210 $20 multicoloured £140 22·00
w. Wmk inverted £600
196/210 *Set of* 15 £225 28·00

*These are from printings which were sent to Hong Kong in March 1973 but not released in London.

†This results in the Queen's face appearing pinkish.

It is believed that No. 206b comes from the last two vertical rows of a sheet, the remainder of which had the pale yellow omitted.

The $1.30 to $20 exist with PVA gum as well as gum arabic. The glazed paper printings are with PVA gum only.

See also Nos. 222, etc.

1963 (4 June). *Freedom from Hunger. As No.* 146 *of Antigua, but additionally inscr in Chinese characters.*
211 $1.30, bluish green 55·00 8·00

1963 (2 Sept). *Red Cross Centenary. As Nos.* 147/8 *of Antigua, but additionally inscr in Chinese characters at right.*
212 10 c. red and black 5·00 30
213 $1.30, red and blue 35·00 8·00

1965 (17 May). *I.T.U. Centenary. As Nos.* 166/7 *of Antigua.*
214 10 c. light purple and orange-yellow 4·00 25
w. Wmk inverted 40·00
215 $1.30, olive-yellow and deep bluish green 25·00 5·50

1965 (25 Oct). *International Co-operation Year. As Nos.* 168/9 *of Antigua.*
216 10 c. reddish purple and turquoise-green 3·00 25
w. Wmk inverted 4·00
217 $1.30, dp bluish green & lavender (*shades*) 20·00 5·50

1966 (24 Jan). *Churchill Commemoration. As Nos.* 170/3 *of Antigua but additionally inscr in Chinese characters.*
218 10 c. new blue 3·00 15
w. Wmk inverted 13·00
219 50 c. deep green 3·50 30
w. Wmk inverted 3·50
220 $1.30, brown 24·00 3·00
221 $2 bluish violet 38·00 10·00
w. Wmk inverted £140
218/21 *Set of* 4 60·00 12·00

1966 (Aug)–**72.** *As Nos.* 196/208 *and* 210 *but wmk W* w **12** (*sideways**). *Chalk-surfaced paper* (5 c. *to* $1) *or glazed, ordinary paper* ($1.30 *to* $20).
222 **40** 5 c. red-orange (5.12.66) 50 80
223 10 c. reddish violet (31.3.67)† 70 30
a. Imperf (horiz pair) £500
w. Wmk Crown to right of CA
224 15 c. emerald (31.3.67)† 2·00 1·50
225 20 c. red-brown 1·75 1·50
a. Glazed, ordinary paper (14.4.72) 8·00 8·00
226 25 c. cerise (31.3.67)† 3·00 3·25
aw. Wmk Crown to right of CA 8·50
b. Glazed, ordinary paper (14.4.72) 14·00 14·00
227 30 c. deep grey-blue (31.3.70) 10·00 1·75
a. Glazed, ordinary paper (14.4.72) 13·00 8·00
228 40 c. deep bluish green (1967) 3·00 1·50
a. Glazed, ordinary paper (14.4.72) 13·00 12·00
229 50 c. scarlet (31.3.67)† 2·50 80
w. Wmk Crown to right of CA (13.5.69) 3·50 1·25
230 65 c. ultramarine (29.3.67)† 6·00 6·50
a. Bright blue (16.7.68) 6·00 6·50
231 $1 sepia (29.3.67)† 12·00 1·50
w. Wmk Crown to right of CA 38·00
232 **41** $1.30, multicoloured (14.4.72) 10·00 2·00
w. Wmk Crown to right of CA (17.11.72) 12·00 2·25
233 $2 multicoloured (13.12.71) 11·00 2·50
a. Ochre (sash) omitted 38·00
w. Wmk Crown to right of CA (17.11.72) 12·00 3·25
234 $5 multicoloured (13.12.71) 65·00 12·00
236 $20 multicoloured (14.4.72) £150 60·00
222/36 *Set of* 14 £250 85·00

*The normal sideways watermark shows Crown to left of CA, *as seen from the back of the stamp.*

†Earliest known postmark dates.

The 5 c. to 25 c., 40 c. and 50 c. exist with PVA gum as well as gum arabic, but the 30 c., and all stamps on glazed paper exist with PVA gum only.

1966 (20 Sept). *Inauguration of W.H.O. Headquarters, Geneva. As Nos. 178/9 of Antigua, but additionally inscr in Chinese characters.*
237 10 c. black, yellow-green and light blue .. 3·00 30
238 50 c. black, light purple and yellow-brown .. 10·00 1·75

1966 (1 Dec). *20th Anniv of U.N.E.S.C.O. As Nos. 196/8 of Antigua, but additionally inscr in Chinese characters.*
239 10 c. slate-violet, red, yellow and orange .. 3·50 20
240 50 c. orange-yellow, violet and deep olive .. 13·00 90
241 $2 black, light purple and orange .. .. 55·00 17·00
239/41 .. .. *Set of* 3 65·00 17·00

42 Rams' Heads on Chinese Lanterns

(Des V. Whiteley. Photo Harrison)

1967 (17 Jan). *Chinese New Year ("Year of the Ram"). T* **42** *and similar horiz design. W w* **12** *(sideways). P* 14½.
242 10 c. rosine, olive-green and light yellow-olive 4·00 50
243 $1.30, emerald, rosine and light yellow-olive 32·00 11·00
Design:—$1.30, Three rams.

44 Cable Route Map

(Des V. Whiteley. Photo Harrison)

1967 (30 Mar). *Completion of Malaysia–Hong Kong Link of SEACOM Telephone Cable. W w* **12**. *P* 12½.
244 **44** $1.30, new blue and red .. .. 17·00 4·50

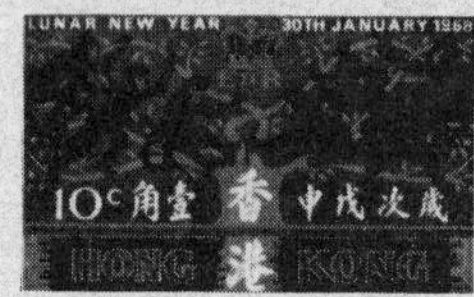

45 Rhesus Macaques in Tree ("Year of the Monkey")

(Des R. Granger Barrett. Photo Harrison)

1968 (23 Jan). *Chinese New Year ("Year of the Monkey"). T* **45** *and similar horiz design. W w* **12** *(sideways). P* 14½.
245 10 c. gold, black and scarlet .. .. .. 4·50 50
246 $1.30, gold, black and scarlet .. .. 30·00 9·50
Design:—$1.30, Family of Rhesus Macaques.

47 *Iberia* (liner) at Ocean Terminal

(Des and litho D.L.R.)

1968 (24 Apr). *Sea Craft. T* **47** *and similar horiz designs. P* 13.
247 10 c. multicoloured .. .. 2·00 15
a. Dull orange and new blue omitted .. £900
248 20 c. cobalt-blue, black and brown .. .. 3·25 1·00
249 40 c. orange, black and mauve .. .. 11·00 9·00
250 50 c. orange-red, black and green .. .. 7·50 75
a. Green omitted £750
251 $1 greenish yellow, black and red .. .. 16·00 4·50
252 $1.30, Prussian blue, black and pink .. 45·00 4·25
247/52 .. .. *Set of* 6 75·00 18·00
Designs:—20 c. Pleasure launch; 40 c. Car ferry; 50 c. Passenger ferry; $1, Sampan; $1.30, Junk.

53 *Bauhinia blakeana*

54 Arms of Hong Kong

(Des V. Whiteley. Photo Harrison)

1968 (25 Sept)–**73**. *W w* **12**. *P* 14 × 14½.
(a) Upright wmk. Chalk-surfaced paper
253 **53** 65 c. multicoloured .. .. .. 9·00 50
aw. Wmk inverted .. .. 17·00
b. Glazed, ordinary paper (3.73) 50·00 13·00
254 **54** $1 multicoloured .. .. .. 9·00 40
(b) Sideways wmk. Glazed, ordinary paper
254*a* **53** 65 c. multicoloured (27.9.72) .. 38·00 15·00
254*b* **54** $1 multicoloured (13.12.71) .. 7·50 2·00
Nos. 253/4 exist with PVA gum as well as gum arabic; Nos. 254*a/b* with PVA gum only.

55 "Aladdin's Lamp" and Human Rights Emblem

(Des R. Granger Barrett. Litho B.W.)

1968 (20 Nov). *Human Rights Year. W w* **12** *(sideways). P* 13½.
255 **55** 10 c. orange, black and myrtle-green .. 1·50 75
256 50 c. yellow, black & dp reddish purple .. 4·50 2·25

56 Cockerel

(Des R. Granger Barrett. Photo Enschedé)

1969 (11 Feb). *Chinese New Year ("Year of the Cock"). T* **56** *and similar multicoloured design. P* 13½.
257 10 c. Type **56** .. .. 5·00 1·00
a. Red omitted £160
258 $1.30, Cockerel (*vert*) .. .. .. 65·00 14·00

58 Arms of Chinese University

59 Earth Station and Satellite

(Des V. Whiteley. Photo Govt Ptg Bureau, Tokyo)

1969 (26 Aug). *Establishment of Chinese University of Hong Kong. P* 13½.
259 **58** 40 c. violet, gold and pale turquoise-blue 7·00 3·00

(Des V. Whiteley. Photo Harrison)

1969 (24 Sept). *Opening of Communications Satellite Tracking Station. W w* **12**. *P* 14½.
260 **59** $1 multicoloured .. .. 24·00 4·50

60 Chow's Head

62 "Expo 70" Emblem

(Des R. Granger Barrett. Photo D.L.R.)

1970 (28 Jan). *Chinese New Year ("Year of the Dog"). T* **60** *and similar design. W w* **12** *(sideways on $1.30). P* 14½×14 *(10 c.) or* 14×14½ *($1.30).*
261 10 c. lemon-yellow, orange-brown and black .. 5·50 1·25
262 $1.30, multicoloured .. .. .. 65·00 14·00
Design: *Horiz*—$1.30, Chow standing.

(Des and litho B.W.)

1970 (14 Mar). *World Fair, Osaka. T* **62** *and similar multicoloured design. W w* **12** *(sideways on 25 c.). P* 13½ × 13 *(15 c.) or* 13 × 13½ *(25 c.).*
263 15 c. Type **62** 65 85
264 25 c. "Expo '70" emblem and junks (*horiz*) 1·40 1·50

64 Plaque in Tung Wah Hospital

65 Symbol

(Des M. F. Griffith. Photo Harrison)

1970 (9 Apr). *Centenary of Tung Wah Hospital. W w* **12** *(sideways*). P* 14½.
265 **64** 10 c. multicoloured 75 25
266 50 c. multicoloured .. .. .. 3·25 1·50
w. Wmk Crown to right of CA .. 4·00
*The normal sideways watermark shows Crown to left of CA, *as seen from the back of the stamp.*

(Des J. Cooter. Litho B.W.)

1970 (5 Aug). *Asian Productivity Year. W w* **12**. *P* 14 × 13½.
267 **65** 10 c. multicoloured .. .. .. 1·00 60

66 Pig

(Des Kan Tai-keung. Photo Govt Ptg Bureau, Tokyo)

1971 (20 Jan). *Chinese New Year ("Year of the Pig"). P* 13½.
268 **66** 10 c. multicoloured .. .. .. 5·00 90
269 $1.30, multicoloured .. .. .. 30·00 11·00

67 "60" and Scout Badge

68 Festival Emblem

(Des Kan Tai-keung. Litho Harrison)

1971 (23 July). *Diamond Jubilee of Scouting in Hong Kong. W w* **12** *(sideways). P* 14×15.
270 **67** 10 c. black, scarlet and yellow 65 10
271 50 c. black, green and blue .. .. 3·25 1·00
272 $2 black, magenta and bluish violet .. 18·00 9·50
270/2 .. .. *Set of* 3 20·00 9·50

(Des Kan Tai-keung. Litho J.W.)

1971 (2 Nov). *Hong Kong Festival. T* **68** *and similar designs. W w* **12** *(sideways on 10 c. and 50 c.). P* 14 *(10 c.) or* 14½ *(others).*
273 **68** 10 c. orange and purple .. .. .. 1·25 20
274 – 50 c. multicoloured .. .. .. 2·50 90
275 – $1 multicoloured .. .. .. 7·50 6·00
273/5 .. .. *Set of* 3 10·00 6·50
Designs: *Horiz* (39 × 23 *mm*)—50 c. Coloured streamers. *Vert* (23 × 39 *mm*)—$1 "Orchid".

69 Stylised Rats

(Des Kan Tai-keung. Photo D.L.R.)

1972 (8 Feb). *Chinese New Year ("Year of the Rat"). W w* **12**. *P* 13½.
276 **69** 10 c. red, gold and black .. .. 3·50 50
277 $1.30, gold, red and black .. .. 32·00 11·00
w. Wmk inverted .. .. .. 45·00

70 Tunnel Entrance

(Des G. Drummond from painting by G. Baxter. Litho Harrison)

1972 (20 Oct). *Opening of Cross-Harbour Tunnel. W w* **12**. *P* 14×15.
278 **70** $1 multicoloured .. .. .. 5·00 2·25
w. Wmk inverted .. .. .. 55·00

71 Phoenix and Dragon

72 Ox

(Des (from photograph by D. Groves) and photo Harrison)

1972 (20 Nov). *Royal Silver Wedding. W w* **12**. *P* 14×15.
279 **71** 10 c. multicoloured 30 15
a. Gold omitted £700
280 50 c. multicoloured .. .. .. 1·10 1·40
a. Dull purple ("50 c", "HONG KONG" and background) double £600
w. Wmk inverted .. .. .. 35·00

(Des R. Granger Barrett. Photo Harrison)

1973 (25 Jan). *Chinese New Year ("Year of the Ox")*. W w **12** (*sideways on* 10 c.). P 14½.
281 **72** 10 c. reddish orange, brown and black .. 2·00 40
282 – $1.30, lt yellow, yellow-orange & black 6·50 6·50
w. Wmk inverted .. .. 8·00
Design:—$1.30, similar to 10 c., but horiz.

73 Queen Elizabeth II **74**

(Des from coinage. Photo ($10 and $20 also embossed) Harrison)

1973 (12 June)–**74**. W w **12** (*sideways** on 15, 30, 40 c. $1.30, 2, 5, 10, $20). P 14½×14 (*Nos.* 283/91) *or* 14×14½ (292/6).
283 **73** 10 c. bright orange 80 50
a. Wmk sideways (from coils) .. 1·75 2·00
284 15 c. yellow-green .. .. .. 7·00 6·00
w. Wmk Crown to left of CA (21.1.74) 9·00 6·50
285 20 c. reddish violet 50 30
w. Wmk inverted .. .. .. 3·00
286 25 c. lake-brown .. .. .. 10·00 6·50
287 30 c. ultramarine .. .. .. 1·00 50
w. Wmk Crown to left of CA (21.1.74) 4·50 1·10
288 40 c. turquoise-blue .. .. .. 2·50 2·25
a. Printed on the gummed side .. £500
289 50 c. light orange-vermilion .. .. 1·25 50
290 65 c. greenish bistre .. .. .. 12·00 11·00
291 $1 bottle-green .. .. .. 2·25 70
292 **74** $1.30, pale yellow and reddish violet 7·00 75
293 $2 pale green and reddish brown .. 8·00 1·00
294 $5 pink and royal blue .. .. 11·00 3·25
a. Imperf (horiz pair) £500
295 $10 pink and deep blackish olive .. 15·00 8·50
296 $20 pink and brownish black .. 25·00 27·00
w. Wmk Crown to right of CA .. ..
283/96 .. .. *Set of* 14 90·00 60·00
*The normal sideways watermark shows Crown to right of CA on the 15 and 30 c., and to left of CA on 40 c. and T **74**, *as seen from the back of the stamp.*
Nos. 295/6 are known with embossing omitted, but it has been reported that such errors can be faked.
See also Nos. 311/24*c* and 340/53.

1973 (14 Nov). *Royal Wedding. As Nos.* 165/6 *of Anguilla, but additionally inscr in Chinese characters.*
297 50 c. ochre 50 15
w. Wmk Crown to right of CA .. .. 25·00
298 $2 bright mauve .. .. .. 2·25 1·50
The normal sideways watermark shows Crown to left of CA, *as seen from the back of the stamp.*

75 Festival Symbols forming Chinese Character

(Des Kan Tai-keung. Litho B.W.)

1973 (23 Nov). *Hong Kong Festival. T* **75** *and similar horiz designs.* W w **12**. P 14½.
299 **75** 10 c. brownish red and bright green .. 40 10
w. Wmk inverted .. .. .. 3·50
300 – 50 c. deep magenta and reddish orange 2·00 90
w. Wmk inverted .. .. .. 6·50
301 – $1 bright green and deep mauve .. 4·75 4·25
299/301 .. .. *Set of* 3 6·50 4·75
Each value has the festival symbols arranged to form a Chinese character. "Hong" on the 10 c.; "Kong" on the 50 c.; "Festival" on the $1.

76 Tiger **77** Chinese Mask

(Des R. Granger Barrett. Litho Harrison)

1974 (8 Jan). *Chinese New Year ("Year of the Tiger")*. W w **12** (*sideways* on* $1.30). P 14½.
302 **76** 10 c. multicoloured .. .. .. 3·50 50
w. Wmk inverted .. .. .. 10·00
303 – $1.30, multicoloured .. .. 11·00 12·00
w. Wmk Crown to left of CA .. 15·00
Design:—$1.30, Similar to T **76**, but vert.
*The normal sideways watermark shows Crown to right of CA, *as seen from the back of the stamp.*

(Des R. Hookham. Litho Enschedé)

1974 (1 Feb). *Arts Festival. Vert designs as T* **77** *showing Chinese opera masks.* W w **12** (*sideways*). P 12 × 12½.
304 **77** 10 c. multicoloured 75 10
305 – $1 multicoloured .. .. .. 6·00 4·25
306 – $2 multicoloured .. .. .. 9·00 8·50
304/6 .. .. *Set of* 3 14·00 11·50
MS307 159×94 mm. Nos. 304/6. Wmk upright. P 14×13 .. .. 60·00 48·00

78 Pigeons with Letters

(Des Kan Tai-keung. Litho Harrison)

1974 (9 Oct). *Centenary of Universal Postal Union. T* **78** *and similar horiz designs.* W w **12** (*sideways* on 10 and 50 c.*). P 14½.
308 10 c. lt greenish blue, lt yell-grn & slate-blk 40 10
aw. Wmk Crown to right of CA .. 3·00
b. No wmk .. .. .. 35·00
309 50 c. deep mauve, orange and slate-black 1·00 40
w. Wmk Crown to right of CA .. 32·00
310 $2 multicoloured .. .. .. 5·25 4·25
w. Wmk inverted .. .. .. 8·00
308/10 .. .. *Set of* 3 6·00 4·25
Designs:—50 c. Globe within letter; $2 Hands holding letters.
*The normal sideways watermark shows Crown to left of CA, *as seen from the back of the stamp.*

1975 (21 Jan)–**82**. *New values (60, 70, 80 and 90 c.) or as Nos.* 283/96 *but* W w **14** (*sideways* on* 10, 20, 25, 50, 65 *c. and* $1).
311 **73** 10 c. bright orange (21.2.75) .. 55 30
a. Wmk upright (from coils) (10.78) 4·25 4·50
312 15 c. yellow-green (21.1.75) .. .. 15·00 9·00
313 20 c. reddish violet (19.3.75) 50 10
a. Deep reddish mauve (21.6.77) .. 1·25 10
b. Deep reddish purple (22.6.79) .. 1·25 10
bw. Wmk Crown to right of CA .. 1·25 20
314 25 c. lake-brown (19.3.75) .. .. 14·00 11·00
315 30 c. ultramarine (9.4.75) 70 30
a. Deep ultramarine (20.4.78) .. 1·50 55
w. Wmk inverted .. .. .. 4·50
316 40 c. turquoise-blue (19.3.75) .. .. 1·25 1·25
w. Wmk inverted .. .. .. 4·00
317 50 c. light orange-vermilion (19.3.75) .. 1·75 50
318 60 c. lavender (4.5.77) .. .. .. 1·75 1·75
w. Wmk inverted .. .. .. 6·00
319 65 c. greenish bistre (19.3.75) .. .. 18·00 13·00
320 70 c. yellow (4.5.77) .. .. .. 1·75 30
a. Chrome-yellow (24.1.80) .. .. 2·75 90
w. Wmk inverted .. .. .. 5·00
321 80 c. bright magenta (4.5.77) .. .. 2·25 2·50
a. Magenta (24.1.80) .. .. 2·75 2·75
bw. Wmk inverted .. .. .. 6·00
321*c* **73** 90 c. sepia (1.10.81) .. .. .. 7·50 1·40
322 $1 bottle-green (19.3.75) .. .. 3·00 60
a. Blackish olive (24.1.80) .. .. 3·00 70
w. Wmk Crown to right of CA .. 3·75
323 **74** $1.30, pale yell & reddish vio (19.3.75) 2·50 30
w. Wmk inverted .. .. .. 3·75
324 $2 pale green & reddish brn (19.3.75) 3·00 1·25
a. Pale green and brown (10.5.82) .. 8·00 3·00
bw. Wmk inverted .. .. .. 5·50
324*c* $5 pink and royal blue (20.4.78) .. 4·75 1·75
ca. Pink & deep ultramarine (10.5.82) 13·00 4·50
cw. Wmk inverted (10.5.82) .. .. 9·00 4·50
324*d* $10 pink & deep blackish olive (20.4.78) 8·00 5·50
dw. Wmk inverted .. .. .. 9·00
324*e* $20 pink and brownish black (20.4.78) 13·00 11·00
ea. Imperf (horiz pair) £550
ew. Wmk inverted .. .. .. 17·00
311/24*e* .. .. *Set of* 18 90·00 55·00
*The normal sideways watermark shows Crown to left of CA, *as seen from the back of the stamp.*
Nos. 324*d/e* are known with the embossing omitted. See note after No. 296.

79 Stylized Hare

(Des Kan Tai-keung. Litho Harrison)

1975 (5 Feb). *Chinese New Year ("Year of the Hare"). T* **79** *and similar horiz design.* P 14½. (*a*) *No wmk.*
325 **79** 10 c. silver and light red .. .. 1·00 75
326 – $1.30, gold and light green .. .. 8·50 11·00
(*b*) W w **12**
327 **79** 10 c. silver and light red .. .. 1·00 60
w. Wmk inverted .. .. .. 38·00
328 – $1.30, gold and light green .. .. 8·00 8·00
w. Wmk inverted .. .. .. 48·00
Design:—$1.30, Pair of hares.

COVER PRICES

Cover factors are quoted at the beginning of each country for most issues to 1945. An explanation of the system can be found on page x. The factors quoted do not, however, apply to philatelic covers.

80 Queen Elizabeth II, the Duke of Edinburgh and Hong Kong Arms **81** Mid-Autumn Festival

(Des PAD Studio. Litho Questa)

1975 (30 Apr). *Royal Visit.* W w **14** (*sideways*). P 13½×14.
329 **80** $1.30, multicoloured .. .. .. 2·75 2·00
330 $2 multicoloured .. .. 3·75 4·00

(Des Tao Ho. Litho De La Rue, Bogotá)

1975 (31 July). *Hong Kong Festivals of* 1975. *T* **81** *and similar vert designs. Multicoloured. No wmk.* P 14.
331 50 c. Type **81** .. .. 2·00 50
332 $1 Dragon-boat Festival .. .. 8·00 2·50
a. Black (oars, etc) omitted £550
b. Printed on the gummed side ..
333 $2 Tin Hau Festival .. .. .. 28·00 7·50
331/3 .. .. *Set of* 3 35·00 9·50
MS334 102×83 mm. Nos. 331/3 .. .. £110 45·00

82 Hwamei **83** Dragon

(Des C. Kuan. Litho Harrison)

1975 (29 Oct). *Birds. T* **82** *and similar vert designs. Multicoloured.* W w **14**. P 14½.
335 50 c. Type **82** .. .. 2·00 50
w. Wmk inverted .. .. .. 5·00
336 $1.30, Chinese Bulbul .. .. .. 8·00 5·00
337 $2 Black-capped Kingfisher .. .. 14·00 12·00
w. Wmk inverted .. .. .. 17·00
335/7 .. .. *Set of* 3 22·00 16·00

(Des Kan Tai-keung. Litho Questa)

1976 (21 Jan). *Chinese New Year ("Year of the Dragon"). T* **83** *and similar horiz design.* W w **14** (*sideways**). P 14½.
338 **83** 20 c. mauve, dull lake and gold .. 75 10
w. Wmk Crown to right of CA .. 50·00
339 – $1.30, light yellow-green, lt red & gold 6·50 3·25
No. 339 is as T **83** but has the design reversed.
*The normal sideways watermark shows Crown to left of CA, *as seen from the back of the stamp.*

1976 (20 Feb–19 Mar). *As Nos.* 283, 285, 287 *and* 293/6 *but without wmk.*
340 **73** 10 c. bright orange (coil stamp) (19.3.76) 24·00 8·50
342 20 c. reddish violet .. .. .. 3·50 1·25
a. Imperf (pair) £550
344 30 c. ultramarine .. .. .. 7·00 2·25
a. Imperf (pair) £650
350 **74** $2 pale green and reddish brown .. 9·00 3·75
351 $5 pink and royal blue .. .. 9·00 7·00
352 $10 pink & dp blackish olive (19.3.76) 75·00 42·00
353 $20 pink and brownish black (19.3.76) £160 60·00
340/53 .. .. *Set of* 7 £250 £110
No. 353 is known with the embossing omitted. See note after No. 296.

84 "60" and Girl Guides Badge **85** "Postal Services" in Chinese Characters

(Des P. Ma. Photo Harrison)

1976 (23 Apr). *Girl Guides Diamond Jubilee. T* **84** *and similar horiz design. Multicoloured.* W w **12**. P 14½.
354 20 c. Type **84** 50 10
w. Wmk inverted .. .. .. 3·00
355 $1.30, Badge, stylised diamond and "60" 5·00 3·50
w. Wmk inverted .. .. .. 9·00

(Des Tao Ho. Litho Harrison)

1976 (11 Aug). *Opening of new G.P.O. T* **85** *and similar vert designs. W* w **14**. *P* 14½.
356 20 c. yellow-green, lt greenish grey & black . . 75 10
w. Wmk inverted . . . . . .
357 $1.30, reddish orge, lt greenish grey & blk 3·75 2·00
358 $2 yellow, light greenish grey and black 6·50 4·50
356/8 . . . . . . *Set of* 3 10·00 6·00
Designs:—$1.30, Old G.P.O.; $2 New G.P.O.

86 Tree Snake on Branch

(Des Jennifer Wong. Litho J.W.)

1977 (6 Jan). *Chinese New Year ("Year of the Snake"). T* **86** *and similar horiz design. W* w **14** (*sideways**). *P* 13½.
359 **86** 20 c. multicoloured 50 15
360 – $1.30, multicoloured . . . . 4·00 4·75
w. Wmk Crown to left of CA . . 8·50
The $1.30 shows a snake facing left.
*The normal sideways watermark shows Crown to right of CA, *as seen from the back of the stamp.*

87 Presentation of the Orb

88 Tram Cars

(Des Hong Kong Govt Services Dept; adapted J.W. Litho Harrison)

1977 (7 Feb). *Silver Jubilee. T* **87** *and similar multicoloured designs. W* w **14** (*sideways on* $2). *P* 14½ × 14 ($2) *or* 14 × 14½ (*others*).
361 20 c. Type **87** 40 10
w. Wmk inverted . . . . . . 30·00
362 $1.30, Queen's visit, 1975 . . . . 1·25 1·25
363 $2 The Orb (*vert*) . . . . . . 1·50 1·50
361/3 . . . . . . *Set of* 3 2·75 2·50

(Des Tao Ho. Litho J.W.)

1977 (30 June). *Tourism. T* **88** *and similar vert designs. Multicoloured. W* w **14**. *P* 13½.
364 20 c. Type **88** 55 10
w. Wmk inverted £500 £200
365 60 c. Star Ferryboat . . . . . . 1·50 2·25
w. Wmk inverted . . . . . . 2·75
366 $1.30, The Peak Railway . . . . 2·50 2·25
w. Wmk inverted . . . . . . 12·00
367 $2 Junk and sampan . . . . . . 3·25 3·75
w. Wmk inverted . . . . . . 6·00
364/7 . . . . . . *Set of* 4 7·00 7·50

89 Buttercup Orchid

90 Horse

(Des Beryl Walden. Litho Questa)

1977 (12 Oct). *Orchids. T* **89** *and similar vert designs. Multicoloured. W* w **14**. *P* 14½.
368 20 c. Type **89** . . . . 1·25 15
369 $1.30, Lady's Slipper Orchid . . . . 4·00 2·25
370 $2 Susan Orchid . . . . . . 6·00 4·25
368/70 . . . . . . *Set of* 3 10·00 6·00

(Des Graphic Atelier Ltd, Hong Kong. Litho Harrison)

1978 (26 Jan). *Chinese New Year ("Year of the Horse"). W* w **14** (*sideways**). *P* 14½.
371 **90** 20 c. magenta, yellow-olive & brn-olive 50 10
w. Wmk Crown to left of CA . . 2·75
372 $1.30, orange, yell-brn & reddish brn 3·50 4·00
*The normal sideways watermark shows Crown to right of CA, *as seen from the back of the stamp.*

NEW INFORMATION

The editor is always interested to correspond with people who have new information that will improve or correct the Catalogue.

91 Queen Elizabeth II

92 Girl and Boy holding Hands

(Des G. Vasarhelyi. Litho Harrison)

1978 (2 June). *25th Anniv of Coronation. W* w **14**. *P* 14×14½.
373 **91** 20 c. magenta and ultramarine . . 40 10
374 $1.30, ultramarine and magenta . . 1·50 2·25
w. Wmk inverted . . . . . . 26·00

(Des Annette Walker. Litho Harrison)

1978 (8 Nov). *Centenary of Po Leung Kuk (child care organisation). T* **92** *and similar horiz design. Multicoloured. W* w **14** (*sideways**). *P* 14½.
375 20 c. Type **92** 30 15
w. Wmk Crown to left of CA . . 30 15
376 $1.30, Ring of children . . . . 1·75 2·00
w. Wmk Crown to left of CA . . 1·75 2·00
*The normal sideways watermark shows the Crown to the right of CA *as seen from the back of the stamp.*

93 Electronics Industry

94 *Precis orithya*

(Litho Harrison)

1979 (9 Jan). *Industries. T* **93** *and similar horiz designs. W* w **14** (*sideways*). *P* 14½.
377 20 c. orange-yellow, olive-yellow & yell-olive 30 10
378 $1.30, multicoloured . . . . . . 1·10 1·75
379 $2 multicoloured . . . . . . 1·10 2·25
377/9 . . . . . . *Set of* 3 2·25 3·75
Designs:—$1.30, Toy industry; $2, Garment industry.

(Des Jane Thatcher. Photo Harrison)

1979 (20 June). *Butterflies. T* **94** *and similar vert designs. Multicoloured. No wmk. P* 14½.
380 20 c. Type **94** . . . . 1·00 10
381 $1 *Graphium sarpedon* . . . . 1·75 80
382 $1.30, *Heliophorus epicles* . . . . 2·50 1·60
383 $2 *Danus genutia* . . . . . . 2·75 3·50
380/3 . . . . . . *Set of* 4 7·00 5·50

HONG KONG 香港 20¢

95 Diagrammatic view of Railway Station

96 Tsui Shing Lau Pagoda

(Des Tao Ho. Litho J.W.)

1979 (1 Oct). *Mass Transit Railway. T* **95** *and similar horiz designs. Multicoloured. W* w **14** (*sideways**). *P* 13½.
384 20 c. Type **95** 80 10
w. Wmk Crown to left of CA . . 3·50
385 $1.30, Diagrammatic view of car . . 2·25 80
w. Wmk Crown to left of CA . . 13·00
386 $2 Plan showing route of railway . . 2·50 1·75
w. Wmk Crown to left of CA . . 50·00
384/6 . . . . . . *Set of* 3 5·00 2·40
*The normal sideways watermark shows Crown to right of CA, *as seen from the back of the stamp.*

(Des D. Leonard. Litho J.W.)

1980 (14 May). *Rural Architecture. T* **96** *and similar designs. W* w **14** (*sideways on* $1.30 *and* $2). *P* 13 × 13½ (20 c.) *or* 13½ × 13 (*others*).
387 20 c. black, magenta and yellow . . 40 20
w. Wmk inverted . . . . . . 24·00
388 $1.30, multicoloured . . . . . . 1·10 1·25
389 $2 multicoloured . . . . . . 1·60 2·50
387/9 . . . . . . *Set of* 3 2·75 3·50
Designs: *Horiz*—$1.30, Village House, Sai O; $2, Ching Chung Koon Temple.

97 Queen Elizabeth the Queen Mother

98 Botanical Gardens

(Des Harrison. Litho Questa)

1980 (4 Aug). *80th Birthday of Queen Elizabeth the Queen Mother. W* w **14** (*sideways*). *P* 14.
390 **97** $1.30, multicoloured . . . . . . 1·00 1·25

(Des D. Chan. Litho J.W.)

1980 (12 Nov). *Parks. T* **98** *and similar vert designs. Multicoloured. W* w **14**. *P* 13½.
391 20 c. Type **98** 40 15
392 $1 Ocean Park 75 60
393 $1.30, Kowloon Park 80 85
394 $2 Country Parks . . . . . . 1·75 2·50
391/4 . . . . . . *Set of* 4 3·25 3·75

99 Red-spotted Grouper

100 Wedding Bouquet from Hong Kong

(Des Jane Thatcher. Litho J.W.)

1981 (28 Jan). *Fishes. T* **99** *and similar horiz designs. Multicoloured. W* w **14** (*sideways**). *P* 13½.
395 20 c. Type **99** 30 15
w. Wmk Crown to left of CA . . 4·00
396 $1 Golden Thread-finned Bream . . 1·00 70
397 $1.30, Scar-breasted Tuskfish . . 1·10 95
398 $2 Blue-barred Orange Parrotfish . . 2·00 3·25
395/8 . . . . . . *Set of* 4 4·00 4·50
*The normal sideways watermark shows Crown to right of CA, *as seen from the back of the stamp.*

(Des J.W. Photo Harrison)

1981 (29 July). *Royal Wedding. T* **100** *and similar vert designs. Multicoloured. W* w **14** (*sideways*). *P* 14.
399 20 c. Type **100** 30 10
400 $1.30, Prince Charles in Hong Kong . . 70 50
401 $5 Prince Charles and Lady Diana Spencer 2·25 2·75
399/401 . . . . . . *Set of* 3 3·00 3·00

101 Suburban Development

102 "Victoria from the Harbour, *c* 1855"

(Des Tao Ho. Litho J.W.)

1981 (14 Oct). *Public Housing. T* **101** *and similar vert designs showing suburban development. W* w **14**. *P* 13½.
402 20 c. multicoloured 20 10
a. Red (jacket and trousers) omitted . . £120
w. Wmk inverted (pair) . . . . . .
403 $1 multicoloured 80 60
404 $1.30, multicoloured . . . . . . 1·10 1·00
405 $2 multicoloured . . . . . . 1·25 2·00
402/5 . . . . . . *Set of* 4 3·00 3·25
MS406 148×105 mm. Nos. 402/5. Wmk inverted 4·25 5·50
w. Wmk upright . . . . . . 25·00 25·00

(Des R. Solley. Litho Questa)

1982 (5 Jan). *Port of Hong Kong, Past and Present. T* **102** *and similar horiz designs. Multicoloured. W* w **14**. *P* 14½.
407 20 c. Type **102** 60 15
408 $1 "West Point, Hong Kong, 1847" . . 1·75 90
409 $1.30, Fleet of Junks . . . . . . 2·25 1·10
410 $2 Liner *Queen Elizabeth 2* at Hong Kong . . 3·00 2·75
407/10 . . . . . . *Set of* 4 7·00 4·50

103 Large Indian Civet

(Des Karen Phillipps. Litho Harrison)

82 (4 May). *Wild Animals. T* **103** *and similar horiz designs.* W w **14** (*sideways**). *P* 14½.

1		20 c. black, salmon-pink and olive-bistre ..	60	15
		w. Wmk Crown to right of CA	13·00	
2		$1 multicoloured	1·25	90
3		$1.30, black, emerald and yellow-orange	1·50	1·10
		w. Wmk Crown to right of CA	18·00	
4		$5 black, orange-brown & greenish yellow	3·00	4·50
1/14		.. .. *Set of* 4	5·50	6·00

Designs:—$1 Chinese Pangolin; $1.30, Chinese Porcupine; $5 dian Muntjac ("Barking Deer").

*The normal sideways watermark shows Crown to left of CA, *seen from the back of the stamp.*

104 Queen Elizabeth II **105**

(Des and photo ($5 to $50 also embossed) Harrison)

982 (30 Aug). *W* w **14** (*sideways* on Nos.* 427/30). *P* 14½×14 (*Nos.* 415/26) *or* 14×14½ (*others*).

15	**104**	10 c. bright carmine, carmine and lemon	70	60
16		20 c. bluish violet, violet and lavender ..	90	70
17		30 c. bluish violet, violet and salmon ..	1·25	30
18		40 c. vermilion and pale blue	1·25	30
19		50 c. chestnut, orange-brn & sage-green	1·25	30
20		60 c. bright purple and brownish grey	2·75	1·40
21		70 c. dp grey-grn, myrtle-grn & orge-yell	2·75	40
		a. Imperf (pair)	£475	
22		80 c. bistre-brown, lt brown & sage-grn	2·75	1·50
23		90 c. bottle-green, deep grey-green and pale turquoise-green	4·50	30
24		$1 reddish orge, red-orge & pale rose	2·50	30
25		$1.30, turquoise-blue and mauve ..	4·00	30
26		$2 ultramarine and flesh	6·50	1·00
27	**105**	$5 dp magenta, brt purple & olive-yell	7·00	2·50
		w. Wmk Crown to right of CA ..	8·00	
28		$10 sepia and grey-brown	8·00	5·00
		w. Wmk Crown to right of CA ..	9·00	
29		$20 deep claret and pale blue ..	14·00	15·00
		w. Wmk Crown to right of CA ..	15·00	
30		$50 deep claret and brownish grey ..	35·00	30·00
		w. Wmk Crown to right of CA ..	42·00	
15/30		.. .. *Set of* 16	80·00	55·00

*The normal sideways watermark shows Crown to left of CA, *seen from the back of the stamp.*

Nos. 415/30 come with a fluorescent security marking, "Hong ong" in Chinese characters encircled by the same in English, rinted over the central oval of the design.

Nos. 415 and 424 also exist from coils.

No. 428 is known with the embossing omitted. See note after No. 96.

For similar stamps without watermark see Nos. 471/87.

106 Table Tennis **107** Dancing

(Des A. Wong. Litho J.W.)

982 (20 Oct). *Sport for the Disabled. T* **106** *and similar horiz designs. Multicoloured. W* w **14**. *P* 14 × 14½.

31		30 c. Type **106**	50	10
32		$1 Racing	75	80
33		$1.30, Basketball	2·75	1·50
34		$5 Archery	5·00	6·50
31/4		.. .. *Set of* 4	8·00	8·00

(Des Tao Ho. Litho J.W.)

983 (26 Jan). *Performing Arts. T* **107** *and similar vert designs. W* w **14** (*sideways*). *P* 14½×14.

35		30 c. cobalt and deep grey-blue	50	10
36		$1.30, rose and brown-purple	2·00	1·25
37		$5 bright green and deep green	6·50	5·50
35/7		.. .. *Set of* 3	8·00	6·00

Designs:—$1.30, "Theatre"; $5 "Music".

108 Aerial View of Hong Kong

(Des local artist. Litho Enschedé)

1983 (14 Mar). *Commonwealth Day. T* **108** *and similar horiz designs. Multicoloured. W* w **14** (*sideways**). *P* 14½×13.

438		30 c. Type **108**	70	10
		w. Wmk Crown to right of CA ..	2·50	
439		$1 *Liverpool Bay* (container ship) ..	1·75	1·25
		w. Wmk Crown to right of CA ..	5·50	
440		$1.30, Hong Kong flag	1·75	1·25
		w. Wmk Crown to right of CA ..	5·00	
441		$5 Queen Elizabeth II and Hong Kong ..	3·50	5·00
438/41		.. .. *Set of* 4	7·00	6·75

*The normal sideways watermark shows Crown to left of CA, *as seen from the back of the stamp.*

109 Victoria Harbour

(Des Tao Ho. Litho Harrison)

1983 (17 Aug). *Hong Kong by Night. T* **109** *and similar horiz designs. Multicoloured. W* w **14** (*sideways**). *P* 14½.

442		30 c. Type **109**	1·25	15
		w. Wmk Crown to right of CA	4·75	
443		$1 Space Museum, Tsim Sha Tsui Cultural Centre	3·75	1·50
444		$1.30, Fireworks display	4·75	2·00
		a. Silver (value and inscr) omitted ..	£900	
445		$5 *Jumbo*, floating restaurant	15·00	8·50
		a. Silver (value and inscr) omitted ..	£1000	
442/5		.. .. *Set of* 4	22·00	11·00

*The normal sideways watermark shows Crown to left of CA, *as seen from the back of the stamp.*

110 Old and New Observatory Buildings

(Des C. Shun Wah. Litho Harrison)

1983 (23 Nov). *Centenary of Hong Kong Observatory. T* **110** *and similar horiz designs. W* w **14** (*sideways*). *P* 14½.

446		40 c. yellow-orange, bistre-brown and black ..	75	10
447		$1 reddish mauve, deep mauve and black ..	2·00	1·75
448		$1.30, new blue, steel-blue and black	2·75	1·75
449		$5 olive-yellow, brown-olive and black ..	8·00	9·00
446/9		.. .. *Set of* 4	12·00	11·00

Designs:—$1 Wind-measuring equipment; $1.30, Thermometer; $5 Ancient and modern seismometers.

111 De Havilland D.H.86 Dragon Express *Dorado* (Hong Kong–Penang Service, 1936)

(Des M. Harris. Litho J.W.)

1984 (7 Mar). *Aviation in Hong Kong. T* **111** *and similar multicoloured designs. W* w **14** (*sideways* on* 40 *c. to* $1.30, *inverted on* $5). *P* 13½.

450		40 c. Type **111**	1·00	15
		w. Wmk Crown to left of CA	4·75	
451		$1 Sikorsky S-42B flying boat (San Francisco–Hong Kong Service, 1937)	2·25	1·75
452		$1.30, Cathay-Pacific Boeing 747 jet leaving Kai Tak Airport	3·25	1·75
453		$5 Baldwin brothers' balloon, 1891 (*vert*)	9·00	10·00
450/3		.. .. *Set of* 4	14·00	12·00

*The normal sideways watermark shows Crown to right of CA, *as seen from the back of the stamp.*

112 Map by Capt E. Belcher, 1836

(Des R. Solley. Litho B.D.T.)

1984 (21 June). *Maps of Hong Kong. T* **112** *and similar horiz designs. Multicoloured. W* w **14** (*sideways*). *P* 14.

454		40 c. Type **112**	1·00	20
455		$1 Bartholomew map of 1929	1·75	1·25
456		$1.30, Early map of Hong Kong waters ..	3·00	1·75
457		$5 Chinese-style map of 1819	11·00	10·00
454/7		.. .. *Set of* 4	15·00	12·00

113 Cockerel

(Des J. Yim. Litho Cartor)

1984 (6 Sept). *Chinese Lanterns. T* **113** *and similar horiz designs showing stylised animals as lanterns. Multicoloured. W* w **14** (*sideways**). *P* 13½×13.

458		40 c. Type **113**	80	15
		w. Wmk Crown to right of CA	9·00	
459		$1 Dog	1·75	1·25
460		$1.30, Butterfly	3·00	1·75
461		$5 Fish	9·00	8·50
458/61		.. .. *Set of* 4	13·00	10·50

*The normal sideways watermark shows Crown to left of CA, *as seen from the back of the stamp.*

114 Jockey on Horse and Nurse with Baby ("Health Care")

(Des M. Harris. Litho Walsall)

1984 (21 Nov). *Centenary of Royal Hong Kong Jockey Club. T* **114** *and similar horiz designs showing aspects of Club's charity work. Multicoloured. W* w **14** (*sideways**). *P* 14½.

462		40 c. Type **114**	1·25	20
463		$1 Disabled man playing handball ("Support for Disabled")	2·00	1·75
464		$1.30, Ballerina ("The Arts")	3·00	2·00
		w. Wmk Crown to right of CA	3·00	
465		$5 Humboldt Penguins ("Ocean Park") ..	9·00	11·00
462/5		.. .. *Set of* 4	14·00	13·50
MS466		178×98 mm. Nos. 462/5	22·00	23·00

*The normal sideways watermark shows Crown to left of CA, *as seen from the back of the stamp.*

115 Hung Sing Temple

(Des M. Harris. Litho J.W.)

1985 (14 Mar). *Historic Buildings. T* **115** *and similar horiz designs. Multicoloured. P* 13½.

467		40 c. Type **115**	60	20
468		$1 St. John's Cathedral	1·75	1·60
469		$1.30, The Old Supreme Court Building ..	2·25	1·75
470		$5 Wan Chai Post Office	9·50	8·50
467/70		.. .. *Set of* 4	12·50	11·00

1985 (13 June)–**87**. *As Nos.* 415/16, 418/30 *and new value* ($1.70). *No wmk. P* 14½×14 (10 *c. to* $2) *or* 14×14½ (*others*).

471	**104**	10 c. brt carm, carm & lemon (23.10.85)	70	70
472		20 c. bluish violet, vio & lavender (6.87)	17·00	15·00
474		40 c. vermilion and pale blue (23.10.85)	90	1·00
475		50 c. chestnut, orange-brown and sage-green (23.10.85)	90	40
476		60 c. brt purple & brnish grey (23.10.85)	1·50	1·10
477		70 c. deep grey-green, myrtle-green and orange-yellow (23.10.85)	1·75	40
478		80 c. bistre-brown, light brown and sage-green (23.10.85)	2·00	1·75
479		90 c. bottle-green, deep grey-green and pale turquoise-green (23.10.85) ..	2·00	50
480		$1 reddish orange, red-orange and pale rose (23.10.85)	1·75	40
		a. Imperf (horiz pair)		
481		$1.30, turquoise-blue and mauve ..	2·25	45
482		$1.70, dull ultramarine, bright blue and bright green (2.9.85)	3·50	1·50
483		$2 ultramarine and flesh (23.10.85) ..	3·75	1·50
484	**105**	$5 deep magenta, bright purple and olive-yellow (23.10.85)	6·50	3·25
485		$10 sepia and grey-brown (23.10.85) ..	7·50	4·00
486		$20 deep claret and pale blue (23.10.85)	10·00	7·50
487		$50 dp claret & brownish grey (23.10.85)	30·00	25·00
471/87		.. .. *Set of* 16	80·00	55·00

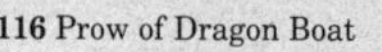

116 Prow of Dragon Boat

117 The Queen Mother with Prince Charles and Prince William, 1984

(Des R. Hookham. Litho Cartor)

1985 (19 June). *10th International Dragon Boat Festival. T* **116** *and similar horiz designs showing different parts of dragon boat. Multicoloured. P* 13½×13.

488 40 c. Type **116** 50 15
489 $1 Drummer and rowers .. .. 1·75 1·25
490 $1.30, Rowers .. .. 3·00 1·60
491 $5 Stern of boat .. .. 9·25 8·00
488/91 .. .. *Set of* 4 13·00 10·00
MS492 190×100 mm. Nos. 488/91. P 13×12 .. 22·00 22·00

(Des C. Abbott. Litho Questa)

1985 (7 Aug). *Life and Times of Queen Elizabeth the Queen Mother. T* **117** *and similar vert designs. Multicoloured. P* 14½×14.

493 40 c. At Glamis Castle, aged 7 .. .. .. 60 10
494 $1 Type **117** .. .. 1·75 1·25
495 $1.30, The Queen Mother, 1970 (from photo by Cecil Beaton) .. .. .. 2·00 1·40
496 $5 With Prince Henry at his christening (from photo by Lord Snowdon).. .. 3·25 4·00
493/6 .. .. *Set of* 4 7·00 6·00

118 Melastoma

(Des N. Jesse. Litho B.D.T.)

1985 (25 Sept). *Native Flowers. T* **118** *and similar horiz designs. Multicoloured. P* 13½.

497 40 c. Type **118** .. .. 1·50 20
498 50 c. Chinese Lily .. .. 1·75 40
499 60 c. Grantham's Camellia .. .. 2·00 90
500 $1.30, Narcissus .. .. 3·25 1·25
501 $1.70, Bauhinia .. .. 3·75 1·50
502 $5 Chinese New Year Flower .. .. .. 7·00 9·00
497/502 .. .. *Set of* 6 17·00 12·00

119 Hong Kong Academy for Performing Arts

(Des N. Jesse. Litho Format)

1985 (27 Nov). *New Buildings. T* **119** *and similar multicoloured designs. P* 15.

503 50 c. Type **119** 80 15
504 $1.30, Exchange Square (*vert*) .. .. 1·75 1·50
505 $1.70, Hong Kong Bank Headquarters (*vert*) .. .. 2·50 1·75
506 $5 Hong Kong Coliseum .. .. 8·00 11·00
503/6 .. .. *Set of* 4 11·50 13·00

120 Halley's Comet in the Solar System

(Des A. Chan. Litho Cartor)

1986 (26 Feb). *Appearance of Halley's Comet. T* **120** *and similar horiz designs. Multicoloured. P* 13½×13.

507 50 c. Type **120** .. .. 1·25 20
508 $1.30, Edmond Halley and Comet .. .. 2·00 1·40
509 $1.70, Comet over Hong Kong .. .. 2·75 1·50
510 $5 Comet passing the Earth .. .. .. 11·00 8·00
507/10 .. .. *Set of* 4 15·00 10·00
MS511 135×80 mm. Nos. 507/10 .. .. 22·00 18·00

(Des A. Theobald. Litho Harrison)

1986 (21 Apr). *60th Birthday of Queen Elizabeth II. Vert designs as T* **110** *of Ascension. Multicoloured. P* 14½×14.

512 50 c. At wedding of Miss Celia Bowes-Lyon, 1931 .. .. 40 10
513 $1 Queen in Garter procession, Windsor Castle, 1977 .. .. 75 60
514 $1.30, In Hong Kong, 1975 .. .. .. 1·00 70
515 $1.70, At Royal Lodge, Windsor, 1980 (from photo by Norman Parkinson) .. 1·10 75
516 $5 At Crown Agents Head Office, London, 1983 .. .. 3·25 4·00
512/16 .. .. *Set of* 5 6·00 5·50

121 Mass Transit Train, Boeing 747 Airliner and Map of World

(Des Agay Ng Kee Chuen. Litho B.D.T.)

1986 (18 July). *"Expo '86" World Fair, Vancouver. T* **121** *and similar horiz designs. Multicoloured. P* 13½.

517 50 c. Type **121** 80 30
518 $1.30, Hong Kong Bank Headquarters and map of world .. .. 1·50 1·00
519 $1.70, Container ship and map of world .. 2·25 1·40
520 $5 Dish aerial and map of world .. .. 6·50 7·00
517/20 .. .. *Set of* 4 10·00 8·75

122 Hand-liner Sampan

123 "The Second Puan Khequa" (attr Spoilum)

(Des Graphic Communications Ltd. Litho B.D.T.)

1986 (24 Sept). *Fishing Vessels. T* **122** *and similar horiz designs, each showing fishing boat and outline of fish. Multicoloured. P* 13½.

521 50 c. Type **122** 80 15
522 $1.30, Stern trawler .. .. 1·50 1·10
523 $1.70, Long liner junk .. .. 2·25 1·40
524 $5 Junk trawler .. .. 7·00 7·50
521/4 .. .. *Set of* 4 10·50 9·00

(Des R. Solley. Litho B.D.T.)

1986 (9 Dec). *19th-century Hong Kong Portraits. T* **123** *and similar vert designs. Multicoloured. P* 14×13½.

525 50 c. Type **123** 55 15
526 $1.30, "Chinese Lady" (19th-century copy) 1·50 1·10
527 $1.70, "Lamqua" (self-portrait) .. .. 1·75 1·40
528 $5 "Wife of Wo Hing Qua" (attr G. Chinnery) .. .. 5·50 5·50
525/8 .. .. *Set of* 4 8·50 7·50

MACHINE LABELS. A single machine operated at the G.P.O. from 30 December 1986 issuing 10 c., 50 c., $1.30 and $1.70 labels showing a carp. These are inscribed "O1". A second machine was installed at Tsim Sha Tsui post office from 18 August 1987 which issued labels coded "O2".

From 1987 a new design was introduced each year to reflect the Chinese calendar. Details of the various issues are as follows:

Year of the Rabbit	18 August 1987	10 c., 50 c., $1.30, $1.70
Year of the Dragon	23 March 1988	10 c., 50 c., $1.30, $1.70
	1 September 1988	10 c., 60 c., $1.40, $1.80
Year of the Snake	24 February 1989	10 c., 60 c., $1.40, $1.80
Year of the Horse	21 February 1990	10 c., 60 c., $1.40, $1.80
Year of the Ram	21 February 1991	10 c., 60 c., $1.40, $1.80
	2 April 1991	10 c., 80 c., $1.80, $2.30
Year of the Monkey	12 March 1992	10 c., 80 c., 90 c., $1.70, $1.80, $2.30, $5
Year of the Cock	10 February 1993	10 c., 80 c., 90 c., $1.70, $1.80, $2.30, $5
	1 November 1993	10 c., $1, $1.90, $2.40
Year of the Dog	1 March 1994	10 c., 80 c., $1, $1.20, $1.30, $1.90, $2, $2.40, $5
Year of the Pig	15 February 1995	10 c., 80 c., $1, $1.20, $1.30, $1.90, $2, $2.40, $5
Year of the Rat	28 February 1996	10 c., $1.20, $1.50, $2.10, $2.30, $2.60, $5
Year of the Ox	12 March 1997	10 c., $1.30, $1.60, $2.50, $2.60, $3.10, $5

From 8 November 1991 the "O1" machine, in addition to th fixed face values, could be used to produce labels of any value i 10 c. steps between 10 c. and $5.

124 Rabbit

(Des Kan Tai-keung. Litho B.D.T.)

1987 (21 Jan). *Chinese New Year ("Year of the Rabbit"). T* **12** *and similar horiz designs showing stylized rabbits. P* 13½.

529 50 c. multicoloured 65 1
530 $1.30, multicoloured .. .. 1·50 1·2
531 $1.70, multicoloured .. .. 1·75 1·4
532 $5 multicoloured .. .. 6·50 6·
529/32 .. .. *Set of* 4 9·50 8·
MS533 133×84 mm. Nos. 529/32 .. .. 32·00 25·

Nos. 530/1 have the "0" omitted from their face values.

125 "Village Square, Hong Kong Island, 1838" (Auguste Borget)

126 Queen Elizabeth II and Central Victoria

(Des J. Yim. Litho B.D.T.)

1987 (23 Apr). *19th-century Hong Kong Scenes. T* **125** *an similar horiz designs. Multicoloured. P* 14.

534 50 c. Type **125** 60 1
535 $1.30, "Boat Dwellers, Kowloon Bay, 1838" (Auguste Borget) .. .. .. 1·75 1·1
536 $1.70, "Flagstaff House, 1846" (Murdoch Bruce) .. .. 2·25 1·4
537 $5 "Wellington Street, late 19th-century" (C. Andrasi) .. .. 7·00 6·5
534/7 .. .. *Set of* 4 10·50 8·0

Two types of Nos. 538/52.

I. Heavy shading under mouth and cheek

II. Lighter shading

(Des R. Hookham. Litho Leigh-Mardon Ltd, Melbourne)

1987 (13 July)–**88.** *T* **126** *and similar vert designs, eac showing Queen Elizabeth II and Hong Kong skylin P* 14½×14 (10 *c. to* $2) *or* 14 ($5 *to* $50). A. *Shading as Type*

538A **126** 10 c. multicoloured 80 9
539A 40 c. multicoloured .. .. .. 1·50 1·4
540A 50 c. multicoloured .. .. .. 1·50 4
541A 60 c. multicoloured .. .. .. 1·75 7
542A 70 c. multicoloured .. .. .. 2·00 8
543A 80 c. multicoloured .. .. .. 2·00 1·5
544A 90 c. multicoloured .. .. .. 2·25 7
545A $1 multicoloured .. .. .. 2·25 7
546A $1.30, multicoloured .. .. 3·00 8
547A $1.70, multicoloured .. .. 3·00 8
548A $2 multicoloured .. .. .. 3·00 1·5
549A – $5 multicoloured .. .. .. 7·50 2·5
550A – $10 multicoloured .. .. .. 8·50 4·7
551A – $20 multicoloured .. .. .. 13·00 13·0
552A – $50 multicoloured .. .. .. 25·00 27·0
538A/52A .. .. .. *Set of* 15 70·00 50·0

B. *Shading as Type* II (1.9.88)

538B **126** 10 c. multicoloured 75 6
539B 40 c. multicoloured .. .. .. 1·50 1·4
540B 50 c. multicoloured .. .. .. 1·50 3
541B 60 c. multicoloured .. .. .. 1·75 6
542B 70 c. multicoloured .. .. .. 2·00 8
543B 80 c. multicoloured .. .. .. 2·00 1·5
544B 90 c. multicoloured .. .. .. 2·25 7
545B $1 multicoloured .. .. .. 8·00 1·2
546B $1.30, multicoloured .. .. 3·00 9
546cB $1.40, multicoloured .. .. 3·00 1·7
547B $1.70, multicoloured .. .. 8·00 1·4
547cB $1.80, multicoloured .. .. 3·00 1·7
548B $2 multicoloured .. .. .. 3·25 9
549B – $5 multicoloured .. .. .. 4·75 2·2
550B – $10 multicoloured .. .. .. 8·50 4·2
551B – $20 multicoloured .. .. .. 15·00 9·5
552B – $50 multicoloured .. .. .. 35·00 16·0
538B/52B .. .. .. *Set of* 17 90·00 40·0

Designs (25×31 *mm*): $5 Kowloon; $10 Victoria Harbour; $20 Legislative Council Building; $50 Government House.

Nos. 538/52 carry the fluorescent security markings as described beneath Nos. 415/30 with the $5 to $50 values showing an additional vertical fluorescent bar at right.

For these stamps as Type II, but with imprint dates, see Nos. 600/15.

127 Hong Kong Flag　**128** Alice Ho Miu Ling Nethersole Hospital, 1887

(Des R. Hookham. Photo Enschedé)

1987 (13 July)–**92.** *Coil Stamps. T* **127** *and similar vert designs. P* 14½×14. (*a*) *Without imprint date*
553 10 c. multicoloured . . 1·00 1·50
554 50 c. bistre, lake and black . . 2·00 3·00

(*b*) *With imprint date*
554*a* 10 c. multicoloured (1.8.89) . . 50 50
554*b* 50 c. bistre, lake and black (1.8.89) . . 1·25 1·50
554*c* 80 c. brt mauve, dp bl-grn & blk (26.3.92) 70 1·00
554*d* 90 c. brt blue, reddish brn & blk (26.3.92) 70 90
554*e* $1.80, brt emer, royal bl & blk (26.3.92) 1·40 1·75
554*f* $2.30, orge-brn, dp vio & blk (26.3.92) 1·60 2·25
554*a/f* . . *Set of* 6 5·50 7·00

Design:—50 c. to $2.30, Map of Hong Kong.

Nos. 553/4*f* carry the fluorescent security marking as described beneath Nos. 415/30.

The printings with imprint date have every fifth stamp in the rolls of 1,000 numbered on the reverse.

Imprint dates: "1989", Nos. 554*a/b*; "1990", No. 554*a*, "1991", Nos. 554*a/f*.

(Des A. Fung. Litho Walsall)

1987 (8 Sept). *Hong Kong Medical Centenaries. T* **128** *and similar horiz designs. Multicoloured. P* 14½.
555 50 c. Type **128** . . 1·00 20
556 $1.30, Matron and nurses, Nethersole Hospital, 1891 . . 2·25 1·40
557 $1.70, Scanning equipment, Faculty of Medicine . . 2·75 1·40
558 $5 Nurse and patient, Faculty of Medicine 8·50 8·00
555/8 . . *Set of* 4 13·00 10·00

129 Casual Dress with Fringed Hem, 220–589

(Des Sumiko Davies. Litho CPE Australia Ltd, Melbourne)

1987 (18 Nov). *Historical Chinese Costumes. T* **129** *and similar horiz designs. Multicoloured. P* 13½.
559 50 c. Type **129** . . 55 10
560 $1.30, Two-piece dress and wrap, 581–960 1·40 1·25
561 $1.70, Formal dress, Song Dynasty, 960–1279 . . 1·75 1·50
562 $5 Manchu empress costume, 1644–1911 . . 5·75 6·50
559/62 . . *Set of* 4 8·50 8·50

130 Dragon　**131** White-breasted Kingfisher

(Des Kan Tai-keung. Litho CPE Australia Ltd, Melbourne)

1988 (27 Jan). *Chinese New Year* (*"Year of the Dragon"*). *T* **130** *and similar horiz designs showing dragons. P* 13½.
563 50 c. multicoloured . . 75 15
564 $1.30, multicoloured . . 1·75 1·25
565 $1.70, multicoloured . . 2·00 1·40
566 $5 multicoloured . . 4·00 5·00
563/6 . . *Set of* 4 7·50 7·00
MS567 134×88 mm. Nos. 563/6 . . 11·00 12·00

(Des Karen Phillipps. Litho CPE Australia Ltd, Melbourne)

1988 (20 Apr). *Hong Kong Birds. T* **131** *and similar vert designs. Multicoloured. P* 13½.
568 50 c. Type **131** . . 1·10 30
569 $1.30, Fukien Niltava . . 2·25 1·40
570 $1.70, Black Kite . . 2·75 1·50
571 $5 Lesser Pied Kingfisher . . 5·00 6·00
568/71 . . *Set of* 4 10·00 8·50

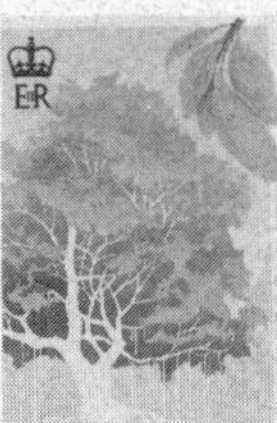

132 Chinese Banyan　**133** Lower Terminal, Peak Tramway

(Des A. Chan. Litho B.D.T.)

1988 (16 June). *Trees of Hong Kong. T* **132** *and similar vert designs. Multicoloured. P* 13½.
572 50 c. Type **132** . . 35 10
573 $1.30, Hong Kong Orchid Tree . . 75 65
574 $1.70, Cotton Tree . . 1·10 85
575 $5 Schima . . 3·50 4·00
572/5 . . *Set of* 4 5·00 5·00
MS576 135×85 mm. Nos. 572/5 . . 11·00 7·50

(Des Lilian Tang. Litho Leigh-Mardon Ltd, Melbourne)

1988 (4 Aug). *Centenary of The Peak Tramway. T* **133** *and similar vert designs. Multicoloured. P* 14½×15.
577 50 c. Type **133** . . 60 10
578 $1.30, Tram on incline . . 1·00 90
579 $1.70, Peak Tower Upper Terminal . . 1·10 90
580 $5 Tram . . 3·50 4·00
577/80 . . *Set of* 4 5·50 5·50
MS581 160×90 mm. Nos. 577/80 . . 8·00 8·00

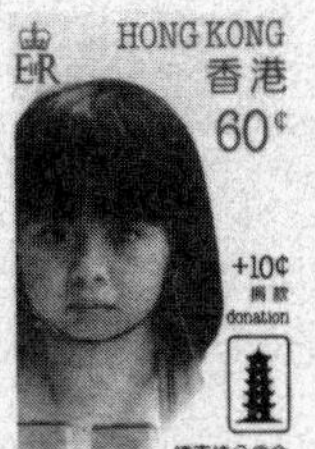

134 Hong Kong Catholic Cathedral　**135** Deaf Girl

(Des C. Buendia. Litho CPE Australia Ltd, Melbourne)

1988 (30 Sept). *Centenary of Hong Kong Catholic Cathedral. P* 14.
582 **134** 60 c. multicoloured . . 1·25 75

(Des M. Tucker. Litho Harrison)

1988 (30 Nov). *Community Chest Charity. T* **135** *and similar vert designs. P* 14½.
583 60 c. + 10 c. brownish black, vermilion and greenish blue . . 60 75
584 $1.40 + 20 c. brownish black, vermilion and bright green . . 80 1·00
585 $1.80 + 30 c. brownish black, vermilion and bright orange . . 1·50 1·60
586 $5 + $1 brownish blk, verm and yell-brn 4·25 5·50
583/6 . . *Set of* 4 6·50 8·00

Designs:—$1.40, Elderly woman; $1.80, Blind boy using braille typewriter; $5 Mother and baby.

136 Snake　**137** Girl and Doll

(Des Kan Tai-keung. Litho Enschedé)

1989 (18 Jan). *Chinese New Year.* (*"Year of the Snake"*). *T* **136** *and similar horiz designs. Multicoloured. P* 13½×14.
587 60 c. Type **136** . . 30 15
a. Booklet pane. Nos. 587 and 589, each ×5 . . 6·00
588 $1.40, Snake and fish . . 1·25 60
589 $1.80, Snake on branch . . 1·75 75
590 $5 Coiled snake . . 5·00 5·00
587/90 . . *Set of* 4 7·50 6·00
MS591 135×85 mm. Nos. 587/90 . . 12·00 7·50

(Des M. Tucker. Litho B.D.T.)

1989 (4 May). *Cheung Chau Bun Festival. T* **137** *and similar vert designs. Multicoloured. P* 13½.
592 60 c. Type **137** . . 45 15
593 $1.40, Girl in festival costume . . 1·10 60
594 $1.80, Paper effigy of god Taai Si Wong . . 1·25 70
595 $5 Floral gateway . . 3·25 3·75
592/5 . . *Set of* 4 5·50 4·75

138 "Twins" (wood carving, Cheung Yee)　**139** Lunar New Year Festivities

(Des Kan Tai-keung. Litho Enschedé)

1989 (19 July). *Modern Art. T* **138** *and similar vert designs. Multicoloured. P* 12×12½.
596 60 c. Type **138** . . 40 15
597 $1.40, "Figures" (acrylic on paper, Chan Luis) . . 1·00 60
598 $1.80, "Lotus" (copper sculpture, Van Lau) 1·25 70
599 $5 "Zen Painting" (ink and colour on paper, Lui Shou-kwan) . . 3·00 3·75
596/9 . . *Set of* 4 5·00 4·75

1989 (1 Aug)–**91.** *As Nos.* 538B/52B, *and new values, with imprint date added to designs. P* 14½×14 (10 *c. to* $2.30) *or* 14 ($5 *to* $50).
600 **126** 10 c. multicoloured . . 50 60
601 40 c. multicoloured . . 1·25 1·50
602 50 c. multicoloured . . 70 30
603 60 c. multicoloured . . 70 30
604 70 c. multicoloured . . 70 50
605 80 c. multicoloured . . 70 40
606 90 c. multicoloured . . 80 40
607 $1 multicoloured . . 80 30
607*a* $1.20, multicoloured (2.4.91) . . 2·75 2·25
608 $1.30, multicoloured . . 1·50 50
609 $1.40, multicoloured . . 1·50 70
609*a* $1.70, multicoloured (2.4.91) . . 2·75 2·25
610 $1.80, multicoloured . . 1·00 60
611 $2 multicoloured . . 1·25 50
611*a* $2.30, multicoloured (2.4.91) . . 2·75 2·25
612 – $5 multicoloured . . 3·50 1·25
613 – $10 multicoloured . . 5·00 3·00
614 – $20 multicoloured . . 7·50 7·00
615 – $50 multicoloured . . 18·00 15·00
600/15 . . *Set of* 19 45·00 35·00

Imprint dates: "1989", Nos. 600/7, 608/9, 610/11, 612/15; "1990", Nos. 600/7, 608/9, 610/11, 612/15; "1991", Nos. 600, 602/7*a*, 609*a*/15.

For miniature sheets containing No. 613 see Nos. **MS**646, **MS**684/5 and **MS**701.

(Des Sumiko Davies. Litho Enschedé)

1989 (6 Sept). *Hong Kong People. T* **139** *and similar vert designs. Multicoloured. P* 13×14½.
616 60 c. Type **139** . . 50 10
617 $1.40, Shadow boxing and horse racing . . 1·25 70
618 $1.80, Foreign-exchange dealer and traditional builder . . 1·60 80
619 $5 Multi-racial society . . 4·00 5·00
616/19 . . *Set of* 4 6·50 6·00

For miniature sheet containing design as $5, but smaller (75×35 mm), see No. **MS**847.

140 University of Science and Technology

(Des I. Leung. Litho CPE Australia Ltd, Melbourne)

1989 (5 Oct). *Building for the Future. T* **140** *and similar square designs. P* 13.
620 60 c. blue-black, orange-yellow & yellow-brn 35 15
621 70 c. black, pale rose and rose . . 40 20
622 $1.30, black, brt yellow-green & blue-grn 80 55
623 $1.40, black, azure and bright blue . . 80 55
624 $1.80, brownish black, pale turquoise-green and turquoise-blue . . 95 80
625 $5 agate, pale red-orange and orange-red 3·25 3·50
620/5 . . *Set of* 6 6·00 5·25

Designs:—70 c. Cultural Centre: $1.30, Eastern Harbour motorway interchange; $1.40, New Bank of China Building; $1.80, Convention and Exhibition Centre; $5 Mass Transit electric train.

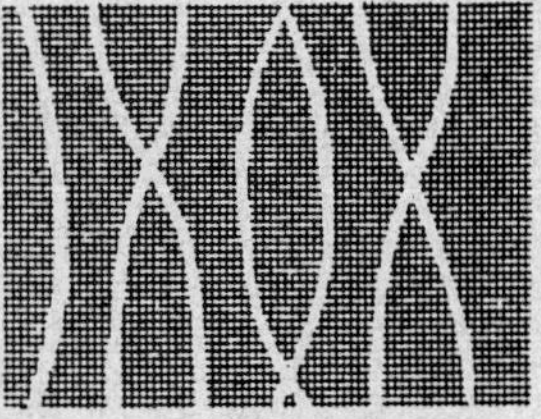

141 Prince and Princess of Wales and Hong Kong Skyline

142

(Des Ng Kee-chuen. Litho Leigh-Mardon Ltd, Melbourne)

1989 (8 Nov). *Royal Visit.* T **141** *and similar vert designs, each showing portrait and different view. Multicoloured.* W **142** *(sideways).* P 14½.

626 60 c. Type **141** 60 15
627 $1.40, Princess of Wales .. .. .. 1·00 60
628 $1.80, Prince of Wales .. .. .. 1·25 95
629 $5 Prince and Princess of Wales in evening dress .. .. 5·00 5·50
626/9 .. .. *Set of* 4 7·00 6·50
MS630 128×75 mm. No. 629 .. .. .. 9·00 8·00

143 Horse

144 Chinese Lobster Dish

(Des Kan Tai-keung. Litho Enschedé)

1990 (23 Jan). *Chinese New Year. ("Year of the Horse").* T **143** *and similar horiz designs.* P 13½×12½.

631 60 c. multicoloured 60 20
a. Booklet pane. Nos. 631 and 633, each×3 .. .. 4·00
632 $1.40, multicoloured .. .. 1·25 1·00
633 $1.80, multicoloured .. .. 1·50 1·25
634 $5 multicoloured .. .. 4·25 4·75
631/4 .. .. *Set of* 4 7·00 6·50
MS635 135×85 mm. Nos. 631/4 .. .. 13·00 10·00

(Des N. Yung and Sumiko Davies. Litho Enschedé)

1990 (26 Apr). *International Cuisine.* T **144** *and similar vert designs showing various dishes. Multicoloured.* P 12½×13.

636 60 c. Type **144** 50 15
637 70 c. Indian 50 20
638 $1.30, Chinese vegetables 80 50
639 $1.40, Thai 80 50
640 $1.80, Japanese .. .. 1·25 70
641 $5 French .. .. 4·00 5·00
636/41 .. .. *Set of* 6 7·00 6·25

145 Air Pollution and Clean Air

146 Street Lamp and Des Voeux Road, 1890

(Litho Leigh-Mardon Ltd, Melbourne)

1990 (5 June). *United Nations World Environment Day.* T **145** *and similar vert designs. Multicoloured.* P 14½.

642 60 c. Type **145** 40 15
643 $1.40, Noise pollution and music 75 50
644 $1.80, Polluted and clean water 90 60
645 $5 Litter on ground and in bin .. .. 2·40 2·75
642/5 .. .. *Set of* 4 4·00 3·50

(Des R. Hookham and I. Leung. Litho Leigh-Mardon Ltd, Melbourne)

1990 (24 Aug). *"New Zealand 1990" International Stamp Exhibition, Auckland. Sheet* 130×75 *mm containing No.* 613. P 14.

MS646 $10 multicoloured .. .. .. 95·00 90·00
The stamp in No. **MS**646 shows the imprint date as "1990".

(Des M. Tucker. Litho Leigh-Mardon Ltd, Melbourne)

1990 (2 Oct). *Centenary of Electricity Supply.* T **146** *and similar horiz designs.* P 14½.

647 60 c. black, olive-bistre & pale orange-brown 40 10
648 $1.40, multicoloured .. .. .. 1·00 80
649 $1.80, black, olive-bistre and deep cobalt 1·10 90
650 $5 multicoloured .. .. 2·50 3·75
647/50 .. .. *Set of* 4 4·50 5·00
MS651 155×85 mm. Nos. 648 and 650 .. .. 5·50 7·00
Designs:—$1.40, Street lamp and *Jumbo* (floating restaurant), 1940; $1.80, Street lamp and pylon, 1960; $5 Street lamp and Hong Kong from harbour, 1980.

147 Christmas Tree and Skyscrapers

(Litho Leigh-Mardon Ltd, Melbourne)

1990 (8 Nov). *Christmas.* T **147** *and similar horiz designs. Multicoloured.* P 14½.

652 50 c. Type **147** 20 10
653 60 c. Dove with holly 20 15
654 $1.40, Firework display 70 40
655 $1.80, Father Christmas hat on skyscraper 90 50
656 $2 Children with Father Christmas .. 1·25 1·25
657 $5 Candy stick with bow and Hong Kong skyline .. .. 2·75 4·00
652/7 .. .. *Set of* 6 5·50 5·75

148 Ram

149 Letter "A", Clock, Teddy Bear and Building Bricks (Kindergarten)

(Des Kan Tai-keung. Litho Enschedé)

1991 (24 Jan). *Chinese New Year. ("Year of the Ram").* T **148** *and similar horiz designs.* P 13½×12½.

658 60 c. multicoloured 25 15
a. Booklet pane. Nos. 658 and 660, each × 3, with margins all round .. .. 4·25
659 $1.40, multicoloured 65 45
660 $1.80, multicoloured 80 60
661 $5 multicoloured .. .. 2·50 3·50
658/61 .. .. *Set of* 4 3·75 4·25
MS662 135×85 mm. Nos. 658/61 .. .. 6·50 7·50

(Litho Enschedé)

1991 (18 Apr). *Education.* T **149** *and similar vert designs. Multicoloured.* P 13½×13.

663 80 c. Type **149** 40 20
664 $1.80, Globe, laboratory flask and mathematical symbols (Primary and Secondary) .. .. 1·00 70
665 $2.30, Machinery (Vocational) .. .. 1·25 1·25
666 $5 Mortar board, computer and books (Tertiary) .. .. 2·75 4·00
663/6 .. .. *Set of* 4 4·75 5·50

150 Rickshaw

151 Victorian Pillar Box and Cover of 1888

(Des C. Tillyer. Litho B.D.T.)

1991 (6 June). 100 *Years of Public Transport.* T **150** *and similar square designs. Multicoloured.* P 14.

667 80 c. Type **150** 30 15
668 90 c. Double-decker bus 55 30
669 $1.70, Harbour ferry 90 60
670 $1.80, Double-deck tram .. .. .. 1·25 60
671 $2.30, Mass Transit electric train .. 1·75 1·75
672 $5 Jetfoil .. .. 3·50 4·50
667/72 .. .. *Set of* 6 7·50 7·00

(Des H. Choi. Litho B.D.T.)

1991 (25 Aug). 150*th Anniv of Hong Kong Post Office (1st issue).* T **151** *and similar vert designs. Multicoloured.* P 14.

673 80 c. Type **151** 40 15
674 $1.70, Edwardian pillar box and cover .. 90 65
675 $1.80, King George V pillar box and cover of 1935 .. .. 1·00 65
676 $2.30, King George VI pillar box and cover of 1938 .. .. 1·40 1·75
677 $5 Queen Elizabeth II pillar box and cover of 1989 .. .. 3·75 4·75
673/7 .. .. *Set of* 5 6·75 7·25
MS678 130×75 mm. $10 As No. 677 .. .. 12·00 14·00
See also Nos. **MS**745 and **MS**899.

152 Bronze Buddha, Lantau Island

153 Monkey

(Litho Questa)

1991 (24 Oct). *Landmarks.* T **152** *and similar vert designs.* P 14.

679 80 c. rosine and black 40 15
680 $1.70, bright emerald and black 90 70
681 $1.80, reddish violet and black .. .. 1·00 70
682 $2.30, new blue and black .. .. 1·25 1·75
683 $5 bright yellow-orange and black .. 3·50 4·50
679/83 .. .. *Set of* 5 6·25 7·00
Designs:—$1.70, Peak Pavilion; $1.80, Clocktower of Kowloon–Canton Railway Station; $2.30, Catholic Cathedral; $5 Wong Tai Sin Temple.

(Des Kan Tai-keung. Litho Leigh-Mardon Ltd, Melbourne)

1991 (16 Nov). *"Phila Nippon '91" International Stamp Exhibition, Tokyo. Sheet* 130×75 *mm containing No.* 613. P 14.

MS684 $10 multicoloured .. .. .. 35·00 25·00
The stamp in No. **MS**684 shows the imprint date as "1991".

(Des Li Shik-kwong. Litho Leigh-Mardon Ltd, Melbourne)

1991 (4 Dec). *Olympic Games, Barcelona* (1992) *(1st issue). Sheet* 130×75 *mm. containing No.* 613. P 14.

MS685 $10 multicoloured .. .. .. 15·00 14·00
The stamp in No. **MS**685 shows the imprint date as "1991".
See also Nos. 696/700 and **MS**722.

(Des Kan Tai-keung. Litho Leigh-Mardon Ltd, Melbourne)

1992 (22 Jan). *Chinese New Year. ("Year of the Monkey").* T **153** *and similar horiz designs.* P 14½.

686 80 c. multicoloured 40 15
a. Booklet pane. Nos. 686 and 688, each × 3, with margins all round .. .. 4·50
687 $1.80, multicoloured 70 55
688 $2.30, multicoloured .. .. 1·25 1·40
689 $5 multicoloured .. .. 2·75 4·00
686/9 .. .. *Set of* 4 4·50 5·50
MS690 135×85 mm. Nos. 686/9 .. .. 8·50 10·00

(Des D. Miller. Litho Leigh-Mardon Ltd, Melbourne)

1992 (11 Feb). 40*th Anniv of Queen Elizabeth II's Accession. Horiz designs as* T **143** *of Ascension. Multicoloured.* P 14½.

691 80 c. Royal barge in Hong Kong harbour .. 30 15
692 $1.70, Queen watching dancing display .. 60 35
693 $1.80, Fireworks display 60 35
694 $2.30, Three portraits of Queen Elizabeth 90 85
695 $5 Queen Elizabeth II .. .. .. 2·00 2·50
691/5 .. .. *Set of* 5 4·00 3·75

154 Running

155 Queen Elizabeth II

(Des Li Shik-kwong. Litho Leigh-Mardon Ltd, Melbourne)

1992 (2 Apr). *Olympic Games, Barcelona (2nd issue).* T **154** *and similar horiz designs.* P 14½.

696 80 c. Type **154** 40 20
697 $1.80, Swimming and javelin 80 80
698 $2.30, Cycling .. .. 1·60 1·75
699 $5 High jump .. .. 2·25 3·25
696/9 .. .. *Set of* 4 4·50 5·50
MS700 130×75 mm. As Nos. 696/9* .. .. 5·50 7·00
* The stamps from No. **MS**700 show the inscriptions in different colours, instead of the black on Nos. 696/9. The designs of the $1.80 and $5 values from the miniature sheet have also been rearranged so that "HONG KONG" and the Royal Cypher occur at the right of the inscription.
For No. **MS**700 additionally inscribed for the opening of the Games see No. **MS**722.

(Des Kan Tai-keung. Litho Leigh-Mardon Ltd, Melbourne)

992 (22 May). *"World Columbian Stamp Expo '92" Exhibition, Chicago. Sheet 130×75 mm containing No. 613, but colours changed. P 14.*

IS701 $10 multicoloured .. .. .. 5·50 7·00

The stamp in No. **MS**701 shows the imprint date as "1992".

(Des I. Leung. Photo Enschedé)

992 (16 June)–**96.** *P* 14½×14 (10 *c. to* $5) *or* 14 ($10, $20, $50).

02 **155** 10 c. magenta, black and pale cerise .. 30 40
 ap. Two phosphor bands (24.4.96) .. 50 60
02*b* 20 c. black, blue-blk & pale bl (1.11.93) 60 70
 bp. Two phosphor bands (24.4.96) .. 50 60
03 50 c. orange-red, black and yellow .. 30 30
 p. Two phosphor bands (24.4.96) .. 50 60
04 60 c. greenish blue, black and light blue 50 45
05 70 c. bright mauve, black and rose-lilac 50 50
06 80 c. cerise, black and rose 30 20
07 90 c. bronze-green, blk & greenish grey 30 20
08 $1 red-brown, black & orange-yellow 35 20
 ap. Two phosphor bands (24.4.96) .. 65 30
08*b* $1.10, deep carmine, black and pale salmon (1.6.95) 35 35
 bp. Two phosphor bands (24.4.96) .. 70 80
09 $1.20, bright violet, black and lilac 35 25
 ap. Two phosphor bands (24.4.96) .. 70 80
09*b* $1.30, blue, brownish black and salmon (1.11.93) .. .. .. 1·00 30
 bp. Two phosphor bands (24.4.96) .. 70 80
09*c* $1.40, brt yellow-grn, blk & greenish yell (two phosphor bands) (2.9.96) 35 30
09*d* $1.50 reddish brn, blk & lt bl (1.6.95) 60 45
 dp. Two phosphor bands (24.4.96) .. 75 85
09*e* $1.60, light green, black and rose-lilac (two phosphor bands) (2.9.96) .. 45 50
10 $1.70, dull ultramarine, blk & pale bl 55 45
11 $1.80, deep magenta, black and grey 85 45
11*a* $1.90, deep blue-green, brownish black and yellow-ochre (1.11.93) 55 50
 ap. Two phosphor bands (24.4.96) .. 85 1·00
'12 $2 turq-blue, black & brt turq-green 1·25 60
 ap. Two phosphor bands (24.4.96) .. 1·00 90
12*b* $2.10, bright crimson, black & pale turquoise-green (1.6.95) 85 60
 bp. One centre phosphor band (24.4.96) .. .. 85 1·00
 bq. Two phosphor bands (2.9.96) .. 2·75 3·00
13 $2.30, blackish brn, blk & rose-pink 80 60
13*a* $2.40, dull ultramarine, black and brownish grey (1.11.93) .. .. 1·50 75
13*b* $2.50, brown-olive, black and lemon (one centre phosphor band) (2.9.96) 55 70
13*c* $2.60, choc, blk & yellow-brn (1.6.95) 75 80
 cp. One centre phosphor band (24.4.96) .. .. 1·10 1·40
13*d* $3.10, orange-brown, black & pale bl (one centre phosphor band) (2.9.96) 65 80
14 $5 bright blue-green, black & lt green 2·00 1·25
 p. One centre phosphor band (24.4.96) .. .. 2·00 2·00
15 – $10 red-brown, black and cinnamon 2·75 2·75
16 – $20 rosine, black and bright salmon 4·00 4·50
17 – $50 grey-black, black and grey .. 8·50 11·00
02/17 .. .. *Set of* 28 28·00 28·00

Nos. 715/17 are as Type **155**, but larger, 26×30 mm, and show large perforation hole at each corner of the stamp.

Nos. 702/17 show "HONG KONG" printed in yellow fluoresence as a security marking. Nos. 715/17 additionally show a orizontal line at foot in green fluorescence.

Nos. 702, 703, 706/7, 709bp, 709*e*, 711, 713, 713*b* and 713*d* lso exist from coils with every fifth stamp numbered on the everse.

For stamps in this design from stamp booklets, printed in thography without watermark or with watermark w **14**, see Jos. 757/65.

For miniature sheets containing designs as Nos. 714 and 715 ee Nos. **MS**723, **MS**745/6, **MS**751, **MS**771, **MS**782, **MS**810/11, **IS**821, **MS**827 and **MS**841/2.

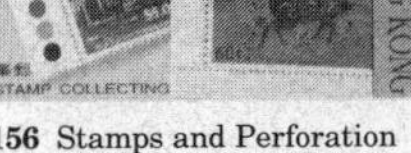

156 Stamps and Perforation Gauge **157** Principal Male Character

(Des Kan Tai-keung. Litho Leigh-Mardon Ltd, Melbourne)

1992 (15 July). *Stamp Collecting. T* **156** *and similar horiz designs. Multicoloured. P* 14½.

718 80 c. Type **156** 30 20
719 $1.80, Handstamp of 1841, 1891 Jubilee overprint and tweezers 60 55
720 $2.30, Stamps of 1946 and 1949 under magnifying glass 85 90
721 $5 2 c. of 1862 and watermark detector 2·00 3·00
718/21 .. .. *Set of* 4 3·25 4·25

(Des Li Shik-kwong. Litho Leigh-Mardon Ltd, Melbourne)

1992 (25 July). *Olympic Games, Barcelona (3rd issue). As No.* **MS**700, *but additionally inscribed* "To Commemorate the Opening of the 1992 Summer Olympic Games 25 July 1992", *in English and Chinese, at foot of sheet.*

MS722 130×75 mm. As Nos. 696/9 .. .. 3·50 4·50

(Des C. Tillyer. Litho Enschedé)

1992 (1 Sept). *"Kuala Lumpur '92" International Stamp Exhibition. Sheet 130×75 mm containing design as No. 715, but litho and colours changed. P 14.*

MS723 $10 dull ultramarine, black and pale blue 4·75 6·00

No. **MS**723 shows "HONG KONG" printed in yellow fluorescence with a horizontal green fluorescent line beneath as a security marking. There is a larger perforation hole at each corner of the stamp.

(Des I. Leung. Litho Enschedé)

1992 (24 Sept). *Chinese Opera. T* **157** *and similar vert designs. Multicoloured. P* 13½.

724 80 c. Type **157** 50 25
725 $1.80, Martial character .. .. 1·00 85
 a. Grey (face value and inscr) omitted .. £750
726 $2.30, Principal female character .. 1·40 1·50
 a. Grey (face value and inscr) omitted .. £750
727 $5 Comic character .. .. .. 2·50 4·00
724/7 .. .. *Set of* 4 4·75 6·00

Nos. 725a and 726a each occur on the bottom row of a sheet and were caused by the upward displacement of the grey colour. One example of each also exists showing the plate number from the bottom margin printed in the design.

158 Hearts

(Des C. Tillyer. Litho Leigh-Mardon Ltd, Melbourne)

1992 (19 Nov). *Greetings Stamps. T* **158** *and similar horiz designs. Multicoloured. P* 14½.

728 80 c. Type **158** 30 20
 a. Booklet pane. Nos. 728×3 and 729/31 with margins all round .. .. 4·00
729 $1.80, Stars 55 60
730 $2.30, Presents 75 95
731 $5 Balloons .. .. 1·60 2·50
728/31 .. .. *Set of* 4 2·75 3·75

159 Cockerel

160 Pipa

(Des Kan Tai-keung. Litho Enschedé)

1993 (7 Jan). *Chinese New Year. ("Year of the Cock"). T* **159** *and similar horiz designs. P* 13½.

732 80 c. multicoloured 30 20
 a. Booklet pane. Nos. 732 and 734, each × 3, with margins all round .. .. 3·75
733 $1.80, multicoloured 70 70
734 $2.30, multicoloured .. .. .. 95 1·10
735 $5 multicoloured .. .. .. 2·25 3·00
732/5 .. .. *Set of* 4 3·75 4·50
MS736 133×84 mm. Nos. 732/5 .. .. 4·75 6·00

(Des Sumiko Davies. Litho Leigh-Mardon Ltd, Melbourne)

1993 (14 Apr). *Chinese String Musical Instruments. T* **160** *and similar vert designs. Multicoloured. Fluorescent paper. P* 14½.

737 80 c. Type **160** 40 20
738 $1.80, Erhu 70 60
739 $2.30, Ruan .. .. 95 1·00
740 $5 Gehu .. .. 2·00 3·00
737/40 .. .. *Set of* 4 3·50 4·25

161 Central Waterfront, Hong Kong in 1954

(Des C. Tillyer. Litho Leigh-Mardon Ltd, Melbourne)

1993 (2 June). *40th Anniv of Coronation. T* **161** *and similar horiz designs. Multicoloured. Fluorescent paper. P* 14.

741 80 c. Type **161** 40 20
742 $1.80, Hong Kong in 1963 .. .. 70 50
743 $2.30, Hong Kong in 1975 .. .. 90 1·00
744 $5 Hong Kong in 1992 .. .. 2·25 2·75
741/4 .. .. *Set of* 4 3·75 4·00

(Des Julia Brown and G. Smith. Litho Enschedé)

1993 (6 July). *150th Anniv of Hong Kong Post Office (2nd issue). Sheet 130×75 mm containing design as No. 715, but litho. P 14.*

MS745 $10 red-brown, black and cinnamon .. 4·50 5·50

No. **MS**745 shows "HONG KONG" printed in yellow fluorescence with a horizontal green fluorescent line beneath as a security marking. There is a larger perforation hole at each corner of the stamp.

(Des Lam Bing-pui. Litho Enschedé)

1993 (12 Aug). *"Hong Kong '94" International Stamp Exhibition. Sheet 115×78 mm containing design as No. 715, but litho and colours changed. P 14.*

MS746 $10 deep purple, black, bistre-yellow and greenish blue .. .. 4·50 5·00

No. **MS**746 shows "HONG KONG" printed in yellow fluorescence with a horizontal green fluorescent line beneath as a security marking. There is a larger perforation hole at each corner of the stamp.

162 University of Science and Technology Building and Student

(Des Lam Bing-pui. Litho Leigh-Mardon Ltd, Melbourne)

1993 (8 Sept). *Hong Kong's Contribution to Science and Technology. T* **162** *and similar horiz designs. Multicoloured. P* 14½.

747 80 c. Type **162** 30 20
748 $1.80, Science Museum building and energy machine exhibit 50 40
749 $2.30, Governor's Award and circuit board 70 90
750 $5 Dish aerials and world map .. .. 1·75 3·00
747/50 .. .. *Set of* 4 2·75 4·00

(Des Lam Bing-pui. Litho Enschedé)

1993 (5 Oct). *"Bangkok '93" International Stamp Exhibition. Sheet 131×75 mm containing design as No. 715, but litho and colours changed. P 14.*

MS751 $10 bright emerald, blackish green and bright blue-green .. .. .. 2·75 3·50

No. **MS**751 shows "HONG KONG" printed in yellow fluorescence with a horizontal green fluorescent line beneath as a security marking. There is a larger perforation hole at each corner of the stamp.

163 Red Calico Egg-fish

(Des N. Young. Litho Leigh-Mardon Ltd, Melbourne)

1993 (17 Nov). *Goldfish. T* **163** *and similar horiz designs. Multicoloured. P* 14½.

752 $1 Type **163** 35 20
753 $1.90, Red Cap Oranda 60 50
754 $2.40, Red and White Fringetail .. .. 90 1·00
755 $5 Black and Gold Dragon-eye .. .. 2·25 3·25
752/5 .. .. *Set of* 4 3·75 4·50
MS756 130×75 mm. Nos. 752/5 .. .. 6·50 7·50

1993 (14 Dec)–**97.** *As Nos.* 702, 708, 709, 709bp, 709*e*, 710/12, 712*b*, 713*a and* 714, *but printed in lithography by Leigh-Mardon Ltd (Nos.* 757, 758, 759 *and* 760/5) *or Enschedé (others). P* 14½×14.

(a) No wmk

757 **155** $1 red-brown, black & orange-yellow 65 65
 a. Booklet pane. No. 757×10 with margins all round .. .. 6·50
757*b* $1.20, brt violet, black & lilac (1.6.95) 60 65
 ba. Booklet pane. No. 757*b*×10 with margins all round .. .. 6·00
757*c* $1.30, blue, deep brown and salmon (two phosphor bands) (2.9.96) .. 45 60
 ca. Booklet pane. No. 757*c*×10 with margins all round .. .. 4·50
 cb. Sheetlet. Nos. 757*c*×4 and 759*e*×2 with margins all round (14.2.97) 4·00
 cc. Booklet pane. As No. 757cb, but with enlarged margins at left and foot (14.2.97) .. .. 7·00
757*d* $1.60, light green, black and rose-lilac (two phosphor bands) (14.2.97) .. 85 1·25
 da. Sheetlet Nos. 757*d*×2 and 759*d*×4 with margins all round .. .. 4·00
 db. Booklet pane. As No. 759da, but with enlarged margins at left and foot .. .. 7·00
758 $1.90, dp blue-green, brownish black and yellow-ochre (28.12.93) .. 80 1·10
 a. Booklet pane. No. 758×10 with margins all round .. .. 8·00
758*b* $2.10, deep claret, black & turquoise-green (1.6.95) .. .. 80 1·00
 ba. Booklet pane. No. 758*b*×10 with margins all round .. .. 8·00
 bb. Two phosphor bands (14.2.97) .. 1·00 1·40
 bc. Sheetlet Nos. 758bb×2 and 759*b*×4 with margins all round 4·00
 bd. Booklet pane. As No. 758bc, but with enlarged margins at left and foot .. .. 7·00
759 $2.40, dull ultramarine, black and brownish grey (28.12.93) .. 85 1·25
 a. Booklet pane. No. 759×10 with margins all round .. .. 8·50

759*b* **155** $2.50, bistre, black and lemon (one centre phosphor band) (2.9.96) .. 60 85
ba. Booklet pane. No. 759*b*×10 with margins all round .. .. 6·00
759*c* $2.60, dp choc, black & brown (1.6.95) 85 1·10
ca. Booklet pane. No. 759*c*×10 with margins all round .. .. 8·50
759*d* $3.10, orge-brown, blk & pale bl (one centre phosphor band) (2.9.96) .. 70 1·25
da. Booklet pane. No. 759*d*×10 with margins all round .. .. 7·00
759*e* $5 bright blue-green, black and light green (one centre phosphor band) (14.2.97) .. .. 1·00 1·50
757/9*e* .. .. *Set of* 11 7·50 10·00

(*b*) W w **14** (12.1.94)

760 **155** 10 c. magenta, black and pale cerise 2·50 3·25
a. Booklet pane. Nos. 760 and 764×5 with margins all round .. 5·50
761 $1 red-brown, black & orange-yellow 60 75
a. Booklet pane. Nos. 761×5 and 765 with margins all round .. 5·50
762 $1.70 dull ultram, black & pale blue 2·50 3·25
a. Booklet pane. Nos. 762 and 763×5 with margins all round .. 5·50
763 $1.80, deep magenta, black and grey 60 75
764 $2 turquoise-blue, blk & brt turq-grn 60 75
765 $5 brt blue-green, black & lt green 2·50 3·25
760/5 .. .. *Set of* 6 8·50 11·00

Nos. 757/65 show "HONG KONG" printed in yellow fluorescence as a security marking.

Nos. 757/9*d* come from definitive booklets and Nos. 760/5 from the Prestige booklet issued to commemorate the 130th anniversary of Hong Kong stamps.

164 Dog

(Des Kan Tai-keung. Litho Leigh-Mardon Ltd, Melbourne)

1994 (27 Jan). *Chinese New Year.* (*"Year of the Dog"*). *T* **164** *and similar horiz designs. P* 14½.
766 $1 multicoloured 30 20
a. Booklet pane. Nos. 766 and 768, each × 3, with margins all round .. .. 4·00
767 $1.90, multicoloured 50 45
768 $2.40, multicoloured 70 90
769 $5 multicoloured .. .. 1·75 2·75
766/9 .. .. *Set of* 4 3·00 3·75
MS770 133×84 mm. Nos. 766/9 .. .. 8·00 6·00

(Des Lam Bing-pui. Litho Leigh-Mardon Ltd, Melbourne)

1994 (18 Feb). *"Hong Kong '94" International Stamp Exhibition. Sheet* 130×75 *mm containing design as No.* 714, *but litho. P* 14½×14.
MS771 **155** $5 bright blue-green, black & lt green 5·00 6·00

No. **MS**771 shows "HONG KONG" printed in yellow fluorescence as a security marking.

165 Modern Police Constables on Traffic Duty

166 Dragon Boat Festival

(Des Li Shik-kwong. Litho Enschedé)

1994 (4 May). 150*th Anniv of Royal Hong Kong Police Force. T* **165** *and similar horiz designs. Multicoloured. P* 13½.
772 $1 Type **165** 30 20
773 $1.20, Marine policeman with binoculars 40 25
774 $1.90, Police uniforms of 1950 .. .. 55 35
775 $2 Tactical firearms unit officer with sub-machine gun 75 55
776 $2.40, Early 20th-century police uniforms 90 90
777 $5 Sikh and Chinese constables of 1900 .. 2·75 3·50
772/7 .. .. *Set of* 6 5·00 5·25

(Des Li Shik-kwong. Litho Questa)

1994 (8 June). *Traditional Chinese Festivals. T* **166** *and similar vert designs. Multicoloured. P* 14½.
778 $1 Type **166** 35 20
779 $1.90, Lunar New Year 60 50
780 $2.40, Seven Sisters Festival .. .. 85 1·10
781 $5 Mid-Autumn Festival .. .. .. 1·75 2·75
778/81 .. .. *Set of* 4 3·25 4·00

(Des C. Tillyer. Litho Enschedé)

1994 (16 Aug). *Conference of Commonwealth Postal Administrations, Hong Kong. Sheet* 134×83 *mm, containing design as No.* 715, *but litho. P* 14.
MS782 $10 red-brown, black and cinnamon .. 5·00 6·00

No. **MS**782 shows "HONG KONG" printed in yellow fluorescence with a horizontal green fluorescent line beneath as a security marking. There is a larger perforation hole at each corner of the stamp.

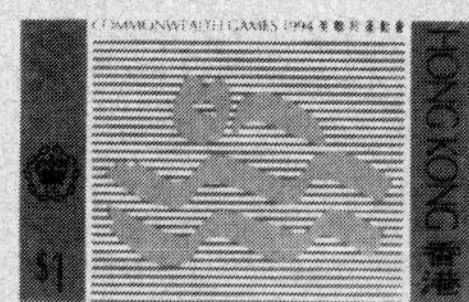

167 Swimming

(Des C. Tillyer. Litho Walsall)

1994 (25 Aug). 15*th Commonwealth Games, Victoria, Canada. T* **167** *and similar horiz designs. Multicoloured. P* 14½.
783 $1 Type **167** 25 20
784 $1.90, Bowls 50 50
785 $2.40, Gymnastics 70 85
786 $5 Weightlifting .. .. 1·60 2·50
783/6 .. .. *Set of* 4 2·75 3·50

168 Dr. James Legge and Students

169 Alcyonium Coral

(Des Lai Wai-kwan. Litho Leigh-Mardon Ltd, Melbourne)

1994 (5 Oct). *Dr. James Legge (Chinese scholar) Commemoration. P* 14½.
787 **168** $1 multicoloured 55 50

(Des Brushstroke Design. Litho Questa)

1994 (17 Nov). *Corals. T* **169** *and similar square designs. Multicoloured. P* 14.
788 $1 Type **169** 35 20
789 $1.90, Zoanthus 60 55
790 $2.40, Tubastrea .. .. 75 1·00
791 $5 Platygyra .. .. 1·75 2·50
788/91 .. .. *Set of* 4 3·00 3·75
MS792 130×75 mm. Nos. 788/91 .. .. 4·50 5·00

170 Pig

(Des Kan Tai-keung. Litho Leigh-Mardon Ltd, Melbourne)

1995 (17 Jan). *Chinese New Year* (*"Year of the Pig"*). *T* **170** *and similar horiz designs. P* 14½.
793 $1 multicoloured 30 30
a. Booklet pane. Nos. 793 and 795, each × 3, with margins all round .. .. 3·25
794 $1.90, multicoloured 60 70
795 $2.40, multicoloured 70 95
796 $5 multicoloured .. .. 1·25 2·00
793/6 .. .. *Set of* 4 2·50 3·50
MS797 130×84 mm. Nos. 793/6 .. .. 4·25 4·50

171 Hong Kong Rugby Sevens

(Des Kan Tai-keung and Roxy Lou Sze-wan. Litho Leigh-Mardon Ltd, Melbourne)

1995 (22 Mar). *International Sporting Events in Hong Kong. T* **171** *and similar horiz designs. Multicoloured. P* 14½.
798 $1 Type **171** 45 20
799 $1.90, The China Sea Yacht Race .. 60 55
800 $2.40, International Dragon Boat Races .. 85 1·00
801 $5 Hong Kong International Horse Races 1·75 2·50
798/801 .. .. *Set of* 4 3·25 3·75

172 Tsui Shing Lau Pagoda

173 Regimental Badge

(Des I. Leung. Recess and litho Enschedé)

1995 (24 May). *Hong Kong Traditional Rural Buildings T* **172** *and similar horiz designs. Multicoloured. P* 13½.
802 $1 Type **172** 30 2
803 $1.90, Sam Tung Uk Village 55 5
804 $2.40, Lo Wai Village .. .. .. 75 1·0
805 $5 Man Shek Tong house .. .. 1·50 2·5
802/5 .. .. *Set of* 4 2·75 3·7

(Des Lam Bing-pui. Litho Leigh-Mardon Ltd, Melbourne)

1995 (16 Aug). *Disbandment of the Royal Hong Kong Regiment. T* **173** *and similar multicoloured designs. P* 14½.
806 $1.20, Type **173** 40 25
807 $2.10, Regimental guidon (*horiz*) 60 55
808 $2.60, Colour of Hong Kong Volunteer Defence Corps, 1928 (*horiz*) 75 85
809 $5 Cap badge of Royal Hong Kong Defence Force, 1951 .. .. 1·25 2·0
806/9 .. .. *Set of* 4 2·75 3·25

(Des C. Tillyer and Valerie Carter. Litho Enschedé)

1995 (1 Sept). *"Singapore '95" International Stamp Exhibition. Sheet* 130×75 *mm, containing design as No.* 715, *but litho and colours changed. P* 14.
MS810 $10 dp mag, yellow-olive, yell & brn-lilac 4·00 5·00

No. **MS**810 shows "HONG KONG" printed in yellow fluorescence with a horizontal green fluorescent line beneath as a security marking. There is a larger perforation hole at each corner of the stamp.

(Des D. Lai. Litho Enschedé)

1995 (9 Oct). 50*th Anniv of End of Second World War. Sheet* 130×75 *mm, containing design as No.* 715, *but litho. P* 14.
MS811 $10 red-brown, black and cinnamon .. 4·00 5·00

No. **MS**811 shows "HONG KONG" printed in yellow fluorescence with a horizontal green fluorescent line beneath as a security marking. There is a larger perforation hole at each corner of the stamp.

174 Bruce Lee

(Des Lau Siu-hong and Wong Kum. Litho Enschedé)

1995 (15 Nov). *Hong Kong Film Stars. T* **174** *and similar horiz designs. Multicoloured. P* 13½.
812 $1.20, Type **174** .. .. 1·50 4
813 $2.10, Leung Sing-por .. .. .. 1·75 1·2
814 $2.60, Yam Kim-fai .. .. .. 2·75 1·4
815 $5 Lin Dai .. .. 2·75 3·0
812/15 .. .. *Set of* 4 8·00 5·5

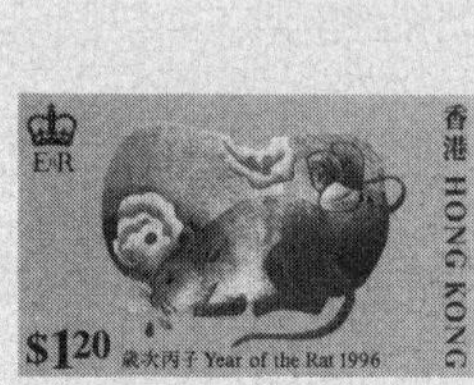

175 Rat

176 Rhythmic Gymnastics

(Des Kan Tai-keung. Litho Enschedé)

1996 (31 Jan). *Chinese New Year* (*"Year of the Rat"*). *T* **175** *and similar horiz designs. P* 13½.
816 $1.20, multicoloured 25 30
a. Booklet pane. Nos. 816 and 818, each × 3, with margins all round .. .. 2·50
817 $2.10, multicoloured 45 55
818 $2.60, multicoloured 50 65
819 $5 multicoloured .. .. 1·25 1·75
816/19 .. .. *Set of* 4 2·25 3·00
MS820 133×83 mm. Nos. 816/19 .. .. 2·50 3·50

(Des Lam Bing-pui. Litho Enschedé)

1996 (23 Feb). *Visit "HONG KONG '97" Stamp Exhibition* (*1st issue*). *Sheet* 130×80 *mm, containing designs as No.* 715, *but litho and colours changed. P* 14.
MS821 $10 yellow-orange, black & bright green 4·50 6·00

No. **MS**821 shows "HONG KONG" printed in yellow fluorescence with a horizontal green fluorescent line beneath as a security marking. There is a large perforation hole at each corner of the stamp.

See also Nos. **MS**827, **MS**841 and **MS**872/3.

(Des B. Kwan. Litho Ashton-Potter America Inc, New York)

1996 (20 Mar). *Olympic Games, Atlanta. T* **176** *and similar vert designs. Multicoloured with Royal Cypher and face values in black and Olympic Rings multicoloured* (*Nos.* 822/5). *Two phosphor bands* ($1.20) *or one side phosphor band* (*others*). *P* 13½.
822 $1.20, Type **176** 25 25
823 $2.10, Diving 45 50

824 $2.60, Athletics 55 75
825 $5 Basketball .. .. 1·25 2·00
822/5 .. .. *Set of* 4 2·25 3·25
MS826 130×75 mm. As Nos. 822/5, but Royal Cypher and Olympic Rings in gold and face values in black (medal in bottom sheet margin) 2·50 3·50

For these designs with Royal Cypher and Olympic Rings in gold see Nos. 832/6

(Des A. Lam. Litho Enschedé)

1996 (18 May). *Visit "HONG KONG '97" Stamp Exhibition (2nd issue). Sheet* 130×80 *mm, containing design as No.* 715, *but litho and colours changed. P* 14.
MS827 $10 brt emer, greenish blk & bluish vio 2·50 3·00

No. **MS**827 shows "HONG KONG" printed in yellow fluorescence with a horizontal green fluorescent line beneath as a security marking. There is a large perforation hole at each corner of the stamp.

177 Painted Pottery Basin, *c.* 4500–3700 B.C.

(Des I. Leung. Litho Enschedé)

1996 (26 June). *Archaeological Discoveries. T* **177** *and similar horiz designs. Multicoloured. Two phosphor bands* ($1.20) *or one side band (others). P* 13½.
828 $1.20, Type **177** 40 25
829 $2.10, Stone "yue" (ceremonial axe), *c.* 2900–2200 B.C. 50 65
830 $2.60, Stone "ge" (halberd), *c.* 2200–1500 B.C. .. .. 60 1·00
831 $5 Pottery tripod, *c.* 25–220 A.D. .. 1·25 2·50
828/31 .. .. *Set of* 4 2·50 4·00

(Des B. Kwan, Litho Ashton-Potter America Inc, New York)

1996 (19 July). *Opening of Centennial Olympic Games, Atlanta. Designs as Nos.* 822/5, *but with Royal Cypher and Olympic Rings in gold and face values in colours quoted. Two phosphor bands* ($1.20) *or one side band (others). P* 14½.
832 $1.20, Type **176** (bright magenta) .. 35 25
833 $2.10, As No. 823 (deep ultramarine) .. 50 60
834 $2.60, As No. 824 (light green) 60 90
835 $5 As No. 825 (orange-vermilion) .. 1·25 2·25
832/5 .. .. *Set of* 4 2·40 3·50
MS836 130×75 mm. As No. **MS**826, but with medal in top margin. P 13½ .. .. 2·50 3·50

The stamps in Nos. **MS**826 and **MS**836 are similar. The miniature sheets differ in the marginal inscriptions and illustrations. No. **MS**826 is inscribed "1996 OLYMPIC GAMES" and has a Gold Medal in the bottom margin. No. **MS**836 is inscribed "TO COMMEMORATE THE OPENING OF THE CENTENNIAL OLYMPIC GAMES 19 JULY 1996" and has the medal in the top margin.

178 Pat Sin Leng Mountain

(Des Lam Bing-pui. Litho Harrison)

1996 (24 Sept). *Mountains. T* **178** *and similar multicoloured designs. Two phosphor bands* ($1.30) *or one side phosphor band (others). P* 13½×14½ ($1.30), 14×14½ ($2.50), 14½×14 ($3.10) *or* 14½×13½ ($5).
837 $1.30, Type **178** 50 35
838 $2.50, Ma On Shan (40×35 *mm*) .. .. 70 1·00
839 $3.10, Lion Rock (35×40 *mm*) .. .. 90 1·40
840 $5 Lantau Peak (25×46½ *mm*) .. .. 1·25 2·25
837/40 .. .. *Set of* 4 3·00 4·50

(Des A. Lam. Litho Enschedé)

1996 (16 Oct). *Visit "HONG KONG '97" Stamp Exhibition (3rd issue). Sheet* 130×80 *mm, containing design as No.* 715 *but litho and colours changed. P* 14½×14.
MS841 $10 apple-green, black and rose-carmine 2·50 3·50

No. **MS**841 shows "HONG KONG" printed in yellow fluorescence with a horizontal green fluorescent line beneath as a security marking. There is a larger perforation hole at each corner of the stamp.

(Des B. Kwan. Litho Enschedé)

1996 (29 Oct). *Hong Kong Team's Achievements at Atlanta Olympic Games. Sheet* 130×75 *mm, containing design as No.* 715 *but litho. P* 14½×14.
MS842 $10 red-brown, black and cinnamon .. 2·50 3·25

No. **MS**842 shows "HONG KONG" printed in yellow fluorescence with a horizontal green fluorescent line beneath as a security marking. There is a larger perforation hole at each corner of the stamp.

179 Main Building, University of Hong Kong, 1912

180 Part of Hong Kong Skyline

(Des T. Li. Recess and litho Ashton-Potter America Inc, New York)

1996 (20 Nov). *Urban Heritage. T* **179** *and similar horiz designs. Multicoloured. Two phosphor bands* ($1.30) *or one phosphor band (others). P* 13½.
843 $1.30, Type **179** 40 30
844 $2.50, Western Market, 1906 .. .. 60 85
845 $3.10, Old Pathological Institute, 1905 .. 65 1·00
846 $5 Flagstaff House, 1846 .. .. .. 80 1·75
843/6 .. .. *Set of* 4 2·25 3·50

(Des A. Lam. Litho Walsall)

1996 (4 Dec). *Serving the Community. Sheet* 130×75 *mm, containing design as No.* 619, *but smaller,* 25×35 *mm. Multicoloured. One phosphor band. P* 13×13½.
MS847 $5 Multi-racial society .. .. .. 1·00 1·25

(Des Kan Tai-keung)

1997 (26 Jan). *T* **180** *and similar vert designs showing different sections of Hong Kong skyline. Two phosphor bands* (10 *c. to* $2.10), *one centre phosphor band* ($2.50 *to* $5) *or phosphorised paper* ($10).

(*a*) *Sheet stamps. Litho Ashton-Potter America Inc, New York. P* 13½×13 (10 *c. to* $5) *or* 14×13½ ($10, $20, $50)
848 10 c. purple and rose-pink 10 10
849 20 c. purple-brown and orange-red .. 10 10
850 50 c. deep green and bright orange .. 10 10
851 $1 greenish blue and orange-yellow .. 15 20
852 $1.20, deep dull green and olive-yellow .. 20 25
853 $1.30, deep violet and apple green .. 20 25
a. Booklet pane. No. 853×10 with margins all round .. .. .. 2·00
854 $1.40, maroon and bright green .. 20 25
855 $1.60, deep purple and bright blue-green 25 30
856 $2 deep olive and greenish blue .. 30 35
857 $2.10, deep turquoise-blue and bright blue 30 35
858 $2.50, violet and bright mauve 40 45
a. Booklet pane. No. 858×10 with margins all round .. .. .. 4·00
859 $3.10, purple and cerise 50 55
a. Booklet pane. No. 859×10 with margins all round .. .. .. 5·00
860 $5 deep magenta and bright orange .. 80 85
861 $10 multicoloured (28×32 *mm*) .. .. 1·60 1·75
862 $20 multicoloured (28×32 *mm*) .. .. 3·25 3·50
863 $50 multicoloured (28×32 *mm*) .. .. 8·00 8·25
848/63 .. .. *Set of* 16 16·50 17·50
MS864 273×53 mm. Nos. 848/57, and as Nos. 858/60 each with one side phosphor band .. 3·50 4·00
MS865 95×72 mm. Nos. 861/3 .. .. 13·00 13·50

(*b*) *Coil stamps. Designs as Nos.* 849, 851, 853, 856 *and* 859/60, *but photo Enschedé. P* 14½×14.
866 10 c. purple and rose-pink 10 10
867 50 c. deep green and bright orange .. 10 10
868 $1.30, deep violet and apple-green .. 20 25
869 $1.60, deep purple and bright blue-green 25 30
870 $2.50, violet and bright mauve 40 45
871 $3.10, purple and cerise 50 55
866/71 .. .. *Set of* 6 1·50 1·75

Nos. 848/71 show "HONG KONG" printed in yellow fluorescence. The perforations on Nos. 848/65 showing alternate small and large holes.

Nos. 866/71 were printed in coils with every fifth stamp numbered on the reverse.

For miniature sheets containing No. 861 see Nos. **MS**872/3 and **MS**892.

(Des Kan Tai-keung. Litho Ashton-Potter America Inc, New York)

1997 (12 Feb). *Visit "HONG KONG '97" Stamp Exhibition (4th issue). Sheet* 130×80 *mm containing design as No.* 861, *but ordinary paper, and with marginal illustration in bluish violet. P* 14×13.
MS872 $10 multicoloured .. .. .. 2·25 3·00

No. **MS**872 shows "HONG KONG" in yellow fluorescence. The perforations show alternate small and large holes.

(Des Kan Tai-keung. Litho Ashton-Potter America Inc, New York)

1997 (16 Feb). *Visit "HONG KONG '97" Stamp Exhibition (5th issue). Sheet* 130×80 *mm, containing design as No.* 861, *but ordinary paper, and with marginal illustration in chestnut. P* 14×13.
MS873 $10 multicoloured .. .. .. 2·25 3·00

No. **MS**873 shows "HONG KONG" in yellow fluorescence. The perforations show alternate small and large holes.

181 Ox

(Des Kan Tai-keung)

1997 (27 Feb). *Chinese New Year ("Year of the Ox"). T* **181** *and similar horiz designs. Two phosphor bands* ($1.30) *or one phosphor band (others).*

(*a*) *Litho Ashton-Potter America Inc, New York. P* 14½
874 $1.30, multicoloured 25 25
875 $2.50, multicoloured 50 55
876 $3.10, multicoloured 75 90
877 $5 multicoloured .. .. 1·25 2·00
874/7 .. .. *Set of* 4 2·50 3·25
MS878 133×84 mm. Nos. 874/7 .. .. 2·50 3·25

(*b*) *Litho Enschedé. P* 13½
879 $1.30, multicoloured 25 25
a. Booklet pane. Nos. 879 and 881 each × 3 5·00
880 $2.50, multicoloured 50 55
881 $3.10, multicoloured 75 90
882 $5 multicoloured .. .. 1·25 2·00
879/82 .. .. *Set of* 4 2·50 3·25
MS883 133×84 mm. Nos. 879/82 .. .. 2·50 3·25

182 Yellow-breasted Bunting

(Des Shek Tak-sheun. Litho Enschedé)

1997 (27 Apr). *Migratory Birds. T* **182** *and similar horiz designs. Multicoloured. Two phosphor bands* ($1.30) *or one phosphor band (others). P* 13½.
884 $1.30, Type **182** 30 35
885 $2.50, Great Knot 50 55
886 $3.10, Falcated Teal 75 90
887 $5 Black-faced Spoonbill .. .. .. 1·25 2·00
884/7 .. .. *Set of* 4 2·50 3·25

183 Hong Kong Stadium

(Des M. Chan)

1997 (18 May). *Modern Landmarks. T* **183** *and similar horiz designs. Multicoloured. Two phosphor bands* ($1.30) *or one phosphor band (others).* (*a*) *Litho Enschedé. P* 13½
888 $1.30, Type **183** 25 25
889 $2.50, Peak Tower 50 55
890 $3.10, Hong Kong Convention and Exhibition Centre .. .. 75 1·00
891 $5 Lantau Bridge .. .. 1·10 2·00
888/91 .. .. *Set of* 4 2·40 3·50
MS892 130×76 mm. No. 891 .. .. .. 1·25 1·75

(*b*) *Photo Walsall. P* 14×14½
893 $1.30, Type **183** 25 25
894 $2.50, Peak Tower 50 55
895 $3.10, Hong Kong Convention and Exhibition Centre .. .. 75 1·00
896 $5 Lantau Bridge .. .. 1·10 2·00
893/6 .. .. *Set of* 4 2·40 3·50
MS897 130×76 mm. No. 896 .. .. .. 1·25 1·75

(Des G. Lai and Leung Ka-shun. Litho Ashton-Potter America Inc, New York)

1997 (1 June). *Paralympic Games, Atlanta* (1996). *Sheet* 130×75 *mm containing design as No.* 861 *but on ordinary paper. P* 14×13.
MS898 $10 multicoloured .. .. .. 2·00 2·75

No. **MS**898 shows "HONG KONG" printed in yellow fluorescence. The perforations show alternate small and large holes.

(Des A. Lam. Litho Courvoisier)

1997 (30 June). *History of the Hong Kong Post Office. Sheet* 130×75 *mm containing design as No.* 677, *but redrawn smaller,* 22×38 *mm. One phosphor band. P* 11½.
MS899 $5 multicoloured .. .. .. 1·40 2·00

Details of the Post Office buildings depicted on the miniature sheet are printed on the reverse.

Hong Kong became a Special Administrative Region of the People's Republic of China on 1 July 1997 when all previous stamp issues, with exception of Nos. 848/71, were withdrawn and invalidated. Later issues are included in the *Part 17 (China)* catalogue.

PRICES OF SETS

Set prices are given for many issues, generally those containing three stamps or more. Definitive sets include one of each value or major colour change, but do not cover different perforations, die types or minor shades. Where a choice is possible the set prices are based on the cheapest versions of the stamps included in the listings.

STAMP BOOKLETS

1903 (Mar). *Black on white cover. Postage rates on front. Stapled.*
SB1 $1 booklet containing twelve 1 c. (No. 62), twelve 2 c. (No. 56), each in blocks of 6, and sixteen 4 c. (No. 57) in blocks of 8 .. .. ..

1904 (1 Jan). *Black on white cover. Postage rates on front. Stapled.*
SB2 $1 booklet containing twelve 1 c. (No. 62), twelve 2 c. (No. 56), each in blocks of 6, and sixteen 4 c. (No. 64) in blocks of 8 .. .. .. £4250

1904. *Black on white cover. Postage rates on front. Stapled.*
SB3 $1 booklet containing twelve 1 c., twelve 2 c. (Nos. 62/3), each in blocks of 6, and sixteen 4 c. (No. 64) in blocks of 8 .. .. £3250

1907–08. *Black on white cover. Stapled.*
SB4 $1 booklet containing twelve 1 c., twelve 2 c. (Nos. 62, 92), each in blocks of 6, and sixteen 4 c. (No. 93) in blocks of 8 .. .. £2750
a. 4 c. in two blocks of 6 and block of 4 (1908) .. £2750

1910. *Black on white cover. Contents on front. Stapled.*
SB5 $1 booklet containing twelve 1 c., twelve 2 c. (Nos. 91/2), each in blocks of 6, and sixteen 4 c. (No. 93) in two blocks of 6 and block of 4 .. £2750

1912. *Black on white cover. Stapled.*
SB6 $1 booklet containing twelve 1 c., twelve 2 c. (Nos 100/1), each in block of 12, and sixteen 4 c. (No. 102) in block of 12 and block of 4 .. .. £2500

1929. *Black on white cover. Stapled.*
SB7 $1 booklet containing twelve 1 c., twelve 2 c. (Nos. 117/18), each in block of 12, and sixteen 4 c. (No. 120) in blocks of 8 .. .. .. £2250

1965 (10 May). *Orange-brown* (No. SB8) *or yellow-green* (No. SB9) *covers. Stitched.*
SB8 $2 booklet containing eight 5 c. and sixteen 10 c. (Nos. 196/7) in blocks of 4 .. .. .. 32·00
SB9 $5 booklet containing twelve 5 c., eight 10 c., eight 20 c. and four 50 c. (Nos. 196/7, 199, 203) in blocks of 4 .. .. £110

1973 (12 June). *Buff* (No. SB10) *or green* (No. SB11) *covers. Stitched.*
SB10 $2 booklet containing twenty 10 c. (No. 283) in blocks of 4 .. .. 30·00
SB11 $5 booklet containing eight 10 c., four 15 c., eight 20 c. and four 50 c. (Nos. 283, 284/5, 289) each in blocks of 4 .. .. 65·00

1975 (27 Jan). *Covers as Nos.* SB10/11. *Stitched.*
SB12 $2 booklet containing twenty 10 c. (No. 311) in blocks of 4 .. .. 30·00
SB13 $5 booklet containing eight 10 c., four 15 c., eight 20 c. and four 50 c. (Nos. 311/13, 317) in blocks of 4 .. .. 60·00

1976 (1 July). *Orange* (No. SB14) *or green* (No. SB15) *covers. Stitched.*
SB14 $2 booklet containing four 10 c. and eight 20 c. (Nos. 311, 313) in blocks of 4 .. .. 25·00
SB15 $5 booklet containing eight 10 c., four 15 c., eight 20 c. and four 50 c. (Nos. 311, 284, 313, 289) in blocks of 4 .. .. 50·00

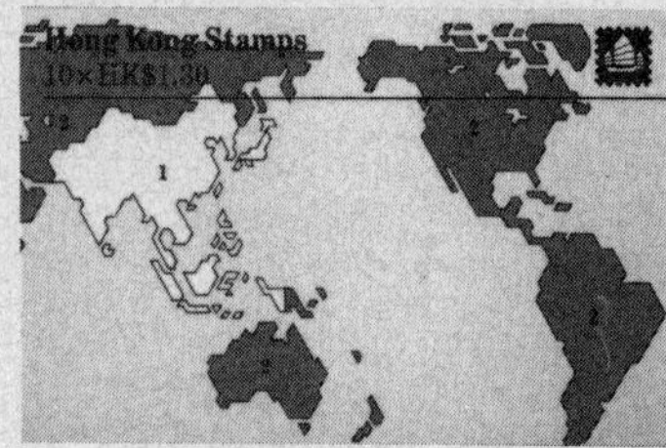

B 1 *World Map*

1985 (1 Apr–Nov). *Multicoloured cover as Type* B **1**. *Stamps attached by selvedge.*
SB16 $13 booklet containing $1.30 (No. 464) in block of 10 .. .. 27·00
a. Containing No. 469 in block of 10 .. .. 22·00
b. Containing No. 490 in block of 10 (June) .. 26·00
c. Containing No. 500 in block of 10 (Sept) .. 27·00
d. Containing No. 504 in block of 10 (Nov) .. 23·00

Supplies of a similar $13 booklet, but containing ten examples of No. 495, were produced for sale by the Crown Agents Stamp Bureau. Such booklets are reported not to have been available from post offices in Hong Kong.

1985 (2 Sept)–**87**. *Multicoloured cover as Type* B **1**. *Stamps attached by selvedge.*
SB18 $17 booklet containing $1.70 (No. 482) in block of 10 .. .. 35·00
a. Containing No. 547 in block of 10 (1987) 28·00

1985 (28 Oct)–**87**. *Multicoloured cover as Type* B **1**, *showing map of Hong Kong. Stamps attached by selvedge.*
SB19 $5 booklet containing 50 c. (No. 475) in block of 10 .. .. 7·00
a. Containing No. 540 in block of 10 (1987) .. 5·50

B **2** Hong Kong Bank Headquarters and Lion's Head
(Illustration further reduced. Actual size 159×86 mm)

1986 (7 Apr). *New Hong Kong Bank Headquarters. Multicoloured cover as Type* B **2**. *Booklet contains text and illustrations on interleaving pages. Stitched.*
SB20 $29 booklet containing 50 c. in block of 24 and $1.70 in block of 10 (Nos. 475, 505) .. 38·00

B **3** Early and Modern Views of the Peak Tramway
(Illustration further reduced. Actual size 161×91 mm)

1988 (26 Aug). *Centenary of The Peak Tramway. Multicoloured cover as Type* B **3**. *Booklet contains text and illustrations on interleaving pages. Stitched.*
SB21 $26 booklet containing No. **MS**581×3 .. .. 22·00

B **4** *(Illustration further reduced. Actual size 145×55 mm)*

1989 (18 Jan). *Year of the Snake. Multicoloured cover as Type* B **4**. *Pane attached by selvedge.*
SB22 $12 booklet containing *se-tenant* pane of 10 (No. 587a) .. .. 6·00

B **5** *(Illustration further reduced. Actual size 140×65 mm)*

1990 (23 Jan). *Year of the Horse. Multicoloured cover as Type* B **5**. *Pane attached by selvedge.*
SB23 $14.50, booklet containing two *se-tenant* panes of 6 (No. 631a) .. .. 8·00

1990 (3 May). *"Stamp World London 90" International Stamp Exhibition. As No.* SB23, *but "Stamp World London 90" emblem printed on cover and top selvedge of each pane.*
SB24 $14.50, booklet. Contents as No. SB23 .. .. 13·00

No. SB24 additionally includes an imperforate black print on gummed paper of the 60 c. and $1.80 values of the New Year issue.

B **6** Hong Kong Skyline at Night
(Illustration further reduced. Actual size 168×86 mm)

1990 (29 Nov). *Centenary of Electricity Supply. Multicoloured cover as Type* B **6**. *Booklet contains text and illustrations on interleaving pages. Stitched.*
SB25 $26 booklet containing No. **MS**651×4 .. .. 25·00

1991 (24 Jan). *Year of the Ram. Multicoloured cover as Type* B **5**. *Pane attached by selvedge.*
SB26 $14.40, booklet containing two *se-tenant* panes of 6 (No. 658a) .. .. 8·50

1992 (22 Jan). *Year of the Monkey. Multicoloured cover as Type* B **5**. *Panes attached by selvedge.*
SB27 $18.60, booklet containing two *se-tenant* panes of 6 (No. 686a) .. .. 9·0(

B **7** "Greetings"
(Illustration further reduced. Actual size 153×67 mm)

1992 (19 Nov). *Greetings Stamps. Multicoloured cover as Type* B **7**. *Panes attached by selvedge.*
SB28 $24 booklet containing two *se-tenant* panes of 6 (No. 728a) and 24 half stamp-size labels .. 8·00

1993 (7 Jan). *Year of the Cock. Multicoloured cover as Type* B **5**. *Panes attached by selvedge.*
SB29 $18.60, booklet containing two *se-tenant* panes of 6 (No. 732a) .. .. 7·50

B **8** Skyscrapers

1993 (14–28 Dec). *Multicoloured cover as Type* B **8**. *Panes attached by selvedge.*
SB30 $10 booklet containing pane of ten $1 (No. 757a) 6·50
SB31 $19 booklet containing pane of ten $1.90 (No. 758a) (cover showing Exhibition Centre) (28 Dec) .. .. 8·00
SB32 $24 booklet containing pane of ten $2.40 (No. 759a) (cover showing historical buildings) (28 Dec) .. .. 8·50

B **9** *(Illustration further reduced. Actual size 160×85 mm)*

1994 (12 Jan). *"A History of Hong Kong Definitive Stamps 1862–1992". Multicoloured cover Type* B **9**. *Booklet contains text and illustrations on panes and on interleaving pages. Stapled.*
SB33 $38 booklet containing three different *se-tenant* panes of 6 (Nos. 760a/2a) .. .. .. 16·00

1994 (27 Jan). *Year of the Dog. Multicoloured cover as Type* B **5**. *Panes attached by selvedge.*
SB34 $20.40, booklet containing two *se-tenant* panes of 6 (No. 766a) .. .. 8·00

1995 (17 Jan). *Year of the Pig. Multicoloured cover as Type* B **5**. *Panes attached by selvedge.*
SB35 $20.40, booklet containing two *se-tenant* panes of 6 (No. 793a) .. .. 6·50

1995 (1 June). *Multicoloured covers as Nos.* SB30/2. *Panes attached by selvedge.*
SB36 $12 booklet containing pane of ten $1.20 (No. 757ba) (Type B **8** cover) .. .. .. 6·00
SB37 $21 booklet containing pane of ten $2.10 (No. 758ba) (cover as No. SB31) .. .. 8·00
SB38 $26 booklet containing pane of ten $2.60 (No. 759ca) (cover as No. SB32) .. .. 8·50

On the initial supply of No. SB36 the inside of the card covers were matt. A printing later in 1995 showed both sides of the cover card glossy.

1996 (31 Jan). *Year of the Rat. Multicoloured cover as Type* B **5**. *Panes attached by selvedge.*
SB39 $22.80, booklet containing two *se-tenant* panes of 6 (No. 816a) .. .. 5·00

1996 (2 Sept). *Multicoloured covers as Nos.* SB30/2. *Panes attached by selvedge.*
SB40 $13 booklet containing pane of ten $1.30 (No. 757ca) (Type B **8** cover) .. .. .. 4·50
SB41 $25 booklet containing pane of ten $2.50 (No. 759ba (cover as No. SB31) .. .. .. 6·00
SB42 $31 booklet containing pane of ten $3.10 (No. 759da) (cover as No. SB32) .. .. 7·00

B 10 Water Front

997 (26 Jan). *Multicoloured covers as Type* B **10**, *each incorporating the design from the stamps included. Panes attached by selvedge.*

B43 $13 booklet containing pane of ten $1.30 (No. 853a) 2·00
B44 $25 booklet containing pane of ten $2.50 (No. 858a) 4·00
B45 $31 booklet containing pane of ten $3.10 (No. 859a) 5·00

B 11 Hong Kong Waterfront
(*Illustration further reduced. Actual size* 183×130 *mm*)

1997 (14 Feb). *Hong Kong Past and Present. Multicoloured cover as Type* B **11**. *Booklet containing text and illustrations on interleaving pages. Stitched.*

SB46 $55 booklet containing three different *se-tenant* panes of 6 (Nos. 757cc, 757db and 758bd) 20·00

1997 (27 Feb). *Year of the Ox. Multicoloured cover as Type* B **5**. *Panes attached by selvedge.*

SB47 $26.40, booklet containing two panes of 6 (No. 879a) 5·00

POSTAGE DUE STAMPS

PRINTERS. Nos. D1/23 were typographed by De La Rue & Co.

D 1 Post-office Scales D 2

1923 (Dec)–**56**. *Wmk Mult Script CA. Ordinary paper. P* 14.

D1 D 1 1 c. brown 2·25 65
a. Wmk sideways (1931) 1·25 3·00
ab. Chalk-surfaced paper (21.3.56) 30 1·00
D2 2 c. green 17·00 5·00
a. Wmk sideways (1928) 10·00 5·00
D3 4 c. scarlet 30·00 7·00
a. Wmk sideways (1928) 27·00 7·00
D4 6 c. yellow 26·00 13·00
a. Wmk sideways (1931) 48·00 28·00
D5 10 c. bright ultramarine 23·00 8·00
a. Wmk sideways (1934) 80·00 16·00
D1/5 *Set of* 5 85·00 30·00
D1a/5a *Set of* 5 £150 50·00
D1/5 Optd "Specimen" *Set of* 5 £225

1938 (Feb)–**63**. *Wmk Mult Script CA (sideways). Ordinary paper. P* 14.

D6 D 1 2 c. grey 13·00 9·00
a. Chalk-surfaced paper (21.3.56) 1·10 10·00
D7 4 c. orange 16·00 6·50
a. Chalk-surfaced paper. *Orange-yellow* (23.5.61) 2·50 9·00
D8 6 c. scarlet 9·50 5·50
D9 8 c. chestnut (26.2.46) 5·50 32·00
D10 10 c. violet 27·00 45
a. Chalk-surfaced paper (17.9.63) 15·00 7·50
D11 20 c. black (26.2.46) 10·00 3·00
D12 50 c. blue (7.47) 38·00 15·00
D6a/12 *Set of* 7 75·00 65·00
D6/12 Perf "Specimen" *Set of* 7 £300

1965 (15 Apr)–**72**. *Chalk-surfaced paper. P* 14.

(*a*) *Wmk* w **12** (*sideways*)

D13 D 1 4 c. yellow-orange 6·50 25·00
D14 5 c. red (13.5.69) 3·25 5·00
a. Glazed paper (17.11.72) 11·00 29·00
D15 10 c. violet (27.6.67) 3·50 4·00
D16 20 c. black (1965) 5·00 4·00
D17 50 c. deep blue (1965) 22·00 9·00
a. Blue (13.5.69) 21·00 9·00
D13/17 *Set of* 5 35·00 42·00

(*b*) *Wmk* w **12** (*upright*)

D18 D 1 5 c. red (20.7.67) 2·00 4·50
D19 50 c. deep blue (26.8.70) 38·00 10·00

The 5 c. is smaller, 21 × 18 mm.

1972 (17 Nov)–**74**. *Glazed, ordinary paper. W* w **12** (*sideways*).

(*a*) *P* 14 × 14½

D20 D 1 10 c. bright reddish violet 6·50 4·25
D21 20 c. grey-black 7·50 6·00
D22 50 c. deep dull blue 4·50 9·50

(*b*) *P* 13½ × 14

D23 D 1 5 c. brown-red (1.5.74) 2·25 5·00
D20/3 *Set of* 4 19·00 22·00

(Typo Walsall)

1976 (19 Mar*)–**78**. *Smaller design* (21 × 17 *mm*) *with redrawn value-tablet. Glazed, ordinary paper. W* w **14**. *P* 14.

D25 D 1 10 c. bright reddish violet 70 3·50
a. Chalk-surfaced paper (15.12.78) 70 1·75
D26 20 c. grey-black 1·00 4·00
a. Chalk-surfaced paper (15.12.78) 70 2·00
D27 50 c. deep dull blue 1·00 4·50
a. Chalk-surfaced paper (15.12.78) 70 2·50
D28 $1 yellow (1.4.76) 11·00 11·00
a. Chalk-surfaced paper (15.12.78) 1·10 3·25
D25/8 *Set of* 4 12·00 21·00
D25a/8a *Set of* 4 2·75 8·50

*This is the London release date. It is believed that the stamps were not released locally until 14 April.

(Typo Walsall)

1986 (11 Jan). *As Nos.* D27a/8a, *but without watermark. P* 14.

D29 D 1 50 c. slate-blue 1·75 4·00
D30 $1 lemon 2·25 4·50

(Des A. Chan. Litho B.D.T.)

1987 (25 Mar). *P* 14×15.

D31 D 2 10 c. light green 10 10
D32 20 c. red-brown 10 10
D33 50 c. bright violet 10 10
D34 $1 yellow-orange 15 20
D35 $5 dull ultramarine 80 85
D36 $10 bright rose-red 1·60 1·75
D31/6 *Set of* 6 2·75 3·00

POSTCARD STAMPS

Stamps specially surcharged for use on Postcards.

PRICES. Those in the left-hand column are for unused examples on complete postcards; those on the right for used examples off card. Examples used on postcards are worth more.

3
CENTS
(P 1)

THREE
(P 2)

1879 (1 Apr). *Nos.* 22 *and* 13 *surch as Type* P **1** *by* D.L.R.

P1 3 3 c. on 16 c. yellow (No. 22) £300 £325
P2 5 c. on 18 c. lilac (No. 13) £275 £325

1879 (Nov). *No.* P2 *handstamped with Type* P **2**.

P3 3 3 c. on 5 c. on 18 c. lilac £5000 £6500

POSTAL FISCAL STAMPS

I. Stamps inscribed "STAMP DUTY"

NOTE. The dated circular "HONG KONG" cancellation with "PAID ALL" in lower segment was used for fiscal purposes, in black, from 1877. Previously it appears in red on mail to the U.S.A., but is usually not used as a cancellation.

F 1

F 2

F 3

1874–1902. *Wmk Crown CC.* (*a*) *P* 15½×15

F1 F 1 $2 olive-green £300 45·00
F2 F 2 $3 dull violet £275 32·00
b. Bluish paper
F3 F 3 $10 rose-carmine £7000 £650

(*b*) *P* 14

F4 F 1 $2 dull bluish green (10.97) £350 £225
F5 F 2 $3 dull mauve (3.02) £400 £350
a. Bluish paper £1500
F6 F 3 $10 grey-green (1892) £10000 £10000
F4/5 Optd "Specimen" *Set of* 2 £400

Nos. F1/3 and F7 exist on various papers, ranging from thin to thick.

All three of the values perforated 15½×15 were authorised for postal use in 1874. The $10 was withdrawn from such use in 1880, the $2 in September 1897 and the $3 in 1902.

The $2 and $3 perforated 14 were available for postal purposes until July 1903. The $10 in grey-green was issued for fiscal purposes in 1892 and is known with postal cancellations.

12
CENTS.
(F 4)

F 5

1880. *No.* F3 *surch with Type* F **4** *by Noronha and Sons, Hong Kong.*

F7 F 3 12 c. on $10 rose-carmine £700 £250

1890 (24 Dec). *Wmk Crown CA. P* 14.

F8 F 5 2 c. dull purple 60·00 14·00

No. F8 was authorised for postal use between 24 and 31 December 1890.

5
DOLLARS
(F 6)

ONE
DOLLAR
(F 7)

F 8

1891 (1 Jan). *Surch with Type* F **6** *by* D.L.R. *Wmk Crown CA. P* 14.

F9 F 3 $5 on $10 purple/*red* (Optd S. £160) £275 95·00

No. F9 was in use for postal purposes until June 1903.

1897 (Sept). *Surch with Type* F **7** *by Noronha and Sons, Hong Kong, and with the value in Chinese characters subsequently applied twice by handstamp as T* **15**.

F10 F 1 $1 on $2 olive-green (No. F1) £180 95·00
a. Both Chinese handstamps omitted £2500 £1800
F11 $1 on $2 dull bluish green (No. F4) (H/S S, £140) £200 £120
a. Both Chinese handstamps omitted £1500 £1100
b. Diagonal Chinese handstamp omitted £9000
c. Vertical Chinese handstamp omitted

1938 (11 Jan). *Wmk Mult Script CA. P* 14.

F12 F 8 5 c. green 50·00 9·50

No. F12 was authorised for postal use between 11 and 20 January 1938 due to a shortage of the 5 c., No. 121.

Forged cancellations are known on this stamp inscribed "VICTORIA 9.AM 11 JA 38 HONG KONG" without side bars between the rings.

II. Stamps overprinted "S.O." (Stamp Office), or "S.D." (Stamp Duty)

S. O. 印 厘
(S 1)

S. D. 印 厘
(S 2)

1891 (1 Jan). *Optd with Types* S **1** *or* S **2**.

S1 S 1 2 c. carmine (No. 33) £750 £275
S2 S 2 2 c. carmine (No. 33) £350 £150
a. Opt inverted † £3750
S3 S 1 10 c. purple/*red* (No. 38) £1000 £350

Examples of No. S1 exist with the "O" amended to "D" in manuscript.

Other fiscal stamps are found apparently postally used, but there is no evidence that this use was authorised.

JAPANESE OCCUPATION OF HONG KONG

Hong Kong surrendered to the Japanese on 25 December 1941. The postal service was not resumed until 22 January 1942 when the G.P.O. and Kowloon Central Office re-opened.

Japanese postmarks used in Hong Kong can be identified by the unique combination of horizontal lines in the central circle and three stars in the lower segment of the outer circle. Dates shown on such postmarks are in the sequence Year/Month/Day with the first shown as a Japanese regnal year number so that Showa 17 = 1942 and so on.

Initially six current Japanese definitives, 1, 2, 3, 4, 10 and 30 s. (Nos. 297, 315/17, 322 and 327). were on sale, but the range gradually expanded to cover all values between ½ s. and 10 y. with Nos. 313/14, 318, 325, 328/31, 391, 395/6, 398/9 and 405 of Japan also available from Hong Kong post offices during the occupation. Philatelic covers exist showing other Japanese stamps, but these were not available from the local post offices. Supply of these Japanese stamps was often interrupted and, during the period between 28 July 1942 and 21 April 1943, circular "Postage Paid" handstamps were sometimes used. A substantial increase in postage rates on 16 April 1945 led to the issue of the local surcharges, Nos. J1/3.

PRICES FOR STAMPS ON COVER

Nos. J1/3 *from* × 7

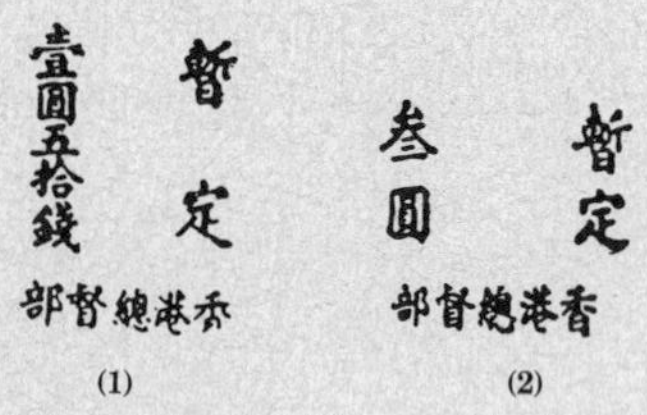

(1) (2)

1945 (16 Apr). *Stamps of Japan surch with T* **1** (*No.* J1) *or as T* **2**.

J1	1.50 yen on 1 s. brown	25·00	21·00
J2	3 yen on 2 s. scarlet	12·00	17·00
J3	5 yen on 5 s. claret	£850	£130

Designs (18½ × 22 *mm*):—1 s. Girl Worker; 2 s. Gen. Nogi; 5 s. Admiral Togo.

No. J3 has four characters of value similarly arranged but differing from T **2**.

BRITISH POST OFFICES IN CHINA

Under the terms of the 1842 Treaty of Nanking China granted Great Britain and its citizens commercial privileges in five Treaty Ports, Amoy, Canton, Foochow, Ningpo and Shanghai. British Consuls were appointed to each Port and their offices, as was usual during this period, collected and distributed mail for the British community. This system was formally recognised by a Hong Kong Government notice published on 16 April 1844. Mail from the consular offices was postmarked when it passed through Hong Kong.

The number of Chinese Treaty Ports was increased to sixteen by the ratification of the Treaty of Peking in 1860 with British postal facilities being eventually extended to the Ports of Chefoo, Hankow, Kiungchow (Hoihow), Swatow, Tainan (Anping) and Tientsin.

As postal business expanded the consular agencies were converted into packet agencies or post offices which passed under the direct control of the Hong Kong postal authorities on 1 May 1868.

In May 1898 the British Government leased the territory of Wei Hai Wei from China for use as a naval station to counter the Russian presence at Port Arthur.

The opening of the Trans-Siberia Railway and the extension of Imperial Penny Postage to the Treaty Port agencies resulted in them becoming a financial burden on the colonial post office. Control of the agencies reverted to the G.P.O., London, on 1 January 1911.

The pre-adhesive postal markings of the various agencies are a fascinating, but complex, subject. Full details can be found in *Hong Kong & the Treaty Ports of China & Japan* by F.W. Webb (reprinted edition J. Bendon, Limassol, 1992) and in various publications of the Hong Kong Study Circle.

From 15 October 1864 the use of Hong Kong stamps on mail from the Treaty Ports became compulsory, although such stamps were, initially, not cancelled (with the exception of Amoy) until they reached Hong Kong where the "B62" killer was applied. Cancellation of mail at the actual Ports commenced during 1866 at Shanghai and Ningpo, spreading to all the agencies during the next ten years. Shanghai had previously used a c.d.s. on adhesives during 1863 and again in 1865–66.

The main types of cancellation used between 1866 and 1930 are illustrated below. The illustrations show the style of each postmark and no attempt has been made to cover differences in type letters or figures, arrangement, diameter or colour.

Until 1885 the vertical and horizontal killers were used to obliterate the actual stamps with an impression of one of the circular date stamps shown elsewhere on the cover. Many of the early postmarks were also used as backstamps or transit marks and, in the notes which follow, references to use are for the first appearance of the mark, not necessarily its first use as an obliterator.

Illustrations in this section are taken from *Hong Kong & the Treaty Ports of China & Japan* by F. W. Webb and are reproduced with the permission of the Royal Philatelic Society, London.

Details of the stamps known used from each post office are taken, with permission, from *British Post Offices in the Far East* by Edward B. Proud, published by Proud-Bailey Co. Ltd.

Postmark Types

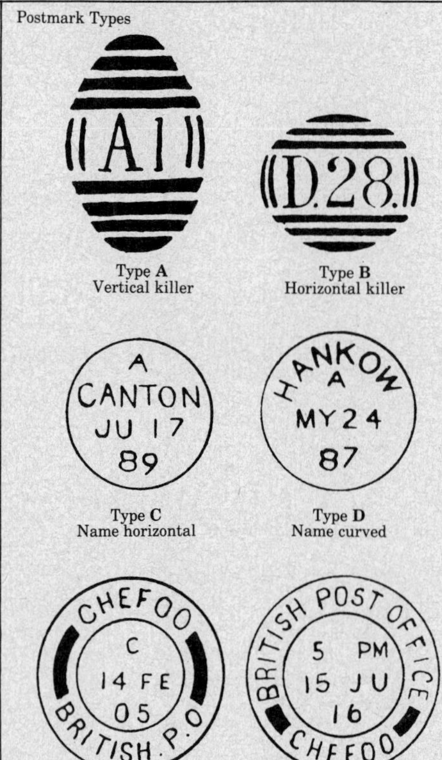

Type **A** Vertical killer

Type **B** Horizontal killer

Type **C** Name horizontal

Type **D** Name curved

Type **E** Double circle Name at top

Type **F** Double circle Name at foot

Type **G** Single circle Name at top

PRICES. The prices quoted in this section are for fine used stamps which show a clear impression of a substantial part of the cancellation.

AMOY

One of the five original Treaty Ports, opened to British trade by the Treaty of Nanking in 1842. A consular postal agency was established in 1844 which expanded in 1876 into two separate offices, one on the off-shore island of Ku Lang Seu and the other in Amoy itself.

Amoy "PAID" (*supplied* 1858) *used* 1859–67
Type **A** ("A1") (*supplied* 1866) *used at Ku Lang Seu* 1869–82
Type **D** (*supplied* 1866) *used* 1867–1922
Type **B** ("D27") (*supplied* 1876) *used at Amoy* 1876–84
Type **C** *used* 1876–94
Type **F** (*supplied* 1913) *used* 1916–22

Stamps of HONG KONG *cancelled at Amoy between* 1864 *and* 1916 *with postmarks detailed above.*

1862. *No wmk* (*Nos.* 1/7).

Z1	2 c. brown	£120
Z2	8 c. yellow-buff	£110
Z3	12 c. pale greenish blue	95·00
Z4	18 c. lilac	60·00
Z5	24 c. green	£120
Z6	48 c. rose	
Z7	96 c. brownish grey	£450

1863–71. *Wmk Crown CC* (*Nos.* 8/19).

Z 8	2 c. brown	28·00
Z 9	4 c. grey	26·00
	a. Perf 12½	
Z10	6 c. lilac	38·00
Z11	8 c. orange	32·00
Z12	12 c. blue	15·00
Z13	18 c. lilac	£450
Z14	24 c. green	38·00
Z15	30 c. vermilion	55·00
Z16	30 c. mauve	10·00
Z17	48 c. rose	35·0
Z18	96 c. olive-bistre	£100
Z19	96 c. brownish grey	£14

1876–77. (*Nos.* 20/1).

Z20	16 c. on 18 c. lilac	£25
Z21	28 c. on 30 c. mauve	£11

1877. *Wmk Crown CC* (*No.* 22).

Z22	16 c. yellow	85·0

1880. (*Nos.* 23/7).

Z23	5 c. on 8 c. orange	£10
Z24	5 c. on 18 c. lilac	90·0
Z25	10 c. on 12 c. blue	90·0
Z26	10 c. on 16 c. yellow	£16
Z27	10 c. on 24 c. green	£10

1880. *Wmk Crown CC* (*Nos.* 28/31).

Z28	2 c. rose	35·00
Z29	5 c. blue	48·00
Z30	10 c. mauve	40·00
Z31	48 c. brown	£110

1882–96. *Wmk Crown CA* (*Nos.* 32/9).

Z31*a*	2 c. rose-lake	
Z32	2 c. carmine	2·75
Z33	4 c. slate-grey	5·50
Z34	5 c. blue	2·75
Z35	10 c. dull mauve	20·00
Z36	10 c. green	3·25
Z37	10 c. purple/*red*	3·25
Z38	30 c. green	21·00

1885. (*Nos.* 40/2).

Z39	20 c. on 30 c. orange-red	8·50
Z40	50 c. on 48 c. yellowish brown	38·00
Z41	$1 on 96 c. grey-olive	65·00

1891. (*Nos.* 43/4, 48/50).

Z42	7 c. on 10 c. green	16·00
Z43	14 c. on 30 c. mauve	70·00
Z44	20 c. on 30 c. green	9·00
Z45	50 c. on 48 c. dull purple	12·00
Z46	$1 on 96 c. purple/*red*	30·00

1891. *50th Anniv of Colony* (*No.* 51).

Z47	2 c. carmine	£75

1898. (*No.* 52).

Z48	$1 on 96 c. black	38·0

1898. (*No.* 55).

Z49	10 c. on 30 c. green	£16

1900–01. *Wmk Crown CA* (*Nos.* 56/61).

Z50	2 c. dull green	2·7
Z51	4 c. carmine	1·9
Z52	5 c. yellow	12·0
Z53	10 c. ultramarine	3·2
Z54	12 c. blue	85·0
Z55	30 c. brown	45·0

1903. *Wmk Crown CA* (*Nos.* 62/76).

Z56	1 c. dull purple and brown	3·2
Z57	2 c. dull green	2·5
Z58	4 c. purple/*red*	1·6
Z59	5 c. dull green and brown-orange	12·0
Z60	8 c. slate and violet	4·5
Z61	10 c. purple and blue/*blue*	2·5
Z62	12 c. green and purple/*yellow*	8·5
Z63	20 c. slate and chestnut	7·0
Z64	30 c. dull green and black	28·0
Z65	50 c. dull green and magenta	45·0
Z67	$2 slate and scarlet	£25
Z68	$3 slate and dull blue	

1904–06. *Wmk Mult Crown CA* (*Nos.* 77/90).

Z71	2 c. dull green	2·5
Z72	4 c. purple/*red*	1·6
Z73	5 c. dull green and brown-orange	9·0
Z74	8 c. slate and violet	7·0
Z75	10 c. purple and blue/*blue*	2·2
Z76	12 c. green and purple/*yellow*	11·0
Z77	20 c. slate and chestnut	6·0
Z78	30 c. dull green and black	18·0
Z79	50 c. green and magenta	16·0
Z83	$5 purple and blue-green	£37

1907–11. *Wmk Mult Crown CA* (*Nos.* 91/9).

Z85	1 c. brown	3·0
Z86	2 c. green	2·5
Z87	4 c. carmine-red	1·6
Z88	6 c. orange-vermilion and purple	9·5
Z89	10 c. bright ultramarine	2·2
Z90	20 c. purple and sage-green	42·0
Z91	30 c. purple and orange-yellow	38·0

1912–15. *Wmk Mult Crown CA* (*Nos.* 100/16).

Z 93	1 c. brown	3·7
Z 94	2 c. green	3·5
Z 95	4 c. red	1·6
Z 96	6 c. orange	2·7
Z 97	8 c. grey	15·0
Z 98	10 c. ultramarine	2·7
Z 99	12 c. purple/*yellow*	13·0
Z100	20 c. purple and sage-green	4·7
Z102	30 c. purple and orange-yellow	10·0
Z103	50 c. black/*green*	7·0
Z104	$1 purple and blue/*blue*	15·0
Z105	$3 green and purple	90·0

POSTCARD STAMPS

1879. (*Nos.* P1/2).
ZP106 3 c. on 16 c. yellow .. £400
ZP107 5 c. on 18 c. lilac .. £450

POSTAL FISCAL STAMPS

1874–1902. *Wmk Crown CC. (a) P* 15½×15 (*Nos.* F1/3)
ZF109 $2 olive-green .. 90·00
ZF110 $3 dull violet .. 80·00

1891. (*No.* F9).
ZF116 $5 on $10 purple/*red* .. £170

1897. (*No.* F10).
ZF118 $1 on $2 olive-green ..

ANPING

Anping is the port for Tainan, on the island of Formosa, opened to British trade in 1860. A British Vice-consulate operated in the port and mail is known postmarked there between 1889 and 1895. Formosa passed under Japanese control in 1895 and British Treaty Port rights then lapsed.

Type **D** *used* 1889–95

Stamps of HONG KONG *cancelled at Anping between* 1889 *and* 1895 *with postmark detailed above.*

1882–91. *Wmk Crown CA* (*Nos.* 32/9).
Z120 2 c. carmine .. £550
Z121 5 c. blue .. £400
Z123 10 c. green .. £550
Z124 10 c. purple/*red* .. £700

1885. (*Nos.* 40/2).
Z126 20 c. on 30 c. orange-red .. £550
Z127 50 c. on 48 c. yellowish brown .. £750

CANTON

A British postal service was organised in Cantom from 1834, but was closed when the foreign communities were evacuated in August 1839. The city was one of the original Treaty Ports and a consular agency was opened there in 1844. The consulate closed during the riots of 1857, being replaced by a temporary postal agency at Whampoa, further down the river. When British forces reached Canton a further temporary agency was set up in 1859, but both closed in July 1863 when the consulate was re-established.

Type **A** ("C1") (*supplied* 1866) *used* 1875–84
Type **C** (*supplied* 1866) *used* 1870–1901
Type **D** *used* 1890–1922

Stamps of HONG KONG *cancelled at Canton between* 1870 *and* 1916 *with postmarks detailed above.*

1862. *No wmk* (*Nos.* 1/7).
Z135 18 c. lilac .. 80·00

1863–71. *Wmk Crown CC* (*Nos.* 8/19).
Z136 2 c. brown .. 27·00
Z137 4 c. grey .. 30·00
Z138 6 c. lilac .. 35·00
Z139 8 c. orange .. 30·00
Z140 12 c. blue .. 15·00
Z142 24 c. green .. 40·00
Z143 30 c. vermilion ..
Z144 30 c. mauve .. 13·00
Z145 48 c. rose .. 50·00
Z147 96 c. brownish grey .. 60·00

1876–77. (*Nos.* 20/1).
Z148 16 c. on 18 c. lilac .. £200
Z149 28 c. on 30 c. mauve .. 85·00

1877. *Wmk Crown CC* (*No.* 22).
Z150 16 c. yellow .. £100

1880. (*Nos.* 23/7).
Z151 5 c. on 8 c. orange .. £110
Z152 5 c. on 18 c. lilac .. 95·00
Z153 10 c. on 12 c. blue .. 90·00
Z154 10 c. on 16 c. yellow .. £170
Z155 10 c. on 24 c. green .. £110

1880. *Wmk Crown CC* (*Nos.* 28/31).
Z156 2 c. rose .. 30·00
Z157 5 c. blue .. 40·00
Z158 10 c. mauve .. 35·00

1882–96. *Wmk Crown CA* (*Nos.* 32/9).
Z159 2 c. rose-lake ..
Z160 2 c. carmine .. 1·50
Z161 4 c. slate-grey .. 6·50
Z162 5 c. blue .. 3·25
Z163 10 c. dull mauve .. 17·00
Z164 10 c. green .. 5·50
Z165 10 c. purple/*red* .. 3·00
Z166 30 c. green .. 22·00

1885. (*Nos.* 40/2).
Z167 20 c. on 30 c. orange-red .. 8·00
Z168 50 c. on 48 c. yellowish brown .. 38·00
Z169 $1 on 96 c. grey-olive .. 65·00

1891. (*Nos.* 43/5, 48/50).
Z170 7 c. on 10 c. green .. 15·00
Z171 14 c. on 30 c. mauve .. 75·00
Z171*a* 20 c. on 30 c. green (No. 45) .. £150
Z172 20 c. on 30 c. green (No. 48) .. 11·00
Z173 50 c. on 48 c. dull purple .. 13·00
Z174 $1 on 96 c. purple/*red* .. 35·00

1891. *50th Anniv of Colony* (*No.* 51).
Z175 2 c. carmine .. £700

1898. (*No.* 52).
Z176 $1 on 96 c. black .. 38·00

1898. (*No.* 55)
Z177 10 c. on 30 c. grey-green ..

1900–01. *Wmk Crown CA* (*Nos.* 56/61).
Z178 2 c. dull green .. 2·75
Z179 4 c. carmine .. 2·50
Z180 5 c. yellow .. 20·00
Z181 10 c. ultramarine .. 2·50
Z182 12 c. blue .. 55·00
Z183 30 c. brown .. 40·00

1903. *Wmk Crown CA* (*Nos.* 62/76).
Z184 1 c. dull purple and brown .. 2·75
Z185 2 c. dull green .. 2·50
Z186 4 c. purple/*red* .. 1·60
Z187 5 c. dull green and brown-orange .. 12·00
Z188 8 c. slate and violet .. 5·50
Z189 10 c. purple and blue/*blue* .. 2·50
Z190 12 c. green and purple/*yellow* .. 9·00
Z191 20 c. slate and chestnut .. 4·50
Z192 30 c. dull green and black .. 25·00

1904–06. *Wmk Mult Crown CA* (*Nos.* 77/90).
Z199 2 c. dull green .. 2·50
Z200 4 c. purple/*red* .. 1·60
Z201 5 c. dull green and brown-orange .. 11·00
Z202 8 c. slate and violet .. 9·00
Z203 10 c. purple and blue/*blue* .. 2·25
Z204 12 c. green and purple/*yellow* .. 13·00
Z205 20 c. slate and chestnut .. 7·50
Z206 30 c. dull green and black .. 16·00
Z207 50 c. green and magenta .. 19·00
Z208 $1 purple and sage-green .. 32·00
Z212 $10 slate and orange/*blue* .. £1000

1907–11. *Wmk Mult Crown CA* (*Nos.* 91/9).
Z213 1 c. brown .. 2·75
Z214 2 c. green .. 2·75
Z215 4 c. carmine-red .. 1·60
Z216 6 c. orange-vermilion and purple .. 10·00
Z217 10 c. bright ultramarine .. 2·25
Z218 20 c. purple and sage-green .. 42·00
Z219 30 c. purple and orange-yellow .. 32·00
Z220 50 c. black/*green* .. 27·00

1912–15. *Wmk Mult Crown CA* (*Nos.* 100/16).
Z222 1 c. brown .. 3·00
Z223 2 c. green .. 2·25
Z224 4 c. red .. 1·40
Z225 6 c. orange .. 2·50
Z226 8 c. grey .. 13·00
Z227 10 c. ultramarine .. 2·50
Z228 12 c. purple/*yellow* .. 10·00
Z229 20 c. purple and sage-green .. 3·75
Z231 30 c. purple and orange-yellow .. 10·00
Z232 50 c. black/*green* .. 3·25
Z235 $3 green and purple .. 90·00

POSTCARD STAMPS

1879. (*Nos.* P1/2).
ZP236 3 c. on 16 c. yellow .. £375
ZP237 5 c. on 18 c. lilac .. £475

POSTAL FISCAL STAMPS

1874–1902. *Wmk Crown CC. (a) P* 15½×15 (*Nos.* F1/3)
ZF238 $2 olive-green .. £110

1891. (*No.* F9).
ZF246 $5 on $10 purple/*red* .. £225

1897. (*No.* F10).
ZF247 $1 on $2 olive-green ..

CHEFOO

Chefoo was opened to British trade in 1860. Although a consulate was established in 1863 no organised postal agency was provided until 1 January 1903 when one was opened at the premises of Curtis Brothers, a commercial firm.

Type **E** (*supplied* 1902) *used* 1903–20
Type **D** (*supplied* 1907) *used* 1907–13
Type **F** *used* 1916–22

Stamps of HONG KONG *cancelled at Chefoo between* 1903 *and* 1916 *with postmarks detailed above.*

1882–96. *Wmk Crown CA* (*Nos.* 32/9).
Z249 5 c. blue .. 19·00

1891. (*Nos.* 43/50)
Z250 20 c. on 30 c. grey-green (No. 48*a*) .. 28·00

1898. (*No.* 52).
Z251 $1 on 96 c. black .. 60·00

1900–01. *Wmk Crown CA* (*Nos.* 56/61).
Z252 2 c. dull green .. 18·00
Z253 4 c. carmine .. 17·00
Z254 5 c. yellow .. 35·00
Z255 10 c. ultramarine .. 18·00
Z257 30 c. brown .. 75·00

1903. *Wmk Crown CA* (*Nos.* 62/76).
Z258 1 c. dull purple and brown .. 7·00
Z259 2 c. dull green .. 6·50
Z260 4 c. purple/*red* .. 6·00
Z261 5 c. dull green and brown-orange .. 14·00
Z262 8 c. slate and violet .. 12·00
Z263 10 c. purple and blue/*blue* .. 7·50
Z264 12 c. green and purple/*yellow* .. 17·00

1904–06. *Wmk Mult Crown CA* (*Nos.* 77/90)
Z273 2 c. dull green .. 5·50
Z274 4 c. purple/*red* .. 5·00
Z275 5 c. dull green and brown-orange .. 11·00
Z276 8 c. slate and violet .. 11·00
Z277 10 c. purple and blue/*blue* .. 5·50
Z278 12 c. green and purple/*yellow* .. 16·00
Z279 20 c. slate and chestnut .. 14·00
Z280 30 c. dull green and black .. 27·00
Z281 50 c. green and magenta .. 32·00
Z283 $2 slate and scarlet .. £150
Z284 $3 slate and dull blue .. £275
Z285 $5 purple and blue-green ..

1907–11. *Wmk Mult Crown CA* (*Nos.* 91/9).
Z287 1 c. brown .. 7·00
Z288 2 c. green .. 6·50
Z289 4 c. carmine-red .. 5·50
Z290 6 c. orange-vermilion and purple .. 17·00
Z291 10 c. bright ultramarine .. 6·00
Z292 20 c. purple and sage-green .. 45·00
Z293 30 c. purple and orange-yellow .. 32·00
Z295 $2 carmine-red and black ..

1912–15. *Wmk Mult Crown CA* (*Nos.* 100/16).
Z296 1 c. brown .. 4·50
Z297 2 c. green .. 5·00
Z298 4 c. red .. 4·00
Z299 6 c. orange .. 8·50
Z301 10 c. ultramarine .. 4·50
Z302 12 c. purple/*yellow* .. 17·00
Z303 20 c. purple and sage-green .. 7·50
Z305 30 c. purple and orange-yellow .. 10·00
Z306 50 c. black/*green* .. 6·00
Z307 $1 purple and blue/*blue* .. 8·00
Z308 $2 carmine-red and grey-black .. 50·00
Z309 $3 green and purple .. 80·00
Z310 $5 green and red/*green* .. £325
Z311 $10 purple and black/*red* .. £190

FOOCHOW

Foochow, originally known as Foochowfoo, was one of the original Treaty Ports opened to British trade in 1842. A British consulate and postal agency was established in June 1844.

Type **A** ("F1") (*supplied* 1866) *used* 1873–84
Type **D** (inscr "FOOCHOWFOO") (*supplied* 1866) *used* 1867–1905
Type **D** (inscr "FOOCHOW") (*supplied* 1894) *used* 1894–1917
Type **E** (inscr "B.P.O.") *used* 1906–10
Type **F** *used* 1915–22

Stamps of HONG KONG *cancelled at Foochow between* 1867 *and* 1916 *with postmarks detailed above.*

1862. *No wmk* (*Nos.* 1/7).
Z312 18 c. lilac .. 90·00

1863–71. *Wmk Crown CC* (*Nos.* 8/19).
Z313 2 c. brown .. 30·00
Z314 4 c. grey .. 30·00
Z315 6 c. lilac .. 40·00
Z316 8 c. orange .. 32·00
Z317 12 c. blue .. 14·00
Z318 18 c. lilac .. £475
Z319 24 c. green .. 50·00
Z320 30 c. vermilion ..
Z321 30 c. mauve .. 11·00
Z322 48 c. rose .. 55·00
Z324 96 c. brownish grey .. 65·00

1876–77. (*Nos.* 20/1).
Z325 16 c. on 18 c. lilac .. £300
Z326 28 c. on 30 c. mauve .. £140

1877. *Wmk Crown CC* (*No.* 22).
Z327 16 c. yellow .. £100

1880. (*Nos.* 23/7).
Z328 5 c. on 8 c. orange .. £325
Z329 5 c. on 18 c. lilac .. £120
Z330 10 c. on 12 c. blue .. £120
Z331 10 c. on 16 c. yellow ..
Z332 10 c. on 24 c. green .. £160

1880. *Wmk Crown CC* (*Nos.* 28/31).
Z333 2 c. rose 28·00
Z334 5 c. blue 48·00
Z335 10 c. mauve 35·00
Z336 48 c. brown £130

1882–96. *Wmk Crown CA* (*Nos.* 32/9).
Z336*a* 2 c. rose-lake
Z337 2 c. carmine 1·50
Z338 4 c. slate-grey 4·50
Z339 5 c. blue 2·50
Z340 10 c. dull mauve 21·00
Z341 10 c. green 9·00
Z342 10 c. purple/*red* 3·00
Z343 30 c. green 27·00

1885. (*Nos.* 40/2).
Z344 20 c. on 30 c. orange-red 9·50
Z345 50 c. on 48 c. yellowish brown 38·00
Z346 $1 on 96 c. grey-olive 65·00

1891. (*Nos.* 43/4, 48/50).
Z348 14 c. on 30 c. mauve 75·00
Z349 20 c. on 30 c. green 15·00
Z350 50 c. on 48 c. dull purple 17·00
Z351 $1 on 96 c. purple/*red* 38·00

1898. (*No.* 52).
Z353 $1 on 96 c. black 48·00

1900–01. *Wmk Crown CA* (*Nos.* 56/61).
Z355 2 c. dull green 2·50
Z356 4 c. carmine 3·00
Z357 5 c. yellow 11·00
Z358 10 c. ultramarine 2·50

1903. *Wmk Crown CA* (*Nos.* 62/76).
Z361 1 c. dull purple and brown 3·25
Z362 2 c. dull green 2·50
Z363 4 c. purple/*red* 1·60
Z364 5 c. dull green and brown-orange 12·00
Z365 8 c. slate and violet 7·00
Z366 10 c. purple and blue/*blue* 2·75
Z367 12 c. green and purple/*yellow* 9·00
Z368 20 c. slate and chestnut 6·00
Z369 30 c. dull green and black 22·00
Z370 50 c. dull green and magenta 32·00

1904–06. *Wmk Mult Crown CA* (*Nos.* 77/90).
Z376 2 c. dull green 2·50
Z377 4 c. purple/*red* 1·60
Z378 5 c. dull green and brown-orange 8·00
Z379 8 c. slate and violet 6·50
Z380 10 c. purple and blue/*blue* 2·75
Z381 12 c. green and purple/*yellow* 12·00
Z382 20 c. slate and chestnut 6·00
Z383 30 c. dull green and black 16·00
Z384 50 c. green and magenta 17·00
Z385 $1 purple and sage-green 30·00

1907–11. *Wmk Mult Crown CA* (*Nos.* 91/9).
Z390 1 c. brown 2·50
Z391 2 c. green 2·50
Z392 4 c. carmine-red 1·60
Z393 6 c. orange-vermilion and purple 10·00
Z394 10 c. bright ultramarine 2·25
Z395 20 c. purple and sage-green 42·00
Z396 30 c. purple and orange-yellow 32·00
Z397 50 c. black/*green* 26·00

1912–15. *Wmk Mult Crown CA* (*Nos.* 100/16).
Z399 1 c. brown 2·75
Z400 2 c. green 2·75
Z401 4 c. red 1·60
Z402 6 c. orange 6·50
Z403 8 c. grey 14·00
Z404 10 c. ultramarine 2·50
Z406 20 c. purple and sage-green 4·00
Z407 25 c. purple and magenta (Type A)
Z408 30 c. purple and orange-yellow 6·00

POSTCARD STAMPS

1879. (*Nos.* P1/2).
ZP413 3 c. on 16 c. yellow £450

POSTAL FISCAL STAMPS

1874–1902. *Wmk Crown CC.* (*a*) *P* 15½×15 (*Nos.* F1/3)
ZF415 $2 olive-green 90·00
ZF416 $3 dull violet 80·00

HANKOW

Hankow, on the Yangtse River 600 miles from the sea, became a Treaty Port in 1860. A British consulate opened the following year, but no organised British postal agency was established until 1872.

Type **D** (*supplied* 1874) *used* 1874–1916
Type **B** ("D29") (*supplied* 1876) *used* 1878–83
Type **F** *used* 1916–22

Stamps of HONG KONG *cancelled at Hankow between* 1874 *and* 1916 *with postmarks detailed above.*

1862. *No wmk* (*Nos.* 1/7).
Z426 18 c. lilac £120

1863–71. *Wmk Crown CC* (*Nos.* 8/19).
Z427 2 c. brown 60·00
Z428 4 c. grey 60·00
Z429 6 c. lilac 75·00
Z430 8 c. orange 60·00
Z431 12 c. blue 22·00
Z432 18 c. lilac £500
Z433 24 c. green 75·00
Z435 30 c. mauve 85·00
Z436 48 c. rose 95·00
Z438 96 c. brownish grey

1876–77. (*Nos.* 20/1).
Z439 16 c. on 18 c. lilac £250
Z440 28 c. on 30 c. mauve £140

1877. *Wmk Crown CC* (*No.* 22).
Z441 16 c. yellow £120

1880. (*Nos.* 23/7).
Z442 5 c. on 8 c. orange £130
Z443 5 c. on 18 c. lilac £110
Z444 10 c. on 12 c. blue £120
Z445 10 c. on 16 c. yellow £200
Z446 10 c. on 24 c. green £140

1880. *Wmk Crown CC* (*Nos.* 28/31).
Z447 2 c. rose 48·00
Z448 5 c. blue 55·00
Z449 10 c. mauve 55·00
Z450 48 c. brown £160

1882–96. *Wmk Crown CA* (*Nos.* 32/9).
Z451 2 c. carmine 4·50
Z452 4 c. slate-grey 9·50
Z453 5 c. blue 5·00
Z454 10 c. dull mauve 38·00
Z455 10 c. green 6·50
Z456 10 c. purple/*red* 5·50
Z457 30 c. green 30·00

1885. (*Nos.* 40/2).
Z458 20 c. on 30 c. orange-red 17·00
Z459 50 c. on 48 c. yellowish brown 42·00
Z460 $1 on 96 c. grey-olive 80·00

1891. (*Nos.* 43/4, 48/50).
Z461 7 c. on 10 c. green 19·00
Z462 14 c. on 30 c. mauve 80·00
Z463 20 c. on 30 c. green 13·00
Z464 50 c. on 48 c. dull purple 13·00
Z465 $1 on 96 c. purple/*red* 38·00

1898. (*No.* 52).
Z467 $1 on 96 c. black 48·00

1898. (*No.* 55).
Z468 10 c. on 30 c. green £160

1900–01. *Wmk Crown CA* (*Nos.* 56/61).
Z469 2 c. dull green 3·25
Z470 4 c. carmine 3·25
Z471 5 c. yellow 14·00
Z472 10 c. ultramarine 4·25
Z473 12 c. blue 75·00
Z474 30 c. brown 42·00

1903. *Wmk Crown CA* (*Nos.* 62/76).
Z475 1 c. dull purple and brown 3·25
Z476 2 c. dull green 3·00
Z477 4 c. purple/*red* 2·50
Z478 5 c. dull green and brown-orange 10·00
Z479 8 c. slate and violet 9·00
Z480 10 c. purple and blue/*blue* 3·00
Z481 12 c. green and purple/*yellow* 10·00
Z482 20 c. slate and chestnut 7·00
Z483 30 c. dull green and black 20·00
Z484 50 c. dull green and magenta 38·00
Z485 $1 purple and sage-green 28·00

1904–06. *Wmk Mult Crown CA* (*Nos.* 77/90).
Z490 2 c. dull green 3·00
Z491 4 c. purple/*red* 2·50
Z492 5 c. dull green and brown-orange 11·00
Z493 8 c. slate and violet 6·50
Z494 10 c. purple and blue/*blue* 3·00
Z495 12 c. green and purple/*yellow* 13·00
Z496 20 c. slate and chestnut 11·00
Z497 30 c. dull green and black 16·00
Z498 50 c. green and magenta 15·00
Z499 $1 purple and sage-green 30·00

1907–11. *Wmk Mult Crown CA* (*Nos.* 91/9).
Z504 1 c. brown 3·00
Z505 2 c. green 3·00
Z506 4 c. carmine-red 1·75
Z507 6 c. orange-vermilion and purple 13·00
Z508 10 c. bright ultramarine 3·00
Z509 20 c. purple and sage-green 50·00
Z510 30 c. purple and orange-yellow 38·00

1912–15. *Wmk Mult Crown CA* (*Nos.* 100/16).
Z513 1 c. brown 3·50
Z514 2 c. green 3·50
Z515 4 c. red 2·50
Z516 6 c. orange 6·50
Z518 10 c. ultramarine 3·00
Z520 20 c. purple and sage-green 8·00
Z522 30 c. purple and orange-yellow 11·00
Z523 50 c. black/*green* 7·00
Z527 $5 green and red/*green* £300

POSTCARD STAMPS

1879. (*Nos.* P1/2).
ZP528 3 c. on 16 c. yellow £650

POSTAL FISCAL STAMPS

1874–1902. *Wmk Crown CC.* (*a*) *P* 15½×15 (*Nos.* F1/3)
ZF529 $2 olive-green £120

(*b*) *P* 14 (*Nos.* F4/6)
ZF532 $2 dull bluish green

KIUNGCHOW (HOIHOW)

Kiungchow, a city on the island of Hainan, and its port of Hoihow was added to the Treaty Port system in 1860. A consular postal agency was opened at Kiungchow in 1876, being transferred to Hoihow in 1878. A second agency was opened at Kiungchow in 1879.

Type **B** ("D28") (*supplied* 1876) *used* 1879–83
Type **D** (inscr "KIUNG-CHOW") (*supplied* 1876) *used* 1879–81

"REGISTERED KIUNG-CHOW" with "REGISTERED" removed (*originally supplied* 1876) *used* 1883–85
Type **D** (inscr "HOIHOW") *used* 1885–1922

Stamps of HONG KONG *cancelled at Kiungchow* (*Hoihow*) *between* 1879 *and* 1916 *with postmarks detailed above.*

1863–71. *Wmk Crown CC* (*Nos.* 8/19).
Z540 2 c. brown £600
Z541 4 c. grey £400
Z542 6 c. lilac £700
Z543 8 c. orange £450
Z544 12 c. blue £425
Z546 24 c. green £600
Z547 30 c. vermilion
Z548 30 c. mauve £550
Z549 48 c. rose £600
Z551 96 c. brownish grey £700

1876–77. (*Nos.* 20/1).
Z552 16 c. on 18 c. lilac £600
Z553 28 c. on 30 c. mauve £475

1877. (*No.* 22)
Z554 16 c. yellow £800

1880. (*Nos.* 23/7).
Z555 5 c. on 8 c. orange £450
Z556 5 c. on 18 c. lilac £450
Z557 10 c. on 12 c. blue £450
Z558 10 c. on 16 c. yellow £850
Z559 10 c. on 24 c. green

1880. *Wmk Crown CC* (*Nos.* 28/31).
Z561 5 c. blue £400
Z562 10 c. mauve £500

1882–96. *Wmk Crown CA* (*Nos.* 32/9).
Z564 2 c. carmine 30·00
Z565 4 c. slate-grey 40·00
Z566 5 c. blue 30·00
Z567 10 c. dull mauve £300
Z568 10 c. green 38·00
Z569 10 c. purple/*red* 30·00
Z570 30 c. green 60·00

1885. (*Nos.* 40/2).
Z571 20 c. on 30 c. orange-red 65·00
Z572 50 c. on 48 c. yellowish brown 70·00
Z573 $1 on 96 c. grey-olive £110

1891. (*Nos.* 43/4, 48/50).
Z574 7 c. on 10 c. green £120
Z576 20 c. on 30 c. green 30·00
Z577 50 c. on 48 c. dull purple 38·00
Z578 $1 on 96 c. purple/*red* 80·00

91. *50th Anniv of Colony (No. 51).*		
579	2 c. carmine	

98. *(No. 52).*		
580	$1 on 96 c. black	£150

00–01. *Wmk Crown CA (Nos. 56/61).*		
583	4 c. carmine	21·00
584	5 c. yellow	48·00
585	10 c. ultramarine	23·00
587	30 c. brown	£100

03. *Wmk Crown CA (Nos. 62/76).*		
588	1 c. dull purple and brown	16·00
589	2 c. dull green	16·00
590	4 c. purple/*red*	11·00
591	5 c. dull green and brown-orange	26·00
592	8 c. slate and violet	24·00
593	10 c. purple and blue/*blue*	13·00
594	12 c. green and purple/*yellow*	30·00
598	$1 purple and sage-green	70·00

04–06. *Wmk Mult Crown CA (Nos. 77/90).*		
603	2 c. dull green	14·00
604	4 c. purple/*red*	11·00
605	5 c. dull green and brown-orange	26·00
606	8 c. slate and violet	18·00
607	10 c. purple and blue/*blue*	12·00
608	12 c. green and purple/*yellow*	30·00
609	20 c. slate and chestnut	35·00
610	30 c. dull green and black	45·00

07–11. *Wmk Mult Crown CA (Nos. 91/9).*		
617	1 c. brown	14·00
618	2 c. green	13·00
619	4 c. carmine-red	11·00
620	6 c. orange-vermilion and purple	29·00
621	10 c. bright ultramarine	12·00
622	20 c. purple and sage-green	55·00

912–15. *Wmk Mult Crown CA (Nos. 100/16).*		
625	1 c. brown	13·00
626	2 c. green	12·00
627	4 c. red	11·00
628	6 c. orange	17·00
629	8 c. grey	
630	10 c. ultramarine	11·00
631	12 c. purple/*yellow*	30·00
632	20 c. purple and sage-green	24·00
633	25 c. purple and magenta (Type A)	50·00
635	50 c. black/*green*	35·00
636	$1 purple and blue/*blue*	40·00

POSTAL FISCAL STAMPS

74–1902. *Wmk Crown CC. (a) P* $15\frac{1}{2}\times15$ *(Nos. F1/3)*		
F641	$2 olive-green	£130
	(b) P 14 (Nos. F4/6)	
F644	$2 dull bluish green	£250

97. *(Nos. F10/11)*		
F650	$1 on $2 olive-green	£225

NINGPO

Ningpo was one of the 1842 Treaty Ports and a consular postal gency was established there in 1844.

Type **A** ("N1") (*supplied* 1866) *used* 1870–82
Type **C** (*supplied* 1866) *used* 1870–99
Type **D** *used* 1899–1922

tamps of HONG KONG *cancelled at Ningpo between* 1866 *and* 1916 *with postmarks detailed above.*

862. *No wmk (Nos. 1/7).*		
652	18 c. lilac	£200

863–71. *Wmk Crown CC (Nos. 8/19).*		
653	2 c. brown	£110
654	4 c. grey	£110
	a. Perf $12\frac{1}{2}$	
655	6 c. lilac	£130
656	8 c. orange	£100
657	12 c. blue	80·00
658	18 c. lilac	
659	24 c. green	£130
660	30 c. vermilion	£140
661	30 c. mauve	70·00
662	48 c. rose	£150
663	96 c. olive-bistre	
664	96 c. brownish grey	£190

876–77. *(Nos. 20/1).*		
665	16 c. on 18 c. lilac	£300
666	28 c. on 30 c. mauve	£150

877. *Wmk Crown CC (No. 22).*		
667	16 c. yellow	£150

880. *(Nos. 23/7).*		
668	5 c. on 8 c. orange	£170
669	5 c. on 18 c. lilac	£160
670	10 c. on 12 c. blue	£170
672	10 c. on 24 c. green	£170

1880. *Wmk Crown CC (Nos. 28/31).*		
Z674	5 c. blue	90·00
Z675	10 c. mauve	90·00
Z676	48 c. brown	£300

1882–96. *Wmk Crown CA (Nos. 32/9).*		
Z677	2 c. carmine	22·00
Z678	4 c. slate-grey	32·00
Z679	5 c. blue	22·00
Z680	10 c. dull mauve	85·00
Z681	10 c. green	24·00
Z682	10 c. purple/*red*	24·00
Z683	30 c. green	48·00

1885. *(Nos. 40/2).*		
Z685	50 c. on 48 c. yellowish brown	55·00

1891. *(Nos. 43/4, 48/50).*		
Z686	7 c. on 10 c. green	27·00
Z687	14 c. on 30 c. mauve	
Z688	20 c. on 30 c. green	19·00
Z689	50 c. on 48 c. dull purple	32·00
Z690	$1 on 96 c. purple/*red*	55·00

1898. *(No. 52).*		
Z692	$1 on 96 c. black	65·00

1898. *(No. 55).*		
Z693	10 c. on 30 c. green	£160

1900–01. *Wmk Crown CA (Nos. 56/61).*		
Z694	2 c. dull green	13·00
Z695	4 c. carmine	12·00
Z697	10 c. ultramarine	13·00

1903. *Wmk Crown CA (Nos. 62/76).*		
Z700	1 c. dull purple and brown	12·00
Z701	2 c. dull green	12·00
Z702	4 c. purple/*red*	9·00
Z703	5 c. dull green and brown-orange	22·00
Z704	8 c. slate and violet	14·00
Z705	10 c. purple and blue/*blue*	10·00
Z706	12 c. green and purple/*yellow*	28·00
Z709	50 c. dull green and magenta	42·00

1904–06. *Wmk Mult Crown CA (Nos. 77/90).*		
Z715	2 c. dull green	12·00
Z716	4 c. purple/*red*	10·00
Z718	8 c. slate and violet	20·00
Z720	12 c. green and purple/*yellow*	30·00
Z721	20 c. slate and chestnut	30·00
Z722	30 c. dull green and black	38·00
Z724	$1 purple and sage-green	45·00

1907–11. *Wmk Mult Crown CA (Nos. 91/9).*		
Z729	1 c. brown	9·50
Z730	2 c. green	9·50
Z731	4 c. carmine-red	8·00
Z733	10 c. bright ultramarine	9·00
Z734	20 c. purple and sage-green	55·00
Z735	30 c. purple and orange-yellow	42·00

1912–15. *Wmk Mult Crown CA (Nos. 100/16).*		
Z738	1 c. brown	10·00
Z739	2 c. green	9·50
Z740	4 c. red	8·50
Z742	8 c. grey	28·00
Z743	10 c. ultramarine	9·50
Z745	20 c. purple and sage-green	
Z749	$1 purple and blue/*blue*	30·00

POSTCARD STAMPS

1879. *(Nos. P1/2).*		
ZP751	3 c. on 16 c. yellow	£550

POSTAL FISCAL STAMPS

1874–1902. *Wmk Crown CC. (a) P* $15\frac{1}{2}\times15$ *(Nos. F1/3)*		
ZF754	$2 olive-green	£140

1881. *(No. F7).*		
ZF760	12 c. on $10 rose-carmine	

1897. *(No. F10).*		
ZF763	$1 on $2 olive-green	

SHANGHAI

Shanghai was one of the original Treaty Ports of 1842 and a packet agency was opened at the British consulate in April 1844. It moved to a separate premises in 1861 and was upgraded to a Post Office in September 1867.

British military post offices operated in Shanghai from 1927 until 1940.

Type **D** (inscr "SHANGHAE" (*supplied* 1861) *used* 1861–99

Sunburst *used* 1864–65
Type **A** ("S1") (*supplied* 1866) *used* 1866–85
Type **D** (inscr "SHANGHAI") (*supplied* 1885) *used* 1886–1906
Type **G** (inscr "B.P.O." at foot) (*supplied* 1904) *used* 1904–21
Type **G** (inscr "Br.P.O." at foot) (*supplied* 1907) *used* 1907–22
Type **E** (figures "I" to "VIII" at foot) *used* 1912–22

Stamps of HONG KONG *cancelled at Shanghai between* 1863 *and* 1916 *with postmarks detailed above.*

1862. *No wmk (Nos. 1/7).*		
Z765	2 c. brown	90·00
Z766	8 c. yellow-buff	75·00
Z767	12 c. pale greenish blue	60·00
Z768	18 c. lilac	48·00
Z769	24 c. green	£100
Z770	48 c. rose	£350
Z771	96 c. brownish grey	£400

1863–71. *Wmk Crown CC (Nos. 8/19).*		
Z772	2 c. brown	7·50
Z773	4 c. grey	6·00
	a. Perf $12\frac{1}{2}$	£275
Z774	6 c. lilac	10·00
Z775	8 c. orange	10·00
Z776	12 c. blue	6·00
Z777	18 c. lilac	£325
Z778	24 c. green	9·00
Z779	30 c. vermilion	15·00
Z780	30 c. mauve	5·50
Z781	48 c. rose	24·00
Z782	96 c. olive-bistre	£650
Z783	96 c. brownish grey	38·00

1876–77. *(Nos. 20/1).*		
Z784	16 c. on 18 c. lilac	£160
Z785	28 c. on 30 c. mauve	50·00

1877. *Wmk Crown CC (No. 22).*		
Z786	16 c. yellow	65·00

1880. *(Nos. 23/7).*		
Z787	5 c. on 8 c. orange	85·00
Z788	5 c. on 18 c. lilac	55·00
Z789	10 c. on 12 c. blue	55·00
Z790	10 c. on 16 c. yellow	£150
Z791	10 c. on 24 c. green	80·00

1880. *Wmk Crown CC (Nos. 28/31).*		
Z792	2 c. rose	19·00
Z793	5 c. blue	32·00
Z794	10 c. mauve	14·00
Z795	48 c. brown	90·00

1882–96. *Wmk Crown CA (Nos. 32/9).*		
Z795*a*	2 c. rose-lake	
Z796	2 c. carmine	90
Z797	4 c. slate-grey	90
Z798	5 c. blue	1·00
Z799	10 c. dull mauve	9·00
Z800	10 c. green	1·40
Z801	10 c. purple/*red*	1·25
Z802	30 c. green	17·00

1885. *(Nos. 40/2).*		
Z803	20 c. on 30 c. orange-red	5·50
Z804	50 c. on 48 c. yellowish brown	27·00
Z805	$1 on 96 c. grey-olive	50·00

1891. *(Nos. 43/44, 46, 48/50).*		
Z806	7 c. on 10 c. green	10·00
Z807	14 c. on 30 c. mauve	55·00
Z807*a*	50 c. on 48 c. dull purple (No. 46)	£275
Z808	20 c. on 30 c. green	5·00
Z809	50 c. on 48 c. dull purple (No. 49)	6·00
Z810	$1 on 96 c. purple/*red*	23·00

1898. *(No. 52).*		
Z812	$1 on 96 c. black	27·00

1898. *(No. 55).*		
Z813	10 c. on 30 c. green	75·00

1900–01. *Wmk Crown CA (Nos. 56/61).*		
Z814	2 c. dull green	90
Z815	4 c. carmine	90
Z816	5 c. yellow	7·00
Z817	10 c. ultramarine	2·00
Z818	12 c. blue	48·00
Z819	30 c. brown	22·00

1903. *Wmk Crown CA* (*Nos.* 62/76).

Z820	1 c. dull purple and brown	60
Z821	2 c. dull green	1·60
Z822	4 c. purple/*red*	45
Z823	5 c. dull green and brown-orange	9·50
Z824	8 c. slate and violet	1·50
Z825	10 c. purple and blue/*blue*	1·50
Z826	12 c. green and purple/*yellow*	4·75
Z827	20 c. slate and chestnut	2·75
Z828	30 c. dull green and black	17·00
Z829	50 c. dull green and magenta	27·00
Z830	$1 purple and sage-green	20·00
Z832	$3 slate and dull blue	£325
Z833	$5 purple and blue-green	£425
Z834	$10 slate and orange/*blue*	£450

1904–06. *Wmk Mult Crown CA* (*Nos.* 77/90).

Z835	2 c. dull green	1·50
Z836	4 c. purple/*red*	50
Z837	5 c. dull green and brown-orange	6·00
Z838	8 c. slate and violet	2·25
Z839	10 c. purple and blue/*blue*	90
Z840	12 c. green and purple/*yellow*	6·50
Z841	20 c. slate and chestnut	2·50
Z842	30 c. dull green and black	13·00
Z843	50 c. green and magenta	7·00
Z844	$1 purple and sage-green	18·00
Z845	$2 slate and scarlet	85·00
Z846	$3 slate and dull blue	£200
Z847	$5 purple and blue-green	£300
Z848	$10 slate and orange/*blue*	£700

1907–11. *Wmk Mult Crown CA* (*Nos.* 91/9).

Z849	1 c. brown	1·00
Z850	2 c. green	1·75
Z851	4 c. carmine-red	50
Z852	6 c. orange-vermilion and purple	3·25
Z853	10 c. bright ultramarine	50
Z854	20 c. purple and sage-green	38·00
Z855	30 c. purple and orange-yellow	19·00
Z856	50 c. black/*green*	14·00
Z857	$2 carmine-red and black	£250

1912–15. *Wmk Mult Crown CA* (*Nos.* 100/16).

Z858	1 c. brown	65
Z859	2 c. green	40
Z860	4 c. red	40
Z861	6 c. orange	1·00
Z862	8 c. grey	7·00
Z863	10 c. ultramarine	40
Z864	12 c. purple/*yellow*	6·00
Z865	20 c. purple and sage-green	1·00
Z867	30 c. purple and orange-yellow	5·00
Z868	50 c. black/*green*	2·00
Z869	$1 purple and blue/*blue*	2·75

POSTCARD STAMPS

1879. (*Nos.* P1/2).

ZP871	3 c. on 16 c. yellow	£325
ZP872	5 c. on 18 c. lilac	£325

POSTAL FISCAL STAMPS

1874–1902. *Wmk Crown CC.* (*a*) *P* 15½×15 (*Nos.* F1/5)

ZF874	$2 olive-green	50·00
ZF875	$3 dull violet	35·00
ZF876	$10 rose-carmine	£600
	(*b*) *P* 14	
ZF877	$2 dull bluish green	£200
ZF878	$3 dull mauve	£350

1881. (*No.* F7).

ZF880	12 c. on $10 rose-carmine	£250

1891. (*No.* F9).

ZF882	$5 on $10 purple/*red*	£100

1897. (*No.* F10/11).

ZF883	$1 on $2 olive-green	£150
ZF884	$1 on $2 dull bluish green	£200

SWATOW

Swatow became a Treaty Port in 1860 and a consular packet agency was opened in the area made available for foreign firms during the following year. In 1867 the original agency was transferred to the Chinese city on the other side of the Han river, but a second agency was subsequently opened in the foreign concession during 1883.

Type **A** ("S2") (*supplied* 1866) *used* 1875–85
Type **C** (*supplied* 1866) *used* 1866–90
Type **D** (*supplied* 1883) *used* 1884–1922
Type **F** *used* 1916–22

Stamps of HONG KONG *cancelled at Swatow between* 1866 *and* 1916 *with postmarks detailed above.*

1862. *No wmk* (*Nos.* 1/7).

Z885	18 c. lilac	£140

1863–71. *Wmk Crown CC* (*Nos.* 8/19).

Z886	2 c. brown	70·00
Z887	4 c. grey	70·00
	a. Perf 12½	
Z888	6 c. lilac	£300
Z889	8 c. orange	75·00
Z890	12 c. blue	32·00
Z891	18 c. lilac	£500
Z892	24 c. green	75·00
Z893	30 c. vermilion	
Z894	30 c. mauve	32·00
Z895	48 c. rose	85·00
Z897	96 c. brownish grey	£450

1876–77. (*Nos.* 20/1).

Z898	16 c. on 18 c. lilac	£300
Z899	28 c. on 30 c. mauve	£130

1877. *Wmk Crown CC* (*No.* 22).

Z900	16 c. yellow	£275

1880. (*Nos.* 23/7).

Z901	5 c. on 8 c. orange	£130
Z902	5 c. on 18 c. lilac	£120
Z903	10 c. on 12 c. blue	£130
Z904	10 c. on 16 c. yellow	£225
Z905	10 c. on 24 c. green	£170

1880. *Wmk Crown CC* (*Nos.* 28/31).

Z906	2 c. rose	60·00
Z907	5 c. blue	60·00
Z908	10 c. mauve	75·00

1882–96. *Wmk Crown CA* (*Nos.* 32/9).

Z910	2 c. carmine	3·75
Z911	4 c. slate-grey	11·00
Z912	5 c. blue	4·25
Z913	10 c. dull mauve	48·00
Z914	10 c. green	5·50
Z915	10 c. purple/*red*	3·75
Z916	30 c. green	28·00

1885. (*Nos.* 40/2).

Z917	20 c. on 30 c. orange-red	8·00

1891. (*No.* 43/4, 48/50).

Z920	7 c. on 10 c. green	15·00
Z921	14 c. on 30 c. mauve	70·00
Z922	20 c. on 30 c. green	13·00
Z923	50 c. on 48 c. dull purple	14·00
Z924	$1 on 96 c. purple/*red*	30·00

1891. *50th Anniv of Colony* (*No.* 51).

Z925	2 c. carmine	£750

1898. (*No.* 52).

Z926	$1 on 96 c. black	42·00

1898. (*No.* 55).

Z927	10 c. on 30 c. green	£130

1900–01. *Wmk Crown CA* (*Nos.* 56/61).

Z928	2 c. dull green	4·25
Z929	4 c. carmine	3·50
Z930	5 c. yellow	13·00
Z931	10 c. ultramarine	4·00
Z933	30 c. brown	32·00

1903. *Wmk Crown CA* (*Nos.* 62/76).

Z934	1 c. dull purple and brown	3·75
Z935	2 c. dull green	3·75
Z936	4 c. purple/*red*	2·75
Z937	5 c. dull green and brown-orange	10·00
Z938	8 c. slate and violet	6·50
Z939	10 c. purple and blue/*blue*	3·75
Z940	12 c. green and purple/*yellow*	8·50
Z941	20 c. slate and chestnut	5·00
Z942	30 c. dull green and black	22·00

1904–06. *Wmk Mult Crown CA* (*Nos.* 77/90).

Z949	2 c. dull green	3·75
Z950	4 c. purple/*red*	2·75
Z951	5 c. dull green and brown-orange	10·00
Z952	8 c. slate and violet	6·50
Z953	10 c. purple and blue/*blue*	3·50
Z954	12 c. green and purple/*yellow*	9·00
Z955	20 c. slate and chestnut	6·50
Z956	30 c. dull green and black	18·00
Z957	50 c. green and magenta	14·00
Z958	$1 purple and sage-green	32·00
Z959	$2 slate and scarlet	£120
Z962	$10 slate and orange/*blue*	£800

1907–11. *Wmk Mult Crown CA* (*Nos.* 91/9).

Z963	1 c. brown	4·25
Z964	2 c. green	4·25
Z965	4 c. carmine-red	3·00
Z966	6 c. orange-vermilion and purple	8·00
Z967	10 c. bright ultramarine	3·50
Z969	30 c. purple and orange-yellow	30·00
Z970	50 c. black/*green*	21·00

1912–15. *Wmk Mult Crown CA* (*Nos.* 100/16).

Z972	1 c. brown	3·00
Z973	2 c. green	3·00
Z974	4 c. red	2·50
Z975	6 c. orange	4·25
Z976	8 c. grey	13·00
Z977	10 c. ultramarine	2·25
Z978	12 c. purple/*yellow*	8·00
Z979	20 c. purple and sage-green	3·75
Z980	25 c. purple and magenta (Type A)	27·00
Z981	30 c. purple and orange-yellow	11·00
Z982	50 c. black/*green*	5·50
Z983	$1 purple and blue/*blue*	10·00

POSTCARD STAMPS

1879. (*Nos.* P1/2).

ZP986	3 c. on 16 c. yellow	£6

POSTAL FISCAL STAMPS

1874–1902. *Wmk Crown CC.* (*a*) *P* 15½×15 (*Nos.* F1/3)

ZF988	$2 olive-green	75·
ZF989	$3 dull violet	65·
	(*b*) *P* 14	
ZF991	$2 dull bluish green	£2

TIENTSIN

Tientsin became a Treaty Port in 1860. A British consula was established in 1861, but no formal postal agency wa organised there until 1882. It was not, however, very successf and was closed during 1890. The British Post Office reopened o 1 October 1906 under the management of the Chines Engineering and Mining Company.

British military post offices operated in Tientsin from 192 until 1940.

Type **E** *used* 1906–13
Type **G** (supplied 1907) *used* 1907–22

Stamps of HONG KONG *cancelled at Tientsin between* 19 *and* 1916 *with postmarks detailed above.*

1903. *Wmk Crown CA* (*Nos.* 62/76).

Z 998	1 c. dull purple and brown	6·
Z 999	5 c. dull green and brown-orange	16·
Z1000	8 c. slate and violet	5·

1904–06. *Wmk Mult Crown CA* (*Nos.* 77/90).

Z1001	2 c. dull green	3·
Z1002	4 c. purple/*red*	2·
Z1003	5 c. dull green and brown-orange	8·
Z1004	8 c. slate and violet	6·
Z1005	10 c. purple and blue/*blue*	2·
Z1006	12 c. green and purple/*yellow*	9·
Z1007	20 c. slate and chestnut	6·
Z1008	30 c. dull green and black	17·
Z1009	50 c. green and magenta	13·
Z1010	$1 purple and sage-green	26·
Z1011	$2 slate and scarlet	£1
Z1013	$5 purple and blue-green	£3
Z1014	$10 slate and orange/*blue*	£8

1907–11. *Wmk Mult Crown CA* (*Nos.* 91/9).

Z1015	1 c. brown	3·
Z1016	2 c. green	2·
Z1017	4 c. carmine-red	1·
Z1018	6 c. orange-vermilion and purple	9·
Z1019	10 c. bright ultramarine	2·
Z1020	20 c. purple and sage-green	42·
Z1021	30 c. purple and orange-yellow	32·
Z1022	50 c. black/*green*	24·

1912–15. *Wmk Mult Crown CA* (*Nos.* 100/16).

Z1024	1 c. brown	2·
Z1025	2 c. green	2·
Z1026	4 c. red	1·
Z1027	6 c. orange	3·
Z1028	8 c. grey	16·
Z1029	10 c. ultramarine	3·
Z1031	20 c. purple and sage-green	5·
Z1033	30 c. purple and orange-yellow	7·
Z1034	50 c. black/*green*	4·
Z1035	$1 purple and blue/*blue*	6·
Z1037	$3 green and purple	85·

WEI HAI WEI

The territory of Wei Hai Wei was leased from the Chinese the British Government from 24 May 1898. At that time the were no organised postal services from the area, although private local post did operate between the port and Chefoo fr 8 December 1898 until 15 March 1899. A Chinese Imperial p office opened in March 1899 to be followed by a British pos agency on the offshore island of Liu Kung Tau on 1 Septemb 1899. A second British agency opened at Port Edward on 1 Ap 1904.

LIU KUNG TAU
15 MAR 1900
POST OFFICE.

Liu Kung Tau oval *used* 1899–1901
Type **D** (inscr "LIU KUNG TAU") (*supplied* 1899) *us* 1901–30

Stamps of HONG KONG *cancelled at Liu Kung Tau betw* 1899 *and* 1916 *with postmarks detailed above.*

1882–96. *Wmk Crown CA* (*Nos.* 32/9).

Z1040	2 c. carmine	27
Z1041	4 c. slate-grey	38
Z1042	5 c. blue	27
Z1043	10 c. purple/*red*	16
Z1044	30 c. green	32

1891. (*Nos.* 48/50).

Z1045	20 c. on 30 c. green	22
Z1046	50 c. on 48 c. dull purple	22

98. (*No.* 52).
047 $1 on 96 c. black .. 45·00

00–01. *Wmk Crown CA* (*Nos.* 56/61).
049 2 c. dull green .. 3·75
050 4 c. carmine .. 3·75
051 5 c. yellow .. 13·00
052 10 c. ultramarine .. 3·75
053 12 c. blue .. 65·00
054 30 c. brown .. 38·00

03. *Wmk Crown CA* (*Nos.* 62/76).
055 1 c. dull purple and brown .. 3·75
056 2 c. dull green .. 3·00
057 4 c. purple/*red* .. 3·00
058 5 c. dull green and brown-orange .. 10·00
059 8 c. slate and violet .. 6·50
060 10 c. purple and blue/*blue* .. 4·75
061 12 c. green and purple/*yellow* .. 14·00
062 20 c. slate and chestnut .. 6·50
063 30 c. dull green and black .. 20·00
064 50 c. dull green and magenta .. 38·00
065 $1 purple and sage-green .. 32·00

04–06. *Wmk Mult Crown CA* (*Nos.* 77/90).
070 2 c. dull green .. 3·50
071 4 c. purple/*red* .. 3·00
073 8 c. slate and violet .. 5·50
076 20 c. slate and chestnut ..
078 50 c. green and magenta .. 27·00

07–11. *Wmk Mult Crown CA* (*Nos.* 91/9).
084 1 c. brown .. 3·50
085 2 c. green .. 3·50
086 4 c. carmine-red .. 2·75
088 10 c. bright ultramarine .. 3·00
089 20 c. purple and sage-green .. 45·00
090 30 c. purple and orange-yellow .. 35·00
091 50 c. black/*green* .. 29·00

12–15. *Wmk Mult Crown CA* (*Nos.* 100/16).
093 1 c. brown .. 3·75
094 2 c. green .. 2·75
095 4 c. red .. 2·50
096 6 c. orange .. 5·50
097 8 c. grey .. 16·00
098 10 c. ultramarine .. 3·00
104 $1 purple and blue/*blue* .. 14·00

POSTAL FISCAL STAMPS

74–1902. *Wmk Crown CC.* (*b*) *P* 14 (*Nos.* F4/6)
106 $2 dull bluish green .. £550

PORT EDWARD
13 JUL 1904
WEI-HAI-WEI

Port Edward rectangle used 1904–08
Type **D** (inscr "WEI-HAI-WEI" at top and "PORT EDWARD" at foot) (*supplied* 1907) used 1907–30

amps of HONG KONG *cancelled at Port Edward between* 1904 *and* 1916 *with postmarks detailed above.*

00–01. *Wmk Crown CA* (*Nos.* 56/61).
109 2 c. dull green .. 38·00
110 10 c. ultramarine .. 40·00

03. *Wmk Crown CA* (*Nos.* 62/76).
111 1 c. dull purple and brown .. 13·00
112 2 c. dull green .. 13·00
113 4 c. purple/*red* .. 11·00
114 5 c. dull green and brown-orange .. 16·00
115 8 c. slate and violet .. 17·00
116 10 c. purple and blue/*blue* .. 14·00
117 12 c. green and purple/*yellow* .. 22·00
118 20 c. slate and chestnut .. 35·00
119 30 c. dull green and black .. 28·00
120 50 c. dull green and magenta .. 32·00
121 $1 purple and sage-green .. 35·00

04–06. *Wmk Mult Crown CA* (*Nos.* 77/90).
126 2 c. dull green .. 7·50
127 4 c. purple/*red* .. 7·00
128 5 c. dull green and brown-orange .. 11·00
129 8 c. slate and violet .. 8·00
132 20 c. slate and chestnut .. 38·00
133 30 c. dull green and black .. 25·00
134 50 c. green and magenta .. 32·00

07–11. *Wmk Mult Crown CA* (*Nos.* 91/9).
140 1 c. brown .. 7·50
141 2 c. green .. 7·50
142 4 c. carmine-red .. 5·00
143 6 c. orange-vermilion and purple ..
144 10 c. bright ultramarine .. 6·00

12–15. *Wmk Mult Crown CA* (*Nos.* 100/16).
151 1 c. brown .. 6·50
152 2 c. green .. 5·00
153 4 c. red .. 3·25
155 8 c. grey .. 14·00
156 10 c. ultramarine .. 3·25
158 20 c. purple and sage-green .. 9·00
161 50 c. black/*green* .. 8·50
162 $1 purple and blue/*blue* .. 9·00

PRICES FOR STAMPS ON COVER

Nos. 1/14	*from* × 50
Nos. 15/17	—
Nos. 18/28	*from* × 30

The overprinted stamps Nos. 1/17 were introduced on 1 January 1917 to prevent currency speculation in the Treaty Ports. They were used in the then-existing agencies of Amoy, Canton, Chefoo, Foochow, Hankow, Hoihow, Ningpo,. Shanghai, Swatow, Tientsin and were also supplied to the British naval base of Wei Hai Wei.

CHINA

(1)

1917 (1 Jan)–**21.** *Stamps of Hong Kong,* 1912–21 (*wmk Mult Crown CA*), *optd with T* 1, *at Somerset House.*

No.	Description	Unused	Used
1	1 c. brown	2·50	1·50
	a. Black-brown	2·00	2·50
	b. Crown broken at right	£250	£300
	c. Wmk sideways	†	£2500
2	2 c. green	2·50	30
3	4 c. carmine-red	3·25	30
4	6 c. orange	3·00	60
5	8 c. slate	8·00	1·25
6	10 c. ultramarine	8·00	30
	y. Wmk inverted and reversed	†	£275
7	12 c. purple/*yellow*	4·50	2·50
8	20 c. purple and sage-green	10·00	60
9	25 c. purple and magenta (A)	7·50	15·00
11	30 c. purple and orange-yellow	22·00	5·00
12	50 c. black/*blue-green* (*olive back*)	40·00	1·50
	a. Emerald surface (1917?)	27·00	8·50
	b. On emerald back (1919)	20·00	5·50
	c. On white back (1920)	£180	45·00
13	$1 reddish purple and bright blue/*blue*	55·00	2·25
	a. Grey-purple and blue/blue (1921)	55·00	6·50
14	$2 carmine-red and grey-black	£170	45·00
15	$3 green and purple	£300	£150
16	$5 green and red/*blue-green* (*olive back*)	£300	£190
17	$10 purple and black/*red*	£750	£375
1/17	*Set of* 16	£1500	£700
12/17	H/S "Specimen" *Set of* 6	£1500	

1922 (Mar)–**27.** *As last, but wmk Mult Script CA.*

No.	Description	Unused	Used
18	1 c. brown	1·75	3·50
19	2 c. green	2·50	2·25
	w. Wmk inverted	90·00	
20	4 c. carmine-rose	3·50	2·00
	a. Lower Chinese character at right broken at top	£130	£110
21	6 c. orange-yellow	3·25	4·25
22	8 c. grey	4·00	13·00
23	10 c. bright ultramarine	5·50	2·25
	w. Wmk inverted	90·00	
24	20 c. purple and sage-green	8·50	5·00
25	25 c. purple and magenta (B)	14·00	60·00
	a. Broken flower	£300	
26	50 c. black/*emerald* (1927) (H/S S. £225)	48·00	£150
27	$1 purple and blue/*blue*	60·00	38·00
28	$2 carmine-red and grey-black	£190	£250
18/28	*Set of* 11	£300	£475

STAMP BOOKLETS

1917. *Black on red cover inscribed* "BRITISH POST OFFICE AGENCIES IN CHINA". *Stapled.*
SB1 $1 booklet containing eight 2 c., six 4 c. and six 10 c. (Nos. 2/3, 6) ..

1922. *Cover as No.* SB1. *Stapled.*
SB2 $1 booklet containing eight 2 c., six 4 c., and six 10 c. (Nos. 19/20, 23) .. £3750

The British P.O.'s in the Treaty Ports closed by agreement with the Chinese on 30 November 1922, but the above overprinted issues continued in use at the Wei Hai Wei offices until they in turn closed on 30 September 1930. Under the terms of the Convention signed with China the Royal Navy continued to use the base at Wei Hai Wei until the mid-1930s.

BRITISH POST OFFICES IN JAPAN

Under the terms of the Anglo-Japanese Treaty of Yedo, signed on 26 August 1858, five Japanese ports were opened to British trade. British consulates were established at Decima (Nagasaki), Kanagawa (Yokohama), Hiogo (Kobe) and Hakodadi (Hakodate). The postage stamps of Hong Kong became available at the Yokohama and Nagasaki consulates during October 1864 and at Hiogo in 1869, although cancellation of mail did not commence until 1866 at Yokohama and Nagasaki or 1876 at Hiogo. Japan became a member of the U.P.U. on 1 June 1877 and all of the British Postal Agencies were closed by the end of 1879.

For illustrations of postmark types see BRITISH POST OFFICES IN CHINA.

HAKODATE

A British consular office existed at Hakodate, but it was never issued with a c.d.s., obliterator or Hong Kong stamps. No British covers are recorded from this consulate prior to opening of the Japanese Post Office.

HIOGO

The Port of Hiogo (Kobe) was first opened to foreigners on 1 January 1868. The British Consular mail service at Hiogo commenced during 1869 to serve the foreigners at Hiogo, Kobe and Osaka. The cities of Hiogo and Kobe later merged to become the single city of Kobe. The consular office at Hiogo closed on 30 November 1879.

Type **B** ("D30") (*supplied* 1876) *used* 1876–79
Type **D** (*supplied* 1876) *used* 1876–79

Stamps of HONG KONG *cancelled at Hiogo between* 1876 *and* 1879 *with postmarks detailed above.*

1863–71. *Wmk Crown CC* (*Nos.* 8/19).
Z 1 2 c. brown .. £3250
Z 2 4 c. grey .. £2250
Z 3 6 c. lilac .. £2750
Z 4 8 c. orange .. £2500
Z 5 12 c. blue .. £3250
Z 6 18 c. lilac ..
Z 7 24 c. green .. £2250
Z 8 30 c. vermilion ..
Z 9 30 c. mauve .. £3250
Z10 48 c. rose .. £3750
Z12 96 c. brownish grey .. £3750

1877. (*Nos.* 20/1).
Z13 16 c. on 18 c. lilac ..

1877. *Wmk Crown CC* (*No.* 22).
Z15 16 c. yellow .. £3000

NAGASAKI

The British Consulate opened in Nagasaki on 14 June 1859, but, with few British residents at the port, the consular staff found it inconvenient to carry out postal duties so that few Nagasaki c.d.s. or "N2" cancellations exist. The postal service was terminated on 30 September 1879.

Type **A** ("N2") (*supplied* 1866) *used* 1876–79
Type **D** (*supplied* 1866) *used* 1876–79

Stamps of HONG KONG *cancelled at Nagasaki between* 1876 *and* 1879 *with postmarks detailed above.*

1863–71. *Wmk Crown CC* (*Nos.* 8/19).
Z16 2 c. brown .. £850
Z17 4 c. grey .. £650
Z18 6 c. lilac .. £750
Z19 8 c. orange .. £650
Z20 12 c. blue .. £750
Z21 18 c. lilac .. £1300
Z22 24 c. green .. £1000
Z24 30 c. mauve .. £950
Z25 48 c. rose .. £1400
Z27 96 c. brownish grey ..

1876–77. (*Nos.* 20/1).
Z28 16 c. on 18 c. lilac .. £1000
Z29 28 c. on 30 c. mauve .. £750

1877. *Wmk Crown CC* (*No.* 22).
Z30 16 c. yellow .. £800

YOKOHAMA

The British Consulate opened in Kanagawa on 21 July 1859, but was relocated to Yokohama where it provided postal services from 1 July 1860 until a separate Post Office was established in July 1867. The British Post Office in Yokohama closed on 31 December 1879.

Type **A** ("Y1") (*supplied* 1866) *used* 1867–79
Type **D** (*supplied* 1866) *used* 1866–79

Stamps of HONG KONG *cancelled at Yokohama between* 1866 *and* 1879 *with postmarks detailed above.*

1862. *No wmk* (*Nos.* 1/8).
Z30*a* 8 c. yellow-buff .. £130
Z31 18 c. lilac .. 65·00

1863–71. *Wmk Crown CC* (*Nos.* 8/19).
Z32 2 c. brown .. 15·00
Z33 4 c. grey .. 15·00
a. Perf $12^1/_2$ .. £450
Z34 6 c. lilac .. 20·00
Z35 8 c. orange .. 21·00
Z36 12 c. blue .. 15·00
Z37 18 c. lilac .. £425
Z38 24 c. green .. 17·00
Z39 30 c. vermilion .. 27·00
Z40 30 c. mauve .. 15·00
Z41 48 c. rose .. 32·00
Z43 96 c. brownish grey .. 42·00

1876–77. (*Nos.* 20/1).
Z44 16 c. on 18 c. lilac .. £200
Z45 28 c. on 30 c. mauve .. 65·00

1877. *Wmk Crown CC* (*No.* 22).
Z46 16 c. yellow .. 85·00

POSTAL FISCAL STAMPS

1874. *Wmk Crown CC. P* $15^1/_2$×15 (*Nos.* F1/3).
ZF47 $2 olive-green .. 65·00
ZF48 $3 dull violet .. 60·00
ZF49 $10 rose-carmine .. £1100

India

PRICES FOR STAMPS ON COVER TO 1945	
Nos. S1/3	*from* × 2
No. 1	†
Nos. 2/26	*from* × 3
Nos. 27/30	—
Nos. 31/4	*from* × 8
Nos. 35/49	*from* × 3
Nos. 50	†
Nos. 51/3	*from* × 4
Nos. 54/65	*from* × 2
Nos. 66/8	*from* × 5
Nos. 69/74	*from* × 3
Nos. 73/277	*from* × 2
Nos. O1/14	*from* × 6
Nos. O15/18	—
No. O19	*from* × 5
Nos. O20/30*a*	*from* × 10
No. O30*b*	†
Nos. O31/133	*from* × 6
Nos. O135/150	*from* × 2

(Currency. 12 pies = 1 anna; 16 annas = 1 rupee)

ISSUE FOR SIND PROVINCE

1

1852 (1 July). "Scinde Dawk." *Embossed.*
S1 **1** ½ a. white £4500 £800
S2 ½ a. blue £12000 £3500
S3 ½ a. scarlet £65000 £8000

These stamps were issued under the authority of Sir Bartle Frere, Commissioner in Sind. They were suppressed in October 1854.

No. S3 is on sealing wax (usually cracked). Perfect copies are very rare.

EAST INDIA COMPANY ADMINISTRATION

2 (*Much reduced*)

3

The ½ a., 1 a. and 4 a. were lithographed in Calcutta at the office of the Surveyor-General. The die was engraved by Mr Maniruddin (spelling uncertain). *Ungummed* paper watermarked as T **2** (the "No. 4" paper) with the Arms of the East India Co in the sheet. The watermark is sideways on the ½ a. and 1 a., and upright on the 4 a. where the paper was trimmed so that only the central portion showing the oval and the arms was used. Imperforate.

1854 (April).
1 **3** ½ a. vermilion £800
a. Deep vermilion £1200

This stamp, with 9½ arches in the side border, was prepared for use and a supply was sent to Bombay, but was not officially issued.

The vermilion shade is normally found on toned paper and the deep vermilion on white.

ILLUSTRATIONS. Types 4/8 are shown twice actual size.

4

1854 (1 Oct). *Die I.*
2 **4** ½ a. blue .. .. 55·00 14·00
a. Printed on both sides .. .. .. † £8000
b. Printed double .. .. .. † £6000
3 ½ a. pale blue .. .. 85·00 19·00
4 ½ a. deep blue .. .. 70·00 19·00
5 ½ a. indigo .. .. £250 65·00

We give the official date of validity. Stamps were on sale to the public from mid September. Actual usage at Toungoo, Burma, is known from mid August.

These stamps were printed between 5 May and 29 July 1854 (Printing 30 millions).

4*a*

Die II
6 **4*a*** ½ a. blue .. .. 50·00 75·00
7 ½ a. indigo .. .. 60·00 85·00

The bulk were printed between 1 and 12 August 1854, with some extra sheets on or before 2 November (Printing about 2 millions).

5

Die III
8 **5** ½ a. pale blue .. .. £750 38·00
8*a* ½ a. blue .. .. £700 35·00
9 ½ a. greenish blue £1500 £160
10 ½ a. deep blue .. .. £950 70·00

These stamps were printed between 3 July and 25 August 1855 (Printing about 4¾ millions).

THE THREE DIES OF THE ½ ANNA

DIE I. *Chignon shading* mostly solid blobs of colour. *Corner ornaments*, solid blue stars with long points, always conspicuous. *Band below diadem* always heavily shaded. *Diadem and jewels.* The middle and right-hand jewels usually show a clearly defined cross. *Outer frame lines.* Stamps with white or faintly shaded chignons and weak frame lines are usually Die I (worn state).

DIE II. *Chignon* normally shows much less shading. A strong line of colour separates hair and chignon. *Corner ornaments.* The right blue star is characteristic (see illustration) but tends to disappear. It never obliterates the white cross. *Band below diadem.* As Die I but heavier, sometimes solid. *Diadem and jewels.* As Die I but usually fainter. *Outer frame lines.* Always strong and conspicuous.

DIE III. *Chignon shading* shows numerous fine lines, often blurred. *Corner ornaments* have a small hollow blue star with short points, which tends to disappear as in Die II. *Band below diadem*, shows light shading or hardly any shading. *Diadem and jewels.* Jewels usually marked with a solid squat star. The ornaments between the stars appear in the shape of a characteristic white "w". *Frame lines* variable.

The above notes give the general characteristics of the three Dies, but there are a few exceptions due to retouching, etc.

6 (*See note below No.* 14)

Die I
11 **6** 1 a. deep red .. .. £375 45·00
12 1 a. red .. .. £225 32·00

Printing of these stamps commenced on 26 July 1854, and continued into August (Printing, see note below No. 14).

7

*Die II: With more lines in the chignon than in Die I, and with white curved line where chignon joins head**
13 **7** 1 a. deep red .. .. £150 48·00
14 1 a. dull red .. .. 42·00 35·00

*Very worn printings of Die II may be found with chignon nearly as white as in Die I.

In stamps of Die I, however, the small blob of red projecting from the hair into the chignon is always visible.

These stamps were printed in August and September 1854 (Total printing, Dies I and II together, about 7¾ millions).

8

Die III. With pointed bust
15 **8** 1 a. red £900 £130
16 1 a. dull red £1400 £180

These stamps were printed between 7 July and 25 August 1855 (Printing, about 1½ millions).

9

NOTE. Our catalogue prices for Four Annas stamps are for cut-square specimens, with clear margins and in good condition. Cut-to-shape copies are worth from 3% to 20% of these prices according to condition.

Four Dies of the Head:—

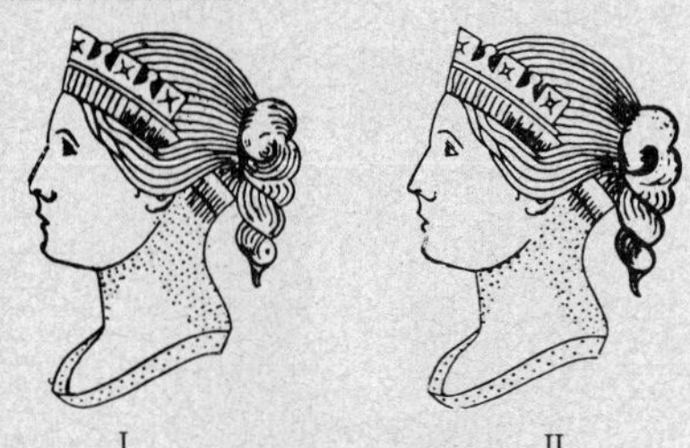

I II

DIE I. Band of diadem and chignon strongly shaded.

DIE II. Lines in band of diadem worn. Few lines in the upper part of the chignon, which, however, shows a strong drawn comma-like mark.

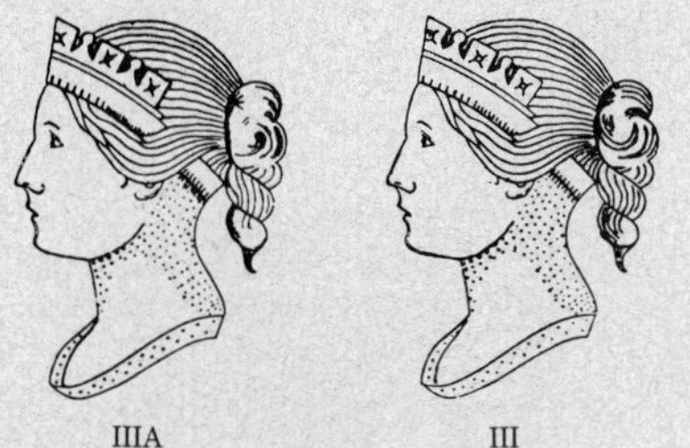

IIIA III

DIE IIIA. Upper part of chignon partly redrawn, showing two short, curved vertical lines in the NE corner. "Comma" has disappeared.

DIE III. Upper part of chignon completely redrawn, but band of diadem shows only a few short lines.

Two Dies of the Frame:—

Die I. Outer frame lines weak. Very small dots of colour, or none at all, in the "R" and "A's". The white lines to the right of "INDIA" are separated, by a line of colour, from the inner white circle.

Die II. Outer frame lines strengthened. Dots in the "R" and "A's" strong. White lines to right of "INDIA" break into inner white circle.

(Des Capt. H. Thuillier)

1854 (15 Oct). *W* **2** *upright, central portion only. Imperf.*

1st *Printing. Head Die I. Frame Die I. Stamps widely spaced and separated by blue wavy line.*

			Un	Used	Us pr
17	**9**	4 a. indigo and red	£4250	£500	£1800
18		4 a. blue and pale red	£4250	£425	£1600
		a. Head inverted	†	£25000/ £80000	†

This printing was made between 13 and 28 Oct 1854 (Printing, 206,040).

Twenty-seven confirmed examples of No. 18a are now known, only three of which are cut-square. The range of prices quoted reflects the difference in value between a sound cut-to-shape stamp and the finest example known.

2nd *Printing. Head Die II. Frame Die I. Stamps widely spaced and separated by blue wavy line.*

19	**9**	4 a. blue and red	£4000	£275	£1000
		a. Blue (head) printed double	†	£6000	†
20		4 a. indigo and deep red ..	£4000	£325	£1200

This printing was made between 1 and 13 Dec 1854 (Printing, 393,960).

No. 19a is only known used cut-to-shape.

3rd *Printing. Head Dies II, IIIA and III. Frame Dies I and II. Stamps, often in bright shades, widely spaced and separated by wavy line.*

21	**9**	4 a. blue and red (*shades*) (Head III, Frame I)	£9000	£1100	£3500
		a. Head II, Frame I	—	£1600	£5000
		b. Head IIIA, Frame I ..	—	£1600	£4750
		c. Head III, Frame II	—	—	£9500

This printing was made between 10 March and 2 April 1855 (Printing, 138,960).

4th *Printing. Head Die III. Frame Die II. Stamps closely spaced 2 to 2½ mm without separating line.*

22	**9**	4 a. deep blue and red	£2750	£275	£850
23		4 a. blue and red	£2500	£225	£750
		a. Blue (head) printed double	†	£4500	†
24		4 a. pale blue and pale red ..	£2750	£300	£900

This printing was made between 3 April and 9 May 1855 (Printing, 540,960).

No. 23a is only known used cut-to-shape.

5th *Printing. Head Die III. Frame Die II. Stamps spaced 4 to 6 mm without separating line.*

25	**9**	4 a. blue and rose-red	£4500	£400	£1600
26		4 a. deep blue and red	£4500	£400	£1600

This printing was made between 4 Oct and 3 Nov 1855 (Printing, 380,064).

Serrated perf about 18, or pin-perf

27	½ a. blue (Die I)	†	£4000	—
28	1 a. red (Die I)	†	£2250	—
29	1 a. red (Die II)	†	£2000	—
30	4 a. blue and red (Die II) ..	†	£9000	—

This is believed to be an unofficial perforation. Most of the known specimens bear Madras circle postmarks (C122 to C126), but some are known with Bombay postmarks. Beware of fakes.

BISECTS. The bisected stamps for issues between 1854 and 1860 were used exclusively in the Straits Settlements during shortages of certain values. Prices quoted are for those with Singapore "B 172" cancellations. Penang marks are considerably rarer.

10

11

(Plate made at Mint, Calcutta. Typo Stamp Office)

1854 (4 Oct). *Sheet wmk sideways, as W* **2** *but with* "No. 3" *at top left. Imperf.*

31	**10**	2 a. green (*shades*)	85·00	23·00
		a. Bisected (1 a.) (1857) (on cover)	†	£95000
34		2 a. emerald-green	£1000	

The 2 a. was also printed on paper with sheet watermark incorporating the words "STAMP OFFICE. One Anna", etc. (*Price £475 unused, £375 used*).

Apart from the rare emerald-green shade, there is a range of shades of No. 31 varying from bluish to yellowish green.

Many stamps show traces of lines external to the design shown in our illustration. Stamps with this frame on all four sides are scarce.

Many reprints of the ½, 1, 2, and 4 a. exist.

PRINTERS. All Indian stamps from No. 35 to 200 were typographed by De La Rue & Co.

1855 (Oct). *Blue glazed paper. No wmk. P* 14.

35	**11**	4 a. black	£400	13·00
		a. Imperf (pair)	£2750	£2750
		b. Bisected (2 a.) (1859) (on cover) ..	†	£7500
36		8 a. carmine (Die I)	£375	11·00
		a. Imperf (pair)	£1800	
		b. Bisected (4 a.) (1859) (on cover) ..	†	£35000

The first supply of the 4 a. was on white paper, but it is difficult to distinguish it from No. 45.

In the 8 a. the paper varies from deep blue to almost white.

For difference between Die I and Die II in the 8 a., see illustrations above No. 73.

1856–64. *No wmk. Paper yellowish to white. P* 14.

37	**11**	½ a. blue (Die I)	48·00	2·75
		a. Imperf (pair)	£325	£950
38		½ a. pale blue (Die I)	40·00	1·25
39		1 a. brown	38·00	1·75
		a. Imperf between (vert pair)		
		b. Imperf (pair)	£750	£1300
		c. Bisected (½ a.) (1859) (on cover) ..	†	£50000
40		1 a. deep brown	55·00	3·00
41		2 a. dull pink	£375	22·00
		a. Imperf (pair)	£1700	
42		2 a. yellow-buff	£160	22·00
		a. Imperf (pair)	£1000	£1800
43		2 a. yellow	£225	24·00
44		2 a. orange	£250	24·00
		a. Imperf (pair)		
45		4 a. black	£180	7·50
		a. Bisected diagonally (2 a.) (1859) (on cover)	†	£16000
		b. Imperf (pair)	£1800	£1800
46		4 a. grey-black	£160	4·75
47		4 a. green (1864)	£800	32·00
48		8 a. carmine (Die I)	£170	14·00
49		8 a. pale carmine (Die I)	£200	14·00
		a. Bisected (4 a.) (1859) (on cover) ..	†	£38000

Prepared for use, but not officially issued

50	**11**	2 a. yellow-green	£700	£800
		a. Imperf (pair)	£1700	

This stamp is known with trial obliterations, and a few are known postally used. It also exists *imperf*, but is not known used thus.

For difference between Die I and Die II in the ½ a., see illustrations above No. 73.

CROWN COLONY

On the 1 November 1858, Her Majesty Queen Victoria assumed the government of the territories in India "heretofore administered in trust by the Honourable East India Company".

12

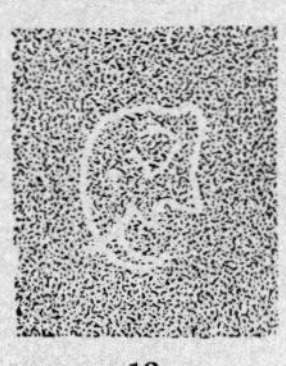

13

1860 (9 May). *No wmk. P* 14.

51	**12**	8 p. purple/*bluish*	£200	85·00
52		8 p. purple/*white*	35·00	4·50
		a. Bisected diagonally (4 p.) (1862) (on cover)	†	£50000
		b. Imperf (pair)	£2000	£3000
53		8 p. mauve	42·00	6·00

1865. *Paper yellowish to white. W* **13**. *P* 14.

54	**11**	½ a. blue (Die I)	7·00	50
		a. Imperf	†	£800
		w. Wmk inverted	—	15·00
55		½ a. pale blue (Die I)	7·00	50
56	**12**	8 p. purple	8·50	8·00
		w. Wmk inverted	30·00	
57		8 p. mauve	9·00	8·00
58	**11**	1 a. pale brown	3·50	50
59		1 a. deep brown	3·00	40
		w. Wmk inverted	40·00	20·00
60		1 a. chocolate	8·50	60
61		2 a. yellow	60·00	3·50
62		2 a. orange	40·00	1·25
		a. Imperf (pair)	†	£3000
63		2 a. brown-orange	21·00	2·00
		w. Wmk inverted	50·00	25·00
64		4 a. green	£325	18·00
		w. Wmk inverted	†	75·00
65		8 a. carmine (Die I)	£1000	75·00
		w. Wmk inverted	£1500	£150

The 8 p. mauve, No. 57, is found variously surcharged "NINE" or "NINE PIE" by local postmasters, to indicate that it was being sold for 9 pies, as was the case during 1874. Such surcharges were made without Government sanction.

The stamps of India, wmk Elephant's Head, surcharged with a crown and value in "cents", were used in the Straits Settlements.

14   POSTAGE (15)   POSTACE (16)

1866 (28 June). *Fiscal stamps as T* **14** *optd. Wmk Crown over* "INDIA". *P* 14 (*at sides only*). (*a*) *As T* **15**.

66	6 a. purple (G.)	£600	£110
	a. Overprint inverted	†	£8500

There are 20 different types of this overprint.

(*b*) *With T* **16**

68	6 a. purple (G.)	£1100	£140

17

18

Die I

Die II

Two Dies of 4 a:—

Die I.—Mouth closed, line from corner of mouth downwards only. Pointed chin.

Die II.—Mouth slightly open; lips, chin, and throat defined by line of colour. Rounded chin.

1866 (Sept)–**1878.** *W* **13**. *P* 14.

69	**17**	4 a. green (Die I)	48·00	2·00
70		4 a. deep green (Die I)	50·00	2·00
71		4 a. blue-green (Die II) (1878) ..	16·00	1·40
72	**18**	6 a. 8 p. slate (5.67)	30·00	18·00
		a. Imperf (pair)	£1700	

Die I (8 a.) (Die I (½ a.)

Die II (8 a.) Die II (½ a.)

868 (1 Jan). *Die II. Profile redrawn and different diadem. W* **13**. *P* 14.

3	**11**	8 a. rose (Die II)	24·00	4·75
		w. Wmk inverted	40·00	
4		8 a. pale rose (Die II)	24·00	4·75

873. *Die II. Features, especially the mouth, more firmly drawn. W* **13**. *P* 14.

5	**11**	½ a. deep blue (Die II)	3·25	50
6		½ a. blue (Die II)	3·25	50
		y. Wmk inverted and reversed	†	50·00

19 20

874 (18 July–1 Sept). *W* **13**. *P* 14.

7	**19**	9 p. bright mauve (18.7.74)	11·00	11·00
8		9 p. pale mauve	11·00	11·00
9	**20**	1 r. slate (1.9.74)	32·00	20·00

21 22

876 (19 Aug). *W* **13**. *P* 14.

0	**21**	6 a. olive-bistre	5·00	2·25
		w. Wmk inverted	50·00	
1		6 a. pale brown	5·00	1·50
2	**22**	12 a. Venetian red	7·00	18·00

EMPIRE

Queen Victoria assumed the title of Empress of India in 1877, and the inscription on the stamps was altered from "EAST INDIA" o "INDIA".

23 24 25

26 27 28

29 30 31

32 33 34

1882 (1 Jan)–**90.** *W* **34**. *P* 14.

84	**23**	½ a. deep blue-green (1883)	3·25	10
85		½ a. blue-green	3·25	10
		a. Double impression	£400	£500
		w. Wmk inverted	—	50·00
86	**24**	9 p. rose (1883)	60	1·50
87		9 p. aniline carmine	90	1·75
88	**25**	1 a. brown-purple (1883)	3·25	30
89		1 a. plum	3·25	30
		w. Wmk inverted	—	50·00
90	**26**	1 a. 6 p. sepia	60	80
91	**27**	2 a. pale blue (1883)	3·25	30
92		2 a. blue	3·25	30
		a. Double impression	£750	£1000
93	**28**	3 a. orange	13·00	5·50
94		3 a. brown-orange (1890)	5·50	50
95	**29**	4 a. olive-green (6.85)	12·00	50
96		4 a. slate-green	12·00	50
		w. Wmk inverted	—	40·00
97	**30**	4 a. 6 p. yellow-green (1.5.86)	14·00	4·00
98	**31**	8 a. dull mauve (1883)	19·00	2·00
99		8 a. magenta	19·00	2·00
100	**32**	12 a. purple/*red* (1.4.88)	6·50	2·50
		w. Wmk inverted	—	60·00
101	**33**	1 r. slate (1883)	12·00	5·00
		w. Wmk inverted	—	50·00
84/101		*Set of* 11	70·00	15·00
97, 100 Handstamped "Specimen"		*Set of* 2	75·00	

No. 92a is from a sheet of 2 a. stamps with a very marked double impression issued in Karachi in early 1898.

(35) 36 37

1891 (1 Jan). *No.* 97 *surch with T* **35** *by Govt Press, Calcutta.*

102	**30**	2½ a. on 4½ a. yellow-green	2·00	60

There are several varieties in this surcharge due to variations in the relative positions of the letters and figures.

1892 (Jan)–**97.** *W* **34**. *P* 14.

103	**36**	2 a. 6 p. yellow-green	1·25	40
104		2 a. 6 p. pale blue-green (1897)	2·50	80
105	**37**	1 r. green and rose	20·00	5·50
106		1 r. green and aniline carmine	7·50	2·00

38 (39) 40

USED HIGH VALUES. It is necessary to emphasise that used prices quoted for the following and all later high value stamps are for postally used copies.

(Head of Queen from portrait by von Angeli)

1895 (1 Sept). *W* **34**. *P* 14.

107	**38**	2 r. carmine and yellow-brown	35·00	11·00
107*a*		2 r. carmine and brown	40·00	13·00
108		3 r. brown and green	25·00	10·00
109		5 r. ultramarine and violet	35·00	23·00
107/9		*Set of* 3	85·00	40·00

1898 (1 Oct). *No.* 85 *surch with T* **39** *by Govt Press, Calcutta.*

110	**23**	¼ on ½ a. blue-green	10	50
		a. Surch double	£160	
		b. Double impression of stamp	£225	

1899. *W* **34**. *P* 14.

111	**40**	3 p. aniline carmine	10	10

1900 (1 Oct)–**02.** *W* **34**. *P* 14.

112	**40**	3 p. grey	50	70
113	**23**	½ a. pale yellow-green	1·25	45
114		½ a. yellow-green	1·25	45
115	**25**	1 a. carmine	1·00	15
116	**27**	2 a. pale violet	3·25	1·00
117		2 a. mauve (1902)	7·00	2·25
118	**36**	2 a. 6 p. ultramarine	3·25	3·75
112/18		*Set of* 5	8·00	5·25

41 42 43

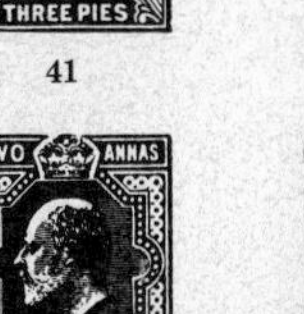

44 45 46

47 48 49

50 51 52

1902 (9 Aug)–**11.** *W* **34**. *P* 14.

119	**41**	3 p. grey	90	10
120		3 p. slate-grey (1904)	90	10
121	**42**	½ a. yellow-green	75	20
122		½ a. green	75	20
123	**43**	1 a. carmine	90	10
124	**44**	2 a. violet (13.5.03)	3·25	40
125		2 a. mauve	2·50	10
126	**45**	2 a. 6 p. ultramarine (1902)	4·00	30
		w. Wmk inverted	†	£110
127	**46**	3 a. orange-brown (1902)	3·75	35
128	**47**	4 a. olive (20.4.03)	3·00	35
129		4 a. pale olive	3·25	35
130		4 a. olive-brown	9·00	3·00
131	**48**	6 a. olive-bistre (6.8.03)	11·00	4·75
132		6 a. maize	10·00	4·50
133	**49**	8 a. purple (*shades*) (8.5.03)	8·00	1·00
134		8 a. claret (1910)	10·00	1·00
135	**50**	12 a. purple/*red* (1903)	7·50	2·00
136	**51**	1 r. green and carmine (1903)	6·50	70
137		1 r. green and scarlet (1911)	30·00	2·00
138	**52**	2 r. rose-red and yellow-brown (1903)	35·00	4·00
139		2 r. carmine and yellow-brown	35·00	4·00
140		3 r. brown and green (1904)	24·00	19·00
141		3 r. red-brown and green (1911)	35·00	22·00
142		5 r. ultramarine and violet (1904)	50·00	35·00
143		5 r. ultramarine and deep lilac (1911)	95·00	45·00
144		10 r. green and carmine (1909)	£100	25·00
146		15 r. blue and olive-brown (1909)	£130	42·00
147		25 r. brownish orange and blue (1909)	£750	£800
119/47		*Set of* 17	£1000	£850

No. 147 can often be found with telegraph cancellation; these can be supplied at one third of the price given above.

1905 (2 Feb). *No.* 122 *surch with T* **39**.

148	**42**	¼ on ½ a. green	55	10
		a. Surch inverted	—	£800

It is doubtful if No. 148a exists unused with genuine surcharge.

53 54

1906 (6 Dec)–**07.** *W* **34**. *P* 14.

149	**53**	½ a. green	2·25	10
150	**54**	1 a. carmine (7.1.07)	1·25	10

55 56 57

58* 59 60

61 62 63

64 65 66

67

"Rs" flaw in right value tablet (R.1/4)

*T **58**. Two types of the 1½ a.; (A) As illustrated. (B) Inscribed "1½ As". "ONE AND A HALF ANNAS".

1911 (Dec)–**22**. *W* **34**. *P* 14.

No.	Type	Description	Unused	Used
151	**55**	3 p. pale grey (1912)	60	20
152		3 p. grey	60	20
153		3 p. slate-grey	60	20
		a. "Rs" flaw	12·00	
154		3 p. blue-slate (1922)	1·90	50
		w. Wmk inverted	10·00	
155	**56**	½ a. yellow-green (1912)	75	15
156		½ a. pale blue-green	75	15
159	**57**	1 a. rose-carmine	2·00	20
160		1 a. carmine	2·00	20
161		1 a. aniline carmine	1·90	15
162		1 a. pale rose-carmine (*chalk-surfaced paper*) (1918)	2·50	40
163	**58**	1½ a. chocolate (Type A) (1919) ..	2·25	30
164		1½ a. grey-brown (Type A)	7·50	2·50
165		1½ a. chocolate (Type B) (1921) ..	2·50	3·25
		w. Wmk inverted	8·00	
166	**59**	2 a. dull purple	2·75	30
167		2 a. mauve	2·75	30
		w. Wmk inverted	15·00	
168		2 a. violet	4·50	40
169		2 a. bright purple (1.19)	4·75	65
170	**60**	2 a. 6 p. ultramarine (1912)	1·90	3·00
171	**61**	2 a. 6 p. ultramarine (1913)	1·75	20
172	**62**	3 a. dull orange	4·75	45
173		3 a. orange-brown	3·00	20
174	**63**	4 a. deep olive (1912)	5·00	45
175		4 a. olive-green	4·75	40
		w. Wmk inverted	15·00	
176	**64**	6 a. bistre (1912)	3·75	90
177		6 a. yellow-bistre	3·75	1·00
178		6 a. deep bistre-brown	16·00	3·50
179	**65**	8 a. purple (1912)	6·00	80
180		8 a. mauve	11·00	95
181		8 a. deep lilac	14·00	1·25
182		8 a. bright aniline mauve	26·00	5·00
183	**66**	12 a. dull claret (1912)	10·00	2·50
184		12 a. claret	7·00	2·25
185	**67**	1 r. brown and green (1913)	17·00	2·00
186		1 r. red-brown and blue-green	12·00	1·50
		w. Wmk inverted	32·00	
187		2 r. carmine and brown (1913)	16·00	1·50
		w. Wmk inverted	45·00	
188		5 r. ultramarine and violet (1913) ..	45·00	6·50
189		10 r. green and scarlet (1913)	70·00	12·00
190		15 r. blue and olive (1913)	90·00	23·00
191		25 r. orange and blue (1913)	£160	30·00
151/91		.. .. *Set of* 19	£350	70·00

Examples of the ½ a. printed double are now believed to be forgeries.

FORGERIES.—Collectors are warned against forgeries of all the later surcharges of India, and particularly the errors.

NINE

PIES

(68)

1921. *T* **57** *surch with T* **68**.

No.	Type	Description	Unused	Used
192		9 p. on 1 a. rose-carmine	60	30
		a. Error. "NINE NINE"	70·00	£120
		b. Error. "PIES PIES"	70·00	£120
		c. Surch double	£140	£170
193		9 p. on 1 a. carmine-pink	1·75	60
194		9 p. on 1 a. aniline carmine	7·00	2·50

In the initial setting of the surcharge No. 192a occurred on R. 2/13–16 of the fourth pane and No. 192b on R. 4/13–16 of the third. For the second setting No. 192a was corrected. Examples of No. 192b still occur but on R. 2/13–16 of the third pane. Later printings showed this corrected also.

1922. *T* **56** *surch with T* **39**.

No.	Type	Description	Unused	Used
195		¼ a. on ½ a. yellow-green	30	35
		a. Surch inverted	9·00	
		b. Surch omitted (in horiz pair with normal)	£190	
196		¼ a. on ½ a. blue-green	1·75	65

1922–26. *W* **34**. *P* 14.

No.	Type	Description	Unused	Used
197	**57**	1 a. chocolate	60	10
198	**58**	1½ a. rose-carmine (Type B) (1926) ..	2·00	30
199	**61**	2 a. 6 p. orange (1926)	4·75	4·25
200	**62**	3 a. ultramarine (1923)	12·00	60
197/200		.. .. *Set of* 4	16·00	4·75

NEW INFORMATION

The editor is always interested to correspond with people who have new information that will improve or correct the Catalogue.

69

70

71

PRINTERS. The following issues of postage and contemporary official stamps were all printed by the Security Printing Press, Nasik, *unless otherwise stated.*

1926–33. *Typo. W* **69**. *P* 14.

No.	Type	Description	Unused	Used
201	**55**	3 p. slate	30	10
		w. Wmk inverted	1·10	30
202	**56**	½ a. green	60	10
		w. Wmk inverted	—	30
203	**57**	1 a. chocolate	50	10
		a. *Tête-bêche* (pair) (1932)	1·25	10·00
		w. Wmk inverted	50	10
204	**58**	1½ a. rose-carmine (Type B) (1929) ..	1·25	10
		w. Wmk inverted	1·50	30
205	**59**	2 a. bright purple	4·50	5·50
		a. Stop under "s" in right value tablet (R. 4/16)	65·00	
206	**70**	2 a. purple	1·00	10
		a. *Tête-bêche* (pair) (1933)	8·00	38·00
		w. Wmk inverted	1·25	30
207	**61**	2 a. 6 p. orange (1929)	1·25	10
		w. Wmk inverted	1·50	40
208	**62**	3 a. ultramarine	6·00	1·00
209		3 a. blue (1928)	5·50	10
		w. Wmk inverted	6·50	60
210	**63**	4 a. pale sage-green	1·50	10
		w. Wmk inverted	—	5·00
211	**71**	4 a. sage-green	6·00	10
		w. Wmk inverted	—	40
212	**65**	8 a. reddish purple	4·00	10
		w. Wmk inverted	6·00	40
213	**66**	12 a. claret	5·00	30
		w. Wmk inverted	7·00	70
214	**67**	1 r. chocolate and green	5·00	45
		a. Chocolate (head) omitted	£3000	
		w. Wmk inverted	8·00	75
215		2 r. carmine and orange	9·00	70
		w. Wmk inverted	11·00	1·40
216		5 r. ultramarine and purple	22·00	1·25
		w. Wmk inverted	—	2·00
217		10 r. green and scarlet (1927)	40·00	2·75
		w. Wmk inverted	65·00	3·75
218		15 r. blue and olive (1928)	38·00	30·00
		w. Wmk inverted	24·00	26·00
219		25 r. orange and blue (1928)	90·00	29·00
		w. Wmk inverted	£100	32·00
201/19		.. .. *Set of* 18	£190	55·00

Examples of the ½ a. printed double are believed to be forgeries.

72 De Havilland D.H.66 Hercules

Missing tree-top (R. 11/6 of 8 a.)

Reversed serif on second "I" of "INDIA"

(Des R. Grant. Litho)

1929 (22 Oct). *Air. W* **69** (*sideways**). *P* 14.

No.	Type	Description	Unused	Used
220	**72**	2 a. deep blue-green	1·75	50
		w. Wmk stars pointing left	1·50	60
221		3 a. blue	1·00	1·40
		w. Wmk stars pointing left	1·25	1·40
222		4 a. olive-green	2·25	85
		w. Wmk stars pointing left	2·75	1·00
223		6 a. bistre	2·25	90
		w. Wmk stars pointing left	2·50	1·00
224		8 a. purple	2·50	1·00
		a. Missing tree-top	80·00	55·00
		b. Reversed serif	£150	80·00
		w. Wmk stars pointing left	3·00	1·00
225		12 a. rose-red	9·00	4·50
		w. Wmk stars pointing left	11·00	4·50
220/5		.. .. *Set of* 6	17·00	8·25

*The normal sideways watermark shows the stars pointing right, *as seen from the back of the stamp.*

73 Purana Qila

(Des H. W. Barr. Litho)

1931 (9 Feb). *Inauguration of New Delhi. T* **73** *and simila[r] horiz designs. W* **69** (*sideways**). *P* 13½×14.

No.	Type	Description	Unused	Used
226		¼ a. olive-green and orange-brown	1·25	2·2
		a. "F" for "P" in "PURANA"	75·00	
		w. Wmk stars pointing left	1·25	2·2
227		½ a. violet and green	1·25	4
		w. Wmk stars pointing left	1·75	4
228		1 a. mauve and chocolate	1·25	2
		w. Wmk stars pointing left	2·00	2
229		2 a. green and blue	1·50	1·5
		w. Wmk stars pointing left	1·75	1·2
230		3 a. chocolate and carmine	2·50	2·5
		w. Wmk stars pointing left	2·50	2·5
231		1 r. violet and green	7·50	20·0
		w. Wmk stars pointing left	7·50	20·0
226/31		.. .. *Set of* 6	14·00	24·0

Designs:—½ a. War Memorial Arch; 1 a. Council House; 2 a The Viceroy's House; 3 a. Government of India Secretariat; 1 r Dominion Columns and the Secretariat.

*The normal sideways watermark shows the stars pointing t[o] the right, *as seen from the back of the stamp.*

79

80

81

82

83

(T **82/3** des T. I. Archer. 9 p. litho and typo; 1¼ a., 3½ a. lith[o] others typo)

1932–36. *W* **69**. *P* 14.

No.	Type	Description	Unused	Used
232	**79**	½ a. green (1934)	1·00	10
		w. Wmk inverted	—	50
233	**80**	9 p. deep green (22.4.32)	30	10
		w. Wmk inverted	75	50
234	**81**	1 a. chocolate (1934)	3·00	10
		w. Wmk inverted	—	50
235	**82**	1 a. 3 p. mauve (22.4.32)	30	10
		w. Wmk inverted	30	30
236	**70**	2 a. vermilion	9·00	3·75
		aw. Wmk inverted	9·00	5·00
236*b*	**59**	2 a. vermilion (1934)	3·75	50
236*c*		2 a. vermilion (*small die*) (1936) ..	4·50	30
		cw. Wmk inverted	—	5·00
237	**62**	3 a. carmine	3·00	10
		w. Wmk inverted	—	1·25
238	**83**	3 a. 6 p. ultramarine (22.4.32) ..	2·50	10
		w. Wmk inverted	2·50	20
239	**64**	6 a. bistre (1935)	7·00	1·50
		w. Wmk inverted	—	10·00
232/9		.. .. *Set of* 9	27·00	5·00

No. 236*b* measures 19×22.6 mm and No. 236*c* 18.4×21.8 mm

84 Gateway of India, Bombay

"Bird" flaw (R.9/3)

1935 (6 May). *Silver Jubilee. T* **84** *and similar horiz designs. Litho. W* **69** (*sideways**). *P* 13½×14.

No.	Type	Description	Unused	Used
240		½ a. black and yellow-green	60	15
		w. Wmk stars pointing left	60	15
241		9 p. black and grey-green	45	20
		w. Wmk stars pointing left	45	30
242		1 a. black and brown	45	15
		w. Wmk stars pointing left	45	10
243		1¼ a. black and bright violet	45	10
		w. Wmk stars pointing left	75	15
244		2½ a. black and orange	2·25	1·40
		w. Wmk stars pointing left	1·50	95
245		3½ a. black and dull ultramarine	3·25	2·75
		a. "Bird" flaw	85·00	60·00
		w. Wmk stars pointing left	3·75	2·75
246		8 a. black and purple	3·25	3·00
		w. Wmk stars pointing left	4·75	3·50
240/6		.. .. *Set of* 7	9·00	6·50

Designs:—9 p. Victoria Memorial Calcutta; 1 a. Rameswaram Temple, Madras; 1¼ a. Jain Temple, Calcutta; 2½ a. Taj Mahal, Agra; 3½ a. Golden Temple, Amritsar; 8 a. Pagoda in Mandalay.

*The normal sideways watermark shows the stars pointing t[o] the right, *as seen from the back of the stamp.*

91 King George VI

92 Dak Runner

93 King George VI

1937 (23 Aug–15 Dec). *Typo. W* **69**. *P* 13½×14 *or* 14×13½ (*T* **93**).

No.	Type	Description	Unused	Used
247	**91**	3 p. slate	50	10
248		½ a. red-brown	1·50	10
249		9 p. green (23.8.37)	4·00	20
250		1 a. carmine (23.8.37)	50	10
		a. *Tête-bêche* (vert pair)	1·00	1·75
		w. Wmk inverted (from booklets)	50	50
251	**92**	2 a. vermilion	2·75	30
252	–	2 a. 6 p. bright violet	75	20
253	–	3 a. yellow-green	4·50	30
254	–	3 a. 6 p. bright blue	3·25	50
255	–	4 a. brown	13·00	20
256	–	6 a. turquoise-green	14·00	80
257	–	8 a. slate-violet	7·50	50
258	–	12 a. lake	18·00	1·10
259	**93**	1 r. grey and red-brown	1·00	15
260		2 r. purple and brown	3·75	30
		w. Wmk inverted	20·00	
261		5 r. green and blue	15·00	50
		w. Wmk inverted	35·00	
262		10 r. purple and claret	15·00	70
263		15 r. brown and green	70·00	55·00
		w. Wmk inverted	75·00	60·00
264		25 r. slate-violet and purple	90·00	17·00
247/64		*Set of* 18	£225	70·00

Designs: *Horiz as T* **92**—2 a. 6 p. Dak bullock cart; 3 a. Dak tonga; 3 a. 6 p. Dak camel; 4 a. Mail train; 6 a. *Strathnaver* (liner); 8 a. Mail lorry; 12 a. Armstrong Whitworth A.W.27 Ensign 1 mail plane (small head).

100a King George VI

101 King George VI **102**

103 Armstrong Whitworth A.W.27 Ensign I Mail Plane (large head)

(T **100a/102** des T. I. Archer. Typo)

1940–43. *W* **69**. *P* 13½×14.

No.	Type	Description	Unused	Used
265	**100a**	3 p. slate	25	10
266		½ a. purple (1.10.42)	40	10
		w. Wmk inverted		
267		9 p. green	40	10
268		1 a. carmine (1.4.43)	40	10
269	**101**	1 a. 3 p. yellow-brown	90	10
		aw. Wmk inverted		
269b		1½ a. dull violet (9.42)	60	10
270		2 a. vermilion	1·25	10
271		3 a. bright violet (1942)	2·25	10
		w. Wmk inverted	—	10·00
272		3½ a. bright blue	70	10
273	**102**	4 a. brown	45	10
274		6 a. turquoise-green	3·00	10
275		8 a. slate-violet	1·50	30
276		12 a. lake	2·75	50
277	**103**	14 a. purple (15.10.40)	18·00	1·25
265/77		*Set of* 14	29·00	2·25

The 1½ a. and 3 a. were at first printed by lithography and were of finer execution and without Jubilee lines in the sheet margins.

105 "Victory" and King George VI

3 PIES

(106)

1946 (2 Jan). *Victory. Litho. W* **69**. *P* 13.

No.	Type	Description	Unused	Used
278	**105**	9 p. yellow-green (8.2.46)	30	30
279		1½ a. dull violet	30	30
280		3½ a. bright blue	75	60
281		12 a. claret (8.2.46)	1·50	55
278/81		*Set of* 4	2·50	1·60

1946 (8 Aug). *Surch with T* **106**.

No.	Type	Description	Unused	Used
282	**101**	3 p. on 1 a. 3 p. yellow-brown	10	15

DOMINION

301 Asokan Capital (Inscr reads "Long Live India")

302 Indian National Flag

303 Douglas DC-4

(Des T. I. Archer. Litho)

1947 (21 Nov–15 Dec). *Independence. W* **69**. *P* 14 × 13½ (1½ *a.*) *or* 13½ × 14 (*others*).

No.	Type	Description	Unused	Used
301	**301**	1½ a. grey-green (15 Dec)	15	10
302	**302**	3½ a. orange-red, blue and green	30	85
		w. Wmk inverted	5·50	5·50
303	**303**	12 a. ultramarine (15 Dec)	1·50	1·75
301/3		*Set of* 3	1·75	2·40

304 Lockheed Constellation

(Des T. I. Archer. Litho)

1948 (29 May). *Air. Inauguration of India-U.K. Air Service. W* **69**. *P* 13½ × 14.

No.	Type	Description	Unused	Used
304	**304**	12 a. black and ultramarine	1·00	2·00

305 Mahatma Gandhi **306**

(Photo Courvoisier)

1948 (15 Aug). *First Anniv of Independence. P* 11½.

No.	Type	Description	Unused	Used
305	**305**	1½ a. brown	1·75	30
306		3½ a. violet	4·25	1·50
307		12 a. grey-green	6·00	60
308	**306**	10 r. purple-brown and lake	55·00	40·00
305/8		*Set of* 4	60·00	40·00

307 Ajanta Panel

308 Konarak Horse

309 Trimurti

310 Bodhisattva

311 Nataraja

312 Sanchi Stupa, East Gate

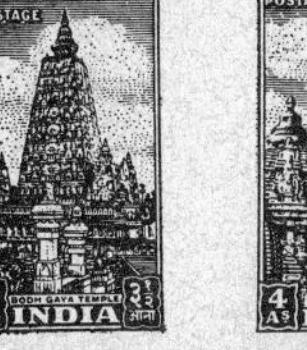
313 Bodh Gaya Temple

314 Bhuvanesvara

315 Gol Gumbad, Bijapur

316 Kandarya Mahadeva Temple

317 Golden Temple, Amritsar

318 Victory Tower, Chittorgarh

319 Red Fort, Delhi

320 Taj Mahal, Agra

321 Qutb Minar, Delhi

322 Satrunjaya Temple, Palitana

(Des T. I. Archer and I. M. Das. Typo (low values), litho (rupee values))

1949 (15 Aug). *W* **69** (*sideways* on* 6 *p.*, 1 *r. and* 10 *r.*). *P* 14 (3 *p. to* 2 *a.*), 13½ (3 *a. to* 12 *a.*), 14×13½ (1 *r. and* 10 *r.*), 13½×14 (2 *r. and* 5 *r.*), 13 (15 *r.*).

No.	Type	Description	Unused	Used
309	**307**	3 p. slate-violet	15	10
		w. Wmk inverted		
310	**308**	6 p. purple-brown	25	10
		w. Wmk star pointing right	3·00	90
311	**309**	9 p. yellow-green	40	10
312	**310**	1 a. turquoise	60	10
313	**311**	2 a. carmine	80	10
		w. Wmk inverted	8·50	90
314	**312**	3 a. brown-orange	1·50	10
315	**313**	3½ a. bright blue	1·50	2·75
316	**314**	4 a. lake	4·00	10
		w. Wmk inverted	12·00	1·00
317	**315**	6 a. violet	1·50	10
		w. Wmk inverted	3·00	45
318	**316**	8 a. turquoise-green	1·50	10
		w. Wmk inverted		
319	**317**	12 a. dull blue	1·50	20
		w. Wmk inverted	4·50	70
320	**318**	1 r. dull violet and green	9·00	10
		w. Wmk star pointing left	18·00	70
321	**319**	2 r. claret and violet	10·00	20
		w. Wmk inverted	22·00	90
322	**320**	5 r. blue-green and red-brown	28·00	90
		w. Wmk inverted	45·00	1·50
323	**321**	10 r. purple-brown and deep blue	45·00	4·75
		a. *Purple-brown and blue*	90·00	3·75
		aw. Wmk star pointing left		
324	**322**	15 r. brown and claret	14·00	17·00
309/24		*Set of* 16	£110	22·00

*The normal sideways watermark has the star pointing to the left on the 6 p. value and to the right on the 1 r. and 10 r. (323*a*) *when seen from the back of the stamp.*

For T **310** with statue reversed see No. 333.

323 Globe and Asokan Capital

1949 (10 Oct). *75th Anniv of U.P.U. Litho. W* **69**. *P* 13.

No.	Type	Description	Unused	Used
325	**323**	9 p. green	1·00	2·00
326		2 a. rose	1·00	2·00
327		3½ a. bright blue	1·75	2·25
328		12 a. brown-purple	3·00	2·50
325/8		*Set of* 4	6·00	8·00

REPUBLIC

324 Rejoicing Crowds

328 As T **310**, but statue reversed

(Des D. J. Keymer & Co. Litho)

1950 (26 Jan). *Inauguration of Republic. T* **324** *and similar designs. W* **69** *(sideways on* 3½ *a.). P* 13.

329		2 a. scarlet	1·00	40
		w. Wmk inverted	11·00	1·60
330		3½ a. ultramarine	1·50	2·75
331		4 a. violet	1·50	65
332		12 a. maroon	3·25	2·25
		w. Wmk inverted	13·00	4·00
329/32		*Set of* 4	6·50	5·50

Designs: *Vert*—3½ a. Quill, ink-well and verse. *Horiz*—4 a. Ear of corn and plough; 12 a. Spinning-wheel and cloth.

1950 (15 July)–**51**. *Typo. W* **69**. *P* 14 (1 *a.*), 13½ (*others*).

333	**328**	1 a. turquoise	2·50	10
		aw. Wmk inverted		
333*b*	**313**	2½ a. lake (30.4.51)	2·50	2·50
333*c*	**314**	4 a. bright blue (30.4.51)	6·00	10
333/*c*		*Set of* 3	10·00	2·50

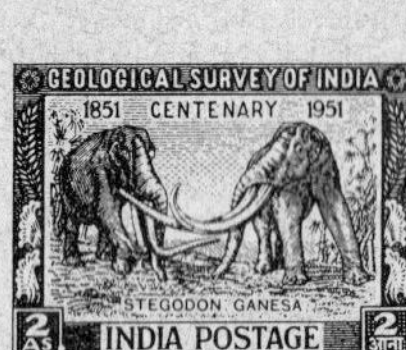

329 *Stegodon ganesa*

330 Torch

1951 (13 Jan). *Centenary of Geological Survey of India. Litho. W* **69**. *P* 13.

334	**329**	2 a. black and claret	2·00	40

1951 (4 Mar). *First Asian Games, New Delhi. Litho. W* **69** *(sideways). P* 14.

335	**330**	2 a. reddish purple and brown-orange	1·00	30
336		12 a. chocolate and light blue	4·00	90

PROCESS. All the following issues were printed in photogravure, *except where otherwise stated.*

331 Kabir

332 Locomotives of 1853 and 1953

1952 (1 Oct). *Indian Saints and Poets. T* **331** *and similar vert designs. W* **69**. *P* 14.

337		9 p. bright emerald-green	30	40
338		1 a. carmine	30	15
339		2 a. orange-red	1·00	20
340		4 a. bright blue	1·25	40
341		4½ a. bright mauve	30	80
342		12 a. brown	2·00	80
337/42		*Set of* 6	4·50	2·50

Designs:—1 a. Tulsidas; 2 a. Meera; 4 a. Surdas; 4½ a. Ghalib; 12 a. Tagore.

1953 (16 Apr). *Railway Centenary. W* **69**. *P* 14½ × 14.

343	**332**	2 a. black	75	10

333 Mount Everest

1953 (2 Oct). *Conquest of Mount Everest. W* **69**. *P* 14½ × 14.

344	**333**	2 a. bright violet	50	10
345		14 a. brown	3·00	25

334 Telegraph Poles of 1851 and 1951

1953 (1 Nov). *Centenary of Indian Telegraphs. W* **69**. *P* 14½ × 14.

346	**334**	2 a. blue-green	30	10
347		12 a. blue	2·50	40

335 Postal Transport, 1854

1954 (1 Oct). *Stamp Centenary. T* **335** *and similar horiz designs. W* **69**. *P* 14½ × 14.

348		1 a. reddish purple	30	20
349		2 a. cerise	30	10
350		4 a. orange-brown	2·75	50
351		14 a. blue	1·50	40
348/51		*Set of* 4	4·25	1·00

Designs:—2, 14 a. "Airmail"; 4 a. Postal transport, 1954.

338 U.N. Emblem and Lotus

1954 (24 Oct). *United Nations Day. W* **69** *(sideways). P* 13.

352	**338**	2 a. turquoise-green	40	30

339 Forest Research Institute

1954 (11 Dec). *Fourth World Forestry Congress, Dehra Dun. W* **69**. *P* 14½ × 14.

353	**339**	2 a. ultramarine	20	10

340 Tractor

344 Woman Spinning

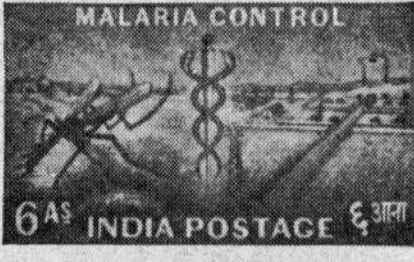

347 "Malaria Control" (Mosquito and Staff of Aesculapius)

1955 (26 Jan). *Five Year Plan. T* **340**, **344**, **347** *and similar designs. W* **69** *(sideways on small horiz designs). P* 14×14½ *(small horiz) or* 14½×14 *(others).*

354		3 p. bright purple	30	10
355		6 p. violet	30	10
356		9 p. orange-brown	40	10
357		1 a. blue-green	45	10
358		2 a. light blue	30	10
359		3 a. pale blue-green	50	10
360		4 a. rose-carmine	50	10
361		6 a. yellow-brown	1·50	10
362		8 a. blue	6·00	10
363		10 a. turquoise-green	2·25	1·50
364		12 a. bright blue	1·75	10
365		14 a. bright green	3·25	20
366		1 r. deep dull green	4·00	10
367		1 r. 2 a. grey	2·00	2·75
368		1 r. 8 a. reddish purple	7·00	4·00
369		2 r. cerise	4·25	10
370		5 r. brown	14·00	30
371		10 r. orange	14·00	4·00
354/71		*Set of* 18	50·00	11·50

Designs: *Horiz (as T* **340**)—6 p. Power loom; 9 p. Bullock-driven well; 1 a. Damodar Valley Dam; 4 a. Bullocks; 8 a. Chittaranjan Locomotive Works; 12 a. Hindustan Aircraft Factory, Bangalore; 1 r. Telephone engineer; 2 r. Rare Earth Factory, Alwaye; 5 r. Sindri Fertiliser Factory; 10 r. Steel plant. *(As T* **347**)—10 a. Marine Drive, Bombay; 14 a. Kashmir landscape; 1 r. 2 a. Cape Comorin; 1 r. 8 a. Mt Kangchenjunga. *Vert (as T* **344**)—3 a. Woman weaving with hand loom.

For stamps as Nos. 366, 369/71 but W **374** see Nos. 413/16.

358 Bodhi Tree

359 Round Parasol and Bodhi Tree

(Des C. Pakrashi (2 a.), R. D'Silva (14 a.))

1956 (24 May). *Buddha Jayanti. W* **69** *(sideways on* 14 *a.). P* 13 × 13½ (2 *a.*) *or* 13½ × 13 (14 *a.*).

372	**358**	2 a. sepia	75	10
373	**359**	14 a. vermilion	4·00	3·50

360 Lokmanya Bal Gangadhar Tilak

361 Map of India

1956 (23 July). *Birth Centenary of Tilak (journalist). W* **69** *P* 13 × 13½.

374	**360**	2 a. chestnut	10	10

(New Currency. 100 naye paise = 1 rupee)

1957 (1 Apr)–**58**. *W* **69** *(sideways). P* 14 × 14½.

375	**361**	1 n.p. blue-green	10	10
376		2 n.p. light brown	10	10
377		3 n.p. deep brown	10	10
378		5 n.p. bright green	4·25	10
379		6 n.p. grey	10	10
379*a*		8 n.p. light blue-green (7.5.58)	5·50	1·25
380		10 n.p. deep dull green	4·25	10
381		13 n.p. bright carmine-red	30	10
381*a*		15 n.p. violet (16.1.58)	3·00	10
382		20 n.p. blue	30	10
383		25 n.p. ultramarine	30	10
384		50 n.p. orange	2·25	10
385		75 n.p. reddish purple	1·25	10
385*a*		90 n.p. bright purple (16.1.58)	3·00	1·50
375/85*a*		*Set of* 14	22·00	2·75

The 8, 15 and 90 n.p. have their value expressed as "nP".
For similar stamps but W **374** see Nos. 399/412.

362 The Rani of Jhansi

363 Shrine

1957 (15 Aug). *Indian Mutiny Centenary. W* **69**. *P* 14½ × 14 (15 *n.p.*) *or* 13 × 13½ (90 *n.p.*).

386	**362**	15 n.p. brown	15	10
387	**363**	90 n.p. reddish purple	1·50	6

364 Henri Dunant and Conference Emblem

365 "Nutrition"

1957 (28 Oct). *19th International Red Cross Conference, New Delhi. W* **69** *(sideways). P* 13½ × 13.

388	**364**	15 n.p. deep grey and carmine	10	1

1957 (14 Nov). *Children's Day. T* **365** *and similar designs W* **69** *(sideways on* 90 *n.p.). P* 14×13½ (90 *n.p.*) *or* 13½×14 *(others).*

389		8 n.p. reddish purple	10	1
390		15 n.p. turquoise-green	10	1
391		90 n.p. orange-brown	25	1
389/91		*Set of* 3	30	3

Designs: *Horiz*—15 n.p. "Education". *Vert*—90 n.p. "Recreation".

OMNIBUS ISSUES

Details, together with prices for complete sets of the various Omnibus issues from the 1935 Silver Jubilee series to date are included in a special section following Zimbabwe at the end of Volume 2.

368 Bombay University **369** Calcutta University

1957 (31 Dec). *Centenary of Indian Universities. T* **368/9** *and similar design. W* **69** *(sideways on T* **368**). *P* 14 × 14½ *(No.* 392) *or* 13½ × 14 *(others).*

392		10 n.p. violet	15	20
393		10 n.p. grey	15	20
394		10 n.p. light brown	30	20
392/4		*Set of* 3	55	55

Design: *Horiz as T* **369**—No. 394, Madras University.

371 J. N. Tata (founder) and Steel Plant **372** Dr. D. K. Karve

1958 (1 Mar). *50th Anniv of Steel Industry. W* **69**. *P* 14½ × 14.
395 **371** 15 n.p. orange-red .. 10 10

1958 (18 Apr). *Birth Centenary of Karve (educationalist). W* **69** *(sideways). P* 14.
396 **372** 15 n.p. orange-brown .. 10 10

373 Westland Wapiti Biplane and Hawker Hunter **374** Asokan Capital

1958 (30 Apr). *Silver Jubilee of Indian Air Force. W* **69**. *P* 14½ × 14.
397 **373** 15 n.p. blue .. 1·00 10
398 90 n.p. ultramarine .. 1·25 1·25

ASOKAN CAPITAL WATERMARK. When the watermark was originally introduced in 1958 the base of each individual capital was 10 mm wide. During 1985 a modified version, with the capital base measurement reduced to 8 mm, was introduced. Examples have been seen on Nos. 921a, 922a, 923a and 928a.

1958–63. *As Nos.* 366, 369/71 *and* 375/85a *but W* **374**.

399	**361**	1 n.p. blue-green (1960)	90	10
		a. Imperf (pair)	£170	
400		2 n.p. light brown (27.10.58)	10	10
401		3 n.p. deep brown (1958)	10	10
402		5 n.p. bright green (27.10.58)	10	10
403		6 n.p. grey (1963)	15	3·25
404		8 n.p. light blue-green (1958)	90	10
405		10 n.p. deep dull green (27.10.58)	15	10
		a. Imperf (pair)	†	—
406		13 n.p. bright carmine-red (1963)	80	3·50
407		15 n.p. violet (10.60)	60	10
408		20 n.p. blue (27.10.58)	30	10
409		25 n.p. ultramarine (27.10.58)	30	10
410		50 n.p. orange (1959)	30	10
411		75 n.p. reddish purple (1959)	40	10
412		90 n.p. bright purple (1960)	5·50	10
413	–	1 r. deep dull green (1959)	3·75	10
414	–	2 r. cerise (1959)	5·50	10
415	–	5 r. brown (1959)	9·00	30
416	–	10 r. orange (1959)	20·00	4·25
399/416		*Set of* 18	42·00	10·50

The 5, 10, 15, 20, 25 and 50 n.p. with serial numbers on the back are coil stamps prepared from sheets for experimenting with coil machines. In the event the machines were not purchased and the stamps were sold over the counter.

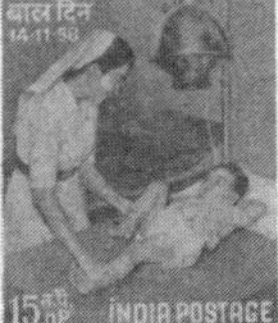

375 Bipin Chandra Pal **376** Nurse with Child Patient

1958 (7 Nov). *Birth Centenary of Pal (patriot). W* **374**. *P* 14 × 13½.
418 **375** 15 n.p. deep dull green .. 10 10

1958 (14 Nov). *Children's Day. W* **374**. *P* 14×13½.
419 **376** 15 n.p. violet .. 10 10

377 Jagadish Chandra Bose **378** Exhibition Gate

1958 (30 Nov). *Birth Centenary of Bose (botanist). W* **374**. *P* 14 × 13½.
420 **377** 15 n.p. deep turquoise-green .. 20 10

1958 (30 Dec). *India 1958 Exhibition, New Delhi. W* **374** *(sideways). P* 14½ × 14.
421 **378** 15 n.p. reddish purple .. 10 10

379 Sir Jamsetjee Jejeebhoy **380** "The Triumph of Labour" (after Chowdhury)

1959 (15 Apr). *Death Centenary of Jejeebhoy (philanthropist). W* **374**. *P* 14 × 13½.
422 **379** 15 n.p. brown .. 10 10

1959 (15 June). *40th Anniv of International Labour Organization. W* **374** *(sideways). P* 14½ × 14.
423 **380** 15 n.p. dull green .. 10 10

381 Boys awaiting admission to Children's Home **382** "Agriculture"

1959 (14 Nov). *Children's Day. W* **374**. *P* 14×14½.
424 **381** 15 n.p. deep dull green .. 10 10
a. Imperf (pair) .. £700

1959 (30 Dec). *First World Agricultural Fair, New Delhi. W* **374**. *P* 13½ × 13.
425 **382** 15 n.p. grey .. 20 10

383 Thiruvalluvar (philosopher)

1960 (15 Feb). *Thiruvalluvar Commemoration. W* **374**. *P* 14 × 13½.
426 **383** 15 n.p. reddish purple .. 10 10

384 Yaksha pleading with the Cloud (from the "Meghaduta") **385** Shakuntala writing a letter to Dushyanta (from the "Shakuntala")

1960 (22 June). *Kalidasa (poet) Commemoration. W* **374**. *P* 13.
427 **384** 15 n.p. grey .. 30 10
428 **385** 1 r. 3 n.p. pale yellow and brown .. 1·40 75

NEW INFORMATION

The editor is always interested to correspond with people who have new information that will improve or correct the Catalogue.

386 S. Bharati (poet) **387** Dr. M. Visvesvaraya

1960 (11 Sept). *Subramania Bharati Commemoration. W* **374**. *P* 14 × 13½.
429 **386** 15 n.p. blue .. 10 10

1960 (15 Sept). *Birth Centenary of Dr. M. Visvesvaraya (engineer). W* **374**. *P* 13 × 13½.
430 **387** 15 n.p. brown and bright carmine .. 10 10

388 "Children's Health"

1960 (14 Nov). *Children's Day. W* **374**. *P* 13½ × 13.
431 **388** 15 n.p. deep dull green .. 10 10

389 Children greeting U.N. Emblem **390** Tyagaraja

1960 (11 Dec). *U.N.I.C.E.F. Day. W* **374**. *P* 13½ × 13.
432 **389** 15 n.p. orange-brown and olive-brown 10 10

1961 (6 Jan). *114th Death Anniv of Tyagaraja (musician). W* **374**. *P* 14×13½.
433 **390** 15 n.p. greenish blue .. 10 10

391 "First Aerial Post" cancellation

392 Air India Boeing 707 Airliner and Humber Sommer Biplane

1961 (18 Feb). *50th Anniv of First Official Airmail Flight, Allahabad-Naini. T* **391/2** *and similar design. W* **374**. *P* 14 *(5 n.p.) or* 13 × 13½ *(others).*

434	5 n.p. olive-drab	1·10	30
435	15 n.p. deep green and grey	1·10	30
436	1 r. purple and grey	3·75	1·60
434/6	*Set of* 3	5·50	2·00

Design: *Horiz as T* **392**—1 r. H. Pecquet flying Humber Sommer plane and "Aerial Post" cancellation.

394 Shivaji on horseback **395** Motilal Nehru (politician)

1961 (17 Apr). *Chatrapati Shivaji (Maratha ruler) Commemoration. W* **374**. *P* 13×13½.
437 **394** 15 n.p. brown and green .. 70 30

1961 (6 May). *Birth Centenary of Pandit Motilal Nehru. W* **374**. *P* 14.
438 **395** 15 n.p. olive-brown and brown-orange .. 10 10

396 Tagore (poet)

397 All India Radio Emblem and Transmitting Aerials

1961 (7 May). *Birth Centenary of Rabindranath Tagore. W* **374**. *P* 13 × 13½.
439 **396** 15 n.p. yellow-orange and blue-green .. 70 30

1961 (8 June). *Silver Jubilee of All India Radio. W* **374**. *P* 13½ × 13.
440 **397** 15 n.p. ultramarine 10 10

398 Prafulla Chandra Ray

399 V. N. Bhatkande

1961 (2 Aug). *Birth Centenary of Ray (social reformer). W* **374**. *P* 14×13½.
441 **398** 15 n.p. grey 10 20

1961 (1 Sept). *Birth Centenary of Bhatkande (composer)* (1960). *W* **374**. *P* 13×13½.
442 **399** 15 n.p. olive-brown 10 10

400 Child at Lathe

401 Fair Emblem and Main Gate

1961 (14 Nov). *Children's Day. W* **374**. *P* 14 × 13½.
443 **400** 15 n.p. brown 10 20

1961 (14 Nov). *Indian Industries Fair, New Delhi. W* **374**. *P* 14 × 14½.
444 **401** 15 n.p. blue and carmine 10 10

402 Indian Forest

1961 (21 Nov). *Centenary of Scientific Forestry. W* **374**. *P* 13 × 13½.
445 **402** 15 n.p. green and brown.. .. .. 30 20

403 Pitalkhora: Yaksha

404 Kalibangan Seal

1961 (14 Dec). *Centenary of Indian Archaeological Survey. W* **374**. *P* 14 × 13½ (15 *n.p.*) *or* 13½ × 14 (90 *n.p.*).
446 **403** 15 n.p. orange-brown 20 10
447 **404** 90 n.p. yellow-olive and light brown .. 40 20

405 M. M. Malaviya

406 Gauhati Refinery

1961 (24 Dec). *Birth Centenary of Malaviya (educationist). W* **374**. *P* 14×13½.
448 **405** 15 n.p. deep slate 10 20

1962 (1 Jan). *Inauguration of Gauhati Oil Refinery. W* **374**. *P* 13×13½.
449 **406** 15 n.p. blue 30 20

407 Bhikaiji Cama

408 Village Panchayati and Parliament Building

1962 (26 Jan). *Birth Centenary of Bhikaiji Cama (patriot). W* **374**. *P* 14.
450 **407** 15 n.p. reddish purple 10 10

1962 (26 Jan). *Inauguration of Panchayati System of Local Government. W* **374**. *P* 13×13½.
451 **408** 15 n.p. bright purple 10 10

409 D. Saraswati (religious reformer)

410 G. S. Vidhyarthi (journalist)

1962 (4 Mar). *Dayanard Saraswati Commemoration. W* **374**. *P* 14.
452 **409** 15 n.p. orange-brown 10 10

1962 (25 Mar). *Ganesh Shankar Vidhyarthi Commemoration. W* **374**. *P* 14×13½.
453 **410** 15 n.p. red-brown 10 10

411 Malaria Eradication Emblem

412 Dr. R. Prasad

1962 (7 Apr). *Malaria Eradication. W* **374**. *P* 13 × 13½.
454 **411** 15 n.p. yellow and claret 10 10

1962 (13 May). *Retirement of President Dr. Rajendra Prasad. W* **374**. *P* 13.
455 **412** 15 n.p. bright purple (*shades*) 20 10

413 Calcutta High Court

416 Ramabai Ranade

1962. *Centenary of Indian High Courts. T* **413** *and similar hori. designs. W* **374**. *P* 14.
456 15 n.p. dull green (1 July) 50 2
457 15 n.p. red-brown (6 August) 50 2
458 15 n.p. slate (14 August) 50 2
456/8 .. .. *Set of* 3 1·40 5
Designs:—No. 457, Madras High Court; No. 458, Bombay High Court.

1962 (15 Aug). *Birth Centenary of Ramabai Ranade (social reformer). W* **374**. *P* 14 × 13½
459 **416** 15 n.p. orange-brown 10 2

417 Indian Rhinoceros

418 "Passing the Flag to Youth"

1962 (1 Oct). *Wild Life Week. W* **374**. *P* 13½ × 14.
460 **417** 15 n.p. red-brown and deep turquoise .. 40 1

INSCRIPTIONS. From No. 461 onwards all designs are inscribed "BHARAT" in Devanagari in addition to "INDIA" in English.

1962 (14 Nov). *Children's Day. W* **374**. *P* 13½ × 13.
461 **418** 15 n.p. orange-red and turquoise-green 15 2

419 Human Eye within Lotus Blossom

420 S. Ramanujan

1962 (3 Dec). *19th International Ophthalmology Congress, New Delhi. W* **374**. *P* 13½ × 13.
462 **419** 15 n.p. deep olive-brown 20 10

1962 (22 Dec). *75th Birth Anniv of Srinivasa Ramanujan (mathematician). W* **374**. *P* 13½×14.
463 **420** 15 n.p. deep olive-brown 60 4

421 S. Vivekananda

Re.1

(**422**)

1963 (17 Jan). *Birth Centenary of Vivekananda (philosopher). W* **374**. *P* 14 × 14½.
464 **421** 15 n.p. orange-brown and yellow-olive .. 15 2

1963 (2 Feb). *No.* 428 *surch with T* **422**.
465 **385** 1 r. on 1 r. 3 n.p. pale yellow & brn .. 30 1

423 Hands reaching for F.A.O. Emblem

424 Henri Dunant (founder) and Centenary Emblem

1963 (21 Mar). *Freedom from Hunger. W* **374**. *P* 13.
466 **423** 15 n.p. grey-blue .. .. .. 1·00 30

963 (8 May). *Red Cross Centenary. W* **374.** *P* 13.
67 **424** 15 n.p. red and grey .. .. 2·50 30
a. Red (cross) omitted £2500

425 Artillery and Helicopter

963 (15 Aug). *Defence Campaign. T* **425** *and similar horiz design. W* **374.** *P* 14.
68 15 n.p. grey-green 40 10
69 1 r. red-brown 70 65
Design:—1 r. Sentry and parachutists.

427 D. Naoroji (parliamentarian)

428 Annie Besant (patriot and theosophist)

963 (4 Sept). *Dadabhai Naoroji Commemoration. W* **374.** *P* 13.
70 **427** 15 n.p. grey 10 10

963 (1 Oct). *Annie Besant Commemoration. W* **374.** *P* 13½×14.
71 **428** 15 n.p. turquoise-green 15 10
No 471 is incorrectly dated "1837". Mrs. Besant was born in 847.

429 Gaur

430 Lesser Panda

963 (7 Oct). *Wild Life Preservation. T* **429/30** *and similar designs. W* **374.** *P* 13½ × 14 (10 *n.p.*) *or* 13 (*others*).
72 10 n.p. black and yellow-orange .. .. .. 75 1·50
73 15 n.p. orange-brown and green .. .. 1·50 60
74 30 n.p. slate and yellow-ochre .. .. 3·75 1·50
75 50 n.p. orange and deep grey-green .. .. 3·50 80
76 1 r. light brown and blue .. .. .. 2·50 50
72/6 .. .. *Set of* 5 11·00 4·50
Designs: *Vert*—30 n.p. Indian elephant. *Horiz* (*as T* **430**)—) n.p. Tiger; 1 r. Lion.

434 "School Meals"

435 Eleanor Roosevelt at Spinning-wheel

963 (14 Nov). *Children's Day. W* **374.** *P* 14 × 13½.
77 **434** 15 n.p. bistre-brown 10 10

963 (10 Dec). 15*th Anniv of Declaration of Human Rights. W* **374.** *P* 13½ × 13.
78 **435** 15 n.p. reddish purple 10 15

436 Dipalakshmi (bronze)

437 Gopabandhu Das (social reformer)

1964 (4 Jan). 26*th International Orientalists Congress, New Delhi. W* **374.** *P* 13 × 13½.
479 **436** 15 n.p. deep ultramarine 20 15

1964 (4 Jan). *Gopabandhu Das Commemoration. W* **374.** *P* 13 × 13½.
480 **437** 15 n.p. deep dull purple 10 10

438 Purandaradasa

1964 (14 Jan). 400*th Death Anniv of Purandaradasa (composer). W* **374.** *P* 13×13½.
481 **438** 15 n.p. light brown 15 10

NETAJI SUBHAS CHANDRA BOSE / SIXTY SEVENTH BIRTH ANNIVERSARY / भारत INDIA

439 S. C. Bose and I. N. A. Badge

440 Bose and Indian National Army

1964 (23 Jan). 67*th Birth Anniv of Subhas Chandra Bose (nationalist). W* **374.** *P* 13.
482 **439** 15 n.p. yellow-bistre 40 20
483 **440** 55 n.p. black, orange and orange-red .. 40 45

441 Sarojini Naidu

442 Kasturba Gandhi

1964 (13 Feb). 85*th Birth Anniv of Sarojini Naidu (poetess). W* **374.** *P* 14.
484 **441** 15 n.p. deep grey-green and purple .. 10 10

1964 (22 Feb). 20*th Death Anniv of Kasturba Gandhi. W* **374.** *P* 14 × 13½.
485 **442** 15 n.p. orange-brown 10 10

443 Dr. W. M. Haffkine (immunologist)

444 Jawaharlal Nehru (statesman)

1964 (16 Mar). *Haffkine Commemoration. W* **374.** *P* 13.
486 **443** 15 n.p. deep purple-brown/*buff* 10 10

(Value expressed as paisa instead of naye paise.)

1964 (12 June). *Nehru Mourning Issue. No wmk. P* 13½ × 13.
487 **444** 15 p. deep slate 10 10

445 Sir Asutosh Mookerjee

446 Sri Aurobindo

1964 (29 June). *Birth Centenary of Sir Asutosh Mookerjee (education reformer). W* **374.** *P* 13½ × 13.
488 **445** 15 p. bistre-brown and yellow-olive .. 10 10

1964 (15 Aug). 92*nd Birth Anniv of Sri Aurobindo (religious teacher). W* **374.** *P* 13×13½.
489 **446** 15 p. dull purple 15 10

447 Raja R. Roy (social reformer)

448 I.S.O. Emblem and Globe

1964 (27 Sept). *Raja Rammohun Roy Commemoration. W* **374.** *P* 13 × 13½.
490 **447** 15 n.p. brown 10 10

1964 (9 Nov). *Sixth International Organization for Standardization General Assembly, Bombay. No wmk. P* 13 × 13½.
491 **448** 15 p. carmine 15 20

449 Jawaharlal Nehru (from 1 r. commemorative coin)

450 St. Thomas (after statue, Ortona Cathedral, Italy)

1964 (14 Nov). *Children's Day. No wmk. P* 14 × 13½.
492 **449** 15 p. slate 10 10

1964 (2 Dec). *St. Thomas Commemoration. No wmk. P* 14 × 13½.
493 **450** 15 p. reddish purple 10 30
No. 493 was issued on the occasion of Pope Paul's visit to India.

451 Globe

452 J. Tata (industrialist)

1964 (14 Dec). 22*nd International Geological Congress. W* **374.** *P* 14 × 13½.
494 **451** 15 p. blue-green 30 30

1965 (7 Jan). *Jamsetji Tata Commemoration. No wmk. P* 13½ × 13.
495 **452** 15 p. dull purple and orange 30 20

453 Lala Lajpat Rai

454 Globe and Congress Emblem

1965 (28 Jan). *Birth Centenary of Lala Lajpat Rai (social reformer). No wmk. P* 13×13½.
496 **453** 15 p. light brown 20 10

1965 (8 Feb). 20*th International Chamber of Commerce Congress, New Delhi. No wmk. P* 13½ × 13.
497 **454** 15 p. grey-green and carmine 15 15

455 Freighter *Jalausha* and Visakhapatnam

456 Abraham Lincoln

1965 (5 Apr). *National Maritime Day. W* **374** *(sideways). P* 14½ × 14.
498 **455** 15 p. blue 30 30

1965 (15 Apr). *Death Centenary of Abraham Lincoln. W* **374**. *P* 13.
499 **456** 15 p. brown and yellow-ochre 15 10

457 I.T.U. Emblem and Symbols

458 "Everlasting Flame"

1965 (17 May). *I.T.U. Centenary. W* **374** *(sideways). P* 14½ × 14.
500 **457** 15 p. reddish purple 90 30

1965 (27 May). *First Anniv of Nehru's Death. W* **374**. *P* 13.
501 **458** 15 p. carmine and blue 15 10

459 I.C.Y. Emblem

460 Climbers on Summit

1965 (26 June). *International Co-operation Year. P* 13½ × 13.
502 **459** 15 p. deep olive and yellow-brown . . 90 60

1965 (15 Aug). *Indian Mount Everest Expedition. P* 13.
503 **460** 15 p. deep reddish purple 20 10

461 Bidri Vase

462 Brass Lamp

466 Electric Locomotive

474 Medieval Sculpture

475 Dal Lake, Kashmir

1965–75. *T* 461/2, 466, 474/5 *and similar designs.*

(a) *W* 374 *(sideways on* 2, 3, 5, 6, 8, 30, 50, 60 *p.,* 2, 5, 10 *r.). P* 14 × 14½ (4, 10, 15, 20, 40, 70 *p.,* 1 *r.) or* 14½ × 14 *(others)*

No.				
504	2 p. red-brown (16.10.67)	. . . .	10	50
505	3 p. brown-olive (16.10.67)	. . . .	10	2·00
505*a*	4 p. lake-brown (15.5.68)	. . . .	10	2·00
506	5 p. cerise (16.10.67)	. . . .	10	10
	a. Imperf (pair)	. . . .	£180	
507	6 p. grey-black (1.7.66)	. . . .	10	2·25
508	8 p. red-brown (15.3.67)	. . . .	30	3·50
509	10 p. new blue (1.7.66)	. . . .	40	10
510	15 p. bronze-green (15.8.65)	. . . .	1·50	10
511	20 p. purple (16.10.67)	. . . .	5·00	10
512	30 p. sepia (15.3.67)	. . . .	15	10
513	40 p. maroon (2.10.68)	. . . .	15	10
514	50 p. blue-green (15.3.67)	. . . .	20	10
515	60 p. deep grey (16.10.67)	. . . .	35	10
516	70 p. chalky blue (15.3.67)	. . . .	60	10
517	1 r. red-brown and plum (1.7.66)	. .	60	10
518	2 r. new blue & deep slate-violet (15.3.67)		2·00	10
519	5 r. deep slate-violet and brown (15.3.67)		2·50	70
520	10 r. black and bronze-green (14.11.65)	. .	13·00	80
504/20	. . . .	*Set of* 18	24·00	10·00

(b) *No wmk. P* 14½ × 14

520*a*	5 p. cerise (12.5.74)	. . . . . .	30	10

(c) *Wmk Large Star and* "INDIA GOVT"† *in sheet. P* 14½ × 14

521	2 p. red-brown (1.3.75)	. . . . . .	50	1·25
	aw. Wmk reversed	. . . . . .	4·00	
521*b*	5 p. cerise (1.3.75)	. . . . . .	75	10

Designs: *Horiz (as T* **466**)—4 p. Coffee berries; 15 p. Plucking tea; 20 p. Hindustan Aircraft Industries Ajeet jet fighter; 40 p. Calcutta G.P.O.; 70 p. Hampi Chariot (sculpture). *(As T* **475**)—5 r. Bhakra Dam, Punjab; 10 r. Atomic reactor, Trombay. *Vert (as T* **461/2**)—5 p. "Family Planning"; 6 p. Konarak Elephant; 8 p. Spotted Deer ("Chital"); 30 p. Indian dolls; 50 p. Mangoes; 60 p. Somnath Temple.

†The arrangement of this watermark in the sheet results in the words and the star appearing upright, inverted or sideways.

Two different postal forgeries exist of No. 511, both printed in lithography and without watermark. The cruder version is roughly perforated 15, but the more sophisticated is perforated 14 × 14½.

See also Nos. 721/38.

479 G. B. Pant (statesman)

480 V. Patel

1965 (10 Sept). *Govind Ballabh Pant Commemoration. P* 13.
522 **479** 15 p. brown and deep green 10 20

1965 (31 Oct). *90th Birth Anniv of Vallabhbhai Patel (statesman). P* 14 × 13½.
523 **480** 15 p. blackish brown 10 30

481 C. Das

482 Vidyapati (poet)

1965 (5 Nov). *95th Birth Anniv of Chittaranjan Das (lawyer and patriot). P* 13.
524 **481** 15 p. yellow-brown 10 10

1965 (17 Nov). *Vidyapati Commemoration. P* 14 × 14½.
525 **482** 15 p. yellow-brown 10 10

483 Sikandra, Agra

484 Soldier, Hindustan Aircraft Industries Ajeet jet fighters and Cruiser *Mysore*

1966 (24 Jan). *Pacific Area Travel Association Conference. New Delhi. P* 13½ × 14.
526 **483** 15 p. slate 10 10

1966 (26 Jan). *Indian Armed Forces. P* 14
527 **484** 15 p. violet 70 30

485 Lal Bahadur Shastri (statesman)

486 Kambar (poet)

1966 (26 Jan). *Shastri Mourning Issue. P* 13 × 13½.
528 **485** 15 p. black 40 10

1966 (5 Apr). *Kambar Commemoration. P* 14 × 14½.
529 **486** 15 p. grey-green 10 10

487 B. R. Ambedkar

488 Kunwar Singh (patriot)

1966 (14 Apr). *75th Birth Anniv of Dr. Bhim Rao Ambedkar (lawyer). P* 14 × 13½.
530 **487** 15 p. purple-brown 10 10

1966 (23 Apr). *Kunwar Singh Commemoration. P* 14 × 13½.
531 **488** 15 p. chestnut 10 10

489 G. K. Gokhale

490 Acharya Dvivedi (poet)

1966 (9 May). *Birth Centenary of Gopal Krishna Gokhale (patriot). P* 13½ × 13.
532 **489** 15 p. brown-purple and pale yellow . . 10 10

1966 (15 May). *Dvivedi Commemoration. P* 13½ × 14.
533 **490** 15 p. drab 10 10

491 Maharaja Ranjit Singh (warrior)

492 Homi Bhabha (scientist) and Nuclear Reactor

1966 (28 June). *Maharaja Ranjit Singh Commemoration P* 14 × 13½.
534 **491** 15 p. purple 30 15

1966 (4 Aug). *Dr. Homi Bhabha Commemoration. P* 14½ × 14.
535 **492** 15 p. dull purple 15 30

493 A. K. Azad (scholar)

494 Swami Tirtha

1966 (11 Nov). *Abul Kalam Azad Commemoration. P* 13½ × 14.
536 **493** 15 p. chalky blue 15 15

1966 (11 Nov). *60th Death Anniv of Swami Rama Tirtha (social reformer). P* 13 × 13½.
537 **494** 15 p. turquoise-blue 20 30

495 Infant and Dove Emblem

496 Allahabad High Court

(Des C. Pakrashi)

1966 (14 Nov). *Children's Day. P* 13 × 13½.
538 **495** 15 p. bright purple 30 20

1966 (25 Nov). *Centenary of Allahabad High Court. P* 14½ × 14
539 **496** 15 p. dull purple 30 30

497 Indian Family **498** Hockey Game

66 (12 Dec). *Family Planning. P* 13.
) **497** 15 p. brown 15 15

66 (31 Dec). *India's Hockey Victory in Fifth Asian Games. P* 13.
1 **498** 15 p. new blue .. .. 1·00 50

499 "Jai Kisan" **500** Voter and Polling Booth

67 (11 Jan). *First Anniv of Shastri's Death. P* 13½ × 14.
2 **499** 15 p. yellow-green 15 30

67 (13 Jan). *Indian General Election. P* 13½ × 14.
3 **500** 15 p. red-brown 15 15

501 Gurudwara Shrine, Patna **502** Taj Mahal, Agra

67 (17 Jan). *300th Birth Anniv* (1966) *of Guru Gobind Singh (Sikh religious leader). P* 14×13½.
4 **501** 15 p. bluish violet 15 15

67 (19 Mar). *International Tourist Year. P* 14½ × 14.
5 **502** 15 p. bistre-brown and orange 15 15

503 Nandalal Bose and "Garuda" **504** Survey Emblem and Activities

67 (16 Apr). *First Death Anniv of Nandalal Bose (painter). P* 14 × 13½.
6 **503** 15 p. bistre-brown 15 15

67 (1 May). *Survey of India Bicentenary. P* 13½ × 13.
7 **504** 15 p. reddish lilac 30 30

505 Basaveswara **506** Narsinha Mehta (poet)

67 (11 May). *800th Death Anniv of Basaveswara (reformer and statesman). P* 13½ × 14.
8 **505** 15 p. orange-red 15 15

67 (30 May). *Narsinha Mehta Commemoration. P* 14 × 13½.
9 **506** 15 p. blackish brown 15 15

507 Maharana Pratap **508** Narayana Guru

1967 (11 June). *Maharana Pratap (Rajput leader) Commemoration. P* 14×14½.
550 **507** 15 p. red-brown 15 15

1967 (21 Aug). *Narayana Guru (philosopher) Commemoration. P* 14.
551 **508** 15 p. brown 15 20

509 President Radhakrishnan **510** Martyrs' Memorial, Patna

1967 (5 Sept). *75th Birth Anniv of Sarvepalli Radhakrishnan (former President). P* 13.
552 **509** 15 p. claret 40 15

1967 (1 Oct). *25th Anniv of "Quit India" Movement. P* 14½ × 14.
553 **510** 15 p. lake 15 15

511 Route Map **512** Wrestling

1967 (9 Nov). *Centenary of Indo-European Telegraph Service. P* 13½ × 14.
554 **511** 15 p. black and light blue 20 20

1967 (12 Nov). *World Wrestling Championships, New Delhi. P* 13½×14.
555 **512** 15 p. purple and light orange-brown .. 30 20

513 Nehru leading Naga Tribesmen **514** Rashbehari Basu (nationalist)

1967 (1 Dec). *4th Anniv of Nagaland as a State of India. P* 13×13½.
556 **513** 15 p. ultramarine 15 15

1967 (26 Dec). *Rashbehari Basu Commemoration. P* 14.
557 **514** 15 p. maroon 15 20

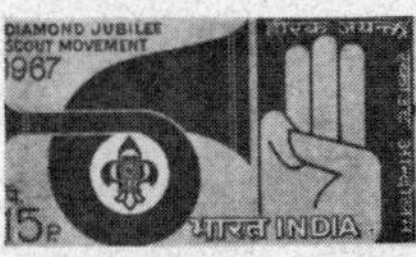

515 Bugle, Badge and Scout Salute

1967 (27 Dec). *60th Anniv of Scout Movement in India. P* 14½×14.
558 **515** 15 p. chestnut 60 30

516 Men embracing Universe **517** Globe and Book of Tamil

1968 (1 Jan). *Human Rights Year. P* 13.
559 **516** 15 p. bronze-green 30 30

1968 (3 Jan). *International Conference-Seminar of Tamil Studies, Madras. P* 13.
560 **517** 15 p. reddish lilac 30 15

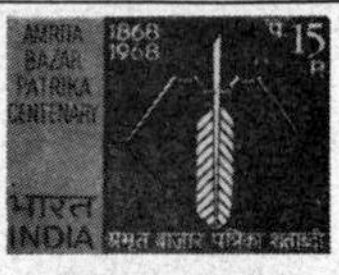

518 U.N. Emblem and Transport **519** Quill and Bow Symbol

1968 (1 Feb). *United Nations Conference on Trade and Development, New Delhi. P* 14½×14.
561 **518** 15 p. turquoise-blue 40 15

1968 (20 Feb). *Centenary of* Amrita Bazar Patrika *(newspaper). P* 13½×14.
562 **519** 15 p. sepia and orange-yellow 15 15

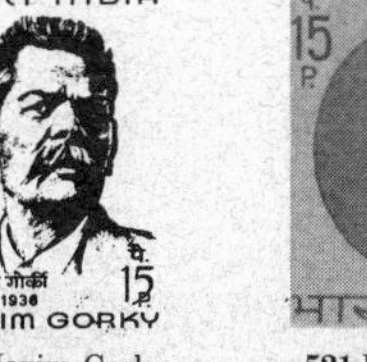

520 Maxim Gorky **521** Emblem and Medal

1968 (28 Mar). *Birth Centenary of Maxim Gorky. P* 13½.
563 **520** 15 p. plum 15 20

1968 (31 Mar). *First Triennale Art Exhibition, New Delhi. P* 13.
564 **521** 15 p. orange, royal blue and light blue 30 20
a. Orange omitted £650

522 Letter-box and "100,000" **523** Stalks of Wheat, Agricultural Institute and Production Graph

(Des C. Pakrashi)

1968 (1 July). *Opening of 100,000th Indian Post Office. P* 13.
565 **522** 20 p. red, blue and black 30 15

1968 (17 July). *Wheat Revolution. P* 13.
566 **523** 20 p. bluish green and orange-brown .. 30 15

524 "Self-portrait" **525** Lakshminath Bezbaruah

(Des from self-portrait)

1968 (17 Sept). *30th Death Anniv of Gaganendranath Tagore (painter). P* 13.
567 **524** 20 p. brown-purple and ochre 30 15

1968 (5 Oct). *Birth Centenary of Lakshminath Bezbaruah (writer). P* 13½ × 14.
568 **525** 20 p. blackish brown 15 15

526 Athlete's Legs and Olympic Rings

1968 (12 Oct). *Olympic Games, Mexico. P* 14½ × 14.
569 **526** 20 p. brown and grey 15 15
570 1 r. sepia and brown-olive 40 15

527 Bhagat Singh and Followers

528 Azad Hind Flag, Swords and Chandra Bose (founder)

1968 (19 Oct). *61st Birth Anniv of Bhagat Singh (patriot). P* 13.
571 **527** 20 p. yellow-brown 20 20

1968 (21 Oct). *25th Anniv of Azad Hind Government. P* 14 × 14½.
572 **528** 20 p. deep blue 20 15

529 Sister Nivedita

530 Marie Curie and Radium Treatment

1968 (27 Oct). *Birth Centenary of Sister Nivedita (social reformer). P* 14×14½.
573 **529** 20p. deep bluish green 30 30

1968 (6 Nov). *Birth Centenary of Marie Curie. P* 14½ × 14.
574 **530** 20 p. slate-lilac .. .. 1·40 50

531 Map of the World

532 Cochin Synagogue

1968 (1 Dec). *21st International Geographical Congress, New Delhi. P* 13.
575 **531** 20 p. new blue 15 15

1968 (15 Dec). *400th Anniv of Cochin Synagogue. P* 13.
576 **532** 20 p. blue and carmine 55 40

533 I.N.S. *Nilgiri* (frigate)

534 Red-billed Blue Magpie

1968 (15 Dec). *Navy Day. P* 13.
577 **533** 20 p. grey-blue .. .. 1·50 40

1968 (31 Dec). *Birds. T* **534** *and similar designs. P* 14 × 14½ (1 *r.*) *or* 14½ × 14 (*others*).
578 20 p. multicoloured 55 40
579 50 p. scarlet, black and turquoise-green .. 1·10 1·50
580 1 r. deep blue, yellow-brown and pale blue .. 1·75 1·00
581 2 r. multicoloured .. .. 1·75 1·50
578/81 .. .. *Set of* 4 4·50 4·00
Designs: *Horiz*—50 p. Brown-fronted Pied Woodpecker; 2 r. Yellow-backed Sunbird. *Vert*—1 r. Slaty-headed Scimitar Babbler.

538 Bankim Chandra Chatterjee

539 Dr. Bhagavan Das

1969 (1 Jan). *130th Birth Anniv of Bankim Chandra Chatterjee (writer). P* 13½.
582 **538** 20 p. ultramarine 15 20

1969 (12 Jan). *Birth Centenary of Dr. Bhagavan Das (philosopher). P* 13½.
583 **539** 20 p. pale chocolate 15 15

540 Dr. Martin Luther King

541 Mirza Ghalib and Letter Seal

1969 (25 Jan). *Martin Luther King Commemoration. P* 13½.
584 **540** 20 p. deep olive-brown 40 20

1969 (17 Feb). *Death Centenary of Mirza Ghalib (poet). P* 14½ × 14.
585 **541** 20 p. sepia, brown-red and flesh 15 15

542 Osmania University

1969 (15 Mar). *50th Anniv of Osmania University. P* 14½ × 14.
586 **542** 20 p. olive-green 15 20

543 Rafi Ahmed Kidwai and Lockheed Constellation Mail Plane

1969 (1 Apr). *20th Anniv of "ALL-UP" Air Mail Scheme. P* 13.
587 **543** 20 p. deep blue 60 30

544 I.L.O. Badge and Emblem

545 Memorial, and Hands dropping Flowers

1969 (11 Apr). *50th Anniv of International Labour Organisation. P* 14½ × 14.
588 **544** 20 p. chestnut 15 20

1969 (13 Apr). *50th Anniv of Jallianwala Bagh Massacre, Amritsar. P* 14×13½.
589 **545** 20 p. rose-carmine 15 20

546 K. Nageswara Rao Pantulu (journalist)

547 Ardaseer Cursetjee Wadia, and Ships

1969 (1 May). *Kasinadhuni Nageswara Rao Pantulu Commemoration. P* 13½ × 14.
590 **546** 20 p. brown 15 20

1969 (27 May). *Ardaseer Cursetjee Wadia (ship-builder) Commemoration. P* 14½×14.
591 **547** 20 p. turquoise-green 40 30

ALTERED CATALOGUE NUMBERS

Any Catalogue numbers altered from the last edition are shown as a list in the introductory pages.

548 Serampore College

549 Dr. Zakir Husain

1969 (7 June). *150th Anniv of Serampore College. P* 13½.
592 **548** 20 p. plum 15 2

1969 (11 June). *President Dr. Zakir Husain Commemoration P* 13.
593 **549** 20 p. sepia 15 2

550 Laxmanrao Kirloskar

1969 (20 June). *Birth Centenary of Laxmanrao Kirloskar (agri culturalist). P* 13.
594 **550** 20 p. grey-black 15 1

551 Gandhi and his Wife

552 Gandhi's Head and Shoulders

553 Gandhi walking (woodcut)

554 Gandhi with Charkha

(Des Suraj Sadan (20 p.), P. Chitnis (75 p.), Indian Security Press (1 r.) and C. Pakrashi (5 r.))

1969 (2 Oct). *Birth Centenary of Mahatma Gandhi. P* 13½ × 1 (20 *p.*), 14 × 14½ (1 *r.*) *or* 13 (*others*).
595 **551** 20 p. blackish brown 60 3
596 **552** 75 p. cinnamon and drab.. .. .. 1·25 9
597 **553** 1 r. blue .. .. 1·25 6
598 **554** 5 r. greyish brown and red-orange .. 4·50 6·5
595/8 .. .. *Set of* 4 7·00 7·5

555 *Ajanta* (bulk carrier) and I.M.C.O. Emblem

1969 (14 Oct). *10th Anniv of Inter-Governmental Maritim Consultative Organization. P* 13.
599 **555** 20 p. violet-blue .. .. 1·50 4

556 Outline of Parliament Building and Globe

557 Astronaut walking beside Space Module on Moon

69 (30 Oct). *57th Inter-Parliamentary Conference, New Delhi. P* 14½ × 14.
0 **556** 20 p. new blue 15 20

69 (19 Nov). *First Man on the Moon. P* 14 × 14½.
1 **557** 20 p. olive-brown 40 30

558 Gurudwara Nankana Sahib (birthplace)

559 Tiger's Head and Hands holding Globe

69 (23 Nov). *500th Birth Anniv of Guru Nanak Dev (Sikh religious leader). P* 13½.
2 **558** 20 p. slate-violet 15 20

69 (24 Nov). *International Union for the Conservation of Nature and Natural Resources Conference, New Delhi. P* 14½ × 14.
3 **559** 20 p. orange-brown and bronze-green . . 30 30

560 Sadhu Vaswani

561 Thakkar Bapa

69 (25 Nov). *90th Birth Anniv of Sadhu Vaswani (educationist). P* 14 × 14½.
4 **560** 20 p. grey 15 15

69 (29 Nov). *Birth Centenary of Thakkar Bapa (humanitarian). P* 13½.
5 **561** 20 p. chocolate 15 20

562 Satellite, Television, Telephone and Globe

563 C. N. Annadurai

70 (21 Jan). *12th Plenary Assembly of International Radio Consultative Committee. P* 13.
6 **562** 20 p. Prussian blue 40 20

70 (3 Feb). *First Death Anniv of Conjeevaram Natrajan Annadurai (statesman). P* 13.
7 **563** 20 p. reddish purple and royal blue . . 15 15

564 M. N. Kishore and Printing Press

565 Nalanda College

70 (19 Feb). *75th Death Anniv of Munshi Newal Kishore publisher). P* 13.
8 **564** 20 p. lake 15 20

70 (27 Mar). *Centenary of Nalanda College. P* 14½ × 14.
9 **565** 20 p. brown 60 40

566 Swami Shraddhanand (social reformer)

567 Lenin

1970 (30 Mar). *Swami Shraddhanand Commemoration. P* 14 × 13½.
610 **566** 20 p. yellow-brown 60 40

1970 (22 Apr). *Birth Centenary of Lenin. P* 13.
611 **567** 20 p. orange-brown and sepia 30 20

568 New U.P.U. H.Q. Building

569 Sher Shah Suri (15th-century ruler)

1970 (20 May). *New U.P.U. Headquarters Building, Berne. P* 13.
612 **568** 20 p. emerald, grey and black 15 20

1970 (22 May). *Sher Shah Suri Commemoration. P* 13.
613 **569** 20 p. deep bluish green 15 20

570 V. D. Savarkar (patriot) and Cellular Jail, Andaman Islands

571 "UN" and Globe

1970 (28 May). *Vinayak Damodar Savarkar Commemoration. P* 13.
614 **570** 20 p. orange-brown 15 20

1970 (26 June). *25th Anniv of United Nations. P* 13.
615 **571** 20 p. light new blue 30 20

572 Symbol and Workers

1970 (18 Aug). *Asian Productivity Year. P* 14½ × 14.
616 **572** 20 p. violet 20 20

573 Dr. Montessori and I.E.Y. Emblem

1970 (31 Aug). *Birth Centenary of Dr. Maria Montessori (educationist). P* 13.
617 **573** 20 p. dull purple 30 30

574 J. N. Mukherjee (revolutionary) and Horse

575 V. S. Srinivasa Sastri

1970 (9 Sept). *Jatindra Nath Mukherjee Commemoration. P* 14½ × 14.
618 **574** 20 p. chocolate 75 30

1970 (22 Sept). *Srinivasa Sastri (educationist) Commemoration. P* 13×13½.
619 **575** 20 p. yellow and brown-purple 30 30

NEW INFORMATION

The editor is always interested to correspond with people who have new information that will improve or correct the Catalogue.

576 I. C. Vidyasagar

577 Maharishi Valmiki

1970 (26 Sept). *150th Birth Anniv of Iswar Chandra Vidyasagar (educationist). P* 13.
620 **576** 20 p. brown and purple 30 30

1970 (14 Oct). *Maharishi Valmiki (ancient author) Commemoration. P* 13.
621 **577** 20 p. purple 30 30

578 Calcutta Port

1970 (17 Oct). *Centenary of Calcutta Port Trust. P* 13½ × 13.
622 **578** 20 p. greenish blue 90 50

579 University Building

1970 (29 Oct). *50th Anniv of Jamia Millia Islamia University. P* 14½ × 14.
623 **579** 20 p. yellow-green 40 40

580 Jamnalal Bajaj

581 Nurse and Patient

1970 (4 Nov). *Jamnalal Bajaj (industrialist) Commemoration. W* 374. *P* 13½×13.
624 **580** 20 p. olive-grey 15 30

1970 (5 Nov). *50th Anniv of Indian Red Cross. W* 374 *(sideways). P* 13 × 13½.
625 **581** 20 p. red and greenish blue 50 40

582 Sant Namdeo

583 Beethoven

1970 (9 Nov). *700th Birth Anniv of Sant Namdeo (mystic). W* 374. *P* 13.
626 **582** 20 p. orange 15 30

1970 (16 Dec). *Birth Bicentenary of Beethoven. P* 13.
627 **583** 20 p. orange and greyish black . . . . 1·50 60

584 Children examining Stamps

585 Girl Guide

1970 (23 Dec). *Indian National Philatelic Exhibition, New Dehli. T* **584** *and similar horiz design. P* 13.
628 20 p. orange and myrtle-green 30 10
629 1 r. orange-brown and pale yellow-brown . . 2·25 80
Design:—1 r. Gandhi commemorative through magnifier.

1970 (27 Dec). *Diamond Jubilee of Girl Guide Movement in India. P* 13.
630 **585** 20 p. maroon 60 30

586 Hands and Lamp (Emblem)

587 Vidyapith Building

1971 (11 Jan). *Centenary of Indian Life Insurance. P* 13.
631 **586** 20 p. sepia and crimson 20 30

1971 (10 Feb). *50th Anniv of Kashi Vidyapith University. P* 14½×14.
632 **587** 20 p. blackish brown 20 30

588 Sant Ravidas

589 C. F. Andrews

1971 (10 Feb). *Sant Ravidas (15th-cent mystic) Commemoration. P* 13.
633 **588** 20 p. lake 30 30

1971 (12 Feb). *Birth Centenary of Charles Freer Andrews (missionary). P* 13×13½.
634 **589** 20 p. chestnut 35 30

590 Acharya Narendra Deo (scholar)

591 Crowd and "100"

1971 (19 Feb). *15th Death Anniv of Acharya Narendra Deo. P* 13.
635 **590** 20 p. dull green 15 30

1971 (10 Mar). *Centenary of Decennial Census. P* 13.
636 **591** 20 p. brown and blue 30 30

592 Sri Ramana Maharishi (mystic)

593 Raja Ravi Varma and "Damayanti and the Swan"

1971 (14 Apr). *21st Death Anniv of Ramana Maharishi. P* 13½.
637 **592** 20 p. orange and sepia 20 30

1971 (29 Apr). *65th Death Anniv of Ravi Varma (artist). P* 13.
638 **593** 20 p. green 40 40

594 Dadasaheb Phalke and Camera

595 "Abhisarika" (Tagore)

1971 (30 Apr). *Birth Centenary of Dadasaheb Phalke (cinematographer). P* 13½×13.
639 **594** 20 p. deep maroon 70 40

1971 (7 Aug). *Birth Centenary of Abanindranath Tagore (painter). P* 14×14½.
640 **595** 20 p. grey, buff-yellow & blackish brown 30 30

596 Swami Virjanand (Vedic scholar)

597 Cyrus the Great and Procession

1971 (14 Sept). *Swami Virjanand Commemoration. P* 13½.
641 **596** 20 p. chestnut 30 40

1971 (12 Oct). *2500th Anniv of Charter of Cyrus the Great. P* 13.
642 **597** 20 p. blackish brown 75 55

598 Globe and Money Box

1971 (31 Oct). *World Thrift Day. P* 14½ × 14.
643 **598** 20 p. blue-grey 20 30

599 Ajanta Caves Painting

600 "Women at Work" (Geeta Gupta)

1971 (4 Nov). *25th Anniv of U.N.E.S.C.O. P* 13.
644 **599** 20 p. red-brown . . . . 1·25 50

(Des from painting by Geeta Gupta)

1971 (14 Nov). *Children's Day. P* 14 × 14½.
645 **600** 20 p. scarlet 20 40

शरणार्थी सहायता REFUGEE RELIEF (601)

Refugee Relief (602)

शरणार्थी सहायता REFUGEE RELIEF (603)

REFUGEE RELIEF (604)

REFUGEE RELIEF (605)

Refugee Relief (606)

Refugee relief (606*a*)

शरणार्थी सहायता Refugee Relief (606*b*)

607 Refugees

1971. *Obligatory Tax. Refugee Relief.*

(*a*) *Provisional issues. No.* 506 *variously optd*

(i) *For all India, optd at Nasik*

646 **601** 5 p. cerise (15 Nov) 50 10
a. Opt double . . . . 2·50

(ii) *For various areas*

647 **602** 5 p. Bangalore . . . . 2·50 1·00
a. Opt double, one inverted . .
648 **603** 5 p. Jaipur . . . . 6·00 1·50
649 **604** 5 p. Rajasthan . . . . 3·25 1·50
a. Error, "RELIEF REFUGEE" . . 12·00
b. Opt inverted . . . .
650 **605** 5 p. New Delhi . . . . . . 14·00 3·25
a. Opt inverted . . . . . . 14·00
650*b* **606** 5 p. Goa . . . . 14·00 3·75
650*c* **606*a*** 5 p. Jabalpur . . . . . . 11·00 3·25
650*d* **606*b*** 5 p. Alwar . . . . . .

(*b*) *Definitive issue. W* 374. *P* 14 × 14½

651 **607** 5 p. carmine (1 Dec) 30 10

From 15 November 1971 until 31 March 1973, the Indian Government levied a 5 p. surcharge on all mail, except postcards and newspapers, for the relief of refugees from the former East Pakistan.

As supplies of the provisional overprint could not be sent to all Indian post offices in time, local postmasters were authorised to make their own overprints. Most of these were applied by rubber stamps and so we do not list them. Those listed have typographed overprints and No. 649 also has a rubber handstamp in native language. Some of the above overprints were also used in areas other than those where they were produced.

608 C. V. Raman (scientist) and Light Graph

1971 (12 Nov). *First Death Anniv of Chandrasekhara Venkat Raman. P* 13.
652 **608** 20 p. orange and deep brown 50 3

609 Visva Bharati Building and Rabindranath Tagore (founder)

1971 (24 Dec). *50th Anniv of Visva Bharati University P* 14½×14.
653 **609** 20 p. sepia and yellow-brown 20 3

610 Cricketers

611 Map and Satellite

1971 (30 Dec). *Indian Cricket Victories. P* 14½ × 14.
654 **610** 20 p. green, myrtle-green and sage-green 2·00 6

1972 (26 Feb). *First Anniv of Arvi Satellite Earth Station P* 13½.
655 **611** 20 p. plum 15 3

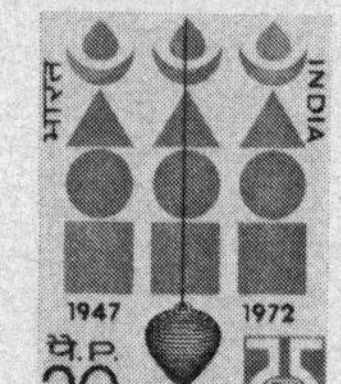

612 Elemental Symbols and Plumb-line

613 Signal Box Panel

1972 (29 May). *25th Anniv of Indian Standards Institution P* 13.
656 **612** 20 p. turquoise-grey and black 15 4

1972 (30 June). *50th Anniv of International Railways Union P* 13.
657 **613** 20 p. multicoloured 50 4
a. Blue omitted . . . . . . 65·00

614 Hockey-player

615 Symbol of Sri Aurobindo

1972 (10 Aug). *Olympic Games, Munich. T* **614** *and similar hor design. P* 13.
658 20 p. deep bluish violet . . . . . . 1·50 2
659 1 r. 45, light turquoise-green & brown-lake 2·00 2·0
Design:—1 r. 45, Various sports.

1972 (15 Aug). *Birth Centenary of Sri Aurobindo (religiou teacher). P* 13½.
660 **615** 20 p. yellow and new blue 20 3

616 Celebrating Independence Day in front of Parliament

617 Inter-Services Crest

72 (15 Aug). *25th Anniversary of Independence* (1st issue). *P* 13.
61 **616** 20 p. multicoloured 15 30
See also Nos. 673/4.

72 (15 Aug). *Defence Services Commemoration. P* 13.
62 **617** 20 p. multicoloured 30 40

618 V. O. Chidambaram Pillai (trade union leader) and Ship

619 Bhai Vir Singh

72 (5 Sept). *Birth Centenary of V. O. Chidambaram Pillai. P* 13.
63 **618** 20 p. new blue and purple-brown .. 75 40

72 (16 Oct). *Birth Centenary of Bhai Vir Singh (poet). P* 13.
64 **619** 20 p. plum 30 40

620 T. Prakasam

621 Vemana

972 (16 Oct). *Birth Centenary of Tanguturi Prakasam (lawyer). P* 13.
65 **620** 20 p. brown 20 40

972 (16 Oct). *300th Birth Anniv of Vemana (poet). W* **374.** *P* 13½ × 14.
66 **621** 20 p. black 20 40

622 Bertrand Russell

623 Symbol of "Asia 72"

972 (16 Oct). *Birth Centenary of Bertrand Russell (philosopher). P* 13½ × 14.
67 **622** 1 r. 45, black .. .. 3·25 2·75

972 (3 Nov). *"Asia '72" (Third Asian International Trade Fair), New Delhi. T* **623** *and similar vert design. W* **374.** *P* 13.
68 20 p. black and orange.. .. .. 10 20
69 1 r. 45, orange and slate-black .. .. 60 1·75
Design:—1 r. 45, Hand of Buddha.

624 V. A. Sarabhai and Rocket

625 Flag of U.S.S.R. and Kremlin Tower

972 (30 Dec). *First Death Anniv of Vikram A. Sarabhai (scientist). P* 13.
70 **624** 20 p. brown and myrtle-green 20 40

972 (30 Dec). *50th Anniv of U.S.S.R. P* 13.
71 **625** 20 p. light yellow and red 20 40

626 Exhibition Symbol

627 "Democracy"

973 (8 Jan). *"Indipex '73" Stamp Exhibition* (1st issue). *P* 13.
72 **626** 1 r. 45, light mauve, gold and black .. 45 1·25
See also Nos. 701/**MS**704.

1973 (26 Jan). *25th Anniv of Independence* (2nd issue). *T* **627** *and similar multicoloured design. P* 13 (20 *p.*) *or* 14½ × 14 (1 *r.* 45).
673 20 p. Type **627** 15 15
674 1 r. 45, Hindustan Aircraft Industries Gnat jet fighters over India Gate (38×20 *mm*) .. .. 1·10 1·60

628 Sri Ramakrishna Paramahamsa (religious leader)

629 Postal Corps Emblem

1973 (18 Feb). *Sri Ramakrishna Paramahamsa Commemoration. P* 13.
675 **628** 20 p. light brown 20 40

1973 (1 Mar). *First Anniv of Army Postal Service Corps. P* 13.
676 **629** 20 p. deep ultramarine and vermilion .. 40 50

630 Flag and Map of Bangladesh

631 Kumaran Asan

(Des C. Pakrashi)

1973 (10 Apr). *"Jai Bangla" (Inauguration of First Bangladesh Parliament). P* 13.
677 **630** 20 p. multicoloured 15 40

1973 (12 Apr). *Birth Centenary of Kumaran Asan (writer and poet). P* 13.
678 **631** 20 p. sepia 20 45

632 Flag and Flames

633 Dr. B. R. Ambedkar (lawyer)

(Des C. Pakrashi)

1973 (13 Apr). *Homage to Martyrs for Independence. P* 13.
679 **632** 20 p. multicoloured 15 40

(Des Charanjit Lal)

1973 (14 Apr). *Bhim Rao Ambedkar Commemoration. P* 13.
680 **633** 20 p. bronze-green and deep purple .. 20 75

634 "Radha-Kishangarh" (Nihal Chand)

635 Mount Everest

1973 (5 May). *Indian Miniature Paintings. T* **634** *and similar vert designs. Multicoloured. P* 13.
681 20 p. Type **634** 30 35
682 50 p. "Dance Duet" (Aurangzeb's period) .. 60 1·50
683 1 r. "Lovers on a Camel" (Nasir-ud-din) .. 1·50 2·75
684 2 r. "Chained Elephant" (Zain-al-Abidin) .. 2·00 3·25
681/4 .. .. *Set of* 4 4·00 7·00

1973 (15 May). *15th Anniv of Indian Mountaineering Foundation. P* 13.
685 **635** 20 p. blue 40 50

636 Tail of Boeing 747

637 Cross, Church of St. Thomas' Mount, Madras

(Des Air-India Art Studies from photograph by Jehangir Gazdar)

1973 (8 June). *25th Anniv of Air-India's International Services. P* 13.
686 **636** 1 r. 45, indigo and carmine-red .. 4·00 4·00

1973 (3 July). *19th Death Centenary of St. Thomas. P* 13.
687 **637** 20 p. blue-grey and agate 20 50

638 Michael Madhusudan Dutt (poet—Death Centenary)

639 A. O. Hume

1973 (21 July). *Centenaries. T* **638** *and similar horiz designs. P* 13.
688 20 p. sage-green and orange-brown .. .. 1·00 65
a. Orange-brown omitted £500
689 30 p. red-brown .. .. 1·25 2·50
690 50 p. deep brown .. .. 1·50 2·50
691 1 r. dull violet and orange-vermilion .. 1·50 1·50
688/91 .. .. *Set of* 4 4·75 6·50
Designs:—30 p. Vishnu Digambar Paluskar (musician—birth centenary); 50 p. Dr G. A. Hansen (centenary of discovery of leprosy bacillus); 1 r. Nicolaus Copernicus (astronomer—5th birth centenary).

1973 (31 July). *Allan Octavian Hume (founder of Indian National Congress) Commemoration. P* 13.
692 **639** 20 p. grey 20 40

640 Gandhi and Nehru

641 R. C. Dutt

(Des C. Pakrashi from photograph)

1973 (15 Aug). *Gandhi and Nehru Commemoration. P* 13.
693 **640** 20 p. multicoloured 20 40

1973 (27 Sept). *Romesh Chandra Dutt (writer) Commemoration. P* 13.
694 **641** 20 p. brown 20 40

642 K. S. Ranjitsinhji

643 Vithalbhai Patel

1973 (27 Sept). *K. S. Ranjitsinhji (cricketer) Commemoration. P* 13.
695 **642** 30p. myrtle-green .. .. 3·50 3·25

1973 (27 Sept). *Vithalbhai Patel (lawyer) Commemoration. P* 13.
696 **643** 50 p. light red-brown 20 65

ALTERED CATALOGUE NUMBERS

Any Catalogue numbers altered from the last edition are shown as a list in the introductory pages.

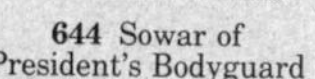

644 Sowar of President's Bodyguard

645 Interpol Emblem

1973 (30 Sept). *Bicentenary of President's Bodyguard. P* 13.
697 **644** 20 p. multicoloured 35 40

1973 (9 Oct). *50th Anniv of Interpol. P* 13.
698 **645** 20 p. brown 30 40

646 Syed Ahmad Khan (social reformer)

647 "Children at Play" (Bela Raval)

1973 (17 Oct). *Syed Ahmad Khan Commemoration. P* 13.
699 **646** 20 p. sepia 20 60

1973 (14 Nov). *Children's Day. P* 13.
700 **647** 20 p. multicoloured 20 30

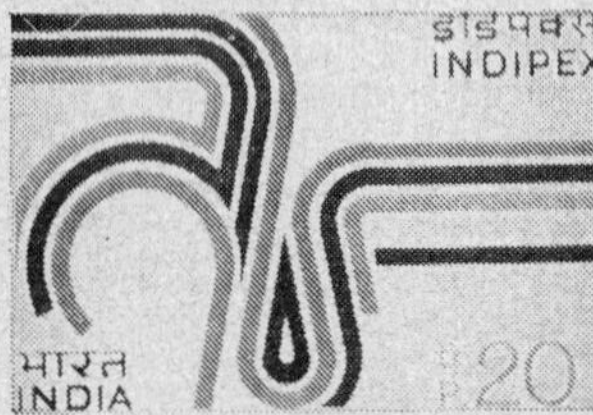

648 Indipex Emblem

1973 (14 Nov). *"Indipex '73" Philatelic Exhibition, New Delhi (2nd issue). T* **648** *and similar multicoloured designs. P* 13½ × 13 (2 *r.*) *or* 13 × 13½ (*others*).
701 20 p. Type **648** 20 30
702 1 r. Ceremonial elephant and 1½ a. stamp of 1947 (*vert*) .. .. 1·25 2·00
703 2 r. Common Peafowl (*vert*) .. .. .. 1·50 2·75
701/3 .. .. *Set of* 3 2·75 4·50
MS704 127 × 127 mm. Nos. 672 and 701/3. Imperf 5·00 8·00

649 Emblem of National Cadet Corps

650 C. Rajagopalachari (statesman)

1973 (25 Nov). *25th Anniv of National Cadet Corps. P* 13.
705 **649** 20 p. multicoloured 20 30

1973 (25 Dec). *Chakravarti Rajagopalachari Commemoration. P* 13.
706 **650** 20 p. olive-brown 20 50

651 "Sun" Mask

652 Chhatrapati

1974 (15 Apr). *Indian Masks. T* **651** *and similar multicoloured designs. P* 13.
707 20 p. Type **651** 15 15
708 50 p. "Moon" mask 30 55
709 1 r. "Narasimha" .. .. 70 1·25
710 2 r. "Ravana" (*horiz*) .. .. 1·00 2·00
707/10 .. .. *Set of* 4 1·90 3·50
MS711 109 × 135 mm. Nos. 707/10 .. .. .. 2·75 6·50

1974 (2 June). *300th Anniv of Coronation of Chhatrapati Shri Shivaji Maharaj. P* 13.
712 **652** 25 p. multicoloured 30 30

653 Maithili Sharan Gupta (poet)

654 Kandukuri Veeresalingam (social reformer)

1974 (3 July). *Indian Personalities* (1*st series*). *T* **653** *and similar vert designs. P* 13.
713 25 p. chestnut 15 45
714 25 p. deep brown 15 45
715 25 p. sepia 15 45
713/15 .. .. *Set of* 3 40 1·25
Portraits:—No. 714, Jainarain Vyas (politician and journalist); No. 715, Utkal Gourab Madhusudan Das (social reformer).

1974 (15 July). *Indian Personalities* (2*nd series*). *T* **654** *and similar vert designs. P* 13.
716 25 p. lake-brown 25 50
717 50 p. dull purple .. .. 55 1·75
718 1 r. chestnut-brown .. .. 70 1·75
716/18 .. .. *Set of* 3 1·40 3·50
Portraits:—50 p. Tipu Sultan; 1 r. Max Mueller (Sanskrit scholar).

655 Kamala Nehru

(Des Charanjit Lal)

1974 (1 Aug). *Kamala Nehru Commemoration. P* 14½ × 14.
719 **655** 25 p. multicoloured 50 50

656 W. P. Y. Emblem

1974 (14 Aug). *World Population Year. P* 13½.
720 **656** 25 p. maroon and buff 20 30

LARGE STAR AND INDIA GOVT WATERMARK. Two types exist of this sheet watermark. The initial arrangement resulted in the stars appearing upright, inverted and sideways, in either direction, within the same sheet.

Printings issued from the beginning of 1980 shows a second type on which the stars in each sheet all point in the same direction. All commemoratives with this watermark used the second type.

657 Spotted Deer

657*b* Bidri Vase

657*a* Vina

Two types of No. 732:

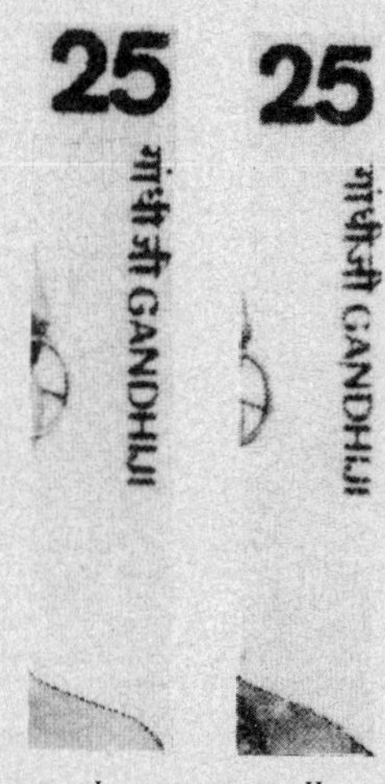

Type I. Left shoulder cut square.
Top of Hindi inscription aligns with edge of shoulder.

Type II. Shoulder ends in point.
Top of English inscription aligns with edge of shoulder. Portrait redrawn slightly smaller.

Two types of No. 736:

I II

Type I. "INDIA" inscription falls below foot of main design. Distance between foot of "2" in face value and top of Hindi inscription 11 mm.

Type II. "INDIA" above foot of design. Distance between "2" and inscription 10½ mm. Inscription redrawn slightly smaller.

1974 (20 Aug)–**83.** *P* 14 × 14½ (10, 20, 50 *p.*) *or* 14½ × 1 (*others*).

(*a*) *Various designs with values expressed with* "p" *or* "Re" *as T* **657**/*a. W* **374** (*sideways*)
721 – 15 p. blackish brown (deep background) (1.10.74) .. .. 3·25 7
722 **657** 25 p. sepia (20.8.74) .. .. .. 75 1·0
a. Imperf (pair) £170
723 **657*a*** 1 r. red-brown and black (1.10.74) .. 2·50 3
a. Black (face value and inscr) omitted £100

(*b*) *Various designs with values expressed in numerals only as i* *T* **657*b***

(i) *Wmk Large Star and* "INDIA GOVT" *in sheet**
724 **657*b*** 2 p. red-brown (*photo*) (1.11.76) .. 70 2·0
724*a* 2 p. pale reddish brn (*litho*) (15.3.79) 70 2·0
725 – 5 p. cerise (as No. 506) (1.11.76) .. 30 1
w. Wmk reversed .. ..
727 **466** 10 p. new blue (5.7.79) .. .. 3·25 5

(ii) *W* **374** (*sideways*† *on* 15, 25, 30, 60 *p.*, 1, 2, 5, 10 *r.*)
729 **466** 10 p. new blue (1.11.76) 30 1
a. Imperf (pair) £100
w. Wmk inverted .. ..
730 – 15 p. blackish brn (light background) (15.7.75) .. .. .. 1·50 1
731 – 20 p. deep dull green (15.7.75) .. 15 1
a. Imperf (horiz pair) £250
732 – 25 p. reddish brown (I) (25.10.78) .. 5·00 1·7
a. Type II (31.5.79) .. .. 5·00 1·7
732*b* – 30 p. sepia (as No. 512) (1.5.79) .. 2·75 5
733 – 50 p. deep violet (15.7.75) .. .. 4·00 1
734 – 60 p. deep grey (as No. 515) (1.11.76) 75 8
735 **657*a*** 1 r. red-brown & grey-blk (15.7.75) 3·25 1
736 – 2 r. violet & blackish brn (I) (15.7.75) 11·00 4
a. Type II (1977) .. .. .. 11·00 4
737 – 5 r. deep slate-violet and brown (as No. 519) (1.11.76) .. .. 1·25 1·0
738 – 10 r. slate and bronze-green (as No. 520) (1.11.76) .. .. .. 1·25 1·2
aw. Wmk capital heads to right .. 2·00 1·2
b. Printed on the gummed side .. 35·00
c. Wmk upright .. .. .. 1·25 1·2
cw. Wmk inverted .. .. 4·25 1·2
d. Perf 13 (22.10.83) .. .. 1·10 1·1
da. Wmk upright .. .. .. 1·10 1·1
dw. Wmk inverted .. .. .. 20·00
721/38 .. .. *Set of* 18 35·00 10·5

Designs: *Vert as T* **657**, **657*b***:—15 p. Tiger; 25 p. Gandhi *Horiz* (20×17 *mm*)—20 p. Handicrafts toy; 50 p. Great Egret ir flight. *Horiz as T* **657*a***:—2 r. Himalayas.

*See note below No. 720. Nos. 724*a* and 727 exist on both types of watermark, Nos. 724 and 725 on the first type only.

†The normal sideways watermark shows the capital heads t left, *as seen from the back of the stamp.*

No. 724*a* can be easily identified by the background of horizontal lines.

From early in 1976 Nos. 730, 731 and 735 were printed from new cylinders, which produced stamps with a slightly smaller design area than that of the original issue.

The 2 r. value with the blackish brown omitted is a chemically produced fake.

For stamps as No. 732, but with face value changed to 30 p., 35 p., 50 p., 60 p. or 1 r. see Nos. 968, 979, 1073, 1320 and 1436.

658 President V. Giri **659** U.P.U. Emblem

(Des Charanjit Lal)

74 (24 Aug). *Retirement of Pres. Giri. P* 13.
39 **658** 25 p. multicoloured 15 30

es C. Pakrashi (25 p.), A. Ramachandran (1 r.), Jyoti Bhatt (2 r.))

74 (3 Oct). *Centenary of Universal Postal Union. T* **659** *and similar designs. P* 13.
40 25 p. violet-blue, royal blue and black .. 40 10
41 1 r. multicoloured .. .. 1·00 1·50
42 2 r. multicoloured .. .. 1·25 2·00
a. Red (inscr etc) omitted £325
0/2 .. .. *Set of* 3 2·40 3·25
S743 108 × 108 mm. Nos. 740/2 .. .. .. 4·50 9·50
Designs: *Horiz*—1 r. Birds and nest, "Madhubani" style. *Vert*—
r. Arrows around globe.

660 Woman Flute-player (sculpture) **661** Nicholas Roerich (medallion by H. Dropsy)

(Des Benoy Sarkar)

974 (9 Oct). *Centenary of Mathura Museum. T* **660** *and similar vert design. P* 13½.
44 25 p. chestnut and blackish brown 50 45
a. Horiz pair. Nos. 744/5 .. .. .. 1·00 1·60
45 25 p. chestnut and blackish brown 50 45
Design:—No. 745, Vidyadhara with garland.
Nos. 744/5 were printed together within the sheet, horizontally
-tenant.

974 (9 Oct). *Birth Centenary of Professor Roerich (humanitarian). P* 13.
46 **661** 1 r. deep blue-green and greenish yellow 50 55

662 Pavapuri Temple **663** "Cat" (Rajesh Bhatia)

(Des Benoy Sarkar)

974 (13 Nov). *2,500th Anniv of Bhagwan Mahavira's attainment of Nirvana. P* 13.
47 **662** 25 p. indigo 40 20

974 (14 Nov). *Children's Day. P* 13.
48 **663** 25 p. multicoloured 60 40

664 "Indian Dancers" (Amita Shah) **665** Territorial Army Badge

974 (14 Nov). *25th Anniv of UNICEF in India. P* 14½ × 14.
49 **664** 25 p. multicoloured 55 45
a. Black (name and value) omitted £325
On No. 749a the background is in greenish black instead of
he intense black of the normal.

(Des Benoy Sarkar)

974 (16 Nov). *25th Anniv of Indian Territorial Army. P* 13.
50 **665** 25 p. black, bright yellow and emerald .. 60 40

666 Krishna as Gopal Bal with Cows (Rajasthan painting on cloth) **667** Symbols and Child's Face

1974 (2 Dec). *19th International Dairy Congress, New Delhi. P* 13½.
751 **666** 25 p. brown-purple and brown-ochre .. 40 30

(Des Benoy Sarkar)

1974 (8 Dec). *Help for Retarded Children. P* 13.
752 **667** 25 p. red-orange and black 40 50

668 Marconi **669** St. Francis Xavier's Shrine, Goa

1974 (12 Dec). *Birth Centenary of Guglielmo Marconi (radio pioneer). P* 13.
753 **668** 2 r. deep slate .. .. 2·00 1·25

1974 (24 Dec). *St Francis Xavier Celebration. P* 13.
754 **669** 25 p. multicoloured 15 30

670 Saraswati (Deity of Language and Learning) **671** Parliament House, New Delhi

1975 (10 Jan). *World Hindi Convention, Nagpur. P* 14 × 14½.
755 **670** 25 p. slate and carmine-red 30 30
For similar stamp see No. 761.

1975 (26 Jan). *25th Anniv of Republic. P* 13.
756 **671** 25 p. grey-black, silver and azure .. 30 30

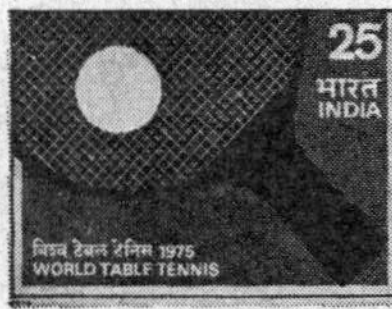

672 Table-tennis Bat

1975 (6 Feb). *World Table-tennis Championships, Calcutta. P* 13.
757 **672** 25 p. black, vermilion and yellow-olive 55 30

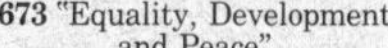

673 "Equality, Development and Peace" **674** Stylised Cannon

(Des Shyama Sarabhai)

1975 (16 Feb). *International Women's Year. P* 13.
758 **673** 25 p. multicoloured 85 45

(Des Benoy Sarkar)

1975 (8 Apr). *Bicentenary of Indian Army Ordnance Corps. P* 13.
759 **674** 25 p. multicoloured 55 45

675 Arya Samaj Emblem **676** Saraswati

1975 (11 Apr). *Centenary of Arya Samaj Movement. P* 13.
760 **675** 25 p. light red-orange & brownish black 30 30

1975 (12 Apr). *World Telugu Language Conference, Hyderabad. P* 14 × 14½.
761 **676** 25 p. black and deep bluish green .. 45 30

677 Satellite "Aryabhata"

1975 (20 Apr). *Launch of First Indian Satellite. P* 13.
762 **677** 25 p. lt blue, deep indigo & dull purple .. 50 40

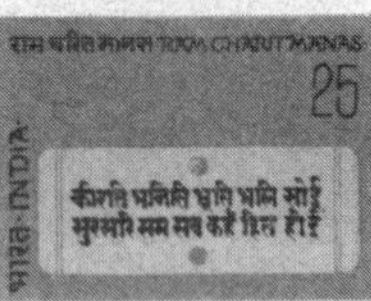

678 Blue-winged Pitta **679** Page from "Ramcharitmanas" Manuscript

(Des J. P. Irani)

1975 (28 Apr). *Indian Birds. T* **678** *and similar multicoloured designs. P* 13.
763 25 p. Type **678** 55 25
764 50 p. Asian Black-headed Oriole .. .. 1·25 1·75
765 1 r. Western Tragopan (*vert*) .. .. .. 2·25 2·75
766 2 r. Himalayan Monal Pheasant (*vert*) .. 2·75 4·50
763/6 .. .. *Set of* 4 6·00 8·25

(Des R. K. Joshi)

1975 (24 May). *4th Centenary of* Ramcharitmanas *(epic poem by Goswami Tulsidas). P* 13.
767 **679** 25 p. black, orange-yellow and vermilion 40 20

680 Young Women within Y.W.C.A. Badge **681** "The Creation"

(Des Benoy Sarkar)

1975 (20 June). *Centenary of Indian Y.W.C.A. P* 13.
768 **680** 25 p. multicoloured 30 30

1975 (28 June). *500th Birth Anniv of Michelangelo. T* **681** *and similar designs showing "Creation" frescoes from Sistine Chapel. P* 14 × 13½.
769 50 p. multicoloured 80 80
a. Block of 4. Nos 769/72 .. .. .. 2·75
ab. Black (inscr & face value) omitted .. £475
770 50 p. multicoloured 80 80
771 50 p. multicoloured 80 80
772 50 p. multicoloured 80 80
769/72 .. .. *Set of* 4 2·75 2·75
T **681** illustrates No. 769. Nos. 770 and 772 are horizontal designs, size 49 × 34 mm.
Nos. 769/72 were printed in *se-tenant* blocks of four within the sheet, forming two composite designs in horizontal pairs.

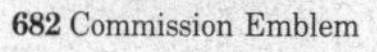

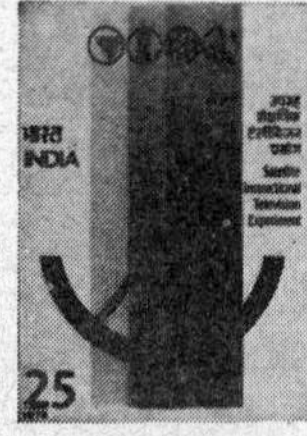

682 Commission Emblem **683** Stylised Ground Antenna

1975 (28 July). *25th Anniv of International Commission on Irrigation and Drainage. P* 13½.
773 **682** 25 p. multicoloured 40 20

(Des Benoy Sarkar)

1975 (1 Aug). *Inauguration of Satellite Instructional Television Experiment. P* 13.
774 **683** 25 p. multicoloured 40 20

684 St. Arunagirinathar **685** Commemorative Text

1975 (14 Aug). *600th Birth Anniv of St. Arunagirinathar. P* 13½.
775 **684** 50 p. dull purple and slate-black .. 1·00 1·00

1975 (26 Aug). *Namibia Day. P* 13½.
776 **685** 25 p. grey-black and rose-red 40 40

686 Mir Anees (poet) **687** Memorial Temple to Ahilyabai Holkar (ruler)

1975 (4 Sept). *Indian Celebrities. P* 13½ *(No. 777) or* 13 *(No. 778).*
777 **686** 25 p. blackish green 25 65
778 **687** 25 p. chestnut 25 65

688 Bharata Natyam **689** Ameer Khusrau

1975 (20 Oct). *Indian Dances. T* **688** *and similar vert designs. Multicoloured. P* 13.
779 25 p. Type **668** 65 20
780 50 p. Orissi .. .. 1·00 1·25
a. Turquoise-green (dress) omitted .. 65·00
781 75 p. Kathak .. .. 1·25 1·50
782 1 r. Kathakali .. .. 1·50 1·25
783 1 r. 50, Kuchipudi .. .. .. 2·25 3·00
784 2 r. Manipuri .. .. 2·25 3·75
779/84 .. .. *Set of* 6 8·00 10·00

1975 (24 Oct). *650th Death Anniv of Ameer Khusrau (poet). P* 13.
785 **689** 50 p. reddish brown and buff .. .. 80 1·50

690 V. K. Krishna Menon **691** Text of Poem

1975 (24 Oct). *First Death Anniv of V. K. Krishna Menon (statesman). P* 13 × 13½.
786 **690** 25 p. olive 50 60

(Des R. K. Joshi)

1975 (24 Oct). *Birth Bicentenary of Emperor Bahadur Shah Zafar. P* 13½×13.
787 **691** 1 r. black, stone and yellow-brown .. 65 90

692 Sansadiya Soudha, New Delhi **693** V. Patel

1975 (28 Oct). *21st Commonwealth Parliamentary Conference, New Delhi. P* 14½ × 14.
788 **692** 2 r. olive .. .. 2·00 2·50

1975 (31 Oct). *Birth Centenary of Vallabhbhai Patel (statesman). P* 13 × 13½.
789 **693** 25 p. slate-green 15 40

694 N. C. Bardoloi **695** "Cow" (Sanjay Nathubhai Patel)

1975 (3 Nov). *Birth Centenary of Nabin Chandra Bardoloi (politician). P* 13 × 13½.
790 **694** 25 p. reddish brown 30 50

1975 (14 Nov). *Children's Day. P* 13½ × 13.
791 **695** 25 p. multicoloured 60 60

696 Original Printing Works, Nasik Road **697** Gurdwara Sisganj (site of martyrdom)

1975 (13 Dec). *50th Anniv of India Security Press. P* 13.
792 **696** 25 p. multicoloured 40 40

1975 (16 Dec). *Tercentenary of the Martyrdom of Guru Tegh Bahadur (Sikh leader). P* 13.
793 **697** 25 p. multicoloured 40 40

698 Theosophical Society Emblem **699** Weather Cock

1975 (20 Dec). *Centenary of the Theosophical Society. P* 13.
794 **698** 25 p. multicoloured 40 40

(Des Benoy Sarkar)

1975 (24 Dec). *Centenary of the Indian Meteorological Department. P* 13 × 13½.
795 **699** 25 p. multicoloured 50 50

700 Early Mail Cart **701** L. N. Mishra (politician)

(Des Benoy Sarkar)

1975 (25 Dec). *"Inpex 75" National Philatelic Exhibition, Calcutta. T* **700** *and similar vert design. P* 13.
796 **700** 25 p. black and lake-brown 50 30
797 – 2 r. grey-brown, brown-purple & black 2·25 3·25
Design:—2 r. Indian Bishop Mark, 1775.

1976 (3 Jan). *First Death Anniv of Lalit Narayan Mishra. P* 13.
798 **701** 25 p. olive-sepia 40 40

702 Tiger **703** Painted Storks

1976 (24 Jan). *Birth Centenary of Jim Corbett (naturalist). P* 13.
799 **702** 25 p. multicoloured .. .. .. 1·00 70

(Des Charanjit Lal)

1976 (10 Feb). *Keoladeo Ghana Bird Sanctuary, Bharatpur. P* 13.
800 **703** 25 p. multicoloured 80 50

704 Vijayanta Tank **705** Alexander Graham Bell

1976 (4 Mar). *Bicentenary of 16th Light Cavalry Regt. P* 13.
801 **704** 25 p. multicoloured .. .. .. 1·40 30

1976 (10 Mar). *Alexander Graham Bell Commemoration. P* 13.
802 **705** 25 p. grey-black and yellow-ochre .. 70 40

706 Muthuswami Dikshitar **707** Eye and Red Cross

1976 (18 Mar). *Birth Bicentenary of Dikshitar (composer). P* 13½
803 **706** 25 p. purple 70 40

(Des Benoy Sarkar)

1976 (7 Apr). *World Health Day. Prevention of Blindness. P* 13.
804 **707** 25 p. reddish brown and dull vermilion .. 80 50

708 "Industries" **709** Type WDM Diesel Locomotive, 1963

(Des Benoy Sarkar)

1976 (30 Apr). *Industrial Development. P* 13.
805 **708** 25 p. multicoloured 30 3

1976 (15 May). *Locomotives. T* **709** *and similar horiz designs. Multicoloured. P* 14½×14.
806 25 p. Type **709** 55 10
807 50 p. Radjustan Malvan Railway Class F/1 steam locomotive, 1895 .. .. 1·50 55
808 1 r. Southern Railway Class WP/1 steam locomotive, 1963 .. .. .. 2·75 1·25
809 2 r. Great Peninsular Railway Class GIP steam locomotive, 1853 .. .. 3·50 2·50
806/9 .. .. *Set of* 4 7·50 4·00

710 Nehru **711**

712

Three types of Nehru portrait (*illustrated actual size*)
Type 710. Portrait measures 24 mm at base. First character above "NEHRU" has two prongs.
Type 711. Whole portrait is larger, measuring 25½ mm at base. Character above "NEHRU" has three prongs.
Type 712. Small portrait, 23 mm at base, with smaller inscription. Character above "NEHRU" has three prongs.

976. *T* **710/12** *and similar vert design.* W **374**. *P* 13½.
10 **710** 25 p. dull violet (27.5.76) .. .. .. 7·50 80
10*a* **711** 25 p. dull violet (9.76) .. .. .. 5·00 80
10*b* **712** 25 p. dull violet (14.11.76) .. .. 4·00 80
11 – 25 p. red-brown (2.10.76) .. .. .. 1·00 30
a. Imperf (pair) .. ..
Design:—No. 811, Gandhi.
For these designs in a smaller size see Nos. 732, 968/9, 979/80 and 073/4 and 1320.

713 "Spirit of 76" (Willard)

714 K. Kamaraj (politician)

976 (29 May). *Bicentenary of American Revolution. P* 13.
12 **713** 2 r. 80, multicoloured .. .. .. 1·25 1·25

976 (15 July). *Kumaraswamy Kamaraj Commemoration. P* 13.
13 **714** 25 p. sepia 15 15

715 "Shooting"

716 Subhadra Kumari Chauhan (poetess)

Des Gopi Gajwani (25 p., 1 r.), Sukumar Shankar (1 r. 50), India Security Press (2 r. 80))

976 (17 July). *Olympic Games, Montreal. T* **715** *and similar vert designs. P* 13.
14 25 p. deep violet and vermilion 30 10
15 1 r. multicoloured .. .. 1·00 90
16 1 r. 50, deep mauve and grey-black .. .. 1·75 2·50
17 2 r. 80, multicoloured .. .. .. 1·75 3·75
14/17 .. .. *Set of* 4 4·25 6·50
Designs:—1 r. Shot-put; 1 r. 50, Hockey; 2 r. 80, Sprinting.

976 (6 Aug). *S. K. Chauhan Commemoration. P* 13.
18 **716** 25 p. grey-blue 15 40

717 Param Vir Chakra Medal

718 University Building, Bombay

(Des Benoy Sarkar)

976 (15 Aug). *Param Vir Chakra Commemoration. P* 13.
19 **717** 25 p. multicoloured 15 50
Examples of No. 819 are found pre-released at Jodhpur on 28 uly 1976.

976 (3 Sept). *60th Anniv of Shreemati Nathibai Damodar Thackersey Women's University. P* 13½.
20 **718** 25 p. bluish violet 30 30

719 Bharatendu Harischandra (writer)

720 S. C. Chatterji

976 (9 Sept). *Harischandra Commemoration. P* 13.
21 **719** 25 p. agate 15 30

976 (15 Sept). *Birth Centenary of Sarat Chandra Chatterji (writer). P* 13.
22 **720** 25 p. grey-black 15 30

721 Planned Family

722 Maharaja Agrasen and Coins

(Des A. K. Nagar)

1976 (22 Sept). *Family Planning. P* 14 × 14½.
823 **721** 25 p. multicoloured 15 30

1976 (24 Sept). *Maharaja Agrasen Commemoration. P* 13.
824 **722** 25 p. red-brown 15 30

723 Swamp Deer

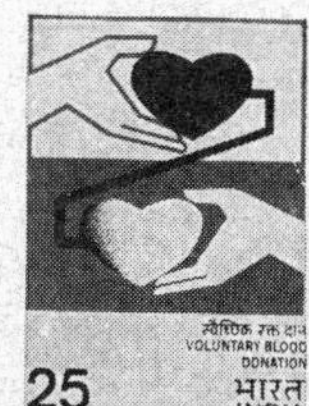

724 Hands holding Hearts

(Des from photos by Rajesh Bedi)

1976 (1 Oct). *Wildlife. T* **723** *and similar multicoloured designs. P* 14 × 14½ (25, 50 *p.*) *or* 14½ × 14 (*others*).
825 25 p. Type **723** 45 40
a. Black (name and year date) omitted .. £425
826 50 p. Lion .. .. 1·25 2·25
827 1 r. Leopard (*horiz*) .. .. 1·75 2·25
828 2 r. Caracal (*horiz*) .. .. 2·00 3·50
825/8 .. .. *Set of* 4 5·00 7·50

(Des B. G. Varma)

1976 (1 Oct). *Voluntary Blood Donation. P* 13.
829 **724** 25 p. yellow-ochre, scarlet and black .. 50 40

725 Suryakant Tripathi ("Nirala")

726 "Loyal Mongoose" (H. D. Bhatia)

1976 (15 Oct). *80th Birth Anniv of "Nirala" (poet). P* 13.
830 **725** 25 p. deep blue 15 30

1976 (14 Nov). *Children's Day. P* 13½ × 14.
831 **726** 25 p. multicoloured 40 40

727 Hiralal Shastri (social reformer)

728 Dr. Hari Singh Gour (lawyer)

1976 (24 Nov). *Shastri Commemoration. P* 13.
832 **727** 25 p. sepia 20 30

1976 (26 Nov). *Dr. Gour Commemoration. P* 13.
833 **728** 25 p. deep reddish purple 20 30

729 Airbus Industrie A300B4

730 Hybrid Coconut Palm

1976 (1 Dec). *Inauguration of Indian Airlines' Airbus Service. P* 14½×14.
834 **729** 2 r. multicoloured .. .. .. 2·25 2·25

1976 (27 Dec). *Diamond Jubilee of Coconut Research. P* 13.
835 **730** 25 p. multicoloured 20 30

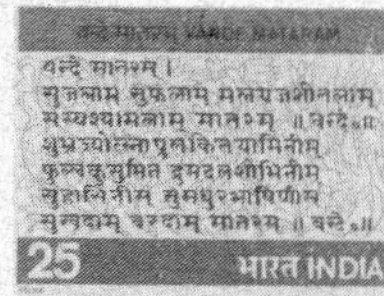

731 First Stanza of *Vande Mataram*

1976 (30 Dec). *Centenary of "Vande Mataram" (patriotic song by B. C. Chatterjee). P* 13.
836 **731** 25 p. multicoloured 20 30

732 Globe and Film Strip

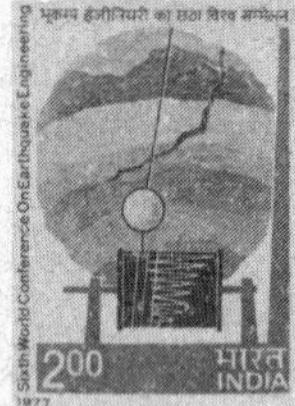

733 Seismograph and Crack in Earth's Crust

1977 (3 Jan). *Sixth International Film Festival of India, New Delhi. P* 13.
837 **732** 2 r. multicoloured .. .. .. 1·10 2·00

1977 (10 Jan). *Sixth World Conference on Earthquake Engineering, New Delhi. P* 13.
838 **733** 2 r. deep plum .. .. 1·00 2·00

734 Tarun Ram Phookun

735 Paramahansa Yogananda (religious leader)

1977 (22 Jan). *Birth Centenary of Tarun Ram Phookun (politician). P* 13.
839 **734** 25 p. blackish brown 15 30

1977 (7 Mar). *Yogananda Commemoration. P* 13.
840 **735** 25 p. reddish orange 40 30

736 Asian Regional Red Cross Emblem

737 Fakhruddin Ali Ahmed

1977 (9 Mar). *First Asian Regional Red Cross Conference, New Delhi. P* 13.
841 **736** 2 r. pink, deep blue and scarlet .. .. 2·00 2·50

1977 (22 Mar). *Death of President Ahmed. P* 13.
842 **737** 25 p. multicoloured 35 35

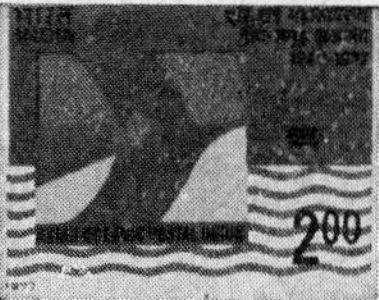

738 Emblem of Asian-Oceanic Postal Union

1977 (1 Apr). *15th Anniv of Asian-Oceanic Postal Union. P* 13.
843 **738** 2 r. multicoloured .. .. .. 1·10 1·75

739 Narottam Morarjee and *Loyalty* (liner)

740 Makhanlal Chaturvedi (writer and poet)

1977 (2 Apr). *Birth Centenary of Morarjee (ship owner). P* 13.
844 **739** 25 p. greenish blue 75 70

1977 (4 Apr). *Chaturvedi Commemoration. P* 13.
845 **740** 25 p. lake-brown 15 30

741 Mahaprabhu Vallabhacharya (philosopher)

742 Federation Emblem

1977 (14 Apr). *Vallabhacharya Commemoration. P* 13.
846 **741** 1 r. sepia 30 40

1977 (23 Apr). *50th Anniv of Federation of Indian Chambers of Commerce and Industry. P* 13.
847 **742** 25 p. dull purple, brown-ochre and buff . . 15 40

744 "Environment Protection"

745 Rajya Sabha Chamber

1977 (5 June). *World Environment Day. P* 13.
848 **744** 2 r. multicoloured . . . . 60 1·25

1977 (21 June). *25th Anniv of Rajya Sabha (Upper House of Parliament). P* 13.
849 **745** 25 p. multicoloured 15 30

746 Lotus

(Des from paintings by J. P. Irani)

1977 (1 July). *Indian Flowers. T* **746** *and similar multicoloured designs. P* $14\frac{1}{2} \times 14$ *(25 p., 2 r.) or* $14 \times 14\frac{1}{2}$ *(others).*
850 25 p. Type **746** 25 15
a. Black (inscription) omitted £325
851 50 p. Rhododendron (*vert*) 45 90
852 1 r. Kadamba (*vert*) . . . . 60 1·00
853 2 r. Gloriosa Lily . . . . 90 2·25
850/3 . . . . *Set of* 4 2·00 3·75

747 Berliner Gramophone

748 Coomaraswamy and Siva

(Des Benoy Sarkar)

1977 (20 July). *Centenary of Sound Recording. P* 13.
854 **747** 2 r. yellow-brown and black . . . . 1·00 2·00

1977 (22 Aug). *Birth Centenary of Ananda Kentish Coomaraswamy (art historian). P* 13.
855 **748** 25 p. multicoloured 40 40

749 Ganga Ram and Hospital

750 Dr. Samuel Hahnemann (founder of homeopathy)

1977 (4 Sept). *50th Death Anniv of Sir Ganga Ram (social reformer). P* $14\frac{1}{2} \times 14$.
856 **749** 25 p. maroon 30 30

1977 (6 Oct). *32nd International Homeopathic Congress, New Delhi. P* 13.
857 **750** 2 r. black and green . . . . 3·50 2·75

751 Ram Manohar Lohia (politician)

752 Early Punjabi Postman

1977 (12 Oct). *R. M. Lohia Commemoration. P* 13.
858 **751** 25 p. red-brown 30 30

1977 (12 Oct). *"Inpex-77" Philatelic Exhibition, Bangalore. T* **752** *and similar horiz design. P* 13 *(25 p.) or* $13\frac{1}{2} \times 14$ *(2 r.).*
859 25 p. multicoloured 50 30
860 2 r. olive-grey/*flesh* . . . . 2·00 2·75
Design:—2 r. "Lion and Palm" essay, 1853.

753 Scarlet "Scinde Dawks" of 1852

754 "Mother and Child" (Khajuraho sculpture)

1977 (19 Oct). *"Asiana 77" Philatelic Exhibition, Bangalore. T* **753** *and similar horiz design. P* 13.
861 1 r. orange, black and yellow . . . . 1·50 1·00
862 3 r. orange, black and light blue . . . . 2·50 3·00
Design:—3 r. Foreign mail arriving at Ballard Pier, Bombay, 1927.

1977 (23 Oct). *15th International Congress of Pediatrics, New Delhi. P* 13.
863 **754** 2 r. reddish brown and grey . . . . 2·25 2·75

755 Statue of Kittur Rani Channamma, Belgaum

756 Symbolic Sun

1977 (23 Oct). *Kittur Rani Channamma (ruler) Commemoration. P* 13.
864 **755** 25 p. grey-green 80 40

1977 (8 Nov). *Union Public Service Commission Commemoration. P* 13.
865 **756** 25 p. multicoloured 35 30

757 Ear of Corn

758 "Cats" (Nikur Dilipbhai Mody)

(Des Benoy Sarkar)

1977 (13 Nov). *"Agriexpo 77" Agricultural Exhibition, Ne Delhi. W* **374** *(sideways). P* 13.
866 **757** 25 p. blue-green 40 4

1977 (14 Nov). *Children's Day. T* **758** *and similar horiz desig Multicoloured. P* 13.
867 25 p. Type **758** 50 3
868 1 r. "Friends" (Bhavsar Ashish Ramanlal) . . 2·25 3·0

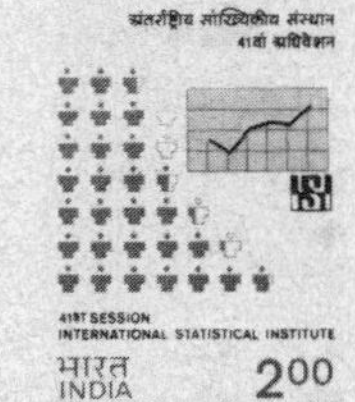

759 Jotirao Phooley (social reformer)

760 Diagram of Population Growth

1977 (28 Nov). *Indian Personalities. T* **759** *and similar ve design. W* **374** *(sideways). P* 13.
869 25 p. brown-olive 30 4
870 25 p. chestnut 30 4
Portrait:—No. 870, Senapti Bapat (patriot).

1977 (13 Dec). *41st Session of International Statistical Institut New Delhi. P* 13.
871 **760** 2 r. blue-green and red . . . . . . 60 1·0

761 Kamta Prasad Guru and Vyakarna (Hindi Grammar)

762 Kremlin Tower and Soviet Flag

1977 (25 Dec). *Kamta Prasad Guru (writer) Commemoratio W* **374** *(sideways). P* $13\frac{1}{2} \times 14$.
872 **761** 25 p. deep brown 20 3

1977 (30 Dec). *60th Anniv of October Revolution. P* 13.
873 **762** 1 r. multicoloured 45 7

763 Climber crossing a Crevice

764 "Shikara" on Lake Dal, Kashmir

1978 (15 Jan). *Conquest of Kanchenjunga (1977). T* **763** *an similar horiz design. Multicoloured. P* 13
874 25 p. Type **763** 10 1
875 1 r. Indian flag near summit 45 8

1978 (23 Jan). *27th Pacific Area Travel Association Conference New Delhi. P* 13.
876 **764** 1 r. multicoloured . . . . 2·00 1·5

765 Children in Library

766 Mother-Pondicherry

1978 (11 Feb). *Third World Book Fair, New Delhi. P* 13.
877 **765** 1 r. chestnut and slate 45 8

1978 (21 Feb). *Birth Centenary of Mother-Pondicherr (philosopher). P* 13.
878 **766** 25 p. brown and light grey 20 3

767 Wheat and Globe

768 Nanalal Dalpatram Kavi (poet)

1978 (23 Feb). *Fifth International Wheat Genetics Symposium, New Delhi. P* 13.
879 **767** 25 p. yellow and blue-green 20 30

1978 (16 Mar). *Nanalal Kavi Commemoration. W* **374** (*sideways*). *P* 13.
880 **768** 25 p. red-brown 20 30

769 Surjya Sen (revolutionary)

770 "Two Vaishnavas" (Jamini Roy)

1978 (22 Mar). *Surjya Sen Commemoration. W* **374** (*sideways*). *P* 13.
881 **769** 25 p. sepia and orange-red 20 30

1978 (23 Mar). *Modern Indian Paintings. T* **770** *and similar vert designs. Multicoloured. P* 14.
882 25 p. Type **770** 20 30
a. Black (face value and inscr) omitted .. £275
883 50 p. "The Mosque" (Sailoz Mookherjea) .. 40 1·25
884 1 r. "Head" (Rabindranath Tagore) .. .. 70 1·50
885 2 r. "Hill Women" (Amrita Sher Gil) .. 90 2·00
882/5 .. .. *Set of* 4 2·00 4·50

771 "Self-portrait" (Rubens)

772 Charlie Chaplin

1978 (4 Apr). *400th Birth Anniv of Rubens. P* 13.
886 **771** 2 r. multicoloured .. .. .. 2·00 3·00

1978 (16 Apr). *Charlie Chaplin Commemoration. P* 13.
887 **772** 25 p. Prussian blue and gold 90 45

773 Deendayal Upadhyaya (politician)

774 Syama Prasad Mookerjee

1978 (5 May). *Deendayal Upadhyaya Commemoration. P* 13.
888 **773** 25 p. olive-brown and pale orange .. 20 40

1978 (6 July). *Syama Prasad Mookerjee (politician) Commemoration. P* 13×13½.
889 **774** 25 p. brown-olive 30 50

775 Airavat (mythological) elephant), Jain Temple, Gujerat (Kachchh Museum)

776 Krishna and Arjuna in Battle Chariot

1978 (27 July). *Treasures from Indian Museums. T* **775** *and similar multicoloured designs. P* 13 × 13½ (25, 50 *p.*) *or* 13½ × 13 (*others*).
890 25 p. Type **775** 30 30
891 50 p. Kalpadruma (magical tree), Besnagar (Indian Museum) .. .. .. 50 1·25
892 1 r. Obverse and reverse of Kushan gold coin (National Museum) (*horiz*) .. .. 70 1·50
893 2 r. Dagger and knife of Emperor Jehangir, Mughal (Salar Jung Museum) (*horiz*) .. 1·00 2·00
890/3 .. .. *Set of* 4 2·25 4·50

1978 (25 Aug). *Bhagawadgeeta (Divine Song of India) Commemoration. P* 13.
894 **776** 25 p. gold and vermilion 20 30

777 Bethune College

778 E. V. Ramasami

1978 (4 Sept). *Centenary of Bethune College, Calcutta. P* 13.
895 **777** 25 p. deep brown and deep green .. 20 30

1978 (17 Sept). *E. V. Ramasami (social reformer) Commemoration. P* 13.
896 **778** 25 p. black 20 20

779 Uday Shankar

780 Leo Tolstoy

1978 (26 Sept). *Uday Shankar (dancer) Commemoration. P* 13.
897 **779** 25 p. reddish brown and stone 20 30

1978 (2 Oct). *150th Birth Anniv of Leo Tolstoy (writer). P* 13.
898 **780** 1 r. multicoloured 30 30

781 Vallathol Narayana Menon

782 "Two Friends" (Dinesh Sharma)

1978 (15 Oct). *Birth Centenary of Vallathol Narayana Menon (poet). P* 13.
899 **781** 25 p. bright purple and brown 15 40

1978 (14 Nov). *Children's Day. P* 13.
900 **782** 25 p. multicoloured 20 40

783 Machine Operator

784 Sowars of Skinner's Horse

1978 (17 Nov). *National Small Industries Fair, New Delhi. P* 13½.
901 **783** 25 p. bronze-green 20 30

1978 (25 Nov). *175th Anniv of Skinner's Horse (cavalry regiment). P* 13.
902 **784** 25 p. multicoloured 60 60

785 Mohammad Ali Jauhar

786 Chakravarti Rajagopalachari

1978 (10 Dec). *Birth Centenary of Mohammad Ali Jauhar (patriot). P* 13.
903 **785** 25 p. olive-green 20 30

1978 (10 Dec). *Birth Centenary of Chakravarti Rajagopalachari (first post-independence Governor-General). P* 13.
904 **786** 25 p. lake-brown 20 30

787 Wright Brothers and Flyer 1

788 Ravenshaw College

1978 (23 Dec). *75th Anniv of Powered Flight. W* **374** (*sideways*). *P* 13 × 13½.
905 **787** 1 r. purple and yellow-ochre 65 30

1978 (24 Dec). *Centenary of Ravenshaw College, Cuttack. P* 14.
906 **788** 25 p. lake and deep green 20 30

789 Schubert

790 Uniforms of 1799, 1901 and 1979 with Badge

1978 (25 Dec). *150th Death Anniv of Franz Schubert (composer). P* 13.
907 **789** 1 r. multicoloured 70 55
a. Black (face value) omitted £650

Two black cylinders were used for the design of No. 907. No. 907a shows the black still present on the portrait.

(Des Charanjit Lal)

1979 (20 Feb). *Fourth Reunion of Punjab Regiment. P* 13.
908 **790** 25 p. multicoloured 90 70

791 Bhai Parmanand

792 Gandhi with Young Boy

1979 (24 Feb). *Bhai Parmanand (scholar) Commemoration. P* 13.
909 **791** 25 p. deep violet-blue 20 30

1979 (5 Mar). *International Year of the Child. T* **792** *and similar vert design. P* 13.
910 25 p. reddish brown and scarlet-vermilion .. 40 30
911 1 r. reddish brown and yellow-orange .. 60 1·50
Design:—1 r. Indian I.Y.C. emblem.

During October 1979 two stamps inscribed "HAPPY CHILD NATION'S PRIDE" with face values of 50 p. and 1 r. were issued to post offices. These were intended for sale as charity labels, without postal validity, the proceeds going to a Child Welfare fund. It would seem that the instructions issued were unclear, however, as some post offices sold these labels as postage stamps and accepted mail franked with them.

793 Albert Einstein

794 Rajarshi Shahu Chhatrapati

1979 (14 Mar). *Birth Centenary of Albert Einstein (physicist). P* 13.
912 **793** 1 r. blue-black 30 50

1979 (1 May). *Rajarshi Shahu Chhatrapati (ruler of Kolhapur State, 1874–1922, and precursor of social reform in India) Commemoration. P* 13.
913 **794** 25 p. deep dull purple 20 30

795 Exhibition Logo

796 Postcards under Magnifying Glass

1979 (2 July). *"India 80" International Stamp Exhibition (1st issue). P* 13.
914 **795** 30 p. deep green and orange 20 30
See also Nos. 942/5 and 955/8.

1979 (2 July). *Centenary of Indian Postcards. P* 13.
915 **796** 50 p. multicoloured 20 40

797 Raja Mahendra Pratap

798 Hilsa, Pomfret and Prawn

799 Rubber Tapping

1979 (15 Aug). *Raja Mahendra Pratap (patriot) Commemoration. P* 13.
916 **797** 30 p. brown-olive 20 40

1979 (3 Sept)–**88.** *Designs as T* **798/9.**

(*a*) *Photo. Wmk Large Star and "INDIA GOVT" in sheet*. P* 14½×14 (15 *p.*) *or* 14×14½ (*others*)
917 2 p. slate-violet (31.3.80) . . . . 75 2·00
918 5 p. new blue (26.11.79) . . . . 1·50 30
919 15 p. deep bluish green (10.3.80) . . . . 2·25 30

(*b*) *Photo. W* **374**† (*sideways*** on 15, 20, 35 *p.*, 1, 2 *r.*, 2 *r.* 25, 2 *r.* 80, 3 *r.* 25 *and* 10 *r.*). *P* 14½×14 (15, 20, 35 *p.*, 1, 2 *r.*), 13 (25 *p.* (*No.* 925*b*), 3 *r.* 25, 10 *r.*) *or* 14×14½ (*others*).
920 2 p. slate-violet (25.3.81) 10 10
921 5 p. new blue (25.3.81) 10 10
a. Perf 13 (5.7.82) 10 10
ab. Wmk sideways (1988) 10 10
aw. Wmk inverted 60 10
922 10 p. deep green (25.1.82) 60 10
a. Perf 13 (5.7.82) 10 10
ab. Printed double . . . .
ac. Wmk sideways (1988) 10 10
923 15 p. deep bluish green (25.3.81) 15 10
a. Perf 13 (5.7.82) 10 10
ab. Wmk upright 50 10
924 20 p. Indian red (25.3.81) 60 10
a. Perf 13 (5.7.82) 10 10
ab. Wmk upright (1988) 10 10
aw. Wmk capital heads to right 60 10
925 25 p. red-brown (26.11.79) 70 10
a. Perf 13 (5.7.82) 30 10
925*b* 25 p. deep blue-green (5.9.85) 70 10
ba. Printed double . . . .
bb. Wmk sideways (1988) 10 10
926 30 p. yellowish green 90 10
a. Perf 13 (6.9.82) 45 10
ab. Wmk sideways (1987) 10 10
aw. Wmk inverted 60 10
927 35 p. cerise (15.9.80) 40 10
a. Perf 13 (5.7.82) 50 20
ab. Wmk upright 70 20
aw. Wmk capital heads to right 60 20
928 50 p. deep violet (25.1.82) . . . . 1·75 10
a. Imperf (pair) . . . . 30·00
b. Perf 13 (5.7.82) 40 10
bb. Imperf between (vert pair) . . . . † —
bw. Wmk inverted . . . . 5·00
c. Wmk sideways (*p* 13) (1988) 10 10
929 1 r. bistre-brown (17.6.80) 40 10
a. Imperf (pair) . . . . 75·00
b. Perf 13 (10.11.83) 10 10
ba. Wmk upright (1987) 30 10
bb. Printed double . . . .
932 2 r. deep rose-lilac (7.12.80) 90 10
a. Perf 13 (10.11.83) 20 10
ab. Wmk upright (1987) 10 10
933 2 r. 25, red and blue-green (25.3.81) . . 1·00 30
aw. Wmk capital heads to right . . 1·75 45
b. Wmk upright . . . . 1·00 30
bw. Wmk inverted . . . .
c. Perf 13 (*wmk upright*) (1983) . . 10 10
ca. Wmk sideways* (1987) . . 75 30
cw. Wmk capital heads to right . .
934 2 r. 80, red and blue-green (25.3.81) . . 50 30
aw. Wmk capital heads to right . .
b. Wmk upright 65 30
934*c* 3 r. 25, reddish orange & bl-grn (23.12.82) 50 30
ca. Wmk upright 10 10
cw. Wmk inverted . . . .
935 5 r. red and emerald (23.11.80) . . 4·50 30
aw. Wmk inverted . . . . 16·00 60
b. Wmk sideways* . . . . 4·50 30
bw. Wmk capital heads to right . .
c. Perf 13×12½ (*wmk upright*) (11.8.83) 60 40
ca. Wmk sideways 90 40
cw. Wmk inverted . . . . 5·50 50
936 10 r. maroon and bright green (24.2.84) . . 50 45
a. Imperf (pair) . . . .
b. Wmk upright (1988) 30 35
920/36 . . . . . . *Set of* 17 3·00 2·25

(*c*) *Litho. Wmk Large Star and "INDIA GOVT" in sheet** (2 *p.*) *or W* **374** (5 *p.*). *P* 14×14½ (2 *p.*) *or* 13 (5 *p.*)
937 2 p. slate-violet (2.2.81) 10 60
938 5 p. new blue (29.11.82) 10 10

Designs: *Horiz as T* **798**—2 p. Adult education class; 10 p. Irrigation canal; 25 p. (No. 925) Chick hatching from egg; 25 p. (No. 925*b*) Village, wheat and tractor; 30 p. Harvesting maize; 50 p. Woman dairy farmer, cows and milk bottles. (36 × 19 *mm*)—10 r. Forest and hillside. *Vert as T* **798**—15 p. Farmer and agriculture symbols; 20 p. Mother feeding child; 35 p. "Family". (17 × 28 *mm*)—1 r. Cotton plant; 2 r. Weaving. *Vert as T* **799**—2 r. 25, Cashew; 2 r. 80, Apples; 3 r. 25, Oranges.

*See note concerning this watermark below No. 720. The 2 p. and 5 p. exist on both types of this watermark, the others on the second type only.

†For notes on the amended version of W **374** see above No. 399. The changes in watermark position from 1987 onwards show the reduced size base.

**The normal sideways watermark shows the capital heads to left, *as seen from the back of the stamp.*

Nos. 920/1 and 923/4 were originally intended for issue on 9 March 1981 and First Day Covers showing this date are known from at least one post office.

At least one sheet of No. 924a exists without an impression from the ink cylinder on the first horizontal row.

No. 937 can be easily identified by the background of horizontal lines.

For 75 p. in same design as No. 927 see No. 1214.

800 Jatindra Nath Das

801 De Havilland D.H.80A Puss Moth

1979 (13 Sept). *50th Death Anniv of Jatindra Nath Das (revolutionary). P* 13.
941 **800** 30 p. blackish brown 20 30

1979 (15 Oct). *Air. "India 80" International Stamp Exhibition (2nd issue). Mail-carrying Aircraft. T* **801** *and similar horiz designs. Multicoloured. P* 14½ × 14.
942 30 p. Type **801** 30 25
943 50 p. Indian Air Force Hindustan Aircraft Industries Chetak helicopter . . 50 45
944 1 r. Indian Airlines Boeing 737 airliner . . 65 75
945 2 r. Air India Boeing 747 airliner . . 75 95
942/5 . . . . . . *Set of* 4 2·00 2·25

802 Early and Modern Lightbulbs

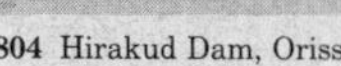
803 Gilgit Record

1979 (21 Oct). *Centenary of Electric Lightbulb. P* 13.
946 **802** 1 r. brown-purple 20 30

1979 (23 Oct). *International Archives Week. P* 14½×14.
947 **803** 30 p. yellow-ochre and sepia 20 50

804 Hirakud Dam, Orissa

805 Fair Emblem

1979 (29 Oct). *50th Anniv, and 13th Congress, of International Commission on Large Dams. P* 13.
948 **804** 30 p. lake-brown and deep blue-green . . 20 30

1979 (10 Nov). *India International Trade Fair, New Delhi. P* 13.
949 **805** 1 r. grey-black and salmon 20 30

806 Child learning to Read

1979 (10 Nov). *International Children's Book Fair, New Delhi. P* 14½ × 14.
950 **806** 30 p. multicoloured 20 30

807 Dove with Olive Branch and I.A.E.A. Emblem

1979 (4 Dec). *23rd I.A.E.A. (International Atomic Energy Agency) Conference, New Delhi. P* 13.
951 **807** 1 r. multicloured 20 4

808 Hindustan Aircraft Industries HAL-26 Pushpak Light Plane and Rohini-1 Glider

809 Gurdwara Baoli Sahib Temple, Goindwal, Amritsar District

(Des R. N. Pasricha)

1979 (10 Dec). *Flying and Gliding. P* 13.
952 **808** 30 p. black, orange-brown and blue . . 1·00 80

1979 (21 Dec). *500th Birth Anniv of Guru Amar Das (Sikh leader). P* 13.
953 **809** 30 p. multicoloured 20 30

810 Ring of People encircling U.N. Emblem and Cogwheel

811 Army Post Office and Postmarks

1980 (21 Jan). *3rd U.N.I.D.O. (United Nations Industrial Development Organisation) General Conference, New Delhi. P* 13.
954 **810** 1 r. multicoloured 20 30

(Des Benoy Sarkar (30, 50 p.), India Security Press (others))

1980 (25 Jan). *"India 80" International Stamp Exhibition (3rd issue). T* **811** *and similar vert designs. No wmk* (1 *r.*) *or Large Star and "INDIA GOVT" in sheet** (*others*). *P* 13.
955 30 p. grey-olive 40 30
956 50 p. bistre-brown and dull olive-bistre . . 70 1·00
957 1 r. Venetian red . . . . . . 80 1·00
958 2 r. olive-brown . . . . . . 80 2·00
955/8 . . . . . . *Set of* 4 2·40 3·75

Designs:—50 p. Money order transfer document, 1879; 1 r. Copper prepayment ticket, 1774; 2 r. Sir Rowland Hill and birthplace at Kidderminster.

*See note below No. 720.

812 Energy Symbols

813 Uniforms of 1780 and 1980, Crest and Ribbon

(Des C. Pakrashi)

30 (17 Feb). *Institution of Engineers (India) Commemoration. Wmk Large Star and "INDIA GOVT" in sheet. P* 13.
9 **812** 30 p. gold and blue 20 30

80 (26 Feb). *Bicentenary of Madras Sappers. P* 13.
0 **813** 30 p. multicoloured 60 50

814 Books

815 Bees and Honey-comb

(Des J. Gupta)

)80 (29 Feb). *4th World Book Fair, New Delhi. Wmk Large Star and "INDIA GOVT" in sheet. P* 13.
51 **814** 30 p. new blue 30 30

(Des M. Bardhan)

980 (29 Feb). *2nd International Apiculture Conference, New Delhi. P* 13.
52 **815** 1 r. deep brown and olive-bistre .. 40 45

816 Welthy Fisher and Saksharta Nicketan (Literacy House), Lucknow

817 Darul-Uloom, Deoband

(Des M. Choudhury)

980 (18 Mar). *Welthy Fisher (teacher) Commemoration. Wmk Large Star and "INDIA GOVT" in sheet. P* 13.
63 **816** 30 p. chalky blue 30 30

(Des Charanjit Lal)

980 (21 Mar). *Darul-Uloom (college), Deoband Commemoration. Wmk Large Star and "INDIA GOVT" in sheet. P* 13.
64 **817** 30 p. deep grey-green 20 30

818 Keshub Chunder Sen

819 Chhatrapati Shivaji Maharaj

980 (15 Apr). *Keshub Chunder Sen (religious and social reformer) Commemoration. Wmk. Large Star and "INDIA GOVT" in sheet. P* 13.
65 **818** 30 p. bistre-brown 20 30

980 (21 Apr). *300th Death Anniv of Chhatrapati Shivaji Maharaj (warrior). P* 13.
66 **819** 30 p. multicoloured 20 30

820 Table Tennis

821 N. M. Joshi

1980 (9 May). *5th Asian Table Tennis Championships, Calcutta. Wmk Large Star and "INDIA GOVT" in sheet. P* 13.
967 **820** 30 p. deep reddish purple 30 30

1980 (27 May). *Designs as Nos. 732 and 810b. Size 17 × 20 mm. W* **374** *(sideways). P* 14½ × 14.
968 30 p. red-brown (Gandhi) .. .. 3·75 80
969 30 p. dull violet (Nehru) .. .. 1·00 40

1980 (5 June). *Narayan Malhar Joshi (trade-unionist) Commemoration. Wmk Large Star and "INDIA GOVT" in sheet. P* 13.
970 **821** 30 p. magenta 60 40

822 Ulloor S. Parameswara Iyer

823 S. M. Zamin Ali

1980 (6 June). *Ulloor S. Parameswara Iyer (poet) Commemoration. Wmk Large Star and "INDIA GOVT" in sheet. P* 13.
971 **822** 30 p. maroon 60 40

1980 (25 June). *Syed Mohammed Zamin Ali (educationist and poet) Commemoration. Wmk Large Star and "INDIA GOVT" in sheet. P* 13.
972 **823** 30 p. bronze-green 20 40

824 Helen Keller

825 High-jumping

1980 (27 June). *Birth Centenary of Helen Keller (campaigner for the handicapped). P* 13.
973 **824** 30 p. black and dull orange 50 40

1980 (19 July). *Olympic Games, Moscow. T* **825** *and similar vert design. Multicoloured. P* 13½ × 14.
974 1 r. Type **825** 40 40
975 2 r. 80, Horse-riding .. .. 1·10 2·25

826 Prem Chand

827 Mother Teresa and Nobel Peace Prize Medallion

1980 (31 July). *Birth Centenary of Prem Chand (novelist). Wmk Large Star and "INDIA GOVT" in sheet. P* 13.
976 **826** 30 p. red-brown 20 40

1980 (27 Aug). *Award of 1979 Nobel Peace Prize to Mother Teresa. Wmk Large Star and "INDIA GOVT" in sheet. P* 13.
977 **827** 30 p. bluish violet 40 30

828 Lord Mountbatten

829 Scottish Church College, Calcutta

1980 (28 Aug). *Lord Mountbatten Commemoration. P* 13.
978 **828** 2 r. 80, multicoloured .. .. 1·75 2·50

1980 (1 Sept)–**82**. *As Nos. 968/9, but new face value. W* **374** *(sideways). P* 14½×14.
979 35 p. red-brown (Gandhi) (16.9.80) 85 30
a. Perf 13 (5.7.82) 85 30
980 35 p. dull violet (Nehru) 30 20
a. Perf 13 (5.7.82) 30 20

(Des C. Pakrashi)

1980 (27 Sept). *150th Anniv of Scottish Church College, Calcutta. Wmk Large Star and "INDIA GOVT" in sheet. P* 13.
981 **829** 35 p. deep rose-lilac 20 30

830 Rajah Annamalai Chettiar

831 Gandhi marching to Dandi

1980 (30 Sept). *Rajah Annamalai Chettiar (banker and educationist) Commemoration. P* 14×14½.
982 **830** 35 p. deep lilac 20 30

(Des S. Ramachandran)

1980 (2 Oct). *50th Anniv of "Dandi March" (Gandhi's defiance of Salt Tax Law). T* **831** *and similar vert design. P* 14½×14.
983 35 p. black, turquoise-blue and gold 20 65
a. Horiz pair. Nos. 983/4 .. .. .. 40 1·25
984 35 p. black, deep mauve and gold 20 65
Design:—No. 983, Type **831**; No. 984, Gandhi picking up handful of salt at Dandi.
No. 984 with the deep mauve omitted is a chemically produced fake.
Nos. 983/4 were printed together, *se-tenant*, in horizontal pairs throughout the sheet.

832 Jayaprakash Narayan

833 Great Indian Bustard

(Des Directorate of Advertising and Visual Publicity, New Delhi)

1980 (8 Oct). *Jayaprakash Narayan (socialist) Commemoration. Wmk Large Star and "INDIA GOVT" in sheet. P* 14×14½.
985 **832** 35 p. chocolate 40 40

(Des J. Irani)

1980 (1 Nov). *International Symposium on Bustards, Jaipur. P* 13.
986 **833** 2 r. 30, multicoloured .. .. .. 1·00 2·00

834 Arabic Commemorative Inscription

(Des B. Makhmoor)

1980 (3 Nov). *Moslem Year 1400 A.H. Commemoration. P* 13.
987 **834** 35 p. multicoloured 15 30

835 "Girls Dancing" (Pampa Paul)

836 Dhyan Chand

1980 (14 Nov). *Children's Day. P* 13½ × 13.
988 **835** 35 p. multicoloured 40 40

1980 (3 Dec). *Dhyan Chand (hockey player) Commemoration. P* 14 × 14½.
989 **836** 35 p. red-brown 80 75

MINIMUM PRICE

The minimum price quote is 10p which represents a handling charge rather than a basis for valuing common stamps. For further notes about prices see introductory pages.

837 Gold Mining

838 M. A. Ansari

1980 (20 Dec). *Centenary of Kolar Gold Fields, Karnataka. P* 13.
990 **837** 1 r. multicoloured .. .. .. 1·10 30

1980 (25 Dec). *Mukhtayar Ahmad Ansari (medical practitioner and politician) Commemoration. Wmk Large Star and* "INDIA GOVT" *in sheet. P* 14×14½.
991 **838** 35 p. dull olive 40 40

839 India Government Mint, Bombay

840 Bride from Tamil Nadu

1980 (27 Dec). *150th Anniv of India Government Mint, Bombay. P* 13.
992 **839** 35 p. black, silver and dull blue 20 30

1980 (30 Dec). *Brides in Traditional Costume. T* **840** *and similar vert designs. Multicoloured. P* 13.

993	1 r. Type **840** ..	40	75
994	1 r. Bride from Rajasthan ..	40	75
995	1 r. Bride from Kashmir ..	40	75
996	1 r. Bride from Bengal ..	40	75
993/6	.. *Set of* 4	1·40	2·75

841 Mazharul Haque

842 St. Stephen's College

1981 (2 Jan). *Mazharul Haque (journalist) Commemoration. Wmk Large Star and* "INDIA GOVT" *in sheet. P* 14×14½.
997 **841** 35 p. chalky blue 20 40

1981 (1 Feb). *Centenary of St. Stephen's College, Delhi. Wmk Large Star and* "INDIA GOVT" *in sheet. P* 14 × 14½.
998 **842** 35 p. dull scarlet 20 40

843 Gommateshwara

844 G. V. Mavalankar

1981 (9 Feb). *Millenium of Gommateshwara (statue at Shravanabelgola). P* 14×14½.
999 **843** 1 r. multicoloured 20 30

1981 (27 Feb). *25th Death Anniv of Ganesh Vasudeo Mavalankar (parliamentarian). P* 14×14½.
1000 **844** 35 p. Venetian red 20 40

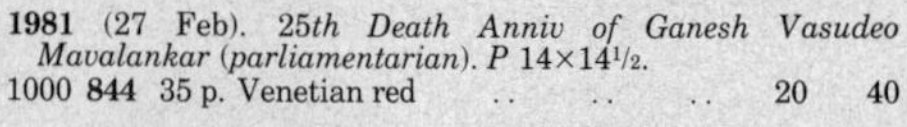

845 Flame of Martyrdom

846 Heinrich von Stephan and U.P.U. Emblem

(Des D. Dey)

1981 (23 Mar). *"Homage to Martyrs". P* 14 × 14½.
1001 **845** 35 p. multicoloured 20 30

1981 (8 Apr). *150th Birth Anniv of Heinrich von Stephan (founder of U.P.U.). P* 14½ × 14.
1002 **846** 1 r. red-brown and new blue 20 50

847 Disabled Child being helped by Able-bodied Child

848 Bhil

(Des K. Raha)

1981 (20 Apr). *International Year for Disabled Persons. P* 14½ × 14.
1003 **847** 1 r. black and blue 20 30

(Des from photographs by A. Pareek (No. 1004), S. Dutta (No. 1005). S. Theodore Baskaran (No. 1006), Kikrumielie Angami (No. 1007))

1981 (30 May). *Tribes of India. T* **848** *and similar vert designs. Multicoloured. P* 14.

1004	1 r. Type **848** ..	40	35
1005	1 r. Dandami Maria ..	40	35
1006	1 r. Toda ..	40	35
1007	1 r. Khlamngam Naga ..	40	35
1004/7	.. *Set of* 4	1·40	1·25

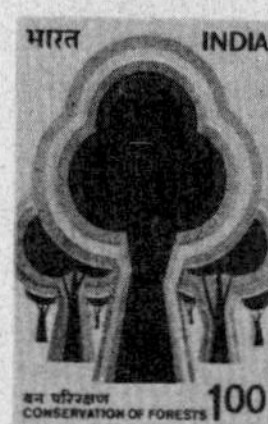

849 Stylised Trees

850 Nilmoni Phukan

(Des M. Bardhan)

1981 (15 June). *Conservation of Forests. P* 14 × 14½.
1008 **849** 1 r. multicoloured 20 30

1981 (22 June). *Nilmoni Phukan (poet) Commemoration. P* 14 × 14½.
1009 **850** 35 p. red-brown 20 40

851 Sanjay Gandhi

852 Launch of "SLV 3" and Diagram of "Rohini"

(Des C. Pakrashi)

1981 (23 June). *First Death Anniv of Sanjay Gandhi (politician). P* 13.
1010 **851** 35 p. multicoloured 40 55

1981 (18 July). *Launch of "SLV 3" Rocket with "Rohini" Satellite. P* 14 × 14½.
1011 **852** 1 r. black, pink and pale blue 30 30

853 Games Logo

854 Flame of the Forest

(Des M. Chaudhury (No. 1013))

1981 (28 July). *Asian Games, New Delhi (1st issue). T* **853** *and similar horiz design. Multicoloured. P* 13½ × 13.

1012	1 r. Type **853** ..	1·25	65
1013	1 r. Games emblem and stylised hockey players ..	1·25	65

See also Nos. 1026, 1033, 1057, 1059 and 1061/6.

(Des from photographs by K. Vaid (35 p., 2 r.), R. Bedi (others))

1981 (1 Sept). *Flowering Trees. T* **854** *and similar vert design. Multicoloured. P* 13 × 13½.

1014	35 p. Type **854** ..	40	
1015	50 p. Crateva ..	75	
1016	1 r. Golden Shower ..	1·00	
1017	2 r. Bauhinia ..	1·40	2·
1014/17	.. *Set of* 4	3·25	3·

855 W.F.D. Emblem and Wheat

856 *Stichophthalma camadeva*

(Des M. Bardhan)

1981 (16 Oct). *World Food Day. P* 14 × 14½.
1018 **855** 1 r. greenish yellow and Prussian blue 20 2

(Des from paintings by M. Mandal)

1981 (20 Oct). *Butterflies. T* **856** *and similar multicoloured designs. P* 13.

1019	35 p. Type **856** ..	90	1
1020	50 p. *Cethosia biblis* ..	1·75	1·4
1021	1 r. *Cyrestis achates (vert)* ..	2·25	7
1022	2 r. *Teinopalpus imperialis (vert)* ..	2·75	5·0
1019/22	.. *Set of* 4	7·00	6·5

857 Bellary Raghava

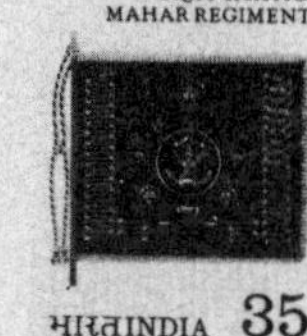

858 Regimental Colour

1981 (31 Oct). *Bellary Raghava (actor) Commemoration. P* 14½ × 14.
1023 **857** 35 p. brown-olive 70

1981 (9 Nov). *40th Anniv of Mahar Regiment. P* 13 × 13½.
1024 **858** 35 p. multicoloured 90

859 "Toyseller" (Kumari Ruchita Sharma)

860 Rajghat Stadium

1981 (14 Nov). *Children's Day. P* 14×14½.
1025 **859** 35 p. multicoloured 75 3

1981 (19 Nov). *Asian Games, New Delhi (2nd issue). P* 13½ × 1
1026 **860** 1 r. multicoloured .. .. .. 1·50 3

861 Kashi Prasad Jayasawal and Yaudheya Coin

862 India and P.L.O. Flags, and People

1981 (27 Nov). *Birth Centenary of Kashi Prasad Jayasawal (lawyer and historian). P* 14 × 14½.
1027 **861** 35 p. chalky blue 50 3

(Des B. Makhmoor)

1981 (29 Nov). *Palestinian Solidarity. P* 14½ × 14.
1028 **862** 1 r. multicoloured .. .. .. 2·00 40

863 I.N.S. *Taragiri* (frigate)

864 Henry Heras and Indus Valley Seal

1981 (4 Dec). *Indian Navy Day*. *P* 14½ × 14.
1029 **863** 35 p. multicoloured .. .. 2·25 1·25

1981 (14 Dec). *Henry Heras (historian) Commemoration*. *P* 14½ × 14.
1030 **864** 35 p. deep rose-lilac 45 30

865 Map of South-East Asia showing Cable Route

866 Stylised Hockey-players and Championship Emblem

1981 (24 Dec). *Inauguration of I.O.C.O.M. (Indian Ocean Commonwealth Cable) Submarine Telephone Cable*. *P* 13½×13.
1031 **865** 1 r. multicoloured .. .. 2·00 35

(Des C. Lal)

1981 (29 Dec). *World Cup Hockey Championship, Bombay*. *P* 13½ × 13.
1032 **866** 1 r. multicoloured 95 30

867 Jawaharlal Nehru Stadium

868 Early and Modern Telephones

1981 (30 Dec). *Asian Games, New Delhi* (3*rd issue*). *P* 13½ × 13.
1033 **867** 1 r. multicoloured 30 20

(Des C. Pakrashi)

1982 (28 Jan). *Centenary of Telephone Services*. *P* 13.
1034 **868** 2 r. black, new blue and olive-grey .. 30 30

869 Map of World

870 Sir J. J. School of Art

1982 (8 Feb). *International Soil Science Congress, New Delhi*. *P* 13.
1035 **869** 1 r. multicoloured 30 20

(Des M. Patel)

1982 (2 Mar). 125*th Anniv of Sir J. J. School of Art, Bombay*. *P* 14 × 14½.
1036 **870** 35 p. multicoloured 20 20

871 "Three Musicians"

872 Deer (stone carving), 5th-century A.D.

1982 (15 Mar). *Birth Centenary of Picasso* (1981). *P* 14.
1037 **871** 2 r. 85, multicoloured .. .. 1·00 50

1982 (23 Mar). *Festival of India. Ancient Sculpture. T* **872** *and similar vert design. Multicoloured. P* 14 × 14½.
1038 2 r. Type **872** 20 40
1039 3 r. 05, Kaliya Mardana (bronze statue), 9th-century A.D. 35 60

873 Radio Telescope, Ooty

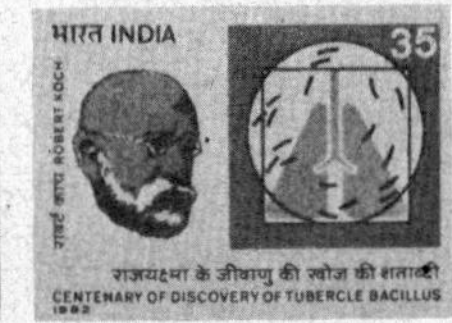

874 Robert Koch and Symbol of Disease

1982 (23 Mar). *Festival of India. Science and Technology*. *P* 13½ × 13.
1040 **873** 3 r. 05, multicoloured 35 40

(Des A. Ramachandran)

1982 (24 Mar). *Centenary of Robert Koch's Discovery of Tubercle Bacillus*. *P* 13½ × 13.
1041 **874** 35 p. deep rose-lilac .. .. 1·40 75

875 Durgabai Deshmukh

876 Blue Poppy

1982 (9 May). *First Death Anniv of Durgabai Deshmukh (social reformer)*. *P* 14½ × 14.
1042 **875** 35 p. blue 60 70

1982 (29 May). *Himalayan Flowers. T* **876** *and similar vert designs. Multicoloured. P* 14.
1043 35 p. Type **876** 65 20
1044 1 r. Showy Inula .. .. 1·50 30
1045 2 r. Cobra Lily .. .. 2·00 2·50
1046 2 r. 85, Brahma Kamal .. .. 2·50 3·25
1043/6 .. .. *Set of* 4 6·00 5·75

877 "Apple" Satellite

878 Bidhan Chandra Roy

1982 (19 June). 1*st Anniv of "Apple" Satellite Launch*. *P* 13½ × 13.
1047 **877** 2 r. multicoloured 50 80

1982 (1 July). *Birth Centenary of Bidhan Chandra Roy (doctor and politician)*. *P* 15 × 14.
1048 **878** 50 p. chestnut .. .. 80 1·10

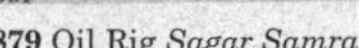

879 Oil Rig *Sagar Samrat*

880 "Bindu" (S. H. Raza)

1982 (14 Aug). 25*th Anniv of Oil and Natural Gas Commission*. *P* 13½ × 13.
1049 **879** 1 r. multicoloured .. .. 1·00 60

1982 (17 Sept). *Festival of India. Contemporary Paintings. T* **880** *and similar vert design. Multicoloured. P* 14×14½.
1050 2 r. Type **880** 40 50
1051 3 r. 05, "Between the Spider and the Lamp" (M. F. Hussain) .. .. .. 60 1·25

881 Red Deer Stag, Kashmir

882 Westland Wapiti Biplane and Mikoyan Gurevich MiG-25

1982 (1 Oct). *Wildlife Conservation*. *P* 13 × 13½.
1052 **881** 2 r. 85, multicoloured .. .. 1·50 1·25

1982 (8 Oct). 50*th Anniv of Indian Air Force*. *P* 13½ × 13.
1053 **882** 1 r. multicoloured .. .. 3·75 1·25

883 J. Tata with De Havilland D.H.80A Puss Moth

884 Police Patrol

1982 (15 Oct). 50*th Anniv of Civil Aviation in India*. *P* 13½ × 13.
1054 **883** 3 r. 25, multicoloured .. .. 3·50 1·60

(Des B. Prakash)

1982 (21 Oct). *Police Commemoration Day*. *P* 13.
1055 **884** 50 p. bronze-green 50 30

885 Coins and Economic Symbols

886 Wrestling Bout

(Des S. Jha)

1982 (23 Oct). *Centenary of Post Office Savings Bank*. *P* 13.
1056 **885** 50 p. brown and cinnamon 20 20

(Des A. Ramachandran)

1982 (30 Oct). *Asian Games, New Delhi* (4*th issue*). *P* 13½ × 14.
1057 **886** 1 r. multicoloured 30 30

887 Troposcatter Communication Link

888 Arjuna shooting Arrow at Fish

1982 (2 Nov). 1*st Anniv of Troposcatter Communication Link between India and U.S.S.R.* *P* 13.
1058 **887** 3 r. 05, multicoloured 30 40

(Des A. Ramachandran)

1982 (6 Nov). *Asian Games, New Delhi* (5*th issue*). *P* 13½ × 14.
1059 **888** 1 r. multicoloured .. .. 1·75 30

PRICES OF SETS

Set prices are given for many issues, generally those containing three stamps or more. Definitive sets include one of each value or major colour change, but do not cover different perforations, die types or minor shades. Where a choice is possible the set prices are based on the cheapest versions of the stamps included in the listings.

889 "Mother and Child" (Deepak Sharma)

890 Stylised Cyclists

1982 (14 Nov). *Children's Day. P* 14 × 14½.
1060 **889** 50 p. multicoloured 30 30

(Des C. Pakrashi (50 p.), B. Prakash (3 r. 25))

1982 (19 Nov). *Asian Games, New Delhi (6th issue). T* **890** *and similar horiz designs. Multicoloured. P* 13.
1061 50 p. Type **890** 10 10
1062 2 r. Javelin-throwing 25 30
1063 2 r. 85, Discus-throwing 30 45
1064 3 r. 25, Football 40 55
1061/4 .. .. *Set of* 4 90 1·25

891 Yachting

892 Chetwode Building

(Des C. Pakrashi)

1982 (25 Nov). *Asian Games, New Delhi (7th issue). T* **891** *and similar horiz design. Multicoloured. P* 13.
1065 2 r. Type **891** 90 30
1066 2 r. 85, Rowing .. .. 1·10 55

1982 (10 Dec). *50th Anniv of Indian Military Academy, Dehradun. P* 13.
1067 **892** 50 p. multicoloured 30 50

893 Purushottamdas Tandon

894 Darjeeling Himalayan Railway

1982 (15 Dec). *Birth Centenary of Purushottamdas Tandon (politician). P* 12½×13.
1068 **893** 50 p. yellow-brown 30 70

1982 (18 Dec). *Centenary of Darjeeling Himalayan Railway. P* 13
1069 **894** 2 r. 85, multicoloured .. .. .. 4·00 4·00

895 Vintage Rail Coach and Silhouette of Steam Locomotive

896 Antarctic Camp

(Des C. Pakrashi)

1982 (30 Dec). *"Inpex 82" Stamp Exhibition. T* **895** *and similar multicoloured design. P* 13 *(50 p.) or* 13½ × 14 *(2 r.).*
1070 50 p. Type **895** 65 85
1071 2 r. 1854 ½ a. stamp and 1947 3½ a. Independence commemorative (33 × 44 *mm*) 1·90 2·25

1983 (9 Jan). *First Indian Antarctic Expedition. P* 13.
1072 **896** 1 r. multicoloured .. .. .. 3·50 2·25

1983 (25 Jan). *As Nos.* 968/9, *but new face value. W* **374** *(sideways*). P* 12½×13.
1073 50 p. red-brown (Gandhi) .. .. .. 3·00 1·50
a. Wmk upright .. .. .. 3·00 1·50
1074 50 p. deep ultramarine (Nehru) .. .. 3·00 1·50
a. Wmk upright .. .. .. 1·50 55
w. Wmk capital heads to right .. 4·00 55

*The normal sideways watermark shows the capital heads to left, *as seen from the back of the stamp.*

897 Roosevelt with Stamp Collection

898 "Siberian (Great White) Cranes at Bharatpur" (Diane Pierce)

1983 (30 Jan). *Birth Centenary of Franklin D. Roosevelt (American statesman) (1982). P* 12½ × 13.
1075 **897** 3 r. 25, bistre-brown .. .. .. 55 1·25

1983 (7 Feb). *International Crane Workshop, Bharatpur. P* 13.
1076 **898** 2 r. 85, multicoloured .. .. .. 2·00 2·50

899 Jat Regiment Uniforms Past and Present

900 Non-aligned Summit Logo

(Des C. Lal)

1983 (16 Feb). *Presentation of Colours to Battalions of the Jat Regiment. P* 13.
1077 **899** 50 p. multicoloured .. .. .. 1·50 1·00

(Des N. Srivastava)

1983 (7 Mar). *7th Non-aligned Summit Conference, New Delhi. T* **900** *and similar horiz design. P* 13.
1078 1 r. bistre, orange-brown and black 20 30
1079 2 r. multicoloured 30 95
Design:—2 r. Nehru.

901 Shore Temple, Mahabalipuram

902 Acropolis and Olympic Emblems

(Des R. Pasricha)

1983 (14 Mar). *Commonwealth Day. T* **901** *and similar horiz design. Multicoloured. P* 13.
1080 1 r. Type **901** 15 30
1081 2 r. Gomukh, Gangotri Glacier .. .. 30 1·25

(Des B. Makhmoor)

1983 (25 Mar). *International Olympic Committee Session, New Delhi. P* 13.
1082 **902** 1 r. multicoloured 30 50

903 "St. Francis and Brother Falcon" (statue by Giovanni Collina)

904 Karl Marx and *Das Kapital*

1983 (4 Apr). *800th Birth Anniv of St. Francis of Assisi. P* 13.
1083 **903** 1 r. bistre-brown 30 30

1983 (5 May). *Death Centenary of Karl Marx. P* 13.
1084 **904** 1 r. brown 20 30

905 Darwin and Map of Voyage

(Des M. Mandal)

1983 (18 May). *Death Centenary* (1982) *of Charles Darwin (naturalist). P* 13.
1085 **905** 2 r. multicoloured .. .. .. 2·25 2·75

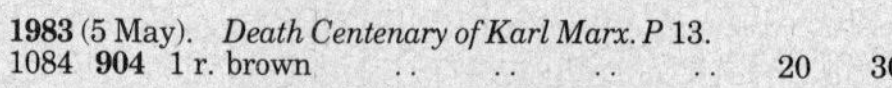

ALTERED CATALOGUE NUMBERS

Any Catalogue numbers altered from the last edition are shown as a list in the introductory pages.

906 Swamp Deer

907 Globe and Satellite

1983 (30 May). *50th Anniv of Kanha National Park. P* 13.
1086 **906** 1 r. multicoloured .. .. .. 1·50 75

(Des M. Mandal)

1983 (18 July). *World Communications Year. P* 13 × 12½.
1087 **907** 1 r. multicoloured 40 40

908 Simon Bolivar

1983 (24 July). *Birth Bicentenary of Simon Bolivar (South American statesman). P* 12½ × 13.
1088 **908** 2 r. multicoloured .. .. .. 1·75 2·00

909 Meera Behn

910 Ram Nath Chopra

(Des C. Pakrashi (No. 1091))

1983 (9 Aug–28 Dec). *India's Struggle for Freedom* (1st *series*). *T* **909** *and similar designs. P* 14×13½ *(No.* 1091) *or* 13 *(others).*
1089 50 p. dull vermilion and dull green .. 90 2·00
a. Horiz pair. Nos. 1089/90 .. .. 1·75 4·00
1090 50 p. lt brown, dull green & dull vermilion 90 2·00
1091 50 p. multicoloured .. .. 90 1·50
1092 50 p. reddish brn, yell-grn & red-orge (18.10) 15 30
1093 50 p. olive-sepia, green and orange (18.10) .. 15 30
1094 50 p. olive-green, yellow-grn & orge (28.12) 15 30
1089/94 .. .. *Set of* 6 2·75 5·75

Designs: *Vert*—No. 1089, Type **909**; No. 1090, Mahadev Desai; No. 1092, Hemu Kalani (revolutionary); No. 1093, Acharya Vinoba Bhave (social reformer); No. 1094, Surendranath Banerjee (political reformer). *Horiz* (43×31 *mm*)—No. 1091, Quit India Resolution.

Nos. 1089/90 were printed together, *se-tenant*, in horizontal pairs throughout the sheet.

See also Nos. 1119/24, 1144/9, 1191/4, 1230/5, 1287/96 and 1345/9.

1983 (17 Aug). *Ram Nath Chopra (pharmacologist) Commemoration. P* 12½ × 13.
1095 **910** 50 p. Venetian red 40 80

911 Nanda Devi Mountain

912 Great Indian Hornbill

1983 (27 Aug). *25th Anniv of Indian Mountaineering Federation. P* 13.
1096 **911** 2 r. multicoloured .. .. .. 1·10 90

(Des J. Irani)

1983 (15 Sept). *Centenary of Natural History Society, Bombay. P* 13.
1097 **912** 1 r. multicoloured .. .. .. 2·50 90

913 View of Garden

914 Golden Langur

1983 (23 Sept). *Rock Garden, Chandigarh. P* 13.
1098 **913** 1 r multicoloured .. .. .. 1·25 85

1983 (1 Oct). *Indian Wildlife. Monkeys. T* **914** *and similar horiz design. Multicoloured. P* 13.
1099 1 r. Type **914**.. .. .. 1·10 50
1100 2 r. Liontail Macaque .. .. .. 2·25 3·00

915 Ghats of Varanasi

916 Krishna Kanta Handique

1983 (3 Oct). *Fifth General Assembly of World Tourism Organization. P* 14 × 13½.
1101 **915** 2 r. multicoloured 40 40

1983 (7 Oct). *Krishna Kanta Handique (scholar) Commemoration. P* 13 × 12½.
1102 **916** 50 p. deep blue 30 70

918 Woman and Child (from "Festival" by Kashyap Premsawala)

920 *Udan Khatola*, First Indian Hot Air Balloon

1983 (14 Nov). *Children's Day. P* 13 × 13½.
1103 **918** 50 p. multicoloured 30 50

1983 (21 Nov). *Bicentenary of Manned Flight. T* **920** *and similar vert design. Multicoloured. P* 13.
1104 1 r. Type **920**.. .. .. 75 20
1105 2 r. Montgolfier balloon .. .. .. 1·00 80

921 Tiger

922 Commonwealth Logo

1983 (22 Nov). *Ten Years of "Project Tiger". P* 13 × 13½.
1106 **921** 2 r. multicoloured .. .. .. 2·50 3·00

(Des K. Raha (1 r.))

1983 (23 Nov). *Commonwealth Heads of Government Meeting, New Delhi. T* **922** *and similar vert design. Multicoloured. P* 13 × 12½.
1107 1 r. Type **922**.. .. .. 10 15
1108 2 r. Early 19th-century Goanese couple .. 25 30

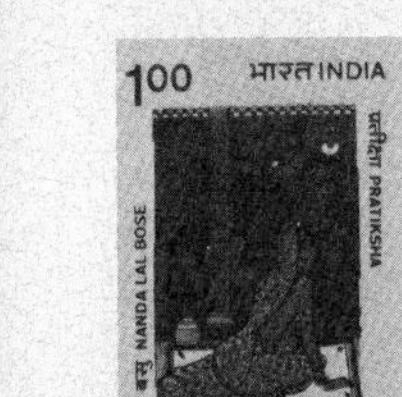

923 "Pratiksha"

925 Lancer in Ceremonial Uniform

1983 (5 Dec). *Birth Cent of Nanda Lal Bose (artist). P* 13 × 12½.
1109 **923** 1 r. multicoloured 30 30

1984 (7 Jan). *Bicentenary of 7th Light Cavalry Regiment. P* 13 × 12½.
1110 **925** 1 r. multicoloured .. .. .. 3·25 1·40

926 Troopers in Ceremonial Uniform, and Tank

927 Society Building and William Jones (founder)

1984 (9 Jan). *Presentation of Regimental Guidon to the Deccan Horse. P* 13 × 13½.
1111 **926** 1 r. multicoloured .. .. .. 3·25 1·40

1984 (15 Jan). *Bicentenary of Asiatic Society. P* 13.
1112 **927** 1 r. emerald and bright purple.. .. 30 50

928 Insurance Logo

929 Hawker Siddeley Sea Harrier

(Des S. Jha)

1984 (1 Feb). *Centenary of Postal Life Insurance. P* 13 × 13½.
1113 **928** 1 r. multicoloured 30 30

(Des Capt. A. Dhir and S. Dheer)

1984 (12 Feb). *President's Review of the Fleet. T* **929** *and similar horiz designs. Multicoloured. P* 13½ × 13.
1114 1 r. Type **929** .. .. 1·40 1·60
a. Block of 4. Nos. 1114/17 .. .. 5·00
1115 1 r. *Vikrant* (aircraft carrier) .. .. 1·40 1·60
1116 1 r. *Vela* (submarine) .. .. .. 1·40 1·60
1117 1 r. *Kashin* (destroyer) .. .. .. 1·40 1·60
1114/17 .. .. *Set of* 4 5·00 5·75
Nos. 1114/17 were printed in *se-tenant* blocks of four within the sheet, forming a composite design.

930 I.L.A. Logo and Hemispheres

(Des J. Irani)

1984 (20 Feb). *12th International Leprosy Congress. P* 13.
1118 **930** 1 r. multicoloured 30 30

(Des C. Pakrashi (Nos. 1119, 1121/4))

1984 (21 Feb–10 May). *India's Struggle for Freedom (2nd series). Vert portraits as T* **909**. *P* 13.
1119 50 p. dp brownish olive, yell-grn & brt orge 30 40
1120 50 p. bistre-brown, emerald & brt orge (23.4) 30 40
1121 50 p. multicoloured (10.5) 50 60
1122 50 p. multicoloured (10.5) 50 60
1123 50 p. multicoloured (10.5) 50 60
1124 50 p. multicoloured (10.5) 50 60
1119/24 .. .. *Set of* 6 2·40 2·75
Designs:—No. 1119, Vasudeo Balvant Phadke (revolutionary); No. 1120, Baba Kanshi Ram (revolutionary); No. 1121, Tatya Tope; No. 1122, Nana Sahib; No. 1123, Begum Hazrat Mahal; No. 1124, Mangal Pandey.

932 "Salyut 7"

(Des R. Pasricha)

1984 (3 Apr). *Indo-Soviet Manned Space Flight. P* 14.
1125 **932** 3 r. multicoloured 55 55

COVER PRICES

Cover factors are quoted at the beginning of each country for most issues to 1945. An explanation of the system can be found on page x. The factors quoted do not, however, apply to philatelic covers.

935 G. D. Birla

936 Basketball

1984 (11 June). *90th Birth Anniv of G. D. Birla (industrialist). P* 13.
1126 **935** 50 p. chocolate 30 70

(Des K. Reha and S. Jha)

1984 (28 July). *Olympic Games, Los Angeles. T* **936** *and similar multicoloured designs. P* 13.
1127 50 p. Type **936** 90 65
1128 1 r. High jumping 75 30
1129 2 r. Gymnastics (*horiz*) .. .. .. 1·00 1·50
1130 2 r. 50, Weightlifting (*horiz*) .. .. 1·25 2·50
1127/30 .. .. *Set of* 4 3·50 4·50

937 Gwalior

938 B.V. Paradkar and Newspaper

1984 (3 Aug). *Forts. T* **937** *and similar multicoloured designs. P* 13½ × 13 (50 *p.,* 2 *r.*) *or* 13 × 13½ (*others*).
1131 50 p. Type **937** 70 55
1132 1 r. Vellore (*vert*) 95 30
1133 1 r. 50, Simhagad (*vert*) .. .. .. 1·75 2·75
1134 2 r. Jodhpur .. .. 2·00 3·00
1131/4 .. .. *Set of* 4 4·75 6·00

1984 (14 Sept). *B. V. Paradkar (journalist) Commemoration. P* 13 × 13½.
1135 **938** 50 p. reddish brown 30 60

939 Dr. D. N. Wadia and Institute of Himalayan Geology, Dehradun

940 "Herdsman and Cattle in Forest" (H. Kassam)

1984 (23 Oct). *Birth Centenary* (1983) *of Dr. D. N. Wadia (geologist). P* 13.
1136 **939** 1 r. multicoloured .. .. .. 1·25 30

1984 (14 Nov). *Children's Day. P* 13 × 13½.
1137 **940** 50 p. multicoloured 75 95

941 Indira Gandhi

(Des C. Lal)

1984 (19 Nov). *Prime Minister Indira Gandhi Commemoration (1st issue). P* 15 × 14.
1138 **941** 50 p. black, lavender and bright orange 2·25 2·25
See also Nos. 1151, 1167 and 1170.

942 Congress Emblem **943** Dr. Rajendra Prasad at Desk

1984 (20 Nov). *12th World Mining Congress, New Delhi. P* 13×13½.
1139 **942** 1 r. black and orange-yellow .. 1·25 30

1984 (3 Dec). *Birth Centenary of Dr. Rajendra Prasad (former President). P* 13.
1140 **943** 50 p. multicoloured .. .. .. 1·00 85

944 Mrinalini (rose) **945** "Fergusson College" (Gopal Deuskar)

1984 (23 Dec). *Roses. T* **944** *and similar vert design. Multicoloured. P* 13.
1141 1 r. 50, Type **944** .. .. 2·00 2·00
1142 2 r. Sugandha .. .. 2·25 2·25

1985 (2 Jan). *Centenary of Fergusson College, Pune. P* 13.
1143 **945** 1 r. multicoloured 55 55

1985 (10 Jan–24 Dec). *India's Struggle for Freedom* (3rd *series). Portraits as T* **909**. *P* 13.
1144 50 p. chestnut, deep green & bright orange 50 60
1145 50 p. chocolate, emerald & brt orange (21.7) 50 60
1146 50 p. reddish brown, emer & red-orge (22.7) 50 60
1147 50 p. olive-sepia, emer & reddish orge (2.12) 50 60
1148 50 p. royal blue, emerald & brt orge (23.12) 50 60
1149 50 p. grey-black, emerald & brt orge (24.12) 50 60
1144/9 .. .. *Set of* 6 2·75 3·25
Designs: *Vert*—No. 1144, Narhar Vishnu Gadgil (politician); No. 1145, Jairamdas Doulatram (journalist); No. 1147, Kakasaheb Kalelkar (author); No. 1148, Master Tara Singh (politician); No. 1149, Ravishankar Maharaj (politician). *Horiz*—No. 1146, Jatindra and Nellie Sengupta (politicians).

947 Gunner and Howitzer from Mountain Battery

1985 (15 Jan). *50th Anniv of Regiment of Artillery. P* 13½×13.
1150 **947** 1 r. multicoloured .. .. .. 3·50 1·50

948 Indira Gandhi making speech

(Des R. Chopra)

1985 (31 Jan). *Indira Gandhi Commemoration* (2nd *issue*). *P* 14.
1151 **948** 2 r. multicoloured .. .. .. 2·50 3·00

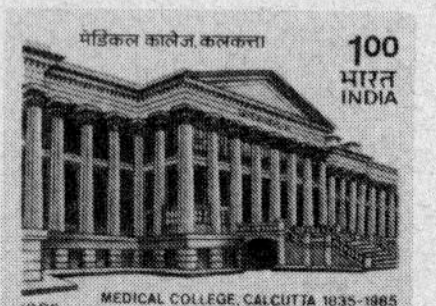
949 Minicoy Lighthouse **950** Medical College Hospital

1985 (2 Feb). *Centenary of Minicoy Lighthouse. P* 13.
1152 **949** 1 r. multicoloured .. .. .. 3·75 85

1985 (20 Feb). *150th Anniv of Medical College, Calcutta. P* 13½×13.
1153 **950** 1 r. yellow, reddish brown and deep reddish purple .. .. .. 2·50 70

951 Medical College, Madras **952** Riflemen of 1835 and 1985, and Map of North-East India

1985 (6 Mar). *150th Anniv of Medical College, Madras. P* 13½×13.
1154 **951** 1 r. yellow-brown and reddish brown .. 2·50 70

(Des A. Sharma)

1985 (29 Mar). *150th Anniv of Assam Rifles. P* 13½×13.
1155 **952** 1 r. multicoloured .. .. .. 3·25 1·25

953 Potato Plant **954** Baba Jassa Singh Ahluwalia

(Des Indian Council of Agricultural Research)

1985 (1 Apr). *50th Anniv of Potato Research in India. P* 13.
1156 **953** 50 p. deep brown and grey-brown .. 1·50 1·60

1985 (4 Apr). *Death Bicentenary* (1983) *of Baba Jassa Singh Ahluwalia (Sikh leader). P* 13.
1157 **954** 50 p. deep reddish purple .. .. 1·50 1·60

955 St. Xavier's College **956** White-winged Wood Duck

1985 (12 Apr). *125th Anniv of St. Xavier's College, Calcutta. P* 13.
1158 **955** 1 r. multicoloured .. .. .. 1·00 50

1985 (18 May). *Wildlife Conservation. White-winged Wood Duck. P* 14.
1159 **956** 2 r. multicoloured .. .. .. 4·50 4·50

957 "Mahara" **958** Yaudheya Copper Coin, c 200 B.C.

1985 (5 June). *Bougainvillea. T* **957** *and similar vert design. Multicoloured. P* 13.
1160 50 p. Type **957** .. .. 1·25 1·75
1161 1 r. "H. B. Singh" .. .. 1·50 1·50

1985 (7 June). *Festival of India* (1st *issue*). *P* 13.
1162 **958** 2 r. multicoloured .. .. .. 2·00 2·00

MINIMUM PRICE

The minimum price quote is 10p which represents a handling charge rather than a basis for valuing common stamps. For further notes about prices see introductory pages.

959 Statue of Didarganj Yakshi (deity) **962** Swami Haridas

1985 (13 June). *Festival of India* (2nd *issue*). *P* 13.
1163 **959** 1 r. multicoloured .. .. .. 1·00 40

1985 (19 Sept). *Swami Haridas (philosopher) Commemoration. P* 13.
1164 **962** 1 r. multicoloured .. .. .. 1·75 1·50
Although not officially issued until 19 September 1985 examples of No. 1164 are known to have circulated from 27 November 1984, the date on which it was originally scheduled for release.

963 Stylised Mountain Road

1985 (10 Oct). *25th Anniv of Border Roads Organization. P* 13.
1165 **963** 2 r. brt carmine, bluish violet & black 2·00 2·25

964 Nehru addressing General Assembly

1985 (24 Oct). *40th Anniv of United Nations Organization. P* 13.
1166 **964** 2 r. multicoloured 90 90

965 Indira Gandhi with Crowd

1985 (31 Oct). *Indira Gandhi Commemoration* (3rd *issue*). *P* 14.
1167 **965** 2 r. brownish black and black .. 2·50 2·75

966 Girl using Home Computer **967** Halley's Comet

1985 (14 Nov). *Children's Day. P* 13½×13.
1168 **966** 50 p. multicoloured 90 90

1985 (19 Nov). *19th General Assembly of International Astronomical Union, New Delhi. P* 13×13½.
1169 **967** 1 r. multicoloured .. .. .. 1·75 1·25

968 Indira Gandhi **969** St. Stephen's Hospital

985 (19 Nov). *Indira Gandhi Commemoration (4th issue). P* 14.
170 **968** 3 r. multicoloured .. .. 2·50 3·00

985 (25 Nov). *Centenary of St. Stephen's Hospital, Delhi. P* 13.
171 **969** 1 r. black and buff 80 40

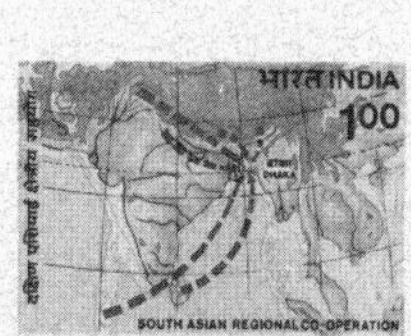
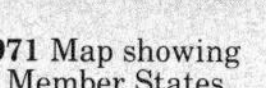

971 Map showing Member States   **972** Shyama Shastri

985 (8 Dec). *1st Summit Meeting of South Asian Association for Regional Co-operation, Dhaka, Bangladesh. T* **971** *and similar multicoloured design. P* 13½×13 (1 *r.*) *or* 14 (3 *r.*).
172 1 r. Type **971** .. .. 1·50 35
173 3 r. Flags of member nations (44×32 *mm*) .. 2·50 3·25

985 (21 Dec). *Shyama Shastri (composer) Commemoration. P* 13.
174 **972** 1 r. multicoloured .. .. .. 2·25 1·50

975 Young Runners and Emblem

(Des J. Irani)

985 (24 Dec). *International Youth Year. P* 13½×13.
175 **975** 2 r. multicoloured .. .. .. 1·25 75

976 Handel and Bach

985 (27 Dec). *300th Birth Annivs of George Frederick Handel and Johann Sebastian Bach (composers). P* 13×13½.
176 **976** 5 r. multicoloured .. .. .. 3·25 3·75

977 A. O. Hume (founder) and Early Congress Presidents   **978** Bombay and Duncan Dry Docks, Bombay

(Des C. Pakrashi)

985 (28 Dec). *Centenary of Indian National Congress. T* **977** *and similar vert designs showing miniature portraits of Congress Presidents. P* 14.
1177 **977** 1 r. black, bright orange, lt green & grey 1·50 1·75
a. Block of 4. Nos. 1177/80 .. .. 5·50
1178 – 1 r. black, bright orange and light green 1·50 1·75
1179 – 1 r. black, bright orange and light green 1·50 1·75
1180 – 1 r. black, bright orange, lt green & grey 1·50 1·75
1177/80 .. .. *Set of* 4 5·50 6·25

Nos. 1178/80 each show sixteen miniature portraits. The individual stamps can be distinguished by the position of the face value and inscription which are at the top on Nos. 1177/8 and at the foot on Nos. 1179/80. No. 1180 shows a portrait of Prime Minister Rajiv Gandhi in a grey frame at bottom right.

(Des Capt. A. Dhir)

1986 (11 Jan). *250th Anniv of Naval Dockyard, Bombay. P* 13½×13.
1181 **978** 2 r. 50, multicoloured .. .. .. 3·25 3·50

979 Hawa Mahal and Jaipur 1904 2 a. Stamp   **980** I.N.S. *Vikrant* (aircraft carrier)

(Des C. Pakrashi (2 r.)

1986 (14 Feb). *"INPEX '86" Philatelic Exhibition, Jaipur. T* **979** *and similar horiz design. Multicoloured. P* 13½×13.
1182 50 p. Type **979** .. .. 1·00 1·00
1183 2 r. Mobile camel post office, Thar Desert 2·25 2·75

(Des A. Sharma)

1986 (16 Feb). *Completion of 25 Years Service by I.N.S.* Vikrant. *P* 13×13½.
1184 **980** 2 r. multicoloured .. .. .. 4·25 4·25

981 Humber Sommer Biplane and Later Mail Planes   **982** Triennale Emblem

(Des R. Pasricha)

1986 (18 Feb). *75th Anniversary of First Official Airmail Flight, Allahabad – Naini. T* **981** *and similar horiz design. Multicoloured. P* 13½×13 (50 *p.*) *or* 13 (3 *r.*).
1185 50 p. Type **981** .. .. 2·25 1·75
1186 3 r. Modern Air India Airbus Industrie A300 mail plane and Humber Sommer biplane (37×24 *mm*) .. .. 4·75 6·00

1986 (22 Feb). *6th Triennale Art Exhibition, New Delhi. P* 13×13½.
1187 **982** 1 r. black, brt purple & orange-yellow 1·50 95

983 Chaitanya Mahaprabhu   **984** Main Building, Mayo College

1986 (13 Mar). *500th Birth Anniv of Chaitanya Mahaprabhu (religious leader). P* 13.
1188 **983** 2 r. multicoloured .. .. .. 2·75 3·50

1986 (12 Apr). *Mayo College (public school), Ajmer, Commem. P* 13½×13.
1189 **984** 1 r. multicoloured .. .. .. 1·50 1·00

985 Two Footballers   **987** Swami Sivananda

(Des Vandana Joshi)

1986 (31 May). *World Cup Football Championship, Mexico. P* 13.
1190 **985** 5 r. multicoloured .. .. .. 4·00 4·00

1986 (14 Aug–30 Dec). *India's Struggle for Freedom (4th series). Vert portraits as T* **909**. *P* 13.
1191 50 p. sepia, emerald and orange-red .. 1·25 1·50
1192 50 p. olive-sepia, emerald & orge-red (26.12) 1·25 1·50
1193 50 p. slate-blk, emer & reddish orge (29.12) 1·25 1·50
1194 50 p. red-brown, emerald & orge-red (30.12) 1·25 1·50
1191/4 .. .. *Set of* 4 4·50 5·50

Designs:—No. 1191, Bhim Sen Sachar; No. 1192, Alluri Seeta Rama Raju; No. 1193, Sagarmal Gopa; No. 1194, Veer Surendra Sai.

1986 (8 Sept). *Birth Centenary of Swami Sivananda (spiritual leader). P* 13.
1195 **987** 2 r. multicoloured .. .. .. 3·00 3·50

988 Volleyball   **989** Madras G.P.O.

(Des Mohinder Dhadwal)

1986 (16 Sept). *Asian Games, Seoul, South Korea. T* **988** *and similar vert design. Multicoloured. P* 13×13½.
1196 1 r. 50, Type **988** .. .. 2·50 2·75
1197 3 r. Hurdling .. .. 3·00 3·75

1986 (9 Oct). *Bicentenary of Madras G.P.O. P* 13.
1198 **989** 5 r. black and Indian red .. .. 4·50 5·00

990 Parachutist   **991** Early and Modern Policemen

(Des Nenu Bagga)

1986 (17 Oct). *225th Anniv of 8th Battalion of Coast Sepoys (now 1st Battalion Parachute Regiment). P* 13×13½.
1199 **990** 3 r. multicoloured .. .. .. 5·00 5·00

(Des A. Ali)

1986 (21 Oct). *125th Anniv of Indian Police. T* **991** *and similar vert design showing early and modern police. P* 13×13½.
1200 1 r. 50, multicoloured .. .. .. 3·50 3·75
a. Horiz pair. Nos. 1200/1 .. .. .. 7·00 7·50
1201 2 r. multicoloured .. .. 3·50 3·75

Nos. 1200/1 were printed together, *se-tenant*, in horizontal pairs with the 2 r. at left, each pair forming a composite design.

992 Hand holding Flower and World Map   **993** "Girl Rock Climber" (Sujasha Dasgupta)

(Des B. Raj)

1986 (24 Oct). *International Peace Year. P* 13½×13.
1202 **992** 5 r. multicoloured .. .. .. 2·25 1·25

1986 (14 Nov). *Children's Day. P* 13×13½.
1203 **993** 50 p. multicoloured .. .. .. 2·25 2·25

994 Windmill

1986 (15 Nov)–**95**. *Science and Technology. T* **994** *and similar designs. W* **374** *(sideways on 75 p., 5, 50 r.). P* 13. *(a) Photo.*
1211 35 p. vermilion (27.2.87) 10 10
a. Wmk sideways 10 10
1212 40 p. rose-red (15.10.88) 10 10
a. Wmk sideways .. .. ..
w. Wmk inverted 90 10
1213 60 p. emerald and scarlet (27.2.87) .. 10 10
a. Wmk sideways 10 10
1214 75 p. orange-vermilion (20.11.90) .. 50 30
a. Wmk upright 30 20
1215 1 r. black and Indian red (18.2.95) .. 15 10
1217 5 r. deep brown & reddish orange (1.1.88) 15 20
a. Wmk upright 40 25
1218 20 r. bistre-brown and blue (30.11.88) .. 55 60
a. Wmk sideways .. .. ..
1219 50 r. black, turquoise-blue and cerise .. 1·40 1·50
a. Wmk upright .. .. .. 1·40 1·50
w. Wmk inverted .. .. ..

(b) Litho

1220 40 p. rose-red (1991) 10 10
w. Wmk inverted .. .. ..
1211/20 .. .. *Set of* 9 2·25 2·25

Designs: *Horiz* (20×17 *mm*)—35 p. Family planning. (37×20 *mm*)—60 p. Indian family; 20 r. Bio gas production. *Vert* (17×20 *mm*)—40 p. Television set, dish aerial and transmitter; 75 p. "Family" (as No. 927). (20×37 *mm*)—1 r. Petrol pump nozzle (Oil conservation); 5 r. Solar energy.

Numbers have been left for further values in this new definitive series.

Postal forgeries of the 5 r., No. 1217, were discovered in the village of Nehru Nagar (Hyderabad) in February 1992. A number of these forgeries, which are on unwatermarked paper and perforated 10½ line, have been found commercially used. Similar forgeries of the 50 r. (No. 1219) have also been seen.

995 Growth Monitoring

996 Tansen

1986 (11 Dec). *40th Anniv of United Nations Children's Fund. T* **995** *and similar horiz design. Multicoloured. P* 13½×13.

1221 50 p. Type **995** .. .. 2·00 2·00
1222 5 r. Immunization .. .. 4·25 6·00

1986 (12 Dec). *Tansen (musician and composer) Commem. P* 13.

1223 **996** 1 r. multicoloured .. .. .. 2·00 60

997 Indian Elephant

998 St. Martha's Hospital

(Des Pratibha Pandey)

1986 (15 Dec). *50th Anniv of Corbett National Park. T* **997** *and similar horiz design. Multicoloured. P* 13½×13.

1224 1 r. Type **997** .. .. 3·50 1·00
1225 2 r. Gharial .. .. 4·00 6·00

1986 (30 Dec). *Centenary of St. Martha's Hospital, Bangalore. P* 13½×13.

1226 **998** 1 r. Prussian blue, vermilion and black 2·00 1·40

999 Yacht *Trishna* and Route Map

1000 Map of Southern Africa and Logo

1987 (10 Jan). *Indian Army Round the World Yacht Voyage,* 1985–7. *P* 13½×13.

1227 **999** 6 r. 50, multicoloured .. .. .. 4·50 4·00

1987 (25 Jan). *Inauguration of AFRICA Fund. P* 14.

1228 **1000** 6 r. 50, black .. .. 4·50 4·75

1001 Emblem

1002 Blast Furnace and Railway Emblem

1987 (11 Feb). *29th Congress of International Chamber of Commerce, New Delhi. P* 13×13½.

1229 **1001** 5 r. bluish violet, new blue and rosine 3·00 1·75

1987 (13 Feb–12 Dec). *India's Struggle for Freedom (5th series). Vert portraits as T* **909**. *P* 13.

1230 60 p. bistre-brown, emerald & reddish orge 2·00 30
1231 60 p. deep violet, emerald & orge-red (18.3) 30 30
1232 60 p. red-brown, dp green & orge-red (21.3) 30 30
1233 60 p. bl, yellowish grn & reddish orge (25.4) 30 30
1234 60 p. yellowish brn, emer & orge-red (17.6) 30 30
1235 60 p. brown, emerald and orange-red (22.8) 30 30
1236 60 p. brown-red, emerald and reddish orange (31.12) 30 30
1230/6 .. .. *Set of* 7 3·50 1·90

Designs:—No. 1230, Hakim Ajmal Khan; No. 1231, Lala Har Dayal; No. 1232, M. N. Roy; No. 1233, Tripuraneni Ramaswamy Chowdary; No. 1234, Dr. Kailas Nath Katju; No. 1235, S. Satyamurti; No. 1236, Pandit Hriday Nath Kunzru.

(Des P. Biswas)

1987 (28 Mar). *Centenary of South Eastern Railway. T* **1002** *and similar multicoloured designs. P* 13×13½ *(vert) or* 13½×13 *(horiz).*

1237 1 r. Type **1002** 40 15
1238 1 r. 50, Tank locomotive, No. 691, 1887 *(horiz)* 45 35
1239 2 r. Electric train on viaduct, 1987 .. 55 60
1240 4 r. Steam locomotive, *c* 1900 *(horiz)* .. 80 1·25
1237/40 .. .. *Set of* 4 2·00 2·10

1003 Kalia Bhomora Bridge, Tezpur, Assam

1004 Madras Christian College

1987 (14 Apr). *Inauguration of Brahmaputra Bridge. P* 13½×13.

1241 **1003** 2 r. multicoloured 30 30

1987 (16 Apr). *150th Anniv of Madras Christian College. P* 13.

1242 **1004** 1 r. 50, black and brown-lake.. .. 20 20

1005 Shree Shree Ma Anandamayee

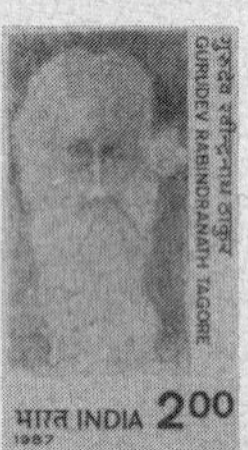

1006 "Rabindranath Tagore" (self-portrait)

1987 (1 May). *Shree Shree Ma Anandamayee (Hindu spiritual leader) Commem. P* 13×13½.

1243 **1005** 1 r. bistre-brown 30 20

1987 (8 May). *Rabindranath Tagore (poet) Commem. P* 14.

1244 **1006** 2 r. multicoloured 40 30

1007 Garwhal Rifles Uniforms of 1887

1008 J. Krishnamurti

1987 (10 May). *Centenary of Garwhal Rifles Regiment. P* 13×13½.

1245 **1007** 1 r. multicoloured 50 20

1987 (11 May). *J. Krishnamurti (philosopher) Commem. P* 13×13½.

1246 **1008** 60 p. sepia 60 90

1009 Regimental Uniforms of 1887

1010 Hall of Nations, Pragati Maidan, New Delhi

1987 (3 June). *Centenary of 37th Dogra Regt (now 7th Battalion (1 Dogra)), Mechanised Infantry Regt. P* 13½×13.

1247 **1009** 1 r. multicoloured 40 20

(Des P. Biswas (Nos. 1248/9), Nenu Bagga (No. **MS**1250)

1987 (15 June)–**89**. *"India–89" International Stamp Exhibition, New Delhi (1st issue). T* **1010** *and similar horiz design. Multicoloured. P* 13½×13.

1248 50 p. Exhibition logo 10 15
a. Booklet pane. No. 1248×4 (20.1.89) 15
1249 5 r. Type **1010** 45 50
a. Booklet pane. No. 1249×4 (20.1.89) 1·50
MS1250 156×58 mm. Nos. 1248/9 *(sold at* 8 *r.)* 70 1·00

Booklet panes Nos. 1248a and 1249a have margins all round.

See also Nos. 1264/8, 1333/4, 1341/2 and 1358/61.

1011 "Sadyah-Snata" Sculpture, Sanghol

1012 Flag and Stylized Birds with "40" in English and Hindi

1987 (3 July). *Festival of India, U.S.S.R. P* 13.

1251 **1011** 6 r. 50, multicoloured .. .. .. 1·00 75

1987 (15 Aug). *40th Anniv of Independence. P* 13×13½.

1252 **1012** 60 p. reddish orange, dp green & new bl 20 20

1013 Sant Harchand Singh Longowal

1014 Guru Ghasidas

1987 (20 Aug). *Sant Harchand Singh Longowal (Sikh leader) Commemoration. P* 13×13½.

1253 **1013** 1 r. multicoloured 40 20

1987 (1 Sept). *Guru Ghasidas (Hindu leader) Commemoration. P* 13.

1254 **1014** 60 p. deep Indian red 20 20

1015 Thakur Anukul Chandra

1016 University of Allahabad

1987 (2 Sept). *Thakur Anukul Chandra (spiritual leader) Commemoration. P* 13×13½.

1255 **1015** 1 r. multicoloured 40 20

1987 (23 Sept). *Centenary of Allahabad University. P* 13.

1256 **1016** 2 r. multicoloured 30 40

1017 Pankha Offering

1018 Chhatrasal on Horseback

1987 (1 Oct). *Phoolwalon Ki Sair Festival, Delhi. P* 13×13½.

1257 **1017** 2 r. multicoloured 30 40

1987 (2 Oct). *Chhatrasal (Bundela ruler) Commemoration. P* 14.

1258 **1018** 60 p. chestnut 30 20

1019 Family and Stylized Houses — 1020 Map of Asia and Logo

987 (5 Oct). *International Year of Shelter for the Homeless. P* 13½×13.
259 **1019** 5 r. multicoloured 45 60

987 (14 Oct). *Asia Regional Conference of Rotary International. T* **1020** *and similar horiz design. P* 13½×13.
260 60 p. chestnut and emerald 15 15
261 6 r. 50, multicoloured 60 80
Design:—6 r. 50, Oral Polio vaccination.

1021 Blind Boy, Braille Books and Computer — 1022 Iron Pillar, Delhi

987 (15 Oct). *Centenary of Service to Blind. T* **1021** *and similar horiz design. P* 13½×13.
262 1 r. multicoloured 15 15
263 2 r. deep blue and new blue 35 30
Design:—2 r. Eye donation.

987 (17 Oct)–89. *"India–89" International Stamp Exhibition, New Delhi (2nd issue). Delhi Landmarks. T* **1022** *and similar horiz designs. Multicoloured. P* 13½×13.
264 60 p. Type **1022** 10 15
a. Booklet pane. No. 1264×4 (20.1.89) 20
265 1 r. 50, India Gate 15 20
a. Booklet pane. No. 1265×4 (20.1.89) 45
266 5 r. Dewan-e-Khas, Red Fort 45 50
a. Booklet pane. No. 1266×4 (20.1.89) 1·50
267 6 r. 50, Old Fort 60 65
a. Booklet pane. No. 1267×4 (20.1.89) 2·00
264/7 .. .. *Set of* 4 1·10 1·40
MS1268 100×86 mm. Nos. 1264/7 (*sold at* 15 *r.*) 1·40 2·00
Booklet panes Nos. 1264a, 1265a, 1266a and 1267a have margins all round.

1023 Tyagmurti Goswami Ganeshdutt — 1024 "My Home" (Siddharth Deshprabha)

1987 (2 Nov). *Tyagmurti Goswami Ganeshdutt (spiritual leader and social reformer) Commemoration. P* 13×13½.
1269 **1023** 60 p. brown-red 20 20

1987 (14 Nov). *Children's Day. P* 13½×13.
1270 **1024** 60 p. multicoloured 30 20

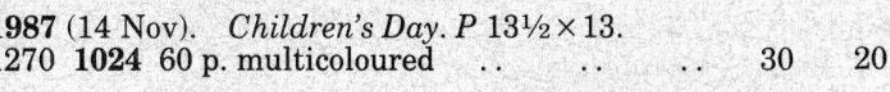

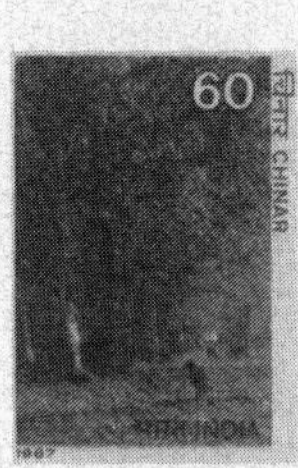

1025 Chinar — 1026 Logo (from sculpture "Worker and Woman Peasant" by V. Mukhina)

(Des O. Ravindran, A. Mehta, T. D. Singh, Sudha Chowdhary)

1987 (19 Nov). *Indian Trees. T* **1025** *and similar multicoloured designs. P* 13×13½ (*vert*) *or* 13½×13 (*horiz*).
1271 60 p. multicoloured 15 15
1272 1 r. 50, multicoloured 20 20
1273 5 r. black, dull yellow-green and chestnut 55 65
1274 6 r. 50, brown, carmine-red & yellow-green 80 80
1271/4 .. .. *Set of* 4 1·40 1·60
Designs: *Horiz*—1 r. 50, Pipal; 6 r. 50, Banyan. *Vert*—5 r. Sal.

1987 (21 Nov). *Festival of U.S.S.R., India. P* 14.
1275 **1026** 5 r. multicoloured 50 50

1027 White Tiger — 1028 Execution of Veer Narayan Singh

1987 (29 Nov). *Wildlife. T* **1027** *and similar multicoloured design. P* 13×13½ (1 *r.*) *or* 13½×13 (5 *r.*).
1276 1 r. Type **1027** 50 15
1277 5 r. Snow Leopard (*horiz*) .. .. .. 1·25 85

(Des S. Samanta)

1987 (10 Dec). *Veer Narayan Singh (patriot) Commemoration. P* 13½×13.
1278 **1028** 60 p. deep brown 20 20

1029 Rameshwari Nehru — 1030 Father Kuriakose Elias Chavara

1987 (10 Dec). *Rameshwari Nehru (women's rights campaigner) Commemoration. P* 13×13½.
1279 **1029** 60 p. red-brown 20 20

1987 (20 Dec). *Father Kuriakose Elias Chavara (founder of Carmelites of Mary Immaculate) Commemoration. P* 13×13½.
1280 **1030** 60 p. bistre-brown 20 20

1031 Dr. Rajah Sir Muthiah Chettiar — 1032 Golden Temple, Amritsar

1987 (21 Dec). *Dr. Rajah Sir Muthiah Chettiar (politician) Commemoration. P* 13.
1281 **1031** 60 p. slate 20 20

1987 (26 Dec). *400th Anniv of Golden Temple, Amritsar. P* 13×13½.
1282 **1032** 60 p. multicoloured 30 20

1033 Rukmini Devi and Dancer — 1034 Dr. Hiralal

1987 (27 Dec). *Rukmini Devi (Bharatanatyam dance pioneer) Commemoration. P* 13½×13.
1283 **1033** 60 p. deep rose-red 30 20

1987 (31 Dec). *Dr. Hiralal (historian) Commemoration. P* 13×13½.
1284 **1034** 60 p. deep violet-blue 20 20

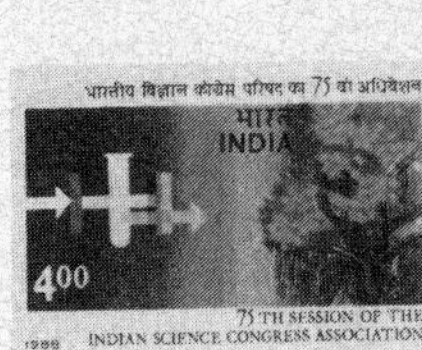

1035 Light Frequency Experiment and Bodhi Tree — 1036 Rural Patient

1988 (7 Jan). *75th Session of Indian Science Congress Association. P* 13.
1285 **1035** 4 r. multicoloured 50 60

(Des M. Sharma)

1988 (28 Jan). *13th Asian Pacific Dental Congress. P* 13×13½.
1286 **1036** 4 r. multicoloured 50 50

1988 (2 Feb–6 Oct). *India's Struggle for Freedom (6th series). Vert portraits as T* **909**. *P* 13.
1287 60 p. black, emerald and reddish orange .. 20 40
1288 60 p. chestnut, emerald & brt orange (4.2) 20 40
1289 60 p. brt carmine, emer & orge-red (27.2) .. 20 40
1290 60 p. blackish purple, emer & brt orge (7.3) 20 40
1291 60 p. plum, dp green & reddish orge (18.6) 20 40
1292 60 p. slate-blk, dp grn & reddish orge (19.6) 20 40
1293 60 p. deep lilac, dp green & orge-red (28.6) 20 40
1294 60 p. dp bluish green, grn & orge-red (6.9) 20 30
1295 60 p. red-brown, emerald & orge-red (6.10) 20 30
1296 60 p. magenta, dp green & brt orange (5.12) 20 30
1287/96 .. .. *Set of* 10 1·75 3·25
Designs:—No. 1287, Mohan Lal Sukhadia; No. 1288, Dr. S. K. Sinha; No. 1289, Chandra Shekhar Azad; No. 1290, G. B. Pant; No. 1291, Dr. Anugrah Narain Singh; No. 1292, Kuladhor Chaliha; No. 1293, Shivprasad Gupta; No. 1294, Sarat Chandra Bose; No. 1295, Baba Kharak Singh; No. 1296, Sheikh Mohammad Abdullah.

1037 U Tirot Singh — 1038 Early and Modern Regimental Uniforms

1988 (3 Feb). *U Tirot Singh (Khasis leader) Commemoration. P* 13×13½.
1297 **1037** 60 p. bistre-brown 20 20

1988 (19 Feb). *Bicentenary of 4th Battalion of the Kumaon Regiment. P* 14.
1298 **1038** 1 r. multicoloured 30 20

1039 Balgandharva — 1040 Soldiers and Infantry Combat Vehicle

1988 (22 Feb). *Birth Centenary of Balgandharva (actor). P* 13×13½.
1299 **1039** 60 p. bistre-brown 20 20

1988 (24 Feb). *Presentation of Colours to Mechanised Infantry Regiment. P* 13½×13.
1300 **1040** 1 r. multicoloured 35 20

1041 B. N. Rau — 1042 Mohindra Government College

1988 (26 Feb). *B. N. Rau (constitutional lawyer) Commemoration. P* 13.
1301 **1041** 60 p. grey-black 20 20

1988 (14 Mar). *Mohindra Government College, Patiala. P* 13×13½.
1302 **1042** 1 r. cerise 20 20

1043 Dr. D. V. Gundappa — 1044 Rani Avantibai

1988 (17 Mar). *Dr. D. V. Gundappa (scholar) Commemoration. P* 13½×13.
1303 **1043** 60 p. slate 20 20

1988 (20 Mar). *Rani Avantibai of Ramgarh Commemoration. P* 13×13½.
1304 **1044** 60 p. cerise 20 20

1045 *Malayala Manorama* Office, Kottayam

1046 Maharshi Dadhichi

1988 (23 Mar). *Centenary of* Malayala Manorama *(newspaper). P* 13.
1305 **1045** 1 r. black and new blue 20 20

1988 (26 Mar). *Maharshi Dadhichi (Hindu saint) Commemoration. P* 13×13½.
1306 **1046** 60 p. Indian red 20 20

1047 Mohammad Iqbal

1048 Samarth Ramdas

(Des Alka Sharma)

1988 (21 Apr). *50th Death Anniv of Mohammad Iqbal (poet). P* 13.
1307 **1047** 60 p. gold and rosine 20 20

1988 (1 May). *Samarth Ramdas (Hindu spiritual leader) Commem. P* 13.
1308 **1048** 60 p. deep yellow-green 20 20

1049 Swati Tirunal Rama Varma

1050 Bhaurao Patil and Class

1988 (2 May). *175th Birth Anniv of Swati Tirunal Rama Varma (composer). P* 13×13½.
1309 **1049** 60 p. deep mauve 20 20

1988 (9 May). *Bhaurao Patil (educationist) Commemoration. P* 13½×13.
1310 **1050** 60 p. reddish brown 20 20

1051 "Rani Lakshmi Bai" (M. F. Husain)

1988 (9 May). *Martyrs from First War of Independence. P* 13×13½.
1311 **1051** 60 p. multicoloured 20 20
a. Myrtle-green (lowest stripe of flag, date, etc) omitted . .

NEW INFORMATION

The editor is always interested to correspond with people who have new information that will improve or correct the Catalogue.

1052 Broad Peak

1053 Child with Grandparents

(Des R. Pasricha (1 r. 50, 4 r.), N. Roerich (5 r.))

1988 (19 May). *Himalayan Peaks. T* **1052** *and similar horiz designs. P* 13½×13.

1312	1 r. 50, reddish lilac, deep violet and blue	35	30
1313	4 r. multicoloured	70	60
1314	5 r. multicoloured	80	70
1315	6 r. 50, multicoloured	95	85
1312/15	. . . . . . *Set of* 4	2·50	2·25

Designs:—4 r. K 2 (Godwin Austen); 5 r. Kanchenjunga; 6 r.50, Nanda Devi.

(Des Neeta Verma)

1988 (24 May). *"Love and Care for Elders". P* 13×13½.
1316 **1053** 60 p. multicoloured 20 20

1054 Victoria Terminus, Bombay

1055 Lawrence School, Lovedale

1988 (30 May). *Centenary of Victoria Terminus Station, Bombay. P* 13½×13.
1317 **1054** 1 r. multicoloured 40 20

1988 (31 May). *130th Anniv of Lawrence School, Lovedale. P* 13.
1318 **1055** 1 r. red-brown and deep green . . 30 20

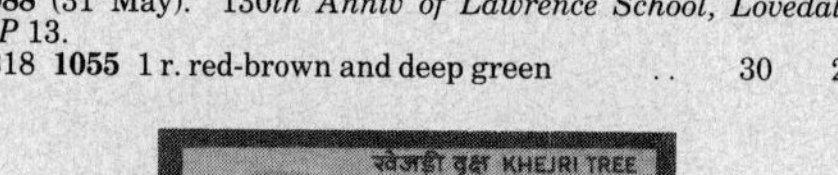

1056 Khejri Tree

1988 (5 June). *World Environment Day. P* 14.
1319 **1056** 60 p. multicoloured 20 15

1988 (15 June). *As No. 732, but new face value. W* **374**. *P* 12½ × 13.
1320 60 p. grey-black (Gandhi) 55 15
a. Wmk sideways 55 15

1057 Rani Durgawati

1058 Acharya Shanti Dev

1988 (24 June). *Rani Durgawati (Gondwana ruler) Commemoration. P* 13.
1322 **1057** 60 p. deep rose-red 20 20

1988 (28 July). *Acharya Shanti Dev (Buddhist scholar) Commemoration. P* 13×13½.
1323 **1058** 60 p. red-brown 20 20

1059 Y. S. Parmar

1988 (4 Aug). *Dr. Yashwant Singh Parmar (former Chief Minister of Himachal Pradesh) Commemoration. P* 13×13½.
1324 **1059** 60 p. slate-violet 20 20

1060 Arm pointing at Proclamation in Marathi

(Des Contract Advertising (India) Ltd)

1988 (16 Aug). *40th Anniv of Independence. Bal Gangadhar Tilak (patriot) Commemoration. T* **1060** *and similar horiz design. Multicoloured. P* 13×13½.
1325 60 p. Type **1060** 20 20
a. Vert pair. Nos. 1325/6 . . . . 40 40
1326 60 p. Battle scene 20 20

Nos. 1325/6 were printed together, *se-tenant*, in vertical pairs throughout the sheet, each pair forming a composite design showing a painting by M. F. Husain.

1061 Durgadas Rathore

1062 Gopinath Kaviraj

1988 (26 Aug). *150th Birth Anniv of Durgadas Rathore (Regent of Marwar). Litho. P* 13×13½.
1327 **1061** 60 p. reddish brown 20 20

1988 (7 Sept). *Gopinath Kaviraj (scholar) Commemoration. P* 13×13½.
1328 **1062** 60 p. bistre-brown 20 20

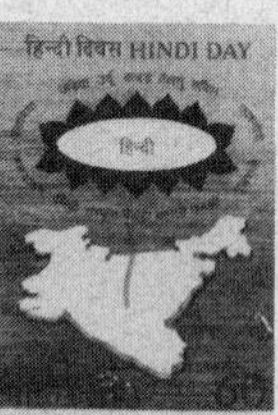

1063 Lotus and Outline Map of India

1064 Indian Olympic Association Logo

1988 (14 Sept). *Hindi Day. P* 13×13½.
1329 **1063** 60 p. orange-verm, grn & reddish brn 20 20

(Des C. Parameswaran (5 p.))

1988 (17 Sept). *"Sports–1988" and Olympic Games, Seoul. T* **1064** *and similar design. P* 13.
1330 60 p. brown-purple 35 15
1331 5 r. multicoloured . . . . . . 1·90 60
Design: *Horiz*—5 r. Various sports.

1065 Jerdon's Courser

1066 *Times of India* Front Page

1988 (7 Oct). *Wildlife Conservation. Jerdon's Courser. P* 13×13½.
1332 **1065** 1 r. multicoloured . . . . . . 1·00 30

(Des C. Meena (4 r.), C. Pakrashi (5 r.))

1988 (9 Oct)–**89**. *"India–89" International Stamp Exhibition, New Delhi (3rd issue). General Post Offices. Horiz designs as T* **1022**. *Multicoloured. P* 13½×13.
1333 4 r. Bangalore G.P.O. 40 35
a. Booklet pane. No. 1333×6 (20.1.89) 2·25
1334 5 r. Bombay G.P.O. 50 45
a. Booklet pane. No. 1334×6 (20.1.89) 2·75

Booklet panes Nos. 1333a and 1334a have margins all round.

(Des A. Nath)

1988 (3 Nov). 150*th Anniv of* The Times of India. *P* 14.
1335 **1066** 1 r. 50, black, gold and lemon .. 20 20

1067 "Maulana Abul Kalam Azad" (K. Hebbar)

1988 (11 Nov). *Birth Centenary of Maulana Abul Kalam Azad (politician). P* 13½×13.
1336 **1067** 60 p. multicoloured 20 20

1068 Nehru

1988 (14 Nov). *Birth Centenary of Jawaharlal Nehru* (1989) (*1st issue*). *T* **1068** *and similar design. P* 13×13½ (60 *p.*) *or* 13½×13 (1 *r.*).
1337 60 p. grey-black, red-orange & deep green 30 15
1338 1 r. multicoloured 35 15
Design: *Vert*—1 r. "Jawaharlal Nehru" (Svetoslav Roerich).
See also No. 1393

1069 Birsa Munda

(Des S. Samantha)

1988 (15 Nov). *Birsa Munda (Munda leader) Commemoration. P* 13½ × 13.
1339 **1069** 60 p. reddish brown 20 20

1070 Bhakra Dam

1988 (15 Dec). 25*th Anniv of Dedication of Bhakra Dam. P* 14.
1340 **1070** 60 p. bright carmine 35 60

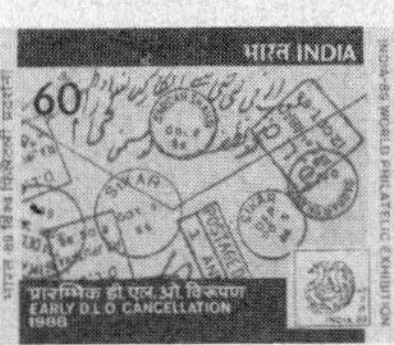

1071 Dead Letter Office Cancellations of 1886

1072 K. M. Munshi

1988 (20 Dec)–89. *"India–89" International Stamp Exhibition, New Delhi* (*4th issue*). *Postal Cancellations. T* **1071** *and similar horiz design. P* 13½×13.
1341 60 p. dp cinnamon, black & carm-vermilion 25 15
a. Booklet pane. No. 1341×6 (20.1.89) 1·40
1342 6 r. 50, orange-brown and black .. .. 1·00 1·00
a. Booklet pane. No. 1342×6 (20.1.89) 5·50
Design:—6 r. 50, Allahabad–Cawnpore travelling post office handstamp of 1864.
Booklet panes Nos. 1341a and 1342a have margins all round.

1988 (30 Dec). *Birth Centenary of K. M. Munshi (author and politician)* (1987). *P* 13½ × 13.
1343 **1072** 60 p. deep olive 20 20

1073 Mannathu Padmanabhan

1074 Lok Sabha Secretariat

1989 (2 Jan). *Mannathu Padmanabhan (social reformer) Commemoration. P* 13 × 13½.
1344 **1073** 60 p. olive-brown 20 20

1989 (2 Jan–11 May). *India's Struggle for Freedom (7th series). Vert portraits as T* **909**. *P* 13.
1345 60 p. blk, dull yellowish grn & reddish orge 20 30
1346 60 p. red-orange, dp grn & dp lilac (8.3.89) 20 50
1347 60 p. grey-black, bottle-green and bright orange (13.4.89) 20 50
1348 60 p. bistre-brown, emerald and reddish orange (13.4.89) 20 50
1349 60 p. brown, dp green & orge-red (11.5.89) 20 30
1345/9 .. .. *Set of* 5 90 1·90
Designs:—No. 1345, Hare Krishna Mahtab; No. 1346, Balasaheb Gangadhar Kher; No. 1347, Raj Kumari Amrit Kaur; No. 1348, Saifuddin Kitchlew; No. 1349, Asaf Ali.

1989 (10 Jan). 60*th Anniv of Lok Sabha Secretariat (formerly Legislative Assembly Department). P* 13½ × 13.
1355 **1074** 60 p. brown-olive 20 20

1075 Goddess Durga seated on Lion (5th-cent terracotta plaque)

1076 Baldev Ramji Mirdha

1989 (11 Jan). 125*th Anniv of Lucknow Museum. P* 14.
1356 **1075** 60 p. deep blue and new blue 20 20

1989 (17 Jan). *Birth Centenary of Baldev Ramji Mirdha (nationalist). P* 13 × 13½.
1357 **1076** 60 p. slate-green 20 20

1077 Girl with Stamp Collection

1078 St. John Bosco and Boy

(Des K. Radhakrishnan (60 p.), M. Jain (1 r. 50))

1989 (20 Jan). *"India–89" International Stamp Exhibition, New Delhi* (*5th issue*). *Philately. T* **1077** *and similar horiz designs. P* 13½×13.
1358 60 p. orge-yellow, rose-red & dp violet-blue 15 10
a. Booklet pane. No. 1358×6 80
1359 1 r. 50, brownish grey, orge-yellow & blk 20 15
a. Booklet pane. No. 1359×6 .. .. 1·10
1360 5 r. dull vermilion and blue 60 50
a. Booklet pane. No. 1360×6 .. .. 3·25
1361 6 r. 50, black, red-brown & turquoise-blue 70 60
a. Booklet pane. No. 1361×6 .. .. 3·75
1358/61 .. .. *Set of* 4 1·50 1·25
Designs:—1 r. 50, Dawk gharry, c. 1842; 5 r. Travancore 1888 2 ch. conch shell stamp; 6 r. 50, Early Indian philatelic magazines.
Booklet panes Nos. 1358a, 1359a, 1360a and 1361a have margins all round.

1989 (31 Jan). *St. John Bosco (founder of Salesian Brothers) Commemoration. P* 13.
1362 **1078** 60 p. carmine 20 20

1079 Modern Tank and 19th-century Sowar

1080 Dargah Sharif, Ajmer

(Des P. Biswas)

1989 (8 Feb). *Third Cavalry Regiment. P* 13½ × 13.
1363 **1079** 60 p. multicoloured 30 20

1989 (13 Feb). *Dargah Sharif (Sufi shrine), Ajmer. P* 13½ × 13.
1364 **1080** 1 r. multicoloured 20 20

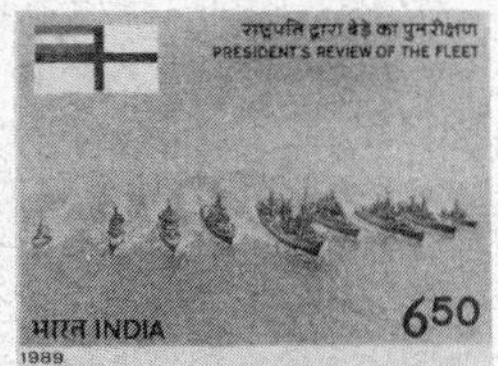

1081 Task Force and Indian Naval Ensign

1989 (15 Feb). *President's Review of the Fleet. P* 14.
1365 **1081** 6 r. 50, multicoloured .. .. 1·25 1·00

1082 Shaheed Laxman Nayak and Barbed Wire Fence

1083 Rao Gopal Singh

1989 (29 Mar). *Shaheed Laxman Nayak Commemoration. P* 13½×13.
1366 **1082** 60 p. dp brown, dp green & red-orange 20 20

1989 (30 Mar). *Rao Gopal Singh Commemoration. P* 13×13½.
1367 **1083** 60 p. olive-brown 20 20

1084 Sydenham College

1085 Bishnu Ram Medhi

1989 (19 Apr). 75*th Anniv of Sydenham College, Bombay* (1988). *P* 13½×13.
1368 **1084** 60 p. grey-black 30 20

1989 (24 Apr). *Birth Centenary of Bishnu Ram Medhi (politician)* (1988). *P* 13.
1369 **1085** 60 p. yellowish green, deep blue-green and orange-red 30 20

1086 Dr. N. S. Hardikar

1087 "Advaita" in Devanagari Script

1989 (13 May). *Birth Centenary of Dr. Narayana Subbarao Hardikar (nationalist). P* 13×13½.
1370 **1086** 60 p. orange-brown 20 20

1989 (17 May). *Sankaracharya (philosopher) Commemoration. P* 14.
1371 **1087** 60 p. multicoloured 20 20

1088 Gandhi Bhavan, Punjab University

1089 Scene from Film *Raja Harischandra*

1989 (19 May). *Punjab University, Chandigarh. P* 13½×13.
1372 **1088** 1 r. light brown and turquoise-blue .. 20 20

1989 (30 May). 75 *Years of Indian Cinema. P* 14.
1373 **1089** 60 p. black and yellow 20 20

1090 Cactus and Cogwheels

1091 Early Class and Modern University Students

1989 (20 June). *Centenary of Kirloskar Brothers Ltd (engineering group). P* 13½×13.
1374 **1090** 1 r. multicoloured 20 20

1989 (27 June). *Centenary of First D.A.V. College. P* 13½×13.
1375 **1091** 1 r. multicoloured 20 20

1092 Post Office, Dakshin Gangotri Base, Antarctica

1093 First Allahabad Bank Building

(Des S. Samantha)

1989 (11 July). *Opening of Post Office, Dakshin Gangotri Research Station, Antarctica. P* 14.
1376 **1092** 1 r. multicoloured 80 20

1989 (19 July). 125*th Anniv of Allahabad Bank* (1990). *P* 14.
1377 **1093** 60 p. maroon and new blue 20 20

1094 Nehru inspecting Central Reserve Police, Neemuch, 1954

1095 Dairy Cow

1989 (27 July). 50*th Anniv of Central Reserve Police Force (formerly Crown Representative's Police). P* 13½×13.
1378 **1094** 60 p. brown 60 20

1989 (18 Aug). *Centenary of Military Farms. P* 13½×13.
1379 **1095** 1 r. multicoloured 50 20

1096 Mustafa Kemal Atatürk

1097 Dr. S. Radhakrishnan

1989 (30 Aug). 50*th Death Anniv of Mustafa Kemal Atatürk (Turkish statesman)* (1988). *P* 13×13½.
1380 **1096** 5 r. multicoloured .. .. .. 1·25 45

1989 (11 Sept). *Birth Centenary of Dr. Sarvepalli Radhakrishnan (former President)* (1988). *P* 13½×13.
1381 **1097** 60 p. grey-black 20 20

1098 Football Match

1099 Dr. P. Subbarayan

1989 (23 Sept). *Centenary of Mohun Bagan Athletic Club. P* 13½×13.
1382 **1098** 1 r. multicoloured 40 20

1989 (30 Sept). *Birth Centenary of Dr. P. Subbarayan (politician). P* 13×13½.
1383 **1099** 60 p. orange-brown 20 20

1100 Shyamji Krishna Varma

1101 Sayajirao Gaekwad III

1989 (4 Oct). *Shyamji Krishna Varma (nationalist) Commemoration. P* 13.
1384 **1100** 60 p. purple-brown, dp grn & orge-red 20 20

1989 (6 Oct). 50*th Death Anniv of Maharaja Sayajirao Gaekwad III of Baroda. P* 13×13½.
1385 **1101** 60 p. brownish grey 20 20

1102 Symbolic Bird with Letter

1103 Namakkal Kavignar

1989 (14 Oct). *"Use Pincode" Campaign. P* 14.
1386 **1102** 60 p. multicoloured 20 20

1989 (19 Oct). *Namakkal Kavignar (writer) Commemoration. P* 13×13½.
1387 **1103** 60 p. brownish black 20 20

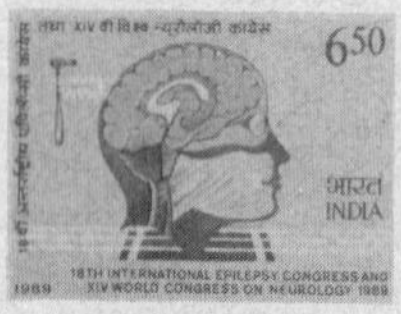

1104 Diagram of Human Brain

1105 Pandita Ramabai and Original Sharada Sadan Building

1989 (21 Oct). 18*th International Epilepsy Congress and* 14*th World Congress on Neurology, New Delhi. P* 13½×13.
1388 **1104** 6 r. 50, multicoloured .. .. 2·25 75

1989 (26 Oct). *Pandita Ramabai (women's education pioneer) Commemoration. P* 13½×13.
1389 **1105** 60 p. light brown 30 20

1106 Releasing Homing Pigeons

1107 Acharya Narendra Deo

1989 (3 Nov). *Orissa Police Pigeon Post. P* 13½×13.
1390 **1106** 1 r. Indian red 50 20

1989 (6 Nov). *Birth Centenary of Acharya Narendra Deo (scholar). P* 13.
1391 **1107** 60 p. brown, emerald and red-orange 20 20

1108 Acharya Kripalani

1989 (11 Nov). *Acharya Kripalani (politician) Commemoration. P* 13½×13.
1392 **1108** 60 p. grey-blk, myrtle-grn & orge-red 20 20

1109 Nehru

(Des S. Debnath)

1989 (14 Nov). *Birth Centenary of Jawaharlal Nehru (2nd issue). P* 14×15.
1393 **1109** 1 r. dull brown, purple-brown and buff. 65 20

1110 Meeting Logo

1111 Sir Gurunath Bewoor

1989 (19 Nov). 8*th Asian Track and Field Meeting, New Delhi. P* 14.
1394 **1110** 1 r. black, reddish orge & yellowish grn 30 20

1989 (20 Nov). *Sir Gurunath Bewoor (former Director-General, Posts and Telegraphs) Commemoration. P* 13×13½.
1395 **1111** 60 p. light brown 20 20

1112 Balkrishna Sharma Navin

1113 Abstract Painting of Houses

1989 (8 Dec). *Balkrishna Sharma Navin (politician and poet) Commemoration. P* 13×13½.
1396 **1112** 60 p. black 20 20

1989 (15 Dec). *Centenary of Bombay Art Society* (1988). *P* 13½×13.
1397 **1113** 1 r. multicoloured 20 20

1114 Lesser Florican

1115 Centenary Logo

1989 (20 Dec). *Wildlife Conservation. Lesser Florican. P* 13×13½.
1398 **1114** 2 r. multicoloured .. .. .. 1·50 55

1989 (29 Dec). *Centenary of Indian Oil Production. P* 14.
1399 **1115** 60 p. red-brown 30 20

1116 Dr. M. G. Ramachandran

1117 Volunteers working at Sukhna Lake, Chandigarh

990 (17 Jan). *Dr. M. G. Ramachandran (former Chief Minister of Tamil Nadu) Commemoration. P* 13×13½.
400 **1116** 60 p. reddish brown 40 20

(Des T. Bedi and S. Singh)

1990 (29 Jan). *Save Sukhna Lake Campaign. P* 13½×13.
1401 **1117** 1 r. multicoloured 20 20

1118 Gallantry Medals

1990 (21 Feb). *Presentation of New Colours to Bombay Sappers. P* 15×14*.
1402 **1118** 60 p. multicoloured 80 80

*On No. 1402 the left hand side of the triangle is perforated 15 and the remaining two sides 14.

1119 Indian Chank Shell and Logo

1120 Penny Black and Envelope

1990 (2 May). *23rd Annual General Meeting of Asian Development Bank, New Delhi. P* 14.
1403 **1119** 2 r. black, brt orange & greenish yell 75 30

(Des M. Deogawanka)

1990 (6 May). *150th Anniv of the Penny Black. P* 13×13½.
1404 **1120** 6 r. multicoloured . . . . . . 1·25 40

1121 Ho Chi-Minh and Vietnamese House

1122 Chaudhary Charan Singh

1990 (17 May). *Birth Centenary of Ho Chi-Minh (Vietnamese leader). P* 13½×13.
1405 **1121** 2 r. reddish brown and yellowish green 30 30

1990 (29 May). *3rd Death Anniv of Chaudhary Charan Singh (former Prime Minister). P* 13.
1406 **1122** 1 r. orange-brown 20 20

1123 Armed Forces' Badge and Map of Sri Lanka

1124 Wheat

1990 (30 July). *Indian Peace-keeping Operations in Sri Lanka. P* 13.
1407 **1123** 2 r. multicoloured 30 30

1990 (31 July). *60th Anniv of Indian Council of Agricultural Research* (1989). *P* 14.
1408 **1124** 2 r. blk, brt yellow-grn & dp bluish grn 30 30

1125 Khudiram Bose

1126 "Life in India" (Tanya Vorontsova)

1990 (11 Aug). *Khudiram Bose (patriot) Commemoration. P* 13×13½.
1409 **1125** 1 r. dull vermilion, dull grn & brn-red 20 20

1990 (16 Aug). *Indo-Soviet Friendship. Children's Paintings. T* **1126** *and similar horiz design. Multicoloured. P* 14.
1410 1 r. Type **1126** . . . . . . 1·50 2·00
a. Horiz pair. Nos. 1410/11 . . . . 3·00 4·00
1411 6 r. 50, "St. Basil's Cathedral and Kremlin, Moscow" (Sanjay Adhikari) 1·50 2·00

Nos. 1410/11 were printed together, *se-tenant*, in horizontal pairs throughout the sheet.

Stamps in similar designs were also issued by U.S.S.R.

1127 K. Kelappan

1128 Girl in Garden

1990 (24 Aug). *K. Kelappan (social reformer) Commemoration. P* 13×13½
1412 **1127** 1 r. reddish brown 20 20

1990 (5 Sept). *Year of the Girl Child. P* 13×13½
1413 **1128** 1 r. multicoloured 50 30

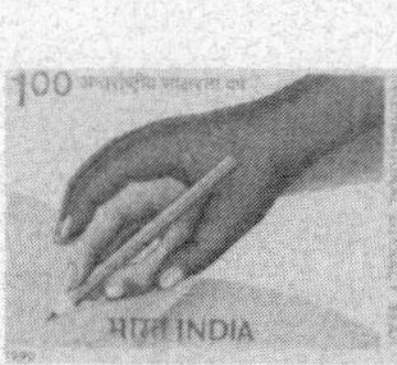

1129 Hand guiding Child's Writing

1130 Woman using Water Pump

1990 (8 Sept). *International Literacy Year. P* 13½×13.
1414 **1129** 1 r. multicoloured 50 30

1990 (10 Sept). *Safe Drinking Water Campaign. P* 13×13½.
1415 **1130** 4 r. black, scarlet-verm & dp bluish grn 1·25 1·75

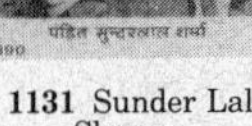

1131 Sunder Lal Sharma

1132 Kabbadi

1990 (28 Sept). *50th Death Anniv of Sunder Lal Sharma (patriot). P* 13×13½.
1416 **1131** 60 p. lake 50 50

(Des C. Pakrashi (Nos. 1418/19), R. Pasricha (No. 1420))

1990 (29 Sept). *11th Asian Games, Peking. T* **1132** *and similar vert designs. Multicoloured. P* 13×13½.
1417 1 r. Type **1132** 40 20
1418 4 r. Athletics . . . . . . 1·50 2·00
1419 4 r. Cycling . . . . . . 1·50 2·00
1420 6 r. 50, Archery . . . . . . 1·75 2·50
1417/20 . . . . . . *Set of* 4 4·75 6·00

1133 A. K. Gopalan

1134 Gurkha Soldier

1990 (1 Oct). *Ayillyath Kuttiari Gopalan (social reformer) Commemoration. P* 13×13½.
1421 **1133** 1 r. red-brown 50 30

(Des R. Pasricha)

1990 (1 Oct). *50th Anniv of 3rd and 5th Battalions, 5th Gurkha Rifles. P* 13.
1422 **1134** 2 r. black and ochre . . . . . . 1·40 1·60

1135 Suryamall Mishran

1136 "Doll and Cat" (Subhash Kumar Nagarajan)

1990 (19 Oct). *75th Birth Anniv of Suryamall Mishran (poet). P* 13 × 13½.
1423 **1135** 2 r. brown and pale orange 50 65

1990 (14 Nov). *Children's Day. P* 13½×13.
1424 **1136** 1 r. multicoloured 60 30

1137 Security Post and Border Guard on Camel

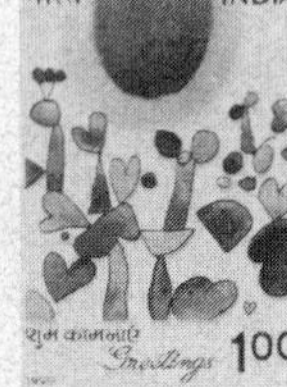

1138 Hearts and Flowers

1990 (30 Nov). *25th Anniv of Border Security Force. P* 13½×13.
1425 **1137** 5 r. greenish blue, yellow-brown & blk 1·50 1·75

(Des R. Pasricha (1 r.))

1990 (17 Dec). *Greetings Stamps. T* **1138** *and similar multicoloured design. P* 13×13½ (1 *r.*) *or* 13½×13 (4 *r.*).
1426 1 r. Type **1138** 20 15
1427 4 r. Ceremonial elephants (*horiz*) 50 65

1139 Bikaner

1140 Bhakta Kanakadas and Udipi Temple

(Des R. Pasricha (4, 5 r.), P. Biswas (6 r. 50))

1990 (24 Dec). *Cities of India. T* **1139** *and similar horiz designs. Multicoloured. P* 13½×13.
1428 4 r. Type **1139** 55 60
1429 5 r. Hyderabad 65 75
1430 6 r. 50, Cuttack . . . . . . 90 1·25
1428/30 . . . . . . *Set of* 3 1·90 2·40

1990 (26 Dec). *Bhakta Kanakadas (mystic and poet) Commemoration. P* 14.
1431 **1140** 1 r. orange-red 55 30

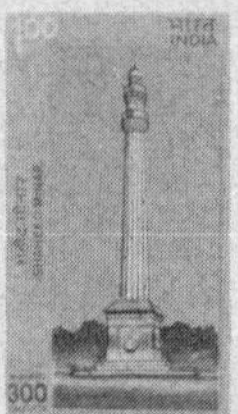

1141 Shaheed Minar Monument

1142 Dnyaneshwari (poet) and Manuscript

1990 (28 Dec). *300th Anniv of Calcutta. T* **1141** *and similar design. P* 14.
1432 1 r. multicoloured 30 20
1433 6 r. black, ochre and rosine . . . . . . 1·25 1·50
Design: *Horiz* (44×36 *mm*)—6 r. Eighteenth-century shipping on the Ganges.

1990 (31 Dec). *700th Anniv of Dnyaneshwari (spiritual epic). P* 13×13½.
1434 **1142** 2 r. multicoloured 30 50

1143 Madan Mohan Malaviya (founder) and University

1144 Road Users

1991 (20 Jan). *75th Anniv of Banaras Hindu University. P* 13½×13.
1435 **1143** 1 r. brown-lake 30 20

1991 (30 Jan). *As No.* 732, *but new face value. W* **374**. *P* 13.
1436 1 r. orange-brown (Gandhi) 10 10
a. Wmk sideways 75
ab. Imperf (pair) . . . . 30·00

(Des J. Das)

1991 (30 Jan). *International Traffic Safety Conference, New Delhi. P* 13½×13.
1437 **1144** 6 r. 50, black, dp blue & orge-vermilion 75 1·00

1145 Exhibition Emblem

1146 Jagannath Sunkersett and Central Railways Headquarters

1991 (12 Feb). *7th Triennale Art Exhibition, New Delhi. P* 13×13½.
1438 **1145** 6 r. 50, multicoloured 60 75

1991 (15 Feb). *125th Death Anniv of Jagannath Sunkersett (educationist and railway pioneer) (1990). P* 13×13½.
1439 **1146** 2 r. royal blue and Indian red 50 60

1147 Tata Memorial Centre

1148 River Dolphin

1991 (28 Feb). *50th Anniv of Tata Memorial Medical Centre. P* 13½×13.
1440 **1147** 2 r. light brown and stone 30 40

1991 (4 Mar). *Endangered Marine Mammals. T* **1148** *and similar horiz design. P* 13½×13.
1441 4 r. red-brown, turquoise-blue & brt green 1·50 1·50
1442 6 r. 50, multicoloured . . . . 2·00 2·00
Design:—6 r. 50, Sea Cow.

1149 Drugs

1150 Hand, Bomb Explosion and Dove

(Des J. Irani)

1991 (5 Mar). *International Conference on Drug Abuse, Calcutta. P* 13×13½.
1443 **1149** 5 r. bluish violet and bright scarlet . . 1·60 1·60

(Des J. Das)

1991 (7 Mar). *World Peace. P* 13×13½.
1444 **1150** 6 r. 50, black, cinnamon & orge-brown 75 1·00

1151 Remote Sensing Satellite "1A"

1152 Babu Jagjivan Ram

1991 (18 Mar). *Launch of Indian Remote Sensing Satellite* "1A". *P* 14.
1445 **1151** 6 r. 50, chestnut and deep violet-blue 60 85

1991 (5 Apr). *Babu Jagjivan Ram (politician) Commemoration. P* 13×13½.
1446 **1152** 1 r. yellow-brown 20 20

1153 Dr. B. R. Ambedkar and Demonstration

1154 Valar Dance

1991 (14 Apr). *Birth Centenary of Dr. Bhimrao Ramji Ambedkar (social reformer). P* 13½×13.
1447 **1153** 1 r. reddish brown and deep dull blue 30 20

1991 (30 Apr). *Tribal Dances. T* **1154** *and similar horiz designs. Multicoloured. P* 13½×13.
1448 2 r. 50, Type **1154** 50 40
1449 4 r. Kayang 70 80
1450 5 r. Hozagiri 80 90
1451 6 r. 50, Velakali . . . . 1·00 1·40
1448/51 . . . . *Set of* 4 2·75 3·25

1155 Ariyakudi Ramanuja Iyengar and Temples

1156 Karpoori Thakur

(Des J. Sharma)

1991 (18 May). *Ariyakudi Ramanuja Iyengar (singer and composer) Commemoration. P* 13½×13.
1452 **1155** 2 r. red-brown and deep bluish green 50 65

(Des L. Sahu)

1991 (30 May). *Jan Nayak Karpoori Thakur (politician and social reformer) Commemoration. P* 13×13½.
1453 **1156** 1 r. reddish brown 20 20

MINIMUM PRICE

The minimum price quote is 10p which represents a handling charge rather than a basis for valuing common stamps. For further notes about prices see introductory pages.

1157 Emperor Penguins

1158 Rashtrapati Bhavan Building, New Delhi

1991 (23 June). *30th Anniv of Antarctic Treaty. T* **1157** *and similar horiz design. Multicoloured. P* 13½×13.
1454 5 r. Type **1157** . . . . 1·75 2·00
a. Horiz pair. Nos. 1454/5 . . . . 3·50 4·00
1455 6 r. 50, Antarctic map and pair of Adelie Penguins . . . . 1·75 2·00
Nos. 1454/5 were printed together, *se-tenant*, in horizontal pairs throughout the sheet, each pair forming a composite design.

(Des P. Biswas)

1991 (25 June). *60th Anniv of New Delhi. T* **1158** *and similar horiz designs. Multicoloured. P* 13½×13.
1456 5 r. Type **1158** . . . . 1·00 1·40
a. Horiz pair. Nos. 1456/7 . . . . 2·00 2·75
1457 6 r. 50, New Delhi monuments . . . . 1·00 1·40
Nos. 1456/7 were printed together, *se-tenant*, in horizontal pairs throughout the sheet, each pair forming a composite design.

1159 Sri Ram Sharma Acharya

1160 "Shankar awarded Padma Vibhushan" (cartoon)

1991 (27 June). *Sri Ram Sharma Acharya (social reformer) Commemoration. P* 13½×13.
1458 **1159** 1 r. turquoise-green and rosine . . 20 20

1991 (31 July). *Keshav Shankar Pillai (cartoonist) Commemoration. T* **1160** *and similar design. P* 13½×13 (4 *r.*) *or* 13×13½ (6 *r.* 50).
1459 4 r. light brown . . . . 1·00 1·40
1460 6 r. 50, deep rose-lilac . . . . . . 1·40 1·75
Design: *Vert*—6 r. 50, "The Big Show".

1161 Sriprakash and Kashi Vidyapith University

1162 Gopinath Bardoloi

1991 (3 Aug). *20th Death Anniv of Sriprakash (politician). P* 13½×13.
1461 **1161** 2 r. red-brown and light brown . . 30 30

1991 (5 Aug). *Birth Centenary of Gopinath Bardoloi (Assamese politician) (1990). P* 13×13½.
1462 **1162** 1 r. deep reddish lilac 20 20

1163 Rajiv Gandhi

(Des R. Chopra)

1991 (20 Aug). *Rajiv Gandhi (Congress Party leader) Commemoration. P* 13.
1463 **1163** 1 r. multicoloured 40 40

1164 Muni Mishrimalji and Memorial

1165 Mahadevi Verma (poetess) and "Varsha"

91 (24 Aug). *Birth Centenary of Muni Mishrimalji (Jain religious leader). P* 13½×13.
64 **1164** 1 r. yellow-brown 30 20

(Des S. Samant)

91 (16 Sept). *Hindu Writers. T* **1165** *and similar horiz design. P* 13½×13.
65 **1165** 2 r. black and light blue 15 25
a. Horiz pair. Nos. 1465/6 .. 30 50
66 – 2 r. black and light blue 15 25
Design:—No. 1466, Jayshankar Prasad (poet and dramatist) d scene from "Kamayani".
Nos. 1465/6 were printed together, *se-tenant*, in horizontal irs throughout the sheet.

1166 Parliament House and C.P.A. Emblem

1167 Frog

(Des P. Biswas)

91 (27 Sept). *37th Commonwealth Parliamentary Association Conference, New Delhi. P* 13½×13.
67 **1166** 6 r. 50, blue and reddish brown .. 40 60

91 (30 Sept). *Greetings Stamps. T* **1167** *and similar vert design. P* 13×13½.
68 1 r. emerald and deep rose-red 20 40
a. Horiz pair. Nos. 1468/9 .. 55 95
69 6 r. 50, deep rose-red and emerald .. 35 55
Design:—6 r. 50, Symbolic bird carrying flower.
Nos. 1468/9 were printed together, *se-tenant*, in horizontal irs throughout the sheet.

1168 *Cymbidium aloifolium*

1169 Gurkha Soldier in Battle Dress

(Des O. Ravindran)

91 (12 Oct). *Orchids. T* **1168** *and similar vert designs. Multicoloured. P* 13×13½.
470 1 r. Type **1168** 30 15
471 2 r. 50, *Paphiopedilum venustum* .. 35 35
472 3 r. *Aerides crispum* 40 50
473 4 r. *Cymbidium bicolour* 50 65
474 5 r. *Vanda spathulata* 55 70
475 6 r. 50, *Cymbidium devonianum* .. 70 1·00
470/5 .. .. *Set of* 6 2·50 3·00

(Des R. Pasricha)

91 (18 Oct) *90th Anniv of 2nd Battalion, Third Gurkha Rifles. P* 13½×13.
476 **1169** 4 r. multicoloured .. .. .. 1·50 1·50

1170 Couple on Horse (embroidery)

1171 Chithira Tirunal and Temple Sculpture

91 (29 Oct). *3rd Death Anniv of Kamaladevi Chattopadhyaya, (founder of All India Handicrafts Board). T* **1170** *and similar vert design. P* 13×13½.
477 1 r. carmine-lake, crimson and yellow .. 40 20
478 6 r. 50, multicoloured .. .. .. 1·50 1·75
Design:—6 r. 50, Traditional puppet.

1991 (7 Nov). *Chithira Tirunal Bala Rama Varma (former Maharaja of Travancore) Commemoration. P* 13½×13.
1479 **1171** 2 r. slate-violet 65 75

1172 "Children in Traditional Costume" (Arpi Snehalbhai Shah)

1173 Mounted Sowar and Tanks

1991 (14 Nov). *Children's Day. P* 13×13½.
1480 **1172** 1 r. multicoloured 70 30

(Des R. Pasricha)

1991 (14 Nov). *70th Anniv of the 18th Cavalry Regiment* (1992). *P* 13½×13.
1481 **1173** 6 r. 50, multicoloured .. .. 2·00 2·50

1174 Kites

1175 Sports on Bricks

1991 (15 Nov). *India Tourism Year. P* 13½×13.
1482 **1174** 6 r. 50, multicoloured .. .. 60 1·00
It was originally intended to release No. 1482 on 28 January 1991, but the issue was postponed until 15 November. Examples are known used from Jaipur on the original date.

1991 (18 Nov). *International Conference on Youth Tourism, New Delhi. P* 13×13½.
1483 **1175** 6 r. 50, multicoloured .. .. 1·10 1·50

1176 "Mozart at Piano" (unfinished painting, J. Lange)

1177 Homeless Family

1991 (5 Dec). *Death Bicentenary of Mozart. P* 13×13½.
1484 **1176** 6 r. 50, multicoloured .. .. 1·50 2·00

(Des N. Srivastav)

1991 (7 Dec). *South Asian Association for Regional Co-operation Year of Shelter. P* 13½×13.
1485 **1177** 4 r. lake-brown and ochre 55 70

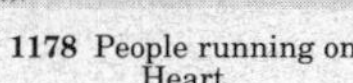

1178 People running on Heart

1179 "Sidhartha with an Injured Bird" (Asit Kumar Haldar)

1991 (11 Dec). *"Run for Your Heart" Marathon, New Delhi. P* 13½×13.
1486 **1178** 1 r. black, slate and bright scarlet .. 20 20

1991 (28 Dec). *Birth Centenary of Asit Kumar Haldar (artist)* (1990). *P* 13×13½.
1487 **1179** 2 r. yellow, Indian red and black .. 30 50

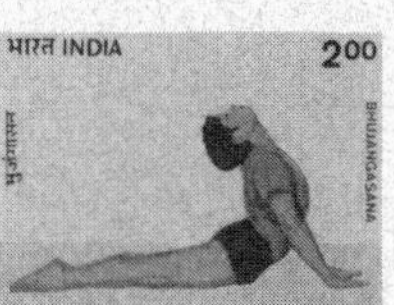

1180 Bhujangasana

1181 Y.M.C.A. Logo

1991 (30 Dec). *Yoga Exercises. T* **1180** *and similar horiz designs. Multicoloured. P* 13½×13.
1488 2 r. Type **1180** 20 25
1489 5 r. Dhanurasana 40 55
1490 6 r. 50, Ustrasana 50 70
1491 10 r. Utthita trikonasana .. .. .. 85 1·25
1488/91 .. .. *Set of* 4 1·75 2·50

1992 (21 Feb). *Centenary of National Council of Y.M.C.As.* (1991). *P* 13×13½.
1492 **1181** 1 r. vermilion and deep dull blue .. 20 20

1182 Madurai Temple Tower and Hooghly River Bridge

1183 Goat Seal from Harappa Culture, 2500 to 1500 B.C.

1992 (1 Mar). *14th Congress of International Association for Bridge and Structural Engineering, New Delhi. T* **1182** *and similar horiz design. P* 13½×13.
1493 **1182** 2 r. bistre-brown, dull vermilion & bl 45 65
a. Horiz pair. Nos. 1493/4 .. 90 1·25
1494 – 2 r. bistre-brown, dull vermilion & bl 45 65
Design:—No. 1494, Gate, Sanchi Stupa and Hall of Nations, New Delhi.
Nos. 1493/4 were printed together, *se-tenant*, in horizontal pairs throughout the sheet.

1992 (2 Mar). *5th International Goat Conference, New Delhi. P* 13×13½.
1495 **1183** 6 r. royal blue and bistre-brown .. 1·50 2·00

1184 Early 19th-century Letter with Mail Pouch and National Archives Building, New Delhi

1185 Krushna Chandra Gajapathi

(Des C. Pakrashi)

1992 (20 Apr). *Centenary of National Archives* (1991). *P* 13½×13.
1496 **1184** 6 r. multicoloured 50 65

1992 (25 Apr). *Krushna Chandra Gajapathi (former Chief Minister of Orissa) Commemoration. P* 13×13½.
1497 **1185** 1 r. deep lilac 15 15

1186 Vijay Singh Pathik

1187 Hang-gliding

1992 (29 Apr). *Vijay Singh Pathik (writer) Commemoration. P* 13×13½.
1498 **1186** 1 r. reddish brown 15 15

(Des R. Pasricha)

1992 (29 Apr). *Adventure Sports. T* **1187** *and similar horiz designs. Multicoloured. P* 13½×13.

1499	2 r. Type **1187**	25	20
1500	4 r. Windsurfing	50	60
1501	5 r. River rafting	60	70
1502	11 r. Skiing	1·25	2·00
1499/1502	*Set of* 4	2·40	3·25

1188 Henry Gidney and Anglo-Indians

1189 Telecommunications Training Centre, Jabalpur

(Des S. Kitson and A. Ali)

1992 (9 May). 50*th Death Anniv of Sir Henry Gidney (ophthalmologist). P* 13½×13.

1503	**1188**	1 r. black and light blue	30	15

1992 (30 May). 50*th Anniv of Telecommunications Training Centre, Jabalpur. P* 13½×13.

1504	**1189**	1 r. bistre	20	15

1190 Sardar Udham Singh

1191 Men's Discus

(Des S. Samanta)

1992 (31 July). *Sardar Udham Singh (patriot) Commemoration. P* 13×13½.

1505	**1190**	1 r. black and light brown	20	15

(Des P. Biswas)

1992 (8 Aug). *Olympic Games, Barcelona. T* **1191** *and similar vert designs. Multicoloured. P* 13×13½.

1506	1 r. Type **1191**	30	10
1507	6 r. Women's gymnastics	80	90
1508	8 r. Men's hockey	1·75	2·00
1509	11 r. Boxing	1·75	2·25
1506/9	*Set of* 4	4·25	4·75

1192 Spinning Wheel Emblem

1193 Treating Casualty

(Des C. Pakrashi)

1992 (9 Aug). 50*th Anniv of "Quit India" Movement. T* **1192** *and similar horiz design. P* 13½×13.

1510	1 r. black and brown-rose	60	30
1511	2 r. black, lake-brown and grey	1·40	1·60

Design:—2 r. Mahatma Gandhi and mantra

1992 (10 Aug). 50*th Anniv of* 60*th Parachute Field Ambulance. P* 13½×13.

1512	**1193**	1 r. multicoloured	1·00	40

1194 Dr. S. R. Ranganathan and Madras University

1195 "Dev Narayan"

1992 (30 Aug). *Birth Centenary of Shiyali Ramamrita Ranganathan (librarian). P* 13½×13.

1513	**1194**	1 r. deep turquoise-blue	55	30

1992 (2 Sept). *Phad Scroll Paintings from Rajasthan. P* 14.

1514	**1195**	5 r. multicoloured	55	70

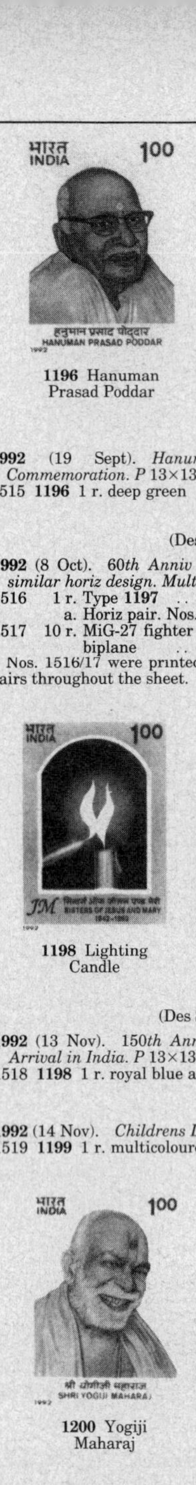

1196 Hanuman Prasad Poddar

1197 Mikoyan Gurevich MiG-29 Fighter and Ilyushin Il-76 Transport

1992 (19 Sept). *Hanuman Prasad Poddar (editor) Commemoration. P* 13×13½.

1515	**1196**	1 r. deep green	15	15

(Des S. Surve)

1992 (8 Oct). 60*th Anniv of Indian Air Force. T* **1197** *and similar horiz design. Multicoloured. P* 13½×13.

1516	1 r. Type **1197**	40	60
	a. Horiz pair. Nos. 1516/17	1·40	1·75
1517	10 r. MiG-27 fighter and Westland Wapiti biplane	1·00	1·25

Nos. 1516/17 were printed together, *se-tenant*, in horizontal pairs throughout the sheet.

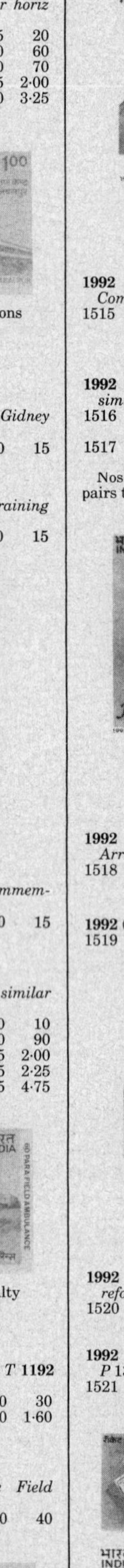

1198 Lighting Candle

1199 "Sun" (Harshit Prashant Patel)

(Des S. Samanta)

1992 (13 Nov). 150*th Anniv of Sisters of Jesus and Mary's Arrival in India. P* 13×13½.

1518	**1198**	1 r. royal blue and light grey	15	15

1992 (14 Nov). *Childrens Day. P* 13½×13.

1519	**1199**	1 r. multicoloured	20	15

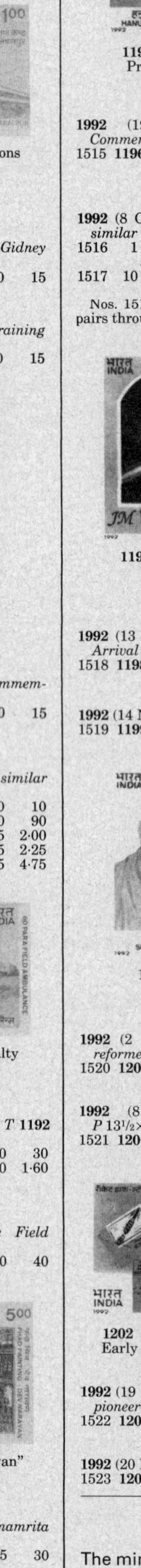

1200 Yogiji Maharaj

1201 Army Service Corps Transport

1992 (2 Dec). *Birth Centenary of Yogiji Maharaj (Hindu reformer). P* 13×13½.

1520	**1200**	1 r. deep ultramarine	30	15

1992 (8 Dec). *Army Service Corps Commemoration. P* 13½×13.

1521	**1201**	1 r. multicoloured	1·00	40

1202 Stephen Smith and Early Rocket Post Covers

1203 Electricity Pylons, Farmers and Crops

1992 (19 Dec). *Birth Centenary of Stephen Smith (rocket mail pioneer)* (1991). *P* 13½×13.

1522	**1202**	11 r. multicoloured	90	1·25

1992 (20 Dec). 25*th Anniv of Haryana State. P* 13½×13.

1523	**1203**	2 r. orange-verm, dp grn & yellow-grn	15	15

MINIMUM PRICE

The minimum price quote is 10p which represents a handling charge rather than a basis for valuing common stamps. For further notes about prices see introductory pages.

1204 Madanlal Dhingra

1205 Osprey

1992 (28 Dec). *Madanlal Dhingra (revolutionary) Commemoration. P* 13×13½.

1524	**1204**	1 r. deep brown, orange-red & dp green	30	1

1992 (30 Dec). *Birds of Prey. T* **1205** *and similar vert design. Multicoloured. P* 13×13½.

1525	2 r. Type **1205**	75	5
	a. Error. 1 r. instead of 2 r.		
1526	6 r. Peregrine Falcon	1·00	1·0
1527	8 r. Lammergeier	1·25	1·6
1528	11 r. Golden Eagle	1·50	1·9
1525/8	*Set of* 4	4·00	4·5

No. 1525a was the original printing of this design incorporating an incorrect Hindi inscription. The stamp was withdrawn before issue and replaced by a 2 r. value with the correct inscription. Three examples of the 1 r. have, however been found in 1992 Year Packs.

1206 Pandit Ravishankar Shukla

1207 William Carey

1992 (31 Dec). *Pandit Ravishankar Shukla (social reformer) Commemoration. P* 13×13½.

1529	**1206**	1 r. deep purple	15	1

1993 (9 Jan). *Bicentenary of William Carey's Appointment as Baptist Missionary to India. P* 13½×13.

1530	**1207**	6 r. multicoloured	90	1·0

1208 Fakirmohan Senapati

1209 Workers and C.S.I.R. Emblem

1993 (14 Jan). *Fakirmohan Senapati Commemoration. P* 13×13½.

1531	**1208**	1 r. Indian red	30	1

1993 (28 Feb). 50*th Anniv of Council of Scientific and Industrial Research. P* 13½×13.

1532	**1209**	1 r. maroon	30	1

1210 Parachute Drop and Field Gun

1211 Westland Wapiti Biplane

1993 (1 Apr). 50*th Anniv of* 9*th Parachute Field Artillery Regiment. P* 13½.

1533	**1210**	1 r. multicoloured	1·00	3

1993 (1 Apr). 60*th Anniv of No.* 1 *Squadron, Indian Air Force. P* 13½.

1534	**1211**	1 r. multicoloured	1·00	3

1212 Rahul Sankrityayan — 1213 Parliament Building and Emblem

1993 (9 Apr). *Birth Centenary of Rahul Sankrityayan (politician).* P 13½×13.
1535 **1212** 1 r. blue-black, cinnamon & yellow-brn .. 15 15

1993 (11 Apr). *89th Inter-Parliamentary Union Conference, New Delhi.* P 13×13½.
1536 **1213** 1 r. blue-black 15 15

1214 Neral Matheran Railway Tank Locomotive, 1905 — 1215 Students and College Building

1993 (16 Apr). *Mountain Locomotives. T* **1214** *and similar horiz designs. Multicoloured.* P 13½×13.
1537 1 r. Type **1214** 60 20
1538 6 r. Darjeeling and Himalayan Railway, 1889 .. .. 1·25 1·25
1539 8 r. Nilgiri Mountain Railway, 1914 .. 1·40 1·60
1540 11 r. Kalka–Simla Railway, 1934 .. 1·90 2·25
1537/40 .. .. *Set of* 4 4·75 4·75

1993 (25 Apr). *Centenary of Meerut College.* P 14.
1541 **1215** 1 r. blue-black and orange-brown .. 15 15

1216 Mahalanobis and Office Block — 1217 Bombay Town Hall

1993 (29 June). *Prasanta Chandra Mahalanobis Commemoration.* P 13.
1542 **1216** 1 r. yellow-brown 15 15

1993 (31 July). *Centenary of Bombay Municipal Corporation.* P 13×13½.
1543 **1217** 2 r. multicoloured 20 30

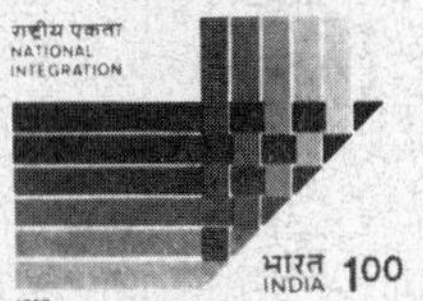

1218 Abdul Ghaffar Khan and Mountainside — 1219 National Integration Emblem

1993 (9 Aug). *Abdul Ghaffar Khan Commemoration.* P 13½×13.
1544 **1218** 1 r. multicoloured 15 15

(Des C. Pakrashi)

1993 (19 Aug). *National Integration Campaign.* P 13½×13.
1545 **1219** 1 r. bright orange and deep green .. 15 15

1220 Dadabhai Naoroji and Houses of Parliament, London — 1221 Swami Vivekananda and Art Institute, Chicago

1993 (26 Aug). *Centenary of Dadabhai Naoroji's Election to the House of Commons.* P 14.
1546 **1220** 6 r. multicoloured 45 60

(Des C. Pakrashi)

1993 (11 Sept). *Centenary of Swami Vivekananda's Chicago Address.* P 13×13½.
1547 **1221** 2 r. reddish orange and grey .. 40 40

1222 *Lagerstroemia speciosa* — 1223 College Building and Emblem

(Des O. Ravindran)

1993 (9 Oct). *Flowering Trees. T* **1222** *and similar vert designs.* P 13×13½.
1548 1 r. rose-carmine, yellow-grn & chocolate 20 15
1549 6 r. multicoloured 40 55
1550 8 r. multicoloured 55 70
1551 11 r. multicoloured .. .. .. 75 1·00
1548/51 .. .. .. *Set of* 4 1·75 2·25
Designs:—6 r. *Cochlospermum religiosum*; 8 r. *Erythrina variegata*; 11 r. *Thespesia populnea*.

1993 (8 Nov). *50th Anniv of College of Military Engineering, Pune.* P 13×13½.
1552 **1223** 2 r. multicoloured 20 30

1224 Dr. Dwaram Venkataswamy Naidu playing Violin — 1225 Children on Elephant

(Des Alka Sharma)

1993 (8 Nov). *Birth Centenary of Dwaram Venkataswamy Naidu (violinist).* P 13×13½.
1553 **1224** 1 r. Indian red 20 20

1993 (14 Nov). *Children's Day.* P 14.
1554 **1225** 1 r. multicoloured 20 20

1226 People with Stress — 1227 Dr. Kotnis performing Operation

1993 (9 Dec). *Heart Care Festival.* P 13½×13.
1555 **1226** 6 r. 50, multicoloured 60 70

1993 (9 Dec). *Dr. Dwarkananth Kotnis (surgeon) Commemoration.* P 13½×13.
1556 **1227** 1 r. blue-black 20 20
a. Printed on the gummed side ..

1228 Tea Symbol — 1229 Papal Seminary Arms and Building

1993 (11 Dec). *Indian Tea Production.* P 13.
1557 **1228** 6 r. deep dull green and bright carmine 50 65

1993 (16 Dec). *Centenary of Papal Seminary, Pune.* P 13½×13.
1558 **1229** 6 r. multicoloured 50 65

1230 Meghnad Saha and Eclipse of the Sun — 1231 Speedpost Letter and Arrows circling Globe

1993 (23 Dec). *Meghnad Saha (astronomer) Commemoration.* P 13×13½.
1559 **1230** 1 r. deep violet-blue 30 20

(Des C. Pakrashi (1 r.))

1993 (25–27 Dec). *"Inpex '93" National Philatelic Exhibition, Calcutta. T* **1231** *and similar horiz design. Multicoloured.* P 13½×13.
1560 1 r. Type **1231** 15 15
1561 2 r. "Custom-house Wharf, Calcutta" (Sir Charles D'Oyly) (27 Dec) 25 35

1232 Dinanath Mangeshkar — 1233 Nargis Dutt

(Des C. Pakrashi)

1993 (29 Dec). *Dinanath Mangeshkar Commemoration.* P 13½×13.
1562 **1232** 1 r. orange-red 15 15

1993 (30 Dec). *Nargis Dutt Commemoration.* P 13.
1563 **1233** 1 r. Indian red 15 15

1234 S.C. Bose inspecting Troops — 1235 Satyendra Nath Bose and Equation

1993 (31 Dec). *50th Anniv of Indian National Army.* P 13½×13.
1564 **1234** 1 r. slate-green, dp green & orange-red 30 20

1994 (1 Jan). *Birth Centenary of Satyendra Nath Bose (scientist).* P 13½×13.
1565 **1235** 1 r. purple-brown 30 15

1236 Dr. Sampurnanand

1994 (10 Jan). *Dr. Sampurnanand (politician) Commemoration.* P 13½×13.
1566 **1236** 1 r. reddish brn, slate-grn & orge-red 15 10

1237 Scene from *Pather Panchali*

1994 (11 Jan). *Satyajit Ray (film director) Commemoration. T* **1237** *and similar multicoloured design. P* 13.
1567 6 r. Type **1237** .. .. 1·00 1·25
a. Horiz pair. Nos. 1567/8 .. .. 2·25 2·75
1568 11 r. Satyajit Ray and Oscar (35×35 *mm*) 1·25 1·50
Nos. 1567/8 were printed together, *se-tenant*, in horizontal pairs throughout the sheet.

1238 Dr. Bhatnagar and University Building

1239 Prajapita Brahma and Memorial

1994 (21 Feb). *Dr. Shanti Swarup Bhatnagar (scientist) Commemoration. P* 13½×13.
1569 **1238** 1 r. deep violet-blue 15 10

1994 (7 Mar). *25th Death Anniv of Prajapita Brahma (social reformer). P* 13½×13.
1570 **1239** 1 r. deep rose-lilac & deep ultramarine 15 10

1240 "Window" (K. Subramanyan)

1241 Agricultural Products and Tea Garden

1994 (14 Mar). *8th Triennale Art Exhibition, New Delhi. P* 13½×13.
1571 **1240** 6 r. salmon, carmine-verm & ultram 40 60

(Des S. Samanta)

1994 (26 Mar). *Centenary of United Planters' Association of Southern India. P* 13×13½.
1572 **1241** 2 r. multicoloured 20 20

1242 Indian Family

1242a Sanchi Stupa

1994 (4 Apr)–**98**. *W* **374** (*sideways on* 5 *r.*). *P* 13.
1573 **1242** 75 p. brown and vermilion (11.7.94) 10 10
a. Wmk sideways (1998) .. ..
1574 – 1 r. cerise & dp bluish grn (11.7.94) 10 10
a. Wmk sideways (1997) .. 10 10
1575 – 3 r. deep claret (21.9.98) .. 15 20
1576 **1242a** 5 r. reddish brown & turquoise-grn 15 20
a. Wmk upright .. ..
Designs: *Horiz* (*as T* **1242**)—1 r. Family outside home. *Vert* (*as T* **1242**)—3 r. Baby and drop of polio vaccine.

1243 Rani Rashmoni on River Bank

1244 Indians releasing Peace Doves

1994 (9 Apr). *Birth Bicentenary of Rani Rashmoni. P* 13½×13.
1589 **1243** 1 r. reddish brown 15 10

(Des S. Kumar)

1994 (13 Apr). *75th Anniv of Jallianwala Bagh Massacre, Amritsar. P* 13½×13.
1590 **1244** 1 r. black and rosine 15 10

1245 Chandra Singh Garhwali

1246 Emblems and National Flag

1994 (23 Apr). *15th Death Anniv of Chandra Singh Garhwali (nationalist). P* 13½×13.
1591 **1245** 1 r. deep olive-green and red-orange 15 10

1994 (1 May). *75th Anniv of International Labour Organization. P* 13½×13.
1592 **1246** 6 r. multicoloured 40 60

1247 Silhouette of Drummer and Logo

1248 Statue of Sepoy

(Des A. Sharma)

1994 (25 May). *50th Anniv of Indian People's Theatre Association. P* 13.
1593 **1247** 2 r. black, yellowish green and gold 15 15

1994 (12 Aug). *Bicentenary of 4th Battalion, The Madras Regiment. P* 13.
1594 **1248** 6 r. 50, multicoloured 55 65

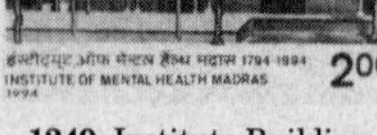

1249 Institute Building and Emblem

1250 Mahatma Gandhi and Indian Flag

(Des C. Pakrashi)

1994 (23 Sept). *Bicentenary of Institute of Mental Health, Madras. P* 13½×13.
1595 **1249** 2 r. deep rose-red and deep blue .. 15 15

(Des S. Samanta and S. Kumar)

1994 (2 Oct). *125th Birth Anniv of Mahatma Gandhi. T* **1250** *and similar multicoloured design. P* 13.
1596 6 r. Type **1250** .. .. 1·00 1·25
a. Horiz pair. Nos. 1596/7 .. .. 2·25 2·75
1597 11 r. Aspects of Gandhi's life on flag (69×34 *mm*) .. .. 1·25 1·50
Nos. 1596/7 were printed together, *se-tenant*, in horizontal pairs throughout the sheet, with the backgrounds forming a composite design.

1251 Symbols of Cancer

1252 Human Resources Emblem

(Des A. Sharma)

1994 (30 Oct). *16th International Cancer Congress, New Delhi. P* 13×13½.
1598 **1251** 6 r. multicoloured 55 65

1994 (8 Nov). *Human Resource Development World Conference, New Delhi. P* 13½×13.
1599 **1252** 6 r. blue, vermilion and azure .. 55 65

COVER PRICES

Cover factors are quoted at the beginning of each country for most issues to 1945. An explanation of the system can be found on page x. The factors quoted do not, however, apply to philatelic covers.

1253 "Me and My Pals" (Namarata Amit Shah)

1254 Family and Emblem

1994 (14 Nov). *Children's Day. P* 13½×13.
1600 **1253** 1 r. multicoloured 10 1

(Des S. Kumar)

1994 (20 Nov). *International Year of the Family. P* 13.
1601 **1254** 2 r. multicoloured 20 1

1255 "Taj Mahal" (illustration from Badsha Nama)

1256 Andaman Teal

1994 (21 Nov). *Khuda Bakhsh Oriental Public Library, Patna Commemoration. P* 14.
1602 **1255** 6 r. multicoloured .. .. .. 4·00 1·0

(Des J. Irani. Litho Madras Security Printers)

1994 (23 Nov). *Endangered Water Birds. T* **1256** *and simila horiz designs. Multicoloured. P* 13½×13.
1603 1 r. Type **1256** .. .. 5·00 2·0
a. Block of 4. Nos. 1603/6 .. .. 30·00
1604 6 r. Eastern White Stork .. .. 8·00 4·0
1605 8 r. Black-necked Crane .. .. 9·00 4·5
1606 11 r. Pink-headed Duck .. .. .. 11·00 6·0
1603/6 .. .. *Set of* 4 30·00 15·0
Nos. 1603/6 were printed together, *se-tenant*, in blocks of throughout the sheet.
It is reported that Nos. 1603/6 were withdrawn shortly afte issue due to technical difficulties.

1257 J. R. D. Tata and Aspects of Industrial Symbols

(Des C. Pakrashi)

1994 (29 Nov). *J. R. D. Tata (industrialist) Commemoratio P* 14.
1607 **1257** 2 r. multicoloured 30 3

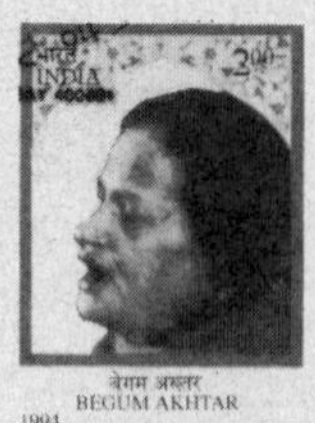

1258 School Building and Computer Class

1259 Begum Akhtar

1994 (30 Nov). *Centenary of Calcutta Blind School. P* 13½×13
1608 **1258** 2 r. rosine, chocolate and cinnamon 20 1

(Litho Madras Security Printers)

1994 (2 Dec). *80th Birth Anniv of Begum Akhtar (singer P* 13×13½.
1609 **1259** 2 r. multicoloured .. .. .. 4·00 4·0
It is reported that No. 1609 was withdrawn shortly after issu due to technical difficulties

1260 College Building

1261 Cavalryman, Infantryman and Dog Handler

94 (4 Dec). *125th Anniv of St. Xavier's College, Bombay. P 13½×13.*

10 **1260** 2 r. purple-brown and azure .. 15 15

94 (14 Dec). *215th Anniv of Remount Veterinary Corps. P 13×13½.*

11 **1261** 6 r. multicoloured 75 60

1262 College Building

1263 Righthand Ornament of Bronze Stand

94 (19 Dec). *Bicentenary of College of Engineering, Guindy, Madras. P 14.*

12 **1262** 2 r. dull vermilion, red-brown & black 15 10

94 (20 Dec). *Centenary of Baroda Museum. T* **1263** *and similar vert design. P 14.*

13 6 r. bistre-yellow and agate .. .. 3·00 75

a. Horiz pair. Nos. 1613/14 .. .. 6·00 1·50

14 11 r. bistre-yellow and agate .. .. 3·00 75

Design:—11 r. Bronze Rishabhanatha statue of Buddha on and.

Nos. 1613/14 were printed together, *se-tenant*, in horizontal airs throughout the sheet.

1264 "200" and Aspects of Postal Service

(Des M. Rajadhyaksha. Litho Calcutta Security Printers, Kanpur)

94 (28 Dec). *Bicentenary of Bombay General Post Office. P 13½×13.*

15 **1264** 6 r. multicoloured .. .. .. 6·00 1·50

1265 Statue of King Rajaraja Chola

1266 Globe and Emblem

(Litho Madras Security Printers)

95 (5 Jan). *8th International Conference-Seminar of Tamil Studies, Thanjavur. P 13×13½.*

16 **1265** 2 r. light blue, ultramarine and black 3·50 75

(Des C. Pakrashi)

95 (7 Jan). *60th Anniv of National Science Academy. P 13×13½.*

17 **1266** 6 r. multicoloured 50 60

1267 Chhotu Ram

1268 Film Reel and Globe

1995 (9 Jan). *Chhotu Ram (social reformer) Commemoration. P 13×13½.*

1618 **1267** 1 r. yellow-brown .. .. .. 1·00 25

(Des S. Kumar. Litho Calcutta Security Printers, Kanpur)

1995 (11 Jan). *Centenary of Cinema. T* **1268** *and similar horiz design. Multicoloured. P 13½×13.*

1619 6 r. Type **1268** 60 70

a. Horiz pair. Nos. 1619/20 .. .. 1·40 1·60

1620 11 r. Film reel and early equipment .. 80 90

Nos. 1619/20 were printed together, *se-tenant*, in horizontal pairs throughout the sheet.

1269 Symbolic Hands and Children

1270 Prithviraj Kapoor and Mask

1995 (12 Jan). *South Asian Association for Regional Cooperation Youth Year. P 13×13½.*

1621 **1269** 2 r. multicoloured 20 20

(Des S. Pawar)

1995 (15 Jan). *50th Anniv of Prithvi Theatre. P 13×13½.*

1622 **1270** 2 r. multicoloured .. .. .. 3·75 75

1271 Field-Marshal Cariappa

1272 Textile Pattern

1995 (15 Jan). *Field-Marshal K. Cariappa Commemoration. P 13×13½.*

1623 **1271** 2 r. multicoloured 30 20

1995 (18 Jan). *"TEX-STYLES INDIA '95" Fair, Bombay. P 13×13½.*

1624 **1272** 2 r. chestnut, pale buff & brt scarlet 20 20

1273 Rafi Ahmed Kidwai

1274 K. L. Saigal, Film Reel and Gramophone

1995 (18 Feb). *Birth Centenary of Rafi Ahmed Kidwai (politician)* (1994). *P 13×13½.*

1625 **1273** 1 r. chestnut 15 10

1995 (4 Apr). *90th Birth Anniv of K. L. Saigal (singer). P 13½×13.*

1626 **1274** 5 r. chestnut, grey and black .. 75 80

1275 R. S. Ruikar

1276 Radio Tower, Globe and Dish Aerial

1995 (1 May). *Birth Centenary of R. S. Ruikar (trade unionist). P 13×13½.*

1627 **1275** 1 r. purple-brown 15 10

(Des S. Kumar. Litho Calcutta Security Printers Ltd, Kanpur)

1995 (17 May). *Centenary of Telecommunications. P 13½×13.*

1628 **1276** 5 r. multicoloured 60 70

1277 Leaves and Symbolic Houses

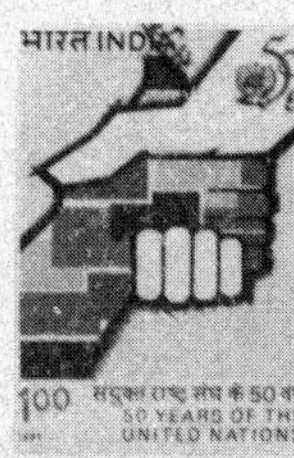

1278 Handshake

(Des D. Banduni. Litho Calcutta Security Printers Ltd, Kanpur)

1995 (23 May). *Delhi Development Authority. P 13½×13.*

1629 **1277** 2 r. multicoloured 20 20

(Des C. Pakrashi. Litho Calcutta Security Printers Ltd, Kanpur)

1995 (26 June). *50th Anniv of United Nations. T* **1278** *and similar vert design. Multicoloured. P 13×13½.*

1630 1 r. Type **1278** 10 10

1631 6 r. Work of U.N. Agencies 45 55

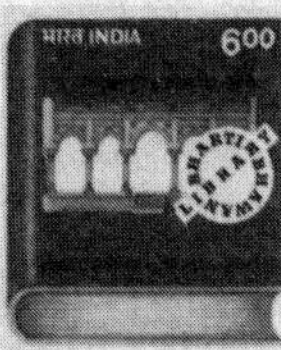

1279 Colonnade on Book Cover

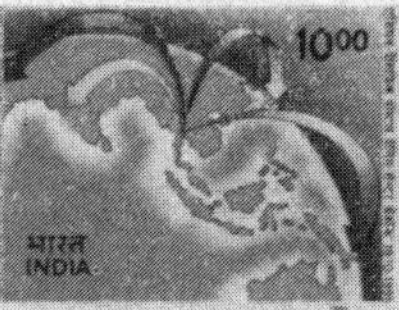

1280 Globe showing South-east Asia

(Des D. Banduni)

1995 (30 Aug). *Centenary of Bharti Bhawan Library, Allahabad. P 14.*

1632 **1279** 6 r. black, chestnut & bright rose-red 55 65

(Des S. Kumar. Litho Calcutta Security Printers Ltd, Kanpur)

1995 (4 Sept). *25th Anniv of Asian-Pacific Postal Training Centre, Bangkok. P 13½×13.*

1633 **1280** 10 r. multicoloured 80 90

1281 "75" and Taurus Formation Sign

1282 Louis Pasteur in Laboratory (from painting by Edelfelt)

1995 (26 Sept). *75th Anniv of Area Army Headquarters, Delhi. P 13×13½.*

1634 **1281** 2 r. multicoloured 30 20

(Des S. Samantha)

1995 (28 Sept). *Death Centenary of Louis Pasteur (chemist). P 13×13½.*

1635 **1282** 5 r. black and stone 60 70

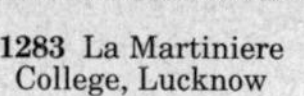

1283 La Martiniere College, Lucknow

1284 Gandhi in South Africa

1995 (1 Oct). *150th Anniv of La Martiniere College, Lucknow. P* 13½×13.
1636 **1283** 2 r. multicoloured 20 20

(Des A. Ainslie)

1995 (2 Oct). *India–South Africa Co-operation. 125th Birth Anniv of Mahatma Gandhi* (1994). *T* **1284** *and similar vert design. P* 13.
1637 1 r. scarlet 25 25
a. Horiz pair. Nos. 1637/8 .. .. 55 55
1638 2 r. scarlet 30 30
MS1639 68×80 mm. Nos. 1637/8 (*sold at* 8 r.) 55 65
a. Printed double .. .. ..
Design:—2 r. Gandhi wearing dhoti.
Nos. 1637/8 were issued together, *se-tenant*, in horizontal pairs throughout the sheet.
Stamps in similar designs were issued by South Africa.

1285 Ears of Grain, "50" and Emblem on Globe

1286 P. M. Thevar

(Des and litho Calcutta Security Printers Ltd, Kanpur)

1995 (16 Oct). *50th Anniv of Food and Agriculture Organization. P* 13½×13.
1640 **1285** 5 r. multicoloured 60 70

1995 (30 Oct). *Pasumpon Muthuramalingam Thevar (social reformer) Commemoration. P* 13.
1641 **1286** 1 r. deep rose-red 15 10

1287 W. C. Rontgen

1288 Children in Circle

1995 (8 Nov). *150th Birth Anniv of W. C. Rontgen (discoverer of X-rays). P* 13×13½.
1642 **1287** 6 r. multicoloured 65 75

1995 (14 Nov). *Children's Day. P* 13×13½.
1643 **1288** 1 r. multicoloured 20 10

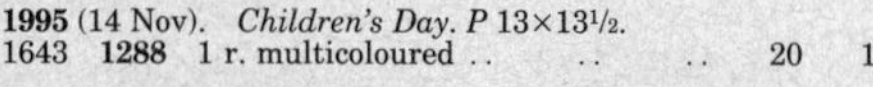

1289 Sitar

1290 Jat War Memorial, Bareilly

1995 (19 Nov). *Communal Harmony Campaign. P* 13.
1644 **1289** 2 r. multicoloured 40 20

1995 (20 Nov). *Bicentenary of Jat Regiments. P* 13.
1645 **1290** 5 r. multicoloured 65 75

1291 Men of Rajputana Rifles

1292 Sant Tukdoji Maharaj and Rural Meeting

1995 (28 Nov). *175th Anniv of 5th (Napier's) Battalion, Rajputana Rifles. P* 13½×13.
1646 **1291** 5 r. multicoloured 70 70

1995 (10 Dec). *Sant Tukdoji Maharaj Commemoration. P* 13½×13.
1647 **1292** 1 r. yellow-brown 15 10
Although dated "1993" No. 1647 was not issued until the date quoted above.

1293 Dr. Yellapragada Subbarow

1294 Pres. Giani Zail Singh

1995 (19 Dec). *Dr. Yellapragada Subbarow (pharmaceutical scientist) Commemoration. P* 13.
1648 **1293** 1 r. orange-brown 30 10

1995 (25 Dec). *First Death Anniv of Pres. Giani Zail Singh. P* 13.
1649 **1294** 1 r. multicoloured 15 10

1295 Dargah of Ala Hazrat Barelvi

1296 Tata Institute Building

(Litho Calcutta Security Printers Ltd, Kanpur)

1995 (31 Dec). *75th Death Anniv of Ala Hazrat Barelvi (Moslem scholar). P* 13×13½.
1650 **1295** 1 r. multicoloured 15 10
a. "1995" omitted from bottom right (R. 2/2) .. .. ..

1996 (9 Feb). *50th Anniv of Tata Institute of Fundamental Research* (1995). *P* 13½×13.
1651 **1296** 2 r. multicoloured 20 20

1297 Kasturba Gandhi

1298 Sectioned Heart

(Des S. Samantha)

1996 (22 Feb). *50th Anniv of the Kasturba Trust. P* 13.
1652 **1297** 1 r. slate, brt green & bright scarlet 15 10

(Litho Calcutta Security Printers Ltd, Kanpur)

1996 (25 Feb). *100 Years of Cardiac Surgery. P* 13×13½.
1653 **1298** 5 r. multicoloured 60 70

NEW INFORMATION

The editor is always interested to correspond with people who have new information that will improve or correct the Catalogue.

1299 C. K. Nayudu

1300 "Vasant" (Spring) (Ragini Basanti)

1996 (13 Mar). *Cricketers. T* **1299** *and similar vert design*
Multicoloured. P 14.
1654 2 r. Type **1299** 20 2
1655 2 r. Vinoo Mankad 20 2
1656 2 r. Deodhar 20 2
1657 2 r. Vijay Merchant 20 2
1654/7 .. .. *Set of* 4 70 7

(Litho Calcutta Security Printers Ltd, Kanpur)

1996 (13 Mar). *Miniature Paintings of the Seasons. T* **1300** *an*
similar vert designs. Multicoloured. P 13½.
1658 5 r. Type **1300** 50 6
1659 5 r. "Greeshma" (Summer) (Jyestha) .. 50 6
1660 5 r. "Varsha" (Monsoon) (Rag Megh Malbar) 50 6
1661 5 r. "Hemant" (Winter) (Pausha) .. 50 6
1658/61 .. .. *Set of* 4 1·75 2·2

1301 Kunjilal Dubey

1302 Morarji Desai

1996 (18 Mar). *Kunjilal Dubey Commemoration. P* 13.
1662 **1301** 1 r. olive-sepia and chocolate .. 15 1

1996 (10 Apr). *Birth Centenary of Morarji Desai (former Prim*
Minister) (1st issue). P 13×13½.
1663 **1302** 1 r. deep rose-red 20 1
See also Nos. 1702

1303 Blood Pheasant

1304 S.K.C.G. College Building

(Des R. Sukumar (Nos. 1663/4), V. Kumar (Nos. 1665/6). Lith
Calcutta Security Printers Ltd, Kanpur)

1996 (10 May). *Himalayan Ecology. T* **1303** *and similar hor*
designs. Multicoloured. P 13½×13.
1664 5 r. Type **1303** 50 6
1665 5 r. Markhor (goat) 50 6
1666 5 r. *Meconopis horridula* (Tsher Gnoin) (plant) 50 6
1667 5 r. *Saussurea simpsoniana* (Sunflower) 50 6
1664/7 .. .. *Set of* 4 1·75 2·2
MS1668 175×105 mm. Nos. 1664/7 (*sold at* 30 *r.*) 2·10 2·1
No. **MS**1668 exists with either blue or white gum.

(Litho Calcutta Security Printers, Kanpur)

1996 (25 May). *Centenary of S.K.C.G. College, Gajapat*
P 13½×13.
1669 **1304** 1 r. brown and cream 15 1

1305 Muhammad Ismail Sahib

1306 Modern Stadium and Ancient Athens

96 (5 June). *Birth Centenary of Muhammad Ismail Sahib (Moslem politician). P* 13×13½.
70 **1305** 1 r. deep reddish purple 15 10

es S. Kumar. Litho Calcutta Security Printers Ltd, Kanpur)
96 (25 June). *Olympic Games, Atlanta. T* **1306** *and similar vert designs. Multicoloured. P* 13×13½.
71 5 r. Type **1306** 35 40
72 5 r. Hand holding Olympic torch .. 35 40

1307 Sister Alphonsa **1308** "Communications"

(Des S. Samanta)

96 (19 July). *50th Death Anniv of Sister Alphonsa. P* 13×13½.
73 **1307** 1 r. black and dull blue 15 10

(Des S. Gujral)

96 (2 Aug). *125th Anniv of Videsh Sanchar Nigam Limited (telecommunications company). P* 14.
74 **1308** 5 r. multicoloured 35 40

1309 Sir Pherozeshah Mehta **1310** Ahilyabai

96 (4 Aug). *150th Birth Anniv of Sir Pherozeshah Mehta (politician). P* 13.
75 **1309** 1 r. deep slate-blue 15 10

(Des S. Samanta)

96 (25 Aug). *Death Bicentenary* (1995) *of Ahilyabai (ruler of Holkar). P* 13×13½.
76 **1310** 2 r. yellow-brown and purple-brown 20 20

1311 Chembai Vaidyanatha Bhagavathar **1312** Red Junglefowl Cockerel

(Des S. Samanta)

96 (28 Aug). *Birth Centenary of Chembai Vaidanatha Bhagavathar (musician). P* 13×13½.
77 **1311** 1 r. chestnut and deep turquoise-green 15 10

es R. Sukumar. Litho Calcutta Security Printers Ltd, Kanpur)

96 (2 Sept). *20th World Poultry Congress, New Delhi. P* 13½×13.
78 **1312** 5 r. multicoloured 50 55

1313 Rani Gaidinliu **1314** Nath Pai

1996 (12 Sept). *Rani Gaidinliu (Naga leader) Commemoration. P* 13.
1679 **1313** 1 r. deep turquoise-blue 15 10

1996 (25 Sept). *25th Death Anniv of Nath Pai (politician). P* 13×13½.
1680 **1314** 1 r. dull blue 15 10

1315 Exhibition Logo **1316** Historic Steam Locomotives

(Des S. Samanta. Litho Calcutta Security Printers Ltd, Kanpur)

1996 (5 Oct). *"INDEPEX '97" International Stamp Exhibition, New Delhi (1st issue). P* 13×13½.
1681 **1315** 2 r. gold and brown-purple 20 20
See also Nos. 1713/16, 1722/5, 1741/4, **MS**1756 and 1758/61.

(Des S. Samanta. Litho Calcutta Security Printers Ltd, Kanpur)

1996 (7 Oct). *25th Anniv of National Rail Museum. P* 13½.
1682 **1316** 5 r. multicoloured 50 55

1317 Jananayak Debeswar Sarmah **1318** Monument and Sikh Sentry

(Des S. Samanta. Litho Calcutta Security Printers Ltd, Kanpur)

1996 (10 Oct). *Birth Centenary of Jananayak Debeswar Sarmah (politician). P* 13×13½.
1683 **1317** 2 r. orange-brown and red-brown .. 20 20

1996 (19 Oct). *150th Anniv of Sikh Regiment. P* 13.
1684 **1318** 5 r. multicoloured 50 55

1319 Dr. Salim Ali **1320** "Indian Village" (child's painting)

1996 (12 Nov). *Birth Centenary of Salim Ali (ornithologist). T* **1319** *and similar square design. Multicoloured. P* 13.
1685 8 r. Type **1319** 70 80
a. Horiz pair. Nos. 1685/6 .. .. 1·60 1·90
1686 11 r. Storks at nest .. .. .. 90 1·10
Nos. 1685/6 were printed together, *se-tenant*, in horizontal pairs with the backgrounds forming a composite design.

1996 (14 Nov). *Children's Day. P* 13½×13.
1687 **1320** 8 r. multicoloured 50 55

1321 Seeds in a Test-tube **1322** Regimental Shrine

1996 (17 Nov). *2nd International Crop Science Congress, New Delhi. P* 13×13½.
1688 **1321** 2 r. multicoloured 20 20

1996 (4 Dec). *Bicentenary of 2nd Battalion, Grenadiers. P* 14.
1689 **1322** 5 r. multicoloured 50 55

1323 Woman writing **1324** Abai Konunbaev

(Des V. Mehra)

1996 (8 Dec). *10th Anniv of South Asian Association for Regional Co-operation (S.A.A.R.C.). P* 13.
1690 **1323** 11 r. multicoloured 65 70

1996 (9 Dec). *150th Birth Anniv of Abai Konunbaev (Kazakh poet)* (1995). *P* 13×13½.
1691 **1324** 5 r. chestnut, purple-brn & slate-lilac 35 40

1325 Buglers in front of Memorial

1996 (16 Dec). *25th Anniv of the Liberation of Bangladesh. P* 14.
1692 **1325** 2 r. multicoloured 20 20

1326 Vivekananda Rock Memorial

(Des S. Samanta. Litho Calcutta Security Printers Ltd, Kanpur)

1996 (26 Dec). *25th Anniv of Vivekananda Rock Memorial, Kanyakumari. P* 13½×13.
1693 **1326** 5 r. multicoloured 50 55
It was originally intended to release No. 1693 on 12 January 1996, but the issue was postponed until 26 December. Examples are known used from Bangalore or Jodhpur on the original date

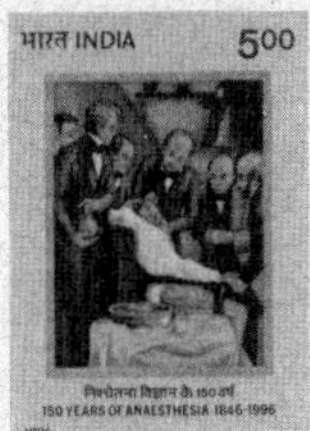

1327 Victorian Doctors performing Operation **1328** Roorkee University Buildings

(Des S. Samanta)

1996 (27 Dec). *150th Anniv of Anaesthetics. P* 13×13½.
1694 **1327** 5 r. multicoloured 50 55

(Des H. Sinvhal)

1997 (1 Jan). *150th Anniv of Roorkee University. P* 13.
1695 **1328** 8 r. multicoloured 60 70

1329 Dr. Vrindavanlal Verma   **1330** Field Post Office

(Des S. Samiti)

1997 (9 Jan). *Dr. Vrindavanlal Verma (writer) Commemoration. P* 13.
1696 **1329** 2 r. dull scarlet 20 20

(Des S. Samanta)

1997 (22 Jan). *25th Anniv of Army Postal Service Corps. P* 13½×13.
1697 **1330** 5 r. multicoloured 35 40

1331 Subhas Chandra Bose   **1332** José Martí

1997 (23 Jan). *Birth Centenary of Subhas Chandra Bose (nationalist). P* 13.
1698 **1331** 1 r. reddish brown 20 10

1997 (28 Jan). *José Martí (Cuban writer) Commemoration. P* 13×13½.
1699 **1332** 11 r. black and flesh 65 70

1333 Conference Logo   **1334** St. Andrew's Church

1996 (15 Feb). *"Towards Partnership between Men and Women in Politics" Inter-Parliamentary Conference, New Delhi. P* 13.
1700 **1333** 5 r. multicoloured 35 40

1997 (25 Feb). *St. Andrew's Church, Egmore, Madras Commemoration. P* 13×13½.
1701 **1334** 8 r. multicoloured 50 55

1335 Morarji Desai   **1336** Shyam Lal Gupt

(Litho Calcutta Security Printers Ltd. Kanpur)

1997 (28 Feb). *Birth Centenary of Morarji Desai (former Prime Minister) (2nd issue). P* 13×13½.
1702 **1335** 1 r. brown and reddish brown . . 10 10

(Des P. Sansthan. Litho Calcutta Security Printers Ltd, Kanpur)

1997 (4 Mar). *Birth Centenary* (1996) *of Shyam Lal Gupt (social reformer). P* 13×13½.
1703 **1336** 1 r. cinnamon and lake-brown . . 10 10

1337 Saint Dnyaneshwar   **1338** Parijati Tree

1997 (5 Mar). *700th Death Anniv of Saint Dnyaneshwar* (1996). *P* 13×13½.
1704 **1337** 5 r. multicoloured 30 35

(Des R. Pasricha. Litho Calcutta Security Printers Ltd, Kanpur)

1997 (8 Mar). *Parijati Tree. T* **1338** *and similar vert design. Multicoloured. P* 13×13½.
1705 5 r. Type **1338** 30 40
a. Horiz pair. Nos. 1705/6 . . . . 60 80
1706 6 r. Parijati flower 30 40
Nos. 1705/6 were printed together, *se-tenant*, in horizontal pairs throughout the sheet.

1339 Monument, Rashtriya Military College   **1340** Ram Manohar Lohia

(Litho Calcutta Security Printers Ltd, Kanpur)

1997 (13 Mar). *75th Anniv of Rashtriya Military College, Dehra Dun. P* 13½.
1707 **1339** 2 r. multicoloured 20 20

(Litho Calcutta Security Printers Ltd, Kanpur)

1997 (23 Mar). *Ram Manohar Lohia Commemoration. P* 13×13½.
1708 **1340** 1 r. multicoloured 10 10

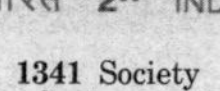

1341 Society Centenary Emblem   **1342** Gyandith Award Winners

(Des J. Irani. Litho Calcutta Security Printers Ltd, Kanpur)

1997 (27 Mar). *Centenary of the Philatelic Society of India. T* **1341** *and similar vert design. Multicoloured. P* 13×13½.
1709 2 r. Type **1341** 20 25
a. Horiz pair. Nos. 1709/10 . . . . 40 50
1710 2 r. Cover of first *Philatelic Journal of India*, 1897 . . . . 20 25
Nos. 1709/10 were printed together, *se-tenant*, in horizontal pairs throughout the sheet.

1997 (28 Mar). *Gyandith Award Scheme. P* 13.
1711 **1342** 2 r. multicoloured 15 15

1343 Madhu Limaye   **1344** Nalanda Monastic University

1997 (1 May). *Madhu Limaye Commemoration. P* 13×13½.
1712 **1343** 2 r. deep dull green 15 15

(Litho Calcutta Security Printers Ltd, Kanpur)

1997 (6 June). *"INDEPEX '97" International Stam Exhibition, New Delhi (2nd issue). Buddhist Cultural Site T* **1344** *and similar horiz designs. Multicoloured. P* 13½×1
1713 2 r. Type **1344** 10 1
a. Block of 4. Nos. 1713/16 . . . . 1·10
1714 6 r. The Bodhi Tree, Bodhgaya 25 3
1715 10 r. Stupa and Pillar, Vaishali 40 4
1716 11 r. Stupa, Kushinagar 40 4
1713/16 . . . . *Set of* 4 1·10 1·2
Nos. 1713/16 were printed together, *se-tenant*, in blocks of throughout the sheet.

1345 Pandit Omkarnath Thakur   **1346** Ram Sewak Yadav

(Des S. Samanta)

1997 (24 June). *Birth Centenary of Pandit Omkarnath Thaku (musician). P* 13×13½.
1717 **1345** 2 r. black and deep dull blue . . 15 1

(Litho Calcutta Security Printers Ltd, Kanpur)

1997 (2 July). *Ram Sewak Yadav (politician) Commemoration P* 13×13½.
1718 **1346** 2 r. brown 15 1

1347 Sibnath Banerjee   **1348** Rukmini Lakshmipathi

(Litho Calcutta Security Printers Ltd, Kanpur)

1997 (11 July). *Birth Centenary of Sibnath Banerjee (trad unionist). P* 13×13½.
1719 **1347** 2 r. brown-lake and purple 15 1

1997 (6 Aug). *Rukmini Lakshmipathi (social reformer Commemoration. P* 13×13½.
1720 **1348** 2 r. reddish brown 15 1

1349 Sri Basaveswara   **1350** Gopalpur-on-Sea Beach

1997 (8 Aug). *Sri Basaveswara (reformer and statesman Commemoration. P* 13×13½.
1721 **1349** 2 r. claret 15 1

1997 (11 Aug). *"INDEPEX '97" International Stamp Exhibition, New Delhi (3rd issue). Beaches. T* **1350** *and similar horiz designs. Multicoloured. P* 13½.
1722 2 r. Type **1350** 10 1
1723 6 r. Kovalam 25 3
1724 10 r. Anjuna 40 4
1725 11 r. Bogmalo 40 4
1722/5 . . . . *Set of* 4 1·10 1·2

1351 Newspaper Masthead   **1352** Shah Nawaz Khan, P. K. Sahgal and G. S. Dhillon

997 (15 Aug). 50*th Anniv of* Swatantra Bharat (*Hindi daily newspaper*). *P* 13½×13.
726 **1351** 2 r. multicoloured 15 15

997 (15 Aug). *I.N.A. Trials Commemoration. P* 13½×13.
727 **1352** 2 r. multicoloured 15 15
No. 1727 is known pre-released at Jaipur on 11 May 1997.

1353 Sir Ronald Ross (bacteriologist)

1354 Firaq Gorakhpuri

997 (20 Aug). *Centenary of the Discovery of the Malaria Parasite by Sir Ronald Ross. P* 13×13½.
728 **1353** 2 r. slate 15 15

997 (28 Aug). *Birth Centenary* (1996) *of Firaq Gorakhpuri* (*poet*). *P* 13×13½.
729 **1354** 2 r. light brown 15 15

1355 Bhaktivedanta Swami

1356 Parachute Regiment Emblem

997 (6 Sept). *Birth Centenary* (1996) *of Bhaktivedanta Swami* (*philosopher*). *P* 13×13½.
730 **1355** 5 r. chestnut 30 35

1997 (7 Sept). *Bicentenary of 2nd* (*Maratha*) *Battalion, Parachute Regiment. P* 13½×13.
1731 **1356** 2 r. multicoloured 15 15

1357 Fossil of *Birbalsahnia divyadarshanii*

1358 Swami Brahmanand

1997 (11 Sept). 50*th Anniv of Birbal Sahni Institute of Paleobotany, Lucknow. Plant Fossils. T* **1357** *and similar vert designs. Multicoloured. P* 13×13½.
1732 2 r. Type **1357** 15 15
1733 2 r. *Glossopteris* 15 15
1734 6 r. *Pentoxylon* (reconstruction) 35 40
1735 10 r. *Williamsonia sewardiana* (model) .. 55 65
1732/5 .. .. *Set of* 4 1·10 1·25

(Litho Calcutta Security Printers, Kanpur)

1997 (14 Sept). *Swami Brahmanand* (*social reformer*) *Commemoration. P* 13×13½.
1736 **1358** 2 r. brownish grey and greenish stone 15 15

1359 "Sir William Jones"

1360 Lawrence School Building and Crest

1997 (28 Sept). 250*th Birth Anniv* (1996) *of Sir William Jones* (*Sanskrit scholar*). *P* 13×13½.
1737 **1359** 4 r. multicoloured 30 30

1997 (4 Oct). 150*th Anniv of Lawrence School, Sanawar. P* 13½×13.
1738 **1360** 2 r. multicoloured 15 15

1361 V. K. Krishna Menon

1362 Policemen and Globe

1997 (6 Oct). *Birth Centenary* (1996) *of V. K. Krishna Menon* (*politician*). *P* 13×13½.
1739 **1361** 2 r. brown-red 15 15

1997 (15 Oct). 66*th General Assembly Session of ICPO Interpol. P* 13½×13.
1740 **1362** 4 r. multicoloured 30 30

1363 Woman from Arunachal Pradesh

1364 Students in Meditation, Astachai

1997 (15 Oct). *"INDEPEX '97" International Stamp Exhibition, New Delhi* (4*th issue*). *Women's Costumes. T* **1363** *and similar vert designs. Multicoloured. P* 13×13½.
1741 2 r. Type **1363** 10 10
a. Block of 4. Nos. 1741/4 .. .. 1·25
1742 6 r. Gujarat costume 25 30
1743 10 r. Ladakh costume 40 45
1744 11 r. Kerala costume 45 50
1741/4 .. .. *Set of* 4 1·25 1·40
Nos. 1741/4 were printed together, *se-tenant*, in blocks of 4 throughout the sheet.

1997 (20 Oct). *Centenary of Scindia School, Gwalior. T* **1364** *and similar horiz design. Multicoloured. P* 14.
1745 5 r. Type **1364** 30 35
a. Horiz pair. Nos. 1745/6 .. .. 60 70
1746 5 r. Gwalior Fort 30 35
Nos. 1745/6 were printed together, *se-tenant*, in horizontal pairs throughout the sheet.

1365 *Ocimum sanctum*

1366 Sant Kavi Sunderdas

1997 (28 Oct). *Medicinal Plants. T* **1365** *and similar vert designs. Multicoloured. P* 14.
1747 2 r. Type **1365** 10 10
a. Block of 4. Nos. 1747/50 .. .. 1·25
1748 5 r. *Curcuma longa* 20 25
1749 10 r. *Rauvolfia serpentina* 40 45
1750 11 r. *Aloe barbadensis* 45 50
1747/50 .. .. *Set of* 4 1·25 1·40
Nos. 1747/50 were printed together, *se-tenant*, in blocks of 4 throughout the sheet.

1997 (8 Nov). 400*th Birth Anniv* (1996) *of Sant Kavi Sunderdas* (*Hindu theologian*). *P* 13×13½.
1751 **1366** 2 r. chestnut 15 15

1367 K. Rama Rao

1368 Jawaharlal Nehru and Child

1997 (9 Nov). *Birth Cent of K. Rama Rao* (*parliamentarian and journalist*). *P* 13×13½.
1752 **1367** 2 r. olive-bistre and bistre-brown .. 15 15

1997 (14 Nov). *Children's Day. P* 13½×13.
1753 **1368** 2 r. multicoloured 15 15

1369 Animals on Globe

1370 Hazari Prasad Dwivedi

1997 (23 Nov). *World Convention on Reverence for All Life, Pune. P* 13×13½.
1754 **1369** 4 r. multicoloured 20 25

1997 (13 Dec). 90*th Birth Anniv of Hazari Prasad Dwivedi* (*scholar*). *P* 13×13½.
1755 **1370** 2 r. brownish grey 15 15

1371 Mother Teresa

1372 Vallabhbhai Patel and Marchers

(Litho Calcutta Security Printers, Kanpur)

1997 (15 Dec). *"INDEPEX '97" International Stamp Exhibition, New Delhi* (5*th issue*). *Mother Teresa Commemoration. Sheet* 81×68 *mm. P* 13×13½.
MS1756 **1371** 45 r. multicoloured 90 95

(Des S. Samanta)

1997 (15 Dec). 47*th Death Anniv of Vallabhbhai Patel* (*politician*). *P* 13×13½.
1757 **1372** 2 r. purple-brown 15 15

1373 Head Post Office, Pune

1374 50th Anniversary Emblem

1997 (15 Dec). *"INDEPEX '97" International Stamp Exhibition, New Delhi* (6*th issue*). *Post Office Heritage. T* **1373** *and similar horiz designs. Multicoloured. P* 13½×13.
1758 2 r. Type **1373** 20 20
a. Block of 4. Nos. 1758/61 .. .. 1·75
1759 6 r. River mail barge 40 45
1760 10 r. Jal Cooper (philatelist) and cancellations 70 75
1761 11 r. *Hindoostan* (paddle-steamer) .. 70 75
1758/61 .. .. *Set of* 4 1·75 1·90
Nos. 1758/61 were printed together, *se-tenant*, in blocks of 4 throughout the sheet.

1997 (16 Dec). 50*th Anniv of Indian Armed Forces. P* 13½×13.
1762 **1374** 2 r. multicoloured 15 15

1375 Dr. Pattabhi Sitaramayya

1376 Father Jerome d'Souza and Cathedral

1997 (17 Dec). *Dr. Pattabhi Sitaramayya* (*politician*) *Commemoration. P* 13×13½.
1763 **1375** 2 r. yellow-brown 15 15

1997 (18 Dec). *Birth Centenary of Father Jerome d'Souza* (*academic*). *P* 13½×13.
1764 **1376** 2 r. red-brown 15 15

1377 Ram Prasad Bismil and Ashfaqullah Khan

1378 Jail Buildings

(Des Alka Sharma)

1997 (19 Dec). *70th Death Anniv of Ram Prasad Bismil and Ashfaqullah Khan (revolutionaries). P* 13.
1765 **1377** 2 r. red-brown 15 15

1997 (30 Dec). *Cellular Jail, Port Blair. P* 13.
1766 **1378** 2 r. multicoloured 15 15

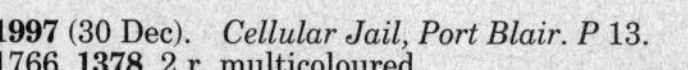

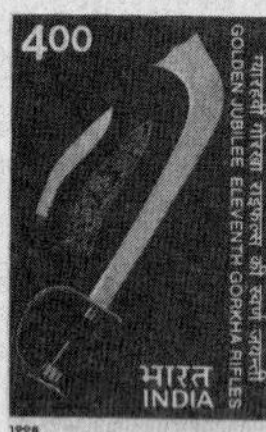

1379 Sword and Kukri

1380 Nahar Singh

1998 (2 Jan). *50th Anniv of 11th Gorkha Rifles. P* 13.
1767 **1379** 4 r. multicoloured 30 35

1998 (9 Jan). *140th Death Anniv of Nahar Singh (Sikh leader) P* 13.
1768 **1380** 2 r. reddish purple 15 15

1381 Nanak Singh

1382 Rotary International Emblem

1998 (10 Jan). *Birth Cent of Nanak Singh (writer)* (1997). *P* 13.
1769 **1381** 2 r. Indian red 15 15

1998 (12 Jan). *Meeting of Rotary International Council on Legislation, Delhi. P* 13½×13.
1770 **1382** 8 r. lemon and blue 50 55

1383 Maharana Pratap

1384 V. S. Khandekar

1998 (19 Jan). *400th Death Anniv of Maharana Pratap (Rajput leader). P* 13×13½.
1771 **1383** 2 r. dull purple 15 15

1998 (19 Jan). *Birth Centenary of V. S. Khandekar (writer). P* 13×13½.
1772 **1384** 2 r. scarlet 15 15

1385 Elephant and Dancers

1386 Jagdish Chandra Jain

1998 (25 Jan). *India Tourism Day. P* 13×13½.
1773 **1385** 10 r. multicoloured 60 65

1998 (28 Jan). *Jagdish Chandra Jain (educationist) Commemoration. P* 13.
1774 **1386** 2 r. chestnut 15 15

1387 Gandhi as a Young Man and Peasants in Fields

1388 A. Vedaratnam

(Des S. Samanta)

1998 (30 Jan). *50th Death Anniv of Mahatma Gandhi. T* **1387** *and similar vert designs. P* 14.
1775 2 r. Type **1387** 10 10
a. Block of 4. Nos. 1775/8 .. .. 1·25
1776 6 r. Woman weaving and Gandhi distributing food .. 25 30
1777 10 r. Gandhi collecting salt 40 45
1778 11 r. Gandhi carrying flag 45 50
1775/8 .. .. *Set of* 4 1·25 1·40

Nos. 1775/8 were printed together, *se-tenant*, in blocks of 4 throughout the sheet with the backgrounds forming a composite design.

1998 (25 Feb). *Birth Centenary* (1997) *of A. Vedaratnam (social reformer). P* 13×13½.
1779 **1388** 2 r. slate-purple 15 15

1389 Anniversary Emblem

1390 Savitribai Phule

1998 (8 Mar). *50th Anniv of Universal Declaration of Human Rights. P* 13×13½.
1780 **1389** 6 r. multicoloured 30 35

1998 (10 Mar). *Death Centenary of Savitribai Phule (educational reformer)* (1997). *P* 13½×13.
1781 **1390** 2 r. deep brown 15 15

1391 Sir Syed Ahmad Khan

1392 Barren Landscape and Living Forest

1998 (27 Mar). *Death Centenary of Sir Syed Ahmed Khan (social reformer). P* 13×13½.
1782 **1391** 2 r. olive-brown 15 15

(Des R. Pasricha)

1998 (1 Apr). *First Assembly Meeting of Global Environment Facility, Delhi. P* 13.
1783 **1392** 11 r. multicoloured 45 50

1393 Ramana Maharshi

1394 College Arms

1998 (14 Apr). *Ramana Maharshi (religious leader) Commemoration. P* 13½×13.
1784 **1393** 2 r. blackish lilac 15 15

1998 (16 Apr). *50th Anniv of Defence Services Staff College, Wellington. P* 14.
1785 **1394** 6 r. deep carmine 30 35

1395 Diesel Train on Viaduct

1998 (1 May). *Konkan Railway. P* 13.
1786 **1395** 8 r. multicoloured 40 45

1396 Narayan Ganesh Goray

1397 Dr. Zakir Husain

1998 (1 May). *Narayan Ganesh Goray (social reformer) Commemoration. P* 13×13½.
1787 **1396** 2 r. red-brown 15 15

1998 (3 May). *Birth Centenary* (1997) *of Dr. Zakir Husain (former President of India). P* 13×13½.
1788 **1397** 2 r. grey-brown 10 15

1398 Mohammed Abdurahiman Shahib

1399 Lokanayak Omeo Kumar Das

1998 (15 May). *Mohammed Abdurahiman Shahib (nationalist) Commemoration. P* 13×13½.
1789 **1398** 2 r. chestnut 10 15

1998 (21 May). *Lokanayak Omeo Kumar Das (writer) Commemoration. P* 14.
1790 **1399** 2 r. bistre-brown 10 15

1400 Vakkom Abdul Khader, Satyendra Chandra Bardhan and Fouja Singh

1401 Bishnu Dey, Tarashankar Bandopadhyay and Ashapurna Devi

1998 (25 May). *Nationalist Martyrs Commemoration. P* 13.
1791 **1400** 2 r. reddish brown and cinnamon .. 10 15

(Des S. Samanta)

98 (5 June). *Bangla Jnanpith Literary Award Winners Commemoration. P* 13.
'92 **1401** 2 r. bistre-brown 10 15

1402 Big Ben, London

1403 Dr. C. Vijiaraghavachariar

98 (8 June). *50th Anniv of First Air India International Flight. T* **1402** *and similar multicoloured design. P* 13×13½.
'93 5 r. Type **1402** 15 20
a. Horiz pair. Nos. 1793/4 .. .. 35 45
'94 6 r. Lockheed Super Constellation airliner, globe and Gateway of India, Bombay (55×35 *mm*) 20 25
Nos. 1793/4 were printed together, *se-tenant*, in horizontal airs throughout the sheet, forming a composite design.

98 (18 June). *Dr. C. Vijiaraghavachariar (lawyer and social reformer) Commemoration. P* 13×13½.
'95 **1403** 2 r. lake-brown 10 15

1404 Anniversary Logo and Savings Stream

1405 Bhagawan Gopinathji

98 (30 June). *50th Anniv of National Savings Organization. T* **1404** *and similar horiz design. Multicoloured. P* 13½×13.
796 5 r. Type **1404** 15 20
a. Vert pair. Nos. 1796/7 .. .. 35 45
797 6 r. Hand dropping coin into jar .. 20 25
Nos. 1796/7 were printed together, *se-tenant*, in vertical pairs hroughout the sheet, each pair forming a composite design.

98 (3 July). *Birth Centenary of Bhagawan Gopinathji (spiritual leader). P* 13.
798 **1405** 3 r. yellow-brown 15 20

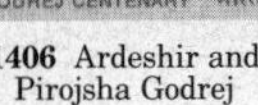

1406 Ardeshir and Pirojsha Godrej

1407 Aruna Asaf Ali

998 (11 July). *Centenary of Godrej (industrial conglomerate). P* 13.
799 **1406** 3 r. emerald 15 20

998 (16 July). *Aruna Asaf Ali (nationalist) Commemoration. P* 13.
800 **1407** 3 r. chestnut 15 20

1408 Iswar Chandra Vidyasagar (educationist) and College

1409 Shivpujan Sahai

998 (29 July). *125th Anniv of Vidyasagar College, Calcutta. P* 13½×13.
801 **1408** 2 r. slate-black 10 15

998 (9 Aug). *Shivpujan Sahai (writer) Commemoration. P* 13½×13.
802 **1409** 2 r. light brown 10 15

1410 Red Fort, Delhi, and Spinning Wheel

1411 Gostha Behari Paul

(Des C. Pakrashi)

1998 (15 Aug). *Homage to Martyrs for Independence. T* **1410** *and similar horiz design. Multicoloured. P* 14.
1803 3 r. Type **1410** 15 20
a. Horiz pair. Nos. 1803/4 .. .. 40 50
1804 8 r. Industrial and scientific development in modern India 25 30
Nos. 1803/4 were printed together, *se-tenant*, in horizontal pairs throughout the sheet.

(Des B. Mirchandani)

1998 (20 Aug). *Gostha Paul (footballer) Commemoration. P* 13.
1805 **1411** 3 r. maroon 15 20

1412 Youth Hostel and Logo

1413 Uniforms, Badge and Tank

(Des S. Samant)

1998 (23 Aug). *50th Anniv of Youth Hostels Association of India. P* 14.
1806 **1412** 5 r. multicoloured 20 25

1998 (15 Sept). *Bicentenary of 4th Battalion, Guards' Brigade (1 Rajput). P* 13½×13.
1807 **1413** 6 r. multicoloured 25 30

1414 Bhai Kanhaiyaji

1415 Emblem and Diagram of Head

1998 (18 Sept). *Bhai Kanhaiyaji (Sikh social reformer) Commemoration. P* 13.
1808 **1414** 2 r. red 10 15

1998 (18 Sept). *20th International Congress of Radiology. P* 13½×13.
1809 **1415** 8 r. multicoloured 30 35

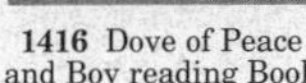

1416 Dove of Peace and Boy reading Book

1417 Dr. Tristao Braganza Cunha

1998 (20 Sept). *26th International Books for Young People Congress. P* 13×13½.
1810 **1416** 11 r. multicoloured 30 35

1998 (26 Sept). *Dr. Tristao Braganza Cunha (nationalist) Commemoration. P* 13×13½.
1811 **1417** 3 r. chocolate 15 20

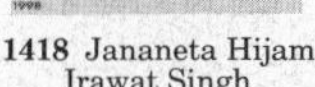

1418 Jananeta Hijam Irawat Singh

1419 Women Aviators and Bi-plane

1998 (30 Sept). *Jananeta Hijam Irawat Singh (social reformer) Commemoration. P* 13×13½.
1812 **1418** 3 r. yellow-brown 15 20

1998 (5 Oct). *Indian Women's Participation in Aviation. P* 13.
1813 **1419** 8 r. chalky blue 25 30

1420 Acharya Tulsi

1998 (20 Oct). *First Death Anniv of Acharya Tulsi (Jain religious leader). P* 13½×13.
1814 **1420** 3 r. red-brown and bright orange .. 15 20

1421 Girl and Bird reading Book

1998 (14 Nov). *Children's Day. P* 13½×13.
1815 **1421** 3 r. multicoloured 15 20

1422 I.N.S. *Delhi* (destroyer)

1423 Mounted Trumpeter

1998 (15 Nov). *Navy Day. P* 13½×13.
1816 **1422** 3 r. multicoloured 15 20

(Litho Calcutta Security Printers Ltd, Kanpur)

1998 (16 Nov). *225th Anniv of President's Bodyguard. P* 13×13½.
1817 **1423** 3 r. multicoloured 15 20

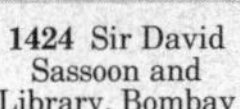

1424 Sir David Sassoon and Library, Bombay

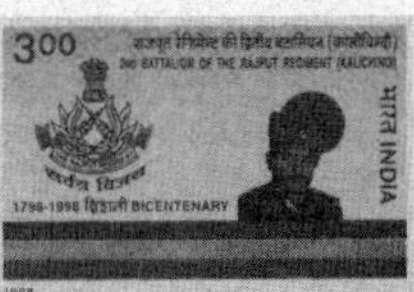

1425 Regimental Arms and Soldier

(Des J. Irani)

1998 (30 Nov). *David Sassoon Library and Reading Room Commemoration. P* 13.
1818 **1424** 3 r. deep ultramarine and pale blue 15 20

(Des S. Chowdhry)

1998 (30 Nov). *Bicent of 2nd Battalion, Rajput Regiment. P* 13.
1819 **1425** 3 r. multicoloured 15 20

1426 Army Postal Service Centre, Kamptee

1998 (2 Dec). *50th Anniv of Army Postal Service Training Centre. P* 13.
1820 **1426** 3 r. multicoloured 15 20

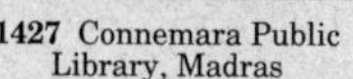

1427 Connemara Public Library, Madras

1428 Neem Tree and Leaves

1998 (5 Dec). *Centenary* (1996) *of Connemara Public Library. P* 13½×13.
1821 **1427** 3 r. yellow-brown and ochre .. 15 20

(Des R. Sukumar. Litho Calcutta Security Printers Ltd, Kanpur)

1998 (10 Dec). *50th Anniv of The Indian Pharmaceutical Congress Association. P* 13×13½.
1822 **1428** 3 r. multicoloured 15 20

1429 Baba Raghav Das

1430 Lt. Indra Lal Roy D.F.C.

1998 (12 Dec). *40th Death Anniv of Baba Raghav Das* (*social reformer*). *P* 13×13½.
1823 **1429** 2 r. slate-violet 10 15

1998 (19 Dec). *Birth Centenary of Indra Lal Roy* (*First World War pilot*). *P* 13×13½.
1824 **1430** 3 r. multicoloured 15 20

1431 Sant Gadge Baba

1432 Rudra Veena (stringed instrument)

(Des B. Mirchandani)

1998 (20 Dec). *Sant Gadge Baba* (*social reformer*) *Commemoration. P* 13×13½.
1825 **1431** 3 r. slate-lilac, new blue and black .. 15 20

(Des S. Samanta)

1998 (29 Dec). *Musical Instruments. T* **1432** *and similar horiz designs. Multicoloured. P* 13½×13.
1826 2 r. Type **1432** 10 15
1827 6 r. Flute 20 25
1828 8 r. Pakhawaj (wooden barrel drum) .. 25 30
1829 10 r. Sarod (stringed instrument) .. 30 35
1826/9 .. .. *Set of* 4 85 1·00

1433 *Chicoreus brunneus* (Murex shell)

1434 Stylised Police Officers

1998 (30 Dec). *Shells. T* **1433** *and similar horiz designs. Multicoloured. P* 13½×13.
1830 3 r. Type **1433** 15 20
1831 3 r. *Cassis cornuta* (Horned Helmet) .. 15 20
1832 3 r. *Cypraea staphylaea* (Cowrie) .. 15 20
1833 11 r. *Lambis lambis* (Common Spider Conch) 30 35
1830/3 .. .. *Set of* 4 75 95

(Des Kamlesahwar. Litho Calcutta Security Printers, Kanpur)

1999 (13 Jan). *50th Anniv of Indian Police Service. P* 13½×13.
1834 **1434** 3 r. multicoloured 15 20

1435 Modern Weapon Systems

1436 Issue of *Orunodoi* (Assamese newspaper) for January, 1846

1999 (26 Jan). *40th Anniv of Defence Research and Development Organization. P* 13.
1835 **1435** 10 r. multicoloured 30 35

1999 (29 Jan). *150th Anniv of Newspapers in Assam. P* 13×13½.
1836 **1436** 3 r. black, orange-yellow & red-orange 15 20

Index to Indian Stamp Designs from 1947

The following index is intended to .cilitate the identification of all Indian .amps from 1947 onwards. Portrait .amps are usually listed under surnames .nly, views under the name of the town or .ty and other issues under the main .bject or a prominent word and date .osen from the inscription. Simple .bbreviations have occasionally been .sorted to and when the same design or .ibject appears on more than one stamp, .nly the first of each series is indicated.

STAMP BOOKLETS

1904. *Black on green* (No. SB1) *or black on pink* (No. SB2) *covers. Stapled.*
SB1 12¼ a. booklet containing twenty-four ½ a. (No. 121) in blocks of 6 .. .. £750
SB2 12¼ a. booklet containing twelve 1 a. (No. 123) in blocks of 6 .. .. £750

1906–11. *Black on green* (No. SB3), *black on pink* (No. SB4) *or black on green and pink* (No. SB5) *match book type covers inscr* "Post Office of India" *and royal cypher of King Edward VII. Stapled.*
SB3 1 r. booklet containing thirty-two ½ a. (No. 149) in blocks of 4 .. .. £425
a. Without "Post Office of India" inscr £375
b. Ditto and showing royal cypher of King George V (1911) £350
SB4 1 r. booklet containing sixteen 1 a. (No. 150) in blocks of 4 (1907) £375
a. Without "Post Office of India" inscr £325
b. Ditto and showing royal cypher of King George V (1911) £350
SB5 1 r. booklet containing sixteen ½ a. and eight 1 a. (Nos. 149/50) in blocks of 4 (1907) £850
a. Without "Post Office of India" inscr £750
b. Ditto and showing royal cypher of King George V (1911) £700

1912–22. *Black on green* (Nos. SB6/7, SB12), *black on pink* (No. SB8), *black on green and pink* (No. SB9), *black on purple* (Nos. SB10) *or black on blue* (No. SB11) *match book type covers with foreign postage rates on back. Stapled.*
SB 6 1 r. booklet containing sixty-four 3 p. (No. 152) in blocks of 4 (blank back cover) £450
SB 7 1 r. booklet containing thirty-two ½ a. (No. 155) in blocks of 4 .. .. £180
a. Blank back cover £180
b. Advertisement contractor's notice on back cover £275
c. Advertisement on back (1922) £275
SB 8 1 r. booklet containing sixteen 1 a. (No. 159) in blocks of 4 .. .. £140
a. Blank back cover £140
b. Advertisements on front flap and back cover (1922) £180
SB 9 1 r. booklet containing sixteen ½ a. and eight 1 a. (Nos. 155, 159) in blocks of 4 (blank back cover) £130
SB10 1 r. 8 a. booklet containing sixteen 1½ a. (No. 163) in blocks of 4 (1919) £300
a. Blank back cover (1921) £300
SB11 2 r. booklet containing sixteen 2 a. (No. 169) in blocks of 4 (blank back cover) (1921) .. £375
a. Black on purple cover with postage rates on back (1922) £375
SB12 2 r. booklet containing sixteen 2 a. (No. 166) in blocks of 4 (1922) £375
a. Black on purple cover £375

1921. *Black on buff match book type cover. Stapled.*
SB13 1 r. 2 a. booklet containing twenty-four 9 p. on 1 a. (No. 192) in blocks of 4 .. .. £100

1922. *Black on brown* (No. SB14) *or black on green and pink* (No. SB15) *match book type covers with foreign postage rates on back. Stapled.*
SB14 1 r. booklet containing sixteen 1 a. (No. 197) in blocks of 4 .. .. £200
a. Advertisement on back £200
b. Advertisements on front flap and back cover
c. Black on lilac cover with blank back .. £200
ca. Advertisements on front flap and back cover £275
d. Black on pink cover with blank back .. £250
SB15 1 r. booklet containing sixteen ½ a. and eight 1 a. (Nos. 155, 197) in blocks of 4 (blank back cover) £400

1926–28. *Black on brown* (No. SB16) *or black on purple* (No. SB17) *match book type covers with foreign postage rates on back. Stapled.*
SB16 1 r. booklet containing sixteen 1 a. (No. 203) in blocks of 4 .. .. 80·00
SB17 2 r. booklet containing sixteen 2 a. (No. 205) in blocks of 4 .. .. £250
a. Containing No. 206 (1928) £300

1929. *Black on brown* (No. SB18) *or black on purple* (No. SB19) *separate leaf covers. Stitched.*
SB18 1 r. booklet containing sixteen 1 a. (No. 203) in blocks of 4 (blank back cover) .. .. 80·00
a. Advertisement contractor's notice on back cover .. .. 80·00
b. Advertisements on front flap and back cover £100
c. Advertisement on back cover £100
SB19 2 r. booklet containing sixteen 2 a. (No. 205) in blocks of 4 (foreign postage rates on back cover) £275
a. Advertisement contractor's notice on back cover £275
b. Containing No. 206 (foreign postage rates on back cover) £325
ba. Advertisement contractor's notice on back cover £325

1932. *Black on brown cover. Stitched.*
SB20 1 r. 4 a. booklet containing sixteen 1¼ a. (No. 235) in blocks of 4 .. .. £250

1934. *Black on buff cover. Stitched.*
SB21 1 r. booklet containing sixteen 1 a. (No. 234) in blocks of 4 .. .. £140

1937. *Black on red cover. Stamps with wmk upright or inverted. Stitched.*
SB22 1 r. booklet containing sixteen 1 a. (No. 250) in blocks of 4 .. .. £140

1980 (Jan) *"India 80" International Stamp Exhibition. Green, orange and blue cover, 80×100 mm. showing stamps. Stapled.*
SB23 33 r. 60, booklet containing twelve 30 p., twelve 50 p., eight 1 r. and eight 2 r. (Nos. 914/15, 942/5, 955/8) in blocks of four .. .. 6·50

1989 (20 Jan). *"India-89" International Stamp Exhibition, New Delhi. Multicoloured cover, showing stamp No. 1248, boatman and Taj Mahal. Stapled.*
SB24 270 r. booklet containing four 50 p., sixteen 60 p., ten 1 r. 50, six 4 r., twenty 5 r. and sixteen 6 r. 50 in panes of four or six each with margins all round (Nos. 1248a, 1249a, 1264a, 1265a, 1266a, 1267a, 1333a, 1334a, 1341a, 1342a, 1358a, 1359a, 1360a, 1361a) 26·00

OFFICIAL STAMPS

Stamps overprinted "POSTAL SERVICE" or "I.P.N." were n[ot] used as postage stamps, and are therefore omitted.

Service.
(O 1)

(Optd by the Military Orphanage Press, Calcutta)

1866 (1 Aug)–**72.** *Optd with Type* O **1**. *P* 14. (*a*) *No wmk.*
O 1 **11** ½ a. blue .. .. — £22
O 2 ½ a. pale blue £900 £11
a. Opt inverted .. .. ..
O 3 1 a. brown .. .. — £15
O 4 1 a. deep brown .. .. .. — £11
O 5 8 a. carmine .. .. 16·00 38·0

(*b*) *Wmk Elephant's Head, T* **13**
O 6 **11** ½ a. blue .. .. £190 22·0
w. Wmk inverted .. .. .. † £10
O 7 ½ a. pale blue .. .. .. £190 12·0
a. Opt inverted .. .. ..
b. No dot on "i" (No. 50 on pane) .. — £25
c. No stop (No. 77 on pane) .. — £20
O 8 **12** 8 p. purple (1.72) .. .. .. 18·00 42·0
a. No dot on "i" £225 £30
b. No stop £225
O 9 **11** 1 a. brown .. .. £190 15·0
O10 1 a. deep brown .. .. .. £190 38·0
a. No dot on "i" .. .. .. — £42
b. No stop .. .. — £35
O11 2 a. orange .. .. £170 75·0
O12 2 a. yellow .. .. £170 75·0
a. Opt inverted .. .. ..
b. Imperf .. ..
w. Wmk inverted £250
O13 4 a. green .. .. £160 70·0
a. Opt inverted .. .. ..
O14 **17** 4 a. green (Die I) £950 £25

A variety with wide and more open capital "S" occurs six time[s] in sheets of all values except No. O8. Price four times the normal.

Reprints exist of Nos. O6, O9 and O14; the latter is Die II instea[d] of Die I.

Reprints of the overprint have also been made, in differen[t] setting, on the 8 pies, purple, no watermark.

O 2

O 6

O 3

O 4

(No. O15 surch at Calcutta, others optd at Madras)

1866 (Oct). *Fiscal stamps, Nos.* O15/18 *with top and bottom inscrs removed, surch or optd. Wmk Crown over* "INDIA".

(*a*) *Surch as in Type* O **2**. *Thick blue glazed paper. Imperf × perf* 14
O15 O **2** 2 a. purple £275 £225

(*b*) *Optd* "SERVICE POSTAGE" *in two lines as in Types* O **3/4** *and similar type. Imperf × perf* 14
O16 O **3** 2 a. purple (G.) £800 £400
O17 O **4** 4 a. purple (G.) £3000 £1100
O18 – 8 a. purple (G.) £3750 £3250
a. Optd on complete stamp (inscr "FOREIGN BILL") .. .. † £9000

(*c*) *Optd* "SERVICE POSTAGE" *in semi-circle. Wmk Large Crown. P* 15½ × 15
O19 O **6** ½ a. mauve/*lilac* (G.) .. .. .. £375 85·00
a. Opt double £2500

So-called reprints of Nos. O15 to O18 are known, but in these the surcharge differs entirely in the spacing, etc., of the words; they are more properly described as Government imitations. The imitations of No. O15 have surcharge in *black* or in *green*. No. O19 exists with reprinted overprint which has a full stop after "POSTAGE".

PRINTERS. The following stamps up to No. O108 were overprinted by De La Rue and thereafter Official stamps were printed or overprinted by the Security Printing Press at Nasik.

Service.
(O 7)

On H. M. S.
(O 8)

On H. S. M.
(O 9)

867–73. *Optd with Type* O **7**. *Wmk Elephant's Head. T* **13**. *P* 14.

O20 **11** ½ a. blue (Die I) .. .. 24·00 40
w. Wmk inverted .. .. .. † 60·00
O21 ½ a. pale blue (Die I) .. .. .. 30·00 1·75
O22 ½ a. blue (Die II) (1873) .. .. £140 60·00
O23 1 a. brown .. .. 30·00 45
w. Wmk inverted .. .. .. † 75·00
O24 1 a. deep brown .. .. .. 32·00 1·75
O25 1 a. chocolate .. .. .. 38·00 1·75
O26 2 a. yellow .. .. 14·00 2·50
O27 2 a. orange .. .. 4·75 2·25
O28 **17** 4 a. pale green (Die I) .. .. 13·00 2·00
O29 4 a. green (Die I) .. .. .. 3·00 1·50
O30 **11** 8 a. rose (Die II) (1868) .. .. 3·25 1·50
O30*a* 8 a. pale rose (Die II) .. .. .. 3·25 1·50
aw. Wmk inverted .. .. .. 30·00 20·00

Prepared for use, but not issued

O30*b* **18** 6 a. 8 p. slate £250

874–82. *Optd with Type* O **8**. (*a*) *In black*.

O31 **11** ½ a. blue (Die II).. .. .. .. 6·50 20
O32 1 a. brown .. .. 10·00 20
O33 2 a. yellow .. .. 45·00 19·00
O33*a* 2 a. orange .. .. 32·00 11·00
O34 **17** 4 a. green (Die I) .. .. .. 11·00 3·00
O35 **11** 8 a. rose (Die II).. .. .. .. 4·75 3·50

(*b*) *Optd in blue-black*

O36 **11** ½ a. blue (Die II) (1877) .. .. £300 38·00
O37 1 a. brown (1882) £500 £110

1883–99. *Wmk Star, T* **34**. *P* 14. *Optd with Type* O **9**.

O37*a* **40** 3 p. aniline carmine (1899) 20 10
O38 **23** ½ a. deep blue-green 80 10
a. Opt double .. .. .. † £1100
O39 ½ a. blue-green 60 10
O40 **25** 1 a. brown-purple .. .. .. 1·50 20
a. Opt inverted £350 £450
aw. Wmk inverted .. .. .. † £550
b. Opt double .. .. .. † £1200
c. Opt omitted (in horiz pair with normal) £1500
O41 1 a. plum 30 10
O42 **27** 2 a. pale blue .. .. 3·75 60
O43 2 a. blue .. .. 4·75 60
O44 **29** 4 a. olive-green .. .. .. 11·00 45
O44*a* 4 a. slate-green .. .. .. 11·00 35
O45 **31** 8 a. dull mauve .. .. .. 14·00 1·00
O46 8 a. magenta .. .. 7·50 50
O47 **37** 1 r. green and rose (1892) .. .. 38·00 3·50
O48 1 r. green and carmine (1892) .. 8·50 40
O37*a*/48 .. .. *Set of* 7 28·00 1·75

1900 *Colours changed. Optd with Type* O **9**.

O49 **23** ½ a. pale yellow-green .. .. .. 1·75 70
O49*a* ½ a. yellow-green .. .. .. 2·50 50
ab. Opt double £900
O50 **25** 1 a. carmine .. .. 2·50 10
a. Opt inverted .. .. .. † £1200
b. Opt double .. .. .. † £1300
O51 **27** 2 a. pale violet .. .. .. 27·00 90
O52 2 a. mauve .. .. 29·00 50
O49/52 .. .. *Set of* 3 28·00 1·00

1902–9. *Stamps of King Edward VII optd with Type* O **9**.

O54 **41** 3 p. grey (1903) .. .. .. 1·75 30
O55 3 p. slate-grey (1905) .. .. 1·75 40
a. No stop after "M" (R. 6/10) .. £130 90·00
O56 **42** ½ a. green .. .. 1·25 30
O57 **43** 1 a. carmine .. .. 1·00 10
O58 **44** 2 a. violet .. .. 4·25 20
O59 2 a. mauve .. .. 3·00 10
O60 **47** 4 a. olive .. .. 7·00 30
O61 4 a. pale olive .. .. 6·50 30
O62 **48** 6 a. olive-bistre (1909) .. .. 1·50 15
O63 **49** 8 a. purple (*shades*) .. .. .. 6·00 85
O64 8 a. claret .. .. 8·00 75
O65 **51** 1 r. green and carmine (1905) .. 4·00 70
O54/65 .. .. *Set of* 8 23·00 2·50

1906. *New types. Optd with Type* O **9**.

O66 **53** ½ a. green 75 10
a. No stop after "M" (R. 6/10) .. 80·00 45·00
O67 **54** 1 a. carmine .. .. 1·50 10
a. No stop after "M" (R. 6/10) .. £130 75·00

On

H. S.

M.

(O 9*a*)

1909. *Optd with Type* O **9***a*.

O68 **52** 2 r. carmine and yellow-brown.. .. 8·00 95
O68*a* 2 r. rose-red and yellow-brown.. .. 8·00 1·10
O69 5 r. ultramarine and violet .. .. 14·00 1·50
O70 10 r. green and carmine .. .. 25·00 10·00
O70*a* 10 r. green and scarlet .. .. 60·00 7·00
O71 15 r. blue and olive-brown .. .. 60·00 32·00
O72 25 r. brownish orange and blue .. .. £140 60·00
O68/72 .. .. *Set of* 5 £225 90·00

SERVICE (O 10)(14 mm)

SERVICE (O 11) (21½ mm)

NINE PIES (O 12)

1912–13. *Stamps of King George V* (*wmk Single Star, T* **34**) *optd with Type* O **10** *or* O **11** (*rupee values*).

O73 **55** 3 p. grey 30 10
O74 3 p. slate-grey 30 10
O75 3 p. blue-slate .. .. 2·50 10
a. Opt omitted (in pair with normal)
O76 **56** ½ a. yellow-green 30 10
a. Overprint double £100
O77 ½ a. pale blue-green 40 10
O80 **57** 1 a. rose-carmine .. .. .. 1·00 10
O81 1 a. carmine .. .. 1·25 10
O82 1 a. aniline carmine .. .. .. 1·25 10
a. Overprint double .. .. .. † £900
O83 **59** 2 a. mauve 55 10
O84 2 a. purple 75 10
O85 **63** 4 a. deep olive .. .. .. 1·00 10
O86 4 a. olive-green .. .. .. 1·00 10
O87 **64** 6 a. yellow-bistre .. .. .. 1·50 2·00
O88 6 a. deep bistre-brown .. .. .. 3·50 3·75
O89 **65** 8 a. purple .. .. 2·25 65
O89*a* 8 a. mauve .. .. 2·25 65
O90 8 a. bright aniline mauve .. .. 25·00 2·25
O91 **67** 1 r. red-brown and blue-green (1913).. 2·50 95
O92 2 r. rose-carmine and brown (1913) .. 3·25 3·75
O93 5 r. ultramarine and violet (1913) .. 12·00 16·00
O94 10 r. green and scarlet (1913) .. .. 40·00 40·00
O95 15 r. blue and olive (1913) .. .. 90·00 £100
O96 25 r. orange and blue (1913) £200 £160
O73/96 .. .. *Set of* 13 £300 £275

1921. *No.* O80 *surch with Type* O **12**.

O97 **57** 9 p. on 1 a. rose-carmine 75 65

1922. *No.* 197 *optd with Type* O **10**.

O98 **57** 1 a. chocolate 85 10

ONE RUPEE (O 13)

ONE RUPEE (O 14)

1925. *Official stamps surcharged.*

(*a*) *Issue of* 1909, *as Type* O **13**

O 99 **52** 1 r. on 15 r. blue and olive .. .. 4·25 3·25
O100 1 r. on 25 r chestnut and blue .. 20·00 60·00
O101 2 r. on 10 r. green and scarlet .. 3·75 3·50
O101*a* 2 r. on 10 r. green and carmine.. .. £200 48·00

(*b*) *Issue of* 1912, *with Type* O **14**

O102 **67** 1 r. on 15 r. blue and olive .. .. 19·00 70·00
O103 1 r. on 25 r. orange and blue .. 5·50 9·00
a. Surch inverted £500

(*c*) *Issue of* 1912, *as Type* O **13**

O104 **67** 2 r. on 10 r. green and scarlet £750

Examples of the above showing other surcharge errors are believed to be of clandestine origin.

ONE ANNA (O 15)

SERVICE ONE ANNA (O 16)

1926. *No.* O62 *surch with Type* O **15**.

O105 **48** 1 a. on 6 a. olive-bistre 30 30

1926. *Postage stamps of* 1911–22 (*wmk Single Star*), *surch as Type* O **16**.

O106 **58** 1 a. on 1½ a. chocolate (A) 20 10
O107 1 a. on 1½ a. chocolate (B) .. .. 1·25 3·50
a. Error. On 1 a. chocolate (197) .. £160
O108 **61** 1 a. on 2 a. 6 p. ultramarine .. 60 80

The surcharge on No. O108 has no bars at top.

Examples of Nos. O106/7 with inverted or double surcharges are believed to be of clandestine origin.

SERVICE (O 17)(13½ mm)

SERVICE (O 18) (19½ mm)

1926–31. *Stamps of King George V* (*wmk Multiple Star, T* **69**) *optd with Types* O **17** *or* O **18** (*rupee values*).

O109 **55** 3 p. slate (1.10.29) 15 10
w. Wmk inverted 75 40
O110 **56** ½ a. green (1931) .. .. .. 4·50 30
w. Wmk inverted .. .. .. — 1·10
O111 **57** 1 a. chocolate 15 10
w. Wmk inverted .. .. .. 1·00 40
O112 **70** 2 a. purple 20 10
w. Wmk inverted 50 30
O113 **71** 4 a. sage-green 40 20
w. Wmk inverted .. .. .. 1·50 50
O115 **65** 8 a. reddish purple 60 10
w. Wmk inverted 60 30
O116 **66** 12 a. claret (1927) .. .. .. 60 1·40
w. Wmk inverted .. .. .. — 2·75
O117 **67** 1 r. chocolate and green (1930) .. 1·90 1·00
w. Wmk inverted .. .. .. 1·90 1·25
O118 2 r. carmine and orange (1930) .. 6·50 6·50
O120 10 r. green and scarlet (1931) .. .. 70·00 48·00
O109/20 .. .. *Set of* 10 75·00 50·00

1930. *As No.* O111, *but optd as Type* O **10** (14 *mm*).

O125 **57** 1 a. chocolate .. .. — 4·00
w. Wmk inverted .. .. .. 85·00 5·00

1932–36. *Stamps of King George V* (*wmk Mult Star, T* **69**) *optd with Type* O **17**.

O126 **79** ½ a. green (1935) 60 10
O127 **80** 9 p. deep green 30 10
O127*a* **81** 1 a. chocolate (1936) .. .. 2·25 10
aw. Wmk inverted .. .. 2·75 40
O128 **82** 1 a. 3 p. mauve 30 10
w. Wmk inverted 40 40
O129 **70** 2 a. vermilion .. .. .. 1·00 2·00
O130 **59** 2 a. vermilion (1935) .. .. 1·25 1·25
O130*a* 2 a. vermilion (*small die*) (1936) .. 1·00 10
O131 **61** 2 a. 6 p. orange (22.4.32) 30 10
w. Wmk inverted .. .. 1·25 50
O132 **63** 4 a. sage-green (1935) .. .. 1·00 10
O133 **64** 6 a. bistre (1936) .. .. .. 20·00 9·50
O126/33 .. .. *Set of* 9 24·00 10·00

1937–39. *Stamps of King George VI optd as Types* O **17** *or* O **18** (*rupee values*).

O135 **91** ½ a. red-brown (1938) .. .. 16·00 15
O136 9 p. green (1937) .. .. .. 16·00 20
O137 1 a. carmine (1937) .. .. .. 2·50 10
O138 **93** 1 r. grey and red-brown (5.38) .. 50 50
O139 2 r. purple and brown (5.38) .. 1·50 2·50
w. Wmk inverted .. .. .. — 20·00
O140 5 r. green and blue (10.38) .. .. 2·50 5·50
O141 10 r. purple and claret (1939) .. 14·00 4·75
O135/41 .. .. *Set of* 7 48·00 12·50

SERVICE 1A (O 19)

INDIA POSTAGE 3 PS SERVICE 3 PS

O 20

1939 (May). *Stamp of King George V, surch with Type* O **19**.

O142 **82** 1 a. on 1¼ a. mauve .. .. .. 10·00 20

(Des T. I. Archer)

1939 (1 June)–42. *Typo. W* **69**. *P* 14.

O143 O **20** 3 p. slate 40 10
O144 ½ a. red-brown .. .. .. 3·50 10
O144*a* ½ a. purple (1942) 30 10
O145 9 p. green 30 10
O146 1 a. carmine 30 10
O146*a* 1 a. 3 p. yellow-brown (1941) .. 3·00 70
O146*b* 1½ a. dull violet (1942) 65 10
O147 2 a. vermilion 60 10
O148 2½ a. bright violet 60 40
O149 4 a. brown 60 10
O150 8 a. slate-violet 90 30
O143/50 .. .. *Set of* 11 10·00 1·50

1948 (15 Aug). *First Anniv of Independence. Nos.* 305/8 *optd as Type* O **17**.

O150*a* **305** 1½ a. brown .. .. .. 42·00 30·00
O150*b* 3½ a. violet £750 £450
O150*c* 12 a. grey-green £2000 £1600
O150*d* **306** 10 r. purple-brown and lake .. £10000

Nos. O150*a*/*d* were only issued to the Governor-General's Secretariat.

SERVICE POSTAGE 3 PS INDIA 3 PS

SERVICE POSTAGE 1 Re INDIA 1 Re

O 21 Asokan Capital O 22

(Des T. I. Archer)

1950 (2 Jan)–51. *Typo* (O **21**) *or litho* (O **22**). *W* **69**. *P* 14.

O151 O **21** 3 p. slate-violet (1.7.50) 10 10
O152 6 p. purple-brown (1.7.50) 10 10
O153 9 p. green (1.7.50) 30 10
O154 1 a. turquoise (1.7.50) 70 10
O155 2 a. carmine (1.7.50) .. .. 1·00 10
w. Wmk inverted .. .. ..
O156 3 a. red-orange (1.7.50) .. .. 3·00 1·75
O157 4 a. lake (1.7.50) .. .. .. 5·00 20
O158 4 a. ultramarine (1.10.51) 50 10
O159 6 a. bright violet (1.7.50) .. .. 3·00 40
O160 8 a. red-brown (1.7.50) .. .. 1·50 10
w. Wmk inverted .. .. .. 8·00
O161 O **22** 1 r. violet .. .. 2·75 10
w. Wmk inverted .. .. ..
O162 2 r. rose-carmine .. .. .. 1·00 60
O163 5 r. bluish green .. .. .. 2·00 1·50
O164 10 r. reddish brown .. .. .. 3·00 16·00
O151/64 .. .. *Set of* 14 21·00 19·00

1957 (1 Apr)–58. *Values in naye paise. Typo* (*t*) *or litho* (*l*). *W* **69**. *P* 14.

O165 O **21** 1 n.p. slate (*l*) 30 10
a. Slate-black (*l*) 30 10
b. Greenish slate (*t*) 10 10
w. Wmk inverted .. .. 3·50 1·25
O166 2 n.p. blackish violet (*t*) 10 10
w. Wmk inverted .. .. ..
O167 3 n.p. chocolate (*t*) 10 10
O168 5 n.p. green (*l*) 10 10
a. Deep emerald (*t*) 45 10

O169	O **21**	6 n.p. turquoise-blue (*t*)	10	10
O170		13 n.p. scarlet (*t*)	10	10
O171		15 n.p. reddish violet (*l*) (6.58)	1·50	1·60
		a. Reddish violet (*t*)	1·25	1·60
O172		20 n.p. red (*l*)	15	40
		a. Vermilion (*t*)	60	10
		aw. Wmk inverted		
O173		25 n.p. violet-blue (*l*)	20	10
		a. Ultramarine (*t*)	2·00	10
O174		50 n.p. red-brown (*l*)	40	10
		a. Reddish brown (*t*)	2·00	90
O165/74		*Set of* 10	2·25	2·00

1958–71. *As Nos.* O165/74*a and* O161/4 *but* W **374** (*upright*). *Litho* (*l*) *or typo* (*t*). *P* 14.

O175	O **21**	1 n.p. slate-black (*t*) (1.59)	10	10
O176		2 n.p. blackish violet (*t*) (1.59)	10	10
O177		3 n.p. chocolate (*t*) (11.58)	10	10
		w. Wmk inverted	3·50	
O178		5 n.p. deep emerald (*t*) (11.58)	10	10
O179		6 n.p. turquoise-blue (*t*) (5.59)	10	10
O180		10 n.p. deep grey-green (*l*) (1963)	1·50	1·25
		a. Deep grey-green (*t*) (1966?)	3·00	3·00
O181		13 n.p. scarlet (*t*) (1963)	55	2·50
O182		15 n.p. deep violet (*t*) (11.58)	10	10
		a. Light reddish violet (*t*) (1961)	2·00	10
O183		20 n.p. vermilion (*t*) (5.59)	30	10
		a. Red (*t*) (1966?)	4·00	80
O184		25 n.p. ultramarine (*t*) (7.59)	10	10
O185		50 n.p. reddish brown (*t*) (6.59)	15	10
		a. Chestnut (*l*) (1966?)	4·00	1·25
O186	O **22**	1 r. reddish violet (*l*) (2.59)	15	10
O187		2 r. rose-carmine (*l*) (1960)	25	10
		a. Wmk sideways.* *Pale rose-carmine* (*l*) (1969?)	45	75
O188		5 r. slate-green (*l*) (7.59)	50	60
		a. Wmk sideways*. *Deep grey-green* (*l*) (1969?)	80	90
O189		10 r. brown-lake (*l*) (7.59)	1·25	80
		a. Wmk sideways* (*l*) (1971)	2·75	3·00
		ab. Printed on the gummed side	38·00	
		aw. Wmk capitals to right	2·75	
O175/89		*Set of* 15	4·50	5·00

*The normal sideways watermark shows the head of the capitals pointing left, *as seen from the back of the stamp.*

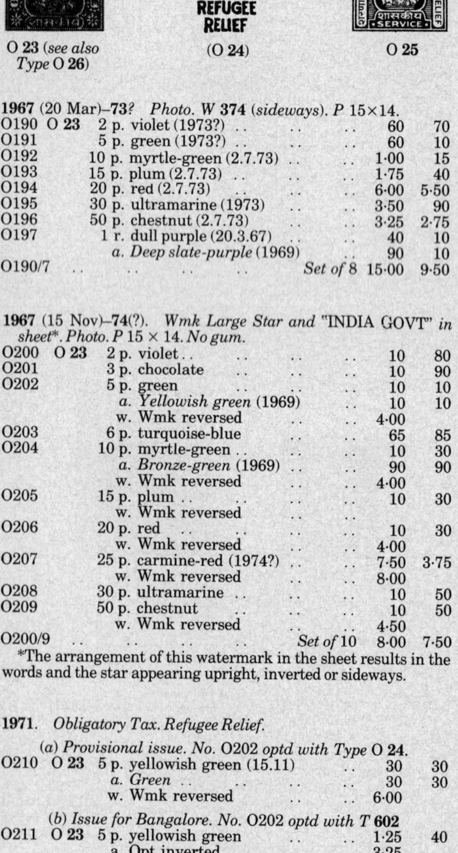

O **23** (*see also* Type O **26**)   (O **24**)   O **25**

1967 (20 Mar)–**73?** *Photo.* W **374** (*sideways*). *P* 15×14.

O190	O **23**	2 p. violet (1973?)	60	70
O191		5 p. green (1973?)	60	10
O192		10 p. myrtle-green (2.7.73)	1·00	15
O193		15 p. plum (2.7.73)	1·75	40
O194		20 p. red (2.7.73)	6·00	5·50
O195		30 p. ultramarine (1973)	3·50	90
O196		50 p. chestnut (2.7.73)	3·25	2·75
O197		1 r. dull purple (20.3.67)	40	10
		a. Deep slate-purple (1969)	90	10
O190/7		*Set of* 8	15·00	9·50

1967 (15 Nov)–**74**(?). *Wmk Large Star and* "INDIA GOVT" *in sheet**. *Photo. P* 15 × 14. *No gum.*

O200	O **23**	2 p. violet	10	80
O201		3 p. chocolate	10	90
O202		5 p. green	10	10
		a. Yellowish green (1969)	10	10
		w. Wmk reversed	4·00	
O203		6 p. turquoise-blue	65	85
O204		10 p. myrtle-green	10	30
		a. Bronze-green (1969)	90	90
		w. Wmk reversed	4·00	
O205		15 p. plum	10	30
		w. Wmk reversed		
O206		20 p. red	10	30
		w. Wmk reversed	4·00	
O207		25 p. carmine-red (1974?)	7·50	3·75
		w. Wmk reversed	8·00	
O208		30 p. ultramarine	10	50
O209		50 p. chestnut	10	50
		w. Wmk reversed	4·50	
O200/9		*Set of* 10	8·00	7·50

*The arrangement of this watermark in the sheet results in the words and the star appearing upright, inverted or sideways.

1971. *Obligatory Tax. Refugee Relief.*

(*a*) *Provisional issue. No.* O202 *optd with Type* O **24**.

O210	O **23**	5 p. yellowish green (15.11)	30	30
		a. Green	30	30
		w. Wmk reversed	6·00	

(*b*) *Issue for Bangalore. No.* O202 *optd with T* **602**

O211	O **23**	5 p. yellowish green	1·25	40
		a. Opt inverted	3·25	
		w. Wmk reversed	8·00	

(*c*) *Issue for Goa. No.* O202 *optd with T* **606**

O212	O **23**	5 p. yellowish green	3·25	90
		w. Wmk reversed	15·00	

(*d*) *Definitive issue. Wmk Large Star and* "INDIA GOVT" *in sheet**. *Litho. P* 15×14. *No gum.*

O213	O **25**	5 p. yellowish green (1.12)	15	15
		a. Yellow-green	15	15
		w. Wmk reversed	6·00	

*See note below No. O209.

The surcharge on mail for the relief of refugees from the former East Pakistan referred to in the note after No. 651 also applied to official mail. The cost of the stamps used by each Government Department was charged against its budget and the additional charge for refugee stamps meant that each Department had to spend less to keep within its budget.

O **26**

O **27**

O **28**

1976 (1 Apr)–**80.** *Redrawn, showing face-value in figures only and smaller Capital with Hindi motto beneath. P* 14 (2, 5, 10 *r.*) *or* 15 × 14 (*others*). (*a*) *Wmk Large Star and* "INDIA GOVT" *in sheet*.* *No gum.*

O214	O **26**	2 p. deep violet-blue	20	85
O215		5 p. yellowish green	10	30
O216		10 p. myrtle-green	15	70
		a. Imperf (pair)		
		b. Deep dull green (1978)	10	70
O217		15 p. deep purple	10	30
O218		20 p. Indian red	15	70
O219		25 p. rose-carmine	55	1·25
		a. Bright crimson (1978)	90	1·25
O220		30 p. chalky blue (1.5.79)	2·00	2·00
O221		35 p. violet (6.12.80)	45	10
O222		50 p. chestnut	2·25	1·25
O223		1 r. deep brownish purple (13.8.80)	3·50	75

(*b*) W **374** (*sideways*)†

O224	O **26**	1 r. deep brownish purple	85	95
O225	–	2 r. rose-red (date?)	2·75	2·75
		aw. Wmk capitals to right	3·00	
		b. Wmk upright	40	1·50
		bw. Wmk inverted	2·00	
O226	–	5 r. deep green (date?)	3·25	3·75
		aw. Wmk capitals to right	3·50	
		b. Wmk upright (1978)	60	2·25
		bw. Wmk inverted		
O227	–	10 r. brown-lake (date?)	1·25	3·50
		a. Wmk upright	3·25	4·50
		aw. Wmk inverted	3·50	
O214/27		*Set of* 14	11·00	14·50

The 2, 5 and 10 r. are larger, size as Type O **22**.

*See note below No. 720. The 2 p. value is only known on the first type of watermark, the 35, 50 p. and 1 r. values on the second and the remaining values on both.

†The normal sideways watermark shows the top of the capitals pointing left, *as seen from the back of the stamp.*

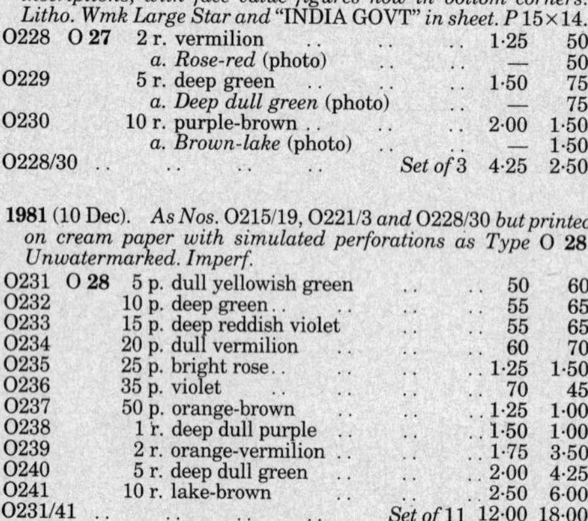

1981 (14 Feb). *Redrawn showing revised border design and inscriptions, with face value figures now in bottom corners. Litho. Wmk Large Star and* "INDIA GOVT" *in sheet. P* 15×14.

O228	O **27**	2 r. vermilion	1·25	50
		a. Rose-red (photo)	—	50
O229		5 r. deep green	1·50	75
		a. Deep dull green (photo)	—	75
O230		10 r. purple-brown	2·00	1·50
		a. Brown-lake (photo)	—	1·50
O228/30		*Set of* 3	4·25	2·50

1981 (10 Dec). *As Nos.* O215/19, O221/3 *and* O228/30 *but printed on cream paper with simulated perforations as Type* O **28**. *Unwatermarked. Imperf.*

O231	O **28**	5 p. dull yellowish green	50	60
O232		10 p. deep green	55	65
O233		15 p. deep reddish violet	55	65
O234		20 p. dull vermilion	60	70
O235		25 p. bright rose	1·25	1·50
O236		35 p. violet	70	45
O237		50 p. orange-brown	1·25	1·00
O238		1 r. deep dull purple	1·50	1·00
O239		2 r. orange-vermilion	1·75	3·50
O240		5 r. deep dull green	2·00	4·25
O241		10 r. lake-brown	2·50	6·00
O231/41		*Set of* 11	12·00	18·00

Some values have been unofficially pin-perforated.

1982 (22 Nov). *As Nos.* 215/23 *and* 228/30. *Photo. Wmk Large Star and* "INDIA GOVT" *in sheet. P* 12½×13.

O242	O **26**	5 p. light green	30	50
O243		10 p. deep dull green	35	70
O244		15 p. blackish purple	35	70
O245		20 p. Indian red	40	70
O246		25 p. cerise	50	1·00
O247		30 p. deep ultramarine	50	1·00
O248		35 p. bluish violet	50	40
O249		50 p. reddish brown	75	1·00
O250		1 r. deep purple-brown	80	1·00
O251	O **27**	2 r. rose-red	1·10	2·00
		a. Vermilion (*litho*)	1·00	2·00
O252		5 r. grey-green	1·50	3·50
O253		10 r. chocolate	2·25	5·00
O242/53		*Set of* 12	8·25	15·00

1984 (16 Apr)–**88.** *As Nos.* O215/23, O228/30 *and new values. Photo.* W **374** (*sideways**). *P* 13.

O254	O **26**	5 p. yellowish green	10	10
		aw. Wmk capitals to right	10	10
		b. Wmk upright	10	10
O255		10 p. deep dull green	10	10
		a. Wmk upright	10	10
O256		15 p. blackish purple	10	10
		a. Wmk upright	10	10
O257		20 p. Indian red	10	10
		a. Wmk upright	10	10
O258		25 p. rose-carmine (1986)	15	10
		a. Wmk upright	15	10
O259		30 p. deep ultramarine	15	10
		a. Wmk upright	15	10
O260		35 p. bluish violet	20	10
		aw. Wmk capitals to left		
		b. Wmk upright	20	10
O262		50 p. reddish brown	20	10
		aw. Wmk capitals to right	20	10
		b. Wmk upright	20	10
O263		60 p. deep brown (15.4.88)	20	10
		a. Wmk upright	20	10
O264		1 r. deep purple-brown	20	10
		aw. Wmk capitals to right	20	10
		b. Wmk upright	20	10
O265	O **27**	2 r. rose-red	25	25
		a. Wmk upright	25	25
O266		5 r. grey-green	40	40
		a. Wmk upright	40	40
O267		10 r. chocolate	65	65
		w. Wmk capitals to right		
O254/67		*Set of* 13	2·25	1·90

*The normal sideways watermark shows the top of the capitals pointing right on the 35 p. and to the left on the other values, *all as seen from the back of the stamp.*

1998 (15 Oct)–**98.** *Litho.* W **374** (*sideways*). *P* 13.

O268	O **26**	40 p. bright violet	10	10
		a. Wmk upright	10	10
		w. Wmk inverted	10	10
O269		50 p. yellow-brown (20.6.98)	10	10
O270		1 r. deep dull purple (20.6.98)	10	10
O271	O **27**	2 r. vermilion (20.6.98)	10	15
O272		5 r. deep grey-green (20.6.98)	15	20
O273		10 r. red-brown (20.6.98)	30	35
O268/73		*Set of* 6	1·00	1·10

INDIA USED ABROAD

In the years following 1858 the influence of the Indian Empire, political, military and economic, extended beyond its borders into neighbouring states, the Arabian Gulf, East Africa and the Far East. Such influence often led to the establishment of Indian civil post offices in the countries concerned where unoverprinted stamps of India were used.

Such offices operated in the following countries. An * indicates that details will be found under that heading elsewhere in the catalogue.

ADEN (SOUTH ARABIAN FEDERATION)*

Unoverprinted stamps of India used from 1854 until 1937.

BAHRAIN*

Unoverprinted stamps of India used from 1884 until 1933.

BRITISH EAST AFRICA (KENYA, UGANDA AND TANGANYIKA)*

Unoverprinted stamps of India used during August and September 1890.

FRENCH INDIAN SETTLEMENTS

The first Indian post office, at Chandernagore, was open by 1784 to be followed by offices in the other four Settlements. By an agreement with the French, dating from 1814, these offices handled mail destined for British India, Great Britain, the British Empire and most other foreign destinations except France and the French colonies. In later years the system was expanded by a number of sub-offices and it continued to operate until the French territories were absorbed into India on 2 May 1950 (Chandernagore) or 1 November 1954.

Chandernagore. Open by 1784. Used numeral cancellations "B86" or "86".
- Sub-offices:
  - Gondalpara (opened 1906)
  - Lakhiganj (opened 1909)
  - Temata (opened 1891)

Karikal. Open by 1794. Used numeral cancellations "C147", "147" or "6/M–21".
- Sub-offices:
  - Ambagarattur (opened 1904)
  - Kottuchari (opened 1901)
  - Nedungaon (opened 1903)
  - Puraiyar Road (opened 1901)
  - Settur (opened 1905)
  - Tirumalrayapatnam (opened 1875 – used numeral cancellation "6/M-21/1")
  - Tiramilur (opened 1898)

Mahe. Open by 1795. Used numeral cancellations "C192" or "9/M-14".

Pondicherry. Opened 1787. Used numeral cancellations "C111", "111" (also used elsewhere), "6/M-19" (also used elsewhere) or "6/M-20".
- Sub-offices:
  - Ariyankuppam (opened 1904)
  - Bahoor (opened 1885)
  - Mudaliarpet (opened 1897)
  - Muthialpet (opened 1885)
  - Pondicherry Bazaar (opened 1902)
  - Pondicherry Railway Station (opened 1895)
  - Olugarai (opened 1907)
  - Vallinur (opened 1875) – used numeral cancellation "M-19/1"

Yanam. Opened 1876. Used numeral cancellation "5/M-4".

IRAN

The British East India Company was active in the Arabian Gulf from the early years of the 17th century with their first factory (trading centre) being established at Jask in 1619. After 1853 this commercial presence was converted into a political arm of the Indian Government culminating in the appointment of a Political Resident to Bushire in 1862.

The first Indian post office in Iran (Persia) opened at Bushire on 1 May 1864 with monthly mail services operating to the Resident there and to the British Legation at Tehran. Further offices in the other Gulf ports followed, but, unless otherwise stated below, all were closed on 1 April 1923.

Abadan. Opened during First World War.
Ahwaz. Opened March 1915.
Bandar Abbas. Opened 1 April 1867. Used numeral cancellations "22" or "1/K-5"
Bushire. Opened 1 May 1864. Used numeral cancellations "308", "26" (also used elsewhere) or "K-5".
Chabbar. Opened 20 August 1913.
Duzdab. Opened 1922. Closed 1927?

Henjam. Opened 21 June 1913
Jask. Opened 1 September 1880
Kuh-Malik-Siah-Ziarat. Opened January 1906. Closed 1924
Linga. Opened 1 April 1867. Used numeral cancellations "21" or "2/K-5".
Maidan-i-Naphtun. Opened during First World War. Closed 1920.
Mirjawa. Opened January 1921. Closed 1930.
Mohammera. Opened 19 July 1892.

IRAQ*

Unoverprinted stamps of India used from 1868 until 1918.

KUWAIT*

Unoverprinted stamps of India used from 1904 until 1923.

MALAYSIA (STRAITS SETTLEMENTS)*

Unoverprinted stamps of India used from 1854 until 1867.

MUSCAT*

Unoverprinted stamps of India used from 1864 until 1947.

NEPAL

A post office was opened in the British Residency at Kathmandu in 1816 following the end of the Gurkha War. Stamps of India were used from 1854, initially with "B137", "137" or "C-37" numeral cancellations. The Residency Post Office continued to provide the overseas mail service after Nepal introduced its own issues in 1881.

In 1920 the Residency Post Office became the British Legation Post Office. On the independence of India in 1947 the service was transferred to the Indian Embassy and continued to function until 1965.

PORTUGUESE INDIA

A British post office was open in Damaun by 1823 and Indian stamps were used there until November 1883, some with "13" and "3/B-19" numeral cancellations.

No other British post offices were opened in the Portuguese territories, but from 1854 Indian stamps were sold by the local post offices. Between 1871 and 1877 mail intended for, or passing through, British India required combined franking of India and Portuguese India issues. After 1877 the two postal administrations accepted the validity of each other's stamps.

SOMALILAND PROTECTORATE*

Unoverprinted stamps of India used from 1887 until 1903.

TIBET

The first Indian post office in Tibet accompanied the Tibetan Frontier Commission in 1903. The Younghusband Military Expedition to Lhasa in the following year operated a number of Field Post Offices which were replaced by civil post offices at Gartok (opened 23 September 1906), Gyantse (opened March 1905), Pharijong (opened 1905) and Yatung (opened 1905). All Indian post offices in Tibet closed on 1 April 1955 except Gartok which, it is believed, did not operate after 1943.

TRUCIAL STATES (DUBAI)*

Unoverprinted stamps of India used from 1909 until 1947.

ZANZIBAR (TANZANIA)*

Unoverprinted stamps of India used from 1875 until 1895.

CHINA EXPEDITIONARY FORCE

Following the outbreak of the Boxer Rising in North China the Peking Legations were besieged by the rebels in June 1900. An international force, including an Indian Army division, was assembled for their relief. The Legations were relieved on 14 August 1900, but operations against the Boxers continued in North China with Allied garrisons at key cities and along the Peking–Tientsin–Shanhaikwan railway. The last Indian Army battalion, and accompanying Field Post Offices, did not leave North China until 1 November 1923.

Field Post Offices accompanied the Indian troops and commenced operations on 23 July 1900 using unoverprinted Indian postage and official stamps. The unoverprinted postage issues were replaced in mid-August by stamps overprinted "C.E.F." to prevent currency speculation. The use of unoverprinted official stamps continued as they were not valid for public postage.

PRICES FOR STAMPS ON COVER	
Nos. C1/10	*from* × 15
No. C10*a*	†
Nos. C11/22	*from* × 8
Nos. C23/34	*from* × 20

C. E. F.

(C 1)

Stamps of India overprinted with Type* C 1, *in black

1900 (16 Aug). *Stamps of Queen Victoria.*

C 1 **40** 3 p. carmine .. .. 40 1·25
a. No stop after "C" (R. 1/2) ..
b. No stop after "F" £130
C 2 **23** ½ a. green 75 30
a. Opt double
b. No stop after "F" £130
C 3 **25** 1 a. plum .. .. 4·00 1·50
a. No stop after "F" £180
C 4 **27** 2 a. ultramarine .. .. .. 3·00 9·00
a. No stop after "F" £180
C 5 **36** 2 a. 6 p. green .. .. .. 2·75 13·00
a. No stop after "F" £250
C 6 **28** 3 a. orange .. .. .. 2·75 16·00
a. Opt double, one albino £120
b. No stop after "F" £250
C 7 **29** 4 a. olive-green .. .. .. 2·75 7·50
a. Opt double, one albino £120
b. No stop after "F" £250
C 8 **31** 8 a. magenta .. .. 2·75 15·00
a. No stop after "F" £300
b. Opt double, one albino £120
C 9 **32** 12 a. purple/*red* .. .. .. 15·00 15·00
a. Opt double, one albino £160
b. No stop after "F" £375
C10 **37** 1 r. green and carmine .. .. 16·00 16·00
a. No stop after "F" £375
C1/10 .. .. *Set of* 10 45·00 85·00

Prepared, but not issued

C10*b* **26** 1 a. 6 p. sepia £200

The missing stop after "F" variety occurs in the ninth row of the upper pane.

1904 (27 Feb).
C11 **25** 1 a. carmine .. .. 27·00 8·00

1905 (16 Sept)–**11.** *Stamps of King Edward VII.*
C12 **41** 3 p. grey (4.11) .. .. .. 4·00 6·50
a. Opt double, one albino £120
b. Opt triple, one albino £375
c. Slate-grey .. .. .. 3·50 6·50
C13 **43** 1 a. carmine .. .. 6·50 70
a. Opt double, one albino £100
C14 **44** 2 a. mauve (11.3.11) .. .. .. 14·00 2·00
a. Opt double, one albino £130
C15 **45** 2 a. 6 p. ultramarine (11.3.11) .. 3·25 5·00
C16 **46** 3 a. orange-brown (11.3.11) .. .. 3·75 4·00
C17 **47** 4 a. olive-green (11.3.11) .. .. 8·50 11·00
C18 **49** 8 a. claret (11.3.11) .. .. .. 8·00 7·50
a. Purple .. .. 55·00 55·00
C19 **50** 12 a. purple/*red* (1909) .. .. 11·00 19·00
a. No stop after "E" £450
C20 **51** 1 r. green and carmine (11.3.11) .. 13·00 28·00
C12/20 .. .. *Set of* 9 65·00 75·00

1908 (Dec)–**09.** "POSTAGE & REVENUE".
C21 **53** ½ a. green (No. 149) (29.9.09) .. .. 1·50 1·25
a. Opt double, one albino £110
C22 **54** 1 a. carmine (No. 150) .. .. 1·50 30
a. Opt double, one albino £150

1914 (5 May)–**22.** *Stamps of King George V. Wmk Star.*
C23 **55** 3 p. slate-grey (7.10.14) .. .. 3·75 22·00
a. Opt double, one albino £200
C24 **56** ½ a. green .. .. 2·75 4·50
C25 **57** 1 a. aniline carmine .. .. .. 3·25 3·25
C26 **58** 1½ a. chocolate (Type A) (9.3.21) .. 21·00 65·00
a. Opt double, one albino £140
C27 **59** 2 a. mauve (11.19) .. .. .. 10·00 48·00
a. Opt triple £425
b. Dull purple .. .. .. 11·00 48·00
C28 **61** 2 a. 6 p. bright blue (2.19) .. .. 8·50 22·00
C29 **62** 3 a. orange-brown (5.22) .. .. 23·00 £180
C30 **63** 4 a. olive-green (5.22) .. .. 19·00 £150
C32 **65** 8 a. mauve (12.21) .. .. .. 20·00 £325
C33 **66** 12 a. claret (8.20) .. .. .. 19·00 £110
C34 **67** 1 r. red-brown and blue-green (10.21) 55·00 £250
C23/34 .. .. *Set of* 11 £160 £1000

Most dates quoted for Nos. C23/34 are those of the earliest recorded postmarks.

On No. C27a two of the overprints are only lightly inked.

BRITISH RAILWAY ADMINISTRATION

As a vital communications link the North China Railway (Peking – Tientsin – Shanhaikwan) was captured by Russian forces during operations against the Boxers. Control of the line was subsequently, in February 1901, assigned to the China Expeditionary Force and a British Railway Administration was set up to run it. By international agreement the line was to provide postal services for the other national contingents and also, to a lesser extent, for the civilian population. Travelling post offices were introduced and, on 20 April 1901, a late letter service for which an additional fee of 5 c. was charged.

Type **32** of China

B.R.A.
5
Five Cents

(BR **35**)

1901 (20 Apr). *No.* 108 *of China surch with Type* BR 35.
BR133 **32** 5 c. on ½ c. brown (Bk.) £325 £100
a. Surch inverted £8000 £2500
b. Surch in green £275 £140
ba. Imperf between (horiz pair) .. † £16000

No. BR133 was used for the collection of the 5 c. late letter fee and was affixed to correspondence by a postal official at the railway station. It was cancelled with a violet circular postmark showing "RAILWAY POST OFFICE" at top and the name of the station (PEKING, TIENTSIN, TONGKU, TONGSHAN or SHANHAIKWAN) at foot. With the exception of official mail it could only be used in combination with Indian stamps overprinted "C.E.F.", stamps from the other allied contingents or of the Chinese Imperial Post (*Price used on cover*: No. BR133 *from* £250. No. BR133b *from* £300).

It is suggested that stamps overprinted in black were used at Tientsin and Tongku with those in green being available at Peking, Tongshan and Shanhaikwan.

The late fee charge was abolished on 20 May 1901 and No. BR133 was then withdrawn. The British Railway Administration continued to run the line, and its travelling post offices, until it was returned to its private owners in September 1902.

INDIAN EXPEDITIONARY FORCES 1914–21

Nos. E1/13 were for use of Indian forces sent overseas during the First World War and its aftermath. Examples were first used in France during September 1914. Other areas where the stamps were used included East Africa, Mesopotamia and Turkey. "I.E.F." overprints ceased to be valid for postage on 15 October 1921.

PRICES FOR STAMPS ON COVER	
Nos. E1/13	*from* × 10

I. E. F.

(E 1)

1914 (Sept). *Stamps of India (King George V) optd with Type* E 1.
E 1 **55** 3 p. slate-grey 15 25
a. No stop after "F" .. .. .. 23·00 26·00
b. No stop after "E" £100 £100
c. Opt double .. .. .. 42·00 30·00
E 2 **56** ½ a. yellow-green 20 20
a. No stop after "F" .. .. .. 70·00 70·00
b. Opt double £140 £250
E 3 **57** 1 a. aniline carmine 50 20
a. No stop after "F" .. .. .. 32·00 35·00
E 4 1 a. carmine .. .. 3·00 3·00
E 5 **59** 2 a. mauve 70 30
a. No stop after "F" .. .. .. 50·00 65·00
b. No stop after "E" £225 £250
E 6 **61** 2 a. 6 p. ultramarine .. .. .. 1·25 2·75
a. No stop after "F" £160 £170
E 7 **62** 3 a. orange-brown 80 70
a. No stop after "F" £150 £160
E 8 **63** 4 a. olive-green 70 70
a. No stop after "F" £225 £250
E 9 **65** 8 a. purple .. .. 1·00 1·75
a. No stop after "F" £225 £250
E10 8 a. mauve .. .. 8·50 12·00
E11 **66** 12 a. dull claret .. .. .. 9·00 13·00
a. No stop after "F" £275 £275
b. Opt double, one albino .. .. 55·00
E12 12 a. claret .. .. 2·25 5·50
E13 **67** 1 r. red-brown and blue-green .. 2·50 4·00
a. Opt double, one albino £100
E1/13 .. .. *Set of* 10 9·00 14·50

The "no stop after F" variety occurred on R. 4/12 of the upper pane, in one printing.

INDIAN CUSTODIAN FORCES IN KOREA

भारतीय
संरक्षा कटक
कोरिया

(K 1)

1953 (17 Oct). *Stamps of India optd with Type* K 1.
K 1 **307** 3 p. slate-violet .. .. .. 1·50 4·50
K 2 **308** 6 p. purple-brown .. .. .. 1·50 4·50
K 3 **309** 9 p. yellow-green .. .. .. 1·75 4·50
K 4 **328** 1 a. turquoise .. .. .. 1·50 4·50
K 5 **311** 2 a. carmine .. .. .. 1·50 4·50
K 6 **313** 2½ a. lake .. .. 1·50 4·75
K 7 **312** 3 a. brown-orange .. .. .. 1·50 4·75
K 8 **314** 4 a. bright blue .. .. .. 2·00 4·75
K 9 **315** 6 a. violet .. .. 8·50 9·00
K10 **316** 8 a. turquoise-green .. .. .. 3·25 9·00
K11 **317** 12 a. dull blue .. .. .. 4·50 17·00
K12 **318** 1 r. dull violet and green .. .. 6·00 17·00
K1/12 .. .. *Set of* 12 30·00 75·00

INDIAN U.N. FORCE IN CONGO

U.N. FORCE
(I N D I A)
CONGO

(U 1)

1962 (15 Jan). *Stamps of India optd with Type* U 1. *W* **69** *(sideways) (13 n.p.) or W* **374** *(others).*
U1 **361** 1 n.p. blue-green .. .. .. 80 2·00
U2 2 n.p. light brown 80 80
U3 5 n.p. bright green 80 55
U4 8 n.p. light blue-green 80 30
U5 13 n.p. bright carmine-red 80 40
U6 50 n.p. orange 80 70
U1/6 .. .. *Set of* 6 4·25 4·25

INDIAN U.N. FORCE IN GAZA (PALESTINE) UNEF

UNEF

(G 1)

1965 (15 Jan). *No.* 492 *of India optd with Type* G 1.
G1 **449** 15 p. slate (C.) .. .. .. 1·25 5·50

INTERNATIONAL COMMISSION IN INDO-CHINA

The International Control Commissions for Indo-China were established in August 1954 as part of the Geneva Declaration which partitioned Vietnam and sought to achieve stable settlements in Cambodia and Laos. The three supervisory commissions were chaired by India with Canada and Poland as the other members. Joint inspection teams of servicemen from the three countries were also provided.

The Indian contingent included a postal unit which handled mail for the three commissions and the inspection teams. The unit arrived in Indo-China on 3 September 1954 and opened field post offices at Saigon (F.P.O. 742), Hanoi (F.P.O. 743), Vientiane (F.P.O. 744) and Phnom Penh (F.P.O. 745).

अन्तर्राष्ट्रीय आयोग कम्बोज (N 1) अन्तर्राष्ट्रीय आयोग लाओस (N 2) अन्तर्राष्ट्रीय आयोग वियत नाम (N 3)

1954 (1 Dec). *Stamps of India. W* **69**.

		(a) Optd as Type N 1, *for use in Cambodia*		
N 1	**307**	3 p. slate-violet	90	7·50
N 2	**328**	1 a. turquoise	90	75
N 3	**311**	2 a. carmine	90	80
N 4	**316**	8 a. turquoise-green	2·00	3·50
N 5	**317**	12 a. dull blue	2·00	4·00
		(b) Optd as Type N 2, *for use in Laos*		
N 6	**307**	3 p. slate-violet	90	7·50
N 7	**328**	1 a. turquoise	90	75
N 8	**311**	2 a. carmine	90	80
N 9	**316**	8 a. turquoise-green	2·00	3·50
N10	**317**	12 a. dull blue	2·00	4·00
		(c) Optd as Type N 3, *for use in Vietnam*		
N11	**307**	3 p. slate-violet	90	7·50
N12	**328**	1 a. turquoise	90	75
N13	**311**	2 a. carmine	90	80
N14	**316**	8 a. turquoise-green	2·00	3·50
N15	**317**	12 a. dull blue	2·00	4·00
N1/15		*Set of* 15	17·00	45·00

1957 (1 Apr). *Stamps of India. W* **69** *(sideways)*.

		(a) Optd as Type N 1, *for use in Cambodia*		
N16	**361**	2 n.p. light brown	75	30
N17		6 n.p. grey	50	30
N18		13 n.p. bright carmine-red	70	40
N19		50 n.p. orange	2·25	1·25
N20		75 n.p. reddish purple	2·25	1·25
		(b) Optd as Type N 2, *for use in Laos*		
N21	**361**	2 n.p. light brown	75	30
N22		6 n.p. grey	50	30
N23		13 n.p. bright carmine-red	70	40
N24		50 n.p. orange	2·25	1·25
N25		75 n.p. reddish purple	2·25	1·25
		(c) Optd as Type N 3, *for use in Vietnam*		
N26	**361**	2 n.p. light brown	75	30
N27		6 n.p. grey	50	30
N28		13 n.p. bright carmine-red	70	40
N29		50 n.p. orange	2·25	1·25
N30		75 n.p. reddish purple	2·25	1·25
N16/30		*Set of* 15	17·00	9·50

F.P.O. 744 (Vientiane) was closed on 25 July 1958 and F.P.O. 745 (Phnom Penh) on 26 June 1958.

1960 (Sept)–**65**. *Stamps of India. W* **374**.

		(a) Optd as Type N 2 *for use in Laos*		
N38	**361**	2 n.p. light brown (15.1.62)	15	2·50
N39		3 n.p. deep brown (1.8.63)	10	20
N40		5 n.p. bright green (1.8.63)	10	15
N41		50 n.p. orange (1965)	3·75	3·75
N42		75 n.p. reddish purple (1965)	3·75	4·00
		(b) Optd as Type N 3, *for use in Vietnam*		
N43	**361**	1 n.p. blue-green	10	20
N44		2 n.p. light brown (15.1.62)	15	2·50
N45		3 n.p. deep brown (1.8.63)	10	20
N46		5 n.p. bright green (1.8.63)	10	15
N47		50 n.p. orange (1965)	3·75	3·75
N48		75 n.p. reddish purple (1965)	3·75	4·00
N38/48		*Set of* 11	14·00	19·00

F.P.O. 744 (Vientiane) re-opened on 22 May 1961.

Examples of the 2 n.p. value overprinted as Type N 1 for use in Cambodia exist, but were never placed on sale there as the Phnom Penh F.P.O. 745 was closed on 26 June 1958. Used examples appear to originate from unauthorised use of the F.P.O. 745 postmark which was in store at Saigon (*Price* 15p, *unused*).

ICC (N 4) ICC (N 5)

1965 (15 Jan). *No.* 492 *of India optd with Type* N 4, *for use in Laos and Vietnam.*

N49	**449**	15 p. slate (C.)	60	3·25

F.P.O. 743 (Hanoi) was closed on 13 July 1966.

1968 (2 Oct). *Nos.* 504/5, 506, 509/10, 515 *and* 517/18 *etc of India optd as Type* N 5, *in red, for use in Laos and Vietnam.*

N50	2 p. red-brown	10	2·25
N51	3 p. brown-olive	10	2·25
N52	5 p. cerise	10	75
N53	10 p. new blue	1·75	1·75
N54	15 p. bronze-green	60	1·75
N55	60 p. deep grey	35	1·25
N56	1 r. red-brown and plum	50	1·75
N57	2 r. new blue and deep slate-violet	1·25	7·50
N50/7	*Set of* 8	4·00	17·00

INDIAN NATIONAL ARMY

The following are stated to have been used in the Japanese occupied areas of India during the drive on Imphal. Issued by the Indian National Army.

Genuine examples are inscribed "PROVISIONAL GOVERNMENT OF FREE INDIA". Forgeries also exist inscribed "PROVISIONAL GOVT. OF FREE INDIA".

Typo in Rangoon. No gum. Perf $11\frac{1}{2}$ or imperf. 1 p. violet, 1 p. maroon, 1 a. green *Price from £50 each unused*

JAPANESE OCCUPATION OF THE ANDAMAN AND NICOBAR ISLANDS

The Andaman Islands in the Bay of Bengal were occupied on the 23 March 1942 and the Nicobar Islands in July 1942. Civil administration was resumed in October 1945.

The following Indian stamps were surcharged with large figures preceded by a decimal point:—

Postage stamps—.3 on ½ a. (No. 248), .5 on 1 a. (No. 250), .10 on 2 a. (No. 236*b*), .30 on 6 a. (No. 274).

Official stamps—.10 on 1 a. 3 p. (No. O146*a*), .20 on 3 p. (No. O143), .20 in red on 3 p. (No. O143).

Prices from £375 each unused

INDIAN CONVENTION STATES

The following issues resulted from a series of postal conventions greed between the Imperial Government and the state administrations of Patiala (1 October 1884), Gwalior, Jind and Nabha 1 July 1885), and Chamba and Faridkot (1 January 1887).

Under the terms of these conventions the British Indian ost Office supplied overprinted British India issues to the state dministrations which, in turn, had to conform to a number of conditions covering the issue of stamps, rates of postage and the xchange of mail.

Such overprinted issues were valid for postage within the state f issue, to other "Convention States" and to destinations in British ndia.

Stamps of Chamba, Gwalior, Jind, Nabha and Patiala ceased to e valid for postage on 1 January 1951, when they were replaced y those of the Republic of India, valid from 1 April 1950.

RULERS OF INDIAN CONVENTION AND FEUDATORY STATES. Details of the rulers of the various states during the eriod when stamps were issued are now provided in a omewhat simplified form which omits reference to minor titles.)ates quoted are of the various reigns, extended to 1971 when he titles of the surviving rulers of the former princely states vere abolished by the Indian Government.

During the absorption of the Convention and Feudatory States there was often an interim period during which the dministration was handed over. In some instances it is only ossible to quote the end of this interim period as the point of ransfer.

Stamps of India overprinted

In the Queen Victoria issues we omit varieties due to broken ype, including the numerous small "A" varieties which may ave come about through damaged type. We do, however, list the mall "G", small "R" and tall "R" in "GWALIOR" as these were efinitely the result of the use of type of the wrong size.

Variations in the length of the words due to unequal spacing when setting are also omitted.

CHAMBA

PRICES FOR STAMPS ON COVER

Nos. 1/27	*from* × 20
Nos. 28/120	*from* × 12
Nos. O1/86	*from* × 25

Raja Sham Singh, 1873–1904

CHAMBA STATE (1)   CHAMBA (2)

1887 (1 Jan)–**95.** *Queen Victoria. Optd with T* **1**.

1 **23** ½ a. blue-green .. 10 35
a. "CHMABA" .. £275 £350
b. "8TATE" .. £550
c. Opt double .. £600
2 **25** 1 a. brown-purple .. 60 90
a. "CHMABA" .. £425 £500
b. "8TATE" .. £900
3 1 a. plum .. 1·25 90
4 **26** 1 a. 6 p. sepia (1895) .. 60 8·00
5 **27** 2 a. dull blue .. 1·00 1·10
b. "CHMABA" .. £1700 £1800
c. "8TATE" .. £1700
6 2 a. ultramarine .. 90 1·10
7 **36** 2 a. 6 p. green (1895) .. 24·00 60·00
8 **28** 3 a. orange (1887) .. 4·50 14·00
9 3 a. brown-orange (1891) .. 60 3·25
a. "CHMABA" .. £4000 £4000
b. Opt inverted
10 **29** 4 a. olive-green .. 2·75 5·00
a. "CHMABA" .. £1200 £1400
b. "8TATE" .. £2250
11 4 a. slate-green .. 3·00 4·00
a. Opt double, one albino .. 50·00
12 **21** 6 a. olive-bistre (1890) .. 2·00 10·00
a. Opt treble, two albino .. 75·00
13 6 a. bistre-brown .. 8·00 10·00
14 **31** 8 a. dull mauve (1887) .. 4·50 7·00
a. "CHMABA" .. £3500 £3500
15 8 a. magenta (1895) .. 3·75 10·00
16 **32** 12 a. purple/*red* (1890) .. 3·75 8·00
a. "CHMABA" .. £5000
b. First "T" in "STATE" inverted .. £5000
c. Opt double, one albino .. 30·00
17 **33** 1 r. slate (1887) .. 26·00 85·00
a. "CHMABA" .. £7500
18 **37** 1 r. green and carmine (1895) .. 4·25 9·00
a. Opt double, one albino .. 40·00
19 **38** 2 r. carmine and yellow-brown (1895) .. 65·00 £190
20 3 r. brown and green (1895) .. 65·00 £170
21 5 r. ultramarine and violet (1895) .. 75·00 £300
a. Opt double, one albino .. £140
1/21 .. *Set of* 15 £225 £750

1900–4. *Colours changed.*

22 **40** 3 p. carmine .. 10 30
a. Opt double, one albino .. 30·00
23 3 p. grey (1904) .. 15 1·50
a. Opt inverted .. 75·00
24 **23** ½ a. pale yellow-green (1902) .. 80 1·60
25 ½ a. yellow-green (1903) .. 10 60
26 **25** 1 a. carmine (1902) .. 10 30
27 **27** 2 a. pale violet (1903) .. 5·00 19·00
22/7 .. *Set of* 5 5·00 19·00

Raja Bhuri Singh, 1904–1919

1903–5. *King Edward VII. Optd with T* **1**.

28 **41** 3 p. pale grey .. 10 85
29 3 p. slate-grey (1905) .. 10 85
30 **42** ½ a. green .. 10 20
31 **43** 1 a. carmine .. 45 20
32 **44** 2 a. pale violet (1904) .. 65 1·75
33 2 a. mauve .. 55 1·60
34 **46** 3 a. orange-brown (1905) .. 2·00 3·00
a. Opt double, one albino .. 30·00
35 **47** 4 a. olive (1904) .. 2·50 10·00
36 **48** 6 a. olive-bistre (1905) .. 2·00 13·00
a. Opt double, one albino .. 30·00
37 **49** 8 a. purple (*shades*) (1904) .. 2·50 12·00
38 8 a. claret .. 5·50 17·00
39 **50** 12 a. purple/*red* (1905) .. 3·50 16·00
a. Opt double, one albino .. 30·00
40 **51** 1 r. green and carmine (1904) .. 4·25 15·00
a. Opt double, one albino .. 40·00
28/40 .. *Set of* 10 16·00 65·00

1907. *Nos.* 149/50 *of India optd with T* **1**.

41 **53** ½ a. green .. 25 2·25
a. Opt double, one albino .. 30·00
42 **54** 1 a. carmine .. 35 2·25

1913. *King George V optd with T* **1**.

43 **55** 3 p. slate-grey .. 10 40
44 **56** ½ a. green .. 20 45
w. Wmk inverted
45 **57** 1 a. rose-carmine .. 3·00 4·50
46 1 a. aniline carmine .. 35 1·50
a. Opt double, one albino .. 30·00
47 **59** 2 a. mauve .. 1·25 5·50
48 **62** 3 a. orange-brown .. 1·50 4·50
49 **63** 4 a. olive .. 1·00 3·00
50 **64** 6 a. olive-bistre .. 90 2·75
51 **65** 8 a. purple .. 1·90 6·50
52 **66** 12 a. dull claret .. 1·60 9·00
53 **67** 1 r. brown and green .. 9·00 16·00
a. Opt double, one albino .. 28·00
43/53 .. *Set of* 10 16·00 45·00

Raja Ram Singh, 1919–1935

1921. *No.* 192 *of India optd with T* **2**.

54 **57** 9 p. on 1 a. rose-carmine .. 80 14·00

1923–27. *Optd with T* **1**. *New values, etc.*

55 **57** 1 a. chocolate .. 80 2·50
56 **58** 1½ a. chocolate (Type A) .. 16·00 75·00
57 1½ a. chocolate (Type B) (1924) .. 60 3·50
58 1½ a. rose-carmine (Type B) (1927) .. 60 12·00
59 **61** 2 a. 6 p. ultramarine .. 50 2·75
60 2 a. 6 p. orange (1927) .. 90 10·00
61 **62** 3 a. ultramarine (1924) .. 1·60 12·00
55/61 .. *Set of* 7 19·00 £100

Nos. 58 and 60 with inverted overprint are of clandestine origin.

CHAMBA STATE (3)   CHAMBA STATE (4)

1927–37. *King George V (Nasik printing, wmk Mult Star). Optd at Nasik with T* **3** *or* **4** *(1 r.).*

62 **55** 3 p. slate (1928) .. 10 65
w. Wmk inverted .. 2·25
63 **56** ½ a. green (1928) .. 20 1·00
w. Wmk inverted .. 60
64 **80** 9 p. deep green (1932) .. 1·25 7·50
65 **57** 1 a. chocolate .. 1·25 25
w. Wmk inverted .. 2·25 35
66 **82** 1 a. 3 p. mauve (1932) .. 75 3·50
w. Wmk inverted .. 2·25 3·50
67 **58** 1½ a. rose-carmine (B) (1932) .. 3·25 3·25
w. Wmk inverted .. 3·25 3·25
68 **70** 2 a. purple (1928) .. 75 1·00
69 **61** 2 a. 6 p. orange (1932) .. 90 11·00
w. Wmk inverted .. 1·00 11·00
70 **62** 3 a. bright blue (1928) .. 80 11·00
71 **71** 4 a. sage-green (1928) .. 55 2·75
72 **64** 6 a. bistre (*wmk inverted*) (1937) .. 25·00 £120
73 **65** 8 a. reddish purple (1928) .. 1·00 6·50
w. Wmk inverted .. 1·00 6·50
74 **66** 12 a. claret (1928) .. 1·10 7·50
75 **67** 1 r. chocolate and green (1928) .. 3·50 16·00
w. Wmk inverted .. 6·50 16·00
62/75 .. *Set of* 14 35·00 £170

The 9 p. exists printed by lithography or typography.

Raja Lakshman Singh, 1935–1971

1935–36. *New types and colours. Optd with T* **3**.

76 **79** ½ a. green .. 55 5·50
77 **81** 1 a. chocolate .. 60 45
78 **59** 2 a. vermilion (No. 236*a*) .. 45 16·00
79 2 a. vermilion (*small die*, No. 236*b*) .. 90·00 £100
80 **62** 3 a. carmine .. 1·25 6·00
81 **63** 4 a. sage-green (1936) .. 1·10 8·50
76/81 .. *Set of* 6 90·00 £120

CHAMBA STATE (5)   CHAMBA (6)   CHAMBA (7)

1938. *King George VI. Nos.* 247/64 *optd with T* **3** *(3 p. to 1 a.), T* **5** *(2 a. to 12 a.) or T* **4** *(rupee values).*

82 **91** 3 p. slate .. 3·25 7·50
83 ½ a. red-brown .. 90 4·25
84 9 p. green .. 4·25 20·00
85 1 a. carmine .. 90 1·25
86 **92** 2 a. vermilion .. 2·75 6·50
87 – 2 a. 6 p. bright violet .. 3·25 14·00
88 – 3 a. yellow-green .. 4·00 15·00
89 – 3 a. 6 p. bright blue .. 4·00 17·00
90 – 4 a. brown .. 13·00 11·00
91 – 6 a. turquoise-green .. 12·00 35·00
92 – 8 a. slate-violet .. 13·00 30·00
93 – 12 a. lake .. 8·00 35·00
94 **93** 1 r. grey and red-brown .. 27·00 42·00
95 2 r. purple and brown .. 42·00 £180
96 5 r. green and blue .. 65·00 £275
97 10 r. purple and claret .. £110 £425
98 15 r. brown and green .. £200 £600
99 25 r. slate-violet and purple .. £225 £700
82/99 .. *Set of* 18 £650 £2000

1942–47. *Optd with T* **6** *(to 12 a), "CHAMBA" only, as in T* **5** *(14 a.) or T* **7** *(rupee values). (a) Stamps of* 1937. *W* **69** *(inverted on 15 r.).*

100 **91** ½ a. red-brown .. 23·00 15·00
101 1 a. carmine .. 26·00 16·00
102 **93** 1 r. grey and red-brown .. 21·00 42·00
103 2 r. purple and brown .. 28·00 £160
104 5 r. green and blue .. 60·00 £170
105 10 r. purple and claret .. 85·00 £325
106 15 r. brown and green .. £180 £500
107 25 r. slate-violet and purple .. £200 £550
100/107 .. *Set of* 8 £550 £1600

(*b*) *Stamps of* 1940–43

108 **100*a*** 3 p. slate .. 60 3·00
109 ½ a. purple (1943) .. 70 2·00
110 9 p. green .. 70 8·00
111 1 a. carmine (1943) .. 90 2·00
112 **101** 1½ a. dull violet (1943) .. 90 5·50
113 2 a. vermilion (1943) .. 1·90 6·00
114 3 a. bright violet .. 7·00 15·00
115 3½ a. bright blue .. 3·50 23·00
116 **102** 4 a. brown .. 5·00 7·00
117 6 a. turquoise-green .. 14·00 35·00
118 8 a. slate-violet .. 13·00 40·00
119 12 a. lake .. 26·00 50·00
120 **103** 14 a. purple (1947) .. 6·00 3·00
108/120 .. *Set of* 13 70·00 £180

The 3 a. exists printed by lithography or typography.

OFFICIAL STAMPS

SERVICE

CHAMBA STATE (O 1)

1887 (1 Jan)–**98.** *Queen Victoria. Optd with Type* O **1**.

O 1 **23** ½ a. blue-green .. 10 10
a. "CHMABA" .. £180 £180
b. "SERV CE"
c. "8TATE" .. £550
d. Thin seriffed "I" in "SERVICE" .. 95·00
O 2 **25** 1 a. brown-purple .. 75 55
a. "CHMABA" .. £325 £325
b. "SERV CE" .. £1800
c. "8TATE" .. £1100
d. "SERVICE" double .. £950 £950
e. "SERVICE" double, one albino .. 40·00
O 3 1 a. plum .. 55 10
a. Thin seriffed "I" in "SERVICE" .. £110
O 4 **27** 2 a. dull blue .. 1·00 80
a. "CHMABA" .. £900 £1100
O 5 2 a. ultramarine (1887) .. 80 1·10
a. Thin seriffed "I" in "SERVICE" .. £170
O 6 **28** 3 a. orange (1890) .. 1·60 8·00
O 7 3 a. brown-orange (1891) .. 1·60 8·00
a. "CHMABA" .. £2000 £2250
b. Thin seriffed "I" in "SERVICE"
c. Opt double, one albino
O 8 **29** 4 a. olive-green .. 1·25 3·00
a. "CHMABA" .. £900 £1100
b. "SERV CE" .. £2250
c. "8TATE" .. £2250
O 9 4 a. slate-green .. 1·10 4·50
a. Thin seriffed "I" in "SERVICE"
O10 **21** 6 a. olive-bistre (1890) .. 3·25 7·50
a. "SERVICE" double, one albino .. 40·00
O11 6 a. bistre-brown
O12 **31** 8 a. dull mauve (1887) .. 2·50 3·75
a. "CHMABA" .. £4000 £4000
O13 8 a. magenta (1895) .. 90 1·60
a. Thin seriffed "I" in "SERVICE" .. £375
O14 **32** 12 a. purple/*red* (1890) .. 7·00 27·00
a. "CHMABA" .. £4500
b. First "T" in "STATE" inverted .. £4750
c. Thin seriffed "I" in "SERVICE"
d. "SERVICE" double, one albino .. 40·00
e. "CHAMBA STATE" double, one albino
O15 **33** 1 r. slate (1890) .. 12·00 80·00
a. "CHMABA" .. £4000
O16 **37** 1 r. green and carmine (1898) .. 5·50 22·00
a. Thin seriffed "I" in "SERVICE"
O1/16 .. *Set of* 10 30·00 £130

Printings up to and including that of December 1895 had the "SERVICE" overprint applied to sheets of stamps already overprinted with Type 1. From the printing of September 1898 onwards both "SERVICE" and "CHAMBA STATE" were overprinted at the same time. Nos. O6, O8 and O12 only exist using the first method, and No. O16 was only printed using the second.

The thin seriffed "I" in "SERVICE" variety occured on R. 19/12 of the September 1898 printing only.

1902–4. *Colours changed. Optd as Type* O **1**.

O17 **40** 3 p. grey (1904) .. 15 45
O18 **23** ½ a. pale yellow-green .. 20 2·50
O19 ½ a. yellow-green .. 2·00 1·10
O20 **25** 1 a. carmine .. 40 40
O21 **27** 2 a. pale violet (1903) .. 8·00 21·00
O17/21 .. *Set of* 4 8·00 21·00

1903–5. *King Edward VII. Stamps of India optd as Type* O **1**.

O22 **41** 3 p. pale grey .. 15 15
a. Opt double, one albino .. 25·00
O23 3 p. slate-grey (1905) .. 10 65
O24 **42** ½ a. yellow-green .. 15 10
O25 **43** 1 a. carmine .. 35 25

O26 **44** 2 a. pale violet (1904) . . . . 2·00 70
O27 2 a. mauve 50 50
O28 **47** 4 a. olive (1905) . . . . 2·50 11·00
O29 **49** 8 a. purple (1905) . . . . 3·00 11·00
O30 8 a. claret . . . . . . 6·00 16·00
a. Opt double, one albino . . 30·00
O31 **51** 1 r. green and carmine (1905) . . 1·40 6·50
O22/31 . . . . . . *Set of* 7 7·25 27·00

The 2 a. mauve King Edward VII, overprinted "On H.M.S.", was discovered in Calcutta, but was not sent to Chamba, and is an unissued variety (*Price un.* £35).

1907. *Nos.* 149/50 *of India, optd with Type* O 1.
O32 **53** ½ a. green 25 75
a. Opt inverted £3750 £3750
b. Opt double, one albino . . 25·00
O33 **54** 1 a. carmine . . . . . . 1·40 1·00

The inverted overprint, No. O32a, was due to an inverted cliché on R. 20/1 which was corrected after a few sheets had been printed.

1913–14. *King George V Official stamps* (*wmk Single Star*) *optd with T* 1.
O34 **55** 3 p. slate-grey 25 65
O35 3 p. grey 20 40
O36 **56** ½ a. yellow-green 10 10
O37 ½ a. pale blue-green 85 30
O38 **57** 1 a. aniline carmine 10 10
O39 1 a. rose-carmine . . . . 3·50 40
O40 **59** 2 a. mauve (1914) . . . . 1·00 8·50
O41 **63** 4 a. olive . . . . . . 1·10 10·00
O42 **65** 8 a. purple . . . . . . 1·60 11·00
O43 **67** 1 r. brown and green (1914) . . 3·25 19·00
a. Opt double, one albino . . 27·00
O34/43 . . . . . . *Set of* 7 6·50 45·00

No. O36 with inverted overprint and No. O39 with double or inverted overprint (on gummed side) are of clandestine origin.

1914. *King George V. Optd with Type* O 1.
O44 **59** 2 a. mauve . . . . . . 10·00
O45 **63** 4 a. olive . . . . . . 9·00

1921. *No.* O97 *of India optd with T* 2 *at top.*
O46 **57** 9 p. on 1 a. rose-carmine . . . . 15 4·50

1925. *As* 1913–14. *New colour.*
O47 **57** 1 a. chocolate . . . . . . 1·40 50

CHAMBA STATE SERVICE (O 2) — CHAMBA STATE SERVICE (O 3)

1927–39. *King George V* (*Nasik printing, wmk Mult Star*), *optd at Nasik with Type* O 2 *or* O 3 (*rupee values*).
O48 **55** 3 p. slate (1928) 40 30
w. Wmk inverted . . . . — 50
O49 **56** ½ a. green (1928) 30 15
O50 **80** 9 p. deep green (1932) . . . . 1·25 6·00
O51 **57** 1 a. chocolate 20 10
w. Wmk inverted . . . . — 20
O52 **82** 1 a. 3 p. mauve (1932) . . . . 4·50 50
w. Wmk inverted . . . .
O53 **70** 2 a. purple (1928) 70 55
O54 **71** 4 a. sage-green (1928) 70 90
O55 **65** 8 a. reddish purple (1930) . . 3·00 6·50
w. Wmk inverted . . . . 4·25
O56 **66** 12 a. claret (1928) . . . . 1·60 15·00
w. Wmk inverted . . . . 6·50
O57 **67** 1 r. chocolate and green (1930) . . 9·50 27·00
O58 2 r. carmine and orange (1939) . . 18·00 £160
O59 5 r. ultramarine and purple (1939) . . 40·00 £225
O60 10 r. green and scarlet (1939) . . 50·00 £200
O48/60 . . . . . . *Set of* 13 £120 £550

1935–39. *New types and colours. Optd with Type* O 2.
O61 **79** ½ a. green . . . . . . 1·00 40
O62 **81** 1 a. chocolate . . . . . . 1·75 45
O63 **59** 2 a. vermilion . . . . . . 2·75 85
O64 2 a. vermilion (*small die*) (1939) . . 1·50 9·00
O65 **63** 4 a. sage-green (1936) . . . . 3·00 2·75
O61/5 . . . . . . *Set of* 5 9·00 12·00

1938–40. *King George VI. Optd with Type* O **2** *or* O **3** (*rupee values*).
O66 **91** 9 p. green . . . . . . 7·50 32·00
O67 1 a. carmine . . . . . . 6·00 1·50
O68 **93** 1 r. grey and red-brown (1940?) . . £500 £750
O69 2 r. purple and brown (1939) . . 50·00 £250
O70 5 r. green and blue (1939) . . 80·00 £325
O71 10 r. purple and claret (1939) . . £120 £500
O66/71 . . . . . . *Set of* 6 £700 £1700

CHAMBA SERVICE (O 4)

1940–43. (*a*) *Official stamps optd with T* 6.
O72 **O 20** 3 p. slate 60 50
O73 ½ a. red-brown . . . . 11·00 1·25
O74 ½ a. purple (1943) . . . . 60 1·40
O75 9 p. green . . . . . . 3·25 5·00
w. Wmk inverted . . . . 11·00 9·00
O76 1 a. carmine (1941) . . . . 60 1·10
O77 1 a. 3 p. yellow-brown (1941) . . 38·00 13·00
O78 1½ a. dull violet (1943) . . . . 3·75 4·25
O79 2 a. vermilion . . . . . . 3·00 3·50
O80 2½ a. bright violet (1941) . . . . 1·75 15·00
O81 4 a. brown . . . . . . 3·25 6·50
O82 8 a. slate-violet . . . . 9·50 38·00
w. Wmk inverted . . . . 8·50 38·00

(*b*) *Postage stamps optd with Type* O 4.
O83 **93** 1 r. grey and red-brown (1942) . . 32·00 £140
O84 2 r. purple and brown (1942) . . 50·00 £200
O85 5 r. green and blue (1942) . . 80·00 £300
O86 10 r. purple and claret (1942) . . £120 £500
O72/86 . . . . . . *Set of* 15 £325 £1100

Chamba became part of Himachal Pradesh on 15 April 1948.

FARIDKOT

For earlier issues, see under INDIAN FEUDATORY STATES

PRICES FOR STAMPS ON COVER

Nos. 1/17	*from* × 30
Nos. O1/15	*from* × 40

Raja Bikram Singh, 1874–1898

FARIDKOT STATE (1)

1887 (1 Jan)–**1900.** *Queen Victoria. Optd with T* 1.
1 **23** ½ a. deep green 75 75
a. "ARIDKOT" . . . .
b. "FAR DKOT" . . . . — £1000
c. Opt double, one albino . . 35·00
2 **25** 1 a. brown-purple . . . . 85 1·75
3 1 a. plum . . . . . . 90 1·00
4 **27** 2 a. blue . . . . . . 2·50 3·25
5 2 a. deep blue . . . . . . 2·50 4·25
6 **28** 3 a. orange . . . . . . 4·25 7·00
7 3 a. brown-orange (1893) . . . . 1·40 2·50
8 **29** 4 a. olive-green . . . . 4·50 12·00
a. "ARIDKOT" £1000
9 4 a. slate-green . . . . 4·50 14·00
10 **21** 6 a. olive-bistre . . . . 18·00 35·00
a. "ARIDKOT" £1600
b. Opt double, one albino . . 35·00
11 6 a. bistre-brown . . . . 1·75 9·50
12 **31** 8 a. dull mauve . . . . 8·00 25·00
a. "ARIDKOT" £2000
13 8 a. magenta . . . . . . 10·00 75·00
a. Opt double, one albino . . 30·00
14 **32** 12 a. purple/*red* (1900) . . . . 29·00 £300
15 **33** 1 r. slate . . . . . . 28·00 £275
a. "ARIDKOT" £2000
16 **37** 1 r. green and carmine (1893) . . 29·00 60·00
a. Opt double, one albino . . 50·00
1/16 . . . . . . *Set of* 10 95·00 £600

The ½ a., 1 a., 2 a., 3 a., 4 a., 8 a. and 1 r. (No. 16) are known with broken "O" (looking like a "C") in "FARIDKOT".

Raja Balbir Singh, 1898–1906

1900. *Optd with T* 1.
17 **40** 3 p. carmine . . . . . . 50 30·00

OFFICIAL STAMPS

SERVICE

FARIDKOT STATE (O 1)

1887 (1 Jan)–**98.** *Queen Victoria. Optd with Type* O 1.
O 1 **23** ½ a. deep green 15 50
a. "SERV CE" £1400
b. "FAR DKOT" . . . .
c. Thin seriffed "I" in "SERVICE" . . £130
d. "FARIDKOT STATE" double, one albino . . . . 30·00
O 2 **25** 1 a. brown-purple . . . . 55 1·00
a. Thin seriffed "I" in "SERVICE" . . £140
b. Opt double, one albino . . 40·00
O 3 1 a. plum 65 90
a. "SERV CE" £1800
O 4 **27** 2 a. dull blue . . . . 1·40 6·00
a. "SERV CE" £1800
O 5 2 a. deep blue . . . . . . 85 8·50
O 6 **28** 3 a. orange . . . . . . 3·75 5·50
a. "SERVICE" double, one albino . .
O 7 3 a. brown-orange (12.98) . . 1·10 24·00
a. Thin seriffed "I" in "SERVICE" . . £350
O 8 **29** 4 a. olive-green . . . . 2·75 14·00
a. "SERV CE" £1800
b. "ARIDKOT" . . . .
c. "SERVICE" treble, two albino . . 60·00
O 9 4 a. slate-green . . . . 7·50 27·00
a. "SERVICE" double, one albino . . 30·00
O10 **21** 6 a. olive-bistre . . . . 24·00 65·00
a. "ARIDKOT" £1100
b. "SERVIC" £1700
c. "SERVICE" double, one albino . . 40·00
d. "FARIDKOT STATE" double, one albino . . . . 40·00
O11 6 a. bistre-brown . . . . 13·00 16·00
O12 **31** 8 a. dull mauve . . . . 4·00 16·00
a. "SERV CE" £1900
O13 8 a. magenta . . . . . . 10·00 75·00
O14 **33** 1 r. slate . . . . . . 38·00 £130
a. "SERVICE" double, one albino . . 55·00
O15 **37** 1 r. green and carmine (12.98) . . 70·00 £375
a. Thin seriffed "I" in "SERVICE" . .
O1/15 . . . . . . *Set of* 9 £120 £500

The ½ a., 1 a., 2 a., 3 a., 4 a., 8 a. and 1 r. (No. O15) are known with the broken "O".

Printings up to and including that of November 1895 had the "SERVICE" overprint applied to sheets already overprinted with Type 1. From December 1898 onwards "SERVICE" and "FARIDKOT STATE" were overprinted at one operation to provide fresh supplies of Nos. O1/3, O7 and O15.

The thin seriffed "I" variety occurs on the December 1898 overprinting only.

This State ceased to use overprinted stamps after 31 March 1901.

GWALIOR

PRICES FOR STAMPS ON COVER

Nos. 1/3	*from* × 10
Nos. 4/11	—
Nos. 12/66	*from* × 5
Nos. 67/128	*from* × 4
Nos. 129/37	*from* × 5
Nos. O1/94	*from* × 12

OVERPRINTS. From 1885 to 1926 these were applied by the Government of India Central Printing Press, Calcutta, and from 1927 at the Security Press, Nasik, *unless otherwise stated.*

Maharaja Jayaji Rao Sindhia, 1843–1886

गवालियर

GWALIOR (1) — GWALIOR गवालियर (2)

GWALIOR — Small "G"
GWALIOR — Small "R"
GWALIOR — Tall "R" (original state)
GWALIOR — Tall "R" (damaged state)

OVERPRINT VARIETIES OF TYPE 2.
Small "G"—Occurs on R.7/11 from June 1900 printing of ½, 1, 2, 3, 4 a. and 3 p. (No. 38), and on an unknown position from May 1901 printing of 2, 3 and 5 r.
Small "R"—Occurs on R. 9/3 from June 1900 printing of 3 p. to 4 a. and on R.2/3 from May 1901 printing of 2, 3 and 5 r.
Tall "R" —Occurs on R.20/2 from printings between June 1900 and May 1907. The top of the letter is damaged on printings from February 1903 onwards.

1885 (1 July)–**97.** *Queen Victoria.* I. *Optd with T* 1.
(*a*) *Space between two lines of overprint* 13 *mm. Hindi inscription* 13 *to* 14 *mm long* (May 1885)
1 **23** ½ a. blue-green . . . . 85·00 16·0
2 **25** 1 a. brown-purple . . . . 60·00 22·0
3 **27** 2 a. dull blue . . . . 50·00 11·0
1/3 . . . . . . *Set of* 3 £180 45·0

A variety exists of the ½ a. in which the space between the two lines of overprint is only 9½ mm but this is probably from a proof sheet.

(*b*) *Space between two lines of overprint* 15 *mm on* 4 *a. and* 6 *a. and* 16 *to* 17 *mm on other values* (June 1885). *Hindi inscription* 13 *to* 14 *mm long*
4 **23** ½ a. blue-green . . . . 35·00
a. Opt double, one albino . . 50·00
b. Hindi inscr 15 to 15½ mm long . . 85·00
ba. Opt double, one albino . . £120
c. Pair. Nos. 4/4b £400
5 **25** 1 a. brown-purple . . . . 42·00
a. Opt double, one albino . . 48·00
b. Hindi inscr 15 to 15½ mm long . . 85·00
ba. Opt double, one albino . . 95·00
c. Pair. Nos. 5/5b £400
6 **26** 1 a. 6 p. sepia . . . . 50·00
b. Hindi inscr 15 to 15½ mm long . . £140
c. Pair. Nos. 6/6b £450
7 **27** 2 a. dull blue . . . . 42·00
b. Hindi inscr 15 to 15½ mm long . . 95·00
c. Pair. Nos. 7/7b £300
8 **17** 4 a. green . . . . . . 60·00
b. Hindi inscr 15 to 15½ mm long . . £140
c. Pair. Nos. 8/8b £500
9 **21** 6 a. olive-bistre . . . . 60·00
a. Opt double, one albino . . 70·00
b. Hindi inscr 15 to 15½ mm long . . £140
ba. Opt double, one albino . . £160
c. Pair. Nos. 9/9b £500
10 **31** 8 a. dull mauve . . . . 55·00
b. Hindi inscr 15 to 15½ mm long . . £140
c. Pair. Nos. 10/10b £500
11 **33** 1 r. slate . . . . . . 55·00
b. Hindi inscr 15 to 15½ mm long . . £140
c. Pair. Nos. 11/11b £500
4/11 . . . . . . *Set of* 8 £350
4b/11b . . . . . . *Set of* 8 £850

The two types of overprint on these stamps occur in the same settings, with about a quarter of the stamps in each sheet showing the long inscription. Nos. 4/7 and 10/11 were overprinted in sheets of 240 and Nos. 8/9 in half-sheets of 160.

II. *Optd with T* 2. *Hindi inscription* 13 *to* 14 *mm long*
(*a*) *In red* (Sept 1885)
12 **23** ½ a. blue-green 30 20
b. Hindi inscr 15 to 15½ mm long . . 45 55
c. Pair. Nos. 12/12b . . . . 8·00 10·00
13 **27** 2 a. dull blue . . . . 9·00 9·50
b. Hindi inscr 15 to 15½ mm long . . 23·00 25·00
c. Pair. Nos. 13/13b £250
14 **17** 4 a. green . . . . . . 16·00 9·00
b. Hindi inscr 15 to 15½ mm long . . £140 75·00
c. Pair. Nos. 14/14b £400

15 **33** 1 r. slate .. .. 7·50 16·00
aw. Wmk inverted .. .. .. 15·00 25·00
b. Hindi inscr 15 to 15½ mm long .. 25·00 55·00
bw. Wmk inverted .. .. .. 38·00 75·00
c. Pair. Nos. 15/15b .. .. .. 45·00 85·00
cw. Wmk inverted .. .. .. 65·00
12/15 .. .. *Set of* 4 29·00 30·00
12b/15b .. .. .. *Set of* 4 £170 £140

No. 14 was overprinted in half-sheets of 160, about 40 stamps having the Hindi inscription 15 to 15½ mm long. The remaining three values were from a setting of 240 containing 166 13 to 14 mm long and 74 15 to 15½ mm long.

Reprints have been made of Nos. 12 to 15, but the majority of the specimens have the word "REPRINT" overprinted upon them.

(*b*) *In black* (1885–97)

16 **23** ½ a. blue-green (1889) .. .. .. 80 1·10
a. Opt double .. .. ..
b. Opt double, one albino .. .. 20·00
c. Hindi inscr 15 to 15½ mm long .. 20 10
ca. Opt double .. .. ..
cb. Opt double, one albino .. .. 60·00
cc. "GWALICR" .. .. .. 85·00 £100
cd. Small "G" .. .. 60·00 48·00
ce. Small "R" .. .. 65·00
cf. Tall "R" .. .. 65·00 65·00
d. Pair. Nos. 16/16c .. .. .. 45·00
17 **24** 9 p. carmine (1891) .. .. .. 27·00 50·00
a. Opt double, one albino .. .. 50·00
c. Hindi inscr 15 to 15½ mm long .. 45·00 65·00
ca. Opt double, one albino .. .. 80·00
d. Pair. Nos. 17/17c £180
18 **25** 1 a. brown-purple 35 15
c. Hindi inscr 15 to 15½ mm long .. 1·40 35
d. Pair. Nos. 18/18c .. .. .. 10·00 11·00
19 1 a. plum (*Hindi inscr 15 to 15½ mm long*) .. .. 1·40 10
a. Small "G" .. .. 70·00 50·00
b. Small "R" .. .. 80·00
c. Tall "R" .. .. 85·00
20 **26** 1 a. 6 p. sepia 30 80
c. Hindi inscr 15 to 15½ mm long .. 65 40
d. Pair. Nos. 20/20c .. .. .. 10·00 13·00
21 **27** 2 a. dull blue .. .. 3·75 80
c. Hindi inscr 15 to 15½ mm long .. 50 10
ca. "R" omitted £450 £450
d. Pair. Nos. 21/21c .. .. .. 95·00
22 2 a. deep blue .. .. 4·50 1·60
c. Hindi inscr 15 to 15½ mm long .. 1·40 30
ca. Small "G" £120 £120
cb. Small "R" £160
cc. Tall "R" £170 £170
d. Pair. Nos. 22/22c £110
23 **36** 2 a. 6 p. yellow-green (*Hindi inscr 15 to 15½ mm long*) (1896) .. .. 4·50 13·00
a. "GWALICR" £475
24 **28** 3 a. orange .. .. 4·00 7·50
a. Opt double, one albino .. .. 40·00
c. Hindi inscr 15 to 15½ mm long .. 40·00 27·00
ca. Opt double, one albino .. ..
d. Pair. Nos. 24/24c £170
25 3 a. brown-orange .. .. .. 16·00 3·00
c. Hindi inscr 15 to 15½ mm long .. 50 15
ca. Opt double, one albino .. .. 30·00
cb. Small "G" £190 £190
cc. Small "R" £350
cd. Tall "R" £160 £160
d. Pair. Nos. 25/25c £150
26 **29** 4 a. olive-green (1889) .. .. .. 3·00 80
c. Hindi inscr 15 to 15½ mm long .. 7·00 2·50
d. Pair. Nos. 26/26c £100
27 4 a. slate-green .. .. 4·00 1·25
c. Hindi inscr 15 to 15½ mm long .. 1·50 45
ca. Opt double, one albino .. .. 50·00
cb. Small "G" £375 £225
cc. Small "R" £375
cd. Tall "R" £250 £250
d. Pair. Nos. 27/27c .. .. .. 32·00
28 **21** 6 a. olive-bistre .. .. 4·50 8·50
c. Hindi inscr 15 to 15½ mm long .. 1·75 8·50
d. Pair. Nos. 28/28c .. .. .. 38·00
29 6 a. bistre-brown .. .. 1·00 4·50
c. Hindi inscr 15 to 15½ mm long .. 3·00 6·00
d. Pair. Nos. 29/29c .. .. .. 18·00
30 **31** 8 a. dull mauve .. .. 7·00 30·00
c. Hindi inscr 15 to 15½ mm long .. 1·75 60
d. Pair. Nos. 30/30c £190
31 8 a. magenta (*Hindi inscr 15 to 15½ mm long*) (1897) .. .. .. 5·00 6·50
32 **32** 12 a. purple/*red* (1891) .. .. .. 3·00 8·00
c. Hindi inscr 15 to 15½ mm long .. 2·50 65
ca. Pair, one without opt .. ..
cb. Tall "R" £600 £475
d. Pair. Nos. 32/32c .. .. .. 55·00
33 **33** 1 r. slate (1889) £100 £300
c. Hindi inscr 15 to 15½ mm long .. 1·40 85
d. Pair. Nos. 33/33c £350
34 **37** 1 r. green and carmine (*Hindi inscr 15 to 15½ mm long*) (1896) .. .. 2·25 2·75
a. Opt double, one albino .. .. 60·00
b. "GWALICR" £700 £850
35 **38** 2 r. carmine and yellow-brown (*Hindi inscr 15 to 15½ mm long*) (1896) .. 5·00 3·00
a. Small "G" £225 £170
b. Small "R" £225 £180
36 3 r. brown and green (*Hindi inscr 15 to 15½ mm long*) (1896) .. .. 7·00 3·50
a. Small "G" £250 £180
b. Small "R" £275 £190
37 5 r. ultramarine and violet (*Hindi inscr 15 to 15½ mm long*) (1896) .. .. 12·00 6·50
a. Small "G" £300 £200
b. Small "R" £325 £225
16/37 .. .. *Set of* 16 60·00 75·00

Printings to 1891 continued to use the setting showing both types, but subsequently a new setting containing the larger overprint only was used.

The ½ a., 1 a., 2 a. and 3 a. exist with space between "I" and "O" of "GWALIOR".

The "GWALICR" error occurs on R. 1/5 in the May 1896 printing only.

Maharaja Madhav Rao Sindhia, 1886–1925

1899–1911. (*a*) *Optd with T* **2** (B).
38 **40** 3 p. carmine 10 20
a. Opt inverted £650 £425
b. Small "G" .. .. 50·00 55·00
d. Small "R" .. .. 60·00
e. Tall "R" .. .. 40·00
f. Opt double, one albino .. .. 30·00
39 3 p. grey (1904) .. .. .. 6·00 60·00
e. Tall "R" £200
f. Opt double, one albino .. .. 50·00
40 **23** ½ a. pale yellow-green (1901) .. .. 20 1·00
e. Tall "R" .. .. 75·00
f. Opt double, one albino .. .. 20·00
40*g* ½ a. yellow-green (1903) .. .. 2·00 1·50
ge. Tall "R" £110
41 **25** 1 a. carmine (1901) 40 35
e. Tall "R" .. .. 85·00
f. Opt double, one albino .. .. 35·00
42 **27** 2 a. pale violet (1903) .. .. .. 60 3·25
e. Tall "R" £130
43 **36** 2 a. 6 p. ultramarine (1903) .. .. 85 3·75
e. Tall "R" £170
38/43 .. .. *Set of* 6 7·25 65·00

(*b*) *Optd as T* **2**, *but "GWALIOR" 13 mm long. Opt spaced 2¾ mm*
44 **38** 3 r. brown and green (1911) £150 £160
45 5 r. ultramarine and violet (1910) .. 55·00 55·00
a. Opt double, one albino .. .. 80·00

1903–11. *King Edward VII. Optd as T* **2**.

A. "GWALIOR" 14 *mm long. Overprint spaced* 1¾ *mm* (1903–06)
46A **41** 3 p. pale grey 45 20
e. Tall "R" .. .. 27·00 29·00
f. Slate-grey (1905) 60 25
fe. Tall "R" .. .. 32·00 35·00
48A **42** ½ a. green 10 10
e. Tall "R" .. .. 26·00 28·00
49A **43** 1 a. carmine 10 10
e. Tall "R" .. .. 30·00 35·00
f. Opt double, one albino .. .. 30·00
50A **44** 2 a. pale violet (1904) 60 60
e. Tall "R" .. .. 70·00
f. Mauve .. .. 1·00 20
fe. Tall "R" .. .. 80·00 80·00
52A **45** 2 a. 6 p. ultramarine (1904) .. .. 15·00 55·00
e. Tall "R" £650
53A **46** 3 a. orange-brown (1904) .. .. 1·00 30
e. Tall "R" £120
54A **47** 4 a. olive .. .. 1·10 40
e. Tall "R" £150 £130
f. Pale olive .. .. 5·50 1·60
fe. Tall "R" £200
56A **48** 6 a. olive-bistre (1904) .. .. .. 2·25 2·75
e. Tall "R" £700
57A **49** 8 a. purple (*shades*) (1905) .. .. 2·75 1·25
e. Tall "R" £300 £190
59A **50** 12 a. purple/*red* (1905) .. .. .. 2·50 12·00
e. Tall "R" £750
60A **51** 1 r. green and carmine (1905) .. .. 1·50 1·75
e. Tall "R" £650
61A **52** 2 r. carmine and yellow-brown (1906) 30·00 42·00
a. Opt double, one albino .. .. 50·00
46A/61A .. .. .. *Set of* 12 50·00 £100

B. "GWALIOR" 13 *mm long. Overprint spaced* 2¾ *mm* (1908–11)
46B **41** 3 p. pale grey .. .. 1·25 10
f. Slate-grey .. .. 1·50 90
49B **43** 1 a. carmine .. .. 1·60 80
50*f*B 2 a. mauve .. .. 1·50 15
52B **45** 2 a. 6 p. ultramarine .. .. .. 60 5·50
53B **46** 3 a. orange-brown .. .. .. 1·60 20
54*f*B 4 a. pale olive .. .. 3·00 50
56B **48** 6 a. olive-bistre .. .. 3·25 80
57B **49** 8 a. purple (*shades*) .. .. .. 4·50 1·50
f. Claret .. .. 11·00 2·25
fa. Opt double, one albino .. .. 40·00
59B **50** 12 a. purple/*red* .. .. 3·00 3·25
f. Opt double, one albino .. .. 50·00
60B **51** 1 r. green and carmine .. .. .. 2·50 1·00
61B **52** 2 r. carmine and yellow-brown .. 7·50 11·00
a. Opt double, one albino .. .. 40·00
62B 3 r. brown and green (1910) .. .. 24·00 40·00
a. Red-brown and green .. .. 60·00 70·00
63B 5 r. ultramarine and violet (1911) .. 17·00 25·00
46B/63B .. .. .. *Set of* 13 60·00 80·00

1907–08. *Nos.* 149 *and* 150 *of India optd as T* **2**.

(*a*) "GWALIOR" 14 *mm long. Overprint spaced* 1¾ *mm*
64 **53** ½ a. green 10 70
e. Tall "R" .. .. 40·00

(*b*) "GWALIOR" 13 *mm long. Overprint spaced* 2¾ *mm* (1908)
65 **53** ½ a. green 40 15
66 **54** 1 a. carmine 75 10

1912–14. *King George V. Optd as T* **2**.
67 **55** 3 p. slate-grey 10 10
a. Opt double .. .. † £750
b. "Rs" flaw .. .. 23·00 27·00
68 **56** ½ a. green 20 10
a. Opt inverted .. .. † £375
69 **57** 1 a. aniline carmine 25 10
a. Opt double .. .. 25·00
70 **59** 2 a. mauve 40 10
w. Wmk inverted .. .. .. † 55·00
71 **62** 3 a. orange-brown 40 15
72 **63** 4 a. olive (1913) 50 60
73 **64** 6 a. olive-bistre 70 75
74 **65** 8 a. purple (1913) 80 30
75 **66** 12 a. dull claret (1914) .. .. .. 95 2·00
76 **67** 1 r. brown and green (1913) .. .. 2·50 40
a. Opt double, one albino .. .. 20·00
b. Opt double £600
77 2 r. carmine-rose and brown (1913) .. 4·50 4·25
a. Opt double, one albino .. .. 50·00
78 5 r. ultramarine and violet (1913) .. 18·00 6·50
a. Opt double, one albino .. .. 70·00
67/78 .. .. *Set of* 12 27·00 14·00

GWALIOR
(3)

1921. *No.* 192 *of India optd with T* **3**.
79 **57** 9 p. on 1 a. rose-carmine 10 40

No. 79 with inverted overprint is of clandestine origin.

1923–7. *Optd as T* **2**. *New colours and values.*
80 **57** 1 a. chocolate 20 10
a. Opt double, one albino .. .. 30·00
81 **58** 1½ a. chocolate (B) (1925) 70 50
82 1½ a. rose-carmine (B) (1927) 15 20
83 **61** 2 a. 6 p. ultramarine (1925) .. .. 1·00 1·75
84 2 a. 6 p. orange (1927) 20 50
85 **62** 3 a. ultramarine (1924) 40 60
80/5 .. .. *Set of* 6 2·40 3·25

No. 82 with inverted overprint is of clandestine origin.

Maharaja George Jivaji Rao Sindhia, 1925–1961

GWALIOR
गवालियर
(4)

GWALIOR
गवालियर
(5)

1928–36. *King George V (Nasik printing, wmk Mult Star), optd at Nasik with T* **4** *or* **5** *(rupee values).*
86 **55** 3 p. slate (1932) 50 10
w. Wmk inverted .. .. 1·00 1·00
87 **56** ½ a. green (1930) .. .. 1·00 10
w. Wmk inverted .. ..
88 **80** 9 p. deep green (1932) .. .. .. 1·25 20
w. Wmk inverted .. .. .. 2·00 60
89 **57** 1 a. chocolate 40 10
w. Wmk inverted .. .. — 50
90 **82** 1 a. 3 p. mauve (1936) 30 10
91 **70** 2 a. purple 45 20
w. Wmk inverted 45 20
92 **62** 3 a. bright blue 60 40
93 **71** 4 a. sage-green 80 90
w. Wmk inverted .. .. .. 1·25 1·60
94 **65** 8 a. reddish purple (*wmk inverted*) .. 1·00 1·10
95 **66** 12 a. claret .. .. 1·10 1·90
96 **67** 1 r. chocolate and green .. .. 1·40 2·50
w. Wmk inverted .. .. .. 2·50 2·50
97 2 r. carmine and orange .. .. 3·00 3·00
w. Wmk inverted .. .. .. 5·00 3·50
98 5 r. ultramarine and purple (*wmk inverted*) (1929) .. .. .. 13·00 20·00
99 10 r. green and scarlet (1930) .. .. 40·00 30·00
100 15 r. blue & olive (*wmk inverted*) (1930) 65·00 48·00
101 25 r. orange and blue (1930) £130 £100
86/101 .. .. *Set of* 16 £225 £180

The 9 p. exists printed by lithography or typography.

1935–36. *New types and colours. Optd with T* **4**.
102 **79** ½ a. green (1936) 20 10
w. Wmk inverted .. .. .. 2·25 1·60
103 **81** 1 a. chocolate 10 10
104 **59** 2 a. vermilion (1936) .. .. .. 35 1·40
102/4 .. .. *Set of* 3 60 1·50

1938–48. *King George VI. Nos.* 247/50, 253, 255/6, *and* 259/64 *optd with T* **4** *or* **5** *(rupee values).*
105 **91** 3 p. slate .. .. 3·25 10
106 ½ a. red-brown .. .. 3·75 10
107 9 p. green (1939) .. .. 32·00 2·50
108 1 a. carmine .. .. 3·25 15
109 – 3 a. yellow-green (1939) .. .. .. 9·00 2·50
110 – 4 a. brown .. .. 38·00 1·50
111 – 6 a. turquoise-green (1939) .. .. 2·50 5·50
112 **93** 1 r. grey and red-brown (1942) .. 5·00 1·50
113 2 r. purple and brown (1948) .. .. 26·00 6·00
114 5 r. green and blue (1948) .. .. 38·00 30·00
115 10 r. purple and claret (1948) .. .. 38·00 38·00
116 15 r. brown and green (1948) £120 £150
117 25 r. slate-violet and purple (1948) .. £110 £120
105/117 .. .. *Set of* 13 £375 £300

1942–5. *King George VI. Optd with T* **4**.
118 **100*a*** 3 p. slate 45 10
w. Wmk inverted .. .. — 12·00
119 ½ a. purple (1943) 45 10
120 9 p. green 45 10
121 1 a. carmine (1943) 40 10
a. Opt double .. .. — £120
122 **101** 1½ a. dull violet .. .. 3·25 20
123 2 a. vermilion 55 20
124 3 a. bright violet .. .. 5·50 30
a. Opt double .. .. — £120
125 **102** 4 a. brown .. .. 1·25 20
126 6 a. turquoise-green (1945) .. .. 20·00 17·00
127 8 a. slate-violet (1944) .. .. .. 2·75 2·75
128 12 a. lake (1943) .. .. 4·50 15·00
118/28 .. .. *Set of* 11 35·00 32·00

The 1½ a. and 3 a. exist printed by lithography or typography.

GWALIOR
गवालियर
(6)

1949 (Apr). *King George VI. Optd with T* **6** *at the Alizah Printing Press, Gwalior.*
129 **100*a*** 3 p. slate 60 50
130 ½ a. purple 60 50
131 1 a. carmine 75 60
132 **101** 2 a. vermilion .. .. 14·00 1·50
133 3 a. bright violet .. .. 35·00 20·00
134 **102** 4 a. brown .. .. 2·25 2·50
135 6 a. turquoise-green .. .. .. 32·00 42·00
136 8 a. slate-violet .. .. 75·00 42·00
137 12 a. lake £275 £120
129/137 .. .. *Set of* 9 £400 £200

OFFICIAL STAMPS

गवालियर

गवालियर

सरविस (O 1)   सरविस (O 2)

1895–96. *Queen Victoria. Optd with Type* O 1.
O 1 **23** ½ a. blue-green 10 10
a. Hindi characters transposed .. 24·00 28·00
b. 4th Hindi character omitted .. £350 40·00
c. Opt double .. .. † £800
O 2 **25** 1 a. brown-purple .. .. 6·00 60
O 3 1 a. plum 65 10
a. Hindi characters transposed .. 38·00 42·00
b. 4th Hindi character omitted .. — 65·00
O 4 **27** 2 a. dull blue .. .. 1·00 35
O 5 2 a. deep blue .. .. 1·00 35
a. Hindi characters transposed .. 60·00 80·00
b. 4th Hindi character omitted .. 80·00 £100
O 6 **29** 4 a. olive-green .. .. 1·50 75
a. Hindi characters transposed .. £425 £425
b. 4th Hindi character omitted .. £1700 £1200
O 7 4 a. slate-green .. .. 1·10 85
a. Hindi characters transposed .. £300
O 8 **31** 8 a. dull mauve .. .. 1·50 1·50
a. Opt double, one albino .. .. 30·00
O 9 8 a. magenta .. .. 1·10 70
a. Hindi characters transposed .. £1100 £1200
b. 4th Hindi character omitted ..
O10 **37** 1 r. green and carmine (1896) .. 3·50 3·00
a. Hindi characters transposed .. £2250
O1/10 .. .. *Set of* 6 6·75 4·50

In the errors listed above it is the last two Hindi characters that are transposed, so that the word reads "Sersiv". The error occurs on R.19/1 in the sheet from the early printings up to May 1896.

1901–04. *Colours changed.*
O23 **40** 3 p. carmine (1902) 30 20
O24 3 p. grey (1904) .. .. 90 1·60
O25 **23** ½ a. pale yellow-green .. .. .. 2·75 15
O26 ½ a. yellow-green 20 10
O27 **25** 1 a. carmine .. .. 3·00 10
O28 **27** 2 a. pale violet (1903) .. .. .. 55 1·50
O23/8 .. .. *Set of* 5 4·50 3·00

1903–08. *King Edward VII. Optd as Type* O 1.
(*a*) *Overprint spaced* 10 *mm* (1903–5)
O29 **41** 3 p. pale grey 30 10
a. Slate-grey (1905) 30 10
O31 **42** ½ a. green .. .. 1·60 10
O32 **43** 1 a. carmine 40 10
O33 **44** 2 a. pale violet (1905) .. .. .. 1·60 50
a. Mauve 90 20
O35 **47** 4 a. olive (1905) .. .. 9·50 90
a. Opt double, one albino .. .. 40·00
O36 **49** 8 a. purple (1905) .. .. 3·00 70
a. Claret .. .. 9·50 3·50
ab. Opt double, one albino .. .. 30·00
O38 **51** 1 r. green and carmine (1905) .. 2·75 1·40
O29/38 .. .. *Set of* 7 17·00 3·00

(*b*) *Overprint spaced* 8 *mm* (1907–8)
O39 **41** 3 p. pale grey .. .. 2·75 15
a. Slate-grey .. .. 4·25 80
O41 **42** ½ a. green .. .. 1·50 15
O42 **43** 1 a. carmine 50 10
O43 **44** 2 a. mauve .. .. 9·00 65
O44 **47** 4 a. olive .. .. 2·50 75
O45 **49** 8 a. purple .. .. 3·25 3·75
O46 **51** 1 r. green and carmine (1908) .. 24·00 9·00
O39/46 .. .. *Set of* 7 40·00 13·00

1907–08. *Nos.* 149 *and* 150 *of India optd as Type* O 1.
(*a*) *Overprint spaced* 10 *mm* (1908)
O47 **53** ½ a. green .. .. 4·25 10
O48 **54** 1 a. carmine .. .. 3·50 15
a. Opt double, one albino .. .. 30·00
(*b*) *Overprint spaced* 8 *mm* (1907)
O49 **53** ½ a. green 65 15
O50 **54** 1 a. carmine .. .. 40·00 3·00

1913–23. *King George V. Optd with Type* O 1.
O51 **55** 3 p. slate-grey 20 10
a. "Rs" flaw .. .. 45·00
O52 **56** ½ a. green 20 10
a. Opt double .. .. 95·00 £140
O53 **57** 1 a. rose-carmine .. .. 6·50 40
a. Aniline carmine 20 10
ab. Opt double .. .. 65·00
O54 1 a. chocolate (1923) .. .. .. 2·25 15
O55 **59** 2 a. mauve 45 20
O56 **63** 4 a. olive 55 80
O57 **65** 8 a. purple 75 80
O58 **67** 1 r. brown and green .. .. .. 14·00 13·00
a. Opt double, one albino .. .. 50·00
O51/8 .. .. *Set of* 8 17·00 14·00

1921. *No.* O97 *of India optd with T* 3.
O59 **57** 9 p. on 1 a. rose-carmine 10 30

1927–35. *King George V* (*Nasik printing, wmk Mult Star*), *optd at Nasik as Type* O 1 (*but top line measures* 13 *mm instead of* 14 *mm*) *or with Type* O 2 (*rupee values*).
O61 **55** 3 p. slate 30 10
w. Wmk inverted 10 50
O62 **56** ½ a. green 10 15
w. Wmk inverted .. .. 1·60
O63 **80** 9 p. deep green (1932) 10 15
O64 **57** 1 a. chocolate 10 10
w. Wmk inverted 50 30
O65 **82** 1 a. 3 p. mauve (1933) 50 15
w. Wmk inverted .. .. 2·25
O66 **70** 2 a. purple 20 15
w. Wmk inverted .. .. 1·60
O67 **71** 4 a. sage-green 50 30
w. Wmk inverted .. .. — 75
O68 **65** 8 a. reddish purple (1928) 50 70
w. Wmk inverted .. .. 1·50 90
O69 **67** 1 r. chocolate and green .. .. 80 1·75
w. Wmk inverted .. .. 1·75 2·25
O70 2 r. carmine and orange (1935) .. 6·00 8·00
O71 5 r. ultramarine and purple (1932) .. 11·00 £120
w. Wmk inverted .. .. 12·00
O72 10 r. green and scarlet (1932) .. .. 85·00 £250
O61/72 .. .. *Set of* 12 95·00 £350

1936–37. *New types. Optd as Type* O 1 (13 *mm*).
O73 **79** ½ a. green 15 15
w. Wmk inverted .. .. — 2·25
O74 **81** 1 a. chocolate 15 15
O75 **59** 2 a. vermilion 20 35
O76 2 a. vermilion (*small die*) .. .. 2·00 1·10
O77 **63** 4 a. sage-green (1937) 50 60
O73/7 .. .. *Set of* 5 2·50 2·10

1938. *King George VI. Optd as Type* O 1 (13 *mm*).
O78 **91** ½ a. red-brown .. .. 6·50 30
O79 1 a. carmine .. .. 1·10 20

गवालियर (O 3)   1A ——— 1A (O 4)

1940–42. *Official stamps optd with Type* O 3.
O80 **O 20** 3 p. slate 50 10
O81 ½ a. red-brown .. .. 3·00 25
O82 ½ a. purple (1942) 50 10
O83 9 p. green (1942) 70 50
O84 1 a. carmine .. .. 2·25 10
O85 1 a. 3 p. yellow-brown (1942) .. 28·00 1·60
w. Wmk inverted .. .. — 12·00
O86 1½ a. dull violet (1942) .. .. .. 1·00 30
O87 2 a. vermilion .. .. 1·00 30
O88 4 a. brown (1942) .. .. 1·25 1·50
O89 8 a. slate-violet (1942) .. .. .. 2·50 5·50
O80/9 .. .. *Set of* 10 35·00 9·00

1941. *Stamp of* 1932 (*King George V*) *optd with Type* O 1 *and surch with Type* O 4.
O90 **82** 1 a. on 1 a. 3 p. mauve .. .. 16·00 2·50
w. Wmk inverted .. .. 21·00 4·50

1942–47. *King George VI. Optd with Type* O 2.
O91 **93** 1 r. grey and red-brown .. .. 8·00 13·00
O92 2 r. purple and brown .. .. .. 20·00 65·00
O93 5 r. green and blue (1943) .. .. 38·00 £350
O94 10 r. purple and claret (1947) £110 £700
O91/4 .. .. *Set of* 4 £160 £1000

Gwalior became part of Madhya Bharat by 1 July 1948.

JIND

For earlier issues, see under INDIAN FEUDATORY STATES

PRICES FOR STAMPS ON COVER	
Nos. 1/4	*from* × 20
Nos. 5/16	—
Nos. 17/40	*from* × 15
Nos. 41/149	*from* × 8
Nos. O1/86	*from* × 15

Raja Raghubir Singh, 1864–1887

JHIND STATE (1)   JEEND STATE (2)   JHIND STATE (3)

1885 (1 July). *Queen Victoria. Optd with T* 1.
1 **23** ½ a. blue-green .. .. 1·25 2·50
a. Opt inverted .. .. 85·00 90·00
2 **25** 1 a. brown-purple .. .. 20·00 28·00
a. Opt inverted £600 £650
3 **27** 2 a. dull blue .. .. 6·50 11·00
a. Opt inverted £500 £550
4 **17** 4 a. green .. .. 40·00 55·00
5 **31** 8 a. dull mauve £375
a. Opt inverted £7500
6 **33** 1 r. slate £400
a. Opt inverted £8500
1/6 .. .. *Set of* 6 £750

The overprint inverted errors occurred on R.10/8 in the setting of 120, although it is believed that one pane of the ½ a. had the overprint inverted on the entire pane. Examples of inverted overprints on the ½ a., 1 a. and 2 a. with the lines much less curved are thought to come from a trial printing.

All six values exist with reprinted overprint. This has the words "JHIND" and "STATE" 8 and 9 mm in length respectively, whereas in the originals the words are 9 and 9½ mm.

1885. *Optd with T* 2.
7 **23** ½ a. blue-green (R.) .. .. .. 75·00
8 **25** 1 a. brown-purple .. .. 80·00
9 **27** 2 a. dull blue (R.) .. .. 80·00
10 **17** 4 a. green (R.) £110
a. Opt double, one albino £140
11 **31** 8 a. dull mauve £110
12 **33** 1 r. slate (R.) £120
7/12 .. .. *Set of* 6 £500

1886. *Optd with T* 3, *in red.*
13 **23** ½ a. blue-green .. .. 19·00
a. "JEIND" for "JHIND" £900
14 **27** 2 a. dull blue .. .. 19·00
a. "JEIND" for "JHIND" £1100
b. Opt double, one albino .. .. 50·00
15 **17** 4 a. green .. .. 35·00
a. Opt double, one albino .. .. 40·00
b. Opt treble, two albino .. .. 60·00
16 **33** 1 r. slate .. .. 38·00
a. "JEIND" for "JHIND" £1600
13/16 .. .. *Set of* 4 £100

1886–99. *Optd with T* 3.
17 **23** ½ a. blue-green 15 10
a. Opt inverted £190
18 **25** 1 a. brown-purple 55 20
a. "JEIND" for "JHIND" £400
b. Opt double, one albino .. .. 30·00
19 1 a. plum (1899) .. .. 1·75 90
20 **26** 1 a. 6 p. sepia (1896) .. .. .. 90 2·25
a. Opt double, one albino .. .. 35·00
21 **27** 2 a. dull blue .. .. 1·00 40
22 2 a. ultramarine .. .. 1·10 50
a. Opt double, one albino .. .. 35·00
23 **28** 3 a. brown-orange (1891) .. .. 1·00 50
24 **29** 4 a. olive-green .. .. 2·25 1·50
25 4 a. slate-green .. .. 2·50 2·50
26 **21** 6 a. olive-bistre (1891) .. .. .. 5·00 12·00
a. Opt double, one albino .. .. 30·00
27 6 a. bistre-brown .. .. 90 6·50
28 **31** 8 a. dull mauve .. .. 3·50 10·00
a. "JEIND" for "JHIND" £1400
29 8 a. magenta (1897) .. .. .. 5·00 16·00
a. Opt double, one albino .. .. 30·00
30 **32** 12 a. purple/*red* (1896) .. .. .. 3·50 15·00
a. Opt double, one albino .. .. 30·00
31 **33** 1 r. slate .. .. 6·00 30·00
32 **37** 1 r. green and carmine (1897) .. 6·50 35·00
33 **38** 2 r. carmine and yellow-brown (1896) .. £200 £600
34 3 r. brown and green (1896) £350 £600
35 5 r. ultramarine and violet (1896) .. £400 £600
17/35 .. .. *Set of* 14 £850 £1700

Varieties exist in which the word "JHIND" measures 10½ mm and 9¾ mm instead of 10 mm. Such varieties are to be found on Nos. 17, 18, 21, 24, 28 and 31.

Raja (Maharaja from 1911) Ranbir Singh, 1887–1959

1900–4. *Colours changed.*
36 **40** 3 p. carmine .. .. 70 1·00
37 3 p. grey (1904) .. .. 15 2·25
38 **23** ½ a. pale yellow-green (1902) .. .. 2·25 3·75
39 ½ a. yellow-green (1903) .. .. .. 5·00 8·50
40 **25** 1 a. carmine (1902) .. .. 20 3·75
a. Opt double, one albino .. .. 25·00
36/40 .. .. *Set of* 4 3·00 9·75

1903–9. *King Edward VII. Optd with T* 3.
41 **41** 3 p. pale grey 10 10
a. Opt double, one albino .. .. 15·00
42 3 p. slate-grey (1905) 20 50
43 **42** ½ a. green .. .. 40 1·25
44 **43** 1 a. carmine .. .. 1·75 1·00
45 **44** 2 a. pale violet .. .. 1·75 1·90
46 2 a. mauve (1906) .. .. 1·25 55
a. Opt double, one albino .. .. 25·00
47 **45** 2 a. 6 p. ultramarine (1909) .. .. 30 4·50
a. Opt double, one albino .. .. 20·00
48 **46** 3 a. orange-brown 35 35
a. Opt double £110 £200
49 **47** 4 a. olive .. .. 5·00 7·50
a. Opt double, one albino .. .. 40·00
50 4 a. pale olive .. .. 4·50 6·50
51 **48** 6 a. bistre (1905) .. .. 4·50 13·00
a. Opt double, one albino .. .. 30·00
52 **49** 8 a. purple (*shades*) .. .. .. 2·00 16·00
53 8 a. claret .. .. 8·50 20·00
54 **50** 12 a. purple/*red* (1905) .. .. .. 1·75 10·00
55 **51** 1 r. green and carmine (1905) .. 2·25 11·00
a. Opt double, one albino .. .. 40·00
41/55 .. .. *Set of* 11 17·00 55·00

1907–9. *Nos.* 149/50 *of India optd with T* 3.
56 **53** ½ a. green 10 20
57 **54** 1 a. carmine (1909) 10 55

1913. *King George V. Optd with T* 3.
58 **55** 3 p. slate-grey .. .. 10 1·60
59 **56** ½ a. green 10 60
60 **57** 1 a. aniline carmine 10 35
61 **59** 2 a. mauve .. .. 15 3·50
62 **62** 3 a. orange-brown .. .. 1·50 8·00
63 **64** 6 a. olive-bistre .. .. 4·00 20·00
58/63 .. .. *Set of* 6 5·50 30·00

JIND STATE (4)   JIND STATE (5)   JIND STATE (6)

1914–27. *King George V. Optd with T* 4.
64 **55** 3 p. slate-grey 40 20
65 **56** ½ a. green .. .. 1·25 15
66 **57** 1 a. aniline carmine 50 15
67 **58** 1½ a. chocolate (Type A) (1922) .. 60 3·00
68 1½ a. chocolate (Type B) (1924) .. 35 1·50
69 **59** 2 a. mauve .. .. 1·00 45
70 **61** 2 a. 6 p. ultramarine (1922) .. .. 35 3·75
71 **62** 3 a. orange-brown .. .. 50 2·00
72 **63** 4 a. olive .. .. 95 4·50
73 **64** 6 a. olive-bistre .. .. 1·10 9·00
74 **65** 8 a. purple .. .. 3·00 5·00
75 **66** 12 a. dull claret .. .. 1·25 9·00
76 **67** 1 r. brown and green .. .. .. 5·50 11·00
a. Opt double, one albino .. .. 25·00
77 2 r. carmine and yellow-brown (1927) .. 4·00 80·00
78 5 r. ultramarine and violet (1927) .. 27·00 £160
64/78 .. .. *Set of* 15 42·00 £250

No. 71 with inverted overprint is of clandestine origin.

1922. *No. 192 of India optd "JIND" in block capitals.*
79 **57** 9 p. on 1 a. rose-carmine .. .. .. 1·25 13·00

1924–27. *Optd with T* **4**. *New colours.*
80 **57** 1 a. chocolate .. .. 2·75 1·00
81 **58** 1½ a. rose-carmine (Type B) (1927) .. 20 1·50
82 **61** 2 a. 6 p. orange (1927) .. .. 30 4·75
83 **62** 3 a. bright blue (1925) .. .. 1·00 3·25
80/3 .. .. *Set of* 4 3·75 9·50
Nos. 81/2 with inverted overprint are of clandestine origin.

1927–37. *King George V (Nasik printing, wmk Mult Star), optd at Nasik with T* **5** *or* **6** *(rupee values).*
84 **55** 3 p. slate 10 10
w. Wmk inverted .. .. .. 1·60
85 **56** ½ a. green (1929) 10 35
86 **80** 9 p. deep green (1932) 40 40
87 **57** 1 a. chocolate (1928) 15 10
w. Wmk inverted .. .. .. — 1·10
88 **82** 1 a. 3 p. mauve (1932) 20 30
89 **58** 1½ a. rose-carmine (Type B) (1930) .. 35 1·40
w. Wmk inverted .. .. .. 90 1·50
90 **70** 2 a. purple (1928) 90 30
w. Wmk inverted .. .. .. 1·00 30
91 **61** 2 a. 6 p. orange (1930) 70
w. Wmk inverted .. .. .. 70 6·50
92 **62** 3 a. bright blue (1930) .. .. 1·75 7·00
w. Wmk inverted .. .. .. 6·00
93 **83** 3 a. 6 p. ultramarine (1937) .. .. 1·50
w. Wmk inverted .. .. .. 50 11·00
94 **71** 4 a. sage-green (1928) .. .. 2·75 1·40
w. Wmk inverted .. .. .. 90 1·40
95 **64** 6 a. bistre (1937) .. .. .. 55 12·00
w. Wmk inverted .. .. .. 3·25
96 **65** 8 a. reddish purple (1930) .. .. 1·75 1·90
w. Wmk inverted .. .. .. 1·75
97 **66** 12 a. claret (1930) .. .. ..
w. Wmk inverted .. .. .. 2·75 13·00
98 **67** 1 r. chocolate and green (1930) .. 2·75 3·00
w. Wmk inverted .. .. ..
99 2 r. carmine and orange (1930) .. 22·00 90·00
w. Wmk inverted .. .. .. 11·00
100 5 r. ultramarine and purple (1928) .. 8·00 26·00
w. Wmk inverted .. .. .. 32·00
101 10 r. green and carmine (1928) .. 10·00 18·00
102 15 r. blue & olive (*wmk inverted*) (1929) 60·00 £375
103 25 r. orange and blue (1929) .. .. 90·00 £450
84/103 .. .. *Set of* 20 £160 £850

1934. *New types and colours. Optd with T* **5**.
104 **79** ½ a. green 30 15
105 **81** 1 a. chocolate 70 20
w. Wmk inverted .. .. .. — 2·25
106 **59** 2 a. vermilion 70 50
107 **62** 3 a. carmine .. .. 1·10 40
108 **63** 4 a. sage-green .. .. .. 1·40 75
104/8 .. .. *Set of* 5 3·75 1·75

1937–38. *King George VI. Nos. 247/64 optd with T* **5** *or T* **6** *(rupee values).*
109 **91** 3 p. slate .. .. 5·50 1·00
110 ½ a. red-brown .. .. .. 60 2·25
111 9 p. green (1937) .. .. .. 60 2·00
112 1 a. carmine (1937) 60 35
113 **92** 2 a. vermilion .. .. 1·50 10·00
114 – 2 a. 6 p. bright violet .. .. 1·00 11·00
115 – 3 a. yellow-green .. .. .. 4·50 9·50
116 – 3 a. 6 p. bright blue .. .. 1·50 11·00
117 – 4 a. brown .. .. 5·50 10·00
118 – 6 a. turquoise-green .. .. .. 3·00 14·00
119 – 8 a. slate-violet .. .. .. 2·00 14·00
120 – 12 a. lake .. .. 1·75 16·00
121 **93** 1 r. grey and red-brown .. .. 14·00 26·00
122 2 r. purple and brown .. .. 16·00 75·00
123 5 r. green and blue .. .. .. 30·00 55·00
124 10 r. purple and claret .. .. 55·00 60·00
125 15 r. brown and green £150 £550
126 25 r. slate-violet and purple £325 £550
109/26 .. .. *Set of* 18 £550 £1200

JIND
(7)

1941–43. *King George VI. Optd with T* **7**. *(a) Stamps of* 1937. *W* **69** *(inverted on* 15 *r.).*
127 **91** 3 p. slate .. .. 9·50 13·00
128 ½ a. red-brown .. .. .. 1·00 40
129 9 p. green .. .. 8·50 10·00
130 1 a. carmine .. .. 1·00 3·00
131 **93** 1 r. grey and red-brown .. .. 8·00 19·00
132 2 r. purple and brown .. .. 16·00 24·00
133 5 r. green and blue .. .. .. 38·00 65·00
134 10 r. purple and claret .. .. 55·00 65·00
135 15 r. brown and green £120 £130
136 25 r. slate-violet and purple £100 £325
127/136 .. .. *Set of* 10 £325 £550

(b) Stamps of 1940–43
137 **100a** 3 p. slate (1942) 50 50
138 ½ a. purple (1943) 50 85
139 9 p. green (1942) .. .. .. 60 2·25
140 1 a. carmine (1942) 65 85
141 **101** 1 a. 3 p. yellow-brown .. .. 1·00 2·75
142 1½ a. dull violet (1942) .. .. 5·00 3·50
143 2 a. vermilion .. .. 1·75 2·50
144 3 a. bright violet (1942) .. .. 11·00 2·75
145 3½ a. bright blue .. .. .. 5·00 5·50
146 **102** 4 a. brown .. .. 3·00 2·50
147 6 a. turquoise-green .. .. .. 3·50 8·50
148 8 a. slate-violet .. .. .. 2·50 8·50
149 12 a. lake .. .. 9·50 8·50
137/149 .. .. *Set of* 13 40·00 45·00
The 1½ a. and 3 a. exist printed by lithography or typography.

OFFICIAL STAMPS

SERVICE (O 14) SERVICE (O 15) JHIND STATE SERVICE (O 16)

1885 (1 July). *Queen Victoria. Nos. 1/3 of Jind optd with Type* O **14**.
O1 **23** ½ a. blue-green 30 30
a. Opt Type 1 inverted .. .. 90·00 55·00
O2 **25** 1 a. brown-purple 30 10
a. Opt Type 1 inverted .. .. 9·00 7·00
O3 **27** 2 a. dull blue .. .. 26·00 35·00
a. Opt Type 1 inverted £800
The three values have had the overprint reprinted in the same way as the ordinary stamps of 1885. See note after No. 6.

1885. *Nos. 7/9 of Jind optd with Type* O **15**.
O7 **23** ½ a. blue-green (R.) .. .. .. 75·00
a. "JEEND STATE" double, one albino £100
O8 **25** 1 a. brown-purple .. .. .. 65·00
O9 **27** 2 a. dull blue (R.) .. .. .. 70·00
O7/9 .. .. *Set of* 3 £190

1886. *Optd with Type* O **16**, *in red.*
O10 **23** ½ a. blue-green .. .. .. 12·00
a. "ERVICE" £2750
b. "JEIND" £500
c. "JHIND STATE" double, one albino 50·00
O11 **27** 2 a. dull blue .. .. 15·00
a. "ERVICE" £1700
b. "JEIND" £800
c. "SERVICE" double, one albino .. 30·00
d. "JHIND STATE" double, one albino 30·00

1886–1902. *Optd with Type* O **16**.
O12 **23** ½ a. blue-green 50 10
a. "JHIND STATE" double, one albino 30·00
O13 **25** 1 a. brown-purple .. .. .. 16·00
a. "ERVICE" .. .. ..
b. "JEIND" £400
c. "SERVICE" double, one albino .. 20·00
O14 1 a. plum (1902) .. .. .. 7·00 20
O15 **27** 2 a. dull blue .. .. 1·50 50
a. "SERVICE" double, one albino .. 30·00
b. "SERVICE" treble, two albino .. 35·00
O16 2 a. ultramarine 50 30
a. "JHIND STATE" double, one albino 35·00
O17 **29** 4 a. olive-green (1892) 85 45
a. "JHIND STATE" double, one albino 30·00
O18 4 a. slate-green .. .. .. 1·40 1·10
O19 **31** 8 a. dull mauve (1892) .. .. 2·75 2·00
O20 8 a. magenta (1897) .. .. .. 2·25 4·50
a. "JHIND STATE" double, one albino 30·00
O21 **37** 1 r. green and carmine (1896) .. 6·00 27·00
a. "SERVICE" double, one albino .. 40·00
b. "JHIND STATE" treble, two albino 50·00
O12/21 .. .. *Set of* 6 15·00 28·00
Varieties mentioned in note after No. 35 exist on Nos. O12, O15, O17 and O20.
Printings up to and including that of October 1897 had the "SERVICE" overprint. Type O **15**, applied to sheets already overprinted with Type **3**. From the printing of December 1899 onwards "SERVICE" and "JHIND STATE" were overprinted at one operation, as Type O **16**, to provide fresh supplies of Nos. O12, O14 and O21.

1902. *Colour changed. Optd with Type* O **16**.
O22 **23** ½ a. yellow-green .. .. .. 1·00 20
a. "V" of "SERVICE" omitted .. 70·00 38·00
No. O22a normally shows a tiny trace of the "V" remaining. Examples showing the letter completely missing are worth much more.

1903–6. *King Edward VII stamps of India optd with Type* O **16**.
O23 **41** 3 p. pale grey 10 10
O24 3 p. slate-grey (1906) 10 10
O25 **42** ½ a. green .. .. 1·90 10
a. "HIND" £2000 £250
b. Opt double, one albino .. .. 25·00
O26 **43** 1 a. carmine 80 10
a. "HIND" .. .. † £200
b. Opt double, one albino .. .. 25·00
O27 **44** 2 a. pale violet .. .. .. 1·25 60
O28 2 a. mauve 30 10
O29 **47** 4 a. olive 40 45
a. Opt double, one albino .. .. 35·00
O30 **49** 8 a. purple (*shades*) .. .. 7·00 5·00
O31 8 a. claret .. .. 2·75 1·50
O32 **51** 1 r. green and carmine (1906) .. 2·50 2·25
O23/32 .. .. *Set of* 7 8·00 4·00

1907. *Nos. 149/50 of India optd with Type* O **16**.
O33 **53** ½ a. green 15 10
O34 **54** 1 a. carmine 30 10

1914–27. *King George V. Official stamps of India optd with T* **4**.
O35 **55** 3 p. slate-grey 10 10
a. "JIND STATE" double, one albino 30·00
O36 **56** ½ a. green 10 10
O37 **57** 1 a. aniline carmine 20 10
O38 1 a. pale rose-carmine 45 10
O39 **59** 2 a. mauve 15 15
O40 **63** 4 a. olive 40 15
O41 **64** 6 a. yellow-bistre (1927) .. .. 45 2·25
O42 **65** 8 a. purple .. .. 30 1·00
O43 **67** 1 r. brown and green .. .. .. 1·00 1·60
a. "JIND STATE" double, one albino 30·00
O44 2 r. carmine and yellow-brown (1927) 10·00 50·00
O45 5 r. ultramarine and violet (1927) .. 17·00 £140
O35/45 .. .. *Set of* 10 27·00 £180
No. O40 with double overprint is of clandestine origin.

1924. *As 1914-27. New colour.*
O46 **57** 1 a. chocolate 40 10

JIND STATE SERVICE (O 17) JIND STATE SERVICE (O 18) JIND SERVICE (O 19)

1927–37. *King George V (Nasik printing, wmk Mult Star), optd with Types* O **17** *or* O **18** *(rupee values).*
O47 **55** 3 p. slate (1928) 10 20
O48 **56** ½ a. green (1929) 10 90
O49 **80** 9 p. deep green (1932) 40 15
O50 **57** 1 a. chocolate 10 10
w. Wmk inverted 50
O51 **82** 1 a. 3 p. mauve (1932) 40 15
w. Wmk inverted 50 30
O52 **70** 2 a. purple (1929) 25 15
O53 **61** 2 a. 6 p. orange (1937) .. .. 45 14·00
O54 **71** 4 a. sage-green (1929) 35 25
w. Wmk inverted .. .. .. 1·00 50
O55 **64** 6 a. bistre (1937) 70
w. Wmk inverted .. .. .. 1·75 12·00
O56 **65** 8 a. reddish purple (1929) .. .. — 1·50
w. Wmk inverted .. .. .. 40 1·25
O57 **66** 12 a. claret (1928) .. .. .. 90 9·50
O58 **67** 1 r. chocolate and green (1928) .. 1·75 2·50
O59 2 r. carmine and orange (1930) .. 27·00 22·00
w. Wmk inverted .. .. .. 22·00
O60 5 r. ultramarine and purple (1929) .. 12·00 £150
O61 10 r. green and carmine (1928) .. 24·00 85·00
w. Wmk inverted .. .. .. 32·00
O47/61 .. .. *Set of* 15 55·00 £275
The 9 p. exists printed by lithography or typography.

1934. *Optd with Type* O **17**.
O62 **79** ½ a. green 20 15
O63 **81** 1 a. chocolate 20 15
O64 **59** 2 a. vermilion 30 15
w. Wmk inverted 30 75
O65 **63** 4 a. sage-green .. .. .. 3·50 30
O62/5 .. .. *Set of* 4 3·75 65

1937–40. *King George VI. Optd with Types* O **17** *or* O **18** *(rupee values).*
O66 **91** ½ a. red-brown (1938) .. .. 48·00 30
O67 9 p. green .. .. 85 6·50
O68 1 a. carmine 55 30
O69 **93** 1 r. grey and red-brown (1940) .. 24·00 42·00
O70 2 r. purple and brown (1940) .. 42·00 £170
O71 5 r. green and blue (1940) .. .. 85·00 £300
O72 10 r. purple and claret (1940) .. £170 £700
O66/72 .. .. *Set of* 7 £325 £1100

1939–43. *(a) Official stamps optd with T* **7**.
O73 **O 20** 3 p. slate 50 60
O74 ½ a. red-brown .. .. .. 1·50 50
O75 ½ a. purple (1943) 60 30
O76 9 p. green .. .. 1·50 7·00
O77 1 a. carmine .. .. 1·50 15
O78 1½ a. dull violet (1942) .. .. 5·00 1·00
O79 2 a. vermilion .. .. .. 2·50 30
w. Wmk inverted .. .. .. — 2·25
O80 2½ a. bright violet .. .. .. 1·50 5·50
O81 4 a. brown .. .. 3·25 1·10
O82 8 a. slate-violet .. .. .. 3·00 2·75

(b) Postage stamps optd with Type O **19**
O83 **93** 1 r. grey and red-brown (1942) .. .. 18·00 40·00
O84 2 r. purple and brown (1942) .. .. 42·00 £120
O85 5 r. green and blue (1942) .. .. 90·00 £275
O86 10 r. purple and claret (1942) £160 £350
O73/86 .. .. *Set of* 14 £300 £700

Jind was absorbed into the Patiala and East Punjab States Union by 20 August 1948.

NABHA

PRICES FOR STAMPS ON COVER

Nos. 1/3	*from* × 15
Nos. 4/6	—
Nos. 10/36	*from* × 12
Nos. 37/117	*from* × 7
Nos. O1/68	*from* × 15

Raja Hira Singh, 1871–1911.

NABHA STATE (1) NABHA STATE (2)

1885 (1 July). *Queen Victoria. Optd with T* **1**.
1 **23** ½ a. blue-green 1·40 3·00
2 **25** 1 a. brown-purple 28·00 £100
3 **27** 2 a. dull blue 9·50 32·00
4 **17** 4 a. green 55·00 £140
5 **31** 8 a. dull mauve £300
6 **33** 1 r. slate £250
1/6 *Set of* 6 £550

All six values have had the overprint reprinted. On the reprints the words "NABHA" and "STATE" both measure 9¼ mm in length, whereas on the originals these words measure 11 and 10 mm respectively. The varieties with overprint double come from the reprints.

1885 (Nov)–**1900**. *Optd with T* **2**. (*a*) *In red.*
10 **23** ½ a. blue-green 20 45
11 **27** 2 a. dull blue 1·40 1·40
a. Opt double, one albino 40·00
12 **17** 4 a. green 24·00 £120
13 **33** 1 r. slate 85·00 £160
a. Opt double, one albino £110
10/13 *Set of* 4 £100 £250

(*b*) *In black* (Nov 1885–97)
14 **23** ½ a. blue-green (1888) 10 10
15 **24** 9 p. carmine (1892) 50 2·25
16 **25** 1 a. brown-purple 95 50
17 1 a. plum 80 40
18 **26** 1 a. 6 p. sepia (1891) 60 1·75
a. "ABHA" for "NABHA" £275
19 **27** 2 a. dull blue (1888) 1·25 80
20 2 a. ultramarine 1·00 70
21 **28** 3 a. orange (1889) 4·50 12·00
a. Opt double, one albino 25·00
22 3 a. brown-orange 1·75 1·10
23 **29** 4 a. olive-green (1888) 3·25 1·40
24 4 a. slate-green 3·25 1·40
25 **21** 6 a. olive-bistre (1889) 3·75 8·50
26 6 a. bistre-brown 1·25 2·00
27 **31** 8 a. dull mauve 1·25 1·60
a. Opt double, one albino 30·00
28 **32** 12 a. purple/*red* (1889) 2·25 3·00
a. Opt double, one albino 27·00
29 **33** 1 r. slate (1888) 6·50 32·00
30 **37** 1 r. green and carmine (1893) 6·00 3·75
a. "N BHA" for "NABHA"
b. Opt double, one albino 40·00
31 **38** 2 r. carmine and yellow-brown (1897) 85·00 £170
a. Opt double, one albino £150
32 3 r. brown and green (1897) 85·00 £200
33 5 r. ultramarine and violet (1897) 85·00 £300
14/33 *Set of* 15 £250 £600

(*c*) *New value. In black* (Nov 1900)
36 **40** 3 p. carmine 10 15

1903–09. *King Edward VII. Optd with T* **2**.
37 **41** 3 p. pale grey 25 15
a. "NAB STA" for "NABHA STATE" £800
b. Opt double, one albino 20·00
37*c* 3 p. slate-grey (1906) 25 15
38 **42** ½ a. green 35 30
a. "NABH" for "NABHA" £950
39 **43** 1 a. carmine 60 60
40 **44** 2 a. pale violet 50 1·60
40*a* 2 a. mauve 1·50 30
40*b* **45** 2 a. 6 p. ultramarine (1909) 17·00 75·00
ba. Opt double, one albino 30·00
41 **46** 3 a. orange-brown 45 30
a. Opt double, one albino 35·00
42 **47** 4 a. olive 1·10 1·75
43 **48** 6 a. olive-bistre 90 9·00
a. Opt double, one albino 20·00
44 **49** 8 a. purple 5·50 14·00
44*a* 8 a. claret 7·50 16·00
45 **50** 12 a. purple/*red* 2·50 16·00
46 **51** 1 r. green and carmine 5·50 8·50
37/46 *Set of* 11 32·00 £110

1907. *Nos.* 149/50 *of India optd with T* **2**.
47 **53** ½ a. green 45 1·10
48 **54** 1 a. carmine 35 70

Maharaja Ripudaman (Gurcharan) Singh, 1911–1928.

1913. *King George V. Optd with T* **2**.
49 **55** 3 p. slate-grey 20 15
50 **56** ½ a. green 20 10
51 **57** 1 a. aniline carmine 45 10
52 **59** 2 a. mauve 45 35
53 **62** 3 a. orange-brown 50 35
54 **63** 4 a. olive 55 90
55 **64** 6 a. olive-bistre 55 4·00
56 **65** 8 a. purple 1·25 3·00
57 **66** 12 a. dull claret 1·10 16·00
58 **67** 1 r. brown and green 6·00 2·75
a. Opt double, one albino 32·00
49/58 *Set of* 10 10·00 25·00

1924. *As* 1913. *New colour.*
59 **57** 1 a. chocolate 2·25 1·25

No. 59 with inverted or double overprint is of clandestine origin.

NABHA STATE (3) NABHA STATE (4)

1927–36. *King George V* (*Nasik printing, wmk Mult Star*), *optd as T* **3** *or* **4** (*rupee values*).
60 **55** 3 p. slate (1932) 60 15
w. Wmk inverted 1·75 1·10
61 **56** ½ a. green (1928) 30 20
61*a* **80** 9 p. deep green (1934) 1·25 1·10
62 **57** 1 a. chocolate 50 15
w. Wmk inverted
63 **82** 1 a. 3 p. mauve (1936) 60 3·50
w. Wmk inverted 60
64 **70** 2 a. purple (1932) 1·40 35
65 **61** 2 a. 6 p. orange (1932) 45 5·50
66 **62** 3 a. bright blue (1930) 1·10 1·00
67 **71** 4 a. sage-green (1932) 1·50 1·40
71 **67** 2 r. carmine and orange (1932) 21·00 70·00
72 5 r. ultramarine and purple (*wmk inverted*) (1932) 70·00 £190
60/72 *Set of* 11 90·00 £250

The 9 p. exists printed by lithography or typography.

Maharaja Partab Singh, 1928–1971

1936–37. *New types and colours. Optd as T* **3**.
73 **79** ½ a. green 30 30
74 **81** 1 a. chocolate 30 30
75 **62** 3 a. carmine (1937) 3·25 8·00
76 **63** 4 a. slate-green (1937) 2·25 2·25
73/6 *Set of* 4 5·50 9·75

NABHA STATE (5) NABHA (6)

1938. *King George VI. Nos.* 247/64 *optd as T* **3** (3 *p. to* 1 *a.*), *T* **5** (2 *a. to* 12 *a.*) *or T* **4** (*rupee values*). *W* **69** (*inverted on* 15 *r.*).
77 **91** 3 p. slate 4·75 30
78 ½ a. red-brown 2·75 50
79 9 p. green 16·00 3·00
80 1 a. carmine 1·25 30
81 **92** 2 a. vermilion 1·00 4·00
82 – 2 a. 6 p. bright violet 1·00 6·50
83 – 3 a. yellow-green 1·10 3·50
84 – 3 a. 6 p. bright blue 1·10 13·00
85 – 4 a. brown 4·50 4·75
86 – 6 a. turquoise-green 2·00 13·00
87 – 8 a. slate-violet 1·90 13·00
88 – 12 a. lake 2·25 15·00
89 **93** 1 r. grey and red-brown 10·00 20·00
90 2 r. purple and brown 19·00 70·00
91 5 r. green and blue 45·00 £140
92 10 r. purple and claret 70·00 £275
93 15 r. brown and green £180 £500
94 25 r. slate-violet and purple £180 £500
w. Wmk inverted £300 £600
77/94 *Set of* 18 £500 £1400

1941–45. *King George VI. Optd with T* **6**. (*a*) *Stamps of* 1937.
95 **91** 3 p. slate (1942) 27·00 2·50
96 ½ a. red-brown (1942) 65·00 3·50
97 9 p. green (1942) 10·00 9·50
98 1 a. carmine (1942) 10·00 2·00
95/8 *Set of* 4 £100 16·00

(*b*) *Stamps of* 1940-43
105 **100*a*** 3 p. slate (1942) 80 45
106 ½ a. purple (1943) 3·75 45
107 9 p. green (1942) 3·00 45
108 1 a. carmine (1945) 80 2·00
109 **101** 1 a. 3 p. yellow-brown 80 1·50
110 1½ a. dull violet (1942) 1·00 1·00
111 2 a. vermilion (1943) 80 2·75
112 3 a. bright violet (1943) 2·00 2·50
113 3½ a. bright blue (1944) 9·50 35·00
114 **102** 4 a. brown 1·60 75
115 6 a. turquoise-green (1943) 7·00 35·00
116 8 a. slate-violet (1943) 5·00 25·00
117 12 a. lake (1943) 4·25 35·00
105/117 *Set of* 13 35·00 £130

The 1½ a. exists printed by lithography or typography.

OFFICIAL STAMPS

SERVICE (O 8) NABHA STATE (O 9)

1885 (1 July). *Nos.* 1/3 *of Nabha optd with Type* O **8**.
O1 **23** ½ a. blue-green 1·50 55
O2 **25** 1 a. brown-purple 30 15
a. Opt Type O 8 double † £1000
O3 **27** 2 a. dull blue 48·00 95·00
O1/3 *Set of* 3 48·00 95·00

The three values have had the overprint reprinted in the same way as the ordinary stamps of 1885.

1885 (Nov)–**97**. *Optd with Type* O **9**. (*a*) *In red.*
O 4 **23** ½ a. blue-green 4·25 3·25
O 5 **27** 2 a. deep blue 50 55

(*b*) *In black* (Nov 1885–97)
O 6 **23** ½ a. blue-green (1888) 10 10
a. "SERVICE." with stop £110 2·25
b. "S ATE" for "STATE"
c. "SERVICE" double, one albino 25·00
O 7 **25** 1 a. brown-purple 75 40
O 8 1 a. plum 75 25
a. "SERVICE." with stop 5·00 75
ab. "SERVICE." with stop, and "NABHA STATE" double † £250
O 9 **27** 2 a. dull blue (1888) 1·40 55
O10 2 a. ultramarine 1·75 85
O11 **28** 3 a. orange (1889) 15·00 48·00
O12 3 a. brown-orange 15·00 48·00
a. "NABHA STATE" double, one albino 40·00
O13 **29** 4 a. olive-green (1888) 1·60 50
O14 4 a. slate-green 1·75 55
O15 **21** 6 a. olive-bistre (1889) 11·00 18·00
a. "SERVICE" double, one albino 30·00
O16 6 a. bistre-brown £600
O17 **31** 8 a. dull mauve (1889) 1·00 70
O18 **32** 12 a. purple/*red* (1889) 4·00 13·00
a. "SERVICE" double, one albino 30·00
b. "NABHA STATE" double, one albino 30·00
O19 **33** 1 r. slate (1889) 26·00 £170
O20 **37** 1 r. green and carmine (1.97) 22·00 50·00
O6/20 *Set of* 10 70·00 £275

Printings up to and including that of August 1895 had the "SERVICE" overprint applied to sheets of stamps already overprinted with Type **2**. From the printing of January 1897 onwards the two parts of the overprint were applied at one operation. This method was only used for printings of the ½ a., 1 a. and 1 r. (O20).

1903–06. *King Edward VII stamps of India optd with Type* O **9**.
O24 **41** 3 p. pale grey (1906) 3·50 15·00
O25 3 p. slate-grey (1906) 65 9·00
a. Opt double, one albino 25·00
O26 **42** ½ a. green 35 10
O27 **43** 1 a. carmine 15 10
O28 **44** 2 a. pale violet 1·25 60
O29 2 a. mauve 1·00 40
a. Opt double, one albino 30·00
O30 **47** 4 a. olive 1·25 50
O32 **49** 8 a. purple (*shades*) 1·10 1·00
a. Opt double, one albino 25·00
O33 8 a. claret 6·50 3·50
O34 **51** 1 r. green and carmine 1·50 2·25
O24/34 *Set of* 7 5·50 12·00

1907. *Nos.* 149/50 *of India optd with Type* O **9**.
O35 **53** ½ a. green 20 35
a. Opt double, one albino 15·00
O36 **54** 1 a. carmine 25 25
a. Opt double, one albino 25·00

1913. *King George V. Optd with Type* O 9.
O37 **63** 4 a. olive 10·00 42·00
O38 **67** 1 r. brown and green 55·00 £275
a. Opt double, one albino 95·00

1913. *Official stamps of India optd with T* **2**.
O39 **55** 3 p. slate-grey 30 5·50
O39*a* 3 p. bluish slate 30 5·50
O40 **56** ½ a. green 15 10
O41 **57** 1 a. aniline carmine 15 10
O42 **59** 2 a. mauve 30 15
O43 **63** 4 a. olive 40 40
O44 **65** 8 a. dull mauve 65 80
O46 **67** 1 r. brown and green 2·75 2·00
O39/46 *Set of* 7 4·25 8·00

NABHA STATE SERVICE (O 10) NABHA SERVICE (O 11)

1932–42?. *King George V* (*Nasik printing, wmk Mult Star*), *optd at Nasik with Type* O **10**.
O47 **55** 3 p. slate 10 15
O48 **81** 1 a. chocolate (1935) 15 15
O49 **63** 4 a. sage-green (1942?) 18·00 2·25
O50 **65** 8 a. reddish purple (1937) 1·00 1·90
O47/50 *Set of* 4 18·00 4·00

1938. *King George VI. Optd as Type* O **10**.
O53 **91** 9 p. green 1·50 2·25
O54 1 a. carmine 8·50 45

1940–43. (*a*) *Official stamps optd with T* **6**.
O55 **O 20** 3 p. slate (1942) 55 60
O56 ½ a. red-brown (1942) 70 30
O57 ½ a. purple (1943) 2·50 45
O58 9 p. green 1·25 20
O59 1 a. carmine (1942) 50 20
O61 1½ a. dull violet (1942) 60 40
O62 2 a. vermilion (1942) 1·25 60
w. Wmk inverted 2·25 1·25
O64 4 a. brown (1942) 3·50 1·75
O65 8 a. slate-violet (1942) 5·50 12·00

(*b*) *Postage stamps optd with Type* O **11**.
O66 **93** 1 r. grey and red-brown (1942) 8·50 27·00
O67 2 r. purple and brown (1942) 23·00 £140
O68 5 r. green and blue (1942) £200 £450
O55/68 *Set of* 12 £225 £550

Nabha was absorbed into the Patiala and East Punjab States Union by 20 August 1948.

PATIALA

PRICES FOR STAMPS ON COVER	
Nos. 1/6	*from* × 10
Nos. 7/34	*from* × 6
Nos. 35/45	*from* × 8
Nos. 46/115	*from* × 4
Nos. O1/84	*from* × 15

Maharaja Rajindra Singh, 1876–1900

PUTTIALLA STATE (1) PUTTIALLA STATE (2) PATIALA STATE (3)

1884 (1 Oct). *Queen Victoria. Optd with T* **1**, *in red.*
1 **23** ½ a. blue-green .. 1·90 2·00
a. Opt double, one sideways .. £1700 £600
b. Opt double, one albino .. 50·00
2 **25** 1 a. brown-purple .. 38·00 38·00
a. Opt double
b. Optd in red and in black .. £600
3 **27** 2 a. dull blue .. 8·50 8·50
4 **17** 4 a. green .. 48·00 48·00
5 **31** 8 a. dull mauve .. £250 £600
a. Opt inverted .. £5000
b. Optd in red and in black .. 70·00 £225
ba. Ditto. Opts inverted .. £3500
c. Opt double, one albino .. £300
6 **33** 1 r. slate .. £110 £350
1/6 .. *Set of* 6 £400 £900

Nos. 5a and 5ba each occur once in the setting of 120. The 8 a. value also exists with a trial overprint (showing the words more curved) reading downwards (*Price* £375 *unused*), which should not be confused with No. 5a.

1885. *Optd with T* **2**. (*a*) *In red.*
7 **23** ½ a. blue-green .. 1·25 20
a. "AUTTIALLA" .. 12·00 17·00
b. "STATE" only
c. Wide spacing between lines .. 3·50 3·75
8 **27** 2 a. dull blue .. 2·75 1·10
a. "AUTTIALLA" .. 25·00
b. Wide spacing between lines .. 12·00 12·00
ba. Ditto "AUTTIALLA" .. £300
9 **17** 4 a. green .. 2·00 1·75
a. Optd in red and in black .. £180
b. Wide spacing between lines .. £225
c. Opt double, one albino .. 30·00
10 **33** 1 r. slate .. 5·50 48·00
a. "AUTTIALLA" .. £350
b. Wide spacing between lines .. £225

(*b*) *In black*
11 **25** 1 a. brown-purple .. 15 15
a. Optd in red and in black .. 4·75 45·00
b. "AUTTIALLA" .. 50·00
ba. Ditto. Optd in red and in black .. £1200
c. Opt double .. £200 £225
d. Wide spacing between lines .. £130
12 **31** 8 a. dull mauve .. 11·00 24·00
a. "AUTTIALLA" .. £300
b. Opt double, one albino .. 50·00
c. Wide spacing between lines .. £225
7/12 .. *Set of* 6 20·00 70·00

The ½, 2 and 4 a. (T **29**), and 1 r. (all overprinted in black), are proofs.

All six values exist with reprinted overprints, and the error "AUTTIALLA STATE" has been reprinted in complete sheets on all values and in addition in black on the ½, 2, 4 a. and 1 r. Nearly all these however, are found with the word "REPRINT" overprinted upon them. On these genuine "AUTTIALLA" errors, which occur on R. 9/12 in the setting of 120, the word "STATE" is 8½ mm long; on the reprints only 7¾ mm.

Nos. 7c, 8b, 9b, 10b, 11d and 12c show 1¼ mm spacing between the two lines of overprint. The normal spacing is ¾ mm.

Nos. 7/8 and 10/12 exist with error "PUTTILLA", but their status is uncertain.

1891–96. *Optd with T* **3**.
13 **23** ½ a. blue-green (1892) .. 10 10
14 **24** 9 p. carmine .. 35 80
15 **25** 1 a. brown-purple .. 70 25
16 1 a. plum .. 1·00 60
a. "PATIALA" omitted .. £170 £325
b. "PA" omitted
c. "PATIA" omitted
d. "PATIAL" omitted
17 **26** 1 a. 6 p. sepia .. 50 45
18 **27** 2 a. dull blue (1896) .. 75 20
19 2 a. ultramarine .. 1·00 55
20 **28** 3 a. brown-orange .. 1·00 35
21 **29** 4 a. olive-green (1896) .. 1·50 40
a. "PATIALA" omitted .. £375 £190
22 4 a. slate-green .. 1·50 40
23 **21** 6 a. bistre-brown .. 1·25 7·00
24 6 a. olive-bistre .. 1·50 12·00
a. Opt double, one albino .. 40·00
25 **31** 8 a. dull mauve
26 8 a. magenta (1896) .. 1·00 7·00
27 **32** 12 a. purple/*red* .. 1·00 8·50
28 **37** 1 r. green and carmine (1896) .. 3·50 29·00
29 **38** 2 r. carmine and yellow-brown (1895) .. 90·00 £475
30 3 r. brown and green (1895) .. £120 £500
a. Opt double, one albino
b. Opt treble, two albino .. £150
31 5 r. ultramarine and violet (1895) .. £150 £550
13/31 .. *Set of* 14 £325 £1400

The errors on the 1 a. plum and 4 a. olive-green occur on R.19/1 in the December 1898 printing. Nos. 16b/d are early stages of the error before the entire word was omitted.

1899–1902. *Colours changed and new value. Optd with T* **3**.
32 **40** 3 p. carmine (1899) .. 10 10
a. Pair, one without opt .. £2500
b. Opt double, one albino .. 30·00
33 **23** ½ a. pale yellow-green .. 55 30
34 **25** 1 a. carmine .. 1·75 60
32/4 .. *Set of* 3 2·00 90

Maharaja Bhupindra Singh, 1900–1938

1903–06. *King Edward VII. Optd with T* **3**.
35 **41** 3 p. pale grey .. 10 15
a. Additional albino opt of Jind Type **3** £200
b. "S" in "STATE" sideways (R.20/1) £850 £850
36 3 p. slate-grey (1906) .. 10 10
37 **42** ½ a. green .. 85 10
38 **43** 1 a. carmine .. 10 10
a. Horiz pair, one without opt .. £850
39 **44** 2 a. pale violet .. 80 65
a. Mauve .. 5·50 75
40 **46** 3 a. orange-brown .. 45 30
41 **47** 4 a. olive (1905) .. 2·25 65
42 **48** 6 a. olive-bistre (1905) .. 2·25 5·00
43 **49** 8 a. purple (1906) .. 2·00 1·10
44 **50** 12 a. purple/*red* (1906) .. 4·00 16·00
45 **51** 1 r. green and carmine (1905) .. 1·60 3·00
35/45 .. *Set of* 10 13·00 24·00

1912. *Nos.* 149/50 *of India optd with T* **3**.
46 **53** ½ a. green .. 10 15
47 **54** 1 a. carmine .. 70 40

1912–26. *King George V. Optd with T* **3**.
48 **55** 3 p. slate-grey .. 15 10
a. "Rs" flaw .. 20·00
49 **56** ½ a. green .. 45 15
50 **57** 1 a. aniline carmine .. 65 15
51 **58** 1½ a. chocolate (Type A) (1922) .. 30 55
52 **59** 2 a. mauve .. 45 35
53 **62** 3 a. orange-brown .. 90 60
54 **63** 4 a. olive .. 1·60 1·40
55 **64** 6 a. yellow-brown .. 2·50 3·25
a. Yellow-bistre .. 80 2·50
56 **65** 8 a. purple .. 1·50 90
57 **66** 12 a. dull claret .. 1·60 5·00
58 **67** 1 r. brown and green .. 3·00 9·00
a. Opt double, one albino .. 30·00
59 2 r. carmine and yellow-brown (1926) 9·00 £100
60 5 r. ultramarine and violet (1926) .. 21·00 £100

1923–6. *As* 1912–26. *New colours.*
61 **57** 1 a. chocolate .. 1·75 30
62 **62** 3 a. ultramarine (1926) .. 1·40 4·50
48/62 .. *Set of* 15 40·00 £200

PATIALA STATE (4)
PATIALA STATE (5)

1928–34. *King George V (Nasik printing, wmk Mult Star) optd at Nasik with T* **4** *or* **5** (*rupee values*).
63 **55** 3 p. slate (1932) .. 1·00 10
w. Wmk inverted .. 2·25 1·00
64 **56** ½ a. green .. 25 10
w. Wmk inverted .. 1·50 1·00
65 **80** 9 p. deep green (1934) .. 70 20
66 **57** 1 a. chocolate .. 70 20
w. Wmk inverted .. 2·25 75
67 **82** 1 a. 3 p. mauve (1932) .. 2·50 15
w. Wmk inverted .. 2·50 1·00
68 **70** 2 a. purple .. 80 30
w. Wmk inverted .. 2·25
69 **61** 2 a. 6 p. orange (1934) .. 2·75 1·25
w. Wmk inverted .. 2·25
70 **62** 3 a. bright blue (1929) .. 1·75 75
71 **71** 4 a. sage-green .. 2·25 65
w. Wmk inverted .. 4·25
72 **65** 8 a. reddish purple (1933) .. 3·50 1·50
73 **67** 1 r. chocolate and green (1929) .. 5·00 5·00
w. Wmk inverted .. — 8·00
74 2 r. carmine and orange .. 16·00
w. Wmk inverted .. 8·00 38·00
63/74 .. *Set of* 12 26·00 42·00

The 9 p. exists printed by lithography or typography.

1935–7. *Optd with T* **4**.
75 **79** ½ a. blue-green (1937) .. 30 20
76 **81** 1 a. chocolate (1936) .. 40 15
77 **59** 2 a. vermilion (No. 236*a*) (1936) .. 30 60
78 **62** 3 a. carmine .. 3·50 3·50
w. Wmk inverted .. 4·25 4·25
79 **63** 4 a. sage-green .. 85 1·25
75/9 .. *Set of* 5 4·75 5·00

PATIALA STATE (6)
PATIALA (7)
PATIALA (8)

1937–8. *King George VI. Nos.* 247/64 *optd with T* **4** (3 *p. to* 1 *a.*), *T* **6** (2 *a. to* 12 *a.*), *or T* **5** (*rupee values*).
80 **91** 3 p. slate .. 25·00 30
81 ½ a. red-brown .. 6·50 20
82 9 p. green (1937) .. 2·25 45
83 1 a. carmine (1937) .. 1·50 20
84 **92** 2 a. vermilion .. 1·50 5·00
85 – 2 a. 6 p. bright violet .. 2·75 11·00
86 – 3 a. yellow-green .. 2·25 4·75
87 – 3 a. 6 p. bright blue .. 3·00 15·00
88 – 4 a. brown .. 16·00 9·00
89 – 6 a. turquoise-green .. 18·00 30·00
90 – 8 a. slate-violet .. 18·00 23·00
91 – 12 a. lake .. 18·00 35·00
92 **93** 1 r. grey and red-brown .. 18·00 32·00
93 2 r. purple and brown .. 27·00 75·00
94 5 r. green and blue .. 38·00 £140
95 10 r. purple and claret .. 55·00 £225
96 15 r. brown and green .. £100 £375
97 25 r. slate-violet and purple .. £130 £450
80/97 .. *Set of* 18 £425 £1300

Maharaja Yadavindra Singh, 1938–1971

1941–6. *King George VI. Optd with T* **7** *or* **8** (*rupee value*).

(*a*) *Stamps of* 1937
98 **91** 3 p. slate .. 8·00 60
99 ½ a. red-brown .. 6·50 25
100 9 p. green .. £130 2·50
w. Wmk inverted
101 1 a. carmine .. 18·00 65
102 **93** 1 r. grey and red-brown (1946) .. 7·50 55·00
98/102 .. *Set of* 5 £150 55·00

(*b*) *Stamps of* 1940–43
103 **100*a*** 3 p. slate (1942) .. 1·40 15
104 ½ a. purple (1943) .. 1·75 15
a. Pair, one without opt .. £4000
105 **100*a*** 9 p. green (1942) .. 1·00 15
a. Vert pair, one without opt .. £2750
106 1 a. carmine (1944) .. 80 10
107 **101** 1 a. 3 p. yellow-brown .. 1·60 1·75
108 1½ a. violet (1942) .. 7·00 1·60
109 2 a. vermilion (1944) .. 6·00 25
110 3 a. bright violet (1944) .. 4·00 75
111 3½ a. bright blue (1944) .. 14·00 21·00
112 **102** 4 a. brown (1944) .. 4·50 1·10
113 6 a. turquoise-green (1944) .. 2·50 14·00
114 8 a. slate-violet (1944) .. 3·00 7·00
115 12 a. lake (1945) .. 9·00 45·00
103/15 .. *Set of* 13 50·00 80·00

The 1½ a. exists printed by lithography or typography.

OFFICIAL STAMPS

SERVICE (O 2)
SERVICE (O 3)

1884 (1 Oct). *Nos.* 1/3 *of Patiala optd with Type* O **2**, *in black.*
O1 **23** ½ a. blue-green .. 9·00 20
O2 **25** 1 a. brown-purple .. 35 10
a. Opt Type **1** inverted .. £1200 £250
b. Opt Type **1** double .. † £100
c. "SERVICE" double .. £1200 £450
d. "SERVICE" inverted .. † £1200
w. Wmk inverted .. † £200
O3 **27** 2 a. dull blue .. £4000 95·00

Essays of No. O3 exist on which "STATE" measures 10 mm long (normal 9 mm) and the words of the Type **1** overprint are more curved. These are rare (*Price* £800 *unused*).

1885–90. (*a*) *No.* 7 *of Patiala optd with Type* O **2**, *in black.*
O4 **23** ½ a. blue-green .. 30 10
a. "SERVICE" double .. † £600
b. "AUTTIALLA" .. 55·00 16·00
ba. "AUTTIALLA", and "SERVICE" double .. † £2250

(*b*) *No.* 11 *of Patiala optd with Type* O **2**, *in black*
O5 **25** 1 a. brown-purple .. 30 10
a. "SERVICE" double .. £1200
b. "SERVICE" double, one inverted .. † £475
c. "AUTTIALLA" .. £500 42·00
d. "PUTTIALLA STATE" double .. † £850

(*c*) *As No.* 7 *of Patiala, but optd in black, and No.* 8, *optd with Type* O **3**
O6 **23** ½ a. blue-green (Bk.) (1890) .. 1·00 10
O7 **27** 2 a. dull blue (R.) .. 30 15
a. "SERVICE" double, one inverted .. 30·00 £160

Stamps as Nos. O4/5, but with Type O **3** (in red on the ½ a.), were prepared for use but not issued, although some were erroneously overprinted "REPRINT". No. O7 with overprint in *black* is a proof. The ½ a "AUTTIALLA" has been reprinted in complete sheets, and can be found with "AUTTIALLA" double.

No. O7 exists with error "PUTTILLA", but its status is uncertain.

SERVICE

PATIALA STATE (O 4)
PATIALA STATE SERVICE (O 5)
PATIALA STATE SERVICE (O 6)

1891 (Nov)–**1900.** *Optd with Type* O **4**, *in black.*
O 8 **23** ½ a. blue-green (9.95) .. 10 10
a. "SERVICE" inverted .. 55·00
b. "I" of "SERVICE" omitted .. £800
c. Second "T" of "STATE" omitted .. £375 £350
O 9 **25** 1 a. plum (10.1900) .. 3·50 10
a. "SERVICE" inverted .. 60·00
O10 **27** 2 a. dull blue (12.98) .. 3·50 1·10
a. Deep blue .. 3·00 1·50
b. "SERVICE" inverted .. 60·00 £150
c. Thin seriffed "I" in "SERVICE" .. £130
O12 **28** 3 a. brown-orange .. 45 1·50
a. "I" of "SERVICE" omitted
O13 **29** 4 a. olive-green .. 40 70
a. Slate-green (9.95) .. 40 20
b. "I" of "SERVICE" omitted
O15 **21** 6 a. bistre-brown .. 85 35
a. Olive-bistre .. £950
O16 **31** 8 a. dull mauve .. 1·40 75
a. Magenta (12.98) .. 80 75
b. "I" of "SERVICE" omitted .. £2250
c. Thin seriffed "I" in "SERVICE" .. £250
O18 **32** 12 a. purple/*red* .. 50 50
a. "I" of "SERVICE" omitted .. £4000
O19 **33** 1 r. slate .. 65 55
a. "I" of "SERVICE" omitted
O8/19 .. *Set of* 9 9·25 4·50

Stamps from the first printing of November 1891 (Nos. O12/13, O15/16, O18/19) had the "SERVICE" overprint, as Type O **3**, applied to sheets already overprinted with Type **3**. Subsequent printings of Nos. O8/10*a*, O13*a* and O16*a* had both overprints applied at one operation as shown on Type O **4**.

The errors with "SERVICE" inverted occur from a trial printing, in two operations, during 1894, which was probably not issued. Some of the "I" omitted varieties may also come from the same trial printing.

1902 (Jan)–**03.** *Optd with Type* O **4**.
O20 **25** 1 a. carmine .. 15 10
O21 **37** 1 r. green and carmine (5.03) .. 5·00 9·00

1903–10. *King Edward VII stamps of India optd with Type* O **4**.
O22 **41** 3 p. pale grey .. 10 10
a. Slate-grey (1909) .. 15 15
O24 **42** ½ a. green .. 10 10
O25 **43** 1 a. carmine .. 10 10
O26 **44** 2 a. pale violet (1905) .. 30 20
a. Mauve .. 20 10

No.	Type	Description	Unused	Used
O28	**46**	3 a. orange-brown	1·60	1·60
O29	**47**	4 a. olive (1905)	50	20
		a. Opt double, one albino	40·00	
O30	**49**	8 a. purple (*shades*)	60	55
		a. Claret (1910)	2·75	1·25
O32	**51**	1 r. green and carmine (1906)	70	70
O22/32		*Set of* 8	3·00	3·00

1907. *Nos.* 149/50 *of India optd with Type* O **4**.

No.	Type	Description	Unused	Used
O33	**53**	½ a. green	10	10
O34	**54**	1 a. carmine	10	10

1913–26. *King George V. Official stamps of India optd with T* **3**.

No.	Type	Description	Unused	Used
O35	**55**	3 p. slate-grey	10	10
		a. Bluish slate (1926)	30	30
O36	**56**	½ a. green	10	10
O37	**57**	1 a. carmine	10	10
O38		1 a. brown (1925)	4·75	90
O39	**59**	2 a. mauve	50	20
O40	**63**	4 a. olive	40	30
O41	**64**	6 a. yellow-bistre (1926)	75	1·75
O42	**65**	8 a. purple	55	45
O43	**67**	1 r. brown and green	1·25	1·40
O44		2 r. carmine and yellow-brown (1926)	11·00	32·00
O45		5 r. ultramarine and violet (1926)	9·00	19·00
O35/45		*Set of* 11	26·00	50·00

1927–36. *King George V (Nasik printing, wmk Mult Star), optd at Nasik with* Type O **5** *or Type* O **6** (*rupee values*).

No.	Type	Description	Unused	Used
O47	**55**	3 p. slate	10	10
		a. Blue opt	1·00	1·00
		w. Wmk inverted	1·60	1·00
O48	**56**	½ a. green (1932)	35	55
		w. Wmk inverted	—	2·25
O49	**57**	1 a. chocolate	15	10
		w. Wmk inverted	1·00	50
O50	**82**	1 a. 3 p. mauve (1932)	30	10
		w. Wmk inverted	2·25	20
O51	**70**	2 a. purple	20	30
O52		2 a. vermilion (1933)	30	35
O53	**61**	2 a. 6 p. orange (1933)	1·50	35
		w. Wmk inverted	50	75
O54	**71**	4 a. sage-green (1935)	40	30
		w. Wmk inverted	1·50	1·00
O55	**65**	8 a. reddish purple (1929)	80	60
		w. Wmk inverted	80	75
O56	**67**	1 r. chocolate and green (1929)	2·75	1·40
		w. Wmk inverted	2·25	1·75
O57		2 r. carmine and orange (1936)	6·50	26·00
O47/57		*Set of* 11	10·50	27·00

1935–9. *New types. Optd with Type* O **5**.

No.	Type	Description	Unused	Used
O58	**79**	½ a. green (1936)	10	10
O59	**81**	1 a. chocolate (1936)	10	30
O60	**59**	2 a. vermilion	15	15
O61		2 a. vermilion (*small die*) (1939)	9·00	2·00
O62	**63**	4 a. sage-green (1936)	95	40
O58/62		*Set of* 5	9·50	2·75

1937–39. *King George VI. Optd with Types* O **5** *or* O **6** (*rupee values*).

No.	Type	Description	Unused	Used
O63	**91**	½ a. red-brown (1938)	75	20
O64		9 p. green (1938)	13·00	50·00
O65		1 a. carmine	75	20
O66	**93**	1 r. grey and red-brown (1939)	1·00	3·75
O67		2 r. purple and brown (1939)	6·00	5·00
O68		5 r. green and blue (1939)	15·00	50·00
O63/8		*Set of* 6	32·00	£100

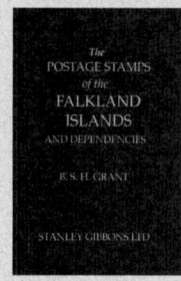

1A ——— 1A (O 7) 1A SERVICE 1A (O 8) PATIALA SERVICE (O 9)

1939–40. *Stamp of* 1932 (*King George V*).

(*a*) *Optd with Types* O **5** *and* O **7**

No.	Type	Description	Unused	Used
O69	**82**	1 a. on 1 a. 3 p. mauve	6·50	1·40
		w. Wmk inverted	6·50	2·00

(*b*) *Optd with T* **4** *and* O **8**

No.	Type	Description	Unused	Used
O70	**82**	1 a. on 1 a. 3 p. mauve (1940)	4·75	1·60
		w. Wmk inverted	4·75	2·25

"SERVICE" measures 9¼ mm on No. O69 but only 8¾ mm on O70.

1939–44. (*a*) *Official stamps optd with T* **7**.

No.	Type	Description	Unused	Used
O71	O **20**	3 p. slate (1940)	45	10
O72		½ a. red-brown	3·25	10
O73		½ a. purple (1942)	45	10
O74		9 p. green	45	20
		w. Wmk inverted		
O75		1 a. carmine	85	10
O76		1 a. 3 p. yellow-brown (1941)	85	25
O77		1½ a. dull violet (1944)	3·25	40
O78		2 a. vermilion (1940)	4·75	15
		w. Wmk inverted		
O79		2½ a. bright violet (1940)	95	65
O80		4 a. brown (1943)	85	1·25
O81		8 a. slate-violet (1944)	1·50	4·00

(*b*) *Postage stamps optd with Type* O **9**.

No.	Type	Description	Unused	Used
O82	**93**	1 r. grey and red-brown (1943)	7·00	7·00
O83		2 r. purple and brown (1944)	15·00	40·00
O84		5 r. green and blue (1944)	21·00	60·00
O71/84		*Set of* 14	55·00	£100

Patiala became part of the Patiala and East Punjab States Union by 20 August 1948.

INDIAN FEUDATORY STATES

These stamps were only valid for use within their respective states, *unless otherwise indicated*.

Postage stamps of the Indian States, current at that date, were replaced by those of the Republic of India on 1 April 1950.

Unless otherwise stated, all became obsolete on 1 May 1950 (with the exception of the "Anchal" stamps of Travancore-Cochin, which remained current until 1 July 1951 or Sept 1951 for the Official issues).

ALWAR

PRICES FOR STAMPS ON COVER

Nos. 1/2	*from* × 25
No. 3	*from* × 50
No. 4	—
No. 5	*from* × 50

Maharao Raja (Maharaja from 1889) Mangal Singh, 1874–1892.

1 (1 a.).

1877. *Litho. Rouletted.*
1 1 ¼ a. steel blue .. .. 13·00 7·00
a. Bright greenish blue .. .. .. 7·00 7·00
b. Ultramarine .. .. 3·25 80
c. Grey-blue (shades) .. .. .. 2·75 70
2 1 a. pale yellowish brown .. .. .. 6·50 4·25
a. Brown (shades) .. .. 2·75 1·25
b. Chocolate .. .. 9·00 8·00
c. Pale reddish brown .. .. .. 2·00 80

Maharaja Jai Singh, 1892–1937

1899–1901. *Redrawn. P* 12. (*a*) *Wide margins between stamps.*
3 1 ¼ a. slate-blue .. .. 5·50 2·25
a. Imperf between (horiz pair) .. £300 £350
b. Imperf between (vert pair) .. £500 £550
4 ¼ a. emerald-green £550

(*b*) *Narrower margins* (1901)
5 1 ¼ a. emerald-green .. .. .. 2·75 2·00
a. Imperf between (horiz pair) .. £190 £225
b. Imperf between (vert pair) .. £200 £225
c. Imperf horiz (vert pair) £200
d. Imperf (pair) £275
e. Pale yellow-green .. .. .. 5·00 2·00
ea. Imperf (pair) £425
eb. Imperf between (horiz pair) .. † £450

In the redrawn type only the bottom outer frameline is thick, whereas in the original 1877 issue the left-hand frameline is also thick, as shown in Type 1.

The stamps of Alwar became obsolete on 1 July 1902.

BAHAWALPUR
See after PAKISTAN

BAMRA

PRICES FOR STAMPS ON COVER

Nos. 1/6	—
Nos. 8/40	*from* × 25

Raja Sudhal Deo, 1869–1903

GUM. The stamps of Bamra were issued without gum.

1 (¼ a.) 1*a* 2 (½ a.)

3 (1 a.) 4 (2 a.) 5 (4 a.)

6 (8 a.)

(*illustrations actual size*)

(Typo Jagannata Ballabh Press, Deogarh)

1888. *Imperf.*
1 1 ¼ a. black/*yellow* £200
a. "g" inverted (R.5/1) £2750
b. Last native character inverted .. £3000
c. Last native character as Type 1*a* .. £3000
2 2 ½ a. black/*rose* .. .. .. 70·00
a. "g" inverted (R.5/1) £1500
3 3 1 a. black/*blue* .. .. .. 42·00
a. "g" inverted (R.5/1) £1300
b. Scroll inverted (R.8/4) £1100
4 4 2 a. black/*green* .. .. .. 65·00 £200
a. "a" omitted (R.8/3) £1500
b. Scroll inverted (R.8/4) £1300
5 5 4 a. black/*yellow* .. .. .. 48·00 £190
a. "a" omitted (R.8/3) £1400
b. Scroll inverted (R.8/4) £1200
6 6 8 a. black/*rose* .. .. .. 38·00
a. "a" omitted (R.8/3) £1200
b. Horiz pair, one printed on back .. £550
c. Scroll inverted (R.8/4) £1000

These stamps were all printed from the same plate of 96 stamps, 12 × 8, but for some values only part of the plate was used. There are 96 varieties of the ½, 4 and 8 a., 72 of the 1 a., 80 of the 2 a. and not less than 88 of the ¼ a.

The scroll ornament can be found pointing to either the right or the left.

There are two forms of the third native character. In the first five horizontal rows it is as in T 1 and in the last three rows as in T 4.

These stamps have been reprinted: the ¼ a. and ½ a. in blocks of 8 varieties (all showing scroll pointing to right), and all the values in blocks of 20 varieties (all showing scroll pointing to left). On the reprints the fourth character is of a quite different shape.

8

1890 (July)–**93.** *Black on coloured paper. Nos.* 24/5 *and* 39/40 *show face value as* "One Rupee". (*a*) "Postage" *with capital* "P".
8 8 ¼ a. on *rose-lilac* .. .. .. 2·75 3·75
a. "Eeudatory" (R. 2/4) .. .. 12·00 20·00
b. "Quatrer" (R. 1/3) .. .. .. 12·00 20·00
c. Inverted "e" in "Postage" (R. 2/3) .. 12·00 20·00
9 ¼ a. on *bright rose* .. .. .. 1·10 1·75
10 ¼ a. on *reddish purple* .. .. .. 1·25 1·60
a. First "a" in "anna" inverted (R. 3/3) 30·00 35·00
b. "AMRA" inverted (R. 4/4) .. .. 45·00 45·00
c. "M" and second "A" in "BAMRA" inverted (R. 4/4) .. .. .. 55·00 55·00
11 ½ a. on *dull green* .. .. .. 1·60 1·90
a. "Eeudatory" (R. 2/4) .. .. 35·00 42·00
12 ½ a. on *blue-green* .. .. .. 3·00 2·75
13 1 a. on *bistre-yellow* .. .. .. 3·25 1·75
a. "Eeudatory" (R. 2/4) .. .. 75·00 80·00
14 1 a. on *orange-yellow* .. .. .. 32·00 32·00
a. "annas" for "anna" £110 £110
15 2 a. on *rose-lilac* .. .. .. 11·00 20·00
a. "Eeudatory" (R. 2/4) £120 £160
16 2 a. on *bright rose* .. .. .. 2·75 3·25
17 2 a. on *dull rose* .. .. .. 7·50 4·75
18 4 a. on *rose-lilac* £550 £700
a. "Eeudatory" (R. 2/4) £3750
19 4 a. on *dull rose* .. .. .. 6·00 3·75
a. "Eeudatory" (R. 2/4) £700 £700
b. "BAMBA" (R. 2/1) £700 £700
20 4 a. on *bright rose* .. .. .. 4·00 5·50
20*a* 4 a. on *deep pink* .. .. .. 12·00 10·00
21 8 a. on *rose-lilac* .. .. .. 16·00 38·00
a. "Foudatory" and "Postagc" (R. 1/2) £150 £200
b. "BAMBA" (R. 2/1) £150 £200
22 8 a. on *bright rose* .. .. .. 9·00 12·00
23 8 a. on *dull rose* .. .. .. 16·00 12·00
24 1 r. on *rose-lilac* .. .. .. 35·00 65·00
a. "Eeudatory" (R. 2/4) £350 £425
b. "BAMBA" (R. 2/1) £250 £300
c. "Postagc" (R. 1/2) £250 £300
25 1 r. on *bright rose* .. .. .. 15·00 18·00
a. Small "r" in "rupee" £180 £180

(*b*) "postage" *with small* "p" (1891–93)
26 8 ¼ a. on *bright rose* .. .. .. 1·10 1·75
27 ¼ a. on *reddish purple* .. .. .. 1·25 1·60
28 ½ a. on *dull green* .. .. .. 2·00 2·25
a. First "a" in "anna" inverted (R. 3/3) 24·00 24·00
29 ½ a. on *blue-green* .. .. .. 3·00 2·75
a. First "a" in "anna" inverted (R. 3/3) 26·00 26·00
30 1 a. on *bistre-yellow* .. .. .. 2·25 1·75
31 1 a. on *orange-yellow* .. .. .. 32·00 32·00
32 2 a. on *bright rose* .. .. .. 2·75 3·25
33 2 a. on *dull rose* .. .. .. 7·50 4·75
34 4 a. on *dull rose* .. .. .. 7·50 3·25
35 4 a. on *bright rose* .. .. .. 4·25 6·00
35*a* 4 a. on *deep pink* .. .. .. 15·00 12·00
36 8 a. on *rose-lilac* .. .. .. 32·00 60·00
37 8 a. on *bright rose* .. .. .. 11·00 13·00
38 8 a. on *dull rose* .. .. .. 16·00 12·00
39 1 r. on *rose-lilac* .. .. .. 50·00 90·00
40 1 r. on *bright rose* .. .. .. 20·00 22·00
a. Small "r" in "rupee" £225 £225
b. Small "r" in "rupee" and native characters in the order 2, 3, 1, 4, 5 (R. 4/4) £1400 £1400

There are 10 settings of Type 8. The first setting (of 20 (4×5)) has capital "P" throughout. The remaining settings (of 16 (4×4)) have capital "P" and small "p" mixed.

For the first setting the 8 a. and 1 r. values were printed within the same block, the ten lefthand stamps being 8 a. values and the ten righthand stamps 1 r.

The various stamps were distributed between the settings as follows:
Setting I—Nos. 8/c, 11/a, 13/a, 15/a, 18/19a, 21, 24/a.
Setting II—Nos. 19, 19b, 21/b, 24, 24b/c, 34, 36, 39
Setting III—Nos. 9, 11, 13, 16, 26, 28, 30, 32
Setting IV—Nos. 20, 22, 25, 35, 37, 40
Setting V—Nos. 10, 10b/c, 20*a*, 27, 35*a*
Setting VI—Nos. 11, 12, 28, 28a, 29/a
Setting VII—Nos. 10/a, 12, 17, 19, 23, 25a, 27, 29, 33/4, 38, 40a/b
Setting VIII—Nos. 17, 33
Setting IX—Nos. 10/a, 12, 14/a, 17, 19, 23, 27, 29, 31, 33/4, 38
Setting X—Nos. 19, 34

There are 4 sizes of the central ornament, which represents an elephant's trunk holding a stick:—(*a*) 4 mm long; (*b*) 5 mm; (*c*) 6½ mm; (*d*) 11 mm. These ornaments are found pointing to right or left, either upright or inverted.

Ornaments (*a*) are found in all settings; (*b*) in all settings from Settings III to X; (*c*) in Settings I and II; and (*d*) only in Setting I.

The stamps of Bamra have been obsolete since 1 January 1895.

BARWANI

PRICES FOR STAMPS ON COVER

Nos. 1/2	*from* × 3
Nos. 3/43	*from* × 5

PROCESS. All Barwani stamps are typographed from clichés, and are in sheets of 4, *unless otherwise indicated*.

Issues to about 1930 were printed by the Barwani State Printing Press, and subsequently by the *Times of India* Press, Bombay.

GUM. Nos. 1/31 were issued without gum.

BOOKLET PANES. Those stamps which were printed in sheets of 4 were issued in stamp booklets, binding holes appearing in the side margin.

Rana Ranjit Singh, 1894–1930

1

2

3

1921 (Mar?). *Clear impression. Medium wove paper. P* 7 *all round.*
1 1 ¼ a. blue-green (dull *to* deep) .. .. 80·00 £225
2 ½ a. dull blue £200 £375
a. Imperf (pair) .. .. .. — £1000

No. 1 also exists perforated on two sides only.

1921 (June?). *Blurred impression. Soft wove paper. P* 7 *on two or three sides.*
3 1 ¼ a. green (*shades*) .. .. .. 17·00 75·00
4 ½ a. ultramarine (dull *to* pale) .. .. 17·00 £100

NOTE. As the small sheets of Barwani stamps were often not perforated all round, many of the earlier stamps are perforated on two or three sides only. Owing to the elementary method of printing, the colours vary greatly in depth, even within a single sheet.

1921. *Clear impression. Vertically laid bâtonné paper. Imperf.*
5 1 ¼ a. green (*shades*) .. .. .. 15·00 45·00
6 ½ a. green (*shades*) .. .. .. 3·75
a. Perf 11 at top or bottom only .. 3·00

It is suggested that No. 5 may be an error due to printing from the wrong plate.

1922 (?). *Clear impression. Thickish glazed wove paper. P* 7 *on two or three sides.*
7 1 ¼ a. dull blue .. .. .. 70·00

1922. *Smooth, soft medium wove paper. P* 7 *on two or three sides.*

(*a*) *Clear impression*
8 1 ¼ a. deep grey-blue .. .. .. 27·00 65·00

(*b*) *Poor impression*
9 1 ¼ a. steel blue .. .. .. 15·00

Examples of No. 9 exist with perforations on all four sides.

1922. *P* 11 *on two or three sides.*

(*a*) *Thick, glazed white wove paper*
10 2 1 a. vermilion (*shades*) .. .. .. 1·60 16·00
a. Imperf between (vert pair) £200
b. Doubly printed £650
11 2 a. purple (*to* violet) .. .. .. 1·90 17·00
a. Doubly printed £225
b. Imperf between (horiz pair) .. £160 £225
c. Imperf between (vert pair) £160

(*b*) *Thick, toned wove paper*
12 2 2 a. purple .. .. .. 11·00 38·00

1922. *Poor impression. Thin, poor wove paper. Pin-perf* 8½ *on two or three sides.*
13 1 ¼ a. grey (*to* grey-blue) .. .. 1·50 32·00
a. Imperf (pair) £200
b. Imperf between (vert pair) £120

1923. *Thin, smooth, unglazed wove paper. P* 11 *on two or three sides.*
14 1 ½ a. green (pale *to* deep) .. .. 1·25 15·00
a. Imperf between (vert pair) £375
15 2 1 a. brown-red £2250 £2250

1923. *Poor impression. Thick, soft wove paper. P* 7.
16 1 ½ a. green (pale *to* deep) .. .. 23·00

No. 16 also exists perforated on two or three sides.

1923 (Mar?). *Poor quality wove paper. P* 7 *on two or three sides.*
17 1 ¼ a. black .. .. .. 55·00 £180
a. Imperf between (horiz pair) .. £1400

1923 (May?). *Horizontally laid bâtonné paper. P* 12.
18 1 ¼ a. rose (*shades*) .. .. .. 90 9·00
a. Imperf between (vert pair) £325
ab. Imperf between (horiz pair) £475
b. Pin perf 6 .. .. .. 95·00 48·00
c. Perf compound of 12 and 6 .. 40·00 50·00
d. Perf 7 .. .. .. £375
da. On wove paper £1300

No. 18 was issued in sheets of 12 (3 panes of 4) and was printed on paper showing a sheet watermark of Britannia and a double-lined inscription. No. 18d was only issued in booklet panes of 4.

1925. *Vertically laid bâtonné paper. P* 11.
19 1 ¼ a. blue (pale *to* deep) .. .. 90 9·00
a. *Tête-bêche* (horiz pair) .. ..

No. 19 was issued in sheets of 8 and was printed on paper with a sheet watermark of a shell and an inscription "SHELL" in double-lined capitals.

1927. *Very poor impression. Thin, brittle wove paper. P* 7.

20 1 ¼ a. milky blue (*shades*) .. .. 9·00 27·00
21 ½ a. yellow-green (*shades*) .. .. 10·00 45·00
a. Imperf between (horiz pair) .. £650
22 3 4 a. orange-brown .. .. 60·00 £250
a. Imperf between (horiz pair) .. £950
20/2 .. .. *Set of* 3 70·00 £275

On Nos. 20/1 the portrait is nearly invisible.

1927. *Thick wove paper. Sewing machine perf* 6–10.

23 3 4 a. yellow-brown .. .. .. 75·00
a. Imperf between (horiz pair) .. £1400
b. Perf 7 .. .. 20·00 £170
c. *Orange-brown* .. .. .. 95·00 £275

1928–32 (?). *Thick glazed paper.* (*a*) *P* 7.

24 1 ¼ a. deep bright blue .. .. 11·00
25 ½ a. bright yellow-green .. .. 21·00

(*b*) *P* 10½ (*rough*) (Nov 1928)

26 1 ¼ a. ultramarine .. .. .. 4·00
a. *Tête-bêche* (horiz pair) .. .. 9·00
b. Horiz pair, one stamp printed on reverse .. ..
27 ½ a. apple-green .. .. .. 4·75
a. *Tête-bêche* (vert pair) .. .. 9·00

(*c*) *P* 11 (*clean-cut*) (1929-32?)

28 1 ¼ a. bright blue .. .. .. 2·25 9·00
a. *Indigo* .. .. .. 1·75 9·00
ab. Imperf between (horiz pair) .. 55·00
b. *Deep dull blue* .. .. .. 1·50 9·00
ba. Imperf between (vert pair) £170
c. *Ultramarine* .. .. .. 2·00 10·00
29 ½ a. myrtle-green .. .. .. 2·75 9·50
a. Imperf between (horiz pair) .. £150
b. *Turquoise-green* .. .. .. 3·50 11·00
ba. Imperf between (vert pair) £325
30 2 1 a. rose-carmine (1931) .. .. 11·00 27·00
a. Imperf between (vert pair) .. .. † £900
31 3 4 a. salmon (*to* orange) (1931) .. .. 50·00 £120
a. Imperf between (horiz pair) .. £1300
28/31 .. .. *Set of* 4 55·00 £150

No. 26 was printed in sheets of 8 (4 × 2) with the two centre pairs *tête-bêche* while No. 27 in similar sheets, had the two horizontal rows *tête-bêche*. Both sheets are always found with one long side imperforate.

Nos. 28/31 were printed in sheets of 8 the two lower values existing either 4 × 2 or 2 × 4 and the two higher values 4 × 2 only. No *tête-bêche* pairs were included in these printings. It is believed that a small printing of No. 31 was produced in sheets of 4, but details are uncertain.

Rana Devi Singh, 1930–1971

4 Rana Devi Singh 5

1932 (Oct)–**47.** *Medium to thick wove paper.*

A. *Close setting* (2½–4½ *mm*). *P* 11, 12 *or compound* (1932–41)

32A 4 ¼ a. slate .. .. .. 1·25 14·00
33A ½ a. blue-green .. .. .. 1·75 14·00
34A 1 a. brown .. .. .. 1·75 13·00
a. Imperf between (horiz pair) .. £1200
35A 2 a. purple (*shades*) .. .. .. 3·25 22·00
36A 4 a. olive-green .. .. .. 6·00 26·00
32A/6A .. .. *Set of* 5 12·50 80·00

B. *Wide setting* (6–7 *mm*). *P* 11 (1945–47)

32B 4 ¼ a. slate .. .. .. 3·25 19·00
33B ½ a. blue-green .. .. .. 2·75 14·00
34B 1 a. brown .. .. .. 7·50 14·00
b. *Chocolate.* Perf 8½ (1947) .. 12·50 35·00
35aB 2 a. rose-carmine £160 £300
36B 4 a. olive-green .. .. .. 20·00 30·00

The measurements given in the heading indicate the vertical spacing between impressions. There are eight settings of this interesting issue: four "Close" where the overall stamp dimensions from centre to centre of perfs vary in width from 21½ to 23 mm and in height from 25 to 27½ mm; three "Wide", width 23–23½ mm and height 29–30 mm and one "Medium" (26½×31 mm) (No. 34B*b* only).

1933–47. *P* 11.

A. *Close setting* (3–4½ *mm*). *Thick, cream-surfaced wove paper* (1933 *and* 1941 (*No.* 38A*a*)

37A 1 ¼ a. black .. .. .. 2·75 40·00
38A ½ a. blue-green .. .. .. 10·00 22·00
a. *Yellowish green* (1941) .. .. 7·00 19·00
39A 2 1 a. brown (*shades*) .. .. 14·00 20·00
42A 3 4 a. sage-green .. .. .. 25·00 55·00

B. *Wide setting* (7–10 *mm*). *Medium to thick wove paper* (1939–47)

37B 1 ¼ a. black (1945) .. .. .. 2·75 23·00
38aB ½ a. yellowish green (1945) .. .. 4·00 25·00
39B 2 1 a. brown (*shades*) .. .. .. 10·00 19·00
a. Perf 8½ (5 mm) (1947) .. .. 11·00 32·00
40B 2 a. bright purple .. .. .. 65·00 £160
41B 2 a. rose-carmine (1945) .. .. 22·00 85·00
42B 3 4 a. sage-green (1941) .. .. 23·00 42·00
a. *Pale sage-green* (1939) .. .. 10·00 30·00

There were two "Close" settings (over-all stamp size 25×29 mm) and five "Wide" settings with over-all sizes 26½–31½ × 31–36½ mm. There was also one "Medium" setting (26½×31 mm) but this was confined to the 1 a. perf 8½, No. 39a.

1938. *P* 11.

43 5 1 a. brown .. .. 25·00 50·00

Stamps printed in red with designs similar to Types **3** and **5** were intended for fiscal use.

STAMP BOOKLETS

Nos. 1/17, 18d/da and 20/5 are believed to have been issued in sewn or stapled booklet, usually containing thirty-two examples of one value in blocks of 4. All these early booklets had plain covers, often in shades of brown. Few complete booklets have survived from this period.

Nos. 32/47, produced by the *Times of India* Press in a series of nine printings between 1932 and 1947, were only issued in booklet form. Booklets from the 1932, 1933, 1937 and 1939 printings had plain card or paper covers in various colours, usually containing eight blocks of 4, except for the 1933 printing, which contained twenty blocks of 4. Booklets from the 1945 printing had plain white tissue covers from the same stock as the interleaving. All these booklets were stapled at left.

The following booklets, from a printing in 1941 and a series of three printings in 1947, had printed covers, produced by a handstamp in the case of Nos. SB14/15.

1941. *Buff, green* (*No.* SB3) *or blue* (*No.* SB7) *card covers inscribed* "BARWANI STATE POSTAGE STAMPS", *booklet value in brackets and number and value of stamps thus* "(Rs 4) 32 2 Annas". *Panes of* 4 *with margin at left only. Stapled.*

(*a*) *Booklets* 59×55 *mm*

SB1 8 a. booklet containing thirty-two ¼ a. (No. 32A) £225
SB2 1 r. booklet containing thirty-two ½ a. (No. 33A) £400
SB3 2 r. booklet containing thirty-two 1 a. (No. 34A) £450
SB4 4 r. booklet containing thirty-two 2 a. (No. 35A) £250
SB5 8 r. booklet containing thirty-two 4 a. (No. 36A) £375

(*b*) *Booklets* 63×60 *mm* (*No.* SB6) *or* 73×72 *mm* (*No.* SB7)

SB6 1 r. booklet containing thirty-two ½ a. (No. 38A*a*) £500
SB7 8 r. booklet containing thirty-two 4 a. (No. 42B) £750

1947. *Grey tissue covers inscribed* "32 STAMPS VALUE....' *Panes of* 4 *with margins all round. Stapled at left.*

(*a*) *Booklets* 70×95 *mm.*

SB 8 1 r. booklet containing thirty-two ½ a. (No. 33B) £475
SB 9 2 r. booklet containing thirty-two 1 a. (No. 34B) £700
SB10 8 r. booklet containing thirty-two 4 a. (No. 36B) £800

(*b*) *Booklets* 76×95 *mm*

SB11 8 a. booklet containing thirty-two ¼ a. (No. 37B) £600
SB12 4 r. booklet containing thirty-two 2 a. (No. 41B) £650
SB13 8 r. booklet containing thirty-two 4 a. (No. 42B*a*) £375

1947. *Buff paper covers with violet handstamp inscribed* "32 STAMPS VALUE Rs 2/-". *Panes of* 4 *with margins all round, Sewn with twine at left.*

SB14 2 r. booklets (71×69 *mm*) containing thirty-two 1 a. (No. 34B*b*) £450
SB15 2 r. booklet (71×73 *mm*) containing thirty-two 1 a. (No. 39B*a*) £350

1947. *Grey tissue covers inscribed* "32 STAMPS VALUE As 8". *Panes of* 4 *with margins all round. Stapled at left.*

SB16 8 a. booklet (70×75 *mm*) containing thirty-two ¼ a. (No. 32B) £140
SB17 8 a. booklet (85×75 *mm*) containing thirty-two ¼ a. (No. 37B) £160

Barwani became part of Madhya Bharat by 1 July 1948

BHOPAL

PRICES FOR STAMPS ON COVER	
Nos. 1/100	*from* × 10
Nos. O301/57	*from* × 15

The correct English inscription on these stamps is "H.H. NAWAB SHAH JAHAN BEGAM". In the case of Nos. 22 and 23 the normal stamps are spelt "BEGAN" and specimens with "BEGAM" are "errors".

As the stamps were printed from lithographic stones on which each unit was drawn separately by hand, numerous errors of spelling occurred. These are constant on all sheets and are listed. Some of our illustrations inadvertently include errors of spelling.

ILLUSTRATIONS. Types **1/3***a* and **6/12***a* are shown actual size.

EMBOSSING. Nos. 1/99 were only valid for postage when embossed with the device, in Urdu, of the ruling Begam. On T **1/3** and **6** to **12***a.* this was intended to fill the central part of the design. Almost all varieties can be found with the embossing inverted or sideways, as well as upright.

Shah Jahan

Sultan Jahan

(*actual size*)

The various basic types were often in concurrent use but for greater convenience the following list is arranged according to types instead of being in strict chronological order.

GUM. Nos. 1/99 were issued without gum.

Nawab Shah Jahan Begam, 16 November 1868–15 June 1901

1 (¼ a.)

1872. *Litho.* (*a*) *Double frame. Sheets of* 20 (5 × 4)

1 1 ¼ a. black £300 £275
a. "BFGAM" (R.3/1) £1000 £1000
b. "BEGAN" (R.2/2, R.4/4) £600 £600
c. "EGAM" (R.4/5) £1000 £1000
2 ½ a. red .. .. 13·00 27·00
a. "BFGAM" (R.3/1) .. .. .. 60·00 95·00
b. "BEGAN" (R.2/2, R.4/4) .. .. 40·00 70·00
c. "EGAM" (R.4/5) .. .. .. 60·00 95·00

2 (½ a.)

(*b*) *Single frame. Sheets of* 20 (4 × 5)

3 2 ¼ a. black .. .. † £4250
4 ½ a. red .. .. 19·00 35·00
a. "NWAB" (R.2/2) .. .. .. 90·00 £140

3 (¼ a.) 3*a* (¼ a.)

1878 (Jan). *All lettered* "EEGAM" *for* "BEGAM". *Sheets of* 20 (4 × 5).

(*a*) *Plate* 1. *Frame lines extend horiz and vert between stamps throughout sheet*

5 3 ¼ a. black .. .. 4·50 8·00

(*b*) *Plate* 2. *Frame lines normal*

5*a* 3*a* ¼ a. black .. .. 4·50 9·50

Apart from the frame line difference between Types **3** and **3***a* the stamps can also be distinguished by the differences in the value tablets, notably the thin vertical line in the centre in Type **3***a* compared with the slightly diagonal and heavier line in Type **3**.

4 (¼ a.) 5 (½ a.)

1878 (June?)–**79.** *Value in parenthesis* (*Nos.* 6/7). *Sheets of* 32 (4 × 8). *Imperf.*

6 4 ¼ a. green (1879) .. .. .. 9·00 15·00
7 ¼ a. green (*perf*) (1879) .. .. .. 7·00 10·00
8 5 ½ a. red .. .. 4·50 9·00
a. "JAHN" (R.5/2) .. .. .. 25·00
b. "NWAB" (R.3/2, R.4/2) .. .. 15·00
c. "EEGAM" (R.1/3) .. .. .. 25·00
9 ½ a. brown .. .. 20·00 30·00
a. "JAHN" (R.5/2) £130
b. "NWAB" (R.3/2, R.4/2) .. .. 80·00
c. "EEGAM" (R.1/3) £130

The ¼ a. shows the "N" of "NAWAB" reversed on R.6/4 and the "N" of "JAHAN" reversed on R.1/2–4 and R.2/2–4.

1880. *T* **5** *redrawn; value not in parenthesis. Sheets of* 32 (4 × 8)

(*a*) *Imperf*

10 ¼ a. blue-green .. .. 4·75
a. "NAWA" (R.2/2–4) .. .. .. 22·00
b. "CHAH" (R.8/3) .. .. .. 60·00
11 ½ a. brown-red .. .. 11·00 14·00

(*b*) *Perf*

12 ¼ a. blue-green .. .. 7·50
a. "NAWA" (R.2/2–4) .. .. .. 32·00
b. "CHAH" (R.8/3) .. .. .. 85·00
13 ½ a. brown-red .. .. 9·00

The ¼ a. shows the "N" of "NAWAB" reversed on R.8/4.

Nos. 12/13 sometimes come with gum.

1884. *T* **5** *again redrawn. Sheets of* 32 (4 × 8), *some with value in parenthesis, others not. Perf.*
4 ¼ a. greenish blue .. .. 2·75 8·50
a. "ANAWAB" (R.8/1–4) .. .. .. 12·00

In this plate there is a slanting dash under and to left of the letters "JA" of "JAHAN," instead of a character like a large comma, as on all previous varieties of this design. With the exception of R.1/1 all stamps in the sheet show "N" of "JAHAN" reversed.

1895. *T* **5** *again redrawn. Sheets of* 8 (2 × 4). *Laid paper.*
15 ¼ a. red (*imperf*) .. .. 3·25 1·10
16 ¼ a. red (*perf*) .. .. — £475

In these cases where the same design has been redrawn several times, and each time in a number of varieties of type, it is not easy to distinguish the various issues. Nos. 6 and 7 may be distinguished from Nos. 10 and 12 by the presence or absence of the parenthesis marks (); 8, 9 and 11 differ principally in colour; 8 and 15 are very much alike, but differ in the value as well as in paper.

6 (1 a.)

1881. *Sheets of* 24 (4 × 6). *Imperf.*
17 **6** ¼ a. black .. .. 3·50 11·00
a. "NWAB" (R.6/2–4) .. .. .. 9·00
18 ½ a. red .. .. 3·00 8·00
a. "NWAB" (R.6/2–4) .. .. .. 8·00
19 1 a. brown .. .. 3·00 9·00
a. "NWAB" (R.6/2–4) .. .. .. 7·00
20 2 a. blue .. .. 1·25 9·00
a. "NWAB" (R.6/2–4) .. .. .. 4·50
21 4 a. buff .. .. 10·00 32·00
a. "NWAB" (R.6/2–4) .. .. .. 28·00
17/21 .. .. *Set of* 5 18·00 55·00

In this issue all values were produced from the same drawing, and therefore show exactly the same varieties of type. The value at foot in this and all the following issues is given in only one form.

7 (½ a.)

1886. *Similar to T* **6** *but normally lettered* (*incorrectly*) "BEGAN"; *larger lettering. Sheets of* 32 (4 × 8). (*a*) *Imperf.*
22 **7** ½ a. pale red .. .. 1·40 6·00
a. "BEGAM" (R.2/1) .. .. .. 9·00
b. "NWAB" (R.3/4) .. .. .. 9·00

(*b*) *Perf*
23 **7** ½ a. pale red £225
a. "BEGAM" (R.2/1) £500
b. "NWAB" (R.3/4) £500

8 (4 a.)

1886. *T* **8**. *T* **6** *redrawn. Sheets of* 24 (4 × 6). *The* "M" *of* "BEGAM" *is an inverted* "W". *The width of the stamps is rather greater than the height.* (*a*) *Wove paper. Imperf.*
24 **8** 4 a. yellow £600
a. "EEGAM" (R.2/3–4, R.3/3–4, R.4/2, R.4/4, R.6/1) £700

(*b*) *Laid paper*
25 **8** 4 a. yellow (*imperf*) .. .. .. 6·50
a. "EEGAM" (R.2/3–4, R.3/3–4, R.4/2, R.4/4, R.6/1) .. .. .. 10·00
26 4 a. yellow (*perf*) .. .. .. 2·75 11·00
a. "EEGAM" (R.2/3–4, R.3/3–4, R.4/2, R.4/4, R.6/1) .. .. .. 5·00 16·00

1889. *T* **6** *again redrawn. Sheets of* 32 (4×8) *lettered* "BEGAN."
27 ¼ a. black (*perf*) .. .. .. 1·00 3·50
a. "EEGAN" (R.7/3) .. .. .. 10·00 20·00
b. Imperf between (horiz pair) £200
28 ¼ a. black (*imperf*) .. .. .. 1·10 3·25
a. "EEGAN" (R.7/3) .. .. .. 12·00 21·00

9 (¼ a.)

1889–90. *T* **9**. *T* **6** *again redrawn. Sheets of* 24 (4 × 6), *all with* "M" *like an inverted* "W". *Wove paper.* (*a*) *Imperf.*
29 **9** ¼ a. black .. .. 1·10 75
30 1 a. brown .. .. 1·00 3·25
a. "EEGAM" (R.2/3) .. .. .. 10·00 18·00
b. "BBGAM" (R.3/1) .. .. .. 10·00 18·00
31 2 a. blue .. .. 75 1·25
a. "BBEGAM" (R.1/2) .. .. .. 6·50 10·00
b. "NAWAH" (R.4/2) .. .. .. 6·50 10·00
32 4 a. orange-yellow .. .. .. 1·25 2·00
29/32 .. .. *Set of* 4 3·75 6·50

(*b*) *Perf*
33 **9** ¼ a. black .. .. 1·10 2·00
34 1 a. brown .. .. 2·75 4·00
a. "EEGAM" (R.2/3) .. .. .. 18·00 24·00
b. "BBGAM" (R.3/1) .. .. .. 18·00 24·00
35 2 a. blue .. .. 85 1·50
a. "BBEGAM" (R.1/2) .. .. .. 6·50 13·00
b. "NAWAH" (R.4/2) .. .. .. 6·50 13·00
36 4 a. orange-yellow .. .. .. 1·60 4·25
33/6 .. .. *Set of* 4 5·50 10·50

Nos. 32 and 36 are nearly square, in many cases rather larger in height than in width.

1891. *As last, but sheets of* 32 (4 × 8).
37 **9** ½ a. red (*imperf*) .. .. 1·10 2·00
38 ½ a. red (*perf*) .. .. 75 3·00

1894–98. *T* **6** *again redrawn;* (*a*) *Sheets of* 24 (4 × 6), *almost all showing a character inside the octagon below, as in T* **9**. *Wove paper.*
39 1 a. deep brown (*imperf*) .. .. .. 4·75 1·75
a. Red-brown .. .. 25·00
b. Printed both sides .. .. .. — £400
41 1 a. deep brown (*perf*) .. .. .. 4·25 1·75

10 (1 a.)

(*b*) *As Nos.* 39/41, *but printed from a new stone showing the lines blurred and shaky. Wove paper. Imperf* (1898)
42 **10** 1 a. purple-brown .. .. .. 2·00 2·75
a. "NAWAH" (R.4/1) .. .. .. 13·00 17·00
43 1 a. purple-brown/*buff* .. .. .. 2·00 2·75
a. "NAWAH" (R.4/1) .. .. .. 13·00 17·00
b. Printed on both sides .. ..

The above are known without embossing.

11 (¼ a.)

1895. *Sheets of* 8 (2 × 4), *lettered* "EEGAM". *White laid paper.*
44 **11** ¼ a. black (*imperf*) .. .. .. 2·00 1·25
a. "A" inserted (R.4/2) .. .. .. 6·50 5·00
45 ¼ a. black (*perf*) .. .. .. 60·00 28·00
a. "NAW B" (R.4/2) £225 £150

On the perf stamp the second "A" in "NAWAB" was missing on R.4/2 in the setting. This letter was later inserted for the imperf printing varying progressively from small to large.

12 (½ a.)

1895. *Narrow label at bottom. Sheets of* 8 (2 × 4), *lettered* "W W" *for* "H H". *Laid paper.*
46 **12** ½ a. black (*imperf*) .. .. 90 1·40

12a

1895. *Sheets of* 8 (2 × 4). *Laid paper.*
47 **12a** ½ a. red (*imperf*) .. .. 1·10 1·25

No. 47 is a combination of Types **1** and **6**, having the double outer frame to the octagon and the value in one form only.

13 (¼ a.)

(**14** (¼ a.)

1884. *Sheets of* 32 (4 × 8). *Perf.*
48 **13** ¼ a. blue-green £130 £160
a. "JAN" (R.2/1–2, R.3/1, R3/3–4, R.4/1–3, R.5/1–3) £130 £160
b. "BEGM" (R.2/3–4) £350
c. "NWAB" and "JAN" (R.3/2) £600
ca. "NWAB" and "JN" (R.5/4) £600
d. "SHAHAN" (R.4/4) £600
e. "JAHA" (R.6/2–4) £275

1895. *T* **14**, *double-lined frame round each stamp. Sheets of* 6 (2 × 3), *lettered* "JAN". *Laid paper.*
49 **14** ¼ a. bright green (*imperf*) .. .. 2·75 8·50

15 (½ a.)

16 (¼ a.)

1884. *Sheets of* 32 (4 × 8). *Laid paper.*
50 **15** ¼ a. blue-green (*imperf*) .. .. .. 90·00 £100
a. "NWAB" (R.1/1) £300
b. "SAH" (R.1/4) £300
c. "NAWA" and "JANAN" (R.3/2) .. £300
51 ¼ a. blue-green (*perf*) .. .. .. 45 2·25
a. "NWAB" (R.1/1) .. .. .. 3·00
b. "SAH" (R.1/4) .. .. .. 3·00
c. "NAWA" and "JANAN" (R.3/2) .. 3·00
d. Imperf between (vert pair) £200
52 ½ a. black (*imperf*) .. .. .. 1·50 1·00
a. "NWAB" (R.1/1) .. .. .. 7·00
b. "SAH" (R.1/4) .. .. .. 7·00
c. "NAWA" and "JANAN" (R.3/2) .. 7·00
53 ½ a. black (*perf*) .. .. 45 1·75
a. "NWAB" (R.1/1) .. .. .. 3·00
b. "SAH" (R.1/4) .. .. .. 3·00
c. "NAWA" and "JANAN" (R.3/2) .. 3·00

The ¼ a. of this issue is in *blue-green*, or *greenish blue*. Both values were printed from the same stone, the value alone being altered. There are therefore the same varieties of each. These are the only stamps of this design on laid paper.

Both values show the "N" of "NAWAB" reversed on R.1/1–4, R.2/1–4, R.3/1–4 and the "N" of "JAHAN" reversed on R.1/1–4, R.2/1–4, R.3/4.

1886. *T* **15** *redrawn. Sheets of* 32 (4 × 8). *Wove paper.*
54 ¼ a. green (*imperf*) .. .. 40 2·00
a. "NAWA" (R.6/3–4) .. .. .. 1·50
b. "NWAB" (R.1/1) .. .. .. 2·50
c. "NWABA" (R.7/4) .. .. .. 2·50
d. "NAWAA" (R.6/2) .. .. .. 2·50
e. "BEGAAM" and "NWABA" (R.7/3) .. 2·50
55 ¼ a. green (*perf*) .. .. 1·25 2·50
a. "NAWA" (R.6/3–4) .. .. .. 6·00
b. "NWAB" (R.1/1) .. .. .. 9·00
c. "NWABA" (R.7/4) .. .. .. 9·00
d. "NAWAA" (R.6/2) .. .. .. 9·00
e. "BEGAAM" and "NWABA" (R.7/3) .. 9·00
f. Imperf between (horiz pair) £130
56 ½ a. red (*imperf*) 45 70
a. "SAH" (R.1/4) .. .. .. 3·50
b. "NAWABA" (R.6/3–4) .. .. .. 2·75

The ¼ a. varies from *yellow-green* to *deep green*.

All examples of the ¼ a. value show the "N" of "NAWAB" reversed. On the same value the "N" of "JAHAN" is reversed on all positions except R.3/2, R.4/1, R.4/3. On the ½ a. both "N"s are always reversed.

1888. *T* 15 *again redrawn. Sheets of* 32 (4 × 8), *letters in upper angles smaller.* "N" *of* "NAWAB" *correct. Wove paper.*
57 ¼ a. deep green (*imperf*) 45 75
a. "SAH" (R.6/2) .. .. 3·50 4·50
b. "NAWA" (R.4/4) .. .. 3·50 4·50
58 ¼ a. deep green (*perf*) .. .. 65 1·40
a. "SAH" (R.6/2) .. .. 4·00
b. "NAWA" (R.4/4) .. .. 4·00
c. Imperf between (vert pair) £180
Nos. 50 to 58 have the dash under the letter "JA" as in No. 14.

1891. *T* 15 *again redrawn. Sheets of* 32 (4 × 8), *lettered* "NWAB." *Wove paper.* (a) *Imperf.*
59 ½ a. red 75 55
a. "SAH" (R.2/4) .. .. 3·50
(*b*) *P* 3 *to* 4½, *or about* 7
60 ½ a. red 60 75
a. "SAH" (R.2/4) .. .. 4·50
Nos. 59 and 60 have the comma under "JA". The "N" of "JAHAN" is reversed on R.1/1–3, R.2/1–2.

1894. *T* 15 *again redrawn; letters in corners larger than in* 1888, *value in very small characters. Sheets of* 32 (4 × 8), *all with* "G" *in left-hand lower corner. Wove paper.*
61 ¼ a. green (*imperf*) 60 60
a. "NAWAH" (R.4/4) .. .. .. 5·50 6·00
b. Value in brackets (R.1/1) .. .. 5·50 6·00
62 ¼ a. green (*perf*) .. .. 1·60 1·50
a. "NAWAH" (R.4/4) .. .. .. 9·00 9·00
b. Value in brackets (R.1/1) .. .. 9·00 9·00
Nos. 61 and 62 have neither the dash nor the comma under "JA".

1896. *T* 16; *oval narrower, stops after* "H.H.", *space after* "NAWAB". *The line down the centre is under the first* "H" *of* "SHAH" *or between* "HA" *instead of being under the second* "H" *or between* "AH". *Sheets of* 32 (4 × 8). *Wove paper. Imperf.*
63 **16** ¼ a. bright green 40 40
a. "SHAN" (R.1/1) .. .. .. 3·00
64 ¼ a. pale green 40 35
a. "SHAN" (R.1/1) .. .. .. 3·00
65 ¼ a. black 30 30
a. "SHAN" (R.1/1) .. .. .. 3·00

1899. *T* 15 *redrawn. Sheets of* 32 (4 × 8), *the first* "A" *of* "NAWAB" *always absent. Numerous defective and malformed letters. Wove paper. Imperf.*
66 ½ a. black .. .. 2·50 3·50
a. "NWASBAHJANNI" (R.2/4) .. .. 15·00 18·00
b. "SBAH" (R.3/3, R.4/3–4, R.5/1–2, R.6/4) 6·50 8·50
c. "SBAN" (R.8/2) .. .. 15·00 18·00
d. "NWIB" (R.3/2) .. .. 15·00 18·00
e. "BEIAM" (R.4/4) .. .. 15·00 18·00
f. "SHH" (R.6/3) .. .. 15·00 18·00
g. "SBAH" and "BBGAM" (R.3/4) .. .. 15·00 18·00
h. "BBGAM" (R.1/3) .. .. 15·00 18·00

17 (8 a.) (**18** (¼ a.)

1890. *T* 17. *Sheets of* 10 (2 × 5). *Single-line frame to each stamp.*
(*a*) *Wove paper*
67 **17** 8 a. slate-green (*imperf*) .. .. 32·00 60·00
a. "HAH" (R.3/1, R.4/1, R.5/1) .. 48·00
b. "JABAN" (R.2/2) .. .. .. 48·00
68 8 a. slate-green (*perf*) .. .. 32·00 60·00
a. "HAH" (R.3/1, R.4/1, R.5/1) .. 48·00
b. "JABAN" (R.2/2) .. .. .. 48·00
(*b*) *Thin laid paper*
69 **17** 8 a. green-black (*imperf*) .. .. 42·00 80·00
a. "HAH" (R.3/1, R.4/1, R.5/1) .. 60·00
b. "JABAN" (R.2/2) .. .. .. 60·00
70 8 a. green-black (*perf*) .. .. 42·00 80·00
a. "HAH" (R.3/1, R.4/1, R.5/1) .. 60·00
b. "JABAN" (R.2/2) .. .. .. 60·00
The "N" of "NAWAB" is reversed on R.5/2 and the "N" of "JAHAN" on R.1/1–2, R.2/2, R.3/2, R.4/2 and R.5/2.

1893. *T* 17 *redrawn. No frame to each stamp, but a frame to the sheet. Sheets of* 10 (2 × 5). (*a*) *Wove paper.*
71 8 a. green-black (*imperf*) .. .. 15·00 15·00
72 8 a. green-black (*perf*) .. .. 20·00 26·00
(*b*) *Thin laid paper. Imperf*
73 8 a. green-black £120 £140

1898. *Printed from a new stone. Lettering irregular. Sheets of* 10 (2×5). *Wove paper. Imperf.*
74 8 a. green-black .. .. 27·00 38·00
a. Reversed "E" in "BEGAM" (R.1/2, R.3/2) 60·00
75 8 a. black .. .. 27·00 38·00
a. Reversed "E" in "BEGAM" (R.1/2, R.3/2) 60·00

1896–1901. *Sheets of* 32 (4×8). (*a*) *Wove paper. Imperf.*
76 **18** ¼ a. black 70 70
(*b*) *Printed from a new stone, lines shaky* (1899)
77 **18** ¼ a. black .. .. 1·50 1·40
(*c*) *The same, on thick wove paper* (1901)
78 **18** ¼ a. black £475 £475

Nawab Sultan Jahan Begam, 16 June 1901–17 May 1926

19 (¼ a.) **20**

1902. *T* 19. *With the octagonal embossed device of the previous issues. Sheets of* 16 (4 × 4) ¼ *a. or* 8 (2 × 4) *others. Thin, yellowish wove paper. Imperf.*
79 **19** ¼ a. rose .. .. 3·75 6·00
80 ¼ a. rose-red .. .. 1·50 3·50
81 ½ a. black .. .. 2·00 4·25
a. Printed both sides £450
82 1 a. brown .. .. 3·00 9·50
83 1 a. red-brown .. .. 2·50 8·50
84 2 a. blue .. .. 5·50 8·00
85 4 a. orange .. .. 45·00 75·00
86 4 a. yellow .. .. 28·00 55·00
87 8 a. lilac .. .. 60·00 £120
88 1 r. rose £160 £200
79/88 .. .. *Set of* 7 £225 £350

1903. *With a circular embossed device. Sheets of* 16 (4×4) ¼ *a.* (*two plates*) *or* 8 (2×4) (*others*). *Wove paper.*
89 **19** ¼ a. rose-red .. .. 80 2·75
a. Laid paper .. .. 50 4·50
90 ¼ a. red .. .. 65 2·50
a. Laid paper .. .. 30 3·50
91 ½ a. black .. .. 60 3·25
a. Laid paper .. .. 65 4·50
92 1 a. brown .. .. 1·00 4·25
a. Laid paper .. .. 60·00
93 1 a. red-brown .. .. 3·25
a. Laid paper .. ..
94 2 a. blue .. .. 2·50 16·00
a. Laid paper £100
95 4 a. orange (*laid paper*) £160 £160
96 4 a. yellow .. .. 14·00 40·00
a. Laid paper .. .. 85·00 80·00
97 8 a. lilac .. .. 35·00 90·00
a. Laid paper £900
98 1 r. rose .. .. 50·00 £120
a. Laid paper £800
89/98 .. .. *Set of* 7 90·00 £250

1903. *No.* 71 *optd with initial of the new Begam, either* 6 *or* 11 *mm long, in red.*
99 8 a. green-black .. .. 70·00 70·00
a. Opt inverted £160 £160
Some of the previous stamps remained on sale (and probably in use) after the issue of the series of 1902, and some of these were afterwards put on sale with the new form of embossing; fresh plates were made of some of the old designs, in imitation of the earlier issues, and impressions from these were also sold with the new embossed device. We no longer list these doubtful items.

(Recess Perkins, Bacon & Co)

1908. *P* 13½.
100 **20** 1 a. green .. .. 2·50 2·50
a. Printed both sides £100
b. Imperf (pair)

The ordinary postage stamps of Bhopal became obsolete on 1 July 1908.

OFFICIAL STAMPS

SERVICE **SERVICE**

(O **1**) (O **2**)

(Recess and optd Perkins, Bacon)

1908–11. *As T* 20, *but inscribed* "H.H. BEGUM'S SERVICE" *at left. No wmk. P* 13 *to* 14. *Overprinted.* (*a*) *With Type* O 1.
O301 ½ a. yellow-green .. .. 1·75 10
a. Imperf (pair) £100
b. Pair, one without overprint £375
c. Opt double, one inverted £110
ca. Ditto. Imperf (pair) £130
d. Opt inverted £120 £120
e. Imperf between (horiz pair) £425
O302 1 a. carmine-red .. .. 3·00 35
a. Opt inverted .. .. 75·00 75·00
b. Imperf (pair) .. .. 90·00
c. Red .. .. 3·75 10
O303 2 a. ultramarine .. .. 19·00 10
a. Imperf (pair) .. .. 55·00
O304 4 a. brown (1911) .. .. 8·50 15
O301/4 .. .. *Set of* 4 29·00 40
(*b*) *With Type* O 2
O305 ½ a. yellow-green .. .. 4·25 40
O306 1 a. carmine-red .. .. 7·00 90
O307 2 a. ultramarine .. .. 3·00 40
a. Opt inverted .. .. 25·00
O308 4 a. brown (1911) .. .. 70·00 40
a. Opt inverted .. .. 20·00 65·00
b. Opt double .. .. 90·00
c. Imperf (pair) .. .. 80·00
d. Imperf (pair) and opt inverted .. .. 80·00
O305/8 .. .. *Set of* 4 75·00 1·90
The two overprints differ in the shape of the letters, noticeably in the "R".

MINIMUM PRICE
The minimum price quote is 10p which represents a handling charge rather than a basis for valuing common stamps. For further notes about prices see introductory pages.

Nawab Mohammad Hamidullah. Khan
17 May 1926 to transfer of administration to India, 1 June 1949

SERVICE

(O **3**)

(O **4**)

(Des T. I. Archer. Litho Indian Govt Ptg Wks, Nasik)

1930 (1 July)–**31.** *Type* O 4 (25½ × 30½ *mm*) *optd with Type* O 3. *P* 14.
O309 O **4** ½ a. sage-green (1931) .. .. 6·00 75
O310 1 a. carmine-red .. .. .. 7·50 15
O311 2 a. ultramarine .. .. .. 7·00 40
O312 4 a. chocolate .. .. .. 6·00 50
O309/12 .. .. *Set of* 4 24·00 1·60
The ½ a., 2 a. and 4 a. are inscribed "POSTAGE" at left.

(Litho Perkins, Bacon)

1932–34. *As Type* O 4 (21 × 25 *mm*), *but inscr* "POSTAGE" *at left. Optd with Type* O 1. (*a*) "BHOPAL STATE" *at right. P* 13.
O313 ¼ a. orange .. .. 2·50 45
a. Perf 11½ (1933) .. .. .. 4·25 20
b. Perf 14 (1934) .. .. .. 10·00 30
c. Perf 13½ (1934) .. .. .. 12·00 30
ca. Vert pair, one without opt £110
(*b*) "BHOPAL GOVT" *at right. P* 13½
O314 ½ a. yellow-green .. .. .. 3·50 10
O315 1 a. carmine-red .. .. .. 6·50 15
a. Vert pair, one without opt £200
O316 2 a. ultramarine .. .. .. 6·50 45
O317 4 a. chocolate .. .. .. 5·00 70
a. Perf 14 (1934) .. .. .. 12·00 40
O313/17 .. .. *Set of* 5 22·00 1·10
No. O317 is comb-perforated and No. O317a line-perforated.

¼ A THREE PIES ONE ANNA

(O **5**) (O **6**) (O **7**)

1935–36. *Nos.* O314, O316 *and* O317 *surch as Types* O **5** *to* O **7**.
O318 O **5** ¼ a. on ½ a. yellow-green (R.) .. 18·00 10·00
a. Surch inverted .. .. £110 75·00
b. Vert pair. Nos. O318/19 .. 28·00 17·00
ba. Ditto. Surch inverted £225 £140
O319 O **6** 3 p. on ½ a. yellow-green (R.) .. 2·50 2·50
a. "THEEE PIES" (R. 7/10) .. 55·00 45·00
b. "THRFE for "THREE" (R. 10/6) 55·00 45·00
c. Surch inverted .. .. 55·00 38·00
O320 O **5** ¼ a. on 2 a. ultramarine (R.) .. 18·00 12·00
a. Surch inverted .. .. £110 60·00
b. Vert pair. Nos. O320/1 .. 28·00 19·00
ba. Ditto. Surch inverted £225 £130
O321 O **6** 3 p. on 2 a. ultramarine (R.) .. 2·75 2·75
a. Surch inverted .. .. 50·00 35·00
b. "THEEE PIES" (R. 7/10) .. 55·00 42·00
ba. Ditto. Surch inverted £375 £375
c. "THRFE" for "THREE" (R. 10/6) 55·00 42·00
ca. Ditto. Surch inverted £375 £375
O322 O **5** ¼ a. on 4 a. chocolate (R.) £600 £180
a. Vert pair. Nos O322 and O324 £850 £325
O323 ¼ a. on 4 a. chocolate (No. O317a, (Blk.) (25.5.36) .. .. 48·00 17·00
a. Vert pair. Nos. O323 and O325 65·00 29·00
O324 O **6** 3 p. on 4 a. chocolate (R.) .. .. 70·00 38·00
a. "THEEE PIES" (R. 7/10) .. £350 £300
c. "THRFE" for "THREE" (R. 10/6) £350 £300
O325 3 p. on 4 a. chocolate (No. O317a) (Blk.) (25.5.36) .. .. 2·50 2·25
a. "THRER" for "THREE" (R. 8/2) £200 £140
b. "FHREE" for "THREE" (R.3/10, 10/1) £225 £180
c. "PISE" for "PIES" (R. 10/10) .. £350 £275
d. "PIFS" for "PIES" (R. 7/9) .. £200 £160
O326 O **7** 1 a. on ½ a. yellow-green (V.) .. 2·50 1·50
a. Surch inverted .. .. 55·00 40·00
b. First "N" in "ANNA" inverted (R. 4/5) .. .. .. 60·00 50·00
ba. Ditto. Surch inverted £375 £350
O327 1 a. on 2 a. ultramarine (R.) .. 2·25 1·75
a. Surch inverted .. .. 60·00 35·00
b. First "N" in "ANNA" inverted (R. 4/5) .. .. .. 60·00 48·00
ba. Ditto. Surch inverted £375 £350
O327*d* 1 a. on 2 a. ultramarine (V.) .. 42·00 42·00
da. Surch inverted .. .. 85·00 85·00
db. First "N" in "ANNA" inverted (R. 4/5) £375 £375
dc. Ditto. Surch inverted £600 £600
O328 1 a. on 2 a. ultram (Blk.) (25.5.36) 70 1·00
a. "ANNO" £900
O329 1 a. on 4 a. chocolate (B.) .. .. 3·00 3·25
a. First "N" in "ANNA" inverted (R. 4/5) .. .. .. 65·00 50·00
b. Perf 14 .. .. .. 6·00 3·25
ba. Ditto. First "N" in "ANNA" inverted (R. 4/5) .. .. £140 75·00
Nos. O318 to O325 are arranged in composite sheets of 100 (10 × 10). The two upper horizontal rows of each value are surcharged as Type O **5** and the next five rows as Type O **6**. The remaining three rows are also surcharged as Type O **6** but in a slightly narrower setting.
The surcharge on No. O323 differs from Type O **5** in the shape of the figures and letter.

O 8

(Des T. I. Archer. Litho Indian Govt Ptg Wks, Nasik (No. O330). Typo Bhopal Govt Ptg Wks (others))

1935–39. *As Type* O **8**.

(a) *Litho. Inscr* "BHOPAL GOVT POSTAGE". *Optd* "SERVICE" (13½ *mm*). *P* 13½
O330 1 a. 3 p. blue and claret — 2·00 30

(b) *Typo. Inscr* "BHOPAL STATE POSTAGE". *Optd* "SERVICE" (11 *mm*). *P* 12
O331 1 a. 6 p. blue and claret (1937) — 1·25 30
a. Imperf between (pair) — £100 £110
b. Opt omitted — 95·00 75·00
c. Opt double, one inverted — £250 £250
d. Imperf (pair) — † 95·00
e. Blue printing double — † 90·00
O332 1 a. 6 p. claret (1939) — 3·50 65
a. Imperf between (pair) — £100 £110
b. Opt omitted — — £200
c. Opt double, one inverted — — £200
d. Opt double — — £225

PRINTERS. From No. O333 all issues were printed by the Bhopal Govt Ptg Wks in typography.

O 9

O 10 The Moti Mahal

1936 (July)–38. *Optd* "SERVICE". *P* 12.
O333 O **9** ¼ a. orange (Br.) — 90 20
a. Imperf between (vert pair) — £120
ab. Imperf between (horiz pair) — † £180
b. Opt inverted — £200 £160
c. Black opt — 7·00 75
ca. Opt inverted — † £200
cb. Opt double — † £190
O334 ¼ a. yellow (Br.) (1938) — 1·90 55
O335 1 a. scarlet — 1·25 10
a. Imperf between (horiz pair) — 85·00 80·00
b. Imperf between (vert pair) — † £150
c. Imperf between (block of four) — £200 £200
d. Imperf vert (horiz pair) — † 90·00

1936–49. *As Type* O **10** (*various palaces*). *P* 12.

(a) *Optd* "SERVICE" (13½ *mm*)
O336 ½ a. purple-brown and yellow-green — 70 50
a. Imperf between (vert pair) — † £120
ab. Imperf between (horiz pair) — † £120
b. Opt double — £180 £120
c. Frame double — 90·00 15·00
d. *Purple-brown and green* (1938) — 70 25

(b) *Optd* "SERVICE" (11 *mm*)
O337 2 a. brown and blue (1937) — 1·25 25
a. Imperf between (vert pair) — † £180
ab. Imperf between (horiz pair) — † £130
b. Opt inverted — £180 £180
c. Pair, one without opt — £350
d. As c. but opt inverted — £500
O338 2 a. green and violet (1938) — 5·50 25
a. Imperf between (vert pair) — † £130
b. Imperf between (vert strip of 3) — 90·00 95·00
c. Frame double — † £140
d. Centre double — † £140
O339 4 a. blue and brown (1937) — 2·50 50
a. Imperf between (horiz pair) — † £350
b. Opt omitted — † £180
c. Opt double — † £120
d. Centre double — † £190
e. *Blue and reddish brown* (1938) — 2·50 55
ea. Frame double — † £140
O340 8 a. bright purple and blue (1938) — 3·50 65
a. Imperf between (vert pair) — † £200
b. Opt omitted — † 95·00
c. Opt double — † £120
d. Imperf vert (horiz pair) and opt omitted — † £170
e. Imperf (pair) and opt omitted — † £170
O341 1 r. blue and reddish purple (Br.) (1938) — 10·00 4·75
a. Imperf horiz (vert pair) — † £750
b. Opt in black (1942) — 12·00 4·00
ba. *Light blue and bright purple* — 32·00 27·00
bb. Laid paper — £400 £425
O336/41 — *Set of* 6 21·00 6·00

(c) *Optd* "SERVICE" (11½ *mm*) *with serifs*
O342 1 r. dull blue and bright purple (Blk.) (1949) — 40·00 65·00
a. "SREVICE" for "SERVICE" (R. 6/6) — £130 £170
b. "SERVICE" omitted — £500

(d) *Optd* "SERVICE" (13½ *mm*) *with serifs*
O343 8 a. bright purple and blue (1949) — 55·00 80·00
a. "SERAICE" for "SERVICE" (R. 6/5) — £225 £325
b. Fig "1" for "I" in "SERVICE" (R. 7/1) — £225 £325

The ½ a. is inscr "BHOPAL GOVT" below the arms, other values have "BHOPAL STATE".

Designs:—(37½ × 22½ *mm*) 2 a. The Moti Masjid; 4 a. Taj Mahal and Be-Nazir Palaces. (39 × 24 *mm*)–8 a. Ahmadabad Palace. (45½ × 27½ *mm*)—1 r. Rait Ghat.

O 11 Tiger

O 13 The Moti Mahal

1940. *As Type* O **11** (*animals*). *P* 12.
O344 ¼ a. bright blue — 2·50 70
O345 1 a. bright purple (Spotted Deer) — 14·00 80

1941. *As Type* O **8** *but coloured centre inscr* "SERVICE"; *bottom frame inscr* "BHOPAL STATE POSTAGE". *P* 12.
O346 1 a. 3 p. emerald-green — 70 70
a. Imperf between (pair) — £300 £300

1944–47. *As Type* O **13** (*various palaces*). *P* 12.
O347 ½ a. green — 85 40
a. Imperf (pair) — † 60·00
b. Imperf between (vert pair) — † £110
c. Doubly printed — † 95·00
O348 2 a. violet — 5·00 2·25
a. Imperf (pair) — † 60·00
c. *Bright purple* (1945) — 1·60 2·00
d. *Mauve* (1947) — 11·00 11·00
e. Error. Chocolate (imperf) — £110 £110
O349 4 a. chocolate — 3·50 1·10
a. Imperf (pair) — † 75·00
b. Imperf vert (horiz pair) — † £140
c. Doubly printed — † £110
O347/9 — *Set of* 3 5·25 3·00

Design inscr "BHOPAL STATE":—2 a. The Moti Masjid; 4 a. Be-Nazir Palaces.

O 14 Arms of Bhopal

(O 15) (O 16)

1944–49. *P* 12.
O350 O **14** 3 p. bright blue — 65 20
a. Imperf between (vert pair) — 75·00 80·00
b. Imperf between (horiz pair) — † £140
c. Stamp doubly printed — 40·00
O351 9 p. chestnut (*shades*) (1945) — 6·50 1·75
a. Imperf (pair) — † £130
b. *Orange-brown* — 2·00 2·50
O352 1 a. purple (1945) — 3·25 80
a. Imperf horiz (vert pair) — † £200
b. *Violet* (1946) — 6·00 1·75
O353 1½ a. claret (1945) — 1·25 40
a. Imperf between (horiz pair) — † £190
b. Imperf between (vert pair)
O354 3 a. yellow — 6·50 7·50
a. Imperf (pair) — † £130
b. Imperf horiz (vert pair) — † £160
c. Imperf vert (horiz pair)
d. *Orange-brown* (1949) — 65·00 60·00
O355 6 a. carmine (1945) — 10·00 28·00
a. Imperf (pair) — † £140
b. Imperf horiz (vert pair) — † £160
c. Imperf vert (horiz pair) — † £160
O350/5 — *Set of* 6 21·00 35·00

1949 (July). *Surch with Type* O **15**. *P* 12.
O356 O **14** 2 a. on 1½ a. claret — 2·25 4·75
a. Stop omitted — 12·00 20·00
b. Imperf (pair) — £150 £170
ba. Stop omitted (pair) — £425 £450
c. "2" omitted (in pair with normal) — £475

The "stop omitted" variety occurs on positions 60 and 69 in the sheet of 81.

1949. *Surch with Type* O **16**. *Imperf.*
O357 O **14** 2 a. on 1½ a. claret — £475 £500
a. Perf 12 — £500 £500

Three different types of "2" occur in the setting of Type O **16**.

BHOR

PRICES FOR STAMPS ON COVER
Nos. 1/2 *from* × 40
No. 3 *from* × 6

GUM. The stamps of Bhor were issued without gum.

Pandit Shankar Rao, 1871–1922

1

2

1879. *Handstamped. Very thick to thin native paper. Imperf.*
1 1 ½ a. carmine (*shades*) — 1·75 3·50
a. *Tête-bêche* (pair) — £600
2 2 1 a. carmine (*shades*) — 3·00 5·00

3

1901. *Typo. Wove paper. Imperf.*
3 3 ½ a. red — 8·00 30·00

BIJAWAR

PRICES FOR STAMPS ON COVER
The stamps of Bijawar are very rare used on cover.

Maharaja Sarwant Singh, 1899–1941

1

2

(Typo Lakshmi Art Ptg Works, Bombay)

1935 (1 July)–36. (a) *P* 11.
1 1 3 p. brown — 4·00 2·75
a. Imperf (pair) — 5·50
b. Imperf between (vert pair) — 80·00
c. Imperf horiz (vert pair) — 50·00
2 6 p. carmine — 4·00 2·75
a. Imperf (pair) — 85·00
b. Imperf between (vert pair) — 80·00
c. Imperf between (horiz pair) — 80·00 £110
d. Imperf horiz (vert pair) — 80·00
3 9 p. violet — 4·25 3·25
a. Imperf (pair) — £140
b. Imperf between (vert pair) — 80·00
c. Imperf between (horiz pair) — 80·00
d. Imperf horiz (vert pair) — 80·00
4 1 a. blue — 4·75 3·75
a. Imperf (pair) — 85·00
b. Imperf between (vert pair) — 85·00
c. Imperf between (horiz pair) — £110
d. Imperf horiz (vert pair) — 85·00
e. Imperf vert (horiz strip of 3) — £130
5 2 a. deep green — 5·00 4·75
a. Imperf (pair) — £100
b. Imperf horiz (vert pair) — 11·00
c. Imperf between (vert pair) — 35·00
d. Imperf between (horiz pair) — 50·00 80·00
1/5 — *Set of* 5 20·00 15·00

(b) *Roul* 7 (1936)
6 1 3 p. brown — 2·50 2·75
a. Printed on gummed side — £400
7 6 p. carmine — 4·00 14·00
8 9 p. violet — 5·50 70·00
9 1 a. blue — 6·50 75·00
10 2 a. deep green — 7·00 80·00
6/10 — *Set of* 5 23·00 £225

1937 (May). *Typo. P* 9.
11 2 4 a. orange — 7·50 55·00
a. Imperf between (vert pair) — £140
b. Imperf (pair) — £200
12 6 a. lemon — 8·00 55·00
a. Imperf between (vert pair) — £140
b. Imperf (pair) — £200
13 8 a. emerald-green — 8·00 70·00
a. Imperf (pair) — £225
14 12 a. greenish blue — 8·00 70·00
a. Imperf (pair) — £250
15 1 r. bright violet — 29·00 £110
a. "1 Rs" for "1 R" (R. 1/2) — 48·00 £300
b. Imperf (pair) — £300
ba. "1 Rs" for "1 R" (R. 1/2) — £850
11/15 — *Set of* 5 55·00 £325

The stamps of Bijawar were withdrawn in 1941.

BUNDI

PRICES FOR STAMPS ON COVER

No. 1	*from* × 2
No. 2	*from* × 4
Nos. 3/53	*from* × 10
Nos. 54/63	*from* × 5
Nos. 64/78	*from* × 2
Nos. 79/92	*from* × 10
Nos. O1/52	*from* × 15
Nos. O53/9	*from* × 20

GUM. Nos. 1/17 were issued without gum.

ILLUSTRATIONS. Types **1/10** and **12/19** are shown actual size.

In Nos. 1 to 17 characters denoting the value are below the dagger, except in Nos. 2a, 11 and 17.

All Bundi stamps until 1914 are imperforate.

Maharao Raja Raghubir Singh, 1889–1927

1

1894 (May). *Each stamp with a distinct frame and the stamps not connected by the framing lines. Three vertical lines on dagger. Laid or wove paper.*

1 **1** ½ a. slate-grey £4500 £1600
a. Last two letters of value below the rest .. .. † £3250

2 (Block of four stamps)

1894 (Dec). *Stamps joined together, with no space between them. Two vertical lines on dagger. Thin wove paper.*

2 **2** ½ a. slate-grey .. .. 29·00 30·00
a. Value at top, name below £170 £190
b. Right upper ornament omitted .. £1300 £1300
c. Last two letters of value below the rest £950 £950
d. Left lower ornament omitted .. £1300 £1300

3

1896 (Nov). *Dagger shorter, lines thicker. Stamps separate. Laid paper.*

3 **3** ½ a. slate-grey .. .. 3·50 7·50
a. Last two letters of value below the rest £300 £375

4 (1 anna)

5 (2 annas)

6 (2 annas)

1897–98. *No shading in centre of blade of dagger. The stamps have spaces between them, but are connected by the framing lines, both vertically and horizontally. Laid paper.*

I. *Blade of dagger comparatively narrow, and either triangular, as in T* **4** *and* **6**, *or with the left-hand corner not touching the bar behind it, as in T* **5** (1897-98)

4 **4** 1 a. Indian red .. .. 7·50 17·00
5 **5** 1 a. red .. .. 7·50 13·00
6 2 a. green .. .. 9·00 18·00
7 **6** 2 a. yellow-green .. .. 9·00 19·00
8 **5** 4 a. green .. .. 38·00 50·00
9 8 a. Indian red .. .. 65·00 £140
10 1 r. yellow/*blue* £150 £275
4/10 .. .. *Set of* 5 £225 £450

7

II. *Blade varying in shape, but as a rule not touching the bar; value above and name below the dagger, instead of the reverse* (Jan 1898)

11 **7** 4 a. emerald-green .. .. .. 24·00
a. Yellow-green .. .. .. 16·00 38·00

8 (½ anna)

9 (8 annas)

III. *Blade wider and (except on the ½ a.) almost diamond shaped; it nearly always touches the bar* (1898–1900)

12 **8** ½ a. slate-grey (5.2.98) .. .. .. 2·25 2·75
13 **9** 1 a. Indian red (7.98) .. .. .. 1·60 1·75
14 2 a. pale green (9.11.98) .. .. .. 6·50 10·00
a. First two characters of value (= two) omitted £1000 £1000
15 8 a. Indian red (7.98) .. .. .. 6·00 11·00
16 1 r. yellow/*blue* (7.98) .. .. .. 20·00 30·00
a. On wove paper .. .. .. 8·00 18·00
12/16a .. .. *Set of* 5 21·00 38·00

10

IV. *Inscriptions as on No. 11; point of dagger to left* (9.11.98)

17 **10** 4 a. green .. .. 17·00 21·00
a. Yellow-green .. .. .. 8·00 12·00

All the above stamps are lithographed in large sheets, containing as many varieties of type as there are stamps in the sheets.

11 Raja protecting Sacred Cows

Type **11** was produced from separate clichés printed as a block of four. The same clichés were used for all values, but not necessarily in the same order within the block. The Devanagri inscriptions, "RAJ BUNDI" at top and the face value at bottom, were inserted into the basic clichés as required so that various differences exist within the 58 settings which have been identified.

The denominations may be identified from the following illustrations. The ½ a., 3 a. and rupee values can be easily distinguished by their colours.

Bottom tablets:—

The nine versions of the inscriptions are as follows:

Top tablet

Type A. Top tablet has inscription in two separate words with a curved line over the first character in the second. The second word has three characters.
Bottom tablet has short line above the first character in the second word.

Type B. Top tablet as Type A, but without the curved line over the first character in the second word.
Bottom tablet as Type A.

Type C. Top tablet as Type B, but with large loop beneath the first character in the second word. This loop is usually joined to the main character, but is sometimes detached as in the illustration.
Bottom tablet as Type A.

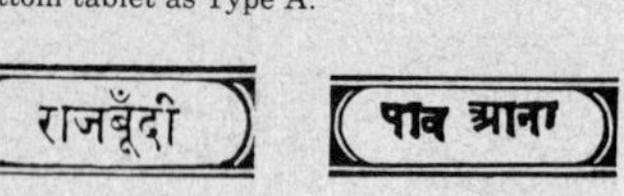

D
Top tablet

E
Bottom tablet

Type D. Top tablet in thinner lettering with the inscription shown as one word of six characters. The fourth character has a curved line above it, as in Type A, and a loop beneath, as in Type C.
Bottom tablet as Type A, but thinner letters.

Type E. Top tablet as Type C.
Bottom tablet shows a redrawn first character to the second word. This has the line at top extending over the entire character.

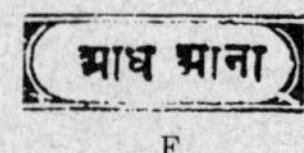

F
Bottom tablet

Type F. Top tablet as Type B.
Bottom tablet as Type E, but first character in second word differs.

Type G. Top tablet as Type C, but without dot over first character in second word. There are now four characters in the second word.
Bottom tablet as Type E.

Type H. Top tablet as Type G, but with characters larger and bolder.
Bottom tablet as Type E, but with characters larger and bolder.

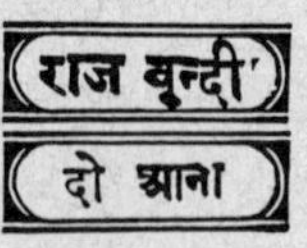

I

Type I. Top tablet as Type H.
Bottom tablet as Type E.

Some settings contained more than one inscription type within the block of four so that *se-tenant* examples are known of Type B with Type C (¼, 1, 2, 4, 8, 10 and 12 a.), Type C with Type E (¼, ½ and 4 a.) and Type E with Type F (½ and 4 a.). Type F only exists from this mixed setting.

1914 (Oct)–**41**. *T* **11**. *Typo. Ungummed paper except for Nos.* 73/8.

I. *Rouletted in colour*

(*a*) *Inscriptions as Type* A. *Thin wove paper* (1916–23)

18 ½ a. black .. .. 2·25 10·00
19 1 a. vermilion .. .. 3·00 16·00
20 2 a. emerald .. .. 2·75 25·00
a. Deep green (coarse ptg on medium wove paper) (1923) .. .. 1·60 9·00
21 2½ a. chrome-yellow (*shades*) (1917).. .. 5·50 25·00
22 3 a. chestnut (1917) .. .. 14·00 27·00

4 a. yellow-green .. .. 17·00
6 a. cobalt (1917) .. .. 17·00 60·00
1 r. reddish violet (1917) .. .. .. 17·00 75·00

A special printing of the 1 a. took place in late 1917 in nnection with the "OUR DAY" Red Cross Society Fund. This ad the "RAJ BUNDI" inscription in the bottom tablet with the ce value below it. The top tablet carried four Devanagri aracters for "OUR DAY". No evidence has been found to ggest that this 1 a. stamp was used for postal purposes (*Price, 70 unused*).

Inscriptions as Type B. *Thin wove or pelure paper* (1914–23)
a ¼ a. cobalt (1916) .. .. 3·00 15·00
¼ a. ultramarine (*shades*) (1917) .. .. 1·75 4·25
a. Indigo (1923) .. .. .. 2·75 6·00
b. Error. Black (1923) .. .. ..
½ a. black .. .. 2·75 6·00
1 a. vermilion (1915) .. .. .. 2·75 9·00
a. Carmine (1923) .. .. .. 6·50 8·50
b. Red (*shades*) (1923) .. .. 4·50 10·00
2 a. emerald (*shades*) (1915) .. .. 4·50 14·00
2½ a. olive-yellow (1917) .. .. .. 5·00 19·00
3 a. chestnut (1917) .. .. .. 4·50 25·00
4 a. apple-green (1915) .. .. .. 3·50 27·00
a 4 a. olive-yellow (1917) £110 £130
6 a. pale ultramarine (*shades*) (1917) .. 8·50 60·00
a. Deep ultramarine (1917) .. .. 7·00
8 a. orange (1915) .. .. .. 7·50 65·00
10 a. olive-sepia (1917) £225 £450
12 a. sage-green (1917) £550
a 1 r. lilac (*shades*) (1915) .. .. .. 24·00

) *Inscriptions as Type* C. *Thin to medium wove paper* (1917–41)
¼ a. ultramarine (*shades*) (1923) .. .. 4·25 5·50
a. Indigo (1923) .. .. .. 4·75 7·00
b. Error. Black (1923) .. .. ..
c. Cobalt (*medium wove paper*) (1937) .. 15·00 15·00
½ a. black .. .. 1·40 4·50
1 a. orange-red .. .. 12·00 17·00
a. Carmine (1923) .. .. .. 10·00 15·00
b. Deep red (*medium wove paper*) (1936) .. 14·00 14·00
2 a. emerald .. .. 7·50 18·00
a. Sage-green .. .. .. 6·50 18·00
4 a. yellow-green (*shades*) .. .. .. 32·00 70·00
a. Olive-yellow .. .. .. 85·00 £120
b. Bright apple-green (*medium wove paper*) (1936) £350 £200
8 a. reddish orange .. .. .. 9·00 48·00
10 a. brown-olive .. .. .. 16·00 60·00
a. Olive-sepia .. .. .. 35·00 85·00
b. Yellow-brown .. .. .. 55·00
12 a. sage-green .. .. .. 8·00 55·00
1 r. lilac .. .. 22·00 80·00
2 r. red-brown and black .. .. 50·00 £130
a. Chocolate and black (*medium wove paper*) (1936) .. .. .. 60·00 £160
3 r. blue and red-brown .. .. .. 75·00 £170
a. Grey-blue and chocolate (*medium wove paper*) (1941) £100
ab. Chocolate (inscriptions) inverted .. £5000
4 r. emerald and scarlet £170 £275
5 r. scarlet and emerald £180 £300

(*d*) *Inscriptions as Type* D. *Thin wove paper* (1918?)
0 2½ a. buff (*shades*) .. .. .. 11·00 35·00
1 3 a. red-brown .. .. .. 18·00 22·00
a. Semi-circle and dot omitted from 4th character .. .. .. 38·00 40·00
2 10 a. bistre .. .. 25·00 75·00
a. 4th character turned to left instead of downwards .. .. .. 45·00
3 12 a. grey-olive .. .. .. 32·00 80·00
a. 4th character turned to left instead of downwards .. .. .. 60·00
b. Blackish green .. .. .. 50·00
ba. 4th character turned to left instead of downwards .. .. .. 80·00

(*e*) *Inscriptions as Type* E. (i) *Medium wove paper* (1930–37)
4 ¼ a. deep slate .. .. .. 15·00 19·00
4a ¼ a. indigo (*thin wove paper*) (1935) .. 14·00 19·00
b. Cobalt (1937) .. .. .. 15·00 15·00
5 ½ a. black .. .. 9·50 11·00
6 1 a. carmine-red .. .. .. 18·00 23·00
7 3 a. chocolate (*shades*) (1936) .. .. 11·00 26·00
8 4 a. yellow-olive (1935) £375 £170
a. Bright apple-green (1936) £375 £170
ab. No tail to 4th character £500 £250

(ii) *Very thick wove paper* (1930–32)
9 ¼ a. indigo (1932) .. .. .. 15·00 20·00
0 ½ a. black .. .. 65·00 70·00
1 1 a. bright scarlet (1931) .. .. 14·00 18·00
a. Carmine-red .. .. .. 50·00 60·00

(iii) *Thin horizontally laid paper* (1935)
2 ¼ a. indigo .. .. 4·00 14·00
3 1 a. scarlet-vermilion .. .. .. 7·00 20·00

Nos. 62 and 63 exist in *tête-bêche* blocks of four on the same or pposite sides of the paper.

(*f*) *Inscriptions as Type* F. *Medium wove paper* (1935)
3a ½ a. black .. .. 70·00
3b 4 a. yellow-olive £650 £400

(*g*) *Inscriptions as Type* G. (i) *Horizontally laid paper* (1935)
4 ½ a. black .. .. 80·00 80·00
a. Vert laid paper .. .. .. 75·00 75·00
5 1 a. scarlet .. .. 70·00 50·00
6 4 a. bright green .. .. .. 20·00 35·00

(ii) *Medium wove paper* (1936)
6a ½ a. black .. .. 4·00 23·00
6b 4 a. yellow-green £950 £475

(*h*) *Inscriptions as Type* H. *Medium wove paper* (1935–41)
7 ¼ a. ultramarine .. .. .. 1·50 7·00
8 ½ a. black (1938) .. .. .. 75·00 75·00
9 1 a. deep red .. .. 5·50 27·00
a. Rosine (1938) .. .. .. 14·00 29·00
0 4 a. emerald (1938) .. .. .. 18·00 27·00
1 4 r. yellow-green and vermilion (1941) .. £180
2 5 r. vermilion and yellow-green (1941) .. £250

No. 70 shows the currency spelt as "ANE" with the last letter issing and an accent over the Devanagri "N".

II. *P* 11.
(*a*) *Inscriptions as Type* H. *Medium wove paper with gum* (1939–41)
73 ¼ a. ultramarine .. .. .. 25·00 38·00
a. Greenish blue (1941) .. .. 1·75 45·00
74 ½ a. black .. .. 28·00 28·00
75 1 a. scarlet-vermilion (1940) .. .. £120 60·00
a. Rose (1940) .. .. .. 12·00 48·00
76 2 a. yellow-green (1941) .. .. 15·00 75·00

(*b*) *Inscriptions as Type* I. *Medium wove paper with gum* (1940)
77 ½ a. black .. .. £120 95·00
78 2 a. bright apple-green .. .. .. 48·00 48·00

FISCAL USE. Collectors are warned that the low values of the later settings of Type **11** were extensively used for fiscal purposes. Stamps which have been fraudulently cleaned of pen-cancels, regummed or provided with forged postmarks are frequently met with. Particular care should be exercised with examples of Nos. 58/*a*, 64/5, 68/70, 74/5*a* and 77.

Maharao Raja Ishwari Singh, 1927–1945

20

1941–44. *Typo. P* 11.
79 **20** 3 p. bright blue .. .. .. 85 3·00
80 6 p. deep blue .. .. .. 2·75 4·25
81 1 a. orange-red .. .. .. 3·00 5·00
82 2 a. chestnut .. .. .. 4·25 11·00
a. Deep brown (*no gum*) (1944) .. 13·00 14·00
83 4 a. bright green .. .. .. 8·00 32·00
84 8 a. dull green .. .. .. 10·00 £110
85 1 r. deep blue .. .. .. 28·00 £160
79/85 .. .. .. *Set of* 7 50·00 £300

The first printing only of Nos. 79/85 is usual with gum; all further printings, including No. 82*a*, are without gum.

Maharao Raja Bahadur Singh, 1945–1971

21 Maharao Raja Bahadur Singh **22** Bundi

(Typo *Times of India* Press, Bombay)

1947. *P* 11.
86 **21** ¼ a. blue-green .. .. .. 1·10 23·00
87 ½ a. violet .. .. .. 1·10 23·00
88 1 a. yellow-green .. .. .. 1·10 23·00
89 – 2 a. vermilion .. .. .. 1·10 42·00
90 – 4 a. orange .. .. .. 1·25 60·00
91 **22** 8 a. ultramarine .. .. .. 2·25
92 1 r. chocolate .. .. .. 13·00
86/92 .. .. .. *Set of* 7 19·00

On the 2 and 4 a. the Maharao is in Indian dress.

OFFICIAL STAMPS

PRICES. Prices for Nos. O1/52 are for unused examples. Used stamps are generally worth a small premium over the prices quoted.

बूंदी
सरविस
(O 1)

BUNDI
SERVICE
(O 2)

BUNDI
SERVICE
(O 3)

1915–41. *T* **11** *handstamped as Types* O 1/3. *Ungummed paper except Nos.* O47/52.

A. *Optd with Type* O 1. B. *Optd with Type* O 2. C. *Optd with Type* O 3.

I. *Rouletted in colour*

		A	B	C
	(*a*) *Inscriptions as Type* A. *Thin wove paper.*			
O 1	½ a. black	£225	†	†
	a. Red opt	£190	†	†
O 1*b*	2 a. emerald	1·75	£200	†
	ba. Deep green (*coarse ptg on medium wove paper*)	6·50	13·00	£170
	bb. Red opt	12·00	11·00	†
O 2	2½ a. chrome-yellow (*shades*)	2·25	10·00	£160
	a. Red opt	£120	£140	†
O 3	3 a. chestnut	2·50	16·00	†
	a. Green opt	£110	†	†
	b. Red opt	£150	£150	†
O 4	6 a. cobalt	24·00	25·00	£180
	a. Red opt	£170	£180	£190
O 5	1 r. reddish violet	38·00	38·00	†
	a. Red opt	£200	£225	†
	(*b*) *Inscriptions as Type* B. *Thin wove or pelure paper*			
O 6	¼ a. ultramarine (*shades*)	1·60	1·75	7·50
	a. Red opt	1·25	4·00	£120
O 7	½ a. black	6·50	4·50	25·00
	a. Red opt	4·25	11·00	£130
O 8	1 a. vermilion	4·00	†	†
	a. Red opt	—	†	†
	b. Carmine	20·00	12·00	50·00
	c. Red (*shades*)	—	6·00	—
O 9	2 a. emerald (*shades*)	21·00	29·00	†
	a. Red opt	—	85·00	†
O 9*b*	3 a. chestnut (R.)	—	†	†
O10	4 a. apple-green	12·00	55·00	£170
	a. Red opt	£180	†	†
O10*b*	4 a. olive-yellow	£170	£180	†
	ba. Red opt	—	£350	†
O11	6 a. pale ultramarine (*shades*)	11·00	£140	†
	a. Red opt	£180	£180	†
	b. Deep ultramarine	50·00	70·00	†
	ba. Red opt	£170	£150	†
O12	8 a. orange	40·00	55·00	£190
	a. Red opt	£190	†	†
O13	10 a. olive-sepia	£160	£200	£375
	a. Red opt	£425	£450	£475
O14	12 a. sage-green	£140	£325	£400
	a. Red opt	†	†	£475
O14*b*	1 r. lilac	£225	†	†
	(*c*) *Inscriptions as Type* C. *Thin to medium wove paper.*			
O15	¼ a. ultramarine (*shades*)	2·00	1·75	14·00
	a. Red opt	90	5·00	†
	b. Green opt	2·50	35·00	†
	c. Cobalt (*medium wove paper*)	48·00	45·00	£190
	ca. Red opt	35·00	16·00	95·00
O16	½ a. black	6·00	3·00	10·00
	a. Red opt	75	8·00	£120
	b. Green opt	3·00	†	†
O17	1 a. orange-red	1·25	—	†
	a. Carmine	19·00	8·00	16·00
	b. Deep red (*medium wove paper*)	32·00	40·00	70·00
	ba. Red opt	†	£100	†
O18	2 a. emerald	4·50	12·00	55·00
	a. Red opt	†	70·00	†
	b. Sage-green	8·00	13·00	75·00
O19	4 a. yellow-green (*shades*)	8·00	60·00	†
	b. Red opt	—	†	†
	c. Olive-yellow	95·00	95·00	†
	ca. Red opt	£200	£200	†
O20	8 a. reddish orange	14·00	24·00	£180
	a. Red opt	£170	£250	†
O21	10 a. brown-olive	40·00	65·00	£250
	a. Red opt	£250	£250	£300
O22	12 a. sage-green	32·00	75·00	£300
	a. Red opt	£350	†	£350
O23	1 r. lilac	£110	†	†
	a. Red opt	£225	†	†
O24	2 r. red-brown and black	£300	£170	†
	a. Red opt	†	£650	†
	b. Chocolate and black (*medium wove paper*)	£450	£450	†
O25	3 r. blue and red-brown	£300	£200	†
	a. Red opt	£650	†	†
	b. Grey-blue & chocolate (*medium wove paper*)	£650	£650	†
	ba. Red opt	£700	†	†
O26	4 r. emerald and scarlet	£275	£300	†
O27	5 r. scarlet and emerald	£275	£300	†
	(*d*) *Inscriptions as Type* D. *Thin wove paper*			
O28	2½ a. buff (*shades*)	15·00	18·00	†
	b. Red opt	£150	—	†
O29	3 a. red-brown	27·00	24·00	†
	a. Variety as No. 51a	48·00	45·00	†
	b. Red opt	†	£225	†
O30	10 a. bistre	32·00	60·00	£325
	a. Variety as No. 52a	60·00	£120	£450
	b. Red opt	£275	£375	†
O31	12 a. grey-olive	48·00	70·00	£275
	a. Variety as No. 53a	80·00	£130	£400
	b. Red opt	£275	£350	†
	ba. Variety as No. 53a	£375	†	†
	(*e*) *Inscriptions as Type* E. (i) *Medium wove paper*			
O32	¼ a. deep slate	30·00	15·00	†
	a. Red opt	27·00	32·00	†
O32*b*	¼ a. indigo (*thin wove paper*)	27·00	32·00	†
	ba. Red opt	26·00	30·00	†
	bb. Green opt	60·00	65·00	†
	c. Cobalt	50·00	50·00	£190
	ca. Red opt	35·00	30·00	90·00
O33	½ a. black	30·00	12·00	†
	a. Red opt	22·00	10·00	†
	b. Green opt	£200	£150	†
O34	1 a. carmine-red	28·00	30·00	£190
O35	3 a. chocolate (*shades*)	£160	£110	£190
	a. Red opt	£325	£325	†
O35*b*	4 a. yellow-olive	†	£350	†
	ba. Bright apple-green	£600	†	†
	(ii) *Very thick wove paper*			
O36	¼ a. indigo	9·00	12·00	†
	a. Red opt	17·00	35·00	†
	b. Green opt	75·00	†	†
O37	½ a. black	75·00	85·00	†
O38	1 a. bright scarlet	13·00	12·00	£170
	a. Carmine-red	85·00	60·00	†
	(iii) *Thin horizontally laid paper*			
O39	¼ a. indigo	65·00	75·00	†
	a. Red opt	5·00	8·00	£150
O40	1 a. scarlet-vermilion	32·00	20·00	†
	a. Red opt	£190	£200	†

Nos. O39/40a exist in *tête-bêche* blocks of four on the same or opposite sides of the paper.

A B C

(f) Inscriptions as Type F. *Medium wove paper*

O40*b* ½ a. black — — †
ba. Red opt £190 £275 †
O40c 4 a. yellow-olive † £475 †

(g) Inscriptions as Type G. (i) *Horizontally laid paper*

O41 ½ a. black (red opt) £110 £110 †
a. Vert laid paper £120 £120 †
ab. Red opt £140 60·00 £250
O42 4 a. bright green £160 £150 †
a. Red opt £180 £225 †

(ii) *Medium wove paper*

O42*b* ½ a. black £160 £170 †
ba. Red opt £200 £200 †

(h) Inscriptions as Type H. *Medium wove paper*

O43 ¼ a. ultramarine 25·00 75·00 †
a. Red opt £160 £200 †
O44 ½ a. black 90·00 £130 †
a. Red opt 75·00 † £325
O45 1 a. rosine £140 £130 £300
O46 4 a. emerald £130 £160 £300
a. Red opt £300 † £325

II. *P* 11. *(a) Inscriptions as Type* H. *Medium wove paper with gum*

O47 ¼ a. ultramarine 45·00 75·00 £110
a. Red opt 65·00 90·00 †
b. *Greenish blue* 70·00 70·00 £160
c. Ditto. Red opt £160 † †
O48 ½ a. black 45·00 55·00 £250
a. Red opt 80·00 £190 £150
O49 1 a. scarlet-vermilion £200 £250 £375
a. Stamp doubly printed † † £850
b. *Rose* £120 £100 £275
O50 2 a. yellow-green £300 £150 £190

(b) Inscriptions as Type I. *Medium wove paper with gum*

O51 ½ a. black £110 £200 £300
a. Red opt £225 £275 †
O52 2 a. bright apple-green £250 £275 £475

Until 1941 it was the general practice to carry official mail free but some of the above undoubtedly exist postally used.

1941. *Nos.* 79 *to* 85 *optd* "SERVICE".

O53 **20** 3 p. bright blue (R.) 3·00 8·00
O54 6 p. deep blue (R.) 10·00 8·00
O55 1 a. orange-red 9·00 7·00
O56 2 a. brown 7·00 8·50
O57 4 a. bright green 24·00 70·00
O58 8 a. dull green 95·00 £300
O59 1 r. deep blue (R.) £120 £325
O53/9 *Set of* 7 £225 £650

Two different types of "R" occur in the "SERVICE" overprint. On five positions in the sheet of 12 the "R" shows a larger loop and a pointed diagonal leg.

Bundi became part of the Rajasthan Union by 15 April 1948.

BUSSAHIR (BASHAHR)

PRICES FOR STAMPS ON COVER
Nos. 1/21 *from* × 8
Nos. 22/23 *from* × 2
Nos. 24/43 *from* × 8

Raja Shamsher Singh, 1850–1914

1 2 3 4 5 6 7 8 (9)

The initials are those of the Tika Raghunath Singh, son of the then Raja, who was the organiser and former director of the State Post Office.

(Litho at the Bussahir Press by Maulvi Karam Bakhsh, Rampur)

1895 (20 June). *Laid paper. Optd with T* **9** *in pale greenish blue* (B.), *rose* (R.), *mauve* (M.) *or lake* (L.). *With or without gum.*

(a) Imperf.

1 1 ¼ a. pink (M.) (1.9.95) £900
a. Monogram in rose £1300
2 2 ½ a. grey (R.) £250
a. Monogram in mauve
3 3 1 a. vermilion (M.) £100
4 4 2 a. orange-yellow (M.) 32·00 £120
a. Monogram in rose 70·00
b. Monogram in lake 48·00
c. Monogram in blue £110
5 5 4 a. slate-violet (M.) 60·00
a. Monogram in rose 80·00
b. Monogram in lake 70·00
c. Without monogram £170
6 6 8 a. red-brown (M.) 60·00 £120
a. Monogram in blue 85·00
b. Monogram in lake
c. Without monogram £160
d. Thick paper 80·00
7 7 12 a. green (L.) £180
a. Monogram in mauve
8 8 1 r. ultramarine (R.) 55·00
a. Monogram in mauve £110
b. Monogram in lake 90·00
c. Without monogram £180

(b) Perf with a sewing machine; gauge and size of holes varying between 7 *and* 11½

9 1 ¼ a. pink (B.) 35·00 75·00
a. Monogram in mauve — £100
b. Without monogram £170 95·00
10 2 ½ a. grey (R.) 15·00 85·00
a. Without monogram £350
11 3 1 a. vermilion (M.) 16·00 75·00
a. Without monogram
12 4 2 a. orange-yellow (B.) 24·00 75·00
a. Monogram in rose
b. Monogram in mauve 65·00
c. Without monogram — £170
13 5 4 a. slate-violet (B.) 16·00 80·00
a. Monogram in rose 24·00 90·00
b. Monogram in mauve 30·00
c. Without monogram 40·00
14 6 8 a. red-brown (M.) 17·00 85·00
a. Monogram in blue 40·00 £120
b. Monogram in rose 60·00
c. Without monogram 95·00
15 7 12 a. green (R.) 50·00 £100
a. Monogram in mauve 85·00
b. Monogram in lake 80·00
c. Without monogram £130
16 8 1 r. ultramarine (R.) 28·00 85·00
a. Monogram in mauve 75·00
b. Without monogram £160 £225
9/16 *Set of* 8 £180 £600

1899. *As* 1895, *but pin-perf or rouletted.*

17 3 1 a. vermilion (M.) £130 £150
18 4 2 a. orange-yellow (M.) 38·00 95·00
a. Monogram in lake 42·00
b. Monogram in rose 60·00
c. Monogram in blue 85·00
d. Without monogram £200
19 5 4 a. slate-violet (L.) £180
a. Monogram in blue
b. Monogram in rose £225
c. Monogram in mauve £225
20 7 12 a. green (R.) £350 £400
21 8 1 r. ultramarine (R.) £350

Nos. 1 to 21 were in sheets of 24. They seem to have been overprinted and perforated as required. Those first issued for use were perforated, but they were subsequently supplied imperf, both to collectors and for use. Nos. 17 to 21 were some of the last supplies. No rule seems to have been observed as to the colour of the overprinted monogram; pale blue, rose and mauve were used from the first. The pale blue varies to greenish blue or blue-green, and appears quite green on the yellow stamps. The lake is possibly a mixture of the mauve and the rose—it is a quite distinct colour and apparently later than the others. Specimens without overprint are either remainders left in the Treasury or copies that have escaped accidentally; they have been found sticking to the backs of others that bore the overprint.

Varieties may also be found doubly overprinted, in two different colours.

10

11

12

T **11**. Lines of shading above and at bottom left and right of shield.
T **12**. White dots above shield and ornaments in bottom corners.

13

14

15

16

(Printed at the Bussahir Press by Maulvi Karam Bakhsh)

1896–97. *Wove paper. Optd with monogram* "R.S.", *T* **9**, *in rose. Recess singly from line-engraved dies. With or without gum. Various perfs.*

22 **10** ¼ a. deep violet (1897) — £600
23 **11** ½ a. grey-blue £450 £160
23*a* ½ a. deep blue (1897) — £225

No. 23 exists sewing-machine perf about 10 and also perf 14½–16. Nos. 22 and 23*a* are pin-perf.

1896–1900. *As Nos.* 22/3, *but lithographed in sheets of variou sizes. No gum.*

(a) Imperf

24 **10** ¼ a. slate-violet (R.) 4·00
a. Monogram in mauve 5·50
b. Monogram in blue 7·50
c. Monogram in lake 11·00
25 **11** ½ a. blue (*shades*) (R.) 4·50 11·0
a. Monogram in mauve 5·00 11·0
b. Monogram in lake 5·50
c. Without monogram
d. Laid paper (B.) 70·00
da. Monogram in lake
26 **13** 1 a. olive (*shades*) (R.) 10·00 25·0
a. Monogram in mauve 23·00
b. Monogram in lake 25·00

(b) Pin-perf or rouletted

27 **10** ¼ a. slate-violet (R.) 12·00 11·00
a. Monogram in lake 15·00 14·00
b. Monogram in mauve — 21·00
28 **11** ½ a. blue (*shades*) (R.) 8·00 22·00
a. Monogram in mauve 10·00 23·00
b. Monogram in lake 20·00 28·00
c. Monogram in blue
d. Laid paper (M.)
29 **13** 1 a. olive (*shades*) (R.) 15·00
a. Monogram in mauve 30·00 30·00
b. Monogram in lake 32·00 32·00
30 **14** 2 a. orange-yellow (B.) £350 £375

The ¼ a. and ½ a. are in sheets of 24, the 1 a. and 2 a. in blocks of 4.

1900–01. ¼ *a.,* 1 *a, colours changed;* ½ *a. redrawn type;* 2 *a. with dash before* "STATE" *and characters in lower left label;* 4 *a. neu value. No gum.*

(a) Imperf

31 **10** ¼ a. vermilion (M.) 3·00 6·0
a. Monogram in blue 3·25 5·5
b. Without monogram
31*c* **12** ½ a. blue (M.) 6·50 16·0
ca. Monogram in rose 21·00
cb. Without monogram 32·00
32 **13** 1 a. vermilion (M.) 2·75 8·5
a. Monogram in blue 4·75 6·0
b. Monogram in lake
c. Without monogram 28·00
33 **15** 2 a. ochre (M.) (9.00) 28·00 60·0
34 2 a. yellow (M.) (11.00) 28·00
a. Monogram in blue 30·00 65·0
b. Without monogram 50·00
35 2 a. orange (B.) (1.01) 35·00 60·0
a. Monogram in mauve 35·00 55·0
b. Without monogram 45·00
36 **16** 4 a. claret (R.) 29·00 75·0
a. Monogram in mauve 40·00 90·0
b. Monogram in blue 50·00 95·0
c. Without monogram 28·00

(b) Pin-perf or rouletted

37 **10** ¼ a. vermilion (M.) 2·25 6·0
a. Monogram in blue 3·00
b. Without monogram
37*c* **12** ½ a. blue (M.) 30·00 40·0
38 **13** 1 a. vermilion (M.) 3·75 8·5
a. Monogram in blue 6·50 7·0
39 1 a. brown-red (M.) (3.01) — £18
40 **15** 2 a. ochre (M.) (9.00) 38·00
a. Monogram in blue
41 2 a. yellow (M.) (11.00) 28·00 50·0
a. Monogram in rose 42·00 65·0
b. Monogram in blue 48·00 75·0
42 2 a. orange (M.) (1.01) 38·00 45·0
a. Monogram in blue 50·00 55·0
b. Without monogram — £12
43 **16** 4 a. claret (R.) 40·00
a. Monogram in blue 45·00 95·0
b. Monogram in mauve 65·00

The ¼ a., ½ a. and 1 a. are in sheets of 24; the 2 a. in sheets o 50 differing throughout in the dash and the characters added a lower left; the 4 a. in sheets of 28.

(17)

The stamps formerly catalogued with large overprint "R.N.S." (T **17**) are now believed never to have been issued for use.

Remainders are also found with overprint "P.S.", the initials o Padam Singh who succeeded Raghunath Singh in the direction o the Post Office, and with the original monogram "R.S." in damaged state, giving it the appearance of a double-lined "R."

The stamps of Bussahir have been obsolete since 1 April 1901. Numerous remainders were sold after this date, and all values were later reprinted in the colours of the originals, or in fancy colours from the original stones, or from new ones. Printings were also made from new types, similar to those of the second issue of the 8 a., 12 a., and 1 r. values, in sheets of 8.

Reprints are frequently found on laid paper.

Collectors are warned against obliterated copies bearing the Rampur postmark with date "19 MA 1900." Many thousand remainders and reprints were thus obliterated for export after the closing of the State Post Office.

CHARKHARI

PRICES FOR STAMPS ON COVER
Nos. 1/4 *from* × 2
Nos. 5/26 *from* × 20
Nos. 27/44 *from* × 3
Nos. 45/53 *from* × 100
Nos. 54/5 *from* × 5
No. 56 *from* × 2

Maharaja Malkhan Singh, 1880–1908

1

1/4 1/2 1 2 4

1/4 1/2 1 2 4

The top row shows the figures of value used in the stamps of 1894-7, and the bottom row those for the 1904 issue. In the 4 a. the figure opes slightly to the right in the first issue, and to the left in the econd.

394. *Typo from a single die. No gum. Imperf.*
1 ¼ anna, rose .. £900 £700
1 annas, dull green .. £1600 £2250
2 annas, dull green .. £1800
4 annas, dull green .. £1200

Nos. 1/2 are known pin-perforated.

897. *Inscr "ANNA". No gum. Imperf.*
1 ¼ a. magenta .. 32·00 40·00
a. Purple .. 2·25 3·00
b. Violet .. 2·25 2·75
½ a. purple .. 2·50 3·50
a. Violet .. 2·50 3·00
1 1 a. blue-green .. 4·50 6·50
a. Turquoise-blue .. 4·00 4·50
b. Indigo .. 10·00 17·00
2 a. blue-green .. 7·50 13·00
a. Turquoise-blue .. 7·00 8·00
b. Indigo .. 10·00 19·00
4 a. blue-green .. 7·50 14·00
a. Turquoise-blue .. 6·00 9·00
b. Indigo .. 20·00 32·00
ba. Figure of value sideways ..
9 .. *Set of* 5 19·00 25·00

Minor varieties may be found with the first "A" in "ANNA" not rinted.

All values are known on various coloured papers, but these are roofs or trial impressions.

904. *Numerals changed as illustrated above. No gum.*
0 1 ¼ a. violet .. 1·75 2·50
1 ½ a. violet .. 3·00 3·50
2 1 a. green .. 5·00 12·00
3 2 a. green .. 20·00 20·00
4 4 a. green .. 13·00 24·00
0/14 .. *Set of* 5 38·00 55·00

Stamps of this issue can be found showing part of the paper-maker's watermark. "Mercantile Script Extra Strong John Haddon & Co.".

Maharaja Jujhar Singh, 1908–1914

2 (Right-hand sword over left)

Type I

POSTAGE STAMP

Type II

ype I. "P" of "POSTAGE" in same size as other letters. "E" small with long upper and lower arms. White dot often appears on one or both of the sword hilts.

ype II. "P" larger than the other letters. "E" large with short upper and lower arms. No dots occur on the hilts.

909–19. *Litho in Calcutta. Wove paper. P* 11. (*a*) *Type* I.
5 2 1 p. chestnut .. 32·00 40·00
a. Pale chestnut .. 2·50 38·00
b. Orange-brown .. 3·00 38·00
6 1 p. turquoise-blue .. 35 45
a. Imperf between (horiz pair) .. £150
b. Greenish blue (1911) .. 70 90
c. Pale turquoise-green .. 90 70
7 ½ a. vermilion .. 1·50 90
a. Deep rose-red .. 80 1·10
8 1 a. sage-green .. 1·75 1·90
a. Yellow-olive .. 1·60 1·25
9 2 a. grey-blue .. 2·50 3·25
a. Dull violet-blue .. 3·00 3·00
20 4 a. deep green .. 3·00 4·00
21 8 a. brown-red .. 6·00 13·00
22 1 r. pale chestnut .. 10·00 26·00
5*a*/22 .. *Set of* 8 24·00 75·00

(*b*) *Type* II
24 2 1 p. turquoise-blue .. 2·00 2·25
25 ½ a. vermilion .. 90 1·10
a. Imperf (pair) .. £425
b. Deep rose-red .. 3·25 3·50
26 1 a. yellow-olive (1919) .. 2·25 2·50
a. Sage-green .. 1·50 1·50
24/6 .. *Set of* 3 4·00 4·25

No. 15, from the original printing, shows an upstroke to the "1", not present on other brown printings of this value.

See also Nos. 31/44.

3

"ـJI" below Swords Right sword overlaps left. Double frame lines.

4

"JI" below Swords. Left sword overlaps right. Single frame line.

1912–17. *Handstamped. Wove paper. No gum. Imperf.*
27 3 1 p. violet .. £375 70·00
a. Dull purple .. — 80·00
28 4 1 p. violet (1917) .. 7·00 5·00
a. Dull purple .. 12·00 5·00
b. *Tête-bêche* (pair) .. 65·00 65·00
c. Laid paper .. — £190
d. Pair, one stamp sideways .. — £100

Maharaja Ganga Singh, 1914–1920

Maharaja Arimardan Singh, 1920–1942

5 (*actual size* 63 × 25 *mm*)

6 (Left-hand sword over right)

1922. *Handstamped. No gum.* (*a*) *Wove paper. Imperf.*
29 5 1 a. violet .. 60·00 75·00
a. Dull purple .. 75·00 85·00

(*b*) *Laid paper. P* 11
30 5 1 a. violet .. 65·00 £100
a. Imperf .. £140 £150

(Typo State Ptg Press, Charkhari)

1930–45. *Wove paper. No gum. Imperf.*
31 6 1 p. deep blue .. 35 11·00
a. Vert pair, top ptd inverted on back, bottom normal upright .. 13·00
b. *Tête-bêche* (vert pair) .. £180
c. Perf 11×imperf (horiz pair) (1939) 30·00 30·00
d. Bluish slate .. 20·00
e. Laid paper (1944) .. — £275
32 1 p. dull *to* light green (*pelure*) (1943) .. 40·00 £140
33 1 p. violet (1943) .. 13·00 £100
a. *Tête-bêche* (vert pair) .. 50·00
34 ½ a. deep olive .. 70 11·00
35 ½ a. red-brown (1940) .. 3·25 22·00
a. *Tête-bêche* (vert pair) .. £325
36 ½ a. black (*pelure*) (1943) .. 45·00 £120
37 ½ a. red (*shades*) (1943) .. 16·00 32·00
a. *Tête-bêche* (vert pair) .. 35·00
b. Laid paper (1944) .. — £275
38 ½ a. grey-brown .. 60·00 75·00
39 1 a. green .. 50 11·00
a. Emerald .. 25·00 42·00
40 1 a. chocolate (1940) .. 5·00 22·00
a. *Tête-bêche* (vert pair) .. 75·00
b. Lake-brown .. — 38·00
41 1 a. red (1940) .. 75·00 55·00
a. Carmine .. — 55·00
b. Laid paper (1944) .. — £300
42 2 a. light blue .. 1·25 15·00
a. *Tête-bêche* (vert pair) .. 9·50
43 2 a. greenish grey (1941?) .. 35·00 48·00
a. *Tête-bêche* (vert pair) .. 70·00
b. Laid paper (1944) .. — £325
c. Greyish green .. 55·00 £100
43*d* 2 a. yellow-green (1945) .. — £425
44 4 a. carmine .. 4·00 18·00
a. *Tête-bêche* (vert pair) .. 14·00

There are two different versions of No. 37a, one with the stamps *tête-bêche* base to base and the other showing them top to top.

7 Imlia Palace

1/2 As.

(8)

(Typo Batliboi Litho Works, Bombay)

1931 (25 June). *T* **7** *and similar designs. P* 11, 11½, 12 *or compound.*
45 ½ a. blue-green .. 80 10
a. Imperf between (horiz pair) .. 35·00 11·00
b. Imperf between (vert pair) .. 35·00
c. Imperf horiz (vert pair) .. 35·00
46 1 a. blackish brown .. 1·00 10
a. Imperf between (horiz pair) .. 11·00 8·00
b. Imperf between (vert pair) .. 12·00 8·00
c. Imperf horiz (vert pair) .. 12·00
47 2 a. violet .. 60 10
a. Imperf between (horiz pair) .. 30·00 25·00
b. Imperf between (vert pair) .. 30·00 25·00
c. Imperf horiz (vert pair) .. 22·00
d. Doubly printed .. 8·50
48 4 a. olive-green .. 80 15
a. Imperf between (vert pair) .. 55·00 55·00
49 8 a. magenta .. 1·00 10
a. Imperf between (horiz pair) .. 38·00 25·00
b. Imperf between (vert pair) .. 38·00
c. Imperf horiz (vert pair) .. 38·00 13·00
50 1 r. green and rose .. 1·40 15
a. Imperf between (vert pair) .. £100 £100
b. Green (centre) omitted .. — £110
51 2 r. red and brown .. 2·25 20
a. Imperf horiz (vert pair) .. 75·00 15·00
52 3 r. chocolate and blue-green .. 6·00 30
a. Imperf between (horiz pair) .. — £150
b. *Tête-bêche* (pair) .. £150 20·00
c. Chocolate (centre) omitted .. 19·00
53 5 r. turquoise and purple .. 7·00 45
a. Imperf between (horiz pair) .. £150
b. Centre inverted .. 42·00 24·00
c. Centre doubly printed .. — 55·00
45/53 .. *Set of* 9 18·00 1·40

Designs:—½ a. The Lake; 2 a. Industrial School; 4 a. Bird's-eye view of City; 8 a. The Fort; 1 r. Guest House. 2 r. Palace Gate; 3 r. Temples at Rainpur; 5 r. Goverdhan Temple.

This issue was the subject of speculative manipulation, large stocks being thrown on the market cancelled-to-order at very low prices and unused at less than face value. The issue was an authorized one but was eventually withdrawn by the State authorities.

1939 (Dec)–**40.** *Nos.* 21/2 *surch as T* **8**.
54 2 ½ a. on 8 a. brown-red (1940) .. 26·00 £110
a. No space between "½" and "As" .. 32·00 £110
b. Surch inverted .. £225
c. "1" of "½" inverted .. £200
55 1 a. on 1 r. chestnut (1940) .. 70·00 £275
a. Surch inverted .. £250
56 "1 ANNA" on 1 r. chestnut .. £500 £550

Maharaja Jaiendra Singh, 1942–1971

Charkhari became part of Vindhya Pradesh by 1 May 1948

COCHIN

(6 puttans = 5 annas. 12 pies = 1 anna; 16 annas = 1 rupee)

Stamps of Cochin were also valid on mail posted to Travancore.

PRICES FOR STAMPS ON COVER	
Nos. 1/3	*from* × 30
Nos. 4/5	*from* × 10
Nos. 6/6*b*	*from* × 3
Nos. 7/9	*from* × 20
Nos. 11/22	*from* × 15
Nos. 26/128	*from* × 8
Nos. O1/105	*from* × 15

Raja Kerala Varma I, 1888–1895

1

2

(Dies eng P. Orr & Sons, Madras; typo Cochin Govt, Ernakulam)

1892 (13 Apr). *No wmk, or wmk large Umbrella in the sheet. P* 12.
1 1 ½ put. buff .. 1·75 2·25
a. Orange-buff .. 1·75 2·00
b. Yellow .. 1·75 2·50
c. Imperf (pair) ..
2 1 put. purple .. 2·00 1·50
a. Imperf between (vert pair) .. † £1800
3 2 2 put. deep violet .. 1·50 1·60
1/3 .. *Set of* 3 4·75 4·50

1893. *Laid paper. P* 12.
4 1 ½ put. orange-buff .. £450 £120
a. Orange .. — £120
b. Yellow .. — £120

WATERMARKS. Prior to the 1911–23 issue, printed by Perkins, Bacon & Co, little attention was paid to the position of the watermark. Inverted and sideways watermarks are frequently found in the 1898 and 1902–03 issues.

1894. *Wmk a small Umbrella on each stamp. P* 12.
5 1 ½ put. buff .. 3·75 2·75
a. Orange .. 1·50 1·10
ab. Imperf (pair) ..
b. Yellow .. 3·00 1·00
6 1 put. purple .. 5·00 4·00
7 2 2 put. deep violet .. 2·75 3·25
a. Imperf (pair) ..
b. Doubly printed .. † —
c. Printed both sides ..
d. *Tête-bêche* (pair) .. £2500
5/7 .. *Set of* 3 8·25 7·50

The paper watermarked with a small umbrella is more transparent than that of the previous issue. The wmk is not easy to distinguish.

The 1 put. in deep violet was a special printing for fiscal use only.

Raja Rama Varma I, 1895-1914

1896 (End). *Similar to T* **1**, *but* 28×33 *mm. P* 12.

(*a*) *Wmk Arms and inscription in sheet*
8 1 put. violet .. 60·00 60·00

(*b*) *Wmk Conch Shell to each stamp*
9 1 put. deep violet .. 16·00 27·00

Nos. 8/9 were intended for fiscal use, but are also known used for postal purposes.

3

4

5

6

1898. *Thin yellowish paper. Wmk small Umbrella on each stamp. With or without gum. P* 12.

No.	Type	Description	Unused	Used
11	**3**	3 pies, blue	1·00	80
		a. Imperf between (horiz pair) ..	£450	
		b. Imperf between (vert pair) ..	£550	
		c. Doubly printed		
12	**4**	½ put. green	1·50	50
		a. Imperf between (horiz pair)		
		b. Stamp sideways (in pair) ..		
13	**5**	1 put. pink	2·75	1·40
		a. *Tête-bêche* (pair)	£2000	£2000
		b. Laid paper	†	£1600
		ba. Laid paper. *Tête-bêche* (pair) ..	†	£6000
		c. Red	1·75	1·25
		d. Carmine-red	3·25	1·40
14	**6**	2 put. deep violet	3·00	1·50
		a. Imperf between (vert pair) ..	£425	
11/14 ..		.. .. *Set of* 4	6·50	3·50

1902–03. *Thick white paper. Wmk small Umbrella on each stamp. With or without gum. P* 12.

No.	Type	Description	Unused	Used
16	**3**	3 pies, blue	40	10
		a. Doubly printed	—	£275
		b. Imperf between (horiz pair) ..	†	£500
17	**4**	½ put. green	75	20
		a. Stamp sideways (in pair) ..	£650	£650
		b. Doubly printed	—	£275
18	**5**	1 put. pink (1903)	1·40	10
		a. *Tête-bêche* (pair)	†	£2750
19	**6**	2 put. deep violet	1·75	30
		a. Doubly printed	£750	£300
16/19		.. .. *Set of* 4	3·75	60

(7) (7*a*)

1909. *T* **3** (*paper and perf of* 1903), *surch with T* **7**. *Wmk is always sideways. No gum.*

No.	Type	Description	Unused	Used
22	**3**	2 on 3 pies, rosy mauve	15	25
		a. Surch T **7** inverted	75·00	75·00
		b. Surch T **7a**	£550	£325
		c. Stamps *tête-bêche*	£110	£130
		d. Stamps and surchs *tête-bêche* ..	£150	£170

Varieties a, c and d were caused by the inversion of one stamp (No. 7) in the plate and the consequent inversion of the corresponding surcharge to correct the error.

Type **7a** was applied by a handstamp to correct the omission of the surcharge on R.3/2 in one setting only.

8 Raja Rama Varma I

8a

(Recess Perkins, Bacon & Co)

1911–13. *Currency in pies and annas. W* **8a**. *P* 14.

No.	Type	Description	Unused	Used
26	**8**	2 p. brown	30	10
		a. Imperf (pair)		
27		3 p. blue	35	10
		a. Perf 14×12½	27·00	2·50
		w. Wmk inverted		
28		4 p. green	1·00	10
		aw. Wmk inverted		
28*b*		4 p. apple-green	2·50	40
		bw. Wmk inverted		
29		9 p. carmine	1·10	10
		a. Wmk sideways		
30		1 a. brown-orange	1·90	10
31		1½ a. purple	4·75	45
32		2 a. grey (1913)	7·50	40
33		3 a. vermilion (1913)	28·00	32·00
26/33		.. .. *Set of* 8	40·00	32·00

COVER PRICES

Cover factors are quoted at the beginning of each country for most issues to 1945. An explanation of the system can be found on page x. The factors quoted do not, however, apply to philatelic covers.

Raja (Maharaja from 1921) Rama Varma II, 1914–1932

9 Raja Rama Varma II **10**

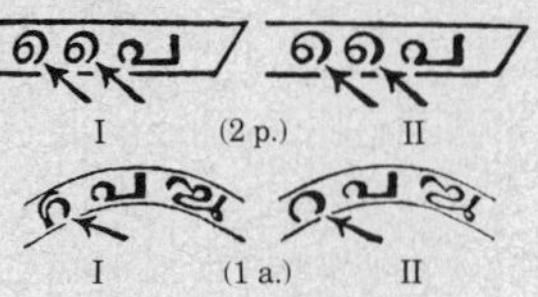

(Recess Perkins, Bacon & Co)

1916–30. *W* **8a**. *P* 13½ *to* 14.

No.	Type	Description	Unused	Used
35	**10**	2 p. brown (Die I) (*a*) (*b*) (*c*)	4·25	10
		a. Imperf (pair)	£475	
		b. Die II (*b*) (*c*) (1930)	1·00	10
36		4 p. green (*a*) (*b*)	95	10
37		6 p. red-brown (*a*) (*b*) (*c*) (1922) ..	1·60	10
38		8 p. sepia (*b*) (1923)	1·40	10
39		9 p. carmine (*a*)	13·00	15
40		10 p. blue (*b*) (1923)	1·90	10
41	**9**	1 a. orange (Die I) (*a*)	10·00	65
		a. Die II (*a*) (*b*) (1922)	8·50	30
42	**10**	1½ a. purple (*b*) (1923)	2·25	15
43		2 a. grey (*a*) (*b*) (*d*)	4·00	10
44		2¼ a. yellow-green (*a*) (*d*) (1922) ..	3·75	2·25
45		3 a. vermilion (*a*) (*b*)	11·00	35
35/45		.. .. *Set of* 11	45·00	3·25

Four different perforating heads were used for this issue: (*a*) comb 13.9; (*b*) comb 13.6; (*c*) line 13.8; (*d*) line 14.2. Values on which each perforation occur are shown above. Stamps with perforation (*a*) are on hand-made paper, while the other perforations are on softer machine-made paper with a horizontal mesh.

2 2 2

Two pies (11) Two pies (12) Two pies (13)

2 2

Two Pies (14) Two Pies (15)

1922–29. *T* **8** (*P* 14), *surch with T* **11/15**.

No.	Type	Description	Unused	Used
46	**11**	2 p. on 3 p. blue	40	30
		a. Surch double	£325	£325
47	**12**	2 p. on 3 p. blue	1·90	70
		a. Surch double	£475	
		b. "Pies" for "pies" (R. 4/8) ..	35·00	18·00
		ba. Surch double		
48	**13**	2 p. on 3 p. blue (6.24)	2·75	35
		a. "Pies" for "pies" (R. 4/8) ..	45·00	16·00
		b. Perf 14×12½	14·00	16·00
		ba. Ditto. "Pies" for "pies" (R. 4/8) ..	£190	£200
49	**14**	2 p. on 3 p. blue (1929)	4·50	5·00
		a. Surch double	£275	
		b. Surch with Type **15**	65·00	95·00
		ba. Ditto. Surch double	£1200	

There are four settings of these overprints. The first (July 1922) consisted of 39 stamps with Type **11**, and 9 with Type **12**, and in Type **11** the centre of the "2" is above the "o" of "Two". In the second setting (May 1924) there were 36 of Type **11** and 12 of Type **12**, and the centre of the figure is above the space between "Two" and "Pies". The third setting (June 1924) consists of stamps with Type **13** only.

The fourth setting (1929) was also in sheets of 48, No. 49b being the first stamp in the fourth row.

ONE ANNA
ഒരു അണ
ANCHAL & REVENUE
(16)

Three Pies
൩ 3
മൂന്നു പൈ
(17)

1928. *Surch with T* **16**.

No.	Type	Description	Unused	Used
50	**10**	1 a. on 2¼ a. yellow-green (*a*)	5·00	12·0
		a. "REVENUF" for "REVENUE" ..	48·00	75·0
		b. Surch double		

1932–33. *Surch as T* **17**. *W* **8a**. *P* 13½.

No.	Type	Description	Unused	Used
51	**10**	3 p. on 4 p. green (*b*)	1·00	8
		a. "r" in "Three" inverted	†	£22
52		3 p. on 8 p. sepia (*b*)	1·00	2·0
53		9 p. on 10 p. blue (*b*)	1·50	2·5
51/3		.. .. *Set of* 3	3·00	4·7

Maharaja Rama Varma III, 1932–1941

18 Maharaja Rama Varma III

(Recess Perkins, Bacon & Co)

1933–38. *T* **18** (*but frame and inscription of* 1 *a. as T* **9**). *W* **8**
P 13 × 13½.

No.	Type	Description	Unused	Used
54	**18**	2 p. brown (1936)	60	2
55		4 p. green	60	1
56		6 p. red-brown	70	1
57	–	1 a. brown-orange	70	1
58	**18**	1 a. 8 p. carmine	3·00	3·7
59		2 a. grey (1938)	3·75	4
60		2¼ a. yellow-green	1·50	1
61		3 a. vermilion (1938)	3·50	1·2
62		3 a. 4 p. violet	1·50	1·4
63		6 a. 8 p. sepia	1·75	9·0
64		10 a. blue	3·00	10·0
54/64 ..		.. .. *Set of* 11	18·00	24·0

For stamps in this design, but lithographed, see Nos. 67/71.

1934. *Surcharged as T* **14**. *W* **8a**. *P* 13½.

No.	Type	Description	Unused	Used
65	**10**	6 p. on 8 p. sepia (R.) (*b*)	75	5
66		6 p. on 10 p. blue (R.) (*b*)	1·75	1·5

"DOUBLE PRINTS". The errors previously listed under thi description are now identified as blanket offsets, a type of variet outside the scope of this catalogue. Examples occur on issues fron 1938 onwards.

SPACING OF OVERPRINTS AND SURCHARGES. Th typeset overprints and surcharges issued from 1939 onwards show considerable differences in spacing. Except for specialists, however these differences have little significance as they occur within th same settings and do not represent separate printings.

(Litho The Associated Printers, Madras)

1938. *W* **8a**. *P* 11.

No.	Type	Description	Unused	Used
67	**18**	2 p. brown	1·00	3
		aw. Wmk inverted		
		b. Perf 13×13½	5·50	6
68		4 p. green	85	1
		aw. Wmk inverted		
		b. Perf 13×13½	8·00	12·0
69		6 p. red-brown	2·25	1
		aw. Wmk inverted	†	—
		b. Perf 13×13½	†	£225
70		1 a. brown-orange	60·00	70·0
		aw. Wmk inverted		
		b. Perf 13×13½	70·00	75·0
71		2¼ a. sage-green	6·00	1
		a. Perf 13×13½	12·00	3·5
67/71		.. .. *Set of* 5	60·00	70·0

Most examples of Nos. 70/b were used fiscally. Collectors are warned against examples which have been cleaned and regummed or provided with forged postmarks.

ANCHAL (19) ANCHAL (19*a*) THREE PIES (20)

SURCHARGED ANCHAL

ONE ANNA THREE PIES ANCHAL (21)

NINE PIES ANCHAL (22)

NINE PIES (23)

SURCHARGED NINE PIES (24)

1939 (Jan). *Nos.* 57 *and* 70 *optd with T* **19/a**.

No.	Type	Description	Unused	Used
72	**18**	1 a. brown-orange (*recess*) (T **19**) ..	1·60	45
73		1 a. brown-orange (*litho*) (T **19**) ..	£250	50
		aw. Wmk inverted	†	—
		b. Perf 13×13½	—	£250
74		1 a. brown-orange (*litho*) (T **19a**) ..	75	1·60
		a. Perf 13×13½	10·00	50

In 1939 it was decided that there would be separate 1 a. stamps for revenue and postal purposes. The "ANCHAL" overprints were applied to stamps intended for postal purposes.

:2–44. *T* **18** *variously optd or surch.*

I. *Recess-printed stamp. No.* 58

3 p. on 1 a. 8 p. carmine (T **20**) .. .. £160 70·00
3 p. on 1 a. 8 p. carmine (T **21**) .. .. 2·00 6·00
6 p. on 1 a. 8 p. carmine (T **20**) .. .. 2·50 16·00
1 a. 3 p. on 1 a. 8 p. carmine (T **21**) .. 1·00 30

II. *Lithographed stamps. Nos.* 68, 70 *and* 70b

3 p. on 4 p. (T **21**) .. .. 5·00 3·00
a. Perf 13×13½ .. .. 13·00 3·00
6 p. on 1 a. (T **22**) £250 £170
a. "SIX PIES" double .. .. † £650
6 p. on 1 a. (T **23**) £225 £150
a. Perf 13×13½ .. .. 85·00 45·00
9 p. on 1 a. (T **22**) .. .. 95·00 £100
9 p. on 1 a. (T **23**) (*p* 13×13½) .. .. £170 28·00
9 p. on 1 a. (T **24**) (*p* 13×13½) .. .. 13·00 4·00

Maharaja Kerala Varma II, 1941–1943

26 Maharaja Kerala Varma II

കൊച്ചിസർക്കാർ

27 (*The actual measurement of this wmk is* 6¼ × 3⅝ *in.*)

(Litho The Associated Printers, Madras)

·43. *Frame of* 1 *a. inscr* "ANCHAL & REVENUE". *P* 13×13½. (*a*) *W* **8***a*.

26 2 p. grey-brown .. .. 1·00 1·60
a. Perf 11 .. .. † £1600
b 4 p. green £450 £225
c 1 a. brown-orange .. .. .. 75·00 90·00
/c .. .. *Set of* 3 £475 £275

(*b*) *W* **27**

26 2 p. grey-brown .. .. .. 25·00 1·60
a. Perf 11 .. .. † £1900
4 p. green .. .. 7·00 15·00
a. Perf 11 .. .. 3·00 3·00
6 p. red-brown .. .. 1·25 10
a. Perf 11 .. .. 8·00 1·40
9 p. ultramarine (*p* 11) .. .. 23·00 1·00
a. Imperf between (horiz pair) .. £1300
1 a. brown-orange £200 £150
a. Perf 11 .. .. 21·00 38·00
2¼ a. yellow-green .. .. .. 18·00 1·50
a. Perf 11 .. .. 24·00 7·00

Part of W **27** appears on many stamps in each sheet, while hers are entirely without wmk.

Although inscribed "ANCHAL (= Postage) & REVENUE" ost examples of Nos. 85*c* and 90/a were used fiscally. Collectors e warned against examples which have been cleaned and gummed or provided with forged postmarks.

Maharaja Ravi Varma 1943-1946

943. *T* **26** *variously optd or surch. P* 13×13½. (*a*) *W* **8***a*

2 3 p. on 4 p. (T **21**) .. .. 50·00 15·00
2*a* 9 p. on 1 a. (T **23**) .. .. 4·25 1·50
2*b* 9 p. on 1 a. (T **24**) .. .. 3·25 1·75
2*c* 1 a. 3 p. on 1 a. (T **21**) .. .. .. — £2750

(*b*) *W* **27**

3 2 p. on 6 p. (T **20**) .. .. 75 2·25
a. Perf 11 .. .. 85 2·25
4 3 p. on 4 p. (T **20**) (*p* 11) .. .. 2·00 10
5 3 p. on 4 p. (T **21**) .. .. 3·00 10
6 3 p. on 6 p. (T **20**) 85 20
a. Perf 11 .. .. 85 35
7 4 p. on 6 p. (T **20**) .. .. 2·75 8·00

No. 92*c* is believed to be an error; a sheet of No. 85*b* having een included in a stock of No. O52 intended to become No. O66.

28 Maharaja Ravi Varma **29**

I

II

(Litho The Associated Printers, Madras)

·944–48. *W* **27**. *No gum.* (*a*) *Type* I. *P* 11.

·8 **28** 9 p. ultramarine (1944) .. .. .. 9·00 1·50

(*b*) *Type* II. *P* 13

98*a* **28** 9 p. ultramarine (1946) .. .. .. 5·50 11·00
ab. Perf 13 × 13½ .. .. 28·00 2·25
99 1 a. 3 p. magenta (1948) .. .. .. 5·00 7·50
a. Perf 13 × 13½ .. .. £150 32·00
100 1 a. 9 p. ultramarine (*shades*) (1948) .. 8·00 10·00
98*a*/100 .. .. *Set of* 3 17·00 18·00

Nos. 98*a*/100 are line-perforated, Nos. 98ab and 99a comb-perforated.

Maharaja Kerala Varma III, 1946–48

(Litho The Associated Printers, Madras)

1946–48. *Frame of* 1 *a. inscr* "ANCHAL & REVENUE". *W* **27**. *No gum* (*except for stamps perf* 11). *P* 13.

101 **29** 2 p. chocolate .. .. 1·25 10
a. Imperf horiz (vert pair) £1200 £1200
c. Perf 11 .. .. 8·00 60
d. Perf 11×13 .. .. £375 £140
102 3 p. carmine 50 10
103 4 p. grey-green .. .. £1600 80·00
104 6 p. red-brown (1947) .. .. .. 20·00 3·00
a. Perf 11 .. .. £150 2·50
105 9 p. ultramarine 50 10
a. Imperf between (horiz pair) .. † £1300
106 1 a. orange (1948) .. .. .. 6·00 25·00
a. Perf 11 .. .. £500
107 2 a. black .. .. 80·00 6·50
a. Perf 11 .. .. £110 5·50
108 3 a. vermilion .. .. 50·00 50
101/8 .. .. *Set of* 8 £1500 £100

Although inscribed "ANCHAL (=Postage) & REVENUE" most examples of No. 106 were used fiscally.

The 1 a. 3 p. magenta, 1 a. 9 p. ultramarine and 2¼ a. yellow-green in Type **29** subsequently appeared surcharged or overprinted for official use. Examples of the 1 a. 3 p. magenta exist without overprint, but may have not been issued in this state (*Price £275 unused*).

30 Maharaja Kerala Varma III

Tail to turban flaw (R. 1/7)

(Litho The Associated Printers, Madras)

1948–50. *W* **27** (*upright or inverted*). *P* 11.

109 **30** 2 p. grey-brown .. .. .. 1·00 15
a. Imperf vert (horiz pair) .. .. † £1200
110 3 p. carmine 75 15
a. Imperf between (vert pair) .. † 31·00
111 4 p. green .. .. 8·50 1·00
a. Imperf vert (horiz pair) £275 £325
112 6 p. chestnut .. .. 11·00 20
a. Imperf vert (horiz pair) £800
113 9 p. ultramarine .. .. 1·75 15
114 2 a. black .. .. 38·00 40
115 3 a. orange-red .. .. 48·00 50
a. Imperf vert (horiz pair) £1500
116 3 a. 4 p. violet (1950) .. .. .. 90·00 £350
a. Tail to turban flaw £250
109/16 .. .. *Set of* 8 £180 £350

Maharaja Rama Varma IV, 1948–1964

31 Chinese Nets

32 Dutch Palace

(Litho The Associated Printers, Madras)

1949. *W* **27**. *P* 11.

117 **31** 2 a. black .. .. 3·00 4·75
a. Imperf vert (horiz pair) £425
118 **32** 2¼ a. green .. .. 2·25 4·25
a. Imperf vert (horiz pair) £425

SIX PIES

ആറ പൈ

(**33**)

പൈ Normal

പൈ Error

Due to similarities between two Malayalam characters some values of the 1948 provisional issue exist with an error in the second word of the Malayalam surcharge. On Nos. 119, 122 and O103 this occurs twice in the setting of 48. No. 125 shows four examples and No. O104b one. Most instances are as illustrated above, but in two instances on the setting for No. 125 the error occurs on the second character.

1949. *Surch as T* **33**. (i) *On* 1944–48 *issue. P* 13.

119 **28** 6 p. on 1 a. 3 p. magenta .. .. 2·75 3·00
a. Incorrect character .. .. .. 23·00 23·00
120 1 a. on 1 a. 9 p. ultramarine (R.) .. 75 90

(ii) *On* 1946–48 *issue*

121 **29** 3 p. on 9 p. ultramarine .. .. .. 7·50 15·00
122 6 p. on 1 a. 3 p. magenta .. .. .. 9·50 11·00
a. Surch double .. .. † £400
b. Incorrect character .. .. .. 65·00 65·00
123 1 a. on 1 a. 9 p. ultramarine (R.) .. 3·00 1·50
a. Surch in black .. .. † £1900
b. Black surch with smaller native characters 7½ mm instead of 10 mm long .. .. † £2500

(iii) *On* 1948–50 *issue*

124 **30** 3 p. on 9 p. ultramarine .. .. .. 1·75 1·75
a. Larger native characters 20 mm instead of 16½ mm long .. .. 2·25 50
ab. Imperf between (vert pair) .. .. † £1100
b. Surch double £400
c. Surch both sides £325
125 3 p. on 9 p. ultramarine (R.) .. .. 2·75 2·25
a. Incorrect character .. .. .. 16·00 13·00
126 6 p. on 9 p. ultramarine (R.) 75 40
119/26 .. .. *Set of* 8 26·00 30·00

The 9 p. ultramarine (T **29**) with 6 p. surcharge (T **33**) in red was prepared for use but not issued (*Price £250 unused*)

1949. *Surch as T* **20**. *W* **27**. *P* 13.

127 **29** 6 p. on 1 a. orange .. .. .. 55·00 £120
128 9 p. on 1 a. orange .. .. .. 65·00 £110

OFFICIAL STAMPS

On C S	ON G C S	ON G C S
(O 1)	(O 2 Small "ON")	(O 3 "G" without serif)

1913. *Optd with Type* O **1** (3 *p.*) *or* O **2** (*others*).

O1 **8** 3 p. blue (R.) £120 10
a. Black opt .. .. † £1000
b. Inverted "S" .. .. — 48·00
c. Opt double .. .. † £500
O2 4 p. green (*wmk sideways*) .. .. 8·00 10
a. Opt inverted .. .. — £250
O3 9 p. carmine .. .. 80·00 10
a. Wmk sideways .. .. .. 15·00 10
w. Wmk inverted .. ..
O4 1½ a. purple .. .. 32·00 10
a. Opt double £425
O5 2 a. grey .. .. 13·00 10
O6 3 a. vermilion .. .. 45·00 30
O7 6 a. violet .. .. 38·00 2·00
O8 12 a. ultramarine .. .. 35·00 5·50
O9 1½ r. deep green .. .. 24·00 45·00
O1/9 .. .. *Set of* 9 £275 50·00

1919–33. *Optd as Type* O **3**.

O10 **10** 4 p. green (*a*) (*b*) .. .. .. 3·25 10
a. Opt double .. .. — £375
O11 6 p. red-brown (*a*) (*b*) (1922) .. .. 5·50 10
a. Opt double .. .. — £350
w. Wmk inverted .. .. † —
O12 8 p. sepia (*b*) (1923) .. .. .. 11·00 10
O13 9 p. carmine (*a*) (*b*) .. .. .. 45·00 10
O14 10 p. blue (*b*) (1923) .. .. .. 12·00 10
O15 1½ a. purple (*a*) (*b*) (1921) .. .. 5·50 10
O16 2 a. grey (*b*) (1923) .. .. .. 38·00 15
O17 2¼ a. yellow-green (*a*) (*b*) (1922) .. 11·00 10
a. Opt double .. .. † £350
O18 3 a. vermilion (*a*) (*b*) (*c*) .. .. 15·00 25
a. Opt inverted .. .. † £350
O19 6 a. violet (*a*) (*b*) (1924) .. .. 29·00 50
O19*a* 12 a. ultramarine (*a*) (*b*) (1929) .. 15·00 2·75
O19*b* 1½ r. deep green (*a*) (*b*) (1933) .. 22·00 80·00
O10/19*b* .. .. *Set of* 12 £190 80·00

All values exist showing a straight-backed "C" variety on R. 4/1.

8

Eight pies

(O 4 27½ mm high)

ON
C G
S

(O 5 Straight back to "C")

ON
C G
S

(O 6 Circular "O"; "N" without serifs)

1923 (Jan)–**24.** *T* **8** *and* **10** *surch with Type* O 4.
O20 8 p. on 9 p. carmine (No. O3) .. .. £325 1·25
a. "Pies" for "pies" (R. 4/8) .. .. £800 55·00
b. Wmk sideways £130 20
ba. "Pies" for "pies" (R. 4/8) .. .. £350 18·00
c. Surch double .. .. .. † £325
O21 8 p. on 9 p. carm (*a*) (*b*) (No. O13) (11.24) 70·00 10
a. "Pies" for "pies" (R. 4/8) .. .. £180 12·00
b. Surch double .. .. .. † £275
c. Opt Type O 3 double .. .. † £275

Varieties with smaller "i" or "t" in "Eight" and small "i" in "Pies" are also known from a number of positions in the setting.

1925 (Apr). *T* **10** *surch as Type* O 4.
O22 10 p. on 9 p. carmine (*b*) (No. O13) .. 65·00 55
b. Surch double .. .. .. † £275
c. Surch 25 mm high (*a*) £160 85
ca. Surch double .. .. .. † £300

1929. *T* **8** *surch as Type* O 4.
O23 10 p. on 9 p. carmine (No. O3a) .. .. £750 7·50
a. Surch double .. .. .. † £350
b. Wmk upright .. .. .. — 40·00

1929–31. *Optd with Type* O 5.
O24 **10** 4 p. green (*b*) (1931) .. .. 22·00 1·10
a. Inverted "S" .. .. .. £130 10·00
O25 6 p. red-brown (*b*) (*c*) (*d*) (1930) .. 13·00 10
a. Inverted "S" .. .. .. 80·00 3·50
O26 8 p. sepia (*b*) (1930) .. .. 6·00 10
a. Inverted "S" .. .. .. 45·00 4·00
O27 10 p. blue (*b*) .. .. .. 6·00 10
a. Inverted "S" .. .. .. 45·00 4·50
O28 2 a. grey (*b*) (1930) .. .. 23·00 15
a. Inverted "S" .. .. .. £100 6·50
O29 3 a. vermilion (*b*) (1930) .. .. 8·00 15
a. Inverted "S" .. .. .. 70·00 7·00
O30 6 a. violet (*b*) (*d*) (1930) .. .. 65·00 3·00
a. Inverted "S" .. .. .. £375 75·00
O24/30 .. .. *Set of* 7 £130 4·25

Pie3

No. O32b

1933. *Nos.* O26/7 *surch as T* **14**, *in red.*
O32 **10** 6 p. on 8 p. sepia (*b*) .. .. 2·00 10
a. Inverted "S" .. .. .. 17·00 4·00
b. "3" for "S" in "Pies" .. ..
O33 6 p. on 10 p. blue (*b*) .. .. 4·00 10
a. Inverted "S" .. .. .. 35·00 3·75

The inverted "S" varieties occur on R.2/1 of one setting of this overprint only.

1933–38. *Recess-printed stamps of* 1933–38 *optd.*

(*a*) *With Type* O **5**

O34 **18** 4 p. green .. .. .. 2·00 10
O35 6 p. red-brown (1934) .. .. 2·25 10
O36 1 a. brown-orange .. .. 9·50 10
O37 1 a. 8 p. carmine .. .. 1·50 20
O38 2 a. grey .. .. .. 9·50 10
O39 2¼ a. yellow-green .. .. 4·00 10
O40 3 a. vermilion .. .. .. 32·00 10
O41 3 a. 4 p. violet .. .. .. 1·50 15
O42 6 a. 8 p. sepia .. .. .. 1·50 20
O43 10 a. blue .. .. .. 1·50 40
O34/43 .. .. *Set of* 10 55·00 1·40

(*b*) *With Type* O **6** (*typo*)

O44 **18** 1 a. brown-orange (1937) .. .. 35·00 45
O45 2 a. grey-black (1938) .. .. 20·00 90
O46 3 a. vermilion (1938) .. .. 10·00 90
O44/6 .. .. *Set of* 3 55·00 2·00

ON
C G
S

(O 7 Curved back to "c")

ON
C G
S

(O 8)

ON
C G
S

(O 9 Circular "O"; N with serifs)

ON
C G
S

(O 10 Oval "O")

ON
C G
S

(O 11)

1938–44. *Lithographed stamps of* 1938. *W* **8***a*, *optd.*

(*a*) *With Type* O **7** *or* O **8** (1 *a*). *P* 11

O47 **18** 4 p. green .. .. .. 19·00 1·50
a. Inverted "S" .. .. .. 24·00 1·50
b. Perf 13×13½ .. .. .. 17·00 1·50
O48 6 p. red-brown .. .. .. 18·00 40
a. Inverted "S" .. .. .. 21·00 50
O49 1 a. brown-orange .. .. .. £250 2·50
O50 2 a. grey-black .. .. .. 14·00 70
a. Inverted "S" .. .. .. 15·00 70

(*b*) *With Type* O **9** (*litho*) *or* O **10** (6 *p.*)

O51 **18** 6 p. red-brown (*p* 13×13½) .. .. 7·00 1·90
O52 1 a. brown-orange .. .. .. 1·00 10
O53 3 a. vermilion .. .. .. 2·75 60

(*c*) *With Type* O **11**

O53*a* **18** 6 p. red-brown £700 £300

The inverted "S" varieties, Nos. O47a, O48a and O50a, occur 21 times in the setting of 48.

1942–43. *Unissued stamps optd with Type* O **10**. *Litho. W* **27**. *P* 11.
O54 **18** 4 p. green .. .. .. 60·00 12·00
a. Perf 13×13½ .. .. .. 1·40 60
O55 6 p. red-brown .. .. .. 90·00 11·00
a. Perf 13×13½ .. .. .. 18·00 90
ab. Optd both sides .. .. † 95·00
O56 1 a. brown-orange .. .. .. 16·00 5·00
a. Perf 13×13½ .. .. .. 1·25 3·75
ab. Optd both sides .. ..
O56*b* 2 a. grey-black (1943) .. .. 48·00 65
ba. Opt omitted .. .. .. † £1100
O56*c* 2¼ a. sage-green (1943) .. .. £900 3·75
O56*d* 3 a. vermilion (1943) .. .. 11·00 3·75

1943. *Official stamps variously surch with T* **20** *or* **21**.

(i) *On* 1½ *a. purple, of* 1919–33

O57 **10** 9 p. on 1½ a. (*b*) (T **20**) .. .. £375 19·00

(ii) *On recess-printed* 1 *a.* 8 *p. carmine of* 1933–44 (*Type* O **5** *opt*)

O58 3 p. on 1 a. 8 p. (T **21**) .. .. .. 4·00 45
O59 9 p. on 1 a. 8 p. (T **20**) .. .. .. £100 26·00
O60 1 a. 9 p. on 1 a. 8 p. (T **20**) .. .. 1·40 1·60
O61 1 a. 9 p. on 1 a. 8 p. (T **21**) 80 30

(iii) *On lithographed stamps of* 1938–44. *P* 11. (*a*) *W* **8***a*

O62 **18** 3 p. on 4 p. (Types O **7** and **20**) (*p* 13×13½) .. .. .. 18·00 4·50
a. Surch double £275 £140
O63 3 p. on 4 p. (Types O **7** and **21**) (*p* 13×13½) .. .. .. 80·00 42·00
O64 3 p. on 1 a. (Types O **9** and **20**) .. 1·75 2·00
O65 9 p. on 1 a. (Types O **9** and **20**) .. £180 45·00
O66 1 a. 3 p. on 1 a. (Types O **9** and **21**) .. £225 90·00

(*b*) *W* **27**

O67 **18** 3 p. on 4 p. (Types O **10** and **20**) (*p* 13×13½) .. .. .. 70·00 45·00
O67*a* 3 p. on 4 p. (Types O **10** and **21**) (*p* 13×13½) £425
O67*b* 3 p. on 1 a. (Types O **10** and **20**) .. £110 60·00
ba. Perf 13×13½ .. .. .. 80·00 60·00

1944. *Optd with Type* O **10**. *W* **27**. *P* 13×13½.
O68 **26** 4 p. green .. .. .. 16·00 2·25
a. Perf 11 .. .. .. £100 4·00
b. Perf 13 .. .. .. £225 65·00
O69 6 p. red-brown 90 10
a. Opt double .. .. .. — 55·00
b. Perf 11 .. .. .. 70 10
ba. Opt double .. .. .. — 55·00
c. Perf 13 .. .. .. 7·00 2·00
O70 1 a. brown-orange .. .. .. £1500 45·00
O71 2 a. black .. .. .. 2·75 40
O72 2¼ a. yellow-green .. .. .. 1·75 40
a. Optd both sides .. .. † £110
O73 3 a. vermilion .. .. .. 4·75 40
a. Perf 11 .. .. .. 3·75 40

Stamps perforated 13 × 13½ are from a comb machine; those perforated 13 from a line perforator.

1944. *Optd with Type* O **10** *and variously surch as Types* **20** *and* **21**. *W* **27**.
O74 **26** 3 p. on 4 p. (T **20**) .. .. 1·25 10
a. Perf 11 .. .. .. 5·00 45
ab. Optd Type O **10** on both sides .. † £110
O75 3 p. on 4 p. (T **21**) .. .. 3·25 30
a. Perf 11 .. .. .. £375 £160
O76 3 p. on 1 a. (T **20**) .. .. 13·00 2·75
O77 9 p. on 6 p. (T **20**) .. .. 5·50 1·25
a. Stamp printed both sides ..
O78 9 p. on 6 p. (T **21**) .. .. 2·50 25
O79 1 a. 3 p. on 1 a. (T **20**) .. .. 4·50 75
O80 1 a. 3 p. on 1 a. (T **21**) .. .. 2·75 10
O74/80 .. .. *Set of* 7 30·00 5·00

1946–47. *Stamps of* 1944–48 (*Head Type II*) *optd with Type* O **10**. *P* 13.
O81 **28** 9 p. ultramarine .. .. .. 2·00 10
a. Stamp printed both sides .. .. † £325
b. Perf 13 × 13½ .. .. .. 3·00 10
O82 1 a. 3 p. magenta (1947) .. .. 1·00 20
a. Opt double .. .. .. 18·00 12·00
b. Optd both sides, opt double on reverse .. .. .. 42·00
O83 1 a. 9 p. ultramarine (1947) 40 60
a. Opt double .. .. ..
O81b/83 .. .. *Set of* 3 3·00 80

1948. *Stamps of* 1946–48 *and unissued values optd with Type* O **2**. *P* 13.
O84 **29** 3 p. carmine 40 10
a. Stamp printed both sides .. .. † —
O85 4 p. grey-green .. .. .. 22·00 4·50
O86 6 p. red-brown .. .. .. 4·25 50
O87 9 p. ultramarine 75 10
O88 1 a. 3 p. magenta .. .. .. 1·60 30
O89 1 a. 9 p. ultramarine .. .. .. 1·40 40
O90 2 a. black .. .. .. 13·00 2·25
O91 2¼ a. yellow-green .. .. .. 15·00 2·25
O84/91 .. .. *Set of* 8 50·00 9·50

1949. *Stamps of* 1948–50 *and unissued values optd with Ty*[p]
O **7**.
O92 **30** 3 p. carmine 60
a. "C" for "G" in opt .. .. 7·50 3·
O93 4 p. green 85
a. Imperf between (pair) .. .. † £10
b. Optd on reverse .. .. 60·00 60·
c. "C" for "G" in opt .. .. 11·00 4·
O94 6 p. chestnut .. .. .. 2·00
a. Imperf between (vert pair) .. † £11
b. "C" for "G" in opt .. .. 16·00 2·
O95 9 p. ultramarine .. .. .. 1·75
a. "C" for "G" in opt .. .. 13·00 3·
O96 2 a. black 85
a. "C" for "G" in opt .. .. 13·00 4·0
O97 2¼ a. yellow-green .. .. .. 2·00 4·0
a. "C" for "G" in opt .. .. 20·00 30·0
O98 3 a. orange-red .. .. .. 1·10 4
a. "C" for "G" in opt .. .. 15·00 7·
O99 3 a. 4 p. violet .. .. .. 26·00 24·
a. "C" for "G" in opt £225 £22
b. Tail to turban flaw £180
O92/9 .. .. *Set of* 8 32·00 26·

The "C" for "G" variety occurs on R. 1/4. Nos. O92/9, O103 and O104b also exist with a flat back to "G" which occurs twi[ce] in each sheet on R. 1/5 and R. 2/8.

No. O93 exists with watermark sideways, but can usual[ly] only be identified when in multiples.

1949. *Official stamps surch as T* **33**. (i) *On* 1944 *issue.*
O100 **28** 1 a. on 1 a. 9 p. ultramarine (R.) .. 60 4

(ii) *On* 1948 *issue*

O101 **29** 1 a. on 1 a. 9 p. ultramarine (R.) .. 15·00 11·0

(iii) *On* 1949 *issue*

O103 **30** 6 p. on 3 p. carmine 35 5
a. Imperf between (vert pair) .. † £75
b. Surch double .. .. .. † £27
c. "C" for "G" in opt .. .. 7·50 8·5
d. Incorrect character .. .. 7·50 8·5
O104 9 p. on 4 p. green (18 *mm long*) .. 55 1·4
a. Imperf between (horiz pair) .. £650
b. Larger native characters, 22 mm long 90 6
ba. Ditto. Imperf between (horiz pair) £650 £65
bb. Incorrect character .. .. 14·00 11·0
c. "C" for "G" in opt .. .. 11·00 16·0
ca. Ditto. Larger native characters, 22 mm long .. .. .. 14·00 11·0
O100/4 .. .. *Set of* 4 15·00 11·5

No. O104 exists with watermark sideways, but can usuall[y] only be identified when in multiples.

1949. *No.* 124*a*, *but with lines of surch* 17½ *mm apart, opt*[d]
"SERVICE".
O105 **30** 3 p. on 9 p. ultramarine 60 5
a. Imperf between (horiz pair) .. † £100

From 1 July 1949 Cochin formed part of the new state [of] Travancore-Cochin. Existing stocks of Cochin issues continue[d] to be used in conjunction with stamps of Travancore surcharge[d] in Indian currency.

DHAR

PRICES FOR STAMPS ON COVER

Nos. 1/4	*from* × 50
No. 5	*from* × 30
No. 6	—
Nos. 7/9	*from* × 50
No. 10	—

Raja (Maharaja from 1877) Anand Rao Puar III, 1857–1898

1

2

अर्धा बलड. अर्धा लबड. आर्धा डबल.

No. 1c No. 1d No. 2

1897–1900. *Type-set. Colour-fugitive paper. With oval handstam*[p] *in black. No gum. Imperf.*
1 **1** ½ p. black/*red* (three characters at bottom left) .. .. 1·90 2·2
a. Handstamp omitted £250
b. Line below upper inscription (R. 2/2) 55·00 55·0
c. Character transposed (R. 2/3) .. 19·00 22·0
d. Character transposed (R. 2/5) .. 55·00
2 ½ p. black/*red* (four characters at bottom left) .. .. 1·75 2·5
a. Handstamp omitted £180
3 ¼ a. black/*orange* .. .. .. 1·50 2·5
a. Handstamp omitted £225
4 ½ a. black/*magenta* .. .. .. 2·75 3·5
a. Handstamp omitted £225 £19
b. Line below upper inscription (R. 2/2) £100 £11
5 1 a. black/*green* .. .. .. 5·50 9·5
a. Handstamp omitted £400
b. Printed both sides .. .. ..
c. Line below upper inscription (R. 2/2) £180 £19
6 2 a. black/*yellow* .. .. .. 20·00 32·0
e. Top right corner ornament transposed with one from top of frame (R. 2/5) £100 £13
1/6 .. .. *Set of* 6 30·00 48·0

Nos. 1/6 were each issued in sheets of 10 (5 × 2), but may, on the evidence of a single sheet of the ½ pice value, have been printed in sheets of 20 containing two of the issued sheets *tête-bêche*.

Research has identified individual characteristics for stamps ·inted from each position in the sheet.

The same research suggests that the type remained assembled ·ring the entire period of production, being amended as necessary provide the different values. Seven main settings have been ·entified with changes sometimes occurring during their use ·hich form sub-settings.

The distribution of stamps between the main settings was as ·llows:

Setting I—½ p.
Setting II—½ a., 1 a.
Setting III—1 a.
Setting IV—½ p., ½ a., 1 a.
Setting V—½ p.
Setting VI—½ p. (No. 2), ¼ a.
Setting VII—2 a.

The listed constant errors all occurred during Setting IV.

In No. 1c the three characters forming the second word in the ·wer inscription are transposed to the order (2) (3) (1) and in No. · to the order (3) (2) (1).

On Nos. 1b, 4b and 5c the line which normally appears above the ·pper inscription is transposed so that it appears below the ·aracters.

All values show many other constant varieties including ·istakes in the corner and border ornaments, and also both ·nstant and non-constant missing lines, dots and characters.

Examples of complete forgeries and faked varieties on genuine ·amps exist.

·aja (Maharaja from 1918) Udaji Rao Puar II, 1898–1926

(Typo at Bombay)

·98–1900. *P* 11 *to* 12.
· 2 ½ a. carmine .. .. 2·75 4·75
a. Imperf (pair) .. .. 35·00
b. Deep rose .. .. 2·25 4·50
· 1 a. claret .. .. 2·50 4·75
· 1 a. reddish violet .. .. 2·75 9·50
a. Imperf between (horiz pair) £400
b. Imperf (pair) £100
· 2 a. deep green .. .. 4·50 17·00
·10 .. .. *Set of* 4 11·00 32·00

The stamps of Dhar have been obsolete since 31 March 1901.

DUNGARPUR

PRICES FOR STAMPS ON COVER
Nos. 1/15 *from* × 2

Maharawal Lakshman Singh, 1918–1971

1 State Arms

(Litho Shri Lakshman Bijaya Printing Press, Dungarpur)

·933–47. *P* 11.
1 1 ¼ a. bistre-yellow .. .. — £110
¼ a. rose (1935) .. .. — £325
¼ a. red-brown (1937) .. .. — £200
1 a. pale turquoise-blue .. .. — 95·00
1 a. rose (1938) .. .. — £1000
1 a. 3 p. deep reddish violet (1935) .. .. — £150
2 a. deep dull green (1947) .. .. .. — £180
4 a. rose-red (1934) .. .. — £350

Nos. 2 and 5 are known in a *se-tenant* strip of 3, the centre ·amp being the 1 a. value.

2

3

4

Maharawal Lakshman Singh

·hree dies of ½ a. (*shown actual size*):

Die I. Size 21×25½ mm. Large portrait (head 5 mm and turban 7½ mm wide), correctly aligned (sheets of 12 and left-hand stamps in subsequent blocks of four *se-tenant* horizontally with Die II)

Die II. Size 20×24½ mm. Large portrait (head 4¾ mm and turban 7 mm wide), but with less detail at foot and with distinct tilt to left (right-hand stamps in sheets of four horizontally *se-tenant* with Die I)

Die III. Size 21×25½ mm. Small portrait (head 4½ mm and turban 6½ mm wide) (sheets of 4)

(Typo L.V. Indap & Co, Bombay)

1939–46. *T* **2** (*various frames*) *and* **3/4**. *Various perfs.*
9 2 ¼ a. orange (*p* 12, 11, 10½ *or* 10) .. £350 48·00
10 ½ a. verm (Die I) (*p* 12, 11 *or* 10½) (1940) £160 35·00
a. Die II (*p* 10½) (1944) .. .. £160 45·00
ab. Horiz pair. Die I and Die II .. £350 £110
b. Die III (*p* 10) (1945) .. .. £225 35·00
c. Imperf between (vert pair) .. † £1600
11 1 a. deep blue (*p* 12, 11, 10½ *or* 10) .. £150 27·00
12 3 1 a. 3 p. brt mauve (*p* 10½ *or* 10) (1944) £400 £140
13 4 1½ a. deep violet (*p* 10) (1946) .. £425 £140
14 2 2 a. brt green (*p* 12, *pin* perf 11½) (1943) £475 £250
15 4 a. brown (*p* 12, 10½ *or* 10) (1940) £400 £110

Stamps perforated 12, 11 and 10½ were printed in sheets of 12 (4×3) which were imperforate along the top, bottom and, sometimes, at right so that examples exist with one or two adjacent sides imperforate. Stamps perforated 10 were printed in sheets of 4 either imperforate at top, bottom and right-hand side or fully perforated.

Dungarpur became part of Rajasthan by 15 April 1948.

DUTTIA (DATIA)

PRICES FOR STAMPS ON COVER
Nos. 1/15 —
Nos. 16/40 *from* × 20

All the stamps of Duttia were impressed with a circular handstamp (as a rule in *blue*) before issue.

This handstamp shows the figure of Ganesh in the centre, surrounded by an inscription in Devanagari reading "DATIYA STET POSTAJ 1893". Stamps could not be used for postage without this control mark.

PROCESS. Nos. 1/15 were type-set and printed singly. Nos. 16/40 were typo from plates comprising 8 or more clichés.

GUM. The stamps of Duttia (*except No.* 25c) were issued without gum.

Maharaja Bhawani Singh, 1857–1907

Rectangular labels each showing a double hand-drawn frame (in black for the 1 a. and in red for the others), face value in black and the Ganesh handstamp are known on thin cream (½ a.), rose (1 a.), orange (2 a.) or pale yellow (4 a.) paper. These are considered by some specialists to be the first stamps of Duttia, possibly issued during 1893, but the evidence for this is inconclusive.

1 (2 a.)

2 (½ a.) Ganesh

3 (4 a.)

1894?. *Rosettes in lower corners. Control handstamp in blue. Imperf.*
1 1 ½ a. black/*green* £5500
2 2 a. grey-blue/*yellow* £2500
a. Handstamp in black £2250

Only two examples of No. 1 have been reported. In both instances the Devanagari inscription was originally 8 a., but was amended in manuscript to ½ a.

1896. *Control handstamp in blue. Imperf.*
3 2 1 a. red £1900 £2000
a. Handstamp in black £1900 £2000

1896. *Control handstamp in blue. Imperf.*
4 3 ¼ a. black/*orange* £2750
a. Without handstamp £1900
5 ½ a. black/*blue-green* £3250
a. Without handstamp £1900
6 2 a. black/*yellow* £1800
a. Without handstamp £4000
7 4 a. black/*rose* £1300

Two types of centre:

I

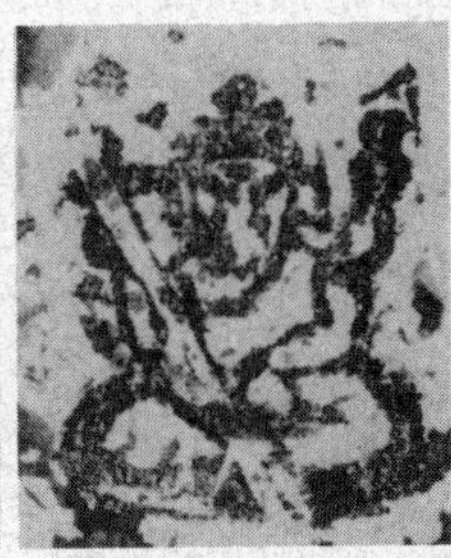

II

Type I. Small Ganesh. Height 13 mm. Width of statue 11 mm. Width of pedestal 8 mm.

Type II. Large Ganesh. Height 13½ mm. Width of statue 11½ mm. Width of pedestal 11½ mm. "Flag" in god's right hand; "angle" above left. All stamps also show dot at top right corner.

1897–98. *Imperf.*
8 2 ½ a. black/*green* (I) (value in one group) 40·00
a. *Tête-bêche* (horiz pair) £850
b. Value in two groups .. .. 15·00 £150
ba. *Tête-bêche* (vert pair) £900
bb. Type II (1898) .. .. .. 16·00
9 1 a. black/*white* (I) .. .. .. 60·00 £170
a. *Tête-bêche* (horiz pair) £900
b. Laid paper .. .. 14·00
ba. *Tête-bêche* (vert pair) £850
c. Type II (1898) .. .. .. 60·00
ca. Laid paper .. .. 16·00
10 2 a. black/*yellow* (I) .. .. .. 20·00 £160
a. *On lemon* .. .. 26·00
b. Type II (1898) .. .. .. 23·00
11 4 a. black/*rose* (I) .. .. .. 17·00 £130
a. *Tête-bêche* (horiz pair) £225
b. *Tête-bêche* (vert pair) £150
c. Doubly printed £1300
d. Type II (1898) .. .. .. 19·00

A used example of the 4 a. is known showing black roulettes at foot.

4 (½ a.)

5 (¼ a.)

1897. *Name spelt* "DATIA." *Imperf.*
12 4 ½ a. black/*green* .. .. .. 55·00 £325
13 1 a. black/*white* £120
14 2 a. black/*yellow* .. .. .. 65·00
a. *Tête-bêche* (vert pair) £3000
15 4 a. black/*rose* .. .. .. 60·00
a. *Tête-bêche* (vert pair) £3000
12/15 .. .. *Set of* 4 £275

1899–1906.

(*a*) *Roulетted in colour or in black, horizontally and at end of rows*
16 5 ¼ a. vermilion .. .. 2·50
a. Rose-red .. .. 1·90
b. Pale rose .. .. 1·60
c. Lake .. .. 3·00 11·00
d. Carmine .. .. 2·75
e. Brownish red .. .. .. 6·50
ea. *Tête-bêche* (pair) £3000
17 ½ a. black/*blue-green* .. .. .. 1·60 11·00
a. On deep green .. .. .. 4·25
b. On yellow-green (pelure) .. .. 4·00 12·00
c. On dull green (1906) .. .. .. 2·50
18 1 a. black/*white* .. .. 1·90 11·00
19 2 a. black/*lemon-yellow* .. .. .. 6·50
a. On orange-yellow .. .. .. 8·50
b. On buff-yellow .. .. .. 2·00 13·00
ba. Handstamp in black .. .. .. 7·50
bb. Without handstamp £130
c. On pale yellow (1906) .. .. .. 2·50 13·00
20 4 a. black/*deep rose* .. .. .. 2·50 12·00
a. *Tête-bêche* (pair) .. .. ..
b. Handstamp in black .. .. .. 10·00
c. Without handstamp £130

(*b*) *Rouletted in colour between horizontal rows, but imperf at top and bottom and at ends of rows*
20c 5 ¼ a. brownish red .. .. .. 30·00
21 1 a. black/*white* .. .. 11·00

One setting of 16 (8×2) of the ¼ a. value (No. 16*e*) showed an inverted cliché at R. 1/2.

1904–5. *Without rouletting.*
22 **5** ¼ a. red .. .. 2·00 20·00
23 ½ a. black/*green* .. .. 12·00
24 1 a. black (1905) .. .. 8·50 24·00

Maharaja Govind Singh, 1907–1955

1911. *P* 13½. *Stamps very wide apart.*
25 **5** ¼ a. carmine .. .. 4·25 30·00
a. Imperf horiz (vert pair) £200
b. Imperf between (horiz pair) £225
c. Stamps closer together (with gum) .. 6·50 22·00
d. As c. Imperf vert (horiz pair) .. £110
25*e* 1 a. black £750

No. 25*e* was mainly used for fiscal purposes (*Price on piece*, £75), but one example has been seen used on a registered postcard.

1912? *Printed close together.* (*a*) *Coloured roulette×imperf*
26 **5** ½ a. black/*green* .. .. 6·50
(*b*) *Printed wide apart. P* 13½×*coloured roulette* (¼ *a.*) *or* 13½×*imperf* (½ *a.*)
27 **5** ¼ a. carmine .. .. 4·50 24·00
28 ½ a. black/*dull green* .. .. 9·50 28·00

1916. *Colours changed. Control handstamp in blue* (*Nos.* 29/33) *or black* (*No.* 34). *Imperf.*
29 **5** ¼ a. deep blue .. .. 5·50 15·00
30 ½ a. green .. .. 4·00 17·00
31 1 a. purple .. .. 3·50 18·00
a. *Tête-bêche* (vert pair) .. .. 22·00
32 2 a. brown .. .. 10·00 22·00
33 2 a. lilac .. .. 5·00 22·00
a. Handstamp in black .. .. 20·00
b. Without handstamp £120
34 4 a. Venetian red (date?) .. .. 65·00

1918. *Colours changed.* (*a*) *Imperf.*
35 **5** ½ a. blue .. .. 2·50 11·00
36 1 a. pink .. .. 2·25 13·00
a. Handstamp in black .. .. 5·00
(*b*) *P* 11½
37 **5** ¼ a. black .. .. 3·50 15·00

1920. *Rouletted.*
38 **5** ¼ a. blue .. .. 1·75 8·00
a. Roul × perf 7 .. .. 35·00 35·00
b. Imperf between (vert pair) £475
c. Without handstamp £110
d. Handstamp in black .. .. 5·00
39 ½ a. pink .. .. 2·00 12·00
a. Roul × perf 7 .. .. £150
b. Without handstamp £150

1920?. *Rough perf about* 7.
40 **5** ½ a. dull red .. .. 9·00 24·00
a. Handstamp in black .. .. 30·00
b. Without handstamp £150

The stamps of Duttia have been obsolete since 1 April 1921.

FARIDKOT

PRICES FOR STAMPS ON COVER

Nos. N1/4	*from* × 10
Nos. N5/6	*from* × 50
Nos. N7/8	—

GUM. The stamps of Faridkot (Nos. N1/8) were issued without gum.

Raja Bikram Singh, 1874-1898

N 1 (1 folus)

N 2 (1 paisa)

N 3

1879–86. *Rough, handstamped impression. Imperf.*
(*a*) *Native thick laid paper*
N1 **N 1** 1 f. ultramarine .. .. 30·00 35·00
N2 **N 2** 1 p. ultramarine .. .. 85·00 90·00
(*b*) *Ordinary laid paper*
N3 **N 1** 1 f. ultramarine .. .. 14·00 16·00
N4 **N 2** 1 p. ultramarine .. .. 55·00 75·00
(*c*) *Wove paper, thick to thinnish*
N5 **N 1** 1 f. ultramarine .. .. 1·50 2·75
a. *Tête-bêche* (pair) £225
N6 **N 2** 1 p. ultramarine .. .. 2·50 6·50
a. Pair, one stamp sideways £800
(*d*) *Thin wove whity brown paper*
N7 **N 2** 1 p. ultramarine .. .. 27·00 29·00
(*e*) *Wove paper*
N8 **N 3** 1 p. ultramarine .. .. 1·25
a. *Tête-bêche* (pair) £200

It is doubtful whether stamps of Type N 3 were ever used for postage.

Impressions of these types in various colours, the ½ a. labels, and the later printings from re-engraved dies, were never in circulation at all.

Faridkot became a convention state and from 1887 used the Indian stamps overprinted which are listed under the Convention States.

HYDERABAD

PRICES FOR STAMPS ON COVER

Nos. 1/3	*from* × 10
Nos. 4/12	—
Nos. 13/60	*from* × 5
Nos. O1/53	*from* × 10

The official title of the State in English was The Dominions of the Nizam and in Urdu "Sarkar-i-Asafia" (State of the successors of Asaf). This Urdu inscription appears in many of the designs.

Nawab Mir Mahbub Ali Khan Asaf Jah VI, 1869–1911

1

2

(Eng Mr. Rapkin. Plates by Nissen & Parker, London. Recess Mint, Hyderabad)

1869 (8 Sept). *P* 11½.
1 **1** 1 a. olive-green .. .. 12·00 6·00
a. Imperf between (horiz pair) .. £110
b. Imperf horiz (vert pair) .. £350 £100
c. Imperf (pair) .. £300 £300

Reprints in the colour of the issue, and also in fancy colours, were made in 1880 on white wove paper, perforated 12½. Fakes of No. 1c are known created by the removal of the outer perforations from examples of Nos. 1a/b.

1870 (16 May). *Locally engraved;* 240 *varieties of each value; wove paper. Recess. P* 11½.
2 **2** ½ a. brown .. .. 4·00 4·00
3 2 a. sage-green .. .. 40·00 35·00

Stamps exist showing traces of lines in the paper, but they do not appear to be printed on true laid paper.

Reprints of both values were made in 1880 on white wove paper, perforated 12½: the ½ a. in grey-brown, yellow-brown, sea-green, dull blue and carmine and the 2 a. in bright green and in blue-green.

3

A
Normal

2 a.

B
Variety

In A the coloured lines surrounding each of the four labels join a coloured circle round their inner edge, in B this circle is missing.

C 3 a. D

C. Normal
D. Character ∧ omitted

Left side of central inscription omitted (Pl 4 R. 2/11)

Dot at top of central inscription omitted

Second dot in bottom label omitted

Centre dot in bottom label omitted

(Plates by Bradbury, Wilkinson & Co. Recess Mint, Hyderabad)

1871–1909. (*a*) *No wmk.* (i) *Rough perf* 11½
4 **3** ½ a. red-brown .. .. 17·00 18·0
5 1 a. purple-brown £100 £11
6 2 a. green (A) £700
7 3 a. ochre-brown .. .. 30·00 40·0
8 4 a. slate £130 £14
9 8 a. deep brown .. ..
10 12 a. dull blue £250
(ii) *Pin perf* 8–9
11 **3** ½ a. red-brown .. .. — £35
12 1 a. drab £300 £15
(iii) *P* 12½
13 **3** ½ a. orange-brown .. .. 1·25 1
a. Imperf vert (horiz pair) .. .. † 80·0
ab. Imperf horiz (vert pair) .. .. † £30
b. Orange .. .. 2·00 1
c. Red-brown .. .. 1·25 1
d. Brick-red .. .. 1·00 1
da. Imperf vert (horiz pair) .. .. † 80·0
db Doubly printed .. .. † £15
e. Rose-red .. .. 1·50 1
ea. Doubly printed .. .. † £18
f. Error. Magenta .. .. 45·00 8·0
g. Left side of central inscription omitted £160 60·0
h. Dot at top of central inscription omitted .. .. 38·00 2·0
14 1 a. purple-brown .. .. 3·75 3·7
a. Doubly printed £300
b. Drab 50 1
ba. Imperf (pair) .. .. — £20
bb. Doubly printed £140
c. Grey-black .. .. 1·00 1
d. Black (1909) .. .. 1·10 1
da. Doubly printed £300
db. Imperf vert (horiz pair) .. .. † £45
dc. Imperf horiz (vert pair) .. .. † £45
e. Dot at top of central inscription omitted .. .. — 90·0
f. Second dot in bottom label omitted 60·00 24·0
15 2 a. green (A) .. .. 2·00 1
a. Deep green (A) .. .. 2·25 4
b. Blue-green (A) .. .. 2·00 4
ba. Blue-green (B) .. .. £170 65·0
c. Pale green (A) .. .. 2·00 1
ca. Pale green (B) .. .. £170 75·0
d. Sage-green (A) (1909) .. .. 1·75 3
da. Sage-green (B) .. .. £120 45·0
e. Dot at top of central inscription omitted .. .. £160 75·0
f. Centre dot in bottom panel omitted 80·00 30·0
16 3 a. ochre-brown (C) .. .. 1·75 1·1
a. Character omitted (D) .. .. £170 70·0
b. Chestnut (C) 85 8
ba. Character omitted (D) .. .. £120 55·0
17 4 a. slate .. .. 4·25 1·7
a. Imperf horiz (vert pair) £600 £60
b. Greenish grey .. .. 3·00 1·7
ba. Imperf vert (horiz pair) £650
c. Olive-green .. .. 3·00 8
18 8 a. deep brown .. .. 1·25 1·9
a. Imperf vert (horiz pair) £650
19 12 a. pale ultramarine .. .. 3·00 4·2
a. Grey-green .. .. 2·50 2·7
13/19 .. .. *Set of* 7 9·75 6·0
(*b*) *W* **7**. *P* 12½
19*b* **3** 1 a. black (1909) .. .. 85·00 9·00
19*c* 2 a. sage-green (A) (1909) .. .. — 75·00
19*d* 12 a. bluish grey (1909?) £750

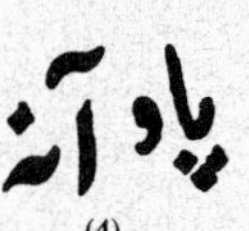
(4)

5

98. *Surch with T* **4.** *P* 12½.
) **3** ¼ a. on ½ a. orange-brown 50 85
a. Surch inverted .. .. .. 27·00 20·00
b. Pair, one without surcharge .. £275
c. Left side of central inscription omitted £100

(Des Khusrat Ullah. Recess Mint, Hyderabad)

900 (20 Sept). *P* 12½.
1 **5** ¼ a. deep blue .. .. 3·75 2·50
a. Pale blue .. .. 3·75 2·50

6

7

(Plates by Allan G. Wyon, London. Recess Mint, Hyderabad)

905 (7 Aug). *W* **7**. *P* 12½.
2 **6** ¼ a. dull blue .. .. 1·25 45
a. Imperf (pair) .. .. .. 28·00 75·00
b. Dull ultramarine .. .. .. 5·00 80
ba. Perf 11 × 12½ .. .. .. 22·00 22·00
c. Pale blue-green .. .. .. 17·00 2·00
3 ½ a. orange .. .. 3·75 35
a. Perf 11 .. ..
b. Vermilion .. .. 1·60 25
ba. Imperf (pair) .. .. .. 26·00 75·00
c. Yellow .. .. 60·00 16·00

908–11. *W* **7**. *P* 12½.
4 **6** ¼ a. grey 45 10
a. Imperf between (horiz pair) .. £180 £180
b. Imperf between (vert pair) .. † £180
c. Perf 11½, 12 .. .. .. 2·00 35
d. Perf 11 .. .. 45·00 20·00
5 ½ a. green .. .. 1·40 10
a. Imperf between (vert pair) .. £170
b. Perf 11½, 12 .. .. .. 3·25 10
c. Perf 13½ .. .. 75·00 35·00
d. Pale green .. .. 1·40 20
da. Perf 11½, 12 .. .. .. 3·25 10
e. Blue-green .. .. 5·00 90
6 1 a. carmine .. .. 1·00 10
a. Perf 11½, 12 .. .. .. 3·75 40
b. Perf 11 .. .. 23·00 8·50
c. Double impression (*perf* 12½×11) ..
7 2 a. lilac .. .. 1·00 20
a. Perf 11½, 12 .. .. .. 3·25 1·10
b. Perf 11 .. .. 2·50 55
c. Perf 13½ .. .. 1·40 15
ca. Imperf between (horiz pair) .. † £275
cb. Rose-lilac .. .. 1·10 10
8 3 a. brown-orange (1909) .. .. 1·10 35
a. Perf 11½, 12 .. .. .. 7·00 2·00
b. Perf 11 .. .. 90 60
c. Perf 13½ .. .. 1·50 30
9 4 a. olive-green (1909) .. .. 1·10 45
a. Perf 11½, 12 .. .. .. 6·50 4·00
b. Perf 11 .. .. 27·00 8·50
ba. Imperf between (pair) £375 £375
c. Perf 13½ 90 30
0 8 a. purple (1911) .. .. .. 3·00 4·00
a. Perf 11½, 12 .. .. ..
b. Perf 11 .. .. 1·75 2·25
c. Perf 13½ .. .. 1·10 35
1 12 a. blue-green (1911) .. .. 70·00 42·00
a. Perf 11½, 12 .. .. .. 8·50 11·00
b. Perf 11 .. ..
c. Perf 13½ .. .. 3·00 1·40

The above perforations also exist compound.

Nawab Mir Osman Ali Khan Asaf Jah VII, 1911–1967

1912. *New plates engraved by Bradbury, Wilkinson & Co. W* **7**. *P* 12½.
2 **6** ¼ a. grey-black .. .. 1·40 10
a. Imperf horiz (vert pair) .. .. † £170
b. Perf 11½, 12 .. .. .. 60 35
c. Perf 11 .. .. 80 15
ca. Imperf between (horiz pair) .. † £170
cb. Imperf between (vert pair) .. † £170
d. Perf 13½ 30 10
3 ¼ a. brown-purple (*shades*) (*p* 13½) .. 50 10
a. Imperf horiz (vert pair) .. .. † £170
4 ½ a. deep green 40 10
a. Imperf between (pair) .. .. † £180
b. Imperf (pair). Laid paper .. .. 80·00 60·00
c. Perf 11½, 12 .. .. .. 5·00 55
d. Perf 11 .. .. 8·00 10
e. Perf 13½ .. ..

The above perforations also exist compound.

In Wyon's ¼ a. stamp the fraction of value is closer to the end of he label than in the B.W. issue. In the Wyon ¼ a. and ½ a. the alue in English and the label below are further apart than in the B.W.

Wyon's ¼ a. measures 19½ × 20 mm and the ½ a. 9½ × 20½ mm; both stamps from the Bradbury plates measure 9¾ × 21½ mm.

8 Symbols

9

1915. *Inscr* "Post & Receipt". *W* **7**. *P* 13½.
35 **8** ½ a. green 60 10
a. Imperf between (pair) .. .. 60·00 65·00
b. Emerald-green .. .. .. 3·00 10
c. Perf 12½ .. .. 5·50 35
ca. Imperf between (pair) .. ..
cb. Imperf (pair) .. .. .. £110 75·00
d. Perf 11 .. .. 60 10
da. Imperf between (pair) .. .. † £160
36 1 a. carmine 80 10
a. Imperf between (pair) £150
b. Scarlet .. .. 1·00 10
ba. Imperf between (horiz pair) .. † £160
bb. Imperf between (vert pair) .. † £160
c. Perf 12½ .. .. 10·00 85
ca. Imperf between (pair) .. ..
cb. Imperf (pair) £150 £130
cc. Scarlet .. ..
d. Perf 11 .. .. 75 20
da. Scarlet .. .. — 15·00

The above perforations also exist compound.
For ½ a. claret, see No. 58.

1927 (1 Feb). *As W* **7**, *but larger and sideways. P* 13½.
37 **9** 1 r. yellow .. .. 9·00 11·00

10 (4 pies)

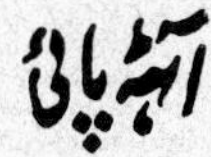
11 (8 pies)

1930 (6 May). *Surch as T* **10** *and* **11**. *W* **7**. *P* 13½.
38 **6** 4 p. on ¼ a. grey-black (R.) .. .. 48·00 15·00
a. Perf 11 .. .. † £200
b. Perf 12½ .. .. † 75·00
39 4 p. on ¼ a. brown-purple (R.) .. 25 10
a. Imperf between (pair) £375 £375
b. Surch double .. .. .. † £170
c. Perf 11 .. .. † £400
d. Black surch £425 £425
40 **8** 8 p. on ½ a. green (R.) 25 10
a. Imperf between (horiz pair) .. † £180
b. Perf 11 .. .. £275 £160
c. Perf 12½ .. .. † £275

12 Symbols

13 The Char Minar

14 Bidar College

(Plates by De La Rue. Recess Stamps Office, Hyderabad)

1931 (12 Nov)–**47**. *T* **12** *to* **14** (*and similar types*). *W* **7**. *Wove paper. P* 13½.
41 **12** 4 p. black 30 10
a. Laid paper (1947) .. .. .. 2·25 4·50
b. Imperf (pair) .. .. .. 48·00 75·00
42 8 p. green 30 10
a. Imperf between (vert pair) .. .. — £550
b. Imperf (pair) .. .. .. 60·00 90·00
c. Laid paper (1947) .. .. .. 3·00 4·00
43 **13** 1 a. brown (*shades*) 30 10
a. Imperf between (horiz pair) .. — £550
44 – 2 a. violet (*shades*) .. .. .. 1·75 10
a. Imperf (pair) £130 £180
45 – 4 a. ultramarine .. .. .. 1·25 30
a. Imperf (pair) £140 £225
46 – 8 a. orange .. .. 3·50 2·25
a. Yellow-orange (1944) .. .. 60·00 30·00
47 **14** 12 a. scarlet .. .. 3·75 8·00
48 – 1 r. yellow .. .. 3·25 2·75
41/8 .. .. *Set of* 8 13·00 12·50

Designs (*as T* **14**): *Horiz*—2 a. High Court of Justice; 4 a. Osman Sagar Reservoir. *Vert*—8 a. Entrance to Ajanta Caves; 1 r. Victory Tower, Daulatabad.

Nos. 41a and 42c have a large sheet watermark "THE NIZAM's GOVERNMENT HYDERABAD DECCAN" and arms within a circle, but this does not appear on all stamps.

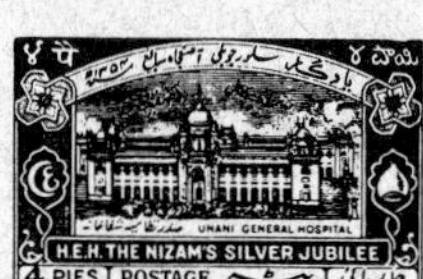

15 Unani General Hospital

16 Family Reunion

(Litho Indian Security Printing Press, Nasik)

1937 (13 Feb). *Various horiz designs as T* **15**, *inscr* "H.E.H. THE NIZAM'S SILVER JUBILEE". *P* 14.
49 4 p. slate and violet 35 75
50 8 p. slate and brown 65 80
51 1 a. slate and orange-yellow 65 55
52 2 a. slate and green .. .. .. 85 2·75
49/52 .. .. *Set of* 4 2·25 4·25

Designs:—8 p. Osmania General Hospital; 1 a. Osmania University; 2 a. Osmania Jubilee Hall.

(Des T. I. Archer. Typo)

1945 (6 Dec). *Victory. W* **7** (*very faint*). *Wove paper. P* 13½.
53 **16** 1 a. blue 10 10
a. Imperf between (vert pair) £500
b. Laid paper 60 60

No. 53b shows the sheet watermark described beneath Nos. 41/8

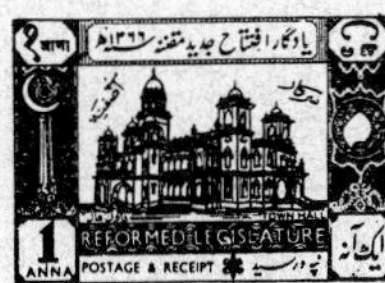

17 Town Hall

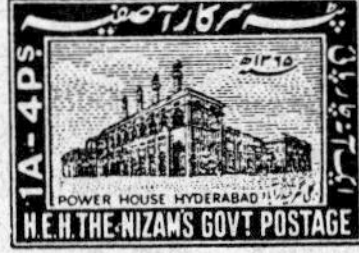

18 Power House, Hyderabad

(Des. T. I. Archer. Litho Government Press)

1947 (17 Feb). *Reformed Legislature. P* 13½.
54 **17** 1 a. black 60 90
a. Imperf between (pair) .. .. — £700

(Des T. I. Archer. Typo)

1947–49. *As T* **18** (*inscr* "H. E. H. THE NIZAM'S GOVT. POSTAGE"). *W* **7**. *P* 13½.
55 1 a. 4 p. green .. .. 65 1·40
56 3 a. greenish blue .. .. .. 75 2·00
a. Bluish green .. .. 1·40 2·25
57 6 a. sepia .. .. 3·00 9·50
a. Red-brown (1949) .. .. .. 18·00 25·00
ab. Imperf (pair) £100
55/7 .. .. *Set of* 3 4·00 11·50

Designs:—3 a. Kaktyai Arch, Warangal Fort; 6 a. Golkunda Fort.

1947. *As* 1915 *issue but colour changed. P* 13½.
58 **8** ½ a. claret .. .. 1·00 50
a. Imperf between (horizontal pair) .. — £275
b. Imperf between (vert pair) .. — £400

An Independence commemorative set of four, 4 p., 8 p., 1 a. and 2 a., was prepared in 1948, but not issued.

1948. *As T* **12** ("POSTAGE" *at foot*). *Recess. W* **7**. *P* 13½.
59 6 p. claret .. .. 5·50 4·50

Following intervention by the forces of the Dominion of India during September 1948 the Hyderabad postal system was taken over by the Dominion authorities, operating as an agency of the India Post Office.

1949. *T* **12** ("POSTAGE" *at top*). *Litho. W* **7**. *P* 13½.
60 **12** 2 p. bistre-brown .. .. .. 1·00 1·60
a. Imperf between (horizontal pair) .. † £600
b. Imperf (pair) £375 £475

No. 60 was produced from a transfer taken from a plate of the 4 p., No. 41, with each impression amended individually.

OFFICIAL STAMPS

Official stamps became valid for postage within India from 1910.

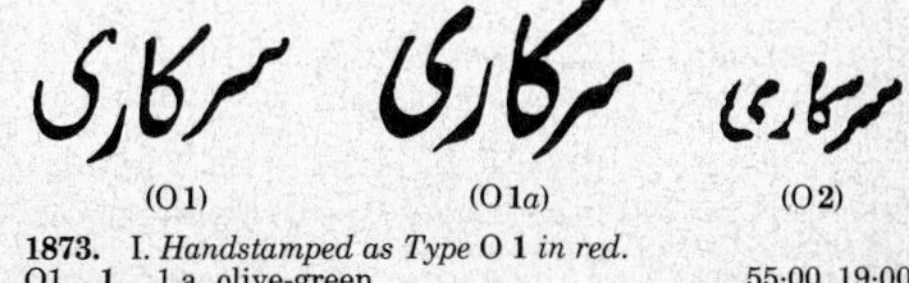
(O 1) (O 1*a*) (O 2)

1873. I. *Handstamped as Type* O **1** *in red.*
O1 **1** 1 a. olive-green .. .. .. 55·00 19·00
a. Black opt .. ..
O2 **2** ½ a. brown .. .. — £375
a. Black opt .. .. — £375
O3 2 a. sage-green .. .. — £400
a. Black opt .. .. — £120

At least ten different handstamps as Type O 1 were used to produce Nos. O1/17. These differ in the size, shape and spacing of the characters. The prices quoted are for the cheapest versions where more than one is known to exist on a particular stamp.

Imitations of these overprints on genuine stamps and on reprints are found horizontally or vertically in various shades of red, in magenta and in black.

II. *T* **3** *handstamped as Type* O **1** *in red.*

(*a*) *Rough perf* 11½
O 4 ½ a. red-brown
a. Black opt — £550
O 5 1 a. purple-brown £700
a. Black opt £120 £150
O 6 2 a. green (A)
a. Black opt — £700
O 7 4 a. slate — £800
a. Black opt
O 8 8 a. deep brown
a. Black opt £800 £800
O 8*b* 12 a. dull blue — £800

(*b*) *Pin perf* 8–9
O 8*c* 1 a. drab (*black opt*) 6·50 85·00

(*c*) *P* 12½
O 9 ½ a. red-brown 8·50 3·25
a. Black opt 5·50 2·25
ab. Left side of central inscription omitted — £110
ac. Dot at top of central inscription omitted — 30·00
O11 1 a. purple-brown 65·00 45·00
a. Black opt — 19·00
O12 1 a. drab 12·00 13·00
a. Black opt 1·40 1·50
ab. Second dot in bottom label omitted 70·00 70·00
O13 2 a. green (*to deep*) (A) 24·00 18·00
a. Black opt 2·75 3·75
ab. Inner circle missing (B) £150
ac. Centre dot in bottom label omitted 85·00 85·00
O14 3 a. ochre-brown 85·00 85·00
a. Black opt 22·00 17·00
O15 4 a. slate 38·00 24·00
a. Black opt 10·00 10·00
O16 8 a. deep brown 40·00 75·00
a. Imperf vert (horiz pair) £550
b. Black opt 28·00 22·00
O17 12 a. blue 60·00 85·00
a. Black opt 32·00 48·00

The use of Official Stamps (Sarkari) was discontinued in 1878, but was resumed in 1909, when the current stamps were overprinted from a new die.

1909–11. *Optd with Type* O **1***a*. (*a*) *On Type* **3**. *P* 12½.
O18 ½ a. orange-brown 80·00 4·00
a. Opt inverted † £325
O19 1 a. black 55·00 10
a. Second dot in bottom label omitted — 6·00
O20 2 a. sage-green (A) 60·00 20
a. Optd on No. 15da (B) — 10·00
b. Stamp doubly printed † £130
c. Centre dot in bottom label omitted — 6·00
O20*d* 3 a. ochre-brown 3·00 1·00
da. Character omitted (D) — £225
O20*e* 4 a. olive-green £275 3·25
ea. Perf 11½, 12 — £250
O20*f* 8 a. deep brown — 27·00
O20*g* 12 a. grey-green — 55·00

(*b*) *On Type* **6** (*Wyon ptgs*). *P* 12½
O21 ½ a. orange — 1·75
a. Vermilion 95·00 15
b. Opt inverted † £225
c. Imperf between (vert pair) † £225
O22 ½ a. green 12·00 10
a. Pale green 12·00 10
b. Opt inverted † 55·00
c. Imperf between (vert pair) † £170
d. Imperf between (horiz pair) † £160
e. Stamp doubly printed † £120
f. Perf 11½, 12 11·00 30
fa. Pale green 11·00 30
fb. Opt inverted † 55·00
g. Perf 11
ga. Pale green
h. Perf 13½ — 50·00
O23 1 a. carmine 32·00 15
a. Opt double £150
b. Perf 11½, 12 45·00 30
ba. Stamp doubly printed — £120
c. Perf 11 — 5·50
O24 2 a. lilac 38·00 30
a. Perf 11½, 12 70·00 4·00
b. Perf 11 £325
O25 3 a. brown-orange 85·00 9·00
a. Opt inverted † £140
b. Perf 11½, 12 £150 20·00
c. Perf 11 £325 32·00
d. Perf 13½ — 55·00
O26 4 a. olive-green (1911) 26·00 30
a. Perf 11½, 12 70·00 3·25
b. Perf 11 — 15·00
O27 8 a. purple (1911) 13·00 1·25
a. Perf 11½, 12 75·00 4·75
b. Perf 11 £325 £100
O28 12 a. blue-green (1911) 9·00 1·00
a. Imperf between (horiz pair) — £600
b. Perf 11½, 12 22·00 2·00
c. Perf 11

(*c*) *On Type* **6** (*Bradbury Wilkinson ptgs*). *P* 11
O28*d* **6** ½ a. deep green £300

1911–12. *Optd with Type* O **2**. (*a*) *Type* **6** (*Wyon printings*). *P* 13½ (8 *a*, 12 *a*.) *or* 12½ (*others*).
O29 ¼ a. grey 38·00 1·00
a. Perf 11½, 12 19·00 30
ab. Imperf between (vert pair) † £190
b. Perf 11 65·00 30·00
c. Perf 13½
O30 ½ a. pale green 28·00 90
a. Perf 11½, 12 — 30
b. Perf 13½
O31 1 a. carmine 85 15
a. Opt inverted — 38·00
b. Imperf horiz (vert pair) † £190
c. Perf 11½, 12 5·50 15
d. Perf 11 75 15
e. Perf 13½
O32 2 a. lilac 4·50 50
a. Perf 11½, 12 16·00 1·75
b. Perf 11 85 20
c. Perf 13½ 5·00 10
ca. Imperf between (horiz pair) † £275
cb. Rose-lilac 1·75 10
O33 3 a. brown-orange 14·00 1·75
a. Opt inverted † 70·00
b. Perf 11½, 12 8·50 1·50
ba. Opt inverted † 75·00
c. Perf 11 22·00 2·00
ca. Opt inverted † 70·00
d. Perf 13½ 14·00 30
da. Opt inverted † 60·00
O34 4 a. olive-green 9·50 1·10
a. Opt inverted — 70·00
b. Perf 11½, 12 4·50 1·60
ba. Opt inverted — 75·00
c. Perf 11 2·00 1·00
d. Perf 13½ 2·25 10
da. Opt inverted † 70·00
O35 8 a. purple 2·75 20
a. Perf 11½, 12
b. Perf 11 £250 32·00
c. Perf 12½ — £275
O36 12 a. blue-green 9·50 40
a. Perf 11½, 12
b. Perf 11
c. Perf 12½

(*b*) *Type* **6** (*Bradbury, Wilkinson printings*). *P* 12½
O37 ¼ a. grey-black 2·00 30
a. Opt inverted † 55·00
b. Pair, one without opt
c. Imperf between (vert pair) † £160
d. Perf 11½, 12 4·50 50
da. Opt inverted † 55·00
db. Pair, one without opt
e. Perf 11 70 30
ea. Opt sideways † 55·00
f. Perf 13½ 1·90 10
fa. Opt inverted † 60·00
fb. Pair, one without opt † £110
fc. Imperf between (horiz pair) † £160
O38 ¼ a. brown-purple (*shades*) (*p* 13½) 1·40 10
a. Imperf horiz (vert pair) † £160
b. Imperf between (horiz pair) † £170
c. Perf 11
O39 ½ a. deep green 2·00 15
a. Opt inverted — 22·00
b. Perf 11½, 12 6·00 75
ba. Pair, one without opt † £120
c. Perf 11 1·90 10
ca. Opt inverted — 25·00
cb. Imperf horiz (vert pair) † £170
d. Perf 13½ 1·25 10
da. Imperf between (horiz pair) † £140
db. Yellow-green — 50

1917–20. *T* **8** *optd with Type* O **2**. *P* 13½.
O40 ½ a. green 1·40 10
a. Opt inverted † 20·00
b. Pair, one without opt † 90·00
c. Imperf between (horiz pair) † £110
d. Imperf between (vert pair) † £140
e. Emerald-green 2·75 40
f. Perf 12½ — 3·50
g. Perf 11 4·75 30
ga. Opt inverted † 22·00
gb. Pair, one without opt
O41 1 a. carmine 2·25 10
a. Opt inverted † 25·00
b. Opt double † 65·00
c. Imperf horiz (vert pair) † £160
d. Stamp printed double
e. Scarlet (1920) 75 10
ea. Stamp printed double † £120
eb. Imperf between (horiz pair) † £140
ec. Imperf between (vert pair) † £140
f. Perf 12½ — 3·50
g. Perf 11 7·50 15
ga. Opt inverted † 16·00
gb. Scarlet (1920) — 20·00

1930–34. *T* **6** *and* **8** *optd as Type* O **2** *and surch at top of stamp, in red, as T* **10** *or* **11**.
O42 4 p. on ¼ a. grey-black (O37*f*) (1934) £190 17·00
O43 4 p. on ¼ a. brown-purple (O38) 65 10
b. Imperf between (horiz pair) † £160
c. Imperf between (vert pair) † £160
d. Imperf horiz (vert pair) † £160
e. Red surch double † 80·00
f. Black opt double † £170
O44 8 p. on ½ a. green (O40) 60 10
c. Imperf between (horiz pair) † £160
ca. Imperf between (vert pair) † £160
d. Red surch double † 80·00
e. Stamp doubly printed † £160
f. Black opt double † £170
O45 8 p. on ½ a. yellow-green (O39*db*) 35·00 45·00

For Nos. O42/5 the red surcharge was intended to appear on the upper part of the stamp, above the official overprint, Type O **2**, but surcharge and overprint are not infrequently found superimposed on one another.

1934–44. *Nos.* 41/8 *optd with Type* O **2**.
O46 4 p. black 85 10
a. Imperf (pair) 60·00
b. Imperf between (vert pair) £500 £500
c. Imperf between (horiz pair) — £500
O47 8 p. green 35 10
a. Opt inverted † £150
b. Imperf between (horiz pair) — £500
c. Opt double † £120
d. Imperf (pair) £120 £150
O48 1 a. brown 50 10
a. Imperf between (vert pair) £400 £400
b. Imperf between (horiz pair) — £400
c. Imperf (pair) £140 £180
d. Opt double — £160
O49 2 a. violet 3·50 10
a. Imperf between (horiz pair) † £850
O50 4 a. ultramarine 1·60 2
a. Opt double † £37
b. Imperf between (vert pair) † £90
O51 8 a. orange (1935) 7·50 5
a. Yellow-orange (1944) — 38·0
O52 12 a. scarlet (1935) 5·50 1·2
O53 1 r. yellow (1935) 12·00 2·0
O46/53 *Set of* 8 29·00 3·7

1947. *No.* 58 *optd with Type* O **2**.
O54 **8** ½ a. claret 9·00 5·0

1949. *No.* 60 *optd with Type* O **2**.
O55 **12** 2 p. bistre-brown 7·00 5·5

1950. *No.* 59 *optd with Type* O **2**.
O56 6 p. claret 8·50 16·0

IDAR

PRICES FOR STAMPS ON COVER

Nos. 1/2*b*	*from* × 2
Nos. 3/6	*from* × 3
Nos. F1/4	*from* × 2

Maharaja Himmat Singh, 1931–1960

1 Maharaja Himmat Singh 2

(Typo M. N. Kothari & Sons, Bombay)

1932 (1 Oct)–**39.** *P* 11. (*a*) *White panels.*
1 **1** ½ a. emerald 11·00 16·0
a. Imperf between (pair) £900
b. Yellow-green 9·50 16·0
ba. Imperf between (horiz pair) £850
c. Pale yellow-green (thick paper) 12·00 18·0

(*b*) *Coloured panels*
2 **1** ½ a. emerald (1939) 15·00 18·0
a. Yellow-green 8·50 18·0
b. Pale yellow-green (thick paper) 21·00 21·0

In No. 2 the whole design is composed of half-tone dots. In No. 1 the dots are confined to the oval portrait.

(Typo P. G. Mehta & Co, Hitmatnagar)

1944 (21 Oct). *P* 12.
3 **2** ½ a. blue-green 1·75 48·0
a. Imperf between (vert pair) £225
b. Yellow-green 1·40 48·0
ba. Imperf between (vert pair) 12·00
4 1 a. violet 1·75 42·0
a. Imperf (pair) £200
b. Imperf vert (horiz pair) £225
5 2 a. blue 2·25 70·0
a. Imperf between (vert pair) 75·00
b. Imperf between (horiz pair) £180
6 4 a. vermilion 2·50 75·0
a. Doubly printed £500
3/6 *Set of* 4 7·00 £200

Nos. 1 to 6 are from booklet panes of 4 stamps, producing single stamps with one or two adjacent sides imperf.

The 4 a. violet is believed to be a colour trial.

POSTAL FISCAL STAMPS

F 1

1940 (?)–**45.** *Typo. P* 11 (*No.* F1) *or* 12 *on two or three sides.*
F1 – 1 a. violet 60·00 95·0
F2 F **1** 1 a. violet (1943) — 95·0
F3 1¼ a. on 1 a. violet 90·00 £19
F4 1¼ a. yellow-green (1945) 13·00
a. Imperf between (vert pair) 30·00
b. Blue-green (1945) 45·00 95·00

No. F1 shows the portrait as Type **1**. Used prices are for examples with postal cancellations. No. F3 shows a handstamped surcharge in Gujerati.

Idar became part of Bombay Province on 10 June 1948.

ALTERED CATALOGUE NUMBERS

Any Catalogue numbers altered from the last edition are shown as a list in the introductory pages.

INDORE

(HOLKAR STATE)

PRICES FOR STAMPS ON COVER	
Nos. 1/15	*from* × 20
Nos. 16/43	*from* × 6
Nos. S1/7	*from* × 40

Maharaja Tukoji Rao Holkar II, 1843–1886

1 Maharaja Tukoji Rao Holkar II

(Litho Waterlow & Sons)

386 (6 Jan). P 15. (*a*) *Thick white paper.*
1 ½ a. bright mauve .. .. 7·00 7·50
(*b*) *Thin white or yellowish paper*
1 ½ a. pale mauve .. .. 1·50 1·10
a. Dull mauve .. .. 1·75 1·75

Maharaja Shivaji Rao Holkar, 1886–1903

2 Type I 2*a* Type II

YPES 2 AND 2a. In addition to the difference in the topline aracter (marked by arrow), the two Types can be distinguished y the difference in the angles of the 6-pointed stars and the appearance of the lettering. In Type I the top characters are smaller and ore cramped than the bottom; in Type II both are in the same style nd similarly spaced.

389 (Sept). *Handstamped. No gum. Imperf.*
2 ½ a. black/*pink* .. .. 25·00 25·00
2*a* ½ a. black/*pink* .. .. 1·90 2·50
a. *Tête-bêche* (pair) £190

Maharaja Shivaji Rao Holkar 4 Maharaja Tukoji Holkar III 5

(Recess Waterlow)

389–92. *Medium wove paper.* P 14 *to* 15.
3 ¼ a. orange (9.2.92) 60 40
a. Imperf between (horiz pair) .. .. † £550
b. Very thick wove paper .. .. 1·25 55
c. Yellow 90 60
½ a. dull violet .. .. 1·50 60
a. Brown-purple 70 15
b. Imperf between (vert pair) £500
1 a. green (7.2.92) 80 50
a. Imperf between (vert pair) £700
b. Very thick wove paper .. .. 75·00
2 a. vermilion (7.2.92) .. .. .. 2·75 1·00
a. Very thick wove paper .. .. 5·00 3·00
8 .. .. *Set of* 4 4·25 1·75

Maharaja Tukoji Rao Holkar III, 1903–1926

(Recess Perkins, Bacon & Co)

904–20. P 13½, 14.
9 4 ¼ a. orange 30 10
0 5 ½ a. lake (1909) .. .. 8·50 10
a. Brown-lake (shades) .. .. .. 9·00 15
b. Imperf (pair) .. .. .. 16·00
1 1 a. green .. .. 1·60 10
a. Imperf (pair) £120
b. Perf 12½ (1920) .. .. .. † 75·00
2 2 a. brown .. .. 7·50 45
a. Imperf (pair) .. .. .. 75·00
3 3 a. violet .. .. 12·00 4·50
4 4 a. ultramarine .. .. 9·00 1·75
a. Dull blue .. .. 5·00 1·10
/14 .. .. *Set of* 6 32·00 5·50

पाव आना.

(6) 7 Maharaja Yeshwant Rao Holkar II

1905 (June). *No.* 6*a surch* "QUARTER ANNA" *in Devanagari, as T* **6**.
15 **3** ¼ a. on ½ a. brown-purple .. .. 3·00 16·00

On 1 March 1908 the Indore State postal service was amalgamated with the Indian Imperial system. Under the terms of the agreement stamps showing the Maharaja would still be used for official mail sent to addresses within the state. Initially Nos. 9/14 were used for this purpose, the "SERVICE" overprints, Nos. S1/7, being withdrawn.

Maharaja Yeshwant Rao Holkar II, 1926–1961

(Recess Perkins, Bacon & Co)

1927–37. P 13 *to* 14.
16 **7** ¼ a. orange (*a*) (*d*) (*e*) 30 10
17 ½ a. claret (*a*) (*d*) (*e*) 30 10
18 1 a. green (*a*) (*d*) (*e*) 80 10
19 1¼ a. green (*c*) (*d*) (1933) .. .. .. 1·25 15
20 2 a. sepia (*a*) .. .. 3·50 90
21 2 a. bluish green (*d*) (1936) .. .. 9·00 60
a. Imperf (pair) .. .. .. 25·00 £100
22 3 a. deep violet (*a*) .. .. .. 1·50 8·50
23 3 a. Prussian blue (*d*) (1935?) .. .. 15·00
a. Imperf (pair) .. .. .. 30·00 £250
24 3½ a. violet (*d*) (1934) .. .. .. 4·50 9·00
a. Imperf (pair) .. .. .. 50·00 £250
25 4 a. ultramarine (*a*) .. .. .. 3·25 3·00
26 4 a. yellow-brown (*d*) (1937) .. .. 21·00 1·50
a. Imperf (pair) .. .. .. 30·00 £180
27 8 a. slate-grey (*a*) .. .. .. 5·50 4·50
28 8 a. red-orange (*d*) (1937) .. .. 15·00 18·00
29 12 a. carmine (*d*) (1934) .. .. .. 5·00 10·00
30 – 1 r. black and light blue (*b*) .. .. 8·00 14·00
31 – 2 r. black and carmine (*b*) .. .. 35·00 35·00
32 – 5 r. black & brown-orange (*b*) .. .. 55·00 60·00

Nos. 30/32 are as Type **7**, but larger, size 23 × 28 mm.

Five different perforating heads were used for this issue: (*a*) comb 13·6; (*b*) comb 13·9; (*c*) line 13·2; (*d*) line 13·8; (*e*) line 14·2. Values on which each perforation occur are indicated above.

Nos. 21a, 23a, 24a and 26a were specifically ordered by the state government in 1933 and are known used for postage *circa* 1938–42. A plate proof of the 1 r. in green and carmine is also known postally used (*Price of pair £32 unused, £275 used*).

Nos. 16/19 and 28/32 also exist as imperforate plate proofs, but these were never sent to India.

QUARTER ANNA

(8)

9

1940 (1 Aug). *Surch in words as T* **8** *by* Times of India *Press, Bombay.*
33 **7** ¼ a. on 5 r. black and brown-orange (*b*) 6·50 75
a. Surch double (Blk. + G.) .. .. † £400
34 ½ a. on 2 r. black and carmine (*b*) .. 10·00 1·60
35 1 a. on 1¼ a. green (*c*) (*d*) (*e*) .. .. 10·00 40
b. Surch inverted (*d*) .. .. .. 90·00
c. Surch double (*c*) £325
33/5 .. .. *Set of* 3 24·00 2·50

(Typo "*Times of India*" Press, Bombay)

1941–46. P 11.
36 **9** ¼ a. red-orange .. .. 2·00 10
37 ½ a. claret .. .. 1·40 10
38 1 a. green .. .. 8·00 10
39 1¼ a. yellow-green .. .. .. 14·00 40
a. Imperf (pair) £190
40 2 a. turquoise-blue .. .. .. 11·00 1·00
41 4 a. yellow-brown (1946) .. .. .. 12·00 9·00
Larger size (23 × 28 *mm*)
42 2 r. black and carmine (1943) .. .. 9·00 95·00
43 5 r. black and yellow-orange (1943) .. 9·00 £130
36/43 .. .. *Set of* 8 60·00 £200

OFFICIAL STAMPS

SERVICE **SERVICE**

(S 1) (S 2)

1904–6. (*a*) *Optd with Type* S **1**.
S1 **4** ¼ a. orange (1906) 10 45
S2 **5** ½ a. lake 10 10
a. Opt inverted .. .. .. 18·00 27·00
b. Opt double .. .. 17·00
c. Imperf (pair) .. .. .. 50·00
d. Brown-lake 10 10
da. Opt inverted .. .. .. 17·00
e. Pair, one without opt £425
S3 1 a. green 10 20
S4 2 a. brown (1905) 30 25
a. Vert pair, one without opt £650
S5 3 a. violet (1906) .. .. .. 1·75 1·50
a. Imperf (pair) £325
S6 4 a. ultramarine (1905) .. .. .. 2·75 1·40
(*b*) *Optd with Type* S **2**
S7 **5** ½ a. lake 10 45
a. Opt double £300
S1/7 .. .. *Set of* 6 4·50 3·50

Types S 1 and S 2 differ chiefly in the shape of the letter "R".

Indore became part of Madhya Bharat by 1 July 1948

JAIPUR

PRICES FOR STAMPS ON COVER	
No. 1	*from* × 3
No. 2	*from* × 2
Nos. 3/5	*from* × 10
Nos. 6/70	*from* × 4
Nos. 71/80	*from* × 6
Nos. O1/34	*from* × 8

Maharaja Sawai Madho Singh II, 1880–1922

1 1*a* 2
Chariot of the Sun God, Surya

Type 1 – Value at sides in small letters and characters. "HALF ANNA", shown as one word except for R. 1/1 and 1/3, measuring between 13½ and 15 mm. Sheets of 12 (4×3) with stamps 2 to 2½ mm apart.

Type 1*a* – Value in large letters and characters. "HALF ANNA", always with a gap between the two words, measuring between 14½ and 15½ mm. Sheets of 24 (4×6) with stamps 3 to 4 mm apart.

Type 2 – Value in large letters and characters. "HALF ANNA" measuring 16 to 17 mm. Both side inscriptions start below the inner frame line. Sheets of 24 (4×6) with stamps 1½ to 2 mm apart.

(Litho Jaipur State Press)

1904 (14 July). *Roughly perf* 14.
1 **1** ½ a. pale blue .. .. 85·00 £120
a. Ultramarine £120 £150
b. Imperf, *ultramarine* £350
2 **1a** ½ a. grey-blue £1100 £200
a. Imperf £350 £550
b. Ultramarine .. .. — £300
3 **2** ½ a. pale blue .. .. 2·75 4·25
a. Deep blue .. .. 3·00 4·25
b. Ultramarine .. .. 3·25 4·50
c. Imperf £300 £300
4 **1** 1 a. dull red .. .. 4·00 11·00
a. Scarlet .. .. 4·00 11·00
5 2 a. pale green .. .. 3·00 10·00
a. Emerald-green .. .. 3·50

Nos. 1b, 2a and 3c are on gummed paper. Imperforate plate proofs also exist for Nos. 1/5, but these are ungummed.

3 Chariot of the Sun God, Surya

(Recess Perkins, Bacon & Co)

1904. P 12.
6 **3** ½ a. blue .. .. 3·00 6·00
a. Perf 12½ .. .. 19·00 13·00
b. Perf comp of 12 and 12½ .. .. 15·00 16·00
7 1 a. brown-red .. .. 45·00 45·00
a. Perf 12½ £110 £110
b. Perf comp of 12 and 12½ £120 £120
c. Carmine .. .. 2·25 3·50
ca. Imperf between (vert pair) £375 £550
cb. Perf comp of 12 and 12½ .. .. 10·00 13·00
8 2 a. deep green .. .. 5·50 10·00
a. Perf 12½ .. .. £110 80·00
b. Perf comp of 12 and 12½ .. .. 25·00 29·00

Nos. 6b, 7b, 7cb and 8b occur on the bottom two rows of sheets otherwise perforated 12.

1905–8. *Wmk* "JAs WRIGLEY & SON Ld. 219" "SPECIAL POSTAGE PAPER LONDON" *or* "PERKINS BACON & Co Ld LONDON" *in sheet.* P 13½.
9 **3** ¼ a. olive-yellow (1906) 55 40
10 ½ a. blue (1906) .. .. 1·75 1·60
a. Indigo 50 40
11 1 a. brown-red (1906) .. .. .. 4·75 4·25
a. Bright red (1908) .. .. .. 1·75 40
12 2 a. deep green (1906) .. .. .. 1·00 75
13 4 a. chestnut .. .. 4·75 2·00
14 8 a. bright violet .. .. 3·00 2·75
15 1 r. yellow .. .. 15·00 16·00
a. Orange-yellow .. .. .. 14·00 16·00
b. Yellow-ochre .. .. .. 17·00 22·00
9/15 .. .. *Set of* 7 23·00 20·00

१ आना

4 Chariot of the Sun God, Surya (5)

(Typo Jaipur State Press)

1911. *Thin wove paper. No gum. Imperf.*
16 4 ¼ a. green .. .. 1·50 2·25
a. Printed double .. .. 5·50
ab. Ditto, one inverted .. ..
b. "¼" inverted in right upper corner (R. 1/2) .. .. 5·00
c. No stop after "STATE" (R. 3/1) .. 5·00
17 ¼ a. greenish yellow 30 55
a. Printed double .. .. 2·00
b. "¼" inverted in right upper corner (R. 1/2) .. .. 1·50
c. No stop after "STATE" (R. 3/1) .. 1·50
18 ½ a. ultramarine 30 55
a. Printed double .. .. 2·00
b. No stop after "STATE" (R. 3/1) .. 75
c. Large "J" in "JAIPUR" (R. 1/2) .. 75
d. "⅓" for "½" at lower left (R. 3/1) .. 1·50
e. "1½ a." at lower right (R. 3/2) .. 1·50
19 ½ a. grey-blue .. .. 1·40 1·40
a. No stop after "STATE" (R. 3/1) .. 2·50
b. Large "J" in "JAIPUR" (R. 1/2) .. 2·50
c. "⅓" for "½" at lower left (R. 3/1) .. 3·50
d. "1½ a." at lower right (R. 3/2) .. 3·50
20 1 a. rose-red 40 60
a. Printed double £180
21 2 a. greyish green .. .. 2·00 5·50
a. Deep green .. .. 2·00 5·50
ab. Printed double £180

Issued in sheets of 6 (2×3). There are three recognised settings. Nos. 18d/e and 19c/d come from Setting B, and Nos. 16b/c, 17b/c, 18b/c and 19a/b from Setting C.

One sheet of the ¼ a. is known in blue.

(Typo Jaipur State Press)

1912–22. *Paper-maker's wmk* "DORLING & CO. LONDON" *in sheet. P* 11.
22 3 ¼ a. pale olive-yellow 30 60
a. Imperf horiz (vert pair) £200 £200
b. Imperf vert (horiz pair) .. .. — £160
23 ¼ a. olive 30 85
a. Imperf between (horiz pair) .. £190
b. Imperf vert (horiz pair) £200
c. Imperf horiz (vert pair) £200
d. *Tête-bêche* (pair) £250
24 ¼ a bistre 30 75
a. Imperf between (horiz pair) .. £190
b. Imperf between (vert pair) .. .. † £275
c. Imperf horiz (vert pair) .. .. † £275
d. Doubly printed .. .. .. † —
25 ½ a. pale ultramarine 90 45
a. Imperf vert (horiz pair) .. .. † £375
b. Blue .. .. 1·00 45
ba. Imperf between (horiz pair) .. £325
26 1 a. carmine (1918) .. .. .. 3·00 3·00
a. Imperf between (vert pair) .. .. † £450
b. Imperf horiz (vert pair) .. .. † £450
27 1 a. rose-red .. .. 1·75 6·00
a. Imperf between (vert pair) .. £475
28 1 a. scarlet (1922) .. .. 1·40 1·40
a. Imperf between (vert pair) .. £475 £475
29 2 a. green (1918) .. .. 3·25 2·75
30 4 a. chocolate .. .. 3·25 5·00
31 4 a. pale brown .. .. 3·50 6·00
a. Imperf vert (horiz pair) £375
22/31 .. .. *Set of* 5 8·25 9·25

Maharaja Sawai Man Singh II 1922–1970

1926. *Surch with T* **5**.
32 3 3 a. on 8 a. bright violet (R.) .. .. 1·00 1·90
a. Surch inverted £170 £140
33 3 a. on 1 r. yellow (R.) .. .. .. 1·75 3·50
a. Surch inverted £350 £170
c. Yellow-ochre .. .. 5·50 7·50

1928. *As* 1913–18 *issue. Wmk* "DORLING & CO. LONDON" (½ *a.*, 1 *a.*, 2 *a.*) *or* "OVERLAND BANK" (*all values*) *in sheet. No gum. P* 12.
34 3 ½ a. ultramarine .. .. 3·00 4·00
a. Perf comp of 12 and 11 .. .. 13·00 8·00
35 1 a. rose-red .. .. 21·00 17·00
a. Imperf between (vert pair) £375
36 1 a. scarlet .. .. 32·00 12·00
a. Perf comp of 12 and 11 .. .. 48·00 24·00
37 2 a. green .. .. 65·00 26·00
a. Perf comp of 12 and 11 .. .. £150 55·00
38 8 a. bright violet £250
39 1 r. orange-vermilion £250 £375

The "OVERLAND BANK" paper has a coarser texture. The ½ a. and 2 a. values also exist on this paper perforated 11, but such stamps are difficult to distinguish from examples of Nos. 25 and 29.

6 Chariot of the Sun God, Surya

7 Maharaja Sawai Man Singh II

8 Sowar in Armour

(Des T. I. Archer. Litho Indian Security Printing Press, Nasik)

1931 (14 Mar). *Investiture of Maharaja. T* **6/8** *and similar designs. No wmk. P* 14.
40 ¼ a. black and deep lake .. .. .. 80 1·10
41 ½ a. black and violet 30 10
42 1 a. black and blue .. .. 4·75 5·00
43 2 a. black and buff .. .. 3·25 5·00
44 2½ a. black and carmine .. .. .. 28·00 42·00
45 3 a. black and myrtle .. .. 10·00 35·00
46 4 a. black and olive-green .. .. .. 12·00 38·00
47 6 a. black and deep blue .. .. .. 6·00 35·00
48 8 a. black and chocolate .. .. .. 10·00 50·00
49 1 r. black and pale olive .. .. .. 23·00 £150
50 2 r. black and yellow-green .. .. 20·00 £160
51 5 r. black and purple .. .. 30·00 £170
40/51 .. .. *Set of* 12 £130 £600

Designs: *Vert*—1 a. Elephant and state banner; 2½ a. Common Peafowl; 8 a. Sireh-Deorhi Gate. *Horiz*—3 a. Bullock carriage; 4 a. Elephant carriage; 6 a. Albert Museum; 1 r. Chandra Mahal; 2 r. Amber Palace; 5 r. Maharajas Jai Singh and Man Singh.

Eighteen of these sets were issued for presentation purposes with a special overprint "INVESTITURE–MARCH 14, 1931" in red (*Price for set of* 12 £2750, *unused*).

10 Maharaja Sawai Man Singh II

One
Rupee

(**11**)

(Des T. I. Archer. Litho Indian Security Printing Press, Nasik)

1932–46. *P* 14. (*a*) *Inscr* "POSTAGE & REVENUE".
52 10 1 a. black and blue 45 50
53 2 a. black and buff .. .. 1·50 1·00
54 4 a. black and grey-green .. .. .. 3·00 5·00
55 8 a. black and chocolate .. .. .. 4·50 8·00
56 1 r. black and yellow-bistre .. .. 15·00 70·00
57 2 r. black and yellow-green .. .. 70·00 £275
52/7 .. .. *Set of* 6 85·00 £325

(*b*) *Inscr* "POSTAGE"
58 7 ¼ a. black and brown-lake 30 15
59 ¾ a. black and brown-red (1943?) .. 4·25 2·50
60 1 a. black and blue (1943?) .. .. 5·00 1·90
61 2 a. black and buff (1943?) .. .. 5·00 2·50
62 2½ a. black and carmine .. .. .. 2·00 1·40
63 3 a. black and green .. .. 1·25 40
64 4 a. black and grey-green (1943?) .. 16·00 75·00
65 6 a. black and deep blue .. .. .. 1·90 17·00
a. Black and pale blue (1946) .. .. 6·50 42·00
66 8 a. black and chocolate (1946) .. .. 13·00 70·00
67 1 r. black and yellow-bistre (1946) .. 20·00 95·00
58/67 .. .. *Set of* 10 60·00 £225

1936. *Nos.* 57 *and* 51 *surch with T* **11**.
68 10 1 r. on 2 r. black and yellow-green (R.) 5·50 60·00
69 – 1 r. on 5 r. black and purple .. .. 5·50 48·00

पाव आना

(**12**)

13 Maharaja and Amber Palace

1938 (Dec). *No.* 41 *surch* "QUARTER ANNA" *in Devanagari, T* **12**.
70 7 ¼ a. on ½ a. black and violet (R.) .. 8·50 12·00

(Recess D.L.R.)

1947 (Dec)–**48.** *Silver Jubilee of Maharaja's Accession to Throne. Various designs as T* **13**. *P* 13½ × 14.
71 ¼ a. red-brown and green (5.48) .. .. 65 2·50
72 ½ a. green and violet .. .. 20 2·25
73 ¾ a. black and lake (5.48) .. .. .. 65 3·00
74 1 a. red-brown and ultramarine .. .. 35 2·25
75 2 a. violet and scarlet .. .. 30 2·50
76 3 a. green and black (5.48) .. .. .. 80 3·50
77 4 a. ultramarine and brown .. .. .. 50 2·25
78 8 a. vermilion and brown .. .. .. 60 3·25
79 1 r. purple and green (5.48) .. .. 1·25 17·00
71/9 .. .. *Set of* 9 4·75 35·00

Designs:—¼ a. Palace Gate; ¾ a. Map of Jaipur; 1 a. Observatory; 2 a. Wind Palace; 3 a. Coat of Arms; 4 a. Amber Fort Gate; 8 a. Chariot of the Sun; 1 r. Maharaja's portrait between State flags.

3 PIES

(**14**)

1947 (Dec). *No.* 41 *surch with T* **14**.
80 7 3 p. on ½ a. black and violet (R.) .. 14·00 22·00
a. "PIE" for "PIES" .. .. .. 40·00 70·00
b. Bars at left vertical .. .. .. 50·00 80·00
c. Surch inverted .. .. 35·00 32·00
d. Surch inverted and "PIE" for "PIES" £150 £140
e. Surch double, one inverted .. .. 48·00 45·00
f. As variety e, but inverted surch showing "PIE" for "PIES" £300 £275

There were three settings of Type **14**, each applied to quarter sheets of 30 (6×5). No. 80a occurs in two of these settings on R.5/5 and one of these settings also shows No. 80b on R.6/1.

OFFICIAL STAMPS

SERVICE (O 1)

SERVICE (O 2)

1928 (13 Nov)–**31.** *T* **3** *typographed. No gum* (*except f Nos.* O6/*a*). *P* 11, 12, *or compound. Wmk* "DORLING & C LONDON" (4 *a.*) *or* "OVERLAND BANK" (*others*). (*a*) *Optd wi Type* O **1**.
O 1 ¼ a. olive .. .. 1·00 1·
a. Bistre .. .. 1·25 1·
O 2 ½ a. pale ultramarine (Blk.) 65
a. Imperf between (horiz pair) £275 £2
b. Imperf between (vert pair) .. .. † £4
c. Opt inverted .. .. † £3
d. Opt double (R. and Blk.) .. .. † £4
O 3 ½ a. pale ultramarine (R.) (13.10.30) .. 2·50
a. Imperf horiz (vert pair) .. ..
b. Stamp doubly printed .. .. ..
O 3*c* 1 a. rose-red 70
d. Imperf between (horiz pair) .. .. † £4
O 4 1 a. scarlet 90
a. Opt inverted £475 £4
b. Imperf between (horiz pair) .. .. † £4
O 5 2 a. green 65
a. Imperf between (vert pair) .. .. † £5
b. Imperf between (horiz pair) £500 £5
O 6 4 a. pale brown (with gum) .. .. 3·25 1·
a. Chocolate (with gum) .. .. .. 2·00 1·
O 7 8 a. bright violet (R.) (13.10.30) .. .. 16·00 48·
O 8 1 r. orange-vermilion .. .. .. 32·00 £1

(*b*) *Optd with Type* O **2**
O 9 ½ a. ultramarine (Blk.) (11.2.31) £180
a. Imperf vert (horiz pair) .. .. † £5
O10 ½ a. ultramarine (R.) (15.10.30) £160
a. Imperf between (vert pair) .. .. † £5
O11 8 a. bright violet (11.2.31) £325 £1
O12 1 r. orange-vermilion (11.2.31) £275 £2

SERVICE (O 3)

आध आना (O 4)

1931–7. *Nos.* 41/3 *and* 46 *optd at Nasik with Type* O **3**, *in red*.
O13 7 ½ a. black and violet 30
O14 – 1 a. black and blue .. .. .. £200 1·
O15 8 2 a. black and buff (1936) .. .. 2·00 4·
O16 – 4 a. black and olive-green (1937) .. 24·00 22·
O13/16 .. .. *Set of* 4 £200 25·

1932. *No.* O5 *surch with Type* O **4**.
O17 3 ½ a. on 2 a. green £120 8

1932–7. *Nos.* 52/6 *optd at Nasik with Type* O **3**, *in red*.
O18 10 1 a. black and blue .. .. .. 1·25
O19 2 a. black and buff .. .. .. 1·75
O20 4 a. black and grey-green (1937) .. £225 5·
O21 8 a. black and chocolate .. .. .. 4·75 1·
O22 1 r. black and yellow-bistre .. .. 13·00 14·
O18/22 .. .. *Set of* 5 £225 18·

1936–46. *Stamps of* 1932–46, *inscr* "POSTAGE".

(*a*) *Optd at Nasik with Type* O **3**, *in red*
O23 7 ¼ a. black and brown-lake (1936) .. 40 1
O24 ¾ a. black and brown-red (1944) .. 1·50 4
O25 1 a. black and blue (1941?) .. .. 7·50 3
O26 2 a. black and buff (date?) .. .. 6·50 1·5
O27 2½ a. black and carmine (1946) .. 9·00 65·0
O28 4 a. black and grey-green (1942) .. 5·00 2·7
O29 8 a. black and chocolate (1943) .. 5·00 4·0
O30 1 r. black and yellow-bistre (date?) .. £100
O23/9 .. .. *Set of* 7 32·00 65·0

(*b*) *Optd locally as Type* O **2** (16 *mm long*), *in black*
O31 7 ¼ a. black and red-brown (1936) .. 65·00 55·0

9 PIES

(O 5)

1947. *No.* O25 *surch with Type* O **5**, *in red*.
O32 7 9 p. on 1 a. black and blue .. .. 2·25 2·5

1947 (Dec). *No.* O13 *surch as T* **14**, *but* "3 PIES" *placed highe*
O33 7 3 p. on ½ a. black and violet (R.) .. 3·50 9·5
a. Surch double, one inverted .. .. 35·00 38·0
ab. "PIE" for "PIES" in inverted surcharge £190 £20
c. Surch inverted .. .. — £100

1949. *No.* O13 *surch* "THREE-QUARTER ANNA" *in Devan agari, as T* **12**, *but with two bars on each side*.
O34 7 ¾ a. on ½ a. black and violet (R.) .. 12·00 12·0
a. Surch double .. .. — £100

There are three different types of surcharge in the setting of 30 which vary in one or other of the Devanagari characters.

Jaipur became part of Rajasthan by 7 April 1949.

JAMMU AND KASHMIR

PRICES FOR STAMPS ON COVER

Nos. 1/73	*from* × 3
Nos. 74/84	*from* × 2
No. 85	—
Nos. 86/9	*from* × 2
Nos. 90/101	*from* × 10
Nos. 101*b*/23	*from* × 5
Nos. 124/36	*from* × 10
Nos. 138/9	*from* × 100
Nos. 140/61*a*	*from* × 15
Nos. 162/8	*from* × 5
No. O1	*from* × 2
Nos. O2/4	*from* × 4
No. O5	—
Nos. O6/14	*from* × 30
Nos. O15/18	—

ILLUSTRATIONS. Designs of Jammu and Kashmir are illustrated actual size.

Maharaja Ranbir Singh, 1857–1885

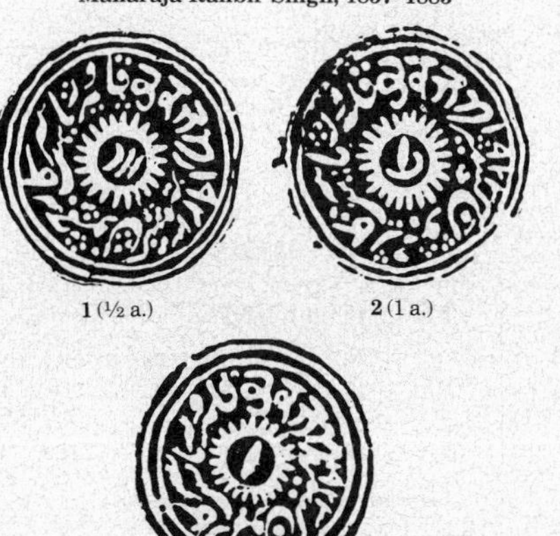

1 (½ a.) 2 (1 a.)

3 (4 a.)

Characters denoting the value (on the circular stamps only) are approximately as shown in the central circles of the stamps illustrated above.

These characters were taken from Punjabi merchants' notation and were not familiar to most of the inhabitants of the state. Type **1** was certainly the ½ anna value, but there has long been controversy over the correct face values of Types **2** and **3**.

The study of surviving material suggests that, to some extent, this confusion involved contemporary post office officials. Although covers posted at Jammu, where the stamps were in use for twelve years, show Type **2** used as the 1 a. value and Type **3** as the 4 a., those originating from Srinagar (Kashmir) during 1866–68 show both Types **2** and **3** used as 1 a. stamps.

In the following listing we have followed contemporary usage at Jammu and this reflects the prevailing opinion amongst modern authorities.

GUM. The stamps of Jammu and Kashmir were issued without gum.

PRICES. Prices for the circular stamps, Nos. 1/49, are for cut-square examples. Cut-to-shape examples are worth from 10% to 20% of these prices, according to condition.

A. *Handstamped in watercolours*

1866 (23 Mar)–**67.** *Native paper, thick to thin, usually having the appearance of laid paper and tinted grey or brown. For Jammu and Kashmir.*

No.	Type		Unused	Used
1	**1**	½ a. grey-black	£160	75·00
2	**2**	1 a. grey-black	£750	£650
3	**3**	4 a. grey-black	£800	
4	**2**	1 a. royal blue	£550	£375
4*a*	**1**	½ a. ultramarine	£2250	£2250
5	**2**	1 a. ultramarine	£275	70·00
6	**3**	4 a. ultramarine	£600	£300
7		4 a. indigo (1867)	£1500	£850

1869–72. *Reissued for use in Jammu only.*

No.	Type		Unused	Used
8	**1**	½ a. red	60·00	£275
9	**2**	1 a. red	£130	£200
10	**3**	4 a. red	50·00	90·00
11	**1**	½ a. orange-red	£450	£475
12	**2**	1 a. orange-red	£140	£225
13	**3**	4 a. orange-red	£110	£160
13*a*		4 a. carmine-red	£700	
13*b*	**2**	1 a. orange (1872)	£550	
13*c*	**3**	4 a. orange (1872)		

1874–76. *Special Printings.*

No.	Type		Unused	Used
14	**1**	½ a. deep black	17·00	£150
		a. *Tête-bêche* (pair)	£350	
15	**2**	1 a. deep black	£200	
16	**3**	4 a. deep black	£200	
17	**1**	½ a. bright blue (1876)	£225	£300
18	**2**	1 a. bright blue (1876)	85·00	£275
19	**3**	4 a. bright blue (1876)	£130	
20	**1**	½ a. emerald-green	65·00	£180
21	**2**	1 a. emerald-green	75·00	£180
22	**3**	4 a. emerald-green	£160	£300
23*a*	**1**	½ a. yellow	£450	£550
24	**2**	1 a. yellow	£550	
25	**3**	4 a. yellow	£350	
25*a*		4 a. deep blue-black (1876)	£850	£500

These special printings were available for use, but little used.

B. *Handstamped in oil colours. Heavy blurred prints*

1877 (June)–**78.** (*a*) *Native paper.*

No.	Type		Unused	Used
26	**1**	½ a. red	24·00	42·00
27	**2**	1 a. red	27·00	£150
28	**3**	4 a. red	£180	£400
29	**1**	½ a. black	23·00	42·00
32		½ a. slate-blue	£100	£170
34	**2**	1 a. slate-blue	20·00	£200
35	**1**	½ a. sage-green	£100	
36	**2**	1 a. sage-green	£110	
37	**3**	4 a. sage-green	£110	

(*b*) *European laid paper, medium to thick*

No.	Type		Unused	Used
38	**1**	½ a. red	—	£600
39	**3**	4 a. red	£325	£350
41	**1**	½ a. black	19·00	42·00
		a. Printed both sides		
		b. *Tête-bêche* (pair)	£250	
44		½ a. slate-blue	30·00	£200
45	**2**	1 a. slate-blue	42·00	£300
46	**3**	4 a. slate-blue	£500	£500
47		4 a. sage-green	£1000	
48	**1**	½ a. yellow	£100	

(*c*) *Thick yellowish wove paper*

No.	Type		Unused	Used
49	**1**	½ a. red (1878)	—	£800

Forgeries exist of the ½ a. and 1 a. in types which were at one time supposed to be authentic.

Reprints and imitations (of which some of each were found in the official remainder stock) exist in a great variety of fancy colours, both on native paper, usually thinner and smoother than that of the originals, and on various thin European *wove* papers, on which the originals were never printed.

The imitations, which do not agree in type with the above illustrations, are also to be found on *laid* paper.

All the reprints, etc. are in oil colours or printer's ink. The originals in oil colour are usually blurred, particularly when on native paper. The reprints, etc. are usually clear.

FOR USE IN JAMMU

½ a. ½ a.

1 a. **4** ½ a.

T **4** to **11** have a star at the top of the oval band; the characters denoting the value are in the upper part of the inner oval. All are dated 1923, corresponding with A.D. 1866.

T **4**. *Printed in blocks of four, three varieties of ½ anna and one of 1 anna.*

1867. *In watercolour on native paper.*

No.		Unused	Used
52	½ a. grey-black	£550	£180
53	1 a. grey-black	£1700	£750
54	½ a. indigo	£225	£200
55	1 a. indigo	£500	£275
56	½ a. deep ultramarine	£190	£130
57	1 a. deep ultramarine	£450	£275
58	½ a. deep violet-blue	£130	70·00
59	1 a. deep violet-blue	£450	£275

1868 (May)–**76.** *In watercolour on native paper.*

No.		Unused	Used
60	½ a. red (*shades*) (1876)	4·50	2·50
61	1 a. red (*shades*) (1876)	10·00	8·00
62	½ a. orange-red	£170	55·00
63	1 a. orange-red	£475	£190
64	½ a. orange (1872)	85·00	90·00
65	1 a. orange (1872)	£1400	£900

1874–6. *Special printings; in watercolour on native paper.*

No.		Unused	Used
66	½ a. bright blue (1876)	£900	£200
67	1 a. bright blue (1876)	£275	£300
68	½ a. emerald-green	£1300	£800
69	1 a. emerald-green	£2250	£1400
69*a*	½ a. jet-black	95·00	£130
69*b*	1 a. jet-black	£1100	£950

1877 (June)–**78.** *In oil colour.* (*a*) *Native paper.*

No.		Unused	Used
70	½ a. red	8·50	5·50
71	1 a. red	24·00	18·00
72	½ a. brown-red (1878)	—	30·00
73	1 a. brown-red (1878)	—	90·00
74	½ a. black	†	£700
75	1 a. black	†	£1600
76	½ a. deep blue-black	†	£1100
77	1 a. deep blue-black	†	£3000

(*b*) *Laid paper (medium or thick)*

No.		Unused	Used
78	½ a. red	—	£750

(*c*) *Thick wove paper*

No.		Unused	Used
79	½ a. red	†	£375
80	1 a. red		

(*d*) *Thin laid, bâtonné paper*

No.		Unused	Used
84	½ a. red	†	£1000
85	1 a. red	£2750	

The circular and rectangular stamps listed under the heading "Special Printings' did not supersede those in *red*, which was the normal colour for Jammu down to 1878. It is not known for what reason other colours were used during that period, but these stamps were printed in 1874 or 1875 and were certainly put into use. The rectangular stamps were again printed in *black* (jet-black, as against the greyish black of the 1867 printings) at that time, and impressions of the two periods can also be distinguished by the obliterations, which until 1868 were in *magenta* and after that in *black*.

There are reprints of these, in *oil* colour, *brown-red* and *bright blue*, on native paper; they are very clearly printed, which is not the case with the originals in *oil* colour.

4*a*

1877 (Sept). *Provisional. Seal obliterator of Jammu handstamped in red watercolour on pieces of native paper, and used as a ½ anna stamp.*

No.	Type		Unused	Used
86	**4*a***	(½ a.) rose-red	—	£900

FOR USE IN KASHMIR

5

1866 (Sept(?)). *Printed from a single die. Native laid paper.*

No.	Type		Unused	Used
87	**5**	½ a. black	£1900	£275

Forgeries of this stamp are commonly found, copied from an illustration in *Le Timbre-Poste*.

6 (½ a.) **7** (1 a.)

1867. *Native laid paper.*

No.	Type		Unused	Used
88	**6**	½ a. black	£950	£130
89	**7**	1 a. black	£1700	£350

Printed in sheets of 25 (5×5), the four top rows being ½ a. and the bottom row 1 a.

8 (¼ a.) **9** (2 a.)

10 (4 a.) **11** (8 a.)

1867–76. *Native laid paper.*

No.	Type		Unused	Used
90	**8**	¼ a. black	1·75	2·00
91	**6**	½ a. ultramarine	1·75	90
92		½ a. violet-blue (1870)	3·50	2·00
93	**7**	1 a. ultramarine	£2750	£1200
94		1 a. orange (7.67)	7·00	7·50
95		1 a. brown-orange (1868)	9·00	7·00
96		1 a. orange-vermilion (1876)	10·00	7·50
97	**9**	2 a. yellow	9·00	11·00
98		2 a. buff	14·00	12·00
99	**10**	4 a. emerald-green	24·00	24·00
		a. *Tête-bêche* (pair)	£850	
100		4 a. sage-green	£225	£110
100*a*		4 a. myrtle-green	£550	£550
101	**11**	8 a. red (1868)	26·00	24·00
		a. *Tête-bêche* (pair)	£850	

Of the above, the ½ a. and 1 a. were printed from the same plate of 25 as Nos. 87/8, the ¼ a. and 2 a. from a new plate of 10 (5 × 2), the top row being ¼ a. and the lower 2 a., and the 4 a. and 8 a. from single dies. Varieties at one time catalogued upon European papers were apparently never put into circulation, though some of them were printed while these stamps were still in use.

Nos. 86 to 101 are in watercolour.

FOR USE IN JAMMU AND KASHMIR

In the following issues there are 15 varieties on the sheets of the 1/8 a., 1/4 a. and 1/2 a.; 20 varieties of the 1 a. and 2 a. and 8 varieties of the 4 a. and 8 a. The value is in the lower part of the central oval.

12 (1/4 a.)

13 (1/2 a.)

14 (1 a.)

15 (2 a.)

16 (4 a.)

17 (8 a.)

1878 (May)–**79.** *Provisional printings.*

I. *Ordinary white laid paper, of varying thickness*

(*a*) *Rough perf* 10 *to* 12 (i) *or* 13 *to* 16 (ii)

101*b* **12** 1/4 a. red (i) .. ..
102 **13** 1/2 a. red (i) .. .. 12·00 14·00
103 **14** 1 a. red (i) £950
104 **13** 1/2 a. slate-violet (i) .. .. .. 70·00 50·00
104*a* **14** 1 a. violet (ii) .. ..
104*b* **15** 2 a. violet (i) £1300

(*b*) *Imperf*

105 **13** 1/2 a. slate-violet (*shades*) .. .. 13·00 12·00
106 **14** 1 a. slate-purple .. .. 19·00 20·00
107 1 a. mauve .. .. 28·00 28·00
108 **15** 2 a. violet .. .. 20·00 20·00
109 2 a. bright mauve .. .. .. 25·00 24·00
110 2 a. slate-blue .. .. 35·00 35·00
111 2 a. dull blue .. .. 70·00 75·00
112 **12** 1/4 a. red .. .. 16·00 13·00
113 **13** 1/2 a. red .. .. 7·00 7·00
114 **14** 1 a. red .. .. 6·50 7·00
115 **15** 2 a. red .. .. 50·00 50·00
116 **16** 4 a. red £130 £110

II. *Medium wove paper.* (*a*) *Rough perf* 10 *to* 12

117 **13** 1/2 a. red .. .. — £160

(*b*) *Imperf*

117*b* **12** 1/4 a. red .. ..
118 **13** 1/2 a. red .. .. 11·00 6·00
119 **14** 1 a. red .. .. 11·00 7·00
120 **15** 2 a. red .. .. 60·00

III. *Thick wove paper. Imperf*

121 **13** 1/2 a. red .. .. 22·00 45·00
122 **14** 1 a. red .. .. 40·00 17·00
123 **15** 2 a. red .. .. 15·00 18·00

Of the above stamps those in red were intended for use in Jammu and those in shades of violet and blue for use in Kashmir.

1879. *Definitive issue. Thin wove paper, fine to coarse.*

(*a*) *Rough perf* 10 *to* 12

124 **13** 1/2 a. red £180 £130

(*b*) *Imperf*

125 **12** 1/4 a. red .. .. 2·25 2·50
126 **13** 1/2 a. red 50 55
a. Bisected (1/4 a.) on postcard .. † £3000
127 **14** 1 a. red .. .. 1·75 2·25
128 **15** 2 a. red .. .. 2·50 3·25
129 **16** 4 a. red .. .. 6·00 6·00
130 **17** 8 a. red .. .. 6·00 7·00

The plates were transferred from Jammu to Srinagar in early 1881 when further printings in red and all orange stamps were produced.

1880 (Mar). *Provisional printing in watercolour on thin bâtonné paper. Imperf.*

130*a* **12** 1/4 a. ultramarine £750 £450

1881–83. *As Nos.* 124 *to* 130. *Colour changed.*

(*a*) *Rough perf* 10 *to* 12

130*b* **13** 1/2 a. orange .. ..

(*b*) *Imperf*

131 **12** 1/4 a. orange .. .. 8·00 9·00
132 **13** 1/2 a. orange .. .. 18·00 12·00
133 **14** 1 a. orange .. .. 16·00 8·50
a. Bisected (1/2 a.) (on cover) .. .. † £3250
134 **15** 2 a. orange .. .. 14·00 8·50
135 **16** 4 a. orange .. .. 24·00 38·00
136 **17** 8 a. orange .. .. 48·00 55·00

Nos. 126a and 133a were used at Leh between April and July 1883.

Nos. 125/30 and 132/6 were re-issued between 1890 and 1894 and used concurrently with the stamps which follow. Such re-issues can be identified by the "three circle" cancellations, introduced in December 1890.

18 (1/8 a.)

1883–94. *New colours. Thin wove papers, toned, coarse to fine, or fine white* (1889). *Imperf.*

138 **18** 1/8 a. yellow-brown 60 90
139 1/8 a. yellow 60 90
140 **12** 1/4 a. sepia 55 40
141 1/4 a. brown 50 40
a. Double impression £1100
142 1/4 a. pale brown 50 40
a. Error. Green .. .. .. 50·00
143 **13** 1/2 a. dull blue .. .. 4·00
144 1/2 a. bright blue .. .. 40·00
145 1/2 a. vermillion 85 35
146 1/2 a. rose 85 55
147 1/2 a. orange-red 80 35
148 **14** 1 a. greenish grey 60 50
149 1 a. bright green 70 70
a. Double impression .. .. ..
150 1 a. dull green 60 50
151 1 a. blue-green 90
152 **15** 2 a. red/*yellow* .. .. 1·00 80
153 2 a. red/*yellow-green* .. .. .. 1·75 2·25
154 2 a. red/*deep green* .. .. .. 9·00 9·00
155 **16** 4 a. deep green .. .. 2·25 3·25
156 4 a. green .. .. 2·50 3·00
157 4 a. pale green .. .. 2·75 3·25
158 4 a. sage-green .. .. 2·75
159 **17** 8 a. pale blue .. .. 4·75 6·50
159*a* 8 a. deep blue .. .. 7·50 8·50
160 8 a. bright blue .. .. 6·50 8·00
161 8 a. indigo-blue .. .. 8·00 9·50
161*a* 8 a. slate-lilac .. .. 10·00 15·00

Well-executed forgeries of the 1/4 a. to 8 a. have come from India, mostly postmarked; they may be detected by the type, which does not agree with any variety on the genuine sheets, and also, in the low values, by the margins being filled in with colour, all but a thin white frame round the stamp. The forgeries of the 8 a. are in sheets of eight like the originals.

Other forgeries of nearly all values also exist, showing all varieties of type. All values are on thin, coarse wove paper.

In February 1890, a forgery, in watercolour, of the 1/2 a. orange on thin wove or on thin laid paper appeared, and many have been found genuinely used during 1890 and 1891 (*Price* £3).

Nos. 143 and 144 were never issued.

Examples of the 1/4 a. brown, 1/2 a. orange-red and 1 a. green on wove paper exist with clean-cut perf 12.

There is a reference in the Jammu and Kashmir State Administration Report covering 1890–91 to the re-introduction of perforating and the machine-gumming of paper at the Jammu printing works.

The few known examples, the 1/4 a. being only recorded used, the others unused or used, would appear to date from this period, but there is, as yet, no direct confirmation as to their status.

Maharaja Partap Singh, 1885–1925

1887–94. *Thin creamy laid paper. Imperf.*

162 **18** 1/8 a. yellow .. .. 35·00 42·00
163 **12** 1/4 a. brown .. .. 9·00 6·00
164 **13** 1/2 a. brown-red (March 1887) .. .. — 60·00
165 1/2 a. orange-red .. .. 6·50 4·75
166 **14** 1 a. grey-green £100 £100
168 **17** 8 a. blue (*Printed in watercolour*) .. £150 £150
a. On wove paper £100 £100

19

T **19** represents a 1/4 a. stamp, which exists in sheets of twelve varieties, in *red* and *black*, on thin wove and laid papers, also in *red* on native paper, but which does not appear ever to have been issued for use. It was first seen in 1886.

The 1/4 a. *brown* and the 4 a. *green* both exist on ordinary white laid paper and the 1/2 a. *red* on native paper. None of these are known to have been in use.

OFFICIAL STAMPS

1878. I. *White laid paper.* (*a*) *Rough perf* 10 *to* 12.

O1 **13** 1/2 a. black .. .. — £1200

(*b*) *Imperf*

O2 **13** 1/2 a. black .. .. 90·00 85·0
O3 **14** 1 a. black .. .. 50·00 55·0
O4 **15** 2 a. black .. .. 50·00 45·0

II. *Medium wove paper. Imperf*

O5 **14** 1 a. black £200

1880–94. *Thin wove papers, toned, coarse to fine, or fine whit* (1889). *Imperf.*

O 6 **12** 1/4 a. black 60 6
a. Double print £180
O 7 **13** 1/2 a. black 15 3
O 8 **14** 1 a. black 20 4
O 9 **15** 2 a. black 30 4
O10 **16** 4 a. black 35 6
O11 **17** 8 a. black .. .. 90 1·0

1887–94. *Thin creamy laid paper. Imperf.*

O12 **12** 1/4 a. black .. .. 4·75 4·7
O13 **13** 1/2 a. black .. .. 2·75 3·0
O14 **14** 1 a. black .. .. 1·50 2·2
O15 **15** 2 a. black .. .. 12·00
O16 **16** 4 a. black .. .. 45·00 50·0
O17 **17** 8 a. black .. .. 28·00 45·0

1889. *Stout white wove paper. Imperf.*

O18 **12** 1/4 a. black £180 £11

The stamps of Jammu and Kashmir have been obsolete sinc 1 November 1894.

JASDAN

PRICES FOR STAMPS ON COVER

Nos. 1/2	*from* × 2
No. 3	*from* × 3
Nos. 4/6	*from* × 4

Darbar Ala Khachar, 1919–1971

1 Sun

(Typo L. V. Indap & Co, Bombay)

1942 (15 Mar)–**47.** *Stamps from booklet panes. Various perfs.*

1 **1** 1 a. deep myrtle-green (*p* 10½×*imperf*) .. £600 £400
2 1 a. light green (*p* 12×*imperf*) £350 £400
3 1 a. light green (*p* 10½×*imperf*) (1943) .. 95·00 £120
4 1 a. pale yellow-green (*p* 8½×*imperf*) .. 11·00 90·00
5 1 a. dull yellow-green (*p* 10) (1946) .. 16·00 £100
6 1 a. bluish green (*p* 9) (1947) .. .. 12·00 90·00

Nos. 1/4 were issued in panes of four with the stamps imperforate on one or two sides; Nos. 5/6 were in panes of eight perforated all round.

A 1 a. rose with the arms of Jasdan in the centre is a fiscal stamp.

Jasdan was merged with the United State of Kathiawar (later Saurashtra) by 15 April 1948.

JHALAWAR

PRICES FOR STAMPS ON COVER

Nos. 1/2	*from* × 25

Maharaj Rana Zalim Singh, 1875–1896

(Figure of an Apsara, "RHEMBA", a dancing nymph of the Hindu Paradise)

1 (1 paisa) **2** (1/4 anna)

1886–90. *Typo in horizontal strips of* 12. *Laid paper. No gum.*

1 **1** 1 p. yellow-green .. .. 3·00 8·00
a. Blue-green .. .. 70·00 28·00
2 **2** 1/4 a. green (*shades*) .. .. .. 70 1·50

The stamps formerly listed as on wove paper are from sheets on laid paper, with the laid paper lines almost invisible.

The Maharaj Rana was deposed in 1896 and much of the state's territory transferred to Kotah on 1 January 1899.

Raj (Maharaj from 1918) Rana Bhawani Singh, 1899–1929

The stamps of Jhalawar have been obsolete since 1 November 1900.

JIND

PRICES FOR STAMPS ON COVER
Nos. J1/34 *from* × 50

ILLUSTRATIONS. Designs of Jind are illustrated actual size.

Raja Raghubir Singh, 1864–1887

J **1** (½ a.)

J **2** (1 a.)

J **3** (2 a.)

J **4** (4 a.)

J **5** (8 a.)

(Litho Jind State Rajah's Press, Sungroor)

1874. *Thin yellowish paper. Imperf.*

J1	J **1**	½ a. blue	5·50	2·50
		a. No frame to value. (Retouched all over)	£225	£140
J2	J **2**	1 a. rosy mauve	7·00	6·00
J3	J **3**	2 a. yellow	1·00	3·00
J4		2 a. brown-buff	£130	75·00
J5	J **4**	4 a. green	18·00	5·00
J6	J **5**	8 a. dull purple	£450	£120
J6*a*		8 a. bluish violet	£160	70·00
J7		8 a. slate-blue	£130	60·00

Nos. J1/7 were produced from two stones. Those from the first stone had rather blurred impressions, but those from the second are clearer with a conspicuous white frame around the value. Nos. J4 and J8/13 were only printed from the second stone.

1876. *Bluish laid card-paper. No gum. Imperf.*

J 8	J **1**	½ a. blue	50	3·00
J 9	J **2**	1 a. purple	1·40	7·00
J10	J **3**	2 a. brown	2·25	9·50
J11	J **4**	4 a. green	1·25	9·50
J11*a*	J **5**	8 a. bluish violet	8·00	20·00
J12		8 a. slate-blue	7·00	10·00
J13		8 a. steel-blue	9·00	15·00

Stocks of the ½ a. (No. J8) and 2 a. (No. J4) were perforated 12 in 1885 for use as fiscal stamps.

J **6** (¼ a.)

J **7** (½ a.)

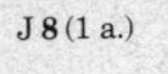
J **8** (1 a.)

J **9** (2 a.)

J **10** (4 a.)

J **11** (8 a.)

(Litho Jind State Rajah's Press, Sungroor)

1882–85. *Types* J **6** *to* J **11**. 25 *varieties of each value. No gum.*

A. *Imperf* (1882–4). (*a*) *Thin yellowish wove paper.*

J15	¼ a. buff (*shades*)	30	1·50
J16	¼ a. red-brown	30	1·25
	a. Doubly printed	42·00	
J17	½ a. lemon	80	1·60
J18	½ a. buff	1·50	1·50
J19	½ a. brown-buff	70	60
J20	1 a. brown (*shades*)	1·60	3·25
J21	2 a. blue	1·50	6·50
J22	2 a. deep blue	2·00	1·00
J23	4 a. sage-green	90	90
J24	4 a. blue-green	1·60	2·75
J25	8 a. red	4·75	4·25

(*b*) *Various thick laid papers*

J26	¼ a. brown-buff	1·25	
J27	½ a. lemon	1·25	
J28	½ a. brown-buff		
J29	1 a. brown	1·25	2·50
J30	2 a. blue	18·00	21·00
J31	8 a. red	2·50	9·00

(*c*) *Thick white wove paper*

J32	¼ a. brown-buff	12·00	
J33	½ a. brown-buff	27·00	
J34	1 a. brown	3·75	
J35	8 a. red	4·75	9·00

B. *Perf* 12 (1885). (*a*) *Thin yellowish wove paper*

J36	¼ a. buff (*shades*)	60	2·50
	a. Doubly printed	85·00	
J37	¼ a. red-brown	3·25	
J38	½ a. lemon	95·00	95·00
J39	½ a. buff	45	3·25
J40	½ a. brown-buff	3·00	4·00
J41	1 a. brown (*shades*)	2·50	4·25
J42	2 a. blue	3·25	8·00
J43	2 a. deep blue	2·75	5·00
J44	4 a. sage-green	5·00	9·00
J45	4 a. blue-green	2·00	
	a. Imperf vert (horiz pair)	£500	
J46	8 a. red	9·00	

(*b*) *Various thick laid papers*

J47	¼ a. brown-buff	6·00	
J48	½ a. lemon	85·00	22·00
J49	1 a. brown	1·50	
J50	2 a. blue	20·00	23·00
J51	8 a. red	2·50	7·00

(*c*) *Thick white wove paper*

J52	1 a. brown		
J53	8 a. red	9·50	

The perforated stamps ceased to be used for postal purposes in July 1885, but were used as fiscals to at least the mid-1920s. Other varieties exist, but they must either be fiscals or reprints, and it is not quite certain that all those listed above were issued as early as 1885.

Jind became a Convention State and from 1 July 1885 used overprinted Indian stamps.

KISHANGARH

PRICES FOR STAMPS ON COVER

Nos. 1/3	—
Nos. 4/91	*from* × 8
Nos. O1/32	*from* × 30

GUM. The stamps of Kishangarh were issued without gum, *except for* Nos. 42/50 and O 17/24.

Maharaja Sardul Singh, 1879–1900

1

1899. *Medium wove paper. Typo from a plate of eight impressions.*

1	**1**	1 a. green (*imperf*)	20·00	50·00
2		1 a. green (*pin-perf*)	60·00	

1900. *Thin white wove paper. Printed from a single die. Imperf.*

3	**1**	1 a. blue	£400

ILLUSTRATIONS. Types **2** to **10*a*** are shown actual size.

2 (¼ a.)

3 (½ a.)

4 (1 a.)

5 (2 a.)
Maharaja Sardul Singh

6 (4 a.)

7 (1 r.)

8 (2 r.)

9 (5 r.)

1899–1901. *Thin white wove paper.* (*a*) *Imperf.*

4	**2**	¼ a. green	£500	
5		¼ a. carmine	6·00	
		a. Rose-pink	75	1·50
6		¼ a. magenta	5·00	5·00
		a. Doubly printed	80·00	
7	**3**	½ a. lilac	95·00	£170
8		½ a. red	£1700	£1100
9		½ a. green	25·00	30·00
10		½ a. pale yellow-olive	38·00	38·00
11		½ a. slate-blue	30·00	30·00
		a. Pair, one stamp sideways	£1000	
		b. Deep blue	5·50	6·50
		c. Light blue	1·25	1·40
12	**4**	1 a. slate	3·75	4·50
		a. Laid paper	38·00	
12*b*		1 a. pink	50·00	£140
13		1 a. mauve	5·00	4·50
		a. Laid paper	32·00	
14		1 a. brown-lilac	1·10	90
		a. Laid paper	28·00	
15	**5**	2 a. dull orange	4·00	4·50
		a. Laid paper	£400	£375
16	**6**	4 a. chocolate	5·00	
		a. Lake-brown	5·00	9·00
		b. Chestnut	5·00	9·00
		c. Laid paper (*shades*)	55·00	55·00
17	**7**	1 r. brown-lilac	20·00	25·00
18		1 r. dull green	18·00	30·00
19	**8**	2 r. brown-red	65·00	85·00
		a. Laid paper	55·00	
20	**9**	5 r. mauve	55·00	65·00
		a. Laid paper	60·00	

(*b*) *Pin-perf* 12½ *or* 14

21	**2**	¼ a. green	£200	£350
		a. Imperf between (pair)	£1000	
22		¼ a. carmine	3·75	4·75
		a. Rose-pink	25	40
		ab. *Tête-bêche* (horiz pair)	£650	
		b. Rose		
23		¼ a. magenta	5·00	7·00
		a. Bright purple		
		ab. Doubly printed		
24	**3**	½ a. green	17·00	22·00
		a. Imperf between (pair)	£160	
25		½ a. pale yellow-olive	13·00	16·00
		a. Imperf vert (horiz pair)	£160	
		b. Imperf between (horiz pair)	†	£250
26		½ a. deep blue	1·75	3·00
		a. Light blue	55	45
		ab. Doubly printed	£100	£100
27	**4**	1 a. slate	4·25	2·75
		a. Laid paper	35·00	18·00
27*b*		1 a. pink	60·00	£160
28		1 a. mauve	85	1·50
		a. Laid paper	35·00	13·00
29		1 a. brown-lilac	75	90
		a. Laid paper	32·00	13·00
30	**5**	2 a. dull orange	4·00	5·00
31	**6**	4 a. chocolate	2·00	5·00
		a. Lake-brown	2·50	5·00
		b. Chestnut	3·50	5·50
		c. Laid paper (*shades*)	45·00	42·00
32	**7**	1 r. dull green	10·00	15·00
		a. Laid paper	70·00	
33		1 r. pale olive-yellow	£650	
34	**8**	2 r. brown-red	38·00	45·00
		a. Laid paper	40·00	
35	**9**	5 r. mauve	32·00	45·00
		a. Laid paper	60·00	

All the above, both imperf and pin-perf, were printed singly, sometimes on paper with spaces marked in pencil. They exist in vertical *tête-bêche* pairs imperf between from the centre of the sheet. *Prices from* 3 × *normal, unused.* No. 22ab is an error.

FISCAL STAMPS. Many of the following issues were produced in different colours for fiscal purposes. Such usage is indicated by the initials "M.C.", punched hole or violet Stamp Office handstamp.

Maharaja Madan Singh, 1900–1926

10 (¼ a.)

10*a* (1 r.)

1901. *Toned wove paper. Pin-perf.*

No.	Type	Description	Unused	Used
36	**10**	¼ a. dull pink	8·00	6·00
37	**4**	1 a. violet	40·00	27·00
38	**10*a***	1 r. dull green	14·00	16·00
36/8		*Set of* 3	55·00	45·00

Nos. 36/8 were printed in sheets of 24. Sheets of the 1 r. were always torn to remove R. 5/4 where the cliché is believed to have been defective.

The 1 a. (No. 37) differs from T 4 in having an inscription in native characters below the words "ONE ANNA".

11 (½ a.)

12 Maharaja Sardul Singh

1903. *Litho. Thick white wove glazed paper. Imperf.*

No.	Type	Description	Unused	Used
39	**11**	½ a. pink	8·00	3·00
		a. Printed both sides	†	£950
40	**12**	2 a. dull yellow	3·00	5·00

12*a* (8 a.)

1904. *Printed singly. Thin paper. Pin-perf.*

No.	Type	Description	Unused	Used
41	**12*a***	8 a. grey	5·00	7·50
		a. *Tête-bêche* (vert pair)	26·00	
		b. Doubly printed	£110	

13 Maharaja Madan Singh 14

(Recess Perkins Bacon & Co)

1904–10. *With gum. P* 12½.

No.	Type	Description	Unused	Used
42	**13**	¼ a. carmine	45	45
		a. Perf 13½ (1910)	45	45
		b. Perf 12×12½	75·00	
43		½ a. chestnut	1·40	75
		a. Perf 13½ (1906)	45	30
44		1 a. blue	3·25	2·00
		a. Perf 13½ (1906)	1·25	1·25
45		2 a. orange-yellow	12·00	7·00
		a. Perf 13½ (1907)	17·00	14·00
46		4 a. brown	18·00	15·00
		a. Perf 13½ (1970)	10·00	13·00
		b. Perf 12	42·00	35·00
47		8 a. violet (1905)	6·00	16·00
48		1 r. green	21·00	27·00
49		2 r. olive-yellow	20·00	95·00
50		5 r. purple-brown	21·00	£120
42/50		*Set of* 9	80·00	£250

Stamps in other colours, all perforated 13½, are colour trials.

1912. *Printed from half-tone blocks. No ornaments to left and right of value in English; large ornaments on either side of value in Hindi. Small stop after* "STATE". (*a*) *Thin wove paper. Rouletted.*

No.	Type	Description	Unused	Used
51	**14**	2 a. deep violet ("TWO ANNA")	3·00	7·50
		a. *Tête-bêche* (vert pair)	8·00	
		b. Imperf (pair)	£275	

No. 51 is printed in four rows, each inverted in respect to that above and below it.

(*b*) *Thick white chalk-surfaced paper. Imperf.*

No.	Type	Description	Unused	Used
52	**14**	2 a. lilac ("TWO ANNA")	£1100	£550

(*c*) *Thick white chalk-surfaced paper. Rouletted in colour (Medallion only in half-tone)*

No.	Type	Description	Unused	Used
53	**14**	¼ a. ultramarine	13·00	13·00

1913. *No ornaments on either side of value in English. Small ornaments in bottom label. With stop after* "STATE". *Thick white chalk-surfaced paper. Rouletted.*

No.	Type	Description	Unused	Used
54	**14**	2 a. purple ("TWO ANNAS")	2·50	5·00

15

No. 59e. This occurs on R. 3/3 on one setting only

2 TWO ANNAS 2 — No. 60. Small figures

2 TWO ANNAS 2 — No. 60b. Large figures

(Typo Diamond Soap Works, Kishangarh)

1913 (Aug). *Thick surfaced paper. Half-tone centre. Type-set inscriptions. Rouletted. Inscr* "KISHANGARH".

No.	Type	Description	Unused	Used
59	**15**	¼ a. pale blue	20	80
		a. Imperf (pair)	7·00	
		b. Roul × imperf (horiz pair)	25·00	
		ba. Imperf between (horiz pair)	42·00	
		c. "OUARTER"	5·00	7·00
		ca. As last, imperf (pair)	28·00	
		cb. As last, roul × imperf	55·00	
		d. "KISHANGAHR"	5·00	7·00
		da. As last, imperf (pair)	28·00	
		db. As last, roul × imperf	55·00	
		dc. As last, imperf between (horiz pair)	85·00	
		e. Character omitted	7·00	7·00
		ea. As last, imperf (pair)	32·00	
60		2 a. purple	7·00	18·00
		a. "KISHANGAHR"	50·00	90·00
		b. Large figures "2"	32·00	55·00

1913–16. *Stamps printed far apart, horizontally and vertically, otherwise as No.* 54, *except as noted below.*

No.	Type	Description	Unused	Used
63	**14**	¼ a. blue	20	45
64		½ a. green (1915)	20	80
		a. Printed both sides	£200	
		b. Imperf (pair)	£150	£150
		c. *Emerald-green* (1916)	1·75	3·50
65		1 a. red	1·00	2·50
		a. Without stop*	1·25	4·50
		ab. Imperf (pair)	£180	
66		2 a. purple ("TWO ANNAS") (1915)	6·00	7·00
67		4 a. bright blue	6·00	8·00
68		8 a. brown	7·00	38·00
69		1 r. mauve	15·00	95·00
		a. Imperf (pair)	£250	
70		2 r. deep green	70·00	£180
71		5 r. brown	85·00	£350
63/71		*Set of* 9	£170	£600

*For this issue, ornaments were added on either side of the English value (except in the ¼ a.) and the inscription in the right label was without stop, except in the case of No. 65.

In Nos. 70 and 71 the value is expressed as "RUPIES" instead of "RUPEES".

Initial printings of the ¼ a., 1 a. and 4 a. values were in sheets of 20 containing two panes of 10 separated by a central gutter margin. Stamps from these sheets measure 20×25½ mm and have heavier screening dots on the perforation margins than on the designs. Subsequent printings of these stamps, and of other values in the set, were from single pane sheets of 20 on which the designs measured 19½×23¾ mm and with the screening dots uniform across the sheet.

Maharaja Yagyanarayan Singh, 1926–1939

16 Maharaja Yagyanarayan Singh 17

1928–36. *Thick surfaced paper. Typo. Pin-perf.*

No.	Type	Description	Unused	Used
72	**16**	¼ a. light blue	60	2·00
73		½ a. yellow-green	2·00	1·10
		a. Deep green	2·50	2·50
		ab. Imperf (pair)	70·00	70·00
		ac. Imperf between (vert or horiz pair)	85·00	85·00
74	**17**	1 a. carmine	60	1·50
		a. Imperf (pair)	£130	95·00
75		2 a. purple	3·00	7·50
75*a*		2 a. magenta (1936)	5·50	11·00
		ab. Imperf (pair)	£190	
76	**16**	4 a. chestnut	1·25	1·75
		a. Imperf (pair)		
77		8 a. violet	3·50	22·00
78		1 r. light green	11·00	42·00
79		2 r. lemon-yellow (1929)	26·00	£130
80		5 r. claret (1929)	30·00	£150
		a. Imperf (pair)	£100	
72/80		*Set of* 9	70·00	£325

The 4 a. to 5 r. are slightly larger than, but otherwise similar to, the ¼ a. and ½ a. The 8 a. has a dotted background covering the whole design.

Maharaja Sumar Singh, 1939–1971

1943–47. *As last, but thick, soft, unsurfaced paper. Poor impression. Typo. Pin-perf.*

No.	Type	Description	Unused	Used
81	**16**	¼ a. pale dull blue (1945)	3·50	8·00
		a. Imperf (pair)	32·00	
82		¼ a. greenish blue (1947)	1·60	6·50
		a. Imperf (pair)	28·00	
83	**16**	½ a. deep green (1944)	90	1·75
		a. Imperf (pair)	25·00	25·00
		b. Imperf between (vert or horiz pair)	42·00	
84		½ a. yellow-green (1946)	4·50	7·00
		a. Imperf (pair)	25·00	25·00
		b. Imperf between (vert or horiz pair)	42·00	
85	**17**	1 a. carmine-red (1944)	6·00	2·50
		a. Double print	£300	
		b. Imperf (pair)	25·00	25·00
		c. Imperf between (vert or horiz pair)	42·00	
		d. Red-orange (1947)	55·00	23·00
		da. Imperf (pair)	90·00	70·00
86		2 a. bright magenta	6·00	12·00
		a. Imperf (pair)	50·00	55·00
87		2 a. maroon (1947)	65·00	16·00
		a. Imperf (pair)	42·00	42·00
		b. Imperf between (vert or horiz pair)	75·00	
88	**16**	4 a. brown (1944)	21·00	16·00
		a. Imperf (pair)		
89		8 a. violet (1945)	45·00	£110
90		1 r. green (1945)	48·00	£120
		a. Imperf (pair)	£160	£250
90*b*		2 r. yellow (date?)		
		ba. Imperf (pair)	£350	
91		5 r. claret (1945)	£400	£425
		a. Imperf (pair)	£275	

OFFICIAL STAMPS

ON
K S
D

(O 1)

1918. *Handstamped with Type* O 1.

(*a*) *Stamps of* 1899–1901. (i) *Imperf*

No.	Type	Description	Unused	Used
O 1	**2**	¼ a. green	—	£160
O 2		¼ a. rose-pink	—	6·00
O 3	**4**	1 a. mauve	—	50·00
O 3*a*		1 a. brown-lilac	38·00	5·50
		ab. Pair, one without opt	—	60·00
O 4	**6**	4 a. chocolate	—	80·00

(ii) *Pin-perf*

No.	Type	Description	Unused	Used
O 5	**2**	¼ a. green	—	£120
O 6		¼ a. rose-pink	2·25	60
		a. Pair, one without opt	70·00	32·00
		b. Stamp doubly printed	90·00	60·00
O 7	**3**	½ a. light blue	£120	35·00
O 8	**4**	1 a. mauve	30·00	1·50
O 9		1 a. brown-lilac	28·00	1·50
O10	**5**	2 a. dull orange	—	£120
O11	**6**	4 a. chocolate	40·00	16·00
		a. Pair, one without opt	—	65·00
O12	**7**	1 r. dull green	£120	90·00
O13	**8**	2 r. brown-red	—	£750
O14	**9**	5 r. mauve	—	£1400

(*b*) *Stamps of* 1903 *and* 1904

No.	Type	Description	Unused	Used
O15	**12**	2 a. dull yellow	55·00	5·00
		a. Stamp printed both sides	†	£750
		b. Red opt	£300	£170
O16	**12*a***	8 a. grey	55·00	22·00
		a. Red opt	—	£150

(*c*) *Stamps of* 1904–5. *P* 13½ (¼ *a. to* 4 *a.*) *or* 12½ (*others*)

No.	Type	Description	Unused	Used
O17	**13**	¼ a. carmine	—	£200
O18		½ a. chestnut	75	35
		a. Pair, one without opt	—	40·00
O19		1 a. blue	7·00	4·00
		a. Red opt	20·00	7·00
		b. Pair, one without opt	—	50·00
O20		2 a. orange-yellow	—	£750
O21		4 a. brown	42·00	18·00
		a. Red opt	50·00	27·00
O22		8 a. violet	£250	£150
		a. Red opt	—	£160
O23		1 r. green	£475	£425
		a. Red opt	—	£400
O24		5 r. purple-brown		

(*d*) *Stamps of* 1913

No.	Type	Description	Unused	Used
O25	**15**	¼ a. pale blue	6·00	
		a. Imperf (pair)	85·00	
		b. Roul × imperf (horiz pair)	£140	
		c. "OUARTER"	22·00	
		ca. As last, imperf (pair)	£130	
		d. "KISHANGAHR"	22·00	
		da. As last, imperf (pair)	£130	
		e. Character omitted	22·00	
		ea. As last, imperf (pair)	£130	
O26	**14**	2 a. purple (No. 54)	—	80·00
		a. Red opt	£110	20·00
O27	**15**	2 a. purple	£350	£375
		a. "KISHANGAHR"	£650	
		b. Large figures "2"	£475	£500

(*e*) *Stamps of* 1913–16

No.	Type	Description	Unused	Used
O28	**14**	¼ a. blue	50	50
		a. Red opt	2·00	1·75
O29		½ a. green	75	75
		a. Pair, one without opt	—	50·00
		b. Red opt	3·25	1·60
		ba. Pair, one without opt	—	£100
O30		1 a. red	8·00	4·50
		a. Without stop	1·00	1·00
		ab. Red opt	—	75·00
O31		2 a. purple	6·00	4·00
		a. Red opt	£110	60·00
		b. Pair, one without opt	—	55·00
O32		4 a. bright blue	20·00	15·00
		a. Red opt	—	30·00

33 14 8 a. brown .. .. 90·00 40·00
a. Red opt .. .. .. — 80·00
34 1 r. lilac £275 £275
35 2 r. deep green .. ..
36 5 r. brown £1200

This overprint is found inverted as often as it is upright; and many other "errors" exist.

Kishangarh became part of Rajasthan by 15 April 1948.

LAS BELA

PRICES FOR STAMPS ON COVER
Nos. 1/12 *from* × 8

Mir Kamal Khan, 1896–1926

1

2

(Litho Thacker & Co, Bombay)

1897–98. *Thick paper. P* 11½.
1 1 ½ a. black on *white* .. .. .. 19·00 12·00

1898–1900. *P* 11½.
2 1 ½ a. black on *greyish blue* (1898) .. 12·00 7·50
3 ½ a. black on *greenish grey* (1899) .. 10·00 6·50
a. "BFLA" for "BELA" £130
b. Imperf between (horiz strip of 3) ..
4 ½ a. black on *thin white surfaced paper* (1899) .. .. .. 22·00 32·00
5 ½ a. black on *slate* (1900) .. .. 24·00 35·00
a. Imperf between (horiz pair) £750

1901–2. *P* 11½.
6 1 ½ a. black on *pale grey* .. .. .. 9·50 7·50
a. "BFLA" for "BELA" .. .. 95·00 £130
7 ½ a. black on *pale green* (1902) .. .. 17·00 18·00
8 2 1 a. black on *orange* .. .. .. 14·00 16·00

There are at least 14 settings of the above ½ a. stamps, the sheets varying from 16 to 30 stamps.

No. 6a occurred on R.3/2 of the July 1901 printing in sheets of 16 (4×4).

1904 (Feb–Nov). *Stamps printed wider apart. P* 11½.
11 1 ½ a. black on *pale blue* .. .. .. 9·50 6·50
a. Imperf between (pair) £650
b. Imperf between (horiz strip of 3) .. £900
c. Perf 12½ (Nov) .. .. .. 12·00 7·50
12 ½ a. black on *pale green* .. .. .. 9·50 6·50
c. Perf 12½ (Nov) .. .. .. 12·00 7·50

There are five plates of the above two stamps, each consisting of 18 (3×6) varieties.

All the coloured papers of the ½ a. show coloured fibres, similar to those in granite paper.

The stamps of Las Bela have been obsolete since 1 April 1907.

MORVI

PRICES FOR STAMPS ON COVER
Nos. 1/19 *from* × 6

Thakur (Maharaja from 1926) Lakhdirji, 1922–48

1

2

3

Maharaja Lakhdirji

1931 (1 April). *Typo. P* 12.

(*a*) *Printed in blocks of four. Stamps* 10 *mm apart* (*Nos.* 1/2) *or* 6½ *mm apart* (*No.* 3). *Perf on two or three sides*
1 1 3 p. deep red .. .. 3·00 14·00
2 ½ a. blue .. .. 20·00 28·00
3 2 a. yellow-brown .. .. 80·00
1/3 .. .. *Set of* 3 95·00

(*b*) *Printed in two blocks of four. Stamps* 5½ *mm apart. Perf on four sides*
4 1 3 p. bright scarlet .. .. .. 4·50 15·00
a. Error. Dull blue .. .. .. 4·00 15·00
b. Ditto. Double print £600
c. Ditto. Printed on gummed side .. £600
5 ½ a. dull blue .. .. 2·25 9·00
a. Chalk-surfaced paper .. .. 1·90 9·00
6 1 a. brown-red .. .. 3·25 18·00
7 2 a. yellow-brown .. .. 4·00 25·00
4/7 .. .. *Set of* 4 12·00 60·00

Nos. 1/3 were supplied to post offices in panes of four sewn into bundles with interleaving.

1932–33. *Horizontal background lines wider apart and portrait smaller than in T* 1. *Typo. P* 11.
8 2 3 p. carmine-rose (*shades*) .. .. 2·00 7·00
9 6 p. green .. .. 4·00 9·00
a. Imperf between (horiz pair) .. £1800
b. Emerald-green .. .. .. 2·75 7·00
10 1 a. ultramarine (*to* deep) .. .. 2·00 7·50
a. Imperf between (vert pair) £1400
11 2 a. bright violet (1933) .. .. .. 10·00 27·00
a. Imperf between (vert pair) £1400
8/11 .. .. *Set of* 4 15·00 42·00

1934. *Typo. London ptg. P* 14.
12 3 3 p. carmine .. .. 1·40 1·60
13 6 p. emerald-green .. .. .. 80 4·00
14 1 a. purple-brown .. .. .. 1·10 8·00
a. Imperf between (horiz pair) .. † £1300
15 2 a. bright violet .. .. .. 2·50 15·00
12/15 .. .. *Set of* 4 5·25 26·00

1935–48. *Typo. Morvi Press ptg. Rough perf* 11.
16 3 3 p. scarlet (*shades*) .. .. .. 70 2·25
a. Imperf between (horiz pair) .. £1300
17 6 p. grey-green .. .. 75 2·00
a. Emerald-green .. .. .. 5·00 22·00
18 1 a. brown .. .. 12·00 14·00
a. Pale yellow-brown .. .. .. 16·00 25·00
b. Chocolate .. .. 22·00 30·00
19 2 a. dull violet (*to* deep) .. .. .. 2·50 15·00
16/19 .. .. *Set of* 4 14·00 30·00

Nos. 17*a*, 18*a* and 18*b* were issued between 1944 and 1948.

Maharaja Mahendra Singh, 1948–1957

Morvi was merged with the United State of Kathiawar (later Saurashtra) by 15 April 1948.

NANDGAON

PRICES FOR STAMPS ON COVER
The stamps of Nandgaon are very rare used on cover.

GUM. The stamps of Nandgaon were issued without gum.

Raja Mahant Balram Das, 1883–1897

1

2 (½ a.)

(Litho at Poona)

1891. *Imperf.*
1 1 ½ a. blue .. .. 3·75 £110
a. Dull blue .. .. 4·00
2 2 a. rose .. .. 17·00 £300

The few covers in existence franked with Nos. 1/2 have undated manuscript cancellations, but other forms are known on loose examples.

The state was under Imperial administration from January 1888 to November 1891 and it is possible that Nos. 1/2 may have appeared in late 1887.

Last character in top line omitted

(Typo Balram Press, Raj-Nandgaon)

1893 (1 Jan)–**94.** *Printed in sheets of* 16 (4×4). *Imperf.*

(*a*) *Stamps printed wide apart* (8 *to* 10 *mm*) *without wavy lines between them. Thin, toned wove paper*
3 2 ½ a. dull *to* deep green .. .. .. 8·00 55·00
4 2 a. red .. .. 7·00 55·00
a. Thick paper .. ..
b. Dull rose .. .. 7·00 55·00

(*b*) *Stamps printed closer together* (4 *to* 7 *mm*) *with wavy lines between them. Thin, white wove paper* (1894)
5 2 ½ a. green .. .. 19·00 42·00
a. Last character in top line omitted (R.4/3) .. .. .. 80·00
b. Thick paper .. ..
ba. Last character in top line omitted ..
6 1 a. rose .. .. 35·00 85·00
a. Thick paper .. ..
b. Thick laid paper .. .. ..
ba. Thin laid paper £200

There were three settings of Type 2 with a number of separate printings made from the third:
Setting I – Nos. 3, 4, 4a, 4*b*, O2
Setting II – Nos. 5, 5b, 6, 6a, 6b
Setting III – Nos. 5, 6ba, O3, O3*a*, O4, O4a, O5 and subsequent reprints

The same clichés were used for all values with the face value inscriptions changed. These exist in two different sizes with both occurring on the ½ a., the small on the 1 a. and the large on the 2 a. except for No. O5 which has the small type.

The ordinary postage stamps of Nandgaon became obsolete on 1 July 1894.

OFFICIAL STAMPS

(O 1)
("M.B.D." = Mahant Balram Das)

1893. *Handstamped with ruler's initials in oval. Type* O **1**, *in purple.*
O1 1 ½ a. blue £350
O2 2 a. rose £600

1894. *Handstamped with Type* O **1** *in purple.*

(*a*) *Stamps printed wide apart* (8 *to* 10 *mm*) *without wavy lines between them. Thin, toned wove paper*
O3 2 2 a. red .. .. 18·00 85·00

(*b*) *Stamps printed closer together* (4 *to* 7 *mm*) *with wavy lines between them. Thin, white wove paper*
O4 2 ½ a. yellow-green .. .. .. 4·50 7·50
a. Sage-green .. .. .. 6·00
O5 1 a. rose (*shades*) .. .. .. 7·00 26·00
a. Thin laid paper .. .. .. 10·00 65·00
O6 2 a. rose (*shades*) .. .. .. 6·00 16·00

Further printings took place in 1895 after the Official stamps were withdrawn from postal use on 31 December 1894. These were all on thin, white wove paper with the ½ a. and 2 a. in slightly different shades and the 1 a. in brown or ultramarine.

There is a forgery of the handstamp, Type O 1, which shows 8 mm between the two ornaments below the initials instead of the normal 4 mm.

NAWANAGAR

PRICES FOR STAMPS ON COVER

No. 1	*from* × 20
No. 2	*from* × 8
Nos. 3/4	*from* × 3
No. 5	—
Nos. 6/12	—
Nos. 13/15	*from* × 100
Nos. 16/18	—

GUM. The stamps of Nawanagar were issued without gum.

Jam Vibhaji 1882–1895

1 (1 docra)

2 (2 docra)

3 (3 docra)

1877. *Typo in sheets of* 32 (4×8 *or* 8×4). *Laid paper.* (*a*) *Imperf*
1 1 1 doc. blue (*shades*) .. .. .. 50 22·00
a. *Tête-bêche* (pair) £1000
b. Doubly printed .. .. .. 80·00

(*b*) *Perf* 12½ (*line*)
2 1 1 doc. slate-blue .. .. 60·00 £100
a. Perf 11 (harrow) .. .. .. 60·00
ab. *Tête-bêche* (pair) £1300

The inverted clichés which cause the *tête-bêche* pairs come from different settings and occur on R. 3/2 (No. 1a) or R. 4/4 (No. 2ab) of sheets of 32 (4×8).

1877. *T* **2** *and* **3**. *Type-set in black. Wove paper. Thick horizontal and vertical frame lines. Stamp* 19 *mm wide.*
3 1 doc. *deep mauve* £3000 £150
a. Stamp 14½–15 mm wide .. .. † £250
b. Stamp 16 mm wide .. .. .. † £190
4 2 doc. *green* £3000 £1500
5 3 doc. *yellow* £3000 £1500

1880. *As last, but thin frame lines, as illustrated. Stamp* 15 *to* 18 *mm wide.*
6 1 doc. *deep mauve* .. .. 2·00 6·50
a. On rose .. .. 2·00
ab. Stamp 14 mm wide .. .. .. 2·00 4·50
7 1 doc. *magenta* (*stamp* 14 *mm wide*) .. 2·00
8 2 doc. *yellow-green* .. .. 2·75 8·50
a. On blue-green .. .. .. 5·00
b. Error. Yellow £325
c. Stamp 14 mm wide .. .. .. 2·75 7·00
ca. On blue-green .. .. .. 6·50

9 3 doc. *orange-yellow* .. .. .. 7·50
  a. On yellow .. .. 3·50 12·00
  ab. On laid paper .. .. .. 85·00
  b. Stamp 14 mm wide. *On yellow* .. 4·00 8·00
  ba. On laid paper .. .. .. 42·00

There are several different settings of each value of this series.

No. 8b occurs in the sheet of the 3 doc. value from one setting only.

4 (1 docra)

1893. *Typo in sheets of* 36. *P* 12. *(a) Thick paper.*

10 4 1 doc. black .. .. 1·60
  a. Imperf (pair) £475
11 3 doc. orange .. .. 2·25

(b) Thick laid paper

12 4 1 doc. black £450

(c) Thin wove paper

13 4 1 doc. black *to* grey .. .. .. 70 3·50
  a. Imperf between (pair) £400
  b. Imperf (pair) £375
14 2 doc. green .. .. 75 4·00
  a. Imperf (pair) £400
  b. Imperf between (vert pair) .. £425
15 3 doc. orange-yellow .. .. .. 1·10 7·00
  a. Imperf between (pair) £425
  b. Orange .. .. 75 6·50
  ba. Imperf (pair) £400
  bb. Imperf vert (horiz pair) £425

(d) Thin, soft wove paper

16 4 1 doc. black .. ..
17 2 doc. deep green .. .. .. 2·50
18 3 doc. brown-orange .. .. .. 3·50

Cancellations for postal purposes were intaglio seals, applied in black. Other forms of cancellation were only used on remainders.

The stamps of Nawanagar became obsolete on 1 January 1895.

NEPAL

Nepal being an independent state, its stamps will be found listed in Part 21 (*South-East Asia*) of this catalogue.

ORCHHA

PRICES FOR STAMPS ON COVER	
Nos. 1/2	—
Nos. 3/7	*from* × 8
Nos. 8/30	*from* × 50
Nos. 31/45	*from* × 4

A set of four stamps, ½ a. red, 1 a. violet, 2 a. yellow and 4 a. deep blue-green, in a design similar to T **2**, was prepared in 1897 with State authority but not put into use. These exist both imperforate and pin-perforated. (*Price for set of* 4, £16 *unused or c.t.o.*)

Maharaja Partab Singh, 1874–1930

1

2

(T **1/2** litho Shri Pratap Prabhakar)

1913. *Background to arms unshaded. Very blurred impression. Wove paper. No gum. Imperf.*

1 1 ½ a. green .. .. 28·00 75·00
2 1 a. red .. .. 19·00

1914–35. *Background shaded with short horizontal lines. Clearer impression. Wove paper. No gum. Imperf.*

3 2 ¼ a. bright ultramarine .. .. .. 1·00 3·00
  a. Grey-blue .. .. 35 3·00
  b. Deep blue .. .. 1·60 3·00
  ba. Laid paper £500
4 ½ a. green (*shades*) .. .. .. 50 3·50
  a. Dull green .. .. 1·50 3·75
  b. Apple-green .. .. 2·25 3·25
5 1 a. scarlet .. .. 2·25 5·50
  a. Laid paper .. .. — £325
  b. Indian red .. .. 1·75 8·00
  c. Carmine .. .. 2·50 3·75
  ca. Laid paper (1935) £190 £250
6 2 a. red-brown (1916) .. .. .. 4·50 18·00
  a. Light brown .. .. .. 10·00 18·00
  b. Chestnut .. .. 18·00 20·00
7 4 a. ochre (1917) .. .. .. 9·00 27·00
  a. Yellow-orange .. .. .. 8·00 27·00
  b. Yellow .. .. 8·00 23·00
3/7 .. .. *Set of* 5 13·50 45·00

There are two sizes of T **2** in the setting of 8 (4 × 2). In each value stamps from the upper row are slightly taller than those from the lower.

Maharaja Vir Singh II, 1930–1956

3 Maharaja Vir Singh II 4

(Typo Lakshmi Art Ptg Wks, Bombay)

1935 (1 Apr). *Thick, chalk-surfaced wove paper. P* 9½, 10, 10×9½, 11, 11×9½, 11½, 11½×11, 11½×12, 12 *or* 12×11.

8 3 ¼ a. purple and slate .. .. .. 1·25 2·00
  a. Imperf between (vert pair) .. ..
  b. Ordinary paper .. .. .. 30 1·25
  ba. Imperf between (vert pair) .. .. 11·00
  bb. Imperf vert (horiz pair) .. .. 65·00
  bc. Imperf horiz (vert pair) .. .. 65·00
9 ½ a. olive-grey and emerald 50 75
  a. Imperf (pair) .. .. .. 75·00
10 ¾ a. magenta and deep myrtle-green .. 50 85
  a. Imperf (pair) .. .. .. 75·00
11 1 a. myrtle-green and purple-brown .. 50 65
  a. Imperf (pair) .. .. .. 65·00 65·00
  b. Imperf horiz (vert pair) .. ..
  c. Imperf vert (horiz pair) .. ..
12 1¼ a. slate and mauve 45 70
  a. Imperf (pair) .. .. .. 75·00 £200
  b. Imperf between (horiz pair) .. 75·00
  c. Frame doubly printed .. .. 75·00
13 1½ a. brown and scarlet 45 75
  a. Imperf between (vert pair) .. .. 75·00
  b. Imperf between (horiz pair) .. 75·00
14 2 a. blue and red-orange 45 75
  a. Imperf (pair) .. .. .. 12·00
  b. Imperf between (horiz pair) .. 75·00
15 2½ a. olive-brown and dull orange .. 65 80
  a. Imperf (pair) .. .. .. 12·00
  b. Imperf between (horiz pair) .. 75·00
16 3 a. bright blue and magenta 65 85
  a. Imperf between (horiz pair) .. 75·00 £100
  b. Imperf (pair) .. .. .. 75·00
17 4 a. deep reddish purple and sage-green 65 2·50
  a. Imperf (pair) .. .. .. 8·50
  b. Imperf between (vert pair) .. .. 75·00
  c. Imperf vert (horiz pair) .. .. 75·00
18 6 a. black and pale ochre .. .. 70 2·50
  a. Imperf (pair) .. .. .. 8·50
19 8 a. brown and purple .. .. .. 1·50 2·75
  a. Imperf (pair) .. .. .. 8·50
  b. Imperf between (vert pair) .. .. 85·00
20 12 a. bright emerald and bright purple .. 1·00 3·00
  a. Imperf (pair) .. .. .. 8·50
  b. Imperf between (vert pair) .. .. 85·00
21 12 a. pale greenish blue and bright purple 23·00 45·00
22 1 r. chocolate and myrtle-green .. .. 80 3·75
  a. Imperf (pair) .. .. .. 9·00
  b. Imperf between (horiz pair) .. 75·00
23 4 1 r. chocolate and myrtle-green .. .. 4·00 9·00
  a. Imperf (pair) .. .. .. 85·00
  b. Imperf between (horiz pair) .. £100
24 3 2 r. purple-brown and bistre-yellow .. 2·75 9·00
  a. Imperf (pair) .. .. .. 9·00
25 3 r. black and greenish blue .. .. 1·50 9·00
  a. Imperf (pair) .. .. .. 9·00
26 4 r. black and brown .. .. .. 2·50 10·00
  a. Imperf (pair) .. .. .. 9·00
27 5 r. bright blue and plum .. .. 3·00 11·00
  a. Imperf (pair) .. .. .. 9·00
28 10 r. bronze-green and cerise .. .. 7·00 17·00
  a. Imperf (pair) .. .. .. 12·00
  b. Imperf between (horiz pair) .. 95·00
29 15 r. black and bronze-green .. .. 12·00 40·00
  a. Imperf (pair) .. .. .. 12·00
30 25 r. red-orange and blue .. .. 16·00 45·00
  a. Imperf (pair) .. .. .. 15·00
8/20, 22/30 .. .. .. *Set of* 22 50·00 £150

Values to 5 r. except the 1 a., are inscribed "POSTAGE", and the remaining values "POSTAGE & REVENUE".

The central portrait of Type **3** is taken from a half-tone block and consists of large square dots. The portrait of Type **4** has a background of lines.

Owing to a lack of proper State control considerable quantities of these stamps circulated at below face value and the issue was subsequently withdrawn, supplies being exchanged for the 1939–42 issue. We are, however, now satisfied that the lower values at least did genuine postal duty until 1939.

Used prices are for stamps cancelled-to-order, postally used examples being worth considerably more.

5 Maharaja Vir Singh II 6

(Litho Indian Security Printing Press, Nasik)

1939–42? *P* 13½ × 14 (*T* **5**) *or* 14 × 13½ (*T* **6**).

31 5 ¼ a. chocolate .. .. 2·25 45·00
32 ½ a. yellow-green .. .. .. 2·50 38·00
33 ¾ a. bright blue .. .. .. 2·50 60·00
34 1 a. scarlet .. .. 2·50 12·00
35 1¼ a. blue .. .. 2·50 60·00
36 1½ a. mauve .. .. 2·75 75·00
37 2 a. vermilion .. .. 2·50 45·00
38 2½ a. turquoise-green .. .. .. 2·50 £130
39 3 a. slate-violet .. .. .. 3·75 70·00
40 5 4 a. slate .. .. 4·75 20·0
41 8 a. magenta .. .. 8·00 £13
42 6 1 r. grey-green .. .. 14·00
43 2 r. bright violet .. .. .. 30·00 £35
44 5 r. yellow-orange .. .. .. 85·00
45 10 r. turquoise-green (1942) £325
46 15 r. slate-lilac (date ?) £2250
47 25 r. claret (date ?) £2250

Orchha became part of Vindhya Pradesh by 1 May 1948.

POONCH

PRICES FOR STAMPS ON COVER	
Nos. 1/2	*from* × 3
Nos. 3/63	*from* × 10
Nos. O1/10	*from* × 30

GUM. The stamps of Poonch were issued without gum, except for some examples of Nos. 7/10.

The stamps of Poonch are all imperforate, and handstamped in watercolours.

ILLUSTRATIONS. Designs of Poonch are illustrated actual size.

Raja Moti Singh, 1852–1892

1

2

1876. *T* **1** (22 × 21 *mm*). *Yellowish white, wove paper.*

1 6 p. red .. .. £3000 95·00

1877. *As T* **1** (19 × 17 *mm*). *Same paper.*

1*a* ½ a. red £5000 £2000

1879. *T* **2** (21 × 19 *mm*). *Same paper.*

2 ½ a. red .. .. — £1800

3 (½ a.)

4 (1 a.)

5 (2 a.) 6 (4 a.)

1880. *Yellowish white, wove paper.*

3 3 ½ a. red .. .. 35·00 15·00
4 4 1 a. red .. .. 60·00 35·00
5 5 2 a. red .. .. £100 75·00
6 6 4 a. red .. .. £110 85·00

1884. *Toned wove bâtonné paper.*

7 3 ½ a. red .. .. 4·00 4·00
8 4 1 a. red .. .. 13·00
9 5 2 a. red .. .. 12·00 15·00
10 6 4 a. red .. .. 24·00 24·00

These are sometimes found gummed.

7 (1 pice)

1884–87. *Various papers. (a) White laid bâtonné or ribbed bâtonné.*

11 7 1 p. red .. .. 13·00 15·00
  a. Pair, one stamp sideways £140
12 3 ½ a. red .. .. 1·60 2·25
13 4 1 a. red .. .. 2·00
14 5 2 a. red .. .. 5·50 7·00
15 6 4 a. red .. .. 7·50

(b) Thick white laid paper

22 7 1 p. red .. .. 32·00
23 3 ½ a. red .. .. 50·00
24 4 1 a. red .. .. 50·00
25 5 2 a. red .. .. 50·00
26 6 4 a. red .. .. 60·00

(c) Yellow wove bâtonné

27 7 1 p. red .. .. 2·25 2·25
a. Pair, one stamp sideways .. 27·00
28 3 ½ a. red .. .. 2·75 3·75
29 4 1 a. red .. .. 24·00
30 5 2 a. red .. .. 5·00 7·00
31 6 4 a. red .. .. 2·25 2·75

(d) Orange-buff wove bâtonné

32 7 1 p. red .. .. 1·40 1·90
a. Pair, one stamp sideways .. 19·00 22·00
b. *Tête-bêche* (pair) .. .. .. 30·00
33 3 ½ a. red .. .. 16·00
34 5 2 a. red .. .. 55·00
35 6 4 a. red .. .. 13·00

(e) Yellow laid paper

36 7 1 p. red .. .. 1·10 2·25
a. Pair, one stamp sideways .. 16·00
b. *Tête-bêche* (pair) .. .. .. 23·00
37 3 ½ a. red .. .. 2·00
38 4 1 a. red .. .. 26·00
39 5 2 a. red .. .. 35·00 35·00
40 6 4 a. red .. .. 28·00

(f) Yellow laid bâtonné

41 7 1 p. red .. .. 8·00 6·00

(g) Buff laid or ribbed bâtonné paper thicker than (d)

42 4 1 a. red .. .. 42·00
43 6 4 a. red .. .. 45·00

(h) Blue-green laid paper (1887)

44 3 ½ a. red .. .. 25·00
45 4 1 a. red .. .. 2·00 3·25
46 5 2 a. red .. .. 21·00
47 6 4 a. red .. .. 40·00

(i) Yellow-green laid paper

48 3 ½ a. red .. ..

(j) Blue-green wove bâtonné

49 7 1 p. red .. .. 28·00 25·00
49*a* 3 ½ a. red £650
50 4 1 a. red .. .. 1·10 2·00

(k) Lavender wove bâtonné

51 4 1 a. red .. .. 55·00
52 5 2 a. red .. .. 1·25 2·00

(l) Blue wove bâtonné

53 7 1 p. red .. .. 1·90 1·40
a. Pair, one stamp sideways .. 18·00
b. *Tête-bêche* (pair) .. .. .. 26·00
54 4 1 a. red £300

(m) Various coloured papers

55 7 1 p. red/*grey-blue laid* .. .. .. 6·00 4·00
56 1 p. red/*lilac laid* .. .. .. 45·00 48·00
a. Pair, one stamp sideways .. £250 £250
b. *Tête-bêche* (pair) £225

1888. *Printed in aniline rose on various papers.*

57 7 1 p. on *blue wove bâtonné* .. .. 3·00
a. *Tête-bêche* (pair) .. .. .. 50·00
58 1 p. on *buff laid* .. .. .. 9·50
59 3 ½ a. on *white laid* .. .. .. 15·00
60 4 1 a. on *green laid* .. .. .. 11·00 12·00
61 1 a. on *green wove bâtonné* .. .. 5·50 5·50
62 5 2 a. on *lavender wove bâtonné* .. 5·00 5·00
63 6 4 a. on *yellow laid* .. .. .. 11·00 12·00
a. Pair, one stamp sideways .. ..
b. *Tête-bêche* (pair) .. .. ..

OFFICIAL STAMPS

Raja Baldeo Singh, 1892–1918

1888. *(a) White laid bâtonné paper.*

O 1 7 1 p. black .. .. 1·60 1·75
a. Pair, one stamp sideways .. .. 12·00 14·00
b. *Tête-bêche* (pair) .. .. .. 15·00
O 2 3 ½ a. black .. .. 1·60 2·50
O 3 4 1 a. black .. .. 1·50 1·60
O 4 5 2 a. black .. .. 2·50 2·50
O 5 6 4 a. black .. .. 4·25 7·00

(b) White toned wove bâtonné paper

O 6 7 1 p. black .. .. 1·60
a. Pair, one stamp sideways .. 25·00
O 7 3 ½ a. black .. .. 2·25 2·25
a. Pair, one stamp sideways .. £800
O 8 4 1 a. black .. .. 13·00 12·00
O 9 5 2 a. black .. .. 5·50 5·50
O10 6 4 a. black .. .. 9·00

RAJASTHAN

Rajasthan was formed in 1948–49 from a number of States in Rajputana; these included Bundi, Jaipur and Kishangarh, whose posts continued to function more or less separately until ordered by the Indian Government to close on 1 April 1950.

PRICES FOR STAMPS ON COVER	
Nos. 1/7	*from* × 15
Nos. 8/10	—
Nos. 11/12	*from* × 5
Nos. 13/14	—
Nos. 15/25	*from* × 4
Nos. 26/42	*from* × 3
No. 43	*from* × 5
Nos. 44/60	*from* × 3
No. 61	*from* × 5
Nos. 62/5	—

BUNDI

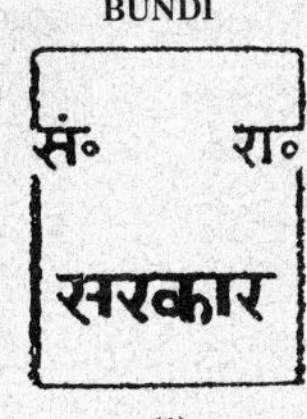

(1)

1949. *Nos. 86/92 of Bundi. (a) Handstamped with T* 1.

A. *In black.* B. *In violet.* C. *In blue*

		A	B	C
1	¼ a. blue-green	4·25	4·00	23·00
	a. Pair, one without opt	£140	†	†
2	½ a. violet	3·00	3·00	25·00
	a. Pair, one without opt	†	£150	†
3	1 a. yellow-green	4·00	9·50	27·00
	a. Pair, one without opt	†	£150	†
4	2 a. vermilion	7·50	20·00	—
5	4 a. orange	27·00	22·00	65·00
6	8 a. ultramarine	3·75	5·50	42·00
7	1 r. chocolate	—	£150	60·00

The above prices are for unused, used stamps being worth about six times the unused prices. Most of these handstamps are known, sideways, inverted or double.

(b) Machine-printed as T 1 *in black*

8 ¼ a. blue-green .. .. ..
9 ½ a. violet .. ..
10 1 a. yellow-green .. .. ..
11 2 a. vermilion .. .. .. 3·50 50·00
a. Opt inverted £250
12 4 a. orange .. .. 2·00 50·00
a. Opt double £225
13 8 a. ultramarine .. .. .. 25·00
a. Opt inverted £425
b. Opt double £375
14 1 r. chocolate .. .. 7·50

JAIPUR

राजस्थान

RAJASTHAN

(2)

1950 (26 Jan). *T* 7 *of Jaipur optd with T* 2.

15 ¼ a. black and brown-lake (No. 58) (B.) .. 3·50 13·00
16 ½ a. black and violet (No. 41) (R.) .. 3·25 14·00
17 ¾ a. black and brown-red (No. 59) (Blue-blk.) 5·50 16·00
a. Opt in pale blue .. .. .. 14·00 32·00
18 1 a. black and blue (No. 60) (R.) .. 4·00 27·00
19 2 a. black and buff (No. 61) (R.) .. 5·50 35·00
20 2½ a. black and carmine (No. 62) (B.) .. 6·50 17·00
21 3 a. black and green (No. 63) (R.) .. 7·00 40·00
22 4 a. black and grey-green (No. 64) (R.) .. 7·00 45·00
23 6 a. black and pale blue (No. 65*a*) (R.) .. 8·00 70·00
24 8 a. black and chocolate (No. 66) (R.) .. 11·00 90·00
25 1 r. black and yellow-bistre (No. 67) (R.) .. 12·00 £130
15/25 .. .. *Set of* 11 65·00 £450

KISHANGARH

1948–49. *Various stamps of Kishangarh handstamped with T* 1 *in red.*

(a) On stamps of 1899–1901

26 ¼ a. rose-pink (No. 5*a*) (B.) £140
26*a* ¼ a. rose-pink (No. 22*a*) .. .. .. — £130
27 ½ a. deep blue (No. 26) £225
29 1 a. brown-lilac (No. 29) .. .. .. 14·00 38·00
b. Imperf (pair) .. .. .. 40·00 80·00
c. Violet handstamp .. .. .. — £200
d. Black handstamp .. .. .. — £250
30 4 a. chocolate (No. 31) .. .. .. 50·00 70·00
a. Violet handstamp .. .. .. — £300
31 1 r. dull green (No. 32) £160 £170
31*a* 2 r. brown-red (No. 34) £190
32 5 r. mauve (No. 35) £180 £180

(b) On stamps of 1904–10

33 13 ½ a. chestnut .. .. — 90·00
33*a* 1 a. blue .. .. — £120
34 4 a. brown .. .. 13·00
a. Blue handstamp £150
35 12*a* 8 a. grey .. .. 70·00 £110
36 13 8 a. violet .. .. 11·00
37 1 r. green .. .. 11·00
38 2 r. olive-yellow .. .. .. 18·00
39 5 r. purple-brown .. .. .. 23·00
a. Blue handstamp £250

(c) On stamps of 1912–16

40 14 ½ a. green (No. 64) .. .. .. — £110
41 1 a. red .. .. — £110
42 2 a. deep violet (No. 51) £225
43 2 a. purple (No. 66) .. .. .. 2·25 5·50
44 4 a. bright blue .. .. .. — £300
45 8 a. brown .. .. 5·00
a. Pair, one without handstamp .. £225
46 1 r. mauve .. .. 10·00
47 2 r. deep green .. .. .. 10·00
48 5 r. brown £200

(d) On stamps of 1928–36

49 16 ½ a. yellow-green .. .. .. 85·00
49*a* 2 a. magenta .. .. — £200
50 4 a. chestnut £130
51 8 a. violet .. .. 6·00 50·00
a. Pair, one without handstamp .. £200
52 1 r. light green .. .. .. 20·00
53 2 r. lemon-yellow .. .. .. 14·00
54 5 r. claret .. .. 15·00

(e) On stamps of 1943–47

55 16 ¼ a. pale dull blue .. .. .. 60·00 60·00
56 ¼ a. greenish blue .. .. .. 38·00 38·00
a. Imperf (pair) £140
57 ½ a. deep green .. .. .. 23·00 25·00
a. Violet handstamp .. .. .. — £130
57*b* ½ a. yellow-green .. .. .. 32·00 35·00
ba. Imperf (pair) £140
bb. Blue handstamp .. .. .. — £130
58 17 1 a. carmine-red .. .. .. 35·00 35·00
a. Violet handstamp .. .. .. — £140
58*b* 1 a. orange-red (*imperf*) .. .. 90·00
ba. Blue handstamp £100
59 2 a. bright magenta £100 £100
60 2 a. maroon (*imperf*) £110
61 16 4 a. brown .. .. 1·75 5·50
62 8 a. violet .. .. 15·00 45·00
63 1 r. green .. .. 6·00
64 2 r. yellow £100
65 5 r. claret .. .. 50·00

A 1 a. value in deep violet-blue was issued for revenue purposes, but is known postally used (*Price* £60 *used*).

RAJPIPLA

PRICES FOR STAMPS ON COVER	
No. 1	*from* × 25
Nos. 2/3	—

Maharana Ganbhir Singh, 1860–1897

1 (1 pice)

2 (2 a.)

3 (4 a.)

1880. *Litho. With or without gum (1 p.) or no gum (others). P* 11 *(1 p.) or* 12½.

1 1 1 p. blue .. .. 1·75 22·00
2 2 2 a. green .. .. 20·00 60·00
a. Imperf between (pair) £550 £550
3 3 4 a. red .. .. 10·00 38·00
1/3 .. .. *Set of* 3 29·00 £110

These stamps became obsolete in 1886.

SHAHPURA

PRICES FOR STAMPS ON COVER	
Nos. 1/4	*from* × 2
No. F1	*from* × 2

DATES. Those quoted are of first known use.

Rajadhiraj Nahar Singh, 1870–1932

RAJ
SHAHPURA
Postage 1 pice

1

RAJ
SHAHPURA
1 pice

2

1914–17. *Typo.*

1 1 1 p. carmine/*bluish grey* (*p* 11) .. .. — £250
2 1 p. carmine/*drab* (*imperf*) (1917) .. .. — £375

Some examples of No. 1 are imperforate on one side or on two adjacent sides.

1920–28. *Typo. Imperf.*

3 2 1 p. carmine/*drab* (1928) .. .. .. — £425
4 1 a. black/*pink* .. .. — £425

POSTAL FISCAL

Rajadhiraj Umaid Singh, 1932–1947

Rajadhiraj Sudarshan Deo, 1947–1971

F 1

1932–47. *Typo. P* 11, $11^1/_2$ *or* 12.
F1 F 1 1 a. red (*shades*) .. .. 40·00 £120
a. Pin-perf 7 (1947) .. .. ..

Nos. F1/a were used for both fiscal and postal purposes. Manuscript cancellations must be assumed to be fiscal, unless on cover showing other evidence of postal use. The design was first issued for fiscal purposes in 1898.

Shahpura became part of Rajasthan by 15 April 1948.

SIRMOOR

PRICES FOR STAMPS ON COVER

The stamps of Sirmoor are very rare used on cover.

Raja Shamsher Parkash, 1886–1898

1 (1 pice)

2

3 Raja Shamsher Parkash

1878 (June)–**80.** *Litho. P* $11^1/_2$.
1 1 1 p. pale green .. .. 8·00 £200
2 1 p. blue (on *laid* paper) (1880) .. .. 4·00 £130
a. Imperf between (pair) £275
b. Imperf (pair) £275

(Litho at Calcutta)

1892. *Thick wove paper. P* $11^1/_2$.
3 2 1 p. yellow-green 60 65
a. Imperf between (vert pair) .. .. 70·00
b. Deep green 50 55
ba. Imperf between (vert pair) .. .. 70·00 70·00
4 1 p. blue 60 60
a. Imperf between (vert pair) .. .. 60·00 60·00
b. Imperf between (horiz pair) .. .. 60·00 60·00
c. Imperf vert (horiz pair) .. .. 60·00
d. Imperf (pair) .. .. .. 75·00

These were originally made as reprints, about 1891, to supply collectors, but there being very little demand for them they were put into use. The design was copied (including the perforations) from an illustration in a dealer's catalogue.

A B
C D

There were seven printings of stamps as Type **3**, all in sheets of 70 (10×7) and made up from groups of transfers which can be traced through minor varieties.

Printings I to V and VII of the 3 p. and 6 p. are as Types A and C (both with large white dots evenly spaced between the ends of the upper and lower inscriptions).

Printing VI is as Type B (small white dots and less space) and Type D (large white dots unevenly positioned between the inscriptions).

(Litho Waterlow)

1885–96. *P* 14 *to* 15.
5 3 3 p. chocolate (A) 55 30
a. Brown (B) (1896) 30 35
6 3 p. orange (A) (1888) .. .. .. 1·50 20
a. Type B (1896) 30 20
ab. Imperf (pair) £550
7 6 p. blue-green (C) .. .. .. 3·75 2·25
a. Green (C) (1888) 95 50
b. Bright green (C) (1891) .. .. 55·00 55·00
c. Deep green (C) (1894) 40 25
d. Yellowish green (D) (1896) .. .. 40 1·50
8 1 a. bright blue .. .. 2·00 2·25
a. Dull blue (1891) .. .. .. 6·00 4·50
b. Steel-blue (1891) .. .. .. 80·00 80·00
c. Grey-blue (1894) .. .. .. 2·25 1·00
d. Slate-blue (1896) .. .. .. 50 1·75
9 2 a. pink .. .. 4·25 10·00
a. Carmine (1894) .. .. .. 3·50 3·00
b. Rose-red (1896) .. .. .. 3·25 4·00

Composition of the various printings was as follows:
Printing I – Nos. 5, 7, 8 and 9
Printing II – Nos. 6 and 7*a*
Printing III – Nos. 6, 7*b* and 8*a*
Printing IV – Nos. 5, 6, 7*a*, and 8*b*
Printing V – Nos. 6, 7*c*, 8*c* and 9*a*
Printing VI – Nos. 5*a*, 6a, 7*d*, 8*d* and 9*b*
Printing VII – Only exists overprinted "On S. S. S." (Nos. 78/81).

NEW INFORMATION

The editor is always interested to correspond with people who have new information that will improve or correct the Catalogue.

4 Indian Elephant

5 Raja Shamsher Parkash

(Recess Waterlow & Sons)

1894–99. *P* 12 *to* 15 *and compounds.*
22 4 3 p. orange-brown .. .. 1·50 30
23 6 p. green 75 30
a. Imperf between (vert pair) £1300
24 1 a. blue .. .. 2·50 70
25 2 a. rose .. .. 1·10 1·00
26 3 a. yellow-green .. .. 14·00 27·00
27 4 a. deep green .. .. 7·00 13·00
28 8 a. deep blue .. .. 10·00 18·00
29 1 r. vermilion .. .. 24·00 42·00
22/9 .. .. *Set of* 8 55·00 90·00

Raja Surindra Bikram Parkash, 1898–1911

(Recess Waterlow & Sons)

1899. *P* 13 *to* 15.
30 5 3 a. yellow-green .. .. 1·60 18·00
31 4 a. deep green .. .. 2·25 12·00
32 8 a. deep blue .. .. 4·25 12·00
33 1 r. vermilion .. .. 8·00 30·00
30/3 .. .. *Set of* 4 14·50 65·00

OFFICIAL STAMPS

NOTE. The varieties occurring in the machine-printed "On S.S.S." overprints may, of course, also be found in the inverted and double overprints, and many of them are known thus.

Roman figures denote printings of the basic stamps (Nos. 7/21). Where more than one printing was overprinted the prices quoted are for the commonest.

I. MACHINE-PRINTED

On
S. S.
S.
(11)

1890. *Optd with T* **11**. (*a*) *In black.*
50 3 6 p. green (C) £850 £850
a. Stop before first "S" .. ..
51 2 a. pink .. .. 50·00 £140
a. Stop before first "S" £130

(*b*) *In red*
52 3 6 p. green (C) .. .. 16·00 2·50
a. Stop before first "S" .. .. 55·00 25·00
53 1 a. bright blue .. .. 38·00 11·00
a. Stop before first "S" .. .. £100 60·00
b. Opt inverted £1000 £550

(*c*) *Doubly optd in red and in black*
53*c* 3 6 p. green (C) £950 £950
ca. Stop before first "S" £2250 £2250

Nos. 50, 52 and 53*c* are from Printing II and the remainder from Printing I.

On
S. S.
S.
(12)

On
S. S.
S.
(13)

1891. *Optd with T* **12**. (*a*) *In black.*
54 3 3 p. orange (A) .. .. 2·25 32·00
a. Opt inverted £400
55 6 p. green (C) .. .. 1·50 1·50
a. Opt double £160
b. No stop after lower "S" .. .. 22·00 22·00
c. Raised stop before lower "S" £150 £110
56 1 a. bright blue £275 £350
57 2 a. pink .. .. 13·00 45·00

(*b*) *In red*
58 3 6 p. green (C) .. .. 25·00 3·00
a. Opt inverted £190 £160
b. Opt double £190 £170
59 1 a. bright blue .. .. 18·00 25·00
a. Opt inverted .. .. .. † £400
b. Opt double .. .. .. † £400
c. No stop after lower "S" £150 £160

(*c*) *In black and red*
59*d* 3 6 p. green (C) £850

Nos. 54/5, 58 and 59*d* are from Printing II and the others from Printing I.

1892–97. *Optd with T* **13**. (*a*) *In black.*
60 3 3 p. orange (A) 50 40
a. Type B .. .. 3·00 60
b. Opt inverted £225
c. First "S" inverted and stop raised .. 5·00 5·00
d. No stop after lower "S" .. .. 5·00 5·00
e. Raised stop after second "S" .. .. 32·00 15·00
f. Vertical pair, Types **12** and **13** .. 90·00
61 6 p. green (C) .. .. 5·00 1·00
a. Deep green (C) .. .. .. 1·60 50
b. First "S" inverted and stop raised .. 30·00 13·00
c. Raised stop after second "S" .. .. 30·00 12·00
d. No stop after lower "S" .. .. 40·00 17·00
e. Opt double £450
62 1 a. steel-blue .. ..
a. Grey-blue .. .. 8·00 1·00
b. Opt double £325
c. First "S" inverted and stop raised .. 30·00 10·00
d. No stop after lower "S" .. .. £120 45·00
e. Raised stop after second "S" .. .. 50·00 12·00
63 2 a. pink .. .. 9·00 15·00
a. Carmine .. .. 7·00 7·00
b. Opt inverted £550 £550
c. First "S" inverted and stop raised .. 35·00 35·00
d. No stop after lower "S" .. .. 35·00 35·00
e. Raised stop after second "S" £150 £150

(*b*) *In red*
64 3 6 p. green (C) .. .. 3·50 50
a. Bright green (C) .. .. .. 6·50 1·00
b. Opt inverted .. .. .. 95·00 85·00
c. First "S" inverted and stop raised .. 19·00 5·00
d. Vertical pair, Types **12** and **13** .. 90·00 90·00
65 1 a. bright blue .. .. 14·00 2·75
a. Steel-blue .. .. 11·00 1·00
b. Opt inverted £180 £140
c. Opt double £225
d. First "S" inverted and stop raised .. 28·00 8·00
e. No stop after lower "S" .. .. 28·00 8·00

(*c*) *Doubly overprinted in black and red*
65*f* 3 6 p. bright green (C) .. .. .. — £800
fa. Green (C). Red opt inverted .. † £1000

The printings used for this issue were as follows:
Printing I – Nos. 63 and 65
Printing II – Nos. 60, 64 and 65*fa*
Printing III – Nos. 60, 64*a* and 65*f*
Printing IV – Nos. 61, 62, 64 and 65*a*
Printing V – Nos. 60, 61*a*, 62*a* and 63*a*
Printing VI – No. 60a

There are seven settings of this overprint, the first of which was a composite setting of 20 (10×2), with examples of Type **12** in the upper row. The inverted "S" and the missing stop occur in the 3rd and 6th settings with the latter also including the raised stop after second "S".

On
S. S.
S.
(14)

On
S. S.
S.
(15)

1896–97. *Optd as T* **14**.
66 3 3 p. orange (B) (1897) .. .. .. 7·50 1·25
a. Comma after first "S" .. .. 42·00 30·00
b. Opt inverted .. .. ..
c. Opt double .. .. .. † £450
67 6 p. deep green (C) .. .. .. 5·50 60
a. Yellowish green (D) .. .. .. — 2·00
b. Comma after first "S" .. .. 42·00 18·00
c. Comma after lower "S" .. .. £130 18·00
d. "S" at right inverted .. .. £130 40·00
68 1 a. grey-blue .. .. 7·00 1·25
a. Comma after first "S" .. .. 60·00 22·00
b. Comma after lower "S" .. .. £150 22·00
c. "S" at right inverted .. .. — 42·00
69 2 a. carmine (1897) .. .. .. 17·00 14·00
a. Comma after first "S" £120 £120

Nos. 66 and 67*a* are from Printing VI and the remainder from Printing V.

There are four settings of this overprint, (1) 23 mm high, includes the comma after lower "S"; (2) and (3) 25 mm high, with variety, comma after first "S"; (4) 25 mm high, with variety, "S" at right inverted.

1898 (Nov). *Optd with T* **15**.
70 3 6 p. deep green (C) .. .. .. £150 7·00
a. Yellowish green (D) .. .. .. £140 5·50
b. Small "S" at right .. .. £250 25·00
c. Comma after lower "S" .. .. — 50·00
d. Lower "S" inverted and stop raised .. — 50·00
71 1 a. grey-blue .. .. £160 11·00
a. Small "S" at right .. .. £275 40·00
b. Small "S" without stop .. .. — £170

No. 70*a* is from Printing VI and the others Printing V.

There are two settings of this overprint. Nos. 70a and 71a/b occur in the first setting, and Nos. 70b/c in the second setting.

On
S. S.
S.
(16)

On
S. S.
S.
(17)

1899 (July). *Optd with T* **16**.
72 3 3 p. orange (B) .. .. £180 6·50
73 6 p. deep green (C) .. .. — 16·00
No. 72 is from Printing VI and No. 73 from Printing V.

1899 (Dec)–**1900**. *Optd as T* **17**.
74 3 3 p. orange (B) .. .. — 4·75
a. Raised stop after lower "S" .. .. † 50·00
b. Comma after first "S" .. .. † £150
c. No stop after first "S" .. .. † 90·00
75 6 p. deep green (C) .. .. — 4·50
a. Yellowish green (D) .. .. .. † 7·00
b. Raised stop after lower "S" .. .. † 50·00
c. Comma after first "S" .. .. † £140
76 1 a. bright blue .. .. † £120
a. Grey-blue .. .. † 6·50
b. Slate-blue .. .. — 8·00
c. Raised stop after lower "S" .. .. † 75·00
d. Comma after first "S" .. .. † £160
e. No stop after first "S" .. .. † 90·00
77 2 a. carmine .. .. — £100
a. Raised stop after lower "S" .. .. † £400

There are two settings of this overprint: (1) 22 mm high, with raised stop variety; (2) 23 mm high, with "comma" and "no stop" varieties.

The printings used for this issue were as follows:
Printing I – No. 76
Printing V – Nos. 75, 76*a* and 77
Printing VI – Nos. 74, 75*a* and 76*b*

On S. S. S.   On S S S
(18)   (19)

(Optd by Waterlow & Sons)

1900. *Optd with T* **18**.
78 3 3 p. orange .. .. 2·00 4·75
79 6 p. green 40 45
80 1 a. blue 35 50
81 2 a. carmine .. .. 3·25 55·00
Nos. 78/81 were from Printing VII which was not issued without the overprint.

II. HANDSTAMPED

The words "On" and each letter "S" struck separately (except for Type **22** which was applied at one operation).

1894. *Handstamped with T* **19**. (*a*) *In black.*
82 3 3 p. orange (A) .. .. 3·00 3·75
a. "On" only .. .. 65·00
83 6 p. green (C) .. .. 5·00 6·00
a. Deep green (C) .. .. 8·00 10·00
b. "On" only .. .. 65·00 65·00
84 1 a. bright blue .. .. 35·00 26·00
a. Dull blue .. .. 11·00 13·00
b. Steel-blue .. ..
c. Grey-blue .. .. 11·00 10·00
d. "On" only .. .. — 90·00
85 2 a. carmine .. .. 16·00 17·00
a. "On" only .. .. 95·00

(*b*) *In red*
86 3 6 p. green (C) .. .. 90·00 95·00
86*a* 1 a. grey-blue £250 £250

The printings used for this issue were as follows:
Printing I – No. 84
Printing III – No. 84*a*
Printing IV – Nos. 83, 84*b* and 86
Printing V – Nos. 82, 83*a*, 84*c*, 85 and 86*a*

1896. *Handstamped with letters similar to those of T* **13**, *with stops, but irregular.*
87 3 3 p. orange (A) .. .. 80·00 65·00
a. Type B .. ..
88 6 p. green (C) .. ..
a. Deep green (C) .. .. 70·00 60·00
b. "On" omitted £130
88*c* 1 a. grey-blue .. .. 85·00 85·00
89 2 a. carmine £140

Printings used for this issue were as follows:
Printing II – No. 88
Printing III – No. 87
Printing IV – No. 88
Printing V – Nos. 87, 88*a*, 88*c* and 89
Printing VI – No. 87a

1897. *Handstamped with letters similar to those of T* **14**, *with stops, but irregular.*
90 3 3 p. orange (B) .. .. 8·00 16·00
91 6 p. deep green (C) .. .. 42·00 48·00
a. "On" only .. .. — 95·00
92 1 a. grey-blue £180 £180
a. "On" only .. .. — 95·00
93 2 a. carmine .. .. 85·00 85·00
No. 90 was from Printing VI and the remainder from Printing V.

1897. *Handstamped with letters similar to those of T* **16**, *with stops, but irregular.*
93*a* 3 6 p. deep green (C) .. .. £100 85·00
No. 93*a* is from Printing V.

ON S S S   on s s s
(20)   (21)

1896. (*a*) *Handstamped with T* **20**.
94 3 3 p. orange (A) .. .. 50·00 55·00
95 2 a. carmine .. .. 55·00 60·00

(*b*) *Handstamped with T* **21**
96 3 3 p. orange (A) £140 £150
97 6 p. bright green (C) .. ..
98 1 a. bright blue £170
a. Dull blue
98*b* 2 a. carmine £180
No. 98 comes from Printing I, No. 98*a* from Printing III, No. 97 possibly from Printing IV and the remainder from Printing V.

On S S S   On S S S
(22)   (23)

(*c*) *Handstamped with T* **22**
99 3 3 p. orange (B) £120
100 6 p. deep green £170
101 1 a. grey-blue £225
101*a* 2 a. carmine £300
No. 99 is from Printing VI and the others from Printing V.

1899. *Handstamped with T* **23**.
102 3 3 p. orange (A) .. .. — £120
a. Type B .. .. 18·00 7·00
103 6 p. green (C) .. ..
a. Deep green (C) .. .. 20·00 14·00
b. Yellowish green (D) .. .. 15·00 16·00
104 1 a. bright blue .. .. — 80·00
a. Grey-blue .. .. 38·00 32·00
105 2 a. pink .. ..
a. Carmine .. .. 38·00 22·00
b. Rose-red .. .. 45·00 30·00
c. "On" only .. .. — £110

Printings used for this issue were as follows:
Printing I – Nos. 104 and 105
Printing IV – Nos. 102 and 103
Printing V – Nos. 102, 103*a*, 104*a* and 105*a*
Printing VI – Nos. 102a, 103*b* and 105*b*

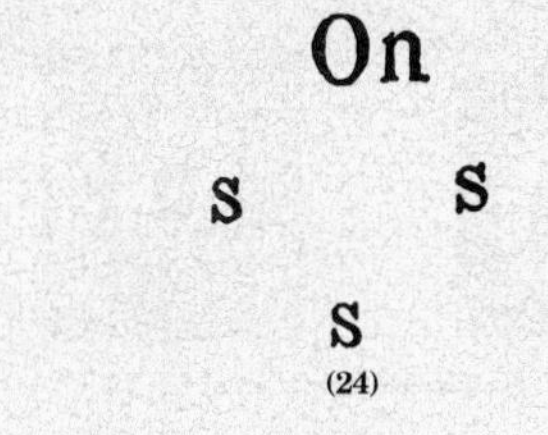
(24)

1901 (?). *Handstamped with T* **24**.
105*d* 3 6 p. yellowish green (D) .. .. .. — £275
From Printing VI

III. MIXED MACHINE-PRINTED AND HANDSTAMPED

1896. (i) *Handstamped "On" as in T* **19**, *and machine-printed opt T* **13** *complete.*
106 3 6 p. green (C) .. .. — £375

(ii) *Handstamped opt as T* **14**, *and machine-printed opt T* **13** *complete*
107 3 6 p. deep green (C) .. ..

No. 106 is from Printing IV and No. 107 from Printing V.

Various other types of these handstamps are known to exist, but in the absence of evidence of their authenticity we do not list them. It is stated that stamps of T **4** were never officially overprinted.

The stamps of Sirmoor have been obsolete since 1 April 1902.

PRICES OF SETS

Set prices are given for many issues, generally those containing three stamps or more. Definitive sets include one of each value or major colour change, but do not cover different perforations, die types or minor shades. Where a choice is possible the set prices are based on the cheapest versions of the stamps included in the listings.

SORUTH

PRICES FOR STAMPS ON COVER

Nos. 1/2	*from* × 5
Nos. 3/4*a*	—
Nos. 5/7	*from* × 2
No. 8	*from* × 3
No. 9	*from* × 2
No. 10	*from* × 5
No. 10*c*	*from* × 2
Nos. 11/13	*from* × 5
Nos. 14/15	*from* × 3
Nos. 16/29	*from* × 20
Nos. 34/6	*from* × 50
Nos. 37/8	*from* × 10
No. 39/41	*from* × 50
Nos. 42/57	*from* × 10
Nos. O1/13	*from* × 20
No. 58	*from* × 15
No. 59	*from* × 6
No. 60	*from* × 10
No. 61	*from* × 6
Nos. O14/22	*from* × 10

The name "Saurashtra" corrupted to "Sorath" or "Soruth", was originally used for all the territory later known as Kathiawar. Strictly speaking the name should have been applied only to a portion of Kathiawar including the state of Junagadh. As collectors have known these issues under the heading of "Soruth" for so long, we retain the name.

The currency was 40 docras = 1 koree but early stamps are inscribed in "annas of a koree", one "anna" being a sixteenth of a koree.

GUM. Nos. 1/47 of Soruth were issued without gum.

JUNAGADH

Nawab Mahabat Khan II, 1857–1882

1

(="Saurashtra Post 1864–65")

1864 (Nov). *Handstamped in water-colour. Imperf.*
1 1 (1 a.) black/*azure* (laid) .. .. .. £650 55·00
2 (1 a.) black/*grey* (laid) .. .. .. £650 50·00
3 (1 a.) black/*azure* (wove) .. .. .. — £150
4 (1 a.) black/*cream* (wove) .. .. .. — £700
4*a* (1 a.) black/*cream* (laid) .. .. .. † £1100

ILLUSTRATIONS. Types **2** to **11** are shown actual size.

2 (1 a.)   3 (1 a.)   4 (4 a.)   5 (4 a.)
No. 8   No. 8a

(Type-set at Junagadh Sarkari Saurashtra Nitiprakash Ptg Press)

1868 (June)–**75**. *T* **2** *to* **5** (*two characters, Devanagri and Gujerati respectively for "1" and "4" as shown in the illustrations*). *Imperf.*

A. *Inscriptions in Gujerati characters*
5 1 a. black/*yellowish* (wove) .. .. .. † £5500

B. *Inscriptions in Devanagri characters* (*as in the illustrations*)

I. *Accents over first letters in top and bottom lines. Wove paper.*
6 1 a. red/*green* .. .. † £2000
7 1 a. red/*blue* .. .. † £2000
8 1 a. black/*pink* .. .. £650 95·00
a. Incorrect character at bottom left (R. 1/4) † £750
9 2 a. black/*yellow* (1869) .. .. .. † £3000

II. *Accents over second letters in top and bottom lines* (1869–75).

(*a*) *Wove paper*

10 2 1 a. black/*pink* .. .. £350 48·00
a. Printed both sides .. .. † —
b. First two characters in last word of bottom line omitted (R. 4/1) .. — £450

(*b*) *Laid paper*

10*c* 3 1 a. black/*white* .. .. † £3000
11 2 1 a. black/*azure* (1870) .. .. .. 70·00 8·00
a. Final character in both top and bottom lines omitted (R. 1/1) ..
b. First two characters in last word of bottom line omitted (R. 4/1) .. — 90·00
c. Doubly printed .. .. .. † £650
12 3 1 a. black/*azure* .. .. £160 17·00
a. Printed both sides .. .. .. † £750
b. Final character in bottom line omitted (R. 1/1) .. .. .. — 90·00
c. Accent omitted from last word in bottom line (R. 5/2, 5/4) .. .. — 70·00
d. Large numeral (R. 4/1) £450 £130
e. First character in middle line omitted (R. 2/4) .. .. — £200
f. Central two characters in middle line omitted (R. 2/4) .. .. .. — £375
13 1 a. red/*white* (1875) .. .. .. 15·00 17·00
a. First two characters in bottom line omitted (R. 5/1) .. .. .. 75·00 95·00
14 4 4 a. black/*white* £110 £180
a. Final character in bottom line omitted (R. 1/1) £400
15 5 4 a. black/*white* £200 £375
a. First two characters in last word of bottom line omitted (R. 4/1) .. £800
b. Final character in bottom line omitted (R. 5/2) £1300

Nos. 10/15 were printed in sheets of 20 (4×5). The same type was used throughout, but changes made to produce the different values resulted in five different settings:

Setting I	Nos. 10, 11, 15
Setting II	Nos. 11/12, 14
Setting III	Nos. 11/12, 14
Setting IV	Nos. 11/12, 15
Setting V	No. 13

The Devanagari (Type **2**) and Gujerati (Type **3**) numerals were mixed in settings II to IV of the 1 a. value, so that *se-tenant* pairs of Nos. 11/12 exist. Horizontally laid paper was used for setting II; vertically laid for settings I and III to V.

Official imitations, consisting of 1 a. carmine-red on white wove and white laid, 1 a. black on blue wove, 4 a. black on white wove, 4 a. black on blue wove, 4 a. red on white laid—all imperforate; 1 a. carmine-red on white laid, 1 a. black on blue wove, 4 a. black on white laid and blue wove—all perforated 12, were made in 1890. Entire sheets of originals have 20 stamps (4×5), the imitations only 4 or 16.

6

7

(Dies eng John Dickinson & Co Ltd, London. Typo Junagadh Sarkari Saurashtra Nitiprakash Ptg Press)

1877. *Imperf.*

(*a*) *Medium laid paper, lines wide apart*
(*b*) *Thick laid paper, lines wide apart*
(*c*) *Thick laid paper, lines close together*

16 6 1 a. green (*a*) 50 30
17 1 a. green (*b*) 50 30
18 1 a. green (*c*) 50 30
a. Printed both sides £450
19 7 4 a. vermilion (*a*) .. .. .. 1·50 1·00
20 4 a. vermilion/*toned* (*b*) .. .. .. 1·50 1·00
a. Printed both sides £475
21 4 a. scarlet/*bluish* (*b*) .. .. .. 2·25 1·75

Nawab Bahadur Khan III, 1882–1892

1886. *P* 12. (*a*) *Wove paper.*

22 6 1 a. green .. .. 1·50 65
a. Imperf (pair) .. .. 50·00 70·00
b. Error. Blue .. .. — £600
c. Imperf horiz (vert pair) £100
23 7 4 a. red .. .. 3·75 7·00
a. Imperf (pair) £130 £160

(*b*) *Toned laid paper*

24 6 1 a. green 15 15
a. Imperf vert (horiz pair) .. .. 90·00
b. Doubly printed .. .. .. † £350
25 1 a. emerald-green .. .. .. 2·25 1·25
a. Error. Blue £600 £600
26 7 4 a. red .. .. 1·25 60
27 4 a. carmine .. .. 2·25 1·75

(*c*) *Bluish white laid paper*

28 6 1 a. green .. .. 2·25 3·25
a. Imperf between (pair) £140
29 4 a. scarlet .. .. 7·50 11·00

There is a very wide range of colours in both values. The laid paper is found both vertical and horizontal.

The 1 a. was originally issued in sheets of 15 (5×3), but later appeared in sheets of 20 (5×4) with marginal inscriptions. No. 22a is known as a double sheet showing two impressions of the plate printed *tête-bêche* on opposite sides of the paper.

The 4 a. was in horizontal strips of 5. No. 19 exists as a sheet of 10 (5×2), with two impressions of the plate printed *tête-bêche*, and No. 23 in a similar sized sheet but with both impressions upright.

Nawab Rasul Khan 1892–1911
Nawab Mahabat Khan III, 1911–1959

(Indian currency)

Three pies.
ત્રણ પાઇ.
(8)

One anna.
એક આનો.
(9)

1913. *Surch in Indian currency with T* **8** *or* **9**. *P* 12.

(*a*) *On yellowish wove paper*

34 6 3 p. on 1 a. emerald 15 20
a. Imperf (pair) £300
b. Imperf between (horiz pair) £250

(*b*) *On white wove paper*

35 6 3 p. on 1 a. emerald 15 20
a. Imperf between (pair) £250 £250
b. Surch inverted .. .. .. 35·00 20·00
c. Surch double .. .. .. † —
36 7 1 a. on 4 a. carmine .. .. .. 1·50 4·00
a. Imperf (pair) .. ..
b. Surch both sides £700
c. Capital "A" in "Anna" .. .. 13·00

(*c*) *On white laid paper*

37 6 3 p. on 1 a. emerald .. .. .. 75·00 30·00
a. Imperf (pair) .. .. .. — £300
b. Larger surch (21 mm long with capital "p" in "Pies") inverted .. .. † £1200
38 7 1 a. on 4 a red .. .. 7·00 38·00
a. Capital "A" in "Anna" £180
b. Surch inverted £650
c. Surch double £650
d. Surch double, one inverted £650

(*d*) *On toned wove paper*

39 7 1 a. on 4 a. red .. .. 1·40 3·75
a. Imperf (pair) £600
b. Capital "A" in "Anna" .. .. 6·00
c. Surch inverted £650
d. Imperf between (horiz pair) .. ..

10

11

(Dies eng Thacker & Co, Bombay. Typo Junagadh State Press)

1914 (1 Sept). *New plates. T* **6/7** *redrawn as T* **10/11**. *Wove paper. P* 12.

40 10 3 p. bright green 35 35
a. Imperf (pair) .. .. .. 4·25 14·00
b. Imperf vert (horiz pair) .. .. 65·00
c. Laid paper .. .. 2·75 1·50
ca. Imperf (pair) .. .. .. 11·00 20·00
41 11 1 a. red 60 95
a. Imperf (pair) .. .. .. 17·00 55·00
b. Imperf between (pair) £350
c. Laid paper .. .. £250 90·00

12 Nawab Mahabat Khan III 13

(Dies eng Popatlal Bhimji Pandya. Typo Junagadh State Press)

1923 (1 Sept). *Blurred impression. Laid paper. Pin-perf* 12.

42 12 1 a. red .. .. 3·00 7·50

Sheets of 16 stamps (8 × 2).

ત્રણ પાઇ
(14)

ત્રણ પાઈ
(14*a*)

1923 (1 Sept). *Surch with T* **14**.

43 12 3 p. on 1 a. red .. .. .. 3·00 7·00
a. Surch with T 14*a* .. .. .. 3·50 9·50

Four stamps in the setting have surch. T 14*a*, i.e. with top of last character curved to right.

1923 (Oct). *Blurred impression. Wove paper. Pin-perf* 12, *small holes.*

44 13 3 p. mauve 35 40

1924. *Clear impression. P* 12, *large holes. Wove paper.*

45 13 3 p. mauve (1.24) 70 35
46 12 1 a. red (4.24) .. .. .. 4·50 5·00
a. Imperf (pair) .. .. .. 40·00
b. Pin perf .. .. 2·25 2·75

The first plate of the 3 p., which printed No. 44, produced unsatisfactory impressions, so it was replaced by a second plate, from which No. 45 comes. Sheets printed from the first plate had very large margins.

The 1 a. is also from a new plate, giving a clearer impression. Sheets of 16 stamps (4×4).

1929. *Clear impression. P* 12, *large holes. Laid paper.*

47 13 3 p. mauve .. .. 3·50 2·50
a. Imperf (pair) .. .. .. 3·00 20·00
b. Perf 11 .. .. 5·00 4·50
ba. Imperf between (horiz pair) .. .. 3·00 17·00

The laid paper shows a sheet watermark of the State Arms within a circular inscription.

15 Junagadh City

16 Lion

17 Nawab Mahabat Khan III

18 Kathi Horse

(Litho Indian Security Printing Press, Nasik)

1929 (1 Oct). *P* 14. *Inscr* "POSTAGE".

49 15 3 p. black and blackish green 60 10
50 16 ½ a. black and deep blue .. .. 4·75 10
51 17 1 a. black and carmine .. .. .. 3·25 85
52 18 2 a. black and dull orange .. .. 8·50 1·75
a. Grey and dull yellow .. .. 25·00 1·75
53 15 3 a. black and carmine .. .. .. 3·00 6·00
54 16 4 a. black and purple .. .. .. 12·00 18·00
55 18 8 a. black and yellow-green .. .. 10·00 18·00
56 17 1 r. black and pale blue .. .. .. 3·75 18·00
49/56 .. .. *Set of* 8 40·00 55·00

1936. *As T* **17**, *but inscr* "POSTAGE AND REVENUE". *P* 14.

57 17 1 a. black and carmine .. .. .. 4·25 90

OFFICIAL STAMPS

SARKARI
(O 1)

1929 (1 Oct). *Optd with Type* O 1, *in vermilion, at Nasik.*

O1 15 3 p. black and blackish green 90 15
a. Red opt 70 10
O2 16 ½ a. black and deep blue .. .. 1·60 10
a. Red opt .. .. 2·50 30
O3 17 1 a. black and carmine (No. 51) .. 2·25 30
a. Red opt .. .. 1·40 15
O4 18 2 a. black and dull orange .. .. 2·50 60
a. Grey and dull yellow .. .. 15·00 60
b. Red opt .. .. 22·00 2·25
O5 15 3 a. black and carmine 60 30
a. Red opt .. .. 14·00 1·50
O6 16 4 a. black and purple .. .. .. 1·75 40
a. Red opt .. .. 18·00 2·00
O7 18 8 a. black and yellow-green .. .. 1·90 1·25
O8 17 1 r. black and pale blue .. .. .. 2·25 13·00
O1/8 .. .. *Set of* 8 11·50 14·00

SARKARI
(O 2)

SARKARI
(O 3)

1932. *Optd with Types* O 2 (3 *a.*, 1 *r.*) *or* O 3 (*others*), *all in red, at Junagadh State Press.*

O 9 15 3 a. black and carmine .. .. .. 70·00 7·00
a. Optd with Type O 3 .. .. 16·00 12·00
O10 16 4 a. black and purple .. .. .. 23·00 15·00
O11 18 8 a. black and yellow-green .. .. 25·00 17·00
O12 17 1 r. black and pale blue .. .. .. 90·00 90·00
a. Optd with Type O 3 .. .. 20·00 55·00

1938. *No.* 57 *optd with Type* O 1, *in vermilion.*

O13 17 1 a. black and carmine .. .. .. 11·00 1·75
a. Brown-red opt .. .. .. 8·50 1·40

The state was occupied by Indian troops on 9 November 1947 following the flight of the Nawab to Pakistan.

UNITED STATE OF SAURASHTRA

The administration of Junagadh state was assumed by the Government of India on 7 November 1947. An Executive Council took office on 1 June 1948.

Under the new Constitution of India the United State of Saurashtra was formed on 15 February 1948, comprising 221 former states and estates of Kathiawar, including Jasdan, Morvi, Nawanagar and Wadhwan, but excluding Junagadh. A referendum was held by the Executive Council of Junagadh which then joined the United State on 20 January 1949. It is believed that the following issues were only used in Junagadh.

The following issues were surcharged at the Junagadh State Press.

POSTAGE & REVENUE

ONE ANNA

(19)

Postage & Revenue

ONE ANNA

(20)

1949. *Stamps of* 1929 *surch. (a) With T* **19** *in red.*
58 **16** 1 a. on ½ a. black and deep blue (6.49) 8·50 4·25
a. Surch double † £400
b. "AFNA" for "ANNA" and inverted "N" in "REVENUE" .. £1500
c. Larger first "A" in "ANNA" .. 80·00 60·00

(*b*) *With T* **20** *in green*
59 **18** 1 a. on 2 a. grey and dull yellow (2.49) 9·00 19·00
a. "evenue" omitted .. .. — £400

No. 58c occurs on position 10.

A number of other varieties occur on No. 58, including: small "V" in "REVENUE" (No. 8); small "N" in "REVENUE" (Nos. 9, 13 and 14); small "E" in "POSTAGE" (No. 12); thick "A" in "POSTAGE" (No. 19); inverted "N" in "REVENUE" and small second "A" in "ANNA" (No. 25); small "O" in "ONE" (No. 26); small "V" and "U" in "REVENUE" (No. 28); small "N" in "ONE" (No. 37).

In No. 59 no stop after "ANNA" is known on Nos. 4, 17, 25, 34 and 38 and small "N" in "ONE" on Nos. 9, 11, 26 and 31.

21

(Typo Waterlow)

1949 (Sept). *Court Fee stamps of Bhavnagar state optd* "SAURASHTRA" *and further optd* "U.S.S. REVENUE & POSTAGE" *as in T* **21**, *in black. Typo. P* 11.
60 **21** 1 a. purple .. .. .. 7·50 8·00
a. "POSTAGE" omitted £225 £180
b. Opt double £250 £300

Minor varieties include small "S" in "POSTAGE" (Nos. 9 and 49); small "N" in "REVENUE" (Nos. 15 and 55); small "U" in "REVENUE" (Nos. 18 and 58); small "V" in "REVENUE" (Nos. 24, 37, 64 and 77); and small "O" in "POSTAGE" (Nos. 31 and 71).

Various missing stop varieties also occur.

POSTAGE & REVENUE
ONE ANNA

(22)

1950 (2 Mar). *Stamp of* 1929 *surch with T* **22**.
61 **15** 1 a. on 3 p. black and blackish green .. 45·00 48·00
a. "P" of "POSTAGE" omitted (R. 8/1) £500 £500
b. "O" of "ONE" omitted £650

Other minor varieties include small second "A" in "ANNA" (No. 2), small "S" in "POSTAGE" with small "V" in "REVENUE" (Nos. 14 and 26) and small "V" in "REVENUE" (Nos. 8 and 11).

OFFICIAL STAMPS

1948 (July–Dec). *Nos.* O4/O7 *surch* "ONE ANNA" (2¼ *mm high*) *by Junagadh State Press.*
O14 **18** 1 a. on 2 a. grey & dull yellow (B.) .. £4000 19·00
O15 **15** 1 a. on 3 a. black and carmine (Aug) .. £1700 42·00
a. Surch double .. .. .. † £1500
O16 **16** 1 a. on 4 a. black and purple (Dec) .. £275 38·00
a. "ANNE" for "ANNA" (R. 5/4) .. £2000 £350
b. "ANNN" for "ANNA" (R. 7/5) .. £2000 £350
O17 **18** 1 a. on 8 a. black & yellow-green (Dec) £250 29·00
a. "ANNE" for "ANNA" (R. 5/4) .. £2000 £275
b. "ANNN" for "ANNA" (R. 7/5) .. £2000 £275

Numerous minor varieties of fount occur in this surcharge.

1948 (Nov). *Handstamped* "ONE ANNA" (4 *mm high*).
O18 **17** 1 a. on 1 r. (No. O8) .. .. .. £900 28·00
O19 1 a. on 1 r. (No. O12a) .. .. .. £325 32·00
a. Optd on No. O12 .. .. .. — 50·00

A used copy of No. O12a is known surcharged in black as on Nos. O14/17. This may have come from a proof sheet.

1949 (Jan). *Postage stamps optd with Type* O **3**, *in red.*
O20 **15** 3 p. black and blackish green .. .. £225 10·00
O21 **16** ½ a. black and deep blue .. .. £500 10·00
O22 **18** 1 a. on 2 a. grey and dull yellow (No. 59) 55·00 18·00

Various wrong fount letters occur in the above surcharges.

MANUSCRIPT OVERPRINTS. Nos. 49, 50, 57, 58, 59 and 60 are known with manuscript overprints reading "Service" or "SARKARI" (in English or Gujerati script), usually in red. Such provisionals were used at Gadhda and Una between June and December 1949 (*Price from £85 each, used on piece*).

The United State of Saurashtra postal service was incorporated into that of India on 31 March 1950. The use of Soruth stamps was permitted until the end of April.

TRAVANCORE

PRICES FOR STAMPS ON COVER	
Nos. 1/77	*from* × 10
Nos. O1/108	*from* × 15

(16 cash = 1 chuckram; 28 chuckrams = 1 rupee)

"Anchel" or "Anchal" = Post Office Department.

The stamps of Travancore were valid on mail posted to Cochin.

PRINTERS. All stamps of Travancore were printed by the Stamp Manufactory, Trivandrum, *unless otherwise stated.*

PRINTING METHODS. The dies were engraved on brass from which electrotypes were made and locked together in a forme for printing the stamps. As individual electrotypes became worn they were replaced by new ones and their positions in the forme were sometimes changed. This makes it difficult to plate the early issues. From 1901 plates were made which are characterised by a frame (or "Jubilee" line) round the margins of the sheets.

Up to the 6 cash of 1910 the dies were engraved by Dharmalingham Asari.

SHADES. We list only the main groups of shades but there are many others in view of the large number of printings and the use of fugitive inks. Sometimes shade variation is noticeable within the same sheet.

Maharaja Rama Varma X, 1885–1924

1 Conch or Chank Shell

1888 (16 Oct). *As T* **1**, *but each value differs slightly. Laid paper. P* 12.
1 **1** 1 ch. ultramarine (*shades*) .. .. 3·25 2·50
2 2 ch. red .. .. 3·25 8·00
3 4 ch. green .. .. 13·00 10·00
1/3 .. .. *Set of* 3 17·00 18·00

The paper bears a large sheet watermark showing a large conch shell surmounted by "GOVERNMENT" in large outline letters, in an arch with "OF TRAVANCORE" at foot in a straight line. Many stamps in the sheet are without watermark.

These stamps on laid paper in abnormal colours are proofs.

2

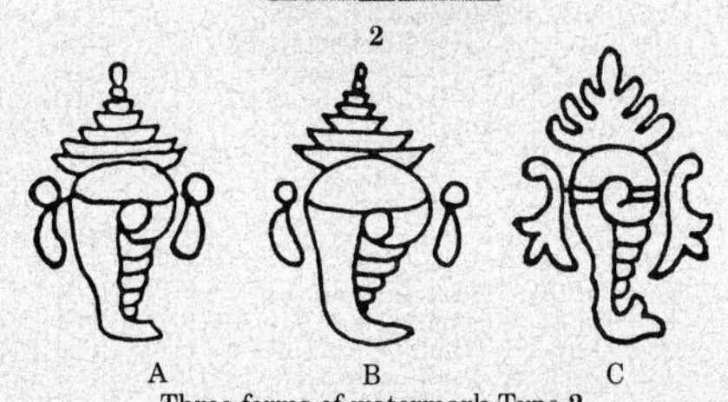

A B C

Three forms of watermark Type **2**.
(*as seen from the back of the stamp*)

WATERMARKS AND PAPERS.

Type A appeared upright on early printings of the 1, 2 and 4 ch. values on odd-sized sheets which did not fit the number of shells. Later it was always sideways with 15 mm between the shells on standard-sized sheets of 84 (14 × 6) containing 60 shells (10 × 6). It therefore never appears centred on the stamps and it occurs on hand-made papers only.

Type B is similar in shape but can easily be distinguished as it is invariably upright, with 11 mm between the shells, and is well centred on the stamps. It also occurs only on handmade papers. It was introduced in 1904 and from 1914, when Type A was brought back into use, it was employed concurrently until 1924.

Type C is quite different in shape and occurs on machine-made papers. There are two versions. The first, in use from 1924 to 1939, has 84 shells 11 mm apart and is always upright and well centred. The second, introduced in 1929 and believed not to have been used after 1930, has 60 shells (12 × 5) 15 mm apart and is invariably badly centred so that some stamps in the sheet are without watermark. This second version is normally found upright, but a few sideways watermark varieties are known and listed as Nos. 35g, 37c, O31j and O32i. We do not distinguish between the two versions of Type C in the lists, but stamps known to exist in the second version are indicated in footnotes. The machine-made paper is generally smoother and of more even texture.

NO WATERMARK VARIETIES. Some of these were formerly listed but we have now decided to omit them as they do not occur in full sheets. They arise in the following circumstances: (*a*) on sheets with wmk A; (*b*) on sheets with the wide-spaced form of wmk C; and (*c*) on late printings of the pictorial issues of 1939–46. They are best collected in pairs, with and without watermark.

DATES OF ISSUE. In the absence of more definite information the dates quoted usually refer to the first reported date of new printings on different watermarks but many were not noted at the time and the dates of these are indicated by a query. Dated postmarks on single stamps are difficult to find.

3

4

5

6

7

8

1889–1904. *Wove paper. Wmk* A (*upright or sideways*). *P* 12 (*sometimes rough*).
4 **1** ½ ch. slate-lilac (1894) .. .. .. 1·90 50
a. Doubly printed .. .. .. † £180
b. Reddish lilac 55 15
ba. Imperf between (vert pair) £180 £180
bb. Doubly printed .. .. .. † £180
c. Purple (1899) .. .. .. 1·00 15
ca. Doubly printed .. .. .. † £180
d. Dull purple (1904) .. .. .. 1·25 15
5 **5** ¾ ch. black (14.3.01) .. .. .. 2·50 70
6 **1** 1 ch. ultramarine .. .. 1·25 15
a. *Tête-bêche* (pair) £2000 £2000
b. Doubly printed .. .. .. † £300
c. Imperf vert (horiz pair) .. .. † £300
d. Imperf between (vert pair) .. .. † £300
e. Pale ultramarine (1892) .. .. 2·25 15
f. Violet-blue (1901) .. .. .. 2·75 35
7 2 ch. salmon (1890) .. .. .. 3·75 85
a. Rose (1891) .. .. 3·00 30
ab. Imperf (pair) .. .. .. † £325
b. Pale pink (1899) .. .. .. 2·50 35
ba. Imperf between (vert pair) £120
bb. Doubly printed £190
c. Red (1904) .. .. 2·50 15
ca. Imperf between (horiz pair) .. .. † £225
8 4 ch. green .. .. 2·75 60
a. Yellow-green (1901) .. .. .. 2·00 40
b. Dull green (1904) .. .. .. 5·50 85
ba. Doubly printed .. .. .. † £300

Nos. 6, 6*d*, 7 and 8 occur with the watermark upright and sideways. No. 7*a* is known only with the watermark upright. The remainder exist only with the watermark sideways.

The sheet sizes were as follows:

½ ch. 56 (14 × 4) except for No. 4*d* which was 84 (14 × 6), initially without border, later with border.

¾ ch. 84 (14 × 6) with border.

1 ch. No. 6, 80 (10 × 8) and later 84 (14 × 6) without border and then with border; No. 6*d*, 96 (16 × 6); No. 6*e*, 84 (14 × 6) with border.

2 ch. No. 7, 80 (10 × 8); No. 7*a*, 70 (10 × 7); Nos. 7*b*, 7*c*, 60 (10 × 6).

4 ch. No. 8, 60 (10 × 6); Nos. 8*a*/*b*, 84 (14 × 6) with border.

After 1904 all stamps in Types **3** to **8** were in standard-sized sheets of 84 (14 × 6) with border.

For later printings watermarked Type A, see Nos. 23/30.

1904–20. *Wmk* B, *upright* (*centred*). *P* 12, *sometimes rough.*
9 **3** 4 ca. pink (11.08) 20 10
a. Imperf between (vert pair) £170 £170
10 **1** 6 ca. chestnut (2.10) 30 10
a. Imperf between (horiz pair) .. † £170
11 ½ ch. reddish lilac 90 10
a. Reddish violet (6.10) 65 10
b. Lilac .. .. 1·00 30
c. "CHUCRRAM" (R. 5/6) .. .. 4·75 3·25
d. Imperf horiz (vert pair) .. .. † £120

No.	T	Description	Unused	Used
12	4	10 ca. pink (1920)	23·00	5·00
13	5	¾ ch. black	1·10	20
14	1	1 ch. bright blue		
		a. Blue	2·75	30
		b. Deep blue	2·75	30
		c. Indigo (8.10)	65	10
		d. Chalky blue (1912)	3·75	60
15		1¼ ch. claret (*shades*) (10.14)	45	45
		a. Imperf between (horiz pair)	£180	£180
16		2 ch. salmon	17·00	6·00
		a. Red (8.10)	50	10
17	6	3 ch. violet (11.3.11)	2·25	20
		a. Imperf between (vert pair)	£170	£170
		b. Imperf between (vert strip of 3)	†	£250
18	1	4 ch. dull green	8·50	3·25
		a. Slate-green	1·10	35
19	7	7 ch. claret (1916)	1·60	45
		a. Error. Carmine-red	—	50·00
20	8	14 ch. orange-yellow (1916)	2·40	1·25
		a. Imperf vert (horiz strip of 3)	£375	

1/**4** (9)   **1 C** (10)

1906. *Surch as T* **9**. *Wmk* B.

No.	T	Description	Unused	Used
21	1	¼ on ½ ch. reddish lilac	30	30
		a. Reddish violet	20	20
		b. Lilac	50	30
		c. "CHUCRRAM" (R.5/6)	3·25	3·25
		d. Surch inverted	38·00	26·00
22		⅜ on ½ ch. reddish lilac	20	35
		a. Reddish violet	20	35
		b. Lilac	20	35
		c. "CHUCRRAM" (R.5/6)	3·25	3·50
		d. Surch inverted	—	38·00
		e. Surch double		
		f. "8" omitted	—	40·00

1914–22. *Reversion to wmk A (sideways). P 12 (sometimes rough).*

No.	T	Description	Unused	Used
23	3	4 ca. pink (1915)	7·00	60
24	4	5 ca. olive-bistre (30.10.21)	50	10
		a. Imperf between (horiz pair)	40·00	45·00
		b. Imperf between (horiz strip of 3)	85·00	90·00
		c. "TRAVANCOPE"	—	8·00
25	1	6 ca. orange-brown (2.15)	4·75	35
26		½ ch. reddish violet (12.14)	2·00	20
		a. "CHUCRRAM" (R.5/6)	8·50	3·25
		b. Imperf between (horiz pair)	£130	
27	4	10 ca. pink (26.10.21)	35	10
28	1	1 ch. grey-blue (5.22)	7·50	1·40
		a. Deep blue	7·50	1·40
29		1¼ ch. claret (12.19)	9·00	30
30	6	3 ch. reddish lilac (8.22)	9·00	1·40

1921 (Mar). *Surch as T* **10**. *Wmk* A.

No.	T	Description	Unused	Used
31	3	1 c. on 4 ca. pink	15	15
		a. Surch inverted	18·00	8·50
32	1	5 c. on 1 ch. grey-blue (R.)	80	10
		a. Deep blue	80	10
		b. Stamp printed both sides		
		c. Imperf between (vert pair)	†	£170
		d. Surch inverted	13·00	7·00
		e. Surch double	38·00	28·00
		f. On wmk B. *Deep blue*	19·00	19·00

ALBINO OVERPRINT VARIETIES. Stamps with overprint double, one albino are frequently found in the provisional and official issues of Travancore, and are only worth a small premium over the normal prices.

Maharaja Bala Rama Varma XI, 1924–1971

1924–39. *Wmk C. Machine-made paper. P* 12.

No.	T	Description	Unused	Used
33	4	5 ca. olive-bistre (18.6.25)	9·50	2·25
		a. Imperf between (horiz pair)	£110	
		b. "TRAVANCOPE"	—	12·00
34		5 ca. chocolate (1930)	2·25	20
		a. Imperf between (horiz pair)	32·00	
		b. Imperf between (vert pair)	†	£100
35	1	6 ca. brown-red (3.24)	4·25	10
		a. Imperf between (horiz pair)	21·00	21·00
		b. Imperf between (vert pair)	80·00	80·00
		c. Printed both sides	50·00	
		d. Perf 12½	4·25	50
		e. Perf comp of 12 and 12½	8·00	4·00
		f. Perf 12½×11	—	70·00
		g. Wmk sideways	—	13·00
36		½ ch. reddish violet (date?)	4·25	4·25
		a. "CHUCRRAM" (R. 5/6)	30·00	
37	4	10 ca. pink (8.24)	1·75	10
		a. Imperf between (horiz pair)	70·00	70·00
		b. Imperf between (vert pair)	20·00	22·00
		c. Wmk sideways (16.9.28)	—	5·00
38	5	¾ ch. black (4.10.32)	8·50	50
39		¾ ch. mauve (16.11.32)	35	10
		a. Imperf between (horiz pair)	†	£110
		b. Perf 12½ (8.37)	8·00	70
		ba. Imperf between (horiz pair)	£100	
		c. Perf comp of 12 and 12½	12·00	5·00
40		¾ ch. reddish violet (1939)	2·75	70
		a. Perf 12½	4·50	50
		b. Perf comp of 12 and 12½	7·50	2·25
		c. Perf 11	—	70·00
		d. Perf comp of 12 and 11	—	70·00
41	1	1 ch. slate-blue (8.26)	2·75	30
		a. Indigo	3·75	20
		b. Imperf between (horiz pair)	†	£150
		c. Imperf between (vert pair)	†	£150
		d. Perf 12½	12·00	1·00
42	1	1½ ch. rose (1932)	2·25	10
		a. Imperf between (horiz strip of 3)	£150	
		b. Perf 12½	20·00	2·75
		c. Perf comp of 12 and 12½	—	25·00
43		2 ch. carmine-red (4.6.29)	4·50	30
44	6	3 ch. violet (4.25)	6·00	15
		a. Imperf between (vert pair)	85·00	85·00
		b. Perf 12½	—	11·00
		c. Perf comp of 12 and 12½	—	23·00
45	1	4 ch. grey-green (5.4.34)	5·50	45
46	7	7 ch. claret (1925)	8·00	1·75
		a. Doubly printed	†	£275
		b. Carmine-red (date?)	65·00	55·00
		c. Brown-purple (1932)	13·00	4·00
		ca. Perf 12½	8·50	14·00
		cb. Perf comb of 12 and 12½	8·50	14·00
46*d*	8	14 ch. orange-yellow (date?)	40·00	
		da. Perf 12½	£170	

It is believed that the 12½ perforation and the perf 12 and 12½ compound were introduced in 1937 and that the 11 perforation came later, probably in 1939.

The 5 ca. chocolate, 6 ca., 10 ca. and 3 ch. also exist on the wide-spaced watermark (60 shells to the sheet of 84).

11 Sri Padmanabha Shrine

12 State Chariot

13 Maharaja Bala Rama Varma XI

(Des M. R. Madhawan Unnithan. Plates by Calcutta Chromotype Co. Typo Stamp Manufactory, Trivandrum)

1931 (6 Nov). *Coronation. Cream or white paper. Wmk C. P* 11½, 12.

No.	T	Description	Unused	Used
47	11	6 ca. black and green	85	85
		a. Imperf between (horiz pair)	£180	£200
48	12	10 ca. black and ultramarine	75	35
		a. Imperf between (vert pair)	†	£325
49	13	3 ch. black and purple	1·75	1·60
47/9		*Set of* 3	3·00	2·50

1 C (14)   **1 C** (15)

16 Maharaja Bala Rama Varma XI and Subramania Shrine

1932 (14 Jan). (i) *Surch as T* **14**. (*a*) *Wmk* A (*sideways*).

No.	T	Description	Unused	Used
50	1	1 c. on 1¼ ch. claret	15	45
		a. Imperf between (horiz pair)	80·00	
		b. Surch inverted	4·25	6·00
		c. Surch double	25·00	25·00
		d. Pair, one without surch	75·00	85·00
		e. "c" omitted	45·00	45·00
51		2 c. on 1¼ ch. claret	15	15
		a. Surch inverted	4·25	6·50
		b. Surch double	25·00	
		c. Surch double, one inverted	55·00	
		d. Surch treble	60·00	
		e. Surch treble, one inverted	70·00	70·00
		f. Pair, one without surch	80·00	80·00
		g. "2" omitted	45·00	45·00
		h. "c" omitted	45·00	45·00
		i. Imperf between (horiz pair)	80·00	
		j. Imperf between (vert pair)	85·00	
		(*b*) *Wmk* B (*upright*)		
52	1	1 c. on 1¼ ch. claret	75	75
		a. Surch inverted	18·00	
		b. Surch double	32·00	
53		2 c. on 1¼ ch. claret	5·50	5·50
		a. Imperf between (horiz pair)	£100	
		(*c*) *Wmk* C		
54	1	1 c. on 1¼ ch. claret	12·00	13·00
		a. Surch inverted	45·00	45·00
55		2 c. on 1¼ ch. claret	18·00	13·00
		(ii) *Surch as T* **10**. *Wmk* B		
56	1	2 c. on 1¼ ch. claret	3·75	12·00

1932 (5 Mar) *Surch as T* **15**. *Wmk* C.

No.	T	Description	Unused	Used
57	4	1 c. on 5 ca. chocolate	15	15
		a. Imperf between (horiz pair)	95·00	
		b. Surch inverted	7·50	10·00
		c. Surch inverted on back only	50·00	
		d. Pair, one without surch	80·00	
		e. "1" omitted	38·00	
		f. "C" omitted	—	38·00
		g. "TRAVANCOPE"	8·50	
58		1 c. on 5 ca. slate-purple	90	15
		a. Surch inverted	†	£150
		b. "1" inverted	65·00	65·00
59		2 c. on 10 ca. pink	15	15
		a. Imperf between (horiz pair)	85·00	
		b. Surch inverted	5·00	7·00
		c. Surch double	18·00	20·00
		d. Surch double, one inverted	48·00	48·00
		e. Surch double, both inverted	35·00	

No. 58 was not issued without the surcharge.

(Plates by Indian Security Printing Press, Nasik. Typo Stamp Manufactory, Trivandrum)

1937 (29 Mar). *Temple Entry Proclamation. T* **16** *and similar horiz designs. Wmk* C. *P* 12.

No.	T	Description	Unused	Used
60		6 ca. carmine	50	65
		a. Imperf between (horiz strip of 3)	£375	
		b. Perf 12½	1·10	1·50
		c. Compound perf	23·00	23·00
61		12 ca. bright blue	1·25	20
		a. Perf 12½	1·75	60
		ab. Imperf between (vert pair)	£350	
		b. Compound perf	35·00	
62		1½ ch. yellow-green	85	60
		a. Imperf between (vert pair)	£275	
		b. Perf 12½	20·00	4·75
		c. Compound perf		
63		3 ch. violet	2·50	1·25
		a. Perf 12½	3·25	1·75
60/3		*Set of* 4	4·50	2·40

Designs:—Maharaja's portrait and temples—12 ca. Sri Padmanabha; 1½ ch. Mahadeva; 3 ch. Kanyakumari.

COMPOUND PERFS. This term covers stamps perf compound of 12½ and 11, 12 and 11 or 12 and 12½, and where two or more combinations exist the prices are for the commonest. Such compounds can occur on values which do not exist perf 12 all round.

17 Lake Ashtamudi

18 Maharaja Bala Rama Varma XI

(Des Nilakantha Pellai. Plates by Indian Security Printing Press, Nasik. Typo Stamp Manufactory, Trivandrum)

1939 (9 Nov). *Maharaja's 27th Birthday. T* **17/18** *and similar designs. Wmk* C. *P* 12½.

No.	T	Description	Unused	Used
64		1 ch. yellow-green	3·00	10
		a. Imperf between (horiz pair)	20·00	
		b. Perf 11	7·00	10
		ba. Imperf between (vert pair)	25·00	32·00
		bb. Imperf between (vert strip of 3)	20·00	32·00
		c. Perf 12	13·00	75
		ca. Imperf between (horiz pair)	20·00	
		cb. Imperf between (vert pair)	26·00	
		d. Compound perf	16·00	1·75
		da. Imperf between (vert pair)	80·00	
65		1½ ch. scarlet	1·40	1·60
		a. Doubly printed	£180	
		b. Imperf between (horiz pair)	25·00	
		c. Imperf between (vert pair)	20·00	
		d. Perf 11	3·00	16·00
		da. Imperf horiz (vert pair)	8·00	
		e. Perf 12	22·00	2·75
		f. Perf 13½	12·00	45·00
		g. Compound perf	30·00	4·00
		h. Imperf (pair)	30·00	
66		2 ch. orange	3·50	60
		a. Perf 11	12·00	35
		b. Perf 12	65·00	3·75
		c. Compound perf	65·00	4·25
67		3 ch. brown	4·50	10
		a. Doubly printed	—	95·00
		b. Imperf between (horiz pair)	32·00	42·00
		c. Perf 11	14·00	30
		ca. Doubly printed	40·00	45·00
		d. Perf 12	27·00	2·00
		da. Imperf between (vert pair)	95·00	95·00
		e. Compound perf	19·00	1·00
68		4 ch. red	3·50	40
		a. Perf 11	22·00	50
		b. Perf 12	19·00	4·50
		c. Compound perf	£100	85·00
69		7 ch. pale blue	5·50	11·00
		a. Perf 11	50·00	21·00
		ab. Blue	50·00	19·00
		b. Compound perf	65·00	24·00
70		14 ch. turquoise-green	5·50	35·00
		a. Perf 11	6·50	60·00
64/70		*Set of* 7	24·00	42·00

Designs: *Vert as T* **18**—1½ ch., 3 ch. Portraits of Maharaja in different frames. *Horiz as T* **17**—4 ch. Sri Padmanabha Shrine; 7 ch. Cape Comorin; 14 ch. Pachipari Reservoir.

19 Maharaja and Aruvikara Falls

2 CASH (20)

(Des Nilakantha Pellai. Plates by Indian Security Printing Press, Nasik. Typo Stamp Manufactory, Trivandrum)

1941 (20 Oct). *Maharaja's 29th Birthday. T* **19** *and similar horiz design. Wmk* C. *P* 12½.

No.	T	Description	Unused	Used
71		6 ca. blackish violet	4·25	10
		a. Perf 11	4·25	10
		ab. Imperf between (vert pair)	20·00	
		ac. Imperf horiz (vert pair)	30·00	42·00
		b. Perf 12	15·00	1·00
		ba. Imperf between (horiz pair)	23·00	
		bb. Imperf between (vert pair)	30·00	
		bc. Imperf between (vert strip of 3)	21·00	
		c. Compound perf	4·50	80

2 ¾ ch. brown .. .. 4·50 15
a. Perf 11 .. .. 6·00 15
ab. Imperf between (horiz pair) .. .. 95·00
ac. Imperf between (vert pair) .. .. 24·00 32·00
ad. Imperf between (vert strip of 3) .. .. 22·00
ae. Block of four imperf between (horiz and vert) £130
b. Perf 12 .. .. 35·00 6·00
c. Compound perf .. .. 8·50 1·10

Design:—¾ ch. Maharaja and Marthanda Varma Bridge, Alwaye.

943 (17 Sept). *Nos. 65, 71 (colour changed) and 72 surch as T* **20**. *P* 12½.
3 2 ca. on 1½ ch. scarlet.. .. .. 1·00 40
a. Imperf between (vert pair) .. .. 32·00
b. "2" omitted £170 £170
c. "CA" omitted £250
d. "ASH" omitted £250
e. Perf 11 .. .. 30 20
ea. "CA" omitted £250
f. Compound perf 55 85
fa. Imperf between (vert pair) .. .. 90·00
fb. "2" omitted £180
'4 4 ca. on ¾ ch. brown .. .. 2·50 90
a. Perf 11 .. .. 2·75 20
b. Perf 12 .. .. — 85·00
c. Compound perf .. .. 3·50 1·00
'5 8 ca. on 6 ca. scarlet .. .. 3·25 10
a. Perf 11 .. .. 2·00 10
ab. Imperf between (horiz pair) .. .. 30·00
b. Perf 12 .. .. — 60·00
c. Compound perf .. .. 9·50 4·75
'3/5 .. .. *Set of* 3 4·25 45

21 Maharaja Bala Rama Varma XI

SPECIAL (22)

Des Nilakantha Pellai. Plates by Indian Security Printing Press, Nasik. Typo Stamp Manufactory, Trivandrum)

1946 (24 Oct). *Maharaja's 34th Birthday. Wmk* C. *P* 12½.
76 **21** 8 ca. carmine .. .. 18·00 2·75
a. Perf 11 .. .. 65 85
b. Perf 12 .. .. 27·00 2·50
ba. Imperf between (horiz pair) .. .. 30·00 42·00
bb. Imperf between (horiz strip of 3) 45·00
c. Compound perf .. .. ..

1946. *No.* O103 *revalidated for ordinary postage with opt T* **22**, *in orange. P* 12½.
77 **19** 6 ca. blackish violet .. .. 6·00 2·00
a. Perf 11 .. .. 27·00 4·75
b. Compound perf .. .. 6·00 4·75

OFFICIAL STAMPS

GUM. Soon after 1911 the Official stamps were issued without gum. Thus only the initial printings of the 1, 2, 3 and 4 ch. values were gummed. As Nos. O38/9, O41/2 and O95 were overprinted on stamps intended for normal postage these, also, have gum.

PRINTINGS. Sometimes special printings of postage stamps were made specifically for overprinting for Official use, thus accounting for Official stamps appearing with watermarks or in shades not listed in the postage issues.

SETTINGS. These are based on the study of complete sheets of 84, and the measurements given are those of the majority of stamps on the sheet. Examples are known showing different measurements as each overprint was set individually in loose type, but these are not included in the listings.

On On
S. S S S
(O 1) (O 2)
Rounded "O"

1911 (16 Aug)–**30.** *Contemporary stamps optd with Type* O 1 (13 *mm wide*). *P* 12, *sometimes rough.* (*a*) *Wmk* B (*upright*) (16.8.11–21).
O 1 3 4 ca. pink (1916) 20 10
a. Opt inverted .. .. † 60·00
b. Opt double .. .. 90·00 70·00
c. "S S" inverted .. .. 24·00 14·00
d. Imperf (pair) £170 £170
e. Stamp doubly printed.. .. .. † £170
O 2 1 6 ca. chestnut (date ?) .. .. .. 29·00 29·00
O 3 ½ ch. reddish lilac (R.) (1919) 70 35
a. "CHUCRRAM" (R.5/6) .. .. 8·00 4·50
O 4 4 10 ca. pink (1921) .. .. 12·00 2·50
a. "O" inverted .. .. 32·00 8·00
b. Left "S" inverted .. .. .. 32·00 8·00
c. Right "S" inverted .. .. .. 32·00 8·00
d. Opt inverted .. .. † 85·00
O 5 1 1 ch. chalky blue (R.) 55 10
a. Imperf between (vert pair) .. .. † £150
b. Opt inverted .. .. 7·00 4·25
c. Opt double .. .. 60·00 50·00
d. "nO" for "On" .. .. 75·00 75·00
e. "O" inverted .. .. 6·50 2·00
f. Left "S" inverted .. .. .. 6·50 2·00
g. Right "S" inverted .. .. .. 6·50 2·00
h. "S S" inverted .. .. — 35·00
O 6 1 2 ch. red 35 10
a. Opt inverted .. .. 8·00 8·00
b. "O" inverted .. .. 7·50 1·25
c. Left "S" inverted .. .. .. 6·00 1·10
d. Right "S" inverted .. .. .. 8·00 1·50
O 7 2 ch. red (B.) (date ?) .. .. .. — 75·00
O 8 6 3 ch. violet 35 10
a. Imperf between (vert pair) £130 £130
b. Imperf vert (horiz pair) £110
c. Opt inverted .. .. 10·00 10·00
d. Opt double .. .. 60·00 60·00
e. Right "S" inverted .. .. .. 4·50 1·00
f. Right "S" omitted .. .. .. 80·00 80·00
g. Left "S" omitted.. .. .. .. 80·00 80·00
O 9 3 ch. violet (B.) (date ?) .. .. .. £100 50·00
O10 1 4 ch. slate-green 55 10
a. Imperf between (pair) £150 £150
b. Opt inverted .. .. 35·00 11·00
c. Opt double .. .. 80·00 80·00
d. "O" inverted .. .. 8·50 2·40
e. Left "S" inverted .. .. .. 7·50 2·40
f. Right "S" inverted .. .. .. 8·00 3·00
g. Left "S" omitted.. .. .. .. 80·00 80·00
O11 4 ch. slate-green (B.) (1921) .. .. — 42·00
a. "O" inverted .. .. — 95·00
b. Left "S" inverted .. .. .. — 95·00
c. Right "S" inverted .. .. .. — 95·00

(*b*) *Wmk* A (*sideways*) (1919–25)
O12 3 4 ca. pink .. .. 3·50 15
a. Imperf (pair) £190 £190
b. Opt inverted .. .. 45·00 15·00
c. "O" inverted .. .. 25·00 7·50
d. Left "S" inverted .. .. .. 25·00 7·50
e. Right "S" inverted .. .. .. 25·00 7·50
O13 4 ca. pink (B.) (1921) .. .. .. 30·00 75
a. "O" inverted .. .. — 18·00
O14 4 5 ca. olive-bistre (1921) 50 10
a. Opt inverted .. .. 11·00 8·50
b. "O" inverted .. .. 4·25 1·25
c. Left "S" inverted .. .. .. 4·25 1·25
d. Right "S" inverted .. .. .. 4·25 1·25
O15 1 6 ca. orange-brown (1921) 30 10
a. Imperf between (vert pair) .. .. † £140
b. Opt inverted .. .. 10·00 8·00
c. Opt double .. .. 55·00 55·00
d. "O" inverted .. .. 5·00 1·40
e. Left "S" inverted .. .. .. 5·00 1·10
f. Right "S" inverted .. .. .. 5·00 1·40
O16 6 ca. orange-brown (B.) (1921) .. .. 8·00 1·25
a. Opt inverted .. .. 85·00 85·00
b. "O" inverted .. .. 40·00 13·00
c. Left "S" inverted .. .. .. 40·00 13·00
d. Right "S" inverted .. .. .. 40·00 13·00
O17 ½ ch. reddish violet (R.) (date?) 85 10
a. Reddish lilac (date?) 85 10
b. Imperf between (horiz pair) .. .. 95·00 95·00
c. Imperf between (vert pair) .. .. 45·00 45·00
d. Stamp doubly printed .. .. .. 48·00
e. Opt inverted .. .. 9·00 3·00
f. Opt double, both inverted .. .. 95·00
g. "CHUCRRAM" (R. 5/6) .. .. .. 6·00 2·75
h. "On" omitted .. .. — 90·00
i. Right "S" inverted .. .. .. — 20·00
j. Right "S" omitted .. .. .. — 90·00
O18 4 10 ca. pink (3.21) 55 10
a. Scarlet (1925?) .. .. — 9·50
b. Opt inverted .. .. — 16·00
c. Opt double .. .. 75·00 60·00
d. "O" inverted .. .. 7·00 2·25
e. Left "S" inverted .. .. .. 6·00 1·50
f. Right "S" inverted .. .. .. 7·00 2·25
g. Imperf between (horiz pair) .. .. — £100
O19 10 ca. pink (B.) (date?) .. .. .. 50·00 12·00
a. Opt inverted .. .. — 65·00
b. "O" inverted .. .. — 40·00
O20 1 1 ch. grey-blue (R.) (date?) .. .. 3·75 60
a. Deep blue .. .. 4·00 80
b. "O" inverted .. .. 28·00 7·50
c. Left "S" inverted .. .. .. 28·00 8·00
d. "On" omitted .. ..
e. Opt inverted .. .. † 42·00
O21 1¼ ch. claret (12.19) 40 10
ca. Stamp doubly printed .. .. .. — £180
b. Opt inverted .. .. 9·00 8·00
c. Opt double .. .. 45·00
d. "O" inverted .. .. 9·50 2·00
e. Left "S" inverted .. .. .. 11·00 2·75
f. Right "S" inverted .. .. .. 11·00 2·75
g. Error. Carmine .. .. 50·00
O22 1¼ ch. claret (B.) (1921) .. .. .. — 50·00
a. "O" inverted .. .. — £110
b. Left "S" inverted .. .. .. — £110
c. Right "S" inverted .. .. .. — £110

(*c*) *Wmk* C (1925–30)
O23 4 5 ca. olive-bistre (1926) 40 35
a. Imperf between (horiz pair) £140 £140
b. Opt inverted .. .. 14·00 11·00
c. "O" inverted .. .. 4·25 2·25
d. Left "S" inverted .. .. .. 4·25 2·25
e. Right "S" inverted .. .. .. 4·25 2·25
O23*f* 5 ca. chocolate (1930) .. .. .. 45·00
fa. Opt inverted .. .. — £100
O24 10 ca. pink (1926) .. .. 3·25 15
a. Imperf between (vert pair) .. .. — £130
b. Opt inverted .. .. 50·00 50·00
c. "O" inverted .. .. 18·00 2·00
d. Left "S" inverted .. .. .. 18·00 2·25
e. Right "S" inverted .. .. .. 18·00 2·25
f. Stamp doubly printed .. .. ..
g. Opt double .. .. † 80·00
O25 1 1¼ ch. claret (1926) .. .. .. 10·00 40
a. "O" inverted .. .. 32·00 3·00
b. Left "S" inverted .. .. .. 38·00 4·75
c. Right "S" inverted .. .. .. 38·00 4·75
d. Opt double .. .. † 80·00
O26 7 7 ch. claret .. .. 1·50 30
a. "O" inverted .. .. 13·00 3·25
b. Left "S" inverted .. .. .. 13·00 3·25
c. Right "S" inverted .. .. .. 13·00 3·25
d. Error. Carmine-red .. .. .. 60·00
O27 8 14 ch. orange-yellow .. .. 2·00 40
a. "O" inverted .. .. 14·00 3·00
b. Left "S" inverted .. .. .. 14·00 3·00
c. Right "S" inverted .. .. .. 14·00 3·75

1926–30. *Contemporary stamps optd with Type* O **2** (16½ *mm wide*). *Wmk* C. *P* 12.
O28 4 5 ca. olive-bistre .. .. 2·25 30
a. Right "S" inverted .. .. .. 12·00 3·75
b. Left "S" inverted .. .. .. 14·00 4·25
O29 5 ca. chocolate (1930) 25 35
a. Imperf between (vert pair) .. .. † £170
b. Opt inverted .. .. 16·00
c. "O" inverted .. .. 3·25 3·25
d. Left "S" inverted .. .. .. 3·25 3·25
O30 1 6 ca. brown-red (date?) .. .. .. 4·25 90
a. "O" inverted .. .. 19·00 5·50
b. Left "S" inverted .. .. .. 19·00 5·50
c. Opt double .. .. † £100
O31 4 10 ca. pink 30 10
a. Imperf between (horiz pair) .. .. 50·00 50·00
b. Imperf between (vert pair) .. .. 40·00 40·00
c. Imperf vert (horiz strip of 3) .. † £100
d. Opt inverted .. .. 9·00 9·00
e. "Ou" for "On" .. .. 38·00 38·00
f. "O" inverted .. .. 4·00 1·50
g. Left "S" inverted .. .. .. 3·50 1·40
h. Right "S" inverted .. .. .. 3·50 1·25
i. Left "S" omitted .. .. .. 35·00 35·00
j. Wmk sideways .. .. 18·00 7·00
O32 1 1¼ ch. claret (*shades*) .. .. .. 1·60 30
a. Imperf between (horiz pair) .. .. 75·00 80·00
b. Imperf between (vert pair) .. .. 80·00 85·00
c. Opt inverted .. .. 20·00 20·00
d. "O" inverted .. .. 16·00 3·50
e. Left "S" inverted .. .. .. 16·00 3·50
f. Right "S" inverted .. .. .. 16·00 3·50
g. Left "S" omitted .. .. .. 90·00 90·00
h. Right "S" omitted .. .. .. 90·00 90·00
i. Wmk sideways .. .. — 7·00
O33 6 3 ch. violet .. .. 8·00 70
a. Opt inverted .. .. † £100
b. "O" inverted .. .. 38·00 16·00
c. "O" omitted .. .. 75·00 75·00
d. "Ou" for "On" £110 £110
e. Left "S" inverted .. .. .. — 28·00
O34 7 7 ch. claret (date?) .. .. .. 95·00 2·00
O35 8 14 ch. orange-yellow .. .. 40·00 85
a. Imperf between (vert pair) £350
b. "O" inverted .. .. 95·00 8·50

The 5 ca. olive-bistre, 3 ch. and 7 ch. exist only with the normal watermark spaced 11 mm; the 5 ca. chocolate and 14 ch. exist only with the wide 15 mm spacing; the 6 ca., 10 ca. and 1¼ ch. exist in both forms.

On On On
S S S S S S
(O 3) (O 4) (O 5)
Italic "S S"

1930. *Wmk* C. *P* 12. (*a*) *Optd with Type* O **3**.
O36 4 10 ca. pink £160 £110
O37 1 1¼ ch. carmine-rose .. .. 3·25 3·25

(*b*) *Optd with Type* O **4**
O38 5 ¾ ch. black (R.) 35 30
a. Left "S" omitted.. .. .. .. 70·00
b. Right "S" omitted .. .. .. 70·00
c. Large roman "S" at left.. .. .. — 70·00

(*c*) *Optd with Type* O **5**
O39 5 ¾ ch. black (R.) 35 15
a. Opt inverted .. .. † £150
b. "n" omitted .. .. 75·00 75·00
O40 1 4 ch. slate-green (R.) .. .. .. 28·00 12·00

On On On
S S S S S S
(O 6) (O 7) (O 8)
Oval "O"

1930–39 (?). *Contemporary stamps overprinted. P* 12.

(*a*) *With Type* O **6** (16 *mm high*) (i) *Wmk* A
O41 3 4 ca. pink .. .. 17·00 32·00
a. Large right "S" as Type O **2** .. 80·00 £130

(ii) *Wmk* B
O42 3 4 ca. pink .. .. 19·00 40·00
a. Large right "S" as Type O **2** .. 90·00 £150

(iii) *Wmk* C
O43 1 6 ca. brown-red (1932) 35 10
a. Opt inverted .. .. 18·00
b. Opt double .. .. 42·00 42·00
c. "O" inverted .. .. 8·00 5·00
O44 4 10 ca. pink .. .. 1·60 1·25
O45 5 ¾ ch. mauve (1933) .. .. .. 3·00 10
a. Imperf between (horiz pair) .. 75·00 50·00
b. Imperf between (horiz strip of 3) † 95·00
c. Imperf between (vert pair) .. † 80·00
d. Stamp doubly printed .. .. † £130
e. Perf 12½ .. .. 6·00 40
f. Perf comp of 12 and 12½ .. .. 12·00 1·40
g. Right "S" inverted .. .. .. — 19·00
O46 1 1¼ ch. carmine-rose .. .. .. 10·00 1·75
a. Opt double .. .. 90·00 70·00
b. Large right "S" as Type O **2** .. 85·00 45·00
O47 4 ch. grey-green .. .. 1·60 3·75

O48 1 4 ch. grey-green (R.) (27.10.30) .. 70 20
a. Imperf between (horiz pair) .. 90·00 90·00
b. Opt double .. .. .. 25·00 25·00
c. "O" inverted .. .. .. 27·00 16·00
d. Large right "S" as Type O 2 .. 40·00 27·00
e. Imperf between (vert pair) .. 90·00
O49 8 14 ch. orange-yellow (1931) .. .. 6·00 1·60
a. Imperf between (vert pair) .. † £110

For the 1½ ch. and 3 ch., and for Nos. O43 and O48/9 but perf 12½, see Nos. O66/70 (new setting combining Types O 6 and O 8).

(*b*) *With Type* O 7 (*14 mm high*). *Wmk* C

O50 3 4 ca. pink .. .. 10·00 25·00
a. "O" inverted .. .. .. 38·00 70·00
O51 4 5 ca. chocolate (1932) .. .. .. 18·00 9·00
a. Opt inverted .. .. .. 65·00 65·00
O52 1 6 ca. brown-red 20 10
a. Imperf between (vert pair) .. 45·00 45·00
b. Opt inverted .. .. .. 26·00
c. Opt double .. .. .. † 55·00
d. "nO" for "On" .. .. .. 90·00 90·00
e. Right "S" inverted .. .. 16·00 11·00
f. Left "S" omitted .. .. .. — 70·00
g. Large "n" as Type O 5 .. .. 19·00 12·00
h. Large italic left "S" as Type O 5 19·00 12·00
i. Perf 12½ .. .. .. — 6·00
j. Perf compound of 12 and 12½ .. — 14·00
O53 ½ ch. reddish violet (1932) 30 15
a. "CHUCRRAM" (R.5/6) .. .. 7·50 5·50
b. "Ou" for "On" .. .. .. 48·00 48·00
c. Left "S" omitted .. .. — 85·00
d. "O" of "On" omitted £120
O54 ½ ch. reddish violet (R.) (1935) .. 20 10
a. Imperf between (vert pair) .. 90·00 90·00
b. "CHUCRRAM" (R.5/6) .. .. 3·00 3·00
c. Left "S" inverted .. .. 18·00 16·00
O55 4 10 ca. pink (date?) .. .. .. 3·00 1·40
a. Imperf between (horiz pair) .. 12·00 16·00
b. Imperf between (vert pair) .. 10·00 15·00
c. "O" inverted .. .. .. 25·00 17·00
d. Right "S" inverted .. .. 25·00 17·00
O56 5 ¾ ch. mauve (1933?) 30 15
a. Imperf between (vert pair) .. † 95·00
b. "Ou" for "On" .. .. .. 50·00 50·00
c. "O" inverted .. .. .. 19·00 16·00
d. Right "S" inverted .. .. — 16·00
e. Opt double .. .. .. † 90·00
f. Perf comp of 12 and 12½ .. 20·00 12·00
O57 1 1 ch. deep blue (R.) (1935) .. .. 1·50 30
a. Slate-blue 90 20
b. Imperf between (horiz pair) .. 85·00 85·00
c. Imperf between (vert pair) .. 25·00 30·00
d. Perf 12½ .. .. .. 8·00 2·75
e. Perf comp of 12 and 12½ .. 15·00 5·00
O58 1¼ ch. claret .. .. 1·25 1·10
O59 1½ ch. rose (1933) 40 10
a. Imperf between (vert pair) .. † £100
b. Opt double .. .. .. 70·00 70·00
c. "O" inverted .. .. .. 3·75 2·50
e. Large "n" as type O 5 .. .. 45·00 22·00
f. Large italic left "S" as Type O 5 45·00 22·00
g. Left "S" inverted .. .. — 19·00
h. Perf 12½ .. .. .. — 8·50
i. Perf comp of 12 and 12½ .. — 16·00
ia. Stamp doubly printed .. .. † £140
O60 6 3 ch. reddish violet (1933) .. .. 1·10 60
a. "O" inverted .. .. .. 15·00 7·00
b. Opt double .. .. .. † 80·00
O61 3 ch. violet (R.) (1934) 70 10
a. Imperf between (horiz pair) .. 65·00 40·00
b. Imperf between (vert pair) .. 55·00 38·00
c. Opt inverted .. .. .. † 40·00
d. "O" inverted .. .. .. 16·00 11·00
e. Perf 12½ .. .. .. — 1·90
ea. Imperf between (vert pair) .. † £130
f. Perf comp of 12 and 12½ .. — 9·50
fa. Imperf between (horiz pair) .. † £130
g. "Ou" for "On" .. .. .. — 65·00
O62 1 4 ch. grey-green (1934) .. .. — £250
O63 4 ch. grey-green (R.) (1935?) 80 20
a. "Ou" for "On" .. .. .. 50·00 40·00
O64 7 7 ch. claret (*shades*) .. .. .. 1·10 30
a. Imperf between (vert pair) .. 26·00 32·00
b. "O" inverted .. .. .. 38·00 18·00
c. Left "S" inverted .. .. 38·00 18·00
d. Perf 12½ .. .. .. — 6·00
e. Perf comp of 12 and 12½ .. — 7·00
ea. Imperf between (vert pair) .. † 80·00
eb. Imperf between (vert strip of 3) .. £100 £100
O65 8 14 ch. orange (1933) .. .. .. 1·60 40
a. Imperf between (horiz pair) .. 28·00 38·00
b. Imperf between (vert pair) .. £100
c. Opt inverted .. .. .. † £250

(*c*) *New setting combining Type* O 8 (*18 mm high*) *in top row with Type* O 6 (*16 mm high*) *for remainder. Wmk* C (*dates?*)

A. *Type* O 8.

O66A 1 6 ca. brown-red .. .. .. 6·00 2·75
a. Perf 12½ .. .. .. 6·00 2·75
O67A 1½ ch. rose .. .. 28·00 4·25
a. Perf 12½ .. .. .. 35·00 7·00
O68A 6 3 ch. violet (R.) .. .. .. 42·00 7·50
a. Perf 12½ .. .. .. 50·00 15·00
b. Perf comp of 12 and 12½ .. 75·00 18·00
O69A 1 4 ch. grey-green (R.) .. .. 45·00 22·00
a. Perf 12½ .. .. .. 40·00 15·00
O70A 8 14 ch. orange-yellow .. .. 40·00 11·00
a. Perf 12½ .. .. .. 42·00 11·00

B. *Type* O 6

O66Ba 1 6 ca. brown-red (*p* 12½) .. .. 2·50 70
ab. Imperf between (vert pair) .. 80·00 80·00
ac. "O" inverted .. .. .. 15·00 8·00
g. Perf comp of 12 and 12½ .. — 14·00
O67B 1½ ch. rose .. .. 7·00 35
a. Perf 12½ .. .. .. 11·00 50
ab. "O" inverted .. .. .. 40·00 15·00
c. Perf comp of 12 and 12½ .. — 17·00
O68B 6 3 ch. violet (R.) .. .. .. 7·50 65
a. Perf 12½ .. .. .. 13·00 75
b. Perf comp of 12 and 12½ .. 22·00 4·75
O69Ba 1 4 ch. grey-green (R.) (*p* 12½) .. 6·50 2·00
ab. Imperf between (horiz pair) .. † £140
ac. "O" inverted .. .. .. 75·00 32·00
O70Ba 8 14 ch. orange-yellow (*p* 12½) .. 9·50 75

Nos. O66/70A/B in vertical *se-tenant* pairs are very scarce.

As with the postage issues it is believed that the 12½ and compound perforations were issued between 1937 and 1939.

1 ch

8 c (O 9)

1 ch Wrong fount "1 c" (R.6/7)

1932. *Official stamps surch as T* 14 *or with Type* O 9. *P* 12.

(*a*) *With opt Type* O 1 (i) *Wmk* A

O71 4 6 c. on 5 ca. olive-bistre .. .. .. 32·00 16·00
a. "O" inverted .. .. .. £100 45·00
b. Left "S" inverted .. .. £100 45·00
c. Right "S" inverted .. .. £100 45·00

(ii) *Wmk* C

O72 4 6 c. on 5 ca. olive-bistre .. .. .. 17·00 6·00
a. "O" inverted .. .. .. 45·00 16·00
b. Left "S" inverted .. .. 45·00 16·00
c. Right "S" inverted .. .. 45·00 16·00
O73 12 c. on 10 ca. pink .. .. .. 95·00

(*b*) *With opt Type* O 2. *Wmk* C

O74 4 6 c. on 5 ca. olive-bistre .. .. .. 1·40 85
a. Opt and surch inverted .. .. 38·00
b. Surch inverted .. .. .. 48·00
c. Left "S" inverted .. .. 12·00 4·50
d. Right "S" inverted .. .. 12·00 4·50
e. "6" omitted .. .. .. — 70·00
O75 6 c. on 5 ca. chocolate 20 25
a. Surch inverted .. .. .. 9·00 9·00
b. Surch double .. .. .. 85·00
c. Surch double, one inverted .. 85·00
d. "O" inverted .. .. .. 3·75 3·75
e. Left "S" inverted .. .. 3·75 3·75
O76 12 c. on 10 ca. pink .. .. .. 1·10 40
a. Opt inverted .. .. .. 10·00 10·00
b. Surch inverted .. .. .. 7·00 7·00
c. Opt and surch inverted .. .. 26·00 26·00
d. Pair, one without surch £225
e. "O" inverted .. .. .. 6·00 3·00
f. Left "S" inverted .. .. 4·75 2·25
g. "Ou" for "On" .. .. .. 65·00 65·00
h. Right "S" inverted .. .. 4·75 2·25
i. "c" omitted (R. 6/1) .. .. 45·00 45·00
O77 1 1 ch. 8 c. on 1¼ ch. claret .. .. 1·75 80
a. Surch inverted .. .. .. † 65·00
b. "O" inverted .. .. .. 8·00 3·50
c. Left "S" inverted .. .. 8·00 3·50
d. Right "S" inverted .. .. 8·00 3·50
e. Wrong fount "1 c" .. .. 22·00 16·00

(*c*) *With opt Type* O 3. *Wmk* C

O78 4 12 c. on 10 ca. pink .. .. .. † £275
O79 1 1 ch. 8 c. on 1¼ ch. carmine-rose .. 45·00 28·00
a. "n" omitted £170
b. Wrong fount "1 c" £160 £110

(*d*) *With opt Type* O 6. *Wmk* C

O80 4 12 c. on 10 ca. pink .. .. .. 75·00 17·00
O81 1 1 ch. 8 c. on 1¼ ch. carmine-rose .. 85·00 15·00
a. Wrong fount "1 c" .. .. £200 65·00
b. "h" omitted .. .. ..
c. Brown-red .. .. .. — 15·00

(*e*) *With opt Type* O 7. *Wmk* C

O82 4 6 c. on 5 ca. chocolate 20 25
a. Opt inverted .. .. .. 60·00 60·00
b. Surch inverted .. .. .. 11·00 12·00
c. Right "S" omitted .. .. 85·00 85·00
d. Two quads for right "S" £450
e. Right "S" inverted .. .. 21·00
O83 12 c. on 10 ca. pink 20 15
a. Opt inverted .. .. .. 7·00 7·00
b. Surch inverted .. .. .. 6·00 6·00
c. Opt and surch inverted .. .. 30·00 30·00
d. Opt double .. .. .. † 75·00
e. "O" inverted .. .. .. 14·00 14·00
f. Right "S" inverted .. .. 14·00 14·00
g. "On" omitted .. .. .. — 80·00
h. "n" omitted .. .. .. — 80·00
i. "c" omitted (R. 6/1) .. .. 28·00 28·00
j. Surch double .. .. .. † 75·00
O84 1 1 ch. 8 c. on 1¼ ch. claret 35 25
a. Imperf between (vert pair) .. † £190
b. Opt omitted .. .. .. † £350
c. Surch inverted .. .. .. 14·00 14·00
d. Surch double .. .. .. 55·00
e. "O" inverted .. .. .. 4·50 2·75
f. Wrong fount "1 c" .. .. 17·00 14·00

SERVICE (O 10) 13 mm ("R" with curved tail)

SERVICE (O 11) 13½ mm ("R" with straight tail)

SERVICE 8 CASH (O 12)

1939–41. *Nos.* 35 *and* 40 *with type-set opt, Type* O 10. *P* 12½.

O85 1 6 ca. brown-red (1941) 70 20
a. Perf 11 .. .. .. 1·10 65
b. Perf 12 .. .. .. 70 30
c. Compound perf .. .. 70 1·10
O86 5 ¾ ch. reddish violet .. .. .. 85·00 48·00
a. Perf 12 .. .. .. 20·00 1·25
b. Compound perf .. .. 80·00 48·00

1939 (9 Nov). *Maharaja's 27th Birthday. Nos.* 64/70 *with type-set opt, Type* O 10. *P* 12½.

O87 1 ch. yellow-green .. .. .. 3·50 25
O88 1½ ch. scarlet .. .. 3·50 75
a. "SESVICE" .. .. .. 75·00 26·00
b. Perf 12 .. .. .. 28·00 5·00
ba. "SESVICE" .. .. .. — 90·00
bb. Imperf between (horiz pair) .. † £120
c. Compound perf .. .. .. 8·50 1·75
O89 2 ch. orange .. .. 3·50 4·00
a. "SESVICE" .. .. .. 95·00 £110
b. Compound perf .. .. .. 65·00 65·00
O90 3 ch. brown .. .. 2·75 20
a. "SESVICE" .. .. .. 55·00 21·00
b. Perf 12 .. .. .. 15·00 45
ba. "SESVICE" .. .. .. £140 42·00
c. Compound perf .. .. .. 6·50 2·75
O91 4 ch. red .. .. 7·00 2·75
O92 7 ch. pale blue .. .. .. 8·00 1·75
O93 14 ch. turquoise-green .. .. .. 10·00 2·75
O87/93 .. .. *Set of* 7 35·00 11·00

1940 (?)–**45.** *Nos.* 40*a and* 42*b optd with Type* O 11 *from stereos. P* 12½.

O94 5 ¾ ch. reddish violet .. .. .. 9·50 20
a. Imperf between (horiz pair) .. 95·00
b. Perf 11 .. .. .. 48·00 1·10
c. Perf 12 .. .. .. 14·00 20
d. Compound perf .. .. 40·00 75
O95 1 1½ ch. rose (1945) .. .. .. 13·00 8·00
a. Perf 12 .. .. .. 4·50 1·00
b. Compound perf .. .. 17·00 12·00

1942 (?). *Nos.* 64/70 *optd with Type* O 11 *from stereos. P* 12½.

O 96 1 ch. yellow-green 70 10
a. Imperf between (vert pair) .. 42·00 45·00
b. Opt inverted .. .. .. † 35·00
c. Opt double .. .. .. 20·00
d. Perf 11 .. .. .. 60 10
da. Imperf between (vert pair) .. 25·00
db. Opt double .. .. .. 80·00 80·00
e. Perf 12 .. .. .. 2·50 50
ea. Imperf between (vert pair) .. 75·00 75·00
eb. Stamp doubly printed £100
ec. Opt inverted .. .. .. † 80·00
ed. Opt double .. .. .. 22·00
f. Compound perf .. .. .. 5·00 1·00
fa. Imperf between (vert pair) .. † £100
O 97 1½ ch. scarlet .. .. .. 2·50 10
a. Imperf between (horiz pair) .. 48·00
b. Perf 11 .. .. .. 1·00 15
ba. Imperf between (vert pair) .. 80·00 80·00
bb. Imperf between (vert strip of 3) 60·00
bc. Imperf between (horiz pair) .. † 85·00
c. Perf 12 .. .. .. 4·00 50
ca. Imperf between (vert strip of 3) £100
d. Compound perf .. .. .. 1·90 30
e. Imperf (pair) .. .. .. 25·00
O 98 2 ch. orange .. .. 1·00 30
a. Perf 11 .. .. .. 6·00 90
ab. Imperf between (vert pair) ..
b. Perf 12 .. .. .. 65·00 65·00
ba. Imperf between (vert pair) .. £250 £250
c. Compound perf .. .. .. 65·00 65·00
O 99 3 ch. brown 60 10
a. Imperf between (vert pair) ..
b. Perf 11 .. .. .. 1·50 10
c. Perf 12 .. .. .. 3·75 1·25
ca. Imperf between (vert pair) .. £190 £190
d. Compound perf .. .. .. 13·00 75
O100 4 ch. red .. .. 1·40 60
a. Perf 11 .. .. .. 2·50 45
b. Perf 12 .. .. .. 12·00 3·25
c. Compound perf .. .. .. 50·00 19·00
O101 7 ch. pale blue .. .. .. 4·75 35
a. Perf 11 .. .. .. 4·00 3·25
b. Perf 12 .. .. .. 16·00 6·00
c. Compound perf .. .. .. 13·00 4·00
d. Blue (*p* 11) .. .. .. 7·50 3·75
da. Perf 12 .. .. .. 6·00 3·75
db. Compound perf .. .. .. 20·00 13·00
O102 14 ch. turquoise-green .. .. .. 9·00 70
a. Perf 11 .. .. .. 9·00 1·50
b. Perf 12 .. .. .. 7·00 2·40
c. Compound perf .. .. .. 45·00 5·50
O96/102 .. .. *Set of* 7 14·00 1·90

1942. *Maharaja's 29th Birthday. Nos* 71/2 *optd with Type* O 11. *P* 12½.

O103 6 ca. blackish violet 40 30
a. Perf 11 .. .. .. 70 70
b. Perf 12 .. .. .. 45·00 4·25
c. Compound perf .. .. .. 1·50 1·00
O104 ¾ ch. brown .. .. 2·75 10
a. Imperf between (vert pair) .. † £225
b. Perf 11 .. .. .. 5·50 10
c. Perf 12 .. .. .. 45·00 1·60
d. Compound perf .. .. .. 6·00 85

1943. *Surch with Type* O 12. *P* 12½.

O105 19 8 ca. on 6 ca. scarlet .. .. .. 1·75 20
a. Perf 11 .. .. .. 1·25 10
ab. Surch inverted .. .. .. † £650
b. Compound perf .. .. .. 5·00 1·25

1945. *Nos.* 73/4 *optd with Type* O 11. *P* 12½.

O106 2 ca. on 1½ ch. scarlet 45 50
a. Perf 11 .. .. .. 45 15
ab. Pair, one without surch £200
b. Compound perf .. .. .. 70 1·00
ba. "2" omitted £180 £180
c. Perf 12 .. .. ..
O107 4 ca. on ¾ ch. brown .. .. .. 2·00 30
a. Perf 11 .. .. .. 1·25 20
b. Compound perf .. .. .. 1·25 1·00

1947. *Maharaja's 34th Birthday. Optd with Type* O 11. *P* 11.

O108 21 8 ca. carmine .. .. 1·50 70
a. Imperf between (horiz pair) .. 35·00
ab. Imperf between (vert pair) .. † £110
b. Opt double .. .. .. † £160
c. Perf 12½ .. .. .. 3·50 1·10
ca. Stamp doubly printed .. .. 30·00
d. Perf 12 .. .. .. 3·50 1·40
da. Stamp doubly printed .. .. 35·00

From 1 July 1949 Travancore formed part of the new State of Travancore-Cochin and stamps of Travancore surcharged in Indian currency were used.

TRAVANCORE-COCHIN

On 1 July 1949 the United State of Travancore and Cochin was formed ("U.S.T.C.") and the name was changed to State of Travancore-Cochin ("T.C.") by the new constitution of India on 26 January 1950.

PRICES FOR STAMPS ON COVER	
Nos. 1/13	*from* × 8
Nos. O1/17	*from* × 15

NO WATERMARK VARIETIES. These were formerly listed but we have now decided to omit them as they do not occur in full sheets. They are best collected in pairs, with and without watermarks.

COMPOUND PERFS. The notes above Type **17** of Travancore also apply here.

VALIDITY OF STAMPS. From 6 June 1950 the stamps of Travancore-Cochin were valid on mail from both Indian and state post offices to destinations in India and abroad.

ONE ANNA
ഒരണ
(1)

2 p. on 6 ca.

രണ്ടു പൈസ — Normal

രണ്ടു പൈസ — 1st character of 2nd group as 1st character of 1st group (Rt pane R.14/2)

1949 (1 July). *Stamps of Travancore surch in* "PIES" *or* "ANNAS" *as T* **1**. *P* 12½.

1 **19** 2 p. on 6 ca. blackish violet (R.) .. .. 1·75 85
a. Surch inverted .. .. 30·00
b. Character error .. .. 95·00 65·00
c. "O" inverted .. .. 23·00 13·00
d. Perf 11 .. .. 1·10 20
da. Imperf between (vert pair) £100 £100
db. Pair, one without surch .. .. 85·00
dc. Character error .. .. 90·00 65·00
dd. "O" inverted .. .. 24·00 13·00
e. Perf 12 .. .. 40 20
ea. Imperf between (horiz pair) .. .. 45·00
eb. Imperf between (vert pair) .. .. 5·00 12·00
ec. Surch inverted .. .. 70·00
ed. Character error .. .. 95·00 65·00
ee. Imperf between (vert strip of 3) .. 29·00
ef. Block of four imperf between (horiz and vert) .. .. 40·00
eg. "O" inverted .. .. 24·00 13·00
f. Perf 14 .. .. † £375
g. Imperf (pair) .. .. 8·50
h. Compound perf .. .. — 29·00

2 **21** 4 p. on 8 ca. carmine .. .. 1·10 30
a. Surch inverted .. .. 35·00
b. "S" inverted .. .. 75·00 38·00
c. Perf 11 .. .. 1·40 30
ca. Imperf between (vert pair) £110 £110
cb. Surch inverted .. .. 70·00
cc. Pair, one without surch .. .. 85·00
cd. "FOUP" for "FOUR" .. .. £110 80·00
ce. "S" inverted .. .. 70·00 38·00
d. Perf 12 .. .. 45 30
da. Imperf between (vert pair) .. .. 17·00
db. Pair, one without surch .. .. 80·00
dc. "FOUP" for "FOUR" .. .. 95·00 75·00
dd. "S" inverted .. .. 80·00 45·00
de. Surch inverted .. .. 90·00
e. Imperf (pair) .. .. 65·00
f. Compound perf .. .. — 29·00
g. Perf 13½ .. .. † £400

3 **17** ½ a. on 1 ch. yellow-green .. .. 2·25 30
a. "NANA" for "ANNA" (Lt pane R.3/3) £110 80·00
b. Inverted "H" in "HALF" .. .. — 70·00
c. Imperf between (vert pair) .. .. † 95·00
d. Perf 11 .. .. 1·50 20
da. Imperf between (vert pair) .. .. 25·00
db. Surch inverted .. .. † £130
dc. "NANA" for "ANNA" (Lt pane R.3/3) £130 90·00
dd. Inverted "H" in "HALF" .. .. — 75·00
e. Perf 12 .. .. 65 40
ea. Imperf between (horiz pair) .. .. 35·00 40·00
eb. Imperf between (vert pair) .. .. 4·50 10·00
ec. Surch inverted .. .. 5·00
ed. "NANA" for "ANNA" (Lt pane R.3/3) £150 95·00
ee. Block of four imperf between (horiz and vert) .. .. 40·00
f. Perf 14 .. .. † £350
g. Imperf (pair) .. .. 8·50 17·00
h. Compound perf .. .. — 27·00

4 **18** 1 a. on 2 ch. orange .. .. 2·50 30
a. Perf 11 .. .. 55 20
ab. Surch double .. .. 48·00
b. Perf 12 .. .. 2·50 50
ba. Imperf between (horiz pair) .. .. 5·50
bb. Imperf between (vert pair) .. .. 4·25 10·00
bc. Block of four imperf between (horiz and vert) .. .. 40·00
c. Perf 13½ .. .. £130 2·00
d. Imperf (pair) .. .. 8·50
e. Compound perf .. .. 30·00 21·00

5 – 2 a. on 4 ch. red (68) .. .. 2·00 60
a. Surch inverted .. .. † £190
b. "O" inverted .. .. 28·00 16·00
c. Perf 11 .. .. 2·00 60
ca. "O" inverted .. .. — 18·00
d. Perf 12 .. .. 1·60 55
da. "O" inverted .. .. 32·00 18·00
e. Compound perf .. .. 32·00 26·00

6 **18** 3 a. on 7 ch. pale blue (69) .. .. 8·00 3·50
a. Perf 11 .. .. 4·50 2·00
ab. *Blue* .. .. 45·00 4·50
ac. "3" omitted .. .. † £350
b. Perf 12 .. .. 7·50 2·75
c. Compound perf .. .. — 45·00
ca. *Blue* .. .. — 60·00

7 – 6 a. on 14 ch. turquoise-green (70) .. 10·00 16·00
a. Accent omitted from native surch (Rt pane R.13/4) £170 £180
b. Perf 11 .. .. 8·00 14·00
ba. Accent omitted from native surch (Rt pane R.13/4) £170 £180
c. Perf 12 .. .. 10·00 16·00
ca. Accent omitted from native surch (Rt pane R. 13/4) £180 £190
d. Compound perf .. .. 23·00 25·00
da. Accent omitted from native surch (Rt pane R.13/4) £250
e. Imperf (pair) .. ..

1/7 .. .. *Set of* 7 14·50 16·00

There are two settings of the ½ a. surcharge. In one the first native character is under the second downstroke of the "H" and in the other it is under the first downstroke of the "A" of "HALF". They occur on stamps perf 12½, 11 and 12 equally commonly and also on the Official stamps.

U. S. T. C. (2) **T.-C.** (3) **SIX PIES** (4)

1949. *No.* 106 *of Cochin optd with T* **2**.

8 **29** 1 a. orange .. .. 4·50 50·00
a. No stop after "S" (R. 1/6) .. .. 65·00
b. Raised stop after "T" (R. 4/1) .. .. 65·00

1950 (1 Apr). *No.* 106 *of Cochin optd with T* **3**.

9 **29** 1 a. orange .. .. 5·50 48·00
a. No stop after "T" .. .. 48·00
b. Opt inverted £180
ba. No stop after "T" £1500

The no stop variety occurs on No. 5 in the sheet and again on No. 8 in conjunction with a short hyphen.

1950 (1 Apr). *No.* 9 *surch as T* **4**.

10 **29** 6 p. on 1 a. orange .. .. 2·50 30·00
a. No stop after "T" (R. 1/5) .. .. 17·00
b. Error. Surch on No. 8 .. .. 25·00
ba. No stop after "S" £200
bb. Raised stop after "T" £200

11 9 p. on 1 a. orange .. .. 1·75 28·00
a. No stop after "T" (R. 1/5) .. .. 17·00
b. Error. Surch on No. 8 .. .. £160
ba. No stop after "S" £600
bb. Raised stop after "T" £600

5 Conch or Chank Shell

6 Palm Trees

(Litho Indian Security Printing Press, Nasik)

1950 (24 Oct). *W* **69** *of India. P* 14.

12 **5** 2 p. rose-carmine .. .. 1·25 1·25
13 **6** 4 p. ultramarine .. .. 2·00 10·00

The ordinary issues of Travancore-Cochin became obsolete on 1 July 1951.

OFFICIAL STAMPS

VALIDITY. Travancore-Cochin official stamps were valid for use throughout India from 30 September 1950.

SERVICE (O 1) **SERVICE** (O 2)

1949–51. *Stamps of Travancore surch with value as T* **1** *and optd* "SERVICE". *No gum. P* 12½. (*a*) *With Type* O **1**.

(i) *Wmk C of Travancore*

O 1 **19** 2 p. on 6 ca. blackish violet (R.) .. 90 20
a. Imperf between (vert pair) .. £110 £110
b. Character error (Rt pane R. 14/2) 32·00 24·00
c. "O" inverted .. .. 20·00 10·00
d. Pair, one without surch .. £100
e. Perf 11 .. .. 70 20
ea. Imperf between (vert pair) .. £110 £110
eb. Character error (Rt pane R. 14/2) 42·00 32·00
ec. "O" inverted .. .. 20·00 11·00
f. Perf 12 .. .. 35 20
fa. Imperf between (horiz pair) .. 7·00 16·00
fb. Imperf between (vert pair) .. 6·00
fc. Character error (Rt pane R.14/2) 35·00 28·00
fd. "O" inverted .. .. 20·00
fe. Block of four imperf between (horiz and vert) .. .. 24·00
g. Imperf (pair) .. .. 8·00 17·00
ga. Character error (Rt pane R. 14/2) £160

O 2 **21** 4 p. on 8 ca. carmine .. .. 1·75 55
a. "FOUB" for "FOUR" (Lt pane R. 2/3) .. .. £140 90·00
b. Perf 11 .. .. 1·60 30
ba. "FOUB" for "FOUR" (Lt pane R. 2/3) .. .. 75·00 32·00
c. Perf 12 .. .. 1·75 55
ca. "FOUB" for "FOUR" (Lt pane R. 2/3) .. .. 85·00 50·00
d. Compound perf .. .. 17·00 17·00

O 3 **17** ½ a. on 1 ch. yellow-green .. 50 25
a. Pair, one without surch .. .. 65·00
b. Surch inverted .. .. 23·00
c. "NANA" for "ANNA" (Lt pane R. 3/3) .. .. £160 55·00
d. Perf 11 .. .. 1·00 25
da. Pair, one without surch .. .. 95·00
db. Surch inverted .. .. 55·00
dc. "NANA" for "ANNA" (Lt pane R. 3/3) .. .. £150 65·00
e. Perf 12 .. .. 7·50 1·90
ea. "NANA" for "ANNA" (Lt pane R. 3/3) £275 £130
eb. Pair, one without surch .. .. 85·00
ec. Surch inverted on back only .. £160
f. Compound perf .. .. — 20·00

O 4 **18** 1 a. on 2 ch. orange .. .. 15·00 5·00
a. Surch inverted .. .. 80·00
b. Pair, one without surch £450
c. Perf 11 .. .. 13·00 7·50

O 5 – 2 a. on 4 ch. red (68) 90 60
b. Perf 11 .. .. 3·75 60
ba. Surch inverted £450
bb. "O" inverted .. .. — 30·00
c. Perf 12 .. .. 4·25 3·50
ca. "O" inverted .. .. — 50·00
cb. Pair, one without surch £180
d. Compound perf .. .. — 27·00
e. Imperf (pair) .. .. 12·00

O 6 – 3 a. on 7 ch. pale blue (69) .. 3·75 1·40
a. Imperf between (vert pair) .. 17·00
b. *Blue* .. .. 28·00 5·00
c. Perf 11 .. .. 2·40 90
ca. *Blue* .. .. 28·00 5·00
d. Perf 12 .. .. 2·25 3·25
da. Imperf between (horiz pair) .. 14·00
db. Imperf between (vert pair) .. 8·00
dc. Block of four imperf between (horiz and vert) .. .. 32·00
dd. *Blue* .. .. 28·00 5·00
e. Imperf (pair) .. .. 11·00

O 7 – 6 a. on 14 ch. turquoise-green (70) .. 10·00 5·50
a. Imperf between (vert pair) .. 27·00
b. Perf 11 .. .. 8·50 4·50
c. Perf 12 .. .. 38·00 6·00
ca. Imperf between (horiz pair) .. 23·00
cb. Imperf between (vert pair) .. 28·00
cc. Block of four imperf between (horiz and vert) .. .. 55·00
d. Imperf (pair) .. .. 14·00

O1/7 .. .. *Set of* 7 23·00 10·00

(ii) *W* **27** *of Cochin*

O 8 **19** 2 p. on 6 ca. blackish violet (R.) .. 30 1·10
a. Type O **1** double .. .. 18·00
b. Perf 11 .. .. 65 1·25
c. Perf 12 .. .. 45 1·10

O 9 – 2 a. on 4 ch. red (68) .. .. 1·10 75
a. Perf 11 .. .. 60 65
ab. Imperf between (vert pair) .. £180 £180
b. Compound perf .. .. — 30·00

(*b*) *With Type* O **2**

(i) *Wmk C of Travancore*

O10 **21** 4 p. on 8 ca. carmine 30 20
a. "FOUB" for "FOUR" (Lt pane R.2/3) 90·00 35·00
b. 2nd "E" of "SERVICE" in wrong fount .. .. — 48·00
c. "S" in "PIES" inverted .. .. — 50·00
d. Imperf between (vert pair) .. † 95·00
e. Perf 11 .. .. 30 20
ea. Imperf between (horiz pair) .. 4·50
eb. Imperf between (vert pair) .. 26·00
ec. "FOUB" for "FOUR" (Lt pane R.2/3) 85·00 32·00
ed. 2nd "E" of "SERVICE" in wrong fount .. .. 95·00 48·00
ee. "S" in "PIES" inverted .. .. — 50·00
ef. Block of four imperf between (horiz and vert) .. .. 30·00
f. Perf 12 .. .. 30 20
fa. Imperf between (horiz pair) .. 3·50
fb. Imperf between (vert pair) .. 2·00
fc. Block of four imperf between (horiz and vert) .. .. 11·00 20·00
fd. "FOUB" for "FOUR" (Lt pane R.2/3) £100 38·00
ff. 2nd "E" of "SERVICE" in wrong fount .. .. 90·00 48·00
fg. "FOUK" for "FOUR" .. .. † £350
g. Perf 13½ .. .. 3·00 1·25
h. Compound perf .. .. 8·00 8·00
i. Imperf (pair) .. .. 6·00
ia. 2nd "E" of "SERVICE" in wrong fount £120

O11 **17** ½ a. on 1 ch. yellow-green .. 50 20
a. "AANA" for "ANNA" (Rt pane R.13/1) .. .. £130 60·00
b. Perf 11 .. .. 30 20
ba. Imperf between (horiz pair) .. 50·00 50·00
bb. Imperf between (vert pair) .. 7·50
bc. Block of four imperf between (horiz and vert) .. .. 45·00
bd. "AANA" for "ANNA" (Rt pane R.13/1) .. .. 70·00 40·00
c. Perf 12 .. .. 50 15
ca. Imperf between (horiz pair) .. 3·50
cb. Imperf between (vert pair) .. 3·50 8·00
cc. "AANA" for "ANNA" (Rt pane R.13/1) .. .. 85·00 50·00
cd. Block of four imperf between (horiz and vert) .. .. 22·00
d. Compound perf .. .. 19·00 14·00
da. "AANA" for "ANNA" (Rt pane R.13/1) .. .. — £150
e. Imperf (pair) .. .. 6·00 14·00

O12 **18** 1 a. on 2 ch. orange 40 30
a. Imperf between (vert pair) .. † £100
ab. Imperf between (horiz pair) .. † £100
b. Perf 11 .. .. 2·00 50
ba. Imperf between (horiz pair) .. 6·00 14·00
bb. Imperf between (vert pair) .. 65·00 65·00
c. Perf 12 .. .. 40 20
ca. Imperf between (horiz pair) .. 5·50
cb. Imperf between (vert pair) .. 3·50 8·50
cc. Block of four imperf between (horiz and vert) .. .. 19·00
d. Compound perf .. .. .. 23·00 16·00
e. Imperf (pair) .. .. .. 14·00
O13 – 2 a. on 4 ch. red (68) .. .. .. 2·25 80
a. "O" inverted (Lt pane R. 14/3) .. 55·00 35·00
b. Perf 11 .. .. 1·50 1·10
ba. "O" inverted (Lt pane R. 14/3) .. 48·00 35·00
c. Perf 12 .. .. 7·00 1·10
ca. Imperf between (vert pair) .. £120 £130
cb. "O" inverted (Lt pane R. 14/3) .. 90·00 35·00
d. Compound perf .. .. .. 23·00 13·00
O14 – 3 a. on 7 ch. pale blue (69) .. .. 5·00 1·10
a. "S" inverted in "SERVICE" (Lt pane R.6/3) .. .. 70·00 32·00
b. First "E" inverted (Lt pane R.7/4) £160 £120
c. "C" inverted (Lt pane R.4/1 and 5/1) 90·00 75·00
d. Second "E" inverted (Lt pane R.3/2) £150 £110
e. Perf 11 .. .. 1·50 1·10
ea. "S" inverted in "SERVICE" (Lt pane R.6/3) .. .. 50·00 32·00
f. Perf 12 .. .. 3·75 1·60
fa. "S" inverted in "SERVICE" (Lt pane R.6/3) .. .. £120 75·00
g. Compound perf .. .. .. — 38·00
h. Imperf (pair) .. .. .. 35·00
O15 – 6 a. on 14 ch. turquoise-green (70) .. 1·50 3·25
a. Accent omitted from native surch 16·00 13·00
b. "S" inverted in "SERVICE" (Lt pane R.6/3) .. .. 70·00 42·00
c. Perf 11 .. .. 11·00 3·25
ca. Accent omitted from native surch 60·00 22·00
cb. "S" inverted in "SERVICE" (Lt pane R.6/3) .. .. £130 50·00
d. Perf 12 .. .. 40·00 4·50
da. Accent omitted from native surch £130 30·00
db. "S" inverted in "SERVICE" (Lt pane R.6/3) .. .. £250 65·00
e. Compound perf .. .. .. 65·00 65·00
O10/15 .. .. .. *Set of* 6 5·00 5·00

(ii) *W* **27** *of Cochin*

O16 **17** ½ a. on 1 ch. yellow-green .. .. 1·10 65
a. Perf 11 .. .. 40 35
b. Perf 12 .. .. 17·00 8·50
c. Compound perf .. .. .. 11·00 3·00
O17 **18** 1 a. on 2 ch. orange 50 65
a. Perf 11 .. .. 50 40
b. Perf 12 .. .. 11·00 4·00
c. Perf 13½ .. .. 2·00 1·00
d. Compound perf .. .. .. 4·75 3·00

Nos. O2, O10, O12 and O17 have the value at top in English and at bottom in native characters with "SERVICE" in between. All others have "SERVICE" below the surcharge.

Type O **2** was overprinted at one operation with the surcharges.

Nos. O10b, O10ed, O10ff and O10ia, show the second "E" of "SERVICE" with serifs matching those on the surcharge.

The "accent omitted" varieties on No. O15 occur on Left pane R. 5/1, 11/4 and Right pane R. 1/4, 12/4, 14/1 and 13/4.

The Official stamps became obsolete in September 1951.

WADHWAN

PRICES FOR STAMPS ON COVER	
No. 1	*from* × 50
No. 2	–
Nos. 3/6	*from* × 50

Thakur Bal Singh, 1885–1910

1

1888–94. *Litho.* (a) *Thin toned wove paper*

1 **1** ½ pice, black (I, III) (*p* 12½ *large holes*) .. 13·00 45·00
a. Imperf between (vert pair) (I) .. ..
b. Pin-perf 6½ irregular (I) .. .. 80·00
c. Compound of 12½ and pin-perf 6½ (I) £140
2 ½ pice, black (II) (*p* 12½ *irregular small holes*) .. .. 30·00

(b) *Medium toned wove paper*

3 **1** ½ pice, black (III) (*p* 12½) .. .. 8·00 35·00
4 ½ pice, black (V) (*p* 12) .. .. 7·00 8·00

(c) *Thick off-white or toned wove paper*

5 **1** ½ pice, black (IV, VI) (*p* 12) (7.92) .. 5·50 6·50
a. Perf compound of 12 and 11 (IV) .. 14·00 35·00
6 ½ pice, black (VII) (*fine impression*) (*p* 12) (1894) .. .. 6·00 19·00

Sheets from the Stone IV printing had at least one horizontal line of perforations gauging 11, normally between the bottom two rows of the sheet.

These stamps were lithographed from seven different stones taken from a single die. Brief details of the individual stones are as follows:

Stone I – No. 1. Sheet size not known, but possibly 28 (4×7). Sheet margins imperforate
Stone II – No. 2. Sheets of 42 (7×6) with imperforate margins
Stone III – Nos. 1 (thin paper) and 3 (medium paper). Sheets of 40 (4×10) with imperforate margins
Stone IV – Nos. 5/a. Sheets of 32 (4×8) with imperforate margins at top and right
Stone V – No. 4. Sheets of 20 (4×5) with imperforate margins at top, right and bottom
Stone VI – No. 5. Sheets of 30 (5×6) with all margins perforated
Stone VII – No. 6. Sheets of 32 (4×8) with all margins perforated. Much finer impression than the other stones

Stamps from stones I and II come with or without the dot before "STATE". Those from the later stones always show the dot. The shading on the pennant above the shield can also be used in stone identification. Stamps from stones I to III show heavy shading on the pennant, but this is less evident on stone IV and reduced further to a short line or dot on stones V to VII. There is a ")" hairline after "HALF" on the majority of stamps from Stone III.

The stamps of Wadhwan became obsolete on 1 January 1895.

Ionian Islands

The British occupation of the Ionian Islands was completed in 1814 and the archipelago was placed under the protection of Great Britain by the Treaty of Paris in 1815. The United States of the Ionian Islands were given local self-government, which included responsibility for the postal services. Crowned-circle handstamps were, however, supplied in 1844, although it is believed these were intended for use on prepaid mail to foreign destinations.

Examples of the Great Britain 1855 1d. red-brown stamp are known used at Corfu, cancelled as No. CC2, but it is believed that these originate from mail sent by the British garrison.

For illustrations of the handstamp types see BRITISH POST OFFICES ABROAD notes, following GREAT BRITAIN.

CEPHALONIA

CROWNED-CIRCLE HANDSTAMPS

CC1 CC 1 CEPHALONIA (19.4.1844) .. *Price on cover* £1000

CORFU

CROWNED-CIRCLE HANDSTAMPS

CC2 CC 1 CORFU (19.4.1844) .. .. *Price on cover* £500
CC3 CC 1 CORFU (G. or B.) (1844) .. *Price on cover* —

ZANTE

CROWNED-CIRCLE HANDSTAMPS

CC4 CC 1 ZANTE (G. or B.) (19.4.1844) .. *Price on cover* £1000

Nos. CC1/2 were later, *circa* 1860/1, struck in green (Cephalonia) or red (Corfu).

It is believed that examples of No. CC4 in black are from an unauthorised use of this handstamp which is now on display in the local museum. A similar handstamp, but without "PAID AT" was introduced in 1861.

PRICES FOR STAMPS ON COVER	
Nos. 1/3	*from* × 10

1

(Recess Perkins, Bacon & Co)

1859 (15 June). *Imperf.*

1	1	(½d.) orange (no wmk)	75·00	£500
2		(1d.) blue (wmk "2")	20·00	£180
3		(2d.) carmine (wmk "1")	15·00	£180

On 30 May 1864, the islands were ceded to Greece, and these stamps became obsolete.

Great care should be exercised in buying used stamps, on or off cover, as forged postmarks are plentiful.

Iraq

Indian post offices were opened at Baghdad and Basra, then part of the Turkish Empire, on 1 January 1868. Unoverprinted stamps of India were used, Baghdad being allocated numeral cancellations "356", "18" and "K-6", and Basra (also spelt Bussorah, Busreh, Busrah, Busra) "357", "19" and "1/K-6".

Both offices closed on 30 September 1914, but Basra re-opened the following month when Indian stamps overprinted "I.E.F." were used.

(Currency. 16 annas = 1 rupee)

I. ISSUES FOR BAGHDAD

PRICES FOR STAMPS ON COVER	
Nos 1/25	*from* × 6

BRITISH OCCUPATION

British and Indian troops occupied the port of Basra on 22 November 1914 to protect the oil pipeline. They then advanced up the rivers, and after a hard campaign took Baghdad from the Turks on 11 March 1917.

IN BRITISH BAGHDAD OCCUPATION 2 Ans

(1)

1917 (1 Sept). *Stamps of Turkey, surch as T* **1** *in three operations.*

(a) Pictorial designs of 1914. *T* **32**, *etc., and* **31**

1 **32**	¼ a. on 2 pa. claret (Obelisk)		90·00	£100
	a. "IN BRITISH" omitted		£4750	
2 **34**	¼ a. on 5 pa. dull purple (Leander's Tower)		65·00	70·00
	a. Value omitted		£4500	
3 **36**	½ a. on 10 pa. green (Lighthouse garden)		£550	£600
4 **31**	½ a. on 10 pa. green (Mosque of Selim)		£850	£1000
5 **37**	1 a. on 20 pa. red (Castle)		£325	£350
	a. "BAGHDAD" double		£1300	
6 **38**	2 a. on 1 pi. bright blue (Mosque)		£110	£140

(b) As (a), but overprinted with small five-pointed Star

7 **37**	1 a. on 20 pa. red (B.)		£170	£190
	a. "OCCUPATION" omitted		£4000	
	b. "BAGHDAD" double		£1300	
8 **38**	2 a. on 1 pi. bright blue (R.)		£2250	£3000

(c) Postal Jubilee stamps (Old G.P.O.). P 12½

9 **60**	½ a. on 10 pa. carmine		£300	£325
	a. Perf 13½		£600	£650
10	1 a. on 20 pa. blue		£2750	
	a. Value omitted		£5500	
	b. Perf 13½		£700	£800
11	2 a. on 1 pi. black and violet		£130	£140
	a. "BAGHDAD" omitted		£4000	
	b. Perf 13½		65·00	75·00

(d) T **30** *(G.P.O., Constantinople) with opt T* **26**.

12 **30**	2 a. on 1 pi. ultramarine		£275	£400
	a. "IN BRITISH" omitted		£5000	

(e) Stamps optd with six-pointed Star and Arabic date "1331" within Crescent. T **53** *(except No. 16, which has five-pointed Star and Arabic "1332", T* **57**)

13 **30**	½ a. on 10 pa. green (R.)		65·00	70·00
14	1 a. on 20 pa. rose		£300	£325
	a. Value omitted		£3750	£3750
	b. Optd with T **26** (Arabic letter "B") also		£4250	£4250
15 **23**	1 a. on 20 pa. rose (No. 554a)		£325	£350
	a. Value omitted		£5000	
16 **21**	1 a. on 20 pa. carmine (No. 732)		£2750	£3500
17 **30**	2 a. on 1 pi. ultramarine (R.)		75·00	90·00
	a. "BAGHDAD" omitted		†	—
18 **21**	2 a. on 1 pi. dull blue (No. 543) (R.)		£130	£140
	a. "OCCUPATION" omitted		£5000	

(f) Stamps with similar opt, but date between Star and Crescent (Nos. 19 and 22, T **54**; *others T* **55**, *five-pointed Star)*

19 **23**	½ a. on 10 pa. grey-green (No. 609a) (R.)		80·00	85·00
	a. "OCCUPATION" omitted		£4250	
20 **60**	½ a. on 10 pa. carmine (*p* 12½) (B.)		£120	£130
	a. Perf 13½		£250	£275
21 **30**	1 a. on 20 pa. rose		75·00	95·00
22 **28**	1 a. on 20 pa. rose (Plate II) (No. 617)		£300	£350
23 **15**	1 a. on 10 pa. on 20 pa. claret (No. 630)		£150	£150
	a. "OCCUPATION" omitted		£4500	£4500
24 **30**	2 a. on 1 pi. ultramarine (R.)		£130	£140
	a. "OCCUPATION" omitted		£4500	
	b. "BAGHDAD" omitted		£4500	
25 **28**	2 a. on 1 pi. ultramarine (Pl. II) (No. 645)		£1000	£1200

The last group *(f)* have the Crescent obliterated by hand in violet-black ink, as this included the inscription, "Tax for the relief of children of martyrs".

II. ISSUES FOR MOSUL

PRICES FOR STAMPS ON COVER	
Nos. 1/8	*from* × 40

BRITISH OCCUPATION

A British and Indian force occupied Mosul on 1 November 1918.

As the status of the vilayet was disputed stocks of "IRAQ IN BRITISH OCCUPATION" surcharges were withdrawn in early 1919 and replaced by Nos. 1/8.

POSTAGE

I.E.F. 'D'

1 Anna — (1) 4 — I 4 — II

Two types of tougra in central design:
(a) Large "tougra" or sign-manual of El Ghazi 7 mm high.
(b) Smaller "tougra" of Sultan Rechad 5½ mm high.

Two types of 4 a. surcharge:
I. Normal "4". Apostrophes on D 3½ mm apart.
II. Small "4" Apostrophes on D 4½ mm apart.

1919 (28 Jan). *Turkish Fiscal stamps surch as T* **1** *by Govt Press, Baghdad. P* 11½ (½ *a.*), 12 (1 *a.*), *or* 12½ (*others*).

1	½ a. on 1 pi. green and red		1·40	1·40
2	1 a. on 20 pa. black/*red (a)*		1·40	1·75
	a. Imperf between (horiz pair)		£600	
	b. Surch double		£500	
	c. "A" of "Anna" omitted		£200	
3	1 a. on 20 pa. black/*red (b)*		4·00	3·00
	b. Surch double		£600	
4	2½ a. on 1 pi. mauve and yellow *(b)*		1·50	1·50
	a. No bar to fraction (R. 2/4)		28·00	40·00
	b. Surch double		£650	
5	3 a. on 20 pa. green *(a)*		1·60	3·00
6	3 a. on 20 pa. green and orange *(b)*		30·00	50·00
7	4 a. on 1 pi. deep violet *(a)* (I)		3·00	3·50
	a. "4" omitted		£1400	
	c. Surch double		£800	
7*d*	4 a. on 1 pi. deep violet *(a)* (II)		7·50	9·50
	da. Surch double, one with "4" omitted		£2250	
8	8 a. on 10 pa. lake *(a)*		4·00	5·00
	a. Surch inverted		£600	£700
	b. Surch double		£500	£600
	c. No apostrophe after "D" (R. 1/5)		24·00	35·00
	d. Surch inverted. No apostrophe after "D"			
	e. "na" of "Anna" omitted		£250	
	f. Error. 8 a. on 1 pi. deep violet		£1700	

No. 4a occurs on some sheets only. No. 8c comes from the first setting only.

Nos. 1/8 were replaced by "IRAQ IN BRITISH OCCUPATION" surcharges during 1921.

In December 1925 the League of Nations awarded the vilayet of Mosul to Iraq.

III. ISSUES FOR IRAQ

PRICES FOR STAMPS ON COVER	
Nos. 1/18	*from* × 4
Nos. 41/154	*from* × 2
Nos. O19/171	*from* × 2

BRITISH OCCUPATION

IN BRITISH IRAQ OCCUPATION 1An.

(1)

A

B

1918 (1 Sept)–**21**. *Turkish pictorial issue of* 1914, *surch as T* **1** *by Bradbury Wilkinson. P* 12.

(a) No wmk. Tougra as A (1 Sept 1918–20)

1	**34**	¼ a. on 5 pa. dull purple		30	80
2	**36**	½ a. on 10 pa. green		30	15
3	**37**	1 a. on 20 pa. red		30	10
4	**34**	1½ a. on 5 pa. dull purple (1920)		2·75	50
5	**38**	2½ a. on 1 pi. bright blue		80	1·25
		a. Surch inverted		£3500	
6	**39**	3 a. on 1½ pi. grey and rose		70	25
		a. Surch double (Bk. + R.)		£1500	£2250
7	**40**	4 a. on 1¾ pi. red-brown and grey		70	25
		a. Centre inverted		†	£14000
8	**41**	6 a. on 2 pi. black and green		1·60	1·25
9	**42**	8 a. on 2½ pi. green and orange		90	60
		a. Surch inverted		†	£9000
10	**43**	12 a. on 5 pi. deep lilac		1·75	2·75
11	**44**	1 r. on 10 pi. red-brown		2·25	1·40
12	**45**	2 r. on 25 pi. yellow-green		7·50	2·50
13	**46**	5 r. on 50 pi. rose		20·00	20·00
14	**47**	10 r. on 100 pi. indigo		45·00	17·00
1/14			*Set of* 14	75·00	42·00
1/3, 5/14 Perf "Specimen"			*Set of* 13	£250	

(b) No wmk. Tougra as B *(one device instead of two)* (1921)

15	**44**	1 r. on 10 pi. red-brown		£100	24·00

(c) Wmk Mult Script CA (sideways on ½ *a.,* 1½ *a.)* (1921)

16	**36**	½ a. on 10 pa. green		80	1·25
17	**34**	1½ a. on 5 pa. dull purple		95	95
18	**45**	2 r. on 25 pi. yellow-green		13·00	11·00
16/18			*Set of* 3	13·00	11·50
16/18 Optd "Specimen"			*Set of* 3	50·00	

Designs: *Horiz*—5 pa. Leander's Tower; 10 pa. Lighthouse-garden, Stamboul; 20 pa. Castle of Europe; 1 pi. Mosque of Sultan Ahmed; 1½ pi. Martyrs of Liberty Monument; 1¾ pi. Fountains of Suleiman; 2 pi. Cruiser *Hamidiye*; 2½ pi. Candilli, Bosphorus; 5 pi. Former Ministry of War; 10 pi. Sweet Waters of Europe; 25 pi. Suleiman Mosque; 50 pi. Bosphorus at Rumeli Hisar; 100 pi. Sultan Ahmed's Fountain.

The original settings of Nos. 1/18 showed the surcharge 27 mm wide, except for the 2½ a. (24 mm), 4 a. (26½ mm), 6 a. (32 mm), 8 a. (30½ mm), 12 a. (33 mm), 1 r. (31½ mm), 2 r. (30 mm) and 5 r. (32 mm). The 6 a., 8 a. and 5 r. also exist from a subsequent setting on which the surcharge was 27½ mm wide.

Nos. 2, 3, 5, 6 and 7/9 are known bisected and used on philatelic covers. All such covers have Makinah or F.P.O. 339 cancellations.

During January 1923 an outbreak of cholera in Baghdad led to the temporary use for postal purposes of the above issue overprinted "REVENUE".

LEAGUE OF NATIONS MANDATE

On 25 April 1920 the Supreme Council of the Allies assigned to the United Kingdom a mandate under the League of Nations to administer Iraq.

The Emir Faisal, King of Syria in 1920, was proclaimed King of Iraq on 23 August 1921.

King Faisal I

23 August 1921–8 September 1933

2 Sunni Mosque, Muadhdham

3 Winged Cherub

4 Allegory of Date Palm

(Des Miss Edith Cheesman (½ a., 1 a., 4 a., 6 a., 8 a., 2 r., 5 r., 10 r.), Mrs. C. Garbett (Miss M. Maynard) (others). Typo (1 r.) or recess (others) Bradbury, Wilkinson)

1923 (1 June)–**25**. *T* **2/4** *and similar designs. Wmk Mult Script CA (sideways on 2 a., 3 a., 4 a., 8 a., 5 r.). P* 12.

41 **2** ½ a. olive-green 50 10
42 – 1 a. brown 85 10
43 **3** 1½ a. lake 40 10
44 – 2 a. orange-buff 40 15
45 – 3 a. grey-blue (1923) 85 15
46 – 4 a. violet .. .. 1·50 30
47 – 6 a. greenish blue .. .. 1·00 30
48 – 8 a. olive-bistre .. .. 1·75 30
49 **4** 1 r. brown and blue-green .. .. .. 2·75 90
50 **2** 2 r. black .. .. 12·00 7·00
51 2 r. olive-bistre (1925) .. .. 30·00 3·25
52 – 5 r. orange .. .. 26·00 13·00
53 – 10 r. lake .. .. 32·00 20·00
41/53 .. .. *Set of* 13 95·00 40·00
41/53 Optd "Specimen" .. .. *Set of* 13 £225

Designs: *Horiz (as T* **2**)—1 a. Gufas on the Tigris. (30×24 *mm*) —2 a. Bull from Babylonian wall-sculpture, 6 a., 10 r. Shiah Mosque, Kadhimain. (34×24 *mm*)—3 a. Arch of Ctesiphon. *Vert (as T* **3**)—4 a., 8 a., 5 r. Tribal Standard, Dulaim Camel Corps.

With the exception of Nos. 49 and 50, later printings of these stamps and of No. 78 are on a thinner paper.

10

11

12

King Faisal I

(Recess Bradbury, Wilkinson)

1927 (1 Apr). *Wmk Mult Script CA. P* 12.

78 **10** 1 r. red-brown (Optd S. £30) .. .. 6·00 50

See note below No. 53.

(Recess Bradbury Wilkinson)

1931 (17 Feb). *Wmk Mult Script CA (sideways on* 1 *r. to* 25 *r.). P* 12.

80 **11** ½ a. green 60 10
81 1 a. red-brown 75 10
82 1½ a. scarlet 60 30
83 2 a. orange 65 10
84 3 a. blue 60 10
85 4 a. slate-purple .. .. 1·25 95
86 6 a. greenish blue .. .. 1·25 60
87 8 a. deep green .. .. 1·25 1·50
88 **12** 1 r. chocolate .. .. 3·00 1·25
89 2 r. yellow-brown .. .. 5·50 3·75
90 5 r. orange .. .. 18·00 30·00
91 10 r. scarlet .. .. 50·00 70·00
92 **10** 25 r. violet £500 £650
80/91 .. .. *Set of* 12 75·00 95·00
80/92 Perf "Specimen" .. .. *Set of* 13 £500

(New Currency. 1000 fils = 1 dinar)

(13) (14)

Normal "SIN" — Error "SAD" (R. 8/16 of second setting)

(Surcharged at Govt Ptg Wks, Baghdad)

1932 (1 Apr). *Nos.* 80/92 *and* 46 *surch in* "Fils" *or* "Dinar" *as T* **13** *or* **14**.

106 **11** 2 f. on ½ a. green (R.) 15 10
107 3 f. on ½ a. green 15 10
a. Surch double £140
b. Surch inverted £140
c. Arabic letter "SAD" instead of "SIN" .. .. .. 20·00 20·00
108 4 f. on 1 a. red-brown (G.) .. .. 1·50 25
109 5 f. on 1 a. red-brown 30 10
a. Inverted Arabic "5" (R. 8/11) .. 27·00 32·00
b. Surch inverted £250
110 8 f. on 1½ a. scarlet 35 30
a. Surch inverted £140
111 10 f. on 2 a. orange 35 10
a. Inverted Arabic "1" (R. 8/13) .. 18·00 18·00
b. No space between "10" and "Fils" 35 10
112 15 f. on 3 a. blue .. .. .. 75 1·00
113 20 f. on 4 a. slate-purple .. .. .. 1·00 1·00
a. Surch inverted £250
114 – 25 f. on 4 a. violet (No. 46) .. .. 1·50 2·75
a. "Flis" for "Fils" (R. 2/1, 10/8, 10/15) £300 £350
b. Inverted Arabic "5" (R. 10/7, 10/14) £350 £450
c. Vars a and b in *se-tenant* pair .. £700
d. Error. 20 f. on 4 a. violet (R. 10/1, 10/9) £1200
115 **11** 30 f. on 6 a. greenish blue .. .. 1·50 60
a. Error. 80 f. on 6 a. greenish blue £1000
116 40 f. on 8 a. deep green .. .. 2·25 2·25
117 **12** 75 f. on 1 r. chocolate .. .. 1·75 2·25
a. Inverted Arabic "5" .. .. 30·00 38·00
118 100 f. on 2 r. yellow-brown .. .. 5·50 3·75
119 200 f. on 5 r. orange .. .. .. 11·00 16·00
120 ½ d. on 10 r. scarlet .. .. .. 48·00 65·00
a. No bar in English "½" £600 £650
b. *Scarlet-vermilion* .. .. .. 48·00 75·00
121 **10** 1 d. on 25 r. violet .. .. .. 80·00 £130
106/121 .. .. *Set of* 16 £130 £200

Nos. 106/13 and 115/16 were in sheets of 160 (16×10), No. 114 sheets of 150 (15×10) and Nos. 117/21 sheets of 100 (10×10). There were three settings of the surcharge for the 3 f. and two settings for the 5, 10, 25, 40, 100 and 200 f. Nos. 109a and 111a come from the first setting and Nos. 107c, 111b and 114a/b come from the second.

No. 109a can be easily identified as it shows the point of the Arabic numeral at the foot of the surcharge.

All 10 f. stamps from the second setting are as No. 111b except for R. 4/7–8 and 15–16 where the spacing is the same as for the first setting (Type **13**).

No. 114d shows "20" instead of "25". Many examples of this error were removed from the sheets before issue. The Arabic value "25" was unaltered.

No. 115a shows the error in the English face value only.

No. 117a occurs on R. 1/2, 1/7 and a third position in the first vertical row not yet identified.

No. 120a occurs on R. 10/1, one position in the first horizontal row and another in the second.

No. 120b was a special printing of No. 91 which does not exist unsurcharged.

15

1932 (9 May). *T* **10** *to* **12**, *but with values altered to* "FILS" *or* "DINAR" *as in T* **15**. *Wmk Mult Script CA (sideways on* 50 *f. to* 1 *d.). P* 12.

138 **11** 2 f. ultramarine 40 10
139 3 f. green 40 10
140 4 f. brown-purple 40 10
141 5 f. grey-green 50 10
142 8 f. scarlet 90 10
143 10 f. yellow 90 10
144 15 f. blue 90 10
145 20 f. orange 90 40
146 25 f. mauve 90 30
147 30 f. bronze-green .. .. .. 1·50 15
148 40 f. violet 90 70
149 **12** 50 f. brown 90 20
150 75 f. dull ultramarine .. .. .. 1·75 1·75
151 100 f. deep green .. .. .. 3·25 70
152 200 f. scarlet .. .. 11·00 3·25
153 **10** ½ d. deep blue .. .. .. 32·00 32·00
154 1 d. claret .. .. 65·00 65·00
138/154 .. .. .. *Set of* 17 £110 95·00
138/54 Perf "Specimen" .. .. *Set of* 17 £180

OFFICIAL STAMPS

ON STATE SERVICE

(O 2)

1920 (1 May)–**23**. *As Nos.* 1/18, *but surch includes additional wording* "ON STATE SERVICE" *as Type* O **2** *in black*.

(a) No wmk. Tougra as A (1920)

O19 **36** ½ a. on 10 pa. blue-green .. .. 3·25 80
O20 **37** 1 a. on 20 pa. red .. .. .. 1·50 60
O21 **34** 1½ a. on 5 pa. purple-brown .. .. 7·50 1·75
O22 **38** 2½ a. on 1 pi. blue .. .. .. 1·50 2·25
O23 **39** 3 a. on 1½ pi. black and rose .. .. 7·50 80
O24 **40** 4 a. on 1¾ pi. red-brown and grey-blue 9·00 2·00
O25 **41** 6 a. on 2 pi. black and green .. .. 11·00 4·75
O26 **42** 8 a. on 2½ pi. yellow-green & orge-brn 10·00 2·75
O27 **43** 12 a. on 5 pi. purple .. .. .. 7·50 4·50
O28 **44** 1 r. on 10 pi. red-brown .. .. 8·00 4·25
O29 **45** 2 r. on 25 pi. olive-green .. .. 16·00 10·00
O30 **46** 5 r. on 50 pi. rose-carmine .. .. 32·00 23·00
O31 **47** 10 r. on 100 pi. slate-blue .. .. 50·00 60·00
O19/31 .. .. .. *Set of* 13 £150 £100

(b) No wmk. Tougra as B *(No. 15) (1922)*

O32 **44** 1 r. on 10 pi. red-brown .. .. .. 19·00 7·00

(c) Wmk Mult Script CA (sideways on ½ *a. to* 8 *a.)* (1921–23)

O33 **36** ½ a. on 10 pa. green 70 70
O34 **37** 1 a. on 20 pa. red .. .. .. 1·75 70
O35 **34** 1½ a. on 5 pa. purple-brown .. .. 1·75 45
O36 **40** 4 a. on 1¾ pi. red-brown and grey-blue 2·00 90
O37 **41** 6 a. on 2 pi. black and green (10.3.23) 11·00 65·00
O38 **42** 8 a. on 2½ pi. yellow-green & orge-brn 3·00 2·00
O39 **43** 12 a. on 5 pi. purple (10.3.23) .. 13·00 55·00
O40 **45** 2 r. on 25 pi. olive-green (10.3.23) .. 42·00 70·00
O33/40 .. .. .. *Set of* 8 65·00 £170
O33/40 Optd "Specimen" .. .. *Set of* 8 £120

Nos. O25/6, O30 and O37/8 only exist from the setting with the surcharge 27½ mm wide.

ON STATE SERVICE

(O 6)

ON
STATE
SERVICE

(O 7)

1923. *Optd with Types* O **6** *(horiz designs) or* O **7** *(vert designs)*.

O54 **2** ½ a. olive-green 80 30
O55 – 1 a. brown 80 10
O56 **3** 1½ a. lake .. .. 1·75 45
O57 – 2 a. orange-buff .. .. 1·75 20
O58 – 3 a. grey-blue .. .. 2·50 85
O59 – 4 a. violet .. .. 3·00 40
O60 – 6 a. greenish blue .. .. 3·75 1·25
O61 – 8 a. olive-bistre .. .. 4·00 1·25
O62 **4** 1 r. brown and blue-green .. .. 5·50 1·25
O63 **2** 2 r. black (R.) .. .. 20·00 8·00
O64 – 5 r. orange .. .. 48·00 25·00
O65 – 10 r. lake .. .. 70·00 48·00
O54/65 .. .. *Set of* 12 £140 75·00
O54/65 Optd "Specimen" .. .. *Set of* 12 £200

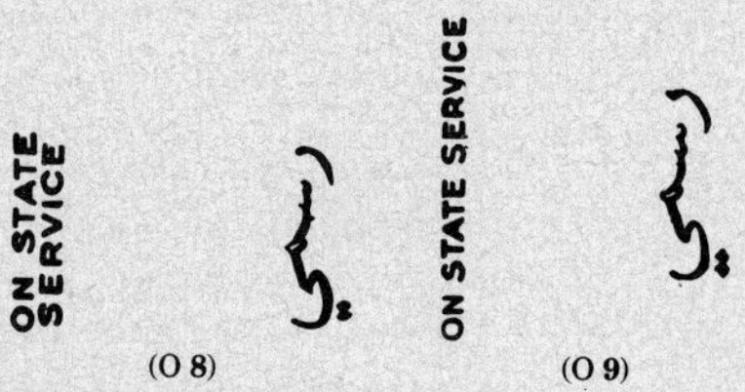

(O 8) (O 9)

1924–25. *Optd with Types* O **8** *(horiz designs) or* O **9** *(vert designs)*.

O66 **2** ½ a. olive-green 75 10
O67 – 1 a. brown 50 10
O68 **3** 1½ a. lake 70 10
O69 – 2 a. orange-buff .. .. 1·00 10
O70 – 3 a. grey-blue .. .. 1·25 10
O71 – 4 a. violet .. .. 3·00 30
O72 – 6 a. greenish blue .. .. 1·75 20
O73 – 8 a. olive-bistre .. .. 2·00 35
O74 **4** 1 r. brown and blue-green .. .. 9·50 1·00
O75 **2** 2 r. olive-bistre (1925) .. .. .. 27·00 3·75
O76 – 5 r. orange .. .. 45·00 42·00
O77 – 10 r. lake .. .. 65·00 42·00
O66/77 .. .. *Set of* 12 £140 80·00
O66/77 Optd "Specimen" .. .. *Set of* 12 £200

1927 (1 Apr). *Optd with Type* O **9**.

O79 **10** 1 r. red-brown (Optd S. £30) .. .. 5·50 1·75

ON STATE SERVICE

ON STATE SERVICE رسمي

رسمي

(O 12) (O 13)

1931. *Optd. (a) As Type* O **12**.

O 93 **11** ½ a. green .. .. 40 2·75
O 94 1 a. red-brown 60 10
O 95 1½ a. scarlet .. .. 4·50 16·00
O 96 2 a. orange 60 10
O 97 3 a. blue 85 70
O 98 4 a. slate-purple 95 90
O 99 6 a. greenish blue .. .. 3·75 14·00
O100 8 a. deep green .. .. 3·75 14·00

(b) As Type O **13**, *horizontally*

O101 **12** 1 r. chocolate .. .. 12·00 13·00
O102 2 r. yellow-brown .. .. 19·00 48·00
O103 5 r. orange .. .. 38·00 85·00
O104 10 r. scarlet .. .. 70·00 £140

(c) As Type O **13**, *vertically upwards*

O105 **10** 25 r. violet £550 £700
O93/104 .. .. *Set of* 12 £140 £300
O93/105 Perf "Specimen" .. .. *Set of* 13 £500

1932 (1 Apr). *Official issues of* 1924–25 *and* 1931 *surch in* "FILS" *or* "DINAR", *as T* **13** *or* **14**.

O122 **11** 3 f. on ½ a. green .. .. .. 3·25 3·25
a. Pair, one without surch £250
O123 4 f. on 1 a. red-brown (G.) .. .. 2·25 10
O124 5 f. on 1 a. red-brown .. .. 2·25 10
a. Inverted Arabic "5" (R. 8/11) .. 40·00 28·00
O125 **3** 8 f. on 1½ a. lake (No. O68) .. .. 3·50 50
O126 **11** 10 f. on 2 a. orange .. .. .. 2·50 10
a. Inverted Arabic "1" (R. 8/13) .. 32·00 25·00
b. "10" omitted .. .. .. † £1500
c. No space between "10" and "Fils" 2·50 10
O127 15 f. on 3 a. blue .. .. .. 3·50 85
O128 20 f. on 4 a. slate-purple .. .. 3·50 1·10
O129 25 f. on 4 a. slate-purple .. .. 3·75 1·25
O130 – 30 f. on 6 a. greenish blue (No. O72) 3·75 1·75
O131 **11** 40 f. on 8 a. deep green .. .. 3·75 3·50
a. "Flis" for "Fils" (R. 7/5, 7/13) .. £200 £275
O132 **12** 50 f. on 1 r. chocolate .. .. 3·75 3·50
a. Inverted Arabic "5" (R. 1/2) .. 65·00 75·00
O133 75 f. on 1 r. chocolate .. .. 5·50 6·00
a. Inverted Arabic "5" .. .. 45·00 55·00
O134 **2** 100 f. on 2 r. olive-bistre (surch at top) 10·00 3·50
a. Surch at foot .. .. .. 11·00 9·00
O135 – 200 f. on 5 r. orange (No. O76) .. 20·00 20·00
O136 – ½ d. on 10 r. lake (No. O77) .. .. 50·00 70·00
a. No bar in English "½" (R. 2/10) £650 £750
O137 **10** 1 d. on 25 r. violet .. .. .. 85·00 £140
O122/37 .. .. .. *Set of* 16 £180 £225

Nos. O122/4, O126/9 and O131 were in sheets of 160 (16×10), Nos. O130, O134 and O136 150 (10×15), No. O135 150 (15×10) and Nos. O125, O132/3 and O137 in sheets of 100 (10×10). There was a second setting of the surcharge for the 3 f. (equivalent to the third postage setting), 10 f. to 25 f., 40 f. to 100 f. and 1 d. Nos. O126c, O131a and O134a come from the second setting.

All 100 f. stamps from the second setting are as No. O134a. For notes on other varieties see below No. 121.

932 (9 May). *Optd. (a) As Type* O **12**.
155 **11** 2 f. ultramarine .. .. 1·00 10
156 3 f. green .. .. 1·00 10
157 4 f. brown-purple .. .. 1·00 10
158 5 f. grey-green .. .. 1·00 10
159 8 f. scarlet .. .. 1·00 10
160 10 f. yellow .. .. 1·75 10
161 15 f. blue .. .. 2·25 10
162 20 f. orange .. .. 2·25 15
163 25 f. mauve .. .. 2·00 15
164 30 f. bronze-green .. .. 3·25 20
165 40 f. violet .. .. 4·25 20

(b) As Type O **13**, *horizontally*
166 **12** 50 f. brown .. .. 3·00 20
167 75 f. dull ultramarine .. .. 2·25 90
168 100 f. deep green .. .. .. 9·00 1·00
169 200 f. scarlet .. .. 18·00 6·50

(c) As Type O **13**, *vertically upwards*
170 **10** ½ d. deep blue .. .. .. 12·00 21·00
171 1 d. claret .. .. 50·00 70·00
155/71 .. .. *Set of* 17 £100 90·00
155/71 Perf "Specimen" .. *Set of* 17 £300

The British Mandate was given up on 3 October 1932 and Iraq became an independent kingdom. Later issues will be found listed in Part 19 (*Middle East*) of this catalogue.

Ireland (Republic)

All the issues of Ireland are listed together here, in this section of the Gibbons Catalogue, purely as a matter of convenience to collectors.

PRICES FOR STAMPS ON COVER TO 1945	
Nos. 1/15	*from* × 5
Nos. 17/21	*from* × 3
Nos. 26/9*a*	*from* × 5
Nos. 30/43	*from* × 4
Nos. 44/6	—
Nos. 47/63	*from* × 5
Nos. 64/6	*from* × 3
Nos. 67/70	*from* × 6
Nos. 71/82	*from* × 2
Nos. 83/8	*from* × 3
Nos. 89/98	*from* × 2
Nos. 99/104	*from* × 3
Nos. 105/37	*from* × 2
Nos. D1/4	*from* × 7
Nos. D5/14	*from* × 6

PROVISIONAL GOVERNMENT

16 January—6 December 1922

Stamps of Great Britain overprinted. T 104/8, W 100; T 109, W 110

Rialtas Sealadac na hÉireann 1922
(1)

Rialtas Sealadac na hÉireann 1922.
(2)

Rialtas Sealadac na hÉireann 1922
(3)

("Provisional Government of Ireland, 1922")

1922 (17 Feb–July). *T* **104** *to* **108** (*W* **100**) *and* **109** *of Great Britain overprinted in black.*

(a) With T **1**, *by Dollard Printing House Ltd. Optd in black**
1 **105** ½d. green 85 40
a. Opt inverted £400 £550
2 **104** 1d. scarlet .. .. 1·25 35
a. Opt inverted £250 £300
b. Opt double, both inverted, one albino £350
c. Opt double .. .. † —
w. Wmk inverted .. .. — £150
3 1d. carmine-red .. .. 2·25 50
4 2½d. bright blue .. .. 1·50 4·50
a. Red opt (1 Apr) .. .. .. 85 3·25
5 **106** 3d. bluish violet .. .. .. 4·00 3·75
6 4d. grey-green .. .. 3·25 9·50
a. Red opt (1 Apr) .. .. .. 8·00 15·00
b. Carmine opt (July) .. .. .. 40·00 65·00
7 **107** 5d. yellow-brown .. .. .. 3·75 8·50
x. Wmk reversed .. .. .. — £200
8 **108** 9d. agate .. .. 10·00 20·00
a. Opt double, one albino .. ..
b. Red opt (1 Apr) .. .. .. 13·00 17·00
c. Carmine opt (July) .. .. .. 80·00 85·00
9 10d. turquoise-blue .. .. .. 8·00 35·00
1/9 .. .. *Set of* 8 28·00 70·00

*All values except 2½d. and 4d. are known with greyish black overprint, but these are difficult to distinguish.

The carmine overprints on the 4d. and 9d. may have been produced by Alex Thom & Co. Ltd. There was a further overprinting of the 2½d. at the same time, but this is difficult to distinguish.

The ½d. with red overprint is a trial or proof printing (*Price* £150).

Bogus inverted T **1** overprints exist on the 2d., 4d., 9d and 1s. values.

(b) With T **2**, *by Alex Thom & Co Ltd.*
10 **105** 1½d. red-brown .. .. .. 1·25 85
a. Error. "PENCF" £350 £275
w. Wmk inverted .. .. .. — £120
x. Wmk reversed .. .. .. — £120
12 **106** 2d. orange (Die I) .. .. .. 2·25 50
a. Opt inverted £180 £250
w. Wmk inverted .. .. .. — £100
x. Wmk reversed .. .. .. — £120
13 2d. orange (Die II) .. .. .. 2·00 50
a. Opt inverted £300 £400
w. Wmk inverted .. .. .. — £120
14 **107** 6d. reddish pur (*chalk-surfaced paper*) 11·00 12·00
15 **108** 1s. bistre-brown .. .. .. 11·00 9·00
10/15 .. .. *Set of* 5 24·00 20·00

Varieties occur throughout the T **2** overprint in the relative positions of the lines of the overprint, the "R" of "Rialtas" being over either the "Se" or "S" of "Sealadac" or intermediately.

(c) With T **3** *by Dollard Printing House Ltd*
17 **109** 2s. 6d. chocolate-brown .. .. 35·00 65·00
18 2s. 6d. reddish brown .. .. 50·00 75·00
19 5s. rose-red .. .. 60·00 £120
21 10s. dull grey-blue £120 £250
17/21 .. .. *Set of* 3 £190 £400

1922 (19 June–Aug). *Optd as T* **2**, *in black, by Harrison & Sons, for use in horiz and vert coils.*
26 **105** ½d. green .. .. 2·25 10·00
27 **104** 1d. scarlet .. .. 2·50 6·00
28 **105** 1½d. red-brown (21.6) .. .. 4·00 32·00
29 **106** 2d. bright orange (Die I) .. .. 18·00 28·00
29*a* 2d. bright orange (Die II) (August) 19·00 25·00
ay. Wmk inverted and reversed .. — £200
26/9*a* .. .. *Set of* 5 40·00 90·00

The Harrison overprint measures 15×17 mm (maximum) against the 14½×16 mm of T **2** (Thom printing) and is a much bolder black than the latter, while the individual letters are taller, the "i" of "Rialtas" being specially outstanding as it extends below the foot of the "R".

The "R" of "Rialtas" is always over the "Se" of "Sealadac".

1922. *Optd by Thom.*

(a) As T **2** *but bolder, in dull to shiny blue-black or red* (June–Nov)
30 **105** ½d. green .. .. 1·75 80
31 **104** 1d. scarlet .. .. 1·00 50
a. "Q" for "O" (No. 357ab) £1200 £1100
b. Reversed "Q" for "O" (No. 357ac) £350 £250
32 **105** 1½d. red-brown .. .. .. 3·25 3·25
33 **106** 2d. orange (Die I) .. .. .. 17·00 2·00
34 2d. orange (Die II) .. .. .. 2·50 50
y. Wmk inverted and reversed .. £120 £120
35 **104** 2½d. blue (R.) .. .. .. 6·00 18·00
36 **106** 3d. violet .. .. 2·25 2·00
y. Wmk inverted and reversed .. 75·00 75·00
37 4d. grey-green (R.) .. .. .. 3·00 4·50
38 **107** 5d. yellow-brown .. .. .. 4·00 8·50
39 6d. reddish pur (*chalk-surfaced paper*) 7·50 3·00
w. Wmk inverted .. .. .. 75·00 50·00
40 **108** 9d. agate (R.) .. .. .. 12·00 15·00
41 9d. olive-green (R.) .. .. .. 4·75 30·00
42 10d. turquoise-blue .. .. .. 25·00 48·00
43 1s. bistre-brown .. .. .. 8·50 11·00
30/43 .. .. *Set of* 14 80·00 £130

Both 2d. stamps exist with the overprint inverted but there remains some doubt as to whether they were issued.

These Thom printings are distinguishable from the Harrison printings by the size of the overprint, and from the previous Thom printings by the intensity and colour of the overprint, the latter being best seen when the stamp is looked through with a strong light behind it.

(b) As with T **3**, *but bolder, in shiny blue-black* (Oct–Dec)
44 **109** 2s. 6d. chocolate-brown £180 £250
45 5s. rose-red £170 £275
46 10s. dull grey-blue £850 £1000
44/6 .. .. *Set of* 3 £1100 £1400

The above differ from Nos. 17/21 not only in the bolder impression and colour of the ink but also in the "h" and "é" of "héireann" which are closer together and horizontally aligned.

Rialtas Sealadac na hÉireann 1922.
(4)

Saorstát Éireann 1922
(5 Wide date)
("Irish Free State 1922")

1922 (21 Nov–Dec). *Optd by Thom with T* **4** (*wider setting*) *in shiny blue-black.*
47 **105** ½d. green .. .. 1·00 1·75
a. Opt in jet-black .. .. .. £100 90·00
48 **104** 1d. scarlet .. .. 3·75 2·50
49 **105** 1½d. red-brown (4 December) .. 3·00 9·00
50 **106** 2d. orange (Die II) .. .. .. 9·00 6·50
51 **108** 1s. olive-bistre (4 December) .. 45·00 48·00
47/51 .. .. *Set of* 5 55·00 60·00

The overprint T 4 measures 15¾ × 16 mm (maximum).

OMNIBUS ISSUES

Details, together with prices for complete sets, of the various Omnibus issues from the 1935 Silver Jubilee series to date are included in a special section following Zimbabwe at the end of Volume 2.

IRISH FREE STATE

6 December 1922—29 December 1937

1922 (Dec)–**23.**

(a) Optd by Thom with T **5**, *in dull to shiny blue-black or red*
52 **105** ½d. green .. .. 1·00 30
a. No accent in "Saorstat" £1000 £900
b. Accent inserted by hand .. .. 85·00 95·00
53 **104** 1d. scarlet 75 40
aa. No accent in "Saorstat" £7000 £5000
a. No accent and final "t" missing .. £6000 £4500
b. Accent inserted by hand £130 £150
c. Accent and "t" inserted £225 £250
d. Reversed "Q" for "O" (No. 357ac) £300 £250
54 **105** 1½d. red-brown .. .. .. 3·25 8·50
55 **106** 2d. orange (Die II) .. .. .. 1·00 1·50
56 **104** 2½d. bright blue (R.) (6.1.23) .. 6·00 7·00
a. No accent £140 £170
57 **106** 3d. bluish violet (6.1.23) .. .. 3·50 11·00
a. No accent £250 £275
58 4d. grey-green (R.) (16.1.23) .. .. 2·75 5·50
a. No accent £150 £170
59 **107** 5d. yellow-brown .. .. .. 3·25 4·75
60 6d. reddish pur (*chalk-surfaced paper*) 2·00 2·00
a. Accent inserted by hand £700 £700
y. Wmk inverted and reversed .. 50·00 30·00
61 **108** 9d. olive-green (R.) .. .. .. 3·00 5·50
a. No accent £250 £275
62 10d. turquoise-blue .. .. .. 16·00 48·00
63 1s. bistre-brown .. .. .. 7·00 10·00
a. No accent £5500 £6500
b. Accent inserted by hand £600 £650
64 **109** 2s. 6d. chocolate-brown .. .. 35·00 55·00
a. Major Re-entry £850 £950
b. No accent £350 £400
c. Accent reversed £425 £475
65 5s. rose-red .. .. 65·00 £120
a. No accent £450 £500
b. Accent reversed £550 £600
66 10s. dull grey-blue £140 £275
a. No accent £2000 £2500
b. Accent reversed £2750 £3500
52/66 .. .. *Set of* 15 £250 £500

The accents inserted by hand are in dull black. The reversed accents are grave (thus "à") instead of acute ("á"). A variety with "S" of "Saorstat" directly over "é" of "éireann", instead of to left, may be found in all values except the 2½d. and 4d. In the 2s. 6d., 5s. and 10s. it is very slightly to the left in the "S" over "é" variety, bringing the "á" of "Saorstat" directly above the last "n" of "éireann".

(b) Optd with T **5**, *in dull or shiny blue-black, by Harrison, for use in horiz or vert coils* (7.3.23)
67 ½d. green .. .. 1·75 9·50
a. Long "1" in "1922" .. .. .. 20·00 48·00
y. Wmk inverted and reversed .. ..
68 1d. scarlet .. .. 4·00 9·50
a. Long "1" in "1922" .. .. .. 75·00 £140
69 1½d. red-brown .. .. 6·00 40·00
a. Long "1" in "1922" .. .. .. 85·00 £225
70 2d. orange (Die II) .. .. .. 6·00 8·50
a. Long "1" in "1922" .. .. .. 26·00 45·00
w. Wmk inverted .. .. .. — £150
67/70 .. .. *Set of* 4 16·00 60·00

In the Harrison overprint the characters are rather bolder than those of the Thom overprint, and the foot of the "1" of "1922" is usually rounded instead of square. The long "1" in "1922" has a serif at foot. The second "e" of "éireann" appears to be slightly raised.

PRINTERS. The following and all subsequent issues to No. 148 were printed at the Government Printing Works, Dublin, *unless otherwise stated.*

6 "Sword of Light"

7 Map of Ireland

8 Arms of Ireland

9 Celtic Cross

10

(Des J. J. O'Reilly, T **6**; J. Ingram, T **7**; Miss M. Girling, T **8**; and Miss L. Williams, T **9**. Typo. Plates made by Royal Mint, London)

1922 (6 Dec)–**34.** *W* **10**. *P* 15×14.
71 **6** ½d. bright green (20.4.23) 85 75
a. Imperf × perf 14, wmk sideways (11.34) .. .. 24·00 45·00
w. Wmk inverted .. .. .. 30·00 15·00
72 **7** 1d. carmine (23.2.23) 90 10
a. Perf 15 × imperf (single perf) (1933) 85·00 £160
c. Perf 15 × imperf (7.34) .. .. 18·00 40·00
cw. Wmk inverted .. .. ..
d. Booklet pane. Three stamps plus three printed labels (21.8.31) .. £225
dw. Wmk inverted .. .. ..
73 1½d. claret (2.2.23) .. .. .. 1·40 1·75
w. Wmk inverted .. .. ..
74 2d. grey-green (6.12.22) .. .. 1·25 10
a. Imperf × perf 14, wmk sideways (11.34) .. .. 42·00 70·00
b. Perf 15 × imperf (1934) £8500 £1500
w. Wmk inverted .. .. .. 20·00 5·00
y. Wmk inverted and reversed .. .. 30·00 7·00

5 8 2½d. red-brown (7.9.23) .. 3·75 3·50
w. Wmk inverted .. 50·00 8·00
5 9 3d. ultramarine (16.3.23) .. 1·75 75
w. Wmk inverted .. 65·00 12·00
7 8 4d. slate-blue (28.9.23) .. 2·00 3·25
w. Wmk inverted .. 75·00 25·00
3 6 5d. deep violet (11.5.23) .. 8·00 9·50
w. Wmk inverted
9 6d. claret (21.12.23) .. 3·75 3·50
w. Wmk inverted .. £110 25·00
) 8 9d. deep violet (26.10.23) .. 13·00 9·00
w. Wmk inverted
1 9 10d. brown (11.5.23) .. 9·00 18·00
w. Wmk inverted
2 6 1s. light blue (15.6.23) .. 17·00 5·50
w. Wmk inverted
1/82 .. *Set of* 12 55·00 50·00

No. 72a is imperf vertically except for a single perf at each top corner. It was issued for use in automatic machines.

See also Nos. 111/22 and 227/8.

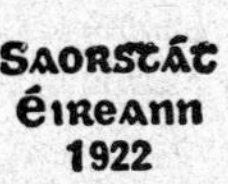

(11 Narrow Date)

12 Daniel O'Connell

1925 (Aug)–28. *T* **109** *of Great Britain (Bradbury, Wilkinson printing) optd at the Government Printing Works, Dublin or by Harrison and Sons. (a) With T* **11** *in black or grey-black* (25.8.25).
3 2s. 6d. chocolate-brown .. 38·00 80·00
a. Wide and narrow date (pair) (1927) .. £250
4 5s. rose-red .. 50·00 £120
a. Wide and narrow date (pair) (1927) .. £400
5 10s. dull grey-blue .. £110 £275
a. Wide and narrow date (pair) (1927) .. £1000
3/5 .. *Set of* 3 £180 £425

The varieties with wide and narrow date *se-tenant* are from what known as the "composite setting," in which some stamps showed the wide date, as T **5**, while in others the figures were close together, as in T **11**.

Single specimens of this printing with wide date may be distinguished from Nos. 64 to 66 by the colour of the ink, which is black or grey-black in the composite setting and blue-black in the Thom printing.

The type of the "composite" overprint usually shows distinct signs of wear.

(*b*) *As T* **5** (*wide date*) *in black* (1927–28)
6 2s. 6d. chocolate-brown (9.12.27) .. 42·00 42·00
a. Circumflex accent over "a" .. £200 £250
b. No accent over "a" .. £350 £375
c. Flat accent on "a" .. £300 £350
7 5s. rose-red (2.28) .. 60·00 80·00
a. Circumflex accent over "a" .. £325 £375
c. Flat accent on "a" .. £400 £450
8 10s. dull grey-blue (15.2.28) .. £150 £170
a. Circumflex accent over "a" .. £800 £900
c. Flat accent on "a" .. £900 £1000
6/8 .. *Set of* 3 £225 £250

This printing can be distinguished from the Thom overprints in all black, by the clear, heavy impression (in deep black) which often shows in relief on the back of the stamp.

The variety showing a circumflex accent over the "a" occurred on R.9/2. The overprint in this position finally deteriorated to such an extent that some examples of the 2s. 6d. were without accent (No. 86b). A new cliché was then introduced with the accent virtually flat and which also showed damage to the "a" and the crossbar of the "t".

(Des L. Whelan. Typo)

1929 (22 June). *Catholic Emancipation Centenary.* W**10.** *P* 15 × 14.
) 12 2d. grey-green .. 50 45
) 3d. blue .. 4·00 8·50
1 9d. bright violet .. 4·00 4·00
9/91 .. *Set of* 3 7·50 11·50

13 Shannon Barrage

14 Reaper

(Des E. L. Lawrenson. Typo)

1930 (15 Oct). *Completion of Shannon Hydro-Electric Scheme.* W **10.** *P* 15 × 14.
2 13 2d. agate .. 80 55

(T **14** and **15** des G. Atkinson. Typo)

1931 (12 June). *Bicentenary of the Royal Dublin Society.* W **10.** *P* 15 × 14.
3 14 2d. blue .. 65 30

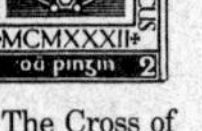

5 The Cross of Cong

16 Adoration of the Cross

17 Hurler

1932 (12 May). *International Eucharistic Congress.* W **10.** *P* 15×14.
94 15 2d. grey-green .. 90 30
w. Wmk inverted
95 3d. blue .. 2·25 5·00

(T **16** to **19** des R. J. King. Typo)

1933 (18 Sept). *"Holy Year".* W **10.** *P* 15 × 14.
96 16 2d. grey-green .. 1·00 15
97 3d. blue .. 2·50 2·00

1934 (27 July). *Golden Jubilee of the Gaelic Athletic Association.* W **10.** *P* 15 × 14.
98 17 2d. green .. 75 45

1935 (Mar–July). *T* **109** *of Great Britain (Waterlow printings) optd as T* **5** *(wide date), at the Government Printing Works, Dublin.*
99 109 2s. 6d. chocolate (No. 450) .. 45·00 48·00
a. Flat accent on "a" (R. 9/2) .. £225 £200
100 5s. bright rose-red (No. 451) .. 80·00 80·00
a. Flat accent on "a" (R. 9/2) .. £300 £250
101 10s. indigo (No. 452) .. £350 £350
a. Flat accent on "a" (R. 9/2) .. £900 £750
99/101 .. *Set of* 3 £425 £425

18 St. Patrick

19 Ireland and New Constitution

1937 (8 Sept). W **10.** *P* 14×15.
102 18 2s. 6d. emerald-green .. £140 65·00
w. Wmk inverted .. £600 £225
103 5s. maroon .. £180 £110
w. Wmk inverted .. £500 £225
104 10s. deep blue .. £140 50·00
w. Wmk inverted
102/4 .. *Set of* 3 £425 £200

See also Nos. 123/5.

EIRE

29 December 1937—17 April 1949

1937 (29 Dec). *Constitution Day.* W **10.** *P* 15×14.
105 19 2d. claret .. 1·00 20
w. Wmk inverted .. — £180
106 3d. blue .. 4·00 3·50

For similar stamps see Nos. 176/7.

20 Father Mathew

(Des S. Keating. Typo)

1938 (1 July). *Centenary of Temperance Crusade.* W **10.** *P* 15×14.
107 20 2d. black .. 1·50 30
w. Wmk inverted
108 3d. blue .. 8·50 6·00

21 George Washington, American Eagle and Irish Harp

22

(Des G. Atkinson. Typo)

1939 (1 Mar). *150th Anniv of U.S. Constitution and Installation of First U.S. President.* W **10.** *P* 15 × 14.
109 21 2d. scarlet .. 1·75 60
110 3d. blue .. 3·25 4·00

SIZE OF WATERMARK. T **22** can be found in various sizes from about 8 to 10 mm high. This is due to the use of two different dandy rolls supplied by different firms and to the effects of paper shrinkage and other factors such as pressure and machine speed.

COVER PRICES

Cover factors are quoted at the beginning of each country for most issues to 1945. An explanation of the system can be found on page x. The factors quoted do not, however, apply to philatelic covers.

White line above left value tablet joining horizontal line to ornament (R. 3/7)

1940–68. *Typo.* W **22.** *P* 15×14 *or* 14×15 (2*s.* 6*d. to* 10*s.*).
111 6 ½d. bright green (24.11.40) .. 2·00 40
w. Wmk inverted .. 50·00 6·50
112 7 1d. carmine (26.10.40) .. 30 10
aw. Wmk inverted .. 1·60 25
b. From coils. Perf 14×imperf (9.40) 65·00 65·00
c. From coils. Perf 15×imperf (20.3.46) .. 40·00 15·00
cw. Wmk inverted .. 40·00 15·00
d. Booklet pane. Three stamps plus three printed labels .. £1500
dw. Wmk inverted
113 1½d. claret (1.40) .. 13·00 30
w. Wmk inverted .. 29·00 7·50
114 2d. grey-green (1.40) .. 30 10
w. Wmk inverted .. 2·25 75
115 8 2½d. red-brown (3.41) .. 9·00 15
w. Wmk inverted .. 19·00 4·00
116 9 3d. blue (12.40) .. 60 10
w. Wmk inverted .. 3·50 50
117 8 4d. slate-blue (12.40) .. 55 10
w. Wmk inverted .. 13·00 2·75
118 6 5d. deep violet (7.40) .. 65 10
w. Wmk inverted .. 26·00 1·50
119 6d. claret (3.42) .. 2·25 50
aw. Wmk inverted .. 18·00 3·00
b. Chalk-surfaced paper (1967) .. 1·25 20
bw. Wmk inverted .. 13·00 2·50
119*c* 8d. scarlet (12.9.49) .. 80 70
cw. Wmk inverted .. 32·00 10·00
120 8 9d. deep violet (7.40) .. 1·50 70
w. Wmk inverted .. 9·50 2·00
121 9 10d. brown (7.40) .. 60 70
aw. Wmk inverted .. 10·00 3·50
121*b* 11d. rose (12.9.49) .. 1·50 2·25
122 6 1s. light blue (6.40) .. 80·00 17·00
w. Wmk inverted .. £600 £150
123 18 2s. 6d. emerald-green (10.2.43) .. 40·00 1·25
aw. Wmk inverted .. 80·00 20·00
b. Chalk-surfaced paper (1968?) .. 1·50 2·25
bw. Wmk inverted .. 28·00 4·00
124 5s. maroon (15.12.42) .. 40·00 3·00
a. Line flaw
bw. Wmk inverted .. £150 30·00
c. Chalk-surfaced paper (1968?) .. 13·00 4·00
ca. Purple .. 6·00 7·50
cb. Line flaw .. 80·00
cw. Wmk inverted .. 35·00 9·00
125 10s. deep blue (7.45) .. 60·00 6·00
aw. Wmk inverted .. £170 65·00
b. Chalk-surfaced paper (1968) .. 19·00 11·00
ba. Blue .. 9·00 16·00
bw. Wmk inverted .. £120 55·00
111/25 .. *Set of* 17 £110 30·00

There is a wide range of shades and also variation in paper used in this issue.

See also Nos. 227/8.

1941
I gCuimhne
Aiséirghe
1916

(**23** *Trans* "In memory of the rising of 1916")

24 Volunteer and G.P.O., Dublin

1941 (12 Apr). *25th Anniv of Easter Rising (1916). Provisional issue. T* **7** *and* **9** *(2d. in new colour), optd with T* **23.**
126 7 2d. orange (G.) .. 1·50 50
127 9 3d. blue (V.) .. 27·00 9·50

(Des V. Brown. Typo)

1941 (27 Oct). *25th Anniv of Easter Rising (1916). Definitive issue.* W **22.** *P* 15 × 14.
128 24 2½d. blue-black .. 70 60

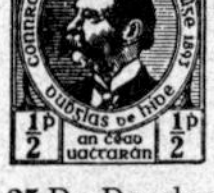

25 Dr. Douglas Hyde

26 Sir William Rowan Hamilton

27 Bro. Michael O'Clery

(Des S. O'Sullivan. Typo)

1943 (31 July). *50th Anniv of Founding of Gaelic League.* W **22.** *P* 15 × 14.
129 25 ½d. green .. 40 30
130 2½d. claret .. 1·25 10

(Des S. O'Sullivan from a bust by Hogan. Typo)

1943 (13 Nov). *Centenary of Announcement of Discovery of Quaternions.* W **22.** *P* 15 × 14.
131 26 ½d. green .. 40 40
w. Wmk inverted
132 2½d. brown .. 1·75 10

(Des R. J. King. Typo)

1944 (30 June). *Tercentenary of Death of Michael O'Clery. (Commemorating the "Annals of the Four Masters"). W* **22** *(sideways*). P* 14×15.
133 **27** ½d. emerald-green 10 10
w. Wmk facing right 55 20
134 1s. red-brown 70 10
w. Wmk facing right .. .. .. 2·25 50

*The normal sideways watermark shows the top of the e facing left, *as seen from the back of the stamp.*

Although issued as commemoratives these two stamps were kept in use as part of the current issue, replacing Nos. 111 and 122.

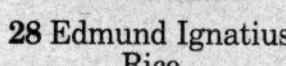

28 Edmund Ignatius Rice

29 "Youth Sowing Seeds of Freedom"

(Des S. O'Sullivan. Typo)

1944 (29 Aug). *Death Centenary of Edmund Rice (founder of Irish Christian Brothers). W* **22.** *P* 15 × 14.
135 **28** 2½d. slate 60 45
w. Wmk inverted .. .. ..

(Des R. J. King. Typo)

1945 (15 Sept). *Centenary of Death of Thomas Davis (founder of Young Ireland Movement). W* **22.** *P* 15 × 14.
136 **29** 2½d. blue .. .. 1·00 25
w. Wmk inverted .. .. .. — £130
137 6d. claret .. .. 7·00 3·75

30 "Country and Homestead"

(Des R. J. King. Typo)

1946 (16 Sept). *Birth Centenaries of Davitt and Parnell (land reformers). W* **22.** *P* 15 × 14.
138 **30** 2½d. scarlet .. .. 1·50 15
139 3d. blue .. .. 3·50 3·50

31 Angel Victor over Rock of Cashel

(Des R. J. King. Recess Waterlow (1d. to 1s. 3d. until 1961), D.L.R. (8d., 1s. 3d. from 1961 and 1s. 5d.))

1948 (7 Apr)–**65.** *Air. T* **31** *and similar horiz designs. W* **22.** *P* 15 *(1s. 5d.) or* 15 × 14 *(others).*
140 **31** 1d. chocolate (4.4.49) .. .. 2·00 3·50
141 – 3d. blue .. .. 4·00 2·25
142 – 6d. magenta .. .. 1·00 1·50
aw. Wmk inverted .. .. ..
142*b* – 8d. lake-brown (13.12.54) .. .. 7·00 7·00
143 – 1s. green (4.4.49) .. .. .. 1·25 1·50
143*a* **31** 1s. 3d. red-orange (13.12.54) .. .. 7·50 1·25
aw. Wmk inverted £550 £250
143*b* 1s. 5d. deep ultramarine (1.4.65) .. 3·50 1·00
140/3*b* .. .. *Set of* 7 24·00 16·00

Designs:—3d., 8d. Lough Derg; 6d. Croagh Patrick; 1s. Glendalough.

35 Theobald Wolfe Tone

(Des K. Uhlemann. Typo)

1948 (19 Nov). *150th Anniv of Insurrection. W* **22.** *P* 15×14.
144 **35** 2½d. reddish purple .. .. .. 1·00 10
w. Wmk inverted .. .. ..
145 3d. violet .. .. 3·25 3·25

REPUBLIC OF IRELAND

18 April 1949

36 Leinster House and Arms of Provinces

37 J. C. Mangan

(Des Muriel Brandt. Typo)

1949 (21 Nov). *International Recognition of Republic. W* **22.** *P* 15 × 14.
146 **36** 2½d. reddish brown .. .. .. 1·50 10
147 3d. bright blue .. .. 5·50 4·00

(Des R. J. King. Typo)

1949 (5 Dec). *Death Centenary of James Clarence Mangan (poet). W* **22.** *P* 15 × 14.
148 **37** 1d. green .. .. 1·50 20
w. Wmk inverted .. .. ..

38 Statue of St. Peter, Rome

39 Thomas Moore

40 Irish Harp

(Recess Waterlow & Sons)

1950 (11 Sept). *Holy Year. W* **22.** *P* 12½.
149 **38** 2½d. violet .. .. 1·00 40
150 3d. blue .. .. 8·00 8·50
151 9d. brown .. .. 8·00 10·00
149/51 .. .. *Set of* 3 15·00 17·00

PRINTERS. Nos. 152 to 200 were recess-printed by De La Rue & Co, Dublin, *unless otherwise stated.*

(Eng W. Vacek)

1952 (10 Nov). *Death Centenary of Thomas Moore (poet). W* **22.** *P* 13.
152 **39** 2½d. reddish purple 50 10
153 3½d. deep olive-green .. .. .. 1·75 2·75

(Des F. O'Ryan. Typo Government Printing Works, Dublin)

1953 (9 Feb). *"An Tostal" (Ireland at Home) Festival. W* **22** *(sideways). P* 14 × 15.
154 **40** 2½d. emerald-green .. .. .. 1·25 35
155 1s. 4d. blue .. .. 15·00 24·00

41 Robert Emmet

42 Madonna and Child (Della Robbia)

43 Cardinal Newman (first Rector)

(Eng L. Downey)

1953 (21 Sept). *150th Death Anniv of Emmet (patriot). W* **22.** *P* 13.
156 **41** 3d. deep bluish green .. .. .. 3·75 15
157 1s. 3d. carmine .. .. 42·00 9·50

(Eng A. R. Lane)

1954 (24 May). *Marian Year. W* **22.** *P* 15.
158 **42** 3d. blue .. .. 1·50 10
159 5d. myrtle-green .. .. 2·75 5·50

(Des L. Whelan. Typo Govt Printing Works, Dublin)

1954 (19 July). *Centenary of Founding of Catholic University of Ireland. W* **22.** *P* 15 × 14.
160 **43** 2d. bright purple .. .. .. 1·50 10
w. Wmk inverted .. .. .. — £180
161 1s. 3d. blue .. .. 16·00 6·00

44 Statue of Commodore Barry

45 John Redmond

46 Thomas O'Crohan

(Des and eng H. Woyty-Wimmer)

1956 (16 Sept). *Barry Commemoration. W* **22.** *P* 15.
162 **44** 3d. slate-lilac .. .. 2·00 10
163 1s. 3d. deep blue .. .. 7·00 9·00

1957 (11 June). *Birth Centenary of John Redmond (politician*
W **22.** *P* 14 × 15.
164 **45** 3d. deep blue .. .. 1·25
165 1s. 3d. brown-purple .. .. .. 10·00 15·

1957 (1 July). *Birth Centenary of Thomas O'Crohan (author*
W **22.** *P* 14 × 15.
166 **46** 2d. maroon .. .. 1·50
a. Wmk sideways .. .. .. †
167 5d. violet .. .. 1·50 5·

47 Admiral Brown

48 "Father Wadding" (Ribera)

49 Tom Clark

(Des S. O'Sullivan. Typo Govt Printing Works, Dublin)

1957 (23 Sept). *Death Centenary of Admiral William Brow*
W **22.** *P* 15 × 14.
168 **47** 3d. blue .. .. 2·25 2
169 1s. 3d. carmine .. .. 30·00 16·0

1957 (25 Nov). *300th Death Anniv of Father Luke Waddin*
(theologian). W **22.** *P* 15.
170 **48** 3d. deep blue .. .. 2·00 1
171 1s. 3d. lake .. .. 17·00 8·5

1958 (28 July). *Birth Centenary of Thomas J. ("Tom") Clark*
(patriot). W **22.** *P* 15.
172 **49** 3d. deep green .. .. 2·50 1
173 1s. 3d. red-brown .. .. 6·50 13·0

50 Mother Mary Aikenhead

51 Arthur Guinness

(Eng Waterlow. Recess Imprimerie Belge de Securité, Bruss
subsidiary of Waterlow & Sons)

1958 (20 Oct). *Death Centenary of Mother Mary Aikenhea*
(foundress of Irish Sisters of Charity). W **22.** *P* 15 × 14.
174 **50** 3d. Prussian blue .. .. .. 1·75
175 1s. 3d. rose-carmine .. .. .. 15·00 10·0

(Typo Govt Printing Works, Dublin)

1958 (29 Dec). *21st Anniv of the Irish Constitution. W* 2
P 15 × 14.
176 **19** 3d. brown .. .. 1·25 1
177 5d. emerald-green .. .. .. 2·25 4·5

1959 (20 July). *Bicentenary of Guinness Brewery. W* **22.** *P* 15.
178 **51** 3d. brown-purple .. .. .. 4·00 1
179 1s. 3d. blue .. .. 14·00 12·0

52 "The Flight of the Holy Family"

(Des K. Uhlemann)

1960 (20 June). *World Refugee Year. W* **22.** *P* 15.
180 **52** 3d. purple 50 1
181 1s. 3d. sepia .. .. 75 3·2

53 Conference Emblem

(Des P. Rahikainen)

1960 (19 Sept). *Europa. W* **22.** *P* 15.
182 **53** 6d. light brown .. .. 4·00 3·0
183 1s. 3d. violet .. .. 10·00 20·0

The ink of No. 183 is fugitive.

NEW INFORMATION

The editor is always interested to correspond wit people who have new information that wi improve or correct the Catalogue.

54 Dublin Airport, De Havilland D.H.84 Dragon Mk 2 *Iolar* and Boeing 720

55 St. Patrick

(Des J. Flanagan and D. R. Lowther)

1961 (26 June). *25th Anniv of Aer Lingus.* W **22.** *P* 15.

184	**54**	6d. blue	1·00	3·25
		w. Wmk inverted		
185		1s. 3d. green	1·50	4·75

(Recess B.W.)

1961 (25 Sept). *Fifteenth Death Centenary of St. Patrick.* W **22.** *P* 14½.

186	**55**	3d. blue	1·25	10
187		8d. purple	2·25	5·50
188		1s. 3d. green	2·50	1·60
186/8		*Set of* 3	5·50	6·50

56 John O'Donovan and Eugene O'Curry

(Recess B.W.)

1962 (26 Mar). *Death Centenaries of O'Donovan and O'Curry (scholars).* W **22.** *P* 15.

189	**56**	3d. carmine	40	10
190		1s. 3d. purple	1·50	2·50

57 Europa "Tree"

(Des L. Weyer)

1962 (17 Sept). *Europa.* W **22.** *P* 15.

191	**57**	6d. carmine-red	50	1·00
192		1s. 3d. turquoise	90	1·50

58 Campaign Emblem

(Des K. Uhlemann)

1963 (21 Mar). *Freedom from Hunger.* W **22.** *P* 15.

193	**58**	4d. deep violet	50	10
194		1s. 3d. scarlet	1·75	2·75

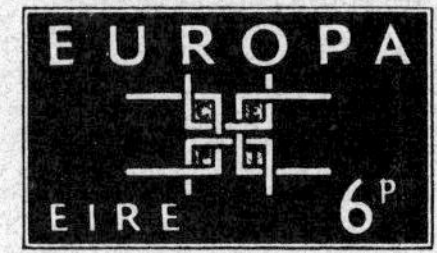

59 "Co-operation"

(Des A. Holm)

1963 (16 Sept). *Europa.* W **22.** *P* 15.

195	**59**	6d. carmine	75	75
196		1s. 3d. blue	2·00	3·75

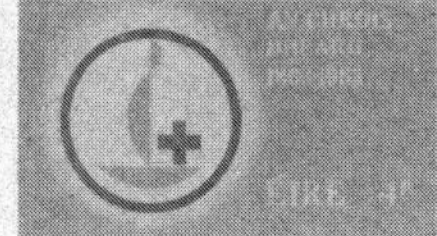

60 Centenary Emblem

(Des P. Wildbur. Photo Harrison & Sons)

1963 (2 Dec). *Centenary of Red Cross.* W **22.** *P* 14½ × 14.

197	**60**	4d. red and grey	50	10
198		1s. 3d. red, grey and light emerald	1·25	2·25

61 Wolfe Tone

(Des P. Wildbur)

1964 (13 Apr). *Birth Bicentenary of Wolfe Tone (revolutionary).* W **22.** *P* 15.

199	**61**	4d. black	75	10
200		1s. 3d. ultramarine	2·25	2·25

62 Irish Pavilion at Fair

(Des A. Devane. Photo Harrison & Sons)

1964 (20 July). *New York World's Fair.* W **22.** *P* 14½ × 14.

201	**62**	5d. blue-grey, brown, violet & yellow-ol	50	10
		a. Brown omitted*	£1200	
202		1s. 5d. blue-grey, brown, turquoise-blue and light yellow-green	2·25	3·75

*No. 201a comes from the top row of a sheet and shows part of the brown cross which would appear in the sheet margin. As the second horizontal row was normal it would appear that the brown cylinder was incorrectly registered.

63 Europa "Flower"

64 "Waves of Communication"

(Des G. Bétemps. Photo Harrison)

1964 (14 Sept). *Europa.* W **22** *(sideways).* *P* 14 × 14½.

203	**63**	8d. olive-green and blue	1·25	1·25
204		1s. 5d. red-brown and orange	3·25	2·75

(Des P. Wildbur. Photo Harrison)

1965 (17 May). *I.T.U. Centenary.* W **22.** *P* 14½ × 14.

205	**64**	3d. blue and green	40	10
206		8d. black and green	1·10	2·00

PRINTERS. Nos. 207 onwards were photogravure-printed by the Stamping Branch of the Revenue Commissioners, Dublin *unless otherwise stated.*

65 W. B. Yeats (poet)

66 I.C.Y. Emblem

(Des R. Kyne, from drawing by S. O'Sullivan)

1965 (14 June). *Yeats' Birth Centenary.* W **22** *(sideways).* *P* 15.

207	**65**	5d. black, orange-brown and deep green	30	10
208		1s. 5d. black, grey-green and brown	2·25	1·75

1965 (16 Aug). *International Co-operation Year.* W **22.** *P* 15.

209	**66**	3d. ultramarine and new blue	60	10
210		10d. deep brown and brown	1·00	3·00

67 Europa "Sprig"

(Des H. Karlsson)

1965 (27 Sept). *Europa.* W **22.** *P* 15.

211	**67**	8d. black and brown-red	1·00	1·00
212		1s. 5d. purple and light turquoise-blue	3·00	3·50

68 James Connolly

69 "Marching to Freedom"

(Des E. Delaney (No. 216), R. Kyne, after portraits by S. O'Sullivan (others))

1966 (12 Apr). *50th Anniv of Easter Rising. T* **68/9** *and similar horiz portraits.* W **22.** *P* 15.

213	3d. black and greenish blue	35	10
	a. Horiz pair. Nos. 213/14	70	2·50
214	3d. black and bronze-green	35	10
215	5d. black and yellow-olive	35	10
	a. Horiz pair. Nos. 215/16	70	2·50
216	5d. black, orange and blue-green	35	10
217	7d. black and light orange-brown	40	2·25
	a. Horiz pair. Nos. 217/18	80	7·50
218	7d. black and blue-green	40	2·25
219	1s. 5d. black and turquoise	40	1·50
	a. Horiz pair. Nos. 219/20	80	9·00
220	1s. 5d. black and bright green	40	1·50
213/20	*Set of* 8	2·75	7·00

Designs:—No. 213, Type **68**; No. 214, Thomas J. Clarke; No. 215, P. H. Pearse; No. 216, Type **69**; No. 217, Eamonn Ceannt; No. 218, Sean MacDiarmada; No. 219, Thomas MacDonagh; No. 220, Joseph Plunkett.

Nos. 213/14, 215/16, 217/18 and 219/20 were each printed together, *se-tenant,* in horizontal pairs throughout the sheet.

76 R. Casement

77 Europa "Ship"

(Des R. Kyne)

1966 (3 Aug). *50th Death Anniv of Roger Casement (patriot).* W **22** *(sideways).* *P* 15.

221	**76**	5d. black	15	10
222		1s. red-brown	30	50

(Des R. Kyne, after G. and J. Bender)

1966 (26 Sept). *Europa.* W **22** *(sideways).* *P* 15.

223	**77**	7d. emerald and orange	35	40
224		1s. 5d. emerald and light grey	90	1·00

78 Interior of Abbey (from lithograph)

79 Cogwheels

1966 (8 Nov). *750th Anniv of Ballintubber Abbey.* W **22.** *P* 15.

225	**78**	5d. red-brown	10	10
226		1s. black	20	25

1966–67. *As Nos.* 116, 118 *but photo. Smaller design* (17×21 *mm). Chalk-surfaced paper.* W **22.** *P* 15.

227	**9**	3d. blue (1.8.67)	40	15
228	**6**	5d. bright violet (1.12.66)	30	15
		w. Wmk inverted (from booklets)	1·75	1·25

No. 228 was only issued in booklets at first but was released in sheets on 1.4.68 in a slightly brighter shade. In the sheet stamps the lines of shading are more regular.

(Des O. Bonnevalle)

1967 (2 May). *Europa.* W **22** *(sideways).* *P* 15.

229	**79**	7d. light emerald, gold and pale cream	30	40
230		1s. 5d. carmine-red, gold and pale cream	70	1·00

COVER PRICES

Cover factors are quoted at the beginning of each country for most issues to 1945. An explanation of the system can be found on page x. The factors quoted do not, however, apply to philatelic covers.

80 Maple Leaves

(Des P. Hickey)

1967 (28 Aug). *Canadian Centennial. W* **22.** *P* 15.

231	**80**	5d. multicoloured	10	10
232		1s. 5d. multicoloured	20	60

81 Rock of Cashel (from photo by Edwin Smith)

1967 (25 Sept). *International Tourist Year. W* **22** (*inverted*). *P* 15.

233	**81**	7d. sepia	15	20
234		10d. slate-blue	15	40

82 1 c. Fenian Stamp Essay **83** 24 c. Fenian Stamp Essay

1967 (23 Oct). *Centenary of Fenian Rising. W* **22** (*sideways*). *P* 15.

235	**82**	5d. black and light green	10	10
236	**83**	1s. black and light pink	20	30

84 Jonathan Swift **85** Gulliver and Lilliputians

(Des M. Byrne)

1967 (30 Nov). *300th Birth Anniv of Jonathan Swift. W* **22** (*sideways*). *P* 15.

237	**84**	3d. black and olive-grey	10	10
238	**85**	1s. 5d. blackish brown and pale blue ..	20	20

86 Europa "Key"

(Des H. Schwarzenbach and M. Biggs)

1968 (29 Apr). *Europa. W* **22.** *P* 15.

239	**86**	7d. brown-red, gold and brown.. ..	25	50
240		1s. 5d. new blue, gold and brown ..	40	1·00

87 St Mary's Cathedral, Limerick

(Des from photo by J. J. Bambury. Recess B.W.)

1968 (26 Aug). *800th Anniv of St. Mary's Cathedral, Limerick. W* **22.** *P* 15.

241	**87**	5d. Prussian blue	10	10
242		10d. yellow-green	20	60

NEW INFORMATION

The editor is always interested to correspond with people who have new information that will improve or correct the Catalogue.

88 Countess Markievicz **89** James Connolly

1968 (23 Sept). *Birth Centenary of Countess Markievicz (patriot). W* **22.** *P* 15.

243	**88**	3d. black	10	10
244		1s. 5d. deep blue and blue	20	20

1968 (23 Sept). *Birth Centenary of James Connolly (patriot). W* **22** (*sideways*). *P* 15.

245	**89**	6d. deep brown and chocolate	15	50
246		1s. blksh grn, apple-grn & myrtle-grn	15	10

90 Stylised Dog (brooch) **91** Stag

92 Winged Ox (Symbol of St. Luke)

93 Eagle (Symbol of St. John The Evangelist)

(Des H. Gerl)

1968–70. *Pence values expressed with* "p". *W* **22** (*sideways* on ½d. to* 1s. *9d.*). *P* 15.

247	**90**	½d. red-orange (7.6.69)	10	30
248		1d. pale yellow-green (7.6.69) ..	15	10
		a. Coil stamp. Perf 14×15 (8.70?) ..	90	3·00
249		2d. light ochre (14.10.68)	50	10
		a. Coil stamp. Perf 14×15 (8.70?) ..	90	3·75
250		3d. blue (7.6.69)	35	10
		a. Coil stamp. Perf 14×15 (8.70?) ..	90	3·75
251		4d. deep brown-red (31.3.69)	30	10
252		5d. myrtle-green (31.3.69)	40	35
253		6d. bistre-brown (24.2.69)	30	10
		w. Wmk e facing right	5·50	1·50
254	**91**	7d. brown and yellow (7.6.69) ..	45	3·50
255		8d. chocolate & orge-brown (14.10.68)	45	1·00
256		9d. slate-blue and olive-green (24.2.69)	50	10
257		10d. chocolate and bluish violet (31.3.69)	1·50	1·50
258		1s. chocolate and red-brown (31.3.69)	40	10
259		1s. 9d. black & lt turquoise-bl (24.2.69)	4·00	1·50
260	**92**	2s. 6d. multicoloured (14.10.68) ..	1·75	30
261		5s. multicoloured (24.2.69)	3·00	1·50
262	**93**	10s. multicoloured (14.10.68)	4·50	3·75
247/62		.. .. *Set of* 16	16·00	12·50

*The normal sideways watermark shows the top of the e facing left, *as seen from the back of the stamp.*

The 1d., 2d., 3d., 5d., 6d., 9d., 1s. and 2s. 6d. exist with PVA gum as well as gum arabic. The coil stamps exist on PVA only, and the rest on gum arabic only.

See also Nos. 287/301, 339/59 and 478/83.

94 Human Rights Emblem **95** Dail Eireann Assembly

1968 (4 Nov). *Human Rights Year. W* **22** (*sideways*). *P* 15.

263	**94**	5d. yellow, gold and black	15	10
264		7d. yellow, gold and red	15	40

(Des M. Byrne)

1969 (21 Jan). *50th Anniv of Dail Eireann (First National Parliament). W* **22** (*sideways*). *P* 15 × 14½.

265	**95**	6d. myrtle-green	15	10
266		9d. Prussian blue	15	30

96 Colonnade **97** Quadruple I.L.O. Emblems

(Des L. Gasbarra and G. Belli; adapted Myra Maguire)

1969 (28 Apr). *Europa. W* **22.** *P* 15.

267	**96**	9d. grey, ochre and ultramarine ..	40	1·1
268		1s. 9d. grey, gold and scarlet	70	1·4

(Des K. C. Däbczewski)

1969 (14 July). *50th Anniv of International Labour Organization. W* **22** (*sideways*). *P* 15.

269	**97**	6d. black and grey	20	1
270		9d. black and yellow	20	2

98 "The Last Supper and Crucifixion" (Evie Hone Window, Eton Chapel)

(Des R. Kyne)

1969 (1 Sept). *Contemporary Irish Art* (1*st issue*). *W* **22** (*sideways*). *P* 15 × 14½.

271	**98**	1s. multicoloured	30	1·50

See also Nos. 280, 306, 317, 329, 362, 375, 398, 408, 452, 470 and 498.

99 Mahatma Gandhi

1969 (2 Oct). *Birth Centenary of Mahatma Gandhi. W* **22.** *P* 15.

272	**99**	6d. black and green	20	10
273		1s. 9d. black and yellow	30	90

100 Symbolic Bird in Tree

(Des D. Harrington)

1970 (23 Feb). *European Conservation Year. W* **22.** *P* 15.

274	**100**	6d. bistre and black	20	10
275		9d. slate-violet and black	25	80

101 "Flaming Sun"

(Des L. le Brocquy)

1970 (4 May). *Europa. W* **22.** *P* 15.

276	**101**	6d. bright violet and silver	30	10
277		9d. brown and silver	45	1·25
278		1s. 9d. deep olive-grey and silver ..	65	2·00
276/8		.. .. *Set of* 3	1·25	3·00

102 "Sailing Boats" (Peter Monamy)
103 "Madonna of Eire" (Mainie Jellett)

(Des P. Wildbur and P. Scott)

970 (13 July). *250th Anniv of Royal Cork Yacht Club.* W **22.** *P* 15.
79 **102** 4d. multicoloured 15 10

970 (1 Sept). *Contemporary Irish Art (2nd issue).* W **22** *(sideways). P* 15.
30 **103** 1s. multicoloured 15 20

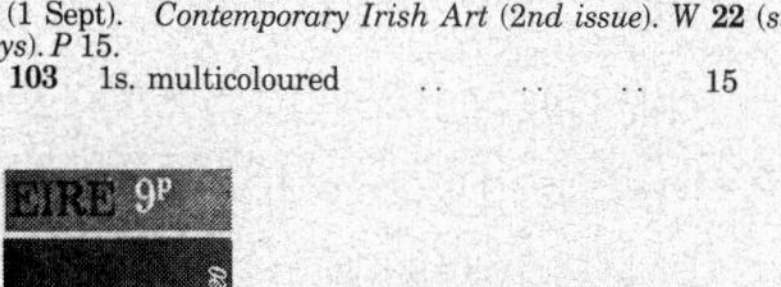

104 Thomas MacCurtain
106 Kevin Barry

(Des P. Wildbur)

970 (26 Oct). *50th Death Anniversaries of Irish Patriots. T* **104** *and similar vert design.* W **22** *(sideways). P* 15.
81 9d. black, bluish violet and greyish black 50 25
a. Pair. Nos. 281/2 1·00 2·50
82 9d. black, bluish violet and greyish black 50 25
83 2s. 9d. black, new blue and greyish black 1·75 1·50
a. Pair. Nos. 283/4 3·75 11·00
84 2s. 9d. black, new blue and greyish black 1·75 1·50
81/4 *Set of* 4 4·50 3·25
Designs:—Nos. 281 and 283, Type **104**; others, Terence lacSwiney.
Nos. 281/2 and 283/4 were each printed together, *se-tenant*, in orizontal and vertical pairs throughout the sheet.

(Des P. Wildbur)

970 (2 Nov). *50th Death Anniv of Kevin Barry (patriot).* W **22** *(inverted). P* 15.
85 **106** 6d. olive-green 40 10
86 1s. 2d. royal blue 55 1·40

106a Stylized Dog (Brooch)
107 "Europa Chain"

Two types of 10 p.:
I. Outline and markings of the ox in lilac.
. Outline and markings in brown.

971 (15 Feb)–**75.** *Decimal Currency. Designs as Nos. 247/62 but with "p" omitted as in T* **106a**. W **22** *(sideways* on 10, 12, 20 and 50p.). P* 15.
287 **106a** ½p. bright green 10 10
a. Wmk sideways 6·00 10·00
ab. Booklet pane of 6 30·00
aw. Wmk e facing right 6·00 10·00
awb. Booklet pane of 6 30·00
288 1p. blue 40 10
a. Coil stamp. Perf 14×14½ 90 60
b. Coil strip. Nos. 288a, 289a and 291a *se-tenant* 1·50
c. Wmk sideways 35 40
ca. Booklet pane of 6 2·00
cb. Booklet pane. No. 288c×5 plus one *se-tenant* label (11.3.74) 2·00
cw. Wmk e facing right 35 40
cwa. Booklet pane of 6 2·00
cwb. Booklet pane. No. 288cw×5 plus one *se-tenant* label (11.3.74) 2·00
289 1½p. lake-brown 15 15
a. Coil stamp. Perf 14×14½ 30 50
b. Coil strip. Nos. 289a, 291a, 294a and 290a *se-tenant* (24.2.72) 1·50
c. Coil strip. Nos. 289a×2, 290a and 295ab *se-tenant* (29.1.74) 1·50
290 2p. myrtle-green 15 10
a. Coil stamp. Perf 14×14½ (24.2.72) 30 40
b. Wmk sideways (27.1.75) 50 50
ba. Booklet pane. No. 290b×5 plus one *se-tenant* label 2·00
bw. Wmk e facing right 50 50
bwa. Booklet pane. No. 290bw×5 plus one *se-tenant* label 2·00

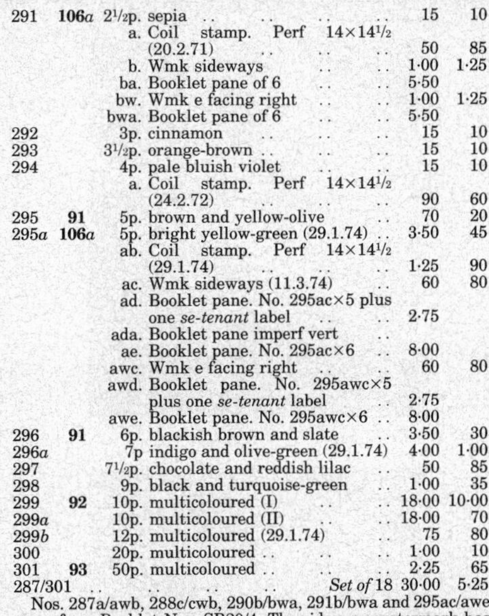
291 **106a** 2½p. sepia 15 10
a. Coil stamp. Perf 14×14½ (20.2.71) 50 85
b. Wmk sideways 1·00 1·25
ba. Booklet pane of 6 5·50
bw. Wmk e facing right 1·00 1·25
bwa. Booklet pane of 6 5·50
292 3p. cinnamon 15 10
293 3½p. orange-brown 15 10
294 4p. pale bluish violet 15 10
a. Coil stamp. Perf 14×14½ (24.2.72) 90 60
295 **91** 5p. brown and yellow-olive 70 20
295a **106a** 5p. bright yellow-green (29.1.74) 3·50 45
ab. Coil stamp. Perf 14×14½ (29.1.74) 1·25 90
ac. Wmk sideways (11.3.74) 60 80
ad. Booklet pane. No. 295ac×5 plus one *se-tenant* label 2·75
ada. Booklet pane imperf vert
ae. Booklet pane. No. 295ac×6 8·00
awc. Wmk e facing right 60 80
awd. Booklet pane. No. 295awc×5 plus one *se-tenant* label 2·75
awe. Booklet pane. No. 295awc×6 8·00
296 **91** 6p. blackish brown and slate 3·50 30
296a 7p indigo and olive-green (29.1.74) 4·00 1·00
297 7½p. chocolate and reddish lilac 50 85
298 9p. black and turquoise-green 1·00 35
299 **92** 10p. multicoloured (I) 18·00 10·00
299a 10p. multicoloured (II) 18·00 70
299b 12p. multicoloured (29.1.74) 75 80
300 20p. multicoloured 1·00 10
301 **93** 50p. multicoloured 2·25 65
287/301 *Set of* 18 30·00 5·25
Nos. 287a/awb, 288c/cwb, 290b/bwa, 291b/bwa and 295ac/awe come from Booklet Nos. SB20/4. The sideways watermark has the top of the e pointing left, and the sideways inverted has it pointing right, *when seen from the back of the stamp.* Stamps with one, or two adjoining, sides imperf come from these booklets.
See also Nos. 339/59 and 478/83.

(Des H. Haflidason; adapted P. Wildbur)

1971 (3 May). *Europa.* W **22** *(sideways). P* 15.
302 **107** 4p. sepia and olive-yellow 50 10
303 6p. black and new blue 1·75 2·25

108 J. M. Synge
109 "An Island Man" (Jack B. Yeats)

(Des R. Kyne from a portrait by Jack B. Yeats)

1971 (19 July). *Birth Centenary of J. M. Synge (playwright).* W **22.** *P* 15.
304 **108** 4p. multicoloured 15 10
305 10p. multicoloured 60 80

(Des P. Wildbur)

1971 (30 Aug). *Contemporary Irish Art (3rd issue). Birth Centenary of J. B. Yeats (artist).* W **22.** *P* 15.
306 **109** 6p. multicoloured 55 55

110 Racial Harmony Symbol
111 "Madonna and Child" (statue by J. Hughes)

(Des P. Wildbur. Litho Harrison)

1971 (18 Oct). *Racial Equality Year. No wmk. P* 14 × 14½.
307 **110** 4p. red 20 10
308 10p. black 50 75

(Des R. Kyne)

1971 (15 Nov). *Christmas.* W **22.** *P* 15.
309 **111** 2½p. black, gold and deep bluish green 10 10
310 6p. black, gold and ultramarine 55 65

112 Heart

(Des L. le Brocquy)

1972 (7 Apr). *World Health Day.* W **22** *(sideways). P* 15.
311 **112** 2½p. gold and brown 30 15
312 12p. silver and grey 1·10 1·75

113 "Communications"

(Des P. Huovinen and P. Wildbur)

1972 (1 May). *Europa.* W **22** *(sideways). P* 15.
313 **113** 4p. orange, black and silver 1·25 25
314 6p. blue, black and silver 3·25 4·75

114 Dove and Moon
115 "Black Lake" (Gerard Dillon)

(Des P. Scott)

1972 (1 June). *The Patriot Dead, 1922–23.* W **22.** *P* 15.
315 **114** 4p. grey-blue, light orange & deep blue 10 10
316 6p. dp yellow-grn, lemon & dp dull grn 45 40

(Des P. Wildbur)

1972 (10 July). *Contemporary Irish Art (4th issue).* W **22** *(sideways). P* 15.
317 **115** 3p. multicoloured 50 35

116 "Horseman" (Carved Slab)
117 Madonna and Child (from Book of Kells)

(Des P. Scott)

1972 (28 Aug). *50th Anniv of Olympic Council of Ireland.* W **22.** *P* 15.
318 **116** 3p. bright yellow, black and gold 15 10
319 6p. salmon, black and gold 55 60

WATERMARK. All issues from here onwards are on unwatermarked paper.

(Des P. Scott)

1972 (16 Oct). *Christmas. P* 15.
320 **117** 2½p. multicoloured *(shades)* 10 10
321 4p. multicoloured 20 10
322 12p. multicoloured 55 65
320/2 *Set of* 3 75 70

118 2d. Stamp of 1922
119 Celtic Head Motif

(Des Stamping Branch of the Revenue Commissioners, Dublin)

1972 (6 Dec). *50th Anniv of the First Irish Postage Stamp. P* 15.
323 **118** 6p. light grey and grey-green 30 60
MS324 72 × 104 mm. No. 323 × 4 6·50 11·00

(Des L. le Brocquy)

1973 (1 Jan). *Entry into European Communities. P* 15.
325 **119** 6p. multicoloured 40 90
326 12p. multicoloured .. .. .. 60 1·10

120 Europa "Posthorn"

(Des L. Anisdahl; adapted R. Kyne)

1973 (30 Apr). *Europa. P* 15.
327 **120** 4p. bright blue 50 10
328 6p. black .. .. 1·25 2·00

121 "Berlin Blues II" (W. Scott) **122** Weather Map

(Adapted by R. Scott)

1973 (9 Aug). *Contemporary Irish Art (5th issue). P* 15 × 14½.
329 **121** 5p. ultramarine and grey-black .. 40 30

(Des R. Ballagh)

1973 (4 Sept). *I.M.O./W.M.O. Centenary. P* 14½ × 15.
330 **122** 3½p. multicoloured 30 10
331 12p. multicoloured .. .. .. 80 2·00

123 Tractor ploughing **124** "Flight into Egypt" (Jan de Cock)

(Des P. Scott)

1973 (5 Oct). *World Ploughing Championships, Wellington Bridge. P* 15 × 14½.
332 **123** 5p. multicoloured 15 10
333 7p. multicoloured 75 50

(Des D. Kiely. Litho ("EIRE" and face value) and photo (3½p.) or photo (12p.))

1973 (1 Nov). *Christmas. P* 15.
334 **124** 3½p. multicoloured 15 10
335 12p. multicoloured .. .. .. 1·10 1·50

125 Daunt Island Lightship and Ballycotton Lifeboat, 1936 **126** "Edmund Burke" (statue by J. H. Foley)

(Des M. Byrne from painting by B. Gribble)

1974 (28 Mar). *150th Anniv of Royal National Lifeboat Institution. P* 15 × 14½.
336 **125** 5p. multicoloured 30 30

(Des P. Wildbur)

1974 (29 Apr). *Europa. P* 14½ × 15.
337 **126** 5p. black and pale violet-blue 75 10
338 7p. black and light emerald .. .. 2·50 2·50

NEW INFORMATION

The editor is always interested to correspond with people who have new information that will improve or correct the Catalogue.

Two types of 50p.:

Type I. Fine screen (Cyls 1)

Type II. Coarse screen (Cyls 2)

1974–83. *Designs as Nos.* 287 *etc. No wmk. P* 15.

339	**106a**	½p. bright green (5.6.78)	30	10
340		1p. blue (14.2.75)	10	10
		a. Coil stamp. Perf 14×14½ (21.3.77)	60	70
		b. Coil strip. Nos. 340a, 341a×2 and 344a *se-tenant* (21.3.77) ..	1·90	
341		2p. myrtle-green (7.4.76)	10	10
		a. Coil stamp. Perf 14×14½ (21.3.77)	40	50
342		3p. cinnamon (14.2.75)	10	10
343		3½p. orange-brown (9.10.74) ..	2·75	4·00
344		5p. bright yellow-green (16.8.74) ..	60	10
		a. Coil stamp. Perf 14 × 14½ (21.3.77)	85	1·40
345	**91**	6p. blackish brn & slate (16.10.74)	1·25	1·75
346	**106a**	6p. slate (17.6.75)	20	10
347	**91**	7p. indigo and olive-green (27.9.74)	90	35
348	**106a**	7p. deep yellow-green (17.6.75) ..	35	10
		a. Booklet pane. No. 348 × 5 plus *se-tenant* label (21.3.77) ..	11·00	
349	**91**	8p. dp brown & dp orge-brn (17.6.75)	75	50
350	**106a**	8p. chestnut (14.7.76)	30	10
351	**91**	9p. black & turquoise-green (12.74)	90	30
352	**106a**	9p. greenish slate (14.7.76) ..	30	10
352a		9½p. vermilion (3.12.79)	35	20
353	**92**	10p. multicoloured (II) (12.74) ..	2·00	30
354	**91**	10p. black and violet-blue (14.7.76)	1·25	10
354a	**106a**	10p. deep mauve (8.6.77)	70	10
355	**91**	11p. black and rose-carmine (14.7.76)	45	30
355a		12p. black and bright green (8.6.77)	75	10
355b	**106a**	12p. yellowish green (26.3.80) ..	30	10
355c	**91**	13p. reddish brn & red-brn (26.3.80)	40	1·25
356	**92**	15p. multicoloured (17.6.74) ..	55	40
356a	**106a**	15p. ultramarine (10.7.80)	40	10
356b	**91**	16p. black & dull yellow-grn (10.7.80)	40	80
356c	**92**	17p. multicoloured (8.6.77)	50	40
357		20p. multicoloured (13.6.74) ..	50	15
358	**93**	50p. multicoloured (I) (12.74) ..	70	30
		a. Type II (1983)	1·75	2·50
359		£1 multicoloured (17.6.75) ..	1·25	30
339/59		.. .. .. *Set of* 29	17·00	10·50

For 18p., 19p., 22p., 24p., 26p. and 29p. values printed by lithography, see Nos. 478/83.

Stamps with one or two sides imperf come from the booklet pane.

127 "Oliver Goldsmith" (statue by J. H. Foley) **128** "Kitchen Table" (Norah McGuiness)

(Des P. Wildbur)

1974 (24 June). *Death Bicentenary of Oliver Goldsmith (writer). P* 14½ × 15.
360 **127** 3½p. black and olive-yellow 20 10
361 12p. black and bright yellowish green .. 90 1·00

(Design adapted by Norah McGuiness. Photo Harrison)

1974 (19 Aug). *Contemporary Irish Art (6th issue). P* 14 × 14½.
362 **128** 5p. multicoloured .. .. .. 35 3(

129 Rugby Players **130** U.P.U. "Postmark"

(Design adapted from Irish Press photograph. Eng C. Slania Recess (3½p.) or recess and photo (12p.) Harrison)

1974 (9 Sept). *Centenary of Irish Rugby Football Union P* 14½ × 14.
363 **129** 3½p. greenish black 30 1
a. *Deep greenish blue* .. .. 7·50 3·5
364 12p. multicoloured .. .. .. 2·25 2·7

No. 363a is from a second printing using a recut plate or which the engraving was deeper.

(Des R. Ballagh)

1974 (9 Oct). *Centenary of Universal Postal Union. P* 14½ × 15.
365 **130** 5p. light yellowish green and black .. 25 1(
366 7p. light ultramarine and black .. 35 8(

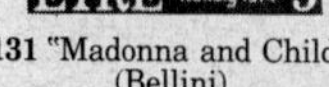

131 "Madonna and Child" (Bellini) **132** "Peace"

(Des P. Wildbur)

1974 (14 Nov). *Christmas. P* 14½ × 15.
367 **131** 5p. multicoloured .. .. .. 15 1(
368 15p. multicoloured .. .. .. 60 9(

(Des Alexandra Wejchert)

1975 (24 Mar). *International Women's Year. P* 14½ × 15.
369 **132** 8p. brt reddish purple & ultramarine .. 25 75
370 15p. ultramarine and bright green .. 50 1·25

133 "Castletown Hunt" (R. Healy)

(Des R. Kyne)

1975 (28 Apr). *Europa. P* 15 × 14½.
371 **133** 7p. grey-black 75 15
372 9p. dull blue-green .. .. .. 1·25 2·50

134 Putting

(Des from photographs by J. McManus. Litho ("EIRE" and face value) and photo).

1975 (26 June). *Ninth European Amateur Golf Team Championship, Killarney. P* 15×14½.
373 **134** 6p. multicoloured (*shades*) 75 45
374 – 9p. multicoloured (*shades*) .. .. 1·50 1·50

The 9p. is similar to T **134** but shows a different view of the putting green.

135 "Bird of Prey" (sculpture by Oisin Kelly) **136** Nano Nagle (founder) and Waifs

(Design adapted by the artist)

975 (28 July). *Contemporary Irish Art (7th issue). P* 15×14½.
'75 **135** 15p. yellow-brown 65 75

(Des Kilkenny Design Workshops)

1975 (1 Sept). *Bicentenary of Presentation Order of Nuns. P* 14½ × 15.
376 **136** 5p. black and pale blue. 20 10
377 7p. black and light stone 30 30

137 Tower of St. Anne's Church, Shandon

138 St. Oliver Plunkett (commemorative medal by Imogen Stuart)

(Des P. Scott)

1975 (6 Oct). *European Architectural Heritage Year. T* **137** *and similar vert design. P* 12½.
378 **137** 5p. blackish brown 20 10
379 6p. multicoloured 40 85
380 – 7p. steel-blue 40 10
381 – 9p. multicoloured 45 80
378/81 . . . . *Set of* 4 1·25 1·75
Design:—Nos. 380/1, Interior of Holycross Abbey, Co. Tipperary.

(Design adapted by the artist. Recess Harrison)

1975 (13 Oct). *Canonisation of Oliver Plunkett. P* 14 × 14½.
382 **138** 7p. black 15 10
383 15p. chestnut 55 45

139 "Madonna and Child" (Fra Filippo Lippi)

140 James Larkin (from a drawing by Sean O'Sullivan)

(Des P. Wildbur)

1975 (13 Nov). *Christmas. P* 15.
384 **139** 5p. multicoloured 15 10
385 7p. multicoloured 15 10
386 10p. multicoloured 45 30
384/6 . . . . *Set of* 3 65 40

(Des P. Wildbur. Litho)

1976 (21 Jan). *Birth Centenary of James Larkin (Trade Union leader). P* 14½×15.
387 **140** 7p. deep bluish green and pale grey . . 20 10
388 11p. sepia and yellow-ochre 40 55

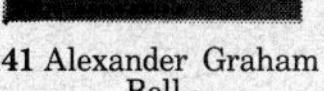

141 Alexander Graham Bell

142 1847 Benjamin Franklin Essay

(Des R. Ballagh)

1976 (10 Mar). *Telephone Centenary. P* 14½ × 15.
389 **141** 9p. multicoloured 20 10
390 15p. multicoloured 45 50

(Des L. le Brocquy; graphics by P. Wildbur. Litho Irish Security Stamp Printing Ltd)

1976 (17 May). *Bicentenary of American Revolution. T* **142** *and similar horiz designs. P* 14½ × 14.
391 7p. ultramarine, light red and silver . . 15 10
a. Silver (inscr) omitted . . . . . . † £225
392 8p. ultramarine, light red and silver . . 20 1·10
393 9p. violet-blue, orange and silver 20 10
394 15p. light rose-red, grey-blue and silver . . 30 75
a. Silver (face-value and inscr) omitted . . £550 £650
391/4 . . . . *Set of* 4 75 1·75
MS395 95 × 75 mm. Nos. 391/4 . . . . 4·50 8·00
a. Silver omitted £1600
Designs:—7p. Thirteen stars; 8p. Fifty stars; 9, 15p. Type **142**.
No. **MS**395 exists with the sheet margins overprinted in blue to commemorate "Stampa 76", the Irish National Stamp Exhibition.

143 Spirit Barrel

(Des P. Hickey)

1976 (1 July). *Europa. Irish Delft. T* **143** *and similar horiz design. Multicoloured. P* 15 × 14.
396 9p. Type **143** 40 20
397 11p. Dish . . . . 70 1·60

144 "The Lobster Pots, West of Ireland" (Paul Henry)

(Des R. McGrath)

1976 (30 Aug). *Contemporary Irish Art (8th issue). P* 15.
398 **144** 15p. multicoloured 60 60

145 Radio Waves

(Des G. Shepherd and A. O'Donnell. Litho De La Rue Smurfit Ltd, Dublin)

1976 (5 Oct). *50th Anniv of Irish Broadcasting Service. T* **145** *and similar vert design. Chalk-surfaced paper. P* 14½×14 *(9p.) or* 14×14½ *(11p.).*
399 9p. light new blue and bottle-green 20 10
400 11p. agate, orange-red and light new blue . . 60 1·00
Design:—11p. Transmitter, radio waves and globe.

146 "The Nativity" (Lorenzo Monaco)

(Des R. McGrath)

1976 (11 Nov). *Christmas. P* 15×14½.
401 **146** 7p. multicoloured 15 10
402 9p. multicoloured 15 10
403 15p. multicoloured 55 55
401/3 . . . . *Set of* 3 75 65

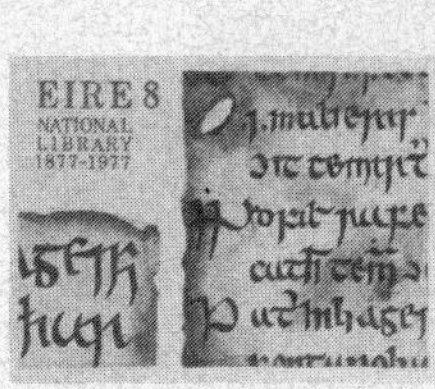

147 16th Century Manuscript

148 Ballynahinch, Galway

(Des P. Hickey)

1977 (9 May). *Centenaries of National Library (8p.) and National Museum (10p.). T* **147** *and similar horiz design. Multicoloured. P* 15 × 14½.
404 8p. Type **147** 30 30
405 10p. Prehistoric stone 40 35

(Des E. van der Grijn. Litho Irish Security Stamp Printing Ltd)

1977 (27 June). *Europa. T* **148** *and similar vert design. Multicoloured. P* 14 × 15.
406 10p. Type **148** 30 25
407 12p. Lough Tay, Wicklow . . . . . . 95 1·50

ALTERED CATALOGUE NUMBERS

Any Catalogue numbers altered from the last edition are shown as a list in the introductory pages.

149 "Head" (Louis le Brocquy)

150 Guide and Tents

(Design adapted by the artist. Litho Irish Security Stamp Ptg Ltd)

1977 (8 Aug). *Contemporary Irish Art (9th issue). P* 14 × 14½.
408 **149** 17p. multicoloured 55 75

(Des R. Ballagh)

1977 (22 Aug). *Scouting and Guiding. T* **150** *and similar horiz design. Multicoloured. P* 15 × 14½.
409 8p. Type **150** 35 10
410 17p. Tent and Scout saluting . . . . . . 75 1·75

151 "The Shanachie" (drawing by Jack B. Yeats)

152 "Electricity" (Golden Jubilee of Electricity Supply Board)

(Des L. Miller (10p.), R. Ballagh (12p.). Litho Irish Security Stamp Printing Ltd)

1977 (12 Sept). *Anniversaries. T* **151** *and similar horiz design. P* 14 × 14½ *(10p.) or* 14½ × 14 *(12p.).*
411 10p. black 25 15
412 12p. black . . . . 35 1·00
Designs and events:—10p. Type **151** (Golden jubilee of Irish Folklore Society; 12p. The philosopher Eriugena (1100th death anniv).

(Des R. Ballagh (10p.), P. Hickey (12p.), B. Blackshaw (17p.). Photo Stamping Branch of the Revenue Commissioners (12p.); Litho Irish Security Stamp Ptg Ltd (others))

1977 (10 Oct). *Golden Jubilees. T* **152** *and similar horiz designs. P* 15 × 14½ *(12p.) or* 15 × 14 *(others).*
413 10p. multicoloured 15 10
414 12p. multicoloured . . . . 30 1·40
415 17p. grey-black and grey-brown 40 85
413/15 . . . . *Set of* 3 75 2·10
Designs:—12p. Bulls (from contemporary coinage) (Jubilee of Agricultural Credit Corporation); 17p. Greyhound (Jubilee of greyhound track racing).

153 "The Holy Family" (Giorgione)

154 Junkers W.33 *Bremen* in Flight

(Des R. McGrath)

1977 (3 Nov). *Christmas. P* 14½ × 15.
416 **153** 8p. multicoloured 15 10
417 10p. multicoloured 15 10
418 17p. multicoloured . . . . . . 55 1·25
416/18 . . . . *Set of* 3 75 1·25

(Des R. Ballagh. Litho Irish Security Stamp Ptg Ltd)

1978 (13 Apr). *50th Anniv of First East–West Transatlantic Flight. P* 14 × 14½.
419 **154** 10p. bright blue and black 20 15
420 – 17p. olive-brown and black . . . . 35 1·10
The 17p. is as T **154**, but shows a different sky and sea.

155 Spring Gentian

156 Catherine McAuley

(Des Wendy Walsh. Litho Irish Security Stamp Ptg Ltd)

1978 (12 June). *Wild Flowers. T* **155** *and similar vert designs. Multicoloured. P* 14 × 15.

421	8p. Type **155**		25	50
422	10p. Strawberry tree		30	15
423	11p. Large-flowered Butterwort		35	70
424	17p. St. Dabeoc's Heath		50	2·00
421/4	.. ..	*Set of* 4	1·25	3·00

(Des R. Ballagh (10p.), R. Kyne (11p.), E. van der Grijn (17p.). Litho Irish Security Stamp Ptg Ltd)

1978 (18 Sept). *Anniversaries and Events. T* **156** *and similar multicoloured designs. P* 14½ × 14 (*11p.*) *or* 14 × 14½ (*others*).

425	10p. Type **156**		20	10
426	11p. Doctor performing vaccination (*horiz*) ..		30	80
427	17p. "Self Portrait"		40	1·10
425/7	.. ..	*Set of* 3	80	1·75

Events:—10p. Birth bicentenary of Catherine McAuley (founder of Sisters of Mercy); 11p. Global eradication of Smallpox; 17p. Birth centenary of Sir William Orpen (painter).

157 Diagram of Drilling Rig 158 Farthing

(Des R. Ballagh. Litho Irish Security Stamp Ptg Ltd)

1978 (18 Oct). *Arrival Onshore of Natural Gas. P* 14 × 14½.

428	**157**	10p. maroon, turquoise-green and bistre	30	30

(Des P. Wildbur and R. Mercer)

1978 (26 Oct). *50th Anniv of Irish Currency. T* **158** *and similar horiz designs. P* 15 × 14½.

429	8p. black, copper and deep bluish green ..		20	20
430	10p. black, silver and blue-green		25	10
431	11p. black, copper and chocolate		25	50
432	17p. black, silver and deep blue		40	1·00
429/32	.. ..	*Set of* 4	1·00	1·60

Designs:—10p. Florin; 11p. Penny; 17p. Half-crown.

159 "The Virgin and Child" (Guercino) 160 Conolly Folly, Castletown

(Des P. Wildbur)

1978 (16 Nov). *Christmas. P* 14½ × 15.

433	**159**	8p. purple-brown, gold and pale turquoise-green	15	10
434		10p. purple-brown, chocolate and pale turquoise-green	15	10
435		17p. purple-brown, deep blue-green and pale turquoise-green	45	1·40
433/5		.. .. *Set of* 3	65	1·40

(Des R. McGrath)

1978 (6 Dec). *Europa. Architecture. T* **160** *and similar horiz design. P* 15 × 14½.

436	10p. lake-brown and red-brown	30	15
437	11p. green and deep green	30	1·00

Design:—11p. Dromoland Belvedere.

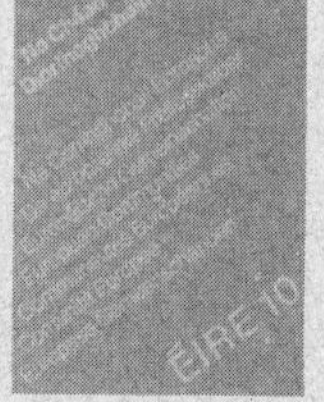

161 Athletes in Cross-country Race 162 "European Communities" (in languages of member nations)

(Des R. Mercer. Litho Irish Security Stamp Ptg Ltd)

1979 (20 Aug). *7th World Cross-country Championships, Limerick. P* 14½ × 14.

438	**161**	8p. multicoloured	20	30

(Des P. Wildbur)

1979 (20 Aug). *First Direct Elections to European Assembly. P* 14½ × 15.

439	**162**	10p. dull turquoise-green	15	15
440		11p. reddish violet	15	35

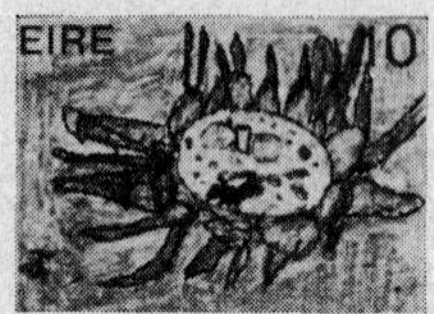

163 Sir Rowland Hill 164 Winter Wren (*Troglodytes troglodytes*)

(Des C. Harrison. Litho Irish Security Stamp Ptg Ltd)

1979 (20 Aug). *Death Centenary of Sir Rowland Hill. P* 14 × 14½.

441	**163**	17p. black, brownish grey and red ..	30	60

(Des Wendy Walsh. Litho Irish Security Stamp Ptg Ltd)

1979 (30 Aug). *Birds. T* **164** *and similar horiz designs. Multicoloured. P* 14½ × 14.

442	8p. Type **164**		40	70
443	10p. Great Crested Grebe (*Podiceps cristatus*)		40	15
444	11p. White-fronted Goose (*Anser albifrons flavirostris*)		45	70
445	17p. Peregrine Falcon (*Falco peregrinus*) ..		70	2·00
442/5	.. ..	*Set of* 4	1·75	3·25

165 "A Happy Flower" (David Gallagher)

(Des P. Wildbur. Litho Irish Security Stamp Ptg Ltd)

1979 (13 Sept). *International Year of the Child. Paintings by Children. T* **165** *and similar multicoloured designs. P* 14 × 14½ (*11p.*) *or* 14½ × 14 (*others*).

446	10p. Type **165**		20	10
447	11p. "Myself and My Skipping Rope" (Lucy Norman) (*vert*)		25	60
448	17p. "Swans on a Lake" (Nicola O'Dwyer) ..		35	85
446/8	.. ..	*Set of* 3	70	1·40

166 Pope John Paul II

(Des P. Byrne. Litho Irish Security Stamp Ptg Ltd)

1979 (29 Sept). *Visit of Pope John Paul II. P* 14½ × 14.

449	**166**	12p. multicoloured	30	20

167 Brother and Child

(Des R. Kyne (9½p.), P. Scott (11p.), R. Mercer (20p.). Photo Stamping Branch of the Revenue Commissioners, Dublin (11p.), Litho Irish Security Stamp Ptg Ltd (others))

1979 (4 Oct). *Commemorations. T* **167** *and similar designs. P* 14½ × 14 (*9½p.*), 14½ × 15 (*11p.*) *or* 14 × 14½ (*others*).

450	9½p. black and pale claret		20	10
451	11p. black, reddish orange and bright blue ..		20	70
452	20p. multicoloured		40	1·40
450/2	.. ..	*Set of* 3	70	2·00

Designs and commemorations: *Horiz*—9½p. Type **167** (Centenary of Hospitaller Order of St. John of God in Ireland); 20p. "Seated Figure" (sculpture by F. E. McWilliam) (Contemporary Irish Art (10th issue)). *Vert*—11p. Windmill and Sun (International Energy Conservation Month).

PRICES OF SETS

Set prices are given for many issues, generally those containing three stamps or more. Definitive sets include one of each value or major colour change, but do not cover different perforations, die types or minor shades. Where a choice is possible the set prices are based on the cheapest versions of the stamps included in the listings.

168 Patrick Pearse, "Liberty" and General Post Office, Dublin 169 Madonna and Child (panel painting from Domnach Airgid Shrine)

(Des R. Ballagh)

1979 (10 Nov). *Birth Centenary of Patrick Pearse (patriot). P* 15 × 14½.

453	**168**	12p. multicoloured	30	15

(Des Ewa Gargulinska)

1979 (15 Nov). *Christmas. P* 14½ × 15.

454	**169**	9½p. multicoloured	15	10
455		20p. multicoloured	30	55

170 Bianconi Long Car, 1836 171 John Baptist de la Salle (founder)

(Des P. Wildbur. Litho Irish Security Stamp Ptg Ltd)

1979 (6 Dec). *Europa. Communications. T* **170** *and similar horiz design. Multicoloured. P* 14½ × 14.

456	12p. Type **170**	20	30
457	13p. Transatlantic cable, Valentia, 1866 ..	30	1·40

(Des P. Wildbur. Litho Irish Security Stamp Ptg Ltd)

1980 (19 Mar). *Centenary of arrival of De La Salle Order. P* 14 × 14½.

458	**171**	12p. multicoloured	30	30

172 George Bernard Shaw 173 Stoat

(Des P. Byrne. Litho Irish Security Stamp Ptg Ltd)

1980 (7 May). *Europa. Personalities. T* **172** *and similar multicoloured design. P* 14 × 14½.

459	12p. Type **172**	40	50
460	13p. Oscar Wilde (28 × 38 *mm*)	40	1·00

(Des Wendy Walsh. Litho Irish Security Stamp Ptg Ltd)

1980 (30 July). *Wildlife. T* **173** *and similar vert designs. Multicoloured. P* 14 × 14½.

461	12p. Type **173**		20	40
462	15p. Arctic Hare		25	15
463	16p. Red Fox		25	60
464	25p. Red Deer		40	1·60
461/4	.. ..	*Set of* 4	1·00	2·50
MS465	73 × 97 mm. Nos. 461/4		1·25	3·00

No. **MS**465 exists with the sheet margins overprinted to commemorate "STAMPA 80", the Irish National Stamp Exhibition, in black or red, and for the Dublin Stamp Show, 1992, in red.

174 Playing Bodhran and Whistle 175 Sean O'Casey

Des J. Dixon and P. Wildbur. Litho Irish Security Stamp Ptg Ltd)

1980 (25 Sept). *Traditional Music and Dance. T* **174** *and similar vert designs. Multicoloured. P* 14 × 14½.
466 12p. Type **174** .. 15 10
467 15p. Playing Uilleann pipes .. 20 15
468 25p. Dancing .. 35 1·10
466/8 .. *Set of* 3 65 1·25

(Des P. Wildbur (12p.), P. Scott (25p.). Litho Irish Security Stamp Ptg Ltd)

1980 (23 Oct). *Commemorations. T* **175** *and similar vert design. P* 14 × 14½.
469 12p. multicoloured .. 15 10
470 25p. black, buff and drab .. 30 55
Designs and commemorations:—12p. Type **175** (Birth centenary of Sean O'Casey (playwright)); 25p. "Gold Painting No. 57" (Patrick Scott) (Contemporary Irish Art (11th issue)).

176 Nativity Scene (painting by Geraldine McNulty)

177 Boyle Air-pump, 1659

(Des P. Wildbur)

1980 (13 Nov). *Christmas. P* 14½ × 15.
471 **176** 12p. multicoloured .. 15 10
472 15p. multicoloured .. 20 10
473 25p. multicoloured .. 40 1·25
471/3 .. *Set of* 3 65 1·25

(Des P. Wildbur. Litho Irish Security Stamp Ptg Ltd)

1981 (12 Mar). *Irish Science and Technology. T* **177** *and similar vert designs. Multicoloured. P* 14 × 14½.
474 12p. Type **177** .. 20 10
475 15p. Ferguson tractor, 1936 .. 25 10
476 16p. Parsons turbine, 1884 .. 25 90
477 25p. Holland submarine, 1878 .. 30 1·25
474/7 .. *Set of* 4 90 2·10

(Litho Irish Security Stamp Ptg Ltd)

1981 (27 Apr)–**82**. *No wmk. P* 14 × 14½.
478 **106***a* 18p. dull claret .. 45 50
479 19p. light blue .. 55 1·75
480 22p. dull turquoise-blue (1.9.81) .. 65 10
481 24p. drab (29.10.81) .. 75 95
482 26p. blue-green (1.4.82) .. 1·50 40
483 29p. purple (1.4.82) .. 1·75 2·00
478/83 .. *Set of* 6 5·00 5·00

178 "The Legend of the Cock and the Pot"

179 Cycling

(Des P. Byrne. Litho Irish Security Stamp Ptg Ltd)

1981 (4 May). *Europa. Folklore. Paintings by Maria Simonds-Gooding. T* **178** *and similar vert design. P* 14 × 14½.
491 18p. black, orange-yellow and carmine .. 25 10
492 19p. black, yellow-orange and yellow .. 35 70
Design:—19p. "The Angel with the Scales of Judgement".

(Des R. Ballagh. Litho Irish Security Stamp Ptg Ltd)

1981 (24 June). *50th Anniv of "An Óige" (Irish Youth Hostel Association). T* **179** *and similar multicoloured designs. P* 14 × 14½ *(15, 30p.) or* 14½ × 14 *(others).*
493 15p. Type **179** .. 30 40
494 18p. Hill-walking (*horiz*) .. 30 10
495 19p. Mountaineering (*horiz*) .. 50 95
496 30p. Rock-climbing .. 50 95
493/6 .. *Set of* 4 1·25 2·25

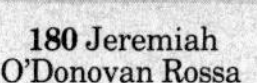

180 Jeremiah O'Donovan Rossa

181 "Railway Embankment" (W. J. Leech)

(Des C. Harrison. Litho Irish Security Stamp Ptg Ltd)

1981 (31 Aug). *150th Birth Anniv of Jeremiah O'Donovan Rossa (politician). P* 14 × 14½.
497 **180** 15p. multicoloured .. 30 30

(Des P. Wildbur. Litho Irish Security Stamp Ptg Ltd)

1981 (31 Aug). *Contemporary Irish Art (12th issue). P* 14½ × 14.
498 **181** 30p. multicoloured .. 60 60

182 James Hoban and White House

183 "Arkle" (steeplechaser)

(Des B. Thompson. Litho Irish Security Stamp Ptg Ltd)

1981 (29 Sept). *150th Death Anniv of James Hoban (White House architect). P* 14½ × 14.
499 **182** 18p. multicoloured .. 30 30

(Des Wendy Walsh and P. Wildbur. Litho Irish Security Stamp Ptg Ltd)

1981 (23 Oct). *Famous Irish Horses. T* **183** *and similar horiz designs. Multicoloured. Ordinary paper (18p.) or chalk-surfaced paper (others). P* 14½ × 14.
500 18p. Type **183** .. 40 1·00
a. Pair. Nos. 500/1 .. 80 2·00
501 18p. "Boomerang" (showjumper) .. 40 1·00
502 22p. "King of Diamonds" (Draught horse) .. 40 30
503 24p. "Ballymoss" (flatracer) .. 40 70
504 36p. "Coosheen Finn" (Connemara pony) .. 60 1·00
500/4 .. *Set of* 5 2·00 3·50
The 18p values were printed together, *se-tenant,* **in horizontal and vertical pairs throughout the sheet.**

184 "Nativity" (F. Barocci)

185 Eviction Scene

(Des P. Wildbur. Litho Irish Security Stamp Ptg Ltd)

1981 (19 Nov). *Christmas. Chalk-surfaced paper. P* 14 × 14½.
505 **184** 18p. multicoloured .. 20 10
506 22p. multicoloured .. 25 10
507 36p. multicoloured .. 45 2·00
505/7 .. *Set of* 3 80 2·00

(Des R. Mercer (18p.), P. Wildbur (22p.). Litho Irish Security Stamp Ptg Ltd)

1981 (10 Dec). *Anniversaries. T* **185** *and similar multicoloured design. Chalk-surfaced paper. P* 14 × 14½ *(18p.) or* 14½ × 14 *(22p.).*
508 18p. Type **185** .. 35 25
509 22p. Royal Dublin Society emblem (*horiz*) .. 40 30
Anniversaries—18p. Centenary of Land Law (Ireland) Act; 22p. 250th of Royal Dublin Society (organization for the advancement of agriculture, industry, art and science).

186 Upper Lake, Killarney National Park

187 "The Stigmatization of St Francis" (Sassetta)

(Des P. Wildbur. Litho Irish Security Stamp Ptg Ltd)

1982 (26 Feb). *50th Anniv of Killarney National Park. T* **186** *and similar horiz design. Multicoloured. P* 14½ × 14.
510 18p. Type **186** .. 35 20
511 36p. Eagle's Nest .. 65 1·60

(Des P. Wildbur (22p.), M. Craig (24p.). Litho Irish Security Stamp Ptg Ltd)

1982 (2 Apr). *Religious Anniversaries. T* **187** *and similar horiz design. Chalk-surfaced paper. P* 14 × 14½ *(22p.) or* 14½ × 14 *(24p.).*
512 22p. multicoloured .. 35 15
513 24p. olive-brown .. 40 80
Designs and anniversaries:—22p. Type **187** (800th birth anniv of St Francis of Assisi (founder of Franciscan Order)); 24p. Francis Makemie (founder of American Presbyterianism) and old Presbyterian Church, Ramelton, Co Donegal (300th anniv of ordination).

188 The Great Famine, 1845–50

189 Pádraic Ó Conaire (writer) (Birth Centenary)

(Des P. Wildbur. Litho Irish Security Stamp Ptg Ltd)

1982 (4 May). *Europa. Historic Events. T* **188** *and similar design. Chalk-surfaced paper. P* 14 × 14½ *(26p.) or* 14½ × 14 *(29p.).*
514 26p. black and stone .. 80 50
515 29p. multicoloured .. 80 2·00
Design: *Horiz*—29p. The coming of Christianity to Ireland.

(Des P. Wildbur. Litho Irish Security Stamp Ptg Ltd)

1982 (16 June). *Anniversaries of Cultural Figures. T* **189** *and similar vert designs. Chalk-surfaced paper. P* 14 × 14½.
516 22p. black and light blue .. 25 30
517 26p. black and sepia .. 30 30
518 29p. black and blue .. 40 1·25
519 44p. black and greenish grey .. 50 1·75
516/19 .. *Set of* 4 1·25 3·25
Designs and anniversaries—26p. James Joyce (writer) (Birth centenary); 29p. John Field (musician) (Birth bicentenary); 44p. Charles Kickham (writer) (Death centenary).

190 Porbeagle Shark (*Lamna nasus*)

191 *St. Patrick* (Galway hooker)

(Des Wendy Walsh and P. Wildbur. Litho Irish Security Stamp Ptg Ltd)

1982 (29 July). *Marine Life. T* **190** *and similar horiz designs. Multicoloured. Chalk-surfaced paper. P* 14½ × 14.
520 22p. Type **190** .. 55 1·25
521 22p. Common European Oyster (*Ostrea edulis*) .. 55 1·25
522 26p. Atlantic Salmon (*Salmo salar*) .. 70 30
523 29p. Dublin Bay Prawn (*Nephrops norvegicus*) .. 70 2·25
520/3 .. *Set of* 4 2·25 4·50

(Des P. Wildbur. Litho Irish Security Stamp Ptg Ltd)

1982 (21 Sept). *Irish Boats. T* **191** *and similar multicoloured designs. Ordinary paper (26p.) or chalk-surfaced paper (others). P* 14 × 14½ *(Nos. 524 and 527) or* 14½ × 14 *(others).*
524 22p. Type **191** .. 60 1·25
525 22p. Currach (*horiz*) .. 60 1·25
526 26p. *Asgard II* (cadet brigantine) (*horiz*) .. 60 30
527 29p. Howth 17 foot yacht .. 60 2·25
524/7 .. *Set of* 4 2·25 4·50

192 "Irish House of Commons" (painting by Francis Wheatley)

193 "Madonna and Child" (sculpture)

(Des P. Wildbur (22p.) or R. Ballagh (26p.). Litho Irish Security Stamp Ptg Ltd)

1982 (14 Oct). *Bicentenary of Grattan's Parliament (22p.) and Birth Centenary of Eamon de Valera (26p.). T* **192** *and similar multicoloured design. P* 14½ × 14 *(22p.) or* 14 × 14½ *(26p.).*
528 22p. Type **192** .. 35 1·25
529 26p. Eamon de Valera (*vert*) .. 40 40

(Des P. Wildbur. Litho Irish Security Stamp Ptg Ltd)

1982 (11 Nov). *Christmas. P* 14 × 14½.
530 **193** 22p. multicoloured .. 30 90
531 26p. multicoloured .. 30 35

NEW INFORMATION

The editor is always interested to correspond with people who have new information that will improve or correct the Catalogue.

194 Aughnanure Castle

195 Ouzel Galley Goblet

(Des M. Craig and P. Wildbur. Litho Irish Security Stamp Ptg Ltd)

1982 (15 Dec)–**90**. *Irish Architecture. T* **194** *and similar designs. Chalk-surfaced paper* (24, 28, 32, 37, 39, 46*p.*, £1 (*No.* 550*b*), £2) *or ordinary paper* (*others*). *P* 15×14 (15, 20, 22, 23, 24, 26, 39, 46, 50*p.*, £1 (*No.* 550), £2, £5) *or* 14×15 (*others*).

532 1p. dull violet-blue (6.7.83) 10 10
a. Chalk-surfaced paper (9.87) .. 40 40
533 2p. deep yellow-green (6.7.83) 20 10
a. Chalk-surfaced paper (27.6.85) .. 50 40
ab. Booklet pane. Nos. 533a, 543a and 545a, each × 2 .. .. 5·50
ac. Booklet pane. Nos. 533a, 543a and 545a, each × 4 .. .. 9·00
ad. Booklet pane. Nos. 533a×2, 535b×3, 544a×3 and 545c×4 (8.9.86) .. 9·00
ae. Booklet pane. Nos. 533a×4, 535b, 544a×2 and 545c×5 (24.11.88) .. 10·00
534 3p. black (6.7.83) 20 10
a. Chalk-surfaced paper (2.88) .. 90 90
535 4p. maroon (16.3.83) 20 10
a. Booklet pane. Nos. 535×3, 543×4 and 1 label (15.8.83) .. .. 2·50
b. Chalk-surfaced paper (9.7.84) .. 40 40
ba. Booklet pane. Nos. 535b×3, 543a×5 and 545a×4 .. .. .. 6·50
c. Perf 13½ (3.5.90) .. .. .. 4·00 4·00
ca. Booklet pane. Nos. 535c×3, 545b, 752ab×2 and 754ab×2 .. 30·00
536 5p. olive-sepia (6.7.83) 30 10
a. Chalk-surfaced paper (8.87) .. 70 30
537 6p. deep grey-blue (16.3.83) 30 15
a. Chalk-surfaced paper (11.85) .. 1·75 1·75
538 7p. dull yellow-green (16.3.83) 30 15
a. Chalk-surfaced paper (3.88) .. 2·00 2·00
539 10p. black (6.7.83) 30 10
a. Chalk-surfaced paper (3.87) .. 85 30
540 12p. purple-brown (6.7.83) 30 30
a. Chalk-surfaced paper (5.87) .. 3·25 3·25
541 15p. deep yellow-green (6.7.83) 45 35
542 20p. deep brown-purple (16.3.83) .. 50 45
a. Chalk-surfaced paper (12.84) .. 1·75 1·75
543 22p. chalky blue 50 10
a. Chalk-surfaced paper (9.7.84) .. 1·75 50
544 23p. yellow-green (16.3.83) 85 80
544*a* 24p. bistre-brown (27.6.85) .. .. 1·25 35
ab. Ordinary paper (9.87) .. .. 3·25 2·00
545 26p. blackish brown 75 10
a. Chalk-surfaced paper (9.7.84) .. 1·25 30
b. Perf 13½ (3.5.90) .. .. .. 5·00 5·00
545*c* 28p. maroon (27.6.85) 75 45
ca. Ordinary paper (10.87) .. .. 9·00 9·00
546 29p. deep yellow-green 90 65
547 30p. black (16.3.83) 70 30
a. Chalk-surfaced paper (3.87) .. 70 90
b. Perf 13½ (3.5.90) .. .. .. 6·00 6·00
ba. Booklet pane. Nos. 547b, 754ab and 774a/5a .. .. 12·00
bb. Booklet pane. Nos. 547b×2, 754ab×2 and 774a .. .. 15·00
547*c* 32p. bistre-brown (1.5.86) .. .. 1·75 2·25
ca. Ordinary paper (9.90) .. .. 5·00 7·00
547*d* 37p. chalky blue (27.6.85) .. .. 90 1·60
547*e* 39p. maroon (1.5.86) .. .. .. 1·75 2·25
548 44p. black and grey 90 90
a. Chalk-surfaced paper (4.85) .. 3·00 3·00
548*b* 46p. olive-green and brownish grey (1.5.86) 4·00 2·00
ba. Ordinary paper (9.87) .. .. 15·00 15·00
549 50p. dull ultramarine and grey (16.3.83) 1·00 65
a. Chalk-surfaced paper (12.84) .. 2·50 90
550 £1 bistre-brown and grey .. .. 3·75 3·00
a. Chalk-surfaced paper (9.84) .. 10·00 7·50
550*b* £1 chalky blue & brownish grey (27.6.85) 3·25 1·25
ba. Ordinary paper (1.88) .. .. 16·00 16·00
550*c* £2 grey-olive and black (26.7.88) .. 4·00 4·50
551 £5 crimson and grey .. .. .. 10·00 5·00
a. Chalk-surfaced paper (8.87) .. 30·00 30·00
532/51 .. .. *Set of* 28 35·00 24·00

Designs: *Horiz* (*as T* **194**)—1p. to 5p. Central Pavilion, Dublin Botanic Gardens; 6p. to 12p. Dr. Steevens' Hospital, Dublin; 28p. to 37p. St. MacDara's Church. (37×21 *mm*)—46p., £1 (No. 550) Cahir Castle: 50p., £2 Casino, Marino; £5 Central Bus Station, Dublin. *Vert* (*as T* **194**)— 15p. to 22p. Type **194**; 23p. to 26p., 39p. Cormac's Chapel. (21×37 *mm*)—44p., £1 (No. 550*b*) Killarney Cathedral.

The following stamps first appeared in booklet panes, but were later issued in sheets: Nos. 533a (7.86), 535b (7.85), 543a (10.84) and 545a (1.85).

Nos. 533ab/ae and 535a/ba show the horizontal edges of the panes imperforate so that 2, 22 and 26p. values from them exist imperforate at top, bottom, left or right, the 4p. at top or bottom the 24p. at right and the 28p. at top.

No. 535ba comes from a £2 Discount booklet and shows "Booklet Stamp" printed over the gum on the reverse of each stamp.

Nos. 535c, 545b and 547b are on ordinary paper and come from the 1990 150th Anniversary of the Penny Black £6 booklet. Examples of Nos. 535c, 545b and 752ab from the right-hand column of booklet pane No. 535ca are imperforate at right (4p.) or top (others). In booklet pane No. 547bb Nos. 547b and 754ab are imperforate at right.

Booklet pane No. 547ba exists with the margins overprinted to commemorate "New Zealand 1990" International Stamp Exhibition Auckland, and No. 547bb with the margins overprinted in blue for "STAMPA 90", the Irish National Stamp Exhibition.

Nos. 550/a were withdrawn without warning on 14 November 1984 after the authorities had discovered forged examples of the £1 stamp used in P.O. savings books. Such forgeries, which it is believed were not used for postal purposes, are line perforated 14.75 or 12 instead of the 14.75×14 comb perforation of the genuine and also show the foot of the "1" rounded instead of square.

(Des P. Wildbur (22p.), C. Harrison (26p.). Litho Irish Security Stamp Ptg Ltd)

1983 (23 Feb). *Bicentenaries of Dublin Chamber of Commerce* (22*p.*) *and Bank of Ireland* (26*p.*). *T* **195** *and similar multi-coloured design. P* 14 × 14½ (22*p.*) *or* 14½ × 14 (26*p.*).

552 22p. Type **195** 30 55
553 26p. Bank of Ireland building (*horiz*) 35 35

196 Pádraig O Siochfhradha (writer and teacher) (Birth cent)

197 Neolithic Carved Pattern, Newgrange Tomb

(Des C. Harrison (26p.), R. Ballagh (29p.). Litho Irish Security Stamp Ptg Ltd)

1983 (7 Apr). *Anniversaries. T* **196** *and similar vert design. Multi-coloured. P* 14 × 14½.

554 26p. Type **196** 50 75
555 29p. Young Boys' Brigade member (Centenary) .. .. 60 1·50

(Des L. le Brocquy (26p.), P. Wildbur (29p.). Litho Irish Security Stamp Ptg Ltd)

1983 (4 May). *Europa. T* **197** *and similar horiz design. P* 14½ × 14.

556 26p. grey-black and gold .. .. .. 1·75 50
557 29p. black, blackish brown and gold .. .. 4·00 5·00

Design:—29p. Sir William Rowan Hamilton's formulae for the multiplication of quaternions.

198 Kerry Blue Terrier

(Des Wendy Walsh and L. Miller. Litho Irish Security Stamp Ptg Ltd)

1983 (23 June). *Irish Dogs. T* **198** *and similar horiz designs. Multicoloured. P* 14½ × 14.

558 22p. Type **198** 65 35
559 26p. Irish Wolfhound 75 45
560 26p. Irish Water Spaniel 75 45
561 29p. Irish Terrier .. .. 95 2·25
562 44p. Irish Setters .. .. 1·40 2·50
558/62 .. .. *Set of* 5 4·00 5·50
MS563 142 × 80 mm. Nos. 558/62 .. .. 6·00 8·00

No. **MS**563 exists with the sheet margins overprinted in blue to commemorate "STAMPA 83", the Irish National Stamp Exhibition.

199 Animals (Irish Society for the Prevention of Cruelty to Animals)

200 Postman with Bicycle

(Des Wendy Walsh (No. 564), B. Murphy (No. 566), K. Uhlemann (No. 567), R. Ballagh (others). Litho Irish Security Stamp Ptg Ltd)

1983 (11 Aug). *Anniversaries and Commemorations. T* **199** *and similar designs. P* 14½ × 14 (*Nos.* 564, 566) *or* 14 × 14½ (*others*).

564 **199** 22p. multicoloured .. .. .. 50 1·00
565 – 22p. multicoloured .. .. .. 50 1·00
566 – 26p. multicoloured 50 60
567 – 26p. multicoloured 50 60
568 – 44p. grey-blue and black .. .. 75 2·00
564/8 .. .. *Set of* 5 2·50 4·75

Designs: *Vert*—No. 565, Sean Mac Diarmada (patriot) (Birth cent); No. 567, "St. Vincent de Paul in the Streets of Paris" (150th anniv of Society of St. Vincent de Paul); No. 568, "Andrew Jackson" (Frank McKelvey) (President of the United States). *Horiz*—No. 566, "100" (Centenary of Industrial Credit Company).

(Des R. Ballagh. Litho Irish Security Stamp Ptg Ltd)

1983 (15 Sept). *World Communications Year. T* **200** *and similar vert design. Multicoloured. P* 14 × 14½.

569 22p. Type **200** .. .. 55 7[illegible]
570 29p. Dish antenna .. .. 70 2·0[illegible]

201 Weaving

202 "La Natividad" (R. van der Weyden)

(Des R. Mercer. Litho Irish Security Stamp Ptg Ltd)

1983 (13 Oct). *Irish Handicrafts. T* **201** *and similar vert designs Multicoloured. P* 14 × 14½.

571 22p. Type **201** 40 50
572 26p. Basketmaking 40 35
573 29p. Irish crochet .. .. 45 1·25
574 44p. Harpmaking .. .. 70 2·00
571/4 .. .. *Set of* 4 1·75 3·50

(Des and litho Irish Security Stamp Ptg Ltd)

1983 (30 Nov). *Christmas. P* 14 × 14½.

575 **202** 22p. multicoloured 35 30
576 26p. multicoloured 40 30

203 Dublin and Kingstown Railway Steam Locomotive *Princess*

(Des C. Rycroft. Litho Irish Security Stamp Ptg Ltd)

1984 (30 Jan). 150*th Anniv of Irish Railways. T* **203** *and similar horiz designs. Multicoloured. Ordinary paper* (23*p.*, 26*p. and miniature sheet*) *or chalk-surfaced paper* (*others*). *P* 15×14.

577 23p. Type **203** .. .. 75 1·25
578 26p. Great Southern Railway steam locomotive *Macha* 75 35
579 29p. Great Northern Railway steam locomotive No. 87 *Kestrel* .. .. .. 85 1·75
580 44p. Coras Iompair Eireann two-car electric unit .. .. 1·10 2·25
577/80 .. .. *Set of* 4 3·00 5·00
MS581 129×77 mm. Nos. 577/80 .. .. 4·75 7·00

No. **MS**581 exists with the sheet margins overprinted in black to commemorate "STAMPA 84", the Irish National Stamp Exhibition.

204 *Sorbus hibernica*

(Des Wendy Walsh and P. Wildbur. Litho Irish Security Stamp Ptg Ltd)

1984 (1 Mar). *Irish Trees. T* **204** *and similar horiz designs. Multi-coloured. P* 15 × 14.

582 22p. Type **204** 65 70
583 26p. *Taxus baccata fastigiata* 70 40
584 29p. *Salix hibernica* .. .. 85 2·00
585 44p. *Betula pubescens* .. .. 1·10 2·75
582/5 .. .. *Set of* 4 3·00 5·25

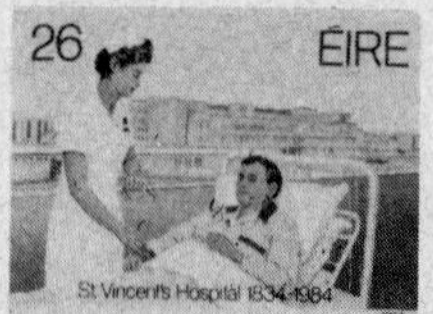

205 St. Vincent's Hospital, Dublin

(Des B. Donegan, adapted by C. Vis (26p.), B. Murphy (44p.). Litho Irish Security Stamp Ptg Ltd)

1984 (12 Apr). 150*th Anniv of St. Vincent's Hospital and Bicentenary of Royal College of Surgeons. T* **205** *and similar horiz design. Multicoloured. P* 15 × 14.

586 26p. Type **205** 50 30
587 44p. Royal College and logo .. .. .. 90 1·50

206 C.E.P.T. 25th Anniversary Logo

(Des J. Larrivière. Litho Irish Security Stamp Ptg Ltd)

1984 (10 May). *Europa*. *P* 15 × 14.
588 **206** 26p. blue, deep dull blue and black .. 1·75 50
589 29p. light green, blue-green and black .. 2·25 2·75

207 Flags on Ballot Box **208** John McCormack

(Des R. Ballagh. Litho Irish Security Stamp Ptg Ltd)

1984 (10 May). *Second Direct Elections to European Assembly*. *P* 15 × 14.
590 **207** 26p. multicoloured 50 70

(Des R. Mercer and J. Sharpe. Litho Irish Security Stamp Ptg Ltd)

1984 (6 June). *Birth Centenary of John McCormack (tenor)*. *P* 14 × 15.
591 **208** 22p. multicoloured 50 70

209 Hammer-throwing

(Des L. le Brocquy and P. Wildbur. Litho Irish Security Stamp Ptg Ltd)

1984 (21 June). *Olympic Games, Los Angeles*. *T* **209** *and similar horiz designs*. *P* 15 × 14.
592 22p. deep mauve, black and gold 35 80
593 26p. violet, black and gold 40 65
594 29p. bright blue, black and gold .. .. 60 1·25
592/4 .. .. *Set of* 3 1·25 2·50
Designs:—26p. Hurdling; 29p. Running.

210 Hurling **211** Galway Mayoral Chain (500th Anniv of Mayoral Charter)

(Des C. Harrison. Litho Irish Security Stamp Ptg Ltd)

1984 (23 Aug). *Centenary of Gaelic Athletic Association*. *T* **210** *and similar multicoloured design*. *P* 15 × 14 (22*p*.) *or* 14 × 15 (26*p*.).
595 22p. Type **210** 50 90
596 26p. Irish football (*vert*) 60 90

(Des P. Wildbur. Litho Irish Security Stamp Ptg Ltd)

1984 (18 Sept). *Anniversaries*. *T* **211** *and similar multicoloured design*. *P* 14 × 15 (26*p*.) *or* 15 × 14 (44*p*.).
597 26p. Type **211** 35 50
598 44p. St. Brendan (from 15th-cent Bodleian manuscript) (1500th birth anniv) (*horiz*) 75 1·50

212 Hands passing Letter **213** "Virgin and Child" (Sassoferrato)

(Litho Irish Security Stamp Ptg Ltd)

1984 (19 Oct). *Bicentenary of the Irish Post Office*. *P* 15 × 14.
599 **212** 26p. multicoloured 60 70

(Des O'Connor O'Sullivan Advertising (17p.), P. Wildbur (others). Litho Irish Security Stamp Ptg Ltd)

1984 (26 Nov). *Christmas*. *T* **213** *and similar multicoloured design*. *Chalk-surfaced paper*. *P* 15 × 14 (17*p*.) *or* 14 × 15 (*others*).
600 17p. Christmas star (*horiz*) 45 80
601 22p. Type **213** .. .. 45 1·25
602 26p. Type **213** 65 40
600/2 .. .. *Set of* 3 1·40 2·25
No. 600 represented a special concession rate for Christmas card postings to addresses within Ireland and Great Britain between 26 November and 8 December 1984.

214 "Love" and Heart-shaped Balloon **215** Dunsink Observatory (Bicentenary)

(Des Susan Dubsky (22p.), Patricia Jorgensen (26p.). Litho Irish Security Stamp Ptg Ltd)

1985 (31 Jan). *Greetings Stamps*. *T* **214** *and similar multicoloured design*. *Chalk-surfaced paper*. *P* 15 × 14 (22*p*.) *or* 14 × 15 (26*p*.).
603 22p. Type **214** 50 75
604 26p. Bouquet of hearts and flowers (*vert*) .. 60 75

(Des R. Ballagh (22, 44p.), K. Thomson (26p.), M. Lunt (37p.). Litho Irish Security Stamp Ptg Ltd)

1985 (14 Mar). *Anniversaries*. *T* **215** *and similar designs*. *Multicoloured*. *Chalk-surfaced paper*. *P* 15 × 14 (26*p*.) *or* 14 × 15 (*others*).
605 22p. Type **215** 50 50
606 26p. "A Landscape at Tivoli, Cork, with Boats" (Nathaniel Grogan) (800th anniv of City of Cork) (*horiz*) .. 50 30
607 37p. Royal Irish Academy (Bicentenary) .. 70 1·75
608 44p. Richard Crosbie's balloon flight (Bicentenary of first aeronautic flight by an Irishman) .. .. 80 1·75
605/8 .. .. *Set of* 4 2·25 3·75

216 *Polyommatus icarus* **217** Charles Villiers Stanford (composer)

(Des I. Loe. Litho Irish Security Stamp Ptg Ltd)

1985 (11 Apr). *Butterflies*. *T* **216** *and similar vert designs*. *Multicoloured*. *Chalk-surfaced paper*. *P* 14 × 15.
609 22p. Type **216** .. .. 1·25 1·00
610 26p. *Vanessa atalanta* .. .. 1·25 70
611 28p. *Gonepteryx rhamni* .. .. .. 1·50 2·75
612 44p. *Eurodryas aurinia* .. .. .. 2·00 3·00
609/12 .. .. *Set of* 4 5·50 6·75

(Des P. Hickey and J. Farrar. Litho Irish Security Stamp Ptg Ltd)

1985 (16 May). *Europa*. *Irish Composers*. *T* **217** *and similar horiz design*. *Multicoloured*. *Chalk-surfaced paper*. *P* 15×14.
613 26p. Type **217** .. .. 2·00 50
614 37p. Turlough Carolan (composer and lyricist) .. .. 4·00 5·50

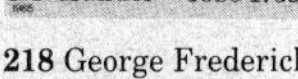

218 George Frederick Handel **219** U.N. Patrol of Irish Soldiers, Congo, 1960 (25th Anniv. of Irish Participation in U.N. Peace-keeping Force)

(Des K. Uhlemann and J. Farrar. Litho Irish Security Stamp Ptg Ltd)

1985 (16 May). *European Music Year*. *Composers*. *T* **218** *and similar vert designs*. *Multicoloured*. *Chalk-surfaced paper*. *P* 14 × 15.
615 22p. Type **218** .. .. 1·25 2·50
a. Pair. Nos. 615/16 .. .. 2·50 5·00
616 22p. Guiseppe Domenico Scarlatti .. .. 1·25 2·50
617 26p. Johann Sebastian Bach .. .. .. 1·50 50
615/17 .. .. *Set of* 3 3·50 5·00
Nos. 615/16 were printed together, *se-tenant*, in horizontal and vertical pairs throughout the sheet.

(Des B. Donegan and J. Farrar (22p.), R. Ballagh (26p.), B. Donegan (44p.). Litho Irish Security Stamp Ptg Ltd)

1985 (20 June). *Anniversaries*. *T* **219** *and similar multicoloured designs*. *Chalk-surfaced paper*. *P* 15 × 14 (22*p*.) *or* 14 × 15 (*others*).
618 22p. Type **219** 65 80
619 26p. Thomas Ashe (patriot) (Birth cent) (*vert*) 65 60
620 44p. "Bishop George Berkeley" (James Lathan) (philosopher) (300th birth anniv) (*vert*) .. .. 1·00 3·00
618/20 .. .. *Set of* 3 2·10 4·00

220 Group of Young People

(Des J. Farrar and N. Mooney. Litho Irish Security Stamp Ptg Ltd)

1985 (1 Aug). *International Youth Year*. *T* **220** *and similar multicoloured design*. *Chalk-surfaced paper*. *P* 15 × 14 (22*p*.) *or* 14 × 15 (26*p*.).
621 22p. Type **220** 55 50
622 26p. Students and young workers (*vert*) .. 55 50

221 Visual Display Unit

(Des B. Donegan (44p.), C. Rycraft (others). Litho Irish Security Stamp Ptg Ltd)

1985 (3 Oct). *Industrial Innovation*. *T* **221** *and similar horiz designs*. *Multicoloured*. *Chalk-surfaced paper*. *P* 15 × 14.
623 22p. Type **221** 65 75
624 26p. Turf cutting with hand tool and with modern machinery 70 55
625 44p. "The Key Man" (Sean Keating) (150th anniv of Institution of Engineers of Ireland) .. .. 1·25 2·50
623/5 .. .. *Set of* 3 2·40 3·50

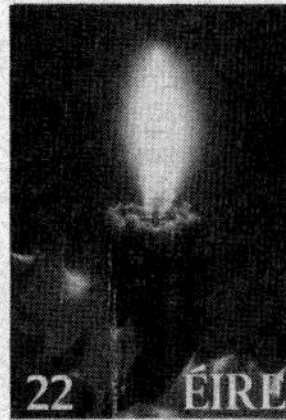

222 Lighted Candle and Holly **223** "Virgin and Child in a Landscape" (Adrian van Ijsenbrandt)

(Des R. Mahon (No. 626). Litho Irish Security Stamp Ptg Ltd)

1985 (26 Nov). *Christmas*. *T* **222** *and designs as T* **223** *showing paintings*. *Multicoloured*. *Chalk-surfaced paper*. *P* 15 × 14 (26*p*.) *or* 14 × 15 (*others*).
626 22p. Type **222** 75 65
a. Sheetlet. No. 626 × 16 .. .. .. 11·00
627 22p. Type **223** .. .. 90 2·50
a. Pair. Nos. 627/8 .. .. 1·75 5·00
628 22p. "The Holy Family" (Murillo) .. .. 90 2·50
629 26p. "The Adoration of the Shepherds" (Louis le Nain) (*horiz*) 90 25
626/9 .. .. *Set of* 4 3·00 5·50
No. 626 was only issued in sheetlets of 16 sold at £3, providing a discount of 52p. off the face value of the stamps.
Nos. 627/8 were printed together, *se-tenant*, in horizontal and vertical pairs throughout the sheet.

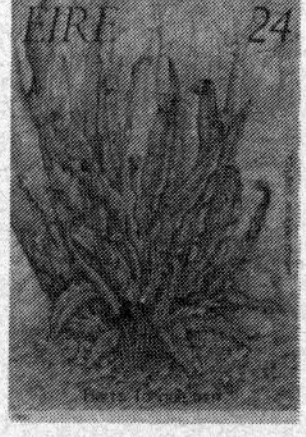

224 Stylised Love Bird with Letter **225** Hart's Tongue Fern

(Des R. Hoek (22p.), T. Monaghan (26p.). Litho Irish Security Stamp Ptg Ltd)

1986 (30 Jan). *Greetings Stamps*. *T* **224** *and similar vert design*. *Multicoloured*. *Chalk-surfaced paper*. *P* 14 × 15.
630 22p. Type **224** 55 90
631 26p. Heart-shaped pillar-box 55 90

(Des I. Loe. Litho Irish Security Stamp Ptg Ltd)

1986 (20 Mar). *Ferns. T* **255** *and similar vert designs. Multicoloured. Chalk-surfaced paper. P* 14 × 15.

632 24p. Type **225** 70 70
633 28p. Rusty-back Fern 80 70
634 46p. Killarney Fern .. .. 1·25 2·10
632/4 .. .. *Set of* 3 2·50 3·25

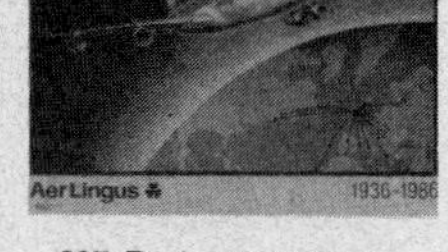

226 "Harmony between Industry and Nature"

227 Boeing 747-200 over Globe showing Aer Lingus Routes

(Des G. van Gelderen. Litho Irish Security Stamp Ptg Ltd)

1986 (1 May). *Europa. Protection of the Environment. T* **226** *and similar multicoloured design. Chalk-surfaced paper. P* 14 × 15 (28*p.*) *or* 15 × 14 (39*p.*).

635 28p. Type **226** .. .. 1·75 50
636 39p. *Vanessa atalanta* (butterfly) and tractor in field ("Preserve hedgerows") (*horiz*) .. .. 3·25 5·00

(Des R. Ballagh. Litho Irish Security Stamp Ptg Ltd)

1986 (27 May). *50th Anniv of Aer Lingus* (*airline*). *T* **227** *and similar horiz design. Multicoloured. Chalk-surfaced paper. P* 15 × 14.

637 28p. Type **227** .. .. 1·40 75
638 46p. De Havilland D.H.84 Dragon Mk 2 *Iolar* (first aircraft) .. .. 1·90 3·00

228 Grand Canal at Robertstown

229 *Severn* (19th-century paddle-steamer)

(Des B. Matthews. Litho Irish Security Stamp Ptg Ltd)

1986 (27 May). *Irish Waterways. T* **228** *and similar multicoloured designs. Chalk-surfaced paper. P* 14 × 15 (28*p.*) *or* 15 × 14 (*others*).

639 24p. Type **228** .. .. 1·00 1·00
640 28p. Fishing in County Mayo (*vert*) .. .. 1·25 1·00
641 30p. Motor cruiser on Lough Derg .. .. 1·50 2·50
639/41 .. .. *Set of* 3 3·25 4·00

(Des C. Rycraft. Litho Irish Security Stamp Ptg Ltd)

1986 (10 July). *150th Anniv of British and Irish Steam Packet Company. T* **229** *and similar horiz design. Multicoloured. P* 15 × 14.

642 24p. Type **229** .. .. 75 1·00
643 28p. M.V. *Leinster* (modern ferry) 85 60

230 Kish Lighthouse and Bell 206B Jet Ranger III Helicopter

231 J. P. Nannetti (first president) and Linotype Operator (Dublin Council of Trade Unions Centenary)

(Des R. Ballagh. Litho Irish Security Stamp Printing Ltd)

1986 (10 July). *Irish Lighthouses. T* **230** *and similar vert design. Multicoloured. P* 14 × 15.

644 24p. Type **230** 75 75
645 30p. Fastnet Lighthouse .. .. .. 1·75 2·75

(Des R. Ballagh (Nos. 646/7), M. Cameron (No. 648), A. Mazer (Nos. 649/50). Litho Irish Security Stamp Ptg Ltd)

1986 (21 Aug). *Anniversaries and Commemorations. T* **231** *and similar designs. Ordinary paper* (24*p.*) *or chalk-surfaced paper* (*others*). *P* 14 × 15 (*Nos.* 646/7, 649) *or* 15 × 14 (*others*).

646 24p. multicoloured 50 90
647 28p. black and brownish grey 60 80
648 28p. multicoloured 60 80
649 30p. multicoloured .. .. 65 1·00
650 46p. multicoloured .. .. 70 1·75
646/50 .. .. *Set of* 5 2·75 4·75

Designs: *Vert*—No. 647, Arthur Griffith (statesman); No. 649, Clasped hands (International Peace Year). *Horiz*—No. 648, Woman surveyor (Women in Society); No. 650, Peace dove (International Peace Year).

232 William Mulready and his Design for 1840 Envelope

233 "The Adoration of the Shepherds" (Francesco Pascucci)

(Des C. Harrison (24p.), A. Mazer from aquatints by M. A. Hayes (others). Litho Irish Security Stamp Ptg Ltd)

1986 (2 Oct). *Birth Bicentenaries of William Mulready* (*artist*) (24*p*). *and Charles Bianconi* (*originator of Irish mail coach service*) (*others*). *T* **232** *and similar multicoloured designs. Chalk-surfaced paper. P* 14 × 15 (28*p.*) *or* 15 × 14 (*others*).

651 24p. Type **232** 65 70
652 28p. Bianconi car outside Hearns Hotel, Clonmel (*vert*) 75 55
653 39p. Bianconi car on the road .. .. 1·25 1·75
651/3 .. .. *Set of* 3 2·40 2·75

(Des C. O'Neill (21p.). Litho Irish Security Stamp Ptg Ltd)

1986 (20 Nov). *Christmas. T* **233** *and similar multicoloured design. Chalk-surfaced paper. P* 15 × 14 (21*p.*) *or* 14 × 15 (28*p.*).

654 21p. Type **233** .. .. 1·10 1·40
a. Sheetlet. No. 654 × 12 .. .. .. 12·00
655 28p. "The Adoration of the Magi" (Frans Francken III) (*vert*) 65 60

No. 654 was only issued in sheetlets of 12 sold at £2.50, providing a discount of 2p. off the face value of the stamps.

234 "Butterfly and Flowers" (Tara Collins)

235 Cork Electric Tram

(Litho Irish Security Stamp Ptg Ltd)

1987 (27 Jan) *Greetings Stamps. Children's Paintings. T* **234** *and similar multicoloured design. Chalk-surfaced paper. P* 15 × 14 (24*p.*) *or* 14 × 15 (28*p.*).

656 24p. Type **234** .. .. 70 1·25
657 28p. "Postman on Bicycle delivering Hearts" (Brigid Teehan) (*vert*) .. .. .. 80 1·25

(Des C. Rycraft. Litho Irish Security Stamp Ptg Ltd)

1987 (4 Mar). *Irish Trams. T* **235** *and similar horiz designs. Multicoloured. Chalk-surfaced paper. P* 15×14.

658 24p. Type **235** 65 65
659 28p. Dublin standard tram No. 291 .. 70 85
660 30p. Howth (Great Northern Railway) tram 80 2·00
661 46p. Galway horse tram .. .. .. 1·25 2·25
658/61 .. .. *Set of* 4 3·00 5·00
MS662 131×85 mm. Nos. 658/61 .. .. 4·25 6·50

No. **MS**662 exists with the sheet margins overprinted in red for "HAFNIA 87" and in black for "STAMPA 87".

236 Ships from Crest (Bicentenary of Waterford Chamber of Commerce)

237 Bord na Mona Headquarters and "The Turf Cutter" sculpture (John Behan), Dublin

(Des K. Uhlemann (24p.), J Farrer (28p.), A. Mazer and Wendy Walsh (30p.), M. Cameron (39p.). Litho Irish Security Stamp Ptg Ltd)

1987 (9 Apr). *Anniversaries. T* **236** *and similar designs. Chalk-surfaced paper. P* 14 × 15 (30*p.*) *or* 15 × 14 (*others*).

663 24p. black, ultramarine and deep grey-green 80 60
664 28p. multicoloured 80 60
665 30p. multicoloured .. .. 85 1·75
666 39p. multicoloured .. .. 90 2·00
663/6 .. .. *Set of* 4 3·00 4·50

Designs: *Horiz*—28p. Canon John Hayes and symbols of agriculture and development (Birth centenary and 50th anniv of Muintir na Tire Programme); 39p. Mother Mary Martin and International Missionary Training Hospital, Drogheda (50th anniv of Medical Missionaries of Mary). *Vert*—30p. *Calceolaria burbidgei* and College crest (300th anniv of Trinity College Botanic Gardens, Dublin).

(Des M. Lunt. Litho Harrison)

1987 (14 May). *Europa. Modern Architecture. T* **237** *and similar horiz design. Multicoloured. P* 15 × 14.

667 28p. Type **237** .. .. 1·50 60
668 39p. St. Mary's Church, Cong .. .. 3·50 5·00

238 Kerry Cow

239 Fleadh Nua, Ennis

(Des B. Driscoll. Litho Irish Security Stamp Ptg Ltd)

1987 (2 July). *Irish Cattle. T* **238** *and similar horiz designs. Multicoloured. Chalk-surfaced paper. P* 15 × 14.

669 24p. Type **238** 70 75
670 28p. Friesian cow and calf 85 60
671 30p. Hereford bullock .. .. 90 2·25
672 39p. Shorthorn bull .. .. 1·00 2·25
669/72 .. .. *Set of* 4 3·00 5·25

(Des R. Ballagh. Litho Irish Security Stamp Ptg Ltd)

1987 (27 Aug). *Festivals. T* **239** *and similar multicoloured designs. Chalk-surfaced paper. P* 14×15 (*vert*) *or* 15 × 14 (*horiz*).

673 24p. Type **239** 65 70
674 28p. Rose of Tralee International Festival .. 70 60
675 30p. Wexford Opera Festival (*horiz*) .. 80 2·00
676 46p. Ballinasloe Horse Fair (*horiz*) .. .. 1·10 2·00
673/6 .. .. *Set of* 4 3·00 4·75

240 Flagon (1637), Arms and Anniversary Ornament (1987) (350th Anniv of Dublin Goldsmiths' Company)

241 Scenes from "The Twelve Days of Christmas" (carol)

(Des B. Donegan (No. 677), R. Ballagh (No. 678), A. Mazer and Breda Mathews (No. 679), Libby Carton (No. 680). Litho Harrison (46p.) or Irish Security Stamp Ptg Ltd (others))

1987 (1 Oct). *Anniversaries and Commemorations. T* **240** *and similar designs. Ordinary paper* (46*p.*) *or chalk-surfaced paper* (*others*). *P* 15 × 14 (*horiz*) *or* 14 × 15 (*vert*).

677 **240** 24p. multicoloured 55 80
678 – 24p. grey and black 55 80
679 – 28p. multicoloured 65 60
680 – 46p. multicoloured .. .. 1·00 1·10
677/80 .. .. *Set of* 4 2·50 3·00

Designs: *Vert*—24p. (No. 678) Cathal Brugha (statesman); 46p. Woman chairing board meeting (Women in Society). *Horiz*—28p. Arms of Ireland and inscription (50th anniv of Constitution).

(Des M. Cameron (21p.), A. Mazer (others). Litho Irish Security Stamp Ptg Ltd)

1987 (17 Nov). *Christmas. T* **241** *and similar multicoloured designs. Chalk-surfaced paper. P* 15 × 14 (21*p.*) *or* 14 × 15 (*others*).

681 21p. Type **241** .. .. 60 1·00
a. Sheetlet. No. 681 × 14 .. .. .. 7·50
682 24p. The Nativity (detail, late 15th-cent Waterford Vestments) (*vert*) .. .. 75 1·00
683 28p. Figures from Neapolitan crib, *c* 1850 (*vert*) 75 80
681/3 .. .. *Set of* 3 1·90 2·50

No. 681 represents a special rate for greetings cards within Ireland and to all E.E.C. countries. It was only issued in sheetlets of 14 stamps and 1 label sold at £2.90, providing an additional discount of 4p. off the face value of the stamps.

242 Acrobatic Clowns spelling "LOVE"

243 "Robert Burke" (Sidney Nolan) and Map of Burke and Wills Expedition Route

(Des M. Cameron (24p.), Aislinn Adams (28p.). Litho Irish Security Stamp Ptg Ltd)

1988 (27 Jan). *Greetings Stamps. T* **242** *and similar multicoloured design. Chalk-surfaced paper. P* 15 × 14 (24*p.*) *or* 14 × 15 (28*p.*).

684 24p. Type **242** 60 60
685 28p. Pillar box and hearts (*vert*) 65 65

(Des A. Mazer. Litho Irish Security Stamp Ptg Ltd)

1988 (1 Mar). *Bicentenary of Australian Settlement. T* **243** *and similar horiz design. Multicoloured. Chalk-surfaced paper. P* 15 × 14.

686 24p. Type **243** 40 60
687 46p. "Eureka Stockade" (mural detail, Sidney Nolan) .. .. 85 1·75

244 Past and Present Buildings of Dublin

245 Showjumping

(Des S. Conlin. Litho Irish Security Stamp Ptg Ltd)

988 (1 Mar). *Dublin Millennium. Chalk-surfaced paper. P* 15×14.
88 **244** 28p. multicoloured 60 55
a. Booklet pane. No. 688 × 4 . . . . 1·75

No. 688a was printed with either Irish or English inscriptions 1 the centre of the pane and came from £2.24 stamp booklets. oose panes could also be purchased from the Philatelic Bureau, Dublin, and its agents. They exist overprinted for "STAMPA 88" n blue on Irish version and red on English) and "Sydpex 88" both green on gold).

(Des Ann Flynn Litho Irish Security Stamp Ptg Ltd)

988 (7 Apr). *Olympic Games, Seoul. T* **245** *and similar horiz design. Multicoloured. Chalk-surfaced paper. P* 15×14.
89 28p. Type **245** . . . . 1·00 1·40
a. Sheetlet. Nos. 689/90, each × 5 . . 9·00
90 28p. Cycling . . . . 1·00 1·40

Nos. 689/90 were printed together, *se-tenant*, in a sheetlet ontaining five of each design and two stamp-size labels.

246 William T. Cosgrave (statesman)

247 Air Traffic Controllers and Airbus Industrie A320

Des R. Ballagh (24p.), J. Farrer (30p.), K. Uhlemann (50p.). Litho Irish Security Stamp Ptg Ltd)

988 (7 Apr). *Anniversaries and Events. T* **246** *and similar designs. Chalk-surfaced paper. P* 14×15 *(vert) or* 15×14 *(horiz).*
91 24p. brownish grey and black 60 45
92 30p. multicoloured . . . . . . 1·00 1·00
93 50p. multicoloured . . . . . . 1·25 1·90
91/3 . . . . . . *Set of* 3 2·50 3·00

Designs: *Horiz*—30p. Members with casualty and ambulance 50th anniv of Order of Malta Ambulance Corps). *Vert*—50p. Barry Fitzgerald (actor) (Birth centenary).

(Des C. Rycraft (28p.), M. Cameron (39p.). Litho Irish Security Stamp Ptg Ltd)

988 (12 May). *Europa. Transport and Communications. T* **247** *and similar horiz design. Multicoloured. Chalk-surfaced paper. P* 15×14.
94 28p. Type **247** . . . . 1·25 55
95 39p. Globe with stream of letters from Ireland to Europe . . . . . . 1·75 2·50

248 *Sirius* (paddle-steamer) (150th anniv of regular transatlantic steamship services)

249 Cottonweed

(Des C. Rycraft. Litho Irish Security Stamp Ptg Ltd)

1988 (12 May). *Transatlantic Transport Anniversaries. T* **248** *and similar horiz design. Multicoloured. Chalk-surfaced paper. P* 15×14.
696 24p. Type **248** 75 50
697 46p. Short S.20 seaplane *Mercury* and Short S.21 flying boat *Maia* (Short-Mayo composite aircraft) in Foynes Harbour (50th anniv of first commercial transatlantic flight) . . 1·50 2·75

(Des Frances Poskitt. Litho Irish Security Stamp Ptg Ltd)

1988 (21 June). *Endangered Flora of Ireland. T* **249** *and similar vert designs. Multicoloured. Chalk-surfaced paper. P* 14×15.
698 24p. Type **249** 65 55
699 28p. Hart's Saxifrage 75 55
700 46p. Purple Milk-Vetch . . . . . . 1·10 2·00
698/700 . . . . . . *Set of* 3 2·25 2·75

250 Garda on Duty

251 Computer and Abacus (Institute of Chartered Accountants in Ireland Centenary)

(Des D. Teskey. Litho Irish Security Stamp Ptg Ltd)

1988 (23 Aug). *Irish Security Forces. T* **250** *and similar horiz designs. Multicoloured. Chalk-surfaced paper. P* 15×14.
701 28p. Type **250** . . . . 60 1·00
a. Strip of 4. Nos. 701/4 . . . . 2·25
702 28p. Army unit with personnel carrier . . 60 1·00
703 28p. Navy and Air Corps members with *Eithne* (helicopter patrol vessel) . . 60 1·00
704 28p. Army and navy reservists . . . . 60 1·00
701/4 . . . . . . *Set of* 4 2·25 3·50

Nos. 701/4 were printed together, both horizontally and vertically *se-tenant*, throughout the sheet of 20 (4×5).

(Des C. Rycraft (24p.), K. King and A. Mazer (46p.). Litho Irish Security Stamp Ptg Ltd)

1988 (6 Oct). *Anniversaries. T* **251** *and similar multicoloured design. Chalk-surfaced paper. P* 14×15 *(24p.) or* 15×14 *(46p.).*
705 24p. Type **251** 40 40
706 46p. *Duquesa Santa Ana* off Donegal *(horiz)* (400th anniv of Spanish Armada) . . 1·25 1·25

252 "President Kennedy" (James Wyeth)

253 St. Kevin's Church, Glendalough

(Des A. Mazer. Litho Irish Security Stamp Ptg Ltd)

1988 (24 Nov). *25th Death Anniv of John F. Kennedy (American statesman). Chalk-surfaced paper. P* 15×14.
707 **252** 28p. multicoloured 70 80

(Des Ann Flynn (21p.), B. Donegan (others). Litho Irish Security Stamp Ptg Ltd)

1988 (24 Nov). *Christmas. T* **253** *and similar vert designs. Multicoloured. Chalk-surfaced paper. P* 14×15.
708 21p. Type **253** 70 70
a. Sheetlet. No. 708 × 14 . . . . 9·00
709 24p. The Adoration of the Magi 50 60
710 28p. The Flight into Egypt 60 55
711 46p. The Holy Family . . . . . . 70 2·00
708/11 . . . . . . *Set of* 4 2·25 3·50

No. 708 represents a special rate for greetings cards within Ireland and to all E.E.C. countries. It was only issued in sheetlets of 14 stamps and 1 label sold at £2.90, providing an additional discount of 4p. off the face value of the stamps.

The designs of Nos. 709/11 are from a 15th-century French Book of Hours.

254 Spring Flowers spelling "Love" in Gaelic

255 Italian Garden, Garinish Island

(Des Susan Dubsky (24p.), A. Mazer (28p.). Litho Irish Security Stamp Ptg Ltd)

1989 (24 Jan). *Greetings Stamps. T* **254** *and similar multicoloured design. Chalk-surfaced paper. P* 15×14 *(24p.) or* 14×15 *(28p.).*
712 24p. Type **254** 60 55
713 28p. "The Sonnet" (William Mulready) *(vert)* 65 55

(Des Frances Poskitt. Litho Irish Security Stamp Ptg Ltd)

1989 (11 Apr). *National Parks and Gardens. T* **255** *and similar horiz designs. Multicoloured. Chalk-surfaced paper. P* 15×14.
714 24p. Type **255** 80 55
715 28p. Lough Veagh, Glenveagh National Park 95 55
716 32p. Barnaderg Bay, Connemara National Park . . . . 1·00 1·25
717 50p. St. Stephen's Green, Dublin . . . . 1·50 1·75
714/17 . . . . . . *Set of* 4 3·75 3·75

256 "Silver Stream", 1908

257 Ring-a-ring-a-roses

(Des C. Rycraft. Litho Irish Security Stamp Ptg Ltd)

1989 (11 Apr). *Classic Irish Cars. T* **256** *and similar horiz designs. Multicoloured. Chalk-surfaced paper. P* 15×14.
718 24p. Type **256** 50 55
a. Booklet pane. Nos. 718/19, each ×2 . . 3·00
b. Booklet pane. Nos. 718/21 . . . . 3·50
719 28p. Benz "Comfortable", 1898 . . . . 50 55
720 39p. "Thomond", 1929 . . . . . . 1·25 1·50
721 46p. Chambers' 8 h.p. model, 1905 . . 1·50 1·60
718/21 . . . . . . *Set of* 4 3·25 3·75

Booklet panes Nos. 718a/b come from £2.41 stamp booklets and stamps from them have one or two adjacent sides imperforate. Such panes were also available loose from the Philatelic Bureau, Dublin, and its agents

(Des C. Harrison. Litho Irish Security Stamp Ptg Ltd)

1989 (11 May). *Europa. Children's Games. T* **257** *and similar horiz design. Multicoloured. Chalk-surfaced paper. P* 15×14.
722 28p. Type **257** . . . . 1·00 75
723 39p. Hopscotch . . . . 1·40 2·25

Nos. 722/3 were each issued in sheets of 10 showing additional illustrations in the left-hand sheet margin.

258 Irish Red Cross Flag (50th anniv)

259 Saints Kilian, Totnan and Colman (from 12th-century German manuscript)

(Des Q Design (24p.), R. Hoek (28p.). Litho Irish Security Stamp Ptg Ltd)

1989 (11 May). *Anniversaries and Events. T* **258** *and similar vert design. Chalk-surfaced paper. P* 14×15.
724 24p. vermilion and black 55 60
725 28p. new blue, black and lemon . . . . 1·10 1·10

Design:—28p. Circle of twelve stars (Third direct elections to European Parliament).

(Des P. Effert. Litho Irish Security Stamp Ptg Ltd)

1989 (15 June). *1300th Death Anniv of Saints Kilian, Totnan and Colman. Chalk-surfaced paper. P* 13½.
726 **259** 28p. multicoloured . . . . . . 80 1·10
a. Booklet pane. No. 726×4 with margins all round . . . . 3·00

A stamp in a similar design was issued by West Germany.

No. 726a exists with text in Irish, English, German or Latin on the pane margin.

260 19th-century Mail Coach passing Cashel

261 Crest and 19th-century Dividers (150th anniv of Royal Institute of Architects of Ireland)

(Des Katie O'Sullivan and B. Donegan. Litho Irish Security Stamp Ptg Ltd)

1989 (27 July). *Bicentenary of Irish Mail Coach Service. Chalk-surfaced paper. P* 15×14.
727 **260** 28p. multicoloured . . . . . . 1·00 75

(Des R. Ballagh (24p.), A. Mazer (28p.), K. Uhlemann (30p.), Carey Clarke (46p.). Litho Irish Security Stamp Ptg Ltd)

1989 (27 July). *Anniversaries and Commemorations. T* **261** *and similar designs. Chalk-surfaced paper. P* 15×14 *(30p.) or* 14×15 *(others).*
728 24p. grey and black 60 55
729 28p. multicoloured 65 55
730 30p. multicoloured . . . . . . 1·40 1·75
731 46p. orange-brown . . . . . . 1·60 1·75
728/31 . . . . . . *Set of* 4 3·75 4·25

Designs: *Vert*—24p. Sean T. O'Kelly (statesman) (drawing by Sean O'Sullivan); 46p. Jawaharlal Nehru (Birth centenary). *Horiz*—30p. Margaret Burke-Sheridan (soprano) (portrait by De Gennaro) and scene from *La Bohème* (Birth centenary).

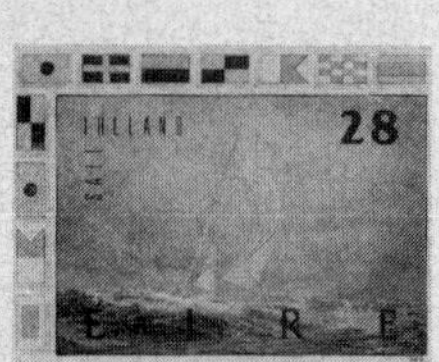

262 "*NCB Ireland* rounding Cape Horn" (Des Fallon)

263 Willow/Red Grouse

(Des I. Caulder. Litho Irish Security Stamp Ptg Ltd)

1989 (31 Aug). *First Irish Entry in Whitbread Round the World Yacht Race. Chalk-surfaced paper. P* 15×14.
732 **262** 28p. multicoloured .. .. 1·25 1·25

(Des R. Ward. Litho Irish Security Stamp Ptg Ltd)

1989 (5 Oct). *Game Birds. T* **263** *and similar square designs. Multicoloured. Chalk-surfaced paper. P* 13½.
733 24p. Type **263** .. .. 1·00 55
734 28p. Lapwing .. .. 1·10 55
735 39p. Woodcock .. .. 1·40 2·25
736 46p. Ring-necked Pheasant .. .. 1·50 2·25
733/6 .. .. *Set of* 4 4·50 5·00
MS737 128×92 mm. Nos. 733/6 .. .. 4·50 5·00
No. **MS**737 exists overprinted on the margins to commemorate "STAMPA 89", the Irish National Stamp Exhibition.

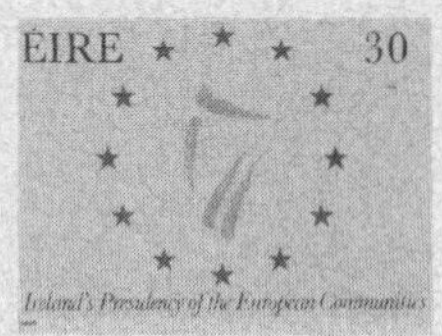

264 "The Annunciation"

265 Logo (Ireland's Presidency of the European Communities)

(Des Jacinta Fitzgerald (21p.), J. McEvoy from 13th-century Flemish Psalter (others). Litho Irish Security Stamp Ptg Ltd)

1989 (14 Nov). *Christmas. T* **264** *and similar vert designs. Multicoloured. Chalk-surfaced paper. P* 14×15.
738 21p. Children decorating crib 75 75
a. Sheetlet. No. 738×14 .. .. 9·50
739 24p. Type **264** 85 60
740 28p. "The Nativity" 90 55
741 46p. "The Adoration of the Magi" .. .. 1·75 2·50
738/41 .. .. *Set of* 4 3·75 4·00
No. 738 represents a special rate for greetings cards within Ireland and to all E.E.C. countries. It was only issued in sheetlets of 14 stamps and 1 label sold at £2.90, providing an additional discount of 4p. off the face value of the stamps.

(Des B. Donegan (30p.), Q Design (50p.). Litho Irish Security Stamp Ptg Ltd)

1990 (9 Jan). *European Events. T* **265** *and similar horiz design. Multicoloured. Chalk-surfaced paper. P* 15×14.
742 30p. Type **265** 75 60
743 50p. Logo and outline map of Ireland (European Tourism Year) .. .. 2·00 3·00

266 Dropping Messages from Balloon

267 Silver Kite Brooch

(Des Aislinn Adams (26p.), Patricia Sleeman and R. Vogel (30p.). Litho Irish Security Stamp Ptg Ltd)

1990 (30 Jan). *Greetings Stamps. T* **266** *and similar vert design. Chalk-surfaced paper. P* 14×15.
744 26p. multicoloured .. .. 1·25 1·25
745 30p. rosine, pale buff and reddish brown .. 1·25 1·25
Design:—30p. Heart and "Love" drawn in lipstick.

PRICES OF SETS

Set prices are given for many issues, generally those containing three stamps or more. Definitive sets include one of each value or major colour change, but do not cover different perforations, die types or minor shades. Where a choice is possible the set prices are based on the cheapest versions of the stamps included in the listings.

Two Types of 20, 28, 52p.:

A. Irish Security Stamp Ptg Ltd printing (coarse background screen. Less distinct centre detail)

B. Enschedé printing (fine background screen. Clear centre detail)

Two Types of £1, £2, £3:

C. Irish Security Stamp Ptg Ltd printing

D. Enschedé printing

(Des M. Craig and Q Design. Litho Walsall (Nos. 748c, 755b), Enschedé (Nos. 751b, 753b, 762b, 763b, 764b, 765b) or Irish Security Stamp Ptg Ltd (others))

1990 (8 Mar)–**97.** *Irish Heritage and Treasures. T* **267** *and similar designs. Chalk-surfaced paper* (5, 20, 26, 28, 30, 32, 37, 38, 41, 44, 50, 52*p.*, £1, £5) *or ordinary paper* (*others*). *P* 14×15 (10, 20, 30, 32*p*, £5) *or* 15×14 (*others*).
746 1p. black and new blue (26.7.90) .. 10 10
a. Chalk-surfaced paper (10.91) .. 30 30
747 2p. black and bright red-orange (26.7.90) 10 10
a. Chalk-surfaced paper (15.11.90) .. 10 10
ab. Booklet pane. Nos. 747a, 748b×3, 752 and 754×2 plus label .. .. 3·00
ac. Booklet pane Nos. 747a×2, 755×2 and 820 (17.10.91) .. .. .. 5·50
748 4p. black and bluish violet (26.7.90) .. 10 10
a. Booklet pane. Nos. 748 and 755a×3 (16.11.95) .. .. 2·00
b. Chalk-surfaced paper (15.11.90) .. 75 1·00
ba. Booklet pane. Nos. 748b×3, 753×4 plus label (17.10.91) .. .. 5·50
bb. Booklet pane. Nos. 748b and 1084×3 (6.3.97) .. .. 1·60
c. Perf 13×13½. Chalk-surfaced paper (24.9.93) 10 10
ca. Booklet pane. Nos. 748c and 755b×3 (4p. at bottom right) .. .. 2·00
cb. Ditto, but 4p., at top left (2.3.94) .. 2·00
749 5p. black and bright green (29.1.91) .. 10 10
a. Ordinary paper (5.92) .. .. 1·00 1·00
750 10p. black and bright red-orange (26.7.90) 20 25
a. Chalk-surfaced paper (9.93) .. 1·00 1·00
751 20p. black and lemon (A) (29.1.91) .. 35 40
a. Ordinary paper (3.92) .. .. 1·50 1·50
b. Type B (Enschedé ptg) (16.11.95) .. 1·00 1·00
752 26p. black and bluish violet 45 50
a. Ordinary paper (5.90) .. .. 2·50 1·50
ab. Perf 13½ (3.5.90) .. .. .. 5·00 5·00
753 28p. black & bright red-orange (A) (3.4.91) 50 55
a. Ordinary paper (5.91) .. .. 2·00 2·00
b. Type B (Enschedé ptg) (16.11.95) .. 1·00 1·00
754 30p. black and new blue 55 60
a. Ordinary paper (5.90) .. .. 1·50 1·50
ab. Perf 13½ (3.5.90) .. .. .. 5·00 5·00
755 32p. black and bright green 60 65
a. Ordinary paper (5.90) .. .. 2·00 2·00
b. Perf 13½×13. Chalk-surfaced paper (24.9.93) 90 90
756 34p. black and lemon (26.7.90) .. .. 1·00 1·00
757 37p. brownish black & brt green (3.4.91) 1·25 1·25
a. Ordinary paper (11.91) .. .. 3·00 3·50
758 38p. black and bluish violet (3.4.91) .. 1·25 1·25
a. Ordinary paper (5.95) .. .. 3·00 3·00
758*b* 40p. black and new blue (14.5.92) .. 1·25 1·25
ba. Chalk-surfaced paper (9.93) .. 3·50 3·50
759 41p. black and bright red-orange .. 70 75
a. Ordinary paper (10.90) .. .. 3·25 3·25
760 44p. agate and lemon (3.4.91) 75 80
760*a* 45p. black and bluish violet (14.5.92) .. 1·25 1·25
761 50p. black and lemon .. .. .. 1·25 1·25
a. Ordinary paper (5.90) .. .. 3·50 3·50
762 52p. black and new blue (A) (3.4.91) .. 1·50 1·50
a. Ordinary paper (2.96) .. .. 12·00 12·00
b. Type B (Enschedé ptg) (16.11.95) .. 1·50 1·75
763 £1 black and lemon (C) .. .. 1·75 1·90
a. Ordinary paper (5.90) .. .. 15·00 4·00
b. Type D (Enschedé ptg) (16.11.95) .. 3·00 3·00
764 £2 black and bright green (C) (26.7.90) 3·50 3·75
a. Chalk-surfaced paper (9.93) .. 9·00 9·00
b. Type D (Enschedé ptg) (chalk-surfaced paper) (16.11.95) .. .. 6·00 6·00
765 £5 black and new blue (C) (29.1.91) .. 9·00 9·25
a. Ordinary paper (10.97) .. .. 30·00 35·00
b. Type D (Enschedé ptg) (16.11.95) .. 15·00 15·00
746/65 .. .. *Set of* 22 25·00 26·00
Designs: *Vert* (*as T* **267**)—1p., 2p. Type **267**; 4p., 5p. Dunamase Food Vessel; 26p., 28p. Lismore Crozier; 34p., 37p., 38p., 40p. Gleninsheen Collar; 41p., 44p., 45p. Silver thistle brooch; 50p., 52p. Broighter Boat. (22×38 *mm*)—£5 St. Patrick's Bell Shrine. *Horiz* (*as T* **267**)—10p. Derrinboy Armlets; 20p. Gold dress fastener; 30p. Enamelled latchet brooch; 32p. Broighter Collar. (38×22 *mm*)—£1 Ardagh Chalice; £2 Tar Brooch.

Nos. 747a and 748b were initially only available from bookle pane No. 747ab, but were subsequently issued in sheet forr during March (4p.) and October (2p.) 1991. Nos. 748c and 755 only occur from booklet panes Nos. 748ca/cb.

With the exception of Nos. 747ac and 748ba each of the liste booklet panes shows either the upper and lower edges (Nos 748a, 748bb) or the three outer edges of the pane imperforate Booklet panes Nos. 535ca and 547bb, which include Nos. 752a and 754ab, and also Nos. 747ac and 748ba each show stamp from the right-hand vertical row imperforate at top, right or a foot depending on the format of the design. The followin variations exist:

2p. Imperf at left (booklet pane No. 747ab)
Imperf at foot (booklet pane No. 747ac)
4p. Imperf at left or right (booklet pane No. 747ab)
Imperf at left (booklet panes Nos. 748a, 748bb)
Imperf at foot (booklet pane No. 748ba)
Imperf at foot and left (*p* 13×13½) (booklet pane No 748ca)
Imperf at right (*p* 13×13½) (booklet pane No. 748cb
26p. Imperf at top (*p* 13½) (booklet pane No. 535ca)
Imperf at foot and left (booklet pane No. 747ab)
28p. Imperf at foot (booklet pane No. 748ba)
30p. Imperf at right (*p* 13½) (booklet pane No. 547bb)
Imperf at top or top and right (booklet pane No 747ab)
32p. Imperf at right (booklet pane No. 747ac)
Imperf at top or foot (booklet pane No. 748a)
Imperf at top, top and right or foot (*p* 13½×13 (booklet pane No. 748ca)
Imperf at top and right, foot and right or foo (*p* 13½×x 13) (booklet pane No. 748cb)

For 4, 28 and 32p. stamps in same designs as Nos. 748, 75 and 755, but printed in photogravure, see Nos. 808/10.

For 32p. value as No. 755, but 27×20 mm and self-adhesive see No. 823.

268 Posy of Flowers

269 Player heading Ball

(Des M. Cameron. Litho Irish Security Stamp Ptg Ltd)

1990 (22 Mar). *Greetings Stamps. T* **268** *and similar vert designs. Multicoloured. P* 14×15.
766 26p. Type **268** .. .. 2·00 2·50
a. Booklet pane. Nos. 766/9 .. .. 7·50
767 26p. Birthday presents .. .. .. 2·00 2·50
768 30p. Flowers, ribbon and horseshoe .. 2·00 2·50
769 30p. Balloons .. .. 2·00 2·50
766/9 .. .. *Set of* 4 7·50 9·00
Nos. 766/9 come from £1.98 discount stamp booklets.
Booklet pane No. 766a exists with the 26p. values at left or right and the right-hand stamp (either No. 767 or 769) imperforate at right. The booklet pane also contains 8 small greetings labels.

(Des C. Harrison. Litho Irish Security Stamp Ptg Ltd)

1990 (5 Apr). *World Cup Football Championship, Italy. T* **269** *and similar vert design. Multicoloured. Chalk-surfaced paper. P* 14×15.
770 30p. Type **269** .. .. 1·50 2·00
a. Sheetlet. Nos. 770/1, each × 4 .. 11·00
771 30p. Tackling .. .. 1·50 2·00
Nos. 770/1 were printed together, *se-tenant*, in a sheetlet of 8 stamps and 1 central stamp-size label.

270 Battle of the Boyne, 1690

(Des S. Conlin. Litho Irish Security Stamp Ptg Ltd)

1990 (5 Apr). *300th Anniv of the Williamite Wars* (*1st issue*). *T* **270** *and similar horiz designs. Multicoloured. Chalk-surfaced paper. P* 13½.
772 30p. Type **270** .. .. 1·00 1·50
a. Pair. Nos. 772/3 .. .. .. 2·00 3·00
773 30p. Siege of Limerick, 1690 .. .. 1·00 1·50
Nos. 772/3 were printed together, *se-tenant*, in horizontal and vertical pairs throughout the sheet.
See also Nos. 806/7.

271 1990 Irish Heritage 30p. Stamp and 1840 Postmark

272 General Post Office, Dublin

(Des Q Design. Litho Irish Security Stamp Ptg Ltd)

90 (3 May). *150th Anniv of the Penny Black. T* **271** *and similar horiz design. Multicoloured. Chalk-surfaced paper. P* 15×14.

4 30p. Type **271** 90 90
a. Ordinary paper .. .. 1·75 2·50
ab. Booklet pane. Nos. 774a/5a, each × 2 8·50
5 50p. Definitive stamps of 1922, 1969, 1982 and 1990 .. .. 1·50 2·00
a. Ordinary paper .. .. 2·50 3·00

Nos. 774a and 775a were only issued in booklets.

In booklet pane No. 774ab one example of each value is perforate at right.

Booklet pane No. 774ab exists with the margins overprinted red in connection with "STAMPA 90", the Irish National amp Exhibition.

For other booklet panes containing Nos. 774a/5a see Nos. 7ba/bb.

(Des P. Keogh. Litho Irish Security Stamp Ptg Ltd)

90 (3 May). *Europa. Post Office Buildings. T* **272** *and similar vert design. Multicoloured. P* 14 × 15.

76 30p. Type **272** .. .. 1·00 60
77 41p. Westport Post Office, County Mayo .. 1·40 2·75

Nos. 776/7 were each printed in sheets of 10 stamps and 2 amp-size labels.

273 Medical Missionary giving Injection

274 Narcissus "Foundling" and Japanese Gardens, Tully

)es I. Calder (26, 50p.), R. Ballagh (30p.). Litho Irish Security Stamp Ptg Ltd)

990 (21 June). *Anniversaries and Events. T* **273** *and similar designs. P* 15×14 (*horiz*) *or* 14×15 (*vert*).

78 26p. multicoloured 90 40
79 30p. black .. .. 1·00 2·25
30 50p. multicoloured .. .. 1·50 1·50
78/80 .. .. *Set of* 3 3·00 3·75

Designs: *Vert*—30p. Michael Collins (statesman) (Birth entenary). *Horiz*—50p. Missionaries working at water pump (rish missionary service).

(Des I. Loe. Litho Irish Security Stamp Ptg Ltd)

990 (30 Aug). *Garden Flowers. T* **274** *and similar vert designs. Multicoloured. P* 14×15.

'81 26p. Type **274** 70 55
a. Booklet pane. Nos. 781/2, each × 2 .. 4·50
b. Booklet pane. Nos. 781/4 .. .. 4·50
'82 30p. *Rosa* × *hibernica* and Malahide Castle gardens 85 80
83 41p. *Primula* "Rowallane Rose" and Rowallane garden .. .. 1·75 2·00
84 50p. *Erica erigena* "Irish Dusk" and Palm House, National Botanical Gardens .. 2·00 2·25
'81/4 .. .. *Set of* 4 4·75 5·00

Both booklet panes show the stamps as horizontal rows of four mperforate at top and at right. Stamps from the right of the ane, 30p. on No. 781a, 50p. on No. 781b, are imperforate at top nd right with the other values imperforate at top only.

No. 781a exists overprinted in blue for Collectors' Road Shows t Waterford and Galway.

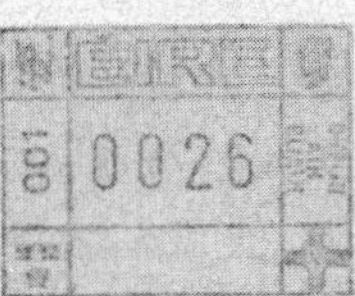

Frama label

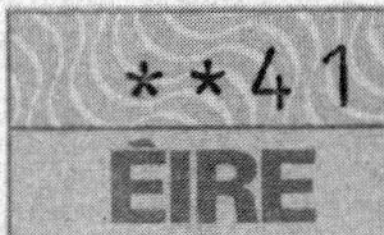

Klussendorf label

Amiel Pitney/Bowes label

MACHINE LABELS. For a trial period of three months from 8)ctober 1990 labels in the above designs, ranging in value from .p. to £99.99, were available from the head post offices at Dublin Frama), Limerick (Klussendorf) and Cork (Amiel Pitney/Bowes). The Amiel Pitney/Bowes machine (Cork) was aken out of service on 31 January 1991. The other two nachines were withdrawn on 31 May 1991.

NEW INFORMATION

The editor is always interested to correspond with people who have new information that will improve or correct the Catalogue.

275 *Playboy of the Western World* (John Synge)

276 Nativity

(Des R. Ballagh. Litho Irish Security Stamp Ptg Ltd)

1990 (18 Oct). *Irish Theatre. T* **275** *and similar horiz designs. Multicoloured. P* 13½.

785 30p. Type **275** .. .. 1·25 1·75
a. Horiz strip of 4. Nos. 785/8 .. .. 4·50
786 30p. *Juno and the Paycock* (Sean O'Casey) 1·25 1·75
787 30p. *The Field* (John Keane) .. .. 1·25 1·75
788 30p. *Waiting for Godot* (Samuel Beckett) .. 1·25 1·75
785/8 .. .. *Set of* 4 4·50 6·00

Nos. 785/8 were printed together in sheets of 20 (4×5), producing horizontal *se-tenant* strips of 4 and vertical *se-tenant* pairs of Nos. 785 and 788 or 786/7.

(Des Pamela Leonard (No. 789), B. Cronin (others). Litho Irish Security Stamp Ptg Ltd)

1990 (15 Nov). *Christmas. T* **276** *and similar vert designs. Multicoloured. Chalk-surfaced paper* (50p.) *or ordinary paper* (*others*). *P* 14×15.

789 26p. Child praying by bed 70 80
a. Sheetlet. No. 789×12 .. .. 7·50
790 26p. Type **276** 70 60
791 30p. Madonna and Child 90 90
792 50p. Adoration of the Magi .. .. 1·60 2·25
789/92 .. .. *Set of* 4 3·50 4·00

No. 789 was only issued in sheetlets of 12 sold at £2.86, providing a discount of 26p. off the face value of the stamps.

277 Hearts in Mail Sack and Postman's Cap

278 Starley "Rover" Bicycle, 1886

(Des Liz Manning (26p.), Louise Mullally (30p.). Litho Irish Security Stamp Ptg Ltd)

1991 (29 Jan). *Greetings Stamps. T* **277** *and similar vert design. Multicoloured. Chalk-surfaced paper. P* 14×15.

793 26p. Type **277** .. .. 85 1·00
794 30p. Boy and girl kissing .. .. .. 90 1·00

(Des E. Patton. Litho Irish Security Stamp Ptg Ltd)

1991 (5 Mar). *Early Bicycles. T* **278** *and similar vert designs. Multicoloured. Chalk-surfaced paper. P* 14×15.

795 26p. Type **278** 80 60
796 30p. Child's horse tricycle, 1875 .. .. 90 1·00
797 50p. "Penny Farthing", 1871 .. .. 1·60 2·00
795/7 .. .. *Set of* 3 3·00 3·25
MS798 113×72 mm. Nos. 795/7 .. .. 3·00 3·25

No. **MS**798 exists with privately-applied marginal overprints for the "Collectorex 91" Exhibition, Dublin, the I.P.T.A. Collectors' Road Show, Birr (both in black) and "STAMPA 91" Exhibition, Dublin (in red or blue).

279 Cuchulainn (statue by Oliver Sheppard) and Proclamation

280 Scene from *La Traviata* (50th anniv of Dublin Grand Opera Society)

(Des I. Calder. Litho Irish Security Stamp Ptg Ltd)

1991 (3 Apr). *75th Anniv of Easter Rising. Chalk-surfaced paper. P* 15×14.

799 **279** 32p. multicoloured .. .. .. 1·25 1·40

(Des K. Uhlemann (28p.), M. Craig and I. Calder (32p.), M. Craig (44p.), M. Craig and Q Design (52p.). Litho Irish Security Stamp Ptg Ltd)

1991 (11 Apr). *"Dublin 1991 European City of Culture". T* **280** *and similar horiz designs. Multicoloured. Chalk-surfaced paper. P* 13½ (52p.) *or* 15×14 (*others*).

800 28p. Type **280** 65 80
a. Booklet pane. Nos. 800/2 .. .. 3·75
b. Booklet pane. Nos. 800/3 .. .. 3·75
801 32p. City Hall and European Community emblem .. .. 85 1·50
802 44p. St. Patrick's Cathedral (800th anniv) 90 1·60
803 52p. Custom House (bicent) (41×24 *mm*) 1·00 1·60
800/3 .. .. *Set of* 4 3·00 5·00

281 *Giotto* Spacecraft approaching Halley's Comet

(Des C. Rycraft. Litho Irish Security Stamp Ptg Ltd)

1991 (14 May). *Europa. Europe in Space. T* **281** *and similar horiz design. Multicoloured. P* 15×14.

804 32p. Type **281** .. .. 1·25 1·00
805 44p. Hubble Telescope orbiting Earth .. 1·75 3·00

Nos. 804/5 were each issued in sheetlets of 10 (2×5) with illustrations of space launches on enlarged left hand margins.

282 Siege of Athlone

283 John A. Costello (statesman)

(Des S. Conlin. Litho Irish Security Stamp Ptg Ltd)

1991 (14 May). *300th Anniv of the Williamite Wars (2nd issue). T* **282** *and similar horiz design. Multicoloured. Chalk-surfaced paper. P* 15×14.

806 28p. Type **282** .. .. 90 1·40
a. Pair. Nos. 806/7 .. .. .. 1·75 2·75
807 28p. Generals Ginkel and Sarsfield (signatories of Treaty of Limerick) .. 90 1·40

Nos. 806/7 were printed together, *se-tenant*, in horizontal and vertical pairs throughout the sheet.

1991 (14 May). *As Nos.* 748, 753 *and* 755, *but printed in photogravure by Enschedé. Chalk-surfaced paper. P* 14×15 (32p.) *or* 15×14 (*others*).

808 4p. black and bluish violet 10 10
a. Booklet pane. Nos. 808×2, 809 and 810×2 plus label .. .. .. 2·00
809 28p. black and reddish orange 55 60
810 32p. black and bright green 65 70
808/10 .. .. *Set of* 3 1·25 1·40

Nos. 808/10 were only available in £1 stamp booklets. Booklet pane No. 808a has imperforate outer edges giving stamps imperforate at left or right (4p.), at left and foot (28p.) and at top and right (32p.).

(Des R. Ballagh (28p.), Q Design (others). Litho Irish Security Stamp Ptg, Ltd)

1991 (2 July). *Anniversaries. T* **283** *and similar designs. Chalk-surfaced paper* (28p.). *P* 15×14 (52p.) *or* 14×15 (*others*).

811 28p. black 70 70
812 32p. multicoloured .. .. 85 1·00
813 52p. multicoloured .. .. 1·40 2·50
811/13 .. .. *Set of* 3 2·75 3·75

Designs: *Vert*—28p. Type **283** (Birth centenary) (drawing by Sean O'Sullivan); 32p. "Charles Stewart Parnell" (Sydney Hall) (Death centenary). *Horiz*—52p. Meeting of United Irishmen (Bicentary).

284 Player on 15th Green, Portmarnock (Walker Cup)

285 Wicklow Cheviot

(Des E. Patton. Litho Irish Security Stamp Ptg Ltd)

1991 (3 Sept). *Golf Commemorations. T* **284** *and similar multicoloured design. Chalk-surfaced paper* (32p.). *P* 15×14 (28p.) *or* 14×15 (32p.).

814 28p. Type **284** .. .. 1·00 75
815 32p. Logo and golfer of 1900 (Centenary of Golfing Union of Ireland) (*vert*) .. 1·25 1·00

(Des Pamela Leonard. Litho Irish Security Stamp Ptg Ltd)

1991 (3 Sept). *Irish Sheep. T* **285** *and similar multicoloured designs. Chalk-surfaced paper. P* 15×14 (52p.) *or* 14×15 (*others*).

816 32p. Type **285** .. .. 1·00 80
817 38p. Donegal Blackface .. .. .. 1·40 1·75
818 52p. Galway (*horiz*) .. .. .. 2·00 3·50
816/18 .. .. *Set of* 3 4·00 5·50

286 Boatyard

287 The Annunciation

(Des C. Rycraft. Litho Irish Security Stamp Ptg Ltd)

1991 (17 Oct). *Fishing Fleet. T* **286** *and similar horiz designs. Multicoloured. Chalk-surfaced paper. P* 15×14.

819 28p. Type **286** 60 65
 a. Booklet pane. Nos. 819/22 .. .. 5·50
 b. Booklet pane. Nos. 819/20 each × 2 .. 5·50
820 32p. Traditional inshore trawlers 70 80
821 44p. Inshore lobster pot boat .. .. 1·60 2·25
822 52p. *Veronica* (fish factory ship) .. .. 2·00 2·50
819/22 .. .. *Set of* 4 4·50 5·50

In booklet pane No. 819a the 32p. and 52p. values are imperforate at right.

Booklet pane No. 819a exists with the gutter margin overprinted in connection with the "PHILANIPPON '91" International Stamp Exhibition, Tokyo.

For a further booklet pane including No. 820 see No. 747ac.

(Litho Printset-Cambec Pty Ltd, Australia (No. 823) or Irish Security Stamp Ptg Ltd (No. 823a))

1991 (31 Oct)–**95.** *As No. 755, but larger, 27×21 mm, and self-adhesive. P* 11½.

823 32p. black and bright green 65 70
 a. Perf 10×9 (8.6.95) 65 80

Examples of No. 823 have rounded perforations at each corner of the stamp and pointed die-cut "teeth". No. 823a shows a perforation at each corner and has rounded teeth. Initially both printers showed the stamps separate on the backing paper, but from September 1996 printings of No. 823a retained the surplus self-adhesive paper around each stamp. Printings from July 1992 contained "reminder" labels inserted 20 stamps and 10 stamps from the end of the coil.

Nos. 823/a were only available in coils of 100, or as strips of 3 from the Philatelic Bureau.

(Des Q. Design (No. 827), T. Gayer (others). Litho Irish Security Stamp Ptg Ltd)

1991 (14 Nov). *Christmas. T* **287** *and similar vert designs. Chalk-surfaced paper. P* 14×15.

827 28p. multicoloured 80 85
 a. Sheetlet. No. 827×13 .. .. .. 10·00
828 28p. dull ultramarine, sage-green and black 75 65
829 32p. scarlet and black 85 75
830 52p. multicoloured .. .. .. 1·60 2·50
827/30 .. .. *Set of* 4 3·50 4·25

Designs:—No. 827, Three Kings; No. 828, Type **287**; No. 829, The Nativity; No. 830, Adoration of the Kings.

No. 827 was only issued in sheetlets of 13 stamps and two labels (at the centre of rows 1 and 2) sold at £3.36 providing a discount of 28p. off the face value of the stamps.

288 Multicoloured Heart

289 Healthy Family on Apple

(Des T. Monaghan (28p.), R. Ballagh (32p.). Litho Irish Security Stamp Ptg Ltd)

1992 (28 Jan). *Greetings Stamps. T* **288** *and similar multicoloured design. P* 15×14 *(28p.) or* 14×15 *(32p.).*

831 28p. Type **288** 85 95
832 32p. "LOVE" at end of rainbow (*vert*) .. 95 1·10

(Des Pamela Leonard. Litho Irish Security Stamp Ptg Ltd)

1992 (25 Feb). *"Healthy Living" Campaign. P* 14×15.

833 **289** 28p. multicoloured 85 85

290 Boxing

(Des C. Harrison. Litho Irish Security Stamp Ptg Ltd)

1992 (25 Feb). *Olympic Games, Barcelona. T* **290** *and similar horiz design. P* 15×14.

834 32p. Type **290** 90 90
835 44p. Sailing .. .. 1·40 2·25
MS836 130×85 mm. Nos. 834/5×2 .. 4·50 5·00
 a. On chalk-surfaced paper £170

No. **MS**836 exists overprinted in black on the margin in connection with the "World Columbian Stamp Expo '92", Chicago. The chalk-surfaced paper variety is only known with this marginal overprint.

291 *Mari* (cog) and 14th-century Map

(Des C. Rycraft. Litho Irish Security Stamp Ptg Ltd)

1992 (2 Apr). *Irish Maritime Heritage. T* **291** *and similar multicoloured design. Chalk-surfaced paper. P* 15×14 *(32p) or* 14×15 *(52p).*

837 32p. Type **291** .. .. 1·00 90
838 52p. *Ovoca* (trawler) and chart (*vert*) .. 1·50 2·75

292 Chamber Logo and Commercial Symbols

293 Cliffs and Cove

(Des E. Patton. Litho Irish Security Stamp Ptg Ltd)

1992 (2 Apr). *Bicentenary of Galway Chamber of Commerce and Industry. Chalk-surfaced paper. P* 15×14.

839 **292** 28p. multicoloured 70 85

(Des Pamela Leonard. Litho Irish Security Stamp Ptg Ltd)

1992 (2 Apr). *Greetings Stamps. T* **293** *and similar vert designs. Multicoloured. Chalk-surfaced paper. P* 14×15.

840 28p. Type **293** .. .. .. 75 1·10
 a. Booklet pane. Nos. 840/3 .. .. 2·75
841 28p. Meadow .. .. 75 1·10
842 32p. Fuchsia and Honeysuckle .. .. 75 1·10
843 32p. Lily pond and dragonfly .. .. 75 1·10
840/3 .. .. *Set of* 4 2·75 4·00

Nos. 840/3 come from £2.40 stamp booklets.

Booklet pane No. 840a exists with the 28p. values at left or right and has the right-hand stamp (either No. 841 or 843) imperforate at right. The booklet pane also contains 8 small greetings labels.

Booklet pane No. 840a exists overprinted on the margin for Regional Stamp Shows at Sligo and Waterford.

MACHINE LABELS. Frama labels in the above design, providing values from 1p. to £99.99, were introduced at head post offices in Dublin (001), Cork (003), Limerick (004) and Galway (005) on 6 April 1992. The system was extended to Bray (008), Killarney (009) and Sligo (007) on 20 July 1992, and to Kilkenny (010) and Waterford (006) on 7 September when a second machine (002) was also provided at Dublin. Both the Dublin machines were relocated to Dublin Airport in August 1994.

294 Fleet of Columbus

(Des S. Conlin. Litho Irish Security Stamp Ptg Ltd)

1992 (14 May). *Europa. 500th Anniv of Discovery of America by Columbus. T* **294** *and similar horiz design. Multicoloured. P* 15×14.

844 32p. Type **294** .. .. 1·25 90
845 44p. Columbus landing in the New World 1·75 2·50

Nos. 844/5 were each issued in sheetlets of 10 (2×5) with illustrated left or right margins.

295 Irish Immigrants

(Des Pamela Leonard. Litho Irish Security Stamp Ptg Ltd)

1992 (14 May). *Irish Immigrants in the Americas. T* **295** *an similar horiz design. Multicoloured. P* 13½.

846 52p. Type **295** .. .. 1·60 1·7
 a. Pair. Nos. 846/7 .. .. .. 3·00 3·5
847 52p. Irish soldiers, entertainers and politicians .. .. 1·60 1·7

Nos. 846/7 were printed together, *se-tenant*, in horizontal an vertical pairs throughout the sheet.

296 Pair of Pine Martens

(Des R. Ward. Litho Irish Security Stamp Ptg Ltd)

1992 (9 July). *Endangered Species. Pine Marten. T* **296** *an similar horiz designs. Multicoloured. P* 15×14.

848 28p. Type **296** .. .. 1·00 7
849 32p. Marten on branch .. .. .. 1·00 8
850 44p. Female with kittens .. .. .. 1·60 1·5
851 52p. Marten catching Great Tit .. .. 2·00 1·7
848/51 .. .. *Set of* 4 5·00 4·2

297 "The Rotunda and New Rooms" (James Malton)

(Des J. McEvoy (28, 44p.), E. Patton (32, 52p.). Litho Iris Security Stamp Ptg Ltd)

1992 (2 Sept). *Dublin Anniversaries. T* **297** *and simila multicoloured designs. Chalk-surfaced paper (32p.). P* 15×1 *(28, 44p.) or* 13½ *(32, 52p.).*

852 28p. Type **297** 70 6
853 32p. Trinity College Library (28×45 *mm*) 1·00 1·0
854 44p. "Charlemont House" .. .. .. 1·10 2·0
855 52p. Trinity College main gate (28×45 *mm*) 1·40 2·2
852/5 .. .. *Set of* 4 3·75 5·5

Anniversaries:—28, 44p. Bicentenary of publication o Malton's "Views of Dublin"; 32, 52p. 400th anniv of founding o Trinity College.

298 European Star and Megalithic Dolmen

299 Farm Produce

(Des R. Ballagh. Litho Irish Security Stamp Ptg Ltd)

1992 (15 Oct). *Single European Market. P* 15×14.

856 **298** 32p. multicoloured 70 8
 a. Booklet pane. No. 856×4 .. 3·00
 b. Booklet pane. No. 856×3 .. 3·00

Three versions of booklet pane No. 856a exist showing th stamps arranged as a block of 4, as singles or in two vertica pairs. The first two versions exist overprinted for "STAMPA '92 (in blue on the block of four pane and in red on the other).

The booklet panes also exist overprinted for Regional Stam Shows at Galway, Dundalk, Kilkenny and Limerick.

(Des. Frances Poskitt. Litho Irish Security Stamp Ptg Ltd)

1992 (15 Oct). *Irish Agriculture. T* **299** *and similar ve designs. Multicoloured. P* 14×15.

857 32p. Type **299** .. .. 1·00 1·2
 a. Horiz strip of 4. Nos. 857/60 .. 3·50
858 32p. Dairy and beef herds .. .. 1·00 1·2
859 32p. Harvesting cereals .. .. .. 1·00 1·2
860 32p. Market gardening .. .. .. 1·00 1·2
857/60 .. .. *Set of* 4 3·50 4·5

Nos. 857/60 were printed together, *se-tenant*, in horizonta strips of 4 throughout the sheet with each strip forming composite design.

ALTERED CATALOGUE NUMBERS

Any Catalogue numbers altered from the last edition are shown as a list in the introductory pages.

300 "The Annunciation" (from illuminated manuscript) **301** Queen of Hearts

Des Frances Poskitt (No. 861), J. McEvoy (others). Litho Irish Security Stamp Ptg Ltd)

1992 (19 Nov). *Christmas. T* **300** *and similar vert designs. Multicoloured. Chalk-surfaced paper. P* 14×15.

861 28p. Congregation entering church .. 80 65
 a. Sheetlet. No. 861×13 .. .. 9·00
862 28p. Type **300** 80 65
863 32p. "Adoration of the Shepherds" (Da Empoli) .. .. 1·10 1·00
864 52p. "Adoration of the Magi" (Rottenhammer) .. .. 1·40 1·50
861/4 .. .. *Set of* 4 3·75 3·50

No. 861 was only issued in sheetlets of 13 stamps and two labels (at the centre of rows 1 and 2) sold at £3.36 providing a discount of 28p. off the face value of the stamps.

(Des C. Harrison (28p.), Q. Design (32p.) Litho Irish Security Stamp Ptg Ltd)

1993 (26 Jan). *Greetings Stamps. T* **301** *and similar multicoloured design. Chalk-surfaced paper. P* 14×15 (28*p.*) *or* 15×14 (32*p.*).

865 28p. Type **301** 75 75
866 32p. Hot air balloon trailing hearts (*horiz*) 85 85

302 "Evening at Tangier" (Sir John Lavery)

(Des. E. Patton. Litho Irish Security Stamp Ptg Ltd)

1993 (4 Mar). *Irish Impressionist Painters. T* **302** *and similar multicoloured designs. Chalk-surfaced paper. P* 13.

867 28p. Type **302** 75 60
 a. Booklet pane. Nos. 867/70 with margins all round .. .. 5·00
 b. Booklet pane. Nos. 867/8 with margins all round .. .. .. 2·75
868 32p. "The Goose Girl" (William Leech) .. 80 65
869 44p. "La Jeune Bretonne" (Roderic O'Conor) (*vert*) .. .. 1·25 1·60
 a. Booklet pane. Nos. 869/70 with margins all round .. .. 2·75
870 52p. "Lustre Jug" (Walter Osborne) (*vert*) 1·75 2·25
867/70 .. .. *Set of* 4 4·00 4·50

Booklet pane No. 867a exists in two slightly different versions, one containing two *se-tenant* pairs and the other the stamps perforated individually.

The booklet panes exist overprinted in the margin in connection with Regional Stamp Shows at Mullingar, Tralee (overprint reads "Summer Regional Show"), Cork and Letterkenny. No. 867b also comes with a blue marginal overprint for "STAMPA 93".

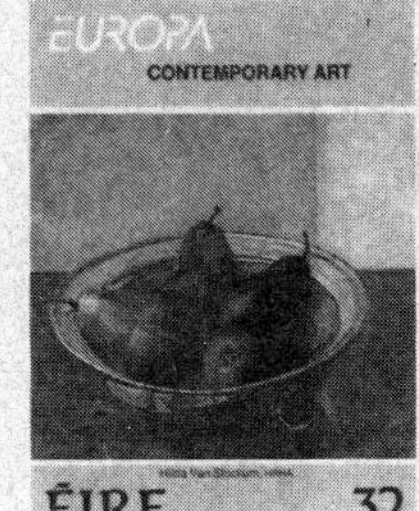

303 Bee Orchid **304** "Pears in a Copper Pan" (Hilda van Stockum)

(Des I. Loe. Litho Irish Security Stamp Ptg Ltd)

1993 (20 Apr). *Irish Orchids. T* **303** *and similar vert designs. Multicoloured. P* 14×15.

871 28p. Type **303** 90 60
872 32p. O'Kelly's Orchid .. .. .. 1·00 80
873 38p. Dark Red Helleborine .. .. 1·60 2·25
874 52p. Irish Lady's Tresses .. .. .. 1·90 2·75
871/4 .. .. *Set of* 4 4·75 5·75
MS875 130×71 mm. Nos. 871/4 .. .. 4·75 6·00

No. **MS**875 exists overprinted in red on the margin in connection with "STAMPA 93". This miniature sheet was also re-issued with a wider upper margin, showing the Irish and Thai flags, for the "Bangkok '93" International Stamp Exhibition. Such sheets were only available from the Philatelic Bureau and the An Post stand at the exhibition.

(Des E. Patton. Litho Irish Security Stamp Ptg Ltd)

1993 (18 May). *Europa. Contemporary Art. T* **304** *and similar vert design. Multicoloured. Chalk-surfaced paper. P* 13.

876 32p. Type **304** 75 75
877 44p. "Arrieta Orzola" (Tony O'Malley) .. 1·10 1·10

Nos. 876/7 were each issued in sheetlets of 10 stamps and two labels (in positions 1 and 4 of the top row).

305 Cultural Activities

(Des K. Uhlemann and B. Donegan. Litho Irish Security Stamp Ptg Ltd)

1993 (8 July). *Centenary of Conradh Na Gaelige (cultural organization). T* **305** *and similar multicoloured design. Chalk-surfaced paper. P* 15×14 (32*p.*) *or* 14×15 (52*p.*).

878 32p. Type **305** 85 75
879 52p. Illuminated manuscript cover (*vert*) .. 1·50 1·50

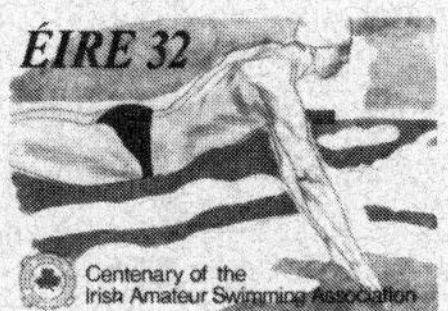

306 Diving

(Des C. Harrison. Litho Irish Security Stamp Ptg Ltd)

1993 (8 July). *Centenary of Irish Amateur Swimming Association. T* **306** *and similar horiz design. Multicoloured. Chalk-surfaced paper. P* 15×14.

880 32p. Type **306** .. .. 1·00 1·25
 a. Horiz pair. Nos. 880/1 .. .. 2·00 2·50
881 32p. Swimming .. .. 1·00 1·25

Nos. 880/1 were printed together, *se-tenant*, in horizontal pairs throughout the sheet.

307 Nurse with Patient and Hospital Buildings (250th anniv of Royal Hospital, Donnybrook)

(Des K. Uhlemann (28p.), Q Design (32p.), C. Rycraft (44p.), P. Monahan (52p.). Litho Irish Security Stamp Ptg Ltd)

1993 (2 Sept). *Anniversaries and Events. T* **307** *and similar multicoloured designs. Chalk-surfaced paper. P* 15×14 (28*p.*, 44*p.*), 14×15 (32*p.*) *or* 13½ (52*p.*).

882 28p. Type **307** 80 60
883 32p. College building and crest (Bicent of St. Patrick's College, Carlow) (*vert*) .. 80 65
884 44p. Map of Neolithic field system, Céide (Opening of interpretative centre) .. 1·25 1·40
885 52p. Edward Bunting (musicologist) (150th death anniv) (25×42 *mm*) .. .. 1·40 1·60
882/5 .. .. *Set of* 4 3·75 3·75

308 Great Northern Railways Gardner at Drogheda **309** The Annunciation

(Des C. Rycraft. Litho Irish Security Stamp Ptg Ltd)

1993 (12 Oct). *Irish Buses. T* **308** *and similar horiz designs. Multicoloured. Chalk-surfaced paper. P* 15×14.

886 28p. Type **308** 60 65
 a. Booklet pane. Nos. 886/7, each × 2 .. 3·25
 b. Booklet pane. Nos. 886/9 .. .. 3·25
887 32p. C.I.E. Leyland Titan at College Green, Dublin 65 70
888 52p. Horse-drawn omnibus at Old Baal's Bridge, Limerick .. .. .. 1·25 1·90
 a. Horiz pair. Nos. 888/9 .. .. 2·50 3·75
889 52p. Char-a-banc at Lady's View, Killarney 1·25 1·90
886/9 .. .. *Set of* 4 3·25 4·50

Nos. 888/9 were printed together, *se-tenant*, in horizontal pairs throughout the sheet.

Booklet panes Nos. 886a/b come from £2.84 stamp booklets and have the outer edges of the pane imperforate.

(Des Pamela Leonard (No. 890), C. Harrison (others). Litho Irish Security Stamp Ptg Ltd)

1993 (16 Nov). *Christmas. T* **309** *and similar multicoloured designs. Chalk-surfaced paper. P* 14×15 (*No.* 890) *or* 15×14 (*others*).

890 28p. The Flight into Egypt (*vert*) 60 65
 a. Sheetlet. No. 890×13 .. .. 5·75
891 28p. Type **309** 60 55
892 32p. Holy Family 70 70
893 52p. Adoration of the shepherds .. .. 1·60 2·25
890/3 .. .. *Set of* 4 3·25 3·75

No. 890 was only issued in sheetlets of 13 stamps and two labels (at the centre of rows 1 and 2) sold at £3.36 providing a discount of 28p. off the face value of the stamps.

310 Airplane skywriting "Love" **311** Smiling Sun

(Des Jean Colton (28p.), E. Rainsberry (32p.) Litho Questa)

1994 (27 Jan). *Greetings Stamps. T* **310** *and similar multicoloured design. Chalk-surfaced paper. P* 15×14 (28*p.*) *or* 14×15 (32*p.*).

894 28p. Type **310** 75 75
895 32p. Couple within heart (*vert*) 85 85

(Des S. Young. Litho Irish Security Stamp Ptg)

1994 (27 Jan). *Greetings Booklet Stamps. T* **311** *and similar vert designs. Multicoloured. P* 14×15.

896 32p. Type **311** 70 85
 a. Booklet pane. No. 896/9 .. .. 2·50
897 32p. Smiling daisy 70 85
898 32p. Smiling heart 70 85
899 32p. Smiling rose 70 85
896/9 .. .. *Set of* 4 2·50 3·00

Nos. 896/9 come from £2.56 stamp booklets.

Booklet pane No. 896a exists with the right-hand stamp (either No. 897 or 899) imperforate at right. Each booklet pane also contains 8 small greeting labels.

The booklet pane also exists overprinted for Regional Stamp Shows at Cork and Letterkenny and from the Dublin International Stamp and Card Show.

(Des S. Young. Litho Irish Security Stamp Ptg Ltd)

1994 (18 Feb). *"Hong Kong '94" International Stamp Exhibition. Chinese New Year ("Year of the Dog"). P* 14×15.

MS900 137×34 mm. Nos. 896/8 .. .. 4·25 4·75

The example of No. 898 in the above miniature sheet is imperforate at right.

312 Stylised Logo of Macra na Feirme (50th anniv)

(Des K. and R. Uhlemann (28p.), Creative Inputs (32p.), E. Patton (38, 52p.). Litho Irish Security Stamp Ptg Ltd)

1994 (2 Mar). *Anniversaries and Events. T* **312** *and similar horiz designs. Chalk-surfaced paper. P* 15×14.

901 28p. gold and deep ultramarine 75 65
902 32p. multicoloured .. .. .. 1·25 75
903 38p. multicoloured .. .. .. 1·25 1·75
904 52p. black, cobalt and bright blue .. 1·40 2·00
901/4 .. .. *Set of* 4 4·25 4·75

Designs: (38×35 *mm*)—32p. "The Taking of Christ" (Caravaggio) (Loan of painting to National Gallery). (37½×27 *mm*)—38p. Sir Horace Plunkett with 19th-century milk carts and modern tankers (Centenary of Irish Co-operative Organisation Society); 52p. Congress emblem (Centenary of Irish Congress of Trade Unions).

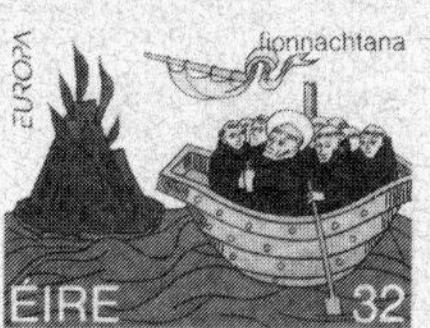

313 St. Brendan visiting Iceland

(Des C. Harrison. Litho Irish Security Stamp Ptg, Ltd)

1994 (18 Apr). *Europa. St. Brendan's Voyages. T* **313** *and similar horiz design. Multicoloured. Chalk-surfaced paper. P* 15×14.

905 32p. Type **313** 75 70
906 44p. St. Brendan discovering Faroe Islands 1·50 2·00
MS907 82×76 mm. Nos. 905/6 .. .. 2·25 2·75

Nos. 905/6 were each issued in sheetlets of 10 (2×5) with enlarged illustrated left margins.

No. **MS**907 also exists overprinted in blue on the margins in connection with "Stampa '94".

314 First Meeting of Dail, 1919

315 Irish and Argentine Footballers

(Des R. Hoek. Litho Irish Security Stamp Ptg Ltd)

1994 (27 Apr). *Parliamentary Anniversaries. T* **314** *and similar horiz design. Multicoloured. Chalk-surfaced paper. P* 15×14.

908 32p. Type **314** (75th anniv) .. .. 90 1·00
a. Booklet pane. Nos. 908/9, each × 2 .. 3·00
b. Booklet pane. Nos. 908/9 .. .. 1·50
909 32p. European Parliament (4th direct elections) .. .. 90 1·00

Booklet panes Nos. 908a/b come from £1.92 stamp booklets and have the outer edges of the panes imperforate. Booklet pane No. 908a contains examples of No. 908 either imperforate at top or at right and foot, and No. 909 imperforate at foot or at top and right. In booklet pane No. 908b No. 908 is imperforate at right and No. 909 fully perforated.

(Des J. Donohoe (Nos. 910/11), E. Patton (others). Litho Irish Security Stamp Ptg, Ltd (Nos. 910/11) or Enschedé (others))

1994 (31 May). *Sporting Anniversaries and Events. T* **315** *and similar multicoloured designs. Chalk-surfaced paper (Nos. 910/11). P* 14×15 *(Nos. 910/11) or* 13×13½ *(others).*

910 32p. Type **315** .. .. 80 1·00
a. Sheetlet. Nos. 910/11, each × 4 .. 6·00
911 32p. Irish and German footballers .. 80 1·00
912 32p. Irish and Dutch women's hockey match (*horiz*) .. .. 1·25 1·00
913 52p. Irish and English women's hockey match (*horiz*) .. .. .. 1·50 2·00
910/13 .. .. *Set of* 4 4·00 4·50

Anniversaries and Events:—Nos. 910/11, World Cup Football Championship, U.S.A.; No. 912, Women's Hockey World Cup, Dublin; No. 913, Centenary of Irish Ladies' Hockey Union.

Nos. 910/11 were printed together, *se-tenant*, in sheetlets of 8 stamps and one central label.

316 *Arctia caja*

317 Statue of Edmund Rice and Class

(Des I. Loe)

1994 (12 July). *Moths. T* **316** *and similar horiz designs. Multicoloured. (a) Litho Irish Security Stamp Ptg Ltd. Chalk-surfaced paper. P* 15×14.

914 28p. Type **316** 65 60
915 32p. *Calamia tridens* 75 70
916 38p. *Saturnia pavonia* .. .. .. 90 1·10
917 52p. *Deilephila elpenor* .. .. .. 1·50 2·00
914/17 .. .. .. *Set of* 4 3·50 4·00
MS918 120×71 mm. Nos. 914/17 .. .. 3·50 4·00

(b) Litho Printset-Cambec Pty Ltd, Australia. Self-adhesive. Chalk-surfaced paper. P 11½

919 32p. *Calamia tridens* .. .. .. 85 1·10
920 32p. Type **316** .. .. 85 1·10
921 32p. *Deilephila elpenor* .. .. .. 85 1·10
922 32p. *Saturnia pavonia* .. .. .. 85 1·10
919/22 .. .. .. *Set of* 4 3·00 4·00

No. **MS**918 also exists with the "Philakorea '94" International Stamp Exhibition, Seoul, logo added at bottom right and also comes overprinted in black for Collectors' Road Show, Sligo, or in red for "Stampa '94".

Nos. 919/22 are smaller, 34×22 mm, and occur, *se-tenant*, in strips of 4 or rolls of 100 with the surplus self-adhesive paper around each stamp removed.

(Des S. Conlin (No. 923), Design Factory (Nos. 925, 927), E. Patton (Nos. 924, 926). Litho Walsall (Nos. 925, 927), Irish Security Stamp Ptg Ltd (others))

1994 (6 Sept). *Anniversaries and Events. T* **317** *and similar multicoloured designs. Chalk-surfaced paper. P* 13½ *(No. 923),* 14 *(Nos. 925, 927),* 14×15 *(Nos. 924) or* 15×14 *(No. 926).*

923 28p. St. Laurence Gate, Drogheda (41½×25 mm) 70 80
924 32p. Type **317** .. .. 75 1·10
925 32p. Edmund Burke (politician) .. .. 75 1·10
926 52p. Vickers FB-27 Vimy and map (*horiz*) 1·25 1·40
927 52p. Eamonn Andrews (broadcaster) .. 1·50 1·50
923/7 .. .. .. *Set of* 5 4·50 5·50

Anniversaries and Events:—No. 923, 800th anniv of Drogheda; No. 924, 150th death anniv of Edmund Rice (founder of Irish Christian Brothers); Nos. 925, 927, The Irish abroad; No. 926, 75th anniv of Alcock and Brown's first Transatlantic flight.

318 George Bernard Shaw (author) and *Pygmalion* Poster

319 The Annunciation (ivory plaque)

(Des R. Ballagh. Litho Irish Security Stamp Ptg Ltd)

1994 (18 Oct). *Irish Nobel Prizewinners. T* **318** *and similar horiz designs. Multicoloured. Chalk-surfaced paper. P* 15×14.

928 28p. Type **318** 60 75
a. Pair. Nos. 928/9 .. .. .. 1·10 1·50
b. Booklet pane. Nos. 928/9 and 930×2 with margins all round .. .. 3·00
c. Booklet pane. Nos. 928/31 with margins all round .. .. .. 3·00
d. Booklet pane. Nos. 928/30 with margins all round .. .. .. 3·00
929 28p. Samuel Beckett (author) and pair of boots 60 75
930 32p. Sean MacBride (human rights campaigner) and peace doves .. 70 75
a. Booklet pane. Nos. 930 and 931×2 with margins all round .. .. .. 3·00
931 52p. William Butler Yeats (poet) and poem 1·10 1·75
928/31 .. .. *Set of* 4 2·75 3·50

Nos. 928/9 were printed together, *se-tenant*, in horizontal and vertical pairs throughout the sheet.

The booklet panes also exist overprinted for Regional Stamp Shows at Waterford, Galway, Athlone and Kilkenny.

(Des Pamela Leonard (No. 932), Q Design (others). Litho Irish Security Stamp Ptg Ltd)

1994 (17 Nov). *Christmas. T* **319** *and similar vert designs. Chalk-surfaced paper. P* 14×15.

932 28p. Nativity 70 60
a. Sheetlet. No. 932×13 .. .. 8·00
933 28p. Type **319** 70 60
934 32p. Flight into Egypt (wood carving) .. 80 70
935 52p. Nativity (ivory plaque) .. .. 1·10 2·00
932/5 .. .. *Set of* 4 3·00 3·50

No. 932 was only issued in sheetlets of 13 stamps and two labels (at the centre of rows 1 and 2) sold at £3.36 providing a discount of 28p. off the face value of the stamps.

320 Tree of Hearts

321 West Clare Railway Steam Locomotive No. 1 *Kilkee* at Kilrush Station

(Des Bridget Flinn. Litho Irish Security Stamp Ptg Ltd)

1995 (24 Jan). *Greetings Stamps. T* **320** *and similar vert designs. Multicoloured. Chalk-surfaced paper. P* 14×15.

936 32p. Type **320** 80 95
a. Booklet pane. Nos. 936/7 .. .. 3·00
937 32p. Teddy bear holding balloon 80 95
938 32p. Clown juggling hearts 80 95
939 32p. Bouquet of flowers 80 95
936/9 .. .. *Set of* 4 3·00 3·50

Nos. 937/9 were only available from £2.56 stamp booklets containing two examples of No. 936a. This pane, which also includes 8 small greetings labels, exists in two different forms with either No. 936 at left and No. 938 at right or No. 937 at left and No. 939 at right. In each instance the right-hand stamp is imperforate at right.

(Des Bridget Flynn. Litho Irish Security Stamp Ptg Ltd)

1995 (24 Jan). *Chinese New Year ("Year of the Pig"). P* 14×15.

MS940 137×74 mm. Nos. 936, 938/9 .. .. 2·25 2·75

The example of No. 939 in the above miniature sheet is imperforate at right.

(Des C. Rycraft. Litho Irish Security Stamp Ptg Ltd)

1995 (28 Feb). *Transport. Narrow Gauge Railways. T* **321** *and similar horiz designs. Multicoloured. Chalk-surfaced paper. P* 15×14.

941 28p. Type **321** 75 60
942 32p. County Donegal Railway tank locomotive No. 2 *Blanche* at Donegal Station 90 90
943 38p. Cork and Muskerry Railway tank locomotive No. 1 *City of Cork* on Western Road, Cork .. .. 1·25 1·75
944 52p. Cavan and Leitrim tank locomotive No. 3 *Lady Edith* on Arigna Tramway .. 1·75 2·50
941/4 .. .. *Set of* 4 4·25 5·25
MS945 127×83 mm. Nos. 941/4 .. .. 4·25 5·25

No. **MS**945 also exists with the "Singapore '95" International Stamp Exhibition logo added.

322 English and Irish Rugby Players

(Des C. Harrison. Litho Walsall)

1995 (6 Apr). *World Cup Rugby Championship, South Africa. T* **322** *and similar horiz design. Multicoloured. Chalk-surfaced paper. P* 14.

946 32p. Type **322** 75 75
947 52p. Australian and Irish players .. 1·25 1·75
MS948 108×77 mm. £1 Type **322** .. .. 2·50 2·75

No. **MS**948 also exists overprinted for Regional Stamp Shows at Limerick and Letterkenny.

323 Peace Dove and Skyscrapers

324 Soldiers of the Irish Brigade and Memorial Cross

(Des R. Ballagh)

1995 (6 Apr). *Europa. Peace and Freedom. T* **323** *and similar horiz design. Multicoloured. Chalk-surfaced paper. (a) Litho Irish Security Stamp Ptg Ltd. P* 15×14.

949 32p. Type **323** 85 75
950 44p. Peace dove and map of Europe and North Africa .. .. 1·40 2·00

(b) Litho Printset Cambec Pty Ltd, Melbourne. Self-adhesive. P 11½

951 32p. Type **323** 90 90
952 32p. As No. 950 .. .. 90 90

Nos. 949/50 were issued in sheetlets of 10 (2×5) with illustrated left margins.

Nos. 951/2 are smaller, 34½×23 mm, and occur, *se-tenant*, in pairs or rolls of 100 with the surplus self-adhesive paper around each stamps removed.

(Des E. Daniels. Photo Belgian Post Office Ptg Wks, Malines)

1995 (15 May). *250th Anniv of Battle of Fontenoy. Chalk-surfaced paper. P* 11½.

953 **324** 32p. multicoloured 80 80

325 Irish Brigade, French Army, 1745

326 Guglielmo Marconi and Original Radio Transmitter

(Des D. McAllister. Litho Irish Security Stamp Ptg Ltd)

1995 (15 May). *Military Uniforms. T* **325** *and similar vert designs. Multicoloured. Chalk-surfaced paper. P* 14×15.

954 28p. Type **325** 70 60
a. Booklet pane. Nos. 954/5, each × 2 .. 3·00
b. Booklet pane. Nos. 954/5 and 957/8 .. 3·00
c. Booklet pane. Nos. 954/5 and 957 .. 3·00
d. Booklet pane. Nos. 954/5 and 958 .. 3·00
955 32p. Tercio Irlanda, Spanish army in Flanders, 1605 .. .. 80 75
956 32p. Royal Dublin Fusiliers, 1914 .. .. 80 75
957 38p. St. Patrick's Battalion, Papal Army, 1860 .. .. 1·10 1·25
958 52p. 69th Regiment, New York State Militia, 1861 .. .. 1·60 1·75
954/8 .. .. *Set of* 5 4·50 4·50

Booklet panes Nos. 954a/b come with the two right-hand stamps (Nos. 954/5 or 955 and 958) imperforate at right.

The booklet panes also exist overprinted for Regional Stamp Shows at Sligo, Waterford and Galway and for "Stampa '95" (two panes).

(Des E. Jünger (No. 959), S. Young (No. 960). Litho Irish Security Stamp Ptg Ltd)

1995 (8 June). *Centenary of Radio. T* **326** *and similar horiz design. Multicoloured. Chalk-surfaced paper. P* 13½.

959 32p. Type **326** .. .. 80 1·00
a. Pair. Nos. 959/60 .. .. .. 1·60 2·00
960 32p. Traditional radio dial .. .. .. 80 1·00

Nos. 959/60 were printed together, *se-tenant*, in horizontal and vertical pairs throughout the sheet.

327 Bartholomew Mosse (founder) and Hospital Building

(Des A. May (No. 961), S. Woulfe Flanagan (No. 962), Q Design (No. 963), Creative Inputs (No. 964). Litho Questa (Nos. 961/2) or Irish Security Stamp Ptg Ltd (others))

1995 (27 July). *Anniversaries. T* **327** *and similar multicoloured designs. Chalk-surfaced paper. P* 15×14 (*Nos.* 961), 14½ (*No.* 962), 14½×14 (*No.* 963) *or* 13½ (*No.* 964).
961 28p. Type **327** (250th anniv of Rotunda Hospital) 70 70
962 32p. St. Patrick's House, Maynooth College (Bicent) (25×41 *mm*) 80 80
963 32p. Laurel wreath and map of Europe (50th anniv of end of Second World War) 80 80
964 52p. Geological map of Ireland (150th anniv of Geological Survey of Ireland) (32½×32½ *mm*) .. .. .. 1·25 1·50
961/4 .. .. *Set of* 4 3·25 3·50

328 Natterjack Toad **329** *Crinum moorei*

(Des I. Loe. Litho Irish Security Stamp Ptg Ltd)

1995 (1 Sept). *Reptiles and Amphibians. T* **328** *and similar horiz designs. Chalk-surfaced paper.* (*a*) *P* 15×14.
965 32p. Type **328** .. .. 1·00 1·25
a. Horiz strip. Nos. 965/8 .. .. 3·50
966 32p. Common Lizards .. .. .. 1·00 1·25
967 32p. Smooth Newts .. .. .. 1·00 1·25
968 32p. Common Frog .. .. .. 1·00 1·25
965/8 .. .. *Set of* 4 3·50 4·50
(*b*) *Self-adhesive. P* 9½.
969 32p. Type **328** .. .. 1·00 1·25
970 32p. Common Lizard .. .. .. 1·00 1·25
971 32p. Smooth Newt .. .. .. 1·00 1·25
972 32p. Common Frog .. .. .. 1·00 1·25
969/72 .. .. *Set of* 4 3·50 4·50
Nos. 965/8 were printed together, *se-tenant*, in horizontal strips of 4 with the backgrounds forming a composite design.
Nos. 969/72 are smaller, 34×23 mm, and occur, *se-tenant*, in strips of 4 or rolls of 100 with the surplus self-adhesive paper around each stamp removed.

(Des Frances Poskitt. Litho Irish Security Stamp Ptg Ltd)

1995 (9 Oct). *Bicentenary of National Botanic Gardens, Glasnevin. Flowers. T* **329** *and similar vert designs. Multicoloured. Chalk-surfaced paper. P* 14×15.
973 32p. Type **329** 85 70
a. Booklet pane. Nos. 973×2 and 974/5 4·50
b. Booklet pane. Nos. 973/5 .. .. 4·50
974 38p. *Sarracenia* × *moorei* .. .. .. 1·10 1·10
975 44p. *Solanum crispum* "Glasnevin" .. 1·50 2·25
973/5 .. .. *Set of* 3 3·00 3·50
Booklet panes Nos. 973a/b come from £2.60 stamp booklets and have the outer edges of the pane imperforate so that examples of each value exist imperforate on one or two sides.

330 Anniversary Logo and Irish United Nations Soldier

(Des Jarlath Hayes. Litho Enschedé)

1995 (19 Oct). *50th Anniv of United Nations. T* **330** *and similar horiz design. Multicoloured. Chalk-surfaced paper. P* 13×13½.
976 32p. Type **330** 80 70
977 52p. Emblem and "UN" .. .. .. 1·25 1·40
Nos. 976/7 were each issued in sheets of 10 (2×5) with enlarged illustrated left margins.

COVER PRICES

Cover factors are quoted at the beginning of each country for most issues to 1945. An explanation of the system can be found on page x. The factors quoted do not, however, apply to philatelic covers.

331 "Adoration of the Shepherds" (illuminated manuscript) (Benedetto Bardone)

332 Zig and Zag on Heart

(Des Q Design. Litho Irish Security Stamp Ptg Ltd)

1995 (16 Nov). *Christmas. T* **331** *and similar horiz designs. Multicoloured. Chalk-surfaced paper. P* 15×14.
978 28p. Adoration of the Magi 70 65
a. Sheetlet. No. 978×13 .. .. 8·25
979 28p. Type **331** 70 65
980 32p. "Adoration of the Magi" (illuminated manuscript) (Bardone) 80 70
981 52p. "The Holy Family" (illuminated manuscript) (Bardone) .. .. 1·40 1·60
978/81 .. .. *Set of* 4 3·25 3·25
No. 978 was only issued in sheetlets of 13 stamps and two labels (at centre of rows 1 and 2) sold at £3.36 providing a discount of 28p. off the face value of the stamps.

(Des Double Z Enterprises. Litho Irish Security Stamp Ptg Ltd)

1996 (23 Jan). *Greetings Stamps. T* **332** *and similar vert designs. Multicoloured. Chalk-surfaced paper. P* 14×15.
982 32p. Type **332** 95 95
a. Booklet pane. Nos. 982/5 .. .. 3·50
983 32p. Zig and Zag waving 95 95
984 32p. Zig and Zag in space suits 95 95
985 32p. Zig and Zag wearing hats 95 95
982/5 .. .. *Set of* 4 3·50 3·50
Nos. 983/5 were only issued in £2.56 stamp booklets. No. 982 was available from sheets and booklets.
Booklet pane No. 982a, which also includes eight small greetings labels, exists in two different forms with either No. 982 or 984 at right. In each instance the right-hand stamp is imperforate at right.

(Des Double Z Enterprises. Litho Irish Security Stamp Ptg Ltd)

1996 (23 Jan). *Chinese New Year* ("*Year of the Rat*"). *Chalk-surfaced paper. P* 14×15.
MS986 130×74 mm. Nos. 982, 984/5 .. .. 3·00 3·00
The example of No. 982 in No. **MS**986 is imperforate at right.
No. **MS**986 also exists overprinted for the Collectors' Road Show at Kilkenny.

333 Wheelchair Athlete **334** Before the Start, Fairyhouse Race Course

(Des C. Harrison. Litho Irish Security Stamp Ptg Ltd)

1996 (1 Feb). *Olympic and Paralympic Games, Atlanta. T* **333** *and similar vert designs. Multicoloured. Chalk-surfaced paper. P* 14×15.
987 28p. Type **333** 70 65
988 32p. Running 80 80
a. Strip of 3. Nos. 988/90 .. .. 2·25
989 32p. Throwing the discus 80 80
990 32p. Single kayak 80 80
987/90 .. .. *Set of* 4 2·75 2·75
Nos. 988/90 were printed together, *se-tenant*, as horizontal and vertical strips of 3 in sheets of 9.

(Des P. Curling and Q Design. Litho Irish Security Stamp Ptg Ltd)

1996 (12 Mar). *Irish Horse Racing. T* **334** *and similar horiz designs. Multicoloured. Chalk-surfaced paper. P* 15×14.
991 28p. Type **334** 70 65
a. Booklet pane. Nos. 991×2 and 992/3 4·25
992 32p. Steeplechase, Punchestown 80 80
a. Pair. Nos. 992/3 .. .. .. 1·60 1·60
b. Booklet pane. Nos. 992/5 .. .. 4·25
c. Booklet pane. Nos. 992×2 and 994 .. 4·25
993 32p. On the Flat, The Curragh 80 80
a. Booklet pane. Nos. 993×2 and 995 .. 4·25
994 38p. Steeplechase, Galway .. .. 1·25 1·25
995 52p. After the race, Leopardstown .. 1·50 1·50
991/5 .. .. *Set of* 4 4·50 4·50
Nos. 992/3 were printed together, *se-tenant*, in horizontal and vertical pairs throughout the sheet.
Booklet pane Nos. 991a, 992b/c and 993a come from £4.92 stamp booklets with the right-hand edge of the panes imperforate. The complete booklet contains two examples of No. 992 and one each of Nos. 991, 993 and 995 imperforate at right.
The booklet panes also exist overprinted for Collectors' Road Shows at Cork (No. 992c), Limerick (No. 991a) or Sligo (No. 993a) and for "Stampa '96" (No. 992c).
For designs as Nos. 992/3 in miniature sheet see No. **MS**1003.

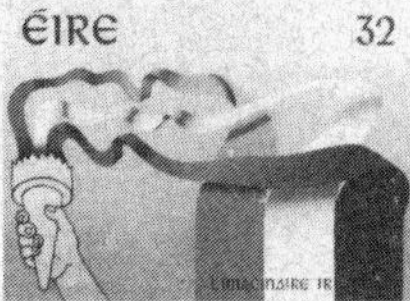

335 Irish and French Coloured Ribbons merging **336** Louie Bennett (suffragette)

(Des R. Ballagh. Litho Irish Security Stamp Ptg Ltd)

1996 (12 Mar). *"L'Imaginaire Irlandais" Festival of Contemporary Irish Arts, France. Chalk-surfaced paper. P* 15×14.
996 **335** 32p. multicoloured 80 80

(Des S. Young)

1996 (2 Apr). *Europa. Famous Women. T* **336** *and similar horiz design. Chalk-surfaced paper.*
(*a*) *Litho Questa. P* 15×14
997 **336** 32p. deep reddish violet 80 70
998 – 44p. myrtle-green .. .. .. 1·10 1·25
(*b*) *Litho Irish Security Stamp Ptg Ltd. Self-adhesive. P* 9½
999 **336** 32p. deep reddish violet .. .. 80 1·00
1000 – 32p. dull green .. .. .. 80 1·00
Design:—Nos. 998, 1000, Lady Augusta Gregory (playwright).
Nos. 997/8 were each issued in sheetlets of 10 (2×5) with enlarged illustrated left margins.
Nos. 999/1000 are smaller, 34×23 mm, and occur, *se-tenant*, in rolls of 100 with the surplus self-adhesive paper around each stamp removed.

337 Newgrange Passage Tomb (Boyne Valley World Heritage Site)

(Des L. Belton (28p.), Q Design (32p.). Litho Walsall)

1996 (2 Apr). *Anniversaries and Events. T* **337** *and similar horiz design. Chalk-surfaced paper. P* 14.
1001 28p. grey-brown and black 85 60
1002 32p. multicoloured 90 90
Designs:—32p. Children playing (50th anniv of U.N.I.C.E.F.).

(Litho Irish Security Stamp Printing Ltd)

1996 (18 May). *"CHINA '96" 9th Asian International Stamp Exhibition, Peking. Sheet* 120×95 *mm containing Nos.* 992/3. *Chalk-surfaced paper. P* 15×14.
MS1003 32p. Steeplechase, Punchestown; 32p. On the Flat, The Curragh .. .. .. 2·25 2·75

338 Stanley Woods **339** Michael Davitt (founder of The Land League)

(Des J. Dunne. Litho Questa)

1996 (30 May). *Isle of Man Tourist Trophy Motorcycle Races. Irish Winners. T* **338** *and similar horiz designs. Multicoloured. Chalk-surfaced paper. P* 14.
1004 32p. Type **338** 80 70
1005 44p. Artie Bell .. .. 1·25 1·40
1006 50p. Alec Bennett .. .. 1·50 1·60
1007 52p. Joey and Robert Dunlop .. .. 1·50 1·60
1004/7 .. .. *Set of* 4 4·50 4·75
MS1008 100×70 mm. 50p. As 52p. .. .. 1·25 1·50
No. **MS**1008 also exists overprinted for "Stampa '96" and for the Collectors' Road Show at Dundalk.

(Des R. Ballagh (28p.), J. Tobin (32p.), C. Harrison (38p.), L. Belton (52p.). Litho Enschedé)

1996 (4 July). *Anniversaries and Events. T* **339** *and similar multicoloured designs. Chalk-surfaced paper. P* 13½×13 (*28p.*) *or* 13×13½ (*others*).
1009 28p. Type **339** (150th birth anniv) .. 70 60
1010 32p. Presidency logo (Ireland's Presidency of European Union) (*horiz*) .. 80 70
1011 38p. Thomas McLaughlin (hydro-electric engineer) and Ardnacrusha Power Station (Birth centenary) (*horiz*) .. 1·00 1·10
1012 52p. Mechanical peat harvester (50th anniv of Bord na Móna) (*horiz*) .. 1·60 1·75
1009/12 .. .. *Set of* 4 3·75 3·75

340 Coastal Patrol Vessel

341 Blind Woman with Child

(Des G. Fallon. Litho Irish Security Stamp Ptg Ltd)

1996 (18 July). *50th Anniv of Irish Naval Service. T* **340** *and similar multicoloured designs. Chalk-surfaced paper. P* 14×15 (52p.) *or* 15×14 (*others*).

1013 32p. Type **340** 80 70
a. Booklet pane. No. 1013×3 .. .. 2·75
b. Booklet pane. Nos. 1013/15 .. 2·75
1014 44p. Corvette .. .. 1·40 1·50
1015 52p. Motor torpedo boat (*vert*) .. .. 1·50 1·60
1013/15 .. .. .. *Set of* 3 3·25 3·50

Booklet panes Nos. 1013a/b come from £2.24 stamp booklets. Stamps from No. 1013a have either one or two adjacent sides imperforate and those from No. 1013b are imperforate at foot (32, 44p.) or at right and foot (52p.).

The booklet panes also exist overprinted for "Stampa '96" (No. 1013b) or for the Collectors' Road Shows at Galway (No. 1013b) and Waterford (No. 1013a).

(Des E. Patton. Litho Irish Security Stamp Ptg Ltd)

1996 (3 Sept). *People with Disabilities. T* **341** *and similar vert design. Multicoloured. Chalk-surfaced paper. P* 14×15.

1016 28p. Type **341** 55 60
a. Pair. Nos. 1016/7 .. .. .. 1·10
1017 28p. Man in wheelchair playing bowls .. 55 60

Nos. 1016/17 were printed together, *se-tenant*, in horizontal and vertical pairs throughout the sheet.

342 Green-winged Teal

(Des R. Ward. Litho Irish Security Stamp Ptg Ltd)

1996 (24 Sept). *Freshwater Ducks. T* **342** *and similar horiz designs. Multicoloured. Chalk-surfaced paper. P* 15×14.

1018 32p. Type **342** 85 70
1019 38p. Common Shoveler .. .. .. 1·00 1·00
1020 44p. European Wigeon .. .. .. 1·25 1·25
1021 52p. Mallard .. .. 1·50 1·50
1018/21 .. .. .. *Set of* 4 4·25 4·00
MS1022 127×85 mm. Nos. 1018/21 .. .. 4·25 4·50

343 Scene from *Man of Aran*

344 Visit of the Magi

(Des J. Reddy. Litho Irish Security Stamp Ptg Ltd)

1996 (17 Oct). *Centenary of Irish Cinema. T* **343** *and similar horiz designs. Multicoloured. Chalk-surfaced paper. P* 13½.

1023 32p. Type **343** 85 90
a. Strip of 4. Nos. 1023/6 .. .. 3·00
1024 32p. *My Left Foot* 85 90
1025 32p. *The Commitments* 85 90
1026 32p. *The Field* 85 90
1023/6 .. .. .. *Set of* 4 3·00 3·25

Nos. 1023/6 were printed together, *se-tenant*, in vertical and horizontal strips of 4 throughout the sheet.

(Des T. Monaghan (No. 1027), E. Patton (others). Litho Irish Security Stamp Ptg Ltd)

1996 (19 Nov). *Christmas. T* **344** *and similar vert designs from 16th-century Book of Hours (Nos. 1028/30). Multicoloured. Chalk-surfaced paper (Nos. 1028/30). P* 14×15.

1027 28p. The Holy Family 75 60
a. Sheetlet. No. 1027×15 .. .. 10·00
1028 28p. Type **344** 60 60
1029 32p. The Annunciation 80 75
1030 52p. The Shepherds receiving news of Christ's birth .. .. 1·40 1·60
1027/30 .. .. .. *Set of* 4 3·25 3·25

No. 1027 was only issued in sheetlets of 15 stamps sold at £3.92 providing a discount of 28p. off the face value of the stamps.

345 Magpie

346 Pair of Doves

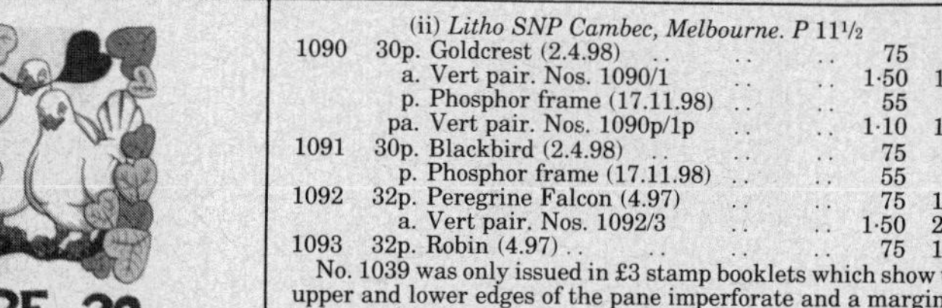

(Des K. Mullarney)

1997 (16 Jan)–**99**. *Birds. T* **345** *and similar multicoloured designs.*

(*a*) *Litho Walsall (Nos.* 1038ac, 1053ac, 1054ac, 1055ac, 1057ac, 1058ac) *or Irish Security Stamp Ptg Ltd (others). Chalk-surfaced paper* (1p., 2p., 4p., 10p., 20p., 30p. (*Nos.* 1039/52), £5) *or ordinary paper (others). P* 15×14 (5p., 28p., 40p., 50p., £1, £5) *or* 14×15 (*others*)

(i) *Size* 21×24 *mm (vert) or* 24×21 *mm (horiz)*

1031 1p. Type **345** (27.8.97) 10 10
1032 2p. Gannet (27.8.97) 10 10
1033 4p. Corncrake (27.8.97) 10 10
a. Ordinary paper (3.98) 20 10
1034 5p. Wood Pigeon (*horiz*) (2.4.98) .. 10 10
a. Chalk-surfaced paper (9.98) .. 20 10
1035 10p. Kingfisher (27.8.97) 20 25
1036 20p. Lapwing (27.8.97) 35 40
1037 28p. Blue Tit (*horiz*) 50 55
a. Chalk-surfaced paper (10.97) .. 50 55
1038 30p. Blackbird (2.4.98) 55 60
a. Chalk-surfaced paper (4.98) .. 80 60
ab. Booklet pane. Nos. 1038a and 1039, each × 5 (4.9.98) .. .. .. 5·50
ac. Perf 14 (phosphor frame) (17.11.98) 55 60
ap. Phosphor frame (16.2.99) 55 60
aq. Sheetlet. Nos. 1038ap, 1039p and 1040/52 (16.2.99) .. .. .. 8·00
ar. Booklet pane. Nos. 1038ap and 1039p, each × 5 (3.99) .. .. .. 5·50
1039 30p. Goldcrest (4.9.98) 55 60
p. Phosphor frame (16.2.99) 55 60
1040 30p. Stonechat (*phosphor frame*) (16.2.99) 55 60
1041 30p. Lapwing (*phosphor frame*) (16.2.99) 55 60
1042 30p. Gannet (*phosphor frame*) (16.2.99) .. 55 60
1043 30p. Corncrake (*phosphor frame*) (16.2.99) 55 60
1044 30p. Type **345** (*phosphor frame*) (16.2.99) 55 60
1045 30p. Kingfisher (*phosphor frame*) (16.2.99) 55 60
1046 30p. Peregrine Falcon (*phosphor frame*) (16.2.99) 55 60
1047 30p. Barn Owl (*phosphor frame*) (16.2.99) 55 60
1048 30p. Robin (*phosphor frame*) (16.2.99) .. 55 60
1049 30p. Song Thrush (*phosphor frame*) (16.2.99) 55 60
1050 30p. Wren (*phosphor frame*) (16.2.99) .. 55 60
1051 30p. Pied Wagtail (*phosphor frame*) (16.2.99) 55 60
1052 30p. Puffin (*phosphor frame*) (16.2.99) .. 55 60
1053 32p. Robin 60 65
a. Chalk-surfaced paper (10.97) .. 60 65
ac. Perf 14 (phosphor frame) (17.11.98) 60 65
1054 35p. Stonechat (2.4.98) 65 70
a. Chalk-surfaced paper (4.98) .. 1·10 70
ac. Perf 14 (phosphor frame) (17.11.98) 65 70
1055 40p. Ringed Plover (*horiz*) (2.4.98) .. 70 75
ac. Perf 14. Chalk-surfaced paper (phosphor frame) (17.11.98) .. 70 75
1056 44p. Puffin 80 85
1057 45p. Song Thrush (2.4.98) 80 85
a. Chalk-surfaced paper (9.98) .. 1·40 85
ac. Perf 14 (phosphor frame) (17.11.98) 80 85
1058 50p. European Sparrow Hawk (*horiz*) (2.4.98) 90 95
a. Chalk-surfaced paper (8.98) .. 1·50 95
ac. Perf 14 (phosphor frame) (17.11.98) 90 95
1059 52p. Barn Owl .. .. 95 1·00

(ii) *Size* 24×45 *mm (vert) or* 45×24 *mm (horiz)*

1060 £1 Greenland White-fronted Goose .. 1·75 1·90
a. Chalk-surfaced paper (11.98) .. 2·50 1·90
1061 £2 Pintail (*horiz*) (2.4.98) .. .. 3·50 3·75
1062 £5 Shelduck (27.8.97) .. .. .. 9·00 9·25
a. Ordinary paper (9.98) .. .. 13·00 9·25
1031/62 .. .. .. *Set of* 32 28·00 30·00

(*b*) *Booklet stamps. Litho Irish Security Stamp Ptg Ltd. Size* 21×17 (5p.) *or* 17×21 *mm (others). Chalk-surfaced paper* (4p., 30p. (*No.* 1083), 32p.) *or ordinary paper (others). P* 14×15 (5p.) *or* 15×14 (*others*)

1080 4p. Corncrake (6.12.97) 10 10
a. Booklet pane. Nos. 1080 and 1085×3 1·75
1081 5p. Wood Pigeon (*horiz*) (2.4.98) .. 10 10
a. Booklet pane. Nos. 1081×2 and 1082×3 plus label .. .. .. 1·75
b. Chalk-surfaced paper (16.2.99) .. 10 10
ba. Booklet pane. Nos. 1081b×2 and 1083×3 plus label .. .. .. 1·75
1082 30p. Blackbird (2.4.98) 55 60
1083 30p. Goldcrest ("all-over" phosphor) (16.2.99) 55 60
1084 32p. Robin (6.3.97) 60 65
1085 32p. Peregrine Falcon (6.12.97) 60 65

(*c*) *Self-adhesive. Size* 25×30 *mm.*

(i) *Litho Irish Stamp Security Ptg Ltd. P* 9×10

1086 30p. Goldcrest (2.4.98) 75 65
a. Vert pair. Nos. 1086/7 .. .. 1·50 1·25
p. Phosphor frame (14.12.98) 55 65
pa. Vert pair. Nos. 1086p/7p .. .. 1·10 1·25
1087 30p. Blackbird (2.4.98) 75 65
p. Phosphor frame (14.12.98) 55 65
1088 32p. Peregrine Falcon (6.3.97) 75 65
a. Vert pair. Nos. 1088/9 .. .. 1·50 1·25
1089 32p. Robin (6.3.97) 75 65

(ii) *Litho SNP Cambec, Melbourne. P* 11½

1090 30p. Goldcrest (2.4.98) 75
a. Vert pair. Nos. 1090/1 .. .. 1·50 1·
p. Phosphor frame (17.11.98) 55
pa. Vert pair. Nos. 1090p/1p .. .. 1·10 1·
1091 30p. Blackbird (2.4.98) 75
p. Phosphor frame (17.11.98) 55
1092 32p. Peregrine Falcon (4.97) .. .. 75 1·
a. Vert pair. Nos. 1092/3 .. .. 1·50 2·
1093 32p. Robin (4.97) .. .. 75 1·

No. 1039 was only issued in £3 stamp booklets which show th upper and lower edges of the pane imperforate and a margin either end.

The sheet stamps with phosphor frames and No. 1038ar sho the actual designs slightly reduced to provide a clear 2 m border on which the phosphor frame appears.

The sheetlet, No. 1038aq, repeats the vertical designs fro other values in the set. The designs showing the Wren and Pi Wagtail only occur in the sheetlet. It also exists overprinted f the Collectors' Road Show at Limerick.

Nos. 748bb (containing No. 1084), 1080a, 1081a and 1081a show the upper and lower edges of the panes imperforate. O booklet pane No. 1081ba the three 30p. have "all-ove phosphor, but this does not extend to the two 5p. stamps or th label.

Nos. 1086/7, 1088/9, 1090/1 and 1092/3 were produced in rol of 100, each containing two designs. Those printed by Iris Stamp Security Ptg Ltd retain the surplus self-adhesive pap around each stamp, but this was removed for those produced Australia.

Nos. 1086p/7p show the actual designs slightly reduced an the inscriptions repositioned to provide a clear 2 mm border o which the phosphor frame appears.

For £2 value in miniature sheet see No. **MS**1131.

(Des Double Z Enterprises. Litho Irish Security Stamp Ptg Lt

1997 (28 Jan). *Greetings Stamps. T* **346** *and similar ve designs. Multicoloured. Chalk-surfaced paper. P* 14×15.

1100 32p. Type **346** 85
a. Booklet pane. Nos. 1100/3 .. .. 3·00
1101 32p. Cow jumping over moon 85
1102 32p. Pig going to market 85
1103 32p. Cockerel 85
1100/3 .. .. .. *Set of* 4 3·00 3·

Nos. 1101/3 were only issued in £2.56 stamp booklets. N 1100 was available from sheets and booklets.

Booklet pane No. 1100a, which also includes eight sma greetings labels, exists in two forms with No. 1101 either at le or right. In each instance the right-hand stamp, No. 1101 or N 1103, is imperforate at right.

(Des Double Z Enterprises. Litho Irish Security Stamp Ptg Lt

1997 (28 Jan). *"HONG KONG '97" International Stam Exhibition. Chinese New Year ("Year of the Ox"). Chal surfaced paper. P* 14×15.

MS1104 124×74 mm. Nos. 1101/3 .. .. 2·40 2·

The example of No. 1103 in No. **MS**1104 is imperforate right.

No. **MS**1104 also exists overprinted for the Collectors' Roa Show at Limerick.

347 Troops on Parade

348 Grey Seals

(Des Q Design. Litho Irish Security Stamp Ptg Ltd)

1997 (18 Feb–6 Dec). *75th Anniv of Irish Free State. T* **347** *an similar horiz designs. Multicoloured. Chalk-surfaced pape P* 15×14.

1105 28p. Page from the "Annals of the Four Masters", quill and 1944 ½d. O'Clery stamp (27 Aug) 55 5
1106 32p. Type **347** 60 6
a. Pair. Nos. 1106/7 .. .. .. 1·25 1·2
1107 32p. The Dail, national flag and Constitution 60 6
1108 32p. Athlete, footballer and hurling players (3 Apr) 60 6
a. Pair. Nos. 1108/9 .. .. .. 1·25 1·2
1109 32p. Singer, violinist and bodhran player (3 Apr) 60 6
1110 32p. Stained glass window and 1929 9d. O'Connell stamp (27 Aug) 60 6
1111 32p. G.P.O., Dublin, and 1923 2d. map stamp (6 Dec) 60 6
1112 52p. Police personnel and Garda badge 1·00 1·2
a. Pair. Nos. 1112/13 .. .. .. 2·00 2·5
1113 52p. The Four Courts and Scales of Justice 1·00 1·2
1114 52p. Currency, blueprint and food-processing plant (3 Apr) .. .. 1·00 1·2
a. Pair. Nos. 1114/15 .. .. .. 2·00 2·5
1115 52p. Books, palette and Seamus Heaney manuscript (3 Apr) .. .. .. 1·00 1·2
1116 52p. Air Lingus airliner and 1965 1s. 5d air stamp (27 Aug) .. .. .. 1·00 9
1105/16 .. .. .. *Set of* 12 8·25 9·0
MS1117 174×209 mm. As Nos. 1105/16, but each with face value of 32p. (6 Dec) .. .. 6·50 7·5

Nos. 1106/7, 1108/9, 1112/13 and 1114/15 were each printe together, *se-tenant*, in horiz or vert pairs throughout the sheets.

Des Rosemary Davis. Litho Irish Security Stamp Ptg Ltd)

97 (6 Mar). *Marine Mammals. T* **348** *and similar multi-oloured designs. Chalk-surfaced paper. P* 14×15 (*28p., 32p.*) *r* 15×14 (*others*).

18 28p. Type **348** 75 60
19 32p. Bottle-nosed Dolphins 85 80
20 44p. Harbour Porpoises (*horiz*) .. .. 1·25 1·40
21 52p. Killer Whale (*horiz*) .. .. .. 1·40 1·50
18/21 .. .. *Set of* 4 3·75 3·75
S1122 150×68 mm. As Nos. 1118/21. P 15 .. 3·75 3·75

No. **MS**1122 also exists overprinted for the Collectors' Road ow at Dublin.

349 Dublin Silver Penny of 997

(Des Creative Inputs. Litho Irish Security Stamp Ptg Ltd)

97 (3 Apr). *Millenary of Irish Coinage. Chalk-surfaced paper. P* 15×14.

23 **349** 32p. multicoloured 65 65

350 "The Children of Lir"

(Des P. Lynch)

97 (14 May). *Europa. Tales and Legends. T* **350** *and similar horiz design. Multicoloured.* (a) *Litho Walsall. Chalk-surfaced paper. P* 14.

24 32p. Type **350** 70 60
25 44p. Oisin and Niamh .. .. 1·00 1·10

b) Litho Irish Security Stamp Ptg Ltd. Self-adhesive. P $9^1/_2$.

26 32p. Type **350** 70 70
a. Horiz pair. Nos. 1126/7 .. .. 1·40 1·40
27 32p. Oisin and Niamh 70 70
24/7 .. .. *Set of* 4 2·75 2·75

Nos. 1124/5 were each issued in sheetlets of 10 (2×5) with larged illustrated left margins.

Nos. 1126/7, which are smaller 36×25 mm, occur in rolls of 0.

351 Emigrants waiting to board Ship

(Des Q Design. Litho Irish Security Stamp Ptg Ltd)

97 (14 May). *150th Anniv of The Great Famine. T* **351** *and similar horiz designs. Chalk-surfaced paper. P* 15×14.

28 28p. dp dull blue, verm & pale yellow-ochre 75 60
29 32p. reddish orange, deep dull blue and pale yellow-ochre 90 70
30 52p. brown, dp dull blue & pale yell-ochre 1·40 1·40
28/30 .. .. *Set of* 3 2·75 2·40

Designs:—32p. Family and dying child; 52p. Irish Society of riends soup kitchen.

(Des K. Mullarney. Litho Irish Security Stamp Ptg Ltd)

97 (29 May). *"Pacific '97" International Stamp Exhibition, San Francisco. Sheet,* 100×70 *mm, containing No.* 1061. *Multicoloured. Chalk-surfaced paper. P* 14.

S1131 £2 Pintail (48×26 *mm*) .. .. 4·50 5·00

352 Kate O'Brien (novelist) (birth centenary) **353** The Baily Lighthouse

(Des Creative Inputs. Litho Irish Security Stamp Ptg Ltd (No. 1133) or Walsall (others))

1997 (1 July). *Anniversaries. T* **352** *and similar vert designs. Multicoloured. Chalk-surfaced paper. P* 14×15 (*No.* 1133), $14^1/_2$ (*No.* 1134) *or* 14 (*others*).

1132 28p. Type **352** 60 60
1133 28p. St. Columba crossing to Iona (stained glass window) (1400th death anniv) 60 60
1134 32p. "Daniel O'Connell" (J. Haverty) (politician) (150th death anniv) (27×49 *mm*) 70 70
1135 52p. "John Wesley" (N. Hone) (founder of Methodism) (250th anniv of first visit to Ireland) .. .. 1·25 1·40
1132/5 .. .. *Set of* 4 2·75 3·00

(Des Design Image. Litho Irish Security Stamp Ptg Ltd)

1997 (1 July). *Lighthouses. T* **353** *and similar multicoloured designs. Chalk-surfaced paper. P* 15×14 (*32p.*) *or* 14×15 (*others*).

1136 32p. Type **353** 70 80
a. Pair. Nos. 1136/7 .. .. .. 1·40 1·60
b. Booklet pane. Nos. 1136×2 and 1137 1·60
c. Booklet pane. Nos. 1136/7, each × 2 2·00
d. Perf 15 .. .. 1·10 1·40
da. Booklet pane. Nos. 1136d/9d .. 4·00
1137 32p. Tarbert 70 80
d. Perf 15 .. .. 1·10 1·40
1138 38p. Hookhead (*vert*) 75 85
d. Perf 15 .. .. 1·10 1·40
da. Booklet pane. Nos. 1138d/9d .. 2·00
1139 50p. The Fastnet (*vert*) .. .. .. 1·10 1·25
d. Perf 15 .. .. 1·10 1·40
1136/9 .. .. *Set of* 4 3·00 3·25

Nos. 1136/7 were printed together, *se-tenant*, in horizontal or vertical pairs throughout the sheet.

Nos. 1136d/9d only exist from booklet panes Nos. 1136da and 1138da.

The booklet panes also exist overprinted for Collectors' Road Shows at Sligo (No. 1136b), Tralee (No. 1138da), Galway (No. 1136c) or Limerick (No. 1136da) and also for "Stampa '97" (Nos. 1136b/c, 1136da and 1138da).

354 Commemorative Cross **355** Dracula and Bat

(Des L. Rafael. Litho Irish Security Stamp Ptg Ltd)

1997 (12 Sept). *Ireland–Mexico Joint Issue. 150th Anniv of Mexican St. Patrick's Battalion. Ordinary paper. P* $13^1/_2$.

1140 **354** 32p. multicoloured 55 60

(Des Passmore Design. Litho Irish Security Stamp Ptg Ltd)

1997 (1 Oct). *Centenary of Publication of Bram Stoker's* Dracula. *T* **355** *and similar multicoloured designs. Chalk-surfaced paper. P* 14×15 (*vert*) *or* 15×14 (*horiz*).

1141 28p. Type **355** 60 55
1142 32p. Dracula and female victim 65 60
1143 38p. Dracula emerging from coffin (*horiz*) 80 80
1144 52p. Dracula and wolf (*horiz*) .. .. 1·10 1·10
1141/4 .. .. *Set of* 4 2·75 2·75
MS1145 150×90 mm. As Nos. 1141/4. P 15 .. 3·25 3·25

A second miniature sheet, 75×55 mm, containing No. 1142, was only available as a promotional item connected with the purchase of funsize bars of various Mars products or at face value from the Philatelic Bureau.

356 "The Nativity" (Kevin Kelly) **357** Christmas Tree

(Des Creative Inputs (Nos. 1146/8). Q. Design (No. 1149). Litho Irish Security Stamp Ptg Ltd)

1997 (18 Nov). *Christmas.* (a) *Stained Glass Windows. T* **356** *and similar vert designs. Multicoloured. Chalk-surfaced paper. P* 14×15.

1146 28p. Type **356** 55 55
1147 32p. "The Nativity" (Sarah Purser and A. E. Child) 60 65
1148 52p. "The Nativity" (A. E. Child) .. .. 95 1·10
1146/8 .. .. *Set of* 3 1·90 2·10

(b) *Self-adhesive booklet stamp. P* 9×10

1149 28p. Type **357** 50 55
a. Booklet pane. No. 1149×20 .. 10·00

No. 1149 as only available from £5.32 stamp booklets.

358 Holding Heart **359** Lady Mary Heath and Avro Avian over Pyramids

(Des B. Asprey. Litho Irish Security Stamp Ptg Ltd)

1998 (26 Jan). *Greetings Stamps* (1*st series*). *T* **358** *and similar vert designs based on the "love is..." cartoon characters of Kim Casali. Multicoloured. Chalk-surfaced paper. P* 14×15.

1150 32p. Type **358** 60 75
a. Booklet pane. Nos. 1150/3 .. .. 2·25
1151 32p. Receiving letter 60 75
1152 32p. Sitting on log 60 75
1153 32p. With birthday presents 60 75
1150/3 .. .. *Set of* 4 2·25 2·75

Nos. 1151/3 were only available from £2.56 stamp booklets containing two examples of No. 1150a. This pane exists in two different forms with either No. 1150 at right and No. 1153 at left or No. 1152 at right and No. 1151 at left. In each instance the right-hand stamp is imperforate at right. No. 1150 is available from both sheets and booklets.

For 30p values in these designs see Nos. 1173/6

(Des B. Asprey. Litho Irish Security Stamp Ptg Ltd)

1998 (26 Jan). *Chinese New Year ("Year of the Tiger"). Chalk-surfaced paper. P* 14×15.

MS1154 124×73 mm. Nos. 1151/3 .. .. 2·25 2·50

The example of No. 1152 in No. **MS**1154 is imperforate at right.

(Des V. Killowry. Litho Irish Security Stamp Ptg Ltd)

1998 (24 Feb). *Pioneers of Irish Aviation. T* **359** *and similar horiz designs. Multicoloured. Chalk-surfaced paper. P* 15×14.

1155 28p. Type **359** 60 55
a. Booklet pane. Nos. 1155/8 .. .. 3·00
b. Booklet pane. Nos. 1155/6 each × 2 3·00
1156 32p. Col. James Fitzmaurice and Junkers W. 33 *Bremen* over Labrador .. 65 60
a. Booklet pane. Nos. 1156×2 and 1157 3·00
b. Booklet pane. Nos. 1156 and 1158×2 3·00
1157 44p. Captain J. P. Saul and Fokker FVIIa/3m *Southern Cross* .. .. 1·00 1·00
1158 52p. Captain Charles Blair and Sikorsky V-s 44 (flying boat) .. .. .. 1·25 1·25
1155/8 .. .. *Set of* 4 3·25 3·00

Booklet panes Nos. 1155b and 1156a/b have margins all round. On No. 1155a there are margins on three sides, but the two right-hand stamps (Nos. 1156 and 1158) are each imperforate at right.

360 Show-jumping

(Des P. Curling. Litho Irish Security Stamp Ptg Ltd)

1998 (2 Apr). *Equestrian Sports. T* **360** *and similar multicoloured designs. Chalk-surfaced paper. P* 14×15 (*45p.*) *or* 15×14 (*others*).

1159 30p. Type **360** 70 60
1160 32p. Three-day eventing 75 65
1161 40p. Gymkhana .. .. 90 1·00
1162 45p. Dressage (*vert*) .. .. 90 1·10
1159/62 .. .. *Set of* 4 3·00 3·00
MS1163 126×84 mm. Nos. 1159/62 .. .. 3·00 3·00

361 Figure of "Liberty"

(Des R. Ballagh. Litho Irish Security Stamp Printing Ltd)

1998 (6 May). *Bicentenary of United Irish Rebellion. T* **361** *and similar horiz designs. Multicoloured. Chalk-surfaced paper. P* 15×14.

1164 30p. Type **361** 75 80
a. Horiz strip of 3. Nos. 1164/6 .. 2·00
1165 30p. United Irishman 75 80
1166 30p. French soldiers 75 80
1167 45p. Wolfe Tone .. .. 1·00 1·25
a. Horiz pair. Nos. 1167/8 .. .. 2·00 2·50
1168 45p. Henry Joy McCracken .. .. .. 1·00 1·25
1164/8 .. .. *Set of* 5 3·75 4·50

Nos. 1164/6 and 1167/8 were each printed together, horizontally *se-tenant*, in strips of 3 (30p.) or in pairs (45p.) throughout sheets of 12.

362 Gathering of the Boats, Kinvara

(Des J. Dunne. Litho Irish Security Stamp Ptg Ltd)

1998 (6 May). *Europa. Festivals. T* **362** *and similar horiz design. Multicoloured. (a) P* 15×14.
1169 30p. Type **362** 70 80
1170 40p. Puck Fair, Killorglin 80 95

(*b*) *Self-adhesive. Chalk-surfaced paper. P* 9½
1171 30p. Type **362** 65 70
1172 30p. Puck Fair, Killorglin 65 70

Nos. 1169/70 were each issued in sheetlets of 10 (2×5) with enlarged illustrated left margins.

Nos. 1171/2, which are smaller 34×23 mm, occur in rolls of 100 with the surplus self-adhesive paper retained.

1998 (6 May). *Greetings Stamps (2nd series). Vert designs as Nos.* 1150/3, *but with changed face value. Multicoloured. Chalk-surfaced paper. P* 14×15.
1173 30p. As No. 1153 .. .. .. 70 80
a. Booklet pane. Nos. 1173/6 .. .. 2·50
1174 30p. As No. 1152 .. .. .. 70 80
1175 30p. As No. 1151 .. .. .. 70 80
1176 30p. Type **358** 70 80
1173/6 .. .. *Set of* 4 2·50 3·00

Nos. 1173/6 were only available from £2.40 stamp booklets containing two examples of No. 1173a. This pane exists in two different forms with either No. 1176 at right and No. 1173 at left or No. 1174 at right and No. 1175 at left. In each instance the right-hand stamp is imperforate at right.

363 Cyclists rounding Bend

(Des C. Harrison. Litho Irish Security Stamp Ptg Ltd)

1998 (2 June). *Visit of "Tour de France" Cycle Race to Ireland. T* **363** *and similar horiz designs. Multicoloured. Chalk-surfaced paper. P* 15×14.
1177 30p. Type **363** 70 70
a. Horiz strip of 4. Nos. 1177/80 .. 2·50
1178 30p. Two cyclists ascending hill 70 70
1179 30p. "Green jersey" cyclist and other competitor 70 70
1180 30p. "Yellow jersey" (race leader) .. 70 70
1177/80 .. .. *Set of* 4 2·50 2·50

Nos. 1177/80 were printed together, *se-tenant*, in horizontal strips of 4 throughout the sheet.

364 Voter and Local Councillors of 1898

365 *Asgard II* (cadet brigantine)

(Des J. Dunne. Litho Irish Security Stamp Ptg Ltd)

1998 (2 June). *Democracy Anniversaries. T* **364** *and similar horiz designs. Multicoloured. Chalk-surfaced paper. P* 15×14.
1181 30p. Type **364** (Cent of Local Government (Ireland) Act) 60 60
1182 32p. European Union flag and harp symbol (25th anniv of Ireland's entry into European Community) 65 65
1183 35p. Woman voter and suffragettes, 1898 (Cent of women's right to vote in local elections) 75 75
1184 45p. Irish Republic flag (50th anniv of Republic of Ireland Act) .. .. 1·00 1·00
1181/4 .. .. *Set of* 4 2·75 2·75

(Des FOR Design. Litho Irish Security Stamp Ptg Ltd)

1998 (20 July). Cutty Sark *International Tall Ships Race, Dublin. T* **365** *and similar multicoloured designs. Chalk-surfaced paper.*

(*a*) *P* 14×15 (30*p*.) *or* 15×14 (45*p*, £1)
1185 30p. Type **365** 55 60
a. Pair. Nos. 1185/6 .. .. .. 1·10 1·25
b. Perf 15 .. .. 55 60
ba. Booklet pane. Nos. 1185b×2 and 1186b with margins all round .. 1·65
1186 30p. U.S.C.G. *Eagle* (cadet barque) .. 55 60
b. Perf 15 .. .. 55 60
ba. Booklet pane. Nos. 1186b/8b with margins all round .. .. .. 1·10
1187 45p. *Boa Esperanza* (caravel) (*horiz*) .. 80 85
b. Perf 15 .. .. 80 85
1188 £1 *Royalist* (training brigantine) (*horiz*) 1·75 1·90
b. Perf 15 .. .. 1·75 1·90
1185/8 .. .. *Set of* 4 3·50 3·75

(*b*) *Self-adhesive. P* 9½
1189 30p. *Boa Esperanza* (*horiz*) 55 60
a. Strip of 4. Nos. 1189/92 .. .. 2·10
1190 30p. Type **365** 55 60
1191 30p. U.S.C.G. *Eagle* 55 60
1192 30p. *Royalist* (*horiz*) 55 60
1189/92 .. .. *Set of* 4 2·10 2·25

Nos. 1185b/8b were only available from £2.65 stamp booklets.

Nos. 1189/92 are smaller, 34×23 or 23×34 mm, and occur, *se-tenant*, in strips of 4 or rolls of 100 with the surplus self-adhesive paper around each stamp retained.

Nos. 1185ba and 1186ba also exist overprinted for "Stampa 98".

366 Ashworth Pillarbox (1856)

367 Mary Immaculate College, Limerick

(Des M. Craig. Litho Irish Security Stamp Ptg Ltd)

1998 (3 Sept). *Irish Postboxes. T* **366** *and similar vert designs. Multicoloured. Chalk-surfaced paper. P* 15×14.
1193 30p. Type **366** 55 60
a. Horiz strip of 4. Nos. 1193/6 .. 2·10
1194 30p. Irish Free State wallbox (1922) .. 55 60
1195 30p. Double pillarbox (1899) 55 60
1196 30p. Penfold pillarbox (1866) 55 60
1193/6 .. .. *Set of* 4 2·10 2·40

Nos. 1193/6 were printed together, *se-tenant*, in horizontal strips of 4 throughout the sheet of 12.

(Des J. McPartlin (45p), E. Patton (others). Litho Irish Security Stamp Ptg Ltd)

1998 (3 Sept). *Anniversaries. T* **367** *and similar multicoloured designs. Chalk-surfaced paper. P* 14×15 (40*p*.) *or* 15×14 (*others*).
1197 30p. Type **367** (centenary) 55 60
1198 40p. Newtown School, Waterford (bicent) (*vert*) 70 75
1199 45p. Trumpeters (50th anniv of Universal Declaration of Human Rights) .. 80 85
1197/9 .. .. *Set of* 3 2·00 2·10

(Des FOR Design. Litho Security Stamp Ptg Ltd)

1998 (4 Sept). *"Portugal '98" International Stamp Exhibition, Lisbon. Sheet,* 101×71 *mm, containing design as No.* 1187. *Chalk-surfaced paper. P* 15×14.
MS1200 £2 *Boa Esperanza* (caravel) (*horiz*) .. 3·50 3·75

368 Cheetah

(Des F. O'Conner. Litho Walsall)

1998 (8 Oct). *Endangered Animals. T* **368** *and similar multicoloured designs. P* 14.
1201 30p. Type **368** 55 60
a. Horiz pair. Nos. 1201/2 .. .. 1·10 1·25
1202 30p. Scimitar-horned Oryx 55 60
1203 40p. Golden Lion Tamarin (*vert*) .. 70 75
1204 45p. Tiger (*vert*) 80 85
1201/4 .. .. *Set of* 4 2·50 2·75
MS1205 150×90 mm. As Nos. 1201/4. P 15 .. 2·50 2·75

Nos. 1201/4 were printed together, *se-tenant*, in horizontal pairs throughout the sheet.

No. **MS**1205 also exists with an enlarged top margin overprinted for "Stampa '98" National Stamp Exhibition, Dublin.

369 The Holy Family

370 Choir Boys

(Des P. Lynch (Nos. 1206/8), J. Laffan (No. 1209))

1998 (17 Nov). *Christmas. (a) Litho Irish Security Stamp Pt Ltd. T* **369** *and similar vert designs. Multicoloured. Chalk-surfaced paper. P* 14×15.
1206 30p. Type **369** 55 60
1207 32p. Shepherds 60 65
1208 45p. Three Kings 80 85
1206/8 .. .. *Set of* 3 1·90 2·1

(*b*) *Litho SNP Cambec, Australia. Self-adhesive. Phosphor frame. P* 11½
1209 30p. Type **370** 55 60
a. Booklet pane. No. 1209×20 .. 10·00

No. 1209, on which the phosphor frame appears greenish yellow under U.V. light, was only available from £5.40 stamp booklets.

371 Puppy and Heart

372 Micheál Mac Liammóir

(Des M. Connor. Litho Irish Security Stamp Ptg Ltd)

1999 (26 Jan). *Greetings Stamps. Pets. T* **371** *and similar vert designs. Multicoloured. Chalk-surfaced paper. Phosphor frame. P* 14×15.
1210 30p. Type **371** 55 60
a. Booklet pane. Nos. 1210/13 .. 2·10
1211 30p. Kitten and ball of wool 55 60
1212 30p. Goldfish 55 60
1213 30p. Rabbit with lettuce leaf 55 60
1210/13 .. .. *Set of* 4 2·10 2·40

Nos. 1211/13, on which the phosphor appears green under U.V. light, were only available from £2.40 stamp booklets containing two examples of No. 1210a. This pane exists in two different forms with either No. 1210 at left and No. 1213 at right or No. 1213 at left and No. 1210 at right. In each instance the right-hand stamp is imperforate at right. No. 1210 is available from both sheets and booklets.

(Des M. Connor. Litho Irish Security Stamp Ptg Ltd)

1999 (26 Jan). *Chinese New Year ("Year of the Rabbit"). Chalk-surfaced paper. Phosphor frame. P* 14×15.
MS1214 124×74 mm. Nos. 1211/13 .. .. 1·60 1·75

The example of No. 1213 is imperforate at right.

(Des Creative Inputs. Litho Irish Security Stamp Ptg Ltd)

1999 (16 Feb). *Irish Actors and Actresses. T* **372** *and similar vert designs. Chalk-surfaced paper. Phosphor frame. P* 14×15.
1215 30p. black and yellow-brown 55 60
1216 45p. black and bright green 80 85
1217 50p. black and ultramarine 90 95
1215/17 .. .. *Set of* 3 2·25 2·40

Designs: 45p. Siobhán McKenna; 50p. Noel Purcell.

373 Irish Emigrant Ship

(Des H. Paine and T. Mann. Litho Irish Security Stamp Ptg Ltd)

1999 (26 Feb). *Ireland–U.S.A. Joint Issue. Irish Emigration. Chalk-surfaced paper. Phosphor frame. P* 15×14.
1218 **373** 45p. multicoloured 80 85

A stamp in a similar design was issued by the U.S.A.

STAMP BOOKLETS

Nos. SB1 to SB24 are stitched. Subsequent booklets have eir panes attached by the selvedge, *unless otherwise stated.*

B 1 Harp and Monogram

B 2 Harp and "EIRE"

31 (21 Aug)–**40.** *Black on red cover as Type* B **1**.
31 2s. booklet containing six ½d., six 2d. (Nos. 71, 74), each in block of 6, and nine 1d. (No. 72) in block of 6 and pane of 3 stamps and 3 labels (No. 72d or 72dw) .. .. .. *From* £1900
Edition Nos.:—31–1, 31–2, 32–3, 33–4, 33–5, 34–6, 34–7, 35–8, 35–9, 36–10, 36–11, 37–12, 37–13, 37–14, 15–38, 16–38, 17–38,
a. Cover as Type B 2
Edition Nos.:—18–39, 19–39, 20–39, 21–40, 22–40

40. *Black on red cover as Type* B **2**.
32 2s. booklet containing six ½d., six 2d. (Nos. 71, 74), each in block of 6, and nine 1d. (No. 72) in block of 6 and pane of 3 stamps and 3 labels (No. 112d or 112dw) £6500
Edition No.:—22–40

940. *Black on red cover as Type* B **2**.
B3 2s. booklet containing six ½d., six 2d. (Nos. 111, 114), each in block of 6, and nine 1d. (No. 112) in block of 6 and pane of 3 stamps and 3 labels (No. 112d or 112dw) £6500
Edition No.:—23–40

941–44. *Black on red cover as Type* B **2**.
B4 2s. booklet containing twelve ½d., six 1d. and six 2d. (Nos. 111/12, 114) in blocks of 6 .. .. £750
Edition Nos.:—24–41, 25–42, 26–44

B 3

945. *Black on red cover as Type* B **3**.
B5 2s. booklet containing twelve ½d., six 1d. and six 2d. (Nos. 111/12, 114) in blocks of 6 .. .. £650
Edition No.:—27–45

946. *Black on buff cover as Type* B **2**.
B6 2s. booklet containing twelve ½d., six 1d. and six 2d. (Nos. 111/12, 114) in blocks of 6 .. .. £475
Edition No.:—28–46

946–47. *Black on buff cover as Type* B **2**.
B7 2s. booklet containing twelve ½d., six 1d. and six 2d. (Nos. 133, 112, 114) in blocks of 6 .. *From* £225
Edition Nos.:—29–46, 30–47

B 4 Harp only

1948–50. *Black on red cover as Type* B **4**.
SB8 2s. 6d. booklet containing six ½d., twelve 1d. and six 2½d. (Nos. 133, 112, 115) in blocks of 6 .. £120
Edition Nos.:—31–48, 32–49, 33–50

1951–53. *Black on buff cover as Type* B **4**.
SB9 2s. 6d. booklet containing six ½d., twelve 1d. and six 2½d. (Nos. 133, 112, 115) in blocks of 6 .. 55·00
Edition Nos.:—34–51, 35–52, 36–53

1954 (24 Nov). *Black on buff cover as Type* B **4**.
SB10 4s. booklet containing six ½d., six 1½d. and twelve 3d. (Nos. 133, 113, 116) in blocks of 6 £110
Edition No.:—37–54

1956 (17 Dec). *Black on buff cover as Type* B **4**.
SB11 4s. booklet containing twelve 1d. and twelve 3d. (Nos. 112, 116) in blocks of 6 .. .. 60·00
Edition No.:—38–56

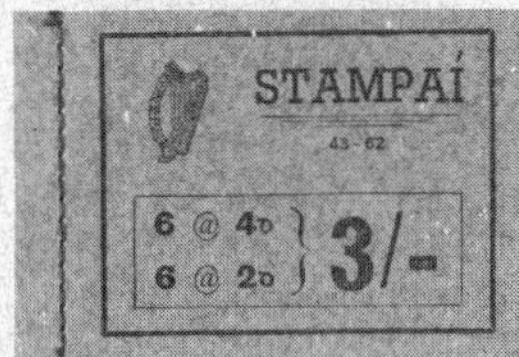

B 5

1958–61. *Black on buff cover as Type* B **5**.
SB12 4s. booklet containing twelve 1d. and twelve 3d. (Nos. 112, 116) in blocks of 6 .. .. 60·00
Edition Nos.:—39–58, 40–59, 41–60, 42–61

1962 (23 Oct)–**63.** *Black on buff cover as Type* B **5**.
SB13 3s. booklet containing six 2d. and six 4d. (Nos. 114, 117) in blocks of 6 .. .. *From* 55·00
Edition Nos.:—43–62, 44–63 (June)

B 6

1964 (Sept). *Red on yellow cover as Type* B **6**.
SB14 3s. booklet containing twelve 1d. and six 4d. (Nos. 112, 117) in blocks of 6 .. .. 35·00

B 7

1966 (1–9 Dec). *Covers as Type* B **7** *in red* (*No.* SB15), *blue* (*No.* SB16) *or green* (*No* SB17).
SB15 2s. 6d. booklet containing six 2d. and six 3d. (Nos. 114, 116) in blocks of 6 (9 Dec) .. 20·00
SB16 2s. 6d. booklet containing six 5d. (No. 228) in block of 6 (9 Dec) .. .. 15·00
SB17 5s. booklet containing twelve 5d. (No. 228) in blocks of 6 .. .. 30·00

B 8

1969 (12 Sept). *Plain blue-green cover as Type* B **8**.
SB18 6s. booklet containing twelve 6d. (No. 253) in blocks of six .. .. 40·00

1971 (15 Feb). *Plain slate-green cover as Type* B **8**.
SB19 30p. booklet containing six ½p., twelve 1p. and six 2½p. in panes of 6 (Nos. 287ab or 287awb, 288ca or 288cwa, 291ba or 291bwa) 32·00

1974 (11 Mar). *Green cover as Type* B **8**.
SB20 50p. booklet containing ten 5p. in panes of 5 stamps and 1 label (No. 295ad or 295adw) 24·00

1974 (11 Mar). *Blue cover as Type* B **8**.
SB21 50p. booklet containing five 1p. in pane of 5 stamps and 1 label (No. 288cb or 288cwb), six 2½p. and six 5p. in panes of 6 (Nos. 291ba or 291bwa, 295ae or 295awe) .. 11·00

1975 (27 Jan). *Covers as Type* B **8**, *in rose* (*No.* SB22) *or light grey* (*No.* SB23).
SB22 40p. booklet containing five 1p., 2p. and 5p. each in panes of 5 stamps and 1 label (Nos. 288cb or 288cwb, 290ba or 290bwa, 295ad or 295awd) .. .. 3·50
SB23 70p. booklet containing ten 2p. and 5p. each in panes of 5 stamps and 1 label (Nos. 290ba or 290bwa, 295ad or 295awd) .. .. 4·50

1977 (21 Mar). *Yellow-olive cover similar to Type* B **8**.
SB24 50p. booklet containing five 1p., 2p. and 7p. each in panes of 5 stamps and 1 label (Nos. 288cb or 288cwb, 290ba or 290bwa, 348a) .. 10·00

B 9 Four Courts

1983 (15 Aug). *Yellow-green cover as Type* B **9**.
SB25 £1 booklet containing *se-tenant* pane of 7 stamps and 1 label (No. 535a) .. .. .. 2·50

No. SB25 was an experimental issue available from two machines, accepting two 50p. coins, at the G.P.O. Dublin, and from the Philatelic Bureau.

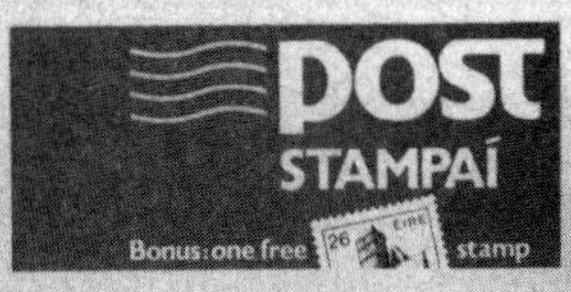

B 10

1984 (9 July). *Dull green, greenish yellow and black cover as Type* B **10**.
SB26 £2 booklet containing *se-tenant* pane of 12 (No. 535ba) .. .. 6·50

No. SB26 actually contains £2.26 worth of stamps, but was sold at a discount of 26p. by the Irish Post Office from 9 July until 10 August.

B 11 Custom House, Dublin, in 19th Century

1985 (27 June). *Yellowish green cover as Type* B **11**.
SB27 £1 booklet containing *se-tenant* pane of 6 (No. 533ab) .. .. 5·50

B 12

1985 (27 June). *Bright green cover as Type* B **12**.
SB28 £2 booklet containing *se-tenant* pane of 12 (No. 533ac) .. .. 9·00

B 13

1986 (8 Sept). *Black, light green and pale yellow cover as Type* B **13**.
SB29 £2 booklet containing *se-tenant* pane of 12 (No. 533ad) .. .. 9·00

B 14 Custom House, Dublin
(Illustration further reduced. Actual size 137×70 mm)

1988 (1 Mar). *Dublin Millenium. Multicoloured cover as Type* B **14**.
SB30 £2.24, booklet containing eight 24p. in panes of 4 (No. 688a) (one inscr in Irish, one in English) 7·00
No. SB30 also exists with the booklet cover overprinted for "SPRING STAMPEX 1988", "7 Internationale Briefmarken-Messe" (Essen), "FINLANDIA 88" and "SYDPEX 88" exhibitions.

1988 (24 Nov). *Maroon and black cover as Type* B **11**, *but showing Courthouse, Cork.*
SB31 £2 booklet containing *se-tenant* pane of 12 (No. 533ae) .. .. 10·00

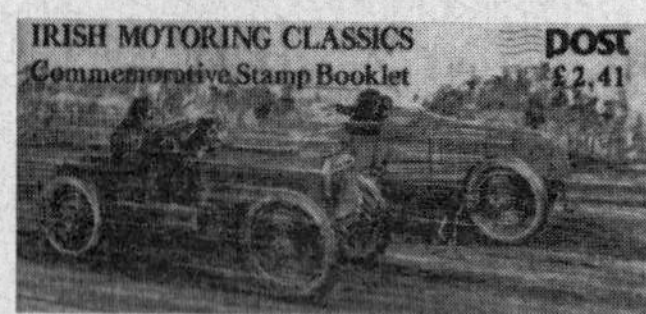

B 15 Gordon Bennett Race, 1903
(Illustration further reduced. Actual size 132×60 mm)

1989 (11 Apr). *Irish Motoring Classics. Multicoloured cover as Type* B **15**.
SB32 £2.41, booklet containing two different *se-tenant* panes of 4 (Nos. 718a/b) .. .. .. 6·50

B 16 8th-century Gilt-silver Brooch
(Illustration further reduced. Actual size 160×100 mm)

1989 (15 June). 1300*th Death Anniv of Saints Kilian, Totnan and Colman. Multicoloured cover as Type* B **16**. *Stitched.*
SB33 £4.48, booklet containing sixteen 28p. in panes of 4 (No. 726a) .. .. 11·00
No. SB33 exists overprinted for "PHILEXFRANCE 89" or "WORLD STAMP EXPO '89".

B 17 *(Illustration further reduced. Actual size 136×74 mm)*

1990 (22 Mar). *Greetings Booklet. Multicoloured cover as Type* B **17**. *Stitched.*
SB34 £1.98, booklet containing two *se-tenant* panes of 4 (No. 766a) and eight greetings labels .. 15·00
No. SB34 was sold at £1.98, providing a discount of 26p. off the face value of the stamps.

B 18 *(Illustration further reduced. Actual size 161×99 mm)*

1990 (3 May). 150th *Anniv of the Penny Black. Multicoloured cover as Type* B **18**. *Stitched.*
SB35 £6 booklet containing *se-tenant* panes of 8, 4 and 5 (Nos. 535ca, 547ba/bb and pane of 4 (No. 774a) 50·00
No. SB25 exists overprinted for "Stamp World London 90" exhibition.

B 19 Garden at Powerscourt, Co. Wicklow
(Illustration further reduced. Actual size 150×75 mm)

1990 (30 Aug). *Garden Flowers. Multicoloured cover as Type* B **19**. *Stitched.*
SB36 £2.59, booklet containing two different *se-tenant* panes of 4 (Nos. 781a/b) .. .. .. 10·00

B 20 7th-century Tara Brooch

1990 (15 Nov). *Irish Heritage. Black and bright blue cover as Type* B **20**.
SB37 £1 booklet containing *se-tenant* pane of 7 stamps and 1 label (No. 747ab) .. .. .. 3·00

B 21 View of Dublin
(Illustration further reduced. Actual size 140×85 mm)

1991 (11 Apr). *"Dublin 1991 European City of Culture". Multicoloured cover as Type* B **21**.
SB38 £2.60, booklet containing two different *se-tenant* panes of 3 (Nos. 800a/b) .. .. .. 8·50

B 22 Ardagh Chalice

1991 (14 May)–**92**. *Covers as Type* B **22**.
SB39 £1 booklet containing *se-tenant* pane of 5 stamps and 1 label (No. 808a) (black and green cover as Type B 22) .. .. 1·75
SB40 £1 booklet containing *se-tenant* pane of 5 stamps and 1 label (No. 808a) (black and orange-yellow cover showing St. Patrick's Bell Shrine) (25.2.92) .. .. 1·75

B 23 *(Illustration further reduced. Actual size 161×99 mm)*

1991 (17 Oct). *Fishing Fleet. Multicoloured cover as Type* B **23**. *Stitched.*
SB41 £5 booklet containing *se-tenant* panes of 5 and 7 and 1 label (Nos. 747ac, 748ba) and two different *se-tenant* panes of 4 (Nos. 819a/b) 20·00

B 24 *(Illustration further reduced. Actual size 138×75 mm)*

1992 (2 Apr). *Greetings Booklet. Multicoloured cover as Typ* B **24**. *Stitched.*
SB42 £2.40, booklet containing two *se-tenant* panes of 4 (No. 840a) and eight greetings labels .. 10·0

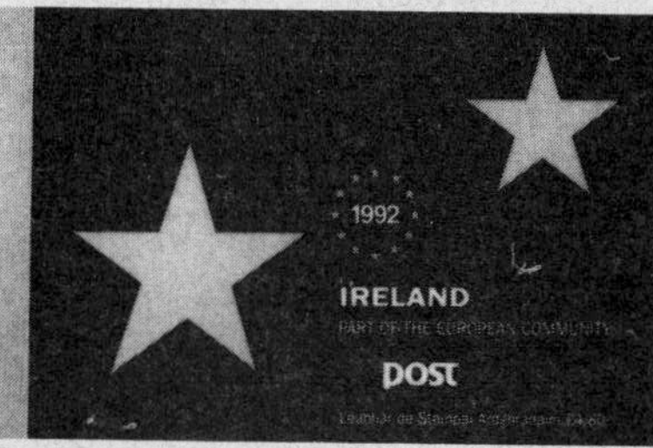

B **25** *(Illustration further reduced. Actual size 161×100 mm)*

1992 (15 Oct). *Single European Market. Deep bluish violet an greenish yellow cover as Type* B **25**. *Stitched.*
SB43 £4.80, booklet containing fifteen 32p. in three panes of 4 (No. 856a) and one pane of 3 (No. 856b) .. .. 11·0

B **26** "Banks of the Seine, near Paris" (N. Hone)
(Illustration further reduced. Actual size 161×100 mm)

1993 (4 Mar). *Irish Impressionist Painters. Multicoloure cover as Type* B **26**. *Stitched.*
SB44 £4.68, booklet containing four *se-tenant* panes (Nos. 867a×2, 867b and 869a) .. .. 11·5

B **27** Lismore Crozier

1993 (24 Sept)–**95**. *Covers as Type* B **27**.
SB45 £1 booklet containing *se-tenant* pane of 4 (No. 748ca) (bright greenish blue cover as Type B 27) .. .. 1·75
SB46 £1 booklet containing *se-tenant* pane of 4 (No. 748cb) (black and bright vermilion cover showing enamelled latchet brooch) (2.3.94) 1·75
SB46*a* £1 booklet containing *se-tenant* pane of 4 (No. 748cb) (black and bright orange-red cover showing Gleninsheen Collar) (28.2.95) .. 1·75
SB46*b* £1 booklet containing *se-tenant* pane of 4 (No. 748a) (black and bright reddish violet cover showing Broighter Collar) (16.11.95) .. 1·75

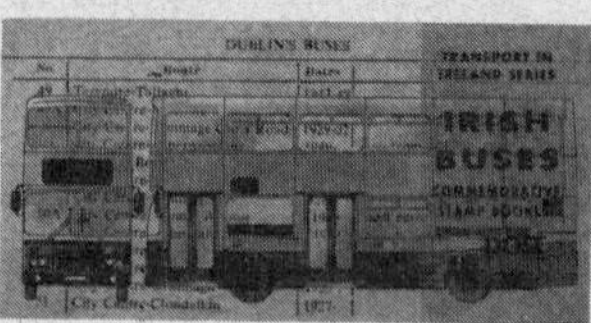

B **28** Front and Side View of Dublin Bus Leyland Olympian
(Illustration further reduced. Actual size 131×61 mm)

1993 (12 Oct). *Irish Buses. Multicoloured cover as Type* B **28**. *Stitched.*
SB47 £2.84, booklet containing two different *se-tenant* panes (Nos. 886a/b) .. .. 8·00

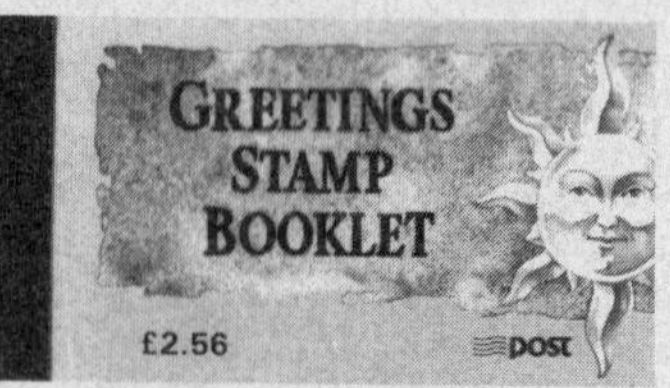

B **29** *(Illustration further reduced. Actual size 138×75 mm)*

1994 (27 Jan). *Greetings Booklet. Multicoloured cover as Type* B **29**. *Stitched.*
SB48 £2.56, booklet containing two *se-tenant* panes of four 32p. (No. 896a) .. .. 8·50

B 30 (*Illustration further reduced. Actual size* 137×60 *mm*)

994 (27 Apr). *Parliamentary Anniversaries. Multicoloured cover as Type* B **30**. *Stitched.*
B49 £1.92, booklet containing two different *se-tenant* panes (Nos. 908a/b) .. .. 7·00

B 31 (*Illustration further reduced. Actual size* 161×101 *mm*)

994 (18 Oct). *Irish Nobel Prizewinners. Multicoloured cover as Type* B **31**. *Stitched.*
B50 £4.84, booklet containing four different *se-tenant* panes (Nos. 928b/d and 930a) .. .. 11·50

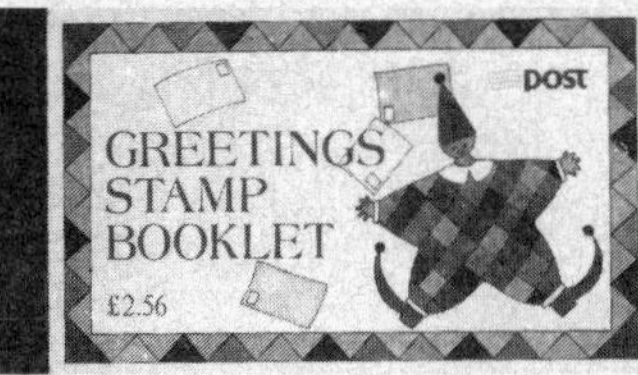

B 32 (*Illustration further reduced. Actual size* 138×75 *mm*)

995 (24 Jan). *Greetings Booklet. Multicoloured cover as Type* B **32**. *Stitched.*
B51 £2.56, booklet containing two *se-tenant* panes of four 32p. (No. 936a) .. .. .. 8·50

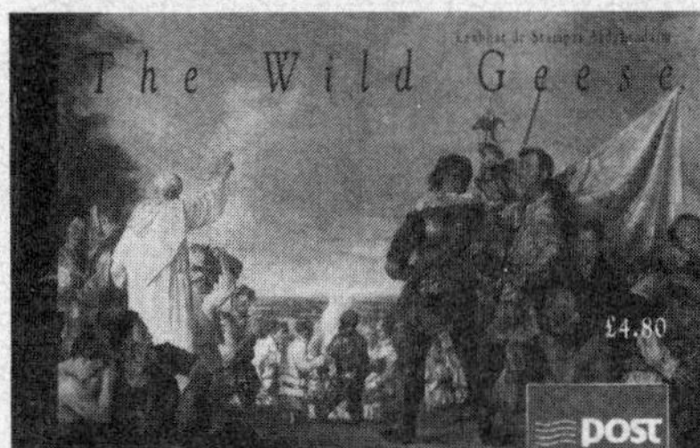

B **33** Blessing before Battle
(*Illustration reduced. Actual size* 161×100 *mm*)

995 (15 May). *Military Uniforms. Multicoloured cover as Type* B **33**. *Stitched.*
B52 £4.80, booklet containing four different *se-tenant* panes (Nos. 954a/d) .. .. 11·50

B 34 (*Illustration reduced. Actual size* 140×82 *mm*)

1995 (9 Oct). *Bicentenary of National Botanic Gardens, Glasnevin. Multicoloured cover as Type* B **34**. *Stitched.*
SB53 £2.60, booklet containing two different *se-tenant* panes (Nos. 973a/b) .. .. 9·00

MINIMUM PRICE

The minimum price quote is 10p which represents a handling charge rather than a basis for valuing common stamps. For further notes about prices see introductory pages.

B **35** (*Illustration reduced. Actual size* 137 x 74 *mm*)

1996 (23 Jan). *Greetings Booklet. Multicoloured cover as Type* B **35**. *Stitched.*
SB54 £2.56, booklet containing two *se-tenant* panes of four 32p. (No. 982a) .. .. .. 10·00

B **36** Steeplechasing
(*Illustration reduced. Actual size* 161×100 *mm*)

1996 (12 Mar). *Irish Horse Racing. Multicoloured cover as Type* B **36**. *Stitched.*
SB55 £4.92, booklet containing four different *se-tenant* panes (Nos. 991a, 992b/c and 993a) .. 16·00

B **37** Coastal Patrol Vessel and Sailor
(*Illustration reduced. Actual size* 150×90 *mm*)

(Des Design Image)

1996 (18 July). *50th Anniv of Irish Naval Service. Multicoloured cover as Type* B **37**. *Stitched.*
SB56 £2.24, booklet containing pane of three 32p. and pane of three values *se-tenant* (Nos. 1013a/b) 5·50

B **38** Farmyard Animals
(*Illustration reduced. Actual size* 137×73 *mm*)

1997 (28 Jan). *Greetings Booklet. Multicoloured cover as Type* B **38**. *Stitched.*
SB57 £2.56, booklet containing two *se-tenant* panes of four 32p. (No. 1100a) .. .. .. 7·50

B **39** Robin

1997 (6 Mar). *Birds. Multicoloured cover as Type* B **39**. *Stamps attached by selvedge.*
SB58 £1 booklet containing pane of 4 (2×2) (No. 748bb) .. .. 1·75

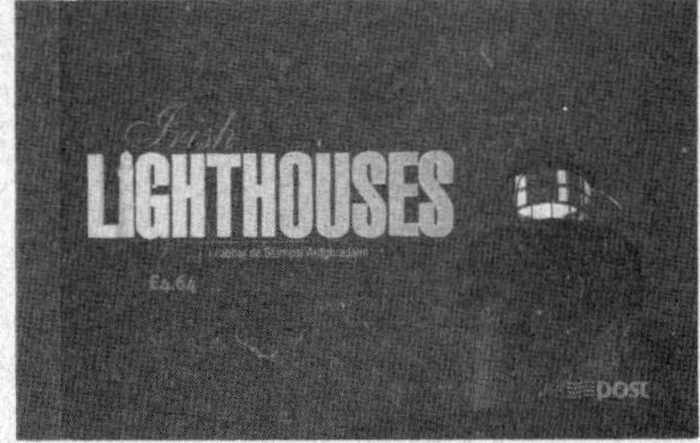

B **40** The Baily Lighthouse
(*Illustration reduced. Actual size* 160×100 *mm*)

1997 (1 July). *Lighthouses. Multicoloured cover as Type* B **40**. *Stitched.*
SB59 £4.64, booklet containing four different, *se-tenant*, panes (Nos. 1136b/c, 1036da and 1038da) .. .. 10·00

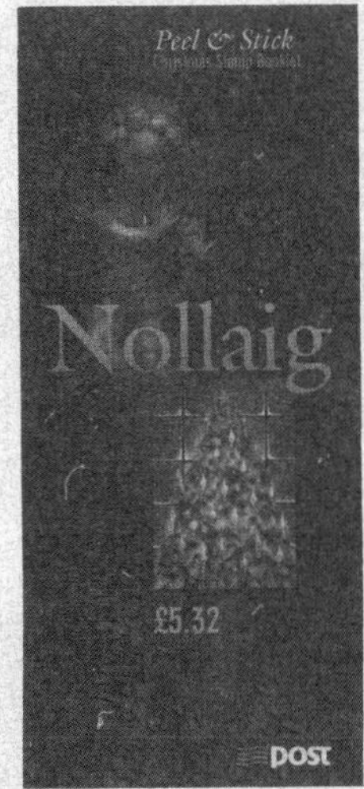

B **41** Christmas Tree

1997 (18 Nov). *Christmas. Multicoloured cover as Type* B **41**. *Self-adhesive.*
SB60 £5.32, booklet containing pane of twenty 28p. (2×10) (No. 1149a) .. .. 10·00

No. SB60 was sold at £5.32 providing a discount of 28p. off the face value of the stamps.

1997 (6 Dec). *Multicoloured cover as Type* B **39** *showing Peregrine Falcon. Stamps attached by selvedge.*
SB61 £1 booklet containing pane of 4 (2×2) (No. 1080a) .. .. 1·75

B **42** On Swing
(*Illustration further reduced. Actual size* 138×74 *mm*)

1998 (26 Jan). *Greetings Booklet. Multicoloured cover as Type* B **42**. *Stitched.*
SB62 £2.56, booklet containing two different *se-tenant* panes of four 32p. (No. 1150a) .. .. 6·50

B **43** Early Aeroplane and Map
(*Illustration further reduced. Actual size* 160×100 *mm*)

1998 (24 Feb). *Pioneers of Irish Aviation. Multicoloured cover as Type* B **43**. *Stitched.*
SB63 $5.20, booklet containing four different, *se-tenant*, panes (Nos. 1155a/b and 1156a/b) 11·00

B 44 Blackbird

1998 (2 Apr). *Multicoloured cover as Type* B **44**. *Stamps attached by selvedge.*

SB64	£1 booklet containing pane of 5 stamps and 1 label (No. 1081a)	1·75

1998 (6 May). *Greetings Booklet. Multicoloured cover as Type* B **42**, *but inscribed* "LETTER POST" *in green border at foot. Stitched.*

SB65	£2.40, booklet containing two different *se-tenant* panes of four 30p. (No. 1173a)	5·00

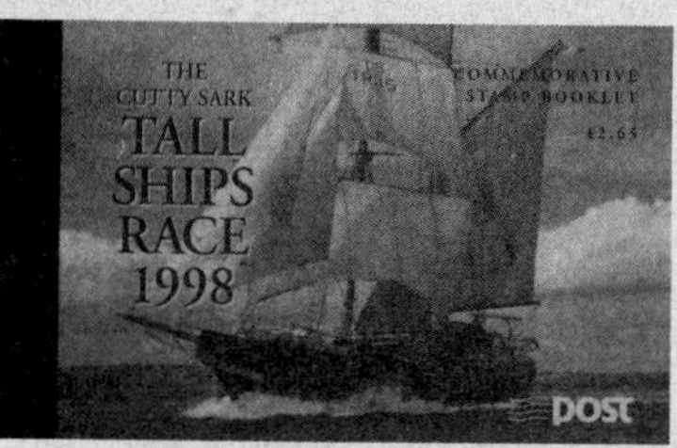

B **45** *Asgard II* (cadet brigantine)
(*illustration reduced. Actual size* 138×89 *mm*)

1998 (20 July). Cutty Sark *International Tall Ships Race, Dublin. Multicoloured cover as Type* B **45**. *Stitched.*

SB66	£2.65, booklet containing two different *se-tenant* panes of 3 (Nos. 1185ba and 1186ba)	4·50

B **46** Blackbird

1998 (4 Sept)–**99.** *Multicoloured cover as Type* B **46**. *Stamps attached by selvedge.*

SB67	£3 booklet containing pane of 10 (5×2) 30p. stamps (No. 1038ab)	5·50
	a. Containing pane No. 1038ar (stamps with phosphor frames) (3.99)	5·50

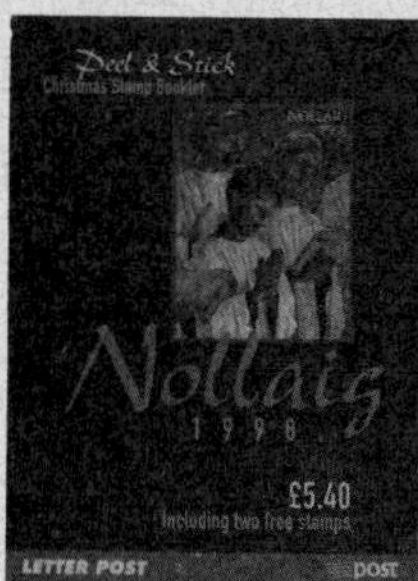

B **47** Choir Boys

1998 (17 Nov). *Christmas. Multicoloured cover as Type* B **47**. *Self-adhesive.*

SB68	£5.40, booklet containing pane of twenty 30p. (5×4) (No. 1209a)	10·00

No. SB68 was sold at £5.40 providing a discount of 60p. off the face value of the stamps.

B **48** Domestic Pets
(*Illustration reduced. Actual size* 139×73 *mm*)

1999 (26 Jan). *Greetings Booklet. Pets. Multicoloured cover as Type* B **48**. *Stitched.*

SB69	£2.40, booklet containing two different *se-tenant* panes of four 30p. (No. 1210a)	4·00

B **49** Goldcrest

1999 (16 Feb). *Multicoloured cover as Type* B **49**. *Stamps attached by selvedge.*

SB70	£1 booklet containing pane of 5 stamps and 1 label (No. 1081ba)	1·75

POSTAGE DUE STAMPS

From 1922 to 1925 Great Britain postage due stamps in both script and block watermarks were used without overprint.

D 1

D 2

D 3

(Des Ruby McConnell. Typo Govt Printing Works, Dublin)

1925 (20 Feb). *W* **10**. *P* 14×15.

D1	D **1**	½d. emerald-green	12·00	16·00
D2		1d. carmine	15·00	3·00
		a. Wmk sideways	£550	£225
		w. Wmk inverted	£225	30·00
D3		2d. deep green	28·00	5·50
		a. Wmk sideways	45·00	15·00
		w. Wmk inverted	70·00	23·00
D4		6d. plum	6·00	6·50
D1/4		*Set of* 4	55·00	28·00

1940–70. *W* **22**. *P* 14×15.

D 5	D **1**	½d. emerald-green (1942)	35·00	22·00
		w. Wmk inverted	£225	£120
D 6		1d. carmine (1941)	1·25	70
		w. Wmk inverted	55·00	6·50
D 7		1½d. vermilion (1953)	1·75	6·50
		w. Wmk inverted	15·00	21·00
D 8		2d. deep green (1940)	2·75	70
		w. Wmk inverted	20·00	6·50
D 9		3d. blue (10.11.52)	2·25	2·75
		w. Wmk inverted	6·00	5·00
D10		5d. blue-violet (3.3.43)	4·50	3·00
		w. Wmk inverted	6·50	7·00
D11		6d. plum (21.3.60)	3·00	2·00
		a. Wmk sideways (1968)	70	85
D12		8d. orange (30.10.62)	8·50	8·00
		w. Wmk inverted	17·00	18·00
D13		10d. bright purple (27.1.65)	8·50	7·50
D14		1s. apple-green (10.2.69)	6·00	9·00
		a. Wmk sideways (1970)	65·00	8·50
D5/14		*Set of* 10	65·00	55·00

1971 (15 Feb). *As Nos.* D5/14, *but with values in decimal currency and colours changed. W* **22.** *P* 14 × 15.

D15	D **1**	1p. sepia	30	60
		a. Wmk sideways	1·75	1·50
		w. Wmk inverted	1·00	1·50
D16		1½p. light emerald	50	1·50
D17		3p. stone	90	1·75
		w. Wmk inverted	1·25	2·00
D18		4p. orange	90	1·25
D19		5p. greenish blue	95	2·50
		w. Wmk inverted	2·00	3·00
D20		7p. bright yellow	40	3·50
		w. Wmk inverted	1·50	3·50
D21		8p. scarlet	40	2·50
D15/21		*Set of* 7	3·75	12·00

1978 (20 Mar). *As Nos.* D17/19, *but no wmk. Chalk-surfaced paper. P* 14×15.

D22	D **1**	3p. stone	1·50	5·00
D23		4p. orange	6·00	8·00
D24		5p. greenish blue	1·50	4·00
D22/4		*Set of* 3	8·00	15·00

1980 (11 June)–**85**. *Photo. Chalk-surfaced paper. P* 15.

D25	D **2**	1p. apple green	30	55
D26		2p. dull blue	30	55
D27		4p. myrtle-green	40	55
D28		6p flesh	40	70
D29		8p. chalky blue	40	75
D30		18p. green	75	1·25
D31		20p. Indian red (22.8.85)	2·25	4·50
D32		24p. bright yellowish green	75	2·00
D33		30p. deep violet blue (22.8.85)	3·00	5·50
D34		50p. cerise (22.8.85)	3·75	6·50
D25/34		*Set of* 10	11·00	20·00

The 1p. to 18p. are on white paper and the 20p., 30p. and 50p. on cream. The 24p. value exists on both types of paper.

(Des Q Design. Litho Irish Security Stamp Ptg Ltd)

1988 (6 Oct). *Chalk-surfaced paper. P* 14 × 15.

D35	D **3**	1p. black, orange-vermilion & lemon	10	10
D36		2p. black, orange-verm & purple-brn	10	10
D37		3p. black, orange-vermilion and plum	10	10
D38		4p. black, orange-vermilion & brt vio	10	10
D39		5p. black, orge-vermilion & royal blue	10	10
D40		17p. black, orange-verm & dp yell-grn	30	35
D41		20p. black, orange-vermilion & slate-bl	35	40
D42		24p. black, orange-verm & dp turq-grn	40	45
D43		30p. black, orange-vermilion & dp grey	50	55
D44		50p. black, orge-verm & brownish grey	90	95
D45		£1 black, orge-vermilion & bistre-brn	1·75	1·90
D35/45		*Set of* 11	4·50	5·00

From 20 September 1993 labels in the above style were use to indicate postage due charges in the Dublin 2 delivery area They are dispensed by a Pitney/Bowes machine, in much th same way as a meter mark, and can show any face valu between 1p. and I£99.99. Such labels are not normall postmarked. Labels with face values of 32p. and 50p. were sol to collectors by the Philatelic Bureau.

THOMOND AND LONG ISLAND

Labels inscribed "Principality of Thomond" appeared on th philatelic market in the early 1960s. Thomond is the name of district in western Ireland. The area does not have its own adminis tration or postal service and the labels were not recognised by th Department of Posts & Telegraphs, Dublin.

Local carriage labels were issued for Long Island, County Cor in April 1973; they were intended to cover the cost of taking ma from the island to the nearest mainland post office. A local servic operated for a few weeks before it was suppressed by the Irish Pos Office. As the stamps were not accepted for national or inter national mail they are not listed here.

Addenda

GREAT BRITAIN

'd to Nos. 1663*a*/4*b*:

(Photo Walsall)

›64*a* **914** (1st) brt orge-red) (2 phosphor bands) (4.4.95))
am. Booklet pane. No. 1664*a*×4 plus commemorative label at right (12.5.99) .. .. .. 1·60

No. 1664am includes a commemorative label for the 50th ›iversary of the Berlin Airlift.

ld to No. 2085:

(Photo Walsall)

085 **1396** 26p. greenish yellow, magenta, new blue, grey-black and silver)
a. Booklet pane. Nos. 2085 and 2089 with margins all round (12.5.99) 80

1407 Prince Edward and Miss Sophie Rhys-Jones

1408

Adapted J. Gibbs from photos by John Swannell. Photo D.L.R.)

999 (15 June). *Royal Wedding. Two phosphor bands. P* 15×14.
096 **1407** 26p. vermilion, black, grey-blk & silver 40 45
2097 **1408** 64p. new blue, black, grey-blk & silver 1·00 1·10

ANGUILLA

184 Roasting Corn-cobs on Fire

(Litho Cot Printery, Ltd, Barbados)

1998 (18 Nov). *Christmas. "Hidden Beauty of Anguilla". T* **184** *and similar horiz designs showing children's paintings. Multicoloured. P* 14.
1021 15 c. Type **184** 10 10
1022 $1 Fresh fruit and market stallholder .. 45 50
1023 $1.50, Underwater scene 65 70
1024 $3 Cacti and view of sea .. .. 1·25 1·40
1021/4 .. .. *Set of* 4 2·40 2·50

185 University of West Indies Centre, Anguilla

(Litho Cartor)

1998 (31 Dec). *50th Anniv of University of West Indies. T* **185** *and similar horiz design. Multicoloured. P* 13½.
1025 $1.50, Type **185** 65 70
1026 $1.90, Man with torch and University arms 80 85

186 Sopwith Camel and Bristol F2B Fighters

(Des R. Vigurs. Litho Cartor)

1998 (31 Dec). *80th Anniv of Royal Air Force. T* **186** *and similar horiz designs. Multicoloured. P* 13½.
1027 30 c. Type **186** 15 20
1028 $1 Supermarine Spitfire Mk II and Hawker Hurricane Mk I 45 50
1029 $1.50, Avro Lancaster 65 70
1030 $1.90, Panavia Tornado F3 and Harrier GR7 .. .. 80 85
1027/30 .. .. *Set of* 4 2·00 2·25

ANTIGUA

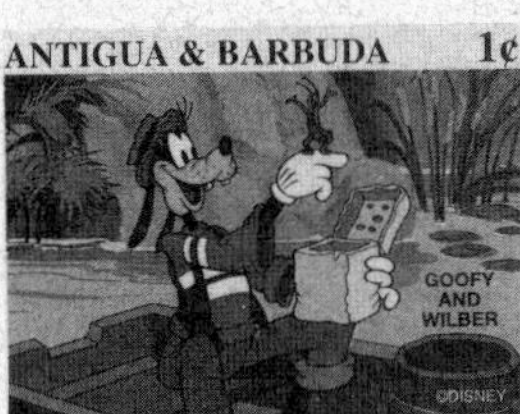

371 Goofy and Wilbur

(Litho Questa)

1997 (17 Feb). *Walt Disney Cartoon Characters. T* **371** *and similar multicoloured designs. P* 14×13½.
2394 1 c. Type **371** 10 10
2395 2 c. Donald and Goofy in boxing ring .. 10 10
2396 5 c. Donald, Panchito and Jose Carioca 10 10
2397 10 c. Mickey and Goofy playing chess .. 10 10
2398 15 c. Chip and Dale with acorns 10 10
2399 20 c. Pluto and Mickey 10 15
2400 $1 Daisy and Minnie eating ice-cream 45 50
2401 $2 Daisy and Minnie at dressing table 85 90
2402 $3 Gus Goose and Donald .. .. 1·25 1·40
2394/402 .. .. *Set of* 9 3·00 3·25
MS2403 Two sheets. (a) 102×127 mm. $6 Goofy. P 14×13½. (b) 127×102 mm. $6 Donald Duck playing guitar (*vert*). P 13½×14 *Set of* 2 *sheets* 5·25 5·50

396 Ford, 1896

1998 (1 Sept). *Classic Cars. T* **396** *and similar horiz designs. Multicoloured. Litho. P* 14.
2687 $1.65, Type **396** 70 75
a. Sheetlet. Nos. 2687/92 .. .. 4·00
2688 $1.65, Ford A, 1903 .. .. .. 70 75
2689 $1.65, Ford T, 1928 .. .. .. 70 75
2690 $1.65, Ford T, 1922 .. .. .. 70 75
2691 $1.65, Ford Blackhawk, 1929 .. .. 70 75
2692 $1.65, Ford Sedan, 1934 .. .. .. 70 75
2693 $1.65, Torpedo, 1911 .. .. .. 70 75
a. Sheetlet. Nos. 2693/8 .. .. 4·00
2694 $1.65, Mercedes 22, 1913 .. .. 70 75
2695 $1.65, Rover, 1920 .. .. .. 70 75
2696 $1.65, Mercedes-Benz, 1956 .. .. 70 75
2697 $1.65, Packard V-12, 1934 .. .. 70 75
2698 $1.65, Opel, 1924 .. .. .. 70 75
2687/98 .. .. *Set of* 12 8·00 9·00
MS2699 Two sheets, each 70×100 mm. (a) $6 Ford, 1908 (60×40 *mm*). (b) $6 Ford, 1929 (60×40 *mm*). P 14×14½ .. *Set of* 2 *sheets* 5·00 5·25

Nos. 2687/92 and 2693/8 were each printed together, *se-tenant*, in sheetlets of 6.

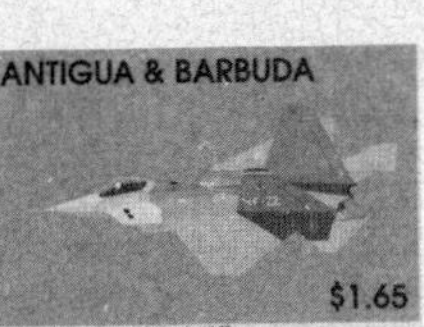

397 Lockheed-Boeing General Dynamics Yf-22

398 Karl Benz (internal-combustion engine)

1998 (22 Sept). *Modern Aircraft. T* **397** *and similar horiz designs. Multicoloured. Litho. P* 14.
2700 $1.65, Type **397** 70 75
a. Sheetlet. Nos. 2700/5 .. .. 4·00
2701 $1.65, Dassault-Breguet Rafale BO 1 .. 70 75
2702 $1.65, MiG 29 .. .. 70 75
2703 $1.65, Dassault-Breguet Mirage 2000D .. 70 75
2704 $1.65, Rockwell B-1B "Lancer" 70 75
2705 $1.65, McDonnell-Douglas C-17A .. 70 75
2706 $1.65, Space Shuttle 70 75
a. Sheetlet. Nos. 2706/11 .. .. 4·00
2707 $1.65, SAAB "Grippen" 70 75
2708 $1.65, Eurofighter EF-2000 .. .. 70 75
2709 $1.65, Sukhoi SU 27 .. .. .. 70 75
2710 $1.65, Northrop B-2 .. .. .. 70 75
2711 $1.65, Lockheed F-117 "Nighthawk" .. 70 75
2700/11 .. .. *Set of* 12 8·00 9·00
MS2712 Two sheets, each 110×85 mm. (a) $6 F18 Hornet. (b) $6 Sukhoi SU 35 *Set of* 2 *sheets* 5·00 5·25

Nos. 2700/5 and 2706/11 were each printed together, *se-tenant*, in sheetlets of 6.

No. **MS**2712b is inscribed "Sukhi" in error.

1998 (10 Nov). *Millennium Series. Famous People of the Twentieth Century. Inventors. T* **398** *and similar multicoloured designs. Litho. P* 14.
2713 $1 Type **398** 45 50
a. Sheetlet. Nos. 2713/20 .. .. 3·50
2714 $1 Early Benz car and Mercedes-Benz racing car (53×38 *mm*) 45 50
2715 $1 Atom bomb mushroom cloud (53×38 *mm*) 45 50
2716 $1 Albert Einstein (theory of relativity) 45 50
2717 $1 Leopold Godowsky Jr. and Leopold Damrosch Mannes (Kodachrome film) 45 50
2718 $1 Camera and transparencies (53×38 *mm*) 45 50
2719 $1 Heinkel He 178 (first turbo jet plane) (53×38 *mm*) 45 50
2720 $1 Dr. Hans Pabst von Ohain (jet turbine engine) 45 50
2721 $1 Rudolf Diesel (diesel engine) 45 50
a. Sheetlet. Nos. 2721/8 .. .. 3·50
2722 $1 Early Diesel engine and forms of transport (53×38 *mm*) 45 50
2723 $1 Zeppelin airship (53×38 *mm*) .. 45 50
2724 $1 Count Ferdinand von Zeppelin (airship pioneer) 45 50
2725 $1 Wilhelm Conrad Rontgen (X-rays) .. 45 50
2726 $1 X-ray of hand (53×38 *mm*) 45 50
2727 $1 Launch of Saturn Rocket (53×38 *mm*) 45 50
2728 $1 Wernher von Braun (rocket research) 45 50
2713/28 .. .. *Set of* 16 7·00 8·00
MS2729 Two sheets, each 106×76 mm. (a) $6 Hans Geiger (Geiger counter). (b) $6 William Shockley (research into semi-conductors) *Set of* 2 *sheets* 5·25 5·50

Nos. 2713/20 and 2721/8 were each printed together, *se-tenant*, in sheetlets of 8 with enlarged illustrated margins.

No. 2713 is inscribed "CARL BENZ" in error.

399 Stylised Americas

400 "Figures on the Seashore"

(Litho Questa)

1998 (18 Nov). *50th Anniv of Organization of American States. P* 13½×14.
2730 **399** $1 multicoloured 45 50

(Des Diana Catherines. Litho Questa)

1998 (18 Nov). *25th Death Anniv of Pablo Picasso (painter). T* **400** *and similar multicoloured designs. P* 14½.
2731 $1.20, Type **400** 50 55
2732 $1.65, "Three Figures under a Tree" (*vert*) 70 75
2733 $1.75, "Two Women running on the Beach" 75 80
2731/3 .. .. *Set of* 3 1·90 2·10
MS2734 126×102 mm. $6 "Bullfight" .. .. 2·50 2·75

401 Dino 246 GT-GTS

(Des F. Rivera. Litho Questa)

1998 (18 Nov). *Birth Centenary of Enzo Ferrari (car manufacturer). T* **401** *and similar horiz designs. Multicoloured. P* 14.
2735 $1.75, Type **401** 75 80
a. Sheetlet. Nos. 2735/7 .. .. 2·25
2736 $1.75, Front view of Dino 246 GT-GTS .. 75 80
2737 $1.75, 365 GT4 BB 75 80
2735/7 .. .. *Set of* 3 2·25 2·40
MS2738 104×72 mm. $6 Dino 246 GT-GTS (91×34 *mm*). P 14×14½ .. .. .. 2·50 2·75

Nos. 2735/7 were printed together, *se-tenant*, in sheetlets of 3.

402 Scout Handshake

403 Mahatma Gandhi

(Litho Questa)

1998 (18 Nov). *19th World Scout Jamboree, Chile.* *T* **402** *and similar horiz designs. Multicoloured. P* 14.

2739	90 c. Type **402**	40	45
2740	$1 Scouts hiking	45	50
2741	$1.20, Scout salute	50	55
2739/41	*Set of* 3	1·25	1·50
MS2742	68×98 mm. $6 Lord Baden-Powell	2·50	2·75

(Des M. Leboeuf. Litho Questa)

1998 (18 Nov). *50th Death Anniv of Mahatma Gandhi.* *T* **403** *and similar vert designs. Multicoloured. P* 14.

2743	90 c. Type **403**	40	45
2744	$1 Gandhi seated	45	50
2745	$1.20, As young man	50	55
2746	$1.65, At primary school in Rajkot, aged 7	70	75
2743/6	*Set of* 4	2·00	2·25
MS2747	100×70 mm. $6 Gandhi with staff	2·50	2·75

404 McDonnell Douglas Phantom F-GR1

(Des D. Miller. Litho Questa)

1998 (18 Nov). *80th Anniv of Royal Air Force.* *T* **404** *and similar horiz designs. P* 14.

2748	$1.75, Type **404**	75	80
	a. Sheetlet. Nos. 2748/51	3·00	
2749	$1.75, Two Sepecat Jaguar GR1As	75	80
2750	$1.75, Panavia Tornado F3	75	80
2751	$1.75, McDonnell Douglas Phantom F-GR2	75	80
2748/51	*Set of* 4	3·00	3·25
MS2752	Two sheets, each 90×68 mm. (a) $6 Golden Eagle (bird) and Bristol F2B Fighter. (b) $6 Hawker Hurricane and EF-2000 Eurofighter *Set of 2 sheets*	5·00	5·25

Nos. 2748/51 were printed together, *se-tenant*, in sheetlets of 4 with enlarged illustrated margins.

405 Brown Pelican

406 Border Collie

(Litho Questa)

1998 (24 Nov). *Sea Birds of the World.* *T* **405** *and similar horiz designs. Multicoloured. P* 14.

2753	15 c. Type **405**	10	10
2754	25 c. Dunlin	10	15
2755	45 c. Atlantic Puffin	20	25
2756	75 c. King Eider	35	40
	a. Sheetlet. Nos. 2756/67	4·00	
2757	75 c. Inca Tern	35	40
2758	75 c. Little Auk ("Dovekie")	35	40
2759	75 c. Ross's Gull	35	40
2760	75 c. Common Noddy ("Brown Noddy")	35	40
2761	75 c. Marbled Murrelet	35	40
2762	75 c. Northern Gannet	35	40
2763	75 c. Razorbill	35	40
2764	75 c. Long-tailed Skua ("Long-tailed Jaegar")	35	40
2765	75 c. Black Guillemot	35	40
2766	75 c. Whimbrel	35	40
2767	75 c. Oystercatcher	35	40
2768	90 c. Pied Cormorant	40	45
2753/68	*Set of* 16	4·75	5·75
MS2769	Two sheets, each 100×70 mm. (a) $6 Black Skimmer. (b) $6 Wandering Albatross *Set of 2 sheets*	5·00	5·25

Nos. 2756/67 were printed together, *se-tenant*, in sheetlets of 12 with the backgrounds forming a composite design.

No. 2759 is inscribed "ROSS' BULL" in error.

(Litho B.D.T.)

1998 (10 Dec). *Christmas. Dogs.* *T* **406** *and similar horiz designs. Multicoloured. P* 13½×14.

2770	15 c. Type **406**	10	10
2771	25 c. Dalmatian	10	15
2772	65 c. Weimaraner	30	35
2773	75 c. Scottish Terrier	35	40
2774	90 c. Long-haired Dachshund	40	45
2775	$1.20, Golden Retriever	50	55
2776	$2 Pekingese	85	90
2770/6	*Set of* 7	2·50	2·75
MS2777	Two sheets, each 75×66 mm. (a) $6 Dalmatian. (b) $6 Jack Russell Terrier *Set of 2 sheets*	5·00	5·25

Barbuda

1998 (25 Mar). *Centenary of Radio. Entertainers. Nos.* 2372/6 *of Antigua optd with T* **111**.

1917	65 c. Kate Smith	30	35
1918	75 c. Dinah Shore	35	40
1919	90 c. Rudy Vallee	40	45
1920	$1.20, Bing Crosby	50	55
1917/20	*Set of* 4	1·60	1·75
MS1921	72×104 mm. $6 Jo Stafford (28×42 *mm*)	2·50	2·75

1998 (25 Mar). *Olympic Games, Atlanta (2nd issue). Previous Medal Winners. Nos.* 2302/24 *of Antigua optd with T* **111** *(Nos.* 1923/4, 1943 *and* **MS**1944a*) or with T* **114**, *but with lines spaced (others).*

1922	65 c. Florence Griffith Joyner (U.S.A.) (Gold – track, 1988)	30	35
1923	75 c. Olympic Stadium, Seoul (1988) (*horiz*)	35	40
1924	90 c. Allison Jolly and Lynne Jewell (U.S.A.) (Gold – yachting, 1988) (*horiz*)	40	45
1925	90 c. Wolfgang Nordwig (Germany) (Gold – pole vaulting, 1972)	40	45
	a. Sheetlet. Nos. 1925/33	3·50	
1926	90 c. Shirley Strong (Great Britain) (Silver – 100 metres hurdles, 1984)	40	45
1927	90 c. Sergei Bubka (Russia) (Gold – pole vault, 1988)	40	45
1928	90 c. Filbert Bayi (Tanzania) (Silver – 3000 metres steeplechase, 1980)	40	45
1929	90 c. Victor Saneyev (Russia) (Gold – triple jump, 1968, 1972, 1976)	40	45
1930	90 c. Silke Renk (Germany) (Gold – javelin, 1992)	40	45
1931	90 c. Daley Thompson (Great Britain) (Gold – decathlon, 1980, 1984)	40	45
1932	90 c. Robert Richards (U.S.A.) (Gold – pole vault, 1952, 1956)	40	45
1933	90 c. Parry O'Brien (U.S.A) (Gold – shot put, 1952, 1956)	40	45
1934	90 c. Ingrid Kramer (Germany) (Gold – Women's platform diving, 1960)	40	45
	a. Sheetlet. Nos. 1934/42	3·50	
1935	90 c. Kelly McCormick (U.S.A.) (Silver – Women's springboard diving, 1984)	40	45
1936	90 c. Gary Tobian (U.S.A.) (Gold – Men's springboard diving, 1960)	40	45
1937	90 c. Greg Louganis (U.S.A.) (Gold – Men's diving, 1984 and 1988)	40	45
1938	90 c. Michelle Mitchell (U.S.A.) (Silver – Women's platform diving, 1984 and 1988)	40	45
1939	90 c. Zhou Jihong (China) (Gold – Women's platform diving, 1984)	40	45
1940	90 c. Wendy Wyland (U.S.A.) (Bronze – Women's platform diving, 1984)	40	45
1941	90 c. Xu Yanmei (China) (Gold – Women's platform diving, 1988)	40	45
1942	90 c. Fu Mingxia (China) (Gold – Women's platform diving, 1992)	40	45
1943	$1.20, 2000 metre tandem cycle race (*horiz*)	50	55
1922/43	*Set of* 21	8·50	9·50
MS1944	Two sheets, each 106×76 mm. (a) $5 Bill Toomey (U.S.A.) (Gold – decathlon, 1968) (*horiz*). (b) $6 Mark Lenzi (U.S.A.) (Gold – Men's springboard diving, 1992) *Set of 2 sheets*	4·75	5·00

1998 (12 May). *World Cup Football Championship, France. Nos.* 2525/39 *of Antigua optd with T* **114**.

1945	60 c. multicoloured	25	30
1946	75 c. agate	35	40
1947	90 c. multicoloured	40	45
1948	$1 agate	45	50
	a. Sheetlet. Nos. 1948/55 and central label	3·50	
1949	$1 agate	45	50
1950	$1 agate	45	50
1951	$1 grey-black	45	50
1952	$1 agate	45	50
1953	$1 agate	45	50
1954	$1 agate	45	50
1955	$1 agate	45	50
1956	$1.20, multicoloured	50	55
1957	$1.65, multicoloured	75	80
1958	$1.75, multicoloured	80	85
1945/58	*Set of* 14	6·50	7·50
MS1959	Two sheets, each 102×127 mm. (a) $6 multicoloured. (b) $6 multicoloured *Set of 2 sheets*	5·25	5·50

1998 (4 June). *Cavalry through the Ages. Nos.* 2359/63 *of Antigua optd with T* **111** *(Nos.* 1960/3*) or T* **114** *(No.* **MS**1964*).*

1960	60 c. Ancient Egyptian cavalryman	25	30
	a. Block of 4. Nos. 1960/3	1·00	
1961	60 c. 13th-century English knight	25	30
1962	60 c. 16th-century Spanish lancer	25	30
1963	60 c. 18th-century Chinese cavalryman	25	30
1960/3	*Set of* 4	1·00	1·25
MS1964	100×70 mm. $6 19th-century French cuirassier (*vert*)	2·75	3·00

1998 (20 July). *50th Anniv of U.N.I.C.E.F. Nos.* 2364/7 *of Antigua optd with T* **114**.

1965	75 c. Girl in red sari	35	40
1966	90 c. South American mother and child	40	45
1967	$1.20, Nurse with child	50	55
1965/7	*Set of* 3	1·25	1·40
MS1968	114×74 mm. $6 Chinese child	2·75	3·00

1998 (20 July). *3000th Anniv of Jerusalem. Nos.* 2368/71 *Antigua optd with T* **111**.

1969	75 c. Tomb of Zachariah and *Verbascum sinuatum*	35	4
1970	90 c. Pool of Siloam and *Hyacinthus orientalis*	40	4
1971	$1.20, Hurva Synagogue and *Ranunculus asiaticus*	50	5
1969/71	*Set of* 3	1·25	1·4
MS1972	66×80 mm. $6 Model of Herod's Temple and *Cercis siliquastrum*	2·75	3·(

1998 (31 Aug). *Diana, Princess of Wales Commemoration. No* 2573/85 *of Antigua optd with T* **114**, *but with lines spaced.*

1973	$1.65, Diana, Princess of Wales	75	8
	a. Sheetlet. Nos. 1973/8	4·50	
1974	$1.65, Wearing hoop earrings (rose-carmine and black)	75	8
1975	$1.65, Carrying bouquet	75	8
1976	$1.65, Wearing floral hat	75	8
1977	$1.65, With Prince Harry	75	8
1978	$1.65, Wearing white jacket	75	8
1979	$1.65, In kitchen	75	8
	a. Sheetlet. Nos. 1979/84	4·50	
1980	$1.65, Wearing black and white dress	75	8
1981	$1.65, Wearing hat (orge-brown & black)	75	8
1982	$1.65, Wearing floral print dress (lake-brown and black)	75	8
1983	$1.65, Dancing with John Travolta	75	8
1984	$1.65, Wearing white hat and jacket	75	8
1973/84	*Set of* 12	9·00	9·5
MS1985	Two sheets, each 70×100 mm. (a) $6 Wearing red jumper. (b) $6 Wearing black dress for Papal audience (lake-brown and black) *Set of 2 sheets*	5·25	5·5

1998 (12 Oct). *Broadway Musical Stars. Nos.* 2384/93 *Antigua optd with T* **111**.

1986	$1 Robert Preston (*The Music Man*)	45	5
	a. Sheetlet. Nos. 1986/94	4·00	
1987	$1 Michael Crawford (*Phantom of the Opera*)	45	5
1988	$1 Zero Mostel (*Fiddler on the Roof*)	45	5
1989	$1 Patti Lupone (*Evita*)	45	5
1990	$1 Raul Julia (*Threepenny Opera*)	45	5
1991	$1 Mary Martin (*South Pacific*)	45	5
1992	$1 Carol Channing (*Hello Dolly*)	45	5
1993	$1 Yul Brynner (*The King and I*)	45	5
1994	$1 Julie Andrews (*My Fair Lady*)	45	5
1986/94	*Set of* 9	4·00	4·5
MS1995	106×76 mm. $6 Mickey Rooney (*Sugar Babies*)	2·50	2·7

1998 (12 Oct). *20th Death Anniv of Charlie Chaplin (film star). Nos.* 2404/13 *of Antigua optd with T* **111**.

1996	$1 Charlie Chaplin as young man	45	5
	a. Sheetlet. Nos. 1996/2004	4·00	
1997	$1 Pulling face	45	5
1998	$1 Looking over shoulder	45	5
1999	$1 In cap	45	5
2000	$1 In front of star	45	5
2001	$1 In *The Great Dictator*	45	5(
2002	$1 With movie camera and megaphone	45	5(
2003	$1 Standing in front of camera lens	45	5(
2004	$1 Putting on make-up	45	5(
1996/2004	*Set of* 9	4·00	4·5(
MS2005	76×106 mm. $6 Charlie Chaplin	2·50	2·75

1998 (23 Nov). *Butterflies. Nos.* 2414/36 *of Antigua optd with T* **114**, *but with lines spaced.*

2006	90 c. *Charaxes porthos*	40	45
2007	$1.10, *Charaxes protoclea protoclea*	50	55
	a. Sheetlet. Nos. 2007/15	4·50	
2008	$1.10, *Byblia ilithyia*	50	55
2009	$1.10, Black-headed Bush Shrike ("Tchagra") (bird)	50	55
2010	$1.10, *Charaxes nobilis*	50	55
2011	$1.10, *Pseudacraea boisduvali trimeni*	50	55
2012	$1.10, *Charaxes smaragdalis*	50	55
2013	$1.10, *Charaxes lasti*	50	55
2014	$1.10, *Pseudacraea poggei*	50	55
2015	$1.10, *Graphium colonna*	50	55
2016	$1.10, Carmine Bee Eater (bird)	50	55
	a. Sheetlet. Nos. 2016/24	4·50	
2017	$1.10, *Pseudacraea eurytus*	50	55
2018	$1.10, *Hypolimnas monteironis*	50	55
2019	$1.10, *Charaxes anticlea*	50	55
2020	$1.10, *Graphium leonidas*	50	55
2021	$1.10, *Graphium illyris*	50	55
2022	$1.10, *Nephronia argia*	50	55
2023	$1.10, *Graphium policenes*	50	55
2024	$1.10, *Papilio dardanus*	50	55
2025	$1.20, *Aethiopana honorius*	50	55
2026	$1.60, *Charaxes hadrianus*	70	75
2027	$1.75, *Precis westermanni*	75	80
2006/27	*Set of* 21	10·50	11·50
MS2028	Three sheets, each 106×76 mm. (a) $6 *Charaxes lactitinctus* (*horiz*). (b) $6 *Eupheadra neophron*. (c) $6 *Euxanthe tiberius* (*horiz*) *Set of 3 sheets*	7·75	8·00

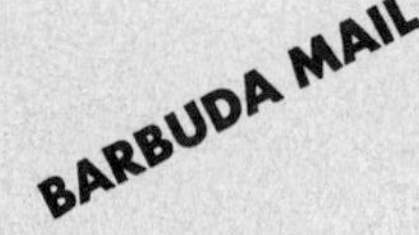

(126)

1998 (23 Dec). *Christmas. Dogs. Nos.* 2770/7 *of Antigua optd with T* **126** *diagonally.*

2029	15 c. Border Collie	10	10
2030	25 c. Dalmatian	10	15
2031	65 c. Weimaraner	30	35
2032	75 c. Scottish Terrier	35	40
2033	90 c. Long-haired Dachshund	40	45
2034	$1.20, Golden Retriever	50	55
2035	$2 Pekingese	85	90
2029/35	*Set of* 7	2·50	2·75
MS2036	Two sheets, each 75×66 mm. (a) $6 Dalmatian. (b) $6 Jack Russell Terrier *Set of 2 sheets*	5·25	5·50

999 (25 Jan). *Lighthouses of the World. Nos.* 2612/20 *of Antigua optd with T* **111**.
037 45 c. Europa Point Lighthouse, Gibraltar .. 20 25
038 65 c. Tierra del Fuego, Argentina (*horiz*) .. 30 35
039 75 c. Point Loma, California, U.S.A. (*horiz*) .. 35 40
040 90 c. Groenpoint, Cape Town, South Africa .. 40 45
041 $1 Youghal, Cork, Ireland 45 50
042 $1.20, Launceston, Tasmania, Australia .. 50 55
043 $1.65, Point Abino, Ontario, Canada (*horiz*) 75 80
044 $1.75, Great Inagua, Bahamas (*horiz*) .. 75 80
037/44 .. .. *Set of* 8 3·50 4·00
IS2045 99×70 mm. $6 Cape Hatteras, North Carolina, U.S.A. .. .. 2·50 2·75

ASCENSION ISLAND

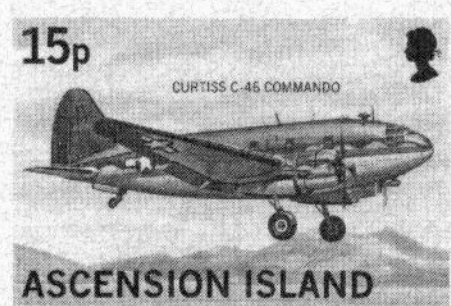

182 Curtiss C-46 Commando

(Des A. Theobald. Litho Questa)

1999 (20 Jan). *Aircraft. T* **182** *and similar horiz designs. Multicoloured. W* w **14** (*sideways*). *P* 14.
760 15p. Type **182** 30 35
761 35p. Douglas C-47 Dakota 70 75
762 40p. Douglas C-54 Skymaster 80 85
763 50p. Consolidated Liberator Mk. V .. 1·00 1·10
760/3 .. .. *Set of* 4 2·75 3·00
MS764 120×85 mm. £1.50, Consolidated Liberator LB-30 .. .. 3·00 3·25

No. **MS**764 also commemorates the 125th birth anniversary of Sir Winston Churchill.

183 *Glengorm Castle* (mail ship), 1929

184 Pair of White Terns ("Fairy Terns")

(Des J. Batchelor. Litho Questa)

1999 (5 Mar). *"Australia '99" World Stamp Exhibition, Melbourne. Ships. T* **183** *and similar horiz designs. Multicoloured. W* w **14** (*sideways*). *P* 15×14.
765 15p. Type **183** 30 35
766 35p. *Gloucester Castle* (mail ship), 1930 .. 70 75
767 40p. *Durham Castle* (mail ship), 1930 .. 80 85
768 50p. *Garth Castle* (mail ship), 1930 .. 1·00 1·10
765/8 .. .. *Set of* 4 2·75 3·00
MS769 121×82 mm. £1 H.M.S. *Endeavour* (Cook) .. .. 2·00 2·10

(Des Doreen McGuiness. Litho Questa)

1999 (27 Apr). *Endangered Species. White Tern ("Fairy Tern"). T* **184** *and similar vert designs. Multicoloured. W* w **16**. *P* 14½.
770 10p. Type **184** 20 25
a. Strip of 4. Nos. 770/3 80
771 10p. On branch 20 25
772 10p. Adult and fledgling 20 25
773 10p. In flight 20 25
770/3 .. .. .. *Set of* 4 80 1·00

Nos. 770/3 were printed in sheets of individual designs, or in sheets of 16 containing the four designs *se-tenant*, both horizontally and vertically.

AUSTRALIA

601 Red Roses

602 Elderly Man and Grandmother with Boy

(Des Nicole Bryant. Litho SNP Ausprint)

1999 (4 Feb). *Greetings Stamp. Romance.* (*a*) *Phosphorised paper. P* 14×14½
1842 **601** 45 c. multicoloured 35 40

(*b*) *Self-adhesive. Phosphor background. P* 11½
1843 **601** 45 c. multicoloured 35 40
a. Booklet pane. No. 1843×10 .. 3·50

No. 1843, on which the phosphor shows pink under U.V. light, was only issued in $4.50, booklets on which the surplus self-adhesive paper was retained.

(Des Lynda Warner. Litho McPherson's Ptg Group, Mulgrave)

1999 (11 Feb). *International Year of Older Persons. T* **602** *and similar horiz design. Multicoloured. P* 14×14½.
1844 45 c. Type **602** 35 40
a. Horiz pair. Nos. 1844/5 70
1845 45 c. Elderly woman and grandfather with boy 35 40

Nos. 1844/5 were printed together, *se-tenant*, as horizontal pairs in sheets of 10.

603 *Polly Woodside* (barque)

604 Olympic Torch and 1956 7½d. Stamp

(Des Beth McKinlay. Litho SNP Ausprint)

1999 (19 Mar). *Sailing Ships. T* **603** *and similar square designs. Multicoloured. Phosphor background* (45 c.) *or phosphorised paper* (*others*). *P* 14½×14.
1846 45 c. Type **603** 35 40
1847 85 c. *Alma Doepel* (topsail schooner) .. 65 70
1848 $1 *Enterprize* replica (topsail schooner) .. 75 80
1849 $1.05, *Lady Nelson* replica (topsail schooner) 80 85
1846/9 .. .. *Set of* 4 2·50 2·75

No. 1846, on which the phosphor appears pink under U.V. light, was printed in sheets with the stamps horizontally *se-tenant* with half stamp-size labels showing the "Australia '99" International Stamp Exhibition emblem.

(Litho SNP Ausprint)

1999 (19 Mar). *Australia—Ireland Joint Issue.* Polly Woodside (*barque*). *Sheet* 137×72 *mm. Multicoloured. Phosphorised paper. P* 14×14½.
MS1850 45 c. Type **603**; 30p. Type **374** of Ireland (*No.* **MS**1850 *was sold at* $1.25 *in Australia*) .. 1·00 1·10

No. **MS**1850 includes the "Australia '99" emblem on the sheet margin and was postally valid in Australia to the value of 45 c. The same miniature sheet was also available in Ireland.

(Litho Ashton-Potter Canada)

1999 (19 Mar). *Australia—Canada Joint Issue.* Marco Polo (*emigrant ship*). *Sheet* 160×95 *mm. Multicoloured. Fluorescent frames. P* 13½ (85 *c.*) *or* 13 (46 *c.*).
MS1851 85 c. As No. 1728; 46 c. Type **701** of Canada (*No.* **MS**1851 *was sold at* $1.30 *in Australia*) .. .. 1·00 1·00

No. **MS**1851, on which the fluorescent frame appears green under U.V. light, includes the "Australia '99" emblem on the sheet margin and was postally valid in Australia to the value of 85 c. The same miniature sheet was also available in Canada.

(Litho SNP Ausprint)

1999 (19 Mar). *"Australia '99" International Stamp Exhibition, Melbourne. Two sheets, each* 142×76 *mm, containing designs as Nos.* 398/403, *but printed litho and all with face value of* 45 c. *P* 14×14½ (*No.* **MS**1852a) *or* 14½×14 (*No.* **MS**1852b).
MS1852 (a) 45 c. deep ultramarine (Type **167**); 45 c. grey-olive (Captain Cook); 45 c. purple-brown (Flinders). (b) 45 c. Indian red (Type **168**); 45 c. deep olive-brown (Bass); 45 c. deep reddish purple (King) .. .. *Set of* 2 *sheets* 2·10 2·25

Designs in No. **MS**1852a are 37×25 mm and those in No. **MS**1852b 24×29 mm.

(Des FHA Image Design. Litho SNP Ausprint)

1999 (22 Mar). *Olympic Torch Commemoration. P* 14½×14.
1853 **604** $1.20, multicoloured 90 95

605 *Correa reflexa* (Native Fuschia)

(Des W. Rankin)

1999 (8 Apr). *Coastal Environment. T* **605** *and similar horiz designs. Multicoloured.*

(*a*) *Litho SNP Ausprint. Phosphorised paper. P* 14×14½
1854 45 c. Type **605** 35 40
a. Block of 4. Nos. 1854/7 .. .. 1·40
1855 45 c. *Hibbertia scandens* (Guinea Flower) 35 40
1856 45 c. *Ipomoea pre-caprae* (Beach Morning Glory) 35 40
1857 45 c. *Wahlenbergia stricta* (Australian Bluebells) 35 40
1854/7 .. .. *Set of* 4 1·40 1·60

(*b*) *Self-adhesive. Litho SNP Ausprint* (*Nos.* 1858/61) *or Pemara* (*Nos.* 1858b/61b). *Phosphor frame. P* 11½
1858 45 c. Type **605** 35 40
a. Booklet pane. Nos. 1858 and 1860, each × 3, and Nos. 1859 and 1861, each × 2 .. .. 3·50
b. Perf 12½×13 .. .. .. 35 40
1859 45 c. *Hibbertia scandens* (Guinea Flower) 35 40
b. Perf 12½×13 .. .. .. 35 40
1860 45 c. *Ipomoea pre-caprae* (Beach Morning Glory) 35 40
b. Perf 12½×13 .. .. .. 35 40
1861 45 c. *Wahlenbergia stricta* (Australian Bluebells) 35 40
b. Perf 12½×13 .. .. .. 35 40
1858/61 .. .. *Set of* 4 1·40 1·60
1858b/61b .. .. *Set of* 4 1·40 1·60

Nos. 1854/7 were printed together, *se-tenant*, in sheets of 50 containing ten of blocks of 4 and ten single stamps.

Nos. 1858/61 and 1858b/61b, on which the phosphor appears pink under U.V. light, were printed in rolls of 100 with the surplus paper around each stamp removed. Nos. 1858/61 also come in $4.50 booklets, containing No. 1858a, on which the surplus paper was retained.

STAMP BOOKLETS

B **60** Red Roses

1999 (4 Feb). *Greetings Stamp. Romance. Multicoloured cover as Type* B **60**. *Self-adhesive.*
SB128 $4.50, booklet containing pane of 10 45 c. (No. 1843a) .. .. 3·50

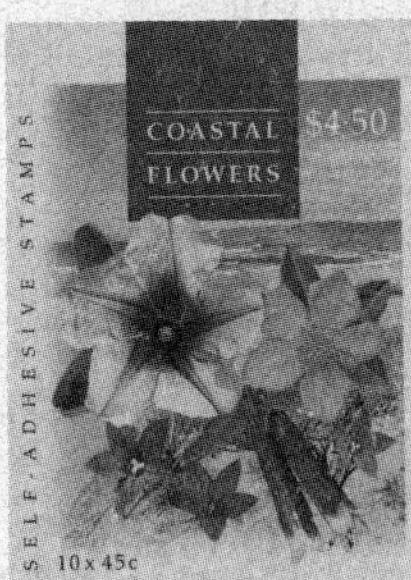

B **61** Flowers on Beach

1999 (8 Apr). *Coastal Flowers. Multicoloured cover as Type* B **61**. *Self-adhesive.*
SB129 $4.50, containing pane of 10 45 c. (No. 1858a) 3·50

Cocos (Keeling) Islands

81 Preparing Food on Beach

(Des Jacqui Young and Sandra Harman. Litho SNP Ausprint)

1999 (11 Feb). *Hari Raya Puasa Festival. T* **81** *and similar vert designs. Multicoloured. P* 14½×14.
359 45 c. Type **81** 35 40
a. Horiz strip of 5. Nos. 359/63 .. .. 1·75
360 45 c. Woman with child and jukongs on beach 35 40
361 45 c. Jukongs and palm fronds 35 40
362 45 c. Two men watching jukongs 35 40
363 45 c. Jukong and white flowers 35 40
359/63 .. .. *Set of* 5 1·75 2·00

Nos. 359/63 were printed together, *se-tenant*, in horizontal strips of 5 throughout the sheet.

COVER PRICES

Cover factors are quoted at the beginning of each country for most issues to 1945. An explanation of the system can be found on page x. The factors quoted do not, however, apply to philatelic covers.

Norfolk Island

200 Short S.23 Sandringham (flying boat)

201 Soft Toy Rabbit

(Des Mary Duke. Litho Photopress International, Norfolk Island)

1999 (28 Jan). *Booklet Stamps. Aircraft. T* **200** *and similar horiz design. Each brown-lake and deep grey-green. Roul* 7.

690 5 c. Type **200** 10 10
 a. Booklet pane of 10 with margins all round 40
691 5 c. DC-4 *Norfolk Trader* 10 10
 a. Booklet pane of 10 with margins all round 40

(Des K. Partridge. Litho Questa)

1999 (9 Feb). *Chinese New Year ("Year of the Rabbit"). Sheet* 80×100 *mm. P* 14.

MS692 **201** 95 c. multicoloured 75 80

202 Hull of *Resolution* under Construction

203 Pacific Black Duck

(Des R. Pennycuick. Litho Cartor)

1999 (19 Mar). *"Australia '99" International Stamp Exhibition, Melbourne. Schooner* Resolution. *T* **202** *and similar horiz designs. Multicoloured. P* 13×13½.

693 45 c. Type **202** 40 40
 a. Booklet pane. Nos. 693/7 plus printed label .. .. 1·90
694 45 c. After being launched 40 40
695 45 c. In Emily Bay 40 40
696 45 c. Off Cascade 40 40
697 45 c. Alongside at Auckland 40 40
693/7 .. .. *Set of* 5 1·90 1·90

Nos. 693/7 were only available in stamp booklets sold for $2.50.

(Des Tracey Yager. Litho Southern Colour Print, Dunedin)

1999 (27 Apr). *"iBRA '99" International Stamp Exhibition, Nuremberg. Sheet* 80×100 *mm. P* 14½.

MS698 **203** $2.50, multicoloured .. .. 1·90 2·00

STAMP BOOKLETS

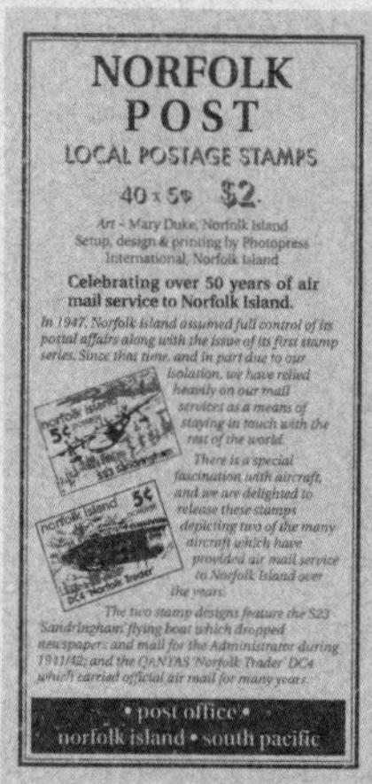

B 7
(*Illustration reduced. Actual size* 92×178 *mm*)

1999 (28 Jan). *Aircraft. Brown-lake and deep grey-green on white cover as Type* B **7**. *Stamps attached by selvedge.*

SB10 $2 booklet containing four panes of ten 5 c. (Nos. 690a/1a, each × 2) .. .. 1·50

B **8** Emily Bay
(*Illustration further reduced. Actual size,* 170×75 *mm*)

1999 (19 Mar). *"Australia '99" International Stamp Exhibition, Melbourne. Schooner Resolution. Multicoloured cover as Type* B **8**. *Stamps attached by selvedge.*

SB11 $2.50, booklet containing pane of five 45 c. and label (No. 693a) .. .. 1·90

BAHAMAS

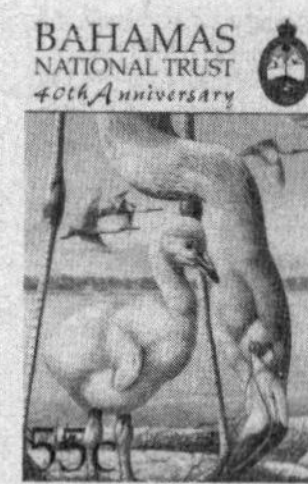

234 Head of Greater Flamingo and Chick

235 Arawak Indian Canoe

(Des A. Robinson. Litho Questa)

1999 (9 Feb). *40th Anniv of National Trust* (*1st issue*). *Inagua National Park. T* **234** *and similar vert designs. Multicoloured. W w* **16**. *P* 14.

1163 55 c. Type **234** 65 70
 a. Horiz strip of 5. Nos. 1163/7 .. 3·25
1164 55 c. Pair with two chicks 65 70
1165 55 c. Greater Flamingos asleep or stretching wings 65 70
1166 55 c. Greater Flamingos feeding 65 70
1167 55 c. Greater Flamingos in flight .. 65 70
1163/7 .. .. *Set of* 5 3·25 3·50

Nos. 1163/7 were printed together, *se-tenant*, in horizontal strips of 5 throughout the sheet with the backgrounds forming a composite design.

(Des D. Miller. Litho Questa)

1999 (9 Mar). *"Australia '99" World Stamp Exhibition, Melbourne. Maritime History. T* **235** *and similar horiz designs. Multicoloured. W w* **14** (*sideways*). *P* 14½.

1168 15 c. Type **235** 20 25
1169 55 c. *Santa Maria* (Columbus), 1492 .. 65 70
1170 60 c. *Queen Anne's Revenge* (Blackbeard), 1716 .. .. 70 75
1171 70 c. *The Banshee* (Confederate paddle-steamer) running blockade 85 90
1168/71 .. .. *Set of* 4 2·40 2·50
MS1172 110×66 mm. $2 Firing on American ships, 1776 .. .. 2·40 2·50

236 Dolphin

(Des A. Robinson. Litho Questa)

1999 (6 Apr). *40th Anniv of National Trust* (*2nd issue*). *Exuma Cays Land and Sea Park. T* **236** *and similar vert designs. Multicoloured. W w* **16**. *P* 14.

1173 55 c. Type **236** 65 70
 a. Horiz strip of 5. Nos. 1173/7 .. 3·25
1174 55 c. Angelfish and Parrotfish 65 70
1175 55 c. Queen Triggerfish 65 70
1176 55 c. Turtle 65 70
1177 55 c. Lobster 65 70
1173/7 .. .. *Set of* 5 3·25 3·50

Nos. 1173/7 were printed together, *se-tenant*, in horizontal strips of 5 throughout the sheet, with the backgrounds forming a composite design.

MINIMUM PRICE

The minimum price quote is 10p which represents a handling charge rather than a basis for valuing common stamps. For further notes about prices see introductory pages.

BANGLADESH

244 Begum Rokeya **245** Anniversary Logo

(Des A. Hussain)

1998 (9 Dec). *Begum Rokeya* (*campaigner for wome education*) *Commemoration. P* 14½×14.

689 **244** 8 t. multicoloured 30

(Des A. Hussain)

1998 (10 Dec). *50th Anniv of Universal Declaration of Huma Rights. P* 14×14½.

690 **245** 10 t. multicoloured 30

1998 (14 Dec). *Martyred Intellectuals* (*7th series*). *Vert desig as T* **148**. *Each grey-black and reddish brown. P* 14×14½.

691 2 t. Md. Khorshed Ali Sarker 10
 a. Sheetlet. Nos. 691/8 80
692 2 t. Abu Yakub Mahfuz Ali 10
693 2 t. S. M. Nural Huda 10
694 2 t. Nazmul Hoque Sarker 10
695 2 t. Md. Taslim Uddin 10
696 2 t. Gulam Mostafa 10
697 2 t. A. H. Nural Alam 10
698 2 t. Timir Kanti Dev 10
699 2 t. Altaf Hossain 10
 a. Sheetlet. Nos. 699/706 80
700 2 t. Aminul Hoque 10
701 2 t. S. M. Fazlul Hoque 10
702 2 t. Mozammel Ali 10
703 2 t. Syed Akbar Hossain 10
704 2 t. Sk. Abdus Salam 10
705 2 t. Abdur Rahman 10
706 2 t. Dr. Shyamal Kanti Lala 10
691/706 .. .. *Set of* 16 1·60 2·4

Nos. 691/8 and 699/706 were each printed together, *se-tenan* in sheetlets of 8, the horizontal rows in each sheetlet bein separated by a row of inscribed labels.

246 Dove of Peace and U.N. Symbols

(Des A. Hussain)

1998 (30 Dec). *50th Anniv of U.N. Peace-keeping Operations* *P* 14×14½.

707 **246** 10 t. multicoloured 30 3

247 Kazi Nazrul Islam

(Des A. Hussain)

1998 (31 Dec). *Birth Centenary* (1999) *of Kazi Nazrul Islam* (*poet*). *P* 14½.

708 **247** 6 t. multicoloured 20 2

BARBADOS

236 Racing Yacht

237 Juvenile Piping Plover in Shallow Water

(Des D. Miller. Litho Cot Printery Ltd)

999 (19 Mar). *"Australia '99" World Stamp Exhibition, Melbourne. Sheet 90×90 mm. W w* **14** *(sideways). P* 14.
S1133 **236** $4 multicoloured .. .. .. 1·50 1·60

(Des J. Pointer. Litho Cot Printery Ltd)

999 (27 Apr). *Endangered Species. Piping Plover. T* **237** *and similar horiz designs. Multicoloured. W w* **14** *(sideways). P* 14.
134 10 c. Type **237** 10 10
135 45 c. Female with eggs 30 35
136 50 c. Male and female with fledglings .. 30 35
137 70 c. Male in shallow water 40 45
134/7 .. .. *Set of* 4 1·10 1·25

BELIZE

222 *Eucharis grandiflora*

(Des Jennifer Toombs. Litho Cartor)

999 (17 Mar). *Easter. Flowers. T* **222** *and similar vert designs. Multicoloured. W w* **14**. *P* 13.
242 10 c. Type **222** 10 10
243 25 c. *Hippeastrum puniceum* 15 20
244 60 c. *Zephyranthes citrina* 35 40
245 $1 *Hymenocallis littoralis* 60 65
242/5 .. .. *Set of* 4 1·10 1·25

BERMUDA

176 Shelly Bay

(Des Sheila Semos. Litho Walsall)

1999 (29 Apr). *Bermuda Beaches. T* **176** *and similar horiz designs. Multicoloured. W w* **14** *(sideways). P* 13×13½.
821 30 c. Type **176** 35 40
822 60 c. Catherine's Bay 70 75
823 65 c. Jobson's Cove 80 85
824 $2 Warwick Long Bay .. .. .. 2·40 2·50
821/4 .. .. *Set of* 4 4·25 4·50

BRITISH INDIAN OCEAN TERRITORY

35 *Westminster* (barque), 1837

(Des J. Batchelor. Litho Walsall)

1999 (1 Feb). *Ships. T* **35** *and similar horiz designs. Multicoloured. W w* **14** *(sideways). P* 13½×14.
224 2p. Type **35** 10 10
225 15p. *Sao Cristovao* (Spanish galleon), 1589 30 35
226 20p. *Sea Witch* (U.S. clipper), 1849 .. 40 45
227 26p. H.M.S. *Royal George* (ship of the line), 1778 .. .. 55 60
228 34p. *Cutty Sark* (clipper), 1883 .. .. 70 75
229 60p. *Mentor* (East Indiaman), 1789 .. 1·25 1·40
230 80p. H.M.S. *Trinculo* (brig), 1809 .. 1·60 1·75
231 £1 *Enterprise* (paddle-steamer), 1825 .. 2·00 2·10
232 £1.15, *Confiance* (French privateer), 1800 2·25 2·40
233 £2 *Kent* (East Indiaman), 1820 .. .. 4·00 4·25
224/33 .. .. *Set of* 10 13·00 14·00

ALTERED CATALOGUE NUMBERS

Any Catalogue numbers altered from the last edition are shown as a list in the introductory pages.

36 *Cutty Sark* (clipper)

(Des J. Batchelor. Litho Questa)

1999 (19 Mar). *"Australia '99" World Stamp Exhibition, Melbourne. Sheet 150×75 mm, containing T* **36** *and similar horiz design. Multicoloured. W w* **16** *(sideways). P* 13½×14.
MS234 60p. Type **36**; 60p. *Thermopylae* (clipper) 2·40 2·50

BRITISH VIRGIN ISLANDS

220 Rock Iguana

(Des R. Watton. Litho Enschedé)

1999 (30 Apr). *Lizards. T* **220** *and similar horiz designs. Multicoloured. W w* **14** *(sideways). P* 15×14.
1014 5 c. Type **220** 10 10
1015 35 c. Pygmy Gecko 40 45
1016 60 c. Slippery Back Skink 70 75
1017 $1.50, Wood Slave Gecko .. .. 1·75 1·90
1014/17 .. .. *Set of* 4 2·75 3·00
MS1018 100×70 mm. 75 c. Doctor Lizard; 75 c. Yellow-bellied Lizard; 75 c. Man Lizard; 75 c. Ground Lizard .. .. 3·50 3·75

BRUNEI

130 Water Village, Bandar Seri Begawan

(Des Siti Zaleha Haji Kaprawi. Litho Cartor)

1999 (23 Feb). *15th Anniv of National Day. T* **130** *and similar vert designs. Multicoloured. P* 13.
606 20 c. Type **130** 15 20
607 60 c. Modern telecommunications and air travel 45 50
608 90 c. Aspects of modern Brunei 70 75
606/8 .. .. *Set of* 3 1·25 1·50
MS609 118×85 mm. Nos. 606/8 .. .. 1·25 1·50
Nos. 606/9 show the Postal Services Department arms in fluorescent ink at the bottom left of each stamp.

CANADA

Add to Nos. 1350/64:

(*b*) *Litho C.B.N. Chalk-surfaced paper. Fluorescent frame. P* 13×13½
1359 – 46 c. mult (19×23 *mm*) (28.12.98) .. 35 40
a. Booklet pane. No. 1359×10 .. 3·50

(*c*) *Coil stamps. Recess C.B.N. Fluorescent frame. P* 10×*imperf*
1365 – 46 c. carmine-red (28.12.98) 35 40

(*d*) *Self-adhesive booklet stamp. Litho Ashton Potter Canada. Chalk-surfaced paper. Fluorescent frame. Die-cut*
1366 – 46 c. multicoloured (28.12.98) 35 40
a. Booklet pane. No. 1366×30 .. 10·50

Design: *Vert*—46 c. (Nos. 1359, 1366) Canadian flag and iceberg.
Booklet pane No. 1359a has the vertical edges of the pane imperforate and margins at top and bottom.

Add to Nos. 1862/3:

No. **MS**1863 also exists with the "CHINA '99" World Stamp Exhibition, Bejing logo, overprinted in gold on the top of the margin.

699 Stylised Mask and Curtain

(Des Y. Paquin and Marie Rouleau. Litho C.B.N.)

1999 (16 Feb). *50th Anniv of Le Théâtre du Rideau Vert. Fluorescent frame. P* 13×12½.
1864 **699** 46 c. multicoloured 35 40

(Des R. Bellemare and P. Leduc. Litho Ashton-Potter Canada)

1999 (24 Feb). *Birds (4th series). Horiz designs as T* **643**. *Multicoloured. Fluorescent frame.* (*a*) *P* 12½×13
1865 46 c. Northern Goshawk 35 40
a. Horiz strip of 4. Nos. 1865/8 .. 1·40
1866 46 c. Red-winged Blackbird 35 40
1867 46 c. American Goldfinch 35 40
1868 46 c. Sandhill Crane 35 40
1865/8 .. .. *Set of* 4 1·40 1·60

(*b*) *Self-adhesive. P* 11½
1869 46 c. Northern Goshawk 35 40
b. Booklet pane. Nos. 1869/72, each × 3 with margins all round .. .. 4·00
1870 46 c. Red-winged Blackbird 35 40
1871 46 c. American Goldfinch 35 40
1872 46 c. Sandhill Crane 35 40
1869/72 .. .. *Set of* 4 1·40 1·60
Nos. 1865/8 were printed together, *se-tenant*, in sheets of 20 (4×5) containing five examples of No. 1865a.
Nos. 1869/72 were only issued in $5.52 stamp booklets on which the surplus self-adhesive paper was retained.

700 "The Raven and the First Men" (B. Reid) and The Great Hall

(Des Barbara Hodgson. Litho C.B.N.)

1999 (9 Mar). *50th Anniv of University of British Columbia Museum of Anthropology. Fluorescent frame. P* 13½.
1873 **700** 46 c. multicoloured 35 40

701 *Marco Polo* (full-rigged ship)

(Des J. Franklin Wright. Litho Ashton-Potter Canada)

1999 (19 Mar). *Canada—Australia Joint Issue.* Marco Polo *(emigrant ship). Multicoloured. Fluorescent frame. P* 13×12½.
1874 46 c. Type **701** 35 40
MS1875 160×95 mm. 85 c. As No. 1728 of Australia. P 13; 46 c. Type **701**. P 13½ (No. **MS**1875 was sold at $1.25 in Canada) .. 1·00 1·10
No. **MS**1875 includes the "Australia '99" emblem on the sheet margin and was postally valid in Canada to the value of 46 c.
The same miniature sheet was also available in Australia.

(Des L. Cable. Litho Ashton-Potter Canada)

1999 (31 Mar). *Scenic Highways (3rd series). Horiz designs as T* **667**. *Multicoloured. Fluorescent frame. P* 12½×13.
1876 46 c. Route 132, Quebec, and hang-glider 35 40
a. Block of 4. Nos. 1876/9 .. .. 1·40
1877 46 c. Yellowhead Highway, Manitoba, and Bison 35 40
1878 46 c. Dempster Highway, Northwest Territories, and Indian village elder 35 40
1879 46 c. The Discovery Trail, Newfoundland, and whale's tailfin 35 40
1876/9 .. .. *Set of* 4 1·40 1·60
Nos. 1876/9 were printed together, *se-tenant*, in sheets of 20 comprising four blocks of 4 and four single stamps.

702 Inuit Children and Landscape

(Des Susan Point and Bonne Zabolotney. Litho Ashton-Potter Canada)

1999 (1 Apr). *Creation of Nunavut Territory. Fluorescent frame. P* $12^1/_2 \times 13$.
1880 **702** 46 c. multicoloured 35 40

703 Elderly Couple on Country Path

(Des Sheila Armstrong-Hodgson, P. Hodgson and S. Peters. Litho C.B.N.)

1999 (12 Apr). *International Year of Older Persons. Fluorescent frame. P* $13^1/_2$.
1881 **703** 46 c. multicoloured 35 40

STAMP BOOKLETS

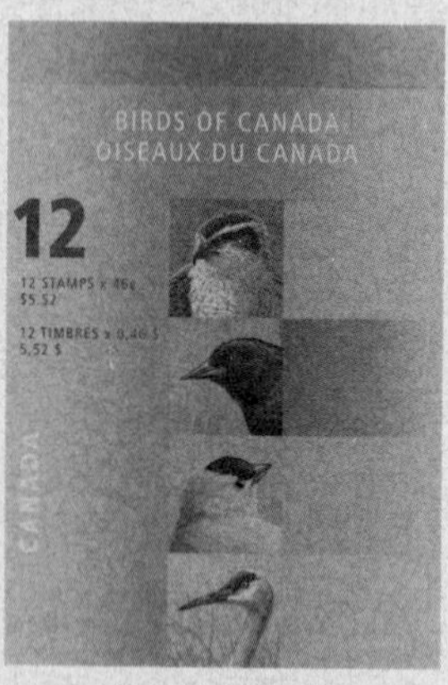

B **62** Birds' Heads
(Illustration reduced. Actual size 110×157 *mm)*

1999 (24 Feb). *Birds* (4*th series*). *Multicoloured cover as Type* B **62**. *Self-adhesive.*
SB231 $5.52, booklet containing pane of 12 46 c. (No. 1869b) .. .. 4·00

CAYMAN ISLANDS

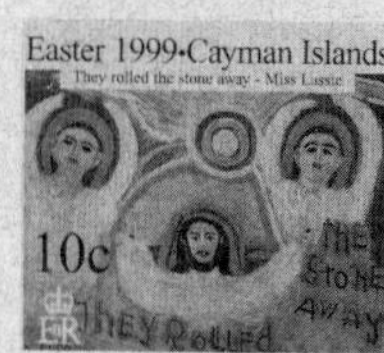

199 "They Rolled the Stone Away" (Miss Lassie)

(Des D. Miller. Litho Cartor)

1999 (26 Mar). *Easter. Paintings by Miss Lassie (Gladwyn Bush). T* **199** *and similar multicoloured designs. W* w **14** *(sideways on horiz designs). P* 13.

872	10 c. Type **199**	15	20
873	20 c. "Ascension" (*vert*)	30	35
874	30 c. "The World Praying for Peace" ..	40	45
875	40 c. "Calvary" (*vert*)	60	65
872/5	.. .. *Set of* 4	1·40	1·60

CYPRUS

322 *Pleurotus eryngii*

(Des S. Vassiliou. Litho Oriental Press, Bahrain)

1999 (4 Mar). *Mushrooms of Cyprus. T* **322** *and similar vert designs. Multicoloured. P* $13^1/_2 \times 13$.

965	10 c. Type **322**	10	10
966	15 c. *Lactarius deliciosus*	35	40
967	25 c. *Sparassis crispa*	60	65
968	30 c. *Morchella elata*	70	75
965/8	.. .. *Set of* 4	1·75	1·90

Turkish Cypriot Posts

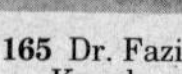

165 Dr. Fazil Kucuk

166 Otello

1999 (15 Jan). 15*th Death Anniv of Dr. Fazil Kucuk (politician). W* **51** *(inverted). P* $14 \times 13^1/_2$.
486 **165** 75000 l. multicoloured 30 40

1999 (30 Jan). *Performance of Verdi's Opera* Otello *in Cyprus. Sheet,* 78×74 *mm, containing T* **166** *and similar vert design. Multicoloured. W* **51** *(inverted). P* $14 \times 13^1/_2$.
MS487 200000 l. Type **166**; 200000 l. Desdemona dead in front of fireplace .. .. .. 1·60 1·75

FALKLAND ISLANDS

203 Prince of Wales (from photo by Clive Arrowsmith)

(Des and litho Walsall)

1999 (13 Mar). *Royal Visit. W* w **16**. *P* $14 \times 13^1/_2$.
837 **203** £2 multicoloured .. .. .. 4·00 4·25

FIJI

276 Wandering Whistling Duck

(Des G. Tavelini. Litho B.D.T.)

1999 (27 Apr). *"iBRA '99" International Stamp Exhibition, Nuremberg. Sheet,* 100×95 *mm, containing T* **276** *and similar vert design. Multicoloured. W* w **14**. *P* $13^1/_2$.
MS1049 $2 Type **276**; $2 Pacific Black Duck .. 2·50 2·75

GIBRALTAR

222 Barbary Macaque

223 Queen Elizabeth II

(Des R. Gorringe. Litho Cartor)

1999 (4 Mar). *Europa. Parks and Gardens. Upper Rock Nature Reserve. T* **222** *and similar vert designs. Multicoloured. P* $13^1/_2 \times 13$.

853	30p. Type **222**	60	65
854	30p. Dartford Warbler	60	65
855	42p. Dusky Grouper	85	90
856	42p. Common Kingfisher	85	90
853/6	.. .. *Set of* 4	2·75	3·00

(Des S. Perera. Litho B.D.T.)

1999 (4 Mar). (*a*) *P* 14 (50*p*., £1, £3) *or* $13^1/_2 \times 13$ (*others*).

857	**223**	1p. reddish purple	10	10
858		2p. olive-sepia	10	10
859		4p. light greenish blue	10	10
860		5p. emerald	10	10
861		10p. orange	20	25
862		12p. rosine	25	30
863		20p. turquoise-green	40	45
864		28p. magenta	55	60
865		30p. reddish orange	60	65
866		40p. deep olive-grey	80	85
867		42p. deep grey-green	85	90
868		50p. bistre	1·00	1·10
869		£1 brownish black	2·00	2·10
870		£3 bright blue	6·00	6·25
		(*b*) *Self-adhesive. P* $9^1/_2$		
871	**223**	(1st) reddish orange	55	60
857/71		.. .. .. *Set of* 14	13·00	13·50

Nos. 868/71 are larger, 25×30 mm.
No. 871 was printed in rolls of 100, on which the surplus self-adhesive paper around each stamp was retained, and was initially sold at 26p.

IRELAND

374 *Polly Woodside* (barque)

(Des V. Killowry. Litho Walsall)

1999 (19 Mar). *Maritime Heritage. T* **374** *and similar multi-coloured designs. Chalk-surfaced paper. Phosphor frame. P* 14.

1219	30p. Type **374**	55	60
1220	35p. *Ilen* (schooner)	65	70
1221	45p. R.N.L.I. Cromer class lifeboat (*horiz*)	80	85
1222	£1 *Titanic* (liner) (*horiz*)	1·75	1·90
1219/22	.. .. *Set of* 4	3·75	4·00
MS1223	150×90 mm. No. 1222×2. No phosphor frame	3·50	3·75

On Nos. 1219/22, the phosphor shows green under U.V. light.
No. **MS**1223 also exists overprinted with the "Australia '99", International Stamp Exhibition, Melbourne, logo in gold.

(Litho SNP Ausprint)

1999 (19 Mar). *Ireland—Australia Joint Issue.* Polly Woodside *(barque). Sheet* 137×72 *mm. Multicoloured. Phosphorised paper. P* $14 \times 14^1/_2$.
MS1224 45 c. Type **603** of Australia; 30p. Type **374** (*No.* **MS**1224 *was sold at* 52*p. in Ireland*) 95 1·00
No. **MS**1224 includes the "Australia '99" emblem on the sheet margin and was postally valid in Ireland to the value of 30p.
The same miniature sheet was also available in Australia.

Note: The first Supplement recording new stamps not in this catalogue or the Addenda appeared in the September 1999 number of *Gibbons Stamp Monthly*.

Index

References to Vol. 1 = **317**
References to Vol. 2 = *Vol. 2 545*

Country — *page*

Notes

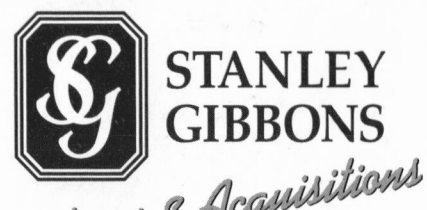